Scott Publishing Co.

SCOTT

911 VANDEMARK ROAD, P. O. Box 828, SIDNEY, OHIO 45365-0828 513-498-0802

W9-BAA-385

Dear Catalogue User:

The big news is that this is the first edition of the Scott standard catalogue to contain values for stamps in the grade of *very fine*. (The change to valuing very fine stamps began with the *1996 United States Specialized Catalogue*, released in November 1996.) In the past we have listed values for stamps of a grade of *fine to very fine*. You will find that the change in grade has significantly affected values throughout the volume, particularly for 19th-century material.

With the 1997 edition of the *Scott Standard Postage Stamp Catalogue*, Scott values also reflect the world market. We have factored the prices stamps sell for in their respective home markets into our values. For example, the editors now take into consideration the price paid in London for a Penny Please study the new visual grading guide on page 9A. It is imperative that you familiarize yourself with the Scott definitions of grading, especially now that there has been a major change. Although everyone grades stamps slightly differently, you need to understand our point of view so you know exactly what grade Scott values represent.

And now, with your permission, I'll ask myself a few key questions.

Why the move to World Market values?

It is time that Scott abandons its isolationist policy of valuing for the U.S. market only. Scott must use values that reflect the world market because overseas buyers have changed the nature of the stamp business. The prices that collectors in the United States pay for stamps is strongly influenced by the home market for the same stamps.

But how does this affect me?

When values of foreign stamps are well below prices paid abroad, many nice stamps are dispatched across the ocean to buyers who are quite willing to pay the higher price. When the next U.S. collector goes to buy the same foreign item, he has to compete not only with the overseas demand but an even thinner supply here in this country. It is a vicious circle.

What stamps are affected?

All stamps are not affected by the change to world market values. Older and scarcer stamps, stamps that are scarce in very fine condition and stamps from countries with a strong home market are most likely to be impacted. Also stamps that are highly sought after as key stamps to a particular area, era or collecting specialty are likely candidates to be affected by the new policy.

Will the change to market values mean that Scott values will be the equivalent in dollars to Stanley Gibbons, Michel, Yvert or other foreign catalogue values?

Good question! Each of these catalogues has its own unique method of valuing stamps. Michel uses reference values that are highly discounted by dealers when selling. So do most of the other overseas catalogues. Scott uses a retail value that represents what a collector might actually expect to pay for a specific stamp in the specified condition.

So what is going on with British stamp values since the last edition of Volume 1B?

In Great Britain, Scott 1, the Penny Black, increases to $3,000 unused and $180 used in very fine, from the 1996 levels of $1,900 unused and $110 used for fine to very fine stamps. The Tuppence Blue, Scott 2, climbs to $5,750 unused and $300 used in very fine, from $5,000 unused and $225 used in fine to very fine, and Scott 3, the 1p red brown on bluish paper of 1841, jumps to $110 unused and $3 used, from $80 unused and $2 used.

In Australia, the Roos are up about 10 percent on average. The 1/2p to 5sh values of the 1913 set with Wide Crown and Wide A watermark, Scott 1-12, push to $698.50 unused, $1,300 never hinged and $316.75 used in very fine, from the 1996 fine to very fine levels of $632 unused, $1,200 never hinged and $281.45 used. The 1915-24 set with Narrow Crown and Narrow A watermark, Scott 45-59, leaps to $490 unused, $1,300 never hinged and $94.15 used, from $446.50 unused, $1,200 never hinged and $87.15 used.

Is Hong Kong still hot?

Yes! Scott 5, the 24¢ unwatermarked Victoria of 1862, jumps to $550 unused and $70 used, from $425 unused and $35 used. The 1865 24¢ Victoria with Crown and CC watermark, Scott 18, forges to $250 unused and $8 used, from $125 unused and $5 used. The 1891 Jubilee Overprint, Scott 66, increases to $225 unused and $80 used, from $190 unused and $32.50 used. Elsewhere in Hong Kong, strong increases abound. The 1903 King Edward VII set with Crown and CA watermark, Scott 71-85, charges to $1,536 unused and $1,052 used, from $830.90 unused and $501.43 used. The 1937 Coronation set, Scott 151-153, bounds to $7.25 unused, $18 never hinged and $3.05 used, from $4.50 unused, $14 never hinged, and 87¢ used. The 1949 UPU issue, Scott 180-183, soars to $60.50 never hinged from $52.25, and the $1.30 Freedom from Hunger of 1963, Scott 218, hops to $40 never hinged from $32.50.

What else?

Ireland's 1922 overprints on the pence denominations, Scott 1-8, climb to $30.55 unused and $49.25 used, from $23.23 unused and $43.55 used, and the "Saorstat Eireann 1922" overprints by Thom, Scott 44-58, leap to $280.90 unused and $472.90 used, from $255.85 unused and $423.80 used. The 1922-23 definitives, Scott 65-76, jump to $71.10 unused and $54.15 used, from $55.86 unused and $28.65 used.

Any editorial changes?

Many minor varieties have been added throughout Volume 1B. Most are shade, missing perforation or overprint varieties.

In Kenya, Uganda and Tanzania, 10 to 100 pound values of the 1922-27 King George V set have been added as majors.

In Mauritius, minors have been added for the latest impressions of Scott 3-6. These impressions have even less detail than those on the "worn impression" minors. In Gambia, four minors for 6p Queen Victoria stamps of the 1869-86 issues with name panel sloping down from left to right have been added as Scott 4b, 10a, 18c and 18d. In Australia, a perf 15x14 minor of the Matthew Flinders $1 of 1966 has been added as Scott 415a, valued at $75 never hinged and $15 used. Also, minors have been added for second types of the 1976 Australian Arms 18¢, Scott 628a, and the 1981 Tasmanian Tiger 24¢, Scott 788a. Two unvalued watermark varieties showing 3 roses and a shamrock have been added in Great Britain, Scott 27b and 39d.

Two more important things.

Set totals for three and four stamp sets have been added throughout Volume 1B. This change will certainly make your life with the catalogue much easier.

Pronunciations for each country return to the standard catalogues this year. Now you'll know how to pronounce Tuvalu.

Happy Collecting,

Stuart Morrissey

Stuart Morrissey, Publisher

Acknowledgments

Our appreciation and gratitude go to the following individuals and organizations who have assisted us in preparing information included in the 1997 Scott Catalogues. Some helpers prefer anonymity. These individuals have generously shared their stamp knowledge with others through the medium of the Scott Catalogue.

Those who follow provided information that is in addition to the hundreds of dealer price lists and advertisements and scores of auction catalogues and realizations which were used in producing the catalogue values. It is from those noted here that we have been able to obtain information on items not normally seen in published lists and advertisements. Support from these people of course goes beyond data leading to catalogue values, for they also are key to editorial changes.

George F. Ackermann
Michael E. Aldrich
A. R. Allison
B. J. Ammel
David J. Armacost
Mike Armus
Robert Ausubel
Don Bakos
Alfredo V. Basurto
Jules K. Beck
Vladimir Berrio-Lemm
Kenneth R. Berry
John Birkinbine II
Rex Dean Bishop
Torbjorn Bjork
John R. Boker, Jr.
George W. Brett
Roger Brody
Randall Brooksbank
Lawrence A. Bustillo
Peter Bylen
A. Bryan Camarda
Nathan Carlin
Dr. Herman J. Cestero, Jr.
E. J. Chamberlin
Richard A. Champagne
Albert F. Chang
Henry Chlanda
Andrew Cronin
James A. Cross
William T. Crowe
Dan Demetriade
Bob Dumaine
William S. Dunn
Victor E. Engstrom
J. A. Farrington
Leon Finik
Henry Fisher
Joseph E. Foley
Marvin Frey
Richard Friedberg
Eugene A. Garrett
Peter Georgiadis
Richard B. Graham
Brian M. Green
Fred F. Gregory
Gary Griffith
Harry Hagendorf
Calvet M. Hahn
Rudolf Hamar
Erich E. Hamm
John B. Head
Dale Hendricks
Clifford O. Herrick
Lee H. Hill, Jr.
W. Wilson Hulme II
Eric Jackson
Michael Jaffe
John I. Jamieson

Peter C. Jeannopoulos
Clyde Jennings
Donald B. Johnstone
Henry Karen
Stanford M. Katz
Lewis Kaufman
Dr. James Kerr
Charles F. Kezbers
Robert Kitson
William Langs
Lester Lanphear III
Richard F. Larkin
Ken Lawrence
Ronald E. Lesher, Sr.
Pedro Llach
William Thomas Lockard
David Mac Donnell
Walter J. Mader
Robert L. Markovits
F. Brian Marshall
Timothy M. Mc Ree
Dr. Hector Mena
Giorgio Migliavacca
Jack Molesworth
Chuck Q. Moo
William E. Mooz
Gary M. Morris
Peter Mosiondz, Jr.
Bruce M. Moyer
Gregg Nelson
Robert Odenweller
John C. Olson
Victor Ostolaza
Souren Panirian
Sheldon Paris
John E. Pearson
Otto Peetoom
Donald J. Peterson
Vernon Pickering
Stanley M. Piller
S. Pinchot
Peter A. Robertson
Jon Rose
Frans H. A. Rummens
Richard H. Salz
Byron Sandfield
Jacques C. Schiff, Jr.
F. Burton Sellers
Jeff Siddiqui
Dr. Hubert Skinner
Roger D. Skinner
Merle Spencer
Sherwood Springer
Richard Stambaugh
Mark Stucker
R. J. Thoden
David Torre
Scott Trepel
Ming W. Tsang

James O. Vadeboncoeur
Xavier Verbeck
Jerome S. Wagshal
Richard A. Washburn
Giana Wayman
Raymond H. Weill
Irwin Weinberg
Larry S. Weiss
William R. Weiss, Jr.
Hans A. Westphal
Greg Winston
Robert F. Yacano
Clarke Yarbrough
Val Zabijaka
Nathan Zankel

A special acknowledgment to Liane and Sergio Sismondo of The Classic Collector for their extraordinary assistance and knowledge sharing that has aided in the preparation of this year's Standard Catalogues.

American Air Mail Society
Stephen Reinhard, PO Box 110,
Mineola, NY 11501

American Philatelic Society
PO Box 8000, State College, PA 16803

American Revenue Association
Bruce Miller, Suite 332, 701 South
First Ave., Arcadia, CA 91006

American Stamp Dealers'
Association
3 School St., Glen Cove, NY 11542

American Topical Association
PO Box 630, Johnstown, PA 15907

Booklet Collectors Club
James Natale, PO Box 2461,
Cinnaminson, NJ 08077-5461

Bureau Issues Association
George V.H. Godin, PO Box 23707,
Belleville, IL 62223

Confederate Stamp Alliance
Richard L. Calhoun, 1749 W. Golf Rd.,
Suite 366, Mt. Prospect, IL 60056

Errors, Freaks, and Oddities
Collectors Club
Jim McDevitt, 138 Lakemont Dr. East,
Kingsland, GA 31548-8921

International Society of Worldwide
Stamp Collectors
2505 Second St.,
Caddo Mills, TX 75135

Junior Philatelists of America
Ellie Chapman, PO Box 850,
Boalsburg, PA 16827-0850

National Duck Stamp Collectors
Society
PO Box 43, Harleysville, PA 19438

No-Value-Identified
Collectors Club
Albert Sauvanet, Le Clos Royal B,
Boulevard des Pas Enchantes, 44230
St. Sebastien-sur-Loire, France

Plate Number Coil Collectors Club
Joann Lenz, 37211 Alper Drive,
Sterling Heights, MI 48312-2203

Precancel Stamp Society
1750 Skippack Pk. #1603,
Center Square, PA 19422

Royal Philatelic Society
41 Devonshire Place,
London, U.K. W1N 1PE

Royal Philatelic Society of Canada
PO Box 929, Station Q,
Toronto ON, CANADA M4T 2P1

United Postal Stationery Society
Joann Thomas, PO Box 48,
Redlands, CA 92373

US Philatelic Classics Society
W. Wilson Hulme II, PO Box 5368,
Naperville, IL 60567-5368

US Possessions Philatelic Society
Charles A. Richmond, PO Box 26724,
Columbus, OH 43226

Society for the New Republics of
the Former USSR
(Armenia, etc.)
Michael Padwee, 163 Joralemon St.,
PO Box 1520, Brooklyn, NY 11201-
1520

American Belgian Philatelic Society
Kenneth L. Costilow,
621 Virginius Dr.,
Virginia Beach, VA 23452-4417

Belize Philatelic Study Circle
Charles R. Gambill, 730 Collingswood,
Corpus Christi, TX 78412

Bermuda Collectors Society
Thomas J. McMahon, 86 Nash Road,
Purdys, NY 10578

Brazil Philatelic Association
Kurt Ottenheimer,
462 West Walnut St.,
Long Beach, NY 11561

British Caribbean Philatelic
Study Group
Gale J. Raymond, PO Box 35695,
Houston, TX 77235

British North America Philatelic
Society
Jerome C. Jarnick, 108 Duncan Drive,
Troy, MI 48098

Burma Philatelic Study Circle
A. Meech, 7208 91st Ave.,
Edmonton, AB, CANADA T6B 0R8

Canal Zone Study Group
Richard H. Salz, 60 27th Ave.,
San Francisco, CA 94121

China Stamp Society
Paul H. Gault, 140 West 18th Ave.,
Columbus, OH 43210

COPAPHIL (Colombia & Panama)
PO Box 2245, El Cajon, CA 92021

Society of Costa Rica Collectors
Dr. Hector Mena, PO Box 14831,
Baton Rouge, LA 70808

SCOTT

1997
Standard Postage
Stamp Catalogue

ONE HUNDRED AND FIFTY-THIRD EDITION IN SIX VOLUMES

VOLUME 1B

GREAT BRITAIN

&

THE BRITISH COMMONWEALTH
IN EUROPE, ASIA, AFRICA AND THE PACIFIC

VICE PRESIDENT/PUBLISHER	Stuart J. Morrissey
EDITOR	James E. Kloetzel
ASSOCIATE EDITOR	William W. Cummings
VALUING EDITOR	Martin J. Frankevicz
NEW ISSUES EDITOR	David C. Akin
COMPUTER CONTROL COORDINATOR	Denise Oder
VALUING ANALYST	Jose R. Capote
EDITORIAL ASSISTANTS	Judith E. Bertrand, Beth Brown
CONTRIBUTING EDITOR	Joyce Nelson
ART/PRODUCTION DIRECTOR	Janine C. S. Apple
PRODUCTION COORDINATOR	Nancy S. Martin
MARKETING/SALES DIRECTOR	William Fay
ADVERTISING	Sabrina D. Morton
CIRCULATION/PRODUCT PROMOTION MANAGER	Tim Wagner

Released May 1996

Copyright© 1996 by

Scott Publishing Co.

911 Vandemark Road, Sidney, OH 45365-0828

A division of AMOS PRESS, INC., publishers of *Linn's Stamp News, Coin World, Cars & Parts* magazine, *Moneycard Collector* and *The Sidney Daily News*.

Table of Contents

See Volume 1A for United States and affiliated territories,
United Nations, Canada and British America.
See Volumes 2, 3, 4 and 5 for nations of Africa, Asia, Europe,
Latin America and their affiliated territories.

Scott Publishing Mission Statement

The Scott Publishing Team exists to serve the recreational,
educational and commercial hobby needs of stamp collectors and dealers.

We strive to set the industry standard for philatelic information and products by developing and
providing goods that help collectors identify, value, organize and present their collections.

Quality customer service is, and will continue to be, our highest priority.
We aspire toward achieving total customer satisfaction.

Croatian Philatelic Society (Croatia and other Balkan areas)
Eck Spahich, 1512 Lancelot Rd., Borger, TX 79007

Cuban Philatelic Society of America
PO Box 450207, Miami, FL 33245-0207

Society for Czechoslovak Philately
Robert T. Cossaboom, PO Box 332, Scott AFB, IL 62225

Estonian Philatleic Soc.
Rudolf Hamar, 1912 Nugget Dr. Felton, CA 95018

Ethiopian Philatelic Society
Huguette Gagnon, PO Box 8110-45, Blaine, WA 98230

Falkland Islands Philatelic Study Group
James Driscoll, PO Box 172, South Dennis, NJ 08245

France & Colonies Philatelic Society
Walter Parshall, 103 Spruce St., Bloomfield, NJ 07003

Germany Philatelic Society
PO Box 779, Arnold, MD 21012-4779

GDR Study Group of German Philatelic Society
Ken Lawrence, PO Box 8040, State College, PA 16803-8040

Great Britain Collectors Club
Frank J. Koch, PO Box 309, Batavia, OH 45103 0309

Hawaiian Philatelic Society
Karen E. Awong, PO Box 10115, Honolulu, HI 96816-0115

Hellenic Philatelic Society of America (Greece and related areas)
Dr. Nicholas Asimakopulos, 541 Cedar Hill Ave., Wyckoff, NJ 07481

International Society of Guatemala Collectors
Mrs. Mae Vignola, 105 22nd Ave., San Francisco, CA 94121

Haiti Philatelic Society
Dwight Bishop, 2385 Cartegena Way, Oceanside, CA 92056

Hong Kong Stamp Society
Dr. An-Min Chung, 120 Deerfield Rd., Broomall, PA 19008

Hungary Philatelic Society
Thomas Phillips, PO Box 1162, Samp Mortar Sta., Fairfield, CT 06432

India Study Circle
John Warren, PO Box 70775, Washington, DC 20024

Society of Indochina Philatelists
Paul Blake, 1466 Hamilton Way, San Jose, CA 95125

Iran Philatelic Study Circle
David J. Armacost, PO Box 33381, Phoenix, AZ 85067

Eire Philatelic Association (Ireland)
Michael J. Conway, 74 Woodside Circle, Fairfield, CT 06430

Society of Israel Philatelists
Howard D. Chapman, 28650 Settlers Lane, Pepper Pike, OH 44124

Italy and Colonies Study Circle
David F. Emery, PO Box 86, Philipsburg, NJ 08865

International Society for Japanese Philately
Kenneth Kamholz, PO Box 1283, Haddonfield, NJ 08033

Korea Stamp Society
William A. Matthews, PO Box 15306, Columbus, OH 43215

Latin American Philatelic Society
Piet Steen, 197 Pembina Ave., Hinton, AB, CANADA T7V 2B2

Cuyahoga Latvian Philatelist Club
Arturs Rubenis, 1460 West Clifton Blvd., Lakewood, OH 44107-3309

Liberian Philatelic Society
William Thomas Lockard, PO Box 267, Wellston, OH 45692

Liechtenstudy USA (Liechtenstein)
Max Rheinberger, 100 Elizabeth St. #112, Duluth, MN 55803

Lithuanian Philatelic Society of New York
Vincent M. Alones, 217 McKee St., Floral Park, NY 11001-1314

Plebiscite-Memel-Saar Study Group
Clay Wallace, 158 Arapaho Circle, San Ramon, CA 94583

Mexico-Elmhurst Philatelic Society International
Juan Jose Vidrio, PO Box 435360, San Ysidro, CA 92143-5360

Nepal & Tibet Philatelic Study Group
Roger D. Skinner, 1020 Covington Rd., Los Altos, CA 94022

American Society of Netherlands Philately
Jan Enthoven, W6428 Riverview Drive, Onalaska, WI 54650

Nicaragua Study Group
Clyde R. Maxwell, Airport Plaza, 2041 Business Center Drive, Suite 101, Irvine, CA 92715

Society of Australasian Specialists / Oceania
Henry Bateman, PO Box 4862, Monroe, LA 71211

Orange Free State Study Circle
J. R. Stroud, 28 Oxford St., Burnham-on-sea, Somerset, U.K. TA8 1LQ

Pakistan Study Circle
Jeff Siddiqui, PO Box 7002, Lynnwood, WA 98046

International Philippine Philatelic Society
Eugene A. Garrett, 446 Stratford Ave., Elmhurst, IL 60126-4123

American Society of Polar Philatelists (Antarctic areas)
Richard Julian, 1153 Fairview Dr., York, PA 17403

Pitcairn Islands Study Group
Nelson A.L. Weller, 2940 Wesleyan Lane, Winston-Salem, NC 27106

Polonus Philatelic Society (Poland)
PO Box 458, Berwyn, IL 60402

International Society for Portuguese Philately
Michael Bryne, Adirondack Stamps, PO Box 13100, Mexico Beach, FL 32410

Rhodesian Study Circle
William R. Wallace, PO Box 16381, San Francisco, CA 94116

Romanian Chapter of Croatian Philatelic Society
Dan Demetriade, PO Box 10182, Detroit, MI 48210

Rossica Society of Russian Philately
Gary Combs, 8241 Chalet Ct., Millersville, MD 21108

Canadian Society of Russian Philately
Andrew Cronin, PO Box 5722, Station A, Toronto, ON, CANADA M5W 1P2

Ryukyu Philatelic Specialist Society
Carmine J. DiVincenzo, PO Box 381, Clayton, CA 94517-0381

St. Helena, Ascension & Tristan Society
Dr. Russell V. Skavaril, 222 East Torrance Road, Columbus, OH 43214 3834

St. Pierre & Miquelon Study Group
David Salovey, Box 464, New York NY 10014-0464

Associated Collectors of El Salvador
Jeff Brasor, 7365 NW 68th Way, Pompano Beach, FL 33067-3918

Sarawak Specialists' Society
Art Bunce, PO Box 2516, Escondido, CA 92033

Arabian Philatelic Association
ARAMCO Box 1929, Dhahran 31311, SAUDI ARABIA

Scandinavian Collectors Club
Robert W. Lang, PO Box 125, Newark, DE 19715-0125

Philatelic Society for Greater Southern Africa
William C. Brooks VI, PO Box 2698, San Bernardino, CA 92406-2698

Slovakia Stamp Society
Jack Benchik, PO Box 555, Notre Dame, IN 46556

Spanish Philatelic Society
Robert H. Penn, RD #3, Box 3349-1, Bangor, PA 18013

American Helvetia Philatelic Society (Switzerland, Liechtenstein)
Richard T. Hall, PO Box 666, Manhattan Beach, CA 90267-0666

Tannu Tuva Collectors Society
Kenneth R. Simon, 513 Sixth Ave. So., Lake Worth, FL 33460-4507

Society for Thai Philately
H.R. Blakeney, PO Box 25644, Oklahoma City, OK 73125

Tonga/Tin Can Mail Study Circle
Tom Jackson, 121 Mullingar Ct. #1A, Schaumburg, IL 60193

Turkey and Ottoman Philatelic Society
Gary F. Paiste, 4249 Berritt St., Fairfax, VA 22030

Tuvalu & Kiribati Philatelic Society
Frank Caprio, PO Box 218071, Nashville, TN 37221

Ukrainian Philatelic & Numismatic Society
Bohdan O. Pauk, PO Box 11184, Chicago, IL 60611-0184

United Nations Philatelists
Alex Bereson, 18 Portola Drive, San Francisco CA 94131-1518

Vatican Philatelic Society
Louis Padavan, PO Box 127, Remsenburg, NY 11960

Yugoslavia Study Group
Michael Lenard, 1514 North 3rd Ave., Wausau, WI 54401

Expertizing Services

American Philatelic Expertizing Service
PO Box 8000, State College, PA 16803

Confederate Stamp Alliance Authorization Service
10833 Greencrest Dr., Baton Rouge, LA 70811

Philatelic Foundation
501 Fifth Ave., Rm. 1901, New York, NY 10017

Professional Stamp Experts
1 Datran Center, Suite 1149, 9100 South Dadeland Blvd., Miami, FL 33156

Information on Catalogue Values, Grade and Condition

Catalogue Value

The Scott Catalogue value is a retail value; that is, an amount you could expect to pay for a stamp in a grade of Very Fine with no faults. Any exceptions to the grade valued will be noted in the text. The general introduction on the following pages and the individual section introductions further explain the type of material that is valued. The value listed for any given stamp is a reference that reflects recent actual dealer selling prices for that item.

Dealer retail price lists, public auction results, published prices in advertising and individual solicitation of retail prices from dealers, collectors and specialty organizations have been used in establishing the values found in this catalogue. Scott Publishing Co. values stamps, but Scott is not a company engaged in the business of buying and selling stamps as a dealer.

Use this catalogue as a guide for buying and selling. The actual price you pay for a stamp may be higher or lower than the catalogue value because of many different factors, including the amount of personal service a dealer offers, or increased or decreased interest in the country or topic represented by a stamp or set. An item may occasionally be offered at a lower price as a "loss leader," or as part of a special sale. You also may obtain an item inexpensively at public auction because of little interest at that time or as part of a large lot.

Copies of stamps that are of a lesser grade than Very Fine, or those with condition problems, trade at lower prices than those given in this catalogue. Stamps of exceptional quality in both grade and condition often command higher prices than those listed.

Values for pre-1900 unused issues are for stamps with at least most of their original gum. On rarer stamps, it may be expected that the original gum will be somewhat more disturbed than it will be on more common issues. Post-1900 unused issues are assumed to have full original gum. From breakpoints in most countries' listings, stamps are valued as never hinged, due to the wide availability of stamps in that condition. These notations are prominently placed in the listings and in the country information preceding the listings. Some countries also feature listings with dual values for hinged and never-hinged stamps.

Grade

A stamp's grade and condition are crucial to its value. The accompanying illustrations show examples of Very Fine stamps from different time periods, along with examples of stamps in Fine to Very Fine and Extremely Fine grades as points of reference.

FINE stamps (illustrations not shown) have designs that are noticeably off center on two sides. Imperforate stamps may have small margins, and earlier issues may show the design touching one edge of the stamp design. For perforated stamps, perfs may barely clear the design on one side, and very early issues normally will have the perforations slightly cutting into the design. Used stamps may have heavier than usual cancellations.

FINE-VERY FINE stamps may be somewhat off center on one side, or slightly off center on two sides. Imperforate stamps will have two margins of at least normal size, and the design will not touch any edge. For perforated stamps, the perfs are well clear of the design, but are still noticeably off center. *However, early issues of a country may be printed in such a way that the design naturally is very close to the edges. In these cases, the perforations may cut into the design very slightly.* Used stamps will not have a cancellation that detracts from the design.

VERY FINE stamps may be slightly off center on one side, but the design will be well clear of the edge. The stamp will present a nice, balanced appearance. Imperforate stamps will have three normal-sized margins. *However, early issues of many countries may be printed in such a way that the perforations may touch the design on one or more sides. Where this is the case, a boxed note will be found defining the centering and margins of the stamps being valued.* Used stamps will have light or otherwise neat cancellations. This is the grade used to establish Scott Catalogue values.

EXTREMELY FINE stamps are close to being perfectly centered. Imperforate stamps will have even margins that are larger than normal. Even the earliest perforated issues will have perforations clear of the design on all sides.

Condition

Grade addresses only centering and (for used stamps) cancellation. *Condition* refers to factors other than grade that affect a stamp's desirability.

Factors that can increase the value of a stamp include exceptionally wide margins, particularly fresh color, the presence of selvage, and plate or die varieties. Unusual cancels on used stamps (particularly those of the 19th century) can greatly enhance their value as well.

Factors other than faults that decrease the value of a stamp include loss of original gum, regumming, a hinge remnant or foreign object adhering to the gum, natural inclusions, straight edges, and markings or notations applied by collectors or dealers.

Faults include missing pieces, tears, pin or other holes, surface scuffs, thin spots, creases, toning, short or pulled perforations, clipped perforations, oxidation or other forms of color changelings, soiling, stains, and such man-made changes as reperforations or the chemical removal or lightening of a cancellation.

Scott Publishing Co. recognizes that there is no formally enforced grading scheme for postage stamps, and that the final price you pay or obtain for a stamp will be determined by individual agreement at the time of transaction.

On the following page are illustrations of Great Britain and British Commonwealth stamps from various time periods, 1840 to the modern era. These stamps have been chosen as being representative of the important different periods of stamp production, and the editors believe the illustrations will prove useful in showing the margin size and centering that will be seen on the various issues.

In addition to the matters of margin size and centering, collectors are reminded that the very fine stamps valued in the Scott catalogues also will possess fresh color and intact perforations, and they will be free from defects.

The three grades shown for each stamp are computer manipulated illustrations from a single digitized master illustration.

1840s 1850s 1850s 1850s 1860s-1870s

Fine-Very Fine

SCOTT CATALOGUES VALUE STAMPS IN THIS GRADE

Very Fine

Extremely Fine

MODERN ISSUES

1870s 1880s 1890s 1910s 1910s

Fine-Very Fine

SCOTT CATALOGUES VALUE STAMPS IN THIS GRADE

Very Fine

Extremely Fine

Understanding the Listings

On the opposite page is an enlarged "typical" listing from this catalogue. Below are detailed explanations of each of the highlighted parts of the listing.

1 **Scott number** — Scott catalogue numbers are used to identify specific items when buying, selling or trading stamps. Each listed postage stamp from every country has a unique Scott catalogue number. Therefore, Germany Scott 99, for example, can only refer to a single stamp. Although the Scott catalogue usually lists stamps in chronological order by date of issue, there are exceptions. When a country has issued a set of stamps over a period of time, those stamps within the set are kept together without regard to date of issue. This follows the normal collecting approach of keeping stamps in their natural sets.

When a country issues a set of stamps over a period of time, a group of consecutive catalogue numbers is reserved for the stamps in that set, as issued. If that group of numbers proves to be too few, capital-letter suffixes, such as "A" or "B," may be added to existing numbers to create enough catalogue numbers to cover all items in the set. A capital-letter suffix indicates a major Scott catalogue number listing. Scott uses a suffix letter only once. Therefore, a catalogue number listing with a capital-letter prefix will not also be found with the same letter (lower case) used as a minor-letter listing. If there is a Scott 16A in a set, for example, there will not also be a Scott 16a.

Suffix letters are not cumulative. A minor variety of Scott 16A would be Scott 16b, not Scott 16Ab. Any exceptions, such as Great Britain Scott 358cp, are clearly indicated.

There are times when a reserved block of Scott catalogue numbers is too large for a set, leaving some numbers unused. Such gaps in the numbering sequence also occur when the catalogue editors move an item's listing elsewhere or have removed it entirely from the catalogue. Scott does not attempt to account for every possible number, but rather attempts to assure that each stamp is assigned its own number.

Scott numbers designating regular postage normally are only numerals. Scott numbers for other types of stamps, such as air post, semipostal, postal tax, postage due, occupation and others have a prefix consisting of one or more capital letters or a combination of numerals and capital letters.

Illustration number — Illustration or design-type numbers are used to identify each catalogue illustration. For most sets, the lowest face-value stamp is shown. It then serves as an example of the basic design approach for other stamps not illustrated. Where more than one stamp use the same illustration number, but have differences in design, the design paragraph or the description line clearly indicates the design on each stamp not illustrated. Where there are both vertical and horizontal designs in a set, a single illustration may be used, with the exceptions noted in the design paragraph or description line.

When an illustration is followed by a lower-case letter in parentheses, such as "A2(b)," the trailing letter indicates which overprint or surcharge illustration applies.

Illustrations normally are 75 percent of the original size of the stamp. An effort has been made to note all illustrations not illustrated at that percentage. Virtually all souvenir sheet illustrations are reduced even more. Overprints and surcharges are shown at 100 percent of their original size, unless otherwise noted. In some cases, the illustration will be placed above the set, between listings or omitted completely. Overprint and surcharge illustrations are not placed in this catalogue for purposes of expertizing stamps.

Paper color — The color of a stamp's paper is noted in italic type when the paper used is not white.

Listing styles — There are two principal types of catalogue listings: major and minor.

Major listings are in a larger type style than minor listings. The catalogue number is a numeral that can be found with or without a capital-letter suffix, and with or without a prefix.

Minor listings are in a smaller type style and have a small-letter suffix or (if the listing immediately follows that of the major number) may show only the letter. These listings identify a variety of the major item. Examples include perforation, color, watermark or printing method differences, multiples (some souvenir sheets, booklet panes and se-tenant combinations), and singles of multiples.

Examples of major number listings include 16, 28A, B97, C13A, 10N5, and 10N6A. Examples of minor numbers are 16a and C13b.

5 **Basic information about a stamp or set** — Introducing each stamp issue is a small section (usually a line listing) of basic information about a stamp or set. This section normally includes the date of issue, method of printing, perforation, watermark and, sometimes, some additional information of note. *Printing method, perforation and watermark apply to the following sets until a change is noted.* Stamps created by overprinting or surcharging previous issues are assumed to have the same perforation, watermark and printing method as the original. Dates of issue are as precise as Scott is able to confirm and often reflect the dates on first-day covers, rather than the actual date of release.

6 **Denomination** — This normally refers to the face value of the stamp; that is, the cost of the unused stamp at the post office at the time of issue. When a denomination is shown in parentheses, it does not appear on the stamp. This includes the non-denominated stamps of the United States, Brazil and Great Britain, for example.

7 **Color or other description** — This area provides information to solidify identification of a stamp. In many recent cases, a description of the stamp design appears in this space, rather than a listing of colors.

8 **Year of issue** — In stamp sets that have been released in a period that spans more than a year, the number shown in parentheses is the year that stamp first appeared. Stamps without a date appeared during the first year of the issue. Dates are not always given for minor varieties.

9 **Value unused and Value used** — The Scott catalogue values are based on stamps that are in a grade of Very Fine unless stated otherwise. Unused values refer to items that have not seen postal, revenue or any other duty for which they were intended. Pre-1900 unused stamps that were issued with gum must have at least most of their original gum. Later issues are assumed to have full original gum. From breakpoints specified in most countries' listings, stamps are valued as never hinged. Stamps issued without gum are noted. Modern issues with PVA or other synthetic adhesives may appear ungummed. Self-adhesive stamps are valued as appearing undisturbed on their original backing paper. For a more detailed explanation of these values, please see the "Catalogue Value," "Condition" and "Understanding Valuing Notations" elsewhere in this introduction.

In some cases, where used stamps are more valuable than unused stamps, the value is for an example with a contemporaneous cancel, rather than a modern cancel or a smudge or other unclear marking. For those stamps that were released for postal and fiscal purposes, the used value represents a postally used stamp. Stamps with revenue cancels generally sell for less.

10 **Changes in basic set information** — Bold type is used to show any changes in the basic data given for a set of stamps. This includes perforation differences from one stamp to the next or a different paper, printing method or watermark.

11 **Total value of a set** — The total value of sets of three or more stamps issued after 1900 are shown. The set line also notes the range of Scott numbers and total number of stamps included in the grouping. *Set value* is the term used to indicate the value of a stamp set when its combined total is less than the sum of the individual stamps. This happens when some of the stamps in a set have the minimum catalogue value.

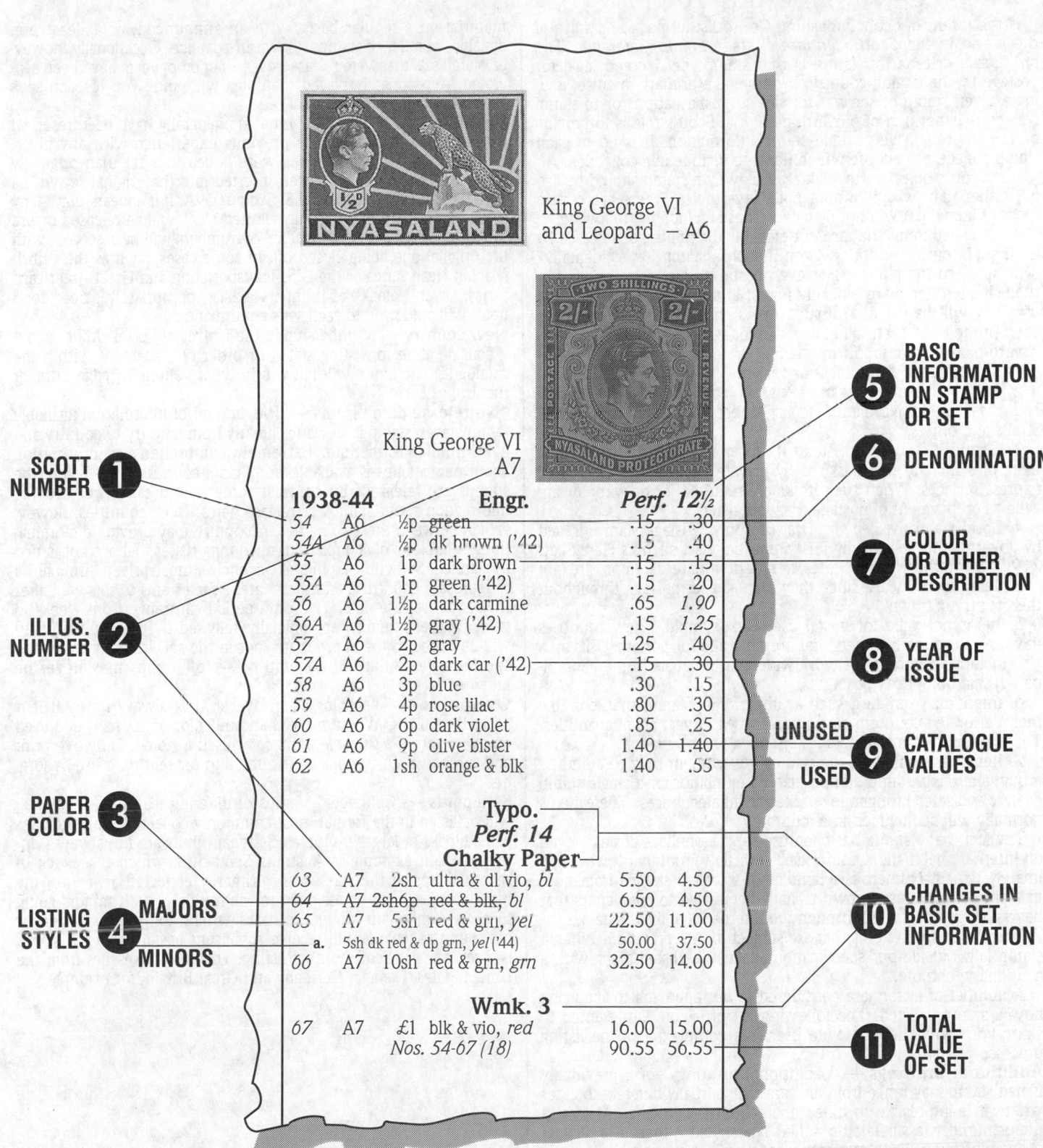

King George VI
and Leopard — A6

King George VI
A7

SCOTT NUMBER ❶

ILLUS. NUMBER ❷

PAPER COLOR ❸

LISTING STYLES ❹ MAJORS / MINORS

BASIC INFORMATION ON STAMP OR SET ❺

DENOMINATION ❻

COLOR OR OTHER DESCRIPTION ❼

YEAR OF ISSUE ❽

UNUSED / USED **CATALOGUE VALUES** ❾

CHANGES IN BASIC SET INFORMATION ❿

TOTAL VALUE OF SET ⓫

				Unused	Used
1938-44			**Engr.**	**Perf. 12½**	
54	A6	½p	green	.15	.30
54A	A6	½p	dk brown ('42)	.15	.40
55	A6	1p	dark brown	.15	.15
55A	A6	1p	green ('42)	.15	.20
56	A6	1½p	dark carmine	.65	1.90
56A	A6	1½p	gray ('42)	.15	1.25
57	A6	2p	gray	1.25	.40
57A	A6	2p	dark car ('42)	.15	.30
58	A6	3p	blue	.30	.15
59	A6	4p	rose lilac	.80	.30
60	A6	6p	dark violet	.85	.25
61	A6	9p	olive bister	1.40	1.40
62	A6	1sh	orange & blk	1.40	.55

Typo.
Perf. 14
Chalky Paper

63	A7	2sh	ultra & dl vio, *bl*	5.50	4.50
64	A7	2sh6p	red & blk, *bl*	6.50	4.50
65	A7	5sh	red & grn, *yel*	22.50	11.00
a.			5sh dk red & dp grn, *yel* ('44)	50.00	37.50
66	A7	10sh	red & grn, *grn*	32.50	14.00

Wmk. 3

67	A7	£1	blk & vio, *red*	16.00	15.00
			Nos. 54-67 (18)	90.55	56.55

Catalogue Listing Policy

It is the intent of Scott Publishing Co. to list all postage stamps of the world in the *Scott Standard Postage Stamp Catalogue*. The only strict criteria for listing is that stamps be decreed legal for postage by the issuing country. Whether the primary intent of issuing a given stamp or set was for sale to postal patrons or to stamp collectors is not part of our listing criteria. Scott's role is to provide basic comprehensive postage stamp information. It is up to each stamp collector to choose which items to include in a collection.

It is Scott's objective to seek reasons why a stamp should be listed, rather than why it should not. Nevertheless, there are certain types of items that will not be listed. These include the following:

1. Unissued items that are not officially distributed or released by the issuing postal authority. Even if such a stamp is "accidentally" distributed to the philatelic or even postal market, it remains unissued. If such items are officially issued at a later date by the country, they will be listed. Unissued items consist of those that have been printed and then held from sale for reasons such as change in government, errors found on stamps or something deemed objectionable about a stamp subject or design.

2. Stamps "issued" by non-existent postal entities or fantasy countries, such as Nagaland, Occusi-Ambeno, Staffa, Sedang, Torres Straits and others.

3. Semi-official or unofficial items not required for postage. Examples include items issued by private agencies for their own express services. When such items are required for delivery, or are valid as prepayment of postage, they are listed.

4. Local stamps issued for local use only. Postage stamps issued by governments specifically for "domestic" use, such as Haiti Scott 219-228, or the United States non-denominated stamps, are not considered to be locals, since they are valid for postage throughout the country of origin.

5. Items not valid for postal use. For example, a few countries have issued souvenir sheets that are not valid for postage. This area also includes a number of worldwide charity labels (some denominated) that do not pay postage.

6. Intentional varieties, such as imperforate stamps that look like their perforated counterparts and are issued in very small quantities. These are often controlled issues intended for speculation.

7. Items distributed by the issuing government only to a limited group, such as a stamp club, philatelic exhibition or a single stamp dealer, and later brought to market at inflated prices. These items normally will be included in a footnote.

The fact that a stamp has been used successfully as postage, even on international mail, is not in itself sufficient proof that it was legitimately issued. Numerous examples of so-called stamps from non-existent countries are known to have been used to post letters that have successfully passed through the international mail system.

There are certain items that are subject to interpretation. When a stamp falls outside our specifications, it may be listed along with a cautionary footnote.

A number of factors are considered in our approach to analyzing how a stamp is listed. The following list of factors is presented to share with you, the catalogue user, the complexity of the listing process.

Additional printings — "Additional printings" of a previously issued stamp may range from an item that is totally different to cases where it is impossible to differentiate from the original. At least a minor number (a small-letter suffix) is assigned if there is a distinct change in stamp shade, noticeably redrawn design, or a significantly different perforation measurement. A major number (numeral or numeral and capital-letter combination) is assigned if the editors feel the "additional printing" is sufficiently different from the original that it constitutes a different issue.

Commemoratives — Where practical, commemoratives with the same theme are placed in a set. For example, the U.S. Civil War Centenniel set of 1961-65 and the Constitution Bicentennial series of 1989-90 appear as sets. Countries such as Japan and Korea issue such material on a regular basis, with an announced, or at least predictable, number of stamps known in advance. Occasionally, however, stamp sets that were released over a period of years have been separated. Appropriately placed footnotes will guide you to each set's continuation.

Definitive sets — Blocks of numbers generally have been reserved for definitive sets, based on previous experience with any given country. If a few more stamps were issued in a set than originally expected, they often have been inserted into the original set with a capital-letter suffix, such as U.S. Scott 1059A. If it appears that many more stamps than the originally allotted block will be released before the set is completed, a new block of numbers will be reserved, with the original one being closed off. In some cases, such as the British Machin Head series or the U.S. Transportation and Great Americans series, several blocks of numbers exist. Appropriately placed footnotes will guide you to each set's continuation.

New country — Membership in the Universal Postal Union is not a consideration for listing status or order of placement within the catalogue. The index will tell you in what volume or page number the listings begin.

"No release date" items — The amount of information available for any given stamp issue varies greatly from country to country and even from time to time. Extremely comprehensive information about new stamps is available from some countries well before the stamps are released. By contrast some countries do not provide information about stamps or release dates. Most countries, however, fall between these extremes. A country may provide denominations or subjects of stamps from upcoming issues that are not issued as planned. Sometimes, philatelic agencies, those private firms hired to represent countries, add these later-issued items to sets well after the formal release date. This time period can range from weeks to years. If these items were officially released by the country, they will be added to the appropriate spot in the set. In many cases, the specific release date of a stamp or set of stamps may never be known.

Overprints — The color of an overprint is always noted if it is other than black. Where more than one color of ink has been used on overprints of a single set, the color used is noted. Early overprint and surcharge illustrations were altered to prevent their use by forgers.

Se-tenants — Connected stamps of differing features (se-tenants) will be listed in the format most commonly collected. This includes pairs, blocks or larger multiples. Se-tenant units are not always symmetrical. An example is Australia Scott 508, which is a block of seven stamps. If the stamps are primarily collected as a unit, the major number may be assigned to the multiple, with minors going to each component stamp. In cases where continuous-design or other unit se-tenants will receive significant postal use, each stamp is given a major Scott number listing. This includes issues from the United States, Canada, Germany and Great Britain, for example.

Special Notices

Classification of stamps

The *Scott Standard Postage Stamp Catalogue* lists stamps by country of issue. The next level of organization is a listing by section on the basis of the function of the stamps. The principal sections cover regular postage, semi-postal, air post, special delivery, registration, postage due and other categories. Except for regular postage, catalogue numbers for all sections include a prefix letter (or number-letter combination) denoting the class to which a given stamp belongs.

The following is a listing of the most commonly used catalogue prefixes.

Prefix....Category
C ....Air Post
M...........Military
P.............Newspaper
N ....Occupation - Regular Issues
O ....Official
Q...........Parcel Post
J..............Postage Due
RA ....Postal Tax
B.............Semi-Postal
E.............Special Delivery
MR ....War Tax

Other prefixes used by more than one country include the following:
H ....Acknowledgment of Receipt
CO.........Air Post Official
CQ.........Air Post Parcel Post
RAC.......Air Post Postal Tax
CF..........Air Post Registration
CB ....Air Post Semi-Postal
CBO.......Air Post Semi-Postal Official
CE ....Air Post Special Delivery
EY..........Authorized Delivery
S ....Franchise
G............Insured Letter
GY ....Marine Insurance
MC ....Military Air Post
MQ........Military Parcel Post
NC.........Occupation - Air Post
NO.........Occupation - Official
NJ ....Occupation - Postage Due
NRA.......Occupation - Postal Tax
NB ....Occupation - Semi-Postal
NE ....Occupation - Special Delivery
QY ....Parcel Post Authorized Delivery
AR ....Postal-fiscal
RAJ ....Postal Tax Due
RAB ....Postal Tax Semi-Postal
F.............Registration
EB..........Semi-Postal Special Delivery
EO ....Special Delivery Official
QE ....Special Handling

New issue listings

Updates to this catalogue appear each month in the *Scott Stamp Monthly* magazine. Included in this update are additions to the listings of countries found in the *Scott Standard Postage Stamp Catalogue* and the *Specialized Catalogue of United States Stamps*, as well as corrections and updates to current editions of this catalogue.

From time to time there will be changes in the final listings of stamps from the *Scott Stamp Monthly* to the next edition of the catalogue. This occurs as more information about certain stamps or sets becomes available.

The catalogue update section of the *Scott Stamp Monthly* is the most timely presentation of this material available. Annual subscriptions to the *Scott Stamp Monthly* are available from Scott Publishing Co., Box 828, Sidney, OH 45365-0828.

Number changes

A listing of catalogue number changes from the previous edition of the catalogue appears at the back of each volume.

Understanding valuing notations

The *minimum catalogue value* of an individual stamp or set is 15 cents. This represents a portion of the costs incurred to a dealer when he prepares an individual stamp for resale. As a point of philatelic-economic fact, the lower the value shown for an item in this catalogue, the greater the percentage of that value is attributed to dealer mark up and profit margin. In many cases, such as the 15-cent minimum value, that price does not cover the labor or other costs involved with stocking it as an individual stamp. The sum of minimum values in a set does not properly represent the value of a complete set primarily composed of a number of minimum-value stamps, nor does the sum represent the actual value of a packet made up of minimum-value stamps. Thus a packet of 1,000 different common stamps — each of which has a catalogue value of 15 cents — normally sells for considerably less than 150 dollars!

The *absence of a retail value* for a stamp does not necessarily suggest that a stamp is scarce or rare. In the U.S. listings, a dash in the value column means that the stamp is known in a stated form or variety, but information is either lacking or insufficient for purposes of establishing a usable catalogue value.

Stamp values in *italics* generally refer to items that are difficult to value accurately. For expensive items, such as those priced at $1,000 or higher, a value in italics indicates that the affected item trades very seldom. For inexpensive items, a value in italics represents a warning. One example is a "blocked" issue where the issuing postal administration may have controlled one stamp in a set in an attempt to make the whole set more valuable. Another example is an item that sold at an extreme multiple of face value in the marketplace at the time of its issue.

One type of warning to collectors that appears in the catalogue is illustrated by a stamp that is valued considerably higher in used condition than it is as unused. In this case, collectors are cautioned to be certain the used version has a genuine and contemporaneous cancellation. The type of cancellation on a stamp can be an important factor in determining its sale price. Catalogue values do not apply to fiscal or telegraph cancels, unless otherwise noted.

Some countries have released back issues of stamps in canceled-to-order form, sometimes covering as much as a 10-year period. The Scott Catalogue values for used stamps reflect canceled-to-order material when such stamps are found to predominate in the marketplace for the issue involved. Notes frequently appear in the stamp listings to specify which items are valued as canceled-to-order, or if there is a premium for postally used examples.

Many countries sell canceled-to-order stamps at a marked reduction of face value. Countries that sell or have sold canceled-to-order stamps at *full* face value include Australia, Netherlands, France and Switzerland. It may be almost impossible to identify such stamps if the gum has been removed, because official government canceling devices are used. Postally used copies of these items on cover, however, are usually worth more than the canceled-to-order stamps with original gum.

Abbreviations

Scott Publishing Co. uses a consistent set of abbreviations throughout this catalogue to conserve space, while still providing necessary information.

COLOR ABBREVIATIONS

amb .....amber	crim.....crimson	ol.........olive
anil ......aniline	cr.........cream	olvn .....olivine
ap ....apple	dk........dark	org.......orange
aqua.....aquamarine	dl.........dull	pck ......peacock
az ....azure	dp........deep	pnksh...pinkish
bis.......bister	db........drab	Prus .....Prussian
bl........blue	emer....emerald	pur.......purple
bld ......blood	gldn .....golden	redsh ...reddish
blk ......black	grysh....grayish	res ....reseda
bril......brilliant	grn.......green	ros ....rosine
brn......brown	grnsh ...greenish	ryl........royal
brnsh ...brownish	hel ....heliotrope	sal........salmon
brnz.....bronze	hn........henna	saph.....sapphire
brt ......bright	ind.......indigo	scar......scarlet
brnt .....burnt	int........intense	sep.......sepia
car ......carmine	lav ......lavender	sien......sienna
cer ......cerise	lem ......lemon	sil ....silver
chlky....chalky	lil........lilac	sl ....slate
cham ...chamois	lt..........light	stl ....steel
chnt.....chestnut	mag .....magenta	turq .....turquoise
choc.....chocolate	man .....manila	ultra.....ultramarine
chr.......chrome	mar......maroon	Ven......Venetian
cit........citron	mv.......mauve	ver.......vermilion
cl.........claret	multi....multicolored	vio ....violet
cob ......cobalt	mlky ....milky	yel ....yellow
cop ......copper	myr......myrtle	yelsh ....yellowish

When no color is given for an overprint or surcharge, black is the color used. Abbreviations for colors used for overprints and surcharges include: "(B)" or "(Blk)," black; "(Bl)," blue; "(R)," red; and "(G)," green.

Additional abbreviations in this catalogue are shown below:

Adm. ....Administration
AFL ....American Federation of Labor
Anniv. ....Anniversary
APS ....American Philatelic Society
Assoc. ....Association
ASSR. ....Autonomous Soviet Socialist Republic
b.....................Born
BEP ....Bureau of Engraving and Printing
Bicent. ....Bicentennial
Bklt...............Booklet
Brit. ....British
btwn...............Between
Bur. ....Bureau
c. or ca............Circa
Cat. ....Catalogue
Cent. ....Centennial, century, centenary
CIO ....Congress of Industrial Organizations
Conf. ....Conference
Cong...............Congress
Cpl. ....Corporal
CTO ....Canceled to order
d.....................Died
Dbl. ....Double
EKU...............Earliest known use
Engr...............Engraved
Exhib..............Exhibition
Expo...............Exposition
Fed. ....Federation
GB..................Great Britain
Gen. ....General
GPO ....General post office
Horiz. ....Horizontal
Imperf..............Imperforate
Impt. ....Imprint

Intl. ....International
Invtd...............Inverted
L......................Left
Lieut., lt. ....Lieutenant
Litho...............Lithographed
LL..................Lower left
LR ....Lower right
mm.................Millimeter
Ms..................Manuscript
Natl. ....National
No. ....Number
NY..................New York
NYC................New York City
Ovpt. ....Overprint
Ovptd. ....Overprinted
P......................Plate number
Perf..................Perforated, perforation
Phil..................Philatelic
Photo...............Photogravure
PO ....Post office
Pr. ....Pair
P.R. ....Puerto Rico
Prec. ....Precancel, precanceled
Pres. ....President
PTT ....Post, Telephone and Telegraph
Rio...................Rio de Janeiro
Sgt. ....Sergeant
Soc. ....Society
Souv. ....Souvenir
SSR.................Soviet Socialist Republic, see ASSR
St.....................Saint, street
Surch...............Surcharge
Typo. ....Typographed
UL ....Upper left
Unwmkd. ....Unwatermarked
UPU ....Universal Postal Union
UR..................Upper Right
US ....United States
USPOD ....United States Post Office Department
USSR...............Union of Soviet Socialist Republics
Vert. ....Vertical
VP ....Vice president
Wmk. ....Watermark
Wmkd. ....Watermarked
WWI ....World War I
WWII ....World War II

Examination

Scott Publishing Co. will not comment upon the genuineness, grade or condition of stamps, because of the time and responsibility involved. Rather, there are several expertizing groups that undertake this work for both collectors and dealers. Neither will Scott Publishing Co. appraise or identify philatelic material. The company cannot take responsibility for unsolicited stamps or covers sent by individuals.

How to order from your dealer

When ordering stamps from a dealer, it is not necessary to write the full description of a stamp as listed in this catalogue. All you need is the name of the country, the Scott catalogue number and whether the desired item is unused or used. For example, "Japan Scott 422 unused" is sufficient to identify the unused stamp of Japan listed as "422 A206 5y brown."

Basic Stamp Information

A stamp collector's knowledge of the combined elements that make a given stamp issue unique determines his or her ability to identify stamps. These elements include paper, watermark, method of separation, printing, design and gum. On the following pages each of these important areas is briefly described.

Paper

Paper is an organic material composed of a compacted weave of cellulose fibers and generally formed into sheets. Paper used to print stamps may be manufactured in sheets, or it may have been part of a large roll (called a web) before being cut to size. The fibers most often used to create paper on which stamps are printed include bark, wood, straw and certain grasses. In many cases, linen or cotton rags have been added for greater strength and durability. Grinding, bleaching, cooking and rinsing these raw fibers reduces them to a slushy pulp, referred to by paper makers as "stuff." Sizing and, sometimes, coloring matter is added to the pulp to make different types of finished paper.

After the stuff is prepared, it is poured onto sieve-like frames that allow the water to run off, while retaining the matted pulp. As fibers fall onto the screen and are held by gravity, they form a natural weave that will later hold the paper together. If the screen has metal bits that are formed into letters or images attached, it leaves slightly thinned areas on the paper. These are called watermarks.

When the stuff is almost dry, it is passed under pressure through smooth or engraved rollers - dandy rolls - or placed between cloth in a press to be flattened and dried.

Stamp paper falls broadly into two types: wove and laid. The nature of the surface of the frame onto which the pulp is first deposited causes the differences in appearance between the two. If the surface is smooth and even, the paper will be of fairly uniform texture throughout. This is known as *wove paper*. Early papermaking machines poured the pulp onto a continuously circulating web of felt, but modern machines feed the pulp onto a cloth-like screen made of closely interwoven fine wires. This paper, when held to a light, will show little dots or points very close together. The proper name for this is "wire wove," but the type is still considered wove. Any U.S. or British stamp printed after 1880 will serve as an example of wire wove paper.

Closely spaced parallel wires, with cross wires at wider intervals, make up the frames used for what is known as *laid paper*. A greater thickness of the pulp will settle between the wires. The paper, when held to a light, will show alternate light and dark lines. The spacing and the thickness of the lines may vary, but on any one sheet of paper they are all alike. See Russia Scott 31-38 for examples of laid paper.

Batonne, from the French word meaning "a staff," is a term used if the lines in the paper are spaced quite far apart, like the printed ruling on a writing tablet. Batonne paper may be either wove or laid. If laid, fine laid lines can be seen between the batons. The laid lines, which are a form of watermark, may be geometrical figures such as squares, diamonds, rectangles or wavy lines.

Quadrille is the term used when the lines in the paper form little squares. *Oblong quadrille* is the term used when rectangles, rather than squares, are formed. See Mexico-Guadalajara Scott 35-37 for examples of oblong quadrille paper.

Paper also is classified as thick or thin, hard or soft, and by color if dye is added during manufacture. Such colors may include yellowish, greenish, bluish and reddish.

Brief explanations of other types of paper used for printing stamps, as well as examples, follow.

Pelure — Pelure paper is a very thin, hard and often brittle paper that is sometimes bluish or grayish in appearance. See Serbia Scott 169-170.

Native — This is a term applied to handmade papers used to produce some of the early stamps of the Indian states. Stamps printed on native paper may be expected to display various natural inclusions that are normal and do not negatively affect value. Japanese paper, originally made of mulberry fibers and rice flour, is part of this group. See Japan Scott 1-18.

Manila — This type of paper is often used to make stamped envelopes and wrappers. It is a coarse-textured stock, usually smooth on one side and rough on the other. A variety of colors of manila paper exist, but the most common range is yellowish-brown.

Silk — Introduced by the British in 1847 as a safeguard against counterfeiting, silk paper contains bits of colored silk thread scattered throughout. The density of these fibers varies greatly and can include as few as one fiber per stamp or hundreds. U.S. revenue Scott R152 is a good example of an easy-to-identify silk paper stamp.

Silk-thread paper has uninterrupted threads of colored silk arranged so that one or more threads run through the stamp or postal stationery. See Great Britain Scott 5-6 and Switzerland Scott 14-19.

Granite — Filled with minute cloth or colored paper fibers of various colors and lengths, granite paper should not be confused with either type of silk paper. Austria Scott 172-175 and a number of Swiss stamps are examples of granite paper.

Chalky — A chalk-like substance coats the surface of chalky paper to discourage the cleaning and reuse of canceled stamps, as well as to provide a smoother, more acceptable printing surface. Because the designs of stamps printed on chalky paper are imprinted on what is often a water-soluble coating, any attempt to remove a cancellation will destroy the stamp. *Do not soak these stamps in any fluid.* To remove a stamp printed on chalky paper from an envelope, wet the paper from underneath the stamp until the gum dissolves enough to release the stamp from the paper. See St. Kitts-Nevis Scott 89-90 for examples of stamps printed on this type of chalky paper.

India — Another name for this paper, originally introduced from China about 1750, is "China Paper." It is a thin, opaque paper often used for plate and die proofs by many countries.

Double — In philately, the term double paper has two distinct meanings. The first is a two-ply paper, usually a combination of a thick and a thin sheet, joined during manufacture. This type was used experimentally as a means to discourage the reuse of stamps.

The design is printed on the thin paper. Any attempt to remove a cancellation would destroy the design. U.S. Scott 158 and other Banknote-era stamps exist on this form of double paper.

The second type of double paper occurs on a rotary press, when the end of one paper roll, or web, is affixed to the next roll to save time feeding the paper through the press. Stamp designs are printed over the joined paper and, if overlooked by inspectors, may get into post office stocks.

Goldbeater's Skin — This type of paper was used for the 1866 issue of Prussia, and was a tough, translucent paper. The design was printed in reverse on the back of the stamp, and the gum applied over the printing. It is impossible to remove stamps printed on this type of paper from the paper to which they are affixed without destroying the design.

Ribbed — Ribbed paper has an uneven, corrugated surface made by passing the paper through ridged rollers. This type exists on some copies of U.S. Scott 156-165.

Various other substances, or substrates, have been used for stamp manufacture, including wood, aluminum, copper, silver and gold foil, plastic, and silk and cotton fabrics.

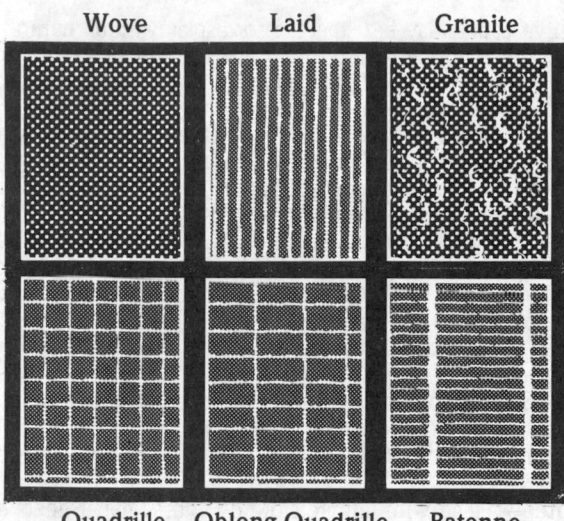

Wove   Laid   Granite

Quadrille   Oblong Quadrille   Batonne

Watermarks

Watermarks are an integral part of some papers. They are formed in the process of paper manufacture. Watermarks consist of small designs, formed of wire or cut from metal and soldered to the surface of the mold or, sometimes, on the dandy roll. The designs may be in the form of crowns, stars, anchors, letters or other characters or symbols. These pieces of metal - known in the paper-making industry as "bits" - impress a design into the paper. The design sometimes may be seen by holding the stamp to the light. Some are more easily seen with a watermark detector. This important tool is a small black tray into which a stamp is placed face down and dampened with a fast-evaporating watermark detection fluid that brings up the watermark image in the form of dark lines against a lighter background. These dark lines are the thinner areas of the paper known as the watermark. Some watermarks are extremely difficult to locate, due to either a faint impression, watermark location or the color of the stamp. There also are electric watermark detectors that come with plastic filter disks of various colors. The disks neutralize the color of the stamp, permitting the watermark to be seen more easily.

 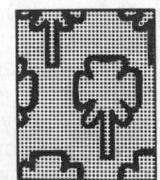

Multiple watermarks of Crown Agents and Burma

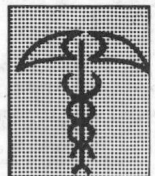  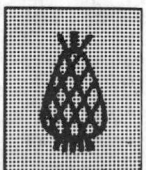

Watermarks of Uruguay, Vatican City and Jamaica

WARNING: Some inks used in the photogravure process dissolve in watermark fluids (Please see the section on Soluble Printing Inks). Also, see "chalky paper."

Watermarks may be found normal, reversed, inverted, reversed and inverted, sideways or diagonal, as seen from the back of the stamp. The relationship of watermark to stamp design depends on the position of the printing plates or how paper is fed through the press. On machine-made paper, watermarks normally are read from right to left. The design is repeated closely throughout the sheet in a "multiple-watermark design." In a "sheet watermark," the design appears only once on the sheet, but extends over many stamps. Individual stamps may carry only a small fraction or none of the watermark.

"Marginal watermarks" occur in the margins of sheets or panes of stamps. They occur on the outside border of paper (ostensibly outside the area where stamps are to be printed). A large row of letters may spell the name of the country or the manufacturer of the paper, or a border of lines may appear. Careless press feeding may cause parts of these letters and/or lines to show on stamps of the outer row of a pane.

Soluble Printing Inks

WARNING: Most stamp colors are permanent; that is, they are not seriously affected by short-term exposure to light or water. Many colors, especially of modern inks, fade from excessive exposure to light. There are stamps printed with inks that dissolve easily in water or in fluids used to detect watermarks. Use of these inks was intentional to prevent the removal of cancellations. Water affects all aniline inks, those on so-called safety paper and some photogravure printings - all such inks are known as *fugitive colors. Removal from paper of such stamps requires care and alternatives to traditional soaking.*

Separation

"Separation" is the general term used to describe methods used to separate stamps. The three standard forms currently in use are perforating, rouletting and die-cutting. These methods are done during the stamp production process, after printing. Sometimes these methods are done on-press or sometimes as a separate step. The earliest issues, such as the 1840 Penny Black of Great Britain (Scott 1), did not have any means provided for separation. It was expected the stamps would be cut apart with scissors or folded and torn. These are examples of imperforate stamps. Many stamps were first issued in imperforate formats and were later issued with perforations. Therefore, care must be observed in buying single imperforate stamps to be certain they were issued imperforate and are not perforated copies that have been altered by having the perforations trimmed away. Stamps issued imperforate usually are valued as singles. However, imperforate varieties of normally perforated stamps should be collected in pairs or larger pieces as indisputable evidence of their imperforate character.

PERFORATION

The chief style of separation of stamps, and the one that is in almost universal use today, is perforating. By this process, paper between the stamps is cut away in a line of holes, usually round, leaving little bridges of paper between the stamps to hold them together. Some types of perforation, such as hyphen-hole perfs, can be confused with roulettes, but a close visual inspection reveals that paper has been removed. The little perforation bridges, which project from the stamp when it is torn from the pane, are called the teeth of the perforation.

As the size of the perforation is sometimes the only way to differentiate between two otherwise identical stamps, it is necessary to be able to accurately measure and describe them. This is done with a perforation gauge, usually a ruler-like device that has dots or graduated lines to show how many perforations may be counted in the space of two centimeters. Two centimeters is the space universally adopted in which to measure perforations.

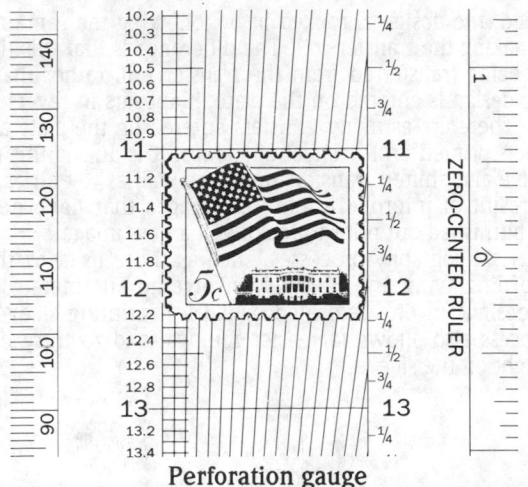

Perforation gauge

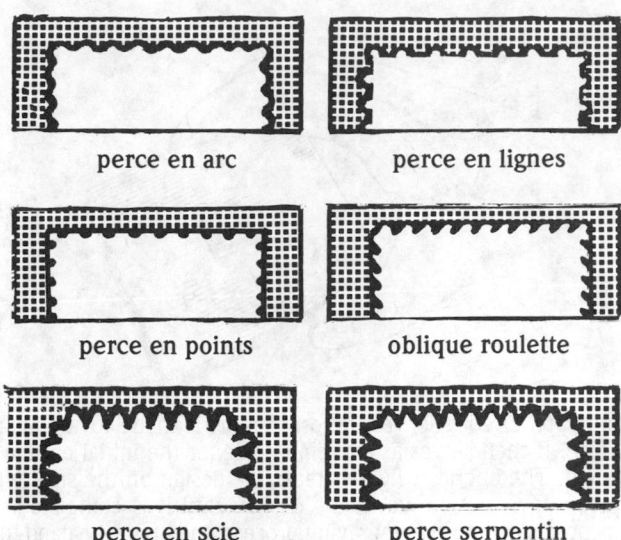

perce en arc   perce en lignes

perce en points   oblique roulette

perce en scie   perce serpentin

To measure a stamp, run it along the gauge until the dots on it fit exactly into the perforations of the stamp. If you are using a graduated-line perforation gauge, simply slide the stamp along the surface until the lines on the gauge perfectly project from the center of the bridges or holes. The number to the side of the line of dots or lines that fit the stamp's perforation is the measurement. For example, an "11" means that 11 perforations fit between two centimeters. The description of the stamp therefore is "perf. 11." If the gauge of the perforations on the top and bottom of a stamp differs from that on the sides, the result is what is known as *compound perforations.* In measuring compound perforations, the gauge at top and bottom is always given first, then the sides. Thus, a stamp that measures 11 at top and bottom and 10 1/2 at the sides is "perf. 11 x 10 1/2." See U.S. Scott 632-642 for examples of compound perforations.

Stamps also are known with perforations different on three or all four sides. Descriptions of such items are clockwise, beginning with the top of the stamp.

A perforation with small holes and teeth close together is a "fine perforation." One with large holes and teeth far apart is a "coarse perforation." Holes that are jagged, rather than clean-cut, are "rough perforations." *Blind perforations* are the slight impressions left by the perforating pins if they fail to puncture the paper. Multiples of stamps showing blind perforations may command a slight premium over normally perforated stamps.

The term *syncopated perfs* describes intentional irregularities in the perforations. The earliest form was used by the Netherlands from 1925-33, where holes were omitted to create distinctive patterns. Beginning in 1992, Great Britain has used an oval perforation to help prevent counterfeiting. Several other countries have started using the oval perfs.

A new type of perforation, still primarily used for postal stationery, is known as microperfs. Microperfs are tiny perforations (in some cases hundreds of holes per two centimeters) that allows items to be intentionally separated very easily, while not accidentally breaking apart as easily as standard perforations. These are not currently measured or differentiated by size, as are standard perforations.

ROULETTING

In rouletting, the stamp paper is cut partly or wholly through, with no paper removed. In perforating, some paper is removed. Rouletting derives its name from the French roulette, a spur-like wheel. As the wheel is rolled over the paper, each point makes a small cut. The number of cuts made in a two-centimeter space determines the gauge of the roulette, just as the number of perforations in two centimeters determines the gauge of the perforation.

The shape and arrangement of the teeth on the wheels varies. Various roulette types generally carry French names:

Perce en lignes - rouletted in lines. The paper receives short, straight cuts in lines. This is the most common type of rouletting. See Mexico Scott 500.

Perce en points - pin-rouletted. This differs from a small perforation because no paper is removed, although round, equidistant holes are pricked through the paper. See Mexico Scott 242-256.

Perce en arc and *perce en scie* - pierced in an arc or saw-toothed designs, forming half circles or small triangles. See Hanover (German States) Scott 25-29.

Perce en serpentin - serpentine roulettes. The cuts form a serpentine or wavy line. See Brunswick (German States) Scott 13-18.

Once again, no paper is removed by these processes, leaving the stamps easily separated, but closely attached.

DIE-CUTTING

The third major form of stamp separation is die-cutting. This is a method where a die in the pattern of separation is created that later cuts the stamp paper in a stroke motion. Although some standard stamps bear die-cut perforations, this process is primarily used for self-adhesive postage stamps. Die-cutting can appear in straight lines, such as U.S. Scott 2522, shapes, such as U.S. Scott 1551, or imitating the appearance of perforations, such as New Zealand Scott 935A and 935B.

Printing Processes

ENGRAVING (Intaglio, Line-engraving, Etching)

Master die - The initial operation in the process of line engraving is making the master die. The die is a small, flat block of softened steel upon which the stamp design is recess engraved in reverse.

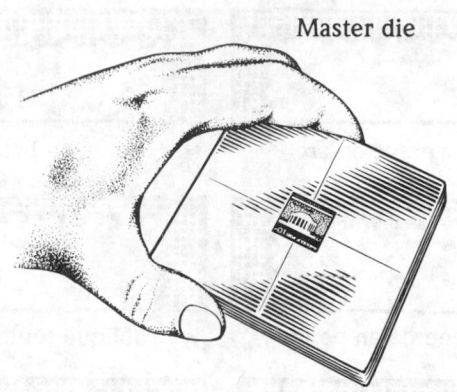

Master die

Photographic reduction of the original art is made to the appropriate size. It then serves as a tracing guide for the initial outline of the design. The engraver lightly traces the design on the steel with his graver, then slowly works the design until it is completed. At various points during the engraving process, the engraver hand-inks the die and makes an impression to check his progress. These are known as progressive die proofs. After completion of the engraving, the die is hardened to withstand the stress and pressures of later transfer operations.

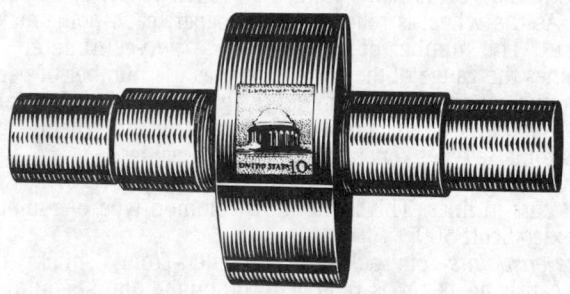

Transfer roll

Transfer roll — Next is production of the transfer roll that, as the name implies, is the medium used to transfer the subject from the master die to the printing plate. A blank roll of soft steel, mounted on a mandrel, is placed under the bearers of the transfer press to allow it to roll freely on its axis. The hardened die is placed on the bed of the press and the face of the transfer roll is applied to the die, under pressure. The bed or the roll is then rocked back and forth under increasing pressure, until the soft steel of the roll is forced into every engraved line of the die. The resulting impression on the roll is known as a "relief" or a "relief transfer." The engraved image is now positive in appearance and stands out from the steel. After the required number of reliefs are "rocked in," the soft steel transfer roll is hardened.

Different flaws may occur during the relief process. A defective relief may occur during the rocking in process because of a minute piece of foreign material lodging on the die, or some other cause. Imperfections in the steel of the transfer roll may result in a breaking away of parts of the design. This is known as a relief break, which will show up on finished stamps as small, unprinted areas. If a damaged relief remains in use, it will transfer a repeating defect to the plate. Deliberate alterations of reliefs sometimes occur. "Altered reliefs" designate these changed conditions.

Plate — The final step in pre-printing production is the making of the printing plate. A flat piece of soft steel replaces the die on the bed of the transfer press. One of the reliefs on the transfer roll is positioned over this soft steel. Position, or layout, dots determine the correct position on the plate. The dots have been lightly marked on the plate in advance. After the correct position of the relief is

determined, the design is rocked in by following the same method used in making the transfer roll. The difference is that this time the image is being transferred from the transfer roll, rather than to it. Once the design is entered on the plate, it appears in reverse and is recessed. There are as many transfers entered on the plate as there are subjects printed on the sheet of stamps. It is during this process that double and shifted transfers occur, as well as re-entries. These are the result of improperly entered images that have not been properly burnished out prior to rocking in a new image.

Modern siderography processes, such as those used by the U.S. Bureau of Engraving and Printing, involve an automated form of rocking designs in on preformed cylindrical printing sleeves. The same process also allows for easier removal and re-entry of worn images right on the sleeve.

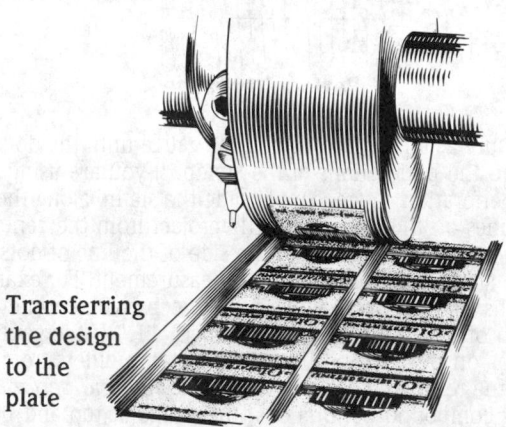

Transferring the design to the plate

Following the entering of the required transfers on the plate, the position dots, layout dots and lines, scratches and other markings generally are burnished out. Added at this time by the siderographer are any required *guide lines, plate numbers* or other *marginal markings.* The plate is then hand-inked and a proof impression is taken. This is known as a plate proof. If the impression is approved, the plate is machined for fitting onto the press, is hardened and sent to the plate vault ready for use.

On press, the plate is inked and the surface is automatically wiped clean, leaving ink only in the recessed lines. Paper is then forced under pressure into the engraved recessed lines, thereby receiving the ink. Thus, the ink lines on engraved stamps are slightly raised, and slight depressions (debossing) occur on the back of the stamp. Prior to the advent of modern high-speed presses and more advanced ink formulations, paper had to be dampened before receiving the ink. This sometimes led to uneven shrinkage by the time the stamps were perforated, resulting in improperly perforated stamps, or misperfs. Newer presses use drier paper, thus both *wet* and *dry printings* exist on some stamps.

Rotary Press — Until 1914, only flat plates were used to print engraved stamps. Rotary press printing was introduced in 1914, and slowly spread. Some countries still use flat-plate printing.

After approval of the plate proof, older *rotary press plates* require additional machining. They are curved to fit the press cylinder. "Gripper slots" are cut into the back of each plate to receive the "grippers," which hold the plate securely on the press. The plate is then hardened. Stamps printed from these bent rotary press plates are longer or wider than the same stamps printed from flat-plate presses. The stretching of the plate during the curving process is what causes this distortion.

Re-entry — To execute a re-entry on a flat plate, the transfer roll is re-applied to the plate, often at some time after its first use on the press. Worn-out designs can be resharpened by carefully burnishing out the original image and re-entering it from the transfer roll. If the

original impression has not been sufficiently removed and the transfer roll is not precisely in line with the remaining impression, the resulting double transfer will make the re-entry obvious. If the registration is true, a re-entry may be difficult or impossible to distinguish. Sometimes a stamp printed from a successful re-entry is identified by having a much sharper and clearer impression than its neighbors. With the advent of rotary presses, post-press re-entries were not possible. After a plate was curved for the rotary press, it was impossible to make a re-entry. This is because the plate had already been bent once (with the design distorted).

However, with the introduction of the previously mentioned modern-style siderography machines, entries are made to the preformed cylindrical printing sleeve. Such sleeves are dechromed and softened. This allows individual images to be burnished out and re-entered on the curved sleeve. The sleeve is then rechromed, resulting in longer press life.

Double Transfer — This is a description of the condition of a transfer on a plate that shows evidence of a duplication of all, or a portion of the design. It usually is the result of the changing of the registration between the transfer roll and the plate during the rocking in of the original entry. Double transfers also occur when only a portion of the design has been rocked in and improper positioning is noted. If the worker elected not to burnish out the partial or completed design, a strong double transfer will occur for part or all of the design.

It sometimes is necessary to remove the original transfer from a plate and repeat the process a second time. If the finished reworked image shows traces of the original impression, attributable to incomplete burnishing, the result is a partial double transfer.

With the modern automatic machines mentioned previously, double transfers are all but impossible to create. Those partially doubled images on stamps printed from such sleeves are more than likely re-entries, rather than true double transfers.

Re-engraved — Alterations to a stamp design are sometimes necessary after some stamps have been printed. In some cases, either the original die or the actual printing plate may have its "temper" drawn (softened), and the design will be re-cut. The resulting impressions from such a re-engraved die or plate may differ slightly from the original issue, and are known as "re-engraved." If the alteration was made to the master die, all future printings will be consistently different from the original. If alterations were made to the printing plate, each altered stamp on the plate will be slightly different from each other, allowing specialists to reconstruct a complete printing plate.

Dropped Transfers — If an impression from the transfer roll has not been properly placed, a dropped transfer may occur. The final stamp image will appear obviously out of line with its neighbors.

Short Transfer — Sometimes a transfer roll is not rocked its entire length when entering a transfer onto a plate. As a result, the finished transfer on the plate fails to show the complete design, and the finished stamp will have an incomplete design printed. This is known as a "short transfer." U.S. Scott No. 8 is a good example of a short transfer.

TYPOGRAPHY (Letterpress, Surface Printing, Flexography, Dry Offset, High Etch)
Although the word "Typography" is obsolete as a term describing a printing method, it was the accepted term throughout the first century of postage stamps. Therefore, appropriate Scott listings in this catalogue refer to typographed stamps. The current term for this form of printing, however, is "letterpress."

As it relates to the production of postage stamps, letterpress printing is the reverse of engraving. Rather than having recessed areas

trap the ink and deposit it on paper, only the raised areas of the design are inked. This is comparable to the type of printing seen by inking and using an ordinary rubber stamp. Letterpress includes all printing where the design is above the surface area, whether it is wood, metal or, in some instances, hardened rubber or polymer plastic.

For most letterpress-printed stamps, the engraved master is made in much the same manner as for engraved stamps. In this instance, however, an additional step is needed. The design is transferred to another surface before being transferred to the transfer roll. In this way, the transfer roll has a recessed stamp design, rather than one done in relief. This makes the printing areas on the final plate raised, or relief areas.

For less-detailed stamps of the 19th century, the area on the die not used as a printing surface was cut away, leaving the surface area raised. The original die was then reproduced by stereotyping or electrotyping. The resulting electrotypes were assembled in the required number and format of the desired sheet of stamps. The plate used in printing the stamps was an electroplate of these assembled electrotypes.

Once the final letterpress plates are created, ink is applied to the raised surface and the pressure of the press transfers the ink impression to the paper. In contrast to engraving, the fine lines of letterpress are impressed on the surface of the stamp, leaving a debossed surface. When viewed from the back (as on a typewritten page), the corresponding line work on the stamp will be raised slightly (embossed) above the surface.

PHOTOGRAVURE (Gravure, Rotogravure, Heliogravure)
In this process, the basic principles of photography are applied to a chemically sensitized metal plate, rather than photographic paper. The design is transferred photographically to the plate through a halftone, or dot-matrix screen, breaking the reproduction into tiny dots. The plate is treated chemically and the dots form depressions, called cells, of varying depths and diameters, depending on the degrees of shade in the design. Then, like engraving, ink is applied to the plate and the surface is wiped clean. This leaves ink in the tiny cells that is lifted out and deposited on the paper when it is pressed against the plate.

Gravure is most often used for multicolored stamps, generally using the three primary colors (red, yellow and blue) and black. By varying the dot matrix pattern and density of these colors, virtually any color can be reproduced. A typical full-color gravure stamp will be created from four printing cylinders (one for each color). The original multicolored image will have been photographically separated into its component colors.

For examples of the first photogravure stamps printed (1914), see Bavaria Scott 94-114.

LITHOGRAPHY (Offset Lithography, Stone Lithography, Dilitho, Planography, Collotype)
The principle that oil and water do not mix is the basis for lithography. The stamp design is drawn by hand or transferred from engraving to the surface of a lithographic stone or metal plate in a greasy (oily) substance. This oily substance holds the ink, which will later be transferred to the paper. The stone (or plate) is wet with an acid fluid, causing it to repel the printing ink in all areas not covered by the greasy substance.

Transfer paper is used to transfer the design from the original stone or plate. A series of duplicate transfers are grouped and, in turn, transferred to the final printing plate.

Photolithography — The application of photographic processes to lithography. This process allows greater flexibility of design, related to use of halftone screens combined with line work. Unlike photogravure or engraving, this process can allow large, solid areas to be printed.

Offset — A refinement of the lithographic process. A rubber-covered blanket cylinder takes the impression from the inked lithographic plate. From the "blanket" the impression is *offset* or transferred to the paper. Greater flexibility and speed are the principal reasons offset printing has largely displaced lithography. The term "lithography" covers both processes, and results are almost identical.

EMBOSSED (Relief) Printing

Embossing, not considered one of the four main printing types, is a method in which the design first is sunk into the metal of the die. Printing is done against a yielding platen, such as leather or linoleum. The platen is forced into the depression of the die, thus forming the design on the paper in relief. This process is often used for metallic inks.

Embossing may be done without color (see Sardinia Scott 4-6); with color printed around the embossed area (see Great Britain Scott 5 and most U.S. envelopes); and with color in exact registration with the embossed subject (see Canada Scott 656-657).

COMBINATION PRINTINGS

Sometimes two or even three printing methods are combined in producing stamps. In these cases, such as Austria Scott 933, the stamp's dual printing technique can be determined by studying the individual characteristics of each printing type (intaglio and offset). A few stamps, such as Singapore Scott 684-684A, combine as many as three of the four major printing types (offset, intaglio and letterpress). When this is done it often indicates the incorporation of security devices against counterfeiting.

INK COLORS

Inks or colored papers used in stamp printing often are of mineral origin, although there are numerous examples of organic-based pigments. As a general rule, organic-based pigments are far more subject to varieties and change than those of mineral-based origin.

The appearance of any given color on a stamp may be affected by many aspects, including printing variations, light, color of paper, aging and chemical alterations.

Numerous printing variations may be observed. Heavier pressure or inking will cause a more intense color, while slight interruptions in the ink feed or lighter impressions will cause a lighter appearance. Stamps printed in the same color by water-based and solvent-based inks can differ significantly in appearance. This affects several stamps in the U.S. Prominent Americans series. Hand-mixed ink formulas (primarily from the 19th century) produced under different conditions (humidity and temperature) account for notable color variations in early printings of the same stamp (see U.S. Scott 248-250, 279B, for example). Different sources of pigment can also result in significant differences in color.

Light exposure and aging are closely related in the way they affect stamp color. Both eventually break down the ink and fade colors, so that a carefully kept stamp may differ significantly in color from an identical copy that has been exposed to light. If stamps are exposed to light either intentionally or accidentally, their colors can be faded or completely changed in some cases.

Papers of different quality and consistency used for the same stamp printing may affect color appearance. Most pelure papers, for example, show a richer color when compared with wove or laid papers. See Russia Scott 181a, for an example of this effect.

The very nature of the printing processes can cause a variety of differences in shades or hues of the same stamp. Some of these shades are scarcer than others, and are of particular interest to the advanced collector.

Luminescence

All forms of tagged stamps fall under the general category of luminescence. Within this broad category is fluorescence, dealing with forms of tagging visible under longwave ultraviolet light, and phosphorescence, which deals with tagging visible only under shortwave light. Phosphorescence leaves an afterglow and fluorescence does not. These treated stamps show up in a range of different colors when exposed to UV light. The differing wavelengths of the light activates the tagging material, making it glow in various colors that usually serve different mail processing purposes.

Intentional tagging is a post-World War II phenomenon, brought about by the increased literacy rate and rapidly growing mail volume. It was one of several answers to the problem of the need for more automated mail processes. Early tagged stamps served the purpose of triggering machines to separate different types of mail. A natural outgrowth was to also use the signal to trigger machines that faced all envelopes the same way and canceled them.

Tagged stamps come many different ways and in different forms. Some tagged stamps have luminescent shapes or images imprinted on them as a form of security device. Others have blocks (United States), stripes, frames (South Africa and Canada), overall coatings (United States), bars (Great Britain and Canada) and many other types. Some types of tagging are even mixed in with the pigmented printing ink (Australia Scott 366, Netherlands Scott 478 and U.S. Scott 1359 and 2443). Each form of tagging has a different purpose, some to give different machines different types of signals, and others as adaptive forms of technological growth.

The means of applying taggant to stamps differs as much as the intended purposes for the stamps. The most common form of tagging is a coating applied to the surface of the printed stamp. Since the taggant ink is frequently invisible except under UV light, it does not interfere with the appearance of the stamp. Another common application is the use of phosphored papers. In this case the paper itself either has a coating of taggant applied before the stamp is printed or has taggant applied during the papermaking process, incorporating it into the fibers. This is currently in use in the United States. A similar form is the application of a fluorescent coating either to the finished paper or during the papermaking process. This type of tagging has been extensively used by Australia and Germany.

Many countries now use tagging in various forms to either expedite mail handling or to serve as a printing security device against counterfeiting. Following the introduction of tagged stamps for public use in 1959 by Great Britain, other countries have steadily joined the parade. Among those are Germany (1961); Canada and Denmark (1962); United States, Australia, France and Switzerland (1963); Belgium and Japan (1966); Sweden and Norway (1967); Italy (1968); and Russia (1969). Since then, many other countries have begun using forms of tagging, including Brazil, China, Czechoslovakia, Hong Kong, Guatemala, Indonesia, Israel, Lithuania, Luxembourg, Netherlands, Penrhyn Islands, Portugal, St. Vincent, Singapore, South Africa, Spain and Sweden to name a few.

In some cases, including United States, Canada, Great Britain and Switzerland, stamps were released both with and without tagging. Many of these were released during each country's experimental period. Tagged and untagged versions are listed for the aforementioned countries and are noted in some other countries' listings. For at least a few stamps, the experimentally tagged version is worth far more than its untagged counterpart, such as the 1963 experimental tagged version of France Scott 1024.

In some cases luminescent varieties of stamps were inadvertently created. Several Russian stamps, for example, sport highly fluorescent ink that was not intended as a form of tagging. Older stamps, such as early U.S. postage dues, can be positively identified by the use of UV light, since the organic ink used has become slightly fluorescent over time. Other stamps, such as Austria Scott 70a-82a (var-

nish bars) and Obock Scott 46-64 (printed quadrille lines), have become fluorescent over time.

Various fluorescent substances have been added to paper to make it appear brighter. These optical brightners, as they are known, greatly affect the appearance of the stamp under UV light. The brightest of these is known as Hi-Brite paper. These paper varieties are beyond the scope of the Scott Catalogue.

Shortwave UV light also is used extensively in expertizing, since each form of paper has its own fluorescent characteristics that are impossible to perfectly match. It is therefore a simple matter to detect filled thins, added perforation teeth and other alterations that involve the addition of paper. UV light also is used to examine stamps that have had cancels chemically removed and for other purposes as well.

Gum

The gum on the back of a stamp may be shiny, dull, smooth, rough, dark, white, colored or tinted. Most stamp gumming adhesives use gum arabic or dextrine as a base. Certain polymers such as polyvinyl alcohol (PVA) have been used extensively since World War II.

The *Scott Standard Postage Stamp Catalogue* does not list items by types of gum. The *Scott Specialized Catalogue of United States Stamps* does differentiate among some types of gum for certain issues.

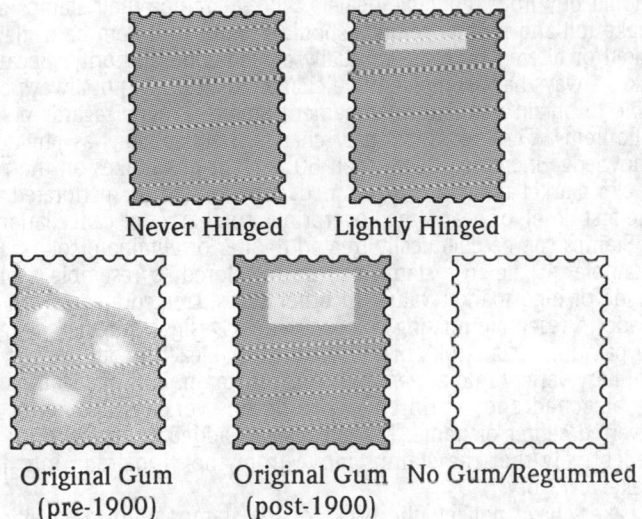

Never Hinged   Lightly Hinged

Original Gum   Original Gum   No Gum/Regummed
(pre-1900)   (post-1900)

For purposes of determining the condition of an unused stamp, Scott Publishing Co. presents the following definitions (with accompanying illustrations): **Never Hinged (NH)** - Full original gum with no hinge mark or disturbance. The presence of an expertizer's mark does not disqualify a stamp from this designation; **Lightly Hinged (LH)** - Full original gum with a light disturbance of the gum from the removal of a peelable hinge; **Original Gum (OG)** - Pre-1900 stamps should have at least most of their original gum. On rarer stamps, it may be expected that the original gum will be somewhat more disturbed than it will be on more common issues. Post-1900 stamps should have full original gum. Original gum will show some disturbance caused by previous hinge, which may be present or entirely removed. **No Gum (NG) or Regummed (RE)** - A stamp with no gum. A regummed stamp is considered the same as a stamp with none of its original gum for purposes of grading.

Reprints of stamps may have gum differing from the original issues. In addition, some countries have used different gum formulas for different seasons. These adhesives have different properties that may become more apparent over time.

Many stamps have been issued without gum, and the catalogue will note this fact. See United States Scott PR33-PR56. Sometimes,

gum may have been removed to preserve the stamp. Germany Scott B68, for example, has a highly acidic gum that eventually destroys the stamps. This item is valued in the catalogue with gum removed.

Reprints and Reissues

These are impressions of stamps (usually obsolete) made from the original plates or stones. If they are valid for postage and reproduce obsolete issues (such as U.S. Scott 102-111), the stamps are *reissues.* If they are from current issues, they are designated as *second, third,* etc., *printing.* If designated for a particular purpose, they are called *special printings.*

When special printings are not valid for postage, but are made from original dies and plates by authorized persons, they are *official reprints. Private reprints* are made from the original plates and dies by private hands. An example of a private reprint is that of the 1871-1932 reprints made from the original die of the 1845 New Haven, Conn., postmaster's provisional. *Official reproductions* or imitations are made from new dies and plates by government authorization. Scott will list those reissues that are valid for postage if they differ significantly from the original printing.

The U.S. government made special printings of its first postage stamps in 1875. Produced were official imitations of the first two stamps (listed as Scott 3-4), reprints of the demonetized pre-1861 issues (Scott 40-47) and reissues of the 1861 stamps, the 1869 stamps and the then-current 1875 denominations. Even though the official imitations and the reprints were not valid for postage, Scott lists all of these U.S. special printings.

Most reprints or reissues differ slightly from the original stamp in some characteristic, such as gum, paper, perforation, color or watermark. Sometimes the details are followed so meticulously that only a student of that specific stamp is able to distinguish the reprint or reissue from the original.

Remainders and Canceled to Order

Some countries sell their stock of old stamps when a new issue replaces them. To avoid postal use, the *remainders* usually are canceled with a punch hole, a heavy line or bar, or a more-or-less regular-looking cancellation. The most famous merchant of remainders was Nicholas F. Seebeck. In the 1880s and 1890s, he arranged printing contracts between the Hamilton Bank Note Co., of which he was a director, and several Central and South American countries. The contracts provided that the plates and all remainders of the yearly issues became the property of Hamilton. Seebeck saw to it that ample stock remained. The "Seebecks," both remainders and reprints, were standard packet fillers for decades.

Some countries also issue stamps *canceled-to-order (CTO),* either in sheets with original gum or stuck onto pieces of paper or envelopes and canceled. Such CTO items generally are worth less than postally used stamps. In cases where the CTO material is far more prevalent in the marketplace than postally used examples, the catalogue value relates to the CTO examples, with postally used examples noted as premium items. Most CTOs can be detected by the presence of gum. However, as the CTO practice goes back at least to 1885, the gum inevitably has been soaked off some stamps so they could pass as postally used. The normally applied postmarks usually differ slightly from standard postmarks, and specialists are able to tell the difference. When applied individually to envelopes by philatelically minded persons, CTO material is known as *favor canceled* and generally sells at large discounts.

Cinderellas and Facsimiles

Cinderella is a catch-all term used by stamp collectors to describe phantoms, fantasies, bogus items, municipal issues, exhibition seals,

local revenues, transportation stamps, labels, poster stamps and many other types of items. Some cinderella collectors include in their collections local postage issues, telegraph stamps, essays and proofs, forgeries and counterfeits.

A *fantasy* is an adhesive created for a nonexistent stamp-issuing authority. Fantasy items range from imaginary countries (Occusi-Ambeno, Kingdom of Sedang, Principality of Trinidad or Torres Straits), to non-existent locals (Winans City Post), or nonexistent transportation lines (McRobish & Co.'s Acapulco-San Francisco Line).

On the other hand, if the entity exists and could have issued stamps (but did not) or was known to have issued other stamps, the items are considered *bogus* stamps. These would include the Mormon postage stamps of Utah, S. Allan Taylor's Guatemala and Paraguay inventions, the propaganda issues for the South Moluccas and the adhesives of the Page & Keyes local post of Boston.

Phantoms is another term for both fantasy and bogus issues.

Facsimiles are copies or imitations made to represent original stamps, but which do not pretend to be originals. A catalogue illustration is such a facsimile. Illustrations from the Moens catalogue of the last century were occasionally colored and passed off as stamps. Since the beginning of stamp collecting, facsimiles have been made for collectors as space fillers or for reference. They often carry the word "facsimile," "falsch" (German), "sanko" or "mozo" (Japanese), or "faux" (French) overprinted on the face or stamped on the back. Unfortunately, over the years a number of these items have had fake cancels applied over the facsimile notation and have been passed off as genuine.

Forgeries and Counterfeits

Forgeries and counterfeits have been with philately virtually from the beginning of stamp production. Over time, the terminology for the two has been used interchangeably. Although both forgeries and counterfeits are reproductions of stamps, the purposes behind their creation differ considerably.

Among specialists there is an increasing movement to more specifically define such items. Although there is no universally accepted terminology, we feel the following definitions most closely mirror the items and their purposes as they are currently defined.

Forgeries (also often referred to as *Counterfeits*) are reproductions of genuine stamps that have been created to defraud collectors. Such spurious items first appeared on the market around 1860, and most old-time collections contain one or more. Many are crude and easily spotted, but some can deceive experts.

An important supplier of these early philatelic forgeries was the Hamburg printer Gebruder Spiro. Many others with reputations in this craft included S. Allan Taylor, George Hussey, James Chute, George Forune, Benjamin & Sarpy, Julius Goldner, E. Oneglia and L.H. Mercier. Among the noted 20th-century forgers were Francois Fournier, Jean Sperati and the prolific Raoul DeThuin.

Forgeries may be complete replications, or they may be genuine stamps altered to resemble a scarcer (and more valuable) type. Most forgeries, particularly those of rare stamps, are worth only a small fraction of the value of a genuine example, but a few types, created by some of the most notable forgers, such as Sperati, can be worth as much or more than the genuine. Fraudulently produced copies are known of most classic rarities and many medium-priced stamps.

In addition to rare stamps, large numbers of common 19th- and early 20th-century stamps were forged to supply stamps to the early packet trade. Many can still be easily found. Few new philatelic forgeries have appeared in recent decades. Successful imitation of well-engraved work is virtually impossible. It has proven far easier to produce a fake by altering a genuine stamp than to duplicate a stamp completely.

Counterfeit (also often referred to as *Postal Counterfeit* or *Postal Forgery*) is the term generally applied to reproductions of stamps that have been created to defraud the government of revenue. Such items usually are created at the time a stamp is current and, in some cases, are hard to detect. Because most counterfeits are seized when the perpetrator is captured, postal counterfeits, particularly used on cover, are usually worth much more than a genuine example to specialists. The first postal counterfeit was of Spain's 4-cuarto carmine of 1854 (the real one is Scott 25). Apparently, the counterfeiters were not satisfied with their first version, which is now very scarce, and they soon created an engraved counterfeit, which is common. Postal counterfeits quickly followed in Austria, Naples, Sardinia and the Roman States. They have since been created in many other countries as well, including the United States.

An infamous counterfeit to defraud the government is the 1-shilling Great Britain "Stock Exchange" forgery of 1872, used on telegraph forms at the exchange that year. The stamp escaped detection until a stamp dealer noticed it in 1898.

Fakes

Fakes are genuine stamps altered in some way to make them more desirable. One student of this part of stamp collecting has estimated that by the 1950s more than 30,000 varieties of fakes were known. That number has grown greatly since then. The widespread existence of fakes makes it important for stamp collectors to study their philatelic holdings and use relevant literature. Likewise, collectors should buy from reputable dealers who guarantee their stamps and make full and prompt refunds should a purchased item be declared faked or altered by some mutually agreed-upon authority. Because fakes always have some genuine characteristics, it is not always possible to obtain unanimous agreement among experts regarding specific items. These students may change their opinions as philatelic knowledge increases. More than 80 percent of all fakes on the philatelic market today are regummed, reperforated (or perforated for the first time), or bear forged overprints, surcharges or cancellations.

Stamps can be chemically treated to alter or eliminate colors. For example, a pale rose stamp can be re-colored to resemble a blue shade of high market value. In other cases, treated stamps can be made to resemble missing color varieties. Designs may be changed by painting, or a stroke or a dot added or bleached out to turn an ordinary variety into a seemingly scarcer stamp. Part of a stamp can be bleached and reprinted in a different version, achieving an inverted center or frame. Margins can be added or repairs done so deceptively that the stamps move from the "repaired" into the "fake" category.

Fakers have not left the backs of the stamps untouched either. They may create false watermarks, add fake grills or press out genuine grills. A thin India paper proof may be glued onto a thicker backing to create the appearance an issued stamp, or a proof printed on cardboard may be shaved down and perforated to resemble a stamp. Silk threads are impressed into paper and stamps have been split so that a rare paper variety is added to an otherwise inexpensive stamp. The most common treatment to the back of a stamp, however, is regumming.

Some in the business of faking stamps have openly advertised fool-proof application of "original gum" to stamps that lack it, although most publications now ban such ads from their pages. It is believed that very few early stamps have survived without being hinged. The large number of never-hinged examples of such earlier material offered for sale thus suggests the widespread extent of regumming activity. Regumming also may be used to hide repairs or thin spots. Dipping the stamp into watermark fluid, or examining it under longwave ultraviolet light often will reveal these flaws.

Fakers also tamper with separations. Ingenious ways to add margins are known. Perforated wide-margin stamps may be falsely represented as imperforate when trimmed. Reperforating is commonly done to create scarce coil or perforation varieties, and to eliminate the naturally occurring straight-edge stamps found in sheet margin

positions of many earlier issues. Custom has made straight-edged stamps less desirable. Fakers have obliged by perforating straight-edged stamps so that many are now uncommon, if not rare.

Another fertile field for the faker is that of overprints, surcharges and cancellations. The forging of rare surcharges or overprints began in the 1880s or 1890s. These forgeries are sometimes difficult to detect, but experts have identified almost all. Occasionally, overprints or cancellations are removed to create non-overprinted stamps or seemingly unused items. This is most commonly done by removing a manuscript cancel to make a stamp resemble an unused example. "SPECIMEN" overprints may be removed by scraping and repainting to create non-overprinted varieties. Fakers use inexpensive revenues or pen-canceled stamps to generate unused stamps for further faking by adding other markings. The quartz lamp or UV lamp and a high-powered magnifying glass help to easily detect removed cancellations.

The bigger problem, however, is the addition of overprints, surcharges or cancellations - many with such precision that they are very difficult to ascertain. Plating of the stamps or the overprint can be an important method of detection.

Fake postmarks may range from many spurious fancy cancellations to a host of markings applied to transatlantic covers, to adding normally appearing postmarks to definitives of some countries with stamps that are valued far higher used than unused. With the increased popularity of cover collecting, and the widespread interest in postal history, a fertile new field for fakers has come about. Some have tried to create entire covers. Others specialize in adding stamps, tied by fake cancellations, to genuine stampless covers, or replacing less expensive or damaged stamps with more valuable ones. Detailed study of postal rates in effect at the time a cover in question was mailed, including the analysis of each handstamp used during the period, ink analysis and similar techniques, usually will unmask the fraud.

Restoration and Repairs

Scott Publishing Co. bases its catalogue values on stamps that are free of defects and otherwise meet the standards set forth earlier in this introduction. Most stamp collectors desire to have the finest copy of an item possible. Even within given grading categories there are variances. This leads to a controversial practice that is not defined in any universal manner: stamp *restoration.*

There are broad differences of opinion about what is permissible when it comes to restoration. Carefully applying a soft eraser to a stamp or cover to remove light soiling is one form of restoration, as is washing a stamp in mild soap and water to clean it. These are fairly accepted forms of restoration. More severe forms of restoration include pressing out creases or removing stains caused by tape. To what degree each of these is acceptable is dependent upon the individual situation. Further along the spectrum is the freshening of a stamp's color by removing oxide build-up or the effects of wax paper left next to stamps shipped to the tropics.

At some point in this spectrum the concept of *repair* replaces that of restoration. Repairs include filling thin spots, mending tears by reweaving or adding a missing perforation tooth. Regumming stamps may have been acceptable as a restoration or repair technique many decades ago, but today it is considered a form of fakery.

Restored stamps may or may not sell at a discount, and it is possible that the value of individual restored items may be enhanced over that of their pre-restoration state. Specific situations dictate the resultant value of such an item. Repaired stamps sell at substantial discounts from the value of sound stamps.

Terminology

Booklets — Many countries have issued stamps in small booklets for the convenience of users. This idea continues to become increasingly popular in many countries. Booklets have been issued in many sizes and forms, often with advertising on the covers, the panes of stamps or on the interleaving.

The panes used in booklets may be printed from special plates or made from regular sheets. All panes from booklets issued by the United States and many from those of other countries contain stamps that are straight edged on the sides, but perforated between. Others are distinguished by orientation of watermark or other identifying features. Any stamp-like unit in the pane, either printed or blank, that is not a postage stamp is considered to be a *label* in the catalogue listings.

Scott lists and values booklet panes only. Complete booklets are listed and valued in only a few cases, such as Grenada Scott 1055 and some forms of British prestige booklets. Individual booklet panes are listed only when they are not fashioned from existing sheet stamps and, therefore, are identifiable from their sheet stamp counterparts.

Panes usually do not have a used value assigned to them because there is little market activity for used booklet panes, even though many exist used and there is some demand for them.

Cancellations — The marks or obliterations put on stamps by postal authorities to show that they have performed service and to prevent their reuse are known as cancellations. If the marking is made with a pen, it is considered a "pen cancel." When the location of the post office appears in the marking, it is a "town cancellation." A "postmark" is technically any postal marking, but in practice the term generally is applied to a town cancellation with a date. When calling attention to a cause or celebration, the marking is known as a "slogan cancellation." Many other types and styles of cancellations exist, such as duplex, numerals, targets, fancy and others. See also "precancels," below.

Coil Stamps — These are stamps that are issued in rolls for use in dispensers, affixing and vending machines. Those coils of the United States, Canada, Sweden and some other countries are perforated horizontally or vertically only, with the outer edges imperforate. Coil stamps of some countries, such as Great Britain and Germany, are perforated on all four sides and may in some cases be distinguished from their sheet stamp counterparts by watermarks, counting numbers on the reverse or other means.

Covers — Entire envelopes, with or without adhesive postage stamps, that have passed through the mail and bear postal or other markings of philatelic interest are known as covers. Before the introduction of envelopes in about 1840, people folded letters and wrote the address on the outside. Some people covered their letters with an extra sheet of paper on the outside for the address, producing the term "cover." Used airletter sheets, stamped envelopes and other items of postal stationery also are considered covers.

Errors — Stamps that have some major, consistent, unintentional deviation from the normal are considered errors. Errors include, but are not limited to, missing or wrong colors, wrong paper, wrong

watermarks, inverted centers or frames on multicolor printing, inverted or missing surcharges or overprints, double impressions, missing perforations and others. Factually wrong or misspelled information, if it appears on all examples of a stamp, are not considered errors in the true sense of the word. They are errors of design. Inconsistent or randomly appearing items, such as misperfs or color shifts, are classified as freaks.

Overprints and Surcharges — Overprinting involves applying wording or design elements over an already existing stamp. Overprints can be used to alter the place of use (such as "Canal Zone" on U.S. stamps), to adapt them for a special purpose ("Porto" on Denmark's 1913-20 regular issues for use as postage due stamps, Scott J1-J7) or to commemorate a special occasion (United States Scott 647-648).

A *surcharge* is a form of overprint that changes or restates the face value of a stamp or piece of postal stationery.

Surcharges and overprints may be handstamped, typeset or, occasionally, lithographed or engraved. A few hand-written overprints and surcharges are known.

Precancels — Stamps that are canceled before they are placed in the mail are known as precancels. Precanceling usually is done to expedite the handling of large mailings and generally allow the affected mail pieces to skip certain phases of mail handling.

In the United States, precancellations generally identified the point of origin; that is, the city and state. This information appeared across the face of the stamp, usually centered between parallel lines. More recently, bureau precancels retained the parallel lines, but the city and state designations were dropped. Recent coils have a service inscription that is present on the original printing plate. These show the mail service paid for by the stamp. Since these stamps are not intended to receive further cancellations when used as intended, they are considered precancels. Such items often do not have parallel lines as part of the precancellation.

In France, the abbreviation *Affranchts* in a semicircle together with the word *Postes* is the general form of precancel in use. Belgian precancellations usually appear in a box in which the name of the city appears. Netherlands precancels have the name of the city enclosed between concentric circles, sometimes called a "lifesaver." Precancellations of other countries usually follow these patterns, but may be any arrangement of bars, boxes and city names.

Precancels are listed in the Scott catalogues only if the precancel changes the denomination (Belgium Scott 477-478); if the precanceled stamp is different from the non-precanceled version (such as untagged U.S. precancels); or if the stamp exists only precanceled (France Scott 1096-1099, U.S. Scott 2265).

Proofs and Essays — Proofs are impressions taken from an approved die, plate or stone in which the design and color are the same as the stamp issued to the public. Trial color proofs are impressions taken from approved dies, plates or stones in colors that vary from the final version. An essay is the impression of a design that differs in some way from the issued stamp. "Progressive die proofs" generally are considered to be essays.

Provisionals — These are stamps that are issued on short notice and intended for temporary use pending the arrival of regular issues. They usually are issued to meet such contingencies as changes in government or currency, shortage of necessary postage values or military occupation.

During the 1840s, postmasters in certain American cities issued stamps that were valid only at specific post offices. In 1861, postmasters of the Confederate States also issued stamps with limited validity. Both of these examples are known as "postmaster's provisionals."

Se-tenant — This term refers to an unsevered pair, strip or block of stamps that differ in design, denomination or overprint.

Unless the se-tenant item has a continuous design (see U.S. Scott 1451a, 1694a) the stamps do not have to be in the same order as shown in the catalogue (see U.S. Scott 2158a).

Specimens — The Universal Postal Union required member nations to send samples of all stamps they released into service to the International Bureau in Switzerland. Member nations of the UPU received these specimens as samples of what stamps were valid for postage. Many are overprinted, handstamped or initial-perforated "Specimen," "Canceled" or "Muestra." Some are marked with bars across the denominations (China-Taiwan), punched holes (Czechoslovakia) or back inscriptions (Mongolia).

Stamps distributed to government officials or for publicity purposes, and stamps submitted by private security printers for official approval, also may receive such defacements.

The previously described defacement markings prevent postal use, and all such items generally are known as "specimens."

Tete Beche — This term describes a pair of stamps in which one is upside down in relation to the other. Some of these are the result of intentional sheet arrangements, such as Morocco Scott B10-B11. Others occurred when one or more electrotypes accidentally were placed upside down on the plate, such as Colombia Scott 57a. Separation of the tete-beche stamps, of course, destroys the tete beche variety.

Currency Conversion

Country	Dollar	Pound	S Franc	Guilder	Yen	Lira	HK Dollar	D-Mark	Fr Franc	Cdn Dollar	Aust Dollar
Australia	1.3568	2.0542	1.1384	0.8207	0.0129	0.0009	0.1755	0.9184	0.2687	0.9948	....
Canada	1.3639	2.0650	1.1444	0.8250	0.0129	0.0009	0.1764	0.9232	0.2701	....	1.0052
France	5.0488	7.6439	4.2363	3.0538	0.0479	0.0032	0.6529	3.4174	....	3.7017	3.7211
Germany	1.4774	2.2368	1.2396	0.8936	0.0140	0.0009	0.1911	....	0.2926	1.0832	1.0889
Hong Kong	7.7325	11.7070	6.4881	4.6770	0.0733	0.0049	....	5.2339	1.5316	5.6694	5.6991
Italy	1584.15	2398.41	1329.21	958.175	15.0156	....	204.869	1072.26	313.768	1161.49	1167.56
Japan	105.50	159.728	88.522	63.812	....	0.0666	13.644	71.409	20.896	77.352	77.757
Netherlands	1.6533	2.5031	1.3872	....	0.0157	0.0010	0.2138	1.1191	0.3275	1.2122	1.2185
Switzerland	1.1918	1.8044	....	0.7209	0.0113	0.0008	0.1541	0.8067	0.2361	0.8738	0.8784
U.K.	0.6605	....	0.5542	0.3995	0.0063	0.0004	0.0854	0.4471	0.1308	0.4843	0.4868
U.S.	....	1.5140	0.8391	0.6049	0.0095	0.0006	0.1293	0.6769	0.1981	0.7332	0.7370

Country	Currency	U.S. $ Equiv.
Aitutaki	New Zealand dollar	.6653
Ascension	British pound	1.5140
Australia	dollar	.7370
Australian Antarctic Territory	dollar	.7370
Bahrain	dinar	2.65
Bangladesh	taka	.0239
Botswana	pula	.3536
British Indian Ocean Territory	British pound	1.5140
Brunei	dollar	.7032
Burma	kyat	.1719
Christmas Island	Australian dollar	.7370
Cocos Islands	Australian dollar	.7370
Cook Islands	New Zealand dollar	.6653
Cyprus	pound	2.141
Fiji	dollar	.6958
Gambia	dalasy	.1015
Ghana	cedi	.00068
Gibraltar	pound	1.5140
Great Britain	pound	1.5140
Alderney	pound	1.5140
Guernsey	pound	1.5140
Jersey	pound	1.5140
Isle of Man	pound	1.5140
Hong Kong	dollar	.1293
India	rupee	.0279
Ireland	Irish pound	1.5713
Kenya	shilling	.0177
Kiribati	Australian dollar	.7370
Kuwait	dinar	3.31
Lesotho	maloti	.274
Malawi	kwacha	.065
Malaysia	dollar	.3948
Maldive Islands	rafiyaa	.085
Malta	pound	2.7563
Mauritius	rupee	.054
Namibia	rand	.27
Nauru	Australian dollar	.7370
Nepal	rupee	.0175
New Zealand	dollar	.6653
Nigeria	naira	.0455
Niue	New Zealand dollar	.6653
Norfolk Island	Australian dollar	.7370
Northern Ireland	British pound	1.5140
Oman	rial	2.597
Pakistan	rupee	.0291
Papua New Guinea	kina	.747
Penrhyn Island	New Zealand dollar	.6653
Pitcairn Islands	New Zealand dollar	.6653
St. Helena	British pound	1.5140
Samoa	dollar	1.00
Scotland	British pound	1.5140
Seychelles	rupee	.20
Zil Elwannyen Sesel	rupee	.20
Sierra Leone	leone	.00109
Singapore	dollar	.70
Solomon Islands	Australian dollar	.7370
South Africa	rand	.27
Sri Lanka	rupee	.0185
Swaziland	emalangeni	.27
Tanzania	shilling	.0018
Tokelau	New Zealand dollar	.6653
Tonga	pa'anga	.7919
Niuafo'ou	pa'anga	.7919
Tristan da Cunha	British pound	1.5140
Tuvalu	Australian dollar	.7370
Uganda	shilling	.00097
Vanuatu	vatu	.0088
Wales	British pound	1.5140
Zambia	kwacha	.001
Zimbabwe	dollar	.107

Source: *Wall Street Journal* Jan. 22, 1996. *Figures reflect values as of Jan. 19, 1996.*

British Commonwealth of Nations
Dominions, Colonies, Territories, Offices and Independent Members

Comprising stamps of the British Commonwealth and associated nations.

A strict observance of technicalities would bar some or all of the stamps listed under Burma, Ireland, Kuwait, Nepal, New Republic, Orange Free State, Samoa, South Africa, South-West Africa, Stellaland, Sudan, Swaziland, the two Transvaal Republics and others but these are included for the convenience of collectors.

1. Great Britain

Great Britain: Including England, Scotland, Wales and Northern Ireland.

2. The Dominions, Present and Past

AUSTRALIA

The Commonwealth of Australia was proclaimed on January 1, 1901. It consists of six former colonies as follows:

New South Wales	Victoria
Queensland	Tasmania
South Australia	Western Australia

Territories belonging to, or administered by Australia: Australian Antarctic Territory, Christmas Island, Cocos (Keeling) Islands, Nauru, New Guinea, Norfolk Island, Papua New Guinea.

CANADA

The Dominion of Canada was created by the British North America Act in 1867. The following provinces were former separate colonies and issued postage stamps:

British Columbia and Vancouver Island	Newfoundland
	Nova Scotia
New Brunswick	Prince Edward Island

FIJI

The colony of Fiji became an independent nation with dominion status on Oct. 10, 1970.

GHANA

This state came into existence Mar. 6, 1957, with dominion status. It consists of the former colony of the Gold Coast and the Trusteeship Territory of Togoland. Ghana became a republic July 1, 1960.

INDIA

The Republic of India was inaugurated on January 26, 1950. It succeeded the Dominion of India which was proclaimed August 15, 1947, when the former Empire of India was divided into Pakistan and the Union of India. The Republic is composed of about 40 predominantly Hindu states of three classes: governor's provinces, chief commissioner's provinces and princely states. India also has various territories, such as the Andaman and Nicobar Islands.

The old Empire of India was a federation of British India and the native states. The more important princely states were autonomous. Of the more than 700 Indian states, these 43 are familiar names to philatelists because of their postage stamps.

CONVENTION STATES

Chamba	Jhind
Faridkot	Nabha
Gwalior	Patiala

NATIVE FEUDATORY STATES

Alwar	Jammu
Bahawalpur	Jammu and Kashmir
Bamra	Jasdan
Barwani	Jhalawar
Bhopal	Jhind (1875-76)
Bhor	Kashmir
Bijawar	Kishangarh
Bundi	Las Bela
Bussahir	Morvi
Charkhari	Nandgaon
Cochin	Nowanuggur
Dhar	Orchha
Duttia	Poonch
Faridkot (1879-85)	Rajpeepla
Hyderabad	Sirmur
Idar	Soruth
Indore	Travancore
Jaipur	Wadhwan

NEW ZEALAND

Became a dominion on September 26, 1907. The following islands and territories are, or have been, administered by New Zealand:

Aitutaki	Ross Dependency
Cook Islands (Rarotonga)	Samoa (Western Samoa)
Niue	Tokelau Islands
Penrhyn	

PAKISTAN

The Republic of Pakistan was proclaimed March 23, 1956. It succeeded the Dominion which was proclaimed August 15, 1947. It is made up of all or part of several Moslem provinces and various districts of the former Empire of India, including Bahawalpur and Las Bela. Pakistan withdrew from the Commonwealth in 1972.

SOUTH AFRICA

Under the terms of the South African Act (1909) the self-governing colonies of Cape of Good Hope, Natal, Orange River Colony and Transvaal united on May 31, 1910, to form the Union of South Africa. It became an independent republic May 3, 1961.

Under the terms of the Treaty of Versailles, South-West Africa, formerly German South-West Africa, was mandated to the Union of South Africa.

SRI LANKA (CEYLON)

The Dominion of Ceylon was proclaimed February 4, 1948. The island had been a Crown Colony from 1802 until then. On May 22, 1972, Ceylon became the Republic of Sri Lanka.

3. Colonies, Past and Present; Controlled Territory and Independent Members of the Commonwealth

Aden	Bechuanaland
Aitutaki	Bechuanaland Prot.
Antigua	Belize
Ascension	Bermuda
Bahamas	Botswana
Bahrain	British Antarctic Territory
Bangladesh	British Central Africa
Barbados	British Columbia and
Barbuda	Vancouver Island
Basutoland	British East Africa
Batum	British Guiana

British Honduras
British Indian Ocean Territory
British New Guinea
British Solomon Islands
British Somaliland
Brunei
Burma
Bushire
Cameroons
Cape of Good Hope
Cayman Islands
Christmas Island
Cocos (Keeling) Islands
Cook Islands
Crete,
  British Administration
Cyprus
Dominica
East Africa & Uganda
  Protectorates
Egypt (see Vol. III)
Falkland Islands
Fiji
Gambia
German East Africa
Gibraltar
Gilbert Islands
Gilbert & Ellice Islands
Gold Coast
Grenada
Griqualand West
Guernsey
Guyana
Heligoland
Hong Kong
Indian Native States
  (see India)
Ionian Islands
Jamaica
Jersey

Kenya
Kenya, Uganda & Tanzania
Kuwait
Labuan
Lagos
Leeward Islands
Lesotho
Madagascar
Malawi
Malaya
  Federated Malay States
  Johore
  Kedah
  Kelantan
  Malacca
  Negri Sembilan
  Pahang
  Penang
  Perak
  Perlis
  Selangor
  Singapore
  Sungei Ujong
  Trengganu
Malaysia
Maldive Islands
Malta
Man, Isle of
Mauritius
Mesopotamia
Montserrat
Muscat
Namibia
Natal
Nauru
Nevis
New Britain
New Brunswick
Newfoundland
New Guinea

New Hebrides
New Republic
New South Wales
Niger Coast Protectorate
Nigeria
Niue
Norfolk Island
North Borneo
Northern Nigeria
Northern Rhodesia
North West Pacific Islands
Nova Scotia
Nyasaland Protectorate
Oman
Orange River Colony
Palestine
Papua New Guinea
Penrhyn Island
Pitcairn Islands
Prince Edward Island
Queensland
Rhodesia
Rhodesia & Nyasaland
Ross Dependency
Sabah
St. Christopher
St. Helena
St. Kitts
St. Kitts-Nevis-Anguilla
St. Lucia
St. Vincent
Samoa
Sarawak
Seychelles
Sierra Leone
Solomon Islands
Somaliland Protectorate
South Arabia
South Australia
South Georgia

Southern Nigeria
Southern Rhodesia
South-West Africa
Stellaland
Straits Settlements
Sudan
Swaziland
Tanganyika
Tanzania
Tasmania
Tobago
Togo
Tokelau Islands
Tonga
Transvaal
Trinidad
Trinidad and Tobago
Tristan da Cunha
Trucial States
Turks and Caicos
Turks Islands
Tuvalu
Uganda
United Arab Emirates
Victoria
Virgin Islands
Western Australia
Zambia
Zanzibar
Zululand

POST OFFICES IN FOREIGN COUNTRIES
Africa
  East Africa Forces
  Middle East Forces
Bangkok
China
Morocco
Turkish Empire

Common Design Types

Pictured in this section are issues where one illustration has been used for a number of countries in the Catalogue. Not included in this section are overprinted stamps or those issues which are illustrated in each country.

EUROPA
Europa Issue, 1956

The design symbolizing the cooperation among the six countries comprising the Coal and Steel Community is illustrated in each country.

Belgium	496-497
France	805-806
Germany	748-749
Italy	715-716
Luxembourg	318-320
Netherlands	368-369

Europa Issue, 1958

"E" and Dove – CD1

European Postal Union at the service of European integration.

1958, Sept. 13

Belgium	527-528
France	889-890
Germany	790-791
Italy	750-751
Luxembourg	341-343
Netherlands	375-376
Saar	317-318

Europa Issue, 1959

6-Link Endless Chain – CD2

1959, Sept. 19

Belgium	536-537
France	929-930
Germany	805-806
Italy	791-792
Luxembourg	354-355
Netherlands	379-380

Europa Issue, 1960

19-Spoke Wheel – CD3

First anniverary of the establishment of C.E.P.T. (Conférence Europeenne des Administrations des Postes et des Telecommunications.)

The spokes symbolize the 19 founding members of the Conference.

1960, Sept.

Belgium	553-554
Denmark	379
Finland	376-377
France	970-971

Germany	818-820
Great Britain	377-378
Greece	688
Iceland	327-328
Ireland	175-176
Italy	809-810
Luxembourg	374-375
Netherlands	385-386
Norway	387
Portugal	866-867
Spain	941-942
Sweden	562-563
Switzerland	400-401
Turkey	1493-1494

Europa Issue, 1961

19 Doves Flying as One – CD4

The 19 doves represent the 19 members of the Conference of European Postal and Telecommunications Administrations C.E.P.T.

1961-62

Belgium	572-573
Cyprus	201-203
France	1005-1006
Germany	844-845
Great Britain	383-384
Greece	718-719
Iceland	340-341
Italy	845-846
Luxembourg	382-383
Netherlands	387-388
Spain	1010-1011
Switzerland	410-411
Turkey	1518-1520

Europa Issue 1962

Young Tree with 19 Leaves – CD5

The 19 leaves represent the 19 original members of C.E.P.T.

1962-63

Belgium	582-583
Cyprus	219-221
France	1045-1046
Germany	852-853
Greece	739-740
Iceland	348-349
Ireland	184-185
Italy	860-861
Luxembourg	386-387
Netherlands	394-395
Norway	414-415
Switzerland	416-417
Turkey	1553-1555

Europa Issue, 1963

Stylized Links, Symbolizing Unity – CD6

1963, Sept.

Belgium	598-599
Cyprus	229-231
Finland	419
France	1074-1075
Germany	867-868
Greece	768-769
Iceland	357-358
Ireland	188-189
Italy	880-881
Luxembourg	403-404
Netherlands	416-417
Norway	441-442

Switzerland	429
Turkey	1602-1603

Europa Issue, 1964

Symbolic Daisy – CD7

5th anniversary of the establishment of C.E.P.T. The 22 petals of the flower symbolize the 22 members of the Conference.

1964, Sept.

Austria	738
Belgium	614-615
Cyprus	244-246
France	1109-1110
Germany	897-898
Greece	801-802
Iceland	367-368
Ireland	196-197
Italy	894-895
Luxembourg	411-412
Monaco	590-591
Netherlands	428-429
Norway	458
Portugal	931-933
Spain	1262-1263
Switzerland	438-439
Turkey	1628-1629

Europa Issue, 1965

Leaves and "Fruit" – CD8

1965

Belgium	636-637
Cyprus	262-264
Finland	437
France	1131-1132
Germany	934-935
Greece	833-834
Iceland	375-376
Ireland	204-205
Italy	915-916
Luxembourg	432-433
Monaco	616-617
Netherlands	438-439
Norway	475-476
Portugal	958-960
Switzerland	469
Turkey	1665-1666

Europa Issue, 1966

Symbolic Sailboat – CD9

1966, Sept.

Andorra, French	172
Belgium	675-676
Cyprus	275-277
France	1163-1164
Germany	963-964
Greece	862-863
Iceland	384-385
Ireland	216-217
Italy	942-943
Liechtenstein	415
Luxembourg	440-441
Monaco	639-640
Netherlands	441-442

Norway	496-497
Portugal	980-982
Switzerland	477-478
Turkey	1718-1719

Europa Issue, 1967

Cogwheels – CD10

1967

Andorra, French	174-175
Belgium	688-689
Cyprus	297-299
France	1178-1179
Greece	891-892
Germany	969-970
Iceland	389-390
Ireland	232-233
Italy	951-952
Liechtenstein	420
Luxembourg	449-450
Monaco	669-670
Netherlands	444-447
Norway	504-505
Portugal	994-996
Spain	1465-1466
Switzerland	482
Turkey	B120-B121

Europa Issue, 1968

Golden Key with C.E.P.T. Emblem CD11

1968

Andorra, French	182-183
Belgium	705-706
Cyprus	314-316
France	1209-1210
Germany	983-984
Greece	916-917
Iceland	395-396
Ireland	242-243
Italy	979-980
Liechtenstein	442
Luxembourg	466-467
Monaco	689-691
Netherlands	452-453
Portugal	1019-1021
San Marino	687
Spain	1526
Turkey	1775-1776

Europa Issue, 1969

"EUROPA" and "CEPT" – CD12

Tenth anniversary of C.E.P.T.

1969

Andorra, French	188-189
Austria	837
Belgium	718-719
Cyprus	326-328
Denmark	458
Finland	483
France	1245-1246
Germany	996-997
Great Britain	585
Greece	947-948
Iceland	406-407
Ireland	270-271

Italy 1000-1001
Liechtenstein 453
Luxembourg 474-475
Monaco 722-724
Netherlands 475-476
Norway 533-534
Portugal 1038-1040
San Marino 701-702
Spain 1567
Sweden 814-816
Switzerland 500-501
Turkey 1799-1800
Vatican 470-472
Yugoslavia 1003-1004

Europa Issue, 1970

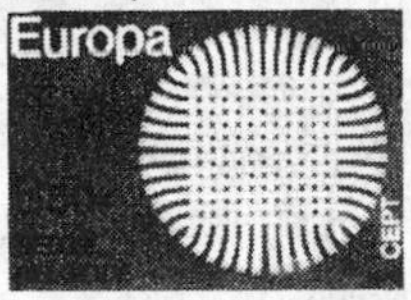

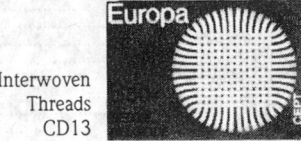

Interwoven Threads
CD13

1970
Andorra, French 196-197
Belgium 741-742
Cyprus 340-342
France 1271-1272
Germany 1018-1019
Greece 985, 987
Iceland 420-421
Ireland 279-281
Italy 1013-1014
Liechtenstein 470
Luxembourg 489-490
Monaco 768-770
Netherlands 483-484
Portugal 1060-1062
San Marino 729-730
Spain 1607
Switzerland 515-516
Turkey 1848-1849
Yugoslavia 1024-1025

Europa Issue, 1971

"Fraternity, Cooperation, Common Effort" – CD14

1971
Andorra, French 205-206
Belgium 803-804
Cyprus 365-367
Finland 504
France 1304
Germany 1064-1065
Greece 1029-1030
Iceland 429-430
Ireland 305-306
Italy 1038-1039
Liechtenstein 485
Luxembourg 500-501
Malta 425-427
Monaco 797-799
Netherlands 488-489
Portugal 1094-1096
San Marino 749-750
Spain 1675-1676
Switzerland 531-532
Turkey 1876-1877
Yugoslavia 1052-1053

Europa Issue, 1972

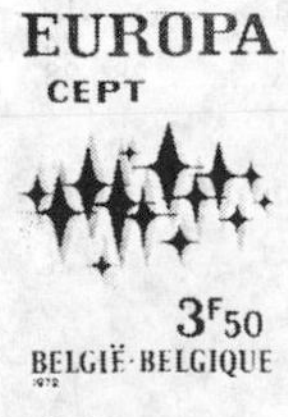

Sparkles, Symbolic of Communications
CD15

1972
Andorra, French 210-211
Andorra, Spanish 62
Belgium 825-826
Cyprus 380-382
Finland 512-513
France 1341
Germany 1089-1090
Greece 1049-1050
Iceland 439-440
Ireland 316-317
Italy 1065-1066
Liechtenstein 504
Luxembourg 512-513
Malta 450-453
Monaco 831-832
Netherlands 494-495
Portugal 1141-1143
San Marino 771-772
Spain 1718
Switzerland 544-545
Turkey 1907-1908
Yugoslavia 1100-1101

Europa Issue, 1973

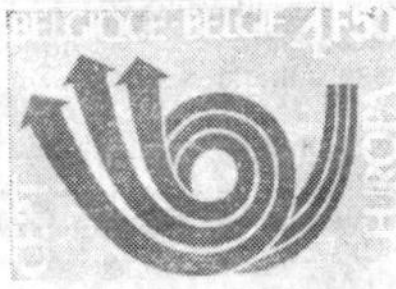

Post Horn and Arrows
CD16

1973
Andorra, French 319-320
Andorra, Spanish 76
Belgium 839-840
Cyprus 396-398
Finland 526
France 1367
Germany 1114-1115
Greece 1090-1092
Iceland 447-448
Ireland 329-330
Italy 1108-1109
Liechtenstein 528-529
Luxembourg 523-524
Malta 469-471
Monaco 866-867
Netherlands 504-505
Norway 604-605
Portugal 1170-1172
San Marino 802-803
Spain 1753
Switzerland 580-581
Turkey 1935-1936
Yugoslavia 1138-1139

BRITISH COMMONWEALTH OF NATIONS

The listings follow established trade practices when these issues are offered as units by dealers. The Peace issue, for example, includes only one stamp from the Indian state of Hyderabad. The U.P.U. issue includes the Egypt set. Pairs are included for those varieties issues with bilingual designs se-tenant.

Silver Jubilee Issue

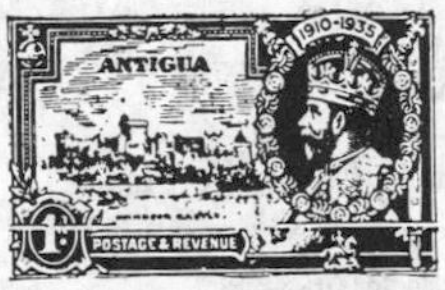

Windsor Castle and King George V
CD301

25th anniversary of the reign of King George V.

1935
Antigua 77-80
Ascension 33-36
Bahamas 92-95
Barbados 186-189
Basutoland 11-14
Bechuanaland Protectorate 117-120
Bermuda 100-103
British Guiana 223-226
British Honduras 108-111
Cayman Islands 81-84
Ceylon 260-263
Cyprus 136-139
Dominica 90-93
Falkland Islands 77-80
Fiji 110-113
Gambia 125-128
Gibraltar 100-103
Gilbert & Ellice Islands 33-36
Gold Coast 108-111
Grenada 124-127
Hong Kong 147-150
Jamaica 109-112
Kenya, Uganda, Tanganyika 42-45
Leeward Islands 96-99
Malta 184-187
Mauritius 204-207
Montserrat 85-88
Newfoundland 226-229
Nigeria 34-37
Northern Rhodesia 18-21
Nyasaland Protectorate 47-50
St. Helena 111-114
St. Kitts-Nevis 72-75
St. Lucia 91 94
St. Vincent 134-137
Seychelles 118-121
Sierra Leone 166-169
Solomon Islands 60-63
Somaliland Protectorate 77-80
Straits Settlements 213-216
Swaziland 20-23
Trinidad & Tobago 43-46
Turks & Caicos Islands 71-74
Virgin Islands 69-72

The following have different designs but are included in the omnibus set:
Great Britain 226-229
Offices in Morocco 67-70, 226-229, 422-425, 508-510
Australia 152-154
Canada 211-216
Cook Islands 98-100
India 142-148
Nauru 31-34
New Guinea 46-47
New Zealand 199-201
Niue 67-69
Papua 114-117
Samoa 163-165
South Africa 68-71
Southern Rhodesia 33-36
South-West Africa 121-124
249 stamps, Never Hinged $925.

Coronation Issue

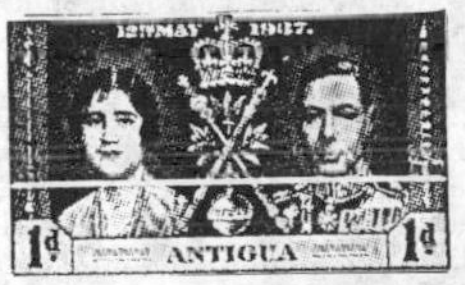

Queen Elizabeth and King George VI
CD302

1937
Aden 13-15
Antigua 81-83
Ascension 37-39
Bahamas 97-99
Barbados 190-192
Basutoland 15-17
Bechuanaland Protectorate 121-123
Bermuda 115-117
British Guiana 227-229
British Honduras 112-114
Cayman Islands 97-99
Ceylon 275-277
Cyprus 140-142
Dominica 94-96
Falkland Islands 81-83
Fiji 114-116
Gambia 129-131
Gibraltar 104-106
Gilbert & Ellice Islands 37-39
Gold Coast 112-114
Grenada 128-130
Hong Kong 151-153
Jamaica 113-115
Kenya, Uganda, Tanganyika 60-62
Leeward Islands 100-102
Malta 188-190
Mauritius 208-210
Montserrat 89-91
Newfoundland 230-232
Nigeria 50-52
Northern Rhodesia 22-24
Nyasaland Protectorate 51-53
St. Helena 115-117
St. Kitts-Nevis 76-78
St. Lucia 107-109
St. Vincent 138-140
Seychelles 122-124
Sierra Leone 170-172
Solomon Islands 64-66
Somaliland Protectorate 81-83
Straits Settlements 235-237
Swaziland 24-26
Trinidad & Tobago 47-49
Turks & Caicos Islands 75-77
Virgin Islands 73-75

The following have different designs but are included in the omnibus set:
Great Britain 234
Offices in Morocco 82, 439, 514
Canada 237
Cook Islands 109-111
Nauru 35-38
Newfoundland 233-243
New Guinea 48-51
New Zealand 223-225
Niue 70-72
Papua 118-121
South Africa 74-78
Southern Rhodesia 38-41
South-West Africa 125-132
202 stamps, Never Hinged $65.

Peace Issue

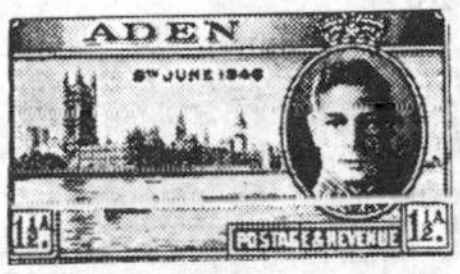

King George VI and Parliament Buildings, London – CD303

Return to peace at the close of World War II.

1945-46
Aden 28-29
Antigua 96-97
Ascension 50-51
Bahamas 130-131
Barbados 207-208
Bermuda 131-132
British Guiana 242-243
British Honduras 127-128
Cayman Islands 112-113
Ceylon 293-294
Cyprus 156-157
Dominica 112-113
Falkland Islands 97-98
Falkland Islands Dep. 1L9-1L10
Fiji 137-138
Gambia 144-145
Gibraltar 119-120
Gilbert & Ellice Islands 52-53
Gold Coast 128-129
Grenada 143-144
Jamaica 136-137
Kenya, Uganda, Tanganyika 90-91
Leeward Islands 116-117
Malta 206-207
Mauritius 223-224
Montserrat 104-105
Nigeria 71-72
Northern Rhodesia 46-47
Nyasaland Protectorate 82-83
Pitcairn Island 9-10
St. Helena 128-129
St. Kitts-Nevis 91-92
St. Lucia 127-128
St. Vincent 152-153
Seychelles 149-150
Sierra Leone 186-187
Solomon Islands 80-81
Somaliland Protectorate 108-109
Trinidad & Tobago 62-63
Turks & Caicos Islands 90-91
Virgin Islands 88-89

The following have different designs but are included in the omnibus set:
Great Britain 264-265
Offices in Morocco 523-524
Aden
Kathiri State of Seiyun 12-13
Qu'aiti State of Shihr and Mukalla 12-13
Australia 200-202
Basutoland 29-31
Bechuanaland Protectorate 137-139
Burma 66-69
Cook Islands 127-130
Hong Kong 174-175
India 195-198
Hyderabad 51
New Zealand 247-257
Niue 90-93
Pakistan-Bahawalpur O16

Federation of the West Indies, April 22, 1958.

1958

Antigua	122-124
Barbados	248-250
Dominica	161-163
Grenada	184-186
Jamaica	175-177
Montserrat	143-145
St. Kitts-Nevis	136-138
St. Lucia	170-172
St. Vincent	198-200
Trinidad & Tobago	86-88

30 stamps, Never Hinged $6.

Freedom from Hunger Issue

Protein Food CD314

United Nations Food and Agricultural Organization's "Freedom from Hunger" campaign.

1963

Aden	65
Antigua	133
Ascension	89
Bahamas	180
Basutoland	83
Bechuanaland Protectorate	194
Bermuda	192
British Guiana	271
British Honduras	179
Brunei	100
Cayman Islands	168
Dominica	181
Falkland Islands	146
Fiji	198
Gambia	172
Gibraltar	161
Gilbert & Ellice Islands	76
Grenada	190
Hong Kong	218
Malta	291
Mauritius	270
Montserrat	150
New Hebrides	93
North Borneo	296
Pitcairn	35
St. Helena	173
St. Lucia	179
St. Vincent	201
Sarawak	212
Seychelles	213
Solomon Islands	109
Swaziland	108
Tonga	127
Tristan da Cunha	68
Turks & Caicos Islands	138
Virgin Islands	140
Zanzibar	280

37 stamps

Red Cross Centenary Issue

Red Cross and Elizabeth II – CD315

Centenary of the International Red Cross.

1963

Antigua	134-135
Ascension	90-91
Bahamas	183-184
Basutoland	84-85
Bechuanaland Protectorate	195-196
Bermuda	193-194
British Guiana	272-273
British Honduras	180-181
Cayman Islands	169-170
Dominica	182-183
Falkland Islands	147-148
Fiji	203-204
Gambia	173-174
Gibraltar	162-163
Gilbert & Ellice Islands	77-78
Grenada	191-192
Hong Kong	219-220
Jamaica	203-204
Malta	292-293

Mauritius	271-272
Montserrat	151-152
New Hebrides	94-95
Pitcairn Islands	36-37
St. Helena	174-175
St. Kitts-Nevis	143-144
St. Lucia	180-181
St. Vincent	202-203
Seychelles	214-215
Solomon Islands	110-111
South Arabia	1-2
Swaziland	109-110
Tonga	134-135
Tristan da Cunha	69-70
Turks & Caicos Islands	139-140
Virgin Islands	141-142

70 stamps

Shakespeare Issue

Shakespeare Memorial Theatre, Stratford-on-Avon – CD316

400th anniversary of the birth of William Shakespeare.

1964

Antigua	151
Bahamas	201
Bechuanaland Protectorate	197
Cayman Islands	171
Dominica	184
Falkland Islands	149
Gambia	192
Gibraltar	164
Montserrat	153
St. Lucia	196
Turks & Caicos Islands	141
Virgin Islands	143

12 stamps

ITU ISSUE

ITU Emblem CD317

Centenary of the International Telecommunication Union.

1965

Antigua	153-154
Ascension	92-93
Bahamas	219-220
Barbados	265-266
Basutoland	101-102
Bechuanaland Protectorate	202-203
Bermuda	196-197
British Guiana	203-204
British Honduras	187-188
Brunei	116-117
Cayman Islands	172-173
Dominica	185-186
Falkland Islands	154-155
Fiji	211-212
Gibraltar	167-168
Gilbert & Ellice Islands	87-88
Grenada	205-206
Hong Kong	221-222
Mauritius	291-292
Montserrat	157-158
New Hebrides	108-109
Pitcairn Islands	52-53
St. Helena	180-181
St. Kitts-Nevis	163-164
St. Lucia	197-198
St. Vincent	224-225
Seychelles	218-219
Solomon Islands	126-127
Swaziland	115-116
Tristan da Cunha	85-86
Turks & Caicos Islands	142-143
Virgin Islands	159-160

64 stamps, Never Hinged $50.

Intl. Cooperation Year Issue

ICY Emblem – CD318

International Cooperation Year, 1965.

1965

Antigua	155-156
Ascension	94-95
Bahamas	222-223
Basutoland	103-104
Bechuanaland Protectorate	204-205
Bermuda	199-200
British Guiana	295-296
British Honduras	189-190
Brunei	118-119
Cayman Islands	174-175
Dominica	187-188
Falkland Islands	156-157
Fiji	213-214
Gibraltar	169-170
Gilbert & Ellice Islands	104-105
Grenada	207-208
Hong Kong	223-224
Mauritius	293-294
Montserrat	176-177
New Hebrides	110-111
Pitcairn Islands	54-55
St. Helena	182-183
St. Kitts-Nevis	165-166
St. Lucia	199-200
Seychelles	220-221
Solomon Islands	143-144
South Arabia	17-18
Swaziland	117-118
Tristan da Cunha	87-88
Turks & Caicos Islands	144-145
Virgin Islands	161-162

62 stamps

Churchill Memorial Issue

Winston Churchill and St. Paul's, London, During Air Attack – CD319

Sir Winston Leonard Spencer Churchill (1874-1965), statesman and World War II leader.

1966

Antigua	157-160
Ascension	96-99
Bahamas	224-227
Barbados	281-284
Basutoland	105-108
Bechuanaland Protectorate	206-209
Bermuda	201-204
British Antarctic Territory	16-19
British Honduras	191-194
Brunei	120-123
Cayman Islands	176-179
Dominica	189-192
Falkland Islands	158-161
Fiji	215-218
Gibraltar	171-174
Gilbert & Ellice Islands	106-109
Grenada	209-212
Hong Kong	225-228
Mauritius	295-298
Montserrat	178-181
New Hebrides	112-115
Pitcairn Islands	56-59
St. Helena	184-187
St. Kitts-Nevis	167-170
St. Lucia	201-204
St. Vincent	241-244
Seychelles	222-225
Solomon Islands	145-148
South Arabia	19-22
Swaziland	119-122
Tristan da Cunha	89-92
Turks & Caicos Islands	146-149
Virgin Islands	163-166

132 stamps

Royal Visit Issue, 1966

Queen Elizabeth II and Prince Philip CD320

Visit to the Caribbean, Feb. 4 - March 6, 1966.

1966

Antigua	161-162
Bahamas	228-229
Barbados	285-286
British Guiana	299-300
Cayman Islands	180-181
Dominica	193-194
Grenada	213-214
Montserrat	182-183
St. Kitts-Nevis	171-172
St. Lucia	205-206
St. Vincent	245-246
Turks & Caicos Islands	150-151
Virgin Islands	167-168

26 stamps

World Cup Soccer Issue

Soccer Player and Jules Rimet Cup CD321

World Cup Soccer Championship, Wembley, England, July 11-30.

1966

Antigua	163-164
Ascension	100-101
Bahamas	245-246
Bermuda	205-206
Brunei	124-125
Cayman Islands	182-183
Dominica	195-196
Fiji	219-220
Gibraltar	175-176
Gilbert & Ellice Islands	125-126
Grenada	230-231
New Hebrides	116-117
Pitcairn Islands	60-61
St. Helena	188-189
St. Kitts-Nevis	173-174
St. Lucia	207-208
Seychelles	226-227
Solomon Islands	167-168
South Arabia	23-24
Tristan da Cunha	93-94

40 stamps

WHO Headquarters Issue

World Health Organization Headquarters, Geneva – CD322

1966

Antigua	165-166
Ascension	102-103
Bahamas	247-248
Brunei	126-127
Cayman Islands	184-185
Dominica	197-198
Fiji	224-225
Gibraltar	180-181
Gilbert & Ellice Islands	127-128
Grenada	232-233
Hong Kong	229-230
Montserrat	184-185
New Hebrides	118-119
Pitcairn Islands	62-63

St. Helena 190-191
St. Kitts-Nevis 177-178
St. Lucia 209-210
St. Vincent 247-248
Seychelles 228-229
Solomon Islands 169-170
South Arabia 25-26
Tristan da Cunha 99-100
44 stamps

UNESCO Anniversary Issue

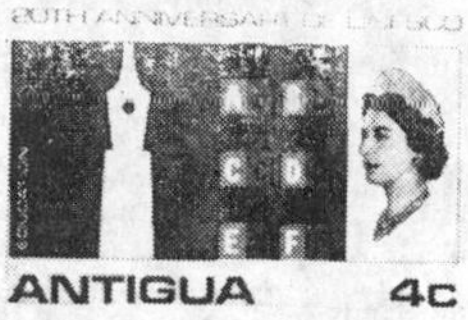

"Education" – CD323

Designs: "Science" (Wheat ears and flask enclosing globe). "Culture" (lyre and columns).

20th anniversary of the United Nations Educational, Scientific and Cultural Organization.

1966-67

Antigua 183-185
Ascension 108-110
Bahamas 249-251
Barbados 287-289
Bermuda 207-209
Brunei 128-130
Cayman Islands 186-188
Dominica 199-201
Gibraltar 183-185
Gilbert & Ellice Islands 129-131
Grenada 234-236
Hong Kong 231-233
Mauritius 299-301
Montserrat 186-188
New Hebrides 120-122
Pitcairn Islands 64-66
St. Helena 192-194
St. Kitts-Nevis 179-181
St. Lucia 211-213
St. Vincent 249-251
Seychelles 230-232
Solomon Islands 171-173
South Arabia 27-29
Swaziland 123-125
Tristan da Cunha 101-103
Turks & Caicos Islands 155-157
Virgin Islands 176-178
81 stamps

Silver Wedding Issue, 1972

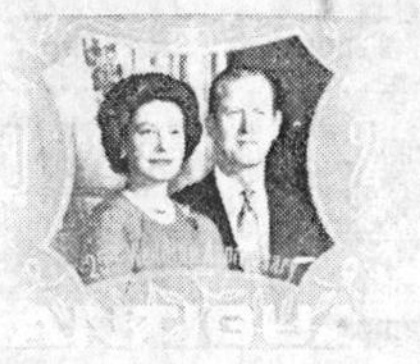

Queen Elizabeth II and Prince Philip
CD324

Designs: borders differ for each country.

1972

Anguilla 161-162
Antigua 295-296
Ascension 164-165
Bahamas 344-345
Bermuda 296-297
British Antarctic Territory 43-44
British Honduras 306-307
British Indian Ocean Territory 48-49
Brunei 186-187
Cayman Islands 304-305
Dominica 352-353
Falkland Islands 223-224
Fiji 328-329
Gibraltar 292-293
Gilbert & Ellice Islands 206-207
Grenada 466-467
Hong Kong 271-272
Montserrat 286-287
New Hebrides 169-170
Pitcairn Islands 127-128
St. Helena 271-272
St. Kitts-Nevis 257-258
St. Lucia 328-329
St.Vincent 344-345
Seychelles 309-310
Solomon Islands 248-249
South Georgia 35-36
Tristan da Cunha 178-179
Turks & Caicos Islands 257-258
Virgin Islands 241-242
60 stamps

Princess Anne's Wedding Issue

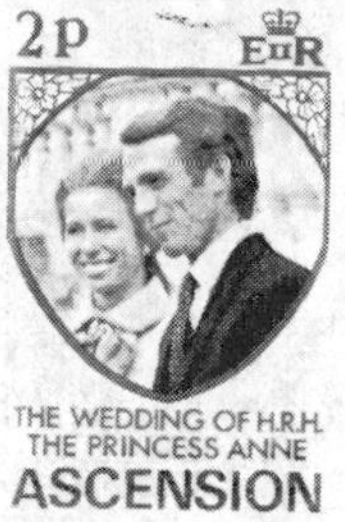

Princess Anne and Mark Phillips
CD325

Wedding of Princess Anne and Mark Phillips, Nov. 14, 1973.

1973

Anguilla 179-180
Ascension 177-178
Belize 325-326
Bermuda 302-303
British Antarctic Territory 60-61
Cayman Islands 320-321
Falkland Islands 225-226
Gibraltar 305-306
Gilbert & Ellice Islands 216-217
Hong Kong 289-290
Montserrat 300-301
Pitcairn Island 135-136
St. Helena 277-278
St. Kitts-Nevis 274-275
St. Lucia 349-350
St. Vincent 358-359
St. Vincent Grenadines 1-2
Seychelles 311-312
Solomon Islands 259-260
South Georgia 37-38
Tristan da Cunha 189-190
Turks & Caicos Islands 286-287
Virgin Islands 260-261
44 stamps

Elizabeth II Coronation Anniversary Issue

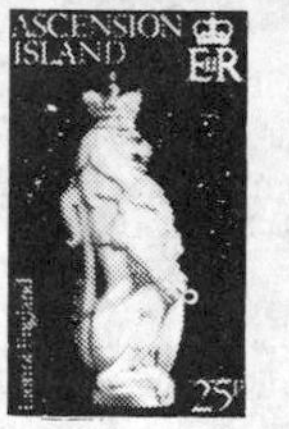

Lion of England
CD326

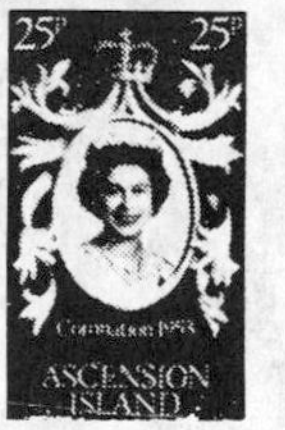

Queen Elizabeth II
CD327

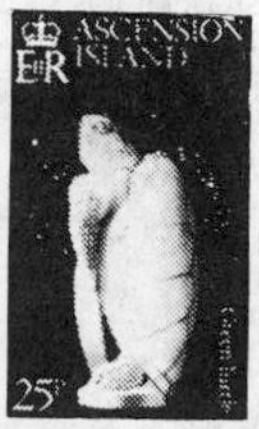

Green Turtle
CD328

Designs: Royal and local beasts in heraldic form and simulated stonework. Portrait of Elizabeth II by Peter Grugeon.

25th anniversary of coronation of Queen Elizabeth II.

1978

Ascension 229
Barbados 474
Belize 397
British Antarctic Territory 71
Cayman Islands 404
Christmas Island 87
Falkland Islands 275
Fiji 384
Gambia 380
Gilbert Islands 312
Mauritius 464
New Hebrides 258
St. Helena 317
St. Kitts-Nevis 354
Samoa 472
Solomon Islands 368
South Georgia 51
Swaziland 302
Tristan da Cunha 238
Virgin Islands 337
20 sheets

Queen Mother Elizabeth's 80th Birthday

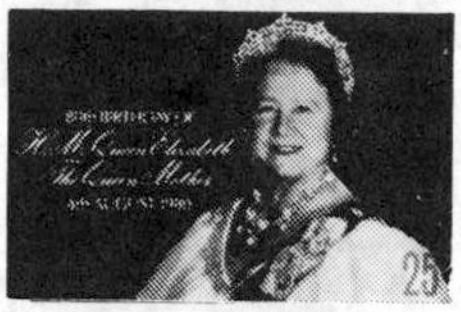

CD330

Designs: Photographs of Queen Mother Elizabeth. Falkland Islands issued in sheets of 50; others in sheets of 9.

1980

Ascension 261
Bermuda 401
Cayman Islands 443
Falkland Islands 305
Gambia 412
Gibraltar 393
Hong Kong 364
Pitcairn Islands 193
St. Helena 341
Samoa 532
Solomon Islands 426
Tristan da Cunha 277
12 stamps

Royal Wedding Issue, 1981

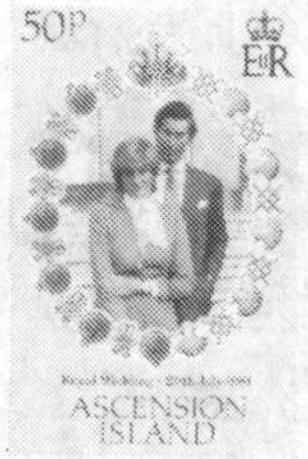

Prince Charles and Lady Diana – CD331

Wedding of Charles, Prince of Wales, and Lady Diana Spencer, St. Paul's Cathedral, London, July 29, 1981.

1981

Antigua 623-625
Ascension 294-296
Barbados 547-549
Barbuda 497-499
Bermuda 412-414
Brunei 268-270
Cayman Islands 471-473
Dominica 701-703
Falkland Islands 324-326
Falkland Islands Dep. 1L59-1L61
Fiji 442-444
Gambia 426-428
Ghana 759-761
Grenada 1051-1053
Grenada Grenadines 440-443
Hong Kong 373-375
Jamaica 500-503
Lesotho 335-337
Maldive Islands 906-908
Mauritius 520-522
Norfolk Island 280-282
Pitcairn Islands 206-208
St. Helena 353-355
St. Lucia 543-545
Samoa 558-560
Sierra Leone 509-517
Solomon Islands 450-452
Swaziland 382-384
Tristan da Cunha 294-296
Turks & Caicos Islands 486-488
Caicos Island 8-10
Uganda 314-316
Vanuatu 308-310
Virgin Islands 406-408

Princess Diana

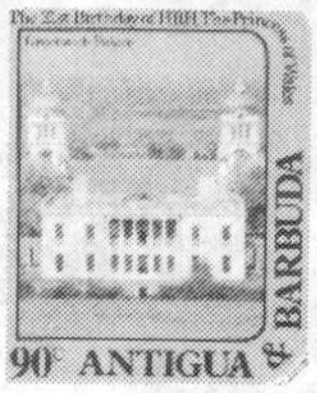

CD332

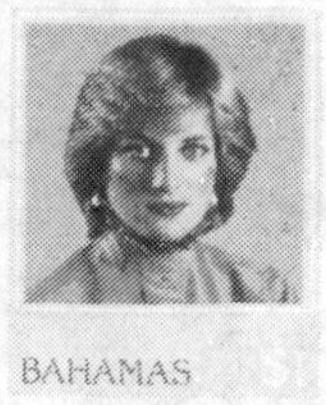

CD333

Designs: Photographs and portrait of Princess Diana, wedding or honeymoon photographs, royal residences, arms of issuing country. Portrait photograph by Clive Friend. Souvenir sheet margins show family tree, various people related to the princess. 21st birthday of Princess Diana of Wales, July 1.

1982

Antigua 663-666
Ascension 313-316
Bahamas 510-513
Barbados 585-588
Barbuda 544-546
British Antarctic Territory 92-95
Cayman Islands 486-489
Dominica 773-776
Falkland Islands 348-351
Falkland Islands Dep. 1L72-1L75
Fiji 470-473
Gambia 447-450
Grenada 1101A-1105
Grenada Grenadines 485-491
Lesotho 372-375
Maldive Islands 952-955
Mauritius 548-551
Pitcairn Islands 213-216
St. Helena 372-375
St. Lucia 591-594
Sierra Leone 531-534
Solomon Islands 471-474
Swaziland 406-409
Tristan da Cunha 310-313
Turks and Caicos Islands 530A-534
Virgin Islands 430-433

250th anniv. of first edition of Lloyd's List (shipping news publication) and of Lloyd's marine insurance.

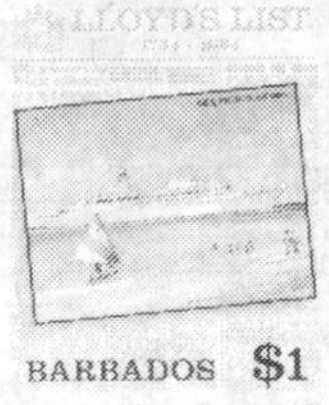

CD335

Designs: First page of early edition of the list; historical ships, modern transportation or harbor scenes.

1984

Ascension 351-354
Bahamas 555-558
Barbados 627-630
Cayes of Belize 10-13
Cayman Islands 522-525
Falkland Islands 404-407
Fiji 509-512
Gambia 519-522
Mauritius 587-590
Nauru 280-283
St. Helena 412-415
Samoa 624-627
Seychelles 538-541
Solomon Islands 521-524
Vanuatu 368-371
Virgin Islands 466-469

Queen Mother 85th Birthday

On Holiday with the Duke of York, Balmoral, 1924 – CD336

Designs: Photographs tracing the life of the Queen Mother, Elizabeth. The high value in each set pictures the same photograph taken of the Queen Mother holding the infant Prince Henry.

1985

Ascension	372-376
Bahamas	580-584
Barbados	660-664
Bermuda	469-473
Falkland Islands	420-424
Falkland Islands Dep.	1L92-1L96
Fiji	531-535
Hong Kong	447-450
Jamaica	599-603
Mauritius	604-608
Norfolk Island	364-368
Pitcairn Islands	253-257
St. Helena	428-432
Samoa	649-653
Seychelles	567-571
Solomon Islands	543-547
Swaziland	476-480
Tristan da Cunha	372-376
Vanuatu	392-396
Zil Elwannyen Sesel	101-105

Queen Elizabeth II, 60th Birthday

CD337

1986, April 21

Ascension	389-393
Bahamas	592-596
Barbados	675-679
Bermuda	499-503
Cayman Islands	555-559
Falkland Islands	441-445
Fiji	544-548
Hong Kong	465-469
Jamaica	620-624
Kiribati	470-474
Mauritius	629-633
Papua New Guinea	640-644
Pitcairn Islands	270-274
St. Helena	451-455
Samoa	670-674
Seychelles	592-596
Solomon Islands	562-566
South Georgia	101-105
Swaziland	490-494
Tristan da Cunha	388-392
Vanuatu	414-418
Zambia	343-347
Zil Elwannyen Sesel	114-118

Royal Wedding

Marriage of Prince Andrew and Sarah Ferguson – CD338

1986, July 23

Ascension	399-400

Bahamas	602-603
Barbados	687-688
Cayman Islands	560-561
Jamaica	629-630
Pitcairn Islands	275-276
St. Helena	460-461
St. Kitts	181-182
Seychelles	602-603
Solomon Islands	567-568
Tristan da Cunha	397-398
Zambia	348-349
Zil Elwannyen Sesel	119-120

Queen Elizabeth II, 60th Birthday

Queen Elizabeth II Inspecting Guard, 1946 – CD339

Designs: Photographs tracing the life of Queen Elizabeth II.

1986

Anguilla	674-677
Antigua	925-928
Barbuda	783-786
Dominica	950-953
Gambia	611-614
Grenada	1371-1374
Grenada Grenadines	749-752
Lesotho	531-534
Maldive Islands	1172-1175
Sierra Leone	760-763
Uganda	495-498

Royal Wedding Issue, 1986

Engagement of Prince Andrew and Sarah Ferguson – CD340

Designs: Photographs of Prince Andrew and Sarah Ferguson during courtship, engagement and marriage.

1986

Antigua	939-942
Barbuda	809-812
Dominica	970-973
Gambia	635-638
Grenada	1385-1388
Grenada Grenadines	758-761
Lesotho	545-548
Maldive Islands	1181-1184
Sierra Leone	769-772
Uganda	510-513

Lloyds of London, 300th Anniv.

CD341

Designs: 17th century aspects of Lloyds, representations of each country's individual connections with Lloyds and publicized disasters insured by the organization.

1986

Ascension	454-457
Bahamas	655-658
Barbados	731-734
Bermuda	541-544
Falkland Islands	481-484
Liberia	1101-1104
Malawi	534-537
Nevis	571-574
St. Helena	501-504
St. Lucia	923-926
Seychelles	649-652
Solomon Islands	627-630
South Georgia	131-134
Trinidad & Tobago	484-487
Tristan da Cunha	439-442
Vanuatu	485-488
Zil Elwannyen Sesel	146-149

Moon Landing, 20th Anniv.

CD342

Designs: Equipment, crew photographs, spacecraft, official emblems and report profiles created for the Apollo Missions. Two stamps in each set are square in format rather than like the stamp shown; see individual country listings for more information.

1989

Ascension Is.	468-472
Bahamas	674-678
Belize	916-920
Kiribati	517-521
Liberia	1125-1129
Nevis	586-590
St. Kitts	248-252
Samoa	760-764
Seychelles	676-680
Solomon Islands	643-647
Vanuatu	507-511
Zil Elwannyen Sesel	154-158

Queen Mother, 90th Birthday

CD343

CD344

Designs: Portraits of Queen Elizabeth, the Queen Mother. See individual country listings for more information.

1990

Ascension Is.	491-492
Bahamas	698-699
Barbados	782-783
British Antarctic Territory	170-171

British Indian Ocean Territory	106-107
Cayman Islands	622-623
Falkland Islands	524-525
Kenya	527-528
Kiribati	555-556
Liberia	1145-1146
Pitcairn Islands	336-337
St. Helena	532-533
St. Lucia	969-970
Seychelles	710-711
Solomon Islands	671-672
South Georgia	143-144
Swaziland	565-566
Tristan da Cunha	480-481
Zil Elwannyen Sesel	171-172

Queen Elizabeth II, 65th Birthday, and Prince Philip, 70th Birthday

CD345   CD346

Designs: Portraits of Queen Elizabeth II and Prince Philip differ for each country. Printed in sheets of 10 + 5 labels (3 different) between. Stamps alternate, producing 5 different triptychs.

1991

Ascension Is.	505-506
Bahamas	730-731
Belize	969-970
Bermuda	617-618
Kiribati	571-572
Mauritius	733-734
Pitcairn Islands	348-349
St. Helena	554-555
St. Kitts	318-319
Samoa	790-791
Seychelles	723-724
Solomon Islands	688-689
South Georgia	149-150
Swaziland	586-587
Vanuatu	540-541
Zil Elwannyen Sesel	177-178

Royal Family Birthday, Anniversary

CD347

Queen Elizabeth II, 65th birthday, Charles and Diana, 10th wedding anniversary: Various photographs of Queen Elizabeth II, Prince Philip, Prince Charles, Princess Diana and their sons William and Henry.

1991

Antigua	1446-1455
Barbuda	1229-1238
Dominica	1328-1337
Gambia	1080-1089
Grenada	2006-2015
Grenada Grenadines	1331-1340
Guyana	2440-2451
Lesotho	871-875
Maldive Islands	1533-1542
Nevis	666-675
St. Vincent	1485-1494
St. Vincent Grenadines	769-778
Sierra Leone	1387-1396
Turks & Caicos Islands	913-922
Uganda	918-927

Queen Elizabeth II's Accession to the Throne 40th Anniversary

CD348

CD349

Various photographs of Queen Elizabeth II with local Scenes.

1992 - CD348

Antigua	1513-1518
Barbuda	1306-1309
Dominica	1414-1419
Gambia	1172-1177
Grenada	2047-2052
Grenada Grenadines	1368-1373
Lesotho	881-885
Maldive Islands	1637-1642
Nevis	702-707
St. Vincent	1582-1587
St. Vincent Grenadines	829-834
Sierra Leone	1482-1487
Turks and Caicos Islands	978-987
Uganda	990-995
Virgin Islands	742-746

1992 - CD349

Ascension Islands	531-535
Bahamas	744-748
Bermuda	623-627
British Indian Ocean Territory	119-123
Cayman Islands	648-652
Falkland Islands	549-553
Gibraltar	605-609
Hong Kong	619-623
Kenya	563-567
Kiribati	582-586
Pitcairn Islands	362-366
St. Helena	570-574
St. Kitts	332-336
Samoa	805-809
Seychelles	734-738
Soloman Islands	708-712
South Georgia	157-161
Tristan da Cunha	508-512
Vanuatu	555-559
Zambia	561-565
Zil Elwannyen Sesel	183-187

Royal Air Force, 75th Anniversary

CD350

1993

Ascension	557-561
Bahamas	771-775
Barbados	842-846
Belize	1003-1008
Bermuda	648-651
British Indian Ocean Territory	136-140
Falkland Is.	573-577
Fiji	687-691
Montserrat	830-834
St. Kitts	351-355

End of World War II, 50th Anniv.

CD351

CD352

1995

Ascension	613-617
Bahamas	824-828
Barbados	891-895
Belize	1047-1050
British Indian Ocean Territory	163-167
Cayman Islands	704-708
Falkland Islands	634-638
Fiji	720-724
Kiribati	662-668
Liberia	1175-1179
Mauritius	803-805
St. Helena	646-654
St. Kitts	389-393
St. Lucia	1018-1022
Samoa	890-894
Solomon Islands	799-803
South Georgia & S. Sandwich Is.	198-200

UN, 50th Anniv.

CD353

1995

Bahamas	839-842
Barbados	901-904
Belize	1055-1058
Jamaica	847-851
Liberia	1187-1190
Mauritius	813-816
Pitcairn Islands	436-439
St. Kitts	398-401
St. Lucia	1023-1026
Samoa	900-903
Tristan da Cunha	568-571
Virgin Islands	807-810

GREAT BRITAIN

'grāt 'bri–t³n

(United Kingdom)

LOCATION — Northwest of the continent of Europe and separated from it by the English Channel
GOVT. — Constitutional monarchy
AREA — 94,511 sq. mi.
POP. — 55,767,387 (1981)
CAPITAL — London

12 Pence = 1 Shilling
20 Shillings = 1 Pound
100 Pence = 1 Pound (1970)

The letters in the corners of the early postage issues indicate position in the horizontal and vertical rows in which that particular specimen was placed.

In the case of illustration A1, this stamp came from the 14th horizontal row (N) and was the 12th stamp (L) from the left in that row. The left corner refers to the horizontal row and the right corner to the vertical row. Thus no two stamps on the plate bore the same combination of letters.

When four corner letters are used (starting in 1858), the lower ones indicate the stamp's position in the sheet and the top ones are the same letters reversed.

Watermarks

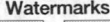

Wmk. 18- Small Crown   Wmk. 19- V R

Wmk. 20- Large Crown   Wmk. 21- Small Garter

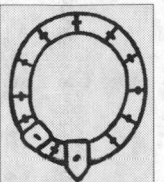 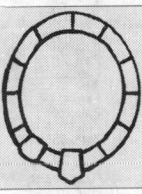

Wmk. 22- Medium Garter   Wmk. 23- Large Garter

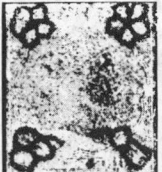 

Wmk. 24- Heraldic Emblems   Wmk. 25- Spray of Rose

Wmk. 26- Maltese Cross

Wmk. 27- "Half Penny" in Script

Wmk. 28- Anchor   Wmk. 29- Orb

Wmk. 30- Imperial Crown   Wmk. 31- Anchor

Wmk. 32- Crown and GvR Multiple   Wmk. 33- Crown and GvR

Wmk. 33 In the normal watermark (sometimes termed the "repeated" watermark) the letters "GvR" are placed one above the other and usually two appear on each stamp. In the multiple watermark the letters "GvR" are condensed, the cyphers are smaller and are so placed that those in each succeeding row are below the spaces between the cyphers in the row above.

Wmk. 34- Large Crown and GvR

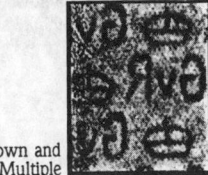

Wmk. 35- Crown and Block GvR Multiple

Wmk. 219- Large Crown and GvR

Wmk. 250- Crown and E8R Multiple

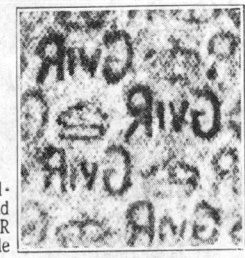

Wmk. 251- Crown and GviR Multiple

Wmk. 259- Crown and Large G VI R

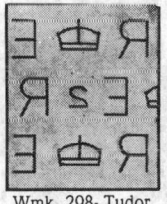 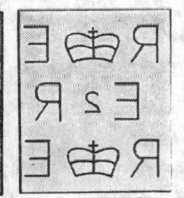

Wmk. 298- Tudor Crown and E 2 R Multiple   Wmk. 308- St. Edward's Crown and E 2 R Multiple

Wmk. 322- St. Edward's Crown Multiple

Values for unused stamps are for examples with original gum as defined in the catalogue introduction. Very fine examples of Nos. 8-56, 58-73, 78-89, 94-95, and the Official overprints on these designs, will have perforations touching the design on at least one side due to the narrow spacing of the stamps on the plates. Stamps with perfs well clear of the design on all four sides range from scarce to rare and command substantially higher prices.

Cancellations on stamps from the 1847 issue to the 1864 issue, and in many cases beyond, are usually heavy. Values quoted are for stamps with better than average cancellations. Stamps with circular date stamps range from scarce to rare and command higher prices.

Queen Victoria
A1   A2

1840, May Wmk. 18 Engr. Imperf.
White Paper

1	A1	1p black	3,000.	180.
2	A1	2p blue	5,750.	300.
a.		2p pale blue	7,500.	400.

No. 1 was printed from 11 plates; No. 2 from 2 plates. The 1p plates 1, 2, 5, 6, 8 and 9 can be found in two or more states.
Issue dates: 1p, May 6; 2p, May 7.
See Nos. 3, 8-9, 11-12, 14, 16, 18, 20, O1.
Compare designs A1-A2 with A8, A10.

1841   **Bluish Paper**

3	A1	1p red brown	110.00	3.00
a.		1p orange brown	300.00	40.00
b.		1p lake red	650.00	250.00
c.		Rouletted 12	4,000.	
d.		"A" missing in lower right corner (position BA, P77)		5,500.
4	A2	2p blue	1,000.	35.00
a.		2p pale blue	1,300.	40.00

No. 3 exists on silk thread paper, but was not regularly issued.
No. 4 was printed from two plates.
See Nos. 10, 13, 15, 17, 19, 21.

During the reigns of Victoria and Edward VIII, many color trials were produced on perfed, gummed and watermarked papers.

A3   A4

With Vertical Silk Threads

1847	Embossed	Unwmk.		
5	A3 1sh green		3,250.	400.00
a.	1sh pale green		3,250.	375.00
	Cut to shape			10.00

Die numbers (on base of bust): 1 and 2.

Nos. 5-7 were printed one stamp at a time on the sheet. Space between the stamps usually is very small. Impressions that touch, or even overlap, are numerous.

Values for Nos. 5-6 are for examples with complete frames and clear white margins on all four sides. Values for No. 7 are for examples with complete design but not necessarily clear margins around the design.

1848

6	A3 10p red brown	2,750.	600.00
	Cut to shape		10.00

Die numbers (on base of bust): 1, 2, 3, 4; also without die number.

1854		Wmk. 19		
7	A4 6p red violet		2,750.	240.00
a.	6p dull violet		2,750.	250.00
b.	6p deep violet		2,750.	250.00
	Cut to shape			8.00

1854-55 Wmk. 18 Engr. Perf. 16
Bluish Paper

8	A1 1p red brown		125.00	3.50
a.	1p yellow brown		190.00	12.00
9	A1 1p red brown, re-engraved ('55)		190.00	15.00
a.	Imperf.			800.00
10	A2 2p blue		1,400.	35.00
a.	2p pale blue		1,500.	50.00

In the re-engraved 1p stamps, the lines of the features are deeper and stronger, the fillet behind the ear more distinct, the shading about the eye heavier, the line of the nostril is turned downward at right and an indentation of color appears between lower lip and chin.

Perf. 14

11	A1 1p red brown ('55)	325.00	20.00
a.	Imperf.		
12	A1 1p red brown, re-engraved ('55)	250.00	20.00
a.	1p orange brown, re-engraved	675.00	75.00
13	A2 2p blue ('55)	2,000.	150.00
a.	Imperf. (P5)		

Wmk. 20 exists in two types. The first includes two vertical prongs, rising from the top of the crown's headband and extending into each of the two balancing midsections. The second type (illustrated), introduced in 1861, omits these prongs.

1855 Wmk. 20 Perf. 16
Bluish Paper

14	A1 1p red brown, re-engraved		
15	A2 2p blue	475.00	32.50
		2,750.	150.00
a.	Imperf. (P5)		2,250.

1855 Bluish Paper Perf. 14

16	A1 1p red brown, re-engraved	110.00	1.00
a.	1p orange brn, re-engraved	275.00	16.00
b.	1p brown rose, re-engraved	175.00	11.00
c.	Imperf.	625.00	625.00
17	A2 2p blue	1,100.	22.50

1856-58 White Paper Perf. 16

18	A1 1p red brown, re-engraved ('57)	650.00	20.00
19	A2 2p blue, thin lines ('58)	3,750.	125.00

Perf. 14

20	A1 1p rose red, re-engraved ('56)	30.00	1.00
a.	Imperf.	575.00	400.00
b.	1p red brown, re-engraved	275.00	27.50
21	A2 2p blue, thin lines ('57)	1,200.	25.00

Queen Victoria — A5

1855 Typo. Wmk. 21

22	A5 4p rose, *bluish*	2,250.	150.
23	A5 4p rose, *white*	3,250.	300.

Compare design A5 with A11, A16, A31.

1856 Wmk. 22

24	A5 4p rose, *bluish*	3,000.	165.
25	A5 4p rose, *white*	1,900.	150.

1857 Wmk. 23

26	A5 4p rose, *white*	675.00	30.00

A6

A7

1856 Wmk. 24

27	A6 6p lilac	500.00	40.00
a.	6p deep lilac	600.00	60.00
b.	Wmk. 3 roses and shamrock		
28	A7 1sh green	675.00	100.00
a.	1sh pale green	625.00	110.00
b.	1sh deep green	1,250.	150.00

Compare design A6 with A13, A18, A22. Compare A7 with A15, A21, A29.

A8

A9

1858-69 Engr. Wmk. 20 Perf. 14

29	A8 2p deep blue (P9)	140.00	3.75
a.	2p blue	140.00	3.75
	Plates 7, 8	400.00	15.00
	Plate 12	650.00	35.00
b.	Imperf. (P9)		3,500.

Lines Above and Below Head Thinner

30	A8 2p blue ('69) (P13)	175.00	5.00
	Plates 14, 15	190.00	9.00
a.	Imperf. (P13)	2,000.	

1860-70

31	A9 1½p lilac rose, *bluish* (P1) ('60)	1,900.	
32	A9 1½p dull rose ('70) (P3)	175.00	17.50
a.	1½p lake red	175.00	17.50
	Plate 1	350.00	27.50
c.	Imperf.		

The 1½p stamps from Plate 1 carry no plate number. The Plate 3 number is in the border at each side above the lower corner letters.
No. 31 was prepared but not issued.
The "OP-PC" variety is a broken letter.

Queen Victoria — A10

1864

33	A10 1p rose red	5.50	.40
a.	1p brick red	5.50	.40
b.	1p lake red	5.50	.40
c.	Imperf. (P116, see footnote)	1,800.	1,250.
	Plate 71	18.00	1.50
	Plate 72	22.50	2.00
	Plate 73	16.00	1.40
	Plate 74	13.00	.40
	Plate 76	25.00	.40
	Plate 77	—	—
	Plate 78	65.00	.40
	Plate 79	20.00	.40
	Plate 80	16.00	.60
	Plate 81	40.00	.75
	Plate 82	80.00	2.25
	Plate 83	110.00	3.50
	Plate 84	45.00	.75
	Plate 85	15.00	.75
	Plate 86	25.00	2.00
	Plate 87	6.50	.40
	Plate 88	110.00	4.75
	Plate 89	25.00	.40
	Plate 90	18.00	.40
	Plate 91	25.00	3.00
	Plate 92	9.50	.50
	Plate 93	25.00	.50
	Plate 94	25.00	2.00
	Plate 95	16.00	.50
	Plate 96	18.00	.40
	Plate 97	9.00	1.25
	Plate 98	9.50	3.00
	Plate 99	16.00	2.50
	Plate 100	22.50	1.00
	Plate 101	32.50	4.50
	Plate 102	13.00	.40
	Plate 103	12.00	1.00
	Plate 104	24.00	2.50
	Plate 105	45.00	3.50
	Plate 106	20.00	.50
	Plate 107	20.00	2.75
	Plate 108	22.50	.90
	Plate 109	50.00	1.40
	Plate 110	15.00	4.50
	Plate 111	22.50	.75
	Plate 112	40.00	.75
	Plate 113	9.50	6.50
	Plate 114	225.00	6.50
	Plate 115	67.50	.75
	Plate 116	50.00	5.00
	Plate 117	11.50	.40
	Plate 118	15.00	.40
	Plate 119	6.50	.50
	Plate 120	5.50	.40
	Plate 121	25.00	5.00
	Plate 122	5.50	.40
	Plates 123-124	8.00	.60
	Plate 125	9.50	1.00
	Plate 127	22.50	1.00
	Plate 129	6.75	4.00
	Plate 130	11.00	1.00
	Plate 131	50.00	10.00
	Plate 132	80.00	12.00
	Plate 133	60.00	6.00
	Plate 134	6.00	.60
	Plate 135	67.50	17.50
	Plate 136	67.50	12.50
	Plate 137	9.50	1.00
	Plate 138	5.75	.60
	Plate 139	16.00	10.00
	Plate 140	5.75	.50
	Plate 141	100.00	6.00
	Plate 142	32.50	17.50
	Plate 143	20.00	9.00
	Plate 144	67.50	12.50
	Plate 145	5.50	1.00
	Plate 146	6.50	3.00
	Plate 147	12.00	1.75
	Plate 148	13.00	1.10
	Plate 149	9.50	3.00
	Plate 150	5.50	.40
	Plate 151	16.00	5.50
	Plate 152	12.00	2.75
	Plate 153	55.00	5.00
	Plate 154	9.50	.40
	Plate 155	11.00	.60
	Plates 156-157	9.50	.40
	Plates 158-160	5.50	.40
	Plate 161	18.00	3.25
	Plate 162	11.00	3.00
	Plates 163-164	9.50	1.25
	Plate 165	13.00	.40
	Plate 166	9.50	3.00
	Plate 167	6.75	.40
	Plate 168	8.00	5.00
	Plate 169	20.00	3.25
	Plate 170	6.50	.40
	Plate 171	5.50	.40
	Plate 172	5.50	.70
	Plate 173	32.50	4.50
	Plate 174	5.50	.40
	Plate 175	22.50	1.25
	Plate 176	16.00	.75
	Plate 177	6.75	.40
	Plate 178	13.00	1.50
	Plate 179	10.50	.90
	Plate 180	10.50	2.50
	Plate 181	9.50	.40
	Plate 182	50.00	2.50
	Plate 183	16.00	1.25
	Plate 184	5.50	.75
	Plate 185	9.50	1.75

Plate 186	21.00	1.00
Plate 187	6.75	.50
Plate 188	13.00	6.00
Plate 189	22.50	3.25
Plate 190	7.50	3.25
Plate 191	5.50	3.25
Plate 192	16.00	.40
Plate 193	5.50	.40
Plate 194	9.50	4.00
Plate 195	9.50	4.00
Plate 196	7.50	2.50
Plate 197	10.50	5.75
Plate 198	5.50	3.00
Plate 199	13.00	3.00
Plate 200	13.00	.50
Plate 201	5.50	2.50
Plate 202	9.25	4.00
Plate 203	6.50	7.50
Plate 204	8.00	1.00
Plate 205	6.75	1.50
Plate 206	6.75	5.75
Plate 207	8.50	5.75
Plate 208	7.50	8.00
Plate 209	10.00	5.75
Plate 210	13.00	7.50
Plate 211	27.50	12.50
Plates 212-213	9.50	6.50
Plate 214	16.00	12.00
Plate 215	16.00	12.00
Plate 216	16.00	12.00
Plate 217	9.50	3.25
Plate 218	6.75	4.00
Plate 219	45.00	47.50
Plate 220	7.00	3.00
Plate 221	19.00	11.00
Plate 222	30.00	22.50
Plate 223	40.00	32.50
Plate 224	47.50	32.50
Plate 225	1,100.	325.00

Plate numbers are contained in the scroll work at the sides of the stamp.

No. 33 was printed from 1864 to 1879.

Thirty-nine plate numbers besides Plate 116 (No. 33c) are also known imperforate. Values for used copies start at $450.

A11

1862   Typo.   Wmk. 23

34 A11 4p vermilion	500.00	30.00
a. Hair lines	550.00	32.50
b. Imperf. (P4)	1,500.	

Hair lines on No. 34a are fine colorless lines drawn diagonally across the corners of the stamp.

A12

A14

A13

A15

1862   Wmk. 24

37 A12 3p pale rose	650.00	100.00
a. 3p deep rose	1,250.	125.00
b. With white dots under side ornaments		3,000.
c. Wmk. 3 roses & shamrock		
39 A13 6p lilac	650.00	25.00
a. 6p deep lilac	825.00	55.00
b. Hair lines	825.00	60.00
c. As "b," imperf. (P4)	1,100.	
d. Wmk. 3 roses & shamrock		
e. As "d," hair lines		
40 A14 9p straw	1,200.	120.00
a. 9p bister	1,200.	125.00
b. Hair lines	10,000.	2,750.
42 A15 1sh green	700.00	50.00
a. 1sh deep green	875.00	110.00
b. As "a," imperf.	1,500.	

Hair lines on Nos. 39b and 40b are fine colorless lines drawn diagonally across the corners of the stamp.

Compare design A14 with A19.

A17

A16

1865   Wmk. 23

43 A16 4p vermilion (P9, 11, 13)	250.00	15.00
a. 4p dull vermilion	250.00	15.00
Plate 7	300.00	20.00
Plate 8	250.00	20.00
Plate 10	325.00	30.00

1865   Wmk. 24

44 A17 3p rose (P4)	425.00	45.00
a. Wmk. 3 roses & shamrock	1,250.	275.00
45 A18 6p lilac (P5)	350.00	30.00
a. 6p deep lilac	425.00	40.00
Plate 6	1,350.	55.00
b. Double impression		6,000.
c. Wmk. 3 roses & shamrock (P5)		300.00
As "c," plate 6		600.00
46 A19 9p straw (P4)	900.00	180.00
Plate 5		12,500.
a. Wmk. 3 roses & shamrock (P4)	2,500.	425.00
47 A20 10p red brn (P1)		21,500.
48 A21 1sh green (P4)	650.00	60.00
b. Wmk. 3 roses & shamrock		400.00
c. Vert. pair, imperf. btwn.		6,250.

No. 46, plate 5, is from a proof sheet.

See Nos. 49-50, 52-54. Compare design A17 with A27.

A19   A20

A21

(No hyphen after SIX) — A22

(Hyphen after SIX) — A18

A23

1867-80   Wmk. 25

49 A17 3p rose (P6)	200.00	12.50
a. 3p deep rose	225.00	17.50
Plate 4	350.00	55.00
Plate 5	200.00	15.00
Plates 7, 8	275.00	15.00
Plate 9	275.00	20.00
Plate 10	275.00	45.00
b. Imperf. (P5,6,8,9)	700.00	
50 A18 6p dull violet (P6)	550.00	30.00
a. bright violet (P6)	550.00	32.50
51 A22 6p brt violet ('69) (P9)	300.00	22.50
a. 6p red violet	325.00	22.50
Plate 8	300.00	22.50
Plate 10		20,000.
b. Imperf. (P8, 9)	750.00	650.00
52 A19 9p bister (P4) ('67)	600.00	100.00
a. Imperf. (P4)	2,250.	
53 A20 10p red brown (P1)	1,000.	140.00
a. 10p deep red brown	1,200.	175.00
Plate 2	20,000.	4,000.
b. Imperf. (P1)	1,850.	
54 A21 1sh green (P4)	350.00	12.50
Plate 5	400.00	12.50
Plate 6	400.00	12.50
Plate 7	600.00	30.00
a. 1sh deep green	475.00	12.50
b. Imperf. (P4)	1,150.	750.00
55 A23 2sh blue (P1)	1,000.	60.00
a. 2sh pale blue	1,500.	90.00
Plate 3		4,500.
b. Imperf. (P1)	2,000.	
56 A23 2sh pale brn (P1) ('80)	6,750.	1,200.

No. 51, plate 10 and No. 53, plate 2, are from proof sheets.

A24

Plate 12, 14 (top right)

Plate 12	250.00	20.00
Plate 14	300.00	32.50
b. Imperf. (P11, 12)	500.00	

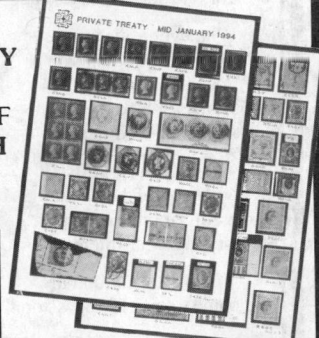

1867   Wmk. 26   Perf. 15½x15

57	A24 5sh rose (P1)	2,750.	250.00
	Plate 2	3,750.	350.00
a.	5sh pale rose	3,250.	250.00
b.	Imperf. (P1)	4,250.	

See No. 90. Compare design A24 with A51.

A25

1870   Engr.   Wmk. 27   Perf. 14

58	A25 ½p rose (P5-6, 11-14)	45.00	6.00
	Plate 1	90.00	10.00
	Plate 3	55.00	12.50
	Plate 4	75.00	7.50
	Plate 8	75.00	4.50
	Plate 9	2,250.	275.00
	Plate 10	65.00	6.00
	Plate 15	55.00	8.00
	Plate 19	80.00	20.00
	Plate 20	90.00	30.00

Plates 1, 4, 5, 6, 8 and 14 are known imperf. Values unused from $1,400, used from $600.

A26    A27

A28    A29

Type A28 has a lined background.

1872-73   Wmk. 25   Typo.

59	A26 6p brown (P11)	350.00	17.50
a.	6p deep brown	425.00	17.50
	Plate 12, #59 or 59a		1,300.
b.	6p pale buff	450.00	45.00
	Plate 12	750.00	55.00
60	A26 6p gray (P12) ('73)	650.00	80.00
a.	Imperf.	1,300.	

1873-80

61	A27 3p rose (shades) (P11, 15-16, 19)	200.00	12.50
	Plates 12, 17, 18	225.00	12.50
	Plate 14	250.00	15.00
	Plate 20	200.00	30.00
62	A28 6p gray (P15, 16)	225.00	17.50
	Plates 13, 14	225.00	20.00
	Plate 17	300.00	35.00
63	A28 6p buff (P13)		10,000.
64	A29 1sh pale green (P12, 13)	250.00	25.00
a.	1sh deep green	325.00	35.00
	Plates 8, 9, 10, 11	325.00	35.00
	Plate 14		15,000.
65	A29 1sh sal (P13) ('80)	1,200.	190.00

No. 64, plate 14, is from a proof sheet.
See Nos. 83, 86-87. For surcharges see Nos. 94-95. For overprints see Nos. O6, O30.

A30

1875   Wmk. 28

66	A30 2½p claret (P1, 2)	250.00	25.00
	Plate 3	425.00	30.00
a.	Bluish paper (P1)	400.00	35.00
	As "a," P2	2,750.	550.00
	As "a," P3		2,000.
b.	Lettered "LH-FL"	8,500.	650.00

1876-80   Wmk. 29

67	A30 2½p claret (P4, 6-9, 11, 14-16)	225.00	12.50
	Plate 3	500.00	27.50
	Plates 5, 12-13	225.00	15.00
	Plate 10	250.00	17.50
	Plate 17	550.00	65.00
68	A30 2½p ultra ('80) (P19, 20)	175.00	10.00
	Plate 17	175.00	17.50
	Plate 18	200.00	12.50

A31    A32

1876-80   Wmk. 23

69	A31 4p vermilion (P15)	650.00	135.00
	Plate 16		
70	A31 4p pale ol grn ('77) (P16)	425.00	100.00
	Plate 15	475.00	100.00
	Plate 17		—
a.	Imperf. (P15)	675.00	
71	A31 4p gray brn (P17) ('80)	625.00	150.00
72	A32 8p brn lilac (P1) ('76)	3,000.	
73	A32 8p org (P1) ('76)	550.00	125.00
a.	Imperf.	1,350.	

No. 72 was never placed in use.
No. 69, plate 16, is from proof sheets.

A33   A34

1878   Wmk. 26   Perf. 15½x15

74	A33 10sh slate (P1)	20,000.	875.
75	A34 £1 brn lilac (P1)	27,500.	1,250.

See Nos. 91-92. Compare design A34 with A52.

A35    A36

A37    A38

A39   A40

1880-81   Wmk. 30   Perf. 14

78	A35 ½p green	17.50	3.25
a.	Imperf.	600.00	
79	A36 1p red brown	6.00	1.25
a.	Imperf.	600.00	
b.	Wmk. 29, error		
80	A37 1½p red brown	80.00	15.00
81	A38 2p lilac rose	100.00	32.50
82	A30 2½p ultra ('81) (P22, 23)	175.00	6.00
	Plate 21	250.00	9.00
a.	Imperf. (P23)	300.00	
83	A27 3p rose ('81) (P21)	190.00	20.00
	Plate 20	275.00	40.00
84	A31 4p gray brown (P17, 18)	175.00	20.00
85	A39 5p dp indigo ('81)	350.00	40.00
86	A28 6p gray (P17, 18)	175.00	20.00
87	A29 1sh sal (P14) ('81)	250.00	40.00
	Plate 13	300.00	40.00
a.	Imperf. (P14)		

See No. 98. For overprints see Nos. O2-O3, O37, O45, O55.
Compare design A35 with A54.

1881

88	A40 1p lilac (14 dots in each angle)	100.00	15.00
89	A40 1p lilac (16 dots in each angle)	1.00	.20
a.	Printed on both sides	525.00	
b.	Imperf., pair	850.00	
c.	Unwmkd.	750.00	
d.	Bluish paper	1,300.	

For overprint see No. O4.

1882-83   Wmk. 31

90	A24 5sh rose, *bluish* (P4)	5,000.	850.
a.	White paper	4,500.	850.

91	A33 10sh slate, *bluish* (P1)	22,500.	1,250.
a.	White paper	25,000.	1,250.
92	A34 £1 brown lilac, *bluish* (P1)	30,000.	2,400.
	White paper	35,000.	2,400.

A41

1882   Wmk. Two Anchors (31)

93	A41 £5 brt orange (P1)	4,500.	1,400.
a.	£5 pale dull orange, *bluish*	17,500.	3,500.
b.	£5 bright orange, *bluish*	17,500.	3,600.

The paper of No. 93b is less bluish than that of No. 93a, and it is a later printing.

Types of 1873-80 Surcharged **3d** in Carmine

1883   Wmk. 30

94	A27 3p on 3p violet	225.00	70.00
95	A28 6p on 6p violet	200.00	65.00

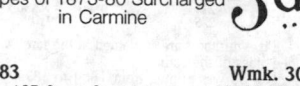
A44

1883   Wmk. 31

96	A44 2sh6p lilac	225.00	55.00
a.	Bluish paper	1,600.	450.00

See British Offices Abroad for overprints on types A44-A133.

These overprints include "M.E.F.," "B.A.," "B.M.A.," "E.A.F.," "CHINA," "Morocco Agencies," "TANGIER," "LEVANT," "PARAS," and "PIASTRE(S)."

A45   A46

A47   A48

A49   A50

1883-84   Wmk. 30

98	A35 ½p slate blue ('84)	8.00	1.50
99	A45 1½p lilac ('84)	55.00	15.00
100	A46 2p lilac ('84)	75.00	27.50
101	A47 2½p lilac ('84)	40.00	3.50
102	A48 3p lilac ('84)	90.00	40.00
103	A49 4p green ('84)	250.00	85.00
104	A45 5p green ('84)	250.00	85.00
105	A50 6p green ('84)	275.00	90.00
106	A50 9p green	525.00	240.00
107	A48 1sh green ('84)	350.00	120.00
	Nos. 98-107 (10)	1,918.	707.50

Values are for copies of good color. Faded copies sell for much less.
No. 104 with line instead of period under "d" was not regularly issued.
Nos. 98-105 and 107 exist imperf. Values from $300 to $600 each.
For overprints see Nos. O5, O7, O27-O29.

A51   A52

1884   **Wmk. 31**

108	A51	5sh carmine rose	400.00	75.
a.		Bluish paper	4,000.	875.
109	A52	10sh ultra	725.00	215.
a.		10sh cobalt	15,000.	3,250.
b.		Bluish paper	12,500.	2,750.
c.		As "a," bluish paper	15,000.	3,500.

For overprints see Nos. O8-O9.

A53

1884   **Wmk. 30**

110	A53	£1 brown violet	11,000.	900.

See Nos. 123-124. For overprints see Nos. O10, O13, O15.

Queen Victoria Jubilee Issue

A54     A55

A56    A57

A58     A59

A60    A61

A62    A63

A64    A65

Two types of 5p:
I - Squarish dots beside "d."
II - Tiny vertical dashes beside "d."

1887-92   **Wmk. 30**

111	A54	½p vermilion	1.00	.30
a.		Printed on both sides		
b.		Double impression	3,750.	
112	A55	1½p violet & grn	9.00	2.00
113	A56	2p grn & car rose	13.50	5.00
a.		2p green & vermilion	275.00	110.00
114	A57	2½p violet, blue	9.00	.50
115	A58	3p violet, yellow	12.50	1.00
a.		3p violet, orange	375.00	135.00

116	A59	4p brown & grn	15.00	6.00
117	A60	4½p car rose & grn ('92)	4.50	14.00
118	A61	5p lilac & bl, II	16.00	4.50
a.		Type I	375.00	35.00
119	A62	6p violet, rose	17.50	4.50
120	A63	9p blue & lilac	35.00	20.00
121	A64	10p car rose & lilac ('90)	32.50	20.00
122	A65	1sh green	125.00	35.00
		Nos. 111-122 (12)	290.50	112.80

See Nos. 125-126. For overprints see Nos. O11-O12, O14, O16-O18, O31-O36, O38, O44, O46-O48, O54, O56-O58, O65-O66.

1888   **Wmk. Three Orbs (29)**

123	A53	£1 brown violet	21,000.	1,300.

1891   **Wmk. 30**

124	A53	£1 green	2,000.	350.

1900   **Wmk. 30**

125	A54	½p blue green	1.00	.30
126	A65	1sh car rose & green	40.00	70.00

No. 125 in bright blue is a color changeling.

King Edward VII
A66   A67

A68   A69

A70    A71

A72   A73

A74   A75

A76    A77

A78

1902-11   **Wmk. 30**   **Perf. 14**

127	A66	½p gray green	.50	.25
128	A66	1p carmine	.30	.25
a.		1p aniline rose ('11)	225.00	100.00
b.		Booklet pane of 6	40.00	
c.		Double impression		
d.		Unwmk.	35.00	35.00
e.		Imperf., pair	7,000.	
129	A67	1½p vio & green	10.00	2.50
130	A68	2p green & car	11.00	3.00
a.		2p green & red	11.00	5.00

131	A66	2½p ultra	3.50	1.50
132	A69	3p vio, yellow	11.00	1.75
133	A70	4p brown & grn	22.50	5.00
134	A71	5p lilac & ultra	11.00	3.00
135	A66	6p dull violet	9.00	3.00
a.		6p red violet	9.00	8.00
b.		6p violet	9.00	9.00
c.		6p black violet	10.50	4.00
136	A72	9p ultra & vio	30.00	20.00
137	A73	10p car rose & violet	30.00	12.00
a.		10p scarlet & violet	32.50	32.50
138	A74	1sh car rose & green	30.00	5.00

Wmk. 31

139	A75	2sh6p dull violet	125.00	40.00
a.		2sh6p dark violet	140.00	40.00
140	A76	5sh car rose	175.00	40.00
a.		5sh carmine	250.00	55.00
141	A77	10sh ultra	325.00	200.00

Wmk. Three Imperial Crowns (30)

142	A78	£1 green	800.00	250.00
		Nos. 127-138 (12)	168.80	57.25

Nos. 129, 130 and 132 to 139 inclusive exist on both ordinary and chalky paper.

See Nos. 143, 144, 146-150. For overprints see Nos. O19-O26, O39-O043, O49-O053, O59-O064, O67-O083.

See British Offices Abroad for overprints on types A44-A133. These overprints include "M.E.F.," "B.A.," "B.M.A.," "E.A.F.," "CHINA," "Morocco Agencies," "TANGIER," "LEVANT," "PARAS," and "PIASTRE(S)."

1904   **Wmk. 30**

143	A66	½p pale yellow green	.50	.25
a.		Booklet pane of 6	30.00	
b.		Booklet pane of 5 + label	175.00	
c.		Double impression	5,000.	
d.		Imperf., pair	2,500.	

Edward VII — A79

1909-10

144	A70	4p orange ('10)	7.00	4.00
145	A79	7p gray ('10)	2.50	3.00

1911   **Perf. 15x14**

146	A66	½p yellow green	20.00	24.00
147	A66	1p carmine	9.00	3.50
148	A66	2½p ultra	10.00	3.50
149	A69	3p violet, yellow	14.00	3.50
a.		3p gray, lemon	3,250.	
150	A70	4p orange	10.00	5.50
		Nos. 146-150 (5)	63.00	40.00

King George V
A80   A81

1911   **Wmk. 30**   **Perf. 15x14**

151	A80	½p yellow green	2.50	.80
a.		Booklet pane of 6	50.00	
b.		Perf. 14 (error)	4,000.	250.00
152	A81	1p carmine	3.00	.50
a.		Booklet pane of 6	50.00	
b.		Perf. 14 (error)	4,750.	

1912, Jan. 1   **Re-engraved**

153	A80	½p yellow green	3.00	.40
154	A81	1p scarlet	1.50	.35
a.		1p aniline scarlet	125.00	47.50

In the re-engraved stamps the lines of the hair and beard are clearer. The re-engraved ½p has 3 lines of shading instead of 4 between the point of neck and frame; in the 1p the body of the lion is nearly covered by lines of shading.

1912, Aug.   **Wmk. 33**   **Perf. 15x14**
Die I (Before Re-engraving)

155	A80	½p yellow green	25.00	25.00
a.		Booklet pane of 6	175.00	
156	A81	1p scarlet	12.50	12.50
a.		Booklet pane of 6	100.00	

Die II (Re-engraved)

157	A80	½p yellow green	2.25	.50
158	A81	1p scarlet	3.50	.35

1912, Oct.   **Wmk. 32**

158A	A80	½p yellow green	4.50	1.75
c.		Imperf., pair	175.00	
158B	A81	1p scarlet	6.25	3.00
d.		Imperf., pair	150.00	

A82

A83

A84

A85

A86

A87

A88

A89

King George V — A90

"Britannia Rules the Waves" A91

TWO PENCE:
Die I - Four horizontal lines above the head. Heavy colored lines above and below the bottom tablet. The inner frame line is closer to the central design than it is to the outer frame line.
Die II - Three lines above the head. Thinner lines above and below the bottom tablet. The inner frame line is midway between the central design and the outer frame line.

1912-13 Wmk. 33 *Perf. 15x14*

159 A82 ½p green .25 .25
a. Double impression —
b. Booklet pane of 6 11.00
160 A83 1p scarlet .20 .25
a. Booklet pane of 6 9.00
b. Tete beche pair
161 A84 1½p red brown 1.00 .25
a. 1½p orange brown 1.25 .25
b. "PENCF" 150.00 75.00
c. Unwmkd. 110.00
d. Booklet pane of 6 22.50
e. Booklet pane of 4 + 2 labels 350.00
162 A85 2p deep orange (I) 1.00 .25
a. 2p deep orange (II) 2.50 1.00
b. Booklet pane of 6 (I) 50.00
c. Booklet pane of 6 (II) 85.00
163 A86 2½p ultra 4.25 .25
164 A87 3p bluish violet 3.50 .25
165 A88 4p slate green 3.50 .65
166 A89 5p yellow brown 4.25 2.50
a. Unwmkd. 450.00
167 A89 6p rose lilac 5.00 .50
a. 6p dull violet 10.00 3.50
b. Perf. 14 60.00 50.00
168 A89 7p olive green 8.75 4.00
169 A89 8p black, *yellow* 25.00 8.50
170 A90 9p black brown 10.00 3.00
171 A90 10p light blue 10.00 12.00
172 A90 1sh bister 12.50 .70
Nos. 159-172 (14) 89.20 33.35

No. 167 is on chalky paper.
See Nos. 177-178, 183, 187-200, 210, 212-220.
Compare design A83 with A97.

See British Offices Abroad for overprints on types A44-A133.
These overprints include "M.E.F.," "B.A.," "B.M.A.," "E.A.F.," "CHINA," "Morocco Agencies," "TANGIER," "LEVANT," "PARAS," and "PIASTRE(S)."

1913-18 Engr. Wmk. 34 *Perf. 11x12*

173 A91 2sh6p lt brown 150.00 60.00
a. 2sh6p black brown 125.00 50.00
174 A91 5sh carmine 300.00 125.00
a. 5sh rose carmine 275.00 125.00
175 A91 10sh lt blue 775.00 275.00
a. 10sh indigo blue 400.00 200.00
176 A91 £1 green 1,100. 500.00

Nos. 173a, 174a, 175a and 176 were printed in 1913 by Waterlow Bros. & Layton; Nos. 173, 174 and 175 were printed in 1915-18 by Thomas De La Rue & Co.
See Nos. 179-181, 222-224.

1913 Wmk. 32 Typo. *Perf. 15x14*
Coil Stamps

177 A82 ½p green 85.00 80.00
178 A83 1p scarlet 180.00 160.00

Type of 1913-18 Retouched

1919 Engr. Wmk. 34 *Perf. 11x12*

179 A91 2sh6p gray brown 75.00 30.00
180 A91 5sh car rose 140.00 40.00
181 A91 10sh blue 250.00 75.00
Nos. 179-181 (3) 465.00 145.00

The retouched stamps usually have a dot above the middle of the top frame. They are 22¾mm high, whereas Nos. 173-176 are 22mm high.
Nos. 179-181 were printed by Bradbury, Wilkinson & Co.

Type of 1912-13

1922 Typo. Wmk. 33 *Perf. 15x14*

183 A90 9p olive green 75.00 11.00

British Empire Exhibition Issue

British Lion and George V — A92

Wmk. 35

1924, Apr. 23 Engr. *Perf. 14*

185 A92 1p vermilion 5.50 6.00
186 A92 1½p dark brown 6.50 8.00
Set, never hinged 29.00

See Nos. 203-204.

Types of 1912-13 Issue

1924 Typo. *Perf. 15x14*

187 A82 ½p green .15 .15
a. Wmk. sideways 5.25 3.25
b. Booklet pane of 6 4.50
c. Double impression 4,250.
188 A83 1p scarlet .24 .15
a. Wmk. sideways 12.00 10.00
b. Booklet pane of 6 6.50
189 A84 1½p red brown .32 .20
a. Tête bêche pair 225.00 125.00
b. Wmk. sideways 3.50 3.00
c. Booklet pane of 6 6.00
d. Bklt. pane of 4 + 2 labels 52.50
190 A85 2p dp orange (II) .90 .50
a. Wmk. sideways 100.00 65.00
b. Unwmkd. 350.00
191 A86 2½p ultra 2.75 .50
a. Unwmkd. 325.00
192 A87 3p violet 3.50 .60
193 A88 4p slate green 4.50 .80
194 A89 5p yel brown 7.00 1.50
195 A89 6p dull violet 2.25 .50
198 A90 9p olive green 9.00 2.00
199 A90 10p dull blue 17.50 11.00
200 A90 1sh bister 13.00 .80
Nos. 187-200 (12) 61.11 18.70
Set, never hinged 150.00

Nos. 187a, 188a, 189b, 190a issued in coils.
Inverted watermarks on the three lowest values are usually from booklet panes.
Nos. 188-189 were issued also on experimental paper with variety of Wmk. 35: closer spacing; letters shorter, rounder.

British Empire Exhibition Issue
Type of 1924, Dated "1925"

1925, May 9 Engr. *Perf. 14*

203 A92 1p vermilion 12.50 10.00
204 A92 1½p brown 25.00 30.00
Set, never hinged 75.00

A93

A94

A95

St. George Slaying the Dragon A96

1929, May 10 Typo. *Perf. 15x14*

205 A93 ½p green 1.50 .90
a. Wmk. sideways 30.00 30.00
b. Booklet pane of 6 22.50
206 A94 1p scarlet 2.25 1.50
a. Wmk. sideways 45.00 37.50
b. Booklet pane of 6 22.50
207 A94 1½p dark brown 1.40 .90
a. Wmk. sideways 30.00 25.00
b. Booklet pane of 6 16.00
c. Booklet pane of 4 + 2 labels 150.00
208 A95 2½p deep blue 10.00 8.50
Nos. 205-208 (4) 15.15 11.80
Set, never hinged 27.50

Nos. 205a, 206a and 207a were issued in coils.

Wmk. 219
Engr. *Perf. 12*

209 A96 £1 black 525.00 425.00
Never hinged 875.00

Universal Postal Union, 9th Congress.

Types of 1924 and

A97

The backgrounds appear to be solid, but under a magnifying glass show the photoengraving screen.

Perf. 14½x14

1934-36 Photo. Wmk. 35

210 A82 ½p dark green .15 .15
a. Wmk. sideways 12.00 1.50
b. Booklet pane of 6 11.00
211 A97 1p carmine .15 .15
a. Wmk. sideways 11.00 4.75
b. Booklet pane of 6 11.00
c. Imperf., pair 950.00
212 A84 1½p red brown .20 .15
a. Imperf., pair 300.00
b. Wmk. sideways 6.00 3.75
c. Booklet pane of 6 5.50
d. Booklet pane of 4 + 2 labels 55.00
213 A85 2p red org ('35) .40 .30
a. Imperf., pair 1,000.
b. Wmk. sideways 65.00 55.00
214 A97 2½p ultra ('35) .70 .50
215 A87 3p dk violet ('35) .90 .50
216 A88 4p dk sl grn ('35) 1.10 .50
217 A89 5p yel brown ('36) 4.00 1.25
218 A90 9p dk ol grn ('35) 10.00 1.65
219 A90 10p Prus blue ('36) 12.50 7.00
220 A90 1sh bister brn ('36) 14.00 .40
Nos. 210-220 (11) 44.10 12.55
Set, never hinged 80.00

The designs in this set are slightly smaller than the 1912-13 issue.
Nos. 210a, 211a, 212b and 213b were issued in coils.

Britannia Type of 1913-18

1934 Engr. Wmk. 34 *Perf. 11x12*

222 A91 2sh6p brown 45.00 7.00
223 A91 5sh carmine 95.00 45.00
224 A91 10sh dark blue 250.00 45.00
Nos. 222-224 (3) 390.00 97.00

Waterlow & Sons. Can be distinguished by the crossed lines in background of portrait. Previous issues have horizontal lines only.

Silver Jubilee Issue

A98

Perf. 14½x14

1935, May 7 Photo. Wmk. 35

226 A98 ½p dark green .20 .15
a. Booklet pane of 4 13.00
227 A98 1p carmine .75 .90
a. Booklet pane of 4 13.00
228 A98 1½p red brown .30 .15
a. Booklet pane of 4 6.50
229 A98 2½p ultramarine 3.50 3.75
a. 2½p Prussian blue 2,750. 2,000.
Never hinged 3,500.
Nos. 226-229 (4) 4.75 4.95
Set, never hinged 8.00

25th anniv. of the reign of George V. Device at right differs on 1½p and 2½p.

Edward VIII — A99

1936 Wmk. 250

230 A99 ½p dark green .15 .15
a. Booklet pane of 6 1.75
231 A99 1p crimson .15 .15
a. Booklet pane of 6 1.75
232 A99 1½p red brown .20 .15
a. Booklet pane of 6 1.75
b. Booklet pane of 4 + 2 labels 15.00
c. Booklet pane of 2 2.00
233 A99 2½p bright ultra .20 .25
Set value .60 .40
Set, never hinged .85

King George VI and Queen Elizabeth A100

Perf. 14½x14

1937, May 13 Wmk. 251

234 A100 1½p purple brown .15 .15
Never hinged .35

Coronation of George VI and Elizabeth.

See British Offices Abroad for overprints on types A44-A133.
These overprints include "M.E.F.," "B.A.," "B.M.A.," "E.A.F.," "CHINA," "Morocco Agencies," "TANGIER," "LEVANT," "PARAS," and "PIASTRE(S)."

King George VI
A101 A102 A103

Nos. 235-240 show face and neck highlighted, background solid.

1937-39

235	A101	½p deep green	.15	.15
a.		Wmk. sideways	.65	.50
b.		Booklet pane of 6	2.75	
c.		Booklet pane of 4	20.00	20.00
d.		Booklet pane of 2	4.50	
236	A101	1p scarlet	.20	.15
a.		Wmk. sideways	7.50	3.00
b.		Booklet pane of 6	6.00	
c.		Booklet pane of 4	60.00	42.50
d.		Booklet pane of 2	4.50	
237	A101	1½p red brown	.20	.15
a.		Wmk. sideways	1.65	.80
b.		Booklet pane of 6	4.50	
c.		Booklet pane of 4 + 2 labels	35.00	
d.		Booklet pane of 2	2.75	
238	A101	2p orange ('38)	.55	.45
a.		Wmk. sideways	40.00	27.50
b.		Booklet pane of 6	22.50	
239	A101	2½p bright ultra	.55	.15
a.		Wmk. sideways	50.00	15.00
b.		Booklet pane of 6	20.00	
c.		Tête bêche pair		
240	A101	3p dk purple ('38)	2.75	.35
241	A102	4p gray green ('38)	.80	.30
a.		Imperf., pair	*800.00*	
242	A102	5p lt brown ('38)	1.40	.30
a.		Imperf., pair	*900.00*	
243	A102	6p rose lilac ('39)	1.40	.30
244	A103	7p emerald ('39)	2.75	.30
a.		Imperf., pair	*650.00*	
245	A103	8p brt rose ('39)	4.00	.35
246	A103	9p dp ol green ('39)	2.75	.35
247	A103	10p royal bl ('39)	2.75	.35
a.		Imperf., pair		
248	A103	1sh brown ('39)	2.75	.20
		Nos. 235-248 (14)	23.00	3.85
		Set, never hinged	35.00	

Nos. 235a, 236a, 237a, 238a and 239a were issued in coils.

Nos. 235c and 236c are watermarked sideways.

The 1½p, 1p, 1½p, 2p and 2½p with watermark inverted are from booklet panes.

See Nos. 258-263, 266, 280-285.

Oman Surcharges

Various definitive and commemorative stamps between Nos. 243 and 372 were surcharged in annas (a), new paisa (np) and rupees (r) for use in Oman. The surcharges do not indicate where the stamps were used.

King George VI and Royal Arms — A104

King George VI — A105

1939-42 Engr. Wmk. 259 *Perf. 14*

249	A104	2sh6p chestnut	30.00	4.50
		Never hinged	50.00	
249A	A104	2sh6p yel green ('42)	3.25	.20
		Never hinged	10.00	
250	A104	5sh dull red	6.75	.90
		Never hinged	13.00	
251	A105	10sh indigo	90.00	14.00
		Never hinged	175.00	
251A	A105	10sh ultra ('42)	11.00	1.90
		Never hinged	35.00	
		Nos. 249-251A (5)	141.00	21.50

See No. 275.

Victoria and George VI — A106

Perf. 14½x14

1940, May 6 Photo. Wmk. 251

252	A106	½p deep green	.15	.15
253	A106	1p scarlet	.25	.25
254	A106	1½p red brown	.40	.20
255	A106	2p orange	.40	.25
256	A106	2½p brt ultra	.60	.50
257	A106	3p dark purple	2.25	2.25
		Nos. 252-257 (6)	4.05	3.60
		Set, never hinged	8.00	

Centenary of the postage stamp.

Type of 1937-39, with Background Lightened

1941-42

258	A101	½p green	.20	.15
a.		Booklet pane of 6	3.50	
b.		Booklet pane of 2	1.25	
c.		Imperf., pair	*850.00*	
d.		Tete beche pair	*1,150.*	
259	A101	1p vermilion	.25	.15
a.		Wmk. sideways ('42)	3.50	4.00
b.		Booklet pane of 2	1.25	
c.		Imperf., pair	*800.00*	
260	A101	1½p lt red brn ('42)	.60	.40
a.		Booklet pane of 2	3.25	
261	A101	2p light orange	.50	.35
a.		Wmk. sideways ('42)	9.00	11.00
b.		Booklet pane of 6	8.00	
c.		Imperf., pair	*1,250.*	
d.		Tete beche pair	1,500.	
262	A101	2½p ultra	.25	.20
a.		Wmk. sideways ('42)	8.00	7.00
b.		Booklet pane of 6	4.00	
c.		Imperf., pair	*900.00*	
d.		Tete beche pair	1,150.	
263	A101	3p violet	1.25	.30
		Nos. 258-263 (6)	3.05	1.55
		Set, never hinged	4.25	

Nos. 259a, 261a and 262a were issued in coils.

Catalogue values for unused stamps in this section, from this point to the end of the section, are for Never Hinged items.

Peace Issue

A107

King George VI and Symbols of Peace and Industry A108

Perf. 14½x14

1946, June 11 Photo. Wmk. 251

264	A107	2½p bright ultra	.15	.15
265	A108	3p violet	.25	.15
		Set value		.20

Return to peace at the close of WW II.

George VI Type of 1939

1947, Dec. 29

266	A103	11p violet brown	3.00	1.00

A109

King George VI and Queen Elizabeth — A110

Perf. 14½x14, 14x14½

1948, Apr. 26

267	A109	2½p brt ultra	.15	.15
268	A110	£1 dp chalky blue	37.50	30.00

25th anniv. of the marriage of King George VI and Queen Elizabeth.

A111

Vraicking (Gathering Seaweed) A112

1948, May 10 *Perf. 14½x14*

269	A111	1p red	.20	.15
270	A112	2½p bright ultra	.25	.20

3rd anniversary of the liberation of the Channel Islands from German occupation.

Sold at post offices in the Channel Islands, but valid for postage throughout Great Britain.

A113

A114

A115

A116

1948, July 29

271	A113	2½p bright ultra	.15	.15
272	A114	3p deep violet	.30	.20
273	A115	6p red violet	.55	.35
274	A116	1sh dark brown	.90	.60
		Nos. 271-274 (4)	1.90	1.30

1948 Olympic Games held at Wembley during July and August.

George VI Type of 1939
Wmk. 259

1948, Oct. 1 Engr. *Perf. 14*

275	A105	£1 red brown	16.00	15.00

A117

A118

A119

A120

Perf. 14½x14

1949, Oct. 10 Photo. Wmk. 251

276	A117	2½p bright ultra	.15	.15
277	A118	3p brt violet	.25	.15
278	A119	6p red violet	.60	.55
279	A120	1sh brown	1.10	1.00
		Nos. 276-279 (4)	2.10	1.85

UPU, 75th anniversary.

Types of 1937

1950-51 Wmk. 251 *Perf. 14½x14*

280	A101	½p light orange	.15	.15
a.		Booklet pane of 2	1.00	
b.		Booklet pane of 4	1.75	
c.		Booklet pane of 6	2.50	
d.		Imperf., pair	*650.00*	
e.		Tete beche pair	*2,200.*	
281	A101	1p ultramarine	.20	.15
a.		Wmk. sideways	.60	.20
b.		Booklet pane of 2	1.20	
c.		Booklet pane of 4	1.75	
d.		Booklet pane of 6	2.50	
e.		Booklet pane of 3 + 3 labels	12.00	
f.		Imperf., pair	*1,250.*	
282	A101	1½p green	.35	.15
a.		Wmk. sideways	1.40	2.00
b.		Booklet pane of 2	1.50	
c.		Booklet pane of 4	3.00	
d.		Booklet pane of 6	3.75	
283	A101	2p lt red brown	.45	.15
a.		Wmk. sideways	1.00	.40
b.		Booklet pane of 6	7.00	
c.		Tete beche pair	*2,250.*	
284	A101	2½p vermilion	.30	.15
a.		Wmk. sideways	1.00	.80
b.		Booklet pane of 6	3.25	
c.		Tete beche pair		
285	A102	4p ultra ('50)	1.40	1.00
		Nos. 280-285 (6)	2.85	1.75

Nos. 281a, 282a, 283a and 284a were issued in coils.

H.M.S. Victory A121

St. George Slaying the Dragon A122

Royal Arms A123

Design: 5sh, White Cliffs, Dover.

Perf. 11x12

1951, May 3 Engr. Wmk. 259

286	A121	2sh6p green	7.50	.65
287	A121	5sh dull red	25.00	1.10
288	A122	10sh ultra	13.00	7.50
289	A123	£1 lt red brown	37.50	11.50
		Nos. 286-289 (4)	83.00	20.75

Britannia, Symbols of Commerce and Prosperity, King George VI — A124

Festival Symbol A125

Perf. 14½x14

1951, May 3 Photo. Wmk. 251

290	A124	2½p scarlet	.15	.15
291	A125	4p bright ultra	.45	.45

Festival of Britain, 1951.

Queen Elizabeth
A126 A127

A128

A129

A130

A131

A132

Type I

Type II

Perf. 14½x14

1952-54 Photo. Wmk. 298

292	A126	½p red orange ('53)	.15	.15
a.		Booklet pane of 2	.70	
b.		Booklet pane of 4	1.25	
c.		Booklet pane of 6	1.50	
293	A126	1p ultra ('53)	.15	.15
a.		Booklet pane of 2	.90	
b.		Booklet pane of 4	1.75	
c.		Booklet pane of 6	2.25	
d.		Booklet pane 3 + 3 labels	35.00	
294	A126	1½p green ('52)	.15	.15
a.		Booklet pane of 2	.70	
b.		Booklet pane of 4	1.25	
c.		Booklet pane of 6 ('53)	1.50	
d.		Wmk. sideways	.30	.25
e.		As "c," imperf. (error)	*750.00*	
295	A126	2p red brown ('53)	.60	.15
a.		Booklet pane of 6	5.00	
b.		Wmk. sideways	1.40	.90
296	A127	2½p scarlet, Type I ('52)	.25	.15
a.		Booklet pane of 6, Type II ('53)	7.00	
b.		Wmk. sideways, Type I ('54)	8.00	8.00
c.		Type II	.60	.55
297	A127	3p dk purple	.85	.20
298	A128	4p ultra ('53)	2.50	.80
299	A129	5p lt brn ('53)	1.25	1.50
300	A129	6p lilac rose	2.50	.50
301	A129	7p emerald	8.00	3.00
302	A130	8p brt rose ('53)	1.65	.80
303	A130	9p dp ol grn	20.00	2.50
304	A130	10p royal blue	16.00	2.50
305	A130	11p vio brown	32.50	15.00
306	A131	1sh brown ('53)	1.50	.28
307	A132	1sh3p dk grn ('53)	4.00	1.75
308	A131	1sh6p dk bl ('53)	12.00	2.50
		Nos. 292-308 (17)	104.05	32.08

Nos. 294d, 295b, 296b issued in coils.

Nos. 292-296 with watermark inverted are from booklets.

Type II stamps of No. 296 come only from booklet panes.

See Nos. 317-333, 353-369.

Compare design A128 with A139.

See regional issues, Guernsey, Jersey and Isle of Man for other stamps showing this portrait of the Queen, which have different frames or devices added to the design.

See British Offices Abroad for overprints on types A44-A133.

These overprints include "M.E.F.," "B.A.," "B.M.A.," "E.A.F.," "CHINA," "Morocco Agencies," "TANGIER," "LEVANT," "PARAS," and "PIASTRE(S)."

Carrickfergus Castle, Ireland — A133

Castles: 5sh, Caernarvon, Wales. 10sh, Edinburgh, Scotland. £1, Windsor, England.

1955 Engr. Wmk. 308 *Perf. 11x12*

309	A133	2sh6p dark brown	11.50	1.50
310	A133	5sh crimson	25.00	3.00
311	A133	10sh brt ultra	75.00	10.00
312	A133	£1 intense blk	125.00	25.00
		Nos. 309-312 (4)	236.50	39.50

See Nos. 371-374, 525-528.

A134

A135

A136

A137

Perf. 14½x14

1953, June 3 Photo. Wmk. 298

313	A134	2½p scarlet	.45	.15
314	A135	4p ultra	1.40	.60
315	A136	1sh3p dark green	5.00	2.25
316	A137	1sh6p dark blue	5.25	2.50
		Nos. 313-316 (4)	12.10	5.50

Types of 1952-54

1955-57 Wmk. 308 *Perf. 14½x14*

317	A126	½p red orange ('56)	.15	.15
a.		Booklet pane of 6	1.50	
b.		Booklet pane of 4	1.25	
d.		Booklet pane of 2	.60	
318	A126	1p ultra ('56)	.15	.15
a.		Bklt. pane of 3 + 3 labels	20.00	
b.		Booklet pane of 6	1.75	
c.		Booklet pane of 4	1.25	
e.		Tete Beche pair	300.00	
f.		Booklet pane of 2	.70	
319	A126	1½p green ('56)	.15	.15
a.		Booklet pane of 6	6.50	
b.		Booklet pane of 4	5.00	
c.		Wmk. sideways ('56)	.25	.65
e.		Tete beche pair	*850.00*	
f.		Booklet pane of 2	1.10	
320	A126	2p red brown ('56)	.20	.15
a.		Wmk. sideways ('56)	.25	.50
b.		Booklet pane of 6	2.50	
d.		Tete beche pair	*250.00*	
e.		Vert. pair, imperf. between	*1,250.*	
f.		As "a," horiz. pair, imperf. between	*1,250.*	
h.		Imperf., pair	250.00	
321	A127	2½p scar, Type I ('56)	.20	.15
a.		Booklet pane of 6, Type II	4.00	
b.		Wmk. sideways, Type I ('56)	1.50	1.00
d.		Type II	.30	.25
e.		Tete beche pair	100.00	
f.		Imperf., pair		
322	A127	3p dk purple ('56)	.20	.15
a.		Booklet pane of 6	4.00	
b.		Booklet pane of 4	5.50	
c.		Wmk. sideways	11.00	9.00
e.		Tete beche pair	*700.00*	
323	A128	4p ultra	1.25	.45
324	A129	5p lt brn ('56)	5.00	3.00
325	A129	6p lilac rose ('56)	3.50	.65
326	A129	7p emerald	45.00	7.00
327	A130	8p brt rose ('56)	5.00	.90
328	A130	9p dp ol grn ('56)	21.00	2.00
329	A130	10p royal bl ('56)	18.00	2.00
330	A130	11p vio brown	.90	.90
331	A131	1sh brown	19.00	.30
332	A132	1sh3p dk grn ('56)	25.00	1.25
333	A131	1sh6p dark blue	20.00	1.00
		Nos. 317-333 (17)	164.70	20.35

Nos. 319c, 320a, 321b, 322c issued in coils.

Nos. 317-322 with watermark inverted are from booklets. See Nos. 353-369.

Black Graphite Lines on Back

1957-59 Wmk. 308

317c	A126	½p red orange	.15	.15
p.		Phosphor. ('59)	4.50	5.50
318d	A126	1p ultra	.30	.30
p.		Phosphor. ('59)	7.00	5.50
319d	A126	1½p green	.85	.60
p.		Phosphor. ('59)	2.50	4.00
320c	A126	2p red brown	2.00	1.25
p.		Phosphor. ('59)	200.00	150.00
321c	A127	2½p scarlet (II)	7.00	4.25
322d	A127	3p dark purple	1.65	.60
		Nos. 317c-322d (6)	11.95	7.15

The vertical black graphite lines were applied to facilitate mail sorting by an electronic machine. The 2p has one line (at right, seen from back), the others two.

Phosphorescent bands were overprinted vertically in Nov. 1959 on the face of the preceding ½p, 1p, 1½p and 2p graphite-lined stamps, plus the 2p, 2½p, 3p, 4p and 4½p graphite-lined stamps with Wmk. 322, in a letter-sorting experiment. These faint bands can be seen best with an ultraviolet lamp; without it they can be seen best on unused stamps.

Scout Emblem and Rolling Hitch Knot
A138

Designs: 4p, Swallows. 1sh3p, Globe encircled by compass.

Perf. 14½x14

1957, Aug. 1 Wmk. 308

334	A138	2½p scarlet	.15	.15
335	A138	4p ultra	.90	.75
336	A138	1sh3p dk green	4.50	4.00
		Nos. 334-336 (3)	5.55	4.90

50th anniv. of the Boy Scout movement and the World Scout Jubilee Jamboree, Sutton Coldfield, Aug. 1-12.

A139

1957, Sept. 12 Photo.

337	A139	4p ultra	.75	.75

46th Conf. of the Inter-Parliamentary Union, London, Sept. 12-19.

Welsh Dragon
A140

Designs: 6p, Flag with British Empire and Commonwealth Games Emblem. 1sh3p, Welsh dragon holding laurel.

1958, July 18 *Perf. 14½x14*

338	A140	3p dk purple	.15	.15
339	A140	6p red lilac	.30	.30
340	A140	1sh3p green	1.65	1.50
		Nos. 338-340 (3)	2.10	1.95

6th British Empire and Commonwealth Games, Cardiff, July 18-26.

Regional Issues of Great Britain for Guernsey, Jersey, Isle of Man, Northern Ireland, Scotland and Wales-Monmouthshire are listed in separate sections following Great Britain Envelopes.

Types of 1952-55

Perf. 14½x14

1958-65 Photo. Wmk. 322

353	A126	½p red orange	.15	.15
a.		Booklet pane of 6	.70	
b.		Booklet pane of 4	.55	
e.		Booklet pane of 4 (3 No. 353 + No. 357) ('63)	7.50	7.50
f.		Tete beche pair	*850.00*	
g.		Booklet pane of 4 (2 Nos. 353 + 2 No. 357) ('64)	2.25	2.25
354	A126	1p ultra ('59)	.15	.15
a.		Booklet pane of 6 ('59)	1.00	
b.		Booklet pane of 4	.75	
e.		Imperf., pair		
f.		Bklt. pane, #2 #354, 2 #358 ('65)	2.25	2.25
355	A126	1½p green	.15	.15
a.		Booklet pane of 6	1.00	
b.		Booklet pane of 4	.75	
356	A126	2p red brown	.15	.15
a.		Wmk. sideways	.30	.20
b.		Booklet pane of 6	6.00	
357	A127	2½p scarlet, type II ('59)	.15	.15
a.		Type I ('61)	.75	.45
b.		Wmk. sideways, type I	.30	.25
c.		Booklet pane of 6, Type II ('59)	1.00	
f.		Tete beche pair, type II		
g.		Booklet pane of 4, type II ('64)	2.50	
h.		Imperf., pair		
358	A127	3p dark purple	.15	.15
a.		Booklet pane of 6	1.75	
b.		Booklet pane of 4	1.25	
e.		Imperf., pair	90.00	
g.		Wmk. sideways	.15	.15
359	A128	4p ultra	.20	.15
b.		Booklet pane of 6 ('65)	3.00	
c.		Booklet pane of 4 ('65)	1.50	
d.		Wmk. sideways	.60	.50
360	A128	4½p henna brown	.15	.15
361	A129	5p light brown	.40	.20
362	A129	6p lil rose ('59)	.25	.15
363	A129	7p emerald	.65	.20
364	A130	8p brt rose ('60)	.55	.15
365	A130	9p dp ol grn ('59)	.65	.15
366	A130	10p royal blue	.55	.20
367	A131	1sh brown	.40	.15
368	A132	1sh3p dk green ('59)	.40	.15
369	A131	1sh6p dark blue	4.00	.25
		Nos. 353-369 (17)	9.10	2.80

Nos. 356a and 357b were issued in coils. The 3p and 4p watermarked sideways may be from a coil or booklet pane of 4.

Booklet panes of this issue have watermarks normal, inverted or sideways.

Part perf. booklet panes exist of No. 353a and No. 354a.

Black Graphite Lines on Back

1958-59 Wmk. 322

353c	A126	½p red orange ('59)	2.50	2.75
d.		Booklet pane of 6	25.00	
354c	A126	1p ultra	1.25	1.25
d.		Booklet pane of 6	12.50	
355c	A126	1½p green ('59)	85.00	37.50
d.		Booklet pane of 6	400.00	
356c	A126	2p red brown	7.75	4.00
cp.		Phosphor. ('59)	6.00	5.00
357d	A127	2½p scarlet (II) ('59)	17.50	11.50
dp.		Phosphor. ('59)	19.00	17.50
e.		Booklet pane of 6	165.00	
358c	A127	3p dark purple	1.00	.75
cp.		Phosphor. ('59)	16.00	10.00
d.		Booklet pane of 6	7.00	
359a	A128	4p ultra ('59)	8.50	6.75
ap.		Phosphor. ('59)	9.00	7.00
360a	A128	4½p henna brown ('59)	9.00	2.50
ap.		Phosphor. ('59)	37.50	27.50
		Nos. 353c-360a (8)	132.50	67.00

The vertical black graphite lines were applied to facilitate mail sorting by an electronic machine. The 2p has one line; the others two. Missing or misplaced lines occur on 1p, 3p and 4p.

Nos. 353c and 354c were issued only in booklets or coils; No. 355c only in booklets.

Phosphorescent Stamps of 1958-65

1960-67 Wmk. 322

353p	A126	½p red orange	.15	.15
354p	A126	1p ultra	.15	.15
355p	A126	1½p green	.15	.15
356p	A126	2p red brown	.15	.15
ap.		Watermark sideways	.15	.15
357p	A127	2½p scarlet (II)	.15	.20
ap.		Type I ('61)	45.00	30.00
358p	A127	3p dark purple	.30	.20
gp.		Watermark sideways	1.25	.50
359p	A128	4p ultramarine	.20	.15
dp.		Watermark sideways	.20	.15
360p	A128	4½p henna brown ('61)	.25	.20
361p	A129	5p lt brown ('67)	.25	.20
362p	A129	6p lilac rose	.25	.15
363p	A129	7p emerald ('67)	.40	.45
364p	A130	8p brt rose ('67)	.40	.40
365p	A130	9p dp ol green ('67)	.65	.30
366p	A130	10p royal blue ('67)	.75	.45
367p	A131	1sh brown ('67)	.40	.20
368p	A132	1sh3p dark green	3.00	.45
369p	A131	1sh6p dark blue ('66)	2.00	.65
		Nos. 353p-369p (17)	9.60	
		Set value		4.10

The 2p, 2½p (II) and 3p were issued with both one and two phosphorescent bands. The less expensive is valued here.

Watermarked sideways, the 2p is from a coil; the 3p and 4p from booklet pane of coil; the ½p, 1p and 1½p from booklet panes (hence unlisted in this state).

Booklet panes of 4 with phosphorescent bands; ½p, 1p, 1½p, 3p (2 bands), 4p, and 1p se-tenant with 3p (1 or 2 bands). Booklet panes of 6 with phosphorescent bands: ½p, 1p, 1½p, 2½p (II) (1 or 2 bands), 3p (1 or 2 bands), 4p.

1959 Engr. Wmk. 322 *Perf. 11x12*

371	A133	2sh6p dk brown	.60	.15
372	A133	5sh crimson	1.50	.40
373	A133	10sh brt ultra	2.50	.80
374	A133	£1 intense black	8.00	3.25
		Nos. 371-374 (4)	12.60	4.60

Postboy on Horseback
A147

Queen Elizabeth II, Oak Leaves and 1660 Post Horn — A148

Perf. 14¹/₂x14, 14x14¹/₂

1960, July 7   Photo.   Wmk. 322
375 A147   3p bright violet   .40   .40
376 A148   1sh3p dark green   3.00   3.00

Tercentenary of the act establishing the General Letter Office (General Post Office).

Symbolic Wheel CD3

Perf. 14¹/₂x14

1960, Sept. 19   Wmk. 322
377 CD3   6p red lilac & grn   1.00   .15
378 CD3   1sh6p dk bl & red brn   4.50   4.00

1st anniv. of the establishment of CEPT.

Symbolic Thrift Plant — A150

Nut Tree, Nest, Squirrel, Owl — A151

Thrift Plant A152

Perf. 14x14¹/₂, 14¹/₂x14

1961, Aug. 28   Photo.   Wmk. 322
379 A150   2¹/₂p scarlet & blk   .15   .15
a.   Black omitted   10,000.
380 A151   3p purple & org   .20   .15
a.   Orange omitted   150.00   75.00
381 A152   1sh6p dk bl & ver   2.00   2.00
Nos. 379-381 (3)   2.35   2.30

Centenary of Post Office Savings Bank.

CEPT Emblem A153

Nineteen Doves Flying as One — CD4

Design: 10p, Queen at right.

1961, Sept. 18   *Perf. 14¹/₂x14*
382 A153   2p red brn, yel & rose   .15   .15
383 CD4   4p ultra, pink & buff   .20   .20
384 CD4   10p dk bl, yel grn & Prus blue   .30   .30
a.   Yellow green omitted   4,000.
b.   Dark blue omitted   4,000.
Nos. 382-384 (3)   .65   .65

Hammer Beam Roof of Westminster Hall — A155

Parliament — A156

Perf. 14¹/₂x14, 14x14¹/₂

1961, Sept. 25   Wmk. 322
385 A155   6p red lil & gold   .30   .20
a.   Gold omitted   425.00
386 A156   1sh3p green & slate   2.00   1.75
a.   Slate (Queen's head) omitted   4,000.

7th Commonwealth Parliamentary Conf.

National Productivity Symbol A157

Designs: 3p, Two arrows and map of the British Isles. 1sh3p, Five arrows pointing up.

Perf. 14¹/₂x14

1962, Nov. 14   Photo.   Wmk. 322
387 A157   2¹/₂p car rose & dk grn   .15   .15
p.   Phosphor.   1.25   1.25
388 A157   3p violet & blue   .20   .15
a.   Queen's head omitted   800.00
p.   Phosphor.   2.75   2.50
389 A157   1sh3p dk grn, car rose & bl   2.00   1.90
a.   Queen's head omitted   3,000.
p.   Phosphor.   25.00   13.00
Nos. 387-389 (3)   2.35   2.20

National Productivity Year. The watermark on Nos. 387-388 is inverted.

Phosphorescent Commemoratives Commemorative stamps between Nos. 387-493 were issued both with and without phosphorescence on the front unless otherwise noted with the issue. Starting with No. 514, commemorative stamps were issued only with phosphorescence on the front unless otherwise noted.

Phosphorescent Regulars Starting in 1967, all small stamps (lower values) of the regular series were issued only with phosphorescence.

Wheat Emblem and People A158

Design: 1sh3p, Caucasian, Negro and Mongol boys.

1963, Mar. 21   Wmk. 322
390 A158   2¹/₂p pink & dp car   .20   .15
p.   Phosphor.   1.60   1.20
391 A158   1sh3p yellow & brn   2.00   1.75
p.   Phosphor.   25.00   17.50

FAO "Freedom from Hunger" campaign.

Paris Postal Conference A159

1963, May 7   Wmk. 322
392 A159   6p purple & green   .35   .35
a.   Green omitted   2,500.
p.   Phosphor.   6.50   3.00

Cent. of the 1st Intl. Postal Conf., Paris, 1863, and Paris Postal Conf., May 7-9, 1963.

Buttercups, Daisies and Bee — A160

Design: 4¹/₂p, Badger, Fawn, woodpecker, lark, titmouse, butterfly, mouse and wild plants.

1963, May 16   *Perf. 14¹/₂x14*
393 A160   3p multicolored   .15   .15
p.   Phosphor.   .50   .60
394 A160   4¹/₂p multicolored   .35   .35
p.   Phosphor.   2.50   1.75

Natl. Nature Week, May 18-25, and the importance of wildlife conservation.

Helicopter Lifting Man from Lifeboat A161

Lifeboat Men A162

Design: 4p, 19th cent. lifeboat under sail.

1963, May 31   Photo.
395 A161   2¹/₂p multicolored   .15   .15
p.   Phosphor.   .80   .55
396 A161   4p multicolored   .70   .65
p.   Phosphor.   1.65   1.25
397 A162   1sh6p multicolored   2.50   2.50
p.   Phosphor.   37.50   27.50
Nos. 395-397 (3)   3.35   3.30

9th Intl. Life-Boat Conf., Edinburgh, June 3-5.

Red Cross Centenary Congress and Elizabeth II — A163

Designs: 1sh3p, Cross at upper left. 1sh6p, Cross in center.

1963, Aug. 15   Wmk. 322
Cross in Red
398 A163   3p purple   .15   .15
a.   Red cross omitted   3,500.
p.   Phosphor.   2.00   1.50
399 A163   1sh3p gray & blue   2.75   2.50
p.   Phosphor.   37.50   22.50
400 A163   1sh6p dull blue & ol bister   3.00   2.75
p.   Phosphor.   35.00   22.50
Nos. 398-400 (3)   5.90   5.40

Red Cross Cent. Cong., Geneva, Sept. 2.

Cable Around World and Under Sea — A164

1963, Dec. 3   *Perf. 14¹/₂x14*
401 A164   1sh6p blue & blk   3.00   2.50
a.   Blue omitted   3,500.
p.   Phosphor.   16.00   14.00

Opening of the Commonwealth Pacific (telephone) cable service, COMPAC.

Puck and Bottom from "A Midsummer Night's Dream," Shakespeare A165

Hamlet Holding Yorick's Skull — A166

First Folio Portrait of Shakespeare and: 6p, Feste the Clown, from "Twelfth Night." 1sh3p, Romeo and Juliet. 1sh6p, Henry V praying at Agincourt.

Perf. 14¹/₂x14

1964, Apr. 23   Photo.   Wmk. 322
402 A165   3p multicolored   .15   .15
p.   Phosphor.   .40   .25
403 A165   6p multicolored   .30   .30
p.   Phosphor.   .70   .75
404 A165   1sh3p multicolored   .65   .75
p.   Phosphor.   5.50   4.50
405 A165   1sh6p multicolored   1.25   1.10
p.   Phosphor.   8.00   7.00

Perf. 11x12
Engr.
406 A166   2sh6p dark gray   1.65   1.50
Nos. 402-406 (5)   4.00   3.80

400th anniv. of the birth of William Shakespeare. No. 406 was not issued with phosphorescence.

Apartment Buildings, London A170

Designs: 4p, Shipyards, Belfast. 8p, Beddgelert Forest Park, Snowdonia. 1sh6p, Dounreay nuclear reactor and sheaves of wheat.

1964, July 1   Photo.   *Perf. 14¹/₂x14*
410 A170   2¹/₂p gray, blk, bl grn & yel   .15   .15
p.   Phosphor.   .30   .30
411 A170   4p blk, vio, pink & ocher   .50   .40
a.   Violet ("4d") omitted   175.00
b.   Ocher omitted   275.00
c.   Violet & ocher omitted   200.00
p.   Phosphor.   .80   .75
412 A170   8p grn, blk, lt brn & emer   1.25   1.00
a.   Green omitted   2,000.
p.   Phosphor.   6.50   5.00
413 A170   1sh6p multicolored   3.25   2.00
p.   Phosphor.   18.00   11.00
Nos. 410-413 (4)   5.15   3.55

20th Intl. Geographical Cong., London, July 20-28.

Spring Gentian A171

1964, Aug. 5   Wmk. 322
414 A171   3p shown   .15   .15
a.   Blue omitted   5,500.
p.   Phosphor.   .30   .25
415 A171   6p Dog rose   .25   .20
p.   Phosphor.   1.50   1.40
416 A171   9p Honeysuckle   1.40   1.40
a.   Light green omitted   5,500.
p.   Phosphor.   7.50   8.00
417 A171   1sh3p Fringed water lily   1.90   .80
p.   Phosphor.   17.50   14.00
Nos. 414-417 (4)   3.70   2.55

10th Intl. Botanical Cong., Edinburgh, Aug. 3-12.

Forth Road Bridge A172

Design: 6p, Bridge and railroad bridge.

1964, Sept. 4   *Perf. 14¹/₂x14*
418 A172   3p blk, lil & blue   .15   .15
419 A172   6p vio blk, grnsh bl & car lake   .50   .45
a.   Greenish blue omitted   2,750.   1,500.
p.   Phosphor.   4.25   4.25

Opening of Forth Road Bridge, Scotland.

Winston Churchill A173

Design: 1sh3p, Large portrait.

1965, July 8 Photo. Wmk. 322

420 A173 4p dk brown & blk .15 .15
p. Phosphor. .45 .40
421 A173 1sh3p gray & black .50 .50
p. Phosphor. 3.50 3.50

Sir Winston Spencer Churchill (1874-1965), statesman and WWII leader.

Seal of Simon de Montfort A174

St. Stephen's Hall, Westminster Hall and Abbey, Engraving by Wenceslaus Hollar, 1647 — A175

1965, July 19 ***Perf. 14½x14***

422 A174 6p dark olive .15 .15
p. Phosphor. .55 .55
423 A175 2sh6p brown black 1.25 1.25

700th anniv. of Parliament. No. 423 was not issued with phosphorescence; size: 58x21mm.

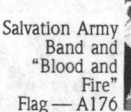

Salvation Army Band and "Blood and Fire" Flag — A176

Design: 1sh6p, Salvation Army officers and flag.

1965, Aug. 9

424 A176 3p dk bl, yel & brt car .15 .15
p. Phosphor. .40 .40
425 A176 1sh6p red, yel & brt bl 1.25 1.10
p. Phosphor. 3.75 3.75

Centenary of the Salvation Army.

Lister's Carbolic Spray — A177

Design: 1sh, Joseph Lister and carbolic acid formula.

1965, Sept. 1

426 A177 4p gray, bluish blk & red brn .15 .15
a. Red brown (tubing) omitted *250.00*
b. Bluish black omitted *1,750.*
p. Phosphor. .20 .15
427 A177 1sh blk, blue & pur 1.00 .95
p. Phosphor. 1.90 1.50

Introduction of antiseptic surgery by Joseph Lister, cent.

Trinidad Folk Dancers, Shrove Monday Carnival A178

Design: 1sh6p, French Canadian folk dancers, Les Feux Follets.

Perf. 14½x14

1965, Sept. 1 Photo. Wmk. 322

428 A178 6p orange & blk .20 .20
p. Phosphor. .40 .30
429 A178 1sh6p brt vio & blk 1.10 1.10
p. Phosphor. 2.50 2.25

1st Commonwealth Arts Festival, Sept. 16-Oct. 2.

Supermarine Spitfire Fighters A179

Anti-Aircraft Gun Battery in Action A180

Designs: No. 431, Pilot in cockpit of Hawker Hurricane fighter. No. 432, Wing tips of Messerschmitt ME-109 and Spitfire. No. 433, Two Spitfires attacking Heinkel HE-111 bomber. No. 434, Spitfire attacking Junkers JU-187B Stuka dive bomber. No. 435, Hurricanes returning over wreckage of Dornier DO-17 Z bomber. 1sh3p, Vapor trails over St. Paul's Cathedral, London.

Perf. 14½x14

1965, Sept. 13 Photo. Wmk. 322

430 A179 4p slate & dk ol .40 .25
431 A179 4p slate & dk ol .40 .25
432 A179 4p sl, dk ol, brt bl & red .40 .25
433 A179 4p slate & dk ol .40 .25
434 A179 4p slate & dk ol .40 .25
435 A179 4p sl, dk ol & brt blue .48 .25
a. Bright blue omitted
436 A180 9p vio bl, org & vio black 2.75 1.75
437 A180 1sh3p brt bl, sl & grnsh gray 2.75 2.50
Nos. 430-437 (8) 7.98 5.75

Phosphorescent

430p A179 4p slate & dark olive .50 .35
431p A179 4p slate & dark olive .50 .35
432p A179 4p sl, dk ol, brt bl & red .50 .35
433p A179 4p slate & dark olive .50 .35
434p A179 4p slate & dark olive .50 .35
435p A179 4p sl, dk ol & brt bl .50 .35
436p A180 9p vio bl, org & vio black 4.50 3.25
437p A180 1sh3p brt bl, slate & grnsh gray 4.00 3.25
Nos. 430p-437p (8) 11.50 8.60

25th anniv. of the Battle of Britain. Nos. 430-435 printed in blocks of 6 (3x2) in sheets of 120.

Post Office Tower and Georgian Buildings — A181

Design: 1sh3p, Post Office Tower and Nash Terrace, Regents Park, horiz.

1965, Oct. 8 ***Perf. 14x14½, 14½x14***

438 A181 3p brt bl, lem & ol green .15 .15
p. Phosphor. .15 .15
439 A181 1sh3p grn, ol grn & blue .45 .40
p. Phosphor. .40 .40

Opening of the Post Office Tower, London.

UN Emblem A182

ICY Emblem A183

1965, Oct. 25 ***Perf. 14½14x14***

440 A182 3p multicolored .15 .15
p. Phosphor. .30 .30
441 A183 1sh6p multicolored .90 .90
p. Phosphor. 2.50 2.50

20th anniv. of the UN and Intl. Cooperation Year, 1965.

"World Telecommunication Stations" — A184

ITU Cent.: 1sh6p, "Radio waves and switchboard."

1965, Nov. 15 Photo. Wmk. 322

442 A184 9p multicolored .35 .35
p. Phosphor. 1.25 1.25
443 A184 1sh6p bl, red, blk, ind & pink .90 .90
a. Pink omitted *500.00*
p. Phosphor. 5.00 4.75

Robert Burns and Saltier Cross of St. Andrew A185

Design: 1sh3p, Alexander Nasmyth portrait of Burns, his signature and symbols of his life. Portrait of Burns on 4p stamp is adaptation of Archibald Skirvings', chalk drawing, 1798.

1966, Jan. 25 ***Perf. 14½x14***

444 A185 4p blue, blk & dk sl .15 .15
p. Phosphor. .20 .20
445 A185 1sh3p org, blk & Prus blue .45 .45
p. Phosphor. 1.25 1.25

Robert Burns (1759-1796), Scottish national poet.

Westminster Abbey A186

Fan Vaulting, Chapel of Henry VII — A187

1966, Feb. 28 Photo. ***Perf. 14½x14***

452 A186 3p blue, blk, & red brn .15 .15
p. Phosphor. .15 .15

Perf. 11x12

Engr.

453 A187 2sh6p black 1.00 1.00

900th anniv. of Westminster Abbey. No. 453 issued only without phosphor.

Landscape near Hassock, Sussex A188

Views: 6p, Antrim, Northern Ireland. 1sh3p, Harlech Castle, Wales. 1sh6p, The Cairngorms (mountains), Scotland.

Perf. 14½x14

1966, May 2 Photo. Wmk. 322

454 A188 4p multicolored .15 .15
p. Phosphor. .15 .15
455 A188 6p multicolored .15 .15
p. Phosphor. .15 .15
456 A188 1sh3p multicolored .30 .30
p. Phosphor. .30 .30
457 A188 1sh6p multicolored .35 .35
p. Phosphor. .35 .35
Set value .85 .75

Soccer Players — A189

Players and Crowd A190

Design: 1sh3p, Goalkeeper and two players.

Perf. 14x14½, 14½x14

1966, June 1 Photo. Wmk. 322

458 A189 4p multicolored .15 .15
p. Phosphor. .15 .15
459 A190 6p bl, sep, red, yel grn & blk .15 .15
a. Black omitted *65.00*
b. Yellow green omitted *1,000.*
c. Red omitted *1,000.*
p. Phosphor. .15 .15
460 A190 1sh3p blk, red, yel, bl & citron .25 .25
a. Blue omitted *175.00*
p. Phosphor. .25 .25
Nos. 458-460 (3) .55
Set value .45

Final games of the 1965-66 World Soccer Championship for the Jules Rimet Cup, Wembley, July 11-30.

See No. 465.

Blackheaded Gull — A191

Perf. 14½x14

1966, Aug. 8 Photo. Wmk. 322

Birds in Natural Colors

461 A191 4p shown .20 .15
p. Phosphor. .20 .20
462 A191 4p Blue tit .20 .15
p. Phosphor. .20 .20
463 A191 4p European robin .20 .15
p. Phosphor. .20 .20
464 A191 4p European blackbird .20 .15
p. Phosphor. .20 .20
a. Block of 4, #461-464 .80 .50
b. Block of 4, #461p-464p .80 .75
Set value .40

Seven colors have been found omitted (singly or in combinations) on Nos. 461-464; green, red, ultramarine, brown, red brown, yellow and black.

No. 458 Inscribed: "ENGLAND WINNERS"

1966, Aug. 18 ***Perf. 14x14½***

465 A189 4p multicolored .15 .15

England's victory in the World Soccer Cup Championship.

Jodrell Bank Radio Telescope A192

Designs: 6p, Automobiles (Jaguar and 3 Mini-Minors). 1sh3p, SR N6 Hovercraft. 1sh6p, Windscale atomic reactor.

1966, Sept. 19 ***Perf. 14½x14***

466 A192 4p yellow & blk .15 .15
p. Phosphor. .15 .15
467 A192 6p org, red & dk bl .15 .15
a. Red (Mini-Minors) omitted *3,500.*
b. Dark blue (Jaguar & imprint) omitted *4,000.*
p. Phosphor. .15 .15
468 A192 1sh3p sl, blk, org & bl .20 .20
p. Phosphor. .35 .35
469 A192 1sh6p multicolored .25 .25
p. Phosphor. .45 .45
Set value .60 .60

British technology.

Battle of Hastings A193

Battle of Hastings from Bayeux Tapestry: No. 471, Two knights on horseback, one killed, one attacking. No. 472, Slain Harold on horseback and knight with shield. No. 473, Knight with shield and axe fighting horseman. No. 474, Knight on foot killing man, and horseman attacking with lance. No. 475, Four knights and two horses in battle scene. 6p, Norman ship. 1sh3p, King Harold's housecarls (body guard) battling Normans.

Photo.; Gold Impressed on 6p, 1sh3p

Perf. 14½x14

1966, Oct. 14 Wmk. 322

Size: 38½x22mm

470 A193 4p multicolored .15 .15
471 A193 4p multicolored .15 .15
472 A193 4p multicolored .15 .15
473 A193 4p multicolored .15 .15
474 A193 4p multicolored .15 .15
475 A193 4p multicolored .15 .15
a. Strip of 6, #470-475 .75
476 A193 6p multi & gold .32 .28

Size: 58x22mm

477 A193 1sh3p multi & gold .75 .65
Set value 1.80 1.35

Phosphorescent

470p A193 4p multicolored .15 .15
471p A193 4p multicolored .15 .15
472p A193 4p multicolored .15 .15
473p A193 4p multicolored .15 .15
474p A193 4p multicolored .15 .15
475p A193 4p multicolored .15 .15
b. Strip of 6, #470p-475p .75
476p A193 6p multi & gold .30 .30
477p A193 1sh3p multi & gold .85 .85
Nos. 470p-477p (8) 2.05 2.05

900th anniv. of the Battle of Hastings.

Eight colors have been found omitted (singly or in pair) on Nos. 470-475 and 470p-477p: gray, orange, blue, dark blue, bright green, olive green, brown and magenta. Also violet on 1sh3p.

Gold Omitted

The variety "Gold (Queen's head) omitted" can be counterfeited by chemically removing the gold.

Christmas — A194

Photo.; Gold Impressed

1966, Dec. 1 ***Perf. 14x14½***

478 A194 3p King .15 .15
b. Green omitted *250.00*
p. Phosphor. .15 .15
479 A194 1sh6p Snowman .25 .25
b. Pink omitted *1,000.*
p. Phosphor. .25 .25

Loading Ship at Dock and Train — A195

Design: 1sh6p, Loading plane from trucks and flags of EFTA members.

Perf. 14½x14

1967, Feb. 20 Photo. Wmk. 322

480 A195 9p blue & multi .15 .15
p. Phosphor. .15 .15
481 A195 1sh6p violet & multi .20 .20
p. Phosphor. .15 .15

European Free Trade Assoc. Tariffs were abolished Dec. 31, 1966, among EFTA members (Austria, Denmark, Finland, Great Britain, Norway, Portugal, Sweden, Switzerland).

Colors omitted include: 9p—yellow, brown, light blue, light violet and green singly; black, brown, light blue and yellow simultaneously. 1sh6p—dark blue, bister, yellow, red, ultramarine and gray. Value range for one-color omissions, $17.50 to $35.

Hawthorn and Wild Blackberry A196

Flowers: No. 489, Morning-glory and viper's bugloss. No. 490, Ox-eye daisy, coltsfoot and buttercup. No. 491, Bluebell, red campion and wood anemone. 9p, Dog violet. 1sh9p, Primrose.

Perf. 14½x14

1967, Apr. 24 Photo. Wmk. 322

488 A196 4p multicolored .15 .15
489 A196 4p multicolored .15 .15
490 A196 4p multicolored .15 .15
491 A196 4p multicolored .15 .15
a. Block of 4, #488-491 .45
492 A196 9p multicolored .30 .25
493 A196 1sh9p multicolored .38 .35
Set value 1.08 .88

Phosphorescent

488p A196 4p multicolored .15 .15
489p A196 4p multicolored .15 .15
490p A196 4p multicolored .15 .15
491p A196 4p multicolored .15 .15
492p A196 9p multicolored .25 .25
493p A196 1sh9p multicolored .35 .35
Set value 1.00 .92

Four colors have been found omitted on Nos. 488-491 and three on 488p-491p: dark brown, red, violet and dull purple.

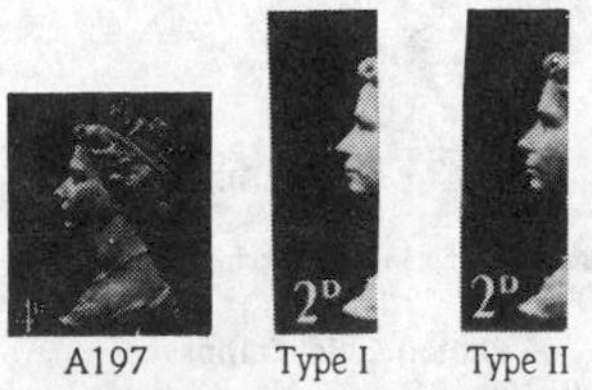

A197 Type I Type II

Two types of 2p:

Type I - Head off-center to right. Foot of "2" 1mm from left margin.

Type II - Head centered. Foot of "2" ½mm from margin.

1967-69 Unwmk. ***Perf. 15x14***

Size: 17½x21½mm

494 A197 ½p brn org ('68) .15 .20
495 A197 1p olive ('68) .15 .15
a. Booklet pane of 6 ('68) 1.00
b. Bklt. pane of 4 (2 No. 495, 2 No. 497) ('68) 2.00
c. Bklt. pane of 6 (4 No. 495, 2 No. 498) ('68) 4.00
d. Coil strip of 5 (1 each Nos. 495, 497, 499; 2 No. 496a) ('69) 3.00 1.25
e. Bklt. pane of 6 (4 No. 495, 2 No. 499) ('69) 3.75
f. Bklt. pane of 15 (6 No. 495, 6 No. 499, 3 No. 500 + recipe) ('69) 14.00
496 A197 2p mar (I) ('68) .15 .15
a. Type II ('69) .20 .15
497 A197 3p dark violet .15 .15
a. Booklet pane of 6 ('68) 12.00
b. Imperf., pair *700.00*
498 A197 4p brown black .15 .15
a. Booklet pane of 4 ('68) 1.00
b. Booklet pane of 6 ('68) 1.50
c. Bklt. pane of 2 + 2 labels ('68) 1.00
d. Imperf., pair
499 A197 4p brt red ('69) .15 .15
a. Booklet pane of 4 ('69) 1.00
b. Booklet pane of 6 ('69) 1.00
c. Bklt. pane of 2 + 2 labels ('69) 1.00
d. Bklt. pane of 15 + recipe ('69) 5.00
500 A197 5p dk blue ('68) .15 .15
a. Booklet pane of 6 ('68) 1.50
b. Bklt. pane of 15 + recipe ('69) 5.00
501 A197 6p magenta ('68) .25 .15
502 A197 7p brt green ('68) .42 .15
503 A197 8p scarlet ('68) .16 .25
504 A197 8p lt grnsh blue ('69) .50 .35
505 A197 9p deep green .42 .15
506 A197 10p gray ('68) .50 .40
507 A197 1sh light violet .45 .15
508 A197 1sh6p ind & grnsh bl .60 .15
a. Greenish blue omitted 110.00
509 A197 1sh9p black & org .50 .15

Perf. 12

Engr.

Size: 27x31mm

510 A197 2sh6p brown ('69) .90 .15
511 A197 5sh dk car ('69) 2.75 .50
512 A197 10sh ultra ('69) 8.25 5.00
513 A197 £1 bluish black ('69) 3.25 1.25
Nos. 494-513 (20) 20.00
Set value 8.85

No. 513 resembles No. 638 on which "£1" is redrawn. On No. 513, "£" has loop at bottom and numeral is a figure "1." On No. 638, "£" lacks loop and numeral is roman like a capital "I."

Nos. 502-505 have denomination at right.

Most of Nos. 494-509 exist with phosphor bands omitted in error.

See Nos. 622-638, 762-775, 887A-903, 969-982, 1071-1087B, 1261-1279, 1396-1409.

For Prestige booklet containing panes #495f, 499d, 500b, see list at end of postage section.

See regional issues, Guernsey, Jersey and Isle of Man for other stamps showing this portrait of the Queen, which have different frames or devices added to the design.

Master Lambton, by Thomas Lawrence — A198

Mares and Foals, by George Stubbs A199

Design: 1sh6p, Children Coming out of School, by Laurence Stephen Lowry.

Photo.; Gold Impressed on 4p, 1sh6p

Perf. 14x14½, 14½x14

1967, July 10 Unwmk.

514 A198 4p multicolored .15 .15
a. Gold (Queen's head & value) omitted *125.00*
515 A199 9p multicolored .15 .15
a. Black (Queen's head & value) omitted *600.00*
b. Yellow omitted *1,000.*
516 A199 1sh6p multicolored .18 .18
a. Blue omitted *150.00*
b. Gray omitted *50.00*
c. Gold (Queen's head) omitted *1,250.*
Set value .35 .35

See Nos. 568-571.

Gipsy Moth IV — A200

1967, July 24 Photo. ***Perf. 14½x14***

517 A200 1sh9p multicolored .15 .15

Sir Francis Chichester's one-man voyage around the world, Aug. 27, 1966-May 28, 1967.

Radar Screen A201

British Discoveries: 1sh, Penicillin mold. 1sh6p, Vickers 10 twin jet engines. 1sh9p, Television camera, vert.

Perf. 14½x14, 14x14½

1967, Sept. 19 Photo. Wmk. 322

518 A201 4p multicolored .15 .15
519 A201 1sh multicolored .15 .15
520 A201 1sh6p multicolored .15 .15
521 A201 1sh9p multicolored .18 .18
a. Gray omitted *250.00*
Set value .45 .45

Madonna and Child, by Murillo — A202

Adoration of the Shepherds, by Le Nain A203

Christmas 1967: 3p, Adoration of the Shepherds, ascribed to School of Seville.

Perf. 14x14½, 14½x14

Photo.; Gold Impressed

1967 Unwmk.

522 A202 3p multicolored .15 .15
a. Gold (Queen's head & value) omitted *55.00*
b. Pink omitted *675.00*
523 A202 4p multicolored .15 .15
a. Gold (Queen's head & value) omitted *60.00*
524 A203 1sh6p multicolored .15 .15
a. Gold (Queen's head & value) omitted
b. Blue omitted *500.00*
Set value .28 .28

Issue dates: 4p, Oct. 18; 3p, 1sh6p, Nov. 27.

Castle Type of 1955

1967-68 Engr. Unwmk. ***Perf. 11x12***

525 A133 2sh6p dk brown ('68) .22 .16
526 A133 5sh crimson ('68) .55 .22
527 A133 10sh brt ultra ('68) 4.00 2.00
528 A133 £1 intense black 3.00 1.00
Nos. 525-528 (4) 7.77 3.38

Aberfeldy Bridge, Perthshire A204

Designs: 4p, Prehistoric Tarr Steps, Exmoor. 1sh6p, Menai Bridge, North Wales, 1826. 1sh9p, Viaduct, Highway M4.

Perf. 14½x14

1968, Apr. 29 Photo. Unwmk.

560 A204 4p gold & multi .15 .15
561 A204 9p gold & multi .15 .15
a. Blue omitted
b. Gold (Queen's head) omitted *125.00*
562 A204 1sh6p gold & multi .15 .15
a. Gold (Queen's head) omitted *125.00*
b. Red omitted
563 A204 1sh9p gold & multi .18 .18
a. Gold (Queen's head) omitted *125.00*
Set value .42 .42

Emmeline Pankhurst Statue — A205

Designs: 4p, Letters "TUC" and faces. 1sh, Sopwith Camel 1914-1918 fighter plane and formation of Lightning jets. 1sh9p, Capt. Cook's "Endeavour" and signature.

1968, May 29

564 A205 4p brt grn, blk, ol & bl .15 .15
565 A205 9p gray, vio & blk .15 .15
566 A205 1sh gray, ol, red, bl & blk .15 .15
567 A205 1sh9p blk & bister .18 .18
Set value .42 .42

Cent. of Trades Union Congress (4p); 50th anniv. of women's suffrage (9p); 50th anniv. of the Royal Air Force (1sh); bicent. of Captain Cook's first discovery voyage (1sh9p)

Paintings Types of 1967

Paintings: 4p, Elizabeth I, c. 1575, artist unknown. 1sh, Pinkie (Miss Sarah Moulton-Barrett) by Sir Thomas Lawrence. 1sh6p, St. Mary le Port, by John Piper. 1sh9p, The Hay Wain (landscape), by John Constable.

Perf. 14x14½, 14½x14

Photo.; Gold Impressed

1968, Aug. 12

568 A198 4p multicolored .15 .15
a. Gold (Queen's head & value) omitted *100.00*
569 A198 1sh multicolored .15 .15
a. Gold (Queen's head & value) omitted *100.00*
570 A198 1sh6p multicolored .15 .15
a. Gold (Queen's head & value) omitted *100.00*
571 A199 1sh9p multicolored .15 .15
a. Gold (Queen's head & value) omitted *250.00*
Set value .40 .40

Sizes: 4p, 27x37½mm; 1sh, 25½x37½mm; 1sh6p, 31x37½mm; 1sh9p, 38x28mm.

Boy and Girl with Rocking Horse A206

Girl Playing with Dolls and Dollhouse A207

Christmas: 1sh6p, Boy with toy train and building blocks.

Perf. 14½x14, 14x14½

1968, Nov. 25 Photo.

572 A206 4p gold & multi .15 .15
a. Gold omitted *2,500.*
573 A207 9p gold & multi .15 .15
a. Yellow omitted *60.00*
574 A207 1sh6p gold & multi .15 .15
Set value .26 .26

Elizabethan Galleon — A208

British Ships: 5p, R.M.S. Queen Elizabeth 2. No. 577, East Indiaman. No. 578, Cutty Sark. No. 579, S.S. Great Britain. No. 580, R.M.S. Mauretania.

1969, Jan. 15 *Perf. 14½x14*

Size: 58x22mm

575 A208 5p multicolored .15 .15
- **a.** Black omitted *1,350.*
- **b.** Gray omitted *100.00*
- **c.** Red omitted 37.50

Size: 38½x22mm

576 A208 9p multicolored .20 .20
- **a.** Red & blue omitted *2,000.*

577 A208 9p multicolored .20 .20
578 A208 9p multicolored .20 .20
- **a.** Strip of 3, #576-578 .60

Size: 58x22mm

579 A208 1sh multicolored .32 .32
580 A208 1sh multicolored .32 .32
- **a.** Pair, #579-580 .75

Nos. 575-580 (6) 1.39 1.39

British seamen and shipbuilders.

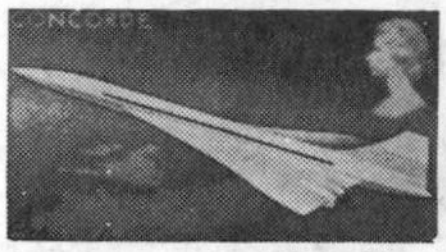

Concorde over Great Britain and France A209

Designs: 9p, Concorde seen from above and from side, flags of France and Great Britain. 1sh6p, Outlines of plane's nose and tail superimposed.

1969, Mar. 3 Photo. *Perf. 14½x14*

581 A209 4p multicolored .15 .15
- **a.** Violet omitted *400.00*
- **b.** Orange omitted *125.00*

582 A209 9p multicolored .15 .15
583 A209 1sh6p multicolored .22 .22
- **a.** Silver omitted *175.00*

Set value .40 .35

First flight of the prototype Concorde plane at Toulouse, France, Mar. 1, 1969.

Alcock, Brown, Daily Mail and Vickers Vimy Plane — A210

"EUROPA" and "CEPT" CD11

Hand Holding Wrench — A212

Flags of NATO Nations Forming one Flag — A213

Vickers-Vimy Plane and Globe — A214

1969, Apr. 2

584 A210 5p multicolored .15 .15
585 CD11 9p multicolored .15 .15
586 A212 1sh multicolored .15 .15
587 A213 1sh6p multicolored .15 .15
- **a.** Black omitted *50.00*
- **b.** Green omitted *50.00*

588 A214 1sh9p multicolored .18 .18

Set value .60 .60

50th anniv. of the 1st non-stop Atlantic flight from Newfoundland to Ireland of Capt. John Alcock and Lt. Arthur Whitten Brown; 10th anniv. of the Conference of European Postal and Telecommunications Administrations; 50th anniv. of the ILO (1sh); 20th anniv. of NATO; 50th anniv. of the first England to Australia flight (1sh9p).

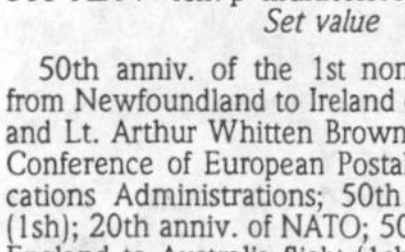

Durham Cathedral A215

British Cathedrals: No. 590, York Minster. No. 591, St. Giles', Edinburgh. No. 592, Canterbury. 9p, St. Paul's. 1sh6p, Liverpool Metropolitan.

Perf. 14½x14

1969, May 28 Photo. Unwmk.

589 A215 5p multicolored .15 .15
590 A215 5p multicolored .15 .15
591 A215 5p multicolored .15 .15
592 A215 5p multicolored .15 .15
- **a.** Block of 4, #589-592 .25 .22

593 A215 9p multicolored .25 .25
- **a.** Black (9d) omitted 80.00

594 A215 1sh6p multicolored .40 .40

Set value .90 .90

King's Gate, Caernarvon Castle, Wales — A216

Celtic Cross, Margam Abbey, Glamorgan — A217

Prince of Wales — A218

Designs: No. 596, Eagle Tower, Caernarvon Castle (2 flags). No. 597, Queen Eleanor's Gate, Caernarvon Castle.

Perf. 14x14½

1969, July 1 Photo. Unwmk.

595 A216 5p silver & multi .15 .15
596 A216 5p silver & multi .15 .15
597 A216 5p silver & multi .15 .15
- **a.** Strip of 3, #595-597 .25 .25

598 A217 9p gold, gray & black .15 .15
599 A218 1sh black & gold .16 .16

Set value .50 .45

Investiture of Prince Charles as Prince of Wales, July 1.

Mahatma Gandhi and Flag of India — A219

1969, Aug. 13 *Perf. 14½x14*

600 A219 1sh6p orange, blk & grn .20 .20

Mohandas K. Gandhi (1869-1948), leader in India's fight for independence.

Emblem of Post Office Bank — A220

International Subscriber Dialing — A221

Automatic Letter Sorting — A222

Design: 1sh, Telecommunications (pulse code modulation graph).

Perf. 13½x14

1969, Oct. 1 Litho. Unwmk.

601 A220 5p blue & multi .15 .15
602 A221 9p ultra & multi .15 .15
603 A221 1sh green & multi .15 .15
604 A222 1sh6p multicolored .22 .22

Set value .52 .52

Technological advancements of the British Post Office, transfer of responsibility from the government to the Post Office Corporation.

Angel — A223

Christmas: 5p, Three shepherds. 1sh6p, The Three Kings.

Photo.; Gold Embossed

1969, Nov. 26 *Perf. 14x15*

605 A223 4p multicolored .15 .15
606 A223 5p multicolored .15 .15
607 A223 1sh6p multicolored .20 .18

Set value .30 .28

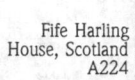

Fife Harling House, Scotland A224

British Rural Architecture: 9p, Cotswold limestone house, Gloucestershire, England. 1sh, Aberaeron town house, Wales. 1sh6p, Irish cottage with Ulster thatching.

Perf. 14x15

1970, Feb. 11 Photo. Unwmk.

Size: 38½x22mm

608 A224 5p multicolored .15 .15
609 A224 9p multicolored .15 .15

Size: 38½x27mm

610 A224 1sh multicolored .16 .16
611 A224 1sh6p multicolored .25 .25

Set value .60 .60

Mayflower Leaving Plymouth, England — A225

Designs: 5p, Signing of the Declaration of Arbroath. 9p, Florence Nightingale and soldiers in Scutari Hospital. 1sh, Earl Grey, Great Britain; Charles Robert, France; Victor Bohmert, Germany; De Keussler, Russia, and document in 4 languages. 1sh9p, Sir William Herschel, Francis Bailey, Sir John Herschel and telescope.

Photo.; Gold Embossed

1970, Apr. 1 *Perf. 14x15*

612 A225 5p red & multi .15 .15
613 A225 9p blue & multi .15 .15
614 A225 1sh lt blue & multi .15 .15
615 A225 1sh6p olive & multi .20 .20
616 A225 1sh9p brt pink & multi .22 .22

Set value .70 .70

650th anniv. of the Declaration of Arbroath (5p); Florence Nightingale (1820-1910), nurse and hospital reformer (9p); Intl.Cooperative Alliance, 75th anniv. (1st); 350th anniv. of Mayflower sailing (1sh6p); sesquicentennial of the Royal Astronomical Soc. (1sh9p).

Missing colors or embossing occur on each denomination.

"The Pickwick Papers," by Dickens A226

Wordsworth's Grasmere, Lake District A227

Designs: No. 618, Mr. and Mrs. Micawber ("David Copperfield"). No. 619, David Copperfield and Betsy Trotwood ("David Copperfield"). No. 620, "Oliver Twist."

Perf. 14x14½

1970, June 3 Photo. Unwmk.

617 A226 5p orange & multi .15 .15
618 A226 5p lilac rose & multi .15 .15
619 A226 5p grnsh blue & multi .15 .15
620 A226 5p lemon & multi .15 .15
- **a.** Block of 4, #617-620 .40 .30

621 A227 1sh6p citron & multi .50 .50

Set value .90 .78

Charles Dickens (1812-70), novelist. William Wordsworth (1770-1850), poet, No. 621.

Decimal Currency Issue

Queen Elizabeth Type of 1967-69

"P" instead of "D"

Type II - Numerals are narrower than originally. Look more upright. "1" and "2" of ½ are aligned vertically.

Perf. 15x14

1970-88 Photo. Unwmk.

Size: 17½x21½mm

622 A197 ½p grnsh blue ('71) .15 .15
- **c.** Coil strip of 5 (2 each #622-623,1 #625) .60
- **f.** Coil strip of 5 (2 #622, 1 each #623, 625, 631) ('75) .75
- **j.** Coil strip of 5 (2 #622, 2 #623, 1 #631B) ('78) .60

623 A197 1p magenta ('71) .15 .15
- **c.** Strip of 3 + 2 labels (2 #623, 632A) .60
- **e.** Type II ('84) .15 .15
- **f.** Syncopated Type C ('93) .15 .15

624 A197 1½p black ('71) .20 .15
625 A197 2p green ('71) .16 .15
- **d.** Syncopated Type C .16 .15

626 A197 2½p brt pink ('71) .16 .15
627 A197 3p ultra ('71) .20 .15
628 A197 3½p gray green ('71) .32 .15
629 A197 4p olive bis ('71) .20 .15
- **c.** Imperf., pair

629A A197 4½p grysh blue ('73) .28 .15
630 A197 5p bluish lilac ('71) .16 .15
630A A197 5½p dk violet ('73) .28 .15
631 A197 6p lt emer ('71) .32 .15
631A A197 6½p Prus blue ('74) .32 .15
631B A197 7p red brn ('75) .32 .15
632 A197 7½p lt red brn ('71) .28 .15
632A A197 8p red ('73) .28 .15
632B A197 8½p yel green ('75) .35 .15
633 A197 9p black & ocher ('71) .65 .25
634 A197 10p org brn & lt org brn ('71) .32 .25

Engr.

Perf. 12

Size: 27x31mm

635 A197 10p car rose 2.75 .60
636 A197 20p olive 1.00 .15
637 A197 50p ultra 1.40 .60
- **p.** Phosphor ('73) 2.50 .60

638 A197 £1 bluish blk ('72) 2.75 1.25

Nos. 622-638 (23) 13.00

Set value 3.60

On No. 638, "£1" is redrawn. The "£" has no loop at bottom and the numeral "I" is roman. On No. 513, "£" has a loop and the numeral is a "1."

Booklet Panes

1970-80

622a	Pane, 2 #622, 2 #625	4.00
622b	Pane of 5 + label	4.50
622d	Pane, 4 #622, 2 #626 ('72)	70.00
622e	Pane, 3 #622, 9 #626 ('72)	25.00
622g	Pane, 2 #622, 3 #623, 1 #631 ('76)	1.00
622h	Pane, 2 #622, 2 #623, 2 #631A, 4 #632B ('76)	5.25
622i	Pane, 2 #622, 2 #623, 1 #631B + label ('78)	.75
623a	Pane, 2 #623, 2 #624	2.00
623b	Pane, 2 #623, 3 #631B, 3 #762 ('77)	3.50
623d	Pane,3 + label2 #623, 632A + label	.50
625a	Pane, 3 #625, 2 #764, 2 #893 + label ('80)	2.25
625b	Pane, 2 #625, 2 #632A, 3 #764 + label	2.50
625c	Pane of 6 + printed margin	1.00
626a	Pane of 4 + 2 labels	5.50
626b	Pane of 5 + label	5.50
626c	Pane, 2 #626, 4 #627	8.00
626d	Pane, 6 #626, 6 #627 ('72)	18.00
627a	Pane of 5 + label	5.00
627b	Pane of 6	5.00
627c	Pane of 12 ('72)	10.00
628a	Pane of 5 + label ('73)	6.00
629b	Pane of 5 + label (#629A) ('74)	6.00
631e	Pane, 10 #631B, 10 #762 ('78)	7.00
632d	Pane, 10 #632A, 10 #764	6.25

Nos. 622h and 623b issued with stamps in two arrangements.

Nos. 622d, 622e, 626d and 627c have a large side margin with inscription about Wedgwood or postal rates.

For Prestige booklets containing panes #622d, 622e, 625e, 626d, 627c, see list at end of postage section.

Athletics A228

1970, July 15 Litho. *Perf. 14x14½*

639 A228	5p	shown	.15	.15
640 A228	1sh6p	Swimming	.32	.32
641 A228	1sh9p	Bicycling	.32	.32
		Nos. 639-641 (3)	.79	.79

9th British Commonwealth Games, Edinburgh, July 16-25.

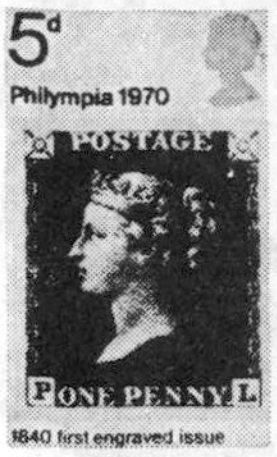

A229

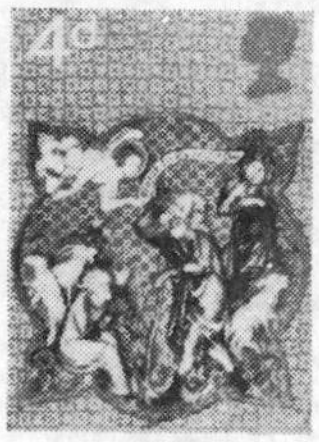

A230

Designs: 5p, Penny black. 9p, 1847 1-shilling stamp, #5. 1sh6p, 1855 4-pence stamp, #22.

1970, Sept. 18 Photo. *Perf. 14x14½*

642 A229	5p	multicolored	.15	.15
643 A229	9p	multicolored	.18	.15
644 A229	1sh6p	multicolored	.32	.30
		Set value	.55	.48

Philympia, London Phil. Exhib., Sept. 18-26.

1970, Nov. 25 Photo. *Perf. 14x14½*

Christmas (Illuminations from 14th Century de Lisle Psalter): 4p, Angel and Shepherds. 5p, Nativity. 1sh6p, Adoration of the Kings.

645 A230	4p	red & multi	.15	.15
646 A230	5p	violet & multi	.15	.15
a.		Imperf., pair	375.00	
647 A230	1sh6p	olive & multi	.35	.35
		Set value	.45	.45

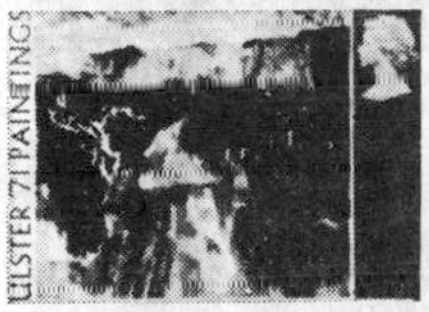

Mountain Road, by T.P. Flanagan A231

Paintings from Northern Ireland: 7½p, Deer's Meadow, by Thomas Carr. 9p, Tollymore Forest Park, by Colin Middleton.

1971, June 16 Photo. *Perf. 14½x14*

648 A231	3p	multicolored	.15	.15
649 A231	7½p	multicolored	.80	.65
650 A231	9p	multicolored	.80	.65
		Nos. 648-650 (3)	1.75	1.45

Ulster '71 Festival, Belfast, May-Oct.

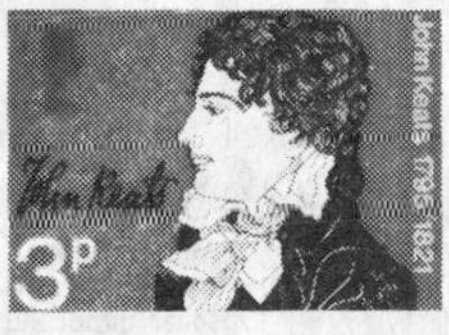

John Keats (1795-1821) A232

Writers and their signatures: 5p, Thomas Gray (1716-71). 7½p, Sir Walter Scott (1771-1832).

1971, July 28 Photo. *Perf. 14½x14*

651 A232	3p	dull bl, blk & gold	.15	.15
652 A232	5p	olive, blk & gold	.38	.30
653 A232	7½p	yel brn, blk & gold	1.00	.95
		Nos. 651-653 (3)	1.53	1.40

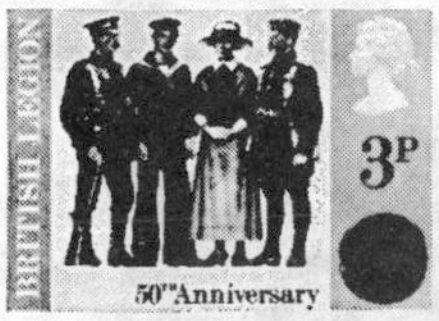

Soldier, Sailor, Airman, Nurse, 1921, and Poppy A233

Designs: 7½p, Roman centurion on horseback, York Castle and coat of arms. 9p, Rugby players 100 years ago, and rose.

1971, Aug. 25

654 A233	3p	ultra & multi	.15	.15
655 A233	7½p	ocher & multi	.70	.45
656 A233	9p	olive & multi	1.00	.85
		Nos. 654-656 (3)	1.85	1.45

50th anniv. of the British Legion (3p); 1900th anniv. of the founding of York (7½p); cent. of the Rugby Football Union (9p).

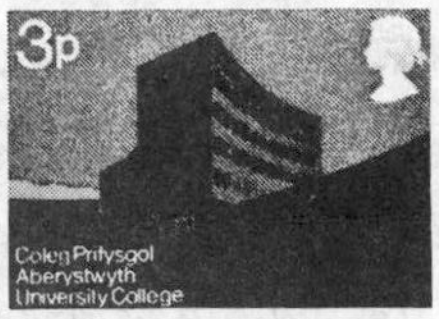

Physical Sciences Building, University College of Wales, Aberystwyth A234

Modern University Buildings: 5p, Faraday Building, Engineering Faculty, University of Southampton. 7½p, Engineering Building, University of Leicester. 9p, Hexagon Restaurant, University of Essex.

1971, Sept. 22 Photo. *Perf. 14½x14*

657 A234	3p	citron & multi	.15	.15
658 A234	5p	rose vio & multi	.40	.30
659 A234	7½p	dp brn & multi	1.00	.65
660 A234	9p	dk blue & multi	1.10	1.10
		Nos. 657-660 (4)	2.65	2.20

No. 658 exists with large "p" in "5p." These are from plate combination 1A1B1C1D and were not officially issued.

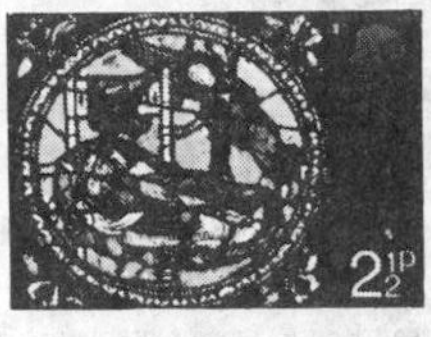

Dream of the Kings — A235

Christmas (from Stained Glass Windows, Canterbury Cathedral): 3p, Adoration of the Kings. 7½p, Journey of the Kings.

1971, Oct. 13

661 A235	2½p	scarlet & multi	.15	.15
662 A235	3p	ultra & multi	.15	.15
663 A235	7½p	green & multi	1.10	.90
		Set value	1.20	1.00

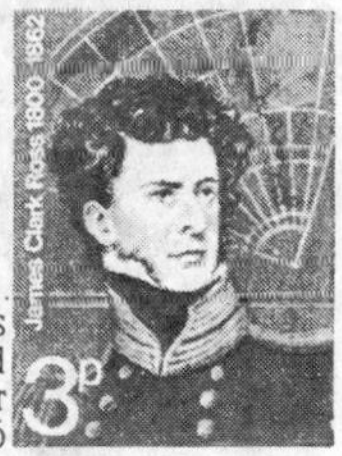

James Clark Ross (1800-1862) and Map of South Polar Sea — A236

British Polar Explorers: 5p, Martin Frobisher (1535-1594), and Desceliers map, 1550. 7½p, Henry Hudson (c. 1560-1611) and Petrus Plancius map, 1592. 9p, Robert Falcon Scott (1868-1912) and map of Antarctica.

1972, Feb. 16 *Perf. 14x14½*

664 A236	3p	dp bister & multi	.15	.15
665 A236	5p	brick red & multi	.28	.28
666 A236	7½p	violet & multi	.60	.60
667 A236	9p	blue & multi	.95	.60
		Nos. 664-667 (4)	1.98	1.63

See Nos. 689-693.

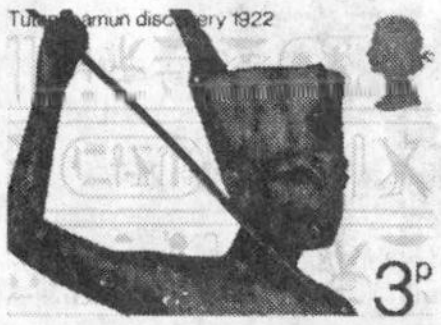

Head of Tutankhamen as Fisherman A237

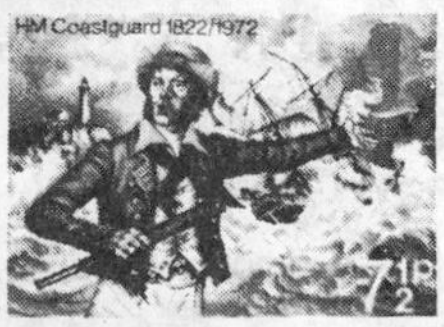

Coast Guard A238

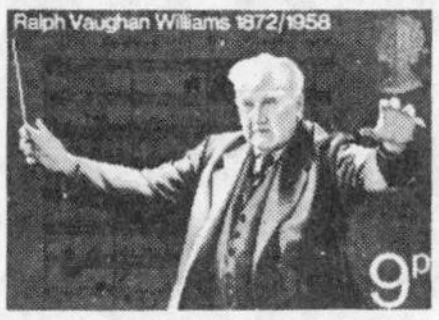

Ralph Vaughan Williams and "Sea Symphony" A239

1972, Apr. 26 Photo. *Perf. 14½x14*

668 A237	3p	gold & multi	.15	.15

Photo.; Queen's Head Gold Embossed

669 A238	7½p	blue & multi	.48	.48
670 A239	9p	multicolored	.70	.70
		Nos. 668-670 (3)	1.33	1.33

50th anniv. of the discovery of the tomb of Tutankhamen by Howard Carter and Lord Carnarvon; sesquicentennial of the British Coast guard; Ralph Vaughan Williams (1872-1958), composer.

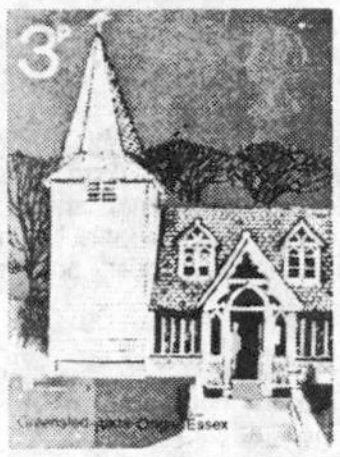

St. Andrew's, Greensted-Juxta-Ongar — A240

Old Village Churches: 4p, All Saints, Earls Barton. 5p, St. Andrew's, Letheringsett. 7½p, St. Andrew's, Helpringham. 9p, St. Mary the Virgin, Huish Episcopi.

Photo.; Queen's Head Gold Embossed

1972, June 21 *Perf. 14x14½*

671 A240	3p	dull blue & multi	.15	.15
672 A240	4p	olive & multi	.28	.20
673 A240	5p	dp grn & multi	.35	.32
674 A240	7½p	red & multi	1.25	1.00
675 A240	9p	blue & multi	1.40	1.25
		Nos. 671-675 (5)	3.43	2.92

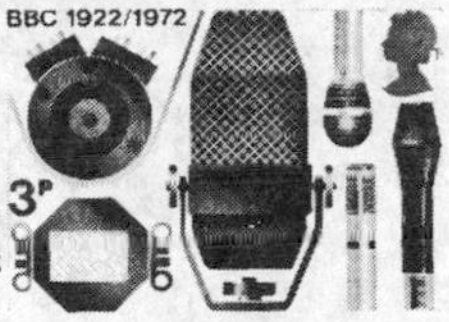

Various BBC Microphones A241

Designs: 5p, Wooden horn loudspeaker 1925. 7½p, Color TV camera, 1972. 9p, Marconi's oscillator and spark transmitter, 1897.

1972, Sept. 13 Photo. *Perf. 14½x14*

676 A241	3p	black, brn & yel	.15	.15
677 A241	5p	henna brn & blk	.32	.25
678 A241	7½p	black & mag	.60	.60
679 A241	9p	black & yel	.90	.90
		Nos. 676-679 (4)	1.97	1.90

Daily broadcasting in the United Kingdom, 50th anniv. (British Broadcasting Corp., #676-678), Marconi-Kemp experiments resulting in the 1st radio transmission across water, 75th anniv. (#679).

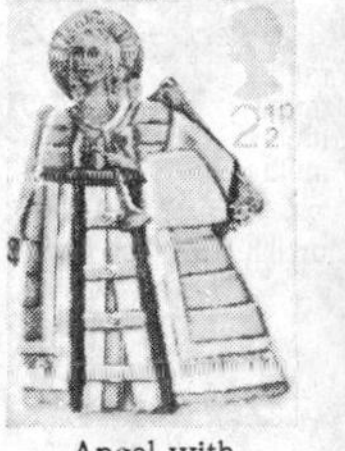

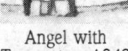

Angel with Trumpet — A242

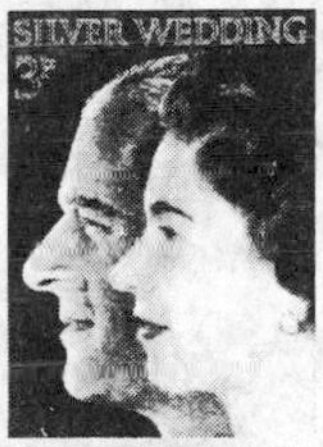

Queen Elizabeth II, Prince Philip — A243

Photo.; Gold Embossed

1972, Oct. 18 *Perf. 14x14½*

680 A242	2½p	shown	.15	.15
681 A242	3p	Angel with lute	.15	.15
682 A242	7½p	Angel with harp	.45	.45
		Set value	.60	.60

Christmas.

1972, Nov. 20 Photo. *Perf. 14x14½*

683 A243	3p	dk blue, sep & sil	.15	.15
684 A243	20p	dk pur, sepia & sil	.70	.70

25th anniv. of the marriage of Queen Elizabeth II and Prince Philip. No. 684 is without phosphor.

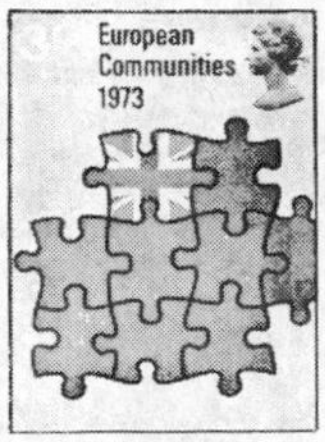

Britain as Part of European Community — A244

1973, Jan. 3

685 A244	3p	brown org & multi	.30	.15
686 A244	5p	blue & multi	.65	.40
687 A244	5p	emerald & multi	.65	.40
a.		Pair, #686-687	1.40	1.00
		Nos. 685-687 (3)	1.60	.95

Britain's entry into the European Community.

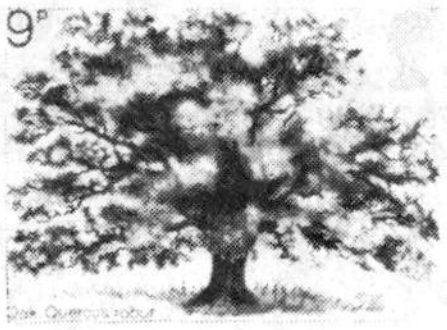

Oak — A245

1973, Feb. 28 Photo. *Perf. 14½x14*

688 A245	9p	multicolored	.42	.42

Tree Planting Year.

Explorer Type of 1972

British Explorers: No. 689, David Livingstone and map of Africa. No. 690, Henry Stanley and map of Africa. 5p, Sir Francis Drake and world map. 7½p, Sir Walter Raleigh and world map. 9p, Charles Sturt and map of Australia.

1973, Apr. 8 Photo. *Perf. 14x14½*

689 A236	3p	multicolored	.15	.15
690 A236	3p	multicolored	.15	.15
a.		Pair, #689-690	.15	.15
691 A236	5p	multicolored	.35	.28
692 A236	7½p	multicolored	.80	.60
693 A236	9p	multicolored	1.10	1.00
		Nos. 689-693 (5)	2.55	2.18

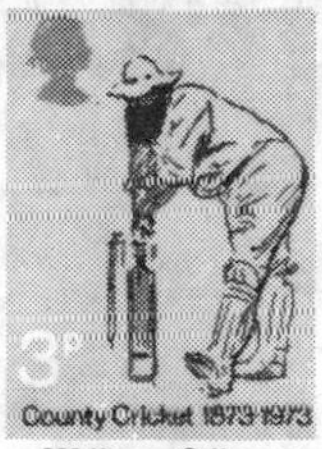

William Gilbert Grace A246

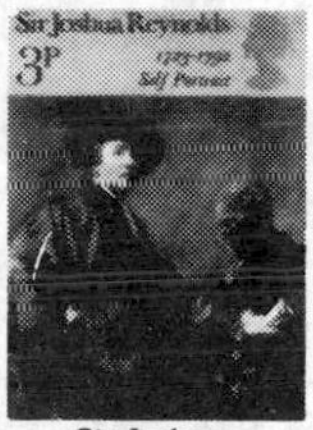

Sir Joshua Reynolds, Self-portrait A247

Designs: Caricatures of William Gilbert Grace, the Great Cricketer, by Harry Furniss.

1973, May 16 Photo. *Perf. 14x14½*

694 A246	3p	brown & black	.15	.15
695 A246	7½p	green & black	1.00	.80
696 A246	9p	blue & black	1.10	1.00
		Nos. 694-696 (3)	2.25	1.95

Centenary of British County Cricket.

1973, July 4 Photo. *Perf. 14x14½*

Paintings: 5p, Sir Henry Raeburn (1756-1823), self-portrait. 7½p, Nelly O'Brien, by Reynolds (1723-92). 9p, Rev. R. Walker (The Skater), by Raeburn.

697 A247	3p	multicolored	.15	.15
698 A247	5p	multicolored	.30	.20
699 A247	7½p	multicolored	.52	.42
700 A247	9p	gray & multi	.55	.48
		Nos. 697-700 (4)	1.52	1.25

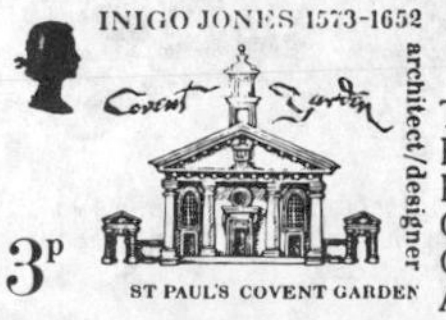

Tuscan Portico, St. Paul's Church, Covent Garden A248

Designs: No. 701, Costumes for Oberon and Titania. No. 703, Prince's Lodging, Newmarket. No. 704, Stage scenery for Oberon.

Litho. and Typo.

1973, Aug. 15 *Perf. 14½x14*

701	A248	3p black, pur & gold	.22	.15
702	A248	3p gold, brn & blk	.22	.15
a.		Pair, #701-702	.45	.30
703	A248	5p black, blue & gold	.75	.70
704	A248	5p gold, olive & blk	.75	.70
a.		Pair, #703-704	1.50	1.50
		Nos. 701-704 (4)	1.94	1.70

400th birth anniv. of Inigo Jones (1573-1652), architect and designer.

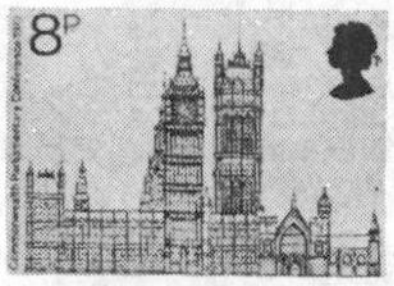

Parliament, from Whitehall
A249

Design: 10p, Parliament from Millbank.

1973, Sept. 12 **Engr. and Typo.**

705	A249	8p buff, gray & blk	.32	.32
706	A249	10p black & gold	.42	.38

Opening by the Queen of the 19th Commonwealth Parliamentary Assoc. Conf., Westminster Hall.

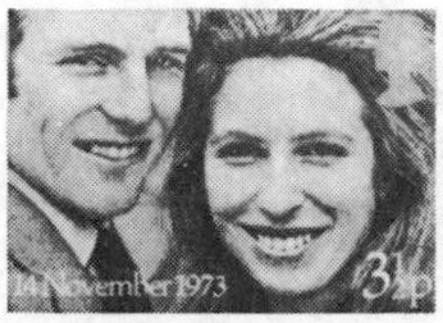

Princess Anne and Mark Phillips
A250

1973, Nov. 14 Photo. *Perf. 14½x14*

707	A250	3½p violet & silver	.15	.15
708	A250	20p brown & silver	.90	.85

Wedding of Princess Anne and Captain Mark Phillips, Nov. 14, 1973.

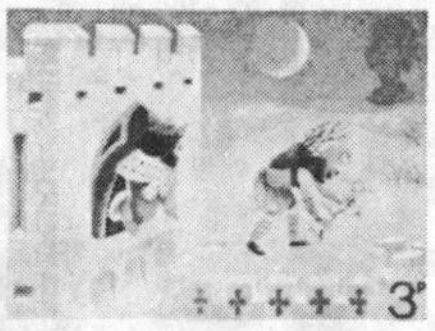

Good King Wenceslas
A251

Christmas: Illustrations for Christmas carol "Good King Wenceslas" showing king and page.

1973, Nov. 28

709	A251	3p shown	.50	.30
710	A251	3p Page looking out of window	.50	.30
711	A251	3p Page leaving castle	.50	.30
712	A251	3p Page in storm	.50	.30
713	A251	3p Page bringing gifts	.50	.30
a.		Strip of 5, #709-713	2.75	1.75
714	A251	3½p Page and peasant	.50	.30
		Nos. 709-714 (6)	3.00	1.80

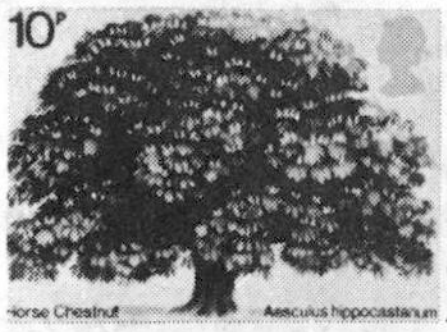

Horse Chestnut
A252

1974, Feb. 27 Photo. *Perf. 14½x14*

715	A252	10p green & multi	.45	.45

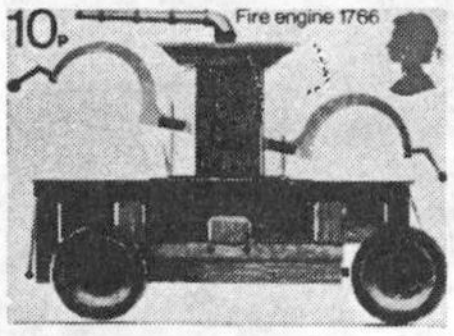

Fire Engine, 1766
A253

Designs: 3½p, First motorized fire engine, 1904. 5½p, Prize winning Sutherland fire engine, 1863. 8p, First steam engine, 1830.

1974, Apr. 24

716	A253	3½p multicolored	.15	.15
717	A253	5½p multicolored	.20	.20
718	A253	8p multicolored	.55	.55
719	A253	10p multicolored	.70	.70
		Nos. 716-719 (4)	1.60	1.60

Fire Prevention (Metropolis) Act, bicent.

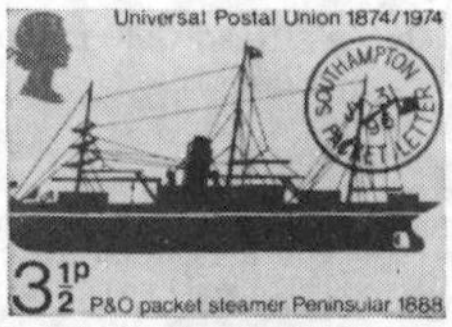

Packet "Peninsular," 1888, and "Southampton Packet Letter" Postmark — A254

Development of Overseas Mail Transport: 5½p, Farnham Biplane and "Aerial Post" postmark. 8p, Truck and pillar box for airmail and "London F.S. Air Mail" postmark. 10p, Imperial Airways flying boat and "Southampton Airport" postmark.

1974, June 12 *Perf. 14½x14*

720	A254	3½p multicolored	.15	.15
721	A254	5½p multicolored	.15	.15
722	A254	8p multicolored	.32	.32
723	A254	10p multicolored	.42	.42
		Nos. 720-723 (4)	1.04	1.04

UPU, Cent.

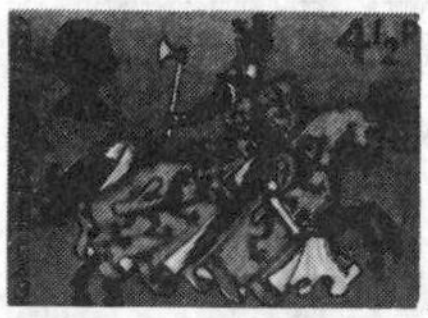

Robert the Bruce
A255

Designs: "Great Britons" on caparisoned chargers.

1974, July 10 *Perf. 14½x14*

724	A255	4½p shown	.15	.15
725	A255	5½p Owain Glyndwr	.24	.24
726	A255	8p King Henry V	.60	.60
727	A255	10p Black Prince	.75	.75
		Nos. 724-727 (4)	1.74	1.74

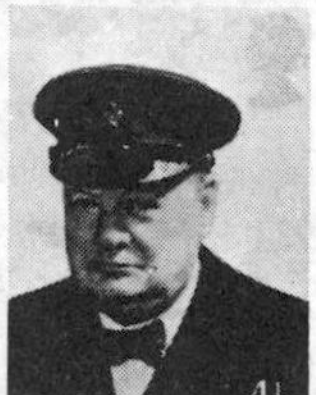

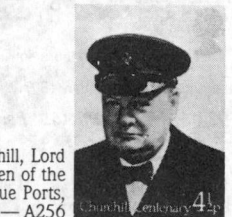

Churchill, Lord Warden of the Cinque Ports, 1942 — A256

Designs (Churchill): 5½p, with bowler and cigar, 1940. 8p, with top hat, as Secretary of War and Air, 1919. 10p, in uniform of South African Light Horse Regiment, 1899.

1974, Oct. 9 Photo. *Perf. 14x14½*

728	A256	4½p silver & multi	.15	.15
729	A256	5½p silver & multi	.40	.40
730	A256	8p silver & multi	.35	.35
731	A256	10p silver & multi	.38	.38
		Nos. 728-731 (4)	1.28	1.28

Sir Winston Spencer Churchill (1874-1965).

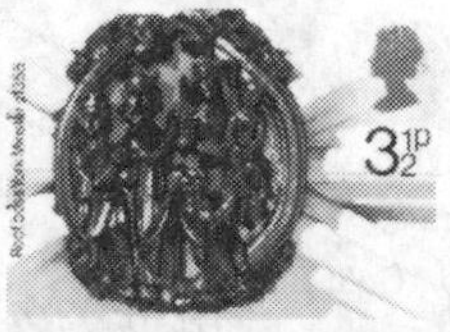

Adoration of the Kings, York Minster, c. 1355
A257

Christmas (Roof Bosses): 4½p, Nativity, St. Helen's, Norwich, c. 1480. 8p, Virgin and Child, Church of Ottery St. Mary, Devonshire, c. 1350. 10p, Virgin and Child, Lady Chapel, Worcester Cathedral, c. 1224.

1974, Nov. 27 *Perf. 14½x14*

732	A257	3½p gold & multi	.15	.15
733	A257	4½p gold & multi	.15	.15
734	A257	8p gold & multi	.28	.28
735	A257	10p gold & multi	.35	.35
		Nos. 732-735 (4)	.93	.93

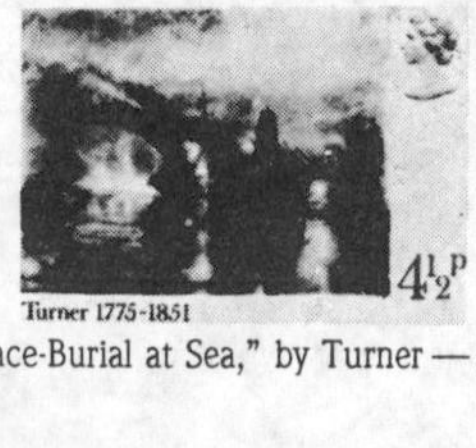

"Peace-Burial at Sea," by Turner — A258

Paintings: 5½p, "Snowstorm-Steamer off a Harbour's Mouth." 8p, "Arsenal, Venice." 10p, "View of St. Laurent."

1975, Feb. 19 Photo. *Perf. 14½x14*

736	A258	4½p multicolored	.15	.15
737	A258	5½p multicolored	.18	.15
738	A258	8p multicolored	.25	.15
739	A258	10p multicolored	.32	.20
		Nos. 736-739 (4)	.90	.65

Birth bicent. of Joseph Mallord William Turner (1775-1851), painter.

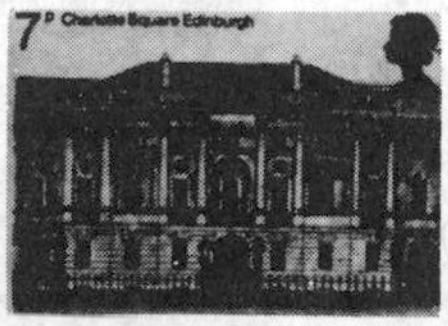

Charlotte Square, Edinburgh
A259

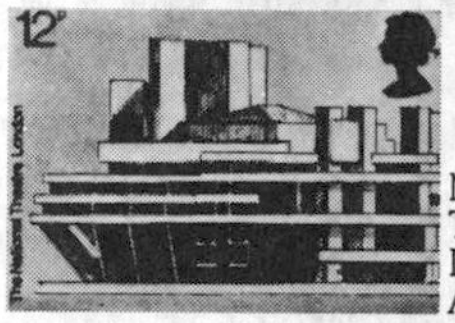

National Theater, London
A260

Designs: No. 740, The Rows, Chester (double-storied medieval shopping streets). 8p, Sir Christopher Wren's Flamsteed House, Royal Observatory, Greenwich. 10p, St. George's Chapel, Windsor.

1975, Apr. 23 *Perf. 14½x14*

740	A259	7p multicolored	.15	.15
741	A259	7p multicolored	.15	.15
742	A259	8p multicolored	.18	.15
743	A259	10p multicolored	.35	.35
744	A260	12p multicolored	.42	.42
		Nos. 740-744 (5)	1.25	1.22

European Architectural Heritage Year 1975. Nos. 740-741 printed se-tenant in sheets of 100. 300th anniv. of Royal Observatory, (No. 742) and 500th anniv. of St. George's Chapel (No. 743).

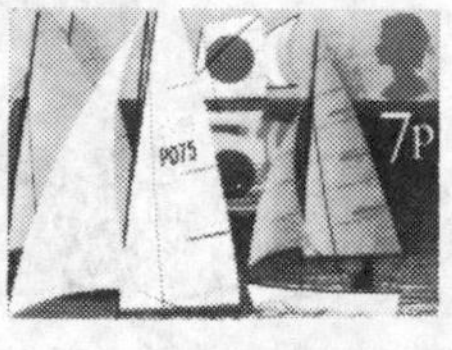

Dinghies
A261

1975, June 11 **Photo. & Engr.**

745	A261	7p shown	.15	.15
746	A261	8p Racing keelboats	.15	.15
747	A261	10p Cruising yachts	.20	.20
748	A261	12p Multihulls	.60	.60
		Nos. 745-748 (4)	1.10	1.10

Royal Thames Yacht Club bicent. and other sailing club anniversaries.

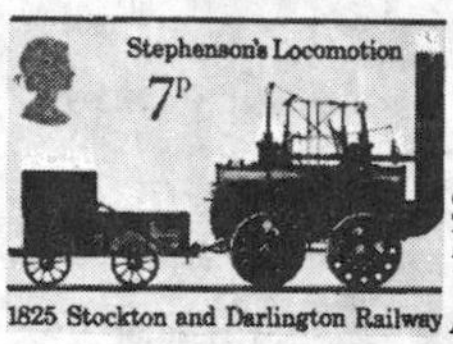

Stephenson's Locomotion, 1825
A262

Locomotives: 8p, Abbotsford, Waverley Class, 1876. 10p, Caerphilly Castle, 1923. 12p, High-speed train, 1975.

1975, Aug. 13 Photo. *Perf. 14½x14*

749	A262	7p multicolored	.24	.15
750	A262	8p multicolored	.25	.22
751	A262	10p multicolored	.45	.45
752	A262	12p multicolored	.55	.55
		Nos. 749-752 (4)	1.49	1.37

Sesquicentennial of public railroads in Great Britain.

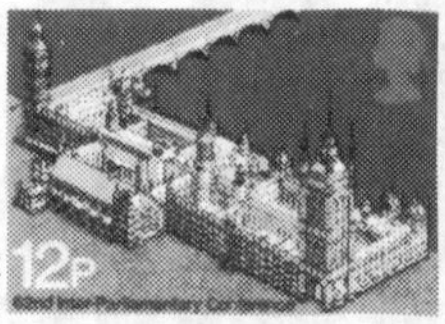

Parliament
A263

1975, Sept. 3

753	A263	12p multicolored	.40	.40

62nd Inter-Parliamentary Conference, London, Sept. 1975.

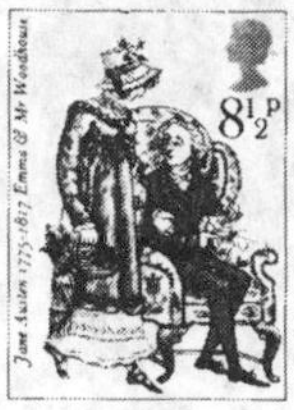

Emma and Mr. Woodhouse from "Emma" — A264

Designs (Illustrations by Barbara Brown of Characters from Jane Austen's Novels): 10p, Catherine Morland from "Northanger Abbey." 11p, Mr. Darcy from "Pride and Prejudice." 13p, Mary and Henry Crawford from "Mansfield Park."

1975, Oct. 22 Photo. *Perf. 14x14½*

754	A264	8½p multicolored	.25	.15
755	A264	10p multicolored	.30	.30
756	A264	11p multicolored	.32	.32
757	A264	13p multicolored	.38	.38
		Nos. 754-757 (4)	1.25	1.15

Jane Austen (1775-1817), novelist.

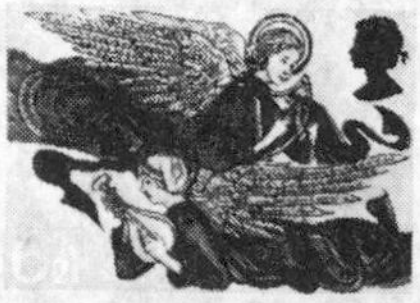

Angels with Lute and Harp — A265

Christmas: 8½p, Angel with mandolin. 11p, Angel with horn. 13p, Angel with trumpet.

1975, Nov. 26 Photo. *Perf. 14½x14*

758	A265	6½p violet & multi	.16	.15
759	A265	8½p multicolored	.22	.18
760	A265	11p multicolored	.42	.42
761	A265	13p ocher & multi	.50	.48
		Nos. 758-761 (4)	1.30	1.23

Redrawn Queen Type of 1970

1976-79 Photo. *Perf. 15x14*

Size: 17½x21½mm

762	A197	9p violet blue	.35	.15
763	A197	9½p bright lilac	.35	.25
764	A197	10p salmon	.32	.15
a.		Bklt. pane of 9 + printed margin ('80)	4.00	
b.		Type II ('84)	*16.00*	*16.00*
765	A197	10½p yellow	.35	.25
766	A197	10½p steel blue ('78)	.65	.50
767	A197	11p pink	.38	.20
768	A197	11½p olive bis ('79)	.45	.40
769	A197	13p gray green ('79)	.60	.40
770	A197	15p deep ultra ('79)	.50	.35
771	A197	20p sepia	.70	.20
772	A197	50p bis brown ('77)	1.75	.35

1977, Feb. 2 *Perf. 14x15*

Size: 27x38mm

773	A197	£1 olive grn & yel	3.00	.60
774	A197	£2 maroon & lt grn	5.50	1.50
775	A197	£5 dk blue & pink	14.00	4.00
		Nos. 762-775 (14)	28.90	9.30

For Prestige booklet containing pane #764a, see list at end of postage section.

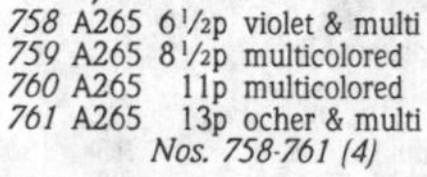

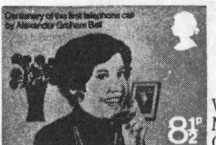

Woman Making Social Call — A266

Designs: 10p, Policeman making emergency call. 11p, District nurse making social welfare call. 13p, Refinery worker making field call.

1976, Mar. 10   Photo.   Perf. 14¹/₂x14

777	A266	8¹/₂p multicolored	.18	.15
778	A266	10p multicolored	.30	.30
779	A266	11p multicolored	.32	.32
780	A266	13p multicolored	.45	.45
		Nos. 777-780 (4)	1.25	1.22

1st telephone call by Alexander Graham Bell, Mar. 10, 1876.

Coal Miner's Hands (Thomas Hepburn) A267

Designs: 10p, Child's hands, textile mill (Robert Owen). 11p, Boy's hand sweeping chimney (Lord Shaftesbury). 13p, Woman's hands holding prison bars (Elizabeth Frey).

1976, Apr. 28   Photo.   Perf. 14¹/₂x14

781	A267	8¹/₂p gray & black	.18	.15
782	A267	10p multicolored	.28	.28
783	A267	11p multicolored	.38	.38
784	A267	13p multicolored	.50	.45
		Nos. 781-784 (4)	1.34	1.26

19th cent. industrial & social reformers: Hepburn formed 1st miners' union in 1831; Owen, improved working conditions in his mill and established schools; Lord Shaftesbury, philanthropist and sponsor of reform work laws; Frey, pioneer of women's prison reforms.

Benjamin Franklin, by Jean-Jacques Caffieri — A268

Elizabeth of Glamis Rose — A269

1976, June 2   Perf. 14x14¹/₂

785 A268 11p multicolored   .40 .40

American Bicentennial.

1976, June 30   Photo.   Perf. 14x14¹/₂

Roses Painted by Kristin Rosenberg.

786	A269	8¹/₂p shown	.18	.15
787	A269	10p Grandpa Dickson	.30	.30
788	A269	11p Rosa Mundi	.40	.32
789	A269	13p Sweet Briar	.50	.40
		Nos. 786-789 (4)	1.38	1.17

Royal National Rose Society, centenary.

Archdruid, Eisteddfod A270

Morris Dancing A271

British Cultural Traditions: 11p, Piper and dancers, Highland gathering. 13p, Woman playing Welsh harp (telyn), Eisteddfod.

1976, Aug. 4   Photo.   Perf. 14x14¹/₂

790	A270	8¹/₂p multicolored	.18	.15
791	A271	10p multicolored	.32	.28
792	A271	11p multicolored	.38	.35
793	A271	13p multicolored	.50	.45
		Nos. 790-793 (4)	1.38	1.18

Squire, from Canterbury Tales — A272

Designs: 10p, Page from Tretyse of Love, c. 1493, set in Caxton typeface. 11p, Philosopher, from The Game and Playe of Chesse, c. 1483. 13p, Printing press and printers, early 16th century woodcut.

Photo.; Queen's Head Gold Embossed
1976, Sept. 29   Perf. 14x14¹/₂

794	A272	8¹/₂p blue & indigo	.20	.18
795	A272	10p olive & dk grn	.35	.30
796	A272	11p gray & black	.40	.40
797	A272	13p ocher & red brn	.48	.48
		Nos. 794-797 (4)	1.43	1.36

500 years of British printing, introduced by William Caxton (1422-1491).

Virgin and Child, Clare Chasuble A273

Christmas (English medieval embroideries): 8¹/₂, Angel with crown. 11p, Angel appearing to the shepherds. 13p, Three Kings bringing gifts, Butler-Bowden cope.

1976, Nov. 24   Photo.   Perf. 14¹/₂x14

798	A273	6¹/₂p multicolored	.15	.15
799	A273	8¹/₂p multicolored	.24	.24
800	A273	11p multicolored	.40	.32
801	A273	13p multicolored	.55	.45
		Nos. 798-801 (4)	1.34	1.16

Racket Sports A274

1977, Jan. 12   Photo.   Perf. 14¹/₂x14

802	A274	8¹/₂p multicolored	.22	.20
803	A274	10p Table tennis	.25	.25
804	A274	11p Squash	.35	.35
805	A274	13p Badminton	.40	.40
		Nos. 802-805 (4)	1.22	1.20

Wimbledon Tennis Championships, cent. and 1977 World Table Tennis Championships, Birmingham.

Steroids Conformational Analysis — A275

Designs: 10p, Vitamin C synthesis (formula and orange). 11p, Starch chromatography. 13p, Salt crystallography.

1977, Mar. 2   Photo.   Perf. 14¹/₂x14

806	A275	8¹/₂p multicolored	.24	.16
807	A275	10p multicolored	.30	.30
808	A275	11p multicolored	.35	.35
809	A275	13p multicolored	.42	.42
		Nos. 806-809 (4)	1.31	1.23

British chemists who won Nobel prize. Derek Barton, 1969 (8¹/₂p); Walter Norman Haworth, 1937 (10p); Archer J. P. Martin and Richard L. M. Synge, 1952 (11p); William and Lawrence Bragg, 1915 (13p).

Queen Elizabeth II — A276

1977   Photo.   Perf. 14¹/₂x14

810	A276	8¹/₂p silver & multi	.24	.20
811	A276	9p silver & multi	.32	.24
812	A276	10p silver & multi	.28	.28
813	A276	11p silver & multi	.35	.35
814	A276	13p silver & multi	.45	.45
		Nos. 810-814 (5)	1.64	1.52

25th anniv. of the reign of Elizabeth II. Issue dates: 9p, June 15. Others, May 11.

Pentagons, Symbolic of Continents and Nations — A277

1977, June 8   Photo.   Perf. 14x14¹/₂

815 A277 13p multicolored   .40 .40

Summit Conference of Commonwealth Heads of Government, London, June 1977.

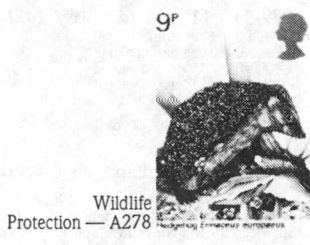

Wildlife Protection — A278

1977, Oct. 5   Photo.   Perf. 14x14¹/₂

816	A278	9p Hedgehog	.35	.25
817	A278	9p Brown hare	.40	.25
818	A278	9p Red squirrel	.50	.25
819	A278	9p Otter	.35	.25
820	A278	9p Badger	.35	.25
a.		Strip of 5, #816-820	2.00	
		Nos. 816-820 (5)	1.95	1.25

THE TWELVE DAYS OF CHRISTMAS
"Two Turtle Doves, Three French Hens. . ." — A279

The Twelve Days of Christmas: No. 822, 4 colly birds, 5 gold rings, 6 geese a-laying. No. 823, 7 swans a-swimming, 8 maids a-milking. No. 824, 9 drummers drumming, 10 pipers piping. No. 825, 11 ladies dancing, 12 lords a-leaping. 9p, A partridge in a pear tree.

1977, Nov. 23   Photo.   Perf. 14x14¹/₂

821	A279	7p multicolored	.20	.15
822	A279	7p multicolored	.20	.15
823	A279	7p multicolored	.20	.15
824	A279	7p multicolored	.20	.15
825	A279	7p multicolored	.20	.15
a.		Strip of 5, #821-825	1.00	
826	A279	9p multicolored	.25	.16
		Nos. 821-826 (6)	1.25	
		Set value		.66

Oil Production Platform, North Sea — A280

Designs: 10¹/₂p, Coal, pithead. 11p, Natural gas, flame. 13p, Electricity-producing nuclear power plant and uranium atom diagram.

1978, Jan. 25   Photo.   Perf. 14x14¹/₂

827	A280	9p multicolored	.30	.18
828	A280	10¹/₂p multicolored	.35	.20
829	A280	11p multicolored	.38	.22
830	A280	13p multicolored	.45	.25
		Nos. 827-830 (4)	1.48	.85

Great Britain's wealth of energy resources.

Tower of London A281

British Architecture: 10¹/₂p, Abbey and Palace, Holyrood House, Edinburgh. 11p, Caernarvon Castle, Wales. 13p, Hampton Court Palace, London.

1978, Mar. 1   Photo.   Perf. 14¹/₂x14

831	A281	9p multicolored	.24	.15
832	A281	10¹/₂p multicolored	.32	.16
833	A281	11p multicolored	.35	.18
834	A281	13p multicolored	.45	.20
a.		Souv. sheet of 4, #831-834	1.65	
		Nos. 831-834 (4)	1.36	.69

No. 834a issued to publicize London 1980 Intl. Stamp Exhib. and sold for 53¹/₂p. The surtax went to exhibition fund.

Gold State Coach — A282

Designs: 10¹/₂p, St. Edward's crown. 11p, Orb. 13p, Imperial State crown.

1978, May 31   Photo.   Perf. 14x14¹/₂

835	A282	9p vio blue & gold	.24	.15
836	A282	10¹/₂p car lake & gold	.28	.16
837	A282	11p dp green & gold	.30	.18
838	A282	13p purple & gold	.35	.20
		Nos. 835-838 (4)	1.17	.69

25th anniv. of coronation of Elizabeth II.

Shire Horse A283

British Horses: 10¹/₂p, Shetland pony. 11p, Merlyn Cymreig Welsh pony. 13p, Thoroughbred.

1978, July 5   Photo.   Perf. 14¹/₂x14

839	A283	9p multicolored	.25	.15
840	A283	10¹/₂p multicolored	.30	.16
841	A283	11p multicolored	.38	.20
842	A283	13p multicolored	.45	.22
		Nos. 839-842 (4)	1.38	.73

"Penny-farthing," 19th Century — A284

British bicycles: 10¹/₂p, 1920 touring bicycles. 11p, Modern small-wheel bicycles. 13p, Road racers.

1978, Aug. 2   Photo.   Perf. 14¹/₂x14

843	A284	9p multicolored	.28	.18
844	A284	10¹/₂p multicolored	.32	.20
845	A284	11p multicolored	.35	.22
846	A284	13p multicolored	.40	.25
		Nos. 843-846 (4)	1.35	.85

Cent. of 1st natl. cycling organizations: British Cycling Fed. and Cyclists Touring Club.

Carolers Around Christmas Tree A285

Christmas: 9p, Christmas waits (watchmen). 11p, 18th century carolers. 13p, Boar's head carol.

1978, Nov. 22   **Photo.**   *Perf. 14½x14*

847	A285	7p multicolored	.20	.15
848	A285	9p multicolored	.25	.15
849	A285	11p multicolored	.35	.18
850	A285	13p multicolored	.42	.20
		Nos. 847-850 (4)	1.22	.68

Old English
Sheepdog
A286

British dogs: 10½p, Welsh springer spaniel. 11p, West Highland white terrier. 13p, Irish setter.

1979, Feb. 7   **Photo.**   *Perf. 14½x14*

851	A286	9p multicolored	.24	.15
852	A286	10½p multicolored	.28	.15
853	A286	11p multicolored	.30	.16
854	A286	13p multicolored	.35	.18
		Nos. 851-854 (4)	1.17	.64

British Wild
Flowers — A287

1979, Mar. 21   **Photo.**   *Perf. 14x14½*

855	A287	9p Primroses	.24	.15
856	A287	10½p Daffodils	.28	.15
857	A287	11p Bluebells	.30	.16
858	A287	13p Snowdrops	.35	.18
		Nos. 855-858 (4)	1.17	.64

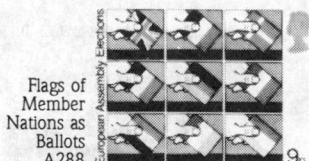

Flags of
Member
Nations as
Ballots
A288

Flags of European Community Members: United Kingdom, Italy, Denmark, Belgium, Fed. Rep. of Germany, France, Netherlands, Ireland, Luxembourg. Positions of hands and flags different on each denomination.

1979, May 9   **Photo.**   *Perf. 14½x14*

859	A288	9p multicolored	.24	.15
860	A288	10½p multicolored	.28	.15
861	A288	11p multicolored	.30	.16
862	A288	13p multicolored	.35	.18
		Nos. 859-862 (4)	1.17	.64

European Parliament, 1st direct elections, 6/7-10.

Saddling of
Mahmoud,
1936 Derby,
by Alfred
Munnings
A289

200th Anniv. of the Derby: 10½p, Liverpool Great National Steeple Chase, 1839, aquatint by F. C. Turner. 11p, First Spring Meeting, Newmarket, 1793, by J. N. Sartorius. 13p, Charles II watching racing at Dorsett Ferry, Windsor, 1684, by Francis Barlow.

1979, June 6   **Photo.**   *Perf. 14½x14*

863	A289	9p multicolored	.24	.15
864	A289	10½p multicolored	.28	.15
865	A289	11p multicolored	.30	.16
866	A289	13p multicolored	.35	.18
		Nos. 863-866 (4)	1.17	.64

Peter Rabbit — A290   Rowland
Hill — A291

Children's books: 10½p, The Wind in the Willows. 11p, Winnie the Pooh. 13p, Alice's Adventures in Wonderland.

1979, July 11   **Photo.**   *Perf. 14x14½*

867	A290	9p multicolored	.32	.18
868	A290	10½p multicolored	.38	.20
869	A290	11p multicolored	.40	.22
870	A290	13p multicolored	.48	.25
		Nos. 867-870 (4)	1.58	.85

International Year of the Child.

1979, Aug. 22   **Photo.**   *Perf. 14x14½*

Designs: 11½p, Bellman, early 19th cent. 13p, London post office and mailman, early 19th cent. 15p, Victorian woman and child mailing letter.

871	A291	10p multicolored	.25	.15
872	A291	11½p multicolored	.30	.15
873	A291	13p multicolored	.32	.18
874	A291	15p multicolored	.40	.22
a.		Souvenir sheet of 4, #871-874	1.40	.90
		Nos. 871-874 (4)	1.27	.70

Sir Rowland Hill (1795-1879), originator of penny postage.
No. 874a issued to publicize London 1980 Intl. Stamp Exhib. and sold for 59½p. The surtax went to exhibition fund.

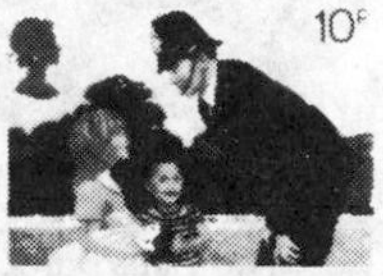

Police Constable
and
Children — A292

Designs: 11½p, Police constable directing traffic. 13p, Police woman on horseback. 15p, River patrol boat.

1979, Sept. 26   **Photo.**   *Perf. 14½x14*

875	A292	10p multicolored	.30	.15
876	A292	11½p multicolored	.35	.18
877	A292	13p multicolored	.38	.18
878	A292	15p multicolored	.45	.25
		Nos. 875-878 (4)	1.48	.76

London Metropolitan Police, 150th anniv.

Three Kings
Following
Star — A293

Christmas: 10p, Angel appearing before the shepherds. 11½p, Nativity. 13p, Joseph and Mary traveling to Bethlehem. 15p, Annunciation.

1979, Nov. 21   **Photo.**   *Perf. 14x14*

879	A293	8p multicolored	.22	.15
880	A293	10p multicolored	.28	.15
881	A293	11½p multicolored	.30	.15
882	A293	13p multicolored	.35	.18
883	A293	15p multicolored	.45	.20
		Nos. 879-883 (5)	1.60	.83

Kingfisher — A294

1980, Jan. 16   **Photo.**   *Perf. 14x14½*

884	A294	10p shown	.30	.15
885	A294	11½p Dipper	.35	.16
886	A294	13p Moorhen	.38	.18
887	A294	15p Yellow wagtail	.45	.22
		Nos. 884-887 (4)	1.48	.71

Redrawn Queen Type of 1970

1980-86   **Photo.**

887A	A197	2p grn, perf. 13½x14, litho. ('80)	.18	.15
b.		Litho., perf. 15x14 ('84)	.30	.15
c.		Litho., perf. 15x14, type II	.50	.25
d.		Photo., perf. 15x14, type II	.15	.15
888	A197	2½p org ver ('81)	.18	.15
889	A197	3p dp lilac rose	.18	.15
a.		Coil strip of 4 (#888, 3 #889)	.75	
b.		Bklt. pane of 9 + label (#889, 2 #969, 6 #972)	4.50	
c.		Photo., perf. 15x14, type II	1.25	.30
d.		Coil strip of 4 (#889, 3 #890f)	.90	.30

Perf. 13½x14

Litho.

890	A197	4p Prus blue	.22	.15
a.		Photo., perf. 15x14 ('81)	.30	.15
b.		Coil strip of 4 (#622, 3 #890a)	1.00	.50
c.		Photo., perf. 15x14, type II ('84)	1.00	.80
e.		Bklt. pane, perf. 15x14, type II ('86)	.50	.20
f.		Dark turq, photo., perf. 15x14, type II ('88)	.22	.15
g.		Coil strip, 4 #887d, 3 #890c	3.25	
891	A197	5p pale lilac ('80)	.22	.20

Perf. 15x14

Photo.

892	A197	11½p dull brn ('81)	.45	.22
a.		Bklt. pane of 6 (#622, #623, 3 #892, #895)	2.25	
b.		Bklt. pane of 8 (3 #888, 2 #890, 3 #892)	2.50	
893	A197	12p yellow green	.50	.40
a.		Bklt. pane, 10 #893, 10 #764	9.00	
b.		Bklt. pane of 9 + printed margin (#625, 4 #764, 4 #893)	4.00	
c.		Bklt. pane of 9 + printed margin ('80)	5.00	
894	A197	13½p brown	.70	.60
895	A197	14p gray blue ('81)	.55	.35
a.		Bklt. pane, 10 #895, 10 #892	10.50	
b.		Bklt. pane, 6 #895, 4 #892	5.25	
896	A197	15½p lt vio ('81)	.60	.35
a.		Bklt. pane of 6 + printed margin ('82)	3.75	
b.		Bklt. pane of 9 + printed margin ('82)	5.50	
897	A197	17p light green	.85	.35
898	A197	17½p lt red brn	.90	.80
899	A197	18p vio blue ('81)	.80	.70
900	A197	20p sepia, perf. 13½x14 ('80)	.85	.40
a.		Litho., perf. 15x14, type II ('86)	1.40	.60
901	A197	22p dark blue	.80	.45
902	A197	25p lilac ('81)	.90	.80

Perf. 13½x14

Litho.

903	A197	75p black	3.50	1.50
a.		Litho., perf. 15x14 ('84)	3.50	1.50
b.		Litho., perf. 15x14, type II	10.00	3.50
c.		Photo., perf. 15x14, type II	2.50	1.10
		Nos. 887A-903 (17)	12.38	7.72

Issue dates: Nos. 887c-887d, 890g, 903b-903c, 1988; Nos. 889c-889d, Oct. 10, 1989.
For Prestige booklets containing panes #889b, 893b, 893c, 896a, 896b, see list at end of postage section.

"Rocket" Locomotive — A295

1980, Mar. 12   **Photo.**   *Perf. 14½x14*

904	A295	12p shown	.35	.15
905	A295	12p 1st, 2nd class cars	.35	.15
906	A295	12p 3rd class and sheep cars	.35	.15
907	A295	12p Flat cars	.35	.15
908	A295	12p Flat car, mail coach	.35	.15
a.		Strip of 5, #904-908	1.75	1.00

Liverpool-Manchester Railroad, 150th anniv. No. 908a has a continuous design.

London
View
A296

INTERNATIONAL STAMP EXHIBITION

1980, Apr. 9   **Engr.**   *Perf. 14½*

909	A296	50p multicolored	1.40	.70
a.		Souvenir sheet	1.65	.95

London 1980, Intl. Stamp Exhib., May 6-14. No. 909a, issued May 7, sold for 75p.

Buckingham
Palace — A297

1980, May 7   **Photo.**   *Perf. 14x14½*

910	A297	10½p shown	.28	.15
911	A297	12p Albert Memorial	.32	.15
912	A297	13½p Royal Opera House	.38	.18
913	A297	15p Hampton Court	.45	.20
914	A297	17½p Kensington Palace	.50	.24
		Nos. 910-914 (5)	1.93	.92

Emily Bronte and "Wuthering
Heights" — A298

Victorian novelists and scenes from their novels: 12p, Charlotte Bronte, "Jane Eyre." 13½p, George Eliot, "The Mill on the Floss." 17½p, Mrs. Gaskell, "North and South." 12p and 13½p show CEPT (Europa) emblem.

1980, July 9   **Photo.**   *Perf. 15x14*

915	A298	12p multicolored	.32	.15
916	A298	13½p multicolored	.38	.18
917	A298	15p multicolored	.45	.20
918	A298	17½p multicolored	.50	.24
		Nos. 915-918 (4)	1.65	.77

A299   A300

1980, Aug. 4   **Photo.**   *Perf. 14x14½*

919	A299	12p multicolored	.42	.15

Queen Mother Elizabeth, 80th birthday.

1980, Sept. 10

English conductors: 12p, Henry Wood, (1869-1944) Conductor. 13½p, Thomas Beecham (1879-1961). 15p, Malcolm Sargent (1895-1967). 17½p, John Barbirolli (1899-1970).

920	A300	12p multicolored	.32	.15
921	A300	13½p multicolored	.38	.18
922	A300	15p multicolored	.45	.20
923	A300	17½p multicolored	.50	.24
		Nos. 920-923 (4)	1.65	.77

Running — A301

1980, Oct. 10 Litho. *Perf. 14x14½*

924 A301 12p shown .32 .15
925 A301 13½p Rugby .38 .18
926 A301 15p Boxing .45 .20
927 A301 17½p Cricket .50 .24
Nos. 924-927 (4) 1.65 .77

Centenaries: Amateur Athletics Assoc.; Welsh Rugby Union; Amateur Boxing Assoc.; 1st cricket test match against Australia.

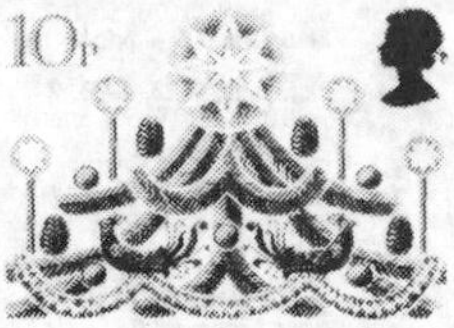
Christmas Tree with Candles A302

Christmas (Traditional Decorations): 12p, Candles, ivy, ribbons. 13½p, Mistletoe, apples. 15p, Paper chain and bell. 17½p, Holly wreath.

1980, Nov. 19 Photo. *Perf. 14½x14*

928 A302 10p multicolored .28 .15
929 A302 12p multicolored .32 .15
930 A302 13½p multicolored .38 .18
931 A302 15p multicolored .45 .20
932 A302 17½ multicolored .50 .24
Nos. 928-932 (5) 1.93 .92

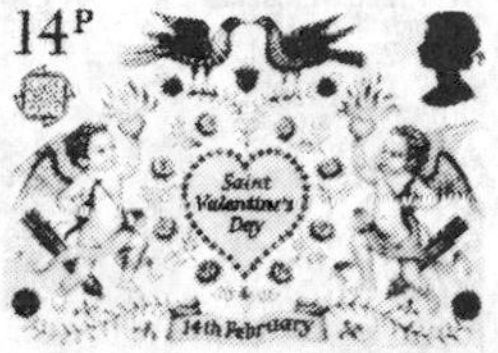
Lovebirds, Angels and Heart (Valentine's Day) — A303

Folklore: 18p, Morris Dancers, 16th century window, Shropshire. 22p, Wheat, fruit, farm couple dancing (Lammastide) 25p, Medieval mummers, 14th century manuscript illustration. 14p and 18p show CEPT (Europa) emblem.

1981, Feb. 6 Photo. *Perf. 14½x14*

933 A303 14p multicolored .45 .24
934 A303 18p multicolored .55 .28
935 A303 22p multicolored .70 .35
936 A303 25p multicolored .80 .40
Nos. 933-936 (4) 2.50 1.27

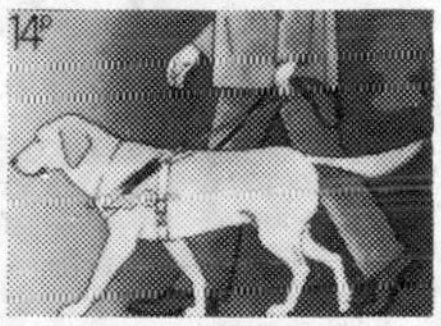
Guide Dog Leading Blind Man — A304

1981, Mar. 25 Photo.

937 A304 14p shown .38 .18
938 A304 18p Sign language .50 .24
939 A304 22p Man in wheelchair .60 .30
940 A304 25p Foot painting .70 .35
Nos. 937-940 (4) 2.18 1.07

International Year of the Disabled.

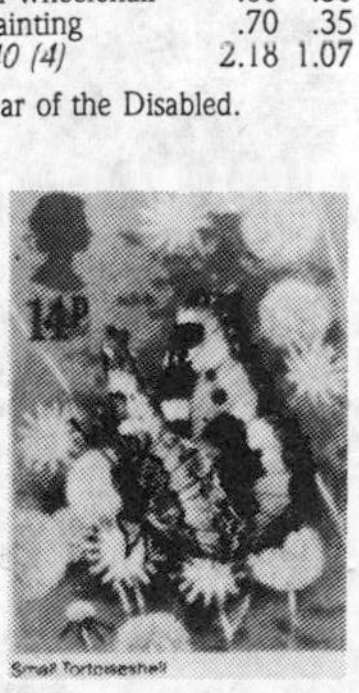
Small Tortoiseshell A305

1981, May 13 *Perf. 14x14½*

941 A305 14p shown .45 .24
942 A305 18p Large blue .55 .28
943 A305 22p Peacock .70 .35
944 A305 25p Checkered skipper .80 .40
Nos. 941-944 (4) 2.50 1.27

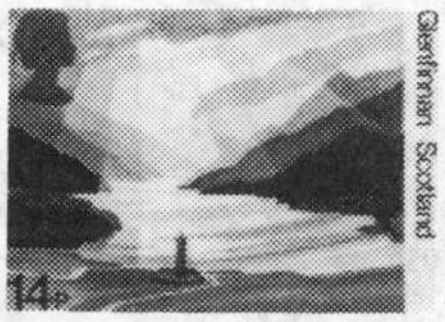
Glenfinnan, Highlands, Scotland A306

50th anniv. of National Trust for Scotland: 18p, Derwentwater, Lake District, England. 20p, Stackpole Head, Dyfed, Wales. 22p, Giant's Causeway, County Antrim, Northern Ireland. 25p, St. Kilda, Scotland.

1981, June 24 Photo. *Perf. 14½x14*

945 A306 14p multicolored .40 .20
946 A306 18p multicolored .52 .25
947 A306 20p multicolored .60 .30
948 A306 22p multicolored .65 .35
949 A306 25p multicolored .75 .38
Nos. 945-949 (5) 2.92 1.48

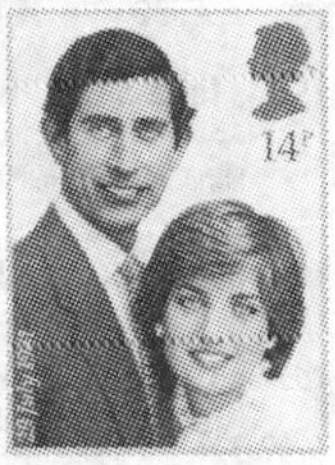
Prince Charles and Lady Diana — A307

1981, July 22 Photo. *Perf. 14x14½*

950 A307 14p multicolored .45 .24
951 A307 25p multicolored .85 .42

Wedding of Charles, Prince of Wales, and Lady Diana Spencer, St. Paul's Cathedral, July 29.

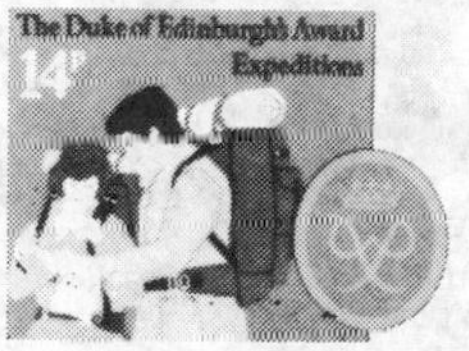

Hikers Reading Map A308

1981, Aug. 12 Litho. *Perf. 14*

952 A308 14p shown .45 .22
953 A308 18p Girl at potter's wheel .55 .28
954 A308 22p Woman administering artificial respiration .70 .35
955 A308 25p Hurdler .80 .40
Nos. 952-955 (4) 2.50 1.25

The Duke of Edinburgh's Awards (expeditions, skills, service, recreation), 25th anniv.

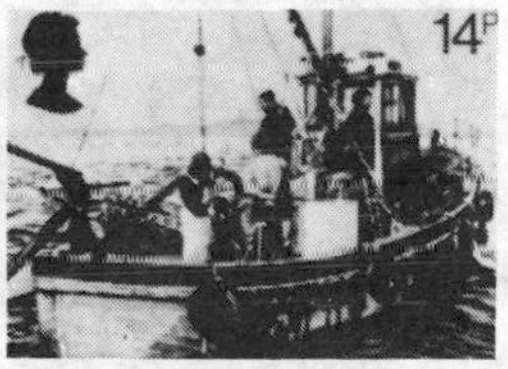
Cockle Dredging A309

1981, Sept. 23 Photo. *Perf. 14½x14*

956 A309 14p shown .40 .20
957 A309 18p Hauling trawl net .52 .25
958 A309 22p Lobster potting .65 .35
959 A309 25p Hauling seine net .75 .38
Nos. 956-959 (4) 2.32 1.18

Fishermen's Year and Royal Natl. Mission to Deep Sea Fishermen centenary.

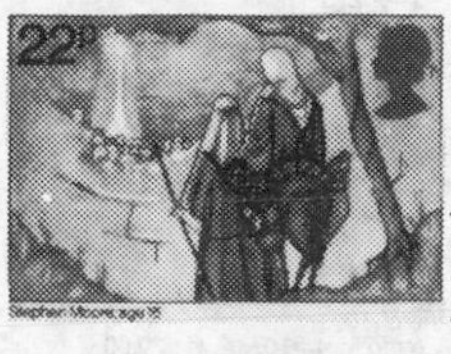
Joseph and Mary Arriving at Bethlehem A310

Christmas: Children's Drawings.

1981, Nov. 18 Photo.

960 A310 11½p Santa Claus .35 .16
961 A310 14p Jesus .40 .20
962 A310 18p Angel .52 .25
963 A310 22p shown .65 .35
964 A310 25p Three Kings .75 .38
Nos. 960-964 (5) 2.67 1.34

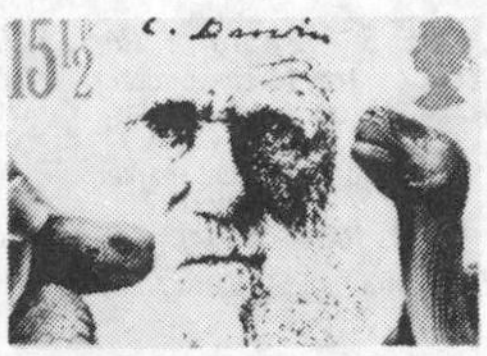
Death Centenary of Charles Darwin (1809-1882) — A311

1982, Feb. 10 Photo.

965 A311 15½p Giant tortoises .45 .22
966 A311 19½p Iguanas .55 .28
967 A311 26p Darwin's finches .80 .38
968 A311 29p Skulls .85 .42
Nos. 965-968 (4) 2.65 1.30

Redrawn Queen Type of 1970

1982-87 Photo. *Perf. 15x14*

969 A197 3½p vio brown, type II ('83) .35 .25
970 A197 5p pink, litho., perf. 13½x14 .60 .20
a. Litho., perf. 15x14 ('84) .70 .20
b. Photo., perf. 15x14, type II ('88) 1.50 .90
971 A197 12½p emerald .42 .25
b. Bklt. pane, 4 #971, 6 #896 6.00
c. Bklt. pane, 10 #971, 10 #896 11.50
d. Bklt. pane, #622, 4 #889, 3 #971 3.00
e. Bklt. pane, 3 #969, 3 #971, 2 #623 7.50
f. Bklt. pane of 6 + printed margin 4.00
g. Bklt. pane, #625, #889, 7 #971 + printed margin 6.00
972 A197 16p dull brown ('83) .55 .25
a. Booklet pane of 10 7.50
b. Bklt. pane, 4 #971, 6 #972 12.00
c. Bklt. pane of 9 + printed margin 5.50
973 A197 16½p fawn 1.00 .75
974 A197 17p blue gray, type II ('83) .55 .30
a. Bklt. pane of 3 + label 2.50
b. Bklt. pane of 9 + printed margin 5.25
c. Bklt. pane, #764b, 7 #974, #1073 + printed margin ('84) 21.00
d. Bklt. pane of 6 + printed margin 20.00
975 A197 19½p olive green 2.75 1.50
976 A197 20½p ultra, type II ('83) 1.25 .90
977 A197 23p orange ver, type II ('83) 1.25 .50
978 A197 26p red 1.00 .52
a. Type II ('87) 6.00 6.00
b. Bklt. pane of 4, No. 978a ('87) 24.00
979 A197 28p deep violet, type II ('83) .85 .60
980 A197 29p brown olive 2.75 1.40
981 A197 31p brt rose lilac, type II ('83) 1.25 .70

Perf. 14x15

Size: 27x38mm

982 A197 £1.30 sl blue & buff 9.50 7.00
Nos. 969-982 (14) 24.07 15.12

See description of type II before #622-638.

No. 971c and a pane of 20 12½p were sold at a discount. Stamps have stars on back.

Nos. 972a, 974a and a pane of ten 17p were sold at a discount. Some panes have "D" or stars on back.

No. 978b has margins on four sides. No. 974b comes with different margins.

For Prestige booklets containing panes #971f, 971g, 972c, 974b, 974c, 974d, see list at end of postage section.

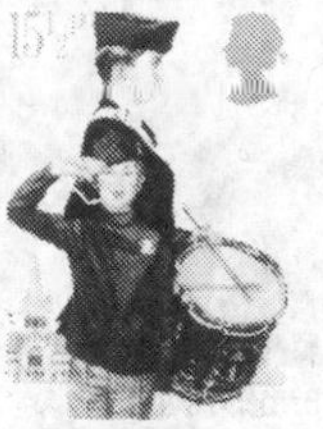
Youth Organizations A312

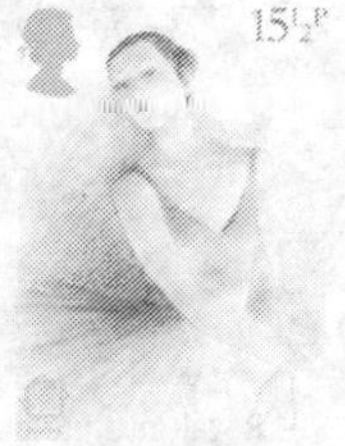
Performing Arts A313

1982, Mar. 24 Photo. *Perf. 14x14½*

983 A312 15½p Boy's Brigade .50 .24
984 A312 19½p Girl's Brigade .65 .32
985 A312 26p Boy Scouts .85 .42
986 A312 29p Girl Guides 1.00 .48
Nos. 983-986 (4) 3.00 1.46

75th anniv. of scouting and 125th birth anniv. of founder Robert Baden-Powell (26p).

1982, Apr. 28 Photo. *Perf. 14x14½*

987 A313 15½p Ballet .50 .24
988 A313 19½p Pantomime .65 .32
989 A313 26p Shakespearean drama .85 .42
990 A313 29p Opera 1.00 .48
Nos. 987-990 (4) 3.00 1.46

Nos. 987-990 show CEPT (Europa) emblem.

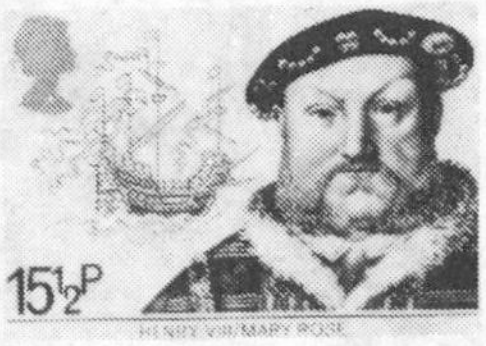
King Henry VIII and the Mary Rose A314

1982, June 16 *Perf. 14½x14*

991 A314 15½p shown .50 .24
992 A314 19½p Admiral Blake, Triumph .65 .32
993 A314 24p Lord Nelson, Victory .75 .35
994 A314 26p Lord Fisher, Dreadnought .85 .42
995 A314 29p Viscount Cunningham, Warspite 1.00 .48
Nos. 991-995 (5) 3.75 1.81

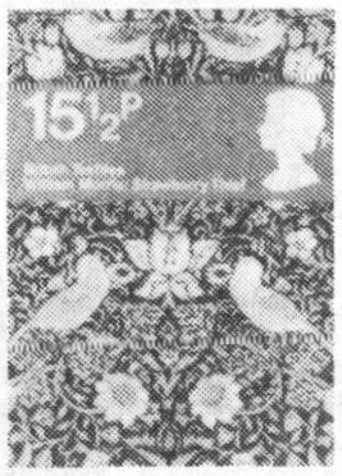
Textile Designs — A315

1982, July 23 Photo. *Perf. 14x14½*

996 A315 15½p Strawberry Thief, 1883 .45 .22
997 A315 19½p Tulips, 1906 .60 .30
998 A315 26p Cherry Orchard, 1930 .80 .38
999 A315 29p Chevron, 1973 .95 .45
Nos. 996-999 (4) 2.80 1.35

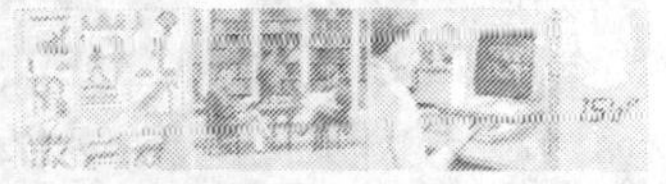
Information Technology — A316

Designs: 15½p, Hieroglyphics, library, word processor. 26p, Viewdata set, satellite, laser pen.

1982, Sept. 8 Photo.

1000 A316 15½p multicolored .50 .24
1001 A316 26p multicolored .85 .42

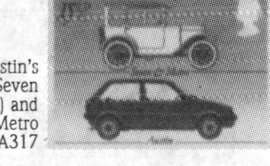

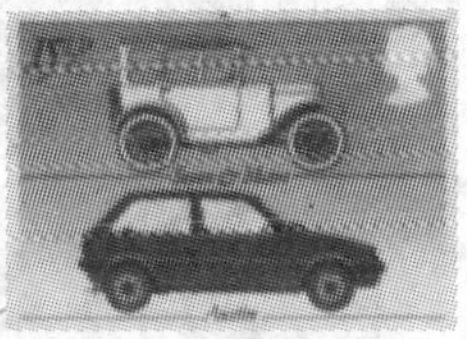
Austin's Seven (1922) and Metro A317

Cars: 19½p, Ford Model T (1913) and Escort. 26p, Jaguar SS (1931) and XJ6 (1967). 29p, Rolls-Royce Silver Ghost (1907) and Silver Spirit (1982).

1982, Oct. 13 Litho. *Perf. 14½x14*

1002 A317 15½p multicolored .45 .38
1003 A317 19½p multicolored .65 .50
1004 A317 26p multicolored .75 .65
1005 A317 29p multicolored 1.00 .75
Nos. 1002-1005 (4) 2.85 2.28

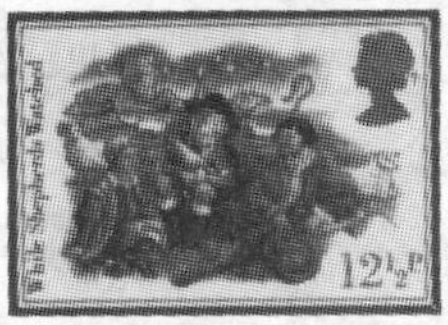
Christmas 1982 A318

Designs: Christmas carols.

1982, Nov. 17 Photo.

1006 A318 12½p While Shepherds Watched .38 .18
1007 A318 15½p The Holly and the Ivy .45 .22
1008 A318 19½p I Saw Three Ships .60 .30
1009 A318 26p We Three Kings .80 .38
1010 A318 29p Good King Wenceslas .95 .45
Nos. 1006-1010 (5) 3.18 1.53

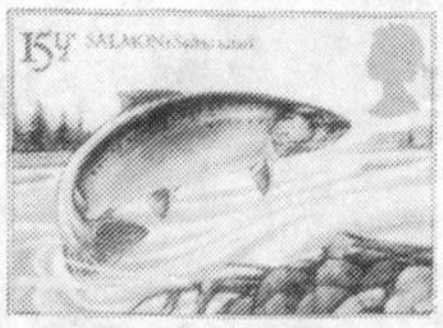

River Fish — A319

1983, Jan. 26 Photo. *Perf. 15x14*

1011 A319 15½p Salmon .40 .25
1012 A319 19½p Pike .55 .35
1013 A319 26p Trout .70 .45
1014 A319 29p Perch .90 .50
Nos. 1011-1014 (4) 2.55 1.55

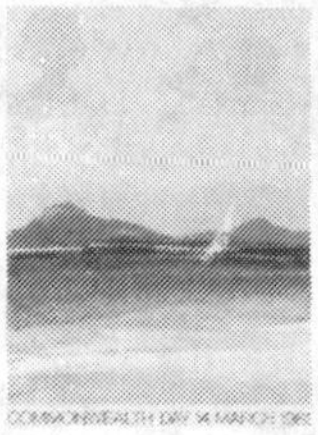

Commonwealth Day — A320

Landscapes by Donald Hamilton Fraser.

1983, Mar. 9 Photo. *Perf. 14x14½*

1015 A320 15½p Tropical island .45 .28
1016 A320 19½p Desert .55 .35
1017 A320 26p Farmland .75 .48
1018 A320 29p Mountains .80 .55
Nos. 1015-1018 (4) 2.55 1.66

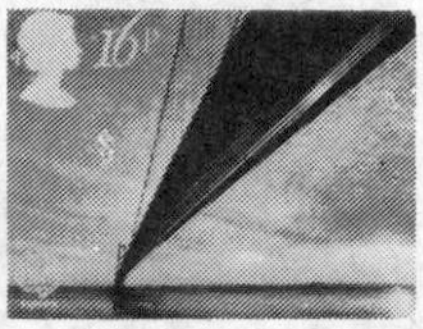

Engineering Achievements (Europa) A321

1983, May 25 Photo. *Perf. 15x14*

1019 A321 16p Humber Bridge .95 .38
1020 A321 20½p Thames Flood Barrier .95 .42
1021 A321 28p Emergency oil rig support vessel Lolair 1.25 .58
Nos. 1019-1021 (3) 3.15 1.38

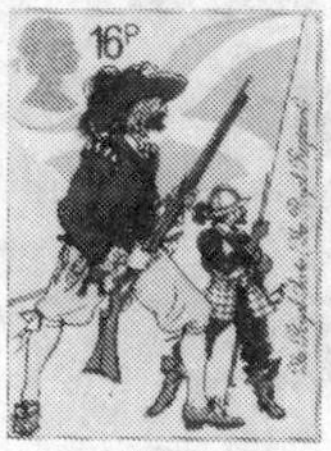

A322

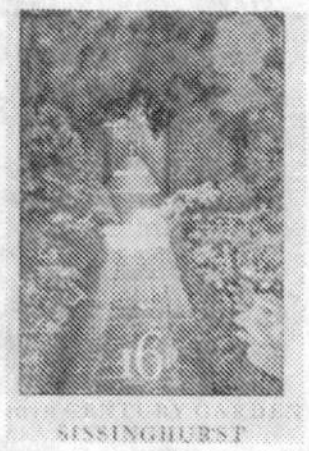

A323

Designs: 16p, The Royal Scots (Royal Regiment). 20½p, Royal Welsh Fusiliers. 26p, Royal Green Jackets. 28p, Irish Guards. 31p, Parachute Regiment.

1983, July 6 *Perf. 14x14½*

1022 A322 16p multicolored .55 .28
1023 A322 20½p multicolored .40 .35
1024 A322 26p multicolored .90 .45
1025 A322 28p multicolored .95 .48
1026 A322 31p multicolored 1.10 .52
Nos. 1022-1026 (5) 3.90 2.08

1983, Aug. 24 Litho. *Perf. 14*

Designs: 16p, 20th cent. garden, Sissinghurst. 20½p, Biddulph Grange, 19th cent. 28p, Blenheim, 18th cent. 31p, Pitmeeden, 17th cent.

1027 A323 16p multicolored .55 .28
1028 A323 20½p multicolored .70 .35
1029 A323 28p multicolored .95 .48
1030 A323 31p multicolored 1.10 .50
Nos. 1027-1030 (4) 3.30 1.61

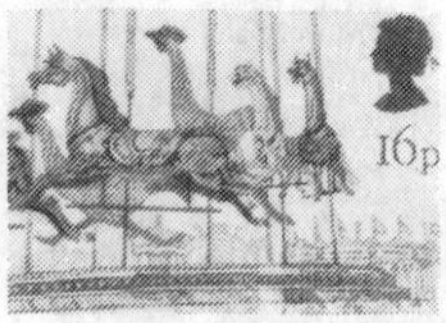

British Fairs A324

1983, Oct. 5 Photo. *Perf. 14½x14*

1031 A324 16p Merry-go-round .55 .28
1032 A324 20½p Animals, rides .70 .35
1033 A324 28p Games .95 .48
1034 A324 31p Ancient market fair 1.00 .50
Nos. 1031-1034 (4) 3.20 1.61

850th anniv. of St. Bartholomew's Fair.

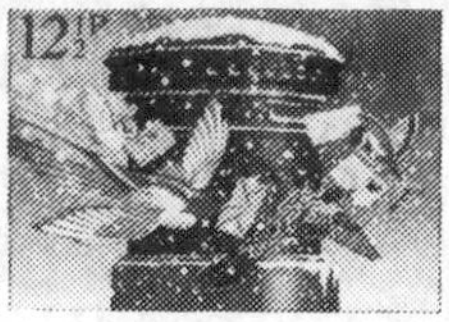

Christmas A325

1983, Nov. 16 Photo.

1035 A325 12½p Birds mailing cards .35 .24
1036 A325 16p Three Kings chimney pots .48 .28
1037 A325 20½p Birds under umbrella .55 .35
1038 A325 28p Birds under street lamp .80 .48
1039 A325 31p Topiary dove .90 .52
Nos. 1035-1039 (5) 3.08 1.87

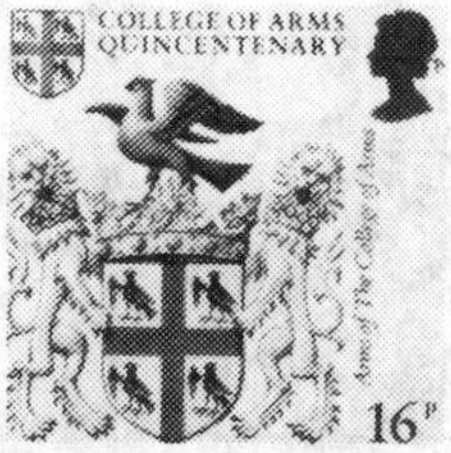

Heraldry A326

Designs: 16p, Arms of The College of Arms. 20½p, Arms of Richard III, founder. 28p, Arms of The Earl Marshal. 31p, Arms of The City of London.

1984, Jan. 17 Photo. *Perf. 14½*

1040 A326 16p multicolored .55 .28
1041 A326 20½p multicolored .70 .35
1042 A326 28p multicolored .95 .48
1043 A326 31p multicolored 1.00 .50
Nos. 1040-1043 (4) 3.20 1.61

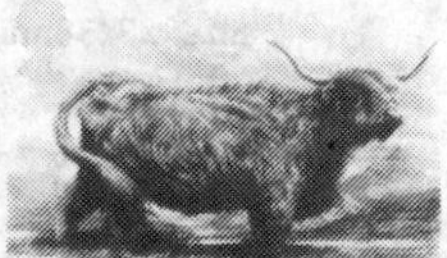

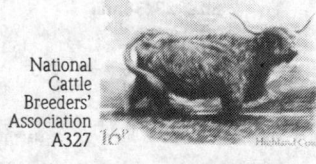

National Cattle Breeders' Association A327

1984, Mar. 6 Litho. *Perf. 15x14½*

1044 A327 16p Highland Cow .50 .25
1045 A327 20½p Chillingham Wild Bull .62 .30
1046 A327 26p Hereford Bull .80 .40
1047 A327 28p Welsh Black Bull .85 .42
1048 A327 31p Irish Moiled Cow .95 .45
Nos. 1044-1048 (5) 3.72 1.82

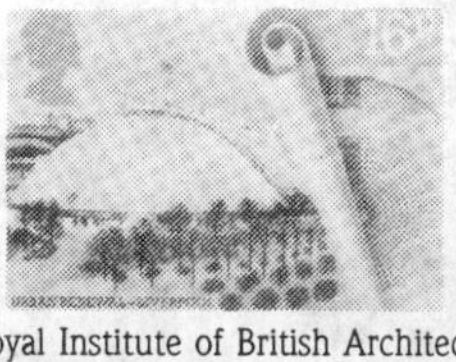

Royal Institute of British Architects Sesquicentennial — A328

Urban renewal projects and plans.

1984, Apr. 3 Photo.

1049 A328 16p Liverpool .55 .28
1050 A328 20½p Durham .70 .35
1051 A328 28p Bristol .95 .48
1052 A328 31p Perth 1.10 .50
Nos. 1049-1052 (4) 3.30 1.61

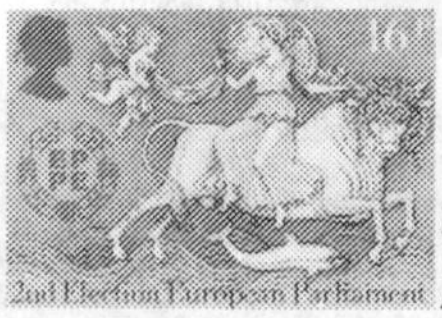

Europa (1959-1984) A329

1984, May 9 Photo. *Perf. 14½x14*

1053 A329 16p Bridge .70 .35
1054 A329 16p Abduction of Europa .70 .35
1055 A329 20½p like No. 1053 .90 .45
1056 A329 20½p like No. 1054 .90 .45
Nos. 1053-1056 (4) 3.20 1.60

Nos. 1054, 1056 also for 2nd Election of the European Parliament.

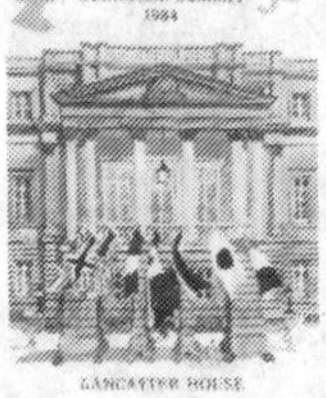

A330

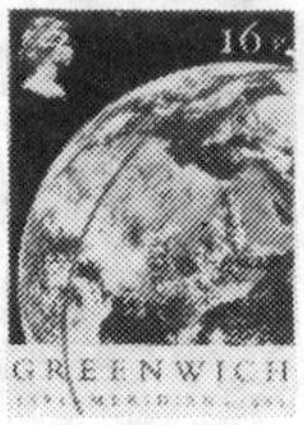

A331

1984, June 5 Photo. *Perf. 14x15*

1057 A330 31p Lancaster House 1.00 .50

London Economic Summit, June 7-9.

1984, June 26 Litho. *Perf. 14x14½*

1058 A331 16p View from Apollo 11 .55 .28
1059 A331 20½p English Channel map .70 .35
1060 A331 28p Greenwich Observatory .95 .48
1061 A331 31p Airy's transit telescope, 1850 1.10 .55
Nos. 1058-1061 (4) 3.30 1.66

Greenwich Meridian centenary.

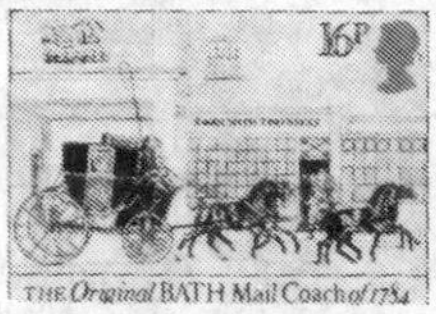

Bath-Bristol-London Mail Coach Bicentenary — A332

18th century drawings by James Pollard.

Photo. & Engr.

1984, July 31 *Perf. 14½x14*

1062 A332 16p Bath, 1784 .55 .25
1063 A332 16p Exeter, 1816 .55 .25
1064 A332 16p Norwich, 1827 .55 .25
1065 A332 16p Holyhead & Liverpool .55 .25
1066 A332 16p Edinburgh, 1831 .55 .25
a. Strip of 5, #1062-1066 3.00
Nos. 1062-1066 (5) 2.75 1.25

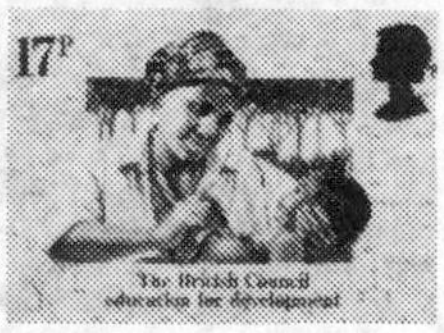

50th Anniv. of British Council A333

1984, Sept. 25 Photo.

1067 A333 17p Education for development .60 .30
1068 A333 22p Promoting the arts .80 .38
1069 A333 31p Technical training 1.10 .55
1070 A333 34p Language & libraries 1.10 .60
Nos. 1067-1070 (4) 3.60 1.83

Redrawn Queen Type of 1970
Type II

1984-88 Photo. *Perf. 15x14*

1071 A197 7p henna brn ('85) 2.00 1.50
1072 A197 12p brt green ('85) .60 .35
a. Bklt. pane of 9 + printed margin 6.00
b. Bklt. pane, 6 #974, 4 #1072 7.00
c. Bklt. pane, 6 #1072, 2 #974, #981 + printed margin *17.00*
d. Bklt. pane, 2 #623e, 4 #1072 *8.00*
1073 A197 13p lt red brown .48 .20
a. Booklet pane of 10 6.00
b. Bklt. pane, 6 #974, 4 #1073 9.00
c. Bklt. pane, 3 #623e, 2 #890, 3 #1073 4.75
d. Bklt. pane, #623e, 2 #970b, 3 #1073 5.00
e. Bklt. pane of 6 + printed margin 3.25
f. Bklt. pane of 9 + printed margin 4.75
g. Bklt. pane, #623e, 2 #970b, 3 #1073 + printed margin ('87) 5.00
h. Booklet pane of 4 ('87) 3.00
i. Litho. ('88) .80 .60
j. Bklt. pane, 2 #890c, 2 #974, 4 #1073, #1084 + printed margin ('85) *17.00*
k. As "e," litho. ('88) 5.00
l. Bklt. pane, 6 #1073i, #1075h, #1078a, #1084a + printed margin 17.50
1074 A197 14p dark blue ('88) .38 .40
a. Booklet pane of 4 *5.00*
b. As "a," imperf. edges *19.00*
c. Booklet pane of 10 5.50
d. As "c," imperf. edges *8.00*
e. Litho. 1.65 .75
f. Booklet pane of 10 #1074e 17.00
g. Litho., perf. 13½x14 ('89) 1.75 .90
1075 A197 18p olive green .55 .50
a. Bklt. pane, #623e, #1073, 2 #1075 3.50
b. Bklt. pane, #1073, 5 #1075 6.00
c. Bklt. pane of 9 + printed margins 5.50
d. Bklt. pane, #623, #978, 2 #1073, 5 #1075 + printed margin *17.50*
e. Booklet pane of 4 ('87) 3.50
f. As "b," imperf. edges ('87) 6.00
g. Booklet pane of 10 ('87) 8.50
h. Litho. ('88) .80 .60
i. Bklt. pane of 6 #1075h + printed margin ('88) 5.00
j. As "c," litho. ('88) 7.75
1076 A197 19p brt orange ('88) .52 .35
a. Bklt. pane, #1074, 2 #1076 + label ('88) 3.75
b. Bklt. pane, 2 #1074, 4 #1076 ('88) *8.00*
c. Booklet pane of 4 *6.00*
d. As "c," imperf. edges *19.00*
e. Booklet pane of 10 7.50
f. As "e," imperf. edges *10.00*
g. Litho. 1.90 .90
h. Booklet pane of 10 #1076g 19.00
i. Litho., perf. 13½x14 ('89) 1.40 1.00
j. Bklt. pane, 2 #1074g, 4 #1076i ('89) 9.25
1077 A197 20p grn blue ('88) .70 .38
1078 A197 22p yel green .70 .55
a. Litho. ('88) 6.50 3.00
1079 A197 23p brt yel grn ('88) .85 .42
1080 A197 24p violet 1.40 .80
1081 A197 27p brown ('88) .95 .75
a. Booklet pane of 4 *8.00*
b. As "a," imperf. edges *27.50*
1082 A197 28p dk ol bister ('88) .95 .50
1083 A197 32p Prus blue ('88) 1.10 .75
1084 A197 34p deep bister 1.10 .80
a. Litho. ('88) 5.00 2.00
1085 A197 35p dark brown ('88) 1.25 1.00

Size: 27x38mm

Perf. 14x15

1086 A197 £1.33 blk & pale rose lil 8.25 6.00
1087 A197 £1.41 ind & buff ('85) 9.00 7.50
1087A A197 £1.50 blk & lt pink ('86) 7.00 3.50
1087B A197 £1.60 indigo & buff ('87) 7.00 3.50
Nos. 1071-1087B (19) 44.78 29.75

Nos. 1073a, 1073h, 1074a, 1074c, 1075e, 1075g, 1076c, 1076e and 1081a have margins on four sides. Nos. 1073g, 1074b, 1074d, 1075f, 1076d, 1076f and 1081b are straight-edged at left and right or top and bottom. In 1989 Nos. 1074b and 1076d were issued straight-edged on three sides.

Panes of 10p stamps with blue stars on back were sold at a discount.

For Prestige booklets containing panes #1072a, 1072c, 1073e, 1073f, 1073j, 1073k, 1073l, 1075c, 1075d, 1075i, 1075j, see list at end of postage section.

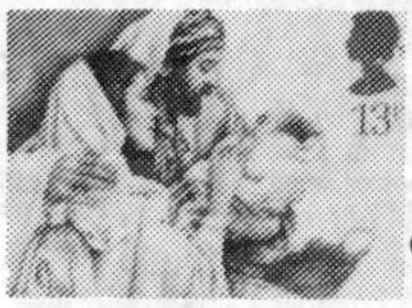

Christmas 1984 — A334

Crayon Sketches by Yvonne Gilbert.

1984, Nov. 20 Photo. *Perf. 15x14*

1088 A334 13p Holy Family .42 .20
1089 A334 17p Arrival in Bethlehem .55 .25
1090 A334 22p Shephard and Lamb .70 .35
1091 A334 31p Virgin and child 1.00 .50
1092 A334 34p Offering Frankincense 1.10 .55
Nos. 1088-1092 (5) 3.77 1.85

Bklt. of 20 13p sold at 30p discount. Stamps have blue stars printed on the back.

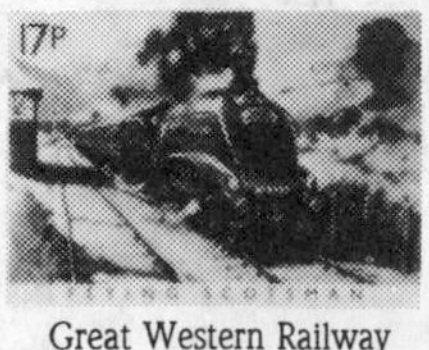

Great Western Railway Sesquicentennial — A335

1985, Jan. 22 Photo. *Perf. 15x14*

1093 A335 17p Flying Scotsman .60 .40
1094 A335 22p Golden Arrow .70 .55
1095 A335 29p Cheltenham Flyer .80 .65

1096 A335 31p Royal Scot 1.25 .75
1097 A335 34p Cornish Riviera 1.25 .95
　　Nos. 1093-1097 (5) 4.60 3.30

Insects — A336

1985, Mar. 12 Photo. *Perf. 15x14¹/₂*
1098 A336 17p Buff tailed bumble
　　　　bee .52 .30
1099 A336 22p Seven spotted lady-
　　　　bird .65 .42
1100 A336 29p Wart-biter bush-crick-
　　　　et .80 .48
1101 A336 31p Stag beetle .90 .48
1102 A336 34p Emperor dragonfly 1.10 .60
　　Nos. 1098-1102 (5) 3.97 2.28

Music Year
(Europa)
A337

British Composers: 17p, Water Music, by George
Frideric Handel. 22p, The Planets Suite, by Gustav
Holst. 31p, The First Cuckoo, by Frederick Delius.
34p, Sea Pictures, by Edward Elgar.

1985, May 14 *Perf. 14¹/₂*
1103 A337 17p Reflections in pool .80 .30
1104 A337 22p View of planets 1.00 .38
1105 A337 31p Roosting cuckoo 1.40 .52
1106 A337 34p Waves, wing 1.50 .60
　　Nos. 1103-1106 (4) 4.70 1.00

Safety at
Sea — A338

1985, June 18 Litho. *Perf. 14*
1107 A338 17p Lifeboat .60 .30
1108 A338 22p Beachy Head Light-
　　　　house, chart .80 .42
1109 A338 31p Marecs-A satellite 1.10 .60
1110 A338 34p Signal buoy, yacht 1.25 .65
　　Nos. 1107-1110 (4) 3.75 1.97

Royal Mail Service,
350th
Anniv. — A339

Designs: 17p, Royal Mail Datapost motorcyclist
and plane. 22p, Postbus on country road. 31p, Parcel service delivery. 34p, Postman delivering mail.

1985, July 30 Photo. *Perf. 14x14¹/₂*
1111 A339 17p multicolored .60 .30
1112 A339 22p multicolored .80 .38
1113 A339 31p multicolored 1.00 .42
1114 A339 34p multicolored 1.25 .55
　　Nos. 1111-1114 (4) 3.65 1.62

Arthurian
Legends
A340

Designs: 17p, Arthur consulting with Merlin.
22p, The Lady of the Lake with the sword "Excali-
bur." 31p, Guinevere and Lancelot fleeing from

Camelot. 34p, Sir Galahad praying during his quest
for the Holy Grail.

1985, Sept. 3 Photo. *Perf. 15x14*
1115 A340 17p multicolored .52 .25
1116 A340 22p multicolored .70 .35
1117 A340 31p multicolored 1.00 .50
1118 A340 34p multicolored 1.10 .55
　　Nos. 1115-1118 (4) 3.32 1.65
500th anniv. of William Caxton's edition of Le
Morte D'Arthur, by Sir Thomas Mallory.

20th Cent. Stars and
Directors of
Film — A341

Photographs: 17p, Peter Sellers (1925-80). 22p,
David Niven (1910-83). 29p, Charlie Chaplin
(1889-1977). 31p, Vivien Leigh (1913-67). 34p, Sir
Alfred Hitchcock (1899-1980), director.

1985, Oct. 8 Photo. *Perf. 14¹/₂*
1119 A341 17p multicolored .60 .25
1120 A341 22p multicolored .80 .35
1121 A341 29p multicolored 1.10 .48
1122 A341 31p multicolored 1.25 .50
1123 A341 34p multicolored 1.40 .55
　　Nos. 1119-1123 (5) 5.15 2.13

Christmas
Pantomime
A342

1985, Nov. 19 Photo. *Perf. 15x14¹/₂*
1124 A342 12p Principal boy .35 .18
　　a. Booklet pane of 20 7.00
1125 A342 17p Genie .50 .25
1126 A342 22p Grande dame .65 .32
1127 A342 31p Good fairy .90 .45
1128 A342 34p Cat 1.00 .50
　　Nos. 1124-1128 (5) 3.40 1.70

No. 1124a has random star design printed on
back.

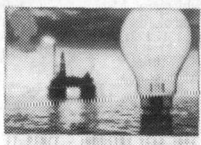

Industry
Year — A343

1986, Jan. 14 Litho. *Perf. 15x14*
1129 A343 17p North Sea oil rig,
　　　　light bulb .55 .28
1130 A343 22p Medical research lab,
　　　　thermometer .70 .35
1131 A343 31p Steel mill, garden
　　　　hoe 1.00 .50
1132 A343 34p Cornfield, bread 1.10 .55
　　Nos. 1129-1132 (4) 3.35 1.68

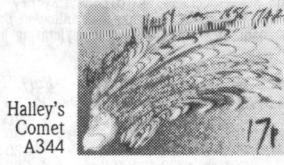

Halley's
Comet
A344

Designs: 17p, Caricature, Edmond Halley (1656-
1742), astronomer. 22p, European Space Agency
Giotto spacecraft pursuing comet. 31p, Comet and
legend, Maybe Twice in a Lifetime. 34p, Comet
orbiting sun.

1986, Feb. 18 Photo.
1133 A344 17p multicolored .55 .28
1134 A344 22p multicolored .70 .35
1135 A344 31p multicolored 1.00 .50
1136 A344 34p multicolored 1.10 .55
　　Nos. 1133-1136 (4) 3.35 1.68

Sixtieth Birthday 17p A345

Queen
Elizabeth II,
60th
Birthday
A346 Sixtieth Birthday 17p

1986, Apr. 21 Photo.
1137 A345 17p multicolored .60 .30
1138 A345 17p multicolored .60 .30
　　a. Pair, #1137-1138 1.25 .60
1139 A346 34p multicolored 1.25 .60
1140 A346 34p multicolored 1.25 .60
　　a. Pair, #1139-1140 2.50 1.25

Europa — A347

1986, May 20 Photo. *Perf. 14¹/₂*
1141 A347 17p Barn owl .60 .30
1142 A347 22p Pine marten .75 .35
1143 A347 31p Wild cat 1.10 .55
1144 A347 34p Natterjack toad 1.25 .60
　　Nos. 1141-1144 (4) 3.70 1.80

Domesday
Book, 900th
Anniv.
A348

1986, June 17 Photo.
1145 A348 17p Peasant .40 .32
1146 A348 22p Freeman .80 .40
1147 A348 31p Knight 1.10 .60
1148 A348 34p Lord 1.25 .65
　　Nos. 1145-1148 (4) 3.55 1.97

Domesday Book, first nationwide survey in British history.

Sports
A349

1986, July 15 Photo. *Perf. 15x14*
1149 A349 17p Track and field .60 .25
1150 A349 22p Rowing .75 .35
1151 A349 29p Weight lifting 1.00 .45
1152 A349 31p Shooting 1.05 .48
1153 A349 34p Field hockey 1.15 .52
　　Nos. 1149-1153 (5) 4.55 2.05

1986 Commonwealth Games, Edinburgh. World
Hockey Cup, London.

A350　　　　　A351

1986, July 22 *Perf. 14x15*
1154 A350 12p multicolored .50 .22
1155 A350 17p multicolored .75 .28
Wedding of Prince Andrew and Sarah Ferguson.

1986, Aug. 19 Litho. *Perf. 14x14¹/₂*
1156 A351 34p multicolored 1.25 .52
Commonwealth Parliamentary Assoc. conf.,
London, Sept.

Royal Air Force
Commanders and
Aircraft — A352

Designs: 17p, Lord Dowding (1882-1970), Hurri-
cane. 22p, Lord Tedder (1890-1967), Hawker
Typhoon. 29p, Lord Trenchard (1873-1956), De
Havilland 9A World War I bomber. 31p, Sir Arthur
Harris (1892-1984), Avro Lancaster. 34p, Lord Por-
tal (1893-1971), De Havilland Mosquito.

1986, Sept. 16 Photo. *Perf. 14¹/₂*
1157 A352 17p multicolored .55 .25
1158 A352 22p multicolored .70 .35
1159 A352 29p multicolored .95 .45
1160 A352 31p multicolored 1.00 .48
1161 A352 34p multicolored 1.10 .52
　　Nos. 1157-1161 (5) 4.30 2.05

Christmas
A353

Customs: 12p, 13p, Glastonbury Thorn. 18p,
Tanad Valley Plygain. 22p, Hebrides Tribute. 31p,
Dewsbury Church Knell. 34p, Hereford Boy
Bishop.

1986, Nov. 18 Photo. *Perf. 15x14¹/₂*
1162 A353 12p multicolored .38 .18
1163 A353 13p multicolored .40 .20
　　a. Pane of 36 14.50
1164 A353 18p multicolored .60 .28
1165 A353 22p multicolored .70 .32
1166 A353 31p multicolored 1.00 .45
1167 A353 34p multicolored 1.10 .50
　　Nos. 1162-1167 (6) 4.18 1.93

No. 1163a printed in two panes of 18 with gutter between, stars on back; folded and sold in discount booklet for £4.30.

Flora — A354

Photographs by Alfred Lammer.

1987, Jan. 20 Photo. *Perf. 14¹/₂*
1168 A354 18p Gaillardia .52 .25
1169 A354 22p Echinops .65 .32
1170 A354 31p Echeveria .90 .45
1171 A354 34p Colchicum 1.00 .50
　　Nos. 1168-1171 (4) 3.07 1.52

Sir Isaac Newton (1642-1727), Physicist,
Mathematician — A355

Manuscripts and principles: 18p, Philosophiae
Naturalis Principia Mathematica, 1687. 22p,
Motion of bodies in ellipses. 31p, Opticks Treatise

of the Refraction, Reflections and Colors of Light. 34p, The System of the World.

1987, Mar. 24 Photo. *Perf. 14*

1172	A355	18p	multicolored	.60	.30
1173	A355	22p	multicolored	.75	.40
1174	A355	31p	multicolored	1.10	.48
1175	A355	34p	multicolored	1.25	.60
			Nos. 1172-1175 (4)	3.70	1.78

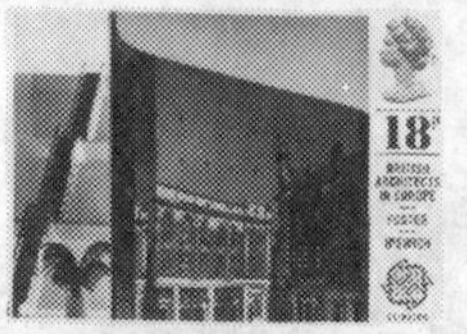

Europa A356

Modern architecture: 18p, Willis Faber & Dumas Building, Ipswich, designed by Norman Foster. 22p, Pompidou Centre, Paris, designed by Richard Rogers and Renzo Piano. 31p, Staatsgalerie, Stuttgart, designed by James Stirling and Michael Wilford. 34p, European Investment Bank, Luxembourg, designed by Sir Denys Lasdun.

1987, May 12 Photo. *Perf. 15x14*

1176	A356	18p	multicolored	.60	.30
1177	A356	22p	multicolored	.75	.38
1178	A356	31p	multicolored	1.05	.52
1179	A356	34p	multicolored	1.15	.58
			Nos. 1176-1179 (4)	3.55	1.78

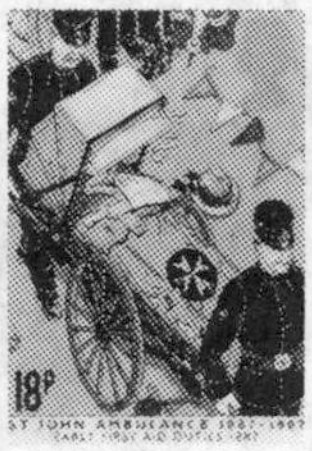

St. John Ambulance, Cent. — A357

First aid.

1987, June 16 Litho. *Perf. 14x14½*

1180	A357	18p	Ambulance, 1887	.62	.30
1181	A357	22p	War victims, 1940	.75	.38
1182	A357	31p	Public event, 1965	1.05	.52
1183	A357	34p	Transplant organ flight, 1987	1.15	.58
			Nos. 1180-1183 (4)	3.57	1.78

Order of the Thistle, Scotland, 300th Anniv. of Revival — A358

Coats of arms: 18p, Lord Lyon, King of Arms, 1687. 22p, Duke of Rothesay, bestowed on Prince Charles in 1974. 31p, Royal Scottish Academy of Painting, Sculpture & Architecture, 1826. 34p, The Royal Society of Edinburgh, 1783.

1987, July 21 Photo. *Perf. 14½*

1184	A358	18p	multicolored	.60	.30
1185	A358	22p	multicolored	.75	.38
1186	A358	31p	multicolored	1.00	.50
1187	A358	34p	multicolored	1.15	.58
			Nos. 1184-1187 (4)	3.50	1.76

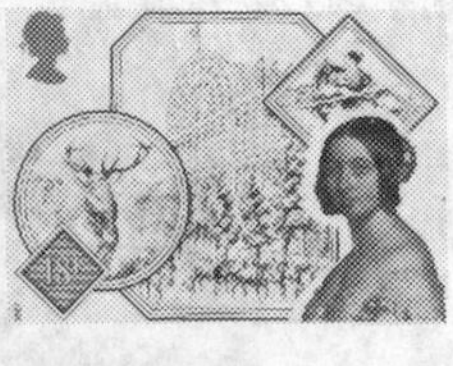

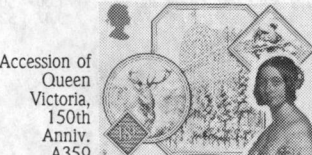

Accession of Queen Victoria, 150th Anniv. A359

Portraits of Victoria and: 18p, Great Exhibition (1851) at the Crystal Palace, Grace Darling's rescue (1838) of the Forfashire's survivors, and Monarch of the Glen, by Sir Edwin Henry Landseer. 22p, Launching of Brunel's ship Great Eastern, portrait of Prince Consort Albert, Mrs. Beeton's Book of Household Management (1889). 31p, The Albert Memorial, Prime Minister Disraeli and 1st ballot ... 34p, The Boer War, Guglielmo Marconi's ... telegraph communications linking Paris ...on (1898), and diamond jubilee emblem.

Photo. & Engr.

1987, Sept. 8 *Perf. 15x14*

1188	A359	18p	multicolored	.60	.30
1189	A359	22p	multicolored	.75	.38
1190	A359	31p	multicolored	1.05	.52
1191	A359	34p	multicolored	1.15	.58
			Nos. 1188-1191 (4)	3.55	1.78

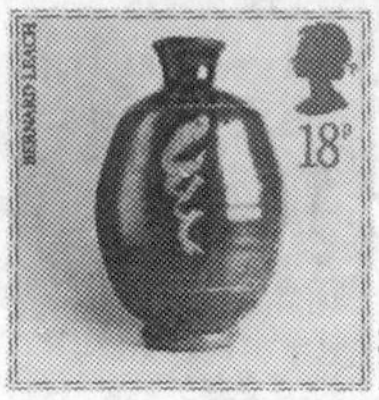

Studio Pottery — A360

1987, Oct. 13 Photo. *Perf. 14½*

1192	A360	18p	Bernard Leach	.60	.30
1193	A360	26p	Elizabeth Fritsch	.85	.42
1194	A360	31p	Lucie Rie	1.05	.52
1195	A360	34p	Hans Coper	1.15	.58
			Nos. 1192-1195 (4)	3.65	1.82

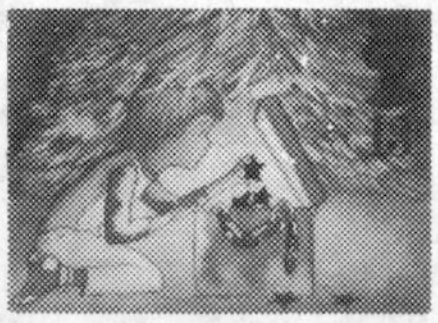

Christmas A361

Childhood memories: 13p, Decorating tree. 18p, Looking out window, Christmas eve. 26p, Sweet dreams. 31p, Reading new book to toys, Christmas morning. 34p, Playing horn, snowman.

1987, Nov. 17 Photo. *Perf. 15x14*

1196	A361	13p	multicolored	.45	.22
a.			Pane of 36	16.25	
1197	A361	18p	multicolored	.60	.30
1198	A361	26p	multicolored	.88	.45
1199	A361	31p	multicolored	1.05	.52
1200	A361	34p	multicolored	1.15	.58
			Nos. 1196-1200 (5)	4.13	2.07

No. 1196a printed in two panes of 18 with gutter between, stars on back; folded and sold in discount booklets for £4.30.

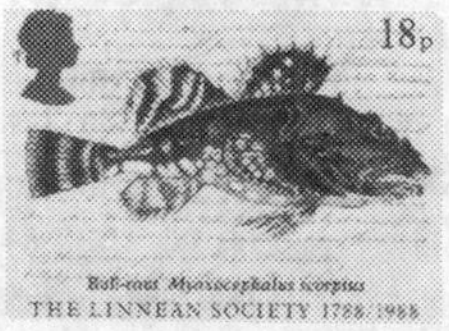

Linnean Society of London, 200th Anniv. A362

1988, Jan. 19 *Perf. 15x14½*

1201	A362	18p	Bull-rout fish	.68	.35
1202	A362	26p	Yellow waterlily	.98	.45
1203	A362	31p	Bewick's swan	1.15	.58
1204	A362	34p	Morel	1.25	.62
			Nos. 1201-1204 (4)	4.06	2.00

Linnaeus (Carl von Linne, 1707-78), inventor of system of taxonomic nomenclature.

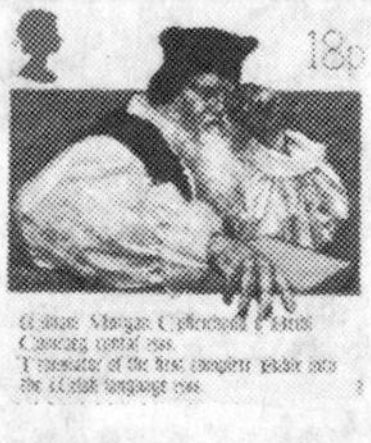

Welsh Bible, 400th Anniv. — A363

1988, Mar. 1 Photo. *Perf. 14½*

1205	A363	18p	William Morgan	.55	.35
1206	A363	26p	William Salesbury	.80	.50
1207	A363	31p	Richard Davies	.95	.58
1208	A363	34p	Richard Parry	1.10	.65
			Nos. 1205-1208 (4)	3.40	2.08

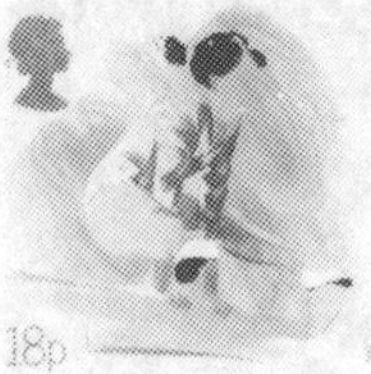

Sports — A364

1988, Mar. 22 Photo. *Perf. 14½*

1209	A364	18p	Balance beam	.55	.32
1210	A364	26p	Downhill skiing	.80	.48
1211	A364	31p	Tennis	.95	.58
1212	A364	34p	Soccer	1.10	.62
			Nos. 1209-1212 (4)	3.40	2.00

Ski Club of Great Britain and centenaries of the British Amateur Gymnastics Assoc., Lawn Tennis Assoc. and the Soccer League.

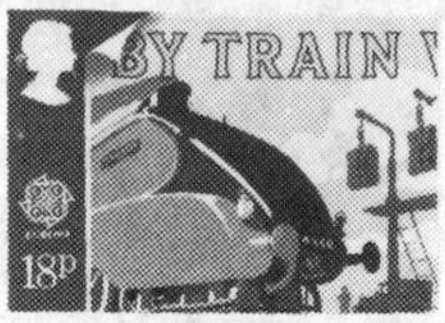

Europa 1988 A365

Transportation and communication, 1938.

1988, May 10 *Perf. 15x14*

1213	A365	18p	Mallard locomotive	.68	.35
1214	A365	26p	Queen Elizabeth ocean liner	.98	.50
1215	A365	31p	Tram No. 1173, Glasgow	1.15	.58
1216	A365	34p	Handley Page aircraft, Croydon Airport	1.25	.62
			Nos. 1213-1216 (4)	4.06	2.05

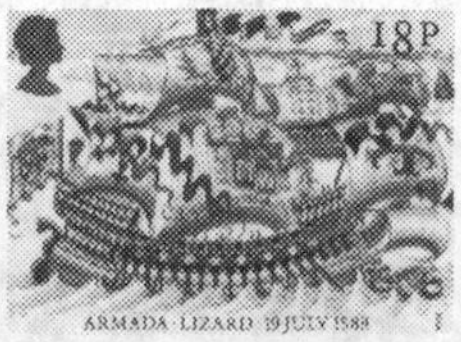

Defeat of the Spanish Armada by the Royal Navy, 400th Anniv. A366

Designs: No. 1217, Armada approaching The Lizard, July 19, 1588. No. 1218, Royal Navy vessels sailing from Plymouth to engage Spaniards in battle, July 21. No. 1219, Battle scene off the Isle of Wight, July 25. No. 1220, Battle scene off Calais, France, July 28-29. No. 1221, Spanish ships foundering in the North Sea storms, July 29-Aug. 2. Printed se-tenant in a continuous design.

1988, July 19

1217	A366	18p	multicolored	.60	.30
1218	A366	18p	multicolored	.60	.30
1219	A366	18p	multicolored	.60	.30
1220	A366	18p	multicolored	.60	.30
1221	A366	18p	multicolored	.60	.30
a.			Strip of 5, Nos. 1217-1221	3.00	1.50
			Nos. 1217-1221 (5)	3.00	1.50

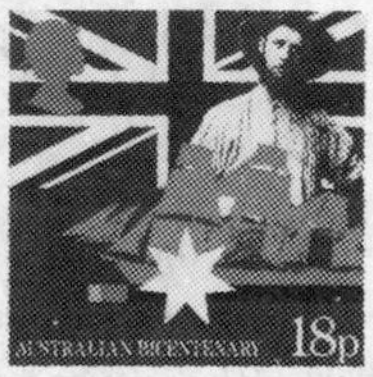

Australia Bicentennial A367

Designs: No. 1222, Colonist, First Fleet vessel. No. 1223, British and Australian parliaments, Queen Elizabeth II. No. 1224, Cricketer W.G. Grace. No. 1225, John Lennon (1940-1980), William Shakespeare (1564-1616) and Sydney Opera House. Stamps of the same denomination printed se-tenant in a continuous design picturing flag of Australia.

1988, June 21 Litho. *Perf. 14½*

1222	A367	18p	multicolored	.70	.35
1223	A367	18p	multicolored	.70	.35
1224	A367	34p	multicolored	1.30	.65
1225	A367	34p	multicolored	1.30	.65
			Nos. 1222-1225 (4)	4.00	2.00

See Australia Nos. 1082-1085.

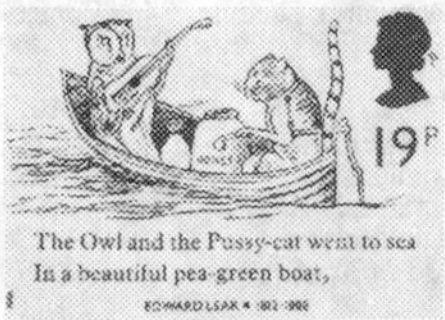

Nonsensical Drawings by Edward Lear (1812-1888) A368

Illustrations and text: 19p, *The Owl and the Pussycat*, 1867. 27p, Self-portrait as a bird, pen-and-ink sketch from a letter. 32p, "C" is for Cat, alphabet book character. 35p, Girl, birds and part of a limerick.

1988, Sept. 6 Photo. *Perf. 15x14*

1226	A368	19p	multicolored	.68	.35
1227	A368	27p	multicolored	.95	.48
1228	A368	32p	multicolored	1.15	.68
1229	A368	35p	multicolored	1.25	.62
a.			Souv. sheet of 4, #1226-1229	9.00	
			Nos. 1226-1229 (4)	4.03	2.13

No. 1229a sold for £1.35. The surtax benefited Stamp World London '90.

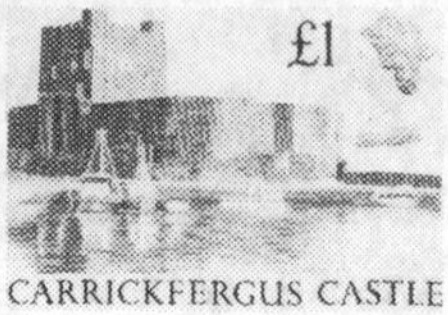

Photographs of Castles by Prince Andrew A369

1988, Oct 18 Engr.

1230	A369	£1	Carrickfergus	2.75	1.75
1231	A369	£1.50	Caernarfon	4.00	2.65
1232	A369	£2	Edinburgh	5.50	3.50
1233	A369	£5	Windsor	13.00	8.75
			Nos. 1230-1233 (4)	25.25	16.65

See Nos. 1445-1448.

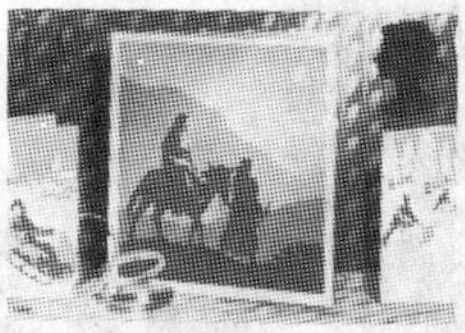

Christmas Cards A370

1988, Nov. 15 Photo. *Perf. 15x14½*

1234	A370	14p	Journey to Bethlehem	.40	.25
1235	A370	19p	Shepherds see star	.60	.35
1236	A370	27p	Magi follow star	.80	.50
1237	A370	32p	Nativity	.95	.58
1238	A370	35p	The Annunciation	1.10	.62
			Nos. 1234-1238 (5)	3.85	2.30

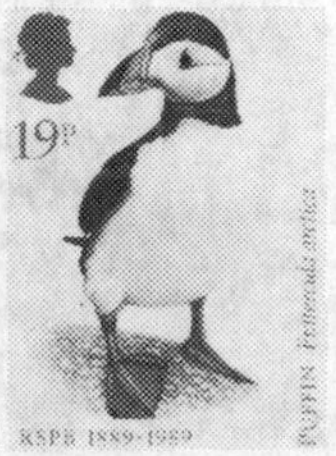

Birds — A371

1989, Jan. 17 *Perf. 14x15*

1239	A371	19p	Puffin	.70	.35
1240	A371	27p	Avocet	.98	.50
1241	A371	32p	Oystercatcher	1.15	.58
1242	A371	35p	Gannet	1.25	.62
			Nos. 1239-1242 (4)	4.08	2.05

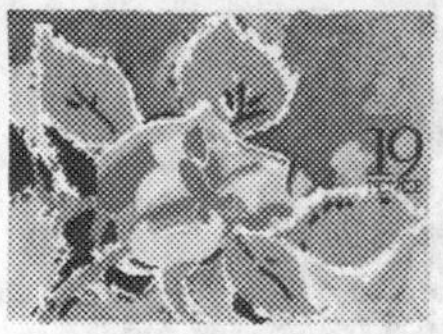

Special Occasions A372

1989, Jan. 31 Photo. *Perf. 15x14*

Booklet Stamps

1243	A372	19p	Rose	2.50	.35
1244	A372	19p	Cupid	2.50	.35
1245	A372	19p	Ships	2.50	.35
1246	A372	19p	Fruit bowl	2.50	.35
1247	A372	19p	Teddy Bear	2.50	.35
a.			Bklt. pane of 10 (2 each #1243-1247) +12 labels	25.00	
			Nos. 1243-1247 (5)	12.50	1.75

Labels inscribed "CONGRATULATIONS," "BEST WISHES," "HAPPY BIRTHDAY," "HAPPY ANNIVERSARY," "WITH LOVE," or "THANK YOU."

No. 1247a is valued with perfs guillotined. Full perfs sell for more.

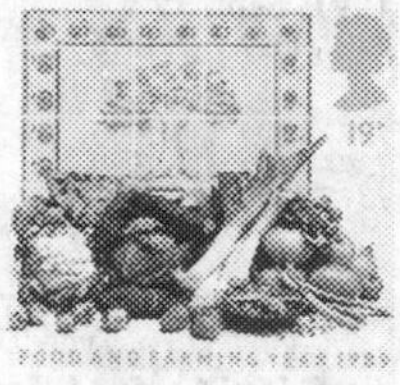

Food and Farming Year — A373

Foods and tile mosaics in agricultural motifs.

1989, Mar. 7 Photo. *Perf. 14½*

1248 A373 19p Fruit and vegetables .55 .35
1249 A373 27p Meat, fish, fruit .80 .50
1250 A373 32p Dairy products 1.10 .60
1251 A373 35p Breads, cake, cereal 1.10 .65
Nos. 1248-1251 (4) 3.55 2.10

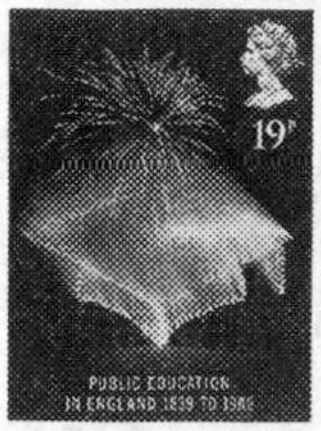

Fireworks — A374

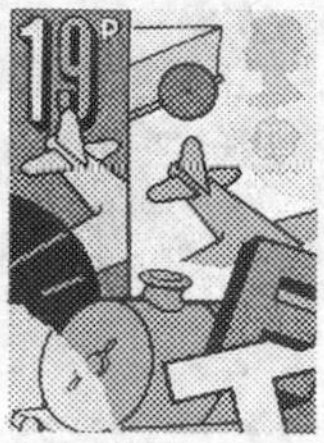

Europa 1989 — A375

1989, Apr. 11 Photo. *Perf. 14x14½*

1252 A374 19p Mortarboard .85 .35
1253 A374 19p "X" on ballot .85 .35
a. Pair, #1252-1253 1.75 .70
1254 A374 35p Posthorn 1.50 .62
1255 A374 35p Globe 1.50 .62
a. Pair, #1254-1255 3.25 1.25
Nos. 1252-1255 (4) 4.70 1.94

Public education in England and Wales, 150th anniv. (#1252); European Parliament 3rd elections (#1253); 26th world congress of Postal Telegraph and Telephone Intl., Brighton, Sept. 18-23 (#1254); Interparliamentary Union Cent. Conf., 82nd session, Sept. 4-9 (#1255).

1989, May 16 *Perf. 14x15*

Children's toys.

1256 A375 19p Airplane, locomotive .68 .35
1257 A375 27p Building-block tower .95 .48
1258 A375 32p Checkerboard, die, ladder, chips 1.15 .58
1259 A375 35p Doll house, boat, robot 1.25 .62
Nos. 1256-1259 (4) 4.03 2.03

Redrawn Queen Type of 1970
Type II

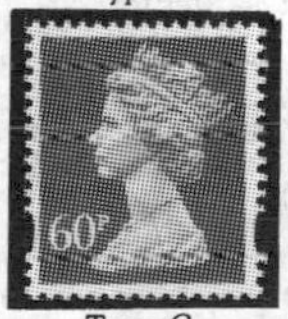

Type C

C. On two longer sides, groups of eleven and two holes separated by an oval hole equal in width to three holes.

1988-95 Photo. *Perf. 15x14*

1260 A197 5p red brown .18 .15
a. Coil strip, 3 #890f, 1 #1260 .90
b. Coil strip, 2 #890f, 2 #1260 .90
c. Syncopated Type C .18 .15
1261 A197 10p brown orange .35 .20
a. Syncopated Type C .35 .20
b. As "a," litho. .35 .20
1262 A197 15p bright blue .45 .25
a. Bklt. pane, #1264, 2 #1262 + label *5.00*
1263 A197 17p dark blue .60 .32
a. Booklet pane of 3 + label *3.00*
b. Booklet pane of 6 3.90
1264 A197 20p brown black .60 .32
a. Booklet pane of 5 + label *8.00*
b. Bklt. pane, #1264, 2 #1262 *5.00*
1265 A197 22p red orange .75 .40
a. Bklt. pane, 2 #1263, 3 #1265 + 3 labels 3.75
b. Booklet pane of 9 7.20
1266 A197 24p orange ver .75 .38
1267 A197 26p olive gray .85 .48
1268 A197 27p violet .90 .50
1269 A197 29p dp rose lilac .85 .45
a. Litho., perf. 13½x14 4.50 3.00
b. Booklet pane of 4, #1269a 18.00
1270 A197 30p olive green .90 .48
a. Syncopated Type C .90 .75
b. As "a," litho. .90 .75
1271 A197 31p ultra 1.00 .58
b. Litho., perf. 13½x14 1.00 .58
c. Booklet pane of 4 4.60
1272 A197 33p emerald 1.10 .62
a. Bklt. pane, 6 #1265, 2 #1272 + label *9.50*
b. Litho. 1.25 .62
c. Litho., perf. 13½x14 .95 .45
d. As "c," booklet pane of 4 3.80
1273 A197 34p royal blue 1.00 .80
1274 A197 37p scarlet, I 1.10 .70
1275 A197 50p olive bister 1.75 .80
1276 A197 2nd dark blue .60 .32
a. Booklet pane of 10 6.50
b. Litho. 1.00 .32
c. Litho., perf. 13½x14 .75 .32
d. Booklet pane of 10, #1276c 7.50
1277 A197 1st orange red .75 .40
a. Booklet pane of 10 8.00
b. Litho. .80 .40
c. Litho., perf. 13½x14 .80 .40
d. Booklet pane of 10, #1277c 8.00
e. Litho., perf. 13x13½ 1.50 1.50
f. Syncopated Type C .65 .52
g. Booklet pane of 10, #1277f 6.50
h. As "b," syncopated Type C .65 .52
i. Booklet pane of 10, #1277h 6.50
j. Bklt. pane of 4 #1277h + label 3.00
k. As "h," min. sheet of 1 .80 .80
1278 A197 2nd bright blue, I 1.00 .40
a. Booklet pane of 10 10.00
b. Litho., perf. 13½x14 1.25 .40
c. Booklet pane of 4, #1278b 5.00
d. Litho. 1.00 .40
e. Booklet pane of 10, #1278d 10.00
f. Booklet pane of 10, #1278b 12.50
g. Bklt. pane of 8 + label 6.75
h. Bklt. pane, 3 each #1277b, 1278d 5.50
i. As "d," syncopated Type C 1.00 .80
j. Booklet pane of 10, #1278i 10.00
k. Photo., syncopated Type C 1.00 .80
l. Booklet pane of 4, #1278k 4.00
1279 A197 1st brown black, I 1.40 .65
a. Booklet pane of 10 14.00
b. Litho., perf. 13½x14 1.65 .65
c. Booklet pane of 4, #1279b 6.75
d. Litho. 1.65 .65
e. Booklet pane of 10, #1279d 16.50
Nos. 1260-1279 (20) 16.88 9.20

Nos. 1278-1279 sold for 14p and 19p until Oct. 2, 1989, after which they were sold for the second class and first class rates. Nos. 1276-1277 were sold for 15p and 20p until Sept. 17, 1990, after which they were sold for the second class and first class rates of 17p and 22p. No. 1277j sold for £1 on day of issue. No. 1277k sold for 25p on date of issue.

No. 1277k was sold in pre-packaged greeting cards at Boots pharmacy. Unfolded examples were later sold by British Philatelic Bureau. Value indicated for No. 1277k is for unfolded example.

No. 1278g contains 2 #1272b, 1 each #1277b, 1278d, 2 each Wales and Monmouthshire #60-61.

Issued: 5p, 7/26; #1278-1279, 8/22/89; 15p, 20p, 24p, 29p, 30p, 34p, 37p, 9/26/89; #1264a-1264b, 10/2/89; 50p, 1990; #1276-1277, 8/7/90; 10p, 17p, 22p, 26p, 27p, 31p, 33p, 9/4/90; #1260a, 11/11/90; #1263b, 1265b, 1272a, 3/19/91; #1278f, 8/6/91; #1260b, 10/2/91; #1277e, 1991; #1272b, 1278g, 3/1/92; #1272c-1272d, 9/8/92; #1260c, 1261a, 6/8/93; #1278f, 8/10/93; #1270a, 1277f, 1278i, 1993; #1277j, 7/27/94; #1277k, 8/17/94; 1261b, 1270b, 4/25/95.

For Prestige booklets containing panes #1263b, 1265b, 1272a, 1278g, 1278h, see list at end of postage section.

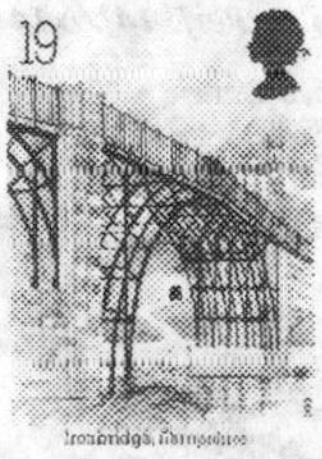

Industrial Archaeology — A376

1989, July 4 Photo. *Perf. 14x15*

1280 A376 19p Ironbridge .68 .35
1281 A376 27p Tin Mine .95 .48
1282 A376 32p Mills 1.15 .58
1283 A376 35p Pontcysyllte Aqueduct 1.25 .62
Nos. 1280-1283 (4) 4.03 2.03

1989, July 25 Souvenir Sheet

1284 Sheet of 4 5.50
a. A376 19p like #1280, horiz. .82
b. A376 27p like #1281, horiz. 1.20
c. A376 32p like #1282, horiz. 1.40
d. A376 35p like #1283, horiz. 1.50

No. 1284 sold for £1.40.

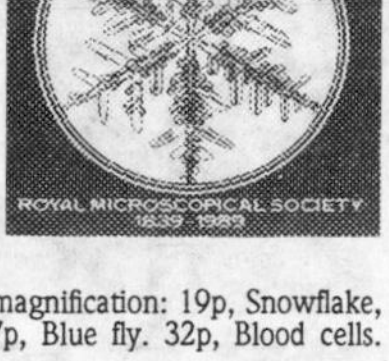

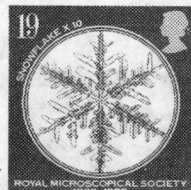

Microscopy A377

Specimens under magnification: 19p, Snowflake, the soc. emblem. 27p, Blue fly. 32p, Blood cells. 35p, Microchip.

1989, Sept. 5 Litho. *Perf. 14½x14*

1285 A377 19p multicolored .55 .35
1286 A377 27p multicolored .80 .48
1287 A377 32p multicolored 1.00 .58
1288 A377 35p multicolored 1.10 .62
Nos. 1285-1288 (4) 3.45 2.03

Royal Microscopical Soc., 150th anniv.

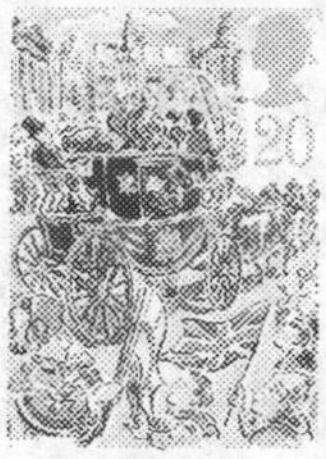

The Lord Mayor's Show, London — A378

Procession of the Lord Mayor's coach from Guildhall to the Law Courts in the Strand: No. 1289, Royal mail coach and The Guildhall. No. 1290, Drummer, cavalrymen and Mansion House. No. 1291, Gold coach, 1757, and The Royal Exchange. No. 1292, Coachman and St. Paul's Cathedral. No. 1293, Drummer, cavalryman and the Law Courts.

1989, Oct. 17 Litho. *Perf. 14x15*

1289 A378 20p multicolored .68 .35
1290 A378 20p multicolored .68 .35
1291 A378 20p multicolored .68 .35
1292 A378 20p multicolored .68 .35
1293 A378 20p multicolored .68 .35
a. Strip of 5, Nos. 1289-1293 3.40 1.75

Ely Cathedral, Cambridgeshire, 800th Anniv. — A379

1989, Nov. 14 Photo. *Perf. 15x14*

1294 A379 15p Gothic arches, 4 peasants .48 .25
Nos. 1294,B2-B5 (5) 3.98 2.87

Christmas.

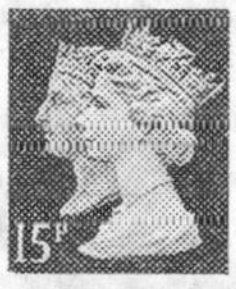

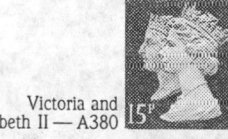

Victoria and Elizabeth II — A380

Two types of 15p:
Type I - Thin numerals.
Type II - Thick numerals.

1990, Jan. 10 Photo. *Perf. 15x14*

1295 A380 15p bright blue .60 .40
a. Litho., perf. 14, type II 1.50 .50
b. Litho., perf. 15x14, type II 1.10 .50
c. Booklet pane of 10, #1295b 11.00
1296 A380 20p black & brn blk .65 .50
a. Souvenir sheet of 1 3.40 3.40
b. Bklt. pane of 5 + label *4.00*
c. Bklt. pane of 6+printed margin 3.90
d. Bklt. pane of 3+label (2 #1295, #1296) *3.00*
e. Bklt. pane of 8+label, rouletted btwn pane and printed margin (#1262, 1264, 1275, 1278-1279, 1295-1297) *22.50*
f. Litho., perf. 14 1.00 .65
g. Bklt. pane of 5 #1296f + label 5.00
h. Litho., perf. 15x14 1.25 .65
i. Booklet pane of 10, #1296h 12.50
1297 A380 29p deep rose lilac 1.10 .70
1298 A380 34p gray blue 1.40 1.00
1299 A380 37p scarlet 1.40 1.00
Nos. 1295-1299 (5) 5.15 3.60

Release of the Penny Black, 150th anniv.

No. 1296a has engraved margin picturing *Britannia Rules the Waves* and Great Britain No. 1 (invalid for postage). Sold for £1.

Issued: #1296e, 1297, Apr. 17; #1296a, May 3.

Nos. 1295b-1295c, 1296h-1296i exist only in booklets.

For Prestige booklet containing panes #1296c, 1296e, see list at end of postage section.

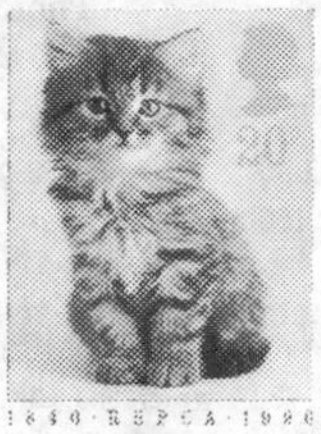

Royal Soc. for the Prevention of Cruelty to Animals, 150th Anniv. — A381

1990, Jan. 23 Litho. *Perf. 14x15*

1300 A381 20p Kitten .62 .30
1301 A381 29p Rabbit .90 .45
1302 A381 34p Duckling 1.05 .52
1303 A381 37p Puppy 1.15 .58
Nos. 1300-1303 (4) 3.72 1.85

Miniature Sheet

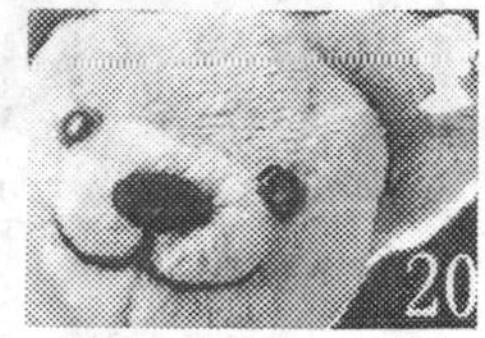

Famous Smiles A382

1990, Feb. 6 Photo. *Perf. 15x14*

1304 A382 20p Teddy bear 1.25 .40
1305 A382 20p Dennis the Menace 1.25 .40
1306 A382 20p Mr. Punch 1.25 .40
1307 A382 20p Cheshire Cat 1.25 .40
1308 A382 20p Man in the Moon 1.25 .40
1309 A382 20p The Laughing Policeman 1.25 .40
1310 A382 20p Clown 1.25 .40
1311 A382 20p Mona Lisa 1.25 .40
1312 A382 20p Queen of Hearts 1.25 .40
1313 A382 20p Stan Laurel 1.25 .40
a. Pane of 10, #1304-1313 13.00 4.00

No. 1313a sold folded and unattached in booklet cover.

See Nos. 1364-1373.

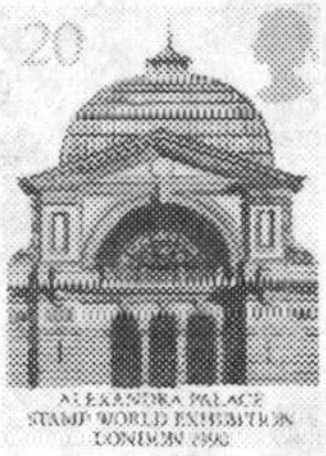

A383

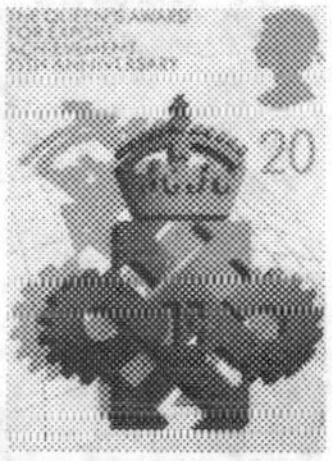

A384

Europa 1990: No. 1314, Alexandra Palace. No. 1315, School of Art, Glasgow. 29p, British Philatelic Bureau, Edinburgh. 37p, Templeton Carpet Factory, Glasgow.

1990, Mar. 6 Photo. *Perf. 14x15*

1314 A383 20p multicolored .68 .35
a. Bklt. pane of 4 + printed margin 5.50
1315 A383 20p multicolored .68 .35
1316 A383 29p multicolored .98 .45
1317 A383 37p multicolored 1.25 .62
Nos. 1314-1317 (4) 3.59 1.77

Stamp World '90, London (No. 1314); Glasgow, European City of Culture (Nos. 1315, 1317).

1990, Apr. 10 Litho.

1318 A384 20p Export .68 .35
1319 A384 20p Technology .68 .35
a. Pair, #1318-1319 1.40
1320 A384 37p like No. 1318 1.25 .62
1321 A384 37p like No. 1319 1.25 .62
a. Pair, #1320-1321 2.50
Nos. 1318-1321 (4) 3.86 1.94

Queen's Awards for Export and Technological Achievement, 25th anniv. Se-tenant pairs have continuous designs.

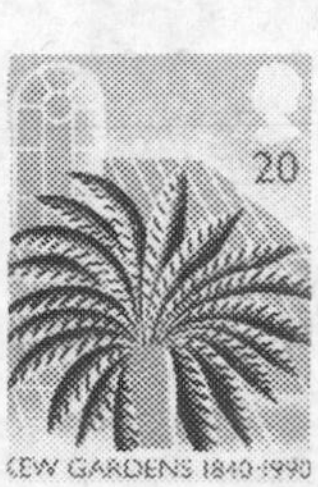

A385

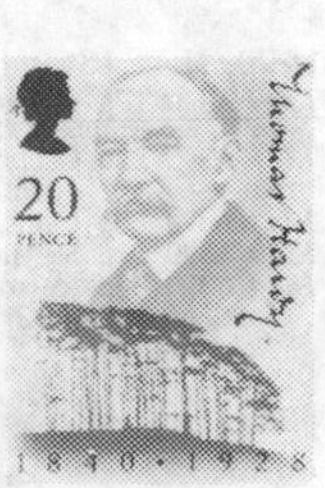

A386

1990, June 5 **Photo.**

1322 A385 20p Cycad .68 .35
1323 A385 29p Stone pine .98 .50
1324 A385 34p Willow tree 1.15 .58
1325 A385 37p Cedar 1.25 .62
Nos. 1322-1325 (4) 4.06 2.05

Kew Gardens, 150th anniv.

1990, July 10 Photo. ***Perf. 14x15***

1326 A386 20p multicolored .68 .35

Thomas Hardy (1840-1928), writer and Clyffe Clump, Dorset.

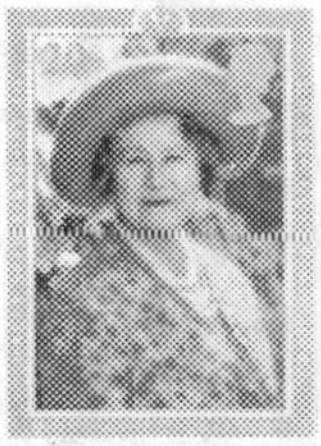
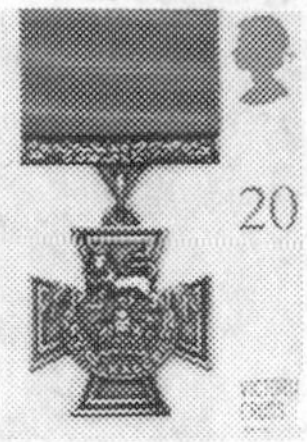

Queen Mother, 90th Birthday — A387

Victoria Cross — A388

Designs: Portraits of Queen Elizabeth, The Queen Mother.

1990, Aug. 2 ***Perf. 14x15, 14½***

1327 A387 20p Recent portrait .68 .35
1328 A387 29p As Queen Consort, 1937 .98 .50
1329 A387 34p As Duchess of York 1.15 .58
1330 A387 37p As Lady Elizabeth Bowes-Lyon 1.25 .62
Nos. 1327-1330 (4) 4.06 2.05

1990, Sept. 11 ***Perf. 14x15, 15x14***

Gallantry Awards: No. 1332, George Cross. No. 1333, Military Cross, Military Medal. No. 1334, Distinguished Flying Cross, Distinguished Flying Medal. No. 1335, Distinguished Service Cross, Distinguished Service Medal. Nos. 1333-1335 horiz.

1331 A388 20p multicolored .68 .35
1332 A388 20p multicolored .68 .35
1333 A388 20p multicolored .68 .35
1334 A388 20p multicolored .68 .35
1335 A388 20p multicolored .68 .35
Nos. 1331-1335 (5) 3.40 1.75

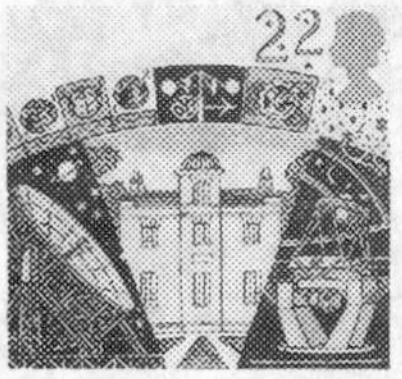

Astronomy A389

Designs: 22p, Armagh Observatory, Jodrell Bank and La Palma telescopes. 26p, Early telescope, celestial diagram. 31p, Greenwich Old Observatory, sextant, chronometer. 37p, Stonehenge, celestial navigation.

1990, Oct. 16 ***Perf. 14***

1336 A389 22p multicolored .75 .38
1337 A389 26p multicolored .90 .45
1338 A389 31p multicolored 1.10 .55
1339 A389 37p multicolored 1.30 .65
Nos. 1336-1339 (4) 4.05 2.03

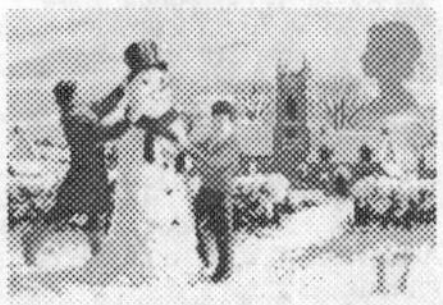

Christmas A390

1990, Nov. 13 Litho. ***Perf. 15x14***

1340 A390 17p Building snowman .55 .32
a. Booklet pane of 20 13.00
1341 A390 22p Carrying Christmas tree .70 .42
1342 A390 26p Caroling .85 .50
1343 A390 31p Sledding 1.10 .62
1344 A390 37p Ice skating 1.25 .72
Nos. 1340-1344 (5) 4.45 2.58

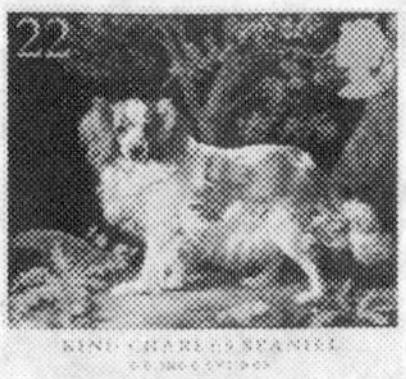

Dogs — A391

Paintings by George Stubbs: 22p, King Charles Spaniel. 26p, A Pointer. 31p, Two Hounds in a Landscape. 33p, A Rough Dog. 37p, Fino and Tiny.

1991, Jan. 8 Photo. ***Perf. 14x14½***

1345 A391 22p multicolored .70 .42
1346 A391 26p multicolored .80 .50
1347 A391 31p multicolored 1.00 .62
1348 A391 33p multicolored 1.10 .65
1349 A391 37p multicolored 1.25 .72
Nos. 1345-1349 (5) 4.85 2.91

Royal Veterinary College bicentennial, National Canine Defense League and Cruft's Dog Show, centennial.

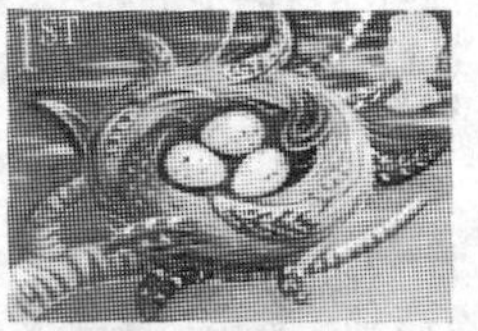

Symbols of Good Luck A392

1991, Feb. 5 Photo. ***Perf. 15x14***

Booklet Stamps

1350 A392 1st shown .85 .42
1351 A392 1st Shooting star, rainbow .85 .42
1352 A392 1st Bird, charm bracelet .85 .42
1353 A392 1st Black cat .85 .42
1354 A392 1st Bluebird, key .85 .42
1355 A392 1st Duck, frog .85 .42
1356 A392 1st Black boot, shamrocks .85 .42
1357 A392 1st Rainbow, pot of gold .85 .42
1358 A392 1st Peacock moths .85 .42
1359 A392 1st Wishing well, sixpence .85 .42
a. Bklt. pane of 10, #1350-1359 8.50
Nos. 1350-1359 (10) 8.50 4.20

No. 1359a printed se-tenant with 12 greetings labels. No. 1359a sold for £2.20 at date of issue.

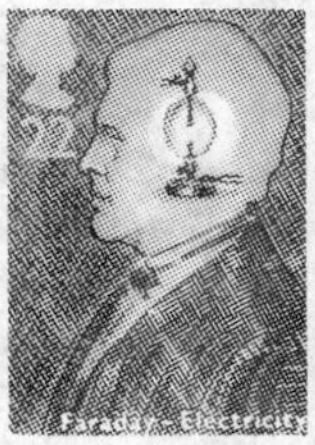

Scientists & Their Technology A393

Designs: No. 1360, Michael Faraday, electricity. No. 1361, Charles Babbage, computers. 31p, Radar, developed by Robert Watson-Watt. 37p, Jet engine developed by Frank Whittle.

1991, Mar. 5 ***Perf. 14x15***

1360 A393 22p multicolored .65 .42
1361 A393 22p multicolored .65 .42
1362 A393 31p multicolored 1.10 .62
1363 A393 37p multicolored 1.25 .72
Nos. 1360-1363 (4) 3.65 2.18

Famous Smiles Type of 1990

1991, Mar. 26 Photo. ***Perf. 15x14***

Booklet Stamps

1364 A382 1st Teddy bear .70 .42
1365 A382 1st Dennis the Menace .70 .42
1366 A382 1st Mr. Punch .70 .42
1367 A382 1st Cheshire Cat .70 .42
1368 A382 1st Man in the Moon .70 .42
1369 A382 1st The Laughing Policeman .70 .42
1370 A382 1st Clown .70 .42
1371 A382 1st Mona Lisa .70 .42
1372 A382 1st Queen of Hearts .70 .42
1373 A382 1st Stan Laurel .70 .42
a. Booklet pane of 10 7.00
Nos. 1364-1373 (10) 7.00 4.20

No. 1373a sold for £2.20 at date of issue. No. 1373a was affixed to booklet cover and was printed se-tenant with 12 greetings labels.

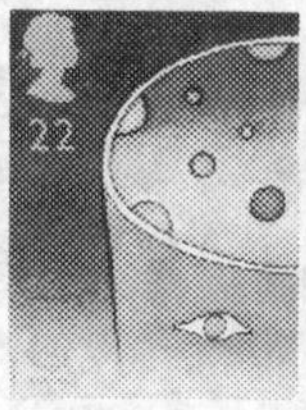
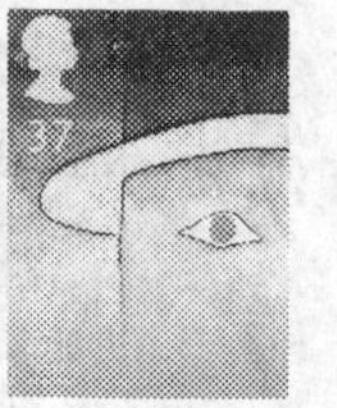

Europa

A394 A395

Illustrations reduced.

1991, Apr. 23 Photo. ***Perf. 14x15***

1374 A394 22p Planets .65 .42
1375 A394 22p Stars .65 .42
a. Pair, #1374-1375 1.40 .85
1376 A395 37p shown 1.25 .72
1377 A395 37p Crescent eye 1.25 .72
a. Pair, #1376-1377 2.50 1.50
Nos. 1374-1377 (4) 3.80 2.28

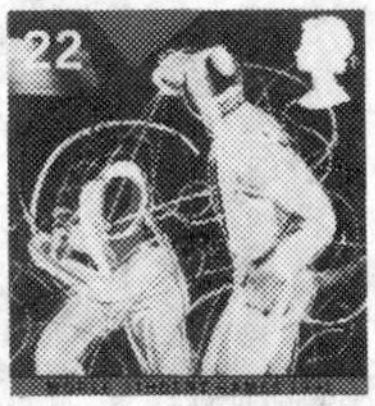

Sports — A396

1991, June 11 Photo. ***Perf. 14½x14***

1378 A396 22p Fencing .72 .35
1379 A396 26p Hurdling .85 .42
1380 A396 31p Diving 1.00 .50
1381 A396 37p Rugby 1.20 .60
Nos. 1378-1381 (4) 3.77 1.87

World Student Games, Nos. 1378-1380. Rugby World Cup, No. 1381.

Roses — A397

1991, July 16 Litho. ***Perf. 14½x14***

1382 A397 22p Silver Jubilee .65 .32
1383 A397 26p Mme Alfred Carriere .80 .40
1384 A397 31p Rosa moyesii .95 .42
1385 A397 33p Harvest Fayre 1.00 .50
1386 A397 37p Mutabilis 1.15 .58
Nos. 1382-1386 (5) 4.55 2.22

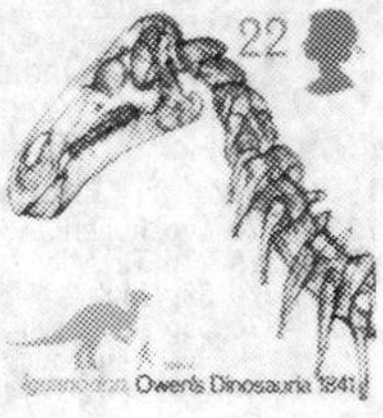

Dinosaurs A398

1991, Aug. 20 Photo. ***Perf. 14½x14***

1387 A398 22p Iguanodon .72 .36
1388 A398 26p Stegosaurus .85 .42
1389 A398 31p Tyrannosaurus 1.00 .50
1390 A398 33p Protoceratops 1.05 .52
1391 A398 37p Triceratops 1.20 .60
Nos. 1387-1391 (5) 4.82 2.40

First use of word "dinosaur" by Sir Richard Owen, 150th anniv.

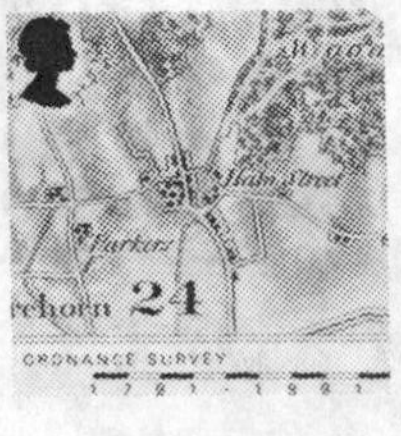

Ordnance Survey Maps, Bicent. A399

Maps of village of Hamstreet, Kent.

1991, Sept. 17 **Litho. & Engr.**

1392 A399 24p 1816 .80 .40

Litho.

1393 A399 28p 1906 .90 .45
1394 A399 33p 1959 1.05 .52
1395 A399 39p 1991 1.25 .62
Nos. 1392-1395 (4) 4.00 1.99

Redrawn Queen Type of 1970
Type II

Perf. 15x14, 15x14 Syncopated Type C (2 Sides; 4p, 19p, 20p, 25p, 29p, 36p, 38p, 41p, 50p, 60p, £1)

1991-95 **Photo., Litho. (60p)**

1395A A197 4p blue .15 .15
1396 A197 6p brt olive green .20 .15
a. Syncopated Type C .18 .15
b. As "a," litho. .18 .15
1399 A197 18p brt yellow green .60 .40
a. Litho. .55 .28
b. As "a," bklt. pane of 6 3.30
1400 A197 19p olive green .60 .30
b. Litho. .55
c. As "b," booklet pane of 6 + printed margin 3.50
1400A A197 20p blue green .60 .30
1401 A197 24p brown .84 .42
a. Bklt. pane, 2 each #623e, 1401 1.80
b. Bklt. pane, 2 #887d, 4 #1401 + 2 labels 3.50
c. Litho. .72 .36
d. As "c," bklt. pane of 6 4.35
e. Bklt. pane, 2 #887c, 4 #1401c + 2 labels 3.50
1402 A197 25p salmon .75 .38
a. Booklet pane of 2 + 2 labels 1.50
b. Booklet pane of 8 6.00
c. Litho. .75 .38
d. As "c," booklet pane of 4 3.00
e. Bklt. pane, #1396b, 1400b, 4 #1402c 3.75
1403 A197 28p blue gray 1.00 .50
1404 A197 29p gray .90 .45
1405 A197 34p brt purple 1.20 .80
1406 A197 35p orange yellow 1.25 .80
a. Syncopated Type C 1.05 .52
b. Litho., syncopated Type C 1.00 .50
c. As "b," booklet pane of 4 4.00
1407 A197 36p blue 1.10 .55
1408 A197 38p red 1.25 .65
1409 A197 39p red lilac 1.35 .80
a. Litho. 1.20 .60
b. Bklt. pane, 1 ea #1277b, 1278d, 2 ea #1399a, 1401c, 1409a *15.00*
c. Bklt. pane, 2 each #1272b, 1278d, 1399a, 1409a + label *15.00*
d. Litho., perf. 13½x14 1.35 .80
e. As "d," bklt. pane of 4 5.50
1410 A197 41p drab 1.25 .65
a. Litho. 1.25 .65
b. As "a," booklet pane of 4 5.00
c. Booklet pane, #1261b, #1270b, 1406b, 1410a, 2 each #1400b, 1402c + label 6.50
1413 A197 50p bister 1.50 .75
1414 A197 60p slate blue 1.75 .85
a. Booklet pane of 4 7.00
1415 A197 £1 violet 3.25 3.25
Nos. 1395A-1415 (18) 19.54 12.15

Issued: 6p, 18p, 24p, 28p, 34p, 35p, 39p, 9/10/91; #1399a, 1401c, 1409a, 1992. #1396a, 4/27/93; #1409c, 8/10/93; #1406a, 1993; 19p, 25p, 29p, 36p, 38p, 41p, 10/26/93; 4p, 20p, 50p, 12/14/93; #1409d-1409e, 9/16/91; #1401e, 2/9/93; #1396b, 1400b, 1402e, 7/26/94; 60p, 8/9/94; #1400c, 1410c, 4/25/95; £1, 8/22/95.

See note after Northern Ireland No. 66.

No. 1414 issued only in booklets.

No. 1415 printed with Iriodin ink, giving stamp design a three dimensional appearance.

For Prestige booklets containing panes #1399b, 1400c, 1401d, 1402e, 1409b, 1409c, 1410c, see list at end of postage section.

This is an expanding set. Numbers will change if necessary.

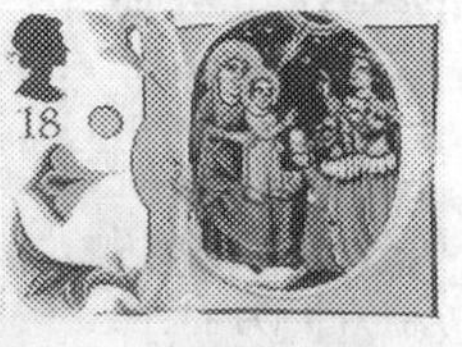

Christmas A400

Illuminated leters from Venetian manuscript "Acts of Mary and Jesus": 18p, "P," Adoration of the Magi. 24p, "M," Mary placing Jesus in manger. 28p, "A," Angel warning Joseph. 33p, "Q," The Annunciation. 39p, "N," Flight into Egypt.

1991, Nov. 12 Photo. ***Perf. 15x14***

1416 A400 18p multicolored .50 .30
a. Booklet pane of 20 10.00
1417 A400 24p multicolored .65 .40
1418 A400 28p multicolored .75 .48
1419 A400 33p multicolored .90 .55
1420 A400 39p multicolored 1.10 .65
Nos. 1416-1420 (5) 3.90 2.38

Animals in Winter
A401

1992, Jan. 14   Photo.   *Perf. 15x14*
1421 A401 18p Fallow deer .60 .30
1422 A401 24p Brown hare .80 .40
1423 A401 28p Fox .95 .48
1424 A401 33p Redwing 1.15 .58
1425 A401 39p Welsh mountain
　　　　　　 sheep 1.35 .65
a.　Booklet pane of 4 5.40
　　Nos. 1421-1425 (5) 4.85 2.41

Issue date: No. 1425a, Mar. 1.

Memories
A402

1992, Jan. 28   Litho.   *Perf. 15x14*
Booklet Stamps
1426 A402 1st Flowers .80 .40
1427 A402 1st Locket .80 .40
1428 A402 1st Key .80 .40
1429 A402 1st Model car .80 .40
1430 A402 1st Compass, 4-leaf clover .80 .40
1431 A402 1st Pocket watch .80 .40
1432 A402 1st Envelope, fountain
　　　　　　 pen .80 .40
1433 A402 1st Buttons, pearls .80 .40
1434 A402 1st Marbles .80 .40
1435 A402 1st Starfish, shovel and
　　　　　　 bucket .80 .40
a.　Bklt. pane of 10, #1426-1435 8.00

No. 1435a printed se-tenant with 12 greeting labels and sold for £2.40 at date of issue.

Queen Elizabeth II's Accession to the Throne, 40th Anniv. A403

Queen Elizabeth II: No. 1436, In coronation regalia. No. 1437, Facing right, wearing garter robes as head of Church of England. No. 1438, Holding infant Prince Andrew. No. 1439, Wearing military uniform at Trooping of the Color. No. 1440, Wearing purple hat.

1992, Feb. 6   Litho.   *Perf. 14¹/₂x14*
1436 A403 24p multicolored .80 .40
1437 A403 24p multicolored .80 .40
1438 A403 24p multicolored .80 .40
1439 A403 24p multicolored .80 .40
1440 A403 24p multicolored .80 .40
a.　Strip of 5, #1436-1440 4.00 2.00

Alfred, Lord Tennyson, Death Cent. — A404

Portraits and illustrations for poems: 24p, The Beguiling of Merlin by Sir Edward Burne-Jones. 28p, April Love by Arthur Hughes. 33p, The Lady of Shalott by John William Waterhouse. 39p, Mariana by Dante Gabriel Rossetti.

1992, Mar. 10   Photo.
1441 A404 24p multicolored .80 .40
1442 A404 28p multicolored .95 .48
1443 A404 33p multicolored 1.15 .58
1444 A404 39p multicolored 1.35 .65
　　Nos. 1441-1444 (4) 4.25 2.11

Castle Type of 1988

Type A Perforations

Nos. 1445-1448 have been re-engraved to show greater detail than on Nos. 1230-1233. The silhouette of the Queen's head on Nos. 1445-1448 is printed in a special ink that changes color from green to gold.
A. On two shorter sides, groups of eight or nine holes separated by an oval hole equal in width to three holes.

Perf. 15x14 Syncopated Type A (2 Sides)
1992-95　　　　　　　　　　**Engr.**
1445 A369 £1 like #1230 2.50 2.00
1446 A369 £1.50 like #1231 3.75 3.10
1447 A369 £2 like #1232 4.75 4.00
1447A A369 £3 like #1230 9.50 9.50
1448 A369 £5 like #1233 12.00 10.00
　　Nos. 1445-1448 (5) 32.50 28.60

Nos. 1445-1447, 1448 were re-issued 12/6/94 with lines strengthened. Castles appear darker than on original issue.
Issued: £3, 8/22/95; others, 3/24/92.

Discovery of America, 500th Anniv. A405

Design: 39p, Sailing ship, Operation Raleigh Grand Regatta.

Litho. & Engr.
1992, Apr. 7　　　　　　*Perf. 14¹/₂*
1449 A405 24p multicolored .80 .40
1450 A405 39p multicolored 1.35 .65

Europa.

Events
A406

Designs: No. 1451, British Olympic Assoc. flag. No. 1452, Flying torch flag of British Paralympic Assoc. No. 1453, British pavilion.

1992, Apr. 7　　　　　　　　　**Litho.**
1451 A406 24p multicolored .80 .40
1452 A406 24p multicolored .80 .40
a.　Pair, #1451-1452 1.60 .80
1453 A406 39p multicolored 1.35 .65
　　Nos. 1451-1453 (3) 2.95 1.45

1992 Summer Olympics (No. 1451) and Paralympics (No. 1452), Barcelona. Expo '92, Seville (No. 1453).

English Civil War, 350th Anniv. — A407

1992, June 16   Photo.   *Perf. 14¹/₂*
1454 A407 24p Pikeman .80 .40
1455 A407 28p Drummer .95 .48
1456 A407 33p Musketeer 1.15 .58
1457 A407 39p Standard bearer 1.35 .65
　　Nos. 1454-1457 (4) 4.25 2.11

Yeoman of the Guard, by Gilbert & Sullivan — A408

Scenes from comic operas: 24p, The Gondoliers. 28p, The Mikado. 33p, The Pirates of Penzance. 39p, Iolanthe.

1992, July 21   Photo.   *Perf. 14¹/₂x14*
1458 A408 18p multicolored .50 .34
1459 A408 24p multicolored .65 .45
1460 A408 28p multicolored .80 .52
1461 A408 33p multicolored .90 .62
1462 A408 39p multicolored 1.10 .75
　　Nos. 1458-1462 (5) 3.95 2.68

Sir Arthur Sullivan, 150th anniv. of birth.

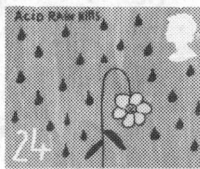

Protect the Environment A409

Children's drawings: 24p, Acid rain kills. 28p, Ozone layer. 33p, Greenhouse effect. 39p, Bird of hope.

1992, Sept. 15   Photo.   *Perf. 14¹/₂*
1463 A409 24p multicolored .65 .45
1464 A409 28p multicolored .80 .52
1465 A409 33p multicolored .90 .62
1466 A409 39p multicolored 1.10 .75
　　Nos. 1463-1466 (4) 3.45 2.34

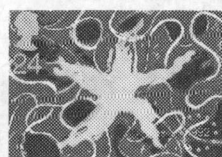

Single European Market A410

1992, Oct. 13   Photo.   *Perf. 15x14*
1467 A410 24p multicolored .78 .78

Christmas A411

Stained glass windows: 18p, Angel Gabriel. 24p, Madonna and Child. 28p, King offering gold crown. 33p, Shepherds. 39p, Kings offering frankincense and myrrh.

1992, Nov. 10   Photo.   *Perf. 15x14*
1468 A411 18p multicolored .55 .28
a.　Booklet pane of 20 11.00
1469 A411 24p multicolored .72 .36
1470 A411 28p multicolored .85 .42
1471 A411 33p multicolored 1.00 .50
1472 A411 39p multicolored 1.20 .60
　　Nos. 1468-1472 (5) 4.32 2.16

Mute Swans — A412

Designs: 18p, Male, St. Catherine's Chapel, Abbotsbury. 24p, Cygnet, reed bed, Abbotsbury Swannery. 28p, Pair, cygnet. 33p, Eggs in nest, Tithe Barn. 39p, Head of young swan.

1993, Jan. 19   Photo.   *Perf. 14x15*
1473 A412 18p multicolored .50 .25
1474 A412 24p multicolored .65 .32
1475 A412 28p multicolored .78 .40
1476 A412 33p multicolored .92 .46
1477 A412 39p multicolored 1.10 .55
　　Nos. 1473-1477 (5) 3.95 1.98

Abbotsbury Swannery, 600th anniv.

Britannia — A413

Perf. 14x14¹/₂ Syncopated, Type B (2 sides)
Litho., Typo. and Embossed
1993, Mar. 2
Granite Paper
B. On two longer sides, groups of six and four holes separated by an oval hole equal in width to three holes.

1478 A413 £10 multicolored 25.00 13.50

Soaking may damage these stamps.

Greetings Stamps A414

Children's Characters: No. 1479, Long John Silver, parrot. No. 1480, Tweedledum, Tweedledee. No. 1481, Just William, Violet Elizabeth. No. 1482, Toad, Mole. No. 1483, Bash Street Kids, teacher. No. 1484, Peter Rabbit, Mrs. Rabbit. No. 1485, Father Christmas, Snowman. No. 1486, Big Friendly Giant, Sophie. No. 1487, Rupert Bear, Bill Badger. No. 1488, Aladdin, Genie.

Perf. 15x14 Syncopated Type A (2 sides)
1993, Feb. 2　　　　　　　　**Litho.**
1479 A414 (1st) multicolored .65 .32
1480 A414 (1st) multicolored .65 .32
1481 A414 (1st) multicolored .65 .32
1482 A414 (1st) multicolored .65 .32
1483 A414 (1st) multicolored .65 .32
1484 A414 (1st) multicolored .65 .32
a.　Booklet pane of 4 2.60
1485 A414 (1st) multicolored .65 .32
1486 A414 (1st) multicolored .65 .32
1487 A414 (1st) multicolored .65 .32
1488 A414 (1st) multicolored .65 .32
a.　Booklet pane of 10, #1479-1488 6.50
　　Nos. 1479-1488 (10) 6.50 3.20

No. 1479-1488 sold for 24p on day of issue. No. 1488a printed se-tenant with 20 greetings labels. See note above No. 1445.
Issue date: No. 1484a, Aug. 10.
For Prestige booklet containing pane #1484a, see list at end of postage section.

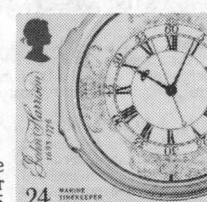

Marine Chronometer No. 4 — A415

Designs: 24p, Face. 28p, Escapement, remontoire and fusee. 33p, Balance spring, temperature compensator. 39p, Back of movement.

1993, Feb. 16   Litho.   *Perf. 14¹/₂*
1489 A415 24p multicolored .65 .32
1490 A415 28p multicolored .78 .40
1491 A415 33p multicolored .90 .45
1492 A415 39p multicolored 1.10 .55
　　Nos. 1489-1492 (4) 3.43 1.72

John Harrison (1693-1776), inventor of marine chronometer.

Orchids
A416

14th World Orchid Conf., Glasgow: 18p, Dendrobium hellwigianum. 24p, Paphiopedilum Maudiae "Magnificum." 28p, Cymbidium lowianum. 33p, Vanda Rothschildiana. 39p, Dendrobium vexillarius.

1993, Mar. 16   Litho.   Perf. 15x14
1493	A416	18p multicolored	.50	.25
1494	A416	24p multicolored	.65	.32
1495	A416	28p multicolored	.78	.40
1496	A416	33p multicolored	.90	.45
1497	A416	39p multicolored	1.10	.55
		Nos. 1493-1497 (5)	3.93	1.97

Contemporary Art — A417

Europa: 24p, Sculpture, Family Group, by Henry Moore. 28p, Print, Kew Gardens, by Edward Bawden. 33p, Painting, St. Francis and the Birds, by Stanley Spencer. 39p, Painting, Still Life, Odyssey 1, by Ben Nicholson.

1993, May 11   Photo.   Perf. 14x14½
1498	A417	24p multicolored	.70	.35
1499	A417	28p multicolored	.85	.42
1500	A417	33p multicolored	1.00	.50
1501	A417	39p multicolored	1.15	.58
		Nos. 1498-1501 (4)	3.70	1.85

Roman Artifacts
A418

Designs: 24p, Gold aureus of Claudius. 28p, Bronze bust of Hadrian. 33p, Gemstone carved with head of Roma. 39p, Mosaic of Christ.

1993, June 15   Photo.   Perf. 14½x14
1502	A418	24p multicolored	.68	.35
1503	A418	28p multicolored	.80	.40
1504	A418	33p multicolored	.95	.48
1505	A418	39p multicolored	1.15	.55
		Nos. 1502-1505 (4)	3.58	1.78

British Canals, Bicent.
A419

Designs: 24p, Grand Junction Canal boats. 28p, Stainforth and Keadby Canal. 33p, Brecknock and Abergavenny Canal boats, horse. 39p, Crinan Canal, steamers and fishing boats.

1993, July 20   Litho.   Perf. 14½x14
1506	A419	24p multicolored	.72	.35
1507	A419	28p multicolored	.85	.42
1508	A419	33p multicolored	1.00	.50
1509	A419	39p multicolored	1.15	.58
		Nos. 1506-1509 (4)	3.72	1.85

Autumn Fruits
A420

1993, Sept. 14   Photo.   Perf. 15x14
1510	A420	18p Horse chestnut	.52	.25
1511	A420	24p Blackberries	.72	.35
1512	A420	28p Filbert	.85	.42

1513	A420	33p Rowanberries	1.00	.50
1514	A420	39p Pears	1.15	.58
		Nos. 1510-1514 (5)	4.24	2.10

Sherlock Holmes — A421

Holmes and: No. 1515, Dr. Watson, The Reigate Squire. No. 1516, Sir Henry, The Hound of the Baskervilles. No. 1517, Lestrade, The Six Napoleons. No. 1518, Mycroft, The Greek Interpreter. No. 1519, Moriarty, The Final Problem.

1993, Oct. 12   Litho.   Perf. 14x14½
1515	A421	24p multicolored	.70	.35
1516	A421	24p multicolored	.70	.35
1517	A421	24p multicolored	.70	.35
1518	A421	24p multicolored	.70	.35
1519	A421	24p multicolored	.70	.35
a.		Strip of 5, #1515-1519	3.50	1.75
		Nos. 1515-1519 (5)	3.50	1.75

A422

Die Cut 14x15, Syncopated Type C
1993, Oct. 19   Litho.
1521	A422	1st orange red	.70	.35
a.		Booklet pane of 20	14.00	

No. 1521 sold for 24p on date of issue. Peelable paper backing is booklet cover.

"A Christmas Carol," by Charles Dickens, 150th Anniv.
A423

Designs: 19p, Tiny Tim, Bob Cratchit. 25p, Mr. & Mrs. Fezziwig. 30p, Scrooge. 35p, Prize Turkey. 41p, Mr. Scrooge's Nephew.

1993, Nov. 9   Photo.   Perf. 15x14
1528	A423	19p multicolored	.55	.28
a.		Booklet pane of 20	11.00	
1529	A423	25p multicolored	.75	.38
1530	A423	30p multicolored	.90	.45
1531	A423	35p multicolored	1.00	.50
1532	A423	41p multicolored	1.25	.60
		Nos. 1528-1532 (5)	4.45	2.21

Age of Steam — A424

Designs: 19p, Tandem locomotives, West Highland Line, North British Railway. 25p, Locomotive #60149, Kings Cross Station, London. 30p, Locomotive #43000 on turntable, Blyth North engine shed. 35p, Locomotive entering station. 41p, Locomotive on bridge over Worcester & Birmingham Canal.

1994, Jan. 18   Photo.   Perf. 14½
1533	A424	19p black & green	.55	.28
1534	A424	25p black & purple	.75	.38
1535	A424	30p black & red brown	.90	.45
1536	A424	35p black & red violet	1.00	.50
1537	A424	41p black & dark blue	1.25	.60
		Nos. 1533-1537 (5)	4.45	2.21

Dan Dare
A425

The Three Bears
A426

Rupert the Bear — A427

Alice in Wonderland
A428

Noggin the Nog — A429

Peter Rabbit
A430

Little Red Riding Hood
A431

Orlando, the Marmalade Cat — A432

Biggles
A433

Paddington
A434

Perf. 15x14 Syncopated, Type A (2 Sides)
1994, Feb. 1   Photo.
Booklet Stamps
1538	A425	(1st) multicolored	.75	.38
1539	A426	(1st) multicolored	.75	.38
1540	A427	(1st) multicolored	.75	.38
1541	A428	(1st) multicolored	.75	.38
1542	A429	(1st) multicolored	.75	.38
1543	A430	(1st) multicolored	.75	.38

1544	A431	(1st) multicolored	.75	.38
1545	A432	(1st) multicolored	.75	.38
1546	A433	(1st) multicolored	.75	.38
1547	A434	(1st) multicolored	.75	.38
a.		Booklet pane of 12, #1538-1547	7.50	

Nos. 1538-1547 sold for 25p on day of issue. No. 1547a was printed se-tenant with 20 greetings labels.

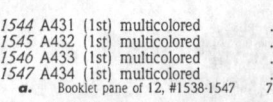

Investiture of Prince of Wales, 25th Anniv.
A435

Watercolor landscapes, by Prince Charles: 19p, Chirk Castle, Clwyd, Wales. 25p, Ben Arkle, Sutherland, Scotland. 30p, Mourne Mountains, County Down, Northern Ireland. 35p, Dersingham, Norfolk, England. 41p, Dolwyddelan, Gwynedd, Wales.

1994, Mar. 1   Photo.   Perf. 15x14
1548	A435	19p multicolored	.55	.28
1549	A435	25p multicolored	.75	.38
1550	A435	30p multicolored	.90	.45
a.		Booklet pane of 4	3.60	
1551	A435	35p multicolored	1.00	.50
1552	A435	41p multicolored	1.25	.60
		Nos. 1548-1552 (5)	4.45	2.21

See note after Northern Ireland No. 66.
For Prestige booklet containing pane #1550a, see list at end of postage section.

British Picture Postcards, Cent. — A436

Seaside characters: 19p, "Bather at Blackpool." 25p, "Where's my Little Lad." 30p, "Wish You Were Here." 35p, "Punch and Judy Show." 41p, "The Tower Crane."

1994, Apr. 12   Litho.   Perf. 14x14½
1553	A436	19p multicolored	.55	.28
1554	A436	25p multicolored	.75	.38
1555	A436	30p multicolored	.90	.45
1556	A436	35p multicolored	1.00	.50
1557	A436	41p multicolored	1.25	.60
		Nos. 1553-1557 (5)	4.45	2.21

Blackpool Tower, cent. (#1553). Tower Bridge, cent. (#1557).

Opening of Channel Tunnel — A437

Designs: Nos. 1558, 1560, British lion, French rooster, meeting over Channel. Nos. 1559, 1561, Joined hands above speeding train.

1994, May 3   Photo.   Perf. 14x14½
1558	A437	25p dk blue & multi	.75	.38
1559	A437	25p dk blue & multi	.75	.38
a.		Pair, #1558-1559	1.50	.75
1560	A437	41p lt blue & multi	1.25	.60
1561	A437	41p multicolored	1.25	.60
a.		Pair, #1560-1561	2.50	1.25
		Nos. 1558-1561 (4)	4.00	1.96

See France Nos. 2421-2424.

D-Day, 50th Anniv. — A438

Photographs from Imperial War Museum's archives: No. 1562, Ground crew reloading FAF Bostons. No. 1563, Coastal bombardment by HMS Warspite. No. 1564, Commandos landing on Gold Beach. No. 1565, Infantry regrouping on Sword Beach. No. 1566, Advancing inland from Ouistreham.

1994, June 6	Litho.	Perf. 14	
1562 A438	25p multicolored	.75	.38
1563 A438	25p multicolored	.75	.38
1564 A438	25p multicolored	.75	.38
1565 A438	25p multicolored	.75	.38
1566 A438	25p multicolored	.75	.38
a.	Strip of 5, #1562-1566	3.75	1.90

Honorable Company of Edinburgh Golfers, 250th Anniv. — A439

Golf courses: 19p, St. Andrews, old course. 25p, Muirfield, 18th hole. 30p, Carnoustie, 15th hole. 35p, Royal Troon, "postage stamp" 8th hole. 41p, Turnberry, 9th hole.

1994, July 5	Photo.	Perf. 14	
1567 A439	19p multicolored	.55	.28
1568 A439	25p multicolored	.75	.38
1569 A439	30p multicolored	.90	.45
1570 A439	35p multicolored	1.00	.50
1571 A439	41p multicolored	1.25	.60
	Nos. 1567-1571 (5)	4.45	2.21

Summertime Events A440

Designs: 19p, Royal Welsh Agricultural Show, Llanelwedd. 25p, Wimbledon. 30p, Yachts on Solent during Cowes Week. 35p, Cricket at Lord's. 41p, Scottish Highland Games, Braemar.

1994, Aug. 2		Perf. 14½x14	
1572 A440	19p multicolored	.55	.28
1573 A440	25p multicolored	.75	.38
1574 A440	30p multicolored	.90	.45
1575 A440	35p multicolored	1.00	.50
1576 A440	41p multicolored	1.25	.60
	Nos. 1572-1576 (5)	4.45	2.21

Medical Discoveries A441

Europa: 25p, Ultrasonic imaging. 30p, Scanning electron microscopy. 35p, Magnetic resonance imaging. 41p, Computed tomography.

1994, Sept. 27	Photo.	Perf. 14x14½	
1577 A441	25p multicolored	.80	.40
1578 A441	30p multicolored	.95	.48
1579 A441	35p multicolored	1.10	.55
1580 A441	41p multicolored	1.25	.62
	Nos. 1577-1580 (4)	4.10	2.05

Christmas A442

School children portraying: 19p, Mary, Joseph, with infant Jesus. 25p, Magi. 30p, Mary holding Jesus. 35p, Shepherds. 41p, Angels.

1994, Nov. 1	Photo.	Perf. 15x14	
1581 A442	19p multicolored	.60	.30
a.	Booklet pane of 20	12.00	
1582 A442	25p multicolored	.80	.40
a.	Booklet pane of 10	8.00	
1583 A442	30p multicolored	.95	.48
1584 A442	35p multicolored	1.10	.55
1585 A442	41p multicolored	1.25	.65
	Nos. 1581-1585 (5)	4.70	2.38

Cats A443

Designs: 19p, Black cat. 25p, Siamese, tabby cats. 30p, Yellow cat. 35p, Calico, Abyssinian cats. 41p, Black & white cat.

1995, Jan. 17	Litho.	Perf. 15x14	
1586 A443	19p multicolored	.60	.30
1587 A443	25p multicolored	.80	.40
1588 A443	30p multicolored	.95	.48
1589 A443	35p multicolored	1.10	.55
1590 A443	41p multicolored	1.25	.65
	Nos. 1586-1590 (5)	4.70	2.38

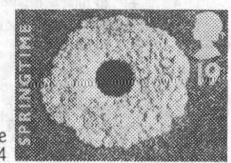

Springtime A444

Sculptures from natural materials, by Andy Goldsworthy: 19p, Dandelions. 25p, Chestnut leaves. 30p, Garlic leaves. 35p, Hazel leaves. 41p, Spring grass.

1995, Mar. 14	Photo.	Perf. 15x14	
1591 A444	19p multicolored	.60	.30
1592 A444	25p multicolored	.80	.40
1593 A444	30p multicolored	.95	.48
1594 A444	35p multicolored	1.10	.55
1595 A444	41p multicolored	1.25	.65
	Nos. 1591-1595 (5)	4.70	2.38

A445

A446

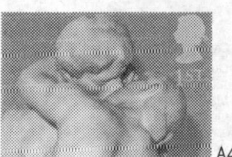

A447

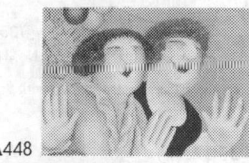

A448

A449

A450

A451

A452

A453

The Art of Greeting A454

Perf. 14 Syncopated Type A (2 Sides)

1995, Mar. 21		Litho.	
1596 A445	1st multicolored	.80	.40
1597 A446	1st multicolored	.80	.40
1598 A447	1st multicolored	.80	.40
1599 A448	1st multicolored	.80	.40
1600 A449	1st multicolored	.80	.40
1601 A450	1st multicolored	.80	.40
1602 A451	1st multicolored	.80	.40
1603 A452	1st multicolored	.80	.40
1604 A453	1st multicolored	.80	.40
1605 A454	1st multicolored	.80	.40
a.	Bklt. pane of 10, #1596-1605	8.00	
	Complete booklet, #1605a + 20 labels	8.00	

Complete booklet sold for £2.50 on day of issue.

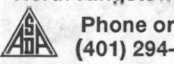

National Trust, Cent. — A455

Designs: 19p, Celebrating 100 years. 25p, Protecting land. 30p, Conserving art. 35p, Saving coast. 41p, Repairing buildings.

1995, Apr. 11	Photo.	Perf. 14x15	
1606 A455	19p multicolored	.60	.30
1607 A455	25p multicolored	.80	.40
a.	Booklet pane of 6	4.80	

1608 A455	30p multicolored	.95	.48
1609 A455	35p multicolored	1.10	.55
1610 A455	41p multicolored	1.25	.65
	Nos. 1606-1610 (5)	4.70	2.38

For Prestige booklet containing panes #1607a, see list at end of postage section.
Issued: #1607a, 4/25/95.

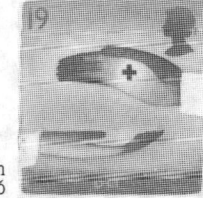

Peace & Freedom A456

Designs: No. 1611, Hands, British Red Cross 1870-1995. No. 1612, British troops, people celebrating liberation of Paris. No. 1613, Dove, outstretched hand, UN, 1945-95. No. 1614, St. Paul's

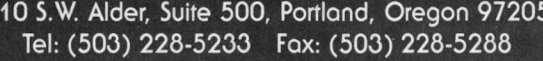

Cathedral, floodlights forming Victory V. 30p, Hands above earth, UN 1945-95.

1995, May 2 Photo. *Perf. 14½x14*

1611	A456	19p multicolored	.60	.30
1612	A456	19p multicolored	.60	.30
1613	A456	25p multicolored	.80	.40
1614	A456	25p multicolored	.80	.40
1615	A456	30p multicolored	.95	.48
		Nos. 1611-1615 (5)	3.75	1.88

End of World War II, 50th anniv. (#1612, 1614), Europa (#1613, 1615).

H. G. Wells (1866-1946), Science Fiction Writer — A457

Novels: 25p, The Time Machine. 30p, The First Men on the Moon. 35p, The War of the Worlds. 41p, The Shape of Things to Come.

1995, June 6 Litho. *Perf. 14½x14*

1616	A457	25p multicolored	.80	.40
1617	A457	30p multicolored	.95	.48
1618	A457	35p multicolored	1.10	.55
1619	A457	41p multicolored	1.25	.65
		Nos. 1616-1619 (4)	4.10	2.08

Opening of Shakespeare's New Globe Theatre A458

Bankside theatres: No. 1620, Swan, 1595. No. 1621, The Rose, 1595. No. 1622, The Globe, 1599. No. 1623, The Hope, 1613. No. 1624, The Globe, 1614.

1995, Aug. 8 Litho. *Perf. 14½x14*

1620	A458	25p multicolored	.80	.40
1621	A458	25p multicolored	.80	.40
1622	A458	25p multicolored	.80	.40
1623	A458	25p multicolored	.80	.40
1624	A458	25p multicolored	.80	.40
a.		Strip of 5, #1620-1624	4.00	2.00

Pioneers of Communication A459

Designs: 19p, Sir Rowland Hill, introduction of uniform penny postage. 25p, Hill as older man, Type A1. 41p, Guglielmo Marconi, early wireless equipment. 60p, Marconi as older man using radiophone, sinking ship.

Litho. & Engr.

1995, Sept. 5 *Perf. 14½*

1625	A459	19p multicolored	.60	.30
1626	A459	25p multicolored	.80	.40
1627	A459	41p multicolored	1.25	.65
1628	A459	60p multicolored	1.90	.95
		Nos. 1625-1628 (4)	4.55	2.30

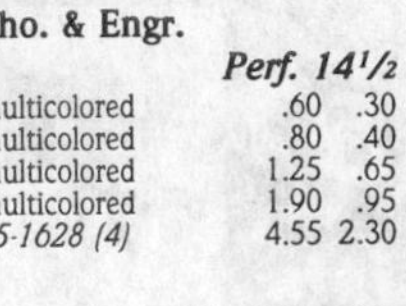

Rugby League, Cent. — A460

1995, Oct. 3 Photo. *Perf. 14x14½*

1629	A460	19p Harold Wagstaff	.60	.30
1630	A460	25p Gus Risman	.80	.40
1631	A460	30p Jim Sullivan	.95	.50
1632	A460	35p Billy Batten	1.10	.55
1633	A460	41p Brian Bevan	1.25	.65
		Nos. 1629-1633 (5)	4.70	2.40

Christmas A461

Designs showing robin in winter scene: 19p, In pillar box. 25p, On fence rail, holly bush. 30p, Standing on snow covered milk bottle. 41p, Sitting on snow covered road sign, blue fence. 60p, Sitting on door knob, Christmas decoration on door.

1995, Oct. 30 Litho. *Perf. 14½x14*

1634	A461	19p multicolored	.60	.30
a.		Booklet pane of 20	12.00	
		Complete booklet, #1634a	12.00	
1635	A461	25p multicolored	.80	.40
a.		Booklet pane of 10	8.00	
		Complete booklet, #1635a	8.00	
1636	A461	30p multicolored	.95	.50
1637	A461	41p multicolored	1.25	.65
1638	A461	60p multicolored	1.90	.95
a.		Booklet pane of 4	7.75	
		Complete booklet, #1638a + 4 labels	7.75	
		Nos. 1634-1638 (5)	5.50	2.80

Robert Burns (1759-1796), Poet — A462

Lines from poems: 19p, "Wee sleeket, cowran, tim'rous beastie." 25p, "O my luve's like a red, red rose." 41p, "Scots, wha hae wi Wallace bled." 60p, "Should auld acquaintance be forgot."

1996, Jan. 25 Litho. *Perf. 14½*

1639	A462	19p multicolored	.60	.30
1640	A462	25p multicolored	.75	.40
1641	A462	41p multicolored	1.25	.65
1642	A462	60p multicolored	1.80	.90
		Nos. 1639-1642 (4)	4.40	2.25

Great Britain new issues through the April 1996 issue of the *Scott Stamp Monthly* appear here.

Prestige Booklets:

12/1/69 - Stamps for Cooks - #495f, 499d, 500b, value, $25 (stitched).

5/24/72 - £1 Wedgwood - #622d, 622e, 626d, 627c, value, $125. This booklet is valued with a F-VF ½p stamp.

6/16/80 - £3 Wedgwood - #625c, 764a, 893b, 893c, value, $15.

5/19/82 - Stanley Gibbons - #896a, 896b, 971f, 971g, value, $20.

9/14/83 - Royal Mint - #889b, 971f, 972c, value, $15.

9/4/84 - Christian Heritage - #974c, 974d, 1073e, value, $45.

1/8/85 - The Times - #974b, 974d, 1073f, 1073j, value, $50.

3/18/86 - British Rail - #974b, 974d, 1072a, 1072c, value, $50.

3/3/87 - P&O Line - #1073e, 1073f, 1075c, 1075d, value, $32.50.

2/9/88 - Financial Times - #1073k, 1073l, 1075i, 1075j, value, $37.50.

3/21/89 - Scots Connection - Scotland #49a, 50a, 50b, 51a, value, $22.50.

3/20/90 - London Life - #1296c, 1296e, 1314a, value, $32.50.

3/19/91 - Agatha Christie - #1263b, 1265b, 1272a, value, $22.50.

3/11/92 - Wales - #1278g, 1425a, Wales & Monmouthshire #60a, 61a, value, $27.50.

10/27/92 - J.R.R. Tolkien - #1399b, 1401d, 1409b, value, $25.

8/10/93 - Beatrix Potter - #1278h, 1409c, 1484a, Northern Ireland #60a, value, $30. Overprints for the Hong Kong exhibition on the cover of this booklet were not official.

7/26/94 - Northern Ireland - #1402e, 1550a, Northern Ireland #66a, 66b, value, $17.50.

4/25/95 - Northern Ireland - #1400c, 1410c, 1607a, Northern Ireland #64a, value, $11.50.

SEMI-POSTAL STAMPS

Catalogue values for unused stamps in this section are for Never Hinged items.

Handicapped Person SP1

Perf. 14½x14

1975, Jan. 22 Photo. Unwmk.

B1	SP1	4½p +1½p blue & lt blue	.22	.22

For the benefit of health and handicap charities. No. B1 is phosphorescent.

Christmas Type of 1989

Ely Cathedral, Cambridgeshire: No. B2, Romanesque arches, west front. No. B3, Central tower. No. B4, Interlocking arches, Romanesque arcades, west transept. No. B5, Peasant, stained-glass window in triple arch, west front.

1989, Nov. 14 Photo. *Perf. 15x14*

B2	A379	15p +1p multicolored	.52	.40
B3	A379	20p +1p multicolored	.68	.50
B4	A379	34p +1p multicolored	1.10	.82
B5	A379	37p +1p multicolored	1.20	.90
		Nos. B2-B5 (4)	3.50	2.62

POSTAGE DUE STAMPS

D1

D2

Perf. 14x14½

1914-22 Typo. Wmk. 33

J1	D1	½p emerald	.50	.25
J2	D1	1p rose	.60	.15
J3	D1	1½p red brown ('22)	55.00	15.00
J4	D1	2p brown black	1.10	.20
J5	D1	3p violet ('18)	3.00	.95
J6	D1	4p gray green ('21)	6.50	.55
J7	D1	5p org brown	4.00	.55
J8	D1	1sh blue	30.00	2.25
		Nos. J1-J8 (8)	100.70	19.90

1924-30 Wmk. 35

J9	D1	½p emerald	.60	.25
J10	D1	1p car rose	.60	.25
J11	D1	1½p red brown	37.50	17.50
J12	D1	2p black brown	2.00	.15
J13	D1	3p violet	3.00	.20
a.		Experimental wmk.	42.50	37.50
J14	D1	4p deep green	11.00	1.75
J15	D1	5p org brown ('30)	24.00	20.00
J16	D1	1sh blue	5.25	.55
J17	D2	2sh6p brown, *yellow*	40.00	1.50
		Nos. J9-J17 (9)	123.95	42.15

The experimental watermark of No. J13a resembles Wmk. 35 but is spaced more closely, with letters short and rounded, crown with flat arch and sides high, lines thicker.

1936-37 Wmk. 250

J18	D1	½p emerald ('37)	2.75	2.25
J19	D1	1p car rose ('37)	1.50	1.10
J20	D1	2p blk brown ('37)	3.75	3.25
J21	D1	3p violet ('37)	1.90	1.75
J22	D1	4p slate green	6.25	2.00
J23	D1	5p bister	7.50	6.50
a.		5p orange brown ('37)	32.50	22.50
J24	D1	1sh blue ('36)	5.25	4.50
J25	D2	2sh6p brn, *yel* ('37)	140.00	8.50
		Nos. J18-J25 (8)	168.90	29.85

1938-39 Wmk. 251

J26	D1	½p emerald	4.00	3.50
J27	D1	1p carmine rose	1.25	.60
J28	D1	2p black brown	1.25	.90
J29	D1	3p violet	5.00	.30
J30	D1	4p slate green	30.00	10.00
J31	D1	5p bister ('39)	5.00	.55
J32	D1	1sh blue	27.50	1.50
J33	D2	2sh6p brown, *yel* ('39)	27.50	3.00
		Nos. J26-J33 (8)	101.50	20.35

Catalogue values for unused stamps in this section, from this point to the end of the section, are for Never Hinged items.

1951-52

J34	D1	½p orange	1.25	1.25
J35	D1	1p violet blue	2.75	.55
J36	D1	1½p green ('52)	2.75	2.00
J37	D1	4p bright blue	13.00	6.50
J38	D1	1sh olive bister	35.00	6.50
		Nos. J34-J38 (5)	54.75	16.80

1954-55 Wmk. 298

J39	D1	½p orange ('55)	3.25	3.25
J40	D1	2p brn black ('55)	3.25	1.50
J41	D1	3p purple ('55)	50.00	21.00
J42	D1	4p brt blue ('55)	16.00	8.50
a.		Imperf., pair	175.00	
J43	D1	5p bister brn ('55)	14.00	10.00
J44	D2	2sh6p dk pur brn, *yel*	110.00	8.00
		Nos. J39-J44 (6)	196.50	52.25

1955-57 Wmk. 308 *Perf. 14x14½*

J45	D1	½p orange ('56)	2.00	2.75
J46	D1	1p ultra ('56)	3.50	.85
J47	D1	1½p green ('56)	3.50	2.00
J48	D1	2p brown blk ('56)	32.50	5.75
J49	D1	3p purple ('56)	5.75	2.00
J50	D1	4p brt blue ('56)	20.00	4.75
J51	D1	5p bister brn ('56)	27.50	2.75
J52	D1	1sh dp olive bister	65.00	2.75
J53	D2	2sh6p dk red brn, *yel* ('57)	150.00	9.50
J54	D2	5sh red, *yellow*	95.00	18.00
		Nos. J45-J54 (10)	404.75	51.10

1959-63 Wmk. 322 *Perf. 14x14½*

J55	D1	½p orange ('61)	.15	.50
J56	D1	1p ultra ('60)	.15	.15
J57	D1	1½p green ('60)	1.00	1.90
J58	D1	2p brown black	.70	.20
J59	D1	3p purple	.40	.15
J60	D1	4p brt blue ('60)	.40	.15
J61	D1	5p bister brn ('62)	.40	.35
J62	D1	6p dp mag ('62)	.40	.25
J63	D1	1sh dp ol bis ('60)	.60	.25
J64	D2	2sh6p dark red brown, *yellow* ('61)	3.50	.45
J65	D2	5sh red, *yellow* ('61)	6.50	.80
J66	D2	10sh ultra, *yel* ('63)	7.50	3.50
J67	D2	£1 blk, *yellow* ('63)	42.50	7.00
		Nos. J55-J67 (13)	64.20	15.65

Nos. J1-J67 are watermarked sideways.

Perf. 14x14½

1968-69 Unwmk. Typo.

J68	D1	2p greenish black	1.00	.25
J69	D1	3p purple	.75	.15
J70	D1	4p bright blue	.90	.25
J71	D1	5p brown org ('69)	8.00	8.00
J72	D1	6p deep magenta	1.50	.40
J73	D1	1sh bister ('69)	2.00	.35
		Nos. J68-J73 (6)	14.15	9.40

1968-69 Photo.

J74	D1	4p bright blue ('69)	5.00	3.50
J75	D1	8p bright red	1.00	.55

D3

D4

Perf. 14x14½

1970-75 Photo. Unwmk.

J79	D3	½p grnsh blue ('71)	.15	.15
J80	D3	1p magenta ('71)	.15	.15
J81	D3	2p green ('71)	.15	.15
J82	D3	3p ultra ('71)	.15	.15
J83	D3	4p olive bister ('71)	.15	.15
J84	D3	5p bluish lilac ('71)	.15	.15
J85	D3	7p brown red ('74)	.30	.25
J86	D4	10p carmine rose	.40	.25
J87	D4	11p slate ('75)	.45	.25
J88	D4	20p olive	.75	.50
J89	D4	50p ultramarine	2.00	1.00
J90	D4	£1 black	4.00	2.25
J91	D4	£5 org & black ('73)	21.00	10.00
		Nos. J79-J91 (13)	29.80	15.40

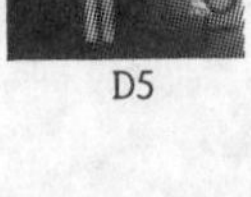

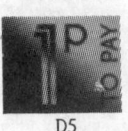

D5

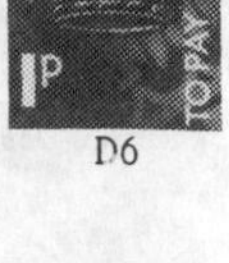

D6

1982, June 9   Photo.   Perf. 14x14½

J92	D5	1p rose carmine	.15	.15
J93	D5	2p ultramarine	.15	.15
J94	D5	3p deep rose lilac	.15	.15
J95	D5	4p dark blue	.15	.15
J96	D5	5p sepia	.15	.15
J97	D5	10p brown	.30	.15
J98	D5	20p dark ol green	.45	.40
J99	D5	25p slate blue	.60	.35
J100	D5	50p black	1.25	.70
J101	D5	£1 vermilion	2.25	1.25
J102	D5	£2 greenish blue	4.25	3.00
J103	D5	£5 yellow bister	11.00	5.50
		Nos. J92-J103 (12)	20.85	12.00

Perf. 15x14 Syncopated, Type C (2 Sides)

1994, Feb. 15   Photo. & Embossed

J104	D6	1p vermilion & org	.15	.15
J105	D6	2p red lilac & red	.15	.15
J106	D6	5p yellow & brown	.15	.15
J107	D6	10p yellow & green	.25	.25
J108	D6	20p green & blue	.60	.60
J109	D6	25p red	.70	.70
J110	D6	£1 violet & red lilac	2.50	2.50
J111	D6	£1.20 blue & green	2.75	2.75
J112	D6	£5 green & black	11.00	11.00
		Nos. J104-J112 (9)	18.25	18.25

OFFICIAL STAMPS

Type of Regular Issue of 1840
"V R" in Upper Corners

1840   Wmk. 18   Imperf.

O1	A1	1p black	6,250.

No. O1 was never placed in use.

Postage stamps perforated with a crown and initials "H.M.O.W.," "O.W.," "B.T." or "S.O." or with only the initials "H.M.S.O." or "D.S.I.R.," were used for official purposes.

Counterfeits exist of Nos. O2-O83.

Inland Revenue
Regular Issues Overprinted in Black:

I.R.   **I. R.**

OFFICIAL   **OFFICIAL**
a   b

Type "a" is overprinted on the stamps of ½ penny to 1 shilling inclusive, type "b" on the higher values.

1882-85   Wmk. 30   Perf. 14

O2	A35	½p green	10.00	2.00
O3	A35	½p slate bl ('85)	22.50	7.50
O4	A40	1p lilac	1.25	.30
a.		"OFFICIAL" omitted		3,500.
b.		Ovpt. lines transposed		
O5	A47	2½p lilac ('85)	95.00	27.50
O6	A28	6p gray	100.00	17.50
O7	A48	1sh green ('85)	3,000.	425.00

Wmk. 31

O8	A51	5sh car rose ('85)	1,250.	400.00
a.		Bluish paper ('85)	2,750.	450.00
O9	A52	10sh ultramarine	2,500.	500.00
a.		10sh cobalt	5,000.	750.00
b.		Bluish paper	6,000.	1,500.

Wmk. Three Imperial Crowns (30)

O10	A53	£1 brown vio	22,500.	5,000.

1888-89   Wmk. 30

O11	A54	½p vermilion	1.25	.30
a.		"I.R." omitted		2,250.
O12	A65	1sh green ('89)	200.00	17.50

1890   Wmk. Three Orbs (29)

O13	A53	£1 brown vio	27,500.	5,000.

1891   Wmk. 30

O14	A57	2½p violet, *blue*	55.00	3.00

Wmk. Three Imperial Crowns (30)

1892

O15	A53	£1 green	3,750.	475.
a.		No period after "R"	10,000.	1,000.

1901   Wmk. 30

O16	A54	½p blue green	4.00	2.25
O17	A62	6p violet, *rose*	100.00	15.00
O18	A65	1sh car rose & green	625.00	90.00

1902-04

O19	A66	½p gray green	14.00	1.00
O20	A66	1p carmine	10.00	.50
O21	A66	2½p ultra	350.00	75.00
O22	A66	6p dull vio ('04)	80,000.	60,000.

O23	A74	1sh car rose & green	450.00	80.00

Wmk. 31

O24	A76	5sh car rose	4,000.	1,750.
O25	A77	10sh ultra	22,500.	15,000.

Wmk. Three Imperial Crowns (30)

O26	A78	£1 green	11,000.	6,500.

Nos. O4, O8, O9 and O15 also exist with overprint in blue black.

Government Parcels

Overprinted **GOVᵀ PARCELS**

1883-86   Wmk. 30

O27	A45	1½p lilac ('86)	100.00	40.00
O28	A46	6p green ('86)	750.00	400.00
O29	A50	9p green	650.00	275.00
O30	A29	1sh salmon (P13)	400.00	110.00
	Plate 14		750.00	165.00

1887-92

O31	A55	1½p violet & green	15.00	2.50
O32	A56	2p green & car rose ('91)	60.00	10.00
O33	A60	4½p carmine rose & green ('92)	95.00	100.00
O34	A62	6p violet, *rose*	42.50	15.00
O35	A63	9p blue & lil ('88)	80.00	20.00
O36	A65	1sh green	175.00	100.00

1897

O37	A40	1p lilac	25.00	7.50
a.		Inverted overprint	1,000.	850.00

1900

O38	A65	1sh car rose & grn	160.00	70.00
a.		Inverted overprint		6,000.

1902

O39	A66	1p carmine	15.00	5.00
O40	A68	2p green & car	50.00	11.00
O41	A66	6p dull violet	110.00	10.00
O42	A72	9p ultra & violet	200.00	42.50
O43	A74	1sh car rose & grn	375.00	70.00
		Nos. O39-O43 (5)	750.00	138.50

Office of Works

Overprinted **O.W. OFFICIAL**

1896

O44	A54	½p vermilion	85.00	37.50
O45	A40	1p lilac	150.00	37.50

1901-02

O46	A54	½p blue green	140.00	50.00
O47	A61	5p lilac & ultra	600.00	175.00
O48	A64	10p car rose & lil	900.00	275.00

1902

O49	A66	½p gray green	300.00	75.00
O50	A66	1p carmine	300.00	75.00
O51	A68	2p green & car	450.00	75.00
O52	A66	2½p ultramarine	500.00	150.00
O53	A73	10p car rose & vio	3,750.	1,400.

Army

Overprinted:

ARMY   **ARMY**

OFFICIAL   **OFFICIAL**
a   b

1896

O54	A54(a)	½p vermilion	1.50	.50
a.		"OFFICIAl"	30.00	16.00
O55	A40(a)	1p lilac	1.25	.60
a.		"OFFICIAl"	30.00	17.50
O56	A57(b)	2½p violet, *blue*	5.00	2.50
		Nos. O54-O56 (3)	7.75	3.60

1900

O57	A54(a)	½p blue green	1.50	2.00

1901

O58	A62(b)	6p violet, *rose*	12.50	4.75

Great Britain Regional issues can be mounted in the Scott Great Britain album.

1902

O59	A66(a)	½p gray green	1.10	.20
O60	A66(a)	1p carmine	1.10	.15
O61	A66(a)	6p dull violet	50.00	21.00
		Nos. O59-O61 (3)	52.20	21.35

Overprinted **ARMY OFFICIAL**

1903

O62	A66	6p dull violet	800.00	500.00

Royal Household

Overprinted **R.H. OFFICIAL**

1902

O63	A66	½p gray green	100.00	80.00
O64	A66	1p carmine	80.00	65.00

Board of Education

Overprinted **BOARD OF EDUCATION**

1902

O65	A61	5p lilac & ultra	375.00	75.00
O66	A65	1sh car rose & grn	1,000.	400.00

1902-04

O67	A66	½p gray green	21.00	2.50
O68	A66	1p carmine	18.00	2.50
O69	A66	2½p ultramarine	350.00	60.00
O70	A71	5p lilac & ultra ('04)	1,750.	800.00
O71	A74	1sh car rose & grn	27,500.	17,500.

Admiralty

Overprinted **ADMIRALTY OFFICIAL**

1903

O72	A66	½p gray green	8.00	2.25
O73	A66	1p carmine	5.00	1.25
O74	A67	1½p vio & green	50.00	30.00
O75	A68	2p green & car	60.00	35.00
O76	A66	2½p ultra	75.00	35.00
O77	A69	3p violet, *yel*	82.50	30.00
		Nos. O72-O77 (6)	280.50	133.50

Overprinted **ADMIRALTY OFFICIAL**

1903

O78	A66	½p gray green	7.50	2.50
O79	A66	1p carmine	5.00	2.50
O80	A67	1½p vio & green	165.00	50.00
O81	A68	2p green & car	425.00	150.00
O82	A66	2½p ultramarine	550.00	300.00
O83	A69	3p violet, *yel*	300.00	50.00

The two types of the "Admiralty Official" overprint differ principally in the shape of the letter "M."

ENVELOPES

Britannia Sending Letters to World
(William Mulready, Designer) — E1

1840

U1	E1	1p black	125.00	175.00
U2	E1	2p blue	200.00	600.00

LETTER SHEETS

U3	E1	1p black	110.00	140.00
U4	E1	2p blue	175.00	550.00

REGIONAL ISSUES

Sold only at post offices within the respective regions, but valid for postage throughout Great Britain. Issues for Guernsey, Jersey and Isle of Man are listed with the Bailiwick issues that follow.

Starting in 1967, all Regional stamps were issued only with phosphorescence.

Catalogue values for unused stamps in this section are for Never Hinged items.

Northern Ireland

A1   A1a

Flax and Red Hand of Ulster
A1b   A2

Perf. 15x14

1958-67   Photo.   Wmk. 322

1	A1	3p dark purple	.15	.15
p.		Phosphor. ('67)	.15	.15
2	A1	4p ultra ('66)	.15	.15
p.		Phosphor. ('67)	.15	.15
3	A1a	6p rose lilac	.30	.15
4	A1a	9p dk green ('67)	.35	.15
5	A1b	1sh3p dark green	.35	.15
6	A1b	1sh6p dark blue ('67)	.35	.15
		Nos. 1-6 (6)	1.65	
		Set value		.60

Nos. 4, 6 and following are phosphorescent.

1968-69   Unwmk.

Design: 1sh6p, Flax plant, Red Right Hand of Ulster and Ulster field gate.

7	A1	4p ultramarine	.18	.15
8	A1	4p olive brown	.15	.15
9	A1	4p bright red ('69)	.32	.15
10	A1	5p dark blue	.20	.15
11	A1b	1sh6p dark blue ('69)	3.50	2.00
		Nos. 7-11 (5)	4.35	
		Set value		2.32

1971-80   Photo.   Perf. 15x14

12	A2	2½p bright pink	1.25	.20
13	A2	3p ultramarine	.60	.15
14	A2	3½p dk ol green ('74)	.30	.15
15	A2	4½p dark blue ('74)	.30	.15
16	A2	5p bluish lilac	2.25	1.25
17	A2	5½p dark violet ('74)	.32	.15
18	A2	6½p Prus blue ('76)	.32	.15
19	A2	7p red brown ('78)	.32	.15
20	A2	7½p light red brown	3.25	1.90
21	A2	8p red ('74)	.35	.25
22	A2	8½p yel green ('76)	.32	.25
23	A2	9p violet blue ('78)	.38	.25
24	A2	10p org brown ('76)	.42	.30

25 A2 10½p steel blue ('78) .55 .30
26 A2 11p red ('76) .55 .35
27 A2 12p yel green ('80) .70 .24
28 A2 13½p dk red brn ('80) .80 .28
29 A2 15p ultra ('80) .70 .30
Nos. 12-29 (18) 13.68 6.77

Issue dates: two phosphorescent bands, 3p, 1971, 3½p, Jan. 1974, 5½p, 1974, 10p, 1976; one center band, 3p, 1974, 3½p, Nov. 1974, 5½p, 1975, 10p, 1980.

1981, Apr. 8 Litho. *Perf. 13½x14*
30 A2 11½p olive gray .95 .75
31 A2 14p gray violet .90 .50
32 A2 18p blue violet 1.00 1.00
33 A2 22p dark blue 1.25 1.00
Nos. 30-33 (4) 4.10 3.25

1982, Feb. 24
34 A2 12½p emerald .60 .40
a. Perf. 15x14 8.00 6.00
35 A2 15½p light violet .95 .75
36 A2 19½p olive green 2.25 2.50
37 A2 26p red 1.10 .90
a. Perf. 15x14 ('87) 1.90 1.00
Nos. 34-37 (4) 4.90 4.55

1983, Apr. 27
38 A2 16p dull brown 1.10 1.25
a. Perf. 15x14 8.00 6.00
39 A2 20½p ultramarine 4.75 2.75
40 A2 28p deep violet 1.25 .90
a. Perf. 15x14 ('87) 1.00 .90
Nos. 38-40 (3) 7.10 4.90

1984, Oct. 23 Litho. *Perf. 15x14*
41 A2 13p pale salmon .60 .35
42 A2 17p light blue gray .95 .50
43 A2 22p yellow green .95 .60
44 A2 31p deep magenta 1.50 1.00
Nos. 41-44 (4) 4.00 2.45

1986, Jan. 7 Litho. *Perf. 15x14*
45 A2 12p green .65 .50

1987, Jan. 6 Photo. *Perf. 15x14*
46 A2 18p olive green .85 .50

1988, Aug. 11 Litho.
47 A2 14p dark blue .52 .35
48 A2 19p bright orange .75 .50
49 A2 23p brt yellow green .95 .60
50 A2 32p Prussian blue 1.40 .80
Nos. 47-50 (4) 3.62 2.25

1989, Nov. 28 Photo. *Perf. 15x14*
51 A2 15p bright blue .48 .35
52 A2 20p brown black .70 .50
53 A2 24p orange vermilion .90 .60
54 A2 34p royal blue 1.25 .90
Nos. 51-54 (4) 3.33 2.35

Two types of crown:
Type 1 - Crown with all pearls individually drawn. Screened background.
Type 2 - Crown with clear outlines, large pearls and strong white line below them. First three pearls are joined. Solid background.

1990, Dec. 4 Litho. *Perf. 15x14*
55 A2 17p dark blue .68 .40
56 A2 22p red orange .85 .60
57 A2 26p olive gray 1.00 .70
58 A2 37p scarlet 1.45 .90
Nos. 55-58 (4) 3.98 2.60

1991, Dec. 3
59 A2 18p brt yellow green .60 .30
a. Perf. 13½x14 ('93) 1.00 .50
60 A2 24p brown .80 .40
a. Bklt. pane, see footnote 4.20
61 A2 28p blue gray .95 .48
62 A2 39p red lilac 1.35 .65
Nos. 59-62 (4) 3.70 1.83

No. 60a contains 1 each of Northern Ireland #59-60, Scotland #61-62, & Wales and Monmouthshire #60-61. Issue date: Aug. 10, 1993.
For Prestige booklet containing pane #60a, see list at end of Great Britain postage section.

Perf. 15x14 Syncopated Type C (2 Sides)

1993-94 Litho.
63 A2 19p olive green .55 .28
64 A2 25p salmon .75 .38
a. Booklet pane, see footnote 4.25
65 A2 30p gray .90 .45
66 A2 41p drab 1.25 .60
a. Bklt. pane of 8, 2 #63, 4 #64, #65-66 + label 6.25
b. Bklt. pane of 4, #63-66 3.50
Nos. 63-66 (4) 3.45 1.71

No. 64a contains 1 each of Northern Ireland 63-64, Scotland #65-66, & Wales and Monmouthshire #64-65 + printed margin.
Issued: #63-66, 12/7/93; #66a-66b, 7/26/94; 64a, 4/25/95.

For Prestige booklet containing panes #66a, 66b, see list at end of Great Britain postage section.

Scotland

St. Andrew's Cross and Thistle — A1

A1a

A1b

Scottish Lion Rampant — A2

Perf. 15x14

1958-67 Photo. Wmk. 322
1 A1 3p dark purple .15 .15
p. Phosphor. .15 .15
2 A1 4p ultra ('66) .15 .15
p. Phosphor. ('67) .15 .15
3 A1a 6p rose lilac .25 .15
p. Phosphor. ('63) .25 .15
4 A1a 9p dark green ('67) .35 .15
5 A1b 1sh3p dark green .35 .15
p. Phosphor. ('63) .35 .15
6 A1b 1sh6p dark blue ('67) .35 .20
Nos. 1-6 (6) 1.60
Set value .70

The 3p with two phosphorescent bands was issued in 1963; with one side band in 1965, and one center band in 1967. The value of No. 1p is for one center band. Nos. 4, 6 and following are phosphorescent.

1967-70 Unwmk.
7 A1 3p purple ('68) .15 .15
8 A1 4p ultramarine .18 .15
9 A1 4p olive brown ('68) .18 .15
10 A1 4p brt red ('69) .18 .15
11 A1 5p dark blue ('68) .28 .15
12 A1a 9p dark green ('70) 7.50 4.75
13 A1b 1sh6p dark blue ('68) 1.40 .85
Nos. 7-13 (7) 9.87 6.35

1971-80 Photo. *Perf. 15x14*
14 A2 2½p bright pink .32 .15
15 A2 3p ultramarine .42 .15
16 A2 3½p dk ol green ('74) .32 .15
17 A2 4½p dark blue ('74) .32 .15
18 A2 5p bluish lilac 2.25 1.25
19 A2 5½p dark violet ('74) .32 .15
20 A2 6½p Prus blue ('76) .32 .15
21 A2 7p red brown ('78) .32 .15
22 A2 7½p light red brown 2.50 1.50
23 A2 8p red ('74) .48 .25
24 A2 8½p yel green ('76) .48 .25
25 A2 9p violet blue ('78) .48 .25
26 A2 10p orange brn ('76) .48 .20
27 A2 10½p steel blue ('78) .48 .40
28 A2 11p red ('76) .48 .40
29 A2 12p yel green ('80) .52 .40
30 A2 13½p dk red brn ('80) .75 .70
31 A2 15p ultra ('80) .60 .50
Nos. 14-31 (18) 11.84 7.15

Issue dates: two phosphorescent bands, 3p, 1971, 3½p, Jan. 1974, 5½p, 1974, 10p, 1976; one center band, 3p, 1974, 3½p, Nov. 1974, 5½p, 1975, 10p, 1980.

1981, Apr. 8 Litho. *Perf. 13½x14*
32 A2 11½p olive gray 1.00 .65
33 A2 14p gray violet .60 .40
34 A2 18p blue violet 1.00 .75
35 A2 22p dark blue 1.10 1.00
Nos. 32-35 (4) 3.70 2.80

1981, Feb. 24
36 A2 12½p emerald .60 .35
37 A2 15½p light violet .90 .60
38 A2 19½p olive green 2.50 2.50
39 A2 26p red 1.10 .90
a. Perf. 15x14 ('87) 1.75 1.00
Nos. 36-39 (4) 5.10 4.35

1983, Apr. 27
40 A2 16p dull brown .80 .45
41 A2 20½p ultramarine 4.50 .75
42 A2 28p deep violet 1.10 .90
a. Perf. 15x14 ('87) 1.10 .90
Nos. 40-42 (3) 6.40 2.10

1984, Oct. 23
43 A2 13p pale salmon .80 .35
44 A2 17p lt blue gray 3.00 2.50
45 A2 22p yellow green 1.15 .65
46 A2 31p deep magenta 1.65 .90
Nos. 43-46 (4) 6.60 4.40

1986-87 *Perf. 15x14*
43a A2 13p ('87) .65 .35
44a A2 17p 4.50 2.50
45a A2 22p ('87) 1.40 .50
46a A2 31p 1.50 .90
Nos. 43a-46a (4) 8.05 4.25

1986, Jan. 7 *Perf. 13½x14*
47 A2 12p green 1.10 .75
a. Perf. 15x14 1.10 .65

Issue date of Nos. 44a, 46a, 47a, Apr. 29.

1987, Jan. 6 Photo. *Perf. 15x14*
48 A2 18p olive green .85 .40

1988, Aug. 11 Litho.
49 A2 14p dark blue .52 .35
a. Bklt. pane of 6+printed margin ('89) 3.15
50 A2 19p brt orange .70 .50
a. Bklt. pane of 6+printed margin ('89) 4.25
b. Bklt. pane of 9+printed margin ('89) 6.30
51 A2 23p brt yellow green 1.00 .60
a. Bklt. pane of 8+label + printed margin (5 14p, 2 19p, 23p) ('89) 5.25
52 A2 32p Prussian blue 1.25 .90
Nos. 48-52 (5) 4.32 2.75

No. 51a has vertical row of rouletting.
For Prestige booklet containing panes #49a, 50a, 50b, 51a, see list at end of Great Britain postage section.

1989, Nov. 28 Photo. *Perf. 15x14*

Two types of lion:
Type 1 - The eye and jaw appear larger and there is no line across the bridge of the nose.
Type 2 - The tongue is thick at the point of entry to the mouth and the eye is linked to the background by a solid line.

53 A2 15p bright blue .48 .35
54 A2 20p brown black .70 .50
55 A2 24p orange vermilion .80 .70
56 A2 34p royal blue 1.10 .90
Nos. 53-56 (4) 3.08 2.45

1990, Dec. 4 Litho. *Perf. 15x14*
57 A2 17p dark blue .68 .40
58 A2 22p red orange .85 .60
59 A2 26p olive gray 1.00 .70
60 A2 37p scarlet 1.45 .90
Nos. 57-60 (4) 3.98 2.60

1991, Dec. 3
61 A2 18p brt yellow green .60 .30
62 A2 24p brown .80 .40
63 A2 28p blue gray .95 .48
64 A2 39p red lilac 1.35 .65
Nos. 61-64 (4) 3.70 1.83

For Prestige booklet containing stamps #61-62, see list at end of Great Britain postage section.

1993 (?) *Perf. 13½x14*
61a A2 18p 1.00 .50
62a A2 24p 1.30 .65
63a A2 28p 1.50 .75
64a A2 39p 2.10 1.05
Nos. 61a-64a (4) 5.90 2.95

See Northern Ireland No. 60a.

Perf. 15x14, Syncopated Type C (2 Sides)

1993, Dec. 7 Litho.
65 A2 19p olive green .55 .28
66 A2 25p salmon .75 .38
67 A2 30p gray .90 .45
68 A2 41p drab 1.25 .60
Nos. 65-68 (4) 3.45 1.71

Wales and Monmouthshire

A1

A1a

A1b

Welsh Dragon
A2

Designs: 6p, 9p, Dragon in rectangular panel at bottom. 1sh3p, 1sh6p, Dragon and leek.

Perf. 15x14

1958-67 Photo. Wmk. 322
1 A1 3p dark purple .15 .15
p. Phosphor. band ('67) .15 .15
2 A1 4p ultra ('66) .18 .15
p. Phosphor. bands ('67) .18 .15
3 A1a 6p rose lilac .40 .30
4 A1a 9p dark green ('67) .32 .15
5 A1b 1sh3p dark green .32 .15
6 A1b 1sh6p dark blue ('67) .32 .20
Nos. 1-6 (6) 1.69 1.10

Nos. 4, 6 and following are phosphorescent.

1967-69 Unwmk.
7 A1 3p dark purple .15 .15
8 A1 4p ultra ('68) .15 .15
9 A1 4p olive brown ('68) .15 .15
10 A1 4p brt red ('69) .18 .15
11 A1 5p dark blue ('68) .22 .15
12 A1b 1sh6p dark blue ('69) 3.25 2.50
Nos. 7-12 (6) 4.10
Set value 2.80

1971-80 Photo. *Perf. 15x14*
13 A2 2½p bright pink .18 .15
14 A2 3p ultramarine .32 .15
15 A2 3½p dk ol green ('74) .28 .15
16 A2 4½p dark blue ('74) .28 .15
17 A2 5p bluish lilac 2.00 1.25
18 A2 5½p dk violet ('74) .32 .15
19 A2 6½p Prus blue ('76) .32 .15
20 A2 7p red brown ('78) .32 .15
21 A2 7½p light red brown 2.75 1.90
22 A2 8p red ('74) .40 .25
23 A2 8½p yel green ('76) .40 .25
24 A2 9p violet blue ('78) .42 .25
25 A2 10p org brown ('76) .42 .30
26 A2 10½p steel blue ('78) .55 .40
27 A2 11p red ('76) .55 .40
28 A2 12p yel green ('80) .60 .40
29 A2 13½p dk red brn ('80) .85 .75
30 A2 15p ultra ('80) .70 .50
Nos. 13-30 (18) 11.66 7.70

Issue dates: two phosphorescent bands, 3p, 1971, 3½p, Jan. 1974, 5½p, 1974, 10p, 1976; one center band, 3p, 1974, 3½p, Nov. 1974, 5½p, 1975, 10p, 1980.

1981, Apr. 8 Litho. *Perf. 13½x14*
31 A2 11½p olive gray .95 .50
32 A2 14p gray violet .70 .40
33 A2 18p blue violet .95 .90
34 A2 22p dark blue 1.10 1.00
Nos. 31-34 (4) 3.70 2.80

1982, Feb. 24
35 A2 12½p emerald .70 .35
a. Perf. 15x14 ('84) 7.00 4.00
36 A2 15½p light violet .95 .50
37 A2 19½p olive green 2.50 2.00
38 A2 26p red 1.00 .80
a. Perf. 15x14 ('87) 4.75 2.50
Nos. 35-38 (4) 5.15 3.65

1983, Apr. 27
39 A2 16p dull brown 1.65 1.00
a. Perf. 15x14 ('84) 1.75 .80
40 A2 20½p ultramarine 4.25 3.75
41 A2 28p deep violet 1.40 .80
a. Perf. 15x14 ('87) 1.25 .70
Nos. 39-41 (3) 7.30 5.55

1984, Oct. 23 Litho. *Perf. 15x14*
42 A2 13p pale salmon .52 .30
43 A2 17p lt blue gray .95 .40
44 A2 22p yellow green .95 .60
45 A2 31p deep magenta 1.25 .90
Nos. 42-45 (4) 3.67 2.20

1986, Jan. 7 Litho. *Perf. 15x14*
46 A2 12p green 1.90 1.10

1987, Jan. 6 Photo. *Perf. 15x14*
47 A2 18p olive green .90 .40

1988, Aug. 11 Litho.
48 A2 14p dark blue .52 .35
a. Bklt. pane of 6+printed margin ('89) 3.15
49 A2 19p brt orange .70 .40
a. Bklt. pane of 6+printed margin ('89) 4.25
b. Bklt. pane of 9+printed margin ('89) 6.30
50 A2 23p brt yellow green 1.00 .60
a. Bklt. pane of 8+label + printed margin (5 14p, 2 19p, 23p) ('89) 5.25
51 A2 32p Prussian blue 1.25 .90
Nos. 48-51 (4) 3.47 2.25

1989, Nov. 28 Photo. *Perf. 15x14*
52 A2 15p bright blue .55 .40
53 A2 20p brown black .70 .50
54 A2 24p orange vermilion .95 .70
55 A2 34p royal blue 1.25 .90
Nos. 52-55 (4) 3.45 2.50

Two types of dragon:
Type 1 - The eye is complete with white dot in the center. Wing tips, tail and tongue are thin.

Type 2 - The eye is joined to the nose by a solid line. Wing tips, tail and tongue are wider than in type 1.

1990, Dec. 4 Litho. *Perf. 15x14*
56 A2 17p dark blue .68 .40
57 A2 22p red orange .85 .60
58 A2 26p olive gray 1.00 .70
59 A2 37p scarlet 1.45 .90
Nos. 56-59 (4) 3.98 2.60

1991, Dec. 3
60 A2 18p brt yellow green .60 .30
a. Booklet pane of 6 3.60
b. Perf. 13 1/2x14 1.00 .50
61 A2 24p brown .80 .40
a. Booklet pane of 6 4.80
b. Perf. 13 1/2x14 1.30 .65
62 A2 28p blue gray .95 .48
63 A2 39p red lilac 1.35 .65
Nos. 60-63 (4) 3.70 1.83

Issued: Nos. 60a, 61a, Mar. 1, 1992. Nos. 60b, 61b, 1993 (?).
For combination booklet panes see Great Britain No. 1278g, Northern Ireland No. 60a.
For Prestige booklets containing panes #60a, 61a and stamps #60-61, see list at end of Great Britain postage section.

Perf. 15x14, Syncopated Type C (2 Sides)

1993, Dec. 7 Litho.
64 A2 19p olive green .55 .28
65 A2 25p salmon .75 .38
66 A2 30p gray .90 .45
67 A2 41p drab 1.25 .60
Nos. 64-67 (4) 3.45 1.71

GUERNSEY

'gərn–zē

LOCATION — A group of islands in the English Channel
GOVT. — Dependent territory (bailiwick) of the British Crown
AREA — 30 sq. mi.
POP. — 53,313 (1981)
CAPITAL — St. Peter Port

The bailiwick includes the islands of Guernsey, Alderney, Sark, Herm, Jethou and Lithou.

Following the establishment of the British General Post Office as a public corporation on October 1, 1969, the post office of the Bailiwick of Guernsey became a separate entity and British postage stamps ceased to be valid.

Catalogue values for unused stamps in this country are for Never Hinged items.

Watermark

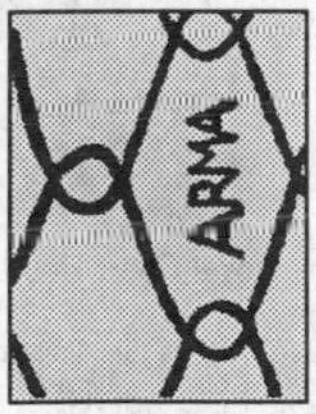

Wmk. 396- Link Fence

British Regional Issue

Guernsey Lily and Crown of William the Conqueror
A1 A2

Perf. 15x14

1958-69 Photo. Wmk. 322
1 A1 2 1/2p rose red ('64) .35 .25
2 A2 3p light purple .35 .20
p. Phoshor. ('67) .15 .15
3 A2 4p ultra ('66) .35 .20
p. Phosphor. ('67) .20 .15

Unwmk.
4 A2 4p ultra ('68) .15 .15
5 A2 4p olive brown ('68) .15 .15
6 A2 4p bright red ('69) .20 .15
7 A2 5p dark blue ('68) .20 .15
Nos. 1-7 (7) 1.75
Set value 1.00

Nos. 4-7 are phosphorescent.
Sold to the general public only at post offices within Guernsey, but valid for postage throughout Great Britain.

Bailiwick Issues

William the Conqueror, Queen Elizabeth II and Map of Bailiwick — A3

Creux Harbor, Sark A4

Designs (Queen Elizabeth II and): 1/2p, Castle Cornet and Edward the Confessor. 1 1/2p, Martello Tower and Henry II. 2p, Arms of Sark and King John. 3p, Arms of Alderney and Edward III. 4p, Guernsey lily and Henry V. 5p, Arms of Guernsey and Queen Elizabeth I. 6p, Arms of Alderney and Charles II. 9p, Arms of Sark and George III. 1sh, Arms of Guernsey and Queen Victoria. 1sh6p, Map of Bailiwick and William I. 1sh9p, Guernsey lily and Queen Elizabeth I. 2sh6p, Martello Tower and King John. 10sh, Braye Harbor, Alderney. £1, St. Peter Port, Guernsey.

Perf. 14 1/2x14

1969-70 Photo. Unwmk.
8 A3 1/2p magenta & blk .15 .15
9 A3 1p ultra & black .15 .15
10 A3 1 1/2p bister & blk .15 .15
11 A3 2p dk blue & multi .15 .15
12 A3 3p deep orange & multi .15 .15
13 A3 4p yel green & multi .15 .15
a. Booklet pane of 1 .40 .40
14 A3 5p vio blue & multi .25 .25
a. Booklet pane of 1 .80 .80
15 A3 6p ol green & multi .30 .30
16 A3 9p plum & multi .50 .50
17 A3 1sh dk olive & multi .80 .80
18 A3 1sh6p blue grn & blk 2.00 2.00
19 A3 1sh9p magenta & multi 3.00 2.00
20 A3 2sh6p purple & blk 8.00 3.25

Perf. 12 1/2
21 A4 5sh multicolored 5.50 4.00
22 A4 10sh multicolored 30.00 27.50
a. Perf. 13 1/2x13 85.00 80.00

Perf. 13 1/2x13
23 A4 £1 multicolored 3.25 3.25
a. Perf. 12 1/2 9.00 8.00
Nos. 8-23 (16) 54.50 44.75

Issued: #22, 23a, 3/5/70; others, 10/1/69.
Nos. 9 and 18 are inscribed "40o 30' N."
See Nos. 28-29, 41-55.

Col. Isaac Brock — A5

Designs: 5p, Sir Isaac Brock as major general. 1sh9p, as ensign, flags of 1789 and 1969. 2sh6p, Regimental coat of arms and flags, horiz.

Perf. 14x13 1/2, 13 1/2x14

1969, Dec. 1 Litho. Unwmk.
24 A5 4p multicolored .35 .20
25 A5 5p black & multi .40 .20
26 A5 1sh9p dp blue & multi 2.25 2.00
27 A5 2sh6p purple & multi 2.50 2.50
Nos. 24-27 (4) 5.50 4.90

Sir Isaac Brock (1769-1812), born on Guernsey, commander of Quebec garrison.

Map Type of 1969 Redrawn

1970, Feb. 4 Photo. *Perf. 14 1/2x14*
28 A3 1p "49o 30'N" .20 .15
a. Booklet pane of 1 .30 .30
29 A3 1sh6p "49o 30'N" 7.00 2.75

No. 28a was issued Dec. 12, 1969, in booklets containing Nos. 13a, 14a, 28a.
Nos. 9 and 18 are inscribed "40o 30' N."

Destroyer "Bulldog" near Castle Cornet — A6

Designs: 5p, Liberation fleet in roadsteads between Guernsey, Herm and Jethou. 1sh6p, Brigadier A. E. Snow reading proclamation of King George VI on steps of Elizabeth College in Guernsey, vert.

1970, May 9 Photo. *Perf. 11 1/2*
30 A6 4p vio blue & lt blue .65 .28
31 A6 5p dp plum & gray .90 .35
32 A6 1sh6p dk brown & bis 4.25 3.50
Nos. 30-32 (3) 5.80 4.13

25th anniv. of Guernsey's liberation from the Germans.

Guernsey Cow — A7

1970, Aug. 12 Photo. *Perf. 11 1/2*
33 A7 4p Tomatoes 1.10 .45
34 A7 5p shown 1.10 .65
35 A7 9p Guernsey bull 10.50 7.50
36 A7 1sh6p Freesias 16.00 8.00
Nos. 33-36 (4) 28.70 16.60

For similar design see No. 68.

St. Anne, Alderney — A8

Christmas (Churches): 5p, St. Peter, Town Church, Guernsey. 9p, St. Peter, Sark, vert. 1sh6p, St. Tugual Chapel, Herm, vert.

1970, Nov. 11 Photo. *Perf. 11 1/2*
37 A8 4p blue, gold & brn .55 .22
38 A8 5p brt grn, gold & brn .65 .25
39 A8 9p rose red, gold & brown 1.90 1.65
40 A8 1sh6p brt purple, gold & brown 3.50 2.50
Nos. 37-40 (4) 6.60 4.62

Decimal Currency Issue
Types of 1969
"p" instead of "d"

Designs: 1/2p, Castle Cornet and Edward the Confessor. 1p, 5p, Map of Bailiwick and William the Conqueror. 1 1/2p, Martello Tower and Henry II. 2p, Guernsey lily and Henry V. 2 1/2p, Arms of Guernsey and Elizabeth I. 3p, Arms of Alderney and Edward III. 3 1/2p, Guernsey lily and Elizabeth I. 4p, Arms of Sark and King John. 6p, Arms of Alderney and Charles II. 7 1/2p, Arms of Guernsey and Queen Victoria. 9p, Arms of Sark and George III. 10p, Martello Tower and King John. 20p, Creux Harbor. 50p, Braye Harbor.

1971 Photo. *Perf. 14 1/2x14*
41 A3 1/2p magenta & blk .15 .15
a. Booklet pane of 1 .15
42 A3 1p ultra & black .15 .15
43 A3 1 1/2p bister & blk .15 .15
44 A3 2p yel green & multi .15 .15
a. Booklet pane of 1 .15
45 A3 2 1/2p vio blue & multi .15 .15
a. Booklet pane of 1 .15
46 A3 3p dp orange & multi .18 .18
47 A3 3 1/2p magenta & multi .20 .20
48 A3 4p dk blue & multi .22 .22
49 A3 5p brt green & multi .28 .28
50 A3 6p dk green & multi .35 .35
51 A3 7 1/2p brn olive & multi .45 .45
52 A3 9p plum & multi 1.10 1.10
53 A3 10p purple & black 1.10 1.10

Perf. 13
54 A4 20p dk red & multi .90 .90
55 A4 50p multicolored 2.50 2.50
Nos. 41-55 (15) 8.03 8.03

Issue dates: #53-55, Jan. 6; others Feb. 15.

Thomas de la Rue, Hong Kong No. 1 — A9

Thomas de la Rue and: 2 1/2p, GB No. 22. 4p, Italy No. 26. 7 1/2p, US Confederate States No. 6.

1971, June 2 Engr. *Perf. 14x13 1/2*
56 A9 2p brown .45 .22
57 A9 2 1/2p carmine .50 .28
58 A9 4p dark green 4.75 2.00
59 A9 7 1/2p violet blue 6.00 2.75
Nos. 56-59 (4) 11.70 5.25

Thomas de la Rue (1793-1866), founder of Thomas de la Rue & Co., Ltd., security printers.

Ebenezer Methodist Church — A10

Historic Churches of Guernsey: 2 1/2p, St. Pierre du Bois. 5p, St. Joseph's, vert. 7 1/2p, St. Philippe de Torteval, vert.

1971, Oct. 27 Photo. *Perf. 11 1/2*
60 A10 2p green, sil & blk .55 .35
61 A10 2 1/2p blue, sil & blk .65 .40
62 A10 5p pur, silver & blk 2.25 1.65
63 A10 7 1/2p red, silver & blk 4.00 3.25
Nos. 60-63 (4) 7.45 5.65

Christmas 1971.

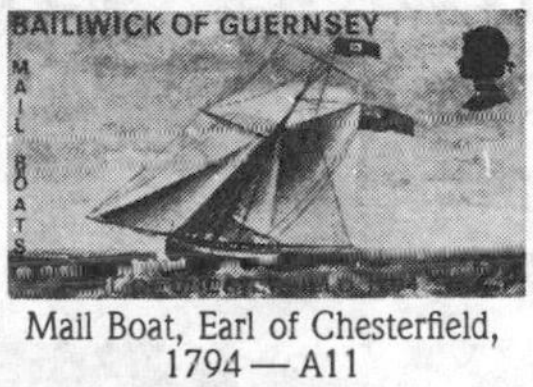

Mail Boat, Earl of Chesterfield, 1794 — A11

1972, Feb. 10 Photo. *Perf. 11 1/2*
64 A11 2p *shown* .16 .16
65 A11 2 1/2p *Dasher, 1827* .18 .18
66 A11 7 1/2p *Ibex, 1891* .75 .75
67 A11 9p *Alberta, 1900* 1.25 1.25
Nos. 64-67 (4) 2.34 2.34

See Nos. 77-80.

Guernsey Bull — A12

1972, May 22 Photo. *Perf. 11 1/2*
68 A12 5p brown & multi 1.25 .90

Guernsey Breeders, 2nd World Conf. For similar designs see Nos. 33-36.

Wild Flowers — A13

1972, May 24
69 A13 2p Sorrel .15 .15
70 A13 2 1/2p Orchis maculata, vert. .16 .15
71 A13 7 1/2p Carpobrotus edulis .80 .75
72 A13 9p Pimpernel, vert. 1.00 .80
Nos. 69-72 (4) 2.11 1.85

Angels, St. Martin's Church — A14

Stained Glass Windows from Guernsey Churches: 2½p, Virgin and Child, St. André's. 7½p, Virgin Mary, St. Sampson's. 9p, Christ Victorious, St. Pierre's.

1972, Nov. 20   Photo.   Perf. 11½

73	A14	2p brick red & multi	.15	.15
74	A14	2½p lt violet & multi	.15	.15
75	A14	7½p yellow & multi	.55	.55
76	A14	9p lt green & multi	.75	.75
		Nos. 73-76 (4)	1.60	1.60

Christmas 1972 and for the 25th anniv. of the marriage of Queen Elizabeth II and Prince Philip.

Mail Boat Type of 1972

1973, Mar. 9   Photo.   Perf. 11½

77	A11	2½p St. Julien, 1925	.15	.15
78	A11	3p Isle of Sark, 1932	.15	.15
79	A11	7½p St. Patrick, 1947	.65	.65
80	A11	9p Sarnia, 1961	.65	.65
		Nos. 77-80 (4)	1.60	1.60

No. 78 is incorrectly inscribed "Isle of Guernsey 1930."

Supermarine Sea Eagle — A15

Airplanes: 3p, Westland Wessex. 5p, De Havilland Rapide. 7½p, Douglas Dakota. 9p, Vickers Viscount.

1973, July 4   Photo.   Perf. 11½

81	A15	2½p multicolored	.15	.15
82	A15	3p multicolored	.15	.15
83	A15	5p multicolored	.22	.22
84	A15	7½p multicolored	.45	.45
85	A15	9p multicolored	.55	.55
		Nos. 81-85 (5)	1.52	1.52

50th anniversary of air service to Guernsey.

The Good Shepherd, St. Michel du Valle — A16

Stained-glass Windows from Guernsey Churches: 3p, Jesus preaching, St. Marie du Castel. 7½p, St. Dominic, Notre Dame du Rosaire. 20p, Virgin and Child, St. Sauveur.

1973, Oct. 24   Photo.   Perf. 11½

86	A16	2½p salmon & multi	.15	.15
87	A16	3p blue & multi	.15	.15
88	A16	7½p yellow & multi	.22	.22
89	A16	20p multicolored	.55	.55
		Nos. 86-89 (4)	1.07	1.07

Christmas 1973.

Princess Anne and Mark Phillips A17

1973, Nov. 14

90	A17	25p blue & multi	.80	.80

Wedding of Princess Anne and Capt. Mark Phillips, Nov. 14, 1973.

"John Lockett," 1875 — A18

Guernsey Lifeboats: 3p, "Arthur Lionel," 1875. 8p, "Euphrosyne Kendal," 1954. 10p, "Arum," 1972.

1974, Jan. 15   Photo.   Perf. 11½
Granite Paper

91	A18	2½p multicolored	.15	.15
92	A18	3p multicolored	.15	.15
93	A18	8p multicolored	.30	.30
94	A18	10p multicolored	.35	.35
		Nos. 91-94 (4)	.95	.95

Sesqui. of Royal Natl. Lifeboat Institution.

A19

Militia
A20

1974-76   Photo.   Perf. 11½
Granite Paper (Nos. 95-107)

95	A19	½p 1815	.15	.15
a.		Bklt. pane of 8 (5 #95, 3 #99)	.40	
b.		Bklt. pane of 16 (4 #95, 6 #99 and 6 #100)	1.25	
96	A19	1p 1825	.15	.15
a.		Bklt. pane of 8 (4 #96, #100, 2 #102, #102A) ('77)	1.00	
b.		Pane of 4 (#96, 2 #98, #102A) ('78)	.80	
97	A19	1½p 1787	.15	.15
98	A19	2p 1815	.15	.15
99	A19	2½p Royal, 1868	.15	.15
100	A19	3p Royal, 1895	.15	.15
101	A19	3½p Royal, 1867	.15	.15
102	A19	4p 1822	.15	.15
102A	A19	5p Royal, 1895	.35	.35
103	A19	5½p Royal, 1833	.18	.18
104	A19	6p Royal, 1832	.20	.20
104A	A19	7p 1822	.40	.40
105	A19	8p Royal, 1868	.25	.25
106	A19	9p 1785	.28	.28
107	A19	10p 1824	.30	.30

Perf. 13x13½, 13½x13

108	A20	20p Royal, 1848, vert.	.55	.55
109	A20	50p Royal, 1868, vert.	1.25	1.25
110	A20	£1 1814	2.50	2.50
		Nos. 95-110 (18)	7.46	7.46

Issued: #95-107, Apr. 2, 1974; #108-110, Apr. 1, 1975; #102A, 104A, May 29, 1976.
Stamps in booklet panes are from special sheets of 80 (two 8x5 panes) which were sold separately.

Bailiwick Seal and UPU Emblem — A21

UPU Cent.: 3p, Map of Guernsey. 8p, UPU Headquarters, Bern, flag of Guernsey. 10p, Legislative Chamber, Parliament.

1974, June 11   Photo.   Perf. 11½
Granite Paper

111	A21	2½p multicolored	.15	.15
112	A21	3p ultra & multi	.15	.15
113	A21	8p multicolored	.28	.28
114	A21	10p multicolored	.35	.35
		Nos. 111-114 (4)	.93	.93

Cradle Rock, by Renoir A22

Paintings by Renoir: 5½p, Moulin-Huet Bay. 8p, Woman at the Shore, vert. 10p, Self-portrait, vert.

1974, Sept. 21   Photo.   Perf. 13

115	A22	3p multicolored	.15	.15
116	A22	5½p multicolored	.15	.15
117	A22	8p multicolored	.22	.20
118	A22	10p multicolored	.35	.32
		Nos. 115-118 (4)	.87	.82

Pierre Auguste Renoir (1841-1919), who painted pictures shown on Nos. 115-117 while visiting Guernsey.

Guernsey Spleenwort — A23

Designs: Guernsey ferns.

1975, Jan. 7   Photo.   Perf. 11½

119	A23	3½p shown	.15	.15
120	A23	4p Sand quillwort	.15	.15
121	A23	8p Guernsey fern	.24	.24
122	A23	10p Least adder's tongue	.30	.30
		Nos. 119-122 (4)	.84	.84

Hauteville, Hugo's House — A24

Victor Hugo Statue, Candie Gardens — A25

Designs: 8p, United Europe Oak, Hauteville (planted by Hugo). 10p, Departure for the Hunt, Aubusson tapestry, Hauteville.

1975, June 6   Photo.   Perf. 11½
Granite Paper

123	A24	3½p dull yel & multi	.15	.15
124	A25	4p lt blue & multi	.15	.15
125	A25	8p yel green & multi	.22	.22
126	A24	10p multicolored	.30	.30
a.		Souvenir sheet of 4, #123-126	1.00	1.00
		Nos. 123-126 (4)	.82	.82

Victor Hugo (1802-85), French writer, political exile in Guernsey (1855-70).

Arms and Map of Guernsey — A26

Designs (Globe with Map of Bailiwick): 6p, Flag of Guernsey. 10p, Flag of Guernsey and arms of Alderney, horiz. 12p, Flag of Guernsey and arms of Sark, horiz.

1975, Oct. 7   Photo.   Perf. 13½

127	A26	4p olive green & multi	.15	.15
128	A26	6p rose lilac & multi	.15	.15
129	A26	10p brt green & multi	.30	.30
130	A26	12p orange & multi	.32	.32
		Nos. 127-130 (4)	.92	.92

Christmas 1975.

Lighthouses — A27

1976, Feb. 10   Photo.   Perf. 11½
Granite Paper

131	A27	4p Les Hanois	.15	.15
132	A27	6p Les Casquets	.16	.16
133	A27	11p Quesnard, Alderney	.35	.35
134	A27	13p Point Robert, Sark	.45	.45
		Nos. 131-134 (4)	1.11	1.11

Guernsey Milk Can — A28

Europa: 25p, Silver christening cup.

1976, May 29   Photo.   Perf. 11½
Granite Paper

135	A28	10p multicolored	.42	.35
136	A28	25p multicolored	.80	.70

Sheets of 9.

Pine Forest, Guernsey — A29

Guernsey Views: 7p, Herm Harbor and Jethou. 11p, Grande Grave Bay, Sark Cliffs, vert. 13p, Trois Vaux Bay, Alderney Cliffs, vert.

1976, Aug. 3   Photo.   Perf. 11½
Granite Paper

137	A29	5p multicolored	.15	.15
138	A29	7p multicolored	.20	.20
139	A29	11p multicolored	.32	.32
140	A29	13p multicolored	.40	.40
		Nos. 137-140 (4)	1.07	1.07

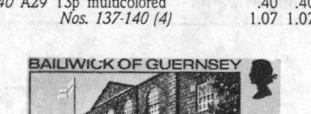

Royal Court House, Guernsey — A30

Christmas (Buildings in the Bailiwick): 7p, Elizabeth College, Guernsey. 11p, La Seigneurie, Sark. 13p, Island Hall, Alderney.

1976, Oct. 14   Photo.   Perf. 11½
Granite Paper

141	A30	5p multicolored	.15	.15
142	A30	7p multicolored	.18	.18
143	A30	11p multicolored	.32	.32
144	A30	13p multicolored	.40	.40
		Nos. 141-144 (4)	1.05	1.05

Guernsey stamps can be mounted in the Scott Channel Islands album.

Elizabeth II with Order of the Garter — A31

Design: 7p, Queen Elizabeth II.

1977, Feb. 8   Photo.   Perf. 12x11½
145 A31 7p blue & multi .20 .20
146 A31 35p purple & multi .90 .90

25th anniv. of the reign of Elizabeth II.

Talbots Valley A32

Design: 25p, Fields and hedges, Talbots Valley.

1977, May 17   Photo.   Perf. 11½
Granite Paper
147 A32 7p multicolored .15 .15
148 A32 25p multicolored .65 .65

Megalithic Tomb, Le Catioroc — A33

Prehistoric monuments: 5p, Menhir (statue), Castel, vert. 11p, Cist (tomb), Alderney. 13p, Menhir, St. Martin, vert.

1977, Aug. 2   Photo.   Perf. 11½
149 A33 5p multicolored .15 .15
150 A33 7p multicolored .18 .18
151 A33 11p multicolored .30 .30
152 A33 13p multicolored .35 .35
   Nos. 149-152 (4) .98 .98

Mobile First Aid Unit A34

Designs: 7p, Mobile radar and rescue coordination unit, for ships in distress. 11p, Marine ambulance "Flying Christine II," vert. 13p, Cliff rescue, vert.

1977, Oct. 25   Photo.   Perf. 11½
153 A34 5p multicolored .15 .15
154 A34 7p multicolored .18 .18
155 A34 11p multicolored .30 .30
156 A34 13p multicolored .35 .35
   Nos. 153-156 (4) .98 .98

St. John Ambulance Assoc. cent. (in GB).

View from Clifton, c. 1830 A35

19th Century Prints, Guernsey: 7p, Market Square, c. 1838. 11p, Petit-Bo Bay, c. 1839. 13p, The Quay, c. 1830.

1978, Feb. 7   Litho.   Perf. 14x13½
157 A35 5p pale green & black .15 .15
158 A35 7p buff & black .20 .20
159 A35 11p pink & black .38 .38
160 A35 13p lt violet & black .38 .38
   Nos. 157-160 (4) 1.11 1.11

See Nos. 236-239.

Memorial to Seamen of Ship Prosperity; Sank 1974 — A36

Europa: 7p, Victoria monument, vert.

1978, May 2   Litho.   Perf. 14½
161 A36 5p multicolored .16 .16
162 A36 7p multicolored .25 .25

Elizabeth II — A37

1978, May 2   Photo.   Perf. 11½
163 A37 20p ultra & black .60 .60

25th anniv. of coronation of Elizabeth II.

Inscribed: "VISIT OF/H.M. THE QUEEN AND/H.R.H. THE DUKE OF EDINBURGH/JUNE 28-29, 1978"

1978, June 28
164 A37 7p emerald & black .30 .30

Gannet A38

Birds: 7p, Firecrest. 11p, Dartford warbler. 13p, Spotted redshank.

1978, Aug. 29   Photo.   Perf. 11½
165 A38 5p multicolored .15 .15
166 A38 7p multicolored .20 .20
167 A38 11p multicolored .35 .35
168 A38 13p multicolored .38 .38
   Nos. 165-168 (4) 1.08 1.08

Solanum — A39

Christmas: 7p, Christmas rose. 11p, Holly, vert. 13p, Mistletoe, vert.

1978, Oct. 31   Photo.   Perf. 11½
169 A39 5p multicolored .15 .15
170 A39 7p multicolored .20 .20
171 A39 11p multicolored .35 .35
172 A39 13p multicolored .38 .38
   Nos. 169-172 (4) 1.08 1.08

1 Double, 1930 — A40

1979, Feb. 13
Granite Paper
173 A40 ½p 1 double, 1930 .15 .15
174 A40 1p 2 doubles, 1899 .15 .15
175 A40 2p 4 doubles, 1902 .15 .15
176 A40 4p 8 doubles, 1959 .15 .15
177 A40 5p 3 pence, 1956 .15 .15
178 A40 6p 5 new pence, 1968 .15 .15
179 A40 7p 50 new pence, 1969 .20 .20
180 A40 8p 10 new pence, 1970 .20 .20
181 A40 9p ½ new penny, 1971 .25 .25
182 A40 10p 1 new penny, 1971 .25 .25
183 A40 11p 2 new pence, 1971 .30 .30
184 A40 12p 1 penny, 1977 .30 .30

185 A40 13p 2 pence, 1977 .35 .35
186 A40 14p 5 pence, 1977 .35 .35
187 A40 15p 10 pence, 1977 .40 .40
188 A40 20p 25 pence, 1977 .55 .55
   Nos. 173-188 (16) 4.05 4.05
   Set value 3.75 3.75

No. 177 is dark brown, No. 182, green & bronze. See Nos. 198B-203A.
Booklets containing 5 each #176, 181, 185 and 2 #176, 3 #181, 5 #185 exist produced from sheets of 30 (two 3x5 panes) and 20 (two 2x5 panes).

Oldest Pillar Box, 1853 Cancel, Truck — A41

Europa: 8p, Telephone, 1897, and telex machine.

1979, May 8   Photo.   Perf. 11½
189 A41 6p multicolored .25 .25
190 A41 8p multicolored .25 .25

Steam Tram, 1879 A42

Public Transportation: 8p, Electric tram, 1896. 11p, Autobus, 1911. 13p, Autobus, 1979.

1979, Aug. 7   Photo.   Perf. 11½
191 A42 6p multicolored .15 .15
192 A42 8p multicolored .24 .24
193 A42 11p multicolored .30 .30
194 A42 13p multicolored .38 .38
   Nos. 191-194 (4) 1.07 1.07

Centenary of public transportation.

Postal Bureau and Headquarters — A43

Designs: 8p, Mail and telegram deliverymen. 13p, Parcel trucks. 15p, Post Office philatelic room.

1979, Oct. 1   Photo.   Perf. 11½
195 A43 6p multicolored .15 .15
196 A43 8p multicolored .18 .18
197 A43 13p multicolored .30 .30
198 A43 15p multicolored .35 .35
   a. Souvenir sheet of 4, Nos. 195-198 1.10 1.10
   Nos. 195-198 (4) .98 .98

Guernsey PO, 10th anniv.; Christmas 1979.

Coin Type of 1979

Designs: 10p, like No. 182. 11½p, ½ pence, 1979. 50p, Battle of Hastings coin, 1966. £1, Queen Elizabeth II 25th anniv., 1977. £2, Queen Elizabeth II 25th wedding anniv., 1972, horiz. £5, Official seal.

1980-81   Photo.   Perf. 11½
198B A40 5p orange brown & multi .15 .15
199 A40 10p orange & bronze .30 .30
200 A40 11½p red & bronze .35 .35

Size: 26x45, 45x26mm
201 A40 50p red org & sil 1.50 1.50
202 A40 £1 green & sil 2.25 2.25
203 A40 £2 blue & silver 4.50 4.50
203A A40 £5 multi ('81) 12.50 12.50
   Nos. 198B-203A (7) 21.55 21.55

No. 177 is dark brown. Booklets containing 5 each #180, 198B, 185 and 4 #180, 5 #198B, 1 #185 exist produced from sheets of 30 (three 2x5 panes or two 3x5 panes).
Issue dates: £5, May 22, others, Feb. 5.

Policewoman Helping Child — A44

Guernsey Police Force, 60th Anniv.: 15p, Policeman on motorcycle. 17½p, Police dog and officer.

1980, May 6   Litho.   Perf. 14
204 A44 7p multicolored .20 .20
205 A44 15p multicolored .42 .42
206 A44 17½p multicolored .48 .48
   Nos. 204-206 (3) 1.10 1.10

Major Gen. John Gaspard Le Marchant — A45

Europa: 13½p, Admiral James Lord de Saumarez (1757-1836).

1980, May 6   Photo.   Perf. 11½
Granite Paper
207 A45 10p multicolored .25 .25
208 A45 13½p multicolored .35 .35

Guernsey Golden Goat — A46

Designs: Various Guernsey golden goats.

1980, Aug. 5   Photo.   Perf. 13
209 A46 7p multicolored .20 .20
210 A46 10p multicolored .30 .30
211 A46 15p multicolored .45 .45
212 A46 17½p multicolored .52 .52
   Nos. 209-212 (4) 1.47 1.47

Sark Cottage, by Peter Le Lievre, 1847 — A47

Christmas 1980 (Le Lievre Paintings): 10p, Moulin Huet, 1850. 13½p, Boats at Sea, 1850. 15p, Cow Lane, 1852, vert. 17½p, Portrait, by Le Lievre's sister, vert.

1980, Nov. 15   Photo.   Perf. 12
Granite Paper
213 A47 7p multicolored .18 .18
214 A47 10p multicolored .25 .25
215 A47 13½p multicolored .35 .35
216 A47 15p multicolored .40 .40
217 A47 17½p multicolored .45 .45
   Nos. 213-217 (5) 1.63 1.63

Common Blue A48

1981, Feb. 24   Photo.   Perf. 14½
218 A48 8p shown .24 .24
219 A48 12p Red Admiral .35 .35
220 A48 22p Small Tortoiseshell .65 .65
221 A48 25p Wall Brown .75 .75
   Nos. 218-221 (4) 1.99 1.99

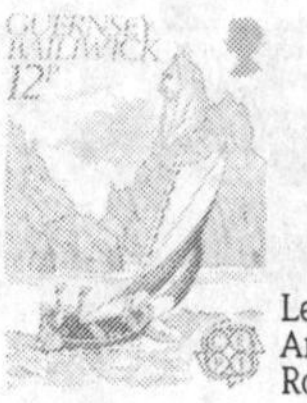

Le Petit Bonhomme Andriou (Head-shaped Rock) — A49

1981, May 22 Litho. *Perf. 14½*

222 A49 12p shown .32 .32
223 A49 18p Guernsey lily .48 .48

Europa.

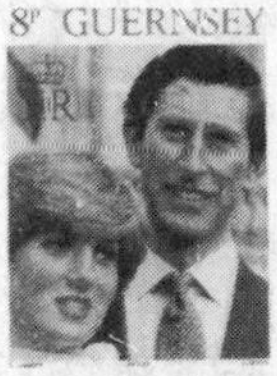

Prince Charles and Lady Diana — A50

Royal Wedding: a, Charles. c, Diana.

1981, July 29 Litho. *Perf. 14½x15*

224 Strip of 3 .70 .70
a.-c. A50 8p any single .22 .22
225 Strip of 3 1.00 1.00
a.-c. A50 12p any single .30 .30

Size: 49x32mm

226 A50 25p Royal family .70 .70
a. Souv. sheet, #224-226, perf. 14x14½ 2.50 2.50
Nos. 224-226 (3) 2.40 2.40

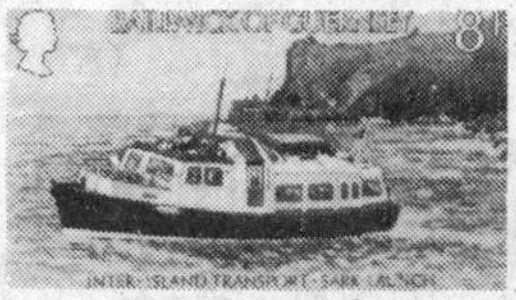

Sark Launch A51

Designs: Interisland transportation.

1981, Aug. 25 Photo. *Perf. 11½*

Granite Paper

227 A51 8p shown .22 .22
228 A51 12p Trislander plane .35 .35
229 A51 18p Hydrofoil .52 .52
230 A51 22p Herm catamaran .65 .65
231 A51 25p Alderney coaster .70 .70
Nos. 227-231 (5) 2.44 2.44

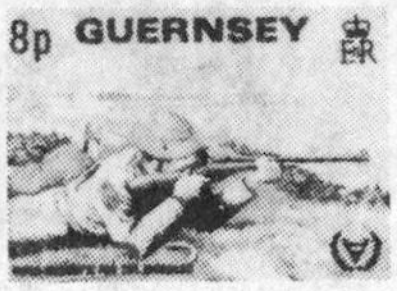

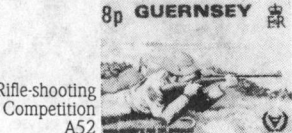

Rifle-shooting Competition A52

1981, Nov. 17 Litho. *Perf. 14*

232 A52 8p shown .22 .22
233 A52 12p Riding .35 .35
234 A52 22p Swimming .60 .60
235 A52 25p Electronics workers .70 .70
Nos. 232-235 (4) 1.87 1.87

Intl. Year of the Disabled.

Print Type of 1978

1982, Feb. 2 Litho. & Engr.

236 A35 8p Jethou .22 .22
237 A35 12p Fermain Bay .35 .35
238 A35 22p The Terres .60 .60
239 A35 25p St. Pierre Port .70 .70
Nos. 236-239 (4) 1.87 1.87

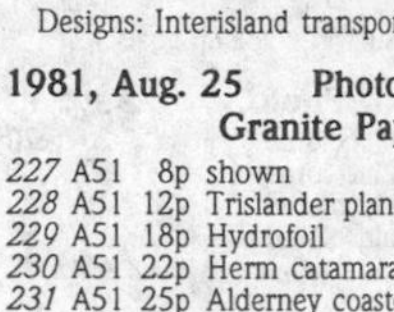

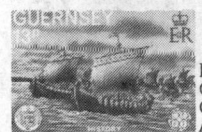

La Societe Guernesiaise Centenary A53

Society Emblem and Activities: 8p, Sir Edgar MacCulloch, founding president. 13p, William the Conqueror's fleet, Battle at Hastings (history). 20p, Sir James Saumarez's Crescent rescued from French fleet (history). 24p, Dragonfly (entomology). 26p, Vale Parish Church bird sanctuary (ornithology). 29p, Samian bowl, King's Road excavation (archaeology). 13p and 20p show CEPT (Europa) emblem.

1982, Apr. 28 Photo. *Perf. 11½*

Granite Paper

240 A53 8p multicolored .24 .24
241 A53 13p multicolored .40 .40
242 A53 20p multicolored .60 .60
243 A53 24p multicolored .75 .75
244 A53 26p multicolored .75 .75
245 A53 29p multicolored .80 .80
Nos. 240-245 (6) 3.54 3.54

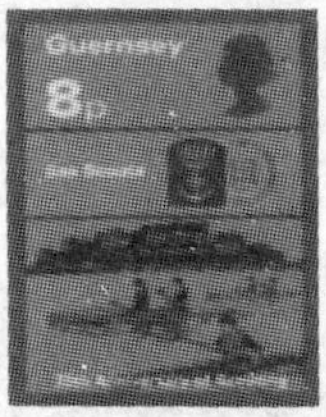

Scouting Year — A54

1982, July 13 Litho. *Perf. 14½*

246 A54 8p Sea scouts, Castle Cornet, St. Peter Port .24 .24
247 A54 13p Boy scouts building bridge .40 .40
248 A54 26p Cub scouts parading .75 .75
249 A54 29p Air scouts reading chart .95 .95
Nos. 246-249 (4) 2.34 2.34

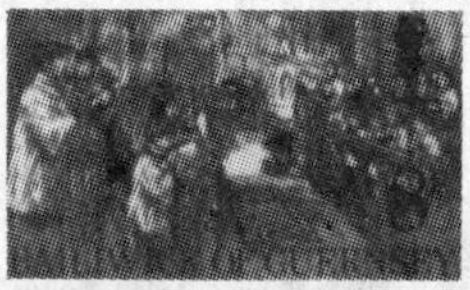

Christmas 1982 A55

1982, Oct. 12 Photo. *Perf. 14½*

250 A55 8p Midnight mass, St. Peter Port Church .22 .22
251 A55 13p Exchanging presents .35 .35
252 A55 24p Dinner .65 .65
253 A55 26p Exchanging cards .70 .70
254 A55 29p Watching Queen's TV greeting .90 .90
Nos. 250-254 (5) 2.82 2.82

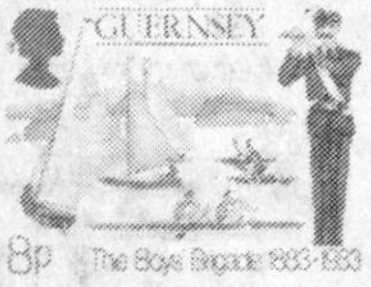

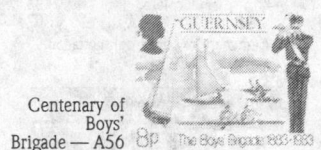

Centenary of Boys' Brigade — A56

Designs: Various brigade activities.

1983, Jan. 18 *Perf. 14*

255 A56 8p multicolored .28 .28
256 A56 13p multicolored .45 .45
257 A56 24p multicolored .80 .80
258 A56 26p multicolored .85 .85
259 A56 29p multicolored 1.10 1.10
Nos. 255-259 (5) 3.48 3.48

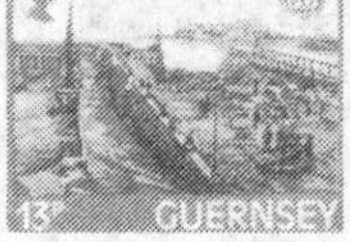

Europa 1983 — A57

Views of St. Peter Port Harbor. Stamps of same denomination se-tenant.

1983, Mar. 14 Photo. *Perf. 11½*

Granite Paper

260 A57 13p multicolored .40 .40
261 A57 13p multicolored .40 .40
262 A57 20p multicolored .60 .60
263 A57 20p multicolored .60 .60
Nos. 260-263 (4) 2.00 2.00

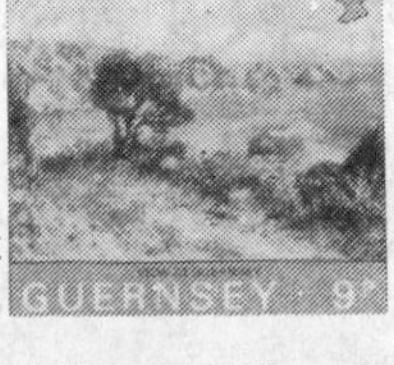

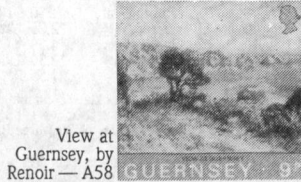

View at Guernsey, by Renoir — A58

Centenary of Renoir's Visit: 13p, Children at the Seashore (26x39mm). 26p, Marine Guernsey. 28p, Moulin Huet Bay through the Trees. 31p, Fog in Guernsey.

Perf. 12, 11½x12 (13p)

1983, Sept. 6 Photo.

Granite Paper

264 A58 9p multicolored .28 .28
265 A58 13p multicolored .40 .40
266 A58 26p multicolored .80 .80
267 A58 28p multicolored .85 .85
268 A58 31p multicolored .95 .95
Nos. 264-268 (5) 3.28 3.28

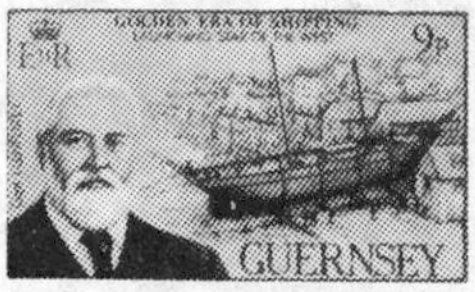

Star of the West, 1869 Merchant Ship, Capt. J.G. Lenfestey A59

1983, Nov. 15 Photo. *Perf. 14½*

269 A59 9p Launching .28 .28
270 A59 13p Leaving St. Peter Port .40 .40
271 A59 26p Rio Grande Bar .80 .80
272 A59 28p St. Lucia .85 .85
273 A59 31p Voyage Map .95 .95
Nos. 269-273 (5) 3.28 3.28

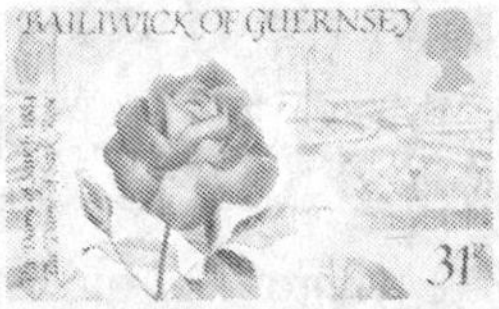

Dame of Sark (Sibyl Hathaway, 1884-1974) — A60

Biographical Scenes: 9p, Portrait, La Seigneurie (residence). 13p, German occupation, 1940-45. 26p, Royal visit, 1957. 28p, Chief Pleas (parliament). 31p, Dame of Sark rose.

1984, Feb. 7 Litho. *Perf. 14½*

274 A60 9p multicolored .28 .28
275 A60 13p multicolored .40 .40
276 A60 26p multicolored .80 .80
277 A60 28p multicolored .85 .85
278 A60 31p multicolored .95 .95
Nos. 274-278 (5) 3.28 3.28

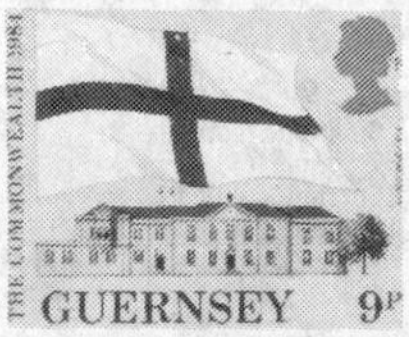

Links with the Commonwealth — A61

Designs: 9p, Flag of Guernsey, Royal Court. 31p, Union Jack, Castle Cornet.

1984, Apr. 10 Litho. *Perf. 14½*

279 A61 9p multicolored .28 .28
280 A61 31p multicolored .95 .95

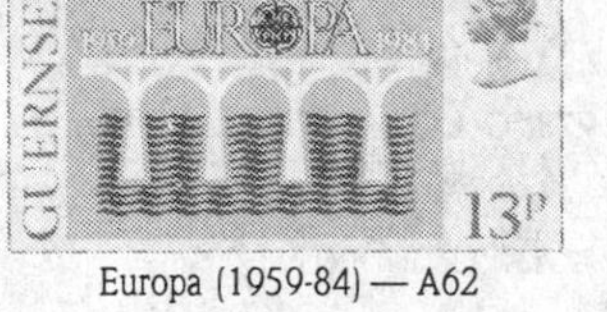

Europa (1959-84) — A62

1984, Apr. 10 *Perf. 15*

281 A62 13p multicolored .50 .50
282 A62 20½p multicolored .75 .75

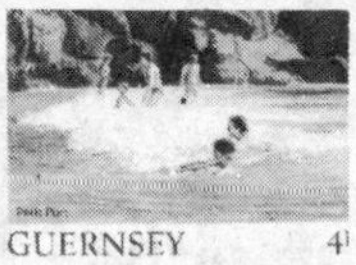

Petit Port — A63

Perf. 15x14½, 14½x15

1984-85 Litho.

283 A63 1p Little Chapel, vert. ('85) .15 .15
284 A63 2p Ft. Grey ('85) .15 .15
285 A63 3p St. Apolline Chapel, vert. .15 .15
286 A63 4p shown .15 .15
287 A63 5p Little Russel ('85) .15 .15
288 A63 6p The Harbour, Herm ('85) .15 .15
289 A63 7p Saints ('85) .16 .16
290 A63 8p St. Saviour, vert. ('85) .20 .20
291 A63 9p Cambridge Berth .22 .22
292 A63 10p Belvoir, Herm .25 .25
a. Min. sheet, 2 2p, 4 4p, 2 5p, 2 10p 1.00
293 A63 11p La Seigneurie, Sark ('85) .25 .25
294 A63 13p St. Saviour's Reservoir .32 .32
a. Min. sheet, 2 4p, 3 9p, 5 13p 2.50
b. Min. sheet, 5 each 4p, 9p, 13p 3.25
295 A63 14p St. Peter Port, vert. .35 .35
a. Min. sheet, 4 9p, 6 14p 3.00
b. Min. sheet, 2 9p, 8 14p 3.50
c. Min. sheet, 5 10p, 5 14p 3.00
296 A63 15p Havelet, vert. ('85) .38 .38
a. Min. sheet, 3p, 2 4p, 4 11p, 3 15p 2.75
b. Min. sheet, 5 each 11p, 15p 3.25
297 A63 20p La Coupee, Sark .52 .52
a. Min. sheet, 4 6p, 4 14p, 2 20p 3.05
b. Min. sheet, 5 14p, 5 20p 4.35
298 A63 30p Grandes Rocques ('85) .75 .75
299 A63 40p St. Torteval Church, vert. 1.10 1.10
300 A63 50p Bordeaux 1.25 1.25
301 A63 £1 Albecq 2.50 2.50
302 A63 £2 L'Ancresse ('85) 4.75 4.75
Nos. 283-302 (20) 13.90 13.90

Issued: 1p, 2p, 5p, 6p, 7p, 8p, 11p, 15p, 30p, £2, 7/23/84; 3p, 4p, 9p, 10p, 13p, 14p, 20p, 40p, 50p, £1, 9/18/84; #292a, 12/2/85; #294a-294b, 9/18/84; #295a-295b, 3/19/85; #295c, 4/1/86; #296a-296b, 3/30/87; #297a-297b, 2/28/89.

Miniature sheets sold folded and unattached in booklet covers.

See Nos. 372-378, 453-454.

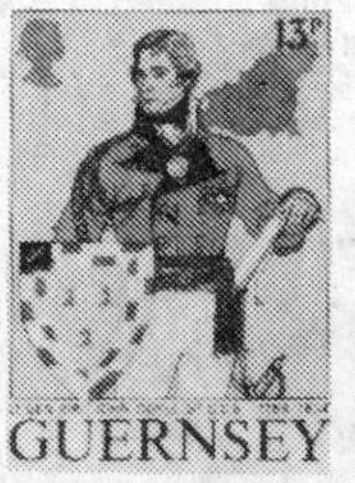

Lieutenant-General John Doyle (1756-1834) A64

Designs: 13p, Portrait by James Ramsey, 1817. 29p, American War of Independence battle. 31p, Land fill, Grand Havre Bay. 39p, Ship approaching Casquets Reef, 1811. 29p, 31p, 39p horiz.

1984, Nov. 20 Photo. *Perf. 11½*

303 A64 13p multicolored .40 .40
304 A64 29p multicolored .95 .95
305 A64 31p multicolored 1.05 1.05
306 A64 34p multicolored 1.10 1.10
Nos. 303-306 (4) 3.50 3.50

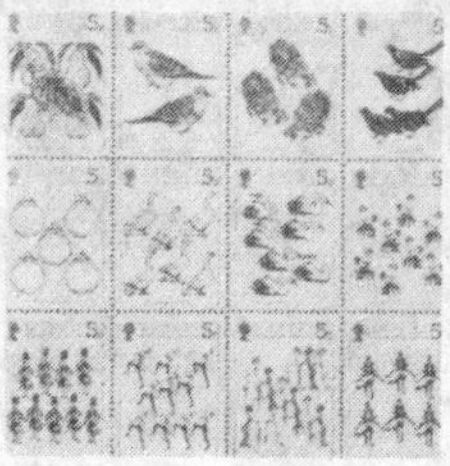

Christmas 1984 A65

Twelve Days of Christmas: a, Partridge in a Pear Tree. b, 2 Turtle Doves. c, 3 French Hens. d, 4 Colly Birds. e, 5 Golden Rings. f, 6 Geese-a-Laying. g, 7 Swans a-Swimming. h, 8 Maids a-Milking. i, 9 Drummers Drumming. j, 10 Pipers Piping. k, 11 Ladies Dancing. l, 12 Lords a-Leaping. Illustration reduced.

1984, Nov. 20 Litho. *Perf. 14½*

307 A65 Sheet of 12 2.25 2.25
a.-l. 5p any single .18 .18

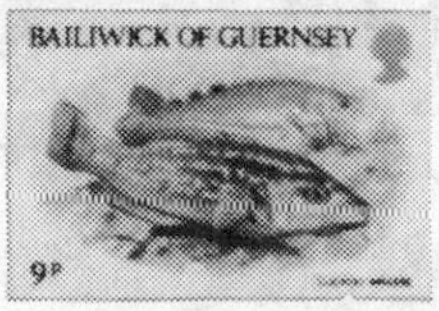

Indigenous Fish — A66

1985, Jan. 22 Photo. *Perf. 12*

308 A66 9p Cockoo Wrasse .35 .35
309 A66 13p Red Gurnard .55 .55
310 A66 29p Red Mullet 1.25 1.25
311 A66 31p Mackerel 1.40 1.40
312 A66 34p Sunfish 1.65 1.65
Nos. 308-312 (5) 5.20 5.20

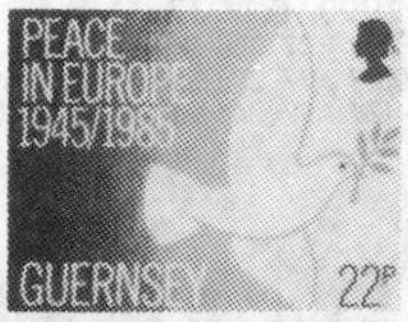

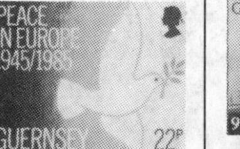

Liberation from German Forces, 40th Anniv. — A67

1985, May 9 Litho. *Perf. 14x14½*

313 A67 22p Peace dove .80 .80

Celebrating the end of the war in Europe (VE-Day).

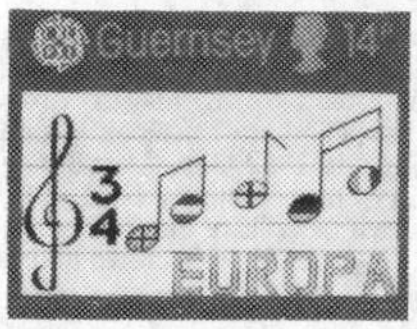

Europa 1985 — A68

Designs: 14p, Musical staff, flags of Great Britain, Netherlands, Germany, Italy, Cross of St. George. 22p, Music, cello, French horn.

1985, May 14 Litho. *Perf. 14½*

314 A68 14p multicolored .45 .45
315 A68 22p multicolored .75 .75

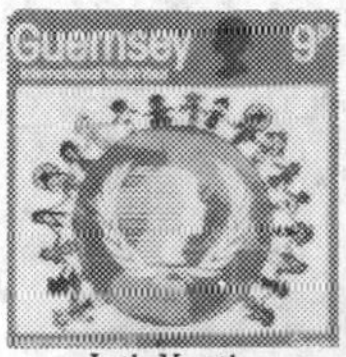

Intl. Youth Year — A69

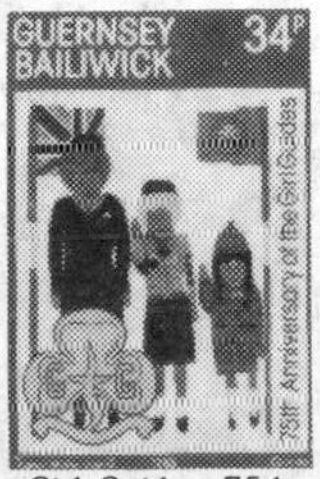

Girl Guides, 75th Anniv. — A70

1985, May 14 Litho. *Perf. 14*

316 A69 9p IYY emblem, circle of children .30 .30
317 A69 31p Girl Guides in camp .95 .95

Children's drawings.

1985, May 14 Litho. *Perf. 14*

318 A70 34p Leader, guide and brownie 1.25 1.25

Child's drawing.

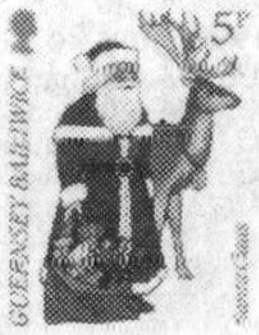

Christmas 1985 — A71

Religious and folk figures: a, Santa Claus. b, Lussibruden. c, Balthasar. d, St. Nicholas. e, La Befana. f, Julenisse. g, Christkind. h, King Wenceslas. i, Shepherd of Les Baux. j, Caspar. k, Baboushka. l, Melchior.

1985, Nov. 19 Litho. *Perf. 12½*

Granite Paper

319 Sheet of 12 *3.75 3.75*
a.-l. A71 5p any single .30 .30

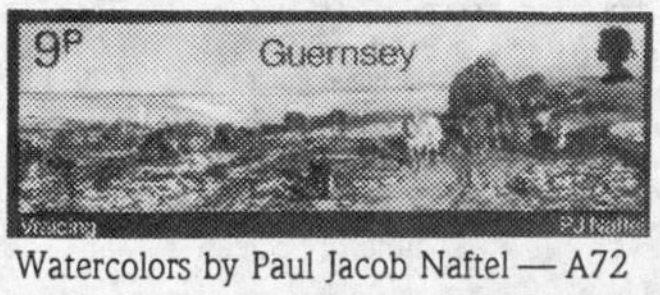

Watercolors by Paul Jacob Naftel — A72

1985, Nov. 19 *Perf. 15x14½*

320 A72 9p Vraicing .30 .30
321 A72 14p Castle Cornet .45 .45
322 A72 22p Rocquaine Bay .70 .70
323 A72 31p Little Russel 1.00 1.00
324 A72 34p Seaweed Gatherers 1.25 1.25
Nos. 320-324 (5) 3.70 3.70

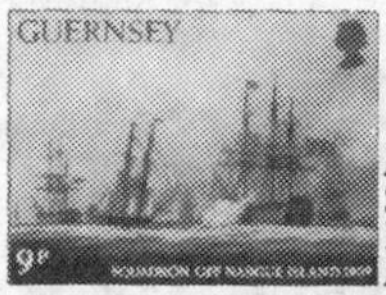

Adm. Lord De Saumarez, 150th Death Anniv. — A73

Designs: 9p, Squadron off Nargue Is., 1809. 14p, Battle of the Nile, 1798. 29p, Battle of St. Vincent, 1797. 31p, HMS Crescent off Cherbourg, 1793. 34p, Battle of the Saints, 1782.

1986, Feb. 4 Litho. *Perf. 12x11½*

Granite Paper

325 A73 9p multicolored .30 .30
326 A73 14p multicolored .50 .50
327 A73 29p multicolored 1.00 1.00
328 A73 31p multicolored 1.10 1.10
329 A73 34p multicolored 1.25 1.25
Nos. 325-329 (5) 4.15 4.15

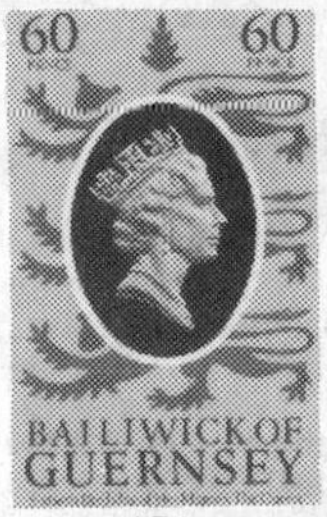

A74

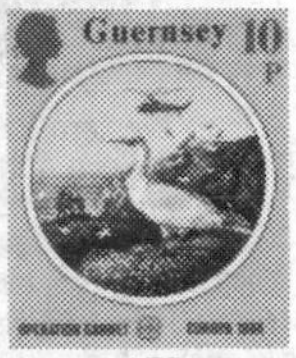

A75

1986, Apr. 21 *Perf. 14*

330 A74 60p multicolored 2.00 2.00

Queen Elizabeth II, 60th birthday.

1986, May 22 *Perf. 11½*

Granite Paper

331 A75 10p Operation Gannet .35 .35
332 A75 14p Whitsun orchid .45 .45
333 A75 22p Guernsey elm .75 .75
Nos. 331-333 (3) 1.55 1.55

Europa 1986.

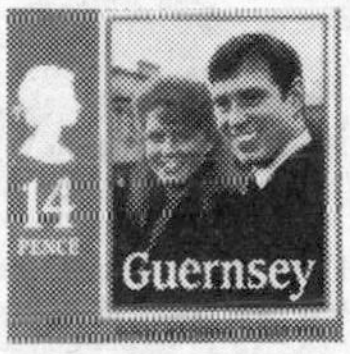

Wedding of Prince Andrew and Sarah Ferguson — A76

1986, July 23 Litho. *Perf. 14*

334 A76 14p Couple .48 .48

Size: 48x32mm

335 A76 34p Couple, diff. 1.25 1.25

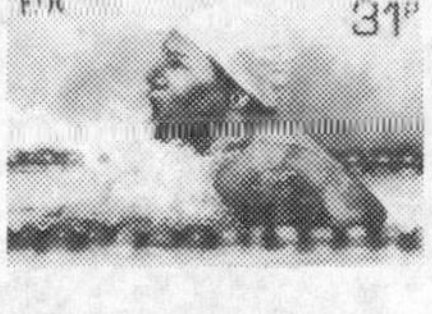

Sports A77

1986, July 24 *Perf. 14½*

336 A77 10p Lawn bowling, vert. .30 .30
337 A77 14p Cricket, vert. .42 .42
338 A77 22p Badminton, vert. .70 .70
339 A77 29p Field hockey, vert. .90 .90
340 A77 31p Swimming 1.00 1.00
341 A77 34p Rifle shooting 1.10 1.10
Nos. 336-341 (6) 4.42 4.42

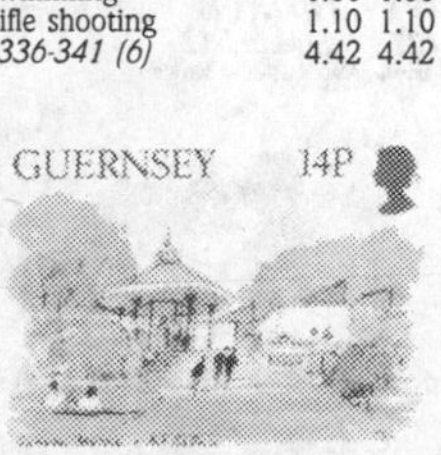

Museums A78

1986, Nov. 18 Litho. *Perf. 14½*

342 A78 14p Guernsey Museum and Art Gallery .40 .40
343 A78 29p Ft. Grey Maritime Museum .80 .80
344 A78 31p Castle Cornet .90 .90
345 A78 34p Natl. Trust of Guernsey Folk Museum 1.00 1.00
Nos. 342-345 (4) 3.10 3.10

Miniature Sheet

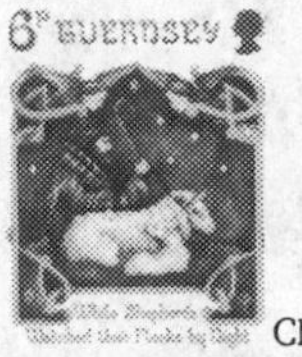

Christmas — A79

Carols: a, "While Shepherds Watched Their Flocks by Night." b, "In the Bleak Mid-Winter." c, "O Little Town of Bethlehem." d, "The Holly and the Ivy." e, "O Little Christmas Tree." f, "Away in a Manger." g, "Good King Wenceslas." h, "We Three Kings of Orient Are." i, "Hark the Herald Angels Sing." j, "I Saw Three Ships." k, "Little Donkey." l, "Jingle Bells."

1986, Nov. 18 *Perf. 12½*

346 Sheet of 12 2.75 2.75
a.-l. A79 6p any single .22 .22

Souvenir Sheet

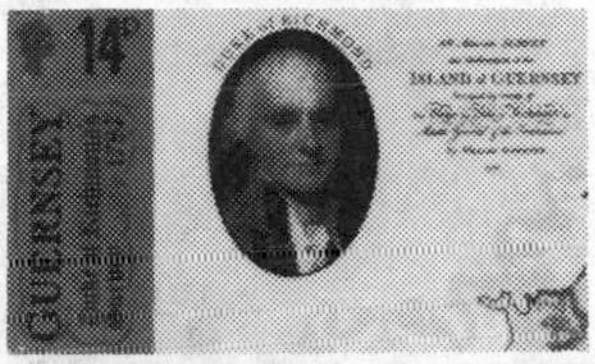

Duke of Richmond, 18th Century Map Detail — A80

1987, Feb. 10 Litho. *Perf. 14½*

347 Sheet of 4 3.35 3.35
a. A80 14p shown .45 .45
b. A80 29p North .90 .90
c. A80 31p Southwest .95 .95
d. A80 34p Southeast 1.05 1.05

Duke of Richmond's survey of Guernsey, bicent.

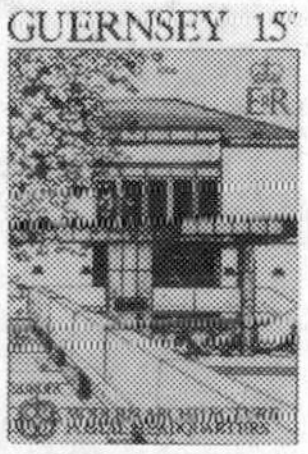

Europa 1987 — A81

Modern architecture.

1987, May 5 Litho. *Perf. 13x13½*

348 A81 15p Postal headquarters .50 .50
349 A81 15p Headquarters, schematic view .50 .50
a. Pair, #348-349 1.00 1.00
350 A81 22p Grammar school entrance .75 .75
351 A81 22p School, schematic view .75 .75
a. Pair, #350-351 1.50 1.50
Nos. 348-351 (4) 2.50 2.50

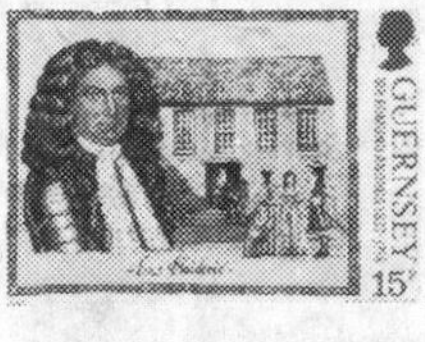

Andros and La Plaiderie Court House, Guernsey A82

Andros and: 29p, Governor's Palace, Virginia. 31p, "Governor Andros and the Boston People," print fron Harper's New Monthly Magazine. 34p, Map of New Amsterdam (New York City).

1987, July 7 *Perf. 12*

Granite Paper

352 A82 15p multicolored .50 .50
353 A82 29p multicolored .95 .95
354 A82 31p multicolored 1.05 1.05
355 A82 34p multicolored 1.15 1.15
Nos. 352-355 (4) 3.65 3.65

Sir Edmund Andros (1637-1714), lieutenant-governor of Guernsey (1704-1706) and statesman of Colonial America (1672-1710).

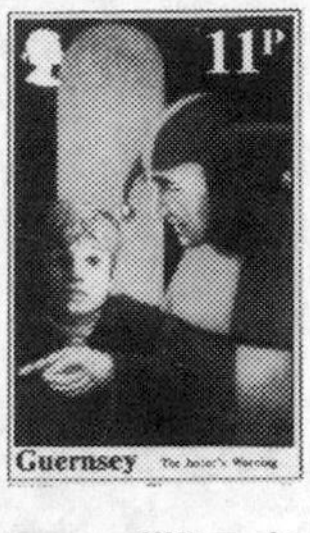

William the Conqueror (c. 1028-1087), King of England (1066-1087) — A83

Designs: 11p, Jester warning young William of a plot to murder him. No. 357, Battle of Hastings. No. 358, King William, his banner at the Battle of Hastings. No. 359, William the Conqueror. No. 360, Abbey at Caen and Queen Matilda of Flanders (d. 1083). 34p, Halley's Comet and regalia of William I.

1987, Sept. 9 *Perf. 13½x14*

356 A83 11p multicolored .35 .35
357 A83 15p multicolored .48 .48
358 A83 15p multicolored .48 .48
a. Pair, #357-358 1.00 1.00
359 A83 22p multicolored .70 .70
360 A83 22p multicolored .70 .70
a. Pair, #359-360 1.40 1.40
361 A83 34p multicolored 1.10 1.10
Nos. 356-361 (6) 3.81 3.81

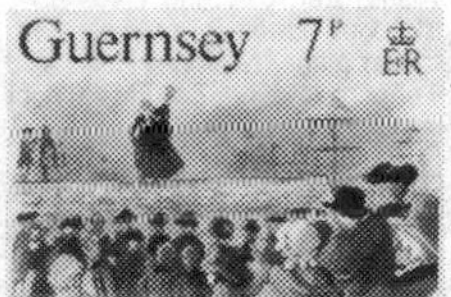

Visit of John Wesley (1703-1791), Religious Reformer, Bicent. A84

Designs: 7p, Preaching at the quay, Alderney. 15p, Preaching at Mon Plaisir. 29p, Preaching at Assembly Rooms, St. Peter Port. 31p, Wesley and La Ville Baudu, an early Methodist meeting place, Vale Parish. 34p, Wesley and Ebenezer Methodist Church, first Methodist chapel, Union Street, 1816.

1987, Nov. 17 Litho. *Perf. 14½*

362 A84 7p multicolored .25 .25
363 A84 15p multicolored .55 .55
364 A84 29p multicolored 1.05 1.05
365 A84 31p multicolored 1.15 1.15
366 A84 34p multicolored 1.25 1.25
Nos. 362-366 (5) 4.25 4.25

Voyage of the Golden Spur, Apr. 12, 1872-Jan. 4, 1874 A85

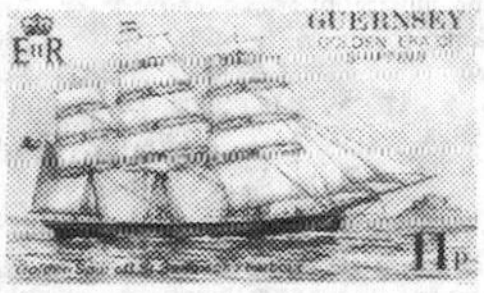

Designs: 11p, Off St. Sampson's Harbor. 15p, Entering Hong Kong Harbor. 29p, Anchored off Macao. 31p, In China Tea Race. 34p, Golden Spur, map of voyage.

1988, Feb. 9 Litho. *Perf. 13½x14*

367 A85 11p multicolored .40 .40
368 A85 15p multicolored .55 .55
369 A85 29p multicolored 1.05 1.05
370 A85 31p multicolored 1.15 1.15
371 A85 34p multicolored 1.25 1.25
Nos. 367-371 (5) 4.40 4.40

Guernsey's Golden Age of Shipping: largest vessel built on Guernsey, the Golden Spur, launched Oct. 15, 1864, wrecked at Haiphong on Feb. 27, 1879.

Landscape Type of 1984

Perf. 14½x15, 15x14½

1987-89 Litho.

372 A63 12p Petit Bot beach, vert. .45 .45
373 A63 16p St. John's Hostel for the Aged .58 .58
a. Min. sheet, 5 each 12p, 16p 5.15
b. Min. sheet, 4 4p, 3 12p, 3 16p 3.75
374 A63 18p Le Variouf, vert. .65 .65
a. Min. sheet, 4p, 6p, 3 12p, 3 18p 3.65
b. Min. sheet, 4 12p, 4 18p 4.40
Nos. 372-374 (3) 1.68 1.68

Nos. 373a-373b and 374a-374b sold unattached in booklet covers.

Coil Stamps

Sizes: 21½x12½mm, 12½x21½mm

Perf. 14x14½, 14½x14

375 A63 11p La Seigneurie, Sark .40 .40
376 A63 12p Petit Bot beach .45 .45
377 A63 15p Havelet, vert. .52 .52

378 A63 16p St. John's Hostel for
the Aged .60 .60
Nos. 375-378 (4) 1.97 1.97

Issued: 11p, 15p, 5/15/87; 12p, 16p, 3/28/88;
18p, 2/28/89.

Waves, Map — A85a

Perf. 14¹/₂x14

1989, Apr. 3 Photo. Coil Stamp
380 A85a (18p) green .58 .58

Inscribed "MINIMUM FIRST CLASS POSTAGE
TO UK PAID." See No. 431.

Europa
1988
A86

Communication and transportation: No. 381,
Bedford Rascal postal van, Lihou Is. rowboat. No.
382, Rowboat, Viscount plane. No. 383, Horse and
buggy, front wheel of bicycle. No. 384, Back wheel
of bicycle, No. 4 coach.

1988, May 10 Litho. Perf. 14¹/₂
381 A86 16p multicolored .52 .52
382 A86 16p multicolored .52 .52
  a. Pair, #381-382 1.10 1.10
383 A86 22p multicolored .75 .75
384 A86 22p multicolored .75 .75
  a. Pair, #383-384 1.50 1.50
  Nos. 381-384 (4) 2.54 2.54

#382a, 384a have continuous designs.

Frederick Corbin
Lukis (1788-
1871),
Archaeologist
A87

Designs: 12p, Entrance to Lukis House, St. Peter
Port, and portrait. 16p, Bound manuscript containing illustrations painted by Lukis's daughter Mary
Anne (born 1822). 29p, Lukis supervising excavation of Le Creux es Faies dolmen at L'Eree, Guernsey. 31p, Rear of Lukis House and garden. 34p,
Artifacts recovered by Lukis and preserved as part
of the museum collection.

1988, July 12 Photo. Perf. 12¹/₂
Granite Paper
385 A87 12p multicolored .42 .42
386 A87 16p multicolored .55 .55
387 A87 29p multicolored 1.00 1.00
388 A87 31p multicolored 1.10 1.10
389 A87 34p multicolored 1.20 1.20
  Nos. 385-389 (5) 4.27 4.27

1988 World
Offshore
Powerboat
Championships
A88

Designs: 16p, Racing boats, Royal Navy helicopter. 30p, Boats racing through Gouliot Passage (separating Sark from Brecqhou). 32p, Boats, helicopter,
St. John's Ambulance rescue ship, vert. 35p, Race
course marked in red on Admiralty Chart, vert.

1988, Sept. 6 Perf. 12
Granite Paper
390 A88 16p multicolored .58 .58
391 A88 30p multicolored 1.05 1.05
392 A88 32p multicolored 1.10 1.10
393 A88 35p multicolored 1.20 1.20
  Nos. 390-393 (4) 3.93 3.93

Publication of *Flora
Sarniensis*,
Bicent. — A89

Designs: 12p, Joshua Gosselin (1739-1813), botanist, and herbarium made by Rollo Sherwill in
1976. No. 395, *Lagurus ovatus* (pressed specimen).
No. 396, *Lagurus ovatus*, diff. No. 397, *Silene gallica quinquevulnera* (pressed specimen). No. 398,
Silene gallica quinquevulnera, diff. 35p, *Limonium
binervosum sarniense serquense.*

1988, Nov. 15 Litho. Perf. 14
394 A89 12p shown .42 .42
395 A89 16p multicolored .55 .55
396 A89 16p multicolored .55 .55
397 A89 23p multicolored .80 .80
398 A89 23p multicolored .80 .80
399 A89 35p multicolored 1.20 1.20
  Nos. 394-399 (6) 4.32 4.32

Miniature Sheet

Ecclesiastical Links to
France and Great
Britain — A90

Church interiors, exteriors and artifacts: a,
Coutances Cathedral, France. b, Notre Dame du
Rosaire Church interior, Guernsey. c, Stained-glass
window, St. Sampson's Church, Guernsey. d, Dol-
de-Bretagne Cathedral, France. e, Bishop's Throne,
Town Church, Guernsey. f, Winchester Cathedral,
England. g, St. John's Cathedral, Portsmouth,
England. h, High Altar, St. Joseph's Church, Guern-
sey. i, Mont Saint-Michel, France. j, Chancel, Vale
Church, Guernsey. k, Lich gate, Forest Church,
Guernsey. l, Marmoutier Abbey, France.

1988, Nov. 15 Perf. 14¹/₂x15
400 Sheet of 12 3.40 3.40
  a.-l. A90 8p any single .28 .28

Christmas 1988.

Europa
1989
A91

Traditional children's toys and games.

1989, Feb. 28 Litho. Perf. 13¹/₂
401 A91 12p Tip cat (Le Cat) .40 .40
402 A91 16p Girl, Cobo Alice doll .52 .52
403 A91 23p Hopscotch (Le
Colimachaon) .75 .75
  Nos. 401-403 (3) 1.67 1.67

Aircraft
A92

1989, May 5
404 A92 12p DH86 Express .40 .40
  a. Booklet pane of 6 2.50
405 A92 12p Southampton .40 .40
406 A92 18p DH89 Rapide .60 .60
  a. Booklet pane of 6 3.75
407 A92 18p Sunderland .60 .60
408 A92 35p BAe 146 1.10 1.10
  a. Booklet pane of 6 7.00
409 A92 35p Shackleton 1.10 1.10
  Nos. 404-409 (6) 4.20 4.20

Guernsey Airport, 50th anniv. (Nos. 404, 406,
408); others, 201st Squadron Affiliation, 50th
anniv.

Visit of Queen
Elizabeth II, May
23-24 — A93

1989, May 23 Perf. 15x14
410 A93 30p Portrait by June Men-
doza 1.00 1.00

Great Western Railway Steamer Service
Between Weymouth and the Channel Isls.,
Cent. — A94

1989, Sept. 5 Litho. Perf. 13¹/₂
411 A94 12p S.S. *Ibex*, 1891 .38 .38
412 A94 18p P.S. *Great Western*,
1872 .55 .55
413 A94 29p S.S. *St. Julien*, 1925 .90 .90
414 A94 34p S.S. *Roebuck*, 1925 1.05 1.05
415 A94 37p S.S. *Antelope*, 1889 1.15 1.15
  a. Souv. sheet of 5, #411-415 4.05 4.05
  Nos. 411-415 (5) 4.03 4.03

Zoological Trust of
Guernsey — A95

1989, Nov. 17 Litho. Perf. 14x13¹/₂
416 A95 18p Two-toed sloth .60 .60
417 A95 29p Capuchin monkey .98 .98
418 A95 32p White-lipped tamarin 1.05 1.05
419 A95 34p Squirrel monkey 1.15 1.15
420 A95 37p Lar gibbon 1.25 1.25
  Nos. 416-420 (5) 5.03 5.03

Animals of the rainforest.

Miniature Sheet

Christmas — A96

Ornaments on tree: a, Star. b, Angel. c, Candles.
d, Robin red breast. e, Presents on sled. f, Caroler.
g, Santa Claus pictured on wooden ornament. h,
Herald and stars pictured on glass ball. i, Presents in
stocking. j, Bell. k, Reindeer. l, Chapel.

1989, Nov. 17 Perf. 13
421 Sheet of 12 4.20 4.20
  a.-l. A96 10p any single .35 .35

Europa
1990
A97

Post offices.

1990, Feb. 27 Litho. Perf. 13¹/₂x14
422 A97 20p Sark, c. 1890 .65 .65
423 A97 20p Sark, 1990 .65 .65
424 A97 24p Arcade, c. 1840 .80 .80
425 A97 24p Arcade, 1990 .80 .80
  Nos. 422-425 (4) 2.90 2.90

Penny
Black,
150th
Anniv.
A98

Designs: 14p, Great Britain No. 1, Maltese Cross
cancellation in red, mail steamer in St. Peter Port
Harbor. 20p, Great Britain No. 3, Maltese Cross
cancellation in black, pedestrians, mailbox at Elm
Grove and Union Street in 1852. 32p, Great Britain
No. 255 bisected, 1940, and military band. 34p,
Guernsey No. 2, crown of William the Conqueror,
Guernsey lily. 37p, Guernsey No. 10, crowd in line
outside Guernsey P.O.

1990, May 3 Litho. Perf. 14
426 A98 14p multicolored .42 .42
427 A98 20p multicolored .60 .60
428 A98 32p multicolored 1.00 1.00
429 A98 34p multicolored 1.00 1.00
430 A98 37p multicolored 1.10 1.10
  a. Souvenir sheet of 5, #426-430 4.25 4.25
  b. No. 430a ovptd. "NZ 1990" emblem,
"FROM LONDON 90 TO NEW
ZEALAND 90" 6.25 6.25
  Nos. 426-430 (5) 4.12 4.12

Map and Waves Type of 1989

1989, Dec. 27 Photo. Perf. 14¹/₂x14
Coil Stamp
431 A85a (14p) ultra & lt ultra .45 .45

Inscribed "MINIMUM BAILIWICK POSTAGE
PAID."

Lord Anson's Circumnavigation of the
World, 250th Anniv. — A99

Designs: 14p, Philip Saumarez writing ship's log.
20p, *Centurion, Gloucester, Severn, Pearle, Wager*
and *Tryal* departing from Portsmouth. 29p, Landfall
at St. Catherine's Is. off Brazil, 1740. 34p, *Tryal*
rounding Cape Horn, 1741. 37p, Camp at Juan
Fernandez, 1741.

1990, July 24 Litho. Perf. 13¹/₂x14
436 A99 14p multicolored .45 .45
437 A99 20p multicolored .65 .65
438 A99 29p multicolored .95 .95
439 A99 34p multicolored 1.10 1.10
440 A99 37p multicolored 1.20 1.20
  Nos. 436-440 (5) 4.35 4.35

Gray
Seal — A100

1990, Oct. 16 Litho. Perf. 14¹/₂
441 A100 20p shown .65 .65
442 A100 26p Bottlenose dolphin .75 .75
443 A100 31p Basking shark 1.00 1.00
444 A100 37p Harbor porpoise 1.20 1.20
  Nos. 441-444 (4) 3.60 3.60

World Wildlife Fund.

Miniature Sheet

Christmas — A101

Winter birds: a, Blue and Great Tits. b, Snow
Bunting. c, Kestrel. d, Starling. e, Greenfinch. f,
Robin. g, Wren. h, Barn owl. i, Mistle Thrush. j,
Heron. k, Chaffinch. l, Kingfisher.

1990, Oct. 16   *Perf. 13½*
445   Sheet of 12   4.00 4.00
a.-l. A101 10p any single   .32 .32

Occupation
Stamp No. N1,
50th Anniv.
A102

1991, Feb. 18   Litho.   *Perf. 13½*
446 A102 37p shown   1.10 1.10
447 A102 53p No. N2   1.65 1.65
448 A102 57p No. N3   1.75 1.75
  a.   Booklet pane of 3, #446-448   4.75

No. 448a printed in three formats with Nos. 446-448 in different order.

Europa — A103

Designs: No. 449, Royal Visit to Guernsey, discovery of Neptune, 1846. No. 450, Royal Visit to Sark, launch of Sputnik, 1957. No. 451, Maiden voyage of ferry Sarnia, first manned space flight, 1961. No. 452, Independence of Guernsey Post Office, first man on moon, 1969.

1991, Apr. 1   Litho.   *Perf. 13½x14*
449 A103 21p multicolored   .65 .65
450 A103 21p multicolored   .65 .65
451 A103 26p multicolored   .85 .85
452 A103 26p multicolored   .85 .85
   Nos. 449-452 (4)   3.00 3.00

Landscape Type of 1984

1991   Litho.   *Perf. 15x14½, 14½x15*
453 A63 21p King's Mills, St.
     Saviours   .60 .60
  a.   Min. sheet (3 each #453, #296, 2
     each #287, #288)   3.50
  b.   Min. sheet (5 each #453, #296)   5.00
454 A63 26p Town Church, St. Peter
     Port   .75 .75

Issue dates: 21p, 26p, Apr. 1. Nos 453a, 453b, Apr. 2. Nos. 453a, 453b sold unattached in booklet covers.

Guernsey Yacht
Club, Cent. — A104

1991, July 2   Litho.   *Perf. 14*
459 A104 15p Guernsey Sailing Trust   .50 .50
460 A104 21p Guernsey Regatta   .70 .70
461 A104 26p Channel Islands Chal-
     lenge   .85 .85
462 A104 31p Rolex Swan Regatta   1.05 1.05
463 A104 37p Old Gaffers Assoc.   1.25 1.25
  a.   Souvenir sheet of 5, #459-463   4.35 4.35
   Nos. 459-463 (5)   4.35 4.35

"Guernsey" and denomination in white on sheet stamps, yellow on souvenir sheet stamps.

Miniature Sheet

Christmas — A105

Children's Paintings: a, Reindeer by Melanie Sharpe. b, Christmas dessert by James Quinn. c, Snowman by Lisa Marie Guille. d, Snowman by Jessica Ede-Golightly. e, Birds by Sharon Le Page. f, Shepherds, sheep, angels by Anna Coquelin. g,

Manger scene by Claudine Lihou. h, Three kings by Jonathan Le Noury. i, Children, angels, star by Marcia Mahy. j, Christmas tree, presents by Laurel Garfield. k, Santa Claus by Rebecca Driscoll. l, Snowman by Ian Lowe.

1991, Oct. 15   Litho.   *Perf. 13*
464   Sheet of 12   4.65 4.65
a.-l. A105 12p any single   .38 .38

Nature
Conservation
A106

Birds and plants: No. 465a, Two oyster catchers. b, Three turnstones. c, Two dunlins, two turnstones. d, Curlew, two turnstones. e, Ringed plover, chicks.

No. 466a, Violet and white flowers. b, Yellow flowers. c, Small yellow flowers. d, Violet, yellow and white flowers. e, Long-stemmed yellow flowers.

1991, Oct. 15   *Perf. 14½*
465   Strip of 5   2.50 2.50
a.-e. A106 15p any single   .50 .50
466   Strip of 5   3.50 3.50
a.-e. A106 21p any single   .70 .70

GUERNSEY
Discovery of America, 500th
Anniv. — A107

1992, Feb. 6   Litho.   *Perf. 13½x14*
467 A107 23p Columbus   .75 .75
468 A107 23p Columbus' signatures   .75 .75
469 A107 28p Map of 1st voyage   .85 .85
470 A107 28p Santa Maria   .85 .85
  a.   Souvenir sheet, #467-470   3.25 3.25
  b.   No. 470a overprinted in brown in
     sheet margin   3.45 3.45
   Nos. 467-470 (4)   3.20 3.20

Europa. No. 470b overprint shows emblem of World Columbian Stamp Expo '92.
Issue date: No. 470b, May 22.

Queen Elizabeth
II's Accession to
Throne, 40th
Anniv. — A108

Various portraits of Queen Elizabeth II.

1992, Feb. 6   Litho.   *Perf. 14*
471 A108 23p multicolored   .70 .70
472 A108 28p multicolored   .85 .85
473 A108 33p multicolored   1.00 1.00
474 A108 39p multicolored   1.25 1.25
   Nos. 471-474 (4)   3.80 3.80

Souvenir Sheet

Guernsey Cows — A109

1992, May 22   Litho.   *Perf. 14*
475 A109 75p multicolored   2.50 2.50

Royal Guernsey Agricultural and Horticultural Society, 150th anniv.

GUERNSEY   Flowers — A110

1992-95   *Perf. 13*
476 A110 1p Stephanotis flori-
     bunda   .15 .15
477 A110 2p Potted hydrangea   .15 .15
478 A110 3p Stock   .15 .15
479 A110 4p Anemones   .15 .15
480 A110 5p Gladiolus   .15 .15
481 A110 6p Gypsophila panicu-
     lata, asparagus
     plumosus   .18 .18
482 A110 7p Guernsey lily   .22 .22
483 A110 8p Enchantment lily   .25 .25
484 A110 9p Clematis freckles   .28 .28
485 A110 10p Alstroemeria   .30 .30
486 A110 16p Standard carnation,
     horiz.   .50 .50
  a.   Perf. 14   .50 .50
  b.   Booklet pane of 8 #486a   4.00
487 A110 20p Spray rose   .60 .60
488 A110 23p Mixed freesia,
     horiz.   .72 .72
  a.   Bklt. pane of 5 #486a, 3 #488c   4.50 4.50
  b.   Booklet pane of 8, #488c   5.75 5.75
  c.   Perf. 14   .70 .70
489 A110 24p Standard rose,
     horiz.   .70 .70
  a.   Perf. 14   .70 .70
  b.   Booklet pane of 8 #489a   5.75
490 A110 25p Iris ideal   .75 .75
  a.   Perf. 14½ on 3 sides   .75 .75
  b.   As "a," booklet pane of 4   3.00
491 A110 28p Lisianthus, horiz.   .85 .85
  a.   Perf. 14   .85 .85
  b.   Booklet pane of 4 #491a   3.50
492 A110 30p Spray chrysanthe-
     mum, horiz.   .95 .95
493 A110 40p Spray carnation   1.25 1.25
494 A110 50p Single freesia, horiz.   1.50 1.50

Size: 39x30mm
Perf. 13½
495 A110 £1 Bouquet, horiz.   3.00 3.00
  a.   Souv. sheet of 1 + label, perf. 13   3.00 3.00
  b.   Souv. sheet of 1 + label, perf. 13   3.25 3.25
496 A110 £2 Chelsea flower
     show, horiz.   6.25 6.25
   Nos. 476-496 (21)   19.05 19.05

PHILAKOREA '94 (#495a). Singapore '95 (#495b).

Issued: 3p, 4p, 5p, 10p, 16p, 20p, 23p, 40p, 50p, £1, 5/22/92; 1p, 2p, 6p, 7p, 8p, 9p, 24p, 28p, 30p, £2, 3/2/93; 25p, 2/18/94; #495a, 8/94; #495b, 9/1/95.
No. 495 dated "1992," No. 495a "1994."
Perf 14 or 14½ stamps issued only in booklets.

Operation
Asterix
A111

1992, Sept. 18   Litho.   *Perf. 13*
498 A111 16p Ship construction   .45 .45
499 A111 23p Loading cargo   .65 .65
500 A111 28p Ship at sea   .80 .80
501 A111 33p Ship on fire   .90 .90
502 A111 39p Ship sinking   1.10 1.10
  a.   Bklt. pane of #498-502 + label   4.00
   Nos. 498-502 (5)   3.90 3.90

No. 502a exists with four different labels.

GUERNSEY
Historic
Trams
A112

Designs: 16p, Tram No. 10 decorated for Battle of Flowers. 23p, No. 10 passing Hougue a la Perre. 28p, Tram No. 1 at St. Sampsons. 33p, First steam tram, St. Peter Port, 1879. 39p, Last electric tram, 1934.

1992, Nov. 17   Litho.   *Perf. 13½x14*
503 A112 16p multicolored   .45 .45
504 A112 23p multicolored   .65 .65
505 A112 28p multicolored   .80 .80
506 A112 33p multicolored   .90 .90
507 A112 39p multicolored   1.10 1.10
   Nos. 503-507 (5)   3.90 3.90

Christmas — A113

Designs: a, Father dressed as Santa. b, Girl pulling end of cracker. c, Mother. d, Champagne, crumpets. e, Turkey. f, Plum pudding. g, Cake. h, Cookies. i, Wine, blue cheese. j, Nuts. k, Ham. l, Cake roll.

1992, Nov. 17   *Perf. 13½*
508   Sheet of 12   4.25 4.25
a.-l. A113 13p any single   .35 .35

24 GUERNSEY   A114

Rupert Bear and friends, created by Mary Tourtel: No. 509: Rupert Bear, Bingo, and dog. No. 510a, 24p, Bill Badger, Willie Mouse, Reggie Rabbit, and Podgy Pig with snowman. No. 510b, 16p, Airplane above castle tower. No. 510c, 24p, Balloonist leaping away from Gregory on sled. No. 510d, 16p, Professor's servant and Autumn Elf. No. 510e, 16p, Algy Pug. No. 510f, 16p, Baby Badger on sled. No. 510g, 24p, Tiger Lily and Edward Trunk.

1993, Feb. 2   Litho.   *Perf. 13½x13*
509 A114 24p multicolored   .75 .75
510 A114   Sheet of 8, #a.-g. &
     #509   4.75 4.75

No. 510 printed in continuous design. Nos. 510b, 510d-510f are 25x26mm.

Contemporary
Art — A115

Europa: No. 511, Tapestry, by Kelly Fletcher. No. 512, The Fish Market, by Sally Reed. No. 513, Dress Shop, King's Road, by Damen Bell. No. 514, Red Abstract, by Molly Harris.

1993, May 7   Litho.   *Perf. 13½x14*
Size: 45x30mm (#512, 513)
511 A115 24p multicolored   .70 .70
512 A115 24p multicolored   .70 .70
513 A115 28p multicolored   .85 .85
514 A115 28p multicolored   .85 .85
   Nos. 511-514 (4)   3.10 3.10

Siege of Castle Cornet, 1643-51 — A116

Designs: 16p, Shipboard arrest of Parliamentarian officials. 24p, Parliamentarian warships firing on castle. 28p, Captured officials fleeing from castle. 33p, Cannon firing from castle into St. Peter Port. 39p, Surrender of castle.

1993, May 7   *Perf. 15x14*
515 A116 16p multicolored   .48 .48
516 A116 24p multicolored   .70 .70
517 A116 28p multicolored   .85 .85
518 A116 33p multicolored   1.00 1.00
519 A116 39p multicolored   1.15 1.15
  a.   Souvenir sheet of 5, #515-519   4.25 4.25
   Nos. 515-519 (5)   4.18 4.18

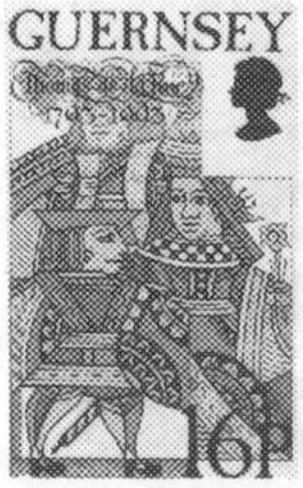

Thomas de la Rue, Printer, Birth Bicent. — A117

Designs: 16p, Playing card king, queen and jack. 24p, Swift reservoir fountain pens. 28p, Envelope folding machine. 33p, Great Britain type A5. 39p, £1 Mauritius bank note, portrait of de la Rue.

1993, July 27 Litho. *Perf. 13½*

520 A117 16p multicolored .48 .48
521 A117 24p multicolored .72 .72
522 A117 28p multicolored .85 .85

Engr.

523 A117 33p rose carmine 1.00 1.00
524 A117 39p green 1.15 1.15
Nos. 520-524 (5) 4.20 4.20

520a Booklet pane of 4 2.00
521a Booklet pane of 4 3.00
522a Booklet pane of 4 3.50
523a Booklet pane of 4 4.00
523a Booklet pane of 4 4.75

Miniature Sheet

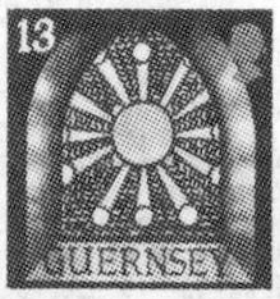

Christmas — A118

Stained glass windows, Chapel of Christ the Healer: a, Sunburst. b, Light from sun. c, Hand of God. d, Doves descending left. e, Christ raising hand. f, Doves descending right. g, Christ Child sitting in temple. h, Christ raising daughter of Jairus from dead. i, "Suffer little children to come unto me." j, Scene from Pilgrim's Progress. k, The Light of the World. l, Archangel of Healing.

1993, Nov. 2 Litho. *Perf. 13x13½*

525 Sheet of 12 4.50 4.50
a.-l. A118 13p any single .38 .38

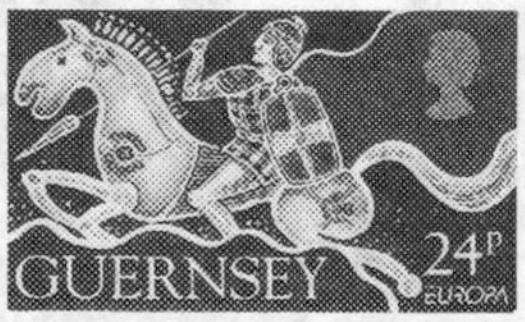

Archaeological Discoveries — A119

Europa: No. 526, Warrior on horseback. No. 527, Burial site, Les Fouaillages. No. 528, Sword, scabbard, spear. No. 529, Cerny-style pots, arrowheads, axe.

1994, Feb. 18 Litho. *Perf. 13½*

526 A119 24p multicolored .75 .75
a. Sheet of 10 with added inscription 7.50 7.50
527 A119 24p multicolored .75 .75
528 A119 30p multicolored .90 .90
529 A119 30p multicolored .90 .90
Nos. 526-529 (4) 3.30 3.30

No. 526a inscribed in sheet margin with Hong Kong '94 emblem and "PHILATELIC EXHIBITION / 18-21 FEBRUARY 1994" in English and Chinese.

Souvenir Sheet

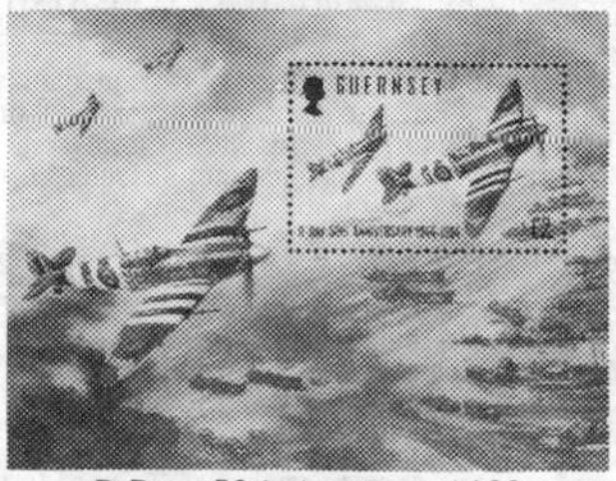

D-Day, 50th Anniv. — A120

Design: £2, Canadian Wing Spitfires flying over Normandy coastline.

1994, June 6 Litho. *Perf. 14*

530 A120 £2 multicolored 6.00 6.00

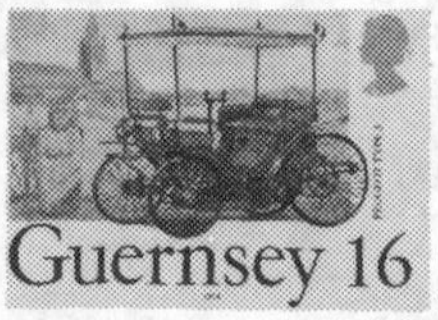

Classic Cars — A121

Designs: 16p, 1894 Peugeot Type 3. 24p, 1903 Mercedes Simplex. 35p, 1906 Humber 14.4hp. 41p, 1936 Bentley 4¼ L. 60p, 1948 MG TC.

1994, July 19 Litho. *Perf. 15x14*

531 A121 16p multicolored .48 .48
532 A121 24p multicolored .75 .75
533 A121 35p multicolored 1.10 1.10
534 A121 41p multicolored 1.25 1.25
535 A121 60p multicolored 1.75 1.75
Nos. 531-535 (5) 5.33 5.33

531a Booklet pane of 4 1.90
532a Booklet pane of 4 3.00
533a Booklet pane of 4 4.50
534a Booklet pane of 4 5.00
535a Booklet pane of 4 7.00

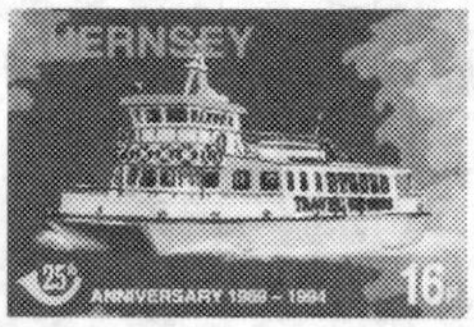

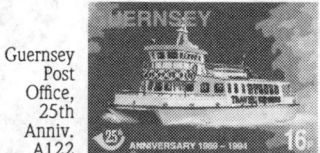

Guernsey Post Office, 25th Anniv. A122

Designs: 16p, Trident ferry. 24p, Handley Page Super Dart Herald of Channel Express. 35p, Aurigny Air Services' JOEY. 41p, Bon Marin de Serk ferry. 60p, Map of Guernsey, Herm, Alderney, Sark.

1994, Oct. 1 Litho. *Perf. 14*

536 A122 16p multicolored .48 .48
537 A122 24p multicolored .75 .75
538 A122 35p multicolored 1.10 1.10
539 A122 41p multicolored 1.25 1.25
540 A122 60p multicolored 1.75 1.75
a. Souvenir sheet, #536-540 5.50 5.50
Nos. 536-540 (5) 5.33 5.33

Miniature Sheets

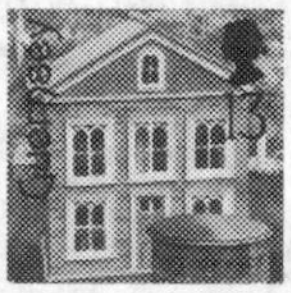
Christmas — A123

Antique toys: No. 541a, Doll house. b, Doll. c, Small teddy bear in carriage. d, Cards, post boxes with candy. e, Top. f, Picture puzzle blocks.

No. 542a, Rocking horse. b, Large teddy bear. c, Tricycle. d, Wooden pull duck. e, Tin plate locomotive. f, Ludo game.

1994, Oct. 1 *Perf. 13*

541 Sheet of 6 2.50 2.50
a.-f. A123 13p any single .42 .42
542 Sheet of 6 4.50 4.50
a.-f. A123 24p any single .75 .75

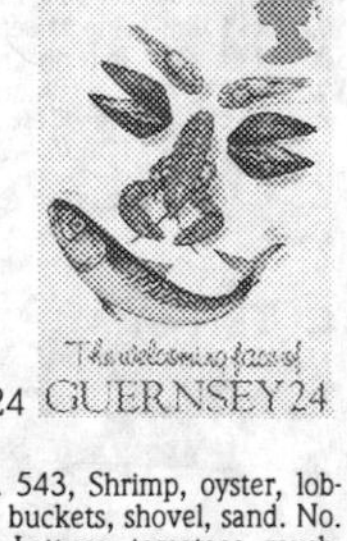

Greetings — A124

Faces formed by: No. 543, Shrimp, oyster, lobster, fish. No. 544, Sand buckets, shovel, sand. No. 545, Flowers. No. 546, Lettuce, tomatoes, mushroom, squash. No. 547, Seaweed, shells. No. 548, Anchor, life preservers. No. 549, Wine, cork, knife, fork. No. 550, Butterflies, caterpillars.

1995, Feb. 2 Litho. *Perf. 14*

543 A124 24p multicolored .75 .75
544 A124 24p multicolored .75 .75
545 A124 24p multicolored .75 .75
546 A124 24p multicolored .75 .75
547 A124 24p multicolored .75 .75
548 A124 24p multicolored .75 .75
549 A124 24p multicolored .75 .75
550 A124 24p multicolored .75 .75
a. Miniature sheet of 8, #543-550 6.00 6.00
Complete booklet, #550a 6.00
Nos. 543-550 (8) 6.00 6.00

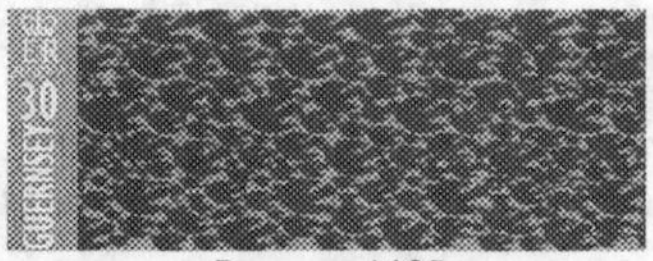

Doves — A125

Europa: 25p, Doves standing. 30p, Doves in flight. Illustration reduced.

1995, May 9 Litho. *Perf. 14*

551 A125 25p green .80 .80
552 A125 30p blue .95 .95

Nos. 551-552 contain a three-dimensional image hidden in the patterns composed of doves.

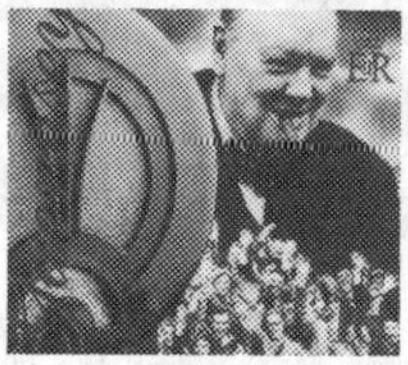
Liberation of Guernsey, 50th Anniv. A126

Designs: 16p, Churchill making broadcast, crowd. 24p, St. Peter Port harbor. 35p, Military band. 41p, Red Cross ship Vega. 60p, Soldier kissing civilian woman.

1995, May 9 *Perf. 13½x14*

553 A126 16p multicolored .48 .48
554 A126 24p multicolored .75 .75
555 A126 35p multicolored 1.10 1.10
556 A126 41p multicolored 1.25 1.25
557 A126 60p multicolored 1.95 1.95
a. Souvenir sheet of 5, #553-557 5.50 5.50
Nos. 553-557 (5) 5.53 5.53

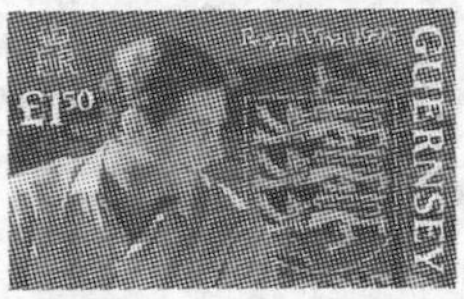

Visit by Prince of Wales A127

1995, May 9 *Perf. 14*

558 A127 £1.50 multicolored 4.50 4.50

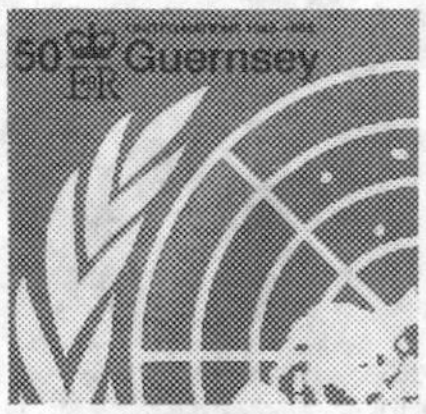

UN, 50th Anniv. A128

Portion of UN emblem, denomination: a, UL. b, UR. c, LL. d, LR.

Litho. & Embossed

1995, Oct. 24 *Perf. 14x13½*

559 Block of 4 6.00 6.00
a.-d. A128 50p any single 1.50 1.50

No. 559 is a continuous design forming complete UN emblem.

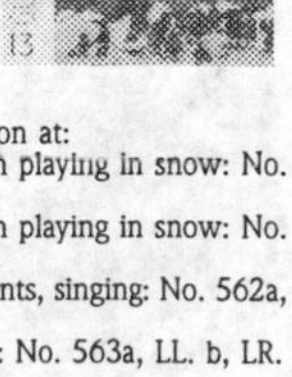

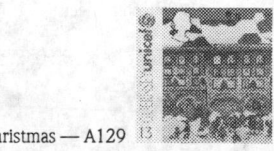

Christmas — A129

Designs, with denomination at:
Shops in the city, children playing in snow: No. 560a, LL. b, LR.
Homes in winter, children playing in snow: No. 561a, LL. b, LR.
Children playing instruments, singing: No. 562a, LL. b, LR.
Children of many nations: No. 563a, LL. b, LR.

1995, Nov. 16 Litho. *Perf. 13½x13*

560 Pair .80 .80
a.-b. A129 13p any single .40 .40
561 Pair .90 .90
a.-b. A129 13p +1p, any single .45 .45
562 Pair 1.50 1.50
a.-b. A129 24p any single .75 .75
563 Pair 1.65 1.65
a.-b. A129 24p +2p, any single .85 .85
Nos. 560-563 (4) 4.85 4.85

Nos. 560-563 are each continuous designs. UNICEF, 50th anniv.

POSTAGE DUE STAMPS

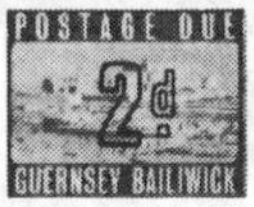

Castle Cornet and St. Peter Port — D1

Perf. 12½x12

1969, Oct. 1 Photo. Unwmk.

Black Numeral

J1 D1 1p deep magenta 1.00 .75
J2 D1 2p yellow green 2.25 1.75
J3 D1 3p red 3.00 2.00
J4 D1 4p ultra 4.00 2.25
J5 D1 5p yellow bister 6.25 3.75
J6 D1 6p greenish blue 8.00 4.50
J7 D1 1sh red brown 21.00 13.00
Nos. J1-J7 (7) 45.50 28.00

Type of 1969
"p" instead of "d"

1971-76

Black Numeral

J8 D1 ½p deep magenta .15 .15
J9 D1 1p yellow green .15 .15
J10 D1 2p red .15 .15
J11 D1 3p ultra .15 .15
J12 D1 4p yellow bister .20 .20
J13 D1 5p greenish blue .25 .25
J14 D1 6p purple ('76) .20 .20
J15 D1 8p orange ('75) .28 .28
J16 D1 10p red brown .50 .50
J17 D1 15p gray ('76) .52 .52
Nos. J8-J17 (10) 2.55 2.55

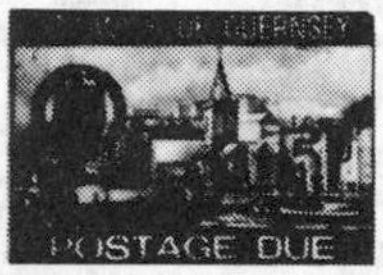

Town Church, St. Peter Port — D2

1977-80 Photo. *Perf. 13½x13*

Arms and Denomination in Black

J18 D2 ½p red brown .15 .15
J19 D2 1p lilac rose .15 .15
J20 D2 2p orange .15 .15
J21 D2 3p red .15 .15
J22 D2 4p greenish blue .15 .15
J23 D2 5p olive green .15 .15
J24 D2 6p greenish blue .18 .18
J25 D2 8p ocher .25 .25
J26 D2 10p dark blue .30 .30
J27 D2 14p green ('80) .45 .45
J28 D2 15p purple .42 .42
J29 D2 16p salmon rose ('80) .55 .55
Nos. J18-J29 (12) 3.05 3.05

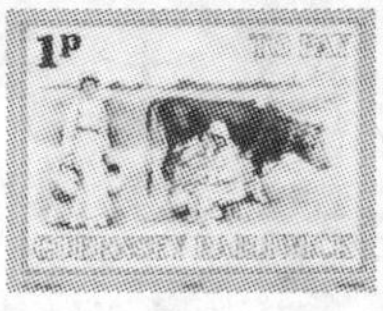

Woman Milking Cow — D3

1982, July 13 Litho. *Perf. 14½*

J30 D3 1p shown .15 .15
J31 D3 2p Vale Mill .15 .15
J32 D3 3p Sark cottage .15 .15
J33 D3 4p St. Peter Port .15 .15
J34 D3 5p Well, Moulin Huet .16 .16
J35 D3 16p Seaweed gathering .45 .45
J36 D3 18p Upper Walk, White Rock .50 .50
J37 D3 20p Cobo Bay .60 .60
J38 D3 25p Saints' Bay .70 .70
J39 D3 30p La Coupee, Sark .95 .95
J40 D3 50p Old Harbor, St. Peter Port 1.40 1.40
J41 D3 £1 Greenhouses, Victoria Tower 3.00 3.00
Nos. J30-J41 (12) 8.36 8.36

OCCUPATION STAMPS

Issued Under German Occupation

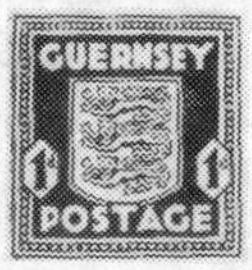

OS1

Rouletted 14x7

1941-44 Typo. Unwmk.

N1	OS1	½p	yellow green	3.50	2.25
N2	OS1	1p	vermilion	2.50	1.75
N3	OS1	2½p	ultramarine	6.00	4.00
			Nos. N1-N3 (3)	12.00	8.00

Issued: ½p, 4/7/41; 1p, 2/18/41; 2½p, 4/4/44.

Numerous shades and papers exist. The rouletting is very crude and may not be measurable. This is not a defect.

Wmk. 396 Chain Link Fence

1942 ***Rouletted 14x7***

Bluish French Bank Note Paper

N4	OS1	½p	green	22.50	*40.00*
N5	OS1	1p	red	17.50	*40.00*

Issue dates: ½p, Mar. 11. 1p, Apr. 9.
Nos. N1-N5 remained valid until Apr. 13, 1946.

ALDERNEY

'ôl–dər–nē

LOCATION — Northernmost of the Channel Islands in the Guernsey Bailiwick
GOVT. — Dependent territory under Bailiwick of Guernsey.
AREA — 3 sq. mi.
POP. — 2086 (est. 1981)
CAPITAL — St. Anne

Part of the Bailiwick of Guernsey, this island began issuing its own stamps.

Catalogue values for unused stamps in this section are for Never Hinged items.

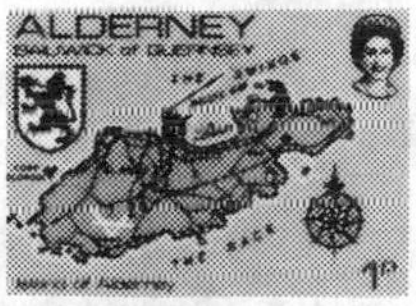

Map of Alderney, Arms — A1

1983, June 14 Litho. ***Perf. 12***

1	A1	1p	shown	.15	.15
2	A1	4p	Hanging Rock	.15	.15
3	A1	9p	States Building	.25	.25
4	A1	10p	St. Anne's Church	.28	.28
5	A1	11p	Yachts, Braye Bay	.30	.30
6	A1	12p	Victoria St., St. Anne	.32	.32
7	A1	13p	Map, arms	.35	.35
8	A1	14p	Ft. Clonque	.40	.40
9	A1	15p	Corblets Bay Port	.42	.42
10	A1	16p	Old Tower, St. Anne	.45	.45
11	A1	17p	Essex Castle Golf Course	.48	.48
12	A1	18p	Ships in Old Harbor	.50	.50
			Nos. 1-12 (12)	4.05	4.05

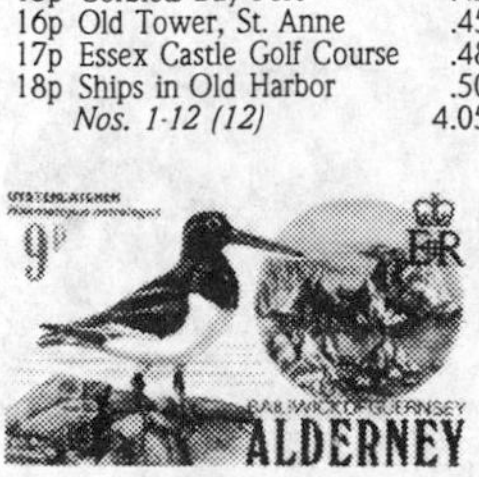

Oystercatcher, Telegraph Bay — A2

1984, June 12 ***Perf. 14½***

13	A2	9p	shown	*2.25*	*1.75*
14	A2	13p	Turnstone, Corblets Bay	*3.75*	*2.75*
15	A2	26p	Ringed plover, Corblets Bay	*6.50*	*4.50*
16	A2	28p	Dunlin, Arch Bay	*6.50*	*4.75*
17	A2	31p	Curlew, Old Harbor	*8.50*	*6.00*
			Nos. 13-17 (5)	*27.50*	*19.75*

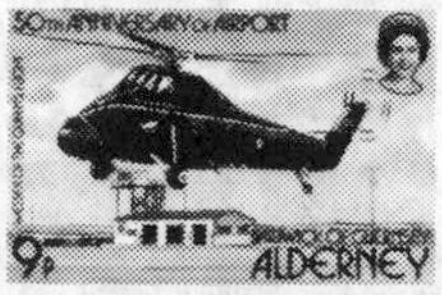

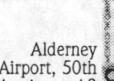

Alderney Airport, 50th Anniv. — A3

Aircraft: 9p, Wessex helicopter of the Queen's Flight, 1984. 13p, Aurigny Air Joey Britten-Norman Trislander, 1981. 29p, Morton Air Services DeHavilland Heron, 1946. 31p, DeHavilland Dragon Rapide, c. 1930. 34p, Saunders-Roe Saro Windhover, 1935.

1985, Mar. 19 ***Perf. 12x11½***

18	A3	9p	multicolored	*2.25*	*1.75*
19	A3	13p	multicolored	*3.25*	*2.75*
20	A3	29p	multicolored	*7.50*	*6.00*
21	A3	31p	multicolored	*7.50*	*6.00*
22	A3	34p	multicolored	*9.00*	*7.00*
			Nos. 18-22 (5)	*29.50*	*23.50*

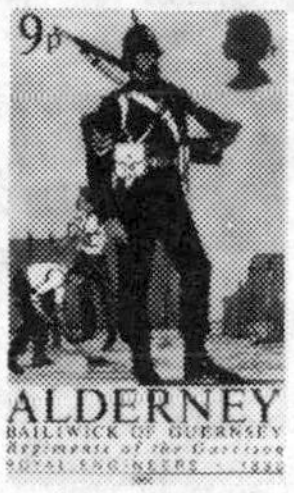

Regimental Uniforms, Alderney Garrison — A4

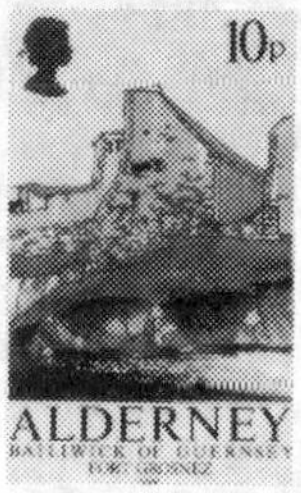

Forts — A5

1985, Sept. 24 ***Perf. 14½***

23	A4	9p	Royal Engineers, 1890	*.85*	*.50*
24	A4	14p	Duke of Albany's Own Highlanders, 1856	*1.10*	*.75*
25	A4	29p	Royal Artillery, 1855	*2.50*	*1.65*
26	A4	31p	South Hampshire Regiment, 1810	*2.75*	*1.75*
27	A4	34p	Royal Irish Regiment, 1782	*3.00*	*1.90*
			Nos. 23-27 (5)	*10.20*	*6.55*

1986, Sept. 23 Litho. ***Perf. 13x13½***

28	A5	10p	Grosnez	1.50	1.50
29	A5	14p	Tourgis	1.75	1.75
30	A5	31p	Clonque	4.00	4.00
31	A5	34p	Albert	4.50	4.50
			Nos. 28-31 (4)	11.75	11.75

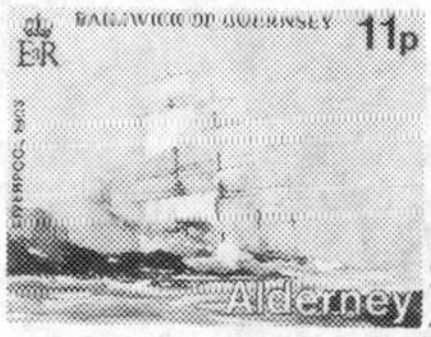

Shipwrecks A6

1987, May 5 Litho. ***Perf. 14½***

32	A6	11p	Liverpool, 1902	*2.75*	*2.75*
33	A6	15p	Petit Raymond, 1906	*3.50*	*3.50*
34	A6	29p	Maina, 1910	*7.75*	*7.75*
35	A6	31p	Burton, 1911	*8.00*	*8.00*
36	A6	34p	Point Law, 1975	*8.50*	*8.50*
			Nos. 32-36 (5)	*30.50*	*30.50*

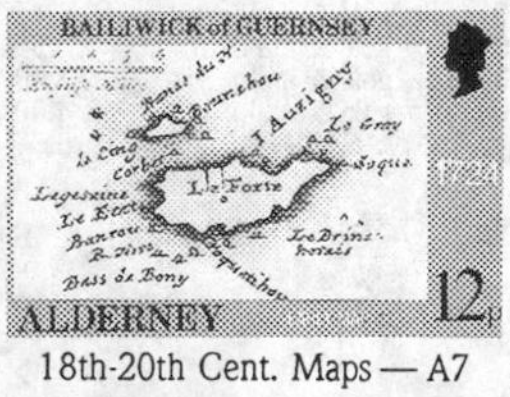

18th-20th Cent. Maps — A7

Designs: 12p, Early map, 1724. 18p, Survey by I.H. Bastide, 1739. 27p, Land survey by F. Goodwin, 1830. 32p, Wartime occupation map, 1943. 35p, Ordnance survey, 1988.

1989, July 7 Litho. ***Perf. 13½x14***

37	A7	12p	multicolored	.45	.45
38	A7	18p	multicolored	.75	.75
39	A7	27p	multicolored	1.10	1.10
40	A7	32p	multicolored	1.25	1.25
41	A7	35p	multicolored	1.40	1.40
			Nos. 37-41 (5)	4.95	4.95

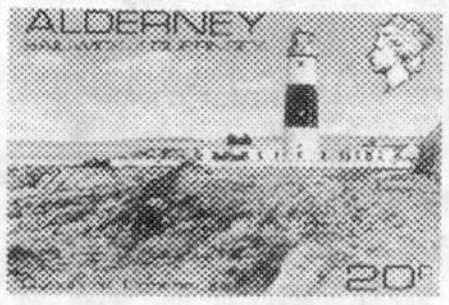

Quesnard Lighthouse A8

Designs: 21p, Inner Harbor, Braye. 23p, The Island Hall, Alderney. 24p, Alderney Railway locomotive, J. T. Daly. 28p, Lifeboat, Louis Marchesi of Round Table.

1989-93 Litho. ***Perf. 15x14***

42	A8	20p	multicolored	.65	.65
43	A8	21p	multicolored	.80	.80
44	A8	23p	multicolored	.80	.80
45	A8	24p	multicolored	.85	.85
46	A8	28p	multicolored	.95	.95
			Nos. 42-46 (5)	4.05	4.05

Issue dates: 20p, Dec. 27. 21p, Apr. 2, 1991. 23p, Feb. 6, 1992. 24p, 28p, Mar. 3, 1993.

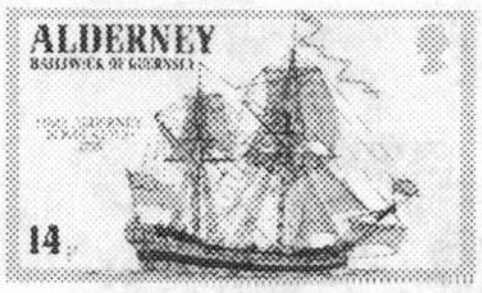

Ships Called HMS *Alderney* A9

1990, May 3 Litho. ***Perf. 13½***

55	A9	14p	Bomb ketch, 1738	.55	.55
56	A9	20p	Sixth-rate, 1742	.75	.75
57	A9	29p	Sloop, 1755	1.10	1.10
58	A9	34p	A-Class submarine, 1945	1.40	1.40
59	A9	37p	Fishery protection vessel, 1979	1.65	1.65
			Nos. 55-59 (5)	5.45	5.45

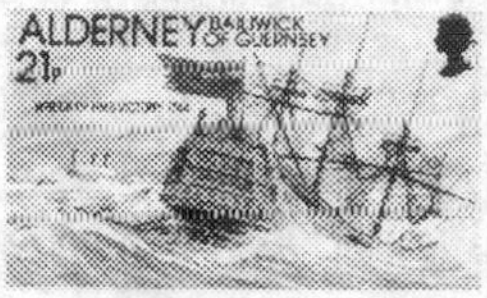

Automation of Casquets Lighthouse — A10

1991, Apr. 20 Litho. ***Perf. 14x13½***

60	A10	21p	Wreck of HMS Victory, 1744	.80	.80
61	A10	26p	Returning by rowboat	.90	.90
62	A10	31p	Helicopter relief	1.10	1.10
63	A10	37p	Lighthouse, birds	1.40	1.40
64	A10	50p	MV Patricia	1.65	1.65
			Nos. 60-64 (5)	5.85	5.85

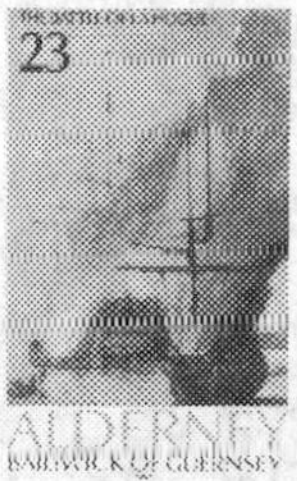

Battle of La Hogue, 300th Anniv. — A11

Designs: 23p, 28p, and 33p, Various details from painting by unknown artist. 50p, Entire painting.

1992, Sept. 18 Litho. ***Perf. 13½***

65	A11	23p	multicolored	.90	.90
66	A11	28p	multicolored	1.10	1.10
67	A11	33p	multicolored	1.25	1.25

Size: 45x30mm

Perf. 14x14½

68	A11	50p	multicolored	1.75	1.75
			Nos. 65-68 (4)	5.00	5.00

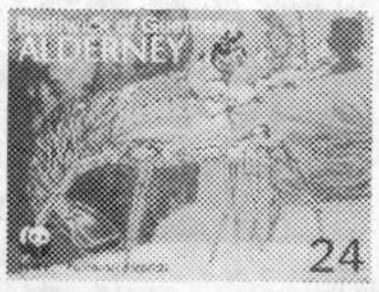

Marine Life — A12

Designs: a, 24p, Palinurus elephas. b, 28p, Metridium senile. c, 33p, Luidia ciliaris. d, 39p, Psammechinus miliaris.

1993, Nov. 2 Litho. ***Perf. 15x14½***

69	A12	Strip of 4, #a.-d.	3.50	3.50

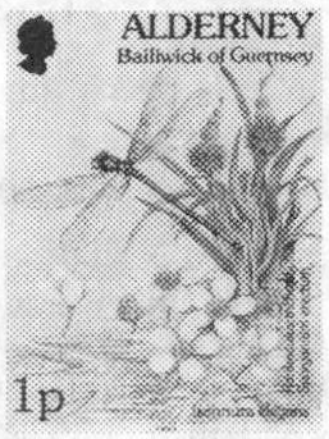

Flora and Fauna — A13

Designs: 1p, Ischnura elegans, ranunculus trichophyllus, sparganium erectum. 2p, Crocidura russula, hypericum linarifolium. 3p, Fulmarus glacialis, carpobrotus edulis. 4p, Colias croceus, trifolium pratense. 5p, Bombus lucorum, orobanche rapum-genistae, cytisus scoparius. 6p, Sylvia undata, cuscuta epithymum, ulex europaeus. 7p, Inachis io, cirsium acaule. 8p, Talpa europaea, endymion non-scripta. 9p, Tettigonia viridissima, ulex europaeus. 10p, Zygaena filipendulae, echium vulgare. 16p, Polyommatus icarus, anacamptis pyramidalis. 20p, Oryctolagus cuniculus, rannunculus repens, pteridium aquilinum. 24p, Larus marinus, romulea columnae. 30p, Fratercula arctica, sedum anglicum. 40p, Saturnia pavonia, rubus fruticosus. 50p, Erinaceus europaeus, oxalis articulata. £1, Sterna hirundo, cynodon dactylon, horiz. £2, Morus bassanus, fucus vesiculosus.

1994-95 Litho. ***Perf. 14***

70	A13	1p	multicolored	.15	.15
71	A13	2p	multicolored	.15	.15
72	A13	3p	multicolored	.15	.15
73	A13	4p	multicolored	.15	.15
74	A13	5p	multicolored	.15	.15
75	A13	6p	multicolored	.18	.18
76	A13	7p	multicolored	.22	.22
77	A13	8p	multicolored	.25	.25
78	A13	9p	multicolored	.28	.28
79	A13	10p	multicolored	.30	.30
80	A13	16p	multicolored	.48	.48
a.			Perf. 14x14½	.48	.48
b.			As "a," booklet pane of 8	4.00	
81	A13	20p	multicolored	.60	.60
82	A13	24p	multicolored	.70	.70
a.			Perf. 14x14½	.70	.70
b.			As "a," booklet pane of 8	5.75	
83	A13	30p	multicolored	.90	.90
84	A13	40p	multicolored	1.25	1.25
85	A13	50p	multicolored	1.50	1.50
86	A13	£1	multicolored	3.00	3.00

Perf. 14x14½

87	A13	£2	multicolored	6.25	6.25
			Nos. 70-87 (18)	16.66	16.66

Issued: £2, 2/28/95; others, 5/5/94.

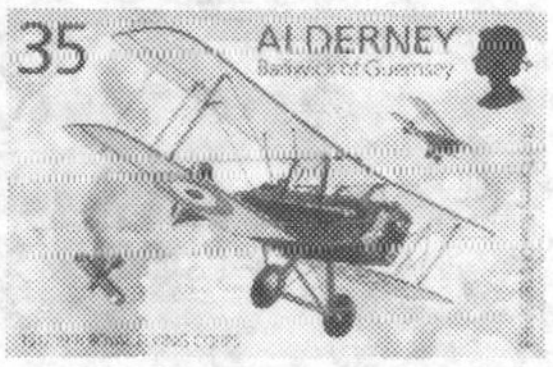

Career of Flt. Lt. Tommy Rose DFC (1895-1968) — A14

Designs: No. 88a, 1917-18 Royal Flying Corps. b, 1939-45 Chief Test Pilot. c, Phillips & Powis (Miles) Aircraft.

No. 89a, Winner, 1935 King's Cup Air Race. b, Winner, 1947 Manx Air Derby. c, UK-Cape-UK Speed Record, 1936.

1995, Sept. 1 Litho. ***Perf. 14x15***

88	A14	35p	Strip of 3, #a.-c.	3.50	3.50
89	A14	41p	Strip of 3, #a.-c.	4.00	4.00

Nos. 88-89 printed in sheets of 12 stamps +h 3 labels.

Souvenir Sheet

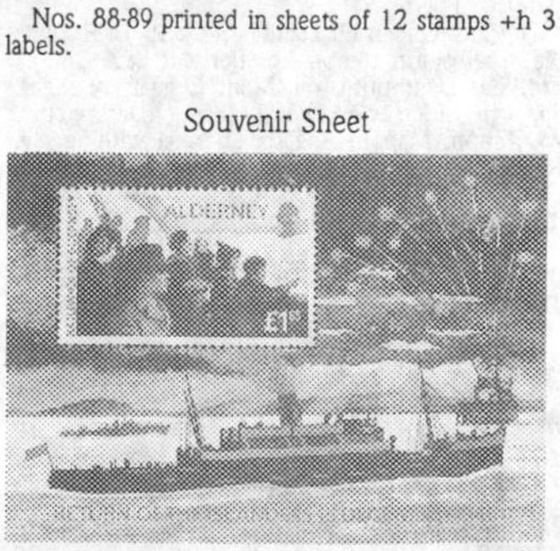

Return of Islanders, 50th Anniv. — A15

Illustration reduced.

1995, Nov. 16 Litho. ***Perf. 13½***

90	A15	£1.65	multicolored	5.25	5.25

JERSEY

jər–zē

LOCATION — Island in the English Channel
GOVT. — Dependent territory (bailiwick) of the British Crown
AREA — 45 sq. mi.
POP. — 76,100 (1980)
CAPITAL — St. Helier

Following the establishment of the British General Post Office as a public corporation on October 1, 1969, the post office of the Bailiwick of Jersey became a separate entity and British postage stamps ceased to be valid.

Catalogue values for unused stamps in this country are for Never Hinged items.

British Regional Issue

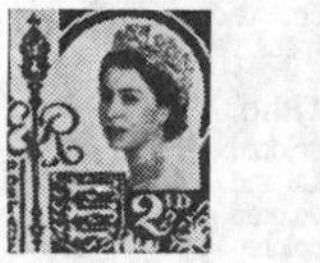

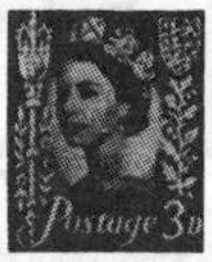

Royal Mace and Arms of Jersey
A1 A2

Perf. 15x14

1958-69 Photo. Wmk. 322

1 A1 2½p rose red ('64) .35 .25
2 A2 3p light purple .35 .15
p. Phosphor. ('67) .15 .15
3 A2 4p ultra ('66) .35 .15
p. Phosphor. ('67) .20 .15

Unwmk.

4 A2 4p olive brown ('68) .20 .15
5 A2 4p brt red ('69) .20 .15
6 A2 5p dark blue ('68) .20 .15
Nos. 1-6 (6) 1.65
Set value .70

Nos. 4-6 are phosphorescent.
Sold to the general public only at post offices within Jersey, but valid for postage throughout Great Britain.

Bailiwick Issues

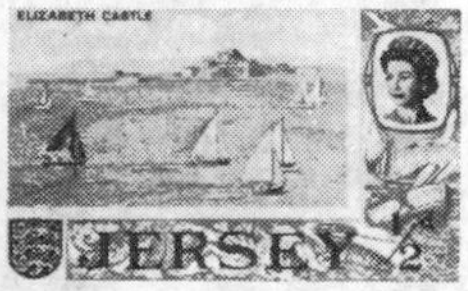

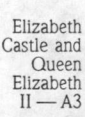

Elizabeth Castle and Queen Elizabeth II — A3

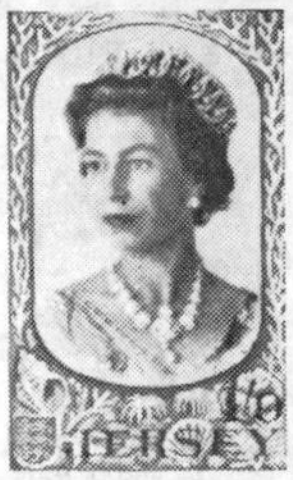

Queen Elizabeth II — A4

Designs (Queen Elizabeth II and): 1p, La Hougue Bie (prehistoric tomb). 2p, Portelet Bay. 3p, La Corbière Lighthouse. 4p, Mont Orgueil by night. 5p, Arms of Jersey and Royal Mace. 6p, Jersey cow. 9p, 1sh6p, Map of English Channel with Jersey. 1sh, Mont Orgueil. 2sh6p, Airport. 5sh, Legislative Chamber. 10sh, Royal Court. £1, Queen Elizabeth II, photograph by Cecil Beaton.

Perf. 14½

1969, Oct. 1 Photo. Unwmk.

7 A3 ½p ocher & multi .35 .35
8 A3 1p brown & multi .15 .15
a. Booklet pane of 1 .40
b. Booklet pane of 2 1.00
9 A3 2p multicolored .15 .15
10 A3 3p dp blue & multi .15 .15
11 A3 4p multicolored .20 .20
a. Booklet pane of 1 .65
b. Booklet pane of 2 1.25
12 A3 5p multicolored .25 .25
a. Booklet pane of 2 2.00
13 A3 6p multicolored .35 .35
14 A3 9p multicolored .45 .45
15 A3 1sh lilac & multi 1.10 1.10
16 A3 1sh6p green & multi 2.25 2.25

Perf. 12

17 A4 1sh9p multicolored 1.75 1.75
18 A3 2sh6p multicolored 7.00 5.00
19 A3 5sh multicolored 15.00 10.00
20 A3 10sh gray & multi 30.00 17.50
a. 10sh green & multi (error) *3,000.*
21 A4 £1 tan & multi 3.50 3.50
Nos. 7-21 (15) 62.65 43.15

See Nos. 34-48, 107-109.

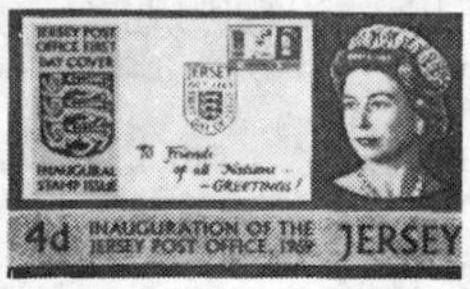

Jersey Post Office First Day Cover A5

1969, Oct. 1 ***Perf. 14½***

22 A5 4p multicolored .25 .20
23 A5 5p blue & multi .30 .20
24 A5 1sh6p brown & multi 2.00 3.25
25 A5 1sh9p emerald & multi 2.50 3.50
Nos. 22-25 (4) 5.05 7.15

Inauguration of independent postal service.

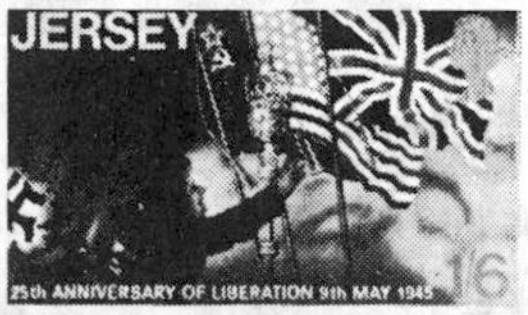

Jersey Woman Reaching for Royal Mace, Flags of USSR, US and Great Britain — A6

Designs: 4p, Lord Coutanche, Bailiff of Jersey, by James Gunn, vert. 5p, Sir Winston Churchill, by D. Van Praag, vert. 1sh9p, Swedish Red Cross ship "Vega."

1970, May 9 Photo. ***Perf. 11½***

26 A6 4p gold & multi .25 .20
27 A6 5p gold & multi .35 .25
28 A6 1sh6p gold & multi 2.25 1.65
29 A6 1sh9p gold & multi 2.75 1.65
Nos. 26-29 (4) 5.60 3.75

25th anniv. of Jersey's liberation from the Germans.

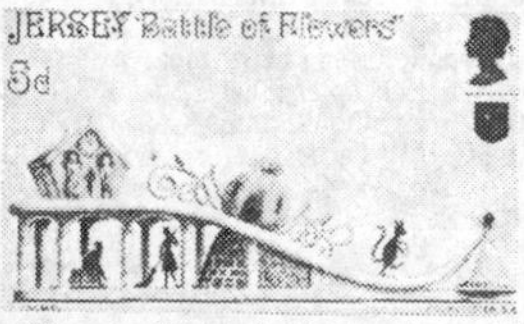

"Rags to Riches" Cinderella — A7

Designs (Parade Floats Made of Flowers): 4p, "A Tribute to Enid Blyton," author of children's books. 1sh6p, "Gourmet's Delight." 1sh9p, "We're the Greatest" (ostriches and trees).

1970, July 28 Photo. ***Perf. 11½***

30 A7 4p gold & multi .45 .30
31 A7 5p gold & multi .60 .45
32 A7 1sh6p gold & multi 11.00 4.25
33 A7 1sh9p gold & multi 12.50 5.50
Nos. 30-33 (4) 24.55 10.50

"Battle of Flowers" annual parade.

Decimal Currency Issue
Types of 1969
"p" instead of "d"

Designs: ½p, Elizabeth Castle. 1p, La Corbiere Lighthouse. 1½p, Jersey cow. 2p, Mont Orgueil by night. 2½p, Arms of Jersey and Royal Mace. 3p, La Hougue Bie. 3½p, Portelet Bay. 4p, 7½p, Map of English Channel and Jersey. 5p, Mont Orgueil by day. 6p, Martello Tower at Archirondel. 9p, Queen Elizabeth II, by Cecil Beaton. 10p, Airport. 20p, Legislative Chamber. 50p, Royal Court.

1970-75 Photo. ***Perf. 14½***

34 A3 ½p ocher & multi ('71) .15 .15
a. Booklet pane of 1 .15
35 A3 1p multicolored ('71) .15 .15
a. Booklet pane of 2 ('75) .15
b. Booklet pane of 4 ('75) .30
36 A3 1½p multicolored ('71) .15 .15
37 A3 2p multicolored ('71) .15 .15
a. Booklet pane of 1 .15
b. Booklet pane of 2 .30
38 A3 2½p multicolored ('71) .15 .15
a. Booklet pane of 1 .30
b. Booklet pane of 2 .40
39 A3 3p brn & multicolored ('71) .15 .15
a. Booklet pane of 1 ('72) .30
b. Booklet pane of 2 ('72) .45
40 A3 3½p multicolored ('71) .20 .20
a. Booklet pane of 1 ('74) .30
b. Booklet pane of 2 ('74) .50
41 A3 4p multicolored ('71) .20 .20
a. Booklet pane of 2 ('75) .50
b. Booklet pane of 4 ('75) .80
42 A3 5p lilac & multi ('71) .25 .25
a. Booklet pane of 2 ('75) .60
b. Booklet pane of 4 ('75) 1.00
43 A3 6p green & multi ('71) .30 .30
44 A3 7½p multicolored ('71) .35 .35
45 A4 9p multicolored ('71) .45 .45

Perf. 12

46 A3 10p multicolored .50 .50
47 A3 20p multicolored .75 .75
48 A3 50p multicolored 1.75 1.75
Nos. 34-48 (15) 5.65 5.65

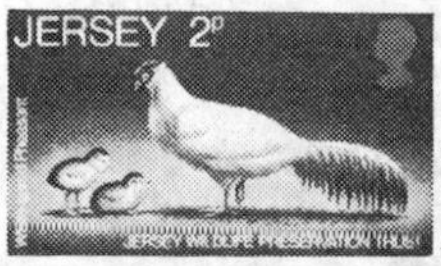

White-eared Pheasant A8

Designs: 2½p, Thick-billed parrots, vert. 7½p, Ursine colobus monkeys, vert. 9p, Ring-tailed lemurs.

1971, Mar. 9 Photo. ***Perf. 11½***

49 A8 2p deep plum & multi .65 .25
50 A8 2½p dark gray & multi .65 .25
51 A8 7½p olive & multi 9.25 3.50
52 A8 9p vio blue & multi 11.00 5.00
Nos. 49-52 (4) 21.55 9.00

Jersey Wildlife Preservation Trust.
See Nos. 65-68.

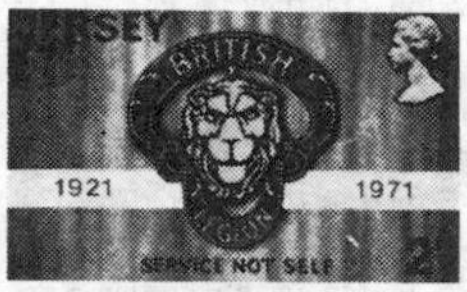

British Legion Emblem A9

Designs: 2½p, Poppy field and poppy emblem. 7½p, Jack Counter (1899-1970) and Victoria Cross. 9p, Flags of France and Great Britain.

1971, June 15 Litho. ***Perf. 14½***

53 A9 2p multicolored .30 .20
54 A9 2½p multicolored .35 .20
55 A9 7½p multicolored 3.00 1.90
56 A9 9p multicolored 3.50 2.50
Nos. 53-56 (4) 7.15 4.80

50th anniversary of the British Legion.

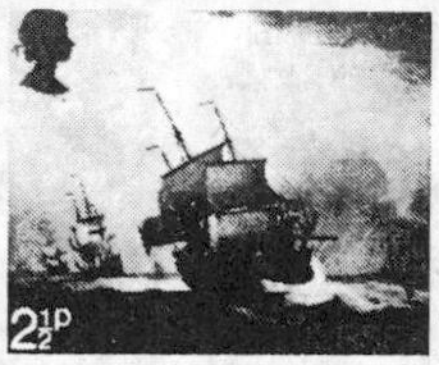

English Fleet in Channel, by Peter Monamy A10

Paintings by Jersey Artists: 2p, Tante Elizabeth (women in farm kitchen), by Edmund Blampied, vert. 7½p, Boyhood of Raleigh (man and boys at seashore), by Sir John Millais. 9p, The Blind Beggar (old man and girl), by W. W. Ouless, vert.

1971, Oct. 5 Photo. ***Perf. 11½***

57 A10 2p gold & multi .45 .30
58 A10 2½p gold & multi .55 .35
59 A10 7½p gold & multi 3.00 2.75
60 A10 9p gold & multi 4.00 4.00
Nos. 57-60 (4) 8.00 7.40

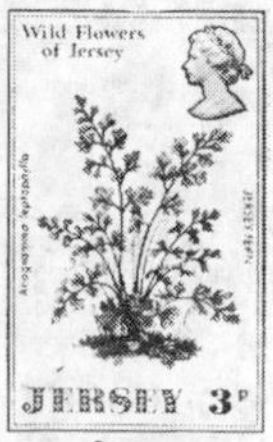

Jersey Fern — A11

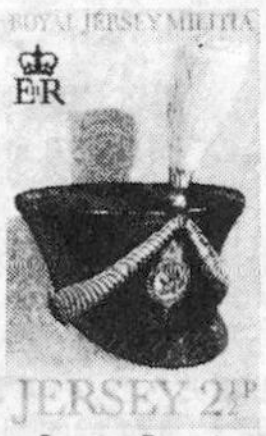

Jersey Royal Artillery Shako — A12

Jersey Wild Flowers: 5p, Thrift. 7½p, Orchid (laxiflora). 9p, Viper's bugloss.

1972, Jan. 18
Flowers in Natural Colors

61 A11 3p brown & blk .30 .15
62 A11 5p lt blue & blk .90 .60
63 A11 7½p lilac & blk 2.75 2.00
64 A11 9p green & blk 3.50 2.75
Nos. 61-64 (4) 7.45 5.50

Wildlife Type of 1971

Designs: 2½p, Cheetahs. 3p, Rothschild's mynahs, vert. 7½p, Spectacled bear. 9p, Tuatara lizards.

1972, Mar. 17 Photo. ***Perf. 11½***
Queen's Head in Gold

65 A8 2½p Prus blue & multi .35 .30
66 A8 3p dk pur & multi .45 .40
67 A8 7½p yel bis & multi 1.75 1.50
68 A8 9p multicolored 2.50 2.25
Nos. 65-68 (4) 5.05 4.45

Jersey Wildlife Preservation Trust.

1972, June 27

69 A12 2½p shown .15 .15
70 A12 3p 2nd North Regiment .20 .15
71 A12 7½p South West Regiment 1.00 .90
72 A12 9p 3rd (South) Light Infantry 1.25 1.10
Nos. 69-72 (4) 2.60 2.30

Royal Jersey Militia shakos of 19th century.

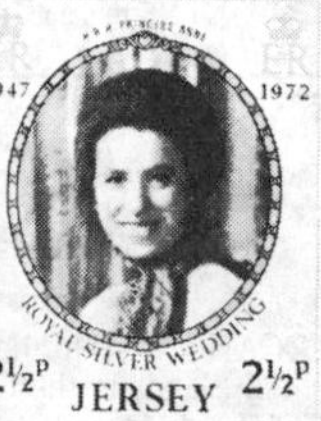

Princess Anne — A13 2½P JERSEY 2½P

Designs: 3p, Queen Elizabeth II and Prince Philip, horiz. 7½p, Prince Charles. 20p, Queen Elizabeth II and family, horiz.

1972, Nov. 1 Photo. ***Perf. 11½***

73 A13 2½p citron & multi .15 .15
74 A13 3p rose & multi .15 .15
75 A13 7½p blue & multi .40 .40
76 A13 20p gray & multi .65 .65
Nos. 73-76 (4) 1.35 1.35

25th anniversary of the marriage of Queen Elizabeth II and Prince Philip.

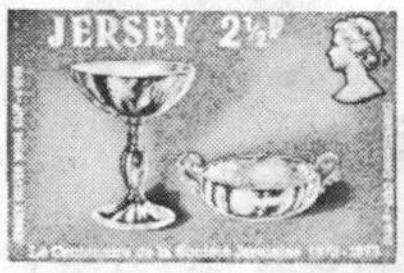

Silver Wine and Christening Cups, 18th Century — A14

Designs: 3p, Gold torque, Bronze Age, vert. 7½p, Seal of Charles II, 1659, vert. 9p, Armorican (Brittany) coins, c. 55 B.C.

1973, Jan. 23 Photo. ***Perf. 11½***

77 A14 2½p ultra & multi .15 .15
78 A14 3p dp car & multi .15 .15
79 A14 7½p org & multi .30 .30
80 A14 9p blue & multi .50 .50
Nos. 77-80 (4) 1.10 1.10

Cent. of the Jersey Soc. Designs are from exhibits in the Soc. museum in St. Helier.

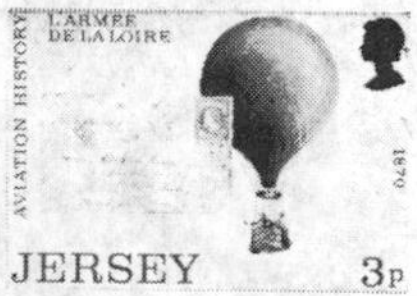

Balloon, Letter to Jersey from Siege of Paris, 1870 — A15

Designs: 5p, Astra seaplane, 1912. 7½p, Supermarine Sea Eagle, 1923. 9p, De Havilland DH86, 1933.

1973, May 16 Photo. ***Perf. 11½***

81 A15 3p brt blue & multi .15 .15
82 A15 5p blue grn & multi .15 .15
83 A15 7½p ultra & multi .40 .40
84 A15 9p vio blue & multi .70 .70
Nos. 81-84 (4) 1.40 1.40

Aviation history connected with Jersey before 1939.

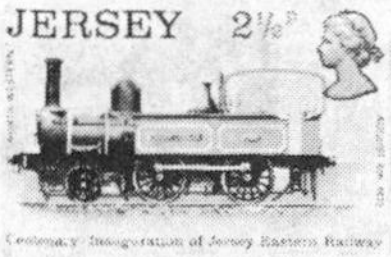

19th Century Locomotives A16

1973, Aug. 6 Photo. *Perf. 11½*

85 A16 2½p North Western .15 .15
86 A16 3p Calvados .15 .15
87 A16 7½p Carteret .55 .55
88 A16 9p Caesarea .75 .75
Nos. 85-88 (4) 1.60 1.60

Centenary of Jersey Eastern Railroad.

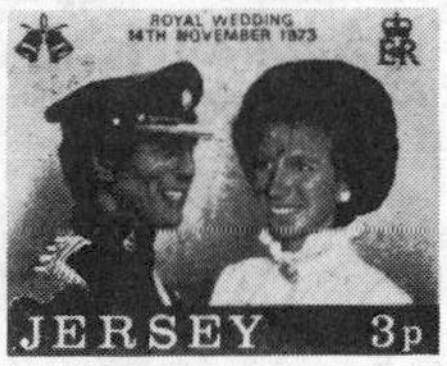

Princess Anne and Mark Phillips A17

1973, Nov. 14 Photo. *Perf. 11½*

89 A17 3p lt blue & multi .15 .15
90 A17 20p pink & multi .95 .95

Wedding of Princess Anne and Capt. Mark Phillips, Nov. 14, 1973.

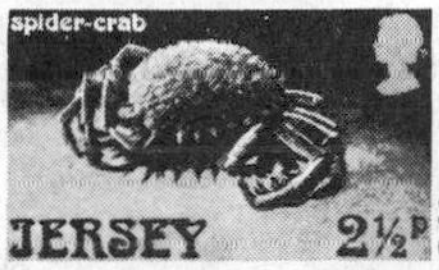

Spider Crab — A18

1973, Nov. 15 Photo. *Perf. 11½*

91 A18 2½p shown .15 .15
92 A18 3p Conger eel .15 .15
93 A18 7½p Lobster .25 .25
94 A18 20p Ormer .60 .60
Nos. 91-94 (4) 1.15 1.15

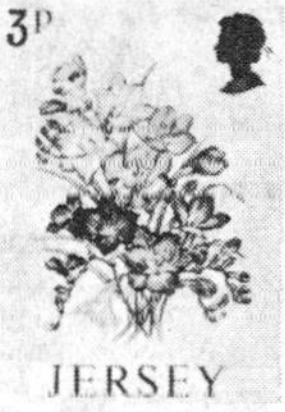

Jersey Spring Flowers — A19

1974, Feb. 13 Photo. *Perf. 12x11½*

95 A19 3p Freesias .15 .15
96 A19 5½p Anemones .20 .20
97 A19 8p Carnations & gladioli .25 .25
98 A19 10p Daffodils & iris .35 .35
Nos. 95-98 (4) .95 .95

First Letter Box, Letter with 1852 Cancel — A20

UPU Cent.: 3p, Postmen, 1862 and 1969. 5½p, Contemporary pillar box and first day cover of No. 101. 20p, BAC 111 and paddle steamer "Aquila," 1874.

1974, June 7 Photo. *Perf. 11½*

99 A20 2½p multicolored .15 .15
100 A20 3p ultra & multi .15 .15
101 A20 5½p olive & multi .20 .20
102 A20 20p gray & multi .70 .70
Nos. 99-102 (4) 1.20 1.20

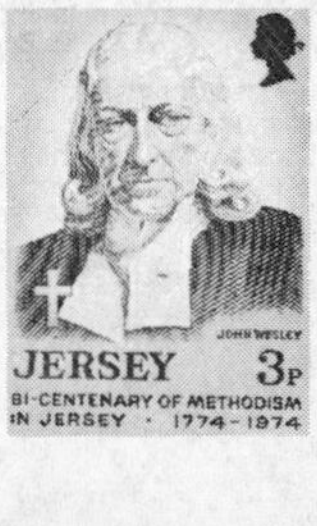

John Wesley — A21

Lithographed and Engraved

1974, July 31 *Perf. 13½x14*

103 A21 3p shown .15 .15
104 A21 3½p Hillary .15 .15
105 A21 8p Wace .25 .25
106 A21 20p Churchill .60 .60
Nos. 103-106 (4) 1.15 1.15

Anniversaries: Methodism in Jersey, bicen.; John Wesley, theologian, founder of Methodism. Sesquicentennial of Royal Natl. Lifeboat Institution, Lt. Col. Sir William Hillary, founder. 800th death anniv. of Canon Wace, poet and chronicler. Sir Winston Churchill.

Type of 1969

Designs: 4½p, Arms of Jersey and Royal Mace. 5½p, Jersey cow. 8p, Mont Orgueil by night.

1974, Oct. 31 Photo. *Perf. 14½*

107 A3 4½p olive & multi .20 .20
108 A3 5½p magenta & multi .25 .25
109 A3 8p yellow & multi .30 .30
Nos. 107-109 (3) .75 .75

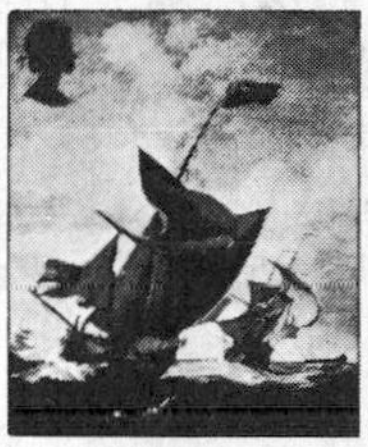

English Yacht, 1660, by Peter Monamy — A22

Marine paintings by Peter Monamy (d. 1749): 5½p, French ship. 8p, Dutch ship, horiz. 25p, Naval battle, 1662.

1974, Nov. 22 Photo. *Perf. 11½*

Size: 31x38, 38x31mm

116 A22 3½p gold & multi .15 .15
117 A22 5½p gold & multi .20 .20
118 A22 8p gold & multi .25 .25

Size: 54x25mm

119 A22 25p gold & multi .70 .70
Nos. 116-119 (4) 1.30 1.30

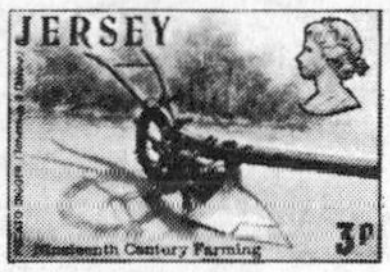

Potato Digger — A23

19th century farming tools: 3½p, Cider apple crusher. 8p, Six-horse plow. 10p, Hay cart.

1975, Feb. 25 Photo. *Perf. 11½*

120 A23 3p multicolored .15 .15
121 A23 3½p multicolored .15 .15
122 A23 8p multicolored .30 .30
123 A23 10p multicolored .35 .35
Nos. 120-123 (4) .95 .95

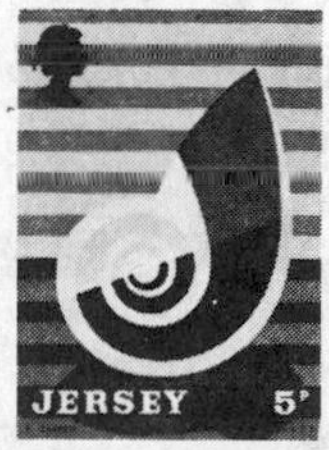

Shell Design as Letter "J" — A24

Designs (Posters): 8p, Beach umbrella. 10p, Beach chair. 12p, Sand castle with Union Jacks and Jersey flag.

1975, June 8 Photo. *Perf. 11½*

124 A24 5p multicolored .15 .15
125 A24 8p multicolored .20 .20
126 A24 10p multicolored .25 .25
127 A24 12p multicolored .35 .35
a. Souvenir sheet of 4 1.00 1.00
Nos. 124-127 (4) .95 .95

Tourist publicity. No. 127a contains Nos. 124-127 in continuous design extending into margin.

Jersey stamps can be mounted in the Scott Channel Islands album.

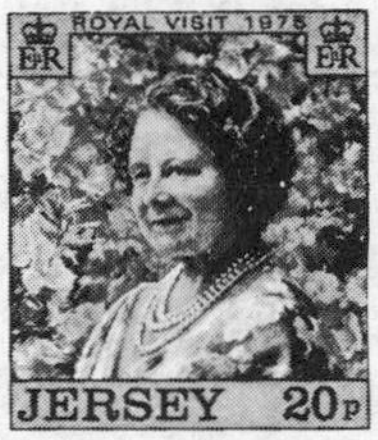

Queen Mother Elizabeth — A25

1975, May 30 Photo. *Perf. 11½*

128 A25 20p multicolored .55 .55

Visit of Queen Mother Elizabeth to Jersey.

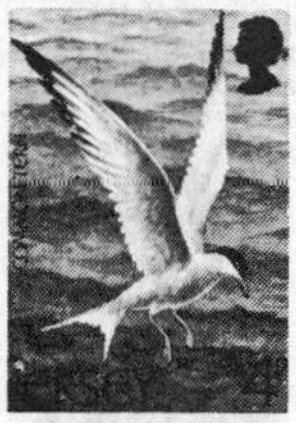

Common Tern — A26

1975, July 28 Photo. *Perf. 11½*

129 A26 4p shown .15 .15
130 A26 5p Storm petrel .15 .15
131 A26 8p Brent geese .25 .25
132 A26 25p Shag .70 .70
Nos. 129-132 (4) 1.25 1.25

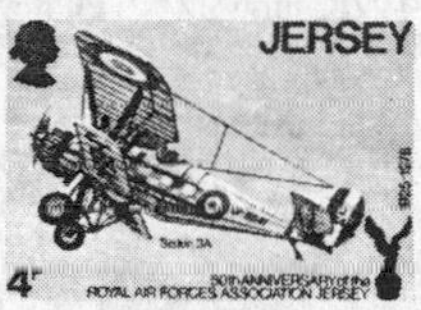

Siskin 3A, 1925 — A27

R.A.F. Planes: 5p, Southampton 1, 1925. 10p, Spitfire 1, 1931. 25p, Gnat T.1, 1962.

1975, Oct. 30 Photo. *Perf. 11½*

133 A27 4p blue & multi .15 .15
134 A27 5p lt green & multi .15 .15
135 A27 10p yellow & multi .30 .30
136 A27 25p ultra & multi .70 .70
Nos. 133-136 (4) 1.30 1.30

Royal Air Force Assoc., Jersey Branch, 50th anniv.

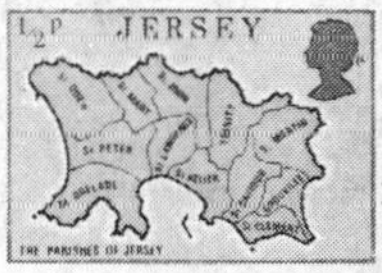

Map of Jersey with 12 Parishes — A28

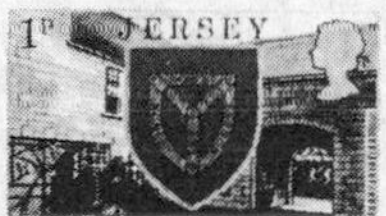

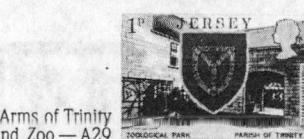

Arms of Trinity and Zoo — A29

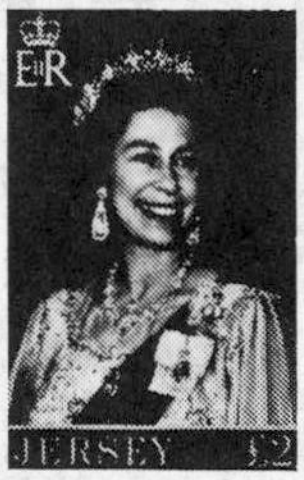

Queen Elizabeth II — A30

Arms and scene: 5p, Church of St. Mary. 6p, Grouville, Seymour Tower. 7p, St. Brelade, La Corbière Lighthouse. 8p, Church of St. Saviour. 9p, St. Helier, Elizabeth Castle. 10p, St. Martin, Gorey Harbor. 11p, St. Peter, Jersey Airport. 12p, St. Ouen, Grosnez Castle. 13p, St. John, Bonne Nuit Harbor. 14p, St. Clement and Le Hocq Tower. 15p, St. Lawrence, Morel Farm. 20p, 12 Parishes, view of harbor. 30p, Jersey flag, map of Island. 40p, Postal Administration emblem, PO Headquarters. 50p, Jersey, Parliament and Royal Court. £1, Flag of Lt.-Governor, Government House.

1976-77 Litho. *Perf. 14½*

Size: 33x23mm

137 A28 ½p lt blue & multi .15 .15
138 A29 1p bister & multi .15 .15
a. Bklt. pane of 2 + 2 labels .15
b. Booklet pane of 4 .25
139 A29 5p rose & multi .15 .15
a. Booklet pane of 4 .75
140 A29 6p vio blue & multi .20 .20
a. Booklet pane of 4 ('78) .80
141 A29 7p fawn & multi .25 .25
a. Booklet pane of 4 1.00
142 A29 8p yel grn & multi .25 .25
a. Booklet pane of 4 ('78) 1.10
143 A29 9p lil rose & multi .30 .30
a. Booklet pane of 4 ('80) 1.25
144 A29 10p ol bis & multi .35 .35
145 A29 11p bl grn & multi .35 .35
146 A29 12p org & multi .40 .40
147 A29 13p blue & multi .40 .40
148 A29 14p yel org & multi .45 .45
149 A29 15p vio & multi .50 .50

Photo.

Perf. 12

Size: 41x26mm, 26x41mm

150 A29 20p gold & multi .65 .65
151 A28 30p gold & multi .90 .90
152 A29 40p gold & multi 1.10 1.10
153 A29 50p gold & multi 1.50 1.50
154 A29 £1 gold & multi 2.25 2.25
155 A30 £2 multicolored ('77) 4.50 4.50
Nos. 137-155 (19) 14.80 14.80

Issue dates: Nos. 137-149, Jan. 29; Nos. 150-154, Aug. 20. No. 155, Nov. 16.

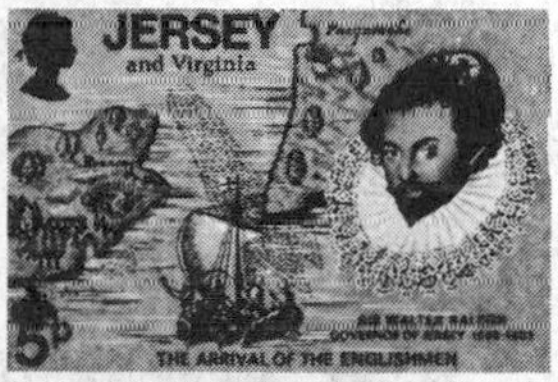

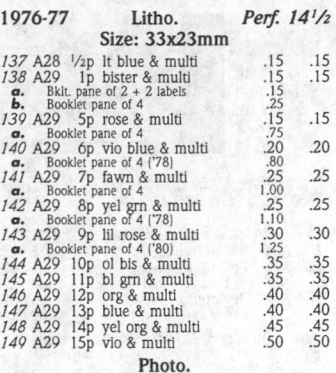

Sir Walter Raleigh and Old Map of Virginia — A31

American Bicentennial: 7p, Sir George Carteret and old map of New Jersey. 11p, Philippe Dauvergne and ships landing on Long Island. 13p, John Singleton Copley and his "Death of Major Pierson."

1976, May 29 Photo. *Perf. 11½*

160 A31 5p multicolored .20 .15
161 A31 7p multicolored .20 .20
162 A31 11p multicolored .30 .30
163 A31 13p multicolored .35 .35
Nos. 160-163 (4) 1.05 1.00

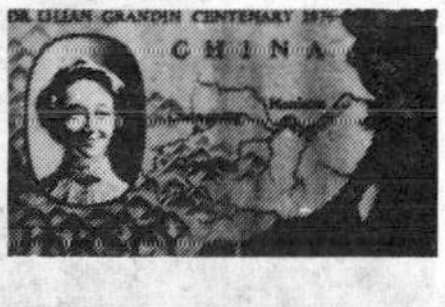

Dr. Grandin, Central and Southern China Map — A32

Designs: 7p, Yangtze River journey. 11p, On horseback to Chaotung. 13p, Dr. Grandin holding infant.

1976, Nov. 25 Photo. *Perf. 11½*

164 A32 5p multicolored .15 .15
165 A32 7p multicolored .20 .20
166 A32 11p multicolored .30 .30
167 A32 13p multicolored .35 .35
Nos. 164-167 (4) 1.00 1.00

Lilian Mary Grandin (1876-1924), Jersey-born missionary doctor in China.

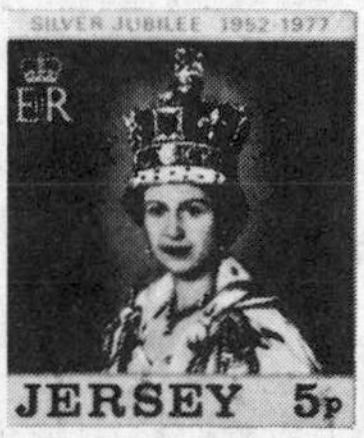

Queen Wearing St. Edward's Crown — A33

Designs: 7p, Queen with Jersey Bailiff Sir Alexander Coutanche, 1957. 25p, Portrait, 1976.

1977, Feb. 7 Photo. *Perf. 11½*

168 A33 5p multicolored .15 .15
169 A33 7p multicolored .15 .15
170 A33 25p multicolored .85 .85
Nos. 168-170 (3) 1.15 1.15

25th anniv. of the reign of Elizabeth II.

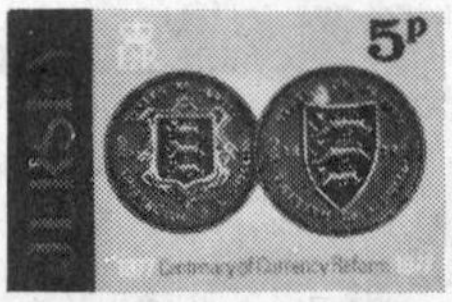

1/13th sh, 1871 and 1/12th sh, 1877
A34

Coins: 7p, 1/12th sh, 1949. 11p, Silver crown, 1966. 13p, Silver £2, 1972.

1977, Mar. 25 Litho. *Perf. 14*

171	A34	5p multicolored	.15	.15
172	A34	7p multicolored	.20	.20
173	A34	11p multicolored	.30	.30
174	A34	13p multicolored	.35	.35
		Nos. 171-174 (4)	1.00	1.00

Centenary of Jersey's currency reform.

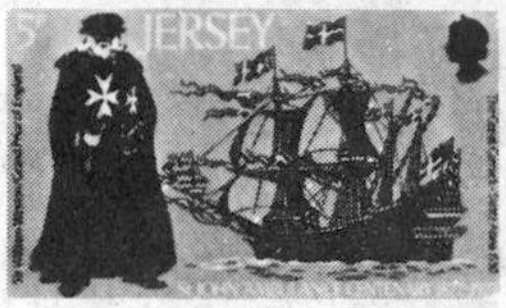

Sir William Weston and Santa Anna, 1530
A35

Designs: 7p, Sir William Drogo and horse-drawn ambulance, 1877. 11p, Duke of Connaught and Jersey ambulance, 1917. 13p, Richard, Duke of Gloucester and ambulance team, 1977.

1977, June 24 Litho. *Perf. 14x13½*

175	A35	5p multicolored	.15	.15
176	A35	7p multicolored	.20	.20
177	A35	11p multicolored	.30	.30
178	A35	13p multicolored	.35	.35
		Nos. 175-178 (4)	1.00	1.00

St. John Ambulance Assoc. cent. (in GB).

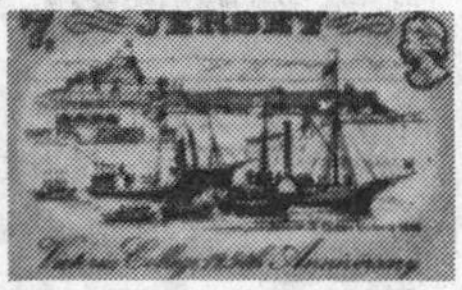

Victoria and Albert Arriving in Jersey, 1846
A36

Designs: 10½p, Victoria College, 1852. 11p, Statue of Sir Galahad near college gate, vert. 13p, College Hall, interior, vert.

1977, Sept. 29 Litho. *Perf. 14½*

179	A36	7p multicolored	.20	.20
180	A36	10½p multicolored	.30	.30
181	A36	11p multicolored	.35	.35
182	A36	13p multicolored	.40	.40
		Nos. 179-182 (4)	1.25	1.25

Jersey Victoria College, 125th anniv.

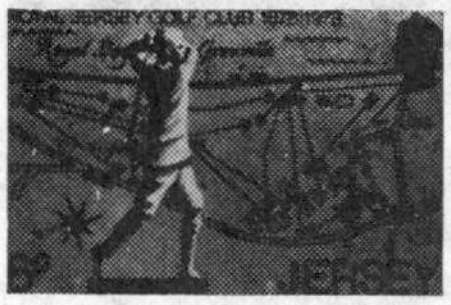

Harry Vardon Statuette, Layout of Golf Course
A37

Designs: 8p, Golf grip and swing perfected by Vardon. 11p, Vardon's putting grip and stance. 13p, Vardon's British and US Open Golf trophies, his book "The Complete Golfer" and biography.

1978, Feb. 28 Litho. *Perf. 14*

183	A37	6p multicolored	.20	.20
184	A37	8p multicolored	.30	.30
185	A37	11p multicolored	.35	.35
186	A37	13p multicolored	.40	.40
		Nos. 183-186 (4)	1.25	1.25

Cent. of Royal Jersey Golf Club and to honor Vardon (1870-1937), Jersey-born golfer.

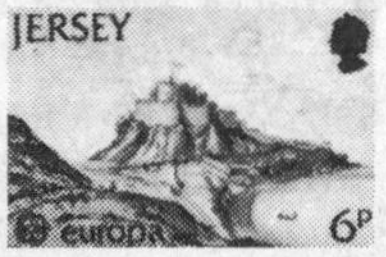

Mont Orgueil — A38

Europa: 8p, St. Aubin's Fort. 10½p, Elizabeth Castle.

1978, May 1 Photo. *Perf. 11½*

187	A38	6p multicolored	.15	.15
188	A38	8p multicolored	.25	.25
189	A38	10½p multicolored	.35	.35
		Nos. 187-189 (3)	.75	.75

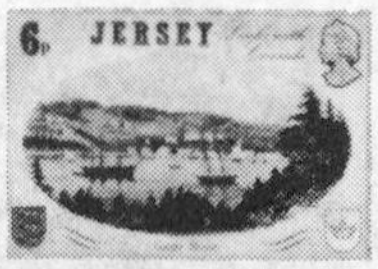

Gaspe Basin, by P. J. Ouless — A39

Designs: 8p, Early map of Gaspe Peninsula, after Capt. Cook. 10½p, Sailing ship Century. 11p, Early map of Jersey. 13p, St. Aubin's Bay Town and Harbor.

1978, June 9 Litho. *Perf. 14x15*

190	A39	6p multicolored	.15	.15
191	A39	8p multicolored	.25	.25
192	A39	10½p multicolored	.25	.25
193	A39	11p multicolored	.30	.30
194	A39	13p multicolored	.40	.40
		Nos. 190-194 (5)	1.35	1.35

Jersey's links with Canada and for CAPEX, Canadian Intl. Phil. Exhib., Toronto, Ont., June 9-18.

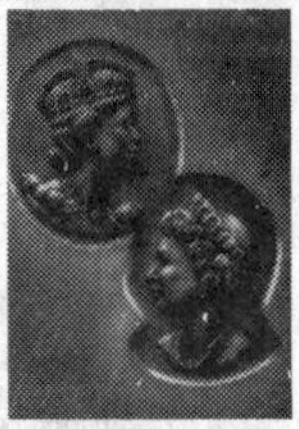

Elizabeth II, Portraits 1953 and 1977 — A40

Design: 8p, Elizabeth II and Prince Philip.

1978, June 27 Photo. *Perf. 11½*

195	A40	8p car, sil & black	.20	.20
196	A40	25p blue, sil & black	.70	.70

25th anniv. of coronation of Queen Elizabeth II and for Royal visit, June 27.

Mail Cutter — A41

Packets: 8p, Flamer, paddle vessel. 10½p, Diana, screw steamer. 11p, Ibex, steamer. 13p, Caesarea, mini-liner.

1978, Oct. 18 Litho. *Perf. 14½x14*

197	A41	6p multicolored	.20	.20
198	A41	8p multicolored	.25	.25
199	A41	10½p multicolored	.30	.30
200	A41	11p multicolored	.35	.35
201	A41	13p multicolored	.40	.40
		Nos. 197-201 (5)	1.50	1.50

First Government packet between Britain and Jersey, bicentenary.

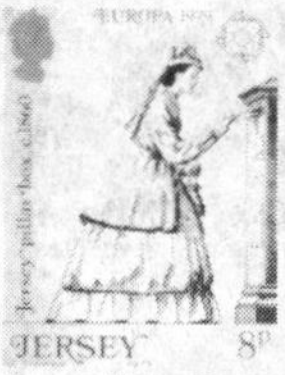

Jersey Pillar Box, 1860 — A42

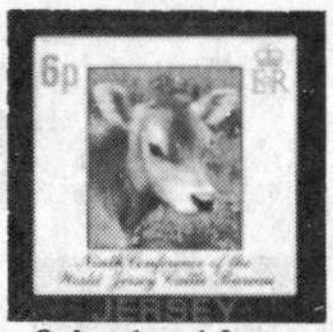

Soft-colored Jersey Heifer — A43

Europa: No. 203, Mailman emptying 1979 mailbox. No. 204, Telephone switchboard, c. 1900. No. 205, Operator working on contemporary telecommunications system.

Perf. 14, 14½x15

1979, Mar. 1 Litho.

202	A42	8p yellow & blk	.15	.15
203	A42	8p carmine & blk	.15	.15
a.		Pair, #202-203	.35	.35
204	A42	10½p violet & blk	.40	.40
205	A42	10½p blue & blk	.40	.40
a.		Pair, #204-205	.80	.80
		Nos. 202-205 (4)	1.10	1.10

Nos. 203a, 205a have continuous design.

1979, Mar. 1

Design: 25p, Milk-laden Jersey cow with First Prize ribbon.

206	A43	6p multicolored	.20	.20
		Size: 48x31mm		
207	A43	25p multicolored	.75	.75

30th anniv. of 1st Intl. Conf. of Jersey Breed Societies and 9th Conf. of the World Jersey Cattle Bureau.

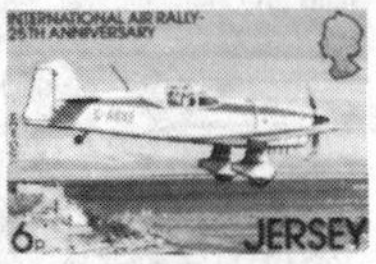

Percival Mew Gull — A44

Planes: 8p, De Havilland Chipmunk. 10½p, Druine D-31 Turbulent. 11p, De Havilland Tiger Moth. 13p, North American Harvard Mk. 4.

1979, Apr. 24 Photo. *Perf. 11½*

208	A44	6p multicolored	.20	.20
209	A44	8p multicolored	.25	.25
210	A44	10½p multicolored	.35	.35
211	A44	11p multicolored	.35	.35
212	A44	13p multicolored	.40	.40
		Nos. 208-212 (5)	1.55	1.55

25th International Air Rally.

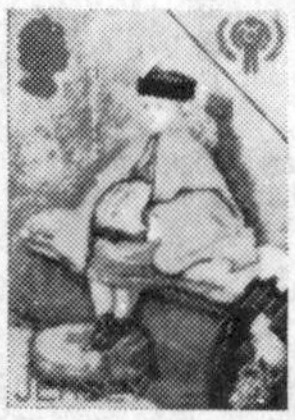

My First Sermon, by Millais — A45

Paintings by Millais: 10½p, Orphan. 11p, The Princes in the Tower. 25p, Jesus in the Home of His Parents, horiz.

1979, Aug. 13 Photo. *Perf. 11½*

Size: 25x35mm

213	A45	8p multicolored	.25	.25
214	A45	10½p multicolored	.30	.30
215	A45	11p multicolored	.30	.30
		Size: 49x30mm		
216	A45	25p multicolored	.70	.70
		Nos. 213-216 (4)	1.55	1.55

IYC and for John Everett Millais (1829-96).

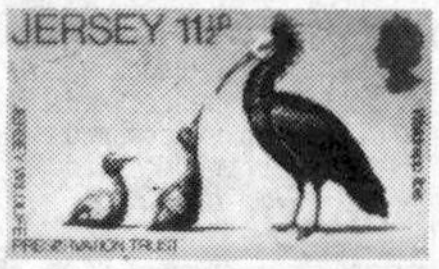

Waldrapp Ibis — A46

1979, Nov. 8 Photo. *Perf. 11½*

217	A46	6p Pink pigeons	.15	.15
218	A46	8p Orangutans	.20	.20
219	A46	11½p shown	.30	.30
220	A46	13p Lowland gorillas	.35	.35
221	A46	15p Rodrigues fruit bats	.40	.40
		Nos. 217-221 (5)	1.40	1.40

Nos. 217-218, 220-221 vertical.

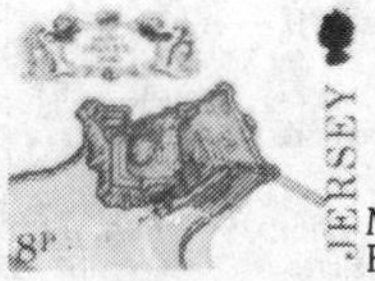

Mont Orgueil Fortress — A47

Fortresses, 300th Anniversary: 11½p, St. Aubin Tower. 13p, Elizabeth. 25p, Map of Jersey showing fortress locations.

1980, Feb. 5 Litho. *Perf. 14½x13½*

222	A47	8p multicolored	.20	.20
223	A47	11½p multicolored	.30	.30
224	A47	13p multicolored	.35	.35
		Perf. 13½x14		
		Size: 37½x26mm		
225	A47	25p multicolored	.65	.65
		Nos. 222-225 (4)	1.50	1.50

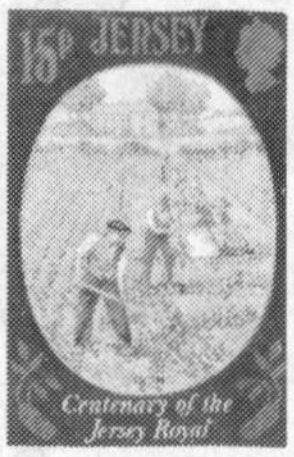

Potato Harvest — A48

Royal Jersey Potato Cent.: 7p, Planting potatoes. 17½p, Loading dock, Weighbridge.

1980, May 6 Litho. *Perf. 14*

226	A48	7p multicolored	.20	.20
227	A48	15p multicolored	.40	.40
228	A48	17½p multicolored	.45	.45
		Nos. 226-228 (3)	1.05	1.05

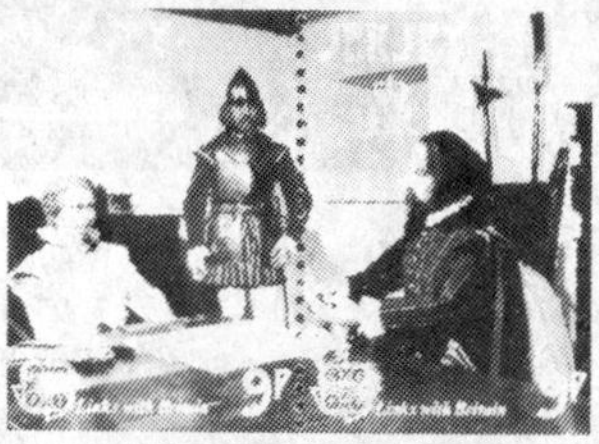

Sir Walter Raleigh and Paul Ivy
A49 A50

Europa (Wax Figures from Mont Orgueil and Elizabeth Castles): No. 230, Charles II and Sir George Carteret, Lady Carteret. Pairs in continuous design.

1980, May 6

229	Pair	.50	.50
a.	A49 9p multicolored	.25	.25
b.	A50 9p multicolored	.25	.25
230	Pair	.75	.75
a.	A49 13½p multicolored	.35	.35
b.	A50 13½p multicolored	.35	.35

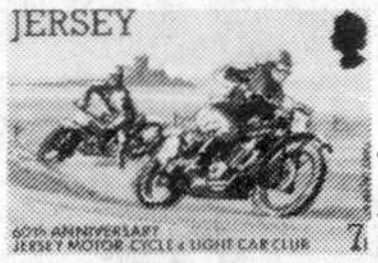

Three-lap Motorcycle Race — A51

1980, July 24 Litho. *Perf. 12*

Granite Paper

231	A51	7p shown	.20	.20
232	A51	9p Intl. road race	.25	.25
233	A51	13½p Motorcycle scrambling	.40	.40
234	A51	15p Sand racing, saloon cars	.45	.45
235	A51	17½p Natl. Hill climb	.50	.50
		Nos. 231-235 (5)	1.80	1.80

Jersey Motorcycle and Light Car Club, 60th anniv.

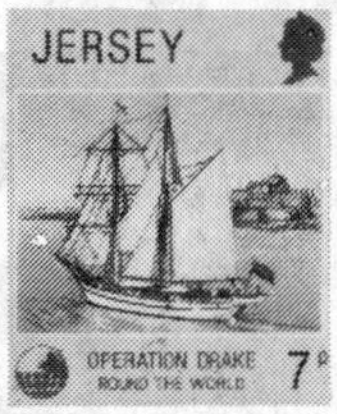

"Eye of the Wind" Leaving St. Helier — A52

Designs: 9p, Medical research, Cuna Indians, Panama. 13½p, Exploration, Papua New Guinea. 14p, Capt. Scott's ship, Antarctica. 15p, Conservation, Sulawesi. 17½p, Marine studies.

1980, Oct. 1 Litho. *Perf. 14½*

236	A52	7p multicolored	.20	.20
237	A52	9p multicolored	.25	.25
238	A52	13½ multicolored	.35	.35
239	A52	14p multicolored	.35	.35
240	A52	15p multicolored	.40	.40
241	A52	17½p multicolored	.45	.45
		Nos. 236-241 (6)	2.00	2.00

Operation Drake, a two-year, round-the-world scientific expedition in tribute to Royal Geographic Society sesquicentennial.

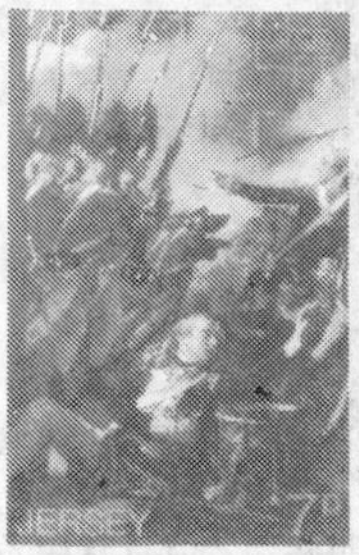

Armed Soldiers and Wounded Drummer — A53

Designs: Details from The Death of Major Peirson, by John Singleton Copley.

1981, Jan. 6 Photo. *Perf. 12½*
Granite Paper

242 A53 7p multicolored .20 .20
243 A53 10p multicolored .30 .30
244 A53 15p multicolored .45 .45
245 A53 17½p multicolored .55 .55
a. Souvenir sheet of 4, #242-245 1.65 1.65
Nos. 242-245 (4) 1.50 1.50

Battle of Jersey bicentenary. No. 245a has continuous design.

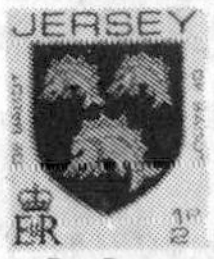

De Bagot Family Arms — A54

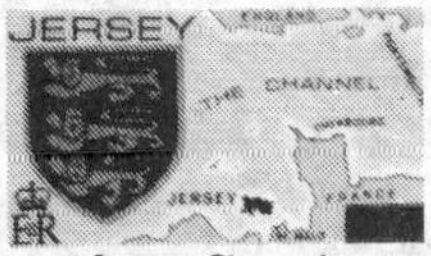

Jersey, Channel Map — A54a

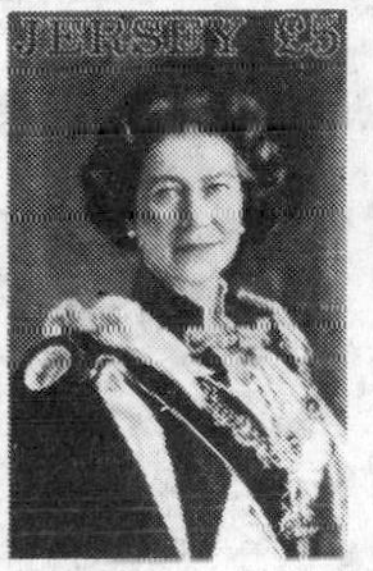

Queen Elizabeth II, by Norman Hepple — A54b

1981-83 Litho. *Perf. 14*

246 A54 ½p shown .15 .15
247 A54 1p De Carteret .15 .15
a. Booklet pane of 6 .30
248 A54 2p La Cloche .15 .15
a. Booklet pane of 6 .50
249 A54 3p Dumaresq .15 .15
a. Booklet pane of 6 .60
250 A54 4p Payn .15 .15
251 A54 5p Janvrin .20 .20
252 A54 6p Poingdestre .20 .20
253 A54 7p Pipon .25 .25
a. Booklet pane of 6 1.50
254 A54 8p Marett .30 .30
a. Booklet pane of 6 ('83) 1.90
255 A54 9p Le Breton .30 .30
256 A54 10p Le Maistre .35 .35
a. Booklet pane of 6 2.25
257 A54 11p Bisson .40 .40
b. Booklet pane of 6 ('83) 2.75
258 A54 12p Robin .40 .40
259 A54 13p Herault .45 .45
260 A54 14p Messervy .50 .50
261 A54 15p Fiott .55 .55
262 A54 20p Badier .75 .75
263 A54 25p L'Arbalestier .90 .90
264 A54 30p Journeaulx 1.10 1.10
265 A54 40p Lempriere 1.25 1.25
266 A54 50p D'Auvergne 1.50 1.50
267 A54a £1 shown 2.25 2.25

Photo.
Perf. 12½x12

268 A54b £5 multi 11.00 11.00
Nos. 246-268 (23) 23.40 23.40

Issued: #246-256, Feb. 24; #257-262, July 28. #263-267, Feb. 23, 1982; £5, Nov. 17, 1983.

1984-88 *Perf. 15x14*

247b A54 1p ('88) .15 .15
248b A54 2p Bklt. pane of 6, ('86) .50
248c A54 2p ('84) .15 .15
249b A54 3p Bklt. pane of 6, ('84) .60
249c A54 3p ('84) .15 .15
250a A54 4p Bklt. pane of 6, ('87) 1.00
250b A54 4p ('88) .15 .15
251a A54 5p ('86) .15 .15
252a A54 6p ('86) .20 .20
255a A54 9p Bklt. pane of 6, ('84) 1.50
255b A54 9p ('84) .25 .25
256b A54 10p Bklt. pane of 6, ('86) 1.80
256c A54 10p ('86) .30 .30
257a A54 11p Bklt. pane of 6, ('87) 2.25
257c A54 11p ('87) .35 .35
258a A54 12p Bklt. pane of 6, ('84) 2.25
258b A54 12p ('88) .35 .35
259a A54 13p ('84) .40 .40
260a A54 14p Bklt. pane of 6, ('86) 2.50
260b A54 14p ('84) .40 .40
261a A54 15p ('87) .40 .40
261b A54 15p Bklt. pane of 6, ('87) 2.75
262a A54 20p ('86) .60 .60
264a A54 30p ('86) .95 .95
265a A54 40p ('87) 1.00 1.00
266a A54 50p ('87) 1.25 1.25

Issued: Nos. 251a, 252a, 262a, 264a, Mar. 4.
Nos. 247a-248a dated "February 1981" or "April 1983"; Nos. 253a, 256a dated "February 1981" or "December 1981." Nos. 250a and 258a also exist dated "May 1988."
See Nos. 381-388.

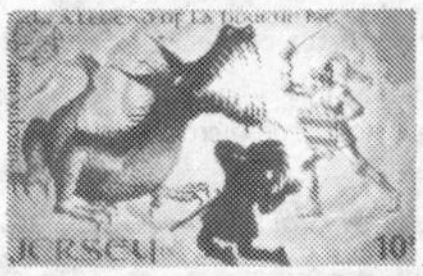

Knight of Hamby Killing the Dragon A55

Europa (Legends): 10p, La Hougue Bie. 18p, Easter Voyage of St. Brelade. No. 272, Servant killing Knight of Hamby. No. 273, Shipwreck of St. Brelade. No. 274, Fish, ships' departure.

1981, Apr. 7 *Perf. 14½*

271 A55 10p multicolored .30 .30
272 A55 10p multicolored .30 .30
a. Pair, #271-272 .60 .60
273 A55 18p multicolored .50 .50
274 A55 18p multicolored .50 .50
a. Pair, #273-274 1.00 1.00
Nos. 271-274 (4) 1.60 1.60

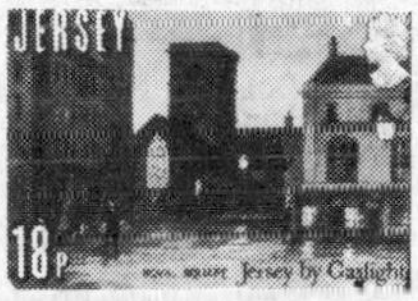

Royal Square by Gaslight A56

1981, May 22 Photo. *Perf. 12*
Granite Paper

275 A56 7p The Harbor .20 .20
276 A56 10p The Quay .30 .30
277 A56 18p shown .50 .50
278 A56 22p Halkett Place .60 .60
279 A56 25p Central Market .70 .70
Nos. 275-279 (5) 2.30 2.30

Gas light sesquicentennial.

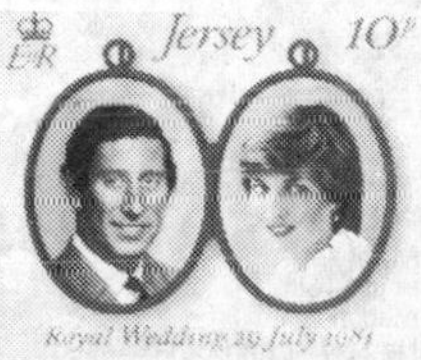

Prince Charles and Lady Diana A57

1981, July 28 Photo. *Perf. 12*
Granite Paper

280 A57 10p multicolored .45 .45
281 A57 25p multicolored 1.10 1.10

Royal Wedding.

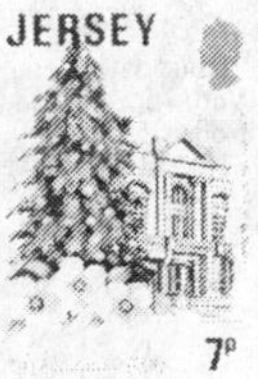

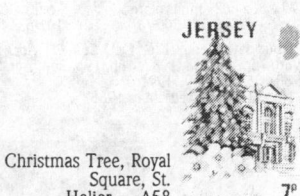

Christmas Tree, Royal Square, St. Helier — A58

1981, Sept. 29 Litho. *Perf. 14½*

282 A58 7p shown .25 .25
283 A58 10p East window, St. Helier's Church, choir .35 .35
284 A58 18p Boxing Day, Jersey Drag Hunt .60 .60
Nos. 282-284 (3) 1.20 1.20

Christmas 1981.

Europa 1982 — A59

Designs: Maps showing formation of Channel Islands resulting from rise in sea level.

1982, Apr. 20 Litho. *Perf. 14½*

285 A59 11p 16,000 BC .30 .30
286 A59 11p 10,000 BC, vert. .30 .30
287 A59 19½p 7,000 BC, vert. .50 .50
288 A59 19½p 4,000 BC .50 .50
Nos. 285-288 (4) 1.60 1.60

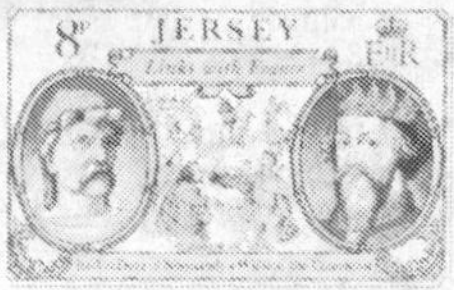

Rollon Duke of Normandy, William the Conqueror, Clameur de Haro (Plea of Injunction) A60

Links with France: No. 290, Kings John and Philippe Auguste, Siege of Rouen. No. 291, Jean Martxell (1694-1753), brandy merchant. No. 292, Victor Hugo. No. 293, Pierre Teilhard de Chardin (1881-1955), theologian. No. 294, Charles Rey (1897-1981), meteorologist.

1982, June 11 Litho. *Perf. 14*

289 A60 8p multicolored .25 .25
290 A60 8p multicolored .25 .25
a. Bklt. pane of 4+label, 2 each #289-290 1.00 1.00
b. Pair, #289-290 .50 .50
291 A60 11p multicolored .35 .35
292 A60 11p multicolored .35 .35
a. Bklt. pane of 4+label, 2 each #291-292 1.40 1.40
b. Pair, #291-292 .70 .70
293 A60 19½p multicolored .65 .65
294 A60 19½p multicolored .65 .65
a. Bklt. pane of 4+label, 2 each #293-294 2.60 2.60
b. Pair, #293-294 1.30 1.30
Nos. 289-294 (6) 2.50 2.50

Issue date: Nos. 290a-294a, Sept. 7. Two versions of Nos. 290a, 292a and 294a exist: the label is inscribed in English or French.

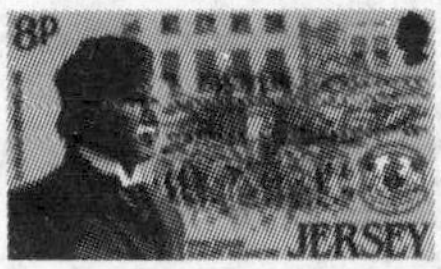

Scouting Year — A61

Designs: 8p, Sir William Smith (Boys Brigade founder). 11p, Liberation parade, 1945, vert. 24p, Boys Brigade annual display, 1903. 26p, The Baden-Powells, 1924, vert. 29p, Scouts.

1982, Nov. 18 Photo. *Perf. 12*
Granite Paper

295 A61 8p multicolored .25 .25
296 A61 11p multicolored .35 .35
297 A61 24p multicolored .75 .75
298 A61 26p multicolored .85 .85
299 A61 29p multicolored .95 .95
Nos. 295-299 (5) 3.15 3.15

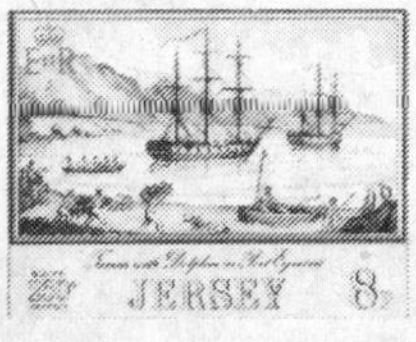

Port Egmont — A62

250th Birth Anniv. of Capt. Philippe de Carteret (1733-97): 18th cent. engravings.

1983, Feb. 15 Litho. *Perf. 14¼*

300 A62 8p shown .25 .25
301 A62 11p Dolphin, Swallow .30 .30
302 A62 19½p Discovering Pitcairn Is. .55 .55
303 A62 24p English Cove, New Ireland .70 .70
304 A62 26p Sinking pirate ship .75 .75
305 A62 29p Endymion .90 .90
Nos. 300-305 (6) 3.45 3.45

No. 19 — A63

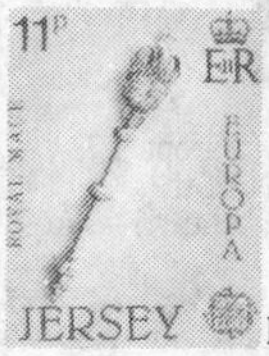

Royal Mace — A64

1983, Apr. 19 Litho.

306 A63 11p shown .40 .40
307 A64 11p shown .40 .40
a. Pair, #306-307 .80 .80
308 A63 19½p No. 20 .70 .70
309 A64 19½p Bailiff's seal .70 .70
a. Pair, #308-309 1.50 1.50
Nos. 306-309 (4) 2.20 2.20

Europa.

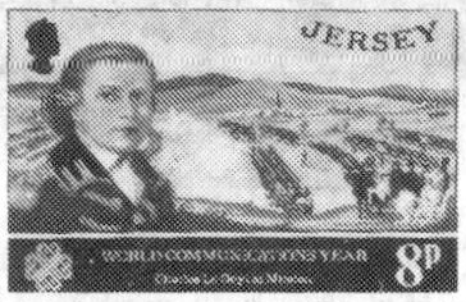

World Communications Year — A65

1st Postmaster Charles William LeGeyt (1733-1827): 8p, Commanding Grenadier Co., 25th Foot, Battle of Minden, 1759. 11p, London-Weymouth mail coach. 24p, PO Mail Packet attacked by French privateer. 25p, Hue St. PO. 29p, St. Helier Harbor.

1983, June 21 Litho. *Perf. 14*

310 A65 8p multicolored .25 .25
311 A65 11p multicolored .35 .35
312 A65 24p multicolored .75 .75
313 A65 26p multicolored .80 .80
314 A65 29p multicolored .95 .95
Nos. 310-314 (5) 3.10 3.10

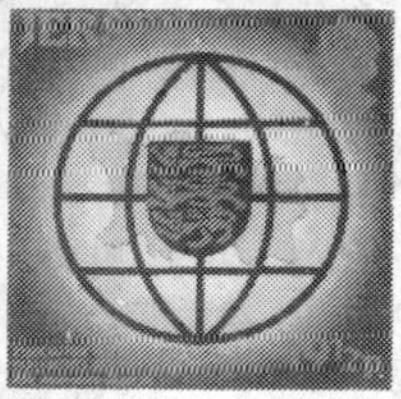

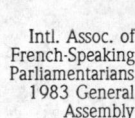

Intl. Assoc. of French-Speaking Parliamentarians 1983 General Assembly A66

1983, June 21 *Perf. 15*

315 A66 19½p multicolored .75 .75

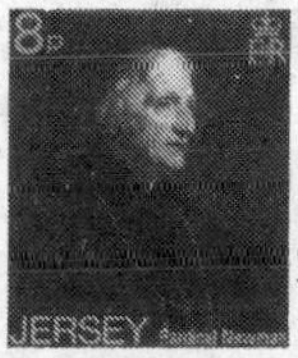

Cardinal Newman, by Walter William Ouless (1848-1933) — A67

1983, Sept. 20 Photo. *Perf. 11½*

316 A67 8p shown .25 .25
317 A67 11p M. De Cazotte and his Daughter .35 .35
318 A67 20½p Thomas Hardy .65 .65

Size: 41x34mm

319 A67 31p David with the Head of Goliath .95 .95
Nos. 316-319 (4) 2.20 2.20

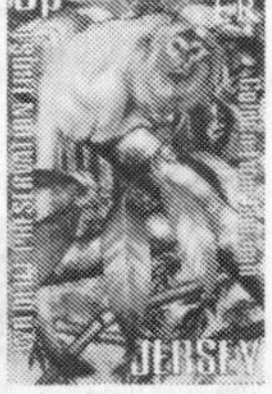

Jersey Wildlife Preservation Trust — A68

1984, Jan. 17 Litho. *Perf. 14*

320 A68 9p Golden Lion Tamarin .30 .30
321 A68 12p Snow Leopard .35 .35
322 A68 20½p Jamaican Boa .65 .65
323 A68 26p Round Island Gecko .80 .80
324 A68 28p Coscoroba Swan .85 .85
325 A68 31p St. Lucia Parrot .95 .95
Nos. 320-325 (6) 3.90 3.90

Europa 1984 (25th Anniv.) — A69

1984, Mar. 12   Perf. 14½x15
326 A69   9p multicolored   .30   .30
327 A69   12p multicolored   .35   .35
328 A69   20½p multicolored   .65   .65
    Nos. 326-328 (3)   1.30   1.30

Souvenir Sheet

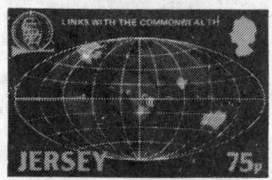

Jersey Links with the Commonwealth — A70

1984, Mar. 12   Perf. 15x14½
329 A70   75p multicolored   2.75   2.75
Commonwealth Postal Administrations Conf.

Royal Natl. Lifeboat Institution Centenary A71

Rescue Scenes (Lifeboats and Ships).

1984, June 1   Litho.   Perf. 14½
330 A71   9p Sarah Brooshoft, Demie de Pas Light   .35   .35
331 A71   9p Hearts of Oak, Maurice Georges   .35   .35
332 A71   12p Elizabeth Rippon, Hanna   .45   .45
333 A71   12p Elizabeth Rippon, Santa Maria   .45   .45
334 A71   20½p Elizabeth Rippon, Bacchus   .75   .75
335 A71   20½p Thomas James King, Cythara   .75   .75
    Nos. 330-335 (6)   3.10   3.10

40th Anniv. of Intl. Civil Aviation Org. — A72

1984, July 24   Litho.   Perf. 14
Granite Paper
336 A72   9p Bristol Type 170   .35   .35
337 A72   12p Airspeed AS-57 Ambassador 2   .45   .45
338 A72   26p De Havilland Heron 1B   .95   .95
339 A72   31p DH-89A Dragon Rapide   1.25   1.25
    Nos. 336-339 (4)   3.00   3.00

Robinson Crusoe, by John Alexander Gilfillan (1793-1864) — A73

Gilfillan Paintings.

1984, Sept. 21   Photo.   Perf. 11½
340 A73   9p shown   .30   .30
341 A73   12p Edinburgh Castle   .40   .40
342 A73   20½p Maori Village   .65   .65
343 A73   26p Australian Landscape   .85   .85
344 A73   28p Waterhouse's Corner, Adelaide   .95   .95
345 A73   31p Capt. Cook at Botany Bay   1.00   1.00
    Nos. 340-345 (6)   4.15   4.15

Christmas 1984 — A74

1984, Nov. 15   Photo.   Perf. 12x11½
346 A74   9p St. Helier orchid   .35   .35
347 A74   12p Mt. Bingham orchid   .45   .45

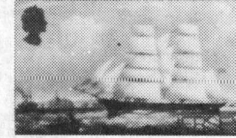

Ship Paintings by Philip John Ouless (1817-85) A75

1985, Feb. 26   Photo.   Perf. 14x14½
348 A75   9p Hebe, 1874   .30   .30
349 A75   12p Gaspe   .35   .35
350 A75   22p London, 1856   .75   .75
351 A75   31p Rambler   1.10   1.10
352 A75   34p Elizabeth Castle   1.25   1.25
    Nos. 348-352 (5)   3.75   3.75

Europa 1985 A76

Performing Arts: 10p, John Ireland, composer (1879-1962). 13p, Ivy St. Helier, actress (1886-1971). 22p, Claude Debussy, composer.

1985, Apr. 23   Litho.   Perf. 14
353 A76   10p multicolored   .35   .35
354 A76   13p multicolored   .45   .45
355 A76   22p multicolored   .80   .80
    Nos. 353-355 (3)   1.60   1.60

Intl. Youth Year — A77

1985, May 30   Litho.   Perf. 14½
356 A77   10p Girls' Brigade   .30   .30
357 A77   13p Girl Guides   .40   .40
358 A77   29p Jersey Youth Service   .85   .85
359 A77   31p Sea Cadet Corps   .95   .95
360 A77   34p Air Training Corps   1.00   1.00
    Nos. 356-360 (5)   3.50   3.50

Railway History — A78

1985, July 16   Photo.   Perf. 12x11½
361 A78   10p Duke of Normandy, Cheapside   .35   .35
362 A78   13p Saddletank, First Tower   .40   .40
363 A78   22p La Moye, Millbrook   .70   .70
364 A78   29p St. Helier's, St. Aubin   .90   .90
365 A78   34p St. Aubyns, Corbiere   1.10   1.10
    Nos. 361-365 (5)   3.45   3.45
Centenary of Jersey's first train from St. Helier to Corbiere.

Huguenot Heritage — A79

300th anniv. of revocation of the Edict of Nantes (religious tolerance) by King Louis XIV of France: No. 366, James Hemery (1814-1849), Dean of Jersey, Rector of St. Helier. No. 367, Francis Henry Jeune, Baron St. Helier, law lord and junior counsel in the Tichbourne case. No. 368, Francois Voisin, merchant. No. 369, Pierre Amiraux, silversmith. No. 370, George Henry Ingouville, Victoria Cross recipient. No. 371, Robert Brohier, co-founder of Schweppes soft-drink company.

1985, Sept. 10   Litho.   Perf. 14
366 A79   10p Memorial window, St. Helier Town Church   .35   .35
   a.   Booklet pane of 4   1.40
367 A79   10p Houses of Parliament, Westminster   .35   .35
   a.   Booklet pane of 4   1.40
368 A79   13p Great Fair, Nijni-Novgorod, Russia   .40   .40
   a.   Booklet pane of 4   1.65
369 A79   13p Silver coffee pot, pitcher   .40   .40
   a.   Booklet pane of 4   1.65
370 A79   22p Naval Battle of Viborg   .65   .65
   a.   Booklet pane of 4   2.75
371 A79   22p Glass bottles, carbonated water commercial patent   .65   .65
   a.   Booklet pane of 4   2.75
    Nos. 366-371 (6)   2.80   2.80

Thomas Benjamin Frederick Davis (1867-1942), Shipping Magnate, Philanthropist A80

Portrait and endowments: 10p, Howard Davis Hall, Victoria College. 13p, Yacht, racing schooner Westward. 31p, Howard Davis Park, St. Helier. 34p, Howard Davis Agricultural Development Farm, Trinity.

1985, Oct. 25   Perf. 13½
372 A80   10p multicolored   .35   .35
373 A80   13p multicolored   .40   .40
374 A80   31p multicolored   1.00   1.00
375 A80   34p multicolored   1.10   1.10
    Nos. 372-375 (4)   2.85   2.85
50th anniv. of Howard Davis Hall, Victoria College, donated by Davis in memory of his son.

Arms Type of 1981-82 and

Elizabeth II, 60th Birthday — A80a

1985-91   Litho.   Perf. 15x14
381 A54   16p Malet   .50   .50
   a.   Booklet pane of 6 ('88)   3.00
382 A54   17p Mabon   .50   .50
383 A54   18p De St. Martin ('88)   .70   .70
384 A54   19p Hamptonne ('88)   .75   .75
386 A54   26p De Bagot ('88)   1.00   1.00
388 A54   75p Remon ('87)   2.50   2.50
     Perf. 11½x12
389 A80a   £1 multicolored   3.00   3.00
     Photo.
     Granite Paper
390 A80a   £2 multicolored   6.00   6.00
    Nos. 381-390 (8)   14.95   14.95
Issue dates: 16p, 17p, Oct. 25. £1, Apr. 21, 1986. 75p, Apr. 23, 1987. 18p, 19p, 26p, Apr. 26, 1988. £2, Mar. 19, 1991.
No. 381a inscribed "May 1988."

Jersey Lily — A81

Lillie Langtry, by Sir John Millais — A82

1986, Jan. 28   Litho.   Perf. 15x14½
391 A81   13p multicolored   .50   .50
392 A82   34p multicolored   1.25   1.25
   a.   Souvenir sheet of 5 (4 13p, 34p)   4.00   4.00
Intl. Flower Gala, June 10-14.

Halley's Comet Sightings A83

Comet and coinciding historic events: 10p, Conquest of England, Bayeux Tapestry, A.D. 912 and 1066 sightings. 22p, Lady Carteret signing New Jersey over to William Penn, 1301, Edmond Halley observing the comet, 1682. 31p, Giotto spacecraft and technology developed in 1910, 1986. Caesarea maiden voyage.

1986, Mar. 4   Litho.   Perf. 13½x13
393 A83   10p multicolored   .35   .35
394 A83   22p multicolored   .80   .80
395 A83   31p multicolored   1.10   1.10
    Nos. 393-395 (3)   2.25   2.25

Europa 1986 — A84

1986, Apr. 21   Perf. 14½
396 A84   10p Viola kitaibeliana   .35   .35
397 A84   14p Matthiola sinuata   .50   .50
398 A84   22p Romulea columnae   .80   .80
    Nos. 396-398 (3)   1.65   1.65
Environmental conservation.

Jersey Natl. Trust, 50th Anniv. A85

1986, June 17   Litho.   Perf. 13½x13
399 A85   10p Le Rat cottage   .35   .35
400 A85   14p The Elms, headquarters   .40   .40
401 A85   22p Morel Farm entrance   .65   .65
402 A85   29p Quetivel Mill   .90   .90
403 A85   31p La Vallette   .95   .95
    Nos. 399-403 (5)   3.25   3.25

Wedding of Prince Andrew and Sarah Ferguson — A86

1986, July 23   Perf. 13½
404 A86   14p multicolored   .45   .45
405 A86   40p multicolored   1.40   1.40

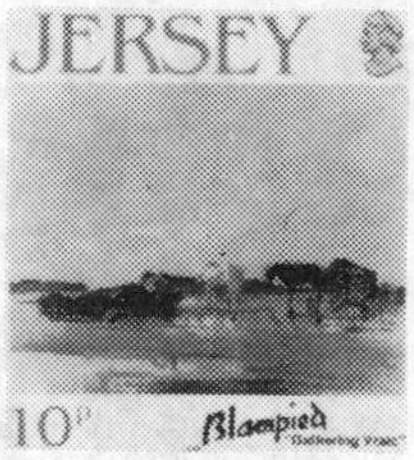

Paintings by Edmund Blampied (1886-1966), Artist — A87

1986, Aug. 28 Litho. *Perf. 14*

406	A87	10p	Gathering Vraic	.35	.35
407	A87	14p	Driving Home in the Rain	.50	.50
408	A87	29p	The Miller	1.00	1.00
409	A87	31p	The Joy Ride	1.10	1.10
410	A87	34p	Tante Elizabeth	1.25	1.25
			Nos. 406-410 (5)	4.20	4.20

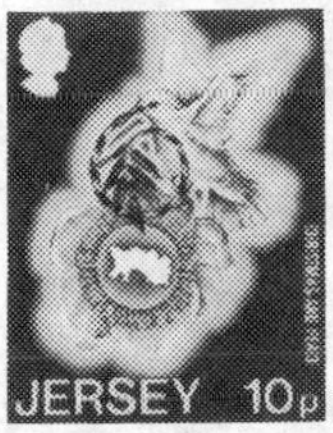

Christmas, Intl. Peace Year — A88

1986, Nov. 4 *Perf. 14½*

411	A88	10p	Dove, map, flower	.35	.35
412	A88	14p	Lovebirds	.45	.45
413	A88	34p	Dove, noise-maker	1.10	1.10
			Nos. 411-413 (3)	1.90	1.90

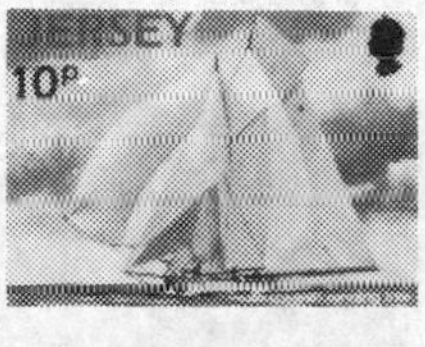

Racing Schooner Westward A89

1987, Jan. 15 Litho. *Perf. 13½*

414	A89	10p	Under full sail	.35	.35
415	A89	14p	T.B. Davis, owner	.45	.45
416	A89	31p	Overhauling Britannia	1.00	1.00
417	A89	34p	Dry dock, St. Helier	1.25	1.25
			Nos. 414-417 (4)	3.05	3.05

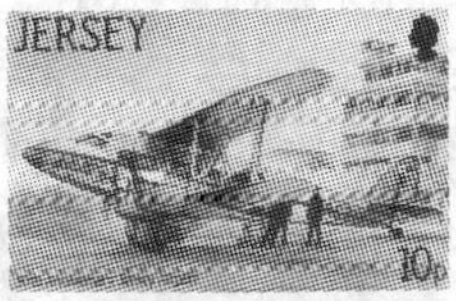

Jersey Airport, 50th Anniv. A90

1987, Mar. 3 Litho. *Perf. 14*

418	A90	10p	DH86 Belcroute Bay	.35	.35
419	A90	14p	Boeing 757, Douglas DC-9	.40	.40
420	A90	22p	Britten Norman Trislander, Islander	.70	.70
421	A90	29p	Short SD330, Vickers Viscount	.85	.85
422	A90	31p	BAC1-11, HPR.7 Dart Herald	.95	.95
			Nos. 418-422 (5)	3.25	3.25

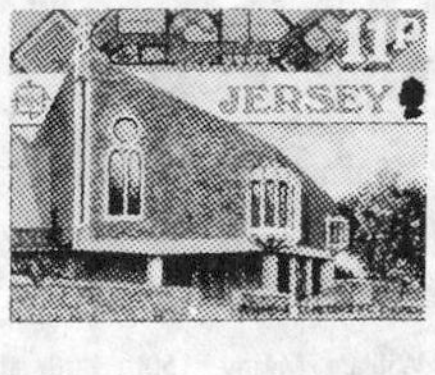

Europa 1987 A91

Modern architecture.

1987, Apr. 23 *Perf. 15x14*

423	A91	11p	St. Mary and St. Peter's Church	.40	.40
424	A91	15p	Villa Devereux	.50	.50

Size: 61x31mm

425	A91	22p	Fort Regent, St. Helier	.70	.70
			Nos. 423-425 (3)	1.60	1.60

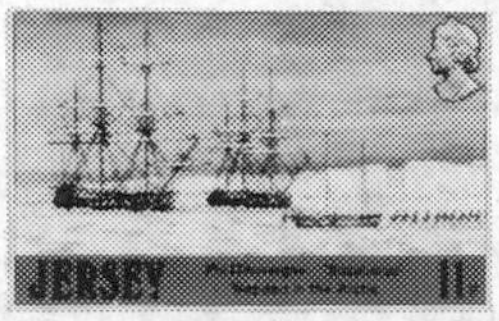

Adm. Philippe D'Auvergne (1754-1816) — A92

Ships: 11p, Racehorse trapped in the Arctic. 15p, Alarm burned at Rhode Island. 29p, Arethusa wrecked off Ushant, France. 31p, Rattlesnake stranded on Trinidad. 34p, Mont Orgueil Castle.

1987, July 9 *Perf. 14*

426	A92	11p	multicolored	.35	.35
427	A92	15p	multicolored	.45	.45
428	A92	29p	multicolored	.90	.90
429	A92	31p	multicolored	.95	.95
430	A92	34p	multicolored	1.00	1.00
			Nos. 426-430 (5)	3.65	3.65

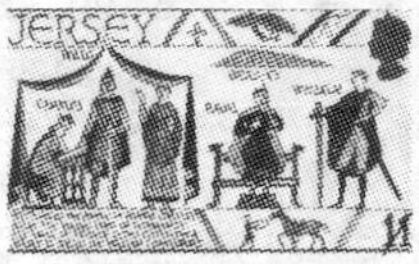

William the Conqueror (c. 1028-87), King of England (1066-87) A93

Designs in the style of the Bayeux Tapestry: 11p, King Charles negotiating peace with the Vikings, 911, and cession of Jersey to Rollo's son William, 933. 15p, Duke Robert I and King Edward ashore Jersey after storm, 1030; Edward's succession to the throne of England, 1042. 22p, William the Conqueror's coronation, 1066, and succession of William II, 1087. 29p, Death of King William Rufus, and Henry defeating Duke Robert to unite England and Normandy, 1106. 31p, Death of Henry, battle for the throne and succession of King Stephen, 1135. 34p, Successions of Henry II, 1154, and John Lackland, 1189.

1987 *Perf. 13½*

431	A93	11p	multicolored	.35	.35
a.			Booklet pane of 4 + label	1.40	
432	A93	15p	multicolored	.50	.50
a.			Booklet pane of 4 + label	2.00	
433	A93	22p	multicolored	.70	.70
a.			Booklet pane of 4 + label	3.00	
434	A93	29p	multicolored	.95	.95
a.			Booklet pane of 4 + label	4.00	
435	A93	31p	multicolored	1.00	1.00
a.			Booklet pane of 4 + label	4.00	
436	A93	34p	multicolored	1.10	1.10
a.			Booklet pane of 4 + label	4.50	
			Nos. 431-436 (6)	4.60	4.60

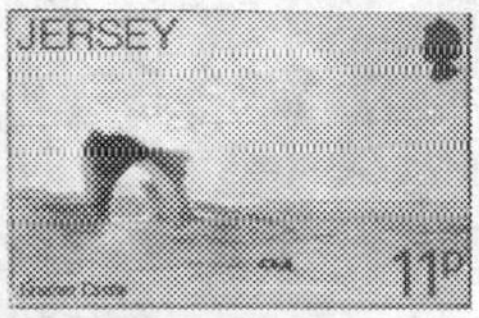

Paintings by John Le Capelain (1812-1848) — A94

1987, Nov. 3 Photo. *Perf. 12x11½*

437	A94	11p	Grosnez Castle	.30	.30
438	A94	15p	St. Aubin's Bay	.45	.45
439	A94	22p	Mt. Orgueil Castle	.60	.60
440	A94	31p	Town Fort and Harbor, St. Helier	.90	.90
441	A94	34p	The Hermitage	1.00	1.00
			Nos. 437-441 (5)	3.25	3.25

Christmas.

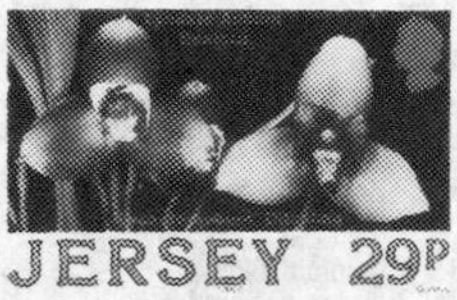

Hybrids, Eric Young Orchid Foundation, Trinity — A95

Nos. 443, 445 are vertical.

1988, Jan. 12 Litho. *Perf. 14*

442	A95	11p	Cymbidium pontac	.40	.40
443	A95	15p	Odontioda Eric Young	.55	.55
444	A95	29p	Lycaste auburn Seaford and Ditchling	1.00	1.00
445	A95	31p	Odontoglossum St. Brelade	1.10	1.10
446	A95	34p	Cymbidium mavourneen Jester	1.25	1.25
			Nos. 442-446 (5)	4.30	4.30

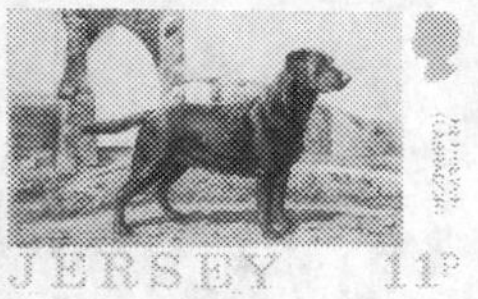

Jersey Dog Club, Cent. A96

1988, Mar. 2

447	A96	11p	Labrador retriever	.45	.45
448	A96	15p	Wire-haired dachshund	.60	.60
449	A96	22p	Pekingese	.85	.85
450	A96	31p	Cavalier King Charles spaniel	1.10	1.10
451	A96	34p	Dalmatian	1.25	1.25
			Nos. 447-451 (5)	4.25	4.25

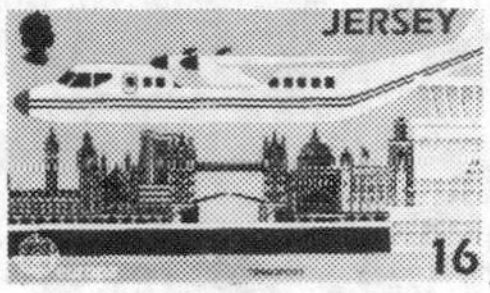

Europa 1988 A97

Transport and communication. Nos. 453 and 455 vert.

1988, Apr. 26 Litho. *Perf. 14x13½*

452	A97	16p	Air transport	.60	.60
453	A97	16p	Air communication	.60	.60
454	A97	22p	Sea transport	.85	.85
455	A97	22p	Sea communication	.85	.85
			Nos. 452-455 (4)	2.90	2.90

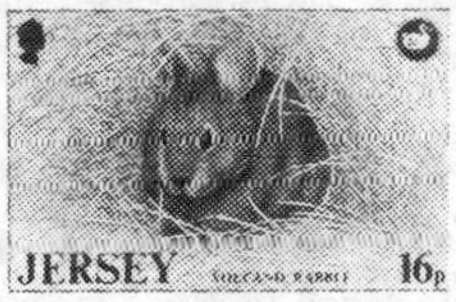

Wildlife Preservation Trust, 25th Anniv. — A98

1988, July 6 Litho.

456	A98	12p	Rodrigues fody, vert.	.40	.40
457	A98	16p	Volcano rabbit	.55	.55
458	A98	29p	White-faced marmoset, vert.	.95	.95
459	A98	31p	Ploughshare tortoise	1.00	1.00
460	A98	34p	Mauritius kestrel, vert.	1.10	1.10
			Nos. 456-460 (5)	4.00	4.00

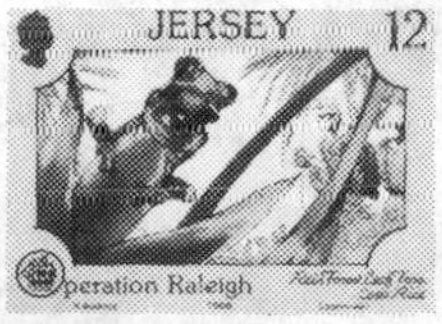

Operation Raleigh A99

Activities: 12p, Rain Forest Leaf Frog, Costa Rica. 16p, Archaeological Survey, Peru. 22p, Glacier Climbing, Chile. 29p, Medical Assistance, Solomon Isls. 31p, Underwater Exploration, Australia. 34p, *Zebu* returns to St. Helier, Jersey.

1988, Sept. 27 Photo. *Perf. 12*

461	A99	12p	multicolored	.45	.45
462	A99	16p	multicolored	.55	.55
463	A99	22p	multicolored	.80	.80
464	A99	29p	multicolored	1.00	1.00
465	A99	31p	multicolored	1.10	1.10
466	A99	34p	multicolored	1.25	1.25
			Nos. 461-466 (6)	5.15	5.15

Operation Raleigh: voyage of the *Zebu*, on which youths were trained with the aim of remotivating them and helping them to earn new self-respect.

WHO 40th anniv. (29p).

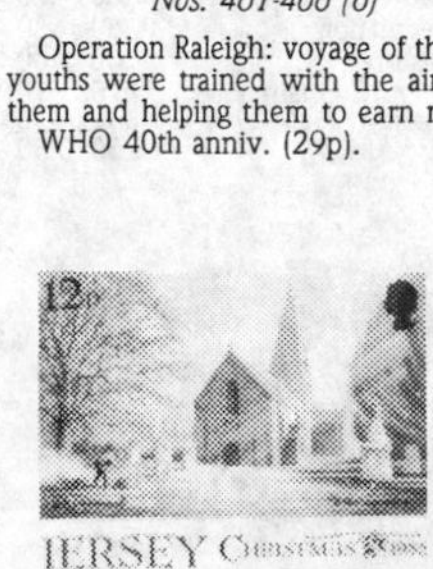

Parish Churches A100

1988, Nov. 15 Litho. *Perf. 14*

467	A100	12p	St. Clement	.45	.45
468	A100	16p	St. Ouen	.55	.55
469	A100	31p	St. Brelade	1.10	1.10
470	A100	34p	St. Lawrence	1.25	1.25
			Nos. 467-470 (4)	3.35	3.35

Christmas. See Nos. 549-552, 610-613.

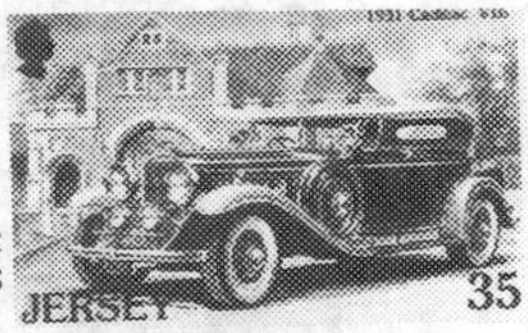

Classic Cars A101

Designs: 12p, 1912 Talbot Tourer, seaweed harvest at Le Hocq. 16p, 1920 De Dion Bouton, Grosnez Castle ruins. 23p, 1926 Austin Chummy, brick kiln at Mont a l'Abbe. 30p, 1926 Ford Model T, harvest of the Jersey royal potato crop. 32p, 1930 Bentley 8-Litre, Guard House and Gate at Government House. 35p, 1931 Cadillac V16 Fleetwood Sports Phaeton, St. Ouen's Manor.

1989, Jan. 31

471	A101	12p	multicolored	.45	.45
472	A101	16p	multicolored	.60	.60
473	A101	23p	multicolored	.85	.85
474	A101	30p	multicolored	1.10	1.10
475	A101	32p	multicolored	1.10	1.10
476	A101	35p	multicolored	1.25	1.25
			Nos. 471-476 (6)	5.35	5.35

See Nos. 604-609.

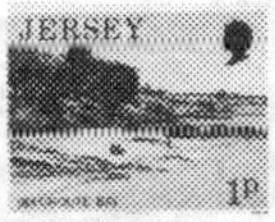

Scenic Views — A102

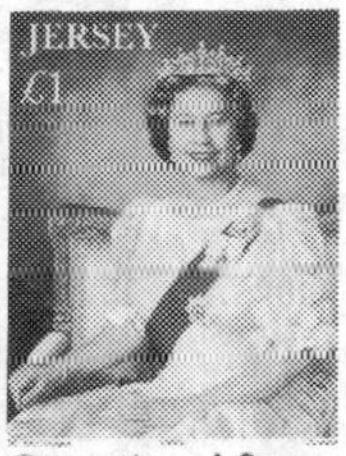

Coronation of Queen Elizabeth II, 40th Anniv. — A102a

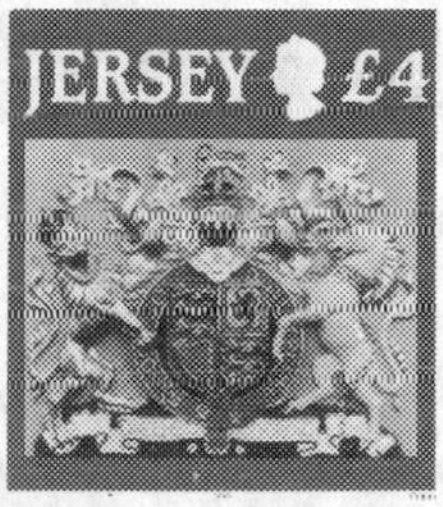

Royal Arms A102b

1989-95 Litho. *Perf. 13½*

477	A102	1p	Belcroute Bay	.15	.15
478	A102	2p	High St., St. Aubin	.15	.15
480	A102	4p	Royal Jersey Golf Course	.15	.15
a.			Booklet pane of 6	.75	.75
481	A102	5p	Portelet Bay	.20	.20
a.			Booklet pane of 6	1.25	1.25
485	A102	10p	Les Charrieres D'Anneport	.40	.40
486	A102	13p	St. Helier Marina	.50	.50
487	A102	14p	St. Ouen's Bay	.50	.50
a.			Booklet pane of 6	3.00	3.00
b.			Booklet pane of 8	4.25	4.25
488	A102	15p	Rozel Harbor	.55	.55
a.			Booklet pane of 6	3.50	3.50
489	A102	16p	St. Aubin's Harbor	.60	.60
a.			Booklet pane of 8	5.00	5.00
490	A102	17p	Jersey Airport	.65	.65
491	A102	18p	Corbiere Lighthouse	.65	.65
a.			Booklet pane of 6	4.00	4.00
492	A102	19p	Val de la Mare	.70	.70
493	A102	20p	Elizabeth Castle	.75	.75
a.			Booklet pane of 6	4.50	4.50
494	A102	21p	Greve de Lecq	.70	.70
495	A102	22p	Samares Manor	.70	.70
a.			Booklet pane of 8	5.75	5.75
496	A102	23p	Bonne Nuit Harbor	.75	.75
497	A102	24p	Grosnez Castle	.80	.80
498	A102	25p	Augres Manor	.80	.80
499	A102	26p	Central Market	.85	.85
500	A102	27p	St. Brelade's Bay	.85	.85
501	A102	30p	St. Ouen's Manor	.95	.95
502	A102	40p	La Hougue Bie	1.25	1.25
503	A102	50p	Mont Orgueil Castle	1.50	1.50
504	A102	75p	Royal Square	2.25	2.25

Perf. 14½

505	A102a	£1	multicolored	3.00	3.00

Perf. 15x14

506 A102b £4 multicolored   13.00 13.00
    Nos. 477-506 (26)   33.35 33.35

Panes issued for Stamp World London '90. Inscribed May 1990.

Issued: 1p-20p, 3/21/89; 21p-27p, 1/16/90; 30p-75p, 3/13/90; #481a, 488a, 493a, 2/12/91; £1, 6/2/93; £4, 1/2/95. Nos. 487b, 489a, 495a were released on May 22, but were not readily available until September 1992. Other booklets, 1990.

This is an expanding set. Numbers will change if necessary.

World Wildlife Fund A103

1989, Apr. 25   Litho.   Perf. 13¹/₂x13

507 A103 13p Large checkered skip-
    per, vert.   .50   .50
508 A103 13p Agile frog   .50   .50
509 A103 17p Green lizard   .60   .60
510 A103 17p Barn owl, vert.   .60   .60
    Nos. 507-510 (4)   2.20 2.20

Europa 1989 — A104

Children's games.

1989, Apr. 25   Perf. 14

511 A104 17p Playpen   .55   .55
512 A104 17p Playground   .55   .55
513 A104 23p Magician, games   .70   .70
514 A104 23p Cricket, rugby, soccer,
    tennis   .70   .70
    Nos. 511-514 (4)   2.50 2.50

Visit of Queen Elizabeth II — A105

1989, May 24   Litho.   Perf. 14¹/₂

515 A105 £1 Ferry Terminal, St. He-
    lier   3.50 3.50

French Revolution, Bicent. A106

Designs: 13p, D'Auvergne meets Louis XVI, 1786. 17p, Storming the Bastille, 1789. 23p, Marie de Bouillon at Navarre, 1790. 30p, Mission from Mont Orgueil, 1795. 32p, Support for the Chouans, 1796. 35p, The last Chouannerie, 1799.

1989, July 7   Perf. 13¹/₂

516 A106 13p multicolored   .45   .45
517 A106 17p multicolored   .55   .55
518 A106 23p multicolored   .75   .75
519 A106 30p multicolored   1.00 1.00
520 A106 32p multicolored   1.10 1.10
521 A106 35p multicolored   1.25 1.25
    Nos. 516-521 (6)   5.10 5.10

Perf. 13¹/₂

516a   Booklet pane of 4   1.90
517a   Booklet pane of 4   2.25
518a   Booklet pane of 4   3.25
519a   Booklet pane of 4   4.25
520a   Booklet pane of 4   4.50
521a   Booklet pane of 4   5.00

Great Western Railway Steamer Service Between Weymouth and the Channel Isls., Cent. — A107

1989, Sept. 5   Litho.   Perf. 13¹/₂x14

522 A107 13p St. Helier, 1925   .40   .40
523 A107 17p Caesarea II, 1910   .50   .50
524 A107 27p Reindeer, 1897   .85   .85
525 A107 32p Ibex, 1891   1.00 1.00
526 A107 35p Lynx, 1889   1.10 1.10
    Nos. 522-526 (5)   3.85 3.85

Paintings by Sarah Louisa Kilpack (1839-1909) — A108

1989, Oct. 24   Litho.   Perf. 13x12¹/₂

527 A108 13p Gorey Harbour   .45   .45
528 A108 17p La Corbiere   .55   .55
529 A108 23p Greve de Lecq   .75   .75
530 A108 32p Bouley Bay   1.10 1.10
531 A108 35p Mont Orgueil   1.10 1.10
    Nos. 527-531 (5)   3.95 3.95

Europa 1990 A109

Post offices.

Perf. 13¹/₂x14, 14x13¹/₂
1990, Mar. 13   Litho.

532 A109 18p Broad Street, 1969   .55   .55
533 A109 18p Mont Millais, 1990   .55   .55
534 A109 24p Hue Street, 1815   .75   .75
535 A109 24p Halkett Place, 1890   .75   .75
    Nos. 532-535 (4)   2.60 2.60

Nos. 532-533 vert.

Festival of Tourism — A110

1990, May 3   Litho.   Perf. 14x13¹/₂

536 A110 18p Battle of Flowers   .60   .60
537 A110 24p Recreation   .80   .80
538 A110 29p History   1.00 1.00
539 A110 32p Salon Culinaire   1.10 1.10
   a. Souvenir sheet of 4, #536-539 3.75 3.75
    Nos. 536-539 (4)   3.50 3.50

News Media A111

1990, June 26   Litho.   Perf. 13¹/₂

540 A111 14p Print (newspapers),
    1784-1889   .50   .50
541 A111 18p The Evening Post,
    1890   .60   .60
542 A111 34p BBC Radio Jersey,
    1982   1.10 1.10

543 A111 37p Channel Television,
    1962   1.25 1.25
    Nos. 540-543 (4)   3.45 3.45

UNESCO World Literacy Year.

Battle of Britain, 50th Anniv. A112

1990, Sept. 4   Perf. 14

544 A112 14p Hawk   .50   .50
545 A112 18p Spitfire   .60   .60
546 A112 24p Hurricane   .80   .80
547 A112 34p Wellington   1.10 1.10
548 A112 37p Lancaster   1.25 1.25
    Nos. 544-548 (5)   4.25 4.25

Parish Churches Type of 1988

1990, Nov. 13   Litho.   Perf. 13¹/₂x14

549 A100 14p St. Helier   .50   .50
550 A100 18p Grouville   .60   .60
551 A100 34p St. Saviour   1.10 1.10
552 A100 37p St. John   1.25 1.25
    Nos. 549-552 (4)   3.45 3.45

Prince's Tower, La Hougue Bie, 1801 A113

Philippe d'Auvergne: 20p, Arrested in Paris, 1802. 26p, Plotting against Napoleon, 1803. 31p, Execution of Cadoudal, 1804. 37p, H.M. Cutter Surly, 1809. 44p, Prince de Bouillon, 1816.

1991, Jan. 22   Litho.   Perf. 13¹/₂

553 A113 15p multicolored   .50   .50
554 A113 20p multicolored   .70   .70
555 A113 26p multicolored   .85   .85
556 A113 31p multicolored   1.00 1.00
557 A113 37p multicolored   1.25 1.25
558 A113 44p multicolored   1.50 1.50
    Nos. 553-558 (6)   5.80 5.80

A114   A115

Europa (Satellites and their functions): No. 559, ERS-1, oceanography. No. 560, Landsat, Earth resources. No. 561, Meteosat, meteorology. No. 562, Olympus, communications.

1991, Mar. 19   Litho.   Perf. 14¹/₂x13

559 A114 20p multicolored   .65   .65
560 A114 20p multicolored   .65   .65
561 A114 26p multicolored   .85   .85
562 A114 26p multicolored   .85   .85
    Nos. 559-562 (4)   3.00 3.00

1991, May 16   Litho.   Perf. 13¹/₂

Anniversaries: 15p, German Occupation Stamps for Jersey, 50th anniv. 20p, Eastern Railway extension to Gorey Pier, 100th anniv. 26p, Jersey Herd Book, 125th anniv. 31p, Victoria Harbor, 150th anniv. 53p, Hospital bequest of Marie Bartlett, 250th anniv.

563 A115 15p multicolored   .50   .50
564 A115 20p multicolored   .65   .65
565 A115 26p multicolored   .85   .85
566 A115 31p multicolored   1.00 1.00
567 A115 53p multicolored   1.75 1.75
    Nos. 563-567 (5)   4.75 4.75

Butterflies & Moths A116

1991, July 9   Litho.   Perf. 13x12¹/₂

568 A116 15p Glanville fritillary   .50   .50
569 A116 20p Jersey tiger   .65   .65
570 A116 37p Small elephant hawk-
    moth   1.10 1.10
571 A116 57p Peacock   1.75 1.75
    Nos. 568-571 (4)   4.00 4.00

See Nos. 727-731.

Overseas Aid — A117

Designs: 15p, Water drilling rig, Ethiopia. 20p, Construction work, Rwanda. 26p, Technical school, Kenya. 31p, Leprosy and eye care, Tanzania. 37p, Agriculture and cultivation aid, Zambia. 44p, Health care and immunization, Lesotho.

1991, Sept. 3   Litho.   Perf. 13¹/₂

572 A117 15p multicolored   .50   .50
573 A117 20p multicolored   .65   .65
574 A117 26p multicolored   .85   .85
575 A117 31p multicolored   1.00 1.00
576 A117 37p multicolored   1.10 1.10
577 A117 44p multicolored   1.65 1.65
    Nos. 572-577 (6)   5.75 5.75

Christmas — A118   Winter Birds — A119

Illustrations by Edmund Blampied from Peter Pan: 15p, This is the place for me. 20p, The Island Come True. 37p, The Never Bird. 53p, The Great White Father.

1991, Nov. 5   Litho.   Perf. 14

578 A118 15p multicolored   .50   .50
579 A118 20p multicolored   .70   .70
580 A118 37p multicolored   1.25 1.25
581 A118 53p multicolored   1.75 1.75
    Nos. 578-581 (4)   4.20 4.20

1992, Jan. 7   Litho.   Perf. 13¹/₂x14

582 A119 16p Pied wagtail   .55   .55
583 A119 22p Firecrest   .75   .75
584 A119 28p Snipe   .95   .95
585 A119 39p Lapwing   1.40 1.40
586 A119 57p Fieldfare   1.90 1.90
    Nos. 582-586 (5)   5.55 5.55

Shanghai Harbor, 1860 A120

William Mesny, 150th birth anniv: No. 588, Running the Taiping blockade, 1862. No. 589, General Mesny, River Gate, 1874. No. 590, Mesny accompanying Gill to Burma, 1877. No. 591, Mesny advises Governor Chang, 1882. No. 592, Mesny, Mandarin First Class, 1886.

1992, Feb. 25   Litho.   Perf. 13¹/₂

587 A120 16p multicolored   .50   .50
588 A120 16p multicolored   .50   .50
589 A120 22p multicolored   .75   .75
590 A120 22p multicolored   .75   .75

591 A120 33p multicolored 1.10 1.10
592 A120 33p multicolored 1.10 1.10
Nos. 587-592 (6) 4.70 4.70

587a Booklet pane of 4 2.00 2.00
588a Booklet pane of 4 2.00 2.00
589a Booklet pane of 4 3.00 3.00
590a Booklet pane of 4 3.00 3.00
591a Booklet pane of 4 4.60 4.60
592a Booklet pane of 4 4.60 4.60

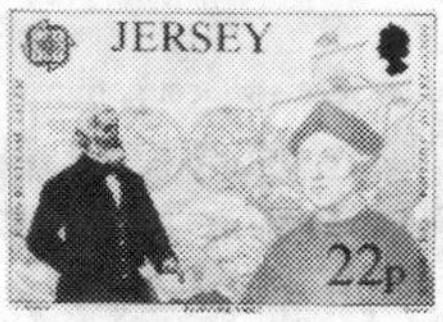

Discovery of America, 500th Anniv. A121

Columbus, ship and: 22p, John Bertram (1796-1882). 28p, Sir George Carteret (1610-1680). 39p, Sir Walter Raleigh (1554-1618).

1992, Apr. 14 Litho. *Perf. 14½*
593 A121 22p multicolored .70 .70
594 A121 28p multicolored .90 .90
595 A121 39p multicolored 1.25 1.25
Nos. 593-595 (3) 2.85 2.85

Europa.

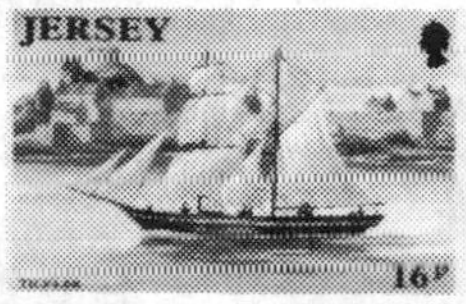

Jersey-Built Sailing Ships A122

1992, Apr. 14 Litho. *Perf. 14*
596 A122 16p Tickler .50 .50
597 A122 22p Hebe .70 .70
598 A122 50p Gemini 1.65 1.65
599 A122 57p Percy Douglas 1.75 1.75
a. Souvenir sheet of 4, #596-599 4.60 4.60
Nos. 596-599 (4) 4.60 4.60

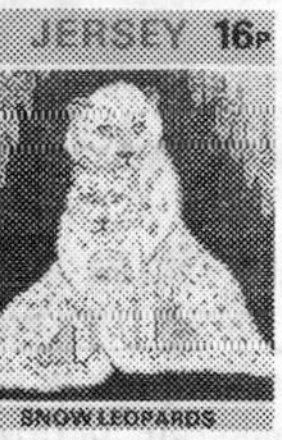

Batik — A123

Designs: 16p, Snow leopards. 22p, Three elements. 39p, Three men in a tub. 57p, Cockatoos.

1992, June 23 Litho. *Perf. 14½*
600 A123 16p multicolored .60 .60
601 A123 22p multicolored .80 .80
602 A123 39p multicolored 1.40 1.40
603 A123 57p multicolored 2.00 2.00
Nos. 600-603 (4) 4.80 4.80

Classic Car Type of 1989

Designs: 16p, 1925 Morris Cowley "Bullnose." 22p, 1932 Rolls Royce 20/25. 28p, 1924 Chenard & Walcker 15. 33p, 1932 Packard 900 Series Light Eight. 39p, 1927 Lanchester 21. 50p, 1913 Buick 30 Roadster.

1992, Sept. 8 Litho. *Perf. 13x12½*
604 A101 16p multicolored .45 .45
605 A101 22p multicolored .65 .65
606 A101 28p multicolored .80 .80
607 A101 33p multicolored 1.00 1.00
608 A101 39p multicolored 1.10 1.10
609 A101 50p multicolored 1.50 1.50
Nos. 604-609 (6) 5.50 5.50

Parish Church Type of 1988

1992, Nov. 3 Litho. *Perf. 13½x14*
610 A100 16p Trinity .45 .45
611 A100 22p St. Mary .65 .65
612 A100 39p St. Martin 1.10 1.10
613 A100 57p St. Peter 1.65 1.65
Nos. 610-613 (4) 3.85 3.85

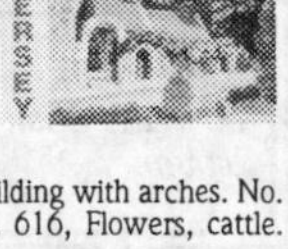

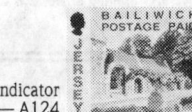

Non-Value Indicator Stamps — A124

Scenic views: No. 614, Building with arches. No. 615, Cemetery, church. No. 616, Flowers, cattle. No. 617, Cattle in pasture.

Beach scenes: No. 618, People lying on beach with umbrella. No. 619, Man with windsurfer. No. 620, Crab facing right. No. 621, Crab, facing left.

Parade floats: No. 622, Smiling face, rainbow. No. 623, Dragon head, Oriental theme. No. 624, Umbrellas, Asian theme. No. 625, Elephant's tusks, African theme.

1993, Jan. 26 Litho. *Perf. 13½*
614 A124 (17p) Bailiwick .50 .50
615 A124 (17p) Bailiwick .50 .50
616 A124 (17p) Bailiwick .50 .50
617 A124 (17p) Bailiwick .50 .50
a. Block of 4, #614-617 2.00 2.00
b. Booklet pane of 8, 2 each #614-617 4.00
618 A124 (23p) UK .65 .65
619 A124 (23p) UK .65 .65
620 A124 (23p) UK .65 .65
621 A124 (23p) UK .65 .65
a. Block of 4, #618-621 2.75 2.75
b. Booklet pane of 8, 2 each #618-621 5.50
622 A124 (28p) European .75 .75
623 A124 (28p) European .75 .75
624 A124 (28p) European .75 .75
625 A124 (28p) European .75 .75
a. Block of 4, #622-625 3.00 3.00
b. Booklet pane of 8, 2 each #622-625 6.00 6.00
Nos. 614-625 (12) 7.60 7.60

The minimum postage rate is represented for each area where mail is delivered.

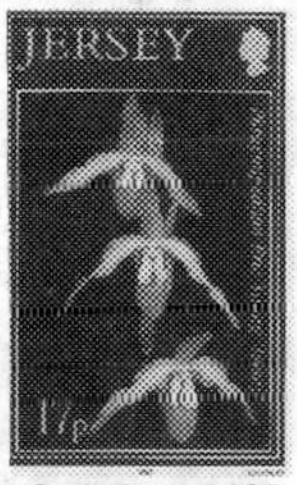

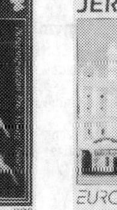

Orchids — A125

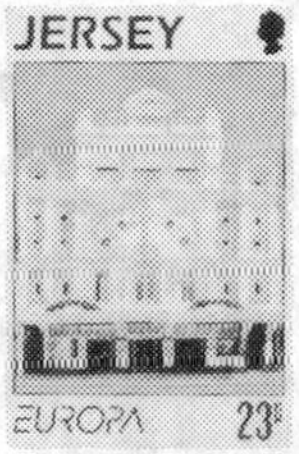

Europa — A126

Designs: 17p, Phragmipedium Eric Young "Jersey." 23p, Odontoglossum Augres "Trinity." 28p, Miltonia Saint Helier "Colomberie." 39p, Phragmipedium pearcei. 57p, Calanthe Grouville "Gorey."

1993, Jan. 26 Litho. *Perf. 14½x13*
626 A125 17p multicolored .50 .50
627 A125 23p multicolored .70 .70
628 A125 28p multicolored .80 .80
629 A125 39p multicolored 1.10 1.10
630 A125 57p multicolored 1.65 1.65
Nos. 626-630 (5) 4.75 4.75

1993, Apr. 1 Litho. *Perf. 13½x14*

Contemporary Art. 23p, Jersey Opera House, by Ian Rolls. 28p, The Ham and Tomato Bap, by Jonathan Hubbard. 39p, Vase of Flowers, by Neil MacKenzie.

631 A126 23p multicolored .70 .70
632 A126 28p multicolored .85 .85
633 A126 39p multicolored 1.10 1.10
Nos. 631-633 (3) 2.65 2.65

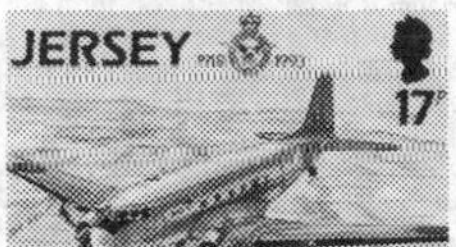

Royal Air Force, 75th Anniv. A127

Designs: 17p, Douglas Dakota. 23p, Wight Seaplane. 28p, Avro Shakleton AEW2. 33p, Gloster Meteor, DeHavilland Vampire. 39p, BAe Harrier GR1A. 57p, Panavia Tornado F3.

1993, Apr. 1 Litho. *Perf. 14*
634 A127 17p multicolored .50 .50
635 A127 23p multicolored .70 .70
636 A127 28p multicolored .85 .85
637 A127 33p multicolored 1.00 1.00
638 A127 39p multicolored 1.10 1.10
639 A127 57p multicolored 1.75 1.75
a. Souvenir sheet of 2, #635, 639 2.50 2.50
Nos. 634-639 (6) 5.90 5.90

Stamps from No. 639a do not have white border.

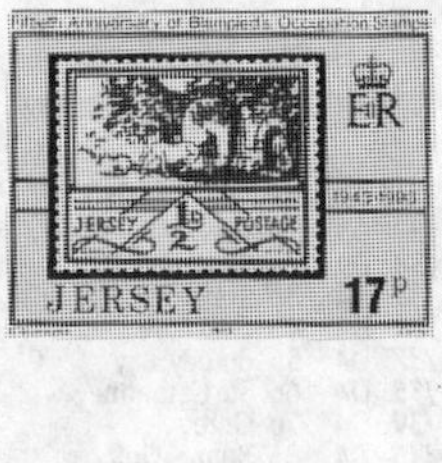

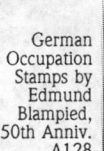

German Occupation Stamps by Edmund Blampied, 50th Anniv. A128

1993, June 2 Litho. *Perf. 13½*
640 A128 17p No. N3 .50 .50
641 A128 23p No. N4 .70 .70
642 A128 28p No. N5 .85 .85
643 A128 33p No. N6 1.00 1.00
644 A128 39p No. N7 1.10 1.10
645 A128 50p No. N8 1.50 1.50
Nos. 640-645 (6) 5.65 5.65

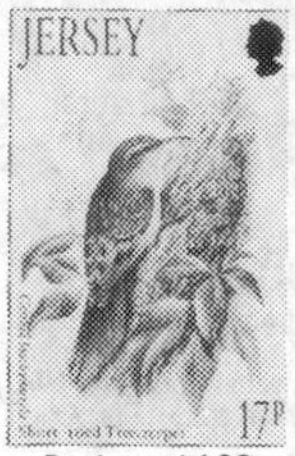

Birds — A129

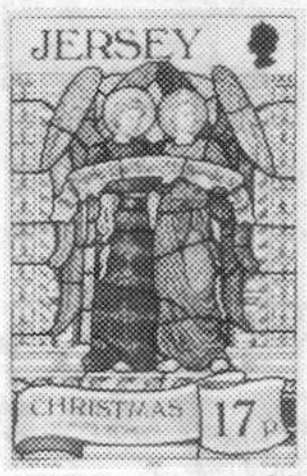

Christmas — A130

1993, Sept. 7 Litho. *Perf. 13½x14*
646 A129 17p Short-toed treecreeper .50 .50
647 A129 23p Dartford warbler .70 .70
648 A129 28p Wheatear .85 .85
649 A129 39p Cirl bunting 1.10 1.10
650 A129 57p Jay 1.75 1.75
Nos. 646-650 (5) 4.90 4.90

1993, Nov. 2 Litho. *Perf. 14½x13*

Stained glass windows by Henry Bosdet, from St. Aubin on the Hill.

651 A130 17p multicolored .50 .50
652 A130 23p multicolored .65 .65
653 A130 39p multicolored 1.10 1.10
654 A130 57p multicolored 1.65 1.65
Nos. 651-654 (4) 3.90 3.90

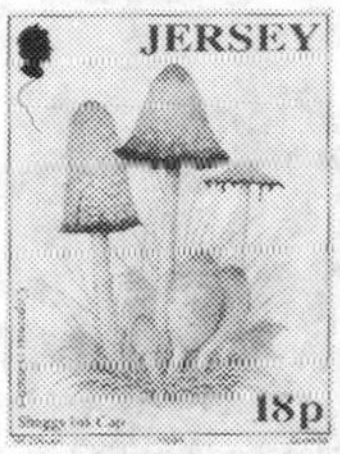

Mushrooms A131

1994, Jan. 11 Litho. *Perf. 14½*
655 A131 18p Shaggy ink cap .50 .50
656 A131 23p Fly agaric .65 .65
657 A131 30p Chanterelle .95 .95
658 A131 41p Parasol mushroom 1.25 1.25
659 A131 60p Latticed stinkhorn 1.75 1.75
Nos. 655-659 (5) 5.10 5.10

Souvenir Sheet

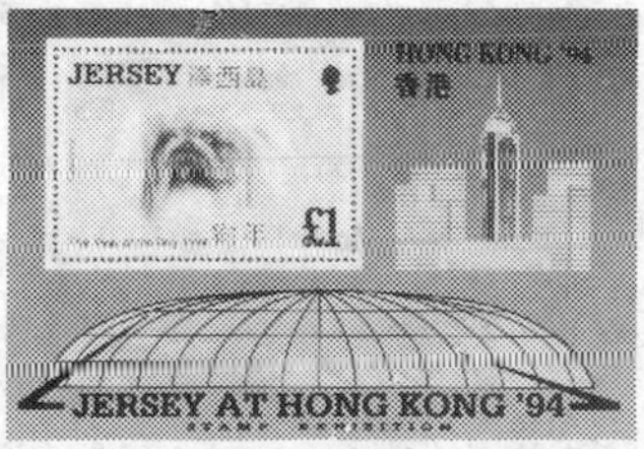

New Year 1994 (Year of the Dog) — A132

1994, Feb. 18 Litho. *Perf. 15x14½*
660 A132 £1 multicolored 3.00 3.00

Hong Kong '94.

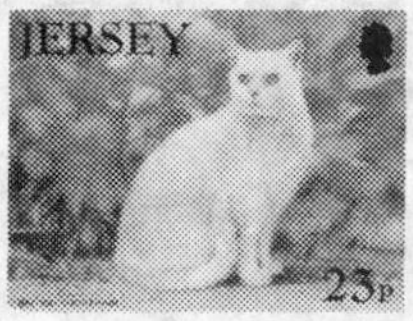

Cats — A133

1994, Apr. 5 Litho. *Perf. 13½*
661 A133 18p Maine coon, vert. .55 .55
662 A133 23p British shorthair .70 .70
663 A133 35p Persian, vert. 1.00 1.00
664 A133 41p Siamese 1.25 1.25
665 A133 60p Non-pedigree, vert. 1.75 1.75
Nos. 661-665 (5) 5.25 5.25

Jersey Cat Club, 21st anniv., and 4th Championship Show.

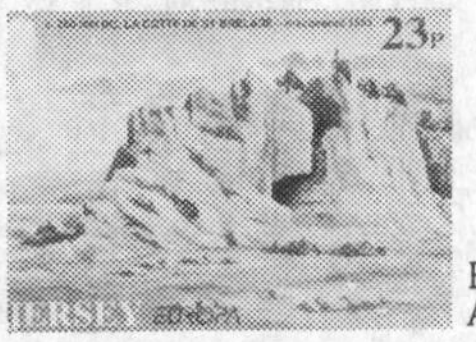

Europa A134

Designs: No. 666, Mammoths on cliff, c. 250,000 B.C. No. 667, Paleolithic hunters dragging mammoth by tusks. No. 668, Neolithic dolmen, "La Hougue Bie," c. 4,000 B.C. No. 669, Exterior of "La Hougue Bie," during construction.

1994, Apr. 5 Litho. *Perf. 13½x14*
666 A134 23p multicolored .70 .70
667 A134 23p multicolored .70 .70
a. Pair, #666-667 1.40 1.40
668 A134 30p multicolored .90 .90
669 A134 30p multicolored .90 .90
a. Pair, #668-669 1.80 1.80
Nos. 666-669 (4) 3.20 3.20

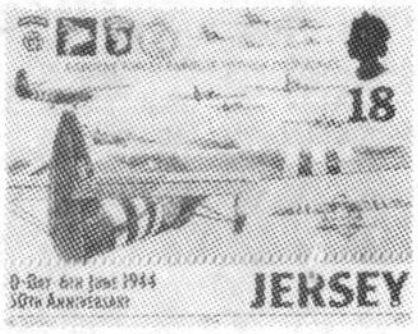

D-Day, 50th Anniv. A135

Designs: No. 670, Airborne Forces enroute to drop zones. No. 671, Allied Fleet of Normandy Coast. No. 672, Coming ashore, Gold Beach. No. 673, Coming ashore, Sword Beach. No. 674, Spitfires on beachead patrol. No. 675, Normandy invasion map.

1994, June 6 Litho. *Perf. 13½*
670 A135 18p multicolored .55 .55
671 A135 18p multicolored .55 .55
a. Bklt. pane, 3 each #670-671 3.30
672 A135 23p multicolored .70 .70
673 A135 23p multicolored .70 .70
a. Bklt. pane, 3 each #672-673 4.25
674 A135 30p multicolored .90 .90
675 A135 30p multicolored .90 .90
a. Bklt. pane, 3 each #674-675 5.50
b. Bklt. pane of 6, #670-675 4.50
Nos. 670-675 (6) 4.30 4.30

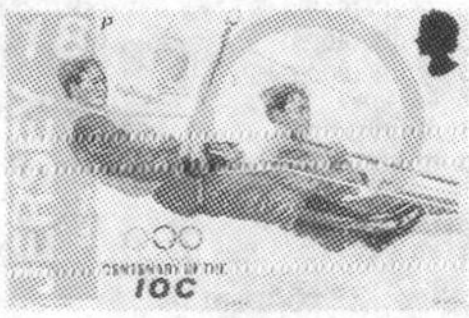

Intl. Olympic Committee, Cent. A136

1994, June 6 *Perf. 14*
676 A136 18p Sailing .55 .55
677 A136 23p Rifle shooting .70 .70
678 A136 30p Hurdles .90 .90
679 A136 41p Swimming 1.25 1.25
680 A136 60p Field hockey 1.75 1.75
Nos. 676-680 (5) 5.15 5.15

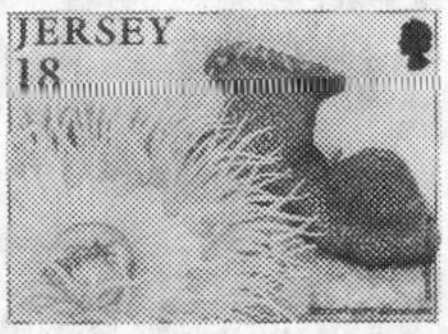

Marine Life — A137

Designs: 18p, Strawberry anemone. 23p, Hermit crab, parasitic anemone. 41p, Velvet swimming crab. 60p, Common jellyfish.

1994, Aug. 2 Litho. *Perf. 13½x13*
681 A137 18p multicolored .60 .60
682 A137 23p multicolored .75 .75
683 A137 41p multicolored 1.25 1.25
684 A137 60p multicolored 1.90 1.90
Nos. 681-684 (4) 4.50 4.50

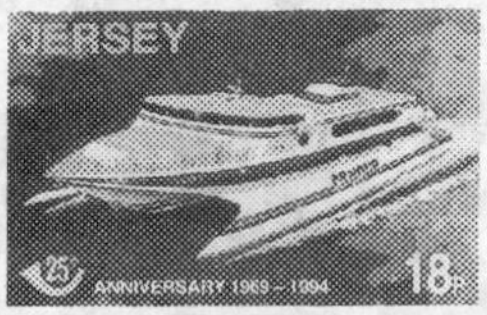

Postal Independence, 25th Anniv. — A138

Designs: 18p, Condor 10 Wavepiercer. 23p, Map of Jersey, postbox. 35p, BEA "Vanguard" aircraft.

41p, Aurigny "Short 360" aircraft. 60p, Sealink vessel "Caesarea."

1994, Oct. 1 Litho. *Perf. 14*

685 A138	18p multicolored	.60	.60
686 A138	23p multicolored	.75	.75
687 A138	35p multicolored	1.10	1.10
688 A138	41p multicolored	1.40	1.40
689 A138	60p multicolored	2.00	2.00
a.	Souvenir sheet, #685-689 + label	5.85	5.85
	Nos. 685-689 (5)	5.85	5.85

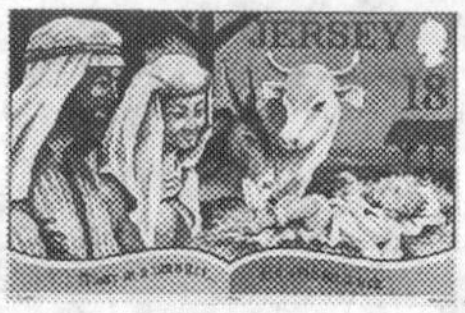

Christmas A139

Christmas carols: 18p, "Away in the manger..." 23p, "Hark! the herald angels sing..." 41p, "While shepherds watched..." 60p, "We three kings of Orient are..."

1994, Nov. 8

690 A139	18p multicolored	.60	.60
691 A139	23p multicolored	.75	.75
692 A139	41p multicolored	1.40	1.40
693 A139	60p multicolored	2.00	2.00
	Nos. 690-693 (4)	4.75	4.75

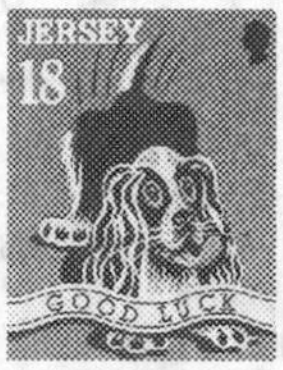

Greetings Stamps — A140

Designs: No. 694, Dog, "Good Luck." No. 695, Rose, "With Love." No. 696, Chick, "Congratulations." No. 697, Bouquet of flowers, "Thank You."
No. 698, Dove, "With love." No. 699, Cat, "Good Luck." No. 700, Carnations, "Thank You." No. 701, Parrot, "Congratulations."
60p, Boar, "Happy New Year."

1995, Jan. 24 Litho. *Perf. 13½x13*

694 A140	18p multicolored	.60	.60
695 A140	18p multicolored	.60	.60
696 A140	18p multicolored	.60	.60
697 A140	18p multicolored	.60	.60
a.	Strip of 4, #694-697	2.50	2.50
698 A140	23p multicolored	.75	.75
699 A140	23p multicolored	.75	.75
700 A140	23p multicolored	.75	.75
701 A140	23p multicolored	.75	.75
a.	Strip of 4, #698-701	3.00	3.00

Size: 25x64mm

702 A140	60p multicolored	2.00	2.00
a.	Booklet pane, #697a, #701a, #702	7.50	
	Booklet, #702a	7.50	
	Nos. 694-702 (9)	7.40	7.40

New Year 1995 (Year of the Boar) (#702).

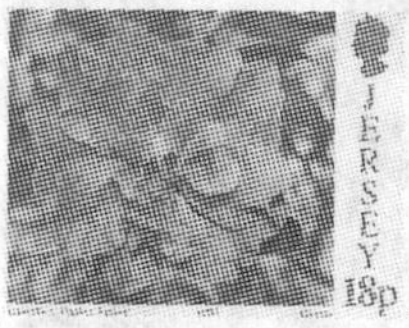

Camellias A141

1995, Mar. 21 Litho. *Perf. 14*

703 A141	18p Captain Rawes	.60	.60
704 A141	23p Brigadoon	.75	.75
705 A141	30p Elsie Jury	.95	.95
706 A141	35p Augusto L Gouveia Pinto	1.10	1.10
707 A141	41p Bella Romana	1.40	1.40
	Nos. 703-707 (5)	4.80	4.80

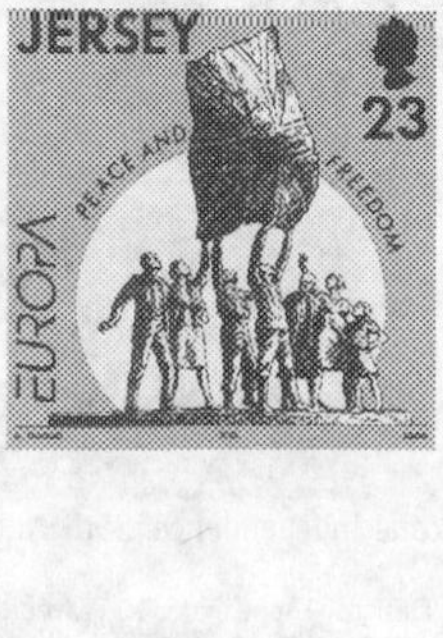

Liberation, by Philip Jackson A142

1995, May 9 Litho. *Perf. 13½*

708 A142	23p gray & black	.75	.75
709 A142	30p pink & black	.95	.95

Europa.

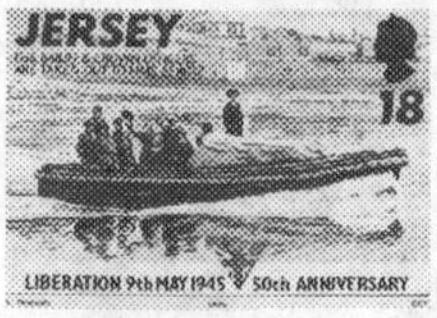

Liberation, 50th Anniv. A143

Designs: No. 710, Bailiff, Crown Officers taken to HMS Beagle. No. 711, Red Cross ship SS Vega. No. 712, Germans surrender on board HMS Beagle. No. 713, First troops of task force 135, Ordinance Yard, St. Helier. No. 714, Royal visitors, June 1945. No. 715, Supplies come ashore from LSTs, Operation Nestegg.
£1, Princess Elizabeth, Queen Elizabeth, Winston Churchill, King George VI, Princess Margaret at Buckingham Palace, VE Day.

1995, May 9 Litho. *Perf. 14½x14*

710 A143	18p multicolored	.60	.60
711 A143	18p multicolored	.60	.60
a.	Booklet pane, 3 each #710-711	3.75	
712 A143	23p multicolored	.75	.75
713 A143	23p multicolored	.75	.75
a.	Booklet pane, 3 each #712-713	4.50	
714 A143	60p multicolored	1.90	1.90
715 A143	60p multicolored	1.90	1.90
a.	Booklet pane, 3 each #714-715	11.50	
	Nos. 711-715 (5)	5.90	5.90

Souvenir Sheet

716 A143	£1 multicolored	3.25	3.25
a.	Booklet pane, #716	3.25	
	Complete booklet, #711a, #713a, #715a, #716a	23.00	

No. 716 contains one 81x29mm stamp.

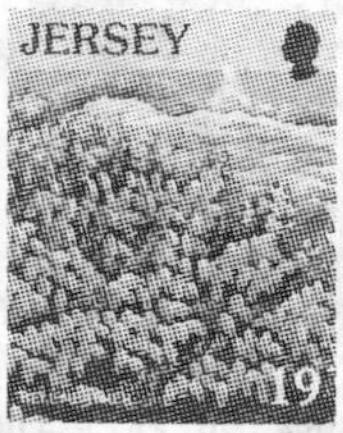

Wild Flowers — A144

1995, July 4 Litho. *Perf. 13½*

717 A144	19p Bell heather	.60	.60
718 A144	19p Sea campion	.60	.60
719 A144	19p Spotted rock-rose	.60	.60
720 A144	19p Thrift	.60	.60
721 A144	19p Sheep's-bit	.60	.60
a.	Strip of 5, #717-721	3.00	3.00
722 A144	23p Field bind-weed	.75	.75
723 A144	23p Common bird's-foot	.75	.75
724 A144	23p Sea holly	.75	.75
725 A144	23p Common centaury	.75	.75
726 A144	23p Dwarf pansy	.75	.75
a.	Strip of 5, #722-726	3.75	3.75
	Nos. 717-726 (10)	6.75	6.75

Butterfly & Moth Type of 1991

1995, Sept. 1 Litho. *Perf. 14*

727 A116	19p Peacock pansy	.60	.60
728 A116	23p Green-barred swallow-tail	.75	.75
729 A116	30p Orange emigrant	.95	.95
730 A116	41p Scarlet mormon	1.25	1.25
731 A116	60p Common birdwing	1.90	1.90
a.	Souvenir sheet of 2, #730-731	3.25	3.25
	Nos. 727-731 (5)	5.45	5.45

Singapore '95 (#731a).

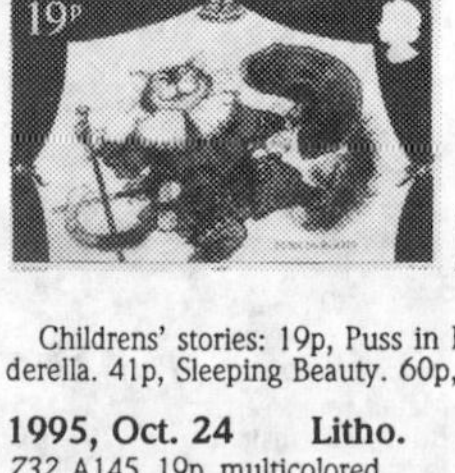

Christmas A145

Childrens' stories: 19p, Puss in Boots. 23p, Cinderella. 41p, Sleeping Beauty. 60p, Aladdin.

1995, Oct. 24 Litho. *Perf. 13½*

732 A145	19p multicolored	.60	.60
733 A145	23p multicolored	.75	.75
734 A145	41p multicolored	1.25	1.25
735 A145	60p multicolored	1.90	1.90
	Nos. 732-735 (4)	4.50	4.50

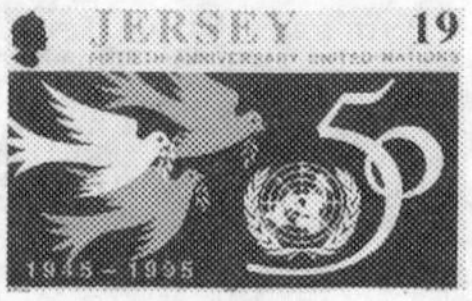

UN, 50th Anniv. A146

1995, Oct. 24 Litho. *Perf. 13x14*

736 A146	19p Doves, emblem	.60	.60
737 A146	23p Olive branch, emblem	.75	.75
738 A146	41p Olive branch, emblem	1.25	1.25
739 A146	60p Doves, emblem	1.90	1.90
	Nos. 736-739 (4)	4.50	4.50

POSTAGE DUE STAMPS

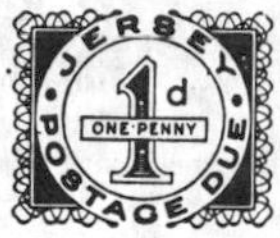

Numeral — D1

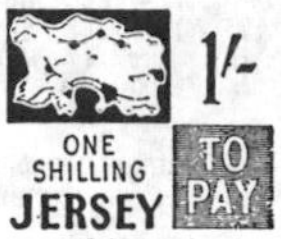

Map of Jersey — D2

Unwmk.

1969, Oct. 1 Litho. *Perf. 14*

J1	D1	1p violet blue	1.25	1.00
J2	D1	2p sepia	1.25	1.00
J3	D1	3p brt carmine	4.00	2.50
J4	D2	1sh emerald	12.00	9.50
J5	D2	2sh6p gray green	20.00	19.00
J6	D2	5sh red orange	37.50	37.50
		Nos. J1-J6 (6)	76.00	70.50

Type of 1969
Decimal Currency

1971-75 Litho. *Perf. 14*

J7	D2	½p black	.15	.15
J8	D2	1p pale violet	.15	.15
J9	D2	2p brown	.15	.15
J10	D2	3p bright pink	.15	.15
J11	D2	4p orange	.15	.15
J12	D2	5p emerald	.15	.15
J13	D2	6p orange ('74)	.15	.15
J14	D2	7p brt yellow ('74)	.20	.20
J15	D2	8p grnsh blue ('75)	.25	.25
J16	D2	10p gray	.30	.30
J17	D2	11p bister ('75)	.35	.35
J18	D2	14p lilac	.40	.40
J19	D2	25p dull green ('74)	.80	.80
J20	D2	50p plum ('75)	1.50	1.50
		Nos. J6-J20 (14)	4.85	4.85

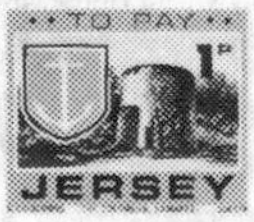

St. Clement Arms, Dovecote, Samares — D3

Arms and Scenes from Jersey Parishes: 2p, St. Lawrence and Handois Reservoir. 3p, St. John and Sorel Point. 4p, St. Ouen and Pinnacle Rock. 5p, St. Peter and Quetivel Mill. 10p, St. Martin and St. Catherine's Breakwater. 12p, St. Helier and St. Helier Harbor. 14p, St. Saviour and Highlands College. 15p, St. Brelade and Beauport Bay. 20p, Grouville and La Hougue Bie. 50p, St. Mary and Perry Farm. £1, Trinity and Bouley Bay.

1978, Jan. 17 Litho. *Perf. 14*

J21	D3	1p brt green & blk	.15	.15
J22	D3	2p orange & blk	.15	.15
J23	D3	3p maroon & blk	.15	.15
J24	D3	4p vermilion & blk	.15	.15
J25	D3	5p dp ultra & blk	.15	.15
J26	D3	10p olive & blk	.25	.25
J27	D3	12p blue & blk	.30	.30
J28	D3	14p red org & blk	.35	.35
J29	D3	15p lilac rose & blk	.40	.40
J30	D3	20p yel green & blk	.50	.50
J31	D3	50p brown & blk	1.25	1.25
J32	D3	£1 violet & blk	2.50	2.50
		Nos. J21-J32 (12)	6.30	6.30

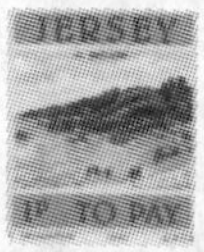

St. Brelade — D4

1982, Sept. 4 Litho. *Perf. 13½x14*

J33	D4	1p shown	.15	.15
J34	D4	2p St. Aubin	.15	.15
J35	D4	3p Rozel	.15	.15
J36	D4	4p Greve de Lecq	.15	.15
J37	D4	5p Bouley Bay	.15	.15
J38	D4	6p St. Catherine	.20	.20
J39	D4	7p Gorey	.25	.25
J40	D4	8p Bonne Nuit	.25	.25
J41	D4	9p La Rocque	.30	.30
J42	D4	10p St. Helier	.30	.30
J43	D4	20p Ronez	.60	.60
J44	D4	30p La Collette	.90	.90
J45	D4	40p Elizabeth Castle	1.10	1.10
J46	D4	£1 Upper Harbor Marina	2.50	2.50
		Nos. J33-J46 (14)	7.15	7.15

OCCUPATION STAMPS

Issued Under German Occupation

OS1

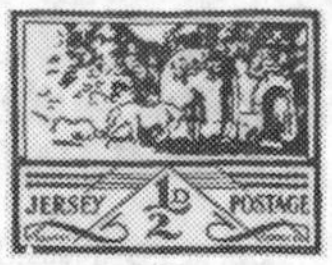

OS2

1941-42 Typo. Unwmk. *Perf. 11*

N1 OS1	½p green	4.50	5.00
N2 OS1	1p vermilion	5.00	*5.00*

Numerous shades and papers exist.
Issue dates: 1p, Apr. 1; ½p, Jan. 29, 1942.

1943-44 *Perf. 13½*

N3 OS2	½p Old Jersey farm	10.00	5.00
N4 OS2	1p Portelet Bay	1.50	.75
a.	On newsprint	2.50	2.50
N5 OS2	1½p Corbiere Lighthouse	2.00	*3.50*
N6 OS2	2p Elizabeth Castle	4.50	3.25
N7 OS2	2½p Mont Orgueil Castle	1.75	2.50
a.	On newsprint	1.25	*2.50*
N8 OS2	3p Gathering seaweed	1.25	*5.00*
	Nos. N3-N8 (6)	21.00	*20.00*

Issued: ½p, 1p, 6/1/43; 1½p, 2p, 6/8/43; 2½p, 3p, 6/29/43; #N4a, 2/28/44; #N7a, 2/25/44.

Nos. N1-N8 remained valid until Apr. 13, 1946.

ISLE OF MAN

'ī(ə)l əv 'man

LOCATION — In the Irish Sea, off Northwest coast of England
GOVT. — Semi-autonomous within the British Commonwealth
AREA — 221 sq. mi.
POP. — 64,679 (1981)
CAPITAL — Douglas

Catalogue values for unused stamps in this section are for Never Hinged items, beginning with Scott 1 in the regular postage section and Scott J1 in the postage due section.

British Regional Issues

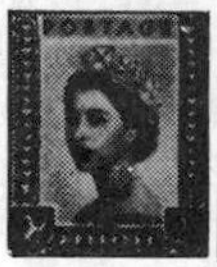

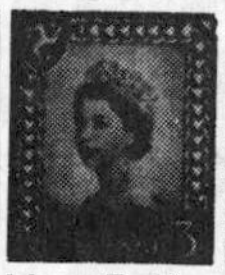

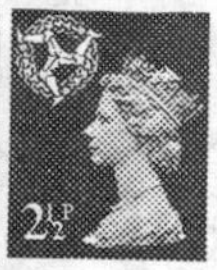

Manx Emblem
A1 A2 A3

Perf. 15x14

1958-69 Photo. Wmk. 322

1 A1	2½p rose red ('64)	.50	.40
2 A2	3p purple	.15	.15
p.	Phosphor. ('68)	.15	.15
3 A2	4p ultra ('66)	1.10	.20
p.	Phosphor. ('67)	.20	.15

Unwmk.

4 A2	4p ultra ('68)	.15	.15
5 A2	4p olive brown ('68)	.15	.15
6 A2	4p bright red ('69)	.55	.25
7 A2	5p dark blue ('68)	.55	.20
	Nos. 1-7 (7)	3.15	
	Set value		1.30

Nos. 4-7 are phosphorescent.
A 1963 printing of No. 2 is on chalky paper.

Isle of Man stamps can be mounted in the Scott Channel Islands album.

1971, July 7 Photo. Unwmk.

8	A3	2½p bright pink	.30	.15
9	A3	3p ultramarine	.35	.15
10	A3	5p bluish lilac	.45	.50
11	A3	7½p light red brown	.60	.60
		Nos. 8-11 (4)	1.70	1.40

Sold to the general public only at post offices within the Isle of Man, but valid for postage throughout Great Britain.

Bailiwick Issues

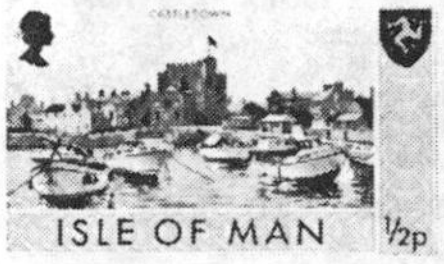
Castletown and Manx Emblem A4

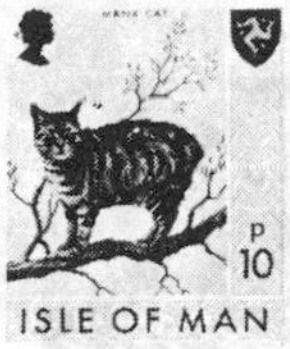
Manx Cat — A5

Perf. 11½

1973, July 5 Photo. Unwmk.

12	A4	½p shown	.15	.15
a.		Booklet pane of 2	2.75	
b.		Booklet pane of 4 ('74)	.90	
13	A4	1p Port Erin	.15	.15
14	A4	1½p Mt. Snaefell	.15	.15
15	A4	2p Laxey Village	.15	.15
a.		Booklet pane of 2	2.75	
16	A4	2½p Tynwald Hill	.15	.15
a.		Booklet pane of 2	.75	
17	A4	3p Douglas Promenade	.15	.15
a.		Booklet pane of 2	.70	
b.		Booklet pane of 4 ('74)	.90	
18	A4	3½p Port St. Mary	.15	.15
a.		Booklet pane of 4 ('74)	1.40	
19	A4	4p Fairy Bridge	.15	.15
20	A4	5p Peel, Castle and shore	.15	.15
21	A4	6p Cregneish Village	.22	.22
22	A4	7½p Ramsey Bay	.30	.30
23	A4	9p Douglas Bay	.32	.32
24	A5	10p shown	.38	.38
25	A5	20p Manx ram	.75	.75
26	A5	50p Manx shearwaters	1.50	1.50
27	A5	£1 Viking longship	3.00	3.00
		Set value	7.25	7.25

See Nos. 52-59.

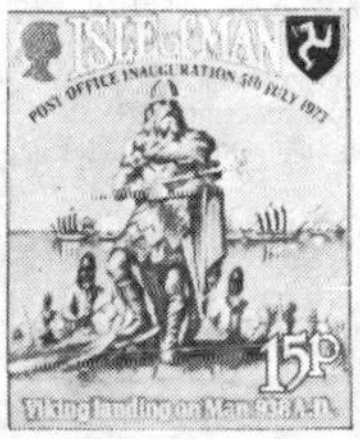
Vikings Landing on Man, 938 — A6

1973, July 5 ***Perf. 14***

28	A6	15p multicolored	.85	.85

Inauguration of postal independence.

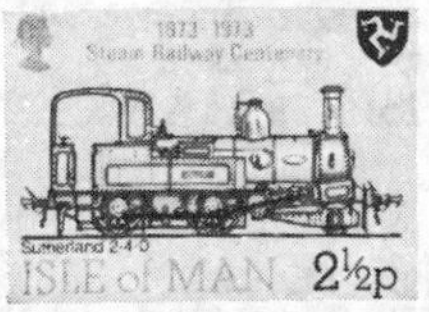
Engine No. 1, Sutherland, 1873 — A7

1973, Aug. 4 ***Perf. 14½x14***

29	A7	2½p shown	.15	.15
30	A7	3p Caledonia, 1885	.15	.15
31	A7	7½p Kissack, 1910	1.00	1.00
32	A7	9p Pender, 1873	1.25	1.25
		Nos. 29-32 (4)	2.55	2.55

Centenary of Manx steam railroad.

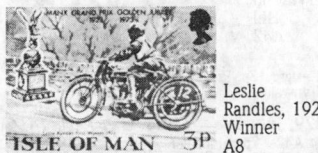

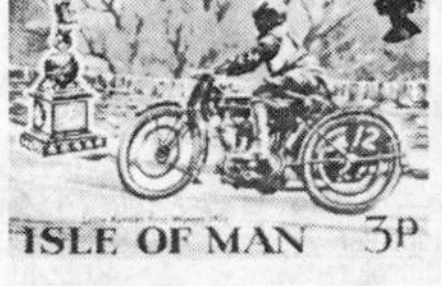
Leslie Randles, 1923 Winner A8

Design: 3½p, Alan Holmes, 1957 double winner.

1973, Sept. 4 Litho. ***Perf. 14***

33	A8	3p multicolored	.25	.25
34	A8	3½p multicolored	.25	.25

Manx Grand Prix Motorcycle Race, 50th anniversary.

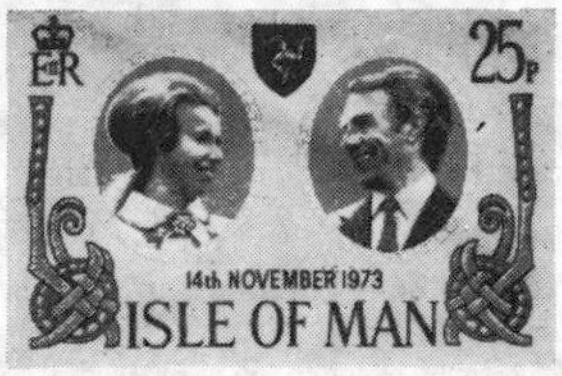
Princess Anne and Mark Phillips — A9

Litho. & Engr.

1973 Nov. 14 ***Perf. 14x13½***

35	A9	25p lt blue & multi	1.00	1.00

Wedding of Princess Anne and Capt. Mark Phillips, Nov. 14, 1973.

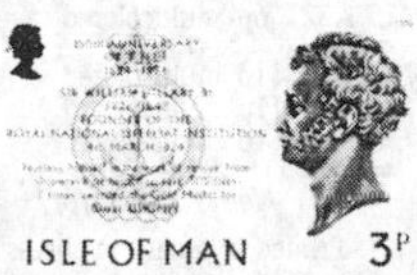
William Hillary, R.N.L.I. Badge — A10

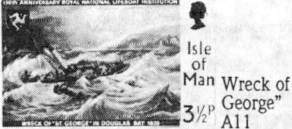

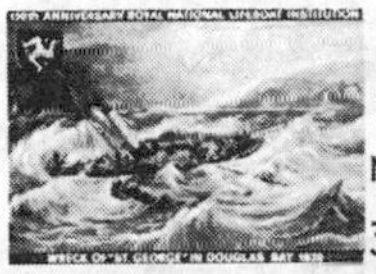
Wreck of "St. George" A11

Designs: 8p, Tower of Refuge and lifeboat "Manchester & Salford." 10p, "Osman Gabriel" at Port Erin. 3½p and 8p are from paintings.

1974, Mar. 4 Photo. ***Perf. 11½***

36	A10	3p black & multi	.15	.15
37	A11	3½p black & multi	.15	.15
38	A11	8p black & multi	.50	.50
39	A11	10p black & multi	.60	.60
		Nos. 36-39 (4)	1.40	1.40

Sesqui. of the founding of the Royal Natl. Lifeboat Institution by Sir William Hillary.

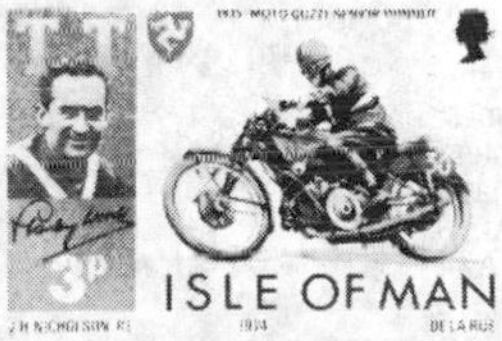
Stanley Woods on Moto Guzzi Motorcycle — A12

Designs: 3½p, Freddie Frith on Norton. 8p, Max Deubel on BMW with sidecar. 10p, Mike Hailwood on Honda.

1974, May 29 Litho. ***Perf. 13***

40	A12	3p yellow grn & multi	.15	.15
41	A12	3½p crimson & multi	.15	.15
42	A12	8p yellow & multi	.32	.28
43	A12	10p ultra & multi	.40	.32
		Nos. 40-43 (4)	1.02	.90

Tourist Trophy Motorcycle Races on the Isle of Man.

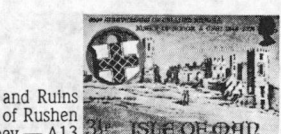

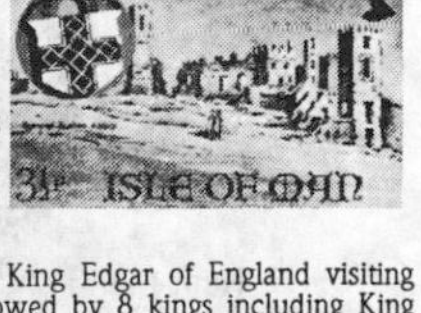
Arms and Ruins of Rushen Abbey — A13

Designs: 4½p, King Edgar of England visiting Chester in boat rowed by 8 kings including King Magnus Haraldson. 8p, Fleet under King Magnus' command and arms he gave to Isle of Man. 10p, Bridge at Avignon, Bishop's mitre and Three Legs of Man.

1974, Sept. 18 Litho. ***Perf. 14***

44	A13	3½p multicolored	.15	.15
45	A13	4½p multicolored	.15	.15
46	A13	8p multicolored	.32	.32
47	A13	10p multicolored	.40	.40
		Nos. 44-47 (4)	1.02	1.02

1,000th death anniv. of Magnus Haraldson, King of Many Islands (Nos. 45-46), and 600th death anniv. of William Russell, Bishop of Sodor and Mann (Nos. 44, 47).

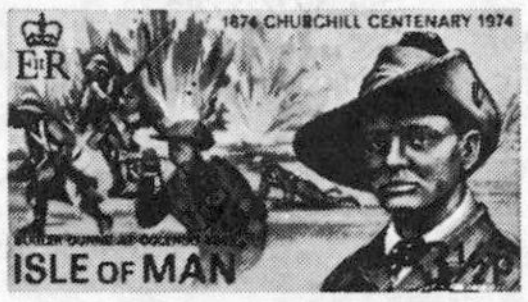
Churchill and "Bugler Dunne at Colenso, 1899" — A14

Sir Winston Churchill: 4½p, Government Buildings, Douglas, and Warrant of Appointment. 8p, Manx A.A. Regiment in action. 20p, Freedom of Douglas Scroll, and casket.

1974, Nov. 22 Photo. ***Perf. 11½***

48	A14	3½p multicolored	.15	.15
49	A14	4½p multicolored	.15	.15
50	A14	8p multicolored	.24	.24
51	A14	20p multicolored	.60	.60
a.		Souvenir sheet of 4, #48-51	1.25	1.25
		Nos. 48-51 (4)	1.14	1.14

Type of 1973

1975 Unwmk. ***Perf. 11½***

52	A4	4½p Tynwald Hill	.20	.20
53	A4	5½p Douglas Promenade	.20	.20
54	A4	7p Laxey Village	.40	.40
55	A4	8p Ramsey Bay	.40	.40
58	A4	11p Monk's Bridge	.45	.45
59	A4	13p Derbyhaven	.55	.55
		Nos. 52-59 (6)	2.20	2.20

Issued: #52, 55, 1/8; #53-54, 5/28; #58-59, 10/29.

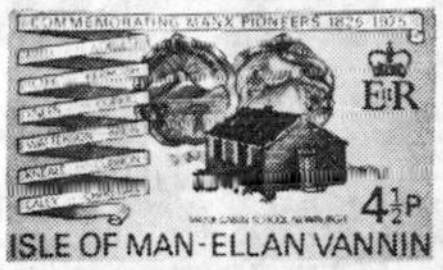
Log Cabin School, Cleveland Medal, Names of Settlers A15

Designs: 5½p, Terminal Tower Building, Cleveland, John Gill and Robert Carran. 8p, Clague House Museum, Margaret and Robert Clague. 10p, Thomas Quayle and S. S. William T. Graves.

1975, Mar. 14 Photo. ***Perf. 11½***

62	A15	4½p multicolored	.15	.15
63	A15	5½p multicolored	.20	.20
64	A15	8p multicolored	.30	.30
65	A15	10p multicolored	.35	.35
		Nos. 62-65 (4)	1.00	1.00

Sesquicentennial of arrival of Manx settlers in Cleveland, Ohio area.

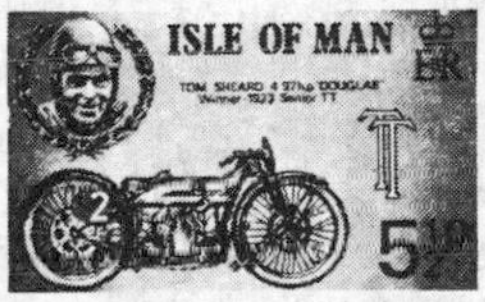
Tom Sheard and "Douglas" A16

Designs: 7p, Walter L. Handley and "Rex-Acme." 10p, Geoffrey Duke and "Gilera." 12p, Peter Williams and "Norton."

1975, May 28 Litho. ***Perf. 13½***

66	A16	5½p bister & multi	.15	.15
67	A16	7p salmon & multi	.20	.20
68	A16	10p lt green & multi	.28	.28
69	A16	12p ultra & multi	.38	.38
		Nos. 66-69 (4)	1.01	1.01

Tourist Trophy Motorcycle races on Isle of Man.

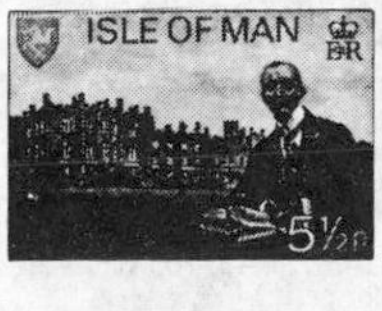
Sir George Goldie and his Birthplace A17

Designs (Sir George Goldie and): 7p, Map of Africa with Niger River basin, vert. 10p, Goldie as president of Royal Geographical Society and Society emblem, vert. 12p, River boats: trading hulk, native canoe, sternwheeler.

1975, Sept. 9 Photo. ***Perf. 11½***

70	A17	5½p multicolored	.15	.15
71	A17	7p multicolored	.20	.20
72	A17	10p multicolored	.28	.28
73	A17	12p multicolored	.38	.38
		Nos. 70-73 (4)	1.01	1.01

Sir George Dashwood Goldie-Taubman (1846-1925), founder of Royal Niger Company.

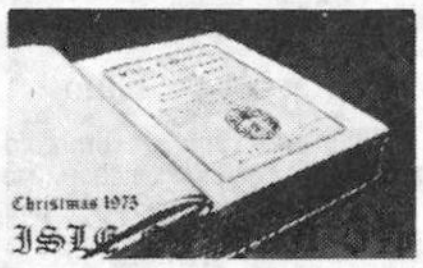
Manx Bible — A18

Bicentenary of Manx Bible and Christmas 1975: 7p, Rev. Philip Moore and Old Ballaugh Church. 11p, Bishop Mark Hildesley and Bishops Court. 13p, Shipwreck off Cumberland Coast with John Kelly holding manuscript above water.

1975, Oct. 29 Litho. ***Perf. 14***

74	A18	5½p multicolored	.15	.15
75	A18	7p multicolored	.20	.20
76	A18	11p multicolored	.30	.30
77	A18	13p multicolored	.32	.32
		Nos. 74-77 (4)	.97	.97

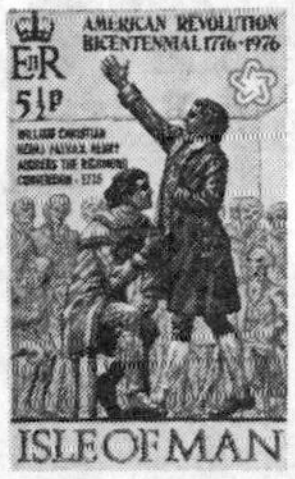
William Christian Listening to Patrick Henry — A19

Designs: 7p, Christian carrying Fincastle Resolutions to Williamsburg. 13p, Col. Patrick Henry and Lt. Col. William Christian of 1st Virginia Regiment. 20p, Christian as frontiersman and Indians.

1976, Mar. 12 Litho. ***Perf. 13½***

78	A19	5½p multicolored	.15	.15
79	A19	7p multicolored	.20	.20
80	A19	13p multicolored	.32	.32
81	A19	20p multicolored	.52	.52
a.		Souv. sheet of 4, #78-81, perf. 14	2.25	2.25
		Nos. 78-81 (4)	1.19	1.19

American Bicentennial. William Christian (1743-1786), patriot, son of a Manx-man and Patrick Henry's brother-in-law.

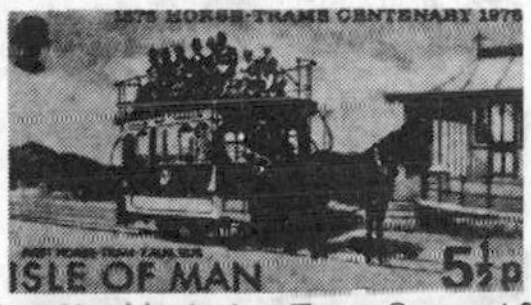
First Double-decker Tram Car — A20

Designs: 7p, Toast-rack tram, 1890. 11p, Horse bus, 1895. 13p, Decorated tram with Queen Elizabeth II and Prince Philip.

1976, May 26 Photo. ***Perf. 11½***

82	A20	5½p multicolored	.15	.15
83	A20	7p multicolored	.18	.18
84	A20	11p multicolored	.28	.28
85	A20	13p multicolored	.30	.30
		Nos. 82-85 (4)	.91	.91

Douglas horse trams, centenary.

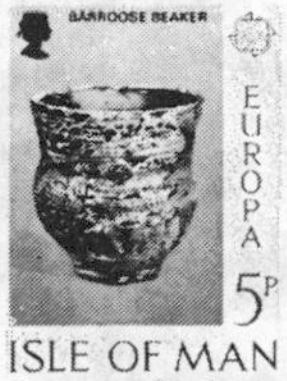
Barroose Beaker, Bronze Age — A21

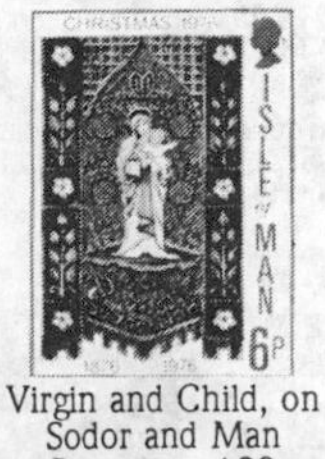
Virgin and Child, on Sodor and Man Banner — A22

Europa (Manx Ceramic Art): No. 87, Souvenir teapot (3-legged man), 19th cent. No. 88, Laxey jug, 1854. No. 89, Cronk Aust food vessel, early Bronze Age. No. 90, Sansbury bowl, 1851. No. 91, Knox urn, 20th cent. Nos. 89-91, horiz.

1976, July 28 Photo. *Perf. 11½*

86	A21	5p multicolored	.32	.32
87	A21	5p multicolored	.32	.32
88	A21	5p multicolored	.32	.32
a.		Strip of 3, #86-88	1.00	1.00
89	A21	10p multicolored	.32	.32
90	A21	10p multicolored	.32	.32
91	A21	10p multicolored	.32	.32
c.		Strip of 3, #89-91	1.00	1.00
		Nos. 86-91 (6)	1.92	1.92

Printed in sheets of 9 (3x3).

1976, Oct. 14 Litho. *Perf. 14x14½*

Virgin and Child on Embroidered Church Banners: 7p, St. Peter's, Onchan, Mothers' Union. 11p, Castletown. 13p, St. Olav's, Ramsey.

92	A22	6p multicolored	.15	.15
93	A22	7p multicolored	.18	.18
94	A22	11p multicolored	.28	.28
95	A22	13p multicolored	.35	.35
		Nos. 92-95 (4)	.96	.96

Christmas 1976 & cent. of Mothers' Union.

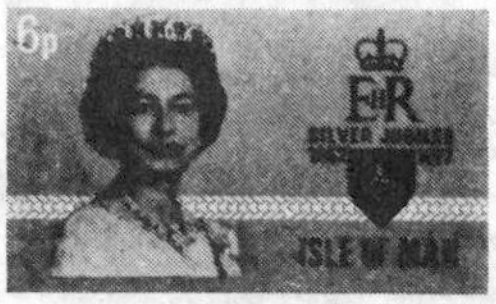

Elizabeth II and Arms of Man A23

Designs: 7p, Queen Elizabeth II and Prince Philip, vert. 25p, Queen, 1976 portrait.

Perf. 13½x14, 14x13½

1977, Mar. 1 Litho. & Engr.

96	A23	6p multicolored	.20	.20
97	A23	7p multicolored	.20	.20
98	A23	25p multicolored	.70	.70
		Nos. 96-98 (3)	1.10	1.10

25th anniv. of the reign of Elizabeth II.

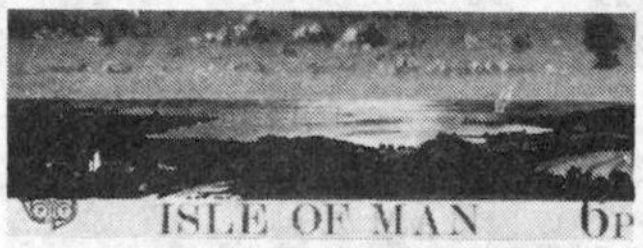

Carrick Bay from Tom-the-Dipper's — A24

Europa: 10p, Looking south from Mooragh Park, Ramsey.

1977, May 25 Litho. *Perf. 14*

99	A24	6p multicolored	.20	.20
100	A24	10p multicolored	.32	.32

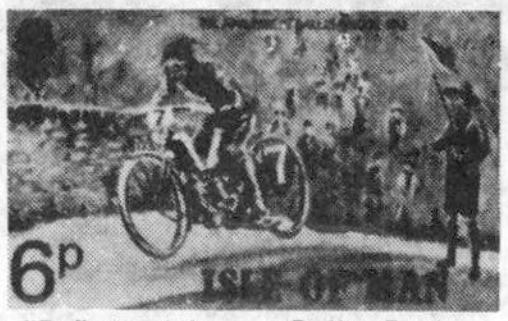

"Pa" Applebee at Ballig Bridge, 1912 — A25

Designs: 7p, Hairpin curve at Governor's Bridge and ambulance attendants. 11p, Boy Scouts tending scoreboards. 13p, John Willams at Windy Corner on Snaefell Mountain, winner of 1976 Open Classic Race.

1977, May 25 *Perf. 13½*

101	A25	6p multicolored	.20	.20
102	A25	7p multicolored	.22	.22
103	A25	11p multicolored	.35	.35
104	A25	13p multicolored	.42	.42
		Nos. 101-104 (4)	1.19	1.19

Tourist Trophy Motorcycle Races, and Boy Scouts, 70th anniv.; St. John Ambulance Assoc. cent. (in GB).

Meeting House, Mt. Morrison — A26

Designs: 7p, John Wesley preaching at Castletown, 1777. 11p, Wesley preaching outside Braddan Church. 13p, Methodist Church on Douglas Promenade, 1976.

1977, Oct. 19 Photo. *Perf. 11½*

Size: 30x24mm

105	A26	6p multicolored	.18	.18

Size: 37½x24mm

106	A26	7p multicolored	.18	.18
107	A26	11p multicolored	.30	.30

Size: 30x24mm

108	A26	13p multicolored	.38	.38
		Nos. 105-108 (4)	1.04	1.04

Bicentenary of John Wesley's first visit to the Isle of Man.

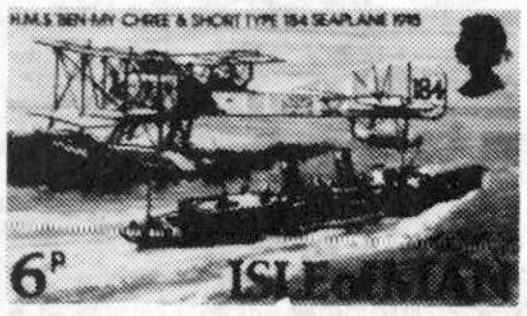

Seaplane and Carrier Ben My Chree — A27

Royal Air Force, 60th Anniv.: 7p, Bristol Scout and carrier Vindex, 1915. 11p, Boulton Paul Defiant over Douglas Bay, 1941. 13p, RAF Jaguar over Ramsey, 1977.

1978, Feb. 28 Litho. *Perf. 13½x14*

109	A27	6p multicolored	.22	.22
110	A27	7p multicolored	.22	.22
111	A27	11p multicolored	.35	.35
112	A27	13p multicolored	.42	.42
		Nos. 109-112 (4)	1.21	1.21

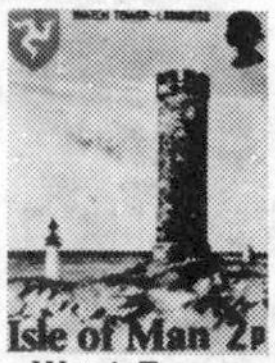

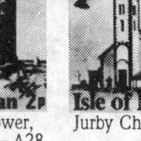

Watch Tower, Langness — A28

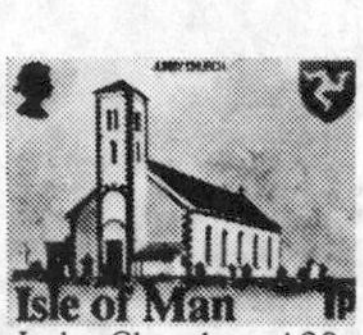

Jurby Church — A29

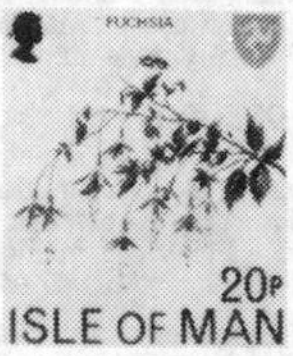

Fuchsia — A30

Landmarks: 6p, Government buildings. 7p, Tynwald Hill. 8p, Milner's Tower. 9p, Laxey Wheel. 10p, Castle Rushen. 11p, St. Ninian's Church. 12p, Tower of Refuge. 13p, St. German's Cathedral. 14p, Point of Ayre Lighthouse. 15p, Corrin's Tower. 16p, Douglas Head Lighthouse. 25p, Manx cat. 50p, Chough (crows). £1, Viking warrior.

1978 Litho. *Perf. 14, 14½*

113	A28	½p multicolored	.15	.15
114	A29	1p multicolored	.15	.15
115	A28	6p multicolored	.15	.15
116	A29	7p multicolored	.15	.15
a.		Perf. 14½	*2.00*	*1.50*
117	A28	8p multicolored	.16	.16
118	A28	9p multicolored	.20	.20
119	A29	10p multicolored	.25	.25
120	A28	11p multicolored	.26	.26
121	A29	12p multicolored	.28	.28
122	A29	13p multicolored	.35	.35
123	A29	14p multicolored	.35	.35
124	A29	15p multicolored	.38	.38
125	A29	16p multicolored	.40	.40
a.		Perf. 14½	*27.50*	*22.50*

Photo.

Perf. 11½

126	A30	20p multicolored	.55	.55
127	A30	25p multicolored	.75	.75
128	A30	50p multicolored	1.40	1.40
129	A30	£1 multicolored	3.00	3.00
		Nos. 113-129 (17)	8.93	8.93

6p exists only perf. 14. ½p-11p, 16p values are for perf. 14, 12p-15p for perf. 14½.

Issued: #113-125, 2/28; #126-129, 10/18.

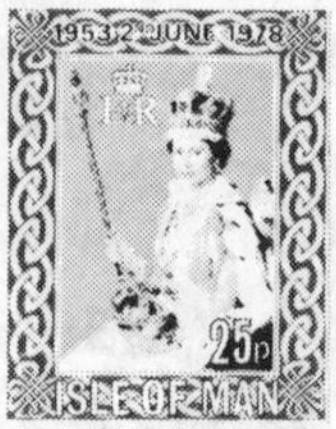

Elizabeth II — A31

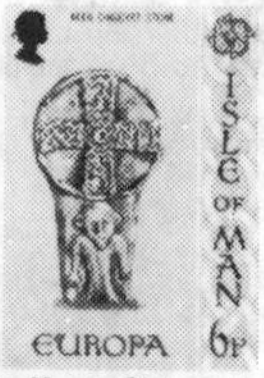

Keeil Chiggyrt Stone — A32

1978, May 24 Litho. *Perf. 14½x14*

130	A31	25p blue & multi	.70	.70

25th anniv. of coronation of Elizabeth II.

1978, May 24 *Perf. 11½*

Europa (Carved Gravestones): No. 132, Wheel-headed cross slab. No. 133, Celtic Wheel cross. No. 134, Thor cross. No. 135, Olaf Liotulfson cross. No. 136, Odd's and Thorleif's crosses.

131	A32	6p multicolored	.15	.15
132	A32	6p multicolored	.15	.15
133	A32	6p multicolored	.15	.15
a.		Strip of 3, #131-133	.45	.45
134	A32	11p multicolored	.24	.24
135	A32	11p multicolored	.24	.24
136	A32	11p multicolored	.24	.24
a.		Strip of 3, #134-136	.72	.72
		Nos. 131-136 (6)	1.17	1.17

Printed se-tenant in sheets of 9 (3x3).

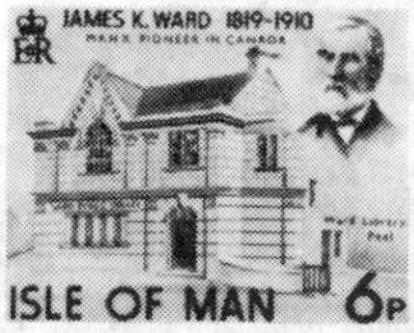

J. K. Ward, Ward Library, Peel — A33

Design: 13p, Lumber camp at Three Rivers and J. K. Ward.

1978, June 10 Litho. *Perf. 13½*

137	A33	6p multicolored	.15	.15
138	A33	13p multicolored	.32	.32

James K. Ward (1819-1910), Manx pioneer in Canada.

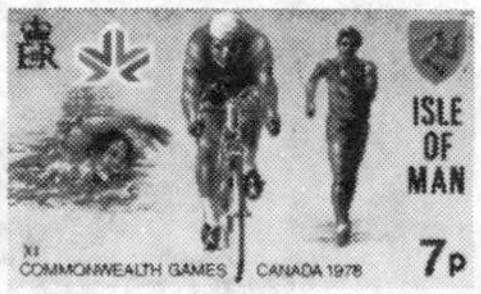

Athletes, Games' Emblem and Manx Arms A34

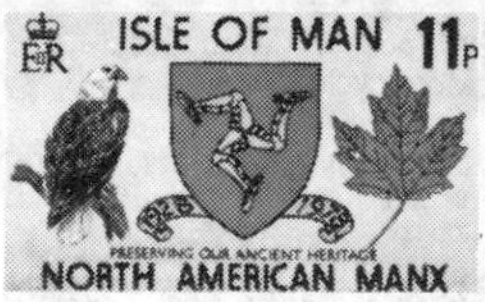

Eagle, Manx Arms, Maple Leaf A35

1978, June 10

139	A34	7p multicolored	.15	.15
140	A35	11p multicolored	.30	.30

11th Commonwealth Games, Edmonton, Aug. 3-12 (7p); North American Manx Soc., 50th anniv. (11p).

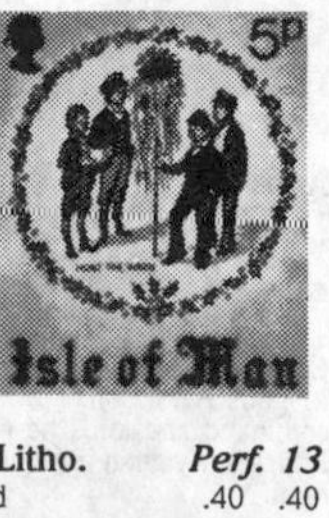

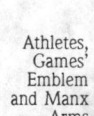

"Hunt the Wren" — A36

1978, Oct. 18 Litho. *Perf. 13*

141	A36	5p multicolored	.40	.40

Christmas 1978.

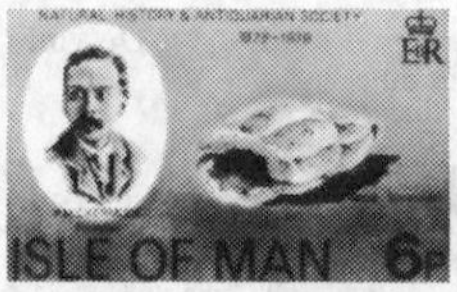

Philip M. C. Kermode and Nassa Kermodei A37

Designs: 7p, Peregrine falcons. 11p, Fulmars. 13p, Asilid fly.

1979, Feb. 27 Litho. *Perf. 14*

142	A37	6p multicolored	.18	.18
143	A37	7p multicolored	.20	.20
144	A37	11p multicolored	.35	.35
145	A37	13p multicolored	.42	.42
		Nos. 142-145 (4)	1.15	1.15

Isle of Man Natural History and Antiquarian Society.

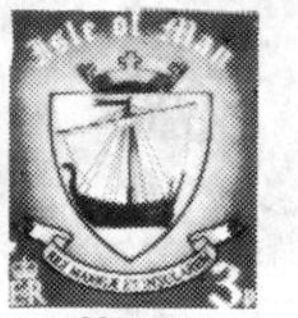
Viking Ship — A38

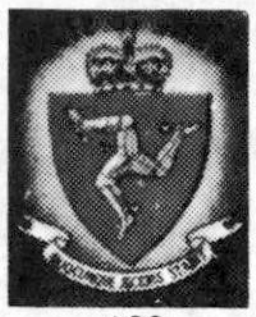
A39

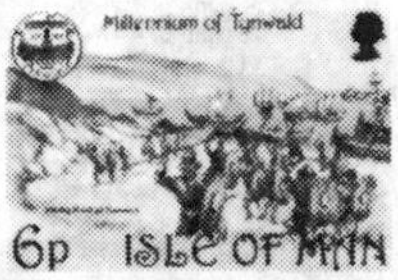

Viking Raid at Garwick — A40

Designs (Tynwald Emblem and): 7p, 10th century meeting at Tynwald. 11p, Tynwald Hill and St. John's Church. 13p, Contemporary Tynwald Day parade.

1979, May 16 Litho. *Perf. 14½x14*

146	A38	3p *Insularem*	.15	.15
a.		Bklt. pane, 4 #146, 2 #147	.60	
b.		*Insularum* ("1980")	.15	.15
c.		Bklt. pane, 4 #146b, 2 #147	.90	
147	A39	4p multicolored	.15	.15
148	A40	6p multicolored	.15	.15
149	A40	7p multicolored	.18	.18
150	A40	11p multicolored	.30	.30
151	A40	13p multicolored	.35	.35
		Nos. 146-151 (6)	1.28	1.28

Millennium of Tynwald, Legislative Council. #146-147 printed se-tenant in sheets of 80.

No. 146a comes in two arrangements.

No. 147 from No. 146c is dated "1980."

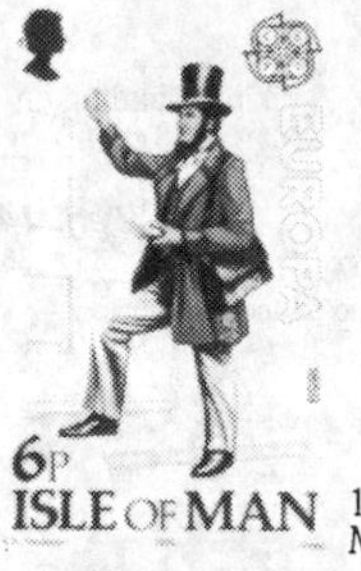

19th Century Mailman — A41

Europa: 11p, Contemporary mailman.

1979, May 16

152	A41	6p multicolored	.15	.15
153	A41	11p multicolored	.30	.30

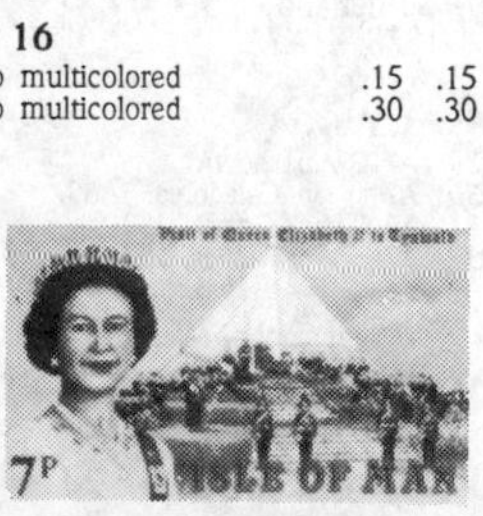

Ceremony on Tynwald Hill A42

Design: 13p, Procession from St. John's Church to Tynwald Hill.

1979, July 5 Litho. *Perf. 14½*

154	A42	7p multicolored	.22	.22
155	A42	13p multicolored	.40	.40

Visit of Queen Elizabeth II for the celebration of millennium of Tynwald.

Girl Holding Teddy Bear — A43

Christmas and IYC: 7p, Children with Santa.

1979, Oct. 19   Litho.   Perf. 13
156 A43 5p multicolored   .16 .16
157 A43 7p multicolored   .25 .25

Capt. John Quilliam and Spencer A44

Capt. Quilliam: 6p, Seized by press gang. 8p, Battle of Trafalgar. 15p, Castle Rushen.

1979, Oct. 19   Perf. 14
158 A44 6p multicolored   .15 .15
159 A44 8p multicolored   .20 .20
160 A44 13p multicolored   .32 .32
161 A44 15p multicolored   .40 .40
    Nos. 158-161 (4)   1.07 1.07

Capt. John Quilliam (1771-1829), British naval hero and member of House of Keys.

"Odin's Raven" A45

1979, Oct. 19   Perf. 14x14 1/2
162 A45 15p multicolored   .42 .42

Voyage of replica Viking longboat across North Sea (Trondheim to Peel), May 27-July 4. See No. 176a.

Conglomerate Arch and Emblem — A46

Langness Emblem and: 8p, Braaid Circle. 12p, Cashtal yn Ard (Neolithic burial ground). 13p, Volcanic rocks, Scarlett. 15p, Sugar-loaf Rock.

1980, Feb. 5   Litho.   Perf. 14 1/2
163 A46 7p multicolored   .25 .25
164 A46 8p multicolored   .30 .30
165 A46 12p multicolored   .35 .35
166 A46 13p multicolored   .40 .40
167 A46 15p multicolored   .45 .45
    Nos. 163-167 (5)   1.75 1.75

Royal Geographical Soc., 150th anniv.

"Mona's Isle I" — A47

1980, May 6   Photo.   Perf. 11 1/2
Granite Paper
168 A47 7p shown   .22 .22
169 A47 8p Douglas I   .25 .25
170 A47 11 1/2p Mona's Queen II, sinking U-boat   .32 .32
171 A47 12p King Orry III   .35 .35
172 A47 13p Ben-My-Chree IV   .38 .38
173 A47 15p Lady of Mann II   .45 .45
    a.   Souvenir sheet of 6, #168-173   2.00 2.00
    Nos. 168-173 (6)   1.97 1.97

Isle of Man Steam Packet Co. sesqui.; London 80 Intl. Stamp Exhib., May 6-14.

Thomas Edward Brown and Characters from his Poems — A48

Europa (Brown (1830-1897), Poet and Scholar): 13 1/2p, Cricket game, Clifton College Bristol.

1980, May 6
174 A48 7p multicolored   .18 .18
175 A48 13 1/2p multicolored   .35 .35

Visit of King Olav V of Norway A49

1980, June 13   Litho.   Perf. 14 1/2
176 A49 12p multicolored   .38 .38
    a.   Souv. sheet of 2, #162, 176   1.10 1.10

Visit of King Olav V of Norway, Aug. 2-7, 1979, and NORWEX 80 stamp exhibition, Oslo, June 13-22.

William Kermode and "Robert Quayle" A50

Kermode Family (First Manx Pioneers in Tasmania): 9p, First homestead, Mona Vale, Merino sheep, 1834. 13 1/2p, Ross Bridge, W. Kermode. 15p, Calendar House, 1868. 17 1/2p, Parliament Buildings, Hobart, Robert Quayle Kermode.

1980, Sept. 29   Litho.
177 A50 7p multicolored   .22 .22
178 A50 9p multicolored   .28 .28
179 A50 13 1/2p multicolored   .45 .45
180 A50 15p multicolored   .48 .48
181 A50 17 1/2p multicolored   .55 .55
    Nos. 177-181 (5)   1.98 1.98

Wren A51

1980, Sept. 29   Litho.   Perf. 13 1/2x14
182 A51 6p shown   .20 .20
183 A51 8p Robin   .28 .28

Wildlife conservation and Christmas 1980.

Luggers, Red Pier, Douglas A52

1981, Feb. 24   Litho.
184 A52 8p shown   .24 .24
185 A52 9p Wanderer saving Lusitania Survivors   .25 .25
186 A52 18p Nickey, Port St. Mary   .52 .52
187 A52 20p Nobby, Ramsey Harbor   .60 .60
188 A52 22p Sunbeam and Zebra, Port Erin   .65 .65
    Nos. 184-188 (5)   2.26 2.26

Royal National Mission to Deep Sea Fishermen centenary.

1p Peregrine Falcon — A53

1980, Sept. 29   Litho.   Perf. 14 1/2x14
Booklet Stamps
189 A53 1p shown   .15 .15
190 A53 5p Loaghtyn ram   .20 .20
    a.   Bklt. pane of 6 (2 each #147, 189, 190)   .85
    Set value   .25 .25

Crosh Cuirn (Cross of Mountain Ash Twigs, Harvest Charm) — A54

Europa: 18p, Bollan fish cross-bone (fishermen's charm).

1981, May 22   Litho.
191 A54 8p multicolored   .25 .25
192 A54 18p multicolored   .55 .55

Col. Mark Wilks, Peel Castle A55

1981, May 22   Perf. 14
193 A55 8p shown   .25 .25
194 A55 20p Wilks, Fort. St. George, Madras   .52 .52
195 A55 22p Wilks, Napoleon   .60 .60
196 A55 25p Wilks at Kirby estate   .65 .65
    Nos. 193-196 (4)   2.02 2.02

Wilks (d. 1831), governor of St. Helena.

Suffragettes Emmeline Goulden Pankhurst and Sophia Jane Goulden A56

1981, May 22   Perf. 14
197 A56 9p multicolored   .28 .28

Centenary of women's suffrage and of House of Keys Election Act (granting widows and unmarried women voting rights).

Prince Charles and Lady Diana A57

1981, July 29   Litho.   Perf. 14
198 A57 9p multicolored   .26 .26
199 A57 25p multicolored   .75 .75
    a.   Souv. sheet, 2 each #198-199   2.50 2.50

Royal Wedding.

Queen Elizabeth II — A58

1981, Sept. 29   Photo.   Perf. 11 1/2
Granite paper
200 A58 £2 multicolored   5.50 5.50

Douglas War Memorial, Poppies, Quote from Laurence Binyon's For the Fallen — A59

1981, Sept. 29
Granite Paper
201 A59 8p shown   .22 .22
202 A59 10p Maj. R.H. Cain, Battle of Arnhem, 1944   .28 .28
203 A59 18p Festival of Remembrance   .50 .50
204 A59 20p Tynwald and Spitfire, Dunkirk, 1940   .55 .55
    Nos. 201-204 (4)   1.55 1.55

Royal British Legion, 60th anniv.

Nativity Stained-glass Window, 1865, St. George's Church, Douglas A60

Design: Christmas pageant, Glencrutchery Special School, Douglas.

1981, Sept. 29   Litho.   Perf. 14 1/2x14
205 A60 7p multicolored   .22 .22
Size: 47x28mm
206 A60 9p multicolored   .28 .28

Christmas and St. George's Church bicen. (7p), IYD (9p).

Scouting Year — A61

Designs: 9p, Cunningham House (Man Scout Headquarters). 10p, Baden-Powell's visit, 1911. 19 1/2p, Portrait (32x41mm., Perf. 14 1/2). 24p, Baden-Powell with scouts, message. 29p, Sign, handshake, globe, emblem.

1982, Feb. 23   Litho.   Perf. 13 1/2x14
207 A61 9p multicolored   .28 .28
208 A61 10p multicolored   .30 .30
209 A61 19 1/2p multicolored   .60 .60
210 A61 24p multicolored   .75 .75
211 A61 29p multicolored   .90 .90
    Nos. 207-211 (5)   2.83 2.83

Europa 1982 A62

Designs: 9p, Bishop Thomas Wilson (1663-1755) and his "The Principles and Duties of Christianity," first book printed in Manx, 1707. 19 1/2p, Visit of Thomas, 2nd Earl of Derby, 1507.

1982, June 1   Photo.   Perf. 12 1/2
Granite Paper
212 A62 9p multicolored   .22 .22
213 A62 19 1/2p multicolored   .52 .52

75th Anniv. of Tourist Trophy Motorcycle Races A63

Designs: Winners on their bikes.

1982, June 1   Litho.   Perf. 14

214	A63	9p	Charlie Collier, 431 Matchless, 1907	.22 .22
215	A63	10p	Freddie Dixon, Douglas, 1923	.28 .28
216	A63	24p	Jimmie Simpson, Norton, 1932	.70 .70
217	A63	26p	Mike Hailwood, Norton, 1961	.75 .75
218	A63	29p	Jock Taylor, 700 Fowler Yamaha, '80	.85 .85
			Nos. 214-218 (5)	2.80 2.80

Isle of Man Steam Packet Co. Mail Contract Sesquicentennial — A64

1982, Oct. 5   Litho.   Perf. 13½x14

219	A64	12p	Mona I	.38 .38
220	A64	19½p	Manx Maid II	.60 .60

Christmas 1982
A65

1982, Oct. 5   Perf. 13x13½

221	A65	8p	Three Kings	.32 .32
222	A65	11p	Robin, Christmas tree, vert.	.45 .45

Souvenir Sheet

Princess Diana and Prince William — A66

1982, Oct. 12

223	A66	50p	multicolored	2.00 2.00

Birth of Prince William of Wales (June 21) and 21st birthday of Princess Diana (July 1).

Marine Birds — A67

1983, Feb. 15   Litho.   Perf. 14½

224	A67	1p	Puffins, Cranstal	.15 .15
225	A67	2p	Gannets, Point of Ayre	.15 .15
226	A67	5p	Lesser black-backed gulls, Santon	.20 .20
227	A67	8p	Cormorants, Maughold Head	.30 .30
228	A67	10p	Kittiwakes, White Strand	.40 .40
229	A67	11p	Shags, Calf of Man	.45 .45
230	A67	12p	Herons, Douglas Foreshore	.50 .50
231	A67	13p	Herring gulls, Peel	.55 .55
232	A67	14p	Razorbills, Calf of Man	.55 .55
233	A67	15p	Great black-backed gulls, Calf of Man	.60 .60
234	A67	16p	Shelducks, Poyll Vaaish	.65 .65
235	A67	18p	Oystercatchers, Langness	.70 .70

1983, Sept. 14   Perf. 14
Size: 39x25mm

236	A67	20p	Arctic terns, Blue Point	.80 .80
237	A67	25p	Guillemots, Calf of Man	1.00 1.00
238	A67	50p	Redshanks, Langness	1.75 1.75
239	A67	£1	Mute swans, Port St. Mary Bay	3.50 3.50
			Nos. 224-239 (16)	12.25 12.25

Centenary of Salvation Army in Isle of Man — A68

Designs: 10p, Citadel opening ceremony, 1932, T.H. Cannell. 12p, Founder William Booth, early meeting place (former Unitarian Church, Douglas). 19½p, Band, Bandmaster Gordon Cowley, 1981. 26p, Lt.-Col. Thomas Bridson, treating lepers in Dutch East Indies.

1983, Feb. 15   Photo.   Perf. 11½
Granite Paper

240	A68	10p	multicolored	.26 .26
241	A68	12p	multicolored	.32 .32
242	A68	19½p	multicolored	.52 .52
243	A68	26p	multicolored	.70 .70
			Nos. 240-243 (4)	1.80 1.80

Europa 1983 — A69

1983, May 18   Perf. 14

244	A69	10p	Laxey Wheel	.26 .26
245	A69	20½p	Designer Robert Casement	.52 .52

King William's College Sesquicentennial — A70

Graduates: 10p, Nick Keig, Yachtsman. 12p, College, arms. 28p, William Bragg, 1915 Nobel Prize winner in physics, ionization spectrometer. 31p, Gen. George Stuart White, Defense of Ladysmith, Boer War.

1983, May 18   Photo.   Perf. 11½
Granite Paper

246	A70	10p	multicolored	.32 .32
247	A70	12p	multicolored	.38 .38
248	A70	28p	multicolored	.95 .95
249	A70	31p	multicolored	1.00 1.00
			Nos. 246-249 (4)	2.65 2.65

World Communications Year and 10th Anniv. of Post Office — A71

1983, July 5   Litho.   Perf. 15

250	A71	10p	New P.O. Headquarters	.35 .35
251	A71	15p	Viking landing, 938	.55 .55

Christmas 1983
A72

1983, Sept. 14   Litho.   Perf. 13x13½

252	A72	9p	Shepherds	.35 .35
253	A72	12p	Three Kings	.45 .45

Karran Fleet — A73

Links with Falkland Islands A74

1984, Feb. 14   Litho.   Perf. 14

254	A73	10p	Manx King, 1884	.35 .35
255	A73	13p	Hope, 1858	.45 .45
256	A73	20½p	Rio Grande, 1868	.70 .70
257	A73	28p	Lady Elizabeth, 1879	1.00 1.00
258	A73	31p	Sumatra, 1858	1.25 1.25
			Nos. 254-258 (5)	3.75 3.75

1984, Feb. 14

259			Sheet of 2, #257, 259a	3.00 3.00
	a.		A74 31p multicolored	1.50 1.50

Europa (1959-1984) A75

1984, Apr. 27   Photo.   Perf. 11½

260	A75	10p	dk yel org, dk brn & buff	.30 .30
261	A75	20½p	blue, dk bl & lt bl	.62 .62

DH-48, Ronaldsway Airport A76

1984, Apr. 27   Litho.   Perf. 14

262	A76	11p	shown	.35 .35
263	A76	13p	DH-86, Calf of Man	.40 .40
264	A76	26p	DC-3, Ronaldsway Airport	.80 .80
265	A76	28p	Vickers Viscount, Douglas	.90 .90
266	A76	31p	Islander, Ronaldsway Airport	1.00 1.00
			Nos. 262-266 (5)	3.45 3.45

50th Anniv. of official airmail service and 40th anniv. of Intl. Civil Aviation Org.

William Cain as Mayor of Melbourne, 1886-87 — A77

1984, Sept. 21   Litho.   Perf. 14½

267	A77	11p	Ballasalla (birthplace)	.32 .32
268	A77	22p	Voyage to Australia	.65 .65
269	A77	28p	Railway, Victoria	.80 .80
270	A77	30p	shown	.85 .85
271	A77	33p	Royal Exhibition Buildings, Melbourne	.95 .95
			Nos. 267-271 (5)	3.57 3.57

William Cain (1831-1914), building contractor and public servant in Australia.

Queen Elizabeth II, CPA Emblem A78

1984, Sept. 21   Perf. 14

272	A78	14p	shown	.42 .42
273	A78	33p	Arms, Elizabeth II	1.00 1.00

30th Conference of Commonwealth Parliamentary Assoc., Sept. 28-Oct. 5.

Christmas — A79

Stained-glass windows.

1984, Sept. 21

274	A79	10p	Birds, Glencrutchery House	.30 .30
275	A79	13p	Arms, Lonan Old Church	.40 .40

75th Anniv. of Girl Guides — A80

Designs: 11p, Cunningham House (headquarters), Mrs. W. and J. Cunningham (early Island Commissioners). 14p, Princess Margaret (president), color guard. 29p, Lady Olave Baden-Powell, headquarters opening. 31p, Uniforms, 1910-85. 34p, Sign, handclasp, trefoil.

1985, Jan. 31   Photo.   Perf. 12

276	A80	11p	multicolored	.40 .40
277	A80	14p	multicolored	.55 .55
278	A80	29p	multicolored	.95 .95
279	A80	31p	multicolored	1.25 1.25
280	A80	34p	multicolored	1.40 1.40
			Nos. 276-280 (5)	4.55 4.55

Elizabeth II — A81

1985, Jan. 31   Litho.   Perf. 14

281	A81	£5	multicolored	14.00 14.00

Europa 1985 — A82

Manx composers and excerpts from their works: No. 282a, "O'Land of our Birth." No. 282b, William H. Gill (1839-1922). No. 283a, Hymn "Crofton;" No. 283b, Dr. John Clague (1842-1908).

1985, Apr. 24   Photo.   Perf. 12

282			Pair	1.10 1.10
	a.-b.		A82 12p any single	.55 .55
283			Pair	1.10 1.10
	a.-b.		A82 22p any single	.55 .55

Motoring A83

Motor races and winning vehicles: No. 284a, 1906 Tourist Trophy Race. No. 284b, 1922 Tourist Trophy Race. No. 285a, 1950 British Empire Trophy Race. No. 285b, 1934 Manin Moar Race. No. 286a, 1984 Tourist Trophy Motorcycle Race (official car). No. 286b, 1981 Rothmans Manx Intl. Rally.

1985, May 25 Litho. *Perf. 14*

284 Pair .70 .70
a.-b. A83 12p any single .35 .35
285 Pair .90 .90
a.-b. A83 14p any single .45 .45
286 Pair 1.90 1.90
a.-b. A83 31p any single .95 .95
Nos. 284-286 (3) 3.50 3.50

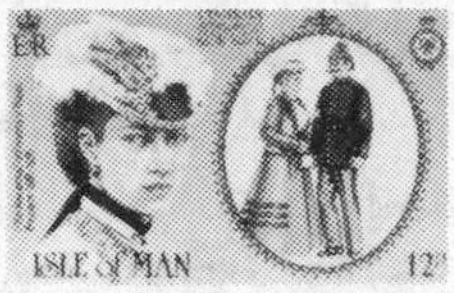

H.R.H. Alexandra (1885-1925), Princess of Wales — A84

SSA presidents: 15p, Queen Mary (1925-1953). 29p, Earl Mountbatten of Burma (1953-1979). 34p, Prince Michael of Kent (1982-).

1985, Sept. 4 Litho. *Perf. 14*

287 A84 12p multicolored .35 .35
288 A84 15p multicolored .45 .45
289 A84 29p multicolored .85 .85
290 A84 34p multicolored 1.00 1.00
Nos. 287-290 (4) 2.65 2.65

Soldier's, Sailors' & Airmen's Families Assoc., cent.

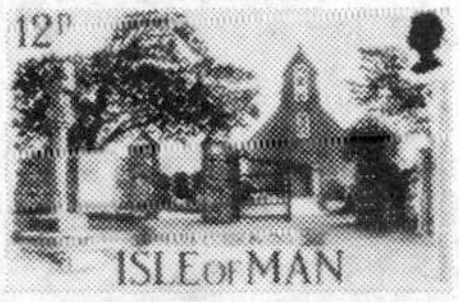

Lt.-Gen. Sir Mark Cubbon, K.C.B. (1785-1861), Commissioner of Mysore — A85

1985, Oct. 2 Litho. *Perf. 14*

291 A85 12p Kirk Maughold Parish Church, 14th century .40 .40
292 A85 22p Portrait, vert. .70 .70
293 A85 45p Equestrian monument, 1866 Bangalore, India, vert. 1.40 1.40
Nos. 291-293 (3) 2.50 2.50

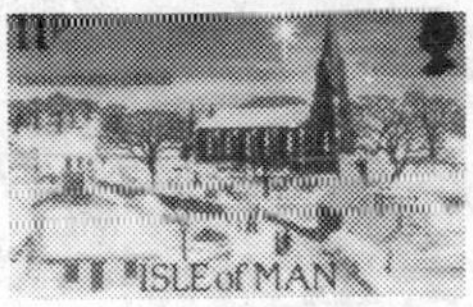

Christmas 1985 A86

1985, Oct. 2 Litho. *Perf. 13½*

294 A86 11p Onchan Parish Church, 1833 .35 .35
295 A86 14p St. John's Church .55 .55
296 A86 31p Bride Parish Church, 1876 1.25 1.25
Nos. 294-296 (3) 2.15 2.15

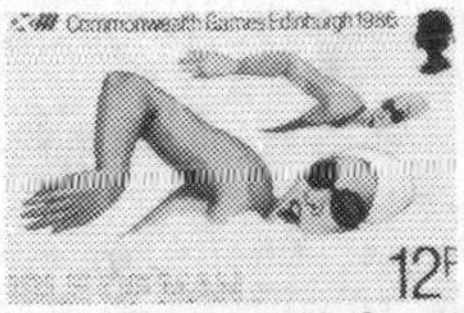

1986 Commonwealth Games, Edinburgh — A87

1986, Feb. 5 Litho. *Perf. 14*

297 A87 12p Women's swimming .40 .40
298 A87 15p Walking .50 .50
299 A87 31p Rifle shooting .95 .95
300 A87 34p Bicycling 1.25 1.25
Nos. 297-300 (4) 3.10 3.10

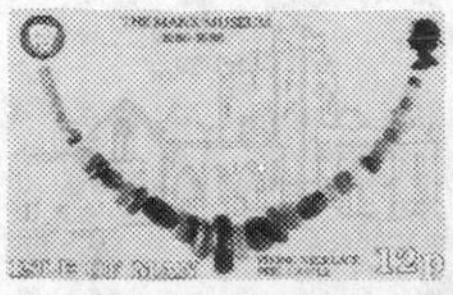

Viking Necklace, Peel Castle A88

Artifacts, architecture: 15p, Meayll Circle burial ground, Rushen. 22p, Prehistoric Cervus giganteus skeleton, Glose-y-Garey, vert. 26p, Norwegian viking longship, vert. 29p, Open-air Museum, Cregneash.

1986, Feb. 5 *Perf. 14½x14, 14x14½*

301 A88 12p multicolored .40 .40
302 A88 15p multicolored .45 .45
303 A88 22p multicolored .65 .65
304 A88 26p multicolored .80 .80
305 A88 29p multicolored 1.00 1.00
Nos. 301-305 (5) 3.30 3.30

Centenaries of Manx Museum and Ancient Monuments Act.

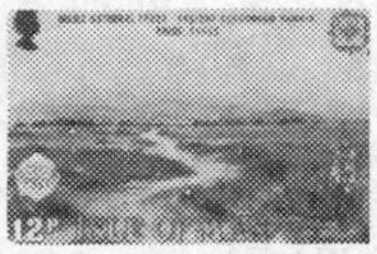

Europa 1986, Manx National Trust — A89

Designs: No. 306a, Bride hills and the Ayres. No. 306b, Calf of Man. No. 307a, Eary Cushlin. No. 307b, St. Michael's Isle.

1986, Apr. 10 Litho. *Perf. 12*

306 Pair .75 .75
a.-b. A89 12p any single .35 .35
307 Pair 1.40 1.40
a.-b. A89 22p any single .70 .70

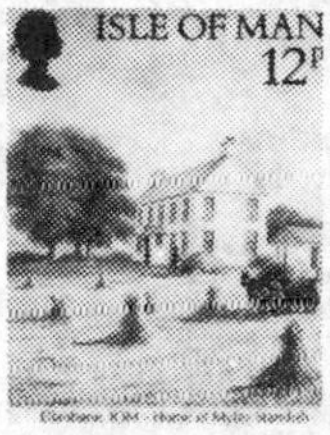

Settling of Plymouth — A90

Designs: 12p, Ellanbane, Isle of Man, Myles Standish's home. 15p, The Mayflower. 31p, Pilgrims landing, 1620. 34p, Capt. Myles Standish (c. 1584-1656).

1986, May 22 *Perf. 13½*

308 A90 12p multicolored .40 .40
309 A90 15p multicolored .50 .50
310 A90 31p multicolored 1.10 1.10
311 A90 34p multicolored 1.25 1.25
a. Souvenir sheet of 2, #310-311, perf. 13x12½ 2.50 2.50
Nos. 308-311 (4) 3.25 3.25

AMERIPEX '86, Chicago, May 22-June 1.

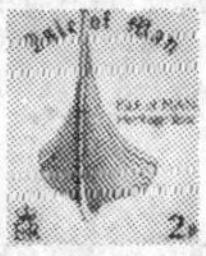

Heritage Year — A91

1986, Apr. 10 Litho. *Perf. 15x14*

312 A91 2p Viking longship bow .15 .15
a. Bklt. pane of 6, 2 #312, 4 #313 3.00
313 A91 10p Celtic cross .80 .80
a. Bklt. pane of 3 + 3 labels 2.00

Issued in booklets only.

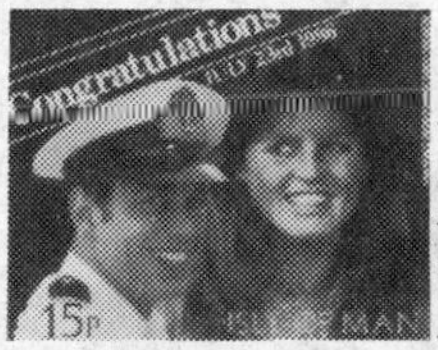

Wedding of Prince Andrew and Sarah Ferguson A92

1986, July 23

314 A92 15p Wedding date .50 .50
315 A92 40p Engagement date 1.25 1.25

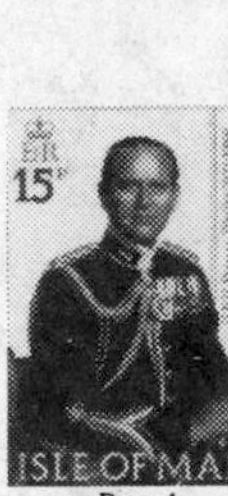

Royal Birthdays — A93

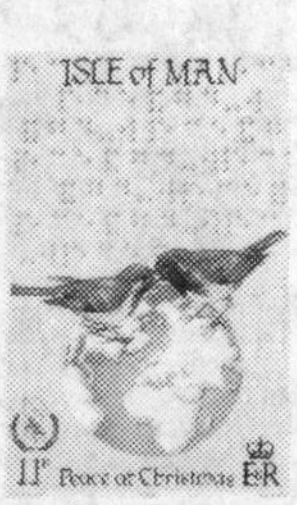

Intl. Peace Year — A94

Designs: No. 316a, Prince Philip, 65. No. 316b, Elizabeth II, 60. No. 317 is the same size as No. 316.

1986, Aug. 28 *Perf. 11½*

316 Pair 1.25 1.25
a.-b. A93 15p any single .60 .60
317 A93 34p Royal couple 1.25 1.25

STOCKHOLMIA '86, Swedish Post Office 350th anniv. Stamps issued in sheets of 6.

1986, Sept. 25 Litho. *Perf. 14*

318 A94 11p Robins, globe, Braille .40 .40
319 A94 14p Hands, dove .45 .45
320 A94 31p Hand-holding, sign language .95 .95
Nos. 318-320 (3) 1.80 1.80

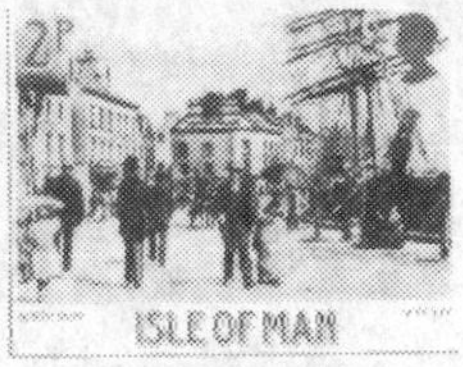

Accession of Queen Victoria to the British Throne, 150th Anniv. A95

Photographs of Victorian Douglas, by John Miller Nicholson.

1987, Jan. 21 Litho. *Perf. 14½*

321 A95 2p North Quay .15 .15
322 A95 3p The Old Fish Market .15 .15
323 A95 10p Breakwater .35 .35
a. Bklt. pane of 8 (2 2p, 2 3p, 4 10p) ('87) 1.90
324 A95 15p Jubilee Clock .55 .55
a. Bklt. pane of 8 (2 2p, 2 3p, 2 10p, 2 15p) ('87) 2.25
325 A95 31p Loch Promenade 1.10 1.10
326 A95 34p Beach 1.25 1.25
Nos. 321-326 (6) 3.55 3.55

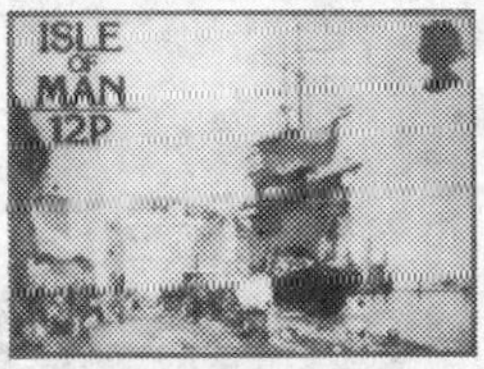

19th Century Paintings by John Miller Nicholson (1840-1913) — A96

Harbor scenes: 12p, The Old Fish Market and Harbor, Douglas. 26p, Red Sails at Douglas. 29p, The Double Corner. 34p, Peel Harbor.

1987, Feb. 18 *Perf. 13½*

327 A96 12p multicolored .40 .40
328 A96 26p multicolored .85 .85
329 A96 29p multicolored .90 .90
330 A96 34p multicolored 1.10 1.10
Nos. 327-330 (4) 3.25 3.25

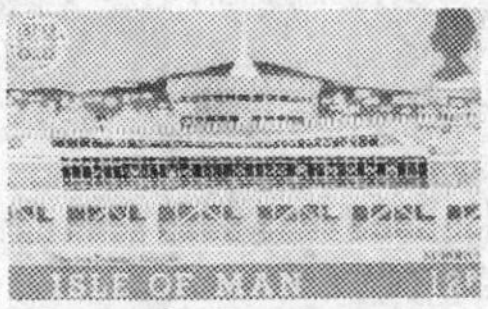

Promenade, Douglas — A97

1987, Apr. 29 Litho. *Perf. 13½*

331 A97 12p Sea Terminal, 1965 .50 .50
332 A97 12p Tower of Refuge, 1832 .50 .50
a. Pair, #331-332 1.00 1.00
333 A97 22p Gaiety Theater, c. 1900 1.00 1.00
334 A97 22p Villa Marina 1.00 1.00
a. Pair, #333-334 2.00 2.00
Nos. 331-334 (4) 3.00 3.00

Europa 1987.

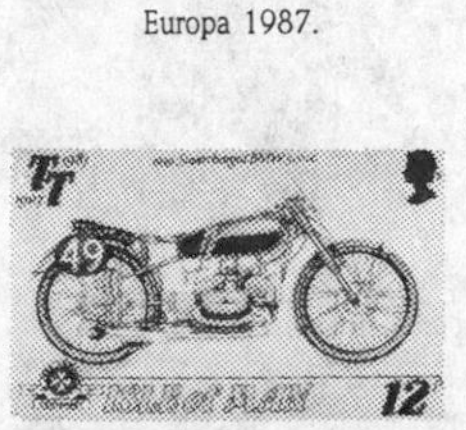

Tourist Trophy Motorcycle Races, 80th Anniv. — A98

1987, May 27 *Perf. 13½x13*

335 A98 12p 1939 Supercharged BMW 500CC .35 .35
336 A98 15p 1953 Manx "Kneeler" Norton 350CC .45 .45
337 A98 29p 1956 MV Agusta 500CC 4 .85 .85
338 A98 31p 1957 Guzzi 500CC V8 .90 .90
339 A98 34p 1967 Honda 250CC 6 1.00 1.00
a. Souv. sheet of 5, #335-339 + 7 labels, perf 14x13½ 3.50 3.50
Nos. 335-339 (5) 3.55 3.55

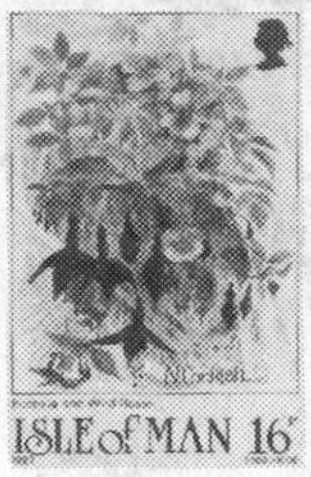

Wildflowers A99

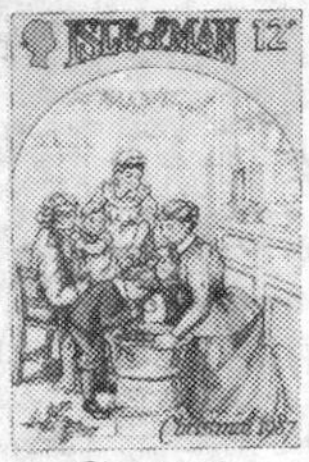

Christmas A100

1987, Sept. 9 Litho. *Perf. 14½x13½*

340 A99 16p Fuchsia, wild roses .50 .50
341 A99 29p Field scabius, ragwort .90 .90
342 A99 31p Wood anemone, celandine .95 .95
343 A99 34p Violets, primroses 1.00 1.00
Nos. 340-343 (4) 3.35 3.35

1987, Oct. 16 *Perf. 14*

Victorian family scenes based on drawings by Alfred Hunt for The Illustrated London News, c. 1870-1890.

344 A100 12p Stirring the pudding .35 .35
345 A100 15p Christmas tree selection .45 .45
346 A100 31p Decorating tree .95 .95
Nos. 344-346 (3) 1.75 1.75

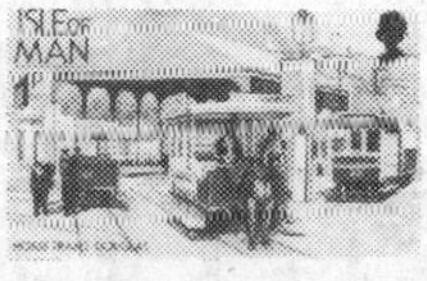

Railways & Tramways A101

Designs: 1p, Horse-drawn "Toast Rack" tram, Douglas Bay, 1884. 2p, No. 5 electric tram, Snaefell Mountain Railway, 1895. 3p, No. 3 open-top double-deck electric tram, Marine Drive-Port Soderick line, Douglas Southern Electric Tramway, 1896. 5p, Tower of Refuge and open tram, Douglas Head Incline Railway. 10p, Electric tram at Maughold Head, 1893, Douglas and Laxey Coast Electric Tramway. 13p, Douglas Cable Car No. 72, 1896. 14p, Manx Northern Railway No. 4 Caledonia, a Dubs 0-6-0T, 1885, at Gob-y-Deigan. 15p, Great Laxey Mine Railway Lewin steam engine Ant pulling coal cars. 16p, Henry B. Loch, first locomotive on the island, Port Erin Breakwater Railway, 1864. 17p, Locomotive No. 1, Ramsey Harbor Tramway. 18p, Engine No. 7 Tynwald, 1880, Foxdale Railway. 19p, Douglas Corp. engine, Baldwin Reservoir Railway. 20p, "Kissack" leaving St. John's for Peel. 25p, "Hutchinson" leaving Douglas Station. 50p, "Polar Bear" of Groudle Glen Railway. £1, The Royal Train.

1988 Litho. *Perf. 13½*

347 A101 1p multicolored .15 .15
348 A101 2p multicolored .15 .15
349 A101 3p multicolored .15 .15
350 A101 5p multicolored .20 .20
351 A101 10p multicolored .35 .35
352 A101 13p multicolored .50 .50
353 A101 14p multicolored .55 .55
354 A101 15p multicolored .55 .55
355 A101 16p multicolored .60 .60
a. Bklt. pane, 2 3p, 13p, 2 16p 1.90
b. Bklt. pane, 4 13p, 6 16p 5.75
356 A101 17p multicolored .60 .60
a. Booklet pane, 2 3p, 2 14p, 17p 2.00
b. Booklet pane, 4 14p, 6 17p 5.75
357 A101 18p multicolored .65 .65
358 A101 19p multicolored .65 .65
e. Bklt. pane, 4 15p, 6 19p 6.00

Perf. 15

358A A101 20p multicolored .70 .70
358B A101 25p multicolored .90 .90
358C A101 50p multicolored 1.75 1.75
358D A101 £1 multicolored 3.50 3.50
Nos. 347-358D (16) 11.95 11.95

Stamps in Nos. 356a, 356b inscribed 1989, No. 358e inscribed 1990. Nos. 358A-358D exist inscribed "1992," Nos. 349, 353, "1989."

Nos. 356a and 356b also exist in special booklet sheets of 50 stamps containing either 10 #356a or 5 #356b.

Issued: 1p-19p, 2/10; #355a-355b, 3/16; 20p-£1, 9/21; #356a, 356b, 10/16/89.

See Nos. 448-459.

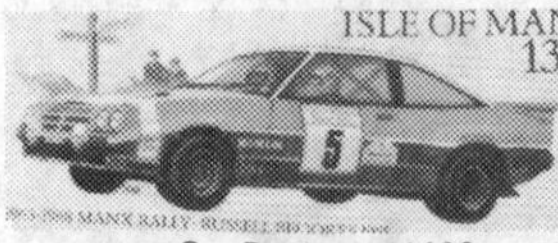
Car Racing — A102

Winning automobiles, drivers: 13p, Vauxhall Opel, Russell Brookes, 1985. 26p, Ford Escort, Ari Vatanen of Finland, 1976. 31p, Repco March 761, Terry Smith, 1980. 34p, Williams/Honda Nigel Mansell, 1986-87.

1988, Feb. 10 *Perf. 13½x14½*

359	A102	13p multicolored	.50	.50
360	A102	26p multicolored	.95	.95
361	A102	31p multicolored	1.15	1.15
362	A102	34p multicolored	1.25	1.25
		Nos. 359-362 (4)	3.85	3.85

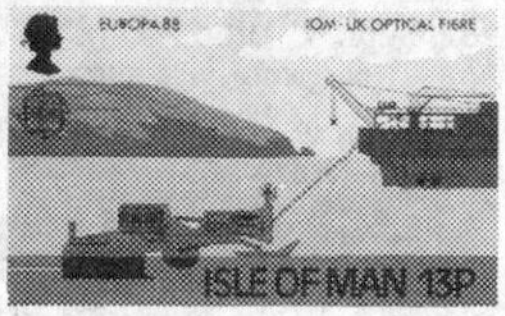
Europa 1988 A103

Telecommunications: No. 363, IOM-UK optical fiber cable-laying plow. No. 364, Cable-laying ship. No. 365, 1st IOM Earth station, Braddan, established by Manx Telecom. No. 366, Intelsat V satellite.

1988, Apr. 14 Litho. *Perf. 14x13½*

363	A103	13p multicolored	.50	.50
364	A103	13p multicolored	.50	.50
a.		Pair, #363-364	1.00	1.00
365	A103	22p multicolored	.80	.80
366	A103	22p multicolored	.80	.80
a.		Pair, #365-366	1.75	1.75
		Nos. 363-366 (4)	2.60	2.60

Submarine cable linking the Isle of Man and Silecroft in Cumbria, 1987 (13p). Nos. 364a, 366a have continuous designs.

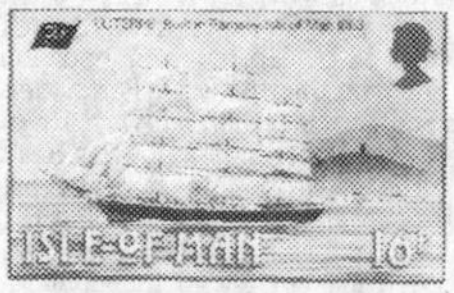
Historic Ships Built on the Isle A104

Isle of Man flag, Australia bicen. emblem or US flag and: 16p, Euterpe, 1863, built in Ramsey. 29p, Vixen leaving Peel for Australia, 1853. 31p, Ramsey, an immigrant ship in Brisbane, 1870. 34p, Star of India (renamed in 1906, was the Euterpe), restored 1960-1976, Maritime Museum at San Diego.

1988, May 11 Litho. *Perf. 14*

367	A104	16p multicolored	.55	.55
368	A104	29p multicolored	1.00	1.00
369	A104	31p multicolored	1.00	1.00
370	A104	34p multicolored	1.10	1.10
a.		Souvenir sheet of 2 (16p, 34p)	1.85	1.85
		Nos. 367-370 (4)	3.65	3.65

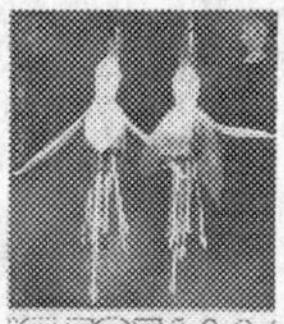
Fuchsia Blossoms — A105

1988, Sept. 21 Litho. *Perf. 13½x14*

371	A105	13p Magellanica	.45	.45
372	A105	16p Pink cloud	.55	.55
373	A105	22p Leonora	.80	.80
374	A105	29p Satellite	1.05	1.05
375	A105	31p Preston Guild	1.10	1.10
376	A105	34p Thalia	1.20	1.20
		Nos. 371-376 (6)	5.15	5.15

British Fuchsia Society, 50th anniv.

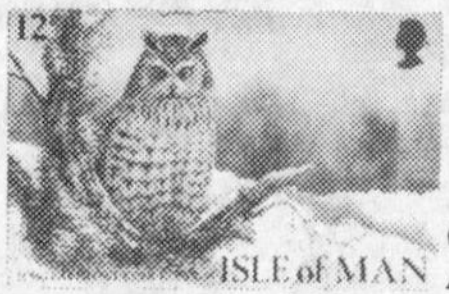
Christmas A106

1988, Oct. 12 *Perf. 14*

377	A106	12p Long-earred owl	.45	.45
378	A106	15p Robin	.55	.55
379	A106	31p Partridge	1.10	1.10
		Nos. 377-379 (3)	2.10	2.10

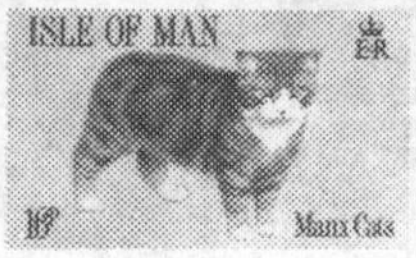
Manx Cats — A107

Various cats.

1989, Feb. 8

380	A107	16p multicolored	.60	.60
381	A107	27p multicolored	1.00	1.00
382	A107	30p multicolored	1.15	1.15
383	A107	40p multicolored	1.50	1.50
		Nos. 380-383 (4)	4.25	4.25

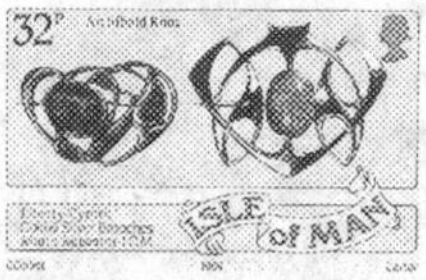
Celtic Works of Art by Archibald Knox (1864-1933) A108

Designs: 13p, Tudric pewter and enamel clock, 1903, vert. 16p, Cross, a watercolor, vert. 23p, Silver tankard, 1902, vert. 32p, Liberty silver and Cymric gold brooches. 35p, Silver jewel box with inlaid turquoise, mother-of-pearl and enamel, 1900.

1989, Feb. 8 Litho. *Perf. 13*

384	A108	13p multicolored	.50	.50
385	A108	16p multicolored	.60	.60
386	A108	23p multicolored	.85	.85
387	A108	32p multicolored	1.15	1.15
388	A108	35p multicolored	1.25	1.25
		Nos. 384-388 (5)	4.35	4.35

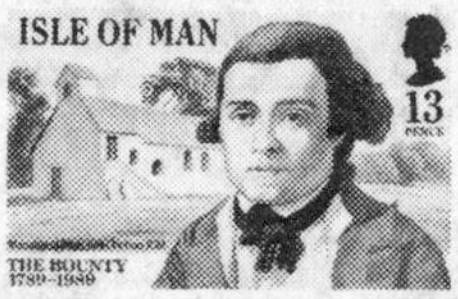
Mutiny on the *Bounty* A109

Designs: 13p, William Bligh, Old Onchan Church. 16p, Bligh and crewmen cast adrift. 30p, Peter Heywood on Tahiti, 1770. 32p, *Bounty* off Pitcairn. 35p, Fletcher Christian on Pitcairn.

1989, Apr. 28 Litho. *Perf. 14*

389	A109	13p multicolored	.45	.45
390	A109	16p multicolored	.60	.60
391	A109	30p multicolored	1.05	1.05
392	A109	32p multicolored	1.15	1.15
393	A109	35p multicolored	1.25	1.25
		Nos. 389-393 (5)	4.50	4.50

Souvenir Sheet

394		Sheet of 3 + label	3.00	3.00
a.		A109 23p Pitcairn Isls. No. 321d	.80	.80
b.		A109 27p Norfolk Is. No. 453	.95	.95
c.		Booklet pane, #394	3.00	
d.		Booklet pane, 1 each #389-394a	5.50	
e.		Booklet pane, 1 each #389-393, #394b	5.50	
f.		Booklet pane, 3 each #394a, #394b	5.25	

See Norfolk Is. Nos. 452-456 and Pitcairn Isls. Nos. 320-322.

No. 394 contains Nos. 393, 394a-394b.

No. 394c is 145x101mm and is rouletted at left.

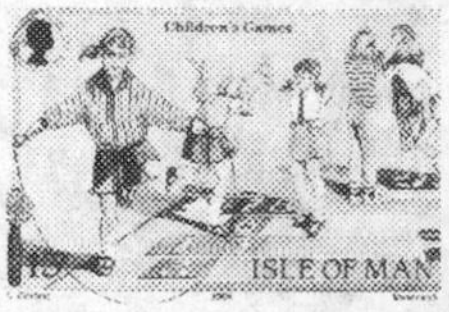
Europa 1989 A110

Children's games: No. 395, Jumping rope, hopscotch, London Bridge is falling down. No. 396, Running, wheelbarrow race, leap frog, piggyback ride. No. 397, Boy building fort, girl blowing soap bubbles, puzzle. No. 398, Doll house, blocks, girl playing with rag doll and puzzle.

1989, May 17 *Perf. 13½*

395	A110	13p multicolored	.45	.45
396	A110	13p multicolored	.45	.45
a.		Pair, #395-396	.90	.90
397	A110	23p multicolored	.80	.80
398	A110	23p multicolored	.80	.80
a.		Pair, #397-398	1.60	1.60
		Nos. 395-398 (4)	2.50	2.50

Nos. 396a, 398a have continuous designs.

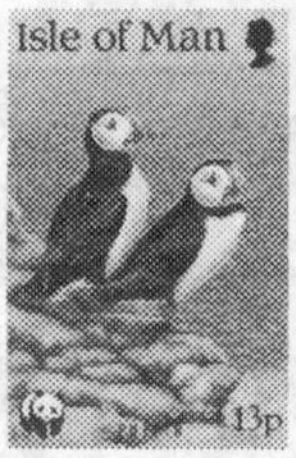
World Wildlife Fund — A111

1989, Sept. 20 Litho. *Perf. 14*

399	A111	13p Puffin	.45	.45
400	A111	13p Black guillemot	.45	.45
401	A111	13p Cormorant	.45	.45
402	A111	13p Kittiwake	.45	.45
a.		Block or strip of 4, #399-402	1.80	1.80
		Nos. 399-402 (4)	1.80	1.80

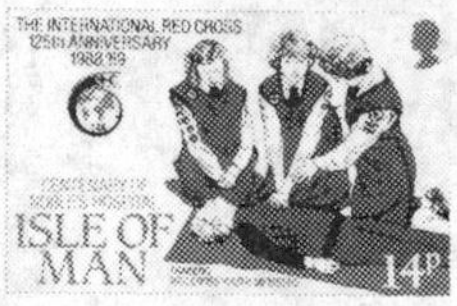
Intl. Red Cross, 125th Anniv. A112

1989, Oct. 16 Litho. *Perf. 14*

403	A112	14p Training youths	.45	.45
404	A112	17p Emblems	.55	.55
405	A112	23p Signing 1st Geneva convention, 1864	.75	.75
406	A112	30p Ambulance services	.95	.95
407	A112	35p Henri Dunant, founder	1.10	1.10
		Nos. 403-407 (5)	3.80	3.80

Noble's Hospital, Douglas, cent.

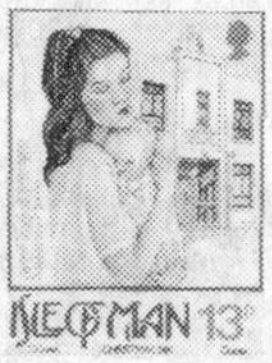
Christmas — A113

1989, Oct. 16 *Perf. 14½x15*

408	A113	13p Maternity home	.40	.40
409	A113	16p Mother and child	.50	.50
410	A113	34p Madonna and child, scripture	1.10	1.10
411	A113	37p Church, baptismal ceremony	1.20	1.20
		Nos. 408-411 (4)	3.20	3.20

Jane Crookall Maternity Home 50th anniv. (13p) and 75th anniv. of the consecration of St. Ninian's Church (37p).

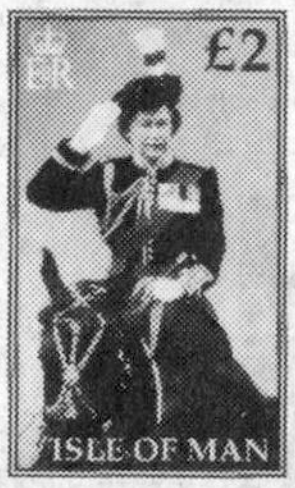
Queen Elizabeth II, Lord of Man, Trooping the Colors — A114

1990, Feb. 14 Litho. *Perf. 14½*

412	A114	£2 multicolored	6.25	6.25

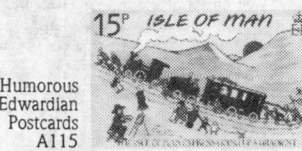

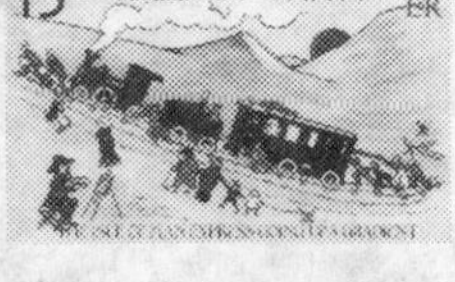
Humorous Edwardian Postcards A115

Designs: 15p, The Isle of Man Express Going Up a Gradient. 19p, A Way We Have in the Isle of Man. 32p, Douglas -- Waiting for the Male Boat. 34p, The Last Toast Rack Home Douglas Parade. 37p, The Last Isle of Man Boat.

1990, Feb. 14 *Perf. 14*

413	A115	15p multicolored	.50	.50
414	A115	19p multicolored	.65	.65
415	A115	32p multicolored	1.10	1.10
416	A115	34p multicolored	1.15	1.15
417	A115	37p multicolored	1.25	1.25
		Nos. 413-417 (5)	4.65	4.65

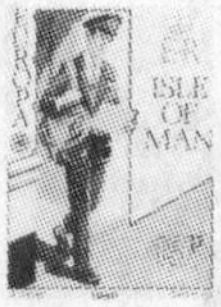
Europa 1990 — A116

Mailmen and post offices.

1990, Apr. 18 Litho. *Perf. 13½*
Size of Nos. 419, 421: 42x28mm

418	A116	15p Mailman, 1990	.50	.50
419	A116	15p Ramsey P.O., 1990	.50	.50
a.		Pair, #418-419	1.00	1.00
420	A116	24p Mailman, c. 1890	.80	.80
421	A116	24p Douglas P.O., c. 1890	.80	.80
a.		Pair, #420-421	1.60	1.60
		Nos. 418-421 (4)	2.60	2.60

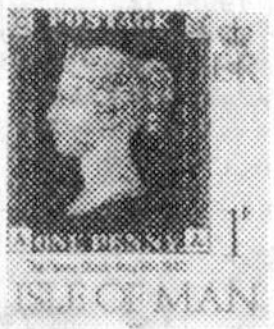
Great Britain No. 1 — A117

Designs: 19p, Wyon Medal. 32p, William Wyon's essay. 34p, Perkins Bacon engine-turned essay of 1839. 37p, Great Britain No. 2.

No. 423 (various Penny Blacks and text): a.-e. Positions AA-AE. f.-j. Positions BA-BE. k.-n. Positions CA-CE. p.-t. Positions DA-DE. u.-y. Positions EA-EE.

Note that A-A top of square on No. 423a, centered on No. 422a.

1990, May 3 Litho. *Perf. 14x13½*

422		Pane of 5	4.20	4.20
a.		A117 1p shown	.15	.15
b.		A117 19p multicolored	.65	.65
c.		A117 32p multicolored	1.10	1.10
d.		A117 34p multicolored	1.15	1.15
e.		A117 37p multicolored	1.25	1.25
g.		Bklt. pane, 2 each #422b-422e)	8.30	
h.		No. 422 ovptd. "From STAMP WORLD LONDON '90 / To NEW ZEALAND '90"	4.20	4.20

Miniature Sheet

423		Sheet of 25	1.50	1.50
a.-y.		A117 1p like #422a, any single	.15	.15
z.		Pane of 8, #a.-d., f.-i.	.40	

Souvenir Sheet

Litho. & Engr.

424	A117	£1 4 Great Britain #1	3.40	3.40
a.		Booklet pane of 1	3.40	3.40

Left margin of #422g, 423z and 424a rouletted.

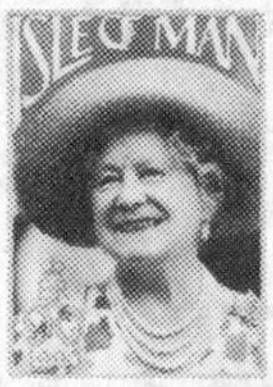
Queen Mother, 90th Birthday — A118

1990, Aug. 4 Litho. *Perf. 13x13½*

425	A118	90p multicolored	2.50	2.50

Sheets of 10 alternating with 10 labels.

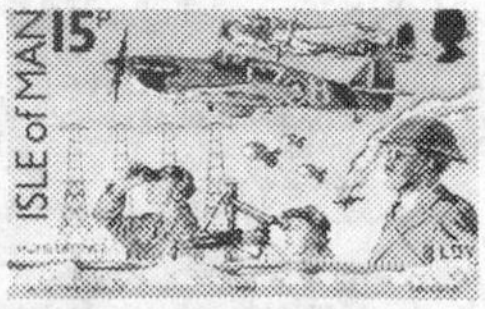
Battle of Britain, 50th Anniv. A119

1990, Sept. 5 Litho. *Perf. 14*

426	A119	15p Home defense	.55	.55
427	A119	15p Air sea rescue	.55	.55
a.		Pair, #426-427	1.10	1.10
428	A119	24p Rearming fighters	.80	.80
429	A119	24p Height of battle	.80	.80
a.		Pair, #428-429	1.65	1.65
430	A119	29p Civil defense	1.00	1.00
431	A119	29p Anti-aircraft defense	1.00	1.00
a.		Pair, #430-431	2.00	2.00
		Nos. 426-431 (6)	4.70	4.70

Sir Winston Churchill (1874-1965) A120

1990, Sept. 5 Perf. 13½
432 A120 19p multicolored .65 .65
433 A120 32p multicolored 1.10 1.10
434 A120 34p multicolored 1.20 1.20
435 A120 37p multicolored 1.30 1.30
Nos. 432-435 (4) 4.25 4.25

Christmas — A121

1990, Oct. 10 Perf. 13x13½
436 A121 14p Mailing letters .50 .50
437 A121 18p Sledding, skating .65 .65
438 A121 34p Snowman 1.10 1.10
439 A121 37p Throwing snowball 1.25 1.25
a. Souvenir sheet of 4, #436-439 3.50 3.50
Nos. 436-439 (4) 3.50 3.50

Denominations on stamps in No. 439a are black.

Manx Photographers A122

Designs: 17p, Henry Bloom Noble, by Marshall Wane. 21p, Douglas, by Frederic Frith & Co. 26p, Studio Portrait, by Hilda Newby. 31p, Cashtal yn Ard, by Christopher Killip. 40p, Peel, by Colleen Corlett.

1991, Jan. 6 Litho. Perf. 14x14½
440 A122 17p multicolored .65 .65
441 A122 21p multicolored .80 .80
442 A122 26p multicolored 1.00 1.00
443 A122 31p multicolored 1.25 1.25
444 A122 40p multicolored 1.50 1.50
Nos. 440-444 (5) 5.20 5.20

Railways and Tramways Type of 1988 with Queen's Head in White

Designs: 18p, TPO Special leaving Douglas Station, 1991. 23p, Double decker horse tram.

1991-92 Litho. Perf. 13½
448 A101 4p like No. 352 .15 .15
456 A101 18p multicolored .65 .65
458 A101 21p like No. 353 .85 .85
a. Souv. sheet, 2 each #448, #458 2.00 2.00
b. Booklet pane 3 #448, 4 #356, 1 #458 3.75
c. Booklet pane, 3 #448, 1 each #356, #458 1.90
459 A101 23p multicolored .80 .80
a. Bklt. pane, 6 #456, 4 #459 7.10
Nos. 448-459 (4) 2.45 2.45

No. 458a for Ninth Conf. of Commonwealth Postal Administrations, Douglas, Isle of Man.
Issue dates: 4p, 21p, Jan. 9. 18p, #458a, July 1. 18p, 23p, Jan. 8, 1992.
No. 458b exists in special booklet sheets containing 5 #458b and 5 each #448, #458.
No. 458b dated 1991.
This is an expanding set. Nos. will change if necessary.

Manx Lifeboats A123

1991, Feb. 13 Perf. 14
463 A123 17p Sir William Hillary .70 .70
464 A123 21p Osman Gabriel .85 .85
465 A123 26p James & Ann Ritchie 1.00 1.00
466 A123 31p The Gough Ritchie 1.25 1.25
467 A123 37p John Batstone 1.40 1.40
Nos. 463-467 (5) 5.20 5.20

Europa — A124

1991, Apr. 24 Litho. Perf. 14
468 A124 17p Satellites .70 .70
469 A124 17p Boats, Ariane rocket .70 .70
a. Pair, #468-469 1.40 1.40
470 A124 26p Satellites, diff. 1.00 1.00
471 A124 26p Space shuttle, jet 1.00 1.00
a. Pair, #470-471 2.00 2.00
Nos. 468-471 (4) 3.40 3.40

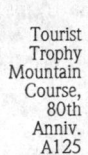 

Tourist Trophy Mountain Course, 80th Anniv. A125

Designs: 17p, Oliver Godfrey, Indian 500cc, Bray Hill, 1911. 21p, Freddie Dixon, Douglas banking sidecar, Ballacraine, 1923. 26p, Bill Ivy, Yamaha 125cc, Waterworks, 1968. 31p, Giacomo Agostini, MV Agusta 500cc, Creg-ny-Baa, 1972. 37p, Joey Dunlop, RVF Honda 750cc, Ballaugh Bridge, 1985.

1991, May 30 Litho. Perf. 14½x13
472 A125 17p multicolored .60 .60
473 A125 21p multicolored .75 .75
474 A125 26p multicolored .90 .90
475 A125 31p multicolored 1.10 1.10
476 A125 37p multicolored 1.25 1.25
a. Souv. sheet of 5, #472-476 + 7 labels 4.75 4.75
b. As "a," ovptd. in black & red in sheet margin 4.75 4.75
Nos. 472-476 (5) 4.60 4.60

No. 476b overprint includes show emblem and "PHILA / NIPPON '91."
Issue date: No. 476b, Nov. 16.

Fire Engines — A126

Designs: 17p, Laxey hand cart. 21p, Douglas horse drawn steamer. 30p, Merryweather Hatfield pump. 33p, Dennis F8 pumping appliance. 37p, Volvo turntable ladder.

1991, Sept. 18 Litho. Perf. 14½
477 A126 17p multicolored .58 .58
478 A126 21p multicolored .75 .75
479 A126 30p multicolored 1.00 1.00
480 A126 33p multicolored 1.10 1.10
481 A126 37p multicolored 1.25 1.25
Nos. 477-481 (5) 4.68 4.68

Swans A127

Designs: No. 482, Mute swans, Douglas Harbor. No. 483, Black swans, Curraghs Wildlife Park. No. 484, Whooper swans, Bishops Dub, Ballaugh. No. 485, Bewick's swans, Eairy Dam, Foxdale. No. 486, Coscaroba swans, Curraghs Wildlife Park. No. 487, Trumpeter swans.

1991, Sept. 18 Perf. 13
482 A127 17p multicolored .60 .60
483 A127 17p multicolored .60 .60
a. Pair, #482-483 1.20 1.20
484 A127 26p multicolored .90 .90
485 A127 26p multicolored .90 .90
a. Pair, #484-485 1.80 1.80
486 A127 37p multicolored 1.30 1.30
487 A127 37p multicolored 1.30 1.30
a. Pair, #486-487 2.60 2.60
Nos. 482-487 (6) 5.60 5.60

Pairs have continuous designs.

Christmas — A128

1991, Oct. 14 Perf. 14x14½
488 A128 16p Three kings .55 .55
489 A128 20p Jesus in manger, Mary .68 .68
490 A128 26p Shepherds .90 .90
491 A128 37p Angels 1.30 1.30
Nos. 488-491 (4) 3.43 3.43

Litho.
Die Cut
Self-Adhesive Booklet Stamps
492 A128 16p like #488 .65 .65
493 A128 20p like #489 .80 .80
a. Bklt. pane, 8 #492, 4 #493 8.50 8.50

Queen Elizabeth II's Accession to the Throne, 40th Anniv. — A129

Various portraits of Queen Elizabeth II.

1992, Feb. 6 Litho. Perf. 14
494 A129 18p multicolored .60 .60
495 A129 23p multicolored .80 .80
496 A129 28p multicolored 1.00 1.00
497 A129 33p multicolored 1.15 1.15
498 A129 39p multicolored 1.35 1.35
Nos. 494-498 (5) 4.90 4.90

Parachute Regiment, 50th Anniv. A130

Designs: No. 499, North Africa & Italy, 1942-43. No. 500, Operation Overlord, Normandy, 1944. No. 501, Operation Market Garden, Arnhem, 1944. No. 502, Operation Varsity, Rhine, 1945. No. 503, Near, Middle and Far East, 1945-68. No. 504, Operation Corporate, Falkland Islands, 1982, and Utrinque Paratus, 1992.

1992, Feb. 6 Perf. 14
499 A130 23p multicolored .80 .80
500 A130 23p multicolored .80 .80
a. Pair, #499-500 1.60 1.60
501 A130 23p multicolored 1.00 1.00
502 A130 23p multicolored 1.00 1.00
a. Pair, #501-502 2.00 2.00
503 A130 39p multicolored 1.40 1.40
504 A130 39p multicolored 1.40 1.40
a. Pair, #503-504 2.80 2.80
Nos. 499-504 (6) 6.40 6.40

Printed in sheets of 8.

Pilgrims' Voyage to America, 1620 — A131

Europa: No. 505, Pilgrims in longboats. No. 506, Speedwell, Delfshaven, Holland. No. 507, Mayflower. No. 508, Speedwell, Dartmouth, England.

1992, Apr. 16 Litho. Perf. 14x13½
505 A131 18p multicolored .60 .60
506 A131 18p multicolored .60 .60
a. Pair, #505-506 1.15 1.15
507 A131 28p multicolored .90 .90
508 A131 28p multicolored .90 .90
a. Pair, #507-508 1.80 1.80
Nos. 505-508 (4) 3.00 3.00

Nos. 506a, 508a have continuous design.

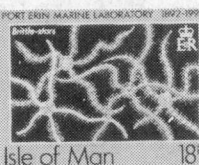

Port Erin Marine Laboratory, Cent. A132

1992, Apr. 16 Perf. 14½
509 A132 18p Brittle stars .60 .60
510 A132 23p Phytoplankton .75 .75
511 A132 28p Herring .90 .90
512 A132 33p Great scallop 1.05 1.05
513 A132 39p Dahlia anemone, delesseria 1.25 1.25
Nos. 509-513 (5) 4.55 4.55

Union Pacific, First Transcontinental Railroad — A133

Designs: No. 514, "Jupiter," 1869. No. 515, "No. 119," 1869. No. 516, "No. 844," 1992. No. 517, "No. 3985," 1992. £1.50, Golden Spike Ceremony, Union Pacific and Central Pacific Railroads, 1869.

1992, May 22 Litho. Perf. 13½x14
514 A133 33p multicolored 1.15 1.15
515 A133 33p multicolored 1.15 1.15
a. Pair, #514-515 + label 2.30 2.30
516 A133 39p multicolored 1.35 1.35
517 A133 39p multicolored 1.35 1.35
a. Pair, #516-517 + label 2.70 2.70
b. Bklt. pane, 1 each #515a, #517a
Nos. 514-517 (4) 5.00 5.00

Souvenir Sheet
518 A133 £1.50 multicolored 5.00 5.00
a. Booklet pane, #518 5.00
b. Booklet pane, 2 #517b, 1 #518a 15.00

World Columbian Stamp Expo '92. No. 518 contains one 60x50mm stamp.
No. 517b exists with two different pairs of labels.
No. 518a has a rouletted white border at left and right.

Manx Harbors — A134

Designs: No. 519, King Orry, Douglas Harbor. 23p, Castletown Harbor. 37p, Port St. Mary Harbor. 40p, Ramsey Harbor. No. 523a, King Orry. b, St. Eloi.
Illustration reduced.

1992, Sept. 18 Litho. Perf. 14½x14
519 A134 18p multicolored .60 .60
520 A134 23p multicolored .75 .75
521 A134 37p multicolored 1.30 1.30
522 A134 40p multicolored 1.40 1.40
Nos. 519-522 (4) 4.05 4.05

Souvenir Sheet
523 Sheet of 2 3.85 3.85
a. A134 18p multicolored .60 .60
b. A134 £1 multicolored 3.25 3.25

Genoa '92. #523 contains 30x24mm stamps.

Christmas — A135

Designs: 17p, Nativity window, St. German's Cathedral, Peel. 22p, Adoration of the Magi panel, St. Matthew's Church. 28p, Nativity window, St. George's Church, Douglas. 37p, Reredos of The Annunciation, St. Mary of the Isle, Douglas. 40p, Good Shepherd window, Trinity Methodist Church, Douglas.

1992, Oct. 13 Litho. Perf. 14½
524 A135 17p multicolored .55 .55
525 A135 22p multicolored .80 .80
526 A135 28p multicolored 1.00 1.00

527	A135	37p multicolored	1.30	1.30
528	A135	40p multicolored	1.40	1.40
		Nos. 524-528 (5)	5.05	5.05

Nigel Mansell, Formula I World Champion, 1992
A136

Williams Renault FW 14B at: 20p, British Grand Prix, 1992. 24p, French Grand Prix, 1992.

1992, Nov. 8   *Perf. 13½*

529	A136	20p multicolored	.70	.70
530	A136	24p multicolored	.85	.85

Ships — A137

British Red Ensign — A137a

Queen Elizabeth II — A137b

1993   **Litho.**   *Perf. 13½*

531	A137	1p HMS Amazon	.15	.15
532	A137	2p Fingal	.15	.15
533	A137	4p Sir Winston Churchill	.15	.15
534	A137	5p Dar Mlodziezy	.15	.15
543	A137	20p Tynwald I	.60	.60
544	A137	21p Ben Veg	.60	.60
545	A137	22p Waverley	.65	.65
546	A137	23p HMY Britannia	.70	.70
547	A137	24p Francis Drake	.70	.70
a.		Booklet pane of 4 #543, 6 #547	6.55	
548	A137	25p Royal Viking Sky	.70	.70
549	A137	26p Lord Nelson	.75	.75
550	A137	27p Europa	.80	.80
551	A137	30p Snaefell V	.80	.80
552	A137	40p Lady of Man	1.10	1.10
553	A137	50p Mona's Queen II	1.40	1.40
553A	A137	£1 QE2, Mona's Queen V	2.75	2.75

Perf. 14½

553B	A137a	£2 multicolored	5.50	5.50
553C	A137b	£5 multicolored	15.00	15.00
		Nos. 531-553C (18)	32.65	32.65

No. 553C has a holographic image. Soaking in water may affect the hologram.

Issued: 1p-5p, 20p-27p, 1/4/93; 30p-£1, 9/15/93; £2, 1/24/94. £5, 7/5/94.

Nos. 543, 547 exist dated "1995."

This is an expanding set. Numbers may change.

Manx Electric Railway, Cent. — A138

Designs: 20p, No. 13 trailer, No. 1 motor car. 24p, No. 19 trailer, No. 9 tunnel car. 28p, No. 59 Royal trailer special saloon car, No. 19 motor car. 39p, No. 33 motor car, No. 45 trailer and No. 13 small van. (Illustration reduced).

1993, Feb. 3   *Perf. 14*

554	A138	20p multicolored	.60	.60
555	A138	24p multicolored	.70	.70
556	A138	28p multicolored	.85	.85
557	A138	39p multicolored	.90	.90
a.		Booklet pane of #554-557	3.00	3.00
		Nos. 554-557 (4)	3.05	3.05

No. 557a exists with four different marginal inscriptions.

Contemporary Art by Bryan Kneale — A139

Europa: No. 558, Statue of Sir Hall Caine. No. 559, Painting, The Brass Bedstead. No. 560, Abstract bronze. No. 561, Drawing of polar bear skeleton.

1993, Apr. 14   **Litho.**   *Perf. 14*

558	A139	20p multicolored	.60	.60
559	A139	20p multicolored	.60	.60
a.		Pair, #558-559	1.20	1.20
560	A139	28p multicolored	.85	.85
561	A139	28p multicolored	.85	.85
a.		Pair, #560-561	1.65	1.65
		Nos. 558-561 (4)	2.90	2.90

Motorcycling Events — A140

Riders and events: 20p, Gold Medalists Graham Oates, Bill Marshall, Intl. Six-Day Trial, 1933, Ariel Square Four. 24p, Geoff Duke, Team Sergeant, Royal Signals Display Team, 1947, Triumph Twin. 28p, Denis Parkinson, winner of Senior Manx Grand Prix, 1953, Manx Norton. 33p, Richard Swallow, winner of Junior Classic Manx Grand Prix, 1991, Aermacchi. 39p, Steve Colley, winner of Scottish Six-Day Trial, 1992, Beta Zero.

1993, June 3   **Litho.**   *Perf. 13½x14*

562	A140	20p multicolored	.65	.65
563	A140	24p multicolored	.70	.70
564	A140	28p multicolored	.85	.85
565	A140	33p multicolored	1.00	1.00
566	A140	39p multicolored	1.15	1.15
a.		Souv. sheet of 5, #562-566 + 4 labels	4.35	4.35
		Nos. 562-566 (5)	4.35	4.35

Butterflies
A141

1993, Sept. 15   **Litho.**   *Perf. 14½*

567	A141	24p Dark green fritillary	.70	.70
568	A141	24p Painted lady	.70	.70
569	A141	24p Holly blue	.70	.70
570	A141	24p Red admiral	.70	.70
571	A141	24p Peacock	.70	.70
a.		Strip of 5, #567-571	3.50	3.50

Christmas — A142

Designs: 19p, Children decorating Christmas tree. 23p, Snowman, girl. 28p, Boy unwrapping presents. 39p, Girl, teddy bear. 40p, Girl with holly basket, boy on sled.

1993, Oct. 12   *Perf. 14*

572	A142	19p multicolored	.55	.55
573	A142	23p multicolored	.65	.65
574	A142	28p multicolored	.80	.80
575	A142	39p multicolored	1.10	1.10
576	A142	40p multicolored	1.10	1.10
		Nos. 572-576 (5)	4.20	4.20

Tourism
A143

Designs: No. 577, Gaiety Theatre, Douglas. No. 578, Field hockey, golf, soccer (#577). No. 579, Yacht racing, artist's hand painting picture of castle (#580). No. 580, TT Motorcycle Races, Red Arrows demonstration squadron. (#581). No. 581, Musical instruments. No. 582, Laxey Wheel, Manx cat. No. 583, Tower of Refuge, beach, sand bucket (#584). No. 584, Cyclist. No. 585, Tynwald Day, classic racing car (#579, 580, 584, 586). No. 586, Santa Claus riding Mince Pie Train, Groudle Glen.

1994, Feb. 18   **Litho.**   *Perf. 13½*
Booklet Stamps

577	A143	24p multicolored	.65	.65
578	A143	24p multicolored	.65	.65
579	A143	24p multicolored	.65	.65
580	A143	24p multicolored	.65	.65
581	A143	24p multicolored	.65	.65
582	A143	24p multicolored	.65	.65
583	A143	24p multicolored	.65	.65
584	A143	24p multicolored	.65	.65
585	A143	24p multicolored	.65	.65
586	A143	24p multicolored	.65	.65
a.		Booklet pane of 10, #577-586	6.50	

Birds
A144

Magpie, Calf of Man Bird Observatory — A145

1994, Feb. 18   *Perf. 14*

587	A144	20p White-throated robin	.55	.55
588	A144	20p Black-eared wheatear	.55	.55
a.		Pair, #587-588	1.10	1.10
589	A144	24p Goldcrest	.65	.65
590	A144	24p Northern oriole	.65	.65
a.		Pair, #589-590	1.30	1.30
591	A144	30p Kingfisher	.85	.85
592	A144	30p Hoopoe	.85	.85
a.		Pair, #591-592	1.75	1.75
		Nos. 587-592 (6)	4.10	4.10

Souvenir Sheet
Perf. 13½x13

593	A145	£1 shown	2.75	2.75

Hong Kong '94 (#593).

Europa
A146

Designs: No. 594, Eubranchus tricolor. No. 595, Loligo forbesii. No. 596, Edward Forbes (1815-54), naturalist. No. 597, Solaster moretonis. No. 598, Adamsia carciniopados on hermit crab. No. 599, Solaster endeca.

1994, May 5   **Litho.**   *Perf. 13x14*

594	A146	20p multicolored	.60	.60
595	A146	20p multicolored	.60	.60
596	A146	20p multicolored	.60	.60
a.		Strip of 3, #594-596	1.80	1.80
597	A146	30p multicolored	.90	.90
598	A146	30p multicolored	.90	.90
599	A146	30p multicolored	.90	.90
a.		Strip of 3, #597-599	2.75	2.75
		Nos. 594-599 (6)	4.50	4.50

D-Day, 50th Anniv.
A147

Designs: No. 600, Transport Ben-My-Chree IV, landing ships, US Maj. Gen. Walter Bedell Smith. No. 601, Transports Victoria, Lady of Mann I, Adm. Sir Bertram Ramsay, RN, Naval Commander. No. 602, Infantry, tanks on Gold, Juno, Sword Beaches, Gen. Montgomery, Commander, 21st Army Group. No. 603, Tanks, landing craft on Gold, Juno, Sword Beaches, Lt. Gen. Sir Miles C. Dempsey, Commander, British 2nd Army. No. 604, US 8th, 9th Air Forces, Air Chief Marshal Sir Trafford Leigh-Mallory, RAF, Air Force Commander. No. 605, Air Chief Marshall Sir Arthur Tedder, RAF, Deputy Supreme Allied Commander, RAF 2nd Tactical Air Force & Bomber Command. No. 606, Landing craft, Omaha, Utah Beaches, Lt. Gen. Omar N. Bradley, Commander, US 1st Army. No. 607, Infantry, tanks on Omaha, Utah Beaches, Gen. Eisenhower, Supreme Allied Commander.

1994, June 6   **Litho.**   *Perf. 14*

600	A147	4p multicolored	.15	.15
601	A147	4p multicolored	.15	.15
a.		Pair, #600-601	.25	.25
602	A147	20p multicolored	.60	.60
603	A147	20p multicolored	.60	.60
a.		Pair, #602-603	1.25	1.25
604	A147	30p multicolored	.90	.90
605	A147	30p multicolored	.90	.90
a.		Pair, #604-605	1.80	1.80
606	A147	41p multicolored	1.25	1.25
607	A147	41p multicolored	1.25	1.25
a.		Pair, #606-607	2.50	2.50
		Nos. 600-607 (8)	5.80	5.80

Nos. 601a, 603a, 605a, 607a are continuous designs.

Postman Pat — A148

Postman Pat at: 1p, Sea Terminal, Douglas. 20p, Laxey Wheel. 24p, Cregneash. 30p, Manx Electric Railway. 36p, Peel Harbor. 41p, Tourist office, Douglas Promenade.
£1, Postman Pat.

1994, Sept. 14 Litho. *Perf. 14½x14*

608	A148	1p multicolored	.15	.15
a.		Booklet pane of 2	.15	
609	A148	20p multicolored	.60	.60
a.		Booklet pane of 2	1.20	
610	A148	24p multicolored	.75	.75
a.		Booklet pane of 2	1.50	
611	A148	30p multicolored	.90	.90
a.		Booklet pane of 2	1.80	
612	A148	36p multicolored	1.10	1.10
a.		Booklet pane of 2	2.25	
613	A148	41p multicolored	1.25	1.25
a.		Booklet pane of 2	2.50	
		Nos. 608-613 (6)	4.75	4.75

Souvenir Sheet

614	A148	£1 multicolored	3.00	3.00
a.		Booklet pane of 1	3.00	3.00

No. 614a is rouletted 9 at left.

A149 A150

1994, Oct. 11 *Perf. 14*

615	A149	10p Cycling	.30	.30
616	A149	20p Alpine skiing	.60	.60
617	A149	24p Swimming	.75	.75
618	A149	35p Steeplechase	1.10	1.10
619	A149	48p Emblem	1.40	1.40
		Nos. 615-619 (5)	4.15	4.15

Intl. Olympic Committee, cent.

1994, Oct. 11

Christmas: 19p, Santa, Mrs. Claus greeting children on Santa Train to Santon, horiz. 23p, Santa Claus on tractor, Postman Pat. 60p, Santa Claus arriving by boat, Port St. Mary, horiz.

620	A150	19p multicolored	.55	.55
621	A150	23p multicolored	.70	.70
622	A150	60p multicolored	1.25	1.25
		Nos. 620-622 (3)	2.50	2.50

Snaefell Mountain Electric Railway, Cent. — A151

Designs: 20p, Opening day, Car No. 2. 24p, Car 3 ascending Laxey Valley, Car 4 in green livery. 35p, Car 5, Car 6. 42p, Caledonia on construction duty, Goods Car 7.
£1, Bungalow Hotel & Station, Snaefell.
Illustration reduced.

1995, Feb. 8 Litho. *Perf. 14*

623	A151	20p multicolored	.65	.65
624	A151	24p multicolored	.80	.80
625	A151	35p multicolored	1.10	1.10
626	A151	42p multicolored	1.40	1.40
		Nos. 623-626 (4)	3.95	3.95

Souvenir Sheet

Perf. 14x13½

627	A151	£1 multicolored	3.25	3.25

No. 627 contains one 61x38mm stamp.

Steam-Powered Vehicles — A152

Designs: 20p, Foden Wagon, 5 ton. 24p, Clayton & Shuttleworth, 7hp, Fowler, 6hp. 30p, Wallis & Steevens, 6hp. 35p, Marshall, 6hp. 41p, Marshall Convertible, 5hp.

1995, Feb. 8 *Perf. 13½*

628	A152	20p multicolored	.65	.65
629	A152	24p multicolored	.80	.80
630	A152	30p multicolored	.95	.95
631	A152	35p multicolored	1.10	1.10
632	A152	41p multicolored	1.25	1.25
		Nos. 628-632 (5)	4.75	4.75

Peace & Freedom — A153

Europa: 20p, Flight of doves forming tidal wave, Tower of Refuge, Douglas Bay. 30p, Dove with olive branch breaking barbed wire.

1995, Apr. 28 Litho. *Perf. 13½*

633	A153	20p multicolored	.65	.65
634	A153	30p multicolored	.95	.95

VE Day, 50th Anniv. A154

Designs: No. 635, Spitfire, tank, 1939-45 Star, African Star. No. 636, France and Germany Star, Italy Star, Hawker Typhoon, artillery. No. 637, Lancaster bomber, aircraft carrier, Air Crew Europe Star, Atlantic Star. No. 638, Pacific Star, Burma Star, Avenger torpedo bomber, soldiers. No. 639, Parliament, Manx flag. No. 640, British flag, crowd celebrating. No. 641, Children celebrating at street party, Manx flag. No. 642, British flag, visit of Queen Elizabeth, King George VI, 1945.

1995, May 8 *Perf. 14*

635	A154	10p multicolored	.32	.32
636	A154	10p multicolored	.32	.32
a.		Pair, #635-636	.65	.65
637	A154	20p multicolored	.65	.65
638	A154	20p multicolored	.65	.65
a.		Pair, #637-638	1.25	1.25
639	A154	24p multicolored	.75	.75
640	A154	24p multicolored	.75	.75
a.		Pair, #639-640	1.50	1.50
641	A154	40p multicolored	1.25	1.25
642	A154	40p multicolored	1.25	1.25
a.		Pair, #641-642	2.50	2.50
		Nos. 635-642 (8)	5.94	5.94

British Motor Car Racing, 90th Anniv. A155

Tourist Trophy Race drivers, cars: 20p, R. Parnell, 1951 Maserati 4 CLT. 24p, S. Moss, 1951 Frazer Nash. 30p, R.J.B. Seaman, 1936 Delage. 36p, Prince Bira, 1937 ERA R2B Romulus. 41p, K. Lee Guinness, 1914 Sunbeam 1. 42p, F. Dixon, 1934 Riley.
£1, John S. Napier, 1905 Arrol Johnston.

1995, May 8

643	A155	20p multicolored	.65	.65
644	A155	24p multicolored	.75	.75
645	A155	30p multicolored	.95	.95
646	A155	36p multicolored	1.10	1.10
647	A155	41p multicolored	1.25	1.25
648	A155	42p multicolored	1.40	1.40
		Nos. 643-648 (6)	6.10	6.10

Souvenir Sheet

649	A155	£1 multicolored	3.25	3.25

No. 649 contains one 47x58mm stamp.

Mushrooms A156

Designs: 20p, Amanita muscaria. 24p, Boletus edulis. 30p, Coprinus disseminatus. 35p, Pleurotus ostreatus. 45p, Geastrum triplex.
£1, Shaggy ink cap, bee orchid.

1995, Sept. 1 Litho. *Perf. 13½x14*

650	A156	20p multicolored	.65	.65
651	A156	24p multicolored	.75	.75
652	A156	30p multicolored	.95	.95
653	A156	35p multicolored	1.10	1.10
654	A156	45p multicolored	1.40	1.40
		Nos. 650-654 (5)	4.85	4.85

Souvenir Sheet

Perf. 14x13½

655	A156	£1 multicolored	3.25	3.25

No. 655 contains one 51x60mm stamp. Singapore '95 (#655).

Thomas the Tank Engine A157

Designs: 20p, Bertie arrives on the quayside. 24p, Mail train and Thomas. 30p, Bertie and trains at Ballasalla. 36p, Viking and Thomas at Port Erin. 41p, The mail gets through. 45p, Race at Laxey Wheel.

1995, Sept. 1 *Perf. 14*

656	A157	20p multicolored	.65	.65
657	A157	24p multicolored	.75	.75
a.		Booklet pane of 2, #656-657	1.40	
658	A157	30p multicolored	.95	.95
a.		Booklet pane of 2, #657-658	1.75	
659	A157	36p multicolored	1.10	1.10
a.		Booklet pane of 2, #658-659	2.05	
660	A157	41p multicolored	1.25	1.25
a.		Booklet pane of 2, #659-660	2.35	
661	A157	45p multicolored	1.40	1.40
a.		Booklet pane of 2, #656, 661	2.05	
b.		Booklet pane of 2, #660-661	2.75	
		Complete booklet, #657a, 658a, 659a, 660a, 661a-661b	12.50	
		Nos. 656-661 (6)	6.10	6.10

Christmas — A158

Designs: 19p, Church, holly. 23p, Bird on holly branch. 42p, Snow crocuses, church. 50p, Antique farming equipment in snow.

1995, Oct. 10 Litho. *Perf. 14x14½*

662	A158	19p multicolored	.60	.60
663	A158	23p multicolored	.70	.70
664	A158	42p multicolored	1.30	1.30
665	A158	50p multicolored	1.50	1.50
		Nos. 662-665 (4)	4.10	4.10

POSTAGE DUE STAMPS

Catalogue values for unused stamps in this section are for Never Hinged items.

D1 D2

Imprint: "1973 Questa"

Perf. 13½

1973, July 5 Litho. Unwmk.

Inscriptions and Coat of Arms in Black and Red

J1	D1	½p yellow	.25	.25
J2	D1	1p buff	.35	.35
J3	D1	2p lt yellow grn	1.25	1.25
J4	D1	3p gray	2.25	2.25
J5	D1	4p dull rose	3.50	3.50
J6	D1	5p light blue	3.75	3.75
J7	D1	10p light violet	8.50	8.50
J8	D1	20p lt grnsh blue	20.00	20.00
		Nos. J1-J8 (8)	39.85	39.85

Imprint: "1973 A Questa"

1973, Sept.

J1a	D1	½p	2.00	1.75
J2a	D1	1p	1.00	.50
J3a	D1	2p	.25	.15
J4a	D1	3p	.20	.15
J5a	D1	4p	.25	.18
J6a	D1	5p	.25	.22
J7a	D1	10p	.50	.40
J8a	D1	20p	1.00	.70
		Nos. J1a-J8a (8)	5.45	4.05

1975, Jan. 8 Litho. *Perf. 14*

Inscriptions and Coat of Arms in Black and Red

J9	D2	½p yellow	.15	.15
J10	D2	1p buff	.15	.15
J11	D2	4p lilac rose	.15	.15
J12	D2	7p blue	.30	.30
J13	D2	9p sepia	.35	.35
J14	D2	10p lilac	.40	.40
J15	D2	50p orange	1.40	1.40
J16	D2	£1 bright green	2.50	2.50
		Nos. J9-J16 (8)	5.40	5.40

D3 D4

1982-92 Litho. *Perf. 15x14*

J17	D3	1p light green	.15	.15
J18	D3	2p bright pink	.15	.15
J19	D3	5p grnsh blue	.20	.20
J20	D3	10p bright lilac	.40	.40
J21	D3	20p gray	.80	.80
J22	D3	50p dull yellow	2.00	2.00
J23	D3	£1 brick red	3.00	3.00
J24	D3	£2 blue	6.50	6.50

Litho.

Perf. 13x13½

J25	D4	£5 multicolored	15.00	15.00
		Nos. J17-J24 (8)	13.20	13.20

Issued: £5, Sept. 16, 1992; others, Oct. 5, 1982.

BRITISH OFFICES ABROAD

OFFICES IN AFRICA

MIDDLE EAST FORCES

For use in Ethiopia, Cyrenaica, Eritrea, the Dodecanese and Somalia

Stamps of Great Britain, 1937-42 Overprinted in Black or Blue Black

M.E.F.

1942-43 Wmk. 251 *Perf. 14½x14*

1	A101	1p scarlet	.15	.15
2	A101	2p orange	.15	.15
3	A101	2½p bright ultra	.15	.15
4	A101	3p dark purple	.15	.15
a.		Double overprint		
5	A102	5p lt brn (Bl Blk) ('43)	.15	.15
a.		Black overprint	.15	.15
6	A102	6p rose lilac ('43)	.25	.25
7	A103	9p dp olive grn ('43)	.30	.30
8	A103	1sh brown ('43)	.30	.30

Wmk. 259
Perf. 14

9	A104	2sh6p yel green ('43)	2.00	2.00
		Nos. 1-9 (9)	3.60	3.60

Same Overprint in Blue Black on Nos. 259, 261, 262 and 263

1943, Jan. 1   **Wmk. 251**

10	A101	1p vermilion	.15	.15
11	A101	2p light orange	.15	.15
12	A101	2½p ultramarine	.15	.15
13	A101	3p violet	.15	.15
		Set value	.40	.40

There were two printings of Nos. 1-4 and 5a, both issued Mar. 2, 1942, and both black. The Cairo printing measures 13½mm, the London printing 14mm.

Nos. 5 and 6-13 compose a third printing, also made in London. On these stamps, issued Jan. 1, 1943, the overprint is 13½mm wide. The 2sh6p overprint is black, the others blue black.

Same Ovpt. in Black on #250, 251A

1947   **Wmk. 259**   **Perf. 14**

14	A104	5sh dull red	7.50	6.25
15	A105	10sh ultramarine	17.50	15.00

In 1950 Nos. 1-15 were declared valid for use in Great Britain. Used values are for copies postmarked in territory of issue. Others sell for about 25 percent less.

POSTAGE DUE STAMPS

Postage Due Stamps of Great Britain Overprinted in **M.E.F.** Blue

1942   **Wmk. 251**   **Perf. 14x14½**

J1	D1	½p emerald	.30	.45
J2	D1	1p carmine rose	.35	.60
J3	D1	2p black brown	.60	1.25
J4	D1	3p violet	1.50	2.50
J5	D1	1sh blue	4.75	9.50
		Nos. J1-J5 (5)	7.50	14.30

No. J1 to J5 were used in Eritrea.

FOR USE IN ERITREA

Catalogue values for unused stamps in this section are for Never Hinged items.

100 Cents = 1 Shilling
Stamps of Great Britain 1937-42 Surcharged

B. M. A. ERITREA

5 CENTS
a

1948, June   **Wmk. 251**   **Perf. 14½x14**

1	A101	5c on ½p green (II)	.15	.15
2	A101	10c on 1p vermilion (II)	.15	.15
3	A101	20c on 2p light org (II)	.20	.20
4	A101	25c on 2½p ultra (II)	.65	.65
5	A101	30c on 3p violet (II)	.20	.20
6	A101	40c on 5p light brown	.25	.25
7	A101	60c on 6p rose lilac	.30	.30
8	A103	75c on 9p deep ol grn	.50	.50
9	A103	1sh on 1sh brown	.50	.50

"B. M. A." stands for British Military Administration.

B. M. A. ERITREA

Great Britain Nos. 249A, 250 and 251A Surcharged

2 SH. 50 CTS.

1948, June   **Wmk. 259**   **Perf. 14**

10	A104	2sh50c on 2sh6p yel grn	6.50	8.25
11	A104	5sh on 5sh dl red	10.00	13.00
12	A105	10sh on 10sh ultra	18.00	21.50

Great Britain No. 245 Surcharged Type "a"

1949   **Wmk. 251**   **Perf. 14½x14**

13	A103	65c on 8p brt rose	1.00	2.00
		Nos. 1-13 (13)	38.40	47.65

Stamps of Great Britain 1937-42 Surcharged

B. A. ERITREA

5 CENTS
c

1950, Feb. 6

14	A101	5c on ½p green (II)	.15	.15
15	A101	10c on 1p ver (II)	.15	.15
16	A101	20c on 2p lt orange (II)	.15	.15
17	A101	25c on 2½p ultra (II)	.15	.15
18	A101	30c on 3p violet (II)	.20	.20
19	A102	40c on 5p light brown	.30	.30
20	A102	50c on 6p rose lilac	.30	.30
21	A103	65c on 8p bright rose	.30	.30
22	A103	75c on 9p deep ol green	.40	.40
23	A103	1sh on 1sh brown	.45	.45

B. A. ERITREA

Great Britain Nos. 249A, 250, 251A Surcharged

2 SH. 50 CTS.

Wmk. 259   **Perf. 14**

24	A104	2sh50c on 2sh6p yel grn	5.00	6.50
25	A104	5sh on 5sh dl red	11.50	13.00
26	A105	10sh on 10sh ultra	25.00	27.50
		Nos. 14-26 (13)	44.05	49.55

Great Britain Nos. 280, 281, 283 and 284 Surcharged Type "c"

Perf. 14½x14

1951, May 3   **Wmk. 251**

27	A101	5c on ½p lt orange	.15	.15
28	A101	10c on 1p ultra	.15	.15
29	A101	20c on 2p lt red brown	.15	.15
30	A101	25c on 2½p vermilion	.25	.25

B. A. ERITREA

Great Britain Nos. 286-288 Surcharged

2 SH. 50 CTS.

1951, May 31   **Wmk. 259**   **Perf. 11x12**

31	A121	2sh50c on 2sh6p grn	3.25	3.25
32	A121	5sh on 5sh dl red	10.00	8.25
33	A122	10sh on 10sh ultra	16.00	20.00
		Nos. 27-33 (7)	29.95	32.20

Surcharge arranged to fit the design on #33.

POSTAGE DUE STAMPS

B. M. A. ERITREA

Great Britain Nos. J26 to J29 and J32 Surcharged

5 CENTS

1948   **Wmk. 251**   **Perf. 14x14½**

J1	D1	5c on ½p emer	10.00	20.00
J2	D1	10c on 1p car rose	10.00	15.00
J3	D1	20c on 2p blk brn	8.00	13.00
J4	D1	30c on 3p violet	12.50	12.00
J5	D1	1sh on 1sh blue	20.00	20.00
		Nos. J1-J5 (5)	60.50	80.00

B. A. ERITREA

Great Britain Nos. J26 to J29 and J32 Surcharged

5 CENTS

1950, Feb. 6

J6	D1	5c on ½p emer	11.00	12.00
J7	D1	10c on 1p car rose	9.25	9.00
a.		"C" of CENTS omitted	1,100.	

J8	D1	20c on 2p blk brn	11.00	10.50
J9	D1	30c on 3p violet	11.00	12.00
J10	D1	1sh on 1sh blue	18.00	20.00
		Nos. J6-J10 (5)	60.25	63.50

EAST AFRICA FORCES

FOR USE IN SOMALIA (ITALIAN SOMALILAND)

12 Pence = 1 Shilling
100 Cents = 1 Shilling
Stamps of Great Britain 1938-42 Overprinted in Blue

E.A.F.

Perf. 14½x14

1943, Jan. 15   **Wmk. 251**

1	A101	1p vermilion	.15	.15
2	A101	2p light orange	.15	.15
3	A101	2½p ultramarine	.15	.15
4	A101	3p violet	.15	.15
5	A101	5p light brown	.20	.20
6	A101	6p rose lilac	.30	.30
7	A103	9p dp olive green	.30	.30
8	A103	1sh brown	.35	.35

On Great Britain No. 249A

1946   **Wmk. 259**   **Perf. 14**

9	A104	2sh6p yellow green	3.50	3.50
		Nos. 1-9 (9)	5.25	5.25

Catalogue values for unused stamps in this section, from this point to the end of the section, are for Never Hinged items.

B. M. A. SOMALIA

Stamps of Great Britain, 1937-42 Surcharged

25 CENTS

Perf. 14½x14

1948, May 27   **Wmk. 251**

10	A101	5c on ½p grn (II)	.15	.15
11	A101	15c on 1½p lt red brn (II)	.90	.90
12	A101	20c on 2p lt org (II)	.22	.22
13	A101	25c on 2½p ultra (II)	.18	.18
14	A101	30c on 3p vio (II)	1.65	4.50
15	A102	40c on 5p lt brown	.35	.35
16	A102	50c on 6p rose lilac	.30	.30
17	A103	75c on 9p dp ol grn	1.40	2.75
18	A103	1sh on 1sh brown	1.65	5.50

B. M. A. SOMALIA

Great Britain Nos. 249A and 250 Surcharged

2 SH. 50 CTS.

Wmk. 259   **Perf. 14**

19	A104	2sh50c on 2sh6p yel grn	6.00	9.00
20	A104	5sh on 5sh dl red	11.50	13.00
		Nos. 10-20 (11)	24.30	36.85

B. A. SOMALIA

Stamps of Great Britain 1937-42 Surcharged

25 CENTS

Perf. 14½x14

1950, Jan. 2   **Wmk. 251**

21	A101	5c on ½p grn (II)	.15	.15
22	A101	15c on 1½p lt red brn (II)	.65	1.25
23	A101	20c on 2p lt org (II)	.60	.60
24	A101	25c on 2½p ultra (II)	.25	.25
25	A101	30c on 3p violet (II)	.80	2.00
26	A102	40c on 5p light brn	.45	.45
27	A102	50c on 6p rose lilac	.80	.80
28	A103	75c on 9p deep ol grn	2.00	2.00
29	A103	1sh on 1sh brown	.48	.80

B. A. SOMALIA

Great Britain Nos. 249A and 250 Surcharged

2 SH. 50 CTS.

Wmk. 259   **Perf. 14**

30	A104	2sh50c on 2sh 6p yel grn	8.00	12.00
31	A104	5sh on 5sh dull red	12.00	20.00
		Nos. 21-31 (11)	24.63	40.30

FOR USE IN TRIPOLITANIA

Catalogue values for unused stamps in this section are for Never Hinged items.

B. M. A. TRIPOLITANIA

Stamps of Great Britain, 1937-42, Surcharged

5 M.A.L.

M.A.L.=Military Authority Lire

Perf. 14½x14

1948, July 1   **Wmk. 251**

1	A101	1 l on ½p green (II)	.18	.18
2	A101	2 l on 1p ver (II)	.15	.15
3	A101	3 l on 1½p lt red brn (II)	.16	.16
4	A101	4 l on 2p lt org (II)	.15	.15
5	A101	5 l on 2½p ultra (II)	.18	.18
6	A101	6 l on 3p violet (II)	.22	.22
7	A102	10 l on 5p lt brown	.22	.22
8	A102	12 l on 6p rose lilac	.30	.30
9	A103	18 l on 9p dp ol grn	.60	1.40
10	A103	24 l on 1sh brown	.90	1.75

B. M. A. TRIPOLITANIA

Great Britain Nos. 249A, 250 and 251A Surcharged

60 M.A.L.

Wmk. 259   **Perf. 14**

11	A104	60 l on 2sh6p yel grn	2.25	7.50
12	A104	120 l on 5sh dl red	11.50	15.00
13	A105	240 l on 10sh ultra	20.00	45.00
		Nos. 1-13 (13)	36.81	72.21

B. A. TRIPOLITANIA

Stamps of Great Britain 1937-42 Surcharged

5 M.A.L.

Perf. 14½x14

1950, Feb. 6   **Wmk. 251**

14	A101	1 l on ½p green (II)	.16	1.75
15	A101	2 l on 1p ver (II)	.15	.15
16	A101	3 l on 1½p lt red brn (II)	.20	1.40
17	A101	4 l on 2p lt org (II)	.15	.70
18	A101	5 l on 2½p ultra (II)	.16	1.00
19	A101	6 l on 3p violet (II)	.16	.70
20	A102	10 l on 5p lt brown	.20	.20
21	A102	12 l on 6p rose lilac	.35	.35
22	A103	18 l on 9p dp ol grn	.55	.55
23	A103	24 l on 1sh brown	.55	.55

B. A. TRIPOLITANIA

Great Britain Nos. 249A, 250 and 251A Surcharged

60 M.A.L.

Wmk. 259 *Perf. 14*

24	A104	60 l on 2sh6p yel grn	5.25	*10.50*
25	A104	120 l on 5sh dl red	10.50	*17.50*
26	A105	240 l on 10sh ultra	19.00	*27.50*
		Nos. 14-26 (13)	37.38	*62.85*

Great Britain Nos. 280-284 Surcharged like Nos. 14-23

Perf. 14½x14

1951, May 3 **Wmk. 251**

27	A101	1 l on ½p lt org	.20	*.80*
28	A101	2 l on 1p ultra	.20	*.80*
29	A101	3 l on 1½p green	.35	*1.50*
30	A101	4 l on 2p lt red brown	.25	*.80*
31	A101	5 l on 2½p ver	.20	*1.25*

B.A. TRIPOLITANIA

Great Britain Nos. 286-288 Surcharged

60 M.A.L.

1951, May 3 Wmk. 259 *Perf. 11x12*

32	A121	60 l on 2sh6p grn	8.00	*12.00*
33	A121	120 l on 5sh dl red	10.00	*18.00*
34	A122	240 l on 10sh ultra	22.50	*32.50*
		Nos. 27-34 (8)	41.70	*67.65*

Surcharge arranged to fit the design on #34.

POSTAGE DUE STAMPS

Great Britain Nos. J26 to J29 and J32, Surcharged

B. M. A TRIPOLITANIA

I M.A.L.

1948 **Wmk. 251** *Perf. 14x14½*

J1	D1	1 l on ½p emer	3.50	*10.00*
J2	D1	2 l on 1p car rose	3.50	*10.00*
J3	D1	4 l on 2p blk brn	4.50	*13.00*
J4	D1	6 l on 3p violet	7.25	*20.00*
J5	D1	24 l on 1sh blue	22.50	*40.00*
		Nos. J1-J5 (5)	41.25	*93.00*

Great Britain Nos. J26 to J29 and J32 Surcharged

B. A TRIPOLITANIA

I M.A.L.

1950, Feb. 6

J6	D1	1 l on ½p emer	5.25	*19.00*
J7	D1	2 l on 1p car rose	5.00	*13.00*
J8	D1	4 l on 2p blk brn	5.00	*15.00*
J9	D1	6 l on 3p violet	8.25	*30.00*
J10	D1	24 l on 1sh blue	25.00	*52.50*
		Nos. J6-J10 (5)	48.50	*129.50*

CHINA

100 Cents = 1 Dollar

Stamps of Hong Kong, 1912-14, Overprinted

CHINA

1917 **Wmk. 3** *Perf. 14*

Ordinary Paper

1	A11	1c brown	.80	.35
2	A11	2c deep green	.60	.15
3	A12	4c scarlet	.52	.15
4	A13	6c orange	1.25	1.00
5	A12	8c gray	1.00	.75
6	A11	10c ultramarine	1.00	.15

Chalky Paper

7	A14	12c violet, *yel*	2.25	1.75
8	A14	20c olive grn & vio	2.00	.60
9	A15	25c red vio & dl vio (on #117)	3.00	3.00
10	A13	30c orange & violet	11.00	1.00
11	A14	50c black, *emerald*	8.00	1.90
a.		50c blk, *blue green*, ol back	18.00	1.25
b.		50c blk, *emerald*, ol back	8.25	1.90
12	A11	$1 blue & vio, *bl*	25.00	1.50
13	A14	$2 black & red	100.00	40.00
14	A13	$3 violet & grn	100.00	95.00
15	A14	$5 red & grn, *bl grn*, ol back	125.00	100.00
16	A13	$10 blk & vio, *red*	325.00	250.00
		Nos. 1-16 (16)	706.42	497.30

Stamps of Hong Kong, 1921-26, Overprinted

CHINA

1922-27 **Wmk. 4**

Ordinary Paper

17	A11	1c brown	.35	.75
18	A11	2c green	.50	.50
19	A12	4c scarlet	.40	.55
20	A13	6c orange	.75	1.50
21	A12	8c gray	1.00	1.50
22	A11	10c ultramarine	.90	.90

Chalky Paper

23	A14	20c ol grn & vio	1.75	2.00
24	A15	25c red violet & dull vio	2.25	*3.50*
25	A14	50c blk, *emerald* ('27)	6.00	*11.00*
26	A11	$1 ultra & vio, *bl*	16.00	18.00
27	A14	$2 black & red	110.00	80.00
		Nos. 17-27 (11)	139.90	120.20

MOROCCO

100 Centimos = 1 Peseta
12 Pence = 1 Shilling
20 Shillings = 1 Pound
100 Centimes = 1 Franc

These stamps were issued for various purposes:
a- For general use at the British Post Offices throughout Morocco.
b- For use in the Spanish Zone of Northern Morocco.
c- For use in the French Zone of Southern Morocco.
d- For use in the International Zone of Tangier.
For convenience these stamps are listed in four groups according to the coinage expressed or surcharged on the stamps, namely:
1- Value expressed in Spanish currency.
2- Value in British currency.
3- Value in French currency.
4- Stamps overprinted "Tangier."

Spanish Currency

Gibraltar Stamps of 1889-95 Overprinted

Morocco Agencies

1898 **Wmk. 2** *Perf. 14*

Black Overprint

1	A11	5c green	.50	.50
2	A11	10c carmine rose	.55	.20
b.		Double overprint	525.00	
3	A11	20c olive green	1.50	1.10
4	A11	25c ultramarine	1.50	.45
5	A11	40c orange brown	2.75	2.75
6	A11	50c violet	15.00	*20.00*
7	A11	1pe bister & blue	9.00	*17.50*
8	A11	2pe blk & car rose	5.75	*17.50*
		Nos. 1-8 (8)	36.55	*60.00*

Dark Blue Overprint

9	A11	40c orange brown	*50.00*	*50.00*
10	A11	50c violet	8.00	12.00
11	A11	1pe bister & blue	*200.00*	*225.00*

Inverted "V" for "A"

1a	A11	5c	19.00	24.00
2a	A11	10c	310.00	375.00
3a	A11	20c	25.00	25.00
4a	A11	25c	100.00	125.00
5a	A11	40c	175.00	200.00
6a	A11	50c	275.00	350.00
7a	A11	1pe	185.00	250.00
8a	A11	2pe	225.00	300.00

Overprinted in Black

(Narrower "M," ear of "g" horiz.)

Morocco Agencies

1899

12	A11	5c green	.25	.15
13	A11	10c carmine rose	.30	.15
14	A11	20c olive green	2.00	.55
15	A11	25c ultramarine	3.25	.75
16	A11	40c orange brown	24.00	13.00
17	A11	50c violet	4.75	2.75
18	A11	1pe bister & blue	14.00	*19.00*
19	A11	2pe blk & car rose	21.00	*35.00*
		Nos. 12-19 (8)	69.55	*71.35*

"M" with long serif

12a	A11	5c	2.75	*3.75*
13a	A11	10c	6.00	*5.00*
14a	A11	20c	15.00	*17.50*
15a	A11	25c	18.00	*17.50*
16a	A11	40c	57.50	*67.50*
17a	A11	50c	80.00	*110.00*
18a	A11	1pe	*100.00*	*125.00*
19a	A11	2pe	250.00	*275.00*

Type of Gibraltar, 1903, with Value in Spanish Currency, Overprinted

1903-05

20	A12	5c gray grn & bl grn	3.00	.75
21	A12	10c violet, *red*	2.50	.15
22	A12	20c gray grn & car rose ('04)	7.75	*22.50*
23	A12	25c vio & blk, *bl*	2.00	.15
24	A12	50c violet	52.50	*80.00*
25	A12	1pe blk & car rose	40.00	*87.50*
26	A12	2pe black & ultra	42.50	*70.00*
		Nos. 20-26 (7)	150.25	*261.05*

"M" with long serif

20a	A12	5c	24.00	24.00
21a	A12	10c	32.50	32.50
22a	A12	20c	52.50	57.50
23a	A12	25c	32.50	37.50
24a	A12	50c	275.00	300.00
25a	A12	1pe	250.00	275.00
26a	A12	2pe	275.00	300.00

1905-06 **Wmk. 3** **Chalky Paper**

27	A12	5c gray grn & bl grn	.50	.45
28	A12	10c violet, *red*	.50	.20
29	A12	20c gray grn & car rose ('06)	1.75	*7.50*
30	A12	25c violet & blk, *bl* ('06)	25.00	6.00
31	A12	50c violet	5.50	*9.00*
32	A12	1pe blk & car rose	25.00	*45.00*
33	A12	2pe black & ultra	13.00	*27.50*
		Nos. 27-33 (7)	71.25	*95.65*

No. 29 is on ordinary paper. Nos. 27 and 28 are on both ordinary and chalky paper.

"M" with long serif

27a	A12	5c	19.00	19.00
28a	A12	10c	19.00	19.00
29a	A12	20c	37.50	42.50
30a	A12	25c	110.00	125.00
31a	A12	50c	140.00	150.00
32a	A12	1pe	225.00	250.00
33a	A12	2pe	225.00	275.00

Numerous other minor overprint varieties exist of Nos. 1-33.

British Stamps of 1902-10 Surcharged in Spanish Currency:

MOROCCO AGENCIES **5 CENTIMOS**
#34-42, 46-48

MOROCCO AGENCIES **3 PESETAS**
#43-45

1907-10 **Wmk. 30**

34	A66	5c on ½p pale grn	.45	.15
35	A66	10c on 1p car	.45	.15
36	A67	15c on 1½p vio & grn	.65	.35
a.		"1" of "15" omitted	3,750.	
37	A68	20c on 2p grn & car	.55	.35
38	A66	25c on 2½p ultra	1.50	.75
39	A70	40c on 4p brn & grn	1.10	*2.00*
40	A70	40c on 4p org ('10)	.45	.90
41	A71	50c on 5p lil & ultra	1.75	1.75
42	A73	1pe on 10p car rose & vio	5.50	*7.50*

Wmk. 31

43	A75	3pe on 2sh6p vio	21.00	21.00
44	A76	6pe on 5sh car rose	37.50	37.50
45	A77	12pe on 10sh ultra	60.00	60.00
		Nos. 34-45 (12)	130.90	132.40

Nos. 36-37, 39-43 are on chalky paper.

Great Britain Nos. 153, 154 and 148 Surcharged

1912 **Wmk. 30** *Perf. 15x14*

46	A80	5c on ½p yel grn	.24	.15
47	A81	10c on 1p scarlet	.45	.15
48	A66	25c on 2½p ultra	15.00	15.00
		Nos. 46-48 (3)	15.69	15.30

British Stamps of 1912-18 Surcharged in Black or Carmine:

MOROCCO AGENCIES **15 CENTIMOS**
c

MOROCCO **AGENCIES** **10 CENTIMOS**
d

MOROCCO AGENCIES **6 PESETAS**
e

1914-18 **Wmk. 33**

49	A82(a)	5c on ½p grn	.15	.15
50	A83(d)	10c on 1p scar	.15	.15
51	A84(c)	15c on 1½p red brn ('15)	.20	.15
52	A85(d)	20c on 2p org (I)	.20	.20
53	A86(d)	25c on 2½p ultra	.55	.55
54	A90(d)	1pe on 10p lt bl	.90	*3.00*

Wmk. 34

Perf. 11x12

55	A91(e)	3pe on 2sh6p lt brn	24.00	*42.50*
a.		3pe on 2sh6p dark brown	24.00	*42.50*
56	A91(e)	6pe on 5sh car	24.00	*55.00*
a.		6pe on 5sh light carmine	125.00	
57	A91(e)	12pe on 10sh dk bl (C)	85.00	*125.00*
a.		12pe on 10sh blue	85.00	*160.00*
		Nos. 49-57 (9)	135.15	*226.70*

Great Britain Nos. 159, 165 Surcharged in Spanish Currency

MOROCCO AGENCIES **3 CENTIMOS**
f

MOROCCO AGENCIES **40 CENTIMOS**
g

1917-23 **Wmk. 33** *Perf. 15x14*

58	A82(f)	3c on ½p green	.30	.35
59	A88(g)	40c on 4p sl green	6.75	*8.25*

Great Britain Nos. 189, 191, 179 Surcharged in Spanish Currency

1926 **Wmk. 35**

60	A84(c)	15c on 1½p red brn	9.75	*11.00*
61	A86(d)	25c on 2½p ultra	1.10	1.40

Wmk. 34

Perf. 11x12

62	A91(e)	3pe on 2sh6p brn	20.00	*40.00*
		Nos. 60-62 (3)	30.85	*52.40*

British Stamps of 1924 Surcharged in Spanish Currency

1929-31 **Wmk. 35** *Perf. 15x14*

63	A82(a)	5c on ½p grn ('31)	.50	*4.00*
64	A83(d)	10c on 1p scar	8.00	*12.00*
65	A85(d)	20c on 2p org (II) ('31)	4.00	4.75
66	A88(g)	40c on 4p sl grn ('30)	.30	.50
		Nos. 63-66 (4)	12.80	*21.25*

Silver Jubilee Issue

Great Britain Nos. 226-229 Surcharged in Blue or Red

MOROCCO **AGENCIES** **5 CENTIMOS**

1935, May 8 *Perf. 14½x14*

67	A98	5c on ½p dk grn	.45	.50
68	A98	10c on 1p car	3.50	3.50
a.		Pair, one reading "CENTIMES"	1,200.	
69	A98	15c on 1½p red brn	.60	.75
70	A98	25c on 2½p ultra (R)	4.50	4.50
		Nos. 67-70 (4)	9.05	9.25

25th anniv. of the reign of King George V.

Great Britain Nos. 210-214, 216, 219 Surcharged in Spanish Currency

1935-37 **Photo.**

71	A82(a)	5c on ½p dk grn ('36)	.20	.15
72	A97(d)	10c on 1p car	.25	.20
73	A84(c)	15c on 1½p red brn	4.00	3.75
74	A85(d)	20c on 2p red org ('36)	.20	.20
75	A97(d)	25c on 2½p ultra ('36)	2.00	1.75
76	A88(d)	40c on 4p dk sl grn ('37)	.20	.30
77	A90(d)	1pe on 10p Prus bl ('37)	.30	.30
		Nos. 71-77 (7)		7.15 6.65

Great Britain Nos. 230-233 Surcharged

MOROCCO **5** **AGENCIES** **CENTIMOS**

"MOROCCO" 14mm

1936 **Wmk. 250**

78	A99	5c on ½p dk green	.15	.15
79	A99	10c on 1p crimson	.15	.15
a.		"Morocco" 15mm long	.25	.25

80 A99 15c on 1½p red brown .15 .15
81 A99 25c on 2½p brt ultra .15 .15
Set value .45 .45

Great Britain #234 Surcharged in Blue

MOROCCO 15 CENTIMOS AGENCIES

Perf. 14½x14

1937, May 13 **Wmk. 251**
82 A100 15c on 1½p purple brn .15 .15

Coronation of George VI and Elizabeth.

Great Britain Nos. 235-237, 239, 241, 244 Surcharged in Blue or Black

MOROCCO AGENCIES
25 CENTIMOS
h

1937-40
83 A101 5c on ½p dp grn (Bl) .15 .15
84 A101 10c on 1p scarlet .15 .15
85 A101 15c on 1½p red brown (Bl) .15 .15
86 A101 25c on 2½p brt ultra .15 .15
87 A102 40c on 4p gray green ('40) .35 .40
88 A103 70c on 7p emer ('40) .55 .55
Set value 1.20 1.35

MOROCCO AGENCIES

Great Britain Nos. 252-254, 256 Surcharged in Blue or Black

5 CENTIMOS

1940, May 6
89 A106 5c on ½p deep grn (Bl) .20 .20
90 A106 10c on 1p scarlet .30 .30
91 A106 15c on 1½p red brn (Bl) .45 .45
92 A106 25c on 2½p brt ultra .50 .50
Nos. 89-92 (4) 1.45 1.45

Centenary of the postage stamp.

Catalogue values for unused stamps in this section, from this point to the end of the section, are for Never Hinged items.

Great Britain Nos. 267 and 268 Surcharged in Black:

25 CENTIMOS

MOROCCO AGENCIES
i

45 PESETAS
MOROCCO AGENCIES
j

Perf. 14½x14, 14x14½

1948, Apr. 26 **Wmk. 251**
93 A109(i) 25c on 2½p .15 .15
94 A110(j) 45pe on £1 25.00 27.50

25th anniv. of the marriage of King George VI and Queen Elizabeth.

Great Britain Nos. 271-274 Surcharged "MOROCCO AGENCIES" and New Value

1948, July 29 *Perf. 14½x14*
95 A113 25c on 2½p brt ultra .15 .15
96 A114 30c on 3p dp vio .20 .20
97 A115 60c on 6p red vio .30 .30
98 A116 1.20pe on 1sh dk brn .60 .60
a. Double surcharge 600.00
Nos. 95-98 (4) 1.25 1.25

1948 Olympic Games, Wembley, July-Aug.
A square of dots obliterates the original denomination on No. 98.

Great Britain Nos. 280-282, 284-285, 247 Surcharged Type "h"

1951-52 **Wmk. 251** *Perf. 14½x14*
99 A101 5c on ½p lt orange 1.40 1.25
100 A101 10c on 1p ultra 2.25 1.00
101 A101 15c on 1½p green 1.75 1.25
102 A101 25c on 2½p ver 1.75 1.25
103 A102 40c on 4p ultra ('52) 1.40 1.25
104 A103 1pe on 10p ryl bl ('52) .45 3.00
Nos. 99-104 (6) 9.00 9.00

Great Britain Nos. 292-293 Surcharged Type "h"

1954-55 **Wmk. 298**
105 A126 5c on ½p red org .15 .15
106 A126 10c on 1p ultra ('55) .20 .20

Great Britain Nos. 317 and 323 Surcharged Type "h"

1956 **Wmk. 308** *Perf. 14x14½*
107 A126 5c on ½p red org .15 .15
108 A128 40c on 4p ultra 1.00 1.00

BRITISH CURRENCY

Stamps of Morocco Agencies were accepted for postage in Great Britain, starting in mid-1950. Copies with contemporaneous Morocco cancellations sell for more.

British Stamps of 1902-11 Overprinted

MOROCCO AGENCIES
a

MOROCCO AGENCIES
b

Overprint "a" 14½mm long

1907-12 **Wmk. 30** *Perf. 14*

Ordinary Paper
201 A66 ½p pale yel grn .90 .55
202 A66 1p carmine 3.25 1.10

Chalky Paper
203 A68 2p green & car 3.00 1.10
204 A70 4p brown & grn 3.50 1.75
205 A70 4p orange ('12) 4.00 3.00
a. Perf. 15x14 8.25 14.00
206 A66 6p dull vio 6.50 3.00
207 A74 1sh car rose & grn 15.00 10.50

Overprinted Type "b"
Wmk. 31
208 A75 2sh6p violet 45.00 47.50
Nos. 201-208 (8) 81.15 68.50

British Stamps of 1912-18 Overprinted Type "a"

Perf. 14½x14, 15x14

1914-21 **Wmk. 33**
209 A82 ½p green ('18) .20 .20
210 A83 1p scarlet ('17) .55 .15
211 A84 1½p red brn ('21) 1.65 8.00
212 A85 2p orange ('18) .80 .20
213 A87 3p violet ('21) 1.75 .28
214 A88 4p slate grn ('21) .70 .50
215 A89 6p dull vio ('21) 4.75 12.00
216 A90 1sh bister ('17) 8.25 1.65

c **MOROCCO AGENCIES**

Wmk. 34 *Perf. 11x12*
217 A91 2sh6p lt brown 30.00 32.50
a. 2sh6p brown 30.00 30.00
b. 2sh6p black brown 30.00 32.50
c. Double overprint 2,250. 1,400.
Nos. 209-217 (9) 48.65 55.48

Same Overprint on Great Britain Nos. 179-180

1925-31
218 A91 2sh6p gray brown 32.50 30.00
219 A91 5sh car rose ('31) 55.00 55.00

British Stamps of 1924 Overprinted Type "a" (14½mm long)

1925-31 **Wmk. 35** *Perf. 15x14*
220 A82 ½p green .70 .55
221 A84 1½p red brn ('31) 8.25 11.00
222 A85 2p dp org (Die II) 1.10 1.10
223 A86 2½p ultra 1.25 2.75
224 A89 6p red vio ('31) 4.50 5.50
225 A90 1sh bister 12.50 4.00
Nos. 220-225 (6) 28.30 24.90

Silver Jubilee Issue

Great Britain Nos. 226-229 Overprinted in Blue or Red

MOROCCO AGENCIES

1935, May 8 *Perf. 14½x14*
226 A98 ½p dark green (Bl) .45 .45
227 A98 1p carmine (Bl) .45 .55
228 A98 1½p red brown (Bl) 2.00 3.75
229 A98 2½p ultramarine (R) 2.25 2.50
Nos. 226-229 (4) 5.15 7.25

25th anniversary of the reign of King George V.

British Stamps of 1924 Overprinted Type "a" (15½mm long)

1935-36
230 A82 ½p green 3.25 6.50
231 A86 2½p ultra 125.00 30.00
232 A88 4p slate green 5.50 16.00
233 A89 6p red violet .55 .80
234 A90 1sh bister 50.00 50.00
Nos. 230-234 (5) 184.30 103.30

British Stamps of 1934-36 Overprinted "MOROCCO AGENCIES"

1935-36
235 A97 1p carmine .20 .25
236 A84 1½p red brown ('36) .75 10.00
237 A85 2p red orange ('36) .15 .20
238 A97 2½p ultra ('36) .80 4.00
239 A87 3p dk violet ('36) .20 .20
240 A88 4p dk slate grn ('36) .20 .20
241 A90 1sh bister brn ('36) .55 .60

Overprinted Type "c"
Wmk. 34
Perf. 11x12
242 A91 2sh6p brown 42.50 24.00
243 A91 5sh carmine ('37) 27.50 30.00
Nos. 235-243 (9) 72.85 69.45

Great Britain Nos. 231, 233 Overprinted

MOROCCO AGENCIES

"MOROCCO" 14mm

1936 **Wmk. 250** *Perf. 14½x14*
244 A99 1p crimson .15 .15
a. "Morocco" 15mm long .75 .75
245 A99 2½p bright ultra .20 .20
a. "Morocco" 15mm long .75 .75

Catalogue values for unused stamps in this section, from this point to the end of the section, are for Never Hinged items.

Great Britain Nos. 258-263, 241-248, 266, 249A-250 Overprinted "MOROCCO AGENCIES" (14½mm long)

1949, Aug. 16 **Wmk. 251**
246 A101 ½p green .25 .25
247 A101 1p vermilion .40 .40
248 A101 1½p lt red brown .60 .60
249 A101 2p lt orange .60 .60
250 A101 2½p ultra .60 .60
251 A101 3p violet .60 .60
252 A102 4p gray green .75 .75
253 A102 5p lt brown 1.10 1.10
254 A102 6p rose lilac 1.00 1.00
255 A103 7p emerald 1.25 1.25
256 A103 8p brt rose 1.65 1.65
257 A103 9p dp olive grn 1.40 1.40
258 A103 10p royal blue 1.65 1.65
259 A103 11p violet brn 1.90 1.90
260 A103 1sh brown 1.90 1.90

"MOROCCO AGENCIES"
17½mm long
Wmk. 259
Perf. 14
261 A104 2sh6p yellow grn 13.00 13.00
262 A104 5sh dull red 25.00 25.00
Nos. 246-262 (17) 53.65 53.65

Great Britain Nos. 280-284, 286-287 Overprinted "MOROCCO AGENCIES" (14½mm long)

Perf. 14½x14

1951, May 3 **Wmk. 251**
263 A101 ½p lt orange .15 .15
264 A101 1p ultra .16 .16
265 A101 1½p green .32 .32
266 A101 2p lt red brown .32 .32
267 A101 2½p vermilion .45 .45

"MOROCCO AGENCIES"
17½mm long
Wmk. 259
Perf. 11x12
268 A121 2sh6p green 11.00 14.00
269 A121 5sh dull red 16.00 20.00
Nos. 263-269 (7) 28.40 35.40

Great Britain Nos. 292-296, 299, 302 and 306 Overprinted "MOROCCO AGENCIES" (14½mm long)

1952-55 **Wmk. 298** *Perf. 14½x14*
270 A126 ½p red orange .15 .15
271 A126 1p ultramarine .15 .15
272 A126 1½p green ('52) .15 .15
273 A126 2p red brown .20 .20
274 A127 2½p scarlet ('52) .28 .28
275 A128 4p ultra ('55) .50 .50
276 A129 5p light brown .60 .60
277 A129 6p lilac rose ('55) .65 .65
278 A130 8p bright rose 1.40 1.40
279 A131 1sh brown 1.10 1.10
Nos. 270-279 (10) 5.18 5.18

Same Ovpt. on Great Britain No. 321

1956 **Wmk. 308** *Perf. 14½x14*
280 A127 2½p scarlet 1.00 1.00

French Currency

British Stamps of 1912-22 Surcharged in French Currency in Red or Black:

MOROCCO AGENCIES
3 CENTIMES
h

MOROCCO AGENCIES
1 FRANC
i

Perf. 14½x14, 15x14

1917-24 **Wmk. 33**
401 A82(h) 3c on ½p green (R) .15 .15
402 A82(h) 5c on ½p green .15 .15
403 A83(h) 10c on 1p scarlet .15 .15
404 A84(h) 15c on 1½p red brn .50 .40
405 A86(h) 25c on 2½p ultra .15 .15
406 A88(h) 40c on 4p sl green .50 .20
407 A89(h) 50c on 5p yellow brown ('23) 1.50 .70
408 A90(h) 75c on 9p olive green ('24) .40 .40
409 A90(i) 1fr on 10p lt blue 1.65 .55
Nos. 401-409 (9) 5.15 2.85

Great Britain No. 179 Surcharged:

MOROCCO AGENCIES

3 FRANCS
k

1924 **Wmk. 34** *Perf. 11x12*
410 A91(k) 3fr on 2sh6p brn 13.00 4.00

British Stamps of 1924 Surcharged in French Currency as in 1917-24

1925-26 **Wmk. 35** *Perf. 15x14*
411 A82(h) 5c on ½p green .30 4.00
412 A83(h) 10c on 1p scarlet .30 .20
413 A84(h) 15c on 1½p red brn .75 1.25
414 A86(h) 25c on 2½p ultra .30 .15
415 A88(h) 40c on 4p sl green .45 .45
416 A89(h) 50c on 5p yel brown .45 .15
417 A90(h) 75c on 9p ol green 1.40 .15
418 A90(i) 1fr on 10p dl blue .65 .15
Nos. 411-418 (8) 4.60 6.50

Great Britain Nos. 180, 198 and 200 Surcharged type "k"

1932 **Wmk. 34** *Perf. 11x12*
419 A91 6fr on 5sh car rose 40.00 40.00

1934 **Wmk. 35** *Perf. 14½x14*
420 A90 90c on 9p ol green 4.25 2.00
421 A90 1.50fr on 1sh bister 4.00 1.50

Great Britain Offices Abroad stamps can be mounted in the Scott Great Britain album.

Silver Jubilee Issue

Great Britain Nos. 226-229 Surcharged in Blue or Red

MOROCCO AGENCIES
5 CENTIMES

1935, May 8 *Perf. 14½x14*

422 A98 5c on ½p dk green .15 .15
423 A98 10c on 1p carmine 1.25 1.50
424 A98 15c on 1½p red brn .50 .50
425 A98 25c on 2½p ultra (R) .50 .50
Nos. 422-425 (4) 2.40 2.65

25th anniv. of the reign of King George V.

British Stamps of 1934-36 Surcharged Types "h" or "k"

Perf. 14½x14

1935-37 **Photo.** **Wmk. 35**

426 A82(h) 5c on ½p dk grn .15 .15
427 A97(h) 10c on 1p car ('36) .15 .15
428 A84(h) 15c on 1½p red brn .60 .60
429 A97(h) 25c on 2½p ultra .15 .15
430 A88(h) 40c on 4p dk sl grn .15 .15
431 A89(h) 50c on 5p yel brn .20 .20
432 A90(h) 90c on 9p dk ol grn .20 .20
433 A90(k) 1fr on 10p Prus bl .20 .20
434 A90(h) 1.50fr on 1sh bister brn ('37) .30 .40

Waterlow Printing

Wmk. 34 *Perf. 11x12*

435 A91(k) 3fr on 2sh6p brn 11.50 8.25
436 A91(k) 6fr on 5sh carmine ('36) 22.50 18.00
Nos. 426-436 (11) 36.10 28.45

Great Britain Nos. 230, 232 Surcharged

MOROCCO 5 AGENCIES
CENTIMES

1936 **Wmk. 250** *Perf. 14½x14*

437 A99 5c on ½p dark green .15 .15
438 A99 15c on 1½p red brown .15 .15
Set value .15 .15

Great Britain No. 234 Surcharged in Blue

MOROCCO AGENCIES
15 CENTIMES

1937, May 13 **Wmk. 251**

439 A100 15c on 1½p purple brn .15 .15

Coronation of George VI and Elizabeth.

MOROCCO
AGENCIES

Great Britain No. 235 Surcharged in Blue

5
CENTIMES

1937

440 A101 5c on ½p deep green .15 .15

For Use in the International Zone of Tangier

Great Britain Nos. 187-190 Overprinted in Black

TANGIER
a

1927 **Wmk. 35** *Perf. 15x14*

501 A82 ½p green .80 .80
502 A83 1p scarlet .80 .15
503 A84 1½p red brown 2.25 1.65
504 A85 2p orange (II) 1.65 .20
Nos. 501-504 (4) 5.50 2.80

Same Overprint on Great Britain Nos. 210-212

1934-35 **Photo.** *Perf. 14½x14*

505 A82 ½p dark green .40 .40
506 A97 1p carmine 1.10 1.25
507 A84 1½p red brown .40 .40
Nos. 505-507 (3) 1.90 2.05

Silver Jubilee Issue

Great Britain Nos. 226-228 Overprinted in Blue

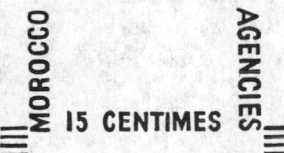

TANGIER TANGIER
b

1935, May 8

508 A98 ½p dark green .75 .75
509 A98 1p carmine 1.65 1.65
510 A98 1½p red brown .65 .65
Nos. 508-510 (3) 3.05 3.05

25th anniv. of the reign of King George V.

Great Britain Nos. 230-232 Overprinted Type "a"

1936 **Wmk. 250**

511 A99 ½p dark green .15 .15
512 A99 1p crimson .15 .15
513 A99 1½p red brown .15 .15
Set value .34 .34

Great Britain No. 234 Overprinted Type "b" in Blue

1937, May 13 **Wmk. 251**

514 A100 1½p purple brown .15 .15

Coronation of George VI and Elizabeth.

Great Britain Nos. 235-237 Overprinted in Blue or Black

TANGIER
c

1937 *Perf. 14½x14*

515 A101 ½p deep green (Bl) .15 .15
516 A101 1p scarlet (Bk) .15 .15
517 A101 1½p red brown (Bl) .15 .15
Set value .30 .30

Great Britain Nos. 252-254 Ovptd. Type "a" in Blue or Black

1940, May 6

518 A106 ½p deep green (Bl) .15 .15
519 A106 1p scarlet (Bk) .25 .25
520 A106 1½p red brown (Bl) .35 .35
Nos. 518-520 (3) .75 .75

Centenary of the postage stamp.

Great Britain Nos. 258 and 259 Overprinted Type "c" in Blue or Black

1944-45

521 A101 ½p green (Bl) .15 .15
522 A101 1p ver (Bk) ('45) .15 .15

Catalogue values for unused stamps in this section, from this point to the end of the section, are for Never Hinged items.

Great Britain Nos. 264-265 Overprinted:

d TANGIER
e TANGIER

1946, June 11

523 A107(d) 2½p bright ultra .20 .20
524 A108(e) 3p violet .25 .25

Return to peace at close of World War II.

Great Britain Nos. 267 and 268 Overprinted Type "a"

Perf. 14½x14, 14x14½

1948, Apr. 26

525 A109 2½p bright ultra .15 .15
a. Pair, one without overprint 1,750.
526 A110 £1 dp chalky bl 27.50 32.50

25th anniv. of the marriage of King George VI and Queen Elizabeth.

Great Britain Nos. 271 to 274 Overprinted Type "a"

1948, July 29 *Perf. 14½x14*

527 A113 2½p bright ultra .20 .16
528 A114 3p deep violet .28 .24
529 A115 6p red violet .40 .32
530 A116 1sh dark brown .80 .70
Nos. 527-530 (4) 1.68 1.42

1948 Olympic Games, Wembley, July-Aug.

Stamps of Great Britain, 1937-47, and Nos. 249A, 250 and 251A Overprinted Type "c"

1949, Jan. 1

531 A101 2p lt org (II) .15 .15
532 A101 2½p ultra (II) .15 .15
533 A101 3p violet (II) .15 .15
534 A102 4p gray green .55 .55
535 A102 5p light brown .52 .52
536 A102 6p rose lilac .35 .35
537 A103 7p emerald .45 .45
538 A103 8p bright rose .60 .60
539 A103 9p deep ol grn .60 .60
540 A103 10p royal blue .80 .80
541 A103 11p violet brn .95 .95
542 A103 1sh brown .55 .55

Wmk. 259

Perf. 14

543 A104 2sh6p yellow grn 4.50 4.50
544 A104 5sh dull red 9.25 9.25
545 A105 10sh ultra 22.50 22.50
Nos. 531-545 (15) 42.07 42.07

Great Britain Nos. 276 to 279 Overprinted Type "a"

Perf. 14½x14

1949, Oct. 10 **Wmk. 251**

546 A117 2½p bright ultra .15 .15
547 A118 3p bright violet .25 .22
548 A119 6p red violet .30 .30
549 A120 1sh brown .60 .60
Nos. 546-549 (4) 1.30 1.27

Great Britain Nos. 280-288 Overprinted Type "c" or "a" (Shilling Values)

1950-51

550 A101 ½p lt orange .15 .15
551 A101 1p ultra .15 .15
552 A101 1½p green .30 .30
553 A101 2p lt red brn .30 .30
554 A101 2½p vermilion .24 .24
555 A102 4p ultra ('50) .70 .70

Wmk. 259

Perf. 11x12

556 A121 2sh6p green 3.50 3.50
557 A121 5sh dull red 7.75 7.75
558 A122 10sh ultra 15.00 15.00
Nos. 550-558 (9) 28.09 28.09

Great Britain Nos. 292-308 Overprinted Type "c"

1952-54 **Wmk. 298** *Perf. 14½x14*

559 A126 ½p red org ('53) .15 .15
560 A126 1p ultra ('53) .15 .15
561 A126 1½p green ('52) .15 .15
562 A126 2p red brn ('53) .15 .15
563 A127 2½p scarlet ('52) .15 .15
564 A127 3p dk pur (Dk Bl) .25 .15
565 A128 4p ultra ('53) .60 .60
566 A129 5p lt brown ('53) 1.25 1.25
567 A129 6p lilac rose .60 .60
568 A129 7p emerald 1.10 1.25
569 A130 8p brt rose ('53) 1.10 1.25
570 A130 9p dp olive grn 1.10 1.25
571 A130 10p royal blue 1.50 1.50
572 A130 11p violet brn 1.50 1.50
573 A131 1sh brown ('53) .75 .80
574 A132 1sh3p dk grn ('53) 1.10 1.25
575 A131 1sh6p dk blue ('53) 1.50 1.50
Nos. 559-575 (17) 13.10 13.65

Stamp and Type of Great Britain 1955 Overprinted Type "a"

Perf. 11x12

1955, Sept. 23 **Engr.** **Wmk. 308**

576 A133 2sh6p dark brown 2.50 3.00
577 A133 5sh crimson 7.50 9.00
578 A133 10sh brt ultra 15.00 18.00
Nos. 576-578 (3) 25.00 30.00

Coronation Issue

Great Britain Nos. 313-316 Overprinted Type "a"

1953, June 3 **Photo.** **Wmk. 298**

579 A134 2½p scarlet .50 .40
580 A135 4p brt ultra .90 .65
581 A136 1sh3p dark green 2.75 1.90
582 A137 1sh6p dark blue 3.25 2.25
Nos. 579-582 (4) 7.40 5.20

Great Britain Nos. 317, 323, 325 and 332 Overprinted Type "c"

1956 **Wmk. 308** *Perf. 14½x14*

583 A126 ½p red orange .15 .15
584 A126 1p ultramarine .30 .15
585 A126 1½p green .55 .50
586 A126 2p red brown .90 .20
587 A127 2½p scarlet .70 .20
588 A127 3p dark purple .70 .35
589 A128 4p ultra 1.40 1.40
590 A129 6p lilac rose .90 .40
591 A132 1sh3p dark green 1.00 *8.50*
Nos. 583-591 (9) 6.60 *11.85*

Great Britain Nos. 317-333 and 309-311 Overprinted "1857-1957 TANGIER"

1957, Apr. 1 **Photo.** **Wmk. 308**

592 A126 ½p red orange .15 .15
593 A126 1p ultramarine .15 .15
594 A126 1½p green .15 .15
595 A126 2p red brown .15 .15
596 A127 2½p scarlet .15 .15
597 A127 3p dark purple .15 .15
598 A128 4p ultramarine .22 .15
599 A129 5p lt brown .22 .15
600 A129 6p lilac rose .30 .20
601 A129 7p emerald .40 .25
602 A130 8p brt rose .40 .25
603 A130 9p dp olive grn .40 .25
a. "TANGIER" omitted *5,500.*
604 A130 10p royal blue .42 .30
605 A130 11p violet brown .60 .40
606 A131 1sh brown .30 .32
607 A132 1sh3p dark green .60 .40
608 A131 1sh6p dark blue .85 .50

Engr.

Perf. 11x12

609 A133 2sh6p dark brown 2.00 1.25
610 A133 5sh crimson 3.25 2.75
611 A133 10sh ultramarine 6.50 5.25
Nos. 592-611 (20) 17.36 13.32

Centenary of British P.O. in Tangier.

Nos. 609-611 are found with hyphen omitted (one stamp in sheet of 40).

British stamps overprinted "Tangier" were discontinued Apr. 30, 1957.

TURKISH EMPIRE

40 Paras = 1 Piaster
12 Pence = 1 Shilling (1905)

40 PARAS (a) 80 PARAS (b)
12 PIASTRES (c) 40 PARAS (d)

Surcharged on Great Britain Nos. 101, 104, 96

1885, Apr. 1 **Wmk. 30** *Perf. 14*

1 A47(a) 40pa on 2½p lilac 60.00 1.00
2 A45(b) 80pa on 5p green 175.00 8.50

Wmk. 31

3 A44(c) 12pi on 2sh6p lilac 35.00 20.00
a. Bluish paper 250.00 125.00
Nos. 1-3 (3) 270.00 29.50

Great Britain Nos. 114, 118 Surcharged

1887 **Wmk. 30**

4 A57(a) 40pa on 2½p vio, *bl* 1.50 .15
a. Double surcharge 3,000. *2,500.*
5 A61(b) 80pa on 5p lil & bl 6.25 .75
a. Small "0" in "80" 85.00 70.00

Great Britain No. 111 Handstamp Surcharged

1893, Feb. 25

6 A54(d) 40pa on ½p ver *500.00 175.00*

No. 6 was a provisional, made and used at Constantinople for five days. Excellent forgeries are known.

Great Britain No. 121 Surcharged

4 PIASTRES
e

1896

7 A64(e) 4pi on 10p car rose & lil 25.00 8.00

British Stamps of 1902 Surcharged

1902-05 **Wmk. 30**

8 A66(a) 40pa on 2½p ultra 5.00 .20
9 A71(b) 80pa on 5p lil & bl 7.00 1.50
a. Small "0" in "80" 275.00 100.00
10 A73(e) 4pi on 10p car rose & vio 3.50 3.25

Wmk. 31

11 A75(c) 12pi on 2sh6p vio ('03) 35.00 30.00
12 A76(c) 24pi on 5sh car rose ('05) 47.50 47.50
Nos. 8-12 (5) 98.00 *82.45*

Great Britain Nos. 131, 134 Surcharged

1 PIASTRE
f

1906 **Wmk. 30**
13 A66(f) 1pi on 2½p ultra 3.50 .18
14 A71(f) 2pi on 5p lil & ultra 10.00 1.75

Nos. 10, 11, 14 are on both ordinary and chalky paper.

Great Britain Nos. 127-135, 138 Overprinted

LEVANT
g

1905
15 A66 ½p pale green .90 .15
16 A66 1p carmine .90 .25
17 A67 1½p violet & grn 6.00 *5.75*
18 A68 2p green & car 1.75 *3.75*
19 A66 2½p ultra 7.75 *16.50*
20 A69 3p violet, *yel* 7.75 *13.00*
21 A70 4p brown & grn 6.50 *11.00*
22 A71 5p lilac & ultra 12.00 *18.00*
23 A66 6p dull violet 9.00 *18.00*
24 A74 1sh car rose & grn 21.00 *30.00*
Nos. 15-24 (10) 73.55 *116.40*

Nos. 17, 18 and 24 are on both ordinary and chalky paper.

No. 18 Surcharged **1 Piastre**

1906, July 2
25 A68 1pi on 2p grn & car 1,500. 650.

British Stamps of 1902-09 Surcharged:

30 PARAS
j

1 PIASTRE 10 PARAS
k

1909
26 A67 30pa on 1½p vio & grn 4.00 .85
27 A69 1pi10pa on 3p vio, *yel* 7.00 *14.00*
28 A70 1pi30pa on 4p brn & grn 5.00 *9.50*
29 A70 1pi30pa on 4p org 8.25 *17.00*
30 A66 2pi20pa on 6p dl violet 12.50 *27.50*
31 A74 5pi on 1sh car rose & grn 3.00 *4.50*
Nos. 26-31 (6) 39.75 *73.35*

No. 29 is on ordinary paper, the others are on chalky paper.

Great Britain Nos. 132, 144, 135 Surcharged:

1¼ PIASTRE
m

2½ PIASTRES
n

1910
32 A69(m) 1¼pi on 3p vio, *yel* .35 .35
33 A70(m) 1¾pi on 4p orange .45 .48
34 A66(n) 2½pi on 6p dl vio .80 .80
Nos. 32-34 (3) 1.60 1.63

There are three different varieties of "4" in the fraction of the 1¾ piastre.

Great Britain Nos. 151-154 Overprinted Type "g"

1911-12 ***Perf. 15x14***
35 A80 ½p yellow green .50 .60
36 A81 1p carmine .75 .90

Re-engraved

37 A80 ½p yel grn ('12) .20 .20
38 A81 1p scarlet ('12) .25 .25

Great Britain No. 148 Surcharged

1 PIASTRE
o

39 A66(o) 1pi on 2½p ultra 1.75 1.50
Nos. 35-39 (5) 3.45 3.45

The surcharge on No. 39 exists in two types with the letters 2½ and 3mm high respectively. The stamp also differs from No. 13 in the perforation.

British Stamps of 1912-13 Surcharged with New Values

1913-14 **Wmk. 33**
40 A84(j) 30pa on 1½p red brown 2.50 *5.25*
41 A86(o) 1pi on 2½p ultra 1.00 .15
42 A87(m) 1¼pi on 3p vio 1.75 *2.75*
43 A88(m) 1¾pi on 4p sl grn 2.50 *3.25*
44 A90(o) 4pi on 10p lt bl 4.00 *7.75*
45 A90(o) 5pi on 1sh bis 17.50 *32.50*
Nos. 40-45 (6) 29.25 *51.65*

British Stamps of 1912-19 Overprinted Type "g"

1913-21
46 A82 ½p green .15 .15
47 A83 1p scarlet .15 *1.25*
48 A85 2p orange ('21) 1.00 *11.00*
49 A87 3p violet ('21) 6.25 *6.00*
50 A88 4p sl grn ('21) 3.75 *7.75*
51 A89 5p yel brn ('21) 7.50 *14.00*
52 A89 6p dl vio ('21) 14.00 *5.25*
53 A90 1sh bister ('21) 8.25 *4.25*

Wmk. 34
Perf. 11x12

54 A91 2sh6p brn ('21) 30.00 *40.00*
Nos. 46-54 (9) 71.05 *89.65*

British Stamps of 1912-19 Surcharged as in 1909-10 and

1½ PIASTRES
p

45 PIASTRES
q

1921 **Wmk. 33** ***Perf. 14½x14***
55 A82(j) 30pa on ½p grn .15 .15
a. Inverted surcharge 100.00
56 A83(p) 1½pi on 1p scar .15 .15
57 A86(p) 3¾pi on 2½p ultra .15 .15
58 A87(p) 4½pi on 3p vio .15 .15
59 A89(p) 7½pi on 5p yel brn .20 .15
60 A90(p) 15pi on 10p lt bl .45 .35
61 A90(p) 18¾pi on 1sh bis 4.25 3.00

Wmk. 34
Perf. 11x12

62 A91(q) 45pi on 2sh6p brown 17.50 *24.00*
63 A91(q) 90pi on 5sh car rose 30.00 32.50
64 A91(q) 180pi on 10sh blue 45.00 35.00
Nos. 55-64 (10) 98.00 95.60

ADEN

'ä–dᵊn

LOCATION — Southern Arabia
GOVT. — Former British colony and protectorate
AREA — 112,075 sq. mi.
POP. — 220,000 (est. 1964)
CAPITAL — Aden

Aden used India stamps before 1937.

In January, 1963, the colony of Aden (the port) and the sheikdoms and emirates of the Western Aden Protectorate formed the Federation of South Arabia. This did not include the Eastern Aden Protectorate with Kathiri and Qu'aiti States. Stamps of Aden, except those of Kathiri and Qu'aiti States, were replaced Apr. 1, 1965, by those of the Federation of South Arabia. See South Arabia, Vol. 1B, and People's Democratic Republic of Yemen, Vol. 5.

12 Pies = 1 Anna
16 Annas = 1 Rupee
100 Cents = 1 Shilling (1951)

Catalogue values for unused stamps in this country are for Never Hinged items, beginning with Scott 28 in the regular postage section and for all of the items in the states' sections.

Dhow — A1

Perf. 13x11½

1937, Apr. 1 **Engr.** **Wmk. 4**
1 A1 ½a lt green .25 .25
2 A1 9p dk green .40 .40
3 A1 1a black brown .40 .32
4 A1 2a red .70 .70
5 A1 2½a blue .90 .75
6 A1 3a car rose 1.65 2.25
7 A1 3½a gray blue 1.40 1.40
8 A1 8a rose lilac 2.25 2.75
9 A1 1r brown 5.00 4.75
10 A1 2r orange yel 8.50 8.00
11 A1 5r rose violet 40.00 40.00
12 A1 10r olive grn 125.00 125.00
Nos. 1-12 (12) 186.45 186.57
Set, never hinged 300.00

Coronation Issue
Common Design Type

1937, May 12 ***Perf. 13½x14***
13 CD302 1a black brown .25 .25
14 CD302 2½a blue .45 .45
15 CD302 3½a gray blue .75 .75
Nos. 13-15 (3) 1.45 1.45
Set, never hinged 2.50

Aidrus Mosque — A2

Designs: ¾a, 5r, Camel Corpsman. 1a, 2r, Aden Harbor. 1½a, 1r, Adenese dhow. 2½a, 8a, Mukalla. 3a, 14a, 10r, Capture of Aden, 1839.

1939-45 **Engr.** **Wmk. 4** ***Perf. 12½***
16 A2 ½a green .20 .15
17 A2 ¾a brown violet .20 .15
18 A2 1a lt blue .20 .15
19 A2 1½a red .40 .15
20 A2 2a dark brown .25 .15
21 A2 2½a brt ultra .40 .15
22 A2 3a rose car & dk brn .40 .15
23 A2 8a orange .25 .15
23A A2 14a lt bl & brn blk ('45) .80 .40
24 A2 1r bright green .90 .45
25 A2 2r rose vio & indigo 3.50 .75
26 A2 5r ol grn & red brn 9.00 2.75
27 A2 10r dk pur & vio brn 10.00 5.50
Nos. 16-27 (13) 27.00 11.05
Set, never hinged 47.50

Catalogue values for unused stamps in this section, from this point to the end of the section, are for Never Hinged items.

Peace Issue
Common Design Type
Perf. 13½x14

1946, Oct. 15 **Engr.** **Wmk. 4**
28 CD303 1½a carmine .15 .15
29 CD303 2½a deep blue .30 .30

Return to peace at end of World War II.

Silver Wedding Issue
Common Design Types

1949, Jan. 17 **Photo.** ***Perf. 14x14½***
30 CD304 1½a scarlet .25 .25

Engraved; Name Typographed
Perf. 11½x11

31 CD305 10r purple 22.50 22.50

25th anniv. of the marriage of King George VI and Queen Elizabeth.

UPU Issue
Common Design Types
Surcharged with New Values in Annas and Rupees

Engr.; Name typo. on Nos. 33-34

1949, Oct. 10 ***Perf. 13½, 11x11½***
32 CD306 2½a on 20c dp ultra .35 .35
33 CD307 3a on 30c dp car .75 .75
34 CD308 8a on 50c org 1.65 1.65
35 CD309 1r on 1sh blue 2.75 2.75
Nos. 32-35 (4) 5.50 5.50

75th anniv. of the formation of the UPU.

Common Design Types pictured in section before Great Britain.

Nos. 18 and 20-27 Surcharged with New Values in Black or Carmine

1951, Oct. 1 **Wmk. 4** ***Perf. 12½***
36 A2 5c on 1a .30 .30
37 A2 10c on 2a .40 .40
38 A2 15c on 2½a .55 .55
a. Double surcharge *500.00*
39 A2 20c on 3a 1.10 1.10
40 A2 30c on 8a (C) 1.10 1.10
41 A2 50c on 8a 1.10 .85
42 A2 70c on 14a 1.40 1.40
43 A2 1sh on 1r 1.75 1.40
44 A2 2sh on 2r 7.00 6.00
45 A2 5sh on 5r 11.00 11.50
46 A2 10sh on 10r 22.50 22.50
Nos. 36-46 (11) 48.20 47.10

Surcharge on No. 40 includes 2 bars.

Coronation Issue
Common Design Type

1953, June 2 **Engr.** ***Perf. 13½x13***
47 CD312 15c dark green & black .35 .35

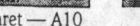

Minaret — A10

Camel Transport — A11

Designs: 15c, Crater. 25c, Mosque. 35c, Dhow. 50c, Map. 70c, Salt works. 1sh, Dhow building. 1sh, 25c, Colony Badge. 2sh, Aden Protectorate levy. 5sh, Crater Pass. 10sh, Tribesman. 20sh, Aden in 1572.

Perf. 12, 12x13½ ('56)

1953-58 **Engr.** **Wmk. 4**
Size: 29x23, 23x29mm
48 A10 5c grn, perf. 12x13½ ('56) .15 .15
a. Perf. 12 .15 .15
49 A11 10c orange .15 .15
50 A11 15c blue green .15 .15
51 A11 25c carmine .15 .15
52 A10 35c dp bl, perf. 12x13½ ('58) .40 .30
a. 35c ultra, perf. 12 .45 .30
53 A10 50c blue, perf. 12x13½ ('56) .25 .22
a. Perf. 12 .35 .32
54 A10 70c gray, perf. 12x13½ ('56) .25 .25
a. Perf. 12 .55 .55
55 A11 1sh pur & sepia .55 .45
55A A11 1sh vio & black ('55) .35 .32
56 A10 1sh25c blk & lt blue ('56) .55 .42
57 A10 2sh car rose & sep 1.50 1.40
57A A10 2sh car & black ('56) 2.25 .55
58 A10 5sh blue & sepia 3.75 3.75
58A A10 5sh dk blue & blk ('56) 2.00 1.50
59 A10 10sh olive & sepia 5.75 7.25
60 A10 10sh ol gray & blk ('54) 4.50 3.25

Size: 36½x27mm
Perf. 13½x13

61 A11 20sh rose vio & dk brn 11.00 9.50
61A A11 20sh lt vio & blk ('57) 7.25 6.25
Nos. 48-61A (18) 40.95 36.01

Various shades from two or more printings exist. No. 60 has heavier shading on tribesman's lower garment than No. 59.

See #66-75. For overprints see #63-64.

Type of 1953
Inscribed: "Royal Visit 1954"

1954, Apr. 27 ***Perf. 12***
62 A11 1sh purple & sepia .40 .40

Nos. 50 and 56 Overprinted in Red

تعديل
الدستور
١٩٥٩
a

REVISED CONSTITUTION 1959
b

1959, Jan. 26 ***Perf. 12, 12x13½***
63 A11(a) 15c dk blue green .25 .25
64 A10(b) 1sh25c blk & lt blue .70 .70

Introduction of a revised constitution.

Freedom from Hunger Issue
Common Design Type
Perf. 14x14½

1963, June 4 **Photo.** **Wmk. 314**
65 CD314 1sh25c green .85 .65

Types of 1953-57
Perf. 12x13½, 12 (#67-69, 73)

1964-65		Engr.	Wmk. 314	
66	A10	5c green ('65)	.18	.20
67	A11	10c orange	.20	.15
68	A11	15c Prus green	.24	.20
69	A11	25c carmine	.42	.18
70	A10	35c dk blue	.70	.42
71	A10	50c dull blue	.70	.38
72	A10	70c gray	.75	.52
73	A11	1sh vio & black	.75	.52
74	A10	1sh25c blk & lt blue	1.50	1.40
75	A10	2sh car & blk ('65)	2.75	3.50
		Nos. 66-75 (10)	8.19	7.47

KATHIRI STATE OF SEIYUN

LOCATION — In Eastern Aden Protectorate
GOVT. — Sultanate
CAPITAL — Seiyun

> Catalogue values for unused stamps in this section are for Never Hinged items.

Sultan Ja'far bin Mansur al Kathiri — A1   Seiyun — A2

Minaret at Tarim — A3

Designs: 2½a, Mosque at Seiyun. 3a, Palace at Tarim. 8a, Mosque at Seiyun, horiz. 1r, South Gate, Tarim. 2r, Kathiri House. 5r, Mosque at Tarim.

1942		Engr.	Wmk. 4	Perf. 14	
1	A1	½a dark green		.25	.25
2	A1	¾a copper brown		.25	.25
3	A1	1a deep blue		.40	.40
		Perf. 13x11½, 11½x13			
4	A2	1½a dark car rose		.45	.45
5	A3	2a black brown		.45	.45
6	A3	2½a deep blue		.45	.45
7	A2	3a dk car rose & dull brn		.55	.55
8	A2	8a orange red		1.10	1.10
9	A3	1r green		1.75	1.75
10	A2	2r rose vio & dk blue		6.25	8.00
11	A3	5r gray green & fawn		9.00	13.00
		Nos. 1-11 (11)		20.90	26.65

For surcharges see Nos. 20-27.

Nos. 4, 6 Ovptd. in Black or Red:

VICTORY
ISSUE
8TH JUNE 1946
a

VICTORY
ISSUE
8TH JUNE
1946
b

Perf. 13x11½, 11½x13

1946, Oct. 15			Wmk. 4	
12	A2 (a)	1½a dark car rose	.18	.18
13	A3 (b)	2½a deep blue (R)	.22	.22
a.		Inverted overprint	425.00	

Victory of the Allied Nations in WWII.

Silver Wedding Issue
Common Design Types

1949, Jan. 17		Photo.	Perf. 14x14½	
14	CD304	1½a scarlet	.28	.28

Engraved; Name Typo.
Perf. 11½x11

15	CD305	5r green	9.00	16.00

25th anniv. of the marriage of King George VI and Queen Elizabeth.

UPU Issue
Common Design Types
Surcharged with New Values in Annas and Rupees

Engr.; Name Typo. on Nos. 17-18

1949, Oct. 10		Perf. 13½, 11x11½		
16	CD306	2½a on 20c dp ultra	.15	.15
17	CD307	3a on 30c dp car	.18	.18
18	CD308	8a on 50c orange	.65	.65
19	CD309	1r on 1sh blue	1.25	1.25
		Nos. 16-19 (4)	2.23	2.23

75th anniv. of the formation of the UPU.

Nos. 3 and 5-11 Surcharged with New Values in Carmine or Black

Perf. 14, 13x11½, 11½x13

1951, Oct. 1		Engr.	Wmk. 4	
20	A1	5c on 1a (C)	.15	.15
21	A3	10c on 2a	.16	.16
22	A3	15c on 2½a	.55	.55
23	A2	20c on 3a	.24	.24
24	A2	50c on 8a	.32	.32
25	A3	1sh on 1r	.90	.80
26	A2	2sh on 2r	2.75	2.50
27	A3	5sh on 5r	6.50	6.00
		Nos. 20-27 (8)	11.57	10.72

Coronation Issue
Common Design Type

1953, June 2			Perf. 13½x13	
28	CD312	15c dk green & blk	.32	.32

Sultan Hussein A10    Qarn Adh Dhabi A11

Designs: 15c, Seiyun scene, horiz. 25c, Minaret at Tarim. 35c, Mosque at Seiyun. 50c, Palace at Tarim, horiz. 1sh, Mosque at Seiyun, horiz. 2sh, South Gate, Tarim. 5sh, Kathiri house, horiz. 10sh, Mosque entrance, Tarim.

1954, Jan. 15		Engr.	Perf. 12½	
29	A10	5c dark brown	.15	.15
30	A10	10c deep blue	.15	.15
		Perf. 13x11½, 11½x13		
31	A11	15c dk blue green	.15	.15
32	A11	25c dk car rose	.15	.15
33	A11	35c deep blue	.15	.15
34	A11	50c dk car rose & dk brn	.15	.15
35	A11	1sh deep orange	.32	.32
36	A11	2sh gray green	.85	.85
37	A11	5sh vio & dk blue	2.25	3.25
38	A11	10sh vio & yel brn	4.50	6.50
		Nos. 29-38 (10)	8.82	11.82

Perf. 11½x13, 13x11½

1964, July 1			Wmk. 314	

Designs: 1sh25c, Seiyun, horiz. 1sh50c, View of Gheil Omer, horiz.

39	A11	70c black	.38	.38
40	A11	1sh25c bright green	.60	.60
41	A11	1sh50c purple	.80	.80
		Nos. 39-41 (3)	1.78	1.78

QUAITI STATE OF SHIHR AND MUKALLA

LOCATION — In Eastern Aden Protectorate
GOVT. — Sultanate
CAPITAL — Mukalla

> Catalogue values for unused stamps in this section are for Never Hinged items.

Sultan Sir Saleh bin Ghalib al Qu'aiti — A1   Mukalla Harbor — A2

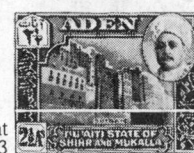

Buildings at Shibam — A3

Designs: 2a, Gateway of Shihr. 3a, Outpost of Mukalla. 8a, View of 'Einat. 1r, Governor's Castle, Du'an. 3r, Mosque in Hureidha. 5r, Meshhed.

1942		Engr.	Wmk. 4	Perf. 14	
1	A1	½a dark green		.35	.15
2	A1	¾a copper brown		.35	.15
3	A1	1a deep blue		.40	.15
		Perf. 13x11½, 11½x13			
4	A2	1½a dk car rose		.40	.15
5	A2	2a black brown		.40	.15
6	A3	2½a deep blue		.40	.15
7	A2	3a dk car rose & dl brn		.45	.15
8	A2	8a orange red		1.00	.32
9	A2	1r green		1.50	.48
10	A3	2r rose vio & dk blue		7.00	2.00
11	A3	5r gray green & fawn		12.00	3.25
		Nos. 1-11 (11)		24.25	7.10

For surcharges see Nos. 20-27.

Nos. 4, 6 Ovptd. in Black or Carmine like Kathiri Nos. 12 13

Perf. 11½x13, 13x11½

1946, Oct. 15				
12	A2 (b)	1½a dk car rose	.15	.15
13	A3 (a)	2½a deep blue (C)	.25	.25

Victory of the Allied Nations in WWII.

Silver Wedding Issue
Common Design Types

1949, Jan. 17		Photo.	Perf. 14x14½	
14	CD304	1½a scarlet	.22	.22

Engraved; Name Typo.
Perf. 11½x11

15	CD305	5r green	7.50	12.50

25th anniv. of the marriage of King George VI and Queen Elizabeth.

UPU Issue
Common Design Types
Surcharged with New Values in Annas and Rupees

Engr.; Name Typo. on Nos. 17 and 18

1949, Oct. 10		Perf. 13½, 11x11½		
16	CD306	2½a on 20c dp ultra	.15	.15
17	CD307	3a on 30c dp car	.35	.35
18	CD308	8a on 50c org	.90	.90
19	CD309	1r on 1sh blue	2.50	2.50
a.		Surcharge omitted	850.00	
		Nos. 16-19 (4)	3.90	3.90

Nos. 3 and 5-11 Surcharged with New Values in Carmine or Black

Perf. 14, 13x11½, 11½x13

1951, Oct. 1		Engr.	Wmk. 4	
20	A1	5c on 1a (C)	.20	.20
21	A2	10c on 2a	.30	.30
22	A3	15c on 2½a	.30	.30
23	A2	20c on 3a	.30	.30
24	A3	50c on 8a	.50	.50
25	A2	1sh on 1r	.90	.90
26	A3	2sh on 2r	2.00	3.00
27	A3	5sh on 5r	6.50	8.00
		Nos. 20-27 (8)	11.00	13.50

Coronation Issue
Common Design Type

1953, June 2		Engr.	Perf. 13½x13	
28	CD312	15c dk blue & black	.40	.40

Qu'aiti State in Hadhramaut

Metal Work — A10

Fisheries — A11

Designs: 10c, Mat making. 15c, Weaving. 25c, Pottery. 35c, Building. 50c, Date cultivation. 90c, Agriculture. 1sh25c, 10sh, Lime burning. 2sh, Dhow building. 5sh, Agriculture.

Perf. 11½x13, 13½x14

1955, Sept. 1		Engr.	Wmk. 4	
29	A10	5c greenish blue	.15	.15
30	A10	10c black	.15	.15
31	A10	15c dk green	.15	.15
32	A10	25c carmine	.15	.15
33	A10	35c ultra	.15	.15
34	A10	50c red orange	.30	.30
35	A10	90c brown	.45	.45
36	A11	1sh purple & blk	.50	.50
37	A11	1sh25c red org & blk	.60	.60
38	A11	2sh dk blue & blk	1.00	1.00
39	A11	5sh green & blk	2.50	2.50
40	A11	10sh car & black	5.25	5.25
		Nos. 29-40 (12)	11.35	11.35

Types of 1955 with Portrait of Sultan Awadh Bin Saleh El Qu'aiti

Design: 70c, Agriculture. Others as before.

1963, Oct. 20			Wmk. 314	
41	A10	5c greenish blue	.15	.15
42	A10	10c black	.15	.15
43	A10	15c dark green	.15	.15
44	A10	25c carmine	.15	.15
45	A10	35c ultra	.25	.25
46	A10	50c red orange	.35	.35
47	A10	70c brown	.60	.60
48	A11	1sh purple & blk	.85	.85
49	A11	1sh25c red org & blk	1.10	1.10
50	A11	2sh dk blue & blk	1.75	1.75
51	A11	5sh green & blk	4.25	4.50
52	A11	10sh carmine & blk	9.50	10.00
		Nos. 41-52 (12)	19.25	20.00

AITUTAKI

ī̇t-ə-'täk-ē

LOCATION — One of the larger Cook Islands, in the South Pacific Ocean northeast of New Zealand
GOVT. — A dependency of the British dominion of New Zealand
AREA — 7 sq. mi.
POP. — 2,335 (1981)

The Cook Islands were attached to New Zealand in 1901. Stamps of Cook Islands were used in 1932-72.
Aitutaki acquired its own postal service in August 1972, though remaining part of Cook Islands.

12 Pence = 1 Shilling
100 Cents = 1 Dollar (1972)

> Catalogue values for unused stamps in this country are for Never Hinged items, beginning with Scott 37.

> Aitutaki stamps can be mounted in the Scott annual New Zealand Dependencies supplement.

Watermark

Wmk. 61- Single-lined NZ and Star Close Together

Stamps of New Zealand Surcharged in Red or Blue:

AITUTAKI.　　　**AITUTAKI.**

Ava Pene.　　　　Tai Pene.
　a　　　　　　　　　b

1903　Engr.　Wmk. 61　Perf. 14
1	A18(a)	½p green (R)	3.00 6.00
2	A35(b)	1p rose (Bl)	3.25 6.25

AITUTAKI.

Rua Pene Ma Te Ava.
　　　　c

AITUTAKI.　AITUTAKI.　AITUTAKI.

Toru Pene.　Ono Pene.　Tai Tiringi.
　d　　　　　e　　　　　f

Perf. 11
3	A22(c)	2½p blue (R)	3.75 8.25
4	A23(d)	3p yellow brn (Bl)	5.50 11.00
5	A26(e)	6p red (Bl)	13.00 27.50
6	A29(f)	1sh scarlet (Bl)	55.00 57.50
a.		1sh orange red (Bl)	55.00 72.50

1912　Typo.　Perf. 14, 14x15
7	A41(a)	½p yellow grn (R)	1.00 2.25

Engr.
Perf. 11
9	A22(c)	2½p deep blue (R)	5.00 6.50

AITUTAKI.　　　AITUTAKI.

Ono Pene.　　　Tai Tiringi.
　g　　　　　　　h

1913-16　　　　　　Typo.
10	A42(b)	1p rose (Bl)	1.50 2.75

Engr.
12	A41(g)	6p car rose (Bl) ('16)	30.00 45.00
13	A41(h)	1sh ver (Bl) ('14)	47.50 67.50

1916-17　Perf. 14x13½, 14x14½
17	A45(g)	6p car rose (Bl)	10.00 19.00
18	A45(h)	1sh ver (Bl) ('17)	27.50 45.00
		Nos. 1-18 (13)	206.00 304.50

New Zealand Stamps of 1909-19 Overprinted in Red or Dark Blue

AITUTAKI.

1917-20　Typo.　Perf. 14x15
19	A43	½p yellow grn ('20)	.60 2.00
20	A42	1p car (Bl) ('20)	.90 2.50
21	A47	1½p gray black	1.75 6.00
22	A47	1½p brown org ('19)	1.40 5.25
23	A43	3p choc (Bl) ('19)	3.75 7.25

Perf. 14x13½, 14x14½
Engr.
24	A44	2½p dull blue ('18)	1.40 6.00
25	A45	3p vio brn (Bl) ('18)	1.75 8.00
26	A45	6p car rose (Bl)	3.75 12.00
27	A45	1sh vermilion (Bl)	10.00 21.00
		Nos. 19-27 (9)	25.30 70.00

Landing of Capt. Cook
A15

Avarua Waterfront
A16

Capt. James Cook — A17

Palm — A18

Houses at Arorangi — A19

Avarua Harbor — A20

1920　Engr.　Unwmk.　Perf. 14
28	A15	½p green & black	.95 2.50
29	A16	1p carmine & black	1.25 3.75
30	A17	1½p brown & blk	2.00 6.00
31	A18	3p dp blue & blk	2.00 7.50
32	A19	6p slate & red brn	6.25 15.00
33	A20	1sh claret & blk	8.25 26.00
		Nos. 28-33 (6)	20.70 60.75

Inverted centers, double frames, etc. are from printers waste.

Rarotongan Chief (Te Po) — A21

1926-27　Wmk. 61　Perf. 14
34	A15	½p green & blk ('27)	1.50 1.65
35	A16	1p carmine & blk	1.50 1.65
36	A21	2½p blue & blk ('27)	6.00 6.75
		Nos. 34-36 (3)	9.00 10.05

> **Catalogue values for unused stamps in this section, from this point to the end of the section, are for Never Hinged items.**

Cook Islands Nos. 199-200, 202, 205-206, 210, 212-213, 215-217 Overprinted

Aitutaki

1972　Photo.　Unwmk.　Perf. 14x13½
37	A34	½c gold & multi	.60 .70
38	A34	1c gold & multi	1.10 1.40
39	A34	2½c gold & multi	5.00 6.00
40	A34	4c gold & multi	1.10 1.10
41	A34	5c gold & multi	7.00 8.75
42	A34	10c gold & multi	6.00 6.25
43	A34	20c gold & multi	1.10 1.10
44	A34	25c gold & multi	1.10 1.10
45	A34	50c gold & multi	7.75 7.75
46	A35	$1 gold & multi	15.00 15.00
47	A35	$2 gold & multi	4.25 4.25
		Nos. 37-47 (11)	50.00 53.40

Overprint horizontal on Nos. 46-47. On $2, overprint is in capitals of different font; size: 21x3mm.
Issued: Nos. 37-46, Aug. 9; No. 47, Nov. 24.

Same Overprint Horizontal in Silver On Cook Islands Nos. 330-332

1972, Oct. 27　　　Perf. 13½
48	A53	1c gold & multi	.15 .15
49	A53	5c gold & multi	.25 .25
50	A53	10c gold & multi	.45 .45
		Nos. 48-50 (3)	.85 .85

Fluorescence

Starting in 1972, stamps carry a "fluorescent security underprinting" in a multiple pattern of New Zealand's coat of arms with "Aitutaki" above, "Cook Islands" below and two stars at each side.

Silver Wedding Type of Cook Islands

1972, Nov. 20　Photo.　Perf. 13½
Size: 29x40mm
51	A54	5c silver & multi	4.75 3.50

Size: 66x40mm
52	A54	15c silver & multi	2.00 1.65

25th anniversary of the marriage of Queen Elizabeth II and Prince Philip. Nos. 51-52 printed in sheets of 5 stamps and one label.

Flower Issue of Cook Islands Overprinted

1972, Dec. 11　Photo.　Perf. 14x13½
53	A34	½c on #199	.15 .15
54	A34	1c on #200	.15 .15
55	A34	2½c on #202	.15 .15
56	A34	4c on #205	.15 .15
57	A34	5c on #206	.20 .20
58	A34	10c on #210	.30 .30
59	A34	20c on #212	.70 .70
60	A34	25c on #213	.90 .90
61	A34	50c on #215	1.75 1.75
62	A35	$1 on #216	3.75 3.75
		Nos. 53-62 (10)	8.20 8.20

See Nos. 73-76.

The Passion of Christ, by Mathias Grunewald — A22

Paintings: No. 63b, St. Veronica, by Rogier van der Weyden. No. 63c, Crucifixion, by Raphael. No. 63d, Resurrection, by della Francesca. No. 64a, Last Supper, by Master of Amiens. No. 64b, Condemnation of Christ, by Hans Holbein, the Elder. No. 64c, Crucifixion, by Rubens. No. 64d, Resurrection, by El Greco. No. 65a, Passion of Christ, by El Greco. No. 65b, St. Veronica, by Jakob Cornelisz. No. 65c, Crucifixion, by Rubens. No. 65d, Resurrection, by Dierik Bouts.

Perf. 13½
1973, Apr. 6　Photo.　Unwmk.
63		Block of 4	.20 .20
a.-d.	A22	1c any single	.15 .15
64		Block of 4	.65 .65
a.-d.	A22	5c any single	.15 .15
65		Block of 4	1.50 1.50
a.-d.	A22	10c any single	.35 .35
		Nos. 63-65 (3)	2.35 2.35

Easter. Printed in blocks of 4 in sheets of 40. Design descriptions in top and bottom margins.

Coin Type of Cook Islands

Queen Elizabeth II Coins: 1c, Taro leaf. 2c, Pineapples. 5c, Hibiscus. 10c, Oranges. 20c, Fairy terns. 50c, Bonito. $1, Tangaroa, Polynesian god of creation, vert.

1973, May 14　　Perf. 13x13½
Size: 37x24mm
66	A55	1c dp car & multi	.15 .15
67	A55	2c blue & multi	.15 .15
68	A55	5c green & multi	.15 .15

Size: 46x30mm
69	A55	10c vio blue & multi	.30 .30
70	A55	20c green & multi	.60 .60
71	A55	50c dp car & multi	1.40 1.40

Size: 32x54½mm
72	A55	$1 blue, blk & sil	2.75 2.75
		Nos. 66-72 (7)	5.50 5.50

Cook Islands coinage commemorating silver wedding anniv. of Queen Elizabeth II.
Printed in sheets of 20 stamps and label showing Westminster Abbey.

Cook Islands Nos. 208, 210, 212 and 215 Overprinted Like Nos. 53-62 and: "TENTH ANNIVERSARY/ CESSATION/ OF/ NUCLEAR TESTING/ TREATY"

1973, July　Photo.　Perf. 14x13½
73	A34	8c gold & multi	.30 .30
74	A34	10c gold & multi	.40 .40
75	A34	20c gold & multi	.90 .90
76	A34	50c gold & multi	2.00 2.00
		Nos. 73-76 (4)	3.60 3.60

Nuclear Test Ban Treaty, 10th anniv., protest against French nuclear testing on Mururoa Atoll.

Princess Anne, Hibiscus A23

Design: 30c, Mark Phillips and hibiscus.

1973, Nov. 14　Photo.　Perf. 13½x14
77	A23	25c gold & multi	.40 .40
78	A23	30c gold & multi	.60 .60
a.		Souvenir sheet of 2, #77-78	1.10 1.10

Wedding of Princess Anne and Capt. Mark Phillips.

Virgin and Child, by Il Perugino — A24

Paintings of the Virgin and Child by various masters.

1973, Dec.　Photo.　Perf. 13
79		Block of 4	.20 .20
a.	A24	1c Van Dyck	.15 .15
b.	A24	1c Bartolommeo Montagna	.15 .15
c.	A24	1c Carlo Crivelli	.15 .15
d.	A24	1c Il Perugino	.15 .15
80		Block of 4	.60 .60
a.	A24	5c Cima da Conegliano	.15 .15
b.	A24	5c Memling	.15 .15
c.	A24	5c Veronese	.15 .15
d.	A24	5c Veronese	.15 .15
81		Block of 4	1.50 1.50
a.	A24	10c Raphael	.35 .35
b.	A24	10c Lorenzo Lotto	.35 .35
c.	A24	10c Del Colle	.35 .35
d.	A24	10c Memling	.35 .35
		Nos. 79-81 (3)	2.30 2.30

Christmas. Printed in blocks of 4 in sheets of 48. Design descriptions in margins.

Murex Ramosus A25

Terebra Maculata — A26

Pacific Shells: 1c, Nautilus macromphalus. 2c, Harpa major. 3c, Phalium strigatum. 4c, Cypraea talpa. 5c, Mitra stictica. 8c, Charonia tritonis. 10c, Murex triremis. 20c, Oliva sericea. 25c, Tritonalia rubeta. 60c, Strombus latissimus. $1, Biplex perca. $5, Cypraea hesitata.

1974-75　　Photo.　Perf. 13
82	A25	½c silver & multi	.15 .15
83	A25	1c silver & multi	.15 .15
84	A25	2c silver & multi	.15 .15
85	A25	3c silver & multi	.15 .15
86	A25	4c silver & multi	.15 .15
87	A25	5c silver & multi	.15 .15
88	A25	8c silver & multi	.20 .15
89	A25	10c silver & multi	.25 .15
90	A25	20c silver & multi	.52 .35
91	A25	25c silver & multi	.65 .45
92	A25	60c silver & multi	1.90 1.10
93	A25	$1 silver & multi	3.75 2.25

Perf. 14

94 A26	$2 silver & multi	5.00	5.00
95 A26	$5 silver & multi	12.00	12.00
	Nos. 82-95 (14)	25.17	22.35

Issue dates: Nos. 82-93, Jan. 31, 1974; $2, Jan. 20, 1975; $5, Feb. 28, 1975.

For overprints see Nos. O1-O16.

William Bligh and "Bounty" A27

1974, Apr. 11 Photo. *Perf. 13*

Size: 38x22mm

96 A27	1c shown	.15	.15
97 A27	1c "Bounty" at sea	.15	.15
98 A27	5c Bligh and "Bounty" off Aitutaki	.32	.32
99 A27	5c Chart of Aitutaki, 1856	.32	.32
100 A27	8c James Cook and "Resolution"	.65	.65
101 A27	8c Maps of Aitutaki and Pacific Ocean	.65	.65
	Nos. 96-101,C1-C6 (12)	6.94	6.94

Capt. William Bligh (1754-1817), European discoverer of Aitutaki, Apr. 11, 1789. Stamps of same denomination printed se-tenant in sheets of 32.

Aitutaki Nos. 1 & 2 Map and UPU Emblem A28

Design: 50c, Aitutaki Nos. 4 and 28, map of Aitutaki and UPU emblem.

1974, July 15 Photo. *Perf. 13½*

102 A28	25c blue & multi	.80	.80
a.	Souvenir sheet of 2, #102-103	2.50	2.50
103 A28	50c blue & multi	1.60	1.60

UPU, cent. Printed in sheets of 5 plus label showing UPU emblem.

Virgin and Child, by Van der Goes — A29

Designs: Paintings of the Virgin and Child.

1974, Oct. 11 Photo. *Perf. 13½*

104 A29	1c shown	.15	.15
105 A29	5c Giovanni Bellini	.15	.15
106 A29	8c Gerard David	.20	.20
107 A29	10c Antonello da Messina	.25	.25
108 A29	25c Joos van Cleve	.70	.70
109 A29	30c Maitre de St. Catherine	.80	.80
a.	Souvenir sheet of 6, #104-109	3.00	3.00
	Nos. 104-109 (6)	2.25	2.25

Christmas. #104-109 printed in sheets of 15 stamps and corner label. See #B1-B6.

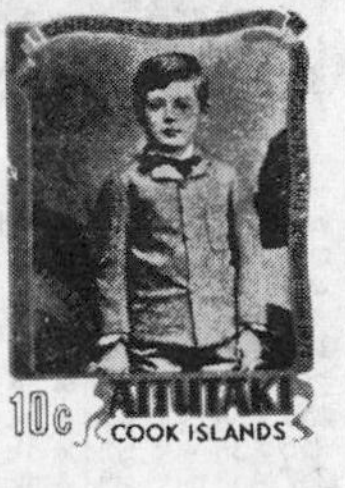

Churchill, Dublin, Age 5 — A30

Designs: Churchill portraits.

1974, Nov. 29 Photo. *Perf. 14*

110 A30	10c shown	.22	.15
111 A30	25c As young man	.55	.35
112 A30	30c Inspecting troops, WWII	.65	.38
113 A30	50c Painting	1.40	.80
114 A30	$1 Giving V sign	2.75	1.65
a.	Souvenir sheet of 5, #110-114 + label, perf. 13½	6.50	5.50
	Nos. 110-114 (5)	5.57	3.33

Sir Winston Churchill (1874-1965). Nos. 110-114 printed in sheets of 5 stamps and corner label.

Emblem US & USSR Flags A31

Design: 50c, Icarus and Apollo Soyuz spacecraft.

1975, July 24 Photo. *Perf. 13x14½*

115 A31	25c multicolored	.75	.75
116 A31	50c multicolored	1.75	1.75
a.	Souvenir sheet of 2	2.50	2.50

Apollo Soyuz space test project (Russo-American cooperation), launching July 15; link-up July 17. Nos. 115 and 116 each printed in sheets of 5 stamps and one label showing area of Apollo splashdowns. No. 116a contains one each of Nos. 115-116 with gold and black border and inscription.

Madonna and Child, by Pietro Lorenzetti — A32

Paintings: 7c, Adoration of the Kings, by Rogier van der Weyden. 15c, Madonna and Child, by Bartolommeo Montagna. 20c, Adoration of the Shepherds.

1975, Nov. 24 Photo. *Perf. 14x13½*

117 A32	Strip of 3	.32	.32
a.	6c St. Francis	.15	.15
b.	6c Madonna and Child	.15	.15
c.	6c St. John the Evangelist	.15	.15
118 A32	Strip of 3	.35	.35
a.	7c One King	.15	.15
b.	7c Madonna and Child	.15	.15
c.	7c Two Kings	.15	.15
119 A32	Strip of 3	.80	.80
a.	15c St. Joseph	.26	.26
b.	15c Madonna and Child	.26	.26
c.	15c St. John the Baptist	.26	.26
120 A32	Strip of 3	1.40	1.40
a.	20c One Shepherd	.42	.42
b.	20c Madonna and Child	.42	.42
c.	20c Two Shepherds	.42	.42
d.	Souv. sheet of 12, #117-120, perf. 13½	4.25	4.25
	Nos. 117-120 (4)	2.87	2.87

Christmas. Nos. 117-120 printed in sheets of 30 (10 strips of 3).

For surcharges see Nos. B7-B10.

Descent from the Cross, detail — A33

Designs (Painting, Flemish School, 16th Century): 30c, Virgin Mary, disciple and body of Jesus. 35c, Mary Magdalene and disciple.

1976, Apr. 5 Photo. *Perf. 13½*

121 A33	15c gold & multi	.18	.18
122 A33	30c gold & multi	.48	.48
123 A33	35c gold & multi	1.25	1.25
a.	Souvenir sheet of 3	2.25	2.25
	Nos. 121-123 (3)	1.91	1.91

Easter. No. 123a contains 3 stamps similar to Nos. 121-123, perf. 13, in continuous design without gold frames and white margins.

Declaration of Independence — A34

Paintings by John Trumbull: 35c, Surrender of Cornwallis at Yorktown. 50c, Washington's Farewell Address. a, "1976 BICENTENARY." b, "UNITED STATES." c, "INDEPENDENCE 1776."

1976, June 1 Photo. *Perf. 13½*

124 A34	Strip of 3	1.65	1.65
a.-c.	30c any single	.52	.52
125 A34	Strip of 3	2.25	2.25
a.-c.	35c any single	.75	.75
126 A34	Strip of 3	3.00	3.00
a.-c.	50c any single	.95	.95
d.	Souvenir sheet of 9 (3x3)	7.00	7.00
	Nos. 124-126 (3)	6.90	6.90

American Bicentennial. Nos. 124-126 printed in sheets of 5 strips of 3 and 3-part corner label showing portrait of John Trumbull, commemorative inscription and portraits of Washington (30c), John Adams (35c) and Jefferson (50c). No. 126d contains 3 strips similar to Nos. 124-126.

Bicycling A35

Montreal Olympic Games Emblem and: 35c, Sailing. 60c, Field hockey. 70c, Running.

1976, July 15 Photo. *Perf. 13x14*

127 A35	15c multicolored	.30	.30
128 A35	35c multicolored	.70	.70
129 A35	60c multicolored	1.10	1.10
130 A35	70c multicolored	1.40	1.40
a.	Souvenir sheet of 4	4.00	4.00
	Nos. 127-130 (4)	3.50	3.50

21st Olympic Games, Montreal, Canada, July 17-Aug. 1. Nos. 127-130 printed in sheets of 5 stamps and label showing coat of Arms and Montreal Olympic Games emblem. No. 130a contains 4 stamps similar to Nos. 127-130 with gold margin around each stamp.

Nos. 127-130a Overprinted Diagonally: "ROYAL VISIT JULY 1976"

1976, July 30

131 A35	15c multicolored	.30	.30
132 A35	35c multicolored	.75	.75
133 A35	60c multicolored	1.10	1.10
134 A35	70c multicolored	1.50	1.50
a.	Souvenir sheet of 4	4.25	4.25
	Nos. 131-134 (4)	3.65	3.65

Visit of Queen Elizabeth II to Montreal and official opening of the Games. Each stamp of No. 134a has diagonal overprint. Sheet margin has additional overprint: "ROYAL VISIT OF H.M. QUEEN ELIZABETH II/OFFICIALLY OPENED 17 JULY 1976."

Annunciation

A36 A37

Designs: Nos. 137-138, Angel appearing to the shepherds. Nos. 139-140, Nativity. Nos. 141-142, Three Kings.

1976, Oct. 18 *Perf. 13½x13*

135 A36	6c dk green & gold	.15	.15
136 A37	6c dk green & gold	.15	.15
137 A36	7c dk brown & gold	.15	.15
138 A37	7c dk brown & gold	.15	.15
139 A36	15c dk blue & gold	.35	.35
140 A37	15c dk blue & gold	.35	.35
141 A36	20c purple & gold	.45	.45
142 A37	20c purple & gold	.45	.45
a.	Souvenir sheet of 8	2.50	2.50
	Nos. 135-142 (8)	2.20	2.20

Christmas. Stamps of same denomination printed se-tenant in sheets of 50. No. 142a contains 8 stamps similar to Nos. 135-142 with white margin around each pair of stamps.

A. G. Bell and 1876 Telephone A38

Design: 70c, Satellite and radar.

1977, Mar. 3 Photo. *Perf. 13½x13*

143 A38	25c rose & multi	.45	.45
144 A38	70c violet & multi	1.50	1.50
a.	Souvenir sheet of 2	2.00	2.00

Centenary of first telephone call by Alexander Graham Bell, Mar. 10, 1876. No. 144a contains a 25c in colors of 70c and 70c in colors of 25c.

Calvary (detail), by Rubens A39

Paintings by Rubens: 20c, Lamentation. 35c, Descent from the Cross.

1977, Mar. 31 Photo. *Perf. 13½x14*

145 A39	15c gold & multi	.38	.38
146 A39	20c gold & multi	.45	.45
147 A39	35c gold & multi	.65	.65
a.	Souv. sheet of 3, #145-147, perf. 13	1.75	1.75
	Nos. 145-147 (3)	1.48	1.48

Easter, and 400th birth anniv. of Peter Paul Rubens (1577-1640), Flemish painter.

Capt. Bligh, "Bounty" and George III — A40

Designs: 35c, Rev. John Williams, George IV, First Christian Church. 50c, British flag, map of Aitutaki, Queen Victoria. $1, Elizabeth II and family on balcony after coronation.

1977, Apr. 21 *Perf. 13½*

148 A40	25c gold & multi	.55	.55
149 A40	35c gold & multi	1.10	1.10
150 A40	50c gold & multi	1.50	1.50
151 A40	$1 gold & multi	3.00	3.00
a.	Souvenir sheet of 4, #148-151	7.50	7.50
	Nos. 148-151 (4)	6.15	6.15

Reign of Queen Elizabeth II, 25th anniv.

For overprint and surcharge see Nos. O11, O15.

Annunciation

A41 A42

Designs: No. 154, Virgin, Child and ox. No. 155, Joseph and donkey (Nativity). No. 156, Three Kings. No. 157, Virgin and Child. No. 158, Joseph. No. 159, Virgin, Child and donkey (Flight into Egypt).

1977, Oct. 14 Photo. *Perf. 13½x14*

152 A41	6c multicolored	.15	.15
153 A42	6c multicolored	.15	.15
154 A41	7c multicolored	.15	.15
155 A42	7c multicolored	.15	.15
156 A41	15c multicolored	.28	.28
157 A42	15c multicolored	.28	.28
158 A41	20c multicolored	.40	.40
159 A42	20c multicolored	.40	.40
a.	Souvenir sheet of 8, #152-159	2.50	2.50
	Nos. 152-159 (8)	1.96	1.96

Christmas. Stamps of same denomination printed se-tenant in sheets of 32.

For surcharges see Nos. B19-B26a.

Hawaiian Wood
Figurine — A43

AITUTAKI
COOK ISLANDS

Designs: 50c, Talbot hunting dog, figure-head of
"Resolution", horiz. $1, Temple figure.

1978, Jan. 19   Litho.   Perf. 13½
160 A43   35c multicolored   .60   .60
161 A43   50c multicolored   .80   .80
162 A43 $1 multicolored   1.50   1.50
   a.   Souvenir sheet of 3, #160-162   3.50   3.50
    Nos. 160-162 (3)   2.90   2.90

Bicentenary of Capt. Cook's arrival in Hawaii.
Nos. 160-162 issued in sheets of 6.

Avignon
Pietà, 15th
Century
A44

Paintings: 15c, Jesus Carrying Cross, by Simone
di Martini. 35c, Christ at Emmaus, by Rembrandt.

1978, Mar. 17   Photo.   Perf. 13½x14
163 A44   15c gold & multi   .25   .25
164 A44   20c gold & multi   .40   .40
165 A44   35c gold & multi   .60   .60
   a.   Souvenir sheet of 3   1.50   1.50
    Nos. 163-165 (3)   1.25   1.25

Easter. No. 165a contains one each of Nos. 163-
165, perf. 13½, and label showing Louvre, Paris.
See Nos. B27-B29.

Elizabeth
II — A45

Virgin and Child,
by Dürer — A46

Souvenir Sheets
1978, June 15   Photo.   Perf. 13½x13
166   Sheet of 6   7.00   7.00
   a.   A45 $1 Yale of Beaufort   1.10   1.10
   b.   A45 $1 shown   1.10   1.10
   c.   A45 $1 Ancestral statue   1.10   1.10
   d.   Souvenir sheet of 6   7.00   7.00

25th anniv. of coronation of Queen Elizabeth II.
No. 166 contains 2 each of Nos. 166a-166c, silver
marginal inscription and coats of arms. No. 166d
contains 2 strips of Nos. 166a-166c separated by
horizontal slate green gutter showing Royal family
on balcony, silver marginal inscription.

1978, Dec. 4   Photo.   Perf. 14½x13
Designs: Various paintings of the Virgin and Child
by Albrecht Dürer.

167 A46   15c multicolored   .22   .22
168 A46   20c multicolored   .30   .30
169 A46   30c multicolored   .55   .55
170 A46   35c multicolored   .70   .70
    Nos. 167-170 (4)   1.77   1.77

Christmas; 450th death anniv. of Albrecht Dürer
(1471-1528), German painter. Nos. 167-170 issued
in sheets of 5 stamps and corner label. See No. B30.

Capt. Cook, by
Nathaniel
Dance — A47

Boy Holding
Hibiscus, IYC
Emblem — A48

Design: 75c, "Resolution" and "Adventure," by
William Hodges.

1979, July 20   Photo.   Perf. 14x13½
171 A47   50c multicolored   1.10   1.10
172 A47   75c multicolored   1.50   1.50
   a.   Souvenir sheet of 2, #171-172   3.00   3.00

Capt. James Cook (1728-1779), explorer, death
bicentenary.

1979, Oct. 1   Photo.   Perf. 14x13½
IYC Emblem and: 35c, Boy playing guitar. 65c,
Boys in outrigger canoe.

173 A48   30c multicolored   .50   .50
174 A48   35c multicolored   .55   .55
175 A48   65c multicolored   1.10   1.10
    Nos. 173-175 (3)   2.15   2.15

See No. B31.

Aitutaki No.
102, Hill,
Penny Black
A49

Designs: Nos. 176, 178-179, 181, paintings of
letter writers, Flemish School, 17th century.

1979, Nov. 14   Photo.   Perf. 13
176 A49   50c Gabriel Metsu   .75   .75
177 A49   50c shown   .75   .75
178 A49   50c Jan Vermeer   .75   .75
179 A49   65c Gerard Terborch   .90   .90
180 A49   65c No. 103 (like No. 177)   .90   .90
181 A49   65c Jan Vermeer   .90   .90
    Nos. 176-181 (6)   4.95   4.95

Souvenir Sheet
182   Sheet of 6   3.00   3.00
   a.   A49 30c like No. 176   .42   .42
   b.   A49 30c like No. 177   .42   .42
   c.   A49 30c like No. 178   .42   .42
   d.   A49 30c like No. 179   .42   .42
   e.   A49 30c like No. 180   .42   .42
   f.   A49 30c like No. 181   .42   .42

Sir Rowland Hill (1795-1879), originator of
penny postage. Nos. 176-178 and 179-181 printed
se-tenant in sheets of 9 (3x3).

Descent from the
Cross,
Detail — A50

Albert
Einstein — A51

Easter: 30c, 35c, Descent from the Cross, by
Quentin Metsys (details).

1980, Apr. 3   Photo.   Perf. 13x13½
183 A50   20c multicolored   .30   .30
184 A50   30c multicolored   .45   .45
185 A50   35c multicolored   .55   .55
    Nos. 183-185 (3)   1.30   1.30

See No. B32.

1980, July 21   Photo.   Perf. 14
186 A51   12c shown   .22   .22
187 A51   12c Formula, atom structure   .22   .22
188 A51   15c Portrait, diff.   .25   .25
189 A51   15c Atomic blast   .25   .25
190 A51   20c Portrait, diff.   .35   .35

191 A51   20c Atomic blast, trees   .35   .35
   a.   Souv. sheet of 6, #186-191, perf. 13   2.50   2.50
    Nos. 186-191 (6)   1.64   1.64

Albert Einstein (1879-1955), theoretical physicist. Stamps of same denomination se-tenant.

Ancestral Figure,
Aitutaki — A52

1980, Sept. 26   Photo.   Perf. 14
192 A52   6c shown   .15   .15
193 A52   6c God image staff, Raro-
       tonga   .15   .15
194 A52   6c Trade adze, Mangaia   .15   .15
195 A52   6c Tangaroa carving, Raro-
       tonga   .15   .15
196 A52   12c Wooden image, Aitutaki   .18   .18
197 A52   12c Hand club, Rarotonga   .18   .18
198 A52   12c Carved mace, Mangaia   .18   .18
199 A52   12c Fisherman's god, Raro-
       tonga   .18   .18
200 A52   15c Ti'i image, Aitutaki   .22   .22
201 A52   15c Fisherman's god, diff.   .22   .22
202 A52   15c Carved mace, Cook Is-
       lands   .22   .22
203 A52   15c Tangaroa, diff.   .22   .22
204 A52   20c Chief's headdress,
       Aitutaki   .30   .30
205 A52   20c Carved mace, diff.   .30   .30
206 A52   20c God image staff, diff.   .30   .30
207 A52   20c like #195   .30   .30
   a.   Souvenir sheet of 16, #192-207   3.50
    Nos. 192-207 (16)   3.40   3.40

Third South Pacific Arts Festival, Port Moresby,
Papua New Guinea. Stamps of same denomination
se-tenant.

Virgin and Child,
Sculptures — A53

1980, Nov. 21   Photo.   Perf. 13x13½
208 A53   15c 13th cent.   .22   .22
209 A53   20c 14th cent.   .30   .30
210 A53   25c 15th cent.   .38   .38
211 A53   35c 15th cent., diff.   .55   .55
    Nos. 208-211 (4)   1.45   1.45

Christmas. See No. B33.

Mourning Virgin, by
Pedro
Roldan — A54

Sturnus
Vulgaris — A55

Easter (Roldan Sculptures): 40c, Christ. 50c,
Mourning St. John.

1981, Mar. 31   Photo.   Perf. 14
212 A54   30c green & gold   .45   .45
213 A54   40c brt purple & gold   .55   .55
214 A54   50c dk blue & gold   .70   .70
    Nos. 212-214 (3)   1.70   1.70

See No. B34.

1981-82   Perf. 14x13½, 13½x14
215 A55   1c shown   .15   .15
216 A55   1c Poephila gouldiae   .15   .15
217 A55   2c Petroica multicolor   .15   .15
218 A55   2c Pachycephala pectoralis   .15   .15
219 A55   3c Falco peregrinus   .15   .15
220 A55   3c Rhipidura rufifrous   .15   .15
221 A55   4c Tyto alba   .15   .15

222 A55   4c Padda oryzivora   .15   .15
223 A55   5c Artamus leucorhynchus   .15   .15
224 A55   5c Vini peruviana   .15   .15
225 A55   6c Columba livia   .20   .20
226 A55   6c Porphyrio porphyria   .20   .20
227 A55   10c Geopelia striata   .35   .35
228 A55   10c Lonchura castane-
       othorax   .35   .35
229 A55   12c Acridotheres tristis   .40   .40
230 A55   12c Egretta sacra   .40   .40
231 A55   15c Diomeda melanophris   .50   .50
232 A55   15c Numenius phaeopus   .50   .50
233 A55   20c Gygis alba   .70   .70
234 A55   20c Pluvialis dominica   .70   .70
235 A55   25c Sula leucogaster   .90   .90
236 A55   25c Anas superciliosa   .90   .90
237 A55   30c Anas acuta   1.00   1.00
238 A55   30c Fregata minor   1.00   1.00
239 A55   35c Stercorarius pomarinus   1.25   1.25
240 A55   35c Conopoderas caffra   1.25   1.25
241 A55   40c Lalage maculosa   1.25   1.25
242 A55   40c Gallirallus philippensis   1.25   1.25
243 A55   50c Vini stepheni   1.65   1.65
244 A55   50c Diomedea epomophora   1.65   1.65
245 A55   70c Ptilinopus victor   2.25   2.25
246 A55   70c Erythrura cyaneovirens   2.25   2.25

Photo.   Perf. 13½
Size: 35x47mm
246A A55 $1 Myiagra azureocapil-
       la   4.25   4.25
246B A55 $2 Myiagra vanikorensis   9.00   9.00
246C A55 $4 Amandava
       amandava   15.00   15.00
246D A55 $5 Halcyon recurviros-
       tris   18.00   18.00
    Nos. 215-246D (36)   68.65   68.65

Issue dates: Nos. 215-230, Apr. 6; Nos. 231-238,
May 8; Nos. 239-246, Jan. 14, 1982; Nos. 246A-
246B, Feb. 15, 1982. Stamps of same denomination se-tenant. Nos. 231-246 horiz.
For surcharges and overprint see Nos. 293-311,
452-454, O40.

Prince Charles
and Lady
Diana — A56

Perf. 13x13½, 13½x13
1981, June 10   Photo.
247 A56   60c Charles, vert.   .75   .75
248 A56   80c Lady Diana, vert.   1.00   1.00
249 A56 $1.40 Shown   1.75   1.75
    Nos. 247-249 (3)   3.50   3.50

Royal Wedding. Issued in sheets of 4.
For overprints see Nos. 265-267. For surcharges
see Nos. 355, 405-407, B35-B37.

1982 World Cup
Soccer — A57

Designs: Various soccer players.

1981, Nov. 30   Photo.   Perf. 14
250 A57   12c Pair, #250a-250b   .40   .40
251 A57   15c Pair, #251a-251b   .48   .48
252 A57   20c Pair, #252a-252b   .65   .65
253 A57   25c Pair, #253a-253b   .80   .80
    Nos. 250-253 (4)   2.33   2.33

See No. B38.

Christmas
A58

Rembrandt Etchings: 15c, Holy Family, 1632,
vert. 30c, Virgin with Child, 1634, vert. 40c, Adoration of the Shepherds, 1654. 50c, Holy Family
with Cat, 1644.

1981, Dec. 10   Perf. 14
254 A58   15c gold & dk brown   .22   .22
255 A58   30c gold & dk brown   .45   .45
256 A58   40c gold & dk brown   .60   .60
257 A58   50c gold & dk brown   .75   .75
    Nos. 254-257 (4)   2.02   2.02

Souvenir Sheets

258	A58 80c + 5c like #254	1.10	1.10
259	A58 80c + 5c like #255	1.10	1.10
260	A58 80c + 5c like #256	1.10	1.10
261	A58 80c + 5c like #257	1.10	1.10

Nos. 258-261 have multicolored margins showing entire etching. Surtax on Nos. 258-261 was for local charities.

21st Birthday of Princess Diana — A59

1982, June 24 Photo. *Perf. 14*

262	A59 70c shown	.75	.75
263	A59 $1 Wedding portrait	1.00	1.00
264	A59 $2 Diana, diff.	2.25	2.25
a.	Souvenir sheet of 3, #262-264	4.50	4.50
	Nos. 262-264 (3)	4.00	4.00

For overprints see Nos. 268-270a.

Nos. 247-249 Overprinted: "21 June 1982 PRINCE WILLIAM OF WALES" or "COMMEMORATING THE ROYAL BIRTH"

1982, July 13 *Perf. 13x13½,13½x13*

265	A56 60c multicolored	1.00	1.00
266	A56 80c multicolored	1.50	1.50
267	A56 $1.40 multicolored	2.50	2.50
	Nos. 265-267 (3)	5.00	5.00

Nos. 262-264a Overprinted: "ROYAL BIRTH 21 JUNE 1982 PRINCE WILLIAM OF WALES"

1982, Aug. 5 *Perf. 14*

268	A59 70c multicolored	1.10	1.10
269	A59 $1 multicolored	1.50	1.50
270	A59 $2 multicolored	3.00	3.00
a.	Souvenir sheet of 3	5.25	5.25
	Nos. 268-270 (3)	5.60	5.60

Christmas — A60

Madonna and Child Sculptures, 12th-15th Cent.

1982, Dec. 10 Photo. *Perf. 13*

271	A60 18c multicolored	.25	.25
272	A60 36c multicolored	.55	.55
273	A60 48c multicolored	.75	.75
274	A60 60c multicolored	.90	.90
	Nos. 271-274 (4)	2.45	2.45

Souvenir Sheet

275	Sheet of 4	2.75	2.75
a.	A60 18c + 2c like 18c	.30	.30
b.	A60 36c + 2c like 36c	.55	.55
c.	A60 48c + 2c like 48c	.75	.75
d.	A60 60c + 2c like 60c	.90	.90

Surtax was for children's charities.

Commonwealth Day — A61

1983, Mar. 14 Photo. *Perf. 13x13½*

276	A61 48c Bananas	.75	.75
277	A61 48c Ti'i statuette	.75	.75
278	A61 48c Boys canoeing	.75	.75
279	A61 48c Capt. William Bligh, Bounty	.75	.75
a.	Block of 4, #276-270	3.00	3.00

Scouting Year — A62

1983, Apr. 18 Photo. *Perf. 14*

280	A62 36c Campfire	.55	.55
281	A62 48c Salute	.75	.75
282	A62 60c Hiking	.90	.90
	Nos. 280-282 (3)	2.20	2.20

Souvenir Sheet
Perf. 13½

283	Sheet of 3	3.00	3.00
a.	A62 36c + 3c like #280	.75	.75
b.	A62 48c + 3c like #281	.90	.90
c.	A62 60c + 3c like #282	1.20	1.20

Surtax was for benefit of Scouting.

Nos. 280 283 Overprinted: "15th WORLD SCOUT JAMBOREE"

1983, July 11 Photo. *Perf. 14*

284	A62 36c multicolored	.55	.55
285	A62 48c multicolored	.75	.75
286	A62 60c multicolored	.90	.90
	Nos. 284-286 (3)	2.20	2.20

Souvenir Sheet

287	Sheet of 3	3.00	3.00
a.	A62 36c + 3c like #284	.75	.75
b.	A62 48c + 3c like #285	.90	.90
c.	A62 60c + 3c like #286	1.20	1.20

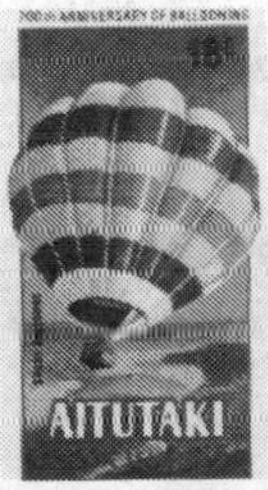

Manned Flight Bicentenary — A63

Modern sport balloons.

1983, July 22 Photo. *Perf. 14x13*

288	A63 18c multicolored	.25	.25
289	A63 36c multicolored	.55	.55
290	A63 48c multicolored	.75	.75
291	A63 60c multicolored	.90	.90
	Nos. 288-291 (4)	2.45	2.45

Souvenir Sheet

292	A63 $2.50 multicolored	3.50	3.50

Nos. 233-246, 246D, 248-249, 263-264 Surcharged

1983, Sept. 22

293	A55 18c on 20c, #233	.36	.36
294	A55 18c on 20c, #234	.36	.36
295	A55 36c on 25c, #235	.72	.72
296	A55 36c on 25c, #236	.72	.72
297	A55 36c on 30c, #237	.72	.72
298	A55 36c on 30c, #238	.72	.72
299	A55 36c on 35c, #239	.72	.72
300	A55 36c on 35c, #240	.72	.72
301	A55 48c on 40c, #241	.95	.95
302	A55 48c on 40c, #242	.95	.95
303	A55 48c on 50c, #243	.95	.95
304	A55 48c on 50c, #244	.95	.95
305	A55 72c on 70c, #245	1.45	1.45
306	A55 72c on 70c, #246	1.45	1.45
307	A56 96c on 80c, #248	1.90	1.90
308	A59 96c on $1, #263	1.90	1.90
309	A56 $1.20 on $1.40, #249	2.40	2.40
310	A59 $1.20 on $2, #264	2.40	2.40

Size: 35x47mm

311	A55 $5.60 on $5, #246D	11.00	11.00
	Nos. 293-311 (19)	31.34	31.34

Nos. 293-306 printed in se-tenant pairs. Nos. 307-308, 310-311 vert.

World Communications Year — A64

1983, Sept. 29 Photo. *Perf. 14*

312	A64 48c shown	.65	.65
313	A64 60c Communications satellite	.85	.85
314	A64 96c Global coverage	1.50	1.50
a.	Souvenir sheet of 3, #312-314	3.00	3.00
	Nos. 312-314 (3)	3.00	3.00

Christmas A65

Raphael Paintings.

1983, Nov. 21 Photo. *Perf. 13½x14*

315	A65 36c Madonna of the Chair	.48	.48
316	A65 48c Alba Madonna	.65	.65
317	A65 60c Connestabile Madonna	.80	.80
	Nos. 315-317 (3)	1.93	1.93

Souvenir Sheet

318	Sheet of 3	2.50	2.50
a.	A65 36c + 3c like #315	.60	.60
b.	A65 48c + 3c like #316	.75	.75
c.	A65 60c + 3c like #317	.90	.90

1983, Dec. 15 *Imperf.*

Size: 46x46mm

319	A65 85c + 5c like #315	1.25	1.25
320	A65 85c + 5c like #316	1.25	1.25
321	A65 85c + 5c like #317	1.25	1.25
	Nos. 319-321 (3)	3.75	3.75

Surtax was for children's charities.

Local Birds — A66

1984 Photo. *Perf. 14*

322	A66 2c as No. 216	.15	.15
323	A66 3c as No. 215	.15	.15
324	A66 5c as No. 217	.15	.15
325	A66 10c as No. 218	.15	.15
326	A66 12c as No. 220	.18	.18
327	A66 18c as No. 219	.25	.25
328	A66 24c as No. 221	.35	.35
329	A66 30c as No. 222	.42	.42
330	A66 36c as No. 223	.50	.50
331	A66 48c as No. 224	.70	.70
332	A66 50c as No. 225	.50	.50
333	A66 60c as No. 226	.65	.65
334	A66 72c as No. 227	.80	.80
335	A66 96c as No. 228	1.10	1.10
336	A66 $1.20 as No. 229	1.25	1.25
337	A66 $2.10 as No. 2230	2.25	2.25
338	A66 $3 as No. 246A	3.25	3.25
339	A66 $4.20 as No. 246B	3.75	3.75
340	A66 $5.60 as No. 246C	4.25	4.25
341	A66 $9.60 as No. 246D	7.25	7.25
	Nos. 322-341 (20)	28.05	28.05

For overprints and surcharges see Nos. O17-O39.

1984 Summer Olympics — A67

1984, July 24 Photo. *Perf. 13x13½*

342	A67 36c Javelin	.32	.32
343	A67 48c Shot put	.45	.45
344	A67 60c Hurdles	.55	.55
345	A67 $2 Handball	1.75	1.75
	Nos. 342-345 (4)	3.07	3.07

Souvenir Sheet

346	Sheet of 4	3.50	3.50
a.	A67 36c + 5c like #342	.38	.38
b.	A67 48c + 5c like #343	.50	.50
c.	A67 60c + 5c like #344	.60	.60
d.	A67 $2 + 5c like #345	1.75	1.75

Surtax was for benefit of local sports.

Nos. 342-345 Overprinted in Gold on Black with Winners' Names, Event, Nationality

1984, Aug. 21 Photo. *Perf. 13x13½*

347	A67 36c multicolored	.32	.32
348	A67 48c multicolored	.45	.45
349	A67 60c multicolored	.55	.55
350	A67 $2 multicolored	1.75	1.75
	Nos. 347-350 (4)	3.07	3.07

Ausipex '84 — A68

1984, Sept. 14 Photo. *Perf. 14*

351	A68 60c William Bligh, map	.55	.55
352	A68 96c Bounty, map	.85	.85
353	A68 $1.40 Stamps, map	1.25	1.25
	Nos. 351-353 (3)	2.65	2.65

Souvenir Sheet

354	Sheet of 3	3.25	3.25
a.	A68 60c + 5c like #351	.65	.65
b.	A68 96c + 5c like #352	1.00	1.00
c.	A68 $1.40 + 5c like #353	1.40	1.40

For overprint see No. 399.

No. 247 Surcharged with Black Bar and New Value in Gold and: "15.9.84 Birth/Prince Henry"

1984, Oct. 10 Photo. *Perf. 13x13½*

355	A56 $3 multicolored	3.00	3.00

Issued in sheets of 4.

A69

A70

1984, Nov. 16 Photo. *Perf. 13*

356	A69 36c Annunciation	.32	.32
357	A69 48c Nativity	.45	.45
358	A69 60c Epiphany	.55	.55
359	A69 96c Flight into Egypt	.90	.90
	Nos. 356-359 (4)	2.22	2.22

Souvenir Sheets
Size: 45x53mm
Imperf

360	A69 90c + 7c like #356	.90	.90
361	A69 90c + 7c like #357	.90	.90
362	A69 90c + 7c like #358	.90	.90
363	A69 90c + 7c like #359	.90	.90

Christmas.

1984, Dec. 10 Photo. *Perf. 13½x14*

364	A70 48c Diana, Henry	.45	.45
365	A70 60c William, Henry	.55	.55
366	A70 $2.10 Family	1.75	1.75
	Nos. 364-366 (3)	2.75	2.75

Souvenir Sheet

367	Sheet of 3	3.00	3.00
a.	A70 96c + 7c like #364	.90	.90
b.	A70 96c + 7c like #365	.90	.90
c.	A70 96c + 7c like #366	.90	.90

Christmas, Birth of Prince Henry, Sept. 15.

Surtax was for benefit of local children's charities.

Audubon Birth Bicentenary — A71

Illustrations of bird species by John J. Audubon.

1985, Mar. 22   Litho.   Perf. 13
368 A71	55c Gray kingbird	.52	.52
369 A71	65c Bohemian waxwing	.60	.60
370 A71	75c Summer tanager	.75	.75
371 A71	95c Cardinal	.95	.95
372 A71	$1.15 White-winged cross-bill	1.10	1.10
	Nos. 368-372 (5)	3.92	3.92

Queen Mother, 85th Birthday A72

Photographs: 55c, Lady Elizabeth Bowes-Lyon, age 7. 65c, Engaged to the Duke of York, 75c, Duchess of York with daughter, Elizabeth. $1.30, Holding the infant Prince Charles. $3, Portrait taken on 63rd birthday.

1985-86   Perf. 13½x13
373 A72	55c multicolored	.50	.50
374 A72	65c multicolored	.60	.60
375 A72	75c multicolored	.70	.70
376 A72	$1.30 multicolored	1.20	1.20
a.	Souvenir sheet of 4, #373-376	3.25	3.25
	Nos. 373-376 (4)	3.00	3.00

Souvenir Sheet
| 377 A72 | $3 multicolored | 2.25 | 2.25 |

Nos. 373-376 printed in sheets of 4.
Issued: #376a, 8/4/86; others, 6/14/85.

Intl. Youth Year A73

Designs: 75c, The Calmady Children, by Thomas Lawrence (1769-1830). 90c, Madame Charpentier's Children, by Renoir (1841-1919). $1.40, Young Girls at Piano, by Renoir.

1985, Sept. 16   Photo.   Perf. 13
378 A73	75c multicolored	.65	.65
379 A73	90c multicolored	.75	.75
380 A73	$1.40 multicolored	1.25	1.25
	Nos. 378-380 (3)	2.65	2.65

Souvenir Sheet
381	Sheet of 3	3.75	3.75
a.	A73 75c + 10c like #378	.95	.95
b.	A73 90c + 10c like #379	1.10	1.10
c.	A73 $1.40 + 10c like #380	1.70	1.70

Surcharged for children's activities.

Adoration of the Magi, by Giotto di Bondone (1276-1337) — A74

1985, Nov. 15   Photo.   Perf. 13½x13
382 A74	95c multicolored	1.10	1.10
383 A74	95c multicolored	1.10	1.10
384 A74	$1.15 multicolored	1.40	1.40
385 A74	$1.15 multicolored	1.40	1.40
	Nos. 382-385 (4)	5.00	5.00

Souvenir Sheet
Imperf
| 386 A74 | $6.40 multicolored | 7.50 | 7.50 |

Christmas, return of Halley's Comet, 1985-86.
Stamps of the same denomination se-tenant.

Halley's Comet A75

Designs: 90c, Halley's Comet, A.D. 684, wood engraving, Nuremberg Chronicles. $1.25, Sighting of 1066, Bayeux Tapestry, detail, c. 1092, France.

$1.75, The Comet Inflicting Untold Disasters, 1456, Lucerne Chronicles, by Diebolt Schilling. $4.20, Melancolia I, engraving by Durer.

1986, Feb. 25   Photo.   Perf. 13½x13
387 A75	90c multicolored	1.00	1.00
388 A75	$1.25 multicolored	1.40	1.40
389 A75	$1.75 multicolored	2.00	2.00
	Nos. 387-389 (3)	4.40	4.40

Souvenir Sheets
390	Sheet of 3 + label	3.30	3.30
a.	A75 95c, like #387	1.10	1.10
b.	A75 95c, like #388	1.10	1.10
c.	A75 95c, like #389	1.10	1.10

Imperf
| 391 A75 | $4.20 multicolored | 4.75 | 4.75 |

Elizabeth II, 60th Birthday — A76

1986, Apr. 21   Perf. 14
| 392 A76 | 95c Coronation portrait | 1.15 | 1.15 |

Souvenir Sheet
Perf. 13½
| 393 A76 | $4.20 Portrait, diff. | 5.00 | 5.00 |

No. 392 printed in sheets of 5 with label picturing U.K. flag and Queen's flag for New Zealand.

Statue of Liberty, Cent. A77

1986, June 27   Photo.   Perf. 14
| 394 A77 | $1 Liberty head | 1.15 | 1.15 |
| 395 A77 | $2.75 Statue | 3.10 | 3.10 |

Souvenir Sheet
Perf. 13½
396	Sheet of 2	2.80	2.80
a.	A77 $1.25 like $1	1.40	1.40
b.	A77 $1.25 like $2.75	1.40	1.40

For surcharges see Nos B44, B49.

Wedding of Prince Andrew and Sarah Ferguson — A78

1986, July 23   Perf. 14
| 397 A78 | $2 multicolored | 2.30 | 2.30 |

Souvenir Sheet
Perf. 13½
| 398 A78 | $5 multicolored | 5.75 | 5.75 |

No. 397 printed in sheets of 5 plus label picturing Westminster Abbey.
For surcharge see No. B48.

No. 354 Ovptd. with Gold Circle over AUSIPEX Emblem, Black and Gold STAMPEX '86 Emblem

1986, Aug. 4   Photo.   Perf. 14
399	Sheet of 3	3.35	3.35
a.	A68 60c + 5c like #351	.70	.70
b.	A68 96c + 5c like #352	1.10	1.10
c.	A68 $1.40 + 5c like #353	1.55	1.55

STAMPEX '86, Adelaide, Aug. 4-10.

Christmas — A79

Paintings by Albrecht Durer: 75c, No. 404a, St. Anne with Virgin and Child. $1.35, No. 404b, Virgin and Child. $1.95, No. 404c, Adoration of the Magi. $2.75, No. 404d, Rosary Festivity.

1986, Nov. 21   Litho.   Perf. 13½
400 A79	75c multicolored	.80	.80
401 A79	$1.35 multicolored	1.45	1.45
402 A79	$1.95 multicolored	2.10	2.10
403 A79	$2.75 multicolored	2.95	2.95
	Nos. 400-403 (4)	7.30	7.30

Souvenir Sheet
| 404 | Sheet of 4 | 7.00 | 7.00 |
| a.-d. | A79 $1.65 any single | 1.75 | 1.75 |

For surcharges see Nos. B39-B44, B46-B47, B50-B54.

Nos. 247-249 Surcharged in Gold and Black

1987, Nov. 20   Photo.   Perf. 13x12½
405 A56	$2.50 on 60c No. 247	3.00	3.00
406 A56	$2.50 on 80c No. 248	3.00	3.00
407 A56	$2.50 on $1.40 No. 249	3.00	3.00
	Nos. 405-407 (3)	9.00	9.00

Issued in sheets of 4 with margin inscriptions overprinted with gold bar and "40th Anniversary of the Royal Wedding / 1947-1987" in black; "OVERPRINTED BY NEW ZEALAND GOVERNMENT PRINTER, / WELLINGTON, NOVEMBER 1987" at left.

A80

The Virgin with Garland, by Rubens — A81

Painting details.

1987, Dec. 10   Photo.   Perf. 13x13½
408 A80	70c UL	.90	.90
409 A80	85c UR	1.10	1.10
410 A80	$1.50 LL	1.95	1.95
411 A80	$1.85 LR	2.35	2.35
	Nos. 408-411 (4)	6.30	6.30

Souvenir Sheets
412	Sheet of 4	5.00	5.00
a.	A80 95c like No. 408	1.25	1.25
b.	A80 95c like No. 409	1.25	1.25
c.	A80 95c like No. 410	1.25	1.25
d.	A80 95c like No. 411	1.25	1.25

Perf. 13
| 413 A81 | $6 multicolored | 7.75 | 7.75 |

Christmas.

1988 Summer Olympics, Seoul — A82

Flags of Korea, Aitutaki, ancient and modern events, and Seoul Games emblem or $50 silver coin issued to commemorate the participation of Aitutaki athletes in the Olympics for the 1st time: 70c, No. 418a, Obverse of silver coin, chariot race, running. 85c, Emblem, running, soccer. 95c, Emblem, boxing, handball. $1.40, No. 418b, Reverse of coin, spearmen, women's tennis.

1988, Aug. 22   Photo.   Perf. 14½x15
414 A82	70c multicolored	.95	.95
415 A82	85c multicolored	1.15	1.15
416 A82	95c multicolored	1.30	1.30
417 A82	$1.40 multicolored	1.90	1.90
	Nos. 414-417 (4)	5.30	5.30

Souvenir Sheet
| 418 | Sheet of 2 | 5.50 | 5.50 |
| a.-b. | A82 $2 any single | 2.75 | 2.75 |

Nos. 414-417 Ovptd. with Names of 1988 Olympic Gold Medalists

a. "FLORENCE GRIFFTH JOYNER / UNITED STATES / 100 M AND 200 M"
b. "GELINDO BORDIN / ITALY / MARATHON"
c. "HITOSHI SAITO / JAPAN / JUDO"
d. "STEFFI GRAF / WEST GERMANY / WOMEN'S TENNIS"

1988, Oct. 10   Litho.   Perf. 14½x15
419 A82 (a)	70c on No. 414	.95	.95
420 A82 (b)	85c on No. 415	1.15	1.15
421 A82 (c)	95c on No. 416	1.30	1.30
422 A82 (d)	$1.40 on No. 417	1.90	1.90
	Nos. 419-422 (4)	5.30	5.30

Griffith is spelled incorrectly on No. 419.

Christmas A83

Paintings by Rembrandt: 55c, Adoration of the Shepherds (detail), National Gallery, London. 70c, Holy Family, Alte Pinakothek, Munich. 85c, Presentation in the Temple, Kunsthalle, Hamburg. 95c, The Holy Family, Louvre, Paris. $1.15, Presentation in the Temple, diff., Mauritshuis, The Hague. $4.50, Adoration of the Shepherds (entire painting).

1988, Nov. 2   Photo.   Perf. 13½
423 A83	55c multicolored	.70	.70
424 A83	70c multicolored	.90	.90
425 A83	85c multicolored	1.10	1.10
426 A83	95c multicolored	1.20	1.20
427 A83	$1.15 multicolored	1.50	1.50
	Nos. 423-427 (5)	5.40	5.40

Souvenir Sheet
Perf. 14
| 428 A83 | $4.50 multicolored | 5.75 | 5.75 |

No. 428 contains one 52x34mm stamp.

A84

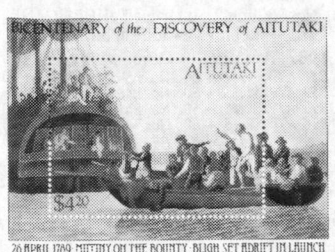

Mutiny on the *Bounty*, 200th Anniv. — A85

1989, July 3   Photo.   Perf. 13½
429 A84   55c Ship, Capt. Bligh   .65   .65
430 A84   65c Breadfruit   .78   .78
431 A84   75c Bligh, chart   .90   .90
432 A84   95c *Bounty* off Aitutaki 1.15 1.15
433 A84 $1.65 Christian, Bligh   2.00 2.00
          Nos. 429-433 (5)   5.48 5.48

Souvenir Sheet

434 A85 $4.20 Castaways   5.00 5.00

Discovery of Aitutaki by William Bligh, bicent.

1st Moon Landing, 20th Anniv. A86

Apollo 11 mission emblem, American flag, eagle, "The Eagle has landed" and: 75c, Astronaut standing on the lunar surface. $1.15, Conducting an experiment in front of the lunar module. $1.80, Carrying equipment. $6.40, Raising the flag.

1989, July 28   Photo.   Perf. 13½x13
435 A86   75c multicolored   .88   .88
436 A86 $1.15 multicolored   1.35 1.35
437 A86 $1.80 multicolored   2.10 2.10
          Nos. 435-437 (3)   4.33 4.33

Souvenir Sheet
Perf. 13½

438 A86 $6.40 multicolored   7.50 7.50

No. 438 contains one 42x31mm stamp.

Christmas — A87

Details from *Virgin in Glory*, by Titian: 70c, Virgin. 85c, Christ child. 95c, Angel. $1.25, Cherubs. $6, Entire painting.

1989, Nov. 20   Photo.   Perf. 13½x13
439 A87   70c multicolored   .82   .82
440 A87   85c multicolored   1.00 1.00
441 A87   95c multicolored   1.10 1.10
442 A87 $1.25 multicolored   1.45 1.45
          Nos. 439-442 (4)   4.37 4.37

Souvenir Sheet
Perf. 13½

443 A87 $6 multicolored   7.00 7.00

No. 443 contains one 45x60mm stamp.

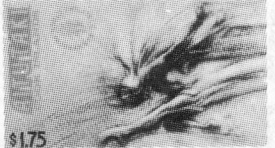
World Environmental Protection — A88

Designs: a, Human comet, World Philatelic Programs emblem. b, Comet tail and "Protect The Endangered Earth!" $3, Human comet, emblem and inscription. (Illustration reduced.)

1990, Feb. 16   Photo.   Perf. 13½x13
444 A88   Pair   4.00 4.00
  a.-b. $1.75 any single   2.00 2.00

Souvenir Sheet

445 A88 $3 multicolored   3.50 3.50

No. 376a Ovptd. "Nineteenth / Birthday" in Black on Gold

Designs: 55c, Lady Elizabeth Bowes-Lyon, 1907. 65c, Lady Elizabeth engaged to Duke of York. 75c, As Duchess of York with daughter Elizabeth. $1.30, As Queen Mother with grandson.

1990, July 16   Litho.   Perf. 13½x13
446   Sheet of 4   3.80 3.80
  a.   A72 55c multicolored   .65   .65
  b.   A72 65c multicolored   .75   .75
  c.   A72 75c multicolored   .90   .90
  d.   A72 $1.30 multicolored   1.50 1.50

Christmas — A89

Paintings: 70c, Madonna of the Basket by Correggio. 85c, Virgin and Child by Morando. 95c, Adoration of the Child by Tiepolo. $1.75, Mystic Marriage of St. Catherine by Memling. $6, Donne Triptych by Memling.

1990, Nov. 28   Litho.   Perf. 14
447 A89   70c multicolored   .85   .85
448 A89   85c multicolored   1.00 1.00
449 A89   95c multicolored   1.15 1.15
450 A89 $1.75 multicolored   2.15 2.15
          Nos. 447-450 (4)   5.15 5.15

Souvenir Sheet

451 A89 $6 multicolored   7.35 7.35

Nos. 246A-246B Overprinted

1990, Dec. 5   Photo.   Perf. 13½
452 A55 $1 multicolored   1.25 1.25
453 A55 $2 multicolored   2.50 2.50

Birdpex '90, 20 Intl. Ornithological Congress, New Zealand.

No. 246D Overprinted
"COMMEMORATING 65TH BIRTHDAY OF H.M. QUEEN ELIZABETH II"

1991, Apr. 22   Photo.   Perf. 13
454 A55 $5 multicolored   5.75 5.75

Christmas — A90

Paintings: 80c, The Holy Family, by Mengs. 90c, Virgin and Child, by Fra Filippo Lippi. $1.05, Virgin and Child, by Durer. $1.75, Adoration of the Shepherds, by De La Tour. $6, The Holy Family, by Michelangelo.

1991, Nov. 13   Litho.   Perf. 14
455 A90   80c multicolored   .90   .90
456 A90   90c multicolored   1.05 1.05
457 A90 $1.05 multicolored   1.20 1.20
458 A90 $1.75 multicolored   2.00 2.00
          Nos. 455-458 (4)   5.15 5.15

Souvenir Sheet

459 A90 $6 multicolored   7.00 7.00

1992 Summer Olympics, Barcelona — A91

1992, July 29   Litho.   Perf. 14
460 A91   95c Hurdles   1.05 1.05
461 A91 $1.25 Weight lifting 1.40 1.40
462 A91 $1.50 Judo   1.75 1.75
463 A91 $1.95 Soccer   2.20 2.20
          Nos. 460-463 (4)   6.40 6.40

6th Festival of Pacific Arts, Rarotonga — A92

Canoes: 30c, Vaka Motu. 50c, Hamatafua. 95c, Alia Kalia Ndrua. $1.75, Hokule'a Hawaiian. $1.95, Tuamotu Pahi.

1992, Oct. 16   Litho.   Perf. 14x15
464 A92   30c multicolored   .35   .35
465 A92   50c multicolored   .55   .55
466 A92   95c multicolored   1.05 1.05
467 A92 $1.75 multicolored   1.95 1.95
468 A92 $1.95 multicolored   2.15 2.15
          Nos. 464-468 (5)   6.05 6.05

Overprinted "ROYAL VISIT"

1992, Oct. 16
469 A92   30c on #464   .35   .35
470 A92   50c on #465   .55   .55
471 A92   95c on #466   1.05 1.05
472 A92 $1.75 on #467   1.95 1.95
473 A92 $1.95 on #468   2.15 2.15
          Nos. 469-473 (5)   6.05 6.05

Christmas A93

Designs: Different details from Virgin's Nativity, by Guido Reni.

1992, Nov. 19   Litho.   Perf. 13½
474 A93   80c multicolored   .90   .90
475 A93   90c multicolored   1.05 1.05
476 A93 $1.05 multicolored   1.15 1.15
477 A93 $1.75 multicolored   1.95 1.95
          Nos. 474-477 (4)   5.05 5.05

Souvenir Sheet

478 A93 $6 like #476   6.60 6.60

No. 478 contains one 39x50mm stamp.

Discovery of America, 500th Anniv. — A94

Designs: $1.25, Columbus being blessed as he departs from Spain. $1.75, Map of Columbus' four voyages. $1.95, Columbus landing in New World.

1992, Dec. 11   Perf. 14x15
479 A94 $1.25 multicolored   1.40 1.40
480 A94 $1.75 multicolored   1.95 1.95
481 A94 $1.95 multicolored   2.15 2.15
          Nos. 479-481 (3)   5.50 5.50

Coronation of Queen Elizabeth II, 40th Anniv. — A95

Designs: a, Queen Victoria, King Edward VII. b, King George V, King George VI. c, Queen Elizabeth II.

1993, June 4   Litho.   Perf. 14
482 A95 $1.75 Strip of 3, #a.-c.   6.00 6.00

Christmas — A96

Religious sculpture: 80c, Madonna and Child, by Nino Pisano. 90c, Virgin on Rosebush, by Luca Della Robbia. $1.15, Virgin with Child and St. John, by Juan Francisco Rustici. $1.95, Virgin with Child, by Michelangelo. $3, Madonna and Child, by Jacopo Della Quercia.

1993, Oct. 29   Litho.   Perf. 14
483 A96   80c multicolored   .90   .90
484 A96   90c multicolored   1.00 1.00
485 A96 $1.15 multicolored   1.25 1.25
486 A96 $1.95 multicolored   2.25 2.25

Size: 32x47mm
Perf. 13½

487 A96 $3 multicolored   3.50 3.50
          Nos. 483-487 (5)   8.90 8.90

1994 Winter Olympics, Lillehammer — A97

Designs: a, Ice hockey. b, Ski jumping. c, Cross-country skiing.

1994, Feb. 11   Litho.   Perf. 14
488 A97 $1.15 Strip of 3, #a.-c.   4.00 4.00

Flowers — A98   Hibiscus A98a

1994   Litho.   Perf. 13½
489 A98   5c   Prostrate morning
                glory   .15   .15
490 A98   10c White frangipani   .15   .15
491 A98   15c Red hibiscus   .16   .16
492 A98   20c Yellow allamanda   .22   .22
493 A98   25c Royal poinciana   .28   .28
494 A98   30c White gardenia   .35   .35

495 A98 50c Pink frangipani .55 .55
496 A98 80c Morning glory .90 .90
497 A98 85c Yellow mallow .95 .95
498 A98 90c Red coral tree 1.00 1.00
499 A98 $1 Cup of gold 1.10 1.10
500 A98 $2 Red cordia 2.25 2.25
501 A98a $3 multicolored 3.75 3.75
502 A98a $5 multicolored 6.25 6.25
Nos. 489-502 (14) 18.06 18.06

Issued: 5-90c, 2/17; $1, $2, 4/29; $3, $5, 11/18. This is an expanding set. Numbers may change.

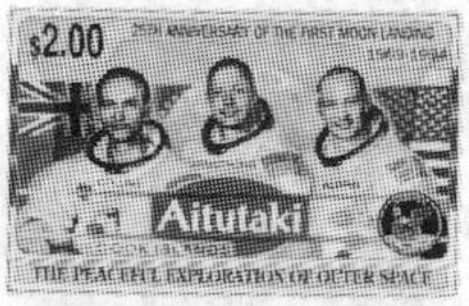

First Manned Moon Landing, 25th Anniv. A99

Designs: No. 506, Astronauts Collins, Armstrong, Aldrin. No. 507, Splash down in South Pacific.

1994, July 20 Litho. *Perf. 14*
506 A99 $2 multicolored 2.25 2.25
507 A99 $2 multicolored 2.25 2.25

Christmas — A100

Paintings: No. 508a, The Madonna of the Basket, by Corregio. b, Virgin & Child with Saints, by Hans Memling. c, The Virgin & Child with Flowers, by Dolci. d, Virgin & Child with Angels, by Bergognone.

No. 509a, The Adoration of the Kings, by Dosso. b, The Virgin & Child, by Bellini. c, The Virgin & Child, by Schiavone. d, Adoration of the Kings, by Dolci.

1994, Nov. 30 Litho. *Perf. 14*
508 A100 85c Block of 4, #a.-d. 3.75 3.75
509 A100 90c Block of 4, #a.-d. 4.00 4.00

End of World War II, 50th Anniv. — A101

Designs: a, Battle of Britain, 1940. b, Battle of Midway, June 1942.

1995, Sept. 4 Litho. *Perf. 13½x13*
510 A101 $4 Pair, #a.-b. 10.50 10.50

No. 510 issued in sheets of 4 stamps.

Queen Mother, 95th Birthday A102

1995, Sept. 14 Litho. *Perf. 13x13½*
511 A102 $4 multicolored 5.25 5.25

UN, 50th Anniv. — A103

1995, Oct. 18 Litho. *Perf. 13½*
512 A103 $4.25 multicolored 5.50 5.50

Year of the Sea Turtle A104

1995, Dec. 1 Litho. *Perf. 14x13½*
513 A104 95c Green turtle 1.25 1.25
514 A104 $1.15 Leatherback turtle 1.50 1.50
515 A104 $1.50 Olive Ridley turtle 2.00 2.00
516 A104 $1.75 Loggerhead turtle 2.25 2.25
Nos. 513-516 (4) 7.00 7.00

SEMI-POSTAL STAMPS

Christmas Type of 1974

Designs: 1c+1c, like #104. 5c+1c, like #105. 8c+1c, like #106. 10c+1c, like #107. 25c+1c, like #108. 30c+1c, like #109.

1974, Dec. 2 Photo. *Perf. 13½*
B1 A29 1c + 1c multicolored .15 .15
B2 A29 5c + 1c multicolored .15 .15
B3 A29 8c + 1c multicolored .20 .20
B4 A29 10c + 1c multicolored .30 .30
B5 A29 25c + 1c multicolored .70 .70
B6 A29 30c + 1c multicolored .75 .75
Nos. B1-B6 (6) 2.25 2.25

Surtax was for child welfare.

Nos. 117-120 Surcharged in Silver

1975, Dec. 19 Photo. *Perf. 14x13½*
B7 A32 Strip of 3 .45 .45
a.-c. 6c+1c any single .15 .15
B8 A32 Strip of 3 .52 .52
a.-c. 7c+1c any single .16 .16
B9 A32 Strip of 3 1.25 1.25
a.-c. 15c+1c any single .40 .40
B10 A32 Strip of 3 1.90 1.90
a.-c. 20c+1c any single .50 .50
Nos. B7-B10 (4) 4.12 4.12

Christmas. The surtax was for children's activities during holiday season.

Nos. 135-142a Surcharged in Silver

1976, Nov. 19 Photo. *Perf. 13½x13*
B11 A36 6c + 1c multicolored .15 .15
B12 A37 6c + 1c multicolored .15 .15
B13 A36 7c + 1c multicolored .15 .15
B14 A37 7c + 1c multicolored .15 .15
B15 A36 15c + 1c multicolored .35 .35
B16 A37 15c + 1c multicolored .35 .35
B17 A36 20c + 1c multicolored .50 .50
B18 A37 20c + 1c multicolored .50 .50
a. Souvenir sheet of 8 3.50 3.50
Nos. B11-B18 (8) 2.30 2.30

Surtax was for child welfare. Stamps of No. B18a each surcharged 2c.

Nos. 152-159a Surcharged in Black

1977, Nov. 15 *Perf. 13½x14*
B19 A41 6c + 1c multicolored .15 .15
B20 A42 6c + 1c multicolored .15 .15
B21 A41 7c + 1c multicolored .15 .15
B22 A42 7c + 1c multicolored .15 .15
B23 A41 15c + 1c multicolored .35 .35
B24 A42 15c + 1c multicolored .35 .35
B25 A41 20c + 1c multicolored .50 .50
B26 A42 20c + 1c multicolored .50 .50
a. Souvenir sheet of 8 3.25 3.25
Nos. B19-B26 (8) 2.30 2.30

Surtax was for child welfare. Stamps of No. B26a each surcharged 2c.

Easter Type of 1978
Souvenir Sheets

Paintings: No. B27, like No. 163. No. B28, like No. 164. No. B29, like No. 165.

1978, Mar. 17 Photo. *Perf. 14*
B27 A44 50c + 5c multicolored .90 .90
B28 A44 50c + 5c multicolored .90 .90
B29 A44 50c + 5c multicolored .90 .90

Nos. B27-B29 contain one stamp 33x25mm.

Christmas Type of 1978
Souvenir Sheet

1978, Dec. 4 Photo. *Perf. 14½x13*
B30 Sheet of 4 2.00 2.00
a. A46 15c + 2c like #167 .28 .28
b. A46 17c + 2c like #168 .30 .30
c. A46 30c + 2c like #169 .52 .52
d. A46 35c + 2c like #170 .60 .60

Year of the Child Type
Souvenir Sheet

1979, Oct. 1 Photo. *Perf. 14x13½*
B31 Sheet of 3 2.50 2.50
a. A48 30c + 3c like #173 .55 .55
b. A48 35c + 3c like #174 .60 .60
c. A48 65c + 3c like #175 1.10 1.10

Easter Type of 1980
Souvenir Sheet

Designs: No. B32 shows entire painting in continuous design. Nos. B32a-B32c similar to Nos. B183-185. Size of Nos. B32a-B32c: 25x50mm.

1980, Apr. 3 Photo. *Perf. 13x13½*
B32 Sheet of 3 1.50 1.50
a. A50 20c + 2c multicolored .35 .35
b. A50 30c + 2c multicolored .50 .50
c. A50 35c + 2c multicolored .60 .60

Christmas Type of 1980
Souvenir Sheet

1980, Nov. 21 Photo. *Perf. 13x13½*
B33 Sheet of 4 1.75 1.75
a. A53 15c + 2c like #208 .28 .28
b. A53 20c + 2c like #209 .35 .35
c. A53 25c + 2c like #210 .45 .45
d. A53 35c + 2c like #211 .60 .60

Easter Type of 1981
Souvenir Sheet

1981, Mar. 31 Photo. *Perf. 13½*
B34 Sheet of 3 2.00 2.00
a. A54 30c + 2c like #212 .45 .45
b. A54 40c + 2c like #213 .60 .60
c. A54 50c + 2c like #214 .80 .80

Nos. 247-249 Surcharged

1981, Nov. 23 Photo. *Perf. 13x13½*
B35 A56 60 + 5c multi 1.00 1.00
B36 A56 80 + 5c multi 1.25 1.25
B37 A56 $1.40 + 5c multi 2.25 2.25
Nos. B35-B37 (3) 4.50 4.50

Intl. Year of the Disabled. Surtax was for the handicapped.

Soccer Type of 1981
Souvenir Sheet

1981, Nov. 30 *Perf. 14*
B38 A57 Sheet of 8, multi 2.50 2.50

No. B38 contains stamps with 2c surtax similar to Nos. 250-253. Surtax was for local sports.

Nos. 400-404 Surcharged "NOVEMBER/21-24 1986/FIRST VISIT TO SOUTH/PACIFIC" and 10c in Silver

1986, Nov. 25 Litho. *Perf. 13½*
B39 A79 75c + 10c multi .60 .60
B40 A79 $1.35 + 10c multi .95 .95
B41 A79 $1.95 + 10c multi 1.50 1.50
B42 A79 $2.75 + 10c multi 2.00 2.00
Nos. B39-B42 (4) 5.05 5.05

Souvenir Sheet

B43 Sheet of 4 5.00 5.00
a.-d. A79 $1.65 +10c on #404a-404d 1.25 1.25

State visit of Pope John Paul II.
For surcharges see Nos. B51-B54.

Nos. 394-395, 397 and 400-403 Surcharged "HURRICANE RELIEF/ + 50c" in Silver or Black

1987, Apr. 29 Litho. *Perf. 13½, 14*
B44 A79 75c + 50c #400 1.40 1.40
B45 A77 $1 + 50c #394 (B) 1.65 1.65
B46 A79 $1.35 + 50c #401 2.25 2.25
B47 A79 $1.95 + 50c #402 2.75 2.75
B48 A78 $2 + 50c #397 2.75 2.75
B49 A77 $2.75 + 50c #395 (B) 3.75 3.75
B50 A79 $2.75 + 50c #403 3.75 3.75
Nos. B44-B50 (7) 18.30 18.30

Nos. B39-B42 Surcharged "HURRICANE RELIEF / +50c" in Silver

1987, Apr. 29 Litho. *Perf. 13½*
B51 A79 75c + 50c No. B39 1.50 1.50
B52 A79 $1.35 + 50c No. B40 2.25 2.25
B53 A79 $1.95 + 50c No. B41 3.00 3.00
B54 A79 $2.75 + 50c No. B42 3.75 3.75
Nos. B51-B54 (4) 10.50 10.50

AIR POST STAMPS

Capt. Bligh Type of 1974

1974, Sept. 9 Litho. *Perf. 13*
Size: 46x26mm
C1 A27 10c Bligh and "Bounty" .40 .40
C2 A27 10c "Bounty" at sea .40 .40
C3 A27 25c Bligh and "Bounty" .85 .85
C4 A27 25c Chart, 1856 .85 .85
C5 A27 30c Cook and "Resolution" 1.10 1.10
C6 A27 30c Maps 1.10 1.10
Nos. C1-C6 (6) 4.70 4.70

Stamps of same denomination printed se-tenant in sheets of 20. See note after No. 101.

OFFICIAL STAMPS

Nos. 83-90, 92-95, 150-151 Overprinted or Surcharged in Black, Silver or Gold

O.H.M.S.

1978-79 Photo. *Perf. 13x13½*
O1 A25 1c multi .15 .15
O2 A25 2c multi .15 .15
O3 A25 3c multi .15 .15
O4 A25 4c multi (G) .15 .15
O5 A25 5c multi .15 .15
O6 A25 8c multi .15 .15
O7 A25 10c multi .15 .15
O8 A25 15c on 60c multi .22 .20
O9 A25 18c on 60c multi .28 .25
O10 A25 20c multi (G) .30 .28
O11 A40 50c multi .75 .70
O12 A25 60c multi .90 .80
O13 A25 $1 multi 1.40 1.25
O14 A26 $2 multi 3.00 2.75
O15 A40 $4 on $1 multi (S) 6.00 5.50
O16 A26 $5 multi 7.25 6.50
Nos. O1-O16 (16) 21.15 19.28

Overprint on 4c, 20c, $1 diagonal.
Issued: #O14-O16, 2/20/79; others, 11/3/78.

Stamps of 1983-84 Ovptd. or Surcharged in Green

O.H.M.S.

or Gold (#O29-O32)

75c

O.H.M.S.

1985, Aug. 9 *Perf. 14, 13x13½*
O17 A66 2c No. 322 .15 .15
O18 A66 5c No. 324 .15 .15
O19 A66 10c No. 325 .15 .15
O20 A66 12c No. 326 .15 .15
O21 A66 18c No. 327 .20 .20
O22 A66 20c on 24c No. 328 .22 .22
O23 A66 30c No. 329 .35 .35
O24 A66 40c on 36c No. 330 .45 .45
O25 A66 50c No. 332 .55 .55
O26 A66 55c on 48c No. 331 .62 .62
O27 A66 60c No. 333 .68 .68
O28 A66 65c on 72c No. 334 .72 .72
O29 A61 75c on 48c No. 276 .85 .85
O30 A61 75c on 48c No. 277 .85 .85
O31 A61 75c on 48c No. 278 .85 .85
O32 A61 75c on 48c No. 279 .85 .85
a. Block of 4, Nos. O29-O32 3.50 3.50
O33 A66 80c on 96c No. 335 .90 .90
Nos. O17-O33 (17) 8.69 8.69

Nos. 336-341, 246C-246D Overprinted or Surcharged Like Nos. O17-O28, O33 in Metallic Green or Blue

1986, Oct. 1 *Perf. 14*
O34 A66 $3 multi 3.10 3.10
O35 A66 $4.20 multi 4.35 4.35
O36 A66 $5.60 multi 5.80 5.80
O37 A66 $9.60 multi 10.00 10.00

1988-91 *Perf. 14*

O38	A66	$1.20 multi	1.50	1.50
O39	A66	$2.10 multi	2.50	2.50

Perf. 13½

O40	A55	$14 on $4 (B)	17.50	17.50
O41	A55	$18 on $5 (B)	22.50	22.50
		Nos. O34-O41 (8)	67.25	67.25

Issue dates: July 2, 1991. Others, June 15.

ASCENSION

ə-'sen(t)-shən

LOCATION — An island in the South Atlantic Ocean, 900 miles from Liberia
GOVT. — A part of the British Crown Colony of St. Helena
AREA — 34 sq. mi.
POP. — 1,625 (1982)

In 1922 Ascension was placed under the administration of the Colonial Office and annexed to the British Crown Colony of St. Helena. The only post office is at Georgetown.

12 Pence = 1 Shilling
20 Shillings = 1 Pound
100 Pence = 1 Pound (1971)

Catalogue values for unused stamps in this country are for Never Hinged items, beginning with Scott 50.

Stamps and Types of St. Helena, 1912-22 Overprinted in Black or Red

ASCENSION

1922 **Wmk. 4** *Perf. 14*

1	A9	½p green & blk	2.25	*5.50*
2	A10	1p green	2.75	*5.50*
3	A10	1½p rose red	5.25	*11.00*
4	A9	2p gray & blk	5.00	*8.50*
5	A9	3p ultra	5.00	*9.00*
6	A10	8p dl vio & blk	12.00	*18.00*
7	A10	2sh ultra & blk, *blue*	70.00	*80.00*
8	A10	3sh vio & blk	125.00	*140.00*

Wmk. 3

9	A9	1sh blk, *gray green* (R)	19.00	*22.50*
		Nos. 1-9 (9)	246.25	300.00

Seal of Colony A3

1924-27 **Typo.** **Wmk. 4** *Perf. 14*

Chalky Paper

10	A3	½p black & gray	.95	1.00
11	A3	1p green & blk	1.10	1.10
12	A3	1½p rose red	2.25	2.25
13	A3	2p bluish gray & gray	2.50	2.50
14	A3	3p ultra	2.50	3.00
15	A3	4p blk & gray, *yel*	15.00	*22.50*
16	A3	5p ol & lil ('27)	9.50	*12.00*
17	A3	6p rose lil & gray	32.50	*45.00*
18	A3	8p violet & gray	11.00	*13.00*
19	A3	1sh brown & gray	13.00	*17.00*
20	A3	2sh ultra & gray, *blue*	47.50	*57.50*
21	A3	3sh blk & gray, *blue*	82.50	*85.00*
		Nos. 10-21 (12)	220.30	*261.85*

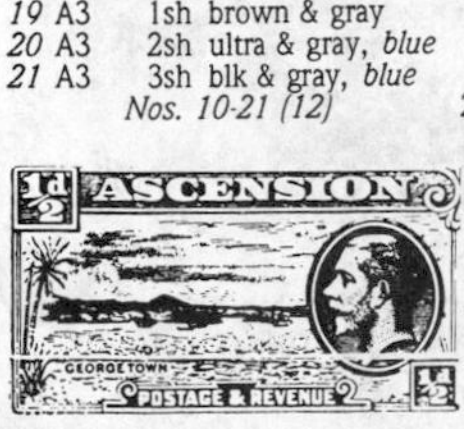

View of Georgetown A4

Ascension stamps can be mounted in the Scott British Africa album.

Map of Ascension — A5

Sooty Tern Breeding Colony A9

Designs: 1½p, Pier at Georgetown. 3p, Long Beach. 5p, Three Sisters. 5sh, Green Mountain.

1934, July 2 **Engr.**

23	A4	½p violet & blk	.20	.55
24	A5	1p lt grn & blk	.65	.65
25	A4	1½p red & black	.80	.80
26	A5	2p org & black	1.65	1.65
27	A4	3p ultra & blk	.95	.95
28	A4	5p blue & black	1.00	1.40
29	A5	8p dk brn & blk	3.25	*8.00*
30	A9	1sh carmine & blk	5.75	*11.00*
31	A5	2sh6p violet & blk	32.50	*50.00*
32	A4	5sh brown & blk	62.50	*65.00*
		Nos. 23-32 (10)	109.25	*140.00*

Silver Jubilee Issue
Common Design Type

1935, May 6 *Perf. 11x12*

33	CD301	1½p car & dk blue	1.75	*5.00*
34	CD301	2p blk & ultra	3.50	*7.00*
35	CD301	5p ind & grn	10.00	*20.00*
36	CD301	1sh brn vio & indigo	20.00	*37.50*
		Nos. 33-36 (4)	35.25	*69.50*

25th anniv. of the reign of King George V.

Coronation Issue
Common Design Type

1937, May 19 *Perf. 13½x14*

37	CD302	1p deep green	.20	.20
38	CD302	2p deep orange	.80	.80
39	CD302	3p bright ultra	1.00	1.00
		Nos. 37-39 (3)	2.00	2.00
		Set, never hinged	3.00	

Georgetown A11

Designs: 1p, 2p, 4p, Green Mountain. 1½p, 2sh6p, Pier at Georgetown. 3p, 5sh, Long Beach. 6p, 10sh, Three Sisters.

1938-49 *Perf. 13½*

Center in Black

40	A11	½p violet	.20	.20
a.		Perf. 13 ('44)	.15	.15
41	A11	1p green	16.00	7.50
41A	A11	1p org yellow, perf. 13 ('42)	.15	.15
b.		Perf. 14 ('49)	.30	.30
c.		Perf. 13½	2.25	2.25
42	A11	1½p red	.50	.50
a.		Perf. 14 ('49)	1.40	1.50
b.		Perf. 13 ('44)	.30	.30
43	A11	2p orange	.35	.35
a.		Perf. 14 ('49)	2.00	*13.00*
b.		Perf. 13 ('44)	.30	.30
44	A11	3p ultra	45.00	22.50
44A	A11	3p black ('40)	2.50	.75
c.		Perf. 13 ('44)	.20	.20
44B	A11	4p ultra, perf. 13 ('44)	1.00	.75
d.		Perf. 13½	.45	.45
45	A11	6p gray blue	.55	.55
a.		Perf. 13 ('44)	1.40	1.40

Perf. 13

46	A11	1sh dk brown ('44)	3.25	1.25
a.		Perf. 13½	1.00	1.00
47	A11	2sh6p car ('44)	10.00	5.00
a.		Perf. 13½	8.50	5.00
48	A11	5sh yel brn ('44)	25.00	6.50
a.		Perf. 13½	16.00	14.00
49	A11	10sh red vio ('44)	45.00	22.50
a.		Perf. 13½	35.00	25.00
		Nos. 40-49 (13)	149.50	68.50
		Set, never hinged	260.00	

See Nos. 54-56.

Catalogue values for unused stamps in this section, from this point to the end of the section, are for Never Hinged items.

Peace Issue
Common Design Type
Perf. 13½x14

1946, Oct. 21 **Engr.** **Wmk. 4**

50	CD303	2p deep orange	.25	.25
51	CD303	4p deep blue	.30	.30

Silver Wedding Issue
Common Design Types

1948, Oct. 20 **Photo.** *Perf. 14x14½*

52	CD304	3p black	.35	.35

Engraved; Name Typographed
Perf. 11½x11

53	CD305	10sh red violet	37.50	*50.00*

Type of 1938

Designs: 1p, Three Sisters. 1½p, Georgetown Pier. 2p, Green Mountain.

1949, June 1 **Engr.** **Wmk. 4** *Perf. 13*

54	A11	1p green & black	.30	.30

Perf. 14

55	A11	1½p lilac rose & blk	.35	.35
a.		Perf. 13	.50	.50
56	A11	2p red & black	.50	.50
		Nos. 54-56 (3)	1.15	1.15

Issue date: No. 55a, Feb. 25, 1953.

UPU Issue
Common Design Types

Engr.; Name Typo. on Nos. 58, 59

1949, Oct. 10 *Perf. 13½, 11x11½*

57	CD306	3p rose carmine	1.00	1.00
58	CD307	4p indigo	2.00	2.00
59	CD308	6p olive	2.50	2.50
60	CD309	1sh slate	5.00	5.00
		Nos. 57-60 (4)	10.50	10.50

Coronation Issue
Common Design Type

1953, June 2 **Engr.** *Perf. 13½x13*

61	CD312	3p gray & black	1.50	1.50

Reservoir A16

Designs: 1p, Map of Ascension. 1½p, Georgetown. 2p, Map showing Ascension between South America and Africa and cable lines. 2½p, Mountain road. 3p, Yellow-billed tropic bird. 4p, Longfinned tuna. 6p, Waves. 7p, Young green turtles. 1sh, Land crab. 2sh6p, Sooty tern (wide-awake). 5sh, Perfect Crater. 10sh, View from Northwest.

1956, Nov. 19 **Wmk. 4** *Perf. 13*

Center in Black

62	A16	½p brown	.15	.15
63	A16	1p lilac rose	.30	.25
64	A16	1½p orange	.30	.20
65	A16	2p carmine	.50	.30
66	A16	2½p orange brown	.60	.50
67	A16	3p blue	.80	.45
68	A16	4p turq blue	.75	.75
69	A16	6p dark blue	1.00	1.00
70	A16	7p olive	1.25	1.25
71	A16	1sh scarlet	1.65	1.40
72	A16	2sh6p brown violet	17.50	10.00
73	A16	5sh bright green	22.50	15.00
74	A16	10sh purple	47.50	27.50
		Nos. 62-74 (13)	94.80	58.75

Brown Booby — A17

Birds: 1½p, Black tern. 2p, Fairy tern. 3p, Red-billed tropic bird in flight. 4½p, Brown noddy. 6p, Sooty tern. 7p, Frigate bird. 10p, Blue-faced booby. 1sh, Yellow-billed tropic bird. 1sh6p, Red-billed tropic bird. 2sh6p, Madeiran storm petrel. 5sh, Red-footed booby (brown phase). 10sh, Frigate birds. £1, Red-footed booby (white phase).

Perf. 14x14½

1963, May 23 **Photo.** **Wmk. 314**

75	A17	1p multicolored	.15	.15
a.		Booklet pane of 4	.30	
76	A17	1½p multicolored	.15	.15
a.		Booklet pane of 4	.50	
b.		Blue omitted	70.00	
77	A17	2p multicolored	.15	.15
a.		Booklet pane of 4	1.10	
78	A17	3p multicolored	.20	.15
a.		Booklet pane of 4	1.25	
79	A17	4½p multicolored	.25	.20
80	A17	6p multicolored	.35	.25
a.		Booklet pane of 4	3.25	
81	A17	7p multicolored	.35	.30
82	A17	10p multicolored	.50	.40
83	A17	1sh multicolored	.55	.50
84	A17	1sh6p multicolored	1.10	1.00
a.		Booklet pane of 4	6.25	
85	A17	2sh6p multicolored	2.75	2.50
86	A17	5sh multicolored	5.50	5.00
87	A17	10sh multicolored	12.50	10.00
88	A17	£1 multicolored	22.50	20.00
		Nos. 75-88 (14)	47.00	40.75

Freedom from Hunger Issue
Common Design Type

1963, June 4 **Wmk. 314**

89	CD314	1sh6p car rose	3.50	2.50

Red Cross Centenary Issue
Common Design Type

1963, Sept. 2 **Litho.** *Perf. 13*

90	CD315	3p black & red	.90	.90
91	CD315	1sh6p ultra & red	6.00	6.00

ITU Issue
Common Design Type
Perf. 11x11½

1965, May 17 **Litho.** **Wmk. 314**

92	CD317	3p mag & violet	.70	.70
93	CD317	6p grnsh bl & brn org	1.65	1.65

Intl. Cooperation Year Issue
Common Design Type

1965, Oct. 25 **Wmk. 314** *Perf. 14½*

94	CD318	1p bl grn & claret	.45	.28
95	CD318	6p lt vio & green	1.75	1.65

Churchill Memorial Issue
Common Design Type

1966, Jan. 24 **Photo.** *Perf. 14*

Design in Black, Gold and Carmine Rose

96	CD319	1p bright blue	.45	.25
97	CD319	3p green	1.50	.85
98	CD319	6p brown	2.00	1.65
99	CD319	1sh6p violet	6.25	4.75
		Nos. 96-99 (4)	10.20	7.50

World Cup Soccer Issue
Common Design Type

1966, July 1 **Litho.** *Perf. 14*

100	CD321	3p multicolored	.70	.55
101	CD321	6p multicolored	1.40	2.25

WHO Headquarters Issue
Common Design Type

1966, Sept. 20 **Litho.** *Perf. 14*

102	CD322	3p multicolored	1.25	1.00
103	CD322	1sh6p multicolored	3.25	3.00

Apollo Satellite Station, Ascension — A18

Wmk. 314

1966, Nov. 7 **Photo.** *Perf. 14*

104	A18	4p purple & black	.15	.15
105	A18	8p blue grn & blk	.25	.16
106	A18	1sh3p brn ol & blk	.48	.30
107	A18	2sh6p brt grnsh blue & black	.95	.70
		Nos. 104-107 (4)	1.83	1.31

Opening of the Apollo communications satellite-earth station, part of the US Apollo program.

UNESCO Anniversary Issue
Common Design Type

1967, Jan. 3 Litho. *Perf. 14*

108 CD323 3p "Education" .70 .65
109 CD323 6p "Science" 2.00 1.75
110 CD323 1sh6p "Culture" 5.00 5.00
Nos. 108-110 (3) 7.70 7.40

BBC Emblem A19

Photo.; Gold Impressed

1967, Dec. 1 Wmk. 314 *Perf. 14½*

111 A19 1p ultra & gold .15 .15
112 A19 3p dk green & gold .15 .15
113 A19 6p brt purple & gold .35 .30
114 A19 1sh6p brt red & gold .80 .70
Nos. 111-114 (4) 1.45 1.30

Opening of the British Broadcasting Company's South Atlantic Relay Station on Ascension Island.

Human Rights Flame and Chain — A20

Perf. 14½x14

1968, July 8 Litho. Wmk. 314

115 A20 6p org, car & blk .22 .15
116 A20 1sh6p gray, mag & blk .45 .42
117 A20 2sh6p brt grn, plum & blk .85 .70
Nos. 115-117 (3) 1.52 1.27

International Human Rights Year.

Blackfish A21

Fish: No. 119, Sailfish. 6p, Oldwife. 8p, Leather jacks. 1sh6p, Yellowtails. 1sh9p, Tuna. 2sh3p, Mako sharks. 2sh11p, Rock hind (jack).

Perf. 13x12½

1968-69 Wmk. 314 Litho.

118 A21 4p brt grnsh bl & blk .30 .18
119 A21 4p red & multi .35 .24
120 A21 6p yel olive & multi .45 .35
121 A21 8p brt rose lil & multi .60 .38
122 A21 1sh6p brown & multi 2.00 1.50
123 A21 1sh9p emer & multi 1.10 .95
124 A21 2sh3p ocher & multi 1.75 1.25
125 A21 2sh11p dp org & multi 3.50 2.25
Nos. 118-125 (8) 10.05 7.10

Issue dates: No. 119, 6p, 1sh6p, 2sh11p, Mar. 3, 1969. Others, Oct. 23, 1968.
See Nos. 130-133.

Arms of R.N.S. Rattlesnake — A22

Coats of Arms of Royal Naval Ships: 9p, Weston. 1sh9p, Undaunted. 2sh3p, Eagle.

Perf. 14x14½

1969, Oct. 1 Photo. Wmk. 314

126 A22 4p multicolored .25 .25
127 A22 9p multicolored .50 .50
128 A22 1sh9p multicolored 1.25 1.25
129 A22 2sh3p multicolored 1.75 1.75
a. Min. sheet of 4, #126-129 6.75 5.75
Nos. 126-129 (4) 3.75 3.75

See Nos. 134-137, 152-159, 166-169.

Fish Type of 1968

Deep-sea fish: 4p, Wahoo. 9p, Coalfish. 1sh9p, Dolphinfishes. 2sh3p, Soldierfish.

1970, Apr. 6 Litho. *Perf. 14*

130 A21 4p bluish grn & multi .55 .35
131 A21 9p org & multi .90 .60
132 A21 1sh9p ultra & multi 1.75 1.40
133 A21 2sh3p gray & multi 3.25 2.00
Nos. 130-133 (4) 6.45 4.35

Naval Arms Type of 1969

Coats of Arms of Royal Naval Ships: 4p, Penelope. 9p, Carlisle. 1sh6p, Amphion. 2sh6p, Magpie.

Perf. 12½x12

1970, Sept. 7 Photo. Wmk. 314

134 A22 4p ultra, gold & blk .25 .25
135 A22 9p lt bl, blk, gold & red .50 .50
136 A22 1sh6p grnsh bl, gold & blk 1.25 1.25
137 A22 2sh6p lt grnsh bl, gold & blk 2.00 2.00
a. Miniature sheet of 4, #134-137 7.50 6.00
Nos. 134-137 (4) 4.00 4.00

Decimal Currency Issue

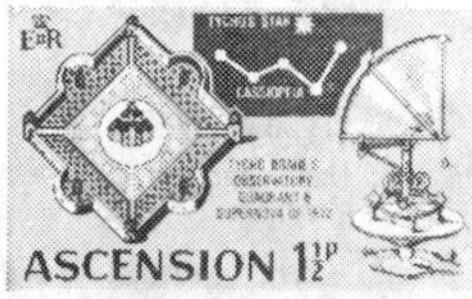

Tycho Brahe's Observatory, Quadrant and Supernova, 1572 — A23

Man into Space: ½p, Chinese rocket, 1232, vert. 1p, Medieval Arab astronomers, vert. 2p, Galileo, his telescope and drawing of moon, 1609. 2½p, Isaac Newton, telescope and apple. 3½p, Harrison's chronometer and ship, 1735. 4½p, First American manned orbital flight (Project Mercury, 1962, vert.). 5p, Reflector of Palomar telescope and ring nebula in Lyra, Messier 57. 7½p, Jodrell Bank telescope. 10p, Mariner 7, 1969, and telescopic view of Mars. 12½p, Sputnik 2 and dog Laika, 1957. 25p, Astronaut walking in space, 1965 (Gemini 4; vert.). 50p, US astronauts and moon landing module, 1969. £1, Future space research station.

1971, Feb. 15 Litho. *Perf. 14½*

138 A23 ½p multicolored .15 .15
a. Booklet pane of 4 .50
139 A23 1p multicolored .15 .15
a. Booklet pane of 4 .75
140 A23 1½p multicolored .20 .20
a. Booklet pane of 4 1.00
141 A23 2p multicolored .20 .20
a. Booklet pane of 4 1.90
142 A23 2½p multicolored .35 .35
a. Booklet pane of 4 2.50
143 A23 3½p multicolored .45 .45
a. Booklet pane of 4 3.50
144 A23 4½p multicolored .60 .60
145 A23 5p multicolored .65 .65
146 A23 7½p multicolored .75 .75
147 A23 10p multicolored 1.00 1.00
148 A23 12½p multicolored 1.40 1.40
149 A23 25p multicolored 2.50 2.50
150 A23 50p multicolored 5.25 5.25
151 A23 £1 multicolored 10.00 10.00
Nos. 138-151 (14) 23.65 23.65

For overprints see Nos. 189-191.

Arms of H.M.S. Phoenix — A24

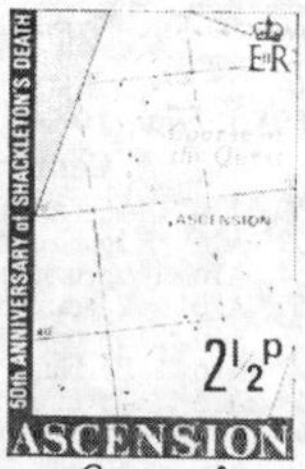

Course of Quest — A25

Coats of Arms of Royal Naval Ships: 4p, Milford. 9p, Pelican. 15p, Oberon.

1971, Nov. 15 Photo. *Perf. 13½x13*

152 A24 2p gold & multi .25 .25
153 A24 4p gold & multi .55 .55
154 A24 9p gold & multi 1.65 1.65
155 A24 15p gold & multi 3.25 3.25
a. Souvenir sheet of 4, #152-155 8.00 10.00
Nos. 152-155 (4) 5.70 5.70

Naval Arms Type of 1969

Coats of Arms of Royal Naval Ships: 1½p, Lowestoft. 3p, Auckland. 6p, Nigeria. 17½p, Bermuda.

1972, May 22 Litho. *Perf. 14x14½*

156 A22 1½p bl, gold & blk .24 .24
157 A22 3p grnsh bl, gold & blk .52 .52
158 A22 6p grn, gold, blk & bl 1.00 1.00
159 A22 17½p lil, gold, blk & red 3.00 3.00
a. Miniature sheet of 4, #156-159 6.00 8.00
Nos. 156-159 (4) 4.76 4.76

1972, Aug. 2 *Perf. 14*

Designs: 4p, Shackleton and "Quest", horiz. 7½p, Shackleton's cabin and Quest in pack ice, horiz. 11p, Shackleton statue, London, and memorial cairn, South Georgia.

160 A25 2½p multicolored .30 .30
161 A25 4p multicolored .50 .50
162 A25 7½p multicolored 1.00 1.00
163 A25 11p multicolored 1.65 1.65
a. Souvenir sheet of 4, #160-163 4.75 4.75
Nos. 160-163 (4) 3.45 3.45

Sir Ernest Henry Shackleton (1874-1922), explorer of Antarctica.

Silver Wedding Issue, 1972
Common Design Type

Design: Queen Elizabeth II, Prince Philip, land crab and shark.

1972, Nov. 20 Photo. *Perf. 14x14½*

164 CD324 2p violet & multi .15 .15
165 CD324 16p car rose & multi .80 .80

Naval Arms Type of 1969

Coats of Arms of Royal Naval Ships: 2p, Birmingham. 4p, Cardiff. 9p, Penzance. 13p, Rochester.

1973, May 28 Litho. Wmk. 314

166 A22 2p blue & multi .60 .42
167 A22 4p yel grn & multi 1.50 1.10
168 A22 9p lt blue & multi 3.00 2.25
169 A22 13p violet & multi 4.25 3.75
a. Min. sheet of 4, #166-169 21.00 24.00
Nos. 166-169 (4) 9.35 7.52

Turtles — A26

1973, Aug. 28 *Perf. 13½*

170 A26 4p Green 1.40 1.10
171 A26 9p Loggerhead 2.75 2.25
172 A26 12p Hawksbill 4.50 3.50
Nos. 170-172 (3) 8.65 6.85

Light Infanty Marine Sergeant, 1900 — A27

Uniforms (Royal Marines): 6p, Private, 1816. 12p, Officer, Light Infantry, 1880. 20p, Color Sergeant, Artillery, 1910.

1973, Oct. 31 *Perf. 14½*

173 A27 2p multicolored .45 .45
174 A27 6p lt green & multi 1.65 1.65
175 A27 12p lt blue & multi 3.25 3.25
176 A27 20p lt lilac & multi 5.50 5.50
Nos. 173-176 (4) 10.85 10.85

Departure of the Royal Marines from Ascension, 50th anniv.

Princess Anne's Wedding Issue
Common Design Type

1973, Nov. 14 *Perf. 14*

177 CD325 2p ocher & multi .15 .15
178 CD325 18p multicolored .75 .75

Letter and UPU Emblem A29

UPU Cent.: 9p, Emblem and Mercury.

Perf. 14½

1974, Mar. 27 Litho. Wmk. 314

179 A29 2p multicolored .20 .20
180 A29 9p vio blue & multi .80 .80

Young Churchill and Blenheim Palace A30

Design: 25p, Churchill and United Nations Headquarters, New York.

1974, Nov. 30 Litho. Unwmk.

181 A30 5p slate grn & multi .26 .26
182 A30 25p purple & multi 1.00 1.00
a. Souvenir sheet of 2, #181-182 2.00 1.75

Sir Winston Churchill (1874-1965), birth centenary.

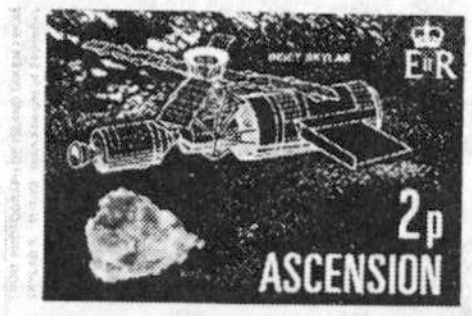

Skylab over Photograph of Ascension Taken by Skylab 3 — A31

Skylab Space Station: 18p, Command module and photo of Ascension from Skylab 4.

1975, Mar. 20 Wmk. 314 *Perf. 14½*

183 A31 2p multicolored .15 .15
184 A31 18p multicolored 1.00 1.00

US Air Force C-141A Starlifter — A32

Aircraft: 5p, Royal Air Force C-130 Hercules. 9p, Vickers VC-10. 24p, U.S. Air Force C-5A Galaxy.

Perf. 13½x14

1975, June 19 Litho. Wmk. 314

185 A32 2p multicolored .22 .22
186 A32 5p multicolored .60 .60
187 A32 9p multicolored 1.10 1.10
188 A32 24p multicolored 3.00 3.00
a. Souvenir sheet of 4, #185-188 8.00 10.00
Nos. 185-188 (4) 4.92 4.92

Wideawake Airfield, Ascension Island.

Nos. 144, 148-149 Overprinted

APOLLO-SOYUZ LINK 1975

1975, Aug. Litho. *Perf. 14½*

189 A23 4½p multicolored .20 .20
190 A23 12½p multicolored .42 .42
191 A23 25p multicolored 1.00 1.00
Nos. 189-191 (3) 1.62 1.62

Apollo Soyuz space test project (Russo-American cooperation), launching July 15; link-up, July 17.

HMS Peruvian and Zenobia Arriving Oct. 22, 1815 A33

Designs: 5p, Water Supply, Dampiers Drip. 9p, First Landing, Oct. 1815. 15p, The Garden on Green Mountain. All designs after paintings by Isobel McManus.

1975, Oct. 22 Wmk. 373 *Perf. 14½*

192 A33 2p lt blue & multi .15 .15
193 A33 5p lt blue & multi .32 .25
194 A33 9p red & multi .52 .50
195 A33 15p red & multi 1.00 .85
Nos. 192-195 (4) 1.99 1.75

British occupation, 160th anniv.

Canaries
A34

Designs: 2p, Fairy tern, vert. 3p, Waxbills. 4p, Black noddy, vert. 5p, Brown noddy. 6p, Common mynah. 7p, Madeira storm petrels, vert. 8p, Sooty terns. 9p, White booby, vert. 10p, Red-footed booby. 15p, Red-throated francolin, vert. 18p, Brown booby, vert. 25p, Red-billed bo'sun bird. 50p, Yellow-billed bo'sun bird. £1, Ascension frigatebird, vert. £2, Boatswain Island Bird Sanctuary and birds.

Perf. 14x14½, 14½x14
1976, Apr. 26   Litho.   Wmk. 373
Size: 35x27mm, 27x35mm

196	A34	1p multicolored	.15	.15
197	A34	2p multicolored	.15	.15
198	A34	3p multicolored	.15	.15
199	A34	4p multicolored	.15	.15
200	A34	5p multicolored	.20	.15
201	A34	6p multicolored	.22	.16
202	A34	7p multicolored	.25	.18
203	A34	8p multicolored	.30	.22
204	A34	9p multicolored	.40	.24
205	A34	10p multicolored	.45	.25
206	A34	15p multicolored	.65	.40
207	A34	18p multicolored	.85	.48
208	A34	25p multicolored	1.25	.65
209	A34	50p multicolored	2.25	1.25
210	A34	£1 multicolored	3.25	2.75

Perf. 13½
Size: 46x33mm

211	A34	£2 multicolored	6.50	5.25
		Nos. 196-211 (16)	17.17	12.58

Great Britain Type A1 with Ascension
Cancel — A35

Designs: 9p, Ascension No. 1, vert. 25p, Freighter Southampton Castle.

1976, May 4   Perf. 13½x14, 14x13½

212	A35	5p lt brn, car & blk	.22	.22
213	A35	9p gray grn, grn & blk	.40	.40
214	A35	25p blue & multi	1.25	1.25
a.		Souvenir sheet of 3	2.75	2.75
		Nos. 212-214 (3)	1.87	1.87

Festival of Stamps 1976. #214a contains one each of Ascension #214, St. Helena #297 and Tristan da Cunha #208.

US Base
A36

Designs: 9p, NASA Station, Devil's Ashpit. 25p, Viking satellite landing on Mars.

Perf. 13½
1976, July 4   Litho.   Wmk. 373

215	A36	8p black & multi	.55	.55
216	A36	9p black & multi	.65	.65
217	A36	25p black & multi	1.50	1.50
		Nos. 215-217 (3)	2.70	2.70

American Bicentennial. No. 215 also for the 20th anniv. of Bahamas Long Range Proving Ground (extension) Agreement.

Queen in Coronation Coach — A37

Designs: 8p, Prince Philip on Ascension Island, 1957, vert. 12p, Queen leaving Buckingham Palace in coronation coach.

Perf. 14x13½, 13½x14
1977, Feb. 7   Litho.   Wmk. 373

218	A37	8p multicolored	.26	.26
219	A37	12p multicolored	.38	.38
220	A37	25p multicolored	.80	.80
		Nos. 218-220 (3)	1.44	1.44

Reign of Queen Elizabeth II, 25th anniv.

Water Pipe in
Tunnel — A38

Designs: 5p, Breakneck Valley wells. 12p, Break tank in pipe line, horiz. 25p, Dam and reservoir, horiz.

1977, June 27   Litho.   Perf. 14½

221	A38	3p multicolored	.16	.16
222	A38	5p multicolored	.25	.25
223	A38	12p multicolored	.60	.60
224	A38	25p multicolored	1.25	1.25
		Nos. 221-224 (4)	2.26	2.26

Water supplies constructed by Royal Marines, 1832 and 1881.

Mars Bay Site, 1877
A39

Designs: 8p, Mars Bay and instrument sites. 12p, Prof. and Mrs. Gill before their tent. 25p, Map of Ascension.

1977, Oct. 3   Litho.   Wmk. 373

225	A39	3p multicolored	.16	.15
226	A39	8p multicolored	.40	.32
227	A39	12p multicolored	.65	.55
228	A39	25p multicolored	1.40	1.10
		Nos. 225-228 (4)	2.61	2.12

Centenary of visit of Prof. David Gill (1843-1914), astronomer, to Ascension.

Elizabeth II Coronation Anniversary Issue

Souvenir Sheet

Common Design Types

Unwmk.

1978, May 21   Litho.   Perf. 15

229		Sheet of 6	3.50	3.50
a.		CD326 25p Lion of England	.55	.55
b.		CD327 25p Elizabeth II	.55	.55
c.		CD328 25p Green turtle	.55	.55

No. 229 contains 2 se-tenant strips of Nos. 229a-229c, separated by horizontal gutter with commemorative and descriptive inscriptions and showing central part of coronation procession with coach.

East Crater (Broken Tooth) — A40

Volcanoes: 5p, Hollands Crater (Hollow Tooth). 12p, Bears Back. 15p, Green Mountain. 25p, Two Boats village.

1978, Sept. 4   Litho.   Perf. 14½

230	A40	3p multicolored	.15	.15
231	A40	5p multicolored	.15	.15
232	A40	12p multicolored	.40	.40
233	A40	15p multicolored	.50	.50
234	A40	25p multicolored	.85	.85
a.		Souvenir sheet, 2 each #230-234	4.75	6.25
b.		Strip of 5, #230-234	2.00	2.00

No. 234b shows panoramic view of volcanic terrain.

Resolution
A41

Capt. Cook's voyages: 8p, Cook's chronometer. 12p, Green turtle. 25p, Cook after Flaxman/Wedgwood medallion.

Litho.; Litho. & Engr. (25p)
1979, Jan. 8   Perf. 11

235	A41	3p multicolored	.15	.15
236	A41	8p multicolored	.32	.26
237	A41	12p multicolored	.55	.42
238	A41	25p multicolored	1.10	.85
		Nos. 235-238 (4)	2.12	1.68

St. Mary's Church,
Georgetown — A42

Designs: 12p, Old map of Ascension Island. 50p, Ascension, by Rembrandt.

Perf. 14½
1979, May 24   Litho.   Wmk. 373

239	A42	8p multicolored	.22	.22
240	A42	12p multicolored	.35	.35
241	A42	50p multicolored	1.50	1.50
		Nos. 239-241 (3)	2.07	2.07

Ascension Day.

Landing Cable at Comfortless Cove — A43

Eastern Telegraph Co., 80th anniv.: 8p, Cable Ship Anglia. 12p, Map showing cables across the Atlantic, vert. 15p, Cable-laying ship. 25p, Cable and earth station.

1979, Sept. 15

242	A43	3p rose car & black	.15	.15
243	A43	8p dk yel grn & black	.22	.22
244	A43	12p yel bister & black	.35	.35
245	A43	15p violet & black	.45	.45
246	A43	25p deep org & black	.70	.70
		Nos. 242-246 (5)	1.87	1.87

Ascension No. 45 — A44

Ascension Stamps: 8p, No. 73. 12p, No. 14, vert. 50p, Hill portrait, vert.

1979, Dec. 17   Wmk. 373   Perf. 14

247	A44	3p multicolored	.15	.15
248	A44	8p multicolored	.18	.18
249	A44	12p multicolored	.25	.25
250	A44	50p multicolored	1.10	1.10
		Nos. 247-250 (4)	1.68	1.68

Sir Rowland Hill (1795-1879), originator of penny postage.

Anogramma
Ascensionis
A45

1980, Feb. 18   Litho.   Perf. 14½

251	A45	3p shown	.15	.15
252	A45	6p Xiphopteris ascensionense	.15	.15
253	A45	8p Sporobolus caespitosus	.20	.20
254	A45	12p Sporobolus durus, vert.	.32	.32
255	A45	18p Dryopteris ascensionis, vert.	.45	.45
256	A45	24p Marattia purpurascens, vert.	.60	.60
		Nos. 251-256 (6)	1.87	1.87

17th Century Bottle Post, London 1980 Emblem — A46

1980, May 1   Wmk. 373   Perf. 14

257	A46	8p shown	.20	.20
258	A46	12p 36-gun frigate, 19th century	.32	.32
259	A46	15p "Garth Castle," 1863	.40	.40
260	A46	50p "St. Helena," Lockheed C141	1.25	1.25
a.		Souvenir sheet of 4, #257-260	2.25	2.50
		Nos. 257-260 (4)	2.17	2.17

London 1980 Intl. Stamp Exhib., May 6-14.

Queen Mother Elizabeth Birthday
Common Design Type

1980, Aug. 11   Litho.   Perf. 14

261	CD330	15p multicolored	.50	.50

Lubbock's Yellowtail
A47

1980, Sept. 15   Litho.   Perf. 13½x14

262	A47	3p shown	.15	.15
263	A47	10p Resplendent angelfish	.30	.30
264	A47	25p Hedgehog butterflyfish	.70	.70
265	A47	40p Marmalade razorfish	1.10	1.10
		Nos. 262-265 (4)	2.25	2.25

Tortoisen, by Thomas Maxon
A48

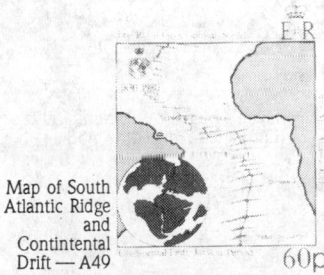

Map of South Atlantic Ridge and Continental Drift — A49

Design: 15p, Wideawake Fair, by Linton Palmer, 1866.

1980, Nov. 17   Perf. 13½, 14 (60p)

266	A48	10p multicolored	.22	.22
267	A48	15p multicolored	.38	.38
268	A49	60p multicolored	1.40	1.40
		Nos. 266-268 (3)	2.00	2.00

Royal Geographical Soc., 50th anniv.

Green Mountain Farm, 1881 — A50

Designs: 15p, Two Boats, 1881. 20p, Green Mountain and Two Boats farms, 1981. 30p, Green Mountain Farm, 1981.

1981, Feb. 15   Litho.   Perf. 14
269 A50	12p multicolored	.30	.30
270 A50	15p multicolored	.40	.40
271 A50	20p multicolored	.50	.50
272 A50	30p multicolored	.85	.85
	Nos. 269-272 (4)	2.05	2.05

Cable and
Wireless
Earth Station
A51

1981, Apr. 27   Litho.   Perf. 14
273	Sheet of 10	3.75	3.75
a.	A51 15p multicolored	.35	.35

Flight of Columbia space shuttle. Gutter contains story of Ascension and space shuttle; margin shows craft and dish antenna.

Poinsettia
A52

1981, May 11   Wmk. 373   Perf. 13½
274 A52	1p shown	.15	.15
275 A52	2p Clustererd wax flower	.15	.15
276 A52	3p Kolanchoe, vert.	.15	.15
277 A52	4p Yellow pops	.15	.15
278 A52	5p Camel's foot creeper	.15	.15
279 A52	8p White oleander	.20	.20
280 A52	10p Ascension lily, vert.	.25	.25
281 A52	12p Coral plant, vert.	.32	.32
282 A52	15p Yellow allamanda	.40	.40
283 A52	20p Ascention euphorbia	.52	.50
284 A52	30p Flame of the forest, vert.	.85	.70
285 A52	40p Bougainvillea	1.00	.95

Size: 42x53mm
286 A52	50p Solanum	1.25	1.10
287 A52	£1 Ladies petticoat	2.75	2.25
288 A52	£2 Red hibiscus	5.25	4.50
	Nos. 274-288 (15)	13.54	11.92

Nos. 275-276, 280, 282-283 and 287 also issued inscribed 1982.
For overprints see Nos. 321-322.

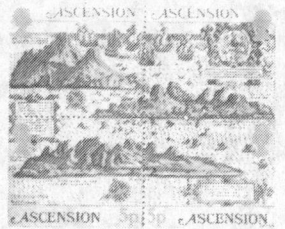

Linschoten's Map of Ascension, 1599
(Illustration reduced) — A53

Maxwell's Map
of Ascension,
1793 — A54

Designs: Old maps of Ascension.

1981, May 22   Perf. 14½
289	A53 Sheet of 4	.60	.60
a.-d.	5p any single	.15	.15
290	A54 10p shown	.30	.30
291	A54 12p Maxwell, 1793, diff.	.38	.38
292	A54 15p Eckberg & Chapman, 1811	.45	.45
293	A54 40p Campbell, 1819	1.25	1.25
	Nos. 289-293 (5)	2.98	2.98

Royal Wedding Issue
Common Design Type

1981, July 22   Wmk. 373   Perf. 14
294 CD331	10p Bouquet	.25	.25
295 CD331	15p Charles	.40	.40
296 CD331	50p Couple	1.25	1.25
	Nos. 294-296 (3)	1.90	1.90

Nos. 294-296 each se-tenant with label.

Man Shining
Cannon — A55

1981, Sept. 14   Litho.   Perf. 14
297 A55	5p shown	.15	.15
298 A55	10p Mountain climbing	.28	.28
299 A55	15p First aid treatment	.42	.42
300 A55	40p Duke of Edinburgh	1.10	1.10
	Nos. 297-300 (4)	1.95	1.95

Duke of Edinburgh's Awards, 25th anniv.

Scouting
Year — A56

1982, Feb. 22   Litho.   Perf. 14
301 A56	10p Parallel rope walking	.28	.28
302 A56	15p 1st Ascension scout flag	.45	.45
303 A56	25p Radio operators	.70	.70
304 A56	40p Baden-Powell	1.10	1.10
a.	Souvenir sheet of 4	2.75	2.75
	Nos. 301-304 (4)	2.53	2.53

No. 304a contains stamps in designs of Nos. 301-304 (30x30mm, perf. 14½, diamond-shape).

Sesquicentennial of Charles Darwin's
Visit — A57

1982, Apr. 19
305 A57	10p Portrait	.25	.25
306 A57	12p Pistols	.32	.32
307 A57	15p Rock crab	.40	.40
308 A57	40p Beagle	1.10	1.10
	Nos. 305-308 (4)	2.07	2.07

40th Anniv.
of
Wideawake
Airfield
A58

1982, June 15   Litho.   Perf. 14
309 A58	5p Fairey Swordfish	.15	.15
310 A58	10p North American B25C Mitchell	.28	.28
311 A58	15p Boeing EC-135N Aria	.45	.45
312 A58	50p Lockheed Hercules	1.40	1.40
	Nos. 309-312 (4)	2.28	2.28

Princess Diana Issue
Common Design Type
Perf. 14½x14

1982, July 1   Wmk. 373
313 CD333	12p Arms	.30	.30
314 CD333	15p Diana	.40	.40
315 CD333	25p Wedding	.60	.60
316 CD333	50p Portrait	1.25	1.25
	Nos. 313-316 (4)	2.55	2.55

Christmas and 50th Anniv. of BBC
Overseas Broadcasting — A59

Anniv. Emblem and: 5p, Bush House (London headquarters). 10p, Atlantic relay station. 25p, Lord Reith, first director general. 40p, King George V delivering Christmas address, 1932.

1982, Dec. 20   Litho.   Perf. 14
317 A59	5p multicolored	.15	.15
318 A59	10p multicolored	.28	.28
319 A59	25p multicolored	.70	.70
320 A59	40p multicolored	1.10	1.10
	Nos. 317-320 (4)	2.23	2.23

Nos. 282-283 Overprinted: "1st
PARTICIPATION / COMMONWEALTH
GAMES 1982"

1982   Perf. 13½
321 A52	15p multicolored	.45	.45
322 A52	20p multicolored	.55	.55

12th Commonwealth Games, Brisbane, Australia, Sept. 30-Oct. 9.

**ASCENSION
ISLAND**

7p   A60

1983, Mar. 1   Perf. 14
323 A60	7p Marasmius echinosphaerus	.25	.25
324 A60	12p Chlorophyllum molybdites	.42	.42
325 A60	15p Leucocoprinus cepaestipes	.55	.55
326 A60	20p Lycoperdon marginatum	.75	.75
327 A60	50p Marasmiellus distantifolius	1.75	1.75
	Nos. 323-327 (5)	3.72	3.72

View of
Georgetown
A61

1983, May 12   Litho.   Perf. 14
328 A61	12p shown	.32	.32
329 A61	15p Farm, Green Mountain	.40	.40
330 A61	20p Boatswain Bird Isld.	.52	.52
331 A61	60p Telemetry Hill	1.65	1.65
	Nos. 328-331 (4)	2.89	2.89

See Nos. 359-362.

Manned Flight Bicentenary — A62

Military Aircraft.

1983, Aug. 1   Wmk. 373   Perf. 14
332 A62	12p Wessex Five helicopter	.32	.32
333 A62	15p Vulcan B2	.40	.40
334 A62	20p Nimrod MR2P	.55	.55
335 A62	60p Victor K2	1.65	1.65
	Nos. 332-335 (4)	2.92	2.92

Introduced
Species
A63

1983, Sept.   Litho.   Wmk. 373
336 A63	12p Iguanid	.30	.30
337 A63	15p Rabbit	.38	.38
338 A63	20p Cat	.50	.50
339 A63	20p Donkey	1.50	1.50
	Nos. 336-339 (4)	2.68	2.68

Tellina
Antonii
Philippi
A64

1983, Nov. 28   Litho.   Perf. 14½
340 A64	7p shown	.18	.18
341 A64	12p Nodipecten nodosus	.30	.30
342 A64	15p Cypraea lurida oceanica	.40	.40
343 A64	20p Nerita ascensionis gmelin	.55	.55
344 A64	50p Micromelo undatus	1.40	1.40
	Nos. 340-344 (5)	2.83	2.83

St. Helena Colony,
150th Anniv. — A65

Designs: First issue inscribed Ascension instead of overprinted.

1984, Jan. 10   Litho.   Perf. 14
345 A65	12p No. 3	.30	.30
346 A65	15p No. 4	.38	.38
347 A65	20p No. 6	.50	.50
348 A65	60p No. 9	1.50	1.50
	Nos. 345-348 (4)	2.68	2.68

Souvenir Sheet

Visit of Prince
Andrew — A66

1984, Apr. 10   Perf. 14½x14
349	Sheet of 2	2.00	2.00
a.	A66 12p Andrew	.25	.25
b.	A66 70p In naval uniform	1.75	1.75

Lloyd's List Issue
Common Design Type

1984, May 28
351 CD335	12p Naval semaphore	.25	.25
352 CD335	15p "Southampton Castle"	.35	.35
353 CD335	20p Pier Head	.45	.45
354 CD335	70p Dane	1.50	1.50
	Nos. 351-354 (4)	2.55	2.55

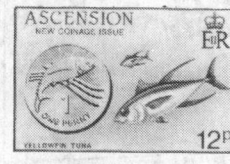

1984 Coins
and Wildlife
A67

1984, June   Perf. 14
355 A67	12p One penny, yellowfin tuna	.30	.30
356 A67	15p Two pence, donkeys	.38	.38
357 A67	20p Fifty pence, green turtle	.50	.50
358 A67	70p One pound, sooty terns	1.75	1.75
	Nos. 355-358 (4)	2.93	2.93

View Type of 1983

1984, Oct.   Litho.   Wmk. 373
359 A61	12p Devil's Riding School	.28	.28
360 A61	15p St. Mary's Church	.35	.35
361 A61	20p Two Boats Village	.48	.48
362 A61	70p Ascension Isld.	1.65	1.65
	Nos. 359-362 (4)	2.76	2.76

Trees — A68

1985, Mar. 8   Litho.   Perf. 14½x14
363 A68	7p Bermuda cypress	.15	.15
364 A68	12p Norfolk Island pine	.30	.30
365 A68	15p Screwpine	.35	.35
366 A68	20p Eucalyptus	.50	.50
367 A68	65p Spore tree	1.65	1.65
	Nos. 363-367 (5)	2.95	2.95

Military Firearms A69

Large guns and insignia: 12p, Thirty-two pounder small bore muzzle loader, c. 1820; Royal Marines hat plate, c. 1816. 15p, Seven-inch rifled muzzle loader, c. 1866; royal cipher. 20p, Seven-pounder rifled muzzle loader, c. 1877; Royal Artillery badge. 70p, HMS Hood 5.5-inch gun; ship crest.

1985, July 21 Wmk. 373 *Perf. 14½*

368 A69 12p multicolored .30 .30
369 A69 15p multicolored .38 .38
370 A69 20p multicolored .52 .52
371 A69 70p multicolored 1.75 1.75
Nos. 368-371 (4) 2.95 2.95

Queen Mother 85th Birthday
Common Design Type

Designs: 12p, With Duke of York, Balmoral, 1924. 15p, With Princes Andrew and Edward. 20p, At Ascot. 70p, Christening of Prince Henry, Windsor Castle. 75p, Leaving the QEII, 1968.

Perf. 14½x14

1985, June 7 Wmk. 384

372 CD336 12p multicolored .25 .25
373 CD336 15p multicolored .28 .28
374 CD336 20p multicolored .40 .40
375 CD336 70p multicolored 1.40 1.40
Nos. 372-375 (4) 2.33 2.33

Souvenir Sheet

376 CD336 75p multicolored 1.55 1.50

Intl. Youth Year, Girl Guides 75th Anniv. — A70

1985, Oct. 4 Wmk. 373

377 A70 12p Guides' banner .30 .30
378 A70 15p First aid .38 .38
379 A70 20p Camping .52 .52
380 A70 70p Lady Baden-Powell 1.75 1.75
Nos. 377-380 (4) 2.95 2.95

Wildflowers A71

Halley's Comet A72

Wmk. 384

1985, Dec. 6 Litho. *Perf. 14*

381 A71 12p Clerodendrum fragrans .30 .30
382 A71 15p Shell ginger .40 .40
383 A71 20p Cape daisy .52 .52
384 A71 70p Ginger lily 1.90 1.90
Nos. 381-384 (4) 3.12 3.12

1986, Mar. 7

Designs: 12p, Newton's reflector telescope. 15p, Edmond Halley, Old Greenwich Observatory. 20p, Short's Gregorian telescope, comet, 1759. 70p, ICE space probe, Ascension satellite tracking station.

385 A72 12p multicolored .30 .30
386 A72 15p multicolored .40 .40
387 A72 20p multicolored .52 .52
388 A72 70p multicolored 1.90 1.90
Nos. 385-388 (4) 3.12 3.12

Queen Elizabeth II 60th Birthday
Common Design Type

Designs: 7p, Infant photograph, 1926. 15p, 1st worldwide Christmas broadcast, 1952. 20p, Garter Ceremony, Windsor Castle, 1983. 35p, Royal Tour, New Zealand, 1981. £1, Visiting Crown Agents' offices, 1983.

1986, Apr. 21 *Perf. 14x14½*

389 CD337 7p scarlet, blk & sil .20 .20
390 CD337 15p ultra, blk & sil .42 .42
391 CD337 20p green & multi .55 .55
392 CD337 35p violet & multi 1.00 1.00
393 CD337 £1 rose vio & multi 2.75 2.75
Nos. 389-393 (5) 4.92 4.92

For overprints see Nos. 431-435.

AMERIPEX '86 — A73

1986, May 22 *Perf. 14½*

394 A73 12p No. 183 .35 .35
395 A73 15p No. 260 .42 .42
396 A73 20p No. 215 .55 .55
397 A73 70p No. 310 2.00 2.00
Nos. 394-397 (4) 3.32 3.32

Souvenir Sheet

398 A73 75p Statue of Liberty, New York Harbor 2.25 2.25

Statue of Liberty, cent.

Royal Wedding Issue, 1986
Common Design Type

Designs: 15p, Couple kissing. 35p, Andrew in navy uniform, helicopter.

Wmk. 384

1986, July 23 Litho. *Perf. 14*

399 CD338 15p multicolored .42 .42
400 CD338 35p multicolored 1.00 1.00

Ships A74

1986, Oct. 14 Wmk. 384 *Perf. 14½*

401 A74 1p Ganymede, c. 1811 .15 .15
402 A74 2p Kangaroo, c. 1811 .15 .15
403 A74 4p Trinculo, c. 1811 .15 .15
404 A74 5p Daring, c. 1811 .15 .15
405 A74 9p Thais, c. 1811 .25 .25
406 A74 10p Pheasant, 1819 .28 .28
407 A74 15p Myrmidon, 1819 .40 .40
408 A74 18p Atholl, 1825 .50 .50
409 A74 20p Medina, 1830 .55 .55
410 A74 25p Saracen, 1840 .70 .70
411 A74 30p Hydra, c. 1845 .80 .80
412 A74 50p Sealark, 1840 1.25 1.25
413 A74 70p Rattlesnake, 1868 1.75 1.75
414 A74 £1 Penelope, 1889 2.75 2.75
415 A74 £2 Monarch, 1897 5.50 5.50
Nos. 401-415 (15) 15.33 15.33

For surcharges see Nos. 502-504.

Edible Bush Fruits A75

1987, Jan. 29 *Perf. 14*

416 A75 12p Cape gooseberry .35 .35
417 A75 15p Prickly pear .45 .45
418 A75 20p Guava .60 .60
419 A75 70p Loquat 2.00 2.00
Nos. 416-419 (4) 3.40 3.40

1st Manned Space Flight, 25th Anniv. — A76

Military Uniforms, 1815-20 — A77

1987, Mar. 30

420 A76 15p Ignition .45 .45
421 A76 18p Lift-off .55 .55
422 A76 25p Reentry .70 .70
423 A76 £1 Splashdown 3.00 3.00
Nos. 420-423 (4) 4.70 4.70

Souvenir Sheet

424 A76 70p Friendship 7 capsule 2.25 2.25

1987, June 29

Designs: a, Captains in full dress, 1st landing on Ascenion. b, Surgeon and sailors at campsite. c, Seaman returning from Dampier's Drip with water supply. d, Midshipman at lookout post. e, Commander and surveyor.

425 Strip of 5 4.00 4.00
a.-e. A77 25p multicolored .80 .80

See Nos. 458, 474, 482, 507.

Butterflies A78

1987, Aug. 10 *Perf. 14½*

426 A78 15p Painted lady .60 .60
427 A78 18p Monarch .75 .75
428 A78 25p Diadem 1.00 1.00
429 A78 £1 Long-tailed blue 3.75 3.75
Nos. 426-429 (4) 6.10 6.10

See Nos. 436-439, 459-462.

Birds — A79

Designs. a, Ascension frigatebirds (males). b, Brown booby, frigatebird, white boobies. c, Frigatebird, white booby. d, Ascension frigatebirds (females). e, Adult frigatebird feeding young.

1987, Oct. 8 Wmk. 373 *Perf. 14*

430 Strip of 5 6.00 6.00
a.-e. A79 25p any single 1.25 1.25

No. 430 has continuous design.

See No. 453.

Nos. 389-393 Ovptd. "40TH WEDDING ANNIVERSARY" in Silver

Perf. 14x14½

1987, Dec. 9 Litho. Wmk. 384

431 CD337 7p scar, blk & sil .22 .22
432 CD337 15p ultra, blk & sil .48 .48
433 CD337 20p green & multi .65 .65
434 CD337 35p violet & multi 1.10 1.10
435 CD337 £1 rose vio & multi 3.25 3.25
Nos. 431-435 (5) 5.70 5.70

40th wedding anniv. of Queen Elizabeth II and Prince Philip.

Insects Type of 1987

1988, Jan. 18 *Perf. 14½*

436 A78 15p Field cricket .60 .60
437 A78 18p Bush cricket .75 .75
438 A78 25p Ladybug 1.00 1.00
439 A78 £1 Burnished brass moth 4.00 4.00
Nos. 436-439 (4) 6.35 6.35

Capt. William Bate (d. 1838), 1st Garrison Commander and Colonial Founder of Ascension A80

Designs: 9p, Bate's Memorial, St. Mary's Church. 15p, Commodore's Cottage, Cross Hill. 18p, North East or Bate's Cottage, 1833. 25p, Landmarks on map. 70p, Bate and 3 soldiers.

1988, Apr. 14 Litho. *Perf. 14*

440 A80 9p multicolored .32 .32
441 A80 15p multicolored .55 .55
442 A80 18p multicolored .65 .65
443 A80 25p multicolored .88 .88
444 A80 70p multicolored 2.50 2.50
Nos. 440-444 (5) 4.90 4.90

Australia Bicentennial Emblem and Ships Named HMS Resolution — A81

1988, June 23 Litho. *Perf. 14*

445 A81 9p 3-Masted squarerigger, 1667 .35 .35
446 A81 18p 3-Masted squarerigger, 1772 .65 .65
447 A81 25p Navy cruiser, 1892 .90 .90
448 A81 65p Battleship, 1916 2.25 2.25
Nos. 445-448 (4) 4.15 4.15

Australia bicentennial.

Nos. 445-448 Overprinted

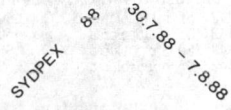

SYDPEX 88 30.7.88 – 7.8.88

Wmk. 384

1988, July 30 Litho. *Perf. 14*

449 A81 9p multicolored .35 .35
450 A81 18p multicolored .68 .68
451 A81 25p multicolored .95 .95
452 A81 65p multicolored 2.45 2.45
Nos. 449-452 (4) 4.43 4.43

SYDPEX '88, July 30-Aug. 7.

Bird Type of 1987

Behaviors of the wideawake tern, Sterna fuscata: a, Two adults, flock overhead. b, Nesting (two birds). c, Nesting (three birds). d, Adult and young. e, Tern flapping its wings.

1988, Aug. 15 *Perf. 14*

453 Strip of 5 6.00 6.00
a.-e. A79 25p any single 1.25 1.25

No. 453 has continuous design.

Lloyds of London, 300th Anniv.
Common Design Type

Designs: 8p, Lloyd's Coffee House, Tower Street, 1688. 18p, Cable ship Alert, horiz. 25p, Satellite recovery in space, horiz. 65p, Ship Good Hope Castle on fire off Ascension, 1973.

Wmk. 373

1988, Oct. 17 Litho. *Perf. 14*

454 CD341 8p multicolored .28 .28
455 CD341 18p multicolored .60 .60
456 CD341 25p multicolored .85 .85
457 CD341 65p multicolored 2.20 2.20
Nos. 454-457 (4) 3.93 3.93

Military Uniforms Type of 1987

Uniforms of the Royal Marines: a, Marines arrive in Ascension (marines), 1821. b, Semaphore station (officer, marine), 1829. c, Octagonal tank (sergeant), 1831. d, Water pipe tunnel (officers), 1833. e, Constructing barracks (officer), 1834.

1988, Nov. 21

458 Strip of 5 5.00 5.00
a.-e. A77 25p multicolored 1.00 1.00

Insect Type of 1987

Perf. 14½

1989, Jan. 16 Litho. Wmk. 384

459 A78 15p Plume moth .60 .60
460 A78 18p Green bottle .70 .70
461 A78 25p Weevil .95 .95
462 A78 £1 Paper wasp 3.75 3.75
Nos. 459-462 (4) 6.00 6.00

ASCENSION ISLAND 15p Land Crabs, Gecarcinus Lagostoma — A82

1989, Apr. 17
463	A82	15p multi	.52 .52
464	A82	18p multi, diff.	.65 .65
465	A82	25p multi, diff.	.88 .88
466	A82	£1 multi, diff.	3.50 3.50
		Nos. 463-466 (4)	5.55 5.55

Miniature Sheet
467	Sheet of 4	5.55 5.55
a.	A82 15p like No. 463	.52 .52
b.	A82 18p like No. 464	.65 .65
c.	A82 25p like No. 465	.88 .88
d.	A82 £1 like No. 466	3.50 3.50

Vignettes of Nos. 467a-467d do not have frame.

Moon Landing, 20th Anniv.
Common Design Type

Apollo 7: 15p, Tracking Station, Ascension Is. 18p, Launch, Cape Kennedy. 25p, Mission emblem. 70p, Expended Saturn IVB stage. £1, Lunar landing profile for the Apollo 11 mission.

1989, July 20   *Perf. 14x13½*
Size of Nos. 469-470: 29x29mm
468	CD342	15p multicolored	.50 .50
469	CD342	18p multicolored	.60 .60
470	CD342	25p multicolored	.85 .85
471	CD342	70p multicolored	2.35 2.35
		Nos. 468-471 (4)	4.30 4.30

Souvenir Sheet
472	CD342	£1 multicolored	3.35 3.35

Souvenir Sheet

A83

1989, July 7   *Perf. 14x13½*
473	A83	75p Emblems, No. 60	2.50 2.50

Miniature Sheet

World Stamp Expo '89, Washington, DC, and PHILEXFRANCE '89, Paris — A84

The Statue of Liberty and scenes from the centenary celebrations, 1986: a, Operation Sail. b, Face. c, Upper body. d, Three crown points. e, Ships in harbor, view of lower Manhattan. f, Ship in port, New York City.

1989, Aug. 21   **Wmk. 373**
474	Sheet of 6	3.00 3.00
a.-f.	A84 25p any single	.50 .50

Devil's Ashpit Tracking Station A85

1989, Sept. 30   **Wmk. 384**   *Perf. 14*
475	Sheet, 5 each #a.-b.	6.75 6.75
a.	A85 18p shown	.55 .55
b.	A85 25p US space shuttle launch	.80 .80

Termination of NASA tracking operations, begun in 1965, at the station.

Shells and Mollusks A86

Wmk. 384
1989, Nov. 6   **Litho.**   *Perf. 14*
476	A86	8p *Strombus latus*	.25 .25
477	A86	18p *Tonna galea*	.58 .58
478	A86	25p *Harpa doris*	.78 .78
479	A86	£1 *Charonia variegata*	3.15 3.15
		Nos. 476-479 (4)	4.76 4.76

Donkeys — A87

Perf. 14 on 3 Sides
1989, Nov. 17   **Litho.**   **Wmk. 384**
Booklet Stamps
480	A87	18p shown	.52 .52
a.		Booklet pane of 6	3.15
481	A87	25p Green turtle	.78 .78
a.		Booklet pane of 4	3.15

No. 480a sold for £1.

Military Type of 1987

Royal Navy equipment, c. 1815-1820: a, Seaman's pistol, hat, cutlass. b, Midshipman's belt buckle, button, sword, hat. c, Surgeon's hat, sword, instrument chest. d, Captain's hat, telescope, sword. e, Admiral's epaulet, megaphone, hat, pocket.

1990, Feb. 12   **Litho.**   *Perf. 14*
482	Strip of 5	4.25 4.25
a.-e.	A77 25p any single	.85 .85

World Wildlife Fund — A88

Frigate birds (*Fregata aquila*): 9p, Family group. 10p, Chick. 11p, Male in flight. 15p, Female and immature in flight.

Perf. 14½x14
1990, Mar. 5   **Litho.**   **Wmk. 373**
483	A88	9p multicolored	.30 .30
484	A88	10p multicolored	.32 .32
485	A88	11p multicolored	.35 .35
486	A88	15p multicolored	.48 .48
		Nos. 483-486 (4)	1.45 1.45

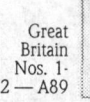 

Great Britain Nos. 1-2 — A89

Exhibition emblem and: 18p, Early Ascension cancellations. 25p, Unloading mail at Wideawake Airfield. £1, Main P.O., Royal Mail van.

1990, May 3   **Litho.**   *Perf. 14*
487	A89	9p shown	.30 .30
488	A89	18p multicolored	.60 .60
489	A89	25p multicolored	.85 .85
490	A89	£1 multicolored	3.35 3.35
		Nos. 487-490 (4)	5.10 5.10

Penny Black 150th anniv., Stamp World London '90.

Queen Mother, 90th Birthday
Common Design Types
1990, Aug. 4   **Wmk. 384**   *Perf. 14x15*
491	CD343	25p Portrait, 1940	.85 .85

Perf. 14½
492	CD344	£1 King, Queen with soldiers	3.35 3.35

Garth Castle, 1910 — A90

Designs: 18p, RMS St. Helena, 1982. 25p, Launching new RMS St. Helena, 1989. 70p, Duke of York launching new RMS St. Helena. £1, New RMS St. Helena.

Perf. 14½
1990, Sept. 13   **Litho.**   **Wmk. 373**
493	A90	9p multicolored	.32 .32
494	A90	18p multicolored	.64 .64
495	A90	25p multicolored	.90 .90
496	A90	70p multicolored	2.50 2.50
		Nos. 493-496 (4)	4.36 4.36

Souvenir Sheet
497	A90	£1 multicolored	3.50 3.50

See St. Helena Nos. 535-539, Tristan da Cunha Nos. 482-486.

Christmas — A91

Sculpture (8p) and paintings of Madonna and Child by: 8p, Felici. 18p, Unknown artist. 25p, Gebhard. 65p, Gritti.

1990, Oct. 24   *Perf. 14*
498	A91	8p multicolored	.28 .28
499	A91	18p multicolored	.64 .64
500	A91	25p multicolored	.90 .90
501	A91	65p multicolored	3.15 3.15
		Nos. 498-501 (4)	4.97 4.97

Nos. 410, 412 & 414 Ovptd. in **BRITISH FOR 175 YEARS** Silver

1991, Feb. 5   **Wmk. 384**   *Perf. 14½*
502	A74	25p on #410	1.00 1.00
503	A74	50p on #412	2.00 2.00
504	A74	£1 on #414	4.00 4.00
		Nos. 502-504 (3)	7.00 7.00

Elizabeth & Philip, Birthdays
Common Design Types
1991, June 18
505	CD345	25p multicolored	.80 .80
506	CD346	25p multicolored	.80 .80
a.		Pair, #505-506 + label	1.60 1.60

Military Uniforms Type of 1987

Royal Marines Equipment 1821-1844: a, Officer's shako, epaulettes, belt plate, button. b, Officer's cap, sword, epaulettes, belt plate. c, Drum Major's shako with cords, staff. d, Sergeant's shako, chevrons, belt plate, canteen. e, Drummer's drum, sticks, shako.

1991, Aug. 1   **Wmk. 373**   *Perf. 14*
507	A77	25p Strip of 5, #a.-e.	4.00 4.00

Atlantic Relay Station, 25th Anniv. A92

Designs: 15p, BBC Atlantic relay station. 18p, English Bay transmitters. 25p, Satellite receiving station, vert. 70p, Antenna support tower, vert.

1991, Sept. 17   **Wmk. 384**   *Perf. 14½*
508	A92	15p multicolored	.50 .50
509	A92	18p multicolored	.60 .60
510	A92	25p multicolored	.85 .85
511	A92	70p multicolored	2.40 2.40
		Nos. 508-511 (4)	4.35 4.35

Christmas — A93

Designs: 8p, St. Mary's Church, exterior. 18p, St. Mary's Church, interior. 25p, Grotto of Our Lady of Ascension, exterior. 65p, Grotto of Our Lady of Ascension, interior.

1991, Oct. 1   *Perf. 14*
512	A93	8p multicolored	.28 .28
513	A93	18p multicolored	.60 .60
514	A93	25p multicolored	.85 .85
515	A93	65p multicolored	2.25 2.25
		Nos. 512-515 (4)	3.98 3.98

Fish A94

Wmk. 373
1991, Dec. 10   **Litho.**   *Perf. 14*
516	A94	1p Blackfish	.15 .15
517	A94	2p Five finger	.15 .15
518	A94	4p Resplendent angelfish	.15 .15
519	A94	5p Silver fish	.16 .16
520	A94	9p Gurnard	.30 .30
521	A94	10p Blue dad	.32 .32
522	A94	15p Cunning fish	.50 .50
523	A94	18p Grouper	.60 .60
524	A94	20p Moray eel	.65 .65
525	A94	25p Hardback soldierfish	.85 .85
526	A94	30p Blue marlin	1.00 1.00
527	A94	50p Wahoo	1.65 1.65
528	A94	70p Yellowfin tuna	2.30 2.30
529	A94	£1 Blue shark	3.35 3.35
530	A94	£2.50 Bottlenose dolphin	8.35 8.35
		Nos. 516-530 (15)	20.48 20.48

Queen Elizabeth II's Accession to the Throne, 40th Anniv.
Common Design Type
Wmk. 373
1992, Feb. 6   **Litho.**   *Perf. 14*
531	CD349	9p multicolored	.30 .30
532	CD349	15p multicolored	.50 .50
533	CD349	18p multicolored	.60 .60
534	CD349	25p multicolored	.85 .85
535	CD349	70p multicolored	2.30 2.30
		Nos. 531-535 (5)	4.55 4.55

Discovery of America, 500th Anniv. — A95

Wmk. 373
1992, Feb. 18   **Litho.**   *Perf. 14*
536	A95	9p STV Eye of the Wind	.30 .30
537	A95	18p STV Soren Larsen	.60 .60
538	A95	25p Pinta, Santa Maria, & Nina	.85 .85
539	A95	70p Columbus, Santa Maria	2.30 2.30
		Nos. 536-539 (4)	4.05 4.05

World Columbian Stamp Expo '92, Chicago and Genoa '92 Intl. Philatelic Exhibitions.

Wideawake Airfield, 50th Anniv. — A96

Wmk. 373

1992, May 5 Litho. *Perf. 14*

540 A96 15p Control tower .50 .50
541 A96 18p Nose hangar .60 .60
542 A96 25p Construction work .85 .85
543 A96 70p Laying fuel pipeline 2.30 2.30
Nos. 540-543 (4) 4.25 4.25

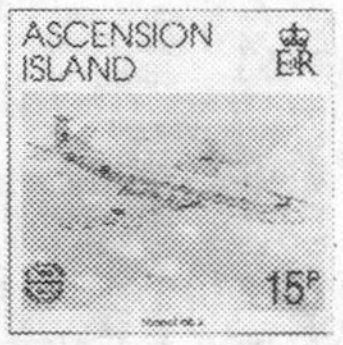

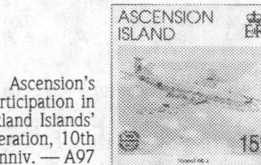

Ascension's Participation in Falkland Islands' Liberation, 10th Anniv. — A97

Designs: #548a, 15p + 3p like #544. b, 18p + 4p like #545. c, 25p + 5p like #546. d, 65p + 13p like #547.

Wmk. 373

1992, June 12 Litho. *Perf. 14*

544 A97 15p Nimrod Mk.2 .50 .50
545 A97 18p VC10 .60 .60
546 A97 25p Wessex HU Mk.5 helicopter .85 .85
547 A97 65p Vulcan B2 2.20 2.20
Nos. 544-547 (4) 4.15 4.15

Souvenir Sheet

548 A97 Sheet of 4, #a.-d. 5.00 5.00

Surtax for Soldiers', Sailors' and Airmen's Families Association.

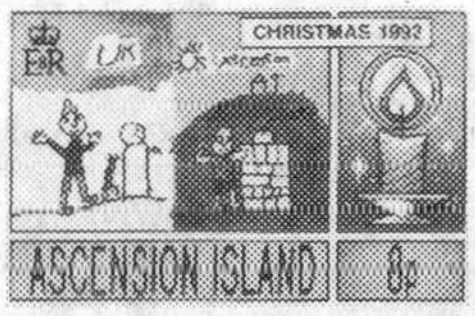

Christmas A98

Children's drawings: 8p, Snowman, rocks, candle. 18p, Underwater Santa, Christmas tree. 25p, Hello, bells. 65p, Nativity Scene, angel.

Wmk. 384

1992, Oct. 13 Litho. *Perf. 14*

549 A98 8p multicolored .30 .30
550 A98 18p multicolored .70 .70
551 A98 25p multicolored .95 .95
552 A98 65p multicolored 2.50 2.50
Nos. 549-552 (4) 4.45 4.45

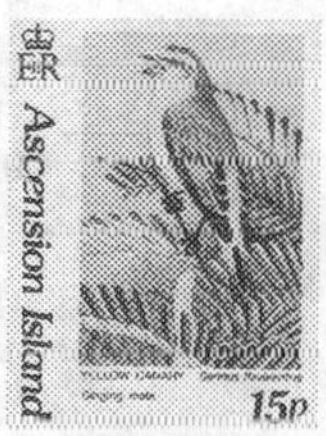

Yellow Canary — A99

Perf. 14½

1993, Jan. 12 Litho. Wmk. 373

553 A99 15p Singing male .45 .45
554 A99 18p Adult male, female .55 .55
555 A99 25p Young calling for food .80 .80
556 A99 70p Mixed flock 2.15 2.15
Nos. 553-556 (4) 3.95 3.95

Royal Air Force, 75th Anniv.

Common Design Type

Designs: 20p, Sopwith Snipe. No. 558, Supermarine Southampton. 30p, Avro Anson. 70p, Vickers Wellington 1C.

No. 561a, Westland Lysander. b, Gloster Meteor. c, DeHavilland Comet. d, British Aerospace Nimrod.

Wmk. 373

1993, Apr. 1 Litho. *Perf. 14*

557 CD350 20p multicolored .58 .58
558 CD350 25p multicolored .72 .72
559 CD350 30p multicolored .85 .85
560 CD350 70p multicolored 2.15 2.15
Nos. 557-560 (4) 4.30 4.30

Souvenir Sheet

561 CD350 25p Sheet of 4, #a.-d. 2.90 2.90

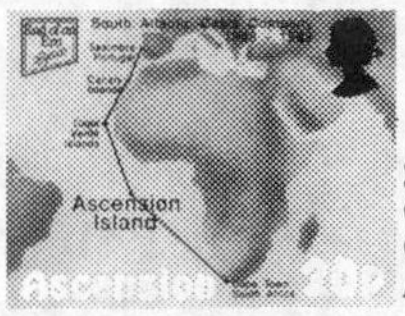

South Atlantic Cable Company, 25th Anniv. — A100

Designs: 20p, Map showing cable route. 25p, Cable ship laying cable. 30p, Map of Ascension. 70p, Cable ship off Ascension.

Perf. 14x14½

1993, June 8 Litho. Wmk. 384

562 A100 20p multicolored .60 .60
563 A100 25p multicolored .75 .75
564 A100 30p multicolored .90 .90
565 A100 70p multicolored 2.10 2.10
Nos. 562-565 (4) 4.35 4.35

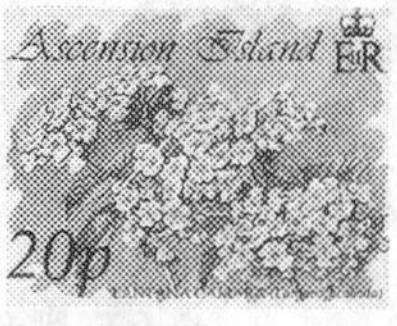

Flowers A101

Perf. 14x14½

1993, Aug. 3 Litho. Wmk. 384

566 A101 20p Lantana camara .60 .60
567 A101 25p Moonflower .75 .75
568 A101 30p Hibiscus .90 .90
569 A101 70p Frangipani 2.10 2.10
Nos. 566-569 (4) 4.35 4.35

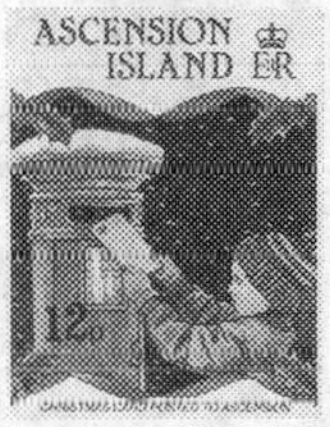

Christmas — A102

Designs: 12p, Child mailing Christmas card. 20p, Mail loaded onto Tristar. 25p, Plane in flight. 30p, Mail unloaded at Wideawake Airfield. 65p, Child reading card, Georgetown.

Perf. 14½x14

1993, Oct. 19 Litho. Wmk. 373

570 A102 12p multicolored .35 .35
571 A102 20p multicolored .60 .60
572 A102 25p multicolored .75 .75
573 A102 30p multicolored .90 .90
574 A102 65p multicolored 2.00 2.00
a. Souvenir sheet of 5, #570-574 4.50 4.50
Nos. 570-574 (5) 4.60 4.60

Stamps from No. 574a show a continuous design, while Nos. 571-574 have white borders on side.

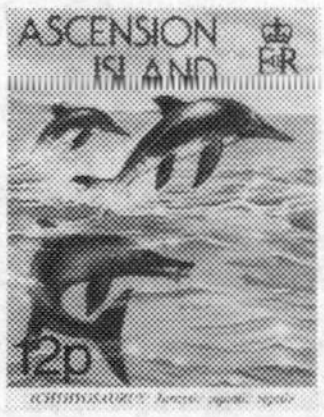

Prehistoric Aquatic Reptiles — A103

1994, Jan. 25 Wmk. 373 *Perf. 14*

575 A103 12p Ichthyosaurus .35 .35
576 A103 20p Metriorhynchus .60 .60
577 A103 25p Mosasaurus .75 .75
578 A103 30p Elasmosaurus .90 .90
579 A103 65p Plesiosaurus 1.90 1.90
Nos. 575-579 (5) 4.50 4.50

Ovptd. with Hong Kong '94 Emblem

1994, Feb. 18

580 A103 12p on #575 .35 .35
581 A103 20p on #576 .60 .60
582 A103 25p on #577 .75 .75
583 A103 30p on #578 .90 .90
584 A103 65p on #579 1.90 1.90
Nos. 580-584 (5) 4.50 4.50

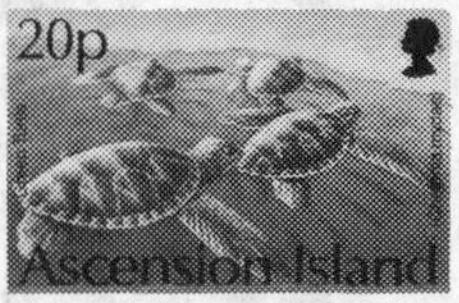

Green Turtle A104

Designs: 20p, Four on beach. 25p, Crawling in sand. No. 587, Crawling from sea. 65p, Swimming.

No. 589a, Side view, crawling from sea. b, Digging nest. c, Hatchlings heading to sea. d, Digging nest, diff.

1994, Mar. 22

585 A104 20p multicolored .60 .60
586 A104 25p multicolored .75 .75
587 A104 30p multicolored .90 .90
588 A104 65p multicolored 1.90 1.90
Nos. 585-588 (4) 4.15 4.15

Souvenir Sheet

589 A104 30p Sheet of 4, #a.-d. 3.50 3.50

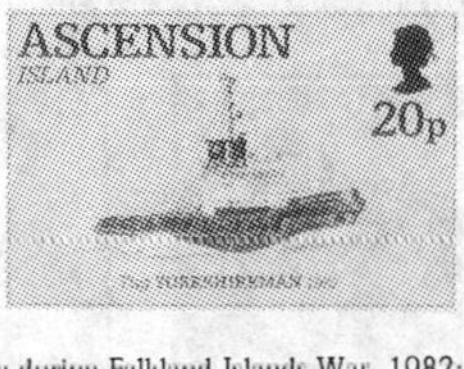

Civilian Ships A105

Ships serving during Falkland Islands War, 1982: 20p, Tug Yorkshireman. 25p, Minesweeper support ship RMS St. Helena. 30p, Oil tanker British ESK. 65p, Cruise liner Uganda, hospital ship.

1994, June 14

590 A105 20p multicolored .60 .60
591 A105 25p multicolored .75 .75
592 A105 30p multicolored .90 .90
593 A105 65p multicolored 1.90 1.90
Nos. 590-593 (4) 4.15 4.15

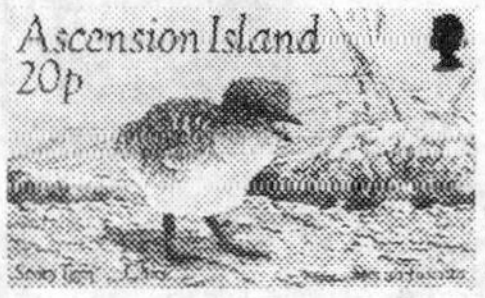

Sooty Tern A106

1994, Aug. 16

594 A106 20p Chick .60 .60
595 A106 25p Juvenile .75 .75
596 A106 30p Brooding adult .90 .90
597 A106 65p Displaying male 1.90 1.90
Nos. 594-597 (4) 4.15 4.15

Souvenir Sheet

598 A106 £1 Dread 3.00 3.00

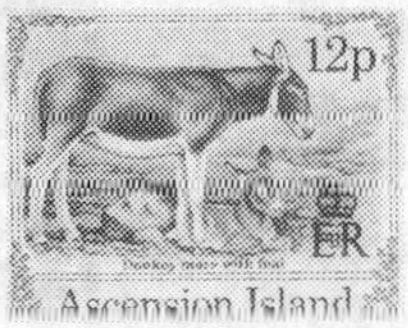

Christmas A107

Donkeys: 12p, Mare with foal. 20p, Young adult. 25p, Foal. 30p, Adult, egrets. 65p, Adult.

1994, Oct. 11 *Perf. 14x14½*

599 A107 12p multicolored .38 .38
600 A107 20p multicolored .60 .60
601 A107 25p multicolored .75 .75
602 A107 30p multicolored .95 .95
603 A107 65p multicolored 2.00 2.00
Nos. 599-603 (5) 4.68 4.68

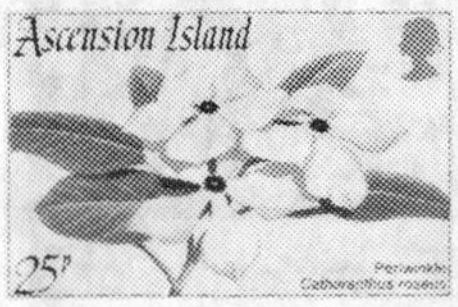

Flowers A108

Designs: 20p, Leonurus japonicus, vert. 25p, Periwinkle. 30p, Four o'clock, vert. 65p, Blood flower.

1995, Jan. 10 *Perf. 14*

604 A108 20p multicolored .60 .60
605 A108 25p multicolored .75 .75
606 A108 30p multicolored .95 .95
607 A108 65p multicolored 2.00 2.00
Nos. 604-607 (4) 4.30 4.30

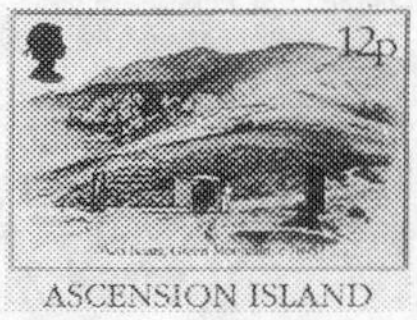

Island Scenes, c. 1895 A109

Designs: 12p, Horse-drawn wagon, Two Boats, Green Mountain. 20p, Island stewards' store. 25p, Royal Navy headquarters, barracks. 30p, Police office. 65p, Pier head.

1995, Mar. 7 Wmk. 384 *Perf. 14½*

608 A109 12p sepia .35 .35
609 A109 20p sepia .60 .60
610 A109 25p sepia .75 .75
611 A109 30p sepia .90 .90
612 A109 65p sepia 2.00 2.00
Nos. 608-612 (5) 4.60 4.60

End of World War II, 50th Anniv.

Common Design Types

Designs: 20p, 5.5-inch guns taken from HMS Hood, 1941. 25p, Fairey Swordfish, first aircraft to land at Ascension. 30p, HMS Dorsetshire patrolling South Atlantic. 65p, HMS Devonshire patrolling South Atlantic.

£1, Reverse of War Medal, 1939-45.

1995, May 8 Wmk. 373 *Perf. 14*

613 CD351 20p multicolored .60 .60
614 CD351 25p multicolored .75 .75
615 CD351 30p multicolored .90 .90
616 CD351 65p multicolored 2.00 2.00
Nos. 613-616 (4) 4.25 4.25

Souvenir Sheet

617 CD352 £1 multicolored 3.00 3.00

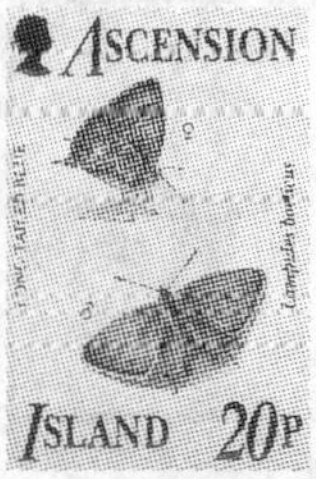

Butterflies — A110

1995, Sept. 1 Wmk. 384

618 A110 20p Long-tailed blue .60 .60
619 A110 25p Painted lady .75 .75
620 A110 30p Diadem .90 .90
621 A110 65p African monarch 2.00 2.00
Nos. 618-621 (4) 4.25 4.25

Souvenir Sheet

622 A110 £1 Red admiral 3.00 3.00

Singapore '95 (#622).

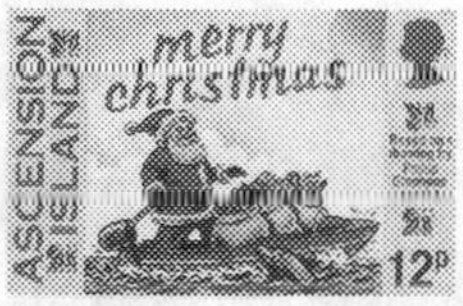

Christmas A111

Designs based on children's drawings: 12p, Santa on boat. 20p, Santa on wall. 25p, Santa in chimney. 30p, Santa on dolphin. 65p, South Atlantic run.

1995, Oct. 10 Wmk. 373

623 A111 12p multicolored .35 .35
624 A111 20p multicolored .60 .60
625 A111 25p multicolored .75 .75
626 A111 30p multicolored .90 .90
627 A111 65p multicolored 2.00 2.00
Nos. 623-627 (5) 4.60 4.60

POSTAGE DUE STAMPS

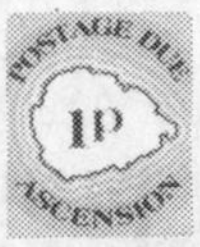

Outline Map of Ascension — D1

1986 Litho. *Perf. 15x14*

J1 D1 1p beige & brown .15 .15
J2 D1 2p orange & brown .15 .15
J3 D1 5p org ver & brn .15 .15
J4 D1 7p violet & black .20 .20

J5 D1 10p ultra & black   .25   .25
J6 D1 25p pale green & blk   .60   .60
        Set value   1.25 1.25

AUSTRALIA

ò–'strāl–yə

LOCATION — Oceania, south of Indonesia, bounded on the west by the Indian Ocean
GOVT. — Self-governing dominion of the British Commonwealth
AREA — 2,967,909 sq. mi.
POP. — 15,276,100 (est. 1982)
CAPITAL — Canberra

Australia includes the former British colonies of New South Wales, Victoria, Queensland, South Australia, Western Australia and Tasmania.

12 Pence = 1 Shilling
20 Shillings = 1 Pound
100 Cents = 1 Dollar (1966)

Catalogue values for unused stamps in this country are for Never Hinged items, beginning with Scott 197 in the regular postage section, Scott C6 in the air post section, Scott J71 in the postage due section, and all of the Australian Antarctic Territory.

Watermarks

Wmk. 8- Wide Crown and Wide A

Wmk. 9- Wide Crown and Narrow A

Wmk. 10- Narrow Crown and Narrow A

Wmk. 11- Multiple Crown and A

Wmk. 12- Crown and Single-lined A

Wmk. 13- Large Crown and Double-lined A

Wmk. 55- Large Crown and NSW

Wmk. 203- Small Crown and A Multiple

Wmk. 228- Small Crown and C of A Multiple

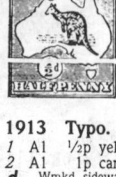
Kangaroo and Map — A1

1913   Typo. Wmk. 8   Perf. 11½, 12

1	A1	½p yellow green	5.00	1.75
2	A1	1p carmine	6.00	.50
d.		Wmkd. sideways	800.00	210.00
3	A1	2p gray	20.00	4.00
4	A1	2½p dark blue	22.50	7.00
5	A1	3p olive bister	37.50	4.50
6	A1	4p orange	45.00	18.00
7	A1	5p orange brown	37.50	25.00
8	A1	6p ultra	42.50	12.00
9	A1	9p purple	37.50	18.00
10	A1	1sh blue green	45.00	11.00
11	A1	2sh brown	150.00	75.00
12	A1	5sh yellow & gray	250.00	140.00
13	A1	10sh pink & gray	600.00	425.00
		Never hinged	725.00	
14	A1	£1 ultra & brown	1,300.	1,000.
		Never hinged	1,500.	
15	A1	£2 dp rose & blk	2,250.	1,400.
		Nos. 1-12 (12)	698.50	316.75
		Set, never hinged	1,300.	

On No. 4 "2½d" is colorless in solid blue background.
See Nos. 38-59, 96-102, 121-129, 206.

King George V A2

Kookaburra (Kingfisher) A3

1913-14   Unwmk. Engr.   Perf. 11

17	A2	1p carmine	4.25	4.25
		Never hinged	5.75	
a.		Vert. pair, imperf. between	2,000.	
18	A3	6p lake brown ('14)	70.00	35.00
		Never hinged	150.00	

See No. 95.

A4

ONE PENNY
Die I - Normal die, having outside the oval band with "AUSTRALIA" a white line and a heavy colored line.
Die Ia - As die I with a small white spur below the right serif at foot of the "1" in left tablet.
Die II - A heavy colored line between two white lines back of the emu's neck. A white scratch crossing the vertical shading lines at the lowest point of the bust.
TWO PENCE
Die I - The numeral "2" is thin. The upper curve is 1mm. across and a very thin line connects it with the foot of the figure.
Die II - The "2" is thicker than in die I. The top curve is 1½mm across and a strong white line connects it with the foot of the figure. There are thin vertical lines across the ends of the groups of short horizontal lines at each side of "TWO PENCE."
THREE PENCE
Die I - The ends of the thin horizontal lines in the background run into the solid color of the various parts of the design. The numerals are thin and the letters of "THREE PENCE" are thin and irregular.
Die II - The oval about the portrait, the shields with the numerals, etc., are outlined by thin white lines which separate them from the horizontal background lines. The numerals are thick and the letters of "THREE PENCE" are heavy and regular.
FIVE PENCE
Die I - The top of the flag of the "5" is slightly curved.
Die II - The top of the flag of the "5" is flat. There are thin white vertical lines across the ends of the short horizontal lines at each side of "FIVE PENCE."

1914-24   Typo. Wmk. 9   Perf. 14

19	A4	½p emerald ('15)	2.50	.40
a.		Thin "½" at right	1,400.	700.00
20	A4	½p orange ('23)	2.50	1.25
21	A4	1p red (I)	4.25	.15
a.		1p carmine rose (I)	8.25	4.75
b.		1p red (Ia)	375.00	4.75

c.		1p carmine (II) ('18)	60.00	30.00
		Never hinged	95.00	
22	A4	1p vio (I) ('22)	3.50	.60
a.		1p red violet	5.50	1.50
		Never hinged	8.00	
23	A4	1p green (I) ('24)	3.50	.20
24	A4	1½p choc ('18)	5.00	.20
a.		1½p red brown	5.50	.20
		Never hinged	12.00	
b.		1½p black brown	4.50	.25
		Never hinged	6.75	
25	A4	1½p emerald ('23)	2.75	.15
26	A4	1½p scarlet ('24)	2.00	.15
27	A4	2p brn org (I) ('20)	5.00	.25
a.		2p orange (I) ('20)	6.50	.30
		Never hinged	19.00	
b.		Booklet pane of 6		
28	A4	2p red (I) ('22)	5.00	.15
29	A4	2p red brn (I) ('24)	15.00	3.75
30	A4	3p ultra (I) ('24)	14.00	2.25
31	A4	4p orange ('15)	17.00	2.25
a.		4p yellow	110.00	16.00
32	A4	4p violet ('21)	15.00	13.00
33	A4	4p lt ultra ('22)	37.50	4.50
34	A4	4p ol bis ('24)	17.50	4.00
35	A4	4½p violet ('24)	17.50	4.00
36	A4	5p org brn (I) ('15)	18.00	3.00
37	A4	1sh4p lt blue ('20)	62.50	19.00
		Never hinged	95.00	
		Nos. 19-37 (19)	250.00	59.25
		Set, never hinged	675.00	

See Nos. 60-76, 113-120, 124.

1915   Perf. 11½, 12

38	A1	2p gray	37.50	7.50
		Never hinged	95.00	
39	A1	2½p dark blue	37.50	15.00
		Never hinged	140.00	
40	A1	6p ultra	125.00	19.00
		Never hinged	275.00	
41	A1	9p violet	125.00	32.50
		Never hinged	275.00	
42	A1	1sh blue green	125.00	20.00
		Never hinged	325.00	
43	A1	2sh brown	375.00	87.50
		Never hinged	900.00	
44	A1	5sh yellow & gray	700.00	165.00
		Never hinged	1,500.	
		Nos. 38-44 (7)	1,525.	346.50

1915-24   Wmk. 10

45	A1	2p gray	15.00	2.75
46	A1	2½p dark blue	13.00	4.00
a.		"1" of fraction omitted	10,000.	3,500.
47	A1	3p olive bister	13.00	4.00
48	A1	6p ultra	35.00	4.00
a.		6p chalky blue	50.00	4.25
49	A1	6p yel brn ('23)	13.00	1.75
50	A1	9p violet	26.00	2.75
a.		9p lilac	22.50	3.25
51	A1	1sh blue grn ('16)	25.00	1.90
a.		Wmkd. sideways ('20)	62.50	62.50
52	A1	2sh brown ('16)	140.00	15.00
53	A1	2sh vio brn ('24)	45.00	10.00
54	A1	5sh yel & gray ('18)	165.00	50.00
a.		Wmkd. sideways	2,500.	2,000.
55	A1	10sh brt pink & gray ('17)	400.00	150.00
		Never hinged	750.00	
a.		Wmkd. sideways	3,500.	2,000.
56	A1	£1 ultra & brn ('16)	1,250.	700.00
a.		£1 ultra & brn org ('16)	1,300.	700.00
b.		Wmkd. sideways	5,000.	2,000.
57	A1	£1 gray ('24)	450.00	275.00
		Never hinged	825.00	
58	A1	£2 dp rose & blk ('19)	2,100.	1,175.
59	A1	£2 rose & vio brn ('24)	1,600.	1,100.
		Nos. 45-54 (10)	490.00	94.15
		Set, never hinged	1,300.	

Perf. 14, 14½, 14½x14
1918-23   Wmk. 11

60	A4	½p emerald	2.00	.50
		Never hinged	4.25	
a.		Thin "½" at right	110.00	45.00
61	A4	1p rose (I)	18.00	9.00
		Never hinged	27.50	
62	A4	1p dl grn (I) ('24)	3.75	3.25
		Never hinged	7.00	
63	A4	1½p choc ('19)	5.00	.70
		Never hinged	11.00	
a.		1½p red brown ('19)	6.75	.80
		Never hinged	12.50	
		Nos. 60-63 (4)	28.75	13.45

1924   Unwmk.   Perf. 14

64	A4	1p green (I)	4.25	3.75
		Never hinged	5.50	
65	A4	1½p carmine	4.25	3.00
		Never hinged	6.75	

1926-30   Perf. 14, 13½x12½   Wmk. 203

66	A4	½p orange	1.40	1.00
a.		Perf. 14 ('27)	5.25	5.25
		Never hinged	6.75	
67	A4	1p green (I)	1.50	.40
a.		1p green (Ia)	47.50	60.00
		Never hinged	65.00	
b.		Perf. 14	2.75	.45
		Never hinged	4.50	
68	A4	1½p rose red ('27)	2.75	.15
c.		Perf. 14 ('26)	6.00	.65
		Never hinged	12.00	
69	A4	1½p red brn ('30)	4.00	2.00
70	A4	2p red brn ('28)	7.00	4.00
a.		Perf. 14 ('27)	24.00	16.00
			40.00	

71 A4	2p red (II) ('30)	4.00	.20
a.	2p red (I) ('30)	5.00	1.65
	Never hinged	12.00	
c.	Unwmkd. (II) ('31)	1,500.	1,000.
72 A4	3p ultra (I)	22.50	2.25
a.	3p ultra (II) ('29)	14.00	1.00
	Never hinged	30.00	
b.	Perf. 14	17.50	4.50
	Never hinged	37.50	
73 A4	4p ol bis ('29)	16.00	.80
a.	Perf. 14 ('28)	42.50	22.50
	Never hinged	85.00	
74 A4	4½p dk vio ('27)	17.00	3.75
a.	Perf. 13½x12½ ('28)	47.50	13.00
	Never hinged	67.50	
75 A4	5p brn buff (II) ('30)	16.00	.95
76 A4	1sh4p pale turq bl ('28)	85.00	20.00
a.	Perf. 14 ('27)	125.00	67.50
	Never hinged	300.00	
	Nos. 66-76 (11)	177.15	35.50
	Set, never hinged	275.00	

For surcharges & overprints see #106-107, O3-O4.

 Parliament House, Canberra — A5

Unwmk.

1927, May 9 Engr. *Perf. 11*

94 A5	1½p brown red	.45	.20
	Never hinged	.85	
a.	Vert. pair, imperf. btwn.	2,750.	2,500.

Opening of Parliament House at Canberra.

Melbourne Exhibition Issue
Kookaburra Type of 1914
1928, Oct. 29

95 A3	3p deep blue	3.75	3.00
	Never hinged	5.25	
a.	Pane of 4	110.00	135.00
	Never hinged	175.00	

No. 95a was issued at the Melbourne Intl. Phil. Exhib. No marginal inscription. Printed in sheets of 60 stamps (15 panes). No. 95 was printed in sheets of 120 and issued Nov. 2 throughout Australia.

Kangaroo-Map Type of 1913
Perf. 11½, 12

1929-30 Wmk. 203 Typo.

96 A1	6p brown	17.50	2.00
	Never hinged	26.00	
97 A1	9p violet	25.00	3.50
	Never hinged	60.00	
98 A1	1sh blue green	22.50	2.25
	Never hinged	65.00	
99 A1	2sh red brown	60.00	9.00
	Never hinged	125.00	
100 A1	5sh yel & gray	175.00	60.00
	Never hinged	325.00	
101 A1	10sh pink & gray	325.00	250.00
	Never hinged	575.00	
102 A1	£2 dl red & blk ('30)	1,800.	400.00
	Nos. 96-102 (7)	2,425.	726.75

For overprint see No. O5.

 Black Swan — A6     Capt. Charles Sturt — A7

Unwmk.

1929, Sept. 28 Engr. *Perf. 11*

103 A6	1½p dull red	.75	.75
	Never hinged	1.40	

Centenary of Western Australia.

1930, June 2

104 A7	1½p dark red	.40	.15
	Never hinged	.45	
105 A7	3p dark blue	3.50	3.00

Capt. Charles Sturt's exploration of the Murray River, cent.

FIVE

Nos. 68 and 74a surcharged

PENCE

1930 Wmk. 203 *Perf. 13½x12½*

106 A4	2p on 1½p rose red	.75	.25
	Never hinged	1.50	
107 A4	5p on 4½p dark violet	5.00	5.00
	Never hinged	10.00	

 "Southern Cross" over Hemispheres A8

Perf. 11, 11½

1931, Mar. 19 Unwmk.

111 A8	2p dull red	.75	.15
	Never hinged	1.10	
112 A8	3p blue	4.75	3.25
	Never hinged	8.00	
	Nos. 111-112, C2 (3)	13.00	10.90

Trans-oceanic flights (1928-1930) of Sir Charles Edward Kingsford-Smith (1897-1935).
See #C3 for similar design. For overprints see #CO1, O1-O2.

Types of 1913-23 Issues
Perf. 13½x12½

1931-36 Typo. Wmk. 228

113 A4	½p orange ('32)	2.00	1.65
	Never hinged	3.00	
114 A4	1p green (I)	.90	.15
	Never hinged	1.90	
115 A4	1½p red brn ('36)	3.75	3.25
	Never hinged	6.50	
116 A4	2p red (II)	1.00	.15
	Never hinged	1.75	
117 A4	3p ultra (II) ('32)	13.00	.30
	Never hinged	19.00	
118 A4	4p ol bis ('33)	16.00	.45
	Never hinged	26.00	
120 A4	5p brn buff (II) ('32)	12.00	.30
	Never hinged	20.00	

Perf. 11½, 12; 13½x12½ (1sh4p)

121 A1	6p yel brn ('36)	15.00	10.00
	Never hinged	20.00	
122 A1	9p violet ('32)	11.00	1.75
	Never hinged	27.50	
124 A4	1sh4p lt blue ('32)	47.50	6.00
	Never hinged	135.00	
125 A1	2sh red brn ('35)	3.50	.90
	Never hinged	5.00	
126 A1	5sh yel & gray ('32)	125.00	18.00
127 A1	10sh pink & gray ('32)	300.00	60.00
128 A1	£1 gray ('32)	400.00	165.00
129 A1	£2 dl rose & blk ('34)	2,000.	300.00
	Nos. 113-129 (15)	2,950.	567.90

For redrawn 2sh see No. 206. For overprints see Nos. O6-O11.

 Sydney Harbor Bridge — A9

Unwmk.

1932, Mar. 14 Engr. *Perf. 11*

130 A9	2p red	1.90	.50
	Never hinged	2.25	
131 A9	3p blue	4.00	3.00
	Never hinged	6.75	
132 A9	5sh gray green	350.00	200.00
	Never hinged	575.00	

Wmk. 228
Perf. 10½
Typo.

133 A9	2p red	1.65	.80
	Never hinged	2.75	

Opening of the Sydney Harbor Bridge on Mar. 19, 1932.
Value for 5sh, used, is for CTO copies.
For overprints see Nos. O12-O13.

 Kookaburra A14    Male Lyrebird A16

1932, June 1 *Perf. 13½x12½*

139 A14	6p light brown	15.00	.50
	Never hinged	25.00	

1932, Feb. 15 Unwmk. *Perf. 11*
Size: 21½x25mm

141 A16	1sh green	37.50	.75
	Never hinged	75.00	

See #175, 300. For overprint see #O14.

 Yarra Yarra Tribesman, Yarra River and View of Melbourne A17

Perf. 10½

1934, July 2 Engr. Wmk. 228

142 A17	2p vermilion	1.10	.40
	Never hinged	1.40	
a.	Perf. 11½	3.75	1.00
	Never hinged	6.50	
143 A17	3p blue	2.50	2.25
	Never hinged	5.25	
a.	Perf. 11½	4.25	2.50
	Never hinged	6.50	
144 A17	1sh black	35.00	15.00
	Never hinged	67.50	
a.	Perf. 11½	40.00	16.00
	Never hinged	72.50	
	Nos. 142-144 (3)	38.60	17.65

Centenary of Victoria.

 Merino Sheep — A18

1934, Nov. 1 *Perf. 11½*

147 A18	2p copper red	2.50	.20
	Never hinged	3.50	
148 A18	3p dark blue	8.50	4.50
	Never hinged	12.00	
149 A18	9p dark violet	35.00	25.00
	Never hinged	67.50	
	Nos. 147-149 (3)	46.00	29.70

Capt. John Macarthur (1767-1834), "father of the New South Wales woolen industry." There are two types of the 2p.

 Cenotaph in Whitehall, London — A19    George V on His Charger "Anzac" — A20

1935, Mar. 18 *Perf. 13½x12½*

150 A19	2p red	.65	.15
		.90	

Perf. 11

151 A19	1sh black	37.50	25.00
	Never hinged	70.00	

Anzacs' landing at Gallipoli, 20th anniv.

1935, May 2 *Perf. 11½*

152 A20	2p red	.20	.15
	Never hinged	.30	
153 A20	3p blue	2.25	1.90
	Never hinged	7.50	
154 A20	2sh violet	35.00	32.50
	Never hinged	55.00	
	Nos. 152-154 (3)	37.45	34.55

25th anniv. of the reign of King George V.

 Amphitrite Joining Cables between Australia and Tasmania — A21

1936, Apr. 1

157 A21	2p red	.35	.15
	Never hinged	.45	
158 A21	3p dark blue	3.25	2.00
	Never hinged	4.75	

Australia/Tasmania telephone link.

 Proclamation Tree and View of Adelaide, 1936 — A22

1936, Aug. 3

159	A22	2p red	.40	.15
		Never hinged	1.10	
160	A22	3p dark blue	3.25	2.75
		Never hinged	5.00	
161	A22	1sh green	11.00	6.50
		Never hinged	20.00	
		Nos. 159-161 (3)	14.65	9.40

Centenary of South Australia.

Gov. Arthur Phillip at Sydney Cove — A23

1937, Oct. 1 *Perf. 13x13½*

163	A23	2p red	.90	.15
		Never hinged	1.90	
164	A23	3p ultra	2.75	1.65
		Never hinged	4.50	
165	A23	9p violet	16.00	11.00
		Never hinged	25.00	
		Nos. 163-165 (3)	19.65	12.80

150th anniversary of New South Wales.

Kangaroo A24

Queen Elizabeth A25

King George VI A26 A27

Koala — A28

Merino Sheep — A29

Kookaburra (Kingfisher) A30

Platypus A31

Queen Elizabeth and King George VI in Coronation Robes A32 A33

King George VI and Queen Elizabeth — A34

Two Types of A25 and A26:

Type I - Highlighted background. Lines around letters of Australia Postage and numerals of value.

Type II - Background of heavy diagonal lines without the highlighted effect. No lines around letters and numerals.

Perf. 13½x14, 14x13½

1937-46 Engr. Wmk. 228

166	A24	½p org, perf. 15x14 ('42)	.15	.15
a.		Perf. 13½x14 ('38)	.70	.25
a.		Never hinged	1.25	
167	A25	1p emerald (I)	.20	.15
168	A26	1½p dull red brn (II)	3.00	2.00
a.		Perf. 15x14 ('41)	4.25	3.50
a.		Never hinged	6.25	
169	A26	2p scarlet (I)	.30	.15
170	A27	3p dp ultra, thin paper ('38)	12.00	.35
a.		3p ultramarine	12.00	.50
a.		Never hinged	30.00	
171	A28	4p grn, perf. 15x14 ('42)	.40	.20
a.		Perf. 13½x14 ('38)	2.50	.90
a.		Never hinged	5.00	
172	A29	5p pale rose vio, perf. 14x15 ('46)	.60	.50
a.		Perf. 14x13½ ('38)	2.50	.55
a.		Never hinged	4.00	
173	A30	6p vio brn, perf. 15x14 ('42)	.60	.15
a.		Perf. 13½x14	5.25	.85
a.		Never hinged	15.00	
b.		6p chocolate, perf. 15x14	1.00	.15
b.		Never hinged	1.50	
174	A31	9p sep, perf. 14x15 ('43)	.90	.15
a.		Perf. 14x13½ ('38)	3.75	.90
a.		Never hinged	7.25	
175	A16	1sh gray grn, perf. 15x14 ('41)	1.10	.15
a.		Perf. 13½x14	17.00	2.00
a.		Never hinged	47.50	
176	A27	1sh4p magenta ('38)	1.50	.45

Perf. 13½

177	A32	5sh dl red brn ('38)	5.00	2.50
178	A33	10sh dl gray vio ('38)	30.00	12.00
179	A34	£1 bl gray ('38)	60.00	27.50
		Nos. 166-179 (14)	115.75	46.40
		Set, never hinged	200.00	

No. 175 measures 17½x21½mm.

See #223A, 293, 295, 298, 300. For surcharge & overprints see #190, M1, M4-M5, M7.

1938-42 *Perf. 15x14*

180	A25	1p emerald (II)	.55	.25
181	A25	1p dl red brn (II) ('41)	.50	.15
181B	A26	1½p bl grn (II) ('41)	.60	.15
182	A26	2p scarlet (II)	.60	.15
182B	A26	2p red vio (II) ('41)	.20	.15
183	A27	3p dk ultra ('40)	12.00	.70
183A	A27	3p dk vio brn ('42)	.20	.15
		Nos. 180-183A (7)	14.65	
		Set value		1.20
		Set, never hinged	35.00	

No. 183 differs from Nos. 170-170a in the shading lines on the king's left eyebrow which go downward, left to right, instead of the reverse. Also, more of the left epaulette shows.

For surcharges & overprint see #188-189, M3.

Coil Perforation

A special perforation was applied to stamps intended for use in coils to make separation easier. It consists of small and large holes (2 small, 10 large, 2 small) on the stamps' narrow side. Some of the stamps so perforated were sold in sheets.

This coil perforation may be found on Nos. 166, 181, 182, 182B, 193, 215, 223A, 231, 257, 315-316, 319, 319a and others.

Nurse, Sailor, Soldier and Aviator — A35

Perf. 13½x13

1940, July 15 Engr. Wmk. 228

184	A35	1p green	.85	.15
		Never hinged	2.00	
185	A35	2p red	.85	.15
		Never hinged	2.00	
186	A35	3p ultra	4.00	2.75
		Never hinged	7.00	
187	A35	6p chocolate	11.00	9.50
		Never hinged	20.00	
		Nos. 184-187 (4)	16.70	12.55

Australia's participation in WWII.

No. 182 Surcharged in Blue 2½d

1941, Dec. 10 *Perf. 15x14*

188	A26	2½p on 2p red	.20	.15
		Never hinged	.25	

No. 183 Surcharged in Blue and Yellow 3½d

189	A27	3½p on 3p dk ultra	.40	.35
		Never hinged	.50	

No. 172a Surcharged in Purple 5½d

Perf. 14x13½

190	A29	5½p on 5p pale rose violet	3.25	3.50
		Never hinged	4.00	
		Nos. 188-190 (3)	3.85	4.00

Queen Elizabeth A36 A37

King George VI A38 A39

George VI and Blue Wrens — A40

Emu — A41

1942-44 Engr. *Perf. 14½x14*

191	A36	1p brown vio ('43)	.15	.15
192	A37	1½p green	.18	.15
193	A38	2p lt rose vio ('44)	.15	.15
194	A39	2½p red	.18	.15
195	A40	3½p ultramarine	.18	.15
196	A41	5½p indigo	.35	.15
		Nos. 191-196 (6)	1.19	
		Set value		.35
		Set, never hinged	1.75	

See #224-225. For overprint see #M2.

Catalogue values for unused stamps in this section, from this point to the end of the section, are for Never Hinged items.

Duke and Duchess of Gloucester — A42

1945, Feb. 19 Engr. *Perf. 14½*

197	A42	2½p brown red	.15	.15
198	A42	3½p bright ultra	.22	.28
199	A42	5½p indigo	.22	.45
		Nos. 197-199 (3)	.59	.88

Inauguration of the Duke of Gloucester as Governor General.

Official Crest and Inscriptions — A43

Dove and Australian Flag A44

Angel of Peace; "Motherhood" and "Industry" A45

1946, Feb. 18 Wmk. 228 *Perf. 14½*

200	A43	2½p carmine	.18	.15
201	A44	3½p deep ultra	.18	.22
202	A45	5½p deep yellow green	.38	.35
		Nos. 200-202 (3)	.74	.72

End of WWII. See #1456-1458.

Sir Thomas Mitchell and Map of Queensland — A46

1946, Oct. 14

203	A46	2½p dark carmine	.15	.15
204	A46	3½p deep ultra	.20	.25
205	A46	1sh olive green	.80	.38
		Nos. 203-205 (3)	1.15	.78

Sir Thomas Mitchell's exploration of central Queensland, cent.

Kangaroo-Map Type of 1913 Redrawn

1945, Dec. Typo. *Perf. 11½*

206	A1	2sh dk red brown	4.50	1.65

The R and A of AUSTRALIA are separated at the base and there is a single line between the value tablet and "Two Shillings." On No. 125 the tail of the R touches the A, while two lines appear between value tablet and "Two Shillings." There are many other minor differences in the design.

For overprint see No. M6.

John Shortland — A47

Pouring Steel — A48

Loading Coal — A49

1947, Sept. Engr. *Perf. 14½x14*

207	A47	2½p brown red	.28	.15

Perf. 14½

208	A48	3½p deep blue	.22	.30
209	A49	5½p deep green	.38	.30
		Nos. 207-209 (3)	.88	.75

150th anniv. of the discovery of the Hunter River estuary, site of Newcastle by Lieut. John Shortland. By error the 2½p shows his father, Capt. John Shortland.

Princess Elizabeth — A50

Perf. 14x14½

1947, Nov. 20 Wmk. 228

210	A50	1p brown violet	.18	.15

See No. 215.

Hereford Bull A51

Crocodile A52

1948, Feb. 16 *Perf. 14½*

211	A51	1sh3p violet brown	1.90	.70
212	A52	2sh chocolate	2.50	.15

See No. 302.

William J. Farrer — A53

Design: No. 214, Ferdinand von Mueller.

1948 *Perf. 14½x14*
213 A53 2½p red .18 .15
214 A53 2½p dark red .24 .15
Set value .15

William J. Farrer (1845-1906), wheat researcher, and Ferdinand von Mueller (1825-1896), German-born botanist.
Issue dates: #213, July 12. #214, Sept. 13.

Elizabeth Type of 1947

1948, Aug. Unwmk. *Perf. 14x14½*
215 A50 1p brown violet .15 .15

Scout in Uniform — A55

Arms of Australia — A56

1948, Nov. 15 Engr. Wmk. 228
216 A55 2½p brown red .18 .15

Pan-Pacific Scout Jamboree, Victoria, Dec. 29, 1948 to Jan. 9, 1949. See No. 249.

1949-50 Wmk. 228 *Perf. 14x13½*
218 A56 5sh dark red 6.00 .15
219 A56 10sh red violet 22.50 .30
220 A56 £1 deep blue 37.50 3.00
221 A56 £2 green ('50) 120.00 12.50
Nos. 218-221 (4) 186.00 15.95

Henry Lawson A57

Outback Mail Carrier and Plane A58

Perf. 14½x14

1949, June 17 Unwmk.
222 A57 2½p rose brown .15 .15

Henry Hertzberg Lawson (1867-1922), author and poet.

1949, Oct. 10
223 A58 3½p violet blue .25 .16

UPU, 75th anniv.

Types of 1938, 1942-44 & A59

Aborigine A59

John Forrest A60

1948-50 Unwmk. *Perf. 14½x14*
223A A24 ½p orange ('49) .15 .15
224 A37 1½p green ('49) .28 .15
225 A38 2p lt rose violet .30 .15

Wmk. 228
226 A59 8½p dark brown ('50) .50 .32
Nos. 223A-226 (4) 1.23
Set value .47

Issue dates: 2p, Dec., ½p, Sept., 1½p, Aug. 29, 8½p, Aug. 14.
See Nos. 248, 303.

1949, Nov. 28 Wmk. 228
227 A60 2½p brown red .15 .15

Forrest (1847-1918), explorer & statesman.

New South Wales A61

Victoria A62

First stamp designs.

Perf. 14½x14

1950, Sept. 27 Unwmk.
228 A61 2½p rose brown .25 .15
229 A62 2½p rose brown .25 .15
a. Pair, #228-229 .65 .40
Set value .20

Cent. of Australian adhesive postage stamps. Issued in sheets of 160 stamps containing alternate copies of Nos. 228 and 229.

Elizabeth A63

George VI A64

A65

A66

1950-51 Engr. Unwmk.
230 A63 1½p deep green .30 .15
231 A63 2p yellow grn ('51) .20 .15
232 A64 2½p violet brn ('51) .20 .15
233 A64 3p dull green ('51) .30 .15
Nos. 230-233 (4) 1.00
Set value .20

Issue dates: 1½p, June 19, 2p, Mar. 28, 2½p, May 23, 3p, Nov. 14.

1950-52 Wmk. 228
234 A64 2½p red .15 .15
235 A64 3p red ('51) .15 .15
236 A65 3½p red brown ('51) .28 .15
237 A65 4½p scarlet ('52) .42 .35
238 A65 6½p choc ('52) .30 .35
238A A65 6½p blue green ('52) .40 .15
239 A66 7½p deep blue ('51) .45 .30
Nos. 234-239 (7) 2.15
Set value 1.20

Issued: 2½p, Apr. 12; 3p, Feb. 28; 7½p, Oct. 31; 3½p, Nov. 28; 4½p, #238, Feb. 20; #238A, Apr. 9.

Sir Edmund Barton A67

Duke of York Opening First Federal Parliament A68

Designs: No. 241, Sir Henry Parkes. 1sh6p, Parliament House, Canberra.

Perf. 14½x14

1951, May 1 Engr. Unwmk.
240 A67 3p carmine .40 .15
241 A67 3p carmine .40 .15
a. Pair, #240, 241 .80 .65
242 A68 5½p deep blue .40 .65
243 A68 1sh6p red brown 1.25 .90
Nos. 240-243 (4) 2.45
Set value 1.65

Founding of the Commonwealth of Australia, 50th anniv.

Edward Hammond Hargraves A69

King George VI A70

Design: No. 245, Charles Joseph Latrobe (1801-1875), first governor of Victoria.

1951, July 2
244 A69 3p rose brown .25 .15
245 A69 3p rose brown .25 .15
a. Pair, #244, 245 .65 .65
Set value .15

Discovery of gold in Australia, cent. (No. 244); Establishment of representative government in Victoria, cent. (No. 245). Sheets contain alternate rows of Nos. 244 and 245.

1952, Mar. 19 Wmk. 228 *Perf. 14½*
247 A70 1sh½p slate blue 1.65 .22

Aborigine Type of 1950 Redrawn

Size: 20½x25mm
248 A59 2sh6p dark brown 3.25 .25

Portrait as on A59; lettering altered and value repeated at lower left. See No. 303.

Scout Type of 1948
Dated "1952-53"
Perf. 14x14½

1952, Nov. 19 Wmk. 228
249 A55 3½p red brown .18 .15

Pan-Pacific Scout Jamboree, Greystanes, Dec. 30, 1952, to Jan. 9, 1953.

Modern Dairy, Butter Production — A71

Perf. 14½

1953, Feb. 11 Unwmk. Typo.
250 A71 3p shown .75 .15
251 A71 3p Wheat .75 .15
252 A71 3p Beef .75 .15
a. Strip of 3, #250-252 6.50 6.50
253 A71 3½p shown .75 .15
254 A71 3½p Wheat .75 .15
255 A71 3½p Beef .75 .15
a. Strip of 3, #253-255 4.50 5.50
Nos. 250-255 (6) 4.50
Set value .60

Both the 3p and 3½p were printed in panes of 50 stamps: 17 Butter, 17 Wheat and 16 Beef. The stamps were issued to encourage food production.

Queen Elizabeth II — A72

Perf. 14½x14

1953-54 Unwmk. Engr.
256 A72 1p purple .16 .15
256A A72 2½p deep blue ('54) .28 .15
257 A72 3p dark green .28 .15

Wmk. 228
258 A72 3½p dark red .28 .15
258B A72 6½p orange ('54) .90 .15
Nos. 256-258B (5) 1.90
Set value .30

Issue dates: 3½p, Apr. 21. 3p, June 17. 1p, Aug. 19. 2½p, 6½p, June 23.
See Nos. 292 and 296.

Coronation Issue

Queen Elizabeth II A73

1953, May 25 Unwmk.
259 A73 3½p rose red .28 .15
260 A73 7½p violet .70 .45
261 A73 2sh dull green 2.25 1.10
Nos. 259-261 (3) 3.23 1.70

Boy and Girl with Calf — A74

1953, Sept. 3 *Perf. 14½*
262 A74 3½p dp green & red brn .25 .15

Official establishment of Young Farmers' Clubs, 25th anniv.

Lieut. Gov. David Collins A75

Tasmania Stamp of 1853 A77

Sullivan Cove, Hobart A76

Design: No. 264, Lieut. Gov. William Paterson (facing left).

1953, Sept. 23 *Perf. 14½x14*
263 A75 3½p red brown .35 .15
264 A75 3½p red brown .35 .15
a. Pair, #263-264 1.25 1.10
265 A76 2sh green 4.25 4.00
Nos. 263-265 (3) 4.95 4.30

Settlement in Tasmania, 150th anniv. Sheets contain alternate rows of Nos. 263 and 264.

1953, Nov. 11 *Perf. 14½*
266 A77 3p red .18 .15

Tasmania's first postage stamps, cent.

Elizabeth II and Duke of Edinburgh — A78

Elizabeth II — A79

Telegraph Pole and Key — A80

1954, Feb. 2 *Perf. 14½x14, 14x14½*
267 A78 3½p rose red .18 .15
268 A79 7½p purple .35 .75
269 A78 2sh green 1.50 1.00
Nos. 267-269 (3) 2.03 1.90

Visit of Queen Elizabeth II and the Duke of Edinburgh, 1954.

1954, Apr. 7 Engr. *Perf. 14*
270 A80 3½p dark red .25 .15

Inauguration of the telegraph in Australia, cent.

Red Cross and Globe — A81

Swan — A82

1954, June 9   *Perf. 14¹/₂x14*
271 A81 3¹/₂p deep blue & red   .18 .15
Australian Red Cross Society.

1954, Aug. 2   **Unwmk.**   *Perf. 14¹/₂*
274 A82 3¹/₂p black   .20 .15
Western Australia's first postage stamp, cent.

Diesel and Early Steam Locomotives A83

1954, Sept. 13   *Perf. 14x14¹/₂*
275 A83 3¹/₂p red brown   .20 .15
Centenary of Australian railroads.

Antarctic Flora and Fauna and Map A84

Olympic Circles and Arms of Melbourne A85

1954, Nov. 17   *Perf. 14*
276 A84 3¹/₂p black   .18 .15
Australia's interest in the Antarctic continent.

1954, Dec. 1
277 A85 2sh dark blue   2.00 1.50
16th Olympic Games to be held in Melbourne Nov.-Dec. 1956. See No. 286.

Globe, Flags and Rotary Emblem — A86

1955, Feb. 23   *Perf. 14x14¹/₂*
278 A86 3¹/₂p carmine   .18 .15
Rotary International, 50th anniv.

Elizabeth II — A87

Top of US Monument, Canberra — A88

1955, Mar. 9   **Wmk. 228**   *Perf. 14¹/₂*
279 A87 1sh¹/₂p dk gray blue   3.50 .25
See No. 301.

1955, May 4   **Unwmk.**   *Perf. 14x14¹/₂*
280 A88 3¹/₂p deep ultra   .18 .15
Friendship between Australia and the US.

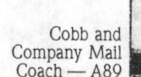

Cobb and Company Mail Coach — A89

1955, July 6   *Perf. 14¹/₂x14*
281 A89 3¹/₂p dark brown   .20 .15
282 A89 2sh brown   2.50 2.00
Pioneers of Australia's coaching era.

World Map, YMCA Emblem A90

Engr. and Typo.

1955, Aug. 10   *Perf. 14*
283 A90 3¹/₂p Prus green & red   .20 .15
Centenary of YMCA.

Florence Nightingale and Modern Nurse — A91

Queen Victoria — A92

1955, Sept. 21   **Engr.**   *Perf. 14x14¹/₂*
284 A91 3¹/₂p red violet   .18 .15
Centenary of Florence Nightingale's work in the Crimea and of the founding of modern nursing.

1955, Oct. 17   *Perf. 14¹/₂*
285 A92 3¹/₂p green   .18 .15
South Australia's first postage stamps, cent.

Olympic Type of 1954

1955, Nov. 30   **Unwmk.**   *Perf. 14*
286 A85 2sh deep green   2.25 1.65
16th Olympic Games at Melbourne, Nov. 22-Dec. 8, 1956.

Queen Victoria, Queen Elizabeth II and Badges of Victoria, New South Wales and Tasmania A93

1956, Sept. 26   *Perf. 14¹/₂x14*
287 A93 3¹/₂p brown carmine   .25 .15
Centenary of responsible government in Victoria, New South Wales and Tasmania.

Melbourne Coat of Arms — A94

Southern Cross, Olympic Torch — A95

Collins Street, Melbourne A96

Design: 2sh, Melbourne across Yarra River.

1956, Oct. 31   **Engr.**   *Perf. 14¹/₂, 14*
288 A94 4p dark carmine   .22 .15

---

289 A95 7¹/₂p ultramarine   .55 .42

Photo.
Perf. 14x14¹/₂
290 A96 1sh multicolored   .75 .38

Perf. 12x11¹/₂
Granite Paper
291 A96 2sh multicolored   1.40 .60
     Nos. 288-291 (4)   2.92 1.55
16th Olympic Games, Melbourne, 11/22-12/8.

A lithographed souvenir sheet incorporating reproductions of Nos. 288-291 in reduced size was of private origin and not postally valid.

Types of 1938-55 and

Queen Elizabeth II — A97

Perf. 14¹/₂x14, 14x15, 15x14, 14¹/₂

1956-57		Engr.	Unwmk.	
292	A72	3¹/₂p dark red	1.00	.15
293	A28	4p green	1.65	.16
294	A97	4p claret ('57)	.30	.15
a.		Booklet pane of 6 ('57)	7.50	
295	A30	6p brown violet	2.75	.16
296	A72	6¹/₂p orange	1.75	.15
297	A97	7¹/₂p violet ('57)	3.00	.35
298	A31	9p sepia	9.00	.52
299	A97	10p gray blue ('57)	2.75	.35
300	A16	1sh gray green	6.00	.35
301	A87	1sh7p redsh brn ('57)	4.50	.35
302	A52	2sh chocolate	12.00	.28
303	A59	2sh6p brown ('57)	9.00	.30
		Nos. 292-303 (12)	53.70	3.07

No. 300 measures 17¹/₂x21¹/₂mm. No. 303 measures 20¹/₂x25mm and is the redrawn type of 1952.
Issued: 3¹/₂p, 7/2; 2sh, 7/21; #293, 6p, 8/18; 6¹/₂p, Sept. 9p, 1sh, 12/13; 2sh6p, 1/30; 10p, 3/6; #294, 1sh7p, 3/13; 7¹/₂p, 11/13.

South Australia Coat of Arms — A99

1957, Apr. 17   **Unwmk.**   *Perf. 14¹/₂*
304 A99 4p brown red   .18 .15
Centenary of responsible government in South Australia.

Caduceus and Map of Australia A100

1957, Aug. 21   *Perf. 14¹/₂x14*
305 A100 7p violet blue   .60 .15
Royal Flying Doctor Service of Australia.

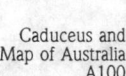

Star of Bethlehem and Praying Child — A101

1957, Nov. 6   **Engr.**
306 A101 3¹/₂p dull rose   .22 .15
307 A101 4p pale purple   .22 .15
Christmas.

Canberra War Memorial, Sailor and Airman A102

Design: No. 309, As No. 308 with soldier and service woman. Printed in alternate rows in sheet.

1958, Feb. 10   **Unwmk.**
308 A102 5¹/₂p brown carmine   1.25 .75
309 A102 5¹/₂p brown carmine   1.25 .75
   a.   Pair, #308-309   3.50 3.50

Sir Charles Kingsford-Smith and "Southern Cross" — A103

1958, Aug. 27   *Perf. 14x14¹/₂*
310 A103 8p brt violet blue   1.00 .90
1st air crossing of the Tasman Sea, 30th anniv. See New Zealand No. 321.

Broken Hill Mine A104

Nativity A105

1958, Sept. 10   *Perf. 14¹/₂x14*
311 A104 4p brown   .25 .15
Broken Hill mining field, 75th anniv.

1958, Nov. 5   *Perf. 14¹/₂x15*
312 A105 3¹/₂p dark red   .15 .15
313 A105 4p dark purple   .22 .15
     Set value   .15
Christmas.

A106   A107   A109

A108   A110

Platypus A111

Tasmanian Tiger A112

Flannel Flower A113

Aboriginal Stockman Cutting Out a Steer A114

Designs: 3p, Queen Elizabeth II facing right. 6p, Banded anteater. 8p, Tiger cat. 9p, Kangaroos. 11p, Rabbit bandicoot. 1sh6p, Christmas bells (flower). 2sh3p, Wattle (flower). 2sh5p, Banksia (flower). 3sh, Waratah (flower).
FIVE PENCE
Die I - Four short lines inside "5" at right of ball; six short lines left of ball; full length line above ball is seventh from bottom. Odd numbered horizontal rows in each sheet are in Die I.
Die II - Five short lines inside "5" at right of ball; seven at left; full length line above ball is eighth from bottom. Even numbered horizontal rows in each sheet are in Die II.

Perf. 14¹/₂x14, 14x14¹/₂, 14¹/₂

1959-64		Engr.	Unwmk.	
314	A106	1p dull violet	.25	.15
315	A107	2p red brown	.35	.15
316	A108	3p bluish green	.25	.15
317	A109	3¹/₂p dark green	.45	.15
318	A109	4p carmine	.35	.15
a.		Booklet pane of 6	25.00	
319	A110	5p dark blue (I)	.65	.15
a.		5p dark blue (II)	.65	.15
b.		Booklet pane of 6 ('60)	12.00	

320	A111	6p chocolate		.65	.15
321	A111	8p red brown		.60	.15
322	A111	9p brown black		2.50	.20
323	A111	11p dark blue		.95	.15
324	A111	1sh slate green		3.75	.15
325	A112	1sh2p dk purple		1.50	.20
326	A113	1sh6p red, *yellow*		2.50	.60
327	A113	2sh dark blue		2.50	.15
328	A113	2sh3p green, *yel*		2.50	.20
328A	A113	2sh3p yellow grn		7.50	1.00
329	A113	2sh5p brown, *yellow*		8.75	.40
330	A113	3sh crimson		3.50	.35

Wmk. 228

331	A114	5sh red brown	25.00	1.00
		Nos. 314-331 (19)	64.50	
		Set value		4.60

Issued: 1p, 4p, 2/2; 3½p, 3/18; 2sh, 4/8; 3p, 5/20; 3sh, 7/15; 1sh, #328, 9/9; 5p, 10/1; 9p, 10/21; 1sh6p, 2/3/60; 2sh5p, 3/16/60; 8p, 5/11/60; 6p, 9/30/60; 11p, 5/3/61; 5sh, 7/26/61; 2p, 1sh2p, 3/21/62; #328A, 10/28/64.

Luminescent Printings

Paper with an orange red phosphorescence (surface coating), was used for some printings of the Colombo Plan 1sh, No. 340, the Churchill 5p, No. 389, and several regular postage stamps. These include 2p, 3p, 6p, 8p, 9p, 11p, 1sh2p, 1sh6p and 2sh3p (Nos. 315, 316, 365, 367, 321, 368, 323, 325, 369, 328A).

Stamps printed only on phosphorescent paper include the Monash 5p, Hargrave 5p, ICY 2sh3p and Christmas 5p (Nos. 388, 390-393) and succeeding commemoratives; the 2sh, 2sh6p and 3sh regular birds (Nos. 370, 372, 373); and most of the regular series in decimal currency.

Ink with a phosphorescent content was used in printing most of the 5p red booklets, No. 366, almost all of the 5p red booklets, No. 366a, most of the decimal 4c regular, No. 397, and its booklet pane, No. 397a, and all of No. 398.

Postmaster Isaac Nichols Boarding Vessel to Receive Mail — A115

1959, Apr. 22 *Perf. 14½x14*
332 A115 4p dark gray blue .25 .15

First post office, Sydney, 150th anniv.

Parliament House, Brisbane, and Queensland Arms — A116

1959, June 5 *Perf. 14x14½*
333 A116 4p dk green & violet .25 .15

Cent. of Queensland self-government.

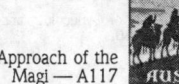

Approach of the Magi — A117

1959, Nov. 4 *Perf. 15x14½*
334 A117 5p purple .25 .15

Christmas.

Girl Guide and Lord Baden-Powell A118

1960, Aug. 18 *Perf. 14½x14*
335 A118 5p dark blue .32 .15

50th anniversary of the Girl Guides.

The Overlanders by Sir Daryl Lindsay — A119

Melbourne Cup and Archer, 1861 Winner — A120

1960, Sept. 21 *Perf. 14½*
336 A119 5p lilac rose .35 .15

Exploration of Australia's Northern Territory, cent.

1960, Oct. 12 **Unwmk.**
337 A120 5p sepia .35 .15

Centenary of the Melbourne Cup.

Queen Victoria A121

Open Bible and Candle A122

1960 Nov. 2 **Engr.** *Perf. 14½*
338 A121 5p dark green .22 .15

Centenary of the first Queensland stamps.

1960, Nov. 9 **Unwmk.**
339 A122 5p maroon .20 .15

Christmas; beginning of 350th anniv. year of the publication of the King James translation of the Bible.

Colombo Plan Emblem — A123

1961, June 30 *Perf. 14x14½*
340 A123 1sh red brown .80 .15

Colombo Plan for the peaceful development of South East Asia countries, 10th anniv.

Dame Nellie Melba, by Sir Bertram Mackennal — A124

1961, Sept. 20 *Perf. 14½*
341 A124 5p deep blue .35 .15

Dame Nellie Melba, singer, birth cent.

Page from Book of Hours, 15th Century — A125

John McDouall Stuart — A126

1961, Nov. 8 *Perf. 14½x14*
342 A125 5p reddish brown .38 .15

Christmas; end of the 350th anniv. year of the publication of the King James translation of the Bible.

1962, July 25 **Unwmk.** *Perf. 14½*
345 A126 5p carmine .35 .15

First south-north crossing of Australia by John McDouall Stuart, cent.

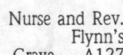

Nurse and Rev. Flynn's Grave — A127

1962, Sept. 5 **Photo.** *Perf. 13½*
346 A127 5p multicolored .35 .15
a. Red omitted 275.00

Australian Inland Mission founded by Rev. John Flynn, 50th anniv.

Woman and Globe — A128

Madonna and Child — A129

1962, Sept. 26 **Engr.** *Perf. 14x14½*
347 A128 5p dark green .35 .15

World Conf. of the Associated Country Women of the World, Melbourne, Oct. 2-12.

1962, Oct. 17 *Perf. 14½*
348 A129 5p deep violet .38 .15

Christmas.

View of Perth and Kangaroo Paw — A130

Arms of Perth — A131

1962, Nov. 1 **Photo.** *Perf. 14*
349 A130 5p multicolored .38 .15
a. Red omitted 450.00

Perf. 14½x14

350 A131 2sh3p emer, blk, red & ultra 5.00 5.00

British Empire and Commonwealth Games, Perth, Nov. 22-Dec. 1.

Elizabeth II — A132

Elizabeth II and Prince Philip — A133

1963, Feb. 18 **Engr.** *Perf. 14½*
351 A132 5p dark green .30 .15
352 A133 2sh3 red brown 5.75 5.00

Visit of Elizabeth II and Prince Philip.

> ***15-Cent Minimum Value***
> *The minimum catalogue value is 15 cents. Separating se-tenant pieces into individual stamps does not increase the value of the stamps since demand for the separated stamps may be small.*

Walter Burley Griffin and Arms of Canberra A134

Red Cross Centenary Emblem A135

1963, Mar. 8 **Unwmk.** *Perf. 14½x14*
353 A134 5p dark green .35 .15

50th anniv. of Canberra; Walter Burley Griffin, American architect, who laid out plan for Canberra.

1963, May 8 **Photo.** *Perf. 13½x13*
354 A135 5p dk blue, red & gray .35 .15

Centenary of the International Red Cross.

Explorers Blaxland, Lawson and Wentworth Looking West from Mt. York — A136

1963, May 28 **Engr.** *Perf. 14½x14*
355 A136 5p dark blue .30 .15

1st crossing of the Blue Mts., 150th anniv.

Globe, Ship, Plane and Map of Australia A137

1963, Aug. 28 **Unwmk.**
356 A137 5p red .35 .15

Importance of exports to Australian economy.

Elizabeth II — A138

Black-backed Magpie and Eucalyptus — A139

Abel Tasman and Ship A144

George Bass, Whaleboat A145

Designs: 6p, Yellow-tailed thornbill, horiz. 1sh6p, Galah on tree stump. 2sh, Golden whistler. 2sh5p, Blue wren and bracken fern. 2sh6p, Scarlet robin, horiz. 3sh, Straw-necked ibis. 5sh, William Dampier and "Roebuck" sailing ship. 7sh6p, Capt. James Cook. 10sh, Matthew Flinders and three-master "Investigator." £2, Admiral Philip Parker King.

1963-65 **Unwmk.** **Engr.** *Perf. 15x14*

365 A138	5p green		.25	.15
a.	Booklet pane of 6 ('64)		20.00	
b.	Pair, imperf. btwn.		3.75	3.75
366 A138	5p red		.25	.15
a.	Booklet pane of 6		25.00	

Photo.

Perf. 13½

367 A139	6p multicolored		.45	.15
a.	Vert. pair, imperf. btwn.			
368 A139	9p multicolored		2.50	1.90
369 A139	1sh6p multicolored		1.25	1.10
370 A139	2sh multicolored		2.50	.38
371 A139	2sh5p multicolored		8.25	2.25
372 A139	2sh6p multicolored		3.75	1.50
a.	Red omitted		1,000.	
373 A139	3sh multicolored		2.50	1.25

Engr.

Perf. 14½x14, 14½x15

374 A144	4sh violet blue		3.75	.55

Wmk. 228

375	A145	5sh red brown	5.25	1.25
376	A144	7sh6p olive green	24.00	15.00
377	A144	10sh deep claret	30.00	7.25
378	A144	£1 purple	50.00	22.50
379	A144	£2 brown black	100.00	90.00
		Nos. 365-379 (15)	234.70	145.38

No. 365a was printed in sheets of 288 which were sold intact by the Philatelic Bureau. These sheets have been broken to obtain pairs and blocks which are imperf. between (see No. 365b).

Issued: #365, 4sh, 10/9/63; 10sh, £1, 2/26/64; 9p, 1sh6p, 2sh5p, 3/11/64; 6p, 8/19/64; 7sh6p, £2, 8/26/64; 5sh, 11/25/64; 2sh, 2sh6p, 3sh, 4/21/65; #366, 6/30/65.

See Nos. 400-401, 406-417.

Star of Bethlehem — A146

1963, Oct. 25 Unwmk. Perf. 14½
380 A146 5p blue .20 .15

Christmas.

Cable Around World and Under Sea — A147

1963, Dec. 3 Photo. Perf. 13½
381 A147 2sh3p gray, ver, blk & blue 6.00 5.00

Opening of the Commonwealth Pacific (telephone) cable service (COMPAC).
See New Zealand No. 364.

Bleriot 60 Plane, 1914 — A148

1964, July 1 Engr. Perf. 14½x14
382 A148 5p olive green .20 .15
383 A148 2sh3p red 5.25 4.75

50th anniv. of the first air mail flight in Australia; Maurice Guillaux, aviator.

Child Looking at Nativity Scene — A149

1964, Oct. 21 Photo. Perf. 13½
384 A149 5p bl, blk, red & buff .20 .15
a. Red omitted 375.00
b. Black omitted 375.00

Christmas.

"Simpson and His Donkey" by Wallace Anderson — A150

1965, Apr. 14 Engr. Perf. 14x14½
385 A150 5p olive bister .20 .15
386 A150 8p dark blue 1.25 .90
387 A150 2sh3p rose claret 5.25 4.75
Nos. 385-387 (3) 6.70 5.80

50th anniv. of the landing of the Australian and New Zealand Army Corps (ANZAC) at Gallipoli, Turkey, Apr. 25, 1915. Private John Simpson Kirkpatrick saved the lives of many wounded soldiers. The statue erected in his honor stands in front of Melbourne's Shrine of Remembrance.

Radio Mast and Satellite Orbiting Earth A151

Winston Churchill A152

1965, May 10 Photo. Perf. 13½
388 A151 5p multicolored .22 .15
a. Black ("5d" and pylon) omitted 650.00

ITU, cent.

1965, May 24
389 A152 5p lt blue, gray & blk .25 .15

Sir Winston Spencer Churchill (1874-1965), statesman and WWII leader.
See New Zealand No. 371.

John Monash and Transmission Tower — A153

Lawrence Hargrave and Sketch for 1902 Seaplane — A154

1965, June 23 Photo. Perf. 13½
390 A153 5p red, yel, blk & lt brn .25 .15

Birth cent. of General Sir John Monash (1865-1931), soldier, Vice-Chancellor of University of Melbourne and chairman of the Victoria state electricity commission.

1965, Aug. 4 Unwmk. Perf. 13½
391 A154 5p multicolored .30 .15
a. Purple (5d) omitted 190.00

50th anniv. of the death of Lawrence Hargrave (1850-1915), aviation pioneer.

ICY Emblem A155

Nativity A156

1965, Sept. 1 Photo. Perf. 13½
392 A155 2sh3p lt blue & green 3.00 2.75

International Cooperation Year.

1965, Oct. 20 Unwmk. Perf. 13½
393 A156 5p multicolored .30 .15
a. Gold omitted 300.00
b. Ultramarine omitted 325.00

Christmas.

Types of 1963-65 and

Elizabeth II — A157

Humbug Fish — A158

Designs: No. 400, Yellow-tailed thornbill, horiz. 6c, blue-faced honeyeater, horiz. 8c, Coral fish. 9c, Hermit crab. 10c Anemone fish. 13c, Red-necked avocet. 15c, Galah on tree stump. 20c, Golden whistler. 24c Azure kingfisher, horiz. 25c, Scarlet robin, horiz. 30c Straw-necked ibis. 40c Abel Tasman and ship. 50c, William Dampier and "Roebuck" sailing ship. 75c, Capt. James Cook. $1, Matthew Flinders and three-master "Investigator." $2, George Bass and whaleboat. $4, Admiral Philip Parker King.

Perf. 14½x14 (A157); 13½ (A158, A139)
Engr. (A157), Photo. (A158, A139)
1966-71

394	A157	1c red brown	.28	.15
395	A157	2c olive green	.50	.15
396	A157	3c Prus green	.68	.15
397	A157	4c red	.15	.15
	a.	Booklet pane of 5 + label	30.00	
398	A157	5c on 4c red ('67)	.75	.15
	a.	Booklet pane of 5 + label ('67)	5.50	
399	A157	5c dk blue ('67)	1.00	.15
	a.	Booklet pane of 5 + label	11.00	
	b.	Booklet pane of 10	55.00	
400	A139	5c lt grn, blk, brn & yel	.22	.15
	a.	Booklet pane of 10	45.00	
401	A139	6c gray, blk, lem & bl	.58	.15
401A	A157	6c orange ('70)	.18	.15
402	A158	7c brn, ver, blk & gray	1.05	.15
402A	A157	7c dp rose lilac ('71)	.22	.15
403	A158	8c multicolored	1.15	.15
404	A158	9c multicolored	1.50	.15
405	A158	10c lt brn, blk, org & bl	1.15	.25
406	A139	13c lt bl grn, blk, gray & red	2.00	.50
	a.	Red omitted	400.00	
407	A139	15c lt grn, blk, gray & rose	3.50	.40
	a.	Gray omitted	1,500.	
408	A139	20c pink, blk, yel & gray	5.75	.15
	a.	Yellow omitted	350.00	
409	A139	24c tan, blk, vio bl & org	1.15	.75
410	A139	25c gray, grn, blk & red	3.50	.15
	a.	Red omitted	750.00	
411	A139	30c lt grn, buff, blk & red	19.00	.50
	a.	Red omitted	575.00	

Engr.
Perf. 14½x14, 14½x15

412	A144	40c violet blue	13.50	.32
413	A145	50c brown red	17.00	.15
414	A144	75c olive green	.88	1.10
415	A144	$1 deep claret	2.50	.32
	a.	Perf 15x14	75.00	15.00
416	A145	$2 purple	7.50	1.10
417	A145	$4 sepia	5.50	4.50
		Nos. 394-417 (26)	91.19	12.14

No. 398 issued in booklets only.
Booklet panes Nos. 399b and 400a were issued for the use of "Australian Defence Forces," as the covers read, in Viet Nam.
Issued: #398, 399, 9/29/67; #401A, 9/28/70; #402A, 10/1/71; #415a, 1973; others, 2/14/66.

Coil Stamps

1966-67 Photo. Perf. 15 Horiz.
418 A157 3c emerald, blk & buff .50 .35
419 A157 4c org red, blk & buff .60 .15
420 A157 5c blue, black & buff .75 .15
Nos. 418-420 (3) 1.85
Set value .56

Issued: 5c, Sept. 29, 1967; others, Feb. 14, 1966.

Rescue — A159

1966 July 6 Photo. Perf. 13½
421 A159 4c blue, ultra & black .30 .15

Royal Life Saving Society, 75th anniv.

Adoration of the Shepherds A160

1966, Oct. 19 Photo. Perf. 13½
422 A160 4c olive & black .24 .15

Christmas.

Dutch Sailing Ship, 17th Century A161

Hands Reaching for Bible A162

1966, Oct. 24 Photo. Perf. 13½
423 A161 4c bl, blk, dp org & gold .24 .15

350th anniv. of Dirk Hartog's discovery of the Australian west coast, and his landing on the island named after him.

1967, Mar. 7 Photo. Perf. 13½
424 A162 4c multicolored .24 .15

British and Foreign Bible Soc., 150th anniv.

Combination Lock and Antique Keys — A163

1967, Apr. 5 Photo. Perf. 13½
425 A163 4c emerald, blk & lt blue .30 .15

150th anniv. of banking in Australia (Bank of New South Wales).

Lions Intl., 50th Anniv. — A164

1967, June 7 Photo. Perf. 13½
426 A164 4c ultra, black & gold .24 .15

YWCA Emblems and Flags — A165

1967, Aug. 21 Photo. Perf. 13½
427 A165 4c dk blue, lt bl & lilac .32 .15

World Council Meeting of the YWCA, Monash University, Victoria, Aug. 14-Sept. 1.

Seated Women Symbolizing Obstetrics and Gynecology, Female Symbol A166

1967, Sept. 20 Photo. Perf. 13½
428 A166 4c lilac, dk blue & blk .24 .15

5th World Congress of Gynecology and Obstetrics, Sydney, Sept. 23-30.

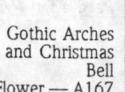 

Gothic Arches and Christmas Bell Flower — A167

Cross, Stars of David and Yin Yang Forming Mandala — A168

1967 Photo. Perf. 13½
429 A167 5c multicolored .24 .15
430 A168 25c multicolored 2.50 2.50
Christmas.
Issue dates: 5c, Oct. 18; 25c, Nov. 27.

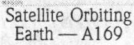

Satellite Orbiting
Earth — A169

Satellite and
Antenna,
Moree,
N.S.W. — A170

Design: 20c, World weather map connecting Washington, Moscow and Melbourne, and computer and teleprinter tape spools.

1968, Mar. 20 Photo. Perf. 13½
431 A169 5c dull yel, red, bl & dk
blue .25 .15
432 A169 20c blue, blk & red 4.00 4.00
433 A170 25c Prus blue, blk & lt
green 4.00 4.00
Nos. 431-433 (3) 8.25 8.15

Use of satellites for weather observations and communications.

Kangaroo Paw,
Western
Australia
A171

Sturt's Desert Rose,
Northern Territory
A171a

State Flowers: 13c, Pink heath, Victoria. 15c, Tasmanian blue gum, Tasmania. 20c, Sturt's desert pea, South Australia. 25c, Cooktown orchid, Queensland. 30c, Waratah, New South Wales.

1968, July 10 Photo. Perf. 13½
Flowers in Natural Colors
434 A171 6c bister & dk brn .40 .20
435 A171 13c lt grnsh blue .52 .15
436 A171 15c dk brn & yel 2.25 .25
437 A171 20c lemon & black 7.25 .15
438 A171 25c light ultra 5.50 .15
439 A171 30c chocolate 1.40 .15
Nos. 434-439 (6) 17.32 1.05

Coil Stamps
1970-75 Perf. 14½ Horiz.
Designs: 5c, Golden wattle, national flower. 7c, 10c, Sturt's desert pea.

439A A171a 2c dk grn & multi .20 .15
439B A171a 4c gray & multi .50 .40
439C A171a 5c gray & multi .20 .15
439D A171a 6c gray & multi 1.10 .50
h. Green omitted 300.00
439E A171a 7c blk, red & grn .35 .15
f. Green omitted 150.00
439G A171a 10c blk, red & grn .30 .15
Nos. 439A-439G (6) 2.65 1.50

Issue dates: 4c, 5c, Apr. 27. 6c, Oct. 28. 2c, 7c, Oct. 1, 1971. 10c, Jan. 15, 1975.

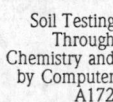

Soil Testing
Through
Chemistry and
by Computer
A172

Hippocrates and
Hands Holding
Hypodermic
A173

1968, Aug. 6 Photo. Perf. 13½
440 A172 5c multicolored .28 .15
441 A173 5c multicolored .28 .15

9th Intl. Congress of Soil Science, University of Adelaide, Aug. 6-16 (No. 440); General Assembly of World Medical Associations, Sydney, Aug. 6-9 (No. 441). Nos. 440-441 printed in sheets of 100 in

two separate panes of 50 connected by a gutter. Each sheet contains 10 gutter pairs.

Runner and Aztec
Calendar Stone
A174

Symbolic
House and
Money
A175

Design: 25c, Aztec calendar stone and Mexican flag, horiz.

1968, Oct. 2
442 A174 5c multicolored .20 .15
443 A174 25c multicolored 2.25 2.00

19th Olympic Games, Mexico City, Oct. 12-27. Nos. 442-443 printed in sheets of 100 in two separate panes of 50 connected by a gutter. Each sheet contains 10 gutter pairs.

1968, Oct. 16
444 A175 5c multicolored .25 .18

11th Triennial Congress of the Intl. Union of Building Societies and Savings Associations, Sydney, Oct. 20-27.

View of Bethlehem and
Church Window — A176

1968, Oct. 23 Photo. Perf. 13½
445 A176 5c lt bl, red, grn & gold .20 .15
a. Red omitted 350.00

Christmas.

Edgeworth David
(1858-1934),
Geologist
A177

Sir Edmund Barton
(1849-1920)
A178

Reginald C. and John R.
Duigan, Aviators — A179

Famous Australians: No. 447, Caroline Chisholm (1808-1877), social worker and reformer. No. 448, Albert Namatjira (1902-1959), aborigine, artist. No. 449, Andrew Barton (Banjo) Paterson (1864-1941), poet and writer.

1968, Nov. 6 Engr. Perf. 15x14
446 A177 5c green, greenish 1.25 .15
a. Booklet pane of 5 + label 6.25
447 A177 5c purple, pink 1.25 .15
a. Booklet pane of 5 + label 6.25
448 A177 5c dark brown, buff 1.25 .15
a. Booklet pane of 5 + label 6.25
449 A177 5c indigo, lt blue 1.25 .15
a. Booklet pane of 5 + label 6.25
Nos. 446-449 (4) 5.00
Set value .48

1969, Oct. 22 Engr. Perf. 15x14
Prime Ministers: No. 451, Alfred Deakin (1856-1919). No. 452, John C. Watson (1867-1941). No. 453, Sir George H. Reid (1845-1918).

450 A178 5c indigo, greenish 1.25 .15
a. Booklet pane of 5 + label 6.25
451 A178 5c indigo, greenish 1.25 .15
a. Booklet pane of 5 + label 6.25
452 A178 5c indigo, greenish 1.25 .15
a. Booklet pane of 5 + label 6.25
453 A178 5c indigo, greenish 1.25 .15
a. Booklet pane of 5 + label 6.25
Nos. 450-453 (4) 5.00
Set value .48

1970, Nov. 16 Engr. Perf. 15x14
Famous Australians: No. 455, Lachlan Macquarie (1761-1824), Governor of New South Wales. No. 456, Adam Lindsay Gordon (1833-1870), poet. No. 457, Edward John Eyre (1815-1901), explorer.

454 A179 6c dark blue 1.25 .15
a. Booklet pane of 5 + label 6.25
455 A179 6c dark brown, salmon 1.25 .15
a. Booklet pane of 5 + label 6.25
456 A179 6c magenta, brt pink 1.25 .15
a. Booklet pane of 5 + label 6.25
457 A179 6c brown red, salmon 1.25 .15
a. Booklet pane of 5 + label 6.25
Nos. 454-457 (4) 5.00
Set value .48

Nos. 446-457 were issued in booklet panes only; all stamps have 1 or 2 straight edges.

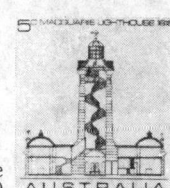

Macquarie
Lighthouse — A180

Perf. 14½x13½
1968, Nov. 27 Engr.
458 A180 5c indigo, buff .35 .15

Macquarie Lighthouse, Outer South Head, Sydney, 150th anniv.

Surveyor George
W. Goyder and
Assistants, 1869;
Building in
Darwin,
1969 — A181

1969, Feb. 5 Photo. Perf. 13½
459 A181 5c black brn & dull yel .24 .15

First permanent settlement of the Northern Territory of Australia, cent.

Melbourne
Harbor
Scene — A182

1969, Feb. 26 Photo. Perf. 13½
460 A182 5c dull blue & multi .24 .15

6th Biennial Conference of the Intl. Assoc. of Ports and Harbors, Melbourne, March 3-8.

Overlapping
Circles — A183

1969, June 5 Photo. Perf. 13½
461 A183 5c gray, vio bl, bl & gold .24 .15

ILO, 50th anniv.

Sugar Cane — A184

Designs (Primary industries): 15c, Eucalyptus (timber). 20c, Wheat. 25c, Ram, ewe and lamb (wool).

1969, Sept. 17 Perf. 13½x13
462 A184 7c blue & multi 1.10 1.10
463 A184 15c emerald & multi 6.50 5.00
464 A184 20c org brn & multi 2.25 .60
465 A184 25c gray, black & yel 1.75 .70
Nos. 462-465 (4) 11.60 7.40

Nativity — A185
Tree of Life — A186

Perf. 13½x13, 13x13½
1969, Oct. 15 Photo.
466 A185 5c multicolored .20 .15
467 A186 25c multicolored 3.50 3.50
Christmas.

Vickers Vimy
Flown by Ross
Smith, England
to Australia
A187

Designs: No. 469, B.E. 2E plane, automobile and spectators. No. 470, Ford truck and surveyors Lieuts. Hudson Fysh and P.J. McGinness.

1969, Nov. 12 Perf. 13x13½
468 A187 5c bl, blk, cop red & ol .60 .35
469 A187 5c bl, blk, cop red & ol .60 .35
470 A187 5c cop red, black & ol .60 .35
a. Strip of 3, #468-470 4.25 3.75
Nos. 468-470 (3) 1.80 1.05

50th anniv. of the first England to Australia flight by Capt. Ross Smith and Lieut. Keith Smith. Nos. 468-470 are printed se-tenant with various combinations possible.

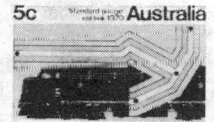

Diesel Locomotive and New Track Linking
Melbourne, Sydney and Brisbane with
Perth — A188

1970, Feb. 11 Photo. Perf. 13x13½
471 A188 5c multicolored .24 .15

Completion of the standard gauge railroad between Sydney and Perth.

EXPO '70
Australian
Pavilion
A189

Design: 20c, Southern Cross and Japanese inscription: "From the country of the south with warm feeling."

1970, Mar. 16 Photo. Perf. 13x13½
472 A189 5c bl, blk, red & brnz .25 .15
473 A189 20c red & black 1.00 .45

EXPO '70 Intl. Exhib., Osaka, Japan, Mar. 15-Sept. 13.

Queen Elizabeth
II and Prince
Philip — A190

Australian
Flag — A191

1970, Mar. 31
474 A190 5c yel bister & black .25 .15
475 A191 30c vio blue & multi 2.25 2.75

Visit of Queen Elizabeth II, Prince Philip and Princess Anne to Australia.

Steer, Alfalfa and Native Spear Grass — A192

1970, Apr. 13 Photo. Perf. 13x13½
476 A192 5c emerald & multi .28 .22

11th Intl. Grasslands Congress, Surfers Paradise, Queensland, Apr. 13-23.

Capt. James Cook and "Endeavour" — A193

Designs: No. 478, Sextant and "Endeavour." No. 479, "Endeavour," landing party and kangaroo. No. 480, Daniel Charles Solander, Sir Joseph Banks, Cook, map and botanical drawing. No. 481, Cook taking possession with Union Jack; "Endeavour" and coral. 30c, Cook, "Endeavour," sextant, kangaroo and aborigines.

1970, Apr. 20 Perf. 13½x13
Size: 24x35½mm
477 A193 5c org brn & multi .50 .15
478 A193 5c org brn & multi .50 .15
479 A193 5c org brn & multi .50 .15
480 A193 5c org brn & multi .50 .15
481 A193 5c org brn & multi .50 .15
a. Strip of 5, #477-481 2.50 2.50

Size: 62x29mm
482 A193 30c org brn & multi 3.50 3.50
a. Souv. sheet of 6, #477-482, imperf. 15.00 15.00
Nos. 477-482 (6) 6.00 4.25

Cook's discovery and exploration of the eastern coast of Australia, 200th anniv.
No. 481a has continuous design.
No. 482a with brown marginal overprint "Souvenir Sheet ANPEX 1970. . ." is of private origin.

Snowy Mountains Hydroelectric Project — A194

Designs: 8c, Ord River hydroelectric project (dam, cotton plant and boll). 9c, Bauxite and aluminum production (mine, conveyor belt and aluminum window frame). 10c, Oil and natural gas (offshore drilling rig and pipelines).

1970, Aug. 31 Photo. Perf. 13x13½
483 A194 7c multicolored 1.65 .38
484 A194 8c multicolored .25 .15
485 A194 9c multicolored .25 .15
486 A194 10c multicolored 1.10 .15
Nos. 483-486 (4) 3.25 .83

Australian economic development.

Flame Symbolizing Democracy and Freedom of Speech — A195

1970, Oct. 2 Photo. Perf. 13½x13½
487 A195 6c green & multi .25 .15

16th Commonwealth Parliamentary Assoc. Conference, Canberra, Oct. 2-9.

Herd of Illawarra Shorthorns and Laboratory A196

1970, Oct. 7 Perf. 13x13½
488 A196 6c multicolored .25 .15

18th Intl. Dairy Cong., Sydney, Oct. 12-16.

Madonna and Child, by William Beasley A197

UN Emblem, Dove and Symbols A198

1970, Oct. 14 Perf. 13½x13
489 A197 6c multicolored .25 .15
Christmas.

1970, Oct. 19
490 A198 6c blue & multi .25 .15
25th anniversary of the United Nations.

Qantas Boeing 707, and Avro 504 — A199

Design: 30c, Sunbeam Dyak powered Avro 504 on ground and Qantas Boeing 707 in the air.

1970, Nov. 2 Perf. 13x13½
491 A199 6c multicolored .24 .15
492 A199 30c multicolored 1.40 1.40

Qantas, Australian overseas airlines, 50th anniv.

Japanese Noh Actor, Australian Dancer and Chinese Opera Character — A200

Designs: 15c, Chinese pipe and trumpet, Australian aboriginal didgeridoo, Thai fiddle, Indian double oboe and Tibetan drums. 20c, Red Sea dhow, Chinese junk, Australian lifeguard's surfboat, Malaysian and South Indian river boats.

1971, Jan. 6 Photo. Perf. 13½x13
493 A200 7c multicolored .60 .15
494 A200 15c multicolored 1.50 1.10
495 A200 20c multicolored 1.50 .80
Nos. 493-495 (3) 3.60 2.05

Link between Australia and Asia; 28th Intl. Congress of Orientalists, Canberra, Jan. 6-12.

Southern Cross — A201

1971, Apr. 21 Photo. Perf. 13½x13½
496 A201 6c multicolored .28 .15

Australian Natives Assoc., cent.

 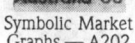 

Symbolic Market Graphs — A202

Rotary Emblem — A203

1971, May 5 Perf. 13½x13
497 A202 6c silver & multi .25 .15
Centenary of Sydney Stock Exchange.

1971, May 17 Perf. 13x13½
498 A203 6c multicolored .25 .15
First Intl. Rotary Convention held in Australia, Sydney, May 16-20.

DH-9A, Australian Mirage Jet Fighters A204

RSPCA Centenary A205

1971, June 9 Perf. 13x13½
499 A204 6c multicolored .35 .15
Royal Australian Air Force, 50th anniv.

1971, July 5 Photo. Perf. 13x13½
Designs: 12c, Man and lamb (animal science). 18c, Kangaroo (fauna conservation). 24c, Seeing eye dog (animals' aid to man).
500 A205 6c blk, brown & org .28 .15
501 A205 12c blk, dk grn & yel .75 .18
502 A205 18c brown & multi .95 .30
503 A205 24c blue & multi 1.25 .50
Nos. 500-503 (4) 3.23 1.13

Royal Society for Prevention of Cruelty to Animals in Australia, cent.

Longnecked Tortoise, Painted on Bark — A206

Aboriginal Art: 25c, Mourners' body paintings, Warramunga tribe. 30c, Cave painting, Western Arnhem Land, vert. 35c, Graveposts, Bathurst and Melville Islands, vert.

Perf. 13x13½, 13½x13
1971, Sept. 29
504 A206 20c multicolored .65 .25
505 A206 25c multicolored .65 .45
506 A206 30c multicolored .90 .35
507 A206 35c multicolored .65 .40
Nos. 504-507 (4) 2.85 1.45

Three Kings and Star — A207

1971, Oct. 13 Photo. Perf. 13½x13½
508 Block of 7 57.50
a. A207 7c brt grn, dk bl (Kings) & lil 10.00 .30
b. A207 7c lil, red brn, grn & dk bl 7.00 .15
c. A207 7c red brown & lilac 2.00 .15
d. A207 7c lilac, red brn & brt grn 3.00 .15
e. A207 7c red brown & dark blue 3.50 .15
f. A207 7c lilac, green & dk blue 22.50 1.40
g. A207 7c brt grn, dk bl & lilac (Kings) 4.00 .15

Christmas. Nos. 508a-508g printed se-tenant in sheets of 50. Each sheet contains 2 green crosses formed by 4 No. 508g and three No. 508a.

7c Australia
Andrew Fisher (1862-1928) — A208

Cameo Brooch — A209

Prime Ministers: No. 515, Joseph Cook (1860-1947). No. 516, William Morris Hughes (1864-1952). No. 517, Stanley Melbourne Bruce (1883-1967).

1972, Mar. 8 Engr. Perf. 15x14
514 A208 7c dark blue .75 .15
a. Booklet pane of 5 + label 4.00
515 A208 7c dark red .75 .15
a. Booklet pane of 5 + label 4.00
516 A208 7c dark blue .75 .15
a. Booklet pane of 5 + label 4.00
517 A208 7c dark red .75 .15
a. Booklet pane of 5 + label 4.00
Nos. 514-517 (4) 3.00
Set value .40

Nos. 514-517 were issued in booklets only; all stamps have one or two straight edges.

1972, Apr. 18 Photo. Perf. 13½
518 A209 7c multicolored .25 .15
Country Women's Assoc., 50th anniv.

Apple and Banana — A210

1972, June 14
519 A210 20c shown 2.00 .50
520 A210 25c Rice 4.00 3.50
521 A210 30c Fish 4.00 .75
522 A210 35c Cattle 11.00 9.00
Nos. 519-522 (4) 21.00 13.75

Worker in Sheltered Workshop — A211

Designs: 18c, Amputee assembling electrical circuit, horiz. 24c, Boy wearing Toronto splint, playing ball.

1972, Aug. 2 Perf. 13½x13½
523 A211 12c green & brown .25 .15
524 A211 18c orange & olive 1.25 .22
525 A211 24c brown & ultra .50 .22
Nos. 523-525 (3) 2.00 .59

Rehabilitation of the handicapped.

Overland Telegraph Line — A212

1972, Aug. 22 Photo. Perf. 13x13½
526 A212 7c dk red, blk & lemon .25 .15

Centenary of overland telegraph line.

Athlete, Olympic Rings — A213

1972, Aug. 28 *Perf. 13½x13*

527 A213	7c shown	.15	.15
528 A213	7c Swimming	.15	.15
529 A213	7c Rowing	.15	.15
530 A213	35c Equestrian	4.50	4.25
	Nos. 527-530 (4)	4.95	4.70

20th Olympic Games, Munich, Aug. 26-Sept. 11.

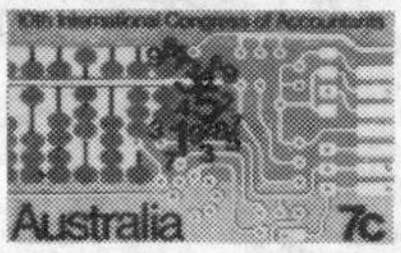

Abacus, Numerals, Computer Circuits A214

1972, Oct. 16 Photo. *Perf. 13x13½*

531 A214	7c multicolored	.20	.15

10th Intl. Congress of Accountants.

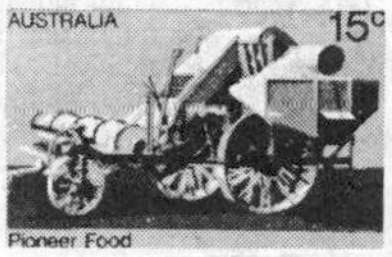

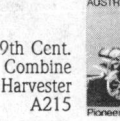

19th Cent. Combine Harvester A215

Perf. 13½x13, 13x13½

1972, Nov. 15 **Photo.**

532 A215	5c Pioneer family, vert.	.16	.15
533 A215	10c Water pump, vert.	.48	.15
534 A215	15c shown	.30	.15
535 A215	40c Pioneer house	.65	.28
536 A215	50c Cobb & Co. coach	1.10	.32
537 A215	60c Early Morse key, vert.	1.00	.55
538 A215	80c Paddle-wheel steamer	1.10	.45
	Nos. 532-538 (7)	4.79	2.05

Australian pioneer life.

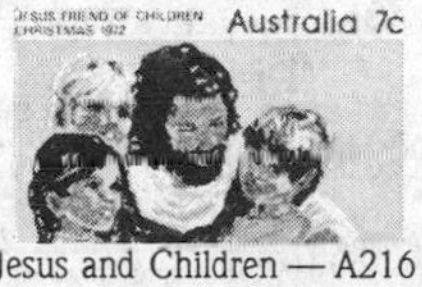

Jesus and Children — A216

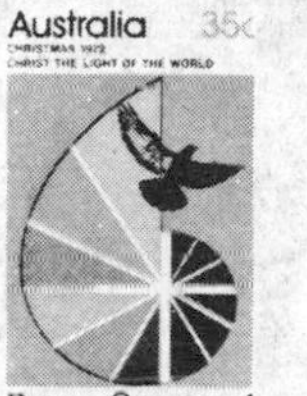

Dove, Cross and "Darkness into Light" — A217

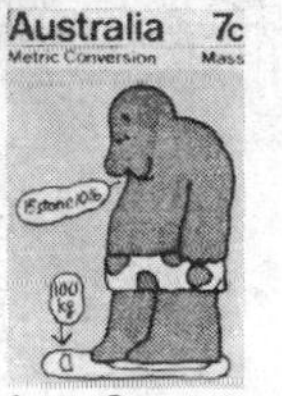

Metric Conversion, Mass — A218

Perf. 14½x14, 13½x13

1972, Nov. 29

539 A216	7c tan & multi	.35	.15
540 A217	35c blue & multi	9.00	9.00

Christmas.

1973, Mar. 7 Photo. *Perf. 14x14½*

Metric conversion: No. 542, Temperature, horiz. No. 543, Length. No. 544, Volume.

541 A218	7c pale vio & multi	.80	.20
542 A218	7c yellow & multi	.80	.20
543 A218	7c yel green & multi	.80	.20
544 A218	7c brt rose & multi	.80	.20
	Nos. 541-544 (4)	3.20	.80

Conversion to metric system.

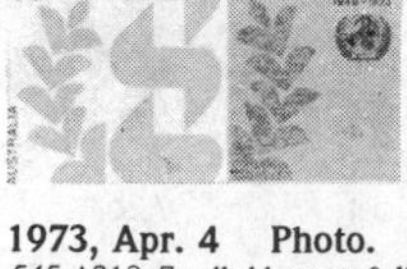

Stylized Caduceus and Laurel — A219

1973, Apr. 4 Photo. *Perf. 14½x14*

545 A219	7c dk bl, emer & lil rose	.25	.15

WHO, 25th anniv.

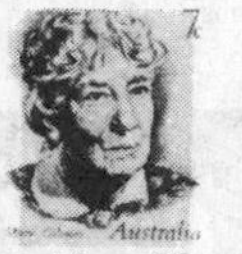

Dame Mary Gilmore, Writer A220

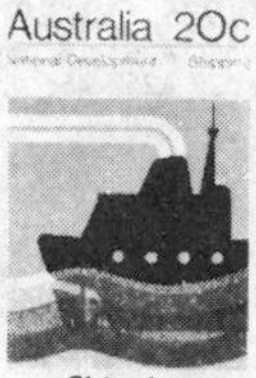

Shipping Industry A221

Famous Australians: No. 547, William Charles Wentworth, explorer. No. 548, Sir Isaac Isaacs, lawyer, first Australian-born Governor-General. No. 549, Marcus Clarke, writer.

Engr. & Litho.

1973, May 16 *Perf. 15x14*

546 A220	7c bister & black	1.25	.15
547 A220	7c bister & black	1.25	.15
548 A220	7c black & violet	1.25	.15
549 A220	7c black & violet	1.25	.15
a.	Block of 4, #546-549	5.00	
	Set value		.48

1973, June 6 Photo. *Perf. 13½x13*

Designs: 25c, Iron ore and steel. 30c, Truck convoy (beef road). 35c, Aerial mapping.

550 A221	20c ultra & multi	2.75	1.65
551 A221	25c red & multi	2.25	2.25
552 A221	30c ol brn & multi	6.00	2.75
553 A221	35c olive & multi	4.00	*4.50*
	Nos. 550-553 (4)	15.00	*11.15*

Australian economic development.

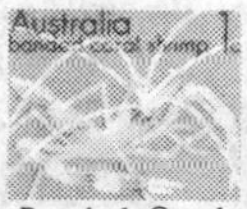

Banded Coral Shrimp A222

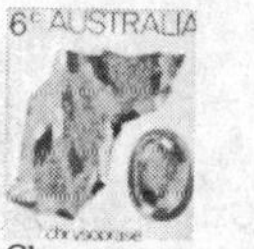

Chrysoprase A223

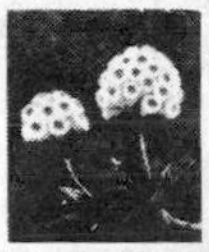
Helichrysum Thomsonii A223a

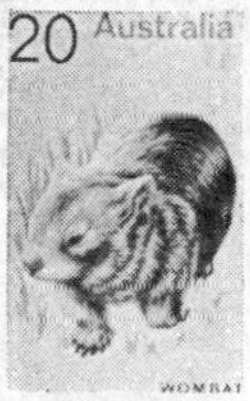

Wombat A224

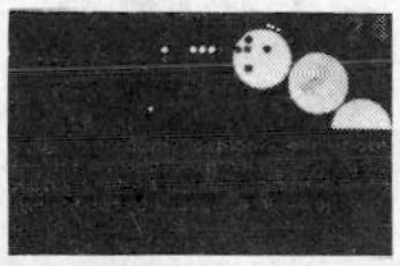
Radio Astronomy A225

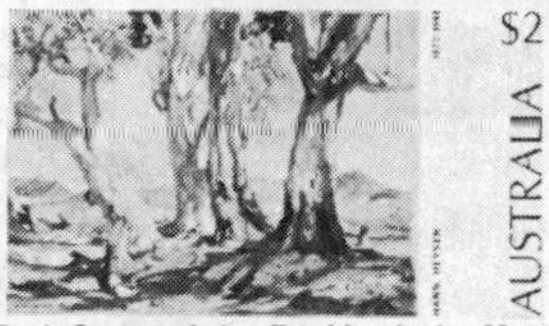

Red Gums of the Far North, by Hans Heysen — A226

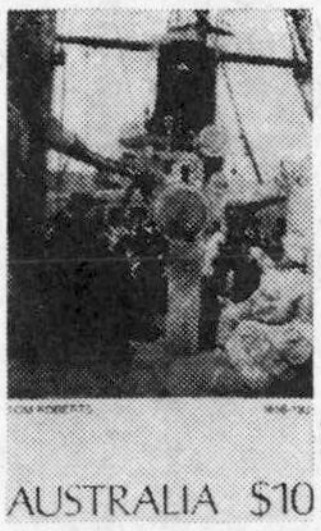

Coming South (Immigrants), by Tom Roberts — A226a

Paintings: $1, Sergeant of Light Horse, by George Lambert. No. 575, On the Wallaby Track. $4, Shearing the Rams, by Tom Roberts. No. 577, McMahon's Point, by Arthur Streeton. No. 578, Mentone.

Perf. 14x15, 15x14 (A222, A223, A223a); Perf. 14x14½ (A224); Perf. 13x13½ (A225, A226, $1)

1973-84 **Photo.**

554 A222	1c shown	.15	.15
555 A222	2c Fiddler crab	.15	.15
556 A222	3c Coral crab	.15	.15
557 A222	4c Mauve stinger	.15	.15
558 A223	6c shown	.15	.15
559 A223	7c Agate	.15	.15
560 A223	8c Opal	.15	.15
561 A223	9c Rhodonite	.15	.15
562 A223	10c Star sapphire ('74)	.15	.15
563 A225	11c Atomic absorption spectrophotometry ('75)	.55	.28
564 A223a	18c shown ('75)	.50	.15
565 A224	20c shown ('74)	.42	.15
566 A225	24c shown ('75)	1.00	.40
567 A224	25c Spiny anteater ('74)	1.25	.35
568 A224	30c Brushtail possum ('74)	.70	.20
569 A225	33c Immunology ('75)	1.00	1.00
570 A223a	45c Callistemon teretifolius, horiz. ('75)	.65	.25
571 A225	48c Oceanography ('75)	1.75	1.10
572 A224	75c Feather-tailed glider ('74)	1.25	.75
573 A226a	$1 multi ('74)	1.50	.25
574 A226	$2 shown ('74)	2.75	.30
575 A226	$2 multi ('81)	2.50	.30
576 A226	$4 multi ('74)	6.50	2.25

Litho.

Perf. 14½

577 A226a	$5 multi ('79)	6.50	2.00
578 A226	$5 multi ('84)	6.00	1.25
579 A226a	$10 shown ('77)	12.00	3.25
	Nos. 554-579 (26)	48.17	15.58

Issued: 1c-9c, 7/11; 20c, 25c, 30c, 75c, 2/13; $1, #574, $4, 4/24; 10c, 10/16; 11c, 24c, 33c, 48c, 5/14; 18c, 45c, 8/27; $10, 10/19; #577, 3/14; #575, 6/17; #578, 4/4.

No. 560 Surcharged in Red = 9c

Perf. 15x14

580 A223	9c on 8c multi ('74)	.24	.15

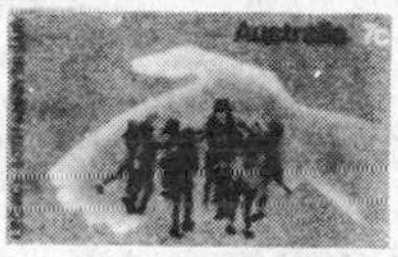

Hand Protecting Playing Children A227

1973, Sept. 5 Photo. *Perf. 13x13½*

581 A227	7c bis brn, grn & plum	.25	.15

50th anniv. of Legacy, an ex-servicemen's organization concerned with the welfare of widows and children of servicemen.

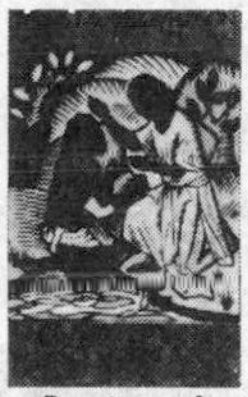
Baptism of Christ A228

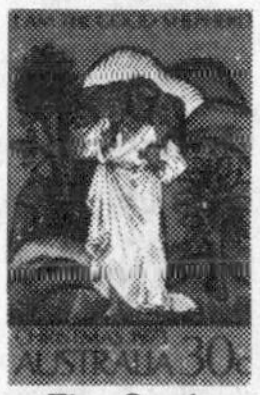

The Good Shepherd A229

1973, Oct. 3 *Perf. 14x14½*

582 A228	7c gold & multi	.30	.15
a.	Perf 14x15	4.00	.60

Perf. 13½

583 A229	30c gold & multi	3.75	4.25

Christmas.

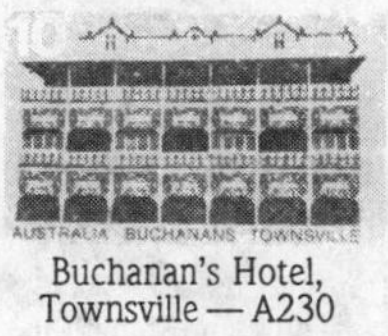

Buchanan's Hotel, Townsville — A230

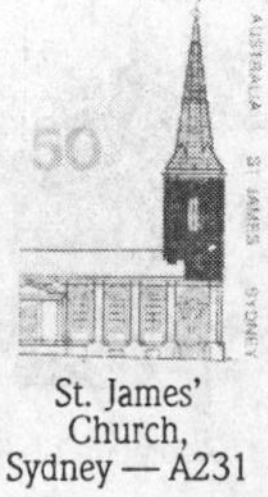

St. James' Church, Sydney — A231

Designs: 7c, Opera House, Sydney. 40c, Como House, Melbourne.

1973, Oct. 17 Photo. *Perf. 14½x14*

584 A230	7c lt blue & ultra	.40	.15
a.	Perf 15x14	4.00	.80
585 A230	10c bister & black	.60	.32

Perf. 13x13½, 13½x13

586 A230	40c dl pink, gray & blk	.75	1.00
587 A231	50c gray & multi	2.00	2.00
	Nos. 584-587 (4)	3.75	3.47

Australian architecture; opening of the Sydney Opera House, Oct. 14, 1973 (No. 584).

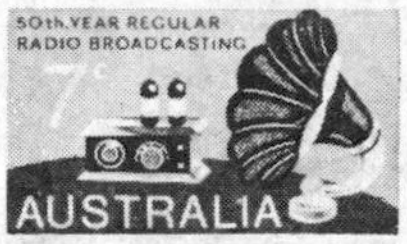

Radio and Gramophone Speaker A232

1973, Nov. 21 Photo. *Perf. 13½x13*

588 A232	7c dull blue, blk & brn	.25	.15

Broadcasting in Australia, 50th anniv.

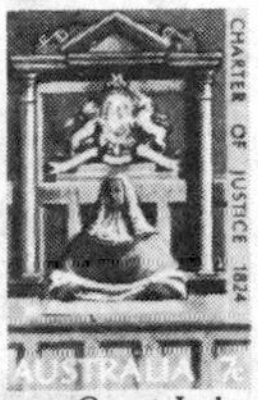

Supreme Court Judge on Bench A233

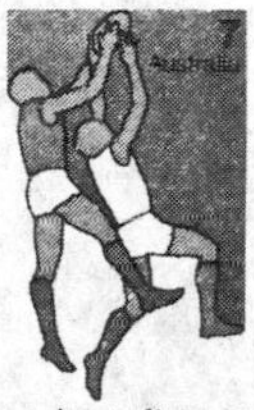

Australian Football A234

1974, May 15 Photo. *Perf. 14x14½*

589 A233	7c multicolored	.25	.15

150th anniv. of the proclamation of the Charter of Justice in New South Wales and Van Diemen's Land (Australia's Third Charter).

1974, July 24 Photo. *Perf. 14x14½*

590 A234	7c shown	.32	.16
591 A234	7c Cricket	.32	.16
592 A234	7c Golf	.32	.16
593 A234	7c Surfing	.32	.16
594 A234	7c Tennis	.32	.16
595 A234	7c Bowls, horiz.	.32	.16
596 A234	7c Rugby, horiz.	.32	.16
	Nos. 590-596 (7)	2.24	1.12

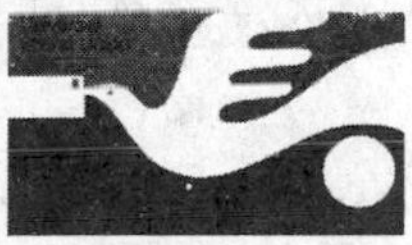
Carrier Pigeon — A235

Designs: 30c, Carrier pigeons, vert.

1974, Oct. 9 Photo. *Perf. 14½x14*

597 A235	7c multicolored	.25	.15
a.	Perf 15x14	.75	.15

Perf. 13½x13

598 A235	30c multicolored	1.00	1.00

UPU, cent. A booklet containing a strip of 5 each of Nos. 597-598 was produced and sold for $4 Australian by the National Stamp Week Promotion Council with government approval.

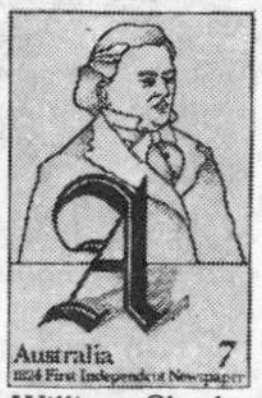

William Charles Wentworth A236

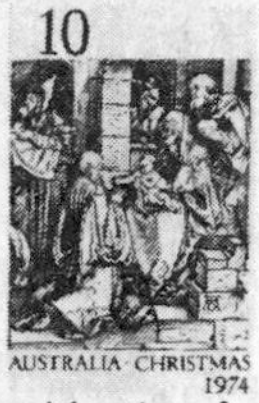

Adoration of the Kings, by Dürer A237

Typo. & Litho.

1974, Oct. 9 *Perf. 14x15*

599 A236	7c bister & black	.35	.15
a.	Perf 14x14½	.90	.25

Sesquicentennial of 1st Australian independent newspaper. W. C. Wentworth and Dr. Robert Wardell were the editors and the "A" is type from masthead of "The Australian."

1974, Nov. 13 Engr. *Perf. 14x14½*

Christmas: 35c, Flight into Egypt, by Albrecht Dürer.

600	A237	10c	buff & black	.22	.15
601	A237	35c	buff & black	.90	.90

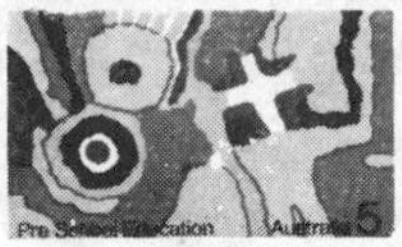

Pre-school Education A238

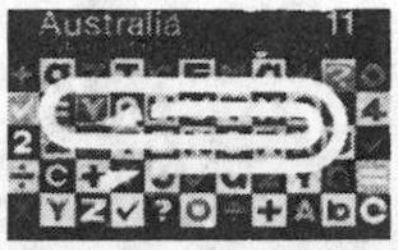

Correspondence Schools A239

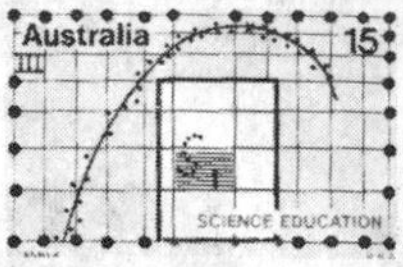

Science Education A240

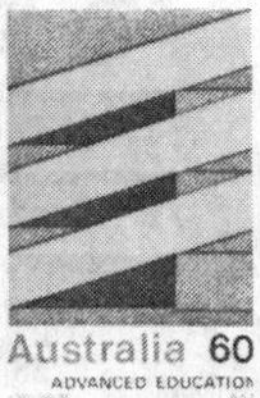

Advanced Education — A241

Perf. 13x13½, 13½x13

1974, Nov. 20 Photo.

602	A238	5c	multicolored	.25	.15
603	A239	11c	multicolored	.38	.28
604	A240	15c	multicolored	.60	.30
605	A241	60c	multicolored	1.25	1.10
			Nos. 602-605 (4)	2.48	1.83

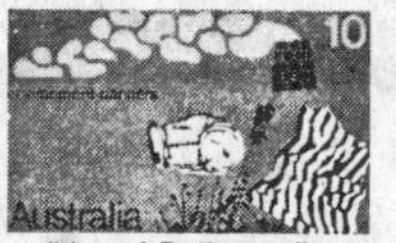

"Avoid Pollution" A242

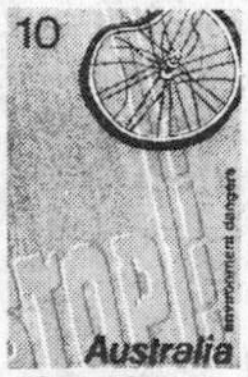

"Road Safety" A243

Design: No. 607, "Avoid bush fires."

1975, Jan. 29 Photo. *Perf. 14½x14*

606	A242	10c	multicolored	.32	.15
a.			Perf. 15x14	7.50	3.75
607	A242	10c	multicolored	.32	.15
a.			Perf. 15x14	1.50	1.00

Perf. 14x14½

608	A243	10c	multicolored	.32	.15
			Nos. 606-608 (3)	.96	.45

Environmental dangers.

Symbols of Womanhood, Sun, Moon A244

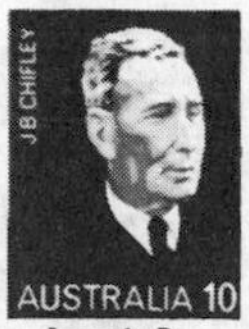

Joseph B. Chifley (1885-1951) A245

1975, Mar. 12 Photo. *Perf. 14x14½*

609	A244	10c	dk vio blue & grn	.28	.15

International Women's Year.

1975, Mar. 26

610	A245	10c	shown	.22	.15
611	A245	10c	John Curtin, 1885-1945	.22	.15
612	A245	10c	Arthur W. Fadden, 1895-1973	.22	.15
613	A245	10c	Joseph A. Lyons, 1879-1939	.22	.15
614	A245	10c	Earle Page, 1880-1963	.22	.15
615	A245	10c	John H. Scullin, 1876-1953	.22	.15
			Nos. 610-615 (6)	1.32	
			Set value		.60

Australian Prime Ministers.

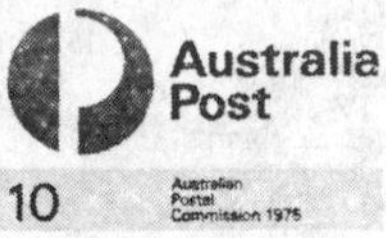

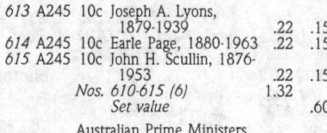

Australian Postal Commission A246

Design: No. 617, Australian Telecommunications Commission.

1975, July 1 Photo. *Perf. 14½x14*

616	A246	10c	red, black & gray	.40	.20
a.			Perf. 15x14	.50	.15
617	A246	10c	yel, black & gray	.40	.20
a.			Pair, #616-617	.95	.75
b.			Perf. 15x14	.50	.15
c.			Pair, #616a, 617b	1.25	1.00

Formation of Australian Postal and Telecommunications Commissions. Printed checkerwise.

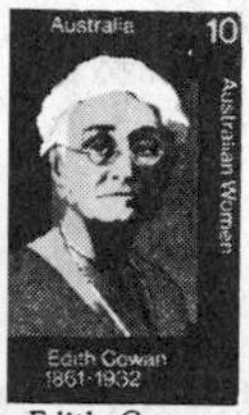

Edith Cowan, Judge and Legislator A247

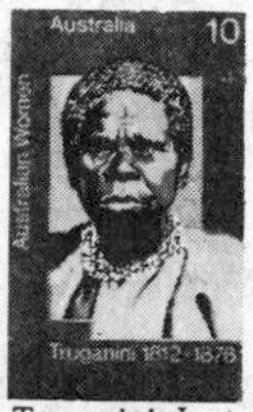

Truganini, Last Tasmanian Aborigine A248

Portraits: No. 619, Louisa Lawson (1848-1920), journalist. No. 620, Ethel Florence (Henry Handel) Richardson (1870-1946), novelist. No. 621, Catherine Spence (1825-1910), teacher, journalist, voting reformer. No. 622, Emma Constance Stone (1856-1902), first Australian woman physician.

1975, Aug. 6 Photo. *Perf. 14x14½*

618	A247	10c	olive grn & multi	.32	.32
a.			Perf 14x15	.35	.35
619	A247	10c	yel bister & multi	.32	.32
a.			Perf 14x15	.35	.35
620	A248	10c	olive & multi	.32	.32
a.			Perf 14x15	.35	.35
621	A248	10c	gray & multi	.32	.32
a.			Perf 14x15	.35	.35
622	A247	10c	violet & multi	.32	.32
623	A248	10c	brown & multi	.32	.32
a.			Perf 14x15	.35	.35
			Nos. 618-623 (6)	1.92	1.92

Famous Australian women.

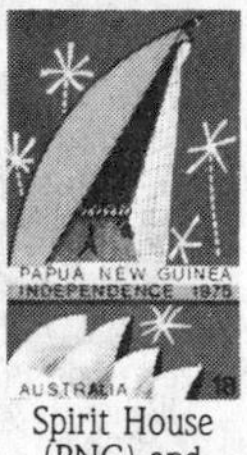

Spirit House (PNG) and Sydney Opera House — A249

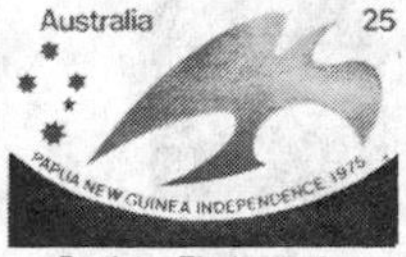

Bird in Flight and Southern Cross — A250

1975, Sept. 16 Photo. *Perf. 13½*

624	A249	18c	multicolored	.40	.15
625	A250	25c	multicolored	.75	.55

Papua New Guinea independence, Sept. 16, 1975.

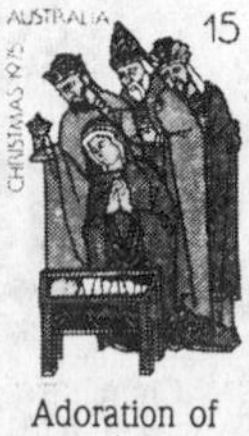

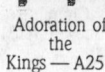

Adoration of the Kings — A251

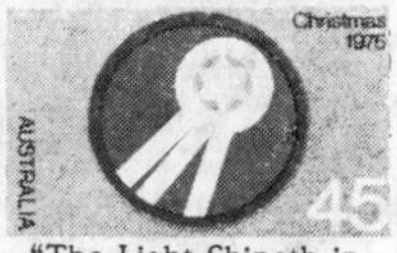

"The Light Shineth in the Darkness" — A252

1975, Oct. 29 Photo. *Perf. 14½x14*

626	A251	15c	multicolored	.28	.15
627	A252	45c	silver & multi	1.65	1.50

Christmas.

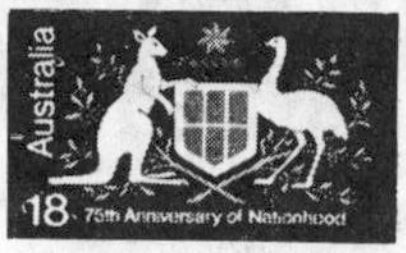

Australian Coat of Arms — A253

Two Types of A253:
Type I - Kangaroo: eye is dot, right paw has 1 toe, left foot has 1 toe. Emu: feet have 1 toe.
Type II - Kangaroo: eye is line, right paw has 3 toes, left foot has 2 toes. Emu: feet have 2 toes.
Other differences exist.

1976, Jan. 5 Photo. *Perf. 14½x14*

628	A253	18c	multicolored, type I	.40	.15
a.			Type II	.75	.25

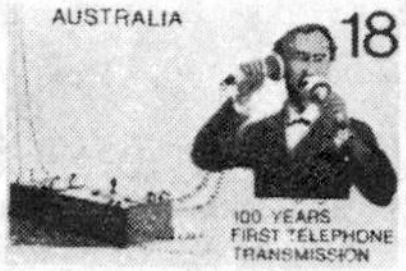

"Williams' Coffin" Telephone, 1878 — A254

1976, Mar. 10 Photo. *Perf. 13½*

629	A254	18c	buff & multi	.35	.18

Centenary of first telephone call by Alexander Graham Bell, Mar. 10, 1876.

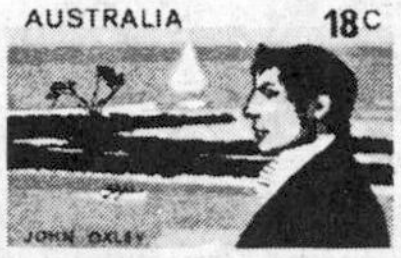

John Oxley — A255

Designs: Australian explorers.

1976, June 9 Photo. *Perf. 13½*

630	A255	18c	shown	.25	.16
631	A255	18c	Hamilton Hume and William Hovell	.25	.16
632	A255	18c	John Forrest	.25	.16
633	A255	18c	Ernest Giles	.25	.16
634	A255	18c	Peter Warburton	.25	.16
635	A255	18c	William Gosse	.25	.16
			Nos. 630-635 (6)	1.50	.96

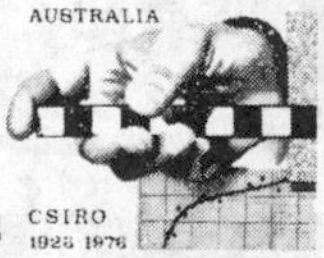

Survey Rule, Graph, Punched Tape — A256

1976, June 15 *Perf. 15x14*

636	A256	18c	multicolored	.30	.18

Commonwealth Scientific and Industrial Research Organization, 50th anniv.

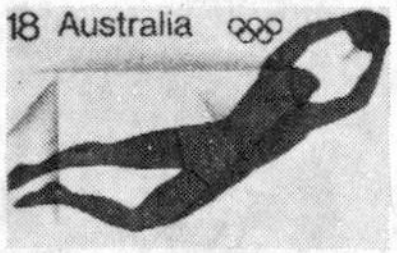

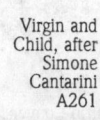

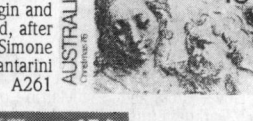

Soccer Goalkeeper A257

Olympic Rings and: No. 638, Woman gymnast, vert. 25c, Woman diver, vert. 40c, Bicycling.

Perf. 13x13½, 13½x13

1976, July 14 Photo.

637	A257	18c	multicolored	.30	.15
638	A257	18c	multicolored	.30	.15
639	A257	25c	multicolored	.45	.40
640	A257	40c	multicolored	.65	.50
			Nos. 637-640 (4)	1.70	1.20

21st Olympic Games, Montreal, Canada, July 17-Aug. 1.

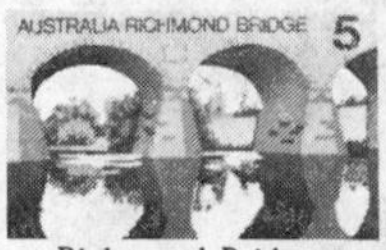

Richmond Bridge, Tasmania A258

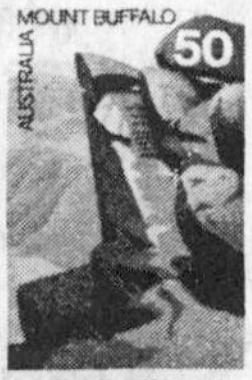

Mt. Buffalo, Victoria A259

Designs: 25c, Broken Bay, New South Wales. 35c, Wittenoom Gorge, Western Australia. 70c, Barrier Reef, Queensland. 85c, Ayers Rock, Northern Territory.

Perf. 14½x14, 14x14½

1976, Aug. 25 Photo.

641	A258	5c	multicolored	.25	.15
642	A258	25c	multicolored	.45	.20
643	A258	35c	multicolored	.42	.30
644	A259	50c	multicolored	.65	.25
645	A258	70c	multicolored	.80	.35
646	A258	85c	multicolored	1.25	1.00
			Nos. 641-646 (6)	3.82	2.25

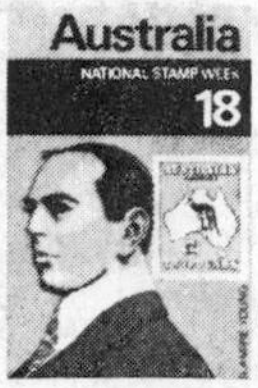

Blamire Young and Australia No. 59 — A260

1976, Sept. 27 Photo. *Perf. 13½*

647	A260	18c	apple green & multi	.35	.15

Miniature Sheet

648			Sheet of 4	1.65	1.50
a.	A260	18c	yellow & dark brown	.38	.35
b.	A260	18c	rose, dk brown & yel	.38	.35
c.	A260	18c	blue, dk brn, rose & yel	.38	.35

Natl. Stamp Week, Sept. 27-Oct. 3. Blamire Young (1862-1935), designer of Australia's 1st issue. No. 648 shows different stages of 4-color printing. The 4th stamp in sheet is identical with No. 647.

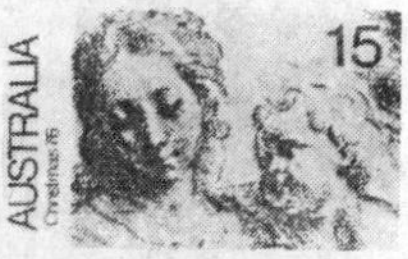

Virgin and Child, after Simone Cantarini A261

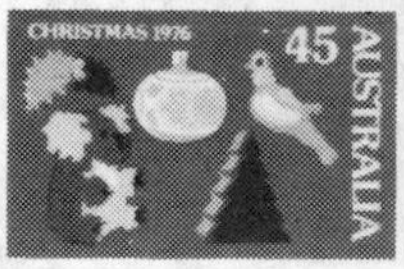

Holly, Toy Koala, Christmas Tree and Decoration, Partridge A262

1976, Nov. 1 Photo. *Perf. 14½x14*

649	A261	15c	brt car & lt blue	.32	.20

Perf. 13½

650	A262	45c	multicolored	.80	.75

Christmas.

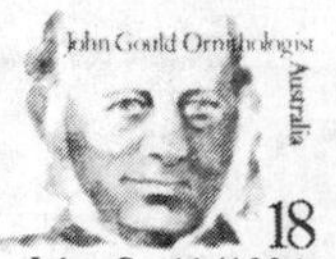

John Gould (1804-1881) Ornithologist A263

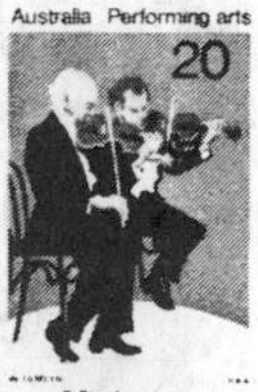

Violinists A264

Famous Australians: No. 652, Thomas Laby (1880-1946), nuclear scientist. No. 653, Sir Baldwin Spencer (1860-1929), anthropologist (aborigines). No. 654, Griffith Taylor (1880-1963), geographer and arctic explorer.

1976, Nov. 10 *Perf. 15x14*

651	A263	18c	shown	.30	.18
652	A263	18c	Laby	.30	.18
653	A263	18c	Spencer	.30	.18
654	A263	18c	Taylor	.30	.18
			Nos. 651-654 (4)	1.20	.72

1977, Jan. 19   Photo.   Perf. 14x14½
655 A264 20c shown .35 .20
656 A264 30c Dramatic scene .42 .20
657 A264 40c Dancer .70 .40
658 A264 60c Opera singer .90 .20
Nos. 655-658 (4) 2.37 1.00

Performing arts in Australia.

Elizabeth II
A265

Wicket Keeper, Slip
Fieldsman
A266

Design: 45c, Elizabeth II and Prince Philip.

1977, Feb. 2
659 A265 18c multicolored .30 .15
660 A265 18c multicolored .75 .75

Reign of Queen Elizabeth II, 25th anniv.

1977, Mar. 9   Photo.   Perf. 13½
Cricket match, 19th century: No. 662, Umpire and batsman. No. 663, Two fieldsmen. No. 664, Batsman and umpire. No. 665, Bowler and fieldsman. 45c, Batsman facing bowler.

661 A266 18c gray & multi .35 .25
662 A266 18c gray & multi .35 .25
663 A266 18c gray & multi .35 .25
664 A266 18c gray & multi .35 .25
665 A266 18c gray & multi .35 .25
a. Strip of 5, #661-665 2.00 2.00
666 A266 45c gray & multi .90 .90
Nos. 661-666 (6) 2.65 2.15

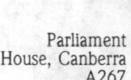

Parliament
House, Canberra
A267

1977, Apr. 13   Perf. 14½x14
667 A267 18c multicolored .40 .15
Parliament House, Canberra, 50th anniv.

Trade Union
Workers
A268

1977, May 9   Photo.   Perf. 13
668 A268 18c multicolored .35 .15
Australian Council of Trade Unions (ACTU), 50th anniv.

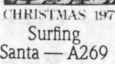

Surfing
Santa — A269

Virgin and
Child — A270

1977, Oct. 31   Photo.   Perf. 14x14½
669 A269 15c multicolored .35 .15
Perf. 13½x13
670 A270 45c multicolored .75 .75
Christmas.

Australian
Flag — A271

1978, Jan. 26   Photo.   Perf. 13x13½
671 A271 18c multicolored .35 .15
Australia Day, 190th anniversary of first permament settlement in New South Wales.

Harry Hawker
and Sopwith
"Camel"
A272

Australian Aviators and their Planes: No. 673, Bert Hinkler and Avro Avian. No. 674, Charles Kingsford-Smith and Fokker "Southern Cross." No. 675, Charles Ulm and "Southern Cross."

1978, Apr. 19   Litho.   Perf. 15½
672 A272 18c ultra & multi .30 .15
673 A272 18c blue & multi .30 .15
674 A272 18c orange & multi .30 .15
675 A272 18c yellow & multi .30 .15
a. Souv. sheet, 2 each #674-675, imperf. 1.65 1.65
Nos. 672-675 (4) 1.20 .60

No. 675a for 50th anniv. of first Trans-Pacific flight from Oakland, Cal., to Brisbane.

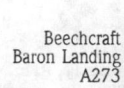

Beechcraft
Baron Landing
A273

1978, May 15   Photo.   Perf. 13½
676 A273 18c multicolored .30 .20
Royal Flying Doctor Service, 50th anniv.

Illawarra Flame
Tree — A274

Sturt's Desert
Rose, Map of
Australia — A275

Australian trees: 25c, Ghost gum. 40c, Grass tree. 45c, Cootamundra wattle.

1978, June 1
677 A274 18c multicolored .18 .15
678 A274 25c multicolored .60 .60
679 A274 40c multicolored .70 1.10
680 A274 45c multicolored .65 1.00
Nos. 677-680 (4) 2.13 2.85

1978, June 19   Litho.   Perf. 15½
681 A275 18c multicolored .35 .18
Establishment of Government of the Northern Territory.

Hooded
Dotterel — A276

Australian birds: 20c, Little grebe. 25c, Spurwing Plover. 30c, Pied oystercatcher. 55c, Lotus bird.

1978   Photo.   Perf. 13½
682 A276 5c multicolored .15 .15
683 A276 20c multicolored .25 .15
684 A276 25c multicolored .35 .15
685 A276 30c multicolored .40 .30
686 A276 55c multicolored .70 .50
Nos. 682-686 (5) 1.85
Set value 1.10

Issued: Nos. 683, 686, July 3; others, July 17.
See Nos. 713-718, 732-739, 768.

Australia No. 95
on Album
Page — A277

Virgin and Child, by
Simon
Marmion — A278

1978, Sept. 25   Litho.   Perf. 15½
687 A277 20c multicolored .38 .15
a. Miniature sheet of 4 1.65 1.65
National Stamp Week; 50th anniv. of Melbourne Intl. Phil. Exhib., Oct. 1928.

1978   Perf. 15
Paintings from National Gallery, Victoria: 15c, Virgin and Child, after Van Eyck. 55c, Holy Family, by Perino del Vaga.

688 A278 15c multicolored .22 .15
689 A278 25c multicolored .50 .52
690 A278 55c multicolored .80 .80
Nos. 688-690 (3) 1.52 1.47

Christmas. Issued: 25c, Oct. 3, others, Nov. 1.

Tulloch
A279

Race horses: 35c, Bernborough, vert. 50c, Phar Lap, vert. 55c, Peter Pan.

Perf. 15x14, 14x15
1978, Oct. 18   Photo.
691 A279 20c multicolored .28 .15
692 A279 35c multicolored .52 .55
693 A279 50c multicolored .75 .80
694 A279 55c multicolored .75 .90
Nos. 691-694 (4) 2.30 2.40

Australian horse racing.

Flag Raising at Sydney
Cove — A280

1979, Jan. 26   Litho.   Perf. 15½
695 A280 20c multicolored .35 .18
Australia Day, Jan. 26.

Passenger
Steamer
Canberra
A281

Ferries and Murray River Steamers: 35c, M.V. Lady Denman. 50c, P.S. Murray River Queen. 55c, Hydrofoil Curl Curl.

1979, Feb. 14   Photo.   Perf. 13½
696 A281 20c multicolored .32 .15
697 A281 35c multicolored .52 .40
698 A281 50c multicolored .75 .65
699 A281 55c multicolored .80 .85
Nos. 696-699 (4) 2.39 2.05

Port Campbell
Australia 20c   A282

Designs: Australian National Parks.

1979, Apr. 9   Litho.   Perf. 15½
700 A282 20c shown .30 .15
701 A282 20c Uluru .30 .15
702 A282 20c Royal .30 .15
703 A282 20c Flinders Ranges .30 .15
704 A282 20c Namburg .30 .15
a. Strip of 5, #700-704 1.50
705 A282 20c Girraween, vert. .30 .15
706 A282 20c Mount Field, vert. .30 .15
a. Pair, #705-706 .60
Nos. 700-706 (7) 2.10
Set value .70

Double
Fairlie — A283

Australian steam locomotives: 35c, Puffing Billy. 50c, Pichi Richi. 55c, Zig Zag.

Perf. 13½, 15x14 (20c)
1979, May 16   Photo.
707 A283 20c multicolored .35 .15
708 A283 35c multicolored .65 .40
709 A283 50c multicolored .90 .75
710 A283 55c multicolored .95 1.00
Nos. 707-710 (4) 2.85 2.30

"Black
Swan" — A284

1979, June 6   Photo.   Perf. 13½
711 A284 20c multicolored .38 .20
150th anniversary of Western Australia.

Children
Playing, IYC
Emblem
A285

1979, Aug. 13   Litho.   Perf. 13½x13
712 A285 20c multicolored .30 .20
International Year of the Child.

Bird Type of 1978
Australian birds: 1c, Zebra finch. 2c, Crimson finch. 15c, Forest kingfisher, vert. 20c, Eastern yellow robin. 40c, Lovely wren, vert. 50c, Flame robin, vert.

1979, Sept. 17   Photo.   Perf. 13½
713 A276 1c multicolored .15 .15
714 A276 2c multicolored .15 .15
715 A276 15c multicolored .30 .15
716 A276 20c multicolored .30 .15
717 A276 40c multicolored .50 .20
718 A276 50c multicolored .70 .20
Nos. 713-718 (6) 2.10
Set value .65

Christmas Letters,
Flag-wrapped
Parcels
A286

Trout Fishing
A287

Christmas: 15c, Nativity, icon. 55c, Madonna and Child, by Buglioni.

1979   Litho.   Perf. 13
719 A286 15c multicolored .15 .15
720 A286 25c multicolored .30 .30
721 A286 55c multicolored .90 .90
Nos. 719-721 (3) 1.35 1.35

Issue dates: 25c, Sept. 24. Others, Nov. 1.

1979, Oct. 24 Photo. *Perf. 14x14½*

Sport fishing: 35c, Angler. 50c, Black marlin fishing. 55c, Surf fishing.

722 A287 20c multicolored .28 .15
723 A287 35c multicolored .48 .48
724 A287 50c multicolored .70 .48
725 A287 55c multicolored .75 .70
Nos. 722-725 (4) 2.21 1.81

Matthew Flinders, Map of Australia A288

1980, Jan. 23 Litho. *Perf. 13½*

726 A288 20c multicolored .30 .15

Australia Day, Jan. 28.

Dingo — A289

1980, Feb. 20 Litho. *Perf. 13½x13*

727 A289 20c shown .30 .20
728 A289 25c Border collie .32 .35
729 A289 35c Australian terrier .60 .40
730 A289 50c Australian cattle dog .80 .70
731 A289 55c Australian kelpie .65 .70
Nos. 727-731 (5) 2.67 2.35

Bird Type of 1978

Perf. 13½, 14x15 (22c), 13x12½ (28c, 60c)

1980 Litho., Photo. (22c)

732 A276 10c Golden-shoulder parrot, vert. .15 .15
a. Perf. 14½x14 1.25 .50
733 A276 22c White-tailed kingfisher, vert. .30 .15
734 A276 28c Rainbow bird, vert. .45 .15
735 A276 35c Regent bower bird, vert. .45 .20
736 A276 45c Masked woodswallow .95 .20
a. Perf. 14x14½ 4.00 2.00
737 A276 60c King parrot, vert. .75 .25
738 A276 80c Rainbow pitta 1.00 .40
739 A276 $1 Western magpie, vert. 1.25 .30
Nos. 732-739 (8) 5.30 1.80

Issued: #733, 734, 737, Mar. 31; others, July 1.

Queen Elizabeth II, 54th Birthday — A290

1980, Apr. 21 Litho. *Perf. 13x13½*

740 A290 22c multicolored .35 .15

Wanderer A291

High Court Building, Canberra A292

1980, May 7 Litho. *Perf. 13x13½*

741 Strip of 5 1.75 1.50
a. A291 22c shown .32 .15
b. A291 22c Stealing sheep .32 .15
c. A291 22c Squatter on horseback .32 .15
d. A291 22c Three troopers .32 .15
e. A291 22c Wanderer's ghost .32 .15

"Waltzing Matilda", poem by Andrew Barton Patterson (1864-1941). No. 741 in continuous design.

1980, May 19

742 A292 22c multicolored .38 .15

Opening of High Court of Australia Building, Canberra, May 26.

Salvation Army Officers — A294

Perf. 13x13½, 13½x13

1980, Aug. 11

747 A294 22c shown .32 .15
748 A294 22c St. Vincent de Paul Society, vert. .32 .15
749 A294 22c Meals on Wheels, vert. .32 .15
750 A294 22c "Life. Be in it." (Joggers, bicyclists) .32 .15
Nos. 747-750 (4) 1.28
Set value .48

Mailman c. 1900 — A295

Holy Family, by Prospero Fontana — A296

1980, Sept. 29 Litho. *Perf. 13x13½*

751 A295 22c Mailbox .35 .16
752 A295 22c shown .35 .16
753 A295 22c Mail truck .35 .16
754 A295 22c Mailman, mailbox .35 .16
755 A295 22c Mailman, diff. .35 .16
a. Souvenir sheet of 3 1.25 1.00
b. Strip of 5, #751-755 1.75 1.00

Natl. Stamp Week, Sept. 29-Oct. 5. #755a contains stamps similar to #751, 753, 755.

1980 *Perf. 13x13½*

Christmas: 15c, Virgin Enthroned, by Justin O'Brien. 60c, Virgin and Child, by Michael Zuern the Younger, 1680.

756 A296 15c multicolored .22 .15
757 A296 28c multicolored .45 .45
758 A296 60c multicolored .90 .65
Nos. 756-758 (3) 1.57 1.25

Issued: 15c, 60c, Nov. 3; 28c, Oct. 1.

CA-6 Wackett Trainer, 1941 — A297

Designs: Australian military training planes.

1980, Nov. 19 *Perf. 13½x14*

759 A297 22c shown .32 .32
760 A297 40c Winjeel, 1955 .60 .60
761 A297 45c Boomerang, 1944 .65 .52
762 A297 60c Nomad, 1975 1.00 .60
Nos. 759-762 (4) 2.57 2.04

Bird Type of 1978

1980, Nov. 17 Litho. *Perf. 13½*

768 A276 18c Spotted catbird, vert. .35 .15

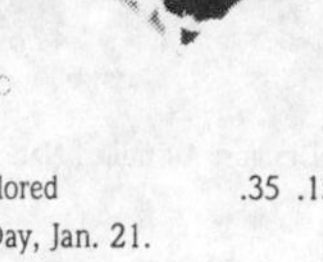

Flag on Map of Australia A298

1981, Jan. 21

771 A298 22c multicolored .35 .15

Australia Day, Jan. 21.

Jockey Darby Munro (1913-1966), by Tony Rafty — A299

Australian sportsmen (Cariactures by Tony Rafty): 35c, Victor Trumper (1877-1915), cricket batsman. 55c, Norman Brookes (1877-1968), tennis player. 60c, Walter Lindrum (1898-1960), billiards player.

1981, Feb. 18 *Perf. 14x13½*

772 A299 22c multicolored .25 .15
773 A299 35c multicolored .45 .45
774 A299 55c multicolored .65 .65
775 A299 60c multicolored .75 .75
Nos. 772-775 (4) 2.10 2.00

Australia No. C2 and Cover — A300

Perf. 13x13½, 13½x13

1981, Mar. 25 Litho.

776 A300 22c Australia No. C2, vert. .30 .25
777 A300 60c shown .90 .80

Australia-United Kingdom official airmail service, 50th anniv.

Map of Australia, APEX Emblem A301

1981, Apr. 6 Photo. *Perf. 13x13½*

778 A301 22c multicolored .30 .15

50th anniv. of APEX (young men's service club).

Queen Elizabeth's Personal Flag of Australia A302

1981, Apr. 21 *Perf. 13*

779 A302 22c multicolored .35 .15

Queen Elizabeth II, 55th birthday.

License Inspected, Forrest Creek, by S.T. Gill — A303

Gold Rush Era (Sketches by S.T. Gill): No. 781, Puddling. No. 782, Quality of Washing Stuff. No. 783, Diggers on Route to Deposit Gold.

1981, May 20 Photo. *Perf. 13x13½*

780 A303 22c multicolored .30 .15
781 A303 22c multicolored .30 .15
782 A303 22c multicolored .30 .15
783 A303 22c multicolored .30 .15
Nos. 780-783 (4) 1.20 .60

Lace Monitor — A303a

Tasmanian Tiger — A304

Two Types of A304:
Type I - Indistinct line at right of ear, stripes even with base of tail.
Type II - Heavy line at right of ear, stripes longer.

1981-83 Litho.

784 A303a 1c shown .15 .15
785 A303a 3c Corroboree frog .15 .15
786 A304 5c Queensland hairy-nosed wombat, vert. .15 .15
787 A303a 15c Eastern snake-necked tortoise .20 .15
788 A304 24c shown, type I .35 .18
a. Type II .35 .18
789 A304 25c Greater bilby, vert. .35 .18
790 A303a 27c Blue Mountains tree frog .40 .20
791 A304 30c Bridled nail-tailed wallaby, vert. .42 .22
792 A303a 40c Smooth knob-tailed gecko .55 .28
793 A304 50c Leadbeater's opossum .85 .40
794 A304 55c Stick-nest rat, vert. .85 .42
795 A303a 65c Yellow-faced whip snake 1.00 .48
796 A303a 70c Crucifix toad 1.10 .55
797 A303a 75c Eastern water dragon 1.10 .55
798 A303a 85c Centralian blue-tongued lizard 1.25 .65
799 A303a 90c Freshwater crocodile 1.40 .70
800 A303a 95c Thorny devil 1.50 .75
Nos. 784-800 (17) 11.77 6.16

Perfs: 1c, 70c, 85c, 95c, 13½; 3c, 15c, 27c, 40c, 50c, 65c, 75c, 90c, 12½x13; 5c, 25c, 30c, 55c, 13x12½; 24c, 13x13½.

Issued: 24c, 7/1/81; 5c, 25c, 30c, 50c, 55c, 7/15/81; 3c, 27c, 65c, 75c, 4/19/82; 15c, 40c, 90c, 6/16/82. 1c, 70c, 85c, 95c, 2/2/83.

1982-84 *Perf. 14x14½, 14½x14*

785a A303a 3c ('84) .32 .15
786a A304 5c ('84) .90 .15
787a A303a 15c ('84) .70 .25
789a A304 25c ('83) 1.10 .20
790a A303a 27c .75 .24
792a A303a 40c ('84) 2.00 .28
793a A304 50c ('83) 1.25 .40
795a A303a 65c ('84) 1.40 .60
797a A303a 75c ('84) 1.50 .80
Nos. 785a-797a (9) 9.92 3.07

Prince Charles and Lady Diana — A305

1981, July 29 Litho. *Perf. 13*

804 A305 24c multicolored .42 .15
805 A305 60c multicolored 1.15 .75

Royal Wedding.

Cortinarius Cinnabarinus A306

Intl. Year of the Disabled A307

Designs: Fungi.

1981, Aug. 19 Litho. *Perf. 13*

806 A306 24c shown .35 .15
807 A306 35c Coprinus comatus .52 .52
808 A306 55c Armillaria luteobubalina .95 .80
809 A306 60c Cortinarius austrovenetus 1.10 1.00
Nos. 806-809 (4) 2.92 2.47

1981, Sept. 16 *Perf. 14x13½*

810 A307 24c multicolored .40 .15

Christmas Bush for His Adorning A308

Globe A309

Christmas (Carols by William James and John Wheeler): 30c, The Silver Stars are in the Sky. 60c, Noeltime.

1981   Litho.   Perf. 13x13½
811 A308 18c multicolored   .35   .15
812 A308 30c multicolored   .50   .35
813 A308 60c multicolored   1.25 1.00
    Nos. 811-813 (3)   2.10 1.50

Issue dates: 30c, Sept. 28; others, Nov. 2.

1981, Sept. 30
814 A309 24c multicolored   .38   .15
815 A309 60c multicolored   1.00   .90

Commonwealth Heads of Government Meeting, Melbourne, Sept. 30-Oct. 7.

Yacht — A310

1981, Oct. 14   Litho.   Perf. 13x13½
816 A310 24c Ocean racer   .45   .15
817 A310 35c Lightweight sharpie .60   .60
818 A310 55c 12-Meter   .90   .60
819 A310 60c Sabot   1.10 1.00
    Nos. 816-819 (4)   3.05 2.35

Australia Day, Jan. 26 — A311

1982, Jan. 20   Litho.   Perf. 13x13½
820 A311 24c multicolored   .40   .15

Sperm Whale — A312

Perf. 13x13½, 13½x13
1982, Feb. 17
821 A312 24c shown   .38   .15
822 A312 35c Southern right whale,
              vert.   .60   .60
823 A312 55c Blue whale, vert.   .90   .75
824 A312 60c Humpback whale   1.00 1.00
    Nos. 821-824 (4)   2.88 2.50

Elizabeth II, 56th   Roses — A314
Birthday — A313

1982, Apr. 21   Perf. 13½
825 A313 27c multicolored   .42   .18

1982, May 19   Perf. 13½
826 A314 27c Marjorie Atherton   .40   .32
827 A314 40c Imp   .65   .60
828 A314 65c Minnie Watson   1.00 1.00
829 A314 75c Satellite   1.10   .95
    Nos. 826-829 (4)   3.15 2.87

50th Anniv. of Australian Broadcasting Commission A315

1982, June 16   Perf. 13½x13
830 A315 27c Announcer, microphone .45 .25
831 A315 27c Emblem   .45   .25
  a.   Pair, #830-831   .90

#830-831 se-tenant in continuous design.

Alice Springs Post Office, 1872 — A316

1982, Aug. 4   Perf. 13½x14, 14x13½
832 A316 27c shown   .38   .16
833 A316 27c Kingston, 1869   .38   .16
834 A316 27c York, 1893   .38   .16
835 A316 27c Flemington, 1890,
              vert.   .38   .16
836 A316 27c Forbes, 1881, vert. .38   .16
837 A316 27c Launceston, 1889,
              vert.   .38   .16
838 A316 27c Rockhampton, 1892,
              vert.   .38   .16
    Nos. 832-838 (7)   2.66 1.12

Christmas — A317

Designs: First Australian Christmas cards, 1881. 21c, horiz.

1982   Litho.   Perf. 14½
839 A317 21c multicolored   .35   .15
840 A317 35c multicolored   .60   .30
841 A317 75c multicolored   1.25 1.10
    Nos. 839-841 (3)   2.20 1.55

Issue dates: 35c, Sept. 15; others, Nov. 1.

12th Commonwealth Games, Brisbane, Sept. 30-Oct. 9 — A318

1982, Sept. 22   Litho.   Perf. 14x14½
842 A318 27c Archery   .45   .15
843 A318 27c Boxing   .45   .15
844 A318 27c Weightlifting   .45   .15
  a.   Souvenir sheet of 3, #842-844 1.50 1.40
845 A318 75c Pole vault   .90   .90
    Nos. 842-845 (4)   2.25 1.35

Natl. Stamp Week — A319

1982, Sept. 27   Perf. 13x13½
846 A319 27c No. 132   .40   .15

A320   A321

Design: Gurgurr (Moon Spirit), Bark Painting by Yirawala Gunwinggu Tribe.

1982, Oct. 12   Perf. 14½
847 A320 27c multicolored   .40   .15

Opening of Natl. Gallery, Canberra.

Perf. 12½x13½
1982, Nov. 17   Photo.
Designs: Various eucalypts (gum trees).

848 A321 1c Pink-flowered marri   .15   .15
849 A321 2c Gungurru   .15   .15
850 A321 3c Red-flowering gum   1.00   .16
851 A321 10c Tasmanian blue gum 1.00   .25

---

852 A321 27c Forrest's marlock   .75   .50
  a.   Bkt. pane of 9 + label (#850-851, 2
         #848-849, 3 #852)   5.00
  b.   Bkt. pane (2 each #848-849, 852) 2.10
    Nos. 848-852 (5)   3.05 1.21

Nos. 848-852 issued in booklets only.

Mimi Spirits Singing and Dancing, by David Milaybuma A322

Aboriginal Bark Paintings: Music and dance of the Mimi Spirits, Gunwinggu Tribe.

1982, Nov. 17   Litho.   Perf. 13½x14
853 A322 27c shown   .40   .25
854 A322 40c Lofty Nabardayal   .65   .65
855 A322 65c Jimmy Galareya   1.00   .75
856 A322 75c Dick Nguleingulei
              Murrumurru   1.10 1.00
    Nos. 853-856 (4)   3.15 2.65

Historic Fire Engines A323

1983, Jan. 12   Perf. 13½x14
857 A323 27c Shand Mason Steam,
              1891   .40   .25
858 A323 40c Hotchkiss, 1914   .65   .65
859 A323 65c Ahrens-Fox PS2, 1929 1.00 1.00
860 A323 75c Merryweather Manu-
              al, 1851   1.10 1.00
    Nos. 857-860 (4)   3.15 2.90

Australia Day — A324

1983, Jan. 26   Litho.   Perf. 14½
861 A324 27c Sirius   .45   .25
862 A324 27c Supply   .45   .25
  a.   Pair, #861-862   .90   .75

A325   A326

1983, Feb. 2   Perf. 14x13½
863 A325 27c multicolored   .40   .15

Australia-New Zealand Closer Economic Relationship agreement (ANZCER).

1983, Mar. 9   Litho.   Perf. 14½
864 A326 27c Equality, dignity   .45   .20
865 A326 27c Social justice, coopera-
              tion   .45   .20
866 A326 27c Liberty, freedom   .45   .20
867 A326 75c Peace, harmony   1.25 1.25
    Nos. 864-867 (4)   2.60 1.85

Commonwealth day.

Queen Elizabeth II, 57th Birthday A327

1983, Apr. 20   Perf. 14½
868 A327 27c Britannia   .40   .15

World Communications Year — A328

1983, May 18   Litho.   Perf. 13½x14
869 A328 27c multicolored   .42   .15

50th Anniv. of Australian Jaycees Youth Organization A329

1983, June 8
870 A329 27c multicolored   .38   .15

St. John Ambulance   Regent
Cent. — A330   Skipper — A331

1983, June 8   Perf. 13½x14
871 A330 27c multicolored   .38   .15

1983   Perf. 13½, 14½x14 (30c)
872 A331 4c shown   .15   .15
873 A331 10c Cairn's birdwing   .15   .15
874 A331 20c Macleay's swallow-
              tail   .28   .15
875 A331 27c Ulysses   .42   .15
875A A331 30c Chlorinda hairstreak .50   .16
876 A331 35c Blue tiger   .52   .22
877 A331 45c Big greasy   .60   .28
878 A331 60c Wood white   .85   .35
879 A331 80c Amaryllis azure   1.00   .40
880 A331 $1 Sword grass brown   1.25   .15
    Nos. 872-880 (10)   5.72 2.16

Issue dates: 30c, Oct. 24; others, June 15.

The Sentimental Bloke, by C.J. Dennis, 1909 — A332

Folktale scenes: a, The bloke. b, Doreen · the intro. c, The stror at coot. d, Hitched. e, The mooch of life.

1983, Aug. 3   Perf. 14½
881   Strip of 5   2.25 1.50
  a.-e. A332 27c multi, any single .45 .30

Kookaburra Bird Wearing Santa Hat — A333

1983   Litho.   Perf. 13½x14
882 A333 24c Nativity   .35   .35
883 A333 35c multicolored   .52   .35
884 A333 85c Holiday beach scene 1.25   .60
    Nos. 882-884 (3)   2.12 1.30

Christmas. Issued: #883, 9/14; #882, 884, 11/2.

Inland Explorers — A334

Clay sculptures by Dianne Quinn: No. 885, Ludwig Leichhardt (1813-48). No. 886, William John Wills (1834-61), Robert O'Hara Burke (1821-61). No. 887, Paul Edmund de Strzelecki (1797-1873). No. 888, Alexander Forrest (1849-1901).

1983, Sept. 26   *Perf. 14¹/₂*
885 A334	30c multicolored	.40	.16
886 A334	30c multicolored	.40	.16
887 A334	30c multicolored	.40	.16
888 A334	30c multicolored	.40	.16
	Nos. 885-888 (4)	1.60	.64

Australia Day — A335

1984, Jan. 26   Litho.   *Perf. 13¹/₂x14*
889 A335   30c Cooks' Cottage   .40 .18

50th Anniv. of Official Air Mail Service — A336

Designs: Pilot Charles Ulm (1898-1934); his plane, "Faith in Australia," and different flight covers.

1984, Feb. 22   Litho.   *Perf. 13¹/₂*
890 A336	45c Australia-New Zealand	1.00	.60
891 A336	45c Australia-Papua New Guinea	1.00	.60
a.	Pair, #890-891	2.00	1.50

Thomson, 1898 — A337

Australian-made vintage cars: b, Tarrant, 1906. c, Australian Six, 1919. d, Summit, 1923. e, Chic, 1924.

1984, Mar. 14   *Perf. 14¹/₂*
892	Strip of 5	2.25	1.50
a.-e.	A337 30c any single	.45	.25

Queen Elizabeth II, 58th Birthday — A338

1984, Apr. 18   *Perf. 14¹/₂*
893 A338   30c multicolored   .42 .18

Clipper Ships — A339

Perf. 14x13¹/₂, 13¹/₂x14
1984, May 23
894 A339	30c Cutty Sark, 1869, vert.	.35	.30
895 A339	45c Orient, 1853	.55	.55
896 A339	75c Sobraon, 1866	.90	.90
897 A339	85c Thermopylae, 1868, vert.	1.10	1.10
	Nos. 894-897 (4)	2.90	2.85

Freestyle Skiing — A340   Coral Hopper — A341

1984, June 6   Litho.   *Perf. 14¹/₂*
898 A340	30c shown	.50	.20
899 A340	30c Slalom, horiz.	.50	.20
900 A340	30c Cross-country, horiz.	.50	.20
901 A340	30c Downhill	.50	.20
	Nos. 898-901 (4)	2.00	.80

Perf. 13¹/₂, 14x14¹/₂ (30c, 33c)
1984-86   Litho.
902 A341	2c shown	.15	.15
903 A341	3c Jimble	.15	.15
904 A341	5c Tasseled anglerfish	.15	.15
905 A341	10c Stonefish	.15	.15
906 A341	20c Red handfish	.25	.15
907 A341	25c Orange-tipped cowrie	.45	.25
908 A341	30c Choat's wrasse	.55	.25
909 A341	33c Leafy sea dragon	.45	.20
910 A341	40c Red velvet fish	.55	.25
911 A341	45c Texile cone shell	.65	.30
912 A341	50c Blue-lined surge-onfish	.90	.50
913 A341	55c Bennett's nudibranch	1.00	.50
914 A341	60c Lionfish	.85	.40
915 A341	65c Stingray	.95	.40
916 A341	70c Blue-ringed octopus	1.00	.50
917 A341	80c Pineapple fish	1.15	.55
918 A341	85c Regal angelfish	1.50	.95
919 A341	90c Crab-eyed goby	1.20	.55
920 A341	$1 Crown of thorns starfish	1.50	.60
	Nos. 902-920 (19)	13.55	6.95

Issued: 2c, 25c, 30c, 50c, 55c, 85c, June 18; 5c, 20c, 40c, 80c, 90c, June 12, 1985; 3c, 10c, 45c, 60c, 65c, 70c, $1, June 11, 1986.

1984 Summer Olympics A342

Event stages.

Perf. 13¹/₂x14, 14x13¹/₂
1984, July 25   Litho.
922 A342	30c Start (facing down)	.45	.20
923 A342	30c Competing (facing right)	.45	.20
924 A342	30c Finish, vert.	.45	.20
	Nos. 922-924 (3)	1.35	.60

Ausipex '84 — A343   Christmas — A344

Designs: No. 926a, Victoria #3. b, New South Wales #1. c, Tasmania #1. d, South Australia #1. e, Western Australia #1. f, Queensland #3.

1984   Litho.   *Perf. 14¹/₂*
925 A343   30c No. 2   .45 .16
Souvenir Sheet
926	Sheet of 7	3.50	3.00
a.-f.	A343 30c any single	.50	.20

#926 contains #925, 926a-926f. Issue dates: #925, Aug. 22; #926, Sept. 21.

1984   Litho.   *Perf. 14x13¹/₂*
927 A344	24c Angel and Child	.30	.25
928 A344	30c Veiled Virgin and Child	.35	.25
929 A344	45c Angel	.50	.40
930 A344	50c Three Kings	.65	.45
931 A344	85c Madonna and Child	1.10	1.00
	Nos. 927-931 (5)	2.90	2.35

Stained-glass windows. Issue dates: 40c, Sept. 17; others, Oct. 30.

European Settlement Bicentenary A345   Settlement of Victoria Sesquicentenary A346

Design: No. 932, Bicentennial Emblem. Rock paintings: No. 933, Stick figures, Cobar Region, New South Wales. No. 934, Bunjil's Cave, Grampians, Western Victoria. No. 935, Quinkan Gallery, Cape York, Queensland. No. 936, Wandjina Spirit and Snake Babies, Gibb River, Western Australia. No. 937, Rock Python, Western Australia. No. 938, Silver Barramundi, Kakadu Natl. Park, Northern Territory. 85c, Rock Possum, Kakadu Natl. Park.

1984, Nov. 7   Litho.   *Perf. 14¹/₂*
932 A345	30c multicolored	.45	.25
933 A345	30c multicolored	.45	.25
934 A345	30c multicolored	.45	.25
935 A345	30c multicolored	.45	.25
936 A345	30c multicolored	.45	.25
937 A345	30c multicolored	.45	.25
938 A345	30c multicolored	.45	.25
939 A345	85c multicolored	1.25	.60
	Nos. 932-939 (8)	4.40	2.35

1984, Nov. 19
940 A346	30c Helmeted honeyeater	.45	.20
941 A346	30c Leadbeater's possum	.45	.20
a.	Pair, #940-941		.90

Australia Day — A347

1985, Jan. 25   Litho.
942 A347	30c Musgrave Ranges, by Sidney Nolan	.45	.20
943 A347	30c The Walls of China, by Russell Drysdale	.45	.20
a.	Pair, #942-943		.90

Intl. Youth Year — A348

1985, Feb. 13   Litho.   *Perf. 14x13¹/₂*
944 A348   30c multicolored   .40 .15

Royal Victorian Volunteer Artillery — A349   District Nursing Service Centenary — A350

Colonial military uniforms: b, Western Australian Pinjarrah Cavalry. c, New South Wales Lancers. d, New South Wales Contingent to the Sudan. e, Victorian Mounted Rifles.

1985, Feb. 25   *Perf. 14¹/₂*
945	Strip of 5	2.25	2.00
a.-e.	A349 33c any single	.45	.16

1985, Mar. 13
946 A350   33c multicolored   .40 .16

Australian Cockatoo A351

Perf. 14 Horiz. on 1 or 2 sides
1985, Mar. 13
947 A351	1c apple grn, yel & buff	.50	.50
948 A351	33c apple grn, yel, & lt grnsh blue	.45	.20
a.	Bklt. pane, 1 #947, 3 #948	2.75	

Issued in booklets only.

A352   A353

1985, Apr. 10   *Perf. 13*
949 A352	33c Abel Tasman, explorer	.55	.32
950 A352	33c The Eendracht	.55	.32
951 A352	33c William Dampier	.55	.32
952 A352	90c Globe and hand	1.50	.90
a.	Souvenir sheet of 4, #949-952	3.50	2.00
	Nos. 949-952 (4)	3.15	1.86

1985, Apr. 22   *Perf. 14x13¹/₂*
949 A353   33c Queen's Badge, Order of Australia   .45 .16

Queen Elizabeth II, 59th birthday.

A354   A356

1985, May 15   Litho.   *Perf. 14x13*
954 A354	33c Soil	.45	.30
955 A354	50c Air	.65	.50
956 A354	80c Water	1.00	.70
957 A354	90c Energy	1.10	.90
	Nos. 954-957 (4)	3.20	2.40

Environmental conservation.

1985, July 17   Litho.   *Perf. 14¹/₂*

Illustrations from classic children's books: a, Elves & Fairies, by Annie Rentoul. b, The Magic Pudding, text and illustrations by Norman Lindsay. c, Ginger Meggs, by James Charles Bancks. d, Blinky Bill, by Dorothy Wall. e, Snugglepot and Cuddlepie, by May Gibbs.

960	Strip of 5	2.25	1.25
a.-e.	A356 33c any single	.40	.18

Electronic Mail — A357

1985, Sept. 18   Litho.
961 A357   33c multicolored   .42 .16

Christmas A358

Angel in a ship, detail from a drawing by Albrecht Durer (1471-1528).

1985, Sept. 18   Litho.
962 A358   45c multicolored   .45 .18

See Nos. 967-970.

Coastal
Shipwrecks
A359

Salvaged antiquities: 33c, Astrolabe from Batavia, 1629. 50c, German beardman (Bellarmine) jug from Vergulde Draeck, 1656. 90c, Wooden bobbins from Batavia, and scissors from Zeewijk, 1727. $1, Silver buckle from Zeewijk.

1985, Oct. 2   Litho.   Perf. 13
963 A359 33c multicolored   .50 .20
964 A359 50c multicolored   .75 .75
965 A359 90c multicolored   1.40 1.25
966 A359 $1 multicolored   1.50 1.00
    Nos. 963-966 (4)   4.15 3.20

Christmas Type of 1985
Illustrations by Scott Hartshorne.

1985, Nov. 1   Litho.   Perf. 14
967 A358 27c Angel with trumpet   .32 .18
968 A358 40c Angel with bells   .40 .24
969 A358 55c Angel with star   .70 .65
970 A358 90c Angel with ornament   1.10 1.10
    Nos. 967-970 (4)   2.52 2.17

Australia
Day — A360

AUSSAT — A361

1986, Jan. 24   Litho.   Perf. 14½
971 A360 33c Aboriginal painting   .42 .16

1986, Jan. 24

Various communications satellites.

972 A361 33c multicolored   .35 .16
973 A361 80c multicolored   1.15 .75

South Australia,
Sesquicent.
A362

1986, Feb. 12   Perf. 13½x14
974 A362 33c Sailing ship Buffalo   .52 .16
975 A362 33c City Sign, sculpture by
        O.H. Hajek   .52 .16
    a.   Pair, #974-975   1.05

Cook's New
Holland
Expedition
A363

1986, Mar. 12   Perf. 13
976 A363 33c Hibiscus merankensis   .45 .30
977 A363 33c Banksia serrata   .45 .30
978 A363 50c Dillenia alata   .68 .68
979 A363 80c Corria reflexa   1.10 .85
980 A363 90c Parkinson   1.25 1.10
981 A363 90c Banks   1.25 1.25
    Nos. 976-981 (6)   5.18 4.48

Australian bicentennial. Sydney Parkinson (d. 1775), artist. Sir Joseph Banks (1743-1820), naturalist.

Halley's Comet
A364

Elizabeth II,
60th Birthday
A365

1986, Apr. 9   Perf. 14x13½
982 A364 33c Radio telescope, trajectory diagram   .42 .18

1986, Apr. 21   Perf. 14½
983 A365 33c multicolored   .42 .18

Horses — A366

1986, May 21
984 A366 33c Brumbies   .50 .28
985 A366 80c Stock horse mustering   1.20 .65
986 A366 90c Show-jumping   1.35 .95
987 A366 $1 Australian pony   1.50 .95
    Nos. 984-987 (4)   4.55 2.83

Click Go the Shears,
Folk Song — A366a

Lines from the song: b, Old shearer stands. c, Ringer looks around. d, Boss of the board. e, Tarboy is there. f, Shearing is all over.

1986, July 21   Litho.   Perf. 14½
987A   Strip of 5   2.75 1.50
    b.-f.   A366a 33c, any single   .55 .18
Amalgamated Shearers' Union, predecessor of the Australian Workers' Union, cent.

Australia
Bicentennial
A367

Settling of Botany Bay penal colony: No. 988, King George III, c. 1767, by A. Ramsay. No. 989, Lord Sydney, secretary of state, 1703-1789, by Gilbert Stuart. No. 990, Capt. Arthur Phillip, 1st penal colony governor, by F. Wheatley, 1786. $1, Capt. John Hunter, governor, 1795-1800, by W. B. Bennett, 1815.

1986, Aug. 6   Litho.   Perf. 13
988 A367 33c multicolored   .50 .30
989 A367 33c multicolored   .50 .30
990 A367 33c multicolored   .50 .30
991 A367 $1 multicolored   1.50 1.00
    Nos. 988-991 (4)   3.00 1.90

Wildlife — A368

Alpine
Wildflowers — A369

Designs: a, Red kangaroo. b, Emu. c, Koala. d, Kookaburra. e, Platypus.

1986, Aug. 13   Perf. 14½x14
992   Strip of 5   2.00 1.25
    a.-e.   A368 36c any single   .40 .15

Rouletted 9½ Vert. on 1 or 2 sides
1986, Aug. 25
Booklet Stamps
993 A369 3c Royal bluebell   .45 .30
994 A369 5c Alpine marsh marigold   1.00 .50
995 A369 25c Mount Buffalo sunray   1.00 .75
996 A369 36c Silver snow daisy   .90 .20
    a.   Bklt. pane, #993, #994, 2 #996   3.25
    b.   Bklt. pane, #993, #995, 2 #996   3.25
    Nos. 993-996 (4)   3.35 1.75

Orchids — A370

America's Cup
Triumph
'83 — A371

1986, Sept. 18   Perf. 14½
997 A370 36c Elythranthera emarginata   .60 .15
998 A370 55c Dendrobium nindii   1.00 .60
999 A370 90c Caleana major   1.65 1.00
1000 A370 $1 Thelymitra variegata   1.75 1.10
    Nos. 997-1000 (4)   5.00 2.85

1986, Sept. 26   Perf. 14x13½
1001 A371 36c Australia II crossing finish line   .60 .25
1002 A371 36c Trophy   .60 .25
1003 A371 36c Boxing kangaroo   .60 .25
    Nos. 1001-1003 (3)   1.80 .75

Intl. Peace
Year — A372

1986, Oct. 22   Litho.   Perf. 14x13½
1004 A372 36c multicolored   .48 .16

Christmas
A373

Kindergarten nativity play: No. 1005, Holy Family, vert. No. 1006, Three Kings, vert. No. 1007, Angels. No. 1008a, Angels, peasants. No. 1008b, Holy Family, angels, vert. No. 1008c, Shepherd, angels, vert. No. 1008d, Three Kings. No. 1008e, Shepherds.

1986, Nov. 3   Litho.
1005 A373 30c multicolored   .50 .18
    a.   Perf 14x13½   1.00 .50
1006 A373 30c multicolored   .60 .24
1007 A373 60c multicolored   1.00 .65
    Nos. 1005-1007 (3)   2.10 1.07

Souvenir Sheet
1008   Sheet of 5   2.50 2.50
    a.-e.   A373 30c any single   .50 .50

Perfs: Nos. 1005-1006, 1008c, 15x14½; Nos. 1007, 1008a 1008e, 14½x15; No. 1008b, 15x14½x15x15; 1008d, 14½x15x14½x14½.

Australia
Day — A374

1987, Jan. 23   Litho.   Perf. 13½x14
1009 A374 36c Flag, circuit board   .42 .16
1010 A374 36c Made in Australia campaign emblem   .42 .16

America's
Cup — A375

Fruits — A376

Views of yachts racing.

1987, Jan. 28   Perf. 15x14½
1011 A375 36c multicolored   .52 .28
1012 A375 55c multicolored   .80 .55
1013 A375 90c multicolored   1.40 .90
1014 A375 $1 multicolored   1.65 .95
    Nos. 1011-1014 (4)   4.37 2.68

1987, Feb. 11   Perf. 14x13½
1015 A376 36c Melons, grapes   .55 .32
1016 A376 65c Tropical fruit   1.00 .60
1017 A376 90c Pears, apples, oranges   1.40 .90
1018 A376 $1 Berries, peaches   1.50 .95
    Nos. 1015-1018 (4)   4.45 2.77

Agricultural
Shows — A377

1987, Apr. 10   Litho.   Perf. 14x13½
1019 A377 36c Livestock   .55 .15
1020 A377 65c Produce   1.00 .60
1021 A377 90c Carnival   1.40 .90
1022 A377 $1 Farmers   1.50 .95
    Nos. 1019-1022 (4)   4.45 2.60

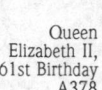

Queen
Elizabeth II,
61st Birthday
A378

1987, Apr. 21   Perf. 13½x14
1023 A378 36c multicolored   .45 .15

First Fleet
Leaving
England — A379

Continuous design: No. 1024a, Convicts awaiting transportation. b, Capt. Arthur Phillip, Mrs. Phillip, longboat on shore. c, Sailors relaxing and working. d, Longboats heading from and to fleet. 4e, Fleet in harbor.

No. 1025a, Longboat approaching Tenerife, The Canary Isls. b, Fishing in Tenerife Harbor. $1, Fleet, dolphins.

1987   Perf. 13
1024   Strip of 5   4.00 4.00
    a.-e.   A379 36c any single   .80 .20
1025   Pair   1.05 1.00
    a.-b.   A379 36c any single   .52 .20
1026 A379 $1 multicolored   1.50 1.50
    Nos. 1024-1026 (3)   6.55 6.50

Australia bicent.; departure of the First Fleet, May 13, 1787; arrival at Tenerife, June 1787.
    Issued: #1024, May 13; #1025-1026, June 3.

1987, Aug. 6

First Fleet arrives at Rio de Janeiro, Aug. 1787: a, Whale, storm in the Atlantic. b, Citrus grove. c, Market. d, Religious procession. e, Fireworks over harbor.

1027   Strip of 5   2.25 2.25
    a.-e.   A379 37c any single   .45 .15

    No. 1027 has a continuous design.

1987, Oct. 13

First Fleet arrives at Cape of Good Hope, Oct. 1787: No. 1028a, British officer surveys livestock and supplies, Table Mountain. No. 1028b, Ships anchored in Table Bay. No. 1029, Fishermen pull in nets as the Fleet approaches the Cape.

1028		Pair	.90	.90
a.-b.	A379	37c any single	.45	.20
1029	A379	$1 multicolored	1.25	.50

No. 1028 has a continuous design.

1988, Jan. 26

Arrival of the First Fleet, Sydney Cove, Jan. 1788: a, Five aborigines on shore. b, Four aborigines on shore. c, Kangaroos. d, White cranes. e, Flag raising.

1030		Strip of 5	2.75	2.75
a.-e.	A379	37c any single	.55	.20

Printed se-tenant in a continuous design.

The Early Years: Sydney Cove and Parramatta Colonies — A380

Details from panorama "View of Sydney from the East Side of the Cove," 1808, painted by convict artist John Eyre to illustrate The Present Picture of New South Wales, published in London in 1811, and paintings in British and Australian museums: a, Government House, 1790, Sydney, by midshipman George Raper. b, Government Farm, Parramatta, 1791, attributed to the Port Jackson Painter. c, Parramatta Road, 1796, attributed to convict artist Thomas Watling. d, The Rocks and Sydney Cove, 1800, an aquatint engraving by Edward Dayes. e, Sydney Hospital, 1803, by George William Evans, an explorer and surveyor-general of New South Wales. Printed se-tenant in a continuous design.

1988, Apr. 13   Litho.   Perf. 13

1031		Strip of 5	3.00	3.00
a.-e.	A380	37c any single	.60	.20

Australia Bicentennial.

The Man from Snowy River, 1890, Ballad by A.B. Paterson — A381

Fauna — A382

Excerpts: a, At the station. b, Mountain bred. c, Terrible descent. d, At their heels. e, Brought them back.

1987, June 24   Perf. 14x13½

1034		Strip of 5	2.75	2.75
a.-e.	A381	36c any single	.55	.30

Printed se-tenant in a continuous design.

1987, July 1   Perf. 14½x14

Designs: a, Possum. b, Cockatoo. c, Wombat. d, Rosella. e, Echidna.

1035		Strip of 5	2.25	2.25
a.-e.	A382	37c any single	.45	.15

Printed se-tenant in a continuous design.

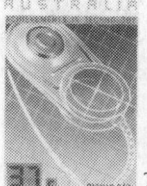

Technology — A383

1987, Aug. 19   Perf. 14½

1036	A383	37c Bionic ear	.38	.18
1037	A383	53c Microchips	.55	.28
1038	A383	63c Robotics	.70	.32
1039	A383	68c Zirconia ceramics	.75	.35
		Nos. 1036-1039 (4)	2.38	1.13

Children A384 37c

1987, Sept. 16

1040	A384	37c Crayfishing	.45	.18
1041	A384	55c Cat's cradle	.65	.28
1042	A384	90c Eating meat pies	1.00	.45
1043	A384	$1 Playing with a joey	1.25	.50
		Nos. 1040-1043 (4)	3.35	1.41

Christmas A385 63c

Carolers: a, Woman, two girls. b, Man, two girls. c, Four children. d, Man, two women, boy. e, Six youths. 37c, three women, two men. Nos. 1044a-1044e are vert.

1987, Nov. 2   Litho.   Perf. 14½

1044		Strip of 5	2.00	2.00
a.-e.	A385	30c any single	.40	.15

Perf. 13½x14

1045	A385	37c multicolored	.45	.20
1046	A385	63c shown	.80	.30
		Nos. 1044-1046 (3)	3.25	2.50

Carols by Candlelight, Christmas Eve, Sidney Myer Bowl, Melbourne.

Aboriginal Crafts — A386

Designs: 3c, Spearthrower, Western Australia. 15c, Shield, New South Wales. No. 1049, Basket, Queensland. No. 1050, Bowl, Central Australia. No. 1051, Belt, Northern Territory.

Perf. 15½ Horiz.

1987, Oct. 13   Photo.

1047	A386	3c multicolored	1.25	1.25
1048	A386	15c multicolored	1.90	1.25
1049	A386	37c multicolored	1.10	.35
a.		Bkt. pane, 2 each #1047, #1049	4.50	
1050	A386	37c multicolored	1.25	.35
1051	A386	37c multicolored	1.25	.35
a.		Bkt. pane, 1 #1048, 3 #1050, 2 #1051	9.00	
		Nos. 1047-1051 (5)	6.75	3.55

Issued only in booklets.

Caricature of Australian Koala and American Bald Eagle — A387

1988, Jan. 26   Perf. 13

1052	A387	37c multicolored	.55	.18

Australia bicentennial. See No. 1086 and US No. 2370.

Living Together — A388 1c

Cartoons.

1988   Perf. 14

1053	A388	1c Religion	.15	.15
1054	A388	2c Industry	.15	.15
1055	A388	3c Local government	.15	.15
1056	A388	4c Trade unions	.15	.15
1057	A388	5c Parliament	.15	.15
1058	A388	10c Transportation	.18	.15
1059	A388	15c Sports	.25	.15
1060	A388	20c Commerce	.35	.15
1061	A388	25c Housing	.42	.15
1062	A388	30c Welfare	.52	.16
1063	A388	37c Postal services	.62	.20
a.		Booklet pane of 10	6.25	
1063B	A388	39c Tourism	.65	.22
c.		Booklet pane of 10	6.50	
1064	A388	40c Recreation	.68	.22
1065	A388	45c Health	.78	.25
1066	A388	50c Mining	.85	.28
1067	A388	53c Primary industry	.90	.30
1068	A388	55c Education	.95	.32
1069	A388	60c Armed Forces	1.05	.35
1070	A388	63c Police	1.10	.35
1071	A388	65c Telecommunications	1.15	.38
1072	A388	68c The media	1.20	.40
1073	A388	70c Science and technology	1.20	.40
1074	A388	75c Visual arts	1.30	.45
1075	A388	80c Performing arts	1.40	.48
1076	A388	90c Banking	1.55	.52
1077	A388	95c Law	1.65	.55
1078	A388	$1 Rescue and emergency services	1.70	.58
		Nos. 1053-1078 (27)	21.20	7.79

Issued: 1c, 2c, 3c, 5c, 30c, 40c, 55c, 60c, 63c, 65c, 68c, 75c, 95c, 3/16; 39c, 9/28; others, 2/17.

Queen Elizabeth II, 62nd Birthday A389 37c

1988, Apr. 21   Perf. 14½

1079	A389	37c multicolored	.58	.20

EXPO '88, Brisbane, Apr. 30-Oct. 30 — A390 37c

1988, Apr. 29   Perf. 13

1080	A390	37c multicolored	.58	.20

Opening of Parliament House, Canberra A391 37c

1988, May 9   Perf. 14½

1081	A391	37c multicolored	.58	.20

Australia Bicentennial A392 37c

Designs: No. 1082, Colonist, clipper ship. No. 1083, British and Australian parliaments, Queen Elizabeth II. No. 1084, Cricketer W.G. Grace. No. 1085, John Lennon (1940-1980), William Shakespeare (1564-1616) and Sydney Opera House. #1083a, 1085a have continuous design picturing flag of Australia.

1988, June 21   Litho.   Perf. 13

1082	A392	37c multicolored	.62	.20
1083	A392	37c multicolored	.62	.20
a.		Pair, #1082-1083	1.25	.75
1084	A392	$1 multicolored	1.65	.55
1085	A392	$1 multicolored	1.65	.55
a.		Pair, #1084-1085	3.50	1.50
		Nos. 1082-1085 (4)	4.54	1.50

See Great Britain Nos. 1222-1225.

Caricature Type of 1988

Design: Caricature of an Australian koala and New Zealand kiwi.

1988, June 21   Litho.   Perf. 13½

1086	A387	37c multicolored	.62	.20

Australia bicentennial. See New Zealand No. 907.

"Dream" Lore on Art of the Desert — A393 37c

Aboriginal paintings from Papunya Settlement in the Flinders University Art Museum: 37c, Bush Potato Country, by Turkey Tolsen Tjupurrula with by David Corby Tjapaltjarri. 55c, Courtship Rejected, by Limpi Puntunka Tjapangati. 90c, Medicine Story, anonymous. $1, Ancestor Dreaming, by Tim Leura Tjapaltjarri.

1988, Aug. 1   Litho.   Perf. 13

1087	A393	37c multicolored	.62	.20
1088	A393	55c multicolored	.90	.75
1089	A393	90c multicolored	1.50	.50
1090	A393	$1 multicolored	1.65	.55
		Nos. 1087-1090 (4)	4.67	2.00

1988 Summer Olympics, Seoul — A394 37c

1988, Sept. 14   Perf. 14½

1091	A394	37c Basketball	.62	.20
1092	A394	65c Running	1.10	.90
1093	A394	$1 Rhythmic gymnastics	1.65	.55
		Nos. 1091-1093 (3)	3.37	1.65

34th Commonwealth Parliamentary Conference, Canberra A395 37c

1988, Sept. 19

1094	A395	37c Scepter and mace	.62	.20

Works in the Contemporary Decorative Arts Collection at the Natl. Gallery — A396 39c

Roulette 9 Horiz.

1988, Sept. 28   Litho.

1095	A396	2c "Australian Fetish," by Peter Tully	2.50	1.75
1096	A396	5c Vase by Colin Levy	2.50	1.75
1097	A396	39c Teapot by Frank Bauer	.75	.35
a.		Bkt. pane of 3 (2c, 2 39c)	4.50	
b.		Bkt. pane of 6 (5c, 5 39c)	6.25	
		Nos. 1095-1097 (3)	5.75	3.85

Nos. 1095-1097 issued in booklets only.

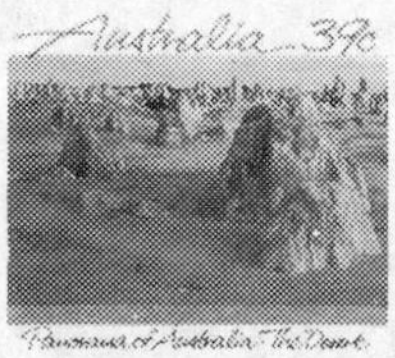

Views — A397

1988, Oct. 17 Photo. *Perf. 13*

1098 A397 39c The Desert .65 .22
1099 A397 55c The Top End .90 .30
1100 A397 65c The Coast 1.10 .38
1101 A397 70c The Bush 1.15 .40
Nos. 1098-1101 (4) 3.80 1.30

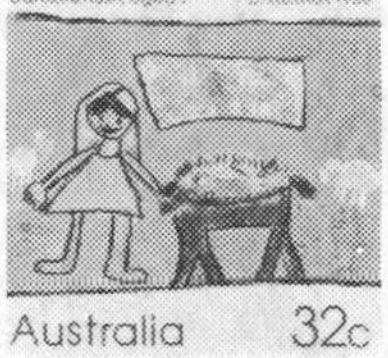

Christmas A398

Children's design contest winning drawings: 32c, Nativity scene, by Danielle Hush, age 7. 39c, Koala wearing a Santa hat, by Kylie Courtney, age 6. 63c, Cockatoo wearing a Santa hat, by Benjamin Stevenson, age 10.

1988, Oct. 31 *Perf. 13½x13*

1102 A398 32c multicolored .55 .18
1103 A398 39c multicolored .65 .22
1104 A398 63c multicolored 1.05 .35
Nos. 1102-1104 (3) 2.25 .75

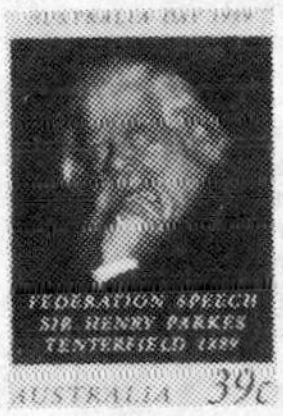

Sir Henry Parkes (1815-1896), Advocate of the Federation of the Six Colonies — A399

1989, Jan. 25 Litho. *Perf. 14x13½*

1105 A399 39c multicolored .70 .22

Australia Day.

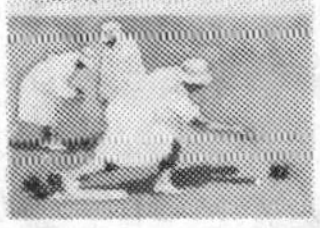

Sports — A400

1989, Feb. 13 *Perf. 14x14½*

1106 A400 1c Bowls .15 .15
a. Perf. 13½x14 ('90) .15 .15
1107 A400 2c Bowling .15 .15
a. Perf. 13x13½ ('91) .15 .15
1108 A400 3c Football .15 .15
1109 A400 39c Fishing .70 .22
a. Booklet pane of 10 7.00
d. Perf. 13x13½ on 3 sides ('90) .70 .22
e. Booklet pane of 10, #1109d 7.00
1109B A400 41c Cycling .62 .20
c. Booklet pane of 10 6.25
1110 A400 55c Kite-flying .98 .32
1111 A400 70c Cricket 1.25 .42
1112 A400 $1.10 Golf 1.95 .65

1990-94

1114 A400 5c Kayaking, canoeing .15 .15
a. Perf. 13x13½ .15 .15
1115 A400 10c Windsurfing .16 .15
a. Perf. 13x13½ .15 .15
1116 A400 20c Tennis .32 .15
a. Perf. 13x13½ .30 .30
1117 A400 65c Rock climbing 1.00 .32
a. Perf. 13x13½ 1.00 1.00
1118 A400 $1 Running 1.55 .52
a. Perf. 13x13½ 1.55 .52

Issued: #1114a, 1115a, 1116a, 1117a, 1118, 1/17/90; #1118a, 1/91; #1115, 1117, 2/92; #1116, 7/93; #1114, 3/94.

1990, Aug. 27

1119 A400 43c Skateboarding .68 .18
a. Booklet pane of 10 6.80

Perf. 13½

1120 A400 $1.20 Hang-gliding 1.90 .48

1991, Aug. 22 *Perf. 14x14½*

1121 A400 75c Netball 1.15 .38
1122 A400 80c Squash 1.25 .40
1123 A400 85c Diving 1.30 .42
1124 A400 90c Soccer 1.40 .45
Nos. 1106-1124 (19) 16.81 5.86

For self-adhesive stamps see #1185-1186.

This is an expanding set. Numbers will change when completed.

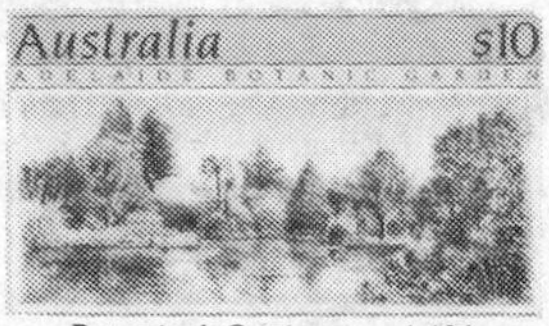

Botanical Gardens — A401

Designs: $2, Nooroo, New South Wales. $5, Mawarra, Victoria. $10, Palm House, Adelaide Botanical Garden. $20, A View of the Artist's House and Garden in Mills Plains, Van Diemen's Land by John Glover.

1989 Litho. & Engr. *Perf. 14*

1132 A401 $2 multicolored 3.00 1.00
a. Perf. 14x13½ ('91) 3.00 1.00
1133 A401 $5 multicolored 7.75 2.50
a. Perf. 14x13½ 8.50 2.50
1134 A401 $10 multicolored 15.00 4.25

Perf. 14½x14

1135 A401 $20 multicolored 27.50 8.00
Nos. 1132-1135 (4) 53.25 15.75

Issued: $10, 4/12; $2, $5, 9/13; $20, 8/15.

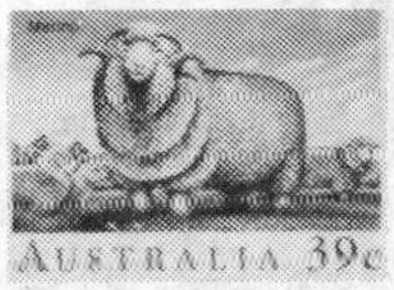

Sheep — A402

1989, Feb. 27 *Perf. 13½x14*

1136 A402 39c Merino .70 .22
1137 A402 39c Poll Dorset .70 .22
1138 A402 85c Polwarth 1.50 .50
1139 A402 $1 Corriedale 1.75 .58
Nos. 1136-1139 (4) 4.65 1.52

World Sheep and Wool Congress, Tasmania, Feb. 27-Mar. 6.

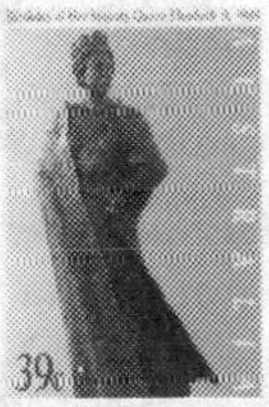

Queen Elizabeth II, 63rd Birthday — A403

1989, Apr. 21 Litho. *Perf. 14½*

1140 A403 39c Statue by John Dowie .65 .22

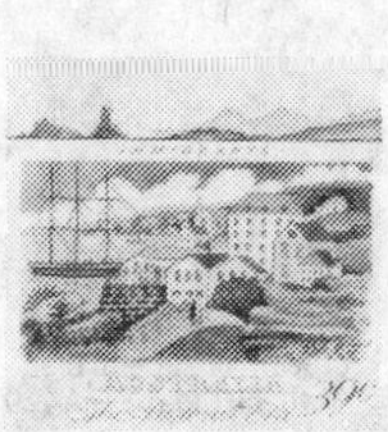

Colonial Australia A404

Pastoral Era: a, Immigrant ship in port, c. 1835. b, Pioneer's hut, wool bales in dray. c, Squatter's homestead. d, Shepherds. e, Explorers.

1989, May 10

1141 Strip of 5 3.25 1.10
a.-e. A404 39c any single .65 .22

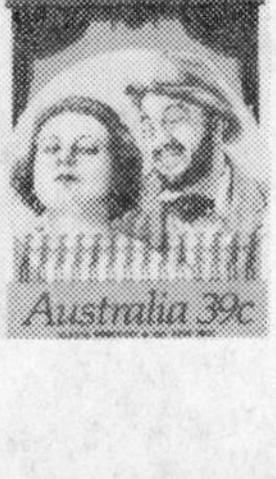

Stars of Stage and Screen — A405

Performers and directors: 39c, Gladys Moncrieff and Roy Rene, the stage, 1920's. 85c, Charles Chauvel and Chips Rafferty, talking films. $1, Nellie Stewart and James Cassius Williamson, the stage, 1890's. $1.10, Lottie Lyell and Raymond Longford, silent films.

1989, July 12 Litho. *Perf. 14½*

1142 A405 39c multicolored .58 .20
a. Perf. 14x13½ ('90) *6.50 6.50*
1143 A405 85c multicolored 1.25 .82
1144 A405 $1 multicolored 1.50 .50
1145 A405 $1.10 multicolored 1.65 .55
Nos. 1142-1145 (4) 4.98 2.07

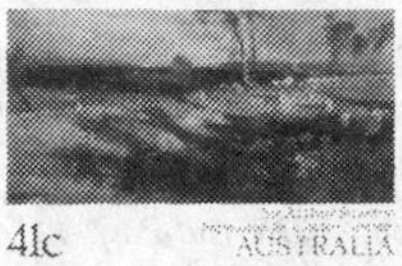

41c Impressionist Paintings A406

Paintings by Australian artists: No. 1146, *Impression for Golden Summer*, by Sir Arthur Streeton. No. 1147, *All on a Summer's Day*, by Charles Conder, vert. No. 1148, *Petit Dejeuner*, by Frederick McCubbin. No. 1149, *Impression*, by Tom Roberts.

Perf. 13½x14, 14x13½

1989, Aug. 23 Litho.

1146 A406 41c shown .62 .20
1147 A406 41c multicolored .62 .20
1148 A406 41c multicolored .62 .20
1149 A406 41c multicolored .62 .20
Nos. 1146-1149 (4) 2.48 .80

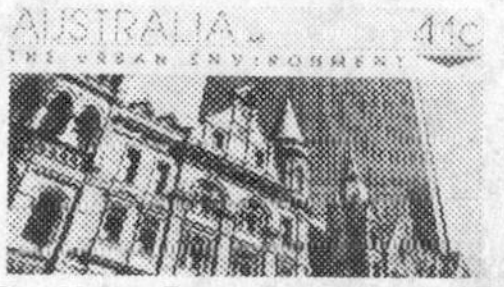

The Urban Environment A407

1989, Sept. 1 Litho. *Perf. 15½*

Booklet Stamps

1150 A407 41c Freeways .70 .25
1151 A407 41c Architecture .70 .25
1152 A407 41c Commuter train .70 .25
a. Bklt. pane of 7, 2 each #1150, 1152 and 3 #1151 5.00
Nos. 1150-1152 (3) 2.10 .75

No. 1152a sold for $3.

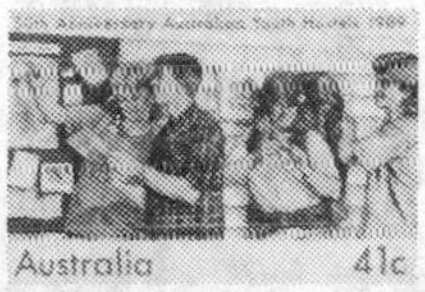

Australian Youth Hostels, 50th Anniv. A408

1989, Sept. 13 *Perf. 14½*

1153 A408 41c multicolored .65 .22

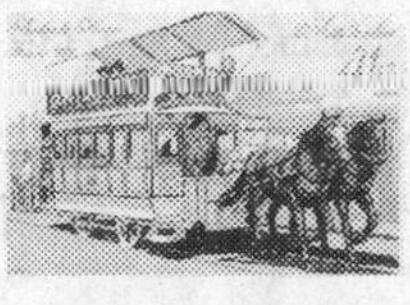

Street Cars — A409

Designs: No. 1154, Horse-drawn tram, Adelaide, 1878. No. 1155, Steam tram, Sydney, 1884. No. 1156, Cable car, Melbourne, 1886. No. 1157, Double-deck electric tram, Hobart, 1893. No. 1158, Combination electric tram, Brisbane, 1901.

1989, Oct. 11 Litho. *Perf. 13½x14*

1154 A409 41c multicolored .65 .22
1155 A409 41c multicolored .65 .22
1156 A409 41c multicolored .65 .22
a. Perf. 14½ on 3 sides 1.30 1.30
b. Booklet pane of 10, #1156a 13.00
1157 A409 41c multicolored .65 .22
1158 A409 41c multicolored .65 .22
Nos. 1154-1158 (5) 3.25 1.10

Purchase of booklet containing No. 1156b included STAMPSHOW '89 admission ticket and a Melbourne one-day transit pass. Sold for $8.

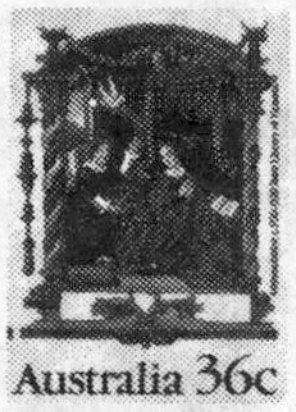

Christmas — A410

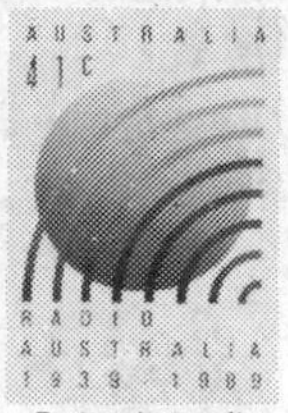

Radio Australia, 50th Anniv. — A411

Illuminations: 36c, Annunciation, from the Nicholai Joseph Foucault Book of Hours, c. 1510-20. 41c, Annunciation to the Shepherds, from the Wharncliffe Hours, c. 1475. 80c, Adoration of the Magi, from Parisian Book of Hours, c. 1490-1500.

1989, Nov. 1 *Perf. 14x13½*

1159 A410 36c multicolored .55 .18
a. Booklet pane of 10 5.50

Perf. 15x14½

1160 A410 41c multicolored .65 .22
1161 A410 80c multicolored 1.25 .42
Nos. 1159-1161 (3) 2.45 .82

1989, Nov. 1 *Perf. 14x13½*

1162 A411 41c multicolored .65 .22

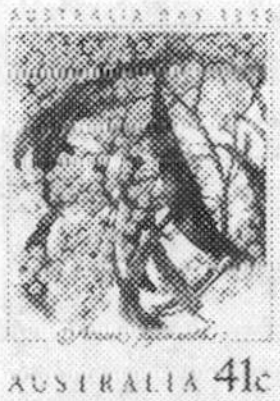

Australia Day — A412

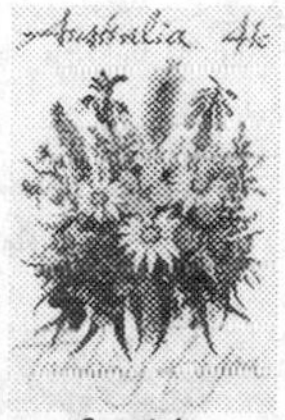

Special Occasions — A413

1990, Jan. 17 Litho. *Perf. 15x14½*

1163 A412 41c Golden wattle .65 .22

1990, Feb. 7 *Perf. 14x13½*

1164 A413 41c Thinking of You .65 .22
a. Booklet pane of 10 6.50
b. Perf. 14½ on 3 sides .65 .16
c. Booklet pane of 10, #1164b 6.50

See No. 1193.

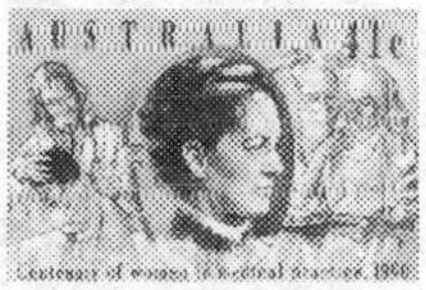

Women Practicing Medicine in Australia, Cent. A414

1990, Feb. 7 *Perf. 14½x15*

1165 A414 41c Constance Stone .65 .22

Dr. Constance Stone, Australia's first woman doctor.

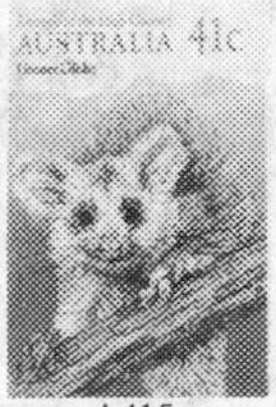

A415

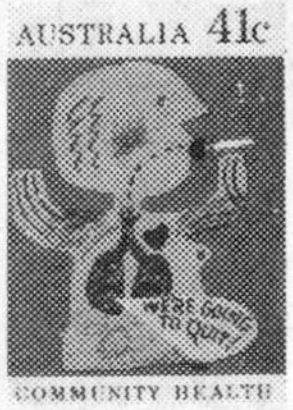

A416

Fauna of the High Country.

1990, Feb. 21 *Perf. 14x13½*

1166 A415 41c Greater glider .65 .22
1167 A415 65c Spotted-tailed quoll 1.00 .32
1168 A415 70c Mountain pygmy-possum 1.10 .35
1169 A415 80c Brush-tailed rock-wallaby 1.25 .42
Nos. 1166-1169 (4) 4.00 1.31

1990, Mar. 14

1170	A416	41c Quit smoking	.65	.22
1171	A416	41c Don't drink and drive	.65	.22
1172	A416	41c Eat right	.65	.22
1173	A416	41c Medical check-ups	.65	.22
		Nos. 1170-1173 (4)	2.60	.88

Community health.

A417   A418

Scenes from WW II, 1940-41: #1174, Anzacs at the front. #1175, Women working in factories, aircraft at the ready. 65c, Veterans and memorial parade. $1, Helicopters picking up wounded, cemetery. $1.10, Anzacs reading mail from home, 5 women watching departure of 2 ships.

1990, Apr. 12   Litho.   *Perf. 14¹/₂*

1174	A417	41c shown	.65	.22
1175	A417	41c multicolored	.65	.22
1176	A417	65c multicolored	1.00	.35
1177	A417	$1 multicolored	1.55	.50
1178	A417	$1.10 multicolored	1.75	.58
		Nos. 1174-1178 (5)	5.60	1.87

Australia and New Zealand Army Corps (ANZAC).

1990, Apr. 19   Litho.   *Perf. 14¹/₂*

1179	A418	41c multicolored	.60	.20

Queen Elizabeth II's 64th birthday.

Penny Black, 150th Anniv. A419

Stamps on stamps: a, New South Wales No. 44. b, South Australia No. 4. c, Tasmania No. 2. d, Victoria No. 120. e, Queensland No. 111A. f, Western Australia No. 3a.

1990, May 1   *Perf. 13¹/₂x14*

1180		Block of 6	3.60	1.20
a.-f.		A419 41c any single	.60	.20
g.		Souvenir sheet of 6	3.60	1.20

The Gold Rush — A420

Designs: a, Off to the diggings. b, The diggings. c, Panning for gold. d, Commissioner's tent. e, Gold escort.

1990, May 16   *Perf. 13*

1181		Strip of 5	3.00	1.00
a.-e.		A420 41c any single	.60	.20

Cooperation in Antarctic Research A421

1990, June 13   Litho.   *Perf. 14¹/₂x14*

1182	A421	41c Glaciology	.62	.20
1183	A421	$1.10 Krill (marine biology)	1.65	.55
a.		Min. sheet of 2, #1182-1183	2.30	.75

See Russia Nos. 5902-5903. For overprint see No. 1198.

Colonial Australia A422

Boom Time: a, Land boom. b, Building boom. c, Investment boom. d, Retail boom. e, Factory boom.

1990, July 12   Litho.   *Perf. 13*

1184		Strip of 5	3.25	1.10
a.-e.		A422 41c any single	.65	.22

Sports Type of 1989

1990-91   Typo.   *Die Cut Perf. 11¹/₂*
Self-Adhesive

1185	A400	41c Cycling	.75	.20
1186	A400	43c Skateboarding	.68	.18
a.		Litho.	.70	.18

Blue background has large dots on No. 1186 and smaller dots on No. 1186a. No. 1186 is on waxed paper backing printed with 0 to 4 koalas. No. 1186a is on plain paper backing printed with one kangaroo.

Issued: 41c, 5/16; #1186, 8/27; #1186a, 1991. This is an expanding set. Numbers will change if necessary.

AUSTRALIA 28c   Salmon Gums by Robert Juniper — A423

Design: 43c, The Blue Dress by Brian Dunlop.

1990, Sept. 3   Litho.   *Perf. 15¹/₂ Vert.*
Booklet Stamps

1191	A423	28c multicolored	.45	.15
a.		Perf. 14¹/₂ vert.	.45	.15
1192	A423	43c multicolored	.68	.18
a.		Bkt. pane, #1191, 4 #1192	3.17	
b.		Perf. 14¹/₂ vert.	.68	.18
c.		Booklet pane, #1191a, 4 #1192b	3.25	

Thinking Of You Type

1990, Sept. 3   *Perf. 14¹/₂*

1193	A413	43c multicolored	.68	.18
a.		Booklet pane of 10	6.80	

Christmas A424

1990, Oct. 31   Litho.   *Perf. 14¹/₂*

1194	A424	38c Kookaburras	.62	.20
a.		Booklet pane of 10	6.20	
1195	A424	43c Nativity, vert.	.70	.22
1196	A424	80c Opossum	1.35	.45
		Nos. 1194-1196 (3)	2.67	.87

Local Government in Australia, 150th Anniv. — A425

1990, Oct. 31

1197	A425	43c Town Hall, Adelaide	.70	.22

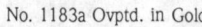

No. 1183a Ovptd. in Gold

WORLD STAMP EXHIBITION
24 AUG - 2 SEPT 1990

1990   Litho.   *Perf. 14¹/₂x14*

1198	A421	Miniature sheet of 2	2.40	1.20

Overprint applied to sheet margin only.

Flags — A426

1991, Jan. 10   Litho.   *Perf. 14¹/₂*

1199	A426	43c National flag	.70	.22
1200	A426	90c White ensign	1.40	.45
1201	A426	$1 Air Force ensign	1.55	.52
1202	A426	$1.20 Red ensign	1.85	.62
		Nos. 1199-1202 (4)	5.50	1.81

Australia Day.

Water Birds A427

1991, Feb. 14

1203	A427	43c Black swan	.70	.22
1204	A427	43c Black-necked stork, vert.	.70	.22
1205	A427	85c Cape Barren goose, vert.	1.30	1.00
1206	A427	$1 Chestnut teal	1.55	.52
		Nos. 1203-1206 (4)	4.25	1.96

Women's Wartime Services, 50th Anniv. A428

50th Anniversaries: No. 1208, Siege of Tobruk. $1.20, Australian War Memorial, Canberra.

1991, Mar. 14   Litho.   *Perf. 14¹/₂*

1207	A428	43c shown	.70	.22
1208	A428	43c multicolored	.70	.22
1209	A428	$1.20 multicolored	1.85	.58
		Nos. 1207-1209 (3)	3.25	1.02

Queen Elizabeth II's 65th Birthday — A429

1991, Apr. 11   Litho.   *Perf. 14¹/₂*

1210	A429	43c multicolored	.70	.22

Insects A430

1991, Apr. 11

1211	A430	43c Hawk moth	.70	.22
1212	A430	43c Cotton harlequin bug	.70	.22
1213	A430	80c Leichhardt's grasshopper	1.25	.40
1214	A430	$1 Jewel beetle	1.55	.50
		Nos. 1211-1214 (4)	4.20	1.34

Australian Photography, 150th Anniv. — A431

Designs: No. 1215a, Bondi, by Max Dupain, 1939. No. 1215b, Gears for the Mining Industry, Vickers Ruwolt Melbourne, by Wolfgang Sievers, 1967. 70c, Wheel of Youth, by Harold Cazneaux, 1929. $1.20, Teacup Ballet, by Olive Cotton, 1935.

1991, May 13   Litho.   *Perf. 14¹/₂*

1215		Pair	1.35	.44
a.-b.		A431 43c any single	.68	.22
1216	A431	70c blk, olive & claret	1.10	.36
1217	A431	$1.20 blk, gray & Prus bl	1.85	.62
		Nos. 1215-1217 (3)	4.30	1.42

Golden Days of Radio — A432   Pets — A433

1991, June 13   Litho.   *Perf. 14¹/₂*

1218	A432	43c Music & variety shows	.68	.22
1219	A432	43c Soap operas	.68	.22
1220	A432	85c Quiz shows	1.30	1.25
1221	A432	$1 Children's stories	1.55	.52
		Nos. 1218-1221 (4)	4.21	2.21

1991, July 25   Litho.   *Perf. 14¹/₂*

1222	A433	43c Puppy	.68	.22
1223	A433	43c Kitten	.68	.22
1224	A433	70c Pony	1.10	.36
1225	A433	$1 Cockatoo	1.50	.50
		Nos. 1222-1225 (4)	3.96	1.30

George Vancouver (1757-1798) and Edward John Eyre (1815-1901), Explorers — A434

1991, Sept. 26   Litho.   *Perf. 14¹/₂*

1226	A434	$1.05 multicolored	1.70	.55
a.		Souvenir sheet of 1	1.70	.55
b.		As "a," overprinted in gold	1.50	.52

Vancouver's visit to Western Australia, 200th anniv. and Eyre's journey to Albany, Western Australia, 150th anniv.

No. 1226b overprinted on sheet margin with show emblem and: "PHILANIPPON / WORLD STAMP / EXHIBITION / TOKYO / 16-24 NOV 1991" followed by Japanese inscription.

Issue date: #1226b, Nov. 16.

Australian Literature of the 1890's A435

Designs: 43c, Seven Little Australians by Ethel Turner. 75c, On Our Selection by Steele Rudd. $1, Clancy of the Overflow by A.B. "Banjo" Paterson, vert. $1.20, The Drover's Wife by Henry Lawson, vert.

1991, Oct. 10

1227	A435	43c multicolored	.68	.22
1228	A435	75c multicolored	1.20	.40
1229	A435	$1 multicolored	1.60	.52
1230	A435	$1.20 multicolored	1.90	.62
		Nos. 1227-1230 (4)	5.38	1.76

Christmas
A436

1991, Nov. 1
1231 A436 38c Shepherd .60 .20
  a. Booklet pane of 20 12.00
1232 A436 43c Baby Jesus .68 .22
1233 A436 90c Wise man, camel 1.40 .45
  Nos. 1231-1233 (3) 2.68 .87

Thinking of
You — A437

1992, Jan. 2 Litho. Perf. 14¹/₂x15
1234 A437 45c Wildflowers .70 .25
  a. Booklet pane of 10 7.00

Threatened
Species — A438

Designs: No. 1235a, Parma wallaby. b, Ghost bat. c, Long-tailed dunnart. d, Little pygmy possum. e, Dusky hopping mouse. f, Squirrel glider.

1992, Jan. 2 Litho. Perf. 14x14¹/₂
1235 Block of 6 3.80 1.35
  a.-f. A438 45c any single .62 .22

Die Cut
Perf. 11¹/₂
Self-Adhesive
1241 A438 45c like #1235a .62 .22
  a. Typo. .62 .22
1242 A438 45c like #1235b .62 .22
  a. Typo. .62 .22
1243 A438 45c like #1235c .62 .22
  a. Typo. .62 .22
1244 A438 45c like #1235d .62 .22
  a. Typo. .62 .22
1245 A438 45c like #1235e .62 .22
  a. Typo. .62 .22
1246 A438 45c like #1235f .62 .22
  a. Typo. .62 .22
  b. Bklt. pane, 2 each #1241-1244, 1 each #1245-1246 6.20
  c. Pane of 5, #1242-1246 3.10
  d. Strip of 6, #1241-1246 3.75
  e. Strip of 6, #1241a-1246a 3.75
  f. #1246c overprinted 3.10

Litho. stamps are sharper in appearance than typo. stamps, most notably on the black lettering. Nos. 1246b and 1246c have tagging bars which make the right portion of the stamps appear toned.
No. 1246f - overprinted in Gold on sheet margin of No. 1246c with emblem of "WORLD COLUMBIAN / STAMP EXPO '92 / MAY 22-31, 1992 - CHICAGO." Issued in May.
See Nos. 1277-1295D, 1406-1407.

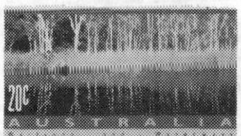

Wetlands — A439

Perf. 14¹/₂ Horiz.
1992, Jan. 2 Photo.
Booklet Stamps
1247 A439 20c Noosa River, Queensland .55 .25
  a. Perf. 14 horiz.
1248 A439 45c Lake Eildon, Victoria .55 .25
  a. Bklt. pane, 1 #1247, 4 #1248 2.75
  b. Perf. 14 horiz.
  c. Bklt. pane, 1 #1247a, 4 #1248b
  Complete booklet, #1248c

Sailing Ships
A440

Perf. 14¹/₂x15, 15x14¹/₂
1992, Jan. 15 Litho.
1249 A440 45c Young Endeavour .70 .24
1250 A440 45c Britannia, vert. .70 .24
1251 A440 $1.05 Akarana, vert. 1.60 .52
1252 A440 $1.20 John Louis 1.80 .60
  a. Sheet of 4, #1249-1252 4.80 4.80
  b. As "a," overprinted 4.80 4.80
  c. As "a," overprinted 4.80 4.80
  Nos. 1249-1252 (4) 4.80 1.60

Australia Day. Discovery of America, 500th anniv. (No. 1252a).
Overprint in gold on sheet margin of No. 1252b contains emblem and "WORLD COLUMBIAN / STAMP EXPO '92 / MAY 22-31, 1992-CHICAGO." No. 1252b issued in May.
Overprint in gold on sheet margin of No. 1252c contains emblem and "GENOVA '92 / 18-27 SEPTEMBER." No. 1252c issued in Sept.

Australian
Battles,
1942 — A441

1992, Feb. 19 Litho. Perf. 14¹/₂
1253 A441 45c Bombing of Darwin .65 .22
1254 A441 75c Milne Bay 1.05 .38
1255 A441 75c Kokoda Trail 1.05 .38
1256 A441 $1.05 Coral Sea 1.50 .52
1257 A441 $1.20 El Alamein 1.70 .60
  Nos. 1253-1257 (5) 5.95 2.10

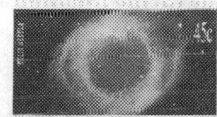

Intl. Space
Year — A442

1992, Mar. 19
1258 A442 45c Helix Nebula .65 .22
1259 A442 $1.05 The Pleiades 1.50 .52
1260 A442 $1.20 Spiral Galaxy NGC 2997 1.70 .60
  a. Sheet of 3, #1258-1260 3.85 3.85
  b. As "a," overprinted 3.85 3.85
  Nos. 1258-1260 (3) 3.85 1.34

Overprint on sheet margin of No. 1260b contains emblem of "WORLD COLUMBIAN / STAMP EXPO '92 / MAY 22-31, 1992-CHICAGO." No. 1260b issued in May.

Queen
Elizabeth II,
66th Birthday
A443

1992, Apr. 9 Perf. 14x14¹/₂
1261 A443 45c Wmk. 228 & #258 .65 .22

Vineyard
Regions
A444

Designs: No. 1262, Hunter Valley New South Wales. No. 1263, North Eastern Victoria. No. 1264, Barossa Valley South Australia. No. 1265, Coonawarra South Australia. No. 1266, Margaret River Western Australia.

1992, Apr. 9
1262 A444 45c multicolored .65 .22
1263 A444 45c multicolored .65 .22
1264 A444 45c multicolored .65 .22
1265 A444 45c multicolored .65 .22
1266 A444 45c multicolored .65 .22
  Nos. 1262-1266 (5) 3.25 1.10

Land Care — A445

Designs: a, Salt action. b, Farm planning. c, Erosion control. d, Tree planting. e, Dune care.

1992, June 11 Litho. Perf. 14¹/₂x14
1267 Strip of 5 3.25 1.10
  a.-e. A445 45c Any single .62 .22

1992 Summer
Olympics and
Paralympics,
Barcelona
A446

1992, July 2 Perf. 14¹/₂
1268 A446 45c Cycling .62 .22
1269 A446 $1.20 Weight lifting 1.75 .60
1270 A446 $1.20 High jump 1.75 .60
  Nos. 1268-1270 (3) 4.12 1.42

Threatened Species Type of 1992
1992-94 Litho. Perf. 14x14¹/₂
1277 A438 30c Saltwater crocodile .42 .15
1278 A438 35c Echidna .50 .18
1279 A438 40c Platypus .55 .18
1280 A438 45c Kangaroo .65 .22
1281 A438 45c Adult kangaroo with joey .65 .22
1282 A438 45c Two adult kangaroos .65 .22
1282A A438 45c Four koalas .65 .22
1282B A438 45c Koala walking .65 .22
1282C A438 45c Koala in tree .65 .22
  d. Block of 6, #1280-1282C 4.00 1.40
  e. Souvenir sheet of 6, #1280-1282C 4.00 4.00
1283 A438 50c Koala .70 .25
1286 A438 60c Common brushtail possum .85 .30
1287 A438 70c Kookaburra .95 .35
1288 A438 85c Pelican 1.25 .40
1289 A438 90c Eastern gray kangaroo 1.25 .40
1290 A438 95c Common wombat 1.35 .45
1292 A438 $1.20 Pink cockatoo 1.65 .55
1293 A438 $1.35 Emu 2.00 .65
  Nos. 1277-1293 (17) 15.37 5.18

PHILAKOREA '94 (#1282e).
Issued: 35c, 50c, 95c, 8/13; 40c, 70c, 90c, $1.20, 8/12/93; 30c, 85c, $1.35, 3/10/94; 45c, 5/12/94; stamps 28/94.
This is an expanding set. Numbers may change.

1994 Litho. Die Cut Perf. 11
Self-Adhesive
1294 A438 45c like #1280 .65 .22
1295 A438 45c like #1281 .65 .22
1295A A438 45c like #1282 .65 .22
1295B A438 45c like #1282A .65 .22
1295C A438 45c like #1282B .65 .22
1295D A438 45c like #1282C .65 .22
  e. Bklt. pane, #1295A, 1295D, 2 each #1294-1295, 1295B-1295C 6.50
  f. Strip of 6, #1294-1295D 4.00
  Nos. 1294-1295D (6) 3.90 1.32

Issued: Nos. 1294-1295D, 5/12/94. This is an expanding set. Numbers may change.

Opening of Sydney
Harbor Tunnel, August
29 — A447

Sydney Harbor Bridge and Tunnel: a, Left side. b, Right side.

1992, Aug. 28 Litho. Perf. 14¹/₂
1296 A447 45c Pair, #a.-b. 1.30 .45
  c. Pair, #d.-e., perf 15¹/₂ 1.30 .45

Buildings in
Western
Australia
Goldfield
Towns — A448

Designs: No. 1297, Warden's Courthouse, Coolgardie. No. 1298, Post Office, Kalgoorlie. $1.05, York Hotel, Kalgoorlie. $1.20, Town Hall, Kalgoorlie.

Sheffield Shield Cricket
Competition,
Cent. — A449

Cricket match, 1890s: 45c, Bowler. $1.20, Batsman, wicket keeper.

1992, Sept. 17 Litho. Perf. 14x14¹/₂
1297 A448 45c multicolored .62 .22
1298 A448 45c multicolored .62 .22
1299 A448 $1.05 multicolored 1.45 .50
1300 A448 $1.20 multicolored 1.65 .58
  Nos. 1297-1300 (4) 4.34 1.52

1992, Oct. 15 Litho. Perf. 14¹/₂
1301 A449 45c multicolored .60 .20
1302 A449 $1.20 multicolored 1.60 .55

Christmas
A450

Designs: 40c, Children dressed as Mary and Joseph with baby carriage. 45c, Boy jumping from bed Christmas morning. $1, Boy and girl singing Christmas carol.

1992, Oct. 30 Litho. Perf. 14x14¹/₂
1303 A450 40c multicolored .55 .55
  a. Booklet pane of 20 11.00
1304 A450 45c multicolored .60 .20
1305 A450 $1 multicolored 1.30 .42
  Nos. 1303-1305 (3) 2.45 1.17

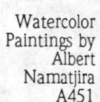

Watercolor
Paintings by
Albert
Namatjira
A451

Designs: No. 1306a, Ghost Gum, Central Australia. b, Across the Plain to Mount Giles.

1993, Jan. 14 Litho. Perf. 14x15
1306 A451 45c Pair, #a.-b. 1.20 .40

Australia Day.

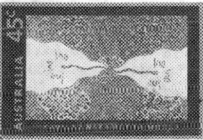

Dreamings
A452

Aboriginal paintings: 45c, Wild Onion Dreaming, by Pauline Nakamarra Woods. 75c, Yam Plants, by Jack Wunuwun, vert. 85c, Goose Egg Hunt, by George Milpurrurru, vert. $1, Kalumpiwarra-Ngulalintji, by Rover Thomas.

Perf. 14x14¹/₂, 14¹/₂x14
1993, Feb. 4 Litho.
1307 A452 45c red & multi .60 .20
1308 A452 75c org yel & multi 1.00 .30
1309 A452 85c buff & multi 1.10 .35
1310 A452 $1 salmon & multi 1.30 .45
  Nos. 1307-1310 (4) 4.00 1.30

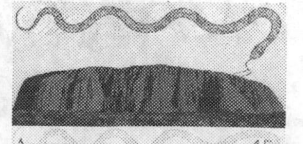

World Heritage Sites in Australia — A453

1993, Mar. 4 Litho. Perf. 14¹/₂x14
1311 A453 45c Uluru (Ayers Rock) .60 .20
1312 A453 85c Fraser Island 1.10 .38
1313 A453 95c Shark Bay 1.25 .40
1314 A453 $2 Kakadu 2.60 .85
  Nos. 1311-1314 (4) 5.55 1.83

World War II Ships
A454

Designs: 45c, Cruiser HMAS Sydney II. 85c, Corvette HMAS Bathurst. $1.05, Destroyer HMAS Arunta. $1.20, Hospital Ship Centaur.

1993, Apr. 7 Litho. *Perf. 14x14½*

1315 A454	45c	multicolored	.60	.20
1316 A454	85c	multicolored	1.15	.28
1317 A454	$1.05	multicolored	1.40	.48
1318 A454	$1.20	multicolored	1.60	.52
		Nos. 1315-1318 (4)	4.75	1.48

A455 A456

1993, Apr. 7 *Perf. 14½x14*

1319 A455 45c multicolored .62 .20

Queen Elizabeth II, 67th birthday.

1993, May 7 Litho. *Perf. 14½x14*

Designs based on 19th century trade union banners: No. 1320, Baker, shoe maker. No. 1321, Stevedore, seamstresses. $1, Blacksmith, telephone operator, cook. $1.20, Carpenters.

1320 A456	45c	multicolored	.60	.20
1321 A456	45c	multicolored	.60	.20
1322 A456	$1	multicolored	1.30	.45
1323 A456	$1.20	multicolored	1.55	.52
		Nos. 1320-1323 (4)	4.05	1.37

Working life in the 1890s.

Trains — A457

Designs: No. 1324, Centenary Special, Tasmania. No. 1325, Spirit of Progress. No. 1326, Western Endeavour. No. 1327, Silver City Comet. No. 1328, Kuranda Tourist Train. No. 1329, The Ghan.

1993, June 1 *Perf. 14x14½*

1324 A457	45c	multicolored	.60	.20
1325 A457	45c	multicolored	.60	.20
1326 A457	45c	multicolored	.60	.20
1327 A457	45c	multicolored	.60	.20
1328 A457	45c	multicolored	.60	.20
1329 A457	45c	multicolored	.60	.20
a.		Block of 6, #1324-1329	3.60	1.20

Die Cut Perf. 12x11½

Self-Adhesive

1330 A457	45c	like No. 1324	.60	.20
1331 A457	45c	like No. 1325	.60	.20
1332 A457	45c	like No. 1326	.60	.20
1333 A457	45c	like No. 1327	.60	.20
1334 A457	45c	like No. 1328	.60	.20
1335 A457	45c	like No. 1329	.60	.20
a.		Strip of 6, #1330-1335	3.60	
b.		Bklt. pane of 10, #1332, 1335, 2 each #1330-1331, 1333-1334	6.00	

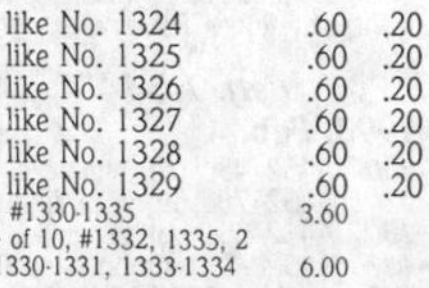

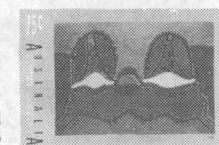

Aboriginal Art — A458

Aboriginal paintings: 45c, Black Cockatoo Feather, by Fiona Foley, vert. 75c, Ngarrgooroon Country, by Hector Jandany. $1, Ngak Ngak, by Ginger Riley. $1.05, Untitled work, by Robert Cole, vert.

Perf. 14½x14, 14x14½

1993, July 1 Litho.

1336 A458	45c	henna brown & multi	.60	.20
1337 A458	75c	brown & multi	1.00	.30
1338 A458	$1	gray & multi	1.30	.42
1339 A458	$1.05	olive & multi	1.35	.45
		Nos. 1336-1339 (4)	4.25	1.37

Dame Enid Lyons, MP, and Sen. Dorothy Tangney
A459

Design: No. 1340, Stylized globe, natl. arms, Inter-Parliamentary Conference emblem.

1993, Sept. 2 Litho. *Perf. 14½*

1340 A459	45c	multicolored	.60	.20
1341 A459	45c	multicolored	.60	.20
a.		Pair, #1340-1341	1.20	.40

90th Inter-Parliamentary Union Conference (#1340). First women in Australian Federal Parliament, 50th anniv. (#1341). Nos. 1340-1341 printed in panes of 25 with 16 #1340 and 9 #1341. Panes with 16 #1341 and 9 #1340 were issued Nov. 19, but were available only through Philatelic Agency.

A460 A461

Dinosaurs: No. 1342, 1348, Ornithocheirus, horiz. No. 1343, 1349, Leaellynasaura. No. 1344, Allosaurus. No. 1345, Timimus. No. 1346, Muttaburrasaurus. No. 1347, Minmi, horiz.

1993, Oct. 1 *Perf. 14x14½, 14½x14*

1342 A460	45c	multicolored	.60	.20
1343 A460	45c	multicolored	.60	.20
1344 A461	45c	multicolored	.60	.20
1345 A461	45c	multicolored	.60	.20

Size: 29x50mm

1346 A461	75c	multicolored	1.00	.35
1347 A461	$1.05	multicolored	1.40	.48
a.		Souvenir sheet of 6, #1342-1347	4.80	4.80
b.		As "a," overprinted	4.80	4.80
c.		As "a," overprinted	4.80	4.80
		Nos. 1342-1347 (6)	4.80	1.63

Self-Adhesive

Die Cut Perf. 11½

1348 A460	45c	multicolored	.60	.20
1349 A460	45c	multicolored	.60	.20
a.		Bklt. pane, 5 each #1348-1349	6.00	

Overprint in gold on sheet margin of No. 1347b contains "BANGKOK 1993" show emblem and "WORLD PHILATELIC / EXHIBITION / BANGKOK 1-10 OCTOBER 1993."

Overprint in gold on sheet margin of No. 1347c contains dinosaur and "Sydney / STAMP & COIN / SHOW / 15-17 October 1993."

Christmas — A462

1993, Nov. 1 Litho. *Perf. 14½x14*

1354 A462	40c	Goodwill	.52	.18
a.		Booklet pane of 20	10.50	
1355 A462	45c	Joy	.60	.20
1356 A462	$1	Peace	1.25	.45
		Nos. 1354-1356 (3)	2.37	.83

Australia Day — A463

Landscape paintings: 45c, Shoalhaven River Bank-Dawn, by Arthur Boyd. 85c, Wimmera (from Mt. Arapiles), by Sir Sidney Nolan. $1.05, Lagoon, Wimmera, by Nolan. $2, White Cockatoos in Paddock with Flame Trees, by Boyd, vert.

Perf. 14½x14, 14x14½

1994, Jan. 13 Litho.

1357 A463	45c	multicolored	.65	.22
1358 A463	85c	multicolored	1.25	.42
1359 A463	$1.05	multicolored	1.50	.50
1360 A463	$2	multicolored	3.00	1.00
		Nos. 1357-1360 (4)	6.40	2.14

See Nos. 1418-1421, 1476-1479.

Royal Life Saving Society, Cent.
A464

1994, Jan. 20 Litho. *Perf. 14x14½*

1361 A464	45c	Vigilance	.65	.22
1362 A464	45c	Education	.65	.22
1363 A464	95c	Drill	1.40	.45
1364 A464	$1.20	Fitness	1.75	.55
		Nos. 1361-1364 (4)	4.45	1.44

Die Cut Perf. 11½

Self-Adhesive

1365 A464	45c	like #1361	.60	.20
1366 A464	45c	like #1362	.60	.20
a.		Pair, #1365-1366	1.25	.40
b.		Booklet pane, 5 #1366a	6.25	

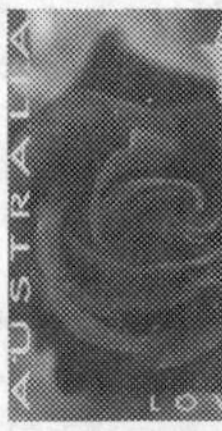

Thinking of You — A465

1994, Feb. 3 Litho. *Perf. 14½x14*

1367 A465	45c	Rose	.60	.20
1368 A465	45c	Tulips	.60	.20
1369 A465	45c	Poppies	.60	.20
a.		Pair, #1368-1369	1.25	.40
b.		Booklet pane, 5 #1369a	6.25	
		Nos. 1367-1369 (3)	1.80	.60

A466 A467

1994, Apr. 8 Litho. *Perf. 14½*

1370 A466 45c multicolored .65 .22

Queen Elizabeth II, 68th birthday.

1994, Apr. 8 *Perf. 14½x14*

1371 A467 95c multicolored 1.25 .45

Opening of Friendship Bridge, Thailand-Laos.

Intl. Year of the Family — A468

Children's paintings of their families: 45c, Bobbie Lea Blackmore. 75c, Kathryn Teoh. $1, Maree McCarthy.

1994, Apr. 14 Litho. *Perf. 14x14½*

1372 A468	45c	multicolored	.65	.22
1373 A468	75c	multicolored	1.10	.35
1374 A468	$1	multicolored	1.50	.50
		Nos. 1372-1374 (3)	3.25	1.07

Australian Women's Right to Vote, Cent. — A469

1994, June 9 Litho. *Perf. 14x14½*

1375 A469 45c multicolored .65 .22

Bunyips Folklore Creatures
A470

Types of Bunyips: No. 1376, Aboriginal legend. No. 1377, Nature Spirit. 90c, Berkeley's Creek. $1.35, Natural history.

1994, July 14 Litho. *Perf. 14x14½*

1376 A470	45c	multicolored	.65	.22
1377 A470	45c	multicolored	.65	.22
a.		Pair, #1376-1377	1.25	.42
1378 A470	90c	multicolored	1.25	.42
1379 A470	$1.35	multicolored	2.00	.65
		Nos. 1376-1379 (4)	4.55	1.51

World War II Prime Ministers
A471

Designs: a, Robert Menzies. b, Arthur Fadden. c, John Curtin. d, Francis (Frank) Forde. e, Joseph Benedict (Ben) Chifley.

1994, Aug. 11

1380	Strip of 5	3.25	1.10
a.-e.	A471 45c any single	.65	.22

Aviation Pioneers — A472

Designs: No. 1381, Lawrence Hargrave, box kites. No. 1382, Ross and Keith Smith, Vickers Vimy. $1.35, Ivor McIntyre, Stanley Globe, Fairey IIID A10-3 seaplane. $1.80, Freda Thompson, DeHavilland Moth Major.

1994, Aug. 29 Engr. *Perf. 12*

1381 A472	45c	multicolored	.65	.22
1382 A472	45c	multicolored	.65	.22
1383 A472	$1.35	multicolored	2.00	.65
1384 A472	$1.80	multicolored	2.50	.82
		Nos. 1381-1384 (4)	5.80	1.91

First England-Australia flight within 30-day time span (#1382). First aerial circumnavigation of Australia (#1383). First woman to fly solo from England-Australia (#1384).

Australian Zoo Animals
A473 A474

Perf. 14x14½, 14½x14

1994, Sept. 28 Litho.

1385 A473	45c	Scarlet macaw	.65	.22
1386 A473	45c	Cheetah, vert.	.65	.22
1387 A474	45c	Fijian crested iguana	.65	.22
1388 A474	45c	Orang-utan	.65	.22

Size: 50x30mm

Perf. 14½x14

1389 A473	$1	Asian elephant	1.50	1.50
a.		Souv. sheet of 5, #1385-1389, perf. 14½	4.25	4.25

b.   As "a," ovptd.   4.25   4.25
c.   As "a," ovptd.   4.25   4.25
d.   As "a," ovptd.   4.25   4.25
e.   As "a," ovptd.   4.25   4.25
    Nos. 1385-1389 (5)   4.10   2.38

Self-Adhesive
Die Cut Perf. 11¹/₂

1390 A473 45c like #1385   .65   .22
1391 A473 45c like #1386   .65   .22
a.   Booklet pane, 6 #1390, 4 #1391   6.50

Overprint in gold on sheet margin:
No. 1389b, show emblem and "Brisbane Stamp Show Zoos / October 21-23, 1994."
No. 1389c, show emblem and "SYDNEY / STAMP / AND / COIN / SHOW / 30/9/94 TO 2/10/94."
No. 1389d, show emblem and "Stampshow '94 Melbourne October 27-30 / National/State Centennial Exhibition 1894-1994."
No. 1389e, show emblem and "STAMP SHOW 94 / Fremantle Convention Centre / 5-6 November 1994."

Christmas
A475

Details from Adoration of the Magi, by Giovanni Toscani: 40c, Madonna and Child, vert. 45c, One of Magi, horse and groom. $1, Joseph receiving frankincense from Magi. $1.80, Entire painting.

1994, Oct. 31   **Litho.**   *Perf. 14¹/₂x14*
1392 A475 40c multicolored   .60   .20
a.   Booklet pane of 20   12.00
    Complete booklet, #1392a   12.00

Perf. 14x14¹/₂
1393 A475 45c multicolored   .70   .25
1394 A475 $1 multicolored   1.60   .40

Size: 50x30mm
1395 A475 $1.80 multicolored   2.75   .80
    Nos. 1392-1395 (4)   5.65   1.65

50th Sydney-Hobart Yacht Race — A476

Designs: a, Yachts bow-on, Sydney Opera House, Harbor Bridge. b, Two yachts abeam.

1994, Oct. 31   *Perf. 14¹/₂*
1396   Pair   1.40   .50
a.-b.   A476 45c any single   .70   .25

Self-Adhesive
Die Cut Perf. 11¹/₂
1397   A476 45c like #1396a   .70   .25
1397A A476 45c like #1396b   .70   .25

A477

1994, Nov. 2   **Litho.**   *Die Cut Perf. 17*
Self-Adhesive
Booklet Stamps
Background Color
1398 A477 45c bluish green   .70   .25
1399 A477 45c blue   .70   .25
1400 A477 45c purple   .70   .25
1401 A477 45c yellow green   .70   .25
1402 A477 45c pale yellow green   .70   .25
1403 A477 45c pale red brown   .70   .25
1404 A477 45c rose   .70   .25
1405 A477 45c orange yellow   .70   .25
a.   Booklet pane of 20   14.00
    Nos. 1398-1405 (8)   5.60   2.00

No. 1405a contains 3 each #1399, 1401, 1403, 1405 and 2 each #1398, 1400, 1402, 1404. No. 1405a was sold in ATM machines, at the Natl. Philatelic Center, and Australian Philatelic Bureau.

Threatened Species Type of 1992
1994, Aug.   **Litho.**   *Die Cut Perf. 11¹/₂*
Self-Adhesive
Size: 53x31mm
1406 A438 45c like #1235a   .70   .25
1407 A438 45c like #1235b   .70   .25
1408 A438 45c like #1235c   .70   .25
1409 A438 45c like #1235d   .70   .25
1410 A438 45c like #1235e   .70   .25

1411 A438 45c like #1235f   .70   .25
a.   Strip of 6, #1406-1411   4.20
    Nos. 1406-1411 (6)   4.20   1.50

Nos. 1406-1411 have computer-generated denomination and inscription "PhilaKorea" at bottom. Inscriptions "AUSTRALIA," animal name and "THREATENED SPECIES" appear beside design instead of above and below it as on No. 1235.

Die Cut Perf. 11
1994, Nov. 17   **Litho.**
Self-Adhesive
Size: 40x27mm
1412 A438 45c like #1280   .70   .25
1413 A438 45c like #1282B   .70   .25
1414 A438 45c like #1282   .70   .25
1415 A438 45c like #1282A   .70   .25
1416 A438 45c like #1281   .70   .25
1417 A438 45c like #1282C   .70   .25
    Nos. 1412-1417 (6)   4.20   1.50

Nos. 1412-1417 have computer-generated denominations and location codes printed at bottom of each stamp. They differ from Nos. 1280-1282C in size and location of inscriptions.
Nos. 1412-1417 can be printed with denominations from 45c-$100. We have listed the 45c value with the NPC (National Philatelic Center) code which is available through the Australian Philatelic Bureau.
Nos. 1412-1417 were issued with "SINGAPORE '95" code on Sept. 1, 1995.

Australia Day Type of 1994
Paintings: No. 1418, Back Verandah, by Russell Drysdale. No. 1419, Skull Springs Country, by Guy Grey-Smith. $1.05, Outcamp, by Robert Juniper. $1.20, Kite Flying, by Ian Fairweather.

1995, Jan. 12   **Litho.**   *Perf. 15x14¹/₂*
1418 A463 45c multicolored   .70   .25
1419 A463 45c multicolored   .70   .25
1420 A463 $1.05 multicolored   1.60   .40
1421 A463 $1.20 multicolored   1.75   .45
    Nos. 1418-1421 (4)   4.75   1.35

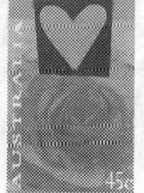

St. Valentine's Day — A478

Designs: a, Red heart. b, Red and gold heart. c, Gold heart.

1995, Feb. 6   **Litho.**   *Perf. 14¹/₂x14*
1422   Strip of 3   2.10   .75
a.-c.   A478 45c any single   .70   .25

Endeavour
A479

Designs: No. 1423a, Captain Cook's Endeavour. b, Replica.

1995, Feb. 9   **Litho.**   *Perf. 14x14¹/₂*
1423   Pair   1.40   .50
a.-b.   A479 45c any single   .70   .25

Booklet Stamps
Size: 44x26mm
Perf. 14 Horiz.
1424 A479 20c like #1423a   .30   .15
1425 A479 45c like #1423b   .70   .25
a.   Booklet pane, 1 #1424, 4 #1425   3.25
    Complete booklet, #1425a   3.25

Natl. Trust, 50th Anniv. — A480

Designs: No. 1426a, Coalport plate, Regency style bracket clock. No. 1426b, 15th-16th cent. x-frame Italian style chair, 19th cent. Steiner doll. $1, Advance Australia teapot, neo-classical parian-ware statuette. $2, China urn, silver bowl.

1995, Mar. 16   **Engr.**   *Perf. 14x14¹/₂*
1426   Pair   1.40   .50
a.-b.   A480 45c any single   .70   .25

1427 A480 $1 red brown & blue   1.50   .50
1428 A480 $2 blue & green   3.00   1.00
    Nos. 1426-1428 (3)   5.90   2.00

Opals — A481

1995, Apr. 5   **Litho.**   *Perf. 14¹/₂x14*
1429 A481 $1.20 Light opal   1.75   .90
1430 A481 $2.50 Black opal   3.75   1.90

Nos. 1429-1430 each contain a holographic image. Soaking in water may affect the hologram.

Australia 45c
A482   A483

1995, Apr. 20   **Litho.**   *Perf. 14¹/₂*
1431 A482 45c multicolored   .65   .22

Queen Elizabeth II, 69th birthday.

1995, Apr. 20   **Litho.**   *Perf. 14¹/₂x14*
Famous Australians from World War II.
1432 A483 45c Sir Edward Dunlop   .65   .22
1433 A483 45c Mrs. Jessie Vasey   .65   .22
1434 A483 45c Tom Derrick   .65   .22
1435 A483 45c Rawdon Hume Middleton   .65   .22
a.   Block of 4, #1432-1435   2.60   .85

Self-Adhesive
Die Cut Perf. 11¹/₂
1436 A483 45c like #1432   .65   .22
1437 A483 45c like #1433   .65   .22
1438 A483 45c like #1434   .65   .22
1439 A483 45c like #1435   .65   .22
a.   Booklet pane, 4 #1436, 2 each #1437-1439   6.50
b.   Strip of 4, #1436-1439   2.60
    Nos. 1432-1439 (8)   5.20   1.76

See Nos. 1452-1455.

UN, 50th Anniv.
A484

1995, May 11   **Litho.**   *Perf. 14x14¹/₂*
1440 A484 45c + label, multi   .65   .22
a.   Block of 4 + 4 labels   2.75   .90

No. 1440 was issued se-tenant with label in blocks of 4 + 4 labels in four designs. In alternating rows, labels appear on left or right side of stamp.

A485   A486

Poster, scene from: No. 1441, The Story of the Kelly Gang, 1906. No. 1442, On Our Selection, 1932. No. 1443, Jedda, 1955. No. 1444, Picnic at Hanging Rock, 1970s. No. 1445, Strictly Ballroom, 1992.

1995, June 8   **Litho.**   *Perf. 14¹/₂x14*
1441 A485 45c multicolored   .65   .22
1442 A485 45c multicolored   .65   .22
1443 A485 45c multicolored   .65   .22
1444 A485 45c multicolored   .65   .22
1445 A485 45c multicolored   .65   .22
a.   Strip of 5, #1441-1445   3.25   1.10

Self-Adhesive
Die Cut Perf. 11¹/₂
1446 A485 45c like #1441   .65   .22
1447 A485 45c like #1442   .65   .22
1448 A485 45c like #1443   .65   .22
1449 A485 45c like #1444   .65   .22
1450 A485 45c like #1445   .65   .22
a.   Strip of 5, #1446-1450   3.25
b.   Booklet pane, 2 each #1446-1450   6.50

Motion Pictures, cent.
By its nature No. 1450b constitutes a complete booklet. The peelable backing serves as a booklet cover.

1995, July 13   **Litho.**   *Perf. 14¹/₂x14*
People with Disabilities: No. 1451a, Person flying kite from wheelchair. b, Blind person playing violin, guide dog.
1451   Pair   1.25   .42
a.-b.   A486 45c any single   .60   .20

Famous Australians from World War II
Type of 1995
1995, Aug. 10   **Litho.**   *Perf. 14¹/₂x14*
1452 A483 45c Leon Goldsworthy   .65   .22
1453 A483 45c Len Waters   .65   .22
1454 A483 45c Ellen Savage   .65   .22
1455 A483 45c Percy Collins   .65   .22
a.   Block of 4, #1452-1455   2.60   .90

Peace Types of 1946
Perf. 14x14¹/₂, 14¹/₂x14
1995, Aug. 10   **Engr.**
1456 A43   45c red brown   .65   .22
1457 A45   45c dark green   .65   .22
1458 A44 $1.50 dark blue   2.25   .75
    Nos. 1456-1458 (3)   3.55   1.19

End of World War II, 50th anniv.

Wildlife
A487

Designs: a, Koalas b, Pandas.

1995, Sept. 1 Litho. *Perf. 14*
1459 Pair 1.30 .40
a.-b. A487 45c any single .65 .20
c. Souv. sheet #1459a, perf. 11x11½ .65 .65
d. Souv. sheet #1459b, perf. 11x11½ .65 .65

See People's Republic of China Nos. 2597-2598.

Australian Medical Discoveries A488

Designs: No. 1461a, Joseph Slattery, Thomas Lyle, Walter Filmer, x-ray pioneers. No. 1461b, Jean Macnamara, Macfarlane Burnet, viruses and immunology. No. 1461C, Fred Hollows, eye care, vert. $2.50, Howard Florey, co-discoverer of penicillin, vert.

Perf. 14x14½, 14½x14
1995, Sept. 7
1461 Pair 1.30 .40
a.-b. A488 45c any single .65 .20
1461C A488 45c multicolored .65 .20
1461D A488 $2.50 multicolored 3.75 1.25
Nos. 1461-1461D (3) 5.70 1.85

No. 1461D exists in sheetlets of 10.

The World Down Under A489

Designs: Nos. 1462a, 1465a, Flatback turtle. Nos. 1462b, 1465b, Flame angelfish, nudibranch. Nos. 1463a, 1465c, Potato cod, giant maori wrasse. Nos. 1463b, 1465d, Giant trevally. Nos. 1464a, 1465e, Black marlin. Nos. 1464b, 1465f, Mako & tiger sharks.

1995, Oct. 3 Litho. *Perf. 14x14½*
1462 Pair 1.30 .40
a.-b. A489 45c any single .65 .20
1463 Pair 1.30 .40
a.-b. A489 45c any single .65 .20
1464 Pair 1.30 .40
a.-b. A489 45c any single .65 .20
Nos. 1462-1464 (3) 3.90 1.20

Miniature Sheet of 6
1465 A489 45c #a.-f. 4.00 1.30
g. Ovptd. in sheet margin 4.00
h. Ovptd. in sheet margin 4.00
i. Ovptd. in sheet margin 4.00
j. Ovptd. in sheet margin 4.00
k. Ovptd. in sheet margin 4.00

Nos. 1462-1464 have pale blue border on three sides. No. 1465 is a continuous design and does not have the pale border. Fish on No. 1465 are printed with additional phosphor ink producing a glow-in-the-dark effect under ultraviolet light.

Overprints in gold in sheet margin of No. 1465 include show emblems and text:

No. 1465g: "ADELAIDE / STAMP AND / COLLECTIBLES / FAIR / 14/10/95 - / 15/10/95."

No. 1465h: "SYDNEY / CENTREPOINT 95 / STAMPSHOW."

No. 1465i: "Brisbane Stamp Show / 20-22 October 1995."

No. 1465j: "Melbourne Stamp & Coin Fair / 27-29 October 1995."

No. 1465k: "Swanpex WA / 28-29 October 1995."

Booklet Stamps
Self-Adhesive
Die Cut Perf. 11½
1466 A489 45c like #1462a .65 .20
1467 A489 45c like #1462b .65 .20
1468 A489 45c like #1463a .65 .20
1469 A489 45c like #1463b .65 .20
1470 A489 45c like #1464a .65 .20
1471 A489 45c like #1464b .65 .20
a. Booklet pane, #1470-1471, 2 each #1466-1469 6.50
b. Strip of 6, #1466-1471 4.00

By its nature, No. 1471a constitutes a complete booklet. The peelable backing serves as a booklet cover.

Christmas — A490

Stained glass windows, Our Lady Help of Christians Church, Melbourne: 40c, Madonna and Child. 45c, Angel carrying banner. $1, Three rejoicing angels.

1995, Nov. 1 Litho. *Perf. 14½x14*
1472 A490 40c multicolored .60 .30
1473 A490 45c multicolored .65 .30
1474 A490 $1 multicolored 1.50 .75
Nos. 1472-1474 (3) 2.75 1.35

Booklet Stamp
Self-Adhesive
Die Cut Perf. 11½
1475 A490 40c multicolored .60 .30
a. Booklet pane of 20 12.00

Madonna and Child on No. 1475 are printed with additional phosphor ink giving parts of the stamp a rough texture.

By its nature, No. 1475a constitutes a complete booklet. The peelable backing serves as a booklet cover, which also contains 20 labels. The complete booklet is available with backing showing two different advertisements.

Australia Day Type of 1994

Paintings by Australian women: 45c, West Australian Banksia, by Margaret Preston, vert. 85c, The Babe is Wise, by Lina Bryans, vert. $1, The Bridge in Curve, by Grace Cossington Smith. $1.20, Beach Umbrellas, by Vida Lahey.

Perf. 14x14½, 14½x14
1996, Jan. 16 Litho.
1476 A463 45c multicolored .65 .20
1477 A463 85c multicolored 1.25 .40
1478 A463 $1 multicolored 1.50 .50
1479 A463 $1.20 multicolored 1.75 .60
Nos. 1476-1479 (4) 5.15 1.70

Heart and Roses A491

1996, Jan. 30 *Perf. 14x14½*
1480 A491 45c gold & multi .65 .20

Australia new issues through the April 1996 issue of the Scott Stamp Monthly appear here.

AIR POST STAMPS

Airplane over Bush Lands — AP1

Unwmk.
1929, May 20 Engr. *Perf. 11*
C1 AP1 3p deep green 7.50 3.00
Never hinged 12.50
a. Booklet pane of 4 ('30) 125.00

Kingsford-Smith Type of 1931

1931, Mar. 19
C2 A8 6p gray violet 7.50 7.50
Never hinged 12.50

AP3

1931, Nov. 4
C3 AP3 6p olive brown 15.00 9.00
Never hinged 22.50

For overprint see No. CO1.

Mercury and Hemispheres AP4

1934, Dec. 1 *Perf. 11*
C4 AP4 1sh6p violet brown 30.00 1.75
Never hinged 75.00

Perf. 13x13½
1937, Oct. 22 Wmk. 228
C5 AP4 1sh6p violet brown 7.50 .25
Never hinged 12.50

Catalogue values for unused stamps in this section, from this point to the end of the section, are for Never Hinged items.

Mercury and Globe — AP5

1949, Sept. 1 *Perf. 14½*
C6 AP5 1sh6p sepia 1.75 .15

1956, Dec. 6 Unwmk.
C7 AP5 1sh6p sepia 16.00 .85

Super-Constellation over Globe — AP6

1958, Jan. 6 *Perf. 14½x14*
C8 AP6 2sh dark violet blue 2.50 1.75

Inauguration of Australian "Round the World" air service.

AIR POST OFFICIAL STAMP

No. C3 Overprinted **OS**

Perf. 11, 11½
1931, Nov. 17 Unwmk.
CO1 AP3 6p olive brown 25.00 *30.00*
Never hinged 40.00

Issued primarily for official use, but to prevent speculation, a quantity was issued for public distribution.

POSTAGE DUE STAMPS

Very fine examples of Nos. J1-J38 will have perforations touching the design on one or more sides due to the narrow spacing of the stamps on the plates. Stamps with perfs clear of the design on all four sides are scarce and will command higher prices.

D1

D2

1902 Typo. Wmk. 55 *Perf. 11½, 12*
J1 D1 ½p emerald 8.25 9.50
J2 D1 1p emerald 16.00 6.50
a. Perf. 11 140.00 45.00
J3 D1 2p emerald 20.00 7.75
J4 D1 3p emerald 30.00 10.00
J5 D1 4p emerald 35.00 10.00
J6 D1 6p emerald 45.00 19.00
J7 D1 8p emerald 125.00 110.00
J8 D1 5sh emerald 250.00 82.50
Nos. J1-J8 (8) 529.25 255.25

The 1p, 2p and 4p, type D1, exist also in perforations compounding 11 with 11½ & 12.

Perf. 11½, 12, 11 and 11 Compound with 11½, 12
1902-04
J9 D2 ½p emerald 7.25 8.25
a. Perf. 11 82.50 65.00
J10 D2 1p emerald 4.50 2.75
a. Perf. 11 110.00 37.50
J11 D2 2p emerald 8.75 3.50
J12 D2 3p emerald 45.00 8.75
J13 D2 4p emerald 45.00 6.00
J14 D2 5p emerald 50.00 16.00
a. Perf. 11 125.00 32.50
J15 D2 6p emerald 72.50 18.00
J16 D2 8p emerald 110.00 40.00
J17 D2 10p emerald 80.00 10.00
J18 D2 1sh emerald 52.50 14.00
a. Perf. 11 175.00 45.00
J19 D2 2sh emerald 72.50 25.00
J20 D2 5sh emerald 225.00 22.50
a. Perf. 11 375.00 150.00
J21 D2 10sh emerald *2,000. 1,050.*
J22 D2 20sh emerald *3,500. 1,900.*
Nos. J9-J20 (12) 773.00 174.75

Perf. 11½, 12 Compound with 11
1906 Wmk. 12
J23 D2 ½p emerald 14.00 10.00
J24 D2 1p emerald 30.00 5.50
a. Perf. 11 165.00 7.50
J25 D2 2p emerald 50.00 10.00
J26 D2 3p emerald 375.00 300.00
J27 D2 4p emerald 77.50 27.50
a. Perf. 11 300.00 110.00
J28 D2 6p emerald 140.00 22.50
Nos. J23-J28 (6) 686.50 375.50

1907 Wmk. 13
J29 D2 ½p emerald 45.00 45.00
J30 D2 1p emerald 72.50 45.00
J31 D2 2p emerald 165.00 100.00
J32 D2 4p emerald 225.00 125.00
J33 D2 6p emerald 325.00 140.00
Nos. J29-J33 (5) 832.50 455.00

D3

D4

1908-09 Wmk. 12
J34 D3 1sh emer ('09) 125.00 16.00
J35 D3 2sh emerald *1,100. 500.00*
J36 D3 5sh emerald 225.00 52.50
J37 D3 10sh emerald *1,900. 775.00*
J38 D3 20sh emerald *5,250. 2,250.*

Perf. 11, 12x12½, 12½, 14
1909 Wmk. 13
J39 D4 ½p green & car 8.75 3.50
J40 D4 1p green & car 11.00 1.65
J41 D4 2p green & car 14.00 1.90
J42 D4 3p green & car 22.50 6.50
J43 D4 4p green & car 25.00 3.75
J44 D4 6p green & car 22.50 3.50
J45 D4 1sh green & car 22.50 2.75
J46 D4 2sh green & car 82.50 14.00
J47 D4 5sh green & car 82.50 14.00
J48 D4 10sh green & car 350.00 300.00
J49 D4 £1 green & car 550.00 325.00
Nos. J39-J49 (11) 1,191. 676.55

1922-25 Wmk. 10 *Perf. 14, 11*
J50 D4 ½p grn & car ('23) 6.50 1.75
J51 D4 1p green & car 6.50 1.90
J52 D4 1½p yellow green & rose ('25) 3.75 3.25
J53 D4 2p green & car 8.00 3.75
J54 D4 3p green & car 15.00 2.75
J55 D4 4p green & car 19.00 2.25
J56 D4 6p green & car 22.50 13.00
Nos. J50-J56 (7) 81.25 28.65

1931-37 Wmk. 228 *Perf. 11, 14*
J57 D4 ½p yel green & rose ('34) 10.00 9.00
J58 D4 1p yel grn & rose 4.00 .75
J59 D4 2p yel grn & rose 4.00 .75
J60 D4 3p yel green & rose ('37) 125.00 42.50
J61 D4 4p yel green & rose ('34) 20.00 2.00
J62 D4 6p yel green & rose ('36) 300.00 300.00
J63 D4 1sh yel green & rose ('34) 50.00 17.50
Nos. J57-J63 (7) 513.00 372.50

D5

Engraved; Value Typo.
1938 *Perf. 14½x14*
J64 D5 ½p green & car .75 1.25
J65 D5 1p green & car 5.00 .50
J66 D5 2p green & car 4.50 .50
J67 D5 3p green & car 15.00 3.50
J68 D5 4p green & car 4.50 .25

J69 D5	6p green & car		45.00	17.50
J70 D5	1sh green & car		20.00	7.50
	Nos. J64-J70 (7)		94.75	31.00

Catalogue values for unused stamps in this section, from this point to the end of the section, are for Never Hinged items.

Type of 1938
Value Tablet Redrawn

Original

Redrawn

Pence denominations: "D" has melon-shaped center in redrawn tablet. The redrawn 3p differs slightly, having semi-melon-shaped "D" center, with vertical white stroke half filling it.

1sh. 1938: Numeral "1" narrow, with six background lines above.

1sh. 1947: Numeral broader, showing more white space around dotted central ornament. Three lines above.

1946-57 **Wmk. 228**

J71	D5	½p grn & car ('56)	2.50	1.40
J72	D5	1p grn & car ('47)	1.25	.25
J73	D5	2p green & car	.75	1.00
J74	D5	3p green & car	4.00	.35
J75	D5	4p grn & car ('52)	5.00	.50
J76	D5	5p grn & car ('48)	7.50	1.25
J77	D5	6p grn & car ('47)	7.50	.65
J78	D5	7p grn & car ('53)	5.00	3.00
J79	D5	8p grn & car ('57)	12.50	11.50
J80	D5	1sh grn & car ('47)	12.50	1.25
		Nos. J71-J80 (10)	58.50	21.15

1953-54

White Tablet, Carmine Numeral

J81	D5	1sh grn & car ('54)	9.00	5.00
J82	D5	2sh green & car	12.50	10.00
J83	D5	5sh green & car	17.50	2.50
		Nos. J81-J83 (3)	39.00	17.50

Issued: 2sh, 5sh, Aug. 26; 1sh, Feb. 17.

Redrawn Type of 1947-57

Two Types of Some Pence Values:

Type I - Background lines touch numeral, "D" and period.

Type II - Lines do not touch numeral, etc.

Second engraving of 1sh has sharper and thicker lines.

Engr.; Value Typo.

1958-60 **Unwmk.** ***Perf. 14½x14***

J86	D5	½p grn & car (II)	2.50	1.10
J87	D5	1p grn & car (II)	2.50	.40
a.		Type I	3.75	.95
J88	D5	3p grn & car (II)	2.50	.75
J89	D5	4p grn & car (I)	5.00	4.00
a.		Type II ('59)	12.00	3.00
J90	D5	5p grn & car (I)	11.00	6.00
a.		Type II ('59)	70.00	22.50
J91	D5	6p grn & car (II)	6.50	1.75
J92	D5	8p grn & car (II)	10.00	15.00
J93	D5	10p grn & car (II)	7.50	3.25

White Tablet, Carmine Numeral

J94	D5	1sh green & car	8.50	2.50
a.		2nd redrawing ('60)	9.00	.60
J95	D5	2sh grn & car	26.00	5.50
		Nos. J86-J95 (10)	82.00	40.25

Issued: 1sh, 9/8/58; 10p, 12/9/59; 2sh, 3/8/60; 3p, 6p, 5/25/60; others, 2/27/58.

MILITARY STAMPS

Nos. 166, 191, 183A, 173, 175, 206 and 177 Overprinted in Black:

B.C.O.F.
JAPAN
1946
a

B.C.O.F.
JAPAN
1946
b

B. C. O. F.
JAPAN
1946
c

Perf. 14½x14, 15x14, 11½, 13½x13

1946-47 **Wmk. 228**

M1	A24(a)	½p orange	2.75	2.75
M2	A36(b)	1p brown vio	2.25	2.25
a.		Blue overprint	100.00	67.50
M3	A27(b)	3p dk vio brn	2.00	.75
M4	A30(a)	6p brn violet	5.00	5.00
M5	A16(a)	1sh gray green	7.50	7.50
M6	A1 (c)	2sh dk red brn	22.50	22.50
M7	A32(c)	5sh dl red brn	110.00	100.00
		Nos. M1-M7 (7)	152.00	140.75

"B.C.O.F." stands for "British Commonwealth Occupation Force."

Issued: #M1-M3, 10/11/46; #M4-M7, 5/8/47.

OFFICIAL STAMPS

Perforated Initials

In 1913-31, postage stamps were perforated "OS" for federal official use. This catalogue does not list varieties with perforated initials.

Overprinted Official stamps are comparatively more difficult to find well centered than the basic issues on which they are printed. This is because poorly centered sheets were purposely chosen to be overprinted.

Overprinted **OS**

On Regular Issue of 1931

1931, May 4 **Unwmk.** ***Perf. 11, 11½***

O1	A8	2p dull red	60.00	22.50
O2	A8	3p blue	175.00	35.00

These stamps were issued primarily for official use but to prevent speculation a quantity was issued for public distribution.

Counterfeit overprints exist.

On Regular Issues of 1928-32

1932 **Wmk. 203** ***Perf. 13½x12½***

O3	A4	2p red (II)	10.00	.90
O4	A4	4p olive bister	30.00	6.00

Perf. 11½, 12

O5	A1	6p brown	67.50	35.00

1932-33 **Wmk. 228** ***Perf. 13½x12½***

O6	A4	½p orange	6.00	1.25
a.		Inverted overprint	3,000.	1,500.
O7	A4	1p green (I)	2.00	.75
O8	A4	2p red (II)	5.00	.60
a.		Inverted overprint		2,250.
O9	A4	3p ultra (II) ('33)	14.00	7.50
O10	A4	5p brown buff	42.50	21.00

Perf. 11½, 12

O11	A1	6p yellow brown	35.00	25.00
		Nos. O6-O11 (6)	104.50	56.10

1932 **Unwmk.** ***Perf. 11, 11½***

O12	A9	2p red	5.50	4.50
O13	A9	3p blue	18.00	18.00
O14	A16	1sh gray green	55.00	32.50
		Nos. O12-O14 (3)	78.50	55.00

AUSTRALIAN ANTARCTIC TERRITORY

Catalogue values for all unused stamps in this section are for Never Hinged items.

All stamps are also valid for postage in Australia.

Edgeworth David, Douglas Mawson and A.F. McKay (1908-09 South Pole Expedition) — A1

Australian Explorers and Map of Antarctica — A2

Designs: 8p, Loading weasel (snow truck). 1sh, Dog team and iceberg, vert. 2sh3p, Emperor penguins and map, vert.

Perf. 14½, 14½x14, 14x14½

1957-59 **Engr.** **Unwmk.**

L1	A1	5p brown	.50	.15
L2	A2	8p dark blue	2.25	1.25
L3	A2	1sh dark green	4.00	2.10
L4	A2	2sh ultra ('57)	3.50	.32
L5	A2	2sh3p green	12.00	6.00
		Nos. L1-L5 (5)	22.25	9.82

Nos. L1 and L2 were printed as 4p and 7p stamps and surcharged typographically in black and dark blue before issuance.

Sizes of stamps: No. L2, 34x21mm; Nos. L3, L5, 21x34mm; No. L4, 43½x25½mm.

1961, July 5 ***Perf. 14½***

L6	A1	5p dark blue	1.10	.18

The denomination on No. L6 is not within a typographed circle, but is part of the engraved design.

Sir Douglas Mawson
A3

Lookout and Iceberg
A4

1961, Oct. 18

L7	A3	5p dark green	.70	.18

50th anniv. of the 1911-14 Australian Antarctic Expedition.

Perf. 13½x13, 13x13½

1966-68 **Photo.** **Unwmk.**

Designs: 1c, Aurora australis and camera dome. 2c, Banding penguins. 5c, Branding of elephant seals. 7c, Measuring snow strata. 10c, Wind gauges. 15c, Weather balloon. 20c, Helicopter. 25c, Radio operator. 50c, Ice compression tests. $1, "Mock sun" (parahelion) and dogs. 20c, 25c, 50c and $1 horizontal.

L8	A4	1c multicolored	.60	.30
L9	A4	2c multicolored	1.10	.45
L10	A4	4c multicolored	1.25	.45
L11	A4	5c multicolored	2.00	1.25
L12	A4	7c multicolored	.60	.35
L13	A4	10c multicolored	2.75	.90
L14	A4	15c multicolored	3.75	3.25
L15	A4	20c multicolored	7.50	4.00
L16	A4	25c multicolored	4.25	4.25
L17	A4	50c multicolored	22.50	8.00
L18	A4	$1 multicolored	30.00	18.00
		Nos. L8-L18 (11)	76.30	41.20

Issue dates: 5c, Sept. 25, 1968. Others, Sept. 28, 1966.

Nos. L8-L18 are on phosphorescent helecon paper. Fluorescent orange is one of the colors used in printing the 10c, 15c, 20c and 50c.

Sastrugi Snow Formation — A5

1971, June 23 **Photo.** ***Perf. 13x13½***

L19	A5	6c shown	.55	.55
L20	A5	30c Pancake ice	6.00	6.00

10th anniv. of the Antarctic Treaty pledging peaceful uses of and scientific cooperation in Antarctica.

Capt. Cook, Sextant, Azimuth Compass — A6

Design: 35c, Chart of Cook's circumnavigation of Antarctica, and "Resolution."

1972, Sept. 13 **Photo.** ***Perf. 13x13½***

L21	A6	7c bister & multi	2.00	.95
L22	A6	35c buff & multi	5.50	6.00

Bicentenary of Capt. James Cook's circumnavigation of Antarctica.

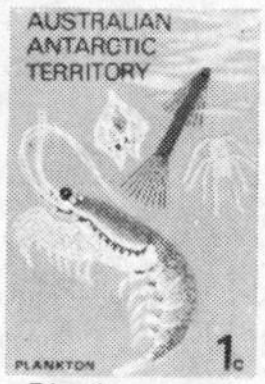

Plankton and Krill Shrimp — A7

Mawson's D.H. Gipsy Moth, 1931 — A8

Food Chain (Essential for Survival): 7c, Adelie penguin feeding on krill shrimp. 9c, Leopard seal pursuing fish, horiz. 10c, Killer whale hunting seals, horiz. 20c, Wandering albatross, horiz. $1, Sperm whale attacking giant squid.

Explorers' Aircraft: 8c, Rymill's DH Fox Moth returning to Barry Island. 25c, Hubert Wilkins Lockheed Vega, horiz. 30c, Lincoln Ellsworth's Northrop Gamma. 35c, Lars Christensen's Avro Avian and Framnes Mountains, horiz. 50c, Richard Byrd's Ford Tri-Motor dropping US flag over South Pole.

Perf. 13½x13, 13x13½

1973, Aug. 15

L23	A7	1c multicolored	.15	.15
L24	A8	5c multicolored	.15	.16
L25	A7	7c multicolored	1.40	.60
L26	A8	8c multicolored	.28	.28
L27	A7	9c multicolored	.25	.25
L28	A7	10c multicolored	3.00	1.25
L29	A7	20c multicolored	.35	.35
L30	A8	25c multicolored	.35	.35
L31	A8	30c multicolored	.35	.35
L32	A8	35c multicolored	.32	.45
L33	A8	50c multicolored	1.25	.85
L34	A7	$1 multicolored	2.25	.85
		Nos. L23-L34 (12)	10.10	5.89

Adm. Byrd, Plane, Mountains
A9

Design: 20c, Adm. Byrd, Floyd Bennett tri-motored plane, map of Antarctica.

1979, June 20 **Litho.** ***Perf. 15½***

L35	A9	20c multicolored	.48	.48
L36	A9	55c multicolored	1.00	.95

50th anniv. of first flight over South Pole by Richard Byrd (1888-1957).

"S.Y. Nimrod"
A10

2c, 5c, 22c, 25c, 40c, 55c, $1 are vertical. No. L41 actually pictures the S.S. Morning.

Perf. 13½x13, 13x13½

1974-81 **Litho.**

L37	A10	1c S.Y. Aurora	.15	.13
L38	A10	2c R.Y. Penola	.15	.15
L39	A10	5c M.V. Thala Dan	.15	.15
L40	A10	10c H.M.S. Challenger	.15	.15
L41	A10	15c shown	.95	.95
L42	A10	15c S.Y. Nimrod, stern view	.25	.22
L43	A10	20c R.R.S. Discovery II	.32	.30
L44	A10	22c R.Y.S. Terra Nova	.28	.28
L45	A10	25c S.S. Endurance	.40	.35
L46	A10	30c S.S. Fram	.50	.50
L47	A10	35c M.S. Nella Dan	.45	.45
L48	A10	40c M.S. Kista Dan	.50	.50
L49	A10	45c L'Astrolabe	.55	.55
L50	A10	50c S.S. Norvegia	.70	.70
L51	A10	55c S.Y. Discovery	.80	.80
L52	A10	$1 H.M.S. Resolution	1.25	.65
		Nos. L37-L52 (16)	7.55	6.85

A11

A12

1982, May 5   Litho.   Perf. 14x13½

L53	A11	27c Mawson, landscape	.35 .35
L54	A11	75c Mawson, map	1.25 1.25

Sir Douglas Mawson (1882-1958), explorer.

1983, Apr. 6   Litho.   Perf. 14½

Local Wildlife: a, Light-mantled sooty albatross. b, Macquarie Isld. shags. c, Elephant seals. d, Royal penguins. e, Antarctic prions.

L55		Strip of 5, multi	2.25 2.25
a.-e.	A12	27c, any single	.45 .45

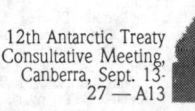

12th Antarctic Treaty Consultative Meeting, Canberra, Sept. 13-27 — A13

1983, Sept. 7   Litho.   Perf. 14½

L56	A13	27c multicolored	.42 .42

South Magnetic Pole Expedition, 75th Anniv. — A14

1984, Jan. 16

L57	A14	30c Prismatic compass	.40 .40
L58	A14	85c Aneroid barometer	1.25 1.25

Dog Team, Mawson Station — A15

1984-87   Litho.   Perf. 14½x15

L60	A15	2c Summer afternoon	.15 .15
L61	A15	5c shown	.15 .15
L62	A15	10c Evening	.15 .15
L63	A15	15c Prince Charles Mts.	.22 .22
L64	A15	20c Morning	.28 .28
L65	A15	25c Sea ice, iceberg	.40 .40
L66	A15	30c Mt. Coates	.48 .48
L67	A15	33c Iceberg Alley, Mawson	.48 .48
L68	A15	36c Winter evening	.50 .50
L69	A15	45c Brash ice, vert.	.65 .65
L70	A15	60c Midwinter shadows	.85 .85
L71	A15	75c Coastline	1.20 1.20
L72	A15	85c Landing field	1.35 1.35
L73	A15	90c Pancake ice, vert.	1.30 1.30
L74	A15	$1 Emperor penguins, Auster Rookery	1.45 1.45
		Nos. L60-L74 (15)	9.61 9.61

Issue dates: 5c, 25c, 30c, 75c, 85c, July 18, 1984. 15c, 33c, 45c, 90c, $1, Aug. 7, 1985, 2c, 10c, 20c, 36c, 60c, Mar. 11, 1987.

A16   A17

1986, Sept. 17   Litho.   Perf. 14x13½

L75	A16	36c multicolored	.55 .55

Antarctic Treaty, 25th anniv.

1988, July 20   Litho.   Perf. 13

Environment, Conservation and Technology: a, Hour-glass dolphins and the *Nella Dan.* b, Emperor penguins and Davis Station. c, Crabeater seal and helicopters. d, Adelie penguins and snow-ice transport vehicle. e, Gray-headed albatross and photographer.

L76		Strip of 5	3.10 1.20
a.-e.	A17	37c any single	.62 .20

Paintings by Sir Sidney Nolan (b. 1917) — A18

1989, June 14   Litho.   Perf. 14x13½

L77	A18	39c Antarctica	.65 .65
L78	A18	39c Iceberg Alley	.65 .65
L79	A18	60c Glacial Flow	1.00 1.00
L80	A18	80c Frozen Sea	1.35 1.35
		Nos. L77-L80 (4)	3.65 3.65

Aurora Australis A19

Design: $1.20, Research ship Aurora Australis.

1991, June 20   Litho.   Perf. 14½

L81	A19	43c multicolored	.68 .22
L82	A19	$1.20 multicolored	1.85 .62

Antarctic Treaty, 30th anniv. (No. L81).

Regional Wildlife A20

Perf. 14x14½, 14½x14

1992-93   Litho.

L83	A20	45c Adelie penguin	.65 .22
L84	A20	75c Elephant seal	1.10 .38
L85	A20	85c Northern giant petrel	1.25 .40
L86	A20	95c Weddell seal	1.40 .45
L86A	A20	$1 Royal penguins	1.45 .48
L87	A20	$1.20 Emperor penguin, vert.	1.75 .58
L88	A20	$1.40 Fur seals	2.00 .70
L89	A20	$1.50 King penguins, vert.	2.20 .75
		Nos. L83-L89 (8)	11.80 3.96

Issued: $1, $1.40, $1.50, 1/14/93; others, 5/14/92.

The Last Huskies A21

1994, Jan. 13   Litho.   Perf. 14½

L90	A21	45c Dog up close, vert.	.65 .22
L91	A21	75c Sled team	1.10 .35
L92	A21	85c Dog seated, vert.	1.25 .42
L93	A21	$1.05 Three dogs	1.50 .50
		Nos. L90-L93 (4)	4.50 1.49

Whales & Dolphins A22

1995, June 15   Litho.   Perf. 14½

L94	A22	45c Humpback whale	.65 .22
L95	A22	45c Hourglass dolphin, vert.	.65 .22
L96	A22	45c Minke whale, vert.	.65 .22
a.		Pair, #L95-L96	1.30 .45
L97	A22	$1 Killer whale	1.40 .48
a.		Souvenir sheet of 4, #L94-L97	3.50 3.50
b.		As "a," ovptd.	3.50 3.50
		Nos. L94-L97 (4)	3.35 1.14

No. L97b is overprinted in gold in sheet margin with Singapore '95 emblem and: "Australia Post Exhibition Sheet No. 2," and, in both Chinese and English, with "Singapore 95 World Stamp Exhibition." Issued 9/1/95.

BAHRAIN

bä–'rān

LOCATION — An archipelago in the Persian Gulf, including the islands of Bahrain, Muharraq, Sitra, Nebi Saleh, Kasasifeh and Arad.
GOVT. — Independent sheikdom
AREA — 255 sq. mi.
POP. — 350,798 (1981)
CAPITAL — Manama

Bahrain was a British-protected territory until it became an independent state on August 15, 1971.

    12 Pies = 1 Anna
    16 Annas = 1 Rupee
    100 Naye Paise = 1 Rupee (1957)
    1000 Fils = 1 Dinar (1966)

> Catalogue values for unused stamps in this country are for Never Hinged items, beginning with Scott 62 in the regular postage section and Scott MR2 in the postal tax section.

Indian Postal Administration

Stamps of India, 1926-32, Overprinted in Black

BAHRAIN
a

Wmk. Multiple Stars (196)

1933, Aug. 10   Perf. 14

1	A46	3p gray	1.40 .15
2	A47	½a green	3.50 .70
3	A68	9p dark green	2.75 .70
4	A48	1a dark brown	4.25 1.65
5	A69	1a3p violet	3.00 .40
6	A60	2a vermilion	3.00 3.25
7	A51	3a blue	14.00 14.00
8	A70	3a6p deep blue	1.50 .60
9	A61	4a olive green	10.50 10.50
10	A54	8a red violet	3.25 1.00
11	A55	12a claret	4.25 1.65

Overprinted in Black
b   **BAHRAIN**

12	A56	1r green & brn	10.00 7.50
13	A56	2r brn org & car rose	30.00 25.00
14	A56	5r dk vio & ultra	80.00 80.00
		Nos. 1-14 (14)	171.40 147.10

Stamps of India, 1926-32, Overprinted Type "a" in Black

1934

15	A72	1a dark brown	2.75 .15
16	A51	3a car rose	3.25 .20
17	A52	4a olive green	4.50 .30
		Nos. 15-17 (3)	10.50 .65

India Nos. 138, 111, 111a Overprinted Type "a" in Black

1935-37   Perf. 13½x14, 14

18	A71	½a green	2.50 .15
19	A49	2a vermilion	17.00 2.00
a.		Small die ('37)	17.00 2.50

India Stamps of 1937 Overprinted Type "a" in Black

1938-41   Wmk. 196   Perf. 13½x14

20	A80	3p slate	1.50 .90
21	A80	½a brown	.15 .15
22	A80	9p green	.25 .20
23	A80	1a carmine	.25 .15
24	A81	2a scarlet	.65 .35
25	A81	3a yel grn ('41)	8.75 2.50
26	A81	3a6p ultra	1.00 2.00
28	A81	4a dk brn ('41)	40.00 30.00
30	A81	8a bl vio ('40)	50.00 35.00
31	A81	12a car lake ('40)	45.00 42.50

Overprinted Type "b" in Black

32	A82	1r brn & slate	1.90 .70
33	A82	2r dk brn & dk vio	12.00 2.50
34	A82	5r dp ultra & dk grn	35.00 13.00
35	A82	10r rose car & dk vio ('41)	60.00 18.00
36	A82	15r dk grn & dk brn ('41)	30.00 24.00
37	A82	25r dk vio & bl vio ('41)	75.00 57.50
		Nos. 20-37 (16)	361.45 229.45

India Stamps of 1941-43 Overprinted Type "a" in Black

1942-44   Wmk. 196   Perf. 13½x14

38	A83	3p slate	.20 .15
39	A83	½a rose vio ('44)	1.00 .15
40	A83	9p lt green ('43)	2.75 3.00
41	A83	1a car rose ('44)	1.00 .30
42	A84	1a3p bister ('43)	2.75 5.00
43	A84	1½a dk pur ('43)	1.75 .90
45	A84	2a scarlet ('43)	.90 .45
46	A84	3a violet ('43)	4.00 1.25
47	A84	3½a ultra	2.25 5.00
48	A85	4a chocolate	.60 .35
49	A85	6a peacock blue	4.00 2.75
50	A85	8a blue vio ('43)	.60 .60
51	A85	12a car lake	1.25 1.25
		Nos. 38-51 (13)	23.05 21.15
		Set, never hinged	45.00

British Postal Administration

See Oman (Muscat) for similar stamps with surcharge of new value only.

Great Britain Nos. 258 to 263, 243 and 248 Surcharged in Black

BAHRAIN

c   **½ ANNA**

1948-49   Wmk. 251   Perf. 14½x14

52	A101	½a on ½p green	.20 .20
53	A101	1a on 1p vermilion	.15 .15
54	A101	1½a on 1½p lt red brn	.15 .15
55	A101	2a on 2p lt orange	.25 .15
56	A101	2½a on 2½p ultra	.35 .35
57	A101	3a on 3p violet	.20 .15
58	A102	6a on 6p rose lilac	.20 .15
59	A103	1r on 1sh brown	1.25 .50

Great Britain Nos. 249A, 250 and 251A Surcharged in Black

BAHRAIN

2 RUPEES

	Wmk. 259		**Perf. 14**
60	A104	2r on 2sh6p yel grn	3.75 3.00
61	A104	5r on 5sh dull red	5.75 5.75
61A	A105	10r on 10sh ultra	32.50 27.50
		Nos. 52-61A (11)	44.75 38.05
		Set, never hinged	70.00

Surcharge bars at bottom on No. 61A.
Issued: 10r, 7/4/49; others, 4/1/48.

> Catalogue values for unused stamps in this section, from this point to the end of the section, are for Never Hinged items.

Silver Wedding Issue

Great Britain Nos. 267 and 268 Surcharged in Black

BAHRAIN   2½ ANNAS

Perf. 14½x14, 14x14½

1948, Apr. 26   Wmk. 251

62	A109	2½a on 2½p	.20 .20
63	A110	15r on £1	37.50 42.50

Three bars obliterate the original denomination on No. 63.

Olympic Issue

Great Britain Nos. 271 to 274 Surcharged "BAHRAIN" and New Value in Black

1948, July 29   Perf. 14½x14

64	A113	2½a on 2½p brt ultra	.20 .20
a.		Double surcharge	425.00 525.00
65	A114	3a on 3p dp vio	.30 .25
66	A115	6a on 6p red vio	.45 .40
67	A116	1r on 1sh dk brn	.90 .75
		Nos. 64-67 (4)	1.85 1.60

A square of dots obliterates the original denomination on No. 67.

UPU Issue
Great Britain Nos. 276 to 279 Surcharged "BAHRAIN," New Value and Square of Dots in Black

1949, Oct. 10 Photo. *Perf. 14½x14*

68 A117 2½a on 2½p brt ultra .30 .30
69 A118 3a on 3p brt vio .45 .35
70 A119 6a on 6p red vio .75 .65
71 A120 1r on 1sh brown 1.90 1.40
Nos. 68-71 (4) 3.40 2.70

Great Britain Nos. 280, 281, 283-285 Surcharged Type "c" in Black

1950-51 Wmk. 251

72 A101 ½a on ½p lt org .20 .20
73 A101 1a on 1p ultra .30 .30
74 A101 1½a on 1½p green .50 *1.25*
75 A101 2a on 2p lt red brn .30 .30
76 A101 2½a on 2½p ver .70 .70
77 A102 4a on 4p ultra .60 .50

BAHRAIN

2 RUPEES

Great Britain Nos. 286-288 Surcharged in Black

Wmk. 259 *Perf. 11x12*

78 A121 2r on 2sh6p green 15.00 5.75
79 A121 5r on 5sh dl red 12.50 8.00
80 A122 10r on 10sh ultra 24.00 17.50
Nos. 72-80 (9) 54.10 34.50

Longer bars, at lower right, on No. 80.
Issue dates: 4a, Nov. 2, 1950; others, May 3, 1951.

Stamps of Great Britain, 1952-54, Surcharged "BAHRAIN" and New Value in Black or Dark Blue

1952-54 Wmk. 298 *Perf. 14½x14*

81 A126 ½a on ½p red org ('53) .25 .25
a. "½" omitted 200.00 *225.00*
82 A126 1a on 1p ultra .25 .15
83 A126 1½a on 1½p grn .25 .25
84 A126 2a on 2p red brn .25 .25
85 A127 2½a on 2½p scar .55 .25
86 A127 3a on 3p dk pur (Dk Bl) .65 .25
87 A128 4a on 4p ultra 1.50 .75
88 A129 6a on 6p lil rose 1.25 .65
89 A132 12a on 1sh3p dk grn 4.00 1.50
90 A131 1r on 1sh6p dk bl 5.50 2.00
Nos. 81-90 (10) 14.45 6.30

Issue dates: Nos. 83, 85, Dec. 5. Nos. 81-82, 84, Aug. 31, 1953. Nos. 87, 89-90, Nov. 2, 1953. Nos. 86, 88, Jan. 18, 1954.

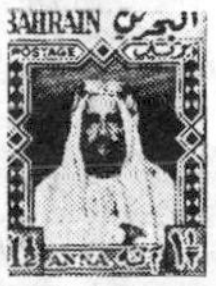

Six stamps of this design picturing Sheik Sulman bin Hamad Al Kalifah were for local use in 1953-57.
Six stamps of similar design (same sheik, "Bahrain" vertical at left) were issued in 1961 for local use.

Coronation Issue
Great Britain Nos. 313-316 Surcharged "BAHRAIN" and New Value in Black

Perf. 14½x14

1953, June 3 Wmk. 298

92 A134 2½a on 2½p scar 1.10 1.10
93 A135 4a on 4p brt ultra 1.75 1.75
94 A136 12a on 1sh3p dk grn 4.00 4.00
95 A137 1r on 1sh6p dk bl 5.25 5.25
Nos. 92-95 (4) 12.10 12.10

Squares of dots obliterate the original denominations on Nos. 94-95.

Great Britain Nos. 309-311 Surcharged "BAHRAIN" and New Value in Black

1955 Wmk. 308 Engr. *Perf. 11x12*

96 A133 2r on 2sh6p dk brn 3.00 1.25
97 A133 5r on 5sh crimson 9.50 4.00
98 A133 10r on 10sh brt ultra 20.00 6.50
Nos. 96-98 (3) 32.50 11.75

Three slightly different types of surcharge are found on the 2r; two on 5r and 10r.

Great Britain Nos. 317, 323, 325, 332-333 Surcharged "BAHRAIN" and New Value

Perf. 14½x14

1956-57 Wmk. 308 Photo.

99 A126 ½a on ½p red org .25 .20
100 A128 4a on 4p ultra 5.00 6.25
101 A129 6a on 6p lil rose .50 .40
102 A132 12a on 1sh3p dk green 6.25 12.00
103 A131 1r on 1sh6p dk bl ('57) 1.50 .75
Nos. 99-103 (5) 13.50 19.60

Great Britain Nos. 317-325, 328, 332 Surcharged "BAHRAIN" and New Value

1957, Apr. 1

104 A129 1np on 5p lt brown .15 .15
105 A126 3np on ½p red org .22 .15
106 A126 6np on 1p ultra .24 .15
107 A126 9np on 1½p green .24 .15
108 A126 12np on 2p red brn .30 .15
109 A127 15np on 2½p scar, type I .35 .15
a. Type II .38 .25
110 A127 20np on 3p dk pur .22 .15
111 A128 25np on 4p ultra .65 .35
112 A129 40np on 6p lil rose .65 .35
113 A130 50np on 9p dp ol grn 1.75 .70
114 A132 75np on 1sh3p dk grn 1.50 .55
Nos. 104-114 (11) 6.27
Set value 2.55

The arrangement of the surcharge varies on different values: there are three bars through value on No. 113.

Jubilee Jamboree Issue
Great Britain Nos. 334-336 Surcharged "BAHRAIN," New Value and Square of Dots in Black

Perf. 14½x14

1957, Aug. 1 Photo. Wmk. 308

115 A138 15np on 2½p scar .35 .35
116 A138 25np on 4p ultra .65 .40
117 A138 75np on 1sh3p dk grn .80 .80
Nos. 115-117 (3) 1.80 1.55

Great Britain No. 357 Surcharged "BAHRAIN/ NP 15 NP" in Black

1960 Wmk. 322 *Perf. 14½x14*

118 A127 15np on 2½p scar, type II 4.50 *7.25*

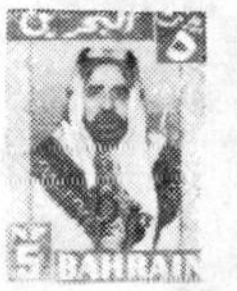

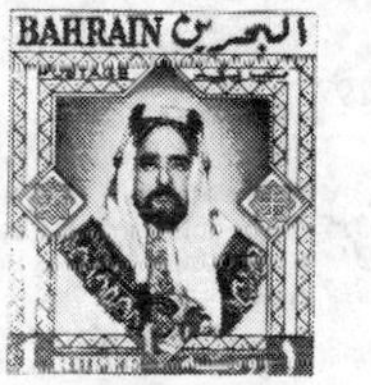

Sheik Sulman bin Hamad Al Khalifah
A1 A2

Perf. 14½x14

1960, July 1 Photo. Unwmk.

119 A1 5np lt ultra .15 .15
120 A1 15np orange .15 .15
121 A1 20np lt violet .20 .15
122 A1 30np olive bister .24 .15
123 A1 40np gray .30 .15
124 A1 50np emerald .32 .15
125 A1 75np red brown .60 .18

Engr.

Perf. 13x13½

126 A2 1r gray .90 .20
127 A2 2r carmine 1.75 .32
128 A2 5r ultra 4.50 1.75
129 A2 10r olive green 12.00 2.25
Nos. 119-129 (11) 21.11 5.60

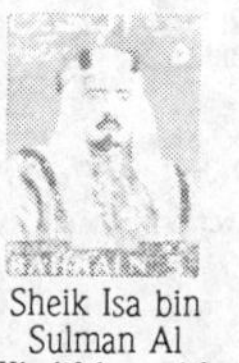

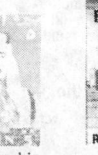

Sheik Isa bin Sulman Al Khalifah — A3

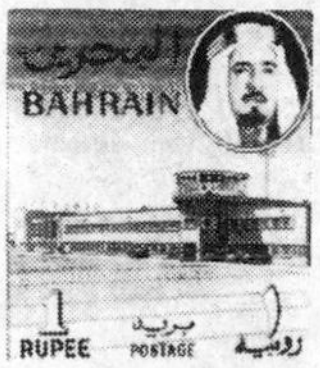

Bahrain Airport — A4

Designs: 5r, 10r, Deep water jetty.

1964, Feb. 22 Photo. *Perf. 14½x14*

130 A3 5np ultra .15 .15
131 A3 15np orange .15 .15
132 A3 20np brt purple .18 .15
133 A3 30np brown olive .24 .15
134 A3 40np slate .24 .15
135 A3 50np emerald .35 .15
136 A3 75np chestnut .60 .38

Engr.

Perf. 13½x13

137 A4 1r black 1.00 .22
138 A4 2r rose red 3.00 .85
139 A4 5r violet blue 7.00 2.25
140 A4 10r dull green 14.00 3.75
Nos. 130-140 (11) 26.91 8.35

Bahrain Postal Administration

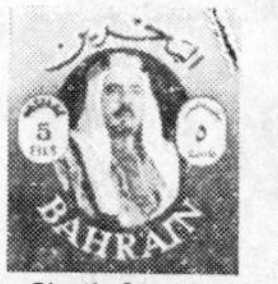

Sheik Isa bin Sulman Al Khalifah — A5

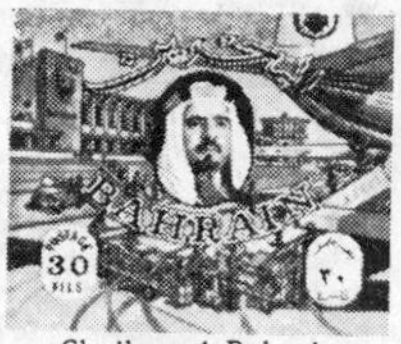

Sheik and Bahrain International Airport — A6

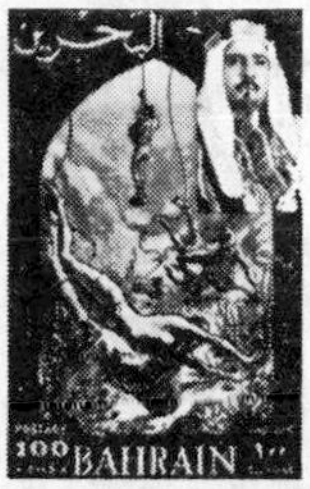

Pearl Divers — A7

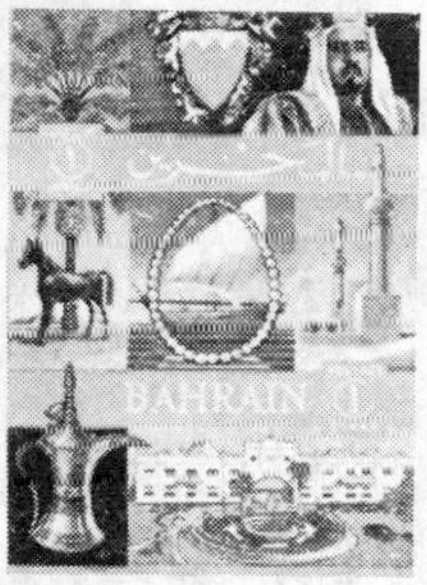

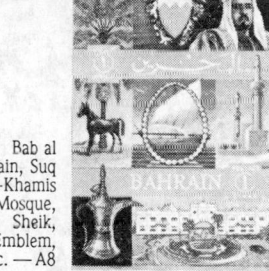

Bab al Bahrain, Suq Al-Khamis Mosque, Sheik, Emblem, etc. — A8

Designs: 50f, 75f, Pier, Mina Sulman harbor. 200f, Falcon and horse race. 500f, "Hospitality," pouring coffee and Sheik's Palace.

Perf. 14½x14

1966, Jan. 1 Photo. Unwmk.

141 A5 5f green .15 .15
142 A5 10f dark red .15 .15
143 A5 15f ultra .15 .15
144 A5 20f magenta .20 .15

Perf. 13½x14

145 A6 30f green & black .28 .16
146 A6 40f blue & black .32 .20
147 A6 50f dp car rose & blk .42 .25
148 A6 75f violet & black .60 .35

Perf. 14½x14

149 A7 100f dk blue & yel 1.00 .50
150 A7 200f dk green & org 3.00 1.00
151 A7 300f red brown & yel 6.25 2.50
152 A8 1d multicolored 12.50 5.00
Nos. 141-152 (12) 25.02 10.56

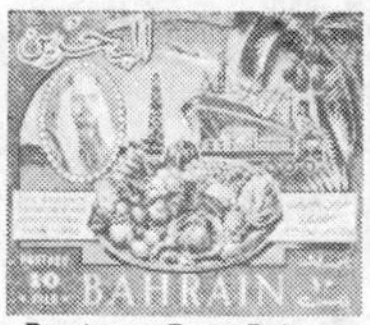

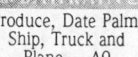

Produce, Date Palm, Ship, Truck and Plane — A9

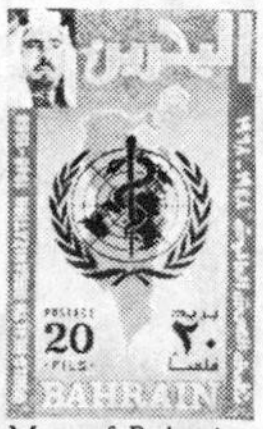

Map of Bahrain and WHO Emblem — A10

1966, Mar. 28 Litho. *Perf. 13x13½*

153 A9 10f red & blue green .32 .32
154 A9 20f green & vio .65 .65
155 A9 40f olive bis & lt bl 1.25 1.25
156 A9 200f vio blue & pink 6.25 6.25
Nos. 153-156 (4) 8.47 8.47

The 6th Bahrain Trade Fair and Agricultural Show.

1968, June Unwmk. *Perf. 13½x14*

157 A10 20f gray & black .55 .55
158 A10 40f blue grn & black 1.40 1.40
159 A10 150f dp rose & black 5.50 5.50
Nos. 157-159 (3) 7.45 7.45

20th anniv. of the WHO.

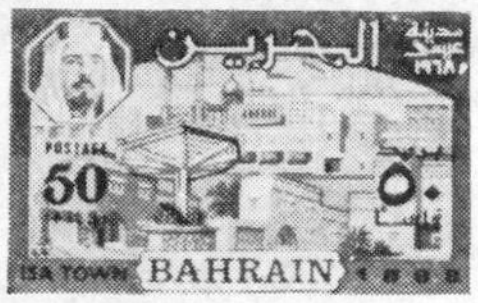

Isa Town A11

1968, Nov. 18 Litho. *Perf. 14½*

160 A11 50f shown 1.65 1.65
161 A11 80f Market 2.50 2.50
162 A11 120f Stadium 4.25 4.25
163 A11 150f Mosque 6.75 6.75
Nos. 160-163 (4) 15.15 15.15

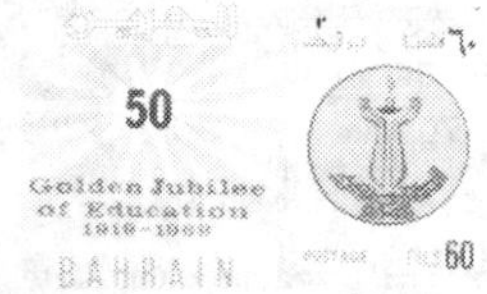

Education Symbol A12

1969, Apr. Litho. *Perf. 13*

164 A12 40f multicolored 1.25 1.25
165 A12 60f multicolored 2.00 2.00
166 A12 150f multicolored 4.25 4.25
Nos. 164-166 (3) 7.50 7.50

50th anniversary of education in Bahrain.

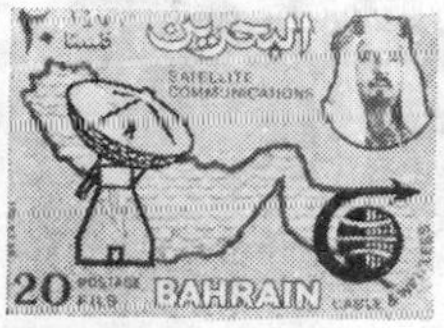

Map of Arabian Gulf, Radar and Emblem A13

Designs: 40f, 150f, Radar installation and emblem of Cable & Wireless Ltd., vert.

Perf. 14x13½, 13½x14

1969, July 14 Litho.

167 A13 20f lt green & multi 1.00 1.00
168 A13 40f vio blue & multi 2.25 2.25
169 A13 100f ocher & multi 5.25 5.25
170 A13 150f rose lilac & multi 9.00 9.00
Nos. 167-170 (4) 17.50 17.50

Opening of the satellite earth station (connected through the Indian Ocean satellite Intelsat III) at Ras Abu Jarjur, July 14.

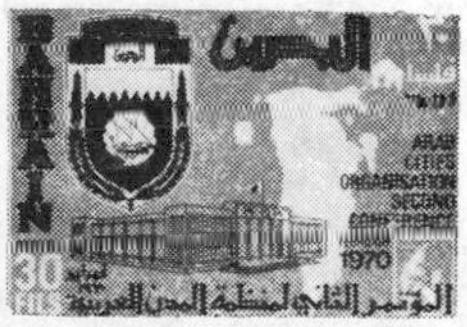

Municipal Building, Arms and Map of Bahrain A14

1970, Feb. 23 Litho. *Perf. 12x12½*

171 A14 30f blue & multi 2.00 2.00
172 A14 150f multicolored 7.00 7.00

2nd Conf. of the Arab Cities' Org.

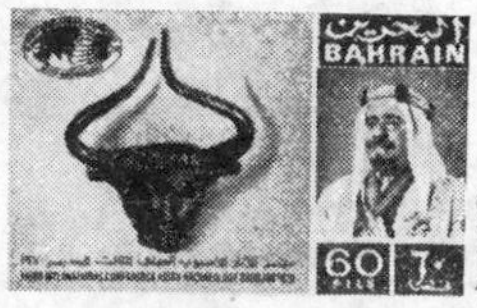

Copper Bull's Head A15

Conference Emblem and: 80f, Gateway to Qalat al Bahrain, 7th century B.C. 120f, Aerial view of grave mounds, Bahrain. 150f, Dilmun seal, 2000 B.C.

1970, Mar. 1 Photo. *Perf. 14½*

173 A15 60f multicolored 2.00 2.00
174 A15 80f multicolored 2.25 2.25
175 A15 120f multicolored 3.50 3.50
176 A15 150f multicolored 4.25 4.25
Nos. 173-176 (4) 12.00 12.00

3rd Intl. Asian Archaeological Conference, Bahrain.

Vickers VC 10, Big Ben and Minaret A16

1970, Apr. 5   Litho.   Perf. 14¹/₂x14
177	A16	30f multicolored	.90	.90
178	A16	60f multicolored	1.90	1.90
179	A16	120f multicolored	6.25	6.25
		Nos. 177-179 (3)	9.05	9.05

1st flight to London from the Arabian Gulf Area by Gulf Aviation Company.

Intl. Education Year Emblem A17

Design: 120f, Education Year emblem and students.

1970, Nov. 1   Litho.   Perf. 14¹/₂x14
180	A17	60f blk, blue & org	3.25	3.25
181	A17	120f multicolored	8.00	8.00

Independent State

Government House, Manama — A18   UN Emblem and Sails — A19

Designs: 30f, "Freedom" with dove and torch, and globe. 120f, 150f, Bahrain coat of arms.

1971, Oct. 2   Photo.   Perf. 14¹/₂x14
182	A18	30f gold & multi	1.65	1.65
183	A18	60f gold & multi	3.25	3.25
184	A18	120f gold & multi	6.50	6.50
185	A18	150f gold & multi	8.25	8.25
		Nos. 182-185 (4)	19.65	19.65

Declaration of Bahrain independence, Aug. 15, 1971.

Perf. 14x14¹/₂, 14¹/₂x14
1972, Feb. 1   Litho.

Designs: 30f, 60f, Dhow with sails showing UN and Arab League emblems, horiz. 150f, as 120f.

186	A19	30f multicolored	1.50	1.50
187	A19	60f red, gray & multi	3.50	3.50
188	A19	120f dull blue & multi	7.00	7.00
189	A19	150f multicolored	8.00	8.00
		Nos. 186-189 (4)	20.00	20.00

Bahrain's admission to the Arab League and the United Nations.

"Your Heart is your Health" — A20

1972, Apr. 7   Litho.   Perf. 14¹/₂x14
190	A20	30f black & multi	3.75	3.75
191	A20	60f gray & multi	7.50	7.50

World Health Day.

UN and FAO Emblems A21

1973, May 12   Litho.   Perf. 12¹/₂x13
192	A21	30f org red, pur & grn	3.75	3.75
193	A21	60f ocher, brn & grn	6.50	6.50

World Food Programs, 10th anniversary.

People of Various Races, Human Rights Flame A22

1973, Nov.   Litho.   Perf. 14x14¹/₂
194	A22	30f blue, blk & brn	3.75	3.75
195	A22	60f lake, blk & brn	7.00	7.00

25th anniversary of the Universal Declaration of Human Rights.

Flour Mill — A23

Designs: 60f, International Airport. 120f, Sulmaniya Medical Center. 150f, ALBA aluminum smelting plant.

1973, Dec. 16   Photo.   Perf. 14¹/₂
196	A23	30f multicolored	1.00	1.00
197	A23	60f multicolored	1.75	1.75
198	A23	120f multicolored	3.50	3.50
199	A23	150f multicolored	4.25	4.25
		Nos. 196-199 (4)	10.50	10.50

National Day.

Letters and UPU Emblem A24

Carrier Pigeon and UPU Emblem A25

Designs: 60f, UPU emblem and letters. 150f, Like 120f.

1974, Feb. 4   Litho.   Perf. 13¹/₂
200	A24	30f blue & multi	1.00	1.00
201	A24	60f emerald & multi	1.75	1.75

Perf. 12¹/₂x13¹/₂
202	A25	120f ultra & multi	3.00	3.00
203	A25	150f yellow & multi	4.25	4.25
		Nos. 200-203 (4)	10.00	10.00

Bahrain's admission to UPU.

Traffic Signals — A26

Jet, Globe, Mail Coach and UPU Emblem A27

1974, May 4   Litho.   Perf. 14¹/₂
204	A26	30f org brown & multi	2.75	2.75
205	A26	60f brt blue & multi	6.25	6.25

International Traffic Day.

1974, Sept. 1   Photo.   Perf. 14x14¹/₂
206	A27	30f multicolored	.55	.55
207	A27	60f multicolored	1.10	1.10
208	A27	120f multicolored	2.25	2.25
209	A27	150f multicolored	2.75	2.75
		Nos. 206-209 (4)	6.65	6.65

Centenary of Universal Postal Union.

National Day Emblem, Sitra Power Station — A28   Woman's Silk Gown — A29

National Day: 120f, 150f, Bahrain dry dock.

1974, Dec. 16   Litho.   Perf. 14¹/₂
210	A28	30f blue & multi	.65	.65
211	A28	60f green & multi	1.10	1.10
212	A28	120f lil rose & multi	2.50	2.50
213	A28	150f ver & multi	3.00	3.00
		Nos. 210-213 (4)	7.25	7.25

Photo.; Gold Embossed
1975, Feb. 1   Perf. 14¹/₂x14

Design: Various women's costumes.

214	A29	30f blue grn & multi	.60	.60
215	A29	60f vio blue & multi	1.00	1.00
216	A29	120f rose red & multi	2.50	2.50
217	A29	150f multicolored	3.00	3.00
		Nos. 214-217 (4)	7.10	7.10

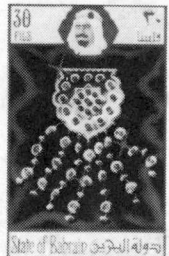   

Pendant — A30   Woman Planting Flower, IWY Emblem — A31

Designs: Various jewelry.

1975, Apr. 1   Photo.   Perf. 14¹/₂x14
218	A30	30f olive & multi	.55	.55
219	A30	60f dp pur & multi	1.25	1.25
220	A30	120f dp car & multi	2.50	2.50
221	A30	150f dp blue & multi	3.25	3.25
		Nos. 218-221 (4)	7.55	7.55

1975, July 28   Litho.   Perf. 14¹/₂

Design: 60f, Educated woman holding IWY emblem.

222	A31	30f multicolored	1.50	1.50
223	A31	60f multicolored	3.50	3.50

International Women's Year.

Miniature Sheet

Arabian Stallion A32

Arabian horses: a, Brown head. b, White mare. c, Mare and foal. d, White head. e, White mare. f, Mare and stallion. g, Bedouins on horseback. #224a, 224b, 224d are vert.

Perf. 14x14¹/₂, 14¹/₂x14
1975, Sept. 1   Photo.
224		Sheet of 8	50.00	32.50
a.-h.		A32 60f any single	5.00	3.50

Flag of Bahrain — A33

Map of Bahrain — A34   Sheik Isa — A35

1976-80   Litho.   Perf. 14¹/₂
225	A33	5f red & ultra	.15	.15
226	A33	10f red & green	.15	.15
227	A33	15f red & black	.15	.15
228	A33	20f red & brown	.15	.15
228A	A34	25f gray & blk ('79)	.15	.15
229	A34	40f blue & black	.25	.25
229A	A34	50f yel grn & blk ('79)	.30	.30
230	A34	60f dl grn & blk ('77)	.35	.35
231	A34	80f rose lil & blk	.45	.45
232	A34	100f lt red brn & blk ('77)	.55	.55
233	A34	150f org & black	.85	.85
234	A34	200f yel & black	1.10	1.10

Engr.
Perf. 12x12¹/₂
235	A35	300f lt grn & grn	1.65	1.65
236	A35	400f pink & red brn	2.25	2.25
237	A35	500f lt bl & dk bl	2.75	2.75
238	A35	1d gray & sepia	5.50	5.00
239	A35	2d rose & vio ('80)	11.50	9.25
240	A35	3d buff & brn ('80)	17.00	14.00
		Nos. 225-240 (18)	45.25	39.50

A later printing of the 100f-200f, and possibly others, has a larger printers imprint at bottom.

Concorde at London Airport — A36

Designs: No. 245, Concorde at Bahrain Airport. No. 246, Concorde over London to Bahrain map. No. 247, Concorde on runway at night.

1976, Jan. 22   Photo.   Perf. 13x14
244	A36	80f gold & multi	2.25	2.25
245	A36	80f gold & multi	2.25	2.25
246	A36	80f gold & multi	2.25	2.25
247	A36	80f gold & multi	2.25	2.25
a.		Souvenir sheet of 4	8.00	8.00
b.		Block of 4, #244-247	9.00	9.00

1st commercial flight of supersonic jet Concorde, London to Bahrain, Jan. 21. No. 247a contains 4 stamps with simulated perfs.

Soldier, Flag and Arms of Bahrain — A37

1976, Feb. 5   Litho.   Perf. 14½
248 A37 40f yellow & multi   2.00 2.00
249 A37 80f lt blue & multi   4.00 4.00
        Defense Force Day.

Sheik Isa, King Khalid, Bahrain and Saudi Flags A38

1976, Mar. 23   Litho.   Perf. 14½
250 A38 40f gold & multi   1.75 1.75
251 A38 80f silver & multi   3.00 3.00
        Visit of King Khalid of Saudi Arabia.

New Housing, Housing Ministry's Seal — A39

1976, Dec. 16   Litho.   Perf. 14½
252 A39 40f rose & multi   1.65 1.65
253 A39 80f blue & multi   3.25 3.25
        National Day.

APU Emblem A40

1977, Apr. 12   Litho.   Perf. 14½
254 A40 40f silver & multi   1.50 1.50
255 A40 80f rose & multi   3.00 3.00
        Arab Postal Union, 25th anniversary.

Miniature Sheet

Dogs on Beach and Dhow A41

Saluki dogs: b, Dog and camels. c, Dog and gazelles. d, Dog and Ruler's Palace. e, Dog's head. f, Heads of two dogs. g, Dog in dunes. h, Playing dogs.

1977, July   Photo.   Perf. 14x14½
256   Sheet of 8   28.00 28.00
a.-h. A41 80f any single   2.75   2.75

Students and Candle A42

1977, Sept. 8   Litho.   Perf. 14½
257 A42 40f multicolored   1.50 1.50
258 A42 80f multicolored   3.00 3.00
        International Literacy Day.

Shipyard and Flags A43

1977, Dec. 16   Litho.   Perf. 14½
259 A43 40f multicolored   1.50 1.50
260 A43 80f multicolored   3.00 3.00
        Inauguration of Arab Shipbuilding and Repair Yard Co.

Antenna, ITU Emblem A44

1978, May 17   Litho.   Perf. 14½
261 A44 40f yellow & multi   1.50 1.50
262 A44 80f silver & multi   3.00 3.00
        10th World Telecommunications Day.

Ganja Dhow A45

Designs: Dhows of the Arabian Gulf. Nos. 267-270 vertical.

Perf. 14x14½, 14½x14
1979, June 16   Photo.
263 A45 100f shown   3.25 3.25
264 A45 100f Zarook   3.25 3.25
265 A45 100f Shu'ai   3.25 3.25
266 A45 100f Jaliboot   3.25 3.25
267 A45 100f Baghla   3.25 3.25
368 A45 100f Sambuk   3.25 3.25
269 A45 100f Boom   3.25 3.25
270 A45 100f Kotia   3.25 3.25
a.   Block of 8, #263-270   26.00 26.00
        Nos. 263-270 (8)   26.00 26.00

Learning to Walk — A46

Hegira, 1,500th Anniv. — A47

IYC Emblem and: 100f, Hands surrounding girl, UN emblem.

1979   Litho.   Perf. 14½
271 A46 50f multicolored   1.50 1.50
272 A46 100f multicolored   3.00 3.00
        International Year of the Child.

1980   Photo.   Perf. 13x13½
273 A47 50f multicolored   .65   .65
274 A47 100f multicolored   1.25 1.25
a.   Miniature sheet of 1   6.00 6.00
275 A47 150f multicolored   2.00 2.00
276 A47 200f multicolored   2.75 2.75
        Nos. 273-276 (4)   6.65 6.65

Falcon A48

Designs: Falcons.

Perf. 13½x14, 14x13½
1980, Nov. 1   Photo.
277   Block of 8   15.00 15.00
a.-h. A48 100f any single   1.75 1.75

IYD Emblem, Sheik Isa — A49

1981, Mar. 21   Litho.   Perf. 14½
278 A49 50f multicolored   1.65 1.65
279 A49 100f multicolored   3.25 3.25
        International Year of the Disabled.

50th Anniversary of Electricity in Bahrain A50

1981, Apr. 26   Litho.   Perf. 14½
280 A50 50f multicolored   1.65 1.65
281 A50 100f multicolored   3.25 3.25

Stone Cutting — A51

1981, July 1   Photo.   Perf. 14x13½
282 A51 50f shown   .75   .75
283 A51 100f Pottery   1.25 1.25
284 A51 150f Weaving   2.75 2.75
285 A51 200f Basket making   3.00 3.00
        Nos. 282-285 (4)   7.75 7.75

Hegira (Pilgrimage Year) — A52

Designs: Various mosques.

1981, Oct. 1   Photo.   Perf. 14x13½
286 A52 50f multicolored   .80   .80
287 A52 100f multicolored   1.65 1.65
288 A52 150f multicolored   2.25 2.25
289 A52 200f multicolored   3.25 3.25
        Nos. 286-289 (4)   7.95 7.95

Sheik Isa, 20th Anniv. of Coronation — A53

1981, Dec. 16   Photo.   Perf. 14x13½
290 A53 15f multicolored   .25   .25
291 A53 50f multicolored   .80   .80
292 A53 100f multicolored   1.75 1.75
293 A53 150f multicolored   2.50 2.50
294 A53 200f multicolored   3.50 3.50
        Nos. 290-294 (5)   8.80 8.80

Wildlife in al Areen Park A54

Designs: a, Gazelle. b, Oryx. c, Dhub lizard. d, Arabian hares. e, Oryxes. f, Reems.

1982, Mar. 1   Photo.   Perf. 13½x14
295   Sheet of 6   14.00 14.00
a.-f. A54 100f any single   2.25 2.25

3rd Session of Gulf Supreme Council, Nov. — A55

1982, Nov. 9   Litho.   Perf. 14½
296 A55 50f blue & multi   .85   .85
297 A55 100f green & multi   2.25 2.25

Opening of Madinat Hamad Housing Development — A56

1983, Dec. 1   Litho.   Perf. 14½
298 A56 50f multicolored   .85   .85
299 A56 100f multicolored   2.25 2.25

Al Khalifa Dynasty Bicentenary — A57

Sheiks or Emblems: a, 500fr, Isa bin Sulman. b, Emblem (tan & multi). c, Isa bin Ali, 1869-1932. d, Hamad bin Isa, 1932-42. e, Sulman bin Hamad, 1942-61. f, Emblem (pale green & multi). g, Emblem (lemon & multi). h, Emblem (light blue & multi). i, Emblem (gray & multi).

1983, Dec. 16   Litho.   Perf. 14½
300   Sheet of 9   9.00 9.00
a.-i. A57 100f any single   .80   .80

Souvenir Sheet
301 A57 500f multicolored   8.50 8.50
        No. 301 contains one stamp 60x38mm.

Gulf Co-operation Council Traffic Week — A58

1984, Apr. 30   Litho.   Perf. 14½
302 A58 15f multicolored   .30   .30
303 A58 50f multicolored   1.00 1.00
304 A58 100f multicolored   2.00 2.00
        Nos. 302-304 (3)   3.30 3.30

1984 Summer Olympics A59

1984, Sept. 15   *Perf. 14¹/₂*
305 A59 15f Hurdles .26 .26
306 A59 50f Equestrian .80 .80
307 A59 100f Diving 1.65 1.65
308 A59 150f Fencing 2.00 2.00
309 A59 200f Shooting 3.50 3.50
Nos. 305-309 (5) 8.21 8.21

Postal Service Cent. A60

1984, Dec. 8   **Photo.**   *Perf. 12x11¹/₂*
310 A60 15f multicolored .40 .40
311 A60 50f multicolored 1.25 1.25
312 A60 100f multicolored 2.25 2.25
Nos. 310-312 (3) 3.90 3.90

Miniature Sheet

Coastal Fish A61

1985, Feb. 10   **Photo.**   *Perf. 13¹/₂x14*
313 Sheet of 10 12.00 12.00
a.-j. A61 100f any single 1.40 1.40

1st Arab Gulf States Week for Social Work A62

1985, Oct. 15   **Litho.**   *Perf. 14¹/₂*
314 A62 15f multicolored .25 .25
315 A62 50f multicolored .85 .85
316 A62 100f multicolored 1.90 1.90
Nos. 314-316 (3) 3.00 3.00

Intl. Youth Year A63

1985, Nov. 16
317 A63 15f multicolored .25 .25
318 A63 50f multicolored .85 .85
319 A63 100f multicolored 1.90 1.90
Nos. 317-319 (3) 3.00 3.00

Bahrain-Saudi Arabia Causeway Opening — A64

1986, Nov.   **Litho.**   *Perf. 14¹/₂*
320 A64 15f Causeway, aerial view .25 .25
321 A64 50f Island .85 .85
322 A64 100f Causeway 1.90 1.90
Nos. 320-322 (3) 3.00 3.00

Sheik Isa, 25th Anniv. as the Emir — A65

1986, Dec. 16
323 A65 15f multicolored .25 .25
324 A65 50f multicolored .85 .85
325 A65 100f multicolored 1.90 1.90
a. Souvenir sheet of 3, #323-325 5.50 5.50
Nos. 323-325 (3) 3.00 3.00

WHO, 40th Anniv. A66

1988, Apr. 30   **Litho.**   *Perf. 14¹/₂*
326 A66 50f multicolored .50 .50
327 A66 150f multicolored 1.40 1.40

Opening of Ahmed Al Fateh Islamic Center A67

1988, June 2   **Litho.**   *Perf. 14¹/₂*
328 A67 50f multicolored .50 .50
329 A67 150f multicolored 1.40 1.40

1988 Summer Olympics, Seoul A68

1988, Sept. 17   **Litho.**   *Perf. 14¹/₂*
330 A68 50f Running .28 .28
331 A68 80f Equestrian .45 .45
332 A68 150f Fencing .80 .80
333 A68 200f Soccer 1.10 1.10
Nos. 330-333 (4) 2.63 2.63

Gulf Cooperation Council Supreme Council 9th Regular Session, Bahrain A69

1988, Dec. 19   **Litho.**   *Perf. 14¹/₂*
334 A69 50f multicolored .50 .50
335 A69 150f multicolored 1.40 1.40

Miniature Sheets

Camels A70

No. 336: a, Close-up of head, rider in background. b, Camel kneeling at rest. c, Two adults, calf. d, Three adults. e, Camel facing right. f, Mount and rider (facing left).
No. 337: a, Man walking in front of camel, oil well. b, Man walking in front of camel. c, Oil well, camel's head. d, Mount and rider (facing forward). e, Mount and rider (facing right). f, Two dromedaries at a run. Nos. 337a-337f vert.

Perf. 13¹/₂x14, 14x13¹/₂
1989, June 15
336 Sheet of 6 6.00 6.00
a.-f. A70 150f any single 1.00 1.00
337 Sheet of 6 6.00 6.00
a.-f. A70 150f any single 1.00 1.00

Sheik Isa — A71

1989, Dec. 16   **Litho.**   *Perf. 13¹/₂x14*
338 A71 25f multicolored .15 .15
339 A71 40f multicolored .24 .24
340 A71 50f multicolored .30 .30
341 A71 60f multicolored .35 .35
342 A71 75f multicolored .45 .45
343 A71 80f multicolored .48 .48
344 A71 100f multicolored .60 .60
345 A71 120f multicolored .72 .72
346 A71 150f multicolored .90 .90
347 A71 200f multicolored 1.20 1.20
a. Souvenir sheet of 10, #338-347 6.00 6.00
Nos. 338-347 (10) 5.39 5.39

Houbara (Bustard) — A72

Designs: a, Two birds facing right. b, Two birds facing each other. c, Chicks. d, Adult, chick. e, Adult, facing right, vert. f, In flight. g, Adult facing right. h, Chick, facing left, vert. i, Adult facing left. j, Adult male, close-up. k, Courtship display. l, Two birds facing left.

1990, Feb. 17   **Photo.**   *Perf. 14*
348 Sheet of 12 10.80 10.80
a.-l. A72 150f any single .90 .90

Gulf Air, 40th Anniv. A73

1990, Mar. 24   **Litho.**   *Perf. 14¹/₂*
360 A73 50f multicolored .30 .30
361 A73 80f multicolored .48 .48
362 A73 150f multicolored .90 .90
363 A73 200f multicolored 1.20 1.20
Nos. 360-363 (4) 2.88 2.88

Chamber of Commerce, 50th Anniv. A74

1990, May 26
364 A74 50f multicolored .30 .30
365 A74 80f multicolored .48 .48
366 A74 150f multicolored .90 .90
367 A74 200f multicolored 1.20 1.20
Nos. 364-367 (4) 2.88 2.88

Intl. Literacy Year A75

1990, Sept. 8   **Litho.**   *Perf. 14¹/₂*
368 A75 50f multicolored .30 .30
369 A75 80f multicolored .48 .48
370 A75 150f multicolored .90 .90
371 A75 200f multicolored 1.20 1.20
Nos. 368-371 (4) 2.88 2.88

Miniature Sheet

Indigenous Birds — A76

Designs: a, Galerida cristata. b, Upupa epops. c, Pycnonotus leucogenys. d, Streptopelia turtur. e, Streptopelia decaocto. f, Falco tinnunculus. g, Passer domesticus, horiz. h, Lanius excubitor, horiz. i, Psittacula krameri.

1991, Sept. 15   **Litho.**   *Perf. 14¹/₂*
372 Sheet of 9 9.00 9.00
a.-i. A76 150f any single 1.10 1.10
See Nos. 382, 407.

Coronation of Sheik Isa, 30th Anniv. A77

Design: Nos. 374, 376, 378, 380, 381a, Portrait at left, leaves.

Litho. & Embossed
1991, Dec. 16   *Perf. 14¹/₂*
373 A77 50f multicolored .35 .35
374 A77 50f multicolored .35 .35
375 A77 80f multicolored .55 .55
376 A77 80f multicolored .55 .55
377 A77 150f multicolored 1.10 1.10
378 A77 150f multicolored 1.10 1.10
379 A77 200f multicolored 1.50 1.50
380 A77 200f multicolored 1.50 1.50
Nos. 373-380 (8) 7.00 7.00

Souvenir Sheet
Perf. 14x14¹/₂
381 Sheet of 2 7.50 7.50
a.-b. A77 500f any single 3.75 3.75
No. 381 contains 41x31mm stamps.

Miniature Sheet
Indigenous Birds Type of 1991

Designs: No. 382a, Ciconia ciconia. b, Merops apiaster. c, Sturnus vulgaris. d, Hypocolius ampelinus. e, Cuculus canorus. f, Turdus viscivorus. g, Coracias garrulus. h, Carduelis carduelis. i, Lanius collurio. j, Turdus iliacus, horiz. k, Motacilla alba, horiz. l, Oriolus oriolus, horiz. m, Erithacus rubecula. n, Luscinia luscinia. o, Muscicapa striata. p, Hirundo rustica.

1992, Mar. 21   **Litho.**   *Perf. 14¹/₂*
382 Sheet of 16 13.50 13.50
a.-p. A76 150f any single .80 .80

Miniature Sheet

Horse Racing A78

Designs: No. 383a, Horses leaving starting gate. b, Trainers leading horses. c, Horses racing around turn. d, Horses in stretch racing by flags. e, Two horses racing by grandstand. f, Five horses galloping. g, Two brown horses racing. h, Black horse, gray horse racing.

1992, May 22
383 Sheet of 8 7.20 7.20
a.-h. A78 150f any single .90 .90

1992
Summer
Olympics,
Barcelona
A79

1992, July 25   Litho.   Perf. 14½
384 A79 50f Equestrian   .35   .35
385 A79 80f Running   .60   .60
386 A79 50f Judo   1.10 1.10
387 A79 200f Cycling   1.40 1.40
    Nos. 384-387 (4)   3.45 3.45

Bahrain
Intl.
Airport,
60th Anniv.
A80

1992, Oct. 27   Litho.   Perf. 14½
388 A80 50f multicolored   .35   .35
389 A80 80f multicolored   .55   .55
390 A80 150f multicolored   1.00 1.00
391 A80 200f multicolored   1.25 1.25
    Nos. 388-391 (4)   3.15 3.15

Children's
Art — A81

Designs: 50f, Girl jumping rope, vert. 80f, Women in traditional dress, vert. 150f, Women stirring kettle. 200f, Fishermen.

1992, Nov. 28   Litho.   Perf. 14½
392 A81 50f multicolored   .30   .30
393 A81 80f multicolored   .50   .50
394 A81 150f multicolored   .95   .95
395 A81 200f multicolored   1.25 1.25
    Nos. 392-395 (4)   3.00 3.00

Inauguration of Expansion of Aluminum
Bahrain — A82

Designs: 50f, Ore funicular. 80f, Smelting pot. 150f, Mill. 200f, Cylindrical aluminum ingots.

1992, Dec. 16
396 A82 50f multicolored   .30   .30
397 A82 80f multicolored   .50   .50
398 A82 150f multicolored   .95   .95
399 A82 200f multicolored   1.25 1.25
    Nos. 396-399 (4)   3.00 3.00

Bahrain
Defense Force,
25th
Anniv. — A83

Designs: 50f, Artillery forces, vert. 80f, Fighters, tanks, and ship, vert. 150f, Frigate. 200f, Jet fighter.

Perf. 13½x13, 13x13½
1993, Feb. 5   Litho.
400 A83 50f multicolored   .30   .30
401 A83 80f multicolored   .50   .50
402 A83 150f multicolored   .95   .95
403 A83 200f multicolored   1.25 1.25
    Nos. 400-403 (4)   3.00 3.00

World Meteorology Day — A84

Designs: 50f, Satellite image of Bahrain, vert. 150f, Infrared satellite map of world. 200f, Earth, seen from space, vert.

1993, Mar. 23   Litho.   Perf. 14½
404 A84 50f multicolored   .45   .45
405 A84 150f multicolored   1.40 1.40
406 A84 200f multicolored   1.75 1.75
    Nos. 404-406 (3)   3.60 3.60

Bird Type of 1991
Miniature Sheet

Designs: a, Ardea purpurea. b, Gallinula chloropus. c, Phalacrocorax nigrogularis. d, Dromas ardeola. e, Alcedo atthis. f, Vanellus vanellus. g, Haematopus ostralegus, horiz. h, Nycticorax nycticorax. i, Sterna caspia, horiz. j, Arenaria interpres, horiz. k, Rallus aquaticus, horiz. l, Anas platyrhynchos, horiz. m, Larus fuscus, horiz.

1993, May 22   Perf. 14½
407   Sheet of 13 + 2 labels 11.00 11.00
 a.-m. A76 150f any single   .85   .85

Gazella Subgutturosa Marica — A85

1993, July 24   Litho.   Perf. 14½
408 A85 25f Calf   .15   .15
409 A85 50f Female standing   .30   .30
410 A85 50f Female walking   .30   .30
411 A85 150f Male   .95   .95
    Nos. 408-411 (4)   1.70 1.70

World Wildlife Federation.

Wild
Flowers — A86   A87

Designs: a, Lycium shawii. b, Alhagi maurorum. c, Caparis spinosa. d, Cistanche phelypae. e, Asphodelus tenuifolius. f, Limonium axillare. g, Cynomorium coccineum. h, Calligonum polygonoides.

1993, Oct. 16   Litho.   Perf. 13½x13
412 A86 150f Sheet of 8, #a.-h. 6.50 6.50

1994, Jan. 22   Litho.   Perf. 14½
Background Color
413 A87 50f yellow   .30   .30
414 A87 80f blue green   .50   .50
415 A87 150f purple   .95   .95
416 A87 200f blue   1.25 1.25
    Nos. 413-416 (4)   3.00 3.00

Intl. Year of the Family.

A88   A89

Butterflies: No. 417a, Lepidochrysops arabicus. b, Ypthima bolanica. c, Eurema brigitta. d, Precis limnoria. e, Aglais urticae. f, Colotis protomedia. g, Salamis anacardii. h, Byblia ilithyia.
No. 418a, Papilio machaon. b, Agrodiaetus loewii. c, Vanessa cardui. d, Papilio demoleus. e, Hamanumida daedalus. f, Funonia orithya. g, Funonia chorimine. h, Colias croceus.

Perf. 13½x13, 13x13½
1994, Mar. 21   Litho.
417 A88 50f Sheet of 8, #a.-h. 2.50 2.50
418 A88 150f Sheet of 8, #a.-h. 7.50 7.50

No. 418 is horiz.

1994, May 8   Litho.   Perf. 14½
419 A89 50f lilac & multi   .30   .30
420 A89 80f yellow & multi   .50   .50
421 A89 150f salmon & multi   .95   .95
422 A89 200f green blue & multi 1.25 1.25
    Nos. 419-422 (4)   3.00 3.00

Intl. Red Cross & Red Crescent Societies, 75th anniv.

1994 World Cup Soccer Championships,
US — A90

Designs: 50f, Goalkeeper. 80f, Heading ball. 150f, Dribbling ball. 200f, Slide tackle.

1994, June 17   Litho.   Perf. 14
423 A90 50f multicolored   .30   .30
424 A90 80f multicolored   .50   .50
425 A90 150f multicolored   .95   .95
426 A90 200f multicolored   1.25 1.25
    Nos. 423-426 (4)   3.00 3.00

Bahrain's
First
Satellite
Earth
Station,
25th
Anniv.
A91

1994, July 14
427 A91 50f blue & multi   .30   .30
428 A91 80f yellow & multi   .50   .50
429 A91 150f violet & multi   .95   .95
430 A91 200f pink, yellow & multi 1.25 1.25
    Nos. 427-430 (4)   3.00 3.00

Education in Bahrain,
75th Anniv. — A92

1994, Nov. 19   Litho.   Perf. 14½
431 A92 50f yellow & multi   .30   .30
432 A92 80f buff & multi   .50   .50
433 A92 150f salmon & multi   .95   .95
434 A92 200f pink & multi   1.25 1.25
    Nos. 431-434 (4)   3.00 3.00

Gulf Cooperation
Council Supreme
Council, 15th
Regular Session,
Bahrain — A93

1994, Dec. 19   Perf. 14
435 A93 50f blue green & multi .30   .30
436 A93 80f brown & multi   .50   .50
437 A93 150f lilac rose & multi .95   .95
438 A93 200f blue & multi   1.25 1.25
    Nos. 435-438 (4)   3.00 3.00

Date Palm
A94

Designs: 80f, Flowering stage. 100f, Dates beginning to ripen. 200f, Dates up close. 250f, Trees from distance.
500f, Pitcher, basket of dates.

1995, Mar. 21   Litho.   Perf. 14
439 A94 80f multicolored   .48   .48
440 A94 100f multicolored   .60   .60
441 A94 200f multicolored   1.25 1.25
442 A94 250f multicolored   1.50 1.50
    Nos. 439-442 (4)   3.83 3.83

Souvenir Sheet
443 A94 500f multicolored   3.00 3.00

No. 443 contains one 65x48mm stamp.

Fight Against
Polio — A95

1995, Apr. 22   Litho.   Perf. 13x13½
444 A95 80f pink & multi   .42   .42
445 A95 200f blue & multi   1.00 1.00
446 A95 250f lt brown & multi 1.40 1.40
    Nos. 444-446 (3)   2.82 2.82

World Health Day.

1st Natl.
Industries
Exhibition
A96

1995, May 15
447 A96 80f blue green & multi .42   .42
448 A96 200f lilac & multi   1.00 1.00
449 A96 250f lt brown & multi 1.40 1.40
    Nos. 447-449 (3)   2.82 2.82

FAO,
50th
Anniv.
A97

Fields of various crops.

1995, June 17   Litho.   Perf. 14
450 A97 80f lilac & multi   .42   .42
451 A97 200f blue & multi   1.00 1.00
452 A97 250f lt pink & multi 1.40 1.40
    Nos. 450-452 (3)   2.82 2.82

Arab League, 50th
Anniv. — A98

1995, Sept. 14   Litho.   Perf. 14½
453	A98	80f pink & multi	.40	.40
454	A98	200f blue & multi	1.10	1.10
455	A98	250f yellow & multi	1.40	1.40
		Nos. 453-455 (3)	2.90	2.90

UN, 50th
Anniv.
A99

1995, Oct. 24   Litho.   Perf. 14½
456	A99	80f yellow & multi	.40	.40
457	A99	100f green & multi	.55	.55
458	A99	200f pink & multi	1.10	1.10
459	A99	250f blue & multi	1.40	1.40
		Nos. 456-459 (4)	3.45	3.45

Miniature Sheet

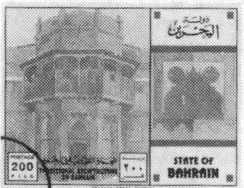

Traditional Architecture — A100

Example of architecture, detail: a, Tower with
balcony. b, Arched windows behind balcony. c,
Double doors under arch. d, Four rows of square
windows above row of arched windows. e, Door
flanked by two windows. f, Three windows.

1995, Nov. 20   Litho.   Perf. 14½
460	A100	200f Sheet of 6, #a.-f.	6.50 6.50

National Day — A101

1995, Dec. 16   Litho.   Perf. 14½
461	A101	80f blue & multi	.40	.40
462	A101	100f green & multi	.55	.55
463	A101	200f violet & multi	1.10	1.10
464	A101	250f blue green & multi	1.40	1.40
		Nos. 461-464 (4)	3.45	3.45

WAR TAX STAMPS

WT1   WT2

1973, Oct. 21   Litho.   Perf. 14½
MR1 WT1 5f sky blue

Catalogue values for all unused
stamps in this section, from this
point to the end of the section, are
for Never Hinged items.

1974   Litho.   Perf. 14½
MR2	WT2 5f light blue	1.75	.25
a.	Perf. 14½x13½		2.50

No. MR2a was issued around 1988.

BANGKOK

'baŋ-ˌkäk

LOCATION — Capital of Siam (Thailand)

Stamps were issued by Great Britain
under rights obtained in the treaty of 1855.
These were in use until July 1, 1885, when
the stamps of Siam were designated as the
only official postage stamps to be used in the
kingdom.

100 Cents = 1 Dollar

Excellent counterfeits of Nos. 1-22 are
plentiful.

Stamps of Straits Settlements
Overprinted in Black   **B**

1882   Wmk. 1   Perf. 14
1	A2	2c brown	2,250.	1,200.
2	A2	4c rose	2,500.	1,200.
a.		Inverted overprint		
3	A6	5c brown violet	300.00	150.00
4	A2	6c violet	225.00	125.00
5	A3	8c yel orange	1,800.	165.00
6	A7	10c slate	200.00	125.00
7	A3	12c blue	500.00	250.00
8	A3	24c green	650.00	125.00
9	A4	30c claret	40,000.	25,000.
10	A5	96c olive gray	4,000.	2,250.

The existence of No. 2a is questioned.
See footnote after No. 20.

1882-83   Wmk. 2
11	A2	2c brown	325.00	250.00
12	A2	2c rose ('83)	40.00	40.00
a.		Inverted overprint	20,000.	10,000.
b.		Double overprint	1,750.	
c.		Triple overprint	10,000.	
13	A2	4c rose	400.00	250.00
14	A2	4c brown ('83)	60.00	60.00
a.		Double overprint		
15	A6	5c ultra ('83)	165.00	165.00
16	A2	6c violet ('83)	100.00	100.00
a.		Double overprint		
17	A3	8c yel orange	125.00	80.00
a.		Inverted overprint	17,500.	10,000.
18	A7	10c slate	125.00	80.00
a.		Double overprint		
19	A3	12c violet brn ('83)	165.00	140.00
20	A3	24c green	3,250.	2,250.

Partial double overprints exist on a number of
values of these issues. They sell for a modest premium over catalogue value depending on how
much of the impression is present.
Stamps known with two clear impressions are:
#2, $6,000 used, #12, $2,750 unused, triple
$10,000 unused, and #14.

1883   Wmk. 1
21	A5	2c on 32c pale red	2,250. 2,250.

On Straits Settlements No. 9

1885   Wmk. 38
22	A7	32c on 2a yel (B+B)	40,000. 50,000.

BANGLADESH

ˌbän-glə-'desh

LOCATION — In southern, central Asia,
touching India, Burma, and the Bay of
Bengal
GOVT. — Republic in the British
Commonwealth
AREA — 55,598 sq. mi.
POP. — 87,052,024 (1981)
CAPITAL — Dacca (Dhaka)

Bangladesh, formerly East Pakistan, broke
away from Pakistan in April 1971, proclaim-
ing its independence. It consists of 14 former eastern districts of Bengal and the former Assam district of Sylhet.

100 Paisas = 1 Rupee

100 Paisas (Poishas) = 1 Taka (1972)

Catalogue values for all unused
stamps in this country are for Never
Hinged items.

Various stamps of Pakistan were
handstamped locally for use in Bangladesh during the first half of 1971.

Map of
Bangladesh
A1

Sheik Mujibur
Rahman
A2

Designs: 20p, "Dacca University Massacre." 50p,
"A Nation of 75 Million People." 1r, Flag of Independence (showing map). 2r, Ballot box. 3r, Broken
chain. 10r, "Support Bangladesh" and map.

Perf. 14x14½
1971, July 29   Litho.   Unwmk.
1	A1	10p red, dk pur & lt bl	.15	.15
2	A1	20p bl, grn, red & yel	.15	.15
3	A1	50p dp org, gray & brn	.15	.15
4	A1	1r red, emer & yel	.25	.25
5	A1	2r lil rose, lt & dk bl	.50	.50
6	A1	3r blue, emer & grn	.70	.70
7	A1	5r dp org, tan & blk	1.25	1.25
8	A1	10r gold, dk bl & lil rose	2.25	2.25
		Nos. 1-8 (8)	5.40	5.40

A set of 15 stamps of types A1 and A2 in new
paisa-taka values and colors was rejected by Bangladesh officials and not issued. Bangladesh representatives in England released these stamps, which
were not valid, on Feb. 1, 1972.
Imperfs of Nos. 1-8 were in the Format International liquidation. They are not errors.

	BANGLADESH
Nos. 1-8 Overprinted in	LIBERATED
Black or Red	বাংলাদেশের মুক্তি

1971, Dec. 20
9	A1	10p multicolored	.15	.15
10	A1	20p multicolored	.15	
11	A1	50p multicolored	.15	
12	A1	1r multicolored	.24	
13	A1	2r multicolored	.48	
14	A1	3r multicolored	.75	
15	A2	5r multicolored (R)	1.10	1.10
16	A1	10r multicolored	2.25	2.25
		Nos. 9-16 (8)	5.27	

Liberation of Bangladesh.
The 10p, 5r and 10r were issued in Dacca, but
Nos. 10-14 were not put on sale in Bangladesh.

Monument
A3

"Independence"
A4

1972, Feb. 21   Litho.   Perf. 13
32	A3	20p green & rose	.30	.30

Martyrs of Bangladesh.

1972, Mar. 26   Photo.   Perf. 13
33	A4	20p maroon & red	.15	.15
34	A4	60p dark blue & red	.20	.20
35	A4	75p purple & red	.20	.20
		Nos. 33-35 (3)	.55	.55

First anniversary of independence.

Doves of
Peace — A5

Flower Growing
from Ruin — A6

1972, Dec. 16   Litho.   Perf. 13
36	A5	20p ocher & multi	.15	.15
37	A5	60p lilac & multi	.20	.20
38	A5	75p yellow green & multi	.25	.25
		Nos. 36-38 (3)	.60	.60

Victory Day, Dec. 16.

1973, Mar. 25   Litho.   Perf. 13
39	A6	20p ocher & multi	.15	.15
40	A6	60p brown & multi	.20	.20
41	A6	1.35t violet blue & multi	.50	.50
		Nos. 39-41 (3)	.85	.85

Martyrs of the war of liberation.

Embroidered
Quilt — A7

Hilsa — A8

Court of
Justice — A9

Designs: 3p, Jute field. 5p, Jack fruit. 10p,
Farmer plowing with ox team. 20p, Dahlia. 25p,
Tiger. 60p, Bamboo and water lilies. 75p, Women
picking tea. 90p, Handicraft. 2t, Coconut harvest,
vert. 5t, Net fishing. 10t, Sixty-dome Mosque.

1973   Litho.   Perf. 14x14½, 14½x14
Size: 21x28mm, 28x21mm
42	A7	2p black	.15	.15
43	A7	3p bright green	.15	.15
44	A7	5p light brown	.15	.15
45	A7	10p black	.15	.15
46	A7	20p olive	.50	.50
47	A7	25p red lilac	1.25	1.25
48	A8	50p rose lilac	1.00	1.00
49	A7	60p gray	.50	.50
50	A7	75p orange	.75	.75
51	A7	90p red brown	.75	.75

Taka Expressed as "TA"
Size: 35x22mm
52	A9	1t violet	2.25	2.25
53	A9	2t greenish gray	3.00	3.00
54	A9	5t grayish blue	4.00	4.00
55	A9	10t rose	4.50	4.50
		Nos. 42-55 (14)	19.10	19.10

See Nos. 82-85, 95-106, 165-176. For overprints
see Nos. O1-O10, O13.

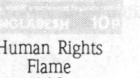

Human Rights
Flame
A10

Family, Chart,
Map of
Bangladesh
A11

1973, Dec. 10   Litho.   Perf. 13x13½

56	A10	10p blue & multi	.15	.15
57	A10	1.25t violet & multi	.35	.35
		Set value	.40	.40

25th anniversary of the Universal Declaration of Human Rights.

1974, Feb. 10   Litho.   Perf. 13½

58	A11	20p blue grn & multi	.15	.15
59	A11	25p brt blue & multi	.15	.15
60	A11	75p red & multi	.20	.20
		Set value	.40	.40

First census in Bangladesh.
For overprints see Nos. 194-196.

Copernicus,
Heliocentric
System
A12

Flag and UN
Headquarters
A13

1974, July 22   Litho.   Perf. 13½

61	A12	25p violet, blk & org	.15	.15
62	A12	75p emerald, blk & org	.40	.40

Nicolaus Copernicus (1473-1543), Polish astronomer.

1974, Sept. 25   Litho.   Perf. 13½

63	A13	25p lilac & multi	.15	.15
64	A13	1t blue & multi	.35	.35

Admission of Bangladesh to the UN.

A14

A15

Designs: 25p, 1.75t, UPU emblem. 1.25t, 5t Mail runner. 25p, 1.25t, country and denomination appear on a yellow background. 1.75t, 5t, blue background.

1974, Oct. 9   Perf. 13½

65	A14	25p multicolored	.15	.15
66	A14	1.25t multicolored	.20	.20
67	A14	1.75t multicolored	.30	.30
68	A14	5t multicolored	.90	.90
a.		Souv. sheet of 4, #65-68, imperf.		
		Nos. 65-68 (4)	1.55	1.55

1974, Nov. 4   Litho.

69	A15	25p Royal bengal tiger	.20	.20
70	A15	50p Tiger cub	.75	.75
71	A15	2t Swimming tiger	2.50	2.50
		Nos. 69-71 (3)	3.45	3.45

"Save the Tiger," World Wildlife Fund.

Type of 1973
Taka Expressed in Bengali

1974-75   Perf. 14½x14, 14x14½
Size: 35x22mm

82	A9	1t violet	1.00	1.00
83	A9	2t grayish green	2.00	2.00
84	A9	5t grayish blue ('75)	2.75	2.75
85	A9	10t rose ('75)	5.00	5.00
		Nos. 82-85 (4)	10.75	10.75

For overprints see Nos. O11-O12, O14.

Family — A16

Children — A17

Family — A18

1974, Dec. 30   Litho.   Perf. 14

86	A16	50p ocher & multi	.15	.15
87	A17	70p claret & multi	.25	.25
88	A18	1.25t multicolored	.35	.35
		Nos. 86-88 (3)	.75	.75

Family planning. The numerals on No. 87 look like "90" but mean "70."

Betbunia Satellite
Earth Station — A19

1975, June 14   Litho.   Perf. 14

89	A19	25p red, black & silver	.15	.15
90	A19	1t vio blue, blk & silver	.20	.30

Opening of Betbunia Satellite Earth Station.

Allegory, IWY
Emblem
A20

1975, Dec. 31   Litho.   Perf. 15

91	A20	50p rose & multi	.15	.15
92	A20	2t lt lilac & multi	.40	.40

International Women's Year.

Types of 1973 Redrawn

1976-77   Litho.   Perf. 15x14½
Size: 18x23mm, 23x18mm

95	A7	5p green	.15	.15
96	A7	10p black	.15	.15
97	A7	20p olive green	.15	.15
98	A7	25p rose lilac	.15	.15
99	A8	50p rose lilac	.15	.15
100	A7	60p gray	.15	.15
101	A7	75p olive	.15	.15
102	A7	90p red brown	.18	.18

Taka Expressed in Bengali
Size: 32x20mm, 20x32mm

103	A9	1t violet	.20	.20
104	A9	2t greenish gray	.45	.45
105	A9	5t grayish blue	1.25	1.25
106	A9	10t rose ('77)	2.50	2.50
		Nos. 95-106 (12)	5.63	5.63
		Set value	5.25	5.25

For overprints see Nos. O16-O25.

Telephones, 1876
and 1976 — A21

Alexander Graham
Bell — A22

1976, Mar. 10   Litho.   Perf. 15

107	A21	2.25t multicolored	.40	.40
108	A22	5t multicolored	.90	.90

Centenary of first telephone call by Alexander Graham Bell, Mar. 10, 1876.

Eye and
Healthful
Food — A23

1976, Apr. 7   Litho.   Perf. 15

109	A23	30p yellow & multi	.15	.15
110	A23	2.25t orange & multi	.35	.35

World Health Day: Foresight prevents blindness.

Liberty
Bell — A24

Designs: 2.25t, Statue of Liberty, New York Skyline. 5t, Mayflower. 10t, Mt. Rushmore, presidents' heads.

1976, May 29   Photo.   Perf. 13½x14

111	A24	30p multicolored	.15	.15
112	A24	2.25t multicolored	.50	.50
113	A24	5t multicolored	1.10	1.10
114	A24	10t multicolored	2.25	2.25
a.		Souv. sheet of 4, #111-114, perf. 13	4.00	4.00
		Nos. 111-114 (4)	4.00	4.00

American Bicentennial. Sheet exists imperf.

Weaver, Chemist,
Farmer, Student and
Emblem — A25

1976, Aug.   Litho.   Perf. 15

115	A25	30p multicolored	.15	.15
116	A25	2.25t multicolored	.35	.35

25th anniversary of Colombo Plan.
For overprint see No. 252.

Hurdles — A26

Montreal Olympic Emblem and: 30p, Running, horiz. 1t, High jump. 2.25t, Swimming, horiz. 3.50t, Gymnastics. 5t, Soccer.

1976, Nov.   Litho.   Perf. 15

117	A26	25p multicolored	.15	.15
118	A26	30p multicolored	.15	.15
119	A26	1t multicolored	.15	.15
120	A26	2.25t multicolored	.35	.35

121	A26	3.50t multicolored	.50	.50
122	A26	5t multicolored	.75	.75
		Nos. 117-122 (6)	2.05	2.05

21st Olympic Games, Montreal, Canada, July 17-Aug. 1.

Coronation
Ceremony — A27

Designs: 2.25t, Queen Elizabeth II. 10t, Queen and Prince Philip.

1977, Feb. 7   Perf. 14x15

123	A27	30p multicolored	.15	.15
124	A27	2.25t multicolored	.35	.35
125	A27	10t multicolored	1.60	1.60
a.		Souv. sheet of 3, #123-125, perf. 14½	2.25	2.25
		Nos. 123-125 (3)	2.10	2.10

25th anniv. of the reign of Elizabeth II.

Qazi Nazrul
Islam — A28

Nazrul
A29

1977, Aug. 29   Litho.   Perf. 14

126	A28	40p lt green & black	.15	.15
127	A29	2.25t multicolored	.30	.30
		Set value	.40	.40

Qazi Nazrul Islam (1899-1976), natl. poet.

Pigeon
Carrying
Letter
A30

1977, Sept. 29   Litho.   Perf. 14

128	A30	30p multicolored	.15	.15
129	A30	2.25t multicolored	.30	.30
		Set value	.35	.35

Asian-Oceanic Postal Union (AOPU), 15th anniversary.

Leopard
A31

40p and 1t are vert.

1977, Nov. 9   Litho.   Perf. 13

130	A31	40p Asiatic black bear	.15	.15
131	A31	1t Axis deer	.20	.20
132	A31	2.25t shown	.40	.40
133	A31	3.50t Gayal	.60	.60
134	A31	4t Elephant	.65	.65
135	A31	5t Bengal tiger	.80	.80
		Nos. 130-135 (6)	2.80	2.80

Campfire, Tent, Scout Emblem — A32

Designs: 3.50t, Emblem, first aid, signaling, horiz. 5t, Scout emblem and oath.

1978, Jan. 22   Litho.   *Perf. 13*
136	A32	40p multicolored	.15	.15
137	A32	3.50t multicolored	.45	.45
138	A32	5t multicolored	.80	.80
		Nos. 136-138 (3)	1.40	1.40

1st National Boy Scout Jamboree, Jan. 22.
For overprint see No. 269.

Champac A33

Flowers and Flowering Trees: 1t, Pudding pipe tree. 2.25t, Flamboyant tree. 3.50t, Water lilies. 4t, Butea. 5t, Anthocephalus indicus.

1978, Mar. 31   Litho.   *Perf. 13*
139	A33	40p multicolored	.15	.15
140	A33	1t multicolored	.15	.15
141	A33	2.25t multicolored	.35	.35
142	A33	3.50t multicolored	.55	.55
143	A33	4t multicolored	.60	.60
144	A33	5t multicolored	.70	.70
		Nos. 139-144 (6)	2.50	2.50

For overprints see Nos. 259A-259F.

Crown, Scepter and Staff of State — A34

Designs: 3.50t, Royal family on balcony. 5t, Queen Elizabeth II and Prince Philip. 10t, Queen in coronation regalia, Westminster Abbey.

1978, May   *Perf. 14*
145	A34	40p multicolored	.15	.15
146	A34	3.50t multicolored	.55	.55
147	A34	5t multicolored	.80	.80
148	A34	10t multicolored	1.50	1.50
a.		Souv. sheet of 4, #145-148, perf. 14½	3.00	3.00
		Nos. 145-148 (4)	3.00	3.00

Coronation of Queen Elizabeth II, 25th anniv.
For overprint see No. 228B.

Alan Cobham's DH50, 1926 A35

Planes: 2.25t, Capt. Hans Bertram's Junkers W33 Atlantis, 1932-33. 3.50t, Wright brothers' plane. 5t, Concorde.

1978, June   Litho.   *Perf. 13*
149	A35	40p multicolored	.15	.15
150	A35	2.25t multicolored	.35	.35
151	A35	3.50t multicolored	.55	.55
152	A35	5t multicolored	.75	.75
		Nos. 149-152 (4)	1.80	1.80

75th anniversary of powered flight.

Holy Kaaba, Mecca — A37

Design: 3.50t, Pilgrims at Mt. Arafat, horiz.

1978, Nov. 9   Litho.   *Perf. 13*
154	A37	40p multicolored	.15	.15
155	A37	3.50t multicolored	.40	.40

Pilgrimage to Mecca.

Jasim Uddin, Poet — A38

1979, Mar. 14   Litho.   *Perf. 14*
156	A38	40p multicolored	.15	.15

Rowland Hill — A39   Moulana Bhashani — A40

Hill and Stamps of Bangladesh: 3.50t, No. 1, horiz. 10t, Unissued UPU stamp of 1974, horiz.

1979, Aug. 27   Litho.   *Perf. 14*
157	A39	40p multicolored	.15	.15
158	A39	3.50t multicolored	.45	.45
159	A39	10t multicolored	1.40	1.40
a.		Souvenir sheet of 3, #157-159	1.75	1.75
		Nos. 157-159 (3)	2.00	2.00

Sir Rowland Hill (1795-1879), originator of penny postage.

1979, Nov. 17   *Perf. 12½*
160	A40	40p multicolored	.15	.15

Moulana Abdul Hamid Khan Bhashani (1880-1976), philosopher and statesman.

A41   A42

IYC Emblem and: 40p, Boys and Hoops. 3.50t, Children jumping. 5t, Boys flying kites.

1979, Dec. 17   Litho.   *Perf. 14x14½*
161	A41	40p multicolored	.15	.15
162	A41	3.50t multicolored	.55	.55
163	A41	5t multicolored	.80	.80
a.		Souv. sheet of 3, #161-163, perf. 14½	1.75	1.75
		Nos. 161-163 (3)	1.50	1.50

International Year of the Child.

Type of 1973

Designs: 5p, Lalbag Fort. 10p, Fenchugan Fertilizer Factory, vert. 15p, Pineapple. 20p, Gas well. 25p, Jute on boat. 30p, Banana tree. 40p, Baitul Mukarram Mosque. 50p, Baitul Mukarram Mosque. 80p, Garh excavations. 1ta, Dotara (musical instrument.) 2t, Karnaphuli Dam.

1979-82   Photo.   *Perf. 14½*
Size: 18x23mm, 23x18mm
165	A7	5p brown ('79)	.15	.15
166	A7	10p Prus blue	.15	.15
167	A7	15p yellow org ('81)	.15	.15
168	A7	20p dk carmine ('79)	.15	.15
169	A7	25p dk blue ('82)	.15	.15
170	A7	30p lt olive grn ('80)	.15	.15
171	A8	40p rose magenta ('79)	.15	.15
172	A9	50p black & gray ('81)	.15	.15
173	A7	80p dk brown ('80)	.15	.15
174	A7	1t red lilac ('81)	.15	.15
175	A7	2t brt ultra ('81)	.28	.28
		Set value	1.00	1.00

For overprints see Nos. O30-O36.

1980, Feb. 23   Litho.   *Perf. 14*
Rotary Intl., 75th Anniv.: 40p, Rotary emblem, diff.
179	A42	40p multicolored	.15	.15
180	A42	5t ultra & gold	.65	.65

For overprints see Nos. 285-286.

Canal Digging A43

1980, Mar.   Litho.   *Perf. 14*
181	A43	40p multicolored	.15	.15

Sher-e-Bangla A.K. Fazlul Huq (1873-1962), Natl. Leader — A44

1980, Apr. 27   Litho.   *Perf. 14*
182	A44	40p multicolored	.15	.15

Early Mail Transport, London 1980 Emblem — A45

1980, May 5
183	A45	1t shown	.15	.15
184	A45	10t Modern mail transport	1.25	1.25
a.		Souvenir sheet of 2, #183-184	1.40	1.40

London 80 Intl. Stamp Exhib., May 6-14.

Dome of the Rock — A46   Adult Education — A47

1980, Aug. 21   Litho.   *Perf. 14½*
185	A46	50p violet rose	.15	.15

For the families of Palestinians.

1980, Aug. 23   *Perf. 13½*
186	A47	50p multicolored	.15	.15

Beach Scene A48

1980, Sept.   Litho.   *Perf. 14*
187	A48	50p shown	.15	.15
188	A48	5t Beach scene, diff.	1.10	1.10
a.		Souvenir sheet of 2, #187-188	1.25	1.25
b.		Pair, #187-188	1.25	1.25

World Tourism Conference, Manila, Sept. 27.
No. 188b has continuous design.
For overprints see Nos. 243-244.

Hegira (Pilgrimage Year) — A49

1980, Nov. 11   Photo.   *Perf. 14*
189	A49	50p multicolored	.15	.15

A50   A51

Design: Deer and Boy Scout emblem.

1981, Jan. 1   Litho.   *Perf. 14*
190	A50	50p multicolored	.15	.15
191	A50	5t multicolored	.75	.75

5th Asia-Pacific and 2nd Bangladesh Scout Jamboree, 1980-1981.

1980, Dec.   Litho.   *Perf. 14*
192	A51	50p multicolored	.15	.15
193	A51	2t multicolored	.45	.45

Begum Roquiah (1880-1932), educator.

Nos. 58-60 Overprinted:
2nd / CENSUS / 1981

1981, Mar. 6   *Perf. 13½*
194	A11	20p multicolored	.15	.15
195	A11	25p multicolored	.15	.15
196	A11	75p multicolored	.15	.15
		Set value	.25	.25

A52   A53

1981, Mar. 16   Litho.   *Perf. 14*
197	A52	1t multicolored	.15	.15
198	A52	15t multicolored	2.00	2.00
a.		Souvenir sheet of 2, #197-198	2.25	2.25

Queen Mother Elizabeth, 80th birthday (1980).

1981, Mar. 26
199	A53	50p Citizen Holding Rifle & Flag	.15	.15
200	A53	2t People, map	.25	.25
		Set value	.32	.32

10th anniversary of independence.

UN Conference on Least-developed
Countries, Paris — A54

1981, Sept. 1   Litho.   Perf. 14x13½
201 A54 50p multicolored   .15 .15

Birth Centenary of
Kemal Ataturk (First
President of
Turkey) — A55

1981, Nov. 10   Litho.   Perf. 14
202 A55 50p Portrait   .15 .15
203 A55 1t Portrait, diff.   .15 .15
    Set value   .20 .20

Intl. Year of
the Disabled
A56

1981, Dec. 26   Litho.   Perf. 14
204 A56 50p Sign language, vert.   .15 .15
205 A56 2t Amputee   .35 .25
    Set value   .33 .33

World Food Day,
Oct. 16 — A57

1981, Dec. 31   Litho.   Perf. 13½x14
206 A57 50p multicolored   .15 .15

A58   A59

1982, May 22   Litho.   Perf. 13½x14
207 A58 50p Boat hauling rice straw .15 .15

10th Anniv. of UN Conf. on Human
Environment.
For overprint see No. 281.

1982, Oct. 9
208 A59 50p K. Hossain   .15 .15

Scouting
Year — A60

1982, Oct. 21   Litho.   Perf. 14
209 A60 50p Emblem, knots   .15 .15
210 A60 2t Baden-Powell, vert.   .45 .45

Capt.
Mohiuddin
Jahangir
A61

Liberation Heroes (Tablet Color): b, Sepoy
Hamidur Rahman (pale green). c, Sepoy Mohammed Mustafa Kamal (rose claret). d, Mohammad
Ruhul Amin (yellow). e, M. Matiur Rahman (olive
bister). f, Lance-Naik Munshi Abdur Rob (brown
orange). g, Lance-Naik Nur Mouhammad (bright
yellow green).

1982, Dec. 16   Litho.   Perf. 14
211   Strip of 7   .60 .60
a.-g. A61 50p multicolored   .15 .15

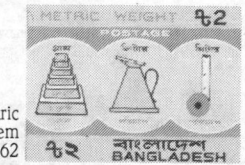

Metric
System
A62

1983, Jan. 10   Litho.   Perf. 14
212 A62 50p Mail scale, vert.   .15 .15
213 A62 2t Weights, measures   .28 .28

TB Bacillus
Centenary — A63

1983, Feb. 20   Litho.   Perf. 14
214 A63 50p Koch   .15 .15
215 A63 1t Slides, microscope   .20 .20

A64

1983, Mar. 14   Litho.   Perf. 14
216 A64 1t Open stage theater   .15 .15
217 A64 3t Boat race   .32 .32
218 A64 10t Snake dance   1.00 1.00
219 A64 15t Tea garden   1.50 1.50
    Nos. 216-219 (4)   2.97 2.97

Commonwealth Day.

Jnantapash
Shahidullah (1885-
1969), Patriot and
Physician — A65

1983, July 10   Litho.   Perf. 14
220 A65 50p multicolored   .15 .15

Birds — A66

1983, Aug. 17   Litho.   Perf. 14
221 A66 50p Copsychus saulari   .15 .15
222 A66 2t Halcyon smyrnensis,
    vert.   .25 .25
223 A66 3.75t Dinopium
    benghalense, vert.   .40 .40

224 A66 5t Carina scutulota   .60 .60
a.   Souvenir sheet of 4, #221-224   1.75 1.75
    Nos. 221-224 (4)   1.40 1.40

No. 224a sold for 13t.

Local
Fish — A67

1983, Oct. 31   Litho.   Perf. 14
225 A67 50p Macrobrachium
    rosengergii   .15 .15
226 A67 2t Stromateus cinereus   .25 .25
227 A67 3.75t Labeo rohita   .40 .40
228 A67 5t Anabas testudineus   .60 .60
a.   Souv. sheet of 4, #225-228, imperf. 1.25 1.25
    Nos. 225-228 (4)   1.40 1.40

No. 228a sold for 13t.

No. 148 Ovptd. "Nov. '83/Visit of Queen"
in Red

1983, Nov. 14   Litho.   Perf. 14
228B A34 10t multicolored   2.50 2.50

World Communications Year — A68

1983, Dec. 21   Litho.   Perf. 14
229 A68 50p Messenger, vert.   .15 .15
230 A68 5t Jet, train, ship, vert.   .60 .60
231 A68 10t Dish antenna, messen-
    ger   1.10 1.10
    Nos. 229-231 (3)   1.85 1.85

Sangsad Bhaban   Mailboat
Conference Hall   A70
A69

1983, Dec. 5   Litho.   Perf. 14
232 A69 50p shown   .15 .15
233 A69 5t Old Dacca Fort   .25 .25
    Set value   .30 .30

14th Islamic Foreign Ministers Conference.

Perf. 11½x12½, 12½x11½
1983, Dec. 21
234 A70 5p shown   .15 .15
235 A70 10p Dacca P.O. interior   .15 .15
236 A70 15p IWTA Terminal   .15 .15
237 A70 20p Sorting mail   .15 .15
238 A70 25p Mail delivery   .15 .15
239 A70 30p Postman at mailbox   .15 .15
240 A70 50p Mobile post office   .15 .15

Size: 30½x1
8½mm
Perf. 12x11½
241 A70 1t Kamalapur Railway
    Station   .15 .15
242 A70 2t Zia Intl. Airport   .20 .20
242A A70 5t Khulna P.O.   .50 .50
    Set value   1.20 1.20

Nos. 235-237, 239-242A horiz.
See #270-271. For overprints see #O37-O46,
O48.

No. 188b Overprinted in English

First Bangladesh National Philatelic Exhibition 1984
50P   ৫০৳

or Bengali in Red

প্রথম বাংলাদেশ জাতীয় ডাকটিকিট প্রদর্শনী - ১৯৮৪

৬৫   ৮৫

1984, Feb. 1   Litho.   Perf. 14
243 A48 50p Beach Scene   .15 .15
244 A48 5t Beach Scene, diff.   .50 .50
a.   Pair, #243-244   1.25 1.25
    Set value   .56 .56

1st Bangladesh Natl. Philatelic Exhibition, 1984.
No. 244a has continuous design.

Girl Examining Stamp Album — A71

1984, May 17   Perf. 14½
245 A71 50p shown   .15 .15
246 A71 7.50t Boy updating collec-
    tion   .75 .75
a.   Souvenir sheet of 2, #245-246   1.25 1.25
b.   Pair, #245-246   .90 .90

#246b has continuous design. #246a sold for 10t.

Dacca Zoo — A72   Postal Life
    Insurance,
    Cent. — A73

1984, July 17   Litho.   Perf. 14
247 A72 1t Sarus crane, gavial   .15 .15
248 A72 2t Peafowl, royal Bengal tiger .20 .20

1984, Dec. 3
249 A73 1t Chicken hawk, hen   .15 .15
250 A73 5t Beneficiaries   .50 .50

Abbasudin Ahmad,
Bengali
Singer — A74

1984, Dec. 24
251 A74 3t multicolored   .30 .30

No. 116 Ovptd. for KHULNAPEX '84
Stamp Exhibition

খুলনাপেক্স — ৮৪

1984, Dec. 29   Litho.   Perf. 15
252 A25 2.25t multicolored   .30 .30

1984
Summer
Olympics,
Los Angeles
A75

1984, Dec. 31   Perf. 14
253 A75 1t Bicycling   .15 .15
254 A75 5t Field hockey   .50 .50
255 A75 10t Volleyball   1.00 1.00
    Nos. 253-255 (3)   1.65 1.65

Islamic Development Bank, 9th Annual
Congress, Dacca — A76

1985, Feb. 2
256 A76   1t Farmer   .15 .15
257 A76   5t Four Bengalis   .50 .50

UN Child Survival   UN Decade for
Campaign — A77   Women — A78

1985, Mar. 14
258 A77   1t Breastfeeding   .20 .20
259 A77   10t Growth monitoring   1.10 1.10

Nos. 139-144 Ovptd. in Bengali for Local
Elections

উপজেলা নির্বাচন ১৯৮৫

1985, May 16   Litho.   Perf. 13
259A A33   40p multicolored   .15 .15
259B A33   1t multicolored   .15 .15
259C A33   2.25t multicolored   .22 .22
259D A33   3.50t multicolored   .32 .32
259E A33   4t multicolored   .38 .38
259F A33   5t multicolored   .45 .45
           Set value   1.00 1.00

1985, July 18   Perf. 14
260   A78   1t shown   .15 .15
261   A78   10t Technology   .90 .90

UN, 40th
Anniv.
A79

1985, Sept. 15
262 A79   1t UN building   .15 .15
263 A79   10t World map, natl. flag .50 .50
          Set value   .56 .56

11th anniv. of UN admission.

Intl. Youth
Year — A80

1985, Nov. 2   Litho.   Perf. 14
264 A80   1t Scissors, pencil   .15 .15
265 A80   5t Hammer, wrenches   .50 .50

Seven Doves,
Council
Emblem — A81

1985, Dec. 8   Litho.   Perf. 14
266 A81   1t shown   .15 .15
267 A81   5t Flags, lotus blossom   .50 .50

1st South Asian Regional Council Summit,
SARC, Dacca.

Shilpacharya Zainul
Abedin (1914-
1976), Founder,
Dacca College of
Art — A82

1985, Dec. 28
268 A82   3t multicolored   .32 .32

No. 138 Overprinted
Reading Up

1985, Dec. 29   Perf. 13
269 A32   5t multicolored   .70 .70

3rd Natl. Scout Jamboree.

Postal Services Type of 1983-84
1986, Jan. 11   Litho.   Perf. 12x11½
           Size: 30½x19mm
270   A70   3t Sorting machine   .30 .30
           Perf. 12x12½
           Size: 33½x22½mm
271   A70   4t Chittagong Port   .55 .55
Issue dates: 3t, Jan. 11, 1986. 4t, Apr. 22, 1993.
For overprint see No. O46.
This is an expanding set. Numbers will change if
necessary.

Fishing Net,
by Safiuddin
Ahmed
A83

Paintings by Bengali artists: 5t, Happy Return, by
Quamrul Hassan. 10t, Levelling the Plowed Field,
by Zainul Abedin.

1986, Apr. 6   Litho.   Perf. 14
275   A83   1t multicolored   .15 .15
276   A83   5t multicolored   .50 .50
277   A83   10t multicolored   1.00 1.00
           Nos. 275-277 (3)   1.65 1.65

1986 World Cup Soccer Championships,
Mexico — A84

1986, June 29   Perf. 15x14
278   A84   1t Stealing the ball   .15 .15
279   A84   10t Goal   1.00 1.00
           Souvenir Sheet
           Imperf
279A A84   20t multicolored   2.00 2.00

No. 279A contains one stamp 62x45mm with
simulated perfs.

Gen. M.A.G. Osmani (1918-1984),
Liberation Forces Commander-in-
Chief — A85

1986, Sept. 10   Litho.   Perf. 14
280 A85   3t multicolored   .55 .55

No. 207 Ovptd. SAARC SEMINAR '86

1986, Dec. 3   Litho.   Perf. 13½x14
281 A58   50p on #207   .15 .15

Intl. Peace Year
A86   A87

1986, Dec. 25   Litho.   Perf. 12x12½
282 A86   1t shown   .15 .15
283 A86   10t City ruins, flower   1.00 1.00
           Souvenir Sheet
284 A87   20t shown   1.65 1.65

Nos. 179-180 Ovptd. or Surcharged
"CONFERENCE FOR DEVELOPMENT
'87"

1987, Jan. 12   Perf. 14
285 A42   1t on 40p multicolored   .15 .15
286 A42   5t multicolored   .50 .50

Language Movement, 35th Anniv. — A88

Illustration reduced.

1987, Feb. 21   Perf. 12½x12
287 A88   3t Protestors   .30 .30
288 A88   3t Memorial   .30 .30

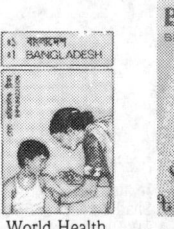

World Health   Bengali New
Day — A89   Year — A90

1987, Apr. 7   Perf. 11½x12
289 A89   1t Child immunization   .15 .15

See No. 318.

1987, Apr. 16   Perf. 12x12½
290 A90   1t Bengali script, embroi-
           dery   .15 .15
291 A90   10t shown   1.00 1.00

Jute Carpet
A91

Exports: 1t, Jute shika (wall hanging, bowl-
holder and mats), vert. 10t, Table lamp and shade,
vert.

Perf. 12x12½, 12½x12
1987, May 18   Litho.
292 A91   1t multicolored   .15 .15
293 A91   5t multicolored   .45 .45
294 A91   10t multicolored   .90 .90
           Nos. 292-294 (3)   1.50 1.50

Ustad Ayet Ali
Khan (1884-
1967),
Composer, and
Surbahar — A92

1987, Sept. 8   Perf. 12x12½
295 A92   5t multicolored   .50 .50

Palanquin
A93

Transportation.

1987, Oct. 24   Litho.   Perf. 12½x12
296 A93   2t shown   .20 .20
297 A93   3t Bicycle rickshaw   .30 .30
298 A93   5t Paddle steamer   .52 .52
299 A93   7t Train   .70 .70
300 A93   10t Ox cart   1.00 1.00
           Nos. 296-300 (5)   2.72 2.72

For overprint see No. 424.

Hossain Shahid
Suhrawardy (1893-
1963),
Politician — A94

1987, Dec. 5   Litho.   Perf. 12x12½
301 A94   3t multicolored   .32 .32

Intl. Year of
Shelter for
the
Homeless
A95

1987, Dec. 15   Perf. 12½x12
302 A95   5t shown   .55 .55
303 A95   5t Prosperous community   .55 .55

Nos. 302-303 are printed se-tenant in a continuous design.

Natl. Democracy, 1st Anniv. — A96

Design: Pres. Hossain Mohammed Ershad addressing parliament.

1987, Dec. 31
304 A96 10t multicolored 1.10 1.10

Woman Tending Crop — A97

1988, Jan. 26
305 A97 3t shown .22 .22
306 A97 5t Milking cow, village .35 .35
Intl. Fund for Agricultural Development (IFAD) Seminar on Loans for Women in Rural Areas.

1988 Summer Olympics, Seoul — A98

1988 Summer Games emblem and Sports: a, Basketball. b, Weight lifting. c, Women's tennis. d, Shooting. e, Boxing.

1988, Sept. 29 Litho. Perf. 11¹/₂
307 Strip of 5 3.00 3.00
a.-e. A98 5t any single .60 .60

Historical Sites — A99

Designs: 1t, Shait Gumbaz Mosque (interior), Bagerhat. 4t, Paharpur Monastery. 5t, Kantanagar Temple, Dinajpur. 10t, Lalbag Fort, Dacca

1988, Oct. 9 Perf. 12¹/₂x12
308 A99 1t multicolored .15 .15
309 A99 4t multicolored .50 .50
310 A99 5t multicolored .62 .62
311 A99 10t multicolored 1.25 1.25
Nos. 308-311 (4) 2.52 2.52

Qudrat-i-Khuda (1900-1977), Scientist — A100

Asia Cup Cricket — A101

1988, Nov. 3 Perf. 12x12¹/₂
312 A100 5t multicolored .55 .55

1988, Nov. 27
313 Strip of 3 1.80 1.80
a. A101 1t Wicketkeeper .15 .15
b. A101 5t Batsman .55 .55
c. A101 10t Bowler 1.10 1.10

Intl. Red Cross and Red Crescent Organizations, 125th Annivs. — A102

1988, Oct. 26 Litho. Perf. 12x12¹/₂
314 A102 5t Emblems, Dunant .65 .65
315 A102 10t Blood donation 1.30 1.30

Dacca G.P.O., 25th Anniv. — A103

1988, Dec. 6 Perf. 12
316 A103 1t Exterior .15 .15
317 A103 5t Sales counter .65 .65

World Health Day Type of 1987

1988, Jan. 16 Litho. Perf. 11¹/₂x12
318 A89 25p Oral rehydration .15 .15

32nd Meeting of the Colombo Plan Consultative Committee, Dacca — A104

1988, Nov. 29 Perf. 12x12¹/₂
319 A104 3t multicolored .32 .32
320 A104 10t multicolored 1.10 1.10

No. 191 Ovptd. ৫ম জাতীয় রোভার মুট ১৯৮৮-৮৯

1989 Litho. Perf. 14
321 A50 5t multicolored .65 .65
Scouting.

No. 277 Ovptd. চতুর্থ দ্বিবার্ষিক এশীয় চারুকলা প্রদর্শনী বাংলাদেশ ১৯৮৯

1989, Mar. 1
322 A83 10t multicolored 1.10 1.10
4th Asiatic Exposition.

A106

A107

1989, Mar. 13 Litho. Perf. 12x12¹/₂
324 A106 10t multicolored 1.10 1.10
Police academy, Sardah, 75th anniv.

1989, Mar. 7 Litho. Perf. 12x12¹/₂
Modernizing water supply services.
325 A107 10t multicolored .95 .95
12th Natl. Science & Technology Week.

A108

French Revolution, Bicent. — A109

Scenes from the revolution: 5t, Close-up of revolutionaries destroying the Bastille, vert. No. 326b, Liberty guiding the people. No. 326c, Women's march on Versailles, vert. No. 327a, Celebration of the Federation on the Champ de Mars. No. 327b, Storming of the Bastille. 25t, Montage of scenes, #326a-326c.

1989, July 12 Perf. 14
326 Sheet of 3 + label 2.65 2.65
a. A108 5t multicolored .52 .52
b.-c. A108 10t any single 1.05 1.05
Perf. 14x15
327 Strip of 2 + label 3.50 3.50
a.-b. A109 17t any single 1.75 1.75
Size: 152x88mm
Imperf
328 A108 25t multicolored 2.65 2.65
Nos. 326-328 (3) 8.80 8.80
Labels picture the revolution anniv. emblem.

Rural Development in Asia and the Pacific (CIRDAP), 10th Anniv. — A110

1989, Aug. 10 Litho. Perf. 12¹/₂x12
329 A110 5t shown .50 .50
330 A110 10t multi, diff. 1.00 1.00
Printed se-tenant in a continuous design.

Child Survival A111

1989, Aug. 22
331 A111 1t shown .15 .15
332 A111 10t Women and children, diff. .95 .95
SOS Children's Village, 40th anniv.

Involvement of the Bangladesh Army in UN Peace-keeping Operations, 1st Anniv. — A112

1989, Sept. 12 Perf. 12x12¹/₂
333 A112 4t shown .38 .38
334 A112 10t Camp, two soldiers .92 .92

2nd Asian Poetry Festival, Dacca — A113

1989, Nov. 17 Litho. Perf. 12x12¹/₂
335 A113 2t multicolored .20 .20
336 A113 10t multicolored 1.00 1.00

State Printing Office A114

1989, Dec. 7 Perf. 13¹/₂
337 A114 10t multicolored 1.00 1.00

Bangladesh Television, 25th Anniv. A115

1989, Dec. 25 Litho. Perf. 12¹/₂x12
338 A115 5t shown .50 .50
339 A115 10t Emblem, flowers, diff. 1.00 1.00

World Wildlife Fund A116

Various gavials, (Gavialis gangeticus).

1990, Jan. 31 Litho. Perf. 14
340 A116 50p shown .15 .15
341 A116 2t Reptile's jaws .20 .20
342 A116 4t 4 reptiles .40 .40
343 A116 10t 2 reptiles resting 1.00 1.00
a. Block of 4, #340-343 1.75 1.75

A117 A118

1990, Feb. 2 Perf. 14
344 A117 6t multicolored .60 .60
Natl. Population Day.

1990, May 6 Perf. 14
345 A118 7t shown .70 .70
346 A118 10t Penny Black, No. 230 1.00 1.00
Penny Black, 150th anniv.

Justice Syed Mahbub Murshed, (1911-1979) — A119

1990, Apr. 3   Litho.   Perf. 12½x12
347 A119 5t multicolored   .50   .50

Intl. Literacy Year — A120

Design: 10t, Boy teaching girl to write.

1990, Apr. 10   Perf. 12x12½
348 A120 6t multicolored   .60   .60
349 A120 10t multicolored   1.00   1.00

Loading Cargo Plane — A121

Curzon Hall — A122

Fertilizer Plant — A123

Postal Academy, Rajshahi — A124

Salimullah Hall — A125

Bangla Academy — A126

1989-93   Perf. 12x11½, 12, 12x12½
350 A121 3t multicolored   .30   .30
351 A122 5t gray blk & red brn   .50   .50
352 A123 10t carmine   1.00   1.00
353 A124 20t multicolored   2.00   2.00
                Perf. 14½x14
354 A125 6t blue gray & yel   .90   .90
                Perf. 14x14½
355 A126 2t brown & green   .60   .60
      Nos. 350-355 (6)   5.30   5.30

   Issue dates: 5t, Mar. 31. 3t, Apr. 30. 10t, 20t,
July 8. 6t, Jan. 30, 1991. 2t, Dec. 3, 1993.
   This is an expanding set. Numbers will change.

World Cup Soccer Championships, Italy — A133

1990, June 12   Litho.   Perf. 14
362 A133 8t shown   .80   .80
363 A133 10t Soccer player, diff.   1.00   1.00
                Size: 115x79mm
                Imperf
364 A133 25t Colosseum, soccer ball   2.50   2.50
      Nos. 362-364 (3)   4.30   4.30

Fruits — A134

1990, July 16   Perf. 12x12½
365 A134 1t Mangifera indica   .15   .15
366 A134 2t Psidium guayava   .20   .20
367 A134 3t Citrullus vulgaris   .30   .30
368 A134 4t Carica papaya   .40   .40
369 A134 5t Artocarpus heterophyl-
              lus   .50   .50
370 A134 10t Averrhoa carambola   1.00   1.00
      Nos. 365-370 (6)   2.55   2.55

UN Conference on Least Developed Nations, Paris A135

1990, Sept. 3   Litho.   Perf. 14
371 A135 10t multicolored   1.20   1.20

Asia-Pacific Postal Training Center, 20th Anniv. — A136

Design: 6t, Map of Western Pacific, letters.

1990, Sept. 10   Perf. 13½x14
372 A136 2t shown   .24   .24
373 A136 6t multicolored   .70   .70
   a.   Pair, #372-373   .94   .94
   No. 373a has continuous design.

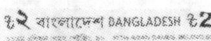

11th Asian Games, Beijing A137

1990, Sept. 22   Perf. 14
374 A137 2t Rowing   .24   .24
375 A137 4t Kabaddi   .48   .48
376 A137 8t Wrestling   .95   .95
377 A137 10t Badminton   1.20   1.20
      Nos. 374-377 (4)   2.87   2.87

Lalan Shah, Poet — A138

1990, Oct. 17   Litho.   Perf. 14
378 A138 6t multicolored   .70   .70

UN Development Program, 40th Anniv. — A139

1990, Oct. 24   Litho.   Perf. 14
379 A139 6t multicolored   .90   .90

Immunization Program — A139a

1990, Nov. 29   Litho.   Perf. 14½x14
379A A139a 2t brown   .28   .28

Butterflies — A140

1990, Dec.   Litho.   Perf. 13½x12
380 A140 6t Danaus chrysippus   .70   .70
381 A140 6t Precis almana   .70   .70
382 A140 10t Ixias pyrene   1.15   1.15
383 A140 10t Danaus plexippus   1.15   1.15
   a.   Block of 4, #380-383   3.70   3.70

UN Decade Against Drugs A141

1991, Jan 1   Litho.   Perf. 14x13½
384 A141 2t Drugs, map   .30   .30
385 A141 4t shown   .60   .60

Third National Census — A142

1991, Mar. 12   Litho.   Perf. 14
386 A142 4t multicolored   .60   .60

Independence, 20th Anniv. A143

Designs: a, Invincible Bangla statue. b, Freedom
Fighter statue. c, Mujibnagar Memorial. d, Eternal
flame. e, National Martyrs' Memorial.

1991, Mar. 26   Perf. 13½
387 A143 4t Strip of 5, #a.-e.   3.00   3.00
   No. 387 printed in continuous design.

Pres. Ziaur Rahman, 10th Death Anniv.
   A144   A145

1991, May 30   Perf. 14
388 A144 50p multicolored   .15   .15
389 A145 2t multicolored   .30   .30
   a.   Souvenir sheet of 2, #388-389   1.50   1.50
          Set value   .38   .38
   No. 389a sold for 10t.

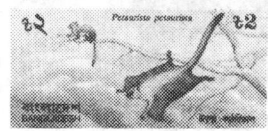

Endangered Animals — A146

1991, June 16   Perf. 12
390 A146 2t Petaurista petaurista   .30   .30
391 A146 4t Presbytis entellus, vert.   .60   .60
392 A146 6t Buceros bicornis, vert.   .90   .90
   a.   Pair, #391-392   1.50   1.50
393 A146 10t Manis crassicaudata   1.50   1.50
   a.   Pair, #390, 393   1.80   1.80
      Nos. 390-393 (4)   3.30   3.30

Kaikobad (1857-1951), Poet — A147

1991, July 21   Litho.   Perf. 14
394 A147 6t multicolored   .90   .90

Rabindranath Tagore, Poet, 50th Anniv. of Death — A148

1991, Aug. 7
395 A148 4t multicolored   .60   .60

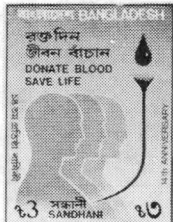

Blood and Eye Donations — A149

1991, Sept. 19
396 A149 3t shown   .90   .90
397 A149 5t Blind man and eye   1.45   1.45

   Sandhani, Medical Students Association, 14th
anniversary.

Shahid Naziruddin, Leader of Democratic Movement, 1st Anniv. of Death — A150

1991, Oct. 10
398 A150 2t multicolored .32 .32

Shaheed Noor Hossain, 4th Death Anniv. — A151

1991, Nov. 10 Litho. Perf. 14
399 A151 2t multicolored .22 .22

Archaeological Treasures of Mainamati — A152

Designs: a, Bronze Stupa with images of Buddha. b, Bowl and pitcher. c, Ruins of Salban Vihara Monastery. d, Gold coins. e, Terra-cotta plaque.

1991, Nov. 26 Litho. Perf. 13½
400 A152 4t Strip of 5, #a.-e. 2.15 2.15

Mass Uprising, First Anniv. A153

1991, Dec. 6 Perf. 14
401 A153 4t multicolored .42 .42

Miniature Sheets

Independence, 20th Anniv. — A154

Martyred intellectuals who died in 1971: No. 402a, A.N.M. Munier Chowdhury. b, Ghyasuddin Ahmad. c, S.M.A. Rashidul Hasan. d, Muhammad Anwar Pasha. e, Dr. Md. Mortaza. f, Shahid Saber. g, Fazlur Rahman Khan. h, Ranada Prasad Saha. i, Adhyaksha Joges Chandra Ghose. j, Santosh Chandra Bhattacharyya.
No. 403a, Dr. Gobinda Chandra Deb. b, A.N.M. Muniruzzaman. c, Mufazzal Haider Chaudhury. d, Dr. Abdul Alim Choudhury. e, Sirajuddin Hossain. f, Shahidulla Kaiser. g, Altaf Mahmud. h, Dr. Jyotirmay Guha Thakurta. i, Dr. Md. Abul Khair. j, Dr. Serajul Haque Khan.
No. 404a, Dr. Mohammad Fazle Rabbi. b, Mir Abdul Quyyum. c, A.N.M. Golam Mostafa. d, Dhirendranath Dutta. e, S.A. Mannan (Ladu Bhai). f, Nizamuddin Ahmad. g, Abul Bashar Chowdhury. h, Selina Parveen. i, Dr. Abul Kalam Azad. j, Saidul Hassan.
No. 404 l, LCDR. Moazzam Hussain. m, Muhammad Habibur Rahman. n, Khandoker Abu Taleb. o, Moshiur Rahman. p, Md. Abdul Muktadir. q, Nutan Chandra Sinha. r, Syed Nazmul Haque. s,

Dr. Mohammed Amin Uddin. t, Dr. N.A.M. Faizul Mohee. u, Sukha Ranjan Somaddar.

1991-93 Litho. Perf. 13½
Sheets of 10
402 A154 2t #a.-j. + 5 labels 2.50 2.50
403 A154 2t #a.-j. + 5 labels 2.50 2.50
404 A154 2t #a.-j. + 5 labels 2.50 2.50
Perf. 14½
404K A154 2t #l.-u. + 5 labels 3.00 3.00
Issued: #402-404, 12/14/91; #404K, 12/14/93. See Nos. 470-471.

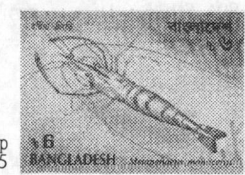

Shrimp A155

1991, Dec. 31 Perf. 14
405 A155 6t Penaeus monodon .75 .75
406 A155 6t Metapenaeus monoceros .75 .75
  a. Pair, #405-406 1.50 1.50

World Environment Day — A157

Design: 4t, Scenes of environmental protection and pollution control, vert.

1992, June 5 Litho. Perf. 14
408 A157 4t multicolored .50 .50
409 A157 10t multicolored 1.25 1.25

Nawab Sirajuddaulah of Bengal (1733-1757) A158

1992, July 2 Litho. Perf. 14
410 A158 10t multicolored 1.25 1.25

Syed Ismail Hossain Sirajee (1880-1931) A159

1992, July 17
411 A159 4t multicolored .48 .48

Tree Week — A160

1992, July 17 Litho. Perf. 14
412 A160 2t Couple planting tree, horiz. .40 .40
413 A160 4t Birds, trees .80 .80

1992 Summer Olympics, Barcelona A161

Olympic rings and: a, 4t, Rowing. b, 6t, Hands holding Olympic torch. c, 10t, Peace doves. d, 10t, Clasped hands.

1992, July 25 Litho. Perf. 14
414 A161 Block of 4, #a.-d. 3.00 3.00

The Star Mosque, 18th Cent. A162

1992, Oct. 29 Litho. Perf. 14½x14
415 A162 10t multicolored 1.25 1.25

Masnad-E-Ala Isa Khan, 393rd Anniv. of Death — A163

1992, Sept. 15 Perf. 14x14½
416 A163 4t multicolored .48 .48

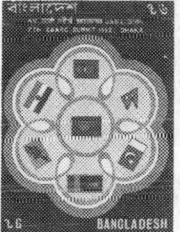

7th SAARC Summit, Dacca — A164

1992, Dec. 5
417 A164 6t Flags of members .75 .75
418 A164 10t Emblem 1.25 1.25

1992 Bangladesh Natl. Philatelic Exhibition — A165

Designs: No. 419a, Elephant and mahout, ivory work, 19th cent. b, Post rider, mail box and postman delivering mail to villager.

1992, Sept. 26 Perf. 14½x14
419 A165 10t Pair, #a.-b. + label 4.50 4.50
  c. Souv. sheet, imperf. 11.00 11.00

No. 419c contains one strip of No. 419 with simulated perforations and sold for 25t.

1992 Intl. Conference on Nutrition, Rome — A166

1992, Dec. 5
420 A166 4t multicolored .48 .48

Meer Nisar Ali Titumeer (1782-1831) — A167

1992, Nov. 19 Litho. Perf. 14½x14
421 A167 10t multicolored 1.75 1.75

Archaeological Relics, Mahasthan — A168

Relics from 3rd century B.C.-15th century A.D.: No. 422a, Terracotta seal and head. b, Terracotta hamsa. c, Terracotta Surya image. d, Gupta stone columns.

1992, Nov. 30 Litho. Perf. 14½x14
422 A168 10t Strip of 4, #a.-d. 3.40 3.40

Canal Digging A169

Designs: a, Workers digging canal. b, Completed project.

1993, Mar. 31 Litho. Perf. 14½x14
423 A169 2t Pair, #a.-b. 1.20 1.20

No.3000vptd. Banglapex '92

1993 Litho. Perf. 12½x12
424 A93 10t multicolored 5.75 5.75

Syed Abdus Samad (1895-1964), Soccer Player — A170

1993, Feb. 2 Perf. 14x14½
425 A170 2t multicolored .65 .65

A171

1993, Apr. 14
426 A171 2t multicolored   2.35 2.35

Haji Shariat Ullah
(1770-1839)
A172

1993, Mar. 10 Litho. Perf. 14x14¹/₂
427 A172 2t multicolored   1.25 1.25

World
Health
Day
A173

1993, Apr. 7 Perf. 14¹/₂x14, 14x14¹/₂
428 A173 6t Prevent accidents   1.30 1.30
429 A173 10t Prevent violence, vert.   2.15 2.15

Compulsory Primary Education — A174

1993, May 26
430 A174 2t Slate, chalk, books   .60 .60
431 A174 2t Hand writing, children, vert.   .60 .60

Nawab Sir Salimullah (1871-
1915) — A175

1993, June 7 Litho. Perf. 14¹/₂x14
432 A175 4t multicolored   1.20 1.20

Fishing
Industry
A176

1993, Aug. 15 Litho. Perf. 14¹/₂x14
433 A176 2t multicolored   .70 .70

Tomb of Sultan Ghiyasuddin Azam
Shah — A177

1993, Dec. 30 Litho. Perf. 14¹/₂x14
434 A177 10t multicolored   2.75 2.75

Scenic
Views
A178

Designs: No. 435, Sunderban. No. 436,
Madhabkunda Waterfall, vert. No. 437, River,
mountains, vert. No. 438, Beach, Kuakata.

Perf. 14¹/₂x14, 14x14¹/₂
1993, Oct. 30
435 A178 10t multicolored   2.00 2.00
436 A178 10t multicolored   2.00 2.00
437 A178 10t multicolored   2.00 2.00
438 A178 10t multicolored   2.00 2.00
   a. Souv. sheet of 4, #435-438, imperf.   10.00 10.00
     Nos. 435-438 (4)   8.00 8.00

No. 438a sold for 50t and has simulated
perforations.

6th Asian Art
Biennial,
Bangladesh
A179

1993, Nov. 7 Litho. Perf. 14x14¹/₂
439 A179 10t multicolored   2.25 2.25

Foy's
Lake
A180

1993, Nov. 6 Perf. 14¹/₂x14
440 A180 10t multicolored   2.25 2.25

Tourism month.

14th Asian
Pacific, 5th
Bangladesh Natl.
Scout Jamboree
A181

1994, Jan. 5 Perf. 14x14¹/₂
441 A181 2t multicolored   2.25 2.25

Oral Rehydration
Solution, 25th
Anniv. — A182

1994, Feb. 5 Litho. Perf. 13¹/₂x14
442 A182 2t multicolored   2.25 2.25

6th SAF
Games,
Dhaka
A183

1993, Dec. 6 Perf. 14x13¹/₂, 13¹/₂x14
443 A183 2t Shot put   .75 .75
444 A183 4t Runners, vert.   1.50 1.50

Mosques
A184

Mosques: 4t, Interior, Chhota Sona, Nawabgonj.
No. 446, Exterior, Chhota Sona. No. 447, Exterior,
Baba Adam's, Munshigonj .

1994, Mar. 30 Litho. Perf. 14x13¹/₂
445 A184 4t multicolored   1.25 1.25
446 A184 6t multicolored   1.75 1.75
447 A184 6t multicolored   1.75 1.75
     Nos. 445-447 (3)   4.75 4.75

ILO, 75th
Anniv.
A185

Designs: 4t, People, oxen working in fields. 10t,
Man rotating gearwheel, vert.

Perf. 14x13¹/₂, 13¹/₂x14
1994, Apr. 11 Litho.
448 A185 4t multicolored   .70 .70
449 A185 10t multicolored   1.75 1.75

Bangla Era, 15th
Cent. — A186

1994, Apr. 14 Perf. 13¹/₂x14
450 A186 2t multicolored   2.50 2.50

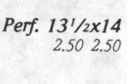

Traditional
Festivals
A187

1994, May 12 Perf. 14x13¹/₂
451 A187 4t Folk Festival   1.25 1.25
452 A187 4t Baishakhi Festival   1.25 1.25

Intl. Year of the
Family — A188

1994, May 15 Perf. 13¹/₂x14
453 A188 10t multicolored   2.50 2.50

Tree Planting
Campaign
A189

1994, June 15 Litho. Perf. 13¹/₂x14
454 A189 4t Family planting trees   1.25 1.25
455 A189 6t Hands, seedlings   1.75 1.75

1994 World Cup
Soccer
Championships,
US — A190

Soccer player's uniform colors: a, Red, yellow &
blue. b, Yellow, green, & red.

1994, June 17 Litho. Perf. 14¹/₂
456 A190 20t Pair, #a.-b. + label   4.00 4.00
     Complete booklet, #456   11.50

Jamuna Multi-Purpose Bridge — A191

1994, July 24 Perf. 14¹/₂x14
457 A191 4t multicolored   2.00 2.00

Birds — A192

Designs: 4t, Oriolus xanthornus. No. 459, Gallus
gallus. No. 460, Dicrurus paradiseus. No. 461,
Dendrocitta vagabunda.

1994, Aug. 31 Perf. 14x14¹/₂
458 A192 4t multicolored   .40 .40
459 A192 6t multicolored   .60 .60
460 A192 6t multicolored   .60 .60
461 A192 6t multicolored   .60 .60
   a. Souvenir sheet, #458-461   2.50 2.50
     Nos. 458-461 (4)   2.20 2.20

No. 461a sold for 25t.

Dr. Mohammad Ibrahim (1911-89), Pioneer in Treatment of Diabetes A193

1994, Sept. 6   Litho.   Perf. 14¹/₂x14
462 A193 2t multicolored   .30 .30

Nawab Faizunnessa Chowdhurani (1834-1903), Social Reformer A194

1994, Sept. 23   Perf. 14x14¹/₂
463 A194 2t multicolored   .30 .30

12th Asian Games, Hiroshima, Japan — A195

1994, Oct. 2   Perf. 14¹/₂x14
464 A195 4t multicolored   .65 .65

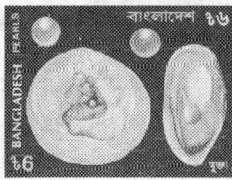

Shells A196

Designs: No. 465, White, pink pearls, oysters. No. 466, Snail, three other shells. No. 467, Scallop, other shells. No. 468, Spiral shaped shells, vert.

Perf. 14¹/₂x14, 14x14¹/₂
1994, Oct. 30   Litho.
465 A196 6t multicolored   .95 .95
466 A196 6t multicolored   .95 .95
467 A196 6t multicolored   .95 .95
468 A196 6t multicolored   .95 .95
      Nos. 465-468 (4)   3.80 3.80

Democracy Demonstration, Death of Dr. Shamsul Alam Khan Milon, 4th Anniv. — A197

1994, Nov. 27   Perf. 14¹/₂x14
469 A197 2t multicolored   .30 .30

Martyred Intellectual Type of 1991
Miniature Sheets of 8

Martyred intellectuals who died in 1971: No. 470a, Dr. Harinath Dey. b, Dr. Lt. Col. A.F. Ziaur Rahman. c, Mamum Mahmud. d, Mohsin Ali Dewan. e, Dr. Lt. Col. N.A.M. Jahangir. f, Shah Abdul Majid. g, Muhammad Akhter. h, Meherunnesa.
No. 471a, Dr. Kasiruddin Talukder. b, Fazlul Haque Choudhury. c, Md. Shamsuzzaman. d, A.K.M. Shamsuddin. e, Lt. Mohammad Anwarul Azim. f, Nurul Amin Khan. g, Mohammad Sadeque. h, Md. Araz Ali.

1994, Dec. 14   Perf. 14¹/₂
470 A154 2t #a.-h. + 4 labels   2.50 2.50
471 A154 2t #a.-h. + 4 lables   2.50 2.50

Cucurbita maxima Duch. Vegetables A199

Perf. 14x14¹/₂, 14¹/₂x14
1994, Dec. 24
472 A199 4t Diplazium esculentum   .32 .32
473 A199 4t Momordica charantia   .32 .32
474 A199 6t Lagenaria siceraria   .48 .48
475 A199 6t Trichosanthes dioica   .48 .48
476 A199 10t Solanum melongena   .80 .80
477 A199 10t Cucurbita maxima   .80 .80
      Nos. 472-477 (6)   3.20 3.20
Nos. 472-476 are vert.

World Tourism Organization, 20th Anniv. — A200

1995, Jan. 2   Perf. 14¹/₂x14
478 A200 10t multicolored   1.00 1.00

Intl. Trade Fair, Dhaka — A201

Designs: 4t, Trade products. 6t, Factories, emblems of industry.

1995, Jan. 7   Litho.   Perf. 14x14¹/₂
479 A201 4t multicolored   .30 .30
480 A201 6t multicolored   .60 .60

Bangladesh Rifles, Bicent. — A202

1995, Jan. 10   Litho.   Perf. 14¹/₂x14
481 A202 2t shown   .30 .30
482 A202 4t Building, battalion .60 .60

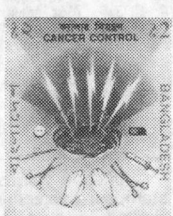

Fight Against Cancer — A203

1995, Apr. 7   Litho.   Perf. 14x14¹/₂
483 A203 2t multicolored   .80 .80

Natl. Diabetes Awareness Day — A204

1995   Perf. 14
484 A204 2t multicolored   .80 .80

OFFICIAL STAMPS

Nos. 42-47, 49-50, 52, 82-84 and 54 Overprinted **SERVICE** in Black or Red

Perf. 14x14¹/₂, 14¹/₂x14
1973-75   Litho.
O1   A7 2p black (R)   .15 .15
O2   A7 3p brt green   .15 .15
O3   A7 5p lt brown   .15 .15
O4   A7 10p black (R)   .15 .15
O5   A7 20p olive   .15 .15
O6   A7 25p red lilac   .15 .15
O8   A7 60p gray (R)   .20 .20
O9   A7 75p orange ('74)   .25 .25
O10 A9 1t violet (#52)   3.25 3.25
O11 A9 1t violet (#82)   .35 .35
O12 A9 2t grayish grn ('74)   .75 .75
O13 A9 5t gray blue (#54)   2.00 2.00
O14 A9 5t grysh bl (#84) ('75) 2.00 2.00
      Nos. O1-O14 (13)   9.70 9.70
Issue date: Apr. 30, 1973.

Nos. 95-101, 103-105 Overprinted "SERVICE" in Black or Red

1976 Litho. Perf. 15x14¹/₂, 14¹/₂x15
O16 A7 5p green   .15 .15
O17 A7 10p black (R)   .15 .15
O18 A7 20p olive   .15 .15
O19 A7 25p rose   .15 .15
O20 A8 50p rose lilac   .18 .18
O21 A7 60p gray (R)   .22 .22
O22 A7 75p olive   .25 .25

Perf. 15
O23 A9 1t violet   .38 .38
O24 A9 2t greenish gray   .75 .75
O25 A9 5t grayish blue   1.90 1.90
      Nos. O16-O25 (10)   4.28 4.28

Nos. 168-169, 171-175 Ovptd. "SERVICE"
1979-82   Photo.   Perf. 14¹/₂
O30 A7 20p dk carmine   .15 .15
O31 A7 25p dk blue ('82)   .15 .15
O32 A9 40p rose magenta   .15 .15
O33 A9 50p gray ('81)   .15 .15
O34 A7 90p dark brown   .15 .15
O35 A7 1t red lilac ('81)   .20 .20
O36 A7 2t brt ultra ('81)   .35 .35
      Set value   1.00 1.00

Nos. 234-242, 271 Ovptd. "Service" in Red, Diagonally Up on No. O43A, 1t, 2t, 4t
Perf. 11¹/₂x12¹/₂, 12¹/₂x11¹/₂
1983, Dec. 21
O37   A70 5p bluish green   .15 .15
O38   A70 10p deep magenta   .15 .15
O39   A70 15p blue   .15 .15
O40   A70 20p dark gray   .15 .15
O41   A70 25p slate   .15 .15
O42   A70 30p gray brown   .15 .15
O43   A70 50p yellow brown   .15 .15
O43A A70 50p yellow brown   .15 .15

Size: 30¹/₂x28¹/₂mm
Perf. 12x11¹/₂
O44   A70 1t ultramarine   .15 .15
O45   A70 2t Prussian blue   .25 .25

Perf. 12
O46   A70 4t blue   .55 .55
      Set value   1.30 1.30
Issue dates: 4t, 1990(?); No. O43A, 1993(?).

No. 241 Ovptd. in Red সার্ভিস

1992, Sept. 16 Litho. Perf. 12x11¹/₂
O48   A70 1t ultramarine   .15 .15

BASUTOLAND

bə-'sü-tə-‚land

LOCATION — An enclave in the state of South Africa
GOVT. — Former British Crown Colony

AREA — 11,716 sq. mi.
POP. — 733,000 (est. 1964)
CAPITAL — Maseru

The Colony, a former independent native state, was annexed to the Cape Colony in 1871. In 1883 control was transferred directly to the British Crown. Stamps of the Cape of Good Hope were used from 1871 to 1910 and those of the Union of South Africa from 1910 to 1933. Basutoland became the independent state of Lesotho on Oct. 4, 1966.

12 Pence = 1 Shilling
100 Cents = 1 Rand (1961)

Catalogue values for unused stamps in this country are for Never Hinged items, beginning with Scott 29 in the regular postage section and Scott J1 in the postage due section.

George V   George VI
A1   A2

Crocodile and River Scene

Perf. 12¹/₂
1933, Dec. 1   Engr.   Wmk. 4
1   A1 ¹/₂p emerald   .20   .60
2   A1 1p carmine   .30   .20
3   A1 2p red violet   .50   1.10
4   A1 3p ultra   .50   1.75
5   A1 4p slate   1.75 2.50
6   A1 6p yellow   2.25 2.50
7   A1 1sh red orange   3.50 5.25
8   A1 2sh6p dk brown   17.50 22.50
9   A1 5sh violet   35.00 50.00
10 A1 10sh olive green   100.00 125.00
      Nos. 1-10 (10)   161.50 211.40

Silver Jubilee Issue
Common Design Type
1935, May 4   Perf. 13¹/₂x14
11 CD301 1p car & blue   .25 .25
12 CD301 2p gray blk & ultra .60 2.00
13 CD301 3p blue & brown   2.50 3.25
14 CD301 6p brt vio & indigo 3.50 6.50
      Nos. 11-14 (4)   6.85 12.00
      Set, never hinged   14.50

Coronation Issue
Common Design Type
1937, May 12   Perf. 13¹/₂x14
15 CD302 1p carmine   .15 .15
16 CD302 2p rose violet .30 .30
17 CD302 3p bright ultra .40 .40
      Nos. 15-17 (3)   .85 .85
      Set, never hinged   1.40

1938, Apr. 1   Perf. 12¹/₂
18 A2 ¹/₂p emerald   .20   .20
19 A2 1p rose car   .20   .15
20 A2 1¹/₂p light blue   .20   .20
21 A2 2p rose lilac   .20   .20
22 A2 3p ultra   .25   .25
23 A2 4p gray   .30   .85
24 A2 6p yel ocher   .35   .40
25 A2 1sh red orange   .55   .60
26 A2 2sh6p black brown 1.75 1.75
27 A2 5sh violet   7.50 7.50
28 A2 10sh olive green   10.00 11.00
      Nos. 18-28 (11)   21.50 23.10
      Set, never hinged   47.50

Catalogue values for unused stamps in this section, from this point to the end of the section, are for Never Hinged items.

Peace Issue
South Africa Nos. 100-102 Overprinted **Basutoland**

Basic stamps inscribed alternately in English and Afrikaans.

1945, Dec. 3   Wmk. 201   Perf. 14
29   A42 1p rose pink & choc, pair   .25 .25
  a.   Single, English   .15 .15
  b.   Single, Afrikaans   .15 .15

30 A43 2p vio & slate blue, pair .30 .30
a. Single, English .15 .15
b. Single, Afrikaans .15 .15
31 A43 3p ultra & dp ultra, pair .45 .45
a. Single, English .15 .15
b. Single, Afrikaans .15 .15
Nos. 29-31 (3) 1.00 1.00

King George VI — A3

King George VI and Queen Elizabeth A4

Princess Margaret Rose and Princess Elizabeth A5

Royal British Family — A6

Perf. 12½

1947, Feb. 17 Wmk. 4 Engr.
35 A3 1p red .15 .15
36 A4 2p green .15 .15
37 A5 3p ultra .15 .15
38 A6 1sh dark violet .25 .25
Set value .45 .45

Visit of the British Royal Family, Mar. 11-12, 1947.

Silver Wedding Issue
Common Design Types

1948, Dec. 1 Photo. *Perf. 14x14½*
39 CD304 1½p brt ultra .15 .15

Engr.; Name Typo.
Perf. 11½
40 CD305 10sh dk brown ol 22.50 *32.00*

UPU Issue
Common Design Types
Engr.; Name Typo. on 3p, 6p
Perf. 13½, 11x11½

1949, Oct. 10 Wmk. 4
41 CD306 1½p blue .28 .28
42 CD307 3p indigo .55 .55
43 CD308 6p orange yel .75 .75
44 CD309 1sh red brown 1.10 1.10
Nos. 41-44 (4) 2.68 2.68

Coronation Issue
Common Design Type

1953, June 3 Engr. *Perf. 13½x13*
45 CD312 2p red violet & black .28 .28

Qiloane Hill — A7

Shearing Angora Goats — A8

Designs: 1p, Orange River. 2p, Mosotho horseman. 3p, Basuto household. 4½p, Maletsunyane falls. 6p, Herdboy with lesiba. 1sh, Pastoral scene. 1sh3p, Plane at Lancers Gap. 2sh6p, Old Fort Leribe. 5sh, Mission cave house.

1954, Oct. 18 Wmk. 4 *Perf. 13½*
46 A7 ½p dk brown & gray .15 .15
47 A7 1p dp grn & gray blk .15 .15
48 A7 2p org & dp blue .25 .25
49 A7 3p car & ol green .30 .30
50 A7 4½p dp blue & ind .65 .65
51 A7 6p dk grn & org brn .60 .60
52 A7 1sh rose vio & dk ol green 1.10 1.10
53 A7 1sh3p aqua & brown 1.40 1.40
54 A7 2sh6p lilac rose & dp ultra 5.00 5.00
55 A7 5sh dp car & black 7.50 7.50
56 A8 10sh dp cl & black 15.00 15.00
Nos. 46-56 (11) 32.10 32.10

See Nos. 72-82, 87-91. For surcharges see Nos. 57, 61-71.

No. 48 Surcharged ½d.

1959, Aug. 1
57 A7 ½p on 2p org & dp blue .20 .20

Chief Moshoeshoe (Moshesh) — A9

Designs: 1sh, Council chamber. 1sh3p, Mosotho on horseback.

Perf. 13x13½

1959, Dec. 15 Wmk. 314
58 A9 3p lt yel, grn & blk .15 .15
59 A9 1sh green & pink .35 .35
60 A9 1sh3p orange & ultra .60 .60
Nos. 58-60 (3) 1.10 1.10

Institution of the Basutoland National Council.

Nos. 46-56 Surcharged with New Value

2½c I **2½c** II **3½c** I **3½c** II
5c I **5c** II **10c** I **10c** II
12½c I **12½c** II
25c I **25c** II **25c.** III
50c I **50c** II **R1** I **R1** II **R1** III

1961, Feb. 14 Wmk. 4 *Perf. 13½*
61 A7 ½c on ½p dk brn & gray .15 .15
a. Double surcharge *250.00*
62 A7 1c on 1p dp grn & gray blk .15 .15
63 A7 2c on 2p org & dp bl .15 .15
a. Inverted surcharge *125.00*
64 A7 2½c on 3p (II) .15 .15
a. Type I .15 .15
b. Inverted surcharge (II) *1,750. 1,000.*
65 A7 3½c on 4½p (I) .15 .15
a. Type II 4.50 4.50
66 A7 5c on 6p (II) .15 .15
a. Type I .15 .15
67 A7 10c on 1sh (I) .22 .22
a. Type II 40.00 40.00
68 A7 12½c on 1sh3p (II) .38 .38
a. Type I .65 .65
69 A7 25c on 2sh6p (I) .65 .65
a. Type II 12.00 12.00
b. Type III .65 .65
70 A7 50c on 5sh (II) 1.40 1.40
a. Type I 2.25 2.25
71 A8 1r on 10sh (III) 2.75 2.75
a. Type I 12.00 12.00
b. Type II 12.00 12.00
Nos. 61-71 (11) 6.30 6.30

Surcharge types on Nos. 64-71 are numbered chronologically.

Types of 1954
Value in Cents and Rands

Designs: ½c, Qiloane Hill. 1c, Orange River. 2c, Mosotho horseman. 2½c, Basuto household. 3½c, Maletsunyane Falls. 5c, Herdboy with lesiba. 10c, Pastoral scene. 12½c, Plane at Lancers Gap. 25c, Old Fort Leribe. 50c, Mission cave house. 1r, Shearing Angora goats.

1961-63 Wmk. 4 Engr. *Perf. 13½*
72 A7 ½c dk brn & gray ('62) .15 .15
73 A7 1c dp grn & gray blk ('62) .15 .15
74 A7 2c org & dp bl ('62) .15 .15
75 A7 2½c car & ol grn .30 .15
76 A7 3½c dp bl & ind ('62) .25 .15
77 A7 5c dk grn & org brn ('62) .40 .30
78 A7 10c rose vio & dk ol ('62) .65 .40
79 A7 12½c aqua & brn ('62) .80 .55
80 A7 25c lilac rose & dp ultra ('62) 1.65 1.00
81 A7 50c dp car & blk ('62) 6.00 4.00

Perf. 11½
82 A8 1r dp cl & blk ('63) 10.00 6.50
Nos. 72-82 (11) 20.50 13.50

See Nos. 87-91. For overprints on stamps and types see Lesotho Nos. 5-14, 20a.

Freedom from Hunger Issue
Common Design Type
Perf. 14x14½

1963, June 4 Photo. Wmk. 314
83 CD314 12½c lilac .50 .40

Red Cross Centenary Issue
Common Design Type

1963, Sept. 2 Litho. *Perf. 13*
84 CD315 2½c black & red .18 .18
85 CD315 12½c ultra & red .70 .70

Queen Type of 1961-63

1964 Engr. *Perf. 13½*
87 A7 1c grn & gray blk .15 .15
88 A7 2½c car & ol green .20 .16
89 A7 5c dk green & org brn .45 .38
90 A7 12½c aqua & brown 1.10 .95
91 A7 50c dp car & black 4.00 3.25
Nos. 87-91 (5) 5.90 4.89

Mosotho Woman and Child — A10

Designs: 3½c, Maseru border post. 5c, Mountains. 12½c, Legislative Building.

Perf. 14x13½

1965, May 10 Photo. Wmk. 314
97 A10 2½c ultra & multi .15 .15
98 A10 3½c blue & bister .16 .15
99 A10 5c blue & ocher .20 .16
100 A10 12½c lt blue, blk & buff .40 .40
Nos. 97-100 (4) .91 .86

Attainment of self-government.

Common Design Types pictured in section before Great Britain.

ITU Issue
Common Design Type

1965, May 17 Litho. *Perf. 11x11½*
101 CD317 1c ver & red lilac .15 .15
102 CD317 20c grnsh bl & org brn .85 .65

Intl. Cooperation Year Issue
Common Design Type

1965, Oct. 25 Wmk. 314 *Perf. 14½*
103 CD318 ½c blue grn & cl .15 .15
104 CD318 12½c lt vio & green .90 .70

Churchill Memorial Issue
Common Design Type

1966, Jan. 24 Photo. *Perf. 14*
Design in Black, Gold and Carmine Rose
105 CD319 1c bright blue .15 .15
106 CD319 2½c green .15 .15
107 CD319 10c brown .50 .50
108 CD319 22½c violet 1.25 1.25
Nos. 105-108 (4) 2.05 2.05

POSTAGE DUE STAMPS

Catalogue values for all unused stamps in this section are for Never Hinged items.

Basutoland stamps can be mounted in the Scott British Africa album.

D1

Coat of Arms — D2

1933-38 Wmk. 4 Typo. *Perf. 14*
J1 D1 1p dark red ('38) .20 .20
a. 1p dark carmine 1.00 1.10
b. Wmk. 4a (error) 67.50
J2 D1 2p lt violet .20 .20
a. Wmk. 4a (error) 67.50

Nos. J1-J2 valued on chalky paper.

1956, Dec. 1
J3 D2 1p carmine .25 .25
J4 D2 2p dark purple .25 .25

Nos. J2-J4 Surcharged with New Value

1961
J5 D2 1c on 1p carmine .15 .15
J6 D2 1c on 2p dk purple .15 .15
J7 D1 5c on 2p lt violet 3.00 3.00
a. Wmk. 4a (error) 275.00
J8 D2 5c on 2p dark pur ("5" 7½mm high) .15 .15
a. "5" 3½mm high 17.50 *25.00*
Nos. J5-J8 (4) 3.45 3.45

Value in Cents

1964 Wmk. 314 *Perf. 14*
J9 D2 1c carmine .15 .15
J10 D2 5c dark purple .20 .20

For overprints see Lesotho Nos. J1-J2.

OFFICIAL STAMPS

Nos. 1-3 and 6 Overprinted "OFFICIAL"

1934 Wmk. 4 Engr. *Perf. 12½*
O1 A1 ½p emerald *3,500. 3,500.*
O2 A1 1p carmine *1,000. 1,500.*
O3 A1 2p red violet *1,500.* 900.
O4 A1 6p yellow 3,500. *2,000.*

Counterfeits exist.

BATUM

LOCATION — A seaport on the Black Sea

Batum is the capital of Adzhar, a territory which, in 1921, became an autonomous republic of the Georgian Soviet Socialist Republic.

Stamps of Batum were issued under the administration of British forces which occupied Batum and environs between December, 1918, and July, 1920, following the Treaty of Versailles.

100 Kopecks = 1 Ruble

Counterfeits exist of Nos. 1-65.

Basic Russian Designs

A8

A11

A14

A15

A19

A1

1919   Unwmk.   Litho.   *Imperf.*

1	A1	5k green	.50	.30
2	A1	10k ultramarine	.50	.30
3	A1	50k yellow	.30	.25
4	A1	1r red brown	.45	.35
5	A1	3r violet	1.75	1.75
6	A1	5r brown	2.75	2.75
		Nos. 1-6 (6)	6.25	5.70

For overprints and surcharges see #13-20, 51-65.

БАТУМ. ОБ.

Russian Stamps of
1909-17 Surcharged

Руб 10 Руб.

1919   On Stamps of 1917

7	A14	10r on 1k orange	25.00	13.50
8	A14	10r on 3k red	12.00	15.00

On Stamp of 1909-12
Perf. 14x14½

9	A14	10r on 5k claret	125.00	125.00

On Stamp of 1917

10	A14	10r on 10k on 7k light blue	110.00	110.00
		Nos. 7-10 (4)	272.00	263.50

БАТУМ. ОБ.

Russian Stamps of
1909-13 Surcharged

Коп 35 Коп.

1919

11	A15	35k on 4k carmine		1,650.
12	A19	35k on 4k dull red		6,500.

This surcharge was intended for postal cards. A few cards which bore adhesive stamps were also surcharged.
Values are for stamps off card and without gum.

Type of 1919 Issue   BRITISH
Overprinted   OCCUPATION

1919   Unwmk.   *Imperf.*

13	A1	5k green	1.25	1.10
14	A1	10k dark blue	1.25	1.10
15	A1	25k orange	1.25	1.10
16	A1	1r pale blue	.90	.85
17	A1	2r salmon pink	.40	.35
18	A1	3r violet	.40	.35
19	A1	5r brown	.40	.35
a.		"OCCIIPATION"	190.00	190.00
20	A1	7r dull red	1.25	1.10
		Nos. 13-20 (8)	7.10	6.30

Russian Stamps of 1909-17 Surcharged in Various Colors:

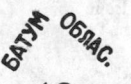

БАТУМ ОБЛАС.   БАТУМЪ
BRITISH
Р 10 Р.   Р. 15 Р.
BRITISH   OCCUPATION
OCCUPATION   ОБЛ.
10r & 50r   15r

On Stamps of 1917

1919-20   *Imperf.*

21	A14(a)	10r on 3k red	25.00	22.50
22	A14(b)	15r on 1k org (R)	50.00	45.00
23	A14(b)	15r on 1k org (Bk)	75.00	65.00
24	A14(b)	15r on 1k org (V)	50.00	45.00
25	A14(a)	50r on 1k org	300.00	300.00
26	A14(a)	50r on 2k green	275.00	250.00

Type "a" on Stamps of 1909-17
Perf. 14x14½

27	A14	50r on 2k green	300.00	300.00
28	A14	50r on 3k red	450.00	450.00
29	A15	50r on 4k car	275.00	275.00
30	A14	50r on 5k claret	275.00	275.00
31	A15	50r on 10k dk blue (R)	650.00	650.00
32	A11	50r on 15k red brn & blue	250.00	250.00

БАТУМ.ОБЛ.
Surcharged   Р.25 Р.
BRITISH
OCCUPATION

On Stamps of 1909-17

33	A14	25r on 5k cl (Bk)	27.50	27.50
34	A14	25r on 5k cl (Bl)	27.50	27.50
35	A14	25r on 10k on 7k lt blue (Bk)	50.00	50.00
36	A14	25r on 10k on 7k lt blue (Bl)	42.50	42.50
37	A11	25r on 20k on 14k bl & rose (Bk)	40.00	40.00
38	A11	25r on 20k on 14k bl & rose (Bl)	40.00	40.00
39	A11	25r on 25k grn & gray vio (Bk)	60.00	60.00
40	A11	25r on 25k grn & gray vio (Bl)	65.00	65.00
41	A8	25r on 50k vio & green (Bk)	20.00	20.00
42	A8	25r on 50k vio & green (Bl)	40.00	40.00
43	A14	50r on 2k green	65.00	65.00
44	A14	50r on 3k red	65.00	65.00
45	A15	50r on 4k car	65.00	65.00
46	A14	50r on 5k claret	70.00	70.00

On Stamps of 1917
Imperf

47	A14	50r on 2k green	95.00	95.00
48	A14	50r on 3k red	150.00	150.00
49	A14	50r on 5k claret	600.00	600.00

On Stamp of 1913
Perf. 13½

50	A19	50r on 4k dull red (Bl)	50.00	50.00

Nos. 3, 13 and 15 Surcharged in Black or Blue:

РУБ 25 ПЕН   R.50R.
BRITISH
OCCUPATION
25 РУБ.25   РУБ.
e   f

1920   *Imperf.*

51	A1(e)	25r on 5k green	20.00	20.00
52	A1(e)	25r on 5k grn (Bl)	22.50	22.50
53	A1(e)	25r on 25k orange	15.00	15.00
54	A1(e)	25r on 25k org (Bl)	60.00	60.00
55	A1(f)	50r on 50k yellow	15.00	15.00
56	A1(f)	50r on 50k yel (Bl)	50.00	50.00
		Nos. 51-56 (6)	182.50	182.50

The surcharges on Nos. 21-56 inclusive are hand-stamped and are known double, inverted, etc.

Tree Type of 1919 Overprinted Like Nos. 13-20

1920

57	A1	1r orange brown	.15	.15
58	A1	2r gray blue	.15	.15
59	A1	3r rose	.15	.15
60	A1	5r black brown	.15	.15
61	A1	7r yellow	.15	.15
62	A1	10r dark green	.15	.15
63	A1	15r violet	.15	.20
64	A1	25r vermilion	.50	.35
65	A1	50r dark blue	.65	.45
		Nos. 57-65 (9)	2.20	
		Set value		1.50

The variety "BPITISH" occurs on #57-65.

BECHUANALAND

ˌbech-'wä-nə-ˌland

(British Bechuanaland)

LOCATION — Southern Africa
GOVT. — A former British Crown Colony, annexed in 1895 to the Cape of Good Hope Colony which became a province in the Union of South Africa.
AREA — 51,424 sq. mi.
POP. — 84,210 (1904)
CAPITAL — Mafeking

12 Pence = 1 Shilling
20 Shillings = 1 Pound

Bechuanaland stamps can be mounted in the Scott British Africa album.

Watermarks

Wmk. 29- Orb   Wmk. 14- VR in Italics

Cape of Good Hope   **British**
Stamps of 1871-85   **Bechuanaland**
Overprinted

1886   Wmk. 1   *Perf. 14*
Black Overprint

1	A6	4p blue	50.00	55.00

Wmk. 2
Black Overprint

3	A6	3p claret	30.00	30.00

Red Overprint

4	A6	½p black	10.00	10.00
a.		Double overprint in red & blk	850.00	

Wmk. Anchor (16)
Black Overprint

5	A6	½p black	6.00	10.00
a.		"ritish"	1,800.	1,800.
6	A6	1p rose	8.00	6.50
b.		"ritish"	1,800.	1,600.
7	A6	2p bister	22.50	10.00
a.		"ritish"	4,500.	4,500.
8	A3	6p violet	60.00	32.50
9	A3	1sh green	215.00	125.00
a.		"ritish"	10,000.	8,000.

There is no period after Bechuanaland in the genuine stamps.

BRITISH

Black Ovpt. on Great
Britain #111

BECHUANALAND

1887   Wmk. 30

10	A54	½p vermilion	.60	1.00
a.		Double overprint	2,250.	

For overprints see Bechuanaland Protectorate Nos. 51-53.

A1

A2   A3

1887   Typo.   Wmk. 29
Country Name in Black

11	A1	1p lilac	12.00	4.75
12	A1	2p lilac	30.00	20.00
13	A1	3p lilac	3.25	4.75
14	A1	4p lilac	35.00	5.50
15	A1	6p lilac	40.00	18.00

Wmk. 14

16	A2	1sh green	30.00	5.00
17	A2	2sh green	45.00	30.00
18	A2	2sh6p green	55.00	40.00
19	A2	5sh green	90.00	90.00
20	A2	10sh green	190.00	225.00

Wmk. 29

21	A3	£1 lilac	900.	725.
22	A3	£5 lilac	2,750.	1,400.
		Pen cancellation		165.

For overprints see Bechuanaland Protectorate Nos. 54-58, 60-66. For surcharge see Cape of Good Hope No. 171.

A4   **1d.**

Surcharge of value in figures

1888
Country Name in Black
Black Surcharge

23	A4	1p on 1p lilac	7.00	5.00
a.		Double surcharge		
		Red Surcharge		
25	A4	2p on 2p lilac	12.50	3.00
a.		"2" with curved tail	200.00	150.00
26	A4	4p on 4p lilac	150.00	160.00
		Green Surcharge		
27	A4	2p on 2p lilac		2,750.
		Blue Surcharge		
27A	A4	6p on 6p lilac		4,500.
		Wmk. 14		
		Black Surcharge		
28	A2	1sh on 1sh green	85.00	47.50

British

One
Half-
Penny

Bechuanaland
No. 29   No. 30

Green Ovpt. on Cape of Good Hope #41

1889   Wmk. 16

29	A4	½p black	4.75	13.00

Vertical overprint, double overprints one inverted or double, and varieties such as "British" omitted probably are from printers waste.

Wmk. 29
Black Surcharge on No. 13

30	A1	½p on 3p lilac & blk	125.00	135.00

Cape of Good Hope Nos. 43-44 Overprinted in Black

1891   Wmk. 16

31	A4	1p rose	10.00	9.50
a.		Horiz. pair, one without overprint	1,500.	
b.		"British" omitted		575.00
c.		"Bechuanaland" omitted	850.00	
32	A4	2p bister	3.00	3.00
a.		Without period	200.00	

See Nos. 38-39.

Stamps of Great Britain   **BRITISH**
Overprinted in Black   **BECHUANALAND**

1891-94   Wmk. 30

33	A40	1p lilac	5.00	1.00
34	A56	2p green & car	3.00	2.50
35	A59	4p brown & green	2.50	.75
36	A62	6p violet, rose	2.50	1.75
37	A65	1sh green ('94)	11.00	13.00
		Nos. 33-37 (5)	24.00	19.00

For surcharges see Cape of Good Hope Nos. 172, 176-177.

Cape of Good Hope Nos. 43-44 Overprinted Like Nos. 31-32 but Reading Down

1893-95   Wmk. 16

38	A6	1p rose	2.50	2.75
a.		No dots over the "i's" of "British"	75.00	75.00
b.		"British" omitted	650.00	
c.		As "a," reading up		750.00
d.		Pair, one without overprint		
39	A6	2p bister ('95)	4.75	2.75
a.		Double overprint	900.00	900.00
b.		No dots over the "i's" of "British"	125.00	125.00
c.		"British" omitted	350.00	325.00
d.		As "b," reading up		

British   Bechuanaland.

Cape of Good Hope No. 42 Overprinted

BRITISH

BECHUANALAND

"BECHUANALAND" 16mm Long
Overprint Lines 13mm Apart

1897

40	A6	½p light green	2.50	5.00

"BECHUANALAND" 15mm Long Overprint Lines 10½mm Apart

41	A6	½p light green	10.00	27.50

"BECHUANALAND" 15mm Long Overprint Lines 13½mm Apart

42	A6	½p light green	17.50	45.00
		Nos. 40-42 (3)	30.00	77.50

BECHUANALAND PROTECTORATE

ˌbech-ˈwä-nə-ˌland prə-ˈtek-t(ə-)rət

LOCATION — In central South Africa, north of the Republic of South Africa, east of South-West Africa and bounded on the north and east by Angola and Southern Rhodesia
GOVT. — Former British Protectorate
AREA — 222,000 sq. mi.
POP. — 540,400 (1964)

Bechuanaland Protectorate became the independent republic of Botswana, Sept. 30, 1966.

12 Pence = 1 Shilling
20 Shillings = 1 Pound
100 Cents = 1 Rand (1961)

Catalogue values for unused stamps in this country are for Never Hinged items, beginning with Scott 137 in the regular postage section and Scott J7 in the postage due section.

Additional Overprint in Black on Bechuanaland No. 10

Protectorate a — Protectorate b — Protectorate c

1888-90 Wmk. 30 Perf. 14

51	A54(a)	½p vermilion	110.00	150.00
a.		Double overprint	575.00	
52	A54(b)	½p vermilion ('89)	2.50	16.00
a.		Double overprint	300.00	
53	A54(c)	½p vermilion	90.00	100.00
a.		Inverted overprint	65.00	80.00
b.		Double overprint	80.00	90.00
c.		As "a," double	600.00	600.00

For surcharge see No. 68.

Bechuanaland Nos. 16-20 Overprinted Type "b" in Black

Wmk. 14

Country Name in Black

54	A2	1sh green	55.00	50.00
a.		First "o" omitted	3,250.	3,000.
55	A2	2sh green	475.00	625.00
a.		First "o" omitted	5,750.	4,250.
56	A2	2sh6p green	500.00	625.00
a.		First "o" omitted	6,000.	4,500.
57	A2	5sh green	1,100.	1,500.
a.		First "o" omitted	6,750.	6,000.
58	A2	10sh green	3,250.	4,000.
a.		First "o" omitted	12,000.	

Bechuanaland Nos. 11-15 Overprinted Type "b" and Surcharged in Black

1888 Wmk. 29

Country Name in Black

60	A1	1p on 1p lilac	5.50	10.00
a.		Short "1"	275.00	300.00
61	A1	2p on 2p lilac	17.50	15.00
a.		"2" with curved tail	300.00	300.00
63	A1	3p on 3p lilac	80.00	110.00
64	A1	4p on 4p lilac	175.00	175.00
65	A1	6p on 6p lilac	50.00	40.00

In #60 the "1" is 2½mm high; in #60a, 2mm.

Value Surcharged in Red

66	A1	4p on 4p lilac	50.00	42.50

A7

Cape of Good Hope Type of 1886 Overprinted in Green

1889 Wmk. 16

67	A7	½p black	3.75	20.00
a.		Double overprint	400.00	475.00
b.		"Bechuanaland" omitted	600.00	600.00

Black Surcharge on Bechuanaland Protectorate No. 52

Wmk. 30

68	A54	4p on ½p ver	15.00	3.00
a.		Inverted surcharge		4,500.

Stamps of Great Britain 1881-87, Overprinted in Black BECHUANALAND PROTECTORATE

1897, Oct.

69	A54	½p vermilion	1.00	1.00
70	A40	1p lilac	3.50	.50
71	A56	2p green & car	2.00	4.00
72	A58	3p violet, *yel*	5.00	7.50
73	A59	4p brown & green	10.00	10.00
74	A62	6p violet, *rose*	17.50	10.50
		Nos. 69-74 (6)	39.00	33.50

For surcharges see Cape of Good Hope Nos. 167-170, 173-175.

Same on Great Britain No. 125

1902, Feb. 25

75	A54	½p blue green	1.50	1.25

Stamps of Great Britain, 1902, Overprinted in Black BECHUANALAND PROTECTORATE

1904-12

76	A66	½p gray green ('06)	3.50	3.50
77	A66	1p car ('05)	4.75	1.25
78	A66	2½p ultra	6.25	5.75
79	A74	1sh scar & grn ('12)	12.00	15.00
		Nos. 76-79 (4)	26.50	25.50

Same on Great Britain No. 143

1908

80	A66	½p pale yel green	2.00	3.00

King Edward VII — A9

Transvaal No. 274 Overprinted

1910 Wmk. 3

81	A9	6p brn org & blk	165.00	210.00

This stamp was issued for fiscal use, although it is known postally used.

Great Britain No. 154 Overprinted Like Nos. 76-79

1912, Sept. Wmk. 30 Perf. 15x14

82	A81	1p scarlet	1.10	1.00

Great Britain Stamps of 1912-13 Overprinted Like Nos. 76-79

1914-24 Wmk. Crown and GvR (33)

83	A82	½p green	.95	1.25
84	A83	1p scarlet	2.50	.30
85	A84	1½p red brn ('20)	1.50	2.00
86	A85	2p orange (I)	2.25	2.25
a.		2p orange (II) ('24)	30.00	3.50
87	A86	2½p ultra	2.50	10.00
88	A87	3p bluish violet	4.75	11.00
89	A88	4p slate green	5.25	9.50
90	A89	6p dull violet	5.75	11.00
91	A90	1sh bister	6.50	12.00
		Nos. 83-91 (9)	31.95	59.30

The dies of No. 86 are the same as in Great Britain 1912-13 issue.

Overprinted BECHUANALAND PROTECTORATE

Wmk. 34 Perf. 11x12

92	A91	2sh6p dk brown	110.00	140.00
a.		2sh6p light brown ('16)	125.00	140.00
93	A91	5sh rose car	150.00	200.00
a.		5sh carmine ('20)	200.00	250.00

Nos. 92, 93 were printed by Waterlow Bros. & Layton; Nos. 92a, 93a were printed by Thomas De La Rue & Co.

Same Overprint On Retouched Stamps of 1919

1920-23

94	A91	2sh6p gray brown	115.00	125.00
95	A91	5sh car rose	150.00	165.00

Great Britain Stamps of 1924 Overprinted like Nos. 76-79

Wmk. Crown and Block GvR Multiple (35)

1925-26 Perf. 15x14

96	A82	½p green	1.00	1.65
97	A83	1p scarlet	1.25	1.65
99	A85	2p deep org (II)	2.50	2.25
101	A87	3p violet	3.25	6.50
102	A88	4p slate green	4.00	12.00
103	A89	6p dull violet	5.25	16.00
104	A90	1sh bister	14.00	21.00
		Nos. 96-104 (7)	31.25	61.05

George V
A11

George VI, Cattle and Baobab Tree
A12

Perf. 12½

1932, Dec. 12 Engr. Wmk. 4

105	A11	½p green	.50	.35
106	A11	1p carmine	.50	.35
107	A11	2p red brown	.50	.45
108	A11	3p ultra	1.00	1.00
109	A11	4p orange	1.00	2.00
110	A11	6p red violet	2.50	1.25
111	A11	1sh blk & ol grn	5.00	5.00
112	A11	2sh black & org	22.50	25.00
113	A11	2sh6p black & car	17.50	20.00
114	A11	3sh black & red vio	25.00	27.50
115	A11	5sh black & ultra	35.00	40.00
116	A11	10sh blk & red brown	85.00	95.00
		Nos. 105-116 (12)	196.00	217.90

Silver Jubilee Issue
Common Design Type

1935, May 4 Perf. 11x12

117	CD301	1p car & blue	.25	.35
118	CD301	2p black & ultra	.55	.45
119	CD301	3p ultra & brown	.55	.60
120	CD301	6p brown vio & ind	1.25	1.25
		Nos. 117-120 (4)	2.60	2.65

Coronation Issue
Common Design Type

1937, May 12 Perf. 13½x14

121	CD302	1p carmine	.15	.15
122	CD302	2p brown	.15	.15
123	CD302	3p brt ultra	.25	.25
		Set value	.45	.45
		Set, never hinged	1.50	

1938, Apr. 1 Perf. 12½

124	A12	½p green	.30	.30
125	A12	1p rose car	.15	.15
126	A12	1½p light blue	.20	.30
127	A12	2p brown	.20	.30
128	A12	3p ultra	.25	.30
129	A12	4p orange	.50	1.00
130	A12	6p rose violet	1.50	2.00
131	A12	1sh blk & ol grn	1.75	2.00
133	A12	2sh6p black & car	9.00	6.50
135	A12	5sh black & ultra	17.50	6.50
136	A12	10sh black & brn	12.00	17.00
		Nos. 124-136 (11)	43.35	36.35
		Set, never hinged	67.50	

Catalogue values for unused stamps in this section, from this point to the end of the section, are for Never Hinged items.

Peace Issue

South Africa Nos. 100-102 Overprinted **Bechuanaland**

Basic stamps inscribed alternately in English and Afrikaans.

1945, Dec. 3 Wmk. 201 Perf. 14

137	A42	1p rose pink & choc, pair	.30	.30
a.		Single, English	.15	.15
b.		Single, Afrikaans	.15	.15
138	A43	2p vio & slate blue, pair	.40	.40
a.		Single, English	.20	.20
b.		Single, Afrikaans	.20	.20
139	A43	3p ultra & dp ultra, pair	.50	.50
a.		Single, English	.25	.25
b.		Single, Afrikaans	.25	.25
		Nos. 137-139 (3)	1.20	1.20

World War II victory of the Allies.

Royal Visit Issue
Types of Basutoland, 1947

Perf. 12½

1947, Feb. 17 Wmk. 4 Engr.

143	A3	1p red	.15	.15
144	A4	2p green	.15	.15
145	A5	3p ultra	.15	.15
146	A6	1sh dark violet	.30	.30
		Set value	.60	.60

Visit of the British Royal Family, Apr. 17, 1947.

Silver Wedding Issue
Common Design Types

1948, Dec. 1 Photo. Perf. 14x14½

147	CD304	1½p brt ultra	.15	.15

Engr.; Name Typo.

Perf. 11½x11

148	CD305	10sh gray black	19.50	30.00

UPU Issue
Common Design Types

Engr.; Name Typo. on 3p and 6p

1949, Oct. 10 Perf. 13½, 11x11½

149	CD306	1½p blue	.25	.25
150	CD307	3p indigo	.35	.35
151	CD308	6p red lilac	.80	.80
152	CD309	1sh olive	1.50	1.50
		Nos. 149-152 (4)	2.90	2.90

Coronation Issue
Common Design Type

1953, June 3 Engr. Perf. 13½x13

153	CD312	2p brown & black	.30	.30

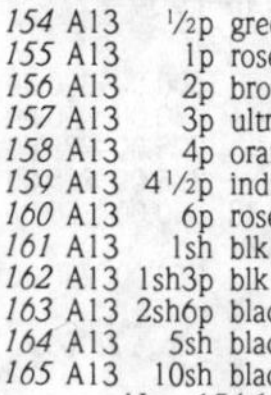

Elizabeth II
A13

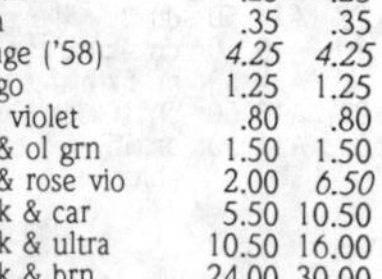

Victoria, Elizabeth II and Water Hole
A14

1955-58 Perf. 13x13½

154	A13	½p green	.25	.25
155	A13	1p rose car	.25	.25
156	A13	2p brown	.25	.25
157	A13	3p ultra	.35	.35
158	A13	4p orange ('58)	4.25	4.25
159	A13	4½p indigo	1.25	1.25
160	A13	6p rose violet	.80	.80
161	A13	1sh blk & ol grn	1.50	1.50
162	A13	1sh3p blk & rose vio	2.00	6.50
163	A13	2sh6p black & car	5.50	10.50
164	A13	5sh black & ultra	10.50	16.00
165	A13	10sh black & brn	24.00	30.00
		Nos. 154-165 (12)	50.90	71.90

For surcharges see Nos. 169-179.

Perf. 14½x14

1960, Jan. 21 Photo. Wmk. 314

166 A14 1p brown & black .15 .15
167 A14 3p car rose & black .16 .16
168 A14 6p ultra & black .32 .32
Nos. 166-168 (3) .63 .63

75th anniv. of the Proclamation of the Protectorate.

Nos. 155-165 Surcharged

1c 1c 3½c 3½c 3½c
I II I II III

5c 5c R1 R1
I II I II

Perf. 13x13½

1961, Feb. 14 Wmk. 4 Engr.

169 1c on 1p (I) .15 .15
a. Type II .15 .15
170 2c on 2p .15 .15
171 2½c on 2p .15 .15
a. Pair, one without surcharge 700.00
172 2½c on 3p .90 .90
173 3½c on 4p (III) .18 .18
a. Type I .52 .52
b. Type II 1.65 1.65
174 5c on 6p (II) .22 .22
a. Type I .75 .75
175 10c on 1sh .32 .32
a. Pair, one without surcharge 700.00
176 12½c on 1sh3p ("12½c" 11¼mm wide) .55 .55
a. "12½c" 12½mm wide .75 .75
177 25c on 2sh6p .90 .90
178 50c on 5sh 1.90 1.90
179 1r on 10sh (II, "R1" at lower center) 4.50 4.50
a. Type II, "R1" at lower left 6.50 6.50
b. Type I 300.00 110.00
Nos. 169-179 (11) 9.92 9.92

Nos. 173a and 173b are found in the same sheet; each comes with "3½c" in both wide and narrow settings.

Surcharge types are numbered chronologically.

African Golden Oriole — A15

Baobab Tree — A16

Designs: 2c, African hoopoe. 2½c, Scarlet-chested sunbird. 3½c, Cape widow bird (Yellow bishop). 5c, Swallow-tailed bee-eater. 7½c, Gray hornbill. 10c, Red-headed weaver. 12½c, Brown-hooded kingfisher. 20c, Woman musician. 35c, Woman grinding corn. 50c, Bechuana ox. 1r, Lion. 2r, Police camel patrol.

Perf. 14x14½, 14½x14

1961, Oct. 2 Photo. Wmk. 314

180 A15 1c lilac, blk & yel .20 .20
181 A15 2c pale ol, blk & org .20 .20
182 A15 2½c bis, blk, grn & dp car .25 .20
183 A15 3½c pink, blk & yel .35 .25
184 A15 5c dl org, blk, grn & bl .45 .30
185 A15 7½c yel grn, blk, red & brn .65 .40
186 A16 10c aqua & multi .80 .50
187 A15 12½c gray, yel, red & blue 1.10 .55
188 A15 20c gray & brn 1.40 1.10
189 A16 25c yel & dk brn 2.50 1.40
190 A15 35c dp org & ultra 2.75 1.75
191 A16 50c lt ol grn & sep 4.00 2.75
192 A15 1r ocher & black 8.25 5.25
193 A15 2r blue & brn 16.00 10.50
Nos. 180-193 (14) 38.90 25.35

Freedom from Hunger Issue
Common Design Type

1963, June 4 *Perf. 14x14½*

194 CD314 12½c green .48 .48

Red Cross Centenary Issue
Common Design Type

1963, Sept. 2 Litho. *Perf. 13*

195 CD315 2½c black & red .20 .20
196 CD315 12½c ultra & red .80 .80

Shakespeare Issue
Common Design Type

1964, Apr. 23 Photo. *Perf. 14x14½*

197 CD316 12½c red brown .28 .28

Notwani River Dam, Gaberones Water Supply A17

Perf. 14½

1965, Mar. 1 Photo. Wmk. 314

198 A17 2½c dark red & gold .15 .15
199 A17 5c deep ultra & gold .15 .15
200 A17 12½c brown & gold .30 .30
201 A17 25c emerald & gold .55 .55
Nos. 198-201 (4) 1.15 1.15

Internal self-government, Mar. 1, 1965.

ITU Issue
Common Design Type
Perf. 11x11½

1965, May 17 Litho. Wmk. 314

202 CD317 2½c ver & dl yel .15 .15
203 CD317 12½c red lil & pale brn .70 .70

Intl. Cooperation Year Issue
Common Design Type

1965, Oct. 25 *Perf. 14½*

204 CD318 1c bl grn & claret .16 .16
205 CD318 12½c lt vio & grn .85 .85

Common Design Types pictured in section before Great Britain.

Churchill Memorial Issue
Common Design Type

1966, Jan. 24 Photo. *Perf. 14*

Design in Black, Gold and Carmine Rose

206 CD319 1c bright blue .15 .15
207 CD319 2½c green .16 .16
208 CD319 12½c brown .65 .65
209 CD319 20c violet 1.10 1.10
Nos. 206-209 (4) 2.06 2.06

Haslar Smoke Generator A18

Perf. 14½

1966, June 1 Photo. Wmk. 314

210 A18 2½c shown .15 .15
211 A18 5c Bugler .15 .15
212 A18 15c Gun site .38 .38
213 A18 35c Regimental cap badge .85 .85
Nos. 210-213 (4) 1.53 1.53

25th anniv. of the Bechuanaland Pioneers and Gunners.

POSTAGE DUE STAMPS

Postage Due Stamps of Great Britain Overprinted

BECHUANALAND PROTECTORATE

On Stamp of 1914-22

1926 Wmk. 33 *Perf. 14x14½*

J1 D1 1p carmine 3.75 40.00

On Stamps of 1924-30
Wmk. 35

J2 D1 ½p emerald 3.75 40.00

Overprinted BECHUANALAND PROTECTORATE

J3 D1 2p black brown 7.25 80.00
Nos. J1-J3 (3) 14.75

D2

1932 Wmk. 4 Typo. *Perf. 14½*

J4 D2 ½p olive green 2.50 *12.50*
J5 D2 1p carmine rose 2.50 *3.50*
J6 D2 2p dull violet 3.50 *12.50*
Nos. J4-J6 (3) 8.50 *28.50*

Catalogue values for unused stamps in this section, from this point to the end of the section, are for Never Hinged items.

Nos. J4-J6 Surcharged

2c 2c
I II

1961, Feb. 14

J7 D2 1c on 1p car rose (II) .15 .15
a. Type I .28 .28
b. Double surcharge (II) 110.00
J8 D2 2c on 2p dull vio (II) .25 .25
a. Type I .35 .35
J9 D2 5c on ½p ol green (I) .52 .52
Nos. J7-J9 (3) .92 .92

Nos. J7, J7a, J8 and J8a are on chalky paper. Nos. J7 and J8 printed on ordinary paper sell for much more.

Denominations in Cents

1961 Wmk. 4 *Perf. 14*

J10 D2 1c carmine rose .15 .15
J11 D2 2c dull violet .16 .16
J12 D2 5c olive green .40 *1.25*
Nos. J10-J12 (3) .71 *1.56*

BOTSWANA

bä-'swä–nə

LOCATION — In central South Africa, north of the Republic of South Africa, east of South-West Africa and bounded on the north and east by Angola and Zimbabwe.
GOVT. — Independent republic
AREA — 222,000 sq. mi.
POP. — 941,027 (1981)
CAPITAL — Gaborone

The former Bechuanaland Protectorate became an independent republic, September 30, 1966, taking the name Botswana.

100 Cents = 1 Rand
100 Thebe = 1 Pula (1976)

Catalogue values for all unused stamps in this country are for Never Hinged items.

National Assembly Building A1

Designs: 5c, Abattoir, Lobatsi. 15c, Dakota plane. 35c, State House, Gaborone.

Unwmk.

1966, Sept. 30 Photo. *Perf. 14*

1 A1 2½c multicolored .15 .15
a. Imperf., pair 200.00
2 A1 5c multicolored .15 .15
3 A1 15c multicolored .35 .35
4 A1 35c multicolored .75 .75
Nos. 1-4 (4) 1.40 1.40

Establishment of Republic of Botswana.

Bechuanaland Protectorate Nos. 180-193 Overprinted

REPUBLIC OF BOTSWANA

Perf. 14x14½, 14½x14

1966, Sept. 30 Wmk. 314

5 A15 1c multicolored .15 .15
6 A15 2c multicolored .15 .15
7 A15 2½c multicolored .15 .15
8 A15 3½c multicolored .15 .15
9 A15 5c multicolored .15 .15
10 A15 7½c multicolored .18 .18
11 A15 10c multicolored .22 .22
12 A15 12½c multicolored 1.25 .28
13 A15 20c gray & brown 1.25 .40
14 A15 25c yel & dk brn .55 .55
15 A15 35c dp org & ultra .70 .70
16 A15 50c lt ol grn & sep 1.75 1.25
17 A15 1r ocher & black 3.25 2.50
18 A15 2r blue & brown 7.00 *8.00*
Nos. 5-18 (14) 16.90 *14.83*

European Golden Oriole — A2

Birds: 2c, African hoopoe. 3c, Groundscraper thrush. 4c, Blue waxbill. 5c, Secretary bird. 7c, Yellow-billed hornbill. 10c, Crimson-breasted shrike. 15c, Malachite kingfisher. 20c, Fish eagle. 25c, Gray lourie. 35c, Scimitar bill. 50c, Knob-billed duck. 1r, Crested barbet. 2r, Didric cuckoo.

Perf. 14x14½

1967, Jan. 3 Photo. Unwmk.

19 A2 1c gray & multi .15 .15
20 A2 2c lt blue & multi .15 .15
21 A2 3c yel green & multi .20 .15
22 A2 4c salmon & multi .32 .25
23 A2 5c pink & multi .35 .28
24 A2 7c slate & multi .50 .40
25 A2 10c emerald & multi .65 .50
26 A2 15c lt green & multi 1.40 1.00
27 A2 20c ultra & multi 1.60 1.25
28 A2 25c green & multi 2.00 1.60
29 A2 35c multicolored 2.50 2.00
30 A2 50c dl yel & multi 3.50 3.00
31 A2 1r dl grn & multi 7.50 6.00
32 A2 2r org brn & multi 14.50 10.00
Nos. 19-32 (14) 35.32 26.73

University Buildings and Graduates A3

1967, Apr. 7 *Perf. 14x14½*

33 A3 3c yel, sepia & dp blue .15 .15
34 A3 7c blue, sepia & dp bl .15 .15
35 A3 15c dull rose, sepia & dp bl .16 .16
36 A3 35c lt vio, sepia & dp bl .38 .38
Nos. 33-36 (4) .84 .84

1st conferment of degrees by the University of Botswana, Lesotho and Swaziland at Roma, Lesotho.

Chobe Bush Bucks A4

Designs: 7c, Sable antelopes. 35c, Fishing on the Chobe River.

1967, Oct. 2 Photo. *Perf. 14*

37 A4 3c multicolored .15 .15
38 A4 7c multicolored .22 .22
39 A4 35c multicolored 1.10 1.10
Nos. 37-39 (3) 1.47 1.47

Publicity for Chobe Game Reserve.

Human Rights Flame and Arms of Botswana A5

Design elements rearranged on 15c, 25c.

1968, Apr. 8 Litho. *Perf. 13½x13*

40 A5 3c brown red & multi .15 .15
41 A5 15c emerald & multi .25 .20
42 A5 25c yellow & multi .40 .30
Nos. 40-42 (3) .80 .65

International Human Rights Year.

Rock Painting — A6

Girl Wearing Ceremonial Beads — A7

Designs: 10c, Baobab Trees, by Thomas Baines (34x25mm). 15c, National Museum and Art Gallery (71½x19mm).

Perf. 13x13½ (3c, 10c); Perf. 12½ (7c); Perf. 12½x13 (15c)

1968, Sept. 30   Litho.

43	A6	3c multicolored	.15 .15
44	A7	7c multicolored	.18 .18
45	A6	10c multicolored	.32 .32
46	A6	15c multicolored	.60 .60
a.		Souv. sheet of 4, #43-46, perf. 13½	2.25 2.25
		Nos. 43-46 (4)	1.25 1.25

Opening of the National Museum and Art Gallery, Gaborone, Sept. 30, 1968.

African Nativity Scene — A8

1968, Nov. 11   Unwmk.   Perf. 13x14

47	A8	1c car & multi	.15 .15
48	A8	2c brown & multi	.15 .15
49	A8	5c green & multi	.15 .15
50	A8	25c dp violet & multi	.55 .50
		Set value	.75 .65

Christmas.

Boy Scout, Botswana Scout Emblem and Lion — A9

Botswana Boy Scout Emblem, Lion and: 15c, Boy Scouts cooking, vert. 25c, Boy Scouts around campfire.

1969, Aug. 21   Litho.   Perf. 13½

51	A9	3c emerald & multi	.15 .15
52	A9	15c lt brown & multi	.75 .75
53	A9	25c dk brown & multi	1.40 1.40
		Nos. 51-53 (3)	2.30 2.30

22nd World Scouting Conf., Helsinki, Finland, Aug. 21-27.

Mother, Child and Star of Bethlehem — A10

Diamond Treatment Plant, Orapa — A11

1969, Nov. 6   Perf. 14½x14

54	A10	1c dk brn & lt blue	.15 .15
55	A10	2c dk brn & apple grn	.15 .15
56	A10	4c dk brn & dull yel	.15 .15
57	A10	35c dk brn & vio blue	.80 .80
a.		Souv. sheet of 4, #54-57, perf. 14½	1.40 1.00
		Set value	1.00 1.00

Christmas.

Perf. 14½x14, 14x14½

1970, Mar. 23

Designs: 7c, Copper and nickel mining, Selebi-Pikwe. 10c, Copper and nickel mining and metal bars, Selebi-Pikwe, horiz. 35c, Orapa diamond mine and diamonds, horiz.

58	A11	3c multicolored	.15 .15
59	A11	7c multicolored	.26 .26
60	A11	10c multicolored	.52 .52
61	A11	35c multicolored	.85 .85
		Nos. 58-61 (4)	1.78 1.78

Botswana development program.

Mr. Micawber and Charles Dickens — A12

Charles Dickens (1812-70), English novelist and: 7c, Scrooge. 15c, Fagin. 25c, Bill Sykes.

1970, July 7   Litho.   Perf. 11

62	A12	3c gray green & multi	.15 .15
63	A12	7c multicolored	.26 .26
64	A12	15c brown & multi	.52 .52
65	A12	25c dp violet & multi	.85 .85
a.		Souvenir sheet of 4, #62-65	3.00 3.00
		Nos. 62-65 (4)	1.78 1.78

UN Headquarters, Emblem — A13

1970, Oct. 24   Litho.   Perf. 11

66	A13	15c ultra, red & silver	.60 .60

United Nations' 25th anniversary.

Toys — A14

1970, Nov. 3   Litho.   Perf. 14

67	A14	1c Crocodile	.15 .15
68	A14	2c Giraffe	.15 .15
69	A14	7c Elephant	.25 .25
70	A14	25c Rhinoceros	1.00 1.00
a.		Souvenir sheet of 4, #67-70	2.25 2.25
		Nos. 67-70 (4)	1.55 1.55

Christmas.

Sorghum A15

1971, Apr. 6   Litho.   Perf. 14

71	A15	3c shown	.15 .15
72	A15	7c Millet	.16 .16
73	A15	10c Corn	.20 .20
74	A15	35c Peanuts	.80 .80
		Nos. 71-74 (4)	1.31 1.31

Ox Head and Botswana Map — A16

King Bringing Gift — A17

Map of Botswana and: 4c, Cogwheels and waves. 7c, Zebra rampant. 10c, Tusk and corn. 20c, Coat of arms of Botswana.

1971, Sept. 30   Perf. 14½x14

75	A16	3c yel grn, blk & brn	.15 .15
76	A16	4c lt blue, blk & bl	.15 .15
77	A16	7c orange & blk	.16 .16
78	A16	10c yellow & multi	.28 .28
79	A16	20c blue & multi	.60 .60
		Nos. 75-79 (5)	1.34 1.34

5th anniversary of independence.

1971, Nov. 11   Perf. 14

Christmas: 2c, King bringing gift. 7c, Kneeling King with gift. 20c, Three Kings and star.

80	A17	2c brt rose & multi	.15 .15
81	A17	3c lt blue & multi	.15 .15
82	A17	7c brt pink & multi	.20 .20
83	A17	20c vio blue & multi	.80 .80
a.		Souvenir sheet of 4, #80-83	1.65 1.65
		Nos. 80-83 (4)	1.30 1.30

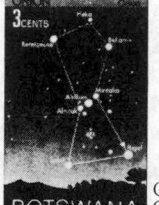

Constellation Orion — A18

Night Sky over Botswana: 7c, Scorpio. 10c, Centaur. 20c, Southern Cross.

1972, Apr. 24   Litho.   Perf. 14

84	A18	3c dp org, bl grn & blk	.25 .25
85	A18	7c org, blue & blk	.50 .50
86	A18	10c org, green & blk	.75 .75
87	A18	20c emer, vio bl & blk	1.50 1.50
		Nos. 84-87 (4)	3.00 3.00

Gubulawayo Cancel and Map of Trail — A19

Cross, Map of Botswana, Bells — A20

Sections of Mafeking-Gubulawayo Trail and: 4c, Bechuanaland Protectorate No. 65. 7c, Mail runners. 20c, Mafeking 638 killer cancellation.

1972, Aug. 21   Perf. 13½x13

88	A19	3c cream & multi	.15 .15
89	A19	4c cream & multi	.18 .18
90	A19	7c cream & multi	.45 .45
91	A19	20c cream & multi	1.50 1.50
a.		Souvenir sheet of 4	6.75 6.75
		Nos. 88-91 (4)	2.28 2.28

84th anniv. of Mafeking to Gubulawayo runner post. No. 91a contains one each of Nos. 88-91, arranged vertically to show map of trail.

Compare with design A89.

1972, Nov. 6   Litho.   Perf. 14

Cross, Map of Botswana and: 3c, Candle. 7c, Christmas tree. 20c, Star and holly.

92	A20	2c yellow & multi	.15 .15
93	A20	3c pale lilac & multi	.15 .15
94	A20	7c yel green & multi	.24 .24

95	A20	20c pink & multi	.60 .60
a.		Souvenir sheet of 4, #92-95	2.00 2.00
		Nos. 92-95 (4)	1.14 1.14

Christmas.

Chariot of the Sun, Trundholm, Denmark A21

WMO Emblem and: 3c, Thor, Norse thunder god, vert. 7c, Ymir, Icelandic frost giant, vert. 20c, Odin on 8-legged horse Sleipnir.

1973, Mar. 23   Litho.   Perf. 14

96	A21	3c orange & multi	.15 .15
97	A21	4c yellow & multi	.16 .16
98	A21	7c ultra & multi	.30 .30
99	A21	20c gold & multi	.90 .90
		Nos. 96-99 (4)	1.51 1.51

Intl. meteorological cooperation, cent.

Livingstone and Boat on Lake Ngwami — A22

Design: 20c, Livingstone and his meeting with Henry Stanley.

1973, Sept. 10   Litho.   Perf. 13½x14

100	A22	3c gray & multi	.15 .15
101	A22	20c yel green & multi	.95 .95

Dr. David Livingstone (1813-1873), medical missionary and explorer.

Shepherd and Flock A23

Christmas: 3c, Ass and foal, African huts, vert. 7c, African mother, child and star, vert. 20c, Tribal meeting (kgotla), symbolic of Wise Men.

1973, Nov. 12   Litho.   Perf. 14½

102	A23	3c multicolored	.15 .15
103	A23	4c multicolored	.15 .15
104	A23	7c multicolored	.24 .24
105	A23	20c multicolored	.70 .70
		Nos. 102-105 (4)	1.24 1.24

Gaborone Campus, Botswana A24

Designs: 7c, Kwaluseni Campus, Swaziland. 20c, Roma Campus, Lesotho. 35c, Map and flags of Botswana, Swaziland and Lesotho.

1974, May 8   Litho.   Perf. 14

106	A24	3c lt blue & multi	.15 .15
107	A24	7c yel green & multi	.15 .15
108	A24	20c yel green & multi	.32 .32
109	A24	35c brt blue & multi	.48 .48
		Nos. 106-109 (4)	1.10 1.10

10th anniversary of the University of Botswana, Lesotho and Swaziland.

UPU Emblem, Mail Vehicles — A25

UPU Cent.: 3c, Post Office, Palapye, c. 1889. 7c, Bechuanaland police camel post, 1900. 20c, 1920 and 1974 planes.

1974, May 22 Litho. *Perf. 13½x14*

110 A25 2c car & multi .15 .15
111 A25 3c green & multi .25 .20
112 A25 7c brown & multi .65 .50
113 A25 20c blue & multi 2.00 1.50
Nos. 110-113 (4) 3.05 2.35

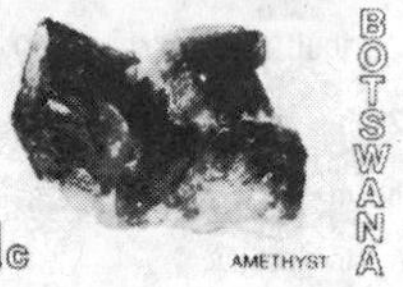

Amethyst A26

Designs: Minerals, precious and semiprecious stones.

1974, July 1 Photo. *Perf. 14x13*

114 A26 1c shown .15 .15
115 A26 2c Agate .16 .16
116 A26 3c Quartz .20 .20
117 A26 4c Niccolite .32 .32
118 A26 5c Moss agate .40 .40
119 A26 7c Agate .60 .60
120 A26 10c Stilbite .85 .85
121 A26 15c Moshaneng banded marble 1.25 1.25
122 A26 20c Gem diamonds 1.65 1.65
123 A26 25c Chrysotile 2.00 2.00
124 A26 35c Jasper 2.75 2.75
125 A26 50c Moss quartz 3.75 3.75
126 A26 1r Citrine 8.00 8.00
127 A26 2r Chalcopyrite 17.00 17.00
Nos. 114-127 (14) 39.08 39.08

For surcharges see Nos. 155-168.

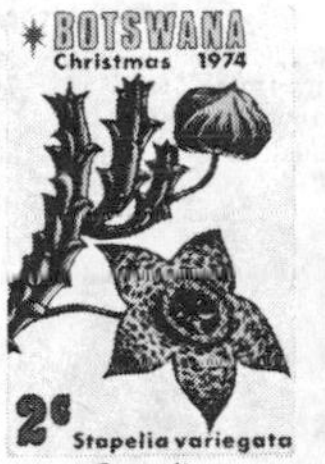

Stapelia Variegata — A27

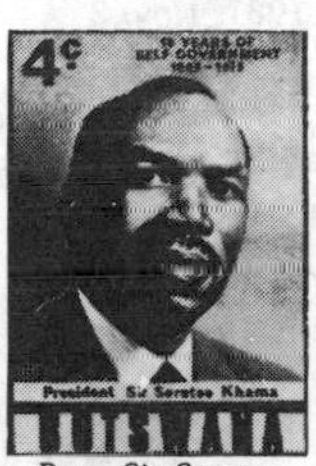

Pres. Sir Seretse Khama — A28

Flowers of Botswana: 7c, Hibiscus lunarifolius. 15c, Ceratotheca triloba. 20c, Nerine laticoma.

1974, Nov. 4 Litho. *Perf. 14*

128 A27 2c multicolored .15 .15
129 A27 7c multicolored .40 .40
130 A27 15c multicolored .90 .90
131 A27 20c multicolored 1.25 1.25
a. Souvenir sheet of 4, #128-131 2.50 2.50
Nos. 128-131 (4) 2.70 2.70

1975, Mar. 24 Photo. *Perf. 13½x13*

132 A28 4c olive & multi .15 .15
133 A28 10c yellow & multi .15 .15
134 A28 20c ultra & multi .30 .30
135 A28 35c brown & multi .50 .50
a. Souvenir sheet of 4, #132-135 1.40 1.40
Nos. 132-135 (4) 1.10 1.10

10th anniv. of self-government.

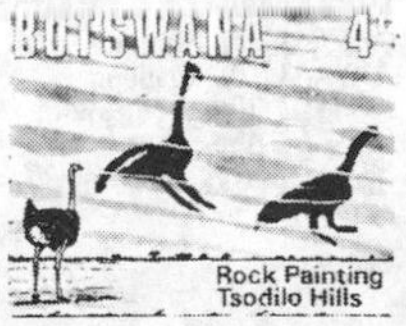

Ostrich and Rock Painting — A29

Paintings and Animals: 10c, Rhinoceros. 25c, Hyena. 35c, Scorpion.

1975, June 23 Litho. *Perf. 14x14½*

136 A29 4c yel green & multi .25 .25
137 A29 10c buff & multi .75 .75
138 A29 25c blue & multi 1.65 1.65
139 A29 35c lilac & multi 2.50 2.50
a. Souvenir sheet of 4, #136-139 6.50 6.50
Nos. 136-139 (4) 5.15 5.15

Rock paintings from Tsodilo Hills.

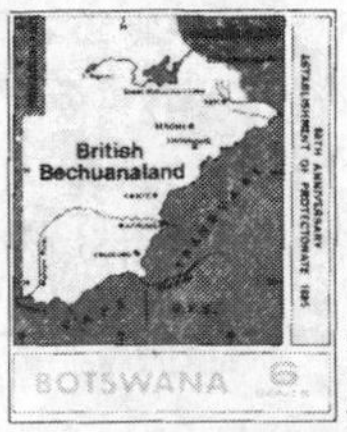

Map of British Bechuanaland A30

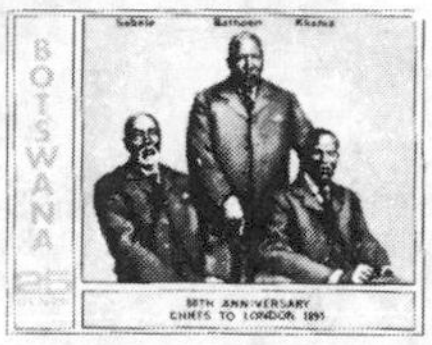

Chiefs Sebele, Bathoen and Khama A31

Design: 10c, Khama the Great and antelope.

Perf. 14½x14, 14x14½

1975, Oct. 31 Litho.

140 A30 6c buff & multi .28 .28
141 A30 10c rose & multi .48 .48
142 A31 25c lt green & multi 1.25 1.25
Nos. 140-142 (3) 2.01 2.01

Establishment of Protectorate, 90th anniv. (6c); Khama the Great (1828-1923), centenary of his accession as chief (10c); visit of the chiefs of the Bakwena, Bangwaketse and Bamangwato tribes to London, 80th anniv. (25c).

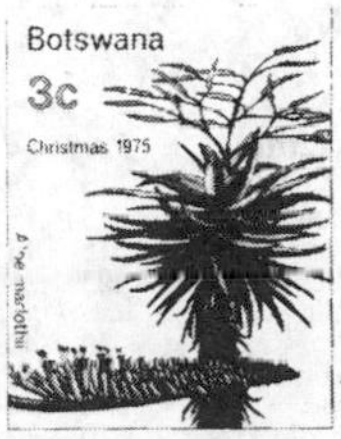

Aloe Marlothii — A32

Christmas: 10c, Aloe lutescens. 15c, Aloe zebrina. 25c, Aloe littoralis.

1975, Nov. 3 Litho. *Perf. 14½x14*

143 A32 3c multicolored .20 .20
144 A32 10c multicolored .50 .50
145 A32 15c multicolored .70 .70
146 A32 25c multicolored 1.40 1.40
Nos. 143-146 (4) 2.80 2.80

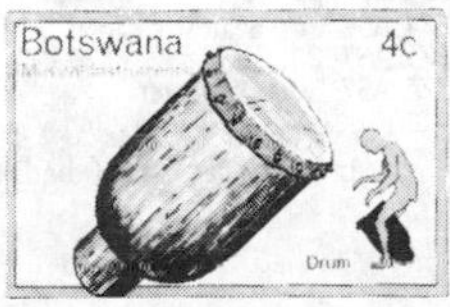

Drum A33

Traditional Musical Instruments: 10c, Hand piano. 15c, Segankuru (violin). 25c, Kudu signal horn.

1976, Mar. 1 Litho. *Perf. 14*

147 A33 4c yellow & multi .15 .15
148 A33 10c lilac & multi .35 .35
149 A33 15c dull yel & multi .60 .60
150 A33 25c lt blue & multi .90 .90
Nos. 147-150 (4) 2.00 2.00

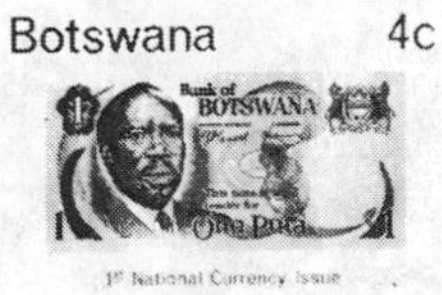

1-pula Bank Note with Seretse Khama A34

Reverse of Bank Notes: 10c, Farm workers. 15c, Antelopes. 25c, National Assembly building.

1976, June 28 Litho. *Perf. 14*

151 A34 4c rose & multi .15 .15
152 A34 10c brt green & multi .25 .25
153 A34 15c yel green & multi .35 .35
154 A34 25c blue & multi .65 .65
a. Souvenir sheet of 4, #151-154 2.25 2.25
Nos. 151-154 (4) 1.40 1.40

First national currency.

Nos. 114-127 Surcharged in Black or Gold

1976, Aug. 23 Photo. *Perf. 14x13*

155 A26 1t on 1c multi .15 .15
156 A26 2t on 2c multi .15 .15
157 A26 3t on 3c multi (G) .15 .15
158 A26 4t on 4c multi .18 .16
159 A26 5t on 5c multi .20 .18
160 A26 7t on 7c multi .28 .25
161 A26 10t on 10c multi .35 .32
162 A26 15t on 15c multi (G) .60 .55
163 A26 20t on 20c multi .80 .75
164 A26 25t on 25c multi 1.10 .90
165 A26 35t on 35c multi 1.25 1.10
166 A26 50t on 50c multi 1.75 1.50
167 A26 1p on 1r multi 3.50 3.25
168 A26 2p on 2r multi (G) 6.75 6.25
Nos. 155-168 (14) 17.21 15.66

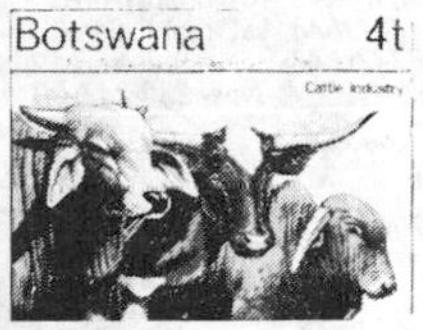

Cattle Industry A35

Designs: 10t, Antelope, tourism, vert. 15t, Schoolhouse and children, education. 25t, Rural weaving, vert. 35t, Mining industry, vert.

1976, Sept. 30 Litho. *Perf. 14x14½*

Textured Paper

169 A35 4t multicolored .15 .15
170 A35 10t multicolored .25 .25
171 A35 15t multicolored .30 .30
172 A35 25t multicolored .50 .50
173 A35 35t multicolored .75 .75
Nos. 169-173 (5) 1.95 1.95

10th anniversary of independence.

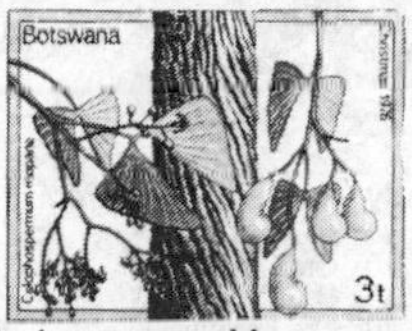

Colophospermum Mopane — A36

Trees: 4t, Baikiaea plurijuga. 10t, Sterculia rogersii. 25t, Acacia nilotica. 40t, Kigelia africana.

1976, Nov. 1 Litho. *Perf. 13*

174 A36 3t multicolored .15 .15
175 A36 4t multicolored .15 .15
176 A36 10t multicolored .35 .35
177 A36 25t multicolored .75 .75
178 A36 40t multicolored 1.25 1.25
Nos. 174-178 (5) 2.65 2.65

Christmas.

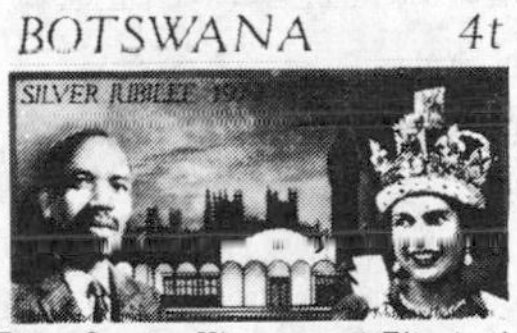

Pres. Seretse Khama and Elizabeth II — A37

Designs: 25t, Coronation coach in procession. 40t, Recognition scene.

1977, Feb. 7 Litho. *Perf. 12*

179 A37 4t multicolored .15 .15
180 A37 25t multicolored .45 .45
181 A37 40t multicolored .75 .75
Nos. 179-181 (3) 1.35 1.35

Reign of Queen Elizabeth II, 25th anniv.

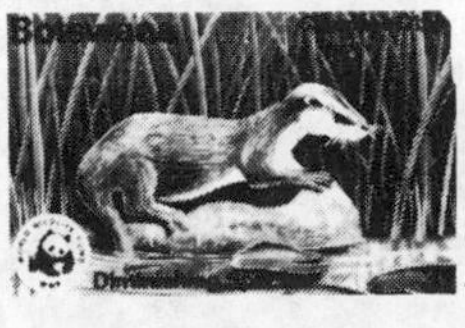
Clawless Otter A38

Wildlife Fund Emblem and: 4t, Serval. 10t, Bat-eared foxes. 25t, Pangolins. 40t, Brown hyena.

1977, June 6 Litho. *Perf. 14*

182 A38 3t multicolored .25 .15
183 A38 4t multicolored .32 .18
184 A38 10t multicolored .65 .40
185 A38 25t multicolored 1.65 1.00
186 A38 40t multicolored 3.25 1.75
Nos. 182-186 (5) 6.12 3.48

Endangered wildlife.

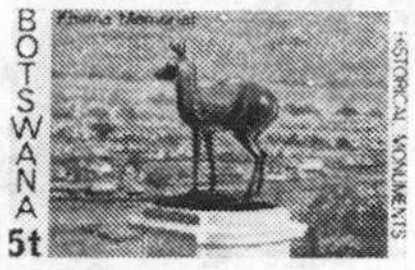

Khama Memorial A39

Designs: 4t, Cwihaba Caves. 15t, Green's (expedition) tree. 20t, Mmajojo ruins. 25t, Ancient morabaraba board. 35t, Matsieng's footprints.

1977, Aug. 22 Litho. *Perf. 14*

187 A39 4t multicolored .15 .15
188 A39 5t multicolored .18 .18
189 A39 15t multicolored .45 .45
190 A39 20t multicolored .55 .55
191 A39 25t multicolored .80 .80
192 A39 35t multicolored 1.10 1.10
a. Souvenir sheet of 6, #187-192 3.50 3.50
Nos. 187-192 (6) 3.23 3.23

Historical sites and national monuments.

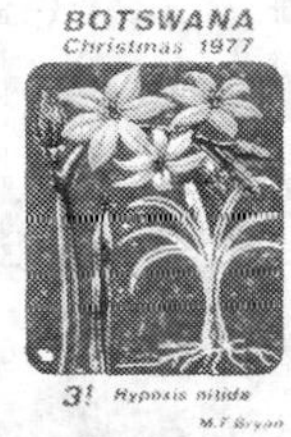

Hypoxis itida — A40

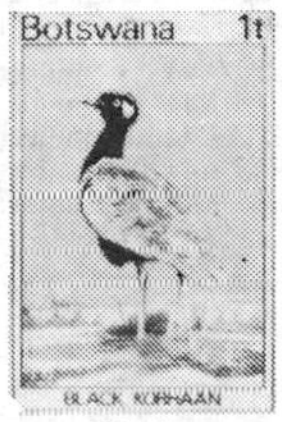

Black Korhaan — A41

Lilies: 5t, Haemanthus magnificus. 10t, Boophane disticha. 25t, Vellozia retinervis. 40t, Ammocharis coranica.

1977, Oct. 31 Litho. *Perf. 14*

193 A40 3t sepia & multi .15 .15
194 A40 5t gray & multi .18 .18
195 A40 10t multicolored .35 .35
196 A40 25t multicolored 1.00 1.00
197 A40 40t multicolored 1.75 1.75
Nos. 193-197 (5) 3.43 3.43

Christmas.

1978, July 3 Photo. *Perf. 14*

Designs: Birds.

198 A41 1t shown .15 .15
199 A41 2t Marabou storks .15 .15
200 A41 3t Red-billed hoopoe .15 .15
201 A41 4t Carmine bee-eaters .15 .15
202 A41 5t African jacana .15 .15
203 A41 7t Paradise flycatcher .16 .16
204 A41 10t Bennett's woodpecker .25 .25
205 A41 15t Red bishop .38 .38
206 A41 20t Crowned plovers .50 .50
207 A41 25t Giant kingfishers .62 .62
208 A41 30t White-faced ducks .75 .75
209 A41 35t Green-backed heron .88 .88
210 A41 45t Black-headed herons 1.12 1.12
211 A41 50t Spotted eagle owl 1.25 1.25
212 A41 1p Gabar goshawk 2.50 2.50
213 A41 2p Martial eagle 5.00 5.00
214 A41 5p Saddlebill storks 10.00 10.00
Nos. 198-214 (17) 24.16 24.16

For surcharges see Nos. 289-290.

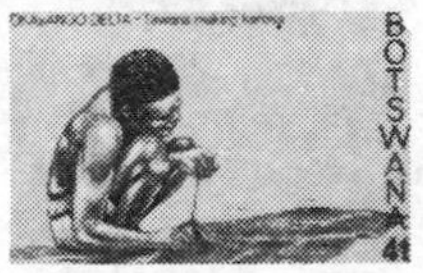

Tawana Making Kaross (garment) A42

Designs: 5t, Map of Okavango Delta. 15t, Bushman collecting roots. 20t, Herero woman milking cow. 25t, Yei pulling mokoro (boat). 35t, Mbukushu fishing.

1978, Sept. 11 Litho. *Perf. 14*

Textured Paper

215 A42 4t multicolored .15 .15
216 A42 5t multicolored .15 .15
217 A42 15t multicolored .20 .20
218 A42 20t multicolored .32 .32
219 A42 25t multicolored .40 .40
220 A42 35t multicolored .52 .52
a. Souvenir sheet of 6, #215-220 2.50 3.00
Nos. 215-220 (6) 1.74 1.74

People of the Okavango Delta.

Caralluma Lutea — A43

Boy at Sip Well — A44

Flowers: 10t, Hoodia lugardii. 15t, Ipomoea transvaalensis. 25t, Ansellia gigantea.

1978, Nov. 6
221	A43	5t multicolored	.16	.16
222	A43	10t multicolored	.32	.32
223	A43	15t multicolored	.48	.48
224	A43	25t multicolored	.80	.80
		Nos. 221-224 (4)	1.76	1.76

Christmas.

1979, Feb. 12   Litho.   Perf. 14
Water Development: 5t, Watering pit. 10t, Hand-dug well and goats. 25t, Windmill, well and cattle. 40t, Modern drilling rig.
225	A44	3t multicolored	.15	.15
226	A44	5t multicolored	.15	.15
227	A44	10t multicolored	.15	.15
228	A44	25t multicolored	.40	.40
229	A44	40t multicolored	.65	.65
		Nos. 225-229 (5)	1.50	1.50

Botswana Pot — A45

Handicrafts: 10t, Clay buffalo. 25t, Woven covered basket. 40t, Beaded bag.

1979, June 4   Litho.   Perf. 14
230	A45	5t multicolored	.15	.15
231	A45	10t multicolored	.16	.16
232	A45	25t multicolored	.42	.42
233	A45	40t multicolored	.65	.65
a.		Souvenir sheet of 4, #230-233	1.65	1.65
		Nos. 230-233 (4)	1.38	1.38

Bechuanaland No. 6, Rowland Hill — A46

Sir Rowland Hill (1795-1879), originator of penny postage, and: 25t, Bechuanaland Protectorate No. 107. 45t, Botswana No. 20.

1979, Aug. 27   Litho.   Perf. 13½
234	A46	5t rose & black	.15	.15
235	A46	25t multicolored	.35	.35
236	A46	45t multicolored	.60	.60
		Nos. 234-236 (3)	1.10	1.10

Children Playing — A47

Design: 10t, Child playing with rag doll, and IYC emblem, vert.

1979, Sept. 24   Perf. 14
237	A47	5t multicolored	.15	.15
238	A47	10t multicolored	.25	.25

International Year of the Child.

Ximenia Caffra — A48

Christmas: 10t, Sclerocarya caffra. 15t, Hexalobus monopetalus. 25t, Ficus soldanella.

1979, Nov. 12   Litho.   Perf. 14
239	A48	5t multicolored	.15	.15
240	A48	10t multicolored	.20	.20
241	A48	15t multicolored	.30	.30
242	A48	25t multicolored	.50	.50
		Nos. 239-242 (4)	1.15	1.15

Flap-Necked Chameleon A49

1980, Mar. 3   Litho.   Perf. 14
243	A49	5t shown	.15	.15
244	A49	10t Leopard tortoise	.18	.18
245	A49	25t Puff adder	.45	.45
246	A49	40t White-throated monitor	.75	.75
		Nos. 243-246 (4)	1.53	1.53

Rock Breaking (Early Mining) — A50

1980, July 7   Litho.   Perf. 13½x14
247	A50	5t shown	.15	.15
248	A50	10t Ore hoisting	.18	.18
249	A50	15t Ore transport	.25	.25
250	A50	20t Ore crushing	.35	.35
251	A50	25t Smelting	.40	.40
252	A50	35t Tools, products	.60	.60
		Nos. 247-252 (6)	1.93	1.93

Chiwele and the Giant — A51

Folktales: 10t, Kgori Is Not Deceived. 30t, Nyambi's Wife and Crocodile. 45t, Clever Hare, horiz.

Perf. 14, 14½ (10t, 30t)
1980, Sept. 8
253	A51	5t multicolored	.15	.15

Size: 28x36mm
254	A51	10t multicolored	.18	.18
255	A51	30t multicolored	.52	.52

Size: 44x26mm
256	A51	45t multicolored	.80	.80
		Nos. 253-256 (4)	1.65	1.65

Game Watching — A52

1980, Oct. 6   Litho.   Perf. 14
257	A52	5t multicolored	.20	.20

World Tourism Conf., Manila, Sept. 27.

Acacia Gerrardii — A53

Christmas: Flowering Trees.

1980, Nov. 3   Litho.   Perf. 14
258	A53	5t shown	.15	.15
259	A53	10t Acacia nilotica	.15	.15
260	A53	25t Acacia erubescens	.32	.32
261	A53	40t Dichrostachys cinerea	.45	.45
		Nos. 258-261 (4)	1.07	1.07

Heinrich von Stephan, Bechuanaland Protectorate No. 150, Botswana No. 111 — A55

Design: 20t, Von Stephan, Bechuanaland Protectorate No. 151, Botswana No. 112.

1981, Jan. 7   Wmk. 373   Perf. 14
266	A55	6t multicolored	.15	.15
267	A55	20t multicolored	.45	.45

Von Stephan (1831-1897), founder of UPU.

Emperor Dragonfly — A56

1981, Feb. 23   Litho.   Perf. 14
268	A56	6t shown	.15	.15
269	A56	7t Praying mantis	.15	.15
270	A56	10t Elegant grasshopper	.15	.15
271	A56	20t Dung beetle	.25	.25
272	A56	30t Citrus swallowtail butterfly	.40	.40
273	A56	45t Mopane worm	.60	.60
a.		Souv. sheet of 6, #268-273	2.00	2.00
		Nos. 268-273 (6)	1.70	1.70

Blind Basket Weaver A57

1981, Apr. 4   Litho.   Perf. 14
274	A57	6t Seamstress	.15	.15
275	A57	20t shown	.30	.30
276	A57	30t Carpenter	.40	.40
		Nos. 274-276 (3)	.85	.85

International Year of the Disabled.

Woman Reading Letter (Literacy Campaign) — A58

1981, June 8
277	A58	6t shown	.15	.15
278	A58	7t Man sending telegram	.15	.15
279	A58	20t Boy, newspaper	.25	.25
280	A58	30t Father and daughter reading	.40	.40
		Nos. 277-280 (4)	.95	.95

Pres. Seretse Khama and Flag — A59

First death anniv. of Pres. Khama: Portrait and local buildings.

1981, July 13
281	A59	6t multicolored	.15	.15
282	A59	10t multicolored	.15	.15
283	A59	30t multicolored	.40	.40
284	A59	45t multicolored	.60	.60
		Nos. 281-284 (4)	1.30	1.30

Cattle in Agricultural Show — A60

1981, Sept. 21   Litho.   Perf. 14½
285	A60	6t Plowing	.15	.15
286	A60	20t shown	.20	.20
287	A60	30t Meat Commission	.35	.35
288	A60	45t Vaccine Institute	.50	.50
		Nos. 285-288 (4)	1.20	1.20

Nos. 209, 204 Surcharged in Black
1981, Sept.   Photo.   Perf. 14
289	A41	25t on 35t multicolored	.30	.30
290	A41	30t on 10t multicolored	.40	.40

Christmas — A61

Designs: Water lilies.

1981, Nov. 2   Litho.
291	A61	6t Nymphaea caerulea	.15	.15
292	A61	10t Nymphoides indica	.15	.15
293	A61	25t Nymphaea lotus	.30	.30
294	A61	40t Ottelia kunenensis	.50	.50
		Nos. 291-294 (4)	1.10	1.10

Children's Drawings — A62

1982, Feb. 15   Litho.   Perf. 14½x14
295	A62	6t Cattle	.15	.15
296	A62	10t Kgotla meeting	.15	.15
297	A62	30t Village	.40	.40
298	A62	45t Huts	.60	.60
		Nos. 295-298 (4)	1.30	1.30

Traditional Houses — A63

1982, May 3   Litho.   Perf. 14
299	A63	6t Common type	.15	.15
300	A63	10t Kgatleng	.15	.15
301	A63	30t Northeastern	.40	.40
302	A63	45t Sarwa	.60	.60
		Nos. 299-302 (4)	1.30	1.30

Red-billed Teals — A64

Perf. 14x14½, 14½x14
1982, July 1   Photo.
303	A64	1t Masked weaver	.15	.15
304	A64	2t Lesser double-collared sunbirds	.15	.15
305	A64	3t White-fronted bee-eaters	.15	.15
306	A64	4t Ostriches	.15	.15
307	A64	5t Grey-headed gulls	.15	.15
308	A64	6t Pygmy geese	.15	.15
309	A64	7t Cattle egrets	.16	.16
310	A64	8t Lanner falcon	.18	.18
311	A64	10t Yellow-billed storks	.22	.22
312	A64	15t shown	.35	.35
313	A64	20t Barn owls	.45	.45
314	A64	25t Hamerkops	.60	.60
315	A64	30t Stilts	.70	.70
316	A64	35t Blacksmith plovers	.80	.80
317	A64	45t Wattled plover	1.00	1.00

318 A64 50t Crowned guinea-fowl 1.10 1.20
319 A64 1p Cape vultures 2.25 2.25
320 A64 2p Augur bustards 4.50 4.50
Nos. 303-320 (18) 13.21 13.31

Nos. 303-311 vert.
For surcharges see Nos. 401-403.

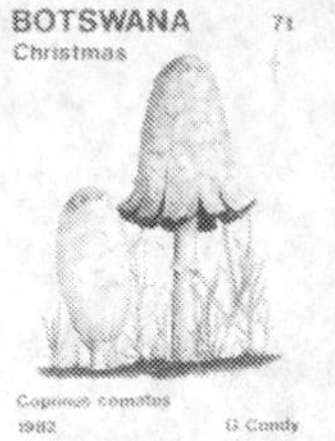

Christmas — A65

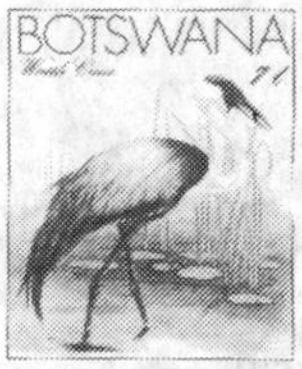

Endangered Species — A67

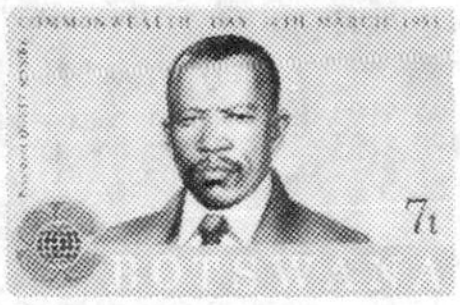

A66

Designs: Mushrooms.

1982, Nov. 2 Litho. *Perf. 14½*
321 A65 7t Shaggy mane .70 .70
322 A65 15t Orange milk 1.50 1.50
323 A65 35t Panther 3.50 3.50
324 A65 50t King boletus 4.75 4.75
Nos. 321-324 (4) 10.45 10.45

1983, Mar. 14 Litho. *Perf. 14*
325 A66 7t Pres. Quett Masire .15 .15
326 A66 15t Dancers .20 .20
327 A66 35t Melbourne Conference Center .50 .50
328 A66 45t Heads of State meeting .60 .60
Nos. 325-328 (4) 1.45 1.45

Commonwealth Day.

1983, Apr. 19 Litho. *Perf. 14x14½*
329 A67 7t Wattle crane .15 .15
330 A67 15t Aloe lutescens .25 .25
331 A67 35t Roan antelope .60 .60
332 A67 50t Hyphaene ventricosa .80 .80
Nos. 329-332 (4) 1.80 1.80

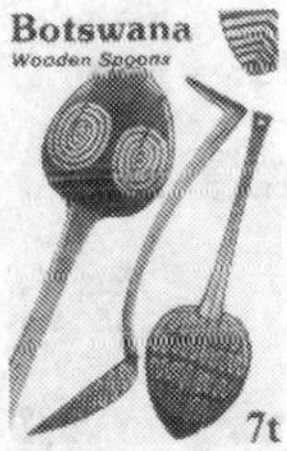

Wooden Spoons — A68

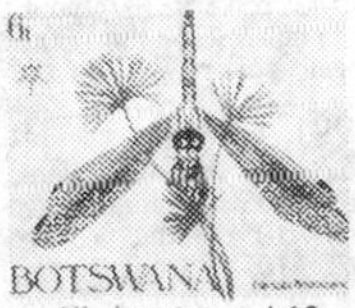

Christmas — A69

1983, July 20 Litho. *Perf. 14*
333 A68 7t shown .15 .15
334 A68 15t Jewelry .28 .28
335 A68 35t Ox-hide milk bag .70 .70
336 A68 50t Decorated knives .90 .90
a. Souvenir sheet of 4, #333-336 2.00 2.00
Nos. 333-336 (4) 2.03 2.03

1983, Nov. 7 Litho. *Perf. 14½x14*

Designs: Dragonflies.

337 A69 6t Pantala flavescens .15 .15
338 A69 15t Anax imperator .30 .30
339 A69 25t Trithemis arteriosa .50 .50
340 A69 45t Chlorolestes elegans .90 .90
Nos. 337-340 (4) 1.85 1.85

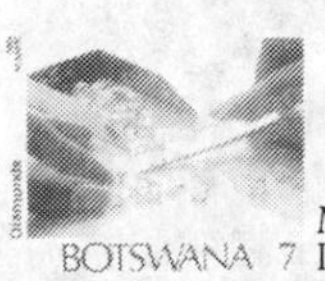

Mining Industry — A70

1984, Mar. 19 Litho. *Perf. 14½*
341 A70 7t Diamonds .15 .15
342 A70 15t Lime .30 .30
343 A70 35t Copper, nickel, vert. .75 .75
344 A70 50t Coal, vert. 1.00 1.00
Nos. 341-344 (4) 2.20 2.20

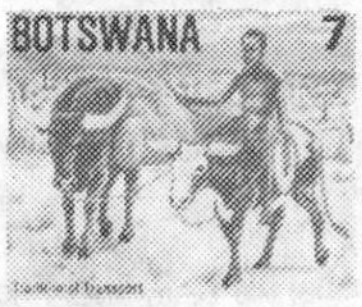

Traditional Transport — A71

1984, June 16 Litho. *Perf. 14½x14*
345 A71 7t Man riding ox .15 .15
346 A71 25t Sled .42 .42
347 A71 35t Wagon .65 .65
348 A71 50t Cart .90 .90
Nos. 345-348 (4) 2.12 2.12

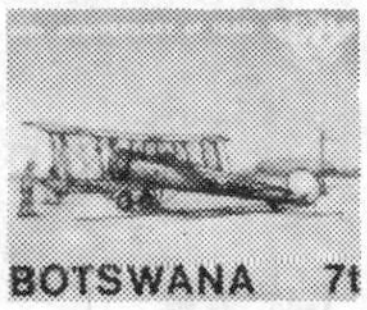

Intl. Civil Aviation Org., 40th Anniv. — A72

1984, Oct. 8 Litho. *Perf. 14x13½*
349 A72 7t Avro 504 .15 .15
350 A72 10t Westland Wessex .15 .15
351 A72 15t Junkers 52-3M .25 .25
352 A72 25t Dragon Rapide .40 .40
353 A72 35t DC-3 .60 .60
354 A72 50t F27 Fokker Friendship .80 .80
Nos. 349-354 (6) 2.35 2.35

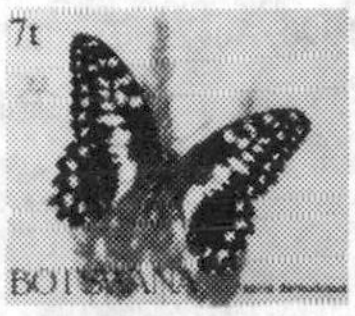

Christmas — A73

Butterflies.

1984, Nov. 5 Litho. *Perf. 14½x14*
355 A73 7t Papilio demodocus .15 .15
356 A73 25t Byblia acheloia .50 .50
357 A73 35t Hypolimnas missipus .75 .75
358 A73 50t Graphium taboranus 1.00 1.00
Nos. 355-358 (4) 2.40 2.40

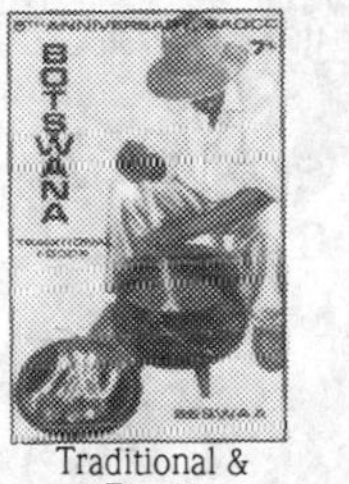

Traditional & Exotic Foods — A74

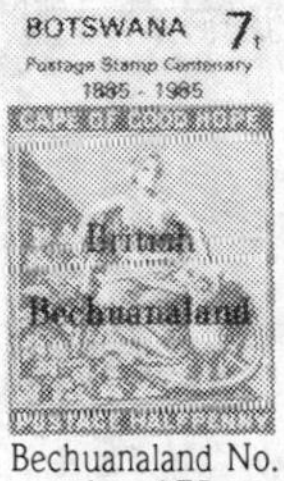

Bechuanaland No. 4 — A75

1985, Mar. 18 Litho. *Perf. 14½*
359 A74 7t Man preparing seswaa .15 .15
360 A74 15t Woman preparing bogobe .20 .20
361 A74 25t Girl eating madilla .32 .32
362 A74 50t Woman collecting caterpillars .65 .65
a. Souvenir sheet of 4, #359-362 1.40 1.40
Nos. 359-362 (4) 1.32 1.32

Southern African Development Coordination Conference, 5th anniv.

1985, June 24

Postage stamp cent.: 15t, Bechuanaland Protectorate No. 72. 25t, Bechuanaland Protectorate No. 106. 35t, Bechuanaland No. 199, 50t, Botswana No. 1, horiz.

363 A75 7t multicolored .15 .15
364 A75 15t multicolored .18 .18
365 A75 25t multicolored .30 .30
366 A75 35t multicolored .42 .42
367 A75 50t multicolored .62 .62
Nos. 363-367 (5) 1.67 1.67

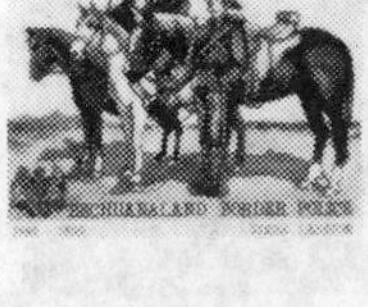

Police Centenary — A76

Designs: 7t, Bechuanaland Border Police, 1885-1895. 10t, Bechuanaland Mounted Police, 1894-1902. 25t, Bechuanaland Protectorate Police, 1903-1966. 50t, Botswana Motorcycle Police, 1966-1985.

1985, Aug. 5 *Perf. 14½x14*
368 A76 7t multicolored .15 .15
369 A76 10t multicolored .15 .15
370 A76 25t multicolored .30 .30
371 A76 50t multicolored .62 .62
Nos. 368-371 (4) 1.22 1.22

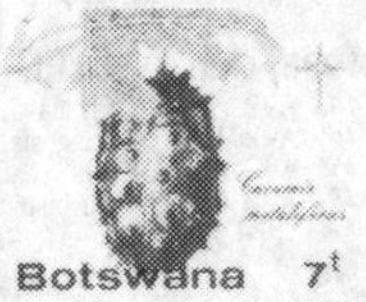

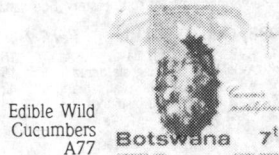

Edible Wild Cucumbers A77

1985, Nov. 4
372 A77 7t Cucumis metuliferus .15 .15
373 A77 15t Acanthosicyos naudinianus .18 .18
374 A77 25t Coccinia sessifolia .30 .30
375 A77 50t Momordica balsamina .62 .62
Nos. 372-375 (4) 1.25 1.25

Christmas.

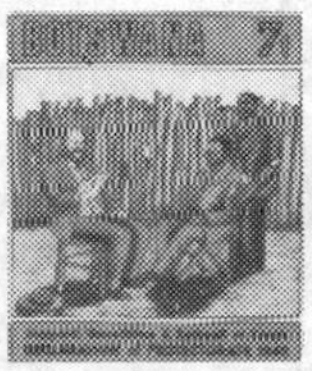

Declaration of Protectorate, Cent. — A78

1985, Dec. 30 Litho. *Perf. 14x14½*
376 A78 7t Heads of state meet .15 .15
377 A78 15t Declaration reading, 1885 .18 .18
378 A78 25t Mackenzie and Khama .30 .30
379 A78 50t Map .62 .62
a. Souvenir sheet of 4, #376-379 1.20 1.20
Nos. 376-379 (4) 1.25 1.25

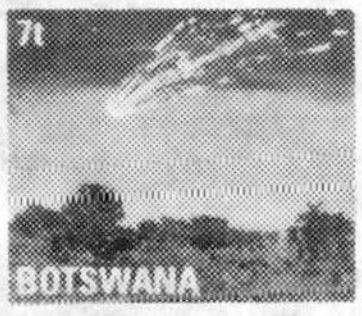

Halley's Comet — A79

1986, Mar. 24 *Perf. 14½x14*
380 A79 7t Comet over Serowe .15 .15
381 A79 15t Over Bobonong .18 .18
382 A79 35t Over Gomare swamps .42 .42
383 A79 50t Over Thamaga, Letlhakeng .62 .62
Nos. 380-383 (4) 1.37 1.37

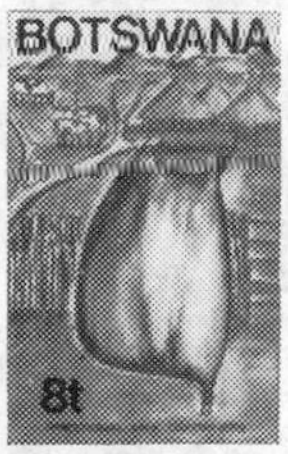

Milk Containers — A80

1986, June 23 *Perf. 14½*
384 A80 8t Leather bag .15 .15
385 A80 15t Ceramic pots .18 .18
386 A80 35t Wood pot .42 .42
387 A80 50t Woman, pots .62 .62
Nos. 384-387 (4) 1.37 1.37

Souvenir Sheet

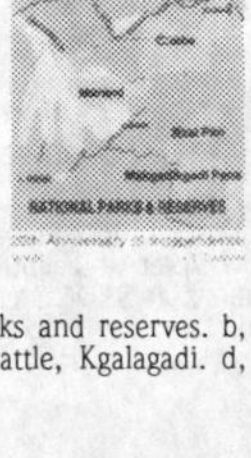

Natl. Independence, 20th Anniv. — A81

Designs: a, Map of natl. parks and reserves. b, Morupule Power Station. c, Cattle, Kgalagadi. d, Natl. Assembly.

1986, Sept. 30 Litho. *Perf. 14½x14*
388 Sheet of 4 .90 .90
a.-d. A81 20t any single .22 .22

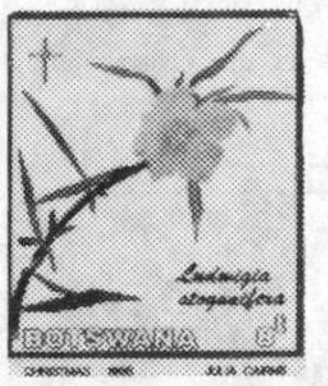

Flowers of the Okavango Swamps — A82

1986, Nov. 3 Litho. *Perf. 14x14½*
389 A82 8t Ludwigia stogonifera .15 .15
390 A82 15t Sopubia mannii .16 .16
391 A82 35t Commelina diffusa .38 .38
392 A82 50t Hibiscus diversifolius .55 .55
Nos. 389-392 (4) 1.24 1.24

Christmas.

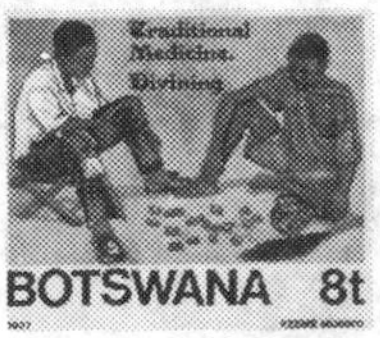

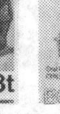

Traditional Medicine A83

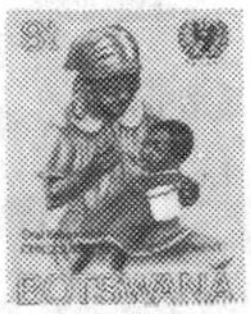

UN Child Survival Campaign A84

1987, Mar. 2 Litho. *Perf. 14½x14*
393 A83 8t Professional diviners .15 .15
394 A83 15t Lightning prevention .18 .18
395 A83 35t Rainmaker .45 .45
396 A83 50t Bloodletting .65 .65
Nos. 393-396 (4) 1.43 1.43

1987, June 1
397 A84 8t Oral rehydration therapy .15 .15
398 A84 15t Growth monitoring .18 .18
399 A84 35t Immunization .45 .45
400 A84 50t Breast-feeding .65 .65
Nos. 397-400 (4) 1.43 1.43

Nos. 308, 311 and 318 Surcharged

Perf. 14x14½,14½x14

1987, Apr. 1 Photo.
401 A64 3t on 6t No. 308 .15 .15
402 A64 5t on 10t No. 311 .15 .15
403 A64 20t on 50t No. 318 .30 .30
Set value .40 .40

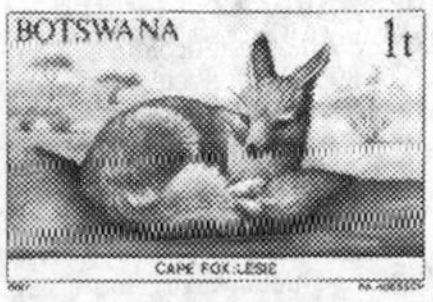

Wildlife Conservation A85

1987, Aug. 3 *Perf. 14*
404 A85 1t Cape fox .15 .15
405 A85 2t Lechwe .15 .15
406 A85 3t Zebra .15 .15
407 A85 4t Duiker .15 .15
408 A85 5t Banded mongoose .15 .15
409 A85 6t Rusty-spotted genet .15 .15
410 A85 8t Hedgehog .15 .15
411 A85 10t Scrub hare .15 .15
412 A85 12t Hippopotamus .15 .15
413 A85 15t Suricate .15 .15
414 A85 20t Caracal .18 .18
415 A85 25t Steenbok .24 .24
416 A85 30t Gemsbok .28 .28
417 A85 35t Square-lipped rhino .32 .32
418 A85 40t Mountain reedbuck .38 .38
419 A85 50t Rock dassie .45 .45
420 A85 1p Giraffe .95 .95
421 A85 2p Tsessebe 1.90 1.90
422 A85 3p Side-striped jackal 2.75 2.75
423 A85 5p Hartebeest 4.75 4.75
Nos. 404-423 (20) 13.70 13.70

For surcharges see Nos. 480-482, 506-509.

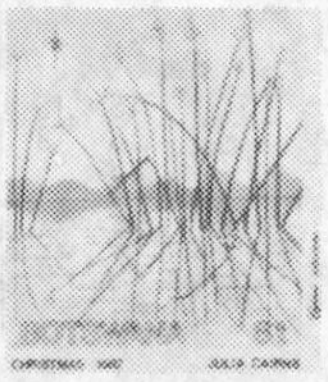
Wetland Grasses — A86

1987, Oct. 26 *Perf. 14x14½*

424 A86	8t Cyperus articulatus	.15	.15
425 A86	15t Miscanthus junceus	.15	.15
426 A86	30t Cyperus alopecuroides	.36	.36
427 A86	1p Typha latifolia	1.20	1.20
a.	Souvenir sheet of 4, #424-427	1.85	1.85
	Nos. 424-427 (4)	1.86	1.86

Christmas, preservation of the Okavango and Kuando-Chobe River wetlands.

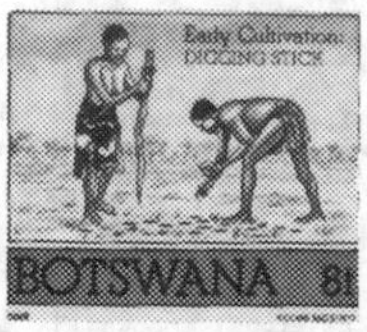

Early Cultivation Techniques A87

1988, Mar. 14 Litho. *Perf. 14½x14*

428 A87	8t Digging stick	.15	.15
429 A87	15t Iron hoe	.18	.18
430 A87	35t Wooden plow	.42	.42
431 A87	50t Communal planting, Lesotla	.60	.60
	Nos. 428-431 (4)	1.35	1.35

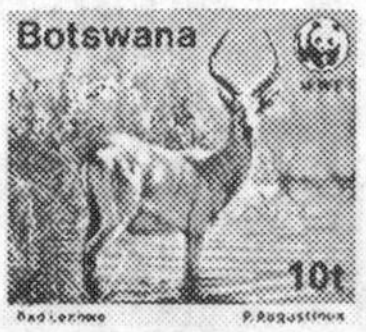

World Wildlife Fund — A88

Designs: WWF emblem and various red lechwe, Kobus leche.

1988, June 6 Litho. *Perf. 14½x14*

432 A88	10t Adult wading	*.22*	*.22*
433 A88	15t Adult, sun	*.35*	*.35*
434 A88	35t Cow, calf	*.75*	*.75*
435 A88	75t Herd	*1.75*	*1.75*
	Nos. 432-435 (4)	*3.07*	*3.07*

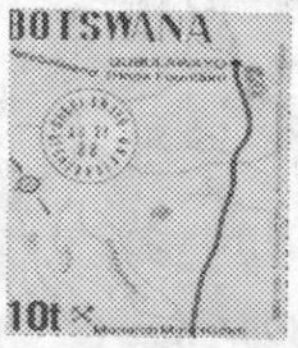

Runner Post, Cent. — A89

Routes and: 10t, Gubulawayo, Bechuanaland, cancellation dated Aug. 21 '88. 15t, Bechuanaland Protectorate No. 65. 30t, Pack traders. 60t, Mafeking killer cancel No. 638.

1988, Aug. 22 Litho. *Perf. 14½*

436 A89	10t multicolored	.15	.15
437 A89	15t multicolored	.18	.18
438 A89	30t multicolored	.35	.35
439 A89	60t multicolored	.65	.65
a.	Souvenir sheet of 4, #436-439	1.30	1.30
	Nos. 436-439 (4)	1.33	1.33

Printed in a continuous design picturing the Mafeking-Gubulawayo route and part of the Shoshong runner post route.

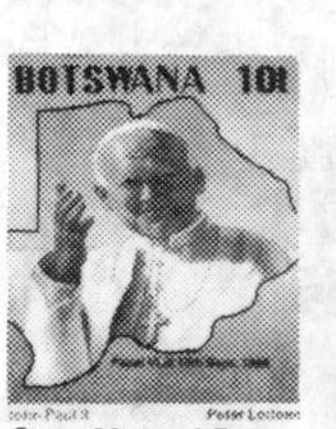

State Visit of Pope John Paul II, Sept. 13 — A90

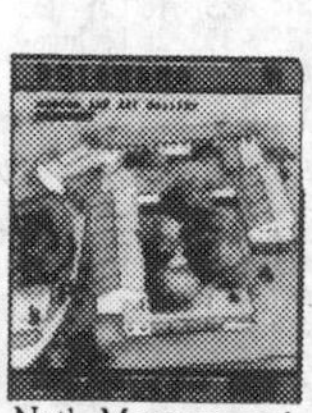
Natl. Museum and Art Gallery, Gaborone, 20th Anniv. — A91

1988, Sept. 13 Litho. *Perf. 14x14½*

440 A90	10t Map, portrait	.15	.15
441 A90	15t Portrait	.15	.15
442 A90	30t Map, portrait, diff.	.35	.35
443 A90	80t Portrait, diff.	.85	.85
	Nos. 440-443 (4)	1.50	1.50

1988, Sept. 30 *Perf. 14½*

444 A91	8t Museum	.15	.15
445 A91	15t Pottery, c. 400-1300	.18	.18
446 A91	30t Buffalo bellows	.35	.35
447 A91	60t Children, mobile museum	.68	.68
	Nos. 444-447 (4)	1.36	1.36

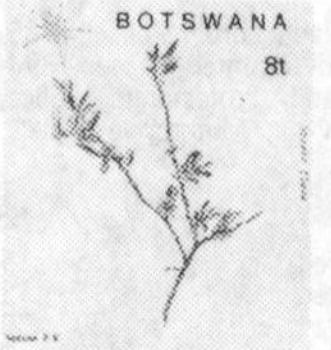

A92

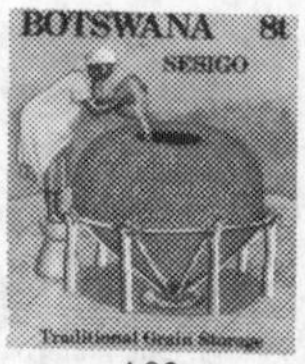

A93

Flowering plants of southeastern Botswana.

1988, Oct. 11 Litho. *Perf. 14x14½*

448 A92	8t Grewia flava	.15	.15
449 A92	15t Cienfuegosia digitata	.15	.15
450 A92	40t Solanum seaforthianum	.42	.42
451 A92	75t Carissa bispinosa	.78	.78
	Nos. 448-451 (4)	1.50	1.50

Christmas.

1989, Mar. 13 Litho. *Perf. 14x14½*

Traditional grain storage.

452 A93	8t Sesigo basket granary	.15	.15
453 A93	15t Letlole daga granary	.15	.15
454 A93	30t Sefalana bisque granary	.30	.30
455 A93	60t Serala granaries	.60	.60
	Nos. 452-455 (4)	1.20	1.20

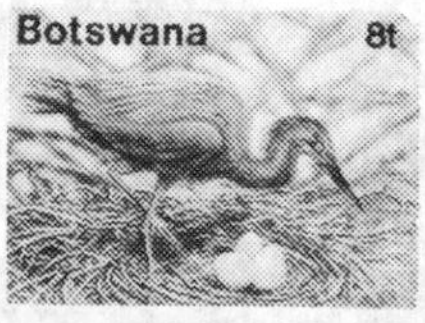

Slaty Egrets — A94

1989, July 5 *Perf. 15x14*

456 A94	8t Nesting	*.15*	*.15*
457 A94	15t Young	*.25*	*.25*
458 A94	30t Adult in flight	*.52*	*.52*
459 A94	60t Two adults	*1.10*	*1.10*
a.	Souvenir sheet of 4, #456-459	*2.00*	*2.00*
	Nos. 456-459 (4)	*2.02*	*2.02*

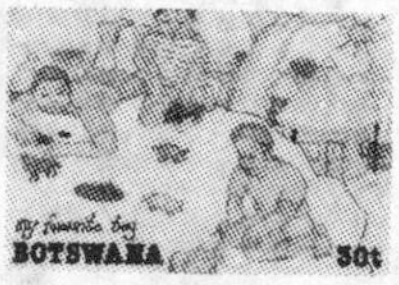

Children's Drawings A95

Perf. 14½x14, 14x14½

1989, Sept. 4

460 A95	10t Ephraim Seeletso	.15	.15
461 A95	15t Neelma Bhatia, vert.	.15	.15
462 A95	30t Thabo Habana	.30	.30
463 A95	1p Thabo Olesitse	1.00	1.00
	Nos. 460-463 (4)	1.60	1.60

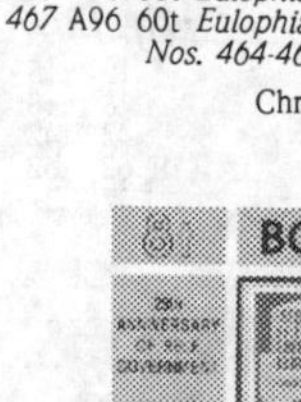

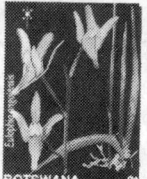

Star and Orchids — A96

1989, Oct. 30 Litho. *Perf. 14x14½*

464 A96	8t *Eulophia angolensis*	*.15*	*.15*
465 A96	15t *Eulophia hereroensis*	*.26*	*.26*
466 A96	30t *Eulophia speciosa*	*.52*	*.52*
467 A96	60t *Eulophia petersii*	*1.10*	*1.10*
	Nos. 464-467 (4)	*2.03*	*2.03*

Christmas.

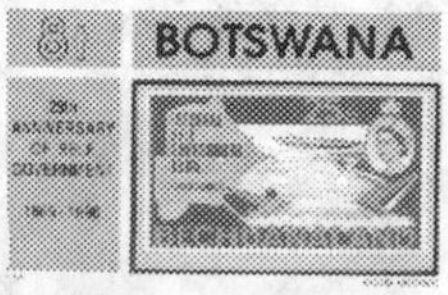

Anniversaries — A97

Designs: 8t, Bechuanaland Protectorate No. 201. 15t, Voter at ballot box. 30t, Map and flags of nations at SADCC conference. 60t, Great Britain No. 1.

1990, Mar. 5 Litho. *Perf. 14½*

468 A97	8t multicolored	.15	.15
469 A97	15t multicolored	.15	.15
470 A97	30t multicolored	.30	.30
471 A97	60t multicolored	.60	.60
	Nos. 468-471 (4)	1.20	1.20

25th anniv. of self government (8t); 1st elections, 25th anniv. (15t); Southern African Development Coordination Conference (SADCC), 10th anniv. (30t); and Penny Black, 150th anniv. (60t).

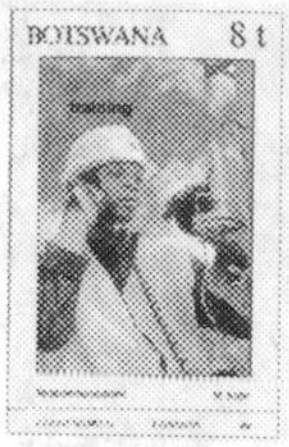

Stamp World London '90 — A98

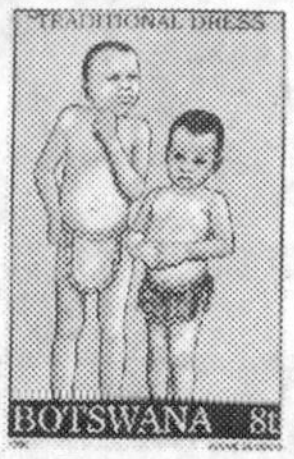

Traditional Dress — A99

Aspects of the telecommunications industry.

1990, May 3

472 A98	8t Training	.15	.15
473 A98	15t Transmission	.15	.15
474 A98	30t Public telephone	.30	.30
475 A98	2p Testing circuitry	2.00	2.00
	Nos. 472-475 (4)	2.60	2.60

1990, Aug. 1 Litho. *Perf. 14*

476 A99	8t Children	.15	.15
477 A99	15t Young woman	.15	.15
478 A99	30t Man	.26	.26
479 A99	2p Adult woman	1.75	1.75
a.	Souvenir sheet of 4, #476-479	2.50	2.50
	Nos. 476-479 (4)	2.31	2.31

Nos. 404 and 412 Surcharged ■ 10t

No. 409 Surcharged 20t ■

1990

480 A85	10t on 1t No. 404	.15	.15
481 A85	20t on 6t No. 409	.20	.20
482 A85	50t on 12t No. 412	.50	.50
	Nos. 480-482 (3)	.85	.85

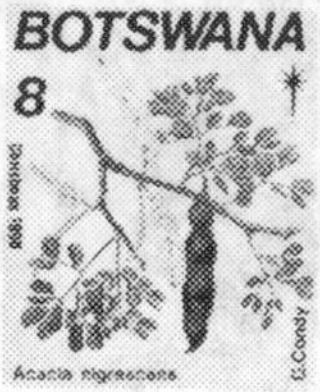

Flowering Trees — A100

1990, Oct. 30 Litho. *Perf. 14*

483 A100	8t Acacia nigrescens	.15	.15
484 A100	15t Peltophorum africanum	.15	.15
485 A100	30t Burkea africana	.26	.26
486 A100	2p Pterocarpus angolensis	1.75	1.75
	Nos. 483-486 (4)	2.31	2.31

Christmas.

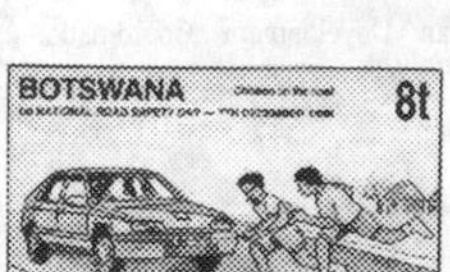

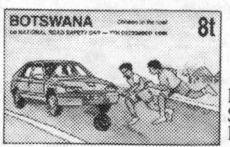

Natl. Road Safety Day — A101

1990, Dec. 7 Litho. *Perf. 14½*

487 A101	8t Children playing on road	.15	.15
488 A101	15t Accident	.18	.18
489 A101	30t Livestock on road	.36	.36
	Nos. 487-489 (3)	.69	.69

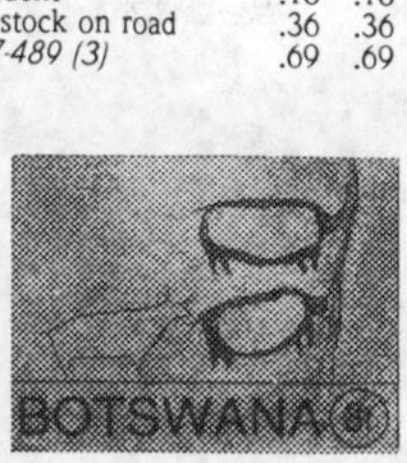

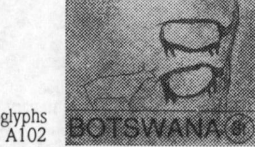

Petroglyphs A102

Various petroglyphs.

1991, Mar. 4 Litho. *Perf. 14x14½*

Textured Paper

490 A102	8t multicolored	.15	.15
491 A102	15t multicolored	.15	.15
492 A102	30t multicolored	.30	.30
493 A102	2p multicolored	2.00	2.00
	Nos. 490-493 (4)	2.60	2.60

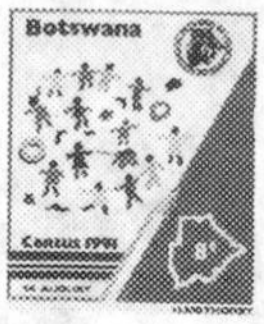

Natl. Census — A103

1991, June 3 Litho. *Perf. 14*

494 A103	8t Children playing	.15	.15

Perf. 14½

495 A103	15t Houses	.18	.18

Perf. 14x14½

496 A103	30t Children in schoolyard	.36	.36
497 A103	2p Children, hospital	2.40	2.40
	Nos. 494-497 (4)	3.09	3.09

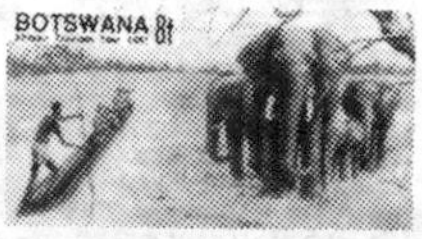

African Tourism Year — A104

1991, Sept. 30 Litho. *Perf. 14*

498 A104	8t Tourists, elephants	.15	.15
499 A104	15t Birds, crocodiles	.18	.18
500 A104	35t Airplane, fish eagles	.40	.40

Size 26x43mm

501 A104	2p Okavango Delta	2.40	2.40
	Nos. 498-501 (4)	3.13	3.13

No. 501 incorporates designs of #498-500.

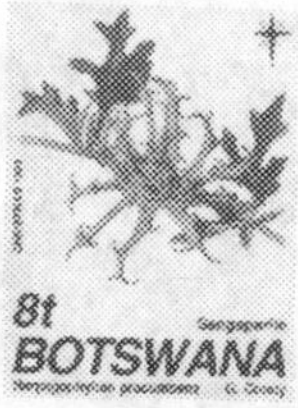

Christmas — A105

Seed pods: 8t, Harpagophytum procumbens. 15t, Tylosema esculentum. 30t, Abrus precatorius. 2p, Kigelia africana.

1991, Nov. 4 Litho. *Perf. 14*

502 A105	8t multicolored	.15	.15
503 A105	15t multicolored	.16	.16
504 A105	30t multicolored	.32	.32
505 A105	2p multicolored	2.25	2.25
	Nos. 502-505 (4)	2.88	2.88

Nos. 406, 409, & 412 Surcharged 8t ■

1992, Mar. 9 Litho. *Perf. 14*

506 A85	8t on 12t No. 412	.15	.15
507 A85	10t on 12t No. 412	.15	.15
508 A85	25t on 6t No. 409	.25	.25
509 A85	40t on 3t No. 406	.38	.38
	Nos. 506-509 (4)	.93	.93

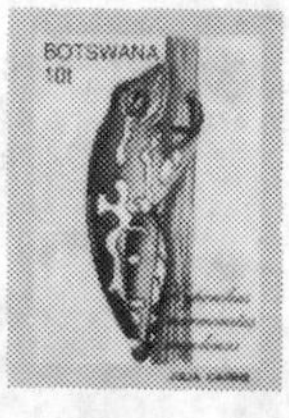

Climbing Frogs — A106

Designs: 8t, Cacosternum boettgeri, horiz. 10t, Hyperolius marmoratus angolensis. 40t, Bufo fenoulheti, horiz. 1p, Hyperolius.

Perf. 14½x14, 14x14½

1992, Mar. 23

510 A106	8t multicolored	.15	.15
511 A106	10t multicolored	.15	.15
512 A106	40t multicolored	.38	.38
513 A106	1p multicolored	.95	.95
	Nos. 510-513 (4)	1.63	1.63

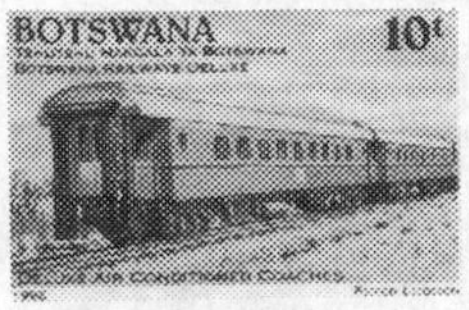

Botswana Railways A107

Designs: 10t, Deluxe air-conditioned coaches. 25t, BD1 locomotive, vert. 40t, Deluxe coach interior, vert. 2p, Locomotive pulling air-conditioned coaches.

1992, June 29 Litho. *Perf. 14*
514 A107 10t multicolored .15 .15
515 A107 25t multicolored .15 .15
516 A107 40t multicolored .20 .20
517 A107 2p multicolored 1.00 1.00
a. Souv. sheet of 4, #514-517 + label 1.40 1.40
Nos. 514-517 (4) 1.50 1.50

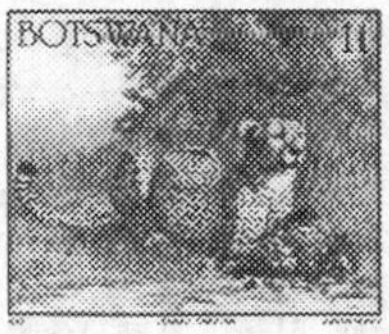

Wild Animals A108

1992, Aug. 3 Litho. *Perf. 14½*
518 A108 1t Cheetah .15 .15
519 A108 2t Spring hares .15 .15
520 A108 4t Blackfooted cat .15 .15
521 A108 5t Striped mouse .15 .15
522 A108 10t Oribi .15 .15
523 A108 12t Pangolin .15 .15
524 A108 15t Aardwolf .15 .15
525 A108 20t Warthog .18 .18
526 A108 25t Ground squirrels .22 .22
527 A108 35t Honey badger .32 .32
528 A108 40t Common mole rat .36 .36
529 A108 45t Wild dogs .40 .40
530 A108 50t Water mongoose .45 .45
531 A108 80t Klipspringer .68 .68
532 A108 1p Lesser bushbaby .90 .90
533 A108 2p Bushveld elephant shrew 1.80 1.80
534 A108 5p Zorilla 4.50 4.50
535 A108 10p Vervet monkey 9.00 9.00
Nos. 518-535 (18) 19.86 19.86

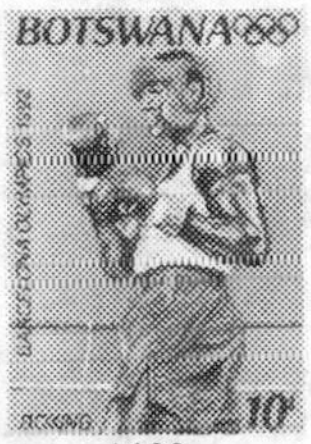

A109

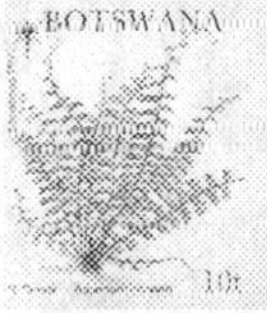

Ferns — A110

1992, Aug. 7 *Perf. 14x15*
536 A109 10t Boxer .15 .15
537 A109 50t Four sprinters .45 .45
538 A109 1p Two boxers .95 .95
539 A109 2p Three runners 1.85 1.85
a. Souvenir sheet of 4, #536-539 3.40 3.40
Nos. 536-539 (4) 3.40 3.40

1992 Summer Olympics, Barcelona.

1992, Nov. 23 Litho. *Perf. 14½*
540 A110 10t Adiantum incisum .15 .15
541 A110 25t Actiniopteris radiata .24 .24
542 A110 40t Ceratopteris cornuta .38 .38
543 A110 1.50p Pellaea calomelanos 1.40 1.40
Nos. 540-543 (4) 2.17 2.17

Christmas.

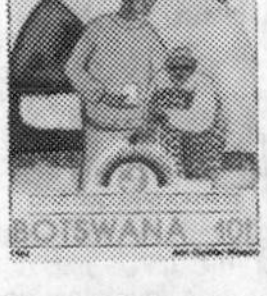

Organizations A111

Designs: 10t, Lions Intl., conquering blindness, vert. 15t, Red Cross Society. 25t, Ecumenical Decade, churches in solidarity with women, vert. 35t, Round Table supporting the deaf. 40t, Rotary Intl., vert. 50t, Botswana Christian Council.

1993, Mar. 29 Litho. *Perf. 14*
544 A111 10t multicolored .15 .15
545 A111 15t multicolored .15 .15
546 A111 25t multicolored .22 .22
547 A111 35t multicolored .32 .32
548 A111 40t multicolored .38 .38
549 A111 50t multicolored .45 .45
Nos. 544-549 (6) 1.67 1.67

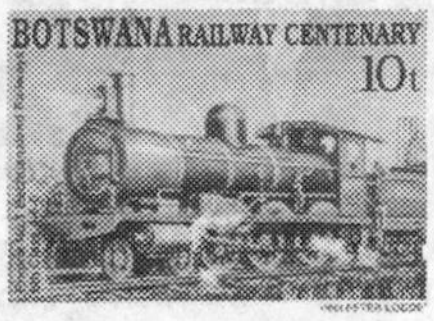

Botswana Railway, Cent. A112

Designs: 10t, Engine No. 1, 6th class 4-6-0, Bechuanaland Railways. 40t, Engine No. 317, 19th class 4-8-2. 50t, Engine No. 256, 12th class 4-8-2. 1.50p, Engine No. 71, 7th class 4-8-0, Rhodesia Railways.

1993, May 24 Litho. *Perf. 15x14*
550 A112 10t multicolored .15 .15
551 A112 40t multicolored .38 .38
552 A112 50t multicolored .48 .48
553 A112 1.50p multicolored 1.45 1.45
a. Souvenir sheet of 4, #550-553 2.50 2.50
Nos. 550-553 (4) 2.46 2.46

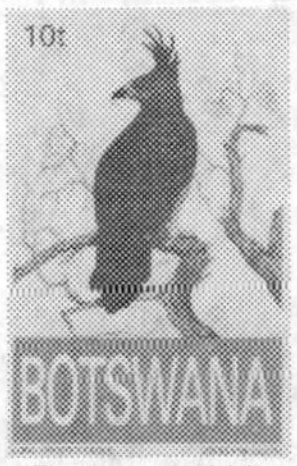

Eagles — A113

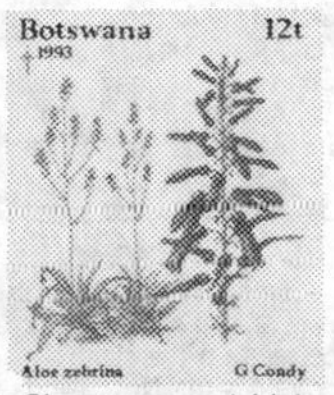

Christmas — A114

1993, Aug. 30 Litho. *Perf. 14½*
554 A113 10t Long crested eagle .15 .15
555 A113 25t Snake eagle .24 .24
556 A113 50t Bateleur eagle .48 .48
557 A113 1.50p Secretary bird 1.50 1.50
Nos. 554-557 (4) 2.37 2.37

1993, Oct. 25 Litho. *Perf. 14x14½*
558 A114 12t Aloe zebrina .15 .15
559 A114 25t Croton megalobotrys .22 .22
560 A114 50t Boophane disticha .45 .45
561 A114 1p Euphorbia davyi .90 .90
Nos. 558-561 (4) 1.72 1.72

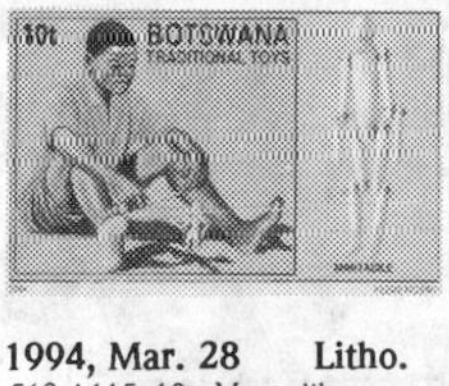

Traditional Children's Toys A115

1994, Mar. 28 Litho. *Perf. 14½*
562 A115 10t Mantadile .15 .15
563 A115 40t Dikgomo tsa mimopa .30 .30
564 A115 50t Sefuu-fuu .38 .38
565 A115 1p Mantlwane .75 .75
Nos. 562-565 (4) 1.58 1.58

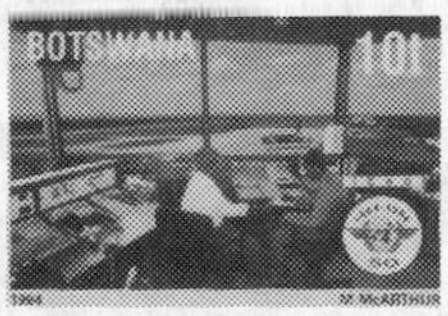

ICAO, 50th Anniv. A116

Perf. 14½x14, 14x14½
1994, June 30 Litho.
566 A116 10t Inside control tower .15 .15
567 A116 25t Fire engine .25 .25
568 A116 40t Baggage carts, vert. .38 .38
569 A116 50t Control tower, vert. .48 .48
Nos. 566-569 (4) 1.26 1.26

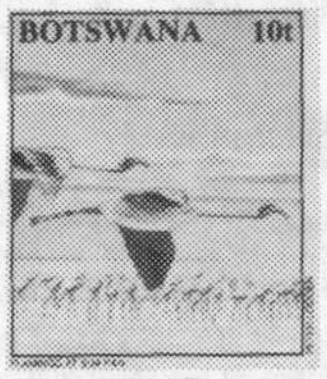

A117

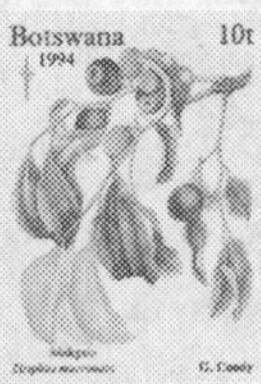

A118

Environmental Protection: 10t, Flamingos, Sua Pan, vert. 35t, Makgadikgadi Pan trees. 50t, Zebra, Makgadikgadi Palm trees, vert. 2p, Map of Makgadikgadi Pans.

1994, Aug. 30 Litho. *Perf. 14*
570 A117 10t multicolored .15 .15
571 A117 35t multicolored .32 .32
572 A117 50t multicolored .48 .48
573 A117 2p multicolored 1.90 1.90
Nos. 570-573 (4) 2.85 2.85

1994, Oct. 24

Edible fruits: 10t, Ziziphus mucronata. 25t, Strychnos cocculoides. 40t, Bauhinia petersiana. 50t, Schinziphyton rautanelii.

574 A118 10t multicolored .15 .15
575 A118 25t multicolored .18 .18
576 A118 40t multicolored .28 .28
577 A118 50t multicolored .35 .35
Nos. 574-577 (4) .96 .96

Christmas.

See Nos. 587-590.

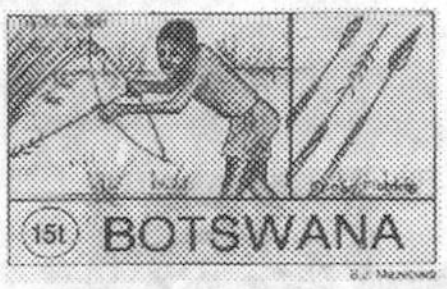

Traditional Fishing A119

1995, Apr. 3 Litho. *Perf. 14*
578 A119 15t Spear .15 .15
579 A119 40t Hook .30 .30
580 A119 65t Net .48 .48
581 A119 80t Basket .60 .60
Nos. 578-581 (4) 1.53 1.53

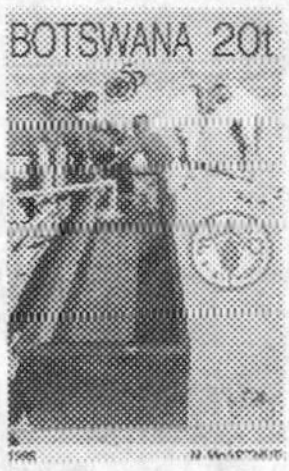

UN, 50th Anniv. — A120

1995, Oct. 16 Litho. *Perf. 14*
582 A120 20t FAO .15 .15
583 A120 50t World Food Program .35 .35
584 A120 80t Development Plan .60 .60
585 A120 1p UNICEF .70 .70
Nos. 582-585 (4) 1.80 1.80

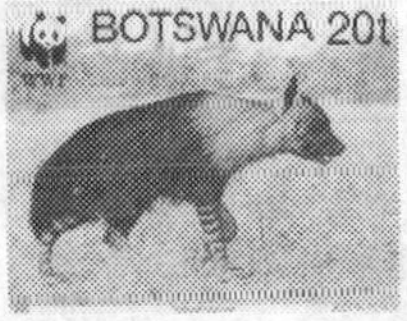

World Wildlife Fund — A121

Hyaena brunnea: a, 20t, Adult walking right. b, 50t, Two young. c, 80t, Adult finding eggs. d, 1p, Two young, adult resting.

1995, Nov. 6
586 A121 Strip of 4, #a.-d. 1.75 1.75

No. 586 was issued in miniature sheets of 4 each.

Christmas Type of 1994

1995, Nov. 27 Litho. *Perf. 14*
587 A118 20t Adenia glauca .15 .15
588 A118 50t Pterodiscus ngamicus .35 .35
589 A118 80t Sesamothamnus lugardii .60 .60
590 A118 1p Fockea multiflora .70 .70
Nos. 587-590 (4) 1.80 1.80

POSTAGE DUE STAMPS

Bechuanaland Protectorate Nos. J10-J12 Overprinted: "REPUBLIC OF / BOTSWANA"

Wmk. 4

1967, Mar. 1 Typo. *Perf. 14*
J1 D2 1c carmine rose .15 *1.00*
J2 D2 2c dull violet .25 *1.50*
J3 D2 5c olive green .60 *2.00*
Nos. J1-J3 (3) 1.00 *4.50*

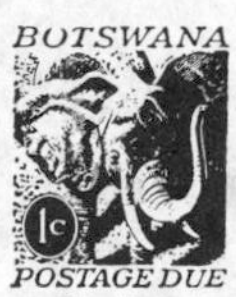

Elephant D1

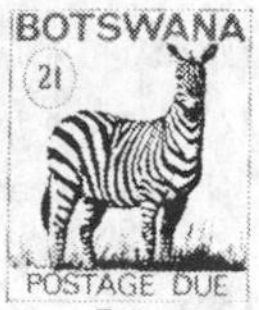

Zebra D2

Perf. 13½
1971, June 9 Litho. Unwmk.
J4 D1 1c carmine rose .24 *.75*
J5 D1 2c violet blue .30 *.90*
J6 D1 6c sepia .52 *1.50*
J7 D1 14c green .95 *2.25*
Nos. J4-J7 (4) 2.01 *5.40*

1978 *Perf. 12½*
J8 D2 1t red orange & black .15 .15
J9 D2 2t emerald & black .15 .15
J10 D2 4t red & black .15 .15
J11 D2 10t dark blue & black .20 .20
J12 D2 16t brown & black .38 .38
Set value .75 .75

1984 *Perf. 14½x14*
J8a D2 1t .15 *.15*
J9a D2 2t .15 *.15*
J10a D2 4t .15 *.15*
J11a D2 10t .20 *.20*
J12a D2 16t .38 *.38*
Set value .75 *.75*

1989, Apr. 1 Litho. *Perf. 14½*
J8b D2 1t .15 .15
J9b D2 2t .15 .15
J10b D2 4t .15 .15
J11b D2 10t .20 .20
J12b D2 16t .38 .38
Set value .75 .75

The design is the same size on the 1984 and 1989 issues, but the paper is wider on the 1989 issue.

BRITISH CENTRAL AFRICA

'bri–tish 'sen–trəl 'a–fri–kə

LOCATION — Central Africa, on the west shore of Lake Nyassa
GOVT. — Former British territory, under charter to the British South Africa Company
AREA — 37,800 sq. mi.
POP. — 1,639,329
CAPITAL — Zomba

In 1907 the name was changed to Nyasaland Protectorate, and stamps so inscribed replaced those of British Central Africa.

12 Pence = 1 Shilling
20 Shillings = 1 Pound

Rhodesia Nos. 2, 4-19 Overprinted in Black **B.C.A.**

1891-95 Unwmk. *Perf. 14*
1 A1 1p black 2.50 2.50
2 A2 2p gray green & ver 2.50 2.50
3 A2 4p red brn & blk 2.00 3.00
4 A1 6p ultramarine 45.00 24.00
5 A1 6p dark blue 5.00 7.50
6 A2 8p rose & blue 12.00 *25.00*
7 A1 1sh bis brown 9.00 9.00
8 A1 2sh vermilion 20.00 *40.00*
9 A1 2sh6p gray lilac 42.50 55.00
10 A2 3sh brn & grn ('95) 42.50 50.00
11 A2 4sh gray & ver ('93) 42.50 *65.00*
12 A1 5sh yellow 45.00 55.00
13 A1 10sh green 85.00 *120.00*
14 A3 £1 blue 600.00 650.00
15 A3 £2 rose red 800.00 *800.00*
16 A3 £5 yel green 1,800. *1,900.*
17 A3 £10 red brown *3,000.* *3,000.*
Nos. 1-13 (13) 355.50 *458.50*

High values with fiscal cancellation are fairly common and can be purchased at a small fraction of the above values. This applies to subsequent issues also.

For surcharge see No. 20.

Rhodesia Nos. 13-14 Surcharged in Black **B.C.A. THREE SHILLINGS.**

1892-93

18 A2	3sh on 4sh gray & ver ('93)	275.00	275.00
19 A1	4sh on 5sh yellow	65.00	75.00

No. 2 Surcharged in Black, with Bar **ONE PENNY.**

1895

20 A2	1p on 2p	7.50	*20.00*
a.	Double surcharge	*3,000.*	*2,000.*

A double surcharge, without period after "Penny," and measuring 16mm instead of 18mm, is from a trial printing.

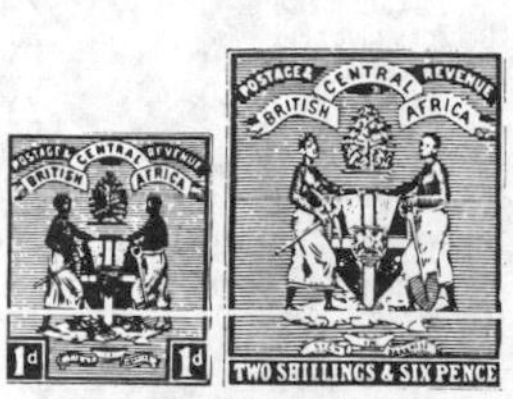

Coat of Arms of the Protectorate
A4 A5

1895 Unwmk. Typo. *Perf. 14*

21	A4	1p black	7.50	5.00
22	A4	2p green & black	12.50	10.00
23	A4	4p org & black	22.50	22.50
24	A4	6p ultra & black	35.00	7.50
25	A4	1sh rose & black	40.00	17.50
26	A5	2sh6p vio & black	100.00	125.00
27	A5	3sh yel & black	65.00	37.50
28	A5	5sh olive & blk	85.00	90.00
29	A5	£1 org & black	650.00	375.00
30	A5	£10 ver & black	*3,250.*	*2,750.*
31	A5	£25 bl grn & blk	*5,750.*	*6,000.*
		Nos. 21-28 (8)	367.50	315.00

1896 Wmk. 2

32	A4	1p black	4.50	4.50
33	A4	2p green & black	12.00	5.75
34	A4	4p org brown & blk	14.00	16.00
35	A4	6p ultra & black	15.00	8.00
36	A4	1sh rose & black	16.00	9.00

Wmk. 1 Sideways

37	A5	2sh6p vio rose & blk	75.00	90.00
38	A5	3sh yel & black	55.00	40.00
39	A5	5sh grn & black	80.00	95.00
40	A5	£1 blue & blk	675.00	475.00
41	A5	£10 ver & blk	*3,750.*	*2,250.*
42	A5	£25 bl grn & blk	*9,500.*	*9,500.*
		Nos. 32-39 (8)	271.50	268.25

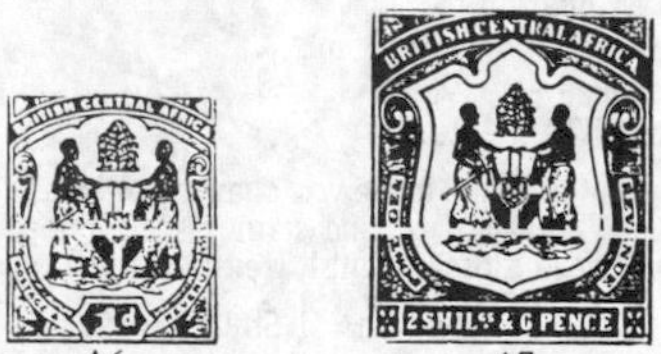

A6 A7

1897-1901 Wmk. 2

43	A6	1p ultra & black	1.00	.60
44	A6	1p rose & violet ('01)	1.25	.90
45	A6	2p yel & black	1.50	.70
46	A6	4p car rose & blk	4.50	2.50
47	A6	4p ol green & violet ('01)	5.00	6.00
48	A6	6p green & black	27.50	4.00
49	A6	6p red brown & violet ('01)	4.00	3.75
50	A6	1sh gray lilac & blk	7.50	6.25

Wmk. 1

51	A7	2sh6p ultra & blk	32.50	35.00
52	A7	3sh gray grn & blk	150.00	175.00
53	A7	4sh car rose & blk	45.00	60.00
54	A7	10sh ol & black	75.00	90.00
55	A7	£1 dp vio & blk	225.00	150.00
56	A7	£10 org & black	*3,500.*	*1,600.*
		Nos. 43-54 (12)	354.75	384.70

No. 52 Surcharged in Red **ONE PENNY**

1897

57 A7	1p on 3s	5.00	7.50
a.	"PNNEY"	1,500.	
b.	"PENN"	900.00	
c.	Double surcharge	750.00	600.00

British Central Africa stamps can be mounted in the Scott British Africa album.

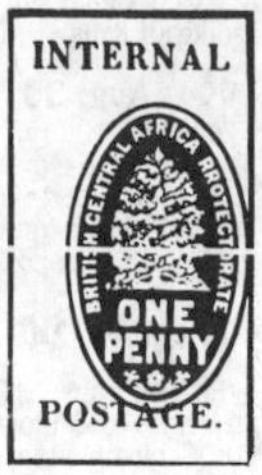

A8

1898, Mar. 11 Unwmk. *Imperf.*

58 A8	1p ver & ultra	1,500.	50.00
a.	Center inverted	*10,000.*	
b.	Double oval		
c.	Pair, one without oval	*6,500.*	
d.	Pair with three ovals		
e.	Initials of P.M. General on back		*450.00*

Perf. 12

59 A8	1p ver & blue	1,500.	15.00

There are two settings of Nos. 58-59, with 30 types of each.

No. 58 issued without gum.

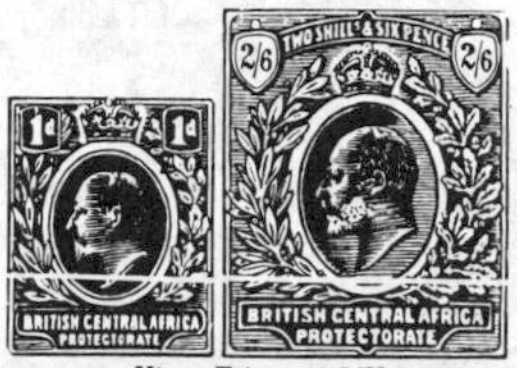

King Edward VII
A9 A10

1903-04 Wmk. 2

60	A9	1p car & black	3.75	.75
61	A9	2p vio & dull vio	3.00	2.50
62	A9	4p blk & gray green	2.25	5.75
63	A9	6p org brn & blk	2.25	4.50
64	A9	1sh pale blue & blk ('04)	2.25	4.00

Wmk. 1

65	A10	2sh6p gray green	27.50	35.00
66	A10	4sh vio & dl vio	47.50	70.00
67	A10	10sh blk & gray green	62.50	110.00
68	A10	£1 scar & blk	175.00	135.00
69	A10	£10 ultra & blk	*3,500.*	*2,750.*
		Nos. 60-68 (9)	326.00	367.50

1907 Wmk. 3

70	A9	1p car & black	2.00	.90
71	A9	2p vio & dull vio	*7,250.*	
72	A9	4p blk & gray grn	*7,250.*	
73	A9	6p org brn & blk	25.00	32.50

Nos. 71-72 were not issued.

British Central Africa stamps were replaced by those of Nyasaland Protectorate in 1908.

BRITISH EAST AFRICA

'bri–tish 'ēst 'a–fri–kə

LOCATION — Formerly included all of the territory in East Africa under British control.

Postage stamps were issued by the British East Africa Company in 1896. Later the territory administered by this company was incorporated in the East Africa and Uganda Protectorate which, together with Kenya, became officially designated Kenya Colony.

16 Annas = 1 Rupee

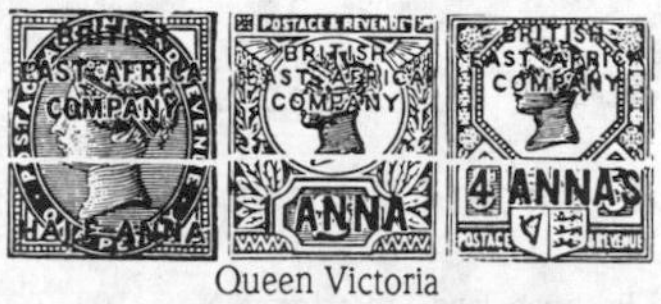

Queen Victoria
A1 A2 A3

1890 Wmk. 30 *Perf. 14*

1	A1	½a on 1p lilac	300.00	200.00
2	A2	1a on 2p grn & car rose	400.00	250.00
3	A3	4a on 5p lilac & bl	450.00	275.00

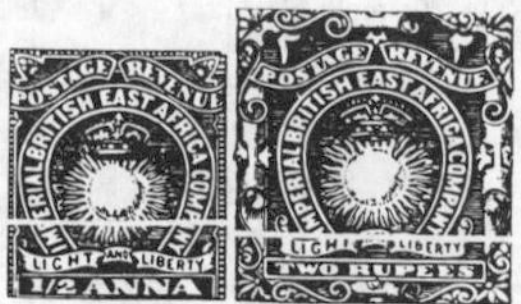

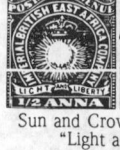

Sun and Crown Symbolical of "Light and Liberty"
A4 A5

1890-94 Unwmk. Litho. *Perf. 14*

14 A4	½a bister brown	1.00	*2.75*
b.	½a deep brown	1.00	*2.50*
c.	As "b," horiz. pair, imperf. btwn.	*1,500.*	750.00
d.	As "b," vert. pair, imperf. btwn.	750.00	475.00
15 A4	1a blue green	1.00	1.00
16 A4	2a vermilion	2.50	1.50
17 A4	2½a black, *yel* ('91)	3.50	3.00
b.	Vert. pair, imperf. btwn.	600.00	400.00
c.	Horiz. pair, imperf. btwn.	800.00	500.00
18 A4	3a black, *red* ('91)	1.25	1.40
b.	Horiz. pair, imperf. btwn.	600.00	400.00
c.	Vert. pair, imperf. btwn.	450.00	350.00
19 A4	4a yellow brown	2.50	2.25
20 A4	4½a brown vio ('91)	2.50	3.25
b.	4½a gray violet ('91)	25.00	7.25
c.	Horiz. pair, imperf. btwn.	1,250.	1,250.
d.	Vert. pair, imperf. btwn.	675.00	450.00
21 A4	5a black, *blue* ('94)	1.10	1.75
22 A4	7½a black ('94)	1.10	1.75
23 A4	8a blue	5.50	7.50
24 A4	8a gray	250.00	325.00
25 A4	1r rose	6.00	7.50
26 A4	1r gray	225.00	225.00
27 A5	2r brick red	10.00	8.00
28 A5	3r gray violet	7.50	6.25
29 A5	4r ultra	12.00	12.50
30 A5	5r gray green	30.00	25.00
	Nos. 14-30 (17)	562.45	635.40

Some of the paper used for this issue had a papermaker's watermark and parts of it often can be seen on the stamps.

Values for Nos. 14c, 14d, 17b, 17c, 18b, 18c, 20c, 20d, unused, are for copies with little or no original gum.

For surcharges and overprints see Nos. 31-53.

1890-91 *Imperf.*

Values for Pairs except No. 19b.

14a	A4	½a	bister brown	600.	350.
14e	A4	½a	deep brown	650.	400.
15a	A4	1a	blue green	800.	475.
16a	A4	2a	vermilion	1,200.	550.
17a	A4	2½a	black, *yellow*	750.	400.
18a	A4	3a	black, *red*	725.	600.
19a	A4	4a	yel brown	1,400.	600.
19b	A4	4a	gray	1,400.	1,400.
20a	A4	4½a	dull violet	1,100.	525.
23a	A4	8a	blue	1,800.	600.
25a	A4	1r	rose	2,400.	625.

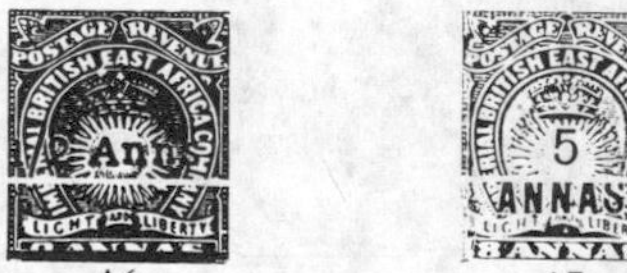

A6 A7

Handstamped Surcharges

1891 *Perf. 14*

31 A6	½a on 2a ver ("A.D.")	2,750.	900.00
a.	Double surcharge		*3,250.*
32 A6	1a on 4a yel brn ("A.B.")	6,000.	1,300.

Nos. 31-32 are initialed in manuscript "A.D." or "A.B." See note below No. 35.

Manuscript Surcharges

1891-95

33 A6	½a on 2a ver ("A.B.")	3,000.	675.00
a.	"½ Annas" ("A.B.")		1,200.
b.	Initialed "A.D."		1,000.
c.	"½ Annas" ("A.D.")		1,600.
34 A6	½a on 3a blk, *red* ("T.E.C.R.")	200.00	50.00
b.	Initialed "A.B."	2,400.	1,100.
34A A6	1a on 3a blk, *red* ("V.H.M.")	3,000.	1,200.
c.	Initialed "T.E.C.R."	3,000.	1,500.
35 A6	1a on 4a yel brn ("A.B.")	2,750.	950.00

The manuscript initials on Nos. 31-35, given in parentheses, stand for Andrew Dick, Archibald Brown, Victor H. Mackenzie (1891) and T.E.C. Remington (1895).

Printed Surcharges

1894

36 A7	5a on 8a blue	52.50	72.50
37 A7	7½a on 1r rose	52.50	72.50

Stamps of 1890-94 Handstamped in Black **BRITISH EAST AFRICA**

1895

38 A4	½a deep brown	60.00	20.00
39 A4	1a blue green	70.00	65.00
40 A4	2a vermilion	125.00	90.00
41 A4	2½a black, *yellow*	110.00	45.00
42 A4	3a black, *red*	42.50	37.50
43 A4	4a yel brown	37.50	37.50
44 A4	4½a gray violet	125.00	85.00
a.	4½a brown violet	750.00	650.00
45 A4	5a black, *blue*	140.00	87.50
b.	Inverted overprint		*2,000.*
46 A4	7½a black	95.00	80.00
47 A4	8a blue	80.00	75.00
b.	Inverted overprint	*2,000.*	
48 A4	1r rose	45.00	47.50
49 A5	2r brick red	250.00	175.00
50 A5	3r gray violet	140.00	125.00
b.	Inverted overprint		
51 A5	4r ultra	125.00	125.00
52 A5	5r gray green	325.00	350.00
	Nos. 38-52 (15)	1,770.	1,445.

Double Overprints

38a	A4	½a		350.	350.
39a	A4	1a		350.	350.
40a	A4	2a		400.	400.
41a	A4	2½a		400.	350.
43a	A4	4a		375.	375.
44b	A4	4½a	gray violet	475.	450.
44c	A4	4½a	brown violet	1,500.	1,400.
45a	A4	5a		700.	650.
46a	A4	7½a		450.	450.
47a	A4	8a		475.	475.
48a	A4	1r		425.	425.
50a	A5	3r		750.	750.
51a	A5	4r		750.	750.
52a	A5	5r		1,100.	1,100.

Surcharged in Red **2½**

1895

53 A4	2½a on 4½a gray vio	90.00	55.00
a.	Double overprint (#44b)	700.00	700.00

Stamps of India 1874-95 Overprinted or Surcharged

British East Africa

2½ **2½** **2½**
a b c

1895 Wmk. Star (39)

54 A17	½a green	3.50	4.00
55 A19	1a maroon	3.50	3.50
56 A20	1a6p bister brn	3.50	3.00
57 A21	2a ultra	3.50	2.25
58 A28	2a6p green	5.00	2.75
59 A20(a)	2½a on 1a6p bis brown	40.00	27.50
a.	"½" without fraction line	70.00	
d.	As "a," "1" of "½" invtd.	750.00	600.00
62 A22	3a orange	7.00	7.50
63 A23	4a olive green	25.00	16.00
64 A25	8a red violet	25.00	32.50
a.	8a red lilac	45.00	50.00
65 A26	12a vio, *red*	18.00	22.50
66 A27	1r gray	55.00	47.50
67 A29	1r car & grn	32.50	55.00
a.	Dbl. ovpt., one sideways	350.00	550.00
68 A30	2r bis & rose	45.00	75.00
69 A30	3r grn & brn	55.00	85.00
70 A30	5r vio & ultra	80.00	120.00
a.	Double overprint	1,800.	

Wmk. Elephant's Head (38)

71 A14	6a bister	21.00	30.00
	Nos. 54-59,62-71 (16)	422.50	534.00

Varieties of the overprint include: "Britlsh," "Brltish," "Bpitish" and "Biitish" for "British", "Afrlca" for "Africa"; "Eas" and "Easa" for "East."

No. 59 is surcharged in bright red; surcharges in brown red were prepared for the UPU, but not regularly issued as stamps. See note following No. 93.

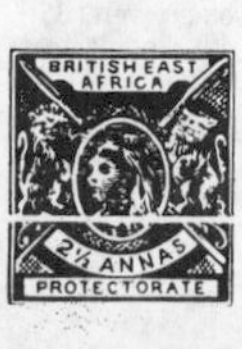

Queen Victoria and British Lions — A8

1896-1903 Engr. Wmk. 2 *Perf. 14*

72	A8	½a yel green	.80	.70
73	A8	1a carmine	2.50	.40
a.		1a red	2.50	.40
74	A8	1a dp rose ('03)	27.50	3.25
75	A8	2a chocolate	3.75	3.25
76	A8	2½a dark blue	4.75	1.00
77	A8	3a gray	2.50	*4.50*
78	A8	4a deep green	5.00	2.50
79	A8	4½a orange	4.00	*8.00*
80	A8	5a dk ocher	6.00	3.50
81	A8	7½a lilac	4.50	*16.00*
82	A8	8a olive gray	2.25	4.00
83	A8	1r ultra	25.00	17.00
a.		1r pale blue	25.00	17.50
84	A8	2r red orange	42.50	22.50
85	A8	3r deep violet	42.50	22.50
86	A8	4r lake	42.50	42.50
87	A8	5r dark brown	42.50	35.00
		Nos. 72-87 (16)	258.55	186.60

Zanzibar Nos. 38-40, 44-46 Overprinted in Black — British East Africa

1897 Wmk. Rosette (71)

88	A2	½a yel grn & red	37.50	37.50
89	A2	1a indigo & red	75.00	75.00
90	A2	2a red brn & red	27.50	18.00
91	A2	4½a org & red	37.50	22.50
92	A2	5a bister & red	37.50	27.50
93	A2	7½a lilac & red	42.50	30.00
a.		Ovptd. on front and back		
		Nos. 88-93 (6)	257.50	210.50

The 1a with red overprint, which includes a period after "Africa", was sent to the UPU, but never placed in use. Nos. 88, 90-93 and 95-100 also exist with period (in black) in sets sent to the UPU. Some experts consider these essays.

Black Ovpt. on Zanzibar #39, 42
New Value Surcharged in Red

1897

95	A2(a)	2½a on 1a	75.00	50.00
a.		Black overprint double	6,500.	
b.		"2" over "1" for "½"	1,200.	
96	A2(b)	2½a on 1a	140.00	90.00
97	A2(c)	2½a on 1a	85.00	55.00
98	A2(a)	2½a on 3a	65.00	45.00
a.		"2" over "1" for "½"	1,200.	
99	A2(b)	2½a on 3a	125.00	85.00
100	A2(c)	2½a on 3a	75.00	50.00
		Nos. 95-100 (6)	565.00	375.00

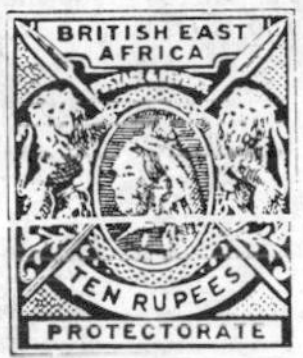

A10

1898 Wmk. 1 Engr.

102	A10	1r ultra	125.00	100.00
a.		1r gray blue	27.50	17.50
103	A10	2r orange	42.50	45.00
104	A10	3r dk violet	42.50	60.00
105	A10	4r carmine	125.00	*150.00*
106	A10	5r black brown	110.00	150.00
107	A10	10r bister	160.00	225.00
108	A10	20r yel green	575.00	1,000.
109	A10	50r lilac	1,900.	2,750.
		Nos. 102-107 (6)	605.00	730.00

The stamps of this country were superseded in 1904 by the stamps of East Africa and Uganda Protectorate.

BRITISH INDIAN OCEAN TERRITORY

'bri–tish 'in–dēən 'ō–chən
'ter–ə–ˌtōr–ē

LOCATION — Indian Ocean
GOVT. — British Dependency
POP. — 558 (1972)

B.I.O.T. was established Nov. 8, 1965. This island group lies 1,180 miles north of Mauritius. It consisted of Chagos Archipelago (chief island: Diego Garcia), Aldabra, Farquhar and Des Roches Islands until June 23, 1976, when the last three named islands were returned to Seychelles.

100 Cents = 1 Rupee
100 Pence = 1 Pound (1990)

Catalogue values for all unused stamps in this country are for Never Hinged items.

Seychelles Nos. 198-202, 204-212 Overprinted — B.I.O.T.

Perf. 14½x14, 14x14½

1968, Jan. 17 Photo. Wmk. 314

Size: 24x31, 31x24mm

1	A17	5c multicolored	.15	.15
2	A17	10c multicolored	.15	.15
3	A17	15c multicolored	.15	.15
4	A17	20c multicolored	.15	.15
5	A17	25c multicolored	.15	.15
6	A18	40c multicolored	.26	.28
7	A18	45c multicolored	.32	.35
8	A17	50c multicolored	.35	.40
9	A17	75c multicolored	.42	.45
10	A18	1r multicolored	1.10	1.25
11	A18	1.50r multicolored	2.00	2.25
12	A18	2.25r multicolored	3.50	3.50
13	A18	3.50r multicolored	5.50	5.50
14	A18	5r multicolored	12.00	12.50

Perf. 13x14

Size: 22½x39mm

15	A17	10r multicolored	24.00	25.00
		Nos. 1-15 (15)	50.20	52.23

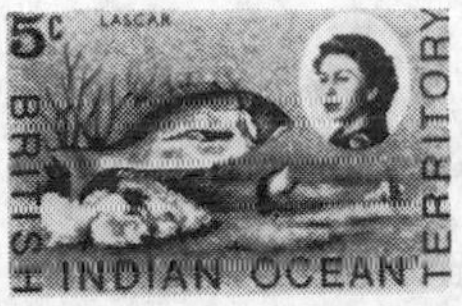

Lascar — A1

Marine Fauna: 10c, Hammerhead shark, vert. 15c, Tiger shark. 20c, Sooty eagle ray. 25c, Butterflyfish, vert. 30c, Robber crab. 40c, Green carangue. 45c, Needlefish, vert. 50c, Barracuda. 60c, Spotted pebble crab. 75c, Parrotfish. 85c, Rainbow runner (fish). 1r, Giant hermit crab. 1.50r, Humphead. 2.25r, Rock cod. 3.50r, Black marlin. 5r, Whale shark, vert. 10r, Lionfish.

Perf. 14x13½, 13½x14; 14 (30c, 60c, 85c)

1968-73 Litho. Wmk. 314

16	A1	5c multicolored	.40	.28
a.		Wmk. upright ('73)	.55	.40
17	A1	10c multicolored	.15	.15
18	A1	15c multicolored	.15	.15
19	A1	20c multicolored	.15	.15
20	A1	25c multicolored	.35	.28
21	A1	30c multi ('70)	.40	.28
22	A1	40c multicolored	.35	.25
23	A1	45c multicolored	2.75	2.25
24	A1	50c multicolored	.35	.32
25	A1	60c multi ('70)	.80	.80
26	A1	75c multicolored	4.00	2.75
27	A1	85c multi ('70)	1.75	1.25
28	A1	1r multicolored	1.40	1.10
29	A1	1.50r multicolored	1.75	1.25
30	A1	2.25r multicolored	14.00	12.50
31	A1	3.50r multicolored	4.00	3.25
32	A1	5r multicolored	6.00	5.25
33	A1	10r multicolored	17.00	12.50
		Nos. 16-33 (18)	55.75	44.76

No. 16 has watermark sideways.

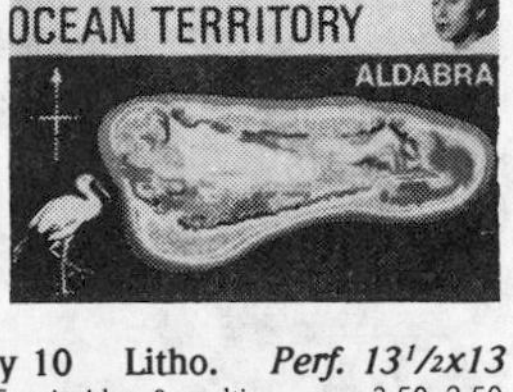

Aldabra Atoll and Sacred Ibis A2

1969, July 10 Litho. *Perf. 13½x13*

34	A2	2.25r vio blue & multi	3.50	2.50

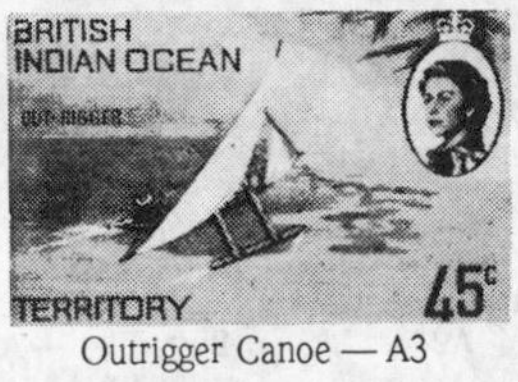

Outrigger Canoe — A3

Designs: 75c, Beaching canoe. 1r, Merchant ship Nordvaer. 1.50r, Yacht, Isle of Farquhar.

Perf. 13½x14

1969, Dec. 15 Litho. Wmk. 314

35	A3	45c multicolored	.52	*.52*
36	A3	75c multicolored	1.00	*.90*
37	A3	1r multicolored	1.50	*1.40*
38	A3	1.50r multicolored	2.50	*2.00*
		Nos. 35-38 (4)	5.52	*4.82*

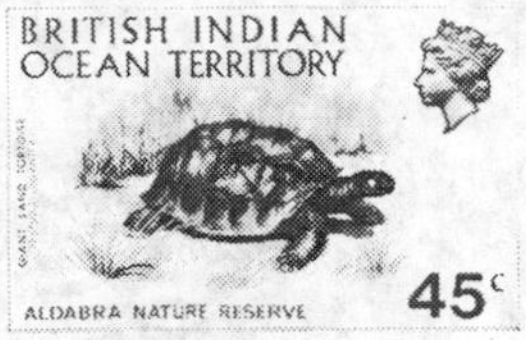

Giant Land Tortoise A4

Designs: 75c, Aldabra lily. 1r, Aldabra tree snail. 1.50r, Dimorphic egrets.

1971, Feb. 1 Litho. Wmk. 314

39	A4	45c multicolored	1.90	1.10
40	A4	75c multicolored	2.50	1.65
41	A4	1r multicolored	5.00	3.25
42	A4	1.50r multicolored	6.50	4.25
		Nos. 39-42 (4)	15.90	10.25

Aldabra Nature Reserve.

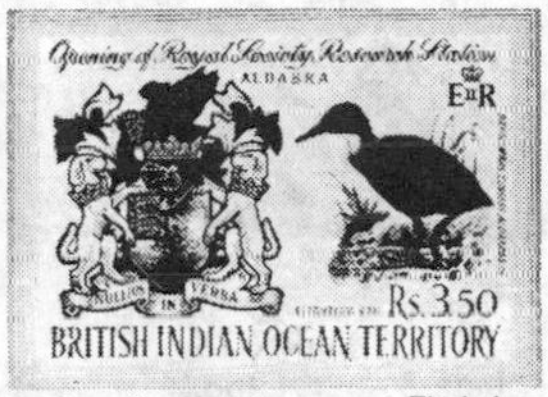

Society Coat of Arms and Flightless Rail — A5

1971, June 30 Litho. *Perf. 13½*

43	A5	3.50r multicolored	10.00	7.00

Opening of Royal Society Research Station at Aldabra.

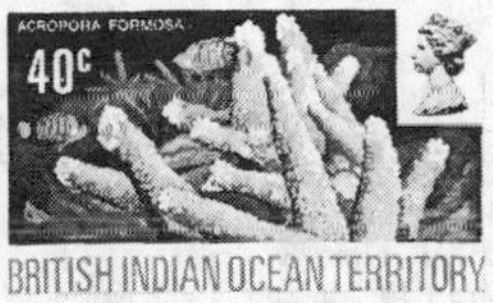

Acropora Formosa A6

Corals: 60c, Goniastrea pectinata. 1r, Fungia fungites. 1.75r, Tubipora musica.

1972, Mar. 1

44	A6	40c blue & multi	.95	.95
45	A6	60c brt pink & multi	1.65	1.65
46	A6	1r blue & multi	3.25	3.25
47	A6	1.75r brt pink & multi	7.25	7.25
		Nos. 44-47 (4)	13.10	13.10

Silver Wedding Issue, 1972
Common Design Type

Design: Queen Elizabeth II, Prince Philip, flightless rail and sacred ibis.

1972, Nov. 20 Photo. *Perf. 14x14½*

48	CD324	95c multicolored	1.10	.50
49	CD324	1.50r violet & multi	1.50	.75

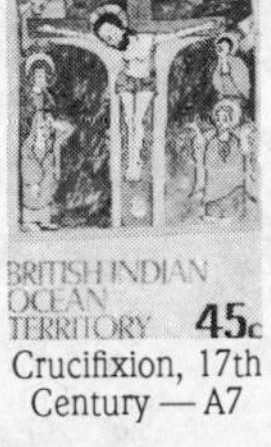

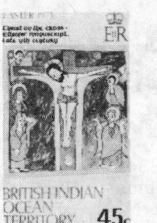

Crucifixion, 17th Century — A7

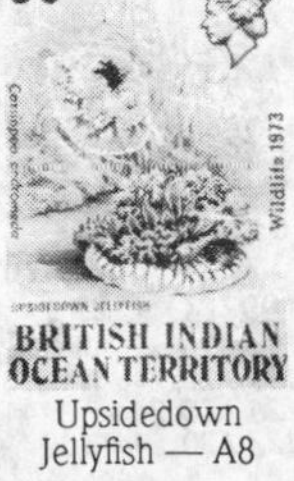

Upsidedown Jellyfish — A8

Paintings, Ethiopian Manuscripts, 17th Century: 75c, 1.50r, Joseph and Nicodemus burying Jesus. 1r, Like 45c.

1973, Apr. 9 Litho. *Perf. 14*

50	A7	45c buff & multi	.45	.28
51	A7	75c buff & multi	.65	.48
52	A7	1r buff & multi	.90	.60
53	A7	1.50r buff & multi	1.50	1.00
a.		Souvenir sheet of 4, #50-53	4.50	3.50
		Nos. 50-53 (4)	3.50	2.36

Easter.

Common Design Types pictured in section before Great Britain.

1973, Nov. 12 Litho. Wmk. 314

54	A8	50c shown	1.40	1.00
55	A8	1r Butterflies	2.25	1.50
56	A8	1.50r Spider	3.75	2.50
		Nos. 54-56 (3)	7.40	5.00

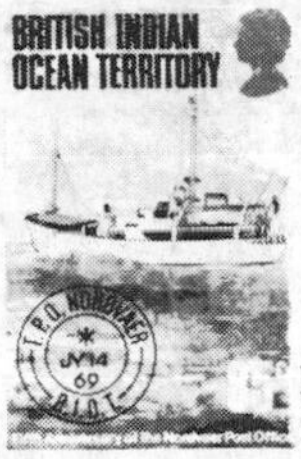

Nordvaer and July 14, 1969 Cancel — A9

Design: 2.50r, Nordvaer offshore and cancel.

1974, July 14

57	A9	85c multicolored	.70	.52
58	A9	2.50r multicolored	1.90	1.25

Nordvaer traveling post office, 5th anniv.

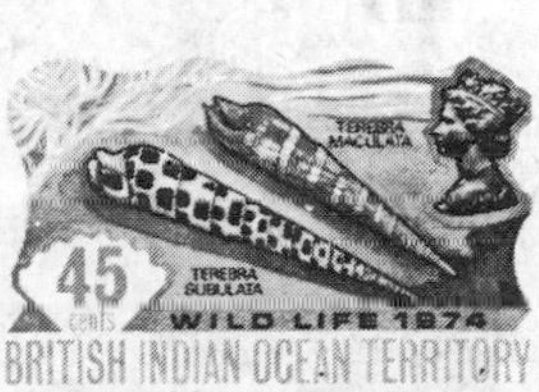

Terebra Maculata and Terebra Subulata — A10

Sea Shells: 75c, Turbo marmoratus. 1r, Drupa rubusidaeus. 1.50r, Cassis rufa.

1974, Nov. 12 Litho. *Perf. 13½x14*

59	A10	45c multicolored	.55	.40
60	A10	75c multicolored	.85	.65
61	A10	1r multicolored	1.40	1.20
62	A10	1.50r multicolored	2.50	2.00
		Nos. 59-62 (4)	5.30	4.25

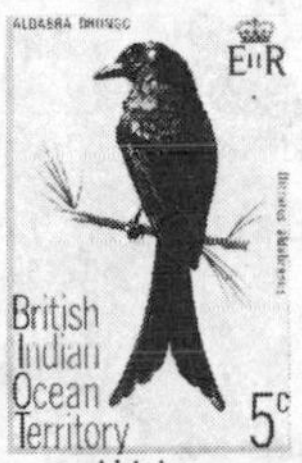

Aldabra Drongo — A11

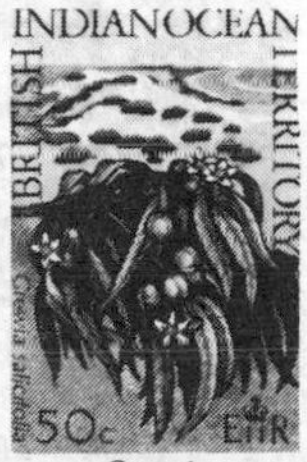

Grewia Salicifolia — A12

Birds: 10c, Malagasy coucal. 20c, Red-headed forest fody. 25c, Fairy tern. 30c, Crested tern. 40c, Brown booby. 50c, Noddy tern. 60c, Gray heron. 65c, Blue-faced booby. 95c, Malagasy white-eye. 1r, Green-backed heron. 1.75r, Lesser frigate bird. 3.50r, White-tailed tropic bird. 5r, Souimanga sunbird. 10r, Malagasy turtledove. Nos. 69, 71-77 horiz.

1975, Feb. 28 Wmk. 314 *Perf. 14*

63	A11	5c buff & multi	.15	*.15*
64	A11	10c lt ultra & multi	.15	*.15*
65	A11	20c dp yel & multi	.18	*.15*
66	A11	25c ultra & multi	.20	*.15*
67	A11	30c dl yel & multi	.30	*.20*
68	A11	40c bis & multi	.38	*.26*
69	A11	50c lt blue & multi	.45	*.38*
70	A11	60c yel & multi	.52	*.42*
71	A11	65c yel grn & multi	.60	*.42*
72	A11	95c cit & multi	.75	*.70*
73	A11	1r bis & multi	.95	*.95*
74	A11	1.75r yel & multi	1.90	*1.40*
75	A11	3.50r blue & multi	3.75	*3.50*
76	A11	5r pale sal & multi	6.25	*4.50*
77	A11	10r brt yel & multi	9.50	*7.00*
		Nos. 63-77 (15)	26.03	*20.33*

1975, July 10   Litho.   Wmk. 314
Native Plants: 65c, Cassia aldabrensis. 1r, Hypoestes aldabrensis. 1.60r, Euphorbia pyrifolia.

78 A12	50c multicolored	.35	.35
79 A12	65c multicolored	.50	.50
80 A12	1r multicolored	.75	.75
81 A12	1.60r multicolored	1.25	1.25
	Nos. 78-81 (4)	2.85	2.85

Nature protection.

Aldabra and Compass Rose — A13

Maps of Islands: 1r, Desroches. 1.50r, Farquhar. 2r, Diego Garcia.

1975, Nov. 8   Litho.   Perf. 13½x14

82 A13	50c blk, blue & grn	.32	.25
83 A13	1r green & multi	.65	.48
84 A13	1.50r blk, ultra & grn	1.00	.70
85 A13	2r blk, lilac & grn	1.40	1.00
a.	Souvenir sheet of 4, #82-85	4.00	3.25
	Nos. 82-85 (4)	3.37	2.43

British Indian Ocean Territory, 10th anniv.

Crimson Speckled Moth A14

Insects: 1.20r, Dysdercus fasciatus. 1.50r, Sphex torridus. 2r, Oryctes rhinoceros.

1976, Mar. 22   Litho.   Wmk. 373

86 A14	65c multicolored	.40	.40
87 A14	1.20r multicolored	.65	.65
88 A14	1.50r multicolored	.90	.90
89 A14	2r multicolored	1.40	1.40
	Nos. 86-89 (4)	3.35	3.35

Exhibition Emblem and No. 37 — A15

1990, May 3   Wmk. 373   Perf. 14

90 A15	15p No. 62	.50	.50
91 A15	20p No. 89	.68	.68
92 A15	34p No. 85	1.15	1.15
93 A15	54p shown	1.85	1.85
	Nos. 90-93 (4)	4.18	4.18

Stamp World London '90.

Birds — A16

1990, May 3   Wmk. 384   Perf. 14

94 A16	15p White-tailed tropic birds	.42	.42
95 A16	20p Turtle doves	.60	.60
96 A16	24p Greater frigate birds	.70	.70
97 A16	30p Little green herons	.90	.90
98 A16	34p Greater sand plovers	1.00	1.00
99 A16	41p Crab plovers	1.25	1.25
100 A16	45p Crested terns	1.40	1.40
101 A16	54p Lesser crested terns	1.65	1.65
102 A16	62p Fairy terns	1.75	1.75
103 A16	71p Red-footed boobies	2.00	2.00
104 A16	80p Indian mynahs	2.50	2.50
105 A16	£1 Madagascar fodies	3.00	3.00
	Nos. 94-105 (12)	17.17	17.17

For overprints see Nos. 145-146.

Queen Mother, 90th Birthday
Common Design Types
Designs: 24p, Lady Elizabeth Bowes-Lyon, 1923. £1, Queen, Princesses Elizabeth & Margaret, 1940.

1990, Aug. 4   Wmk. 384   Perf. 14x15

| 106 CD343 | 24p multicolored | .80 | .80 |

Perf. 14½

| 107 CD344 | £1 brown & black | 3.35 | 3.35 |

British Indian Ocean Territory, 25th Anniv. — A17

1990, Nov. 8   Litho.   Perf. 14

| 108 A17 | 20p Flag | .78 | .78 |
| 109 A17 | 24p Coat of arms | .95 | .95 |

Souvenir Sheet

| 110 A17 | £1 Map | 4.00 | 4.00 |

Govt. Services A18

Wmk. 373
1991, June 3   Litho.   Perf. 14

111 A18	20p Postal service	.70	.70
112 A18	24p Royal Marines	.85	.85
113 A18	34p Police station, officers	1.20	1.20
114 A18	54p Customs service	1.90	1.90
	Nos. 111-114 (4)	4.65	4.65

Visiting Ships A19

1991, Nov. 8

115 A19	20p Survey ship Experiment, 1786	.70	.70
116 A19	24p US Brig Pickering, 1819	.85	.85
117 A19	34p SMS Emden, 1914	1.20	1.20
118 A19	54p HMS Edinburgh, 1988	1.90	1.90
	Nos. 115-118 (4)	4.65	4.65

Queen Elizabeth II's Accession to the Throne, 40th Anniv.
Common Design Type
Wmk. 373
1992, Feb. 6   Litho.   Perf. 14

119 CD349	15p multicolored	.50	.50
120 CD349	20p multicolored	.70	.70
121 CD349	24p multicolored	.85	.85
122 CD349	34p multicolored	1.20	1.20
123 CD349	54p multicolored	1.90	1.90
	Nos. 119-123 (5)	5.15	5.15

Aircraft A20

Wmk. 384
1992, Oct. 23   Litho.   Perf. 14

124 A20	20p Catalina	.75	.75
125 A20	24p Nimrod	.92	.92
126 A20	34p P-3 Orion	1.30	1.30
127 A20	54p B-52	2.10	2.10
	Nos. 124-127 (4)	5.07	5.07

Christmas — A21

Paintings: 5p, The Mystical Marriage of St. Cathrin, by Correggio. 24p, Madonna and Child by unknown artist. 34p, Madonna and Child by unknown artist, diff. 54p, The Birth of Jesus, by Kaspar Jele.

1992, Nov. 27   Perf. 14½

128 A21	5p multicolored	.18	.18
129 A21	24p multicolored	.80	.80
130 A21	34p multicolored	1.15	1.15
131 A21	54p multicolored	1.85	1.85
	Nos. 128-131 (4)	3.98	3.98

Coconut Crab A22

Wmk. 384
1993, Mar. 3   Litho.   Perf. 14

132 A22	10p Crab, coconut	.30	.30
133 A22	10p Large crab	.30	.30
134 A22	10p Two crabs	.30	.30
135 A22	15p Crab on tree trunk	.45	.45
	Nos. 132-135 (4)	1.35	1.35

World Wildlife Fund.

Royal Air Force, 75th Anniv.
Common Design Type
Designs: No. 136, Vickers Virginia. 24p, Bristol Bulldog. 34p, Short Sunderland. 54p, Bristol Blenheim IV.
No. 140a, Douglas Dakota. b, Gloster Javelin. c, Blackburn Beverley. d, Vickers VC10.

1993, Apr. 1   Wmk. 373

136 CD350	20p multicolored	.58	.58
137 CD350	24p multicolored	.70	.70
138 CD350	34p multicolored	1.00	1.00
139 CD350	54p multicolored	1.55	1.55
	Nos. 136-139 (4)	3.83	3.83

Souvenir Sheet

| 140 CD350 | 20p Sheet of 4, #a.-d. | 2.30 | 2.30 |

Flowers — A23

Christmas: 20p, Stachytarpheta urticifolia. 24p, Ipomea pes-caprae. 34p, Sida pusilla. 54p, Catharanthus roseus.

Perf. 14½
1993, Nov. 22   Litho.   Wmk. 373

| 141-144 A23 | Set of 4 | 3.75 | 3.75 |

Nos. 96, 105 Ovptd. with Hong Kong '94 Emblem

Wmk. 384
1994, Feb. 18   Litho.   Perf. 14

| 145 A16 | 24p multicolored | .65 | .65 |
| 146 A16 | £1 multicolored | 2.75 | 2.75 |

A24   Butterflies — A25

18th Cent. Maps and Charts: a, 20p, Sketch of Diego Garcia. b, 24p, Plan of harbor, Chagos Island or Diego Garcia, by Lt. Archibald Blair. c, 34p, Chart of Chagos Archipelago, by Lt. Blair. d, 44p, Plan of part of Chagos Island or Diego Garcia, from survey made by the Drake. e, 54p, Plan of Chagos Island or Diego Garcia, by M. Aa Fontaine.

1994, June 1   Wmk. 373

| 147 A24 | Strip of 5, #a.-e. | 5.25 | 5.25 |

1994, Aug. 16   Wmk. 384

148 A25	24p Junonia villida	.80	.80
149 A25	30p Petrelaea dana	1.00	1.00
150 A25	56p Hypolimnas misippus	1.75	1.75
	Nos. 148-150 (3)	3.55	3.55

Sharks A26

1994, Nov. 1   Wmk. 373

151 A26	15p Nurse	.45	.45
152 A26	20p Silver tip	.60	.60
153 A26	24p Black tip reef	.75	.75
154 A26	30p Oceanic white tip	.95	.95
155 A26	35p Black tip	1.10	1.10
156 A26	41p Smooth hammerhead	1.25	1.25
157 A26	46p Lemon	1.40	1.40
158 A26	55p White tip reef	1.75	1.75
159 A26	65p Tiger	2.00	2.00
160 A26	74p Indian sand tiger	2.25	2.25
161 A26	80p Great hammerhead	2.50	2.50
162 A26	£1 Great white	3.00	3.00
	Nos. 151-162 (12)	18.00	18.00

End of World War II, 50th Anniv.
Common Design Types
Designs: 20p, War graves, memorial cross, Diego Garcia. 24p, 6-inch naval gun, Cannon Point. 30p, Sunderland flying boat, 230 Squadron. 56p, HMIS Clive.
£1, Reverse of War Medal 1939-45.

Wmk. 373
1995, May 8   Litho.   Perf. 14

163 CD351	20p multicolored	.52	.52
164 CD351	24p multicolored	.65	.65
165 CD351	30p multicolored	.80	.80
166 CD351	56p multicolored	1.50	1.50
	Nos. 163-166 (4)	3.47	3.47

Souvenir Sheet

| 167 CD352 | £1 multicolored | 2.75 | 2.75 |

Game Fish A27

1995, Oct. 6   Wmk. 384

168 A27	20p Dolphinfish	.60	.60
169 A27	24p Sailfish	.75	.75
170 A27	30p Wahoo	.95	.95
171 A27	56p Striped marlin	1.75	1.75
	Nos. 168-171 (4)	4.05	4.05

BRUNEI

'brü-,nī

LOCATION — On the northwest coast of Borneo
GOVT. — Independent state
AREA — 2,226 sq. mi.
POP. — 191,770 (1981)
CAPITAL — Bandar Seri Begawan

Brunei became a British protectorate in 1888. A treaty between the sultan and the British Government in 1979 provided for independence in 1983.

100 Cents (Sen) = 1 Dollar

Catalogue values for unused stamps in this country are for Never Hinged items, beginning with Scott 62.

Watermark

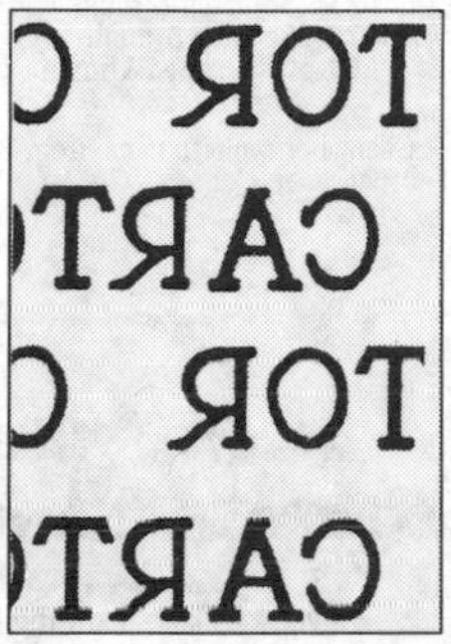

Wmk. 385 - CARTOR

Labuan Stamps of 1902-03 Overprinted or Surcharged in Red:

BRUNEI.

BRUNEI. **TWO CENTS.**

1906 Unwmk. *Perf. 12 to 16*

1	A38	1c violet & blk	14.00	*32.50*
a.		Black overprint	*2,000.*	*2,750.*
2	A38	2c on 3c brn & blk	1.50	*5.00*
a.		"BRUNEI." double	*4,250.*	*3,000.*
3	A38	2c on 8c org & blk	16.00	*55.00*
a.		"TWO CENTS." double	*5,750.*	
b.		"TWO CENTS." omitted, in pair with normal	*6,000.*	
4	A38	3c brown & blk	16.00	*55.00*
5	A38	4c on 12c yel & black	1.75	*4.75*
6	A38	5c on 16c org brn & green	20.00	*42.50*
7	A38	8c orange & blk	7.00	*17.00*
8	A38	10c on 16c org brn & green	7.00	*15.00*
9	A38	25c on 16c org brn & green	72.50	*110.00*
10	A38	30c on 16c org brn & green	72.50	*100.00*
11	A38	50c on 16c org brn & green	72.50	*100.00*
12	A38	$1 on 8c org & blk	72.50	*100.00*
		Nos. 1-12 (12)	373.25	*636.75*

The 25c surcharge reads: "25 CENTS."

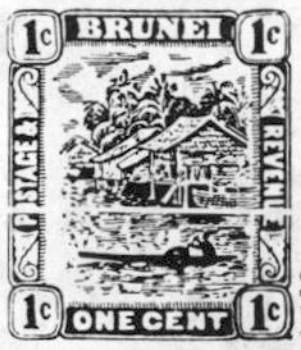

Scene on Brunei River — A1

Two Types of 1908 1c, 3c:
Type I - Dots form bottom line of water shading. (Double plate.)
Type II - Dots removed. (Single plate.)

1907-21 Engr. Wmk. 3 *Perf. 14*

13	A1	1c yel green & blk	1.50	*2.75*
14	A1	1c green (II) ('08)	.40	*.40*
a.		Type I ('19)	*.60*	*1.50*
15	A1	2c red & black	1.50	*3.00*
16	A1	2c brn & blk ('11)	.60	*1.40*
17	A1	3c red brn & blk	12.50	*15.00*
18	A1	3c car (I) ('08)	.85	*1.50*
a.		Type II ('17)	*12.50*	*17.50*
19	A1	4c lilac & blk	5.00	*9.00*
20	A1	4c claret ('12)	4.00	*.50*
21	A1	5c ultra & blk	37.50	*50.00*
22	A1	5c org & blk ('08)	3.50	4.00
23	A1	5c orange ('16)	1.75	2.25
24	A1	8c orange & blk	5.50	*20.00*
25	A1	8c blue ('08)	4.25	6.25
26	A1	8c ultra ('16)	2.00	2.25
27	A1	10c dk green & blk	9.00	*15.00*
28	A1	10c violet, *yel* ('12)	1.00	1.25
29	A1	25c yel brn & blue	19.00	*30.00*
30	A1	25c violet ('12)	1.90	*4.00*
31	A1	30c black & pur	19.00	*30.00*
32	A1	30c org & red vio ('12)	6.50	*12.50*
33	A1	50c brown & grn	19.00	*30.00*
34	A1	50c blk, *grn* ('12)	19.00	30.00
35	A1	50c blk, *grnsh bl* ('21)	5.50	*13.50*
36	A1	$1 slate & red	62.50	*75.00*
37	A1	$1 red & blk, *bl* ('12)	25.00	*50.00*
38	A1	$5 lake, *grn* ('08)	67.50	*125.00*
39	A1	$25 blk, *red* ('08)	400.00	*400.00*
		Nos. 13-38 (26)	335.75	*534.55*

Used value for No. 39 is for CTO. CTOs dated before Dec. 1941 cost more.

Stamps of 1908-21 Overprinted in Black: "MALAYA-BORNEO EXHIBITION, 1922" in Four Lines

1922

14b	A1	1c green	2.25	*17.00*
16a	A1	2c brown & black	5.00	*21.00*
18b	A1	3c carmine	6.75	*30.00*
20a	A1	4c claret	5.25	*35.00*
23a	A1	5c orange	10.00	*45.00*
28a	A1	10c violet, *yellow*	8.75	*45.00*
30a	A1	25c violet	19.00	*67.50*
35a	A1	50c greenish blue	60.00	*125.00*
37a	A1	$1 red & black, *blue*	92.50	*165.00*
		Nos. 14b-37a (9)	209.50	*550.50*

Industrial fair, Singapore, Mar. 31-Apr. 15.

Type of 1907 Issue

1924-37 Wmk. 4

43	A1	1c black ('26)	.20	.30
44	A1	2c deep brown	.70	*2.75*
45	A1	2c green ('33)	.25	.25
46	A1	3c green	.70	*3.75*
47	A1	4c claret brown	1.90	.65
48	A1	4c orange ('29)	.50	.40
49	A1	5c orange	.65	.75
50	A1	5c lt gray ('31)	3.50	*5.75*
51	A1	5c brown ('33)	1.75	.15
52	A1	8c ultra ('27)	2.50	*4.25*
53	A1	8c gray ('33)	2.75	.45
54	A1	10c violet, *yel* ('37)	6.25	*15.00*
55	A1	25c dk violet ('31)	4.00	*9.00*
56	A1	30c org & red vio ('31)	4.75	*12.50*
57	A1	50c black, *grn* ('31)	6.00	*10.50*
58	A1	$1 red & blk, *bl* ('31)	25.00	*55.00*
		Nos. 43-58 (16)	61.40	*121.45*

For overprints see Nos. N1-N20.

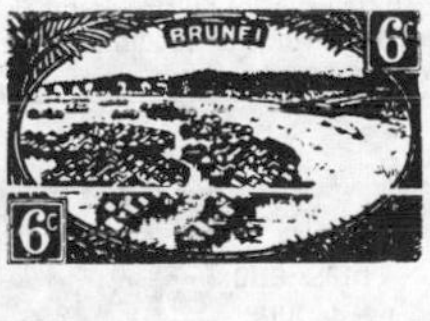

Dwellings in Town of Brunei — A2

1924-31

59	A2	6c black	3.50	*8.25*
60	A2	6c red ('31)	2.75	*9.00*
61	A2	12c blue	5.00	*7.50*
		Nos. 59-61 (3)	11.25	*24.75*

See note after Nos. N1-N19.

Catalogue values for unused stamps in this section, from this point to the end of the section, are for Never Hinged items.

Types of 1907-24

1947-51 Engr. *Perf. 14*

62	A1	1c brown	.15	.15
63	A1	2c gray	.15	.15
a.		Perf. 14½x13½ ('50)	*1.75*	*2.50*
64	A2	3c dark green	.35	.35
65	A1	5c deep orange	.15	.15
a.		Perf. 14½x13½ ('50)	*7.25*	*9.00*
66	A2	6c gray black	1.75	1.75
67	A1	8c scarlet	.20	.20
a.		Perf. 13 ('51)	*.20*	*.20*
68	A1	10c violet	.20	.20
a.		Perf. 14½x13½ ('50)	*1.75*	*3.00*
69	A1	15c brt ultra	3.75	3.75
70	A1	25c red violet	.35	.35
a.		Perf. 14½x13½ ('51)	*.60*	*1.25*
71	A1	30c dp org & gray blk	.45	.45
a.		Perf. 14½x13½ ('51)	*.55*	*1.25*
72	A1	50c black	.45	.45
a.		Perf. 13 ('50)	*3.50*	*12.00*
73	A1	$1 scar & gray blk	1.25	1.25
74	A1	$5 red org & grn ('48)	15.00	*15.00*
75	A1	$10 dp claret & gray blk ('48)	30.00	*42.50*
		Nos. 62-75 (14)	54.20	*66.70*

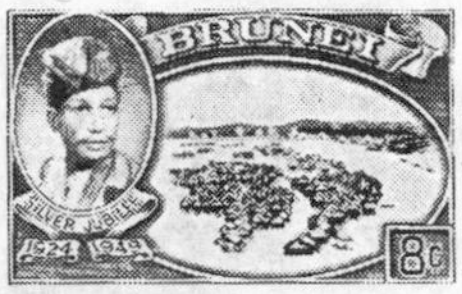

Sultan Ahmed and Pile Dwellings A3

1949, Sept. 22 Wmk. 4 *Perf. 13*

76	A3	8c car & black	1.60	1.60
77	A3	25c red orange & pur	1.60	1.60
78	A3	50c blue & black	2.00	2.00
		Nos. 76-78 (3)	5.20	5.20

25th anniv. of the reign of Sultan Ahmed Tajudin Akhazul Khair Wad-din.

UPU Issue
Common Design Types
Engr.; Name Typo. on 15c and 25c
1949, Oct. 10 *Perf. 13½, 11x11½*

79	CD306	8c rose car	.50	.50
80	CD307	15c indigo	.75	.75
81	CD308	25c red lilac	1.25	1.25
82	CD309	50c slate	2.50	2.50
		Nos. 79-82 (4)	5.00	5.00

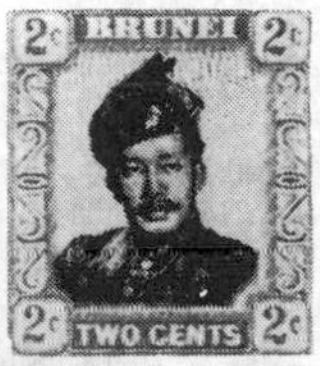

Sultan Omar Ali Saifuddin — A4

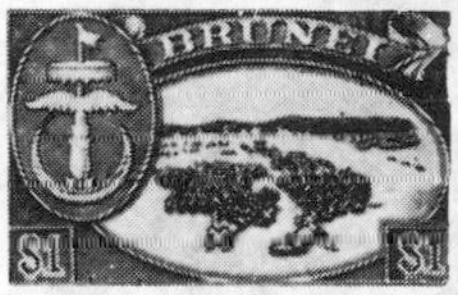

River Kampong A5

Perf. 13½x13
1952, Mar. 1 Engr. Wmk. 4
Center in Black

83	A4	1c black	.15	.15
84	A4	2c red orange	.15	.15
85	A4	3c red brown	.15	.15
86	A4	4c green	.15	.15
87	A4	6c gray	.20	.15
88	A4	8c carmine	.25	.20
89	A4	10c olive brown	.25	.15
90	A4	12c violet	.30	.25
91	A4	15c blue	.40	.20
92	A4	25c purple	.60	.50
93	A4	50c ultramarine	.90	.60

Perf. 13

94	A5	$1 dull green	2.25	1.00
95	A5	$2 red	3.50	3.00
96	A5	$5 deep plum	11.00	9.00
		Nos. 83-96 (14)	20.25	15.65

See Nos. 101-114.

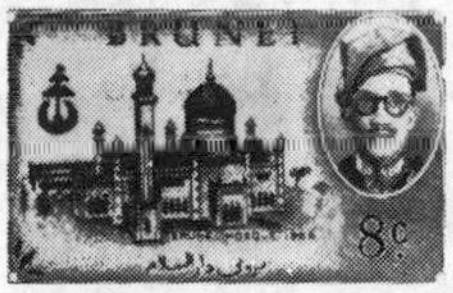

Mosque and Sultan Omar — A6

1958, Sept. 24 Wmk. 314 *Perf. 13*
Center in Black

97	A6	8c dull green	.25	.30
98	A6	15c carmine rose	.30	.25
99	A6	35c rose violet	.50	.75
		Nos. 97-99 (3)	1.05	1.30

Opening of the Brunei Mosque.

Freedom from Hunger Issue
Common Design Type with Portrait of Sultan Omar
1963, June 4 Photo. *Perf. 14x14½*

100	CD314	12c sepia	1.50	1.50

Types of 1952
Wmk. 314 Upright
1964-70 Engr. *Perf. 13½x13*
Center in Black

101	A4	1c black	.15	.15
102	A4	2c red orange	.15	.15
103	A4	3c red brown	.15	.15
104	A4	4c green	.15	.15
105	A4	6c black	.20	.15
106	A4	8c dk carmine	.30	.15
107	A4	10c olive brown	.25	.20
108	A4	12c violet	.40	.20
109	A4	15c blue	.40	.25
110	A4	25c purple	.75	.28
111	A4	50c ultramarine	1.60	1.00

Perf. 13

112	A5	$1 dull green ('68)	3.00	2.00
113	A5	$2 red ('70)	10.00	6.50
114	A5	$5 deep plum ('70)	20.00	16.50
		Nos. 101-114 (14)	37.50	27.83

Nos. 101-112 were reissued in 1968-70 on whiter, glazed paper; the $2 and $5 are only on this paper.

Wmk. 314 Sideways
1972-73 *Perf. 13½x13*
Center in Black

102a	A4	2c red orange	.20	.20
103a	A4	3c red brown	.25	.25
104a	A4	4c green	.30	.30
105a	A4	6c black	.45	.45
106a	A4	8c dark carmine	.60	.60
107a	A4	10c olive brown	.75	.75
108a	A4	12c violet	.90	.90
109a	A4	15c blue	1.25	1.25
		Nos. 102a-109a (8)	4.70	4.70

The stamps with watermark sideways are on the whiter, glazed paper.
Issue dates: 2c, 8c, May 9, 1973, others, Nov. 17, 1972.

The following six sets are Common Design Types but with the portrait of Sultan Omar.

ITU Issue
Perf. 11x11½
1965, May 17 Litho. Wmk. 314

116	CD317	4c red lil & org brn	.15	.15
117	CD317	75c orange & emer	1.40	1.40

Intl. Cooperation Year Issue
1965, Oct. 25 *Perf. 14½*

118	CD318	4c blue grn & claret	.15	.15
119	CD318	15c lt violet & grn	.70	.70

Churchill Memorial Issue
1966, Jan. 24 Photo. *Perf. 14*

120	CD319	3c multicolored	.25	.15
121	CD319	10c multicolored	.65	.35
122	CD319	15c multicolored	1.00	.60
123	CD319	75c multicolored	3.50	2.50
		Nos. 120-123 (4)	5.40	3.60

World Cup Soccer Issue
1966, July 4 Litho. *Perf. 14*

124	CD321	4c multicolored	.15	.15
125	CD321	75c multicolored	1.25	1.25

WHO Headquarters Issue
1966, Sept. 20 Litho. *Perf. 14*

126	CD322	12c multicolored	.25	.20
127	CD322	25c multicolored	.75	.75

UNESCO Anniversary Issue
1966, Dec. 1 Litho. Wmk. 314

128	CD323	4c "Education"	.15	.15
129	CD323	15c "Science"	.45	.45
130	CD323	75c "Culture"	2.25	2.25
		Nos. 128-130 (3)	2.85	2.85

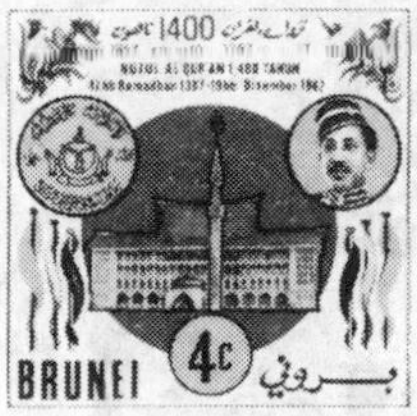

State Religious Building and Sultan Hassanal Bolkiah — A7

1967, Dec. 19 Photo. *Perf. 12½*

131	A7	4c violet & multi	.15	.15
132	A7	10c red & multi	.15	.15
133	A7	25c orange & multi	.35	.35
134	A7	50c lt violet & multi	.65	.65
		Nos. 131-134 (4)	1.30	1.30

A three-stamp set (12c, 25c, 50c) showing views of the new Language and Communications Headquarters was prepared and announced for release in April, 1968. The Crown Agents distributed sample sets, but the stamps were not issued. Later, Nos. 144-146 were issued instead.

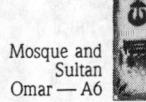

Sultan Hassanal Bolkiah, Brunei Mosque and Flags — A8

Sultan Hassanal Bolkiah Installation: 12c, Sultan, Mosque and flags, horiz.

1968, July 9   Photo.   Unwmk.
135	A8	4c green & multi	.15 .15
136	A8	12c dp bister & multi	.30 .30
137	A8	25c violet & multi	.75 .75
		Nos. 135-137 (3)	1.20 1.20

Sultan Hassanal Bolkiah — A9

Wmk. 314
1968, July 15   Litho.   Perf. 12
138	A9	4c multicolored	.15 .15
139	A9	12c multicolored	.20 .20
140	A9	25c multicolored	.40 .50
		Nos. 138-140 (3)	.75 .85

Sultan Hassanal Bolkiah's birthday.

Coronation of Sultan Hassanal Bolkiah, Aug. 1, 1968 — A10

1968, Aug. 1   Photo.   Perf. 14½x14
141	A10	4c Prus blue & multi	.15 .15
142	A10	12c rose lilac & multi	.25 .25
143	A10	25c multicolored	.50 .50
		Nos. 141-143 (3)	.90 .90

A11

Hall of Language and Culture — A12

Perf. 13½, 12½x13½ (A12)
1968, Sept. 29   Wmk. 314
144	A11	10c blue grn & multi	.15 .25
145	A12	15c ocher & multi	.20 .30
146	A12	30c ultra & multi	.45 .75
		Nos. 144-146 (3)	.80 1.30

Opening of the Hall of Language and Culture and of the Broadcasting and Information Department Building. Nos. 144-146 are overprinted "1968" and 4 bars over the 1967 date. They were not issued without this overprint.

Human Rights Flame and Struggling Man — A13

Unwmk.
1968, Dec. 16   Litho.   Perf. 14
147	A13	12c green, yel & blk	.15 .15
148	A13	25c ultra, yel & blk	.35 .35
149	A13	75c dk plum, yel & blk	.90 .90
		Nos. 147-149 (3)	1.40 1.40

International Human Rights Year.

Sultan and WHO Emblem A14

1968, Dec. 19   Litho.   Perf. 14
150	A14	4c lt blue, org & blk	.15 .15
151	A14	15c brt purple, org & blk	.22 .22
152	A14	25c olive, org & blk	.38 .38
		Nos. 150-152 (3)	.75 .75

20th anniv. of the WHO.

Sultan Hassanal Bolkiah, Pengiran Shahbandar and Oil Rig — A15

Perf. 14x13
1969, July 10   Photo.   Wmk. 314
153	A15	12c green & multi	.20 .20
154	A15	40c dk rose brn & multi	.60 .60
155	A15	50c violet & multi	.75 .75
		Nos. 153-155 (3)	1.55 1.55

Installation of Pengiran Shahbandar as Second Minister (Di-Galong Sahibol Mal).

Royal Assembly Hall and Council Chamber — A16

Design: 50c, Front view of buildings.

Unwmk.
1969, Sept. 23   Litho.   Perf. 15
156	A16	12c multicolored	.15 .15
157	A16	25c multicolored	.35 .35
158	A16	50c violet & pink	.65 .65
		Nos. 156-158 (3)	1.15 1.15

Opening of the Royal Assembly Hall and Council Chamber.

Youth Center — A17

1969, Dec. 20   Litho.   Wmk. 314
159	A17	6c lt org, blk & dull vio	.15 .15
160	A17	10c cit, blk & dl Prus grn	.15 .15
161	A17	30c yel green, blk & brn	.45 .45
		Nos. 159-161 (3)	.75 .75

Opening of Youth Center, Mar. 15, 1969.

Helicopter and Emblem A18

Designs: 10c, Soldier and emblem, vert. 75c, Patrol boat and emblem.

1971, May 31   Litho.   Perf. 14
162	A18	10c green & multi	.38 .15
163	A18	15c Prus blue & multi	.45 .25
164	A18	75c lt ultra & multi	2.75 1.75
		Nos. 162-164 (3)	3.58 2.15

10th anniv. of Royal Brunei Malay Reg.

50th Anniv. of the Royal Brunei Police Force — A19

1971, Aug. 14   Perf. 14½
165	A19	10c Superintendent	.40 .25
166	A19	15c Constable	.50 .32
167	A19	50c Traffic policeman	2.25 1.60
		Nos. 165-167 (3)	3.15 2.17

Sultan, Heir Apparent and View of Brunei — A20

Portraits and: 25c, View of Brunei with Mosque. 50c, Mosque and banner.

1971, Aug. 27   Litho.   Wmk. 314
168	A20	15c multicolored	.38 .22
169	A20	25c multicolored	.75 .55
170	A20	50c multicolored	1.40 1.10
		Nos. 168-170 (3)	2.53 1.87

Installation of Sultan Hassanal Bolkiah's brother Muda Omar Ali Saifuddin as heir apparent (Perdana Wazir).

Brass and Copper Goods A21

Designs: 12c, Basketware. 15c, Leather goods. 25c, Silverware. 50c, Brunei Museum.

1972, Feb. 29   Perf. 13½x14
Size: 37x21mm
Portrait in Black
171	A21	10c brn, sal & yel grn	.15 .15
172	A21	12c org, yel & green	.18 .15
173	A21	15c dk grn, emer & org	.25 .22
174	A21	25c brown, org & sl	.70 .60

Size: 58x21mm
175	A21	50c dull blue & multi	1.50 1.10
		Nos. 171-175 (5)	2.78 2.22

Opening of Brunei Museum.

Queen Elizabeth II, Sultan and View — A22

Queen Elizabeth II, Sultan Hassanal Bolkiah and: 15c, View of Brunei. 25c, Mosque and barge. 50c, Royal Assembly Hall.

1972, Feb. 29   Photo.   Perf. 13x13½
176	A22	10c lt brown & multi	.24 .20
177	A22	15c lt blue & multi	.35 .30
178	A22	25c lt green & multi	.70 .60
179	A22	50c dull purple & multi	2.00 2.00
		Nos. 176-179 (4)	3.29 3.10

Visit of Queen Elizabeth II, Feb. 29.

Bangunan Secretariat (Government Buildings) — A23

Sultans Omar Ali Saifuddin and Hassanal Bolkiah: 15c, Istana Darul Hana (Sultan's residence). 25c, View of capital. 50c, View of new Mosque.

1972, Oct. 4   Litho.   Perf. 13½
180	A23	10c org, blk & green	.15 .15
181	A23	15c green & multi	.25 .25
182	A23	25c ultra & multi	.50 .50
183	A23	50c rose red & multi	1.00 1.00
		Nos. 180-183 (4)	1.90 1.90

Change of capital's name from Brunei to Bandar Seri Begawan, Oct. 4, 1970.

Beverley Plane Landing — A24

Design: 25c, Blackburn Beverley plane dropping supplies by parachute, vert.

Perf. 14x13½, 13½x14
1972, Nov. 15   Litho.
184	A24	25c blue & multi	1.65 1.65
185	A24	75c ultra & multi	4.00 4.00

Opening of Royal Air Force Museum, Hendon, London.

Silver Wedding Issue, 1972
Common Design Type

Design: Queen Elizabeth II, Prince Philip; girl and boy with traditional gifts.

1972, Nov. 20   Photo.   Perf. 14x14½
186	CD324	12c multi	.40 .15
187	CD324	75c multi	1.25 1.25

INTERPOL Emblem and Headquarters, Paris — A25

Design: 50c, similar to 25c.

1973, Sept. 7   Litho.   Perf. 14x14½
188	A25	25c emerald & multi	.75 .75
189	A25	50c multicolored	1.50 1.50

50th anniv. of Intl. Criminal Police Org. (INTERPOL).

Princess Anne and Mark Phillips — A26

1973, Nov. 14   Litho.   Perf. 13½
190	A26	25c vio blue & multi	.20 .20
191	A26	50c red lilac & multi	.40 .40

Wedding of Princess Anne and Capt. Mark Phillips, Nov. 14, 1973.

Churchill
Painting
Outdoors
A27

Sultan Hassanal
Bolkiah
A28

Design: 50c, Churchill making "V" sign.

Perf. 14x13½
1973, Dec. 31   Litho.   Wmk. 314
192 A27 12c car rose & multi   .15   .15
193 A27 50c dk green & multi   .55   .55

Winston Churchill Memorial Exhibition.

Wmk. 314 Sideways
1974, July 15   Photo.   Perf. 13x15
194 A28   4c blue grn & multi   .15   .15
195 A28   5c dull blue & multi   .15   .15
196 A28   6c olive grn & multi   .15   .15
197 A28 10c lt violet & multi   .15   .15
  b.   Watermark upright ('76)   .15   .15
198 A28 15c brown & multi   .15   .15
199 A28 20c buff & multi   .16   .15
  b.   Watermark upright ('76)   .16   .16
200 A28 25c olive & multi   .18   .16
  b.   Watermark upright ('76)   .20   .18
201 A28 30c multicolored   .22   .20
202 A28 35c gray & multi   .25   .22
203 A28 40c multicolored   .32   .28
204 A28 50c yel brn & multi   .38   .32
205 A28 75c multicolored   .60   .50
206 A28 $1 dull org & multi   .75   .65
207 A28 $2 multicolored   1.65 1.40
208 A28 $5 silver & multi   3.50 3.25
209 A28 $10 gold & multi   8.25 8.25
    Nos. 194-209 (16)   17.01 16.13

Issue date: Nos. 197b-200b, Apr. 12.

1975, Aug. 13   Wmk. 373
194a A28   4c   .15   .15
195a A28   5c   .15   .15
196a A28   6c   .15   .15
197a A28 10c   .15   .15
198a A28 15c   .15   .15
199a A28 20c   .16   .16
200a A28 25c   .20   .20
201a A28 30c   .24   .24
202a A28 35c   .28   .28
203a A28 40c   .32   .32
204a A28 50c   .40   .40
205a A28 75c   .60   .60
206a A28 $1   .80   .80
207a A28 $2   1.60 1.60
208a A28 $5   4.00 4.00
209a A28 $10   8.00 8.00
    Nos. 194a-209a (16)   17.35 17.35

For surcharge see No. 225.

Brunei
Airport
A29

Design: 75c, Sultan Hassanal Bolkiah in uniform and jet over airport.

Perf. 14x14½, 12½x13 (75c)
1974, July 18   Litho.   Wmk. 314
Size: 44x28mm
215 A29 50c multicolored   1.00 1.00
Size: 47x36mm
216 A29 75c multicolored   1.35 1.35

Opening of Brunei Airport.

UPU
Emblem
A30

1974, Oct. 28   Perf. 14½
217 A30 12c orange & multi   .15   .15
218 A30 50c blue & multi   .50   .50
219 A30 75c emerald & multi   .75   .75
    Nos. 217-219 (3)   1.40 1.40

Centenary of Universal Postal Union.

Winston
Churchill
A31

Design: 75c, Churchill smoking cigar.

1974, Nov. 30   Wmk. 373   Perf. 14
220 A31 12c vio blue, blue & gold   .15   .15
221 A31 75c dk green, black & gold   .90   .90

Sir Winston Churchill (1874-1965).

Boeing 737
Planes at
Airport
A32

Designs: 35c, Boeing 737 over Bandar Seri Begawan Mosque. 75c, Boeing 737 in flight. All planes with crest of Royal Brunei Airlines.

Perf. 12½x12
1975, May 14   Unwmk.
222 A32 12c multicolored   .30   .25
223 A32 35c multicolored   1.00   .75
224 A32 75c multicolored   2.00 2.00
    Nos. 222-224 (3)   3.30 3.00

Inauguration of Royal Brunei Airlines.

No. 196a Surcharged in
Silver

Perf. 13x15
1976, Aug. 16   Photo.   Wmk. 373
225 A28 10c on 6c multicolored   .25   .25

British Royal Coat of
Arms — A33

Designs: 20c, Imperial State Crown. 75c, Elizabeth II.

Wmk. 373
1977, June 7   Litho.   Perf. 14
226 A33 10c dk blue & multi   .15   .15
227 A33 20c purple & multi   .20   .20
228 A33 75c yellow & multi   .65   .65
    Nos. 226-228 (3)   1.00 1.00

25th anniv. of the reign of Elizabeth II.

Coronation of
Elizabeth II — A34

Designs: 20c, Elizabeth II with coronation regalia. 75c, Departure from Westminster Abbey (coach).

1978, June 2   Litho.   Perf. 13½x13
229 A34 10c multicolored   .15   .15
230 A34 20c multicolored   .20   .20
231 A34 75c multicolored   .65   .65
    Nos. 229-231 (3)   1.00 1.00

25th anniv. of coronation of Elizabeth II.

Sultan's Coat of
Arms — A35

Struggling Man,
Human Rights
Flame — A36

Coronation of Sultan Hassanal Bolkiah, 10th Anniv.: 20c, Coronation ceremony. 75c, Royal crown.

1978, Aug. 1   Wmk. 373   Perf. 12
232 A35 10c multicolored   .15   .15
233 A35 20c multicolored   .22   .22
234 A35 75c multicolored   .90   .75
  a.   Souvenir sheet of 3, #232-234 5.00 3.50
    Nos. 232-234 (3)   1.27 1.08

1978, Dec. 10   Litho.   Perf. 14
235 A36 10c red, black & yel   .15   .15
236 A36 20c violet, black & yel   .18   .18
237 A36 75c olive, black & yel   .65   .65
    Nos. 235-237 (3)   .98   .98

Universal Declaration of Human Rights, 30th anniversary.

Children
and IYC
Emblem
A37

International Year of the Child 1979

1979, June 30   Wmk. 373   Perf. 14
238 A37 10c shown   .15   .15
239 A37 $1 IYC emblem   .90   .90

Telisai
Earth
Satellite
Station
A38

Designs: 20c, Radar screen and satellite. 75c, Cameraman, telex operator, telephone.

1979, Sept. 23   Litho.   Perf. 14½x14
240 A38 10c multicolored   .15   .15
241 A38 20c multicolored   .18   .18
242 A38 75c multicolored   .75   .75
    Nos. 240-242 (3)   1.08 1.05

Hajeer
Emblem — A39

1979, Nov. 21
243 A39 10c multicolored   .15   .15
244 A39 20c multicolored   .20   .20
245 A39 75c multicolored   .75   .75
  a.   Souvenir sheet of 3, #243-245 2.50 2.50
    Nos. 243-245 (3)   1.10 1.10

Hegira, 1400th anniversary.

Installation
Ceremony — A40

1980   Litho.   Perf. 14
246 A40 10c shown   .15   .15
247 A40 10c Ceremony, diff.   .15   .15
248 A40 75c Jefri Bolkiah   .60   .60
249 A40 75c Sufri Bolkiah   .60   .60
    Nos. 246-249 (4)   1.50 1.50

Installation of Jefri Bolkiah and Sufri Bolkiah as Wizars (Ministers of State for Royalty) 1st anniv. Issue dates: Nos. 246, 248, Nov. 8; others, Dec. 6.

Umbrella — A41

1981, Jan. 19   Litho.   Perf. 12x11½
255 A41 10c shown   .15   .15
256 A41 15c Dagger, shield   .18   .18
257 A41 20c Spears   .25   .25
258 A41 30c Gold pouch   .35   .35

Size: 22½x40mm
Perf. 14x13½
259 A41 50c Headdress   .60   .60
  a.   Souvenir sheet of 5, #255-259 2.25 2.25
    Nos. 255-259 (5)   1.53 1.53

13th World
Telecommunications
Day — A42

1981, May 17   Litho.   Perf. 13x13½
260 A42 10c car rose & black   .15   .15
261 A42 75c dp violet & black   .75   .75

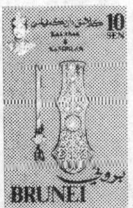

Dagger and Case — A43

Perf. 12½x12, 12 (75c)
1981, July 15   Litho.
Deep Rose Lilac Background
262 A43 10c shown   .15   .15
263 A43 15c Rifle, powder pouch   .15   .15
264 A43 20c Spears   .18   .18
265 A43 30c Sword, tunic, shield   .30   .30
266 A43 50c Horns   .50   .50

Size: 28½x45mm
267 A43 75c Gold bowl, table   .75   .75
    Nos. 262-267 (6)   2.03 2.03

See Nos. 278-289.

Royal Wedding Issue
Common Design Type
1981, July 29   Perf. 14
268 CD331 10c Bouquet   .15   .15
269 CD331 $1 Charles   .65   .65
270 CD331 $2 Couple   1.25 1.25
    Nos. 268-270 (3)   2.05 2.05

World Food
Day — A44

Intl. Year of the
Disabled — A45

1981, Oct. 16   Litho.   Perf. 12
271 A44 10c Fishermen .15 .15
272 A44 $1 Produce .80 .80

1981, Dec. 16   Wmk. 373   Perf. 12
273 A45 10c Blind man .15 .15
274 A45 20c Sign language .16 .16
275 A45 75c Man in wheelchair .60 .60
Nos. 273-275 (3) .91 .91

TB Bacillus
Centenary
A46

1982, Mar. 24   Perf. 12, 13½ (75c)
276 A46 10c Lungs .15 .15
277 A46 75c Bacillus, microscope .60 .60

Type of 1981

1982, May 31   Litho.   Perf. 12½x12
Deep Magenta Background
278 A43 10c shown .15 .15
279 A43 15c Pedestal urn .15 .15
280 A43 20c Silver bowl .20 .20
281 A43 30c Candle .30 .30
282 A43 50c Gold pipe .50 .50

Size: 28x44mm
Perf. 13½
283 A43 75c Silver pointer .75 .75
Nos. 278-283 (6) 2.05 2.05

1982, July 15   Litho.   Perf. 12½x12
Violet Background
284 A43 10c Urn .15 .15
285 A43 15c Crossed banners .15 .15
286 A43 20c Golden fan .20 .20
287 A43 30c Lid .30 .30
288 A43 50c Sword, sheath .50 .50
Size: 28x44mm
Perf. 12
289 A43 75c Golden chalice pole .75 .75
Nos. 284-289 (6) 2.05 2.05

A47

1983, Mar. 14   Litho.   Perf. 13½
290 A47 10c Flag .15 .15
291 A47 20c Natl. palace .20 .20
292 A47 75c Oil drilling .75 .75
293 A47 $2 Sultan Bolkiah 2.00 2.00
a. Block of 4, #290-293 3.05 3.05

Commonwealth Day.

World Communications Year — A48

1983, July 15   Litho.   Perf. 13½
294 A48 10c Mail delivery .15 .15
295 A48 75c Typewriter, phone .80 .80
296 A48 $2 Dish antenna, satellite,
    TV 2.00 2.00
Nos. 294-296 (3) 2.95 2.95

Opening
of
Hassanal
Bolkiah
National
Stadium
A49

$1

1983, Sept. 23   Litho.   Perf. 12
297 A49 10c Soccer, vert. .15 .15
298 A49 75c Runners, vert. 1.00 1.00
299 A49 $1 shown 1.25 1.25
Nos. 297-299 (3) 2.40 2.40
Size, Nos. 297-298: 26x33mm.

Fishing Industry — A50

1983, Sept. 23   Litho.   Perf. 13½
300 A50 10c Shrimp, lobster .15 .15
301 A50 50c Pacific jacks .60 .60
302 A50 75c Parrotfish, flatfish .90 .90
303 A50 $1 Tuna 1.25 1.25
Nos. 300-303 (4) 2.90 2.90

State Assembly
Building — A51

Map of Southeast Asia, Flag — A52

Sultan Hassanal
Bolkiah — A53

1984, Jan. 1   Litho.   Perf. 13
304 A51 10c shown .15 .15
305 A51 20c State Secretariat build-
    ing .25 .25
306 A51 35c New Law Court .40 .40
307 A51 50c Liquid natural gas well .60 .60
308 A51 75c Omar Ali Saifuddin
    Mosque .90 .90
309 A51 $1 Sultan's Palace 1.20 1.20
310 A52 $3 shown 3.60 3.60
a. Souvenir sheet of 7, #304-310 7.25 7.25
Nos. 304-310 (7) 7.10 7.10

Souvenir Sheets
311 Sheet of 4, Constitution sign-
    ing, 1959 1.25 1.25
a.-d. A53 25c any single .25 .25
312 Sheet of 4, Brunei U.K.
    Friendship Agreement, 1979 1.25 1.25
a.-d. A53 25c any single .25 .25

Forestry Resources — A54

1984, Apr. 21   Litho.   Perf. 13½
313 A54 10c Forests, enrichment
    planting .15 .15
314 A54 50c Irrigation canal .60 .60
315 A54 75c Recreation forest .90 .90
316 A54 $1 Wildlife 1.20 1.20
Nos. 313-316 (4) 2.85 2.85

Philakorea
1984 — A55

Litho. & Engr.
1984, Oct. 22   Perf. 13
317 A55 10c No. 93 .15 .15
a. Souvenir sheet of 1 .15 .15
318 A55 75c No. 27 .90 .90
a. Souvenir sheet of 1 .90 .90
319 A55 $2 1895 local stamp 2.50 2.50
a. Souvenir sheet of 1 2.50 2.50
Nos. 317-319 (3) 3.55 3.55

Brunei Admission
to Intl.
Organizations
A56

1985, Sept. 23   Litho.   Perf. 13
320 A56 50c UN .45 .45
321 A56 50c Commonwealth .45 .45
322 A56 50c ASEAN .45 .45
323 A56 50c OIC .45 .45
a. Souv. sheet of 4, #320-323 + label 2.00 2.00
Nos. 320-323 (4) 1.80 1.80

Intl. Youth
Year — A57

1985, Oct. 17   Perf. 12
324 A57 10c shown .15 .15
325 A57 75c Industry, education .55 .55
326 A57 $1 Public Service .70 .70
Nos. 324-326 (3) 1.40 1.40

Intl. Day of
Solidarity with
the Palestinian
People — A58

1985, Nov. 29   Perf. 12x12½
327 A58 10c lt blue & multi .15 .15
328 A58 50c pink & multi .55 .55
329 A58 $1 lt green & multi 1.10 1.10
Nos. 327-329 (3) 1.80 1.80

Natl. Scout
Jamboree, Dec. 14-
20 — A59

Sultan Hassanal
Bolkiah — A60

1985, Dec. 14   Perf. 13½
330 A59 10c Scout handshake .15 .15
331 A59 20c Semaphore .18 .18
332 A59 $2 Jamboree emblem 1.75 1.75
Nos. 330-332 (3) 2.08 2.08

1985-86   Wmk. 233   Perf. 13½x14½
333 A60 10c multi .15 .15
334 A60 15c multi .15 .15
335 A60 20c multi .18 .18
336 A60 25c multi .22 .22
337 A60 35c multi ('86) .32 .32
338 A60 40c multi ('86) .36 .36
339 A60 50c multi ('86) .45 .45
340 A60 75c multi ('86) .68 .68

Size: 35x42mm
Perf. 14
341 A60 $1 multi ('86) .90 .90
342 A60 $2 multi ('86) 1.75 1.75
343 A60 $5 multi ('86) 4.50 4.50
344 A60 $10 multi ('86) 9.00 9.00
Nos. 333-344 (12) 18.66 18.66
Issued: #333-336, Dec. 23; #337-340, Jan. 15;
#341-343, Feb. 23; #344, Mar. 29.

Admission to Intl.
Organizations
A61

Wmk. Cartor (385)
1986, Apr. 30   Litho.   Perf. 13
345 A61 50c WMO .45 .45
346 A61 50c ITU .45 .45
347 A61 50c UPU .45 .45
348 A61 50c ICAO .45 .45
a. Souv. sheet of 4, #345-348 + label 1.80 1.80
Nos. 345-348 (4) 1.80 1.80

Royal Brunei Armed Forces, 25th Anniv.
A62

1986, May 31   Unwmk.   Perf. 13½
349 Strip of 4 1.40 1.40
a. A62 10c In combat .15 .15
b. A62 20c Communications .18 .18
c. A62 50c Air and sea defense .45 .45
d. A62 75c On parade, Royal Palace .68 .68

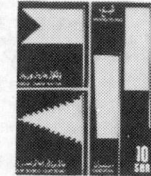

Royal Ensigns — A63

Designs: No. 350, Tunggul charok buritan,
Pisang-pisang, Alam bernaga, Sandaran. No. 351,
Dadap, Tunggul kawan, Ambal, Payong ubor-ubor,
Sapu-sapu ayeng and Rawai lidah. No. 352, Ula-ula
besar, Payong haram, Sumbu layang. No. 353,
Payong ubor-ubor tiga ringkat and Payong tinggi.
No. 354, Panji-panji, Chogan istiadat, Chogan
ugama. No. 355, Lambang duli yang maha mulia
and Mahligai.

1986   Litho.   Perf. 12½
350 A63 10c multicolored .15 .15
351 A63 10c multicolored .15 .15
352 A63 75c multicolored .68 .68
353 A63 75c multicolored .68 .68
354 A63 $2 multicolored 1.75 1.75
355 A63 $2 multicolored 1.75 1.75
Nos. 350-355 (6) 5.16 5.16

Intl. Peace
Year — A64

1986, Oct. 24   Litho.   Perf. 12
356 A64 50c Peace doves .48 .48
357 A64 75c Hands .68 .68
358 A64 $1 Peace symbols .88 .88
Nos. 356-358 (3) 2.04 2.04

Natl. Anti-Drug Campaign Posters — A65

Brass Artifacts — A66

1987, Mar. 15   Litho.   Perf. 12
359 A65 10c Jail   .15   .15
360 A65 75c Noose   .65   .65
361 A65 $1 Execution   .88   .88
  Nos. 359-361 (3)   1.68 1.68

1987, July 15
362 A66 50c Kiri (kettle)   .45   .45
363 A66 50c Langguai (bowl)   .45   .45
364 A66 50c Badil (cannon)   .45   .45
365 A66 50c Pelita (lamp)   .45   .45
  Nos. 362-365 (4)   1.80 1.80

See Nos. 388-391.

Dewan Bahasa Dan Pustaka, 25th Anniv. — A67

Illustration reduced.

1987, Sept. 29   Perf. 13½x13
366 A67   Strip of 3   1.75 1.75
  a.   10c multicolored   .15   .15
  b.   50c multicolored   .30   .30
  c. $2 multicolored   1.25 1.25

Language and Literature Bureau.

ASEAN, 20th Anniv. — A68

1987, Aug. 8   Litho.   Perf. 14x13½
367 A68 20c Map   .18   .18
368 A68 50c Year dates   .45   .45
369 A68 $1 Flags, emblem   .90   .90
  Nos. 367-369 (3)   1.53 1.53

World Food Day A70

Fruit: a, Artocarpus odoratissima. b, Canarium odontophyllum mig. c, Litsea garciae. d, Mangifera foetida lour.

1987, Oct. 31   Perf. 12½
370   Strip of 4   1.80 1.80
  a.-d. A70 50c any single   .45   .45

See Nos. 374, 405, 423, 457-460.

Intl. Year of Shelter for the Homeless A71

Various houses.

1987, Nov. 28   Litho.   Perf. 13
371 A71 50c multi   .48   .48
372 A71 75c multi, diff.   .70   .70
373 A71 $1 multi, diff.   .95   .95
  Nos. 371-373 (3)   2.13 2.13

Fruit Type of 1987
Without FAO Emblem, Dated 1988

Fruit: a, Durio. b, Durio oxleyanus. c, Durio graveolens (cross section at L). d, Durio graveolens (cross section at R).

1988, Jan. 30   Litho.   Perf. 12
374   Strip of 4   2.00 2.00
  a.-d. A70 50c, any single   .50   .50

Opening of Malay Technology Museum — A72

1988, Feb. 29   Perf. 12½x12
375 A72 10c Wooden lathe   .15   .15
376 A72 75c Water wheel, buffalo   .75   .75
377 A72 $1 Bird caller in blind   1.00 1.00
  Nos. 375-377 (3)   1.90 1.90

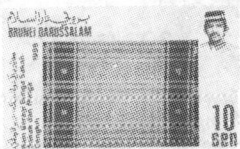

Handwoven Cloth — A73

Designs: 10c, Kain Beragi Bunga Sakah-Sakah Dan Bunga Cengkih. 20c, Kain Jong Sarat. 25c, Kain Si Pugut. 40c, Kain Si Pugut Bunga Berlapis. 75c, Kain Si Lobang Bangsi Bunga Belitang Kipas.

1900, Apr. 1   Litho.   Perf. 12
378 A73 10c multicolored   .15   .15
379 A73 20c org brown & blk   .20   .20
380 A73 25c multicolored   .25   .25
381 A73 40c multicolored   .40   .40
382 A73 75c multicolored   .75   .75
  a.   Souvenir sheet of 5, #378-382 + label 1.70 1.70
  Nos. 378-382 (5)   1.75 1.75

1988, Sept. 29   Litho.   Perf. 12
Designs: 10c, Kain Beragi. 20c, Kain Bertabur. 25c, Kain Sukma Indra. 40c, Kain Si Pugut Bunga Bersusup. 75c, Kain Beragi Si Lobang Bangsi Bunga Cendera Kesuma.
383 A73 10c multicolored   .15   .15
384 A73 20c multicolored   .20   .20
385 A73 25c multicolored   .25   .25
386 A73 40c multicolored   .40   .40
387 A73 75c multicolored   .75   .75
  a.   Souvenir sheet of 5, #383-387 1.70 1.70
  Nos. 383-387 (5)   1.75 1.75

Brass Artifacts Type of 1987

1988, June 30   Litho.   Perf. 12
388 A66 50c Celapa (repousse box)   .50   .50
389 A66 50c Gangsa (footed plate)   .50   .50
390 A66 50c Periok (lidded pot)   .50   .50
391 A66 50c Lampong (candlestick)   .50   .50
  Nos. 388-391 (4)   2.00 2.00

Coronation of Sultan Hassanal Bolkiah, 20th Anniv. — A74

1988, Aug. 1   Litho.   Perf. 14
392 A74 20c shown   .20   .20
393 A74 75c Reading from the Koran .75   .75
  Size: 26x62mm
  Perf. 12½x13
394 A74 $2 In full regalia   2.00 2.00
  a.   Souvenir sheet of 3, #392-394 3.00 3.00
  Nos. 392-394 (3)   2.95 2.95

Eradicate Malaria, WHO 40th Anniv. A75

1988, Dec. 17   Litho.   Perf. 14x13½
395 A75 25c Mosquito   .25   .25
396 A75 35c Extermination   .35   .35
397 A75 $2 Microscope, infected blood cells 2.10 2.10
  Nos. 395-397 (3)   2.70 2.70

Natl. Day — A76

1989, Feb. 23   Litho.   Perf. 12
  Size of 60c: 22x54½mm
398 A76 20c Sultan Bolkiah, officials .20 .20
399 A76 30c Honor guard   .30   .30
400 A76 60c Fireworks, palace, vert. .60 .60
401 A76 $2 Religious ceremony   2.00 2.00
  a.   Souvenir sheet of 4, #398-401 3.20 3.20
  Nos. 398-401 (4)   3.10 3.10

Independence from Britain, 5th anniv.

Solidarity with the Palestinians A77

1989, Apr. 1   Litho.   Perf. 13½
402 A77 20c shown   .20   .20
403 A77 75c Map, flag   .75   .75
404 A77 $1 Dome of the Rock   1.00 1.00
  Nos. 402-404 (3)   1.95 1.95

Fruit Type of 1987
Without FAO Emblem, Dated 1989

Designs: a, Daemonorops fissa. b, Eleiodoxa conferia. c, Salacca zalacca. d, Calamus ornatus.

1989, Oct. 31   Litho.   Perf. 12
405   Strip of 4   2.50 2.50
  a.-d. A70 60c any single   .82   .82

Oil and Gas Industry, 60th Anniv. A79

1989, Dec. 28   Perf. 13½
406 A79 20c Drill   .22   .22
407 A79 60c Tanker   .65   .65
408 A79 90c Refinery   1.00 1.00
409 A79 $1 Rail transport   1.10 1.10
410 A79 $2 Offshore rig   2.20 2.20
  Nos. 406-410 (5)   5.17 5.17

Brunei Museum, 25th Anniv. A80

1990, Jan. 1   Litho.   Perf. 12x12½
411 A80 30c Exhibits   .30   .30
412 A80 60c Official opening, 1965 .60   .60
413 A80 $1 Museum exterior   1.00 1.00
  Nos. 411-413 (3)   1.90 1.90

Intl. Literacy Year — A81

1990, July 15   Litho.   Perf. 12x12½
414 A81 15c multicolored   .16   .16
415 A81 90c multicolored   .95   .95
416 A81 $1 multicolored   1.10 1.10
  Nos. 414-416 (3)   2.21 2.21

Tarsier — A82

Fight Against AIDS — A83

1990, Sept. 29   Litho.   Perf. 12
417 A82 20c shown   .22   .22
418 A82 60c Eating leaves   .68   .68
419 A82 90c Climbing tree   1.00 1.00
  Nos. 417-419 (3)   1.90 1.90

1990, Dec. 1   Litho.   Perf. 13
420 A83 20c shown   .22   .22
421 A83 30c AIDS transmission   .35   .35
422 A83 90c Tombstone, skulls   1.00 1.00
  Nos. 420-422 (3)   1.57 1.57

Fruit Type of 1987
Without FAO Emblem, Dated 1990

Fruit: a, Willoughbea (uncut core). b, Willoughbea (core cut in half). c, Willoughbea angustifolia.

1990, Dec. 31   Perf. 12½
423   Strip of 3   2.05 2.05
  a.-c. A70 60c any single   .68   .68

Proboscis Monkey — A84

1991, Mar. 30   Litho.   Perf. 13½x14
424 A84 15c shown   .18   .18
425 A84 20c Head, facing   .22   .22
426 A84 50c Sitting on branch   .60   .60
427 A84 60c Adult with young   .70   .70
  Nos. 424-427 (4)   1.70 1.70

Teacher's Day A85

Design: 90c, Teacher at blackboard.

1991, Sept. 23   Litho.   Perf. 13½x14
428 A85 60c multicolored   .70   .70
429 A85 90c multicolored   1.05 1.05

Brunei Beauty A86

1991, Oct. 1   Litho.   Perf. 13
430 A86 30c Three immature   .35   .35
431 A86 60c Female   .70   .70
432 A86 $1 Adult male   1.20 1.20
  Nos. 430-432 (3)   2.25 2.25

Footnotes near stamp listings often refer to other stamps of the same design.

Happy Family
Campaign — A87

1991, Nov. 30   Litho.   *Perf. 13*
433 A87 20c Family, graduating son   .25   .25
434 A87 60c Mothers, children   .70   .70
435 A87 90c Adults, children, heart   1.05   1.05
    Nos. 433-435 (3)   2.00   2.00

World Health
Day — A88

1992, Apr. 7   Litho.   *Perf. 13*
436 A88 20c multicolored   .25   .25
437 A88 50c multi, diff.   .58   .58
     Size: 48x28mm
438 A88 75c multi, diff.   .90   .90
    Nos. 436-438 (3)   1.73   1.73

Brunei-Singapore and Brunei-Malaysia-
Philippines Fiber Optic Submarine
Cables — A89

1992, Apr. 28   Litho.   *Perf. 12*
439 A89 20c Map   .25   .25
440 A89 30c Diagram   .35   .35
441 A89 90c Submarine cable   1.05   1.05
    Nos. 439-441 (3)   1.65   1.65

Visit
ASEAN
Year
A90

Designs: a, 20c, Sculptures. b, 60c, Judo exhibition. c, $1, Sculptures, diff.

1992, June 30   Litho.   *Perf. 13¹/₂x14*
442 A90 Strip of 3, #a.-c.   2.00   2.00

ASEAN, 25th
Anniv. — A91

1992, Aug. 8   Litho.   *Perf. 14*
443 A91 20c shown   .25   .25
444 A91 60c Building   .70   .70
445 A91 90c Views of member states   1.05   1.05
    Nos. 443-445 (3)   2.00   2.00

1992, Oct. 5   *Perf. 14x13¹/₂*

Sultan in various forms of dress and: No. 446a,
Coronation procession. b, Airport. c, New Law
Court, Sultan's Palace. d, Ship and Brunei Univer-
sity. e, Mosque, buildings.

446 A92 25c Strip of 5, #a.-e.   1.50   1.50

Sultan Hassanal Bolkiah's Accession to the
Throne, 25th Anniv.

Birds — A93

Designs: No. 447, Crested wood partridge, vert.
No. 448, Long-tailed parakeet, vert. No. 449,
Chestnut-breasted malkoha. No. 450, Asian para-
dise flycatcher, vert. No. 451, Magpie robin, vert.
No. 452, White-rumped shama. No. 453, Great
argus pheasant, vert. No. 454, Malay lorikeet, vert.
No. 455, Black and red broadbill, vert.

   Perf. 14x13¹/₂, 13¹/₂x14

1992-93   Litho.
447 A93 30c multicolored   .38   .38
448 A93 30c multicolored   .38   .38
449 A93 30c multicolored   .38   .38
450 A93 60c multicolored   .75   .75
451 A93 60c multicolored   .75   .75
452 A93 60c multicolored   .75   .75
453 A93 $1 multicolored   1.20   1.20
454 A93 $1 multicolored   1.20   1.20
455 A93 $1 multicolored   1.20   1.20
    Nos. 447-455 (9)   6.99   6.99

Issue dates: Nos. 447, 450, 453, Dec. 30, 1992.
Nos. 448, 451, 454, Jan. 27, 1993. Others, May 3,
1993.

Natl. Day, 10th
Anniv. — A94

10th anniv. emblem and: a, 10c, Natl. flag. b,
20c, Hands supporting inscription. c, 30c, Natl. day
emblems, 1985-93. d, 60c, Emblem with star,
crossed swords.

1994, June 16   Litho.   *Perf. 13*
456 A94 Strip of 4, #a.-d.   1.50   1.50

Fruit Type of 1987
Without FAO Emblem, Dated 1994

Designs: No. 457, Nephelium mutabile. No. 458,
Nephelium xerospermoides. No. 459, Nephelium
spp. No. 460, Nephelium macrophyllum.

1994, Aug. 8   Litho.   *Perf. 13¹/₂x13*
457 A70 60c multicolored   .75   .75
458 A70 60c multicolored   .75   .75
459 A70 60c multicolored   .75   .75
460 A70 60c multicolored   .75   .75
    Nos. 457-460 (4)   3.00   3.00

A95   A96

World Stop Smoking Day: 10c, Cigarette, lung,
fetus over human figure. 15c, People throwing
away tobacco, cigarettes, pipe. $2, Arms around
world crushing out cigarettes.

1994, Sept. 1   Litho.   *Perf. 13¹/₂x13*
461 A95 10c multicolored   .15   .15
462 A95 15c multicolored   .20   .20
463 A95 $2 multicolored   2.50   2.50
    Nos. 461-463 (3)   2.85   2.85

1994, Oct. 7   *Perf. 13¹/₂*

Girl Guides in Brunei, 40th anniv.: a, Leader. b,
Girl receiving award. c, Girl reading. d, Girls in
various costumes. e, Girls camping out.

464 A96 40c Strip of 5, #a.-e.   2.50   2.50

Royal Brunei
Airlines, 20th
Anniv. — A97

Airplanes: 10c, Twin-engine propeller. 20c, Passenger jet attached to tow bar. $1, Passenger jet in
air.

1994, Nov. 18   Litho.   *Perf. 13¹/₂*
465 A97 10c multicolored   .15   .15
466 A97 20c multicolored   .28   .28
467 A97 $1 multicolored   1.25   1.25
    Nos. 465-467 (3)   1.68   1.68

Intl. Day Against
Drug Abuse — A98

Healthy people wearing traditional costumes:
20c, 60c, $1.

1994, Dec. 30   Litho.   *Perf. 13¹/₂*
468 A98 Strip of 3, #a.-c.   2.25   2.25

No. 468 is a continuous design.

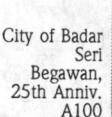 

City of Badar
Seri
Begawan,
25th Anniv.
A100

Aerial view of city: 30c, In 1970. 50c, In 1980,
with details of significant buildings. $1, In 1990.

1995, Oct. 4   Litho.   *Perf. 13¹/₂*
481 A100 30c multicolored   .40   .40
482 A100 60c multicolored   .70   .70
483 A100 $1 multicolored   1.40   1.40
    Nos. 481-483 (3)   2.50   2.50

UN, 50th
Anniv. — A101

UN headquarters: 20c, Delegates in General
Assembly. 60c, Security Council. 90c, Exterior.

1995, Oct. 24   *Perf. 14¹/₂x14*
484 A101 20c multicolored   .30   .30
485 A101 60c multicolored   .85   .85
     Size: 27x44mm
486 A101 90c multicolored   1.30   1.30
    Nos. 484-486 (3)   2.45   2.45

University of Brunei,
10th Anniv. — A102

Designs: 30c, Students in classroom. 50c, Campus buildings. 90c, Sultan in procession.

1995, Oct. 28   *Perf. 13x13¹/₂*
487 A102 30c multicolored   .40   .40
488 A102 50c multicolored   .70   .70
489 A102 90c multicolored   1.30   1.30
    Nos. 487-489 (3)   2.40   2.40

OCCUPATION STAMPS

Issued under Japanese Occupation
Stamps and Types of 1908-37
Handstamped in Violet, Red Violet, Blue or
Red

大日本帝国政府

   Perf. 14, 14x11¹/₂ (#N7)
1942-44   **Wmk. 4**
N1 A1 1c black   6.50   11.00
N2 A1 2c green   65.00   100.00
N3 A1 2c dull orange   3.50   6.00
N4 A1 3c green   27.50   65.00
N5 A1 4c orange   5.00   14.00
N6 A1 5c brown   5.50   14.00
N7 A2 6c slate gray   65.00   140.00
N8 A2 6c red   525.00   500.00
N9 A1 8c gray (RV)   575.00   825.00
N10 A2 8c carmine   5.00   10.00
N11 A1 10c violet, *yel*   10.00   17.50
N12 A2 12c blue   10.00   17.50
N13 A2 15c ultra   10.00   17.50
N14 A1 25c dk violet   22.50   65.00
N15 A1 30c org & red vio   110.00   275.00
N16 A1 50c blk, *green*   27.50   80.00
N17 A1 $1 red & blk, *bl*   50.00   100.00
           Wmk. 3
N18 A1 $5 lake, *green*   800.   750.
N19 A1 $25 black, *red*   1,000.   1,500.

Overprints vary in shade. Nos. N3, N7, N10 and
N13 without overprint are not believed to have
been regularly issued.

大日本

参弗

帝国郵便

No. 43 Surcharged in
Red

1944   **Wmk. 4**   *Perf. 14*
N20 A1 $3 on 1c black   3,250.   3,250.
   a.   On No. N1   3,250.   3,250.

BURMA

ˈbər–mə

Myanmar

LOCATION — Bounded on the north by
China; east by China, Laos and Thailand;
south and west by the Bay of Bengal,
Bangladesh and India.
GOVT. — Republic
AREA — 261,789 sq. mi.
POP. — 35,313,905 (1983)
CAPITAL — Rangoon

Burma was part of India from 1826 until
April 1, 1937, when it became a self-governing unit of the British Commonwealth
and received a constitution. On January 4,
1948, Burma became an independent
nation.

    12 Pies = 1 Anna
    16 Annas = 1 Rupee
    100 Pyas = 1 Kyat (1953)

Catalogue values for unused
stamps in this country are for Never
Hinged items, beginning with Scott
35 in the regular postage section
and Scott O28 in the official
section.

Watermarks

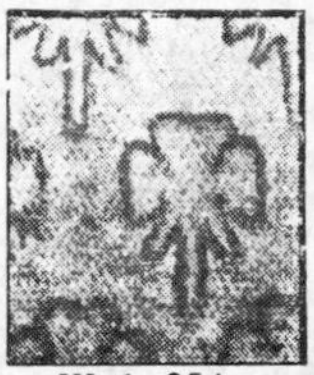

Wmk. 254-
Elephant Heads

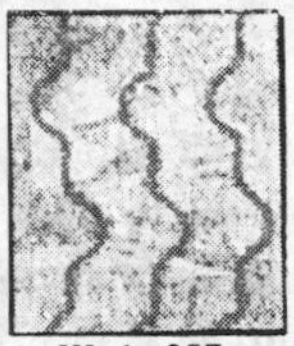

Wmk. 257-
Curved Wavy
Lines

Stamps of India 1926-36 Overprinted **BURMA**

1937, Apr. 1 Wmk. 196 *Perf. 14*

1 A46 3p slate .15 .15
2 A71 ½a green .15 .15
3 A68 9p dark green .20 .15
4 A72 1a dark brown .15 .15
5 A49 2a ver (small die) .15 .15
6 A57 2a6p buff .15 .15
7 A51 3a carmine rose .40 .15
8 A70 3a6p deep blue .40 .15
9 A52 4a olive green .45 .15
10 A53 6a bister .40 .25
11 A54 8a red violet .90 .15
12 A55 12a claret 1.50 .50

Overprinted **BURMA**

13 A56 1r green & brown 5.00 .75
14 A56 2r brn org & car rose 7.50 2.50
15 A56 5r dk violet & ultra 10.00 3.00
16 A56 10r car & green 27.50 6.00
17 A56 15r ol green & ultra 125.00 60.00
18 A56 25r blue & ocher 250.00 150.00
Nos. 1-18 (18) 430.00 224.50

For overprints see #1N1-1N3, 1N25-1N26, 1N47.

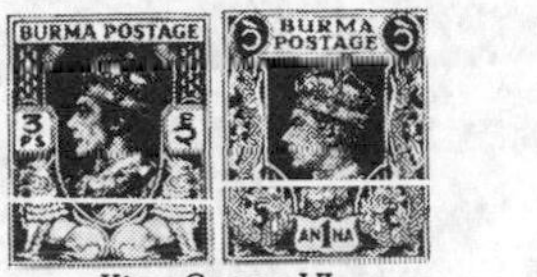

King George VI
A1 A2

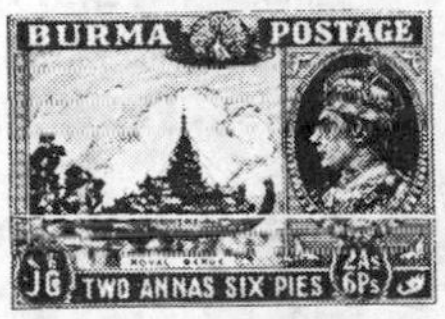

Royal
Barge — A3

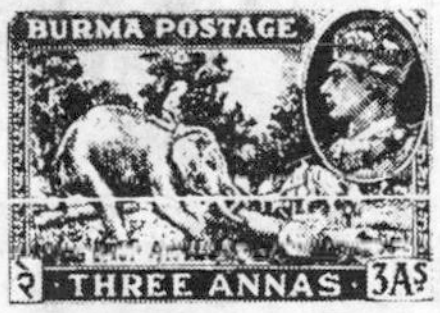

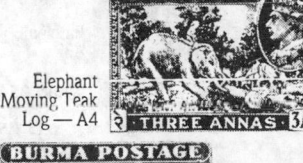

Elephant
Moving Teak
Log — A4

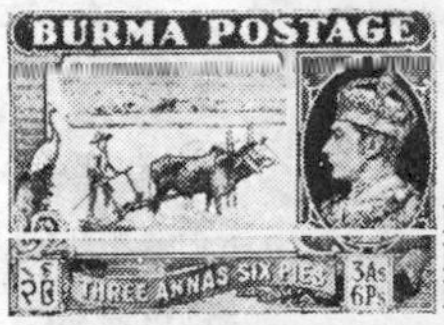

Farmer
Plowing Rice
Field — A5

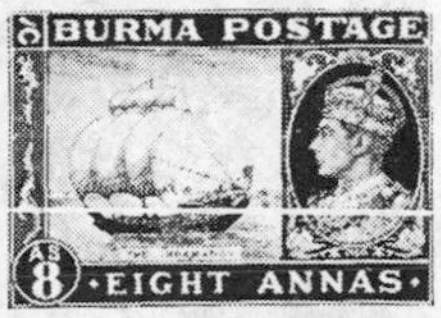

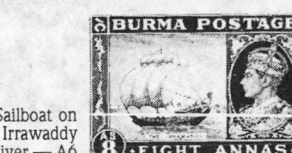

Sailboat on
Irrawaddy
River — A6

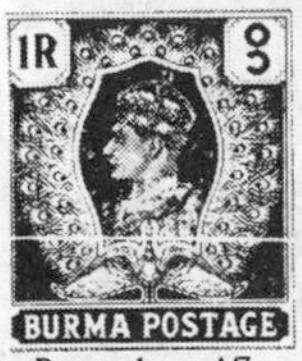

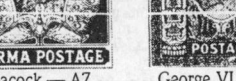

Peacock — A7

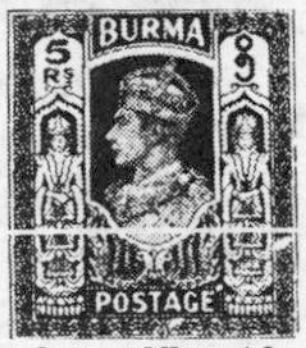

George VI — A8

Perf. 13½x14

1938-40 Litho. Wmk. 254

18A A1 1p red orange ('40) .75 .25
19 A1 3p violet .15 .15
20 A1 6p ultramarine .15 .15
21 A1 9p yel green .50 .30
22 A2 1a brown violet .15 .15
23 A2 1½a turquoise green .15 .15
24 A2 2a carmine .25 .15

Perf. 13

25 A3 2a6p rose lake .75 .40
26 A4 3a dk violet 2.25 .45
27 A5 3a6p dp blue & brt bl 1.25 *2.50*
28 A2 4a slate blue, perf. 13½x14 .15 .15
29 A6 8a slate green 1.25 .15

Perf. 13½

30 A7 1r brt ultra & dk violet 2.00 .25
31 A7 2r dk vio & red brown 4.75 1.25
32 A8 5r car & dull vio 20.00 7.50
33 A8 10r gray grn & brn 40.00 30.00
Nos. 18A-33 (16) 74.50 43.95

See Nos. 51-65. For overprints and surcharges see Nos. 34-50, O15-O27, 1N4-1N11, 1N28-1N30, 1N37-1N46, 1N48-1N49.

No. 25 Surcharged in Black

COMMEMORATION
POSTAGE STAMP
6th MAY 1840

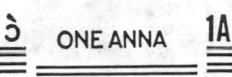

ONE ANNA 1A

1940, May 6 *Perf. 13*

34 A3 1a on 2a6p rose lake 1.00 .80

Centenary of first postage stamp.

Catalogue values for unused stamps in this section, from this point to the end of the section, are for Never Hinged items.

Nos. 18A to 33 Overprinted in Black:

MILY ADMN
a

MILY ADMN
b

1945

35 A1(a) 1p red orange .15 .15
36 A1(a) 3p violet .15 .15
37 A1(a) 6p ultramarine .15 .15
38 A1(a) 9p yel green .15 .15
39 A2(a) 1a brown violet .15 .15
40 A2(a) 1½a turq green .15 .15
41 A2(a) 2a carmine .15 .15
42 A3(b) 2a6p rose lake .45 .45
43 A4(b) 3a dk violet .75 .15
44 A5(b) 3a6p dp bl & brt bl .15 .15
45 A2(a) 4a slate blue .15 .15
46 A6(b) 8a slate green .15 .20
47 A7(b) 1r brt ultra & dk violet .30 .40
48 A7(b) 2r dk vio & red brown .30 .75
49 A8(b) 5r car & dull vio .75 .80
50 A8(b) 10r gray grn & brn 1.50 1.50
Nos. 35-50 (16) 5.55 5.60

Types of 1938

Perf. 13½x14

1946, Jan. 1 Litho. Wmk. 254

51 A1 3p brown .15 .15
52 A1 6p violet .15 .15
53 A1 9p dull green .15 .15
54 A2 1a deep blue .15 .15
55 A2 1½a salmon .15 .15
56 A2 2a rose lake .15 .15

Perf. 13

57 A3 2a6p greenish blue .25 .15
58 A4 3a blue violet 4.50 1.50
59 A5 3a6p ultra & gray blk .15 .15
60 A2 4a rose lil, perf. 13½x14 .15 .15
61 A6 8a deep magenta 1.50 .20

Perf. 13½

62 A7 1r dp mag & dk vio .90 .25
63 A7 2r salmon & red brn 5.00 1.50
64 A8 5r red brn & dk grn 5.00 5.00
65 A8 10r dk vio & car 5.00 5.00
Nos. 51-65 (15) 23.35 14.80

For overprints see Nos. 70-84, O28-O42.

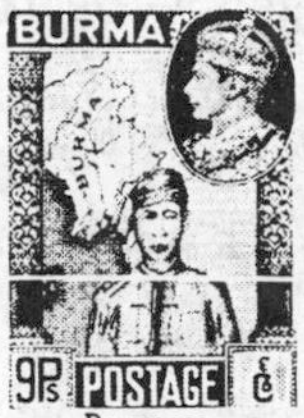

Burmese
Man — A9

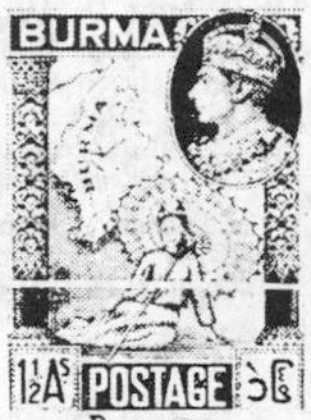

Burmese
Woman — A10

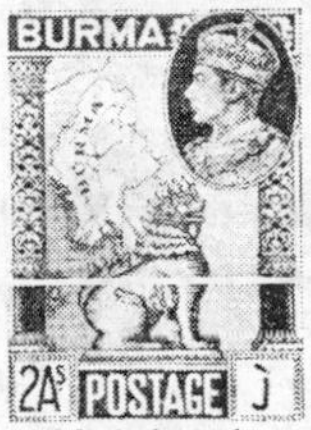

Mythological
Chinze — A11

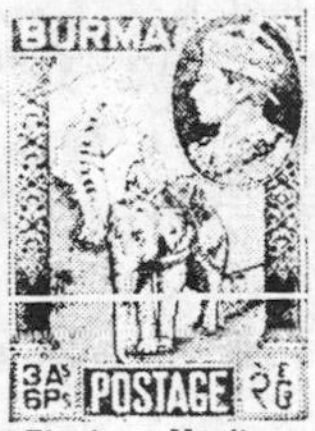

Elephant Hauling
Teak — A12

1946, May 2 *Perf. 13*

66 A9 9p peacock green .15 .15
67 A10 1½a brt violet .15 .15
68 A11 2a carmine .15 .15
69 A12 3a6p ultramarine .15 .15
Set value .40 .40

Victory of the Allied Nations in WWII.

Nos. 51 to 65 Overprinted in Black ကြားဖြတ် အစိုးရ။

1947, Oct. 1 *Perf. 13½x14, 13, 13½*

70 A1 3p brown .15 .15
71 A1 6p violet .15 .15
72 A1 9p dull green .15 .15
a. Inverted overprint 8.00 8.00
73 A2 1a deep blue .15 .15
74 A2 1½a salmon .15 .15
75 A2 2a rose lake .15 .15
76 A3 2a6p greenish bl .15 .15
77 A4 3a blue violet .15 .15
78 A5 3a6p ultra & gray blk .15 .15
79 A2 4a rose lilac .15 .15
80 A6 8a dp magenta .20 .20
81 A7 1r dp mag & dk vio .40 .30
82 A7 2r sal & red brn .80 .55
83 A8 5r red brn & dk grn 1.00 .75
84 A8 10r dk vio & car 1.75 1.50
Set value 5.00 4.00

The overprint is slightly larger on Nos. 76 to 78 and 80 to 84. The Burmese characters read "Interim Government."

Other denominations are known with the overprint inverted or double.

Issues of the Republic

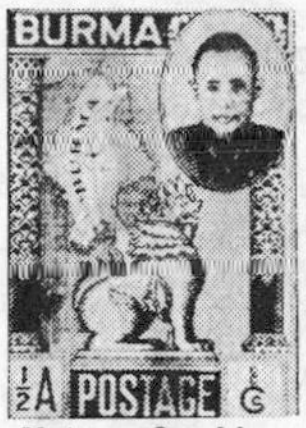

U Aung San Map
and Chinze — A13

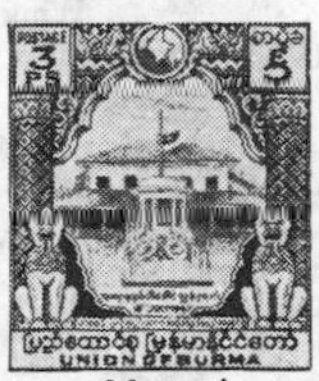

Martyrs'
Memorial — A14

Perf. 12½x12

1948, Jan. 6 Litho. Unwmk.

85 A13 ½a emerald .15 .15
86 A13 1a deep rose .15 .15
87 A13 2a carmine .15 .15
88 A13 3½a blue .15 .15
89 A13 8a lt chocolate .20 .20
Set value .60 .50

Attainment of independence, Jan. 4, 1948.

1948, July 19 Engr. *Perf. 14x13½*

90 A14 3p ultramarine .15 .15
91 A14 6p green .15 .15
92 A14 9p dp carmine .15 .15
93 A14 1a purple .15 .15
94 A14 2a lilac rose .15 .15
95 A14 3½a dk slate green .15 .15
96 A14 4a yel brown .15 .15
97 A14 8a orange red .15 .15
98 A14 12a claret .16 .15
99 A14 1r blue green .20 .16
100 A14 2r deep blue .48 .35
101 A14 5r chocolate 1.25 .80
Set value 2.50 1.90

1st anniv. of the assassination of Burma's leaders in the fight for independence.

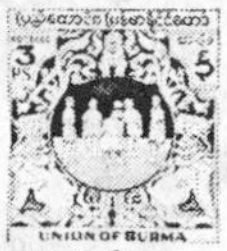

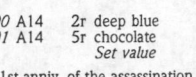

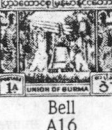

Ball Game
(Chinlon)
A15

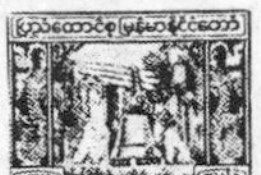

Bell
A16

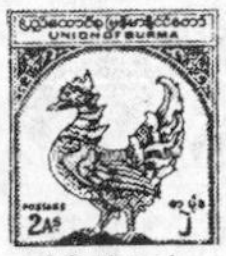

Mythical
Bird — A17

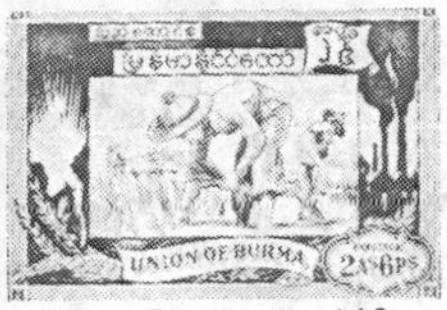

Rice Planting — A18

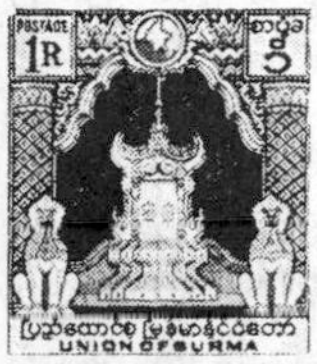

Throne — A19

Designs: 6p, Dancer. 9p, Musician. 3a, Spinning. 3a6p, Royal Palace. 4a, Cutting teak. 8a, Plowing rice field.

Perf. 12½ (A15-A17), 12x12½ (A18), 13 (A19)

1949, Jan. 4

102 A15 3p ultramarine .15 .15
103 A15 6p green .15 .15
104 A15 9p carmine .15 .15
105 A16 1a red orange .15 .15
106 A17 2a orange .15 .15
107 A18 2a6p lilac rose .15 .15
108 A18 3a purple .15 .15
109 A18 3a6p dk slate grn .15 .15
110 A16 4a chocolate .15 .15
111 A18 8a carmine .16 .15
112 A19 1r blue green .35 .20
a. Perf. 14 2.50
113 A19 2r deep blue .80 .32
114 A19 5r chocolate 1.65 .70
115 A19 10r orange red 3.25 1.00
Nos. 102-115 (14) 7.56
Set value 2.85

See Nos. 122-135, 139-152, O56-O67.

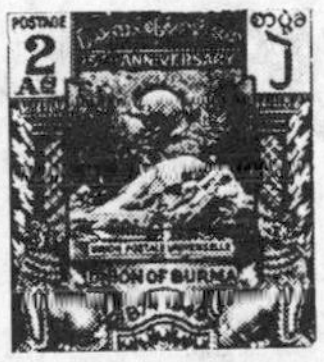

UPU Monument,
Bern — A20

1949, Oct. 9 Unwmk. *Perf. 13*

116 A20 2a orange .15 .15
117 A20 3½a olive grn .15 .15
118 A20 6a lilac .16 .15
119 A20 8a crimson .24 .16
120 A20 12½a ultra .32 .16
121 A20 1r blue green .52 .50
Nos. 116-121 (6) 1.54 1.27

75th anniv. of the UPU.

Types of 1949

Designs as before.

Perf. 13½x14, 14x13½, 13

1952-53 Litho. Wmk. 254

122 A15 3p brown orange .15 .15
123 A15 6p deep plum .15 .15
124 A15 9p blue .15 .15
125 A16 1a violet bl .15 .15
126 A17 2a green ('52) .15 .15
127 A18 2a6p green .15 .15
128 A18 3a sal pink ('52) .15 .15
129 A18 3a6p brown orange .15 .15
130 A16 4a vermilion .15 .15
131 A18 8a lt blue ('52) .15 .15
132 A19 1r rose violet .24 .15
133 A19 2r yel green .52 .26
134 A19 5r ultramarine 1.65 .85
135 A19 10r aquamarine 3.25 1.65
Nos. 122-135 (14) 7.16
Set value 3.50

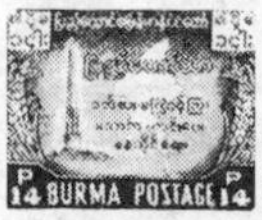

Map of Burma and Monument — A21

1953, Jan. 4 *Perf. 14*
136 A21 14p green .15 .15

Perf. 13
Size: 36½x26mm
137 A21 20p salmon pink .15 .15
138 A21 25p ultramarine .15 .15
Set value .25 .20

Fifth anniversary of independence.
For surcharge see No. 166.

Types of 1949

Designs: 2p, Dancer. 3p, Musician. 20p, Spinning. 25p, Royal Palace. 30p, Cutting teak. 50p, Plowing rice field.

1954, Jan. 4 *Perf. 14x13½, 13, 14*
139 A15 1p brown orange .15 .15
140 A15 2p plum .15 .15
141 A15 3p blue .15 .15
142 A16 5p ultramarine .15 .15
143 A18 10p yel green .15 .15
144 A17 15p green .15 .15
145 A18 20p vermilion .15 .15
146 A18 25p lt red org .15 .15
147 A16 30p vermilion .15 .15
148 A18 50p blue .24 .15
149 A19 1k rose violet .50 .15
150 A19 2k green 1.00 .15
151 A19 5k ultramarine 2.75 .15
152 A19 10k light blue 5.00 .26
Nos. 139-152 (14) 10.84
Set value 1.00

For overprints and surcharges see Nos. 163-165, 173-175, O68-O79, O80-O81, O83, O85, O87.

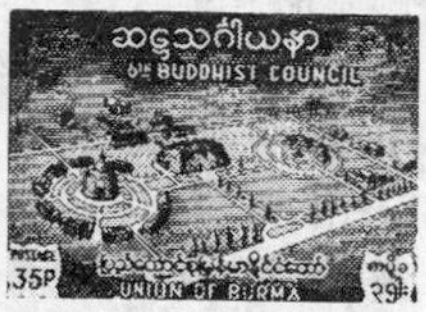

Peace Pagoda, Monks' Hostels and Meeting-cave A22

Designs: 10p, Sangha (community) of Cambodia. 15p, Council meeting. 50p, Sangha of Thailand. 1k, Sangha of Ceylon. 2k, Sangha of Laos.

1954 **Typo.** *Perf. 13*
153 A22 10p deep blue .15 .15
154 A22 15p deep claret .15 .15
155 A22 35p dark brown .15 .15
156 A22 50p green .16 .15
157 A22 1k carmine .32 .16
158 A22 2k violet .60 .40
Set value 1.30 .80

6th Buddhist Council, Rangoon, 1954-56.

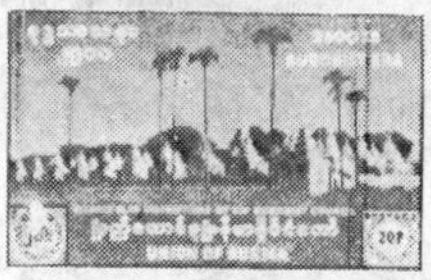

Marble Markers of 5th Buddhist Council A23

Designs: 40p, Thatbyinnyu Pagoda. 60p, Shwedagon Pagoda, Rangoon. 1.25k, Aerial View of 6th Buddhist Council, Yegu.

Perf. 11x11½
1956, May 24 **Litho.** **Unwmk.**
159 A23 20p blue & gray olive .15 .15
160 A23 40p blue & brt yel grn .15 .15
161 A23 60p green & lemon .16 .15
162 A23 1.25k gray blue & yel .32 .20
Nos. 159-162 (4) .78
Set value .45

2500th anniv. of the Buddhist Era.

Nos. 146, 149-150 Surcharged or Overprinted

မြို့မန္တလာ-နှစ်တရာ
၁၂၂၁-၁၃၂၁
15 P ၁၅ပြား

1959, Nov. 9 **Wmk. 254** *Perf. 13, 14*
163 A18 15p on 25p lt red org .15 .15
164 A19 1k rose violet .30 .16
165 A19 2k green .55 .45
Nos. 163-165 (3) 1.00
Set value .65

Centenary of Mandalay, former capital.
The two lines of overprint are 4mm apart on No. 163; 7mm on Nos. 164-165.

No. 136 Surcharged: ၁၅ပြား

1961, June *Perf. 14*
166 A21 15p on 14p green .32 .16

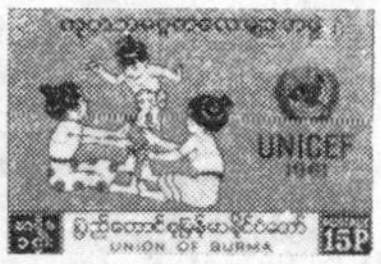

Children — A24

Unwmk.
1961, Dec. 11 **Litho.** *Perf. 13*
167 A24 15p claret & rose claret .15 .15

15th anniversary of UNICEF.

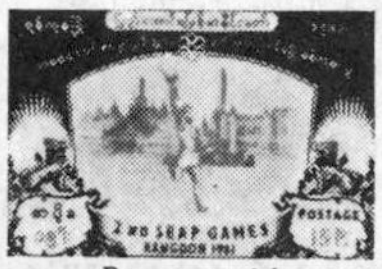

Runner with Torch — A25

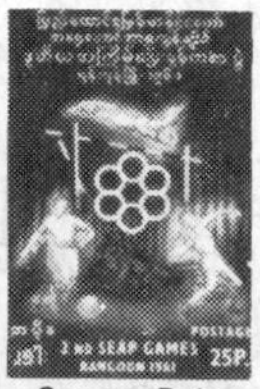

Soccer, Pole Vault and Shot Put — A26

Designs: 50p, Women runners. 1k, Hurdling, weight lifting, boxing, bicycling and swimming.

1961, Dec. 11 **Photo.** *Perf. 14x13*
168 A25 15p red & ultra .15 .15
169 A26 25p dk green & ocher .15 .15
170 A26 50p vio blue & pink .20 .15
171 A25 1k brt green & yel .35 .25
Nos. 168-171 (4) .85
Set value .50

2nd South East Asia Peninsular Games, Rangoon.

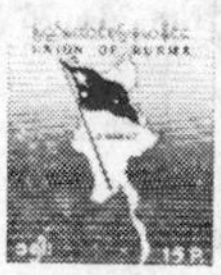

Map and Flag of Burma — A27

Wmk. 254
1963, Mar. 2 **Engr.** *Perf. 13*
172 A27 15p red .20 .15

First anniversary of new government.

Nos. 143 and 148 Overprinted in Violet or Red: "FREEDOM FROM HUNGER"

1963, Mar. 21 **Litho.**
173 A18 10p yel green (V) .15 .15
174 A18 50p blue (R) .20 .15
Set value .30 .20

FAO "Freedom from Hunger" campaign.

No. 145 Overprinted
အလုပ်သမားနေ့
၁၉၆၃

1963, May 1
175 A18 20p vermilion .15 .15

Issued for May Day.

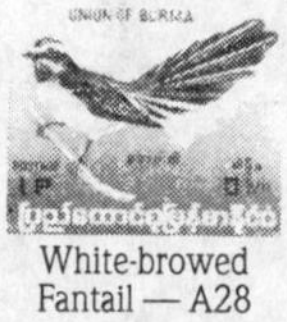

White-browed Fantail — A28

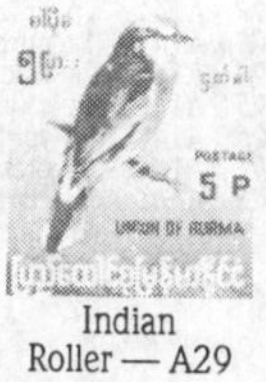

Indian Roller — A29

Birds: 20p, Red-whiskered bulbul. 25p, Crested serpent eagle. 50p, Sarus crane. 1k, Malabar pied hornbill. 2k, Lineated kalij pheasant. 5k, Green peafowl.

Unwmk.
1964, Apr. 16 **Photo.** *Perf. 13*
Size: 25x21mm
176 A28 1p gray .15 .15
177 A28 2p carmine rose .15 .15
178 A28 3p blue green .15 .15
Size: 22x26½mm
179 A29 5p violet blue .15 .15
180 A29 10p orange brn .15 .15
181 A29 15p olive .15 .15
Size: 35x25mm
182 A28 20p rose & brn .16 .15
Size: 27x36½mm, 36½x27mm
183 A29 25p yel & brown .20 .15
184 A29 50p red, blk & gray .50 .15
185 A29 1k gray, ind & yel 1.00 .15
186 A28 2k pale ol, ind & red 2.00 .32
187 A29 5k citron, dk bl & red 4.75 .65
Nos. 176-187 (12) 9.51
Set value 1.50

See Nos. 197-208. For overprints see Nos. O82, O84, O86, O88-O93, O94-O115.

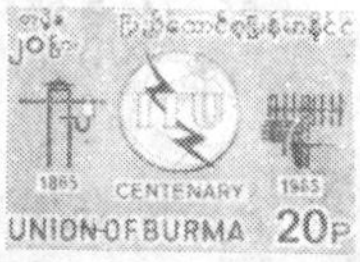

ITU Emblem, Old and New Communication Equipment — A30

1965, May 17 **Litho.** *Perf. 15*
Size: 32x22mm
188 A30 20p bright pink .15 .15
Perf. 13
Size: 34x24½mm
189 A30 50p dull green .25 .25
Set value .35 .30

Centenary of the ITU.

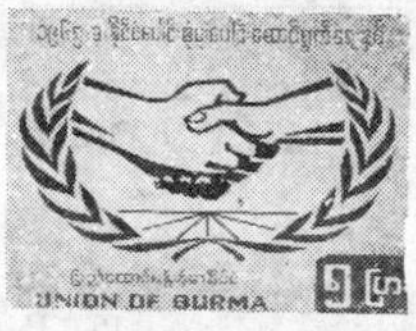

ICY Emblem A31

1965, July 1 **Unwmk.** *Perf. 13*
190 A31 5p violet blue .15 .15
191 A31 10p brown orange .15 .15
192 A31 15p olive .15 .15
Set value .20 .15

International Cooperation Year.

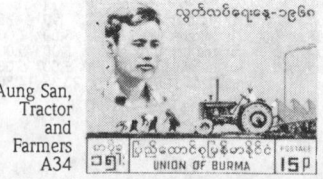

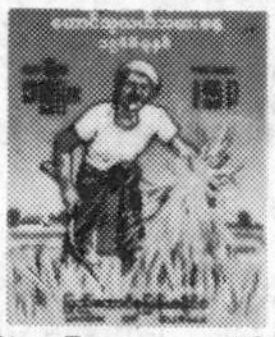
Rice Farmer — A32

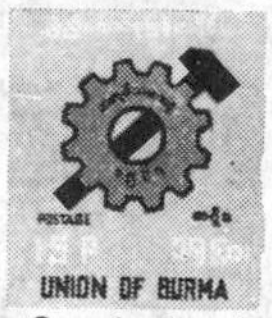

Cogwheel and Hammer — A33

1966, Mar. 2
193 A32 15p multicolored .15 .15

Issued for Farmers' Day.

1967, May 1 **Litho.** **Unwmk.**
194 A33 15p lt blue, yel & black .15 .15

Issued for Labor Day, May 1.

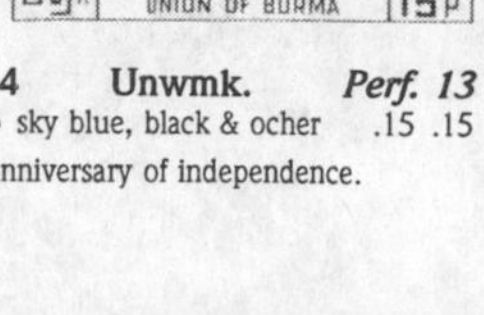

Aung San, Tractor and Farmers A34

1968, Jan. 4 **Unwmk.** *Perf. 13*
195 A34 15p sky blue, black & ocher .15 .15

20th anniversary of independence.

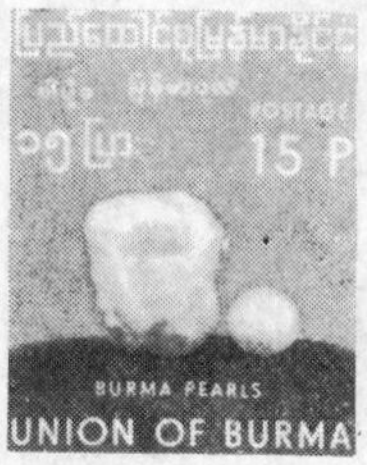

Largest Burmese Pearl — A35

1968, Mar. 4 **Litho.** *Perf. 13½x13*
196 A35 15p blue, ultra, gray & yel .15 .15

Burmese pearl industry.

Bird Types of 1964 in Changed Sizes; Designs as Before

Unwmk.
1968, July 1 **Photo.** *Perf. 14*
Size: 21x17mm
197 A28 1p gray .15 .15
198 A28 2p carmine rose .15 .15
199 A28 3p blue green .15 .15
Size: 23½x28mm
200 A29 5p violet blue .15 .15
201 A29 10p orange brown .15 .15
202 A29 15p olive .15 .15
Size: 38½x21, 21x38½mm
203 A28 20p rose & brown .15 .15
204 A29 25p yel & brown .16 .15
205 A29 50p ver, blk, & gray .32 .15
206 A29 1k gray, ind & yel .65 .15
207 A28 2k dull cit, ind & red 1.40 .24
208 A29 5k yel, dk blue & red 3.25 .55
Nos. 197-208 (12) 6.83
Set value 1.25

For overprints see Nos. O92-O102.

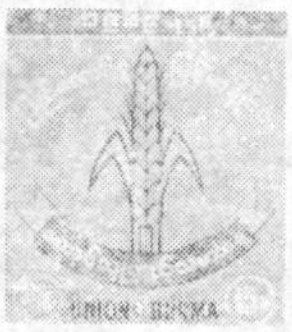
Wheat — A36

1969, Mar. 2 **Litho.** *Perf. 13*
209 A36 15p blue, emerald & yel .15 .15

Issued for Peasant's Day.

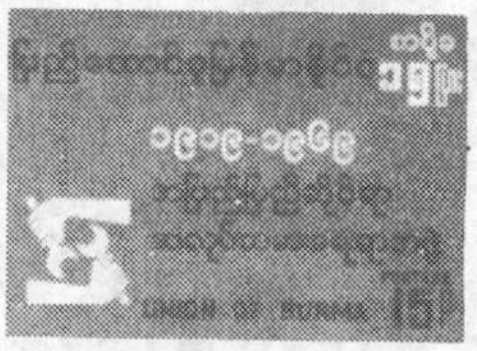

ILO Emblem A37

1969, Oct. 29 **Photo.** **Wmk. 254**
210 A37 15p dk blue grn & gold .15 .15
211 A37 50p dp carmine & gold .15 .15
Set value .20 .20

50th anniv. of the ILO.

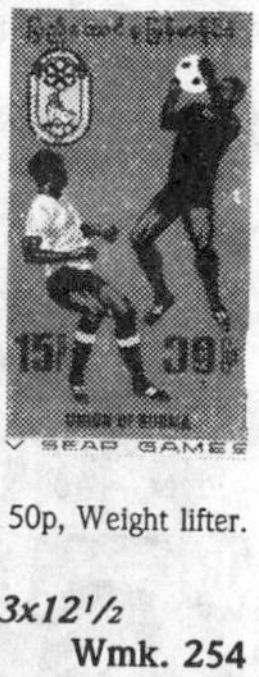
Soccer — A38

Designs: 25p, Runner, horiz. 50p, Weight lifter. 1k, Women's volleyball.

Perf. 12½x13, 13x12½
1969, Dec. 1 **Litho.** **Wmk. 254**
212 A38 15p brt olive & multi .15 .15
213 A38 25p brown & multi .15 .15
214 A38 50p brt green & multi .25 .15
215 A38 1k blue, yel grn & blk .45 .30
Nos. 212-215 (4) 1.00
Set value .60

5th South East Asia Peninsular Games, Rangoon.

Burmese Flags and Marching
Soldiers — A39

1970, Mar. 27   *Perf. 13*
216 A39 15p multicolored   .15 .15

Issued for Armed Forces Day.

Solar System
and UN
Emblem
A40

1970, June 26   Photo.   Unwmk.
217 A40 15p lt ultra & multi   .15 .15

25th anniversary of the United Nations.

Scroll,
Marchers,
Peacock
Emblem
A41

Designs: 25p, Students' boycott demonstration.
50p, Banner and marchers at Shwedagon Camp.

1970, Nov. 23   Litho.   *Perf. 13x13½*
218 A41 15p ultra & multi   .15 .15
219 A41 25p multicolored   .15 .15
220 A41 50p lt blue & multi   .24 .15
    Set value   .45 .22

For the 50th National Day (Students' 1920
uprising).

Workers, Farmers, Technicians — A42

Designs: 15p, Burmese of various races, and
flags. 25p, Hands holding document. 50p, Red
party flag.

1971, June 28   Litho.   *Perf. 13½*
221 A42 5p blue & multi   .15 .15
222 A42 15p blue & multi   .15 .15
223 A42 25p blue & multi   .15 .15
224 A42 50p blue & multi   .22 .15
a.   Souvenir sheet of 4, #221-224   .45 .45
    Set value   .45 .25

1st Congress of Burmese Socialist Program Party.

Child Drinking
Milk — A43

UNICEF, 25th Anniv.: 50p, Marionettes.

1971, Dec. 11   *Perf. 14½*
225 A43 15p lt ultra & multi   .15 .15
226 A43 50p emerald & multi   .30 .15
    Set value   .25

Aung San, Independence Monument,
Pinlon — A44

Union Day, 25th Anniv.: 50p, Bogyoke Aung San
and people in front of Independence Monument.
1k, Map of Burma with flag pointing to Pinlon, vert.

1972, Feb. 12   *Perf. 14*
227 A44 15p ocher & multi   .15 .15
228 A44 50p blue & multi   .24 .15
229 A44 1k green, ultra & red   .40 .20
    Set value   .70 .35

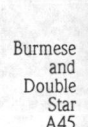 

Burmese
and
Double
Star
A45

1972   Litho.   *Perf. 14*
230 A45 15p bister & multi   .15 .15

Revolutionary Council, 10th anniversary.

"Your Heart is your
Health" — A46

1972, Apr. 7   *Perf. 14x14½*
231 A46 15p yellow, red & black   .15 .15

World Health Day.

Burmese of
Various
Ethnic
Groups
A47

1973, Feb. 12   Litho.   *Perf. 14*
232 A47 15p multicolored   .15 .15

1973 census.

Casting Vote — A48

Natl. Referendum. 10p, Voters holding map of
Burma. 15p, Farmer and soldier holding ballots,
vert.

Perf. 14x14½, 14½x14
1973, Dec. 15   Litho.
233 A48 5p deep org & black   .15 .15
234 A48 10p blue & multi   .15 .15
235 A48 15p blue & multi   .15 .15
    Set value   .15 .15

Open-air
Meeting
A49

Designs: 15p, Regional flags. 1k, Scales of justice
and Burmese emblem.

1974, Mar. 2   Photo.   *Perf. 13*
Size: 80x26mm
236 A49 15p blue & multi   .15 .15
Size: 37x25mm
237 A49 50p blue & multi   .20 .15
238 A49 1k lt blue, bis & blk   .40 .26
    Set value   .65 .45

First meeting of People's Parliament.

Messenger
Bird and UPU
Emblem
A50

UPU Cent.: 20p, Mother reading letter to child,
vert. 50p, Simulated block of stamps, vert. 1k, Burmese doll, vert. 2k, Mailman delivering letter to
family.

1974, May 22
239 A50 15p grn, lt grn & org   .15 .15
240 A50 20p multicolored   .15 .15
241 A50 50p green & multi   .22 .15
242 A50 1k ultra & multi   .48 .25
243 A50 2k blue & multi   .95 .50
    Nos. 239-243 (5)   1.95
    Set value   .95

Children   Man and Woman
A51   A52

Designs: 3p, Girl. 5p, 15p, Man and woman.
10p, Children (like 1p). 50p, Woman with fan. 1k,
Seated woman. 5k, Drummer.

Perf. 13, 13x13½ (#248-251)
1974-78   Photo.
244 A51 1p rose & lilac rose   .15 .15
245 A51 3p dk brown & pink   .15 .15
246 A51 5p pink & violet   .15 .15
246A A51 10p Prus blue ('78)   .15 .15
247 A51 15p lt green & olive   .15 .15
248 A52 20p lt blue & multi   .15 .15
249 A52 50p ocher & multi   .24 .15
250 A52 1k brt rose & multi   .48 .28
251 A52 5k ol green & multi   2.00 1.40
    Set value   3.00 2.00

For different country names see Nos. 298-303.

IWY
Emblem,
Woman and
Globe — A53

IWY: 2k, Symbolic flower, globe and IWY
emblem, vert.

1975, Dec. 15   Photo.   *Perf. 13½*
252 A53 50p green & black   .18 .15
253 A53 2k black & blue   .70 .48

Burmese with
Raised
Fists — A54

Constitution Day: 50p, Demonstrators with banners and emblem. 1k, People and map of Burma,
emblem.

1976, Jan. 3   *Perf. 14*
254 A54 20p blue & black   .15 .15
255 A54 50p blue, blk & brn   .22 .15
Size: 56x20mm
256 A54 1k blue & multi   .45 .20
    Nos. 254-256 (3)   .82
    Set value   .40

Students,   Abacus
Campaign   A56
Emblem
A55

Intl. Literacy Year: 50p, Campaign emblem. 1k,
Emblem, book and globe.

1976, Sept. 8   Photo.   *Perf. 14*
257 A55 10p salmon & black   .15 .15
258 A56 15p blue grn & multi   .15 .15
259 A56 50p ultra, org & blk   .24 .15
260 A55 1k multicolored   .60 .30
    Set value   .95 .55

Steam   Diesel Train
Locomotive — A57   Emerging from
         Tunnel — A58

Cent. of Burma's Railroad: 20p, Early train and
oxcart. 25p, Old and new trains approaching station. 50p, Railroad bridge.

1977, May 1   *Perf. 13½*
261 A57 15p multicolored   .15 .15
Size: 38x26, 26x38mm
262 A57 20p multicolored   .15 .15
263 A57 25p multicolored   .15 .15
264 A57 50p multicolored   .26 .15
265 A58 1k multicolored   .52 .25
    Set value   1.00 .60

Karaweik
Pagoda
A59

Design: 1k, Karaweik Pagoda, front view.

1977
266 A59 50p light brown   .20 .15
Size: 78x25mm
267 A59 1k multicolored   .35 .25

Jade Dragon — A60

Precious Jewelry: 20p, Gold bird with large pearl.
50p, Hand holding pearl necklace with pendant.
1k, Gold dragon, horiz.

1978   Photo.   *Perf. 13*
268 A60 15p green & yel grn   .15 .15
269 A60 20p multicolored   .15 .15
270 A60 50p multicolored   .30 .20
Size: 55x20mm
Perf. 14
271 A60 1k multicolored   .50 .30
    Set value   .95 .60

Satellite over Map of Asia — A61

1979, Feb., 12   Photo.   Perf. 13
272 A61 25p multicolored   .15 .15

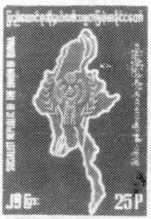

IYC Emblem in Map of Burma — A62

Weather Balloon, WMO Emblem — A63

1979, Dec.   Photo.   Perf. 13½
273 A62 25p multicolored   .16 .15
274 A62 50p multicolored   .32 .16
   International Year of the Child.

1980, Mar. 23   Photo.   Perf. 13½
275 A63 25p multicolored   .16 .15
276 A63 50p Weather satellite, cloud   .32 .16
   World Meteorological Day.

Weight Lifting, Olympic Rings A64

1980, Dec.   Litho.   Perf. 14
277 A64 20p shown   .15 .15
278 A64 50p Boxing   .20 .15
279 A64 1k Soccer   .40 .25
   Nos. 277-279 (3)   .75
     Set value   .44
22nd Summer Olympic Games, Moscow, July 19-Aug. 3.

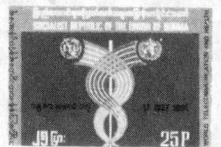

13th World Telecommunications Day — A65

1981, May 17   Photo.   Perf. 13½
280 A65 25p orange & black   .15 .15

World Food Day — A66

1981, Oct. 16   Photo.   Perf. 13½
281 A66 25p Livestock, produce   .15 .15
282 A66 50p Farmer, rice, produce   .20 .15
283 A66 1k Emblems   .40 .25
   Nos. 281-283 (3)   .75
     Set value   .46

Intl. Year of the Disabled A67

1981, Dec. 12
284 A67 25p multicolored   .15 .15

World Communications Year — A68

1983, Sept. 15   Litho.   Perf. 14½x14
285 A68 15p pale blue & black   .15 .15
286 A68 25p dull lake & black   .15 .15
287 A68 50p pale brn, blk & lake   .30 .20
288 A68 1k buff, blk, beige & yel grn   .60 .40
   Nos. 285-288 (4)   1.20
     Set value   .77

Fish, Ship, Globe, FAO Emblem — A69

1983, Oct. 16   Photo.   Perf. 14x14½
289 A69 15p brt blue, bister & blk   .15 .15
290 A69 25p yel grn, pale org & blk   .15 .15
291 A69 50p org, pale grn & blk   .30 .20
292 A69 1k yel, ultra & black   .60 .40
   Nos. 289-292 (4)   1.20
     Set value   .77
   World Food Day.

Stylized Trees, Hemispheres and Log — A70

1984, Oct. 16   Perf. 14½x14
293 A70 15p org, black & blue   .15 .15
294 A70 25p pale yel, blk & lt vio   .15 .15
295 A70 50p pale pink, blk & lt grn   .30 .20
296 A70 1k yel, blk & lt rose vio   .60 .40
   Nos. 293-296 (4)   1.20
     Set value   .77
   World Food Day.

Intl. Youth Year — A71

1985, Oct. 15   Perf. 14x14½
297 A71 15p multicolored   .15 .15

Types of 1974
Inscribed: Union of Burma

Design: 15p, Man and woman. 50p, Woman with fan. 1k, Woman seated.

1989   Photo.   Perf. 13½
298 A51 15p olive & lt green   .15 .15
299 A52 50p violet & brown   .25 .25
300 A52 1k multicolored   .52 .52
   Nos. 298-300 (3)   .92 .92
Issued: 15p, June 26; 50p, June 12; 1k, Sept. 6.

Inscribed: Union of Myanmar

1989   Photo.   Perf. 13½
301 A51 15p olive & lt green   .15 .15
302 A52 50p violet & brown   .25 .25
303 A52 1k multicolored   .52 .52
   Nos. 301-303 (3)   .92 .92
Issued: 15p, May 26; 50p, May 12.

Fountain, Natl. Assembly Park — A74

Illustration reduced.

1990, May 27   Litho.   Perf. 14½x14
304 A74 1k multicolored   .52 .52
State Law and Order Restoration Council.

A75   A76

1990, Dec. 20   Litho.   Perf. 14x14½
305 A75 2k multicolored   .82 .82
UN Development Program, 40th anniv.

1991, Jan. 26
306 A76 50p Nawata ruby   .28 .28

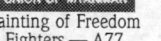

Painting of Freedom Fighters — A77

Bronze Statue — A78

1992, Jan. 4   Litho.   Perf. 14x14½
307 A77 50p multicolored   .20 .20
308 A78 2k multicolored   .80 .80

A79   A80

1992, Apr. 10   Litho.   Perf. 14x14½
309 A79 50p multicolored   .52 .52
National Sports Festival.

1992, Dec. 1   Litho.   Perf. 14x14½
310 A80 50p red   .35 .35
World Campaign Against AIDS.

A81   Artifacts — A82

1992, Dec. 5   Litho.   Perf. 14x14½
Background Color
311 A81 50p pink   .20 .20
312 A81 1k yellow   .42 .42
313 A81 3k orange   1.25 1.25
314 A81 5k green   2.05 2.05
   Nos. 311-314 (4)   3.92 3.92
Intl. Conference on Nutrition, Rome.

1993, Sept. 1   Litho.   Perf. 14½x14
315 A82 5k Bird   1.65 1.65
316 A82 10k shown   3.25 3.25

Natl. Assembly — A83

1993, Jan. 1   Litho.   Perf. 14x14½
317 A83 50p multicolored   .16 .16
318 A83 3k multicolored   1.00 1.00

Equestrian Festival A84

1993, Oct. 23   Litho.   Perf. 14½x14
319 A84 3k multicolored   1.00 1.00

A85   A86

1994, June 5   Litho.   Perf. 14
320 A85 4k multicolored   1.50 1.50
Environment day.

1994, Sept. 15   Litho.   Perf. 14
321 A86 3k multicolored   1.25 1.25
Union of Solidarity & Development, 1st anniv.

Armed Forces, 50th Anniv. A87

1995, Mar. 27   Litho.   Perf. 14½x14
322 A87 50p multicolored   .22 .22

Prevent Drug Abuse — A88

1995   Litho.   Perf. 14
323 A88 2k multicolored   .80 .80

OFFICIAL STAMPS

BURMA

Stamps of India, 1926-34, Overprinted in Black

SERVICE

1937 Wmk. 196 *Perf. 14*

O1	A46	3p gray	.25	.15
O2	A71	½a green	.50	.15
O3	A68	9p dark green	.50	.20
O4	A72	1a dark brown	.40	.15
O5	A49	2a vermilion	.50	.25
O6	A57	2a6p buff	.75	.40
O7	A52	4a olive grn	.75	.40
O8	A53	6a bister	1.50	1.75
O9	A54	8a red violet	.90	.45
O10	A55	12a claret	.75	.80

BURMA

Overprinted

SERVICE

O11	A56	1r green & brown	5.00	1.50
O12	A56	2r buff & car rose	10.00	8.00
O13	A56	5r dk vio & ultra	30.00	15.00
O14	A56	10r car & green	90.00	*40.00*
		Nos. O1-O14 (14)	141.80	*69.20*

For overprint see No. 1N27.

Regular Issue of 1938 Overprinted in Black **SERVICE**

Perf. 13½x14, 13, 13½

1939 Wmk. 254

O15	A1	3p violet	.15	.15
O16	A1	6p ultramarine	.15	.15
O17	A1	9p yel green	.15	.15
O18	A2	1a brown violet	.15	.15
O19	A2	1½a turquoise green	.15	.15
O20	A2	2a carmine	.15	.15
O21	A2	4a slate blue	1.25	.30

Overprinted **SERVICE**

O22	A3	2a6p rose lake	3.50	1.00
O23	A6	8a slate green	5.50	1.25
O24	A7	1r brt ultra & dk vio	10.00	1.25
O25	A7	2r dk vio & red brn	12.50	2.00
O26	A8	5r car & dull vio	27.50	12.50
O27	A8	10r gray grn & brn	50.00	17.00
		Nos. O15-O27 (13)	111.15	36.20

For overprints see Nos. 1N12-1N16, 1N31-1N36, 1NO1.

Catalogue values for unused stamps in this section, from this point to the end of the section, are for Never Hinged items.

Nos. 51-56, 60 Overprinted Like Nos. O15-O21

1946 *Perf. 13½x14*

O28	A1	3p brown	.15	.15
O29	A1	6p violet	.15	.15
O30	A1	9p dull green	.15	.15
O31	A2	1a deep blue	.15	.15
O32	A2	1½a salmon	.15	.15
O33	A2	2a rose lake	.15	.15
O34	A2	4a rose lilac	.15	.15

Nos. 57, 61-65 Ovptd. Like Nos. O22-O27

Perf. 13, 13½

O35	A3	2a6p greenish blue	.15	.15
O38	A6	8a deep magenta	.15	*1.00*
O39	A7	1r dp mag & dk vio	.50	*1.50*
O40	A7	2r salmon & red brn	4.00	*12.50*
O41	A8	5r red brn & dk grn	7.50	*15.00*
O42	A8	10r dk violet & car	12.50	*22.50*
		Nos. O28-O42 (13)	25.85	*53.70*

Nos. O28 to O42 Overprinted in Black ကြားဖြတ် အစိုးရ။

1947

O43	A1	3p brown	.15	.15
O44	A1	6p violet	.15	.15
O45	A1	9p dull green	.15	.15
O46	A2	1a deep blue	.15	.15
O47	A2	1½a salmon	.15	.15
O48	A2	2a rose lake	.15	.15
O49	A3	2a6p greenish bl	.15	.15
O50	A2	4a rose lilac	2.00	.75
O51	A6	8a dp magenta	2.25	1.50
O52	A7	1r dp mag & dk vio	4.50	1.50
O53	A7	2r sal & red brn	*7.50*	*5.00*
O54	A8	5r red brn & dk grn	*10.00*	*12.50*
O55	A8	10r dk vio & car	*12.50*	*15.00*
		Nos. O43-O55 (13)	*39.80*	*37.30*

The overprint is slightly larger on Nos. O49 and O51 to O55. The Burmese characters read "Interim Government."

Issues of the Republic

Nos. 102 to 106 and 109 to 115 Overprinted in Carmine or Black အစိုးရကိစ္စ

a. Overprint 13mm long.
b. Overprint 15mm long.

1949 Unwmk. *Perf. 12½, 13*

O56	A15(a)	3p ultra (C)	.15	.15
O57	A15(a)	6p green (C)	.15	.15
O58	A15(a)	9p carmine	.15	.15
O59	A16(a)	1a red orange	.15	.15
O60	A17(a)	2a orange	.15	.15
O61	A18(b)	3a6p dk sl grn (C)	.15	.15
O62	A16(a)	4a chocolate	.15	.15
O63	A18(b)	8a carmine	.16	.15
O64	A19(b)	1r blue green (C)	.32	.24
O65	A19(b)	2r dp blue (C)	.65	.40
O66	A19(b)	5r chocolate	1.65	1.25
O67	A19(b)	10r orange red	3.25	2.50
		Nos. O56-O67 (12)	7.08	
		Set value		4.85

Same Overprint in Black on Nos. 139-142, 144-152

Perf. 14x13½, 13, 14

1954-57 Wmk. 254

O68	A15(a)	1p brown org	.15	.15
O69	A15(a)	2p plum	.15	.15
O70	A15(a)	3p blue	.15	.15
O71	A16(a)	5p ultra	.15	.15
O72	A17(a)	15p green	.15	.15
O72A	A18(b)	20p vel ('57)	.15	.15
O73	A18(b)	25p lt red org	.15	.15
O74	A16(a)	30p vermilion	.15	.15
O75	A18(b)	50p blue	.20	.15
O76	A19(b)	1k rose violet	.40	.15
O77	A19(b)	2k green	.85	.20
O78	A19(b)	5k ultra	1.65	.32
O79	A19(b)	10k light blue	3.25	.45
		Nos. O68-O79 (13)	7.55	
		Set value		1.50

No. 141 Ovptd. Service

1964 Litho. *Perf. 14*

O80	A15	3p blue		

Nos. 139, 141-142, 144, 177-179, 181, 183 Ovptd. အစိုးရကိစ္စ

1964-65

Overprint: 11½mm

O81	A15	1p brown orange		
O82	A28	2p carmine rose ('65)		
O83	A15	3p blue		
O84	A28	3p blue green ('65)		
O85	A16	5p ultramarine		
O86	A28	5p violet blue ('65)		
O87	A17	15p green		
O88	A28	15p olive ('65)		
O89	A29	25p yellow & brown ('65)		

အစိုးရကိစ္စ #176-178 Ovptd. — အစိုးရကိစ္စ #181 Ovptd.

1966

Overprint: 15mm

O90	A28	1p black		
O91	A28	2p carmine rose		
O92	A28	3p blue green		

Overprint: 12mm

O93	A28	15p olive		

Nos. 176-179, 181-187 Overprinted in Black or Red အစိုးရကိစ္စ

1967 Unwmk. Photo. *Perf. 13*

Overprint: 15mm

Size: 25x21mm

O94	A28	1p gray	.15	.15
O95	A28	2p carmine rose	.15	.15
O96	A28	3p blue green	.15	.15

Size: 22x26½mm

O97	A29	5p violet blue	.15	.15
O98	A29	15p olive	.15	.15

Size: 35x25mm

O99	A28	20p rose & brown	.15	.15

Size: 27x36½mm, 36½x27mm

O100	A29	25p yel & brown (R)	.15	.15
O101	A29	50p red, blk & gray	.26	.15
O102	A29	1k gray, ind & yel (R)	.52	.15
O103	A28	2k pale ol, ind & red (R)	1.10	.30
O104	A29	5k cit, dk bl & red (R)	2.75	.65
		Nos. O94-O104 (11)	5.68	
		Set value		1.50

Similar Overprint on Nos. 197-200, 202-208 in Black or Red

1968 Unwmk. *Perf. 14*

Size: 21x17mm

Overprint: 13mm

O105	A28	1p gray	.15	.15
O106	A28	2p carmine rose	.15	.15
O107	A28	3p blue green	.15	.15

Size: 23½x28mm

Overprint: 15mm

O108	A29	5p violet blue	.15	.15
O109	A29	15p olive	.15	.15

Size: 38½x21mm, 21x38½mm

Overprint: 14mm

O110	A28	20p rose & brn	.15	.15
O111	A29	25p yel & brown (R)	.15	.15
O112	A29	50p ver, blk & gray	.26	.15
O113	A29	1k gray, ind & yel (R)	.52	.15
O114	A28	2k dl cit, ind & red (R)	1.10	.24
O115	A29	5k yel, dk bl & red (R)	2.75	.55
		Nos. O105-O115 (11)	5.68	
		Set value		1.25

OCCUPATION STAMPS

Issued by Burma Independence Army (in conjunction with Japanese occupation officials)

Stamps of Burma, 1937-40, Overprinted in Blue, Black Blue, Black or Red

Henzada Issue

Nos. 1, 3 and 5 Overprinted in Blue or Black

Henzada Type I

1942, May Wmk. 196 *Perf. 14*

1N1	A46	3p slate	5.00	*7.50*
1N2	A68	9p dark green	17.50	*25.00*
1N3	A49	2a vermilion	50.00	*75.00*

On 1938-40 George VI Issue

Perf. 13½x14

Wmk. 254

1N4	A1	1p red org	75.00	*87.50*
1N5	A1	3p violet	17.50	*35.00*
1N6	A1	6p ultra	15.00	*30.00*
1N7	A1	9p yel green	200.00	
1N8	A2	1a brown vio	5.00	*7.50*
1N9	A2	1½a turq green	12.50	*17.50*
1N10	A2	2a carmine	15.00	*17.50*
1N11	A2	4a slate blue	30.00	*37.50*

On Official Stamps of 1939

1N12	A1	3p violet	50.00	*62.50*
1N13	A1	6p ultra	45.00	*62.50*
1N14	A2	1½a turq green	65.00	*87.50*
1N15	A2	2a carmine	150.00	150.00
1N16	A2	4a slate blue	200.00	250.00

Authorities believe this overprint was officially applied only to postal stationery and that the adhesive stamps existing with it were not regularly issued. It has been called "Henzada Type II."

Myaungmya Issue

1937 George V Issue Overprinted in Black

Myaungmya Type I

1942, May Wmk. 196 *Perf. 14*

1N25	A68	9p dk green	50.00	62.50
1N26	A70	3a6p deep blue	25.00	32.50

On Official Stamp of 1937, No. O8

1N27	A53	6a bister	50.00	62.50

On 1938-40 George VI Issue

Perf. 13½x14

Wmk. 254

1N28	A1	9p yel green	100.00	125.00
1N29	A2	1a brown vio	175.00	225.00
1N30	A2	4a sl blue (blk ovpt. over red)	100.00	125.00

On Official Stamps of 1939

1N31	A1	3p violet	15.00	15.00
1N32	A1	6p ultra	7.50	10.00
1N33	A2	1a brown vio	7.50	10.00
1N34	A2	1½a turq green	400.00	
1N35	A2	2a carmine	15.00	20.00
1N36	A2	4a slate blue	12.50	17.50

1938-40 George VI Issue Overprinted

Myaungmya Type II

1942, May

1N37	A1	3p violet	12.50	*20.00*
1N38	A1	6p ultra	25.00	*30.00*
1N39	A1	9p yel green	10.00	*15.00*
1N40	A2	1a brown vio	10.00	12.50
1N41	A2	2a carmine	15.00	20.00
1N42	A2	4a slate blue	15.00	*25.00*

Nos. 30-31 Overprinted

Myaungmya Type III

1N43	A7	1r brt ultra & dk vio	150.00	
1N44	A7	2r dk vio & red brn	110.00	

Pyapon Issue

No. 5 and 1938-40 George VI Issue Overprinted

1942, May

1N45	A1	6p ultra	75.00	
1N46	A2	1a brown vio	65.00	50.00
1N47	A49	2a vermilion	75.00	
1N48	A2	2a carmine	45.00	62.50
1N49	A2	4a slate blue	150.00	*200.00*
		Nos. 1N45-1N49 (5)	410.00	

Counterfeits of the peacock overprints exist.

The Scott Catalogue value is a retail value; that is, what you could expect to pay for the stamp in a grade of Very Fine. The value listed reflects recent actual dealer selling prices.

OCCUPATION OFFICIAL STAMP

Myaungmya Issue
Burma No. O23 Overprinted in Black

1942, May　　Wmk. 254　　Perf. 13

1NO1　A6　8a slate green　　50.00　62.50

Overprint characters translate: "Office use." Two types of overprint differ mainly in base of peacock which is either 5mm or 8mm.

ISSUED UNDER JAPANESE OCCUPATION

Yano Seal — OS1

Wmk. ABSORBO DUPLICATOR and Outline of Elephant in Center of Sheet
Handstamped

1942, June 1　　　　　Perf. 12x11
Without Gum

2N1　OS1　1(a) vermilion　　30.00　37.50

This stamp is the handstamped impression of the personal chop or seal of Shizuo Yano, chairman of the committee appointed to re-establish the Burmese postal system. It was prepared in Rangoon on paper captured from the Burma Government Offices. Not every stamp shows a portion of the watermark.

Farmer Plowing — OS2

Vertically Laid Paper
Without Gum
Wmk. ELEPHANT BRAND and Outline of Trumpeting Elephant Covering Several Stamps

1942, June 15　　Litho.　　Perf. 11x12

2N2　OS2　1a scarlet　　20.00　25.00

See illustration OS4.

Same, Surcharged with New Value
1942, Oct. 15

2N3　OS2　5c on 1a scarlet　　12.50　10.50

Rice Harvest — A83

Power Plant — A85

General Nogi — A84

Admiral Togo — A86

Diamond Mountains, Korea — A89

Meiji Shrine, Tokyo — A90

Yomei Gate, Nikko — A91

Mount Fuji and Cherry Blossoms — A94

Torii of Miyajima Shrine — A96

Stamps of Japan, 1937-42, Handstamp Surcharged with New Value in Black

1942, Sept.　　Wmk. 257　　Perf. 13

2N4	A83	¼a on 1s fawn	12.50	15.00
2N5	A84	½a on 2s crim	12.50	15.00
2N6	A85	¾a on 3s green	20.00	20.00
2N7	A86	1a on 5s brn lake	17.50	20.00
2N8	A89	3a on 7s dp green	30.00	32.50
2N9	A86	4a on 4s dk green	22.50	27.50
a.		4a on 4s + 2s dk green (#B5)	75.00	87.50
2N10	A90	8a on 8s dk pur & pale vio	100.00	100.00
a.		Red surcharge	140.00	150.00
2N11	A91	1r on 10s lake	12.50	15.00
2N12	A94	2r on 20s ultra	30.00	35.00
a.		Red surcharge	37.50	37.50
2N13	A96	5r on 30s pck bl	10.00	10.00
a.		Red surcharge	15.00	15.00
		Nos. 2N4-2N13 (10)	267.50	290.00

Numerous double, inverted, etc., surcharges exist.

Re-surcharged in Black
1942, Oct. 15

2N14	A83	1c on ¼a on 1s	25.00	25.00
2N15	A84	2c on ½a on 2s	25.00	25.00
2N16	A85	3c on ¾a on 3s	30.00	32.50
a.		"3C." in blue	75.00	100.00
2N17	A86	5c on 1a on 5s	40.00	40.00
a.		"3C." in blue	125.00	
2N18	A89	10c on 3a on 7s	45.00	45.00
2N19	A86	15c on 4a on 4s	10.50	10.50
2N20	A90	20c on 8a on 8s (#2N10)	110.00	90.00
a.		On #2N10a	125.00	100.00
		Nos. 2N14-2N20 (7)	285.50	268.00

No. 2N16a was issued in the Shan States. Done locally, numerous different handstamps of each denomination can exist.

Stamps of Japan, 1937-42, Handstamp Surcharged with New Value in Black
1942, Oct. 15

2N21	A83	1c on 1s fawn	10.00	12.50
2N22	A84	2c on 2s crim	17.50	20.00
2N23	A85	3c on 3s green	20.00	25.00
a.		"3C." in blue	75.00	87.50
2N24	A86	5c on 5s brn lake	20.00	25.00
a.		"5C." in violet	87.50	100.00
2N25	A89	10c on 7s dp grn	25.00	30.00
2N26	A86	15c on 4s dk grn	10.00	12.50
2N27	A90	20c on 8s dk pur & pale vio	70.00	60.00
		Nos. 2N21-2N27 (7)	172.50	185.00

Nos. 2N23a and 2N24a were issued in the Shan States.

Burma State Government Crest — OS3

Unwmk.
1943, Feb. 15　　Litho.　　Perf. 12
Without Gum

2N29	OS3	5c carmine	10.00	12.50
a.		Imperf.	12.50	15.00

This stamp was intended to be used to cover the embossed George VI envelope stamp and generally was sold affixed to such envelopes. It is also known used on private envelopes.

Farmer Plowing — OS4

1943, Mar.　　　　　　Typo.
Without Gum

2N30	OS4	1c deep orange	1.00	1.00
2N31	OS4	2c yel green	1.00	1.50
2N32	OS4	3c blue	1.00	1.00
a.		Laid paper	10.00	10.00
2N33	OS4	5c carmine	.50	.65
a.		Small "5c"	3.00	4.00
b.		Imperf.		
2N34	OS4	10c violet brown	.75	.90
2N35	OS4	15c red violet	.25	.25
a.		Laid paper	10.00	
2N36	OS4	20c dull purple	.25	.75
2N37	OS4	30c blue green	.25	.75
		Nos. 2N30-2N37 (8)	5.00	6.80

Small "c" in Nos. 2N34 to 2N37.

Burmese Soldier Carving "Independence" OS5

Farmer Rejoicing OS6

Boy with Burmese Flag — OS7

Hyphen-hole Perf., Pin-Perf. x Hyphen-hole Perf.

1943, Aug. 1　　　　　Typo.

2N38	OS5	1c orange	1.00	2.00
a.		Perf. 11	3.50	4.00
2N39	OS6	3c blue	1.00	2.00
a.		Perf. 11	3.50	4.00
2N40	OS7	5c rose	1.00	2.00
a.		Perf. 11	3.50	4.00
		Nos. 2N38-2N40 (3)	3.00	6.00

Declaration of the independence of Burma by the Ba Maw government, Aug. 1, 1943.

Burmese Girl Carrying Water Jar — OS8

Elephant Carrying Teak Log — OS9

Watch Tower of Mandalay Palace — OS10

1943, Oct. 1　　Litho.　　Perf. 12½

2N41	OS8	1c dp salmon	3.00	4.50
2N42	OS8	2c yel green	.15	.50
2N43	OS8	3c violet	.15	.38
2N44	OS9	5c rose	.20	.38
2N45	OS9	10c blue	.25	.25
2N46	OS9	15c vermilion	.15	.38
2N47	OS9	20c yel green	.20	.50
2N48	OS9	30c brown	.25	.50
2N49	OS10	1r vermilion	.25	1.25
2N50	OS10	2r violet	.30	2.00
		Nos. 2N41-2N50 (10)	4.90	10.64

No. 2N49 exists imperforate. Canceled to order copies of Nos. 2N42-2N50 same values as unused.

Bullock Cart — OS11

Shan Woman — OS12

1943, Oct. 1　　　　　Perf. 12½

2N51	OS11	1c brown	22.50	35.00
2N52	OS11	2c yel green	22.50	35.00
2N53	OS11	3c violet	20.00	30.00
2N54	OS11	5c ultra	4.50	12.00
2N55	OS12	10c blue	20.00	35.00
2N56	OS12	20c rose	22.50	35.00
2N57	OS12	30c brown	22.50	35.00
		Nos. 2N51-2N57 (7)	134.50	217.00

For use only in the Shan States. Perak No. N34 also used in Shan States. CTO's ½ used value.

ဗမာနိုင်ငံတော်

Surcharged in Black

၁ ဆင့်။

1944, Nov. 1

2N58	OS11	1c brown	1.75	2.00
2N59	OS11	2c yel green	.15	.50
a.		Inverted surcharge	150.00	200.00
2N60	OS11	3c violet	1.00	1.75
2N61	OS11	5c ultra	.50	.65
2N62	OS12	10c blue	1.00	1.50
2N63	OS12	20c rose	.25	.65
2N64	OS12	30c brown	.30	.65
		Nos. 2N58-2N64 (7)	4.95	7.70

Top line of surcharge reads: "Bama naing ngan daw" (Burma State). Bottom line repeats denomination in Burmese. Surcharge applied when the Shan States came under Burmese government administration, Dec. 24, 1943. CTO's same value as unused.

BUSHIRE

bü-'shir

LOCATION — On Persian Gulf

Bushire is a Persian port which British troops occupied Aug. 8, 1915.

20 Chahis (or Shahis) = 1 Kran
10 Krans = 1 Toman

Watermark

Wmk. 161 - Lion

ISSUED UNDER BRITISH OCCUPATION

Basic Iranian Designs

Shah Ahmed — A32

Imperial Crown — A33

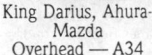

King Darius, Ahura-
Mazda
Overhead — A34

Ruins of
Persepolis — A35

BUSHIRE

Iranian Stamps of
1911-13 Overprinted in
Black

**Under British
Occupation.**

Perf. 11½, 11½x11
Typo. & Engr.

			Unwmk.	
1915, Aug. 15				
N1	A32	1c green & org	27.50	27.50
N2	A32	2c red & sepia	27.50	27.50
N3	A32	3c gray brn & grn	30.00	27.50
N4	A32	5c brown & car	250.00	250.00
N5	A32	6c green & red brn	22.50	22.50
N6	A32	9c yel brn & vio	25.00	27.50
a.		Double overprint		
N7	A32	10c red & org brn	25.00	25.00
N8	A32	12c grn & ultra	30.00	30.00
N9	A32	1k ultra & car	40.00	25.00
a.		Double overprint	5,250.	
N10	A32	24c vio & grn	42.50	30.00
N11	A32	2k grn & red vio	175.00	125.00
N12	A32	3k vio & blk	150.00	165.00
N13	A32	5k red & ultra	65.00	70.00
N14	A32	10k ol bis & cl	75.00	75.00
		Nos. N1-N14 (14)	985.00	927.50

Nos. N1-N14, except No. N4, exist without period after "Occupation." This variety sells for more.

Forged overprints exist of Nos. N1-N29.
The Bushire overprint exists on Iran No. 537 but is considered a forgery.

On Iranian Stamps of 1915
Perf. 11, 11½

			Wmk. 161	
1915, Sept.				
N15	A33	1c car & indigo	350.	350.
N16	A33	2c blue & car	4,750.	6,000.
N17	A33	3c dk grn	350.	400.
N18	A33	5c red	4,000.	4,250.
N19	A33	6c ol grn & car	3,000.	3,500.
N20	A33	9c yel brn & vio	500.	525.
N21	A33	10c bl grn & yel brn	800.	900.
N22	A33	12c ultra	950.	1,250.
N23	A34	1k sil, yel brn & gray	350.	375.
N24	A33	24c yel brn & dk brn	450.	400.
N25	A34	2k sil, bl & rose	300.	350.
N26	A34	3k sil, vio & brn	400.	425.
N27	A34	5k sil, vio & brn	450.	450.
a.		Inverted overprint		
N28	A35	1t gold, pur & blk	325.	375.
N29	A35	3t gold, cl & red brn	2,500.	2,750.

Persia resumed administration of Bushire post office Oct. 16, 1915.

CAMEROONS

ˌka-mə-ˈrün

LOCATION — West coast of Africa, north of equator
GOVT. — Former British Mandate
AREA — 34,081 sq. mi.
POP. — 868,637 (estimated)
CAPITAL — Buea

Prior to World War I, Cameroons (Kamerun) was a German Protectorate. It was occupied during the War by Great Britain and France and in 1922 was mandated to these countries by the League of Nations. Stamps of Nigeria were used in the British part until 1960. The northern section of the British Cameroons became part of the independent state of Nigeria in 1960, and the southern section became a United Kingdom Trust Territory. After a referendum, this U.K.T.T. joined the independent State of Cameroun to form the Federal Republic of Cameroun, Oct. 1, 1961.

Stamps of the German Protectorate, the French Mandate, the independent state and the Cameroun Federal Republic are listed in Volume 2.

Catalogue values for unused stamps in this country are for Never Hinged items, beginning with Scott 66.

Watermark

Wmk. 125-
Lozenges

Issued under British Occupation

Kaiser's Yacht "Hohenzollern"
A3   A4

C. E. F.

Stamps of German
Cameroun Surcharged

½ d.

**Wmk. 125 (5, 10, 20pf and 5m);
Unwmk. (Other Values)**
1915   *Perf. 14, 14½*
Blue Surcharge

53	A3	½ on 3pf brown	6.00	11.00
54	A3	½ on 5pf green	2.50	5.00
a.		Double surcharge	400.00	300.00
b.		Black surcharge	12.50	10.00
55	A3	1p on 10pf car	2.50	5.00
a.		"1" with thin serifs	10.50	13.00
b.		Double surcharge	175.00	175.00
c.		Black surcharge	22.50	30.00
d.		As "c," "1" with thin serifs	60.00	70.00

Black Surcharge

56	A3	2p on 20pf ultra	2.75	10.00
57	A3	2½p on 25pf org & blk, yel	12.00	21.00
a.		Double surcharge	3,500.	
58	A3	3p on 30pf org & blk, sal	9.00	21.00
59	A3	4p on 40pf lake & blk	9.00	21.00
60	A3	6p on 50pf pur & blk, sal	9.00	21.00
61	A3	8p on 80pf lake & blk, rose	9.00	21.00

C. E. F.

Surcharged

1 s.

Perf. 14½x14

62	A4	1sh on 1m car	140.00	275.00
a.		"S" inverted	650.00	1,000.
63	A4	2sh on 2m blue	140.00	275.00
a.		"S" inverted	650.00	1,000.
64	A4	3sh on 3m blk vio	140.00	275.00
a.		"S" inverted	650.00	1,000.
b.		Double surcharge	4,000.	
65	A4	5sh on 5m sl & car	150.00	275.00
a.		"S" inverted	650.00	1,000.
		Nos. 53-65 (13)	631.75	1,236.

The letters "C. E. F." are the initials of "Cameroons Expeditionary Force."

Catalogue values for unused stamps in this section, from this point to the end of the section, are for Never Hinged items.

United Kingdom Trust Territory

Stamps and Type of
Nigeria, 1953,
Overprinted in Red

**CAMEROONS
U.K.T.T,**

Perf. 13½, 14

			Wmk. 4	Engr.
1960, Oct. 1				
		Size: 35½x22½mm		
66	A17	½p red org & black	.15	.15
67	A17	1p ol gray & black	.15	.15
68	A17	1½p blue green	.15	.15
69	A17	2p gray (II)	.15	.15
70	A17	3p purple & black	.15	.15
71	A17	4p ultra & black	.15	.15
72	A17	6p blk & org brn, perf. 14	.20	.20
a.		Perf. 13x13½ ('61)	.20	.20
73	A17	1sh brown vio & blk	.30	.30
		Size: 40½x24½mm		
74	A17	2sh6p green & black	.75	.75
75	A17	5sh ver & black	1.50	1.50
76	A17	10sh red brn & blk	3.00	3.00
		Size: 42x31½mm		
77	A17	£1 violet & black	5.75	5.75
		Nos. 66-77 (12)	12.40	12.40

Nos. 66-77 were withdrawn in Northern Cameroons on May 31, 1961, when that territory joined Nigeria and in Southern Cameroons Sept. 30, 1961, when that territory joined the Cameroun Federal Republic.

CAPE OF GOOD HOPE

ˈkāp əv ˈgu̇d ˈhōp

LOCATION — In the extreme southern part of South Africa
GOVT. — Former British Colony
AREA — 276,995 sq mi. (1911)
POP. — 2,564,965 (1911)
CAPITAL — Cape Town

Cape of Good Hope joined with Natal, the Transvaal and the Orange River Colony in 1910, forming the Union of South Africa.

12 Pence = 1 Shilling

Watermarks

Wmk. 15-
Anchor

Wmk. 16- Anchor

"Hope"
Seated
A1

Printed by Perkins, Bacon & Co.
Wmk. 15

			Engr.	*Imperf.*
1853, Sept. 1				
		Bluish Paper		
1	A1	1p brick red	2,750.	200.
a.		Deeply blued paper	3,500.	275.
2	A1	4p blue	1,250.	100.
a.		Deeply blued paper	2,250.	175.

Counterfeits exist.

1855-58

		White Paper		
3	A1	1p rose ('57)	425.	200.
a.		1p dull red	550.	
4	A1	4p blue	275.	45.
5	A1	6p pale lilac ('58)	700.	200.
a.		6p rose lilac	1,700.	300.
b.		6p grayish lilac on bluish paper	4,250.	
c.		6p slate purple on bluish paper	3,750.	1,000.
d.		Half used as 3p on cover		
6	A1	1sh yellow grn ('58)	2,500.	175.
a.		1sh dark green	225.	475.
b.		Half used as 6p on cover		

Nos. 3-6 are known rouletted unofficially. Counterfeits exist.

No. 4 was reproduced by the collotype process in an unwatermarked souvenir sheet distributed at the London Intl. Stamp Exhib. 1950.

A2

Printed by Saul Solomon & Co.

1861		**Laid Paper**	Unwmk.	**Typo.**
7	A2	1p vermilion	13,500.	2,000.
a.		1p carmine	22,500.	3,000.
b.		1p red	30,000.	4,500.
c.		1p milky blue (error)		27,500.
d.		1p pale blue (error)		30,000.
9	A2	4p milky blue	10,000.	1,750.
a.		4p pale blue	10,000.	2,000.
b.		4p blue	12,500.	2,800.
c.		4p dark blue	80,000.	4,500.
d.		Right corner retouched		6,000.
e.		4p vermilion (error)	125,000.	65,000.
g.		4p carmine (error)		80,000.

Nos. 7 and 9 are usually called Wood Blocks. The plates were made locally and composed of clichés mounted on wood. The errors were caused by a cliché of each value being mounted in the plate of the other value.

In 1883 plate proofs of both values on white paper, usually called "reprints," were made. The 1p is in dull orange red; the 4p in dark blue. These are known canceled, as a few were misused as stamps. The proofs do not include the errors.
Counterfeits exist.

Printed by De La Rue & Co.

			Wmk. 15	Engr.
1863-64				
12	A1	1p brown red	325.00	225.00
a.		1p dark carmine	100.00	225.00
13	A1	4p dark blue	110.00	42.50
a.		4p slate blue	2,250.	475.00
14	A1	6p purple	165.00	375.00
15	A1	1sh emerald	325.00	425.00
a.		1sh pale emerald	1,000.	

Nos. 12-15 can be distinguished from Nos. 3-6 not only by colors but because Nos. 12-15 often appear in a granular ink or with the background lightly printed in whole or part.

No. 12a, Wmk. 1, is believed to be a proof.
Counterfeits exist.

"Hope" and Symbols of Colony

A3   A6

Frame Line Around Stamp

1864-65		Typo.	Wmk. 1	Perf. 14	
16	A3	1p rose ('65)		70.00	11.00
17	A3	4p blue ('65)		90.00	1.75
a.		4p pale blue		90.00	1.90
b.		4p dull ultramarine		225.00	45.00
18	A3	6p bright violet		90.00	1.75
a.		6p dull violet		150.00	8.00
19	A3	1sh yellow green		90.00	1.75
a.		1sh blue green		90.00	2.50
		Nos. 16-19 (4)		340.00	16.25

Imperf. stamps are believed to be proofs.
For surcharges, see Nos. 20-21, N3.
For types A3 and A6 with manuscript surcharge of 1d or overprints "G. W." or "G," see Griqualand West listings.

Stamps of 1864 Surcharged in Red or Black:

Four Pence.   ONE PENNY.

a   b

1868-74			Red Surcharge	
20	A3(a)	4p on 6p	125.00	10.00
a.		"Peuce" for "Pence"	1,800.	900.00
b.		"Fonr" for "Four"		750.00
21	A3(b)	1p on 6p ('74)	275.00	50.00
a.		"E" of PENNY omitted		675.00

Space between words and bars varies from 12½-16mm on #20, and 16½-18mm on #21.

1876			Black Surcharge	
22	A3 (b)	1p on 1sh green	32.50	22.50

Without Frame Line Around Stamp

1871-81			Perf. 14	
23	A6	½p gray black ('75)	5.00	4.00
24	A6	1p rose ('72)	20.00	.50
25	A6	3p lilac rose ('80)	150.00	13.00
26	A6	3p claret ('81)	75.00	2.25
27	A6	4p blue ('76)	75.00	.65
a.		4p ultramarine	190.00	37.50
28	A6	5sh orange	175.00	8.25
		Nos. 23-28 (6)	500.00	28.65

For surcharges see Nos. 29-32, 39, 55.

THREE PENCE

No. 27 Surcharged in Red

1879				
29	A6	3p on 4p blue	70.00	2.50
a.		"THE.EE"	1,800.	425.00
b.		"PENCB"	1,700.	275.00
c.		Double surcharge	8,000.	3,000.
d.		As "a," double surcharge		

Type of 1871 Surcharged in Black   THREEPENCE

1880				
30	A6	3p on 4p lilac rose		37.50	1.65

No. 25 Surcharged in Black

3   3

e   f

31	A6(e)	3p on 3p lilac rose	95.00	4.00
a.		Inverted surcharge	7,500.	1,000.
32	A6(f)	3p on 3p lilac rose	32.50	1.10
a.		Inverted surcharge	750.00	37.50

1882-83			Wmk. 2	
33	A6	½p gray black	4.00	.50
34	A6	1p rose	20.00	.25
35	A6	2p bister	47.50	.25
36	A6	3p claret	5.00	.75
37	A3	6p bright violet	48.00	.90
38	A6	5sh orange ('83)	775.00	200.00

For overprint see Rhodesia No. 49.

Nos. 26 and 36 Surcharged in Black

One Half-penny.

1882			Wmk. 1	
39	A6	½p on 3p claret	1,750.	145.00
a.		Hyphen omitted		3,500.

		Wmk. 2		
40	A6	½p on 3p claret	5.50	2.50
a.		"ENN"	2,000.	900.00
b.		"PENN"	1,000.	700.00
c.		Hyphen omitted	475.00	350.00

1884-98			Wmk. 16	
41	A6	½p gray black ('86)	.80	.15
42	A6	½p green ('96)	.95	.15
43	A6	1p rose ('85)	.80	.15
44	A6	2p bister	2.00	.15
45	A6	2p choc brown ('97)	1.65	1.50
46	A6	3p red violet ('98)	1.65	.40
47	A6	4p blue ('90)	2.75	.15
48	A6	4p pale ol grn ('97)	2.50	.60
49	A3	6p violet	1.95	.20
50	A6	1sh green ('85)	60.00	3.50
51	A6	1sh blue grn ('94)	22.50	1.00
52	A6	1sh yel buff ('96)	5.50	.60
53	A6	5sh orange ('87)	40.00	2.75
54	A6	5sh brown org ('96)	40.00	3.50
		Nos. 41-54 (14)	183.05	14.80

For surcharges see Nos. 58, 162, 165-166. For overprints see Rhodesia Nos. 43, 45-48.

Type of 1871 Surcharged in Black   **2½d**

1891, Mar.				
55	A6	2½p on 3p vio rose	1.00	.80
a.		"1" of "½" has straight serif	50.00	32.50

Hope Seated — A13

1892-96				
56	A13	2½p olive green	2.75	.15
57	A13	2½p ultra ('96)	2.25	.15
		Set value		.25

For surcharge see No. N4. For overprint see Orange River Colony No. 55.

ONE PENNY.

No. 44 Surcharged in Black

1893, Mar.				
58	A6	1p on 2p bister	1.25	.25
a.		Double surcharge		400.00
b.		No period after "PENNY"	40.00	13.00

Hope Standing A15   Table Mountain and Bay; Coat of Arms A16

1893-1902				
59	A15	½p green ('98)	.25	.15
60	A15	1p rose	.25	.15
61	A15	3p red violet ('02)	3.50	.70
		Nos. 59-61 (3)	4.00	
		Set value		.85

For surcharges see Nos. 163-164, N2. For overprints see Orange River Colony #54, 56, Rhodesia #44, Transvaal #236-236A.

1900, Jan.				
62	A16	1p carmine rose	.70	.15

King Edward VII — A17

Various frames.

1902-04			Wmk. 16	
63	A17	½p emerald	.65	.20
64	A17	1p car rose	.40	.20
65	A17	2p brown ('04)	1.50	.40
66	A17	2½p ultra ('04)	2.50	2.25
67	A17	3p red violet ('03)	3.50	.30
68	A17	4p ol green ('03)	1.50	.30
69	A17	6p violet ('03)	4.25	.80
70	A17	1sh bister	4.25	.40
71	A17	5sh brown org ('03)	40.00	7.50
		Nos. 63-71 (9)	58.55	12.35

Imperf. stamps are proofs.

Cape of Good Hope stamps were replaced by those of Union of South Africa.

ISSUED IN MAFEKING

Excellent forgeries of Nos. 162-179 are known.

Stamps of Cape of Good Hope Surcharged

MAFEKING, 1d. BESIEGED.

1900, Mar. 24				
162	A6	1p on ½p grn	165.	47.50
163	A15	1p on ½p grn	175.	52.50
164	A15	3p on 1p rose	165.	47.50
165	A6	6p on 3p red vio	—	275.00
166	A6	1sh on 4p pale ol green	5,750.	325.00

MAFEKING 3d. BESIEGED.

Stamps of Bechuanaland Protectorate Surcharged

1900			Wmk. 30	
167	A54	1p on ½p ver	165.	47.50
a.		Inverted surcharge		4,000.
168	A40	3p on 1p lilac	900.	52.50
a.		Double surcharge		11,500.
169	A56	6p on 2p grn & car	1,300.	250.00
170	A58	6p on 3p vio, yel	3,750.	250.00
a.		Inverted surcharge		15,000.
b.		Double surcharge		

The lettering of "Mafeking Besieged" shows varying breaks in various letters, and may have either a period or no punctuation after "Mafeking."

On Stamps of Bechuanaland

		Wmk. 29		
171	A1	6p on 3p violet	425.	62.50

		Wmk. 30		
172	A59	1sh on 4p brn & grn	1,250.	65.00
a.		Double surch., one inverted		15,000.
b.		Triple surcharge		15,000.
c.		Inverted surcharge		5,750.
d.		Double surcharge		15,000.

MAFEKING 3d. BESIEGED.

Stamps of Bechuanaland Protectorate Surcharged

1900				
173	A40	3p on 1p lilac	900.	55.
a.		Double surcharge		7,250.
174	A56	6p on 2p grn & car	1,200.	65.
175	A62	1sh on 6p vio, rose	3,500.	85.

On Stamps of Bechuanaland

176	A62	1sh on 6p vio, rose	12,000.	650.
177	A65	2sh on 1sh green	6,250.	300.

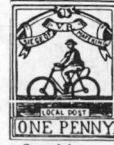 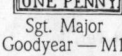   

Sgt. Major Goodyear — M1   Gen. Robert S. S. Baden-Powell — M2

Cape of Good Hope stamps can be mounted in the Scott British Africa album.

Wmk. OCEANA FINE Photographic Print

1900, Apr.			Perf. 12	
		Laid Paper		
178	M1	1p blue, blue	900.	275.
179	M2	3p blue, blue,		
		18½mm wide	1,250.	350.
a.		Horiz. pair, imperf. between		
b.		Double impression		12,000.
c.		Reversed design	—	25,000.
180	M2	3p blue, blue, 21mm wide	7,500.	925.

The color of the paper varies from pale to deep blue.

OCEANA FINE is a sheet watermark and does not appear on every stamp.

Imperfs of No. 178 are proofs.

There is one used pair of No. 179a privately owned.

Issued: #178, Apr. 6; #179-180, Apr. 10.

ISSUED IN VRYBURG

Under Boer Occupation

Cape of Good Hope Stamps of 1884-96 Surcharged   **½ PENCE Z.A.R.**

Two Types of Surcharge:
Type I - Surcharge 10mm high. Space between lines 5½mm.
Type II - Surcharge 12mm high. Space between lines 7½mm.

1899, Nov.			Wmk. 16	Perf. 14	
N1	A6	½p on ½p emer (I)		200.	85.
a.		Type II		1,750.	700.
N2	A15	1p on 1p rose (I)		225.	100.
a.		Type II		2,000.	750.
N3	A3	2p on 6p vio (II)		2,500.	475.
N4	A13	2½p on 2½p ultra (I)		1,900.	425.
a.		Type II		10,000.	4,500.

"Z.A.R." stands for Zuid Afrikaansche Republiek (South African Republic).

Under British Occupation

Transvaal Stamps of 1895-96 Handstamped   **V. R. SPECIAL POST**

1900			Unwmk.	Perf. 12½	
N5	A13	½p green			2,750.
N6	A13	1p rose & grn	9,000.	3,000.	
N7	A13	2p brown & grn			
N8	A13	2½p ultra & grn			

CEYLON

si-'län

LOCATION — An island in the Indian Ocean separated from India by the Gulf of Manaar
GOVT. — Independent republic within the British Commonwealth
AREA — 25,332 sq. mi.
POP. — 12,670,000 (est. 1971)
CAPITAL — Colombo

Ceylon changed its name to Republic of Sri Lanka on May 22, 1972. Issues of Sri

Lanka are listed under that name in this volume.

12 Pence = 1 Shilling
100 Cents = 1 Rupee (1872)

Values for unused stamps are for examples with original gum as defined in the catalogue introduction except for Nos. 2, 5, 8-9 which seldom have any remaining trace of their original gum. Many unused stamps of Ceylon, especially between Nos. 59 and 274, have toned gum or tropical stains. Values quoted are for stamps with fresh gum. Toned stamps have lower values, and common stamps with toned gum are worth very little.

Very fine examples of Nos. 1-14, will be cut square, will have small margins, but will show an intact design. Inferior examples with the design partly cut away will sell for much less, and examples with large margins will command higher prices. Very fine examples of Nos. 17-58b will have perforations just cutting into the design on one or more sides due to the narrow spacing of the stamps on the plates and to imperfect perforating methods. Stamps with perfs clear on all four sides are extremely scarce and will command substantially higher prices.

Catalogue values for unused stamps in this country are for Never Hinged items, beginning with Scott 290 in the regular postage section and Scott B1 in the semi-postal section.

Watermarks

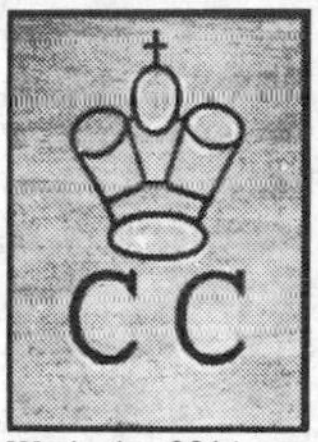

Wmk. 1a- 22½mm high, Oval Letters

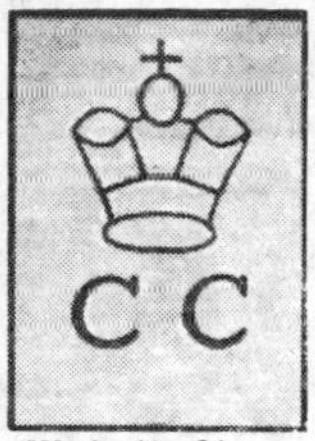

Wmk. 1b- 21mm high, Round Letters

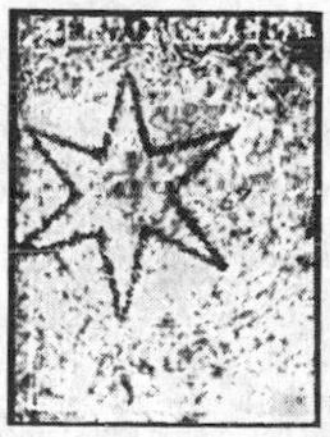

Wmk. 6- Large Star

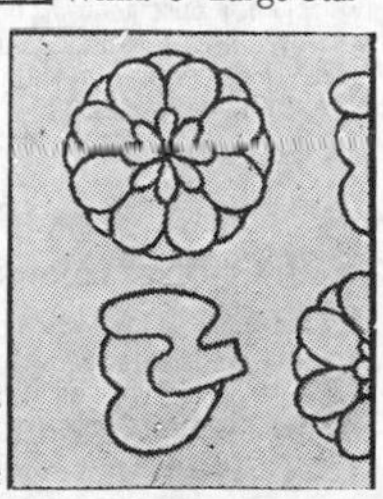

Wmk. 290- Lotus and "Sri" Multiple

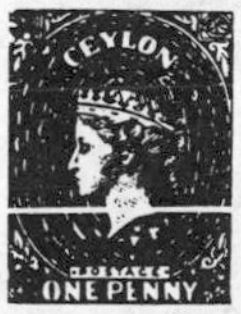

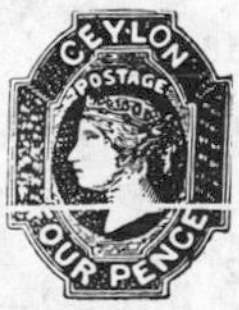

Queen Victoria

A1 A2

1857 Engr. Wmk. 6 *Imperf.*
Blued Paper

1	A1	1p blue		150.00
2	A1	6p plum	10,000.	450.00

Beware of copies of No. 25b with perfs removed to resemble No. 1.

1857-59
White Paper

3	A1	1p blue	625.00	20.00
4	A1	2p deep green	140.00	50.00
a.		2p yellow green	350.00	90.00
5	A2	4p dl rose ('59)	75,000.	4,500.
6	A1	5p org brown	2,000.	150.00
6A	A1	6p plum	2,000.	125.00
7	A1	6p brown	6,000.	350.00
8	A2	8p brown ('59)	22,500.	1,500.
9	A2	9p lil brn ('59)	30,000.	1,000.
10	A1	10p vermilion	850.00	200.00
11	A1	1sh violet	4,500.	200.00
12	A2	1sh9p green ('59)	750.00	750.00
a.		1sh9p yellow green	3,500.	2,000.
13	A2	2sh blue ('59)	5,500.	1,200.

Stamps of type A2 frequently have repaired corners.

Nos. 3-4 exist unofficially rouletted.

No. 5 was reproduced by the collotype process in a souvenir sheet distributed at the London International Stamp Exhibition 1950. The paper is unwatermarked.

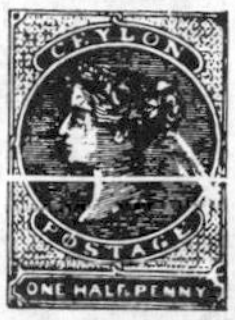

A3

1857-58 Typo. Unwmk.

14	A3	½p lilac ('58)	175.00	150.00
15	A3	½p lilac, *bluish*	4,000.	450.00

No. 14 exists unofficially rouletted.

Nos. 14-15, 38 are printed on surface-glazed paper. Values are for stamps without cracking of the surface, and examples showing cracking should be discounted.

Clean-Cut Perf. 14 to 15½

1861 Wmk. 6 Engr.

17	A1	1p blue	75.00	15.00
18	A1	2p yel green	75.00	22.50
19	A2	4p dull rose	1,500.	225.00
20	A1	5p org brown	65.00	8.50
20A	A1	6p brown	1,200.	65.00
b.		6p bister brown		110.00
21	A2	8p brown	1,250.	325.00
22	A2	9p lilac brown	4,000.	200.00
23	A1	1sh violet	60.00	14.00
24	A2	2sh blue	1,700.	350.00

Rough Perf. 14 to 15½

25	A1	1p blue	55.00	5.50
b.		Blued paper	300.00	15.00
26	A1	2p yel green	35.00	40.00
27	A2	4p rose red	175.00	40.00
28	A1	6p bister brown	1,000.	80.00
a.		6p deep brown	500.00	60.00
29	A2	8p brown	1,000.	300.00
30	A2	8p yel brown	1,000.	250.00
31	A2	9p olive brown	350.00	27.50
32	A2	9p deep brown	50.00	30.00
33	A1	10p vermilion	160.00	20.00
a.		Imperf. vert., pair		—
34	A1	1sh violet	200.00	12.50
35	A2	1sh9p green	425.00	
36	A2	2sh blue	500.00	82.50

The 1sh9p green was never placed in use.

1863 *Perf. 12½*

37	A1	10p vermilion	200.00	13.00

1864 Typo. Unwmk.

38	A3	½p lilac	175.00	150.00

See note following No. 15.

1863 Engr. *Perf. 13*

39	A1	1p blue	70.00	8.00
40	A1	5p car brown	825.00	125.00
41	A1	6p brown	75.00	19.00
42	A2	9p brown	700.00	60.00
43	A1	1sh grayish violet	1,600.	70.00

Parts of the papermaker's sheet watermark, "T. H. SAUNDERS 1862," may be found on some copies of Nos. 39-43.

Perf. 12

44	A1	1p blue	700.00	90.00
a.		Horiz. pair, imperf. btwn.		6,000.

Two Types of Watermark Crown and CC (1)

1863-67 Typo. Wmk. 1a *Perf. 12½*

45	A3	½p lilac	20.00	13.00

Engr.

46	A1	1p blue	50.00	3.50
a.		1p dark blue	50.00	3.75
c.		Perf. 11½	1,800.	150.00
47	A1	2p gray green	30.00	6.00
48	A1	2p emerald	90.00	70.00
48A	A1	2p yel green	9,000.	325.00
49	A1	2p olive	200.00	200.00
50	A2	4p rose	150.00	40.00
51	A1	5p car brown	90.00	35.00
52	A1	5p olive green	650.00	175.00
e.		5p deep sage green	1,750.	250.00
53	A1	6p choc brown	60.00	7.00
a.		6p brown	60.00	8.00
c.		Perf. 13	1,250.	85.00
54	A2	8p red brown	40.00	20.00
55	A2	9p brown	200.00	20.00
c.		Perf. 13	2,500.	400.00
56	A1	10p orange	1,600.	160.00
a.		10p vermilion	900.00	35.00
58	A2	2sh blue	140.00	20.00

The ½p, 1p blue, 2p olive, 4p and 5p green exist imperf.

Wmk. 1b

46d	A1	1p blue	60.00	5.00
e.		1p dark blue	60.00	5.00
49d	A1	2p orange yellow	25.00	4.00
e.		2p olive yellow	25.00	5.00
f.		2p olive green	125.00	30.00
50b	A2	4p rose	25.00	10.00
52b	A1	5p myrtle green	35.00	5.00
c.		5p olive green	60.00	6.75
d.		5p bronze green	17.50	24.00
53d	A1	6p chocolate brown	17.50	24.00
e.		6p brown	35.00	9.00
54a	A2	8p red brown	30.00	35.00
55a	A2	9p dark brown	22.50	5.00
b.		9p bister brown	200.00	25.00
56b	A1	10p orange	40.00	7.00
c.		10p orange red	24.00	5.50
d.		10p vermilion	1,250.	125.00
57	A1	1sh purple	50.00	6.25
58a	A2	2sh deep blue	60.00	7.00
b.		2sh indigo	90.00	12.50

The 1p blue and 6p brown exist imperf.

For overprints see Nos. O2, O4-O7.

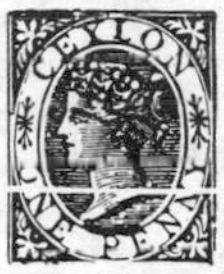

A4

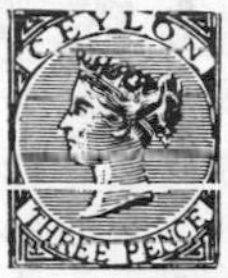

A5

1866 Typo. Wmk. 1 *Perf. 12½*

59	A5	3p rose	160.00	60.00
a.		Imperf., pair	550.00	

For overprint see No. O3.

1868 *Perf. 14*

61	A4	1p blue	10.00	4.25
62	A5	3p rose	40.00	20.00

For overprint see No. O1.

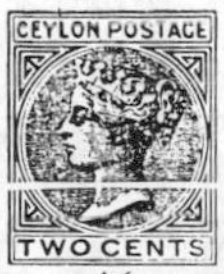

A6

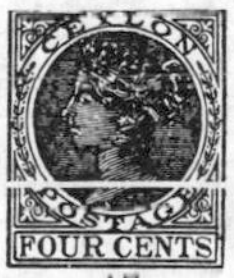

A7

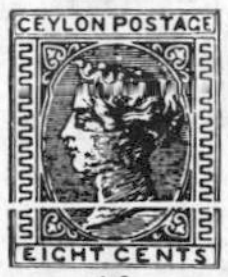

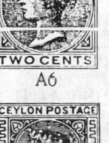

A8

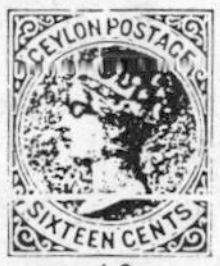

A9

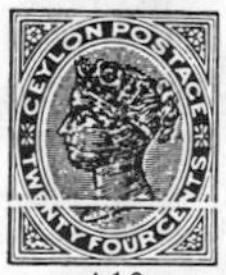

A10

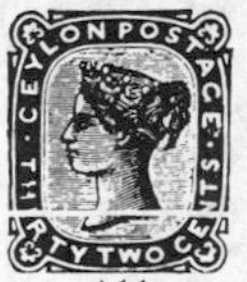

A11

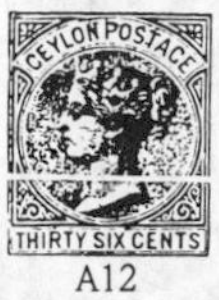

A12

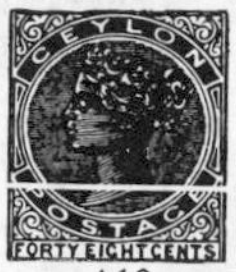

A13

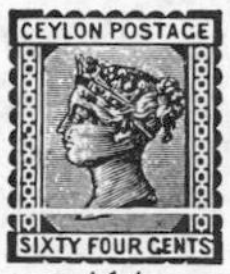

A14

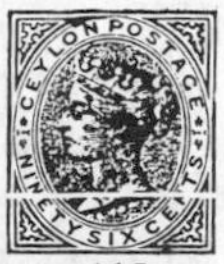

A15

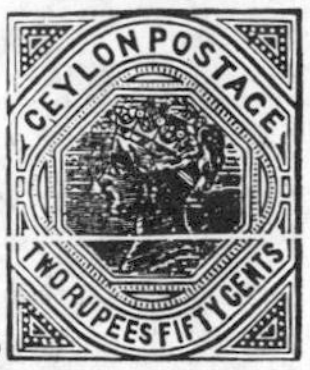

A16

1872-80 *Perf. 14*

63	A6	2c brown	5.00	1.50
64	A7	4c gray	22.50	1.50
65	A7	4c lil rose ('80)	42.50	1.50
66	A8	8c orange	37.50	5.00
a.		8c orange yellow	22.50	5.00
67	A9	16c violet	50.00	2.75
68	A10	24c green	30.00	2.00
69	A11	32c slate bl ('77)	85.00	13.00
70	A12	36c blue	65.00	15.00
71	A13	48c rose	60.00	5.00
72	A14	64c red brn ('77)	170.00	55.00
73	A15	96c olive gray	150.00	25.00
		Nos. 63-73 (11)	717.50	127.25

For surcharges see #83-84, 94A-110, 112-114. For types surcharged see #124-129.

1872 *Perf. 12½*

74	A6	2c brown	1,750.	100.00
75	A7	4c gray	850.00	165.00

1879 *Perf. 14x12½*

77	A6	2c brown	350.00	50.00
78	A7	4c gray	625.00	20.00
79	A8	8c orange	325.00	32.50

Perf. 12½x14

82	A16	2r50c claret	475.00	240.00

The 32c and 64c are known perf. 14x12½, but were not regularly issued.

No. 82, perf. 12½, was not regularly issued.

See Nos. 142, 158. For surcharges see Nos. 111, 115, 130. For types surcharged see Nos. 160-161.

SIXTEEN

Nos. 68, 72 Surcharged **16**

CENTS

1882 *Perf. 14*

83	A10	16c on 24c green	18.00	6.00
84	A14	20c on 64c red brn	8.50	3.00
a.		Double surcharge		1,150.

1883-99 Wmk. 2

85	A6	2c pale brown	40.00	1.50
86	A6	2c green ('84)	1.25	.15
a.		Perf. 12	1,600.	
87	A6	2c org brn ('99)	1.00	.25
88	A7	4c lilac rose	1.50	.20
89	A7	4c rose ('84)	2.30	10.00
a.		Perf. 12	1,600.	
90	A7	4c brt rose ('98)	6.00	6.00
91	A7	4c yellow ('99)	1.25	2.25
92	A8	8c orange	3.50	6.00
93	A9	16c violet	1,000.	125.00
94	A10	24c purple brown	900.00	
b.		Perf. 12	1,750.	

Nos. 86a, 89a, 94 and 94b were never placed in use. A 48c brown, perf. 12, was prepared but not issued.

For surcharges and overprints see Nos.116-123, 143-151D, 155-156. O8-O9.

Issues of 1872-82 Surcharged:

Postage &

FIVE
CENTS

Revenue
a

TEN
CENTS
b

Twenty
Cents
c

One Rupee
Twelve
Cents
d

1885 **Wmk. 1** *Perf. 14*

94A A9 (a) 5c on 16c
95 A10 (a) 5c on 24c *1,250.* *90.00*
96 A11 (a) 5c on 32c *50.00* *15.00*
a. Inverted surcharge *800.00*
97 A12 (a) 5c on 36c *125.00* *7.50*
a. Inverted surcharge *1,000.*
98 A13 (a) 5c on 48c *575.00* *35.00*
99 A14 (a) 5c on 64c *50.00* 4.50
a. Double surcharge *650.00*
100 A15 (a) 5c on 96c *275.00* *50.00*
101 A9 (b) 10c on 16c *1,100.*
102 A10 (b) 10c on 24c *300.00* *75.00*
103 A12 (b) 10c on 36c *300.00* *125.00*
104 A14 (b) 10c on 64c *250.00* *75.00*
105 A10 (b) 20c on 24c *35.00* 13.00
106 A11 (c) 20c on 32c *30.00* *30.00*
107 A11 (c) 25c on 32c 9.75 4.00
108 A13 (c) 28c on 48c *30.00* 5.00
a. Double surcharge *800.00*
109 A12 (b) 30c on 36c 8.00 7.50
a. Inverted surcharge *200.00* *100.00*
110 A15 (b) 56c on 96c 15.00 10.00

Perf. 12½

111 A16 (d) 1r12c on 2r50c *300.00* *75.00*

Perf. 14x12½

112 A11 (a) 5c on 32c *275.00* *35.00*
113 A14 (a) 5c on 64c *250.00* *25.00*
114 A14 (b) 10c on 64c *40.00* *60.00*
a. Vert. pair, imperf. btwn. *2,250.*

Perf. 12½x14

115 A16 (d) 1r12c on 2r50c *60.00* *30.00*

Perf. 14

Wmk. 2

116 A7 (a) 5c on 4c lil rose — —
a. Inverted surcharge —
117 A7 (a) 5c on 4c rose *12.50* 2.50
a. Inverted surcharge *250.00*
118 A8 (a) 5c on 8c org *37.50* 5.00
a. Inverted surcharge *1,000.*
b. Double surcharge *750.00*
119 A9 (a) 5c on 16c vio *50.00* 7.00
a. Inverted surcharge *150.00*
120 A10 (a) 5c on 24c pur brn — *500.00*
121 A9 (b) 10c on 16c vio *2,750.* *600.00*
122 A10 (b) 10c on 24c pur brn 9.00 4.00
123 A9 (b) 15c on 16c vio 8.00 4.25

Some authorities believe Nos. 116, 116a to be forgeries. A 5c on 24c green is known to exist and is considered to be a forgery.

Types of 1872-80 Surcharged

5 CENTS
e

10 CENTS **1 R. 12 C.**
f g

1885-87

124 A 8 (e) 5c on 8c lilac *7.00* 1.50
125 A10 (f) 10c on 24c pur brn 8.00 4.00
126 A 9 (f) 15c on 16c org *30.00* 4.25
127 A11 (f) 28c on 32c sl bl 12.00 2.00
128 A12 (f) 30c on 36c ol grn *25.00* 12.50
129 A15 (f) 56c on 96c ol gray *27.50* 7.50

Wmk. 1 Sideways

130 A16 (g) 1r12c on 2r50c cl 27.50 *60.00*
Nos. 124-130 (7) *137.00* 91.75

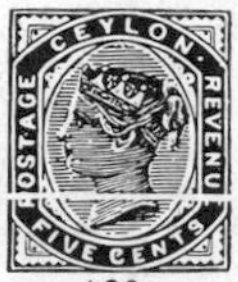
A23

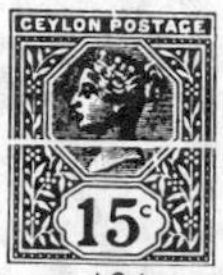
A24

FIVE CENTS
Type I - Thin lines in background. Hair and curl clear.
Type II - Thicker lines in background. Heavier shading under chin.

1886 **Wmk. 2**

131 A23 5c lilac, type I 1.25 .15
a. Type II 1.25 .15

For overprint see No. O12.

1886-1900

132 A24 3c org brn & green ('93) 1.25 .30
133 A24 3c green ('00) .90 .30
134 A24 6c rose & blk ('99) .75 .30
135 A24 12c ol grn & car ('00) 2.25 2.50
136 A24 15c olive green 1.75 .30
137 A24 15c ultra ('00) 1.50 1.50
138 A24 25c brown 1.25 .90
a. 25c brown, value in ol yel 80.00 70.00
139 A24 28c slate 2.25 1.40
140 A24 30c vio & org brown ('93) 2.50 1.25
141 A24 75c blk & org brown ('00) 4.25 4.00
Nos. 132-141 (10) 18.65 12.75

Numeral tablet of 3c, 12c and 75c has lined background with colorless value and "c."
For surcharges see Nos. 152-154, 157, 159. For overprints see Nos. O10-O11, O13-O17.

1887 **Wmk. 1**

142 A16 1r12c claret 15.00 12.50

For overprint see No. O18.

Issue of 1883-84 Surcharged **TWO CENTS**

1888-90 **Wmk. 2**

143 A7 2c on 4c lilac rose .45 .35
a. Inverted surcharge 7.00 7.00
b. Double surcharge, one inverted 32.50
144 A7 2c on 4c rose .45 .30
a. Inverted surcharge 7.00 7.00
b. Double surcharge 25.00

Surcharged **TWO**

145 A7 2c on 4c lilac rose .60 .25
a. Inverted surcharge 17.50 17.50
b. Double surcharge 27.50 22.50
c. Double surcharge, one inverted 12.00 12.00
146 A7 2c on 4c rose 1.00 .20
a. Double surcharge, one inverted 22.50 22.50
b. Double surcharge 22.50 22.50
c. Inverted surcharge 45.00

Surcharged **2 Cents**

147 A7 2c on 4c lilac rose 40.00 27.50
a. Inverted surcharge 35.00
b. Double surcharge, one inverted 80.00
148 A7 2c on 4c rose 1.40 .75
a. Inverted surcharge 8.50 8.00
b. Double surcharge, one inverted 8.00 8.00
c. Double surcharge

Surcharged **Two Cents**

149 A7 2c on 4c lilac rose 40.00 27.50
a. Inverted surcharge 70.00 30.00
150 A7 2c on 4c rose 1.10 .70
a. Inverted surcharge 7.00 5.50
b. Double surcharge 17.50 17.50
c. Double surcharge, one inverted 8.00 5.50

Surcharged **2 Cents**

151 A7 2c on 4c rose 2.50 .60
a. Inverted surcharge 6.50 5.50
b. Double surcharge 35.00 35.00
c. Double surch., one invtd. 13.00 8.00
i. "S" of "Cents" inverted 40.00
151D A7 2c on 4c lilac rose 30.00 22.00
e. Inverted surcharge 47.50 40.00
f. Double surcharge 32.00
g. Double surch., one invtd. 40.00 40.00
h. "S" of "Cents" inverted

Counterfeit errors of surcharges of Nos. 143 to 151D are prevalent.

No. 136 Surcharged **POSTAGE** **Five Cents** **REVENUE**

1890

152 A24 5c on 15c ol green 1.00 1.00
a. "Five" instead of "Five" 70.00 60.00
b. "REVENUE" omitted 80.00 65.00
c. Inverted surcharge 12.00 12.00
d. Double surcharge 90.00 90.00
e. As "a," inverted surcharge — *750.00*
f. Inverted "s" in "Cents" 30.00 35.00
g. As "f," inverted surcharge *750.00*
h. As "b," inverted "s" in "Cents" *450.00*

Nos. 138-139 Surcharged **FIFTEEN CENTS**

1891

153 A24 15c on 25c brown 7.50 7.00
154 A24 15c on 28c slate 7.00 7.00

Nos. 88, 89 and 139 Surcharged **3 Cents**

1892

155 A7 3c on 4c lilac rose .50 .60
156 A7 3c on 4c rose 1.40 1.50
a. Double surcharge, one inverted
157 A24 3c on 28c slate .50 .65
a. Double surcharge 55.00
Nos. 155-157 (3) 2.40 2.75

Type of 1879

1898

158 A16 2r50c violet, *red* 22.50 26.00

No. 136 Surcharged in Black **Six Cents**

1899

159 A24 6c on 15c olive green .40 .40

Surcharged Type "g" in Black

1899 **Wmk. 1**

160 A16 1r50c on 2r50c gray 20.00 32.50
161 A16 2r25c on 2r50c yel 27.50 45.00

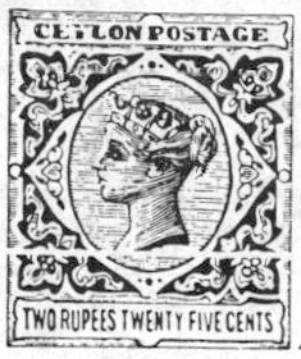
A35

1900 **Wmk. 1**

162 A35 1r50c car rose 12.00 *30.00*
163 A35 2r25c dull blue 25.00 *50.00*

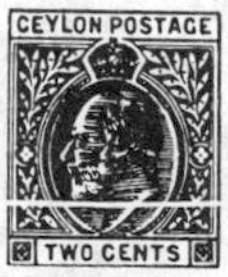
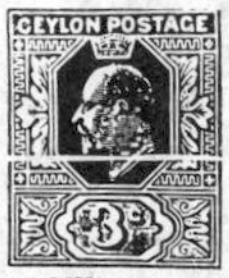
King Edward VII
A36 A37

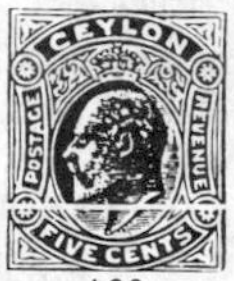
A38

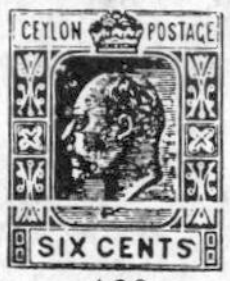
A39

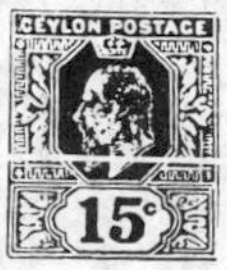
A40

1903-05 **Wmk. 2**

166 A36 2c org brown .90 .15
167 A37 3c green .90 .60
168 A37 4c yel & blue 1.10 *2.00*
169 A38 5c dull lilac 1.25 .20
170 A39 6c car rose 4.00 1.10
171 A37 12c ol grn & car 2.75 *5.00*
172 A40 15c ultra 4.75 1.50
173 A40 25c bister 3.00 *5.50*
174 A40 30c vio & green 2.75 *3.00*
175 A37 75c bl & org ('05) *2.50* 12.50
176 A40 1r50c gray ('04) 47.50 37.50
177 A40 2r25c brn & grn ('04) 42.50 32.50
Nos. 166-177 (12) 113.90 101.55

For overprints see Nos. O19-O24.

1904-10 **Wmk. 3**

178 A36 2c orange brown .45 .15
a. 2c orange 1.25 .50
179 A37 3c green .60 .15
180 A37 4c yel & blue .50 .40
181 A38 5c dull lilac 1.50 .55
a. Booklet pane of 12
182 A39 6c car rose .90 .15
183 A40 10c ol grn & vio ('10) 1.25 .90
184 A37 12c ol grn & car 1.25 1.10
185 A40 15c ultra .75 .40
186 A40 25c bister ('05) 5.00 2.50
187 A40 25c slate ('10) 2.00 .50
188 A40 30c vio & grn ('05) 2.00 .95
189 A40 50c brown ('10) 3.25 4.75
190 A37 75c bl & org ('05) 4.25 5.00
191 A40 1r vio, *yel* ('10) 6.25 6.50
192 A40 1r50c gray ('05) 13.00 *6.50*
193 A40 2r scar, *yel* ('10) 13.00 *17.00*
194 A40 2r25c brn & grn 15.00 *18.00*
195 A40 5r blk, *grn* ('10) 32.50 *42.50*
196 A40 10r blk, *red* ('10) 57.50 *100.00*
Nos. 178-196 (19) 160.95 *208.00*

No. 181 exists on ordinary and chalky paper.

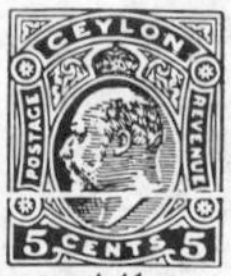
A41

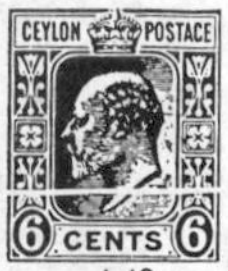
A42

1908

197 A41 5c deep red violet 2.00 .15
a. Booklet pane of 12
198 A42 6c carmine rose .70 .20
Set value .25

1911, July 5

199 A40 3c green 1.00 .15

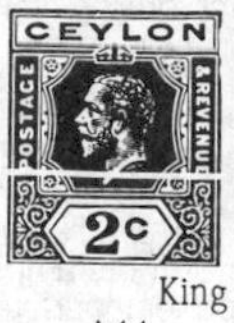
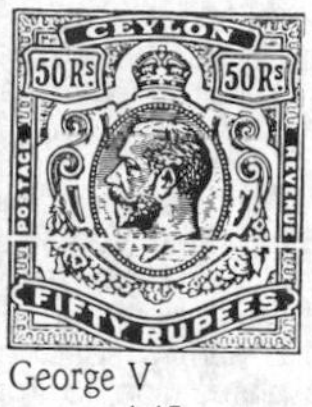
King George V
A44 A45

3 AND 6 CENTS
Type I - Small "c" after value, 2¼mm wide and 2mm high.
Type II - Large "c" after value, 2½mm wide and 2¼mm high.
1, 5 AND 9 CENTS are Type II, other denominations Type I.

Die I

For description of the dies, see back of this section of the Catalogue.

1912-25 **Wmk. 3**

200 A44 1c dp brn (Die Ib) ('20) .75 .15
201 A44 2c brown org .25 .15
202 A44 3c dp grn (Die Ia, type II) 2.00 .35
a. 3c deep green, die I, type I 3.25 .80
203 A44 5c red violet .70 .45
204 A44 6c car (Die Ib, type II) .95 .60
a. 6c carmine, die I, type I 1.75 .35
b. As "a," bklt. pane of 6
205 A44 10c olive green 2.50 1.25
206 A44 15c ultra 1.25 .90

Chalky Paper

207 A44 25c yel & ultra 1.50 1.25
208 A44 30c green & vio 3.50 1.65
209 A44 50c black & scar 1.00 1.25
210 A44 1r violet, *yel* 1.65 *2.25*
211 A44 2r blk & red, *yel* 2.50 *5.75*
212 A44 5r blk, *green* 12.00 *16.00*
a. 5r black, *bl grn*, olive back 11.00 *17.00*
b. 5r black, *emer* (Die II) ('20) 40.00 60.00
213 A44 10r vio & blk, *red* 42.50 55.00
a. Die II ('20) 50.00 65.00
214 A44 20r blk & red, *bl* 67.50 55.00
215 A45 50r dull violet 375.00
216 A45 100r gray black 1,400.
217 A45 500r gray green *4,250.*
218 A45 1000r vio, *red* ('25) *16,000.*
Nos. 200-214 (15) 140.55 142.00

Although Nos. 217 and 218 were theoretically available for postage it is not probable that they were ever used for other than fiscal purposes.
The 1r through 100r with revenue cancellations sell for minimal prices.
For surcharge & overprints see #223, MR1-MR3.

Die I
Surface-colored Paper

1913-14

220 A44 1r violet, *yellow* 1.25 *2.25*
221 A44 2r black & red, *yel* 1.90 *6.25*
222 A44 5r black, *green* 10.00 *19.00*
Nos. 220-222 (3) 13.15 *27.50*

No. 203 Surcharged **ONE CENT**

1918

223 A44 1c on 5c red violet .15 .15

For overprint see No. MR4.

Die I

1921-33 **Wmk. 4**

Ordinary Paper

225 A44 1c dp brn (Die Ib) ('27) .35 .25
226 A44 2c brn org (Die II) .25 .15
227 A44 3c green (Die Ia, type II) .65 .50
228 A44 3c slate (Die Ia, type II) ('22) .25 .15
229 A44 5c red vio (Die I) .25 .15
230 A44 6c carmine (Die Ib, type II) .65 .50

No.	Type	Description	Unused	Used
231	A44	6c vio (Die Ib, type II) ('22)	.25	.15
232	A44	9c red, *yel* (Die II) ('26)	.35	.25
233	A44	10c olive green	.65	.25
a.		Die II	.65	.40
234	A44	12c scarlet ('25)	2.75	3.00
a.		Die II	.70	1.00
235	A44	15c ultramarine	2.25	4.25
236	A44	15c green, *yel* ('22)	1.10	.70
a.		Die II	1.10	.30
237	A44	20c ultra ('22)	2.25	3.25
a.		Die II	1.10	.20
238	A44	25c yel & blue	.70	1.00
a.		Die II	2.00	.85

For surcharges see Nos. 248-249.

Chalky Paper

No.	Type	Description	Unused	Used
239	A44	30c green & violet	1.25	1.75
a.		Die II	1.40	.85
240	A44	50c blk & scar (Die II)	.90	.55
a.		Die I	40.00	52.50
241	A44	1r violet, *yel*	12.00	14.00
a.		Die II	6.75	12.00
242	A44	2r blk & red, *yel* (Die II)	3.25	4.50
243	A44	5r blk, *emer*, (Die II)	17.00	24.00
244	A44	20r blk & red, *bl*, (Die II)	72.50	65.00
245	A45	50r dull vio	325.00	
246	A45	100r gray black	1,750.	
247	A45	100r ultra & dl vio ('27)	1,600.	
		Nos. 225-244 (20)	119.60	124.35

Nos. 228, 231 Surcharged

2 Cents.

1926

No.	Type	Description	Unused	Used
248	A44	2c on 3c slate	.35	.25
a.		Double surcharge	40.00	40.00
b.		Bar omitted	27.50	
249	A44	5c on 6c violet	.25	.25
a.		Double surcharge		

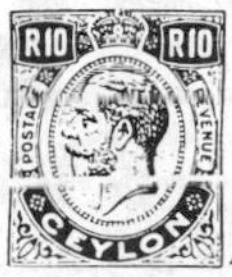

A46

1927-29 Chalky Paper Wmk. 4

No.	Type	Description	Unused	Used
254	A46	1r red vio & dl vio ('28)	2.50	.85
255	A46	2r car & green ('29)	3.50	1.25
256	A46	5r brn vio & grn ('28)	12.00	10.00
257	A46	10r org & green	24.00	30.00
258	A46	20r ultra & dl vio	55.00	65.00
		Nos. 254-258 (5)	97.00	107.10

Silver Jubilee Issue

Common Design Type

1935, May 6 Engr. *Perf. 13½x14*

No.	Type	Description	Unused	Used
260	CD301	6c gray blk & ultra	.25	.25
261	CD301	9c indigo & green	.40	.45
262	CD301	20c brown & blue	2.00	1.75
263	CD301	50c brt vio & ind	2.50	4.00
		Nos. 260-263 (4)	5.15	6.45

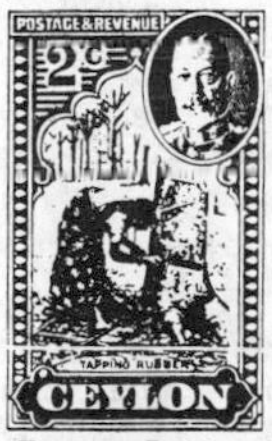

Tapping Rubber Tree — A47

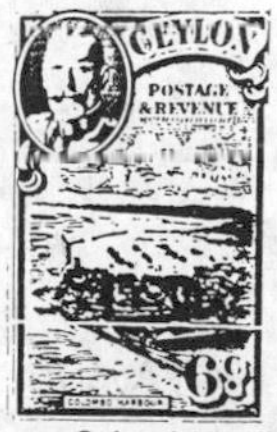

Colombo Harbor — A49

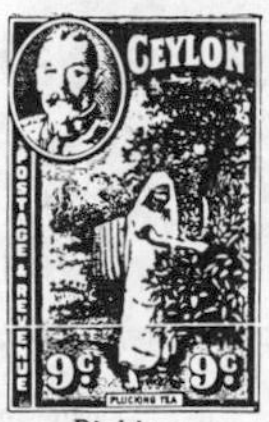

Picking Tea — A50

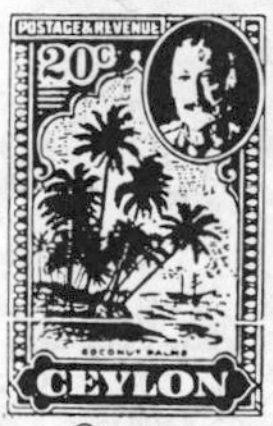

Coconut Palms — A53

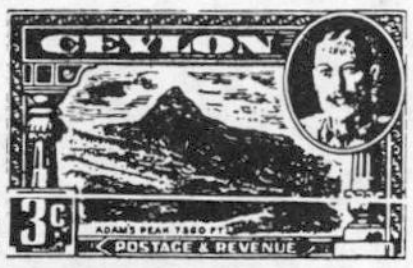

Adam's Peak — A48

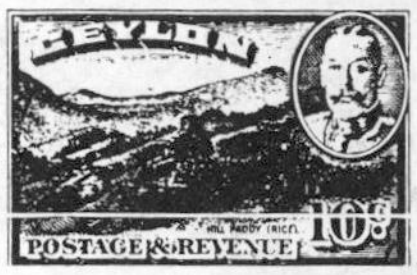

Rice Terraces A51

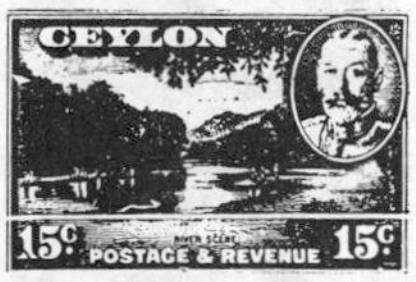

River Scene — A52

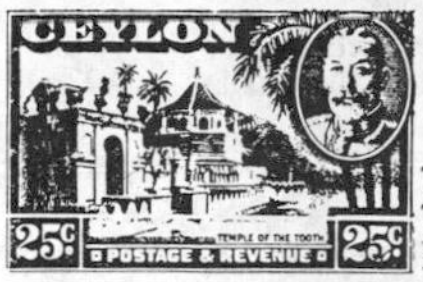

Temple of the Tooth, Kandy — A54

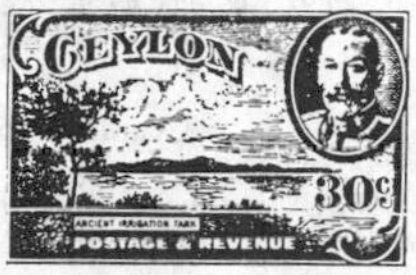

Ancient Reservoir A55

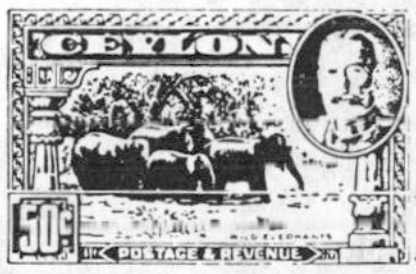

Wild Elephants A56

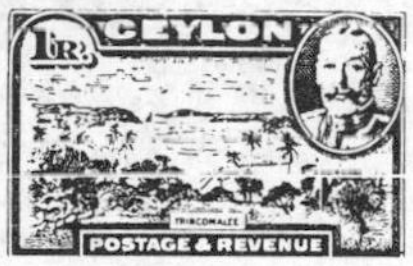

View of Trincomalee A57

Perf. 11x11½, 11½x11; 11½x13, 13x11½ (A47, A48, A53); 14 (A56)

1935-36 Wmk. 4

No.	Type	Description	Unused	Used
264	A47	2c car rose & blk	.20	.15
a.		Perf. 14	6.00	.50
265	A48	3c olive & black	.30	.15
a.		Perf. 14	16.00	.50
266	A49	6c blue & black	.20	.15
267	A50	9c org red & ol grn	.50	.16
268	A51	10c dk vio & blk	.60	.20
269	A52	15c grn & org brn	.95	.25
270	A53	20c ultra & black	1.75	.50
271	A54	25c choc & dk ultra	1.25	.35
272	A55	30c green & lake	2.25	.75
273	A56	50c dk vio & blk	7.50	1.50
274	A57	1r brown & vio	7.00	2.75
		Nos. 264-274 (11)	22.50	6.91

Issued: 2c, 15c, 25c, 5/1/35; 10c, 6/1/35; 1r, 7/1/35; 30c, 8/1/35; 3c, 10/1/35; 6c, 9c, 20c, 50c, 1/1/36.

Coronation Issue

Common Design Type

1937, May 12 *Perf. 11x11½*

No.	Type	Description	Unused	Used
275	CD302	6c dark carmine	.30	.15
a.		Booklet pane of 10		
276	CD302	9c deep green	1.00	1.00
a.		Booklet pane of 10	150.00	
277	CD302	20c deep ultra	1.60	1.50
		Nos. 275-277 (3)	2.90	2.65

Types of 1935 with "Postage & Revenue Removed" and Picturing George VI and:

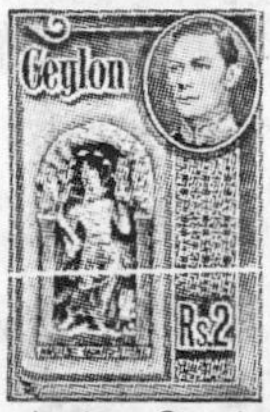

Ancient Guard Stone — A68

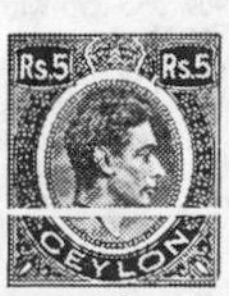

George VI — A69

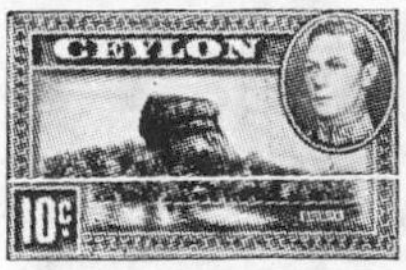

Sigiriya (Lion Rock) — A61

Perf. 11x11½, 11½x11; 12 (#278-279, 286)

1938-52 Engr. Wmk. 4

No.	Type	Description	Unused	Used
278	A47	2c car rose & blk ('49)	.15	.15
a.		Perf. 13½x13 ('38)	6.00	.15
b.		Perf. 13½ ('38)	.15	.15
c.		Perf. 11x11½ ('44)	.15	.15
d.		Perf. 11½x13 ('38)	1.75	.15
279	A48	3c dk grn & blk ('46)	.15	.15
a.		Perf. 13x13½ ('38)	100.00	2.50
b.		Perf. 14 ('41)	25.00	.40
c.		Perf. 13½ ('38)	.15	.15
d.		Perf. 11½x11 ('42)	.15	.15
e.		Perf. 13x11½	1.75	.15
280	A49	6c blue & black	.15	.15
281	A61	10c blue & black	.15	.15
282	A52	15c red brn & grn	.15	.15
283	A50	20c dull bl & blk	.15	.15
284	A54	25c choc & dk ultra	.15	.15
285	A55	30c dk grn & rose car	.55	.15
286	A56	50c dk vio & blk ('46)	.50	.15
a.		Perf. 14 ('42)	4.25	1.25
b.		Perf. 13x11½ ('38)	62.50	25.00
c.		Perf. 13x13½ ('38)	125.00	1.75
d.		Perf. 13½ ('38)	.75	.20
e.		Perf. 11½x11 ('42)	.45	.15
287	A57	1r dk brn & bl vio	1.20	.35
288	A68	2r dark car & blk	1.75	.90

Typo. *Perf. 14*

No.	Type	Description	Unused	Used
289	A69	5r brn vio & grn	5.00	1.25
289A	A69	10r yel org & dl grn ('52)	40.00	25.00
		Nos. 278-289 (12)	10.05	
		Set value		3.10

No. 289A differs from type A69 in having "REVENUE" inscribed vertically at either side of the frame. This revenue 10r was valid for postage Dec. 1, 1952-Mar. 14, 1954.

See #292, 295. For surcharges see #290-291.

Catalogue values for unused stamps in this section, from this point to the end of the section, are for Never Hinged items.

No. 283 Surcharged in Black

3 CENTS

1940, Nov. 5 *Perf. 11x11½*

No.	Type	Description	Unused	Used
290	A63	3c on 20c dull bl & blk	.25	.25

No. 280 Surcharged with New Value and Bars

1941, May 10

No.	Type	Description	Unused	Used
291	A60	3c on 6c blue & black	.15	.15

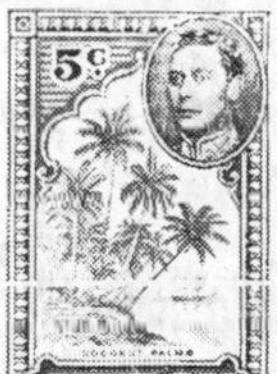

Coconut Palms — A70

1943-47 Wmk. 4 Engr. *Perf. 12*

No.	Type	Description	Unused	Used
292	A70	5c red org & ol grn ('47)	.15	.15
a.		Perf. 13½ ('43)	.15	.15

Peace Issue

Common Design Type

1946, Dec. 10 *Perf. 13½x14*

No.	Type	Description	Unused	Used
293	CD303	6c deep blue	.15	.15
294	CD303	15c brown	.15	.15
		Set value	.23	.23

Guard Stone Type of 1938

1947, Mar. 15 *Perf. 11x11½*

No.	Type	Description	Unused	Used
295	A68	2r violet & black	1.50	.55

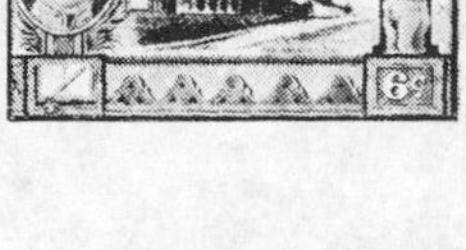

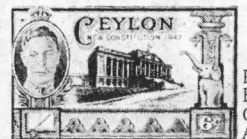

Parliament Building, Colombo A71

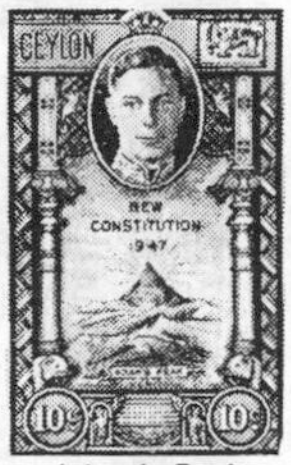

Adam's Peak A72

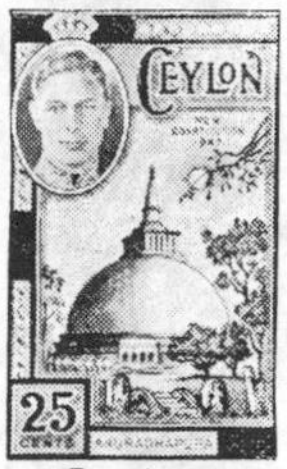

Dagoba at Anuradhapura A74

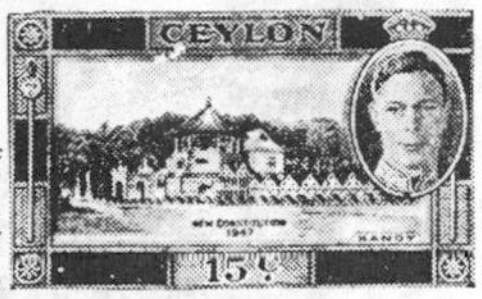

Temple of the Tooth, Kandy A73

1947, Nov. 25 *Perf. 11x12, 12x11*

No.	Type	Description	Unused	Used
296	A71	6c deep ultra & black	.15	.15
297	A72	10c car, orange & black	.15	.15
298	A73	15c red vio & grnsh blk	.16	.15
299	A74	25c brt green & bister	.20	.20
		Set value	.56	.56

New constitution of 1947.

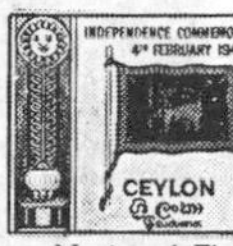

National Flag A75

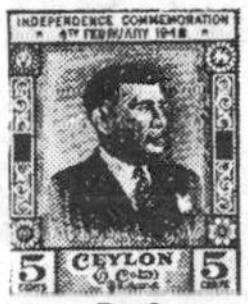

D. S. Senanayake A76

Engr., Flag Typo. (A75); Engr. (A76)

Perf. 12½x12, 12x12½, 13x12½

1949 Wmk. 4

No.	Type	Description	Unused	Used
300	A75	4c org brn, car & yel	.15	.15
301	A76	5c dark green & brn	.15	.15

Wmk. 290

No.	Type	Description	Unused	Used
302	A75	15c red org, car & yel	.16	.15
303	A76	25c dp blue & brown	.28	.15
		Set value	.64	.42

Size of No. 302: 28x22¼mm.

1st anniv. of Ceylon's independence.

Issued: #300-301, Feb. 4; #302-303, Apr. 5.

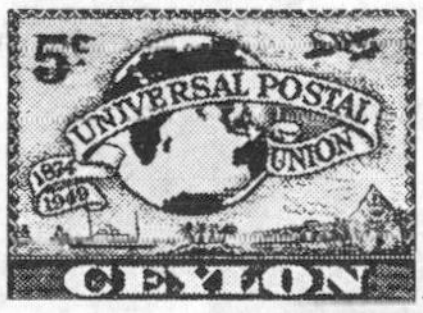

A77

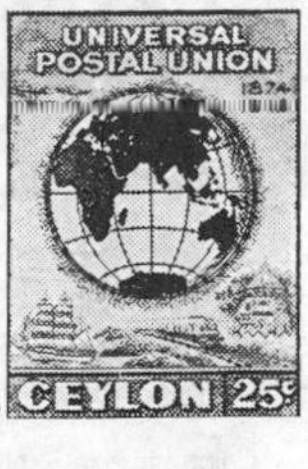

A78

Design: 15c, Lion Rock and UPU symbols.

Wmk. 290

1949, Oct. 10 Engr. *Perf. 12*

No.	Type	Description	Unused	Used
304	A77	5c dk green & brown	.22	.15
305	A77	15c dark car & black	.65	.25
306	A78	25c ultra & black	.90	.25
		Nos. 304-306 (3)	1.77	.65

75th anniv. of the UPU.

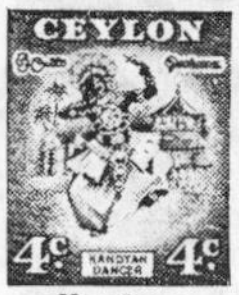

Kandyan Dancer A79

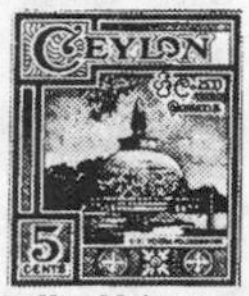

Kiri Vehera, Polonnaruwa A80

Vesak
Orchid — A81   Sigiriya — A82

Ratmalana, Plane — A83

Vatadage Ruins
at Madirigiriya
A84

1950, Feb. 4   Perf. 12x12½
307 A79 4c bright red & choc   .15 .15
308 A80 5c green   .15 .15
   a. Booklet pane of 10   .60
309 A81 15c pur & blue green   .18 .15
310 A82 30c carmine & yel   .18 .15
   Perf. 11x11½, 11½x11
311 A83 75c red org & blue   .40 .15
   a. Booklet pane of 4   2.00
312 A84 1r red brn & dp blue   .50 .20
    Nos. 307-312 (6)   1.56
    Set value   .56
     See Nos. 340-345.

Coconut
Palms — A85   Star
                     Orchid — A86

1951-52 Unwmk. Photo. Perf. 11½
313 A85 10c gray & dark green   .20 .15
314 A86 35c dk grn & rose brn ('52) .50 .15
   a. Corrected inscription ('54) .30 .15
    Set value   .15

On No. 314a a dot has been added above the
third character in the second line of the Tamil
inscription.
Issue dates: 10c, Aug. 1; 35c, Feb. 1.
See No. 351.

Mace and
Symbols of
Industry
A87

1952, Feb. 23   Wmk. 290
    Perf. 12½x14
315 A87 5c green   .15 .15
316 A87 15c brt ultramarine   .30 .25
    Set value   .30

Colombo Plan Exhibition, February 1952.

Coronation Issue

Queen Elizabeth II — A88

1953, June 2   Engr.   Perf. 12½x12½
317 A88 5c green   .15 .15

Royal
Procession
A89

1954, Apr. 10   Perf. 13x12½
318 A89 10c deep blue   .15 .15
    Visit of Queen Elizabeth II and the Duke of Edin-
burgh, 1954.

Sambar in
Ruhuna
National
Park — A90   Rubber
                    Trees — A91

Designs: 3c, Ancient guard stone. 6c and 10r,
Harvesting rice. 25c, Sigiriya fresco. 50c, Outrigger
fishing canoe. 85c, Tea Picker. 2r, Gal Oya dam. 5r,
Bas-relief, "The Lovers."

1954   Unwmk.   Photo.   Perf. 11½
    Size: 21x25½mm
319 A90 2c green & brown   .15 .15
320 A90 3c violet & black   .15 .15
321 A90 6c yel grn & blk brn   .15 .15
322 A90 25c vio bl, bl & brn orange .16 .15
    Size: 25½x21mm
323 A91 40c black brown   .25 .15
324 A91 50c indigo   .25 .15
  Size: 23x32½mm, 32½x23mm
325 A90 85c dk grn & gray   .45 .18
326 A91 2r blue & blk brn   1.75 .32
327 A91 5r dp org & blk brn   4.50 .80
328 A90 10r brown   10.00 2.25
    Nos. 319-328 (10)   17.81
    Set value   3.90
     See Nos. 346-356.
Issued: 25c, 50c, 5r, 10r, 3/15; others, 5/15.
Nos. 327-328 with revenue cancellations sell for
minimal prices.

King Coconuts
A92   Symbols of Agriculture
             A93

1954, Dec. 1
329 A92 10c brown & orange   .15 .15
    See No. 349.

    Perf. 14x14½
1955, Dec. 10   Wmk. 290
330 A93 10c orange & brown   .15 .15
    Royal Agricultural and Food Exhibition.

House of
Representatives
A94

1956, Mar. 26   Unwmk.   Perf. 11½
    Granite Paper
331 A94 10c deep green   .15 .15
    25th anniv. of Prime Minister Sir John Kote-
lawala's entry into the Ceylon Legislature.

Arrival of Vijaya
in Ceylon — A95

Dharmachakra
Encircling
Globe — A96

1956, May 23   Granite Paper
332 A95 3c dull vio gray & saph .15 .15
333 A96 15c ultramarine   .25 .15
    Set value   .31 .15
    Birth of Buddha, 2500th anniv. See #B1-B2.

Methods of
Transportation — A97

Designs: 35c, 85c, Ceylon's first stamp and coat
of arms.

1957, Apr. 1   Photo.   Perf. 12½x13
334 A97 4c blue green & ver   .18 .15
335 A97 10c blue & vermilion   .22 .15
    Perf. 11½
    Granite Paper
336 A97 35c blue, yel & brown   .35 .15
337 A97 85c dull grn, yel & brn   .65 .55
    Nos. 334-337 (4)   1.40
    Set value   .79
    Ceylon's 1st postage stamps, cent.

Nos. B1-B2 Overprinted with Black Bars
and Squares

1958, Jan. 15   Unwmk.
    Granite Paper
338 SP1 4c dp blue & lt yel   .15 .15
   a. Inverted overprint   12.50
   b. Double overprint   12.50
339 SP1 10c dk gray, yel & brt pink .15 .15
   a. Inverted overprint   20.00
    Set value   .15 .15

The overprint obliterates the surtax and inscription at right.

Types of 1950-54 Redrawn
    Perf. 12x12½
1958-59   Engr.   Wmk. 290
340 A79 4c brt red & chocolate   .15 .15
341 A80 5c green   .15 .15
342 A81 15c purple & blue grn   .15 .15
343 A82 30c car & yel ('59)   .15 .15
    Perf. 11½x11
344 A83 75c red org & bl ('59)   .28 .15
    Perf. 11x11½
345 A84 1r red brn & dp blue   .38 .15
    Set value   .97 .40
Issued: 4c, 5/14; 5c, 15c, 1r, 10/1; 30c, 75c,
5/1.
For surcharge see No. 368.

1958-59 Unwmk. Photo. Perf. 11½
    Granite Paper
346 A90 2c green & brown   .15 .15
347 A90 3c violet & black   .15 .15
348 A90 6c yel grn & blk brn   .15 .15
349 A92 10c brown & orange   .15 .15
350 A90 25c vio bl, bl & brn or-
    ange   .15 .15
351 A86 35c dk grn & rose brn   .22 .15
352 A91 50c indigo   .25 .15
353 A90 85c dark green & gray   1.90 .15
354 A91 2r blue & blk brn   .75 .25
355 A90 5r dp org & blk brn   1.90 .60
356 A90 10r brown   3.75 1.25
    Nos. 346-356 (11)   9.52
    Set value   2.55

Designs and sizes of Nos. 340-356 remain as
before, but wording has been changed to be
predominantly Singhalese. "Ceylon" appears in
small letters only in English and Tamil.
Nos. 355-356 with revenue cancellations sell for
minimal prices.
Issue dates: 35c, 50c, July 15. 10c, Oct. 1. 85c,
May 1, 1959. Others, May 14, 1958.

Hands Reaching
for UN
Symbol — A98

    Perf. 13x12½
1958, Dec. 10   Photo.   Unwmk.
357 A98 10c red brown & red   .15 .15
358 A98 85c Prus green & red   .50 .45
    10th anniv. of the signing of the Universal Decla-
ration of Human Rights.

Pirivena
Universities and
Founders
A99

1959, Dec. 31
359 A99 10c brt ultra & dp org   .15 .15
    Institution of Pirivena Universities; founders Hik-
kaduwe Sri Sumangala Nayaka Thero and
Ratmalane Sri Dharmaloka Nayake Thero.

Uprooted Oak
Emblem
A100   Prime Minister
              Bandaranaike
              A101

1960, Apr. 7   Photo.   Perf. 11½
    Granite Paper
360 A100 4c chocolate & gold   .15 .15
361 A100 25c vio blue & gold   .18 .15
    Set value   .26 .17
World Refugee Year, July 1, 1959-June 30, 1960.

1961, Jan. 8   Granite Paper
Two types:
  I - Gray hair at temple.
  II - Dark hair at temple (redrawn).
362 A101 10c vio bl & gray bl (I) .15 .15
   a. Type II   .40 .25
Solomon West Ridgeway Dias Bandaranaike,
assassinated Sept. 26, 1959.

Badge of
Singhalese
Scouts
A102   Malaria
              Eradication
              Emblem
              A103

1962, Feb. 26   Unwmk.   Perf. 11½
    Granite Paper
363 A102 35c dark blue & ocher   .30 .15
    Boy Scouts of Ceylon, 50th anniv.

    Perf. 14½x14
1962, Apr. 7   Photo.   Wmk. 290
364 A103 25c lt sep, red org & brn .15 .15
    WHO drive to eradicate malaria.

Monoplane 1938,
and De Havilland
Comet
IV — A104

1963, Feb. 28   Unwmk.   Perf. 11½
    Granite Paper
365 A104 50c lt grnsh blue & blk .30 .18
    25th anniv. of Ceylonese airmail service.

Stylized Vase and Wheat Emblem — A105

1963, Mar. 21
Granite Paper
366 A105 5c blue & orange ver .20 .15
367 A105 25c olive & brown .50 .15
Set value .15

FAO "Freedom from Hunger" campaign.

ශත
2
சதம்

No. 340 Surcharged

Perf. 12x12¹/₂
1963, June 1 Engr. Wmk. 290
368 A79 2c on 4c brt red & choc .15 .15
a. Inverted surcharge 25.00
b. Double surcharge 17.50

Rural
Life — A106

1963, July 5 Photo. Perf. 14x14¹/₂
369 A106 60c dull red & black .30 .18

50th anniv. of the Cooperative Movement.

Landscape and Elephant
A107

1963, Dec. 2 Wmk. 290
370 A107 5c blue & black .15 .15

National Conservation Week.

S.W.R.D.
Bandaranaike
A108

Anagarika
Dharmapala
A109

Perf. 11¹/₂
1963, Sept. 26 Unwmk. Engr.
Granite Paper
371 A108 10c blue .15 .15

Redrawn

1964, July 1 Photo.
Granite Paper
372 A108 10c grnsh gray & bl vio .15 .15

Frame redrawn on No. 372; inscription in bottom panel replaced by ornament. For surcharge see No. 389.

1964, Sept. 16 Unwmk. Perf. 11¹/₂
Granite Paper
373 A109 25c gray brn & dull yel .15 .15

Anagarika Dharmapala, Buddhist missionary, birth cent.

Ceylon Jungle
Fowl — A110

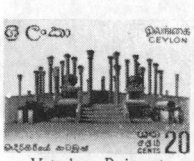

Vatadage Ruins at
Madirigiriya — A111

Tea
Picker — A112

Designs: 5c, Hill myna. 15c, Blue peafowl. 75c, Asiatic black-headed oriole. 5r, Girls, working in rice field. 10r, Map of Ceylon on scroll, showing agricultural development stations.

Wmk. 290, Unwmkd. (20c)
1964-69 Photo. Perf. 14, 11¹/₂ (20c)
374 A110 5c brt bl, blk, yel & grn .15 .15
375 A110 15c yel, grn, blk, brt bl & rose .15 .15
376 A111 20c dk red brn, buff .15 .15
377 A110 60c yel & multi .40 .15
a. Blue omitted 50.00
b. Red omitted 50.00
378 A110 75c ol, blk, org & brn .48 .15
a. Souvenir sheet of 4 2.00
b. As "a," overprinted 1.00
379 A112 1r brown & grn .32 .15
c. Brown omitted 125.00
379A A111 5r multicolored 1.50 .35
379B A112 10r brown & multi 3.25 .80
Nos. 374-379B (8) 6.40
Set value 1.55

No. 378a contains four imperf. stamps with simulated perforations similar to Nos. 374-375 and 377-378.
No. 378b is overprinted "First National Stamp Exhibition 1967" in two lines of black capitals.
No. 376 is on granite paper.
Issue dates: 20c, 1r, Oct. 1. 5c, 15c, 60c, 75c, Feb. 5, 1966. 5r, Aug. 15, 1969. 10r, Oct. 1, 1969. See No. 325.

Exhibition
Buildings,
Cogwheels
A113

1964, Dec. 1 Unwmk. Perf. 11
"Industrial Exhibition" in Singhalese and English
380 A113 5c multicolored .15 .15

"Industrial Exhibition" in Singhalese and Tamil
381 A113 5c multicolored .15 .15
a. Pair, #380-381 .16 .15
Set value .16 .15

1965 Industrial Exhibition.

Railroad Trains,
1864-1964
A114

Wmk. 290
1964, Dec. 21 Photo. Perf. 14
"Railway Centenary" in Singhalese and English
382 A114 60c lil rose, bl & yel grn .60 .20

"Railway Centenary" in Singhalese and Tamil
383 A114 60c lil rose, bl & yel grn .60 .20
a. Vertical pair, #382-383 1.25 .50

Centenary of Ceylonese railroads.

ITU Emblem,
Old and New
Communication
Equipment
A115

1965, May 17 Perf. 14
384 A115 2c ultra & red .15 .15
385 A115 30c brown & red .50 .30

ITU, centenary.

ICY Emblem
A116

1965, June 26 Unwmk. Perf. 11¹/₂
Granite Paper
386 A116 3c rose car & dk bl .15 .15
387 A116 50c gold, rose car & blk .50 .40

International Cooperation Year.

Municipal
Council
Building
A117

1965, Oct. 29 Photo. Perf. 11¹/₂
Granite Paper
388 A117 25c gray & green .15 .15

Centenary of Colombo Municipal Council.

No. 372 Surcharged **5** ■

1965, Dec. 18 Photo. Perf. 11¹/₂
389 A108 5c on 10c .15 .15

D. S.
Senanayake
A118

View and Arms of
Kandy
A119

1966, Mar. 22 Unwmk. Perf. 11¹/₂
Granite Paper
390 A118 10c bright green .15 .15

D. S. Senanayake, first prime minister of Ceylon, 14th death anniv. See No. 418.

Perf. 14x13¹/₂
1966, June 15 Photo. Wmk. 290
391 A119 25c multicolored .15 .15

Centenary of Kandy Municipal Council.

Opening of
WHO
Headquarters,
Geneva — A120

Unwmk.
1966, Oct. 8 Litho. Perf. 14
392 A120 4c multicolored .15 .15
393 A120 1r multicolored .50 .50

Rice, Map of
Ceylon, FAO
Emblem
A121

UNESCO Emblem
A122

Design: 30c, Rice and globe.

1966, Oct. 25 Photo. Perf. 11¹/₂
Granite Paper
394 A121 6c dk green, org & brn .15 .15
395 A121 30c brt blue, org & brn .22 .15
Set value .27 .20

Intl. Rice Year under sponsorship of the FAO.

1966, Nov. 3 Litho. Perf. 12
396 A122 3c tan & multi .15 .15
397 A122 50c brt green & multi .25 .20
Set value .30 .25

20th anniv. of UNESCO.

Map of Ceylon
and UNESCO
Emblem
A123

Worshippers at
Buddhist Shrine
A124

1966, Dec. 1 Unwmk. Perf. 14
398 A123 2c yel brn, yel & blue .15 .15
399 A123 2r multicolored .60 .45

Intl. Hydrological Decade (UNESCO), 1965-74.

1967, Jan. 2 Photo. Perf. 12
Designs: 20c, Muhintale Rock. 35c, Sacred Bo Tree. 60c, Adam's Peak.
400 A124 5c multicolored .15 .15
401 A124 20c multicolored .15 .15
402 A124 35c multicolored .15 .15
403 A124 60c multicolored .24 .15
Set value .50 .32

1st anniv. of the Poya Holiday System, Buddhist holiday replacing Sunday.

Dutch
Ramparts,
Clock Tower
and Arms of
Galle — A125

1967, Jan. 5 Litho. Perf. 14x13¹/₂
404 A125 25c dk green & multi .15 .15

Centenary of Galle Municipal Council.

Tea Research
A126

Designs: 40c, Tea tasting (cup and loose tea). 50c, Tea picking. 1r, Tea export (crate and freighter).

1967, Aug. 1 Unwmk. Perf. 13¹/₂
405 A126 4c multicolored .15 .15
406 A126 40c multicolored .16 .15
407 A126 50c multicolored .20 .15
408 A126 1r multicolored .40 .24
Set value .55

Centenary of the Ceylonese tea industry.

Elephant and
ITY Emblem
A127

1967, Aug. 15 Litho.
409 A127 45c multicolored .40 .15

Intl. Tourist Year.

Girl Guide,
Jubilee Emblem
and Flag — A128

1967, Sept. 19 Perf. 12x12¹/₂
410 A128 3c green & multi .15 .15
411 A128 25c org yel & multi .20 .20
Set value .35 .25

Ceylon Girl Guide Assoc., 50th anniv.

Henry S. Olcott and Buddhist Flag — A129

Perf. 13¹/₂
1967, Dec. 12   Unwmk.   Litho.
412 A129 15c multicolored   .15 .15
Colonel Henry S. Olcott (1832-1907), an American who reorganized the Buddhist hierarchy and school system in Ceylon and was the first president of the Theosophical Society.

Independence Memorial, Colombo A130

Design: 1r, Flag of Ceylon and mace.

1968, Feb. 4   Wmk. 290   Perf. 14
413 A130 5c multicolored   .15 .15
414 A130 1r multicolored   .40 .30
      Set value   .45 .35
20th anniversary of independence.

D. B. Jayatilaka — A131

1968, Feb. 14   Photo.
415 A131 25c brown   .15 .15
Sir Don Baron Jayatilaka (1868-1944), Buddhist leader and scholar.

Hygiene Institute, Kalutara A132

Perf. 11¹/₂x12
1968, Apr. 4   Litho.   Wmk. 290
416 A132 50c multicolored   .15 .15
WHO, 20th anniversary.

Jet over Colombo Terminal A133

1968, Aug. 5   Perf. 13¹/₂
417 A133 60c org brn, dk bl & org   .22 .15
Opening of Colombo Airport.

D. S. Senanayake — A134

1968, Sept. 23   Photo.   Perf. 14
418 A134 10c deep green   .15 .15
See No. 390.

Open Koran — A135

1968, Oct. 14   Photo.   Perf. 14
419 A135 25c org brn, blk, blue & emerald   .15 .15
1,400th anniversary of the Koran.

Human Rights Flame — A136

Perf. 12¹/₂x13¹/₂
1968, Dec. 10   Unwmk.
420 A136 2c multicolored   .15 .15
421 A136 20c multicolored   .15 .15
422 A136 40c multicolored   .15 .15
423 A136 2r multicolored   .55 .48
      Set value   .82 .67
International Human Rights Year.

Ceylon Buddhist Headquarters, Colombo A137

1968, Dec. 19   Litho.   Perf. 13¹/₂
424 A137 5c multicolored   .15 .15
50th anniv. of the All-Ceylon Buddhist Congress.
   A multicolored 50c showing the Sri Padmaya (Sacred Footprint) on Adam's Peak was prepared but the issuance order was countermanded on Dec. 18. Some were sold in ignorance of the withdrawal order.

E. W. Perera — A138

"Strength in Saving" — A139

Wmk. 290
1969, Feb. 17   Photo.   Perf. 14
425 A138 60c brown   .30 .20
E. W. Perera, member of Legislative Council.

1969, Mar. 20
426 A139 3c blue, yel & black   .15 .15
National Savings Movement, 25th anniv.

Seat of Enlightenment under Bodhi Tree — A140

Design: 6c, Buduresmala (disk symbolic of six-fold Buddha rays).

Wmk. 290
1969, Apr. 10   Litho.   Perf. 15
427 A140 4c orange & multi   .15 .15
428 A140 6c gold & multi   .15 .15
429 A140 35c scarlet & multi   .18 .15
      Set value   .28 .22
Vesak Day, which commemorates the birth, enlightenment and death of Buddha.
For surcharges see Nos. 463, 466.

Alexander Ekanayake Goonesingha — A141

1969, Apr. 29   Photo.   Perf. 14x14¹/₂
430 A141 15c org yel & multi   .15 .15
Alexander Ekanayake Goonesingha (1891-1967), trade unionist, political leader and diplomat.

ILO, 50th Anniv. — A142

1969, May 4   Perf. 14¹/₂x14
431 A142 5c grnsh bl & black   .15 .15
432 A142 25c car rose & black   .20 .15
      Set value   .25 .15

Convocation Hall, University of Ceylon — A143

Elephant Lamp (Ath Pana) — A144

Designs: 35c, "Lamp of Education," globe and flags. 50c, Uranium atom diagram. 60c, Symbols of science education. 1r, Aerial view of Sigiriya rock fortress.

Unwmk.
1969, Aug. 1   Litho.   Perf. 14
Inscribed: "SIYAWASA"
433 A143 4c yellow & multi   .15 .15
434 A144 6c multicolored   .15 .15
435 A144 35c multicolored   .15 .15
436 A144 50c red & multi   .16 .15
437 A143 60c blue & multi   .18 .15
438 A144 1r yel & multi   .32 .20
      Set value   .88 .54
Centenary of public education and archaeological research.
For surcharges see Nos. 464-467.

Wild Water Buffalo — A145

Designs: 15c, Slender loris. 50c, Axis deer. 1r, Leopard.

Perf. 14x13¹/₂
1970, May 11   Litho.   Unwmk.
439 A145 5c lt blue & multi   .15 .15
440 A145 15c buff & multi   .16 .15
441 A145 50c salmon & multi   .48 .16
442 A145 1r gray & multi   1.00 .42
   Nos. 439-442 (4)   1.79
      Set value   .68

Symbols of Agriculture and Industry — A146

1970, June 17
443 A146 60c multicolored   .15 .15
Asian Productivity Year.

Inauguration of UPU Headquarters, Bern — A147

1970, Aug. 14   Litho.   Unwmk.
444 A147 50c org, black & blue   .20 .15
445 A147 1.10r red, black & blue   .44 .22

Caduceus and Oil Lamp — A148

1970, Sept. 1   Perf. 13¹/₂x14
446 A148 5c multicolored   .15 .15
447 A148 45c gray & multi   .30 .15
      Set value   .35 .20
Centenary of the Ceylon Medical School.

Victory March and S.W.R.D. Bandaranaike A149

1970, Sept. 25   Perf. 14
448 A149 10c red & multi   .15 .15
For surcharge, see No. 465.

UN Emblem and Dove A150

Keppetipola Dissawe A151

1970, Oct. 24   Photo.   Perf. 12¹/₂x14
449 A150 2r dp orange & multi   .60 .38
25th anniversary of the United Nations.

1970, Nov. 26   Litho.   Perf. 14x14¹/₂
450 A151 25c multicolored   .15 .15
   The 152nd anniversary of the execution of Keppetipola Dissawe, leader of the Great Rebellion of 1817-18.

Ola Leaf Manuscript and Education Year Emblem — A152

1970, Dec. 21   Photo.   Perf. 13
451 A152 15c brown & multi   .15 .15
International Education Year.

Charles Henry
de
Soysa — A153

Edward Henry
Pedris — A154

1971, Mar. 3   Litho.   Perf. 14x13½
452 A153 20c orange & multi   .15 .15
de Soysa (1836-90), philanthropist who founded hospitals and schools.

1971, July 8   Litho.   Perf. 14x14½
453 A154 25c blue & multi   .15 .15
Edward Henry Pedris (1888-1925), patriot.

A 5c stamp for the 10th Conf. of World Fellowship of Buddhists, Ceylon, May 9-13, was not issued without "1972" overprint. See Sri Lanka No. 471.

Lenin (1870-1924)
A156

Cumaratunga
Munidasa
A157

1971, Aug. 31   Perf. 14½
455 A156 40c dp car & multi   .16 .15

1971, Oct. 29   Perf. 14
Poets and Philosophers: No. 457, Ananda Coomaraswamy (1887-1947). No. 458, Rev. S. Mahinda Thero (1905-1951). No. 459, Anada Rajakaruna (1885-1957). No. 460, Arumuga Navalar (1822-1878).
456 A157 5c brown   .15 .15
457 A157 5c slate   .15 .15
458 A157 5c deep orange   .15 .15
459 A157 5c dp vio blue   .15 .15
460 A157 5c brown red   .15 .15
  Set value   .15 .15

CARE Package
A158

1971, Dec. 28   Perf. 14x13
461 A158 50c purple, blue & pink   .20 .15
25th anniv. of CARE, a US-Canadian Cooperative for American Relief Everywhere.

Map of Ceylon,
Colombo Plan
Emblem
A159

1971, Dec. 28   Litho.   Perf. 14x14½
462 A159 20c multicolored   .15 .15
20th anniversary of the Colombo Plan.

Issues of 1969-70 Surcharged

5 X 5   ■   15   ●
a   b   c

25   ■   25
d   e

Wmk. 290, Unwmkd.
1971, Dec. 5   Perf. 15, 14
463 A140 (a) 5c on 4c (#427)   .20 .20
464 A143 (b) 5c on 4c (#433)   .15 .15
465 A149 (c) 15c on 10c (#448)   .15 .15
466 A140 (d) 25c on 6c (#428)   .20 .20
467 A144 (e) 25c on 6c (#434)   .20 .20
  Set value   .80 .80
Nos. 463-466 exist with surcharge inverted.

WHO Emblem
and
Heart — A160

1972, May 2   Unwmk.   Perf. 13x13½
468 A160 25c multicolored   .15 .15
"Your heart is your health," World Health Day.

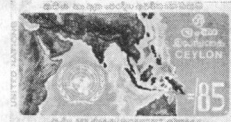

UN Emblem, Map Showing Asian Highway
A161

1972, May 2   Perf. 13x12½
469 A161 85c lt blue & multi   .40 .27
Economic Commission for Asia and the Far East (ECAFE), 25th anniversary.

Sri Lanka
Succeeding issues, inscribed "Sri Lanka," are listed under that name in this volume.

SEMI-POSTAL STAMPS

Catalogue values for unused stamps in this section are for Never Hinged items.

Lamp and
Dharmachakra — SP1

Design: 10c+5c, Hand of Peace.

Perf. 11½
1956, May 10   Unwmk.   Photo.
Granite Paper
B1 SP1 4c + 2c dp bl & lt yel   .28 .28
B2 SP1 10c + 5c dk gray, yel & brt   .45 .38
        pink
2500th anniv. of the birth of Buddha. The surtax went to the Buddha Jayanti Fund. For overprints, see Nos. 338-339.

WAR TAX STAMPS

Nos. 201, 202, 202a and 203   **WAR**
Overprinted   **STAMP**

Die I
1918   Wmk. 3   Perf. 14
MR1 A44 2c brown orange   .15 .15
  a.   Double overprint   40.00 35.00
  b.   Inverted overprint   40.00 35.00
MR2 A44 3c dp grn (Die Ia, type   .15 .15
        II)
  a.   3c dp green (Die I, type I)   .15 .15
  b.   Double overprint (Die I)   80.00 80.00
MR3 A44 5c red violet   .15 .15
  a.   Double overprint   30.00 30.00
  b.   Inverted overprint   40.00 40.00
  Set value   .30 .30

Same Overprint on No. 223
MR4 A44 1c on 5c red violet   .15 .15
  a.   Double overprint

OFFICIAL STAMPS

Regular Issues Overprinted **SERVICE**

1869   Wmk. 1   Perf. 12½, 14
Black Overprint
O1 A4 1p blue   50.00
O2 A1 2p yellow   50.00
O3 A5 3p rose   80.00
O4 A2 8p red brown   70.00
O5 A1 1sh gray lilac   100.00
Red Overprint
O6 A1 6p brown   67.50
O7 A2 2sh blue   95.00
  a.   Imperf.   625.00
  Nos. O1-O7 (7)   512.50
Nos. O1-O7 were never placed in use.
The overprint measures 15mm on #O1, O3.

Regular Issues Overprinted   **On**
in Black or Red   **Service**

1895-1900   Wmk. 2   Perf. 14
O8 A6 2c green   6.00 .25
O9 A6 2c org brn ('00)   .70 .30
O10 A24 3c org brn & grn   7.00 .60
O11 A24 3c green ('00)   1.25 .60
O12 A23 5c lilac   .90 .25
O13 A24 15c olive green   7.00 .30
O14 A24 15c ultra ('00)   7.00 .60
O15 A24 25c brown   7.00 .60
O16 A24 30c vio & org brn   9.00 .30
O17 A24 75c blk & org brn (R)   5.50 1.50
        ('99)
Wmk. 1
O18 A16 1r12c claret   50.00 35.00
  Nos. O8-O18 (11)   101.35 40.30

1903-04   Wmk. 2
O19 A36 2c orange brown   2.00 1.75
O20 A37 3c green   1.75 1.75
O21 A38 5c dull lilac   2.00 .85
O22 A40 15c ultramarine   11.00 3.25
O23 A40 25c bister   32.50 32.50
O24 A40 30c violet & green   12.50 2.25
  Nos. O19-O24 (6)   61.75 42.35

CHRISTMAS ISLAND

ˈkris—məs ˈī—lənd

LOCATION — In the Indian Ocean, 230 miles south of Java
GOVT. — A territory of Australia
AREA — 135 sq. mi.
POP. — 3,000 (est. 1983)

Australia took over Christmas Island from Singapore in 1958.

Catalogue values for all unused stamps in this country are for Never Hinged items.

Queen Elizabeth II — A1

Engr.; Name and Value Typo. in Black
1958, Oct. 15   Unwmk.   Perf. 14½
1 A1 2c yellow orange   .15 .15
2 A1 4c brown   .25 .20
3 A1 5c lilac   .30 .25
4 A1 6c dull blue   .35 .30
5 A1 8c gray brown   .60 .40
6 A1 10c violet   .75 .50
7 A1 12c carmine rose   .80 .60
8 A1 20c ultramarine   2.50 2.00
9 A1 50c yellow green   15.00 6.50
10 A1 $1 greenish blue   20.00 10.00
  Nos. 1-10 (10)   40.70 20.90

Map of
Island — A2

Island Scene — A3

Designs: 4c, Moonflower. 5c, Robber crab. 8c, Phosphate train. 10c, Crane loading phosphate.

12c, Flying fish cove. 20c, Loading ship. 50c, Frigate bird. $1, Yellow-billed tropic bird.

Perf. 14x14½, 14½x14
1963, Aug. 28   Engr.
11 A2 2c orange   .15 .15
12 A2 4c red brown   .20 .15
13 A2 5c rose lilac   .25 .20
14 A3 6c slate   .25 .20
15 A2 8c black   .60 .25
16 A2 10c violet   .40 .25
17 A3 12c dull red   .60 .40
18 A3 20c dark blue   1.40 1.00
19 A3 50c green   3.00 1.25
Size: 35x21mm
20 A3 $1 orange yellow   7.00 3.25
  Nos. 11-20 (10)   13.85 7.10

"Simpson and His
Donkey" by Wallace
Anderson — A3a

1965, Apr. 14   Photo.   Perf. 13½x13
21 A3a 10c brt grn, sepia & blk   .95 .95
ANZAC issue. See note after Australia No. 387.

Moorish
Goddess — A4

Fish: 1c, Golden striped grouper. 3c, Forceps fish. 4c, Queen triggerfish. 5c, Regal angelfish. 9c, Surgeonfish. 10c, Turkeyfish. 15c, Saddleback butterflyfish. 20c, Clown butterflyfish. 30c, Ghost pipefish. 50c, Lined surgeonfish. $1, Meyer's butterflyfish.

1968-70   Photo.   Perf. 13½
22 A4 1c multicolored   .15 .15
23 A4 2c multicolored   .25 .25
24 A4 3c multicolored   .30 .30
25 A4 4c multicolored   .40 .40
26 A4 5c multicolored   .45 .45
27 A4 9c multicolored   1.00 1.00
28 A4 10c multicolored   1.10 1.10
29 A4 15c multi ('70)   9.50 9.50
30 A4 20c multicolored   3.25 3.25
31 A4 30c multi ('70)   9.50 9.50
32 A4 50c multicolored   11.00 11.00
33 A4 $1 multicolored   21.00 21.00
  Nos. 22-33 (12)   57.90 57.90

Christmas Issues

"Hark the
Herald Angels
Sing" — A5

Virgin and
Child, by
Morando — A6

Adoration of the
Shepherds, Seville
School — A7

1969, Nov. 10   Photo.   Perf. 13½
34 A5 5c dk blue, gold, buff & red   .55 .55

1970, Oct. 26   Photo.   Perf. 14x14½
Design: 3c, The Ansidei Madonna, by Raphael.
35 A6 3c gold & multi   .25 .25
36 A6 5c silver & multi   .40 .40

1971, Oct. 4

Design: 20c, Adoration of the Shepherds, by Guido Reni.

37	A7	6c black & multi	.65	.65
38	A7	20c dark blue & multi	2.00	2.00

"Flying Fish," 1887 — A8

Ships and Map of Christmas Island: 1c, "Eagle," 1714. 2c, "Redpole," 1890. 3c, "Hoi Houw," 1959. 4c, "Pigot," 1771. 5c, "Valetta," 1968. 7c, "Asia," 1805. 8c, "Islander," 1929-60. 9c, "Imperieuse," 1888 (incorrectly inscribed "Imperious"). 10c, "Egeria," 1887. 20c, "Thomas," 1615. 25c, "Gordon," 1864. 30c, "Cygnet," 1688. 35c, "Triadic," 1958. 50c, "Amethyst," 1857. $1, "Royal Mary," 1643.

1972-73 Photo. *Perf. 14½x13½*

39	A8	1c yel green & multi	.15	.15
40	A8	2c lt red brn & multi	.15	.15
41	A8	3c dp rose & multi	.15	.15
42	A8	4c multicolored	.20	.15
43	A8	5c multicolored	.25	.20
44	A8	6c lilac & multi	.25	.25
45	A8	7c lt green & multi	.25	.25
46	A8	8c blue & multi	.30	.30
47	A8	9c org & multi	.40	.30
48	A8	10c lem & multi	.40	.30
49	A8	20c tan & multi	.85	.75
50	A8	25c multicolored	.90	.85
51	A8	30c multicolored	1.00	.90
52	A8	35c tan & multi	1.00	.90
53	A8	50c ultra & multi	1.10	1.00
54	A8	$1 yellow & multi	3.00	2.75
		Nos. 39-54 (16)	10.35	9.35

Issued: 6c, 7c, 8c, 20c, 2/5/72; 1c, 2c, 3c, $1, 6/5/72; 4c, 5c, 9c, 50c, 2/6/73; 10c, 25c, 30c, 35c, 6/4/73.

"Joy" — A9

Christmas: Nos. 55, 57, "Peace," angel facing right.

1972, Oct. 2 Litho. *Perf. 14½*

55	A9	3c black & multi	.85	.80
56	A9	3c black & multi	.85	.80
a.		Pair, #55-56	1.75	1.75
57	A9	7c black & multi	1.25	1.10
58	A9	7c black & multi	1.25	1.10
a.		Pair, #57-58	2.50	2.50
		Nos. 55-58 (4)	4.20	3.80

Mother and Child, Christmas Island Map — A10

1973, Oct. 2 Photo. *Perf. 14½x13½*

59	A10	7c blue & multi	1.25	1.25
60	A10	25c brt green & multi	5.75	5.75

Christmas.

Mother and Child with Star and Cross — A11

1974, Oct. 2 Photo. *Perf. 13½x14½*

61	A11	7c black & lilac rose	.70	.70
62	A11	30c black & yellow	4.00	4.00

Christmas.

Flight into Egypt — A12

1975, Oct. 2 Photo. *Perf. 14½x13½*

63	A12	10c gold, black & yel	.55	.55
64	A12	35c gold, vio blk & rose	1.90	1.90

Christmas.

Star of Bethlehem and Dove
A13 A14

1976, Oct. 2 Photo. *Perf. 13½*

65	A13	10c red & multi	.35	.35
66	A14	10c red & multi	.35	.35
a.		Pair, #65-66	.70	.70
67	A13	35c blue & multi	1.40	1.40
68	A14	35c blue & multi	1.40	1.40
a.		Pair, #67-68	3.00	3.00
		Nos. 65-68 (4)	3.50	3.50

Christmas.

Andrew Clunies-Ross (first settler) — A15

Famous Visitors: 1c, William Dampier, explorer, buccaneer. 2c, Capt. Willem de Vlamingh, Dutch explorer. 3c, Vice Adm. John F. L. P. Maclear, Royal Navy. 4c, John Murray, oceanographer, scientist. 5c, Adm. Pelham Aldrich and crew collecting specimen. 7c, Joseph Jackson Lister, naturalist, and arenga listeri plant. 8c, Adm. William Henry May. 9c, Henry Nicholas Ridley, botanist. 10c, George Clunies-Ross, pioneer phosphate miner. 20c, Capt. Joshua Slocum. 45c, Charles William Andrews, zoologist, and frigate birds. 50c, Karl Richard Hanitsch, zoologist, and fruit pigeon. 75c, Victor W. W. Saunders Purcell, Sinologist. $1, Fam Choo Beng, educator. $2, Harold Spencer-Jones, astronomer.

1977-78 Photo. *Perf. 14x13½*

69	A15	1c multicolored	.15	.15
70	A15	2c multicolored	.15	.15
71	A15	3c multicolored	.15	.15
72	A15	4c multicolored	.15	.15
73	A15	5c multicolored	.15	.15
74	A15	6c multicolored	.15	.15
75	A15	7c multicolored	.15	.15
76	A15	8c multicolored	.15	.15
77	A15	9c multicolored	.15	.15
78	A15	10c multicolored	.20	.20
79	A15	20c multicolored	.35	.35
80	A15	45c multicolored	.50	.50
81	A15	50c multicolored	.65	.65
82	A15	75c multicolored	1.00	1.00
83	A15	$1 multicolored	1.40	1.40
84	A15	$2 multicolored	2.00	2.00
		Nos. 69-84 (16)	7.45	7.45

Issue dates: 1c, 6c, 9c, $1, Apr. 30, 1977. 2c, 3c, 4c, $2, Feb. 22, 1978. 5c, 7c, 45c, 50c, May 31, 1978. 8c, 10c, 20c, 75c, Sept. 1, 1978.

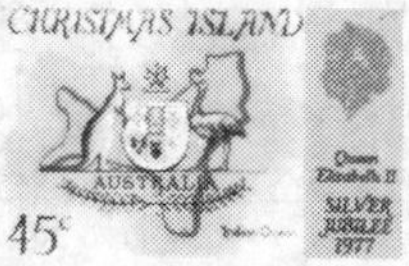

Australian Arms, Map of Christmas Island — A16

1977, June 2 Litho. *Perf. 14½x13½*

85	A16	45c multicolored	1.25	1.25

25th anniv. of reign of Elizabeth II.

> *Christmas Island stamps can be mounted in the Scott Australia Dependencies album.*

Souvenir Sheet

Partridge in a Pear Tree — A17

Twelve Days of Christmas: a, Partridge in a pear tree. b, 2 turtle doves. c, 3 French hens. d, 4 calling birds. e, 5 gold rings. f, 6 geese. g, 7 swans. h, 8 maids a-milking. i, 9 ladies dancing. j, 10 lords a-leaping. k, 11 pipers piping. l, 12 drummers drumming.

Unwmk.

1977, Oct. 20 Litho. *Perf. 14*

86		Sheet of 12	2.75	2.75
a.-l.		A17 10c, single stamp	.20	.20
m.		Wmk. 373 ('78)	2.25	2.25

Christmas.

Elizabeth II Coronation Anniversary

Common Design Types

Souvenir Sheet

1978, Apr. 21 Litho. *Perf. 15*

87		Sheet of 6	4.75	4.75
a.		CD326 45c White swan of Bohun	.75	.75
b.		CD327 45c Elizabeth II	.75	.75
c.		CD328 45c Abbott's booby	.75	.75

No. 87 contains 2 se-tenant strips of Nos. 87a-87c, separated by horizontal gutter with commemorative and descriptive inscriptions.

Souvenir Sheet

Christ Child — A18

Song of Christmas: a, Christ Child. b, Herald angels. c, Redeemer. d, Israel. e, Star. f, Three Wise Men. g, Manger. h. "All He stands for." i, "Shepherds came."

1978, Oct. 2 Litho. *Perf. 14*

88	A18	Sheet of 9	1.75	1.75
a.-i.		10c single stamp	.18	.18

Christmas. Each stamp design incorporates one letter of "Christmas."

IYC Emblem, Oriental Children — A19

Design: IYC emblem and children of different races holding hands, continuous design.

1979, Apr. 20 Litho. *Perf. 14*

89		Strip of 5	2.25	2.25
a.		A19 20c single stamp	.40	.40

International Year of the Child.

Rowland Hill and No. 25 — A20

Designs: Sir Rowland Hill (1795-1879), originator of penny postage, and Christmas Island stamps: a, No. 1. b, No. 11. c, No. 21. d, No. 25. e, No. 34.

1979, Aug. 27 Litho. *Perf. 13x13½*

90		Strip of 5	1.75	1.75
a.-e.		A20 20c any single	.30	.30

Three Kings Bearing Gifts — A21

Christmas: 55c, Virgin and Child, globe.

1979, Oct. 22 Litho. *Perf. 14x14½*

91	A21	20c multicolored	.35	.35
92	A21	55c multicolored	.90	.90

25 Years of Golf — A22

1980, Feb. 12 Litho. *Perf. 14½x14*

93	A22	20c shown	.30	.30
94	A22	55c Clubhouse	.80	.80

Surveyor, Phosphate Industry — A23

1980, May 5 Litho. *Perf. 14x14½*

95	A23	15c shown	.25	.25
96	A23	22c Drilling for samples	.38	.38
97	A23	40c Sample analysis	.70	.70
98	A23	55c Mine planning	.90	.90

1980, July 14

99	A23	15c Jungle clearing	.25	.25
100	A23	22c Overburden removal	.38	.39
101	A23	40c Open cut mining	.70	.70
102	A23	55c Restoration	.90	.90

1981, Feb. 9

103	A23	22c Screening and stockpiling	.38	.38
104	A23	28c Loading train	.50	.50
105	A23	40c Rail transport	.70	.70
106	A23	60c Drying	1.00	1.00

1981, May 4

107	A23	22c Crushing	.38	.38
108	A23	28c Pipeline	.50	.50
109	A23	40c Bulk storage	.70	.70
110	A23	60c Loading ship	1.00	1.00
		Nos. 95-110 (16)	9.62	9.63

Souvenir Sheet

Virgin and Child — A24

1980, Oct. 6 Litho. *Perf. 13½x13*

111		Sheet of 6	3.00	3.00
a.		A24 15c Angel	.25	.25
b.		A24 22c shown	.35	.35
c.		A24 60c Angel	.85	.85
d.		A24 15c Angel holding soldier	.25	.25
e.		A24 22c Kneeling woman and man	.35	.35
f.		A24 60c Chinese, Indian, European children	.85	.85

Christmas. No. 111 contains 2 strips of 3 (Nos. 111a-111c and 111d-111f) with gutter between.

Cryptoblepharus Egeriae — A25

Designs: Reptiles.

1981, Aug. 10 Litho. *Perf. 13x13½*

112 A25 24c shown .35 .35
113 A25 30c Emoia nativitata .50 .50
114 A25 40c Lepidodactylus listeri .60 .60
115 A25 60c Cyrtodactylus nov. .85 .85
Nos. 112-115 (4) 2.30 2.30

Souvenir Sheet

Nativity — A26

1981, Oct. 19 Litho. *Perf. 14½x14*

116 Sheet of 4 2.50 2.50
a. A26 18c Angels, star .30 .30
b. A26 24c shown .40 .40
c. A26 40c Children praying to Jesus .70 .70
d. A26 60c Children praying .90 .90

Christmas.

Reef Heron — A27

1982-83 Litho. *Perf. 14*

117 A27 1c shown .15 .15
118 A27 2c Noddies .15 .15
119 A27 3c Glossy swiftlet .15 .15
120 A27 4c Imperial pigeon .15 .15
121 A27 5c Christmas Isld. silver-eyes .15 .15
122 A27 10c Thrush .15 .15
123 A27 25c Silver bosunbird .35 .35
124 A27 30c Christmas Isld. emerald doves .42 .42
125 A27 40c Brown boobies .60 .60
126 A27 50c Red-footed boobies .75 .75
127 A27 65c Christmas Isld. frigatebird 1.00 1.00
128 A27 75c Golden bosunbirds 1.10 1.10
129 A27 80c Nankeen kestrel, vert. 1.25 1.25
130 A27 $1 Christmas Isld. hawk owl, vert. 1.50 1.50
131 A27 $2 Goshawk, vert. 2.75 2.75
132 A27 $4 Abbott's boobies, vert. 6.00 6.00
Nos. 117-132 (16) 16.62 16.62

Issue dates: 1c, 2c, 25c $4, Mar. 8. 3c, 4c, 10c, $2, June 14. 40c, 50c, 65c, 75c, Aug. 23. 5c, 30c, 80c, $1, Feb. 21, 1983.

Christmas — A28

25th Anniv. of Boat Club — A29

Designs: Paper sculptures. Nos. 135-137 se-tenant.

1982, Oct. 18 Litho. & Embossed

135 A28 27c Joseph .40 .40
136 A28 50c Angel .65 .65
137 A28 75c Wise Man 1.00 1.00
Nos. 135-137 (3) 2.05 2.05

Perf. 14x14½, 14½x14
1983, May 2 Litho.

Designs: Various boating activities.

138 A29 27c multicolored .40 .40
139 A29 35c multicolored .55 .55
140 A29 50c multi, horiz. .85 .85
141 A29 75c multi, horiz. 1.10 1.10
Nos. 138-141 (4) 2.90 2.90

25th Anniv. of Australian Territory A30

1983, Oct. 1 Litho. *Perf. 14*

142 A30 24c Maps, golden bosun bird, kangaroo .35 .35
143 A30 30c Map, flag .40 .40
144 A30 85c Boeing 727, maps 1.25 1.25
Nos. 142-144 (3) 2.00 2.00

Christmas — A31

Designs: Christmas candles.

1983, Oct. 31 Litho. *Perf. 13½x13*

145 A31 24c multicolored .35 .35
146 A31 30c multicolored .40 .40
147 A31 85c multicolored 1.25 1.25
Nos. 145-147 (3) 2.00 2.00

Red Land Crab — A32

1984, Feb. 20 Litho. *Perf. 14x14½*

148 A32 30c Feeding .55 .55
149 A32 40c Migration .75 .75
150 A32 55c Developmental stages 1.00 1.00
151 A32 85c Adult female, young 1.50 1.50
Nos. 148-151 (4) 3.80 3.80

Local Fungi — A33

1984, Apr. 30 *Perf. 13½x14½*

152 A33 30c Leucocoprinus fragilissimus .60 .60
153 A33 40c Microporus xanthopus .85 .85
154 A33 45c Trogia anthidepas .90 .90
155 A33 55c Haddowia longipes 1.10 1.10
156 A33 85c Phillipsia domingensis 1.65 1.65
Nos. 152-156 (5) 5.10 5.10

Cricket on Christmas Isld., 25th Anniv. — A34

1984, July 23 Litho. *Perf. 14*

157 A34 30c Runout .60 .60
158 A34 40c Catch at point .80 .80
159 A34 55c Batsman 1.10 1.10
160 A34 85c Batsman hitting 1.65 1.65
Nos. 157-160 (4) 4.15 4.15

Souvenir Sheet

Christmas; Ausipex '84 A35

1984, Sept. 21 Litho. *Perf. 13½*

161 Sheet of 3 3.50 3.50
a. A35 30c Father Christmas arriving .60 .60
b. A35 55c Distributing gifts 1.10 1.10
c. A35 85c Waving good-bye 1.75 1.75

Crabs — A36

1985 Litho. *Perf. 13x13½*

162 A36 30c Birgus latro .55 .55
163 A36 33c Cardiosoma hirtipes .60 .60
164 A36 33c Gecarcoidea natalis .60 .60
165 A36 40c Ocypode ceratophthalma .75 .75
166 A36 45c Ceonobita rugosa .80 .80
167 A36 45c Metasesarma rousseauxi .80 .80
168 A36 55c Coenobita brevimana 1.10 1.10
169 A36 60c Geograpsus stormi 1.10 1.10
170 A36 60c Grapsus tenuicrustatus 1.10 1.10
171 A36 85c Geograpsus grayi 1.65 1.65
172 A36 90c Ocypode cordimana 1.75 1.75
173 A36 90c Geograpsus crinipes 1.75 1.75
Nos. 162-173 (12) 12.55 12.55

Issued: 30c, 40c, 55c, 85c, 1/30; #163, 166, 169, 172, 4/29; #164, 167, 170, 173, 7/22.

Once in Royal David's City — A37

Songs: 33c, While Shepherds Watched Their Flocks by Night. 45c, Away in a Manger. 60c, We Three Kings of Orient Are. 90c, Hark! The Herald Angels Sing.

1985, Oct. 28 Litho. *Perf. 14x14½*

174 A37 27c multicolored .50 .50
175 A37 33c multicolored .65 .65
176 A37 45c multicolored .85 .85
177 A37 60c multicolored 1.10 1.10
178 A37 90c multicolored 1.65 1.65
a. Strip of 5, #174-178 5.00 5.00

Christmas.

Halley's Comet — A38

1985, Apr. 30 Litho. *Perf. 14*

179 A38 33c Over island .58 .58
180 A38 45c Edmond Halley .75 .75
181 A38 60c Over phosphate shipping 1.10 1.10
182 A38 90c Over Flying Fish Cove 1.60 1.60
Nos. 179-182 (4) 4.03 4.03

Indigenous Flowers — A39

1986, June 30 Litho. *Perf. 14*

183 A39 33c Ridley's orchid .58 .30
184 A39 45c Hanging flower .75 .40
185 A39 60c Hoya 1.10 .60
186 A39 90c Sea hibiscus 1.60 .85
Nos. 183-186 (4) 4.03 2.15

Royal Wedding Issue, 1986
Common Design Type

Designs: 33c, Couple in Buckingham Palace garden. 90c, Andrew operating helicopter.

1986, July 23 Litho. *Perf. 14½x14*

187 CD338 33c multicolored .65 .65
188 CD338 90c multicolored 1.75 1.75

Christmas A40

Santa Claus at Christmas Island.

1986, Sept. 30 Litho. *Perf. 13x13½*

189 A40 30c Speedboating .50 .50
190 A40 36c At the beach .60 .60
191 A40 55c Fishing .85 .85
192 A40 70c Golfing 1.10 1.10
193 A40 $1 Sleeping in hammock 1.60 1.60
Nos. 189-193 (5) 4.65 4.65

Visiting Ships, Cent. A41

1987, Jan. 21 *Perf. 14½*

194 A41 36c Flying Fish .55 .55
195 A41 90c Egeria 1.40 1.40

Wildlife A42

1987-89 Litho. *Perf. 14*

196 A42 1c Blind snake .15 .15
197 A42 2c Blue-tailed skink .15 .15
198 A42 3c Insectivorous bat .15 .15
199 A42 5c Green cricket .15 .15
200 A42 10c Christmas Is. fruit bat .15 .15
201 A42 25c Gecko .30 .30
202 A42 30c Praying mantis .35 .35
203 A42 36c Hawk owl .42 .42
204 A42 40c Bull-mouth helmet shell .50 .50
204A A42 41c Nudibranch ('89) .60 .60
205 A42 50c Textile cone shell .60 .60
206 A42 65c Brittle-stars .75 .75
207 A42 75c Royal angelfish .90 .90
208 A42 90c Christmas Is. white butterfly 1.10 1.10
209 A42 $1 Mimic butterfly 1.25 1.25
210 A42 $2 Shrew 2.50 2.50
211 A42 $5 Green turtle 6.00 6.00
a. Sheet of 16, #196-211 18.00 18.00
Nos. 196-211 (17) 16.02 16.02

Issue dates: 1c, 2c, 25c, $5, Mar. 25; 3c, 10c, 36c, $2, June 24; 40c, 50c, 65c, 75c, Aug. 26. 5c, 30c, 90c, $1, Mar. 1, 1988. 41c, Sept. 1, 1989.

Stamps contained in No. 211a inscribed "1988" at bottom.

For overprint see Nos. 246-247.

Souvenir Sheet

Santa Claus Delivering Presents — A43

Illustration reduced.

1987, Oct. 7 Litho. *Perf. 13½*

212 A43 Sheet of 4 3.85 3.85
a. 30c multicolored .45 .45
b. 37c multicolored .55 .55
c. 90c multicolored 1.35 1.35
d. $1 multicolored 1.50 1.50

Christmas. Nos. 212a-212d printed in a continuous design.

Australia Bicentennial A44

Designs: a, First Fleet sighted by 5 Aborginals on land. b, Four Aboriginals on land, one in canoe. c, Ships entering bay, kangaroos. d, Europeans land. e, Flag raising.

1988, Jan. 26 Litho. *Perf. 13*

213 Strip of 5 3.50 3.50
a.-e. A44 37c any single .70 .70

Nos. 213a-213e printed in a continuous design. See Cocos Islands No. 172.

Annexation of the
Island, Cent. — A45

1988, June 8   **Litho.**   *Perf. 14½*
214	A45	37c Capt William Henry May	.55	.55
215	A45	53c Annexation ceremony	.78	.78
216	A45	95c HMS Imperieuse	1.40	1.40
217	A45	$1.50 Building cairn of stones	2.20	2.20
		Nos. 214-217 (4)	4.93	4.93

Settlement of
Christmas Is.,
Cent. — A46

Transportation: 37c, Horse and cart, 1910. 55c, Phosphate mining, 1910. 70c, Steam locomotive, 1914. $1, Arrival of first aircraft, 1957.

1988, Aug. 24   **Litho.**   *Perf. 14½*
218	A46	37c multicolored	.52	.52
219	A46	55c multicolored	.80	.80
220	A46	70c multicolored	1.00	1.00
221	A46	$1 multicolored	1.50	1.50
		Nos. 218-221 (4)	3.82	3.82

Christmas
Presents — A47

1988, Nov. 15   *Perf. 14x14½*
222	A47	32c Bucket, shovel, boat	.48	.48
223	A47	39c Snorkeling equipment	.60	.60
224	A47	90c Toy soldier, doll, stuffed animals	1.40	1.40
225	A47	$1 Race car, truck, plane	1.50	1.50
		Nos. 222-225 (4)	3.98	3.98

Chinese New
Year — A48

1989, Jan. 31   *Perf. 14½*
226	A48	39c Good harvest	.60	.60
227	A48	70c Prosperity	1.15	1.15
228	A48	90c Good fortune	1.40	1.40
229	A48	$1 Progress	1.55	1.55
		Nos. 226-229 (4)	4.70	4.70

Sir John
Murray (1841-
1914),
Oceanographer
A49

1989, Mar. 16   *Perf. 14½x14*
230	A49	39c Portrait	.58	.58
231	A49	80c Murray Hill (map)	1.20	1.20
232	A49	$1 Murray's equipment	1.50	1.50
233	A49	$1.10 HMS Challenger	1.60	1.60
		Nos. 230-233 (4)	4.88	4.88

Malay-Hari Raya Folk
Celebration — A50

1989, May 31   *Perf. 14*
234	A50	39c Children	.62	.62
235	A50	55c Tambourine player	.90	.90
236	A50	80c Girl	1.30	1.30
237	A50	$1.10 Minaret	1.75	1.75
		Nos. 234-237 (4)	4.57	4.57

Ferns — A51   Christmas — A52

1989, Aug. 16
238	A51	41c *Huperzia phlegmaria*	.62	.62
239	A51	65c *Asplenium polydon*	.98	.98
240	A51	80c *Davallia denticulata*	1.20	1.20
241	A51	$1.10 *Asplenium nidus*	1.65	1.65
		Nos. 238-241 (4)	4.45	4.45

1989, Oct. 4   **Litho.**   *Perf. 14½x15*

Biblical scenes: 36c, Joseph. 41c, Manger. 80c, Shepherds see star. $1.10, Magi riding camels.
242	A52	36c multi	.55	.55
243	A52	41c multi	.65	.65
244	A52	80c multi	1.25	1.25
245	A52	$1.10 multi	1.70	1.70
		Nos. 242-245 (4)	4.15	4.15

Nos. 204A and 209 Overprinted

1989, Oct. 18   **Litho.**   *Perf. 14*
246	A42	41c multicolored	.65	.65
247	A42	$1 multicolored	1.55	1.55

STAMPSHOW '89, Melbourne.

1st Sighting of Christmas
Is., 375th Anniv. — A53

Sightings of the island: 41c, John Milward, master of the British East India ship *Thomas*, 1615. $1.10, William Mynors, captain of *Royal Mary*, 1643.

1990, Jan. 31   **Litho.**   *Perf. 14x15*
248	A53	41c multicolored	.65	.65
249	A53	$1.10 multicolored	1.70	1.70

Transport
Through the
Ages — A55

Perf. 14x13½, 13½x14
1990		**Litho.**		**Unwmk.**
254	A55	1c Phosphate transport	.15	.15
255	A55	2c Phosphate train	.15	.15
256	A55	3c Rail car, vert.	.15	.15
257	A55	5c Road train	.15	.15
258	A55	10c Trishaw, vert.	.15	.15
259	A55	15c Terex	.22	.22
260	A55	25c Long bus	.38	.38
261	A55	30c Passenger rake, vert.	.45	.45
262	A55	40c Passenger barge, vert.	.60	.60
263	A55	50c Kolek canoe	.75	.75

264	A55	65c Flying doctor, ambulance	1.00	1.00
265	A55	75c Tradestore van	1.15	1.15
266	A55	90c Vintage truck	1.40	1.40
267	A55	$1 Water tanker	1.50	1.50
268	A55	$2 Traction engine	3.00	3.00
269	A55	$5 Steam locomotive, flat car	7.50	7.50
		Nos. 254-269 (16)	18.70	18.70

Issue dates: 1c, 3c, 10c, 25c, 30c, 40c, 50c, $5, Apr. 18. Others, Aug. 22.

World Wildlife
Fund — A56

Abbott's boobies *(Sula abbotti)*: 20c, Adult (facing left). 29c, Adult (facing right). No. 273, Adults, nest, hatchling. No. 274a, Adult landing on tree branch. No. 274b, Adult resting on branch. No. 274c, Adult, young in nest.

Perf. 14x14½
1990, June 6		**Litho.**		**Unwmk.**
270	A56	10c shown	.15	.15
271	A56	20c multicolored	.30	.30
272	A56	29c multicolored	.45	.45
273	A56	41c multicolored	.62	.62
		Nos. 270-273 (4)	1.52	1.52

Souvenir Sheet
Perf. 14½
274		Sheet of 3	1.90	1.90
a.-c.		A56 41c any single	.62	.62
d.		Overprinted in purple	1.90	1.90
e.		Overprinted in green	1.90	1.90

No. 274d overprint reads "WORLD STAMP EXHIBITION / AUCKLAND, NEW ZEALAND, 24 AUGUST-2 SEPTEMBER 1990."
No. 274e overprint reads "BIRDPEX '90 National Philatelic Exhibition / University of Canterbury Christchurch NZ 6-9 Dec 1990 / In Conjunction / With The 20th International Ornithological Congress" and Bird's head.
Issued: No. 274d, Aug. 24; No. 274e, Dec. 6.

Centenary of Visit by Botanist Henry
Ridley — A57

1990, July 11   **Litho.**   *Perf. 14½*
275	A57	41c No. 77	.62	.62
276	A57	75c Ridley, vert.	1.15	1.15

Christmas
A58

Flowers.

1990, Oct. 3   **Litho.**   *Perf. 14½*
294	A58	38c Corymborkus veratrifolia	.62	.62
295	A58	43c Hoya aldrichii	.72	.72
296	A58	80c Quisqualis indica	1.35	1.35
297	A58	$1.20 Barringtonia racemosa	2.00	2.00
		Nos. 294-297 (4)	4.69	4.69

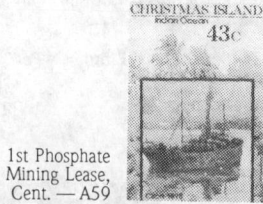

1st Phosphate
Mining Lease,
Cent. — A59

1991, Feb. 13   **Litho.**   *Perf. 14½*
298	A59	43c Freighter	.65	.65
299	A59	43c Loading rail cars	.65	.65
300	A59	85c Shay locomotive	1.30	1.30

301	A59	$1.20 Bucket shovel	1.85	1.85
302	A59	$1.70 Reforestation	2.60	2.60
a.		Strip of 5, #298-302	7.05	7.05

Island Police
Force — A60

1991, Apr. 17   **Litho.**   *Perf. 14½*
303	A60	43c Community relations	.65	.65
304	A60	43c Traffic control	.65	.65
305	A60	90c Customs and quarantine	1.40	1.40
306	A60	$1.20 Search and rescue	1.85	1.85
a.		Souvenir sheet of 4, #303-306	4.55	4.55
		Nos. 303-306 (4)	4.55	4.55

Maps — A61

1991, June 19   **Litho.**   *Perf. 14*
307	A61	43c 1991	.65	.65
308	A61	75c Goos Atlas, 1666	1.05	1.05
309	A61	$1.10 Apres De Manevillette, 1745	1.55	1.55
310	A61	$1.20 Comberford, 1667	1.70	1.70
		Nos. 307-310 (4)	4.95	4.95

Trees
A62

1991, Aug. 21   **Litho.**   *Perf. 14*
311	A62	43c Bruguiera gymnorrhiza	.65	.65
312	A62	70c Syzygium operculatum	1.00	1.00
313	A62	85c Ficus microcarpa	1.20	1.20
314	A62	$1.20 Arenga listeri	1.70	1.70
		Nos. 311-314 (4)	4.55	4.55

Christmas
A63

Drawings of "What Christmas Means to Me" by: No. 315a, S'ng Yen Luiw. b, Liew Ann Nee. c, Foo Pang Chuan. d, Too Lai Peng. e, Jesamine Wheeler. 43c, Ho Puay Ha. $1, Ng Hooi Hua. $1.20, Yani Kawi.

1991, Oct. 2   **Litho.**   *Perf. 14½*
315		Strip of 5	2.75	2.75
a.-e.		A63 38c any single	.55	.55
316	A63	43c multicolored	.65	.65
317	A63	$1 multicolored	1.45	1.45
318	A63	$1.20 multicolored	1.70	1.70
		Nos. 315-318 (4)	6.55	6.55

A64   Shells — A65

War Time Evacuation, 50th Anniv.: No. 319, Conference to decide upon evacuation. No. 320,

Europeans awaiting barge. $1.05, Barge approaching waiting ship. $1.20, Remaining population waving to TSS Islander.

1992, Feb. 19 Litho. *Perf. 14½*

319	A64	45c multicolored	.65	.65
320	A64	45c multicolored	.65	.65
321	A64	$1.05 multicolored	1.50	1.50
322	A64	$1.20 multicolored	1.70	1.70
		Nos. 319-322 (4)	4.50	4.50

1992 Litho. *Perf. 15x14½*

327	A65	5c Cypraea tigris	.15	.15
328	A65	10c Cypraea caput-serpentis	.15	.15
329	A65	15c Lambis scorpius	.22	.22
330	A65	20c Chlamys pallium	.28	.28
330A	A65	25c Engina mendicaria	.36	.36
331	A65	30c Drupa ricinus	.42	.42
332	A65	40c Distorsio reticulata	.58	.58
333	A65	45c Turbo petholatus	.65	.65
334	A65	50c Cantharus pulcher	.72	.72
335	A65	60c Conus capitaneus	.85	.85
336	A65	70c Turbo lajonkairii	1.00	1.00
337	A65	80c Lambis chiragra	1.15	1.15
338	A65	90c Angaria delphinus	1.30	1.30
339	A65	$1 Vasum ceramicum	1.45	1.45
340	A65	$2 Tonna perdix	2.90	2.90
342	A65	$5 Drupa rubusidaea	7.25	7.25
		Nos. 327-342 (16)	19.43	19.43

Issued: 10c, 20c, 30c, 45c, 60c, 80c, $1, $2, 4/15; 5c, 15c, 25c, 40c, 50c, 70c, 90c, $5, 8/19.
For overprint see No. 348.
This is an expanding set. Numbers may change.

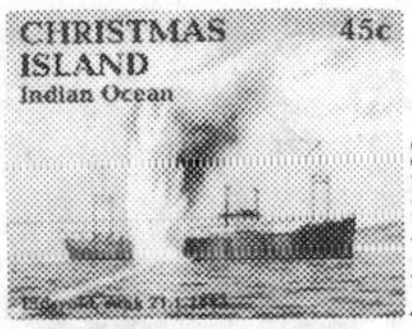

Sinking of Eidsvold and Nissa Maru, 50th Anniv. — A66

Designs: 45c, Eldsvold hit by torpedo. 80c, Eidsvold sinking. $1.05, Nissa Maru hit by torpedo. $1.20, Nissa Maru sinking.

1992, June 17 Litho. *Perf. 14x13½*

343	A66	45c multicolored	.65	.65
344	A66	80c multicolored	1.15	1.15
345	A66	$1.05 multicolored	1.55	1.55
346	A66	$1.20 multicolored	1.75	1.75
		Nos. 343-346 (4)	5.10	5.10

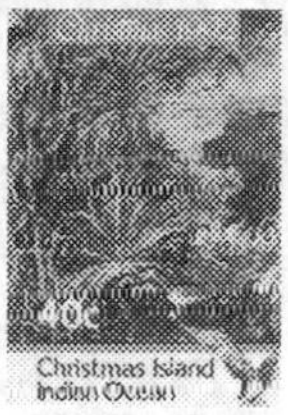

Christmas — A67

Coastline, booby birds: a, 40c, Plants on shore, birds. b, 40c, Birds, rocks offshore. c, 45c, Birds on shore. d, $1.05, Birds in flight, coastline. e, $1.20, Forest, rocky coastline.

1992, Oct. 7 Litho. *Perf. 14½*

347	A67	Strip of 5, #a.-e.		5.00 5.00

No. 342 Ovptd. in Red Violet 

1992, Sept. 1 Litho. *Perf. 15x14½*

348	A65	$5 on #342	7.25	7.25

Kuala Lumpur Philatelic Exhibition.

Starting with No. 349, Christmas Island stamps are valid for postage on items mailed in Australia and Australian stamps are valid on items posted on Christmas Island.

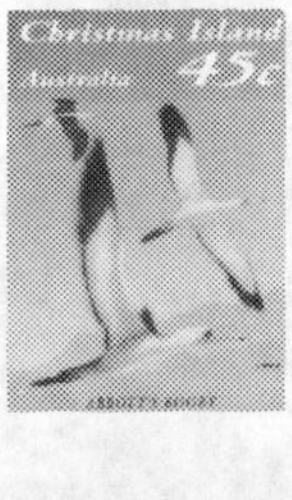

Seabirds — A68

Designs: a, Abbott's booby. b, Christmas Island frigatebird. c, Common noddy. d, Golden bosunbird. e, Brown booby.

1993, Mar. 4 Litho. *Perf. 14½x14*

349	A68	45c Strip of 5, #a.-e.	3.15	3.15
f.		Souvenir sheet of 5, #a.-e.	3.15	3.15
g.		As "f," overprinted	3.15	3.15
h.		As "f," overprinted	3.15	3.15

No. 349g Ovptd. in Gold in sheet margin with Taipei '93 emblem and: "ASIAN INTERNATIONAL INVITATION STAMP EXHIBITION / TAIPEI '93" in Chinese and English.

No. 349h Ovptd. in Gold in Sheet Margin with "INDOPEX '93 / 6TH ASIAN INTERNATIONAL PHILATELIC EXHIBITION 1993 / PAMERAN INTERNASIONAL PENGUMPULAN / KEENAM DI ASIA TAHUN 1993" and show emblem.

Issued: #349g, 4/93; #349h, 5/29/93.

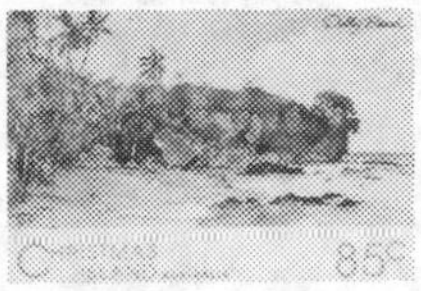

Scenic Views — A69

1993, June 1 *Perf. 14x14½*

350	A69	85c Dolly Beach	1.25	1.25
351	A69	95c Blow holes	1.40	1.40
352	A69	$1.05 Merrial Beach	1.50	1.50
353	A69	$1.20 Rain forest	1.75	1.75
		Nos. 350-353 (4)	5.90	5.90

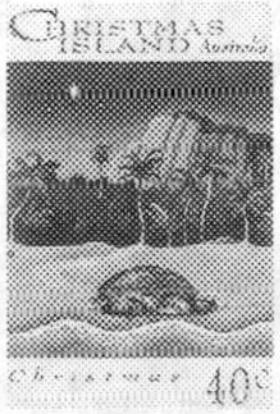

Christmas — A70

1993, Sept. 2 Litho. *Perf. 14½x14*

354	A70	40c Turtle on beach	.55	.55
355	A70	45c Crabs, wave	.60	.60
356	A70	$1 Frigatebird, rainforest	1.40	1.40
		Nos. 354-356 (3)	2.55	2.55

Naming of Christmas Island, 350th Anniv. A71
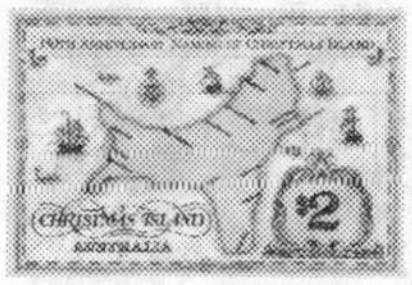

1993, Dec. 1 Litho. *Perf. 14x14½*

357	A71	$2 multicolored	2.75	2.75

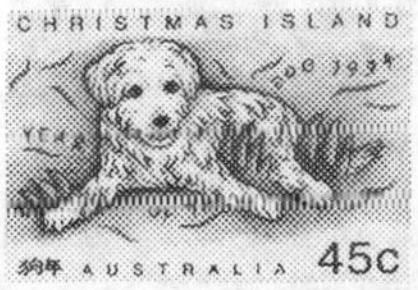

New Year 1994 (Year of the Dog) — A72

1994, Jan. 20 Litho. *Perf. 14x14½*

358	A72	45c shown	.60	.60
359	A72	45c Pekingese	.60	.60
a.		Pair, #358-359	1.25	1.25
b.		Souvenir sheet of 1, #359a	1.25	1.25
c.		As "b," overprinted	1.25	1.25
d.		As "b," overprinted	1.25	1.25
e.		As "b," overprinted	1.25	1.25
f.		As "b," overprinted	1.25	1.25

No. 359c Ovptd. in gold in sheet margin with dog and "Melbourne / STAMP & COIN SHOW / 11-13 February 1994;" No. 359d with "HONG KONG '94 STAMP EXHIBITION" and show emblem; No. 359e with "Canberra /Stamp Show '94 / 19-21 March / 1994" and show emblem; COIN SHOW 1994 / JUNE 11, 12, 13."

Issued: #359c, 2/11/94; #359d, 2/18/94; #359e, 3/19/94; #359f, 1995.

Christmas Island Railway Steam Locomotives A73
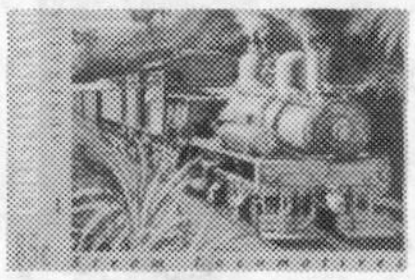

1994, May 19 Litho. *Perf. 14x14½*

360	A73	85c Locomotive No. 4	1.25	1.25
361	A73	95c Locomotive No. 9	1.40	1.40
362	A73	$1.20 Locomotive No. 1	1.75	1.75
		Nos. 360-362 (3)	4.40	4.40

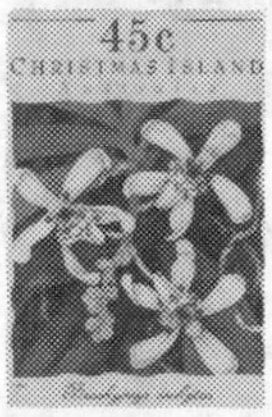

Orchids — A74

Designs: a, Brachypeza archytas. b, Thelasis capitata. c, Corymborkis veratrifolia. d, Flickingeria nativitatis. e, Dendrobium crumenatum.

1994, Aug. 16 Litho. *Perf. 14½x14*

363	A74	45c Strip of 5, #a.-e.	3.25	3.25

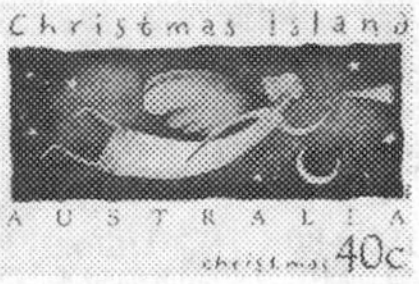

Christmas A75

1994, Sept. 8 Litho. *Perf. 14x14½*

364	A75	40c Angel	.60	.60
365	A75	45c Wise man	.70	.70
366	A75	80c Bethlehem	1.25	1.25
		Nos. 364-366 (3)	2.55	2.55

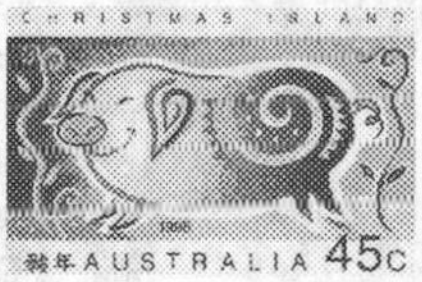

New Year 1995 (Year of the Boar) — A76

Design: 85c, Stylized boar, diff.

1995, Jan. 12 Litho. *Perf. 14x14½*

367	A76	45c shown	.70	.70
368	A76	85c multicolored	1.25	1.25
a.		Souvenir sheet, #367-368	2.00	2.00
b.		As "a," overprinted	2.00	2.00

No. 368b ovptd. in gold in sheet margin with outline of boar and: "STAMP & COIN FAIR / ROYAL EXHIBITION BUILDING / MELBOURNE VIC. 3000 . 10-12 FEB 1995."

Christmas Island Golf Course, 40th Anniv. — A77
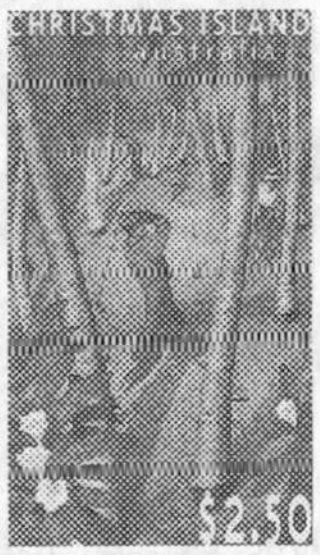

1995, May 11 Litho. *Perf. 14*

369	A77	$2.50 multicolored	3.75	3.75

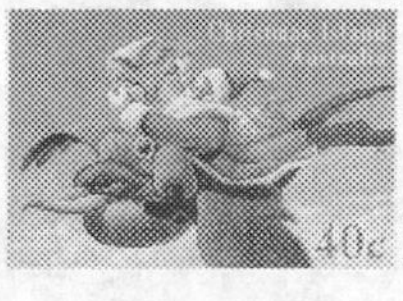

Christmas A78

Santa Claus riding great frigatebird: 40c, Reading map. 45c, Dropping presents. 80c, Waving.

1995, Sept. 14 Litho. *Perf. 14x14½*

370	A78	40c multicolored	.60	.60
371	A78	45c multicolored	.70	.70
372	A78	80c multicolored	1.25	1.25
		Nos. 370-372 (3)	2.55	2.55

End of World War II, 50th Anniv. A79
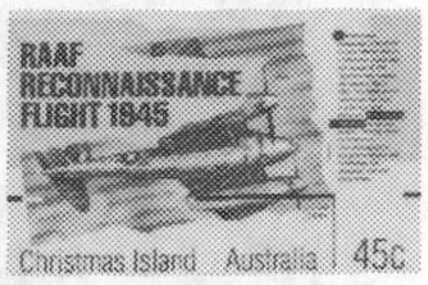

Designs: #373a, RAAF reconnaissance flight, 1945. #373b, Arrival of HMS Rother, 1945.

Perf. 14x14½

1995, Oct. 12 Litho. & Engr.

373		Pair	1.40	1.40
a.-b.		A79 45c any single	.70	.70

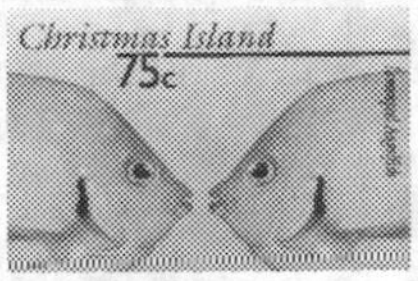

Angelfish A80

1995, Oct. 12 Litho.

374	A80	75c Lemonpeel	1.10	1.10
375	A80	$1 Emperor	1.50	1.50

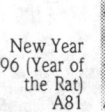

New Year 1996 (Year of the Rat) A81
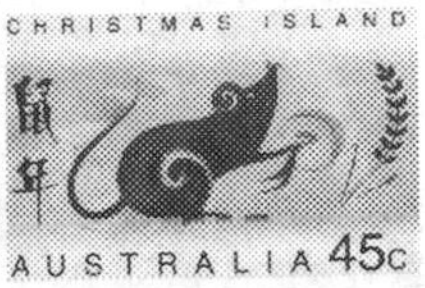

Stylized rats: No. 376, Facing right. No. 377, Facing left.

1996, Jan. 9 Litho. *Perf. 14x14½*

376	A81	45c gold & multi	.70	.70
377	A81	45c gold & multi	.70	.70
a.		Pair, #376-377	1.40	1.40
b.		Souvenir sheet, #377a	1.40	1.40

COCOS ISLANDS

'kō-kəs 'ī-ləndz

(Keeling Islands)

LOCATION — Indian Ocean, 1,330 miles northwest of Australia, 580 miles south west of Java
GOVT. — A territory of Australia
AREA — 6 sq. mi.
POP. — 579 (1983)

Of 27 small coral islands making up two atolls, two islands are inhabited. Cocos Islands stamps are also valid within Australia.

12 Pence = 1 Shilling
100 Cents = 1 Dollar (1969)

Catalogue values for all unused stamps in this country are for Never Hinged items.

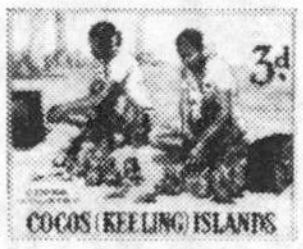

Copra Industry — A1

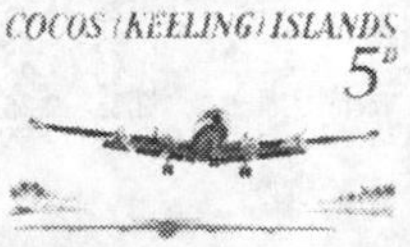

Super Constellation — A2

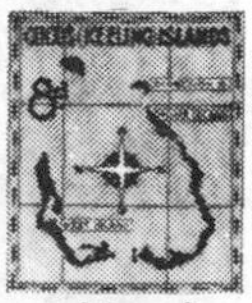

Map of Islands — A3

Designs: 1sh, Coco palms. 2sh, Sailboat (dukong). 2sh3p, Fairy tern.

Perf. 14½

1963, June 11 Unwmk. Engr.

1	A1	3p dk red brown	4.00	1.90
2	A2	5p vio blue	1.50	1.10
3	A3	8p red	7.75	2.90

4	A1	1sh green	5.00	1.50
5	A3	2sh dull purple	14.00	5.50
6	A2	2sh3p green	27.50	15.00
		Nos. 1-6 (6)	59.75	27.90

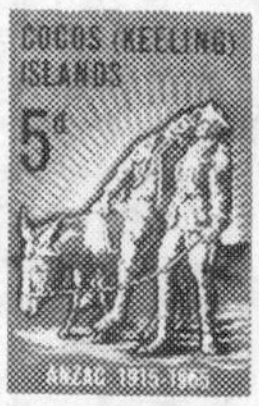
COCOS (KEELING) ISLANDS
5d
ANZAC 1915-1965

"Simpson and His Donkey" by Wallace Anderson — A3a

1965, Apr. 14 Photo. *Perf. 13½x13*

7	A3a	5p brt grn, sepia & blk	1.00	.90

ANZAC issue. See note after Australia No. 387.

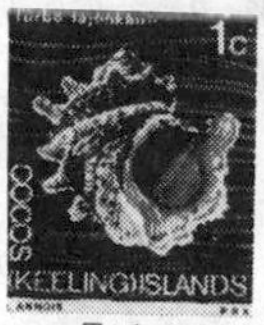
1c
COCOS
(KEELING)ISLANDS

Turbo Lajonkairii A4

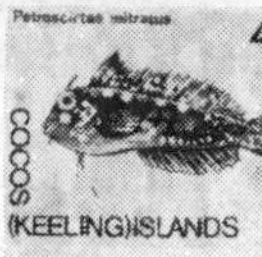
4c
COCOS
(KEELING)ISLANDS

Blenny A5

Designs: 2c, Tridacna crocea (shell). 3c, Tridacna derasa (shell). 5c, Porites cocosensis (coral). 6c, Flyingfish. 10c, Banded rail (bird). 15c, Java sparrow. 20c, Red-tailed tropic bird. 30c, Sooty tern. 50c, Eastern reef heron. $1, Great frigate bird.

Perf. 13½

1969, July 9 Unwmk. Photo.

Size: 21½x27mm, 26½x22mm

8	A4	1c multicolored	.15	.15
9	A4	2c multicolored	.80	.65
10	A5	3c multicolored	.20	.15
11	A5	4c multicolored	.25	.20
12	A5	5c multicolored	.30	.25
13	A5	6c multicolored	.50	.40
14	A5	10c multicolored	1.25	1.10
15	A5	15c multicolored	1.00	.80
16	A5	20c multicolored	1.00	.80
17	A5	30c multicolored	1.75	1.40
18	A5	50c multicolored	3.00	1.75

Size: 21½x34mm

19	A4	$1 multicolored	5.00	5.00
		Nos. 8-19 (12)	15.20	12.65

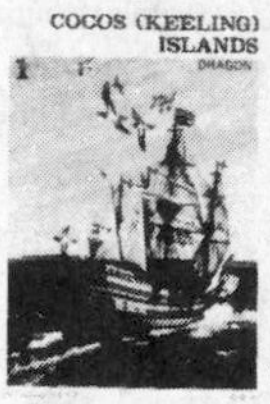
COCOS (KEELING) ISLANDS

"Dragon" — A6

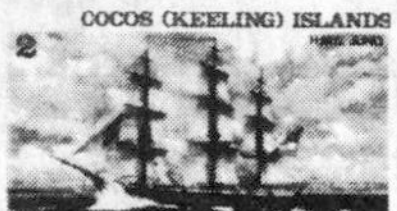
COCOS (KEELING) ISLANDS

"Juno" — A7

Perf. 13½x13, 13x13½

1976, Mar. 29 Photo.

20	A6	1c shown	.15	.15
21	A7	2c shown	.15	.15
22	A7	5c "Beagle"	.20	.20
23	A7	10c "Sydney"	.25	.25
24	A7	15c "Emden"	.50	.50
25	A7	20c "Ayesha"	.60	.60
26	A6	25c "Islander"	.85	.85
27	A6	30c "Cheshire"	.95	.95
28	A7	35c "Jukung"	1.25	1.25
29	A7	40c "Scotia"	.85	.85
30	A6	50c "Orontes"	1.25	1.25
31	A6	$1 Royal Yacht "Gothic"	2.25	2.25
		Nos. 20-31 (12)	9.25	9.25

Historic ships.

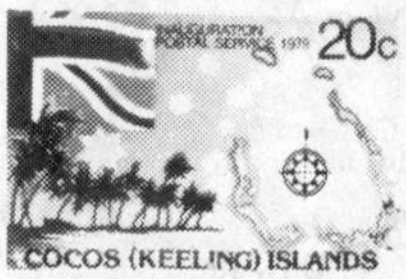
20c
COCOS (KEELING) ISLANDS

Flag, Southern Cross, Islands' Map — A8

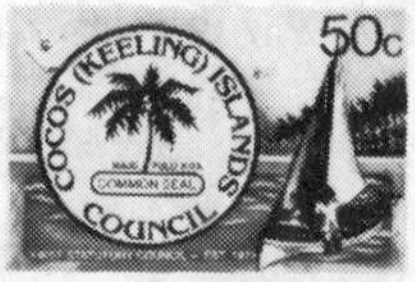
50c
COCOS (KEELING) ISLANDS
COMMON SEAL
COUNCIL

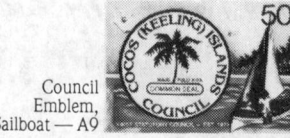

Council Emblem, Sailboat — A9

1979, Sept. 3 Litho. *Perf. 15½*

32	A8	20c multicolored	.30	.30
33	A9	50c multicolored	.80	.80

Inauguration of Cocos Islands' postal service (20c), and establishment of Cocos Islands Council (50c).

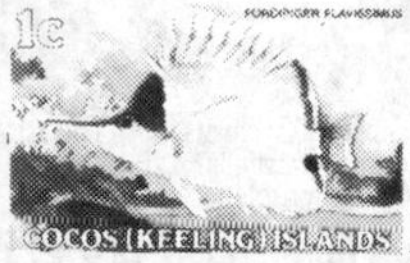
1c
COCOS (KEELING) ISLANDS

Forcipiger Flavissimus A10

Fish: 2c, Chaetodon ornatissimus. 5c, Anthias. 10c, Meyer's coralfish. 15c, Halichoeres. 20c, Amphiprion clarkii. 22c, Balistapus undulatus. 25c, Maori wrasse. 28c, Macropharyngodon meleagris. 30c, Chaetodon madagascariensis. 35c, Centropyge colini. 40c, Bodianus axillaris. 50c, Corisgaimardi. 55c, Spotted wrasse. 60c, Epinepnelus tauvina. $1, Paracanthurus hepatus. $2, Striped butterflyfish.

1979-80 Litho. *Perf. 15½*

34	A10	1c multicolored	.15	.15
35	A10	2c multicolored	.15	.15
36	A10	5c multicolored	.15	.15
37	A10	10c multi ('80)	.20	.20
38	A10	15c multicolored	.30	.30
39	A10	20c multicolored	.40	.40
40	A10	22c multi ('80)	.35	.35
41	A10	25c multi ('80)	.50	.50
42	A10	28c multi ('80)	.45	.45
43	A10	30c multicolored	.60	.60
44	A10	35c multicolored	.65	.65
45	A10	40c multicolored	.70	.70
46	A10	50c multicolored	1.00	1.00
47	A10	55c multi ('80)	1.10	1.10
48	A10	60c multi ('80)	.50	.50
49	A10	$1 multicolored	1.00	1.00
50	A10	$2 multi ('80)	2.00	2.00
		Nos. 34-50 (17)	10.20	10.20

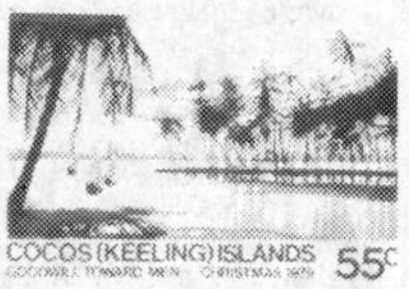
COCOS (KEELING) ISLANDS
55c

Sailboats in Lagoon — A11

Christmas: 25c, Yachts and seagulls, vert.

1979, Oct. 22 Litho. *Perf. 15½*

51	A11	25c multicolored	.35	.35
52	A11	55c multicolored	.80	.80

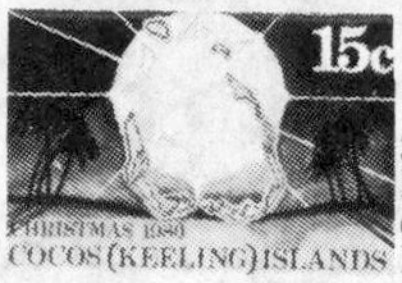
15c
CHRISTMAS 1980
COCOS (KEELING) ISLANDS

Star of Bethlehem, Map of Cocos Islands — A12

Christmas (Map of Cocos Islands and): 28c, Three kings. 60c, Nativity.

1980, Oct. 22 Litho. *Perf. 13½x13*

53	A12	15c multicolored	.25	.25
54	A12	28c multicolored	.40	.40
55	A12	60c multicolored	.80	.80
		Nos. 53-55 (3)	1.45	1.45

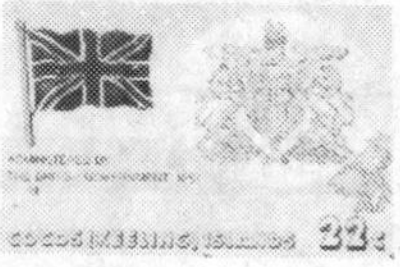
COCOS (KEELING) ISLANDS
22c

Flag and Arms of Great Britain — A13

Australian Territory Status, 25th Anniv. (British Flag and Arms of Past Administrators): No. 57, Ceylon, 1878, 1942-1946. No. 58, Straits Settlements, 1886. No. 59, Singapore, 1946. No. 60, Australia (flag), 1955.

1980, Nov. 24 Litho. *Perf. 13½x13*

56	A13	22c multicolored	.35	.35
57	A13	22c multicolored	.35	.35
58	A13	22c multicolored	.35	.35
59	A13	22c multicolored	.35	.35
60	A13	22c multicolored	.35	.35
a.		Strip of 5, Nos. 56-60	1.75	1.75

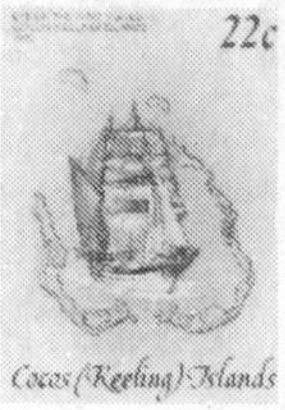
22c
Cocos (Keeling) Islands

Eye of the Wind, Map of Cocos Islands — A14

Perf. 13x13½, 13½x13

1980, Dec. 18

61	A14	22c shown	.35	.35
62	A14	28c Expedition routes, horiz.	.40	.40
63	A14	35c Francis Drake, Golden Hinde	.70	.70
64	A14	60c Prince Charles, Eye of the Wind	.65	.65
		Nos. 61-64 (4)	2.10	2.10

Operation Drake circumnavigation.

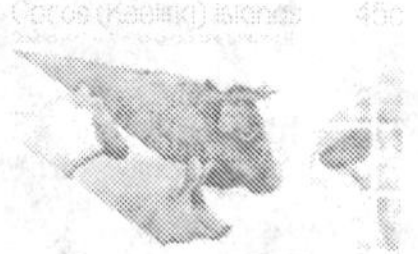

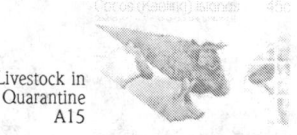

Livestock in Quarantine A15

1981, May 12 Litho. *Perf. 13½x13*

65	A15	22c Aerial view of station	.30	.30
66	A15	45c shown	.65	.65
67	A15	60c Livestock, diff.	.80	.80
		Nos. 65-67 (3)	1.75	1.75

West Island Quarantine Station opening.

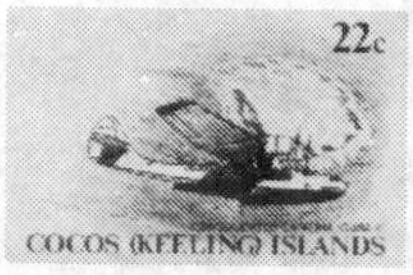
22c
COCOS (KEELING) ISLANDS

Catalina Guba II A16

Inauguration of Air Service to Indian Ocean: No. 69, Avro Lancastrian. No. 70, Douglas DC4 Skymaster, Lockheed Constellation. No. 71, Lockheed Electra. No. 72, Boeing 727.

1981, June 23 Litho. *Perf. 13½x13*

68	A16	22c multicolored	.40	.40
69	A16	22c multicolored	.40	.40
70	A16	22c multicolored	.40	.40
71	A16	22c multicolored	.40	.40
72	A16	22c multicolored	.40	.40
a.		Strip of 5, #68-72	2.10	2.10

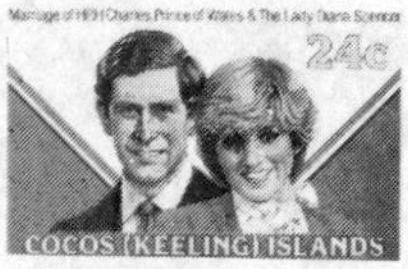
24c
COCOS (KEELING) ISLANDS

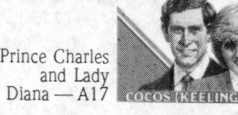

Prince Charles and Lady Diana — A17

1981, July 29 Litho. *Perf. 13½x13*

73	A17	24c multicolored	.50	.50
74	A17	60c multicolored	1.00	1.00

Royal Wedding.

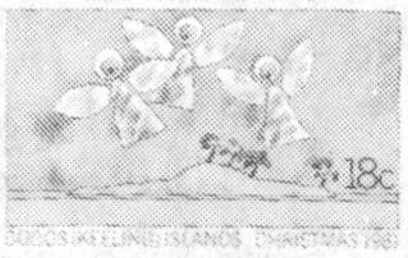
18c

Angels We Have Heard on High — A18

Christmas: Carols.

1981, Oct. 22 Photo. *Perf. 13½x13*

75	A18	18c shown	.30	.30
76	A18	30c Shepherds Why this Jubilee	.50	.50
77	A18	60c Come to Bethlehem and See Him	1.00	1.00
		Nos. 75-77 (3)	1.80	1.80

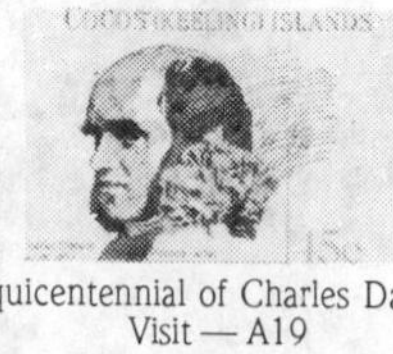
COCOS (KEELING) ISLANDS
15c

Sesquicentennial of Charles Darwin's Visit — A19

1981, Dec. 28 Litho. *Perf. 13½x13*

78	A19	24c Coral	.35	.35
79	A19	45c Darwin, coral	.60	.60
80	A19	60c Beagle, coral	.80	.80
		Nos. 78-80 (3)	1.75	1.75

Souvenir Sheet

81		Sheet of 2	1.10	1.10
a.		A19 24c Atoll	.55	.55
b.		A19 24c Atoll, diff.	.55	.55

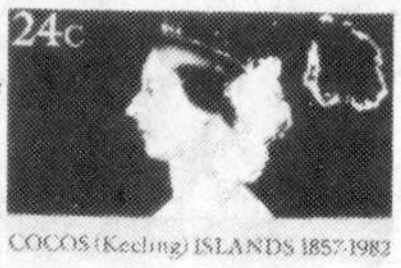
24c
COCOS (Keeling) ISLANDS 1857-1982

125th Anniv. of Annexation to the British Dominions A20

1982, Mar. 31 Litho. *Perf. 13½x14*

82	A20	24c Queen Victoria	.40	.40
83	A20	45c British flag	.70	.70
84	A20	60c Capt. Fremantle	1.00	1.00
		Nos. 82-84 (3)	2.10	2.10

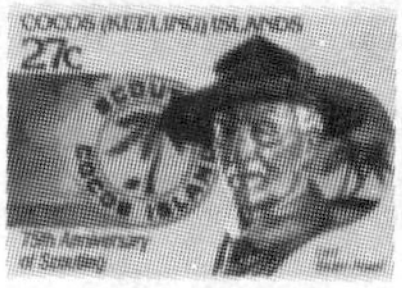
COCOS (KEELING) ISLANDS
27c
75th Anniversary of Scouting

Scouting Year — A21

Perf. 13½x14, 14x13½

1982, July 21 Litho.

85	A21	27c Baden-Powell	.45	.45
86	A21	75c Emblem, map, vert.	1.40	1.40

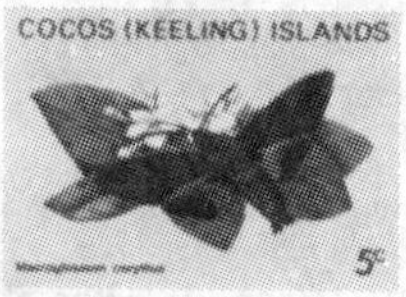
COCOS (KEELING) ISLANDS
5c

Macroglossum Corythus A22

1982, Sept. 6

87	A22	1c Presic villida, vert.	.15	.15
88	A22	2c Cephonodes picus	.15	.15
89	A22	5c shown	.15	.15
90	A22	10c Chasmina candida, vert.	.15	.15
91	A22	20c Nagia linteola	.30	.30
92	A22	25c Eublemma rivula, vert.	.45	.45
93	A22	30c Eurrhyparodes tricoloralis, vert.	.50	.50
94	A22	35c Hippotion boerhaviae	.70	.70
95	A22	40c Euploea core corinna, vert.	.70	.70
96	A22	45c Psara hipponalis	.80	.80
97	A22	50c Danaus chrysippus	.85	.85
98	A22	55c Hypolimas misippus, vert.	1.00	1.00
99	A22	60c Spodoptera litura, vert.	1.00	1.00
100	A22	$1 Achaea janata, vert.	1.25	1.25
101	A22	$2 Hippotion velox	2.75	2.75
102	A22	$3 Utetheisa pulchelloides	4.00	4.00
		Nos. 87-102 (16)	14.90	14.90

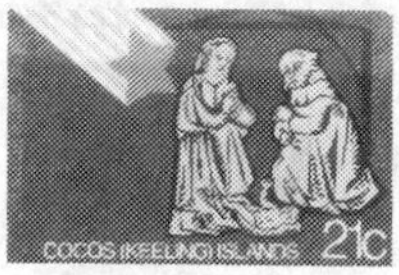
COCOS (KEELING) ISLANDS
21c

Christmas A23

1982, Oct. 25 *Perf. 13x13½*

104	A23	21c Holy Family	.40	.40
105	A23	35c Angel	.50	.50
106	A23	75c Flight into Egypt	1.10	1.10
		Nos. 104-106 (3)	2.00	2.00

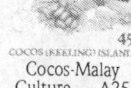

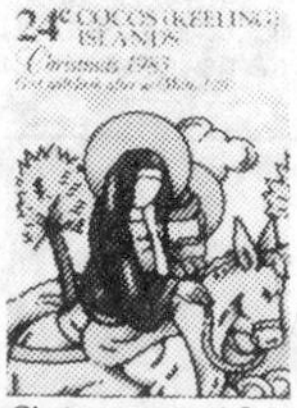

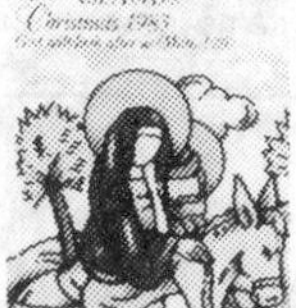
24c
COCOS (KEELING) ISLANDS
Christmas 1983

Christmas — A24

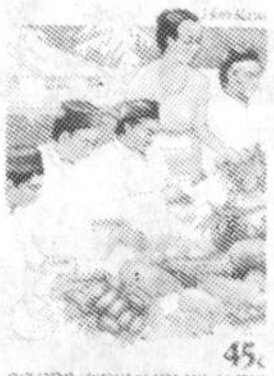
45c
COCOS (KEELING) ISLANDS

Cocos-Malay Culture — A25

The Birth of Christ: a, God Will Look After Us; b, Our Baby King Jesus; c, Your Saviour is Born; d, Wise Men Followed the Star; e, And Worship the Lord.

1983, Oct. 31   Litho.   Perf. 14x13½
107   Strip of 5   2.00   2.00
a.-e.   A24 24c any single   .40   .40

1984, Jan. 27   Litho.   Perf. 14x13½
Festive Occasions.
108   A25   45c   Hari Raya   1.00   1.00
109   A25   75c   Melenggok dance   1.75   1.75
110   A25   85c   Wedding   1.90   1.90
    Nos. 108-110 (3)   4.65   4.65

75th Anniv. of
Barrel Mail
(1909-1955)
A26

Designs: 35c, Mail distribution, Direction Isld.
55c, Jukongs retrieving barrels from ocean liner.
70c, Morea receiving outgoing barrel mail, 1909.
$1, Barrel mail recovery.

1984, Apr. 20   Litho.   Perf. 13½x14
111   A26   35c   multicolored   .75   .75
112   A26   55c   multicolored   1.25   1.25
113   A26   70c   multicolored   1.50   1.50
    Nos. 111-113 (3)   3.50   3.50

Souvenir Sheet
114   A26 $1   multicolored   2.25   2.25

375th Anniv. of Islands'
Discovery — A27

1984, July 10   Litho.   Perf. 14x13½
115   A27   30c   Capt. William Keeling   .65   .65
116   A27   65c   The Hector   1.40   1.40
117   A27   95c   Astrolabe   2.00   2.00
118   A27 $1.10   Map, 1666   2.25   2.25
    Nos. 115-118 (4)   6.30   6.30

AUSIPEX
'84 — A28

Designs: 45c, Malay Settlement, Home Island.
55c, West Island Air Strip, settlement. $2, Jukong
ships racing, Melbourne Exhibition Center.

1984, Sept. 21   Litho.   Perf. 13½
119   A28   45c   multicolored   1.60   1.60
120   A28   55c   multicolored   2.00   2.00

Souvenir Sheet
121   A28 $2   multicolored   4.25   4.25

Christmas
A29

1984, Oct. 31   Litho.   Perf. 13½
122   A29   24c   Fish   .55   .55
123   A29   35c   Butterfly   .80   .80
124   A29   55c   Bird   1.25   1.25
    Nos. 122-124 (3)   2.60   2.60

Souvenir Sheet

Act of Self-Determination — A30

Integration with Australia: a, Australians welcoming Cocos islanders. b, Australian flag over the
islands.

1984, Nov. 30   Litho.   Perf. 13½x14
125   Sheet of 2   2.40   2.40
a.-b.   A30 30c any single   1.10   1.10

Crafts — A31

1985, Jan. 30   Perf. 14x13½
126   A31   30c   Boat building   .70   .70
127   A31   45c   Blacksmith   1.00   1.00
128   A31   55c   Woodcarving   1.40   1.40
    Nos. 126-128 (3)   3.10   3.10

Cable-laying
Ships — A32

1985, Apr. 24   Perf. 13½x14
129   A32   33c   Scotia   .90   .90
130   A32   65c   Anglia   1.50   1.50
131   A32   80c   Patrol   2.50   2.50
    Nos. 129-131 (3)   4.90   4.90

Birds
A33

1985, July 17   Perf. 13½
132   A33   33c   Redfooted booby, vert.   .75   .75
133   A33   60c   Nankeen night heron   1.25   1.25
134   A33 $1   Buff-banded rail   2.50   2.50
a.   "Block" of 3, #132-134   4.50   4.50

Nos. 132-134 printed in a continuous design.

Seashells — A34

1985-86   Litho.   Perf. 13½x14
135   A34   1c   Trochus maculatus   .15   .15
136   A34   2c   Smaragdia rangiana   .15   .15
137   A34   3c   Chama   .15   .15
138   A34   4c   Cypraea moneta   .15   .15
139   A34   5c   Drupa morum   .15   .15
140   A34   10c   Conus miles   .15   .15
141   A34   15c   Terebra maculata   .20   .20
142   A34   20c   Fragum fragum   .25   .25
143   A34   30c   Turbo lajonkairii   .35   .35
144   A34   33c   Mitra fissurata   .40   .40
145   A34   45c   Lambis lambis   .45   .45
146   A34   50c   Tridacna squamosa   .55   .55
147   A34   60c   Cypraea histrio   .80   .80
148   A34 $1   Phillidia varicosa   1.40   1.40
149   A34 $2   Halgerda tessellata   3.25   3.25
150   A34 $3   Harminoea
        cymbalum   4.00   4.00
    Nos. 135-150 (16)   12.55   12.55

Issue dates: 1c, 5c, 33c, $1, Sept. 18. 2c, 3c,
10c, $3, Jan. 29, 1986. 15c-30c, 40c, Apr. 30,
1986. 4c, 50c, 60c, $2, July 30, 1986.
For surcharges see #225, 228-229, 231-233.

Souvenir Sheet

Christmas
A35

Designs: a, Star LR. b, Star LL. c, Star UR. d, Star
UL.

1985, Oct. 30   Perf. 13½x14
151   Sheet of 4   3.00   3.00
a.-d.   A35 27c any single   .75   .75

Darwin's Visit to the
Islands — A36

1986, Apr. 1   Litho.   Perf. 14x13½
152   A36   33c   Charles Darwin   .75   .75
153   A36   60c   Map of voyage   1.40   1.40
154   A36 $1   HMS Beagle   2.25   2.25
    Nos. 152-154 (3)   4.40   4.40

Christmas
A37

1986, Oct. 20   Litho.   Perf. 13½x14
155   A37   30c   Coconut palm, holly   .60   .60
156   A37   90c   Shell, ornament   1.75   1.75
157   A37 $1   Tropical fish, bell   2.00   2.00
    Nos. 155-157 (3)   4.35   4.35

Sailboats
A38

Se-tenant in a continuous design: a, Jukong. b,
Ocean racers. c, Sarimanok. d, Ayesha.

1987, Jan. 28
158   Strip of 4   2.00   2.00
a.-d.   A38 36c any single   .50   .50

Island
Views — A39

1987, Apr. 8
159   A39   70c   Direction Is.   1.00   1.00
160   A39   90c   West Is.   1.40   1.40
161   A39 $1   Golf course, Cocos   1.50   1.50
    Nos. 159-161 (3)   3.90   3.90

Communications — A40

1987, July 29   Litho.   Perf. 13½x14
162   A40   70c   Radio   1.05   1.05
163   A40   75c   Air service   1.10   1.10
164   A40   90c   Satellite   1.35   1.35
165   A40 $1   Airmail   1.50   1.50
    Nos. 162-165 (4)   5.00   5.00

Industries
A41

1987, Sept. 16
166   A41   45c   Batik printing   .70   .70
167   A41   65c   Boat building   .95   .95
168   A41   75c   Copra production   1.10   1.10
    Nos. 166-168 (3)   2.75   2.75

Industrial activities of the Cocos Malay people.

Christmas — A42

1987, Oct. 28   Perf. 14x13½
169   A42   30c   Peace on Earth   .40   .40
170   A42   90c   Unity   1.25   1.25
171   A42 $1   Goodwill Towards All   1.40   1.40
    Nos. 169-171 (3)   3.05   3.05

Australia
Bicentennial
A43

Arrival of the First Fleet, Sydney Cove, Jan.
1788: a, Five aboriginals on shore. b, Four
aboriginals on shore, one in canoe. c, Ships entering
bay, kangaroos. d, Europeans land, white cranes. e,
Flag raising.

1988, Jan. 26   Litho.   Perf. 13
172   Strip of 5   3.00   3.00
a.-e.   A43 37c any single   .60   .60

No. 172 has a continuous design. See Christmas
Is. No. 213.

Life Cycle of the
Coconut — A44

1988, Apr. 13   Litho.   Perf. 14x13½
173   A44   37c   Flower   .60   .60
174   A44   65c   Small nut stage   1.00   1.00
175   A44   90c   Mature nuts   1.40   1.40
176   A44 $1   Seedlings   1.55   1.55
a.   Souvenir sheet of 4, #173-176   4.55   4.55
    Nos. 173-176 (4)   4.55   4.55

For surcharge see No. O1.

Cocos
Postage
Stamps,
25th Anniv.
A45

1988, June 15   Litho. & Engr.   Perf. 15x14
177   A45   37c   No. 1   .55   .55
178   A45   55c   No. 4   .85   .85
179   A45   65c   No. 2   .95   .95
180   A45   70c   No. 3   1.10   1.10
181   A45   90c   No. 5   1.40   1.40
182   A45 $1   No. 6   1.50   1.50
    Nos. 177-182 (6)   6.35   6.35

For overprint and surcharge see #216, 236.

Flowering Plants — A46

1988-89 Litho. *Perf. 14x13½*

183 A46	1c	Pisonia grandis	.15	.15
184 A46	2c	Cocos nucifera	.15	.15
185 A46	5c	Morinda citrifolia	.15	.15
186 A46	10c	Cordia subcordata	.15	.15
189 A46	30c	Argusia argentea	.40	.40
190 A46	37c	Calophyllum inophyllum	.50	.50
191 A46	40c	Barringtonia asiatica	.50	.50
192 A46	50c	Caesalpinia bonduc	.65	.65
194 A46	90c	Terminalia catappa	1.25	1.25
195 A46	$1	Pemphis acidula	1.40	1.40
197 A46	$2	Scaevola sericea	2.75	2.75
198 A46	$3	Hibiscus tiliaceus	4.00	4.00
		Nos. 183-198 (12)	12.05	12.05

Issued: 1c, 5c, 37c, $3, July 29; 2c, 10c, 30c, $2, Jan. 18, 1989; 40c, 50c, 90c, $1, Apr. 19, 1989.

For self-adhesive sheet of 3 see No. 217.

Souvenir Sheet

1988, July 30

199 A46 $3 like No. 198 *5.00 5.00*

SYDPEX '88.

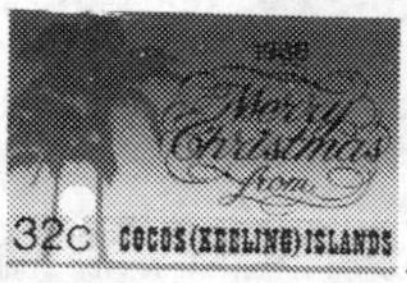

Christmas A47

1988, Oct. 12 Litho. *Perf. 13½x14*

200 A47	32c	multicolored	.35	.35
201 A47	90c	multicolored	1.00	1.00
202 A47	$1	multicolored	1.10	1.10
		Nos. 200-202 (3)	2.45	2.45

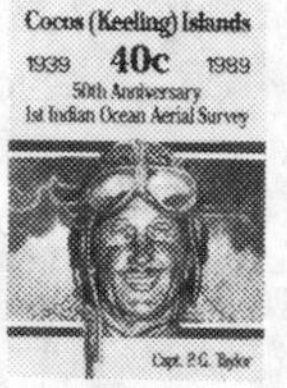

1st Aerial Survey of the Indian Ocean Air Route, 50th Anniv. — A48

Designs: 40c, P.G. Taylor, pilot. 70c, *Guba II* seaplane and crew. $1, *Guba II* landing off Direction Island. $1.10, Unissued 5p stamp of Australia, 1939.

1989, July 19 Litho. *Perf. 14x13½*

203 A48	40c	multicolored	.60	.60
204 A48	70c	multicolored	1.05	1.05
205 A48	$1	multicolored	1.50	1.50
206 A48	$1.10	multicolored	1.65	1.65
		Nos. 203-206 (4)	4.80	4.80

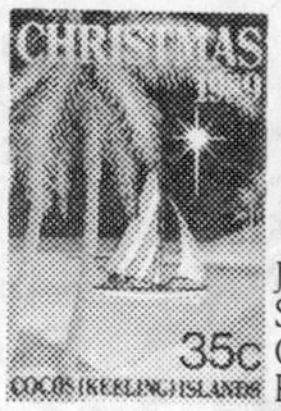

Jukong, Traditional Sailing Vessel of the Cocos Malay People — A49

1989, Oct. 18 Litho. *Perf. 14x13½*

207 A49	35c	multicolored	.55	.55
208 A49	80c	multicolored	1.25	1.25
209 A49	$1.10	multicolored	1.70	1.70
		Nos. 207-209 (3)	3.50	3.50

Christmas.

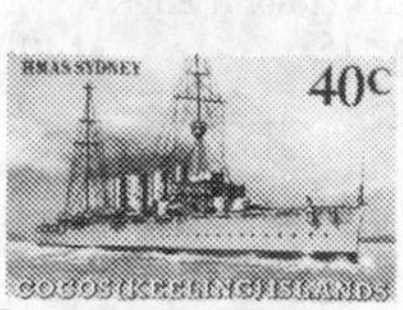

Naval Engagement of the HMAS *Sydney* and the German Raider SMS *Emden*, 75th Anniv. — A50

Designs: 40c, HMAS *Sydney*. 70c, SMS *Emden*. $1, Steam launch belonging to the *Emden*. $1.10, HMAS *Sydney* and naval crest.

1989, Nov. 9 Litho. *Perf. 13½x14*

210	Strip of 4 + label	5.00	5.00
a.	A50 40c multicolored	.60	.60
b.	A50 70c multicolored	1.10	1.10
c.	A50 $1 multicolored	1.55	1.55
d.	A50 $1.10 multicolored	1.70	1.70
e.	Souvenir sheet of 4, #210a-210d	5.00	5.00

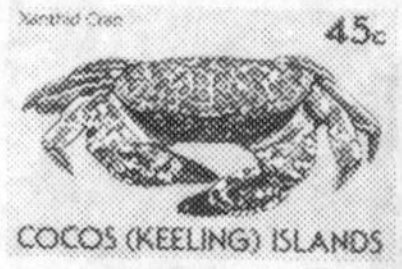

Crabs — A52

1990, May 31 Litho. *Perf. 14½*

212 A52	45c	Xanthid	.70	.70
213 A52	75c	Ghost	1.10	1.10
214 A52	$1	Red-backed mud crab	1.50	1.50
215 A52	$1.30	Coconut, vert.	1.95	1.95
		Nos. 212-215 (4)	5.25	5.25

No. 180 Overprinted in Red

NZ 1990
NEW ZEALAND
1990
24 AUG
•
2 SEP
AUCKLAND

Litho. & Engr.

1990, Aug. 24 *Perf. 15x14*

216 A45 70c gray, black & red 1.15 1.15

Flowering Plants Type of 1988

1990, Aug. 24 Photo. *Rouletted 9½*

Self-Adhesive

217	Sheet of 3	5.00	5.00
a.	A46 10c like No. 186	.15	.15
b.	A46 90c like No. 194	1.50	1.50
c.	A46 $2 like No. 197	3.35	3.35

World Stamp Exhibition, New Zealand 1990. Nos. 217a-217c inscribed 1990.

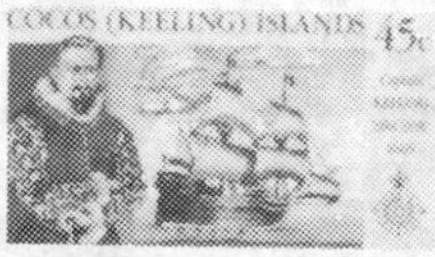

Explorers and Their Ships A54

Designs: 45c, Capt. Keeling, Hector, 1609. 75c, Capt. Fitzroy, Beagle, 1836. $1, Capt. Belcher, Samarang, 1846. $1.30, Capt. Fremantle, Juno, 1857.

1990, Aug. 24 Litho. *Perf. 14½*

218 A54	45c	violet brown	.75	.75
219 A54	75c	pale bl & vio brn	1.25	1.25
220 A54	$1	pale yel & vio brn	1.65	1.65
221 A54	$1.30	buff & vio brn	2.15	2.15
a.		Souv. sheet of 4, #218-221, imperf.	5.80	5.80
		Nos. 218-221 (4)	5.80	5.80

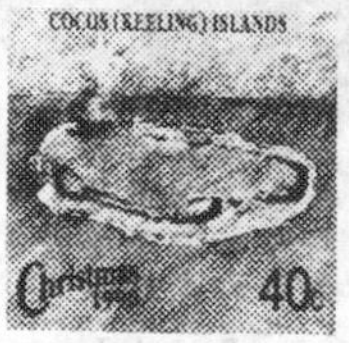

Christmas — A55

1990, Dec. 12 Litho. *Rouletted 5*

222 A55	40c	Star at left	.60	.60
a.		Bklt. pane of 10 + 2 labels	7.50	
223 A55	70c	Star in center	1.10	1.10
a.		Bklt. pane, 4 #222, 2 #223 + 6 labels	5.75	
224 A55	$1.30	Star at right	2.15	2.15
		Nos. 222-224 (3)	3.85	3.85

Nos. 140, 141, 143, 146-147, 179 Surcharged in Blue or Black

LOCAL
POSTAGE PAID

Perf. 13½x14, 15x14

1990-91 Litho., Litho. & Engr.

225 A34	(1c)	on 30c #143	*.55*	*.55*
228 A34	(43c)	on 10c #140	*1.10*	*1.10*
229 A34	(43c)	on 10c #140	*1.10*	*1.10*
231 A34	70c	on 60c #147 (bk)	*1.65*	*1.65*
232 A34	80c	on 50c #146 (bk)	*1.90*	*1.90*
233 A34	$1.20	on 15c #141 (bk)	*3.00*	*3.00*
236 A45	$5	on 65c #179	*12.50*	*12.50*
		Nos. 225-236 (7)	*21.80*	*21.80*

Issue dates: No. 236, Dec. 11, 1990. No. 228, Dec. 18, 1990. Nos. 225, 229, 231-233, Jan. 1991.

Obliterator consists of diagonal lines on No. 228, crosshatched lines on No. 229.

Additional text in surcharges reads: "MAINLAND / POSTAGE PAID" (Nos. 228-229), "ZONE 1 / POSTAGE PAID" (No. 231), "ZONE 2 / POSTAGE PAID" (No. 232), "ZONE 5 / POSTAGE PAID" (No. 233).

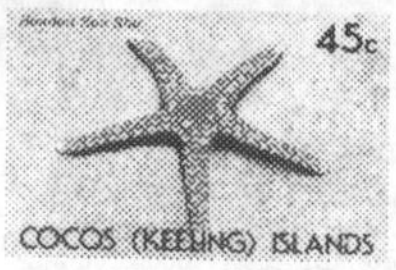

Beaded Sea Star — A56

1991, Feb. 28 Litho. *Perf. 14½*

237 A56	45c	shown	.75	.75
238 A56	75c	Feather star	1.25	1.25
239 A56	$1	Slate pencil urchin	1.65	1.65
240 A56	$1.30	Globose sea urchin	2.15	2.15
		Nos. 237-240 (4)	5.80	5.80

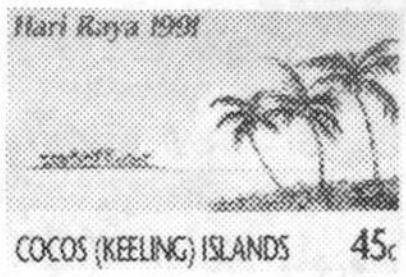

Hari Raya — A57

1991, Mar. Litho. *Perf. 14½*

241 A57	45c	multicolored	.75	.75
242 A57	75c	multi, diff.	1.25	1.25
243 A57	$1.30	multi, diff.	2.15	2.15
		Nos. 241-243 (3)	4.15	4.15

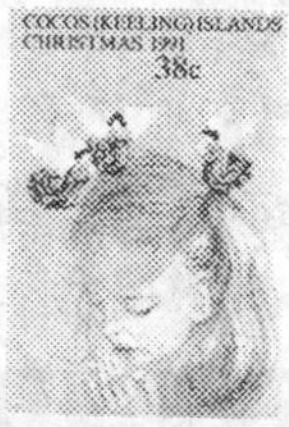

Christmas — A58

1991, Nov. 6 Litho. *Perf. 15½*

244 A58	38c	Child praying	.60	.60
245 A58	43c	Child sleeping	.70	.70
246 A58	$1	Child singing	1.60	1.60
247 A58	$1.20	Child in wonder	1.90	1.90
		Nos. 244-247 (4)	4.80	4.80

Souvenir Sheet

248	Sheet of 4	4.80	4.80
a.	A58 38c Two children	.60	.60
b.	A58 43c Three girls	.70	.70
c.	A58 $1 Boy, two girls	1.60	1.60
d.	A58 $1.20 Boy, girl	1.90	1.90

Nos. 248a-248d are in a continuous design depicting a children's choir.

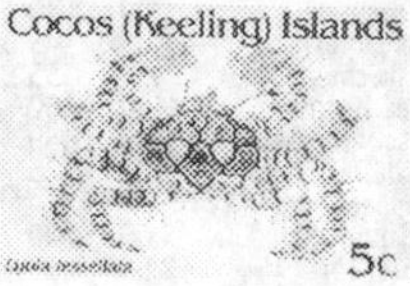

Crustaceans A59

Designs: 5c, Lybia tessellata. 10c, Pilodius areolatus. 20c, Trizopagurus strigatus. 30c, Lophozozymus pulchellus. 40c, Thalamitoides quadridens. 45c, Calcinus elegans, vert. 50c, Clibarius humilis. 60c, Trapezia rufopunctata, vert. 80c, Pylopaguropsis magnimanus, vert. $1, Trapezia ferruginea, vert. $2, Trapezia guttata, vert. $3, Trapezia cymodoce, vert.

1992 Litho. *Perf. 14½*

249 A59	5c	multicolored	.15	.15
250 A59	10c	multicolored	.15	.15
251 A59	20c	multicolored	.30	.30
252 A59	30c	multicolored	.45	.45
253 A59	40c	multicolored	.60	.60
254 A59	45c	multicolored	.65	.65
255 A59	50c	multicolored	.70	.70
256 A59	60c	multicolored	.85	.85
257 A59	80c	multicolored	1.10	1.10
258 A59	$1	multicolored	1.40	1.40
259 A59	$2	multicolored	2.75	2.75
260 A59	$3	multicolored	4.25	4.25
		Nos. 249-260 (12)	13.35	13.35

Issue dates: 10c, 30c, 50c, 80c, $1, $2, Aug. 11; others, Feb. 28.

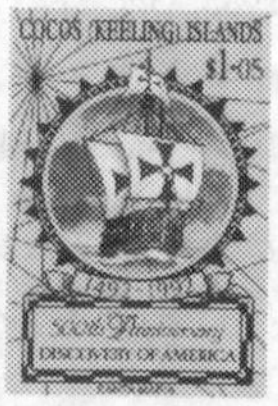

Discovery of America, 500th Anniv. — A60

1992, May 22 Litho. *Perf. 14½*

261 A60 $1.05 multicolored 1.50 1.50

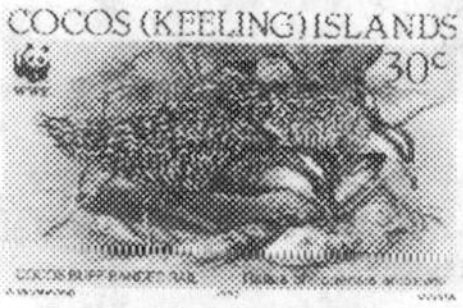

Buff-banded Rail — A61

Designs: No. 262a, 10c, Bird looking for food. b, 15c, Adult with chick. c, 30c, Two adults eating. d, 45c, Adult with eggs, hatchling.

No. 263a, 45c, Two birds, one in water. b, 85c, Chick in nest. c, $1.20, Bird's head.

1992, June 18 Litho. *Perf. 14*

262 A61 Strip of 4, #a.-d. 1.40 1.40

Souvenir Sheet

263 A61 Sheet of 3, #a.-c. 3.50 3.50

World Wildlife Fund (#262).

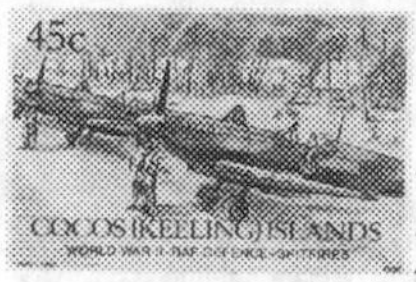

World War II, 50th Anniv. — A62

Designs: 45c, Royal Air Force Spitfire fighters. 85c, Japanese bombing of Kampong. $1.20, Sunderland reconnaissance flying boat.

1992, Oct. 13 Litho. *Perf. 14½*

264 A62	45c	multicolored	.60	.60
265 A62	85c	multicolored	1.15	1.15
266 A62	$1.20	multicolored	1.60	1.60
		Nos. 264-266 (3)	3.35	3.35

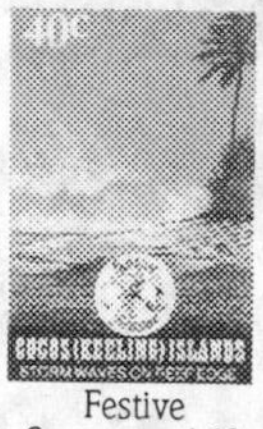

Festive Season — A63

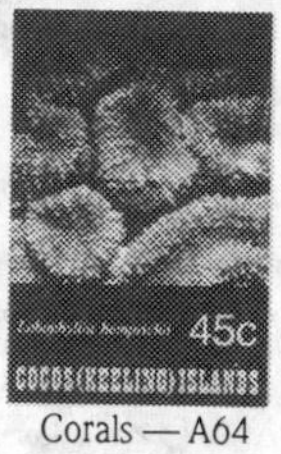

Corals — A64

Designs: 40c, Storm waves on reef edge. 80c, Direction Island. $1, Moorish idols among coral.

1992, Nov. 10 Litho. *Perf. 15x14½*

267 A63	40c	multicolored	.50	.50
268 A63	80c	multicolored	1.05	1.05
269 A63	$1	multicolored	1.35	1.35
		Nos. 267-269 (3)	2.90	2.90

1993, Jan. 28 Litho. *Perf. 14½*

270 A64	45c	Lobophyllia hemprichii	.60	.60
271 A64	85c	Pocillopora eydouxi	1.10	1.10
272 A64	$1.05	Fungia scutaria	1.35	1.35
273 A64	$1.20	Sarcophyton sp.	1.55	1.55
		Nos. 270-273 (4)	4.60	4.60

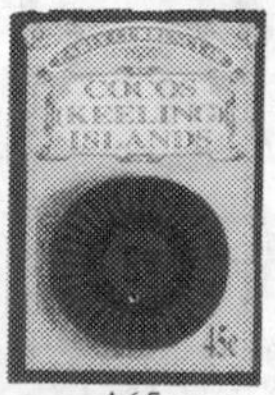

A65

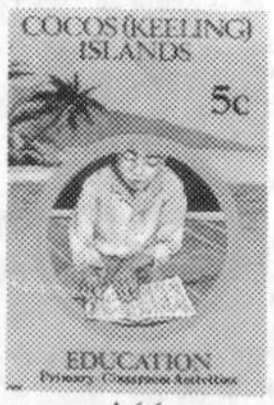

A66

Island Currency Tokens: 45c, 5r token, 1968. 85c, Island scene token, 1968. $1.05, 150r token, 1977. $1.20, Token, 1910.

1993, Mar. 30 Litho. *Perf. 15x14½*

274 A65	45c multicolored	.55	.55
275 A65	85c multicolored	1.05	1.05
276 A65	$1.05 multicolored	1.30	1.30
277 A65	$1.20 multicolored	1.50	1.50
	Nos. 274-277 (4)	4.40	4.40

1993, June 1 Litho. *Perf. 14½*

Education: 5c, Primary classroom activities. 45c, Secondary studies. 85c, Crafts, traditional basket weaving. $1.05, Office staff, higher education. $1.20, Marine officers, coxswain's training.

278 A66	5c multicolored	.15	.15
279 A66	45c multicolored	.55	.55
280 A66	85c multicolored	1.05	1.05
281 A66	$1.05 multicolored	1.30	1.30
282 A66	$1.20 multicolored	1.50	1.50
	Nos. 278-282 (5)	4.55	4.55

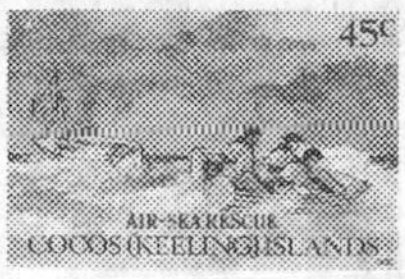

Air-Sea Rescue Service — A67

Designs: 45c, Men in lifeboat. 85c, Westwind Seascan. $1.05, R.J. Hawke inter-island ferry.

1993, Aug. 17 Litho. *Perf. 14½*

283 A67	45c multicolored	.60	.60
284 A67	85c multicolored	1.10	1.10
285 A67	$1.05 multicolored	1.40	1.40
a.	Souvenir sheet of 3, #283-285	3.25	3.25
	Nos. 283-285 (3)	3.10	3.10

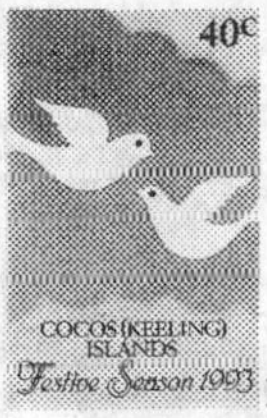

Festive Season — A68

1993, Oct. 24 Litho. *Perf. 14½*

286 A68	40c pink & multi	.50	.50
287 A68	80c blue & multi	1.00	1.00
288 A68	$1 yellow & multi	1.25	1.25
	Nos. 286-288 (3)	2.75	2.75

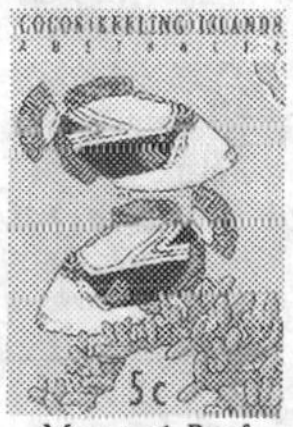

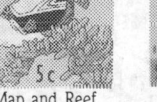

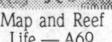

Map and Reef Life — A69

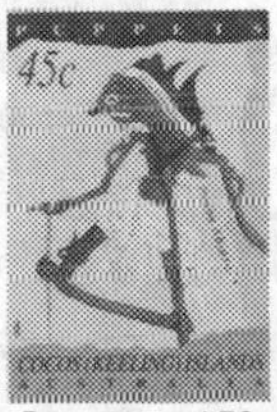

Puppets — A70

Reef triggerfish: No. 289a, Two fish, purple coral (b). b, Three fish. c, Two fish, d, Two fish, red coral (e). e, One fish.

Green turtles: No. 290a, Eggs, turtles. b, Two turtles (c). c, Group of baby turtles. d, Baby turtle. e, Fish, large turtle.

Pyramid butterflyfish: No. 291a, Three fish. b, Two small, one large fish, coral (c). c, One small, one large fish, coral (d). d, Three fish, coral (e). e, Coral, one fish.

Junkongs sailing craft: No. 292a, One boat, red sail. b, Two boats, one blue & white sail, one red sail. c, One boat, yellow sail. d, Two boats sailing away. e, Two boats, one red sail, one white & blue sail.

1994, Feb. 17 Litho. *Perf. 14½x14*

289 A69	5c Strip of 5, #a.-e.	.30	.30
290 A69	10c Strip of 5, #a.-e.	.65	.65
291 A69	20c Strip of 5, #a.-e.	1.25	1.25
292 A69	45c Strip of 5, #a.-e.	3.00	3.00
f.	Sheet of 20, #289-292	5.25	5.25

No. 292 also produced in sheets of 20.

1994, June 16 Litho. *Perf. 14½x14*

293 A70	45c Prabu Abjasa	.60	.60
294 A70	90c Prabu Pandu	1.25	1.25
295 A70	$1 Judistra	1.40	1.40
296 A70	$1.35 Abimanju	1.90	1.90
	Nos. 293-296 (4)	5.15	5.15

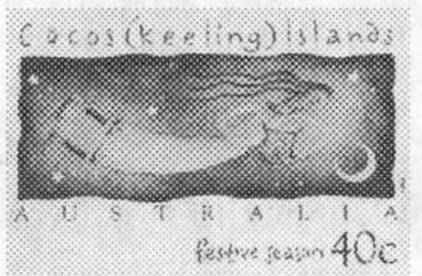

Christmas A71

1994, Oct. 31 Litho. *Perf. 14x14½*

297 A71	40c Angel	.60	.60
298 A71	45c Wise man	.65	.65
299 A71	80c Bethlehem	1.25	1.25
	Nos. 297-299 (3)	2.50	2.50

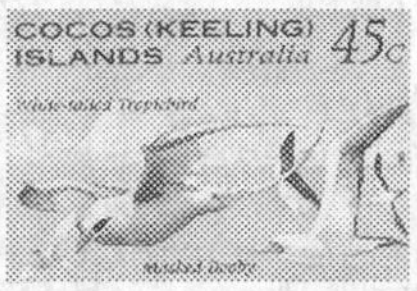

Seabirds A72

Designs: 45c, White-tailed tropicbird, masked booby. 85c, Great frigatebird, white tern.

1995, Mar. 16 Litho. *Perf. 14x14½*

300 A72	45c multicolored	.65	.65
301 A72	85c multicolored	1.25	1.25
a.	Souvenir sheet of 2, #300-301	1.90	1.90
b.	As "a," ovptd.	2.00	2.00

No. 301b ovptd. in gold in sheet margin with Jakarta '95 exhibition emblem and: "8th Asian International Philatelic Exhibition / PARMERAN FILATELI INTERNASIONAL ASIA VIII."

No. 301b issued 8/19/95.

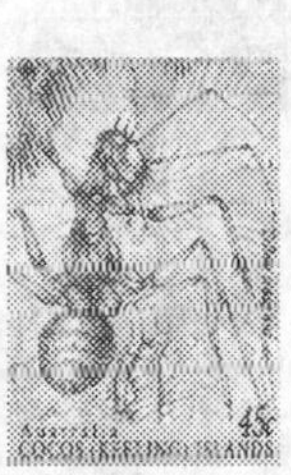

Insects — A73

Designs: No. 302a, Yellow crazy ant. b, Aedes mosquito. c, Hawk moth. d, Scarab beetle. e, Laux aniid fly.

$1.20, Common eggfly butterfly.

1995, July 13 Litho. *Perf. 14½x14*

302 A73	45c Strip of 5, #a.-e.	3.25	3.25
303 A73	$1.20 multicolored	1.75	1.75

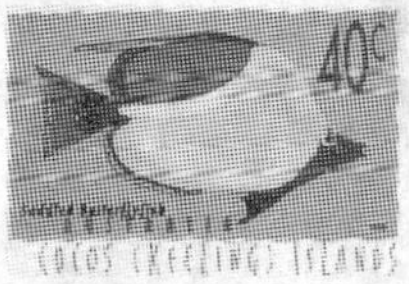

Fish — A74

Designs: 40c, Saddled butterflyfish. 80c, Blue tang. $1.05, Longnosed butterflyfish.

1995 Litho. *Perf. 14x14½*

308 A74	40c multicolored	.60	.60
312 A74	80c multicolored	1.25	1.25
314 A74	$1.05 multicolored	1.60	1.60
	Nos. 308-314 (3)	3.45	3.45

Issued: 40c, 80c, $1.05, 11/1/95. This is an expanding set. Numbers may change.

OFFICIAL STAMPS

No. 175 Ovptd. and Surcharged in Dark Blue

OFFICIAL PAID MAINLAND

1991, Jan. 25 Litho. *Perf. 14x13½*

O1 A44	(43c) on 90c multi	35.00

No. O1 was not sold to public unused. Used value is for canceled to order copy.

COOK ISLANDS

'kůk 'ī–lənds

(Rarotonga)

LOCATION — South Pacific Ocean, northeast of New Zealand
GOVT. — Internal self-government, linked to New Zealand
AREA — 117 sq. mi.
POP. — 17,754 (1981)
CAPITAL — Rarotonga

Fifteen islands in Northern and Southern groups extend over 850,000 square miles of ocean.

Separate stamp issues used by Aitutaki (1903-32 and 1972 onward) and Penrhyn Islands (1902-32 and 1973 onward). Niue is included geographically, but administered separately. It continues to issue separate stamps.

12 Pence = 1 Shilling
20 Shillings = 1 Pound
100 Cents = 1 Dollar (1967)

Catalogue values for unused stamps in this country are for Never Hinged items, beginning with Scott 127 in the regular postage section, Scott B1 in the semi-postal section, Scott C1 in the air post section, Scott CB1 in the air post semi-postal section and Scott O16 in the official section.

Watermarks

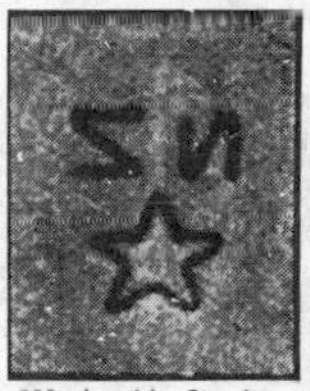

Wmk. 61- Single-lined N Z and Star Close Together

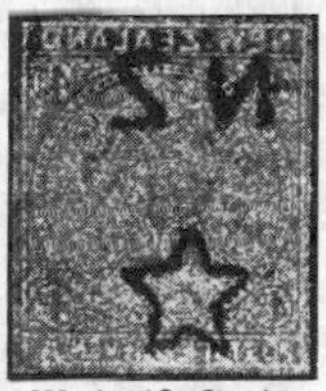

Wmk. 62- Single lined N Z and Star Wide Apart

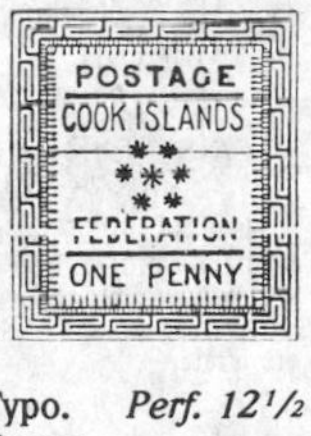

A1

1892 Unwmk. Typo. *Perf. 12½*

Toned Paper

1 A1	1p black	20.00	20.00
2 A1	1½p violet	35.00	35.00
3 A1	2½p blue	35.00	35.00
4 A1	10p carmine	150.00	140.00
	Nos. 1-4 (4)	240.00	230.00

White Paper

5 A1	1p black	22.50	22.50
a.	Vert. pair, imperf. between	9,000.	
6 A1	1½p violet	35.00	35.00
7 A1	2½p blue	40.00	37.50
8 A1	10p carmine	150.00	140.00
	Nos. 5-8 (4)	247.50	235.00

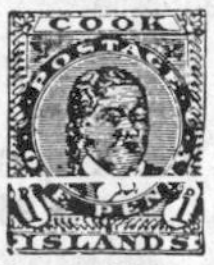

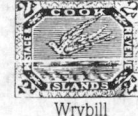

Queen Makea Takau — A2

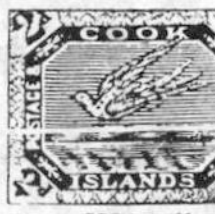

Wrybill (Torea) — A3

1893-94 Wmk. 62 *Perf. 12x11½*

9 A2	1p brown	40.00	*47.50*
10 A2	1p blue ('94)	4.00	2.50
11 A2	1½p brt violet	5.00	3.50
12 A2	2½p rose	22.50	*20.00*
13 A2	5p olive gray	12.50	10.00
14 A2	10p green	50.00	*47.50*
	Nos. 9-14 (6)	134.00	*131.00*

Perf. 11½ examples of Nos. 9-14 are from a part of the normal perf. 12x11½ sheets. They were caused by a partial deviation of the original perforating.

1898-1900 *Perf. 11*

15 A3	½p blue ('00)	3.50	5.00
a.	"d" omitted at upper right	1,350.	
16 A2	1p brown	6.50	10.00
17 A2	1p blue	2.50	3.50
18 A2	1½p violet	4.50	4.50
19 A3	2p chocolate	6.00	6.00
20 A2	2½p car rose	7.50	7.50
21 A2	5p olive gray	19.00	21.00
22 A3	6p red violet	14.00	17.50
23 A2	10p green	22.50	25.00
24 A3	1sh car rose	40.00	50.00
	Nos. 15-24 (10)	126.00	150.00

No. 17 Surcharged in Black

ONE HALF PENNY

1899

25 A2	½p on 1p blue	40.00	45.00
a.	Double surcharge	1,000.	1,000.
b.	Inverted surcharge	1,000.	1,000.

No. 16 Overprinted in Black

1901

26 A2	1p brown	160.00	150.00
a.	Inverted overprint	1,750.	1,750.
c.	Double overprint	1,750.	2,000.

Some single stamps were overprinted by favor. Other varieties could exist.

Types of 1893-98

1902 Unwmk.

27 A3	½p green	4.00	5.00
a.	Vert. pair, imperf. horiz.	1,000.	
28 A2	1p rose	5.00	6.00
29 A2	2½p dull blue	14.00	*20.00*
	Nos. 27-29 (3)	23.00	*31.00*

1902 Wmk. 61 *Perf. 11*

30 A3	½p green	1.10	2.00
31 A2	1p rose	2.25	*1.90*
32 A2	1½p brt violet	2.00	4.25
33 A3	2p chocolate	3.00	*6.00*
b.	Perf. 11x14	*500.00*	
34 A2	2½p dull blue	3.00	*4.00*
35 A2	5p olive gray	27.50	*25.00*
36 A3	6p purple	25.00	*17.00*
37 A2	10p blue green	40.00	*50.00*
38 A3	1sh car rose	40.00	*40.00*
a.	Perf. 11x14	*325.00*	
	Nos. 30-38 (9)	143.85	*150.15*

The 2p exists with value omitted.

1909-19 *Perf. 14, 14x14½, 14½x14*

39 A3	½p green ('11)	2.00	*5.50*
40 A2	1p red	2.00	*2.25*
41 A2	1½p purple ('15)	5.00	2.00
42 A3	2p dp brown ('19)	4.50	*20.00*
43 A2	10p dp green ('18)	11.00	*37.50*
44 A3	1sh car rose ('19)	22.50	*37.50*
	Nos. 39-44 (6)	47.00	*104.75*

Nos. 39-40 are on both ordinary and chalky paper; Nos. 41-44 on chalky paper.

RAROTONGA

New Zealand Stamps of 1909-19 Surcharged in Dark Blue or Red

APA PENE

1919 Typo. *Perf. 14x13½, 14x14½*

48 A43	½p yel green (R)	.15	.40
a.	Pair, one without surcharge		
49 A42	1p carmine	.25	.75
50 A47	1½p brown org (R)	.20	.30
51 A43	2p yellow (R)	.90	1.75
52 A43	3p chocolate	2.25	2.50

Engr.

53 A44	2½p dull blue (R)	1.00	2.00
54 A45	3p violet brown	1.50	1.75
55 A45	4p purple	1.50	2.50
56 A44	4½p dark green	.90	*4.00*
57 A45	6p car rose	1.50	*4.00*
58 A44	7½p red brown	1.50	*4.00*
59 A45	9p ol green (R)	1.75	*6.00*
60 A45	1sh vermilion	2.75	*7.50*
	Nos. 48-60 (13)	16.15	*37.45*

The Polynesian surcharge restates the denomination of the basic stamp.

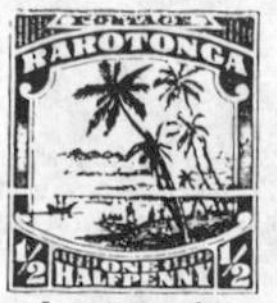
Landing of Capt. Cook A4

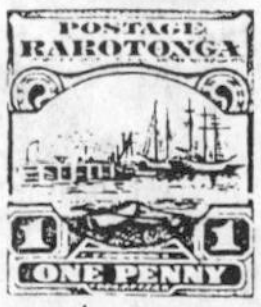
Avarua Waterfront A5

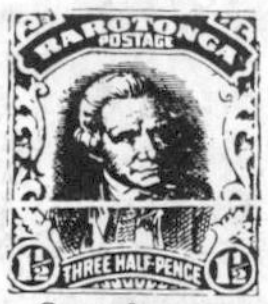
Capt. James Cook — A6

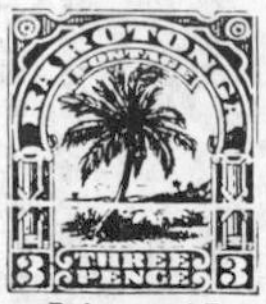
Palm — A7

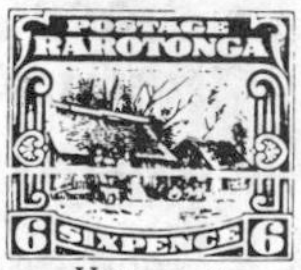
Houses at Arorangi — A8

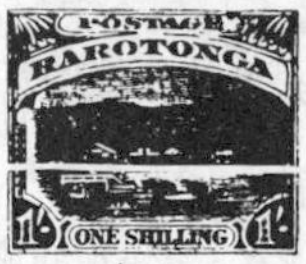
Avarua Harbor — A9

1920 Unwmk. Engr. *Perf. 14*

61	A4	1/2p green & black	2.00	4.00
62	A5	1p car & black	1.40	2.50
a.		Center inverted	550.00	
63	A6	1 1/2p blue & black	4.00	5.00
64	A7	3p red brn & blk	3.25	6.50
65	A8	6p org & red brn	3.25	6.50
66	A9	1sh vio & black	4.50	10.00
		Nos. 61-66 (6)	18.40	34.50

The stamps overprinted or inscribed "Rarotonga" were used throughout the Cook Islands.
For surcharges see Nos. 78, 79.

New Zealand Postal-Fiscal Stamps of 1906-13 Overprinted in Red or Dark Blue

a **RAROTONGA**

Perf. 14, 14 1/2, 14x14 1/2

1921 Typo. Wmk. 61

67	PF1	2sh blue (R)	22.50	35.00
68	PF1	2sh6p brown	20.00	35.00
69	PF1	5sh green (R)	22.50	35.00
70	PF1	10sh claret	45.00	70.00
71	PF2	£1 rose	75.00	90.00
		Nos. 67-71 (5)	185.00	265.00

Types of 1920 Issue

1924-26 Engr. *Perf. 14*

72	A4	1/2p yel grn & black	.80	.70
73	A5	1p carmine & black	2.25	1.75

Issued: 1/2p, May 13, 1926; 1p, Nov. 10, 1924.

New Zealand Stamps of 1926 Overprinted Type "a" in Red

1926-28 Typo. *Perf. 14, 14 1/2x14*

74	A56	2sh blue ('27)	12.00	20.00
a.		2sh dark blue	14.00	19.00
75	A56	3sh violet ('28)	18.00	30.00

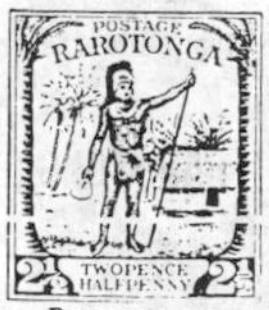
Rarotongan Chief (Te Po) — A10

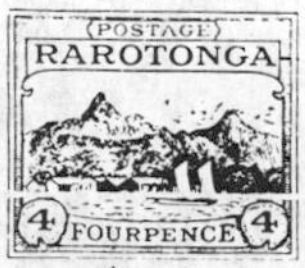
Avarua Harbor — A11

1927, Oct. 15 Engr. *Perf. 14*

76	A10	2 1/2p dk bl & red brn	2.00	2.50
77	A11	4p dull vio & bl grn	4.50	4.75

No. 63 Surcharged in Red **TWO PENCE**

1931 Unwmk.

78	A6	2p on 1 1/2p blue & blk	4.00	2.00

Same Surcharge on Type of 1920

Wmk. 61

79	A6	2p on 1 1/2p blue & blk	1.50	3.00

No. 79 was not issued without surcharge.

New Zealand Postal-Fiscal Stamps of 1931-32 Overprinted Type "a" in Blue or Red

1931, Nov. 12 Typo.

80	PF5	2sh6p dp brown (Bl)	9.00	10.00
81	PF5	5sh green (R)	15.00	18.00
82	PF5	10sh dk car (Bl)	35.00	37.50
83	PF5	£1 pink (Bl) ('32)	65.00	75.00
		Nos. 80-83 (4)	124.00	140.50

See Nos. 103-108, 124A-126C.

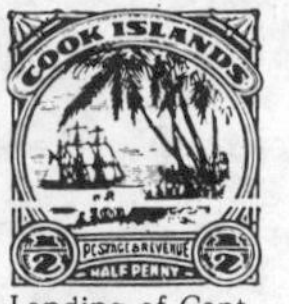
Landing of Capt. Cook — A12

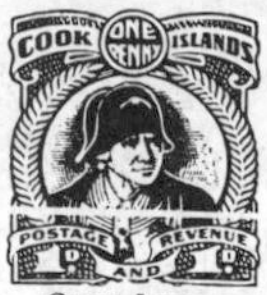
Capt. James Cook — A13

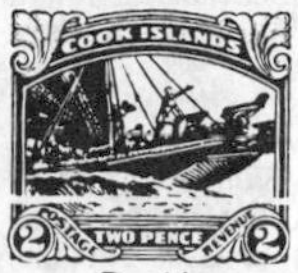
Double Canoe — A14

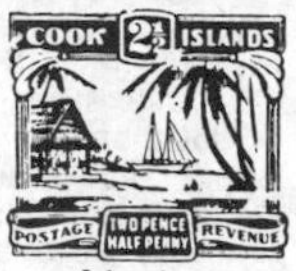
Islanders Unloading Ship — A15

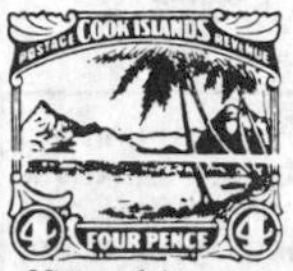
View of Avarua Harbor — A16

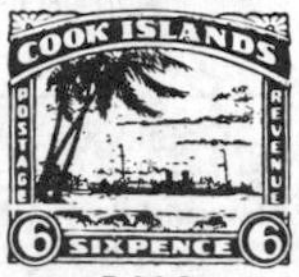
R.M.S. Monowai — A17

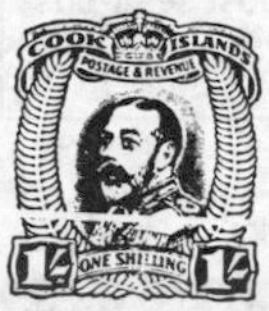
King George V — A18

Unwmk.

1932, Mar. 16 Engr. *Perf. 13*

Center in Black

84	A12	1/2p deep green	.40	.55
a.		Perf. 14	20.00	25.00
85	A13	1p brown lake	.45	.55
a.		Center inverted	1,500.	1,750.
b.		Perf. 14	9.00	12.50
86	A14	2p brown	7.50	7.50
b.		Perf. 14	6.00	13.00
87	A15	2 1/2p dark ultra	5.75	35.00
b.		Perf. 14	11.00	35.00

Perf. 14

88	A16	4p ultra	15.00	40.00
a.		Perf. 13	17.00	37.50
b.		Perf. 14x13	32.50	80.00
89	A17	6p orange	22.50	45.00
a.		Perf. 13	24.00	45.00
90	A18	1sh deep violet	6.50	16.00
		Nos. 84-90 (7)	58.10	144.60

Nos. 84 to 90 were available for postage in Aitutaki, Penrhyn and Rarotonga and replaced the special issues for those islands.
Inverted centers of the 1p and 2p are from printers waste.

1933-36 Wmk. 61 *Perf. 14*

91	A12	1/2p dp grn & blk	.20	.25
92	A13	1p dk car & black ('35)	.35	.45
93	A14	2p brn & blk ('36)	.45	.60
94	A15	2 1/2p dk ultra & blk	.55	.65
95	A16	4p blue & black	1.00	1.25
96	A17	6p org & blk ('36)	1.25	1.65
97	A18	1sh dp vio & black ('36)	16.00	18.00
		Nos. 91-97 (7)	19.80	22.85

See Nos. 116-121.

Silver Jubilee Issue

Types of 1932 Overprinted in Black or Red

SILVER JUBILEE OF KING GEORGE V. 1910 - 1935.

1935, May 7

98	A13	1p dk car & brn red	.25	.30
99	A15	2 1/2p dk ultra & bl (R)	.80	.90
100	A17	6p dull org & green	3.75	4.00
		Nos. 98-100 (3)	4.80	5.20

The vertical spacing of the overprint is wider on No. 100.

New Zealand Stamps of 1926 Overprinted in Black

b **COOK ISLANDS**

1936, July 15 Typo. *Perf. 14*

101	A56	2sh blue	12.50	14.00
102	A56	3sh violet	15.00	17.50

New Zealand Postal-Fiscal Stamps of 1931-35 Overprinted Type "b" in Black or Red

1932-36

103	PF5	2sh6p brown ('36)	8.50	12.50
104	PF5	5sh grn (R) ('36)	10.00	12.50
105	PF5	10sh dk car ('36)	16.00	27.50
106	PF5	£1 pink ('36)	27.50	35.00
107	PF5	£3 lt grn (R)	110.00	200.00
108	PF5	£5 dk blue (R)	150.00	175.00
		Nos. 103-108 (6)	322.00	462.50

Issue dates: Mar. 1932, July 15, 1936.

New Zealand Stamps of 1937 Overprinted in Black **COOK IS'DS.**

Perf. 14x13 1/2

1937, June 1 Engr. Wmk. 253

109	A78	1p rose carmine	.15	.15
110	A78	2 1/2p dark blue	.20	.20
111	A78	6p vermilion	.30	.30
		Nos. 109-111 (3)	.65	.65

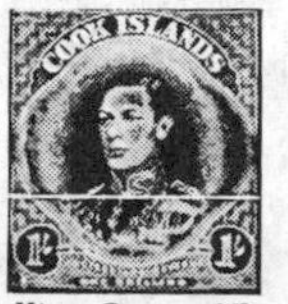
King George VI A19

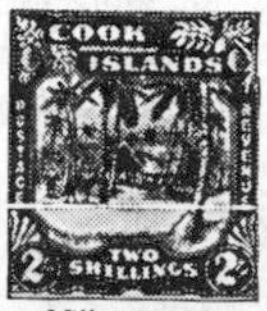
Village and Palms A20

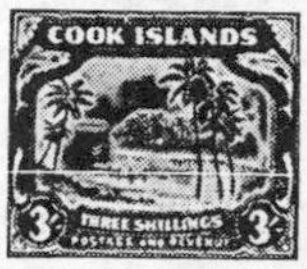
Coastal Scene with Canoe — A21

1938, May 2 Wmk. 61 *Perf. 14*

112	A19	1sh dp violet & blk	1.90	1.90
113	A20	2sh dk red brn & blk	7.00	7.00
114	A21	3sh yel green & blue	16.00	16.00
		Nos. 112-114 (3)	24.90	24.90

See Nos. 122-124.

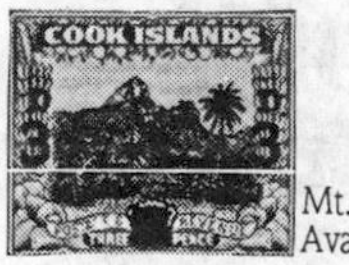
Mt. Ikurangi behind Avarua — A22

Perf. 13 1/2x14

1940, Sept. 2 Engr. Wmk. 253

115	A22	3p on 1 1/2p violet & blk	.15	.15

Types of 1932-38

1944-46 Engr. *Perf. 14*

116	A12	1/2p dk ol grn & blk ('45)	.25	.25
117	A13	1p dk car & blk ('45)	.16	.16
118	A14	2p brn & blk ('46)	.75	.75
119	A15	2 1/2p dk bl & blk ('45)	.25	.25
120	A16	4p blue & black	.38	.38
121	A17	6p org & black	.55	.55
122	A19	1sh dp vio & blk	.75	.75
123	A20	2sh dk red brn & blk	1.90	1.90
124	A21	3sh yel green & blue ('45)	2.75	2.75
		Nos. 116-124 (9)	7.74	7.74

New Zealand Nos. AR76, AR78, AR85 and Type of 1931 Postal-Fiscal Stamps Overprinted Type "b" in Black or Red

1943-50 Wmk. 253 Typo. *Perf. 14*

124A	PF5	2sh6p brn ('46)	3.25	4.00
125	PF5	5sh green (R)	4.75	8.00
126	PF5	10sh dp pink ('48)	14.00	20.00
126A	PF5	£1 pink ('47)	17.50	24.00
126B	PF5	£3 lt grn (R) ('46)	90.00	140.00
126C	PF5	£5 dk bl (R) ('50)	150.00	225.00
		Nos. 124A-126C (6)	279.50	421.00

For surcharges see Nos. 192-194.

Catalogue values for unused stamps in this section, from this point to the end of the section, are for Never Hinged items.

Peace Issue

New Zealand Nos. 248, 250, 254 and 255 Overprinted in Black or Blue:

COOK ISLANDS — c
COOK — d
ISLANDS

Perf. 13x13 1/2, 13 1/2x13

1946, June 1 Engr.

127	A94 (c)	1p emerald	.15	.15
128	A96 (d)	2p rose vio (Bl)	.20	.20
129	A100(c)	6p org red & red brn	.30	.30
130	A101(c)	8p brn lake & blk (Bl)	.35	.35
		Nos. 127-130 (4)	1.00	1.00

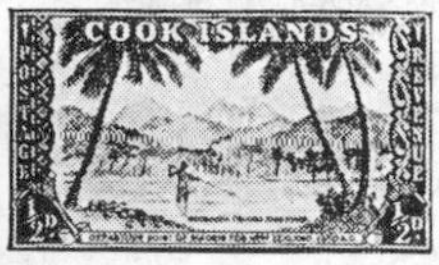
Ngatangiia Channel, Rarotonga A23

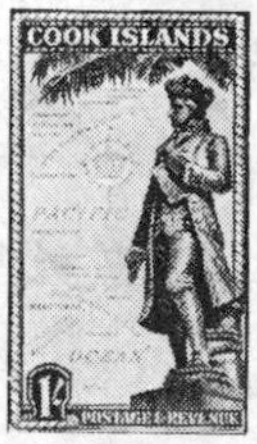
Capt. James Cook Statue and Map of Cook Islands — A24

Designs: 1p, Cook and map of Hervey Isls. 2p, Rev. John Williams, his ship Messenger of Peace, and map of Rarotonga. 3p, Aitutaki map and palms. 5p, Mail plane landing at Rarotonga airport. 6p, Tongareva (Penrhyn) scene. 8p, Islander's house, Rarotonga. 2sh, Thatched house, mat weaver. 3sh, Steamer Matua offshore.

Perf. 13 1/2x13, 13x13 1/2

1949, Aug.1 Engr. Wmk. 253

131	A23	1/2p brown & violet	.15	.50
132	A23	1p green & orange	.60	.60
133	A23	2p carmine & brn	.40	.75
134	A23	3p ultra & green	.35	.75
135	A23	5p purple & grn	1.90	1.90
136	A23	6p car rose & blk	1.00	1.25
137	A23	8p orange & olive	1.40	3.00
138	A24	1sh chocolate & bl	2.25	2.25
139	A24	2sh rose car & brn	5.25	9.00
140	A24	3sh bl grn & lt ultra	6.00	10.00
		Nos. 131-140 (10)	19.30	30.00

For surcharge see No. 147.

Coronation Issue

Type of New Zealand

1953, May 25 Photo. *Perf. 14x14 1/2*

145	A113	3p brown	.45	.45
146	A114	6p slate black	.90	.90

No. 135 Surcharged with New Value and Two Dots

1960, Apr. 1 Engr. *Perf. 13 1/2x13*

147	A23	1sh6p on 5p purple & grn	.50	.75

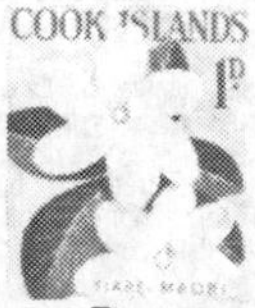
Tiare Maori — A25

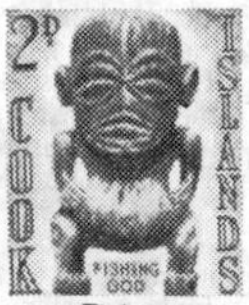
Fishing God — A26

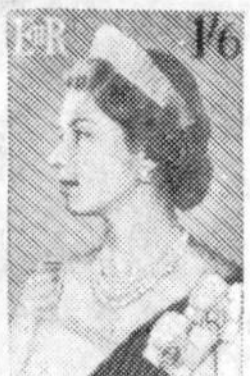
Queen Elizabeth II — A27

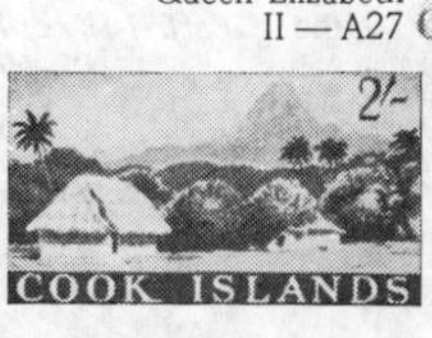
Island Scene — A28

Designs: 3sh, Administration building, Mangaia. 5sh, Ship in Rarotonga harbor. (3p, 5p, 6p, 1sh, horizontal.)

Perf. 13½x13, 13x13½

1963, June 4 Litho.; Engr.; (1sh6p)

148 A25	1p	shown	.15	.15
149 A26	2p	shown	.15	.16
150 A25	3p	Frangipani	.20	.25
151 A26	5p	Fairy tern	.32	.35
152 A25	6p	Hibiscus	.35	.40
153 A26	8p	Bonito	.52	.60
154 A25	1sh	Oranges	.80	1.00
155 A27	1sh6p	shown	1.60	2.50
156 A28	2sh	gray & brown	2.50	3.25
157 A28	3sh	emer & black	3.50	4.50
158 A28	5sh	ultra & brown	5.00	6.00
		Nos. 148-158 (11)	15.09	19.16

For overprints see Nos. 167-169. For surcharges see Nos. 179-181, 183-184, 186-190.

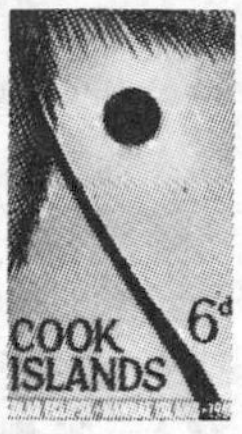

Solar Eclipse and Palm Tree — A29

1965, May 31 Litho. *Perf. 13x13½*

159 A29	6p	black, lt blue & yel	.30	.30

Observation of the solar eclipse on Manuae Island, May 30, 1965.
For surcharge see No. 185.

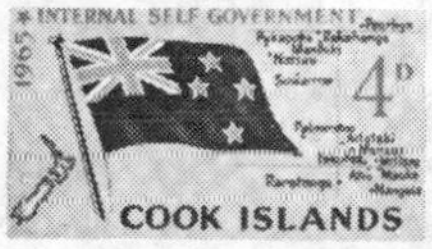

Flag of New Zealand and Map of Cook Islands — A30

Designs: 10p, London Missionary Society Chruch and graveyard. 1sh, Reading of Proclamation of Cession, Oct. 8, 1900, and Queen Elizabeth II. 1sh9p, Nikao School and flag of New Zealand.

Perf. 13½x13

1965, Sept. 16 Litho. Wmk. 253

160 A30	4p	blue & red	.15	.15
161 A30	10p	multicolored	.40	.40
162 A30	1sh	multicolored	.45	.45
163 A30	1sh9p	multicolored	.75	.75
		Nos. 160-163 (4)	1.75	1.75

Establishment of internal self-government.
For surcharges see Nos. 182, 191.

Nos. 160-162 and 156-158 Overprinted in Red: "In Memoriam / Sir Winston Churchill / 1874-1965"

1966, Jan. 24 Litho. Wmk. 253

164 A30	4p	blue & red	.35	.25
165 A30	10p	multicolored	.75	.65
a.		Inverted overprint	225.00	
166 A30	1sh	multicolored	.85	.75
167 A28	2sh	gray & brown	2.00	1.75
168 A28	3sh	emer & black	3.00	2.75
169 A28	5sh	ultra & brown	5.00	4.50
		Nos. 164-169 (6)	11.95	10.65

Statesman and WWII leader.

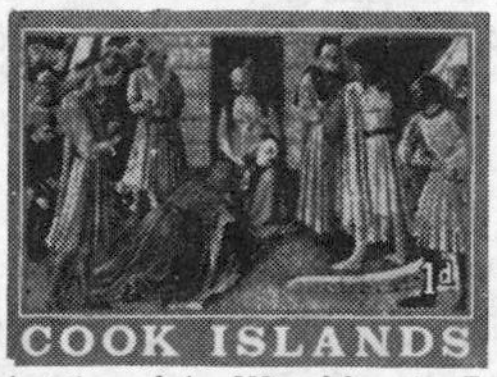

Adoration of the Wise Men, by Fra Angelico — A31

Paintings: 2p, Nativity, by Hans Memling, vert. 4p, Adoration of the Wise Men, by Velazquez. 10p, Adoration of the Wise Men, by Hieronymus Bosch. 1sh6p, Adoration of the Shepherds, by Jose Ribera, vert.

Perf. 13x14½, 14½x13

1966, Nov. 28 Photo. Unwmk.

170 A31	1p	multicolored	.15	.15
171 A31	2p	multicolored	.15	.15
172 A31	4p	multicolored	.18	.15
173 A31	10p	multicolored	.40	.32
174 A31	1sh6p	multicolored	.75	.55
		Nos. 170-174 (5)	1.63	1.32

Christmas. Issued in sheets of 6 with ornamental gold border.

Perf. 13x12, 12x13

170a A31	1p		.22	.15
171a A31	2p		7.00	3.50
172a A31	4p		.45	.35
173a A31	10p		1.10	1.10
174a A31	1sh6p		2.25	1.75
		Nos. 170a-174a (5)	11.02	6.85

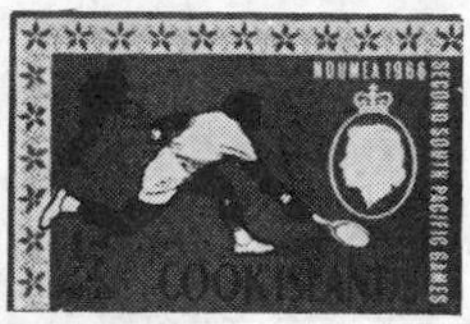

Tennis and Queen Elizabeth A32

Sport: 1p, Women's basketball and Games' emblem. 4p, Boxing and team emblem. 7p, Soccer and Queen Elizabeth II.

1967, Jan. 12 *Perf. 13½*

175 A32	½p	brt olive & multi	.15	.15
176 A32	1p	brt blue & multi	.15	.15
177 A32	4p	purple & multi	.15	.15
178 A32	7p	red & multi	.20	.20
		Nos. 175-178,C10-C11 (6)	1.65	1.65

Second South Pacific Games, Noumea, New Caledonia, Dec. 8-18, 1966.

Nos. 148-155, 157-161 Surcharged with New Value or Black or Red

2½c I **2½c** II

1967

179 A25	1c on 1p		1.75	1.75
180 A26	2c on 2p		.15	.15
181 A25	2½c on 3p (I)		.15	.15
a.	Type II		.15	.15
182 A30	3c on 4p		.15	.15
183 A26	4c on 5p		.35	.35
184 A25	5c on 6p		.15	.15
185 A29	5c on 6p		1.00	.65
186 A26	7c on 8p		.20	.20
187 A25	10c on 1sh		.28	.28
188 A27	15c on 1sh6p (R)		2.00	1.00
189 A28	30c on 3sh (R)		6.50	5.00
190 A28	50c on 5sh (R)		4.25	2.75
191 A30	$1 on 10p (R)		14.00	10.00
	Nos. 179-191 (13)		30.93	22.58

Issued: 2c, 2½c, 3c, 5c, 7c, 10c, 4/3; others 5/4.
No. 191 is surcharged "10/ $1.00" and 3 bars over old value.
Numerous varieties of surcharge include wrong-font "c," thin numerals, etc.

Nos. 126A, 126B and 126C Surcharged in Red

Wmk. 253

1967, June 6 Typo. *Perf. 14*

192 PF5	$2 on £1	pink	100.00	100.00
193 PF5	$6 on £3	lt green	125.00	125.00
194 PF5	$10 on £5	dk blue	200.00	200.00
		Nos. 192-194 (3)	425.00	425.00

Frequently found with stained gum.

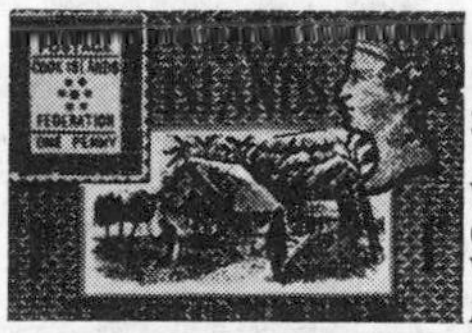

Stamp of 1892, Village and Queen Victoria A33

Designs: 3c (4p), PO, Rarotonga, and Elizabeth II. 8c (10p), View of Avarua, Rarotonga, and 10p stamp of 1892. 18c (1sh9p), Map of Cook Islands, DC-3, S.S. Moana Roa and Capt. Cook.

Perf. 13½

1967, July 3 Photo. Unwmk.

195 A33	1c (1p)	multi	.15	.15
196 A33	3c (4p)	multi	.20	.20
197 A33	8c (10p)	multi	.40	.40
198 A33	10c (1sh9p)	multi	.80	.80
a.		Souvenir sheet of 4, #195-198	1.50	1.50
		Nos. 195-198 (4)	1.55	1.55

75th anniv. of the 1st Cook Islands stamps. Issued in sheets of 8 stamps and 1 label with inscription in yellow margin.

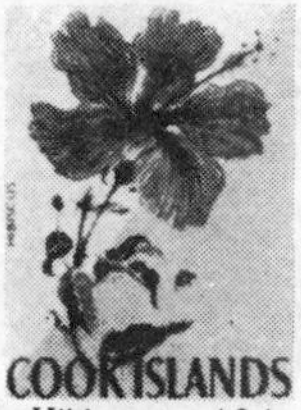

Hibiscus — A34

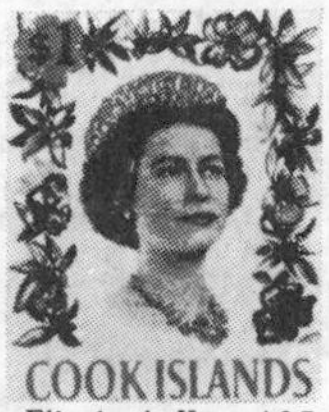

Elizabeth II — A35

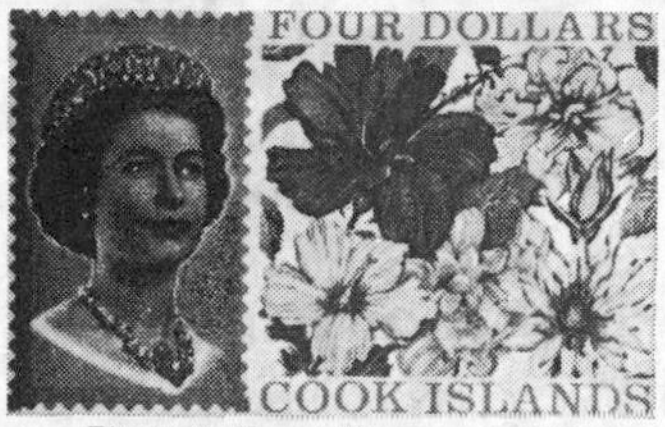

Elizabeth II and Flowers — A36

Flowers: 1c, Rose of Sharon. 2c, 15c, Frangipani. 2½c, Butterfly pea. 3c, Suva queen and Queen Elizabeth II. 4c, Water lily. 5c, Bauhania. 6c, Yellow hibiscus. 8c, Alamanda and Queen Elizabeth II. 9c, Stephanotis. 10c, Flaymboyant poinciana. 20c, Thunbergia. 25c, Canna lily and Queen Elizabeth II. 30c, Poinsettia. 50c, Gardenia.

1967-69 Photo. *Perf. 14x13½*

199 A34	½c	gold & multi	.15	.15
200 A34	1c	gold & multi	.15	.15
201 A34	2c	gold & multi	.15	.15
202 A34	2½c	gold & multi	.15	.15
203 A34	3c	gold & multi	.15	.15
204 A34	4c	*Walter Lily*	1.75	1.75
205 A34	4c	*Water Lily*	.15	.15
206 A34	5c	gold & multi	.15	.15
207 A34	6c	gold & multi	.15	.15
208 A34	8c	gold & multi	.16	.16
209 A34	9c	gold & multi	.20	.20
210 A34	10c	gold & multi	.22	.22
211 A34	15c	gold & multi	.35	.35
212 A34	20c	gold & multi	.50	.50
213 A34	25c	gold & multi	.60	.60
214 A34	30c	gold & multi	.75	.75
215 A34	50c	gold & multi	1.10	1.10
216 A35	$1	gold & multi	2.25	2.25
217 A35	$2	gold & multi	3.50	3.50
218 A36	$4	multi ('68)	6.50	6.50
219 A36	$6	multi ('68)	10.00	10.00
219A A36	$8	multi ('69)	11.00	11.00
220 A36	$10	multi ('68)	15.00	15.00
		Nos. 199-220 (23)	55.08	55.08

The $4 exists with "FOUR DOLLARS" in two widths: 32½mm and 33½mm.
Nos. 214-215 were surcharged "Plus 20c United Kingdom Special Mail Service" in 5 lines of capitals for use during the 1971 British mail strike. The strike ended Mar. 8, the day the 50c+20c, was released.
For surcharges see Nos. 290-291, 305-309, B1-B13, B17-B18, B20. For overprints see Nos. 277-283, 302-304, 315, 351-356, O1-O15.

Fluorescence

Since 1968 a number of stamps have been issued with a "fluorescent security underprinting" in a multiple coat of arms pattern. Some issues have this underprint, some do not.
Stamps issued both with and without the underprint are Nos. 199-203, 205-220, 283, 290-291.
From Nos. 292-296 onward, all stamps have this underprint unless otherwise noted.

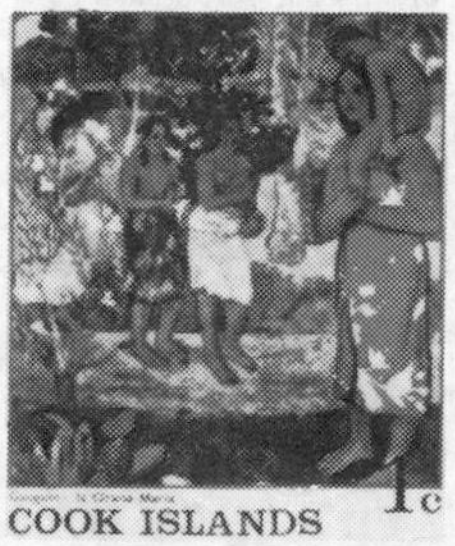

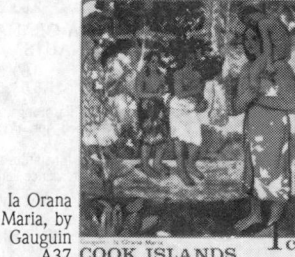

Ia Orana Maria, by Gauguin A37

Gauguin Paintings: 3c, Riders on the Beach. 5c, Still Life with Flowers. 8c, Whispered Words. 15c, Maternity. 22c, Why Are You Angry?

1967, Oct. 23 Photo. *Perf. 13½*

221 A37	1c	gold & multi	.15	.15
222 A37	3c	gold & multi	.15	.15
223 A37	5c	gold & multi	.15	.15
224 A37	8c	gold & multi	.15	.15
225 A37	15c	gold & multi	.30	.30
226 A37	22c	gold & multi	.45	.45
a.		Souvenir sheet of 6, #221-226	1.50	1.40
		Set value	1.10	1.10

#221-226 are printed in sheets of 6 (3x2).

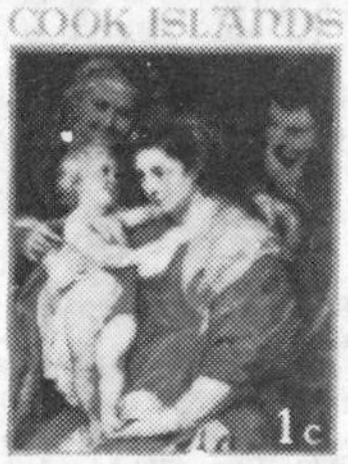

Holy Family by Rubens — A38

Paintings: 3c, Adoration of the Magi, by Albrecht Durer. 4c, The Lucca Madonna, by Jan Van Eyck. 8c, Adoration of the Shepherds, by Jacopo da Bassano. 15c, Nativity, by El Greco. 25c, Madonna and Child, by Antonio Allegri da Correggio.

1967, Dec. 4 *Perf. 12x13*

227 A38	1c	gold & multi	.15	.15
228 A38	3c	gold & multi	.15	.15
229 A38	4c	gold & multi	.15	.15
230 A38	8c	gold & multi	.18	.18
231 A38	15c	gold & multi	.35	.35
232 A38	25c	gold & multi	.65	.65
		Set value	1.40	1.40

Christmas.

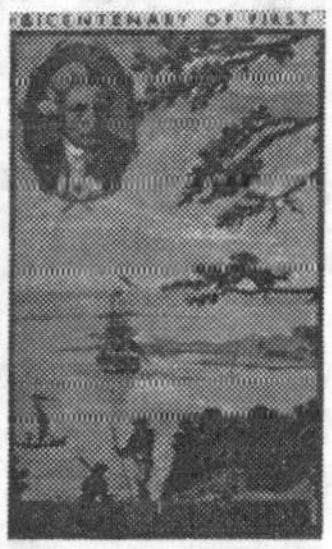

Capt. Cook and Matavai Bay, Tahiti, by Sydney Parkinson — A39

Designs: 1c, Ships off Huahine Island, Tahiti, by John and James Clevely. 2c, town and harbor of Kamchatka, by John Webber, and Queen Elizabeth II. 4c, "The Ice Islands" (Antarctica), by William Hodges.

1968, Sept. 12 Photo. *Perf. 13*

233 A39	½c	gold & multi	.15	.15
234 A39	1c	gold & multi	.15	.15
235 A39	2c	gold & multi	.15	.15
236 A39	4c	gold & multi	.20	.20
		Set value	.39	.39

Bicent. of Capt. Cook's 1st voyage of discovery. Printed in sheets of 10 stamps and 2 labels (3x4). Labels show portraits of Elizabeth II and Cook.

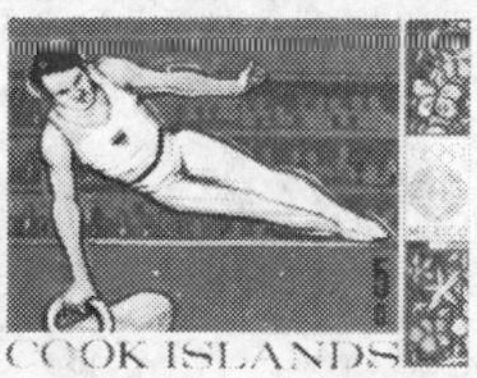

Gymnast A40

1968, Oct. 21

237 A40	1c	Sailing	.15	.15
238 A40	5c	shown	.15	.15
239 A40	15c	High jump	.22	.22
240 A40	20c	Woman diver	.30	.30
241 A40	30c	Bicyclist	.45	.45
242 A40	50c	Woman hurdler	.75	.75
		Nos. 237-242 (6)	2.02	2.02

19th Olympic Games, Mexico City, Oct. 12-27. Printed in sheets of 10 stamps and 2 labels (3x4).

Cook Islands stamps can be mounted in the Scott New Zealand Dependencies album.

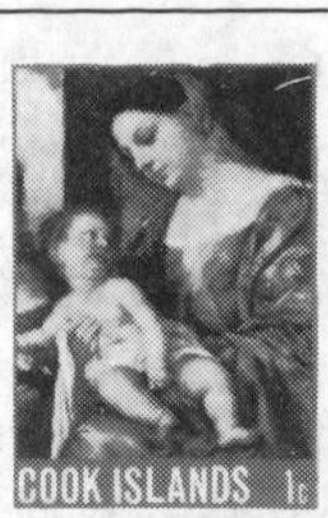

Virgin and Child, by Titian — A41

Paintings: 4c, Holy Family, by Raphael. 10c, Madonna of the Rosary, by Murillo. 20c, Adoration of the Magi, by Memling. 30c, Adoration of the Magi, by Ghirlandajo.

1968, Dec. 2 Photo. *Perf. 13*

243	A41	1c gold & multi	.15	.15
244	A41	4c gold & multi	.15	.15
245	A41	10c gold & multi	.15	.15
246	A41	20c gold & multi	.30	.30
247	A41	30c gold & multi	.45	.45
a.		Souvenir sheet of 5, #243-247 + label	1.75	1.75
		Set value	1.00	1.00

Issued in sheets of 6 (2x3).

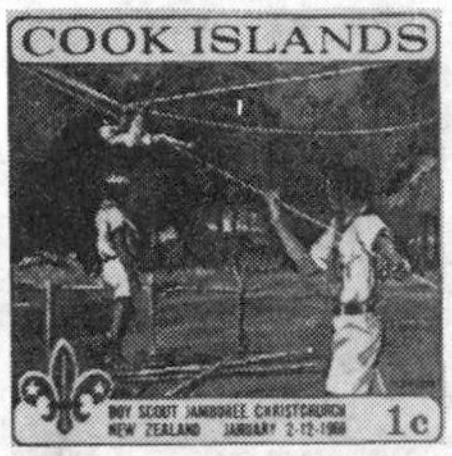

Training on Ropeway A42

Designs: ½c, Boy Scouts cooking over campfire. 5c, Training with signal flags, and Queen Elizabeth II. 10c, Erecting a hut. 20c, Planting a tree. 30c, Lord Baden-Powell, lake and mountains (visit to Rarotonga in 1935).

1969, Feb. 6 Photo. *Perf. 13½*

248	A42	½c multicolored	.15	.15
249	A42	1c multicolored	.15	.15
250	A42	5c multicolored	.15	.15
251	A42	10c multicolored	.25	.25
252	A42	20c multicolored	.50	.50
253	A42	30c multicolored	.75	.75
		Set value	1.70	1.70

5th Natl. Boy Scout Jamboree, Christchurch, New Zealand, Jan. 2-12.
Issued in sheets of 10 stamps and 2 labels (4x3).

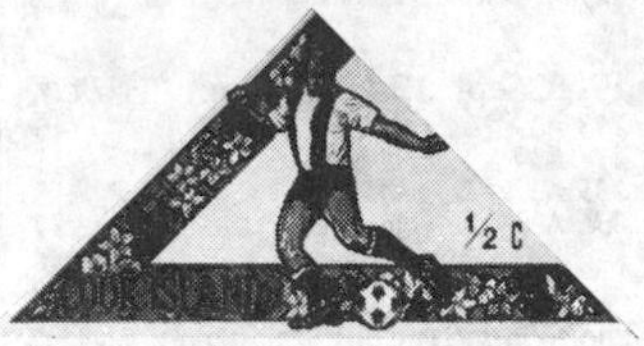

Soccer — A43

Sports: No. 255, Pole vault. No. 256, Weight lifting. No. 257, Basketball, Elizabeth II. No. 258, Long jump. No. 259, Tennis. No. 260, Running. No. 261, Javelin, Elizabeth II. No. 262, Boxing. No. 263, Golf.

Perf. 13½x13

1969, July 7 Photo. Unwmk.

254	A43	½c gold & multi	.15	.15
255	A43	½c gold & multi	.15	.15
256	A43	1c gold & multi	.15	.15
257	A43	1c gold & multi	.15	.15
258	A43	4c gold & multi	.15	.15
259	A43	4c gold & multi	.15	.15
260	A43	10c gold & multi	.20	.20
261	A43	10c gold & multi	.20	.20
262	A43	15c gold & multi	.35	.35
263	A43	15c gold & multi	.35	.35
a.		Souvenir sheet of 10, #254-263 + 2 labels	2.00	2.00
		Set value	1.40	1.40

3rd South Pacifc Games, Port Moresby, Papua and New Guinea, Aug. 13-23.
Stamps of the same denomination are printed se-tenant in sheets of 10.

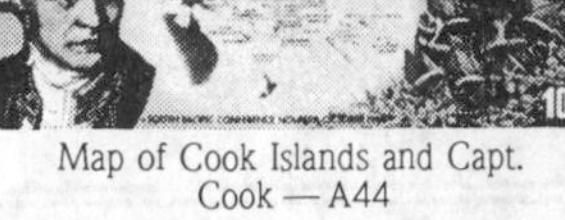

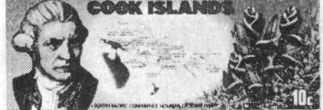

Map of Cook Islands and Capt. Cook — A44

Map of Cook Islands and: 5c, Premier Albert Henry of New Zealand. 25c, Coat of arms of New Zealand. 30c, Queen Elizabeth II.

1969, Oct. 8 Photo. *Perf. 13*

264	A44	5c red & multi	.15	.15
265	A44	10c lemon & multi	.35	.35
266	A44	25c green & multi	.85	.85
267	A44	30c blue & multi	1.00	1.00
		Nos. 264-267 (4)	2.35	2.35

South Pacific Conf., Noumea, Oct. 1969.

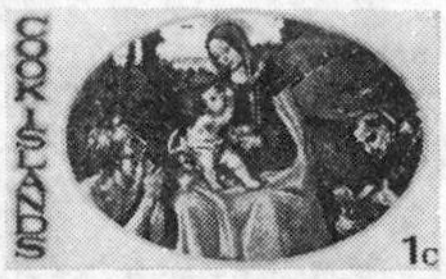

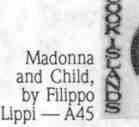

Madonna and Child, by Filippo Lippi — A45

Paintings: 4c, Holy Family, by Baccio della Porta. 10c, Madonna and Child, by Anton Raphael Mengs. 20c, Madonna and Child, by Le Maitre de Flemalle. 30c, Madonna and Child by Correggio.

1969, Nov. 21 Photo. *Perf. 13½*

268	A45	1c buff & multi	.15	.15
269	A45	4c buff & multi	.15	.15
270	A45	10c buff & multi	.22	.22
271	A45	20c buff & multi	.45	.45
272	A45	30c buff & multi	.65	.65
a.		Souvenir sheet of 5, #268-272 + label	1.75	1.75
		Nos. 268-272 (5)	1.62	1.62

Issued in sheets of 8 stamps, one label with portrait of Queen Elizabeth II.

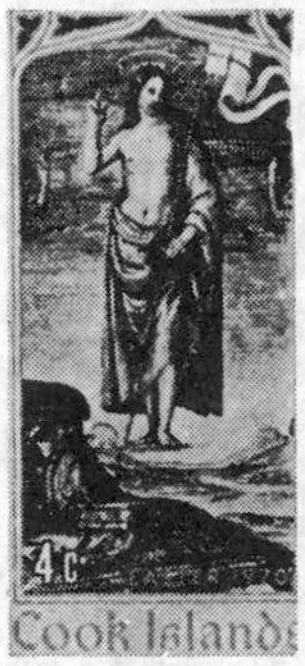

Resurrection of Christ, by Raphael — A46

The Resurrection of Christ by: 8c, Dirk Bouts. 20c, Albert Altdorfer. 25c, Murillo.

1970, Mar. 12 Photo. *Perf. 13½*

Size: 25½x56mm

273	A46	4c gold & multi	.15	.15
274	A46	8c gold & multi	.20	.20
275	A46	20c gold & multi	.50	.50
276	A46	25c gold & multi	.60	.60
a.		Souv. sheet of 4, #273-276 + 2 labels	1.50	1.50
		Nos. 273-276 (4)	1.45	1.45

Easter 1970.
Printed in sheets of 8 stamps and a label (3x3) showing portrait of Queen Elizabeth II and name of painting and painter.
See Nos. 316-318.

Nos. 205, 208, 211-212, 214, 217 Overpinted: "KIA ORANA / APOLLO 13 /ASTRONAUTS / Te Atua to / Tatou Irinakianga"

1970, Apr. *Perf. 14x13½*

277	A34	4c gold & multi	.15	.15
278	A34	8c gold & multi	.15	.15
279	A34	15c gold & multi	.16	.16
280	A34	20c gold & multi	.22	.22
281	A34	30c gold & multi	.35	.35
282	A35	$2 gold & multi	2.00	2.00

No. 218 Overprinted: "KIA ORANA / APOLLO 13 /ASTRONAUTS"

283	A36	$4 gold & multi	5.00	5.00
		Nos. 277-283 (7)	8.03	8.03

Splashdown of Apollo 13 west of Rarotonga, Apr. 17, 1970. Nos. 277-282 were issued Apr. 17; No. 283, Apr. 30.
Values for Nos. 283, 290-291 are for stamps with fluorescence. Stamps without fluorescence sell for more.

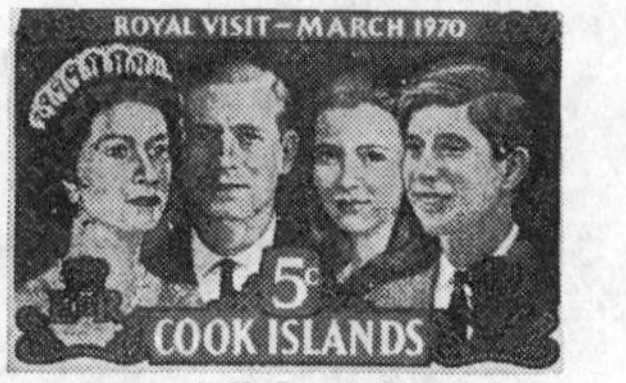

Queen Elizabeth II, Prince Philip, Princess Anne and Prince Charles — A47

Design: 30c, Wedgwood bust of Capt. Cook and "Endeavour." $1, Royal visit commemorative coin, obverse and reverse.

1970, June 12 Photo. *Perf. 13½*

284	A47	5c gold & multi	.20	.20
285	A47	30c gold & multi	1.40	1.25
286	A47	$1 gold & multi	4.50	4.00
a.		Souvenir sheet of 3, #284-286 + label	7.50	7.00
		Nos. 284-286 (3)	6.10	5.45

Visit of the British royal family.

Nos. 284-286 Overprinted in Silver or Black: "Fifth Anniversary Self-Government August 1970"

1970, Aug. 27 Photo. *Perf. 13½*

287	A47	5c gold & multi (S)	.18	.15
288	A47	30c gold & multi	1.00	.90
289	A47	$1 gold & multi	3.50	3.00
		Nos. 287-289 (3)	4.68	4.05

5th anniv. of self-government. The overprint on No. 287 is arranged in one line around 3 sides of the design; the overprint on Nos. 288-289 is in 3 horizontal lines.

Nos. 219A-220 Surcharged

FOUR

DOLLARS

$4.00

1970, Nov. 11 Photo. *Perf. 14x13½*

290	A36	$4 on $8 multi	*14.50*	*14.50*
291	A36	$4 on $10 multi	*10.00*	*10.00*

In each sheet of 15, 3 stamps have 2 surcharged bars instead of one. See second note after No. 283.

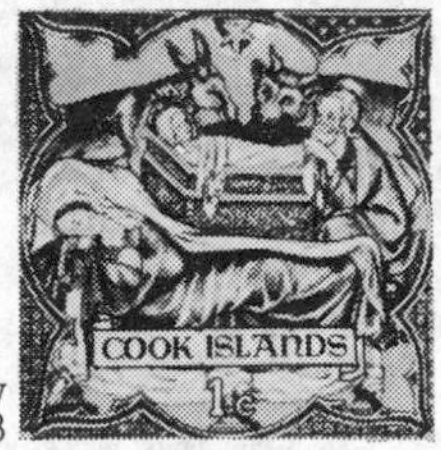

Nativity A48

Illuminations from 14th Century Robert de Lisle Psalter: 4c, Angel and shepherds. 10c, The Circumcision. 20c, The Adoration of the Kings. 30c, The Presentation at the Temple.

1970, Nov. 30 Photo. *Perf. 13½*

292	A48	1c gold & multi	.15	.15
293	A48	4c gold & multi	.15	.15
294	A48	10c gold & multi	.25	.25
295	A48	20c gold & multi	.50	.50
296	A48	30c gold & multi	.75	.75
a.		Souvenir sheet of 5, #292-296 + label	2.00	2.00
		Nos. 292-296 (5)	1.80	1.80

Christmas.
Issued in sheets of 5 stamps and a label (3x2) showing portrait of Queen Elizabeth II and source of design.

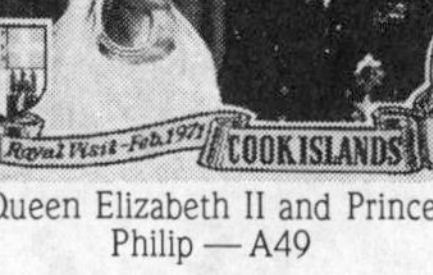

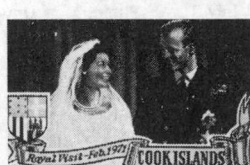

Queen Elizabeth II and Prince Philip — A49

Designs: 4c, Royal family at Balmoral. 10c, Prince Philip sailing. 15c, Prince Philip as polo player. 25c, Prince Philip and royal yacht.

1971, Mar. 11 Litho. *Perf. 13½*

297	A49	1c brt blue & multi	.15	.15
298	A49	4c brt blue & multi	.25	.25
299	A49	10c brt blue & multi	.65	.65
300	A49	15c brt blue & multi	1.00	1.00
301	A49	25c brt blue & multi	1.75	1.75
a.		Souv. sheet of 5, #297-301 + 2 labels	5.00	5.00
		Nos. 297-301 (5)	3.80	3.80

Visit of Prince Philip, Duke of Edinburgh to Rarotonga, Feb. 27, 1971. Printed in sheets of 10 stamps and 2 labels showing Queen Elizabeth II commemorative coin and a portrait of Prince Philip.

Nos. 210, 213-214 Overprinted

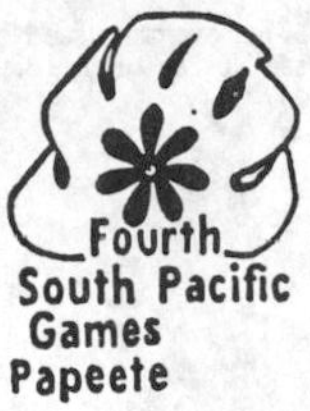

1971, Sept. 8 Photo. *Perf. 14x13½*

302	A34	10c gold & multi	.15	.15
303	A34	25c gold & multi	.30	.30
304	A34	30c gold & multi	.40	.40
		Nos. 302-304 (3)	.85	.85

4th South Pacific Games, Papeete, French Polynesia, Sept. 8-19.

Nos. 202, 205, 208-209 and 211 Surcharged with New Value and Three Bars

1971, Oct. 20

305	A34	10c on 2½c multi	.28	.28
306	A34	10c on 4c multi	.28	.28
307	A34	10c on 8c multi	.28	.28
308	A34	10c on 9c multi	.28	.28
309	A34	10c on 15c multi	.28	.28
		Nos. 305-309 (5)	1.40	1.40

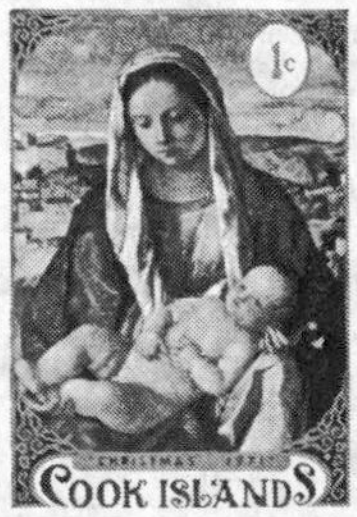

Madonna and Child, by Bellini — A50

Christmas: Paintings of the Madonna and Child, by Giovanni Bellini.

1971, Nov. 30 *Perf. 13½*

310	A50	1c gold & multi	.15	.15
311	A50	4c gold & multi	.15	.15
312	A50	10c gold & multi	.25	.25
313	A50	20c gold & multi	.50	.50
314	A50	30c gold & multi	.75	.75
a.		Souvenir sheet of 5, #310-314 + label	2.50	2.25
		Nos. 310-314 (5)	1.80	1.80

See No. B14.

No. 216 Overprinted: "SOUTH PACIFIC / COMMISSION / FEB. 1947-1972"

1972, Feb. 17 Photo. *Perf. 14x13½*

315	A35	$1 gold & multi	2.00	1.75

South Pacific Commission, 25th anniv.

Easter Type of 1970

Illuminations from 14th century Robert de Lisle Psalter: 5c, St. John. 10c, Christ crucified. 20c, Virgin Mary.

1972, Mar. 6 Photo. *Perf. 13½*

Size: 21x68mm

316	A46	5c gold & multi	.15	.15
317	A46	10c gold & multi	.25	.25
318	A46	30c gold & multi	.90	.90
a.		Souvenir sheet of 3, #316-318	2.25	2.00
		Nos. 316-318 (3)	1.30	1.30

Printed in sheets of 12.
For surcharges see Nos. B15-B16, B19.

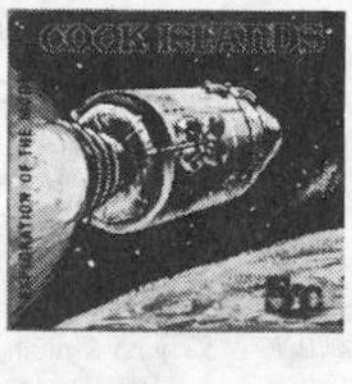

Rocket over Moon — A51

1972, Apr. 17

319	A51	5c shown	.15	.15
320	A51	5c Earth over moon	.15	.15
321	A51	10c Landing module and astronaut	.20	.20
322	A51	10c Astronaut collecting moon rocks	.20	.20
323	A51	25c Earth and rocket over moon	.50	.50
324	A51	25c Lunar rover and astronaut	.50	.50
325	A51	30c Helicopter over raft in Pacific	.65	.65
326	A51	30c Capsule and parachutes	.65	.65
a.		Souvenir sheet of 8	4.50	4.25
		Nos. 319-326 (8)	3.00	3.00

Apollo moon explorations. Stamps of the same denomination are printed se-tenant in sheets of 12.
No. 326a contains one each of Nos. 319-326 arranged in 2 blocks of 4 divided by a map showing splashdown area of Apollo X, XII and XIII.
For surcharges see Nos. B21-B28a.

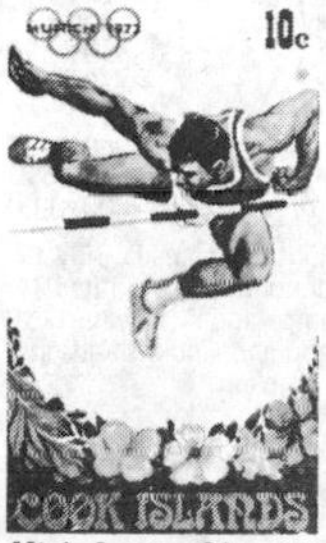

High Jump, Olympic Rings A52

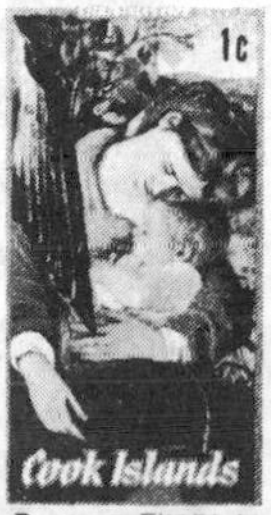

Rest on Flight to Egypt, by Caravaggio A53

1972, June 26

327	A52	10c shown	.35	.35
328	A52	25c Running	.90	.90
329	A52	30c Boxing	1.00	1.00
a.		Souvenir sheet of 3, #327-329 + label	3.00	3.00
		Nos. 327-329 (3)	2.25	2.25

20th Olympic Games, Munich, Aug. 26-Sept. 10. Sheets of 8 stamps and label.
See No. B29.

1972, Oct. 11 Photo. *Perf. 13½*

Paintings: 5c, Virgin of the Swallows, by Guercino. 10c, Virgin with Green Cushion, by Andrea Solario. 20c, Virgin and Child, by Lorenzo di Credi. 30c, Virgin and Child, by Giovanni Bellini.

330	A53	1c gold & multi	.15	.15
331	A53	5c gold & multi	.15	.15
332	A53	10c gold & multi	.28	.28
333	A53	20c gold & multi	.55	.55
334	A53	30c gold & multi	.90	.90
a.		Souvenir sheet of 5, #330-334 + label	2.50	2.50
		Nos. 330-334 (5)	2.03	2.03

Christmas. See No. B30.

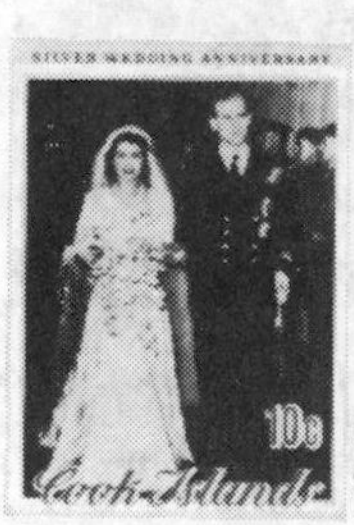

Princess Elizabeth and Prince Philip — A54

Designs: 5c, Wedding ceremony, Westminster Abbey. 15c, Bridal portrait. 30c, Official wedding picture of royal family.

1972, Nov. 20

Size: 29x40mm

335	A54	5c silver & multi	.15	.15
336	A54	10c silver & multi	.30	.30

Size: 40x40mm

337	A54	15c silver & multi	.50	.50

Size: 66x40mm

338	A54	30c silver & multi	1.00	1.00
		Nos. 335-338 (4)	1.95	1.95

25th anniversary of the marriage of Queen Elizabeth II and Prince Philip.
Nos. 335-337 printed in sheets of 8 stamps and one label; No. 338 in sheets of 6.

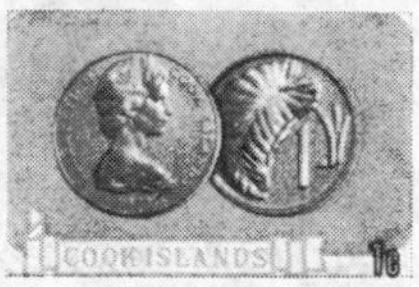

1c Coin with Queen Elizabeth II and Taro Leaf — A55

Queen Elizabeth II Coins: 2c, Pineapples. 5c, Hibiscus. 10c, Oranges. 20c, Fairy terns. 50c, Bonito. $1, Tangaroa, Polynesian god of creation, vert.

1973, Mar. 15 Photo. *Perf. 13x13½*

Size: 37x24mm

339	A55	1c dp car, blk & gold	.15	.15
340	A55	2c blue, blk & gold	.15	.15
341	A55	5c green, blk & gold	.15	.15

Size: 46x30mm

342	A55	10c vio, blue, blk & sil	.22	.22
343	A55	20c dk green, blk & sil	.45	.45
344	A55	50c dp car, black & sil	1.10	1.10

Size: 32x54½mm

345	A55	$1 blue, blk & silver	2.25	2.25
		Nos. 339-345 (7)	4.47	4.47

Coinage commemorating silver wedding anniversary of Queen Elizabeth II.
Printed in sheets of 20 stamps and label showing Westminster Abbey.

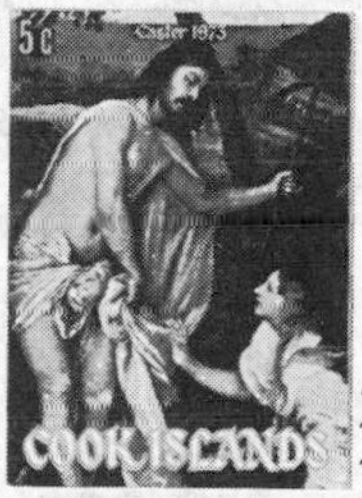

"Noli me Tangere," by Titian — A56

Paintings: 10c, Descent from the Cross, by Rubens. 30c, The Lamentation of Christ, by Dürer.

1973, Apr. 9

346	A56	5c gold & multi	.15	.15
347	A56	10c gold & multi	.25	.25
348	A56	30c gold & multi	.75	.75
a.		Souvenir sheet of 3, #346-348	1.75	1.75
		Nos. 346-348 (3)	1.15	1.15

Easter. Printed in sheets of 15 stamps and one label.
See Nos. 378-380, B31-B33, B39-B41.

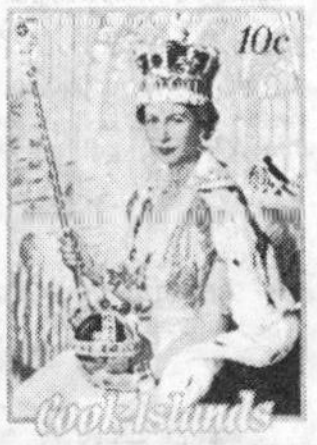

Queen Elizabeth II in Coronation Regalia — A57

1973, June 1 Photo. *Perf. 14x13½*

349	A57	10c gold & multi	2.00	1.25

Souvenir Sheet

Perf. 13½x14½

350	A57	50c gold & multi	6.00	4.00

20th anniv. of the coronation of Queen Elizabeth II. No. 349 printed in sheets of 5 stamps and one label.

Nos. 206, 208, 210, 212-214 Overprinted: "TENTH ANNIVERSARY / CESSATION OF / NUCLEAR TESTING / TREATY"

1973, July 25 Photo. *Perf. 14x13½*

351	A34	5c gold & multi	.15	.15
352	A34	8c gold & multi	.20	.20
353	A34	10c gold & multi	.25	.25
354	A34	20c gold & multi	.50	.50
355	A34	25c gold & multi	.65	.65
356	A34	30c gold & multi	.75	.75
		Nos. 351-356 (6)	2.50	2.50

Nuclear Test Ban Treaty, 10th anniv. and as protest against French nuclear testing on Mururoa atoll.

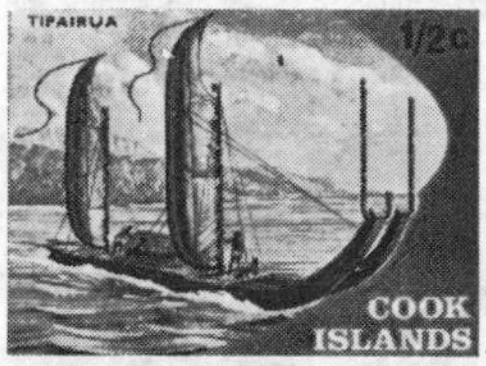

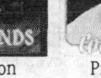

Tipairua A58

Designs: Historic South Pacific sailing vessels.

1973, Sept. 17 Photo. *Perf. 13½x13*

357	A58	½c shown	.15	.15
358	A58	1c Wa'a Kaulua	.15	.15
359	A58	1½c Tainui	.15	.15
360	A58	5c War canoe	.15	.15
361	A58	10c Pahi	.25	.25
362	A58	15c Amatasi	.40	.40
363	A58	25c Vaka	.65	.65
		Set value	1.58	1.58

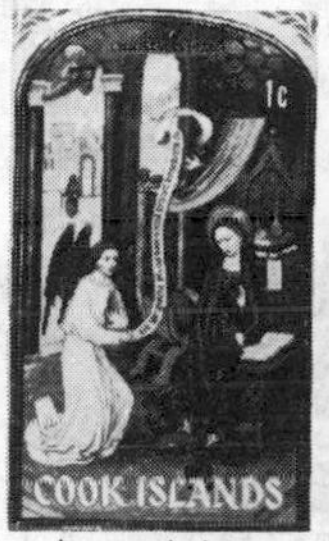

Annunciation A59

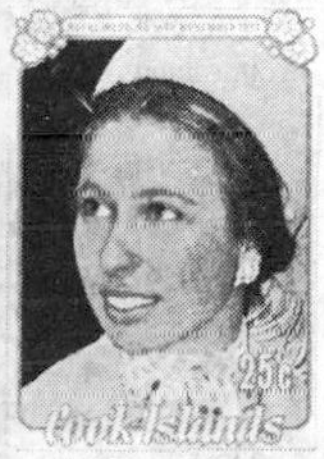

Princess Anne A60

Designs from 15th Century Prayer Book: 5c, The Visitation. 10c, Adoration of the Shepherds. 20c, Adoration of the Kings. 30c, Slaughter of the Innocents.

1973, Oct. 30 Photo. *Perf. 13x13½*

364	A59	1c multicolored	.15	.15
365	A59	5c multicolored	.15	.15
366	A59	10c multicolored	.18	.18
367	A59	20c multicolored	.40	.40
368	A59	30c multicolored	.65	.65
a.		Souvenir sheet of 5, #364-368 + label	1.75	1.50
		Nos. 364-368 (5)	1.53	1.53

Christmas. See Nos. B34-B38.

1973, Nov. 14 Photo. *Perf. 14*

369	A60	25c shown	.40	.40
370	A60	30c Mark Phillips	.60	.60
371	A60	50c Princess and Mark Phillips	1.00	1.00
a.		Souvenir sheet of 3, #369-371 + label	2.50	2.50
		Nos. 369-371 (3)	2.00	2.00

Wedding of Princess Anne and Capt. Mark Phillips.

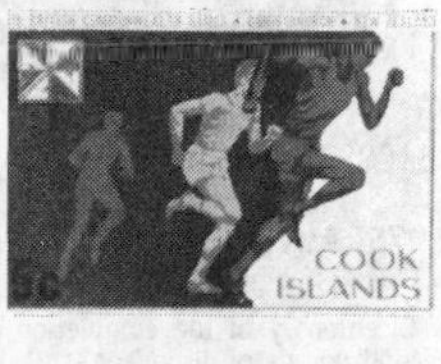

Running and Games Emblem A61

Games Emblem and: 1c, Diving, vert. 3c, Boxing, vert. 10c, Weight lifting. 30c, Bicycling. 50c, Discobolus, vert.

1974, Jan. 24 Photo. *Perf. 14*

372	A61	1c multicolored	.15	.15
373	A61	3c multicolored	.15	.15
374	A61	5c multicolored	.15	.15
375	A61	10c multicolored	.25	.25
376	A61	30c multicolored	.75	.75
		Set value	1.25	1.25

Souvenir Sheet

377	A61	50c multicolored	1.25	1.25

10th British Commonwealth Games, Christchurch, New Zealand, Jan. 24-Feb. 2. No. 377 contains one stamp 35x45mm.

Easter Type of 1973
Dated "1974"

Paintings: 5c, Jesus Carrying Cross, by Raphael. 10c, Jesus in the Arms of God, by El Greco. 30c, Descent from the Cross, by Caravaggio.

1974, Mar. 25 *Perf. 13½x13*

378	A56	5c gold & multi	.15	.15
379	A56	10c gold & multi	.25	.25
380	A56	30c gold & multi	.65	.65
a.		Souvenir sheet of 3, #378-380	1.40	1.40
		Nos. 378-380 (3)	1.05	1.05

Easter. See Nos. B39-B41.

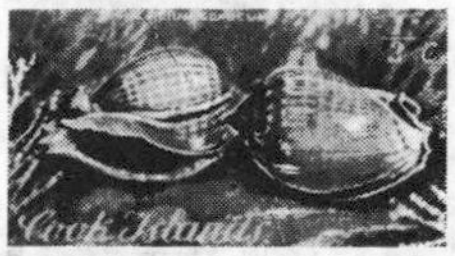

Phallicium Glaucum A62

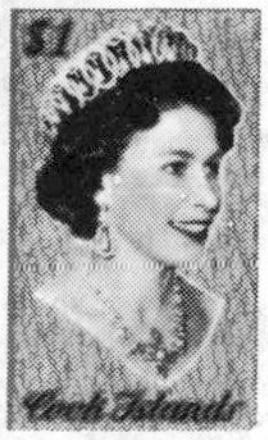

Queen Elizabeth II — A63

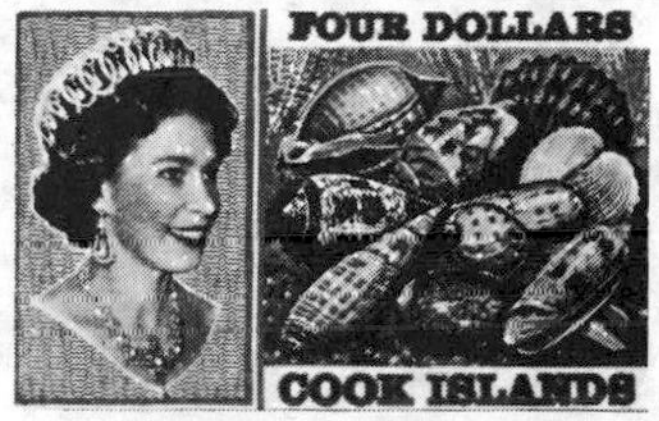

Queen and Shells — A64

Designs: Cook Islands sea shells. The designs of the 2c, 5c, 10c and 30c include portrait of Queen Elizabeth II.

1974-75 Photo. *Perf. 13½*

381	A62	½c shown	.15	.15
382	A62	1c Vasum turbinellus	.15	.15
383	A62	1½c Corculum cardissa	.15	.15
384	A62	2c Terebellum terebellum	.15	.15
385	A62	3c Aulica vespertilio	.15	.15
386	A62	4c Strombus gibberulus	.15	.15
387	A62	5c Cymatium pileare	.15	.15
388	A62	6c Cyprae caputserpentis	.15	.15
389	A62	8c Bursa granularis	.18	.16
390	A62	10c Tenebra muscaria	.22	.20
391	A62	15c Mitra mitra	.32	.30
392	A62	20c Natica alapillonis roding	.42	.38
393	A62	25c Gloripallium pallium	.55	.45
394	A62	30c Conus miles	.65	.55
395	A62	50c Conus textile	1.10	1.00
396	A62	60c Oliva sericea roding	1.25	1.10
397	A63	$1 multicolored	1.90	1.90
398	A63	$2 multi ('75)	3.75	3.75

Perf. 14x13½

399	A64	$4 multi ('75)	5.50	5.50
400	A64	$6 multi ('75)	8.75	8.75
401	A64	$8 multi ('75)	11.00	11.00
402	A64	$10 multi ('75)	15.00	15.00
		Nos. 381-402 (22)	51.79	51.24

Issued: 50c, 60c, $1, 8/26; $2, 1/27; $4, 3/17; $6, 4/29; $8, 5/30; $10, 6/30; others, 5/17.
For surcharges see Nos. 488-498, 526-528. For overprints see Nos. 991, O16-O26, O30-O31.

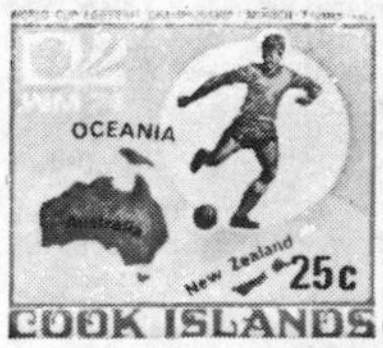

Soccer Player and Map of Oceania — A65

Designs: 50c, Munich stadium and map of Oceania. $1, Soccer player, Munich stadium and World Cup.

1974, July 5 Photo. *Perf. 13½*

Size: 31x29mm

403	A65	25c multicolored	.45	.45
404	A65	50c multicolored	.90	.90

Size: 68x28½mm

405	A65	$1 multicolored	1.75	1.75
a.		Souvenir sheet of 3, #403-405	3.75	3.75
		Nos. 403-405 (3)	3.10	3.10

World Cup Soccer Championship, Munich, June 13-July 7. Nos. 403-405 printed in sheets of 8 and commemorative label.

$2.50 Capt. Cook
Silver Coin — A66

Commemorative Silver Coins: $7.50, $7.50 coin with Queen Elizabeth II on obverse; Capt. Cook, map of Islands and "Resolution" on reverse. $2.50 coin shows "Resolution," "Adventure" and globe on reverse.

1974, July 22   Photo.   Perf. 14
406 A66 $2.50 sil, vio & blk   9.25   7.25
407 A66 $7.50 grn, sil & blk   25.00   22.50
  a. Souvenir sheet of 2, #406-407   40.00   35.00

Bicentenary of Capt. Cook's 2nd voyage of discovery. Nos. 406-407 printed in sheets of 5 and commemorative label.

Cook Islands Nos. 1, 49, 62, 66, 77 — A67

Stamps of Cook Islands: 25c, DC-3 over old Rarotonga landing strip, and No. 19. 30c, Rarotonga Post Office, UPU emblem and No. 65. 50c, UPU emblem and Nos. 1, 19, 49, 62, 65-66 and 77.

1974, Sept. 16 Photo.   Perf. 13½x14
408 A67 10c gold & multi   .22   .22
409 A67 25c gold & multi   .55   .55
410 A67 30c gold & multi   .65   .65
411 A67 50c gold & multi   1.20   1.20
  a. Souv. sheet of 4, #408-411, perf.
       13½   2.75   2.75
       Nos. 408-411 (4)   2.62   2.62

Cent. of UPU. Nos. 408-411 printed in sheets of 8 and commemorative label.

Virgin and Child, with St. John, by Raphael — A68

Paintings: 5c, Holy Family, by Andrea del Sarto. 10c, Nativity, by Correggio. 20c, Holy Family, by Rembrandt. 30c, Nativity, by Van der Weyden.

1974, Oct. 15   Photo.   Perf. 13½
412 A68 1c multicolored   .15   .15
413 A68 5c multicolored   .15   .15
414 A68 10c multicolored   .20   .20
415 A68 20c multicolored   .45   .45
416 A68 30c multicolored   .65   .65
  a. Souvenir sheet of 5, #412-416 + label 1.65 1.65
       Nos. 412-416 (5)   1.60   1.60

Christmas 1974. Nos. 412-416 printed in sheets of 15 and one label showing Queen Elizabeth II. See Nos. B42-B46.

Churchill and Blenheim Palace A69

Sir Winston Churchill (1874-1965) and: 10c, Parliament. 25c, Chartwell. 30c, Buckingham Palace. 50c, St. Paul's Cathedral.

1974, Nov. 20   Photo.   Perf. 14
417 A69 5c violet & multi   .15   .15
418 A69 10c maroon & multi   .25   .25
419 A69 25c dk blue & multi   .65   .65
420 A69 30c brown & multi   .85   .85
421 A69 50c multicolored   1.65   1.65
  a. Souvenir sheet of 5, #417-421 + label 3.75 3.75
       Nos. 417-421 (5)   3.55   3.55

Nos. 417-421 printed in sheets of 5 stamps and one label showing $100 commemorative gold coin.

Vasco Nunez de Balboa A70

Designs: 5c, Ferdinand Magellan and route around South America. 10c, Juan Sebastian del Cano and ship. 25c, Andres de Urdaneta and ship. 25c, Miguel Lopez de Legaspi and ship.

1975, Feb. 3   Perf. 13½
422 A70 1c multicolored   .15   .15
423 A70 5c multicolored   .15   .15
424 A70 10c multicolored   .45   .30
425 A70 25c multicolored   1.25   1.00
426 A70 30c multicolored   1.50   1.10
       Nos. 422-426 (5)   3.50   2.70

16th century explorers of the Pacific Ocean.

Apollo and Apollo-Soyuz Emblem — A71

Apollo-Soyuz Emblem and: No. 428, Soyuz. No. 429, Aleksei A. Leonov and Valery N. Kubasov. No. 430, Donald K. Slayton, Vance D. Brand and Thomas P. Stafford. No. 431, Cosmonaut inside Soyuz capsule. No. 432, American astronauts inside Apollo capsule.

1975, July 15   Photo.   Perf. 13½
427 A71 25c multicolored   .50   .50
428 A71 25c multicolored   .50   .50
429 A71 30c multicolored   .60   .60
430 A71 30c multicolored   .60   .60
431 A71 50c multicolored   1.00   1.00
432 A71 50c multicolored   1.00   1.00
  a. Souvenir sheet of 6, #427-432   4.25   4.25
       Nos. 427-432 (6)   4.20   4.20

Apollo Soyuz space test project (Russo-American space cooperation), launching July 15; link-up, July 17. Stamps of same denomination printed se-tenant in sheets of 18 stamps and 2 labels showing flags.

$100 Gold Commemorative Coin — A72

1975, Aug. 8   Photo.   Perf. 13½x13
433 A72 $2 gold & dp violet   6.00   5.75

Bicentenary of the completion of Capt. Cook's second voyage of discovery.

Cook Islands' Flag, Map of Islands and New Zealand A73

Prime Minister Sir Albert Henry — A74

Design: 25c, View of Rarotonga and flag.

1975, Aug. 8   Perf. 13½x13, 13x13½
434 A73 5c gold & multi   .15   .15
435 A74 10c gold & multi   .25   .20
436 A73 25c gold & multi   .65   .50
       Nos. 434-436 (3)   1.05   .85

Tenth anniversary of self-government.

Virgin and Child, 15th Century, Flemish — A75

Paintings: 10c, Madonna in the Field, by Raphael. 15c, Holy Family, by Raphael. 20c, Adoration of the Shepherds, by J. B. Mayno. 35c, Annunciation, by Murillo.

1975, Dec. 1   Photo.   Perf. 13½
437 A75 6c gold & multi   .15   .15
438 A75 10c gold & multi   .20   .20
439 A75 15c gold & multi   .30   .30
440 A75 20c gold & multi   .40   .40
441 A75 35c gold & multi   .65   .65
  a. Souvenir sheet of 5, #437-441 + label 1.75 1.75
       Nos. 437-441 (5)   1.70   1.70

Christmas. See Nos. B47-B51.

Descent from the Cross, by Raphael A76

Paintings: 15c, Pieta, by Veronese. 35c, Pieta, by El Greco.

1976, Mar. 29   Photo.   Perf. 13½
442 A76 7c gold & multi   .15   .15
443 A76 15c gold & multi   .28   .28
444 A76 35c gold & multi   .70   .70
  a. Souvenir sheet of 3, #442-444   1.10   1.10
       Nos. 442-444 (3)   1.13   1.13

Easter. Nos. 442-444 printed in sheets of 20 with label showing Queen Elizabeth II. See Nos. B52-B54.

Benjamin Franklin and "Resolution" — A77

Designs: $2, Capt. James Cook and "Resolution." $3, Cook, "Resolution" and Franklin.

1976, May 29   Photo.   Perf. 13½
445 A77 $1 gold & multi   5.50   3.00
446 A77 $2 gold & multi   11.50 6.25

Souvenir Sheet
Perf. 13
447 A77 $3 gold & multi   14.00 8.00

American Bicentennial. No. 447 contains one stamp 73x31mm. Nos. 445-446 printed in sheets of 5 and corner label with Franklin's request to assist Capt. Cook.
For overprint see No. O29.

Nos. 445-447 Overprinted
"Royal Visit July 1976"

1976, July 6   Photo.   Perf. 13½
448 A77 $1 gold & multi   2.50   2.00
449 A77 $2 gold & multi   6.25   5.75

Souvenir Sheet
Perf. 13
450 A77 $3 gold & multi   13.00 9.00

Visit of Queen Elizabeth II and Prince Philip to the United States.

High Hurdles
A78   A79

1976, July 22   Perf. 13½
451 A78 7c shown   .15   .15
452 A79 7c shown   .15   .15
453 A79 15c Field hockey   .25   .25
454 A79 15c Field hockey   .25   .25
455 A79 30c Fencing   .50   .50
456 A79 30c Fencing   .50   .50
457 A78 35c Soccer   .60   .60
458 A79 35c Soccer   .60   .60
  a. Souvenir sheet of 8, #451-458   3.25   3.25
       Nos. 451-458 (8)   3.00   3.00

21st Olympic Games, Montreal, Canada, July 17-Aug. 1. Stamps of same denomination printed se-tenant in sheets of 10 stamps and 2 labels (4x3), showing flags of New Zealand and Cook Islands and Montreal Olympic Games emblem.

The Visitation — A80

Designs: 10c, Virgin and Child. 15c, Adoration of the Shepherds. 20c, Adoration of the Kings. 35c, Holy Family. After painted Renaissance altar sculptures.

1976, Oct. 12 Photo.   Perf. 14x13½
459 A80 6c gold & multi   .15   .15
460 A80 10c gold & multi   .18   .18
461 A80 15c gold & multi   .25   .25
462 A80 20c gold & multi   .35   .35
463 A80 35c gold & multi   .60   .60
  a. Souvenir sheet of 5, #459-463 + label 1.75 1.75
       Nos. 459-463 (5)   1.53   1.53

Christmas. Nos. 459-463 printed in sheets of 20 with label showing Queen Elizabeth II. See Nos. B55-B59.

$5 Silver Coin, 1976 A81

1976, Nov. 15 Photo.   Perf. 13½
464 A81 $1 multicolored   3.00   2.25

National Wildlife and Conservation Day. Issued in sheets of 5 stamps and commemorative label. See Nos. 502, 536.

Elizabeth II in Coronation Vestments — A82

Designs: No. 465, Crown. No. 467, Westminster Abbey. No. 468, Coach in procession. No. 469, Queen and Prince Philip after coronation. No. 470, Investiture of Sir Albert Henry, Premier of Cook Islands, 1974.

1977, Feb. 7 Photo. *Perf. 13½x13*

465 A82 25c silver & multi .50 .40
466 A82 25c silver & multi .50 .40
467 A82 50c silver & multi 1.25 1.00
468 A82 50c silver & multi 1.25 1.00
469 A82 $1 silver & multi 2.50 2.00
470 A82 $1 silver & multi 2.50 2.00
a. Souv. sheet of 6, #465-470, perf. 13 8.75 7.50
Nos. 465-470 (6) 8.50 6.80

Reign of Queen Elizabeth II, 25th anniv. Stamps of same denomination printed se-tenant in sheets of 8 (4x2).
For overprints see Nos. O27-O28.

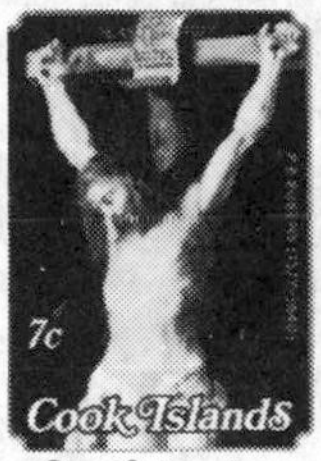

Crucifixion, by Rubens — A83

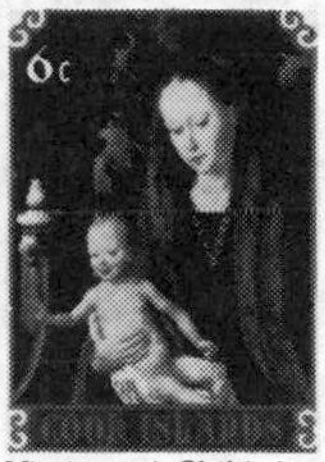

Virgin and Child, by Memling — A84

Paintings by Rubens: 15c, Christ Between the Thieves. 35c, Descent from the Cross.

1977, Mar. 28 Photo. *Perf. 14x13½*

471 A83 7c gold & multi .15 .15
472 A83 15c gold & multi .20 .20
473 A83 35c gold & multi .50 .50
a. Souv. sheet of 3, #471-473, perf 13 .90 .90
Nos. 471-473 (3) .85 .85

Easter 1977, and 400th birth anniv. of Peter Paul Rubens (1577-1640), Flemish painter. Nos. 471-473 printed in sheets of 24 stamps and corner label with portrait of Queen Elizabeth II and description.
See Nos. B60-B62.

1977, Oct. 3 Photo. *Perf. 13½*

Virgin and Child by: 10c, Hans Memling. 15c, Geertgen Tot Sin Jans. 20c, Carlo Crivelli. 35c, School of Henry Blex.

474 A84 6c gold & multi .15 .15
475 A84 10c gold & multi .15 .15
476 A84 15c gold & multi .20 .20
477 A84 20c gold & multi .28 .28
478 A84 35c gold & multi .50 .50
a. Souvenir sheet of 5, #474-478 + label 1.25 1.25
Nos. 474-478 (5) 1.28 1.28

Christmas. Nos. 474-478 printed in sheets of 24 and label. See Nos. B63-B67.

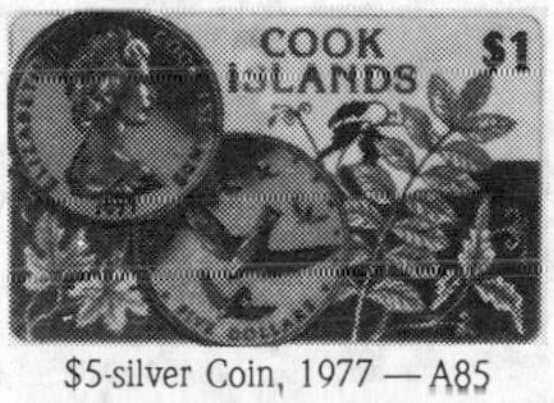

$5-silver Coin, 1977 — A85

1977, Nov. 15 Photo. *Perf. 13½*

479 A85 $1 silver & multi 3.50 1.65

National Wildlife Conservation Day. No. 479 issued in sheets of 5 and one label.

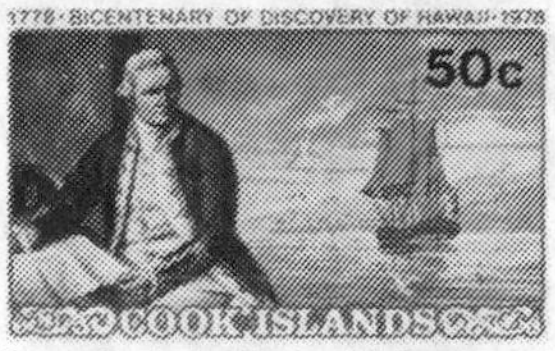

Capt. Cook, by Nathaniel Dance and "Resolution" — A86

Designs: $1, "Capt. Cook Landing at Owyhee" and Capt. Cook. $2, Cook Islands $200 commemorative coin, 1978, and Cook Monument, Hawaii, 1825.

1978, Jan. 20 Litho. *Perf. 13½*

480 A86 50c gold & multi .75 .75
481 A86 $1 gold & multi 1.50 1.50
482 A86 $2 gold & multi 3.00 3.00
a. Souvenir sheet of 3, #480-482 6.00 6.00
Nos. 480-482 (3) 5.25 5.25

Bicentennial of Capt. Cook's arrival in Hawaii.
Nos. 480-482 issued in sheets of 5 with corner label showing ship off Hawaiian coast.
For overprints see Nos. 499-501a.

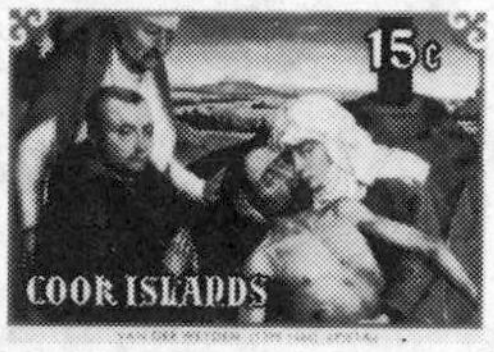

Pieta, by Rogier van der Weyden A87

Paintings, National Gallery, London: 35c, Burial of Jesus, by Michelangelo. 75c, Jesus at Emmaus, by Caravaggio.

1978, Mar. 20 Photo. *Perf. 13½x13*

483 A87 15c gold & multi .22 .22
484 A87 35c gold & multi .50 .50
485 A87 75c gold & multi 1.10 1.10
a. Souvenir sheet of 3, #483-485 + label 1.40 1.40
Nos. 483-485 (3) 1.82 1.82

Easter. Nos. 483-485 printed in sheets of 5 and corner label showing National Gallery.
See Nos. B68-B70.

Souvenir Sheets

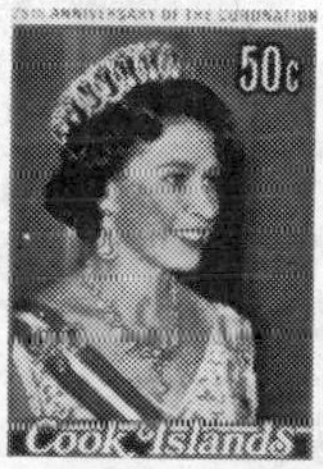

Elizabeth II — A88

1978, June 6 Photo. *Perf. 13*

486 Sheet of 4 + 2 labels 1.65 1.65
a. A88 50c shown .65 .65
b. A88 50c Lion of England .65 .65
c. A88 50c Imperial State Crown .65 .65
d. A88 50c Tangaroa figure .65 .65
487 Sheet of 4 + label 2.50 2.50
a. A88 70c like 486a .85 .85
b. A88 70c Scepter with Cross .85 .85
c. A88 70c St. Edward's Crown .85 .85
d. A88 70c Rarotongan staff god .85 .85
e. Souv. sheet of 8, #486a-487d + label 5.50 5.50

Coronation of Queen Elizabeth II, 25th anniv.

Nos. 381, 383, 388-389, 393-396 Surcharged with New Value and Three Bars in Silver, Black or Gold

1978, Nov. 10 Photo. *Perf. 13½*

488 A62 5c on 1½c multi (S) .15 .15
489 A62 7c on ½c multi .20 .20
490 A62 10c on 6c multi (G) .28 .28
491 A62 10c on 8c multi (G) .28 .28
492 A62 15c on ½c multi .42 .42
493 A62 15c on 25c multi (S) .42 .42
494 A62 15c on 30c multi .42 .42
495 A62 15c on 50c multi (S) .42 .42
496 A62 15c on 60c multi (G) .42 .42
497 A62 17c on ½c multi .48 .48
498 A62 17c on 50c multi (S) .48 .48
Nos. 488-498 (11) 3.97 3.97

See Nos. 526-528.

Nos. 480-482a Overprinted in Black on Silver Panel: "1728--250th ANNIVERSARY OF COOK'S BIRTH--1978"

1978, Nov. 13 Litho. *Perf. 13½*

499 A86 50c gold & multi .75 .75
500 A86 $1 gold & multi 1.50 1.50
501 A86 $2 gold & multi 3.00 3.00
a. Souvenir sheet of 3, #499-501 6.00 6.00
Nos. 499-501 (3) 5.25 5.25

250th anniv. of Capt. Cook's birth. Similar overprint in 4 lines was applied to labels. Label of No. 501a overprinted only with dates 1728, 1978.

Coin Type of 1976

Design: $1, $5 Silver coin, 1978 (Polynesian warbler).

1978, Nov. 15 Photo. *Perf. 13½*

502 A81 $1 multicolored 2.25 2.00

National Wildlife and Conservation Day. Sheets of 24 containing 4 panes of 6.

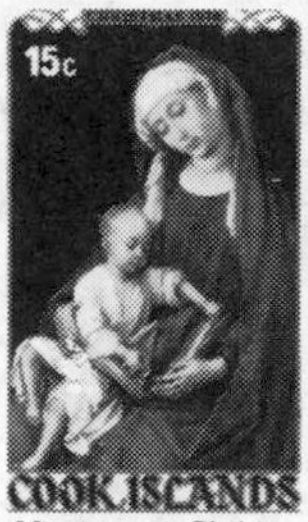

Virgin and Child, by Rogier van der Weyden — A89

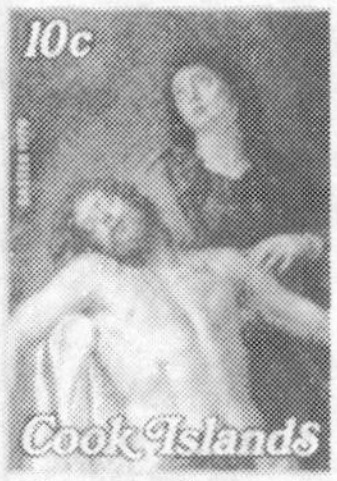

Pieta, by Gaspar de Crayer — A90

Virgin and Child by: 17c, Carlo Crivelli. 35c, Murillo.

1978, Dec. 8 Photo. *Perf. 13*

503 A89 15c multicolored .20 .20
504 A89 17c multicolored .25 .25
505 A89 35c multicolored .50 .50
a. Souvenir sheet of 3, #503-505 1.25 1.25
Nos. 503-505 (3) .95 .95

Christmas. See Nos. B71-B73.

1979, Apr. 5 Photo. *Perf. 13*

Descent from the Cross, by Gaspar de Crayer (Details): 12c, St. John. 15c, Mary Magdalene. 20c, Cherubs.

506 A90 10c multicolored .15 .15
507 A90 12c multicolored .18 .18
508 A90 15c multicolored .24 .24
509 A90 20c multicolored .50 .50
Nos. 506-509 (4) 1.07 1.07

Easter. See No. B74.

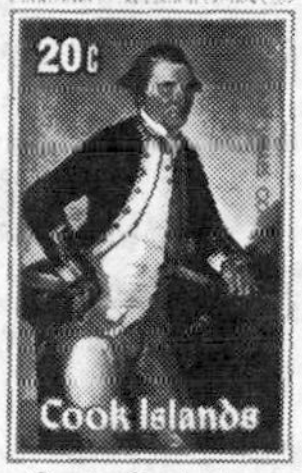

Capt. Cook, by John Weber — A91

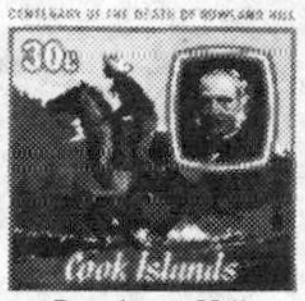

Rowland Hill, Postrider — A92

Designs: 30c, Resolution, by Henry Roberts. 35c, Endeavour. 50c, Death of Capt. Cook, by George Carter.

1979, July 23 Photo. *Perf. 14x13½*

510 A91 20c multicolored .35 .35
511 A91 30c multicolored .50 .50
512 A91 35c multicolored .60 .60
513 A91 50c multicolored .80 .80
a. Souvenir sheet of 4 2.00 2.00
Nos. 510-513 (4) 2.25 2.25

Capt. Cook (1728-1779), explorer. No. 513a contains 4 stamps similar to Nos. 510-513 with black frames.

1979, Sept. 10 *Perf. 14½*

Sir Rowland Hill (1795-1879), originator of penny postage, and: No. 515, Stagecoach. No. 516, Automobile. No. 517, Streamlined train. No. 518, Cap-Horniers, sailing ship. No. 519, River steamer. No. 520, Liner Deutschland. No. 521, Liner United States. No. 522, Balloon Neptune. No. 523, Junkers F13. No. 524, Graf Zeppelin. No. 525, Concorde.

514 A92 30c multicolored .30 .30
515 A92 30c multicolored .30 .30
516 A92 30c multicolored .30 .30
517 A92 30c multicolored .30 .30
518 A92 35c multicolored .35 .35
519 A92 35c multicolored .35 .35
520 A92 35c multicolored .35 .35
521 A92 35c multicolored .35 .35
522 A92 50c multicolored .50 .50
523 A93 50c multicolored .50 .50
524 A93 50c multicolored .50 .50
525 A93 50c multicolored .50 .50
a. Souvenir sheet of 12, #514-525 5.00 5.00
Nos. 514-525 (12) 4.60 4.60

Stamps of same denomination printed se-tenant in sheets of 40.

Nos. 381, 383, 396 Surcharged in Gold or Silver

1979, Sept. 12 Photo. *Perf. 13½*

526 A62 6c on ½c multi .18 .18
527 A62 10c on 1½c multi (S) .28 .28
528 A62 15c on 60c multi .42 .42
Nos. 526-528 (3) .88 .88

Nos. 526-528 have 3 thick bars of equal length over old value.

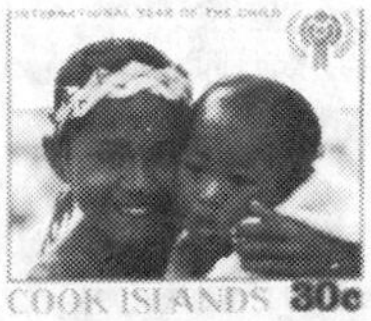

Girl and Baby, IYC Emblem — A93

IYC Emblem and: 50c, Boy playing tree drum. 65c, Children dancing.

1979, Oct. 10 *Perf. 13*

529 A93 30c multicolored .42 .42
530 A93 50c multicolored .70 .70
531 A93 65c multicolored .90 .90
Nos. 529-531 (3) 2.02 2.02

See No. B75.

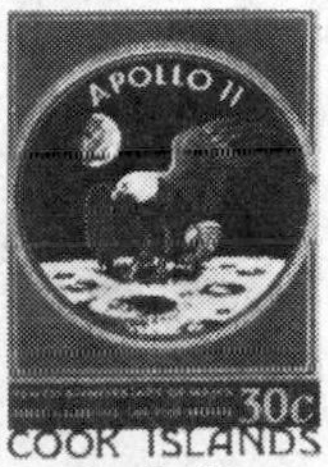

Apollo 11 Emblem — A94

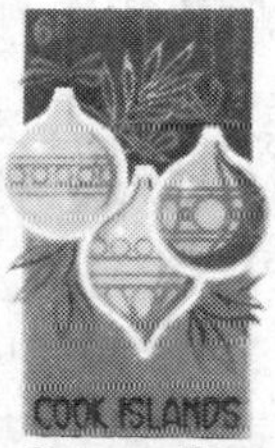

Christmas Tree Ornaments — A95

Designs: 50c, Apollo 11 crew, lunar map. 60c, Astronaut walking on moon. 65c, Splashdown.

1979, Nov. 7 *Perf. 14*

532 A94 30c multicolored .40 .40
533 A94 50c multicolored .60 .60
534 A94 60c multicolored .75 .75
535 A94 65c multicolored .85 .85
a. Souv. sheet of 4, #532-535, perf. 13 3.00 3.00
Nos. 532-535 (4) 2.60 2.60

Apollo 11 moon landing, 10th anniv.

Coin Type of 1976

Design: $1, $5 Silver coin, 1979 (Raratonga fruit dove).

Perf. 13½x14½

1979, Nov. 15 Photo.

536 A81 $1 multicolored 2.00 2.00

National Wildlife and Conservation Day.

1979, Dec. 14 *Perf. 14*

Christmas (Flowers and): 10c, Star. 12c, Bells and candle. 15c, Ancestral statue.

537 A95 6c multicolored .15 .15
538 A95 10c multicolored .15 .15
539 A95 12c multicolored .15 .15
540 A95 15c multicolored .20 .20
Nos. 537-540,B76-B79 (8) 1.53 1.53

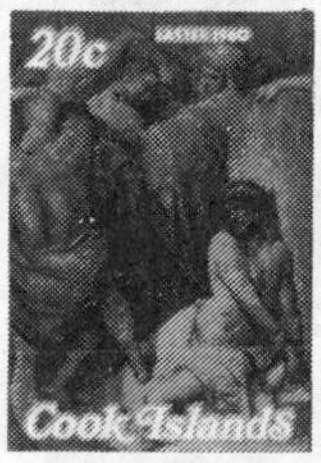

Flagellation, by Dore — A96

Bible illustrations by Gustave Dore, 1833-1883.

1980, Mar. 31 Photo. *Perf. 13*

541 A96 20c shown .28 .28
542 A96 20c Jesus Wearing Crown of Thorns .28 .28
543 A96 30c Jesus Mocked .45 .45
544 A96 30c Jesus Falls .45 .45
545 A96 35c The Crucifixion .50 .50
546 A96 35c Descent from the Cross .50 .50
Nos. 541-546 (6) 2.46 2.46

Easter. Stamps of same denomination se-tenant.
See Nos. 553, B80-B86.

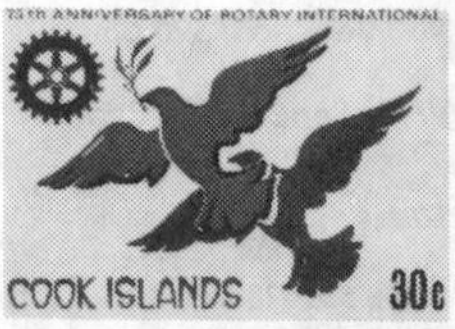

Doves with Olive Branch, Rotary Emblem
A97

1980, May 27 Photo. *Perf. 14*

547	A97	30c shown	.45	.45
548	A97	35c Flowers	.50	.50
549	A97	50c Flags, globe	.70	.70
		Nos. 547-549 (3)	1.65	1.65

Rotary International, 75th anniv. See No. B87

Easter Type of 1980 and:

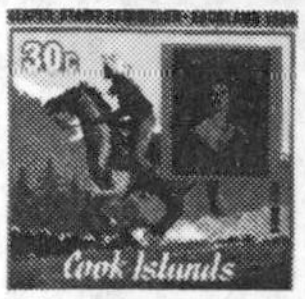

New Zealand No. 1 and Postrider — A98

Designs (Four different designs for each denomination, stamp of New Zealand): 30c, #1; coach, automobile and train. 35c, #2; sailing ship, river steamer, early transatlantic liner and ocean liner. 50c, #3; 1870-71 mail balloon, 1919 plane, Graf Zeppelin and Concorde.

1980, Aug. 22 Photo. *Perf. 14*

550		Block of 4	1.50	1.25
a.		A98 30c single stamp	.35	.30
551		Block of 4	2.00	1.75
a.		A98 35c single stamp	.50	.42
552		Block of 4	3.00	2.50
a.		A98 50c single stamp	.75	.60
b.		Souvenir sheet of 12	7.50	6.50
		Nos. 550-552 (3)	6.50	5.50

Souvenir Sheet

Perf. 13

553	A96	Sheet of 6, #541-546	5.00	3.50

ZEAPEX '80, New Zealand Intl. Stamp Exhib., Auckland, Aug. 23-31. Stamps of same denomination se-tenant in blocks of 4, sheets of 40. No. 552b contains stamps of Nos. 550-552 arranged se-tenant horizontally (4x3). No. 553 has black on gold overprint: "ZEAPEX / '80 / Auckland / +10c" in margin.

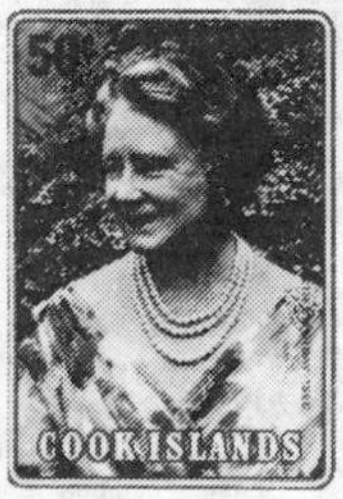

Queen Mother Elizabeth, 80th Birthday — A99

1980, Sept. 22 Photo. *Perf. 13*

554	A99	50c multicolored	1.50	1.00

Souvenir Sheet

555	A99	$2 multicolored	2.75	2.75

No. 554 issued in sheets of 9 (3x3).

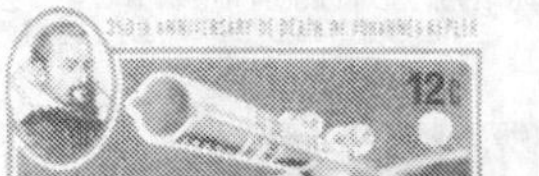

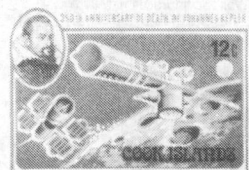

Johannes Kepler, Spacecraft — A100

Designs: Nos. 557, 562, Kepler, spacecraft (diff.). No. 563, Kepler, lunar rover, astronaut on moon. Nos. 558-561, Jules Verne, various scenes from From Earth to Moon, vert. Stamps of same denomination se-tenant.

1980, Nov. 7 Photo. *Perf. 13*

556	A100	12c multicolored	.25	.25
557	A100	12c multicolored	.25	.25
558	A100	20c multicolored	.25	.25
559	A100	20c multicolored	.25	.25
560	A100	30c multicolored	.65	.65
561	A100	30c multicolored	.65	.65
a.		Souvenir sheet of 4, #558-561	2.25	2.25
562	A100	50c multicolored	1.10	1.10
563	A100	50c multicolored	1.10	1.10
a.		Souv. sheet of 4, #556-557, 562-563	2.75	2.75
		Nos. 556-563 (8)	4.50	4.50

Death anniversaries of Johannes Kepler, German astronomer and Jules Verne, French science fiction writer.

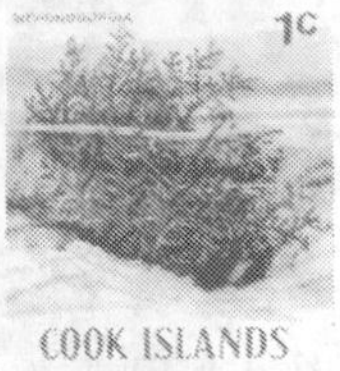

Burning Bush Coral — A101

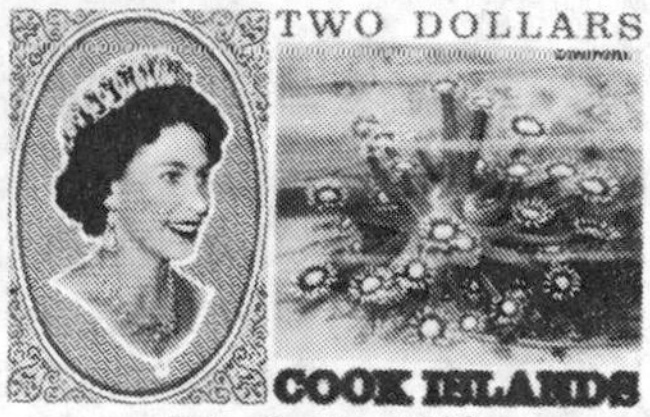

Daisy Coral — A102

1980-82 *Perf. 13½x13*

564	A101	1c Siphonogorgia	.15	.15
565	A101	1c Pavona practorta	.15	.15
566	A101	1c Stylaster echinatus	.15	.15
567	A101	1c Tubastraea	.15	.15
568	A101	3c Millepora alcicornis	.15	.15
569	A101	3c Junceella gemmaea	.15	.15
570	A101	3c Fungia fungites	.15	.15
571	A101	3c Heliofungia actiniformis	.15	.15
572	A101	4c Distichopora violacea	.15	.15
573	A101	4c Stylaster	.15	.15
574	A101	4c Gonipora	.15	.15
575	A101	4c Caulastraea echinulata	.15	.15
576	A101	5c Ptilosarcus gurneyi	.15	.15
577	A101	5c Stylophora pistillata	.15	.15
578	A101	5c Melithaea squamata	.15	.15
579	A101	5c Porites andrewsi	.15	.15
580	A101	6c Lobophyllia bemprichii	.15	.15
581	A101	6c Palauastrea ramosa	.15	.15
582	A101	6c Bellonella indica	.15	.15
583	A101	6c Pectinia alcicornis	.15	.15
584	A101	8c Sarcophyton digitatum	.16	.16
585	A101	8c Melithaea albitincta	.16	.16
586	A101	8c Plerogyra sinuosa	.16	.16
587	A101	8c Dendrophyllia gracilis	.16	.16
588	A101	10c like #564	.20	.20
589	A101	10c like #565	.20	.20
590	A101	10c like #566	.20	.20
591	A101	10c like #567	.20	.20
592	A101	12c like #568	.24	.24
593	A101	12c like #569	.24	.24
594	A101	12c like #570	.24	.24
595	A101	12c like #571	.24	.24
596	A101	15c like #572	.28	.28
597	A101	15c like #573	.28	.28
598	A101	15c like #574	.28	.28
599	A101	15c like #575	.28	.28
600	A101	20c like #576	.35	.35
601	A101	20c like #577	.35	.35
602	A101	20c like #578	.35	.35
603	A101	20c like #579	.35	.35
604	A101	25c like #580	.50	.50
605	A101	25c like #581	.50	.50
606	A101	25c like #582	.50	.50
607	A101	25c like #583	.50	.50
608	A101	30c like #584	.60	.60
609	A101	30c like #585	.60	.60
610	A101	30c like #586	.60	.60
611	A101	30c like #587	.60	.60
612	A101	35c like #564	.65	.65
613	A101	35c like #565	.65	.65
614	A101	35c like #566	.65	.65
615	A101	35c like #567	.65	.65
616	A101	50c like #568	.90	.90
617	A101	50c like #569	.90	.90
618	A101	50c like #570	.90	.90
619	A101	50c like #571	.90	.90
620	A101	60c like #572	1.10	1.10
621	A101	60c like #573	1.10	1.10
622	A101	60c like #574	1.10	1.10
623	A101	60c like #575	1.10	1.10
624	A101	70c like #576	1.25	1.25
625	A101	70c like #577	1.25	1.25
626	A101	70c like #578	1.25	1.25
627	A101	70c like #579	1.25	1.25
628	A101	80c like #580	1.40	1.40
629	A101	80c like #581	1.40	1.40
630	A101	80c like #582	1.40	1.40
631	A101	80c like #583	1.40	1.40
632	A101	$1 like #584	1.50	1.50
633	A101	$1 like #585	1.50	1.50
634	A101	$1 like #586	1.50	1.50
635	A101	$1 like #587	1.50	1.50

Perf. 14x13½

636	A102	$2 like #574	4.75	4.75
637	A102	$3 like #571	6.75	6.75
638	A102	$4 like #577	8.75	8.75
639	A102	$6 like #566	13.00	13.00
640	A102	$10 like #585	20.00	20.00
		Nos. 564-640 (77)	92.77	92.77

Issued: 1-8c, 11/21/80; 10-30c, 12/19/80; 35-60c, 3/16/81; 70c, 80c, 4/13/81; $1, 5/20/81; $2, $3, 11/27/81; $4, $6, 1/11/82; $10, 3/5/82.

Stamps of same denomination se-tenant in continuous design.

For surcharges see Nos. 710-731, 738-741, 743, 811-815, 929-936, 938-945, 947-950, 952-959, 961-964, 978-979, 984-986, B109-B111, O49, O53. For overprints see Nos. 992, 1049.

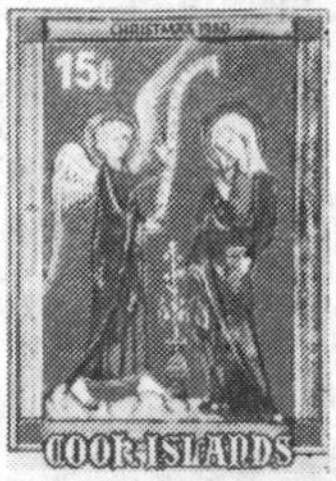

Annunciation, 13th Century Prayerbook Illustration — A102a

1980, Dec. 1 Photo. *Perf. 14*

652	A102a	15c shown	.20	.20
653	A102a	30c Visitation	.42	.42
654	A102a	40c Nativity	.50	.50
655	A102a	50c Epiphany	.70	.70
a.		Souvenir sheet of 4, #652-655	2.00	2.00
		Nos. 652-655 (4)	1.82	1.82

Christmas. See Nos. B88-B91.

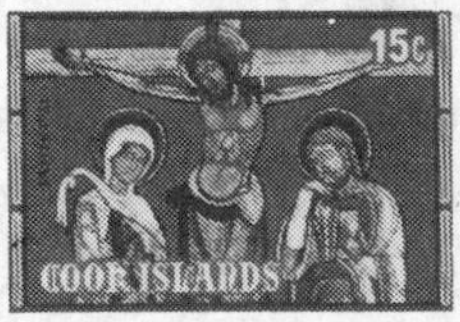

Crucifixion, 12th Cent. Prayerbook Illustration
A103

1981, Apr. 10 *Perf. 14*

656	A103	15c shown	.22	.22
657	A103	25c Placing in Tomb	.38	.38
658	A103	40c Marys at the Tomb	.60	.60
		Nos. 656-658 (3)	1.20	1.20

Easter. See Nos. B92-B95.

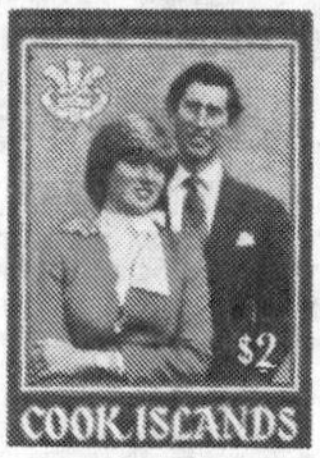

Prince Charles and Lady Diana — A104

1981, July 29 Photo. *Perf. 14*

659	A104	$1 Charles	1.75	1.75
660	A104	$2 shown	3.50	3.50
a.		Souv. sheet of 2, #659-660	5.00	5.00

Royal Wedding. Issued in sheets of 4.

See Nos. B97-B98. For overprints and surcharges see Nos. 679-680A, 837, 980-981, B97-B98.

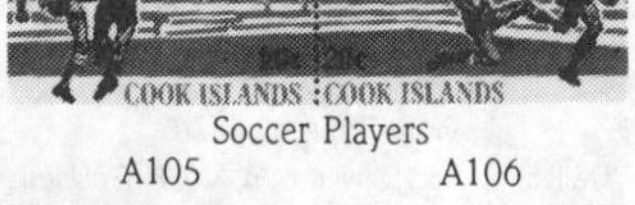

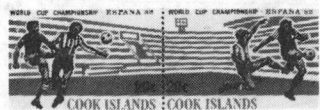

Soccer Players

A105 A106

Designs: Various soccer players.

1981, Oct 20 Photo. *Perf. 14*

661	A105	20c multicolored	.25	.25
662	A106	20c multicolored	.25	.25
663	A105	30c multicolored	.40	.40
664	A106	30c multicolored	.40	.40
665	A105	35c multicolored	.50	.50
666	A106	35c multicolored	.50	.50
667	A105	50c multicolored	.65	.65
668	A106	50c multicolored	.65	.65
		Nos. 661-668 (8)	3.60	3.60

ESPANA '82 World Cup Soccer Championships. Stamps of same denomination se-tenant in continuous design. See No. B96.

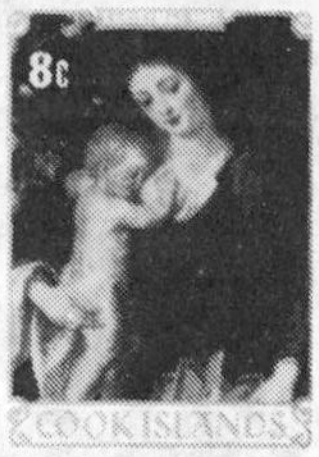

Virgin and Child, by Rubens — A107

Christmas: Rubens Paintings.

1981, Dec. 14 Photo. *Perf. 14x13½*

669	A107	8c shown	.15	.15
670	A107	15c Coronation of St. Catherine	.20	.20
671	A107	40c Adoration of the Shepherds	.50	.50
672	A107	50c Adoration of the Kings	.60	.60
		Nos. 669-672 (4)	1.45	1.45

Souvenir Sheets

1982, Jan. 18

673	A107	75c +5c like #669	1.10	1.10
674	A107	75c +5c like #670	1.10	1.10
675	A107	75c +5c like #671	1.10	1.10
676	A107	75c +5c like #672	1.10	1.10

Surtax was for school children. See No. B99.

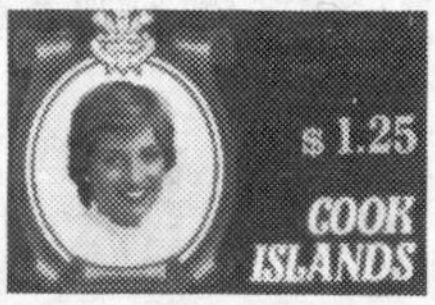

21st Birthday of Princess Diana
A108

1982, June 21 Photo. *Perf. 14*

677	A108	$1.25 Portrait	2.50	2.50
677A	A108	$1.25 1 July 1982	2.50	2.50
678	A108	$2.50 Wedding portrait	5.00	5.00
b.		Souvenir sheet of 2	6.50	6.50
678A	A108	$2.50 1 July 1982	5.00	5.00
		Nos. 677-678A (4)	15.00	15.00

No. 678b contains $1.25 and $2.50 stamps inscribed in two lines: 21st Birthday 1 July 1982. Perf. 13½.

See Nos. 681-682A. For surcharges and overprints see Nos. 742-742A, 833-836, 982-983.

Nos. 659-660a Overprinted: "ROYAL BIRTH 21 JUNE 1982" or "PRINCE WILLIAM OF WALES"

1982, July 12

679	A104	$1 Royal Birth	1.50	1.50
679A	A104	$1 Prince William	1.50	1.50
680	A104	$2 Royal Birth	2.75	2.75
b.		Souvenir sheet of 2	6.00	6.00
680A	A104	$2 Prince William	2.75	2.75
		Nos. 679-680A (4)	8.50	8.50

For surcharges see Nos. 987-990.

Type A108 Inscribed: "Royal Birth" and/or "21 June 1982"

1982, Aug. 3

681	A108	$1.25 Royal Birth	1.75	1.75
681A	A108	$1.25 21 June 1982	1.75	1.75
682	A108	$2.50 Royal Birth	3.50	3.50
b.		Souvenir sheet of 2	5.00	5.00
682A	A108	$2.50 21 June 1982	3.50	3.50
		Nos. 681-682A (4)	10.50	10.50

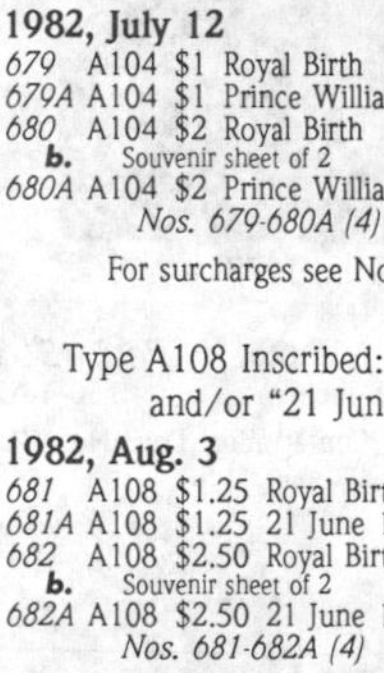

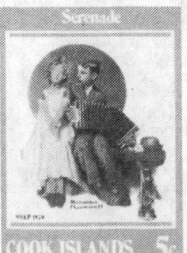

Serenade, by Norman Rockwell (1894-1978)
A109

1982, Sept. 10 Photo. *Perf. 14*

683 A109 5c shown .15 .15
684 A109 10c The Hikers .15 .15
685 A109 20c The Doctor and the Doll .30 .30
686 A109 30c Home From Camp .45 .45
Nos. 683-686 (4) 1.05 1.05

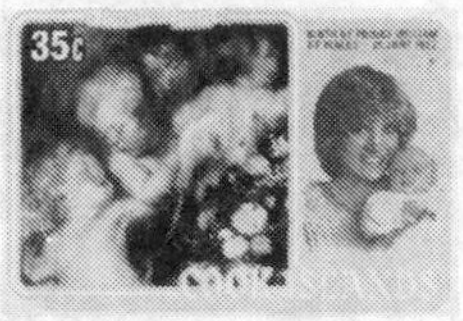

Christmas A110

Princess Diana Holding Prince William. Various Details from Virgin with Garlands, by Rubens.

1982, Nov. 30 Photo. *Perf. 14*

687 A110 35c multicolored .50 .50
688 A110 48c multicolored .65 .65
689 A110 60c multicolored .75 .75
690 A110 $1.70 multicolored 2.25 2.25
Nos. 687-690 (4) 4.15 4.15

Souvenir Sheets

Perf. 13½

691 Sheet of 4 3.50 3.50
a. A110 60c like 35c .85 .85
b. A110 60c like 48c .85 .85
c. A110 60c like #689 .85 .85
d. A110 60c like $1.70 .85 .85
692 A110 75c + 5c like 35c 1.50 1.50
693 A110 75c + 5c like 48c 1.50 1.50
694 A110 75c + 5c like 60c 1.50 1.50
695 A110 75c + 5c like $1.70 1.50 1.50

No. 691 contains 4 stamps (27x32mm., showing only painting details) plus 2 labels showing Diana and William. Nos. 692-695 show Diana and William (27x39mm), multicolored margins show painting details. Surtax was for child welfare.

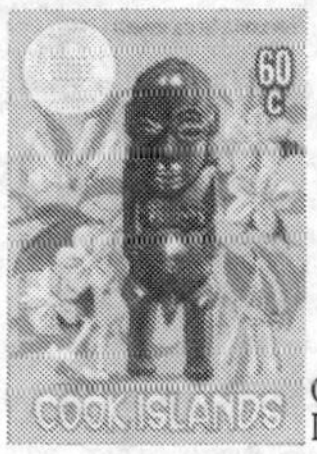

Commonwealth Day — A111

1983, Mar. 14 Photo. *Perf. 14*

696 A111 60c Tangaroa statue .65 .65
697 A111 60c Rarotonga oranges .65 .65
698 A111 60c Rarotonga Airport .65 .65
699 A111 60c Prime Minister Thomas Davis .65 .65
Nos. 696-699 (4) 2.60 2.60

Nos. 696-699 se-tenant.
For overprints see Nos. O46-O49.

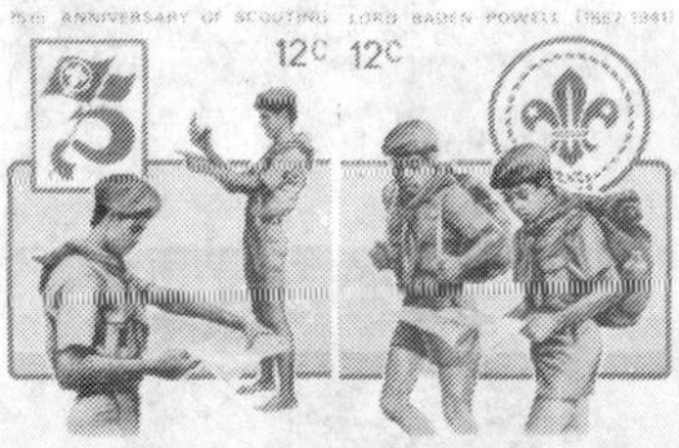

Scouting Year
A112 A113

1983, Apr. 5 Photo. *Perf. 13x13½*

700 Pair, shown .35 .35
a. A112 12c multicolored .16 .16
b. A113 12c multicolored .16 .16
701 Pair, Camping 1.10 1.10
a. A112 36c multicolored .50 .50
b. A113 36c multicolored .50 .50
702 Pair, Rope swing 1.40 1.40
a. A112 48c multicolored .70 .70
b. A113 48c multicolored .70 .70
703 Pair, Tree planting 1.75 1.75
a. A112 60c multicolored .85 .85
b. A113 60c multicolored .85 .85
Nos. 700-703 (4) 4.60 4.60

Souvenir Sheet

704 Sheet of 8 4.50 4.50
a. 12c + 2c pair like #700 .40 .40
b. 36c + 2c pair like #701 1.00 1.00
c. 48c + 2c pair like #702 1.40 1.40
d. 60c + 2c pair like #703 1.65 1.65

No. 704 contains Nos. 704a-704d.

Nos. 700-704 Overprinted: "XV WORLD JAMBOREE ALBERTA CANADA 1983"

1983, July 4 Photo. *Perf. 13x13½*

705 Pair, #a.-b. .35 .35
706 Pair, #a.-b. 1.10 1.10
707 Pair, #a.-b. 1.40 1.40
708 Pair, #a.-b. 1.75 1.75
Nos. 705-708 (4) 4.60 4.60

Souvenir Sheet

709 Sheet of 8 5.00 5.00
a. 12c + 2c pair like #705 .42 .42
b. 36c + 2c pair like #706 1.10 1.10
c. 48c + 2c pair like #707 1.50 1.50
d. 60c + 2c pair like #708 1.90 1.90

Nos. 584-587, 596-599, 608-611, 604-607, 624-627, 660, 639 Surcharged in Black or Gold

Perf. 13½x13, 14x13½, 14

1983, Aug. 12 Photo.

710 A101 18c on 8c #584 .40 .40
711 A101 18c on 8c #585 .40 .40
712 A101 18c on 8c #586 .40 .40
713 A101 18c on 8c #587 .40 .40
714 A101 36c on 15c #596 .65 .65
715 A101 36c on 15c #597 .65 .65
716 A101 36c on 15c #598 .65 .65
717 A101 36c on 15c #599 .65 .65
718 A101 36c on 30c #608 .65 .65
719 A101 36c on 30c #609 .65 .65
720 A101 36c on 30c #610 .65 .65
721 A101 36c on 30c #611 .65 .65
722 A101 48c on 25c #604 1.00 1.00
723 A101 48c on 25c #605 1.00 1.00
724 A101 48c on 25c #606 1.00 1.00
725 A101 48c on 25c #607 1.00 1.00
726 A101 72c on 70c #624 1.50 1.50
727 A101 72c on 70c #625 1.50 1.50
728 A101 72c on 70c #626 1.50 1.50
729 A101 72c on 70c #627 1.50 1.50
730 A104 96c on $2 #660 (G) 2.00 2.00
731 A102 $5.60 on $6 #639 (G) 12.50 12.50
Nos. 710-731 (22) 31.30 31.30

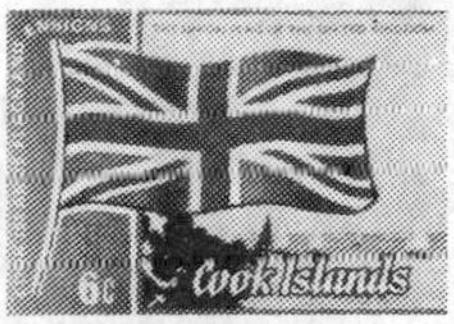

A114

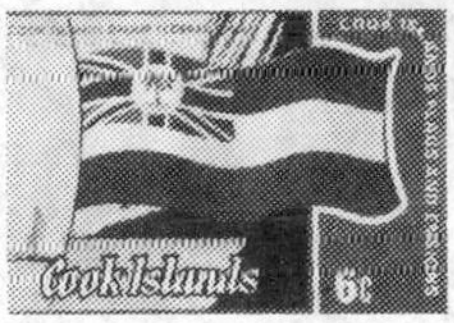

A115

1983, Sept. 9 *Perf. 14*

732 Pair .15 .15
a. A114 6c Gt. Britain .15 .15
b. A115 6c Cook Islds. Group Federal flag .15 .15
733 Pair .25 .25
a. A114 12c Raratonga ensign .15 .15
b. A115 12c New Zealand .15 .15
734 Pair .30 .30
a. A114 15c Cook Islds, 1973-79 .15 .15
b. A115 15c Cook Islds, 1983 .15 .15
c. Souvenir sheet of 6, #732-734 .75 .75
735 Pair .45 .45
a. A114 20c like #732a .20 .20
b. A115 20c like #732b .20 .20
736 Pair .60 .60
a. A114 30c like #733a .30 .30
b. A115 30c like #733b .30 .30
737 Pair .70 .70
a. A114 35c like #734a .35 .35
b. A115 35c like #734b .35 .35
c. Souvenir sheet of 6, #735-737 1.75 1.75
Nos. 732-737 (6) 2.45 2.45

Nos. 732-737 have different background landscapes; Nos. 735-737 airmail with silver background. Nos. 734c, 737c perf. 13½.

Nos. 612-615, 640, 678-678A Surcharged in Black or Gold

Perf. 13½x13, 14x13½, 14

1983, Aug. 30 Photo.

738 A101 36c on 35c #612 .65 .65
739 A101 36c on 35c #613 .65 .65
740 A101 36c on 35c #614 .65 .65
741 A101 36c on 35c #615 .65 .65
742 A108 96c on $2.50 #678 (G) 2.00 2.00
742A A108 96c on $2.50 #678A 2.00 2.00
743 A102 $5.60 on $10 #640 (G) 10.00 10.00
Nos. 738-743 (7) 16.60 16.60

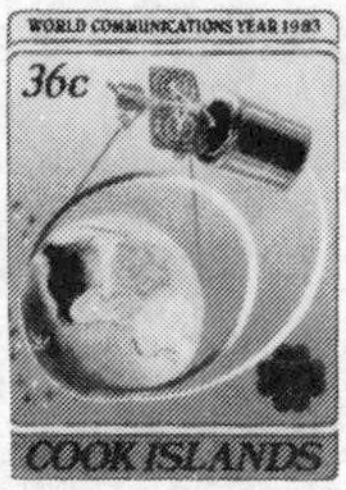

Satellite Earth Station — A116

Designs: Various satellites in orbit.

1983, Oct. 10 Litho. *Perf. 13½*

744 A116 36c multicolored .50 .50
745 A116 48c multicolored .65 .65
746 A116 60c multicolored .75 .75
747 A116 96c multicolored 1.25 1.25
Nos. 744-747 (4) 3.15 3.15

Souvenir Sheet

748 A116 $2 multicolored 3.50 3.50

World Communications Year.

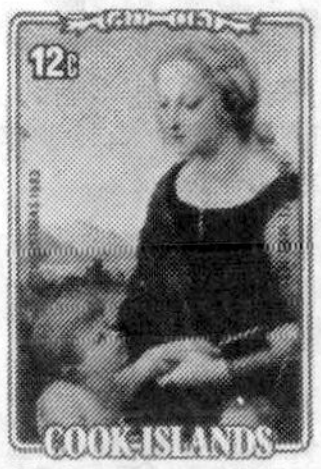

Christmas — A117

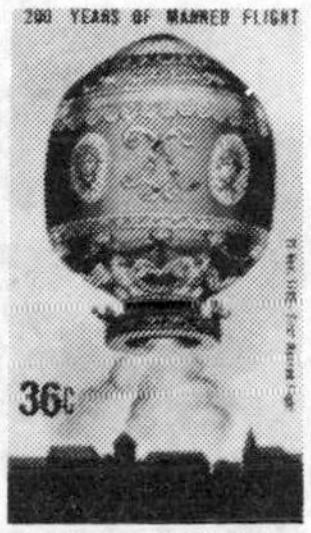

Manned Flight Bicent. — A118

Raphael Paintings: 12c, La Belle Jardiniere. 18c, Madonna and Child with Five Saints. 36c, Madonna and Child with Saint John. 48c, Madonna of the Fish. 60c, Madonna of the Baldacchino.

1983 Photo. *Perf. 14*

749 A117 12c multicolored .15 .15
750 A117 18c multicolored .22 .22
751 A117 36c multicolored .45 .45
752 A117 48c multicolored .55 .55
753 A117 60c multicolored .75 .75
Nos. 749-753 (5) 2.12 2.12

Souvenir Sheets

Perf. 13½

754 Sheet of 5 3.25 3.25
a. A117 12c + 3c like #749 .24 .24
b. A117 18c + 3c like #750 .32 .32
c. A117 36c + 3c like #751 .60 .60
d. A117 48c + 3c like #752 .78 .78
e. A117 60c + 3c like #753 .95 .95
755 A117 85c + 5c like #749 1.35 1.35
756 A117 85c + 5c like #750 1.35 1.35
757 A117 85c + 5c like #751 1.35 1.35
758 A117 85c + 5c like #752 1.35 1.35
759 A117 85c + 5c like #753 1.35 1.35

Nos. 749-753 issued in sheets of 5 + label. Surtax was for children's charities.
Issued: #749-754, Nov. 14; others, Dec. 9.

1984, Jan. 16 Photo. *Perf. 13*

Various balloons.

760 A118 36c 1st manned flight, 1783 .50 .50
761 A118 48c Ascent of Adorne, Strasbourg, 1784 .65 .65
762 A118 60c 1785 .75 .75
763 A118 72c Man on horse, 1785 1.10 1.10
764 A118 96c Godard's aerial acrobatics, 1850 1.25 1.25
Nos. 760-764 (5) 4.25 4.25

Souvenir Sheets

765 A118 $2.50 Blanchard & Jefferies, 1785 4.00 4.00
766 Sheet of 5 10.25 10.25
a. A118 36c + 5c like 36c 1.25 1.25
b. A118 48c + 5c like 48c 1.55 1.55
c. A118 60c + 5c like 60c 2.00 2.00
d. A118 72c + 5c like 72c 2.25 2.25
e. A118 96c + 5c like 96c 3.00 3.00

#765 contains 1 stamp 30x48mm, perf. 13½.

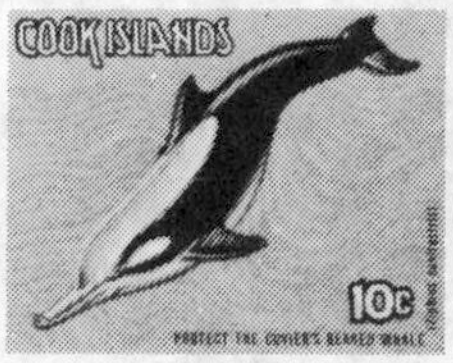

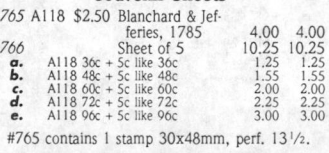

Save the Whales Campaign A119

1984, Feb. 10 Photo. *Perf. 13*

767 A119 10c Cuvier's beaked whale .18 .18
768 A119 18c Risso's dolphin .30 .30
769 A119 20c True's beaked whale .32 .32
770 A119 24c Long-finned pilot whale .40 .40
771 A119 30c Narwhal .50 .50
772 A119 36c Beluga whale .60 .60
773 A119 42c Common dolphin .70 .70
774 A119 48c Commerson's dolphin .75 .75
775 A119 60c Bottle-nosed dolphin 1.00 1.00
776 A119 72c Sowerby's whale 1.25 1.25
777 A119 96c Common porpoise 1.50 1.50
778 A119 $2 Boutu 3.25 3.25
Nos. 767-778 (12) 10.75 10.75

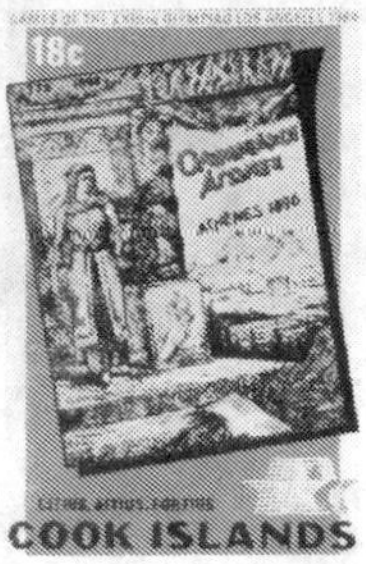

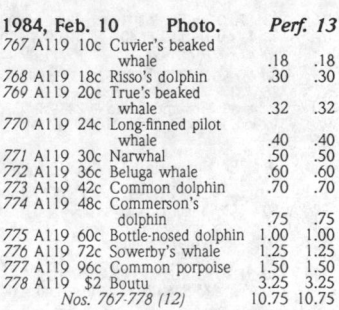

1984 Summer Olympics — A120

Posters of Various Summer Olympics. 72c, 96c, $1.20 airmail.

1984, Mar. 8 Photo. *Perf. 13½*

779 A120 18c Athens, 1896 .28 .28
780 A120 24c Paris, 1900 .36 .36
781 A120 36c St. Louis, 1904 .55 .55
782 A120 48c London, 1948 .72 .72
783 A120 60c Tokyo, 1964 .90 .90
784 A120 72c Berlin, 1936 1.10 1.10
785 A120 96c Rome, 1960 1.50 1.50
786 A120 $1.20 Los Angeles, 1932 1.80 1.80
Nos. 779-786 (8) 7.21 7.21

For overprints see Nos. 826-828.

Nos. 636-640 Surcharged and:

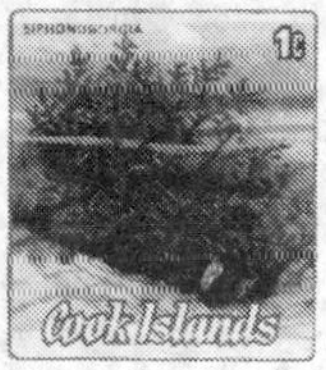

Coral — A121

1984 *Perf. 13½x13*

787 A121 1c Siphonogorgia .15 .15
788 A121 2c Millepora alcicornis .15 .15
789 A121 3c Distichopora violacea .15 .15
790 A121 5c Ptilosarcus gurneyi .15 .15
791 A121 10c Lobophyllia bemprichii .15 .15
792 A121 12c Sarcophyton digitatum .18 .18
793 A121 14c Pavona praetorta .22 .22
794 A121 18c Junceela gemmacea .28 .28
795 A121 20c Stylaster .30 .30
796 A121 24c Stylophora pistillata .36 .36
797 A121 30c Palauastrea ramosa .45 .45
798 A121 36c Melithaea albitincta .55 .55
799 A121 40c Stylaster echinatus .60 .60
800 A121 42c Fungia fungites .65 .65
801 A121 48c Gonipora .72 .72
802 A121 50c Melithaea squamata .75 .75
803 A121 52c Bellonella indica .78 .78
804 A121 55c Plerogyra sinuosa .82 .82
805 A121 60c Tubastraea .90 .90
806 A121 70c Heliofungia actinformis 1.05 1.05
807 A121 85c Caulastraea echinulata 1.30 1.30
808 A121 96c Porites andrewsi 1.45 1.45
809 A121 $1.10 Pectinia alcicornis 1.65 1.65
810 A121 $1.20 Dendrophyllia gracilis 1.80 1.80

Perf. 14x13½

Size: 59½x38½mm

811 A102 $3.60 on $2 #636 4.50 4.50
812 A102 $4.20 on $3 #637 5.00 5.00
813 A102 $5 on $4 #638 6.00 6.00

814 A102 $7.20 on $6 #639 8.00 8.00
815 A102 $9.60 on $10 #640 10.00 10.00
Nos. 787-815 (29) 49.06 49.06

Issued: #787-801, 3/23; #802-810, 5/15; #811-813, 6/28; #814, 7/20; #815, 8/10.
For surcharges & overprints see #924-928, 937, 946, 951, 960, 965-967, B105-B108, O32-O45.

Nos. 784-786 Overprinted With Winners

1984, Aug. 24 Photo. *Perf. 13½*

826 A120 72c Team Dressage, Germany .75 .75
827 A120 96c Daley Thompson, U.K. 1.00 1.00
828 A120 $1.20 Carl Lewis, USA 1.25 1.25
Nos. 826-828 (3) 3.00 3.00

1984 Summer Olympics. Nos. 826-828 airmail.

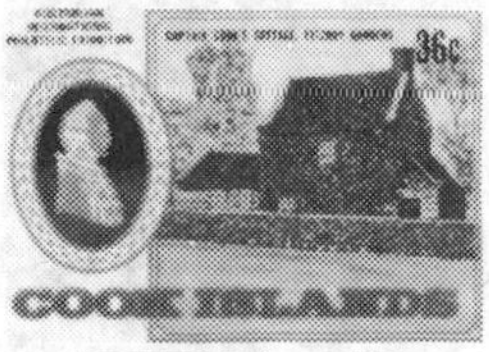

AUSIPEX '84 — A123

1984, Sept. 20

829 A123 36c Captain Cook's cottage .40 .40
830 A123 48c The Endeavour .50 .50
831 A123 60c Cook's landing .60 .60
832 A123 $2 Portrait, by John Webber 2.00 2.00
a. Souvenir sheet of 4, #829-832, 90c each 4.00 4.00
b. Sheet of 4, STAMPEX '86 emblem 4.00 4.00
Nos. 829-832 (4) 3.50 3.50

No. 832b issued Aug. 4, 1986, for STAMPEX '86, Adelaide, Aug. 4-10; margin ovptd. with exhibition emblem, stamp picturing James Cook ovptd. with gold circle and black "Stampex 86 / Adelaide."

No. 659 Ovptd. "Royal Birth/Prince Henry/15 Sept. 1984" and Surcharged in Silver.

Nos. 677-677A, 678-678A Ovptd.: "Commemorating -/15 Sept. 1984" or "Birth H.R.H./Prince Henry" and Surcharged in Gold.

1984, Oct. 15 Photo. *Perf. 14*

833 A108 $1.25 No. 677 1.00 1.00
834 A108 $1.25 No. 677A 1.00 1.00
835 A108 $2.50 No. 678 2.25 2.25
836 A108 $2.50 No. 678A 2.25 2.25
837 A104 $3 on $1 No. 659 2.75 2.75
Nos. 833-837 (5) 9.25 9.25

Nos. 833-836 printed in sheets of 4, two each of same denomination. #837 printed in sheets of 4.

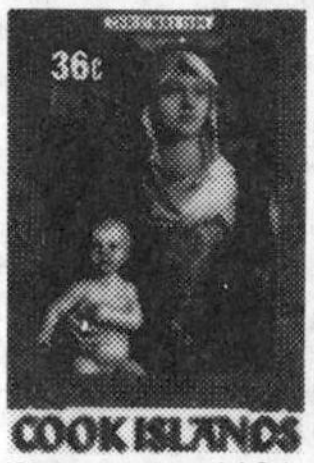

Christmas — A124

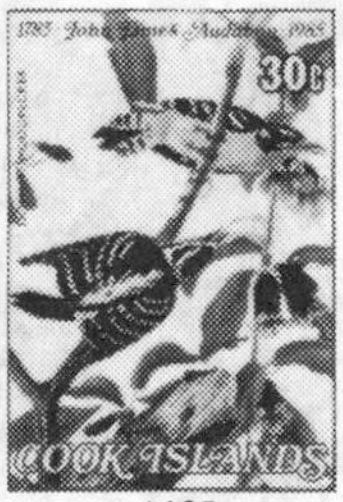

A125

Paintings: 36c, Virgin on Throne with Child, by Giovanni Bellini (c. 1430-1516). 48c, Virgin and Child, 15th century, artist unknown. 60c, Virgin and Child with Saints, by Alvise Vivarini (c. 1446-1505). 96c, Virgin and Child with Angels, by Hans Memling (c. 1435-1494). $1.20, Adoration of the Magi, by Giovanni Tiepolo (1696-1770).

1984

838 A124 36c multicolored .48 .48
839 A124 48c multicolored .65 .65
840 A124 60c multicolored .80 .80
841 A124 96c multicolored 1.25 1.25
842 A124 $1.20 multicolored 1.50 1.50
Nos. 838-842 (5) 4.68 4.68

Souvenir Sheets

Perf. 13½

843 Sheet of 5 4.00 4.00
a. A124 36c +5c like #838 .45 .45
b. A124 48c +5c like #839 .55 .55
c. A124 60c +5c like #840 .65 .65
d. A124 96c +5c like #841 1.10 1.10
e. A124 $1.20 +5c like #842 1.25 1.25
844 A124 95c + 5c like #838 1.25 1.25
845 A124 95c + 5c like #839 1.25 1.25
846 A124 95c + 5c like #840 1.25 1.25
847 A124 95c + 5c like #841 1.25 1.25
848 A124 95c + 5c like #842 1.25 1.25

Surtax of No. 843 for children's organizations, of Nos. 844-848 for youth education.
Issued: #838-843, Nov. 21; #844-848, Dec. 10.

1985, Apr. 23 *Perf. 13x13½*

Illustrations of North American bird species by artist, naturalist John J. Audubon.

849 A125 30c Downy woodpecker .28 .28
850 A125 55c Black-throated blue warbler .52 .52
851 A125 65c Yellow-throated warbler .60 .60
852 A125 75c Chestnut-sided warbler .70 .70
853 A125 95c Dickcissel .90 .90
854 A125 $1.15 White-crowned sparrow 1.00 1.00
Nos. 849-854 (6) 4.00 4.00

Souvenir Sheets

855 A125 $1.30 Red-cockaded woodpecker 1.25 1.25
856 A125 $2.80 Seaside sparrow 2.50 2.50
857 A125 $5.30 Zenaida dove 5.00 5.00

Audubon birth bicentenary.

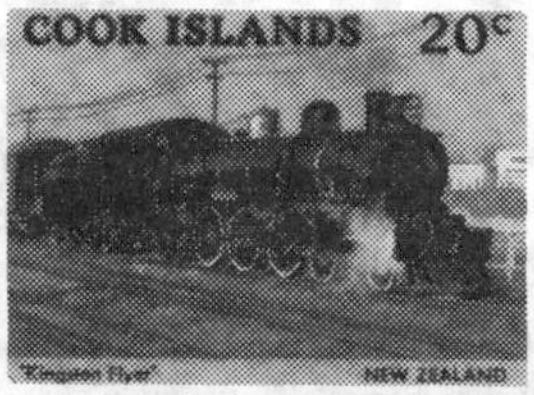

Locomotives — A126

1985, May 14 Litho. *Perf. 14x13½*

858 A126 20c Kingston Flyer, New Zealand .20 .20
859 A126 55c Class 640, Italy .52 .52
860 A126 65c Gotthard, Switzerland .60 .60
861 A126 75c Union Pacific 6900, USA .70 .70
862 A126 95c Super Continental, Canada .90 .90
863 A126 $1.15 TGV, France 1.00 1.00
864 A126 $2.20 Flying Scotsman, U.K. 2.00 2.00
865 A126 $3.40 Orient Express, Europe 3.00 3.00
Nos. 858-865 (8) 8.92 8.92

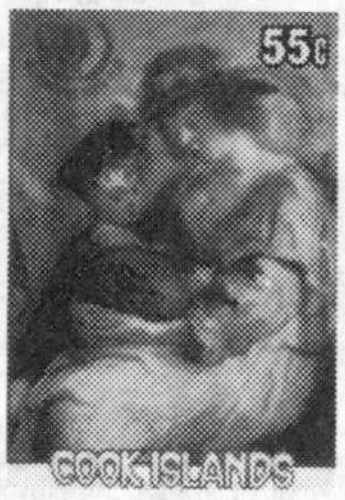

Intl. Youth Year — A127

Paintings: 55c, Helena Fourment, by Rubens. 65c, Vigee-Lebrun and Daughter, by Elizabeth Vigee-Lebrun (1755-1842). 75c, On the Terrace, by Renoir. $1.30, Young Mother Sewing, by Mary Cassatt (1845-1926).

1985, June 6 Photo. *Perf. 13x13½*

866 A127 55c multicolored .50 .50
867 A127 65c multicolored .60 .60
868 A127 75c multicolored .70 .70
869 A127 $1.30 multicolored 1.15 1.15
Nos. 866-869 (4) 2.95 2.95

Souvenir Sheet

870 Sheet of 4 3.50 3.50
a. A127 55c + 10c like #866 .60 .60
b. A127 65c + 10c like #867 .70 .70
c. A127 75c + 10c like #868 .80 .80
d. A127 $1.30 + 10c like #869 1.25 1.25

Surtax for youth organizations.

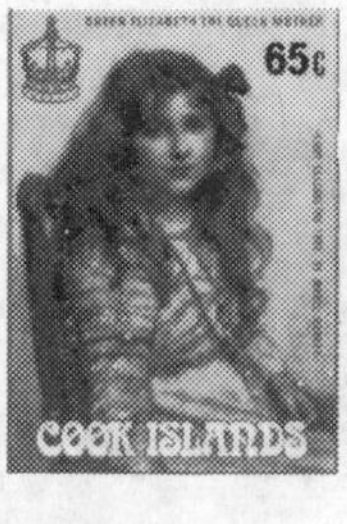

Queen Mother, 85th Birthday — A128

Portraits: 65c, Lady Elizabeth, 1908, by Mable Hankey. 75c, Duchess of York, 1923, by Savely Sorine. $1.15, Duchess of York, 1925, by Philip De Laslo. $2.80, $5.30, Queen Elizabeth, 1938, by Sir Gerald Kelly.

1985, June 28

871 A128 65c multi .45 .45
872 A128 75c multi .50 .50
873 A128 $1.15 multi .80 .80
874 A128 $2.80 multi 1.75 1.75
874A Sheet of 4 ('86) 2.25 2.25
b.-e. A128 55c, like #871-874 .55 .55
Nos. 871-874A (5) 5.75 5.75

Souvenir Sheet

875 A128 $5.30 multi 4.75 4.75

Nos. 871-874 printed in sheets of four.
#874A issued Aug. 4, 1986, for 86th birthday. June 28, 1985.
For surcharges see Nos. B114, B116, B122, B134, B140.

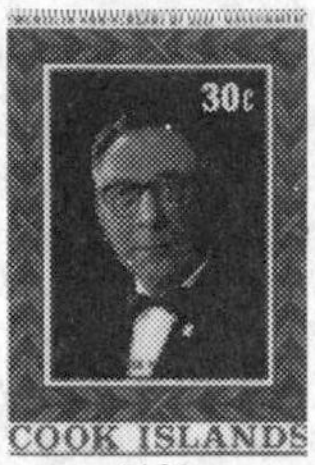

A129

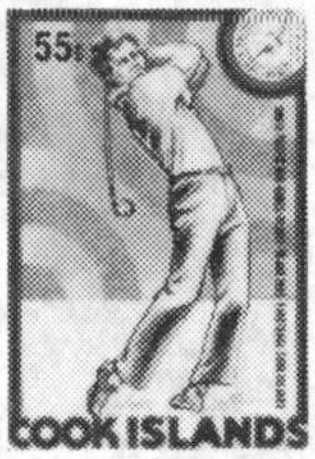

A130

Portraits of prime ministers.

1985, July 29

876 A129 30c Albert Henry, 1965-78 .32 .32
877 A129 50c Sir Thomas Davis, 1978-83 .55 .55
878 A129 65c Geoffrey Henry, 1983 .70 .70
Nos. 876-878 (3) 1.57 1.57

Souvenir Sheet

879 Sheet of 3 1.75 1.75
a. A129 55c like #876 .58 .58
b. A129 55c like #877 .58 .58
c. A129 55c like #878 .58 .58

Self-government, 20th anniv.

1985, July 29 *Perf. 14*

880 A130 55c Golf .65 .65
881 A130 65c Rugby .70 .70
882 A130 75c Tennis .80 .80
Nos. 880-882 (3) 2.15 2.15

Souvenir Sheet

883 Sheet of 3 3.50 3.50
a. A130 55c + 10c like #880 1.10 1.10
b. A130 65c + 10c like #881 1.10 1.10
c. A130 75c + 10c like #882 1.10 1.10

South Pacific Mini Games, Rarotonga, July 31-Aug. 10. Surtax for the benefit of the Mini Games.

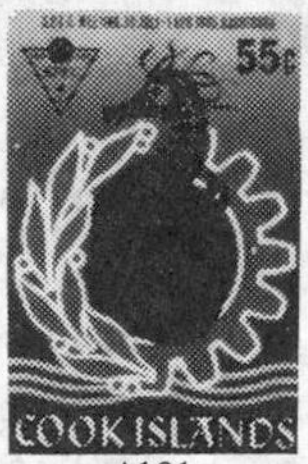

A131

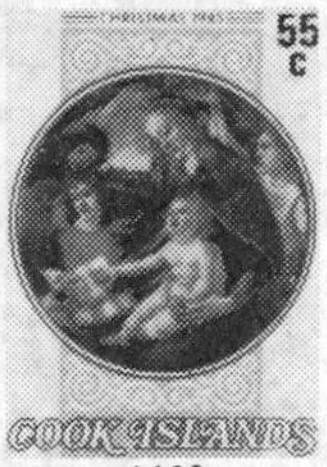

A132

Seahorse & conf. emblems: 55c, South Pacific Bureau for Economic Cooperation. 65c, No. 887b, South Pacific Forum. 75c, No. 887c, Pacific Islands Conf.

1985, July 29 *Perf. 14*

884 A131 55c blk, scar & gold .60 .60
885 A131 65c blk, vio & gold .70 .70
886 A131 75c blk, brt grn & gold .80 .80
Nos. 884-886 (3) 2.10 2.10

Souvenir Sheet

887 50c Sheet of 3, #a.-c. 2.00 2.00

Pacific islands conf., Rarotonga, July 30-Aug. 10.

1985

Virgin and Child paintings by Botticelli.

888 A132 55c Madonna of the Magnificent .65 .65
889 A132 65c Madonna with Pomegranate .78 .78
890 A132 75c Madonna with Child & Six Angels .90 .90
891 A132 95c Madonna & Child with St. John 1.15 1.15
Nos. 888-891 (4) 3.48 3.48

Souvenir Sheets

Perf. 13½

892 A132 $2.75 Sheet of 4 2.50 2.50
a. A132 50c like #888 .60 .60
b. A132 50c like #888 .60 .60
c. A132 50c like #890 .60 .60
d. A132 50c like #891 .60 .60

Imperf

893 A132 $1.20 like #888 1.50 1.50
894 A132 $1.45 like #889 1.75 1.75
895 A132 $2.20 like #890 2.75 2.75
896 A132 $2.75 like #891 3.25 3.25

Christmas. Issue dates: Nos. 888-892, Nov. 18. Nos. 893-896, Dec. 9.

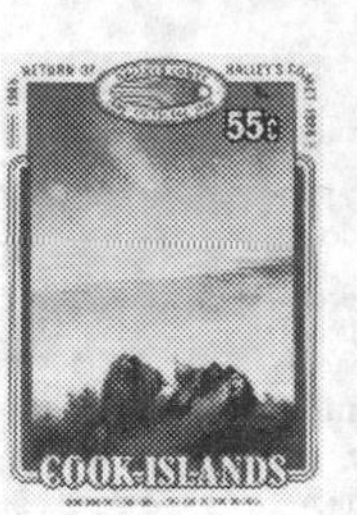

Halley's Comet — A133

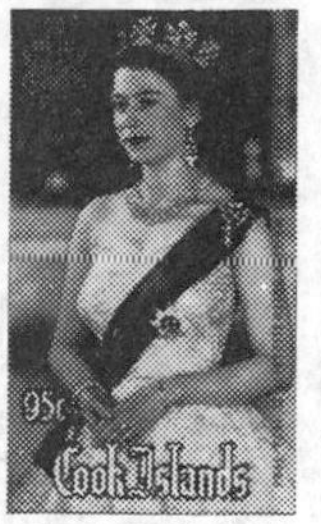

Elizabeth II, 60th Birthday — A134

Paintings: 55c, No. 902a, The Eve of the Deluge, by John Martin (1789-1854). 65c, No. 902b, Lot and His Daughters, by Lucas van Leyden (1494-1533). 75c, No. 902c, Auspicious Comet, 1587, anonymous. $1.25, No. 902d, Events Following Charles I, by Herman Saftleven (1609-1658). $2, No. 902e, Ossian Receiving Napoleonic Officers, by Anne Louis Girodet-Trioson (1764-1824). $4, Halley's Comet over the Thames, 1759, by Samuel Scott (1702-1772).

1986, Mar. 13 Photo. *Perf. 14*

897 A133 55c multicolored .52 .52
898 A133 65c multicolored .62 .62
899 A133 75c multicolored .72 .72
900 A133 $1.25 multicolored 1.25 1.25
901 A133 $2 multicolored 2.00 2.00
Nos. 897-901 (5) 5.11 5.11

Souvenir Sheets

Perf. 13½

902 Sheet of 5 + label 3.50 3.50
a.-e. A133 70c, each single .68 .68
903 A133 $4 multicolored 4.50 4.50

For surcharges see Nos. B113, B115, B117, B123, B129.

1986, Apr. 21 *Perf. 13x13½*

Various portraits.

904 A134 95c multi 1.15 1.15
905 A134 $1.25 multi 1.50 1.50
906 A134 $1.50 multi 1.75 1.75
Nos. 904-906 (3) 4.40 4.40

Souvenir Sheets

907 A134 $1.10 like #904 1.25 1.25
908 A134 $1.95 like #905 2.25 2.25
909 A134 $2.45 like #906 3.00 3.00

For surcharges see Nos. 972-974, B118, B124, B127, B136-B137, B139.

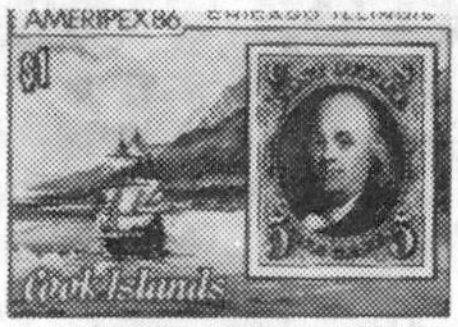

AMERIPEX '86 — A135

Designs: $1, US No. 1, The Resolution, Rarotonga. $1.50, Downtown Chicago. $2, No. 398, Benjamin Franklin, The Resolution.

1986, May 21 Photo. *Perf. 14*

910 A135 $1 multi 1.40 1.40
911 A135 $1.50 multi 2.00 2.00
912 A135 $2 multi 2.75 2.75
Nos. 910-912 (3) 6.15 6.15

For surcharges see Nos. B119, B128, B130.

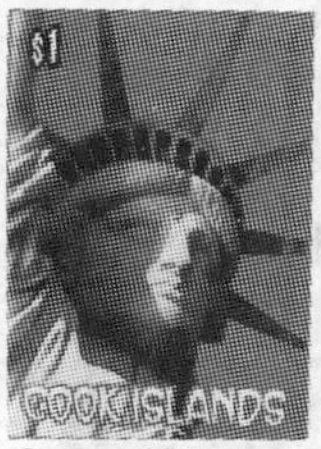

Statue of Liberty, Cent. — A136

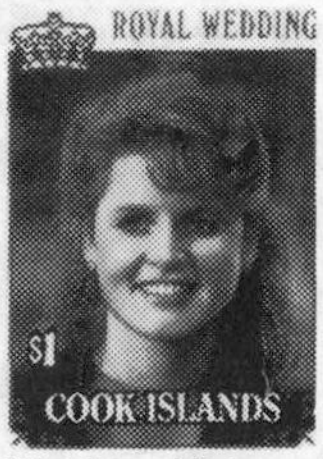

Wedding of Prince Andrew and Sarah Ferguson — A137

1986, July 4

913 A136	$1 Head		1.10	1.10
914 A136	$1.25 Torch		1.40	1.40
915 A136	$2.75 Liberty Is.		3.00	3.00
	Nos. 913-915 (3)		5.50	5.50

For surcharges see Nos. B120, B125, B132.

1986, July 23

916 A137	$1 Sarah Ferguson	1.10	1.10
917 A137	$2 Prince Andrew	2.20	2.20

Size: 60x33½mm

Perf. 13½x13

918 A137	$3 Couple	3.30	3.30
	Nos. 916-918 (3)	6.60	6.60

Nos. 916-918 each printed in sheets of 4.
For surch. see #975-977, B121, B131, B135.

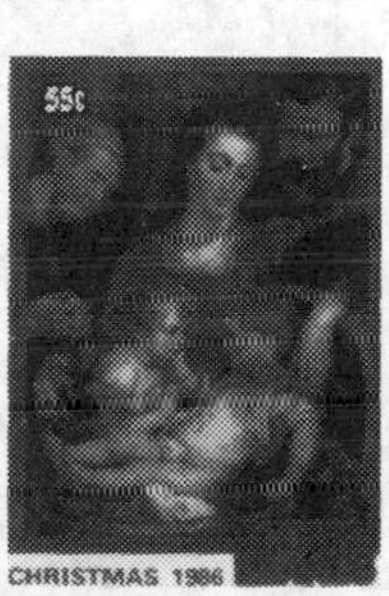

Christmas A138

Paintings by Rubens: 55c, No. 922a, The Holy Family. $1.30, $6.40, No. 922b, Virgin with Garland. $2.75, No. 922c, Adoration of Magi.

1986, Nov. 17 Litho. *Perf. 13½*

919 A138	55c multi	.60	.60
920 A138	$1.30 multi	1.40	1.40
921 A138	$2.75 multi	2.90	2.90
	Nos. 919-921 (3)	4.90	4.90

Souvenir Sheets

922	Sheet of 3	7.50	7.50
a.-c.	A138 $2.40, any single	2.50	2.50
923 A138	$6.40 multi	6.75	6.75

No. 922 contains 3 stamps 38½x49mm.
For surcharges see Nos. B100-B104, B126, B133, B138, B141.

Stamps of 1980-86 Surcharged in Black, Black and Gold or Gold

1987, Feb. Litho. *Perfs. as before*

924 A121	5c on 1c #787	.15	.15
925 A121	5c on 2c #788	.15	.15
926 A121	5c on 3c #789	.15	.15
927 A121	5c on 12c #792	.15	.15
928 A121	5c on 14c #793	.15	.15
929 A101	10c on 15c #596	.15	.15
930 A101	10c on 15c #597	.15	.15
931 A101	10c on 15c #598	.15	.15
932 A101	10c on 15c #599	.15	.15
933 A101	10c on 15c #604	.15	.15
934 A101	10c on 25c #605	.15	.15
935 A101	10c on 25c #606	.15	.15
936 A101	10c on 25c #607	.15	.15
937 A121	18c on 24c #796	.20	.20
938 A101	18c on 12c #592	.20	.20
939 A101	18c on 12c #593	.20	.20
940 A101	18c on 12c #594	.20	.20
941 A101	18c on 12c #595	.20	.20
942 A101	18c on 20c #600	.20	.20
943 A101	18c on 20c #601	.20	.20
944 A101	18c on 20c #602	.20	.20
945 A101	18c on 20c #603	.20	.20
946 A121	55c on 52c #803	.65	.65
947 A101	55c on 35c #612	.65	.65
948 A101	55c on 35c #613	.65	.65
949 A101	55c on 35c #614	.65	.65
950 A101	55c on 35c #615	.65	.65
951 A121	65c on 42c #800	.75	.75
952 A101	65c on 50c #616	.75	.75
953 A101	65c on 50c #617	.75	.75
954 A101	65c on 50c #618	.75	.75
955 A101	65c on 50c #619	.75	.75
956 A101	65c on 60c #620	.75	.75
957 A101	65c on 60c #621	.75	.75
958 A101	65c on 60c #622	.75	.75
959 A101	65c on 60c #623	.75	.75
960 A121	75c on 48c #801	.90	.90
961 A101	75c on 70c #624	.90	.90
962 A101	75c on 70c #625	.90	.90
963 A101	75c on 70c #626	.90	.90
964 A101	75c on 70c #627	.90	.90
965 A121	95c on 96c #808	1.10	1.10
966 A121	95c on $1.10 #809	1.10	1.10
967 A121	95c on $1.20 #810	1.10	1.10
968 A123	$1.30 on 36c #829 (B&G)	1.50	1.50
969 A123	$1.30 on 48c #830 (B&G)	1.50	1.50
970 A123	$1.30 on 60c #831 (B&G)	1.50	1.50
971 A123	$1.30 on $2 #832 (G)	1.50	1.50
972 A134	$2.80 on 95c #904 (G)	3.25	3.25
973 A134	$2.80 on $1.25 #905 (G)	3.25	3.25
974 A134	$2.80 on $1.50 #906 (G)	3.25	3.25
975 A137	$2.80 on $1 #916 (B&G)	3.25	3.25
976 A137	$2.80 on $2 #917 (B&G)	3.25	3.25
977 A137	$2.80 on $3 #918 (B&G)	3.25	3.25
978 A102	$6.40 on $4 #638	7.00	7.00
979 A102	$7.20 on $6 #639	8.00	8.00
980 A104	$9.40 on $1 #659 (G)	11.00	11.00
981 A104	$9.40 on $2 #660 (G)	11.00	11.00
982 A108	$9.40 on $2.50 #678 (G)	11.00	11.00
983 A108	$9.40 on $2.50 #678A (G)	11.00	11.00
	Nos. 924-983 (60)	106.05	106.05

Issued: 5c, #937, 946, 951, 960, 95c, $6.40, $7.20, 2/10; 10c, #938-945, 947-950, 952-959, 961-964, 2/11; $12.30, $2.80, $9.40, 2/12.
For surcharge see No. B111.

Stamps of 1980-82 Surcharged in Black (A102) or Gold (A104)

1987, June 17 Photo. *Perfs. as before*

984 A102	$2.80 on $2 #636	3.50	3.50
985 A102	$5 on $3 #637	6.15	6.15
986 A102	$9.40 on $10 #640	11.50	11.50
987 A104	$9.40 on $1 #679	11.50	11.50
988 A104	$9.40 on $1 #679A	11.50	11.50
989 A104	$9.40 on $2 #680	11.50	11.50
a.	Souv. sheet of 2 (on #680b)	22.50	22.50
990 A104	$9.40 on $2 #680A	11.50	11.50
	Nos. 984-990 (7)	67.15	67.15

No. 989a contains 2 stamps (Nos. 679-680), each surcharged $9.20.

Nos. 399 and 638 Ovptd. "ROYAL / WEDDING / FORTIETH / ANNIVERSARY" in Black on Gold Bar

1987, Nov. 20 Photo. *Perf. 14x13½*

991 A64	$4 on #399	4.90	4.90
992 A102	$4 on #638	4.90	4.90

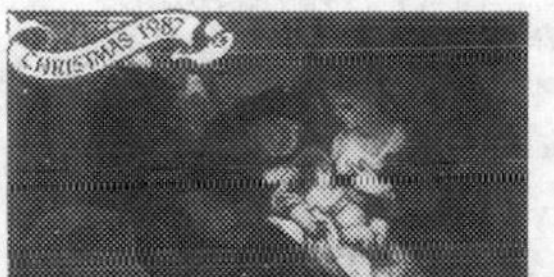

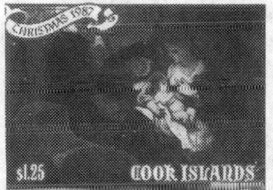

Christmas — A139

The Holy Family, religious paintings by Rembrandt in European museums: $1.25, No. 996a, The Louvre, Paris. $1.50, No. 996b, $6, The Holy Family with Angels, The Hermitage, Leningrad. $1.95, No. 996c, The Alte Pinakothek, Munich.

1987, Dec. 7 Photo. *Perf. 13½*

993 A139	$1.25 multi	1.55	1.55
994 A139	$1.50 multi	1.85	1.85
995 A139	$1.95 multi	2.40	2.40
	Nos. 993-995 (3)	5.80	5.80

Souvenir Sheets

996	Sheet of 3	4.40	4.40
a.-c.	A139 $1.15 any single	1.45	1.45

Perf. 13x13½

997 A139	$6 multi	7.75	7.75

Size of Nos. 996a-996c: 49½x38½mm. No. 997 contains 1 stamp 39½x31½mm.

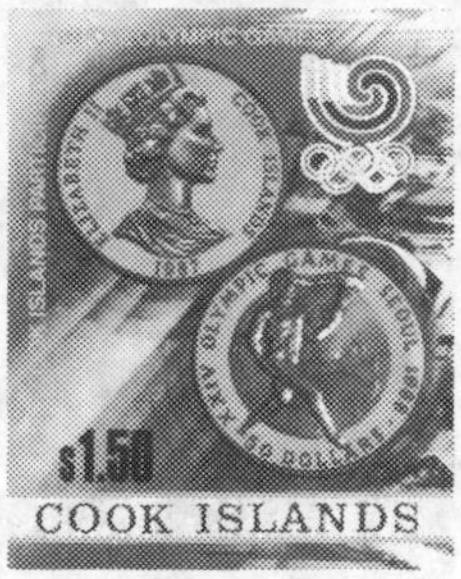

1988 Summer Olympics, Seoul A140

Designs: a, Cook Islands commemorative silver coin (obverse and reverse) issued on Aug. 20, 1987, for the '88 Summer Games. b, Seoul Olympic Park, torch and emblem. c, Steffi Graf, women's tennis champion, and '88 gold medal.

1988, Apr. 26 Photo. *Perf. 13½x14*

998	Strip of 3	6.00	6.00
a.-c.	A140 $1.50 multicolored	2.00	2.00

Souvenir Sheet

Perf. 13½

999 A140	$10 multi	13.00	13.00

Participation of national athletes in the Olympics for the first time, introduction of tennis as an Olympic gold-medal event.
No. 999 contains one stamp 114x47mm combining the designs of Nos. 998a-998c.

Nos. 998-999 Ovptd. for Olympic Winners
a. "MILOSLAV MECIR CZECHOSLOVAKIA GOLD MEDAL WINNER MEN'S TENNIS"
b. "TIM MAYOTTE UNITED STATES GABRIELA SABATINI ARGENTINA SILVER MEDAL WINNERS"
c. "GOLD MEDAL WINNER STEFFI GRAF WEST GERMANY"
d. "GOLD MEDAL WINNER SEOUL OLYMPIC GAMES STEFFI GRAF - WEST GERMANY"

1988, Oct. 12 Photo. *Perf. 13½x14*

1000	Strip of 3	5.85	5.85
a.-c.	A140 $1.50 multicolored	2.00	2.00

Souvenir Sheet

Perf. 13½

1001 A140(d)	$10 on No. 999	13.00	13.00

Margin of No. 1001 ovptd.: "STEFFI GRAF, WINNER OF AUSTRALIAN OPEN 24 JULY 1988, FRENCH OPEN / 4 JUNE 1988, WIMBLEDON 2 JULY 1988, U.S. OPEN 10 SEPTEMBER 1988. / FIRST GRAND SLAM WINNER IN 18 YEARS. GOLD MEDAL WINNER SEOUL / OLYMPICS 1 OCTOBER 1988."

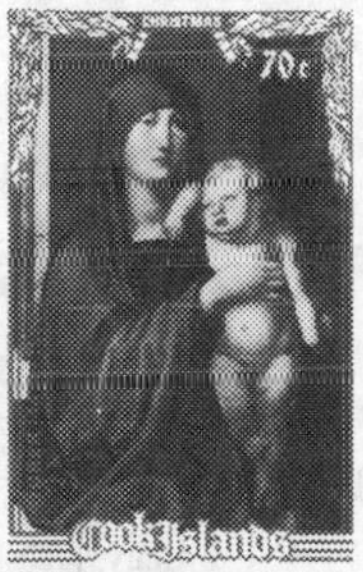

Christmas A141

Paintings by Albrecht Durer: 70c, Virgin and Child. 85c, Virgin and Child, diff. 95c, Virgin and Child, diff. $1.25, Virgin and Child, diff. $6.40, The Nativity.

1988, Nov. 11 *Perf. 13½*

1002 A141	70c multi	.90	.90
1003 A141	85c multi	1.10	1.10
1004 A141	95c multi	1.20	1.20
1005 A141	$1.25 multi	1.60	1.60
	Nos. 1002-1005 (4)	4.80	4.80

Souvenir Sheet

1006 A141	$6.40 multi	6.50	6.50

No. 1006 contains one stamp 45x60mm.

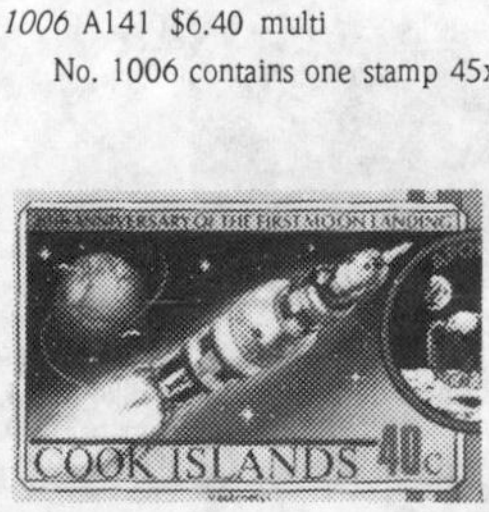

Scene and Left Half of Mission Emblem A142

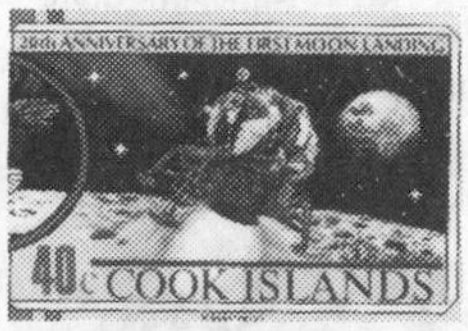

Scene and Right Half of Mission Emblem A143

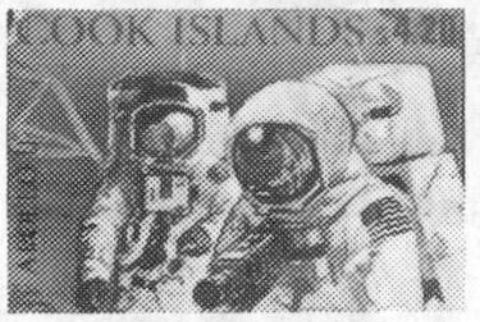

1st Moon Landing, 20th Anniv. A144

1989, July 14 Photo. *Perf. 13*

1007 A142	40c	Launch vehicle in space	.45	.45
1008 A143	40c	*Eagle* landing on Moon	.45	.45
1009 A142	55c	Astronaut descending ladder	.62	.62
1010 A143	55c	Astronaut on Moon	.62	.62
1011 A142	65c	Seismic experiment	.75	.75
1012 A143	65c	Solar wind experiment	.75	.75
1013 A142	75c	Liftoff from Moon	.85	.85
1014 A143	75c	Splashdown and recovery	.85	.85
		Nos. 1007-1014 (8)	5.34	5.34

Souvenir Sheet

1015 A144	$4.20 Armstrong and Aldrin	5.00	5.00

Stamps of the same denomination printed se-tenant in continuous designs.

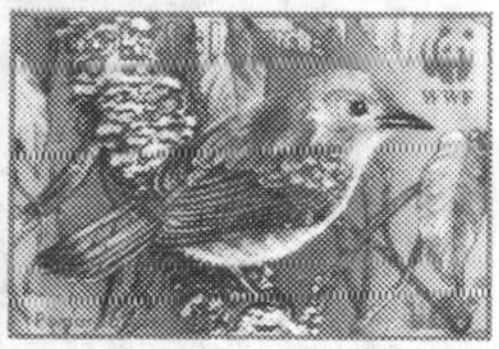
World Wildlife Fund A145

Endangered bird species.

1989, Oct. 4 Photo. *Perf. 13½x13*

1016 A145	15c	*Pomarea dimidiata*	.18	.18
1017 A145	20c	*Pomarea dimidiata* (two)	.24	.24
1018 A145	65c	*Ptilinopus rarotongensis* (two)	.78	.78
1019 A145	70c	*Ptilinopus rarotongensis*	.82	.82
		Nos. 1016-1019 (4)	2.02	2.02

Souvenir Sheets Without WWF Emblem

Perf. 13½

1020 A145	$1 like 15c	1.20	1.20
1021 A145	$1.25 like 20c	1.45	1.45
1022 A145	$1.50 like 65c	1.75	1.75
1023 A145	$1.75 like 70c	2.00	2.00

World Wildlife Fund. Nos. 1020-1023 are airmail and contain one stamp (size: 52x34mm); multicolored decorative margins continue the designs.
For overprints see Nos. C24-C27.

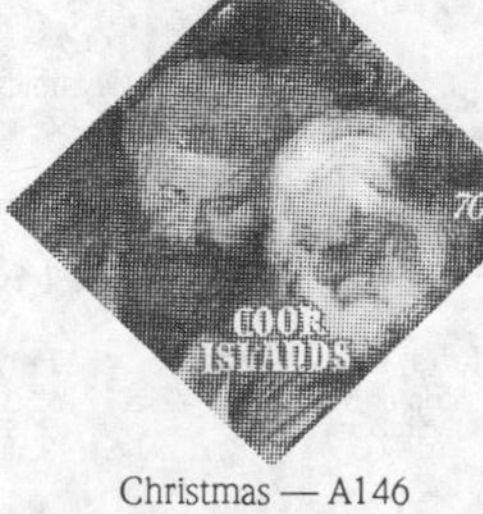

Christmas — A146

Details of *Adoration of the Magi*, by Rubens: 70c, Witnesses. 85c, Madonna. 95c, Christ child. $1.50, Attendant. $6.40, Entire painting.

1989, Nov. 24 Photo. *Perf. 13½x13*

1024 A146	70c multicolored	.82	.82
1025 A146	85c multicolored	1.00	1.00
1026 A146	95c multicolored	1.10	1.10
1027 A146	$1.50 multicolored	1.75	1.75
	Nos. 1024-1027 (4)	4.67	4.67

Souvenir Sheet
Perf. 13½
1028 A146 $6.40 multicolored   7.00 7.00

No. 1028 contains one 45x60mm stamp.

Religious History — A147

Designs: 70c, John Williams, LMS Mission Church. 85c, Bernardine Castanie, Roman Catholic Church. 95c, Osborne J.P. Widstoe, Church of Jesus Christ of Latter Day Saints. $1.60, J.E. Caldwell, Seventh Day Adventist Church.

1990, Feb. 19   Photo.   *Perf. 13½x13*
1029 A147 70c multicolored   .85 .85
1030 A147 85c multicolored   1.00 1.00
1031 A147 95c multicolored   1.10 1.10
1032 A147 $1.60 multicolored   2.00 2.00
   Nos. 1029-1032 (4)   4.95 4.95

Souvenir Sheet
Perf. 13½
1033   Sheet of 4   4.50 4.50
  a.   A147 90c like 70c   1.10 1.10
  b.   A147 90c like 85c   1.10 1.10
  c.   A147 90c like 95c   1.10 1.10
  d.   A147 90c like $1.60   1.10 1.10

No. 1033 contains 4 36x36mm stamps.

Penny Black, 150th Anniv. — A148

Paintings: 85c, No. 1038a, *Woman Writing a Letter*, by Gerard Terborch (1617-1681). $1.15, No. 1038b, *Portrait of George Gisze*, by Hans Holbein the Younger. $1.55, No. 1038c, *Portrait of Mrs. John Douglas*, by Thomas Gainsborough. $1.85, No. 1038d, *Portrait of a Gentleman*, by Albrecht Durer.

1990, May 2   Photo.   *Perf. 13½*
1034 A148 85c multicolored   1.00 1.00
1035 A148 $1.15 multicolored   1.35 1.35
1036 A148 $1.55 multicolored   1.75 1.75
1037 A148 $1.85 multicolored   2.15 2.15
   Nos. 1034-1037 (4)   6.25 6.25

Souvenir Sheet
1038   Sheet of 4   4.80 4.80
  a.-d.   A148 $1.05 any single   1.20 1.20

The margin of No. 1038 pictures the Stamp World '90 emblem and Great Britain #1-2.

1992 Olympics A149

Designs: a. Summer Games, Barcelona (runners). b. Eternal flame, commemorative coin obverse (Queen Elizabeth II) and reverse (athletes). c. Winter Games, Albertville (skier).

1990, June 15   Photo.   *Perf. 14*
1039   Strip of 3   6.50 6.50
  a.-c.   A149 $1.85 any single   2.15 2.15

Queen Mother, 90th Birthday — A150

1990, July 20   Photo.   *Perf. 13½*
1040 A150 $1.85 multicolored   2.15 2.15

Souvenir Sheet
1041 A150 $6.40 multicolored   7.50 7.50

Christmas A151

Paintings: 70c, Adoration of the Magi by Memling. 85c, The Holy Family by Lotto. 95c, Madonna and Child with Saints John and Catherine by Titian. $1.50, The Holy Family by Titian. $6.40, Madonna and Child Enthroned, Surrounded by Saints by Vivarini.

1990, Nov. 29   Litho.   *Perf. 14*
1042 A151 70c multicolored   .85 .85
1043 A151 85c multicolored   1.05 1.05
1044 A151 95c multicolored   1.15 1.15
1045 A151 $1.50 multicolored   1.85 1.85
   Nos. 1042-1045 (4)   4.90 4.90

Souvenir Sheet
1046 A151 $6.40 multicolored   7.75 7.75

Souvenir Sheet

1992 Olympic Games — A152

Illustration reduced.

1991, Feb. 12   *Perf. 13½*
1047 A152 $6.40 multicolored   7.75 7.75

Discovery of America 500th Anniv. (in 1992) — A153

1991, Feb. 14   Photo.   *Perf. 13½x13*
1048 A153 $1 multicolored   1.25 1.25

No. 640 Ovptd. "65th BIRTHDAY" in Gold

1991, Apr. 22   Litho.   *Perf. 14x13½*
1049 A102 $10 multicolored   12.00 12.00

Christmas A154

Paintings: 70c, Adoration of the Child, by Delle Notti. 85c, Birth of the Virgin, by Murillo. $1.15, Adoration of the Shepherds, by Rembrandt. $1.50, Adoration of the Shepherds, by Le Nain. $6.40, Madonna and Child, by Fra Filippo Lippi, vert.

1991, Nov. 12   Litho.   *Perf. 14*
1050 A154 70c multicolored   .80 .80
1051 A154 85c multicolored   1.00 1.00
1052 A154 $1.15 multicolored   1.35 1.35
1053 A154 $1.50 multicolored   1.75 1.75
   Nos. 1050-1053 (4)   4.90 4.90

Souvenir Sheet
1054 A154 $6.40 multicolored   7.50 7.50

Marine Life — A155

A155a

1992-94   Litho.   *Perf. 14½x13½*
1058 A155 5c Red-breasted maori wrasse   .15 .15
1059 A155 10c Blue sea star   .15 .15
1062 A155 15c Black & gold angelfish   .18 .18
1064 A155 20c Spotted pebble crab   .24 .24
1065 A155 25c Black-tipped cod   .30 .30
1066 A155 30c Spanish dancer   .38 .38
1071 A155 50c Royal angelfish   .58 .58
1076 A155 80c Squirrel fish   .95 .95
1077 A155 85c Red pencil sea urchin   1.00 1.00
1078 A155 90c Red-spot rainbow fish   1.05 1.05
1080 A155 $1 Black-lined maori wrasse   1.15 1.15
1081 A155 $2 Longnose butterflyfish   2.25 2.25
1082 A155a $3 Red-spot rainbow fish   3.50 3.50
1083 A155 $5 Blue sea star   5.50 5.50
1085 A155a $7 Royal angelfish   8.00 8.00
1087 A155a $10 Spotted pebble crab   11.00 11.00
1089 A155a $15 Red pencil sea urchin   18.00 18.00
   Nos. 1058-1089 (17)   54.38 54.38

Issued: 85c, 90c, $1, $2, 3/23/92; $3, $5, 10/25/93; $7, 12/6/93; $10, 1/31/94; $15, 9/9/94; others, 1/22/92.

See Nos. 1154-1176 for stamps with buff border. For overprints see Nos. O54-O65.

This is an expanding set. Numbers may change.

Discovery of America, 500th Anniv. — A157

1992   Litho.   *Perf. 14x14½*
1107 A157 $6 multicolored   7.00 7.00

Souvenir Sheet
Perf. 15x14
1107A A157 $10 Coming ashore   12.00 12.00

Issue dates: #1107, May 22. #1107A, Sept. 21. No. 1107A contains one 40x30mm stamp.

1992 Summer Olympics, Barcelona — A158

Designs: No. 1108a, $50 coin, soccer players. b, Flags of Spain, Cook Islands, Barcelona medal. c, $10 coin, basketball players. No. 1109a, Runners. b, $10, $50 coins. c, Cyclists. $6.40, Javelin.

1992, July 24   Litho.   *Perf. 13*
1108 A158 $1.75 Strip of 3, #a.-c.   6.00 6.00
1109 A158 $2.25 Strip of 3, #a.-c.   7.50 7.50

Souvenir Sheet
1110 A158 $6.40 multicolored   7.25 7.25

6th Festival of Pacific Arts, Rarotonga — A159

Designs: 80c, UNESCO poster. 85c, $1, & $1.75, Different carvings of Rarotongan fertility god, Tangaroa.

1992, Oct. 16   Litho.   *Perf. 15x14*
1111 A159 80c multicolored   .95 .95
1112 A159 85c multicolored   1.00 1.00
1113 A159 $1 multicolored   1.15 1.15
1114 A159 $1.75 multicolored   2.00 2.00
   Nos. 1111-1114 (4)   5.10 5.10

Ovptd. "ROYAL VISIT"

1992, Oct. 16
1115 A159 80c on #1111   .95 .95
1116 A159 85c on #1112   1.00 1.00
1117 A159 $1 on #1113   1.15 1.15
1118 A159 $1.75 on #1114   2.00 2.00
   Nos. 1115-1118 (4)   5.10 5.10

Endangered Wildlife Type of 1992

1992   Litho.   *Perf. 14*
1119 A156 $1.15 Jackass penguin   1.30 1.30
1120 A156 $1.15 Asian lion   1.30 1.30
1121 A156 $1.15 Peregrine falcon   1.30 1.30
1122 A156 $1.15 Persian fallow deer   1.30 1.30
1123 A156 $1.15 Key deer   1.30 1.30
1124 A156 $1.15 Alpine ibex   1.30 1.30
   Nos. 1119-1124 (6)   7.80 7.80

Issued: #1119, 11/2; #1120, 11/3; #1121, 11/4; #1122, 11/5; #1123, 11/6; #1124, 11/7.

Endangered Wildlife A156

1992   Litho.   *Perf. 14*
1095 A156 $1.15 Tiger   1.35 1.35
1096 A156 $1.15 Asiatic elephant   1.35 1.35
1097 A156 $1.15 Grizzly bear   1.35 1.35
1098 A156 $1.15 Black rhinoceros   1.35 1.35
1099 A156 $1.15 Chimpanzee   1.35 1.35
1100 A156 $1.15 Asian bighorn   1.35 1.35
1101 A156 $1.15 Heavisides dolphin   1.30 1.30
1102 A156 $1.15 Eagle owl   1.30 1.30
1103 A156 $1.15 Bee hummingbird   1.30 1.30
1104 A156 $1.15 Eastern cougar   1.30 1.30
1105 A156 $1.15 European otter   1.30 1.30
1106 A156 $1.15 Red kangaroo   1.30 1.30
   Nos. 1095-1106 (12)   15.90 15.90

Issued: #1095, 4/6; #1096, 4/7; #1097, 4/8; #1098, 4/9; #1099, 4/10; #1100, 4/11; #1101, 7/13; #1102, 7/14; #1103, 7/15; #1104, 7/16; #1105, 7/17; #1106, 7/18.

See Nos. 1119-1124, 1134-1138.

Christmas
A160

Paintings by El Parmigianino: 70c, Worship of Shepherds. 85c, $6.40, Virgin with Long Neck. $1.15, Virgin with Rose. $1.90, St. Margaret's Virgin.

1992, Nov. 20	Litho.	Perf. 13½	
1125 A160	70c multicolored	.80	.80
1126 A160	85c multicolored	.95	.95
1127 A160	$1.15 multicolored	1.30	1.30
1128 A160	$1.90 multicolored	2.15	2.15
Nos. 1125-1128 (4)		5.20	5.20

Souvenir Sheet

1129 A160	$6.40 multicolored	7.25	7.25

No. 1129 contains one 36x47mm stamp.

Queen Elizabeth II's Accession to the Throne, 40th Anniv. — A161

Various portraits of Queen Elizabeth II.

1992, Dec. 10	Litho.	Perf. 14	
1130 A161	80c multicolored	.90	.90
1131 A161	$1.15 multicolored	1.30	1.30
1132 A161	$1.50 multicolored	1.70	1.70
1133 A161	$1.95 multicolored	2.20	2.20
Nos. 1130-1133 (4)		6.10	6.10

Endangered Wildlife Type of 1992

1993	Litho.	Perf. 14	
1134 A156	$1.15 English mandrill	1.30	1.30
1135 A156	$1.15 Gorilla	1.30	1.30
1136 A156	$1.15 Vanessa atlanta	1.30	1.30
1137 A156	$1.15 Sichuan takin	1.30	1.30
1138 A156	$1.15 Ring tailed lemur	1.30	1.30
Nos. 1134-1138 (5)		6.50	6.50

Issued: #1134, Feb. 1; #1135, Feb. 2; #1136, Feb. 3; #1137, Feb. 4; #1138, Feb. 5.

Coronation of Queen Elizabeth II, 40th Anniv. — A162

Designs: $1, Coronation ceremony. $2, Coronation portrait. $3, Queen, family on balcony, Buckingham Palace.

1993, June 2	Litho.	Perf. 14	
1139 A162	$1 multicolored	1.15	1.15
1140 A162	$2 multicolored	2.30	2.30
1141 A162	$3 multicolored	3.45	3.45
Nos. 1139-1141 (3)		6.90	6.90

Christmas — A163

Paintings: 70c, Virgin with Child, by Filippo Lippi. 85c, Bargellini Madonna, by Lodovico Carracci. $1.15, Virgin of the Curtain, by Raphael. $2.50, Holy Family, by Il Bronzino. $4, Saint Zachary Virgin, by Il Parmigianino.

1993, Nov. 8	Litho.	Perf. 14	
1142 A163	70c multicolored	.80	.80
1143 A163	85c multicolored	1.00	1.00
1144 A163	$1.15 multicolored	1.25	1.25
1145 A163	$2.50 multicolored	3.00	3.00

Size: 32x47mm
Perf. 13½

1146 A163	$4.00 multicolored	4.75	4.75
Nos. 1142-1146 (5)		10.80	10.80

1994 Winter Olympics, Lillehammer — A164

Illustration reduced.

1994, Feb. 11	Litho.	Perf. 13½x14	
1147 A164	$5 multicolored	5.50	5.50

1994 World Cup Soccer Championships, US — A165

Illustration reduced.

1994, June 17	Litho.	Perf. 14	
1148 A165	$4.50 multicolored	5.00	5.00

First Manned Moon Landing, 25th Anniv. — A166

Apollo 11 emblem and: No. 1149a, First step onto Moon, US flag. No. 1149b, Astronaut carrying experiment packs on Moon. No. 1150a, Astronaut, US flag. No. 1150b, Flag, reflection shown in astronaut's visor.

1994, July 20			
1149 A166	$2.25 Pair, #a.-b. + label	5.00	5.00
1150 A166	$2.25 Pair, #a.-b. + label	5.00	5.00

Living Reef Type of 1992

1994	Litho.	Perf. 14½x13½	
	Size: 41x31mm		
	Buff & Multicolored		
1154 A155	5c like #1058	.15	.15
1158 A155	15c like #1062	.18	.18
1160 A155	20c like #1064	.25	.25
1161 A155	25c like #1065	.30	.30
1162 A155	30c like #1066	.35	.35
1167 A155	50c like #1071	.60	.60
1172 A155	80c like #1076	.95	.95
1173 A155	85c like #1077	1.00	1.00
1174 A155	90c like #1078	1.10	1.10
1176 A155	$1 like #1080	1.25	1.25
Nos. 1154-1176 (10)		6.13	6.13

Issued: 5c, 15c, 20c, 25c, 30c, 50c, 80c, 85c, 90c, $1, 10/24/94. This is an expanding set. Numbers may change.

Miniature Sheet

The Return of Tommy Tricker — A167

Scenes from film: a, Three people in canoe. b, Traditional dancers. c, Couple walking on beach. d, Aerial view of island. e, Girls performing hand gestures. f, Girls walking along sand bar.

1994, Nov. 23	Litho.	Perf. 14	
1191 A167	85c Sheet of 6, #a.-f.	6.00	6.00

Christmas — A168

Paintings: No. 1192a, The Virgin and Child, by Morales. b, Adoration of Kings, by Gerard David. c, Adoration of Kings, by Vinc Foppa. d, The Madonna & Child with St. Joseph & Infant Baptist, by Baroccio.
No. 1193a, Madonna with Iris, in style of Durer. b, Adoration of Shepherds, by Le Nain. c, The Virgin and Child, by follower of Leonardo. d, The Mystic Nativity, by Botticelli.

1994, Nov. 30	Litho.	Perf. 14	
1192 A168	85c Block of 4, #a.-d.	4.25	4.25
1193 A168	$1 Block of 4, #a.-d.	5.00	5.00

Robert Louis Stevenson (1850-94), Writer — A169

Adventure scenes from books: a, "Treasure Island." b, "David Balfour." c, "Dr. Jekyll and Mr. Hyde." d, "Kidnapped."

1994, Dec. 12		Perf. 14x15	
1194 A169	$1.50 Block of 4, #a.-d.	7.75	7.75

UN, 50th Anniv. — A170

1995, July 17	Litho.	Perf. 13x13½	
1195 A170	$4.75 multicolored	6.25	6.25

No. 1195 was issued in sheets of 4.

FAO, 50th Anniv. — A171

1995, Oct. 12	Litho.	Perf. 13½	
1196 A171	$4.50 multicolored	6.00	6.00

No. 1196 was issued in sheets of 4.

Queen Mother, 95th Birthday — A172

1995, Aug. 31			
1197 A172	$5 multicolored	6.75	6.75

End of World War II, 50th Anniv. — A173

Designs: a, German surrender, Rheims. b, Japanese surrender, Tokyo Bay.

1995, Sept. 4		Perf. 13	
1198 A173	$3.50 Pair, #a.-b.	9.50	9.50

No. 1198 was issued in sheets of 4 stamps.

Year of the Sea Turtle — A174

Designs: 85c, Green turtle in water. $1, Hawksbill turtle in water. $1.75, Green turtle nesting. $2.25, Hawksbill turtle hatchlings leaving nest.

1995, Nov. 20	Litho.	Perf. 14	
1199 A174	85c multicolored	1.10	1.10
1200 A174	$1 multicolored	1.40	1.40
1201 A174	$1.75 multicolored	2.25	2.25
1202 A174	$2.25 multicolored	3.00	3.00
Nos. 1199-1202 (4)		7.75	7.75

1996 Summer Olympics, Atlanta A175

1996, Jan 12	Litho.	Perf. 14	
1203 A175	85c Discus	1.10	1.10
1204 A175	$1 Torch bearer	1.40	1.40
1205 A175	$1.50 Sprinting	2.00	2.00
1206 A175	$1.85 Gymnastics	2.50	2.50
1207 A175	$2.10 Archery	2.75	2.75
1208 A175	$2.50 Javelin	3.25	3.25
Nos. 1203-1208 (6)		13.00	13.00

SEMI-POSTAL STAMPS

Catalogue values for unused stamps in this section are for Never Hinged items.

Nos. 203-204, 223, 210, 213, 215-216 Surcharged

HURRICANE RELIEF PLUS 2c

Perf. 14x13½, 13½

1968, Feb. 12		Photo.	
B1 A34	3c + 1c multi	.15	.15
B2 A34	4c + 1c multi	.15	.15
B3 A37	5c + 2c multi	.15	.15
B4 A34	10c + 2c multi	.22	.22
B5 A34	25c + 5c multi	.40	.40
B6 A34	50c + 10c multi	.90	.90
B7 A35	$1 + 10c multi	1.75	1.75
Nos. B1-B7 (7)		3.72	3.72

Surtax for the victims of hurricane of Dec. 15-18, 1967. The surcharge on No. B3 is printed on a

silver rectangle. The surcharge on No. B7 is in smaller type with serifs, measuring 7½mm in depth.

Nos. 210, 213-214 Surcharged in Ultramarine

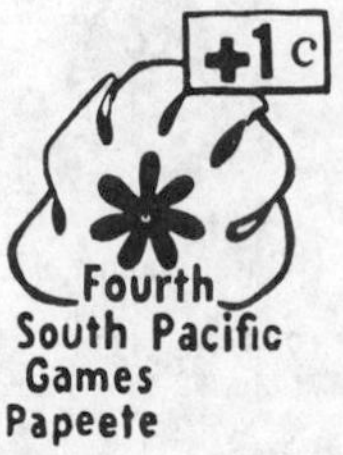

1971, Sept. 8 Photo. *Perf. 14x13½*

B8	A34 10c + 1c multi	.25	.25
B9	A34 10c + 3c multi	.25	.25
B10	A34 25c + 1c multi	.65	.65
B11	A34 25c + 3c multi	.65	.65
B12	A34 30c + 1c multi	.75	.75
B13	A34 30c + 3c multi	.75	.75
	Nos. B8-B13 (6)	3.30	3.30

4th South Pacific Games, Papeete, French Polynesia, Sept. 8-19.

Christmas Type of Regular Issue
Souvenir Sheet

Design: 50c+5c, Holy Family in a Garland of Flowers, by Jan Brueghel and Pieter van Avont.

1971, Nov. 30 Photo. *Perf. 13½*

B14	A50 50c + 5c gold & multi	1.75	1.75

No. B14 contains one stamp 45x40mm.

Nos. 316-318, 211, 213 and 215 Surcharged in Red or Black

HURRICANE RELIEF PLUS 2c (a) — Hurricane Relief Plus 5c (b)

1972, Mar. 30 Photo. *Perf. 13½*

B15	A46(a) 5c + 2c multi (R)	.15	.15
B16	A46(a) 10c + 2c multi (R)	.20	.20
B17	A34(b) 15c + 5c multi	.35	.35
B18	A34(b) 25c + 5c multi	.65	.65
B19	A46(a) 30c + 5c multi (R)	.75	.75
B20	A34(b) 50c + 10c multi	1.40	1.40
	Nos. B15-B20 (6)	3.50	3.50

Surtax for victims of hurricane of Mar. 22-26.

Nos. 319-326a with Surcharge Similar to Type "a"

1972, May 24 Photo. *Perf. 13½*

B21	A51 5c + 2c multi	.15	.15
B22	A51 5c + 2c multi	.15	.15
B23	A51 10c + 2c multi	.20	.20
B24	A51 10c + 2c multi	.20	.20
B25	A51 25c + 2c multi	.50	.50
B26	A51 25c + 2c multi	.50	.50
B27	A51 30c + 2c multi	.75	.75
B28	A51 30c + 2c multi	.75	.75
a.	Souvenir sheet of 8	3.50	3.50
	Nos. B21-B28 (8)	3.20	3.20

Surtax for victims of hurricane of Mar. 22-26. Stamps of No. B28a each surcharged 3c.

Olympic Type of Regular Issue
Souvenir Sheet

Design: 50c+5c, Pierre de Coubertin and Olympic rings.

1972, June 26

B29	A52 50c + 5c multi	3.25	3.25

Christmas Type of Regular Issue
Souvenir Sheet

Design: 50c+5c, Nativity, by Correggio.

1972, Oct. 11 Photo. *Perf. 13½*

B30	A53 50c + 5c multi	2.25	2.00

No. B30 contains one stamp 30x40mm.

Easter Type of Regular Issue
Souvenir Sheets

1973, Apr. 30 Photo. *Perf. 13½x14*

B31	A56 50c + 5c like #346	1.10	1.10
B32	A56 50c + 5c like #347	1.10	1.10
B33	A56 50c + 5c like #348	1.10	1.10
	Nos. B31-B33 (3)	3.30	3.30

Surtax was for school children.

Christmas Type of Regular Issue
Souvenir Sheets

1973, Dec. 3 Photo. *Perf. 13x13½*

B34	A59 50c + 5c like #364	.75	.75
B35	A59 50c + 5c like #365	.75	.75
B36	A59 50c + 5c like #366	.75	.75
B37	A59 50c + 5c like #367	.75	.75
B38	A59 50c + 5c like #368	.75	.75
	Nos. B34-B38 (5)	3.75	3.75

Surtax was for school children.

Easter Type of 1973
Dated "1974"
Souvenir Sheets

1974, Apr. 22 *Perf. 13½x14*

B39	A56 50c + 5c like #378	1.00	1.00
B40	A56 50c + 5c like #379	1.00	1.00
B41	A56 50c + 5c like #380	1.00	1.00
	Nos. B39-B41 (3)	3.00	3.00

Christmas Type of 1974
Souvenir Sheets

1974 Photo. *Perf. 13½x13*

B42	A68 50c + 5c like #412	.75	.75
B43	A68 50c + 5c like #413	.75	.75
B44	A68 50c + 5c like #414	.75	.75
B45	A68 50c + 5c like #415	.75	.75
B46	A68 50c + 5c like #416	.75	.75
	Nos. B42-B46 (5)	3.75	3.75

Christmas Type of 1975
Souvenir Sheets

1975, Dec. 1 *Perf. 13½*

B47	A75 75c + 5c like #437	1.10	1.10
B48	A75 75c + 5c like #438	1.10	1.10
B49	A75 75c + 5c like #439	1.10	1.10
B50	A75 75c + 5c like #440	1.10	1.10
B51	A75 75c + 5c like #441	1.10	1.10
	Nos. B47-B51 (5)	5.50	5.50

Size of stamps: 23x40mm.

Easter Type of 1976
Souvenir Sheets

1976, May 3 Photo. *Perf. 13½*

B52	A76 60c + 5c like #442	1.00	1.00
B53	A76 60c + 5c like #443	1.00	1.00
B54	A76 60c + 5c like #444	1.00	1.00
	Nos. B52-B54 (3)	3.00	3.00

Size of stamps: 36x36mm.

Christmas Type of 1976
Souvenir Sheets

1976, Nov. 2 Photo. *Perf. 14x13½*

B55	A80 75c + 5c like #459	1.25	1.25
B56	A80 75c + 5c like #460	1.25	1.25
B57	A80 75c + 5c like #461	1.25	1.25
B58	A80 75c + 5c like #462	1.25	1.25
B59	A80 75c + 5c like #463	1.25	1.25
	Nos. B55-B59 (5)	6.25	6.25

Easter Type of 1977
Souvenir Sheets

1977, Apr. 18 Photo. *Perf. 13½x14*

B60	A83 60c + 5c like #471	1.00	1.00
B61	A83 60c + 5c like #472	1.00	1.00
B62	A83 60c + 5c like #473	1.00	1.00
	Nos. B60-B62 (3)	3.00	3.00

Size of stamps: 30x42mm.

Christmas Type of 1977
Souvenir Sheets

1977, Oct. 31 Photo. *Perf. 14x13½*

B63	A84 75c + 5c like #474	1.10	1.10
B64	A84 75c + 5c like #475	1.10	1.10
B65	A84 75c + 5c like #476	1.10	1.10
B66	A84 75c + 5c like #477	1.10	1.10
B67	A84 75c + 5c like #478	1.10	1.10
	Nos. B63-B67 (5)	5.50	5.50

Easter Type of 1978
Souvenir Sheets

1978, Apr. 10 Photo. *Perf. 14x13½*

B68	A87 60c + 5c like #483	.85	.75
B69	A87 60c + 5c like #484	.85	.75
B70	A87 60c + 5c like #485	.85	.75
	Nos. B68-B70 (3)	2.55	2.25

Christmas Type of 1978
Souvenir Sheets

1979, Jan. 12 Photo. *Perf. 13*

B71	A89 75c + 5c like #503	.90	.90
B72	A89 75c + 5c like #504	.90	.90
B73	A89 75c + 5c like #505	.90	.90
	Nos. B71-B73 (3)	2.70	2.70

Easter Type of 1979
Souvenir Sheet

1979, Apr. 5 Photo. *Perf. 13*

B74	Sheet of 4	1.00	1.00
a.	A90 10c + 2c like #506	.16	.16
b.	A90 12c + 2c like #507	.20	.20
c.	A90 15c + 2c like #508	.25	.25
d.	A90 20c + 2c like #509	.35	.35

IYC Type of 1979
Souvenir Sheet

1979, Oct. 10

B75	Sheet of 3	2.25	2.25
a.	A93 30c + 5c like #529	.45	.45
b.	A93 50c + 5c like #530	.75	.75
c.	A93 65c + 5c like #531	.90	.90

Christmas Type of 1979

1980, Jan. 15 Photo. *Perf. 14*

B76	A95 6c + 2c like #537	.15	.15
B77	A95 10c + 2c like #538	.20	.20
B78	A95 12c + 2c like #539	.25	.25
B79	A95 15c + 2c like #540	.28	.28
	Nos. B76-B79 (4)	.88	.88

Easter Type of 1980
Souvenir Sheets

1980, Mar. 31 Photo. *Perf. 13*

B80	Sheet of 6	2.25	2.25
a.	A96 20 + 2c like #542	.25	.25
b.	A96 20 + 2c like #541	.25	.25
c.	A96 30 + 2c like #543	.40	.40
d.	A96 30 + 2c like #544	.40	.40
e.	A96 35 + 2c like #545	.45	.45
f.	A96 35 + 2c like #546	.45	.45

1980, Apr. 23

B81	A96 75c + 5c like #541	1.00	1.00
B82	A96 75c + 5c like #542	1.00	1.00
B83	A96 75c + 5c like #543	1.00	1.00
B84	A96 75c + 5c like #544	1.00	1.00
B85	A96 75c + 5c like #545	1.00	1.00
B86	A96 75c + 5c like #546	1.00	1.00
	Nos. B81-B86 (6)	6.00	6.00

Surtax was for school children.

Rotary Type of 1980
Souvenir Sheet

1980, May 27 Photo. *Perf. 14*

B87	Sheet of 3	1.75	1.75
a.	A97 30c + 3c like #547	.45	.45
b.	A97 35c + 3c like #548	.55	.55
c.	A97 50c + 3c like #549	.75	.75

Christmas Type of 1980
Souvenir Sheets

1981, Jan. 9 Photo. *Imperf.*

B88	A102a 75c + 5c like #652	1.00	1.00
B89	A102a 75c + 5c like #653	1.00	1.00
B90	A102a 75c + 5c like #654	1.00	1.00
B91	A102a 75c + 5c like #655	1.00	1.00
	Nos. B88-B91 (4)	4.00	4.00

Easter Type of 1981
Souvenir Sheets

1981, Apr. 10 Photo. *Perf. 13½*

B92	Sheet of 3	1.50	1.50
a.	A103 15c + 2c like #656	.25	.25
b.	A103 25c + 2c like #657	.50	.50
c.	A103 40c + 2c like #658	.75	.75

1981, Apr. 28 *Imperf.*

B93	A103 75c + 5c like #656	1.50	1.50
B94	A103 75c + 5c like #657	1.50	1.50
B95	A103 75c + 5c like #658	1.50	1.50
	Nos. B93-B95 (3)	4.50	4.50

Surtax was for school children.

Espana '82 Type of 1981
Souvenir Sheet

1981 Photo. *Perf. 13½*

B96	Sheet of 8	3.75	3.75
a.	A105 20c + 3c multicolored	.25	.25
b.	A106 20c + 3c multicolored	.25	.25
c.	A105 30c + 3c multicolored	.40	.40
d.	A106 30c + 3c multicolored	.40	.40
e.	A105 35c + 3c multicolored	.50	.50
f.	A106 35c + 3c multicolored	.50	.50
g.	A105 50c + 3c multicolored	.70	.70
h.	A106 50c + 3c multicolored	.70	.70

Royal Wedding Type of 1981
Nos. 659-660a Surcharged in Black

1981, Nov. 10 Photo. *Perf. 14*

B97	A104 $1 + 5c multi	2.25	2.25
B98	A104 $2 + 5c multi	4.50	4.50
a.	Souvenir sheet of 2	7.50	7.50

Intl. Year of the Disabled. No. B98a contains Nos. B97-B98 each with 10c surtax, which was for benefit of the disabled; black overprint in margin.

Christmas Type of 1981
Souvenir Sheet

1981, Dec. 14 Photo. *Perf. 13½*

B99	Sheet of 4	3.50	3.50
a.	A107 8c + 3c like #669	.25	.25
b.	A107 15c + 3c like #670	.40	.40
c.	A107 40c + 3c like #671	1.10	1.10
d.	A107 50c + 3c like #672	1.40	1.40

Surtax was for school children.

Nos. 919-923 Surcharged "FIRST PAPAL VISIT TO SOUTH PACIFIC / POPE JOHN PAUL II / *NOV 21-24 1986* " and Value in Silver

1986, Nov. 21 Litho. *Perf. 13½*

B100	A138 55c + 10c multi	.70	.70
B101	A138 $1.30 + 10c multi	1.50	1.50
B102	A138 $2.75 + 10c multi	3.00	3.00
	Nos. B100-B102 (3)	5.20	5.20

Souvenir Sheets

B103	Sheet of 3	8.00	8.00
a.-c.	A138 $2.40 + 10c on Nos. 922a-922c, any single	2.65	2.65
B104	A138 $6.40 + 50c multi	7.25	7.25

No. B103 ovptd. in margin "VISIT TO SOUTH PACIFIC / OF POPE JOHN PAUL II" and "FIRST PAPAL VISIT / NOVEMBER 21-24 1986." No. B104 ovptd. around margin only, "*FIRST PAPAL VISIT TO SOUTH PACIFIC NOVEMBER 21-24 1986" and "PRE-CHRISTMAS VISIT OF HIS HOLINESS POPE JOHN PAUL II."

For surcharge see No. B112.

Stamps of 1982 and 1987 Surcharged "HURRICANE RELIEF" in Sans-serif Capitals Plus New Value

1987, June 30 Photo. *Perfs. as before*

B105	A121 55c +25c on #946	1.00	1.00
B106	A121 65c +25c on #951	1.10	1.10
B107	A121 75c +25c on #960	1.25	1.25
B108	A121 95c +25c on #965	1.50	1.50
B109	A101 $2.80 +50c on #636	4.10	4.10
B110	A101 $5 +50c on #637	6.75	6.75
B111	A102 $6.40 +50c on #978	8.50	8.50
	Nos. B105-B111 (7)	24.20	24.20

Stamps of 1985-86 Surcharged "HURRICANE RELIEF / +50c" in Silver or Black

1987 *Perfs. as before*

B112	A138 55c +50c on #B100	1.30	1.30
B113	A133 55c +50c on #897 (B)	1.30	1.30
B114	A128 65c +50c on #871	1.40	1.40
B115	A133 65c +50c on #898	1.40	1.40
B116	A128 75c +50c on #872	1.50	1.50
B117	A133 75c +50c on #899	1.50	1.50
B118	A134 95c +50c on #908 (B)	1.80	1.80
B119	A135 $1 +50c on #910	1.85	1.85
B120	A136 $1 +50c on #913	1.85	1.85
B121	A137 $1 +50c on #916	1.85	1.85
B122	A128 $1.15 +50c on #873	2.00	2.00
B123	A133 $1.25 +50c on #900	2.15	2.15
B124	A134 $1.25 +50c on #905	2.15	2.15
B125	A136 $1.25 +50c on #914 (B)	2.15	2.15
B126	A138 $1.30 +50c on #920	2.20	2.20
B127	A134 $1.50 +50c on #906 (B)	2.50	2.50
B128	A135 $1.50 +50c on #911 (B)	2.50	2.50
B129	A133 $2 +50c on #901 (B)	3.10	3.10
B130	A135 $2 +50c on #912 (B)	3.10	3.10
B131	A137 $2 +50c on #917	3.10	3.10
B132	A136 $2.75 +50c on #915	4.00	4.00
B133	A138 $2.75 +50c on #921	4.00	4.00
B134	A128 $2.80 +50c on #874	4.10	4.10
B135	A137 $3 +50c on #918	4.30	4.30
	Nos. B112-B135 (24)	57.10	57.10

Souvenir Sheets

B136	A134 $1.10 +50c on #907 (B)	2.00	2.00
B137	A134 $1.95 +50c on #908	3.00	3.00
B138	on #922 (sheet of 3)	10.80	10.80
a.-c.	A138 $2.40 +50c, any single	3.60	3.60
B139	A134 $2.45 +50c on #909 (B)	3.65	3.65
B140	A128 $5.30 +50c on #875	7.15	7.15
B141	A138 $6.40 +50c on #923	8.50	8.50
	Nos. B136-B141 (6)	35.10	35.10

Issue dates: Nos. B112-B117, B119-B120, B122-B123, B125-B126, B128, B130, B132-B134, B138, B141-B142, June 30. Others July 31.

AIR POST STAMPS

Catalogue values for unused stamps in this section are for Never Hinged items.

Stamps of 1936-63 Overprinted and Surcharged 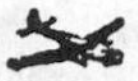 **Airmail**

Perf. 13x13½, 13½x13
Litho., Engr.

1966, Apr. 22 Wmk. 253

C1 A25 6p on #152 .25 .20
C2 A26 7p on 8p #153 .30 .25
C3 A25 10p on 3p #150 .40 .35
C4 A25 1sh on #154 .50 .45
C5 A27 1sh6p on #155 .75 .65
C6 A28 2sh3p on 3sh #157 1.25 1.00
C7 A28 5sh on #158 2.00 1.75
C8 A28 10sh on 2sh #156 4.00 4.00

Typo. *Perf. 14*
C9 PF5 £1 on #106 15.00 14.00
Nos. C1-C9 (9) 24.45 22.65

The position of the airplane in relationship to "Airmail" varies. The surcharges are printed on silver ovals.

2nd So. Pacific Games' Type of Regular Issue

Sport: 10p, Women runners and Games' emblem. 2sh3p, Runner and team emblem.

Perf. 13½
1967, Jan. 12 Unwmk. Photo.
C10 A32 10p org & multi .25 .25
C11 A32 2sh3p multi .75 .75

Capt. Cook Type of Regular Issue

Designs: 6c, The "Resolution" and "Discovery" Beating Through the Ice, by Webber. 10c, The Island of Otaheite, by Hodges, and Queen Elizabeth II. 15c, View of Karakakooa (Kealakekua), Hawaii, by Webber. 25c, The Landing at Middleburg, Tonga, by Hodges, and Captain Cook. (All horizontal.)

1968, Sept. 12 Photo. *Perf. 13*
C12 A39 6c gold & multi .25 .25
C13 A39 10c gold & multi .40 .40
C14 A39 15c gold & multi .50 .50
C15 A39 25c gold & multi 1.00 1.00
Nos. C12-C15 (4) 2.15 2.15

See note after No. 236.

Christmas Type of 1979

1979, Dec. 14 Photo. *Perf. 14*
C16 A95 20c like #537 .25 .25
C17 A95 25c like #538 .35 .35
C18 A95 30c like #539 .40 .40
C19 A95 35c like #540 .50 .50
Nos. C16-C19 (4) 1.50 1.50

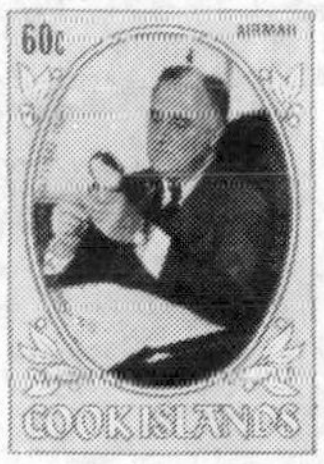

Franklin D. Roosevelt (1882-1945) — AP1

Portraits: 80c, Benjamin Franklin (1706-1790). $1.40, George Washington (1732-1799), by Gilbert Stuart.

1982, Sept. 30 Photo. *Perf. 14*
C20 AP1 60c multicolored .90 .90
C21 AP1 80c multicolored 1.10 1.10
C22 AP1 $1.40 multicolored 2.00 2.00
a. Souvenir sheet of 3 4.25 4.25
Nos. C20-C22 (3) 4.00 4.00

No. C22a contains Nos. C20-C22, perf. 13½ with portraits in square frames.

No. C22 Overprinted in Gold and Black

1983, Aug. 12 Photo. *Perf. 14*
C23 AP1 96c on $1.40 multi 2.00 2.00

Endangered Bird Species Type Souvenir Sheets

Nos. 1020-1023 overprinted 

1990, Dec. 5 Litho. *Perf. 13½*
C24 A145 $1 Flycatcher 1.25 1.25
C25 A145 $1.25 Flycatchers 1.50 1.50
C26 A145 $1.50 Fruit dove 1.85 1.85
C27 A145 $1.75 Fruit doves 2.15 2.15
Nos. C24-C27 (4) 6.75 6.75

Birdpex '90, 20th Intl. Ornithological Cong., New Zealand.

AIR POST SEMI-POSTAL STAMPS

Catalogue values for unused stamps in this section are for Never Hinged items.

Christmas Type of 1979

1980, Jan. 15 Photo. *Perf. 14*
CB1 A95 20c + 4c like #C16 .40 .40
CB2 A95 25c + 4c like #C17 .45 .45
CB3 A95 30c + 4c like #C18 .50 .50
CB4 A95 35c + 4c like #C19 .60 .60
Nos. CB1-CB4 (4) 1.95 1.95

OFFICIAL STAMPS

Flower Issue of 1967-69 Overprinted or Surcharged in Black on Silver [redacted] [redacted]

1975 Photo. Unwmk. *Perf. 14x13½*
O1 A34 1c multi (#200) .15
O2 A34 2c multi (#201) .15
O3 A34 3c multi (#203) .15
O4 A34 4c multi (#205) .15
O5 A34 5c on 2½c multi (#202) .16
O6 A34 8c multi (#208) .25
O7 A34 10c on 6c multi (#207) .28
O8 A34 18c on 20c multi (#212) .40
O9 A34 25c on 9c multi (#209) .60
O10 A34 30c on 15c multi (#211) .80
O11 A34 50c multi (#215) 1.25
O12 A35 $1 multi (#216) 2.75
O13 A35 $2 multi (#217) 4.75
O14 A36 $4 multi (#218) 8.00
O15 A36 $6 multi (#219) 10.00
Nos. O1-O15 (15) 29.84

No. O1-O15 were not sold to the public unused. Arrangement of surcharge varies on different denominations.

Silver panel on Nos. O14-O15 measures 26½x6mm and is rounded at both ends.

Issue dates: 1c-$2, Mar. 17, $4-$6, May 19.

Catalogue values for unused stamps in this section, from this point to the end of the section, are for Never Hinged items.

Nos. 381-382, 389, 393-396, 469-470, 446 Overprinted or Surcharged in Silver or Black **O.H.M.S.**

Photo., Litho.
1978, Oct. 19 *Perf. 13½*
O16 A62 1c multi (S) .15 .15
O17 A62 2c on ½c multi .15 .15
O18 A62 5c on ½c multi .15 .15
O19 A62 10c on 8c multi (S) .15 .15
O20 A62 15c on 50c multi (S) .20 .15
O21 A62 18c on 60c multi (S) .25 .20
O22 A62 25c multicolored .35 .25
O23 A62 30c multi (S) .40 .30
O24 A62 35c on 60c multi (S) .50 .35
O25 A62 50c multi (S) .65 .50
O26 A62 60c multi (S) .75 .60
O27 A82 $1 multi (S) 1.30 1.00
O28 A82 $1 multi (S) 1.30 1.00
O29 A77 $2 multicolored 2.50 2.00
O30 A64 $4 multi ('79) 5.00 4.00
O31 A64 $6 multi ('79) 7.00 6.50
Nos. O16-O31 (16) 20.80 17.45

Diagonal overprint on Nos. O27-O28. Overprint on No. O29: 19x4mm.

Nos. 790-791, 795, 797, 799, 805, 807, 809-810 Ovptd. or Surcharged "O.H.M.S." in Silver

1985, July 10 Photo. *Perf. 13½x13*
O32 A121 5c multi .15 .15
O33 A121 10c multi .15 .15
O34 A121 20c multi .20 .20
O35 A121 30c multi .30 .30
O36 A121 40c multi .40 .40
O37 A121 55c on 85c multi .55 .55
O38 A121 60c multi .60 .60
O39 A121 $1.10 multi 1.10 1.10
O40 A121 $2 on $1.20 multi 2.00 2.00
Nos. O32-O40 (9) 5.45 5.45

Nos. 792-794, 802, 806, 696-699 and 637-640 Ovptd. or Surcharged "O.H.M.S." in Silver, Gold (75c) or Black and Silver ($5, $18)

1986-90 Photo. ***Perfs. as Before***
O41 A121 12c multi .15 .15
O42 A121 14c multi .16 .16
O43 A121 18c multi .22 .22
O44 A121 50c multi .60 .60
O45 A121 70c multi .85 .85
O46 A111 75c on 60c #696 .90 .90
O47 A111 75c on 60c #697 .90 .90
O48 A111 75c on 60c #698 .90 .90
O49 A111 75c on 60c #699 .90 .90
O50 A102 $5 on $3 multi 6.00 6.00
O51 A102 $9 on $4 multi 10.50 10.50
O52 A102 $14 on $6 multi 16.25 16.25
O53 A102 $18 on $10 multi 21.00 21.00
Nos. O41-O53 (13) 59.33 59.33

Issue dates: $9, May 30, 1989. $14, July 12, 1989. $18, June 4, 1990. Others May 5, 1986.

Nos. 1058-1059, 1062, 1064-1066, 1071, 1076-1078, 1080-1081 Ovptd. "O.H.M.S." in Silver

Perf. 14½x13½
1995, Feb. 24 Litho.
O54 A155 5c multicolored .15 .15
O55 A155 10c multicolored .15 .15
O56 A155 15c multicolored .18 .18
O57 A155 20c multicolored .25 .25
O58 A155 25c multicolored .30 .30
O59 A155 30c multicolored .35 .35
O60 A155 50c multicolored .60 .60
O61 A155 80c multicolored .95 .95
O62 A155 85c multicolored 1.00 1.00
O63 A155 90c multicolored 1.10 1.10
O64 A155 $1 multicolored 1.40 1.40
O65 A155 $2 multicolored 2.75 2.75
Nos. O54-O65 (12) 9.18 9.18

Issued: 5c-90c, 2/24/95; $1-$2, 5/15/95

CRETE

'krēt

LOCATION — An island in the Mediterranean Sea south of Greece
GOVT. — Joint administration of France, Great Britain, Italy and Russia
AREA — 3,235 sq. mi.
POP. — 301,273 (1900)
CAPITAL — Canea

Formerly Crete was a province of Turkey. After an extended period of civil wars, France, Great Britain, Italy and Russia intervened and declaring Crete an autonomy, placed it under the administration of Prince George of Greece as High Commissioner.

Stamps issued for use in the Russian Sphere of Administration and by the Cretan government are listed in Vol. 2.

40 Paras = 1 Piaster

British Sphere of Administration District of Heraklion (Candia)

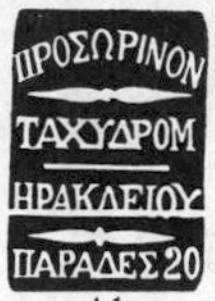

A1

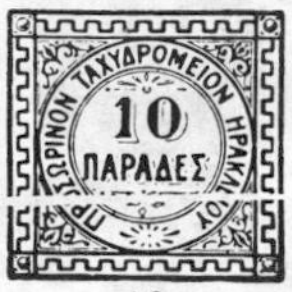

A2

Handstamped
1898 Unwmk. ***Imperf.***
1 A1 20pa violet 400.00 275.00

1898 Litho. *Perf. 11½*
2 A2 10pa blue 8.00 2.50
a. Horiz. pair, imperf. btwn.
b. Imperf., pair 250.00
3 A2 20pa green 8.00 2.50
a. Imperf., pair 250.00

1899
4 A2 10pa brown 8.00 2.50
a. Horiz. pair, imperf. btwn.
b. Imperf., pair 250.00
5 A2 20pa rose 8.00 2.50
a. Imperf., pair 250.00

Used values for Nos. 2-5 are for stamps canceled by the straight-line "Heraklion" town postmark.

Stamps canceled with any other postmark used for postal duty are scarce and worth much more.

Counterfeits exist of Nos. 1-5.

Reprints exist of Nos. 2-5.

CYPRUS

'sī-prəs

LOCATION — An island in the Mediterranean Sea off the coast of Turkey
GOVT. — Republic
AREA — 3,572 sq. mi.
POP. — 645,500 (1982)
CAPITAL — Nicosia

The British Crown Colony of Cyprus became a republic in 1960.

Turkey invaded Cyprus in 1974 resulting in the the northern 40% of the island becoming the Turkish Republic of Northern Cyprus. No other country recognizes this division of the island.

See Turkey in Volume 5.

12 Pence = 1 Shilling
40 Paras = 1 Piaster
9 Piasters = 1 Shilling
20 Shillings = 1 Pound
1000 Milliemes = 1 Pound (1955)
100 Cents = 1 Cyprus Pound (1983)

Catalogue values for unused stamps in this country are for Never Hinged items, beginning with Scott 156 in the regular postage section and Scott RA1 in the postal tax section.

Values for unused stamps are for examples with original gum as defined in the catalogue introduction. Very fine examples of Nos. 1, 2 and 7-10 will have perforations touching the design on at least one or more sides due to the narrow spacing of the stamps on the plates and to imperfect perforation methods. Stamps with perfs clear on all four sides are scarce and will command higher prices.

Watermark

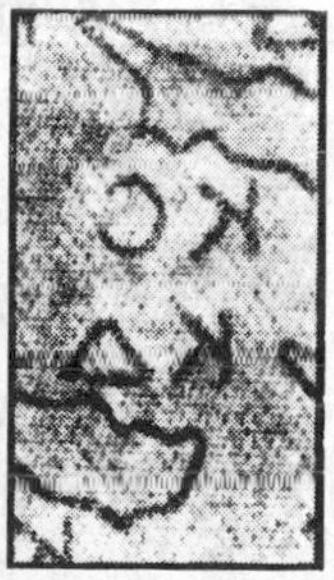
Wmk. 344- Map of Cyprus and KC/K Delta

Queen Victoria — A1

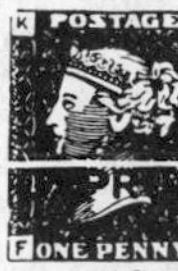

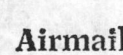

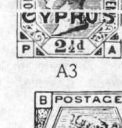

A2

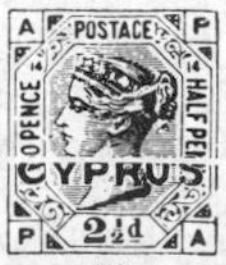

A3

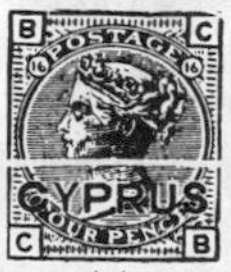

A4

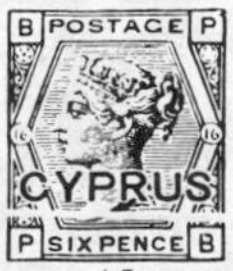

A5

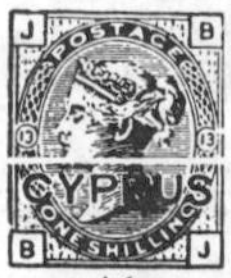

A6

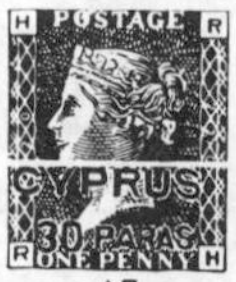

A7

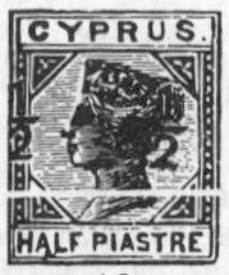

A9

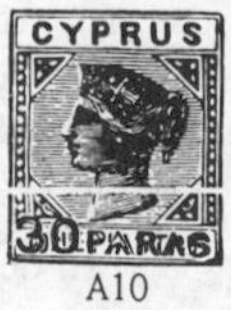

A10

Various Watermarks as in Great Britain (20, 23, 25, 27 & 29)

1880 *Perf. 14*

1	A1	½p rose (Plate 15)	80.00	80.00
		Plate 12	160.00	225.00
		Plate 19	3,500.	950.00
b.		Double overprint (P 15)		*8,000.*
2	A2	1p red (P 201, 215-217)	7.50	*27.50*
		Plate 174	1,000.	1,000.
		Plate 181	250.00	150.00
		Plate 184	10,000.	3,000.
		Plates 193, 196	600.00	
		Plate 205	30.00	30.00
		Plate 208	75.00	40.00
		Plate 218	11.00	*35.00*
		Plate 220	800.00	525.00
b.		Double overprint (P 218)	6,000.	
		Double overprint (P 208)	*9,000.*	
c.		Pair, one without ovpt. (P 208)	*12,000.*	
3	A3	2½p claret (P 14)	2.00	4.00
		Plate 15	4.00	*14.00*
4	A4	4p lt ol grn (P 16)	125.00	*225.00*
5	A5	6p ol gray (P 16)	500.00	650.00
6	A6	1sh green (P 13)	600.00	450.00

Black Surcharge

7	A7	30 paras on 1p red (P 216)	90.00	95.00
		Plate 201	110.00	95.00
		Plate 217	150.00	135.00
		Plate 220	125.00	125.00
b.		Double surch., one invtd. (P 220)	1,250.	1,500.
		Double surch., one invtd. (P 216)	2,750.	

No. 2 Surcharged

HALF-PENNY

18mm Long

1881

8	A2	½p on 1p (201, 216)	60.00	70.00
		Plate 174	110.00	*225.00*
		Plate 181	90.00	125.00
		Plate 205	60.00	75.00
		Plate 208	135.00	*225.00*
		Plate 215	500.00	525.00
		Plate 217	650.00	525.00
		Plate 218	350.00	425.00
		Plate 220	200.00	250.00

HALF-PENNY

16mm Long

9	A2	½p on 1p (P 201)	125.00	150.00
		Plate 216	300.00	350.00
a.		Double surcharge (P 201)	2,500.	

HALF-PENNY

13mm Long

10	A2	½p on 1p red (P 215, 218)	40.00	60.00
		Plate 205	150.00	
		Plate 217	85.00	65.00
c.		Double surcharge (P 215)	600.00	600.00
		Double surcharge (P 205)	675.00	
e.		Triple surcharge (P 215)	675.00	
		Triple surcharge (P 205)	*2,750.*	
		Triple surcharge (P 217)		
		Triple surcharge (P 218)	*2,250.*	
h.		Quadruple surch. (P 205, 215)	*2,750.*	
j.		"CYPRUS" double (P 218)	*5,000.*	

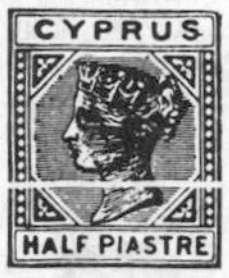

A8

1881, July **Typo.** **Wmk. 1**

11	A8	½pi emerald green	175.00	45.00
12	A8	1pi rose	350.00	32.50
13	A8	2pi ultramarine	450.00	30.00
14	A8	4pi olive green	900.00	275.00
15	A8	6pi olive gray	1,300.	450.00

Postage and revenue stamps of Cyprus with "J.A.B." (the initials of Postmaster J.A. Bulmer) in manuscript, or with "POSTAL SURCHARGE" (with or without "J. A. B."), were not Postage Due stamps but were employed for accounting purposes between the chief PO at Larnaca and the sub-offices.

See Nos. 19-25, 28-37. For surcharges see Nos. 16-18, 26-27.

Black Surcharge

1882 **Wmk. 1**

16	A9	½pi on ½pi grn	475.00	75.00
17	A10	30pa on 1pi rose	1,500.	110.00

1884 **Wmk. 2**

18	A9	½pi on ½pi green	120.00	12.00
a.		Double surcharge		2,750.

See Nos. 26, 27.

1882-94 **Die B**

For explanation of Dies A and B, see back of this section of the Catalogue.

19	A8	½pi green	2.50	.60
20	A8	30pa violet	2.00	2.50
21	A8	1pi rose	7.25	1.75
22	A8	2pi blue	10.00	1.25
23	A8	4pi olive green	24.00	15.00
24a	A8	6pi	140.00	450.00
25a	A8	12pi	125.00	*250.00*
		Nos. 19-25a (7)	310.75	721.10

Die A

19a	A8	½pi	7.00	.50
b.		½pi emerald	*4,000.*	350.00
20a	A8	30pa lilac	55.00	17.50
21a	A8	1pi	60.00	3.50
22a	A8	2pi	90.00	1.65
23a	A8	4pi	165.00	22.50
24	A8	6pi olive gray	35.00	10.00
25	A8	12pi brown org	165.00	25.00
		Nos. 19a-25 (7)	577.00	70.65

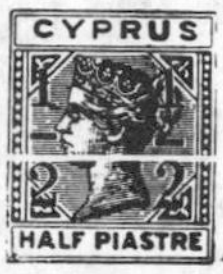

A11

Type I - Figures "½" 8mm apart.
Type II - Figures "½" 6mm apart.
The space between the fraction bars varies from 5½ to 8½mm but is usually 6 or 8mm.

Black Surcharge Type I

1886 **Wmk. 2**

26	A11	½pi on ½pi grn	225.00	15.00
a.		Type II	225.00	65.00
b.		Double surcharge, type II		

Wmk. 1

27	A11	½pi on ½pi grn	*6,500.*	425.00
a.		Type II	*10,000.*	

No. 27a probably is a proof.

1894-96 **Wmk. 2**

28	A8	½pi grn & car rose	3.00	.40
29	A8	30pa violet & green	2.50	.50
30	A8	1pi rose & ultra	3.25	.40
31	A8	2pi ultra & mar	3.75	.75
32	A8	4pi ol green & vio	9.00	4.00
33	A8	6pi ol gray & grn	7.50	8.00
34	A8	9pi brown & rose	15.00	10.00
35	A8	12pi brn org & blk	15.00	*40.00*
36	A8	18pi slate & brown	45.00	40.00
37	A8	45pi dk vio & ultra	100.00	125.00
		Nos. 28-37 (10)	204.00	229.05

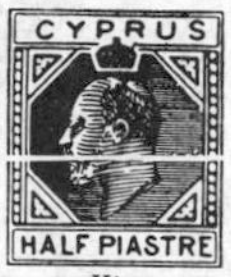

King Edward VII — A12

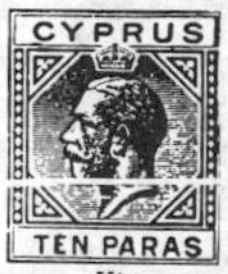

King George V — A13

1903 **Typo.**

38	A12	½pi grn & car rose	.95	.30
39	A12	30pa violet & green	.45	.45
40	A12	1pi carmine rose & ultra	5.50	.55
41	A12	2pi ultra & mar	11.00	1.75
42	A12	4pi ol green & vio	14.00	6.50
43	A12	6pi ol brown & grn	27.50	32.50
44	A12	9pi brn & car rose	55.00	75.00
45	A12	12pi org brn & blk	5.00	8.50
46	A12	18pi black & brown	55.00	60.00
47	A12	45pi dk vio & ultra	190.00	*275.00*
		Nos. 38-47 (10)	364.40	460.55

1904-07 **Wmk. 3**

48	A12	5pa bis & blk ('07)	.30	.20
49	A12	10pa org & grn ('07)	.35	.20
50	A12	½pi grn & car rose	4.25	.20
51	A12	30pa violet & green	1.75	.80
52	A12	1pi car rose & ultra	1.10	.35
53	A12	2pi ultra & maroon	5.50	.35
54	A12	4pi ol grn & red vio	7.75	3.25
55	A12	6pi ol brn & green	12.00	5.75
56	A12	9pi brn & car rose	3.25	3.25
57	A12	12pi org brn & blk	18.00	14.00
58	A12	18pi black & brown	26.00	11.00
59	A12	45pi dk vio & ultra	57.50	57.50
		Nos. 48-59 (12)	137.75	96.85

1912

61	A13	10pa orange & green	1.65	.20
62	A13	½pi grn & car rose	1.10	.20
63	A13	30pa violet & green	1.10	.20
64	A13	1pi car & ultra	2.75	.55
65	A13	2pi ultra & maroon	4.00	.55
66	A13	4pi ol grn & red vio	2.00	1.10
67	A13	6pi ol brn & green	2.00	2.00
68	A13	9pi brn & car rose	14.00	15.00
69	A13	12pi org brn & blk	6.75	14.00
70	A13	18pi black & brown	16.00	10.00
71	A13	45pi dl vio & ultra	47.50	55.00
		Nos. 61-71 (11)	98.85	98.80

1921-23 **Wmk. 4**

72	A13	10pa orange & grn	.60	.30
73	A13	10pa gray & yellow	3.50	9.00
74	A13	30pa violet & grn	2.25	.30
75	A13	30pa green	1.50	.30
76	A13	1pi rose & ultra	6.25	8.50
77	A13	1pi violet & car	4.00	2.00
78	A13	1½pi orange & blk	4.00	4.00
79	A13	2pi ultra & red vio	5.50	5.00
80	A13	2pi rose & ultra	5.50	7.50
81	A13	2¾pi ultra & red vio	7.25	*9.75*
82	A13	4pi ol grn & red vio	3.50	2.25
83	A13	6pi ol brn & green	8.50	13.00
84	A13	9pi brn & carmine	14.00	*14.00*
85	A13	18pi black & brn	52.50	67.50
86	A13	45pi dl vio & ultra	140.00	150.00
		Nos. 72-86 (15)	258.85	293.40

Wmk. 3

87	A13	10sh grn & red, *yel*	325.	*675.*
88	A13	£1 vio & black, *red*	1,050.	*1,500.*

Years of issue: Nos. 73, 75, 77-78, 80-81, 87-88, 1923. Others, 1921.

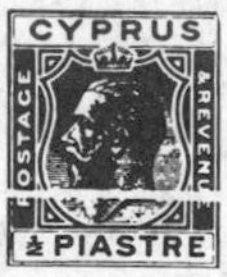

A14

1924-28 **Chalky Paper** **Wmk. 4**

89	A14	¼pi gray & brn org	.25	.15
90	A14	½pi gray blk & blk	1.00	*3.50*
91	A14	½pi grn & dp grn ('25)	1.00	.15
92	A14	¾pi grn & dp grn	1.00	.15
93	A14	¾pi gray blk & blk ('25)	1.10	.15
94	A14	1pi brn vio & org brown	.50	.15
95	A14	1½pi org & black	1.00	.55
96	A14	1½pi carmine ('25)	1.50	.30
97	A14	2pi car & green	1.50	*4.00*
98	A14	2pi org & black ('25)	2.75	2.50
99	A14	2½pi ultra ('25)	2.25	.20
100	A14	2¾pi ultra & dull vio	1.25	1.00
101	A14	4pi ap grn & vio	1.25	1.25
102	A14	4½pi black & yel, *emer*	2.00	2.50
103	A14	6pi grn ol & grn	2.25	2.75
104	A14	9pi brn & dk vio	2.25	2.50
105	A14	12pi org brn & blk	6.25	*27.50*
106	A14	18pi blk & org	12.50	6.75
		Revenue cancel		.15
107	A14	45pi gray vio & ultra	22.50	25.00
		Revenue cancel		.40
108	A14	90pi grn & red, *yel*	55.00	*85.00*
		Revenue cancel		1.00
109	A14	£5 blk, *yel* ('28)	3,250.	*5,500.*
		Revenue cancel		125.00

Wmk. 3

110	A14	£1 vio & black, *red*	300.00	350.00
		Revenue cancel		2.75
		Nos. 89-108 (20)	119.10	*166.05*

Nos. 96 and 99 are on ordinary paper.

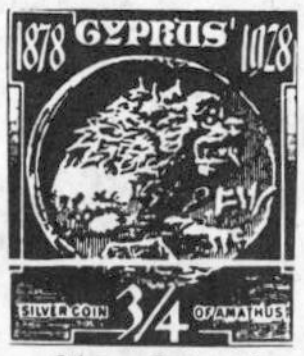

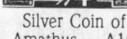

Silver Coin of Amathus — A15

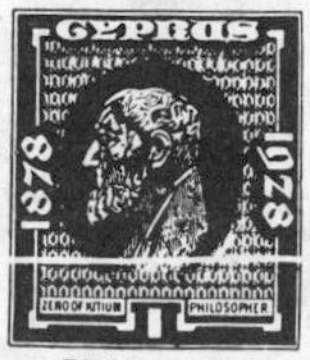

Philosopher Zeno — A16

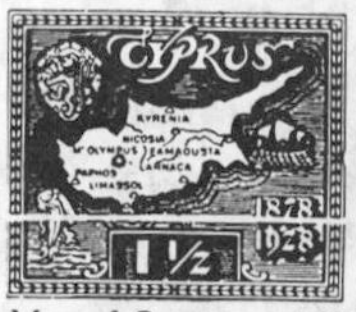

Map of Cyprus — A17

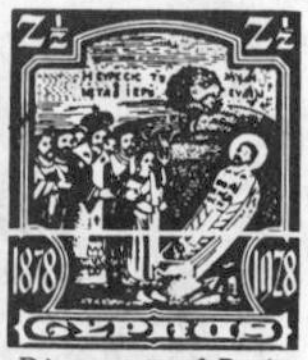

Discovery of Body of St. Barnabas — A18

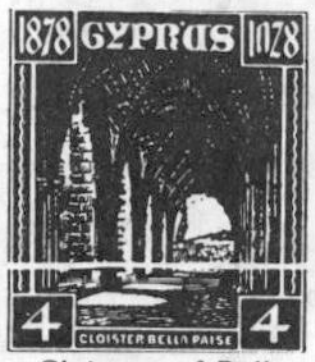

Cloisters of Bella Paise Monastery — A19

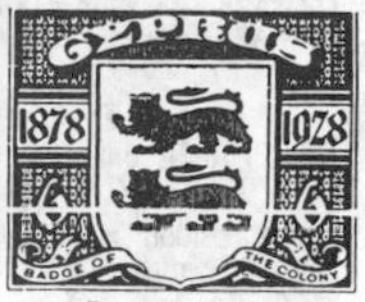

Badge of the Colony — A20

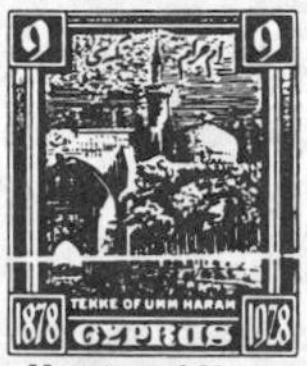

Hospice of Umm Haram at Larnaca — A21

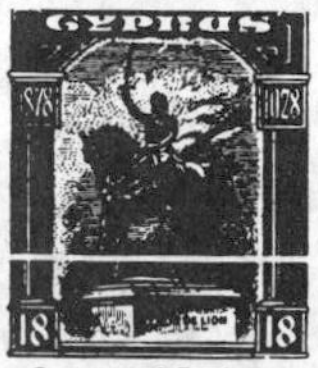

Statue of Richard Coeur de Lion, London — A22

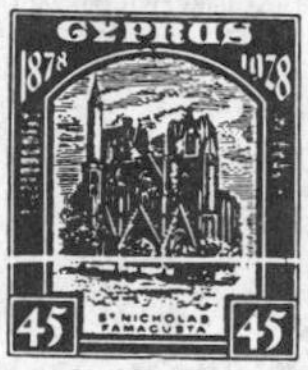

St. Nicholas Cathedral, Famagusta — A23

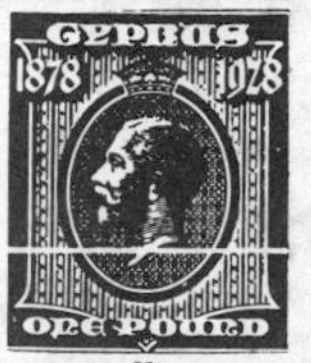

King George V — A24

1928, Feb. 1 **Engr.** **Wmk. 4** *Perf. 12*

114	A15	¾pi dark violet	1.00	.35
115	A16	1pi Prus bl & blk	1.25	.95
116	A17	1½pi red	3.50	2.25
117	A18	2½pi ultramarine	1.00	*2.00*
118	A19	4pi dp red brown	4.25	*7.50*
119	A20	6pi dark blue	4.25	*10.00*
120	A21	9pi violet brown	5.00	*9.00*
121	A22	18pi dk brn & blk	12.50	*18.00*
122	A23	45pi dp blue & vio	25.00	*35.00*
123	A24	£1 ol brn & deep blue	200.00	*275.00*
		Nos. 114-123 (10)	257.75	*360.05*

50th year of Cyprus as a British colony.

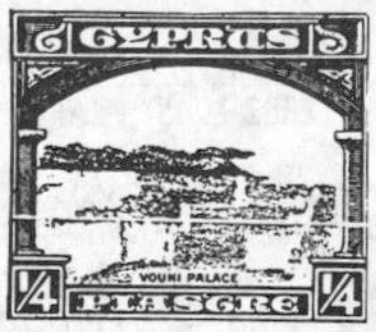

Ruins of Vouni Palace — A25

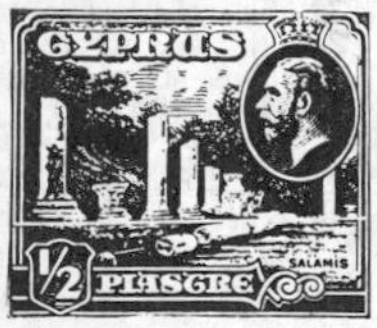

Columns at Salamis — A26

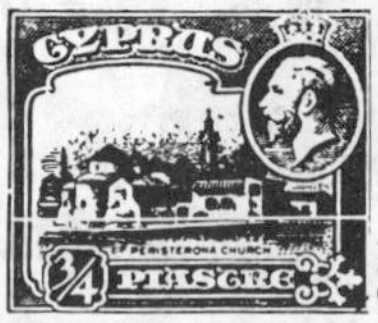

Peristerona Church — A27

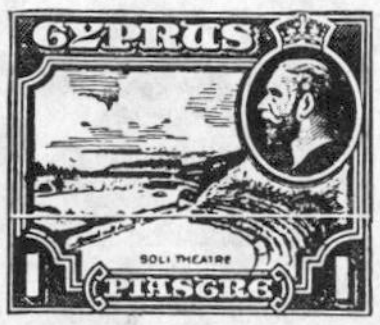
Soli Theater — A28

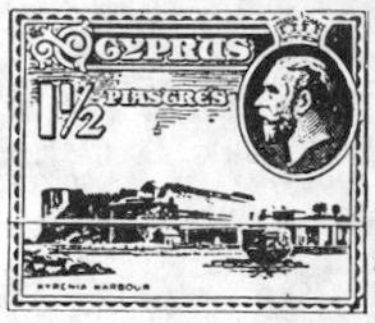
Kyrenia Castle and Harbor — A29

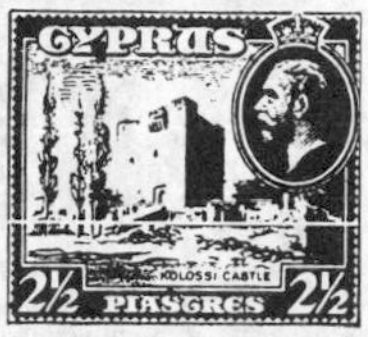
Kolossi Castle — A30

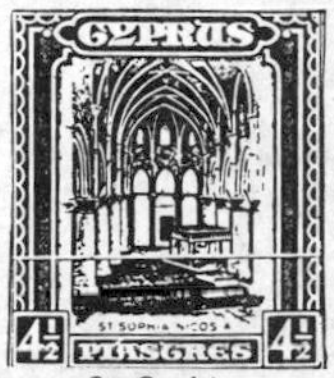
St. Sophia Cathedral — A31

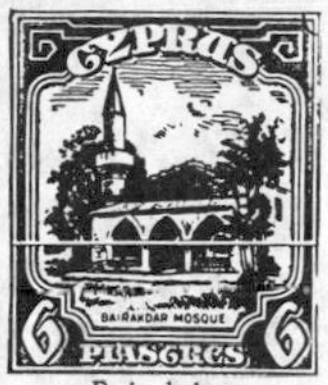
Bairakdar Mosque — A32

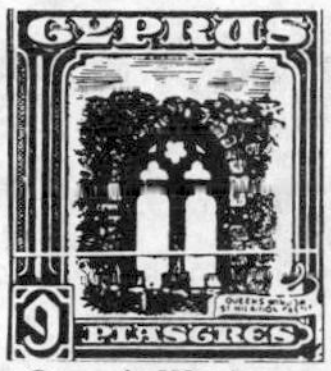
Queen's Window, St. Hilarion Castle — A33

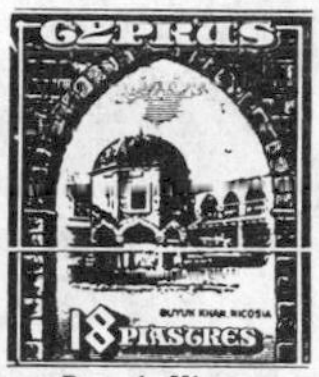
Buyuk Khan, Nicosia — A34

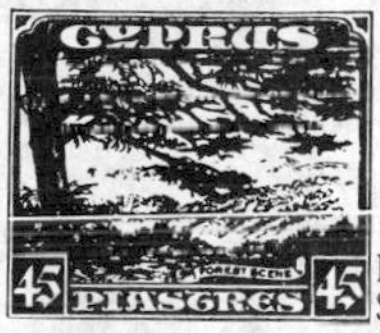
Forest Scene — A35

1934, Dec. 1 Engr. *Perf. 12½*

125	A25	¼pi	yel brn & ultra	.20	.20
a.			Vert. pair, imperf. between	9,000.	
126	A26	½pi	green	.20	.20
a.			Vert. pair, imperf. between	12,500.	8,000.
127	A27	¾pi	violet & blk	.20	.20
128	A28	1pi	brown & blk	.25	.20
a.			Vert. pair, imperf. between	7,500.	8,000.
b.			Horiz. pair, imperf. btwn.	10,000.	
129	A29	1½pi	rose red	.25	.25
130	A30	2½pi	dark ultra	.40	.40
131	A31	4½pi	dk car & blk	5.00	.85
132	A32	6pi	blue & black	4.50	5.50
133	A33	9pi	dl vio & blk brown	4.50	5.50
134	A34	18pi	ol grn & black	26.00	27.50
135	A35	45pi	blk & emer	47.50	52.50
			Nos. 125-135 (11)	89.00	93.30

Silver Jubilee Issue
Common Design Type

1935, May 6 *Perf. 11x12*

136	CD301	¾pi	gray blk & ultra	.55	.25
137	CD301	1½pi	car & dk bl	3.25	3.00
138	CD301	2½pi	ultra & brn	2.75	4.25
139	CD301	9pi	brn vio & ind	11.00	19.00
			Nos. 136-139 (4)	17.55	26.50
			Set, never hinged	35.00	

Coronation Issue
Common Design Type

1937, May 12 *Perf. 11x11½*

140	CD302	¾pi	dark gray	.35	.15
141	CD302	1½pi	dark carmine	.50	.60
142	CD302	2½pi	deep ultra	.85	1.25
			Nos. 140-142 (3)	1.70	2.00
			Set, never hinged	3.25	

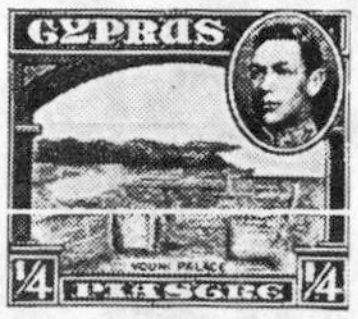
Ruins of Vouni Palace — A36

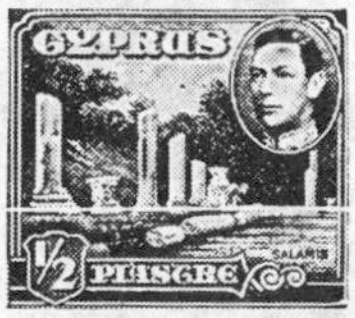
Columns at Salamis — A37

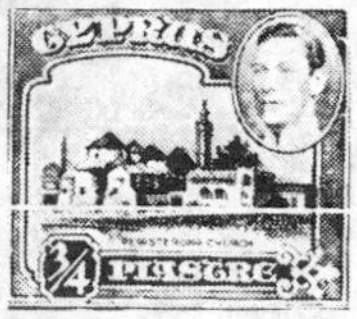
Peristerona Church — A38

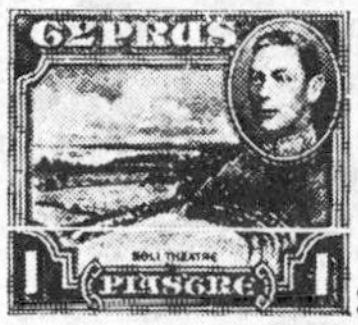
Soli Theater — A39

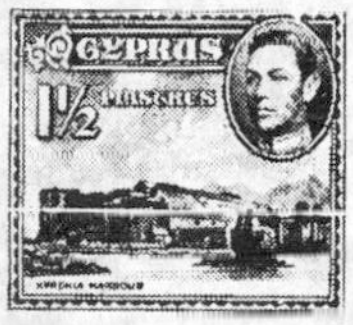
Kyrenia Castle and Harbor — A40

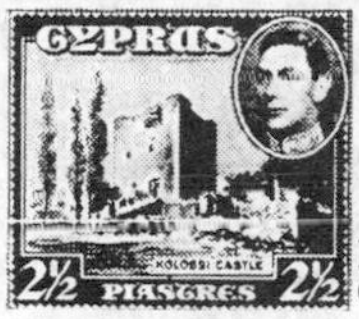
Kolossi Castle — A41

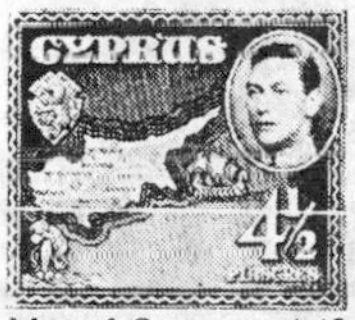
Map of Cyprus — A42

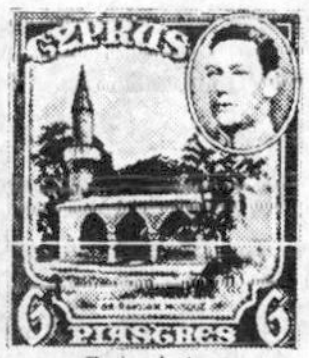
Bairakdar Mosque — A43

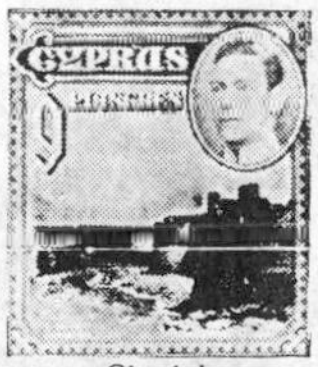
Citadel, Famagusta — A44

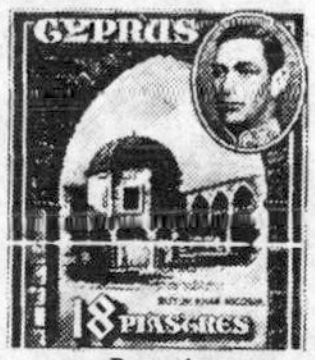
Buyuk Khan — A45

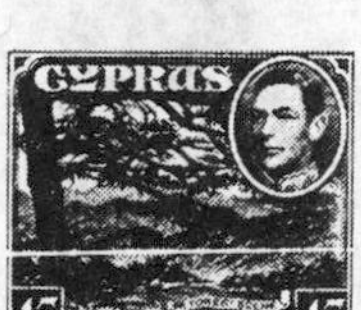
Forest Scene A46

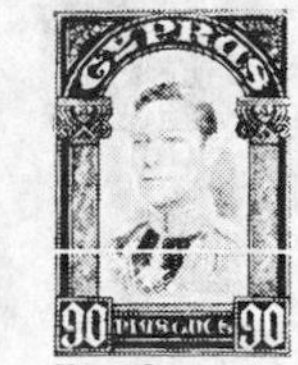
King George VI A47

1938-44 Wmk. 4 *Perf. 12½*

143	A36	¼pi	yel brn & ultra	.15	.15
144	A37	½pi	green	.15	.15
145	A38	¾pi	violet & blk	3.50	.15
146	A39	1pi	orange	.18	.15
a.			Perf. 13½x12½ ('44)	200.00	22.50
147	A40	1½pi	rose carmine	.45	.35
147A	A40	1½pi	lt vio ('43)	.18	.15
147B	A38	2pi	carmine & blk ('42)	.18	.15
c.			Perf. 12½x13½ ('44)	1.40	3.00
148	A41	2½pi	ultramarine	4.00	3.50
148A	A41	3pi	dp ultra ('42)	.28	.15
149	A42	4½pi	gray	.28	.15
150	A43	6pi	blue & black	.48	.25
151	A44	9pi	dk vio & blk	.40	.22
152	A45	18pi	ol grn & blk	1.40	.65
153	A46	45pi	blk & emer	3.50	1.50
154	A47	90pi	blk & brt vio	16.00	13.00
155	A47	£1	ind & dl red	30.00	18.00
			Nos. 143-155 (16)	61.13	38.67
			Set, never hinged	120.00	

See Nos. 164-166.

Catalogue values for unused stamps in this section, from this point to the end of the section, are for Never Hinged items.

Peace Issue
Common Design Type

1946, Oct. 21 Engr. *Perf. 13½x14*

156	CD303	1½pi	purple	.15	.15
157	CD303	3pi	deep blue	.15	.15
			Set value	.25	.25

Silver Wedding Issue
Common Design Types

1948, Dec. 20 Photo. *Perf. 14x14½*

158	CD304	1½pi	purple	.15	.15

Engr.; Name Typo.
Perf. 11½x11

159	CD305	£1	dark blue	45.00	45.00

UPU Issue
Common Design Types
Perf. 13½, 11x11½

1949, Oct. 10 Engr. Wmk. 4

160	CD306	1½pi	violet	.40	.40
161	CD307	2pi	deep carmine	.65	.65
162	CD308	3pi	indigo	1.25	1.25
163	CD309	9pi	rose violet	3.00	2.75
			Nos. 160-163 (4)	5.30	5.05

Types of 1938-43

1951, July 2 Engr. *Perf. 12½*

164	A37	½pi	purple	.20	.15
165	A40	1½pi	deep green	.30	.15
166	A41	4pi	deep ultra	.50	.15
			Nos. 164-166 (3)	1.00	
			Set value		.26

Coronation Issue
Common Design Type

1953, June 2 *Perf. 13½x13*

167	CD312	1½pi	brt grn & black	.50	.35

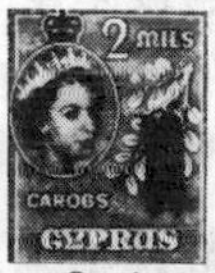
Carobs A48

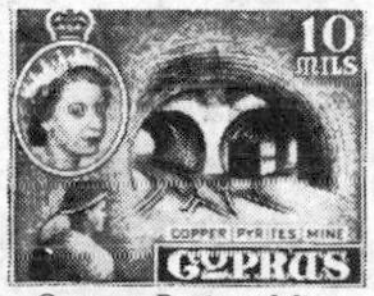
Copper Pyrites Mine A49

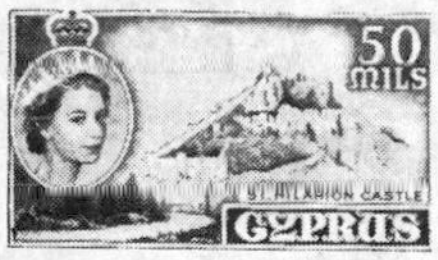
St. Hilarion Castle — A50

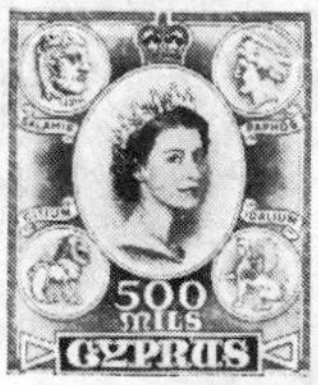
Queen Elizabeth II and Cyprian Coin Devices — A51

Designs: 3m, Grapes. 5m, Oranges. 15m, Troodos forest. 20m, Aphrodite beach. 25m, Coin of Paphos. 30m, Kyrenia. 35m, Harvest in Mesaoria. 40m, Famagusta harbor. 100m, Hala Sultan Tekke. 250m, Kanakaria church. £1, Queen Elizabeth II and devices of Byzantium, Lusignan, Ottoman Empire and Venice.

Perf. 11½

1955, Aug. 1 Engr. Wmk. 4

168	A48	2m	chocolate	.15	.15
169	A48	3m	violet blue	.15	.15
170	A48	5m	orange	.15	.15
171	A49	10m	gray grn & chocolate	.15	.15
172	A49	15m	indigo & olive	.25	.15
173	A49	20m	ultra & brown	.25	.15
174	A49	25m	aquamarine	.40	.24
175	A49	30m	carmine & blk	.25	.15
176	A49	35m	aqua & orange	.35	.28
177	A49	40m	choc & dk grn	.55	.35

Perf. 13½

178	A50	50m	red brn & aqua	1.00	.30
179	A50	100m	bl green & mag	2.75	.65
180	A50	250m	vio brn & dk blue gray	6.50	4.00

Perf. 11x11½

181	A51	500m	lilac rose & grnsh gray	20.00	10.00
182	A51	£1	grnsh gray & brn red	32.50	22.50
			Revenue cancel		1.00
			Nos. 168-182 (15)	65.40	39.37

Republic

Nos. 168-182 Overprinted in Dark Blue

ΚΥΠΡΙΑΚΗ
ΔΗΜΟΚΡΑΤΙΑ
KIBRIS
CUMHURIYETİ

1960, Aug. 16 Ovpt. 10x6½mm

183	A48	2m	chocolate	.15	.15
184	A48	3m	violet blue	.15	.15
185	A48	5m	orange	.18	.15

Overprint 12½x11mm

186	A49	10m	gray grn & choc	.25	.15
187	A49	15m	indigo & ol	.40	.20
188	A49	20m	ultra & brn	.40	.20
a.			Double overprint		6,000.
189	A49	25m	aquamarine	.60	.35
190	A49	30m	car & black	.75	.30
a.			Double overprint		6,000.
191	A49	35m	aqua & org	.85	.45
192	A49	40m	choc & dk green	1.10	.65

2-line overprint 2½mm apart

193	A50	50m	red brown & aqua	1.25	.75
194	A50	100m	bl grn & mag	3.00	2.00
195	A50	250m	vio brn & dk blue gray	10.50	6.00

2-line overprint 22mm apart

196	A51	500m	lil rose & grnsh gray	37.50	18.00
197	A51	£1	grnsh gray & brn red	92.50	45.00
			Nos. 183-197 (15)	149.58	74.50

The overprint, in Greek and Turkish, reads "Republic of Cyprus."

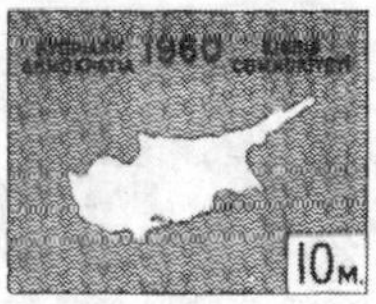
Map of Cyprus — A52

Perf. 11½

1960, Aug. 16 Wmk. 314 Engr.

198	A52	10m	brown & green	.35	.32
199	A52	30m	blue & brown	1.50	.95
200	A52	100m	purple & black	3.50	3.25
			Nos. 198-200 (3)	5.35	4.52

Independence of Republic of Cyprus.

Europa Issue, 1961

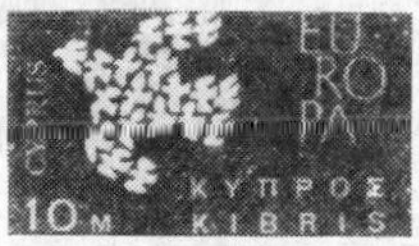
Nineteen Doves Flying as One — CD4

Perf. 14x13½

1962, Mar. 19 Litho. Unwmk.

201	CD4	10m	lilac	.15	.15
202	CD4	40m	deep ultra	.38	.32
203	CD4	100m	emerald	.75	.75
			Nos. 201-203 (3)	1.28	1.22

Admission of Cyprus to Council of Europe.

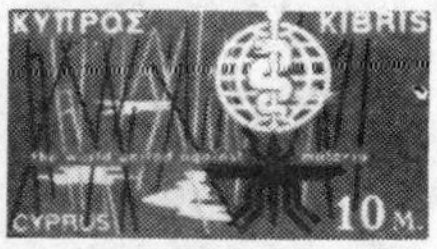
Malaria Eradication Emblem A54

1962, May 14 *Perf. 14x13½*

204	A54	10m	gray green & blue	.25	.18
205	A54	30m	red brown & black	.95	.80

WHO drive to eradicate malaria.

Iron Age Jug — A55

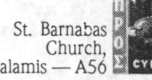

St. Barnabas Church, Salamis — A56

Designs: 5m, Grapes. 10m, Head of Apollo. 15m, St. Sophia Church, Nicosia. 30m, Temple of Apollo. 35m, Head of Aphrodite. 40m, Skiing on Mt. Troodos. 50m, Ruins of Gymnasium, Salamis. 100m, Hala Sultan Tekke (sheep, Salt Lake Larnaca and tomb). 250m, Bella Paise Monastery. 500m, Cyprus mouflon. £1, St. Hilarion Castle.

Perf. 13¹/₂x14, 14x13¹/₂

1962, Sept. 17   **Wmk. 344**

206	A55	3m dk brn & sal	.15	.15
207	A55	5m dull green & red lilac	.15	.15
208	A55	10m dk slate grn & yel green	.15	.15
209	A55	15m dk brn & rose vio	.20	.15
210	A56	25m salmon & brn	.35	.20
211	A55	30m lt bl & dk bl	.52	.25
212	A55	35m dk bl & pale grn	.75	.42
213	A55	40m vio bl & dk bl	.95	.55
214	A55	50m olive bis & dk grn	1.40	.50
215	A55	100m brn & yel brn	2.75	1.25
216	A55	250m tan & black	10.00	4.00
217	A55	500m brown & olive	27.50	13.00
218	A56	£1 gray & green	35.00	27.50
		Nos. 206-218 (13)	79.87	48.27

Wmk. 344 is found in two positions: normal or inverted on vertical stamps, and reading up or down on horizontal stamps.

For overprints see Nos. 232-236, 265-268. For surcharge see No. 273.

Europa Issue, 1962
Common Design Type
Perf. 14x13¹/₂

1963, Jan. 28   **Wmk. 344**
Size: 36x20mm

219	CD5	10m ultra & black	.45	.30
220	CD5	40m red & black	3.25	2.25
221	CD5	150m green & black	13.00	6.00
		Nos. 219-221 (3)	16.70	8.55

Cypriot Farm Girl — A57

Cub Scout and Tents — A58

Design: 75m, Statue of Demeter, goddess of agriculture.

1963, Mar. 21   *Perf. 13¹/₂x14*

222	A57	25m blk, ultra & ocher	.85	.85
223	A57	75m dk car, gray & blk	3.50	3.50

FAO "Freedom from Hunger" campaign.

1963, Aug. 21   **Wmk. 344**

Designs: 20m, Sea Scout. 150m, Boy Scout and mouflon.

224	A58	3m multicolored	.15	.15
225	A58	20m multicolored	.75	.50
226	A58	150m multicolored	3.75	3.75
a.		Souvenir sheet of 3	125.00	95.00
		Nos. 224-226 (3)	4.65	4.40

50th anniv. of the Boy Scout movement in Cyprus. #226a contains 3 imperf. stamps similar to #224-226 with simulated perforations. Sold for 250m.

Red Cross Nurse — A59

Children's Home, Kyrenia A60

Perf. 13¹/₂x14, 14x13¹/₂

1963, Sept. 9 **Litho.** **Wmk. 344**

227	A59	10m multicolored	.28	.16
228	A60	100m multicolored	3.25	1.75

Intl. Red Cross, cent.

Europa Issue, 1963

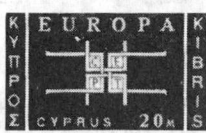

Stylized Links, Symbolizing Unity — CD6

1963, Nov. 4   *Perf. 14x13¹/₂*

229	CD6	20m multicolored	.80	.65
230	CD6	30m multicolored	.95	.70
231	CD6	100m multicolored	11.00	6.25
		Nos. 229-231 (3)	12.75	7.60

Nos. 208, 211, 213-215 Overprinted in Ultramarine

1964

1964, May 5 *Perf. 13¹/₂x14, 14x13¹/₂*

232	A55	10m dk sl grn & yel grn	.15	.15
233	A55	30m lt blue & dk blue	.35	.26
234	A55	40m vio bl & dull bl	.55	.45
235	A55	50m ol bis & dk grn	.75	.55
236	A55	100m brn & yel brown	1.75	1.65
		Nos. 232-236 (5)	3.55	3.06

Decision by the UN and its Security Council to help restore the country to normality and to seek a solution of its problems.

Clay Mask and Soli Theater A62

Designs: 35m, Curium theater. 50m, Salamis theater. 100m, Performance of "Othello" in front of Othello Tower.

1964, June 15   *Perf. 13¹/₂x14*

237	A62	15m multicolored	.16	.15
238	A62	35m multicolored	.42	.32
239	A62	50m multicolored	.60	.45
240	A62	100m multicolored	1.50	1.10
		Nos. 237-240 (4)	2.68	2.02

400th anniversary of Shakespeare's birth.

Boxers — A63

14th century B.C. art: 10m, Runners, vert. 75m, Chariot.

1964, July 6 *Perf. 13¹/₂x14, 14x13¹/₂*

241	A63	10m brn, bis & blk	.15	.15
242	A63	25m gray bl, bl & brn	.40	.32
243	A63	75m brick red, blk & brn	1.25	1.00
a.		Souvenir sheet of 3	8.00	5.75
		Nos. 241-243 (3)	1.80	1.47

18th Olympic Games, Tokyo, Oct. 10-25, 1964. No. 243a contains three imperf. stamps similar to Nos. 241-243 with gray marginal inscription. Sheet sold for 250m; the difference between face value and selling price went for the promotion of classical athletics in Cyprus.

Symbolic Daisy — CD7

Satyr Drinking Wine, 5th Century B.C. Statuette — A65

Modern Winery A66

Europa Issue, 1964
Perf. 13¹/₂x14

1964, Sept. 14 **Litho.** **Wmk. 344**

244	CD7	20m bis brn & red brn	.50	.45
245	CD7	30m lt blue & dk blue	.70	.65
246	CD7	150m green & ol green	8.75	5.50
		Nos. 244-246 (3)	9.95	6.60

CEPT, 5th anniv. The 22 petals of the flower symbolize the 22 members of the organization.

Perf. 14x13¹/₂, 13¹/₂x14

1964, Oct. 26   **Wmk. 344**

Cypriot Wine Industry: 10m, Dionysus and Acme drinking wine, 3rd century mosaic. 50m, Commandaria wine, Knight Templar and Kolossi Castle.

247	A66	10m multicolored	.15	.15
248	A65	40m multicolored	.75	.45
249	A65	50m multicolored	1.25	.65
250	A66	100m multicolored	4.00	2.00
		Nos. 247-250 (4)	6.15	3.25

Pres. John F. Kennedy (1917-1963) — A67

Perf. 14x13¹/₂

1965, Feb. 15 **Litho.** **Wmk. 344**

251	A67	10m violet blue	.15	.15
252	A67	40m green	.55	.38
253	A67	100m rose claret	1.65	1.00
a.		Souvenir sheet of 3	4.00	3.00
		Nos. 251-253 (3)	2.35	1.53

No. 253a contains 3 imperf. stamps similar to Nos. 251-253 with simulated perforations. Sold for 250m, 100m going to charitable organizations in Cyprus.

Old Couple — A68

Mother and Children by A. Diamantis — A69

Design: 45m, Man with broken leg (accident insurance).

1965, Apr. 12   *Perf. 13¹/₂x14*

254	A68	30m dull green & tan	.50	.25
255	A68	45m dk vio bl, bl & gray	1.00	.75

Perf. 13¹/₂x12¹/₂

256	A69	75m buff & red brown	3.00	1.50
		Nos. 254-256 (3)	4.50	2.50

Introduction of Social Insurance Law.

ITU Emblem, Old and New Communication Equipment — A70

1965, May 17 **Litho.** *Perf. 14x13¹/₂*

257	A70	15m brn, yel & black	.50	.20
258	A70	60m grn, lt grn & black	3.25	1.40
259	A70	75m dk & lt bl & black	4.75	1.90
		Nos. 257-259 (3)	8.50	3.50

ITU, cent.

ICY Emblem A71

1965, May 17   **Wmk. 344**

260	A71	50m multicolored	1.50	.75
261	A71	100m multicolored	2.50	1.50

International Cooperation Year.

Europa Issue, 1965

Leaves and Fruit — CD8

Perf. 14x13¹/₂

1965, Sept. 27 **Litho.** **Wmk. 344**

262	CD8	5m org, org brn & black	.18	.16
263	CD8	45m lt grn, org brn & black	2.00	1.40
264	CD8	150m gray, org brn & black	5.50	4.50
		Nos. 262-264 (3)	7.68	6.06

Nos. 206, 208, 211 and 216 Overprinted in Dark Blue

**U. N.
Resolution
on Cyprus
18 Dec. 1965**

Perf. 13¹/₂x14, 14x13¹/₂

1966, Jan. 31

265	A55	3m dk brn & salmon	.15	.15
266	A55	10m dk sl grn & yel green	.18	.15
267	A56	30m lt bl & dk blue	.40	.35
268	A56	250m tan & black	3.00	2.75
		Nos. 265-268 (4)	3.73	3.40

UN General Assembly's resolution to mediate the dispute between Greeks and Turks on Cyprus, Dec. 18, 1965.

St. Barnabas, Ancient Icon — A73

Chapel over Tomb of St. Barnabas A74

Bishop Anthemios of Constantine Dreaming of St. Barnabas, Discovering Tomb, etc. — A75

Design: 15m, Discovery of body of St. Barnabas (scene as in type A18).

Perf. 13x14, 14x13

1966, Apr. 25	**Litho.**	**Wmk. 344**	
269 A73	15m multicolored	.15	.15
270 A74	25m multicolored	.30	.28
271 A73	100m multicolored	1.50	1.25

Size: 110x91mm

Imperf

272 A75	250m multicolored	7.25	6.00
	Nos. 269-272 (4)	9.20	7.68

1900th anniv. of the death of St. Barnabas.

No. 206 Surcharged with New Value and Three Bars

Perf. 13¹/₂x14

1966, May 30		**Wmk. 344**	
273 A55	5m on 3m dk brn & salmon	.15	.15

Gen. K. S. Thimayya A76

1966, June 6		**Perf. 14x13¹/₂**	
274 A76	50m tan & black	.50	.40

In memory of Gen. Kodendera Subayya Thimayya (1906-1965), commander of the UN Peace-keeping Force on Cyprus.

Europa Issue, 1966

EUROPA

Symbolic Sailboat — CD9

Perf. 13¹/₂x14

1966, Sept. 26	**Litho.**	**Wmk. 344**	
275 CD9	20m multicolored	.18	.15
276 CD9	30m multicolored	.32	.28
277 CD9	150m multicolored	2.75	2.75
	Nos. 275-277 (3)	3.25	3.18

Stavrovouni Monastery A78

St. Nicholas Cathedral, Famagusta A79

Ingot Bearer, Bronze Age — A80

Designs: 5m, St. James' Church, Tricomo, vert. 10m, Zeno of Citium, marble bust, vert. 15m, Ship from 7th cent. BC vase, horiz. 20m, Silver coin, 4th cent. BC (head of Hercules with lion skin). 25m, Sleeping Eros (1st cent. marble statue; horiz.). 35m, Hawks on 11th cent. gold and enamel scepter from Curium. 40m, Marriage of David (7th cent. silver disc). 50m, Silver coin of Alexander the Great showing Hercules and Zeus, horiz. 100m, Bird catching fish on 7th cent. BC jug. 500m, The Rape of Ganymede (3rd cent. mosaic). £1, Aphrodite (1st cent. marble statue).

Perf. 12x12¹/₂, 12¹/₂x12

1966, Nov. 21	**Litho.**	**Wmk. 344**	
278 A78	3m bl, dl yel, grn & black	.15	.15
279 A78	5m dk bl, ol & blk	.15	.15
280 A78	10m olive & black	.15	.15

Perf. 14x13¹/₂, 13¹/₂x14

281 A79	15m org brn, blk & red brn	.15	.15
282 A79	20m red brn & blk	.15	.15
283 A79	25m red brn, gray & black	.15	.15
284 A79	30m aqua, tan & blk	.20	.15
285 A79	35m dk car, yel & blk	.28	.20
286 A79	40m brt bl, gray & blk	.35	.15
287 A79	50m org brn, gray & blk	.55	.22
288 A79	100m gray, buff, blk & red	1.40	.60

Perf. 13x14

289 A80	250m dull yel, grn & blk	3.50	1.75
290 A80	500m multicolored	9.00	4.75
291 A80	£1 gray, lt gray & black	21.00	12.00
	Nos. 278-291 (14)	37.18	20.72

Electric Power Station, Limassol — A81

Arghaka-Maghounda Dam — A82

Designs: 35m, Troodos Highway. 50m, Cyprus Hilton Hotel. 100m, Ships in Famagusta Harbor.

Perf. 14x13¹/₂, 13¹/₂x14

1967, Apr. 10	**Litho.**	**Wmk. 344**	
292 A81	10m lt brn, dark brn & yellow	.15	.15
293 A82	15m lt blue, blue & green	.15	.15
294 A82	35m dark gray, indigo & dark grn	.30	.24
295 A82	50m gray, olive & blue	.50	.32
296 A82	100m gray, indigo & blue	1.40	1.00
	Nos. 292-296 (5)	2.50	1.86

1st development program, 1962-66, completion.

Europa Issue, 1967
Common Design Type

1967, May 2		**Perf. 13x14**

Size: 21x37mm

297 CD10	20m yel grn & olive	.28	.22
298 CD10	30m rose vio & pur	.40	.32
299 CD10	150m pale brn & brn	2.00	1.65
	Nos. 297-299 (3)	2.68	2.19

Javelin Thrower, Map of Eastern Mediterranean and "Victory" — A83

Map of Eastern Mediterranean, Victory Statue and: 35m, Runner. 100m, High jumper. 250m, Amphora, map of Eastern Mediterranean and Victory statue.

Perf. 13¹/₂x13

1967, Sept. 4	**Litho.**	**Wmk. 344**	
300 A83	15m multicolored	.15	.15
301 A83	35m multicolored	.30	.26
302 A83	100m multicolored	.70	.60

Size: 97x77mm

Imperf

303 A83	250m multicolored	2.50	2.25
	Nos. 300-303 (4)	3.65	3.26

Cyprus-Crete-Salonika Athletic Games.

Marble Forum at Salamis, Church of St. Barnabas and Bellapais Abbey A84

ITY Emblem and: 40m, Famagusta Beach. 50m, Plane and Nicosia International Airport. 100m, Youth Hostel and skiing on Mt. Troodos.

Perf. 13¹/₂x13

1967, Oct. 16	**Litho.**	**Wmk. 344**	
304 A84	10m multicolored	.15	.15
305 A84	40m multicolored	.30	.22
306 A84	50m multicolored	.48	.32
307 A84	100m multicolored	1.00	.90
	Nos. 304-307 (4)	1.93	1.59

Intl. Tourist Year, 1967.

St. Andrew, 6th Century Mosaic — A85

Crucifixion, 15th Century — A86

The Three Kings, 15th Century Fresco — A87

1967, Nov. 8		**Perf. 13x13¹/₂**	
308 A85	25m multicolored	.18	.18
309 A86	28m multicolored	.28	.28
310 A87	75m multicolored	.50	.50
	Nos. 308-310 (3)	.96	.96

St. Andrew's Monastery, cent. (25m); Exhibition of Art of Cyprus, Paris, Nov. 7, 1967-Jan. 3, 1968 (50m); 20th anniv. of UNESCO (75m).

Human Rights Flame and Stars — A88

Designs: 90m, Human Rights flame and UN emblem. 250m, Scroll showing Article One of the Declaration of Human Rights.

Perf. 13¹/₂x14

1968, Mar. 18	**Litho.**	**Wmk. 344**	
311 A88	50m multicolored	.24	.24
312 A88	90m multicolored	.65	.65

Size: 110x90mm

Imperf

313 A88	250m multicolored	2.25	2.25
	Nos. 311-313 (3)	3.14	3.14

Intl. Human Rights Year.

Europa Issue, 1968
Common Design Type

1968, Apr. 29		**Perf. 14x13¹/₂**
314 CD11	20m multicolored	.20 .15
315 CD11	30m dk car rose, gray brn & blk	.35 .22
316 CD11	150m multicolored	1.75 1.40
	Nos. 314-316 (3)	2.30 1.77

Boy Holding Milk, UNICEF Emblem A89

Aesculapius and WHO Emblem — A90

Perf. 14x13¹/₂, 13¹/₂x14

1968, Sept. 2		**Wmk. 344**	
317 A89	35m dk red, lt brn & blk	.18	.18
318 A90	50m gray ol, blk & grn	.28	.28

21st anniv. of UNICEF (No. 317), 20th anniv. of the WHO (No. 318).

Discus Thrower — A91

ILO Emblem — A92

Designs: 25m, Runners. 100m, Stadium, Mexico City, horiz.

Perf. 13¹/₂x14, 14x13¹/₂

1968, Oct. 24		**Litho.**	
319 A91	10m multicolored	.15	.15
320 A91	25m vio blue & multi	.15	.15
321 A91	100m blue & multi	.70	.70
	Nos. 319-321 (3)	1.00	1.00

19th Olympic Games, Mexico City, Oct. 12-27.

Perf. 12x13¹/₂

1969, Mar. 3		**Wmk. 344**	
322 A92	50m bl, vio bl & org brn	.20	.20
323 A92	90m gray, blk & org brn	.55	.55

ILO, 50th anniv.

Cyprus stamps can be mounted in the Scott British Europe album.

Ancient Map of Cyprus A93

Design: 50m, Medieval map of Cyprus.

Perf. 13¹/₂x13

1969, Apr. 7   Wmk. 344
324 A93   35m multicolored   .35 .28
325 A93   50m olive & multi   .35 .28

1st Intl. Congress of Cypriot Studies.

Europa Issue, 1969

"EUROPA" and "CEPT" CD12

1969, Apr. 28   Litho.   Perf. 14x13¹/₂
326 CD12 20m bl, blk & gray   .16 .15
327 CD12 30m cop red, blk &
            ocher   .32 .16
328 CD12 150m grn, blk & yel   1.40 1.00
       Nos. 326-328 (3)   1.88 1.31

CEPT, 10th anniv.

European Roller — A95

Birds: 15m, Audouin's gull. 20m, Cyprus warbler. 30m, Eurasian jay, vert. 40m, Hoopoe, vert. 90m, Eleonora's falcon, vert.

Perf. 13¹/₂x12, 12x13¹/₂

1969, July 7   Wmk. 344
329 A95   5m multicolored   .15 .15
330 A95   15m multicolored   .22 .16
331 A95   20m multicolored   .25 .16
332 A95   30m multicolored   .38 .24
333 A95   40m multicolored   .55 .35
334 A95   90m multicolored   1.75 1.40
       Nos. 329-334 (6)   3.30 2.45

Nativity, Mural, 1192 A96

Christmas: 45m, Nativity, mural in Church of Ayios Nicolaos tis Steghis, 14th century. 250m, Virgin and Child between Archangels Michael and Gabriel, mosaic in Church of Panayia Angeloktistos, 6th-7th centuries. Design of 20m is a mural in Church of Panayia tou Arakos, Lagoudhera.

1969, Nov. 24 Litho. Perf. 13¹/₂x13
335 A96   20m multicolored   .16 .15
336 A96   45m multicolored   .40 .35

Size: 109x89mm
                                  Imperf
337 A96   250m dk blue & multi   5.00 3.75
       Nos. 335-337 (3)   5.56 4.25

Mahatma Gandhi A97

1970, Jan. 26   Perf. 14x13¹/₂
338 A97   25m multicolored   .16 .15
339 A97   75m multicolored   .55 .50

Birth cent. of Mohandas K. Gandhi (1869-1948), leader in India's struggle for independence.

Europa Issue, 1970

Interwoven Threads CD13

1970, May 4   Litho.   Wmk. 344
340 CD13 20m brn, yel & org   .18 .15
341 CD13 30m brt bl, yel & org   .30 .24
342 CD13 150m brt rose lil, yel &
            orange   1.75 1.50
       Nos. 340-342 (3)   2.23 1.89

Landscape with Flowers — A99

Designs: Various landscapes with flowers.

Perf. 13x14

1970, Aug. 3   Litho.   Wmk. 344
343 A99   10m multicolored   .15 .15
344 A99   50m multicolored   .38 .35
345 A99   90m multicolored   1.10 1.10
       Nos. 343-345 (3)   1.63 1.60

European Nature Conservation Year.

Education Year Emblem — A100

Grapes and Partridge (Mosaic) A101

UN Emblem, Dove, Globe and Wheat A102

Perf. 13x14, 14x13

1970, Sept. 7   Litho.   Wmk. 344
346 A100   5m tan, blk & brn   .15 .15
347 A101 15m multicolored   .15 .15
348 A102 75m multicolored   .48 .42
       Set value   .64 .55

Intl. Education Year (No. 346); 50th General Assembly of the Intl. Vine and Wine Office (No. 347); 25th anniv. of the UN (No. 348).

Virgin and Child, Mural from Podhithou Church, 16th Century A103

Perf. 14x14¹/₂

1970, Nov. 23   Photo.   Unwmk.
349 A103 Strip of three   .45 .45
  a.   25m Left angel   .15 .15
  b.   25m Virgin and Child   .15 .15
  c.   25m Right angel   .15 .15
350 A103 75m multicolored   .45 .45

Christmas.
Design of No. 349 is same as No. 350, but divided by perforation into 3 stamps with 25m denomination each. Size of No. 349: 71x46mm; size of No. 350: 42x31mm.

Cotton Napkin A104

Festive Costume A105

Drinking Cup, 7th Cent. B.C. — A106

Mouflon from Mosaic Pavement, 3rd Century A107

Cypriot Art: 5m, St. George, bas-relief on pine board, 19th cent. 20m, kneeling donors, painting, Church of St. Mamas, 1465. 25m, Mosaic head, 5th cent. A.D. 30m, Athena mounting horse-drawn chariot, terracotta figurine, 5th cent. B.C. 40m, Shepherd playing pipe, 14th cent. fresco. 50m, Woman's head, limestone, 3rd cent. B.C. 75m, Angel, mosaic, 6th cent. 90m, Mycenaean silver bowl, 14th cent. B.C. 500m, Woman and tree, decoration from amphora, 7th-6th cent. B.C. £1, God statue (horned helmet), from Enkomi, 12th cent. B.C., vert.

**Perf. 12¹/₂x13¹/₂ (A104), 13x14
(A105), 14x13 (A106), 13 ¹/₂x13,
13x13¹/₂ (A107)**

1971, Feb. 22   Litho.   Wmk. 344
351 A104   3m blk, red & brn   .15 .15
352 A104   5m citron, red brn &
            black   .15 .15
353 A105 10m multicolored   .15 .15
354 A106 15m bister brn, blk &
            slate   .15 .15
355 A105 20m slate, red brn &
            black   .15 .15
356 A105 25m multicolored   .15 .15
357 A106 30m multicolored   .18 .15
358 A105 40m gray & multi   .30 .18
359 A105 50m bl, bis & blk   .35 .24
360 A105 75m cit & multi   .55 .38
361 A106 90m multicolored   .80 .60
362 A107 250m lt red brn, brn &
            black   3.50 2.25
363 A107 500m tan & multi   5.50 5.00
364 A107   £1 multicolored   10.00 8.50
       Nos. 351-364 (14)   22.08 18.20

For surcharges see Nos. 403, 444, RA1. For overprints see Nos. 424-427.

Europa Issue, 1971

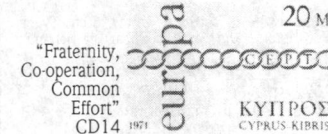

"Fraternity, Co-operation, Common Effort" CD14

1971, May 3   Litho.   Perf. 14x13¹/₂
Size: 36¹/₂x23¹/₂mm
365 CD14 20m lt bl, vio bl & blk   .16 .15
366 CD14 30m brt yel grn, grn &
            blk   .28 .22
367 CD14 150m yel, grn & blk   1.65 1.50
       Nos. 365-367 (3)   2.09 1.87

Archbishop Kyprianos, 1821 — A109

Paintings: 30m, Young Greek Taking Oath, horiz. 100m, Bishop Germanòs of Patras Declaring Greek Independence.

Perf. 13x13¹/₂, 13¹/₂x13
1971, July 9   Wmk. 344
368 A109 15m multicolored   .15 .15
369 A109 30m multicolored   .15 .15
370 A109 100m multicolored   .70 .55
       Nos. 368-370 (3)   1.00
       Set value   .70

150th anniversary of Greek independence.

Arch and Castle A110

Tourist Publicity: 25m, Decorated gourd and sun over shore, vert. 60m, Mountain road, vert. 100m, Village church.

Perf. 13¹/₂x13, 13x13¹/₂
1971, Sept. 20
371 A110 15m vio bl & multi   .15 .15
372 A110 25m ocher & multi   .15 .15
373 A110 60m green & multi   .35 .35
374 A110 100m blue & multi   .70 .70
       Nos. 371-374 (4)   1.35 1.35

Virgin and Child A111

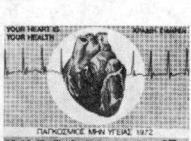

Heart and Electrocardiogram A112

1971, Nov. 22   Perf. 13¹/₂x14
375 A111 10m shown   .15 .15
376 A111 50m The Three Kings   .45 .35
377 A111 100m Shepherds   .90 .70
  a.   Strip of 3, Nos. 375-377   1.50 1.50

Christmas.

1972, Apr. 11   Perf. 13¹/₂x12¹/₂
378 A112 15m bister & multi   .15 .15
379 A112 50m brown & multi   .40 .38
       Set value   .50 .46

"Your heart is your health," World Health Day.

Europa Issue 1972

Sparkles, Symbolic of Communications CD15

1972, May 22   Perf. 12¹/₂x13¹/₂
380 CD15 20m brn, org & fawn   .35 .20
381 CD15 30m pur, org & lilac   .50 .45
382 CD15 150m dk ol, org & brt
            green   2.50 2.25
       Nos. 380-382 (3)   3.35 2.90

Archery, Olympic and Motion Emblems A114

1972, July 24   Perf. 14x13¹/₂
383 A114 10m shown   .15 .15
384 A114 40m Wrestling   .38 .35
385 A114 100m Soccer   1.10 1.00
       Nos. 383-385 (3)   1.63 1.50

20th Olympic Games, Munich, Aug. 26-Sept. 11.

Apollo, Silver Stater, Marion, 5th Century B.C. — A115

Silver Staters of Cyprus: 30m, Eagle's head, Paphos, c. 460 B.C. 40m, Pallas Athena, Lapithos, 388-387 B.C. 100m, Sphinx (obverse) and lotus flower (reverse), Idalion, c. 460 B.C.

		1972, Sept. 25	Litho.	Wmk. 344
		Coins in Silver		
386	A115	20m lt grnsh bl & blk	.15	.15
387	A115	30m pale bl & silver	.20	.18
388	A115	40m ol bister & black	.32	.30
389	A115	100m pale brn & blk	1.25	1.10
		Nos. 386-389 (4)	1.92	1.73

Bathing the Christ Child — A116

Christmas: 20m, The Three Kings. 100m, Nativity. 250m, The Nativity, 1466, mural in Church of the Holy Cross, Platanistasa. The designs of the 10m, 20m, 100m, show details from mural shown entirely on 250m.

		1972, Nov. 20	Litho.	Perf. 13¹/₂x14
390	A116	10m multicolored	.15	.15
391	A116	20m multicolored	.22	.22
392	A116	100m multicolored	1.40	1.25
		Size: 110x90mm		
		Imperf		
393	A116	250m multicolored	4.50	4.25
		Nos. 390-393 (4)	6.27	5.87

Landscape, Troodos Mountains A117

Design: 100m, FIS Congress emblem and map of Cyprus.

		Perf. 14x13¹/₂		
		1973, Mar. 13		Wmk. 344
394	A117	20m blue & multi	.18	.18
395	A117	100m blue & multi	.80	.80

29th Meeting of the Intl. Ski Fed. (FIS), Nicosia, June 1973.

Europa Issue 1973

Post Horn of Arrows CD16

		1973, May 7		Size: 37x21mm
396	CD16	20m dl bl & multi	.22	.18
397	CD16	30m multicolored	.45	.35
398	CD16	150m multicolored	2.25	2.00
		Nos. 396-398 (3)	2.92	2.53

Archbishop's Palace, Nicosia A119

Traditional Architecture: 30m, Konak, Nicosia, 18th century, vert. 50m, House, Gourri, 1850, vert. 100m, House, Rizokarpaso, 1772.

		1973, July 23		Perf. 14x13, 13x14
399	A119	20m multicolored	.16	.15
400	A119	30m multicolored	.32	.30
401	A119	50m multicolored	.50	.42
402	A119	100m multicolored	.95	.85
		Nos. 399-402 (4)	1.93	1.72

No. 354 Surcharged

20M
=

		1973, Sept. 24		Perf. 14x13
403	A106	20m on 15m multi		.22	.22

Cyprus Scout Emblem — A120 KΥΠΡΟΣ 10M

Cyprus Airways Emblem — A122 KΥΠΡΟΣ 50M

EEC Emblem A121 25M

Designs: 35m, FAO emblem. 100m, INTERPOL emblem.

		1973, Sept. 24		Perf. 13x14, 14x13
404	A120	10m brn ol & buff	.15	.15
405	A121	25m pur, bl & plum	.20	.18
406	A121	35m grn, gray grn & citron	.30	.28
407	A122	50m black & blue	.45	.42
408	A120	100m brown & fawn	.90	.85
		Nos. 404-408 (5)	2.00	1.88

60th anniv. of Cyprus Boy Scout Organ.; association of Cyprus with EEC; 10th anniv. of FAO; 25th anniv. of Cyprus Airways; 50th anniv. of Intl. Criminal Police Organization.

Archangel Gabriel — A123

Virgin and Child — A124

Christmas: 100m, Panaya tou Araka Church, horiz. Designs of 10m, 20m are from wall paintings in Arakas Church.

		1973, Nov. 26		Wmk. 344
409	A123	10m multicolored	.15	.15
410	A124	20m multicolored	.15	.15
411	A124	100m multicolored	1.00	.90
		Nos. 409-411 (3)	1.30	1.20

Grapes A125

Rape of Europa A126

		1974, Mar. 18	Litho.	Perf. 13x14
412	A125	25m shown	.15	.15
413	A125	50m Grapefruit	.38	.35
414	A125	50m Oranges	.38	.35
415	A125	50m Lemons	.38	.35
a.		Strip of 3, #413-415	1.25	1.25
		Nos. 412-415 (4)	1.29	1.20

Europa Issue 1974

1974, Apr. 29

Design shows a silver stater of Marion, second half of 5th century B.C.

416	A126	10m org brn & multi	.15	.15
417	A126	40m multicolored	.38	.38
418	A126	150m dk car & multi	1.40	1.40
		Nos. 416-418 (3)	1.93	1.93

Solon, 3rd Century Mosaic A127

Designs: 10m, Front page of "History of Cyprus," by Archimandrite Kyprianos, 1788, vert. 100m, St. Neophytos, mural, vert. 250m, Maps of Cyprus and Greek Islands, by Abraham Ortelius, 1584.

		1974, July 22	Litho.	Wmk. 344
419	A127	10m multicolored	.15	.15
420	A127	25m multicolored	.16	.15
421	A127	100m multicolored	.70	.70
		Size: 110x90mm		
		Imperf		
422	A127	250m multicolored	2.00	1.90
		Nos. 419-422 (4)	3.01	2.90

2nd Intl. Congress of Cypriot Studies, Nicosia, Sept. 15-21. No. 422 has simulated perforations.

SECURITY
COUNCIL
RESOLUTION
353
20 JULY 1974

Nos. 353, 358-359, 362 Overprinted

		Perf. 13x14, 13¹/₂x13		
		1974, Oct. 14		Litho.
424	A105	10m multicolored	.15	.15
425	A105	40m multicolored	.35	.30
426	A105	50m multicolored	.40	.38
427	A107	100m multicolored	2.25	2.00
		Nos. 424-427 (4)	3.15	2.83

UN Security Council Resolution No. 353 to end hostilities on Cyprus. Overprint is in 3 lines on No. 427.

Virgin and Child, 1466 A129

Adoration of the Kings, c. 1500 — A130

Christmas: 100m, Flight into Egypt, mural, Monastery Church of Ayios Meophytos, c. 1500. (50m is from same church). Mural on 10m is in Church of Stavros tou Ahiasmati.

		Perf. 14x13, 13x14		
		1974, Dec. 2		Wmk. 344
429	A129	10m multicolored	.15	.15
430	A130	50m multicolored	.25	.22
431	A129	100m multicolored	.65	.55
		Nos. 429-431 (3)	1.05	
		Set value		.82

Disabled Persons, Emblem — A131

Council of Europe Flag — A132

		1975, Feb. 17	Unwmk.	Perf. 14¹/₂
432	A131	30m ocher & ultra	.25	.22
433	A132	100m multicolored	.85	.75

8th European Meeting of the Intl. Society for the Rehabilitation of Disabled Persons (30m; design shows society's emblem); 25th anniv. of Council of Europe (100m).

First Mail Coach in Cyprus A133

		1975, Feb. 17		
434	A133	20m multicolored	.15	.15
435	A133	50m ultra & multi	1.50	.50

Centenary (in 1974) of UPU.

The Distaff, by Michael Kashalos — A134

Europa (Paintings): 30m, Still Life, by Christoforos Savva. 150m, Virgin and Child of Liopetri, by Georghios P. Georghiou.

		Perf. 13¹/₂x14¹/₂		
		1975, Apr. 28		Photo.
436	A134	20m multicolored	.15	.15
437	A134	30m multicolored	.20	.15
438	A134	150m multicolored	1.00	.85
a.		Strip of 3, #436-438	1.35	1.35

Red Cross Flag over Cyprus — A135

Nurse and Nurses Emblem — A136

Steatite Female Figure, c. 3000 B.C. — A137

		Perf. 12¹/₂x13¹/₂, 13¹/₂x12¹/₂		
		1975, Aug. 4	Litho.	Wmk. 344
439	A135	25m blue green & red	.16	.15
440	A136	30m dp blue & lt grn	.22	.20
441	A137	75m multicolored	.55	.48
		Nos. 439-441 (3)	.93	.83

Cyprus Red Cross, 25th anniv.; Intl. Nurses' Day 1975; IWY.

Submarine Cable — A138

International Telephone — A139

		Perf. 12¹/₂x13¹/₂, 13¹/₂x12¹/₂		
		1975, Oct. 13		Litho.
442	A138	50m multicolored	.25	.22
443	A139	100m purple & org	.50	.42

Telecommunications achievements.

No. 351 Surcharged

10M
=

		1976, Jan. 5		Perf. 12¹/₂x13¹/₂
444	A104	10m on 3m multi	.15	.15

Vessel in Shape of Woman, 19th Century — A140

Composite Vessel, 2100-2000 B.C. — A141

Europa: 100m, Byzantine goblet, 15th cent.

Perf. 13x14

1976, May 3   Litho.   Wmk. 344
445 A140 20m violet & multi   .15   .15
446 A141 60m gray & multi   .40   .40
447 A140 100m brown & multi   .65   .65
       Nos. 445-447 (3)   1.20 1.20

Self-help Housing A142

Cyprus Airways Jet — A143

Designs: 25m, Women sewing in front of tents. 30m, Aforestation.

1976, May 3   Perf. 14x13
448 A142 10m multicolored   .15   .15
449 A142 25m multicolored   .15   .15
450 A142 30m multicolored   .15   .15
451 A143 60m multicolored   .35   .35
       Set value   .70   .70

Re-activation of the economy.

Terracotta Statue, 7th-6th Centuries B.C. — A144

Bronze Plate with Inscription, Idalion, 5th Century B.C. — A145

Designs: 10m, Limestone head of bearded man, 5th cent. B.C. 20m, Gold necklace, Lamboussa, 6th cent. A.D. 25m, Terracotta warrior on horseback, 7th cent. B.C. 30m, Limestone figure, priest of Aphrodite, 5th cent. B.C. 50m, Mycenaean crater, 13th cent. B.C. 60m, Limestone sarcophagus, Amathus, 550-500 B.C. 100m, Gold bracelet, Lamboussa, 6th cent. A.D. 250m, Silver dish, Lamboussa, 6th cent. A.D. 500m, Bronze stand, 12th cent. B.C. £1, Marble statue of Artemis, Larnaca, 4th cent. B.C.

Perf. 12x13¹/₂

1976, June 7   Wmk. 344
       Size: 22x33mm
452 A144 5m brn & multi   .15   .15
453 A144 10m gray & multi   .15   .15
       Size: 24x37mm, 37x24mm
       Perf. 13x14, 14x13
454 A144 20m red & multi   .15   .15
455 A144 25m lt brn & blk   .15   .15
456 A144 30m green & multi   .15   .15
457 A145 40m nbis gray & blk   .20   .18
458 A145 50m brn & multi   .22   .20
459 A145 60m dk brown & multi   .28   .25
460 A145 100m crim & multi   .48   .45

Size: 28x40mm
       Perf. 13x12¹/₂
461 A144 250m dk bl & multi   1.10 1.00
462 A144 500m yel & multi   2.25 2.25
463 A144 £1 slate & multi   4.75 4.50
       Nos. 452-463 (12)   10.03 9.58

George Washington — A146

1976, July 5   Perf. 13x13¹/₂
464 A146 100m multicolored   .70   .60

American Bicentennial.

Montreal Olympic Games Emblem — A147

Various Sports A148

Design: 100m, like 60m, with different sports.

1976, July 5   Unwmk.   Perf. 14
465 A147 20m yel, blk & dk car   .15   .15
466 A148 60m ultra & multi   .38   .38
467 A148 100m lilac & multi   .60   .60
       Nos. 465-467 (3)   1.13 1.13

21st Olympic Games, Montreal, Canada, July 17-Aug. 1.

Children in Library A149

Low-cost Housing Development A150

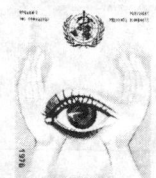

Hands Shielding Eye — A151

Perf. 13¹/₂x14, 13x13¹/₂

1976, Sept. 27   Litho.   Wmk. 344
468 A149 40m black & multi   .28   .28
469 A150 50m multicolored   .24   .20
470 A151 80m ultra & multi   .40   .35
       Nos. 468-470 (3)   .92   .83

Books for Children (40m); Habitat, UN Conference on Human Settlements, Vancouver, Canada, May 31-June 11 (50m); World Health Day: Foresight prevents blindness (80m).

Archangel Michael — A152

Christmas: 15m, Archangel Gabriel. 150m, Nativity. Icons in Ayios Neophytis Monastery, 16th century.

1976, Nov. 15   Unwmk.   Perf. 12¹/₂
471 A152 10m multicolored   .15   .15
472 A152 15m multicolored   .15   .15
473 A152 150m multicolored   .95   .85
       Set value   1.10 1.00

Landscape, by A. Diamantis A154

Europa (Paintings): 60m, Trees and Meadow, by T. Kanthos. 120m, Harbor, by V. Ioannides.

Perf. 13¹/₂x13

1977, May 2   Litho.   Unwmk.
475 A154 20m multicolored   .15   .15
476 A154 60m multicolored   .48   .45
477 A154 120m multicolored   .90   .80
       Nos. 475-477 (3)   1.53 1.40

Cyprus No. 196 — A155

Perf. 13x13¹/₂

1977, June 13   Litho.   Wmk. 344
478 A155 120m multicolored   .65   .48

25th anniv. of reign of Queen Elizabeth II.

Silver Tetradrachm of Demetrios Poliorcetes — A156

Ancient Coins of Cyprus: 10m, Bronze coin of Emperor Trajan. 60m, Silver Tetradrachm of Ptolemy VIII. 100m, Gold octadrachm of Arsinoe II.

1977, June 13   Unwmk.   Perf. 14
479 A156 10m multicolored   .15   .15
480 A156 40m multicolored   .22   .20
481 A156 60m multicolored   .35   .32
482 A156 100m multicolored   .52   .52
       Nos. 479-482 (4)   1.24 1.19

Archbishop Makarios (1913-1977), Pres. of Cyprus — A157

Designs: 20m, Archbishop in full vestments. 250m, Head.

Handicrafts A158

Perf. 13x14

1977, Sept. 10   Litho.   Unwmk.
483 A157 20m multicolored   .15   .15
484 A157 60m multicolored   .30   .15
485 A157 250m multicolored   1.10 1.00
       Nos. 483-485 (3)   1.55 1.30

Sputnik over Earth — A159

Designs: 40m, Map of Cyprus. 60m, Gold medals and sports emblems.

Perf. 13¹/₂x12

1977, Oct. 17   Wmk. 344
486 A158 20m multicolored   .15   .15
487 A158 40m multicolored   .20   .18
488 A158 60m multicolored   .30   .28
489 A159 80m multicolored   .45   .38
       Nos. 486-489 (4)   1.10   .99

Revitalization of handicrafts (20m); Man and the biosphere (40m); Gold medals won by secondary school students in France for long jump and 200 meter race (60m); 60th anniv. of Bolshevik Revolution (80m).

Nativity A160

Christmas (Children's Drawings): 10m, Three Kings following the star. 150m, Flight into Egypt.

Perf. 14x13¹/₂

1977, Nov. 21   Litho.   Unwmk.
490 A160 10m multicolored   .15   .15
491 A160 40m multicolored   .20   .18
492 A160 150m multicolored   .75   .70
       Nos. 490-492 (3)   1.10 1.03

Demetrios Libertis (1866-1937) — A161

Design: 150m, Vasilis Michaelides (1849-1917).

1978, Mar. 6   Wmk. 344   Perf. 14x13
493 A161 40m bister & olive   .22   .20
494 A161 150m gray, ver & blk   .70   .65

Cypriot poets.

Chrysorrhogiatissa Monastery — A162

Europa: 75m, Kolossi Castle. 125m, Municipal Library, Paphos.

Perf. 14¹/₂x13

1978, Apr. 24   Litho.   Unwmk.
495 A162 25m multicolored   .15   .15
496 A162 75m multicolored   .35   .35
497 A162 125m multicolored   .60   .60
       Nos. 495-497 (3)   1.10 1.10

Makarios as Archbishop 1950-1977 — A163

"The Great Leader" — A164

Archbishop Makarios: 25m, Exiled, Seychelles, 1956-1957. 50m, President of Cyprus, 1960-1977. 75m, Soldier of Christ. 100m, Freedom fighter.

Perf. 14x14¹/₂

		1978, Aug. 3	Litho.	Unwmk.
498	A163	15m multicolored	.15	.15
499	A163	25m multicolored	.15	.15
500	A163	50m multicolored	.30	.30
501	A163	75m multicolored	.42	.42
502	A163	100m multicolored	.60	.60

Size: 110x80mm

Imperf

503	A164	300m multicolored	6.00	5.00
		Nos. 498-503 (6)	7.62	6.62

Archbishop Makarios, President of Cyprus.

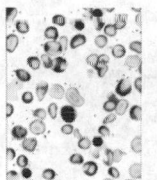

Blood Cells with Low Hemoglobin A165

Bust of Aristotle A166

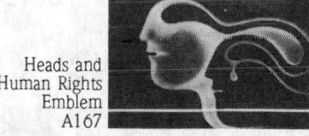

Heads and Human Rights Emblem A167

Wilbur and Orville Wright, Flyer I A168

Perf. 13x14, 14x13

		1978, Oct. 23	Unwmk.	Litho.
504	A165	15m multicolored	.15	.15
505	A166	35m multicolored	.20	.20
506	A167	75m black	.40	.40
507	A168	125m multicolored	.55	.55
		Nos. 504-507 (4)	1.30	1.30

Anemia prevention (15m); 2300th birth anniv. of Aristotle (35m); 30th anniv. of Universal Declaration of Human Rights (75m); 75th anniv. of first powered flight (125m).

Kiti Icon Stand — A169

Christmas: 35m, Athienou icon stand. 150m, Omodhos icon stand.

1978, Dec. 4   **Perf. 14x14¹/₂**

508	A169	15m multicolored	.15	.15
509	A169	35m multicolored	.18	.18
510	A169	150m multicolored	.75	.75
		Nos. 508-510 (3)	1.08	1.08

Venus Statue from Soli A170

Design: 125m, Birth of Venus, by Botticelli (detail).

1979, Mar. 12   **Litho.**   **Perf. 14x13¹/₂**

511	A170	75m multicolored	.35	.35
512	A170	125m multicolored	.55	.55

Mail Coach, Envelope and Truck A171

Europa: 75m, Old telephone, dish antenna and satellite. 125m, Steamship, jet and envelopes.

1979, Apr. 30   **Litho.**   **Perf. 14x13¹/₂**

513	A171	25m multicolored	.15	.15
514	A171	75m multicolored	.35	.35
515	A171	125m multicolored	.55	.55
		Nos. 513-515 (3)	1.05	1.05

Peacock Wrasse — A172

Designs: 50m, Black partridge, vert. 75m, Cyprus cedar, vert. 125m, Mule.

Perf. 13¹/₂x12¹/₂, 12¹/₂x13¹/₂

		1979, June 25		Litho.
516	A172	25m multicolored	.15	.15
517	A172	50m multicolored	.24	.22
518	A172	75m multicolored	.35	.32
519	A172	125m multicolored	.55	.50
		Nos. 516-519 (4)	1.29	1.19

Children Holding Globe, UNESCO Emblem — A173

Dove, Magnifying Glass, Album A174

Lord Kitchener, Map of Cyprus A175

Smiling Child, IYC Emblem A176

Soccer A177

Rotary Emblem — A178

1979, Oct. 1   **Litho.**   **Perf. 12¹/₂**

520	A173	15m multicolored	.15	.15
521	A174	25m multicolored	.15	.15
522	A175	50m multicolored	.24	.24
523	A176	75m multicolored	.32	.28
524	A177	100m multicolored	.48	.45
525	A178	125m multicolored	.55	.48
		Nos. 520-525 (6)	1.89	1.75

Intl. Bureau of Education, Geneva, 50th anniv.; Cyprus Philatelic Society, 20th anniv.; Horatio Herbert Kitchener's survey of Cyprus, cent.; IYC; European Soccer Assoc., 25th anniv.; Rotary Club of Cyprus, 75th anniv.

Jesus, Icon, 12th Century — A179

Christmas (Icons): 35m, Nativity, 16th cent. 150m, Virgin and Child, 12th cent.

Perf. 13¹/₂x14, 13x14

		1979, Nov. 5		Litho.
		Sizes: 24x37mm; 27x40mm (35m)		
526	A179	15m multicolored	.15	.15
527	A179	35m multicolored	.20	.18
528	A179	150m multicolored	.70	.60
		Nos. 526-528 (3)	1.05	.93

Cyprus No. 1, Nicosia Cancel A180

Cyprus Stamp Centenary: 125m, #3, Kyrenia cancel. 175m, #6, Larnaca cancel. 500m, #1-6.

1980, Mar. 17   **Litho.**   **Perf. 14x13**

529	A180	40m multicolored	.22	.22
530	A180	125m multicolored	.65	.65
531	A180	175m multicolored	.95	.95

Size: 105x85mm

Imperf

532	A180	500m multicolored	3.00	3.00
		Nos. 529-532 (4)	4.82	4.82

Holy Cross, St. Barnabas Church, Ayiasmati — A181

Europa: 125m, Zenon of Citium, Ny Carsberg Glyptothek, Copenhagen.

1980, Apr. 28   **Perf. 12¹/₂**

533	A181	40m multicolored	.20	.20
534	A181	125m multicolored	.62	.62

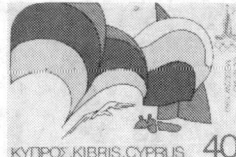

Sailing, Moscow '80 Emblem A182

1980, June 23   **Litho.**   **Perf. 14x13**

535	A182	40m shown	.20	.20
536	A182	125m Swimming	.62	.62
537	A182	200m Gymnast	1.00	1.00
		Nos. 535-537 (3)	1.82	1.82

22nd Summer Olympic Games, Moscow, July 19-Aug. 3.

Gold Necklace A183

Clay Amphora A184

Designs: Archaeological finds on Cyprus, 12th century B.C. to 3rd century A.D. 15m, 40m, 150m, 500m, horiz.

Perf. 13¹/₂x14, 14x13¹/₂

		1980, Sept. 15	Litho.	Wmk. 344
538	A183	10m shown	.15	.15
539	A184	15m Bronze cow	.15	.15
540	A184	25m shown	.15	.15
541	A184	40m Lion, gold ring	.15	.15
542	A184	50m Bronze cauldron	.15	.15
543	A184	75m Stele	.25	.25
544	A184	100m Clay jug	.35	.35
545	A184	125m Warrior, terracotta bust	.40	.40
546	A184	150m Lions attacking bull	.50	.50
547	A184	175m Faience and enamel vase	.60	.60
548	A184	200m Warrior god, bronze	.65	.65
549	A184	500m Stone bowl	1.75	1.75
550	A183	£1 Ivory plaque	3.25	3.25
551	A183	£2 Leda and the swan, mosaic	7.00	7.00
		Nos. 538-551 (14)	15.50	15.50

For surcharges see Nos. 584, 600-611.

Cyprus Flag — A185

Archbishop Makarios — A187

Treaty Signing Establishing Republic, 20th Anniversary — A186

1980, Oct. 1   **Perf. 13¹/₂x14, 14x13**
552 A185 40m multicolored   .20   .20
553 A186 125m multicolored   .62   .62
554 A187 175m multicolored   .90   .90
      Nos. 552-554 (3)   1.72 1.72

Dove and Woman A188

Perf. 14x13
1980, Nov. 29   Litho.   Wmk. 344
555 A188 40m shown   .20   .20
556 A188 125m Dove and man   .62   .62
   a.   Pair, #555-556   .82   .82

Intl. Palestinian Solidarity Day.

Pulpit, Tripiotis Church, Nicosia — A189

Christmas: 100m, Iconostatis (Holy Door), Panayia Church, Paralimni. 125m, Pulpit, Ayios Lazaros Church, Larnaca.

1980, Nov. 29   Perf. 13¹/₂x14
557 A189 25m multicolored   .15   .15
      Size: 24x37mm
558 A189 100m multicolored   .50   .50
      Size: 21x37mm
559 A189 125m multicolored   .62   .62
      Nos. 557-559 (3)   1.27 1.27

Europa Issue 1981

Folk Dance — A190

1981, May 4   Photo.   Perf. 14
560 A190 40m shown   .20   .20
561 A190 175m Dance, diff.   .90   .90

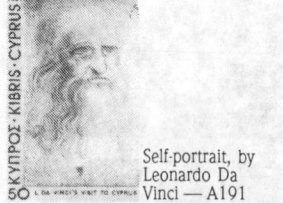

Self-portrait, by Leonardo Da Vinci — A191

The Last Supper, by Da Vinci — A192

Perf. 13¹/₂x14, 12¹/₂x13¹/₂
1981, June 15   Wmk. 344   Litho.
562 A191 50m shown   .25   .25
563 A192 125m shown   .65   .65
564 A191 175m Lace pattern, Milan
             Cathedral   .90   .90
      Nos. 562-564 (3)   1.80 1.80

Da Vinci's visit to Cyprus, 500th anniv.

Ophrys Kotschyi — A193

Designs: Orchids.

1981, July 6   Perf. 13¹/₂x14
565 A193 25m shown   .18   .18
566 A193 50m Orchis puntulata   .35   .35
567 A193 75m Ophrys argolica ele-
             gantis   .50   .50
568 A193 150m Epipactis veratrifolia 1.00 1.00
   a.   Block of 4, #565-568   2.15 2.15

Prince Charles and Lady Diana, St. Paul's Cathedral A194

Perf. 14x13
1981, Sept. 28   Wmk. 344
569 A194 200m multicolored   1.00 1.00

Royal wedding.

Heinrich von Stephan (1831-1897), UPU Founder — A195

World Food Day (Oct. 16) A196

Intl. Year of the Disabled A197

European Campaign for Urban Renaissance — A198

1981, Sept. 28
570 A195 25m multicolored   .18   .18
571 A196 40m multicolored   .22   .22
572 A197 125m multicolored   .65   .65
573 A198 150m multicolored   .75   .75
      Nos. 570-573 (4)   1.80 1.80

Our Lady of the Angels, Transfiguration Church, Palekhori A199

Christmas (Frescoes): 100m, Christ, Madonna of Arakas Church, Lagoudera, vert. 125m, Baptism of Christ, Our Lady of Assinou Church, Nikitari.

1981, Nov. 16   Perf. 12¹/₂
574 A199 25m multicolored   .15   .15
575 A199 100m multicolored   .42   .42
576 A199 150m multicolored   .50   .50
      Nos. 574-576 (3)   1.07 1.07

Bathing Aphrodite, Sculpture, Soloi, 250 B.C. — A200

Design: 175m, Aphrodite Emerging from the Water, by Titian, 16th cent.

Perf. 13¹/₂x14
1982, Apr. 12   Litho.   Wmk. 344
577 A200 125m multicolored   .60   .60
578 A200 175m multicolored   .85   .85

Europa Issue 1982

Liberation by Emperor Nicephorus II Phocas, 965 A.D. — A201

Perf. 12¹/₂
1982, May 3   Photo.   Unwmk.
579 A201 40m shown   .15   .15
580 A201 175m Conversion of Sergius
             Paulus, 45 A.D.   .65   .65

Mosaic Chrismon A202

Cultural Heritage: 125m, King of Palaepaphos (High Priest of Aphrodite), sculpture, vert. 225m, Theseus Struggling with the Minotaur, mosaic.

1982, July 5   Litho.   Wmk. 344
581 A202 50m multicolored   .20   .20
582 A202 125m multicolored   .50   .50
583 A202 225m multicolored   .95   .95
      Nos. 581-583 (3)   1.65 1.65

No. 543 Surcharged

1982, Sept. 6   Litho.   Perf. 13¹/₂x14
584 A184 100m on 75m multi   .38   .38

Scouting Year A203

Christmas A204

Perf. 13¹/₂x12¹/₂, 12¹/₂x13¹/₂
1982, Nov. 8   Wmk. 344
585 A203 100m Emblem, horiz.   .40   .40
586 A203 125m Baden-Powell   .50   .50
587 A203 175m Camp site, horiz. .70   .70
      Nos. 585-587 (3)   1.60 1.60

Perf. 12¹/₂, 13¹/₂x14 (100m)
1982, Dec. 6
Designs: 25m, 250m, Christ Giving Holy Communion (bread, 25m: wine, 250m) to the Apostles, St. Neophytos Monastery Church, Paphos, horiz. 100m, Chalice, Church of St. Savvas, Nicosia.

588 A204 25m multicolored   .15   .15
589 A204 100m multicolored   .45   .45
590 A204 250m multicolored   1.10 1.10
      Nos. 588-590 (3)   1.70 1.70

A204a KYΠPOΣ-KIBRIS-CYPRUS 50

1983, Mar. 14   Perf. 14x13¹/₂
591 A204a 50m Cyprus Forest In-
              dustries, Ltd.   .20   .20
592 A204a 125m Mosaic, 3rd cent. .50   .50
593 A204a 150m Dancers   .60   .60
594 A204a 175m Royal Exhibition
              Building, Mel-
              bourne   .70   .70
      Nos. 591-594 (4)   2.00 2.00

Commonwealth Day.

Europa A205

Designs: 50m, Cyprosyllabic script funerary stele, 6th cent. B.C. 200m, Copper ore, Enkomi ingot, 1400-1250 BC, bronze jug, 2nd cent.

1983, May 3   Photo.   Perf. 14¹/₂x14
595 A205 50m multicolored   .18   .18
596 A205 200m multicolored   .80   .80

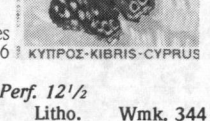

Local Butterflies A206

Perf. 12¹/₂
1983, June 28   Litho.   Wmk. 344
597 A206 60m Pararge aegeria   .30   .30
598 A206 130m Aricia medon   .65   .65
599 A206 250m Glaucopsyche pa-
             phos   1.25 1.25
      Nos. 597-599 (3)   2.20 2.20

Nos. 538-549 Surcharged
Perf. 13¹/₂x14, 14x13¹/₂
1983, Oct. 3   Litho.   Wmk. 344
600 A183 1c on 10m multi   .15   .15
601 A184 2c on 15m multi   .15   .15
602 A184 3c on 25m multi   .15   .15
603 A184 4c on 40m multi   .16   .16
604 A184 5c on 50m multi   .20   .20
605 A184 6c on 75m multi   .24   .24
606 A184 10c on 100m multi   .40   .40
607 A184 13c on 125m multi   .52   .52
608 A184 15c on 150m multi   .60   .60
609 A184 20c on 200m multi   .80   .80
610 A184 25c on 175m multi   1.00 1.00
611 A184 50c on 500m multi   2.00 2.00
      Nos. 600-611 (12)   6.37 6.37

Electricity Authority of Cyprus, 30th Anniv. — A207

World Communications Year — A208

Intl. Maritime Org., 25th Anniv. — A209

Universal Declaration of Human Rights, 35th Anniv. — A210

Nicos Kazantzakis, 100th Birth Anniv. — A211

Archbishop Makarios III, 70th Birth Anniv. — A212

1983, Oct. 31   Litho.   Perf. 13½x14
612	A207	3c multicolored	.15	.15
613	A208	6c multicolored	.22	.22
614	A209	13c multicolored	.48	.48
615	A210	15c multicolored	.55	.55
616	A211	20c multicolored	.75	.75
617	A212	25c multicolored	.90	.90
		Nos. 612-617 (6)	3.05	3.05

Christmas — A213

Designs: 4c, Belfry, St. Lazaros Church, Larnaca. 13c, Belfry, St. Varvara Church, Kaimakli, Nicosia. 20c, Belfry, St. Ioannis Church, Larnaca.

1983, Dec. 12   Perf. 12½x14
618	A213	4c multicolored	.15	.15
619	A213	13c multicolored	.48	.48
620	A213	20c multicolored	.70	.70
		Nos. 618-620 (3)	1.33	1.33

Waterside Cafe at the Marina, Larnaca A214

19th Century engravings. Size of 6c: 41x27mm; 75c, 110x85mm.

Perf. 14½x14 (6c), 14, Imperf. (75c)
1984, Mar. 6
621	A214	6c shown	.22	.22
622	A214	20c Bazaar, Larnaca	.70	.70
623	A214	30c East Gate, Nicosia	1.00	1.00
624	A214	75c St. Lazarus Church Interior, Larnaca	2.75	2.75
		Nos. 621-624 (4)	4.67	4.67

Europa (1959-1984) A215

1984, Apr. 30   Wmk. 344   Perf. 12½
625	A215	6c multicolored	.28	.28
626	A215	15c multicolored	.65	.65

1984 Summer Olympics A216

1984, June 18   Litho.   Perf. 14
627	A216	3c Running	.15	.15
628	A216	4c Olympic column	.16	.16
629	A216	13c Swimming	.52	.52
630	A216	20c Gymnastics	.80	.80
		Nos. 627-630 (4)	1.63	1.63

Turkish Invasion, 10th Anniv. A217

1984, July 20   Litho.   Perf. 14x13½
631	A217	15c Prisoners, barbed wire	.60	.60
632	A217	20c Map	.85	.85

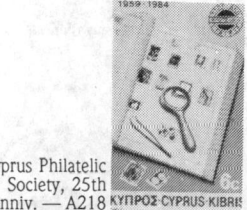

Cyprus Philatelic Society, 25th Anniv. — A218

Cyprus Soccer Assoc., 50th Anniv. A219

George Papanicolaou (1883-1962), Cancer Researcher — A220

Medieval Map — A221

1984, Oct. 15   Wmk. 344   Perf. 12½
633	A218	6c multicolored	.18	.18
634	A219	10c multicolored	.30	.30
635	A220	15c multicolored	.50	.50
636	A221	25c multicolored	.95	.95
		Nos. 633-636 (4)	1.93	1.93

Intl. Symposium of Cyprus Cartography and First Intl. Symposium on Medieval Paleography (25c).

Christmas — A222

1984, Nov. 26   Litho.   Perf. 12½
637	A222	4c St. Mark	.15	.15
638	A222	13c Gospel page (St. Mark)	.48	.48
639	A222	20c St. Luke	.75	.75
		Nos. 637-639 (3)	1.38	1.38

Landscapes A223

Perf. 15x14, 14x15
1985, Mar. 18   Litho.
640	A223	1c Autumn at Platania	.15	.15
641	A223	2c Ayia Napa Monastery	.15	.15
642	A223	3c Phine Village	.15	.15
643	A223	4c Kykko Monastery	.15	.15
644	A223	5c Beach at Makronissos	.16	.16
645	A223	6c Village Street, Omodhos, vert.	.18	.18
646	A223	10c Sea view	.30	.30
647	A223	13c Water sports	.40	.40
648	A223	15c Beach at Protaras	.48	.48
649	A223	20c Forestry, vert.	.60	.60
650	A223	25c Sunrise at Protaras, vert.	.90	.75
651	A223	30c Village houses, Pera Orinis	1.25	.90
652	A223	50c Apollo Hylates Sanctuary	2.50	1.50
653	A223	£1 Troodos Mountain, vert.	5.00	5.00
654	A223	£5 Personification of Autumn, Dionyssos House, vert.	19.00	15.00
		Nos. 640-654 (15)	31.37	25.87

For surcharges see Nos. 684-685, 712.

Europa A224

Designs: 6c, Ceramic figures playing the double flute, lyre and tambourine, 7th-6th century B.C. 15c, Cypriot violin, lute, flute, the Fourth Women's Dance from the Cyprus Suite.

1985, May 6   Litho.   Perf. 12½
655	A224	6c multicolored	.22	.22
656	A224	15c multicolored	.55	.55

Republic of Cyprus, 25th Anniv. — A225

UN 40th Anniv. — A229

Natl. Liberation Movement, 30th Anniv. — A226

Intl. Youth Year A227

Solon Michaelides (1905-1979), Conductor, European Music Year — A228

Perf. 14½ (#657), 14½x14, 15 (#661)
1985, Sept. 23   Litho.
657	A225	4c multicolored	.15	.15
658	A226	6c multicolored	.22	.22
659	A227	13c multicolored	.48	.48
660	A228	15c multicolored	.55	.55
661	A229	20c multicolored	.75	.75
		Nos. 657-661 (5)	2.15	2.15

Christmas — A230

Murals of the St. Ioannis Lampadistis Monastery, Kalopanyiotis: 4c, Virgin Mary's Visit to Elizabeth. 13c, The Nativity. 20c, The Candlemas, Church of Our Lady of Assinous, Nikitari.

1985, Nov. 18   Litho.   Perf. 12½
662	A230	4c multicolored	.15	.15
663	A230	13c multicolored	.52	.52
664	A230	20c multicolored	.80	.80
		Nos. 662-664 (3)	1.47	1.47

Hellenistic Platinum Spoon A231

Designs: 20c, Ionian helmet, foot of a sculpture. 25c, Union of Eros and Intellect personified, abstract. 30c, Statue profile.

1986, Feb. 17   Perf. 15x14
665	A231	15c multicolored	.60	.60
666	A231	20c multicolored	.80	.80
667	A231	25c multicolored	1.00	1.00
668	A231	30c multicolored	1.25	1.25
a.		Souvenir sheet of 4, #665-668	9.00	9.00
		Nos. 665-668 (4)	3.65	3.65

Construction of the New Archaeological Museum, Nicosia. Department of Antiquities, 50th anniv. No. 668a sold for £1.

Europa Issue

Mouflon, Cedar Trees A232

1986, Apr. 28   Litho.   Perf. 14x13
669	A232	7c shown	.30	.30
670	A232	17c Flamingos, Larnaca Salt Lake	.80	.80

Seashells A233

1986, July 1   Perf. 14x13½
671	A233	5c Chlamys pesfelis	.24	.24
672	A233	7c Charonia variegata	.30	.30
673	A233	18c Murex brandaris	.60	.60
674	A233	25c Cypraea spurca	.85	.85
		Nos. 671-674 (4)	1.99	1.99

Overseas Cypriots Year A234

Halley's Comet A235

Anniversaries and events.

Perf. 13¹/₂x13

1986, Oct. 13   Litho.   Wmk. 344
675 A234 15c multicolored   .90   .90
676 A235 18c shown   1.10 1.10
677 A235 18c Comet tail, Edmond
                 Halley   1.10 1.10
  a.   Pair, #676-677   2.25 2.25
         Nos. 675-677 (3)   3.10 3.10

No. 677a has continuous design.

Road Safety A236

1986, Nov. 10   Perf. 14x13
678 A236 5c Pedestrian crossing   .20   .20
679 A236 7c Helmet, motorcycle
                 controls   .28   .28
680 A236 18c Seatbelt, rearview mir-
                 ror   .70   .70
         Nos. 678-680 (3)   1.18 1.18

Intl. Peace Year, Christmas — A237

Nativity frescoes (details): 5c, Church of Panayia tou Araka. 15c, Church of Panayia tou Moutoulla. 17c, Church of St. Nicholaos tis Steyis.

1986, Nov. 24   Perf. 13¹/₂x14
681 A237 5c multicolored   .25   .25
682 A237 15c multicolored   .75   .75
683 A237 17c multicolored   .85   .85
         Nos. 681-683 (3)   1.85 1.85

Nos. 645 and 647 Surcharged
Perf. 14x15, 15x14

1986, Oct. 13   Litho.   Wmk. 344
684 A223 7c on 6c multi   .30   .30
685 A223 18c on 13c multi   .75   .75

Miniature Sheet

ΚΥΠΡΟΣ CYPRUS KIBRIS

Troodos Churches on UNESCO World Heritage List — A238

Churches and frescoes: a, Assinou, Nikitari. b, Moutoulla, Moutoullas. c, Podithou, Galata. d, Ayios Ioannis Lampadistis, Kalopanayiotis. e, Timios Stavros, Pelentri. f, Stavros Ayiasmati, Platanistassa. g, Archangelos Pedoula, Pedoulas. h, Ayios Nicolaos tis Steyis, Kakopetria. i, Araka, Lagoudera.

Perf. 12¹/₂

1987, Apr. 22   Photo.   Unwmk.
686   Sheet of 9   6.00 6.00
  a.-i. A238 15c any single   .65   .65

Europa Issue

Modern Architecture A239

Perf. 14x13¹/₂

1987, May 11   Litho.   Wmk. 344
687 A239 7c Central Bank of Cyprus .28   .28
688 A239 18c Cyprus Communications
                 Authority   .75   .75

Ships Named Kyrenia A240

1987, Oct. 3
689 A240 2c The Kyrenia, Kyrenia
                 Castle   .15   .15
690 A240 3c Kyrenia II, Perama
                 Shipyard   .15   .15
691 A240 15c Kyrenia II, Paphos   .22   .22
692 A240 17c Kyrenia II, NY Harbor .75   .75
         Nos. 689-692 (4)   1.27 1.27

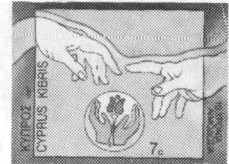

Blood Donation Coordinating Committee, 10th Anniv. A241

European Campaign for Countryside A242

TROODOS '87 — A243

Perf. 14x13¹/₂

1987, Nov. 2   Litho.   Wmk. 344
693 A241 7c multicolored   .30   .30
694 A242 15c multicolored   .65   .65
695 A243 20c multicolored   .85   .85
         Nos. 693-695 (3)   1.80 1.80

Christmas A244

1987, Nov. 30   Perf. 14
696 A244 5c Babe in a manger   .22   .22
697 A244 15c Ornament   .65   .65
698 A244 17c Fruit bowl   .72   .72
         Nos. 696-698 (3)   1.59 1.59

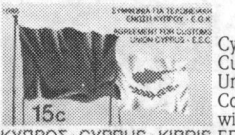

Cyprus Customs Union in Cooperation with the EEC — A245

Perf. 13x13¹/₂

1988, Jan. 11   Wmk. 344
699 A245 15c Natl. and EEC flags   .65   .65
700 A245 18c Maps   .80   .80

A246

Europa (Communication and transportation): No. 701, Electronic mail (Intelpost). No. 702, Cellular

---

telephone system. No. 703, Cyprus Airways, technology vs. ecology (jet, 3 flamingos). No. 704, Cyprus Airways (jet, 4 flamingos).

1988, May 9   Perf. 14x14¹/₂
701 A246 7c multicolored   .32   .32
702 A246 7c multicolored   .32   .32
  a.   Pair, #701-702   .65   .65
703 A246 18c multicolored   .82   .82
704 A246 18c multicolored   .82   .82
  a.   Pair, #703-704   1.65 1.65
         Nos. 701-704 (4)   2.28 2.28

1988 Summer Olympics, Seoul — A247

Unwmk.
1988, June 27   Photo.   Perf. 12
Granite Paper
705 A247 5c Sailing   .22   .22
706 A247 7c Track   .32   .32
707 A247 10c Marksmanship   .45   .45
708 A247 20c Judo   .90   .90
         Nos. 705-708 (4)   1.89 1.89

Non-Aligned Foreign Minister's Conference — A248

Designs: 10c, Natl. coat of arms. 50c, Jawaharlal Nehru, Tito, Gamal Abdel Nasser and Makarios III (1913-77).

Perf. 14x13¹/₂

1988, Sept. 5   Litho.   Wmk. 344
709 A248 1c shown   .15   .15
710 A248 10c multicolored   .45   .45
711 A248 50c multicolored   2.15 2.15
         Nos. 709-711 (3)   2.75 2.75

No. 643 Surcharged   **15c =**

1988, Oct. 3   Litho.   Perf. 15x14
712 A223 15c on 4c multi   .85   .85

Christmas — A249   A250

Perf. 13¹/₂x14

1988, Nov. 28   Litho.   Wmk. 344
713 A249 5c Candlemas   .22   .22
714 A249 15c Madonna and child   .65   .65
715 A249 17c Adoration of the Magi .75   .75
         Nos. 713-715 (3)   1.62 1.62

1988, Dec. 10
716 A250 25c lt ultra & int blue 1.10 1.10
UN Declaration of Human Rights, 40th anniv.

3rd Games of Small European States, Nicosia A251

Perf. 13¹/₂

1989, Apr. 10   Litho.   Unwmk.
717 A251 1c Discus   .15   .15
718 A251 5c Javelin   .22   .22
719 A251 15c Wrestling   .65   .65
720 A251 18c Running   .80   .80

Size: 110x80mm
Imperf
721 A251 £1 Mythological woman,
                 laurel, bird   4.40 4.40
         Nos. 717-721 (5)   6.22 6.22

Various Children's Games A252

Perf. 13x13¹/₂

1989, May 8   Unwmk.
722 A252 7c multi (5 boys)   .30   .30
723 A252 7c multi (6 boys)   .30   .30
  a.   Pair, #722-723   .60   .60
724 A252 18c multi (6 boys)   .80   .80
725 A252 18c multi (5 boys)   .80   .80
  a.   Pair, #724-725   1.60 1.60
         Nos. 722-725 (4)   2.20 2.20

Europa.

French Revolution, Bicent. — A253

Perf. 11¹/₂

1989, July 7   Litho.   Unwmk.
Granite Paper
726 A253 18c multicolored   .80   .80

 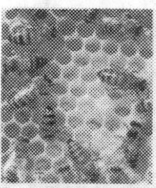

A254   A255

1989, Sept. 4   Perf. 13¹/₂
727 A254 15c multicolored   .62   .62
728 A255 30c multicolored   1.25 1.25

15c for Interparliamentary Union, cent. 30c for 9th Non-Aligned Summit Conf., Belgrade.

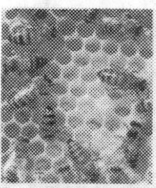 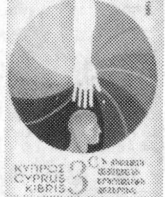

Apiculture — A256   Annivs. & Events — A257

1989, Oct. 15   Perf. 13¹/₂x14
729 A256 3c Honeycomb   .15   .15
730 A256 10c Gathering nectar   .42   .42
731 A256 15c Gathering nectar,
                 diff.   .62   .62
732 A256 18c Queen, worker bees   .75   .75
         Nos. 729-732 (4)   1.94 1.94

1989, Nov. 13

Designs: 3c, Armenian earthquake. 5c, Cyprus Philatelic Society. 7c, European Cancer Year. 17c, World Food Day.

733 A257 3c multicolored .15 .15
734 A257 5c multicolored .20 .20
735 A257 7c multicolored .28 .28
736 A257 17c multicolored .68 .68
Nos. 733-736 (4) 1.31 1.31

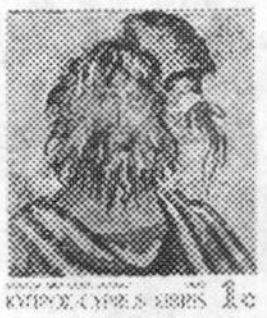
A258

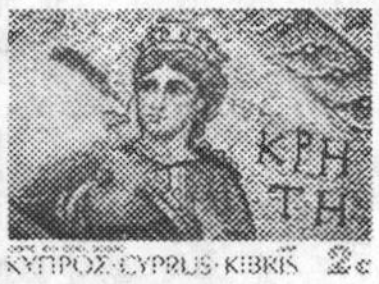
A259

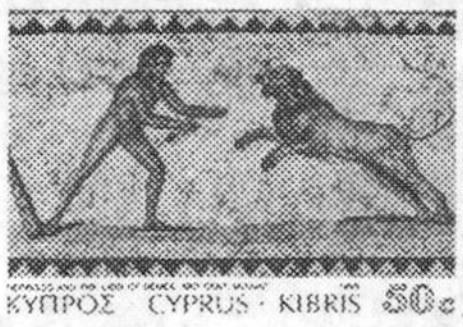
Mosaics, 3rd-5th Cent. A260

Details: 1c, Winter, from *The Four Seasons,* House of Dionysos. 2c, Personification of Crete, from *Theseus Slaying the Minotaur,* Villa of Theseus. 3c, Centaur and Maenad, from *The Dionysiac Procession,* House of Aion, vert. 4c, *Poseidon and Amymone,* House of Dionysos. 5c, Leda, from *Leda and the Swan,* House of Aion. 7c, Apollon, from *Apollo and Marsyas,* House of Aion. 10c, Hermes and Dionysos, from *Hermes Presenting Dionysos to Tropheus,* House of Aion, vert. 15c, Cassiopeia, from *Cassiopeia and the Nereids,* House of Aion. 18c, *Orpheus Playing the Lyre,* House of Orpheus. 20c, Nymphs preparing bath, from *Hermes Presenting Dionysos to Tropheus,* vert. 25c, Amazon holding double ax and reins, House of Orpheus, vert. 40c, Doris, one of 3 Nereids in *Cassiopeia and the Nereids.* 50c, Hercules and the lion, from *The First Labor of Hercules,* House of Orpheus. £1, *Apollon and Daphne,* House of Dionysos. £3, Cupid hunting, Villa of Theseus.

Perf. 13, 13x13½ (2c, 4c, 18c, 40c), 13½x13 (3c, 10c, 20c, 25c)

1989, Dec. 29

737 A258 1c multicolored .15 .15
738 A259 2c multicolored .15 .15
739 A259 3c multicolored .15 .15
740 A259 4c multicolored .16 .16
741 A258 5c multicolored .20 .20
742 A258 7c multicolored .28 .28
743 A259 10c multicolored .40 .40
744 A258 15c multicolored .60 .60
745 A259 18c multicolored .75 .75
746 A259 20c multicolored .80 .80
747 A259 25c multicolored 1.00 1.00
748 A259 40c multicolored 1.60 1.60

Perf. 13½x14

749 A260 50c multicolored 2.00 2.00
750 A260 £1 multicolored 4.00 4.00
751 A260 £3 multicolored 12.00 12.00
Nos. 737-751 (15) 24.24 24.24

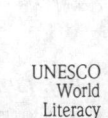

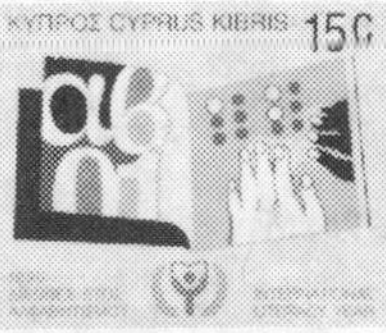
UNESCO World Literacy Year — A261

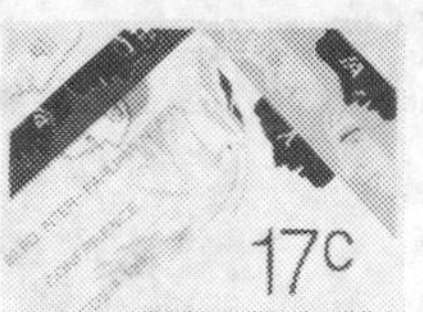
83rd Interparliamentary Conference, Nicosia — A262

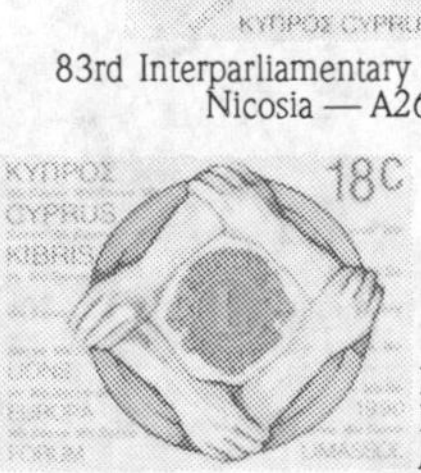
Lions Europa Forum A263

Anniversaries & events.

1990, Apr. 3 ***Perf. 14x13½***

752 A261 15c multicolored .65 .65
753 A262 17c multicolored .72 .72
754 A263 18c multicolored .75 .75
Nos. 752-754 (3) 2.12 2.12

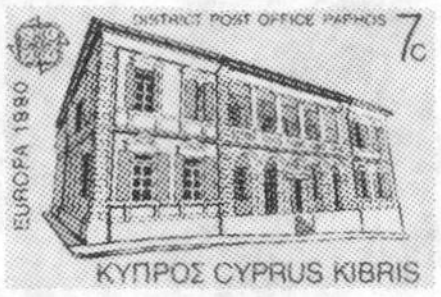
Europa A264

Post Offices.

1990, May 10 Litho. ***Perf. 13x13½***

755 A264 7c Paphos .30 .30
756 A264 18c Limassol City Center .75 .75

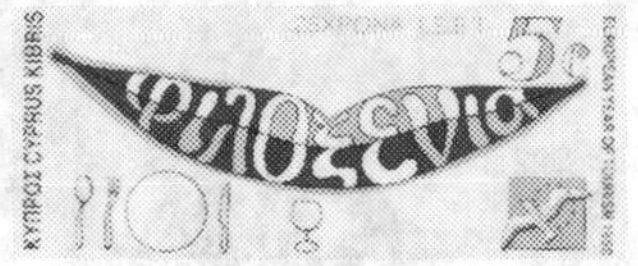
European Year of Tourism — A265

Designs: 5c, Hotel and Catering Institute, 25th anniv. 7c, Holy Church of St. Lazarus, 1100th anniv. 15c, Female silhouette, butterflies. 18c, Male silhouette, birds.

1990, July 9 ***Perf. 14***

757 A265 5c multicolored .20 .20
758 A265 7c multicolored .30 .30
759 A265 15c multicolored .65 .65
760 A265 18c multicolored .75 .75
Nos. 757-760 (4) 1.90 1.90

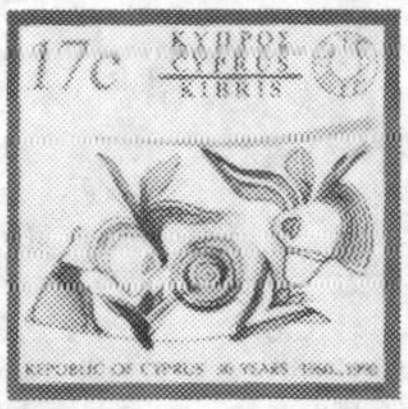
Republic of Cyprus, 30th Anniv. A266

1990, Sept. 29 Photo. ***Perf. 11½***

761 A266 15c Sun .65 .65
762 A266 17c shown .72 .72
763 A266 18c Fish .75 .75
764 A266 40c Birds, flowers 1.75 1.75

Size: 90x90mm

Imperf

765 A266 £1 Stylized bird 4.25 4.25
Nos. 761-765 (5) 8.12 8.12

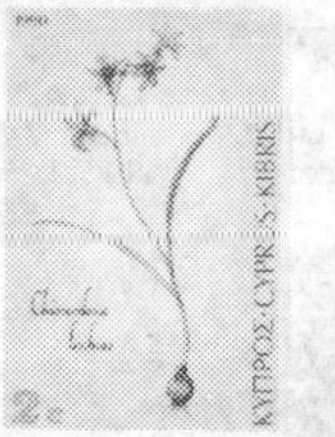
Flowers — A267

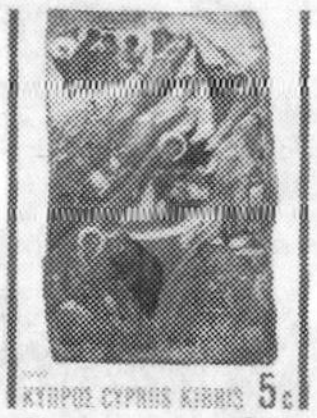
Christmas — A268

1990, Nov. 5 Litho. ***Perf. 13½x13***

766 A267 2c Chionodoxa lochiae .15 .15
767 A267 3c Pancrayium maritimum .15 .15
768 A267 5c Paeonia mascula .22 .22
769 A267 7c Cyclamen cyprium .32 .32
770 A267 15c Tulipa cypria .68 .68
771 A267 18c Crocus cyprius .80 .80
Nos. 766-771 (6) 2.32 2.32

1990, Dec. 3 ***Perf. 13½x14***

772 A268 5c Nativity .22 .22
773 A268 15c Virgin and Child .66 .66
774 A268 17c Nativity, diff. .75 .75
Nos. 772-774 (3) 1.63 1.63

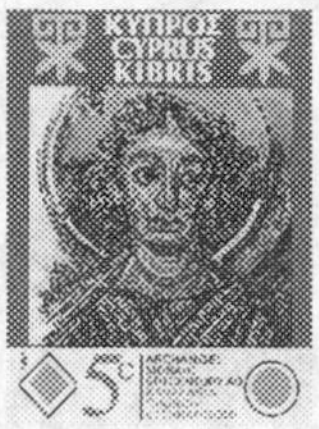
Mosaics From Kanakaria Church — A269

1991, Mar. 28 Photo. ***Perf. 12***

Granite Paper

775 A269 5c Archangel .22 .22
776 A269 15c Christ Child .66 .66
777 A269 17c St. James .75 .75
778 A269 18c St. Matthew .80 .80
Nos. 775-778 (4) 2.43 2.43

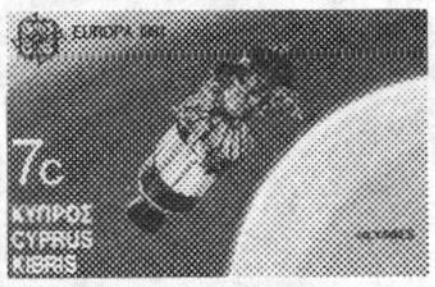
Europa A270

1991, May 6 Litho. ***Perf. 13x13½***

779 A270 7c Spacecraft Ulysses .30 .30
780 A270 18c Spacecraft Giotto .80 .80

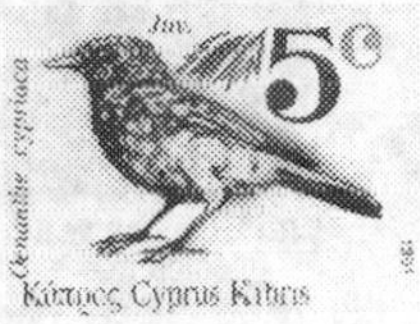
Oenanthe Cypriaca (Cyprus Wheatear) A271

1991, July 4 Litho. ***Perf. 13½***

781 A271 5c Juvenile bird .22 .22
782 A271 7c Autumn plumage .30 .30
783 A271 15c Male bird .65 .65
784 A271 30c Female bird 1.30 1.30
Nos. 781-784 (4) 2.47 2.47

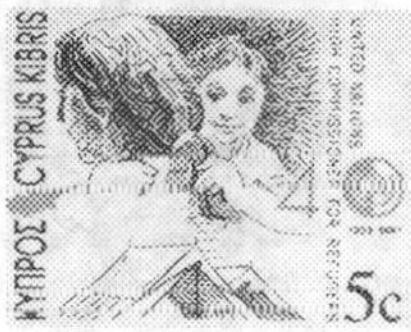
UN High Commissioner for Refugees, 40th Anniv. A272

1991, Oct. 7 Litho. ***Perf. 14x13½***

785 A272 5c shown .22 .22
786 A272 15c Legs .65 .65
787 A272 18c Faces .80 .80
Nos. 785-787 (3) 1.67 1.67

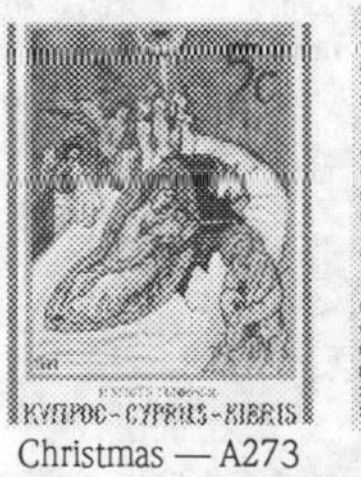
Christmas — A273

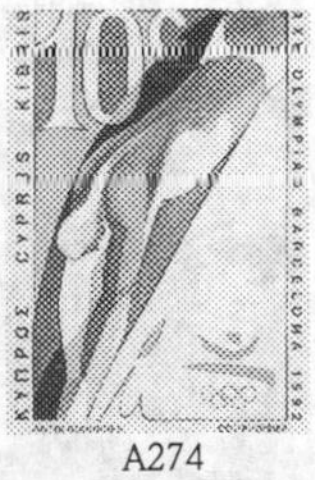
A274

1991, Nov. 25 Litho. ***Perf. 13½***

788 A273 5c Nativity scene .22 .22
789 A273 15c St. Basil .65 .65
790 A273 17c Baptism of Jesus .75 .75
a. Strip of 3, #788-790 1.65 1.65

Strips of 3 are from sheets of 9.

1992, Apr. 3 Litho. ***Perf. 12***

Granite Paper

791 A274 10c Swimming .42 .42
792 A274 20c Long jump .85 .85
793 A274 30c Running 1.30 1.30
794 A274 35c Discus 1.50 1.50
Nos. 791-794 (4) 4.07 4.07

1992 Summer Olympics, Barcelona.

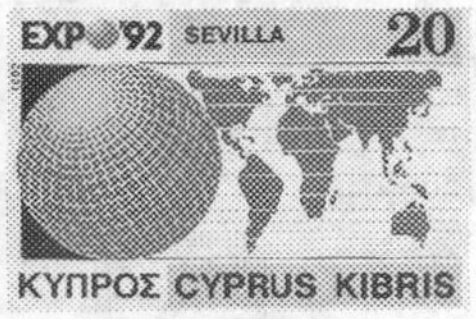
Expo '92, Seville A275

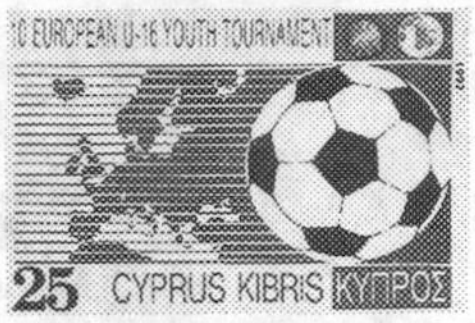
10th Youth Under 16 European Soccer Tournament — A276

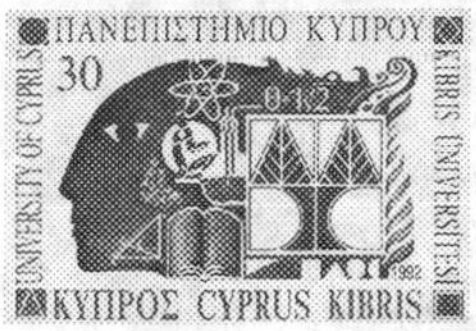
Opening of University of Cyprus A277

1992, Apr. 20 Litho. ***Perf. 14***

795 A275 20c multicolored .85 .85
796 A276 25c multicolored 1.10 1.10
797 A277 30c multicolored 1.30 1.30
Nos. 795-797 (3) 3.25 3.25

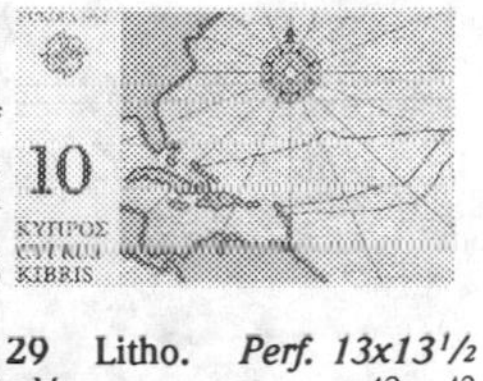
Discovery of America, 500th Anniv. A278

1992, May 29 Litho. ***Perf. 13x13½***

798 A278 10c Map .42 .42
799 A278 10c Embarkation at Palos .42 .42
a. Pair, #798-799 .85 .85
800 A278 30c Three ships 1.30 1.30
801 A278 30c Columbus 1.30 1.30
a. Pair, #800-801 2.60 2.60
Nos. 798-801 (4) 3.44 3.44

Europa.

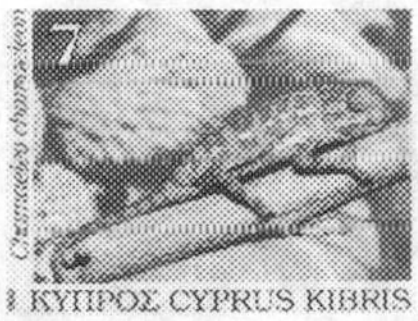
Reptiles A279

Designs: 7c, Chamaeleo chamaeleon. 10c, Lacerta laevis troodica. 15c, Mauremys caspica. 20c, Coluber cypriensis.

1992, Sept. 14 Litho. ***Perf. 14x13½***

802 A279 7c multicolored .32 .32
803 A279 10c multicolored .48 .48
804 A279 15c multicolored .70 .70
805 A279 20c multicolored .95 .95
Nos. 802-805 (4) 2.45 2.45

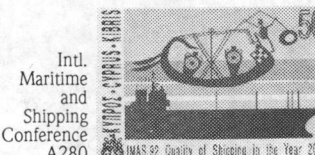

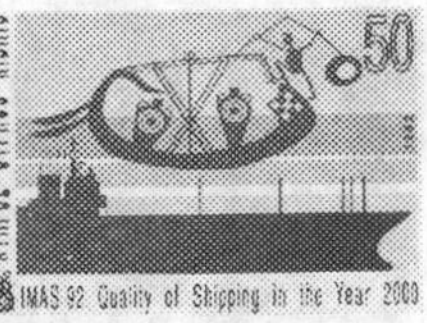
Intl. Maritime and Shipping Conference A280

Unwmk.

1992, Nov. 9 Litho. ***Perf. 14***

806 A280 50c multicolored 2.20 2.20

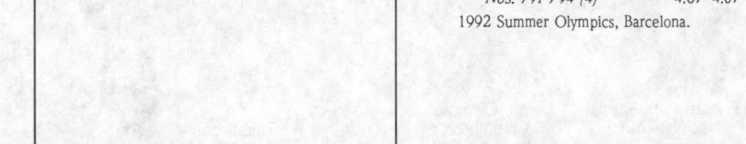

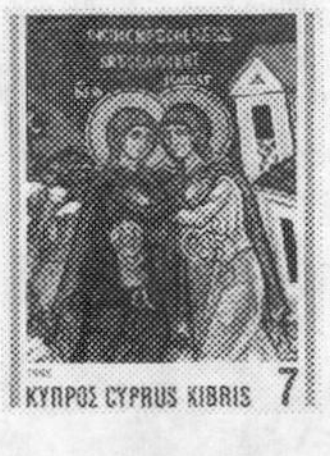
Christmas — A281

Church wall paintings: 7c, , "Virgin Mary Greeting Elizabeth," Church of Timios Stavros, Pelendri. 15c, "The Virgin and Child," Church of Panayia tou Araka. 20c, "Holy Mother Odigitria," Church of Ayios Nicolaos tis Steyis.

1992, Nov. 9   *Perf. 13¹/₂x14*

807	A281	7c multicolored	.32	.32
808	A281	15c multicolored	.70	.70
809	A281	20c multicolored	.95	.95
		Nos. 807-809 (3)	1.97	1.97

Pancyprian Gymnasium, Cent. — A282

1993, Feb. 15   Litho.   *Perf. 14*

810	A282	10c multicolored	.40	.40

Europa A283

Designs: 10c, Bronze sculpture, Motherhood, by N. Dymiotis (1930-1990), vert. 30c, Applique, Motherhood, by Savva (1924-1968).

1993, Apr. 3   *Perf. 13¹/₂x14, 14x13¹/₂*

811	A283	10c multicolored	.40	.40
812	A283	30c multicolored	1.20	1.20

13th European Cup for Women Athletes —A284

Scouting in Cyprus, 80th Anniv. — A285

Water Skiing Moufflon Encouragement Cup — A286

Archbishop Makarios III, 80th Anniv. of Birth A287

Perf. 13¹/₂x14, 14x13¹/₂

1993, May 24   Litho.

813	A284	7c multicolored	.30	.30
814	A285	10c multicolored	.45	.45
815	A286	20c multicolored	.90	.90
a.		Inscribed "MUFFLON"	35.00	
816	A287	25c multicolored	1.10	1.10
		Nos. 813-816 (4)	2.75	2.75

Fish — A288

1993, Sept. 6   Litho.   *Perf. 14x13¹/₂*

817	A288	7c Holocentrus ruber	.28	.28
818	A288	15c Scorpaena scrofa	.60	.60
819	A288	20c Serranus scriba	.80	.80
820	A288	30c Balistes capriscus	1.25	1.25
		Nos. 817-820 (4)	2.93	2.93

Maritime Cyprus A289

1993, Oct. 4   *Perf. 14*

821	A289	25c multicolored	1.00	1.00

12th Commonwealth Summit Conference — A290

1993, Oct. 4   *Perf. 14x13¹/₂*

822	A290	35c red brown & tan	1.40	1.40
823	A290	40c olive brown & tan	1.65	1.65

Christmas — A291

Designs: 7c, Carved wooden cross, Stavrovouni Monastery. 20c, Crucifixion, cross from Lefkara Church. 25c, Nativity, cross from Pedoulas Church, horiz.

1993, Nov. 22   Litho.   *Perf. 13¹/₂x14*

824	A291	7c multicolored	.28	.28
825	A291	20c multicolored	.80	.80

Perf. 14x13¹/₂

826	A291	25c multicolored	1.00	1.00
		Nos. 824-826 (3)	2.08	2.08

Copper Industry A292

Europa: 10c, Early smelting of copper. 30c, Map, boat, copper ingot.

1994, Mar. 1   Litho.   *Perf. 13x13¹/₂*

827	A292	10c multicolored	.40	.40
828	A292	30c multicolored	1.25	1.25

Persons with Special Needs — A293

Intl. Olympic Committee, Cent. — A294

 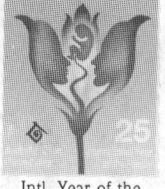

World Gymnasiade, Nicosia — A295

Intl. Year of the Family — A296

1994, May 9   Litho.   *Perf. 13*

829	A293	7c multicolored	.28	.28
830	A294	15c multicolored	.60	.60
831	A295	20c multicolored	.80	.80
832	A296	25c multicolored	1.00	1.00
		Nos. 829-832 (4)	2.68	2.68

Turkish Invasion and Occupation of Cyprus, 20th Anniv. A297

1994, June 27   Litho.   *Perf. 14*

833	A297	10c Human rights	.40	.40
834	A297	50c Cultural heritage	2.00	2.00

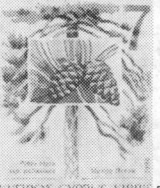

Trees — A298

Designs: 7c, Pinus nigra. 15c, Cedrus libani. 20c, Quercus alnifolia. 30c, Arbutus andrachne.

1994, Oct. 10   Litho.   *Perf. 13¹/₂*

835	A298	7c multicolored	.28	.28
836	A298	15c multicolored	.60	.60
837	A298	20c multicolored	.80	.80
838	A298	30c multicolored	1.25	1.25
		Nos. 835-838 (4)	2.93	2.93

ICAO, 50th Anniv. A299

1994, Nov. 21   Litho.   *Perf. 14*

839	A299	30c multicolored	1.25	1.25

Christmas A300

Designs: 7c, Virgin Mary (Vlahernitissa). 20c, Nativity. 25c, Archangel Michael.

1994, Nov. 21   *Perf. 13¹/₂*

840	A300	7c multicolored	.28	.28
841	A300	20c multicolored	.80	.80
842	A300	25c multicolored	1.00	1.00
		Nos. 840-842 (3)	2.08	2.08

Traditional Costumes — A301

Costumes: 1c, Female, Phapos. 2c, Bridal, Karpass. 3c, Female, Phapos, diff. 5c, Female, Messaoria. 7c, Bridegroom's. 10c, Shepherd's, Messaoria. 15c, Festive female, Nicosia. 20c, Festive female, Karpass. 25c, Female, Mountain-Pitsillia. 30c, Festive female, Karpass, diff. 35c, Rural male. 40c, Plain festive male, Messaoria. 50c, Urban male. £1, Urban festive female, Sarka.

1994, Dec. 27   Litho.   *Perf. 13¹/₂x13*

843	A301	1c multicolored	.15	.15
844	A301	2c multicolored	.15	.15
845	A301	3c multicolored	.15	.15
846	A301	5c multicolored	.22	.22
847	A301	7c multicolored	.30	.30
848	A301	10c multicolored	.45	.45
849	A301	15c multicolored	.65	.65
850	A301	20c multicolored	.90	.90
851	A301	25c multicolored	1.10	1.10
852	A301	30c multicolored	1.25	1.25
853	A301	35c multicolored	1.40	1.40
854	A301	40c multicolored	1.75	1.75
855	A301	50c multicolored	2.25	2.25
856	A301	£1 multicolored	4.50	4.50
		Nos. 843-856 (14)	15.22	15.22

Third Intl. Congress of Cypriot Studies — A302

Excavations: 20c, Hearth room, Ashlar building, Paliotaverna. 30c, Hall, Agios Demetrios area, Kalavasos.
£1, Old Nicosia Archbishoρic building, 18th cent.

1995, Feb. 27   Litho.   *Perf. 14*

859	A302	20c multicolored	.90	.90
860	A302	30c multicolored	1.40	1.40

Size: 107x71mm

Imperf

861	A302	£1 multicolored	4.50	4.50
		Nos. 859-861 (3)	6.80	6.80

A303   A304

Liberation Monument, Nicosia: a, People walking left. b, Statue of Liberty, prisoners leaving prison. c, People walking right.

1995, Mar. 31   Litho.   *Perf. 13x14*

862		Strip of 3	2.75	2.75
a.-c.		A303 20c any single	.90	.90

No. 862 is a continuous design.
Formation of EOKA (Natl. Organization of Cypriot Struggle), 40th anniv.

1995, May 8   Litho.   *Perf. 13¹/₂*

Europa: 10c, Concentration camp prisoners, dove, rainbow, map of Europe. 30c, Prisoner, dove.

863	A304	10c multicolored	.45	.45
864	A304	30c multicolored	1.25	1.25

Liberation of the concentration camps, 50th anniv.

Health A305

Designs: 7c, Proper nutrition, exercise, vert. 10c, Fight against AIDS. 15c, Fight against illegal drugs. 20c, Stop smoking campaign, vert.

1995, June 26 Litho. *Perf. 13½*

865	A305	7c multicolored	.30	.30
866	A305	10c multicolored	.45	.45
867	A305	15c multicolored	.70	.70
868	A305	20c multicolored	.95	.95
		Nos. 865-868 (4)	2.40	2.40

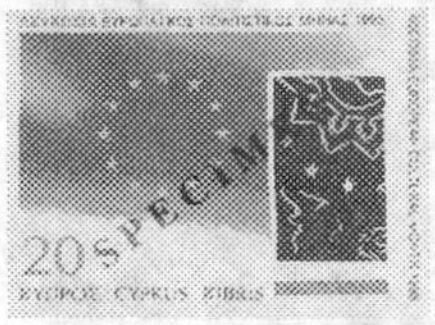

European Cultural Month A306

1995, Sept. 18 Litho. *Perf. 13x13½*

869	A306	20c shown	.95	.95
870	A306	25c Map of Europe, building	1.25	1.25

Souvenir Sheet

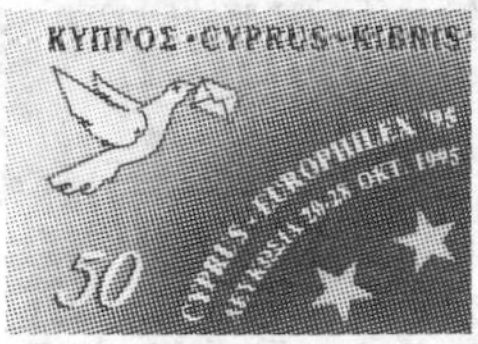

Eurofilex '95 A307

Designs: a, Dove carrying letter, stars. b, Stars, exhibition emblem. Illustration reduced.

1995, Sept. 18 Litho. *Perf. 14*

871	A307	Sheet of 2	4.25	4.25
a.-b.		50c any single	2.10	2.10

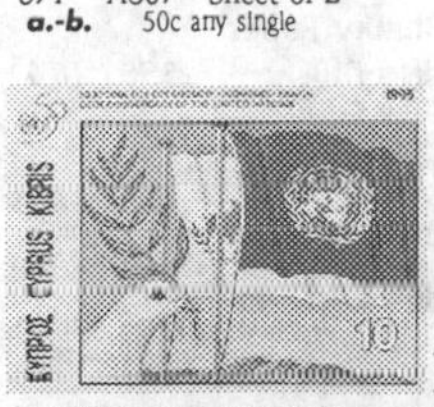

UN, 50th Anniv. A308

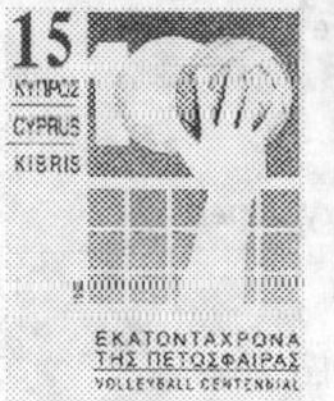

Volleyball, Cent. — A309

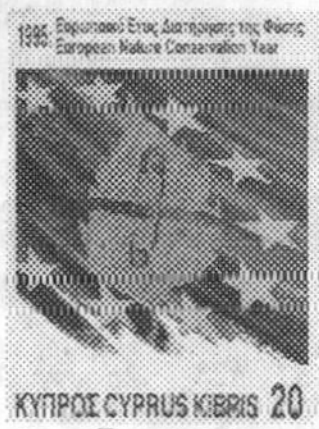

European Conservation Year — A310

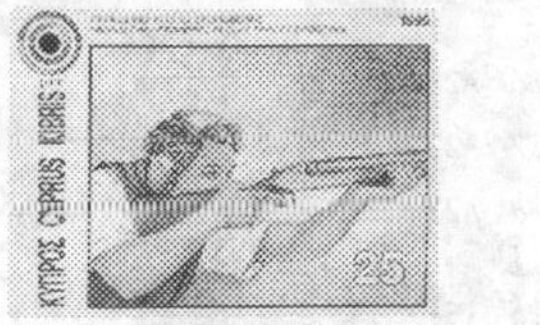

World Clay Target Shooting Championships — A311

Perf. 13x13½, 13½x13

1995, Oct. 24 Litho.

872	A308	10c multicolored	.45	.45
873	A309	15c multicolored	.65	.65
874	A310	20c multicolored	.90	.90
875	A311	25c multicolored	1.10	1.10
		Nos. 872-875 (4)	3.10	3.10

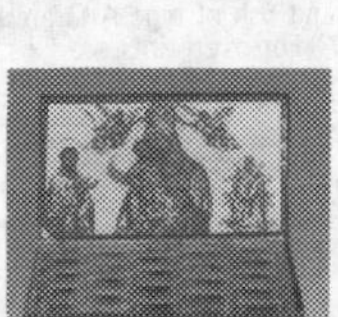

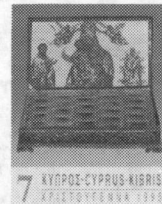

Christmas — A312

Various reliquaries, Kykko Monastery.

1995, Nov. 27 Litho. *Perf. 13½x13*

876	A312	7c multicolored	.30	.30
877	A312	20c multicolored	.90	.90
878	A312	25c multicolored	1.10	1.10
		Nos. 876-878 (3)	2.30	2.30

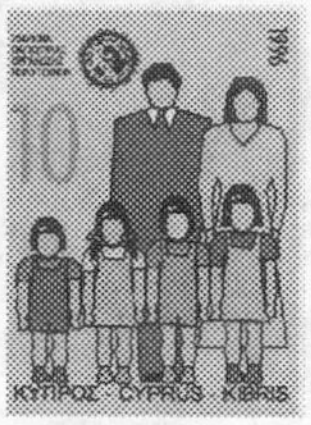

A313

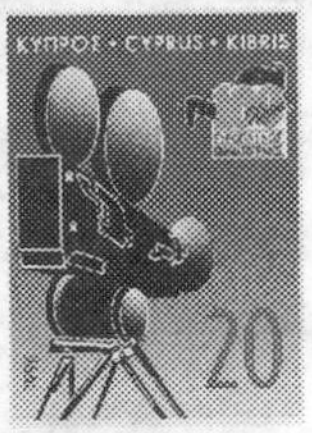

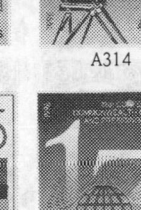

A314

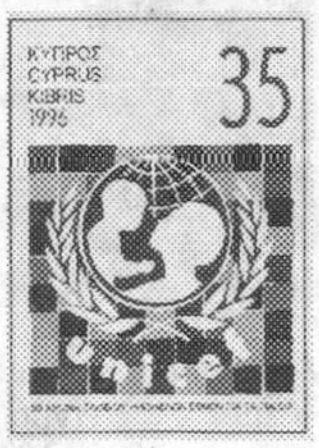

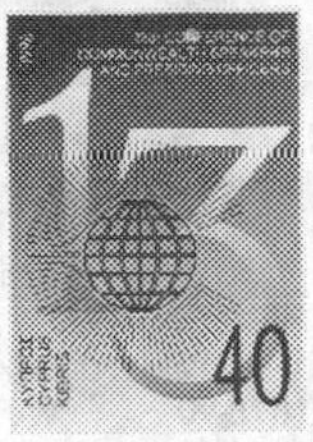

Anniversaries and Events

A315 A316

1996, Jan. 4 Litho. *Perf. 13½x13*

879	A313	10c multicolored	.40	.40
880	A314	20c multicolored	.80	.80
881	A315	35c multicolored	1.50	1.50
882	A316	40c multicolored	1.75	1.75
		Nos. 879-882 (4)	4.45	4.45

Pancyprian Organization of Large Families, 25th anniv. (#879). Motion pictures, cent. (#880). UNICEF, 50th anniv. (#881). 13th Conf. of Commonwealth Speakers and Presiding Officers (#882).

POSTAL TAX STAMPS

Catalogue values for unused stamps in this section are for Never Hinged items.

No. 352 Surcharged

REFUGEE
FUND
ΤΑΜΕΙΟΝ
ΠΡΟΣΦΥΓΩΝ
GOCMENLER
FONU

10M

Perf. 12x12½

1974, Dec. 2 Wmk. 344

RA1	A104	10m on 5m multi	.15	.15

Nos. RA1-RA12 for the Refugee Fund.

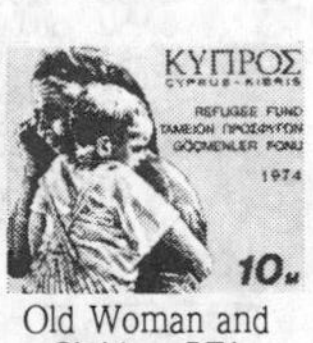

Old Woman and Child — PT1

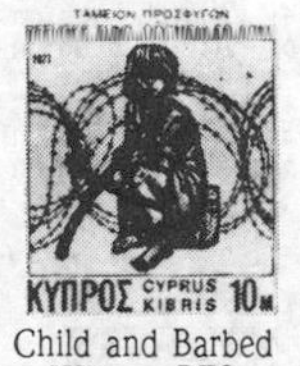

Child and Barbed Wire — PT2

1974, Oct. 1 *Perf. 12½x13½*

RA2	PT1	10m gray & black	.15	.15

Perf. 13x12½

1977, Jan. 10 Litho. Wmk. 344

RA3	PT2	10m black	.15	.15

Inscribed 1984

1984, June 18 *Perf. 13x12½*

RA4	PT2	1c black	.15	.15

There are two types of No. RA4.

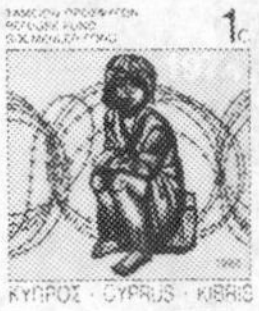

Inscribed 1988 — PT3

1988-95 *Perf. 13x12½*

RA5	PT3	1c black & pale gray	.15	.15
		Perf. 11½x12		
RA6	PT3	1c Inscribed 1989	.15	.15
RA7	PT3	1c Inscribed 1990	.15	.15
		Unwmk.		
		Perf. 13		
RA8	PT3	1c Inscribed 1991	.15	.15
RA9	PT3	1c Inscribed 1992	.15	.15
RA10	PT3	1c Inscribed 1993	.15	.15
RA11	PT3	1c Inscribed 1994	.15	.15
		Perf. 14½x13½		
RA12	PT3	1c Inscribed 1995	.15	.15
		Set value	.50	.50

Issued: #RA5, 9/12/88; #RA6, 9/4/89; #RA7, 9/29/90; #RA8, 10/7/91; #RA9, 11/9/92; #RA10, 1993; #RA11, 11/21/94; #RA12, 1995.

EAST AFRICA AND UGANDA PROTECTORATES

'ēst 'a-fri-kə and ü-'gan-də prə-'tek-t(ə-)rəts

LOCATION — Central East Africa, bordering on the Indian Ocean
GOVT. — Former British Protectorate
AREA — 350,000 sq. mi. (approx.)
POP. — 6,503,507 (approx.)
CAPITAL — Mombasa

This territory, formerly administered by the British East Africa Colony, was divided between Kenya Colony and the Uganda Protectorate. See Kenya, Uganda and Tanzania.

16 Annas = 1 Rupee
100 Cents = 1 Rupee (1907)

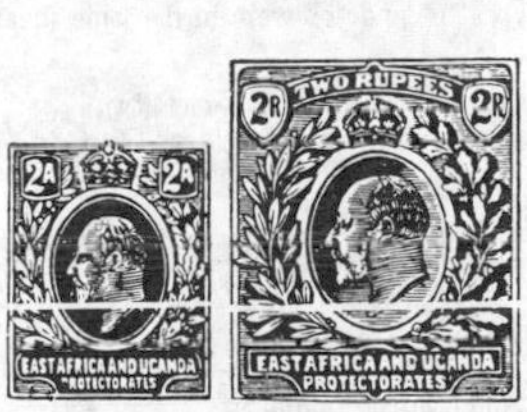

King Edward VII

A1 A2

1903 Typo. Wmk. 2 *Perf. 14*

1	A1	½a gray green	2.00	2.50
2	A1	1a car & black	1.90	.50
3	A1	2a vio & dull vio	7.00	7.00
4	A1	2½a ultramarine	15.00	*30.00*
5	A1	3a gray grn & brn	12.50	*27.50*
6	A1	4a blk & gray grn	13.50	13.50
7	A1	5a org brn & blk	15.00	*32.50*
8	A1	8a pale blue & blk	15.00	*25.00*
		Wmk. 1		
9	A2	1r gray green	12.50	*35.00*
10	A2	2r vio & dull vio	40.00	37.50
11	A2	3r blk & gray grn	65.00	*85.00*
12	A2	4r lt green & blk	75.00	*80.00*
13	A2	5r car & black	80.00	*125.00*
14	A2	10r ultra & black	110.00	125.00
15	A2	20r ol gray & blk	650.00	*700.00*
16	A2	50r org brn & blk	1,500.	*1,250.*
		Nos. 1-14 (14)	463.40	*625.00*

Nos. 9 and 14 are on both ordinary and chalky paper.

1904-07 Wmk. 3 Chalky Paper

17	A1	½a gray green	3.50	1.00
18	A1	1a car & black	2.50	.20
19	A1	2a vio & dull vio	2.50	1.10
20	A1	2½a ultramarine	6.50	*16.00*
a.		2½a blue	6.00	*15.00*
21	A1	3a gray grn & brn	3.50	*20.00*
22	A1	4a blk & gray grn	8.00	*13.00*
23	A1	5a org brn & blk	6.00	*13.00*
24	A1	8a pale blue & blk	6.00	7.50
25	A2	1r gray green	21.00	*45.00*
26	A2	2r vio & dl vio	25.00	*40.00*
27	A2	3r blk & gray grn	37.50	*70.00*
28	A2	4r lt green & blk	45.00	*110.00*
29	A2	5r car & black	50.00	*70.00*
29A	A2	10r ultra & black	150.00	150.00
30	A2	20r ol gray & blk	450.00	500.00
30A	A2	50r org brn & blk	1,200.	*1,200.*
		Nos. 17-29 (13)	217.00	*406.80*

Nos. 17-19, 21-24 are on both ordinary and chalky paper. No. 20 is on ordinary paper.

1907-08

31	A1	1c brown ('08)	.25	.15
32	A1	3c gray green	2.50	.20
33	A1	6c carmine	2.00	.30
34	A1	10c citron & violet	*7.50*	*7.50*
35	A1	12c red vio & dl vio	4.00	2.50
36	A1	15c ultramarine	5.50	7.25
37	A1	25c blk & blue green	4.25	3.50
38	A1	50c org brn & green	6.50	9.50
39	A1	75c pale bl & gray blk ('08)	5.25	*14.00*
		Nos. 31-39 (9)	37.75	44.90

Nos. 31, 32, 33 and 36 are on ordinary paper.
There are two dies of the 6c differing very slightly in many details.

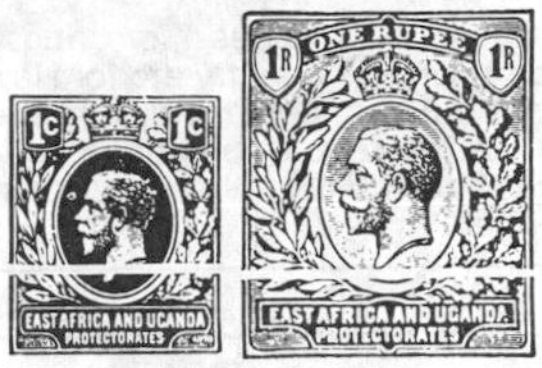

King George V

A3 A4

1912-18 Ordinary Paper Wmk. 3

40	A3	1c black	.25	.15
41	A3	3c green	1.75	.15
a.		Booklet pane of 6		
42	A3	6c carmine	.45	.15
a.		Booklet pane of 6		
43	A3	10c orange	1.75	.20
44	A3	12c gray	2.25	.40
45	A3	15c ultramarine	2.25	.30
		Chalky Paper		
46	A3	25c scar & blk, *yel*	.40	.45
47	A3	50c violet & black	1.25	.75
48	A3	75c black, *green*	1.25	11.00
a.		75c black, *emerald*	9.00	25.00
b.		75c blk, *blue grn*, olive back	5.25	4.50
c.		75c blk, *emerald*, olive back	35.00	*90.00*
49	A4	1r black, *green*	1.50	4.00
a.		1r black, *emerald*	5.00	30.00
50	A4	2r blk & red, *bl*	17.50	*27.50*
51	A4	3r gray grn & vio	17.50	40.00
52	A4	4r grn & red, *yel*	40.00	80.00
53	A4	5r dl vio & ultra	40.00	*85.00*
54	A4	10r grn & red, *grn*	65.00	*110.00*
55	A4	20r vio & blk, *red*	325.00	200.00
56	A4	20r bl & violet, *blue* ('18)	300.00	200.00
57	A4	50r gray grn & rose red	700.00	700.00
58	A4	100r blk & vio, *red*	*3,500.*	*2,000.*
59	A4	500r red & grn, *grn*		
		Nos. 40-54 (15)	193.10	360.05

1914 Surface-colored Paper

60	A3	25c scarlet & blk, *yel*	1.25	1.75
61	A3	75c black, *green*	1.90	*4.75*

Stamps of types A3 and A4 with watermark 4 are listed under Kenya, Uganda and Tanzania.
The 1r through 50r with revenue cancellations sell for minimal prices. The 100r and 500r were available for postage but were nearly always used fiscally.
For surcharge see No. 62.

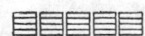

No. 42 Surcharged

4 cents

1919

62	A3	4c on 6c carmine	.25	.15
a.		Double surcharge	125.00	150.00
b.		Without squares over old value	25.00	25.00
c.		Pair, one without surcharge	500.00	*550.00*
d.		Inverted surcharge	150.00	175.00

For later issues see Kenya, Uganda and Tanzania.
For stamps of East Africa and Uganda overprinted "G. E. A." see German East Africa in this volume.

East Africa and Uganda Protectorates stamps can be mounted in the Scott British Africa album.

FIJI

'fē-(,)jē

LOCATION — Group of about 844 islands (106 inhabited) in the South Pacific Ocean east of Vanuatu
GOVT. — Independent nation in British Commonwealth
AREA — 7,078 sq. mi.
POP. — 646,561 (1981)
CAPITAL — Suva

A British colony since 1874, Fiji became fully independent in 1970.

12 Pence = 1 Shilling
20 Shillings = 1 Pound
100 Cents = 1 Dollar (1872-74, 1969)

Catalogue values for unused stamps in this country are for Never Hinged items, beginning with Scott 137 in the regular postage section and Scott B1 in the semi-postal section.

Values for unused stamps are for examples with original gum as defined in the catalogue introduction except for Nos. 1-10 which are valued without gum. Additionally, Nos. 1-10 are valued with roulettes showing on two or more sides, but expect small faults which do not detract from the appearance of the stamps. Very few examples of Nos. 1-10 will be found free of faults and these will command substantial premiums.

Watermark

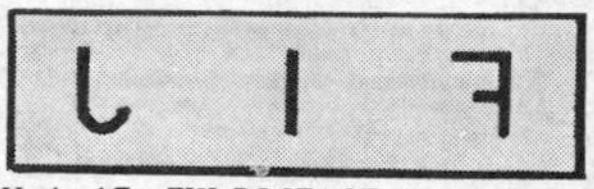

Wmk. 17 - FIJI POSTAGE Across Center Row of Sheet

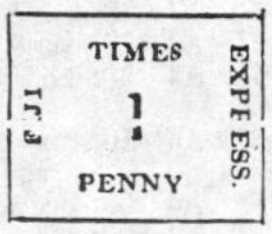

A1

1870 Unwmk. Typeset *Rouletted*
Quadrille Paper

1	A1	1p black, *pink*	2,750.	3,000.
2	A1	3p black, *pink*	2,750.	2,500.
3	A1	6p black, *pink*	2,250.	2,750.
5	A1	1sh black, *pink*	1,700.	2,250.

1871 Laid Batonne Paper

6	A1	1p black, *pink*	950.	1,500.
7	A1	3p black, *pink*	1,500.	2,000.
8	A1	6p black, *pink*	1,300.	1,500.
9	A1	9p black, *pink*	1,500.	2,000.
10	A1	1sh black, *pink*	1,500.	1,400.

This service was established by the *Fiji Times,* a weekly newspaper, for the delivery of the newspaper. Since there was no postal service to the other islands, delivery of letters to agents of the newspaper on the islands was offered to the public.

Nos. 1-5 were printed in the same sheet, one vertical row of each. Nos. 6-10 were printed in the same sheet, one horiz. row each of 1p, 6p, 1sh, and one horiz. row with three 3p and three 9p.

Most used examples have pen cancels.

Up to three sets of imitations exist. One on pink laid paper, pin-perforated, measuring 22½x16mm. Originals measure 22½x18½mm. A later printing was made on pink wove paper.

Forgeries also exist plus fake cancellations.

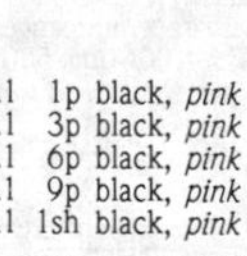

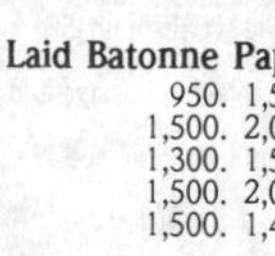

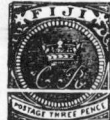

Crown and "CR" (Cakobau Rex)

A2 A3

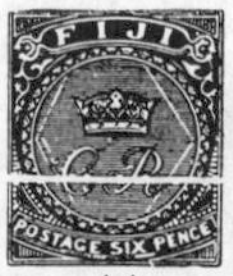

A4

1871 Typo. Wmk. 17 *Perf. 12½*
Wove Paper

15	A2	1p blue	62.50	125.00
16	A3	3p green	110.00	325.00
17	A4	6p rose	150.00	250.00
		Nos. 15-17 (3)	322.50	700.00

Sheets of 50 (10x5).
For overprints and surcharges see Nos. 18-39.

Stamps of 1871 Surcharged in Black

Two
Cents

1872, Jan. 13

18	A2	2c on 1p blue	25.00	40.00
19	A3	6c on 3p green	60.00	60.00
20	A4	12c on 6p rose	75.00	75.00
		Nos. 18-20 (3)	160.00	175.00

Nos. 18-20 with Additional Overprint in Black:

V.R.
b

V.R.
c

1874, Oct. 10

21	A2(b)	2c on 1p blue	750.	200.
22	A2(c)	2c on 1p blue	650.	180.
a.		Invtd. "A" instead of "V"		1,500.
b.		Period after "R" is a Maltese Cross		1,500.
23	A3(b)	6c on 3p green	1,500.	850.
24	A3(c)	6c on 3p green	1,000.	550.
a.		Inverted "A"	3,000.	
b.		Period after "R" is a Maltese Cross		
25	A4(b)	12c on 6p rose	550.	250.
a.		"V.R." inverted	4,000.	
26	A4(c)	12c on 6p rose	500.	175.
a.		Inverted "A"		1,350.
b.		Period after "R" is a Maltese Cross		1,350.
c.		"V.R." inverted		3,750.

Types "b" and "c" were in the same sheet.

Nos. 23-26 with Additional Surcharge in Black or Red 2d.

1875

27	A3(b)	2p on 6c on 3p	1,250.	550.
a.		Period btwn. "2" and "d"		
b.		"V.R." double		3,250.
28	A3(b)	2p on 6c on 3p (R)	500.	200.
a.		Period btwn. "2" and "d"		
29	A3(c)	2p on 6c on 3p	950.	325.
a.		Inverted "A"	2,500.	1,250.
b.		Period after "R" is a Maltese Cross	2,500.	1,250.
c.		No period after "2d"	2,500.	1,250.
30	A3(c)	2p on 6c on 3p (R)	375.	225.
a.		Inverted "A"	1,750.	725.
b.		Period after "R" is a Maltese Cross	1,750.	725.
c.		No period after "2d"	1,850.	725.
31	A4(b)	2p on 12c on 6p	1,000.	650.
a.		Period btwn. "2" and "d"		
b.		No period after "2d"		
c.		"2d, VR" double		3,000.
32	A4(c)	2p on 12c on 6p	1,000.	500.
a.		Inverted "A"	1,350.	650.
b.		No period after "2d"		
c.		"2d, VR" double		3,000.

Types of 1871 Overprinted or Surcharged in Black:

e

Two Pence
f

1876, Jan. 31 Unwmk. Wove Paper

33	A2(e)	1p ultramarine	50.00	50.00
a.		Inverted surcharge		
b.		Dbl. impression of stamp	1,000.	
34	A3(e+f)	2p on 3p dk grn	32.50	50.00
a.		Dbl. surch. "Two Pence"		
35	A4(e)	6p rose	50.00	47.50
b.		Surcharge inverted		
c.		Dbl. impression of stamp		
		Nos. 33-35 (3)	132.50	147.50

1877 Laid Paper

36	A2(e)	1p ultramarine	12.50	20.00
a.		Horiz. pair, imperf. vert.	1,100.	
37	A3(e+f)	2p on 3p dk grn	50.00	50.00
38	A3(e+f)	4p on 3p lilac	75.00	25.00
a.		Horiz. pair, imperf. vert.	850.00	
39	A4(e)	6p rose	45.00	25.00
a.		Horiz. pair, imperf. vert.	675.00	
		Nos. 36-39 (4)	182.50	120.00

Many of the preceding stamps are known imperforate. They are printer's waste and were never issued.

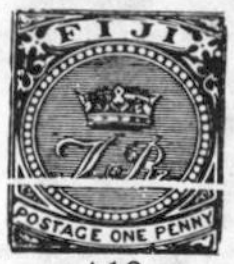

A12

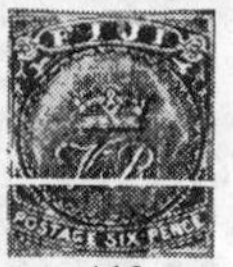

A13

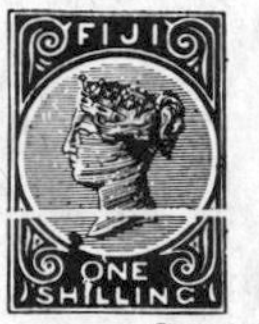

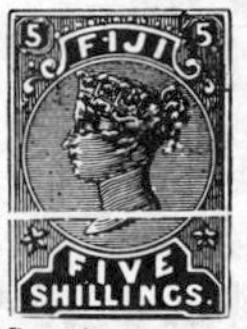

Queen Victoria
A14 A15

Perf. 10-13½ & Compound
1878-90 Wove Paper Typo.

40	A12	1p ultra ('79)	4.00	2.00
a.		1p blue	30.00	6.50
41	A12	2p green	8.00	1.75
b.		2p ultramarine (error)		
42	A12	4p brt vio ('90)	6.50	6.50
a.		4p mauve	7.50	9.00
43	A13	6p brt rose ('80)	5.75	4.75
a.		Printed on both sides	900.00	750.00
44	A14	1sh yel brn ('81)	25.00	8.00
a.		1sh deep brown	50.00	14.00

Litho.

45	A15	5sh blk & red brn ('82)	50.00	50.00
		Nos. 40-45 (6)	99.25	73.00

Facsimiles of the 5sh were officially made in 1900, differing in shades and detail of design from No. 45. They exist imperf., perf. 10 and 12; are all canceled "SUVA" and usually dated "15 Dec., 00."

No. 41b was not put on sale. All copies were supposed to be destroyed.

For surcharges see Nos. 46-52.

Surcharged type "f" in Black

1878-90 Typo.

46	A12	2p on 3p green	4.75	*9.00*
47	A12	4p on 1p vio ('90)	20.00	12.50
48	A12	4p on 2p lilac ('83)	35.00	7.25
		Nos. 46-48 (3)	59.75	28.75

Nos. 40-43 Surcharged in Black:

½d.
g

2½d.
h

5d
j

FIVE PENCE
k

1891-92 *Perf. 10*

49	A12(g)	½p on 1p ('92)	37.50	55.00
50	A12(h)	2½p on 2p	37.50	50.00
a.		Wider space (2mm) between "2" and "½"	150.00	150.00
51	A12(j)	5p on 4p ('92)	50.00	65.00
52	A13(k)	5p on 6p ('92)	50.00	65.00
a.		"FIVE" and "PENCE" 3mm apart	60.00	65.00
		Nos. 49-52 (4)	175.00	235.00

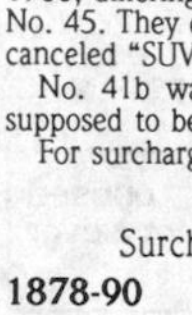

A18

Fijian Canoe — A19

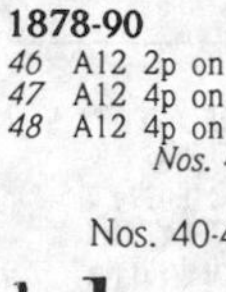

A20

1891-96 *Perf. 10-12 & Compound*

53	A18	½p grnsh blk ('92)	2.25	3.50
a.		½p gray	2.50	5.00
54	A19	1p black ('93)	3.75	3.50
55	A19	1p lilac rose ('96)	3.00	1.00
56	A19	2p green ('93)	4.25	.85
a.		Perf. 10x12 ('94)		325.00
57	A20	2½ red brown	5.00	5.00
58	A19	5p ultra ('93)	6.25	6.25
		Nos. 53-58 (6)	24.50	20.10

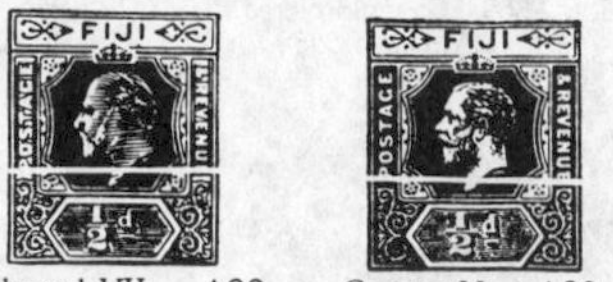

Edward VII — A22 George V — A23

1903, Feb. 1 Wmk. 2 *Perf. 14*

59	A22	½p gray grn & pale grn	.60	.40
60	A22	1p vio & blk, *red*	7.00	.30
61	A22	2p vio & orange	.50	.50
62	A22	2½p vio & ultra, *bl*	9.50	*12.00*
63	A22	3p vio & red vio	1.40	*3.50*
64	A22	4p violet & blk	1.65	*3.00*
65	A22	5p vio & green	1.65	*4.00*
66	A22	6p vio & car rose	3.00	*4.75*
67	A22	1sh grn & car rose	12.00	*17.00*
68	A22	5sh green & blk	27.50	*47.50*
69	A22	£1 gray & ultra	350.00	*475.00*
		Revenue cancel		60.00
		Nos. 59-68 (10)	64.80	*92.95*

Numerals of 2p, 4p, 6p and 5sh of type A22 are in color on plain tablet.

1904-12 Wmk. 3
Ordinary Paper

70	A22	½p green ('04)	5.00	2.00
71	A22	1p vio & black, *red* ('04)	12.50	.25
72	A22	1p carmine ('06)	3.25	.30
73	A22	2½p ultra ('10)	3.75	*5.00*

Chalky Paper

74	A22	6p violet ('10)	5.75	*10.00*
75	A22	1sh grn & car rose ('09)	22.50	*35.00*
76	A22	1sh black, *green* ('11)	4.00	*8.25*
77	A22	5sh grn & scarlet, *yel* ('11)	35.00	*40.00*
78	A22	£1 vio & black, *red* ('12)	300.00	325.00
		Nos. 70-77 (8)	91.75	*100.80*

Die I

For description of Dies I and II see back of this section of the Catalogue.

1912-23
Ordinary Paper

79	A23	¼p brown ('16)	.20	.22
80	A23	½p green	.45	.45
81	A23	1p scarlet	.70	.15
a.		1p carmine ('16)	1.10	.52
82	A23	2p gray ('14)	1.40	.55
83	A23	2½p ultra ('14)	4.75	5.00
84	A23	3p violet, *yel*	1.50	1.50
a.		Die II ('21)	1.50	1.75
85	A23	4p black & red, *yel* ('14)	2.25	2.25
a.		Die II ('23)	6.25	*15.00*

Chalky Paper

86	A23	5p dl vio & ol grn ('14)	3.50	4.00
87	A23	6p dl vio & red vio ('14)	2.75	2.75
88	A23	1sh black, *green*	3.50	3.50
a.		1sh black, *blue green,* ol back	2.75	3.00
b.		1sh black, *emerald* ('21)	2.75	2.75
c.		Die II ('22)	4.25	*8.25*
89	A23	2sh 6p black & red, *blue*	16.00	*21.00*
90	A23	5sh grn & scar, *yellow*	22.50	*35.00*
91	A23	£1 vio & black, *red*	260.00	300.00
a.		Die II ('21)	260.00	300.00
		Revenue cancel		45.00

Surface-colored Paper

92	A23	1sh black, *green*	2.00	2.00
		Nos. 79-90,92 (13)	61.50	*78.37*

Numerals of ¼p, 1½p, 2p, 4p, 6p, 2sh, 2sh6p and 5sh of type A23 are in color on plain tablet.

For overprints see Nos. MR1-MR2.

Die II

1922-27 Wmk. 4
Ordinary Paper

93	A23	¼p dark brown	1.10	*8.50*
94	A23	½p green	.70	.65
95	A23	1p rose red	1.40	1.65
96	A23	1p violet ('27)	.45	.25
97	A23	1½p rose red ('27)	3.00	2.75
98	A23	2p gray	1.40	.25
99	A23	3p ultra ('23)	.70	.65
100	A23	4p blk & red, *yel*	3.00	3.50
101	A23	5p dl vio & ol green	2.25	1.10
102	A23	6p dl vio & red violet	2.25	2.50

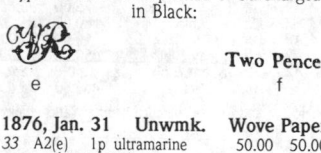

Chalky Paper

103	A23	1sh blk, *emerald*	2.25	2.50
104	A23	2sh vio & ultra, *bl* ('27)	17.00	*27.50*
105	A23	2sh6p blk & red, *bl*	13.00	*22.50*
106	A23	5sh grn & scar, *yellow*	40.00	*52.50*
		Nos. 93-106 (14)	88.50	*126.80*

Silver Jubilee Issue
Common Design Type

1935, May 6 ***Perf. 13½x14***

110	CD301	1½p carmine & blue	.42	.42
111	CD301	2p gray blk & ultra	.70	.70
112	CD301	3p blue & brown	1.75	2.00
113	CD301	1sh brt vio & indigo	2.75	2.50
		Nos. 110-113 (4)	5.62	5.62

Coronation Issue
Common Design Type

1937, May 12 ***Perf. 11x11½***

114	CD302	1p dark violet	.15	.15
115	CD302	2p gray black	.25	.25
116	CD302	3p indigo	.30	.30
		Nos. 114-116 (3)	.70	.70

Outrigger Canoe — A24

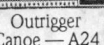

Fijian Village — A25

Outrigger Canoe — A26

Map of Fiji Islands — A27

Canoe and Arms of Fiji — A28

Sugar Cane — A29

Spear Fishing at Night — A30

Arms of Fiji — A31

Suva Harbor — A32

River Scene — A33

Fijian House — A34

Papaya Tree — A35

Bugler — A36

Designs: No. 121, Government buildings. 8p, 1sh5p, 1sh6p, Arms of Fiji.

Perf. 13½, 12½ (1p)

1938-55 **Engr.** **Wmk. 4**

117	A24	½p green	.15	.20
c.		Perf. 14 ('41)	6.25	2.75
d.		Perf. 12 ('48)	.15	*1.10*
118	A25	1p blue & brn	.15	.15
119	A26	1½p rose car (empty canoe)	5.50	.25
120	A27	2p grn & org brn (no "180 degree")	15.00	.30
121	A27	2p mag & grn	.15	.40
a.		Perf. 12 ('46)	.15	.40

Perf. 12½, 13x12 (6p), 14 (8p)

122	A28	3p dp ultra	.25	.15
123	A29	5p rose red & blue	15.00	8.00
124	A29	5p rose red & yel grn	.15	.25
125	A27	6p blk (no "180 degree")	21.00	8.75
126	A31	8p rose car	.25	.20
a.		Perf. 13 ('50)	.20	*1.40*
127	A30	1sh black & yel	.25	.25

Perf. 14

128	A31	1sh5p car & black	.15	.15
128A	A31	1sh6p ultra	1.40	1.25
b.		Perf. 13 ('55)	.40	*12.00*

Perf. 12½

129	A32	2sh vio & org	.60	.30
130	A33	2sh6p brn & grn	.60	.70
131	A34	5sh dk vio & grn	.70	1.00
131A	A35	10sh emer & brn org	12.50	*32.50*
131B	A36	£1 car & ultra	17.50	*40.00*
		Nos. 117-131B (18)	91.30	*94.80*

Issued: 1sh5p, 6/13/40; 5p, 10/1/40; #121, 5/19/42; 8p, 11/15/48; 10sh, £1, 3/13/50; 1sh6p, 8/1/50; others, 4/5/38.

Types of 1938-40
Redrawn

Perf. 13½ (1½p, 2p, 6p), 14 (2½p)

1940-49 **Wmk. 4**

132	A26	1½p rose car (man in canoe)	.35	*1.65*
a.		Perf. 12 ('49)	.30	*1.00*
b.		Perf. 14 ('42)	5.25	*12.50*
133	A27	2p grn & org brn ("180 degree")	5.50	*12.50*
134	A27	2½p grn & org brn	.20	.30
a.		Perf. 12 ('48)	.20	.40
b.		Perf. 13½ ('44)	.15	.30
135	A27	6p blk ("180 degree")	.90	1.25
a.		Perf. 12 ('47)	.45	.50
		Nos. 132-135 (4)	6.95	15.70

No. 132, type A26, has a man sitting in the canoe.

Nos. 133-135, type A27, have 180 degree added to the lower right hand corner of the design.

Issued: 2½p, Jan. 6, 1942; others Oct. 1, 1940.

No. 133 Surcharged in Black

2½d.

1941, Feb. 10 ***Perf. 13½***

136	A27	2½p on 2p grn & org brn	.20	.20
		Never hinged	.35	

Catalogue values for unused stamps in this section, from this point to the end of the section, are for Never Hinged items.

Peace Issue
Common Design Type

1946, Aug. 17 ***Perf. 13½***

137	CD303	2½p bright green	.15	.15
138	CD303	3p deep blue	.15	.15

Silver Wedding Issue
Common Design Types

1948, Dec. 17 **Photo.** ***Perf. 14x14½***

139	CD304	2½p dark green	.30	.50

Engr.; Name Typo.

Perf. 11½x11

140	CD305	5sh blue violet	16.00	13.00

UPU Issue
Common Design Types

Engr.; Name Typo. on 3p, 8p

Perf. 13½, 11x11½

1949, Oct. 10 **Wmk. 4**

141	CD306	2p red violet	.50	.40
142	CD307	3p indigo	.85	1.00
143	CD308	8p dp carmine	1.50	1.50
144	CD309	1sh6p blue	3.00	3.00
		Nos. 141-144 (4)	5.85	5.90

Coronation Issue
Common Design Type

1953, June 2 ***Perf. 13½x13***

145	CD312	2½p dk green & blk	.90	.90

Type of 1938-40 with Portrait of Queen Elizabeth II Inscribed: "Royal Visit 1953"

1953, Dec. 16 ***Perf. 13***

146	A31	8p carmine lake	.25	.25

Visit of Queen Elizabeth II and the Duke of Edinburgh, 1953.

Types of 1938 50 with Portrait of Queen Elizabeth II, and:

A39

Loading Copra — A40

Designs: 1sh6p, Sugar cane train. 2sh, Bananas for export. 5sh, Gold industry.

Perf. 11½, 11½x11, 12, 12½, 13

1954-56 **Engr.**

147	A24	½p green	.15	.15
148	A39	1p grnsh blue	.15	.15
149	A39	1½p brown	.15	.15
150	A27	2p mag & green	.25	.15
151	A39	2½p blue vio	1.00	.50
152	A40	3p purple & brn	.42	.15
154	A27	6p black	.45	.30
155	A31	8p carmine lake	.60	.38
156	A30	1sh black & yel	1.25	.65
157	A40	1sh6p grn & dp ultra	3.00	1.50
158	A40	2sh brt car & black	3.25	1.50
159	A33	2sh6p brn & bl grn	1.40	.80
160	A40	5sh dp ultra & yel	12.50	2.75
161	A35	10sh emer & brn org	25.00	17.50
162	A36	£1 car & ultra	35.00	14.00
		Nos. 147-162 (15)	84.57	40.63

Issue dates: 2p, 1sh, 2sh6p, Feb. 1, 1954. ½p, 6p, 8p, 10sh, £1, July 1, 1954. 1p, June 1, 1956. 1½p, 2½p, 3p, 1sh6p, 2sh, 5sh, Oct. 1, 1956.

Types of 1954-56 and:

Nautilus Shells — A41

Hibiscus — A42

Kandavu Parrot — A43

Designs: ½p, 2p, 2½p, Queen Elizabeth II (A39). 1p, Queen, turtles in bottom panels. 6p, Fijian beating drum (lali). 10p, Yaqona ceremony. 1sh, South Pacific map. 2sh6p, Nadi Airport. 10sh, Cutting sugar cane. £1, Arms of Fiji.

Perf. 11½ (A39, A41); 11½x11 (A40); 14½x14 (A42); 14x14½ (A43)

Engr. (A39, A40, A41); others Photo.

1959-63 **Wmk. 4**

163	A39	½p green ('61)	.15	.15
164	A41	1p dk blue ('62)	.15	.15
165	A41	1½p dk brown ('62)	.20	.18
166	A39	2p crim rose ('61)	.35	.32
167	A39	2½p brown org ('62)	.65	.60
168	A40	6p blk & car rose ('61)	.80	.75
169	A42	8p gray, red, yel & grn ('61)	1.00	.90
170	A40	10p car & brn ('63)	1.90	1.40
171	A40	1sh dk bl & bl ('61)	.60	.50
172	A40	2sh6p pur & blk ('61)	2.50	2.50
173	A43	4sh dk grn, red, bl & emer	3.00	2.25
174	A40	10sh sep & emer ('61)	11.00	10.50
175	A40	£1 org & blk ('61)	32.50	22.50
		Nos. 163-175 (13)	54.80	42.70

Issued: 4sh, 7/13; 8p, 8/1; ½p, 2p, 6p, 1sh, 2sh6p, 10sh, £1, 11/14; 1p, 1½p, 2½p, 12/3; 10p, 4/1.

For type overprinted see No. 205.

Types of 1954-63 and:

Elizabeth II — A44

Designs: 1sh6p, 180th meridian and International Date Line. 2sh, White orchids. 5sh, Orange dove.

Perf. 11½ (A41); 12½ (A44); 11½x11 (A40); 14x14½ (A43)

Engr. (A40, A41); others Photo.

1962-67 **Wmk. 314**

176	A41	1p dark blue ('64)	.65	.55
177	A39	2p crim rose ('65)	.75	.65
178	A44	3p rose cl & multi	.18	.15
179	A40	6p blk & car rose ('64)	.95	.52
180	A42	9p ultra, red, yel & grn ('63)	.95	.42
181	A40	10p car & brn ('64)	.95	.65
183	A40	1sh dk bl & bl ('66)	1.65	1.10
183	A43	1sh6p dk bl & multi	1.95	.95
184	A42	2sh gold, yel grn & grn	2.75	1.10
185	A40	2sh6p pur & blk ('65)	1.95	1.25
186	A43	4sh grn & multi, wmk. sideways ('67)	2.50	2.25
a.		As #186, wmk. upright ('64)	3.50	3.25
b.		4sh dark green & multi ('66)	4.00	3.25
187	A43	5sh dk gray, yel & red	7.25	3.50
188	A40	10sh sep & emer ('64)	11.00	10.50
189	A40	£1 org & blk ('64)	20.00	13.00
		Nos. 176-189 (14)	53.48	36.59

Issued: 3p, 1sh6p, 2sh, 5sh, Dec. 3; 9p, #186a, Apr. 1; 1p, 10p, 10sh, Jan. 14; 6p, £1, June 9; 2p, 2sh6p, Aug. 3; #186b, Mar. 1; #186, Feb. 16.

Nos. 178 and 171 Overprinted: "ROYAL VISIT 1963"

1963, Feb. 1

196	A44	3p multicolored	.20	.20
197	A40	1sh dark blue & blue	.65	.65

Visit of Elizabeth II & Prince Philip, Feb. 3.

Freedom from Hunger Issue
Common Design Type

1963, June 4 **Photo.** ***Perf. 14x14½***

198	CD314	2sh ultramarine	5.50	3.50

Running A45

Designs: 9p, Throwing the discus, vert. 1sh, Field hockey, vert. 2sh6p, Women's high jump.

Perf. 14½x14, 14x14½

1963, Aug. 6 **Wmk. 314**

199	A45	3p yel, blk & brn	.22	.22
200	A45	9p violet, blk & brn	.40	.40
201	A45	1sh green, blk & brn	.52	.52
202	A45	2sh6p blue, blk & brn	1.65	1.65
		Nos. 199-202 (4)	2.79	2.79

1st So. Pacific Games, Suva, Aug. 29-Sept. 7.

Red Cross Centenary Issue
Common Design Type

1963, Sept. 2 **Litho.** ***Perf. 13***

203	CD315	2p black & red	.38	.32
204	CD315	2sh ultra & red	4.50	3.75

Type of 1959-63
Overprinted

COMPAC CABLE IN SERVICE DECEMBER 1963

1963, Dec. 2   Engr.   Perf. 11¹/₂x11
205 A40 1sh dark blue & blue   .95 .95
Opening of the Commonwealth Pacific (telephone) Cable service, COMPAC.

Fiji Scout Badge — A46

Scouts of India, Fiji and Europe Tying Knot — A47

1964, Aug. 3   Photo.   Perf. 12¹/₂
206 A46 3p multicolored   .18 .18
207 A47 1sh ocher & purple   .95 .95
50th anniv. of the founding of the Fiji Boy Scouts.

Amphibian "Aotearoa," 1939 — A48

Map of Fiji and Tonga Islands and Plane — A49

Design: 6p, Heron plane.

1964, Oct. 24   Perf. 12¹/₂, 14¹/₂
208 A48 3p brt red & black   .16 .16
209 A48 6p ultra & red   .38 .38
210 A49 1sh grnsh blue & black   .75 .75
    Nos. 208-210 (3)   1.29 1.29
Fiji-Tonga airmail service, 25th anniv.

ITU Issue
Common Design Type
Perf. 11x11¹/₂
1965, May 17   Litho.   Wmk. 314
211 CD317 3p blue & rose red   .35 .35
212 CD317 2sh yel & bister   3.00 3.00

Intl. Cooperation Year Issue
Common Design Type
1965, Oct. 25   Perf. 14¹/₂
213 CD318 2p blue grn & cl   .32 .32
214 CD318 2sh6p lt vio & grn   2.00 1.75

Churchill Memorial Issue
Common Design Type
1966, Jan. 24   Photo.   Perf. 14
Design in Black, Gold and Carmine Rose
215 CD319 3p brt blue   .28 .28
216 CD319 9p green   .90 .90
217 CD319 1sh brown   1.10 1.10
218 CD319 2sh6p violet   3.00 3.00
    Nos. 215-218 (4)   5.28 5.28

World Cup Soccer Issue
Common Design Type
1966, July 1   Litho.   Perf. 14
219 CD321 2p multicolored   .28 .28
220 CD321 2sh multicolored   2.00 1.40

H.M.S. Pandora and Split Island, Rotuma A50

Designs: 10p, Rotuma chiefs, Pandora, and Rotuma's position in Pacific. 1sh6p, Rotuma islanders welcoming Pandora.

1966, Aug. 29   Photo.   Perf. 14x13
221 A50 3p multicolored   .15 .15
222 A50 10p multicolored   .35 .35
223 A50 1sh6p multicolored   .70 .70
    Nos. 221-223 (3)   1.20 1.20
175th anniv. of the discovery of Rotuma, a group of eight islands forming part of the colony of Fiji.

WHO Headquarters Issue
Common Design Type
1966, Sept. 20   Litho.   Perf. 14
224 CD322 6p multicolored   .52 .45
225 CD322 2sh6p multicolored   3.75 2.50

Woman Runner A51

Designs: 9p, Shot put, vert. 1sh, Diver.

1966, Dec. 8   Photo.   Perf. 14x14¹/₂
226 A51 3p ol, black & lt brn   .15 .15
227 A51 9p brt blue, blk & brn   .30 .30
228 A51 1sh blue green & multi   .48 .48
    Nos. 226-228 (3)   .93 .93
2nd South Pacific Games, Noumea, New Caledonia, Dec. 8-18.

Common Design Types
pictured in section before Great Britain.

Military Band — A52

Intl. Tourist Year: 9p, Reef diving. 1sh, Beqa fire walkers. 2sh, Liner Oriana and Mt. Rama volcano.

1967, Oct. 20   Perf. 14x13
229 A52 3p multi & gold   .15 .15
230 A52 9p multi & silver   .28 .28
231 A52 1sh multi & gold   .32 .32
232 A52 2sh multi & silver   .75 .60
    Nos. 229-232 (4)   1.50 1.35

Admiral Bligh, H.M.S. Providence and Old Map of "Feejee" A53

Designs: 1sh, Bligh's longboat being chased by double canoe and map of Fiji Islands. 2sh6p, Bligh's tomb, St. Mary's Cemetery, Lambeth, London.

Perf. 15x14, 12¹/₂x13 (1sh)
1967, Dec. 7   Photo.   Wmk. 314
Size: 35x21mm
233 A53 4p emer, blk & yel   .15 .15
Size: 54x20mm
234 A53 1sh brt bl, brn org & blk   .28 .28
Size: 35x21mm
235 A53 2sh6p sepia & multi   .70 .70
    Nos. 233-235 (3)   1.13 1.13
150th anniv. of the death of Adm. William Bligh (1754-1817), captain of the Bounty and principal discoverer of the Fiji Islands.

Simmonds "Spartan" Seaplane A54

Designs: 6p, Fiji Airways Hawker-Siddeley H748 and emblems of various airlines. 1sh, Fokker "Southern Cross," Capt. Charles Kingsford-Smith, his crew and Southern Cross constellation. 2sh, Lockheed Altair "Lady Southern Cross."

Perf. 14x14¹/₂
1968, June 5   Wmk. 314
236 A54 2p green & black   .15 .15
237 A54 6p brt blue, car & blk   .18 .18
238 A54 1sh dp violet & green   .35 .35
239 A54 2sh orange brn & dk blue   .70 .70
    Nos. 236-239 (4)   1.38 1.38
40th anniv. of the first Trans-Pacific Flight through Fiji under Capt. Charles Kingsford-Smith.

Fijian Bures — A55

Eastern Reef Heron — A56

Designs: 1p, Passion fruit flowers. 2p, Nautilus pompilius shell. 4p, Hawk moth. 6p, Reef butterflyfish. 9p, Bamboo raft (bilibili). 10p, Tiger moth. 1sh, Black marlin. 1sh6p, Orange-breasted honey eaters. 2sh, Ringed sea snake, horiz. 2sh6p, Outrigger canoes (takia), horiz. 3sh, Golden cowrie shell. 4sh, Emperor gold mine and gold ore. 5sh, Bamboo orchids, horiz. 10sh, Tabua (ceremonial whale's tooth). £1, Coat of Arms and Queen Elizabeth II, horiz.

Perf. 13¹/₂ (A55), 14 (A56)
1968, July 15   Photo.   Wmk. 314
240 A55 ¹/₂p multicolored   .15 .15
241 A55 1p multicolored   .15 .15
242 A55 2p multicolored   .15 .15
243 A55 3p multicolored   .15 .15
244 A55 4p multicolored   .18 .18
245 A55 6p multicolored   .28 .28
246 A55 9p multicolored   .45 .45
247 A55 10p multicolored   .60 .60
248 A56 1sh multicolored   .65 .65
249 A56 1sh6p multicolored   .75 .75
250 A56 2sh multicolored   .90 .90
251 A56 2sh6p multicolored   1.25 1.25
252 A55 3sh multicolored   1.50 1.50
253 A56 4sh multicolored   1.75 1.75
254 A56 5sh multicolored   2.75 2.75
255 A56 10sh multicolored   5.25 5.25
256 A56 £1 red & multi   10.00 10.00
    Nos. 240-256 (17)   26.91 26.91
See Nos. 260-276.

WHO Emblem, Map of Fiji and Nurses — A57

WHO Emblem and: 9p, Medical team loading patient on stretcher on dinghy and medical ship "Vuniwai." 3sh, People playing on beach.

1968, Dec. 9   Litho.   Perf. 14
257 A57 3p blue green & multi   .15 .15
258 A57 9p brt blue & multi   .30 .30
259 A57 3sh dk blue & multi   .90 .90
    Nos. 257-259 (3)   1.35 1.35
WHO, 20th anniv.

Types of 1968
Values in Cents and Dollars

Designs: 1c, Passion fruit flowers. 2c, Nautilus pompilius shell. 3c, Reef heron. 4c, Hawk moth. 5c, Reef butterflyfish. 6c, Fijian bures. 8c, Bamboo raft. 9c, Tiger moth. 10c, Black marlin. 15c, Orange-breasted honey-eater. 20c, Ringed sea snake, horiz. 25c, Outrigger canoes (takia), horiz. 30c, Golden cowrie shell. 40c Emperor gold mine and gold ore. 50c, Bamboo orchids, horiz. $1, Tabua (ceremonial whale's tooth). $2, Coat of Arms and Queen Elizabeth II, horiz.

Perf. 13¹/₂ (A55), 14 (A56)
1969, Jan. 13   Photo.   Wmk. 314
260 A55 1c multicolored   .15 .15
261 A55 2c multicolored   .15 .15
262 A56 3c multicolored   .15 .15
263 A56 4c multicolored   .15 .15
264 A55 5c multicolored   .16 .15
265 A55 6c multicolored   .18 .15
266 A55 8c multicolored   .25 .18
267 A55 9c multicolored   .32 .25

268 A56 10c multicolored   .38 .28
269 A56 15c multicolored   1.90 1.25
270 A56 20c multicolored   .95 .55
271 A56 25c multicolored   1.10 .75
272 A55 30c multicolored   3.25 1.10
273 A56 40c multicolored   2.25 1.50
274 A56 50c multicolored   3.75 1.90
275 A56 $1 multicolored   5.75 3.75
276 A56 $2 red & multi   9.50 7.75
    Nos. 260-276 (17)   30.34 20.16
For overprints & surcharges see #286-288, B5-B6.

Fiji Soldiers and Map of Solomon Islands A58

Designs: 10c, Flags of Fiji Military Force, soldiers in full and battle dress. 25c, Cpl. Sefanaia Sukanaivalu and Victoria Cross.

1969, June 23   Wmk. 314   Perf. 14
277 A58 3c emerald & multi   .15 .15
278 A58 10c red & multi   .25 .25
279 A58 25c black & multi   .65 .65
    Nos. 277-279 (3)   1.05 1.05
25th anniv. of the Fiji Military Forces campaign in the Solomon Islands and of the posthumous award of the Victoria Cross to Cpl. Sefanaia Sukanaivalu.

Yachting — A59

Designs: 4c, Javelin. 20c, Winners and South Pacific Games medal.

1969, Aug. 18   Photo.   Perf. 14¹/₂x14
280 A59 4c red, brown & blk   .15 .15
281 A59 8c blue & black   .22 .22
282 A59 20c olive grn, blk & ocher .55 .55
    Nos. 280-282 (3)   .92 .92
3rd South Pacific Games, Port Moresby, Papua New Guinea, Aug. 13-23.

Students in Laboratory A60

Designs: 2c, Map of South Pacific and mortarboard. 8c, Site of University at Royal New Zealand Air Force Seaplane Station, Laucala Bay, RNZAF badge and Sunderland flying boat.

1969, Nov. 10   Perf. 14x14¹/₂
283 A60 2c multicolored   .15 .15
284 A60 8c red & multi   .22 .22
285 A60 25c dk green & multi   .70 .70
    Nos. 283-285 (3)   1.07 1.07
Inauguration of the University of the South Pacific, Laucala Bay, Suva.

Nos. 261, 268 and 271 Overprinted:
"ROYAL VISIT / 1970"

1970, Mar. 4   Perf. 13¹/₂, 14
286 A55 2c multicolored   .15 .15
287 A56 10c multicolored   .35 .35
288 A55 25c multicolored   .90 .90
    Nos. 286-288 (3)   1.40 1.40
Visit of Queen Elizabeth II, Prince Philip and Princess Anne, Mar. 4-5.

Nuns Sitting under Chaulmoogra Tree, and Chaulmoogra Fruit — A61

Designs: 10c, Paintings by Semisi Maya (former patient). No. 290, Cascade, vert. No. 291, Sea urchins, vert. 30c, Aerial view of Makogai Hospital.

Perf. 14x14½, 14½x14

1970, May 25 Photo. Wmk. 314

289	A61	2c brt pink & multi	.15	.15
290	A61	10c gray green & blk	.28	.28
291	A61	10c blue, car & blk	.28	.28
a.		Pair, #290-291	.60	.60
292	A61	30c orange & multi	.75	.75
		Nos. 289-292 (4)	1.46	1.46

Closing of the Leprosy Hospital on Makogai Island in 1969.

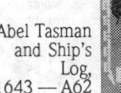

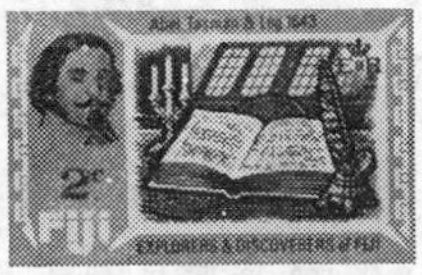
Abel Tasman and Ship's Log, 1643 — A62

Designs: 3c, Capt. James Cook and "Endeavour." 8c, Capt. William Bligh and longboat, 1789. 25c, Man of Fiji and Fijian ocean-going canoe.

1970, Aug. 18 Litho. *Perf. 13x12½*

293	A62	2c blue green & multi	.28	.15
294	A62	3c gray green & multi	.55	.20
295	A62	8c multicolored	1.25	.70
296	A62	25c dull lilac & multi	3.50	2.25
		Nos. 293-296 (4)	5.58	3.30

Discoverers and explorers of Fiji Islands.

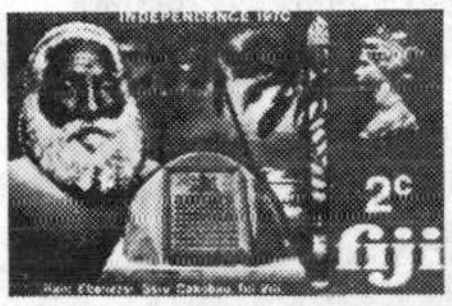
King Cakobau and Cession Stone at Lavuka A63

Designs: 3c, Chinese, Fijian, Indian and European children. 10c, Prime Minister Ratu Sir Kamisese Mara and flag of Fiji. 25c, Fijian male dancer and Indian female dancer.

1970, Oct. 10 Wmk. 314 *Perf. 14*

297	A63	2c multicolored	.15	.15
298	A63	3c multicolored	.15	.15
299	A63	10c multicolored	.32	.26
300	A63	25c multicolored	.90	.65
		Nos. 297-300 (4)	1.52	
		Set value		1.04

Fijian independence.

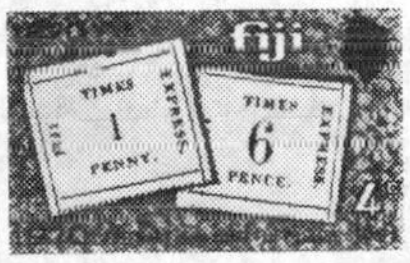
Fiji Nos. 1 and 3 — A64

Designs: 15c, Fiji Nos. 15, 44, 59, 81, 127 and 166. 20c, Fiji Times Office, Levuka, and General Post Office, Suva.

1970, Nov. 2 Photo. *Perf. 14½x14*

Size: 35x21mm

301	A64	4c multicolored	.15	.15

Size: 60x21½mm

302	A64	15c multicolored	.45	.45

Size: 35x21mm

303	A64	20c multicolored	.70	.70
		Nos. 301-303 (3)	1.30	1.30

Centenary of first postage stamps of Fiji.

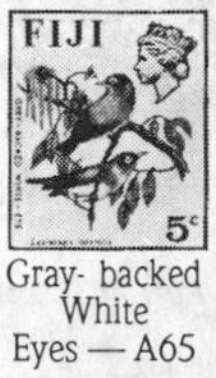
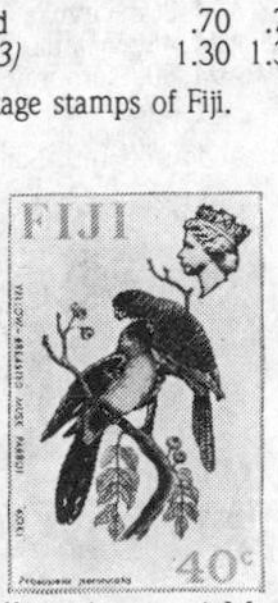
Gray-backed White Eyes — A65 Yellow-breasted Musk Parrots — A66

Designs: 1c, Cirrhopetalum umbellatum. 2c, Cardinal honey eaters. 3c, Calanthe furcata. 4c, Bulbophyllum. 6c, Phaius tancarvilliae. 8c, Blue-crested broadbills. 10c, Acanthephippium vitiense. 15c, Dendrobium tokai. 20c, Slaty flycatchers. 25c, Kandavu honey eaters. 30c, Dendrobium gordonii. 50c, White-throated pigeon. $1, Collared lories (kula). $2, Dendrobium platygastrium. (Orchids shown on 1c, 3c, 4c, 6c, 10c, 15c, 30c, $2.)

Wmk. 314 Upright

1971-72 Litho. *Perf. 13½x14*

305	A65	1c blk & multi ('72)	.15	.15
306	A65	2c carmine & multi	.15	.15
307	A65	3c multi ('72)	.20	.15
308	A65	4c blk & multi ('72)	.26	.20
309	A65	5c brown & multi	.42	.26
310	A65	6c lt bl & multi ('72)	.45	.30
311	A65	8c black & multi	.52	.35
312	A65	10c multi ('72)	.55	.38
313	A56	15c multi ('72)	.75	.55
314	A65	20c gray & multi	.95	.60

Perf. 14

315	A66	25c sepia & multi	1.50	.95
316	A66	30c grn & multi ('72)	1.90	.95
317	A66	40c blue & multi	2.50	1.50
318	A66	50c gray & multi	3.00	1.90
319	A66	$1 red & multi	6.25	3.75
320	A66	$2 multi ('72)	12.50	7.25
		Nos. 305-320 (16)	32.05	19.39

Issued: 5c, 20c, 40c, 50c, 8/6; 2c, 8c, 25c, $1, 11/22; 1c, 10c, 30c, $2, 1/4; 3c, 4c, 6c, 15c, 6/23.

1972-74 Wmk. 314 Sideways

306c	A65	2c	('73)	.16	.15
307a	A65	3c	('73)	.24	.16
308a	A65	4c	('73)	.28	.18
309a	A65	5c	('73)	.32	.24
310a	A65	6c	('73)	.38	.28
311a	A65	8c	('73)	.52	.38
313a	A65	15c	('73)	.95	.70
314a	A65	20c		1.40	.95
315a	A66	25c	('73)	1.65	1.10
317a	A66	40c	('74)	2.75	1.90
318a	A66	50c	('74)	3.75	2.25
319a	A66	$1		7.00	4.75
320a	A66	$2		14.00	9.25
		Nos. 306c-320a (13)		33.40	22.29

Issued: 20c, $1, $2, 11/17; 3c, 5c, 3/8; 4c, 6c, 8c, 15c, 25c, 4/11; 2c, 12/12; 40c, 50c, 3/15.

1975-77 Wmk. 373

305b	A65	1c		.15	.15
306d	A65	2c		.18	.15
307b	A65	3c		.25	.20
308b	A65	4c	('76)	.35	.30
309b	A65	5c		.30	.24
310b	A65	6c	('76)	.35	.28
311b	A65	8c	('76)	.50	.35
312b	A65	10c		.80	.60
313b	A65	15c	('76)	1.25	.90
314b	A65	20c	('77)	1.50	1.00
316b	A66	30c	('76)	2.50	1.75
317b	A66	40c	('76)	2.25	1.50
318b	A66	50c	('76)	2.75	2.00
319b	A66	$1	('76)	6.00	4.50
320b	A66	$2	('76)	12.00	9.00
		Nos. 305b-320b (15)		31.03	22.82

Issued: 1c, 2c, 3c, 5c, 10c, 4/9; 20c, 7/15; others, 9/3.

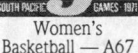

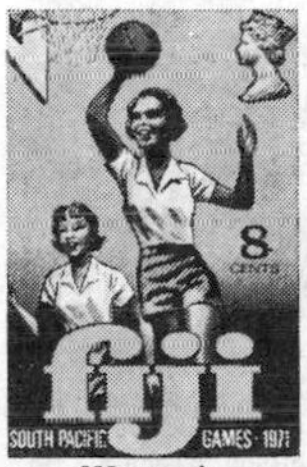
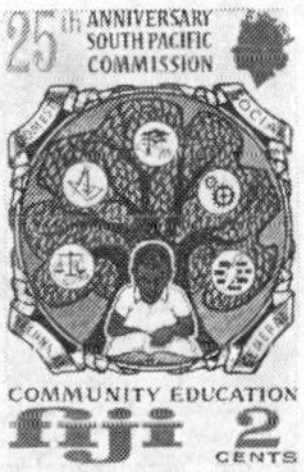
Women's Basketball — A67 Community Education — A68

1971, Sept. 6 Wmk. 314 *Perf. 14*

321	A67	8c shown	.30	.30
322	A67	10c Running	.35	.35
323	A67	25c Weight lifting	.90	.90
		Nos. 321-323 (3)	1.55	1.55

4th South Pacific Games, Papeete, French Polynesia, Sept. 8-19.

1972, Feb. 7

Designs: 4c, Public health. 50c, Economic growth (farm scenes).

324	A68	2c bright rose & multi	.15	.15
325	A68	4c gray & multi	.15	.15
326	A68	50c bright blue & multi	1.50	1.50
		Nos. 324-326 (3)	1.80	1.80

South Pacific Commission, 25th anniv.

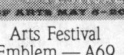

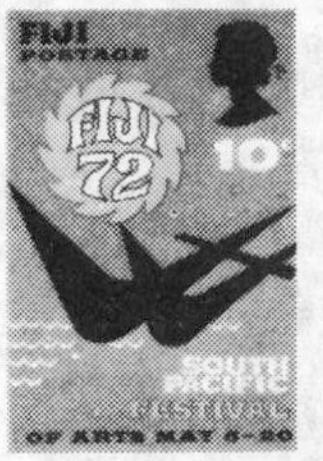
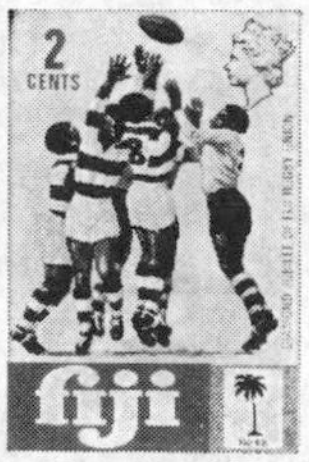
Arts Festival Emblem — A69 Rugby — A70

1972, Apr. 10

327	A69	10c blue, org & black	.32	.32

South Pacific Festival of Arts, May 6-20.

Silver Wedding Issue, 1972

Common Design Type

Design: Queen Elizabeth II, Prince Philip, flowers and shells.

1972, Nov. 20 Photo. *Perf. 14x14½*

328	CD324	10c slate grn & multi	.28	.28
329	CD324	25c red lilac & multi	.60	.60

1973, Mar. 9 Litho. *Perf. 14*

330	A70	2c shown	.15	.15
331	A70	8c Tackle	.38	.38
332	A70	25c Kicking ball	1.10	1.10
		Nos. 330-332 (3)	1.63	1.63

60th anniversary of Fiji Rugby Union.

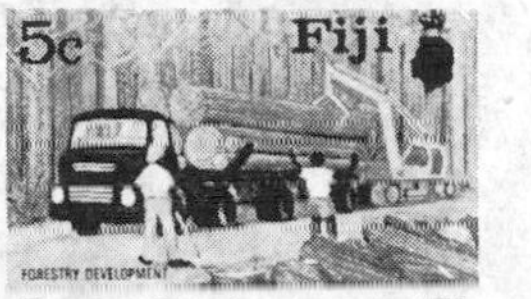
Forestry Development — A71

Development projects: 8c, Irrigation of rice field. 10c, Low income housing. 25c, Highway construction.

1973, July 23 *Perf. 14*

333	A71	5c multicolored	.16	.16
334	A71	8c multicolored	.22	.22
335	A71	10c multicolored	.30	.30
336	A71	25c multicolored	.80	.80
		Nos. 333-336 (4)	1.48	1.48

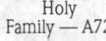

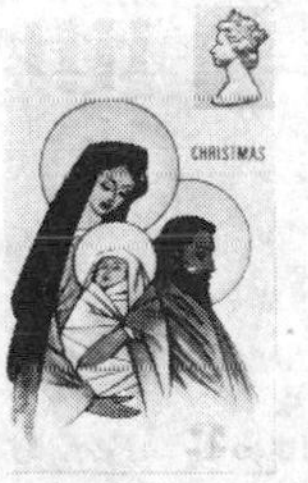
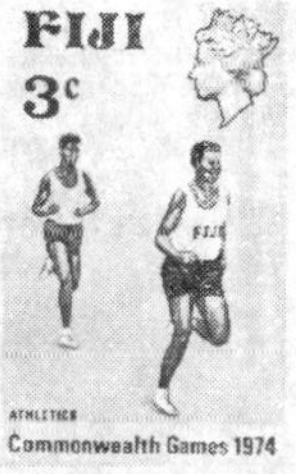
Holy Family — A72 Runners — A73

Festivals: 10c, Diwali (Candles; Indian New Year). 20c, Id-Ul-Fitar (Friendly greeting and mosque; Moslem, Ramadan). 25c, Chinese New Year (dragon dance).

1973, Oct. 26 *Perf. 14x14½*

337	A72	3c blue & multi	.15	.15
338	A72	10c purple & multi	.32	.32
339	A72	20c emerald & multi	.65	.65
340	A72	25c red & multi	.95	.95
		Nos. 337-340 (4)	2.07	2.07

Festivals celebrated by various groups in Fiji.

1974, Jan. 7

341	A73	3c shown	.15	.15
342	A73	8c Boxing	.18	.18
343	A73	50c Lawn bowling	2.25	1.25
		Nos. 341-343 (3)	2.58	1.58

10th British Commonwealth Games, Christchurch, N.Z., Jan. 24-Feb. 2.

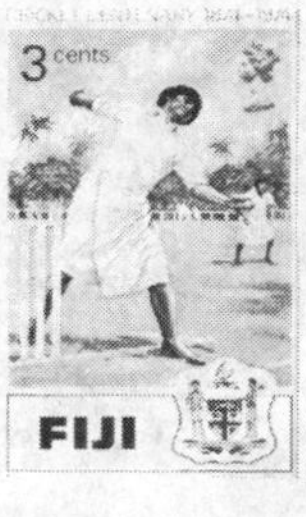
Centenary of Cricket in Fiji — A74

Designs: 3c, Bowler. 25c, Batsman and wicket-keeper. 40c, Fielder, horiz.

Perf. 14x14½, 14½x14

1974, Feb. 21 Litho.

344	A74	3c multicolored	.18	.15
345	A74	25c multicolored	1.25	.65
346	A74	40c multicolored	2.00	1.10
		Nos. 344-346 (3)	3.43	1.90

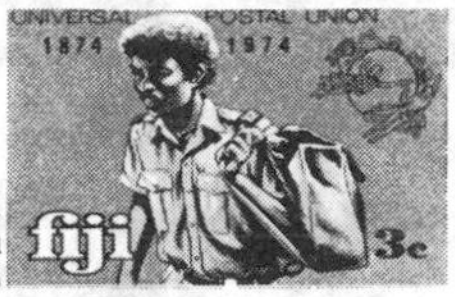
Mailman and UPU Emblem A75

UPU Emblem and: 8c, Loading mail on ship. 30c, Post office and truck. 50c, Jet.

1974, May 22 Wmk. 314 *Perf. 14*

347	A75	3c orange & multi	.16	.15
348	A75	8c multicolored	.38	.30
349	A75	30c lt blue & multi	.90	.70
350	A75	50c multicolored	1.50	1.25
		Nos. 347-350 (4)	2.94	2.40

Centenary of the Universal Postal Union.

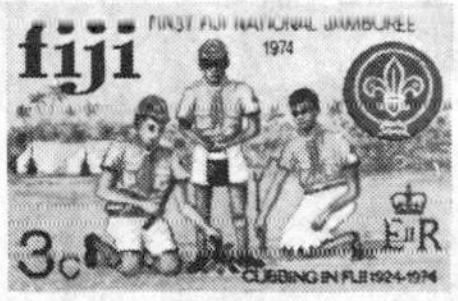
Cub Scouts A76

Designs: 10c, Boy Scouts reading map. 40c, Scouts and Fiji flag, vert.

1974, Aug. 30

351	A76	3c multicolored	.15	.15
352	A76	10c multicolored	.45	.45
353	A76	40c multicolored	1.65	1.65
		Nos. 351-353 (3)	2.25	2.25

First National Boy Scout Jamboree, Lautoka, Viti Levu Island.

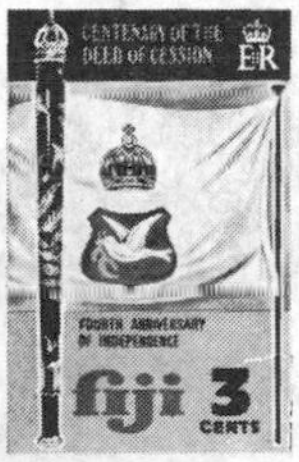
Cakobau Club and Flag — A77

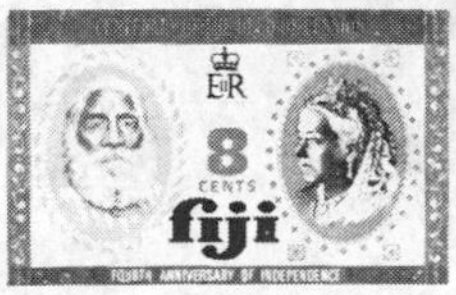
King Cakobau, Queen Victoria A78

Design: 50c, Signing ceremony at Levuka.

1974, Oct. 9 Litho. *Perf. 13½x13*

354	A77	3c multicolored	.15	.15
355	A78	8c multicolored	.25	.25
356	A78	50c multicolored	1.65	1.65
		Nos. 354-356 (3)	2.05	2.05

Deed of Cession, cent. and 4th anniv. of independence.

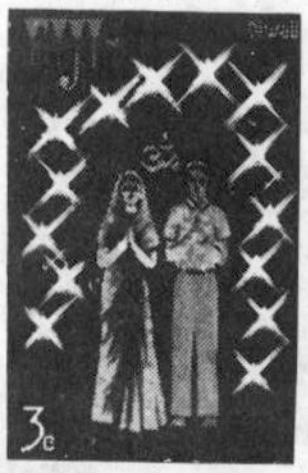

Diwali, Hindu Festival of Lights — A79

Designs: 15c, Id-Ul-Fitar (women exchanging greetings under moon). 25c, Chinese New Year (girl twirling streamer, and fireworks). 30c, Christmas (man and woman singing hymns, and star).

1975, Oct. 31 Wmk. 373 *Perf. 14*

357 A79 3c black & multi .15 .15
358 A79 15c black & multi .45 .45
359 A79 25c black & multi .75 .75
360 A79 30c black & multi .90 .90
a. Souvenir sheet of 4, #357-360 5.50 4.25
Nos. 357-360 (4) 2.25 2.25

Festivals celebrated by various groups in Fiji.

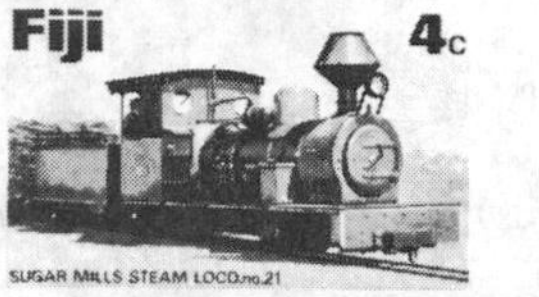

Steam Locomotive No. 21 — A80

Sugar mill trains: 15c, Diesel locomotive No. 8. 20c, Diesel locomotive No. 1. 30c, Free passenger train.

1976, Jan. 26 Litho. *Perf. 14½*

361 A80 4c yellow & multi .24 .16
362 A80 15c salmon & multi .65 .50
363 A80 20c multicolored .85 .65
364 A80 30c blue & multi 1.25 1.10
Nos. 361-364 (4) 2.99 2.41

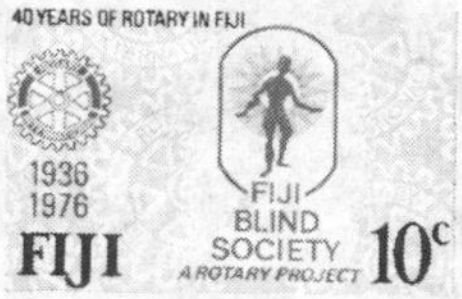

Fiji Blind Society and Rotary Emblems A81

Rotary Intl. of Fiji, 40th Anniv.: 25c, Ambulance and Rotary emblems.

Perf. 13x13½

1976, Mar. 26 Wmk. 373

365 A81 10c lt green, brn, ultra .32 .32
366 A81 25c multicolored .80 .80

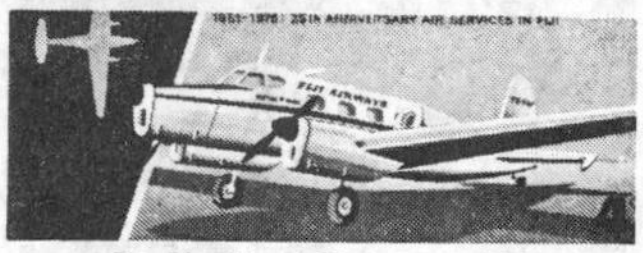

De Havilland Drover — A82

Planes: 15c, BAC One-Eleven. 25c, Hawker-Siddeley 748. 30c, Britten Norman Trislander.

1976, Sept. 1 Litho. *Perf. 14*

367 A82 4c multicolored .22 .22
368 A82 15c multicolored .60 .42
369 A82 25c multicolored 1.40 .70
370 A82 30c multicolored 1.65 .90
Nos. 367-370 (4) 3.87 2.24

Fiji air service, 25th anniversary.

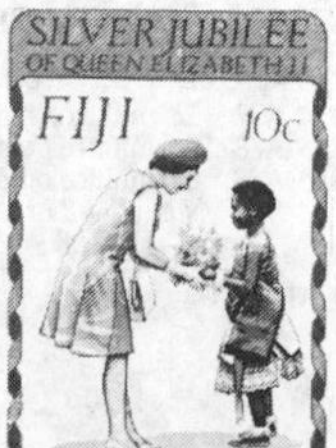

Queen's Visit, 1970 — A83

Designs: 25c, King Edward's Chair. 30c, Queen wearing cloth-of-gold supertunica.

1977, Feb. 7 Litho. *Perf. 14x13½*

371 A83 10c silver & multi .16 .16
372 A83 25c silver & multi .42 .42
373 A83 30c silver & multi .60 .60
Nos. 371-373 (3) 1.18 1.18

25th anniv. of reign of Elizabeth II.

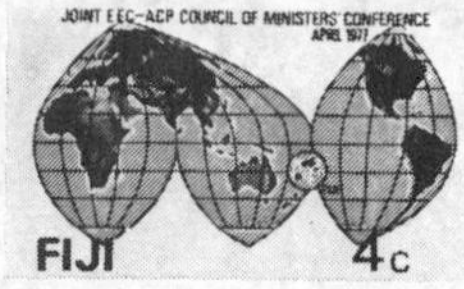

World Map, Sinusoidal Projection A84

Design: 30c, Map showing Fiji Islands.

Perf. 14½

1977, Apr. 12 Litho. Wmk. 373

374 A84 4c multicolored .15 .15
375 A84 30c multicolored 1.00 .70

First Joint Council of Ministers Conference of the European Economic Community (EEC) and of African, Caribbean and Pacific States (ACP).

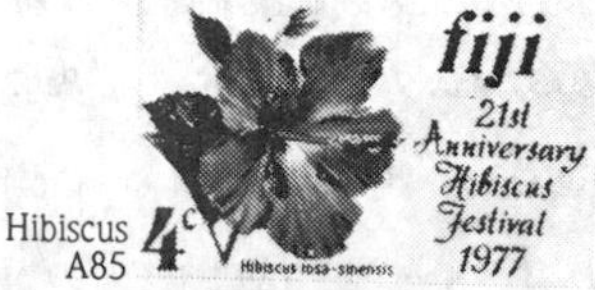

Hibiscus A85

1977, Aug. 27 Wmk. 373 *Perf. 14*

376 A85 4c red .15 .15
377 A85 15c orange .42 .35
378 A85 30c pink .90 .70
379 A85 35c yellow 1.10 .90
Nos. 376-379 (4) 2.57 2.10

Fiji Hibiscus Festival, 21st anniversary.

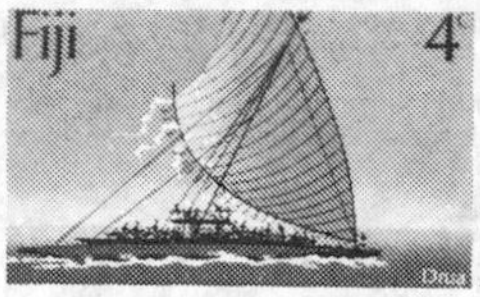

Drua, Double Canoe A86

Canoes: 15c, Tabilai. 25c, Takia, dugout outrigger canoe. 40c, Camakau.

1977, Nov. 7 Litho. *Perf. 14½*

380 A86 4c multicolored .15 .15
381 A86 15c multicolored .42 .35
382 A86 25c multicolored .70 .60
383 A86 40c multicolored 1.10 1.00
Nos. 380-383 (4) 2.37 2.10

Elizabeth II Coronation Anniversary Issue

Common Design Types

Souvenir Sheet

Unwmk.

1978, Apr. 21 Litho. *Perf. 15*

384 Sheet of 6 3.00 3.00
a. CD326 25c White hart of Richard II .48 .48
b. CD327 25c Elizabeth II .48 .48
c. CD328 25c Banded iguana .48 .48

No. 384 contains 2 se-tenant strips of Nos. 348a-348c, separated by horizontal gutter.

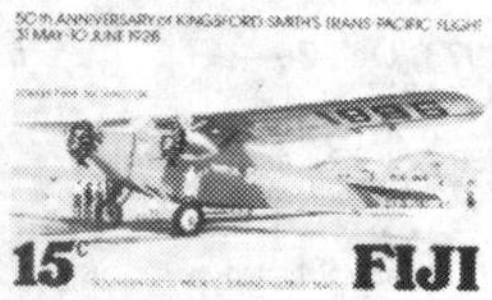

Southern Cross on Naselai Beach A87

Designs: 4c, Fiji Defence Force surrounding Southern Cross. 25c, Wright Flyer. 30c, Bristol F2B.

1978, June 26 Wmk. 373 *Perf. 14½*

385 A87 4c multicolored .15 .15
386 A87 15c multicolored .42 .32
387 A87 25c multicolored .75 .60
388 A87 30c multicolored 1.10 .75
Nos. 385-388 (4) 2.42 1.82

50th anniv. of Kingsford-Smith's Trans-Pacific flight, May 31-June 10, 1928 (4c, 15c); 75th anniv. of Wright brothers' first powered flight, Dec. 17, 1903 (25c); 60th anniv. of Royal Air Force, Apr. 1, 1918 (30c).

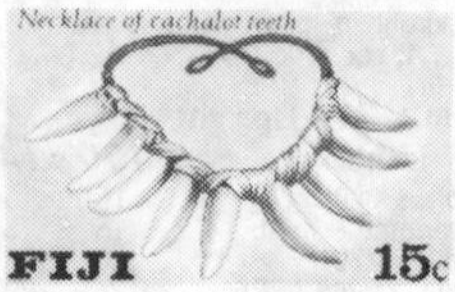

Necklace of Sperm Whale Teeth A88

Fiji artifacts: 4c, Wooden oil dish in shape of man, vert. 25c, Twin water bottles. 30c, Carved throwing club (Ula), vert.

1978, Aug. 14 Litho. *Perf. 14*

389 A88 4c multicolored .15 .15
390 A88 15c multicolored .25 .25
391 A88 25c multicolored .45 .45
392 A88 30c multicolored .55 .55
Nos. 389-392 (4) 1.40 1.40

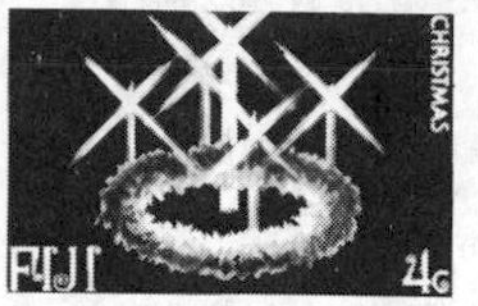

Christmas Wreath and Candles A89

Festivals: 15c, Diwali (oil lamps). 25c, Id-Ul-Fitr (fruit, coffeepot and cups). 40c, Chinese New Year (paper dragon).

1978, Oct. 30 *Perf. 14*

393 A89 4c multicolored .15 .15
394 A89 15c multicolored .30 .30
395 A89 25c multicolored .48 .48
396 A89 40c multicolored .80 .80
Nos. 393-396 (4) 1.73 1.73

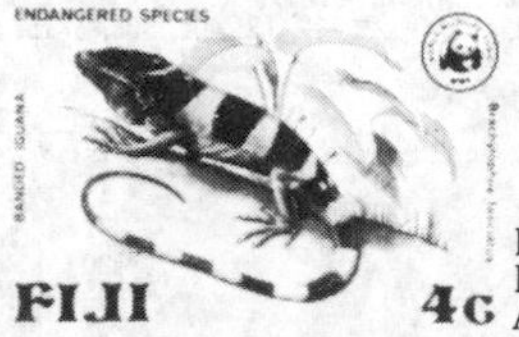

Banded Iguana A90

Endangered species and Wildlife Fund emblem: 15c, Tree frog. 25c, Long-legged warbler. 30c, Pink-billed parrot finch.

1979, Mar. 19 Litho. Wmk. 373

397 A90 4c multicolored .15 .15
398 A90 15c multicolored .45 .45
399 A90 25c multicolored .70 .70
400 A90 30c multicolored .85 .85
Nos. 397-400 (4) 2.15 2.15

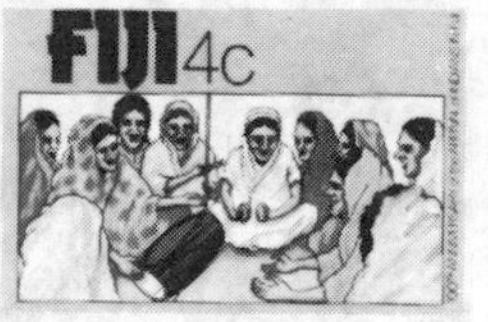

Indian Women Making Music A91

Designs: 15c, Indian men sitting around kava bowl. 30c, Indian sugar cane and houses. 40c, Sailing ship Leonidas and map of South Pacific.

1979, May 11 Wmk. 373 *Perf. 14*

401 A91 4c multicolored .15 .15
402 A91 15c multicolored .24 .24
403 A91 30c multicolored .48 .48
404 A91 40c multicolored .65 .65
Nos. 401-404 (4) 1.52 1.52

Arrival of Indians as indentured laborers, cent.

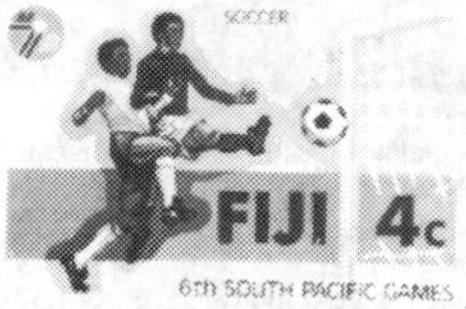

Soccer A92

Games Emblem and: 15c, Rugby. 30c, Tennis. 40c, Weight lifting.

1979, July 2 Litho. *Perf. 14*

405 A92 4c multicolored .15 .15
406 A92 15c multicolored .30 .30
407 A92 30c multicolored .60 .60
408 A92 40c multicolored .80 .80
Nos. 405-408 (4) 1.85 1.85

6th South Pacific Games.

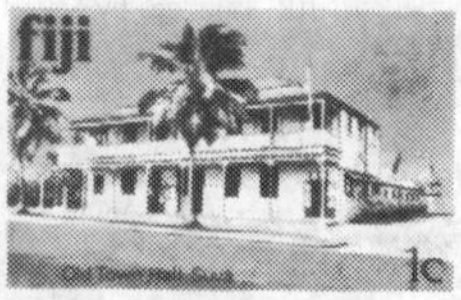

Old Town Hall, Suva A93

Designs: 2c, Dudley Church, Suva. 3c, Telecommunications building, Suva. 4c, 5c, Lautoka Mosque. 6c, GPO, Suva. 8c, 12c, Levuka Public School. 10c, Visitors' Bureau, Suva. 15c, Colonial War Memorial Hospital Suva. 18c, Labasa Sugar Mill. 20c, Rewa Bridge, Nausori. 30c Sacred Heart Cathedral, Suva, vert. 35c Grand Pacific Hotel, Suva. 45c, Shiva Temple, Suva. 50c Serua Island Village. $1, Solo Lighthouse, vert. $2, Baker memorial Hall, Nausori. $5, Government House.

1979-91 Wmk. 373 *Perf. 14*

409 A93 1c multicolored .15 .15
410 A93 2c multicolored .15 .15
411 A93 3c multicolored .15 .15
411B A93 4c multicolored .15 .15
412 A93 5c multicolored .15 .15
413 A93 6c multicolored .15 .15
414 A93 10c multicolored .18 .18
415 A93 12c multicolored .20 .20
416 A93 15c multicolored .26 .26
417 A93 18c multicolored .30 .30
418 A93 20c multicolored .35 .35
419 A93 30c multicolored .40 .40
420 A93 35c multicolored .48 .48
421 A93 45c multicolored .60 .60
422 A93 50c multicolored .70 .70

Perf. 14x13½, 13½x14

Size: 29x45mm, 45x29mm

423 A93 $1 multicolored 1.40 1.40
424 A93 $2 multicolored 2.75 2.75

Size: 48x31mm

425 A93 $5 multicolored 6.75 6.75
Nos. 409-425 (18) 15.27 15.27

Issue dates: 5c, 6c, 12c, 18c, 35c-$2, Dec. 22, 1980. No. 411B, Nov. 1991. Others, Nov. 11.

2c, 5c, 6c reissued inscribed 1983; 2c, 10c, 15c inscribed 1991; 2c, 12c, 20c, 50c, $1 inscribed 1994.

1986-91 Wmk. 384

409a A93 1c .15 .15
410a A93 2c .15 .15
411a A93 3c .15 .15
411c A93 4c .15 .15
413A A93 8c .15 .15
414a A93 10c .18 .18
416a A93 15c .20 .20
418a A93 20c .35 .35
420a A93 35c .45 .45
422a A93 50c .65 .65
423a A93 $1 1.30 1.30
Nos. 409a-423a (11) 3.88 3.88

Issue dates: 2c, Apr. 1986. 8c, Dec. 1, 1986. 3c, Jan. 6, 1988. 3c, 4c, 20c, June 1, 1988. 10c, Mar. 1, 1990. 1c, 15c, 35c, 50c, $1, Mar. 11, 1990.

2c reissued inscribed 1988; 20c inscribed 1990; 1c, 2c, 3c, 4c, 10c, 15c, 35c, 50c, $1 inscribed 1991.

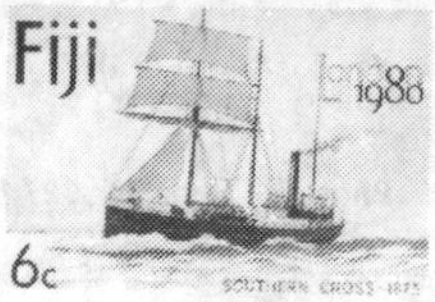

Southern Cross, 1873, London 1980 Emblem A94

1980, Apr. 28 Wmk. 373 *Perf. 13½*

426 A94 6c shown .15 .15
427 A94 20c Levuka, 1910 .32 .32
428 A94 45c Matua, 1936 .70 .70
429 A94 50c Oronsay, 1951 .80 .80
Nos. 426-429 (4) 1.97 1.97

London 80 Intl. Stamp Exhib., May 6-14.

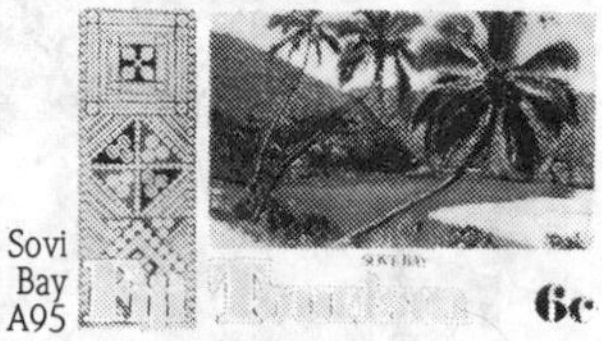

Sovi Bay A95

1980, Aug. 18 *Perf. 13½x14*

430 A95 6c shown .15 .15
431 A95 20c Yanuca Island, evening scene .30 .30
432 A95 45c Dravuni Beach .65 .65
433 A95 50c Wakaya Island .75 .75
Nos. 430-433 (4) 1.85 1.85

Opening of Parliament, 1979 A96

1980, Oct. 6　Litho.　Perf. 13
434 A96　6c shown　.15　.15
435 A96　20c Coat of arms, vert.　.28　.28
436 A96　45c Fiji flag　.60　.60
437 A96　50c Elizabeth II, vert.　.70　.70
　　Nos. 434-437 (4)　1.73　1.73

Independence, 10th anniversary.

Coastal Scene, by Semisi Maya A97

Intl. Year of the Disabled: Paintings and portrait of disabled artist Semisi Maya.

1981, Apr. 21　Wmk. 373　Perf. 14
438 A97　6c shown　.15　.15
439 A97　35c Underwater Scene　.50　.50
440 A97　50c Maya Painting, vert.　.70　.70
441 A97　60c Peacock, vert.　.85　.85
　　Nos. 438-441 (4)　2.20　2.20

Royal Wedding Issue
Common Design Type

1981, July 22　Wmk. 373　Perf. 14
442 CD331　6c Bouquet　.15　.15
443 CD331　45c Charles　.60　.60
444 CD331　$1 Couple　1.25　1.25
　　Nos. 442-444 (3)　2.00　2.00

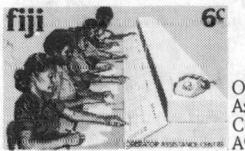

Operator Assistance Center A98

1981, Aug. 7　Litho.　Perf. 14
445 A98　6c shown　.15　.15
446 A98　35c Microwave station, map　.65　.65
447 A98　50c Satellite earth station　.90　.90
448 A98　60c Cableship Retriever　1.10　1.10
　　Nos. 445-448 (4)　2.80　2.80

World Food Day — A99

1981, Sept. 21　Litho.　Perf. 14½x14
449 A99　20c multicolored　.40　.40

Ratu Sir Lala Sukuna, First Legislative Council Speaker A100

1981, Oct. 19　Litho.　Perf. 14
450 A100　6c shown　.15　.15
451 A100　35c Mace, flag　.55　.55
452 A100　50c Suva Civic Center　.75　.75
　　Nos. 450-452 (3)　1.45　1.45

Souvenir Sheet
453 A100　60c Emblem, participants' flags　.90　.90

27th Commonwealth Parliamentary Assoc. Conf., Suva.

World War II Aircraft A101

1981, Dec. 7　Litho.　Perf. 14
454 A101　6c Bell P-39 Aircobra　.15　.15
455 A101　18c Consolidated PBY-5 Catalina　.32　.32
456 A101　35c Curtiss P-40 Warhawk　.65　.65
457 A101　60c Short Singapore　1.00　1.00
　　Nos. 454-457 (4)　2.12　2.12

Scouting Year A102

1982, Feb. 22　Litho.　Perf. 14½
458 A102　6c Building　.15　.15
459 A102　20c Sailing, vert.　.32　.32
460 A102　45c Campfire　.75　.75
461 A102　60c Baden-Powell, vert.　1.00　1.00
　　Nos. 458-461 (4)　2.22　2.22

Disciplined Forces A103

1982, May 10　Wmk. 373　Perf. 14
462 A103　12c UN checkpoint　.20　.20
463 A103　30c Construction project　.50　.50
464 A103　40c Police, car　.65　.65
465 A103　70c Navy ship　1.25　1.25
　　Nos. 462-465 (4)　2.60　2.60

1982 World Cup A104

1982, June 15　Litho.　Perf. 14
466 A104　6c Fiji Soccer Assoc. emblem　.15　.15
467 A104　18c Flag, ball　.30　.30
468 A104　50c Stadium　.80　.80
469 A104　90c Emblem　1.50　1.50
　　Nos. 466-469 (4)　2.75　2.75

Princess Diana Issue
Common Design Type

1982, July 1　Perf. 14½x14
470 CD333　20c Arms　.32　.32
471 CD333　35c Diana　.55　.55
472 CD333　45c Wedding　.70　.70
473 CD333　$1 Portrait　1.50　1.50
　　Nos. 470-473 (4)　3.07　3.07

October Royal Visit — A105

1982, Nov. 1　Litho.　Perf. 14
474 A105　6c Duke of Edinburgh　.15　.15
475 A105　45c Elizabeth II　.80　.80

Souvenir Sheet
476　　Sheet of 3　2.75　2.75
c.　A105 $1 Britannia　1.65　1.65

No. 476 contains Nos. 474-475 and 476c.

Christmas A106

1982, Nov. 22　Perf. 14x14½
477 A106　6c Holy Family　.15　.15
478 A106　20c Adoration of the Kings　.40　.40
479 A106　35c Carolers　.75　.75
　　Nos. 477-479 (3)　1.30　1.30

Souvenir Sheet
480 A106　$1 Faith, from The Three Virtues, by Raphael　2.00　2.00

Red-throated Lory — A107

Parrots.

1983, Feb. 14　Litho.　Perf. 14
481 A107　20c shown　.50　.50
482 A107　40c Blue-crowned lory　1.00　1.00
483 A107　55c Sulphur-breasted musk parrot　1.40　1.40
484 A107　70c Red-breasted musk parrot　1.75　1.75
　　Nos. 481-484 (4)　4.65　4.65

A108

1983, Mar. 14
485 A108　8c Traditional house　.15　.15
486 A108　25c Barefoot firewalkers　.42　.42
487 A108　50c Sugar cane crop　.85　.85
488 A108　80c Kava Yagona ceremony　1.40　1.40
　　Nos. 485-488 (4)　2.82　2.82

Commonwealth Day.

Manned Flight Bicentenary A109

1983, July 18　Wmk. 373　Perf. 14
489 A109　8c Montgolfiere, 1783　.15　.15
490 A109　20c Wright Flyer　.35　.35
491 A109　25c DC-3　.42　.42
492 A109　40c DeHavilland Comet　.70　.70
493 A109　50c Boeing 747　.85　.85
494 A109　58c Columbia space shuttle　1.00　1.00
　　Nos. 489-494 (6)　3.47　3.47

Cordia Subcordata A110

Earth Satellite Station, Fijian Playing Lali A111

Flowers.

1983, Sept. 26　Litho.　Perf. 14
495 A110　8c shown　.15　.15
496 A110　25c Gmelina vitiensis　.42　.42
497 A110　40c Carruthersia scandens　.70　.70
498 A110　$1 Amylotheca insularum　1.75　1.75
　　Nos. 495-498 (4)　3.02　3.02

See Nos. 505-508.

Perf. 14x13½
1983, Nov. 7　Wmk. 373
499 A111　50c multicolored　.85　.85

Dacryopinax Spathularia — A112

Various fungi.

1984, Jan. 9　Perf. 14x13½, 13½x14
500 A112　8c shown　.22　.22
501 A112　15c Podoscypha involuta　.40　.40
502 A112　40c Lentinus squarrosulus　1.10　1.10
503 A112　50c Scleroderma flavidum　1.50　1.50
504 A112　$1 Phillipsia domingensis　2.75　2.75
　　Nos. 500-504 (5)　5.97　5.97

Flower Type of 1983

1984　Litho.　Perf. 14x14½
505 A110　15c Pseuderanthemum laxiflorum　.30　.30
506 A110　20c Storkiella vitiensis　.40　.40
507 A110　50c Paphia vitiensis　1.00　1.00
508 A110　70c Elaeocarpus storkii　1.40　1.40
　　Nos. 505-508 (4)　3.10　3.10

Lloyd's List Issue
Common Design Type
Perf. 14½x14

1984, May 7　Wmk. 373
509 CD335　8c Tui Lau on reef　.15　.15
510 CD335　40c Tofua　.70　.70
511 CD335　55c Canberra　1.00　1.00
512 CD335　60c Suva Wharf　1.10　1.10
　　Nos. 509-512 (4)　2.95　2.95

Souvenir Sheet

1984 UPU Congress — A113

1984, June 14　Litho.　Perf. 14½
513 A113　25c Map　.52　.52

Ausipex '84 — A114

1984, Sept. 17　Wmk. 373　Perf. 14
514 A114　8c Yalavou cattle　.15　.15
515 A114　25c Wailoa Power Station, vert.　.48　.48
516 A114　40c Boeing 737　.75　.75
517 A114　$1 Cargo ship Eua Kavenga　1.90　1.90
　　Nos. 514-517 (4)　3.28　3.28

Christmas A115

1984, Nov. 5　Litho.　Perf. 14
518 A115　8c Church on hill　.15　.15
519 A115　20c Sailing　.38　.38
520 A115　25c Santa, children, tree　.45　.45
521 A115　40c Going to church　.75　.75
522 A115　$1 Family, tree, vert.　1.90　1.90
　　Nos. 518-522 (5)　3.63　3.63

Butterflies A116

1985, Feb. 4 — Perf. 14
523 A116 8c Monarch .25 .25
524 A116 25c Common eggfly .80 .80
525 A116 40c Long-tailed blue, vert. 1.25 1.25
526 A116 $1 Meadow argus, vert. 3.25 3.25
Nos. 523-526 (4) 5.55 5.55

EXPO '85, Tsukuba,
Japan — A117

1985, Mar. 18 Litho. Perf. 14
527 A117 20c Outrigger canoe,
Toberua Isl. .35 .35
528 A117 25c Wainivula Falls .42 .42
529 A117 50c Mana Island .85 .85
530 A117 $1 Sawa-I-Lau Caves 1.75 1.75
Nos. 527-530 (4) 3.37 3.37

Queen Mother 85th Birthday Issue
Common Design Type
Perf. 14¹/₂x14
1985, June 7 Wmk. 384
531 CD336 8c Holding Prince Andrew .16 .16
532 CD336 25c With Prince Charles .50 .50
533 CD336 40c On Oaks Day, Ep-
som Races .80 .80
534 CD336 50c Holding Prince Henry 1.00 1.00
Nos. 531-534 (4) 2.46 2.46

Souvenir Sheet
535 CD336 $1 In Royal Wedding
Cavalcade, 1981 2.00 2.00

Shallow
Water
Fish
A118

1985, Sept. 23 Perf. 14¹/₂
536 A118 40c Horned squirrel fish .70 .70
537 A118 50c Yellow-banded goatfish .85 .85
538 A118 55c Fairy cod .95 .95
539 A118 $1 Peacock rock cod 1.75 1.75
Nos. 536-539 (4) 4.25 4.25

Sea Birds — A119

1985, Nov. 4 Perf. 14
540 A119 15c Collared petrel .32 .32
541 A119 20c Lesser frigate bird .45 .45
542 A119 50c Brown booby 1.10 1.10
543 A119 $1 Crested tern 2.50 2.50
Nos. 540-543 (4) 4.37 4.37

Queen Elizabeth II 60th Birthday Issue
Common Design Type
Designs: 20c, With the Duke of York at the Royal
Tournament, 1936. 25c, On Buckingham Palace
balcony, wedding of Princess Margaret and
Anthony Armstrong-Jones, 1960. 40c, Inspecting
the Guard of Honor, Suva, 1982. 50c, State visit to
Luxembourg, 1976. $1, Visiting Crown Agents'
offices, 1983.

Perf. 14x14¹/₂
1986, Apr. 21 Wmk. 384
544 CD337 20c scar, blk & sil .38 .38
545 CD337 25c ultra & multi .48 .48
546 CD337 40c green & multi .75 .75
547 CD337 50c violet & multi .95 .95
548 CD337 $1 rose vio & multi 1.85 1.85
Nos. 544-548 (5) 4.41 4.41

Intl. Peace
Year — A120

Halley's
Comet — A121

1986, June 23 Wmk. 373 Perf. 14¹/₂
549 A120 8c shown .15 .15
550 A120 40c Dove .75 .75

1986, July 7 Perf. 13¹/₂
551 A121 25c Newton's reflector telescope .48 .48
552 A121 40c Comet over Lomaiviti .75 .75
553 A121 $1 Comet nucleus, Giotto
probe 1.85 1.85
Nos. 551-553 (3) 3.08 3.08

Reptiles and Amphibians — A122

1986, Aug. 1 Perf. 14¹/₂
554 A122 8c Ground frog .15 .15
555 A122 20c Burrowing snake .38 .38
556 A112 25c Spotted gecko .48 .48
557 A122 40c Crested iguana .75 .75
558 A122 50c Blotched skink .92 .92
559 A122 $1 Speckled skink 1.85 1.85
Nos. 554-559 (6) 4.53 4.53

Ancient War
Clubs — A123

Cone
Shells — A124

1986, Nov. 10 Wmk. 384 Perf. 14
560 A123 25c Gatawaka .45 .45
561 A123 40c Siriti .65 .65
562 A123 50c Bulibuli .85 .85
563 A123 $1 Culacula 1.65 1.65
Nos. 560-563 (4) 3.60 3.60

1987, Feb. 26 Litho. Perf. 14x14¹/₂
564 A124 15c Weasel .35 .35
565 A124 20c Pertusus .48 .48
566 A124 25c Admiral .60 .60
567 A124 40c Leaden .95 .95
568 A124 50c Imperial 1.25 1.25
569 A124 $1 Geography 2.50 2.50
Nos. 564-569 (6) 6.13 6.13

Souvenir Sheet

Tagimoucia Flower — A125

1987, Apr. 23 Wmk. 373 Perf. 14¹/₂
570 A125 $1 multicolored 1.85 1.85

No. 570 Overprinted with CAPEX '87
Emblem
1987, June 13
571 A125 $1 multicolored 1.85 1.85

Intl. Year
of Shelter
for the
Homeless
A126

1987, July 20 Perf. 14
572 A126 55c Hut .80 .80
573 A126 70c Government housing 1.10 1.10

Beetles
A127

1987, Sept. 7 Wmk. 384
574 A127 20c Bulbogaster ctenosto-
moides .35 .35
575 A127 25c Paracupta flaviventris .45 .45
576 A127 40c Cerambyrhynchus
schoenherri .70 .70
577 A127 50c Rhinoscapha lagopyga .85 .85
578 A127 $1 Xixuthrus heros 1.75 1.75
Nos. 574-578 (5) 4.10 4.10

Christmas — A128

1987, Nov. 19
579 A128 8c Holy Family, vert. .15 .15
580 A128 40c Shepherds see star .55 .55
581 A128 50c Three Kings follow
star .65 .65
582 A128 $1 Adoration of the Magi 1.25 1.25
Nos. 579-582 (4) 2.60 2.60

World Expo
'88, Apr.
30-Oct. 30,
Brisbane,
Australia
A129

1988, Apr. 27 Litho. Perf. 14
583 A129 30c Windsurfing .45 .45

Intl.
Council of
Women,
Cent.
A130

1988, June 14
584 A130 45c Fiji Nouna .62 .62

Pottery
A131

Wmk. 384, 373 (69c)
1988, Aug. 29 Litho. Perf. 13¹/₂
585 A131 9c Lapita (bowl) .15 .15
586 A131 23c Kuro (cooking pot) .32 .32
587 A131 58c Saqa (ritual drinking
vessel) .75 .75
588 A131 63c Saqa, diff. .85 .85
589 A131 69c Ramarama (oil lamp) .90 .90
590 A131 75c Kuro, diff., vert. 1.00 1.00
Nos. 585-590 (6) 3.97 3.97

Fiji Tree
Frog — A132

Indigenous
Flowering
Plants — A133

1988, Oct. 3 Wmk. 384 Perf. 14
591 A132 18c multi .45 .45
592 A132 23c multi, diff. .60 .60
593 A132 30c multi, diff. .75 .75
594 A132 45c multi, diff. 1.25 1.25
Nos. 591-594 (4) 3.05 3.05

World Wildlife Fund.

1988, Nov. 21 Wmk. 373
595 A133 9c Dendrobium mohlianum .15 .15
596 A133 30c Dendrobium cattilare .42 .42
597 A133 45c Degeneria vitiensis .62 .62
598 A133 $1 Degeneria roseiflora 1.40 1.40
Nos. 595-598 (4) 2.59 2.59

Intl. Red Cross and Red Crescent Orgs.,
125th Anniv. — A134

1989, Feb. 6 Wmk. 384
599 A134 58c Battle of Solferino,
1859 .80 .80
600 A134 63c Jean-Henri Dunant,
vert. .85 .85
601 A134 69c Medicine .95 .95
602 A134 $1 Anniv. emblem, vert. 1.40 1.40
Nos. 599-602 (4) 4.00 4.00

Epic Voyage of
William
Bligh — A135

Designs: 45c, Plans (line drawing) of the
Bounty's launch. 58c, Diary and inscription on artifacts "The cup I eat my miserable allowance out
of." 80c, Silhouette, lightning, quote "O Almighty
God, relieve us. . ." $1, Map of Bligh's Islands,
launch and compass rose.

1989, Apr. 28 Perf. 14¹/₂
603 A135 45c multicolored .65 .65
604 A135 58c multicolored .85 .85
605 A135 80c multicolored 1.15 1.15
606 A135 $1 multicolored 1.45 1.45
Nos. 603-606 (4) 4.10 4.10

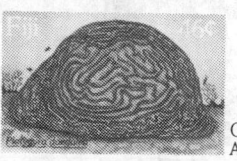

Coral
A136

1989, Aug. 21 Wmk. 373 Perf. 14
607 A136 46c Platygyra daedalea .60 .60
608 A136 60c Caulastrea furcata .80 .80
609 A136 75c Acropora echinata 1.00 1.00
610 A136 90c Acropora humilis 1.20 1.20
Nos. 607-610 (4) 3.60 3.60

Nos. 609-610 vert.

1990 World Cup Soccer Championships,
Italy — A137

Various Fijian soccer players.

1989, Sept. 25	**Wmk. 384**	*Perf. 14¹/₂*		
611	A137	35c shown	.45	.45
612	A137	63c multi, diff.	.85	.85
613	A137	70c multi, diff.	.92	.92
614	A137	85c multi, diff.	1.15	1.15
		Nos. 611-614 (4)	3.37	3.37

Christmas — A138

1989, Nov. 1		**Wmk. 373**		
615	A138	9c Church service	.15	.15
616	A138	45c *Delonix regia* tree	.60	.60
617	A138	$1 Holy family	1.35	1.35
618	A138	$1.40 Tree, Fijian children	1.90	1.90
		Nos. 615-618 (4)	4.00	4.00

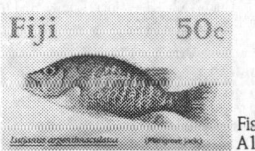

Fish
A139

1990, Apr. 23	**Litho.**	**Wmk. 384**		
619	A139	50c Mangrove jack	.68	.68
620	A139	70c Orange-spotted therapon perch	.95	.95
621	A139	85c Spotted scat	1.15	1.15
622	A139	$1 Flagtail	1.35	1.35
		Nos. 619-622 (4)	4.13	4.13

Souvenir Sheet

Stamp World London '90 — A140

1990, May 1				
623	A140	Sheet of 2	4.00	4.00
a.		$1 No. 243	1.35	1.35
b.		$2 No. 249	2.65	2.65

Soil
Conservation
A141

Designs: 50c, Vertiver grass contours. 70c, Mulching. 90c, Contour cultivation. $1, Proper land use, vert.

1990, July 23	**Litho.**	**Wmk. 373**		
625	A141	50c multicolored	.65	.65
626	A141	70c multicolored	.90	.90
627	A141	90c multicolored	1.20	1.20
628	A141	$1 multicolored	1.30	1.30
		Nos. 625-628 (4)	4.05	4.05

Trees — A142

1990, Oct. 2				
629	A142	25c Dacrydium nidulum	.32	.32
630	A142	35c Decussocarpus vitiensis	.45	.45
631	A142	$1 Agathis vitiensis	1.30	1.30
632	A142	$1.55 Santalum yasi	2.00	2.00
		Nos. 629-632 (4)	4.07	4.07

Christmas
A143

Christmas carols: 10c, Hark! The Herald Angels Sing. 35c, Silent Night. 65c, Joy to the World! $1, The Race that Long in Darkness Pined.

1990, Nov. 26	**Wmk. 373**	*Perf. 14*		
633	A143	10c multicolored	.15	.15
634	A143	35c multicolored	.45	.45
635	A143	65c multicolored	.85	.85
636	A143	$1 multicolored	1.30	1.30
		Nos. 633-636 (4)	2.75	2.75

Scenic
Views — A144

1991, Feb. 25		**Wmk. 384**		
637	A144	35c Sigatoka sand dunes	.45	.45
638	A144	50c Monu, Monuriki Islands	.65	.65
639	A144	65c Ravilevu Nature Reserve	.82	.82
640	A144	$1 Colo-I-Suva Forest Park	1.30	1.30
		Nos. 637-640 (4)	3.22	3.22

Discovery
of Rotuma
Island,
Bicent.
A145

1991, Aug. 8	**Wmk. 373**	*Perf. 14*		
641	A145	54c HMS Pandora	.70	.70
642	A145	70c Map of Rotuma Island	.85	.85
643	A145	75c Natives	.95	.95
644	A145	$1 Mt. Solroroa, Uea Island	1.25	1.25
		Nos. 641-644 (4)	3.75	3.75

Crabs — A146

Designs: 38c, Scylla serrata. 54c, Metopograpsus messor. 96c, Parasesarma erythrodactyla. $1.65, Cardisoma carnifex.

1991, Sept. 26		*Perf. 14¹/₂x14*		
645	A146	38c multicolored	.48	.48
646	A146	54c multicolored	.70	.70
647	A146	96c multicolored	1.20	1.20
648	A146	$1.65 multicolored	2.10	2.10
		Nos. 645-648 (4)	4.48	4.48

Christmas
A147

Designs: 11c, Mary, Joseph travelling to Bethlehem. 75c, Manger scene. 96c, Jesus being blessed at temple in Jerusalem. $1, Baby Jesus.

1991, Oct. 31	**Wmk. 384**	*Perf. 14*		
649	A147	11c multicolored	.15	.15
650	A147	75c multicolored	.95	.95
651	A147	96c multicolored	1.20	1.20
652	A147	$1 multicolored	1.25	1.25
		Nos. 649-652 (4)	3.55	3.55

Air Pacific,
40th Anniv.
A148

Airplanes: 54c, Dragon Rapide, Harold Gatty, founder. 75c, Douglas DC3. 96c, ATR 42. $1.40, Boeing 767.

1991, Nov. 18		*Perf. 14¹/₂*		
653	A148	54c multicolored	.70	.70
654	A148	75c multicolored	.95	.95
655	A148	96c multicolored	1.20	1.20
656	A148	$1.40 multicolored	1.75	1.75
		Nos. 653-656 (4)	4.60	4.60

Expo
'92,
Seville
A149

Designs: 27c, Traditional dance and costumes. 75c, Faces of people. 96c, Train and gold bars. $1.40, Cruise ship in port.

		Perf. 14¹/₂x14		
1992, Mar. 23		**Wmk. 373**		
657	A149	27c multicolored	.35	.35
658	A149	75c multicolored	.95	.95
659	A149	96c multicolored	1.20	1.20
660	A149	$1.40 multicolored	1.75	1.75
		Nos. 657-660 (4)	4.25	4.25

Inter-Islands Shipping — A150

1992, June 22		*Perf. 14*		
661	A150	38c Tabusoro	.50	.50
662	A150	54c Degei II	.70	.70
663	A150	$1.40 Dausoko	1.75	1.75
664	A150	$1.65 Nivanga	2.00	2.00
		Nos. 661-664 (4)	4.95	4.95

1992 Summer Olympics,
Barcelona — A151

1992, July 30		*Perf. 13¹/₂*		
665	A151	20c Running	.25	.25
666	A151	86c Yachting	1.10	1.10
667	A151	$1.34 Swimming	1.65	1.65
668	A151	$1.50 Judo	1.90	1.90
		Nos. 665-668 (4)	4.90	4.90

Levuka
A152

Designs: 30c, European War Memorial. 42c, Map. 59c, Beach Street. 77c, Sacred Heart Church, vert. $2, Deed of Cession Site, vert.

1992, Sept. 21		*Perf. 14¹/₂*		
669	A152	30c multicolored	.40	.40
670	A152	42c multicolored	.58	.58
671	A152	59c multicolored	.78	.78
672	A152	77c multicolored	1.05	1.05
673	A152	$2 multicolored	2.70	2.70
		Nos. 669-673 (5)	5.51	5.51

Intl. Planned Parenthood Federation, 40th
Anniv. — A153

1992, Nov. 2		*Perf. 15x14¹/₂*		
674	A153	77c Globe	1.05	1.05
675	A153	$2 Family	2.70	2.70

Christmas — A154

Bible interpretations: 12c, "God so loved the world..." 77c, "We love because God first loved us." 83c, "It is more blessed to give..." $2, "Every good gift..."

1992, Nov. 17				
676	A154	12c multicolored	.16	.16
677	A154	77c multicolored	1.05	1.05
678	A154	83c multicolored	1.15	1.15
679	A154	$2 multicolored	2.75	2.75
		Nos. 676-679 (4)	5.11	5.11

Peace
Corps in
Fiji, 25th
Anniv.
A155

Designs: 59c, Voluntary service. 77c, Fiji/US friendship. $1, Education. $2, Income generating business through volunteer help.

		Perf. 14¹/₂		
1993, Feb. 22	**Litho.**	**Wmk. 373**		
680	A155	59c multicolored	.80	.80
681	A155	77c multicolored	1.05	1.05
682	A155	$1 multicolored	1.40	1.40
683	A155	$2 multicolored	2.75	2.75
		Nos. 680-683 (9)	7.08	7.08

Hong Kong Rugby
Sevens — A156

Designs: 77c, Players performing traditional Cibi Dance. $1.06, Two players, map of Fiji, Hong Kong, and Australia. $2, Stadium, players in scrum.

		Perf. 14x15		
1993, Mar. 26	**Litho.**	**Wmk. 384**		
684	A156	77c multicolored	1.00	1.00
685	A156	$1.06 multicolored	1.50	1.50
686	A156	$2 multicolored	2.75	2.75
		Nos. 684-686 (3)	5.25	5.25

Royal Air Force, 75th Anniv.
Common Design Type

Designs: 59c, Gloster Gauntlet. 77c, Armstrong Whitworth Whitley. 83c, Bristol F2b. $2, Hawker Tempest.

No. 691a, Vickers Vildebeest. b, Handley Page Hampden. c, Vickers Vimy. d, British Aerospace Hawk.

1993, Apr. 1   **Perf. 14**

687	CD350	59c multicolored	.85	.85
688	CD350	77c multicolored	1.10	1.10
689	CD350	83c multicolored	1.15	1.15
690	CD350	$2 multicolored	2.75	2.75
		Nos. 687-690 (4)	5.85	5.85

Souvenir Sheet

691	CD350	$1 Sheet of 4, #a.-d.	5.50	5.50

Nudibranchs — A157

1993, July 27   **Wmk. 373**
Litho.   **Perf. 14**

692	A157	12c Chromodoris fidelis	.16	.16
693	A157	42c Halgerda carlsoni	.58	.58
694	A157	53c Chromodoris lochi	.75	.75
695	A157	83c Glaucus atlanticus	1.15	1.15
696	A157	$1 Phyllidia bourguini	1.38	1.38
697	A157	$2 Hexabranchus sanguineus	2.75	2.75
		Nos. 692-697 (6)	6.77	6.77

Tropical Fruit — A158

1993, Oct. 25   **Perf. 13½**
Litho.   **Wmk. 373**

698	A158	30c Mango	.42	.42
699	A158	42c Guava	.60	.60
700	A158	$1 Lemon	1.40	1.40
701	A158	$2 Soursop	2.75	2.75
		Nos. 698-701 (4)	5.17	5.17

Souvenir Sheet

Hong Kong '94 — A159

Butterflies: a, Caper white. b, Blue branded king crow. c, Vagrant. d, Glasswing.

1994, Feb. 18   **Perf. 14½x13**
Litho.   **Wmk. 373**

702	A159	$1 Sheet of 4, #a.-d.	5.50	5.50

Easter — A160

Designs: 59c, The Last Supper. 77c, The Crucifixion, vert. $1, The Resurrection. $2, Jesus showing his wounds to his disciples, vert.

Edible Seaweeds — A161

Perf. 14x15, 15x14
1994, Mar. 31   **Litho.**   **Wmk. 373**

703	A160	59c multicolored	.80	.80
704	A160	77c multicolored	1.10	1.10
705	A160	$1 multicolored	1.25	1.25
706	A160	$2 multicolored	2.75	2.75
		Nos. 703-706 (4)	5.90	5.90

Designs: 42c, Codium bulbopilum. 83c, Coulerpa racemosa. $1, Hypnea pannosa. $2, Gracilaria.

Wmk. 384
1994, June 6   **Perf. 14**

707	A161	42c multicolored	.55	.55
708	A161	83c multicolored	1.10	1.10
709	A161	$1 multicolored	1.40	1.40
710	A161	$2 multicolored	2.75	2.75
		Nos. 707-710 (4)	5.80	5.80

Souvenir Sheet

White-Collared Kingfisher — A162

Designs: a, On branch. b, In flight.

Perf. 13½
1994, Aug.   **Litho.**   **Wmk. 373**

711	A162	$1.50 Sheet of 2, #a.-b.	4.00	4.00
c.		Overprinted in sheet margin	4.25	4.25

Overprint on No. 711c consists of exhibition emblem and "JAKARTA '95."
Issued: #711, 8/16; #711c, 8/19.

Souvenir Sheet

Singpex '94 — A163

Neoveitchia storckii: a, Complete tree. b, Fruits, inflorescence.

1994, Aug. 31   **Wmk. 384**   **Perf. 14**

712	A163	$1.50 Sheet of 2, #a.-b.	4.00	4.00

First Catholic Missionaries in Fiji, 150th Anniv. — A164

Wmk. 373
1994, Dec. 16   **Litho.**   **Perf. 14**

713	A164	23c Father Ioane Batita	.30	.30
714	A164	31c Local catechist	.40	.40
715	A164	44c Sacred Heart Cathedral	.55	.55
716	A164	63c Lomary Church	.80	.80

717	A164	81c Pope Gregory XVI	1.00	1.00
718	A164	$2 Pope John Paul II	2.50	2.50
		Nos. 713-718 (6)	5.55	5.55

Souvenir Sheet

Ecotourism in Fiji — A165

Designs: a, Waterfalls, banded iguana. b, Mountain trekking, Fiji tree frog. c, Bilibili River trip, kingfisher. d, Historic sites, flying fox.

Wmk. 373
1995, Mar. 27   **Litho.**   **Perf. 14**

719	A165	81c Sheet of 4, #a.-d.	5.00	5.00

End of World War II, 50th Anniv.
Common Design Types

Designs: 13c, Fijian regiment guarding crashed Japanese Zero Fighter. 63c, Kameli Airstrip, Solomon Islands, built by Fijian regiment. 87c, Corp. Sukanaivalu VC, Victoria Cross. $1.12, HMS Fiji. $2, Reverse side of War Medal 1939-45.

Perf. 13½
1995, May 8   **Litho.**   **Wmk. 373**

720	CD351	13c multicolored	.18	.18
721	CD351	63c multicolored	.90	.90
722	CD351	87c multicolored	1.25	1.25
723	CD351	$1.12 multicolored	1.65	1.65
		Nos. 720-723 (4)	3.98	3.98

Souvenir Sheet
Perf. 14

724	CD352	$2 multicolored	2.75	2.75

Birds — A166

1995   **Litho.**   **Wmk. 373**   **Perf. 13**

725	A166	1c Red-headed parrotfinch	.15	.15
726	A166	2c Golden whistler	.15	.15
727	A166	3c Ogea flycatcher	.15	.15
728	A166	4c Peale's pigeon	.15	.15
729	A166	6c Blue-crested broadbill	.15	.15
730	A166	13c Island thrush	.20	.20
731	A166	23c Many-colored fruit dove	.30	.30
732	A166	31c Mangrove heron	.40	.40
733	A166	44c Purple swamphen	.60	.60
734	A166	63c Fiji goshawk	.85	.85
735	A166	81c Kadavu fantail	1.10	1.10
736	A166	87c Collared lory	1.25	1.25
737	A166	$1 Scarlet robin	1.40	1.40
738	A166	$2 Peregrine falcon	2.75	2.75
739	A166	$3 Barn owl	4.00	4.00
739A	A166	$5 Yellow-breasted musk parrot	7.25	7.25
		Nos. 725-739A (16)	20.85	20.85

Issued: 13c, 23c, 31c, 44c, 63c, 81c, $2, $3, 7/25/95; 1c, 2c, 3c, 4c, 6c, 87c, $1, $5, 11/7/95.
This is an expanding set. Numbers may change.

Souvenir Sheet

Singapore '95 — A167

Orchids: a, Arundina graminifolia. b, Phaius tankervilliae.

Wmk. 373
1995, Sept. 1   **Litho.**   **Perf. 14**

740	A167	$1 Sheet of 2, #a.-b.	3.00	3.00

Independence, 25th Anniv. — A168

Designs: 81c, Pres. Kamisese Mara, Parliament Building. 87c, Fijian youth. $1.06, Playing rugby. $2, Air Pacific Boeing 747.

Wmk. 373
1995, Oct. 4   **Litho.**   **Perf. 14**

741	A168	81c multicolored	1.10	1.10
742	A168	87c multicolored	1.25	1.25
743	A168	$1.06 multicolored	1.50	1.50
744	A168	$2 multicolored	2.75	2.75
		Nos. 741-744 (4)	6.60	6.60

Christmas — A169

Paintings: 10c, Praying Madonna with the Crown of Stars, from Correggio Workshop. 63c, Madonna and Child with Crowns on porcelain. 87c, The Holy Virgin with the Holy Child and St. John, after Titian. $2, The Holy Family and St. John, from Rubens Workshop.

Wmk. 373
1995, Nov. 22   **Litho.**   **Perf. 13**

745	A169	10c multicolored	.15	.15
746	A169	63c multicolored	.90	.90
747	A169	87c multicolored	1.25	1.25
748	A169	$2 multicolored	2.75	2.75
		Nos. 745-748 (4)	5.05	5.05

SEMI-POSTAL STAMPS

Catalogue values for unused stamps in this section are for Never Hinged items.

Children at Play — SP1

Rugby Player — SP2

Perf. 13x13½
1951, Sept. 17   **Engr.**   **Wmk. 4**

B1	SP1	1p + 1p brown	.25	.25
B2	SP2	2p + 1p deep green	.32	.32

Bamboo River Raft — SP3

Design: 2½p+½p, Cross of Lorraine.

1954, Apr. 1   **Perf. 11x11½**

B3	SP3	1½p + ½p green & brn	.25	.25
B4	SP3	2½p + ½p black & org	.32	.32

Nos. 269 and 272 Surcharged

HURRICANE RELIEF +5c

1972, Dec. 4 Photo. *Perf. 14, 13½*

B5	A56	15c + 5c multi	.52	.52
B6	A55	30c + 10c multi	1.10	1.10

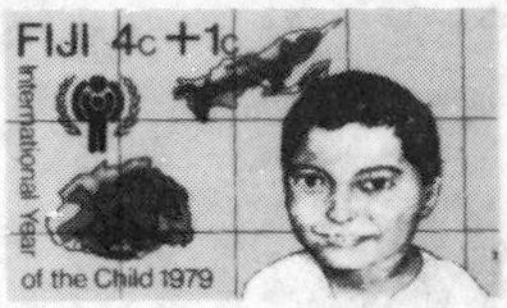

Indian Boy, Map of Fiji
SP4

Map of Fiji and: 15c+2c, European girl. 30c+3c, Chinese girl. 40c+4c, Fijian boy.

Perf. 14½

1979, Sept. 17 Litho. Wmk. 373

B7	SP4	4c + 1c multicolored	.15	.15
B8	SP4	15c + 2c multicolored	.26	.26
B9	SP4	30c + 3c multicolored	.50	.50
B10	SP4	40c + 4c multicolored	.70	.70
		Nos. B7-B10 (4)	1.61	1.61

The surtax was for IYC fund.

POSTAGE DUE STAMPS

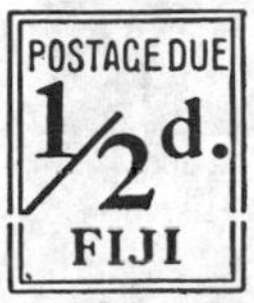

D1

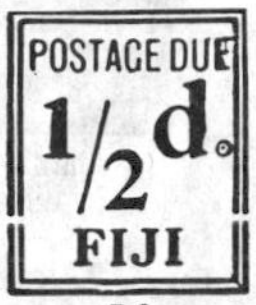

D2

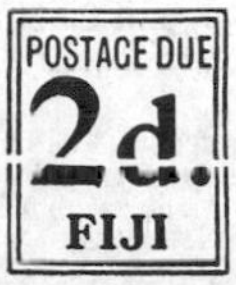

D3

1917 Unwmk. Typeset *Perf. 11*

Laid Papers; Without Gum

J1	D1	½p black	500.00	425.00
J2	D2	½p black	550.00	300.00
J3	D3	1p black	250.00	85.00
J4	D3	2p black	275.00	72.50
J5	D3	3p black	400.00	100.00
J6	D3	4p black	675.00	425.00
		Nos. J1-J6 (6)	2,650.	1,407.

There were 2 printings of No. J3. In the 1st the stamps were 25mm wide including the margins. In the 2nd the clichés were set a little closer, and the stamps were 23mm wide.

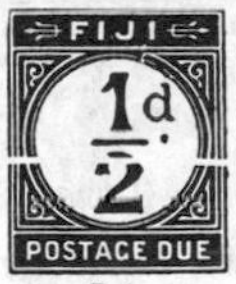

D4

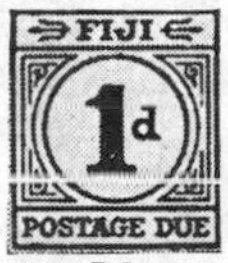

D5

1918, June 1 Typo. Wmk. 3 *Perf. 14*

J7	D4	½p black	3.75	*6.00*
J8	D4	1p black	3.75	*4.75*
J9	D4	2p black	4.75	*7.25*
J10	D4	3p black	6.00	*8.50*
J11	D4	4p black	7.25	*12.00*
		Nos. J7-J11 (5)	25.50	*38.50*

1940 Wmk. 4 *Perf. 12½*

J12	D5	1p bright green	4.00	*25.00*
J13	D5	2p bright green	5.75	*25.00*
J14	D5	3p bright green	7.50	*30.00*
J15	D5	4p bright green	8.00	*32.50*
J16	D5	5p bright green	10.00	*32.50*
J17	D5	6p bright green	5.50	*35.00*
J18	D5	1sh dk carmine	13.00	*55.00*
J19	D5	1sh6p dk carmine	13.00	*80.00*
		Nos. J12-J19 (8)	66.75	*315.00*

WAR TAX STAMPS

Regular Issue of 1912-16 Overprinted **WAR STAMP**

Die I

1916 Wmk. 3 *Perf. 14*

MR1	A23	½p green	.15	.35
a.		Inverted overprint	450.00	
b.		Double overprint		
MR2	A23	1p scarlet	.35	.40
a.		1p carmine	12.50	15.00
b.		Pair, one without ovpt.	*10,000.*	
c.		Inverted overprint	400.00	

#MR2b may exist only in horiz. strips of 12.

GAMBIA

'gam-bē-ə

LOCATION — Extending inland from the mouth of the Gambia River on the west coast of Africa
GOVT. — Republic in British Commonwealth
AREA — 4,068 sq. mi.
POP. — 695,886 (1983)
CAPITAL — Banjul

The British Crown Colony and Protectorate of Gambia became independent in 1965 and a republic in 1970.

12 Pence = 1 Shilling
100 Bututs = 1 Dalasy (1971)

Catalogue values for unused stamps in this country are for Never Hinged items, beginning with Scott 144.

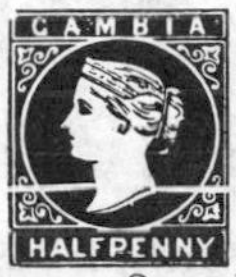

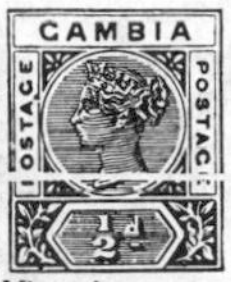

Queen Victoria
A1 A2

Typographed and Embossed

1869, Jan. Unwmk. *Imperf.*

1	A1	4p pale brown	375.	200.
a.		4p brown	400.	165.
2	A1	6p blue	375.	165.
a.		6p pale blue	*3,000.*	*2,000.*

1874, Aug. Wmk. 1

3	A1	4p brown	350.	175.
a.		4p pale brown	325.	175.
4	A1	6p blue	300.	175.
a.		6p deep blue	300.	200.
b.		Panel sloping down from left to right	475.	275.

The name panel sloping down variety is from a top right corner position. A top left corner position exists with a less noticeable sloping of the panel down from right to left; it is worth less.

1880, June *Perf. 14*

5	A1	½p orange	4.00	6.50
6	A1	1p maroon	3.25	4.50
7	A1	2p rose	17.50	9.00
8	A1	3p ultra	40.00	25.00
9	A1	4p brown	140.00	10.00
10	A1	6p blue	75.00	40.00
a.		Panel sloping down from left to right	225.00	150.00
11	A1	1sh green	225.00	150.00
		Nos. 5-11 (7)	504.75	245.00

The watermark on Nos. 5-11 exists both upright and sideways.
See footnote following No. 4.

1886-87 Wmk. 2 Sideways

12	A1	½p green ('87)	1.00	*1.25*
13	A1	1p rose car ('87)	1.25	*2.00*
a.		1p maroon		*16,000.*
14		2p deep orange	2.00	*5.50*
b.		2p orange	7.50	5.50
15	A1	2½p ultramarine	3.75	3.50
16	A1	3p slate	2.00	*6.00*
17	A1	4p brown	2.25	2.25
18	A1	6p slate green	8.50	*20.00*
a.		6p pale olive green	50.00	27.50
b.		6p bronze green	20.00	*27.50*
c.		As "a," panel sloping down from left to right	120.00	75.00
d.		As "b," panel sloping down from left to right	55.00	80.00
19	A1	1sh violet	5.50	*12.50*
a.		1sh purple	6.50	*15.00*
		Nos. 12-19 (8)	26.25	*53.00*

See footnote following No. 4.

1898, Jan. Typo. Wmk. 2

20	A2	½p gray green	1.75	1.75
21	A2	1p carmine rose	1.50	1.50
22	A2	2p brn org & pur	2.75	*4.00*
23	A2	2½p ultramarine	1.75	*3.00*
24	A2	3p red vio & ultra	6.50	*12.00*
25	A2	4p brown & ultra	6.00	*18.00*
26	A2	6p ol grn & car rose	9.00	*15.00*
27	A2	1sh vio & green	17.50	*40.00*
		Nos. 20-27 (8)	46.75	*95.25*

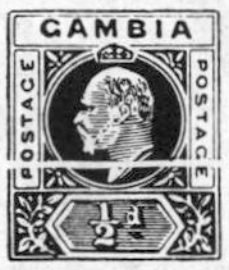

King Edward VII — A3

1902-05 *Perf. 14*

28	A3	½p green	.75	*1.25*
29	A3	1p car rose	1.25	.50
30	A3	2p org & pur	2.50	2.50
31	A3	2½p ultramarine	12.50	10.00
32	A3	3p red vio & ultra	7.50	7.50
33	A3	4p brn & ultra	3.50	*12.50*
34	A3	6p ol grn & rose	4.50	*7.50*
35	A3	1sh bluish vio & green	32.50	*40.00*
36	A3	1sh6p grn & red, *yel*	12.50	*17.50*
37	A3	2sh black & org	17.50	*27.50*
38	A3	2sh6p pur & brn, *yel*	17.50	*35.00*
39	A3	3sh red & grn, *yel*	25.00	*35.00*
		Nos. 28-39 (12)	137.50	*196.75*

Numerals of 5p, 7½p, 10p, 1sh6p, 2sh, 2sh6p and 3sh of type A3 are in color on plain tablet.
Issue dates: 1p, Mar. 13. ½p, 3p, Apr. 19. 2p, 2½p, 4p, 6p, 1sh, 2sh, June 14. 1sh6p, 2sh6p, 3sh, Apr. 6, 1905.
For surcharges, see Nos. 65-66.

1904-09 Wmk. 3

41	A3	½p green	.50	.35
42	A3	1p car rose	.45	.25
a.		1p carmine ('09)	3.00	2.00
43	A3	2p org & pur ('06)	6.25	5.00
44	A3	2p gray ('09)	1.10	1.10
45	A3	2½p ultramarine	1.45	1.50
46	A3	3p red vio & ultra	3.75	4.00
47	A3	3p vio, *yel* ('09)	3.25	2.50
48	A3	4p brn & ultra ('06)	12.00	15.00
49	A3	4p blk & red, *yel* ('09)	1.25	1.90
50	A3	5p gray & black	6.25	7.50
51	A3	5p org & vio ('09)	1.90	2.25
52	A3	6p ol grn & rose ('06)	12.00	12.75
53	A3	6p dull vio ('09)	1.50	1.90
54	A3	7½p blue grn & red	5.25	7.50
55	A3	7½p brn & ultra ('09)	1.90	3.00
56	A3	10p ol bis & red	15.00	16.50
57	A3	10p ol grn & car rose ('09)	2.00	2.75
58	A3	1sh violet & grn	19.00	25.00
59	A3	1sh blk, *grn* ('09)	2.50	3.75
60	A3	1sh 6p vio & grn ('09)	6.25	7.50
61	A3	2sh black & org	50.00	62.50
62	A3	2sh vio & bl, *bl* ('09)	9.50	12.00
63	A3	2sh 6p blk & red, *bl* ('09)	16.00	19.00
64	A3	3sh yel & grn ('09)	28.00	30.00
		Nos. 41-64 (24)	207.05	245.50

Nos. 38-39 Surcharged in Black:

HALF PENNY

a

ONE PENNY

b

Type a (I) - The word "PENNY" is 5mm from the horizontal bars.
Type a (II) - "PENNY" is 4mm from the bars.

1906, Apr. Wmk. 2

65	A3	½p on 2sh6p, type I	50.00	55.00
a.		Type II	50.00	55.00
66	A3	1p on 3sh	62.50	67.50
a.		Double surcharge	*1,900.*	*4,500.*

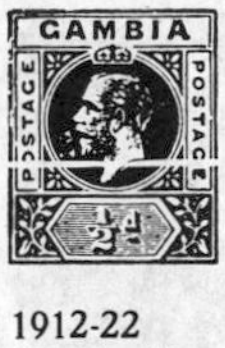

King George V — A4

1912-22 Wmk. 3

70	A4	½p green	.25	.25
71	A4	1p scarlet	.75	.15
a.		1p carmine	.25	.15
72	A4	1½p ol brn & grn	.45	.55
73	A4	2p gray	.40	.55
74	A4	2½p ultramarine	1.50	.80
75	A4	3p violet, *yel*	.40	.55
76	A4	4p blk & red, *yel*	.55	.90
77	A4	5p orange & vio	1.25	1.50
78	A4	6p dl vio & red violet	.80	1.00
79	A4	7½p brn & ultra	.80	1.00
80	A4	10p ol grn & car rose	1.50	*3.50*
81	A4	1sh blk, *green*	.65	.80
a.		1sh black, *emerald*	1.00	1.10
82	A4	1sh6p vio & green	5.50	7.00
83	A4	2sh vio & bl, *bl*	5.50	7.00
84	A4	2sh6p blk & red, *bl*	7.00	11.00
85	A4	3sh yel & green	8.50	14.00
86	A4	5sh grn & red, *yel* ('22)	35.00	*42.50*
		Nos. 70-86 (17)	70.80	*93.05*

Numerals of 1½p, 5p, 7½p, 10p, 1sh6p, 2sh, 2sh6p, 3sh, 4sh and 5sh of type A3 are in color on colorless tablet. No. 86 is on chalky paper.

1921-22 Wmk. 4

87	A4	½p green	.25	*1.65*
88	A4	1p carmine	.70	*.80*
89	A4	1½p ol grn & bl grn	2.75	*5.50*
90	A4	2p gray	1.50	*2.75*
91	A4	2½p ultramarine	.75	*1.90*
92	A4	5p org & violet	2.50	*5.50*
93	A4	6p dl vio & red vio	3.25	*5.50*
94	A4	7½p brn & ultra	4.00	*8.25*
95	A4	10p yel grn & car rose	5.00	*11.00*
96	A4	4sh blk & red ('22)	35.00	*60.00*
		Nos. 87-96 (10)	55.70	*102.85*

No. 96 is on chalky paper.

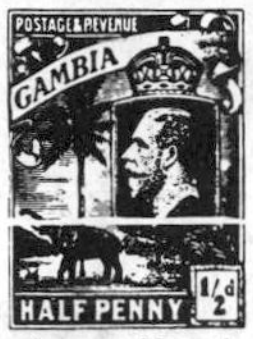

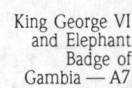

George V and Elephant — A5

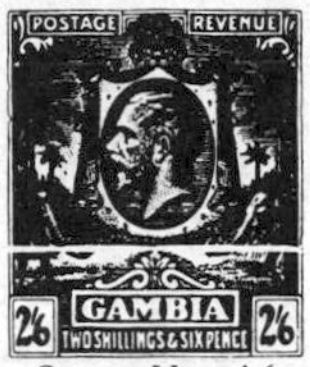

George V — A6

1922-27 Engr. Wmk. 4

Head and Shield in Black

102	A5	½p green	.45	.15
103	A5	1p brown	.60	.15
104	A5	1½p carmine	.70	.15
105	A5	2p gray	.85	.70
106	A5	2½p orange	.80	*2.75*
107	A5	3p ultramarine	.75	.55
108	A5	4p car, *org* ('27)	3.00	3.25
109	A5	5p yellow green	1.75	*5.00*
110	A5	6p claret	1.10	1.10
111	A5	7½p vio, *yel* ('27)	6.00	*7.00*
112	A5	10p blue	4.00	*8.25*
113	A6	1sh vio, *org* ('24)	2.00	1.65
114	A6	1sh6p blue	7.75	*8.00*
115	A6	2sh vio, *blue*	2.75	4.00
116	A6	2sh6p dark green	3.25	*10.00*
117	A6	3sh aniline vio	9.50	*16.50*
a.		3sh black purple	165.00	*350.00*
118	A6	4sh brown	3.50	*11.00*
119	A6	5sh dk grn, *yel* ('26)	9.50	*19.00*
120	A6	10sh yellow green	60.00	*80.00*
		Nos. 102-120 (19)	118.25	*179.20*

1922, Sept. 1 Wmk. 3

Head & Shield in Black

121	A5	4p carmine, *yel*	1.65	*1.50*
122	A5	7½p violet, *yel*	1.65	*3.75*
123	A6	1sh violet, *orange*	4.50	*10.00*
124	A6	5sh dk green, *yel*	24.00	*57.50*
		Nos. 121-124 (4)	31.80	*72.75*

Silver Jubilee Issue
Common Design Type

1935, May 6 Wmk. 4 *Perf. 11x12*

125	CD301	1½p carmine & bl	.35	.35
126	CD301	3p ultra & brn	.85	.85
127	CD301	6p ol grn & lt bl	1.75	1.75
128	CD301	1sh brn vio & ind	1.75	1.75
		Nos. 125-128 (4)	4.70	4.70

Coronation Issue
Common Design Type

1937, May 12 *Perf. 11x11½*

129	CD302	1p brown	.15	.15
130	CD302	1½p dark carmine	.15	.15
131	CD302	3p deep ultra	.20	.20
		Set value	.40	.40

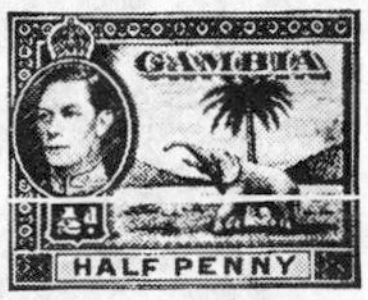

King George VI and Elephant Badge of Gambia — A7

1938-46 *Perf. 12*

132	A7	½p bl grn & blk	.15	.15
133	A7	1p brn & red vio	.15	.15
134	A7	1½p rose red & brn lake	.15	.15
134A	A7	1½p gray black & ultra ('44)	.15	.15
135	A7	2p gray black & ultra	.65	.65
135A	A7	2p rose red & brn lake ('43)	.15	.15
136	A7	3p blue & brt bl	.15	.15
136A	A7	5p dk vio brn & olive ('41)	.18	.18
137	A7	6p plum & ol grn	.50	.50
138	A7	1sh vio & sl blk	.75	.75

138A A7 1sh3p bl & choc ('46) .40 .40
139 A7 2sh bl & dp rose 1.10 1.10
140 A7 2sh6p sl grn & sep 1.25 1.25
141 A7 4sh dk vio & red orange 3.75 3.25
142 A7 5sh org red & dk blue 4.00 4.00
143 A7 10sh blk & yel org 8.75 8.75
Nos. 132-143 (16) 22.23 21.73

Issue dates: 5p, Mar. 13. No. 135A, Oct. 1. No. 134A, Jan. 2. 1sh3p, Nov. 28. Others, Apr. 1.

Catalogue values for unused stamps in this section, from this point to the end of the section, are for Never Hinged items.

Peace Issue
Common Design Type

1946, Aug. 6 Engr. *Perf. 13½*
144 CD303 1½p black .15 .15
145 CD303 3p deep blue .20 .20

Silver Wedding Issue
Common Design Types

1948, Dec. 24 Photo. *Perf. 14x14½*
146 CD304 1½p black .15 .15

Perf. 11½x11
Engr.; Name Typo.
147 CD305 £1 purple 12.50 *17.50*

UPU Issue
Common Design Types
Engr.; Name Typo. on 3p, 6p
Perf. 13½, 11x11½

1949, Oct. 10 Wmk. 4
148 CD306 1½p slate .30 .30
149 CD307 3p indigo .55 .55
150 CD308 6p red lilac 1.10 1.10
151 CD309 1sh violet 2.00 2.00
Nos. 148-151 (4) 3.95 3.95

Coronation Issue
Common Design Type

1953, June 2 Engr. *Perf. 13½x13*
152 CD312 1½p dk blue & black .20 .20

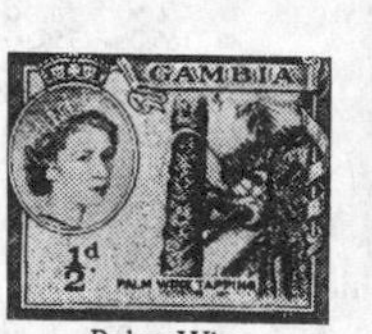
Palm Wine Tapping — A8

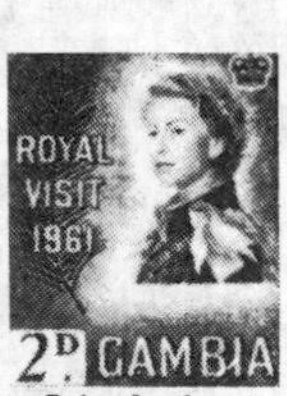
Palm Leaf and Elizabeth II, by Annigoni — A9

Designs: 1p, 1sh3p, Cutter. 1½p, 5sh, Wollof woman. 2½p, 2sh, Barra canoe. 3p, 10sh, "Lady Wright." 4p, 4sh, James Island. 1sh, 2sh6p, Woman farming. £1, Elephant badge of Gambia.

1953, Nov. 2 *Perf. 13½*
153 A8 ½p dk green & car .15 .15
154 A8 1p dk brn & ultra .15 .15
155 A8 1½p gray & dk brn .15 .15
156 A8 2½p car & black .30 .30
157 A8 3p pur & indigo .32 .32
158 A8 4p dp blue & blk .25 .25
159 A8 6p dp plum & brn .25 .25
160 A8 1sh green & yel brn .50 .50
161 A8 1sh3p blue & vio bl .65 .65
162 A8 2sh car & indigo 1.60 1.60
163 A8 2sh6p brn & bl grn 1.75 1.75
164 A8 4sh brn org & dp bl 2.75 2.75
165 A8 5sh ultra & red brn 3.25 3.25
166 A8 10sh dk yel green & ultra 5.75 5.75
167 A8 £1 black & bl grn 12.50 12.50
Nos. 153-167 (15) 30.32 30.32

Perf. 11½
1961, Dec. 2 Wmk. 314 Engr.

Design: 3p, 6p, Map of West Africa.

168 A9 2p lilac & green .15 .15
169 A9 3p brown & Prus grn .15 .15
170 A9 6p car rose & dk blue .15 .15
171 A9 1sh3p green & violet .35 .35
Nos. 168-171 (4) .80 .80

Visit of Elizabeth II to Gambia, Dec., 1961.

Freedom from Hunger Issue
Common Design Type

1963, June 4 Photo. *Perf. 14x14½*
172 CD314 1sh3p car rose .50 .50

Red Cross Centenary Issue
Common Design Type

1963, Sept. 2 Litho. *Perf. 13*
173 CD315 2p black & red .15 .15
174 CD315 1sh3p ultra & red .75 .75

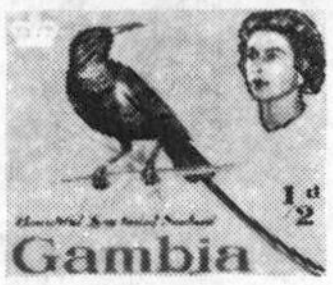
Beautiful Long-tailed Sunbird — A10

Birds: 1p, Yellow-mantled whydah. 1½p, Cattle egret. 2p, Yellow-bellied parrot. 3p, Ring-necked parakeet. 4p, Amethyst starling. 6p, Village weaver. 1sh, Rufous-crowned roller. 1sh3p, Red-eyed turtle dove. 2sh6p, Double-spurred francolin. 5sh, Palm-nut vulture. 10sh, Orange-cheeked waxbill. £1, Emerald cuckoo.

Perf. 12½x13
1963, Nov. 4 Photo. Wmk. 314
Multicolored Design & Inscription
175 A10 ½p rose buff .15 .15
176 A10 1p gray green .15 .15
177 A10 1½p pale violet .20 .15
178 A10 2p buff .15 .15
179 A10 3p light gray .32 .28
180 A10 4p lt yel green .55 .50
181 A10 6p light blue .65 .55
182 A10 1sh pale grysh grn 1.10 1.00
183 A10 1sh3p light blue 2.75 1.75
184 A10 2sh6p pale green 3.75 3.00
185 A10 5sh blue 6.75 5.50
186 A10 10sh tan 13.00 10.00
187 A10 £1 pale rose 32.50 21.00
Nos. 175-187 (13) 62.02 44.18

For overprints, see Nos. 188-191, 193-205.

Nos. 176, 179, 182 and 183 Overprinted: "SELF GOVERNMENT/1963"

1963, Nov. 7
188 A10 1p multicolored .15 .15
189 A10 3p multicolored .15 .15
190 A10 1sh multicolored .30 .30
191 A10 1sh3p multicolored .40 .40
Set value .85 .85

Shakespeare Issue
Common Design Type

1964, Apr. 23 Photo. *Perf. 14x14½*
192 CD316 6p ultramarine .22 .22

Nos. 175-187 Overprinted: "INDEPENDENCE / 1965"

Perf. 12½x13
1965, Feb. 18 Photo. Wmk. 314
Multicolored Design & Inscription
193 A10 ½p rose buff .15 .15
194 A10 1p gray green .15 .15
195 A10 1½p pale violet .15 .15
196 A10 2p buff .15 .15
197 A10 3p light gray .15 .15
198 A10 4p lt yel green .18 .18
199 A10 6p light blue .22 .22
200 A10 1sh pale grysh grn .40 .40
201 A10 1sh3p light blue .55 .55
202 A10 2sh6p pale green 1.10 1.10
203 A10 5sh blue 2.25 2.25
204 A10 10sh tan 3.50 3.50
205 A10 £1 pale rose 6.75 6.75
Nos. 193-205 (13) 15.70 15.70

In the overprint, "1965" is flush at left side under "Independence" on the ½p, 1½p, 6p, 1sh3p and 2sh6p; it is centered on the others.

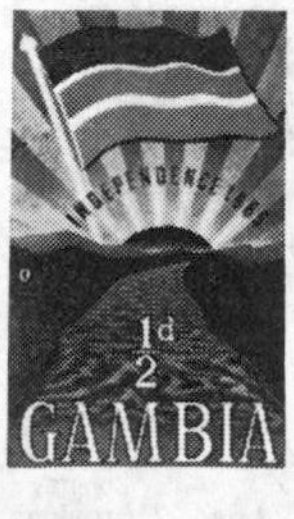
Flag of Gambia over Gambia River — A11

Design: 2p, 1sh6p, Coat of arms.

1965, Feb. 18 Unwmk. *Perf. 14*
206 A11 ½p slate & multi .15 .15
207 A11 2p lt brown & multi .15 .15
208 A11 7½p dk brown & multi .15 .15
209 A11 1sh6p lt green & multi .30 .30
Set value .56 .56

Gambia's Independence.

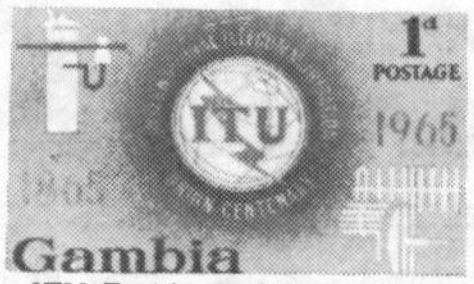
ITU Emblem, Old and New Communication Equipment — A12

1965, May 17 Photo. *Perf. 14½x14*
210 A12 1p dull blue & silver .15 .15
211 A12 1sh6p violet & gold .65 .65

Cent. of the ITU.

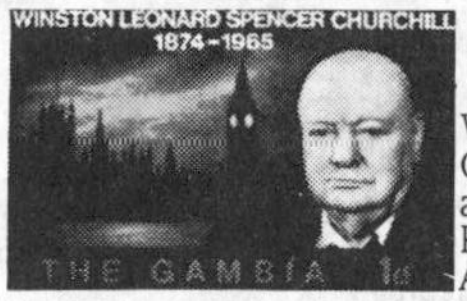
Winston Churchill and Parliament A13

1966, Jan. 24 *Perf. 14x14½*
212 A13 1p multicolored .15 .15
213 A13 6p multicolored .30 .30
214 A13 1sh6p multicolored .85 .85
Nos. 212-214 (3) 1.30 1.30

Sir Winston Leonard Spencer Churchill, statesman and WWII leader.

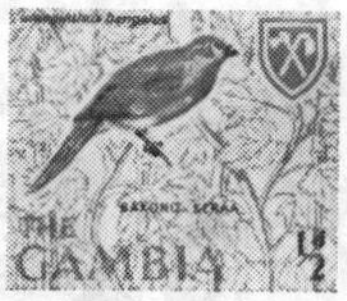
Red-cheeked Cordon Bleu and Emblem — A14

Birds: 1p, White-faced tree duck. 1½p, Red-throated bee eater. 2p, Pied kingfisher. 3p, Yellow-crowned bishop. 4p, Fish eagle. 6p, Bruce's green pigeon. 1sh, Blue-bellied roller. 1sh6p, African pigmy kingfisher. 2sh6p, Spur-winged goose. 5sh, Little woodpecker. 10sh, Violet plantain eater. £1, Pintailed whydah, vert.

Perf. 12½x13
1966, Feb. 18 Photo. Unwmk.
Size: 29x25mm
Multicolored Design & Inscription
215 A14 ½p gray .15 .15
216 A14 1p bluish green .15 .15
217 A14 1½p yel green .15 .15
218 A14 2p rose lilac .65 .32
219 A14 3p lilac .15 .15
220 A14 4p blue .15 .15
221 A14 6p gray .20 .20
222 A14 1sh light green .32 .32
223 A14 1sh6p bright blue .50 .50
224 A14 2sh6p tan .80 .80
225 A14 5sh gray green 1.50 1.50
226 A14 10sh ocher 3.00 3.00

Perf. 14x14½
Size: 25x39mm
227 A14 £1 pink 5.00 5.00
Nos. 215-227 (13) 12.72 12.39

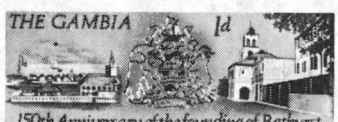

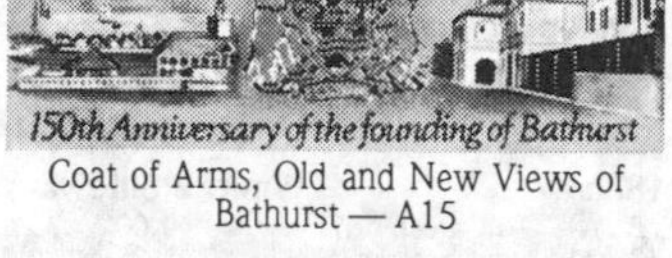
Coat of Arms, Old and New Views of Bathurst — A15

Photo.; Silver Impressed (Arms)
1966, June 24 *Perf. 14½x14*
228 A15 1p orange & dk brn .15 .15
229 A15 2p lt ultra & dk brn .15 .15
230 A15 6p emer & dk brown .16 .16
231 A15 1sh6p brt pink & dk brn .40 .40
Set value .70 .70

150th anniv. of the founding of Bathurst.

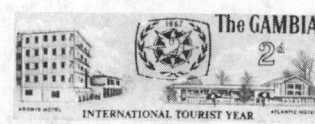

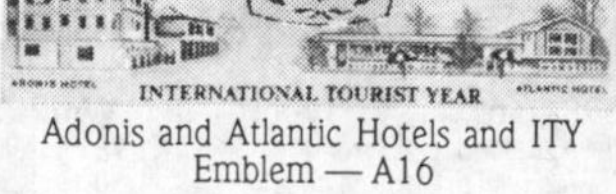
Adonis and Atlantic Hotels and ITY Emblem — A16

Photo.; Silver Impressed (Emblem)
1967, Dec. 20 *Perf. 14½x14*
232 A16 2p lt yel green & brn .15 .15
233 A16 1sh orange & brown .20 .20
234 A16 1sh6p lilac rose & brn .30 .30
Set value .55 .55

International Tourist Year.

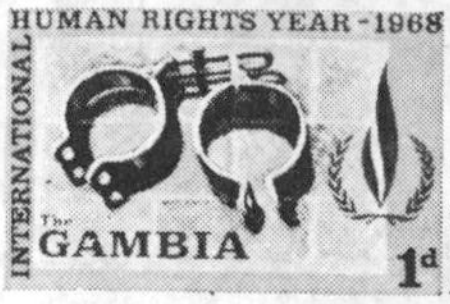
Handcuffs and Human Rights Flame A17

Intl. Human Rights Year: 1sh, Fort Bullen. 5sh, Methodist Church.

1968, July 15 Photo. *Perf. 14x13*
235 A17 1p gold & multi .15 .15
236 A17 1sh gold & multi .15 .15
237 A17 5sh gold & multi .90 .90
Nos. 235-237 (3) 1.20 1.20

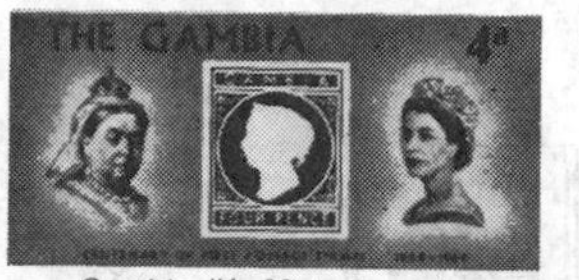
Gambia #1, Victoria and Elizabeth II — A18

Designs: 6p, Gambia #2, Victoria & Elizabeth II. 2sh6p, Gambia #1-2, Elizabeth II.

Photo. and Embossed
Perf. 14x13½
1969, Jan. 20 Wmk. 314
238 A18 4p dull yel & dk brn .15 .15
239 A18 6p dp yel grn & bl .18 .18
240 A18 2sh6p dk bl gray, brn & bl .90 .90
Nos. 238-240 (3) 1.23 1.23

Centenary of Gambian postage stamps.

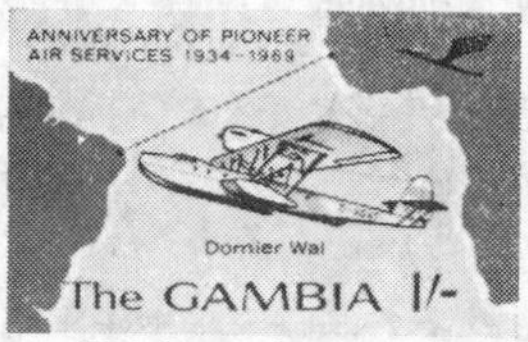
Dornier Wal, Route Gambia to Brazil and Lufthansa Emblem — A19

Designs: 2p, Plane and ship Westfalen, route Gambia to Brazil and Lufthansa emblem. 1sh6p, Zeppelin, route Gambia to Brazil and Lufthansa emblem.

Perf. 13½x14
1969, Dec. 15 Litho. Unwmk.
241 A19 2p pink, org red & blk .15 .15
242 A19 1sh buff, dl yel & blk .30 .30
243 A19 1sh6p lt bl, ultra & blk .75 .75
Nos. 241-243 (3) 1.20 1.20

35th anniversary of pioneer air services.

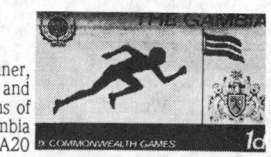

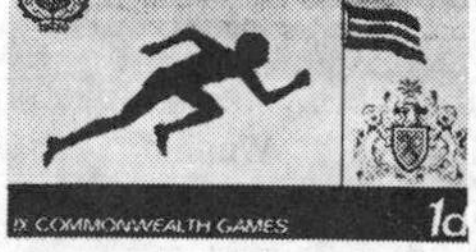
Runner, Flag and Arms of Gambia A20

1970, July 16 *Perf. 14½x14*
Flag in Red, Blue & Green
244 A20 1p pink & brown .15 .15
245 A20 1sh ultra & brown .20 .20
246 A20 5sh green & brown 1.00 1.00
Nos. 244-246 (3) 1.35 1.35

9th Commonwealth Games, Edinburgh, Scotland, July 16-25.

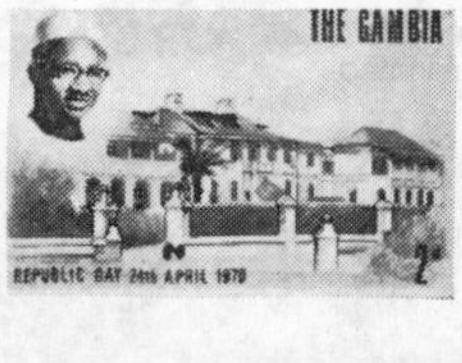
Pres. Jawara and State House A21

Republic Day, Apr. 24, 1970: 1sh, Pres. Sir Dauda Kairaba Jawara, vert. 1sh6p, Pres. Jawara and Gambia flag, vert.

1970, Nov. 2   Litho.   Perf. 14
247 A21   2p gray & multi   .15 .15
248 A21   1sh multicolored   .20 .20
249 A21   1sh6p pink & multi   .30 .30
          Set value   .55 .55

Methodist Church, Georgetown — A22

Designs: 1sh, Map of Africa and cross, vert. 1sh6p, John Wesley.

1971, Apr. 16   Unwmk.   Perf. 14
250 A22   2p multicolored   .15 .15
251 A22   1sh vio blue & multi   .20 .20
252 A22   1sh6p green & multi   .40 .40
          Set value   .65 .65

Establishment of Methodist Mission, 150th anniv.

Yellowfin Tuna A23

Fish from Gambian Waters: 4b, Peters' mormyrid. 6b, Tropical two-wing flying fish. 8b, African sleeper goby. 10b, Yellowtail snapper. 13b, Rock hind. 25b, West African eel cat. 38b, Tiger shark. 50b, Electric catfish. 63b, Swamp eel. 1.25d, Smalltooth sawfish. 2.50d, Barracuda. 5d, Brown bullhead.

1971, July 1   Litho.   Perf. 14
Fish in Natural Colors
253 A23   2b blue   .15 .15
254 A23   4b lemon   .15 .15
255 A23   6b lt blue green   .15 .15
256 A23   8b orange brown   .15 .15
257 A23   10b lt Prus blue   .15 .15
258 A23   13b orange yel   .15 .15
259 A23   25b green   .28 .28
260 A23   38b brick red   .35 .35
261 A23   50b Prus blue   .60 .48
262 A23   63b blster   .70 .70
263 A23   1.25d yel green   1.50 1.50
264 A23   2.50d deep rose   3.00 3.00
265 A23   5d ultramarine   6.50 6.50
          Nos. 253-265 (13)   13.83 13.71

Mungo Park, Scottish Landscape, Map of Gambia Basin — A24

Map of Gambia River Basin and: 25b, Park traveling in dugout canoe. 37b, Park's death under attack at Busa Rapids.

**   Perf. 13½x14**
1971, Sept. 10   Litho.   Unwmk.
270 A24   4b ultra & multi   .15 .15
271 A24   25b yel green & multi   .35 .35
272 A24   37b brick red & multi   .55 .55
          Nos. 270-272 (3)   1.05 1.05

Mungo Park (1771-1806), Scottish explorer of the Gambia and Niger Rivers.

Radio Gambia and Pres. Jawara A25

Designs: 25b, Map showing area reached by Radio Gambia. 37b, Like 4b.

1972, July 1   Perf. 14
273 A25   4b black & dull yel   .15 .15
274 A25   25b black, blue & red   .40 .40
275 A25   37b black & yel green   .60 .60
          Nos. 273-275 (3)   1.15 1.15

Radio Gambia, 10th anniv., May 1.

High Jump A26

1972, Aug. 31   Perf. 13½
276 A26   4b emerald & multi   .15 .15
277 A26   25b lt ultra & multi   .25 .25
278 A26   37b red & multi   .40 .40
          Set value   .70 .70

20th Olympic Games, Munich, Aug. 26-Sept. 11.

Mandingo Woman — A27

Designs: 25b, Musician playing Mandingo 21-stringed lute (kora). 37b, Map of Mali empire and area of Mandingo language.

1972, Oct. 18   Litho.   Perf. 14x14½
279 A27   2b rose red & multi   .15 .15
280 A27   25b lt ultra & multi   .35 .35
281 A27   37b emerald & multi   .50 .50
          Nos. 279-281 (3)   1.00 1.00

International Conference on Mandingo Studies, London, June 30-July 3.

Ship Model with Lanterns A28

Christmas: 2b, Lighted ship (lantern) carried by boys.

1972, Dec. 1   Litho.   Perf. 13x13½
282 A28   2b violet & multi   .15 .15
283 A28   1.25d blue & multi   1.50 1.50

Peanuts, FAO Emblem — A29

1973, Mar. 31   Litho.   Perf. 14½x14
284 A29   2b red & multi   .15 .15
285 A29   25b lt blue & multi   .40 .40
286 A29   37b emerald & multi   .65 .65
          Nos. 284-286 (3)   1.20 1.20

Freedom from Hunger, 2nd UN development campaign.

Planting and Drying Rice — A30   Oil Palms — A31

Cassava A32

1973, Apr. 30   Perf. 14½x14
287 A30   2b shown   .15 .15
288 A30   25b Sorghum (Guinea corn) .30 .30
289 A30   37b Rice crop   .50 .50

1973, July 16
290 A31   2b shown   .15 .15
291 A31   25b Limes   .32 .32
292 A31   37b Oil palm fruits   .55 .55

1973, Oct. 15
293 A32   2b shown   .15 .15
294 A32   50b Cotton   .70 .70
          Nos. 287-294 (8)   2.82 2.82

Gambian agriculture.

OAU Emblem — A33

1973, Nov. 1   Unwmk.   Perf. 13½x13
295 A33   4b green, yel & black   .15 .15
296 A33   25b dp mag, yel & black   .40 .40
297 A33   37b blue, yel & black   .60 .60
          Nos. 295-297 (3)   1.15 1.15

10th anniv. of the OAU.

Red Cross — A34

**   Perf. 14½x14**
1973, Nov. 30   Wmk. 314
298 A34   4b red & black   .15 .15
299 A34   25b ultra, red & black   .40 .40
300 A34   37b emer, red & black   .60 .60
          Nos. 298-300 (3)   1.15 1.15

25th anniv. of Gambia Red Cross Soc.

Flag of Gambia and Arms of Banjul — A35

**   Perf. 13½x13**
1973, Dec. 17   Litho.   Unwmk.
301 A35   4b yel green & multi   .15 .15
302 A35   25b ver & multi   .35 .35
303 A35   37b lt ultra & multi   .50 .50
          Nos. 301-303 (3)   1.00 1.00

Change of name of Bathurst to Banjul and of St. Mary's Island to Banjul Island.

UPU Emblem — A36

1974, Aug. 24   Litho.   Perf. 13½x13
304 A36   4b lilac & multi   .15 .15
305 A36   37b blue & multi   .65 .65

Centenary of Universal Postal Union.

Churchill at Harrow — A37   Churchill in Uniform of 4th Hussars — A38

Designs: 50b, Churchill as Prime Minister.

1974, Nov. 30   Litho.   Perf. 13½
306 A37   4b multicolored   .15 .15
307 A38   37b multicolored   .40 .40
308 A38   50b multicolored   .65 .65
          Nos. 306-308 (3)   1.20 1.20

Sir Winston Churchill (1874-1965).

WPY Emblem, Races of Man — A39

Symbolic Designs and WPY Emblem: 37b, Races multiplying and dividing like atom. 50b, World population.

1974, Dec. 16   Litho.   Perf. 14
309 A39   4b multicolored   .15 .15
310 A39   37b multicolored   .35 .35
311 A39   50b multicolored   .50 .50
          Nos. 309-311 (3)   1.00 1.00

World Population Year.

Dr. Schweitzer and Hospital, Lambarene A40

Portrait and: 50b, Dr. Schweitzer examining patient. 1.25d, Dr. Schweitzer in boat on Ogowe River.

1975, Jan. 14   Litho.   Perf. 14
312 A40   10b multicolored   .15 .15
313 A40   50b multicolored   .42 .42
314 A40   1.25d multicolored   1.10 1.10
          Nos. 312-314 (3)   1.67 1.67

Dr. Albert Schweitzer (1875-1965), medical missionary, birth centenary.

Peace Dove A41

Designs: 10b, Gambia flag. 50b, Gambia coat of arms. 1.25d, Map of Gambia and Gambia River.

1975, Feb. 18   Perf. 13
315 A41   4b multicolored   .15 .15
316 A41   10b multicolored   .15 .15
317 A41   50b multicolored   .40 .40
318 A41   1.25d multicolored   1.00 1.00
          Nos. 315-318 (4)   1.70 1.70

10th anniversary of independence.

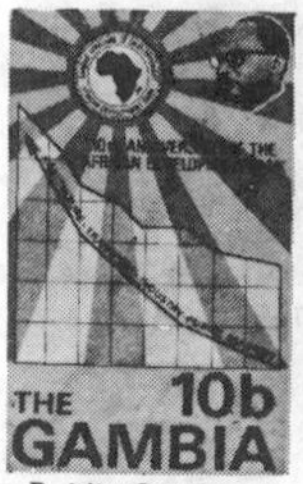

Public Services Graph, A.D.B. Emblem
A42

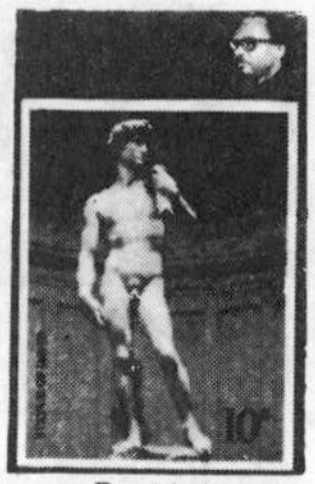

David, by Michelangelo
A43

African Development Bank Emblem and: 50b, Plant symbolizing growth of Africa, fed by Development Bank. 1.25d, A.D.B. emblem surrounded by symbols of water, education, roads and hospitals.

1975, Mar. 31 Litho. *Perf. 14*

319	A42	10b multicolored	.15	.15
320	A42	50b multicolored	.40	.40
321	A42	1.25d multicolored	1.00	1.00
		Nos. 319-321 (3)	1.55	1.55

African Development Bank, 10th anniv.

1975, Nov. 14 *Perf. 14½*

Bas-reliefs by Michelangelo: 50b, Madonna of the Steps. 1.25d, Battle of the Centaurs, horiz.

322	A43	10b dull blue & multi	.15	.15
323	A43	50b sepia & multi	.40	.40
324	A43	1.25d green & multi	1.00	1.00
		Nos. 322-324 (3)	1.55	1.55

Michelangelo Buonarroti (1475-1564), Italian painter, sculptor and architect.

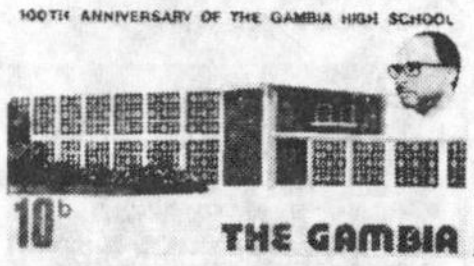

Gambia High School
A44

Designs: 50b, Pupil in laboratory and school emblem. 1.50d, School emblem.

1975, Nov. 17

325	A44	10b multicolored	.15	.15
326	A44	50b multicolored	.40	.40
327	A44	1.50d multicolored	1.00	1.00
		Nos. 325-327 (3)	1.55	1.55

Gambia High School, centenary.

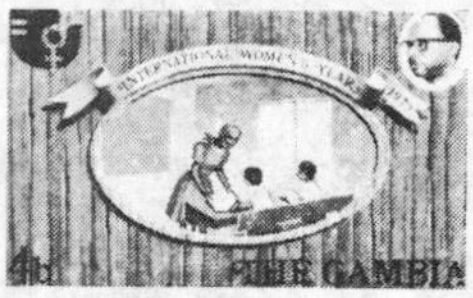

Teacher and IWY Emblem
A45

Intl. Women's Year: 10b, Women planting rice. 50b, Nurse holding baby. 1.50d, Woman traffic officer.

1975, Dec. 15 Litho. *Perf. 14½*

328	A45	4b yellow & multi	.15	.15
329	A45	10b multicolored	.15	.15
330	A45	50b multicolored	.60	.60
331	A45	1.50d blue & multi	1.50	1.50
		Nos. 328-331 (4)	2.40	2.40

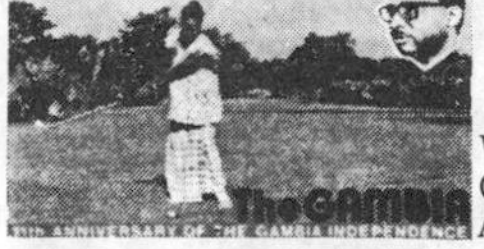

Woman Golfer
A46

Designs: 50b, Golfer addressing ball. 1.50d, Golfer finishing iron shot.

1976, Feb. 18 Litho. *Perf. 14½*

332	A46	10b multicolored	.15	.15
333	A46	50b multicolored	.85	.70
334	A46	1.50d multicolored	2.25	2.00
		Nos. 332-334 (3)	3.25	2.85

11th anniversary of independence.

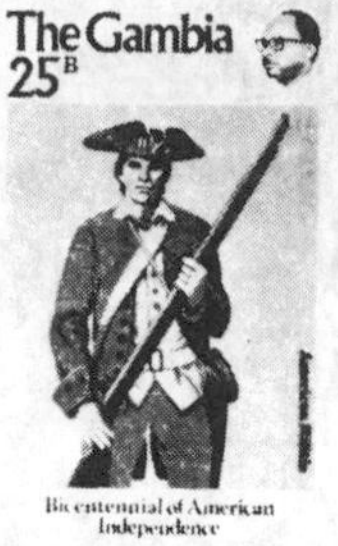

American Militiaman — A47

American Bicent.: 50b, Continental Army soldier. 1.25d, Declaration of Independence.

1976, May 15 Litho. *Perf. 14x13½*

335	A47	25b multicolored	.25	.22
336	A47	50b multicolored	.55	.45
337	A47	1.25d multicolored	1.40	1.40
a.		Souvenir sheet of 3, #335-337	3.25	3.25
		Nos. 335-337 (3)	2.20	2.07

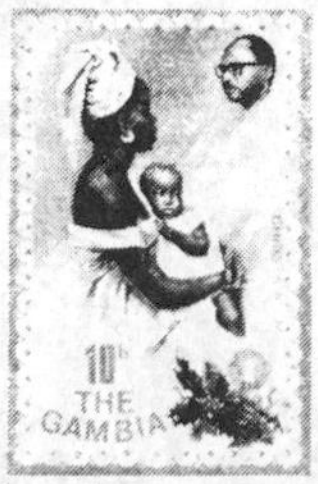

Mother and Child, Christmas Decoration — A48

1976, Oct. 28 Litho. *Perf. 14*

338	A48	10b lt ultra & multi	.15	.15
339	A48	50b rose & multi	.50	.50
340	A48	1.25d yel grn & multi	1.40	1.40
		Nos. 338-340 (3)	2.05	2.05

Christmas.

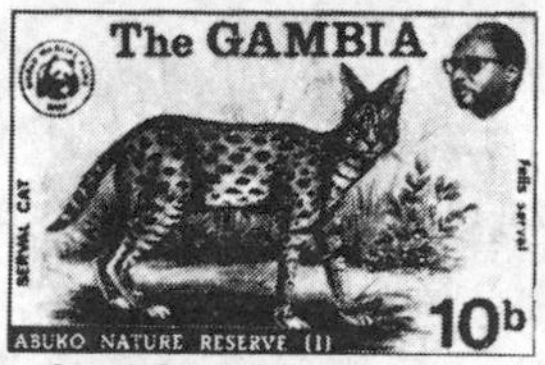

Serval Cat and Wildlife Fund Emblem — A49

Designs: 25b, Harnessed antelope. 50b, Sitatunga. 1.25d, Leopard.

1976, Nov. 29 *Perf. 13½x14*

341	A49	10b multicolored	.22	.15
342	A49	25b multicolored	.70	.38
343	A49	50b multicolored	1.10	.70
344	A49	1.25d multicolored	2.75	1.75
a.		Souvenir sheet of 4, #341-344	7.50	4.00
		Nos. 341-344 (4)	4.77	2.98

Abuko Nature Reserve.

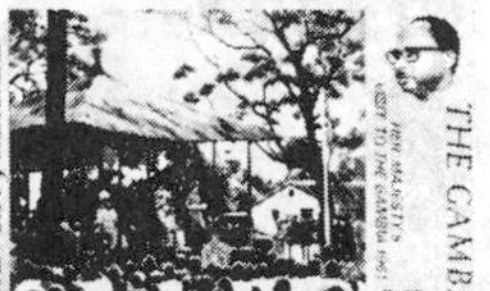

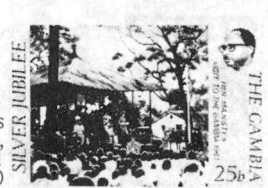

Queen's Visit, 1961
A50

Designs: 50b, The spurs and jeweled sword. 1.25d, The oblation of the sword.

1977, Feb. 7 Litho. *Perf. 13½x14*

345	A50	25b multicolored	1.25	1.25
346	A50	50b multicolored	1.75	1.25
347	A50	1.25d multicolored	5.50	2.25
		Nos. 345-347 (3)	8.50	4.75

25th anniv. of the reign of Elizabeth II.

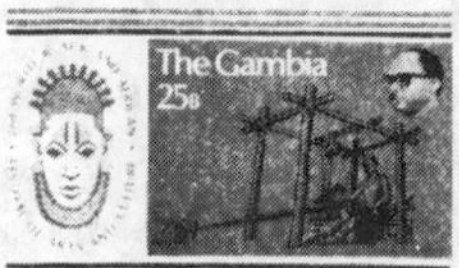

Festival Emblem and Weaver
A51

1977, Jan. 12 Litho. *Perf. 14*

348	A51	25b multicolored	.25	.25
349	A51	50b multicolored	.45	.45
350	A51	1.25d multicolored	1.10	1.10
a.		Souvenir sheet of 3, #348-350	2.50	2.50
		Nos. 348-350 (3)	1.80	1.80

2nd World Black and African Festival, Lagos, Nigeria, Jan. 15-Feb. 12.

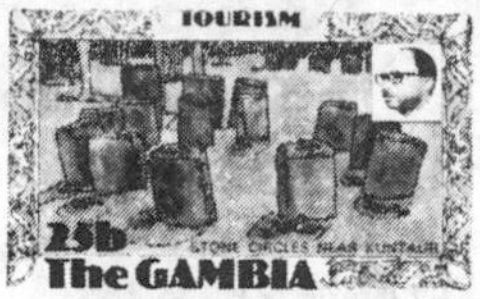

Stone Circles, near Kuntaur
A52

Tourism: 50b, Ruins of Fort on James Island. 1.25d, Mungo Park Monument.

1977, Feb. 18 Litho. *Perf. 14½*

351	A52	25b multicolored	.25	.25
352	A52	50b multicolored	.50	.50
353	A52	1.25d multicolored	1.10	1.10
		Nos. 351-353 (3)	1.85	1.85

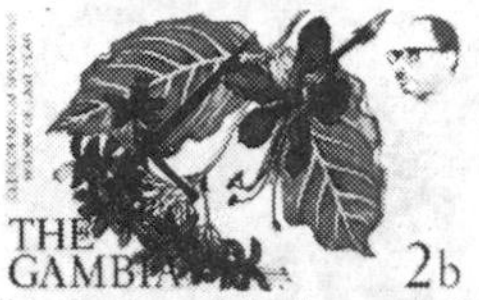

Clerodendrum Splendens — A53

Flowers and Shrubs: 4b, White water lily. 6b, Fireball lily. 8b, Mussaenda elegans. 10b, Broad-leaved ground orchid. 13b, Fiber plant. 25b, False kapok. 38b, Baobab. 50b, Coral tree. 63b, Gloriosa lily. 1.25d, Bell-flowered mimosa. 2.50d, Kindin dolo. 5d, African tulip tree. 6b, 8b, 10b, 13b, 25b, 38b, 1.25d, 2.50d, vertical.

1977, July 1 Litho. *Perf. 14½*

354	A53	2b multicolored	.15	.15
355	A53	4b multicolored	.15	.15
356	A53	6b multicolored	.15	.15
357	A53	8b multicolored	.15	.15
358	A53	10b multicolored	.15	.15
359	A53	13b yellow & multi	.15	.15
a.		Pale olive background	.15	.15
360	A53	25b multicolored	.20	.20
361	A53	38b multicolored	.28	.28
362	A53	50b multicolored	.38	.38
363	A53	63b multicolored	.48	.48
364	A53	1.25d multicolored	1.00	1.00
365	A53	2.50d multicolored	2.00	2.00
366	A53	5d multicolored	4.00	4.00
		Nos. 354-366 (13)	9.24	9.24

For surcharges see Nos. 390A-390C.

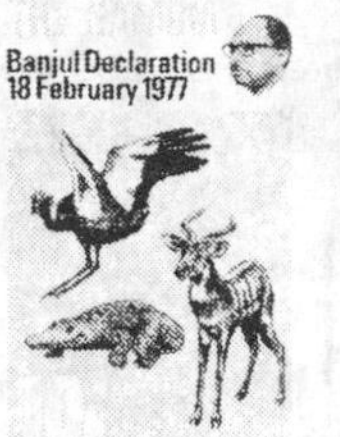

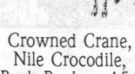

Crowned Crane, Nile Crocodile, Bush Buck — A54

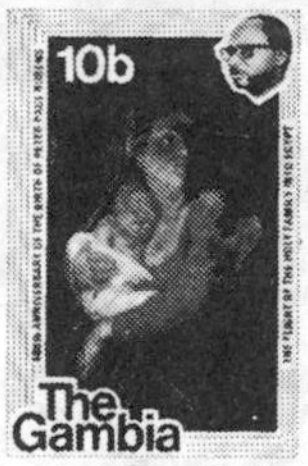

Madonna, Flight into Egypt, by Rubens — A55

Designs: 25b, Banjul Declaration, excerpt, flag colors. 50b, Banjul Declaration. 1.25d, Climbing lily, butterfly and moth.

1977, Oct. 15 Litho. *Perf. 14*

367	A54	10b lt blue & black	.15	.15
368	A54	25b multicolored	.30	.25
369	A54	50b multicolored	.55	.50
370	A54	1.25d red & black	1.40	1.10
		Nos. 367-370 (4)	2.40	2.00

Banjul Declaration, for the conservation of flora and fauna, Feb. 18, 1977.

1977, Dec. 15 Litho. *Perf. 14x13½*

Rubens Paintings: 25b, Education of Mary by St. Ann. 50b, Child's head. 1d, Madonna surrounded by saints.

371	A55	10b multicolored	.15	.15
372	A55	25b multicolored	.25	.25
373	A55	50b multicolored	.60	.60
374	A55	1d multicolored	1.40	1.40
		Nos. 371-374 (4)	2.40	2.40

Peter Paul Rubens (1577-1640). Nos. 371-374 printed in sheets of 5 stamps and decorative label.

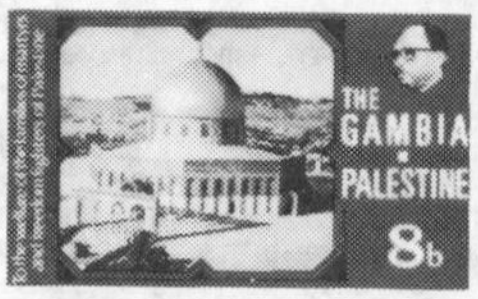

Dome of the Rock, Jerusalem
A56

1978, Jan. 3 Litho. *Perf. 14½*

375	A56	8b olive green & multi	*.90*	*.90*
376	A56	25b red & multi	*3.75*	*3.75*

Palestinian fighters and their families.

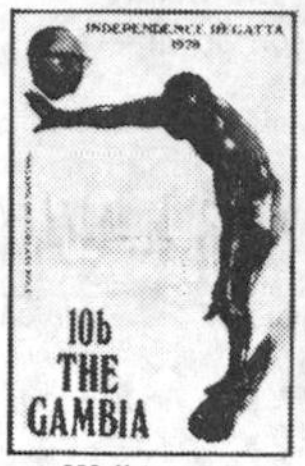

Walking on Greased Pole — A57

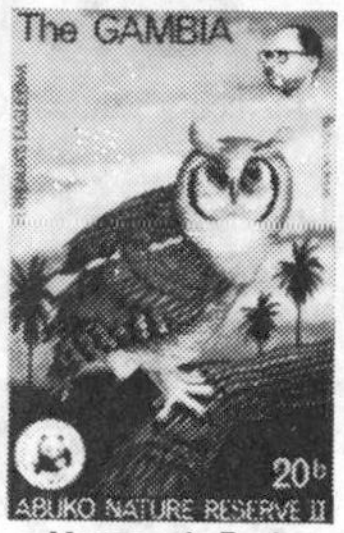

Verreaux's Eagle Owl — A58

Designs: 50b, Pillow fight on greased pole. 1.25d, Rowers in long boat.

1978, Feb. 18 *Perf. 14*

377	A57	10b multicolored	.15	.15
378	A57	50b multicolored	.50	.50
379	A57	1.25d multicolored	1.40	1.40
		Nos. 377-379 (3)	2.05	2.05

Independence Regatta celebrating 13th anniversary of independence.

Elizabeth II Coronation Anniversary Issue

Souvenir Sheet

Common Design Types

1978, Apr. 15 Litho. *Perf. 15*

380	Sheet of 6	4.00	4.00
a.	CD326 1d White grayhound of Richmond	.65	.65
b.	CD327 1d Elizabeth II	.65	.65
c.	CD328 1d Lion	.65	.65

No. 380 contains 2 se-tenant strips of Nos. 380a-380c, separated by horizontal gutter with commemorative and descriptive inscriptions.

1978, Oct. 28 Litho. *Perf. 14x13½*

Birds of Prey and Wildlife Fund Emblem: 25b, Lizard buzzard. 50b, West African harrier hawk. 1.25d, Long-crested hawk eagle.

381	A58	20b multicolored	.70	.50
382	A58	25b multicolored	.80	.60
383	A58	50b multicolored	1.50	1.25
384	A58	1.25d multicolored	3.50	3.00
		Nos. 381-384 (4)	6.50	5.35

Abuko Nature Reserve.

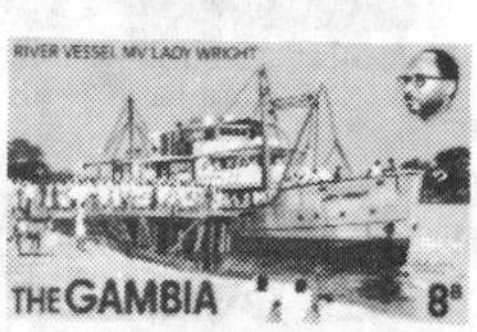

MV Lady Wright
A59

New river vessels: 25b, River vessel Lady Chilel Jawara. 1d, Cross section of Lady Chilel Jawara.

1978, Dec. 1 Litho. *Perf. 14½*

385	A59	8b multicolored	.15	.15
386	A59	25b multicolored	.45	.35
387	A59	1d multicolored	1.75	1.50
		Nos. 385-387 (3)	2.35	2.00

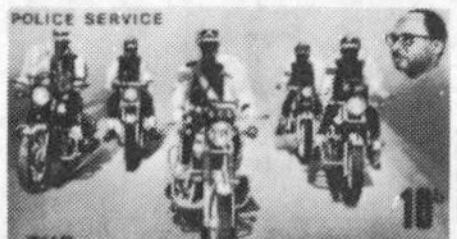

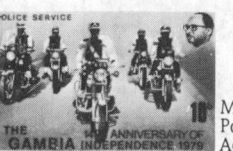

Motorized Police
A60

1979, Feb. 18 Litho. *Perf. 14*

388	A60	10b shown	.15	.15
389	A60	50b Fire engine	.65	.65
390	A60	1.25d Ambulance	1.60	1.60
		Nos. 388-390 (3)	2.40	2.40

14th anniversary of independence.

Nos. 359, 363-364 Surcharged

1979		Litho.		Perf. 14½	
390A	A53	25b on 13b multi		.22	.22
390B	A53	25b on 63b multi		.22	.22
390C	A53	25b on 1.25d multi		.22	.22
		Nos. 390A-390C (3)		.66	.66

Issue dates: No. 390A, Mar. 5; others, Mar. 26.

Ramsgate Sands, by William P. Frith — A61

Designs: 10b, 25b, IYC emblem and details from painting shown on 1d. 25b, vert.

1979, May 25		Litho.		Perf. 14	
		Size: 38x21mm, 21x38mm			
391	A61	10b multicolored		.15	.15
392	A61	25b multicolored		.22	.22
		Size: 56x21mm			
393	A61	1d multicolored		.90	.90
		Nos. 391-393 (3)		1.27	1.27

International Year of the Child.

Gambia No. 15, Maltese Cross Postmark A62

Gambian Stamps and Maltese Cross Postmark: 25b, No. 1. 50b, No. 208. 1.25d, No. 125.

1979, Aug. 16		Litho.		Perf. 14½	
394	A62	10b multicolored		.15	.15
395	A62	25b multicolored		.15	.15
396	A62	50b multicolored		.40	.40
397	A62	1.25d multicolored		1.00	1.00
a.		Souvenir sheet of 1		1.25	1.25
		Nos. 394-397 (4)		1.70	1.70

Sir Rowland Hill (1795-1879), originator of penny postage.

Abuko Earth Station, Construction — A63

Telecommunications: 50b, Newly opened station. 1d, Intelsat satellites orbiting earth.

1979, Sept. 20		Litho.		Perf. 14	
398	A63	25b multicolored		.25	.25
399	A63	50b multicolored		.50	.50
400	A63	1d multicolored		1.00	1.00
		Nos. 398-400 (3)		1.75	1.75

Apollo 11 Liftoff — A64

1979, Oct. 17		Litho.		Perf. 14	
401	A64	25b shown		.25	.25
402	A64	38b Orbiting moon		.38	.38
403	A64	50b Splashdown		.50	.50
a.		Souvenir booklet		4.00	
b.		Pane of 6 (2 each of 25b, 38b, 50b)		1.90	
c.		Pane of 6 (2d Lunar module)		1.75	
		Nos. 401-403 (3)		1.13	1.13

Apollo 11 moon landing, 10th anniversary. No. 403a contains Nos. 403b-403c printed on peelable, self-adhesive paper backing with Apollo 11 emblems on back. Stamps and panes are die-cut and have 1 to 3 sides rouletted 9½.

Large Spotted Acraea, Wildlife Fund Emblem A65

Wildlife Fund Emblem and Butterflies: 50b, Yellow pansy. 1d, Veined swallowtail. 1.25d, Foxy charaxes.

1980, Jan. 3		Litho.		Perf. 13½x14	
404	A65	25b multicolored		.32	.32
405	A65	50b multicolored		.65	.65
406	A65	1d multicolored		1.40	1.40
407	A65	1.25d multicolored		1.65	1.65
a.		Souvenir sheet of 4, #404-407		5.25	5.25
		Nos. 404-407 (4)		4.02	4.02

Abuko Nature Reserve.

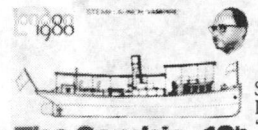

Steam Launch "Vampire" A66

1980, May 6		Litho.		Perf. 14½	
408	A66	10b shown		.15	.15
409	A66	25b "Lady Denham"		.25	.25
		Perf. 13½x14½			
		Size: 49x21mm			
410	A66	50b "Mansa Kila Ba"		.50	.50
411	A66	1.25d "Prince of Wales"		1.25	1.25
		Nos. 408-411 (4)		2.15	2.15

London 80 Intl. Stamp Exhib., May 6-14. For surcharge see No. 497A.

Queen Mother Elizabeth Birthday Issue
Common Design Type

1980, Aug. 4		Litho.		Perf. 14	
412	CD330	67b multicolored		.60	.60

Phoenician Trading Vessel — A67

1980, Oct. 2		Litho.		Perf. 14½	
413	A67	8b shown		.15	.15
414	A67	67b Egyptian seagoing ship		.52	.52
415	A67	75b Portuguese caravel		.60	.60
416	A67	1d Spanish galleon		.80	.80
		Nos. 413-416 (4)		2.07	2.07

Virgin and Child, by Francesco de Mura — A68

Christmas: 67b, Praying Virgin with Crown of Stars, by Correggio. 75b, Rest on the Flight, after Correggio.

1980, Dec. 18		Litho.		Perf. 14	
417	A68	8b multicolored		.15	.15
418	A68	67b multicolored		.52	.52
419	A68	75b multicolored		.60	.60
		Nos. 417-419 (3)		1.27	1.27

New Atlantic Hotel, Conference Emblem A69

1981, Feb. 18		Litho.		Perf. 14	
420	A69	25b shown		.25	.25
421	A69	75b Ancient stone circle		.75	.75
422	A69	85b Conference emblem		.85	.85
		Nos. 420-422 (3)		1.85	1.85

World Tourism Conference, Manila, Sept. 27 and 16th anniversary of independence.

13th World Telecomunications Day — A70

1981, May 17		Litho.		Perf. 14	
423	A70	50b No. 399		.35	.35
424	A70	50b No. 313		.35	.35
425	A70	85b ITU, WHO emblems		.60	.60
		Nos. 423-425 (3)		1.30	1.30

Royal Wedding Issue
Common Design Type

1981, July 22		Litho.		Perf. 13½x13	
426	CD331	75b Bouquet		.55	.55
427	CD331	1d Charles		.75	.75
428	CD331	1.25d Couple		.90	.90
		Nos. 426-428 (3)		2.20	2.20

For surcharges see Nos. 439, 497C.

Planting Rice Seedlings A71

1981, Sept. 4		Litho.		Perf. 14	
429	A71	10b shown		.15	.15
430	A71	50b Spraying		.40	.40
431	A71	85b Winnowing and drying		.65	.65
		Nos. 429-431 (3)		1.20	1.20

West African Rice Development Assoc., 10th anniv.

Abuko Nature Reserve A72

Designs: Wildlife Fund emblem and reptiles.

1981, Nov. 17		Litho.		Perf. 14	
432	A72	40b Bosc's monitor		.40	.40
433	A72	60b Dwarf crocodile		.60	.60
434	A72	80b Royal python		.80	.80
435	A72	85b Chameleon		.85	.85
		Nos. 432-435 (4)		2.65	2.65

30th Anniv. of West African Examinations Council — A73

1982, Mar. 16		Litho.		Perf. 14	
436	A73	60b Test room		.40	.40
437	A73	85b 1st high school		.55	.55
438	A73	1.10d Council office		.75	.75
		Nos. 436-438 (3)		1.70	1.70

No. 426 Surcharged

1982, Apr. 19		Litho.		Perf. 13½x13	
439	CD331	60b on 75b multi		3.50	

Scouting Year — A74

1982, May				Perf. 14	
440	A74	85b Tree planting		.55	.55
441	A74	1.25d Woodworking		.80	.80
442	A74	1.27d Baden-Powell		.90	.90
		Nos. 440-442 (3)		2.25	2.25

1982 World Cup A75

1982, June 13		Litho.		Perf. 14	
443	A75	10b Team		.15	.15
444	A75	1.10d Players		.75	.75
445	A75	1.25d Stadium		.80	.80
446	A75	1.55d Cup		1.00	1.00
a.		Souvenir sheet of 4, #443-446		2.75	2.75
		Nos. 443-446 (4)		2.70	2.70

For surcharge see No. 497B.

Princess Diana Issue
Common Design Type

1982, July 1				Perf. 14½x14	
447	CD333	10b Arms		.15	.15
448	CD333	85b Diana		.65	.65
449	CD333	1.10d Wedding		.85	.85
450	CD333	2.50d Portrait		1.75	1.75
		Nos. 447-450 (4)		3.40	3.40

For surcharge see No. 479D.

Economic Community of West African States Development A76

Designs: 10b, Yundum Experimental Farm. 60b, Banjul/Kaolack Microwave Tower. 90b, Soap Factory, Denton Bridge Banjul. 1.25d, Control Tower, Yundum.

1982, Nov. 5		Litho.		Perf. 14x14½	
451	A76	10b multicolored		.15	.15
452	A76	60b multicolored		.45	.45
453	A76	90b multicolored		.70	.70
454	A76	1.25d multicolored		.90	.90
		Nos. 451-454 (4)		2.20	2.20

Kassina Cassinoides A77

1982, Dec.		Litho.		Perf. 14	
455	A77	10b shown		.15	.15
456	A77	20b Hylarana galamensis		.15	.15
457	A77	85b Euphlyctis occipitalis		.60	.60
458	A77	2d Kassina senegalensis		1.40	1.40
		Nos. 455-458 (4)		2.30	2.30

A78

1983, Mar. 14		Wmk. 373		Perf. 12	
459	A78	10b Globe showing Gambia		.15	.15
460	A78	60b Batik cloth		.35	.35
461	A78	1.10d Bagging peanuts		.60	.60
462	A78	2.10d Flag		1.10	1.10
		Nos. 459-462 (4)		2.20	2.20

Commonwealth Day.

Sisters of St. Joseph of Cluny Centenary — A79

1983, Apr. 8 Litho. *Perf. 14*

463 A79 10b Founder Anne Marie Javouhey, vert. .15 .15
464 A79 85b Javouhey with children, house .60 .60

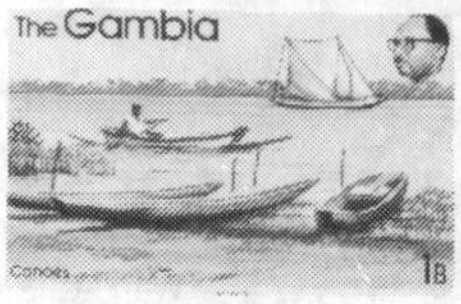

River Boats A80

1983, July 11 Litho. *Perf. 14*

465 A80 1b Canoes .15 .15
466 A80 2b Upstream ferry .15 .15
467 A80 3b Dredging vessel .15 .15
468 A80 4b Harbor launch .15 .15
469 A80 5b Freighter .15 .15
470 A80 10b 60-foot launch .15 .15
471 A80 20b Multi-purpose vessel .15 .15
472 A80 30b Large sailing canoe .16 .16
473 A80 40b Passenger-cargo ferry .22 .22
474 A80 50b Cargo liner, diff. .28 .28
475 A80 75b Fishing boats .40 .40
476 A80 1d Peanut river train .52 .52
477 A80 1.25d Groundnutter .65 .65
478 A80 2.50d Banjul-Barra ferry 1.40 1.40
479 A80 5d Binlang Bolong 2.75 2.75
480 A80 10d Passenger-cargo ferry, diff. 5.25 5.25
Nos. 465-480 (16) 12.68 12.68

For overprints see Nos. 523-524.

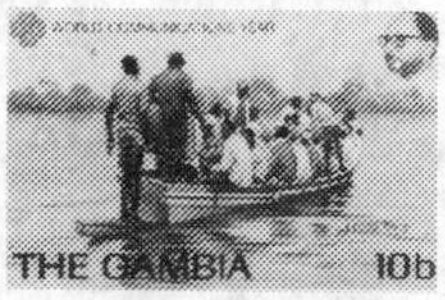

World Communications Year — A81

1983, Oct. 10

481 A81 10b Local ferry .15 .15
482 A81 85b GPO telex, Banjul .65 .65
483 A81 90b Radio Gambia .70 .70
484 A81 1.10d Loading mail, Yundum Airport .85 .85
Nos. 481-484 (4) 2.35 2.35

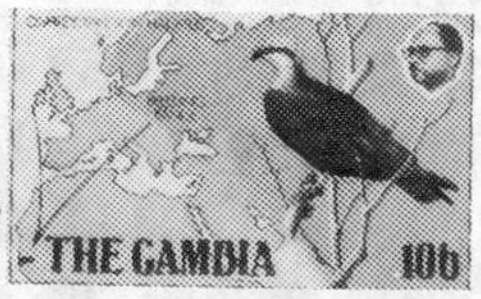

Osprey, Breeding Range A82

Designs: Birds, Maps of Europe and Africa.

1983, Sept. 12 Litho. *Perf. 14*

485 A82 10b multicolored .15 .15
486 A82 60b multicolored .48 .48
487 A82 85b multicolored .70 .70
488 A82 1.10d multicolored .90 .90
Nos. 485-488 (4) 2.23 2.23

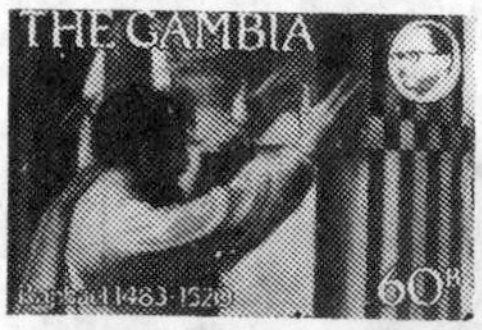

Raphael, 500th Birth Anniv. A83

Details from St. Paul Preaching at Athens.

1983, Nov. 1 Litho. *Perf. 14*

489 A83 60b multicolored .30 .30
490 A83 85b multicolored .40 .40
491 A83 1d multicolored .50 .50
Nos. 489-491 (3) 1.20 1.20

Souvenir Sheet

492 A83 2d multi, vert. 1.00 1.00

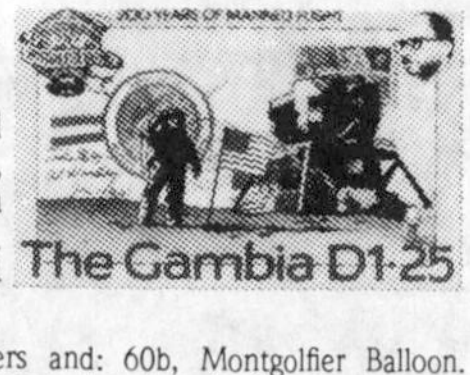

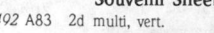

Manned Flight, 200th Anniv. A84

Flown covers and: 60b, Montgolfier Balloon. 85b, British Caledonian Aircraft. 96b, Junkers Airplane. 1.25d, Lunar module. 4d, Zeppelin.

1983, Dec. 12 Litho. *Perf. 14*

493 A84 60b multicolored .55 .55
494 A84 85b multicolored .75 .75
a. Bklt. pane, 2 each #493, 494 2.75
495 A84 90b multicolored .80 .80
496 A84 1.25d multicolored 1.10 1.10
a. Bklt. pane, 2 each #495, 496 4.00
Nos. 493-496 (4) 3.20 3.20

Souvenir Sheet

497 A84 4d multicolored 7.00 7.00

No. 497 issued in booklet containing Nos. 497, 494a, 496a.

Nos. 411, 445, 428 and 449 Surcharged with Black Bars and New Value

1983, Dec. 14 Litho. *Perfs. as before*

497A A66 1.50d on 1.25d, #411
497B A75 1.50d on 1.25d, #445
497C CD331 2d on 1.25d, #428
497D CD333 2d on 1.10d, #449

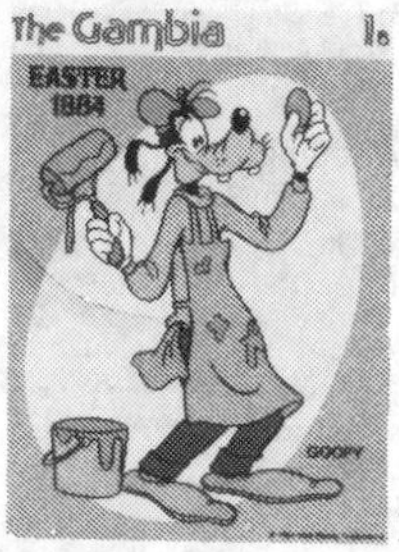

Easter — A85

Various Disney characters painting Easter eggs.

1984, Apr. 15 Litho. *Perf. 11*

498 A85 1b multicolored .15 .15
499 A85 2b multicolored .15 .15
500 A85 3b multicolored .15 .15
501 A85 4b multicolored .15 .15
502 A85 5b multicolored .15 .15
503 A85 10b multicolored .15 .15
504 A85 60b multicolored .40 .40
505 A85 90b multicolored .60 .60
506 A85 5d multicolored 3.50 3.50
Set value 4.75 4.75

Souvenir Sheet

Perf. 14

507 A85 5d multicolored 3.50 3.50

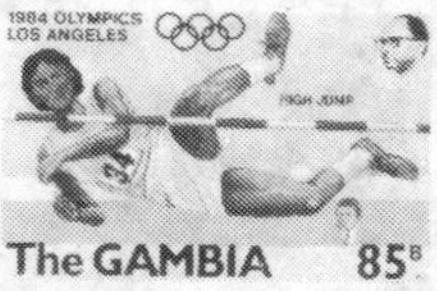

1984 Summer Olympics A86

1984, Mar. 30 Litho. *Perf. 14*

508 A86 60b Shot put, vert. .35 .35
509 A86 85b High jump .48 .48
510 A86 90b Wrestling, vert. .50 .50
511 A86 1d Gymnastics, vert. .55 .55
512 A86 1.25d Swimming .70 .70
513 A86 2d Diving 1.10 1.10
Nos. 508-513 (6) 3.68 3.68

Souvenir Sheet

514 A86 5d Yachting, vert. 3.00 3.00

For overprints see Nos. 570-576.

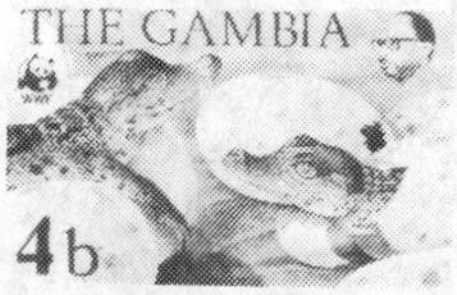

Nile Crododile A87

1984, May 23

515 A87 4b Young hatching .15 .15
516 A87 6b Adult carrying young .15 .15
517 A87 90b Adult .52 .52
518 A87 1.50d Adult, diff. .90 .90
a. Souvenir sheet of 4, #514-518 1.50 1.50
Nos. 515-518 (4) 2.72 2.72

Lloyd's List Issue

Common Design Type

1984, June 1 Litho. *Perf. 14*

519 CD335 60b Banjul Port .35 .35
520 CD335 85b Bulk cargo carrier .50 .50
521 CD335 90b Sinking of the Dagomba .52 .52
522 CD335 1.25d 19th-cent. frigate .70 .70
Nos. 519-522 (4) 2.07 2.07

Nos. 478-479 Overprinted: "19th UPU / CONGRESS HAMBURG"

1984, June 19 Litho. *Perf. 14*

523 A80 2.50d multicolored 1.50 1.50
524 A80 5d multicolored 3.00 3.00

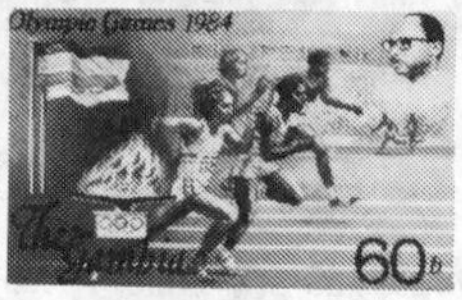

1984 Summer Olympics A88

1984, July 28 Litho. *Perf. 14*

525 A88 60b Running .36 .36
526 A88 85b Long jump .52 .52
527 A88 90b Running, diff. .55 .55
528 A88 1.25d Long jump, diff. .75 .75
Nos. 525-528 (4) 2.18 2.18

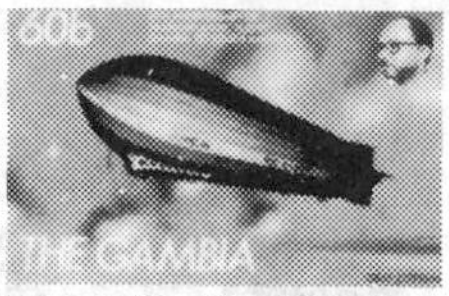

Gambia-South America Transatlantic Flight, 50th Anniv. — A89

1984, Nov. 1 Litho. *Perf. 14*

529 A89 60b Graf Zeppelin D-LZ127 .30 .30
530 A89 85b Dornier Wal on S.S. Westfalen .50 .50
531 A89 90b Dornier DO-18 D-ABYM .52 .52
532 A89 1.25d Dornier Wal D-2069 .70 .70
Nos. 529-532 (4) 2.02 2.02

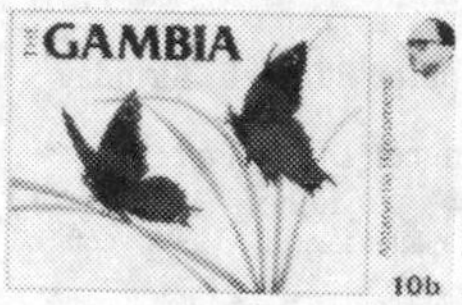

Butterflies and Marine Life — A90

1984, Nov. 27

533 A90 10b Antanartia hippomene .15 .15
534 A90 55b Penaeus duorarum .30 .30
535 A90 75b Caretta caretta .45 .45
536 A90 85b Pseudacraea eurytus .48 .48
537 A90 90b Charaxes lactitinctus .50 .50
538 A90 1.50d Physalia .85 .85
539 A90 2.35d Uca pugilator 1.25 1.25
540 A90 3d Graphium pylades 1.50 1.50
Nos. 533-540 (8) 5.48 5.48

Souvenir Sheets

541 A90 5d Eurema hapale 2.75 2.75
542 A90 5d Cowrie snail 2.75 2.75

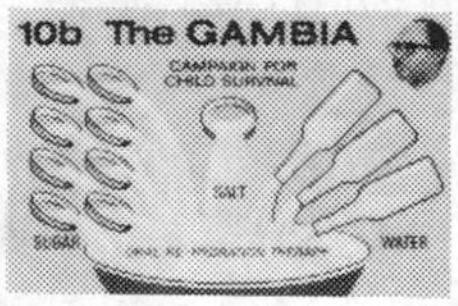

UN Child Survival Campaign A91

1985, Feb. 27

543 A91 10b Oral rehydration therapy .15 .15
544 A91 85b Growth monitoring .50 .50
545 A91 1.10d Breast-feeding .65 .65
546 A91 1.50d Universal immunization .90 .90
Nos. 543-546 (4) 2.20 2.20

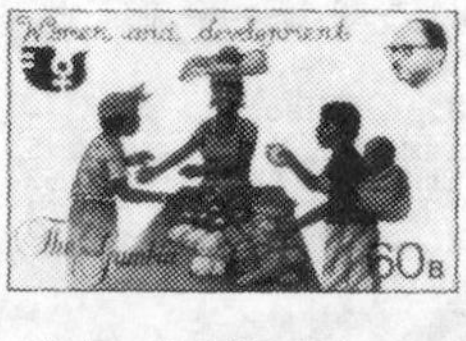

UN Decade for Women A92

Design: 1d, 1.25d, Woman working in office.

1985, Mar. 11

547 A92 60b multicolored .30 .30
548 A92 85b multicolored .45 .45
549 A92 1d multicolored .55 .55
550 A92 1.25d multicolored .65 .65
Nos. 547-550 (4) 1.95 1.95

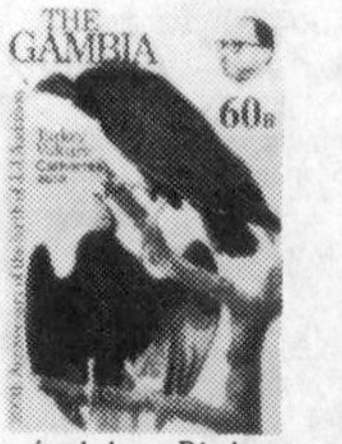

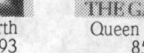

Audubon Birth Bicent. — A93

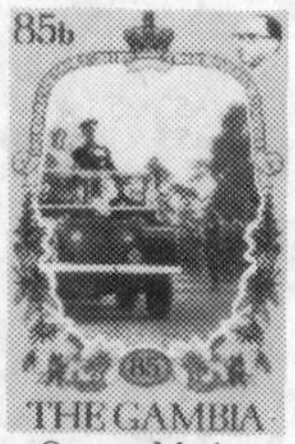

Queen Mother, 85th Birthday — A94

Illustrations of North American bird species by John J. Audubon (1785-1851).

1985, July 15

551 A93 60b Cathartes aura .32 .32
552 A93 85b Anhinga anhinga .50 .50
553 A93 1.50d Butoroides striatus .90 .90
554 A93 5d Aix sponsa 3.00 3.00
Nos. 551-554 (4) 4.72 4.72

Souvenir Sheet

555 A93 10d Gavia immer 5.50 5.50

1985, July 24

556 A94 85b Inspecting troops .50 .50
557 A94 3d Portrait 1.65 1.65
558 A94 5d Portrait, diff. 3.00 3.00
Nos. 556-558 (3) 5.15 5.15

Souvenir Sheet

559 A94 10d On parade with Prince Charles 5.50 5.50

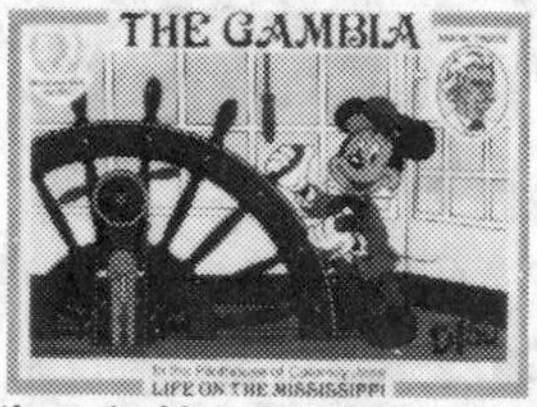

Life on the Mississippi, by Mark Twain (1835-1910) — A95

Walt Disney characters. The 60b, 85b, 2.35d, 5d show scenes from "Faithful John" by the Grimm Brother.

1985, Oct. 30

560 A95 60b Portrait .30 .30
561 A95 85b Treasure .40 .40
562 A95 1.50d Helm of Calamity Jane .90 .90
563 A95 2d Antebellum Mansion, Missouri Shore 1.20 1.20
564 A95 2.35d Music 1.20 1.20
565 A95 2.50d Measuring Channel Depth, Natchez 1.40 1.40
566 A95 3d Card Game aboard the Gold Dust 1.65 1.65
567 A95 5d Statue 2.50 2.50
Nos. 560-567 (8) 9.55 9.55

Souvenir Sheet

568 A95 10d Landing, St. Louis 5.00 5.00
569 A95 10d Goofy 5.00 5.00

Nos. 508-514 Ovptd. "GOLD MEDALIST" or "GOLD MEDAL," Name of Winner and Country

Designs: 60b, Claudia Losch, West Germany, women's shot put. 85b, Ulrike Meyfarth, West Germany, women's high jump. 90b, Pasquale Passarelli, West Germany, 126-pound Greco-Roman wrestling. 1d, Li Ning, China, men's gymnastic floor exercises. 1.25d, Michael Gross, West Germany, men's 100-meter butterfly and 200-meter freestyle swimming. 2d, Sylvie Bernier, Canada, women's springboard diving. 5d, US, Star Class yachting.

1985, Nov. 11 *Perf. 14*

570 A86 60b multicolored .28 .28
571 A86 85b multicolored .40 .40
572 A86 90b multicolored .48 .48
573 A86 1d multicolored .50 .50
574 A86 1.25d multicolored .65 .65
575 A86 2d multicolored 1.00 1.00
Nos. 570-575 (6) 3.31 3.31

Souvenir Sheet

576 A86 5d multicolored 2.50 2.50

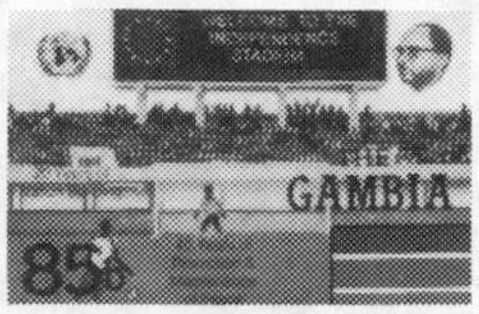

UN 40th Anniv. A97

Views of Banjul.

1985, Nov. 15

577 A97 85b Independence Stadium .45 .45
578 A97 2d Central Bank 1.10 1.10
579 A97 4d Port 2.25 2.25
580 A97 6d Oyster Creek Bridge 3.50 3.50
Nos. 577-580 (4) 7.30 7.30

Natl. independence, 20th anniv.

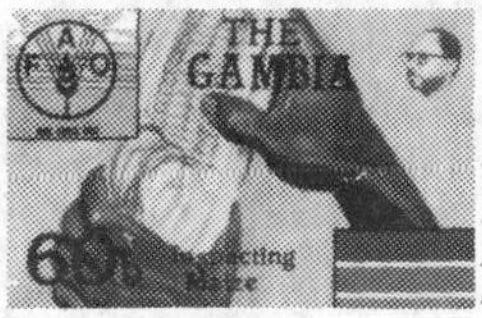

UN FAO, 40th Anniv. A98

1985, Nov. 15

581 A98 60b Corn .30 .30
582 A98 1.10d Paddy .60 .60
583 A98 3d Cow, calf 1.75 1.75
584 A98 5d Fruit 2.75 2.75
Nos. 581-584 (4) 5.40 5.40

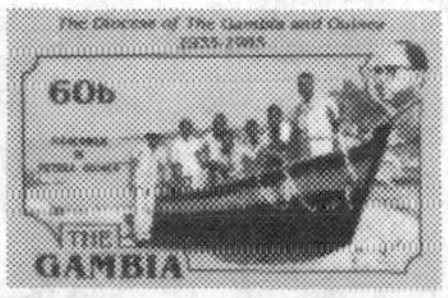

Diocese of Gambia and Guinea, 50th Anniv. A99

Designs: 60b, Fishermen, Fotoba, Guinea. 85b, St. Mary's Primary School, Banjul. 1.10d, St. Mary's Cathedral, Banjul. 1.50d, Mobile Dispensary at Christy, Kunda, 1935-45.

1985, Dec. 24

585 A99 60b multicolored .30 .30
586 A99 85b multicolored .45 .45
587 A99 1.10d multicolored .60 .60
588 A99 1.50d multicolored .90 .90
Nos. 585-588 (4) 2.25 2.25

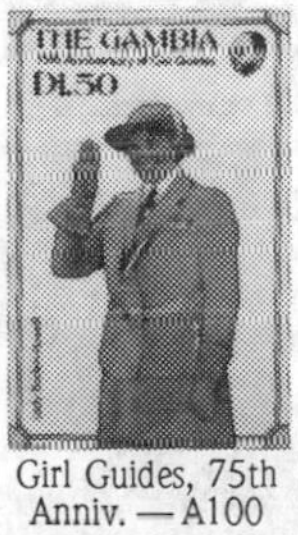

Girl Guides, 75th Anniv. — A100

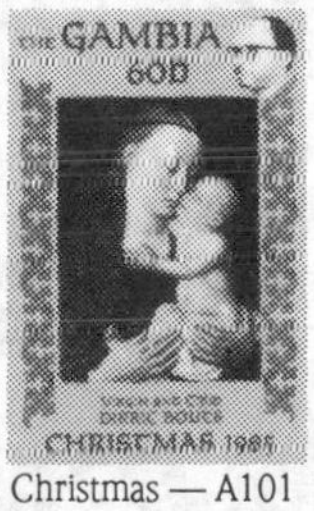

Christmas — A101

1985, Dec. 27

589 A100 60b Application, horiz. .30 .30
590 A100 85b 2nd Bathurst, horiz. .45 .45
591 A100 1.50d Lady Baden-Powell .90 .90
592 A100 5d Rosamond Fowlis, leader 2.75 2.75
Nos. 589-592 (4) 4.40 4.40

Souvenir Sheet

593 A100 10d Guides 5.50 5.50

1985, Dec. 27 *Perf. 15*

Painting details: 60b, Virgin and Child, by Dirck Bouts (c. 1400-1475). 85b, The Annunciation, by Robert Campin (c. 1378-1444). 1.50d, Adoration of the Shepherds, by Gerard David (c. 1460-1523). 5d, The Nativity, by Gerard David. 10d, Adoration of the Magi, by Hieronymus Bosch (1450-1516).

594 A101 60b multicolored .30 .30
595 A101 85b multicolored .45 .45
596 A101 1.50d multicolored .90 .90
597 A101 5d multicolored 2.75 2.75
Nos. 594-597 (4) 4.40 4.40

Souvenir Sheet

598 A101 10d multicolored 5.50 5.50

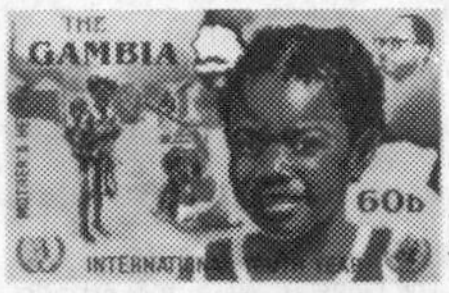

Intl. Youth Year — A102

1985, Dec. 31 *Perf. 14*

599 A102 60b Mother's helper .30 .30
600 A102 85b Wrestling .45 .45
601 A102 1.10d Griot storyteller .60 .60
602 A102 1.50d Crocodile pool .90 .90
Nos. 599-602 (4) 2.25 2.25

Souvenir Sheet

603 A102 5d Cow herder 2.75 2.75

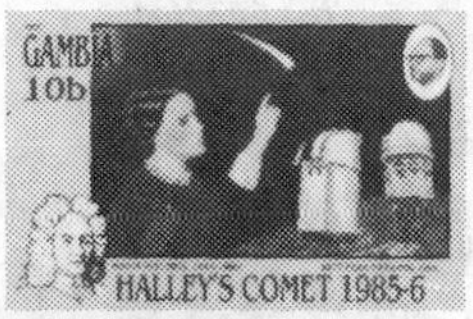

A103

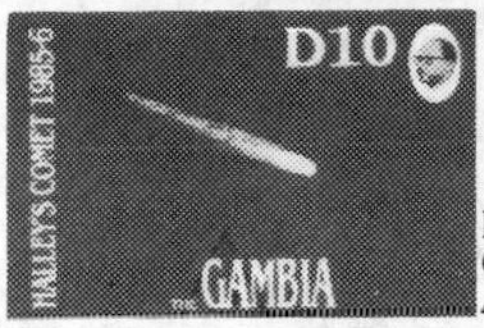

Halley's Comet A104

Designs: 10b, Maria Mitchell (1818-1889), American astronomer, Kitt Peak Natl. Observatory, Papago Indian Reservation, Arizona. 20b, Apollo 11, Neil Armstrong steps on moon, 1969. 75b, Skylab 4, Kohoutek Comet, 1973. 1d, NASA Infrared Astronomical Satellite, 1983. 2d, Comet sighting, 1577, Turkish art. No. 609, NASA Intl. Cometary Explorer satellite. No. 610, Comet.

1986, Mar.

604 A103 10b multicolored .15 .15
605 A103 20b multicolored .15 .15
606 A103 75b multicolored .40 .40
607 A103 1d multicolored .60 .60
608 A103 2d multicolored 1.10 1.10
609 A103 10d multicolored 5.50 5.50
Nos. 604-609 (6) 7.90 7.90

Souvenir Sheet

610 A104 10d multicolored 5.75 5.75

For overprints see Nos. 650-656.

Queen Elizabeth II, 60th Birthday
Common Design Type

Designs: 1d, Royal family at Royal Tournament, 1936. 2.50d, Christening, 1983. No. 613, State visit to West Germany, 1978. No. 614, At Balmoral, 1935.

1986, Apr. 21

611 CD339 1d lt yel bis & blk .60 .60
612 CD339 2.50d pale green & multi 1.40 1.40
613 CD339 10d dl lil & multi 5.50 5.50
Nos. 611-613 (3) 7.50 7.50

Souvenir Sheet

614 CD339 10d tan & black 5.50 5.50

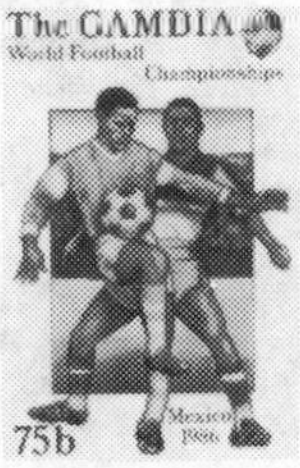

1986 World Cup Soccer Championships, Mexico — A105

1986, May 2

615 A105 75b Block .45 .45
616 A105 1d Kneeing the ball .60 .60
617 A105 2.50d Kick 1.40 1.40
618 A105 10d Heading the ball 5.50 5.50
Nos. 615-618 (4) 7.95 7.95

Souvenir Sheet

619 A105 10d Goalie catching ball 5.50 5.50

For overprints see Nos. 639-643.

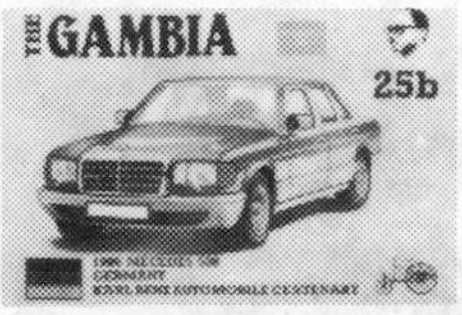

AMERIPEX '86 A106

Exhibition emblem, automobiles and flags: 25b, 1986 Mercedes 500, Germany. 75b, 1935 Cord 810, US. 1d, 1957 Borgward Isabella Coupe, Germany. 1.25d, 1985-6 Lamborghini Countach, Italy. 2d, 1955 Ford Thunderbird, US. 2.25d, 1956 Citroen DS19, France. 5d, 1936 Bugatti Atlante, France. 10d, 1936 Horch 853, Germany. No. 628, 1913 Benz 8/20, Germany. No. 629, 1924 Steiger 10/50, Germany.

1986, May 22 *Perf. 15*

620 A106 25b multi .15 .15
621 A106 75b multi .40 .40
622 A106 1d multi .60 .60
623 A106 1.25d multi .70 .70
624 A106 2d multi 1.10 1.10
625 A106 2.25d multi 1.25 1.25
626 A106 5d multi 2.75 2.75
627 A106 10d multi 5.50 5.50
Nos. 620-627 (8) 12.45 12.45

Souvenir Sheets

628 A106 12d multi 6.75 6.75
629 A106 12d multi 6.75 6.75

Karl Benz automobile cent.

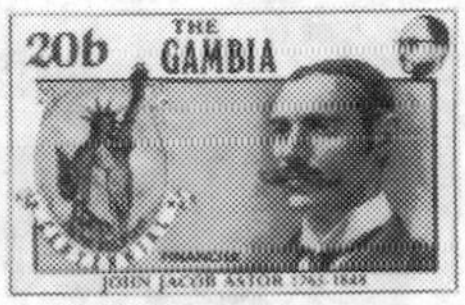

Statue of Liberty, Cent. A107

Statue and famous emigrants: 20b, John Jacob Astor (1763-1848), financier. 1d, Jacob Riis (1849-1914), journalist. 1.25d, Igor Sikorsky (1889-1972), aeronautics engineer. 5d, Charles Boyer (1899-1978), actor. 10d, Statue, vert.

1986, June 10 *Perf. 14*

630 A107 20b multicolored .15 .15
631 A107 1d multicolored .60 .60
632 A107 1.25d multicolored .70 .70
633 A107 5d multicolored 2.75 2.75
Nos. 630-633 (4) 4.20 4.20

Souvenir Sheet

634 A107 10d multicolored 5.50 5.50

Royal Wedding Issue, 1986
Common Design Type

Designs: 1d, Engagement of Prince Andrew and Sarah Ferguson. 2.50d, Andrew. 4d, Andrew in flight uniform, other helicopter pilot. 7d, Couple, diff.

1986, July 23

635 CD340 1d multi .60 .60
636 CD340 2.50d multi 1.40 1.40
637 CD340 4d multi 2.25 2.25
Nos. 635-637 (3) 4.25 4.25

Souvenir Sheet

638 CD340 7d multi 4.00 4.00

Nos. 615-619 Overprinted "WINNERS / Argentina 3 / W. Germany 2" in Gold

1986, Sept. 16 **Litho.** *Perf. 14*

639 A105 75b multicolored .40 .40
640 A105 1d multicolored .60 .60
641 A105 2.50d multicolored 1.50 1.50
642 A105 10d multicolored 5.50 5.50
Nos. 639-642 (4) 8.00 8.00

Souvenir Sheet

643 A105 10d multicolored 5.50 5.50

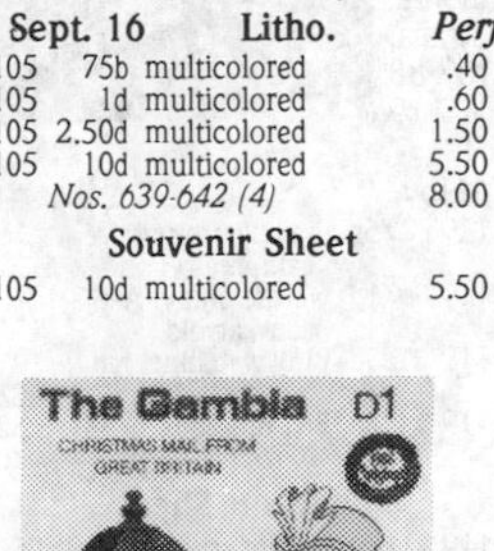

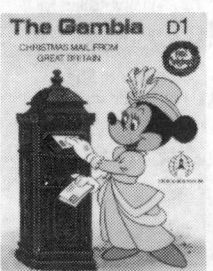

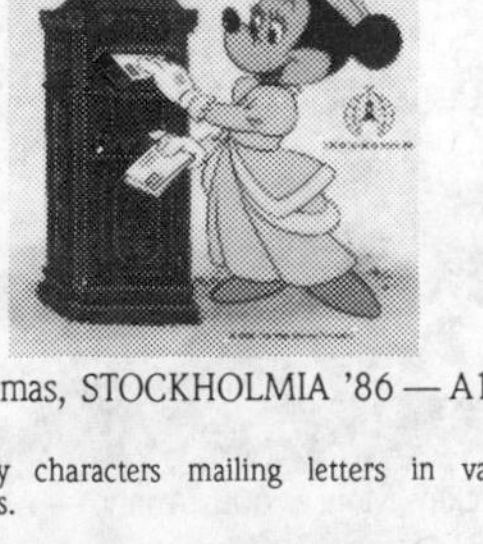

Christmas, STOCKHOLMIA '86 — A108

Disney characters mailing letters in various countries.

1986, Nov. 4 *Perf. 11*

644 A108 1d Great Britain .30 .30
645 A108 1.25d United States .40 .40
646 A108 2d France .60 .60
647 A108 2.35d Australia .70 .70
648 A108 5d Germany 1.60 1.60
Nos. 644-648 (5) 3.60 3.60

Souvenir Sheet

649 A108 10d Sweden 3.00 3.00

Nos. 604-610 Ovptd. with Halley's Comet Logo in Silver

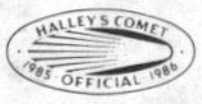

1986, Oct. 21 **Litho.** *Perf. 14*

650 A103 10b multicolored .15 .15
651 A103 20b multicolored .15 .15
652 A103 75b multicolored .22 .22
653 A103 1d multicolored .30 .30
654 A103 2d multicolored .55 .55
655 A103 10d multicolored 3.00 3.00
Nos. 650-655 (6) 4.37 4.37

Souvenir Sheet

656 A104 10d multicolored 3.00 3.00

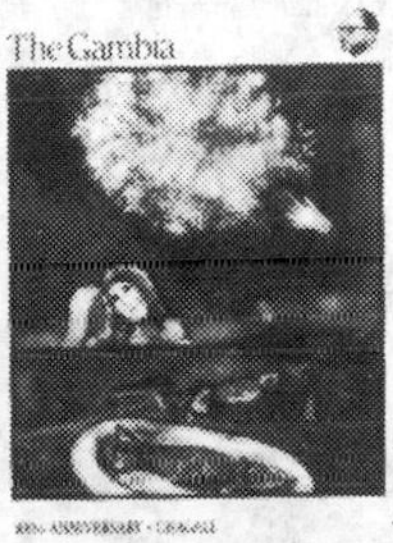

Marc Chagall (1887-1985), Artist — A109

Paintings, ceramicware, sculpture: 75b, Snowing. 85b, The Boat, 1957. 1d, Maternity, 1913. 1.25d, The Flute Player. 2.35d, Lovers and the Beast, 1957. 4d, Fishes at Saint Jean. 5d, Entering the Ring, 1968. 10d, Three Acrobats, 1956. No. 665, The Sabbath. No. 666, The Cattle Driver.

1987, Feb. 6 **Litho.**

657 A109 75b multi .20 .20
658 A109 85b multi .22 .22
659 A109 1d multi .25 .25
660 A109 1.25d multi .32 .32
661 A109 2.35d multi .60 .60
662 A109 4d multi 1.00 1.00
663 A109 5d multi 1.25 1.25
664 A109 10d multi 2.50 2.50

Sizes: 110x95mm, 110x68mm

Imperf

665 A109 12d multi 3.00 3.00
666 A109 12d multi 3.00 3.00
Nos. 657-666 (10) 12.34 12.34

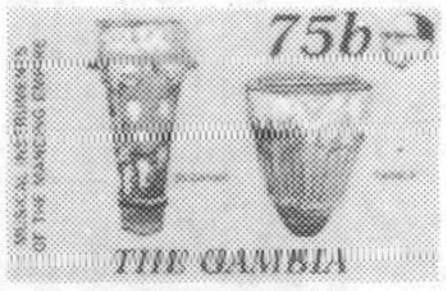

Musical Instruments A110

Various instruments from the Mandingo Empire.

1987, Jan. 21 **Litho.** *Perf. 15*

667 A110 75b Bugarab, tabala .22 .22
668 A110 1d Balaphong, fiddle .30 .30
669 A110 1.25d Bolongbato, konting .35 .35
670 A110 10d Koras 2.75 2.75
Nos. 667-670 (4) 3.62 3.62

Souvenir Sheet

671 A110 12d Sabarrs 3.25 3.25

Nos. 669-670 vert.
For overprints see Nos. 750, 856-860.

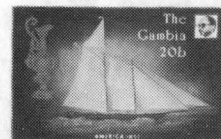

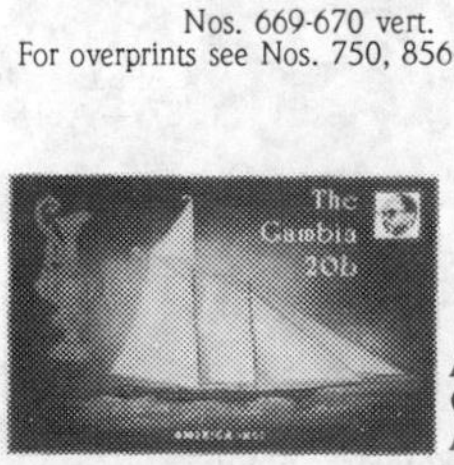

America's Cup A111

1987, Apr. 3 *Perf. 14*

672 A111	20b	America, 1851	.15	.15
673 A111	1d	Courageous, 1974	.32	.32
674 A111	2.50d	Volunteer, 1887	.80	.80
675 A111	10d	Intrepid, 1967	3.25	3.25
		Nos. 672-675 (4)	4.52	4.52

Souvenir Sheet

676 A111	12d	Australia II, 1983	4.25	4.25

For overprint see No. 751.

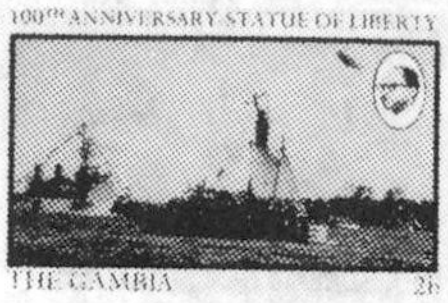

Statue of Liberty, Cent. A112

Photographs of restoration and unveiling in 1986.

1987, Apr. 9 **Litho.**

677 A112	1b	Shoulder, torch	.15	.15
678 A112	2b	Operation Sail flotilla	.15	.15
679 A112	3b	Tall ship, ships	.15	.15
680 A112	5b	Luxury liner, aircraft carrier	.15	.15
681 A112	50b	Statue's coiffure	.15	.15
682 A112	75b	Coiffure, diff.	.22	.22
683 A112	1d	Workmen scaling statue	.28	.28
684 A112	1.25d	Back of statue	.35	.35
685 A112	10d	Front of Statue	2.75	2.75
686 A112	12d	Side of statue	3.50	3.50
		Nos. 677-686 (10)	7.85	7.85

Nos. 677, 681-686 vert.

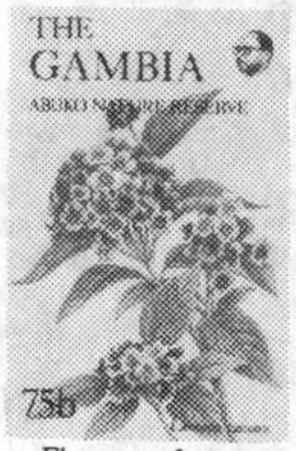

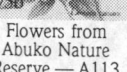

Flowers from Abuko Nature Reserve — A113

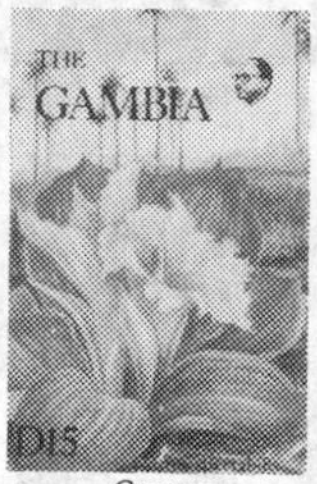

Costus Spectabilis — A114

1987, May 25

687 A113	75b	Lantana camara	.22	.22
687A A113	1d	Clerodendrum thomsoniae	.30	.30
688 A113	1.50d	Haemanthus multiflorus	.45	.45
688A A113	1.70d	Gloriosa simplex	.50	.50
689 A113	1.75d	Combretum microphyllum	.50	.50
689A A113	2.25d	Eulophia guineensis	.65	.65
689B A113	5d	Erythrina senegalensis	1.50	1.50
690 A113	15d	Dichrostachys glomerata	4.25	4.25
		Nos. 687-690 (8)	8.37	8.37

Souvenir Sheets

691 A114	15d	shown	4.25	4.25
691A A114	15d	Strophanthus preussii	4.25	4.25

For overprint see No. 752.

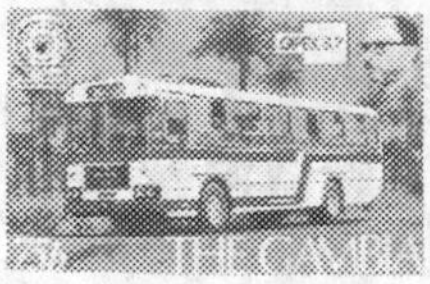

CAPEX '87 — A115

Various buses.

1987, June 15

692 A115	20b	multi, vert.	.15	.15
693 A115	75b	multi	.26	.26
694 A115	1d	multi	.38	.38
695 A115	10d	multi, vert.	3.50	3.50
		Nos. 692-695 (4)	4.29	4.29

Souvenir Sheet

696 A115	12d	multi	3.75	3.75

For overprint see No. 749.

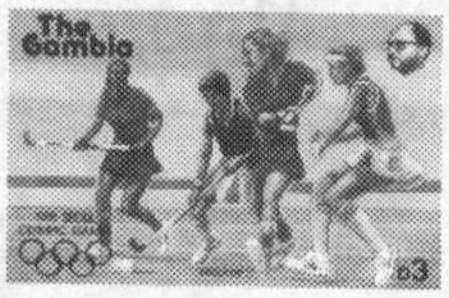

1988 Summer Olympics, Seoul A116

1987, July 3

697 A116	50b	Women's basketball	.16	.16
698 A116	1d	Volleyball	.30	.30
699 A116	3d	Field hockey	.90	.90
700 A116	10d	Handball	3.00	3.00
		Nos. 697-700 (4)	4.36	4.36

Souvenir Sheet

701 A116	15d	Soccer	4.75	4.75

Nos. 697-698 vert.

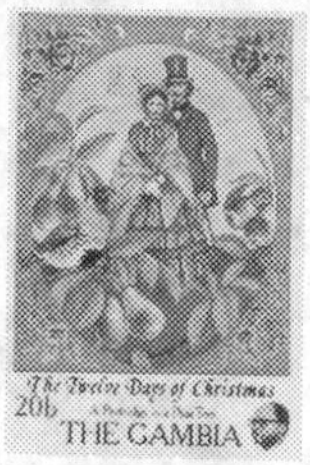

A117

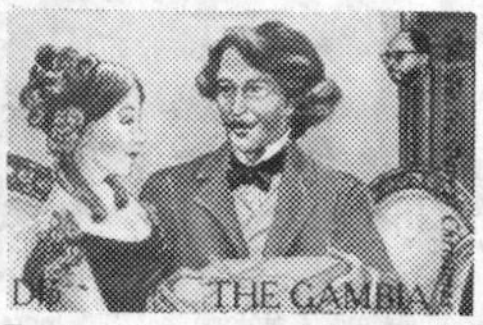

The Twelve Days of Christmas, Medieval Counting Song — A118

Designs: 20b, Partridge in a pear tree. 40b, 2 turtle doves. 60b, 3 French hens. 75b, 4 calling birds. 1d, 5 golden rings. 1.25d, 6 geese a-laying. 1.50d, 7 swans a-swimming. 2d, 8 maids a-milking. 3d, 9 ladies dancing. 5d, 10 lords a-leaping. 10d, 11 pipers piping. 12d, 12 drummers drumming.

Miniature Sheet

1987, Nov. 2 **Litho.** *Perf. 14*

702	Sheet of 12	11.00	11.00
a.	A117 20b multicolored	.15	.15
b.	A117 40b multicolored	.15	.15
c.	A117 60b multicolored	.16	.16
d.	A117 75b multicolored	.20	.20
e.	A117 1d multicolored	.30	.30
f.	A117 1.25d multicolored	.35	.35
g.	A117 1.50d multicolored	.45	.45
h.	A117 2d multicolored	.55	.55
i.	A117 3d multicolored	.90	.90
j.	A117 5d multicolored	1.40	1.40
k.	A117 10d multicolored	2.75	2.75
l.	A117 12d multicolored	3.25	3.25

Souvenir Sheet

703 A118	15d	multi	4.75	4.75

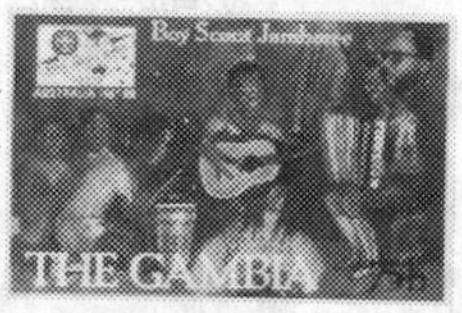

16th Boy Scout Jamboree, Australia, 1987-88 A119

1987, Nov. 9

704 A119	75b	Singing around campfire	.22	.22
705 A119	1d	Nature study, African katydid	.30	.30
706 A119	1.25d	Bird watching, red-tailed tropicbird	.38	.38
707 A119	12d	Boarding bus	3.50	3.50
		Nos. 704-707 (4)	4.40	4.40

Souvenir Sheet

708 A119	15d	Nature study	4.50	4.50

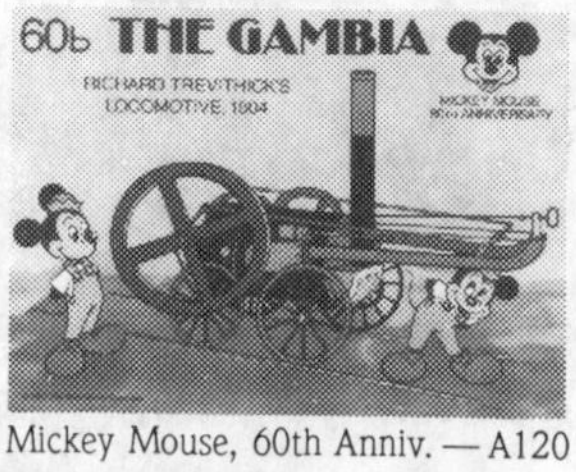

Mickey Mouse, 60th Anniv. — A120

Disney animated characters and historic locomotives: 60b, Richard Trevithick's locomotive, 1804. 75b, Empire State Express 999, 1893. 1d, George Stephenson's Rocket, 1829. 1.25d, Santa Fe Mountain 2-10-2, 1920. 2d, Class GG-1 Pennsylvania, 1933. 5d, Stourbridge Lion, 1829. 10d, Best Friend of Charleston, 1830. 12d, M10001 Union Pacific, 1934. No. 717, Tres Grande Vitesse-SNCF, 1981, France. No. 718, The General, Western & Atlantic, 1855.

1987, Dec. 9 **Litho.** *Perf. 14x13½*

709 A120	60b	multicolored	.18	.18
710 A120	75b	multicolored	.22	.22
711 A120	1d	multicolored	.30	.30
712 A120	1.25d	multicolored	.38	.38
713 A120	2d	multicolored	.60	.60
714 A120	5d	multicolored	1.50	1.50
715 A120	10d	multicolored	3.00	3.00
716 A120	12d	multicolored	3.60	3.60
		Nos. 709-716 (8)	9.78	9.78

Souvenir Sheets

717 A120	15d	multicolored	4.25	4.25
718 A120	15d	multicolored	4.25	4.25

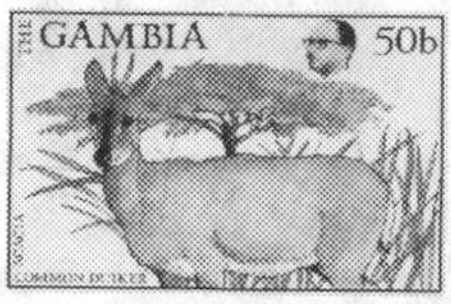

Fauna and Flora A121

1988, Feb. 9 **Litho.** *Perf. 15*

719 A121	50b	Duiker, acacia	.15	.15
720 A121	75b	Red-billed hornbill, casuarina	.22	.22
721 A121	90b	West African dwarf crocodile, rice	.28	.28
722 A121	1d	Leopard, papyrus	.30	.30
723 A121	1.25d	Crested cranes, millet	.38	.38
724 A121	2d	Waterbuck, baobab tree	.60	.60
725 A121	3d	Oribi, Senegal palm	.90	.90
726 A121	5d	Hippopotamus, papaya	1.50	1.50
		Nos. 719-726 (8)	4.33	4.33

Souvenir Sheets

727 A121	12d	Great white pelican	3.60	3.60
728 A121	12d	Red-throated bee-eater	3.60	3.60

Nos. 720, 722, 724, 726 and 728 vert.

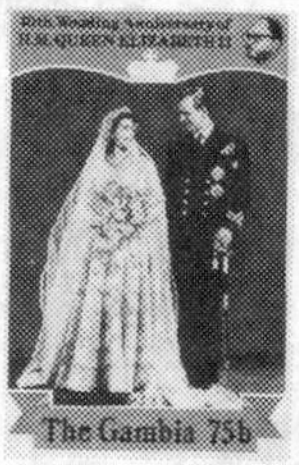

40th Wedding Anniv. of Queen Elizabeth II and Prince Philip — A122

1988, Mar. 15 *Perf. 14*

729 A122	75b	Wedding portrait, 1947	.22	.22
730 A122	1d	Couple at leisure	.30	.30
731 A122	3d	Wedding portrait, diff.	.90	.90
732 A122	10d	Couple, c. 1987	3.00	3.00
		Nos. 729-732 (4)	4.42	4.42

Souvenir Sheet

733 A122	15d	Wedding party	4.50	4.50

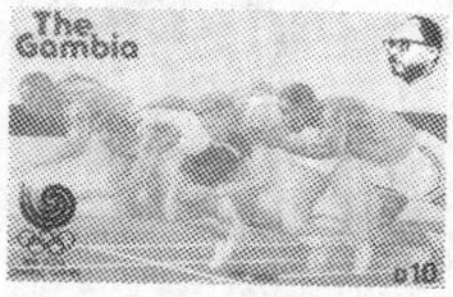

1988 Summer Olympics, Seoul A123

1988, May 3 **Litho.** *Perf. 14*

734 A123	1d	Archery, vert.	.30	.30
735 A123	1.25d	Boxing, vert.	.38	.38
736 A123	5d	Gymnastics, vert.	1.50	1.50
737 A123	10d	100-Meter sprint	3.00	3.00
		Nos. 734-737 (4)	5.18	5.18

Souvenir Sheet

738 A123	15d	Award ceremony, Olympic stadium	4.50	4.50

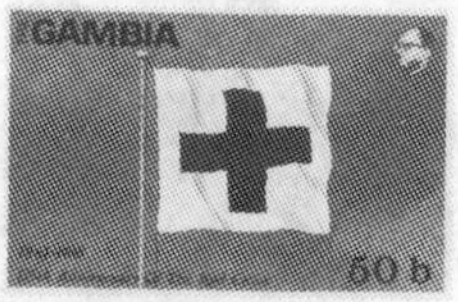

Anniversaries & Events — A124

Designs: 50b, Red Cross flag. 75b, Friendship 7, piloted by John Glenn, 1963. 1d, British Airways Concorde jet. 1.25d, Spirit of St. Louis, piloted by Charles Lindbergh, 1927. 2d, X-15, piloted by Major William Knight, 1967. 3d, Bell X-1, piloted by Capt. Charles Yeager, 1947. 10d, Spanish galleon, British warship, 1588. 12d, The Titanic. No. 747, Kangaroo and joey. No. 748, Cathedral, modern church, vert.

1988, May 15

739 A124	50b	multicolored	.16	.16
740 A124	75b	multicolored	.24	.24
741 A124	1d	multicolored	.32	.32
742 A124	1.25d	multicolored	.38	.38
743 A124	2d	multicolored	.62	.62
744 A124	3d	multicolored	.95	.95
745 A124	10d	multicolored	3.10	3.10
746 A124	12d	multicolored	3.75	3.75
		Nos. 739-746 (8)	9.52	9.52

Souvenir Sheets

747 A124	15d	multicolored	4.50	4.50
748 A124	15d	multicolored	4.50	4.50

Intl. Red Cross, 125th anniv. (50b); first American in space, 25th anniv. in 1987 (75b); 1st London-New York scheduled Concorde flight, 10th anniv. in 1987 (1d); first solo transatlantic flight, 60th anniv. in 1987 (1.25d); fastest speed flown, 6.72 Mach, 20th anniv. in 1987 (2d); 1st supersonic flight, 40th anniv. in 1987 (3d); defeat of the Spanish Armada, 400th anniv. (10d); maiden voyage of the Titanic, 75th anniv. in 1987 (12d); founding of Australia, bicentennial (No. 747); and founding of Berlin, 750th anniv. in 1987 (No. 748).

Nos. 694, 670, 675 and 690 Ovptd. for Philatelic Exhibitions

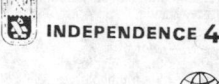

a INDEPENDENCE 40

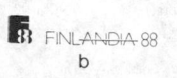

FINLANDIA 88 b

Praga '88 c

d OLYMPHILEX '88

1988, Apr. 19 **Litho.** *Perf. 14, 15*

749 A115(a)	1d	multi	.32	.32
750 A110(b)	10d	multi	3.10	3.10
751 A111(c)	10d	multi	3.25	3.25
752 A113(d)	15d	multi	4.75	4.75
		Nos. 749-752 (4)	11.42	11.42

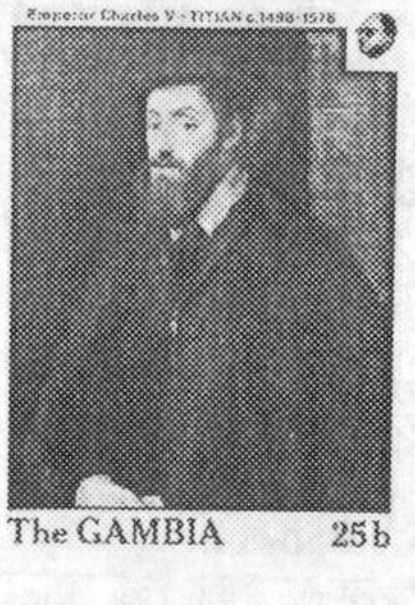

Paintings by Titian — A125

Designs: 25b, Emperor Charles V, 1549. 50b, St. Margaret and the Dragon, 1565. 60b, Ranuccio Farnese, 1542. 75b, Tarquin and Lucretia, 1570. 1d, The Knight of Malta, c. 1550. 5d, Spain Succouring Faith, 1571. 10d, Doge Francesco Venier, 1555. 12d, Doge Grimani Before the Faith, c. 1555-1576. No. 761, Jealous Husband, 1511. No. 762, Venus Blindfolding Cupid, 1560.

1988, July 7 **Litho.** *Perf. 13½x14*

753 A125	25b	multicolored	.15	.15
754 A125	50b	multicolored	.16	.16
755 A125	60b	multicolored	.20	.20
756 A125	75b	multicolored	.25	.25
757 A125	1d	multicolored	.32	.32
758 A125	5d	multicolored	1.60	1.60
759 A125	10d	multicolored	3.10	3.10
760 A125	12d	multicolored	3.75	3.75
		Nos. 753-760 (8)	9.53	9.53

Souvenir Sheets

761 A125	15d	multicolored	4.50	4.50
762 A125	15d	multicolored	4.50	4.50

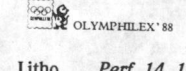

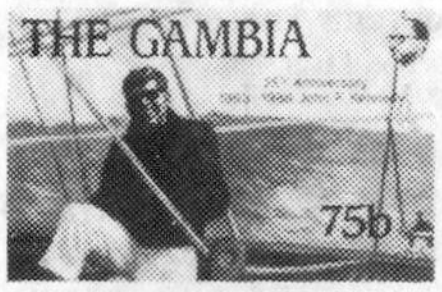

Tribute to John F. Kennedy A126

1988, Sept. 1 Litho. *Perf. 14*

763	A126	75b	Sailing	.22	.22
764	A126	1d	Peace Corps enactment	.30	.30
765	A126	1.25d	Public address, vert.	.38	.38
766	A126	12d	Grave, Arlington Natl. Cemetery	3.60	3.60
			Nos. 763-766 (4)	4.50	4.50

Souvenir Sheet

767	A126	15d	Kennedy, vert.	4.50	4.50

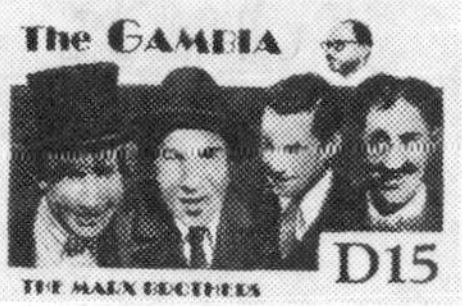

Entertainers A127

Designs: 20b, Emmett Lee Kelly (1898-1979), clown. 1d, Gambia Natl. Ensemble. 1.25d, Jackie Gleason (1916-87), comedian, and The Honeymooners cast. 1.50d, Stan Laurel (1890-1965) and Oliver Hardy (1892-1957), film comedy team. 2.50d, Yul Brynner (c. 1920-1985), actor. 3d, Cary Grant (1904-86), actor. 10d, Danny Kaye (1918-87), comedian, actor. 20d, Charlie Chaplin (1889-1977), comedian, actor. No. 776, Harpo (1893-1964), Chico (1891-1961), Zeppo (1901-1979) and Groucho (1890-1977) Marx, comedy team. No. 777, Fred Astaire (1899-1987) and Rita Hayworth (1918-1987), dancers and film stars. Nos. 768-775 vert.

1988, Nov. 9 Litho.

768	A127	20b	multi	.15	.15
769	A127	1d	multi	.30	.30
770	A127	1.25d	multi	.38	.38
771	A127	1.50d	multi	.45	.45
772	A127	2.50d	multi	.75	.75
773	A127	3d	multi	.90	.90
774	A127	10d	multi	3.00	3.00
775	A127	20d	multi	6.00	6.00
			Nos. 768-775 (8)	11.93	11.93

Souvenir Sheets

776	A127	15d	multi	4.50	4.50
777	A127	15d	multi	4.50	4.50

Kelly's name is spelled incorrectly; Brynner's and Grant's dates are incorrect.

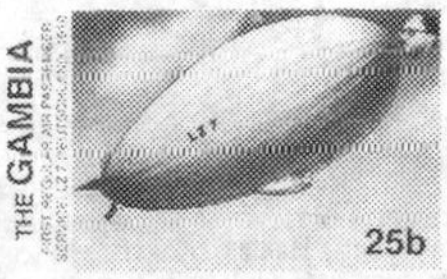

Zeppelin LZ7 Deutschland, 1910 — A128

Transportation innovations: 50b, Stephenson's Locomotion, 1825. 75b, General Motors Sun Racer, 1987. 1d, Sprague's Premiere, 1888. 1.25d, Gold Rush bicycle, 1986. 2.50d, 1st Liquid-fuel rocket, invented by Robert Goddard, 1925. 10d, Orukter Amphibolos, 1805. 12d, Sovereign of the Seas, 1988. No. 786, USS Nautilus, 1954, vert. No. 787, Fulton's Nautilus, early 19th cent.

1988, Nov. 21 Litho. *Perf. 14*

778	A128	25b	multi	.15	.15
779	A128	50b	multi	.15	.15
780	A128	75b	multi	.22	.22
781	A128	1d	multi	.30	.30
782	A128	1.25d	multi	.38	.38
783	A128	2.50d	multi	.75	.75
784	A128	10d	multi	3.00	3.00
785	A128	12d	multi	3.60	3.60
			Nos. 778-785 (8)	8.55	8.55

Souvenir Sheets

786	A128	15d	multi	4.50	4.50
787	A128	15d	multi	4.50	4.50

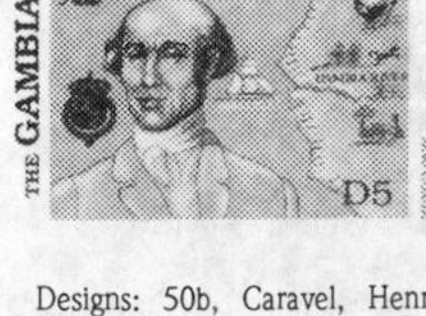

Discovery of America, 500th Anniv. (in 1992) A129

Designs: 50b, Caravel, Henry the Navigator (1394-1460), Prince of Portugal, and coat of arms, vert. 75b, Jesse Ramsden's sextant, map of Africa, arms, vert. 1d, Hour glass, 15th cent., and map, vert. 1.25d, Henry and Vasco da Gama, vert. 2.50d, Da Gama and 15th cent. caravel, vert. 5d, Mungo Park (1771-1806), Scottish explorer, arms and map of Gambia River. 10d, Map of west African coast, 1563. 12d, Portuguese caravel, arms. No. 796, Caravel off the Gambian coast, 15th cent., vert. No. 797, European ship off Gambian coast, 15th cent., vert.

1988, Dec. 1 Litho. *Perf. 14*

788	A129	50b	multi	.15	.15
789	A129	75b	multi	.22	.22
790	A129	1d	multi	.30	.30
791	A129	1.25d	multi	.38	.38
792	A129	2.50d	multi	.75	.75
793	A129	5d	shown	1.50	1.50
794	A129	10d	multi	3.00	3.00
795	A129	12d	multi	3.60	3.60
			Nos. 788-795 (8)	9.90	9.90

Souvenir Sheets

796	A129	15d	multi	4.50	4.50
797	A129	15d	multi	4.50	4.50

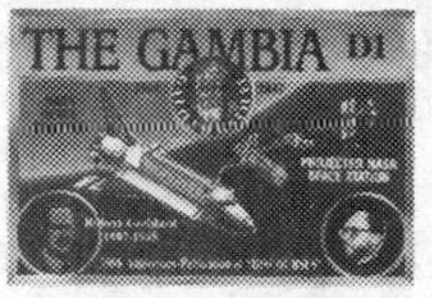

Space Achievements — A130

Galileo and: 50b, Futuristic aerospace plane and Ernst Mach (1838-1916), Austrian physicist, vert. 75b, OAO III astronomical satellite and Niels Bohr (1885-1962), Danish physicist and Nobel lauerate in 1922, vert. 1d, NASA space shuttle, future space station and Robert Goddard (1882-1945), American rocket scientist. 1.25d, Flyby of probe past Jupiter, 1979, and Edward Barnard (1857-1923), American astronomer who discovered Jupiter's 5th satellite in 1892. 2d, Voyager, 1st circumnavigation of the world without refueling, 1987, and the Wright Brothers. 3d, Precision measurement of the distance between the Earth and the Moon by laser and Albert A. Michelson (1852-1931), Nobel lauerate in 1907 for research on the speed of light. 10d, HEAO-2 Einstein orbital satellite and Albert Einstein, vert. 20d, Hubble Space Telescope and George Hale (1868-1938), American astronomer, vert. No. 806, Moon Ganymede passing the Great Red Spot on Jupiter. No. 807, Apollo and Neil Armstrong, 1st man on the Moon, July 20, 1969, vert.

1988, Dec. 12 *Perf. 14*

798	A130	50b	multi	.15	.15
799	A130	75b	multi	.22	.22
800	A130	1d	multi	.30	.30
801	A130	1.25d	multi	.38	.38
802	A130	2d	multi	.60	.60
803	A130	3d	multi	.90	.90
804	A130	10d	multi	3.00	3.00
805	A130	20d	multi	6.00	6.00
			Nos. 798-805 (8)	11.55	11.55

Souvenir Sheets

806	A130	15d	multi	4.50	4.50
807	A130	15d	multi	4.50	4.50

350th anniv. of the publication of Discourses, by Galileo.

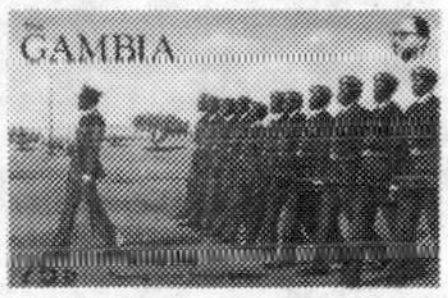

Army Day A131

1989, Feb. 10 Litho. *Perf. 14*

808	A131	75b	Troops on parade	.22	.22
809	A131	1d	Regimental flags	.30	.30
810	A131	1.25d	Drummer, vert.	.38	.38
811	A131	10d	Atlantic Shooting Cup winner, vert.	3.00	3.00
812	A131	15d	Assault course, vert.	4.50	4.50
813	A131	20d	105-mm gun	6.00	6.00
			Nos. 808-813 (6)	14.40	14.40

Buying Sets

It is often less expensive to purchase complete sets than individual stamps that make up the set. Set values are provided for many such sets.

Miniature Sheet

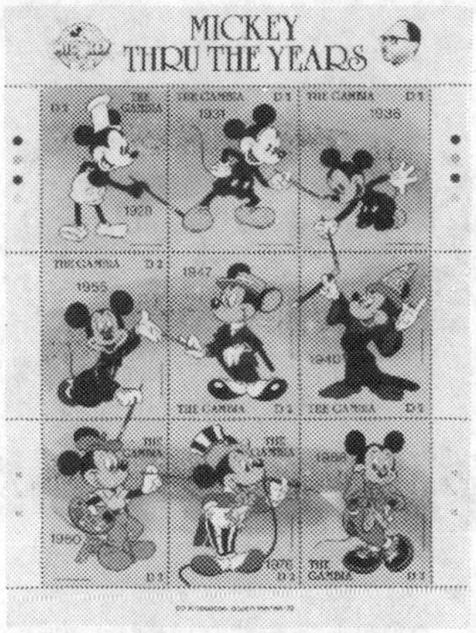

Mickey Mouse, 60th Anniv. (in 1988) — A132

Mickey Mouse through the years: a, 1928. b, 1931. c, 1936. d, 1955. e, 1947. f, 1940. g, 1960. h, 1976. i, 1988. 15d, Birthday party.

1989, Apr. 6 Litho. *Perf. 13x13½*

814	A132		Sheet of 9	5.40	5.40
a.-i.		2d	any single	.60	.60

Size: 139x110mm

Imperf

815	A132	15d	multi	4.50	4.50

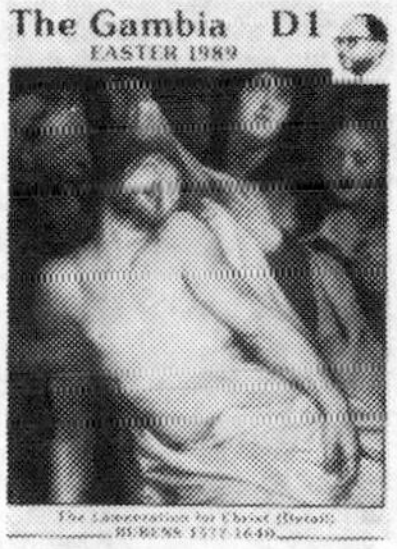

Easter — A133

Paintings by Rubens: 50b, Le Coup de Lance, 1620. 75b, The Flagellation of Christ, 1617. 1d, The Lamentation for Christ, c. 1617. 1.25d, Descent from the Cross, c. 1611. 2d, The Holy Trinity, c. 1617. 5d, The Doubting Thomas. 10d, Lamentation over Christ, 1614. 12d, Lamentation over Christ with the Virgin and St. John, c. 1613. No. 824, The Last Supper, c. 1631. No. 825, The Raising of the Cross, c. 1610.

1989, Apr. 14 *Perf. 13½x14*

816	A133	50b	multi	.16	.16
817	A133	75b	multi	.24	.24
818	A133	1d	multi	.32	.32
819	A133	1.25d	multi	.40	.40
820	A133	2d	multi	.65	.65
821	A133	5d	multi	1.60	1.60
822	A133	10d	multi	3.20	3.20
823	A133	12d	multi	3.85	3.85
			Nos. 816-823 (8)	10.42	10.42

Souvenir Sheets

824	A133	15d	multi	4.75	4.75
825	A133	15d	multi	4.75	4.75

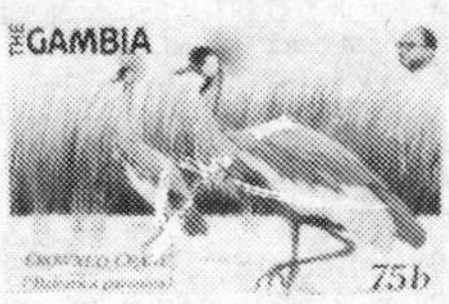

Indigenous Birds A134

1989, Apr. 24 *Perf. 14*

826	A134	20b	African emerald cuckoo	.15	.15
827	A134	60b	Gray-headed bush shrike	.20	.20
828	A134	75b	Crowned crane	.24	.24
829	A134	1d	Secretary bird	.32	.32
830	A134	2d	Red-billed hornbill	.65	.65
831	A134	5d	Superb sunbird	1.60	1.60
832	A134	10d	Little owl	3.20	3.20
833	A134	12d	Bateleur eagle	3.85	3.85
			Nos. 826-833 (8)	10.21	10.21

Souvenir Sheets

834	A134	15d	Red-billed fire finch	4.75	4.75
835	A134	15d	Ostriches	4.75	4.75

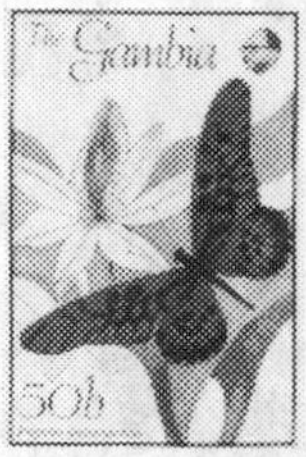

Indigenous Butterflies — A135

1989, May 15

836	A135	50b	Papilio antimachus	.16	.16
837	A135	75b	Euphaedra neophron	.24	.24
838	A135	1d	Aterica rabena	.32	.32
839	A135	1.25d	Salamis parhassus	.40	.40
840	A135	5d	Precis rhadama	1.60	1.60
841	A135	10d	Papilio demodocus	3.20	3.20
842	A135	12d	Charaxes etesippe	3.85	3.85
843	A135	15d	Danaus formosa	4.75	4.75
			Nos. 836-843 (8)	14.52	14.52

Souvenir Sheets

844	A135	15d	Euphaedra ceres	4.75	4.75
845	A135	15d	Cymothoe pluto	4.75	4.75

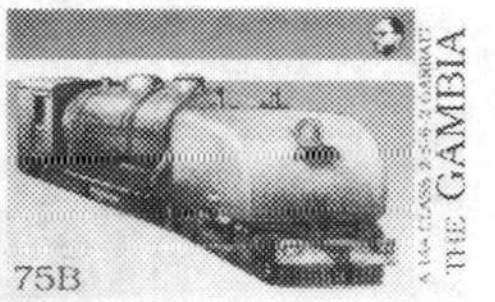

Trains of Africa A136

Designs: 50b, Nigerian coal train, 1959. 75b, 14A Class 2-6-6-2 Garratt. 1d, British (Pacific) in Sudan. 1.25d, American 0-8-0, 1925. 5d, Scottish 4-8-2, 1955. 7d, Scottish 4-8-2, 1926. 10d, British 4-6-0. 12d, American-made 2-6-0 in Ghana. No. 854, British 2-8-2 Class 25 facing forward, vert. No. 855, Class 25 facing left, vert.

1989, June 15 Litho. *Perf. 14*

846	A136	50b	multi	.16	.16
847	A136	75b	multi	.24	.24
848	A136	1d	multi	.32	.32
849	A136	1.25d	multi	.40	.40
850	A136	5d	multi	1.60	1.60
851	A136	7d	multi	2.25	2.25
852	A136	10d	multi	3.20	3.20
853	A136	12d	multi	3.85	3.85
			Nos. 846-853 (8)	12.02	12.02

Souvenir Sheets

854	A136	15d	multi	4.75	4.75
855	A136	15d	multi	4.75	4.75

Nos. 667-671 Ovptd. "PHILEXFRANCE / '89"

1989, June 23 Litho. *Perf. 15*

856	A110	75b	multi	.24	.24
857	A110	1d	multi	.32	.32
858	A110	1.25d	multi	.40	.40
859	A110	10d	multi	3.25	3.25
			Nos. 856-859 (4)	4.21	4.21

Souvenir Sheet

860	A110	12d	multi	3.85	3.85

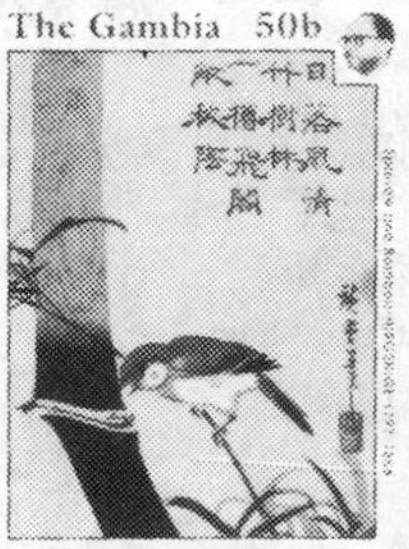

Paintings by Japanese Artists A137

Paintings by Hiroshige unless noted otherwise: 50b, Sparrow and Bamboo. 75b, Peonies and a Canary, by Hokusai. 1d, Crane and Marsh Grasses. 1.25d, Crossbill and Thistle, by Hokusai. 2d, Cuckoo and Azalea, by Hokusai. 5d, Parrot on a Pine Branch. 10d, Mandarin Ducks in a Stream. 12d, Bullfinch and Drooping Cherry, by Hokusai. No. 869, Tit and Peony, horiz. No. 870, Peony and Butterfly, by Shigenobu, horiz.

1989, July 7 *Perf. 13½x14, 14x13½*

861	A137	50b	multi	.16	.16
862	A137	75b	multi	.24	.24
863	A137	1d	multi	.32	.32
864	A137	1.25d	multi	.40	.40
865	A137	2d	multi	.65	.65
866	A137	5d	multi	1.60	1.60

867 A137 10d multi 3.20 3.20
868 A137 12d multi 3.85 3.85
Nos. 861-868 (8) 10.42 10.42

Souvenir Sheets

869 A137 15d multi 4.75 4.75
870 A137 15d multi 4.75 4.75

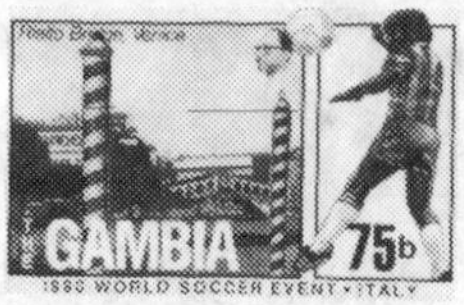

1990 World Cup Soccer Championships, Italy — A138

Various athletes and Italian landmarks: 75b, Rialto Bridge, Venice. 1.25d, The Baptistery, Pisa. 7d, Casino San Remo. 12d, The Colosseum, Rome. No. 875, St. Mark's Cathedral, Venice, vert. No. 876, Piazza Colonna, Rome.

1989, Aug 25 *Perf. 14*

871 A138 75b multi .22 .22
872 A138 1.25b multi .35 .35
873 A138 7d multi 2.00 2.00
874 A138 12d multi 3.50 3.50
Nos. 871-874 (4) 6.07 6.07

Souvenir Sheets

875 A138 15d multi 4.25 4.25
876 A138 15d multi 4.25 4.25

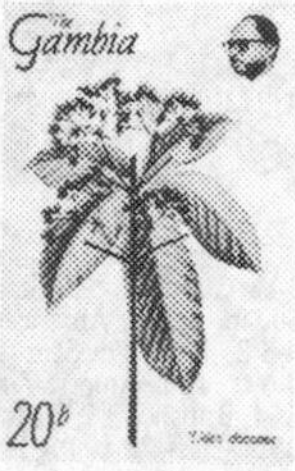

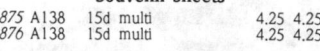

Medicinal Plants — A139

1989, Sept. 18 Litho. *Perf. 14*

877 A139 20b *Vitex doniana* .15 .15
878 A139 50b *Ricinus communis* .15 .15
879 A139 75b *Palisota hirsuta* .22 .22
880 A139 1d *Smilax kraussiana* .28 .28
881 A139 1.25d *Aspilia africana* .35 .35
882 A139 5d *Newbouldia laevis* 1.40 1.40
883 A139 8d *Monodora tenuifolia* 2.25 2.25
884 A139 10d *Gossypium arboreum* 2.75 2.75
Nos. 877-884 (8) 7.55 7.55

Souvenir Sheets

885 A139 15d *Kigelia africana* 4.00 4.00
886 A139 15d *Spathodea campanulata* 4.00 4.00

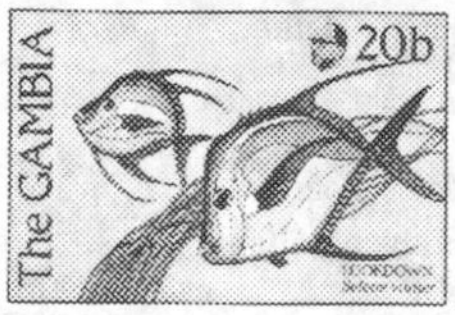

Fish A140

1989, Oct. 19 Litho. *Perf.*

887 A140 20b Lookdown .15 .15
888 A140 75b Boarfish .24 .24
889 A140 1d Gray triggerfish .32 .32
890 A140 1.25d Skipjack tuna .40 .40
891 A140 2d Bermuda chub .65 .65
892 A140 4d Atlantic manta 1.25 1.25
893 A140 5d Striped mullet 1.60 1.60
894 A140 10d Ladyfish 3.20 3.20
Nos. 887-894 (8) 7.81 7.81

Souvenir Sheet

895 A140 15d Porcupinefish 4.25 4.25
896 A140 15d Shortfin makos 4.25 4.25

Souvenir Sheet

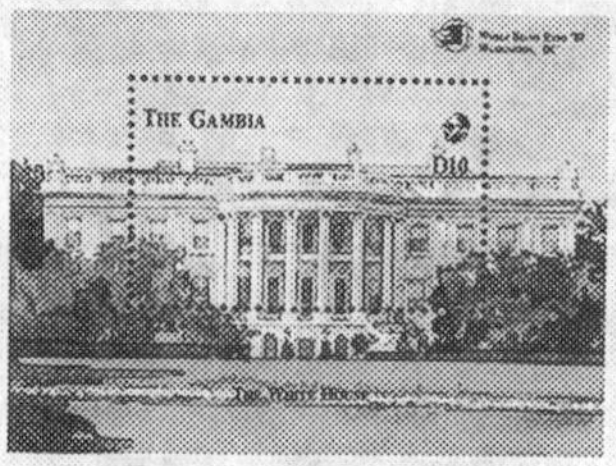

The White House, Washington, DC — A141

1989, Nov. 17 Litho. *Perf. 14*

897 A141 10d multicolored 3.35 3.35

World Stamp Expo '89.

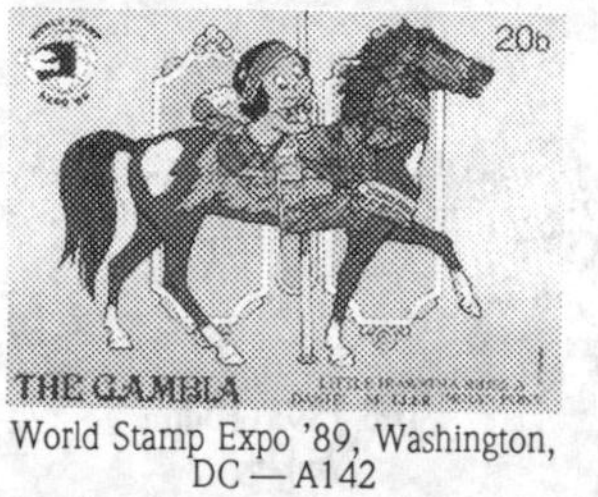

World Stamp Expo '89, Washington, DC — A142

Disney characters riding carousel horses: 20b, Daniel Muller Indian pony. 50b, Herschell-Spillman steed. 75b, Gustav Dentzel stander. 1d, Muller armored stander. 1.25d, Jumper from the Smithsonian Collection. 2d, Illion "American Beauty." 8d, Zalar jumper. 10d, Parker buckling. No. 906, Philadelphia Toboggan Co. Carousel, Elitch Gardens, Denver, CO. No. 907, PTC Roman chariot.

1989, Nov. 29 Litho. *Perf. 14x13½*

898 A142 20b multicolored .15 .15
899 A142 50b multicolored .16 .16
900 A142 75b multicolored .24 .24
901 A142 1d multicolored .32 .32
902 A142 1.25d multicolored .40 .40
903 A142 2d multicolored .65 .65
904 A142 8d multicolored 2.60 2.60
905 A142 10d multicolored 3.15 3.15
Nos. 898-905 (8) 7.67 7.67

Souvenir Sheets

906 A142 12d multicolored 3.00 3.00
907 A142 12d multicolored 3.00 3.00

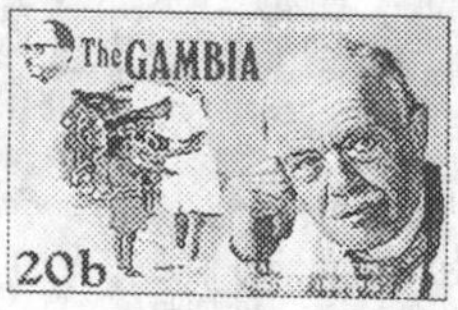

Nobel Prize Winners for Physiology and Great Medical Pioneers A143

Designs: 20b, Charles Nicolle (1866-1936), France, 1928 Prize, discovered transmission of typhus by body lice. 50b, Paul Ehrlich (1854-1915), Germany, 1908 Prize, immunology research. 75b, Selman Waksman (1888-1973), Russian-American, 1952 Prize, discovered antibiotic streptomycin, used to treat tuberculosis. 1d, Edward Jenner (1749-1823), Great Britain, discovered smallpox vaccine. 1.25d, Robert Koch (1843-1910), 1905 Prize, isolated the tubercle bacillus. 5d, Sir Alexander Fleming (1881-1955), Scotland, 1945 Prize, developed penicillin. 8d, Max Theiler (1899-1972), US, 1951 Prize, developed yellow fever vaccine. 10d, Louis Pasteur (1822-1895), France, proved the germ theory of infection. No. 916, C-9 Nightingale Aeromedical Airlift. No. 917, Hughes Vicking helicopter used in airlift.

1989, Dec. 12 *Perf. 14*

908 A143 20b multicolored .15 .15
909 A143 50b multicolored .16 .16
910 A143 75b multicolored .25 .25
911 A143 1d multicolored .35 .35
912 A143 1.25d multicolored .42 .42
913 A143 5d multicolored 1.65 1.65
914 A143 8d multicolored 2.50 2.50
915 A143 10d multicolored 3.25 3.25
Nos. 908-915 (8) 8.73 8.73

Souvenir Sheets

916 A143 15d multicolored 4.25 4.25
917 A143 15d multicolored 4.25 4.25

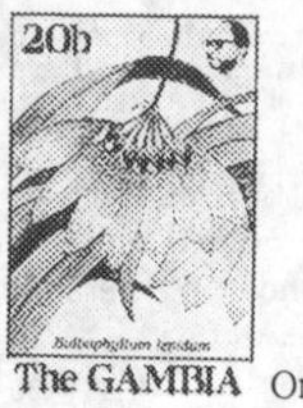

The GAMBIA Orchids — A144

1989, Dec. 18 *Perf. 14*

918 A144 20b *Bulbophyllum lepidum* .15 .15
919 A144 75b *Tridactyle tridactylites* .24 .24
920 A144 1d *Vanilla imperialis* .32 .32
921 A144 1.25d *Oeceoclades maculata* .40 .40
922 A144 2d *Polystachya affinis* .65 .65
923 A144 4d *Ancistrochilus rothschildianus* 1.25 1.25
924 A144 5d *Angraecum distichum* 1.60 1.60
925 A144 10d *Liparis guineensis* 3.15 3.15
Nos. 918-925 (8) 7.76 7.76

Souvenir Sheets

926 A144 15d *Eulophia guineensis* 4.25 4.25
927 A144 15d *Plectrelminthus caudatus* 4.25 4.25

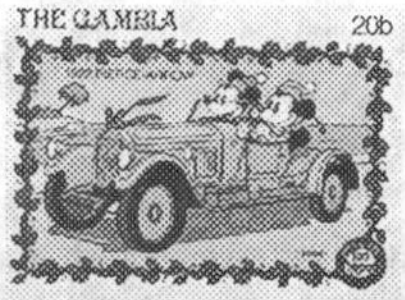

Christmas A145

Disney characters and classic automobiles: 20b, 1922 Pierce Arrow. 50b, 1919 Spyker. 75b, 1929 Packard. 1d, 1920 Daimler. 1.25d, 1924 Hispano Suiza. 2d, Opel Laubfrosch, 1924-27. 10d, 1927 Vauxhall 30/98. 12d, 1923 Peerless. No. 936, 1930 Bentley Supercharged, Santa Claus. No. 937, 1928 Stutz Blackhawk Speedster, picnic.

1989, Dec. 19 Litho. *Perf. 14*

928 A145 20b multicolored .15 .15
929 A145 50b multicolored .16 .16
930 A145 75b multicolored .24 .24
931 A145 1d multicolored .32 .32
932 A145 1.25d multicolored .40 .40
933 A145 2d multicolored .65 .65
934 A145 10d multicolored 3.15 3.15
935 A145 12d multicolored 3.75 3.75
Nos. 928-935 (8) 8.82 8.82

Souvenir Sheets

936 A145 15d multicolored 4.75 4.75
937 A145 15d multicolored 4.75 4.75

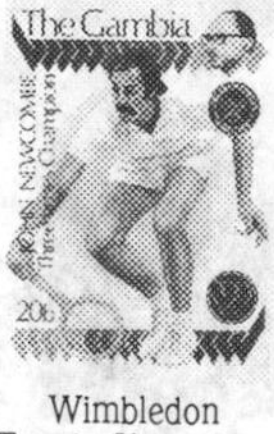

Wimbledon Tennis Champions A146

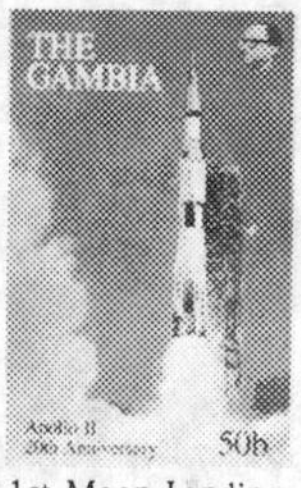

1st Moon Landing, 20th Anniv. (in 1989) A147

1990, Jan. 2 Litho. *Perf. 15x14½*

938 A146 20b John Newcombe .15 .15
939 A146 20b G.W. Hillyard .15 .15
940 A146 50b Roy Emerson .15 .15
941 A146 50b Dorothy Chambers .15 .15
942 A146 75b Donald Budge .18 .18
943 A146 75b Suzanne Lenglen .18 .18
944 A146 1d Laurence Doherty .22 .22
945 A146 1d Helen Wills Moody .22 .22
946 A146 1.25d Bjorn Borg .30 .30
947 A146 1.25d Maureen Connolly .30 .30
948 A146 4d Jean Borotra .90 .90
949 A146 4d Maria Bueno .90 .90
950 A146 5d Anthony Wilding 1.10 1.10
951 A146 5d Louise Brough 1.10 1.10
952 A146 7d Fred Perry 1.75 1.75
953 A146 7d Margaret Court 1.75 1.75
954 A146 10d Bill Tilden 2.25 2.25
955 A146 10d Billie Jean King 2.25 2.25
956 A146 12d Rod Laver 2.75 2.75
957 A146 12d Martina Navratilova 2.75 2.75
Nos. 938-957 (20) 19.50 19.50

Stamps of the same denomination printed se-tenant.

Souvenir Sheets

958 A146 15d Rod Laver, diff. 3.75 3.75
959 A146 15d Martina Navratilova, diff. 3.75 3.75

1990, Feb. 16 *Perf. 14*

Designs: 20b, *Eagle* lunar module descending, horiz. 50b, Apollo 11 liftoff. 75b, Astronaut descending ladder, horiz. 1d, Astronaut, US flag over Sea of Tranquillity, horiz. 1.25d, Mission emblem. 1.75d, Crew, horiz. 8d, Lunar module, Sea of Tranquillity, horiz. 12d, Recovery of command module *Columbia* after splashdown. No. 968, Neil Armstrong returning to *Eagle*. No. 969, View of Earth.

960 A147 20b multicolored .15 .15
961 A147 50b multicolored .15 .15
962 A147 75b multicolored .18 .18
963 A147 1d multicolored .25 .25
964 A147 1.25d multicolored .32 .32
965 A147 1.75d multicolored .40 .40
966 A147 8d multicolored 1.90 1.90
967 A147 12d multicolored 2.75 2.75
Nos. 960-967 (8) 6.10 6.10

Souvenir Sheets

968 A147 15d multicolored 3.75 3.75
969 A147 15d multicolored 3.75 3.75

Miniature Sheet

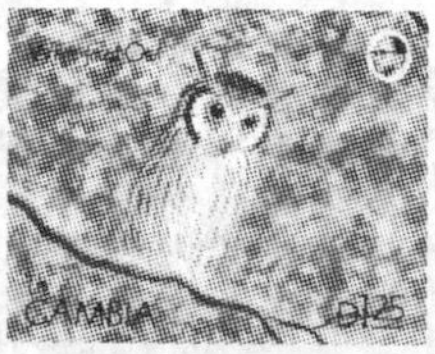

Birds of Africa A148

Designs: a, White-faced owl. b, Village weaver. c, Red-throated bee eater. d, Brown harrier eagle. e, Red bishop. f, Scarlet-chested sunbird. g, Red-billed hornbill. h, Mosque swallow. i, White-faced tree duck. j, African fish eagle. k, Great white pelican. l, Carmine bee eater. m, Hadada ibis. n, Crocodile plover. o, Yellow-bellied sunbird. p, African skimmer. q, Woodland kingfisher. r, Jacana. s, Pygmy goose. t, Hamerkop.

1990, Apr. 12 Litho. *Perf. 14*

970 Sheet of 20 6.50 6.50
a.-t. A148 1.25d any single .32 .32

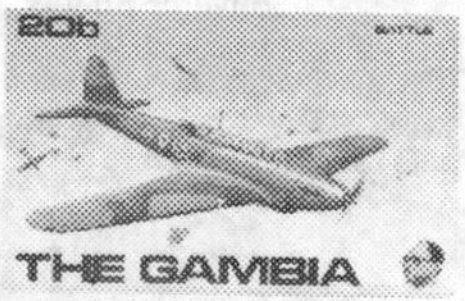

RAF World War II Fighter Planes A149

Designs: 10b, Bristol Blenheim Mk-1. 20b, Battle. 50b, Blenheim 4. 60b, Wellington 1C. 75b, Whitley 5. 1d, Hampden Mk-1. 1.25d, Spitfire 1A and Hurricane 1. 2d, Avro Manchester. 3d, Stirling. 5d, Handley Page Halifax B-2. 10d, Lancaster B-3. 12d, Mosquito B-4. No. 983, Lancaster B-3 over Hamburg. No. 984, Spitfire 1, Battle of Britain.

1990, Apr. 18 *Perf. 14*

971 A149 10b multicolored .15 .15
972 A149 20b multicolored .15 .15
973 A149 50b multicolored .15 .15
974 A149 60b multicolored .15 .15
975 A149 75b multicolored .20 .20
976 A149 1d multicolored .26 .26
977 A149 1.25d multicolored .32 .32
978 A149 2d multicolored .50 .50
979 A149 3d multicolored .75 .75
980 A149 5d multicolored 1.25 1.25
981 A149 10d multicolored 2.50 2.50
982 A149 12d multicolored 3.00 3.00
Nos. 971-982 (12) 9.38 9.38

Souvenir Sheets

983 A149 15d multicolored 4.00 4.00
984 A149 15d multicolored 4.00 4.00

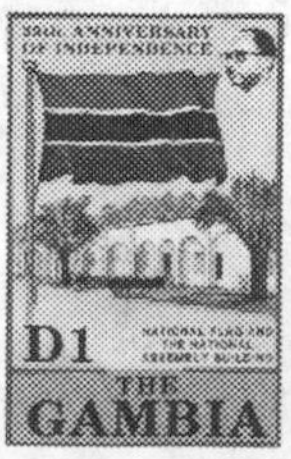

Independence, 25th Anniv. — A150

Designs: 3d, Sir Dawda Jawara, President. 12d, Jet and map showing airport. 18d, National arms.

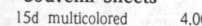

1990, June 5 Litho. *Perf. 14*

985 A150 1d multicolored .20 .20
986 A150 3d multicolored .60 .60
987 A150 12d multicolored 2.50 2.50
Nos. 985-987 (3) 3.30 3.30

Souvenir Sheet

988 A150 18d multicolored 3.75 3.75

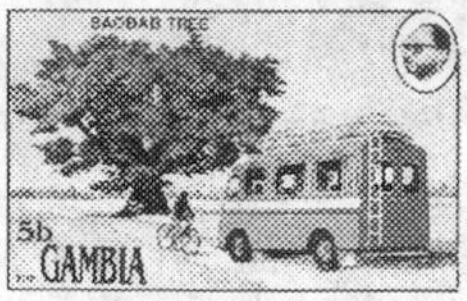

Baobab Tree A151

1990, June 14 Litho. *Perf. 14*

989 A151 5b shown .15 .15
990 A151 10b Woodcarving .15 .15
991 A151 20b Pres. Jawara .15 .15
992 A151 50b Map .15 .15
993 A151 75b Batik fabric .18 .18
994 A151 1d Bakau Beach Resort .25 .25
995 A151 1.25d Tendaba Camp .30 .30
996 A151 2d Shrimp industry .48 .48
997 A151 5d Peanut oil mill 1.25 1.25
998 A151 10d Pottery, kora 2.50 2.50
999 A151 15d Ansellia Africana orchid 3.75 3.75
1000 A151 30d Ancient stone rings, Euryphene gambiae 7.25 7.25
Nos. 989-1000 (12) 16.56 16.56

Nos. 990, 999 vert.

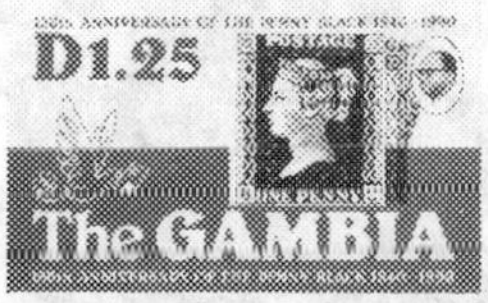

Penny Black, 150th Anniv. A152

1990, June 18

1001 A152 1.25d brt bl & blk .35 .35
1002 A152 12d dark red & blk 3.50 3.50

Souvenir Sheet

1003 A152 15d sil, bis & blk 4.25 4.25

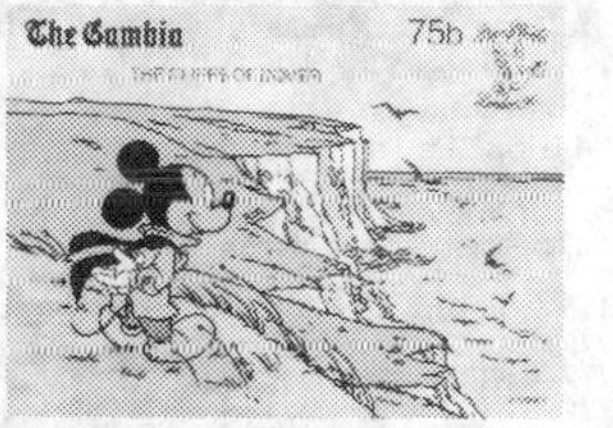

Mickey Visits England — A153

Walt Disney characters at: 20b, 10 Downing Street. 50b, Trafalgar Square. 75b, Cliffs of Dover. 1d, Tower of London. 5d, Hampton Court Palace. 8d, Magdalen Tower, Oxford University. 10d, Old London Bridge. 12d, Rosetta Stone, British Museum. No. 1012, Picadilly Circus. No. 1013, Houses of Parliament and Big Ben on the River Thames.

1990, June 19 *Perf. 14x13½*

1004 A153 20b multicolored .15 .15
1005 A153 50b multicolored .16 .16
1006 A153 75b multicolored .24 .24
1007 A153 1d multicolored .32 .32
1008 A153 5d multicolored 1.60 1.60
1009 A153 8d multicolored 2.60 2.60
1010 A153 10d multicolored 3.20 3.20
1011 A153 12d multicolored 3.85 3.85
Nos. 1004-1011 (8) 12.12 12.12

Souvenir Sheets

1012 A153 18d multicolored 5.00 5.00
1013 A153 18d multicolored 5.00 5.00

Stamp World London '90. Nos. 1004-1005, 1007, 1009 vert.

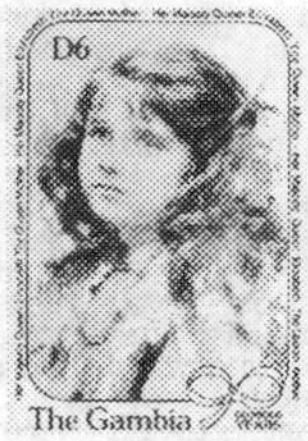

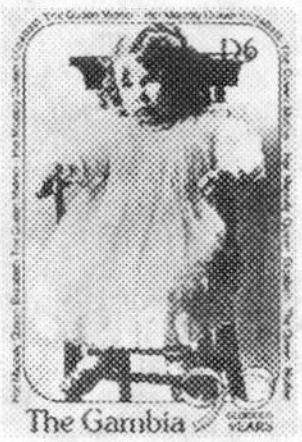

Queen Mother's 90th Birthday
A154 A155

1990, July 19 *Perf. 14*

1014 A154 6d shown 1.65 1.65
1015 A155 6d Young girl, diff. 1.65 1.65
1016 A155 6d shown 1.65 1.65
Nos. 1014-1016 (3) 4.95 4.95

Souvenir Sheet

1017 A154 18d like No. 1014 5.00 5.00

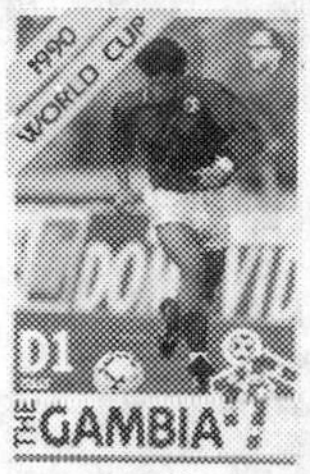

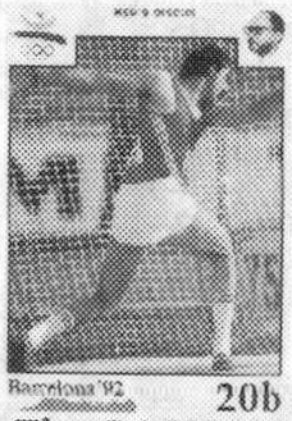

A156 A157

Players from participating countries.

1990, Sept. 24 Litho. *Perf. 14*

1018 A156 1d Italy .32 .32
1019 A156 1.25d Argentina .40 .40
1020 A156 3d Costa Rica .95 .95
1021 A156 5d UAE 1.60 1.60
Nos. 1018-1021 (4) 3.27 3.27

Souvenir Sheets

1022 A156 18d Holland 5.00 5.00
1023 A156 18d Romania 5.00 5.00

World Cup Soccer Championships, Italy.

1990, Nov. 1 Litho. *Perf. 14*

1024 A157 20b Men's discus .15 .15
1025 A157 50b Men's 100-meter race .15 .15
1026 A157 75b Women's 400-meter race .20 .20
1027 A157 1d Men's 200-meter race .28 .28
1028 A157 1.25d Rhythmic gymnastics .35 .35
1029 A157 3d Soccer .85 .85
1030 A157 10d Men's marathon 3.00 3.00
1031 A157 12d Tornado class sailing 3.50 3.50
Nos. 1024-1031 (8) 8.48 8.48

Souvenir Sheets

1032 A157 15d Parade of flags 4.00 4.00
1033 A157 15d Stadium, card section 4.00 4.00

1992 Summer Olympics, Barcelona.

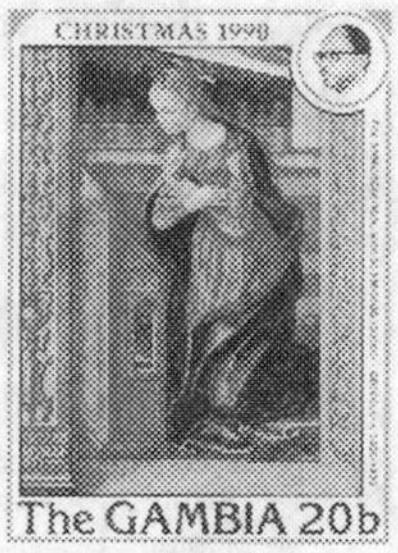

Christmas A158

Entire paintings or different details from: 20b, 7d, The Annunciation with St. Emidius by Crivelli. 50b, The Annunciation by Campin. 75b, The Solly Madonna by Raphael. 1.25d, The Tempi Madonna by Raphael. 2d, Madonna of the Linen Window by Raphael. 10d, The Orleans Madonna by Raphael. 15d, Madonna and Child by Crivelli. No. 1042, The Niccolini-Cowper Madonna by Raphael.

1990, Dec. 24 Litho. *Perf. 13½x14*

1034 A158 20b multicolored .15 .15
1035 A158 50b multicolored .15 .15
1036 A158 75b multicolored .18 .18
1037 A158 1.25d multicolored .35 .35
1038 A158 2d multicolored .55 .55
1039 A158 7d multicolored 1.90 1.90
1040 A158 10d multicolored 2.75 2.75
1041 A158 15d multicolored 4.00 4.00
Nos. 1034-1041 (8) 10.03 10.03

Souvenir Sheet

1042 A158 15d multicolored 4.00 4.00

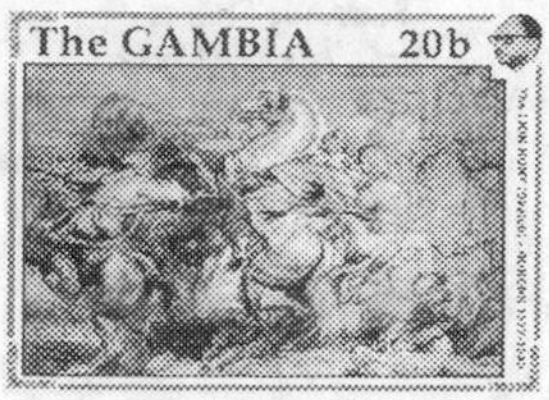

Peter Paul Rubens (1577-1640), Painter — A159

Entire paintings or different details from: 20b, 75b, 10d, No. 1054, The Lion Hunt. 1d, 1.25d, 3d, 15d, The Tiger Hunt. 5d, No. 1055, The Boar Hunt. No. 1056, The Crocodile and Hippopotamus Hunt. No. 1057, Saint George Slays the Dragon, vert.

1990, Dec. 24 Litho. *Perf. 14x13½*

1046 A159 20b multicolored .15 .15
1047 A159 75b multicolored .22 .22
1048 A159 1d multicolored .30 .30
1049 A159 1.25d multicolored .40 .40
1050 A159 3d multicolored .90 .90
1051 A159 5d multicolored 1.50 1.50
1052 A159 10d multicolored 3.00 3.00
1053 A159 15d multicolored 4.50 4.50
Nos. 1046-1053 (8) 10.97 10.97

Souvenir Sheets

1054 A159 15d multicolored 4.00 4.00
1055 A159 15d multicolored 4.00 4.00
1056 A159 15d multicolored 4.00 4.00
1057 A159 15d multicolored 4.00 4.00

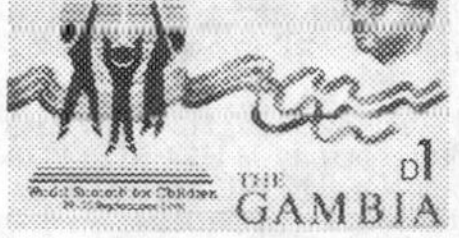

World Summit for Children A160

1991, Jan. 7 Litho. *Perf. 14*

1058 A160 1d multicolored .32 .32

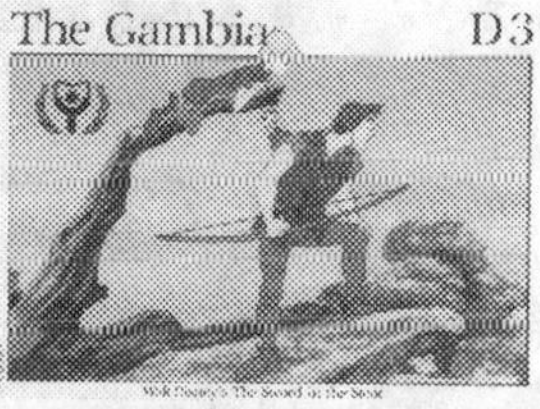

Intl. Literacy Year — A161

Walt Disney characters in "The Sword in the Stone": No. 1059a, Wart and Sir Kay. b, Merlin reading book. c, Wart learning geography. d, Wart writing on blackboard. e, Wart as bird, Madam Mim. f, Merlin and Madam Mim. g, Mim as dragon. h, Wart pulling sword from stone. i, Wart as King of England. No. 1060, Merlin, Wart in forest, vert. No. 1061, Knight trying to remove sword from stone, vert.

1991, Feb. 14 Litho. *Perf. 14x13½*

1059 A161 3d Min. sheet of 9, #1059a-1059i 8.50 8.50

Souvenir Sheets

1060 A161 20d multicolored 6.40 6.40
1061 A161 20d multicolored 6.40 6.40

Miniature Sheets

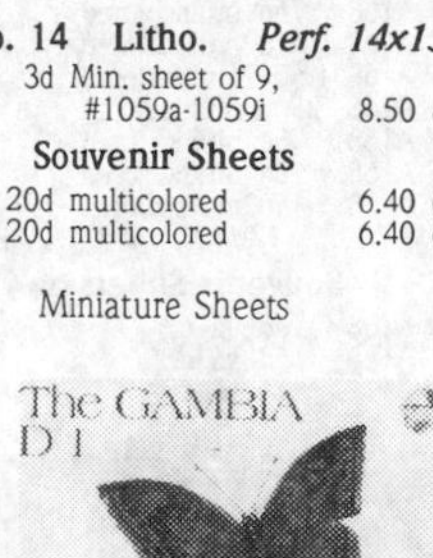

Wildlife A162

No. 1062: a, Bebearia senegalensis. b, Graphium ridleyanus. c, Precis antilope. d, Charaxes ameliae. e, Addax. f, Sassaby. g, Civet. h, Green monkey. i, Spurwing goose. j, Red-billed hornbill. k, Osprey. l, Glossy ibis. m, Egyptian plover. n, Golden-tailed woodpecker. o, Green woodhoopoe. p, Gaboon viper.

No. 1063: a, Red-billed firefinch. b, Leaflove. c, Piacpiac. d, Emerald cuckoo. e, Red colobus monkey. f, African elephant. g, Duiker. h, Giant eland. i, Oribi. j, West African dwarf crocodile. k, Crowned crane. l, Jackal. m, Yellow-throated longclaw. n, Abyssinian ground hornbill. o, Papilio hesperus. p, Papilio antimachus.

No. 1064: a, Martial eagle. b, Red-cheeked cordon-bleu. c, Red bishop. d, Great white pelican. e, Patas monkey. f, Vervet monkey. g, Roan antelope. h, Western hartebeest. i, Waterbuck. j, Warthog. k, Spotted hyena. l, Olive baboon. m, Palla decius. n, Acraea pharsalus. o, Neptidopsis ophione. p, Acraea caecilia.

No. 1065, African spoonbill, vert. No. 1066, Lion, vert. No. 1067, Buffalo weaver, vert.

1991, May 31 Litho. *Perf. 14*

Sheets of 16

1062 A162 1d #a.-p. 4.75 4.75
1063 A162 1.50d #a.-p. 7.25 7.25
1064 A162 5d #a.-p. 24.00 24.00
Nos. 1062-1064 (3) 36.00 36.00

Souvenir Sheets

1065 A162 18d multicolored 5.40 5.40
1066 A162 18d multicolored 5.40 5.40
1067 A162 18d multicolored 5.40 5.40

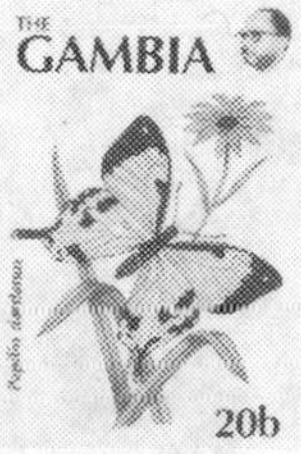

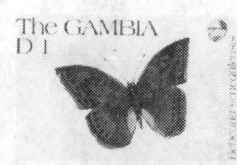

20b Butterflies — A163

Designs: 20b, Papilio dardanus. 50b, Bematistes poggei. 1d, Vanessa cardiu. 1.50d, Amphicallia tigris. 3d, Hypolimnes dexithea. 8d, Acraea egina. 10d, Salmis temora. 15d, Precis octavia. No. 1076, Danaus chrysippus. No. 1077, Charaxes jasius. No. 1078, Papilio demodocus. No. 1079, Papilio nireus.

1991, June 1 Litho. *Perf. 14*

1068 A163 20b multicolored .15 .15
1069 A163 50b multicolored .15 .15
1070 A163 1d multicolored .30 .30
1071 A163 1.50d multicolored .45 .45
1072 A163 3d multicolored .90 .90
1073 A163 8d multicolored 2.40 2.40
1074 A163 10d multicolored 3.00 3.00
1075 A163 15d multicolored 4.50 4.50
Nos. 1068-1075 (8) 11.85 11.85

Souvenir Sheets

1076 A163 18d multicolored 5.40 5.40
1077 A163 18d multicolored 5.40 5.40
1078 A163 18d multicolored 4.65 4.65
1079 A163 18d multicolored 4.65 4.65

While Nos. 1078-1079 have same release date as Nos. 1068-1077, the dollar value of Nos. 1078-1079 were lower when they were released.

Royal Family Birthday, Anniversary

Common Design Type

1991, Aug. 12 Litho. *Perf. 14*

1080 CD347 20b multi .15 .15
1081 CD347 50b multi .15 .15
1082 CD347 75b multi .22 .22
1083 CD347 1d multi .30 .30
1084 CD347 1.25d multi .38 .38
1085 CD347 1.50d multi .45 .45
1086 CD347 12d multi 3.60 3.60
1087 CD347 15d multi 4.50 4.50
Nos. 1080-1087 (8) 9.75 9.75

Souvenir Sheets

1088 CD347 18d Elizabeth, Philip 5.40 5.40
1089 CD347 18d Diana, sons, Charles 5.40 5.40

20b, 75b, 1.50d, 15d, No. 1089, Charles and Diana, 10th wedding anniversary. Others, Queen Elizabeth II, 65th birthday.

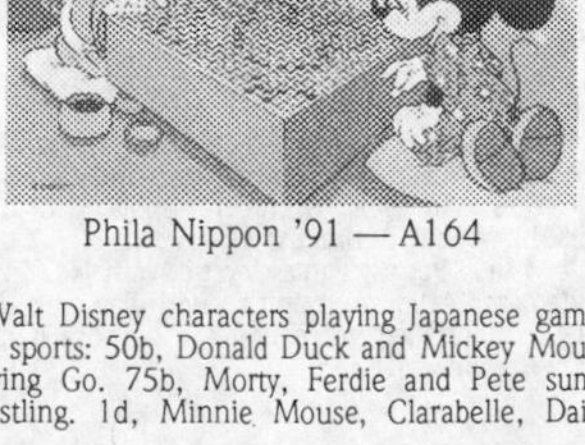

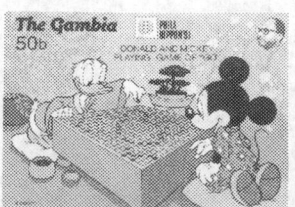

Phila Nippon '91 — A164

Walt Disney characters playing Japanese games and sports: 50b, Donald Duck and Mickey Mouse playing Go. 75b, Morty, Ferdie and Pete sumo wrestling. 1d, Minnie Mouse, Clarabelle, Daisy

Duck playing battledore and shuttlecock. 1.25d, Goofy, Mickey at Okinawa bullfight, vert. 5d, Mickey as a Hawk Hunter Tagari, vert. 7d, Mickey, Minnie, and Donald play Jan-Ken-Pon, vert. 10d, Goofy as archer. 15d, Morty, Ferdie fly Japanese kites, vert. No. 1098, Goofy batting in Japanese baseball game, vert. No. 1099, Mickey, Scrooge McDuck playing Japanese football, vert. No. 1100, Mickey fly fishing, vert. No. 1101, Mickey climbing Mt. Fuji, vert.

Perf. 14x13½, 13½x14

1991, Aug. 22 Litho.

1090	A164	50b	multicolored	.15	.15
1091	A164	75b	multicolored	.22	.22
1092	A164	1d	multicolored	.30	.30
1093	A164	1.25d	multicolored	.38	.38
1094	A164	5d	multicolored	1.50	1.50
1095	A164	7d	multicolored	2.10	2.10
1096	A164	10d	multicolored	3.00	3.00
1097	A164	15d	multicolored	4.50	4.50
	Nos. 1090-1097 (8)			12.15	12.15

Souvenir Sheets

1098	A164	20d	multicolored	6.00	6.00
1099	A164	20d	multicolored	6.00	6.00
1100	A164	20d	multicolored	6.00	6.00
1101	A164	20d	multicolored	6.00	6.00

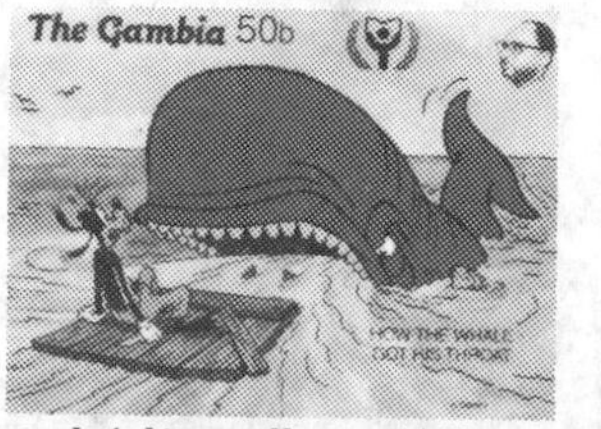

Intl. Literacy Year — A165

Walt Disney characters in scenes from Rudyard Kipling's "Just So Stories": 50b, How the Whale Got His Throat. 75b, How the Camel Got His Hump. 1d, How the Leopard Got His Spots. 1.25d, The Elephant's Child. 1.50d, Singsong of Old Man Kangaroo. 7d, The Crab that Played with the Sea. 10d, The Cat that Walked by Himself. 15d, The Butterfly that Stamped. No. 1110, How the Alphabet was Made, vert. No. 1111, The Beginning of the Armadillos. No. 1112, How the First Letter was Written, vert. No. 1113, How the Rhinoceros Got His Skin.

1991, Aug. 28 Litho. *Perf. 14x13½*

1102	A165	50b	multicolored	.15	.15
1103	A165	75b	multicolored	.22	.22
1104	A165	1d	multicolored	.30	.30
1105	A165	1.25d	multicolored	.38	.38
1106	A165	1.50d	multicolored	.45	.45
1107	A165	7d	multicolored	2.10	2.10
1108	A165	10d	multicolored	3.00	3.00
1109	A165	15d	multicolored	4.50	4.50
	Nos. 1102-1109 (8)			11.10	11.10

Souvenir Sheets

Perf. 13½x14, 14x13½

1110	A165	20d	multicolored	6.00	6.00
1111	A165	20d	multicolored	6.00	6.00
1112	A165	20d	multicolored	4.50	4.50
1113	A165	20d	multicolored	4.50	4.50

While Nos. 1112-1113 have the same issue date as Nos. 1102-1111, the dollar value of Nos. 1112-1113 was lower when they were released.

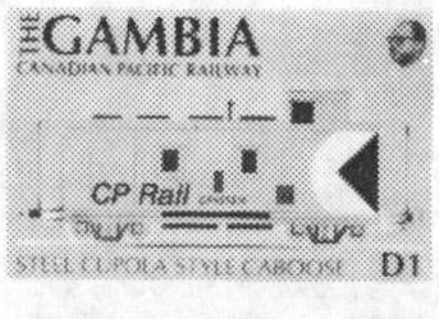

Train Cabooses A166

Designs: No. 1114a, Steel cupola, Canadian Pacific. b, Four-wheel, Cumberland and Pennsylvania. c, Mexican slim gauge. d, All steel cupola, Northern Pacific. e, Four-wheel, Morristown & Erie. f, Streamlined cupola, Burlington Northern. g, Caboose coach, McCloud River. h, Wide vision, Santa Fe. i, Wide vision, Frisco.

No. 1115a, Narrow gauge, Oahu Railway. b, Standard brake-van, British Railways. c, Wide view steel, Union Pacific. d, Four-wheel, Belt Railway of Chicago. e, Four-wheel, McCloud River. f, Logging, Angelina County Lumber Co. g, Narrow gauge, Coahuila & Zacatecas. h, Three-foot gauge, United Railways of Yucatan. i, Steel cupola, Rio Grande.

No. 1116a, Four-wheel, Colorado & Southern. b, Transfer, Santa Fe. c, Wooden cupola, Canadian National. d, Transfer steel, Union Pacific. e, Caboose coach, Virginia & Truckee. f, Standard brake-van, British. g, Narrow gauge, Intl. Railways of Central America. h, Steel cupola, Northern Pacific. i, Wood, Burlington Northern.

No. 1117, Pennsylvania electric, vert. No. 1118, Unidentified caboose, trainman with flag, vert. No. 1119, Unidentified green wooden caboose behind yellow freight car.

1991, Sept. 12 Litho. *Perf. 14x13½*

Sheets of 9

1114	A166	1d	#a.-i.	3.00	3.00
1115	A166	2d	#a.-i.	4.00	4.00
1116	A166	1.50d	#a.-i.	3.00	3.00
	Nos. 1114-1116 (3)			10.00	10.00

Souvenir Sheets

Perf. 12x13, 13x12

1117	A166	20d	multicolored	6.00	6.00
1118	A166	20d	multicolored	4.50	4.50
1119	A166	20d	multicolored	4.50	4.50

While Nos. 1115-1116 and 1118-1119 have the same issue date as Nos. 1114 and 1117, the dollar value of Nos. 1115-1116 and 1118-1119 was lower when they were released.

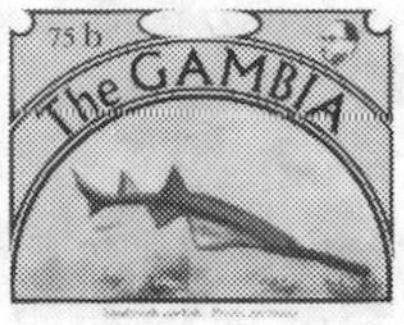

Fish — A167

1991, Oct. 28 Litho. *Perf. 14x14½*

1120	A167	20b	Tiger shark	.15	.15
1121	A167	25b	Common jewel fish	.15	.15
1122	A167	50b	Five spot fish	.15	.15
1123	A167	75b	Smalltooth saw-fish	.22	.22
1124	A167	1d	Five spot tilapia	.30	.30
1125	A167	1.25d	Dwarf jewel fish	.28	.28
1126	A167	1.50d	Five spot jewel fish	.45	.45
1127	A167	3d	Bumphead	.90	.90
1128	A167	10d	Egyptian mouth-brooder	3.00	3.00
1129	A167	15d	Burton's mouth-brooder	3.25	3.25
	Nos. 1120-1129 (10)			8.85	8.85

Souvenir Sheets

1130	A167	18d	Great barracuda	4.00	4.00
1131	A167	18d	Yellowtail snap-per	4.00	4.00

While Nos. 1120-1122, 1125, 1129-1131 have the same issue date as Nos. 1123-1124, 1126-1128 the dollar value of Nos. 1120-1122, 1125, 1129-1130 was lower when they were released.

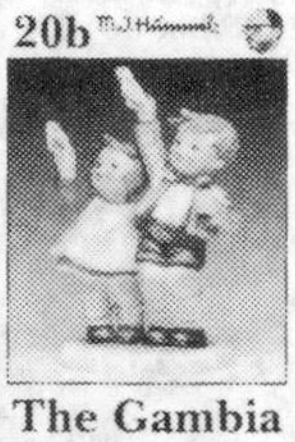

Hummel Figurines — A168

Designs: 20b, No. 1141a, Girl and boy waving handkerchiefs. 75b, No. 1140a, Boy and girl under umbrella. 1d, No. 1140b, Two girls wearing scarfs. 1.50d, No. 1140c, Girl and boy in window with flower box. 2.50d, No. 1141b, Two girls with basket. 5d, No. 1141c, Boy wearing long pants, boy wearing shorts. 10d, No. 1141d, Two girls on fence. 15d, No. 1140d, Boy with stick, girl with bag.

1991, Nov. 4 Litho. *Perf. 14*

1132	A168	20b	multicolored	.15	.15
1133	A168	75b	multicolored	.22	.22
1134	A168	1d	multicolored	.30	.30
1135	A168	1.50d	multicolored	.45	.45
1136	A168	2.50d	multicolored	.75	.75
1137	A168	5d	multicolored	1.50	1.50
1138	A168	10d	multicolored	3.00	3.00
1139	A168	15d	multicolored	4.50	4.50
	Nos. 1132-1139 (8)			10.87	10.87

Souvenir Sheets of 4

1140	A168	4d	#a.-d.	4.80	4.80
1141	A168	5d	#a.-d.	6.00	6.00

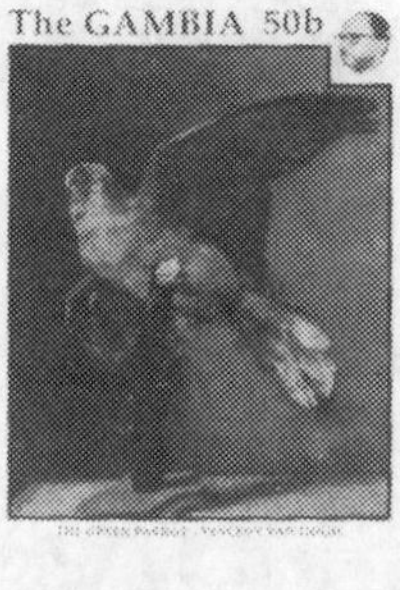

Paintings by Vincent Van Gogh — A169

Designs: 20b, The Old Cemetery Tower at Nuenen in the Snow, horiz. 25b, Head of a Peasant Woman with White Cap. 50b, The Green Parrot. 75b, Vase with Carnations. 1d, Vase with Red Gladioli. 1.25b, Beach at Scheveningen in Calm Weather, horiz. 1.50d, Boy Cutting Grass with a Sickle, horiz. 2d, Coleus Plant in a Flowerpot. 3d, Self-portrait, spring-summer 1887. 4d, Self-portrait. 5d, Self-portrait, diff. 6d, Self-portrait, spring 1887. 8d, Still Life with a Bottle, Two Glasses, Cheese and Bread. 10d, Still Life with Cabbage, Clogs and Potatoes, horiz. 12d, Montmartre: The Street Lamps. 15d, Head of a Peasant Woman with Brownish Cap. No. 1158, Arles: View From the Wheat Fields. No. 1159, Autumn Landscape. No. 1160, Montmartre: Quarry, The Mills, horiz. No. 1161, The Potato Eaters, horiz.

Perf. 13½x14, 14x13½

1991, Dec. 5 Litho.

1142	A169	20b	multicolored	.15	.15
1143	A169	25b	multicolored	.15	.15
1144	A169	50b	multicolored	.15	.15
1145	A169	75b	multicolored	.22	.22
1146	A169	1d	multicolored	.22	.22
1147	A169	1.25d	multicolored	.38	.38
1148	A169	1.50d	multicolored	.35	.35
1149	A169	2d	multicolored	.60	.60
1150	A169	3d	multicolored	.70	.70
1151	A169	4d	multicolored	1.20	1.20
1152	A169	5d	multicolored	1.50	1.50
1153	A169	6d	multicolored	1.35	1.35
1154	A169	8d	multicolored	2.40	2.40
1155	A169	10d	multicolored	2.25	2.25
1156	A169	12d	multicolored	2.75	2.75
1157	A169	15d	multicolored	4.50	4.50

Size: 127x102mm

Imperf

1158	A169	20d	multicolored	6.00	6.00
1159	A169	20d	multicolored	6.00	6.00
1160	A169	20d	multicolored	4.50	4.50
1161	A169	20d	multicolored	4.50	4.50
	Nos. 1142-1161 (20)			39.87	39.87

While Nos. 1142-1143, 1146, 1148, 1150, 1153, 1155-1156, 1160-1161 have the same issue date as Nos. 1144-1145, 1147, 1149, 1151-1152, 1154, 1157-1159, the dollar value of Nos. 1142-1143, 1146, 1148, 1150, 1153, 1155-1156, 1160-1161 was lower when they were released.

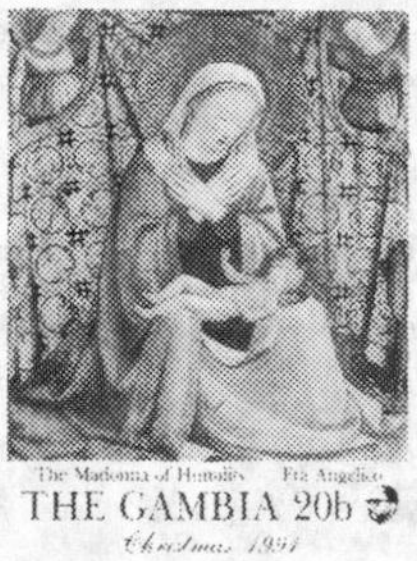

Christmas A170

Paintings by Fra Angelico: 20b, The Madonna of Humility. 50b, Madonna and Child with Angels. 75b, The Virgin and Child with Angels. 1d, Annunciation. 1.25d, Presentation in the Temple. 5d, Annunciation, diff. 10d, Madonna della Stella. 15d, Naming of St. John the Baptist. No. 1170, Annunciation and Adoration of the Magi. No. 1171, Coronation of the Virgin.

1991, Dec. 23 *Perf. 12*

1162	A170	20b	multicolored	.15	.15
1163	A170	50b	multicolored	.15	.15
1164	A170	75b	multicolored	.22	.22
1165	A170	1d	multicolored	.30	.30
1166	A170	1.25d	multicolored	.38	.38
1167	A170	5d	multicolored	1.50	1.50
1168	A170	10d	multicolored	3.00	3.00
1169	A170	15d	multicolored	4.50	4.50
	Nos. 1162-1169 (8)			10.20	10.20

Souvenir Sheets

Perf. 14½

1170	A170	20d	multicolored	6.00	6.00
1171	A170	20d	multicolored	6.00	6.00

Queen Elizabeth II's Accession to the Throne, 40th Anniv.

Common Design Type

1992, Feb. 6 Litho. *Perf. 14*

1172	CD348	20b	multicolored	.15	.15
1173	CD348	50b	multicolored	.15	.15
1174	CD348	1d	multicolored	.22	.22
1175	CD348	15d	multicolored	3.25	3.25
	Nos. 1172-1175 (4)			3.77	3.77

Souvenir Sheets

1176	CD348	20d	Queen at left, yacht	4.50	4.50
1177	CD348	20d	Queen at right, boat	4.50	4.50

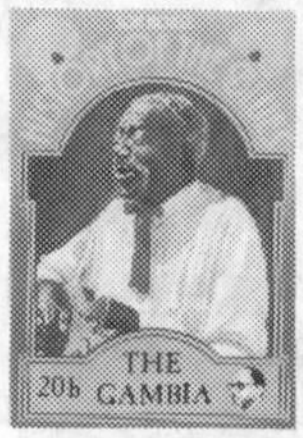

Famous Blues Musicians — A171

1992, Feb. 12 *Perf. 14*

1178	A171	20b	Son House	.15	.15
1179	A171	25b	W. C. Handy	.15	.15
1180	A171	50b	Muddy Waters	.15	.15
1181	A171	75b	Lightnin Hopkins	.18	.18
1182	A171	1d	Ma Rainey	.22	.22
1183	A171	1.25d	Mance Lipscomb	.28	.28
1184	A171	1.50d	Mahalia Jackson	.35	.35
1185	A171	2d	Ella Fitzgerald	.45	.45
1186	A171	3d	Howlin Wolf	.70	.70
1187	A171	5d	Bessie Smith	1.10	1.10
1188	A171	7d	Leadbelly	1.55	1.55
1189	A171	10d	Joe Willie Wilkins	2.25	2.25
	Nos. 1178-1189 (12)			7.53	7.53

Souvenir Sheets

1190	A171	20d	Gambian string drummer	4.50	4.50
1191	A171	20d	Elvis Presley	4.50	4.50
1192	A171	20d	Billie Holiday	4.50	4.50

While all stamps have the same issue date the dollar value of some was lower when they actually were released.

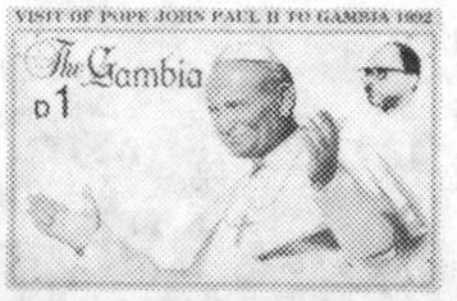

A172

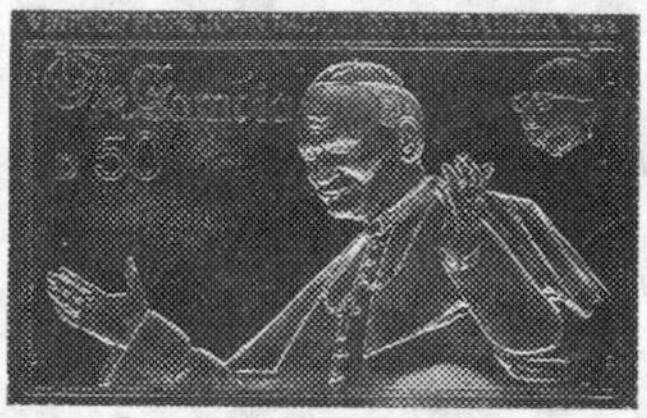

Papal Visit, 1992 — A172a

Designs: 1d, Pope John Paul II. 1.25d, Pope, Pres. Dwada Jawara. 20d, Flags, Papal arms. 25d, Pope at Mass.

Illustration A172a reduced.

1992, Feb. 23 Litho. *Perf. 14*

1193	A172	1d	multicolored	.22	.22
1194	A172	1.25d	multicolored	.28	.28
1195	A172	20d	multicolored	4.50	4.50
	Nos. 1193-1195 (3)			5.00	5.00

Souvenir Sheet

1196	A172	25d	multicolored	5.50	5.50

Embossed

Perf. 12

Without Gum

Size: 65x43mm

1196A	A172a	50d	gold

No. 1196A was not available until late 1993, exists imperf on large card.

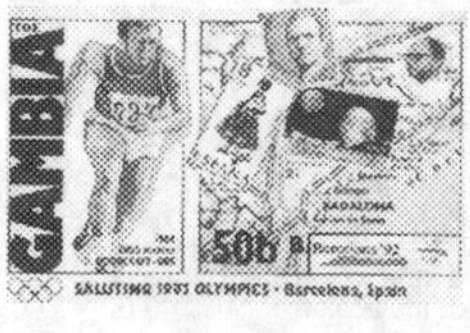

1992 Summer Olympics, Barcelona A173

Designs: 20b, Map and Nadia Comaneci, gymnastics, Romania, 1976. 50b, D. Moorcraft, 5000 meters, Great Britain, 1984. 75b, M. Nemeth, javelin, Hungary, 1976. 1d, J. Pedraza, 20k walking, Mexico, 1968. 1.25d, Map, Spanish Arms and flag, Yachting soling class, Brazil, 1984. 1.50d, Spanish building, Field hockey, East Germany, 1984. 12d, Map and Michael Jordan, basketball, US, 1984. 15d, V. Borzov, 100 meters, USSR, 1972. No. 1201, Flamenco dancer, vert. No. 1206, Map and Bull.

1992, Mar. 6 Litho. *Perf. 14*

1197	A173	20b	multicolored	.15	.15
1198	A173	50b	multicolored	.15	.15
1199	A173	75b	multicolored	.22	.22

1200	A173	1d multicolored	.30	.30
1201	A173	1.25d multicolored	.28	.28
1202	A173	1.50d multicolored	.35	.35
1203	A173	12d multicolored	2.75	2.75
1204	A173	15d multicolored	4.50	4.50
		Nos. 1197-1204 (8)	8.70	8.70

Souvenir Sheet

1205	A173	20d multicolored	6.00	6.00
1206	A173	20d multicolored	4.50	4.50

While Nos. 1197, 1201-1203, 1206 have the same issue date as Nos. 1198-1200, 1204-1205, the value of Nos. 1197, 1201-1203, 1206 was lower when they were released.

Easter — A174

Paintings: 20b, Christ Presented to the People, by Rembrandt. 50b, Christ Carrying the Cross, by Mathias Grunewald. 75b, The Crucifixion, by Mathias Grunewald. 1d, The Crucifixion, by Rubens. 1.25d, The Road to Calvary (detail), by Tintoretto. 1.50d, The Road to Calvary (entire), by Tintoretto. 15d, The Crucifixion, by Masaccio. 20d, Descent from the Cross (detail), by Rembrandt. No. 1215, Crowning with Thorns (detail), by Titian. No. 1216, Crowning with Thorns, by Anthony Van Dyck.

1992, Apr. 16		Litho.	Perf. 13½	
1207	A174	20b multicolored	.15	.15
1208	A174	50b multicolored	.15	.15
1209	A174	75b multicolored	.18	.18
1210	A174	1d multicolored	.25	.25
1211	A174	1.25d multicolored	.28	.28
1212	A174	1.50d multicolored	.35	.35
1213	A174	15d multicolored	3.50	3.50
1214	A174	20d multicolored	4.50	4.50
		Nos. 1207-1214 (8)	9.36	9.36

Souvenir Sheets

1215	A174	25d multicolored	5.75	5.75
1216	A174	25d multicolored	5.75	5.75

World Columbian Stamp Expo, Chicago A175

Walt Disney characters in Chicago: 50b, Mickey at Navy pier. 1d, Mickey floats by Wrigley Building. 1.25d, Donald graduates from University of Chicago. 12d, Goofy at Chicago's Adler Planetarium. No. 1221, Goofy above Chicago at the Hancock Center, horiz.

1992, Apr. 8		Litho.	Perf. 13½x14	
1217	A175	50b multicolored	.15	.15
1218	A175	1d multicolored	.22	.22
1219	A175	1.25d multicolored	.28	.28
1220	A175	12d multicolored	2.75	2.75
		Nos. 1217-1220 (4)	3.40	3.40

Souvenir Sheet
Perf. 14x13½

1221	A175	18d multicolored	4.00	4.00

No. 1220 has name spelled "Alder."

Granada '92 — A176

Mickey Mouse as Columbus: 20b, With map. 75b, Ideas rejected. 1.50d, Explores America. 15d, Returns to Spain. No. 1231, Embarks for America.

1992, Apr. 8			Perf. 13½x14	
1227	A176	20b multicolored	.15	.15
1228	A176	75b multicolored	.18	.18
1229	A176	1.50d multicolored	.35	.35
1230	A176	15d multicolored	3.50	3.50
		Nos. 1227-1230 (4)	4.18	4.18

Souvenir Sheet

1231	A176	18d multicolored	4.00	4.00

Flowers — A177

1992, July 21		Litho.	Perf. 14	
1237	A177	20b Hibiscus	.15	.15
1238	A177	50b Calabash nutmeg	.15	.15
1239	A177	75b Silk cotton tree	.18	.18
1240	A177	1d Oncoba	.25	.25
1241	A177	1.25d Paintbrush plant	.28	.28
1242	A177	1.50d Tree gardenia	.38	.38
1243	A177	2d Glory bower	.45	.45
1244	A177	5d Ashanti blood	1.25	1.25
1245	A177	10d African peach	2.50	2.50
1246	A177	12d Butterfly bush	2.90	2.90
1247	A177	15d Crepe ginger	3.75	3.75
1248	A177	18d Spider tresses	4.00	4.00
		Nos. 1237-1248 (12)	16.24	16.24

Souvenir Sheets

1249	A177	20d Water lily	4.50	4.50
1250	A177	20d Bougainvillea	5.00	5.00
1251	A177	20d Baobab tree	5.00	5.00
1252	A177	20d Climbing pea	5.00	5.00

While Nos. 1240, 1242, 1244, 1247, 1250 have the same release date as Nos. 1237, 1241, 1243, 1248-1249, their values in relation to the dollar were higher when they were released.

Riverboats — A178

Riverboat and waterway: 20b, Joven Antonia, Gambia River. 50b, Dresden, Elbe River. 75b, Medway Queen, Medway River. 1d, Lady Wright, Gambia River. 1.25d, Devin, Vltava River. 1.50d, Lady Chilel, Gambia River. 5d, Robert Fulton, Hudson River. 10d, Coonawarra, Murray River. 12d, Nakusp, Columbia River. 15d, Lucy Ashton, Firth of Clyde. No. 1263, Rudesheim, Rhine River. No. 1264, City of Cairo, Mississippi River.

1992, Aug. 3		Litho.	Perf. 14	
1253	A178	20b multicolored	.15	.15
1254	A178	50b multicolored	.15	.15
1255	A178	75b multicolored	.16	.16
1256	A178	1d multicolored	.22	.22
1257	A178	1.25d multicolored	.28	.28
1258	A178	1.50d multicolored	.35	.35
1259	A178	5d multicolored	1.10	1.10
1260	A178	10d multicolored	2.20	2.20
1261	A178	12d multicolored	2.65	2.65
1262	A178	15d multicolored	3.50	3.50
		Nos. 1253-1262 (10)	10.76	10.76

Souvenir Sheets

1263	A178	20d multicolored	4.50	4.50
1264	A178	20d multicolored	4.50	4.50

Miniature Sheet

World War II in the Pacific A179

Designs: a, USS Pennsylvania. b, Japanese attack begins. c, USS Ward sinking Japanese submarine. d, Ford Naval Air Station under attack. e, News bulletin announcing attack. f, Front page of Honolulu Star-Bulletin. g, Japanese invade Guam. h, US recovers Wake Island. i, Doolittle raids Japan from USS Hornet. j, Battle of Midway.

1992		Litho.	Perf. 14½x15	
1265	A179	2d Sheet of 10, #a.-j.	4.50	4.50

1992 Summer Olympics, Barcelona A180

Designs: 20b, Women's double sculls. 50b, Kayak, vert. 75b, Women's precision rapid-fire shooting. 1d, Judo, vert. 1.25d, Javelin, vert. 1.50d, Gymnastics, vault, vert. 3d, Windsurfing, vert. 5d, High jump. No. 1274, Women's 200-meter backstroke. No. 1275, Table tennis.

1992, Aug. 10		Litho.	Perf. 14	
1266	A180	20b multicolored	.15	.15
1267	A180	50b multicolored	.15	.15
1268	A180	75b multicolored	.18	.18
1269	A180	1d multicolored	.25	.25
1270	A180	1.25d multicolored	.30	.30
1271	A180	1.50d multicolored	.35	.35
1272	A180	3d multicolored	.75	.75
1273	A180	5d multicolored	1.20	1.20
		Nos. 1266-1273 (8)	3.33	3.33

Souvenir Sheets

1274	A180	18d multicolored	4.50	4.50
1275	A180	18d multicolored	4.50	4.50

1992 Winter Olympics, Albertville — A181

Designs: 2d, Downhill skiing, vert. 10d, Fourman bobsled, vert. 12d, Ski jumping, vert. 15d, Slalom skiing.
No. 1280, Men's 500 meter speedskating. No. 1281, Pairs figure skating, vert.

1992, Aug. 10		Litho.	Perf. 14	
1276-1279	A181	Set of 4	10.00	10.00

Souvenir Sheets

1280-1281	A181	18d each	4.50	4.50

Dinosaurs — A182

1992, Sept. 21		Litho.	Perf. 14	
1283	A182	20b Dryosaurus	.15	.15
1284	A182	25b Saurolophus	.15	.15
1284A	A182	50b Allosaurus	.15	.15
1284B	A182	75b Fabrosaurus	.18	.18
1284C	A182	1d Deinonychus	.25	.25
1285	A182	1.25d Cetiosaurus	.32	.32
1286	A182	1.50d Camptosaurus	.38	.38
1286A	A182	2d Ornithosuchus	.50	.50
1287	A182	3d Spinosaurus	.75	.75
1288	A182	5d Ornithomimus	1.25	1.25
1289	A182	10d Kentrosaurus	2.50	2.50
1290	A182	12d Schlermochus	3.00	3.00
		Nos. 1283-1290 (12)	9.58	9.58

Souvenir Sheets

1291	A182	25d like #1284A	6.00	6.00
1292	A182	25d like #1286A	6.00	6.00
1292A	A182	25d like #1285	6.00	6.00

Genoa '92.

Walt Disney's Goofy, 60th Anniv. — A183

Scenes from Disney cartoon films: 50b, Orphan's Benefit, 1934, 1941. 75b, Moose Hunters, 1937. 1d, Mickey's Amateurs, 1937. 1.25d, Lonesome Ghosts, 1937. 5d, Boat Builders, 1938. 7d, The Whalers, 1938. 10d, Goofy and Wilbur, 1939. 15d, Saludos Amigos, 1941. No. 1301, The Band Concert, 1935, vert. No. 1302, Goofy today, vert.

1992		Litho.	Perf. 14x13½	
1293	A183	50b multicolored	.15	.15
1294	A183	75b multicolored	.18	.18
1295	A183	1d multicolored	.22	.22
1296	A183	1.25d multicolored	.30	.30
1297	A183	5d multicolored	1.10	1.10
1298	A183	7d multicolored	1.75	1.75
1299	A183	10d multicolored	2.50	2.50
1300	A183	15d multicolored	3.50	3.50
		Nos. 1293-1300 (8)	9.70	9.70

Souvenir Sheets
Perf. 13½x14

1301	A183	20d multicolored	4.50	4.50
1302	A183	20d multicolored	5.00	5.00

Discovery of America, 500th Anniv. A184

Designs: 5d, Santa Maria. 12d, Pinta, Santa Maria, and Nina. 18d, Tree branch, green-winged macaw, vert.

1992, Oct.		Litho.	Perf. 14	
1303	A184	5d multicolored	1.10	1.10
1304	A184	12d multicolored	2.75	2.75

Souvenir Sheet

1305	A184	18d multicolored	4.00	4.00

Golf — A186

Pres. Jarwara playing golf and: 20b, Map, flag of Australia. 1d, Trophy, Gambian flag. 1.50d, Gambian flag. 2d, Map, flag of Japan. 3d, Map, flag of US. 5d, Trophy, 1985, Gambian flag (small portrait only). No. 1312, Map, flag of Scotland. 12d, Map, flag of Italy. No. 1312B, Pres. Jawara about to tee off. No. 1312C, Gambian flag (small portrait), horiz.

1992		Litho.	Perf. 14	
1306	A186	20b multicolored	.15	.15
1307	A186	1d multicolored	.25	.25
1308	A186	1.50d multicolored	.38	.38
1309	A186	2d multicolored	.48	.48
1310	A186	3d multicolored	.75	.75
1311	A186	5d multicolored	1.25	1.25
1312	A186	10d multicolored	2.50	2.50
1312A	A186	12d multicolored	3.00	3.00
		Nos. 1306-1312A (8)	8.76	8.76

Souvenir Sheets

1312B	A186	10d multicolored	2.50	2.50
1312C	A186	18d multicolored	4.00	4.00

No. 1306, Royal Melbourne Golf Course, Australia. No. 1309, Shinonoseki Golf Course, Japan. No. 1310, US Open, Pebble Beach. No. 1312, St. Andrew's Golf Course, Scotland. No. 1312A, Italian Open, Monticello, Milan.
Issued: 20b, 2d, 5d, #1312, 1312B, Dec. 8; others, Oct.

Souvenir Sheet

Ellis Island, New York City — A187

1992, Oct. 28 Litho. *Perf. 14*
1313 A187 18d multicolored 4.50 4.50

Postage Stamp Mega Event '92, New York City.

The Gambia · Christmas 1992
Raphael - THE HOLY FAMILY 50b Christmas A188

Details or entire paintings: 50b, The Holy Family, by Raphael. 75b, Madonna and Child with St. Elizabeth and the Infant St. John (Small Holy Family), by Raphael. 1d, The Holy Family as the Little Holy Family, by Raphael. 1.25d, Escape to Egypt, by Broederlam. 1.50d, Flight Into Egypt, by Isenbrant. No. 1319, The Flight into Egypt, by Cosimo Tura. No. 1320, Flight into Egypt, by Master of Hoogstraelen. No. 1321, The Holy Family, by El Greco. 4d, The Holy Family, by Bernard Van Orley. 5d, Holy Family with Infant Jesus Sleeping, by Charles Le Brun. 10d, Rest on the Flight to Egypt, by Gentileschi. 12d, Rest on the Flight to Egypt, by Orazio Gentileschi. No. 1326, The Holy Family, by Giorgione. No. 1327, Rest on the Flight to Egypt, by Simone Cantarino. No. 1328, The Flight to Egypt, by Vittore Carpaccio.

1992, Nov. 3 Litho. *Perf. 13¹/₂x14*
1314 A188 50b multicolored .15 .15
1315 A188 75b multicolored .16 .16
1316 A188 1d multicolored .25 .25
1317 A188 1.25d multicolored .30 .30
1318 A188 1.50d multicolored .40 .40
1319 A188 2d multicolored .45 .45
1320 A188 2d multicolored .50 .50
1321 A188 2d multicolored .50 .50
1322 A188 4d multicolored 1.00 1.00
1323 A188 5d multicolored 1.25 1.25
1324 A188 10d multicolored 2.50 2.50
1325 A188 12d multicolored 2.75 2.75
  Nos. 1314-1325 (12) 10.21 10.21

Souvenir Sheets
1326 A188 25d multicolored 5.50 5.50
1327 A188 25d multicolored 6.00 6.00
1328 A188 25d multicolored 6.00 6.00

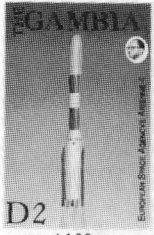

A189 A190

A191

A192

A193 D7

Anniversaries and Events
A194 A195

Designs: No. 1329, Ariane 4 rocket. No. 1330, Berlin airlift, Konrad Adenauer. No. 1331, LZ127 Graf Zeppelin. 6d, Jentink's duiker. 7d, World map. 9d, Wolfgang Amadeus Mozart. No. 1335, America's Cup yacht Enterprise, 1930. No. 1336, Imperial parrot. No. 1337, Lions Intl. emblem. No. 1338, American Space shuttle. 15d, Prisoners of war returning home, Adenauer. 18d, First rigid airship, LZ1. No. 1341, European Space Agency's Hermes space shuttle. No. 1342, Scene from "The Marriage of Figaro." No. 1343, Face of Adenauer. No. 1344, Count Ferdinand von Zeppelin. No. 1345, Earth as seen from space.

1992-93 Litho. *Perf. 14*
1329 A189 2d multicolored .50 .50
1330 A191 2d multicolored .50 .50
1331 A191 2d multicolored .50 .50
1332 A192 6d multicolored 1.50 1.50
1333 A193 7d multicolored 1.75 1.75
1334 A191 9d multicolored 2.25 2.25
1335 A194 10d multicolored 2.50 2.50
1336 A191 10d multicolored 2.50 2.50
1337 A195 10d multicolored 2.50 2.50
1338 A189 12d multicolored 3.00 3.00
1339 A191 15d multicolored 3.75 3.75
1340 A191 18d multicolored 4.50 4.50
  Nos. 1329-1340 (12) 25.75 25.75

Souvenir Sheets
1341 A189 18d multicolored 4.50 4.50
1342 A190 18d multicolored 4.50 4.50
1343 A191 18d multicolored 4.50 4.50
1344 A191 18d multicolored 4.50 4.50
1345 A192 18d multicolored 4.50 4.50

Intl. Space Year (#1329, 1338, 1341). Wolfgang Amadeus Mozart, bicent. of death (#1334, 1342). Konrad Adenauer, 25th anniv. of death (#1330, 1339, 1343). Count Zeppelin, 75th anniv. of death (#1331, 1340, 1344). Earth Summit, Rio de Janeiro (#1332, 1336, 1345). Intl. Conf. on Nutrition, Rome (#1333). America's Cup yacht race (#1335). Lions Intl., 75th anniv. (#1337).

Issue dates: Nos. 1333, 1335, 1339, 1343, Jan. 1993. Others, Dec. 1992.

Peace Corps, 25th Anniv. A196

1993, Feb.
1346 A196 2d multicolored .50 .50

Elvis Presley, 15th Anniv. of Death (in 1992) — A197

Designs: a, Portrait. b, With guitar. c, Holding microphone.

1993
1347 A197 3d Strip of 3, #a.-c. 2.25 2.25

Miniature Sheets

Mighty Casey
Baseball Films — A198

Movie and stars: No. 1348a, Casey at the Bat, Wallace Beery, 1927, Elliott Gould, 1986. b, Babe Comes Home, Anna Q. Nilsson, Babe Ruth, 1927. c, Elmer the Great, Joe E. Brown, 1933. d, The Naughty Nineties, Bud Abbott and Lou Costello, 1945. e, Take Me Out to the Ball Game, Frank Sinatra, Gene Kelly, Esther Williams, 1949. f, Damn Yankees, Tab Hunter, Gwen Verdon, 1958. g, The Pride of St. Louis, Dan Dailey, 1952. h, Brewster's Millions, John Candy, Richard Pryor, 1985.

No. 1349a, The Jackie Robinson Story, Jackie Robinson, Ruby Dee, 1950. b, Bang the Drum Slowly, Robert DeNiro, 1973. c, The Bingo Long Traveling All-Stars & Motor Kings, James Earl Jones, Billy Dee Williams, 1976. d, Bull Durham, Kevin Costner, Susan Sarandon, 1988. e, Eight Men Out, eight actors, 1988. f, Field of Dreams, Ray Liotta, 1989. g, Major League, Charlie Sheet, 1989. h, Mr. Baseball, Tom Selleck, 1992.

No. 1350, The Babe, John Goodman, 1992. No. 1351, The Natural, Robert Redford, vert. No. 1351A, The Winning Team, Ronald Reagan. No. 1351B, A League of Their Own, Tom Hanks, Madonna, vert.

1993, Mar. 25 Litho. *Perf. 13*
1348 A198 3d Sheet of 8, #a.-h. 6.00 6.00
1349 A198 3d Sheet of 8, #a.-h. 6.00 6.00

Souvenir Sheet
1350 A198 20d multicolored 5.00 5.00
1351 A198 20d multicolored 5.00 5.00
1351A A198 20d multicolored 5.00 5.00
1351B A198 20d multicolored 5.00 5.00

Miniature Sheets

Louvre Museum, Bicent.
THE GAMBIA D3 A199

Details from paintings, by Jacques-Louis David (1748-1825): Nos. 1352a-b, Oath of the Horatii (diff. details). c, The Love of Paris & Helen. d, Rape of the Sabine Women. e, Leonidas of Thermopylae. f-h, Napoleon Crowning Josephine (left, center, right).

Details from paintings, by Antoine (c. 1588-1648) and Louis (1593-1648) Le Nain: No. 1353a, Inside Home of Peasants. b-c, The Tobacco Smokers (diff. details). d, The Cart. e, Peasants' Meal. f-g, Interior Portraits (diff. details). h, The Forge.

Details or entire paintings, by Leonardo Da Vinci: No. 1354a, St. John the Baptist. b, Virgin of the Rocks. c, Bacchus. d, Woman from the Court of Milan. e, The Virgin of the Rocks (detail). f, Mona Lisa. g, Mona Lisa (detail of hands). h, Two Horsemen, Study of the Horse.

No. 1355, Allegory of Victory, by Mathieu Le Nain (1607-1677). No. 1356, The Artist and Her Daughter, by Elisabeth Vigee-Lebrun (1755-1842).

1993, Jan. 7 Litho. *Perf. 12*
1352 A199 3d Sheet of 8, #a.-h. 6.00 6.00
1353 A199 3d Sheet of 8, #a.-h. 6.00 6.00
1354 A199 3d Sheet of 8, #a.-h. 6.00 6.00

Souvenir Sheets
Perf. 14¹/₂
1355 A199 20d multicolored 5.00 5.00
1356 A199 20d multicolored 5.00 5.00

Nos. 1355-1356 each contain one 55x88mm stamp.

Miniature Sheet

Animals of West Africa — A200

Designs: No. 1358a, Giraffe. b, Baboon. c, Caracal. d, Large-spotted genet. e, Bushbuck. f, Red-fronted gazelle. g, Red-flanked duiker. h, Cape buffalo. i, African civet. j, Side-striped jackal. k, Ratel. l, Striped polecat.

No. 1359a, Vervet. b, Blackish-green guenon. c, Long-tailed pangolin. d, Leopard. e, Elephant. f, Hunting dog. g, Spotted hyena. h, Lion. i, Hippopotamus. j, Nile crocodile. k, Aardvark. l, Warthog.

1993, Apr. 5 Litho. *Perf. 14*
1358 A200 2d Sheet of 12, #a.-l. 9.00 9.00
1359 A200 5d Sheet of 12, #a.-l. 9.00 9.00

Souvenir Sheet
1360 A200 20d like #1359b 5.00 5.00

No. 1360 printed in continuous design with black frameline around stamp. A number has been reserved for an additional value in this set.

Long-Tailed Pangolin — A201

Pangolin in various positions on tree limb.

1993, Apr. 5
1362 A201 1.25d multicolored .32 .32
1363 A201 1.50d multicolored .38 .38
1364 A201 2d multicolored .50 .50
1365 A201 5d multicolored 1.25 1.25
  Nos. 1362-1365 (4) 2.45 2.45

Souvenir Sheet
1366 A201 20d like #1363 5.00 5.00

World Wildlife Federation.

Birds
A202 A203

Designs: 1.25d, Osprey. 1.50d, Egyptian vulture, horiz. 2d, Martial eagle. 3d, Ruppell's griffon vulture, horiz. 5d, Auger buzzard. 8d, Greater kestrel. 10d, Secretary bird. 15d, Bateleur eagle, horiz.

No. 1375a, Rose-ringed parakeet. b, Variable sunbird. c, Red-billed hornbill. d, Red-billed fire-finch. e, Common go-away bird. f, Crimson-breasted shrike. g, Gray-headed bush-shrike. h, Nicator. i, Egyptian plover. j, Congo peacock. k, Greater painted snipe. l, Crowned crane.
#1376, Verreaux's eagle. #1377, Tawny owl.

1993, Apr. 15 Litho. *Perf. 14*
1367 A202 1.25d multicolored .32 .32
1368 A202 1.50d multicolored .38 .38
1369 A202 2d multicolored .50 .50
1370 A202 3d multicolored .75 .75
1371 A202 5d multicolored 1.25 1.25
1372 A202 8d multicolored 2.00 2.00
1373 A202 10d multicolored 2.50 2.50
1374 A202 15d multicolored 3.75 3.75
  Nos. 1367-1374 (8) 11.45 11.45

Miniature Sheet
1375 A203 2d Sheet of 12, #a.-l. 6.00 6.00

Souvenir Sheets

1376 A202 20d multicolored 5.00 5.00
1377 A202 20d multicolored 5.00 5.00

Nos. 1376-1377 each contain one 56x42mm stamp.

Aviation Anniversaries — A204

Designs: No. 1379, Guyot balloon, 1785, vert. No. 1380, Dr. Hugo Eckener, zeppelin LZ3 in flight. No. 1381, Sopwith Snipe. No. 1382, Eckener, LZ3 moored to ground. 8d, Eckener, Graf Zeppelin. 10d, Balloon, Comte D'Artois, 1785, vert. 15d, Royal Aircraft Factory S.E.5. No. 1386, Avro 504K. No. 1387, Eckener, LZ3 in flight, diff. No. 1388, Blanchard's flying ship, 1785, vert.

1993, May Litho. *Perf. 14*

1379	A204	2d	multicolored	.50	.50
1380	A204	2d	multicolored	.50	.50
1381	A204	5d	multicolored	1.25	1.25
1382	A204	5d	multicolored	1.25	1.25
1383	A204	8d	multicolored	2.00	2.00
1384	A204	10d	multicolored	2.50	2.50
1385	A204	15d	multicolored	3.75	3.75
			Nos. 1379-1385 (7)	11.75	11.75

Souvenir Sheets

1386 A204 20d multicolored 5.00 5.00
1387 A204 20d multicolored 5.00 5.00
1388 A204 20d multicolored 5.00 5.00

Dr. Hugo Eckener, 125th birth anniv. (#1380, 1382, 1383, 1387). Royal Air Force, 75th anniv. (#1381, 1385, 1386).

Nos. 1379, 1384, 1388 are airmail.

Coronation of Queen Elizabeth II, 40th Anniv. — A205

Designs: a, 2d, Official coronation photograph. b, 5d, Orb and Scepter. c, 8d, Winston Churchill. d, 10d, Queen during Trooping of the Color.

20d, Portrait, by Joe King, 1972.

1993, June 2 *Perf. 13½x14*

1389 A205 Sheet, 2 each #a.-d. 12.50 12.50

Souvenir Sheet

Perf. 14

1390 A205 20d multicolored 5.00 5.00

No. 1390 contains one 28x42mm stamp.

Miniature Sheet

A206

Benz Automobiles: a, 1894 Benz Velo. b, 1894 Benz. c, 1885 Benz. d, 1905 Benz Mannheim. e, 1892 Benz. f, 1900 Benz, blue. g, 1911 Benz. h, 1893 Benz Velo. i, 1900 Benz, black. j, 1900 Benz, red. k, 1911 Benz, front view. l, 1885 Benz, rear view.

20d, 1900 Benz, diff.

Ford automobiles: No. 1392a, Henry Ford, age 30, 1910 Model T. b, 1896, green seat. c, Henry Ford with Barney Oldfield and 1902 racing car, 999. d, 1896, Henry Ford with bicycle. e, 1903 Model A. f, 1908 Model T, top down. g, 1908 Model T, top up. h, 1906 Model K. i, 1931 Model A. j, 1906 Model A. k, 1906 Model N. l, 1905 Model F.

No. 1394, 1896, red seat.

1993, June 7 *Perf. 14*

1391 A206 2d Sheet of 12, #a.-l. 6.00 6.00
1392 A206 2d Sheet of 12, #a.-l. 6.00 6.00

Souvenir Sheet

1393 A206 20d multicolored 5.00 5.00
1394 A206 20d multicolored 5.00 5.00

1st Benz 4-wheel automobile, cent. (#1391, 1393).

1st engine by Henry Ford, cent. (#1392, 1394).

Miniature Sheets

Entertainers — A207

Designs: No. 1395a, Buddy Holly. b, Otis Redding. c, Bill Haley. d, Dinah Washington. e, Musical instruments. f, Ritchie Valens. g, Clyde McPhatter. h, Elvis Presley.

#1396a-1396i, Various pictures of Madonna.

#1397a-1397i, Various pictures of Elvis Presley.

#1398a-1398i, Various pictures of Marilyn Monroe.

1993, July 26 Litho. *Perf. 14*

1395	A207	3d	Sheet of 8, #a.-h.	6.00	6.00
1396	A207	3d	Sheet of 9, #a.-i.	6.75	6.75
1397	A207	3d	Sheet of 9, #a,-i.	6.75	6.75
1398	A207	3d	Sheet of 9, #a.-i.	6.75	6.75
			Nos. 1395-1398 (4)	26.25	26.25

Cats and Dogs A208

Cats: No. 1399a, Siamese. b, Colorpoint longhair. c, Burmese. d, Birman. e, Snowshoe. f, Tonkinese. g, Foreign shorthair. h, Balinese. i, Oriental shorthair. j, Foreign shorthair, diff. k, Colorpoint longhair, diff. l, Colorpoint longhair, diff.

No. 1401, Colorpoint shorthair, vert. No. 1402, Burmese, vert.

Dogs: No. 1400a, Shih tzu. b, Skye terrier. c, Berner laufhund. d, Boxer. e, Welsh corgi (Queen Elizabeth II). f, Dumfrieshire. g, Lurcher. h, Welsh corgi (Princess Anne). i, Pekinese. j, Papillon. k, Otterhound. l, Pug.

No. 1403, Long-haired dachshund. No. 1404, Cairn terrier.

1993, Sept. 13 Litho. *Perf. 14*

1399 A208 2d Sheet of 12, #a.-l. 6.00 6.00
1400 A208 2d Sheet of 12, #a.-i. 6.00 6.00

Souvenir Sheets

1401 A208 20d multicolored 5.00 5.00
1402 A208 20d multicolored 5.00 5.00
1403 A208 20d multicolored 5.00 5.00
1404 A208 20d multicolored 5.00 5.00

Taipei '93 — A209

Designs: No. 1405, Fawang Si Pagoda, Song Shan Mt., Henan. No. 1406, Wanshoubao Pagoda, Shashi. No. 1407, Red Pavilion, Shibaozhai. No. 1408, Songyue Si Pagoda, Song Shan Mt., Henan. No. 1409, Bond Center, Hong Kong. No. 1410, Tianning Si Pagoda, Beijing. No. 1411, Xuanzhuang Pagoda, Xian, Shenxi. No. 1412, Forbidden City, Beijing.

Tang Dynasty funerary objects: No. 1413a, Camel. b, Horse and female rider. c, Camel, diff. d, Yellow-glazed horse. e, Camel, diff. f, Horse with saddle.

Pottery: No. 1414a, Vase. b, Small wine cup. c, Fahua type Mei-ping vase. d, Urn vase, export ware. e, Tureen. f, Lidded Potiche.

No. 1415, Standing Buddhas, Hallway of Upper Huayan Si Temple, Datong. No. 1416, Seated Buddha, Main Hall, Shanhua Si Temple, Datong, horiz.

1993, Sept. 27 Litho. *Perf. 14*

1405	A209	20b	multicolored	.15	.15
1406	A209	20b	multicolored	.15	.15
1407	A209	2d	multicolored	.50	.50
1408	A209	2d	multicolored	.50	.50
1409	A209	5d	multicolored	1.25	1.25
1410	A209	5d	multicolored	1.25	1.25
1411	A209	15d	multicolored	3.75	3.75
1412	A209	15d	multicolored	3.75	3.75
			Nos. 1405-1412 (8)	11.30	11.30

Miniature Sheets

1413 A209 5d Sheet of 6, #a.-f. 7.50 7.50
1414 A209 5d Sheet of 6, #a.-f. 7.50 7.50

Souvenir Sheets

1415 A209 18d multicolored 4.50 4.50
1416 A209 18d multicolored 4.50 4.50

With Bangkok '93 Emblem

Designs: No. 1417, Sanctuary of Prasat Phanom Wan. No. 1418, Lai Kham Vihan, Chiang Mai. No. 1419, Spirit Shrine, Bangkok. No. 1420, Walking Buddha, Wat Phra Si Ratana Mahathat. No. 1421, Buddha, Sukhothai's Wat Mahathat. No. 1422, Gopura of Prasat Phanom Rung. No. 1423, Prang of Prasat Hin Phimai. No. 1424, Slender Chedis, Wat Yai Chai, Mongkon.

Thai painting: No. 1425a, Early Fruit Stand. b, Scene in Chinese Style, Wat Bovornivet. c, Buddha Descends from Tauatimsa. d, Sang Thong Tales, Lai Kham Vihan. e, The Damned in Hell, Wah Suthat. f, King Sanjaya Travels on Elephant, Wat Suwannaram.

Thai Buddha sculpture: No. 1426a, U Thong C, 14th-15th cent. b, Adorned Seated, 17th cent. c, Phra Chai, 19th cent. d, Bronze, 14th cent. e, U Thong A, bronze. f, Crowned, 14th-15th cent.

No. 1427, Ceramics, horiz. No. 1428, Character in Khon, dance drama.

1993

1417	A209	20b	multicolored	.15	.15
1418	A209	20b	multicolored	.15	.15
1419	A209	2d	multicolored	.50	.50
1420	A209	2d	multicolored	.50	.50
1421	A209	5d	multicolored	1.25	1.25
1422	A209	5d	multicolored	1.25	1.25
1423	A209	15d	multicolored	3.75	3.75
1424	A209	15d	multicolored	3.75	3.75
			Nos. 1417-1424 (8)	11.30	11.30

Miniature Sheets

1425 A209 5d Sheet of 6, #a.-f. 7.50 7.50
1426 A209 5d Sheet of 6, #a.-f. 7.50 7.50

Souvenir Sheets

1427 A209 18d multicolored 4.50 4.50
1428 A209 18d multicolored 4.50 4.50

With Indopex '93 Emblem

Designs: No. 1429, Pura Taman Ayun (garden temple), Mongwi, Bali. No. 1430, Natl. monument with statue of Prince Diponegoro, Jakarta. No. 1431, Candi Jawi, East Java. No. 1432, Guardian at Singosari Palace, East Java. No. 1433, Monument of Irian Jaya, (liberation), Jakarta. No. 1434, Central Temple, Prambanan complex, Lara Djonggrang. No. 1435, "Date of the Year Temple," Panataran complex, East Java. No. 1436, Brahma & Siva Temples, Loro Jonggrang, Java.

Masks: No. 1437a, Telek Luh. b, Jero Gde. c, Barong Macan. d, Monkey. e, Mata Gde. f, Jauk Kras.

Paintings: No. 1438a, Tree Mask, Soedibio, 1978. b, Dry Lizard, Hendra Gunawan, 1977. c, The Corn Eater, Sudjana Kerton, 1988. d, Night Watchman, Djoko Pekik, 1988. e, Hunger, Kerton, 1984. f, Arje Player, Soedjojono, 1971.

No. 1439, Stone carving, Brahma & Gods, Borobudur, Java, horiz. No. 1440, Effigies of the Dead, Torajaland, horiz.

1993, Sept. 27 Litho. *Perf. 14*

1429	A209	20b	multicolored	.15	.15
1430	A209	20b	multicolored	.15	.15
1431	A209	2d	multicolored	.50	.50
1432	A209	2d	multicolored	.50	.50
1433	A209	5d	multicolored	1.25	1.25
1434	A209	5d	multicolored	1.25	1.25
1435	A209	15d	multicolored	3.75	3.75
1436	A209	15d	multicolored	3.75	3.75
			Nos. 1429-1436 (8)	11.30	11.30

Miniature Sheets

1437 A209 5d Sheet of 6, #a.-f. 7.50 7.50
1438 A209 5d Sheet of 6, #a.-f. 7.50 7.50

Souvenir Sheets

1439 A209 18d multicolored 4.50 4.50
1440 A209 18d multicolored 4.50 4.50

Miniature Sheet

Casey at the Bat — A210

Nos. 1441-1443: Characters and scenes from Disney's animated film Casey at the Bat.

1993, Oct. 25 Litho. *Perf. 14x13½*

1441 A210 2d Sheet of 9, #a.-i. 4.50 4.50

Souvenir Sheets

1442 A210 20d multicolored 5.00 5.00

Perf. 13½x14

1443 A210 20d multi, vert. 5.00 5.00

Picasso (1881-1973) A211

Copernicus (1473-1543) A212

Paintings: 2d, Woman with a Comb, 1906. 5d, The Mirror, 1932. 7d, Woman on a Pillow, 1969. 18d, The Three Dancers, 1925.

1993, Oct. 7 Litho. *Perf. 14*

1444-1446 A211 Set of 4 3.50 3.50

Souvenir Sheet

1447 A211 18d multicolored 4.50 4.50

1993, Oct. 7 *Perf. 14*

Designs: 5d, Early astronomical instrument. 10d, Telescope.

1448-1449 A212 Set of 2 3.75 3.75

Souvenir Sheet

Perf. 12x13

1450 A212 18d Copernicus 4.50 4.50

Polska '93 — A213

Paintings: 2d, Pont-Nuef, Paris, by Rudzka-Cybisowa, 1932. No. 1452, 10d, Honegger's Liturgical Symphony, by Bogusz, 1973. No. 1453, 10d, Niedzica castle. 18d, When You Enter Here, Whisper My Name Soundlessly, by Waniek, 1973.

1993, Oct. 7 *Perf. 14*

1451-1453 A213 Set of 3 5.50 5.50

Souvenir Sheet

1454 A213 18d multicolored 4.50 4.50

1994 World Cup Soccer Championships, US — A214

Players, country: 1.25d, Hannich, Hungary; Stopyra, France. 1.50d, Labd, Morocco; Lineker, England. 2d, Segota, Canada; Morozov, Russia. 3d, Roger Milla, Cameroun. 5d, Rodax, Australia; Weiss, Czech Republic. 10d, Claesen, Belgium; Bossis & Amoros, France. 12d, Candida, Brazil; Ramirez, Costa Rica. 15d, Silva, Brazil; Platini, France. No. 1463, Muller, Brazil; McDonald, Ireland,

horiz. No. 1463A, Buchwald and Matthaeus, Germany; Maradona, Argentina, horiz.

1993, Nov. 22 *Perf. 13½x14*

1455	A214	1.25d	multicolored	.32	.32
1456	A214	1.50d	multicolored	.38	.38
1457	A214	2d	multicolored	.50	.50
1458	A214	3d	multicolored	.75	.75
1459	A214	5d	multicolored	1.25	1.25
1460	A214	10d	multicolored	2.50	2.50
1461	A214	12d	multicolored	3.00	3.00
1462	A214	15d	multicolored	3.75	3.75
	Nos. 1455-1462 (8)			12.45	12.45

Souvenir Sheets

Perf. 13

1463	A214	25d	multicolored	6.25	6.25
1463A	A214	25d	multicolored	6.25	6.25

Christmas A215

Designs: 25b, 2d (No. 1467), 15d, Details or entire painting, Adoration of the Magi, by Rubens.

Details or entire woodcut by Durer: 1d, Holy Family with Joachim & Anna. 1.50d, The Annunciation, Life of the Virgin. 2d (No. 1468), The Virgin Mary Worshipped by Albrecht Bonstetten. 7d, Virgin on a Throne, Crowned by an Angel. 10d, The Holy Family with Two Angels in a Portico (detail).

Souvenir Sheets: No. 1472, 20d, Adoration of the Magi, by Rubens. No. 1473, 20d, The Holy Family with Two Angels in a Portico, (entire), by Durer, horiz.

1993, Dec. 1 *Perf. 13½x14, 14x13½*

1464-1473	A215	Set of 10	20.00	20.00

Fine Art — A216

Paintings by Rembrandt: 50b, A Man in a Cap. No. 1476, Man with a Gold Helmet. 7d, A Franciscan Monk. 15d, The Apostle Paul. 20d, Dr. Tulp Demonstrating the Anatomy of the Arm, horiz.

Paintings by Matisse: 1.50d, Portrait of Pierre Matisse. No. 1477, Portrait of Auguste Pellerin (II). 5d, Andre Derain. 12d, The Young Sailor (II). No. 1483, Pianist and Checker Players, horiz.

1993, Dec. 15 *Perf. 13½x14*

1474	A216	50b	multicolored	.15	.15
1475	A216	1.50d	multicolored	.38	.38
1476	A216	2d	multicolored	.50	.50
1477	A216	2d	multicolored	.50	.50
1478	A216	5d	multicolored	1.25	1.25
1479	A216	7d	multicolored	1.75	1.75
1480	A216	12d	multicolored	3.00	3.00
1481	A216	15d	multicolored	3.75	3.75
	Nos. 1474-1481 (8)			11.28	11.28

Souvenir Sheets

Perf. 14x13½

1482	A216	20d	multicolored	5.00	5.00
1483	A216	20d	multicolored	5.00	5.00

Winter Sports A217

Disney characters portraying sports: 50b, Ski ballet. 75b, Pairs figure skating. 1d, Speed skating. 1.25d, Biathlon. 4d, 4-Man bobsled. 5d, Luge. 7d, Figure skating. 10d, Downhill skiing. 15d, Ice hockey.

No. 1493, Cross country skiing. No. 1494, Mogul skiing.

1993, Dec. 20 *Perf. 13½x14*

1484-1492	A217	Set of 9	11.00	11.00

Souvenir Sheets

1493-1494	A217	20d each	5.00	5.00

A218

Hong Kong '94 — A219

Stamps, painting, Spring Garden-1846, by M. Bruce: No. 1495, Hong Kong #357, left detail. No. 1496, Right detail, #1000.

Museum of Qin Figures, Shaanxi Province, Tomb of First Emperor: No. 1497a, Qin warriors, horses. b, Warrior in battle dress. c, Armor clad warrior. d, Chariot driver. e, Dog. f, Qin warriors.

No. 1498, Show emblem, Hong Kong #253, vert.

1994, Feb. 18 **Litho.** *Perf. 14*

1495	A218	1.50d multicolored	.38	.38
1496	A218	1.50d multicolored	.38	.38
a.		Pair, #1495-1496	.75	.75

Miniature Sheet

1497	A219	1.50d Sheet of 6, #a.-f.	2.25	2.25

Souvenir Sheet

1498	A218	20d multicolored	5.00	5.00

Nos. 1495-1496 issued in sheets of 5 pairs. No. 1496a is a continuous design.

New Year 1994 (Year of the Dog) (#1497e, #1498).

New Year 1994 (Year of the Dog) — A220

Disney characters: 25b, Pluto the Racer. 50b, Fifi. 75b, Pluto, Jr. 1.25d, Goofy and Bowser. 1.50d, Butch. 2d, Toliver. 3d, Ronnie. 5d, Primo. 8d, Pluto's kid brother. 10d, Army mascot. 12d, Pluto and Dinah's pups. 18d, Bent Tail, Junior.

No. 1511, Pluto, Dinah. No. 1512, Eega Beeva, Dog Pflip, Goofy, horiz. No. 1513, Dinah's pups, Pluto.

1994, Apr. 11 **Litho.** *Perf. 13½x14*

1499-1510	A220	Set of 12	16.00	16.00

Souvenir Sheets

1511	A220	20d multicolored	5.00	5.00

Perf. 14x13½, 13½x14

1512	A220	20d multicolored	5.00	5.00
1513	A220	20d multicolored	5.00	5.00

Orchids A221

Designs: 1d, Oeceoclades maculata. 1.25d, Angraecum distichum. 2d, Plectrelminthus caudatus. 5d, Tridactyle tridactylites. 8d, Bulbophyllum lepidum. 10d, Angraecum eburneum. 12d, Eulophia guineensis. 15d, Angraecum eichleranum.

No. 1522, Ancistrochilus rothschildianus. No. 1523, Vanilla imperialis.

1994, May 1 *Perf. 14*

1514	A221	1d	multicolored	.25	.25
1515	A221	1.25d	multicolored	.32	.32
1516	A221	2d	multicolored	.50	.50
1517	A221	5d	multicolored	1.25	1.25
1518	A221	8d	multicolored	2.00	2.00
1519	A221	10d	multicolored	2.50	2.50
1520	A221	12d	multicolored	3.00	3.00
1521	A221	15d	multicolored	3.75	3.75
	Nos. 1514-1521 (8)			13.57	13.57

Souvenir Sheets

1522	A221	25d	multicolored	6.25	6.25
1523	A221	25d	multicolored	6.25	6.25

Easter A222

Disney characters celebrate Easter: 25b, 4d, 8d, 12d, Ludwig von Drake. 50b, Minnie, Daisy. 3d, Mickey. 5d, Donald. 10d, Goofy.

#1532, Von Drake. #1533, Mickey, Minnie.

1994, Apr. 11 **Litho.** *Perf. 13½x14*

1524-1531	A222	Set of 8	11.50	11.50

Souvenir Sheets

1532-1533	A222	20d each	5.00	5.00

Miniature Sheets of 6 or 8

Sierra Club, Cent. A223

Various views of: No. 1534a-1534b, Prince William Sound. c-d, The Serengeti. e-f, Ross Island.

No. 1535: a-c, Briksdal Fjord, vert. d-f, Yosemite, vert.

No. 1536: a-b, Tibetan Plateau, vert. c-d, Yellowstone, vert. e, Ross Island, vert. f, The Serengeti, vert. g, Mount Erebus, vert. h, Ansel Adams Wilderness, vert.

No. 1537: a-b, Ansel Adams Wilderness. c-d, Mount Erebus. e, Prince William Sound. f, Yellowstone. g, Tibetan Plateau. h, Sierra Club emblem.

1994, Apr. 25 *Perf. 14*

1534-1535	A223	5d #a.-f., each	7.50	7.50
1536-1537	A223	5d #a.-h., each	10.00	10.00

Miniature Sheets of 12

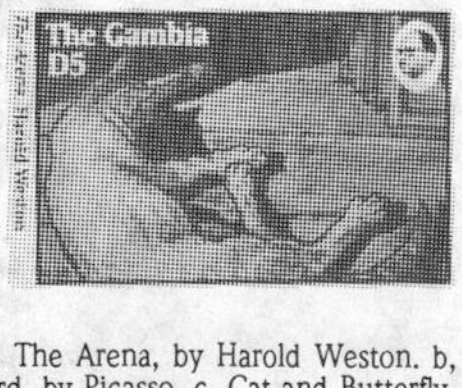

Paintings of Cats A224

No. 1538: a, The Arena, by Harold Weston. b, Cat Killing a Bird, by Picasso. c, Cat and Butterfly, by Hokusai. d, Winter: Cat on a Cushion, by Steinlen. e, Rattown Tigers, by Prang. f, Cat on the Floor, by Steinlen. g, Cat and Kittens. h, Cats Looking Over a Fence, by Prang. i, Little White Kittens into Mischief, by Ives. j, Cat Bathing, by Hiroshige. k, Playtime, by Tuck. l, Summer: Cat on a Balustrade, by Steinlen.

No. 1539, vert.: a, Girl with a Kitten, by Perronneau. b, Still Life with Cat and Fish, by Chardin. c, Tinkle a Cat. d, Naughty Puss! e, Cats, by Steinlen. f, Girl in Red with Cat and Dog, by Phillips. g, Cat, Butterfly and Begonia, by Haronobu. h, Cat and Kitten, by Higgins. i, Woman with a Cat, by Renoir. j, Minnie from Outskirts of Village, by Thrall. k, The Fisher, by Tuck. l, Artist and His Family, by Vaenius.

No. 1540, The Morning Rising, by Lepicie. No. 1541, The Graham Children, by Hogarth, vert.

1994, July 11 **Litho.** *Perf. 14*

1538-1539	A224	5d #a.-l, each	15.00	15.00

Souvenir Sheets

1540-1541	A224	20d each	5.00	5.00

Monkeys — A225

Designs: 1d, Patas. 1.50d, Collared mangabey. 2d, Black and white colobus. 5d, Mona. 8d, Kirk's colobus. 10d, Vervet. 12d, Red colobus. 15d, Guinea baboon.

Heads of: No. 1550, Collared mangabey. No. 1551, Guinea baboon.

1994, Aug. 1 **Litho.** *Perf. 14*

1542-1549	A225	Set of 8	12.00	12.00

Souvenir Sheets

1550-1551	A225	25d each	5.50	5.50

D-Day, 50th Anniv. A226

Designs: 50b, Free Dutch sloop Soema joins attack. 75b, HMS Belfast fires on beach defenses. 1d, USS Texas hits Point Du Hoc. 2d, Free French cruiser George Leygues.

20d, HMS Ramillies.

1994, Aug. 16

1552-1555	A226	Set of 4	1.00	1.00

Souvenir Sheet

1556	A226	20d multicolored	4.50	4.50

Miniature Sheet of 9

First Manned Moon Landing, 25th Anniv. A227

Designs: a, Yuri Gagarin. b, Valentina Tereshkova. c, Ham (chimpanzee). d, Alexei Leonov. e, Neil Armstrong. f, Svetlana Y. Savitskaya. g, Marc Garneau. h, Vladimir Komarov. i, Ulf Merbold.

30d, Neil Armstrong, Edwin "Buzz" Aldrin, Michael Collins at press conference.

1994, Aug. 16

1557	A227	2d #a.-i.	4.00	4.00

Souvenir Sheet

1558	A227	30d multicolored	6.00	6.00

A228

PHILAKOREA '94 — A229

Designs: 50b, Kungnakchon Hall, Naejangsa. 2d, Kettle of Popchusa. 3d, Pomun Tourist Resort.

Paper screen panels, episode from Sanguozhi, 18th cent. Choson Dynasty: a, Warriors on horseback. b, Soldiers atop fort. c, Shooting with bows

and arrows. d, Bowing before horse & rider. e, Fight on horseback. f, h, Charging on horses. g, Trudging through valley. i, j, Living peacefully.

20d, Traditional tombstone guardian, Taenung, vert.

1994, Aug. 16 *Perf. 14, 13½ (#1562)*
1559-1561 A228 Set of 3 ... 1.10 1.10
Miniature Sheet of 10
1562 A229 1d #a.-j. ... 2.00 2.00
Souvenir Sheet
1563 A228 20d multicolored ... 4.00 4.00

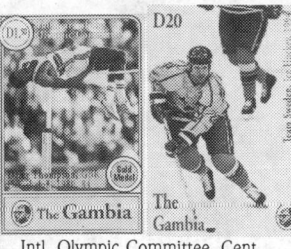

Intl. Olympic Committee, Cent.
A230   A231

Designs: 1.50d, Daley Thompson, Great Britain, decathalon, 1980, 1984. 5d, Heide Marie Rosendohl, Germany, long jump, 1972.
20d, Team Sweden, ice hockey, 1994.

1994, Aug. 16 *Perf. 14*
1564 A230 1.50d multicolored ... .30 .30
1565 A230 5d multicolored ... 1.00 1.00
Souvenir Sheet
1566 A231 20d multicolored ... 4.00 4.00

Butterflies
A232

Designs: 1d, Mylothris rhodope. 1.25d, Iolaphilus menas. 2d, Neptis nemetes. 5d, Antanartia delius. 8d, Acraea caecilia. 10d, Papilio nireus. 12d, Pipilio menestheus. 15d, Iolaphilus julus.
No. 1575, Colotis evippe. No. 1576, Bematistes epaea.

1994, Aug. 18 *Perf. 14*
1567-1574 A232 Set of 8 ... 11.00 11.00
Souvenir Sheets
1575-1576 A232 25d each ... 5.00 5.00

1994 World Cup Soccer Championships, US — A233

Designs: 50b, Bobby Charlton, England. 75b, Ferenc Puskas, Hungary. 1d, Paolo Rossi, Italy. 2d, Biri Biri, Gambian playing for Spain. 3d, Diego Maradona, Argentina. 8d, Johan Cruyff, Netherlands. 10d, Franz Beckenbauer, Germany. 15d, Thomas Dooley, US.
No. 1585, Pele, Brazil. No. 1586, Gordon Banks, England.

1994, Sept. 1
1577-1584 A233 Set of 8 ... 8.00 8.00
Souvenir Sheets
1585-1586 A233 25d each ... 5.00 5.00

Miniature Sheets of 9

Mushrooms
A234

Designs: No. 1587a, Agaricus campestris. b, Lepista nuda. c, Podaxis pistillaris. d, Oudemansiella radicata. e, Schizophyllum commune. f, Chlorophyllum molybdites. g, Hypholoma fasciculare. h, Mycena pura. i, Ganoderma lucidum.
No. 1588a, Suillus luteus. b, Bolbitius vitellinus. c, Clitocybe nebularis. d, Omphalotus olearius. e, Auricularia auricula. f, Macrolepiota rhacodes. g, Volvariella volvacea. h, Psilocybe coprophila. i, Suillus granulatus.
No. 1589, Cyathus striatus. No. 1590, Leucoagaricus naucina.

1994, Sept. 30
1587-1588 A234 5d #a.-i. each ... 9.00 9.00
Souvenir Sheets
1589-1590 A234 20d each ... 4.00 4.00

Expectant Madonna with St. Joseph - Anon., 15th Cent. French
Christmas 1994
THE GAMBIA   50b   A235
Christmas

French paintings: 50b, Expectant Madonna with St. Joseph, by unknown artist. 75b, Rest of the Holy Family, by Louis Le Nain. 1d, Rest on the Flight into Egypt, by Antoine Watteau. No. 1594, 2d, Noon, by Claude Lorrain. No. 1595, 2d, Rest on the Flight into Egypt, by Francois Boucher. No. 1596, 2d, Rest on the Flight into Egypt, by Jean-Honore Fragonard. 10d, The Holy Family, by Nicolas Poussin. 12d, Mystical Marriage of St. Catherine, by Pierre-Francois Mignard.
No. 1599, The Nativity by Torchlight, by Louis Le Nain. No. 1600, Adoration of the Shepherds, by Mathieu Le Nain.

1994, Dec. 5 *Litho.* *Perf. 13½x14*
1591-1598 A235 Set of 8 ... 6.75 6.75
Souvenir Sheets
1599-1600 A235 25d each ... 5.75 5.75

Miniature Sheet of 9

Gambia

Marilyn Monroe (1926-62), Actress — A236

Designs: No. 1601a-1601i, Various portraits. No. 1602, Wearing red dress. No. 1603, Wearing long, dangling earrings.

1995, Jan. 8 *Litho.* *Perf. 14*
1601 A236 4d #a.-i. ... 7.25 7.25
Souvenir Sheets
1602-1603 A236 25d each ... 5.00 5.00

Miniature Sheet of 9

GAMBIA

Elvis Presley (1935-77), Entertainer A237

Portraits: a, As child. b, Singing, later years. c, With mother. d, With wife, Priscilla. e, With gold medallion. f, Wearing army uniform. g, Singing, younger years. h, Wearing hat. i, With daughter, Lisa Marie.

1995, Jan. 8
1604 A237 4d #a.-i. ... 7.25 7.25

Miniature Sheets of 12

THE GAMBIA D2
Pteranodon

Dinosaurs — A238

No. 1605: a, Pteranodon. b, Archaeopteryx. c, Rhamphorhynchus. d, Ornithomimus. e, Stegosaurus. f, Heterodontosaurus. g, Lystrosaurus. h, Euoplocephalus. i, Coelophysis. j, Staurilosaurus. k, Giantoperis. l, Diarthrognathus.
No. 1606: a, Archaeopteryx, diff. b, Vangehuanosaurus. c, Ceolophysis, diff. d, Plateosaurus. e, Baryonyx. f, Ornitholestes. g, Dryosaurus. h, Estemmenosuchus. i, Macroplata. j, Shonisaurus. k, Muraeonosaurus. l, Archelon.
No. 1607, Bactrosaurus. No. 1608, Tyrannosaurus, vert. No. 1609, Triceratops, vert. No. 1610, Spinosaurus.

1995 *Litho.* *Perf. 14*
1605 A238 2d #a.-l. ... 5.25 5.25
1606 A238 3d #a.-l. ... 8.00 8.00
Souvenir Sheets
1607 A238 20d multi ... 4.50 4.50
1608 A238 22d multi ... 4.75 4.75
1609-1610 A238 25d each ... 5.50 5.50

Miniature Sheet of 4

New Year 1995 (Year of the Boar) — A239

Stylized boars. Chinese inscriptions in: a, Green. b, Blue violet. c, White. d, Black.
10d, Three boars.

1995, May 4 *Perf. 14½*
1611 A239 3d #a.-d. ... 2.75 2.75
Souvenir Sheet
1612 A239 10d multicolored ... 2.25 2.25

The GAMBIA D2
GREAT WHITE EGRET

Water Birds A240

Designs: 2d, Great white egret. 8d, Hammerkop. 10d, Shoveler. 12d, Crowned crane.
No. 1617a, Pintail. b, Fulvous tree duck (a). c, Garganey. d, White-faced tree duck. e, White-backed duck. f, Egyptian goose. g, Pigmy goose. h, Little bittern (k). i, Redshank. j, Ringed plover. k, Black-winged stilt. l, Squacco heron (k).
No. 1618, Ferruginous duck. No. 1619, Moorhen.

1995, May 8 *Perf. 14*
1613-1616 A240 Set of 4 ... 7.00 7.00
Miniature Sheet of 12
1617 A240 3d #a.-l. ... 8.00 8.00
Souvenir Sheets
1618-1619 A240 25d each ... 5.50 5.50

THE GAMBIA

ECOWAS — A241

Designs: 2d, Free movement of people in Gambia. 5d, Captain Yaya AJJ Jammeh, Chairman of Arm Force Provisional Ruling Council, Head of State.

1995, May 30 *Litho.* *Perf. 14*
1620 A241 2d multicolored ... .45 .45
1621 A241 5d multicolored ... 1.10 1.10

THE GAMBIA D8
LEATHER BACK TURTLE

Marine Life A242

No. 1622, vert: a, Multicolored parrot fish. b, Sparisoma viride. c, Queen parrot fish. d, Bicolor parrot fish.
No. 1623: a, Leatherback turtle. b, Tiger shark. c, Surgeon fish. d, Emperor angelfish. e, Blue parro fish. f, Triggerfish. g, Sea horse. h, Lionfish. i, Moray eel. j, Red fin butterflyfish. k, Octopus. l, Ray.
No. 1624, Holacanthus ciliaris. No. 1625, Angelichthys isabelita.

1995, June 20
1622 A242 8d Strip of 4, #a.-d. ... 7.00 7.00
Miniature Sheet of 12
1623 A242 3d #a.-l. ... 8.00 8.00
Souvenir Sheets
1624-1625 A242 25d each ... 5.50 5.50

GAMBIA D3
1945-1995

UN, 50th Anniv. — A243

Designs: No. 1626a, 3d, Girls. b, 5d, Woman helping girl at blackboard. c, 8d, Girl writing on blackboard.
25d, Nurse holding baby on scales.

1995, July 6
1626 A243 Strip of 3, #a.-c. ... 3.50 3.50
Souvenir Sheet
1627 A243 25d multicolored ... 5.50 5.50

Miniature Sheet of 8

World War II Motion Pictures A244

Movie stars: No. 1628a, Peter Lawford. b, Gene Tierney. c, Dana Andrews. c, Groucho, Gummo Marx. d, James Stewart. e, Chico, Harpo Marx. f, Tyrone Power. g, Cary Grant, Ingrid Bergman. h, Veronica Lake.
Motion pictures: No. 1629, A Lady Fights Back No. 1630, Desert Victory.

1995, July 6
1628 A244 3d #a.-h + label ... 5.25 5.25
Souvenir Sheets
1629-1630 A244 25d each ... 5.50 5.50

Miniature Sheet of 6

The Gambia D5

VJ Day, 50th Anniv. A245

No. 1631: a, Fairey Firefly. b, Fairey Barracuda II. c, Vickers Supermarine Seafire II. d, HMS Repulse. e, HMS Illustrious. f, HMS Exeter.
25d, Bomber being shot down by 3-stack cruiser.

1995, Aug. 1
1631 A245 5d #a.-f. + label ... 6.75 6.75
Souvenir Sheet
1632 A245 25d multicolored ... 5.50 5.50

FAO, 50th Anniv. — A246

Carrying sacks of grain: No. 1633a, 3d, Woman in pink. b, 5d, Two people. c, 8d, Man. 25d, Fisherman with net.

1995, Aug. 1   Litho.   Perf. 14
1633 A246   Strip of 3, #a.-c.   3.50 3.50
Souvenir Sheet
1634 A246 25d multicolored   5.50 5.50
No. 1633 is a continuous design.

Nobel Prize Winners — A247

Recipients: 2d, Kenichi Fukui, chemistry, 1981. 3d, Gustav Stresemann, peace, 1929. 5d, Thomas Mann, literature, 1929. 8d, Albert Schweitzer, peace, 1952. 12d, Leo Esaki, physics, 1973. 15d, Lech Walsea, peace, 1983.
No. 1635a, Marie Curie, chemistry, 1911. b, Adolf Butenandt, chemistry, 1939. c, Tonegawa Susumu, medicine, 1987. d, Nelly Sachs, literature, 1966. e, Kawabata Yasunari, literature, 1968. f, Yukawa Hideki, physics, 1949. g, Paul Ehrlich, medicine, 1908. h, Sato Eisaku, peace, 1974. i, Carl von Ossietzky, peace, 1935.
15d, Willy Brandt, peace, 1971.

1995, Aug. 1
1634A-1634F A247   Set of 6   10.00 10.00
Miniature Sheet of 9
1635 A247   5d #a.-i.   10.00 10.00
Souvenir Sheet
1636 A247 25d multicolored   5.50 5.50

Rotary Intl., 50th Anniv. A248

Designs: 15d, Paul Haris, Rotary emblem. 20d, Natl. flag, Rotary emblem.

1995, Aug. 1
1637 A248 15d multicolored   3.25 3.25
Souvenir Sheet
1638 A248 20d multicolored   4.50 4.50

Miniature Sheets of 3

1995 Boy Scout Jamboree, Holland — A249

How to tie the lariat: No. 1639a, shown. b, Second step. c, Completed.
How to tie bowline: No. 1640a, 12d, First step. b, 10d, Second step. c, 5d, Completed.
No. 1641, Bowline used to lift injured scout. No. 1642, Hitch used in lifesaving lift.

1995, Aug. 1
1639   A249   2d #a.-c.   1.40 1.40

1640   A249   #a.-c.   6.00 6.00
Souvenir Sheets
1641-1642 A249 25d each   5.50 5.50

Queen Mother, 95th Birthday A250

No. 1643: a, Drawing. b, Bright blue hat, dress. c, Formal portrait. d, Green hat, dress. 25d, Pale blue & white dress, blue hat.

1995, Aug. 1   Perf. 13½×14
1643 A250   5d Strip or block of 4, #a.-d.   4.50 4.50
Souvenir Sheet
1644 A250 25d multicolored   5.50 5.50
No. 1643 was issued in sheets of 8 stamps.

1996 Summer Olympics, Atlanta — A251

Designs: 1d, Bruce Jenner, US, decathlon. 1.25d, Greg Louganis, US, diving. 1.50d, Michael Gross, Germany 50-meter butterfly. 2d, Vasily Alexeev, USSR, weight lifting. 3d, Patrick Ewing, US, Juan Antonio Corbalan, Spain, basketball. 5d, Men's volleyball, US v. Brazil. 10d, John Svenden, West Germany, Armando Fernandez, US, water polo. 15d, Pertti Karppinen, Finland, single sculls.
No. 1653, vert: a, Stefano Cerioni, Italy, fencing. b, Alberto Covo, Italy, 10,000-meter run. c, Mary Lou Retton, US, women's gymnastics. d, Vladimir Artemov, USSR, men's gymnastics. e, Florence Griffith-Joyner, US, 400-meter relay. f, Brazil, soccer. g, Nelson Valis, US, 1000-meter sprint cycling. h, Cheryl Miller, US, women's basketball.
No. 1654, Karen Stives, US, equestrian. No. 1655, Edwin Moses, US, 400-meter hurdles, vert.

1995, Aug. 17
1645-1652 A251   Set of 8   8.50 8.50
Miniature Sheet of 8
1653   A251   3d #a.-h.   5.25 5.25
Souvenir Sheets
1654-1655 A251 25d each   5.50 5.50
Volleyball, cent. (#1650).

Rotary, Intl., 90th Anniv., 1995 Boy Scout Jamboree, Holland A252

Designs: 2d, Gambia Rotary contributing to education. No. 1657, 5d, Wood Badge course, Yundum, 1980. No. 1658, 5d, M.J.E. Sambou, organizing scout commissioner, vert.

1995, Sept. 5
1656-1658 A252   Set of 3   2.75 2.75

Flowers — A253

Designs: 2d, Zantedeschia rehmannii. 5d, Euadenia eminens. 10d, Passiflora vitifolia. 15d, Dietes grandiflora.
No. 1663: a, Canarina abyssinica. b, Nerine bowdenii. c, Zantedeschia aethiopica. d, Aframomum sceptrum. e, Schotia brachypetala. f, Catharanthus roseus. g, Protea grandiceps. h, Plumbago capensis. i, Uncarina grandidieri.
No. 1664: a, Kigelia africana. b, Hibiscus schizopetalus. c, Dombeya mastersii. d, Agapanthus orientalis. e, Strelitzia reginae. f, Spathodea campanulata. g, Rhodolaena bakeriana. h, Gazania rigens. i, Ixianthes retzioides.
No. 1665, Eulophia quartiniana. No. 1666, Gloriosa simplex.

1995, Oct. 2   Litho.   Perf. 14
1659-1662 A253   Set of 4   7.00 7.00
Miniature Sheets of 9
1663-1664 A253   3d #a.-i., each   6.00 6.00
Souvenir Sheets
1665-1666 A253 25d each   5.50 5.50

SOS Children's Villages A254

Designs: No. 1667, 2d, Children playing near houses. No. 1668, 2d, Aid worker with child, vert. 5d, Children.

1995, Oct. 9   Litho.   Perf. 14
1667-1669 A254   Set of 3   2.00 2.00

Miniature Sheets of 9

Entertainers A255

Rock & roll stars: No. 1670: a, Roy Orbison. b, Mick Jagger. c, Bruce Springsteen. d, Jimi Hendrix. e, Bill Haley. f, Gene Vincent. g, Buddy Holly. h, Jerry Lee Lewis. i, Chuck Berry.
Nos. 1671a-1671i, Various pictures of James Dean.
No. 1672, James Dean. No. 1673, Elvis Presley.

1995, Dec. 1   Litho.   Perf. 13½x14
1670-1671 A255   3d #a.-i.   6.00 6.00
Souvenir Sheets
1672-1673 A255 25d each   5.50 5.50
Motion pictures, cent. (#1671-1672).

Christmas A256

Details or entire paintings: 75b, Madonna of the Valley. 1d, Madonna, by Giotto. 2d, The Flight into Egypt, by Luca Giordano. 5d, The Epiphany, by Bondone. 8d, Virgin & Child, by Burgkmair. 12d, Madonna, by Bellini.
No. 1680, Mother and Child, by Rubens. No. 1681, The Christ, by Carpaccio.

1995, Dec. 18
1674-1679 A256   Set of 6   6.25 6.25
Souvenir Sheets
1680-1681 A256 25d each   5.50 5.50

Banjul Intl. Airport A257

1995, Dec. 21   Litho.   Perf. 14
1682-1685 A257   1d, 2d, 3d, 5d, set of 4   2.50 2.50

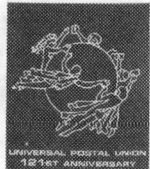

UPU, 121st Anniv. — A258

1995, Dec. 21
1686-1689 A258   1d, 2d, 3d, 7d, set of 4   2.75 2.75

Marine Life A259

Designs: 2d, Commerson's dolphin. 5d, Narwhal. 8d, True's beaked whale. 10d, Rough-toothed dolphin.
Dolphins: No. 1694a, Northern rightwhale. b, Spotted. c, Common. d, Pacific white-sided. e, Atlantic humpbacked. f, Atlantic white-sided. g, White-beaked. h, Striped. i, Risso's.
Whales: No. 1695a, Bryde's. b, Sperm. c, Humpback. d, Sei. e, Blue. f, Gray. g, Fin. h, Killer. i, Right.
No. 1696, Beluga, clymene dolphin. No. 1697, Bowhead whale, dall's porpoise, blue shark.

1995, Dec. 22
1690-1693 A259   Set of 4   5.50 5.50
Miniature Sheets of 9
1694-1695 A259   3d #a.-i., each   6.00 6.00
Souvenir Sheets
1696-1697 A259 25d each   5.50 5.50

Cowboys and American Indians — A260

Disney characters portraying Amerian Indians or in western scenes: 15b, Pete, Seminole. 20b, Donald, Chinook. 25b, Huey, Dewey, Louie, Blackfoot. 30b, Sharp shooter Minnie. 40b, Bull-riding Donald. 50b, Cattle-branding Mickey. 2d, Donald, Tlingit. 3d, Bronco-busting Mickey. 12d, Trick-roping Grandma Duck. No. 1707, 15d, Goofy the ranch hand. No. 1708, 15d, Mickey, Pomo. 20d, Minnie, Goofy, Navaho.
No. 1710, Minnie, Massachusetts Tribe. No. 1711, Pluto singing, vert. No. 1712, Donald with rope around neck, vert. No. 1712, Minnie, Shoshoni, vert.

1995, Dec. 22   Perf. 14x13½
1698-1709 A260   Set of 12   15.00 15.00
Souvenir Sheets
1710-1713 A260 25d each   5.50 5.50

New Year 1996 (Year of the Rat) — A261

Various stylized rats: Nos. 1714a, 63b. b, 75b. c, 1.50d. d, 4d.

No. 1715a, like #1714a. b, like #1714d. c, like #1714c. d, like #1714b.
No. 1716, Two rats.

1996, Jan. 2			Perf. 14¹/₂	
1714	A261	Strip of 4, #a.-d.	1.50	1.50
		Miniature Sheet		
1715	A261	3d Sheet of 4, #a.-d.	2.75	2.75
		Souvenir Sheet		
1716	A261	10d multicolored	2.25	2.25

No. 1714 was issued in sheets of 16 stamps.

GERMAN EAST AFRICA

'jər–mən 'ēst 'a–fri–kə

LOCATION — East Africa, bordering on the Indian Ocean
GOVT. — Former German Colony
AREA — 384,180 sq. mi.
POP. — 7,651,106
CAPITAL — Dar-es-Salaam

Following World War I, the greater part of this German Colonial possession was mandated to Great Britain. The British ceded to the Belgians the provinces of Ruanda and Urundi (Belgian East Africa.) The Kionga triangle was awarded to the Portuguese and became part of the Mozambique Colony. The remaining area became the British Mandated Territory of Tanganyika.

12 Pence = 1 Shilling
100 Cents = 1 Rupee (1917)

ISSUED UNDER BRITISH OCCUPATION

Stamps of Nyasaland Protectorate, 1913-15 Overprinted **N. F.**

1916		Wmk. 3	Perf. 14	
N101	A3	¹/₂p green	1.40	4.25
a.		Double overprint (R & Bk)		
N102	A3	1p carmine	.70	2.00
N103	A3	3p violet, *yel*	7.00	12.00
a.		Double overprint		8,500.
N104	A3	4p scar & blk, *yel*	24.00	37.50
N105	A3	1sh black, *green*	24.00	37.50
		Nos. N101-N105 (5)	57.10	93.25

"N.F." stands for "Nyasaland Force."

Stamps of East Africa and Uganda, 1912-14, Overprinted in Black or Red **G.E.A.**

1917				
N106	A3	1c black (R)	.15	.50
N107	A3	3c blue green	.15	.15
N108	A3	6c carmine	.15	.15
N109	A3	10c brown orange	.15	.15
a.		Inverted overprint		
N110	A3	12c gray	.30	.90
N111	A3	15c ultramarine	.25	1.50
N112	A3	25c scar & blk, *yel*	.25	2.00
N113	A3	50c violet & blk	2.50	3.00
N114	A3	75c blk, *bl grn*, olive back (R)	.90	3.50
a.		75c black, *emerald* (R)	1.10	3.00

Overprinted **G.E.A.**

N115	A4	1r blk, *green*(R)	1.25	4.50
a.		1r black, *emerald* (R)	1.75	12.50
N116	A4	2r blk & red, *bl*	3.50	12.50
N117	A4	3r gray grn & vio	5.50	17.50
N118	A4	4r grn & red, *yel*	12.50	37.50
N119	A4	5r dl vio & ultra	17.50	47.50
N120	A4	10r grn & red, *grn*	42.50	80.00
a.		10r grn & red, *emerald*	47.50	125.00
N121	A4	20r vio & blk, *red*	110.00	200.00
N122	A4	50r gray grn & red	500.00	675.00
		Nos. N106-N120 (15)	87.55	211.35

See Tanganyika for "G.E.A." overprints on stamps inscribed "East Africa and Uganda Protectorates" with watermark 4.

GHANA

'gä–nə

LOCATION — West Africa between Benin and Ivory Coast

GOVT. — Republic
AREA — 92,010 sq. mi.
POP. — 12,827,000 (est. 1983)
CAPITAL — Accra

Ghana is the former British colony of Gold Coast, which achieved independence March 6, 1957. It includes the former trusteeship territory of British Togoland.

12 Pence = 1 Shilling
20 Shillings = 1 Pound
100 Pesewas = 1 Cedi (1965, 1972)
100 New Pesewas = 1 New Cedi (1967)

Used Values in Italics
In 1961 the government canceled all remainder stocks, using cancellations which closely resemble genuine postmarks. Catalogue values in italics (in Ghana) are for canceled-to-order stamps. Postally used copies are worth more.

Catalogue values for all unused stamps in this country are for Never Hinged items.

Watermark

Wmk. 325 Stars and G Multiple

Kwame Nkrumah, Map and Palm-nut Vulture — A1

1957, Mar. 6		Wmk. 4	Photo.	
1	A1	2p rose red	.15	.15
2	A1	2¹/₂p green	.15	.15
3	A1	4p brown	.15	.15
4	A1	1sh3p dark blue	.20	.15
		Set value	.36	.18

Independence, Mar. 6, 1957.
For overprints see Nos. 28-31.

Stamps of Gold Coast, 1952-54, Overprinted in Black or Red **GHANA INDEPENDENCE 6ᵀᴴ MARCH. 1957.**

1957, Mar. 6			Engr.	
5	A14	¹/₂p yel brown & car	.15	.15
6	A14	1p deep blue (R)	.15	.15
7	A14	1¹/₂p green	.15	.15
8	A14	3p rose	.15	.15
9	A15	6p org & black (R)	.15	.15
10	A14	1sh red org & black	.15	.15
11	A14	2sh rose car & ol brn	.25	.15
12	A14	5sh gray & red vio	.60	.25
13	A15	10sh olive grn & black	1.25	.35
		Set value	2.40	.95

Nos. 5-6 exist in vertical coils.
See Nos. 25-27.

Viking Ship and Angelfish A2

Designs: 1sh3p, Medieval galleon and swordfish. 5sh, Modern cargo ship and flyingfish.

1957, Dec. 27		Engr.	Unwmk.	
14	A2	2¹/₂p emerald	.15	.15
15	A2	1sh3p dark blue	.45	.45
16	A2	5sh red lilac	1.75	1.75
		Nos. 14-16 (3)	2.35	2.35

Black Star Line inauguration.

Ambassador Hotel — A3

Design: 2¹/₂p, Opening of Parliament. 1sh3p, National monument.

		Perf. 14x14¹/₂, 14¹/₂x14		
1958, Mar. 6		Photo.	Wmk. 4	
		Flags in Original Colors		
17	A3	¹/₂p car rose & black	.15	.15
18	A3	2¹/₂p org yel, red & blk	.15	.15
19	A3	1sh3p blue & black	.18	.18
20	A4	2sh multicolored	.30	.25
		Set value	.58	.53

First anniversary of Independence.

Map of Africa — A5

Map and Torch — A6

1958, Apr. 15			Perf. 13¹/₂x14¹/₂	
21	A5	2¹/₂p multicolored	.15	.15
22	A5	3p multicolored	.15	.15
23	A6	1sh multicolored	.15	.15
24	A6	2sh6p multicolored	.30	.25
		Set value	.56	.45

1st conf. of Independent African States, Accra, Apr. 15-22.

Gold Coast Nos. 151-152 and 154 Overprinted Like Nos. 5-13

		Perf. 11¹/₂x12, 12x11¹/₂		
1958, May 26		Engr.	Wmk. 4	
25	A15	2p chocolate	.15	.15
26	A15	2¹/₂p red	.15	.15
27	A14	4p deep blue	.18	.15
		Set value	.32	.26

Nos. 25-27 were prepared in 1957 and some were sold without authorization. The set was officially released in 1958.

Ghana Nos. 1-4 Overprinted: "Prime Minister's Visit U. S. A. and Canada"

1958, July 18		Photo.	Perf. 14x14¹/₂	
28	A1	2p rose red	.15	.15
29	A1	2¹/₂p green	.15	.15
30	A1	4p brown	.15	.15
31	A1	1sh3p dark blue	.18	.18
		Set value	.37	.36

Prime Minister Kwame Nkrumah's visit to the US and Canada, July, 1958.

Palm-nut Vulture over Globe — A7

"Britannia" Plane — A8

Designs: 2sh, Stratocruiser and albatross. 2sh6p, Palm-nut vulture and jet plane, horiz.

		Perf. 14x14¹/₂, 14¹/₂x14		
1958, July 15				
32	A7	2¹/₂p multicolored	.15	.15
33	A8	1sh3p multicolored	.20	.18
34	A8	2sh multicolored	.25	.20
35	A7	2sh6p olive bister & blk	.35	.30
		Nos. 32-35 (4)	.95	.83

Inauguration of Ghana Airways.

A9

		Perf. 14x14¹/₂		
1958, Oct. 24		Wmk. 4	Litho.	
36	A9	2¹/₂p multicolored	.15	.15
37	A9	1sh3p multicolored	.20	.18
38	A9	2sh6p multicolored	.25	.20
		Set value	.51	.43

United Nations Day, Oct. 24.

A10

		Perf. 14x14¹/₂		
1959, Feb. 12		Photo.	Wmk. 325	
		Lincoln Memorial and Kwame Nkrumah.		
39	A10	2¹/₂p dp plum & brt pink	.15	.15
40	A10	1sh3p dp blue & lt bl	.20	.18
41	A10	2sh6p ol gray & org yel	.28	.25
a.		Souv. sheet of 3, #39-41, imperf.	2.25	2.25
		Set value	.54	.48

Lincoln's birth sesquicentennial.

Kente Cloth with Traditional Symbols A11

Symbol of Greeting — A12

Designs: 2¹/₂p, Talking drums and elephant horn-blower. 2sh, Map of Africa, flag and palm tree.

		Perf. 14¹/₂x14, 14x14¹/₂		
1959, Mar. 6		Photo.	Wmk. 325	
42	A11	¹/₂p multicolored	.15	.15
43	A11	2¹/₂p multicolored	.15	.15
44	A12	1sh3p multicolored	.22	.18
45	A11	2sh multicolored	.30	.25
		Set value	.64	.54

Independence, 2nd anniversary.

Flags of Independent States of Africa and Globe — A13

1959, Apr. 15   Perf. 14¹/₂x14
46	A13	2¹/₂p multicolored	.15	.15
47	A13	8¹/₂p multicolored	.18	.18
		Set value	.24	.23

Africa Freedom Day, Apr. 15.

Kente Cloth and "God's Omnipotence" Symbol — A13a

Nkrumah Statue, Accra — A14

Shell Ginger — A15

Cacao — A16

"God's Omnipotence" Symbol — A16a

Blackwinged Red Bishop — A17

Designs: 1¹/₂p, Ghana timber. 2p, Volta river. 4p, Diamond and mine. 11p, Golden spider lily. 2sh6p, Great blue turaco. 5sh, Tiger orchid. 10sh, Jewelfish (tropical African cichlid).

Perf. 11¹/₂x12, 12x11¹/₂, 14x14¹/₂, 14¹/₂x14

1959, Oct. 5   Photo.   Wmk. 325
Size: 30¹/₂x21mm, 21x30¹/₂mm
48	A13a	¹/₂p multi (God's Omnipotence)		
49	A14	1p multicolored	.15	.15

Size: 26¹/₂x37mm, 37x26¹/₂mm
50	A15	1¹/₂p multicolored	.15	.15
51	A16	2p multicolored	.15	.15
52	A16	2¹/₂p multicolored	.15	.15
53	A16a	3p multi (God's Omnipotence)	.15	.15
54	A16	4p multicolored	.15	.15
55	A17	6p multicolored	.22	.15
a.		Booklet pane of 4	.90	
56	A15	11p multicolored	.30	.15
57	A15	1sh multicolored	.25	.15
58	A17	2sh6p multicolored	.60	.28
59	A15	5sh multicolored	1.25	.60

Size: 45x26mm
60	A16	10sh multicolored	2.50	1.50
		Nos. 48-60 (13)	6.17	
		Set value		2.95

Nos. 48 and 53 inscribed "God's Omnipotence." Nos. 95-96 inscribed "Gye Nyame." See Nos. C1-C2. For surcharges see Nos. 216-217, 219-225, 277-283.

Map and Gold Cup — A18

Designs: 1p, Soccer players, vert. 3p, Flags and goalkeeper in stadium. 8p, Soccer player at goal. 2sh6p, Kwame Nkrumah Gold Cup, vert.

1959, Oct. 15   Perf. 14¹/₂x14, 14x14¹/₂
61	A18	¹/₂p multicolored	.15	.15
62	A18	1p multicolored	.15	.15
63	A18	3p multicolored	.15	.15
64	A18	8p multicolored	.20	.15
65	A18	2sh6p multicolored	.65	.28
		Set value	1.00	.50

West African Soccer Competitions.

Prince Philip — A19

Perf. 14¹/₂x14

1959, Nov. 24   Photo.   Wmk. 325
66	A19	3p brt pink & black	.15	.15

Visit of Prince Philip.

Talking Drums — A20

Designs: 6p, 1sh3p, Ghana flag and UN emblem, vert. 2sh6p, Pile of Ceremonial Stools and "UNTC," vert.

Perf. 14¹/₂x14, 14x14¹/₂

1959, Dec. 10
Flag in Original Colors
67	A20	3p violet & org yel	.15	.15
68	A20	6p Prus green & blk	.15	.15
69	A20	1sh3p grnsh bl, blk & vio	.22	.15
70	A20	2sh6p dark blue & black	.45	.30
		Set value	.85	.52

United Nations Trusteeship Council.

Three Flying Eagles — A21

Designs: 3p, Three clusters of fireworks. 1sh3p, Ghana flag forming "3" and dove. 2sh, Ghana flag forming triple sail of symbolic ship.

Perf. 13¹/₂x14¹/₂

1960, Mar. 6   Wmk. 325
71	A21	¹/₂p multicolored	.15	.15
72	A21	3p multicolored	.15	.15
73	A21	1sh3p multicolored	.25	.15
74	A21	2sh multicolored	.40	.20
		Set value	.81	.40

Independence, 3rd anniversary.

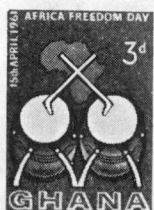

Flags Forming "A" and Map — A22

Designs: 6p, Letter "F." 1sh, "D."

1960, Apr. 15   Photo.   Wmk. 325
Flags in Original Colors
75	A22	3p green, red & black	.15	.15
76	A22	6p rose & black	.15	.15
77	A22	1sh blue, black & red	.20	.15
		Set value	.40	.20

Africa Freedom Day, Apr. 15.

President Kwame Nkrumah — A23

Olympic Rings and Hand Holding Torch — A24

Designs: 1sh3p, Flag and star. 2sh, Hand holding torch. 10sh, Coat of Arms and flag of Ghana, horiz.

Perf. 14x14¹/₂, 14¹/₂x14

1960, July 1   Litho.
78	A23	3p multicolored	.15	.15
79	A23	1sh3p multicolored	.28	.22
80	A23	2sh multicolored	.45	.35
81	A23	10sh multicolored	1.75	1.50
a.		Souv. sheet of 4, #78-81, imperf.	2.75	2.75
		Nos. 78-81 (4)	2.63	2.22

Declaration of the Republic, July 1, 1960.

1960, Aug. 15   Photo.   Wmk. 325
Design: 1sh3p, 2sh6p, Runner, Map of Africa and Olympic Rings, horiz.
82	A24	3p multicolored	.15	.15
83	A24	6p multicolored	.15	.15
84	A24	1sh3p multicolored	.18	.15
85	A24	2sh6p multicolored	.40	.30
		Set value	.79	.62

17th Olympic Games, Rome, Aug. 25-Sept. 11.

Map and Arch — A25

UN Emblem and Ghana Flag — A26

Designs: 3p, Flag and Kwame Nkrumah, horiz. 6p, Star and Nkrumah.

1960, Sept. 21   Photo.
86	A25	3p multicolored	.15	.15
87	A25	6p multicolored	.15	.15
88	A25	1sh3p multicolored	.28	.20
		Set value	.49	.37

Founder's Day, Sept. 21, birthday of Dr. Kwame Nkrumah.

1960, Dec. 10   Perf. 14x14¹/₂
Designs: 6p, Flame and emblem. 1sh3p, UN Emblem.
89	A26	3p multicolored	.15	.15
90	A26	6p multicolored	.15	.15
91	A26	1sh3p multicolored	.20	.15
		Set value	.36	.24

Human Rights Day, Dec. 10, 1960.

Talking Drums and Map — A27

Designs: 6p, Map of Africa showing 25 independent states. 2sh, Map of Africa and flags of independent nations in 1958, horiz.

Red-fronted Gazelle — A28

Perf. 14x14¹/₂, 14¹/₂x14

1961, Apr. 15   Wmk. 325
92	A27	3p multicolored	.15	.15
93	A27	6p multicolored	.15	.15
94	A27	2sh multicolored	.40	.28
		Nos. 92-94 (3)	.70	
		Set value		.45

Africa Freedom Day, Apr. 15, 1961.

Types of 1959 Redrawn and

Perf. 11¹/₂x12, 14¹/₂x14

1961, Apr. 29   Photo.   Wmk. 325
95	A13a	¹/₂p "Gye Nyame"	.15	.15
96	A16a	3p "Gye Nyame"	.15	.15
a.		Booklet pane of 4	.35	

Perf. 14x14¹/₂
97	A28	£1 multicolored	4.50	2.75
		Nos. 95-97 (3)	4.80	3.05

Nos. 95-96 are the same sizes as Nos. 48 and 53 which are inscribed "God's Omnipotence." For surcharges see Nos. 218, 226, 284.

Column, Eagle and Star — A29

Dove with Olive Branch — A30

World Map, Chain and Olive Branch A31

Designs: 1sh3p, Symbolic flower and star. 2sh, Star and 3 Ghana flags.

1961, July 1   Perf. 14x14¹/₂
98	A29	3p multicolored	.15	.15
99	A29	1sh3p multicolored	.30	.22
100	A29	2sh multicolored	.50	.30
		Nos. 98-100 (3)	.95	
		Set value		.57

First anniversary of the Republic.

Perf. 14x14¹/₂, 14¹/₂x14

1961, Sept. 1
Design: 5sh, Rostrum and olive branch.
101	A30	3p green	.15	.15
102	A31	1sh3p dark blue	.25	.18
103	A31	5sh rose carmine	1.00	.80
		Nos. 101-103 (3)	1.40	1.13

Conference of Non-aligned Nations, Belgrade, Sept. 1961.

Kwame Nkrumah and Globe — A32

Designs: 1sh3p, Kente cloth and Nkrumah, vert. 5sh, Kwame Nkrumah, vert.

Perf. 14¹/₂x14, 14x14¹/₂

1961, Sept. 21   Wmk. 325
104	A32	3p multicolored	.15	.15
a.		Souvenir sheet of 4, imperf.	.60	.60
105	A32	1sh3p multicolored	.35	.28
a.		Souvenir sheet of 4, imperf.	1.75	1.75
106	A32	5sh multicolored	1.65	1.40
a.		Souvenir sheet of 4, imperf.	10.00	10.00
		Nos. 104-106 (3)	2.15	1.80

Founder's Day.
The souvenir sheets contain four imperf. stamps each with simulated perforations.

Elizabeth II and Map of Africa — A33

1961, Nov. 10 *Perf. 14½x14*

Gold Inscriptions: Design in Black, Red, Yellow & Green

107	A33	3p claret	.15	.15
108	A33	1sh3p Prussian blue	.28	.18
109	A33	5sh violet blue	1.10	.90
a.		Souvenir sheet of 4	6.00	6.00
		Nos. 107-109 (3)	1.53	1.23

Visit of Queen Elizabeth II to Ghana, Nov. 10-22.
No. 109a contains four imperf. copies of No. 109 with simulated perforations.

Map of Tema Harbor and Ships — A34

Perf. 14x13

1962, Feb. 10 **Litho.** **Unwmk.**

110	A34	3p multicolored	.15	.15

Opening of Tema Harbor, as part of Volta River Project.

Dove Flying over Map of Africa — A35

1962, Mar. 6 *Perf. 13x14*

111	A35	3p multicolored	.15	.15

Conference of African heads of state at Casablanca, 1st anniv. See Nos. C5-C6.

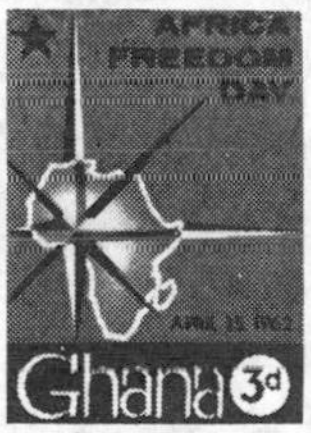

"Freedom" Illuminating Africa — A36

"Five Continents at Peace" — A37

Perf. 14x14½

1962, Apr. 15 **Photo.** **Wmk. 325**

112	A36	3p multicolored	.15	.15
113	A36	6p multicolored	.15	.15
114	A36	1sh3p multicolored	.28	.20
		Set value	.51	.38

Africa Freedom Day, Apr. 15.

1962, June 21 **Wmk. 325**

Designs: 6p, Atom bomb blast in shape of skull. 1sh3p, Peace dove and globe.

115	A37	3p deep rose & black	.15	.15
116	A37	6p black & dk red	.20	.15
117	A37	1sh3p greenish blue	.50	.35
		Nos. 115-117 (3)	.85	
		Set value		.54

Accra Assembly of Africans for a "World Without Bomb," June 21-28.

Patrice Lumumba A38

1962, June 30 *Perf. 14½x14*

118	A38	3p black & orange	.15	.15
119	A38	6p maroon, grn & blk	.15	.15
120	A38	1sh3p dk grn, pink & blk	.40	.22
		Nos. 118-120 (3)	.70	
		Set value		.39

1st anniv. (on Feb. 12) of the death of Patrice Lumumba, premier of Congo.

Arch and Star — A39

Kwame Nkrumah — A40

Designs: 6p, Torch in flag colors and globe. 1sh3p, Palm-nut vulture trailing flag, horiz.

Perf. 13x13½, 13½x13

1962, July 1 **Unwmk.**

121	A39	3p multicolored	.15	.15
122	A39	6p multicolored	.25	.20
123	A39	1sh3p multicolored	.65	.50
		Nos. 121-123 (3)	1.05	.85

Second anniversary of the republic.

1962, Sept. 21 **Litho.** *Perf. 13x14*

Designs: 3p, Nkrumah medal. 1sh3p, Nkrumah's head and stars. 2sh, Hands with trowel and building block.

124	A40	1p multicolored	.15	.15
125	A40	3p multicolored	.15	.15
126	A40	1sh3p ultra & black	.35	.25
127	A40	2sh multicolored	.55	.30
		Set value	1.04	.66

Founder's Day, Nkrumah's 53rd birthday.

Malaria Eradication Emblem — A41

Wheat Emblem and Globe — A42

Perf. 14x14½

1962, Dec. 1 **Photo.** **Wmk. 325**

128	A41	1p carmine rose	.15	.15
129	A41	4p yellow green	.15	.15
130	A41	6p olive bister	.18	.15
131	A41	1sh3p violet	.35	.25
a.		Souvenir sheet of 4, imperf.	.90	.90
		Set value	.70	.52

WHO drive to eradicate malaria.
No. 131a contains one each of Nos. 128-131, with simulated perforation.

Perf. 14x14½, 14½x14

1963, Mar. 21 **Wmk. 325**

Designs: 4p, Hands holding Wheat Emblem, horiz. 1sh3p, Globe, horiz.

132	A42	1p multicolored	.15	.15
133	A42	4p multicolored	.15	.15
134	A42	1sh3p multicolored	.25	.18
		Set value	.38	.29

FAO "Freedom from Hunger" campaign.

Map of Africa in Sun — A43

Cross, Flag and Centenary Emblem — A44

Designs: 4p, Symbolic wood carving, horiz. 1sh3p, Map of Africa and ceremonial fire. 2sh6p, Gazelle and flag.

1963, Apr. 15 **Photo.**

135	A43	1p crimson & gold	.15	.15
136	A43	4p orange, blk & red	.15	.15
137	A43	1sh3p multicolored	.28	.20
138	A43	2sh6p multicolored	.55	.40
		Set value	.96	.70

Africa Freedom Day, Apr. 15.

Perf. 14x14½, 14½x14

1963, May 28 **Wmk. 325**

Designs: 1½p, Centenary emblem, horiz. 4p, Family and emblem, horiz. 1sh3p, Emblem and globe.

139	A44	1p multicolored	.15	.15
140	A44	1½p multicolored	.15	.15
141	A44	4p multicolored	.15	.15
142	A44	1sh3p multicolored	.25	.18
a.		Souvenir sheet of 4, imperf.	.50	.50
		Set value	.42	.32

Cent. of the founding of the Intl. Red Cross.
No. 142a contains one each of Nos. 139-142, with simulated perforation.

A45

Designs: 4p, Three flags. 1sh3p, Map of Africa with Ghana, vert. 2sh6p, Torch, vert.

Perf. 14½x14, 14x14½

1963, July 1 **Photo.**

143	A45	1p multicolored	.15	.15
144	A45	4p multicolored	.15	.15
145	A45	1sh3p multicolored	.25	.18
146	A45	2sh6p multicolored	.50	.35
		Set value	.88	.62

The 3rd anniversary of the republic.

Dancers, Fireworks and Nkrumah A46

Designs: 1p, Nkrumah and streamer, vert. 4p, Nkrumah and flag, vert. 5sh, Wisdom symbol.

Perf. 14x14½, 14½x14

1963, Sept. 21

147	A46	1p multicolored	.15	.15
148	A46	4p multicolored	.15	.15
149	A46	1sh3p multicolored	.22	.15
150	A46	5sh multicolored	.90	.60
		Set value	1.25	.85

Founder's Day, Nkrumah's 54th birthday.

Ramses II at Abu Simbel — A47

Designs: 1½p, Rock painting, bird and fish, horiz. 2p, Queen Nefertari, horiz. 4p, Sphinx of Wadi es-Sebua. 1sh3p, Statues of Ramses II at Abu Simbel, horiz.

1963, Nov. 1 **Unwmk.** *Perf. 11½x11*

151	A47	1p multicolored	.15	.15
152	A47	1½p multicolored	.15	.15
153	A47	2p multicolored	.15	.15
154	A47	4p multicolored	.15	.15
155	A47	1sh3p multicolored	.55	.40
		Set value	.88	.65

UNESCO world campaign to save historic monuments in Nubia.

Steam and Diesel Engines A48

Perf. 14½x14

1963, Nov. 1 **Wmk. 325**

156	A48	1p multicolored	.15	.15
157	A48	6p multicolored	.25	.15
158	A48	1sh3p multicolored	.60	.50
159	A48	2sh6p multicolored	1.50	1.25
		Nos. 156-159 (4)	2.50	2.05

The 60th anniversary of Ghana's railroads.

Eleanor Roosevelt and Flame — A49

IQSY Emblem and Satellites — A50

Designs: 6p, Mrs. Roosevelt and flag. 1sh3p, Mrs. Roosevelt, flag, flame and Ghanaian symbols, horiz.

Perf. 11½x11, 11x11½

1963, Dec. 10 **Unwmk.**

160	A49	1p multicolored	.15	.15
161	A49	4p multicolored	.15	.15
162	A49	6p multicolored	.18	.15
163	A49	1sh3p multicolored	.35	.25
		Set value	.70	.48

Eleanor Roosevelt; 15th anniv. of the Universal Declaration of Human Rights.

> Imperforates
> Starting in 1964, certain sets of Ghana exist imperf.

1964, June 1 **Photo.** *Perf. 14*

164	A50	3p multicolored	.15	.15
165	A50	6p multicolored	.18	.15
166	A50	1sh3p multicolored	.35	.25
a.		Souvenir sheet of 4	1.50	1.50
		Nos. 164-166 (3)	.68	
		Set value		.39

Intl. Quiet Sun Year, 1964-65. No. 166a contains 4 imperf. stamps similar to No. 166 with simulated perforations.
See Nos. 186-188.

Harvest on State Farm — A51

Designs: 6p, Oil refinery, Tema. 1sh3p, Communal labor. 5sh, Ghana flag and people.

1964, July 1 *Perf. 13x14*

167	A51	3p multicolored	.15	.15
168	A51	6p multicolored	.18	.15
169	A51	1sh3p multicolored	.35	.25
170	A51	5sh multicolored	1.10	1.00
a.		Souvenir sheet of 4	2.00	2.00
		Nos. 167-170 (4)	1.78	1.55

4th anniv. of the Republic. No. 170a contains four stamps similar to Nos. 167-170 with simulated perforations.

Dove, Globe, Olive Branch and Flag — A52

Designs: 6p, Map of Africa and quill pen, vert. 1sh3p, Knotted rope and map of Africa. 5sh, Hands planting symbolic tree, vert.

1964, July 6 *Perf. 14*

171	A52	3p multicolored	.15	.15
172	A52	6p black & red	.15	.15
173	A52	1sh3p blue & multi	.28	.20
174	A52	5sh yel & multi	1.10	.75
		Nos. 171-174 (4)	1.68	
		Set value		1.07

Signing of the African Unity Charter, 1st anniv.

Nkrumah and Hibiscus — A53

Boxing — A54

Perf. 14x14½

1964, Sept. 21 Photo. Wmk. 325

Design in Brown, Green and Rose Red

175	A53	3p light blue	.15	.15
176	A53	6p yellow	.15	.15
177	A53	1sh3p gray	.28	.25
178	A53	2sh6p emerald	.55	.40
a.		Souvenir sheet of 4	2.50	2.25
		Nos. 175-178 (4)	1.13	
		Set value		.76

Founder's Day, Nkrumah's 55th birthday.

No. 178a contains four of No. 178 with simulated perforation.

1964, Oct. 25 *Perf. 14½x14*

Sport: 1p, Hurdling, horiz. 2½p, Running, horiz. 4p, Broad jump. 6p, Soccer. 1sh3p, Athlete with Olympic torch. 5sh, Banners and Tokyo Olympic emblem, horiz.

179	A54	1p yellow & multi	.15	.15
180	A54	2½p multicolored	.15	.15
181	A54	3p red & multi	.15	.15
182	A54	4p blue & multi	.15	.15
183	A54	6p multicolored	.15	.15
184	A54	1sh3p blue & multi	.28	.20
185	A54	5sh gray & multi	1.10	.80
a.		Souvenir sheet of 3	3.00	3.00
		Set value	1.80	1.30

18th Olympic Games, Tokyo, Oct. 10-25.

No. 185a contains stamps similar to Nos. 183-185 with simulated perforation.

Quiet Sun Year Type of 1964

1964, Oct. Unwmk. Photo. *Perf. 14*

186	A50	3p gray, bl, grn, yel & red	1.25	1.25
187	A50	6p pink, bl, grn, yel & red	2.50	2.50
188	A50	1sh3p tan, bl, grn, yel, & red	4.00	4.00
		Nos. 186-188 (3)	7.75	7.75

Each issued in sheets of 12, with star-strewn blue border inscribed "Ghana International Quiet Sun Year." Stamps arranged in square surrounding vignette of New York World's Fair Unisphere in blue.

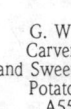

G. W. Carver and Sweet Potato A55

Design: 1sh3p, Albert Einstein, theory of relativity formula and atom symbol.

1964, Dec. 7 Wmk. 325 *Perf. 14½*

189	A55	6p grn & dk blue	.18	.15
190	A55	1sh3p Prus bl & claret	.35	.25
191	A55	5sh org ver & brn blk	1.50	1.25
a.		Souvenir sheet of 3	2.25	2.00
		Nos. 189-191 (3)	2.03	1.65

Human Rights Day; Albert Einstein (1878-1955) and George Washington Carver (1864-1943), scientists.

No. 191a commemorates UNESCO Week and contains one each of Nos. 189-191 with simulated perforations.

Secretary Bird — A56

Designs: 1p, Elephant, vert. 2½p, Purple wreath, vert. 3p, Gray parrot, vert. 4p, Blue-naped mousebird. 6p, African tulip tree flowers. 1sh3p, Amethyst starling. 2sh6p, Hippopotamuses.

Perf. 11½x11, 11x11½

1964, Dec. 14 Photo. Unwmk.

192	A56	1p blue & multi	.15	.15
193	A56	1½p org & multi	.15	.15
194	A56	2½p lt green & multi	.20	.15
a.		Souv. sheet of 3, #192-194, imperf.	1.00	1.00
195	A56	3p lt green & multi	.20	.18
196	A56	4p multicolored	.28	.20
197	A56	6p multicolored	.28	.15
198	A56	1sh3p multicolored	.50	.35
199	A56	2sh6p multicolored	1.00	.60
a.		Souv. sheet of 5, #195-199, imperf.	3.00	3.00
		Nos. 192-199 (8)	2.76	
		Set value		1.62

ICY Emblem — A57

1965, Feb. 15 Litho. *Perf. 14x13*

Design in Black, Red and Green

200	A57	1p gray	.15	.15
201	A57	4p bister	.15	.15
202	A57	6p tan	.18	.15
203	A57	1sh3p light green	.45	.30
a.		Souvenir sheet of 4	1.75	1.75
		Set value	.80	.56

Intl. Cooperation Year. No. 203a contains 4 imperf. stamps similar to No. 203.

ITU Emblem, Old and New Communication Equipment — A58

1965, Apr. 12 *Perf. 13½*

204	A58	1p multicolored	.15	.15
205	A58	6p multicolored	.15	.15
206	A58	1sh3p multicolored	.28	.18
207	A58	5sh multicolored	1.10	.90
a.		Souvenir sheet of 4	1.75	1.75
		Nos. 204-207 (4)	1.68	1.38

Cent. of the ITU. No. 207a contains 4 imperf. stamps similar to Nos. 204-207 with simulated perforations.

Lincoln's Home, Springfield, Ill. — A59

Designs: 1sh3p, Inaugural Address and Lincoln. 2sh, Lincoln and his signature. 5sh, Adaptation of 1869 U.S. Lincoln stamp (No. 122).

Perf. 12½

1965, Apr. Wmk. 325 Photo.

208	A59	6p multicolored	.15	.15
209	A59	1sh3p multicolored	.28	.18
210	A59	2sh multicolored	.42	.35
211	A59	5sh red & black	1.10	.75
a.		Souvenir sheet of 4	2.00	1.50
		Nos. 208-211 (4)	1.95	1.43

Centenary of death of Abraham Lincoln.

No. 211a contains one each of Nos. 208-211 with simulated perforation.

5-Pesewa Coin, Nkrumah's Head — A60

Coins: 10pa, 10 pesewas. 25pa, 25 pesewas. 50pa, 50 pesewas.

Perf. 11x13

1965, July 19 Unwmk. Litho.

Coin in Silver and Black

Size: 45x32mm

212	A60	5pa red, grn & lt grn	.15	.15
213	A60	10pa red, grn, & pink	.25	.20

Size: 62x39mm

214	A60	25pa red, grn, & pink	.70	.55

Size: 71x43½mm

215	A60	50pa red, grn & lt grn	1.40	1.10
		Nos. 212-215 (4)	2.50	2.00

Introduction of decimal currency.

Regular Issue of 1959-61 Surcharged in Red, Blue, Brown, Black or White with New Value and: "Ghana New Currency / 19th July, 1965"

Perf. 12x11½, 14½x14, 14x14½

1965, July 19 Photo. Wmk. 325

216	A14	1pa on 1p (R)	.15	.15
217	A16	2pa on 2p (Bl)	.15	.15
218	A16a	3pa on 3p (#96, Br)	.15	.15
219	A16	4pa on 4p (Bl)	.15	.15
220	A17	6pa on 6p (Bk)	.18	.15
221	A15	11pa on 11p (W)	.25	.15
222	A15	12pa on 1sh (Bl)	.28	.15
223	A17	30pa on 2sh6p (Bl)	1.00	.45
224	A15	60pa on 5sh (Bl)	1.75	.90
225	A16	1.20c on 10s (Bl)	3.25	2.25
226	A28	2.40c on £1 (Bl)	7.25	5.75
		Nos. 216-226 (11)	14.56	10.40

The two lines of the overprint are diagonal on the 1pa, 11pa, 12pa, 60pa, 1.20c and 2.40c.

The surcharge exists double or inverted on six or more denominations.

Summit Conference, Accra — A61

Map of Africa and Flags — A62

Designs: 2pa, "OAU" and three heads (triangle pointing up). 5pa, Symbol of African Unity. 15pa, Sunburst and map of Africa. 24pa, Map of Africa.

Perf. 14, 14½x14

1965, Oct. 21 Photo.

Ghana Flag in Red, Black & Green

227	A61	1pa multicolored	.15	.15
228	A61	2pa multicolored	.15	.15
229	A61	5pa multicolored	.15	.15
230	A62	6pa orange & black	.18	.15
231	A62	15pa light blue & blk	.50	.30
232	A62	24pa lt ultra & green	.75	.65
		Nos. 227-232 (6)	1.88	
		Set value		1.20

Summit Conference of the Organization for African Unity, Accra, Oct. 1965.

Soccer Goalkeeper A63

Designs: 15pa, Soccer player and cup, vert. 24pa, Two soccer players and cup.

Perf. 14x13, 13x14

1965, Nov. 15 Unwmk.

233	A63	6pa ocher & multi	.15	.15
234	A63	15pa multicolored	.25	.15
235	A63	24pa lt blue & multi	.50	.30
		Nos. 233-235 (3)	.90	
		Set value		.47

African Soccer Cup competition.

For overprints see Nos. 244-246.

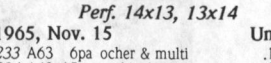

John F. Kennedy and Eternal Flame — A64

Various Kennedy portraits.

1965, Dec. 15 Wmk. 325 *Perf. 12½*

236	A64	6pa blk, yel, gold & grn	.18	.15
237	A64	15pa vio, crim & brt grn	.55	.35
238	A64	24pa dp pur & blk	.90	.90
239	A64	30pa vio brn & blk	1.25	1.25
a.		Souvenir sheet of 4 ('66)	3.75	3.00
		Nos. 236-239 (4)	2.88	2.65

President John F. Kennedy (1917-1963).

No. 239a contains four imperf. stamps similar to Nos. 236-239.

Generators, Volta River Project A65

Designs: 15pa, Dam and Lake Volta. 24pa, "Ghana" forming dam. 30pa, Grain.

Perf. 11x11½

1966, Jan. 22 Unwmk.

240	A65	6pa sepia & multi	.15	.15
241	A65	15pa multicolored	.40	.30
242	A65	24pa multicolored	.60	.38
243	A65	30pa brt blue & blk	.85	.60
		Nos. 240-243 (4)	2.00	1.43

Opening of the Volta River dam and electric power station at Akosombo.

Nos. 233-235 Overprinted Diagonally: "Black Stars Retain Africa Cup / 21st Nov. 1965"

1966, Feb. 7 *Perf. 14x13, 13x14*

244	A63	6pa ocher & multi	.20	.15
245	A63	15pa multicolored	.45	.35
246	A63	24pa lt bl & multi	.70	.45
		Nos. 244-246 (3)	1.35	.95

Ghana's soccer victory, Nov. 21, 1965.

Inauguration of WHO Headquarters, Geneva A66

Designs: 24pa, 30pa, WHO Headquarters from the west and WHO emblem.

Perf. 14x14½

1966, July 1 Photo. Wmk. 325

247	A66	6pa multicolored	.15	.15
248	A66	15pa multicolored	.35	.25
249	A66	24pa multicolored	.55	.32
250	A66	30pa multicolored	.70	.50
a.		Souvenir sheet of 4	2.00	1.75
		Nos. 247-250 (4)	1.75	1.22

No. 250a contains 4 imperf. stamps similar to Nos. 247-250 with simulated perforations.

Herring, Fishermen and Flag — A67

Designs: 15pa, Flatfish and canoes. 24pa, Spadefish and schooner. 30pa, Red snapper and fishing trawler "Shama." 60pa, Mackerel and steamer.

1966, Aug. 10   Unwmk.   *Perf. 14x13*
251 A67	6pa ocher & multi	.18	.15
252 A67	15pa yel grn & multi	.40	.25
253 A67	24pa ver & multi	.65	.28
254 A67	30pa blue & multi	1.00	.40
a.	Souvenir sheet of 4	3.50	2.00
255 A67	60pa green & multi	1.40	.85
	Nos. 251-255 (5)	3.63	1.93

1966 Freedom from Hunger campaign "Young World Against Hunger."
No. 254a contains 4 imperf. stamps similar to No. 254.

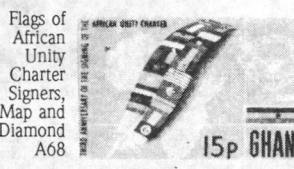

Flags of African Unity Charter Signers, Map and Diamond
A68

Designs: 6p, Ghana flag and links enclosing map of Africa, vert. 24p, Ship's wheel enclosing map of Africa, and cacao pod.

1966, Sept.   Unwmk.   *Perf. 13x13¹/₂*
256 A68	6pa brt blue & multi	.18	.15
257 A68	15pa blue & multi	.55	.40
258 A68	24pa dp green & multi	.90	.55
	Nos. 256-258 (3)	1.63	1.10

Signing of the African Unity Charter, 3rd anniv.

Soccer Player and Rimet Cup — A69

Various Soccer Scenes.

Perf. 14¹/₂x14
1966, Nov. 14   Photo.   Wmk. 325
259 A69	5pa brown & multi	.15	.15
260 A69	15pa blue & multi	.35	.25
261 A69	24pa green & multi	.55	.32
262 A69	30pa brt rose & multi	.75	.50
263 A69	60pa lilac & multi	1.50	1.00
a.	Souvenir sheet of 4	5.00	5.00
	Nos. 259-263 (5)	3.30	2.22

World Cup Soccer Championship, Wembley, England, July 11-30.
No. 263a contains 4 imperf. stamps similar to No. 263 with simulated perforations.

UNESCO Emblem A70

1966, Dec. 23   Wmk. 325   *Perf. 14¹/₂*
264 A70	5pa multicolored	.15	.15
265 A70	15pa multicolored	.35	.25
266 A70	24pa multicolored	.52	.45
267 A70	30pa multicolored	.70	.50
268 A70	60pa multicolored	1.40	1.00
a.	Souvenir sheet of 5	3.25	2.25
	Nos. 264-268 (5)	3.12	2.30

UNESCO, 20th anniv. No. 268a contains 5 imperf. stamps similar to Nos. 264-268 with simulated perforations.

Packing Cases and Fair Emblem A71

Fair Emblem and: 15pa, World map and trade routes to Accra. 24pa, Freighters and loading crane, vert. 36pa, Hand holding cargo net.

1967, Feb. 1   *Perf. 14¹/₂x14, 14x14¹/₂*
269 A71	5pa multicolored	.15	.15
270 A71	15pa multicolored	.45	.25
271 A71	24pa multicolored	.60	.50
272 A71	36pa multicolored	1.10	.75
	Nos. 269-272 (4)	2.30	1.65

International Trade Fair, Accra, Feb. 1-19.

Eagle and Flag — A72

1967, Feb. 24   Photo.   *Perf. 14x14¹/₂*
Flag in Red, Yellow, Black and Green
273 A72	1np gray bl & dk brn	.15	.15
274 A72	4np ocher & dk brn	.20	.20
275 A72	12¹/₂np ol grn & dk brn	.65	.65
276 A72	25np dl cl & dk brn	1.50	1.50
a.	Souvenir sheet of 4, #273-276	3.25	2.50
	Nos. 273-276 (4)	2.50	2.50

1st anniv. of the revolution which overthrew the regime of Kwame Nkrumah.
No. 276a has dull claret marginal inscriptions. An imperf. sheet similar to No. 276a has solid margins of dull claret, colorless inscriptions. Value $2.

Nos. 51, 54-58, 60 and 97 Surcharged in Black, Red or White
Perf. 14¹/₂x14, 14x14¹/₂
1967, Feb. 27
Size: 30¹/₂x21mm, 21x30¹/₂mm
277 A16	1¹/₂np on 2p (B)	9.00	3.00
278 A16	3¹/₂np on 4p (R)	.18	.15
279 A17	5np on 6p (R)	.20	.15
280 A15	9np on 11p (W)	.32	.16
281 A15	10np on 1sh (W)	.33	.22
282 A17	25np on 2sh6p (R)	2.50	1.50

Size: 45x26mm
283 A16	1nc on 10sh (R)	9.00	7.25
284 A28	2nc on £1 (R)	15.75	14.00
	Nos. 277-284 (8)	37.30	26.43

Corn — A73   Forest Kingfisher — A74

African Lungfish A75

Designs: 2np, Ghana Mace (golden staff). 2¹/₂np, Commelina flower. 4np, Rufous-crowned roller, vert. 6np, Akosombo Dam, Volta River. 8np, Adomi Bridge, Volta River. 9np, Chemeleon. 10np, Quay No. 2, Tema Harbor. 20np, Cape hare. 50np, Black-winged stilt. 1nc, Chief's ceremonial stool. 2nc, Frangipani. 2.50nc, State Chair.

Perf. 11¹/₂x12, 12x11¹/₂ (A73), 14x14¹/₂, 14¹/₂x14 (A74-A75)
1967   Photo.   Wmk. 325
286 A73	1np multicolored	.15	.15
287 A74	1¹/₂np multicolored	.15	.15
288 A74	2np multicolored	.15	.15
289 A74	2¹/₂np multicolored	.15	.15
290 A75	3np multicolored	.15	.15
291 A73	4np multicolored	.15	.15
292 A75	6np multicolored	.15	.15
293 A73	8np multicolored	.15	.15
294 A75	9np multicolored	.15	.15
295 A75	10np multicolored	.15	.15
296 A74	20np blue	.30	.22
297 A74	50np multicolored	.90	.75
298 A74	1nc multicolored	1.90	1.25
299 A74	2nc multicolored	3.75	2.75
300 A74	2.50nc multicolored	4.75	3.25
	Nos. 286-300 (15)	13.10	9.72

For overprints & surcharges see #356-370, 858, 1091, 1092A-1092C, 1092E-1093, 1095, 1096B.

Kumasi Fort, 1896 A76

Castles on Ghana Coast: 12¹/₂np, Christiansborg Castle, 1659, and British galleon. 20np, Elmina Castle, 1482, and Portuguese galleon. 25np, Cape Coast Castle, 1664, and Spanish galleon.

1967, June 12   *Perf. 14¹/₂*
301 A76	4np grnsh bl & multi	.15	.15
302 A76	12¹/₂np red org & multi	.55	.38
303 A76	20np brt grn & multi	1.10	.60
304 A76	25np lt red brn & multi	1.50	.75
	Nos. 301-304 (4)	3.30	1.88

Orbiter 1 Landing on Moon — A77

Designs: 4np, Luna 10 on the moon, and globe. 12¹/₂np, Astronaut walking in space.

1967, Aug. 16   Unwmk.   *Perf. 13¹/₂*
305 A77	4np multicolored	.15	.15
306 A77	10np multicolored	.30	.22
307 A77	12¹/₂np multicolored	.38	.30
a.	Souvenir sheet of 3	1.50	1.50
	Nos. 305-307 (3)	.83	.67

Achievements in space. Issued in Ghana in sheets of 30. Sheets of 12 with ornamented, inscribed border also exist; these were sold in Ghana in 1968.
No. 307a contains 3 imperf. stamps similar to Nos. 305-307.

Boy Scouts at Campfire A78

Designs: 10np, Hiking Boy Scout. 12¹/₂np, Lord Baden-Powell.

1967, Sept. 18   Photo.   *Perf. 14x13¹/₂*
308 A78	4np multicolored	.15	.15
309 A78	10np multicolored	.40	.30
310 A78	12¹/₂np multicolored	.50	.40
a.	Souvenir sheet of 3	1.10	.90
	Nos. 308-310 (3)	1.05	.85

50th anniv. of the Ghana (Gold Coast) Boy Scouts. Issued in Ghana in sheets of 30. Sheets of 12 with ornamented, inscribed border also exist; these were sold in Ghana in 1968.
No. 310a contains 3 imperf. stamps similar to Nos. 308-310 with simulated perforations.

UN Secretariat Building — A79

Design: 50np, 2.50nc, UN Headquarters.

1967, Oct. 24   Litho.   *Perf. 13¹/₂x13*
311 A79	4np multicolored	.15	.15
312 A79	10np multicolored	.25	.15
313 A79	50np multicolored	.65	.65
314 A79	2.50nc multicolored	5.50	5.50
a.	Souvenir sheet	6.75	6.75
	Nos. 311-314 (4)	6.55	6.45

United Nations Day. No. 314a contains one imperf. stamp similar to No. 314 with simulated perforations.

Leopard — A80

Designs: 12¹/₂np, Christmas butterfly. 20np, Nubian carmine bee-eaters. 50np, Waterbuck.

Perf. 12¹/₂
1967, Dec. 28   Wmk. 325   Photo.
315 A80	4np multicolored	.15	.15
316 A80	12¹/₂np multicolored	.35	.20
317 A80	20np multicolored	.75	.40
318 A80	50np multicolored	1.75	1.10
a.	Souvenir sheet of 3	3.00	2.00
	Nos. 315-318 (4)	3.00	1.85

Intl. Tourist Year. No. 318a contains 3 imperf. stamps similar to Nos. 316-318 with simulated perforations.

Convoy Entering Accra A81

Designs: 12¹/₂np, Victory parade. 20np, Waving crowd. 40np, Singing and dancing crowd.

Unwmk.
1968, Feb. 24   Litho.   *Perf. 14*
319 A81	4np sal & multi	.15	.15
320 A81	12¹/₂np multicolored	.40	.30
321 A81	20np multicolored	.65	.50
322 A81	40np yel & multi	1.40	1.10
	Nos. 319-322 (4)	2.60	2.05

2nd anniversary of Feb. 24th Revolution.

Cacao Beans and Microscope A82

Designs: 4np, 25np, Cacao tree and beans, microscope.

Perf. 14¹/₂x14
1968, Mar. 18   Photo.   Wmk. 325
323 A82	2¹/₂np grn & multi	.15	.15
324 A82	4np gray & multi	.15	.15
325 A82	10np scar & multi	.20	.20
326 A82	25np multicolored	.50	.50
a.	Souvenir sheet of 4	1.10	1.10
	Set value	.83	.81

Issued to publicize Ghana's cocoa production. Sheets of 30.
No. 326a contains four imperf. stamps similar to Nos. 323-326 with simulated perforations.
Nos. 323-326 also exist in sheets of 12 believed not to have been on sale in Ghana.

Lt. Gen. E. K. Kotoka A83

Designs: Various portraits of Lt. Gen. Kotoka. 40np vertical.

1968, Apr. 17 Unwmk. *Perf. 14*

327 A83	4np pur & multi	.15	.15
328 A83	12½np grn & multi	.45	.45
329 A83	20np multicolored	.90	.90
330 A83	40np gray & multi	1.75	1.75
	Nos. 327-330 (4)	3.25	3.25

Lt. Gen. Emmanuel Kwasi Kotoka (1926-967), leader of the Revolution of 1966 against Nkrumah.

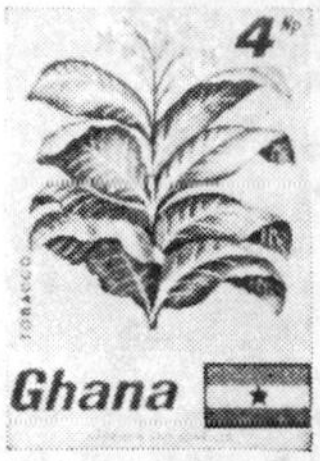
Tobacco — A84

Designs: 5np, Crested porcupine. 12½np, Tapped rubber tree. 20np, Cymothoe sangaris butterfly. 40np, Charaxes ameliae butterfly.

1968, Aug. Photo. *Perf. 14x14½*

331 A84	4np multicolored	.15	.15
332 A84	5np multicolored	.15	.15
333 A84	12½np multicolored	.45	.45
334 A84	20np multicolored	.75	.75
335 A84	40np multicolored	1.50	1.50
a.	Souvenir sheet of 4	3.00	3.00
	Nos. 331-335 (5)	3.00	3.00

No. 335a contains 4 stamps similar to Nos. 331, 332-335 with simulated perforations.

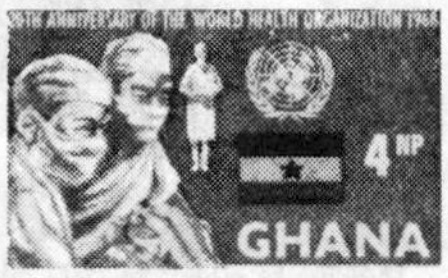
Surgical Team A85

1968, Nov. 11 *Perf. 14x13*

336 A85	4np grn & multi	.15	.15
337 A85	12½np multicolored	.45	.30
338 A85	20np pur & multi	.70	.65
339 A85	40np bl & multi	1.65	1.50
a.	Souvenir sheet of 4	3.25	3.25
	Nos. 336-339 (4)	2.95	2.60

WHO, 20th anniv. No. 339a contains 4 imperf. stamps similar to Nos. 336-339.

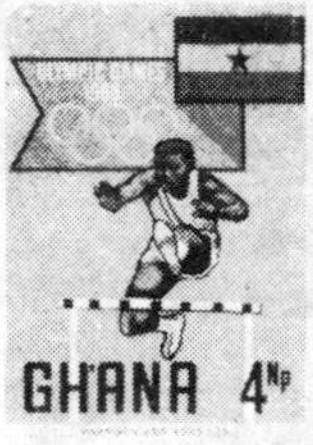
Hurdling — A86

Designs: 12½np, Boxing. 20np, Torch bearer, flags and Olympic rings. 40np, Soccer.

1968, Dec. Unwmk. *Perf. 14x14½*

340 A86	4np gray & multi	.15	.15
341 A86	12½np gray & multi	.35	.25
342 A86	20np ultra & multi	.70	.60
343 A86	40np gray & multi	1.40	1.25
a.	Souvenir sheet of 4	3.50	3.50
	Nos. 340-343 (4)	2.60	2.25

19th Olympic Games, Mexico City, Oct. 12-27, 1968. No. 343a contains 4 imperf. stamps with simulated perforations similar to Nos. 340-343.

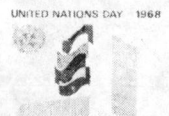

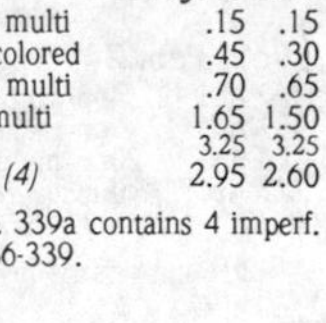
UN Headquarters and Flags — A87

UN Day, 1968: 12np, UN emblem and Ghanaian staff and stool. 20np, UN Headquarters, New York, UN emblem and Ghana flag. 40np, UN emblem surrounded by flags.

1969, Feb. 1 Litho. *Perf. 13x13½*

344 A87	4np multicolored	.15	.15
345 A87	12½np pink & multi	.35	.22
346 A87	20np blk & multi	.75	.50
347 A87	40np lt bl & multi	1.40	1.20
a.	Souvenir sheet of 4	3.50	3.00
	Nos. 344-347 (4)	2.65	2.07

No. 347a contains 4 imperf. stamps with simulated perforations similar to #344-347.

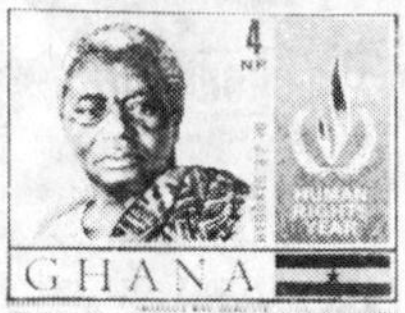
Joseph Boakye Danquah A88

Design: 12½np, 20np, Dr. Martin Luther King, Jr., Human Rights flame and flag of Ghana.

1969, Mar. 7 Photo. *Perf. 14½x14*

348 A88	4np gray & multi	.15	.15
349 A88	12½np multicolored	.45	.30
350 A88	20np blue & multi	.85	.80
351 A88	40np grn & multi	1.50	1.50
a.	Souvenir sheet of 4	3.25	3.25
	Nos. 348-351 (4)	2.95	2.75

Intl. Human Rights Year, Rev. Martin Luther King, Jr. (1929-1968), American civil rights leader, and Joseph Boakye Danquah (1895-1965), lawyer, writer and Ghanaian political leader.

No. 351a contains 4 imperf. stamps with simulated perforations similar to #348-351.

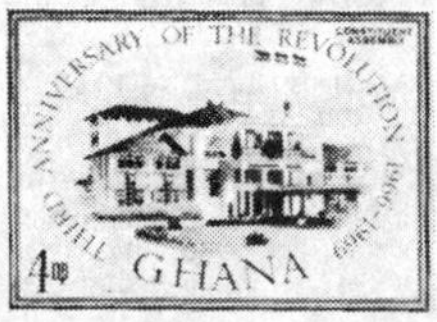
Parliament A89

Design: 12½np, 40np, Coat of Arms.

1969, Sept. Wmk. 325 *Perf. 14½x14*

352 A89	4np multicolored	.15	.15
353 A89	12½p multicolored	.45	.30
354 A89	20np multicolored	.75	.70
355 A89	40np multicolored	1.50	1.40
a.	Souvenir sheet of 4	3.00	3.00
	Nos. 352-355 (4)	2.85	2.55

3rd anniv. of the revolution. No. 355a contains 4 imperf. stamps with simulated perforations similar to Nos. 352-355.

Nos. 286-300 Overprinted in Black, Yellow or Red

NEW CONSTITUTION
1969

Perf. 11½x12, 12x11½ (A73), 14x14½, 14½x14 (A74-A75)

1969, Oct. 1 Photo. Wmk. 325

356 A73	1np multicolored	.15	.15
357 A74	1½np multicolored	.15	.15
358 A73	2np multicolored	.15	.15
359 A73	2½np multicolored	.15	.15
360 A75	3np multicolored	.15	.15
361 A73	4np multi (Y)	.15	.15
362 A75	6np multicolored	.15	.15
363 A73	8np multicolored	.16	.15
364 A75	9np multicolored	.16	.15
365 A75	10np multicolored	.20	.16
366 A74	20np blue	.50	.45
367 A74	50np multicolored	1.75	1.25
368 A74	1nc multicolored	2.25	1.90
369 A74	2nc multi (R)	5.25	4.50
370 A74	2.50nc multicolored	6.75	5.25
	Nos. 356-370 (15)	18.07	14.86

Overprint vertical on vertical stamps.

The 4np also exists with overprint in black and in red.

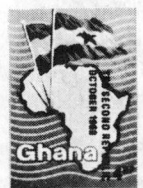

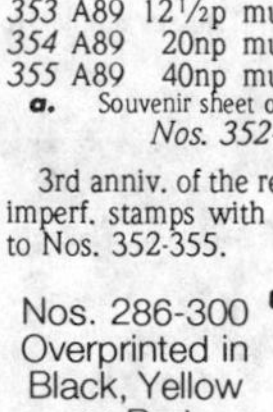
Map of Africa, Two Ghana Flags Rising from Ghana — A90

Designs: 12½np, "2" with laurel and star. 20np, Three hands and egg (symbol of rebirth) and Kente cloth. 40np, like 4np.

Unwmk.

1969, Dec. 4 Litho. *Perf. 14*

371 A90	4np multicolored	.15	.15
372 A90	12½np bl & multi	.40	.30
373 A90	20np multicolored	.75	.70
374 A90	40np bl & multi	1.50	1.40
	Nos. 371-374 (4)	2.80	2.55

Inauguration of the 2nd Republic, Oct. 1969.

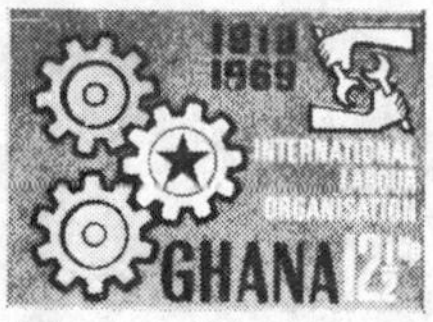
Cogwheels and ILO Emblem A91

Perf. 14½x14

1970, Jan. 5 Photo. Wmk. 325

375 A91	4np rose red & multi	.15	.15
376 A91	12½np multicolored	.45	.30
377 A91	20np multicolored	.75	.65
a.	Souvenir sheet of 3	1.75	1.10
	Nos. 375-377 (3)	1.35	1.10

ILO, 50th anniv. No. 377a contains 3 imperf. stamps similar to Nos. 375-377 with simulated perforations.

Nos. 375-377 printed in sheets of 12.

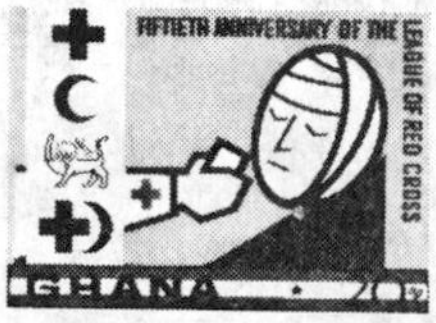
Red Cross Helping Wounded A92

Designs: 4np, Red Cross and globe, vert. 12½np, Henri Dunant, Red Cross, Red Crescent, Lion and Sun emblems. 40np, Red Cross and first aid.

1970, Feb. 2 *Perf. 14x14½, 14½x14*

378 A92	4np gold & multi	.15	.15
379 A92	12½np gold & multi	.30	.15
380 A92	20np blue & multi	.60	.25
381 A92	40np multicolored	1.25	.50
a.	Souvenir sheet of 4	2.25	2.00
	Nos. 378-381 (4)	2.30	
	Set value		.91

League of Red Cross Societies, 50th anniv. No. 381a contains 4 imperf. stamps similar to Nos. 378-381 with simulated perforations.

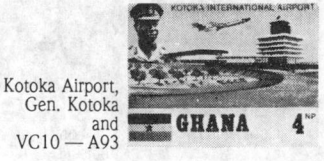

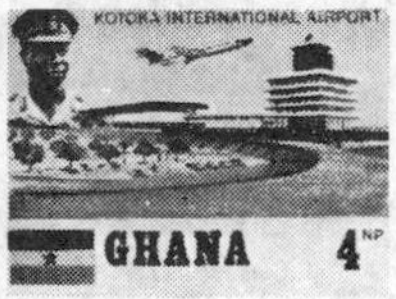
Kotoka Airport, Gen. Kotoka and VC10 — A93

Designs: 12½np, Control tower and tail section of VC10. 20np, Bird's eye view of airport and runway. 40np, Flags in front of Kotoka Airport.

Perf. 13x14

1970, Apr. Unwmk. Litho.

382 A93	4np multicolored	.15	.15
383 A93	12½np multicolored	.35	.20
384 A93	20np multicolored	.65	.50
385 A93	40np multicolored	1.25	1.00
	Nos. 382-385 (4)	2.40	1.85

Inauguration of Kotoka Airport.

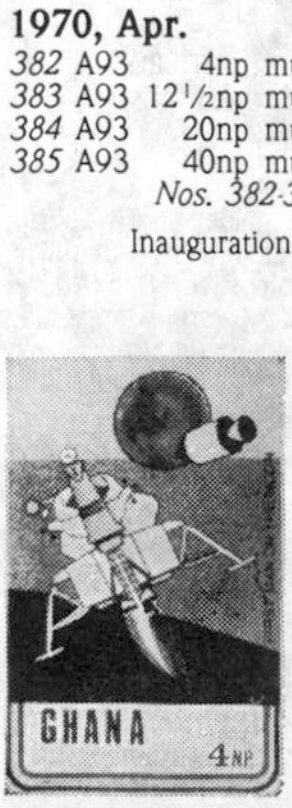
Lunar Landing Module and Spacecraft — A94

Designs: 12½np, Neil A. Armstrong stepping onto the moon. 20np, Scientific experiments on the moon, horiz. 40np, Neil A. Armstrong, Michael Collins and Edwin E. Aldrin, Jr., after return to earth, horiz.

1970, June 15 Litho. *Perf. 12½*

386 A94	4np multicolored	.30	.25
387 A94	12½np multicolored	1.50	1.25
388 A94	20np multicolored	1.75	1.50
389 A94	40np multicolored	6.00	5.00
a.	Souvenir sheet of 4	9.00	8.00
	Nos. 386-389 (4)	9.55	8.00

See note after US No. C76. No. 389a contains 4 imperf. stamps similar to Nos. 386-389. Exists with and without simulated perfs.

Nos. 386-389 and 389a were overprinted "PHILYMPIA/LONDON 1970" in black or silver in Sept. 1970. They are believed not to have been regularly issued.

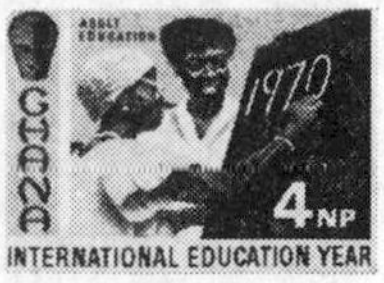
Adult Education A95

Education Year Emblem and: 12½np, Children of various races studying together. 20np, "Ntesie" symbol of wisdom and knowledge. 40np, Nursery school children.

1970, Aug. 10 Litho. *Perf. 13x12½*

390 A95	4np blue & multi	.15	.15
391 A95	12½np blue & multi	.32	.25
392 A95	20np blue & multi	.52	.40
393 A95	40np blue & multi	1.00	.80
	Nos. 390-393 (4)	1.99	1.60

Issued for International Education Year.

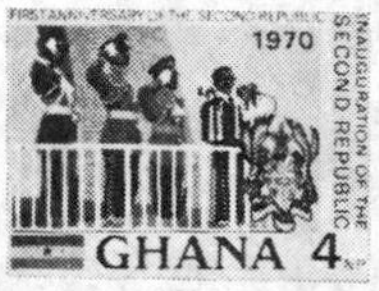
Inauguration of Second Republic — A96

Designs: 12½np, Mace and words of proclamation by K. A. Busia. 20np, Mace and globe with doves. 40np, Opening of Parliament of Second Republic.

1970, Oct. 1 Litho. *Perf. 13*

398 A96	4np multicolored	.15	.15
399 A96	12½np multicolored	.40	.30
400 A96	20np multicolored	.65	.50
401 A96	40np lt bl & multi	1.25	1.10
	Nos. 398-401 (4)	2.45	2.05

First anniversary of the Second Republic.

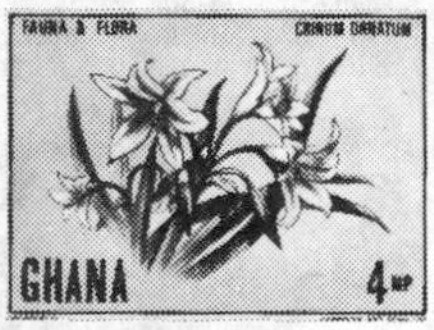
Amaryllis A97

Perf. 14½x14

1970 Photo. Wmk. 325

402 A97	4np shown	.15	.15
403 A97	12½np Lioness	.30	.15
404 A97	20np African orchid	.75	.30
405 A97	40np Elephant	1.50	.75
	Nos. 402-405 (4)	2.70	1.35

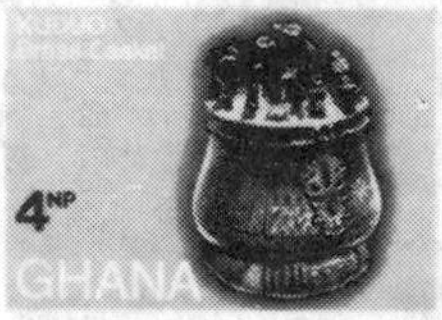
Kuduo Brass Casket A98

Designs: 12½np, Akan traditional house, Danmum. 20np, Larabanga Mosque. 40np, Akan funerary clay head.

1970, Dec. 7 Litho. *Perf. 14½x14*

406 A98	4np gray & multi	.15	.15
407 A98	12½np blue & multi	.32	.25
408 A98	20np multicolored	.52	.40
a.	Souvenir sheet of 4	2.25	2.25
409 A98	40np blue & multi	1.00	.90
	Nos. 406-409 (4)	1.99	1.70

No. 408a contains stamps similar to Nos. 406 and 408, a 12½np (Pompeii Basilica) and a 40np (Pompeii scene). Simulated perforation.

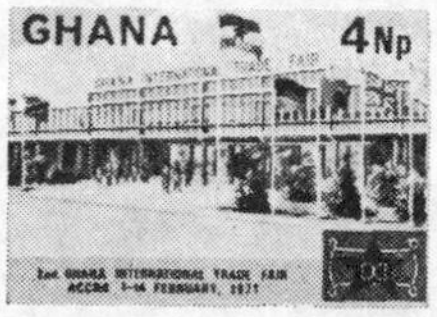

Fair Building and Emblem A99

Fair Emblem and: 12½np, Drugstore merchandise. 20np, Automotives and tools. 40np, Cranes and trucks. 50np, Cargo, ship and plane, vert.

Perf. 14½x14, 14x14½

1971, Feb. 5 Photo. Wmk. 325

410 A99	4np	multicolored	.15	.15
411 A99	12½np	lilac & multi	.28	.28
412 A99	20np	blue & multi	.45	.45
413 A99	40np	multicolored	.90	.90
414 A99	50np	multicolored	1.10	1.10
		Nos. 410-414 (5)	2.88	2.88

2nd Ghana International Trade Fair, Accra, Feb. 1-14, 1971.

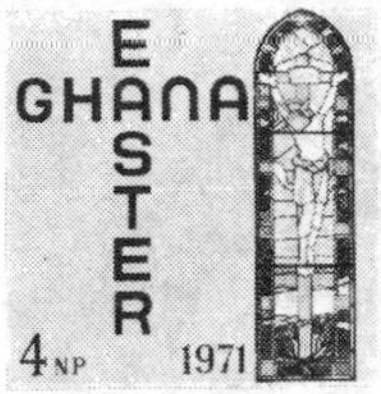

Crucifixion A100

Easter: 12½np, Jesus and disciples. 20np, Resurrection.

Perf. 13½

1971, May 19 Litho. Unwmk.

415 A100	4np	multicolored	.15	.15
416 A100	12½np	multicolored	.40	.35
417 A100	20np	multicolored	.75	.70
		Nos. 415-417 (3)	1.30	1.20

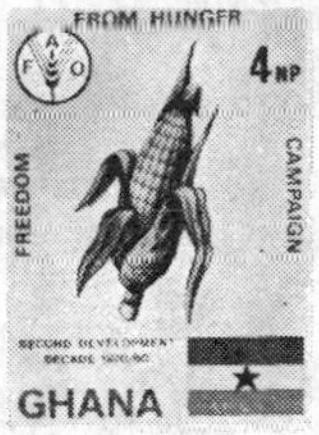

Corn and FAO Emblem — A101

Perf. 14x14½

1971, June Wmk. 325 Photo.

418 A101	4np	lilac & multi	.28	.20
419 A101	12½np	lt bl & multi	1.10	.65
420 A101	20np	multicolored	2.00	1.25
		Nos. 418-420 (3)	3.38	2.10

Freedom from Hunger, second development decade, 1970-1980.

The overprint "In Memoriam / Lord Boyd ORR / 1880-1971" was applied to Nos. 418-420 in October, 1971. The 4np was also surcharged "60NP."

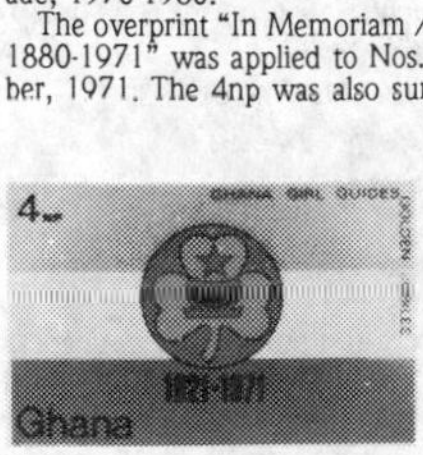

Girl Guide Emblem on Flag of Ghana A102

Emblem and: 12½np, Mrs. Elsie Ofuatey-Kodjoe, national founder. 20np, Girl Guides at play. 40np, Campfire and tent. 50np, Girl Guides signalling.

Unwmk.

1971, July 22 Litho. *Perf. 14*

421 A102	4np	multicolored	.15	.15
422 A102	12½np	yel & multi	.28	.28
423 A102	20np	sal & multi	.50	.50
424 A102	40np	multicolored	1.00	1.00
425 A102	50np	lilac & multi	1.25	1.10
a.		Souvenir sheet of 5	3.00	2.75
		Nos. 421-425 (5)	3.18	3.03

50th anniversary of the Girl Guides of Ghana. No. 425a contains 5 imperf. stamps similar to Nos. 421-425.

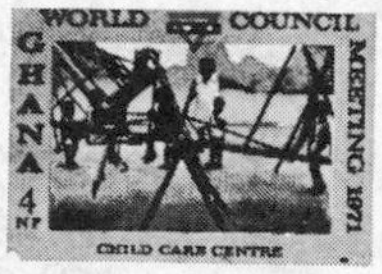

Child Care Center — A103

YWCA Emblem and: 12½np, World Council Meeting and map of Ghana. 20np, Typing class. 40np, Building fund day.

1971, Aug. 5 *Perf. 13*

426 A103	4np	multicolored	.15	.15
427 A103	12½np	ultra & multi	.30	.30
428 A103	20np	blue & multi	.50	.50
429 A103	40np	yel & multi	.90	.90
a.		Souvenir sheet of 4	2.50	2.50
		Nos. 426-429 (4)	1.85	1.85

World Council Meeting of Young Women's Christian Association, Accra, Aug. 5. No. 429a contains 4 stamps similar to Nos. 426-429 with simulated perforations.

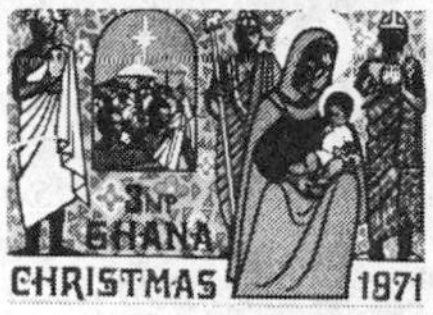

African Nativity Scene A104

Christmas: 1np, Fireworks, vert. 6np, Flight into Egypt.

Perf. 14x14½, 14½x14

1971, Nov. Photo. Wmk. 325

433 A104	1np	multicolored	.15	.15
434 A104	3np	orange & multi	.15	.15
435 A104	6np	blue & multi	.18	.15
		Set value	.30	.25

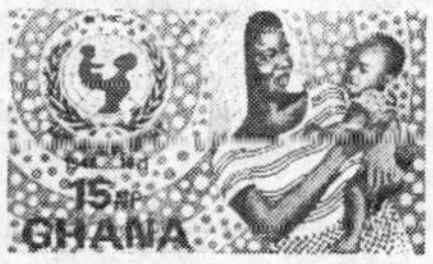

UNICEF Emblem, and Child — A105

UNICEF Emblem and: 5np, Infant weighed in net scale, vert. 30np, Student midwife, vert. 50np, Boy in day care center.

Perf. 13½x13, 13x13½

1971, Dec. 20 Litho. Unwmk.

436 A105	5np	grn & multi	.15	.15
437 A105	15np	yel & multi	.45	.40
438 A105	30np	pink & multi	.85	.70
439 A105	50np	blue & multi	1.65	1.50
a.		Souvenir sheet of 4	3.50	3.50
		Nos. 436-439 (4)	3.10	2.75

25th anniv. of UNICEF. No. 439a contains 4 stamps with simulated perforations similar to Nos. 436-439.

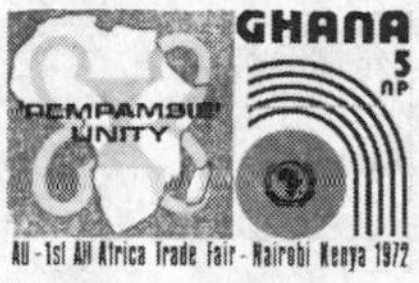

Fair Emblem, Map of Africa, Symbol of Unity — A106

Fair Emblem and: 15np, Horn of Plenty. 30np, Fireworks over Africa. 60np, 1nc, Names of participating nations over map of Africa.

1972, Feb. 23 Litho. *Perf. 14*

440 A106	5np	lt brn & multi	.18	.15
441 A106	15np	lt bl & multi	.65	.50
442 A106	30np	green & multi	1.40	1.25
443 A106	60np	yel & multi	2.00	1.90
444 A106	1nc	lt bl & multi	3.50	3.25
		Nos. 440-444 (5)	7.73	7.05

First All-Africa Trade Fair, Nairobi, Kenya, Feb. 23-Mar. 5.

Nos. 440-444 were overprinted "BELGICA 72" in red for release June 24, 1972. The regularity of this issue has been questioned.

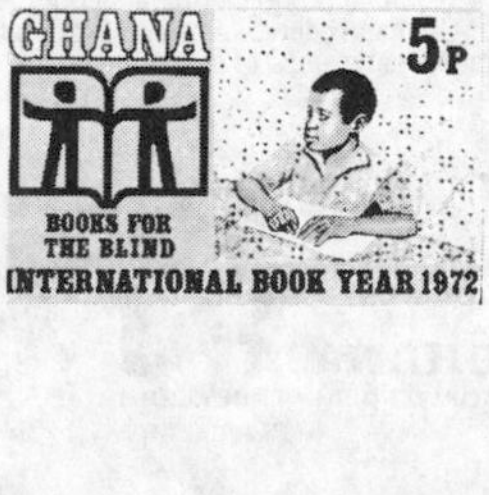

Books for the Blind A107

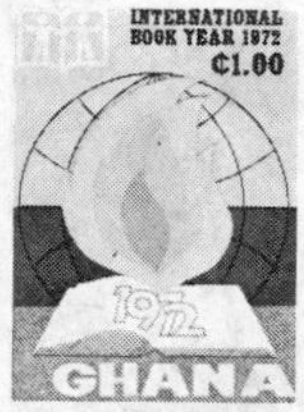

Book and Flame of Knowledge — A108

Book Year Emblem and: 15p, Books for Children ("Anansi and Snake the Postman"). 30p, Books for Recreation (Accra Central Library). 50p, Books for Students (2 students).

1972, Apr. 21 *Perf. 13½*

445 A107	5p	blue & multi	.15	.15
446 A107	15p	yel & multi	.35	.35
447 A107	30p	lilac & multi	.75	.75
448 A107	50p	green & multi	1.10	1.10
449 A108	1ce	blue & multi	1.75	1.75
a.		Souvenir sheet of 5	4.50	4.25
		Nos. 445-449 (5)	4.10	4.10

Intl. Book Year. No. 449a contains one each of Nos. 445-449 with simulated perforations.

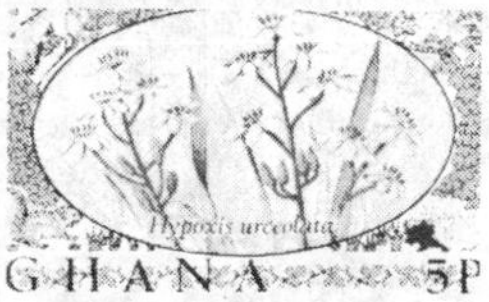

Star Grass A109

1972, July 3 Litho. *Perf. 13½*

450 A109	5p	shown	.15	.15
451 A109	15p	Mona monkey	.35	.25
452 A109	30p	Amaryllis	1.00	.50
453 A109	1ce	Side-striped squirrel	3.50	1.75
		Nos. 450-453 (4)	5.00	2.65

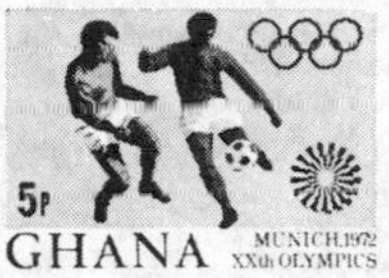

Olympic Emblems, Soccer — A110

1972, Sept. 5 Litho. *Perf. 13½x13*

454 A110	5p	shown	.15	.15
455 A110	15p	Running	.38	.25
456 A110	30p	Boxing	.75	.55
457 A110	50p	Long jump	1.25	1.00
458 A110	1ce	High jump	2.75	2.25
		Nos. 454-458 (5)	5.28	4.20

Souvenir Sheet

459		Sheet of 2	4.50	2.50
a.	A110	40p like 30p	.75	.50
b.	A110	60p like 5p	1.10	.75

20th Olympic Games, Munich, Aug. 26-Sept. 11.

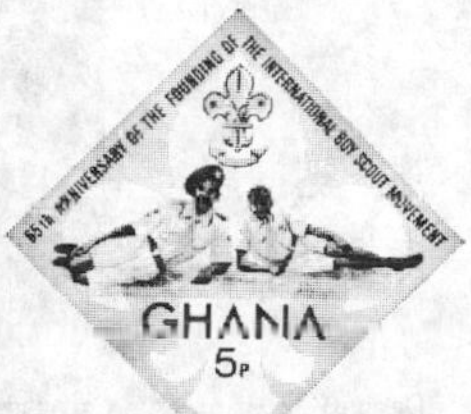

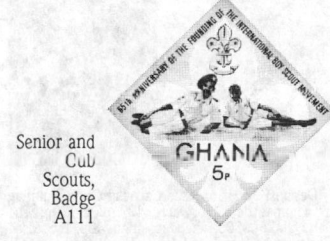

Senior and Cub Scouts, Badge A111

Designs: 15p, Scout in front of tent. 30p, 40p, Sea Scouts in canoe. 50p, Cub Scouts with den mother. 60p, 1ce, Scouts studying.

1972, Oct. Litho. *Perf. 14*

460 A111	5p	blue grn & multi	.15	.15
461 A111	15p	ocher & multi	.40	.30
462 A111	30p	lilac & multi	.80	.65
463 A111	50p	multicolored	1.25	1.10
464 A111	1ce	blue & multi	2.50	2.25
		Nos. 460-464 (5)	5.10	4.45

Souvenir Sheet

Perf. 13½

465		Sheet of 2	3.75	3.75
a.	A111	40p brown & multi	.60	.38
b.	A111	60p green & multi	.90	.55

Boy Scout Movement, 65th anniversary.

For overprints see Nos. 484-489.

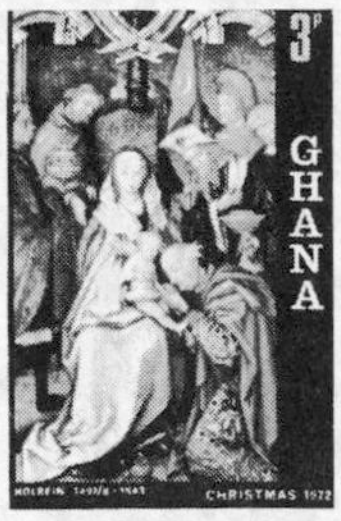

Virgin and Child, by Holbein the Younger — A112

Paintings: 1p, Holy Night, by Correggio. 15p, Virgin and Child, by Andrea Rico. 30p, Melchior. 60p, Virgin and Child with Caspar. 1ce, Balthasar. 30p, 60p, 1ce, are from early 16th century stained glass windows.

1972, Dec. 2 *Perf. 14x13½*

466 A112	1p	black & multi	.15	.15
467 A112	3p	black & multi	.15	.15
468 A112	15p	black & multi	.28	.20
469 A112	30p	black & multi	.55	.45
470 A112	60p	black & multi	1.25	.90
471 A112	1ce	black & multi	2.25	1.50
a.		Souvenir sheet of 3	4.00	3.00
		Nos. 466-471 (6)	4.63	3.35

Christmas. No. 471a contains one each of Nos. 469-471 with simulated perforations.

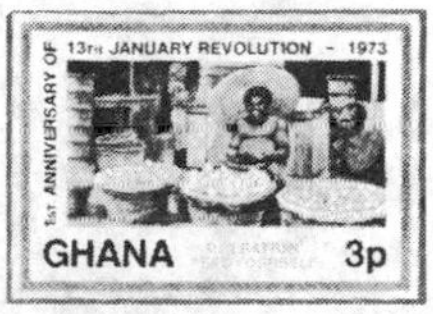

Market A113

Designs: 1p, Unity Declaration at Kumasi Durbar. 5p, Woman with child selling bananas, vert. 15p, Farmer at rest and produce, vert. 30p, Market. 40p, 1ce, Farmer cutting palm nuts with cutlass. 60p, Miners.

Perf. 14x13½, 13½x14

1973, Apr. Litho.

472 A113	1p	multicolored	.15	.15
473 A113	3p	multicolored	.15	.15
474 A113	5p	multicolored	.15	.15
475 A113	15p	multicolored	.40	.35
476 A113	30p	multicolored	.75	.70
477 A113	1ce	multicolored	2.50	2.40
		Nos. 472-477 (6)	4.10	3.90

Souvenir Sheet

478		Sheet of 2	3.00	2.75
a.	A113	40p multicolored	.80	.50
b.	A113	60p multicolored	1.20	.75

Operation "Feed Yourself" and for 1st anniv. of the Oct. 13 Revolution.

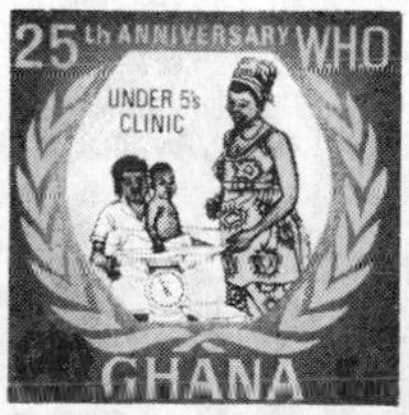

Children's Clinic — A114

WHO Emblem and: 15p, Radiology. 30p, Immunization. 50p, Fight against malnutrition (starving child). 1ce, WHO Headquarters, Geneva.

1973, July *Perf. 14x13½*

479 A114	5p	rose red & multi	.15	.15
480 A114	15p	blue & multi	.28	.28
481 A114	30p	bister & multi	.60	.55
482 A114	50p	green & multi	1.00	.90
483 A114	1ce	multicolored	2.00	1.75
		Nos. 479-483 (5)	4.03	3.63

WHO, 25th anniversary.

Nos. 460-465 Overprinted: "1st WORLD SCOUTING CONFERENCE IN AFRICA"

1973, July Litho. *Perf. 14*

484 A111	5p	green & multi	.15	.15
485 A111	15p	ocher & multi	.35	.35
486 A111	30p	lilac & multi	.75	.70
487 A111	50p	multicolored	1.25	1.10
488 A111	1ce	blue & multi	2.50	2.25
		Nos. 484-488 (5)	5.00	4.55

Souvenir Sheet

Perf. 13½

489		Sheet of 2	3.25	3.00
a.	A111	40p brown & multi	.90	.60
b.	A111	60p green & multi	1.25	.90

24th Boy Scout World Conference (1st in Africa), Nairobi, Kenya, July 16-21.

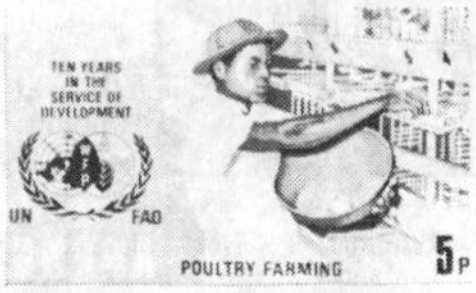

Poultry Farming A115

FAO/UN Emblem and: 15p, 40p, Tractor. 50p, Cacao harvest. 60p, 1ce, FAO Headquarters, Rome.

1973 Litho. *Perf. 14½x14*

490	A115	5p blue & multi	.15	.15
491	A115	15p blue & multi	.50	.45
492	A115	50p blue & multi	1.50	1.35
493	A115	1ce blue & multi	3.00	2.75
		Nos. 490-493 (4)	5.15	4.70

Souvenir Sheet

494		Sheet of 2	3.00	2.75
a.	A115	40p blue & multi	.80	.50
b.	A115	60p blue & multi	1.20	.75

World Food Program, 10th anniversary.

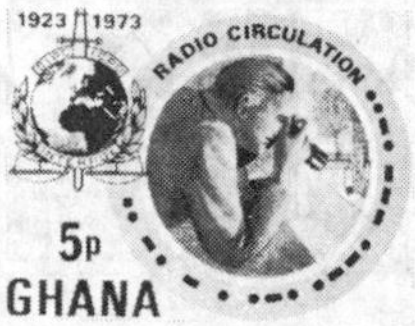

INTERPOL Emblem, Observer A116

INTERPOL Emblem and: 30p, Judge's wig, poison bottle, handcuffs. 50p, photograph and fingerprint. 1ce, Corpse and question mark.

1973 *Perf. 13x13½*

495	A116	5p emerald & multi	.15	.15
496	A116	30p rose red & multi	.65	.60
497	A116	50p ultra & multi	1.00	.90
498	A116	1ce gray & multi	2.25	2.00
		Nos. 495-498 (4)	4.05	3.65

50th anniv. the Intl. Criminal Police Org. (INTERPOL).

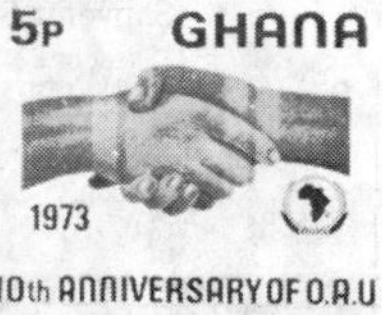

Handclasp and "OAU" — A117

"OAU" and: 30p, Africa Hall, Addis Ababa. 50p, OAU emblem (map of Africa). 1ce, "X" in Ghana flag colors.

1973, Oct. 22 Litho. *Perf. 14x14½*

499	A117	5p lt bl, blk & brn	.15	.15
500	A117	30p bluish grn, blk & brn	.65	.60
501	A117	50p pink, black & ol	1.00	.90
502	A117	1ce multicolored	2.25	2.00
		Nos. 499-502 (4)	4.05	3.65

Org. for African Unity, 10th anniv.

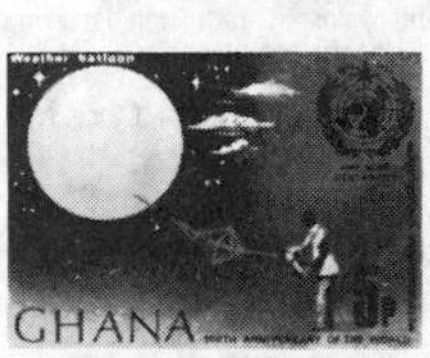

Weather Balloon, WMO Emblem A118

WMO Emblem and: 15p, 40p, Tiros weather satellite. 30p, 60p, Computer weather map. 1ce, Radar cloud scanner.

1973, Nov. 16

503	A118	5p multicolored	.15	.15
504	A118	15p multicolored	.30	.25
505	A118	30p multicolored	.60	.50
506	A118	1ce multicolored	1.75	1.50
		Nos. 503-506 (4)	2.80	2.40

Souvenir Sheet

507		Sheet of 2	2.50	2.25
a.	A118	40p multicolored	.75	.40
b.	A118	60p multicolored	1.10	.60

Intl. meteorological cooperation, cent.

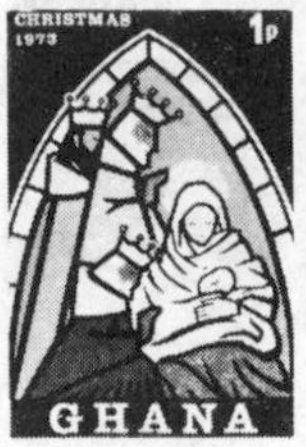

Adoration of the Kings — A119

Christmas: 3p, 40p, Madonna and Child (contemporary). Nos. 510, 511d, Madonna and Child, by Murillo. No. 511, 60p, Adoration of the Kings, by Tiepolo. No. 511b as 1p.

1973, Dec. 10 *Perf. 14*

508	A119	1p black & multi	.15	.15
509	A119	3p gray & multi	.15	.15
510	A119	30p multicolored	.90	.90
511	A119	50p multicolored	1.75	1.75
		Nos. 508-511 (4)	2.95	2.95

Souvenir Sheet

Imperf

511A		Sheet of 4	2.75	2.75
b.	A119	30p black & multi	.45	.45
c.	A119	40p gray & multi	.60	.60
d.	A119	50p multicolored	.75	.75
e.	A119	60p multicolored	.90	.90

No. 511A has simulated perforations.

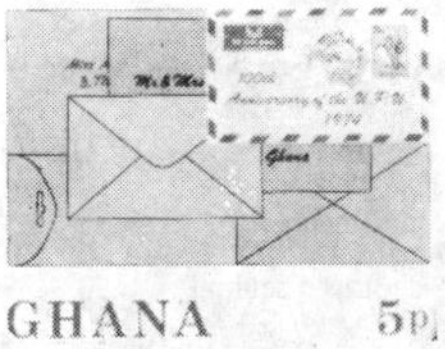

Various Envelopes A120

UPU Emblem and: 9p, 30p, UPU Headquarters, Bern. 40p, 50p, Airmail envelope with Ghana No. 296. 60p, 1ce, Ghana No. 296.

1974, May Litho. *Perf. 14½*

512	A120	5p blue, blk & org	.15	.15
513	A120	9p blue, blk & org	.15	.15
514	A120	50p blue, blk & org	.90	.80
515	A120	1ce blue, blk & org	1.90	1.75
		Nos. 512-515 (4)	3.10	2.85

Souvenir Sheet

515A		Sheet of 4	3.00	2.75
b.	A120	20p blue, blk & org	.25	.25
c.	A120	30p blue, blk & org	.50	.50
d.	A120	40p blue, blk & org	.75	.75
e.	A120	50p blue, blk & org	.90	.90

Centenary of Universal Postal Union.
For overprints see Nos. 521-524A.

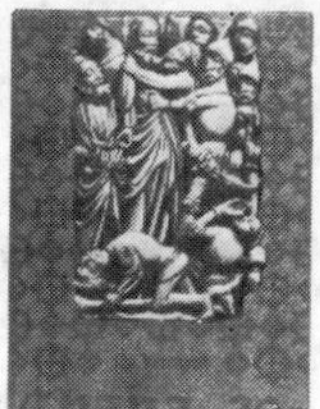

The Betrayal — A121

Designs: 5p, 15p, Jesus Carrying Cross, painting by Thomas de Coloswar, 1427. 20p, 30p, The Betrayal. 25p, 50p, The Deposition. 40p, 1ce, Risen Christ and Mary Magdalene. The designs (except 5p, 15p) are from 15th century English ivory carvings.

1974, Apr. Litho. *Perf. 14*

516	A121	5p black & multi	.15	.15
517	A121	30p sil, ultra & brn	.48	.48
518	A121	50p sil, red & brn	.80	.80
519	A121	1ce silver, ol & brn	1.60	1.60
		Nos. 516-519 (4)	3.03	3.03

Souvenir Sheet

Imperf

520		Sheet of 4	1.65	1.65
a.	A121	15p black & multi	.22	
b.	A121	20p silver, ultra & brn	.30	
c.	A121	25p silver, red & brn	.38	
d.	A121	40p silver, olive & brn	.60	

Easter. No. 520 contains 4 stamps with simulated perforations.

Nos. 512-515A Overprinted "INTERNABA 1974"

1974, June 7 *Perf. 14½*

521	A120	5p blue, blk & org	.15	.15
522	A120	9p blue, blk & org	.20	.15
523	A120	50p blue, blk & org	1.35	1.00
524	A120	1ce blue, blk & org	2.75	2.00
		Nos. 521-524 (4)	4.45	3.30

Souvenir Sheet

524A		Sheet of 4	3.75	3.00
b.	A120	20p blue, blk & org	.28	.28
c.	A120	30p blue, blk & org	.52	.52
d.	A120	40p blue, blk & org	.75	.75
e.	A120	60p blue, blk & org	1.00	1.00

INTERNABA 1974 International Philatelic Exhibition, Basel, June 7-16.
Overprint is applied to individual stamps of No. 524A.

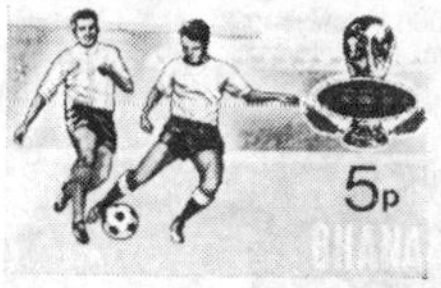

Soccer and World Cup Emblem A122

Designs: Various soccer scenes and world cup emblem.

1974, June 17 Litho. *Perf. 14½, 13*

525	A122	5p multicolored	.15	.15
526	A122	30p multicolored	.55	.45
527	A122	50p multicolored	.90	.80
528	A122	1ce multicolored	1.75	1.60
		Nos. 525-528 (4)	3.35	3.00

Souvenir Sheet

Perf. 14½

529		Sheet of 4	3.75	3.25
a.	A122	25p multicolored	.40	
b.	A122	40p multicolored	.65	
c.	A122	55p multicolored	.90	
d.	A122	60p multicolored	1.00	

World Cup Soccer Championship, June 13-July 7.
Nos. 525-528 were issued in sheets of 30, perf. 14½, and in sheets of 5 plus label, perf. 13.
For overprints, see Nos. 535-539, 549-553.

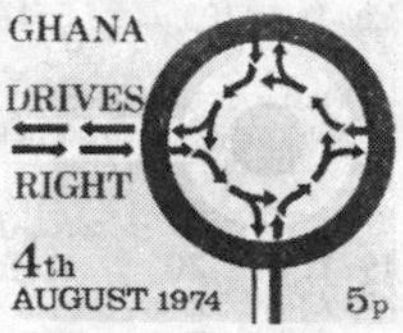

Traffic Diagram at Traffic Circle — A123

Designs: 15p, Traffic sign "Two-way traffic." 30p, "Change to right hand drive!," vert. 50p, Warning hands sign, vert. 1ce, 2 hands and car symbolizing traffic change, vert.

1974, July 16 *Perf. 13½*

Size: 35x28½mm

530	A123	5p yel grn, red & blk	.15	.15
531	A123	15p lilac, red & blk	.25	.18

Size: 28½x41mm

Perf. 14½

532	A123	30p multicolored	.50	.40
533	A123	50p multicolored	.80	.65
534	A123	1ce red, green & blk	1.75	1.50
		Nos. 530-534 (5)	3.45	2.88

Publicity for change to right-hand driving, Aug. 4, 1974.

Nos. 525-529 Overprinted: "WEST GERMANY WINNERS"

1974, Aug. 30 Litho. *Perf. 14½, 13*

535	A122	5p multicolored	.15	.15
536	A122	30p multicolored	.65	.65
537	A122	50p multicolored	1.10	1.10
538	A122	1ce multicolored	2.00	2.00
		Nos. 535-538 (4)	3.90	3.90

Souvenir Sheet

539		Sheet of 4	3.75	3.25
a.	A122	25p multicolored	.40	
b.	A122	40p multicolored	.65	
c.	A122	55p multicolored	.90	
d.	A122	60p multicolored	1.00	

World Cup Soccer Championship, 1974, victory of German Federal Republic. Overprint is applied to individual stamps of No. 539.

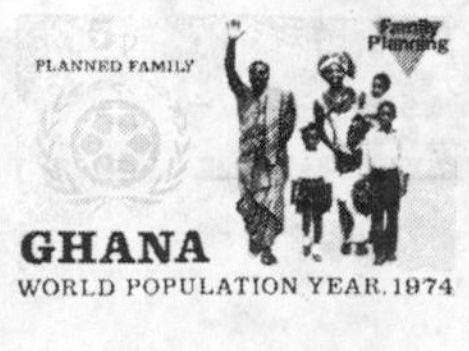

Family and WPY Emblem A124

1974, Sept. 27 *Perf. 12½*

540	A124	5p shown	.15	.15
541	A124	30p Clinic	.50	.40
542	A124	50p Immunization of children	.80	.75
543	A124	1ce Census	1.75	1.75
		Nos. 540-543 (4)	3.20	3.05

World Population Year.

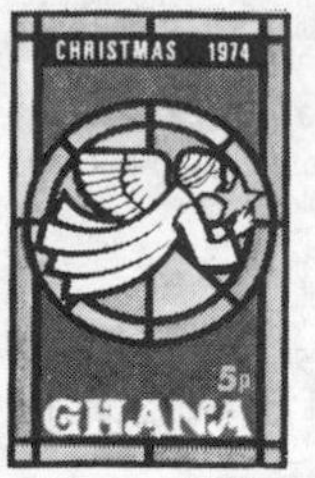

Angel — A125

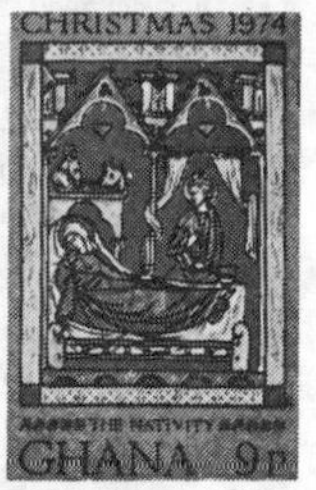

Nativity — A127

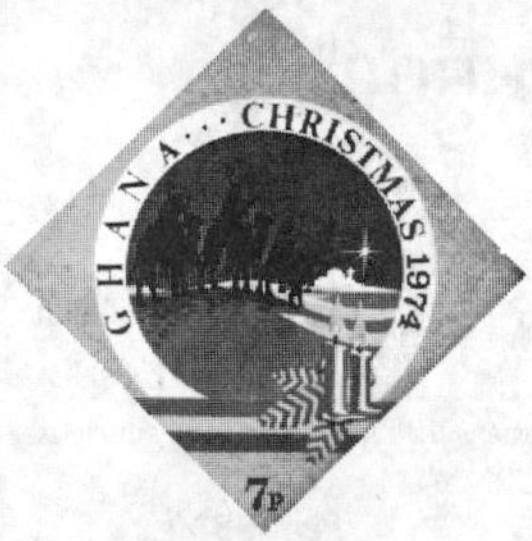

Three Kings, Candles — A126

Design: 60p, 1ce, Annunciation.

Perf. 13½, 14 (7p)

1974, Dec. 19 Litho.

544	A125	5p red & multi	.15	.15
545	A126	7p blue & multi	.15	.15
546	A127	9p orange & multi	.20	.15
547	A127	1ce orange & multi	2.50	2.50
		Nos. 544-547 (4)	3.00	2.95

Souvenir Sheet

Imperf

548		Sheet of 4	2.75	2.75
a.	A125	15p red & multi	.22	
b.	A126	30p blue & multi	.45	
c.	A127	45p orange & multi	.70	
d.	A127	60p orange & multi	.90	

Christmas. No. 548 contains 4 stamps with simulated perforations.

Nos. 525-529 Overprinted "APOLLO / SOYUZ / JULY 15, 1975"

1975, Aug. 15 Litho. *Perf. 14½, 13*

549	A122	5p multicolored	.15	.15
550	A122	30p multicolored	.52	.40
551	A122	50p multicolored	1.00	.80
552	A122	1ce multicolored	2.00	1.60
		Nos. 549-552 (4)	3.67	2.95

Souvenir Sheet

Perf. 14½

553		Sheet of 4	3.75	3.75
a.	A122	25p multicolored	.40	
b.	A122	40p multicolored	.65	
c.	A122	55p multicolored	.90	
d.	A122	60p multicolored	1.00	

Apollo Soyuz space test project (Russo-American cooperation), launching July 15, link-up, July 17.
Overprint is applied to individual stamps of No. 553.
Nos. 549-552 with perf. 13 are from the sheets of 5 plus label.

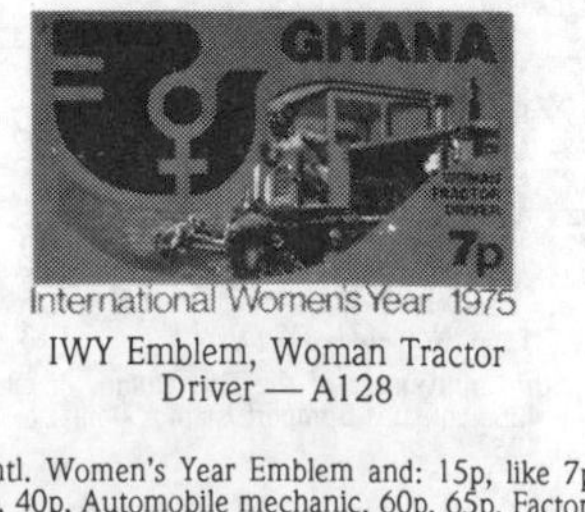

IWY Emblem, Woman Tractor Driver — A128

Intl. Women's Year Emblem and: 15p, like 7p. 30p, 40p, Automobile mechanic. 60p, 65p, Factory workers. 80p, 1ce, Cocoa research.

1975, Sept. 3 Litho. *Perf. 14*

554	A128	7p multicolored	.15	.15
555	A128	30p lt violet & multi	.55	.55
556	A128	60p multicolored	1.10	1.10
557	A128	1ce lilac & multi	1.75	1.75
		Nos. 554-557 (4)	3.55	3.55

Souvenir Sheet
Imperf

558 Sheet of 4 3.75 3.75
a. A128 15p Prus green & multi .22
b. A128 40p light violet & multi .60
c. A128 65p dull green & multi 1.00
d. A128 80p lilac & multi 1.20

Intl. Women's Year. No. 558 contains 4 stamps with simulated perforations.

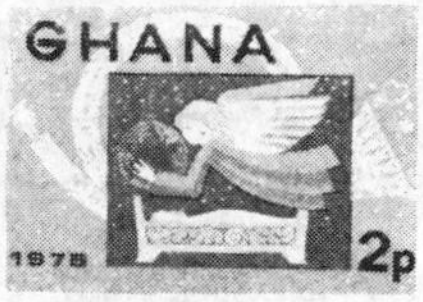

Angel over Child in Crib — A129

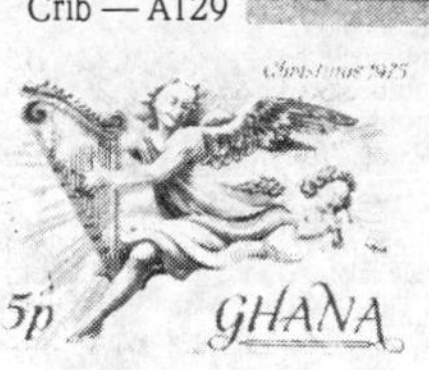

Angel with Harp — A130

Designs: 7p, 40p, Angels with lute and bell. 30p, 65p, Angel with viol. 1ce, 80p, Angels with trumpets. 15p, like 5p.

1975, Dec. 31 Litho. *Perf. 14x13½*
559 A129 2p org & multi .15 .15
560 A130 5p yel, brown & grn .15 .15
561 A130 7p yel, brown & grn .15 .15
562 A130 30p yel, brown & grn .48 .25
563 A130 1ce yel, brown & grn 1.60 1.00
Nos. 559-563 (5) 2.53
Set value 1.42

Souvenir Sheet
Imperf

564 Sheet of 4 3.50 3.50
a. A130 15p yellow, green & brown .25
b. A130 40p yellow, green & brown .25
c. A130 65p yellow, green & brown 1.10
d. A130 80p yellow, green & brown 1.25

Christmas. No. 564 has simulated perforations.

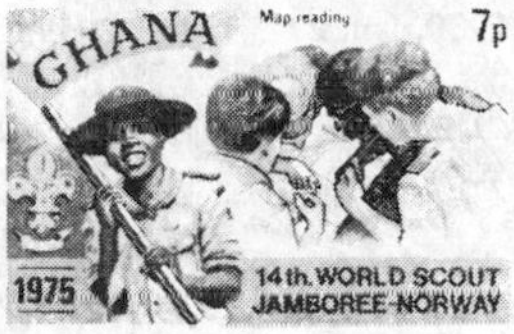

Boy Scouts Reading Map A131

Designs: 30p, 40p, Sailing. 60p, 65p, Hiking. 80p, 1ce, Life saving (swimmers). 15p, like 7p.

1976, Jan. 5 *Perf. 13½x14*
565 A131 7p ocher & multi .15 .15
566 A131 30p blue & multi .45 .22
567 A131 60p green & multi .90 .45
568 A131 1ce multicolored 1.50 .90
Nos. 565-568 (4) 3.00 1.72

Souvenir Sheet

569 Sheet of 4 3.50 3.50
a. A131 15p ocher & multi .25
b. A131 40p blue & multi .65
c. A131 65p green & multi 1.10
d. A131 80p rose claret & multi 1.25

Nordjamb 75, 14th World Boy Scout Jamboree, Lillehammer, Norway, July 29-Aug. 7.
For overprints, see Nos. 578-582.

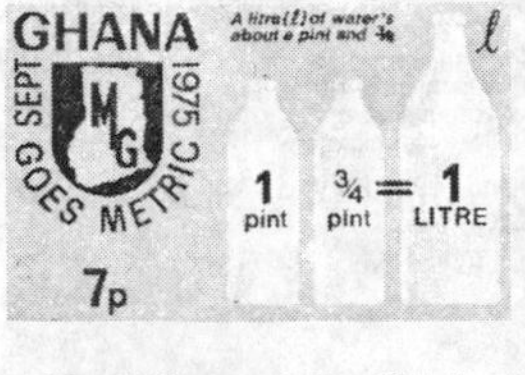

1¾ Pints Equal 1 Liter A132

Map of Ghana and: 30p, "2¼ lbs of jam a little more than a kilogram." 60p, "A meter of cloth will be a little more than 3 foot 3." 1ce, Thermometer, ice and boiling tea kettle.

1976, Jan. 5 Litho. *Perf. 14x13½*
570 A132 7p bluish gray & blk .15 .15
571 A132 30p vio blue & multi .45 .22
572 A132 60p ocher & multi .90 .45
573 A132 1ce multicolored 1.50 .90
Nos. 570-573 (4) 3.00 1.72

Introduction of metric system, Sept. 1975.

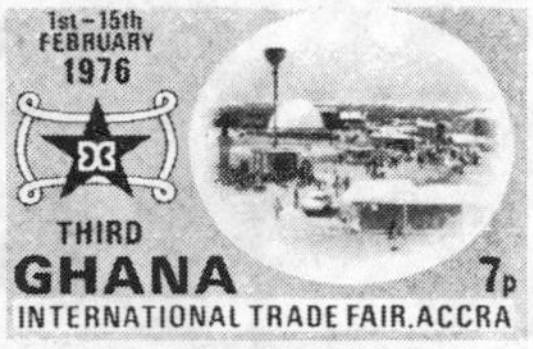

Fair Grounds — A133

Designs: Various exhibition halls.

1976, Apr. 6 Litho. *Perf. 14*
574 A133 7p multicolored .15 .15
575 A133 30p yellow & multi .45 .22
576 A133 60p multicolored .90 .45
577 A133 1ce salmon & multi 1.50 .90
Nos. 574-577 (4) 3.00 1.72

International Trade Fair, Accra, Feb. 1-15.

Nos. 565-569 Overprinted in Violet Blue: 'INTERPHIL' 76 BICENTENNIAL EXHIBITION

1976, May 29 Litho. *Perf. 13½x14*
578 A131 7p ocher & multi .15 .15
579 A131 30p blue & multi .55 .22
580 A131 60p green & multi 1.10 .45
581 A131 1ce multicolored 1.50 .90
Nos. 578-581 (4) 3.30 1.72

Souvenir Sheet

582 Sheet of 4 3.50 2.25
a. A131 15p ocher & multi .25
b. A131 40p blue & multi .65
c. A131 65p green & multi 1.10
d. A131 80p rose claret & multi 1.25

Interphil 76 International Philatelic Exhibition, Philadelphia, Pa., May 29-June 6. Overprint applied to individual stamps of No. 582.

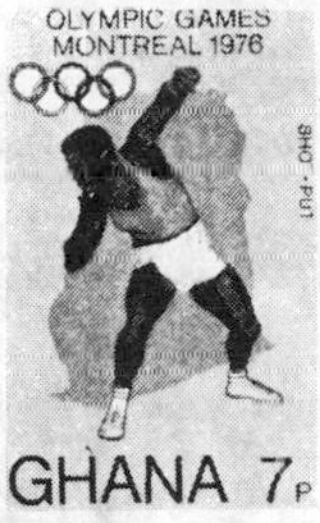

Shot Put — A134

Olympic Rings, Map of Ghana and: 15p, like 7p. 30p, 40p, Soccer. 60p, 65p, Women's 1500 meters. 80p, 1ce, Boxing.

1976, Aug. 9 Litho. *Perf. 14x13½*
583 A134 7p lt blue & multi .15 .15
584 A134 30p yellow & multi .48 .25
585 A134 60p multicolored 1.00 .48
586 A134 1ce yellow & multi 1.60 1.00
Nos. 583-586 (4) 3.23 1.88

Souvenir Sheet

587 Sheet of 4 3.50 3.50
a. A134 15p light blue & multi .25
b. A134 40p yellow & multi .65
c. A134 65p emerald & multi 1.00
d. A134 80p yellow & multi 1.25

21st Olympic Games, Montreal, Canada, July 17-Aug. 1.
For overprints see Nos. 606-610.

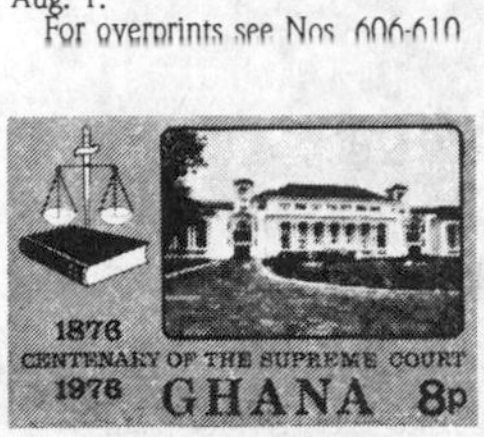

Supreme Court, Accra A135

Designs: Various views of Supreme Court Building, Scales of Justice, law book.

1976, Sept. 7 Litho. *Perf. 14*
588 A135 8p lilac & multi .15 .15
589 A135 30p blue & multi .50 .50
590 A135 60p ver & multi 1.00 1.00
591 A135 1ce multicolored 1.75 1.75
Nos. 588-591 (4) 3.40 3.40

Ghana Supreme Court, centenary.

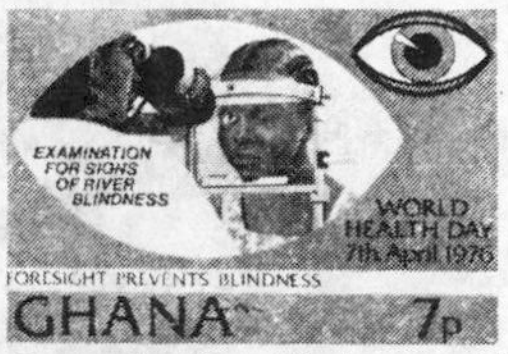

Examination for River Blindness — A136

Designs: 30p, Ghanaian entomologist with microscope. 60p, Flowers. 1ce, Boatmen checking effectiveness of black fly larvae insecticide.

1976, Oct. 28 Litho. *Perf. 14½x14*
592 A136 7p multicolored .15 .15
593 A136 30p multicolored .50 .50
594 A136 60p multicolored 1.00 1.00
595 A136 1ce multicolored 1.75 1.75
Nos. 592-595 (4) 3.40 3.40

World Health Day. Prevention of blindness.

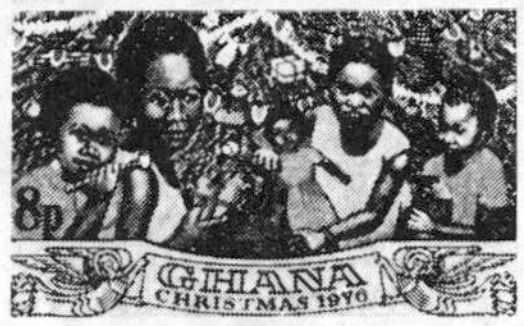

Children with Gifts and Christmas Tree — A137

Designs: 6p, 15p, Children with firecrackers. 30p, 65p, Family at Christmas dinner. 40p, 80p, 1ce, like 8p.

1976, Dec. 15 Litho. *Perf. 13½*
596 A137 6p multicolored .15 .15
597 A137 8p multicolored .15 .15
598 A137 30p multicolored .55 .55
599 A137 1ce multicolored 1.75 1.75
Nos. 596-599 (4) 2.60 2.60

Souvenir Sheet
Imperf

600 Sheet of 4 3.50 3.50
a. A137 15p multicolored .22
b. A137 40p multicolored .60
c. A137 65p multicolored 1.00
d. A137 80p multicolored 1.25

Christmas. No. 600 has simulated perfs.

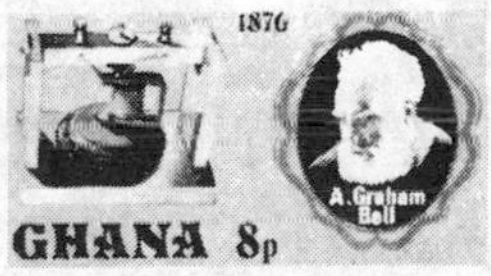

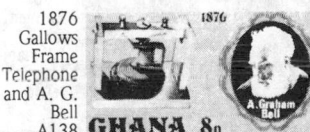

1876 Gallows Frame Telephone and A. G. Bell A138

A. G. Bell and: 15p, like 8p. 30p, 40p, 1895 telephone. 60p, 65p, 1929 telephone. 80p, 1ce, 1976 telephone.

1976, Dec. 17 *Perf. 14½*
601 A138 8p multicolored .15 .15
602 A138 30p multicolored .50 .25
603 A138 60p multicolored 1.10 .50
604 A138 1ce multicolored 1.75 .90
Nos. 601-604 (4) 3.50 1.80

Souvenir Sheet
Perf. 13

605 Sheet of 4 3.50 3.50
a. A138 15p multicolored .22
b. A138 40p multicolored .60
c. A138 65p multicolored 1.00
d. A138 80p multicolored 1.20

Centenary of first telephone call by Alexander Graham Bell, Mar. 10, 1876.
For overprints, see Nos. 616-620.

Nos. 583-587 Overprinted:
a. EAST GERMANY / WINNERS
b. U.S.S.R. WINNERS
c. U.S.A. WINNERS

1977, Feb. 22 Litho. *Perf. 14x13½*
606 A134(a) 7p multicolored .15 .15
607 A134(a) 30p multicolored .40 .20
608 A134(b) 60p multicolored .80 .40
609 A134(c) 1ce multicolored 1.75 .65
Nos. 606-609 (4) 3.10 1.40

Souvenir Sheet

610 Sheet of 4 3.50 2.50
a. A134(a) 15p multicolored .35
b. A134(a) 40p multicolored .75
c. A134(b) 65p multicolored 1.10
d. A134(c) 80p multicolored 1.25

1976 Montreal Olympic Games' winners.

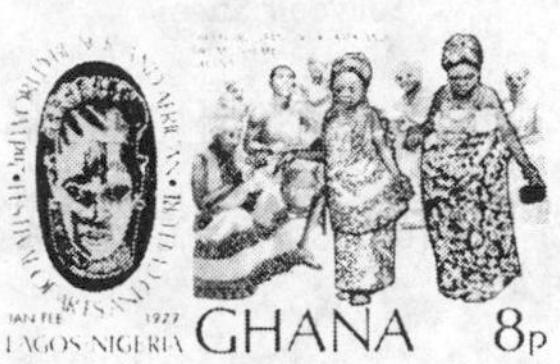

Klama Dance, Dipo Tribe — A139

Festival Emblem and: 15p, like 8p. 30p, 40p, African artifacts. 60p, 65p, Acon dance. 80p, 1ce, Mud, straw and wooden huts.

1977, Mar. 24 Litho. *Perf. 14x13½*
611 A139 8p multicolored .15 .15
612 A139 30p multicolored .45 .22
613 A139 60p multicolored .90 .45
614 A139 1ce multicolored 1.50 .75
Nos. 611-614 (4) 3.00 1.57

Souvenir Sheet

615 Sheet of 4 3.50 2.50
a. A139 15p multicolored .35
b. A139 40p multicolored .75
c. A139 65p multicolored 1.10
d. A139 80p multicolored 1.25

2nd World Black and African Festival of Arts and Culture, Lagos, Nigeria, Jan. 15-Feb. 12.

Nos. 601-605 Overprinted: "PRINCE CHARLES / VISITS GHANA / 17th TO 25th / MARCH, 1977"

1977, June 2 Litho. *Perf. 14½*
616 A138 8p multicolored .15 .15
617 A138 30p multicolored .40 .18
618 A138 60p multicolored .90 .35
619 A138 1ce multicolored 1.40 .60
Nos. 616-619 (4) 2.85 1.28

Souvenir Sheet
Perf. 13

620 Sheet of 4 3.50 2.50
a. A138 15p multicolored .35
b. A138 40p multicolored .75
c. A138 65p multicolored 1.10
d. A138 80p multicolored 1.25

Visit of Prince Charles, Mar. 17-25. Overprint applied to individual stamps of No. 620.

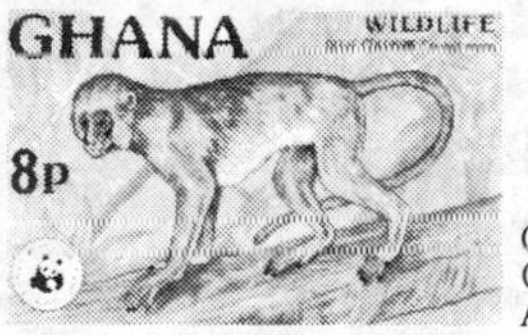

Olive Colobus A140

Wildlife Fund Emblem and: 15p, like 8p. 20p, 40p, Ebien palm squirrel. 30p, 65p, African wild dog. 60p, 80p, West African manatee.

1977, June 22 Litho. *Perf. 13½x14*
621 A140 8p multicolored .15 .15
622 A140 20p multicolored .35 .15
623 A140 30p multicolored .30 .20
624 A140 60p multicolored 1.00 .40
Nos. 621-624 (4) 1.80 .90

Souvenir Sheet

625 Sheet of 4 3.50 2.50
a. A140 15p multicolored .35
b. A140 40p multicolored .75
c. A140 65p multicolored 1.10
d. A140 80p multicolored 1.25

Wildlife protection.

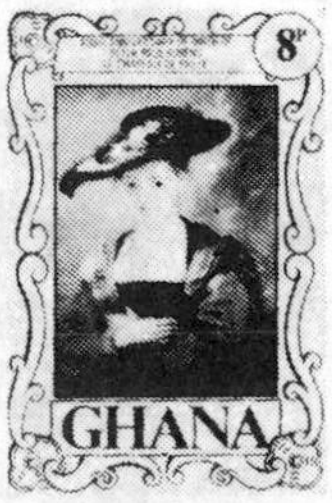

Suzanne Fourment in Velvet Hat, by Rubens — A141

Paintings: 15p, like 8p. 30p, 40p, Isabella of Portugal, by Titian. 60p, 65p, Duke and Duchess of Cumberland, by Gainsborough. 80p, 1ce, Rubens and his wife Isabella, by Rubens.

1977, Sept. Litho. *Perf. 14x13½*
626 A141 8p lt blue & multi .16 .16
627 A141 30p lt blue & multi .60 .60
628 A141 60p lt blue & multi 1.20 1.20
629 A141 1ce lt blue & multi 2.00 2.00
Nos. 626-629 (4) 3.96 3.96

Souvenir Sheet

630	Sheet of 4	4.25	4.25
a.	A141 15p light blue & multi	.30	
b.	A141 40p light blue & multi	.80	
c.	A141 65p light blue & multi	1.30	
d.	A141 80p light blue & multi	1.60	

Painters, birth annivs.: Peter Paul Rubens (1577-1640); Titian (1477-1576); Thomas Gainsborough (1727-1788).

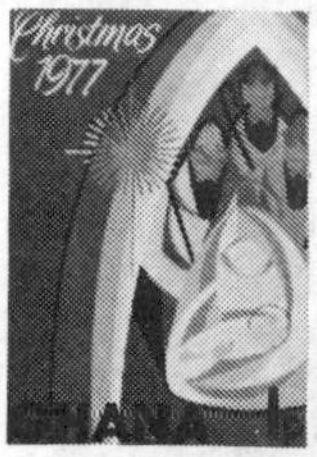

Adoration of the Kings — A142

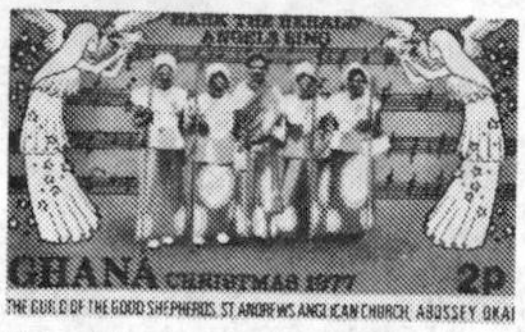

Guild of the Good Shepherd, Abossey Okai — A143

Designs: 6p, 40p, Methodist Church, Wesley, Accra. 8p, Virgin and Child, and Star. 15p, like 2p. 30p, 65p, Holy Spirit Cathedral, Accra. 80p, 1ce, Ebenezer Presbyterian Church, Osu, Accra. Type A143 designs include score of "Hark the Herald Angels Sing."

Perf. 14x14½, 14

1977, Dec. 30 **Litho.**

631	A142 1p multicolored	.15	.15
632	A143 2p multicolored	.15	.15
633	A143 6p multicolored	.15	.15
634	A142 8p multicolored	.15	.15
635	A143 30p multicolored	.48	.25
636	A143 1ce multicolored	1.60	.80
	Nos. 631-636 (6)	2.68	
	Set value		1.25

Souvenir Sheet

Imperf

637	Sheet of 4	3.75	3.75
a.	A143 15p multicolored	.25	
b.	A143 40p multicolored	.65	
c.	A143 65p multicolored	1.00	
d.	A143 80p multicolored	1.40	

Christmas. No. 637 has simulated perfs.

No. 631-637 Overprinted: "REFERENDUM 1978 VOTE EARLY"

Perf. 14x14½, 14

1978, Mar. 28 **Litho.**

638	A142 1p multicolored	.15	.15
639	A143 2p multicolored	.15	.15
640	A143 6p multicolored	.15	.15
641	A142 8p multicolored	.15	.15
642	A143 30p multicolored	.48	.25
643	A143 1ce multicolored	1.60	.80
	Nos. 638-643 (6)	2.68	
	Set value		1.25

Souvenir Sheet

Imperf

644	Sheet of 4	*30.00*	
a.	A143 15p multicolored	*1.50*	
b.	A143 40p multicolored	*3.75*	
c.	A143 65p multicolored	*6.00*	
d.	A143 80p multicolored	*7.50*	

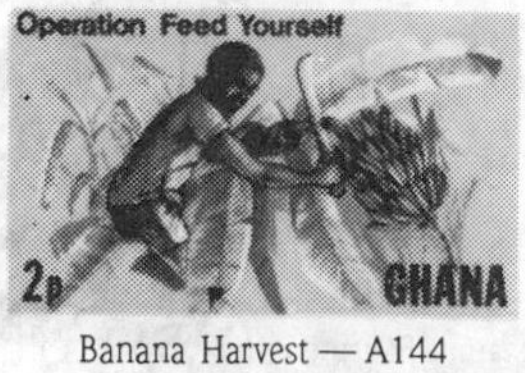

Banana Harvest — A144

Designs: 8p, Vegetable garden. 30p, Produce market. 60p, Fishing. 1ce, Tractor.

1978, May 15 *Perf. 14*

645	A144 2p multicolored	.15	.15
646	A144 8p multicolored	.15	.15
647	A144 30p multicolored	.45	.22
648	A144 60p multicolored	.90	.45
649	A144 1ce multicolored	1.50	.75
	Nos. 645-649 (5)	3.15	
	Set value		1.50

Operation feed yourself.

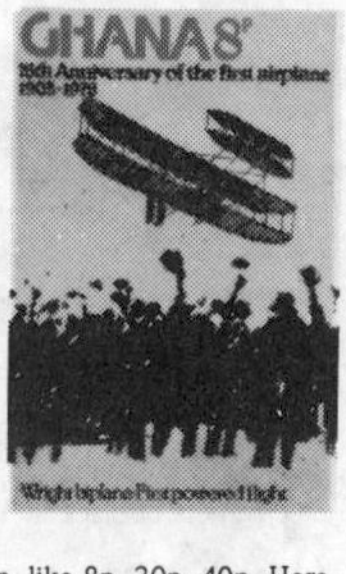

Wright Biplane and Crowd — A145

Planes and Crowd: 15p, like 8p. 30p, 40p, Heracles, 1st practical airliner. 60p, 65p, D. H. Comet, 1st jet airliner. 80p, 1ce, Concorde, 1st supersonic airliner.

1978, June 6 **Litho.** *Perf. 14x13½*

650	A145 8p multicolored	.15	.15
651	A145 30p multicolored	.45	.22
652	A145 60p multicolored	.90	.45
653	A145 1ce multicolored	1.50	.75
	Nos. 650-653 (4)	3.00	1.57

Souvenir Sheet

654	Sheet of 4	3.00	3.00
a.	A145 15p multicolored	.22	
b.	A145 40p multicolored	.60	
c.	A145 65p multicolored	1.00	
d.	A145 80p multicolored	1.10	

75th anniversary of first powered flight. The cheering crowd forms a continuing design on Nos. 650-654.

Nos. 650-653, 654a-654d Overprinted: "CAPEX 78 / JUNE 9-18 1978"

1978, June 9

655	A145 8p multicolored	.15	.15
656	A145 30p multicolored	.48	.25
657	A145 60p multicolored	1.00	.48
658	A145 1ce multicolored	1.60	.80
	Nos. 655-658 (4)	3.23	1.68

Souvenir Sheet

659	Sheet of 4	3.00	3.00
a.	A145 15p multicolored	.22	
b.	A145 40p multicolored	.60	
c.	A145 65p multicolored	.90	
d.	A145 80p multicolored	1.10	

CAPEX, Canadian International Philatelic Exhibition, Toronto, Ont., June 9-18.

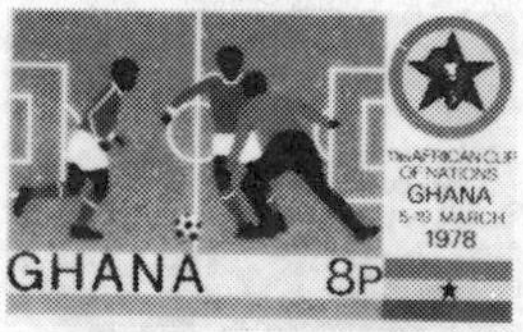

Soccer, Africa Cup Emblem and Ghana Flag A146

Designs: 15p, like 8p. 30p, 40p, Three soccer players, Africa Cup emblem, Ghana flag. 60p, 65p, Two soccer players. Argentina '78 emblem, Argentine flag. 80p, 1ce, Goalkeeper, Argentina '78 emblem and Argentine flag.

1978, July 1 **Litho.** *Perf. 13½x14*

660	A146 8p multicolored	.15	.15
661	A146 30p multicolored	.45	.22
662	A146 60p multicolored	.90	.45
663	A146 1ce multicolored	1.50	.75
	Nos. 660-663 (4)	3.00	1.57

Souvenir Sheet

664	Sheet of 4	3.00	3.00
a.	A146 15p multicolored	.22	
b.	A146 40p multicolored	.60	
c.	A146 65p multicolored	.90	
d.	A146 80p multicolored	1.10	

11th African Cup of Nations, Ghana, Mar. 5-19, and 11th World Cup Soccer Championship, Argentina, June 1-25.

Nos. 660-661, 664a-664b Overprinted: "GHANA WINNERS"

Nos. 662-663, 664c-664d Overprinted: "ARGENTINA WINS"

1978, Aug. 21 **Litho.** *Perf. 13½x14*

665	A146 8p multicolored	.15	.15
666	A146 30p multicolored	.45	.22
667	A146 60p multicolored	.90	.45
668	A146 1ce multicolored	1.50	.75
	Nos. 665-668 (4)	3.00	1.57

Souvenir Sheet

669	Sheet of 4	3.00	3.00
a.	A146 15p multicolored	.22	
b.	A146 40p multicolored	.60	
c.	A146 65p multicolored	.90	
d.	A146 80p multicolored	1.10	

Winners, 11th African Cup and 11th World Cup Soccer Championships.

Overprint on 60p and 65p is in two lines.

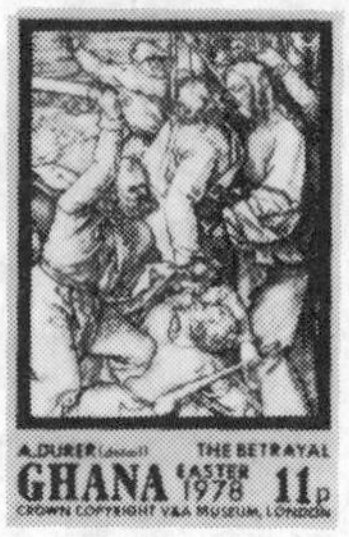

The Betrayal, by Dürer — A147

Etchings by Albrecht Dürer: 39p, The Crucifixion. 60p, The Deposition. 1ce, The Resurrection.

1978, Sept. 1 **Litho.** *Perf. 14x13½*

670	A147 11p lilac & black	.15	.15
671	A147 39p salmon & black	.28	.28
672	A147 60p orange & black	.40	.40
673	A147 1ce yel green & black	.65	.65
	Nos. 670-673 (4)	1.48	1.48

Easter.

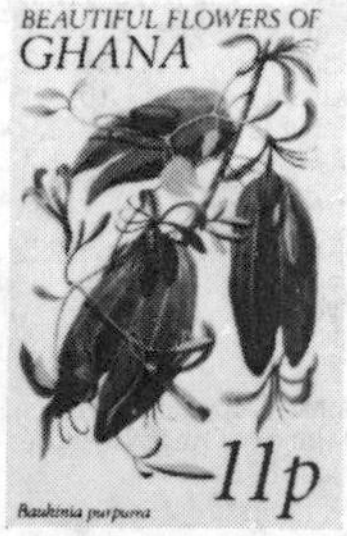

Bauhinia Purpurea — A148

Flowers: 39p, Cassia fistula. 60p, Frangipani. 1ce, Jacaranda mimosifolia.

1978, Nov. 20 **Litho.** *Perf. 14x13½*

674	A148 11p multicolored	.15	.15
675	A148 39p multicolored	.25	.20
676	A148 60p multicolored	.50	.30
677	A148 1ce multicolored	.75	.50
	Nos. 674-677 (4)	1.65	1.15

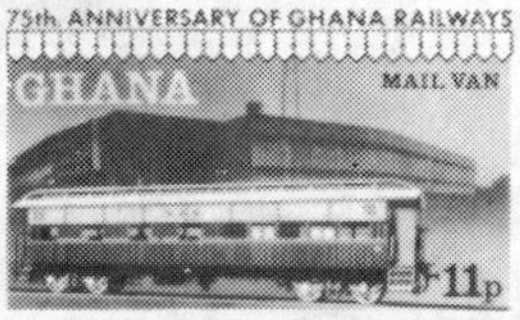

Mail Railroad Car A149

Ghana railroad, 75th Anniv.: 39p, Pay and bank car. 60p, Locomotive, 1922. 1ce, Diesel locomotive, 1960.

1978, Dec. 4 **Litho.** *Perf. 13½*

678	A149 11p multicolored	.15	.15
679	A149 39p multicolored	.50	.40
680	A149 60p multicolored	1.00	.60
681	A149 1ce multicolored	1.50	1.00
	Nos. 678-681 (4)	3.15	2.15

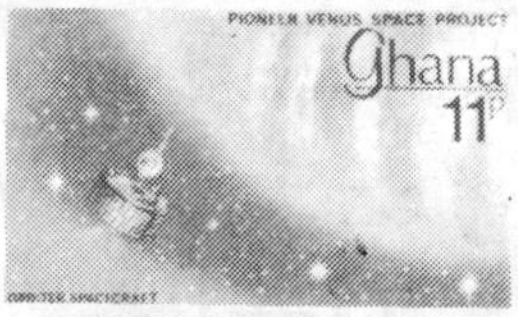

Orbiter Spacecraft — A150

Designs: 15p, like 11p. 39p, 40p, Multiprobe spacecraft. 60p, 65p, Orbiter and Multiprobe circling Venus. 2ce, 3ce, Radar chart of Venus.

1979, July 5 **Litho.** *Perf. 14x13½*

682	A150 11p multicolored	.15	.15
683	A150 39p multicolored	.35	.35
684	A150 60p multicolored	.50	.50
685	A150 3ce multicolored	2.50	2.50
	Nos. 682-685 (4)	3.50	3.50

Souvenir Sheet

Imperf

686	Sheet of 4	3.25	3.25
a.	A150 15p multicolored	.15	
b.	A150 40p multicolored	.40	
c.	A150 65p multicolored	.65	
d.	A150 2ce multicolored	2.00	

Pioneer Venus Space Project.

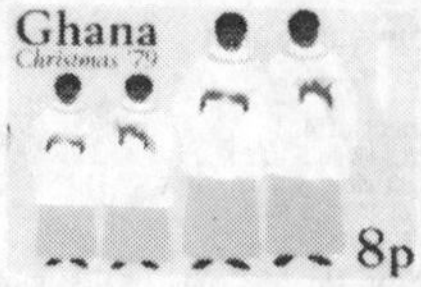

O Come All Ye Faithful A152

Christmas Carols: 10p, O Little Town of Bethlehem. 15p, 65p, We Three Kings of Orient Are. 20p, I Saw Three Ships Come Sailing By. 25p, like 8p. No. 696, 1ce, Away in a Manger. 4ce, No. 698d, Ding Dong Merrily on High.

1979, Dec. 20 *Perf. 14½*

692	A152 8p multicolored	.15	.15
693	A152 10p multicolored	.15	.15
694	A152 15p multicolored	.16	.15
695	A152 20p multicolored	.22	.15
696	A152 2ce multicolored	2.25	1.10
697	A152 4ce multicolored	4.00	2.00
	Nos. 692-697 (6)	6.93	3.70

Souvenir Sheet

698	Sheet of 4	4.00	2.00
a.	A152 25p multicolored	.25	.15
b.	A152 65p multicolored	.60	.35
c.	A152 1ce multicolored	1.00	.50
d.	A152 2ce multicolored	2.00	1.00

Christmas.

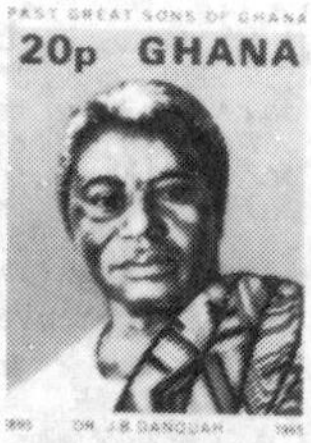

J.B. Danquah (1895-1965) — A153

National Leaders: 65p, John Mensah Sarbah (1864-1910). 80p, J.E.K. Aggrey (1875-1925). 2ce, Kwame Nkrumah (1909-1972). 4ce, G.E. Grant (1878-1956).

1980, Jan. 21 **Litho.** *Perf. 13½x14*

699	A153 20p multicolored	.22	.15
700	A153 65p multicolored	.75	.35
701	A153 80p multicolored	.80	.40
702	A153 2ce multicolored	2.25	1.10
703	A153 4ce multicolored	4.25	2.25
	Nos. 699-703 (5)	8.27	4.25

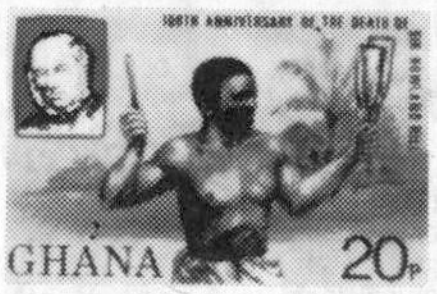

Man with Clack Bells, Hill — A154

Hill and: 25p, Man with clack bells. 50p, 65p, Chief, elephant staff. 1ce, 2ce, Drummer. 4ce, 5ce, Chief, ivory staff.

1980, Mar. 12 **Litho.** *Perf. 14½*

704	A154 20p multicolored	.15	.15
705	A154 65p multicolored	.50	.25
706	A154 2ce multicolored	1.50	.75
707	A154 4ce multicolored	3.00	1.50
	Nos. 704-707 (4)	5.15	2.65

Souvenir Sheet

708	Sheet of 4	5.75	3.00
a.	A154 25p multicolored	.18	.15
b.	A154 50p multicolored	.35	.25
c.	A154 1ce multicolored	.75	.50
d.	A154 5ce multicolored	3.75	2.00

Sir Rowland Hill (1795-1879), originator of penny postage.

For overprints see Nos. 714-718.

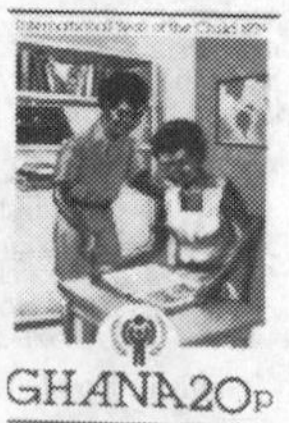

Students, IYC Emblem — A155

IYC Emblem and: 25p like 20p. 50p, 65p, Boys playing soccer. 1ce, 2ce, Boys in canoe. 3ce, 4ce, Mother and child.

1980, Apr. 2   Litho.   *Perf.* 15
709 A155 20p multicolored .15 .15
710 A155 65p multicolored .50 .25
711 A155 2ce multicolored 1.50 .75
712 A155 4ce multicolored 3.00 1.50
Nos. 709-712 (4) 5.15 2.65

Souvenir Sheet
713   Sheet of 4 6.50 3.00
a. A155 25p multicolored .35 .18
b. A155 50p multicolored .75 .35
c. A155 1ce multicolored 1.40 .55
d. A155 3ce multicolored 4.00 1.90

Intl. Year of the Child (in 1979).
For overprints see Nos. 719-723.

Nos. 704-708 Overprinted: "LONDON
1980" / 6th-14th May 1980

1980, May 6   Litho.   *Perf.* 14½
714 A154 20p multicolored .15 .15
715 A154 65p multicolored .50 .25
716 A154 2ce multicolored 1.50 .75
717 A154 4ce multicolored 3.00 1.50
Nos. 714-717 (4) 5.15 2.65

Souvenir Sheet
718   Sheet of 4 5.75 3.00
a. A154 25p multicolored .22 .15
b. A154 50p multicolored .45 .22
c. A154 1ce multicolored .85 .45
d. A154 5ce multicolored 4.00 2.00

London 1980 Intl. Stamp Exhib., May 6-14.
Sheet margin overprinted: Earl's Court 6th-14th
May "London 1980."

Nos. 709-713 Overprinted: "PAPAL VISIT"
/ 8th-9th May / 1980

1980, May 8   *Perf.* 15
719 A155 20p multicolored .15 .15
720 A155 65p multicolored .50 .25
721 A155 2ce multicolored 1.50 .75
722 A155 4ce multicolored 3.00 1.50
Nos. 719-722 (4) 5.15 2.65

Souvenir Sheet
723   Sheet of 4 6.00 3.00
a. A155 25p multicolored .30 .15
b. A155 50p multicolored .60 .30
c. A155 1ce multicolored 1.25 .60
d. A155 3ce multicolored 3.75 1.65

Visit of Pope John Paul II to Ghana, May 8-9.

Parliament
House
A156

1980, Aug. 4   Litho.   *Perf.* 14
724 A156 20p shown .15 .15
725 A156 65p Supreme Court .60 .25
726 A156 2ce The Castle 1.50 .75
Nos. 724-726 (3) 2.25 1.15

Souvenir Sheet
727   Sheet of 3 3.25 1.65
a. A156 25p like #724 .18 .15
b. A156 1ce like #725 .75 .30
c. A156 3ce like #726 2.25 1.10

Third Republic.

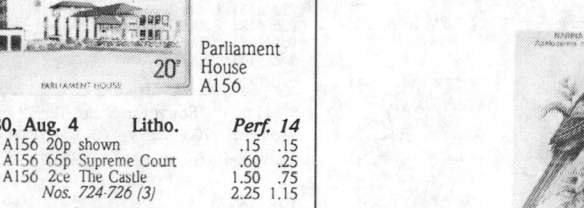

Map of West
African
Member
Countries, Flag
of Ghana,
Jet — A157

1980, Nov. 5   Litho.   *Perf.* 14½
728 A157 20p shown .15 .15
729 A157 65p Dish antenna .42 .22
730 A157 80p Cogwheels .55 .25
731 A157 2ce Corn 1.40 .65
Nos. 728-731 (4) 2.52 1.27

5th Anniversary of ECOWAS (Economic Community of West African States).

A158   A159

1980, Nov. 26
732 A158 20p "OAU" .15 .15
733 A158 65p OAU Banner, Maps .45 .22
734 A158 80p Waves on map of Africa .55 .25
735 A158 2ce Flag, banner, map 1.40 .65
Nos. 732-735 (4) 2.55 1.27

Org. for African Unity summit conference, Lagos,
Nigeria, Apr. 28-29.

1980, Dec. 10   *Perf.* 14
Christmas (Fra Angelico Paintings): 15p, 25p,
Adoration of the Magi. 20p, 50p, Virgin and Child
Enthroned with Four Angels. 1ce, 2ce, Virgin and
Child Enthroned with Eight Angels. 3ce, 4ce,
Annunciation.

736 A159 15p multicolored .15 .15
737 A159 20p multicolored .15 .15
738 A159 2ce multicolored 1.00 .60
739 A159 4ce multicolored 2.00 1.00
Nos. 736-739 (4) 3.30 1.80

Souvenir Sheet
740   Sheet of 4 2.75 1.50
a. A159 25p multicolored .15 .15
b. A159 50p multicolored .30 .15
c. A159 1ce multicolored .40 .30
d. A159 3ce multicolored 1.50 .90

Nurse
Weighing
Newborn,
Rotary
Emblem
A160

1980, Dec. 18
741 A160 20p shown .16 .15
742 A160 65p Map of Ghana and
world .60 .30
743 A160 2ce Helping hands, world
map 1.65 1.00
744 A160 4ce Food distribution 3.75 1.65
Nos. 741-744 (4) 6.16 3.10

Souvenir Sheet
745   Sheet of 4 4.25 2.25
a. A160 25p like #741 .22 .15
b. A160 50p like #742 .42 .22
c. A160 1ce like #743 .80 .42
d. A160 3ce like #744 2.50 1.40

Rotary International, 75th anniv.

Narina
Trogon — A161

1981, Jan. 12   Litho.   *Perf.* 14
746 A161 20p shown .15 .15
747 A161 65p White-crowned robin-
chat .50 .25
748 A161 2ce Swallow-tailed bee-eater 1.50 .75
749 A161 4ce Long-tailed parakeet 3.00 1.50
Nos. 746-749 (4) 5.13 2.63

Souvenir Sheet
750   Sheet of 4 5.25 2.75
a. A161 25p like #746 .30 .15
b. A161 50p like #747 .60 .30
c. A161 1ce like #748 1.10 .55
d. A161 3ce like #749 3.25 1.60

Pope John Paul II, Pres. Limann,
Archbishop of Canterbury — A162

1981, Mar. 3   Litho.   *Perf.* 14
751 A162 20p multicolored .30 .15
752 A162 65p multicolored 1.00 .50
753 A162 80p multicolored 1.20 .60
754 A162 2ce multicolored 3.00 1.50
Nos. 751-754 (4) 5.50 2.75

Visit of Pope John Paul II, May 8-10, 1980.

Earth Satellite
Station — A163

1981, Sept. 28   Litho.   *Perf.* 14
755 A163 20p shown .15 .15
756 A163 65p Satellites orbiting
earth .40 .40
757 A163 80p Satellite .50 .50
758 A163 4ce Satellite, earth 2.25 2.25
Nos. 755-758 (4) 3.30 3.30

Souvenir Sheet
758A   Sheet of 4 3.25 3.25
b. A163 25p like #755 .16 .16
c. A163 50p like #756 .35 .35
d. A163 1ce like #757 .70 .70
e. A163 3ce like #758 1.75 1.75

Earth Satellite Station commission.

Royal Wedding Issue
Common Design Type
1981   Litho.   *Perf.* 14
759 CD331 20p Couple .15 .15
759A CD331 65p like 20p .35 .35
760 CD331 80p Charles .45 .45
760A CD331 1ce like 80p .60 .60
760B CD331 3ce like 4ce 1.65 1.65
761 CD331 4ce Royal yacht Britannia 2.25 2.25
Nos. 759-761 (6) 5.45 5.45

Souvenir Sheet
762   CD331 7ce St. Paul's Cathedral 3.50 3.50

Nos. 759-761 each printed se-tenant with label
showing heraldic design.
Issue dates: 20p, 80p, 4ce, 7ce, July 8. 65p, 1ce,
3ce, Sept. 16.
For surcharges see Nos. 859, 866, 871, 880,
1168-1169, 1195-1197.

1981, Sept. 16   Litho.   *Perf.* 14
763 CD331 2ce like 4cc 1.50 1.50
764 CD331 5ce like 20p 3.75 3.75
a. Bklt. pane, 2 each #763-764 11.00 11.00

Nos. 763-764 issued only in booklets.

World
Food
Day
A164

1981, Oct. 16   Litho.   *Perf.* 14
765 A164 20p Women pounding fufu .15 .15
766 A164 65p Plucking cocoa .50 .50
767 A164 80p Preparing banku .65 .65
768 A164 2ce Processing garri 1.50 1.50
Nos. 765-768 (4) 2.80 2.80

Souvenir Sheet
769   Sheet of 4 3.50 3.50
a. A164 25p like #765 .15 .15
b. A164 50p like #766 .35 .35
c. A164 1ce like #767 .75 .75
d. A164 3ce like #768 2.25 2.25

Angelic Musicians
Play for Mary and
Child, by Aachener
Altares (1480-1520)
A165

Christmas (Paintings): 15p, The Betrothal of St.
Catherine of Alexandria, by Lucas Cranach (1472-
1553). 65p, Child Jesus Embracing His Mother, by
Gabriel Metsu (1629-1667). 80p, Virgin and Child,
by Fra Filippo Lippi (1406-1469). $2, The Virgin
with Infant Jesus, by Barnaba da Modena (1361-
1383). $4, The Immaculate Conception, by
Bartolome Murillo (1618-1682). $6, Virgin and
Child, by Hans Memling (1430-1494).

1981, Nov. 26   *Perf.* 14
770 A165 15p multicolored .15 .15
771 A165 20p multicolored .15 .15
772 A165 65p multicolored .45 .45

773 A165 80p multicolored .50 .50
774 A165 $2 multicolored 1.40 1.40
775 A165 $4 multicolored 2.50 2.50
Nos. 770-775 (6) 5.15 5.15

Souvenir Sheet
776 A165 $6 multicolored 4.00 4.00

Intl. Year of
the Disabled
A166

1982, Feb. 8   Litho.   *Perf.* 14
777 A166 20p Blind man .15 .15
778 A166 65p Woman, crutch .50 .50
779 A166 80p Girl reading Braille .60 .60
780 A166 4ce Couple 3.00 3.00
Nos. 777-780 (4) 4.25 4.25

Souvenir Sheet
781 A166 6ce Group 4.75 4.75

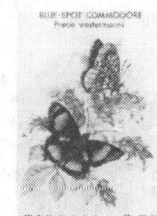

Clawless
Otter — A167

Blue-spot
Commodore — A168

1982, Feb. 22
782 A167 20p shown .15 .15
783 A167 65p Bushbuck .50 .50
784 A167 80p Aardvark .60 .60
785 A167 1ce Scarlet bell tree .75 .75
786 A167 2ce Glory lilies 1.50 1.50
787 A167 4ce Blue peas 3.00 3.00
Nos. 782-787 (6) 6.50 6.50

Souvenir Sheet
788 A167 5ce Chimpanzees 3.75 3.75

1982, Apr. 27   Litho.   *Perf.* 14
789 A168 20p shown .15 .15
790 A168 65p Emperor swallowtail .50 .50
791 A168 2ce Orange admiral 1.50 1.50
792 A168 4ce Giant charaxes 3.00 3.00
Nos. 789-792 (4) 5.15 5.15

Souvenir Sheet
Perf. 14½
793   Sheet of 4 3.75 3.75
a. A168 25p like #789 .18 .18
b. A168 50p like #790 .35 .35
c. A168 1ce like #791 .75 .75
d. A168 3ce like #792 2.25 2.25

Scouting
Year — A169

1982, June 1   Litho.   *Perf.* 15
794 A169 20p Tree planting .15 .15
795 A169 65p Camping .50 .50
796 A169 80p Sailing .60 .60
797 A169 3ce Watching elephant 2.25 2.25
Nos. 794-797 (4) 3.50 3.50

Souvenir Sheet
798 A169 5ce Baden-Powell, vert. 3.75 3.75

For surcharges see Nos. 867, 870, 875, 877.

Kpong Hydroelectric Dam
Opening — A170

1982, June 28   Litho.   *Perf.* 14
799 A170 20p Cranes, lifts .15 .15
800 A170 65p Construction .50 .50
801 A170 80p Turbines .60 .60
802 A170 2ce Aerial view 1.50 1.50
Nos. 799-802 (4) 2.75 2.75

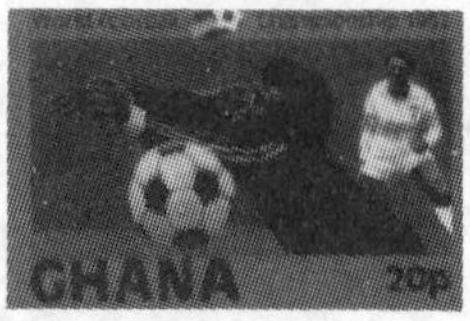

1982 World Cup A171

Perf. 15, 14¹/₂x15 (30p, No. 807, 1ce, 3ce)

1982, July 19 **Litho.**

803 A171 20p multi .15 .15
804 A171 30p multi, like 20p .22 .22
805 A171 65p multi .50 .50
806 A171 80p multi, like 65p .60 .60
807 A171 80p multi, diff. .60 .60
808 A171 1ce multi, like #807 .75 .75
809 A171 3ce multi 2.25 2.25
810 A171 4ce multi, like 3ce 3.00 3.00
Nos. 803-810 (8) 8.07 8.07

Souvenir Sheet

811 A171 6ce multi 4.50 4.50

Nos. 804, 807-809 in sheets of 5 plus label.
For overprints & surcharges see #826-834, 861-862, 864-865, 868-869, 872-873, 878-879, 912-917.

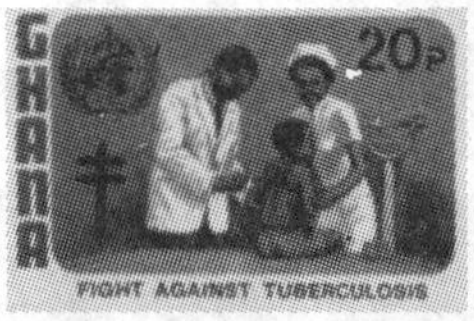

TB Bacillus Centenary A172

1982, Aug. 9 ***Perf. 14***

812 A172 20p Child immunization .15 .15
813 A172 65p Koch, Berlin .50 .50
814 A172 80p Koch, Africa .60 .60
815 A172 1ce Looking through microscope .75 .75
816 A172 2ce Koch, 1905 Nobel medal 1.50 1.50
Nos. 812-816 (5) 3.50 3.50

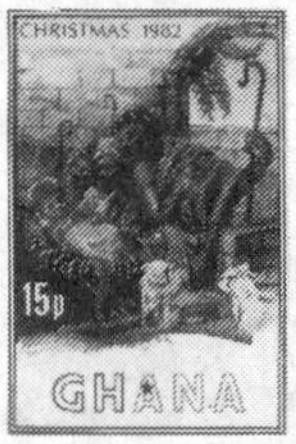

Christmas — A173

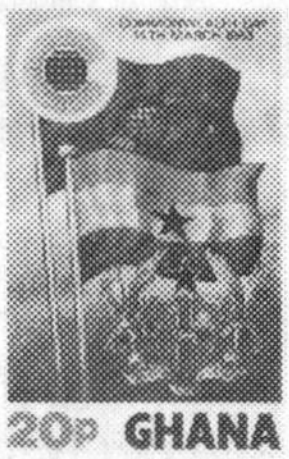

A173a

1982, Dec. **Litho.** ***Perf. 15***

817 A173 15p Angel with banner .15 .15
818 A173 20p Holy Family .15 .15
819 A173 65p Three Kings .50 .50
820 A173 4ce Nativity 3.00 3.00
Nos. 817-820 (4) 3.80 3.80

Souvenir Sheet

821 A173 6ce Nativity, diff. 4.50 4.50

1983, Mar. 10 **Litho.** ***Perf. 15***

822 A173a 20p Flags .15 .15
823 A173a 55p Aerial view .40 .40
824 A173a 80p Minerals .60 .60
825 A173a 3ce Eagle 2.25 2.25
Nos. 822-825 (4) 3.40 3.40

Commonwealth Day. For surcharges see Nos. 860, 863, 874, 876.

Nos. 803-811 Overprinted in Gold: "WINNER ITALY / 3-1"

1983, June **Litho.**

826 A171 20p multicolored .15 .15
827 A171 30p multicolored .18 .18
828 A171 65p multicolored .40 .40
829 A171 80p multi, on #806 .48 .48
830 A171 80p multi, on #807 .48 .48
831 A171 1ce multicolored .60 .60
832 A171 3ce multicolored 1.75 1.75
833 A171 4ce multicolored 2.50 2.50
Nos. 826-833 (8) 6.54 6.54

Souvenir Sheet

834 A171 6ce multicolored 3.50 3.50

Italy's victory in 1982 World Cup.
For surcharges see Nos. 862, 865, 869, 873, 879, 913, 915, 917.

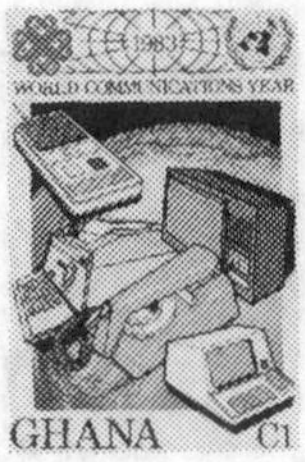

World Communications Year — A173b

1983, Dec. 13 **Litho.** ***Perf. 14***

835 A173b 1ce shown .50 .50
836 A173b 1.40ce Dish antenna .65 .65
837 A173b 2.30ce Cable ship 1.20 1.20
838 A173b 3ce Switchboard 1.50 1.50
839 A173b 5ce Control tower 2.50 2.50
Nos. 835-839 (5) 6.35 6.35

Souvenir Sheet

840 A173b 6ce Satellite 3.00 3.00

For surcharges see Nos. 1107-1111.

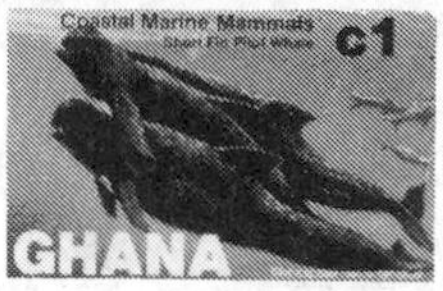

Coastal Marine Mammals A173c

1983, Nov. 15 **Litho.** ***Perf. 15***

841 A173c 1ce Short fin pilot whale .40 .40
842 A173c 1.40ce Gray dolphin .50 .50
843 A173c 2.30ce False killer whale .80 .80
844 A173c 3ce Spinner dolphin 1.20 1.20
845 A173c 5ce Atlantic humpback dolphin 1.75 1.75
Nos. 841-845 (5) 4.65 4.65

Souvenir Sheet

846 A173c 6ce White Alantic humpback dolphin 2.25 2.25

For surcharges see Nos. 918-920.

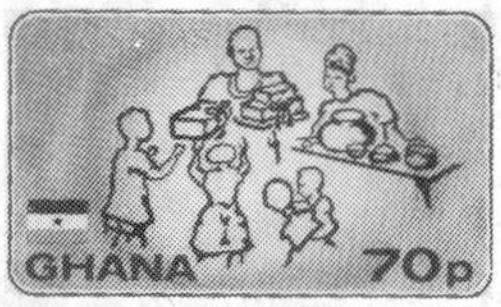

A174

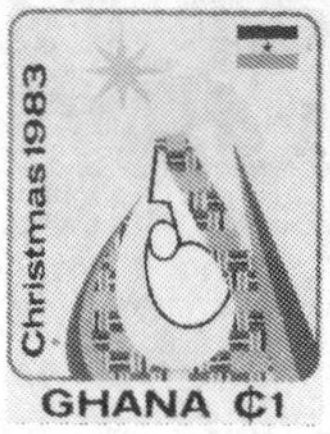

Christmas — A175

Perf. 14x13¹/₂, 14¹/₂x14

1983, Dec. 28

852 A174 70p Children receiving gifts .15 .15
853 A175 1ce Nativity .15 .15
854 A175 1.40ce Children playing .15 .15
855 A175 2.30ce Family praying .15 .15
856 A174 3ce Bongo drums, festivities .18 .18
Set value .52 .52

Souvenir Sheet

857 A175 6ce like #855 .38 .38

Surcharges
Many inverts, doubles, etc., exist on the surcharged stamps that follow.

Previous Issues Surcharged

1984, Feb. 8

858 A74 1ce on 20np #296 .15 .15
859 CD331 1ce on 20p #759 .15 .15
860 A173a 1ce on 20p #822 .15 .15
861 A171 1ce on 20p #803 .15 .15
862 A171 1ce on 20p #826 .15 .15
863 A173a 9ce on 55p #823 .65 .65
864 A171 9ce on 65p #805 .65 .65
865 A171 9ce on 65p #828 .65 .65
866 CD331 9ce on 80p #760 .65 .65
867 A169 10ce on 20p #794 .70 .70
868 A171 10ce on 80p #806 .70 .70
869 A171 10ce on 80p #830 .70 .70
870 A169 19ce on 65p #795 1.40 1.40
871 CD331 20ce on 4ce #761 1.45 1.45
872 A171 20ce on 4ce #810 1.45 1.45
873 A171 20ce on 4ce #833 1.45 1.45
874 A173a 30ce on 80p #824 2.00 2.00
875 A169 30ce on 3ce #797 2.00 2.00
876 A173a 50ce on 3ce #825 3.50 3.50
Nos. 858-876 (19) 18.70 18.70

Souvenir Sheets

877 A169 60ce on 5ce #798 4.25 4.25
878 A171 60ce on 6ce #811 4.25 4.25
879 A171 60ce on 6ce #834 4.25 4.25
880 CD331 60ce on 7ce #762 4.25 4.25

For surcharges on this issue see #1092A-1092C.

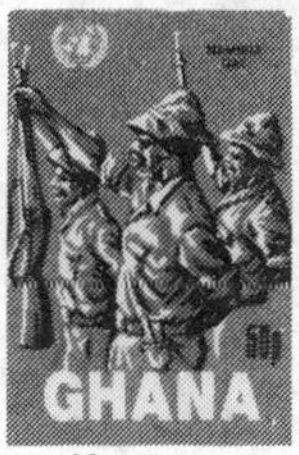

Namibia Day — A176

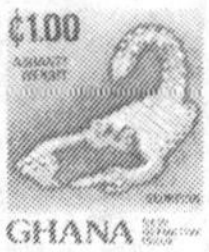

Scorpion Weight — A177

1984, Jan. 26 ***Perf. 14***

881 A176 50p Soldiers raising rifles .15 .15
882 A176 1ce Soldiers, tank .15 .15
883 A176 1.40ce Machete cutting chains .15 .15
884 A176 2.30ce Namibian woman .20 .20
885 A176 3ce Soldiers in combat .24 .24
Set value .68 .68

1983, Dec. 12 **Litho.** ***Perf. 14***

886 A177 5p Banded Jewelfish, horiz. .15 .15
887 A177 10p Banded Jewelfish, map, horiz. .15 .15
888 A177 20p Blood lily .15 .15
889 A177 50p Mounted warrior (gold statuette) .15 .15
890 A177 1ce shown .15 .15
891 A177 2ce Jet, horiz. .16 .16
892 A177 3ce White-collared mangabey .24 .24
893 A177 4ce Pigmy bush baby .32 .32
894 A177 5ce Nigerian iris .40 .40
895 A177 10ce Gray-backed warbler .80 .80
Set value 2.15 2.15

For surcharges see Nos. 1089A-1090, 1092, 1092D, 1093A-1094A, 1096-1096A.

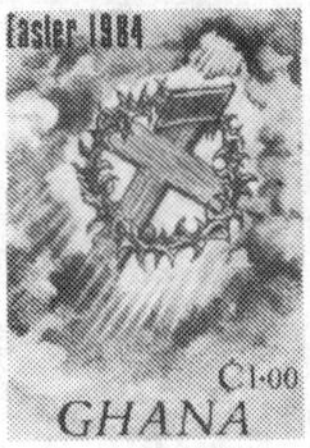

Easter — A178

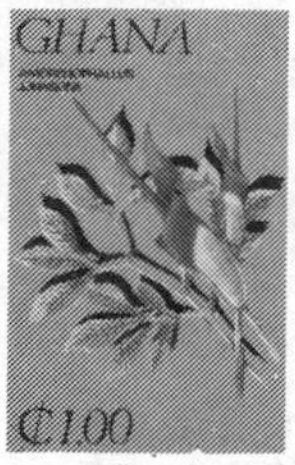

Local Flowers — A179

1984, Apr. **Litho.** ***Perf. 14¹/₂***

906 A178 1ce Cross, crown of thorns .15 .15
907 A178 1.40ce Jesus praying .15 .15
908 A178 2.30ce Jesus going to Jerusalem .18 .18
909 A178 3ce Jesus entering Jerusalem .24 .24
910 A178 50ce Jesus with Disciples 4.00 4.00
Nos. 906-910 (5) 4.72 4.72

Souvenir Sheet

911 A178 60ce Cross, crown of thorns 4.50 4.50

Nos. 804, 807, 809, 827, 830, 832 Surcharged

1984, Feb. 8 **Litho.**

912 A171 9ce on 3ce #809 .72 .72
913 A171 9ce on 3ce #832 .72 .72
914 A171 10ce on 30p #804 .80 .80
915 A171 10ce on 30p #827 .80 .80
916 A171 20ce on 80p #807 1.60 1.60
917 A171 20ce on 80p #830 1.60 1.60
Nos. 912-917 (6) 6.24 6.24

Nos. 844-846 Surcharged and Overprinted in Red with UPU Emblem and: "19th U.P.U. CONGRESS-HAMBURG"

1984 **Litho.** ***Perf. 14¹/₂***

918 A173c 10ce on 3ce multi .70 .70
919 A173c 50ce on 5ce multi 3.50 3.50

Souvenir Sheet

920 A173c 60ce on 6ce multi 4.25 4.25

1984, July **Litho.** ***Perf. 14***

921 A179 1ce Amorphophallus johnsonii .15 .15
922 A179 1.40ce Pancratium trianthum .15 .15
923 A179 2.30ce Eulophia cucullata .18 .18
924 A179 3ce Amorphophallus abyssinicus .24 .24
925 A179 50ce Chlorophytum togoense 4.00 4.00
Nos. 921-925 (5) 4.72 4.72

Souvenir Sheet

926 A179 60ce like 1ce 5.00 5.00

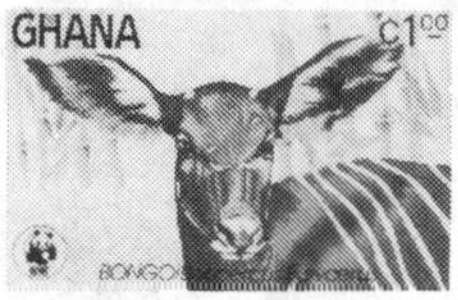

Endangered Species A180

1984, Aug. ***Perf. 14***

927 A180 1ce Bongo .15 .15
928 A180 2.30ce Males locking horns .18 .18
929 A180 3ce Family .24 .24
930 A180 20ce Herd 1.60 1.60
Nos. 927-930 (4) 2.17 2.17

Souvenir Sheets

931 A180 70ce Kob 6.00 6.00
932 A180 70ce Bushbuck 6.00 6.00

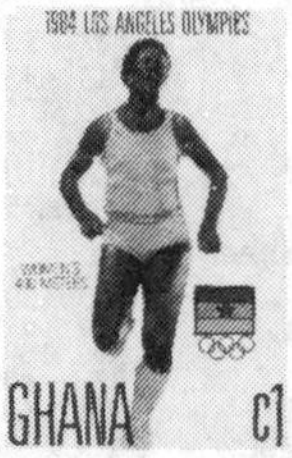

1984 Summer Olympics — A181

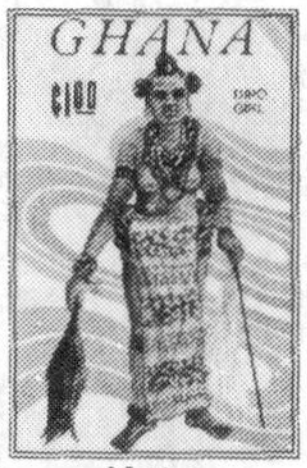

Native Dancers — A182

1984, Aug. ***Perf. 15***

933 A181 1ce Running .15 .15
934 A181 1.40ce Boxing .15 .15
935 A181 2.30ce Field hockey .18 .18
936 A181 3ce Hurdles .24 .24
937 A181 50ce Rhythmic gymnastics 4.00 4.00
Nos. 933-937 (5) 4.72 4.72

Souvenir Sheet

938 A181 70ce Soccer 6.00 6.00

For surcharges see #945-950, 1112-1116.

1984, Sept. ***Perf. 14***

939 A182 1ce Dipo .15 .15
940 A182 1.40ce Adowa .15 .15
941 A182 2.30ce Agbadza .18 .18
942 A182 3ce Damba .24 .24
943 A182 50ce Dipo, diff. 4.00 4.00
Nos. 939-943 (5) 4.72 4.72

Souvenir Sheet

944 A182 70ce Mandolin player 6.00 6.00

Nos. 933-938 Ovptd. in Gold with Winner and Country

1984, Dec. 3 **Litho.** ***Perf. 15***

945 A181 1ce Valerie Brisco-Hooks, US .15 .15
946 A181 1.40ce US winners .15 .15
947 A181 2.30ce Pakistan, (field hockey) .15 .15
948 A181 3ce Edwin Moses, US .15 .15
949 A181 50ce Lauri Fung, Canada 2.00 2.00
Nos. 945-949 (5) 2.60 2.60

Souvenir Sheet

950 A181 70ce France 2.75 2.75

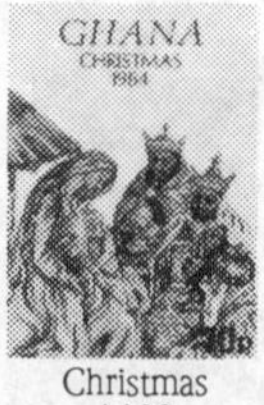

Christmas A183

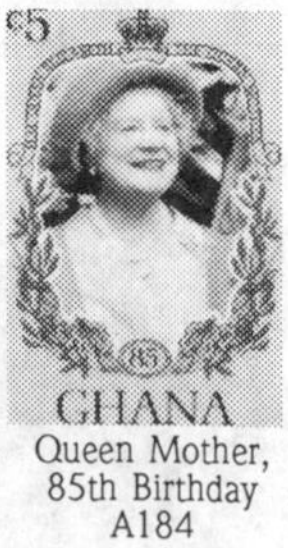

Queen Mother, 85th Birthday A184

1984, Nov. 19 — Perf. 12x12½
951 A183 70p Adoration of the
Magi .15 .15
952 A183 1ce Chorus of angels .15 .15
953 A183 1.40ce Adoration of the
shepherds .15 .15
954 A183 2.30ce Flight into Egypt .15 .15
955 A183 3ce King holding Christ .15 .15
956 A183 50ce Adoration of the
angels 2.00 2.00
Set value 2.35 2.35

Souvenir Sheet
957 A183 70ce like 70p 2.75 2.75

1985
Portraits.
958 A184 5ce multicolored .20 .20
959 A184 8ce like 5ce .32 .32
960 A184 12ce multicolored .48 .48
961 A184 20ce like 12ce .80 .80
962 A184 70ce multicolored 2.75 2.75
963 A184 100ce like 70ce 4.00 4.00
Nos. 958-963 (6) 8.55 8.55

Souvenir Sheet
964 A184 110ce multicolored 4.50 4.50
Issue dates: 5ce, 12ce, 100ce, 110ce, July 29.
8ce, 20ce, 70ce, Dec.
Nos. 959, 961-962 issued in sheets of 5 + label.
For surcharges see Nos. 1117-1119A, 1198-
1200, 1311-1317.

Id-El-Fitr Islamic
Festival — A185

Intl. Youth
Year — A186

1985, Aug. 1
965 A185 5ce Entering mosque .20 .20
966 A185 8ce Prayer rug .32 .32
967 A185 12ce Mosque .48 .48
968 A185 18ce Public Koran reading .72 .72
969 A185 50ce Map, Banda Nkwanta
Mosque 2.00 2.00
Nos. 965-969 (5) 3.72 3.72

1985, Aug. 9
970 A186 5ce Street clean-up .20 .20
971 A186 8ce Tree planting .32 .32
972 A186 12ce Food production .48 .48
973 A186 100ce Education 4.00 4.00
Nos. 970-973 (4) 5.00 5.00

Souvenir Sheet
974 A186 110ce like 8ce 4.50 4.50

Motorcycle
Centenary
A187

1985, Sept. 9
975 A187 5ce 1984 Honda Inter-
ceptor .20 .20
976 A187 8ce 1938 DKW .32 .32
977 A187 12ce 1923 BMW R 32 .48 .48
978 A187 100ce 1900 NSU 4.00 4.00
Nos. 975-978 (4) 5.00 5.00

Souvenir Sheet
979 A187 110ce 1973 Zundapp 4.50 4.50

Audubon Birth
Bicent. — A188

1985, Oct. 16
980 A188 5ce York-tailed flycatcher .20 .20
981 A188 8ce Barred owl .32 .32
982 A188 12ce Black-throated mango .48 .48

---

983 A188 100ce White-crowned pigeon 4.00 4.00
Nos. 980-983 (4) 5.00 5.00

Souvenir Sheet
984 A188 110ce Downy woodpecker 4.50 4.50
For surcharges see Nos. 1124-1127.

UN, 40th
Anniv.
A189

1985, Oct. 24 — Perf. 14½x14
985 A189 5ce UN building .20 .20
986 A189 8ce UN building, diff. .32 .32
987 A189 12ce Dove .48 .48
988 A189 18ce General Assembly .72 .72
989 A189 100ce Flags 4.00 4.00
Nos. 985-989 (5) 5.72 5.72

Souvenir Sheet
990 A189 110ce UN No. 36 4.50 4.50

UNCTAD,
20th Anniv.
A190

1985, Nov. 4 — Perf. 14
991 A190 5ce Coffee .20 .20
992 A190 8ce Cocoa .32 .32
993 A190 12ce Lumber .48 .48
994 A190 18ce Bauxite mining .72 .72
995 A190 100ce Gold mining 4.00 4.00
Nos. 991-995 (5) 5.72 5.72

Souvenir Sheet
Perf. 15x14
996 A190 110ce Produce 4.50 4.50

UN Child
Survival
Campaign
A191

1985, Dec. 16 — Perf. 14
997 A191 5ce Weighing .20 .20
998 A191 8ce Oral rehydration
therapy .32 .32
999 A191 12ce Breast-feeding .48 .48
1000 A191 100ce Immunization 4.00 4.00
Nos. 997-1000 (4) 5.00 5.00

Souvenir Sheet
Perf. 15x14
1001 A191 110ce Emblem, pinwheel 4.50 4.50

AMERIPEX
'86 — A192

Perf. 14½x14, 14x14½
1986, Oct. 27 — Litho.
1002 A192 5ce Young collectors .15 .15
1003 A192 25ce Earth, jet .75 .75
1004 A192 100ce Stewardess, vert. 3.00 3.00
Nos. 1002-1004 (3) 3.90 3.90

Souvenir Sheet
1005 A192 150ce Young collectors,
diff. 4.50 4.50

INTER-TOURISM '86, Nov. 8-17 — A193

Designs: 5ce, Kejetia Roundabout, Jumasi. 15ce,
Fort St. Jago, Elmina. 25ce, Warriors. 100ce, Chief,
retinue. 150ce, Elephants.

1986, Nov. 10 — Perf. 14
1006 A193 5ce multi .15 .15
1007 A193 15ce multi .45 .45
1008 A193 25ce multi .75 .75
1009 A193 100ce multi 3.00 3.00
Nos. 1006-1009 (4) 4.35 4.35

Souvenir Sheet
Perf. 15x14
1010 A193 150ce multi 4.50 4.50

1986 World Cup
Soccer
Championships,
Mexico — A194

Fertility
Dolls — A195

Various soccer plays.

1987, Jan. 16 — Litho. — Perf. 14x14½
1011 A194 5ce multi .15 .15
1012 A194 15ce multi .45 .45
1013 A194 25ce multi .75 .75
1014 A194 100ce multi 3.00 3.00
Nos. 1011-1014 (4) 4.35 4.35

Souvenir Sheet
1015 A194 150ce multi 4.50 4.50
For surcharges see Nos. 1120-1123D.

1987, Jan. 22
Various dolls.
1016 A195 5ce multi .15 .15
1017 A195 15ce multi .45 .45
1018 A195 25ce multi .75 .75
1019 A195 100ce multi 3.00 3.00
Nos. 1016-1019 (4) 4.35 4.35

Souvenir Sheet
1020 A195 150ce like #1016 4.50 4.50

Intl. Peace
Year
A196

Perf. 14½x14, 14x14½
1987, Mar. 2 — Litho.
1021 A196 5ce Children playing .15 .15
1022 A196 25ce Plow .75 .75
1023 A196 100ce Earth, doves, vert. 3.00 3.00
Nos. 1021-1023 (3) 3.90 3.90

Souvenir Sheet
1024 A196 150ce Dove, plow, vert. 4.50 4.50

GIFEX
'87 — A197

1987, Mar. 10 — Perf. 14
1025 A197 5ce Lumber, house
construction .15 .15
1026 A197 15ce Furniture .30 .30
1027 A197 25ce Tree stumps .50 .50
1028 A197 200ce Logs, art objects 4.00 4.00
Nos. 1025-1028 (4) 4.95 4.95
Ghana Intl. Forestry Exposition, Accra.

A198

Halley's
Comet
A199

Designs: 5ce, Mikhail Vasilyevich Lomonosov
(1711-1765), Russian scientist, and the Chamber of
Curiosities. 25ce, Landing of the US probe Surveyor
on the Moon's surface, 1966. 200ce, Wedgewood
memorial to Sir Isaac Newton, the appearance of
Halley's Comet in 1790 and US astronauts Armstrong and Aldrin landing Eagle on the Moon in
1969. 250ce, Comet over Fishermen near Chris-
tianborg Castle,

1987, Apr. 8 — Perf. 14½x14
1029 A198 5ce multi .15 .15
1030 A198 25ce multi .50 .50
1031 A198 200ce multi 4.00 4.00
Nos. 1029-1031 (3) 4.65 4.65

Souvenir Sheet
1032 A199 250ce multi 5.00 5.00
For surcharges see Nos. 1128-1131,

Solidarity with South
Africans for Abolition
of Apartheid — A200

1987, May 18 — Perf. 14x14½
1033 A200 5ce Liberated prisoner .15 .15
1034 A200 15ce Miner, gold ingots .30 .30
1035 A200 25ce Zulu warrior .50 .50
1036 A200 100ce Nelson Mandela,
shackles 2.00 2.00
Nos. 1033-1036 (4) 2.95 2.95

Souvenir Sheet
1037 A200 150ce Mandela, map, star 3.00 3.00

Traditional
Musical
Instruments
A201

1987, July 13 — Perf. 14½x14
1038 A201 5ce Horns .15 .15
1039 A201 15ce Xylophone .30 .30
1040 A201 25ce String instruments .50 .50
1041 A201 100ce Drums 2.00 2.00
Nos. 1038-1041 (4) 2.95 2.95

Souvenir Sheet
1042 A201 200ce Percussion instruments 3.00 3.00

Intl. Year of
Shelter for
the Homeless
A202

1987, Sept. 21 — Litho. — Perf. 14
1043 A202 5ce Public well .15 .15
1044 A202 15ce Home construction .30 .30
1045 A202 25ce Village, bridge, car .50 .50
1046 A202 100ce Village, electric
power lines 2.00 2.00
Nos. 1043-1046 (4) 2.95 2.95

Festivals — A203

Designs: Preparation of Kpokpoi, Homowo Festival. 15ce, Hunters with catch, Aboakyir Festival. 25ce, Chief dancing, Odwira Festival. 100ce, Chief held aloft in a palanquin, Yam Festival.

1988, Jan. 6 Litho. *Perf. 15*

1047	A203	5ce multi		.15	.15
1048	A203	15ce multi		.30	.30
1049	A203	25ce multi		.50	.50
1050	A203	100ce multi		2.00	2.00
		Nos. 1047-1050 (4)		2.95	2.95

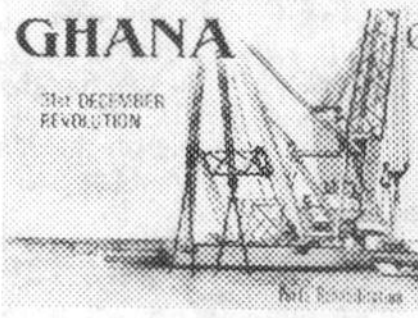

December 31, 1981 Revolution — A203a

1988, Jan. 26 Litho. *Perf. 13*

1050A	A203a	5ce	Ports	.15	.15
1050B	A203a	15ce	Railways	.45	.45
1050C	A203a	25ce	Cocoa industry	.80	.80
1050D	A203a	100ce	Mining industry	3.00	3.00
			Nos. 1050A-1050D (4)	4.40	4.40

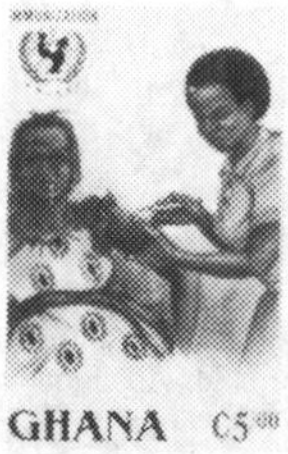

UN Universal Immunization Campaign — A204

Child Survival Campaign emblem and: 5ce, Nurse immunizing woman. 15ce, Child receiving intramuscular vaccine. 25ce, Youth crippled by polio. 100ce, Nurse handing infant to mother.

1988, Feb. 1 *Perf. 15*

1051	A204	5ce multi	.15	.15
1052	A204	15ce multi	.30	.30
1053	A204	25ce multi	.50	.50
1054	A204	100ce multi	2.00	2.00
		Nos. 1051-1054 (4)	2.95	2.95

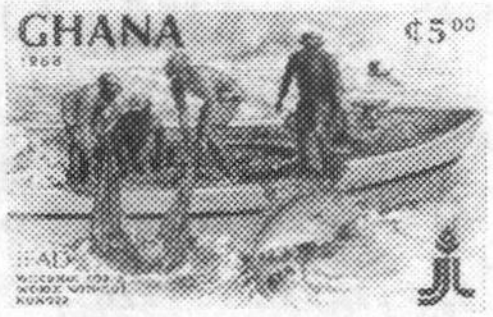

Intl. Fund for Agricultural Development — A204a

1988, Apr. 14 *Perf. 13*

1054A	A204a	5ce	Fishing	.15	.15
1054B	A204a	15ce	Harvesting	.45	.45
1054C	A204a	25ce	Cattle	.80	.80
1054D	A204a	100ce	Granary	3.00	3.00
			Nos. 1054A-1054D (4)	4.40	4.40

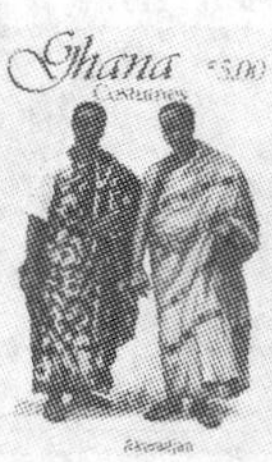

Tribal Costumes — A205

1988, May 9 Litho. *Perf. 14*

1055	A205	5ce	Akwadjan	.15	.15
1056	A205	25ce	Banaa	.22	.22
1057	A205	250ce	Agwasen	2.25	2.25
			Nos. 1055-1057 (3)	2.62	2.62

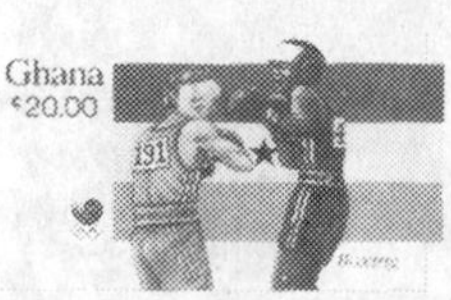

1988 Summer Olympics, Seoul A206

1988, Oct. 10

1058	A206	20ce	Boxing	.20	.20
1059	A206	60ce	Running	.60	.60
1060	A206	80ce	Discus	.80	.80
1061	A206	100ce	Javelin	1.00	1.00
1062	A206	350ce	Weight lifting	3.50	3.50
			Nos. 1058-1062 (5)	6.10	6.10

Souvenir Sheet

1063	A206	500ce	like 80ce	5.00	5.00

For overprints see Nos. 1084-1089.

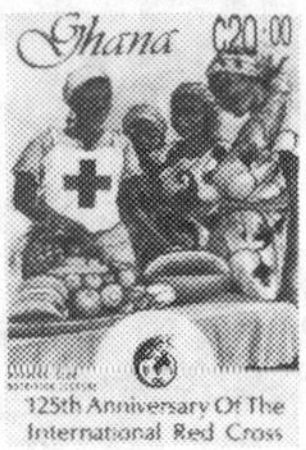

Intl. Red Cross, 125th Anniv. — A207

1988, Dec. 14 Litho. *Perf. 14*

1064	A207	20ce	Nutrition	.20	.20
1065	A207	50ce	Voluntary service	.50	.50
1066	A207	60ce	Disaster relief (flood)	.60	.60
1067	A207	200ce	Medical assistance	2.00	2.00
			Nos. 1064-1067 (4)	3.30	3.30

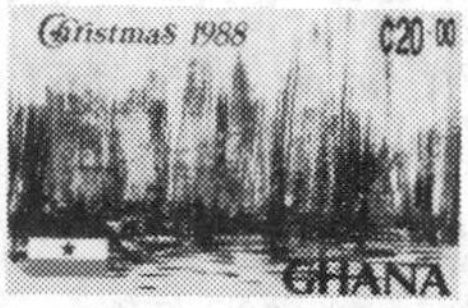

Christmas Symbolism A208

1988, Dec. 19 Litho. *Perf. 14*

1068	A208	20ce	shown	.20	.20
1069	A208	60ce	Mother and child, vert.	.60	.60
1070	A208	80ce	Mother, child, tree, vert.	.80	.80
1071	A208	100ce	Magi follow star	1.00	1.00
1072	A208	350ce	Abstract, diff., vert.	3.50	3.50
			Nos. 1068-1072 (5)	6.10	6.10

Souvenir Sheet

1073	A208	500ce	Mother and child, diff., vert.	5.00	5.00

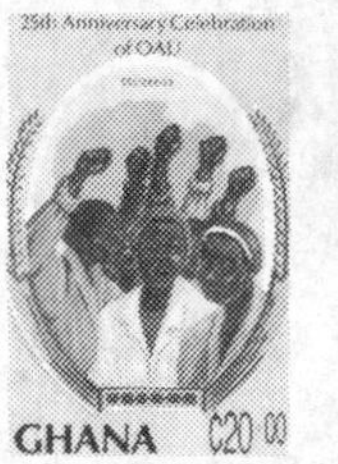

Organization of African Unity, 25th Anniv. — A209

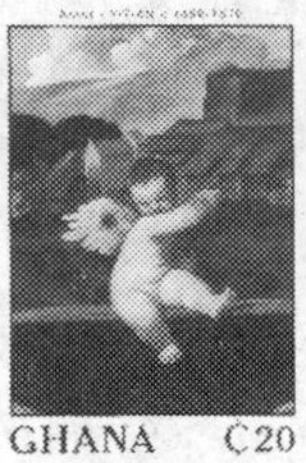

Titian, 500th Birth Anniv. (in 1988) — A210

1989, Jan. 3

1074	A209	20ce	Solidarity	.20	.20
1075	A209	50ce	OAU, Addis Ababa	.50	.50
1076	A209	60ce	Haile Selassie, Ethiopia	.60	.60
1077	A209	200ce	Kwame Nkrumah, Ghana	2.00	2.00
			Nos. 1074-1077 (4)	3.30	3.30

"Selassie" is spelled incorrectly on No. 1076. Nos. 1076-1077 horiz.

1989, Jan. 16

1078	A210	20ce	Amor, 1515	.20	.20
1079	A210	60ce	The Appeal	.60	.60
1080	A210	80ce	Bacchus and Ariadne, c. 1523	.80	.80
1081	A210	100ce	Portrait of a Musician, c. 1518	1.00	1.00
1082	A210	350ce	Philip II Seated	3.50	3.50
			Nos. 1078-1082 (5)	6.10	6.10

Souvenir Sheet

1083	A210	500ce	Portrait of a Gentleman, c. 1550	5.00	5.00

Nos. 1058-1063 Ovptd. with Winners' Names

1989, Jan. 23

1084	A206	20ce	"A. ZUELOW / DDR / 60 KG"	.20	.20
1085	A206	60ce	"G. BORDIN / ITALY / MARATHON"	.60	.60
1086	A206	80ce	"J. SCHULT / DDR"	.80	.80
1087	A206	100ce	"T. KORJUS / FINLAND"	1.00	1.00
1088	A206	350ce	"B. GUIDIKOV / BULGARIA / 75 KG"	3.50	3.50
			Nos. 1084-1088 (5)	6.10	6.10

Souvenir Sheet

1089	A206	500ce	multi	5.00	5.00

1988 Summer Olympics, Seoul. Margin of No. 1089 ovptd. "GOLD / J. SCHULT DDR / SILVER / R. OUBARTAS USSR / BRONZE / R. DANNEBERG W. GERMANY."

Stamps of 1967-1984 Surcharged

1988-91

1089A	A177	20ce	on 50p #889		
1090	A177	20ce	on 1ce #890	.20	.20
1091	A75	50ce	on 10np #295	.50	.50
1092	A177	50ce	on 10p #887	.50	.50
1092A	A74	50ce	on 1ce #858		
1092B	A74	50ce	on 1ce #858		
1092C	A74	50ce	on 1ce #858		
1092D	A177	50ce	on 1ce #890		
1092E	A73	60ce	on 1np #286		
1093	A73	60ce	on 4np #291	.60	.60
1093A	A177	60ce	on 3ce #892		
1094	A177	80ce	on 5p #886	.80	.80
1094A	A177	80ce	on 5ce #894		
1095	A74	100ce	on 20np #296	1.00	1.00
1096	A177	100ce	on 20p #888	1.00	1.00
1096A	A177	100ce	on 3ce #892		
1096B	A75	200ce	on 6np #292		

Surcharge has no decimal on No. 1092A, is vertical on No. 1092B and horizontal on No. 1092C.

No. 1090 also exists with 5mm spacing between block and $20.00.

Unauthorized surchages exist.

Issue dates: Nos. 1089A, 1096B, July 1, 1988. Nos. 1092A, 1092B, 1092D, 1092E, 1094A, 1096A, 1990. No. 1092C, 1991. Others, 1989.

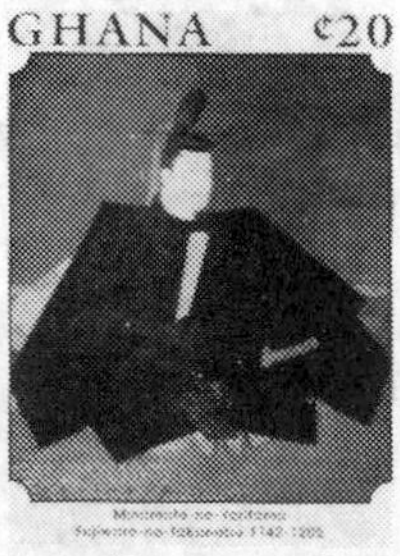

Minamoto-no-Yoritomo, by Fujiwara-no-Takanobu (1142-1205) — A211

Paintings: 50ce, Takami Senseki, by Watanabe Kazan (1793-1841). 60ce, Ikkyu Sojum, by Bokusai, Muromachi period. 75ce, Nakamura Kuranosuka, by Ogata Korin (1658-1716). 125ce, Portrait of a Lady, Kyoto branch of Kano school, Momoyama period. 150ce, Portrait of Zemmui, anonymous, 12th cent. 200ce, Ono no Komachi, the Poetess, by Hokusai. No. 1104, Kobo Daisi as a Child, anonymous, Kamakura period. No. 1105, Portrait of Kodai-no-Kimi, attributed to Fujiwara-no-Nobuzane, 12th cent. No. 1106, Portrait of Emperor Hanazono, by Fujiwara-no-Goshin, 14th cent.

1989, Aug. 21 Litho. *Perf. 13½x14*

1097	A211	20ce shown	.18	.18
1098	A211	50ce multi	.45	.45
1099	A211	60ce multi	.52	.52
1100	A211	75ce multi	.68	.68
1101	A211	125ce multi	1.10	1.10
1102	A211	150ce multi	1.35	1.35
1103	A211	200ce multi	1.75	1.75
1104	A211	500ce multi	2.65	2.65
		Nos. 1097-1104 (8)	8.68	8.68

Souvenir Sheets

1105	A211	500ce multi	4.45	4.45
1106	A211	500ce multi	4.45	4.45

Hirohito (1901-1989) and enthronement of Akihito as emperor of Japan.

Nos. 835-838 and 840 Surcharged

1989, July 3 Litho. *Perf. 14*

1107	A173b	60ce on 1ce	.42	.42
1108	A173b	80ce on 1.40ce	.58	.58
1109	A173b	200ce on 2.30ce	1.45	1.45
1110	A173b	300ce on 3ce	2.15	2.15
		Nos. 1107-1110 (4)	4.60	4.60

Souvenir Sheet

1111	A173b	500ce on 6ce	3.75	3.75

Nos. 933-936 and 938 Surcharged

1989, July 3 *Perf. 15*

1112	A181	60ce on 1ce	.42	.42
1113	A181	80ce on 1.40ce	.58	.58
1114	A181	200ce on 2.30ce	1.45	1.45
1115	A181	300ce on 3ce	2.15	2.15
		Nos. 1112-1115 (4)	4.60	4.60

Souvenir Sheet

1116	A181	600ce on 70ce	4.35	4.35

Nos. 958, 960 and 963-964 Surcharged

1989, Nov. 20 Litho. *Perf. 14*

1117	A184	80ce on 5ce #958	.65	.65
1118	A184	250ce on 12ce #960	2.00	2.00
1119	A184	300ce on 100ce #963	2.35	2.35
		Nos. 1117-1119 (3)	5.00	5.00

Souvenir Sheet

1119A	A184	500ce on 110ce #964	4.00	4.00

Nos. 1011-1013 and 1015 Surcharged

1989 Litho. *Perf. 14x14½*

1120	A194	60ce on 5ce #1011	.48	.48
1121	A194	200ce on 15ce #1012	1.60	1.60
1122	A194	300ce on 25ce #1013	2.40	2.40
		Nos. 1120-1122 (3)	4.48	4.48

Souvenir Sheet

1123	A194	600ce on 150ce #1015	4.00	4.00

C60 ═══

Nos. 1120-1123 Surcharged

WINNERS
Argentina 3
W. Germany 2

1989 Litho. *Perf. 14x14½*

1123A	A194	60ce on 5ce	.48	.48
1123B	A194	200ce on 15ce	1.60	1.60
1123C	A194	300ce on 25ce	2.40	2.40
		Nos. 1123A-1123C (3)	4.48	4.48

Souvenir Sheet

1123D	A194	600ce on 150ce	4.00	4.00

Nos. 980-982 and 984 Surcharged

1989, Nov. 20 Litho. *Perf. 14*

1124	A188	80ce on 5ce #980	.65	.65
1125	A188	100ce on 8ce #981	.80	.80
1126	A188	300ce on 12ce #982	2.35	2.35
		Nos. 1124-1126 (3)	3.80	3.80

Souvenir Sheet

1127	A188	500ce on 110ce #984	4.00	4.00

Nos. 1029-1032 Surcharged

1989, Nov. 20 *Perf. 14½x14*

1128	A198	60ce on 5ce #1029	.35	.35
a.		With comet logo	.35	.35
1129	A198	80ce on 25ce #1030	.48	.48
a.		With comet logo	.48	.48
1130	A198	500ce on 200ce #1031	3.00	3.00
a.		With comet logo	3.00	3.00
		Nos. 1128-1130 (3)	3.83	3.83
		Nos. 1128a-1130a (3)	3.83	3.83

Souvenir Sheet

1131	A199	750ce on 250ce #1032	5.00	5.00
a.		With comet logo	5.00	5.00

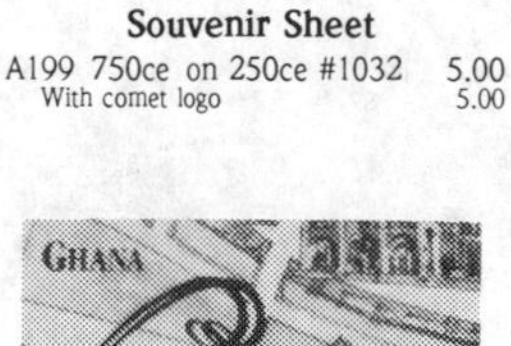

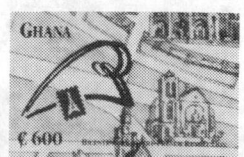

PHILEXFRANCE '89, French Revolution Bicent. — A212

Emblems, French arms and flags: 20ce, Tube-mounted field carriage, flag of 1643 to 1790. 60ce, Infantryman, flag of 1789. 80ce, Handgun, flag of 1789, diff. 350ce, Musket, flag of 1794 to 1814 and 1848 to present. Nos. 1132-1135 vert.

1989, Sept. 22 Litho. *Perf. 14*

1132 A212 20ce multi .16 .16
1133 A212 60ce multi .48 .48
1134 A212 80ce multi .62 .62
1135 A212 350ce multi 2.75 2.75
Nos. 1132-1135 (4) 4.01 4.01

Souvenir Sheet

1136 A212 600ce shown 4.75 4.75

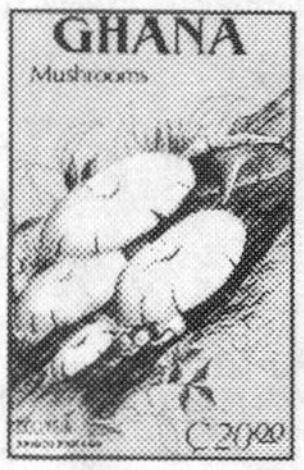

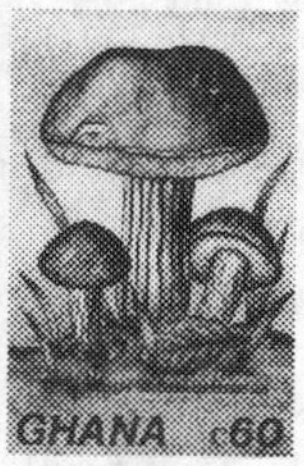

Mushrooms
A213 A214

1989, Oct. 2 Litho. *Perf. 14*

1137 A213 20ce Collybia .16 .16
1138 A213 50ce Lawyer's wig .40 .40
1139 A214 60ce *Xerocomus subtomentosus* .48 .48
1140 A213 80ce Wood belwits .65 .65
1141 A214 150ce *Suillus placidus* 1.20 1.20
1142 A214 200ce *Lepista nuda* 1.60 1.60
1143 A213 300ce Fairy rings 2.40 2.40
1144 A213 500ce Field mushroom 4.00 4.00
Nos. 1137-1144 (8) 10.89 10.89

Souvenir Sheets

1145 A213 600ce Three *Amanita* species 4.75 4.75
1146 A214 600ce Three *Boletus* species 4.75 4.75

Souvenir Sheet

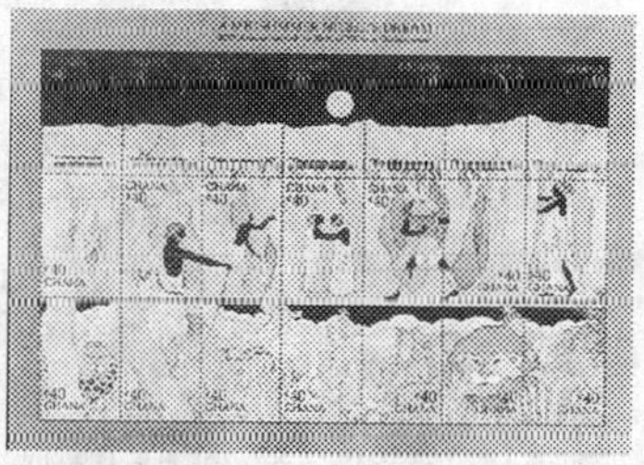

A Midsummer Night's Dream, by Shakespeare — A215

Designs: a, "The course of true love never did run smooth." b, "Love looks not with the eye but with the mind." c, "Nature here shows art." d, "Things growing are not ripe till their season." e, "He is defiled that draws a sword on thee." f, "It is not enough to speak but to speak true." g, "Thou art wise as thou art beautiful." h, Leopard behind trees. i, Theseus. j, Boy holding flower, trees. k, Oberon and Titania among trees. l, Bottom wearing head of a jackass. m, Bottom's leg, leopard behind trees. n, Hippolyta. o, Leopard, tree trunk. p, Tree trunk, foliage, lower portion of Theseus's robe. q, Wisps of fragrance, clouds, hills, foliage. r, Wisps of fragrance, flowering plants. s, Flowering plants. t, Lion, foliage. u, Lion's mane, foliage.

1989, Oct. 9 *Perf. 13½x13*

1147 A215 Sheet of 21 6.75 6.75
a.-u. 40ce any single .32 .32

425th Birth anniv. of William Shakespeare, playwright.

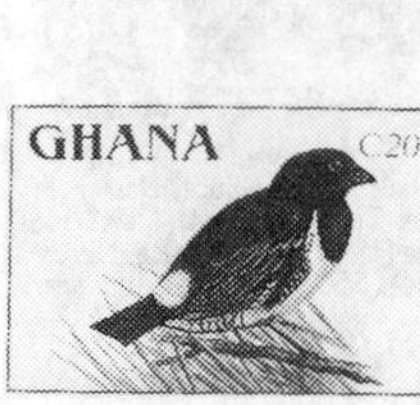

Birds
A216

1989, Oct. 16 *Perf. 14*

1148 A216 20ce *Spermestes cuculatus* .16 .16
1149 A216 50ce *Motacilla aguimp* .40 .40
1150 A216 60ce *Halcyon malimbicus* .48 .48
1151 A216 80ce *Ispidina picta* .65 .65
1152 A216 150ce Striped kingfisher 1.20 1.20
1153 A216 200ce Shikra 1.60 1.60
1154 A216 300ce Gray parrot 2.40 2.40
1155 A216 500ce Black kite 4.00 4.00
Nos. 1148-1155 (8) 10.89 10.89

Souvenir Sheets

1156 A216 600ce Four birds 4.75 4.75
1157 A216 600ce Three birds 4.75 4.75

Nos. 1152-1156 vert.

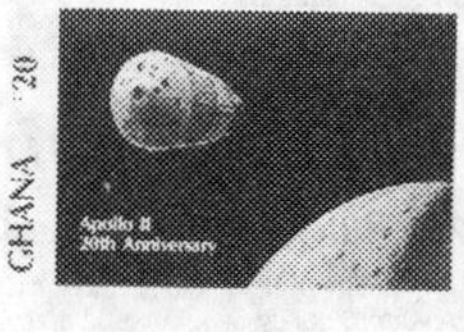

1st Moon Landing, 20th Anniv. A217

Highlights of the Apollo 11 mission.

1989, Nov. 6 *Perf. 14*

1158 A217 20ce *Columbia* .16 .16
1159 A217 80ce Footprint .65 .65
1160 A217 200ce Aldrin on Moon 1.60 1.60
1161 A217 300ce Splashdown 2.40 2.40
Nos. 1158-1161 (4) 4.81 4.81

Souvenir Sheets

1162 A217 500ce Liftoff, vert. 4.00 4.00
1163 A217 500ce Earth, vert. 4.00 4.00

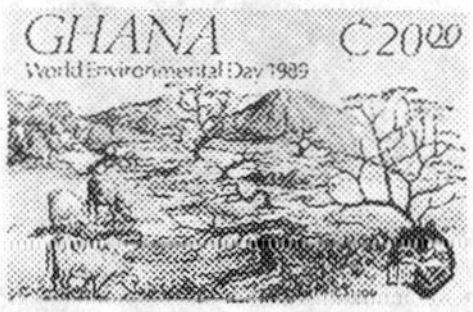

World Environment Day — A218

1989, Nov. 20 Litho. *Perf. 14*

1164 A218 20ce Desertification .16 .16
1165 A218 60ce Bush fires .50 .50
1166 A218 400ce Industrial pollution 3.25 3.25
1167 A218 500ce Soil erosion 4.00 4.00
Nos. 1164-1167 (4) 7.91 7.91

Nos. 760 and 761 Surcharged

1989, Nov. 20 *Perf. 14*

1168 CD331 100ce on 80p .80 .80
1169 CD331 500ce on 4ce 4.75 4.75

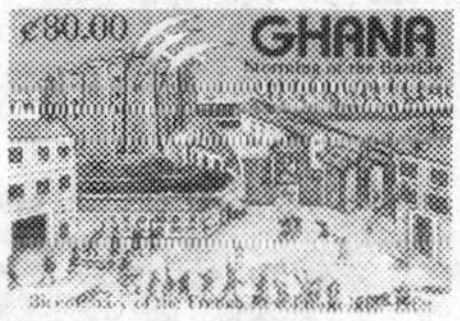

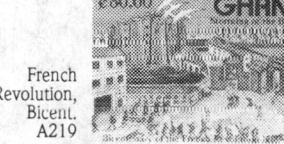

French Revolution, Bicent. A219

Designs: 20ce, Storming of the Bastille, vert. 60ce, Declaration of Human Rights and Citizenship, vert. 80ce, Storming of the Bastille, diff. 200ce, *Departure of the Volunteers in 1792*, high relief on the Arc de Triomphe, 1833-35, by Francis Rude. 350ce, Planting the Liberty Tree.

Perf. 14x13½, 13½x14

1989, Sept. 22

1170 A219 20ce multicolored .16 .16
1171 A219 60ce multicolored .48 .48
1172 A219 80ce multicolored .65 .65
1173 A219 200ce multicolored 1.60 1.60
1174 A219 350ce multicolored 2.75 2.75
Nos. 1170-1174 (5) 5.64 5.64

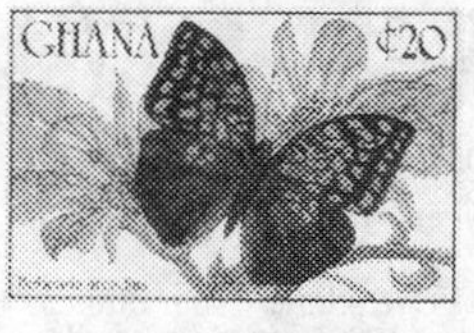

Butterflies
A220

1990, Feb. 15 Litho. *Perf. 14*

1175 A220 20ce *Bebearia arcadius* .16 .16
1176 A220 60ce *Charaxes laodice* .48 .48
1177 A220 80ce *Euryphura porphyrion* .65 .65
1178 A220 100ce *Neptis nicomedes* .80 .80
1179 A220 150ce *Citrinophila erastus* 1.20 1.20
1180 A220 200ce *Epitola honorius* 1.60 1.60
1181 A220 300ce *Precis westermanni* 2.40 2.40
1182 A220 500ce *Cymothoe hypatha* 4.00 4.00
Nos. 1175-1182 (8) 11.29 11.29

Souvenir Sheets

1183 A220 600ce *Telipna bimacula* 4.75 4.75
1184 A220 600ce *Pentila phidia* 4.75 4.75

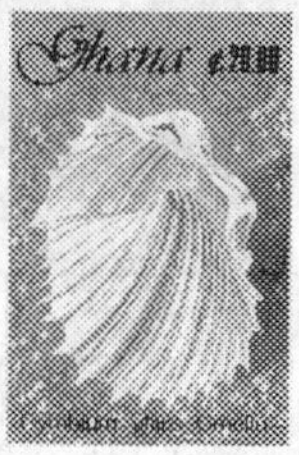

Seashells — A221

1990, Feb. 20 *Perf. 14x14½*

1185 A221 20ce *Cymbium glans* .15 .15
1186 A221 60ce *Cardium costatum* .35 .35
1187 A221 80ce *Conus genuanus* .50 .50
1188 A221 200ce *Ancilla tankervillei* 1.20 1.20
1189 A221 350ce *Tectarius coronatus* 2.15 2.15
Nos. 1185-1189 (5) 4.35 4.35

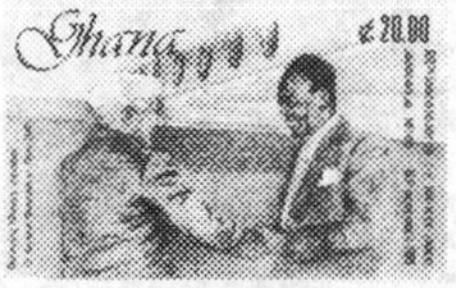

Jawaharlal Nehru, 1st Prime Minister of Independent India — A222

Designs: 20ce, Greeting Pres. Kwame Nkrumah of Ghana. 60ce, Addressing Afro-Asian conference. 80ce, Return from tour of China, vert. 200ce, Releasing dove during a children's celebration in New Delhi, vert. 350ce, Portrait, vert.

Perf. 14½x14, 14x14½

1990, Mar. 27 Litho.

1190 A222 20ce shown .15 .15
1191 A222 60ce multicolored .35 .35
1192 A222 80ce multicolored .45 .45
1193 A222 200ce multicolored 1.15 1.15
1194 A222 350ce multicolored 2.00 2.00
Nos. 1190-1194 (5) 4.10 4.10

Nos. 759A and 760A-760B Surcharged

1990 *Perf. 14*

1195 CD331 80ce on 65p .80 .80
1196 CD331 100ce on 1cc 1.00 1.00
1197 CD331 300ce on 3cc 3.00 3.00
Nos. 1195-1197 (3) 4.80 4.80

Nos. 961, 959 and 962 Surcharged

1990

1198 A184 80ce on 20ce .80 .80
1199 A184 200ce on 8ce 2.00 2.00
1200 A184 250ce on 70ce 2.50 2.50
Nos. 1198-1200 (3) 5.30 5.30

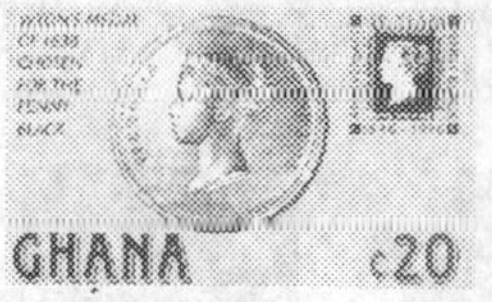

Penny Black, 150th Anniv. A223

Great Britain No. 1 and: 20ce, City Medal containing portrait of Victoria by William Wyon adapted for use on the Penny Black. 60ce, No. 1208, Bath mail coach. 80ce, Leeds Mail coach. 200ce, Heath's engraving, based on the Wyon portrait. 350ce, Penny Black master die. 400ce, London mail coach. No. 1207, Printers and flat-bed presses of Perkins, Bacon & Petch, 1840.

1990, May 3 *Perf. 13½x14*

1201 A223 20ce shown .16 .16
1202 A223 60ce multicolored .48 .48
1203 A223 80ce multicolored .65 .65
1204 A223 200ce multicolored 1.60 1.60
1205 A223 350ce multicolored 2.80 2.80
1206 A223 400ce multicolored 3.20 3.20
Nos. 1201-1206 (6) 8.89 8.89

Souvenir Sheets

1207 A223 600ce multicolored 4.75 4.75
1208 A223 600ce multicolored 4.75 4.75

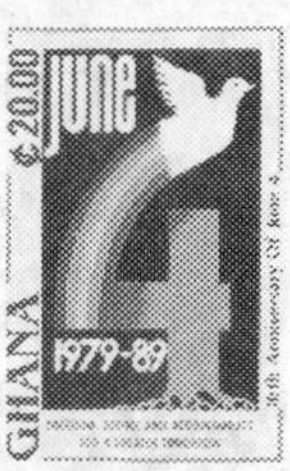

June 4, Revolution, 10th Anniv. (in 1989) — A224

1990, June 5 Litho. *Perf. 14½x14*

1209 A224 20ce shown .16 .16
1210 A224 60ce Pineapple, lobsters .48 .48
1211 A224 80ce Corn, cacao beans .65 .65
1212 A224 200ce Mining 1.60 1.60
1213 A224 350ce Scales, sword 2.80 2.80
Nos. 1209-1213 (5) 5.69 5.69

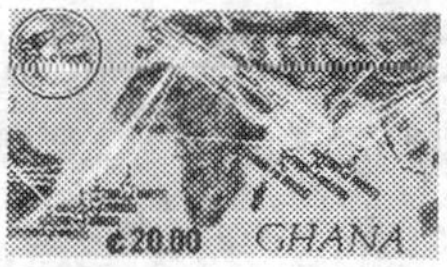

Intelsat, 25th Anniv. A225

Satellites over: 60ce, Pacific Ocean. 80ce, Pacific, diff. 200ce, South Atlantic. 350ce, Pacific, Indian Oceans.

1990, July 12 *Perf. 14x14½*

1214 A225 20ce multicolored .16 .16
1215 A225 60ce multicolored .48 .48
1216 A225 80ce multicolored .65 .65
1217 A225 200ce multicolored 1.60 1.60
1218 A225 350ce multicolored 2.80 2.80
Nos. 1214-1218 (5) 5.69 5.69

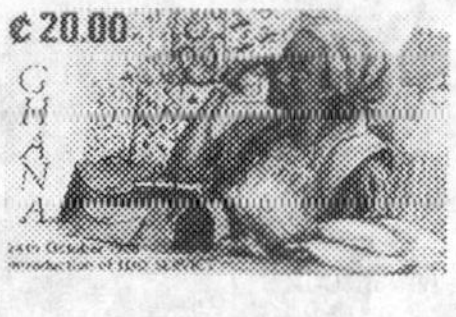

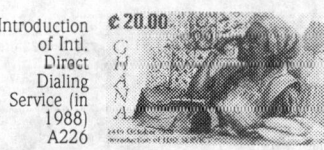

Introduction of Intl. Direct Dialing Service (in 1988) A226

1990, July 16

1219 A226 20ce shown .16 .16
1220 A226 60ce Man using telephone .48 .48
1221 A226 80ce Man using pay telephone .65 .65
1222 A226 200ce Telephone booths 1.60 1.60
1223 A226 350ce Satellite dish 2.80 2.80
Nos. 1219-1223 (5) 5.69 5.69

Miniature Sheet

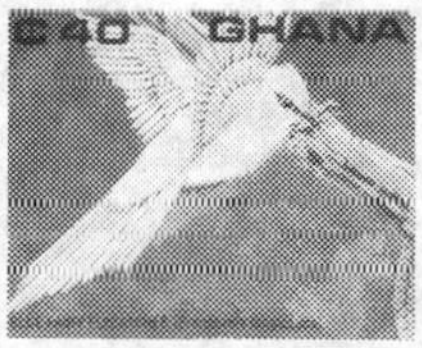

African Tropical Rain Forest A227

Designs: No. 1224a, Blue fairy flycatcher. b, Boomslang. c, Superb sunbird. d, Bateleur eagle. e, Yellow-casqued hornbill. f, Salamis temora. g, Potto. h, Leopard. i, Bongo. j, Gray parrot. k, Okapi. l, Gorilla. m, Flap-necked chameleon. n, West African dwarf crocodile. o, Python. p, Giant pangolin. q, Pseudacraea boisduvali. r, African crested porcupine. s, Rosy-columned aerangis. t, Cymothoe sangaris.

No. 1225, Leopard, vert.

1990, Oct. 25 Litho. *Perf. 14x14½*

1224 Sheet of 20 6.40 6.40
a.-t. A227 40ce any single .32 .32

Souvenir Sheet

1225 A227 600ce multicolored 4.80 4.80

Miniature Sheet

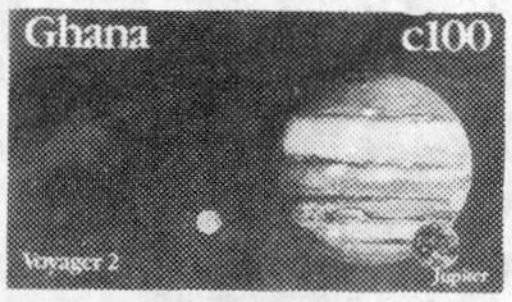

Voyager 2 A228

Photographs from Voyager 2: No. 1226a, Jupiter. b, Neptune, Triton. c, Ariel, moon of Uranus. d, Saturn, Mimas. e, Saturn. f, Rings of Saturn. g, Neptune. h, Uranus, Miranda. i, Volcano on Io.

1990, Dec. 13 Litho. *Perf. 14*

1226 A228 100ce Sheet of 9, #1226a-1226i 7.20 7.20

Souvenir Sheets

1227 A228 600ce Voyager 2 liftoff, vert. 4.80 4.80
1228 A228 600ce Voyager 2, vert. 4.80 4.80

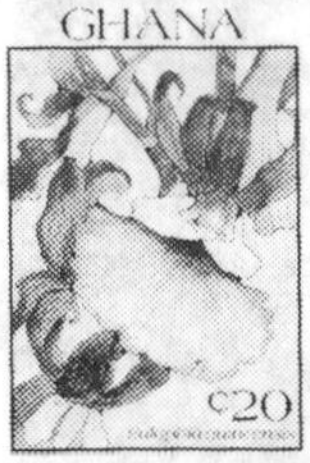

Orchids — A229

Designs: 20ce, Eulophia guineensis. 40ce, Eurychone rothschildiana. 60ce, Bulbophyllum barbigerum. 80ce, Polystachya galeata. 200ce, Diaphananthe kamerunensis. 300ce, Podangis dactyloceras. 400ce, Ancistrochilus rothschildianus. 500ce, Rangaeris muscicola. No. 1237, Bolusiella imbricata. No. 1238, Diaphananthe rutila.

1990, Dec. 17

1229 A229 20ce multicolored .16 .16
1230 A229 40ce multicolored .32 .32
1231 A229 60ce multicolored .48 .48
1232 A229 80ce multicolored .65 .65
1233 A229 200ce multicolored 1.60 1.60
1234 A229 300ce multicolored 2.40 2.40
1235 A229 400ce multicolored 3.20 3.20
1236 A229 500ce multicolored 4.00 4.00
Nos. 1229-1236 (8) 12.81 12.81

Souvenir Sheets

1237 A229 600ce multicolored 4.80 4.80
1238 A229 600ce multicolored 4.80 4.80

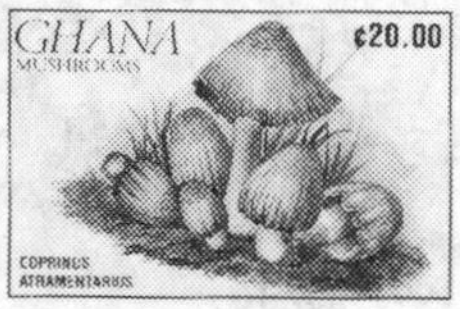

Mushrooms A230

Designs: 20ce, Coprinus atramentarius. 50ce, Marasmius oreades. 60ce, Oudamansiella radicata. 80ce, Cep. 150ce, Hebeloma crustuliniforme. 200ce, Coprinus micaceus. 300ce, Lepiota procera. 500ce, Amanita phalloides.

1990, Dec. 18

1239 A230 20ce multicolored .16 .16
1240 A230 50ce multicolored .40 .40
1241 A230 60ce multicolored .48 .48
1242 A230 80ce multicolored .65 .65
1243 A230 150ce multicolored 1.20 1.20
1244 A230 200ce multicolored 1.60 1.60
1245 A230 300ce multicolored 2.40 2.40
a. Min. sheet of 4, #1240, 1243-1245 5.60 5.60
1246 A230 500ce multicolored 4.00 4.00
a. Min. sheet of 4, #1239, 1241-1242, 1246 4.29 4.29

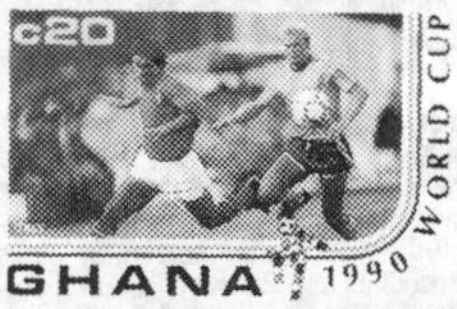

World Cup Soccer Championships, Italy — A231

Players from participating countries.

1990, Dec. 18 Litho. *Perf. 14*

1247 A231 20ce Italy .16 .16
1248 A231 50ce Egypt .40 .40
1249 A231 60ce Cameroun .48 .48
1250 A231 80ce Romania .65 .65
1251 A231 100ce Yugoslavia .80 .80
1252 A231 150ce Cameroun, vert. 1.20 1.20
1253 A231 400ce South Korea 3.20 3.20
1254 A231 600ce West Germany 4.80 4.80
Nos. 1247-1254 (8) 11.69 11.69

Souvenir Sheets

1255 A231 800ce UAE 6.50 6.50
1256 A231 800ce Colombia 6.50 6.50

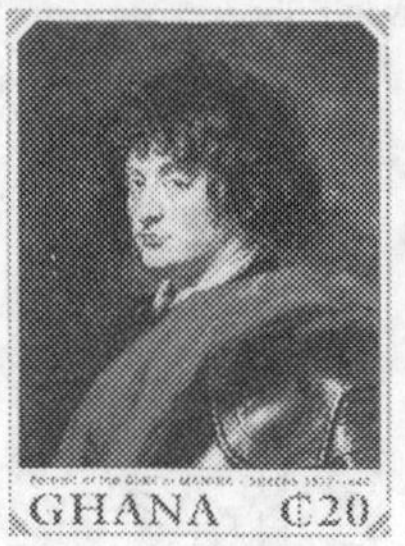

Peter Paul Rubens (1577-1640), Painter A232

Portraits by Rubens: 20ce, Duke of Mantua. 50ce, Jan Brant. 60ce, Young man. 80ce, Michel Ophovius. 100ce, Caspar Gevaerts. 200ce, Head of a warrior (detail). 300ce, Bearded man. 400ce, Paracelsus. No. 1265, Archduke Ferdinand. No. 1266, Warrior with Two Pages.

1990, Dec. 24 Litho. *Perf. 14*

1257 A232 20ce multicolored .16 .16
1258 A232 50ce multicolored .40 .40
1259 A232 60ce multicolored .48 .48
1260 A232 80ce multicolored .64 .64
1261 A232 100ce multicolored .80 .80
1262 A232 200ce multicolored 1.60 1.60
1263 A232 300ce multicolored 2.40 2.40
1264 A232 400ce multicolored 3.20 3.20
Nos. 1257-1264 (8) 9.68 9.68

Souvenir Sheets

1265 A232 600ce multicolored 4.80 4.80
1266 A232 600ce multicolored 4.80 4.80

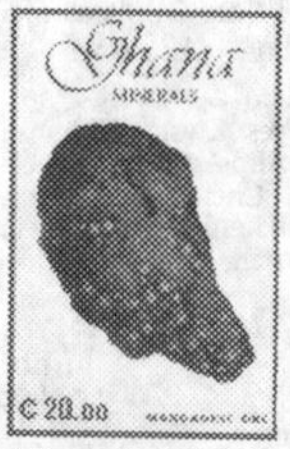

Minerals — A233

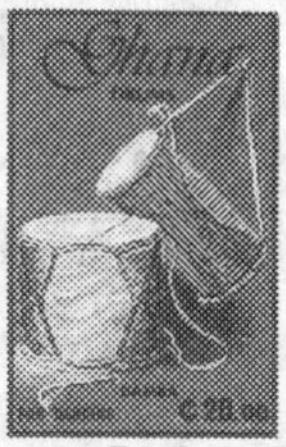

Tribal Drums — A234

1991, May 2 Litho. *Perf. $14^1/_2$x14*

1267 A233 20ce Manganese ore .16 .16
1268 A233 60ce Iron ore .48 .48
1269 A233 80ce Bauxite ore .64 .64
1270 A233 200ce Gold ore 1.60 1.60
1271 A233 350ce Diamond 2.80 2.80
Nos. 1267-1271 (5) 5.68 5.68

Souvenir Sheet

1272 A233 600ce Diamonds 4.80 4.80

1991, May 9

1273 A234 20ce Damba .16 .16
1274 A234 60ce Atumpan .48 .48
1275 A234 80ce Kroboto .64 .64
1276 A234 200ce Asafo 1.60 1.60
1277 A234 350ce Obonu 2.80 2.80
Nos. 1273-1277 (5) 5.68 5.68

Souvenir Sheet

1278 A234 600ce Single drum 4.80 4.80

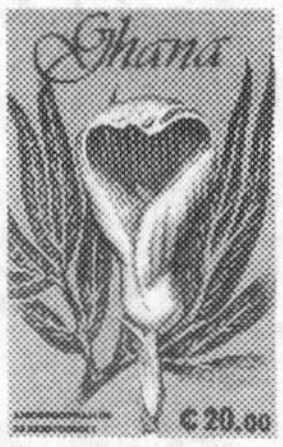

Flowers — A235

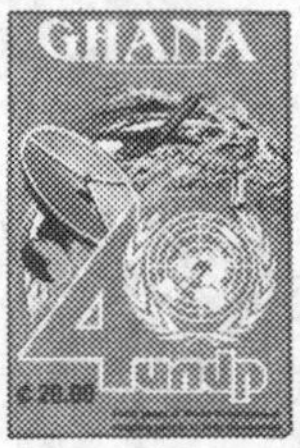

A236

1991, May 15

1279 A235 20ce Amorphophallus dracontioides .16 .16
1280 A235 60ce Anchomanes difformis .48 .48
1281 A235 80ce Kaemferia nigerica .64 .64
1282 A235 200ce Aframomum sceptrum 1.60 1.60
1283 A235 350ce Amorphophallus flavovirens 2.80 2.80
Nos. 1279-1284 (6) 10.48 10.48

Souvenir Sheet

1284 A235 600ce White flowers 4.80 4.80

1991, May 17 Litho. *Perf. $14^1/_2$x14*

1285 A235 20ce Urginea indica .16 .16
1286 A235 60ce Hymenocallis littoralis .48 .48
1287 A235 80ce Crinum jagus .64 .64
1288 A235 200ce Dipcadi tacazzeanum 1.60 1.60
1289 A235 350ce Haemanthus rupestris 2.80 2.80
Nos. 1285-1289 (5) 5.68 5.68

Souvenir Sheet

1290 A235 600ce Red flowers 4.80 4.80

1991, June 21 Litho. *Perf. $13^1/_2$x14*

Designs: 20ce, Satellite transmissions, airplane. 60ce, Scientific research, honey bee. 80ce, Literacy instruction. 200ce, Agricultural development. 350ce, Industry.

1291 A236 20ce multicolored .16 .16
1292 A236 60ce multicolored .48 .48
1293 A236 80ce multicolored .64 .64
1294 A236 200ce multicolored 1.60 1.60
1295 A236 350ce multicolored 2.80 2.80
Nos. 1291-1295 (5) 5.68 5.68

UN Development Program, 40th anniv.

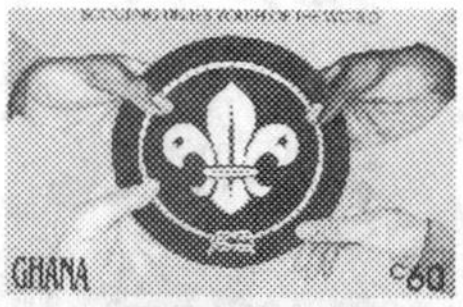

Lord Robert Baden-Powell (1857-1941), Founder of Boy Scouts — A237

Designs: 20ce, Sketch by Baden-Powell used in first scouting handbook, vert. 50ce, Portrait, vert. 80ce, Scout handbook illustration by Norman Rockwell. 100ce, Native runner, Cape of Good Hope #178. 200ce, Scouts aiding victims after V-1 attack, London, 1944. 500ce, Scout praying, vert. 600ce, Emblem, Cape of Good Hope #178 used. No. 1304, Cover with Cape of Good Hope #178 from Mafeking, 1900. No. 1305, Campsites, 17th World Scout Jamboree, Korea, 1991.

1991, July 16 Litho. *Perf. 14*

1296 A237 20ce buff & black .16 .16
1297 A237 50ce multicolored .40 .40
1298 A237 60ce multicolored .48 .48
1299 A237 80ce black & buff .64 .64
1300 A237 100ce multicolored .80 .80
1301 A237 200ce multicolored 1.60 1.60
1302 A237 500ce multicolored 4.00 4.00
1303 A237 600ce multicolored 4.80 4.80
Nos. 1296-1303 (8) 12.88 12.88

Souvenir Sheets

1304 A237 800ce multicolored 6.40 6.40
1305 A237 800ce multicolored 6.40 6.40

For overprints see Nos. 1567-1572.

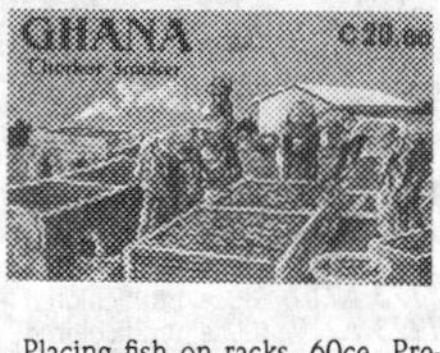

Chorkor Smoker A238

Designs: 20ce, Placing fish on racks. 60ce, Preparing smokers. 80ce, Preparing fish. 200ce, Preparing racks for smoker. 350ce, Placing racks in smoker.

1991, July 22 Litho. *Perf. 14x$14^1/_2$*

1306 A238 20ce multicolored .16 .16
1307 A238 60ce multicolored .48 .48
1308 A238 80ce multicolored .64 .64
1309 A238 200ce multicolored 1.60 1.60
1310 A238 350ce multicolored 2.80 2.80
Nos. 1306-1310 (5) 5.68 5.68

Nos. 958-964 Overprinted "90th Birthday / 4th August 1990" and Surcharged

Perf. 14, $12^1/_2$x12 (#1312-1313, 1315)

1991, July 22

1311 A184 20ce on 5ce #958 .16 .16
1312 A184 20ce on 8ce #959 .16 .16
1313 A184 40ce on 20ce #961 .32 .32
1314 A184 60ce on 12ce #960 .48 .48
1315 A184 80ce on 70ce #962 .64 .64
1316 A184 150ce on 100ce #963 1.20 1.20
Nos. 1311-1316 (6) 2.96 2.96

Souvenir Sheet

1317 A184 200ce on 110ce #964 1.60 1.60

Nos. 1312-1313, 1315 issued in sheets of 5 + label. Overprint is vertical on stamp in No. 1317, horizontal on sheet margin.

The status of this issue is uncertain.

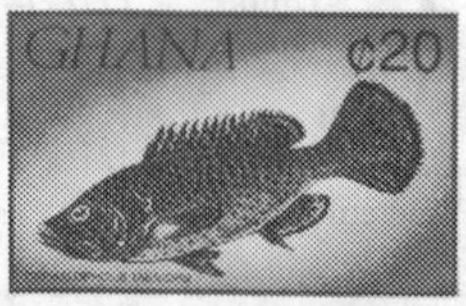

Fish A239

1991, July 29 Litho. *Perf. 14*

1318 A239 20ce Cephalopholis taeniops .16 .16
1319 A239 50ce Synodontis sorex .40 .40
1320 A239 80ce Balistes forcipatus .40 .40
1321 A239 100ce Petrocephalus bane .50 .50
1322 A239 200ce Syngnathus rastellatus 1.00 1.00
1323 A239 300ce Gymnarchus niloticus 2.40 2.40
1324 A239 400ce Hemichromis bimaculatus 3.20 3.20
1325 A239 500ce Sphyrna zygaena 2.50 2.50
Nos. 1318-1325 (8) 10.56 10.56

Souvenir Sheets

1326 A239 800ce Bagrus bayad 6.40 6.40
1327 A239 800ce Dactyloptena orientalis 4.00 4.00

While Nos. 1320-1322, 1325, 1327 have the same issue date as Nos. 1318-1319, 1323-1324, 1326, the value of Nos. 1320-1322, 1325, 1327 was lower when they were released.

For overprints see Nos. 1573-1578.

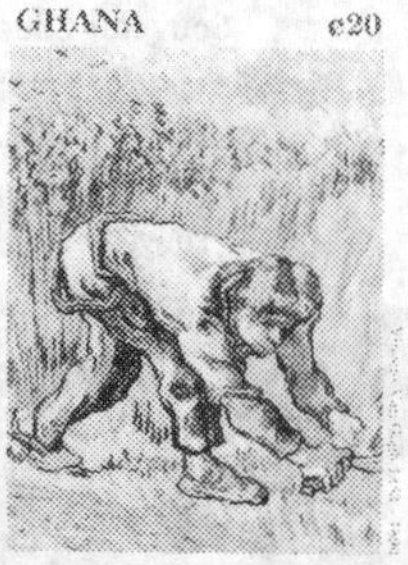

Paintings by Vincent Van Gogh A240

Designs: 20ce, Reaper with Sickle. 50ce, The Thresher. 60ce, The Sheaf Binder. 80ce, The Sheep Shearers. 100ce, Peasant Woman Cutting Straw. 200ce, The Sower. 500ce, The Plow and the Harrow, horiz. 600ce, The Woodcutter. No. 1336, Evening: The Watch. No. 1337, Evening: The End of the Day.

Perf. 13x$13^1/_2$, $13^1/_2$x13

1991, Aug. 12 Litho.

1328 A240 20ce multicolored .16 .16
1329 A240 50ce multicolored .40 .40
1330 A240 60ce multicolored .48 .48
1331 A240 80ce multicolored .64 .64
1332 A240 100ce multicolored .80 .80
1333 A240 200ce multicolored 1.60 1.60
1334 A240 500ce multicolored 4.00 4.00
1335 A240 600ce multicolored 4.80 4.80
Nos. 1328-1335 (8) 12.88 12.88

Size: 106x80mm

Imperf

1336 A240 800ce multicolored 6.40 6.40
1337 A240 800ce multicolored 6.40 6.40

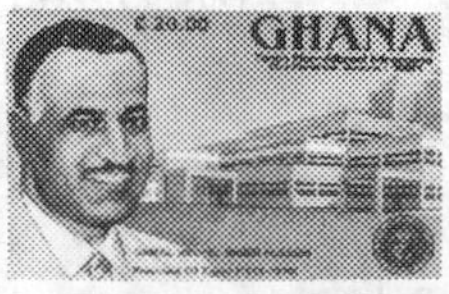

10th Non-aligned Ministers Conference, Accra A241

Natl. Leaders: 20ce, Nasser, Egypt (1952-1970). 60ce, Tito, Yugoslavia (1945-1980). 80ce, Nehru, India (1947-1964). 200ce, Nkrumah, Ghana (1957-1966). 350ce, Sukarno, Indonesia (1945-1967).

1991, Sept. 2 *Perf. $13^1/_2$x14*

1338 A241 20ce multicolored .16 .16
1339 A241 60ce multicolored .48 .48
1340 A241 80ce multicolored .64 .64
1341 A241 200ce multicolored 1.60 1.60
1342 A241 350ce multicolored 2.80 2.80
Nos. 1338-1342 (5) 5.68 5.68

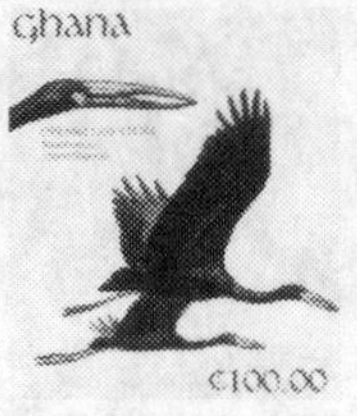

Birds of Ghana — A242

Designs: No. 1343a, Melba finch. b, Orange-cheeked waxbill. c, Paradise flycatcher. d, Blue plantain-eater, e, Red bishop. f, Splendid glossy starling. g, Red-headed lovebird. h, Palm swift. i, Narina trogon. j, Tawny eagle. k, Bateleur eagle. l, Hoopoe. m, Secretary bird. n, White-backed vulture. o, Bare-headed rockfowl. p, Ground hornbill.

No. 1344a, Openbilled stork. b, African spoonbill. c, Pink-backed pelican. d, Little bittern. e, King reed-hen. f, Saddlebill stork. g, Glossy ibis. h, White-faced tree duck. i, Black-headed heron. j, Hammerkop. k, African darter. l, Woolly-necked stork. m, Yellow-billed stork. n, Black-winged stilt. o, Goliath heron. p, Lily trotter.

No. 1345a, Shikra. b, Abyssinian roller (c, g). c, Carmine bee-eater (g). d, Pintailed whydah (h). e, Purple glossy starling. f, Yellow-backed whydah (j). g, Pel's fishing owl. h, Verreaux's touraco (l). i, Red-cheeked cordon-bleu. j, Olive-bellied sunbird. k, Red-billed hornbill. l, Red-billed quelea. m, Crowned crane (i). n, Blue quail. o, Egyptian vulture (p). p, Helmeted guineafowl.

No. 1346, Marabou stork. No. 1347, Saddlebill stork, diff. No. 1348, African river eagle.

1991, Oct. 14 Litho. *Perf. 14½x14*

Sheets of 16

1343	A242	80ce	#a.-p.	7.25	7.25
1344	A242	100ce	#a.-p.	10.00	10.00
1345	A242	100ce	#a.-p.	12.75	12.75
			Nos. 1343-1345 (3)	30.00	30.00

Souvenir Sheets

1346	A242	800ce	multicolored	5.00	5.00
1347	A242	800ce	multicolored	5.00	5.00
1348	A242	800ce	multicolored	5.00	5.00

While No. 1344 has the same issue date as No. 1345, the value of No. 1344 was lower when it was released.

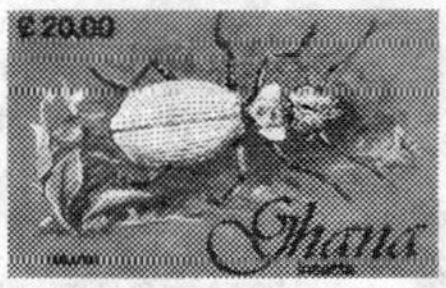

Insects A243

1991, Oct. 25 *Perf. 14x13½*

1349	A243	20ce	Nularda	.16	.16
1350	A243	50ce	Zonocrus	.40	.40
1351	A243	60ce	Gryllotalpa africana	.48	.48
1352	A243	80ce	Weevil	.64	.64
1353	A243	100ce	Coenagrion	.80	.80
1354	A243	150ce	Sahlbergella	1.20	1.20
1355	A243	200ce	Anthia	1.60	1.60
1356	A243	350ce	Megacephala	2.80	2.80
			Nos. 1349-1356 (8)	8.08	8.08

Souvenir Sheet

Perf. 13x12

1357	A243	600ce	Lacetus	4.80	4.80

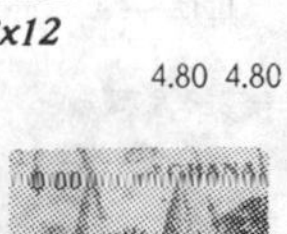

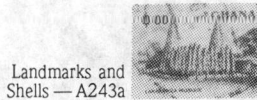

Landmarks and Shells — A243a

Designs: 50ce, Boti Falls, vert. 60ce, Larabanga Mosque. 80ce, Fort Sebastian, Shama. 100ce, Cape Coast Castle. 200ce, Leucodon cowrie. 400ce, Achatina achatina.

1991 Litho. *Perf. 13½*

1357A	A243a	50ce	multicolored
1357B	A243a	60ce	multicolored
1357C	A243a	80ce	multicolored
1357D	A243a	100ce	multicolored
1357E	A243a	200ce	multicolored
1357F	A243a	400ce	multicolored

Issue dates: 50ce, Nov. 21. Others, Dec. 12.

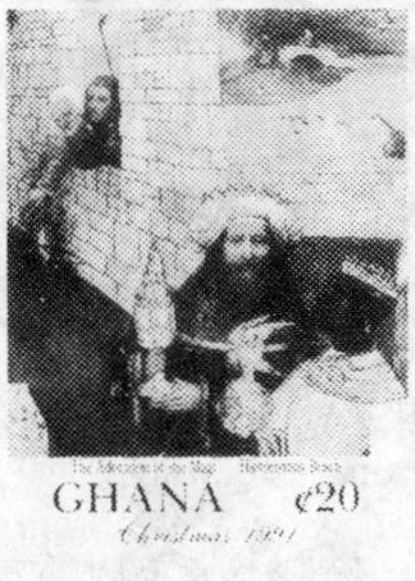

Adoration of the Magi by Hieronymus Bosch — A244

Details or entire paintings: 50ce, The Annunciation by Robert Campin. 60ce, Virgin and Child by Dirk Bouts. 80ce, Presentation in the Temple by Hans Memling. 100ce, The Virgin and Child Enthroned with an Angel and a Donor by Memling. 200ce, The Virgin and Child with Saints and a Donor by Jan van Eyck. 400ce, St. Luke Painting the Virgin by Rogier van der Weyden. 700ce, Virgin and Child by Bouts, diff. No. 1366, The Annunciation by Memling. No. 1367, The Virgin and Child Standing in a Niche by van der Weyden.

1991, Dec. 23 *Perf. 12*

1358	A244	20ce	multicolored	.16	.16
1359	A244	50ce	multicolored	.40	.40
1360	A244	60ce	multicolored	.48	.48
1361	A244	80ce	multicolored	.64	.64
1362	A244	100ce	multicolored	.80	.80
1363	A244	200ce	multicolored	1.60	1.60
1364	A244	400ce	multicolored	3.20	3.20
1365	A244	700ce	multicolored	5.60	5.60
			Nos. 1358-1365 (8)	12.88	12.88

Souvenir Sheets

Perf. 14½

1366	A244	800ce	multicolored	6.40	6.40
1367	A244	800ce	multicolored	6.40	6.40

Christmas.

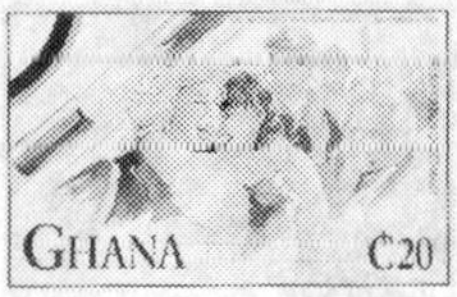

Reunification of Germany — A245

Designs: 20ce, Opening of German border, Nov. 9, 1989. 60ce, Signing of Two Plus Four Treaty, Sept. 12, 1990. 80ce, Opening of Brandenburg Gate, Dec. 22, 1989. 800ce, German leaders, Unity Day, Oct. 3, 1990.

No. 1371b, USSR Pres. Mikhail Gorbachev, vert. c, Chancellor Helmut Kohl, vert. d, Map of West Germany, vert. e, Map of East Germany, vert. 1000ce, Currency union, July 1, 1990.

No. 1371g, Doves. h, German Chancellor Helmut Kohl, Foreign Minister Hans-Dietrich Genscher.

1992, Feb. 17 Litho. *Perf. 14*

1368	A245	20ce	multicolored	.15	.15
1369	A245	60ce	multicolored	.42	.42
1370	A245	80ce	multicolored	.55	.55
1371	A245	1000ce	multicolored	6.85	6.85
			Nos. 1368-1371 (4)	7.97	7.97

Souvenir Sheets

1371A	A245	300ce	Sheet of 4, #b.-e.	7.50	7.50
1371F	A245	400ce	Sheet of 2, #g.-h.	2.50	2.50
1372	A245	800ce	multicolored	5.50	5.50

While No. 1371F has the same issue date as No. 1371A, the dollar value of No. 1371F was lower when it was released.

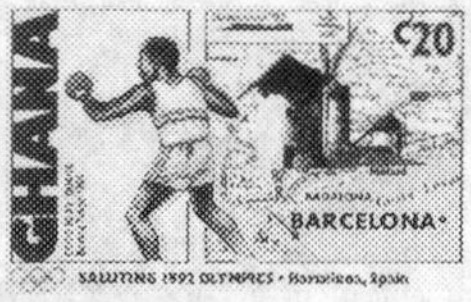

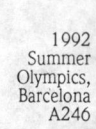

1992 Summer Olympics, Barcelona A246

Map and: 20ce, Eddie Blay, boxing, Ghana, 1964. 60ce, Mike Ahey, track, Ghana, 1964-1972. 80ce, T. Wilson, ski jumping, US, 1988. 100ce, East German 4-Man bobsled, 1988. 200ce, Greg Louganis, diving, US, 1984. 300ce, L. Visser, speed skating, Netherlands, 1988. 350ce, J. Passler, biathlon, Italy, 1988. 400ce, Mary Lou Retton, gymnastics, US, 1984. 500ce, Jurgen Hingsen, decathlon, Germany, 1984. 600ce, R. Neubert, heptathlon, West Germany, 1984. No. 1380, Jai alai player, vert. No. 1381, Windmill.

1992, Mar. 3 Litho. *Perf. 14*

1373	A246	20ce	multi	.15	.15
1373A	A246	60ce	multi	.18	.18
1374	A246	80ce	multi	.50	.50
1375	A246	100ce	multi	.60	.60
1376	A246	200ce	multi	1.25	1.25
1377	A246	300ce	multi	1.85	1.85
1378	A246	350ce	multi	2.15	2.15
1378A	A246	400ce	multi	1.20	1.20
1378B	A246	500ce	multi	1.50	1.50
1379	A246	600ce	multi	3.70	3.70
			Nos. 1373-1379 (10)	13.08	13.08

Souvenir Sheets

1380	A246	800ce	multi	5.00	5.00
1381	A246	800ce	multi	5.00	5.00

While Nos. 1373A, 1378A-1378B have the same issue date as rest of the set the dollar value of Nos. 1373A, 1378A-1378B were lower when they were released.

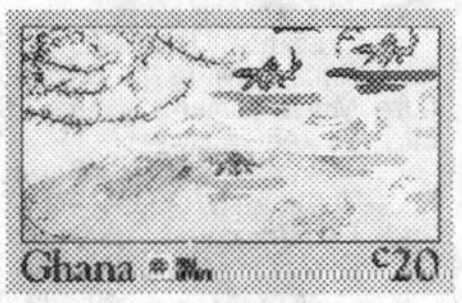

Phila Nippon '91 A247

1992, Feb. 16 Litho. *Perf. 14*

1382	A247	20ce	shown	.15	.15
1383	A247	60ce	Torii of Itsukushima Jingu shrine	.38	.38
1384	A247	80ce	Geisha	.50	.50
1385	A247	100ce	Samurai residence	.60	.60
1386	A247	200ce	Bonsai tree	1.20	1.20
1387	A247	400ce	Olympic sports hall	2.40	2.40
1388	A247	500ce	Great Buddha	3.10	3.10
1389	A247	600ce	Nagoya castle	3.70	3.70
			Nos. 1382-1389 (8)	12.03	12.03

Souvenir Sheets

1390	A247	800ce	Takamatsu castle	5.00	5.00
1391	A247	800ce	Heian shrine	5.00	5.00

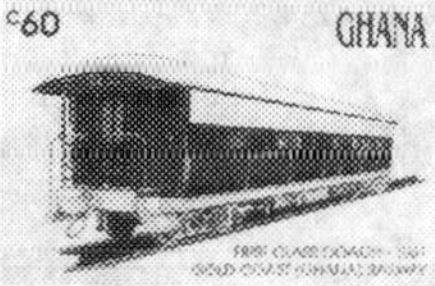

Ghana Natl. Railways A248

Designs: 20c, Engine, 1903, Gold Coast Railway. 50c, Diesel passenger locomotive, Ghana Railways Corp. 60ce, First class coach, 1931 Gold Coast Railway. 80ce, Official inspection coach, Gold Coast Railway. 100ce, Engine No. 401 on turntable. 200c, Twin-bogie cocoa wagon, 1921, Gold Coast Railway. 500ce, Engine No. 223, "Prince of Wales." 600ce, Twin-bogie cattle wagon, Gold Coast Railway. No. 1396, German-made locomotive, Gold Coast Railway. No. 1397, Beyer-Garratt #301, 1943, Gold Coast Railway.

1992, Mar. 2

1392	A248	20ce	multicolored	.15	.15
1393	A248	50ce	multicolored	.32	.32
1394	A248	60ce	multicolored	.38	.38
1395	A248	80ce	multicolored	.50	.50
1396	A248	100ce	multicolored	.65	.65
1397	A248	200ce	multicolored	1.30	1.30
1398	A248	500ce	multicolored	3.10	3.10
1399	A248	600ce	multicolored	3.70	3.70
			Nos. 1392-1399 (8)	10.10	10.10

Souvenir Sheets

1400	A248	800ce	multicolored	5.00	5.00
1401	A248	800ce	multicolored	5.00	5.00

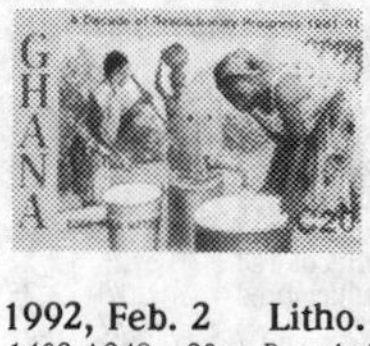

Decade of Revolutionary Progress — A249

1992, Feb. 2 Litho. *Perf. 14x13½*

1402	A249	20ce	Bore hole water	.15	.15
1403	A249	50ce	Mining industry	.30	.30
1404	A249	60ce	Small scale industry	.38	.38
1405	A249	80ce	Timber industry	.50	.50
1406	A249	200ce	Cocoa rehabilitation	1.25	1.25
1407	A249	350ce	Rural electrification	2.15	2.15
			Nos. 1402-1407 (6)	4.73	4.73

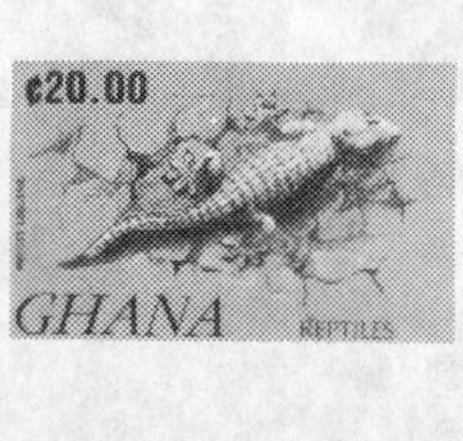

Reptiles A251

1992, Mar. 30 Litho. *Perf. 14*

1414	A251	20ce	Angides lugubris	.15	.15
1415	A251	50ce	Kinixys erosa	.30	.30
1416	A251	60ce	Agama agama	.38	.38
1417	A251	80ce	Chameleo gracilis	.50	.50
1418	A251	100ce	Naja melanleuca	.60	.60
1419	A251	200ce	Crocodylus niloticus	1.20	1.20
1420	A251	400ce	Chelonia mydas	2.40	2.40
1421	A251	500ce	Varanus exanthematicus	3.00	3.00
			Nos. 1414-1421 (8)	8.53	8.53

Souvenir Sheet

1422	A251	600ce	Snake & tortoise	3.60	3.60

Numbers have been reserved for additional values in this set.

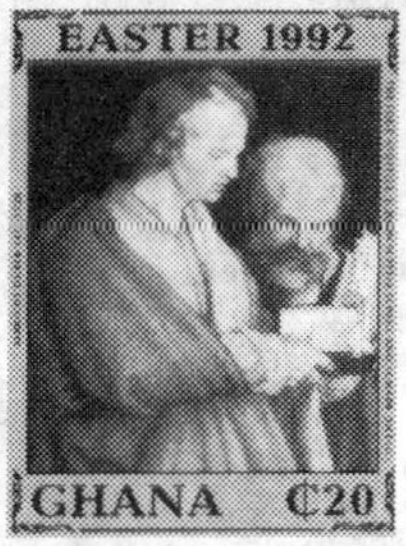

Easter — A252

Details from paintings: 20ce, The Four Apostles: Sts. John, Peter, Paul & Mark, by Durer. 50ce, The Last Judgment, by Rubens. 60ce, The Four Apostles: Sts. John, Peter, Paul and Mark, diff. by Durer. 80ce, The Last Judgment, diff. by Rubens. 100ce, Crucifixion, by Rubens. 200ce, The Last Judgment, diff. by Rubens. 500ce, Christum Videre, by Rubens. 600ce, The Last Judgment, diff. by Rubens. No. 1432, Last Communion of St. Francis of Assisi, by Rubens. No. 1432A, Scourging the Money Changers from the Temple, by El Greco, horiz.

1992, Mar. 13 *Perf. 13½x14*

1424	A252	20ce	multi	.15	.15
1425	A252	50ce	multi	.30	.30
1426	A252	60ce	multi	.38	.38
1427	A252	80ce	multi	.50	.50
1428	A252	100ce	multi	.60	.60
1429	A252	200ce	multi	1.20	1.20
1430	A252	500ce	multi	3.00	3.00
1431	A252	600ce	multi	3.60	3.60
			Nos. 1424-1431 (8)	9.73	9.73

Souvenir Sheets

1432	A252	800ce	multi	4.80	4.80

Perf. 14x13½

1432A	A252	800ce	multi	4.80	4.80

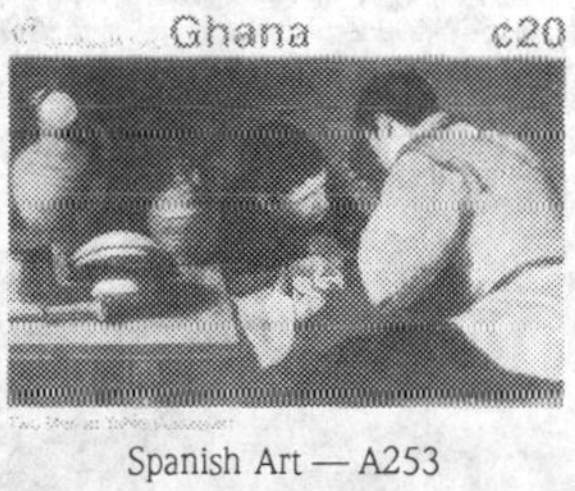

Spanish Art — A253

Paintings by Velazquez: 20ce, Two Men at Table. 60ce, Christ in the House of Mary and Martha (detail). 80ce, The Supper at Emmaus. 100ce, Three Muscians. 200ce, Old Woman Cooking Eggs, vert. 400ce, Old Woman Cooking Eggs (detail), vert. 500ce, The Surrender of Breda (detail) diff., vert. 700ce, The Surrender of Breda (detail), vert.

No. 1441, They Still Say that Fish is Expensive, by Joaquin Sorolla y Bastida. No. 1442, The Water-seller of Seville.

1992, May 4 *Perf. 13½*

1433	A253	20ce	multicolored	.15	.15
1434	A253	60ce	multicolored	.30	.30
1435	A253	80ce	multicolored	.40	.40
1436	A253	100ce	multicolored	.60	.60
1437	A253	200ce	multicolored	1.20	1.20
1438	A253	400ce	multicolored	2.00	2.00
1439	A253	500ce	multicolored	2.50	2.50
1440	A253	700ce	multicolored	4.25	4.25

Size: 120x95mm

Imperf

1441	A253	900ce	multicolored	5.50	5.50
1442	A253	900ce	multicolored	4.50	4.50
			Nos. 1433-1442 (10)	21.40	21.40

Granada '92. While Nos. 1434-1435, 1438-1439, 1442 have the same issue date as Nos. 1433, 1436-1437, 1440-1441, the value in relation to the dollar of Nos. 1434-1435, 1438-1439, 1442 was lower when they were released.

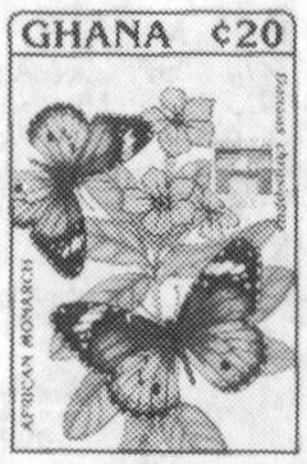

Butterflies — A254

1992, May 25 Litho. *Perf. 14*

1443	A254	20ce	African monarch	.15	.15
1444	A254	60ce	Mocker swallowtail	.35	.35
1445	A254	80ce	Painted lady	.50	.50
1446	A254	100ce	Mountain beauty	.60	.60
1447	A254	200ce	Blue temora	1.20	1.20
1448	A254	400ce	Foxy charaxes	2.40	2.40
1449	A254	500ce	Blue pansy	3.00	3.00
1450	A254	700ce	Golden pansy	4.20	4.20
			Nos. 1443-1450 (8)	12.40	12.40

Souvenir Sheets

1451	A254	900ce	Gaudy commodore	5.50	5.50
1452	A254	900ce	Christmas butterfly	5.50	5.50

Genoa '92. For overprints see Nos. 1471-1480.

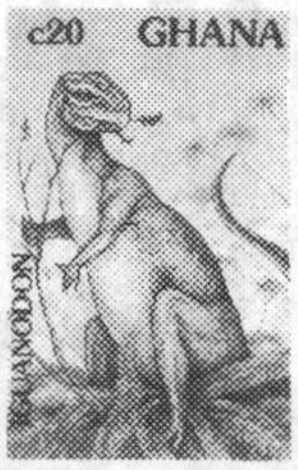

Dinosaurs — A255

1992, June 1 Litho. *Perf. 14*

1453	A255	20ce	Iguanodon	.15	.15
1454	A255	50ce	Anchisaurus	.30	.30
1455	A255	60ce	Heterodontosaurus	.38	.38
1456	A255	80ce	Ouranosaurus	.40	.40
1457	A255	100ce	Anatosaurus	.60	.60
1458	A255	200ce	Elaphrosaurus	1.00	1.00
1459	A255	500ce	Coelophysis	2.50	2.50
1460	A255	600ce	Rhamphorynchus	3.60	3.60
			Nos. 1453-1460 (8)	8.93	8.93

Souvenir Sheets

1461	A255	1500ce	like #1459	9.00	9.00
1462	A255	1500ce	like #1458	7.50	7.50

While Nos. 1453, 1456, 1458-1459 and 1462 have the same issue date as Nos. 1454-1455, 1457, 1460-1461, their value in relation to the dollar was lower when they were released.

Miniature Sheet

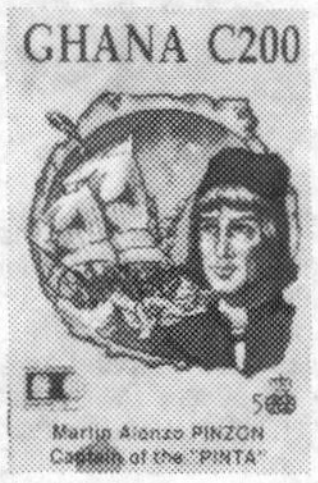

Discovery of America, 500th Anniv. — A256

Designs: No. 1463a, Capt. Martin Alonzo Pinzon, Pinta. b, Capt. Vicente Yanez Pinzon, Nina. c, Columbus, Fr. Marchena in La Rabida, 1485. d, Columbus in cabin. e, Land sighted, Oct. 12, 1492. f, Columbus lands on Samana Cay. g, Shipwreck of Santa Maria. h, Columbus returns to Spanish Court, 1493. No. 1464, Columbus, ship.

1992, July Litho. *Perf. 14*

1463	A256	200ce	Sheet of 8, #a.-h.	9.60	9.60

Souvenir Sheet

1464	A256	500ce	multicolored	3.00	3.00

World Columbian Stamp Expo '92, Chicago.

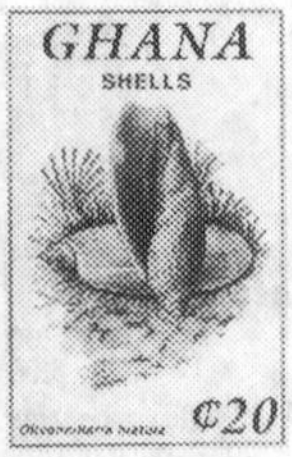

Shells — A257

1992, Oct. 5 Litho. *Perf. 14*

1465	A257	20ce	Olivancillaria hiatula	.15	.15
1465A	A257	20ce	Tympanotonus fuscatus	.15	.15
1466	A257	60ce	Donax rugosus	.30	.30
1466A	A257	60ce	Murex cornutus	.30	.30
1467	A257	80ce	Sigaretus concavus	.40	.40
1467A	A257	80ce	Tivela tripla	.40	.40
1468	A257	200ce	Pila africana	1.00	1.00
1468A	A257	200ce	Cypraea stercoraria	1.00	1.00
1469	A257	350ce	Thais hiatula	1.75	1.75
1469A	A257	350ce	Cassis tesselata	1.75	1.75
			Nos. 1465-1469A (10)	7.20	7.20

Souvenir Sheet

1470	A257	600ce	Natica favel	3.00	3.00
1470A	A257	600ce	Semifusos morio	3.00	3.00

Nos. 1443-1452 Ovptd. "40th / Anniversary / of the / Accession / of / HM Queen / Elizabeth II / 1952-1992" in Silver

1992, Aug. 10 Litho. *Perf. 14*

1471	A254	20ce	on #1443	.15	.15
1472	A254	60ce	on #1444	.30	.30
1473	A254	80ce	on #1445	.40	.40
1474	A254	100ce	on #1446	.50	.50
1475	A254	200ce	on #1447	1.00	1.00
1476	A254	400ce	on #1448	2.00	2.00
1477	A254	500ce	on #1449	2.50	2.50
1478	A254	700ce	on #1450	3.50	3.50
			Nos. 1471-1478 (8)	10.35	10.35

Souvenir Sheets

1479	A254	900ce	on #1451	4.50	4.50
1480	A254	900ce	on #1452	4.50	4.50

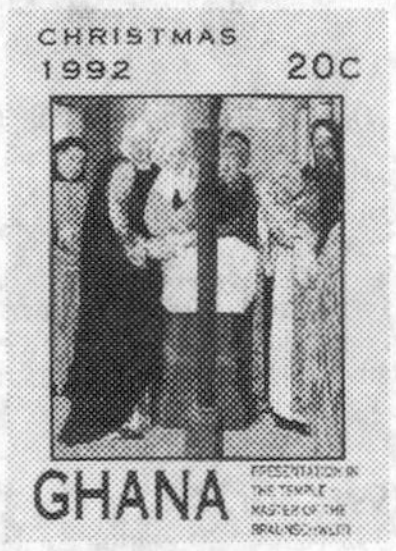

Christmas A259

Details or entire paintings: 20ce, Presentation in the Temple, by Master of Brunswick. 50ce, Presentation in the Temple, by Master of St. Severin. 60ce, The Visitation, by Sebastiano del Piombo. 80ce, The Visitation, by Giotto. 100ce, The Circumcision, by Studio of Giovanni Bellini. 200ce, The Circumcision, by Workshop of Benvenuto Garofalo. 500ce, The Visitation, by Workshop of Rogier van der Weyden. 800ce, The Visitation, by Workshop of Rogier Van der Weyden. No. 1491, The Visitation, by Giotto. No. 1492, The Presentation in the Temple, by Bartolo di Fredi.

1992 Litho. *Perf. 13½x14*

1483	A259	20ce	multicolored	.15	.15
1484	A259	50ce	multicolored	.24	.24
1485	A259	60ce	multicolored	.28	.28
1486	A259	80ce	multicolored	.35	.35
1487	A259	100ce	multicolored	.45	.45
1488	A259	200ce	multicolored	.90	.90
1489	A259	500ce	multicolored	2.25	2.25
1490	A259	800ce	multicolored	3.75	3.75
			Nos. 1483-1490 (8)	8.37	8.37

Souvenir Sheet

1491	A259	900ce	multicolored	4.50	4.50
1492	A259	900ce	multicolored	4.50	4.50

No. 1492 exists imperf.

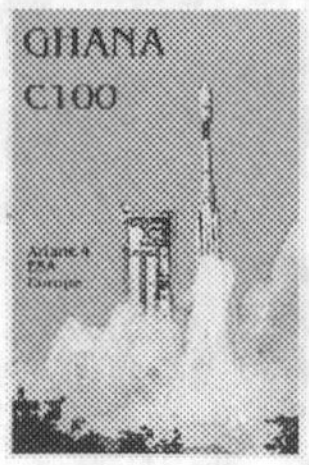

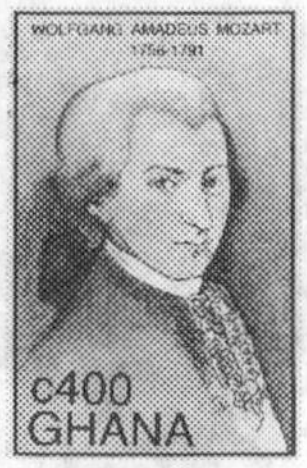

Anniversaries and Events
A260 A261

Designs: 20ce, LZ3, floating hangar at Lake Constance, horiz. 100ce, Lift-off of Ariane 4 rocket, horiz. 200ce, Leopard in tree, horiz. 300ce, Roman Colosseum, fruits and vegetables, horiz. 400ce, Wolfgang Amadeus Mozart. 600ce, Lift-off of H-1 rocket, Japan. 800ce, LZ10, Schwaben, horiz. No. 1501, Scene from "The Marriage of Figaro." No. 1502, Space shuttle, US. No. 1503, Count Ferdinand von Zeppelin. No. 1504, Bongo, horiz.

1992, Dec. Litho. *Perf. 14*

1493	A260	20ce	multicolored	.15	.15
1494	A260	100ce	multicolored	.50	.50
1495	A260	200ce	multicolored	1.00	1.00
1496	A260	300ce	multicolored	1.50	1.50
1497	A261	400ce	multicolored	2.00	2.00
1499	A260	600ce	multicolored	3.00	3.00
1500	A260	800ce	multicolored	4.00	4.00
			Nos. 1493-1500 (7)	12.15	12.15

Souvenir Sheets

1501	A261	900ce	multicolored	4.50	4.50
1502	A260	900ce	multicolored	4.50	4.50
1503	A260	900ce	multicolored	4.50	4.50
1504	A260	900ce	multicolored	4.50	4.50

Count Ferdinand von Zeppelin, 75th anniv. of death (#1493, 1500, 1503). Intl. Space Year (#1494, 1499, 1502). UN Earth Summit, Rio de Janeiro (#1495, 1504). WHO, Intl. Conference on Nutrition, Rome (1496). Mozart, bicent. of death (in 1991) (#1497, 1501).

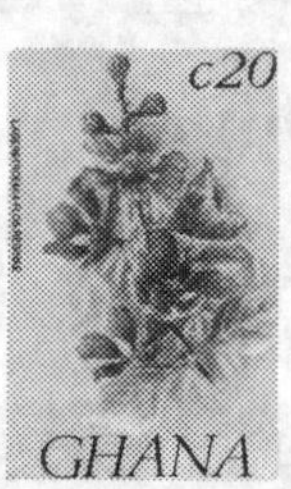

Flowers — A262

Designs: Nos. 1505, 1514d (100ce), Lagerstroemia flos-reginae. No. 1506, Clerodendrum thomsoniae. Nos. 1507, 1514c (50ce), Spathodea campanulata. No. 1508, Cassia fistula. Nos. 1509, 1514e (150ce), Mellitea ferrugenea. Nos. 1510, 1514j (300ce), Hildegardia barteri. Nos. 1511, 1514i (150ce), Ipomoea asarifolia. No. 1512, Petrea volubilis. Nos. 1513, 1514f (300ce), Ritchiea reflexa. Nos. 1514, 1514h (100ce), Bryphyllum pinnatum.

1993, Mar. 1 Litho. *Perf. 14*

1505	A262	20ce	multicolored	.15	.15
1506	A262	20ce	multicolored	.15	.15
1507	A262	60ce	multicolored	.30	.30
1508	A262	60ce	multicolored	.30	.30
1509	A262	80ce	multicolored	.40	.40
1510	A262	80ce	multicolored	.40	.40
1511	A262	200ce	multicolored	1.00	1.00
1512	A262	200ce	multicolored	1.00	1.00
1513	A262	350ce	multicolored	1.75	1.75
1514	A262	350ce	multicolored	1.75	1.75
			Nos. 1505-1514 (10)	7.20	7.20

Souvenir Sheets

1514A	A262		Sheet of 4, #c.-f.	3.00	3.00
1514B	A262		Sheet of 4, #g.-j.	3.00	3.00

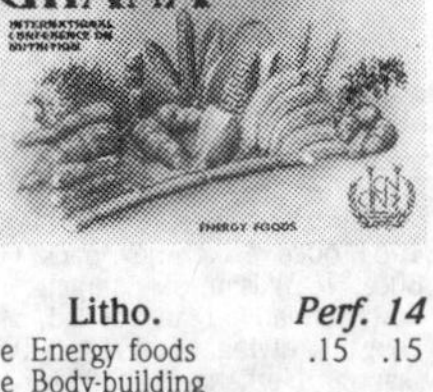

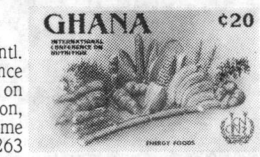

Intl. Conference on Nutrition, Rome A263

1993, Jan. Litho. *Perf. 14*

1515	A263	20ce	Energy foods	.15	.15
1516	A263	60ce	Body-building foods	.30	.30
1517	A263	80ce	Protective foods	.40	.40
1518	A263	200ce	Disease prevention	1.00	1.00
1519	A263	400ce	Food quality control, preservation	2.00	2.00
			Nos. 1515-1519 (5)	3.85	3.85

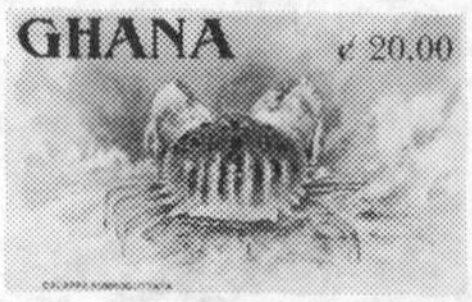

Crabs A264

Designs: 20ce, Clappa rubroguttata. 60ce, Cardisoma amatum. 80ce, Maia squinado. 400ce, Ocypoda cursor. 800ce, Grapus grapus.

1993, Feb. *Perf. 14x13½*

1520	A264	20ce	multicolored	.15	.15
1521	A264	60ce	multicolored	.30	.30
1522	A264	80ce	multicolored	.40	.40
1523	A264	400ce	multicolored	2.00	2.00
a.			Souv. sheet of 4, #1520-1523	2.80	2.80
1524	A264	800ce	multicolored	4.00	4.00
			Nos. 1520-1524 (5)	6.85	6.85

Miniature Sheet of 8

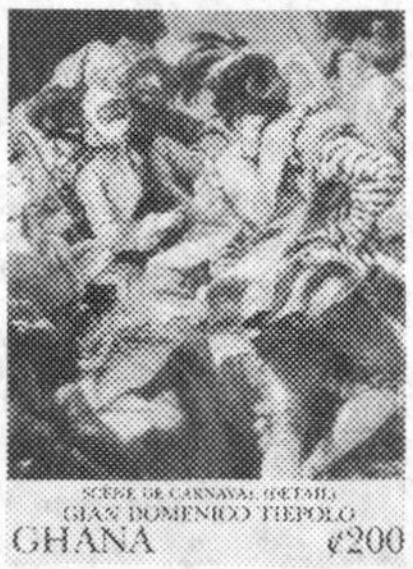

Louvre Museum, Bicent. A265

Details or entire paintings, by Giovanni Domenico Tiepolo (1727-1804) (a-e) and Giovanni Battista Tiepolo (1696-1770) (f-h). No. 1525: a-c, Carnival Scene, (left, center, right). d-e, Tooth Puller, (left, right). f, Rebecca at the Well. g-h, Presenting Christ to the People, (left, right).

700ce, Chancellor Seguier, by Le Brun, horiz.

1993, Mar. 1 Litho. *Perf. 12*

1525	A265	200ce	#a.-h. + label	8.25	8.25

Souvenir Sheet

Perf. 14½

1526	A265	700ce	multicolored	3.75	3.75

No. 1526 contains one 55x88mm stamp.

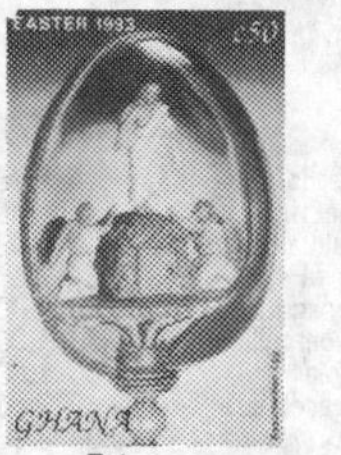

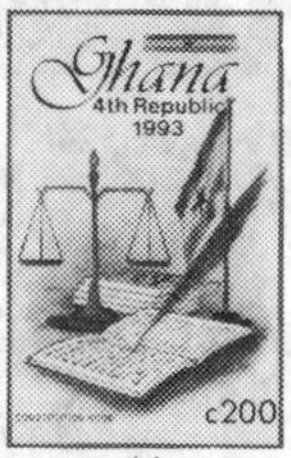

Faberge Eggs — A266 4th Republic — A268

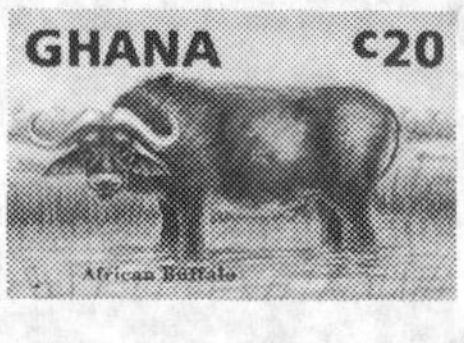

Wild Animals A267

Easter: 50ce, Resurrection Egg. 80ce, Imperial Red Cross Egg with Resurrection Triptych. 100ce, Imperial Uspensky Cathedral Egg. 150ce, Imperial Red Cross Egg with portraits. 200ce, Orange Tree Egg. 250ce, Rabbit Egg. 400ce, Imperial Coronation Egg. 900ce, Silver-gilt enamel Easter Egg. No. 1535, Spring Flower Egg. No. 1536, Egg charms, horiz.

1993, Apr. 26 *Perf. 14*

1527	A266	50ce	multicolored	.25	.25
1528	A266	80ce	multicolored	.40	.40
1529	A266	100ce	multicolored	.50	.50
1530	A266	150ce	multicolored	.75	.75
1531	A266	200ce	multicolored	1.00	1.00
1532	A266	250ce	multicolored	1.25	1.25
1533	A266	400ce	multicolored	2.00	2.00
1534	A266	900ce	multicolored	4.50	4.50
			Nos. 1527-1534 (8)	10.65	10.65

Souvenir Sheets

1535	A266	1000ce	multicolored	5.00	5.00
1536	A266	1000ce	multicolored	5.00	5.00

1993, May 24 Litho. *Perf. 14*

1537	A267	20ce African buffalo	.15	.15
1538	A267	50ce Giant forest hog	.25	.25
1539	A267	60ce Potto	.30	.30
1540	A267	80ce Bay duiker	.40	.40
1541	A267	100ce Royal antelope	.50	.50
1542	A267	200ce Serval	1.00	1.00
1543	A267	500ce Golden cat	2.50	2.50
1544	A267	800ce Megaloglossus woermanni	4.00	4.00
		Nos. 1537-1544 (8)	9.10	9.10

Souvenir Sheets

1545	A267	900ce Dormouse	4.50	4.50
1546	A267	900ce White collared mangabey	4.50	4.50

1993, May Litho. *Perf. 14*

Designs: 50ce, Kwame Nkrumah Mausoleum, horiz. 100ce, Kwame Nkrumah Conference Center, horiz. 200ce, Constitution book. 350ce, Independence Square. 400ce, Christiansborg Castle.

1547	A268	50ce multicolored	.25	.25
1548	A268	100ce multicolored	.50	.50
1549	A268	200ce multicolored	1.00	1.00
1550	A268	350ce multicolored	1.75	1.75
1551	A268	400ce multicolored	2.00	2.00
		Nos. 1547-1551 (5)	5.50	5.50

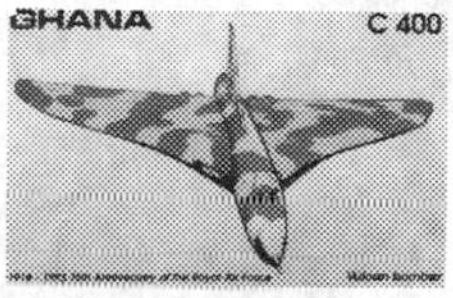

A269

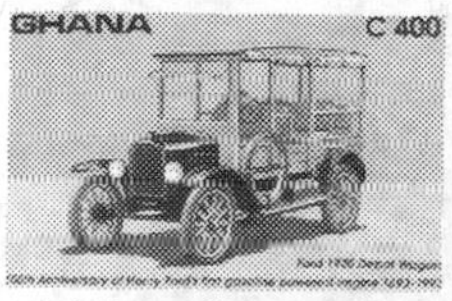

Aviation and Automotive Anniversaries — A270

Designs: 50ce, Graf Zeppelin over Alps, vert. No. 1552, Mercedes Benz 300 SLR in 1955 Mille Miglia. No. 1553, LZ7 Deutschland. No. 1554, Vulcan bomber. No. 1555, Ford Tri-motor. No. 1556, 1920 Ford Depot Wagon. No. 1557, Nieuport 27, vert. No. 1558, Graf Zeppelin taking aboard letters, vert. No. 1559, 1970 Ford Mach 1 Mustang.

No. 1560, LZ10 Schwaben. No. 1561, Mercedes wins 1937 Monaco Grand Prix. No. 1562, Graf Zeppelin over Rome. No. 1563, 1955 Mercedes Benz Type 196. No. 1564, Early US air mail flight. No. 1565, S.E.5A, 1918. No. 1566, 1910 Ford Super T, 999.

1993 Litho. *Perf. 14*

1551A	A269	50ce multicolored	.25	.25
1552	A270	150ce multicolored	.75	.75
1553	A269	150ce multicolored	.75	.75
1554	A269	400ce multicolored	2.00	2.00
1555	A269	400ce multicolored	2.00	2.00
1556	A270	400ce multicolored	2.00	2.00
1557	A269	600ce multicolored	3.00	3.00
1558	A269	600ce multicolored	3.00	3.00
1559	A270	600ce multicolored	3.00	3.00
1560	A269	800ce multicolored	4.00	4.00
1561	A270	800ce multicolored	4.00	4.00
		Nos. 1551A-1561 (11)	24.75	24.75

Souvenir Sheets

1562	A269	1000ce multicolored	5.00	5.00
1563	A270	1000ce multicolored	5.00	5.00
1564	A269	1000ce multicolored	5.00	5.00
1565	A269	1000ce multicolored	5.00	5.00
1566	A270	1000ce multicolored	5.00	5.00

Capt. Hugo Eckener, 125th birth anniv. (#1551A, 1553-1554, 1562). Benz's first four-wheeled vehicle, cent. (#1552, 1561, 1563). Royal Air Force, 75th anniv. (#1554, 1557, 1564). Henry Ford's first gasoline powered engine, cent. (#1556, 1559, 1566).

No. 1564 contains one 57x42mm stamp. Nos. 1563, 1566 contains one 85x28mm stamp.

Issued: #1555-1556, 1558-1559, 1565-1566, May. #1551A-1554, 1557, 1560-1564, June.

Nos. 1300-1305 Ovptd. 40TH ANNIVERSARY OF CORONATION H.M. ELIZABETH II

1993 Litho. *Perf. 14*

1567	A237	100ce multicolored	.50	.50
1568	A237	200ce multicolored	1.00	1.00
1569	A237	500ce multicolored	2.50	2.50
1570	A237	600ce multicolored	3.00	3.00
		Nos. 1567-1570 (4)	7.00	7.00

Souvenir Sheet

1571	A237	800ce on #1304	4.00	4.00
1572	A237	800ce on #1305	4.00	4.00

Nos. 1321, 1323-1327 Ovptd. a. in Black "35 YEARS OF / ROTARY INTERNATIONAL / GHANA 1958" or b. in Red "GHANA / RED CROSS SOCIETY / FOUNDED 1932"

1993

1573	A239(a)	100ce multi	.50	.50
1574	A239(b)	300ce multi	1.50	1.50
1575	A239(b)	400ce multi	2.00	2.00
1576	A239(a)	500ce multi	2.50	2.50
		Nos. 1573-1576 (4)	6.50	6.50

Souvenir Sheets

1577	A239(a)	800ce on #1326	4.00	4.00
1578	A239(b)	800ce on #1327	4.00	4.00

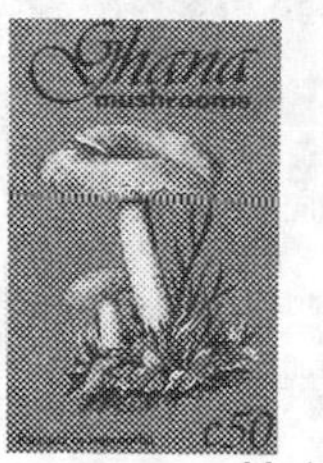

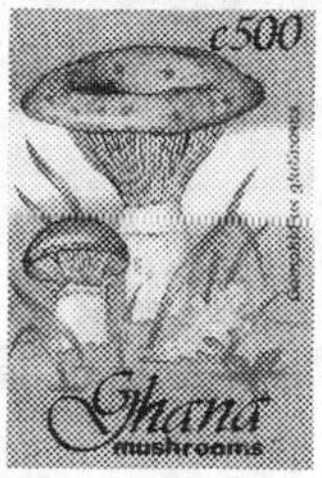

Mushrooms
A271 A272

Designs: 20ce, Cantharellus cibarius. 50ce, Russula cyanoxantha. 60ce, Clitocybe rivulosa. No. 1581, Boletus chrysenteron. No. 1582, Cortinarius elatior. No. 1583, Mycena galericulata. No. 1584, Boletus edulis. No. 1585, Tricholoma gambosum. No. 1586, Lepista saeva. 250ce, Gyroporus castaneus. No. 1589, Nolanea sericea. No. 1590, Hygrophorus puiceus. 500ce, Gomphidius glutinosus. No. 1592, Russula olivacea. 1000ce, Russula aurata.

No. 1594a, 100ce, Cantharellus cibarius. b, 150ce, Cortinarius elatior. c, 300ce, Tricholoma gambosum. d, 600ce, Hygrophorus puiceus.

No. 1595a, 50ce, like #1581. b, 100ce, like #1583. c, 150ce, like #1584. d, 1000ce, like #1589.

1993, July 30 Litho. *Perf. 14*

1579	A271	20ce multicolored	.15	.15
1580	A271	50ce multicolored	.25	.25
1581	A271	60ce multicolored	.30	.30
1582	A271	80ce multicolored	.40	.40
1583	A271	80ce multicolored	.40	.40
1584	A271	200ce multicolored	1.00	1.00
1585	A271	200ce multicolored	1.00	1.00
1586	A272	200ce multicolored	1.00	1.00
1587	A272	250ce multicolored	1.25	1.25
1588	A271	300ce multicolored	1.50	1.50
1589	A271	350ce multicolored	1.75	1.75
1590	A271	350ce multicolored	1.75	1.75
1591	A272	500ce multicolored	2.50	2.50
1592	A272	600ce multicolored	3.00	3.00
1593	A272	1000ce multicolored	5.00	5.00
		Nos. 1579-1593 (15)	21.25	21.25

Souvenir Sheets

1594	A271	Sheet of 4, #a.-d.	6.00	6.00
1595	A271	Sheet of 4, #a.-d.	6.50	6.50

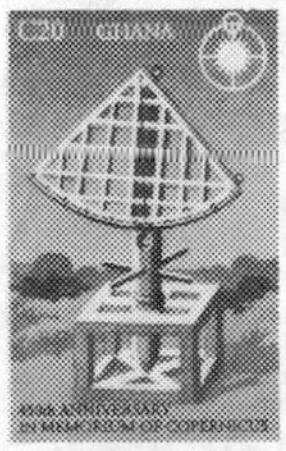

Copernicus (1473-1543)
A273

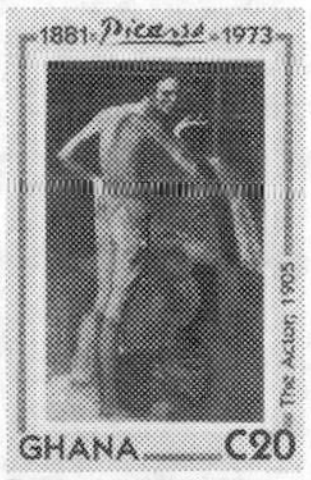

Picasso (1881-1973)
A274

Designs: 20ce, Early astronomical instrument. 200ce, Telescope. No. 1598, Copernicus, long hair. No. 1599, Copernicus, shorter hair.

1993, Oct. 19 Litho. *Perf. 13½x14*

1596	A273	20ce multicolored	.15	.15
1597	A273	200ce multicolored	1.00	1.00

Souvenir Sheets

Perf. 12x13

1598	A273	1000ce multicolored	5.00	5.00
1599	A273	1000ce multicolored	5.00	5.00

1993, Oct. 19 *Perf. 14*

Paintings: 20ce, The Actor, 1905. 80ce, Portrait of Allen Stein, 1906. 800ce, Seated Male Nude, 1908-09.

1600-1602	A274	Set of 3	4.75	4.75

Souvenir Sheet

1603	A274	900ce Guernica, 1937	4.75	4.75

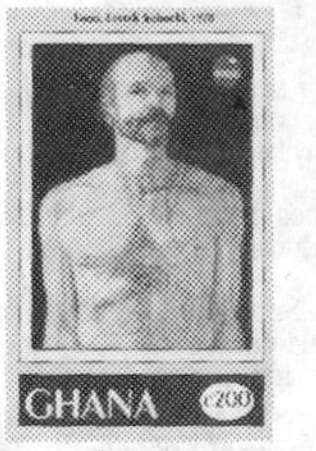

Polska '93 — A275

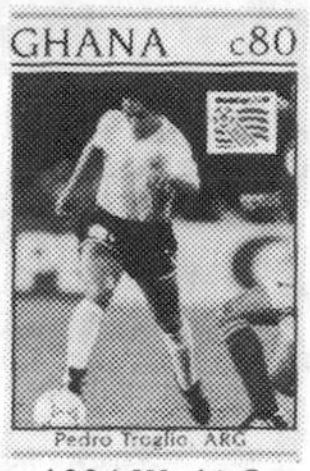

1994 World Cup Soccer, US — A276

Paintings: 200ce, Tatoo, by Sobocki, 1978. 600ce, Prison, by Blonder, 1934. 1000ce, Baijka o Czlowieku Szczesliwym, by Mickalak, 1925, horiz.

1993, Oct. 19

1604-1605	A275	Set of 2	4.00	4.00

Souvenir Sheet

1606	A275	1000ce multicolored	5.00	5.00

1993, Dec. 1 *Perf. 13½x14*

Designs: 50ce, Abedi Pele, Ghana. 80ce, Pedro Troglio, Argentina. 100ce, Fernando Alvez, Uruguay. 200ce, Franco Baresi, Italy. 250ce, Gomez, Colombia; Katanec, Yugoslavia. 600ce, Diego Maradona, Argentina. 800ce, Hasek, Czech Republic; Wynalda, US. 1000ce, Lothar Matthaeus, Germany.

No. 1615, Giuseppe Giannini, Italy. No. 1616, Rabie Yassein, Egypt; Ruud Gullit, Holland.

1607	A276	50ce multicolored	.25	.25
1608	A276	80ce multicolored	.42	.42
1609	A276	100ce multicolored	.52	.52
1610	A276	200ce multicolored	1.00	1.00
1611	A276	250ce multicolored	1.25	1.25
1612	A276	600ce multicolored	3.00	3.00
1613	A276	800ce multicolored	4.25	4.25
1614	A276	1000ce multicolored	5.25	5.25
		Nos. 1607-1614 (8)	15.94	15.94

Souvenir Sheets

Perf. 13

1615	A276	1200ce multicolored	6.00	6.00
1616	A276	1200ce multicolored	6.00	6.00

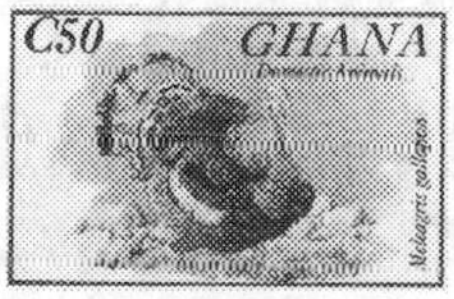

Domestic Animals A277

Designs: 50ce, Meleagris gallopvo. 100ce, Capra hircus. 150ce, Carina moschata. 200ce, Eguus asinus. 250ce, Male gallus gallus. 300ce, Sus vittatus. 400ce, Numida meleagris. 600ce, Canis domesticus. 800ce, Female gallus gallus. 1000ce, Ovis aries.

No. 1627a, 100ce, like No. 1618. b, 250ce, like No. 1624. c, 350ce, like 1622. d, 500ce, like No. 1626.

No. 1628a, 100ce, like No. 1623. b, 250ce, like No. 1621. c, 350ce, like No. 1625. d, 500ce, like No. 1617.

1993, Dec. 8 *Perf. 14*

1617-1626	A277	Set of 10	15.00	15.00

Souvenir Sheets

1627	A277	multicolored	5.00	5.00
1628	A277	multicolored	5.00	5.00

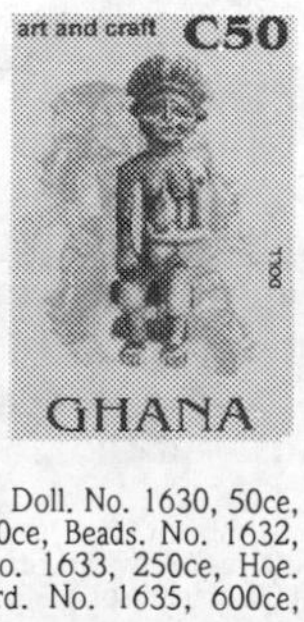

Arts and Crafts — A278

Designs: No. 1629, 50ce, Doll. No. 1630, 50ce, Pot and lid. No. 1631, 200ce, Beads. No. 1632, 200ce, Snake charmers. No. 1633, 250ce, Hoe. No. 1634, 250ce, Scabbard. No. 1635, 600ce, Pipe. No. 1636, 600ce, Deer. No. 1637, 1000ce, Mask. No. 1638, 1000ce, Doll with baby.

No. 1639a, 100ce, like #1629. b, 250ce, like #1631. c, 350ce, like #1633. d, 500ce, like #1635.

No. 1640a, 100ce, like #1630. b, 250ce, like #1632. c, 350ce, like #1634. d, 500ce, like #1636.

1994, Jan. 24 Litho. *Perf. 14*

1629-1638	A278	Set of 10	12.50	12.50

Souvenir Sheets

1639	A278	multicolored	5.00	5.00
1640	A278	multicolored	5.00	5.00

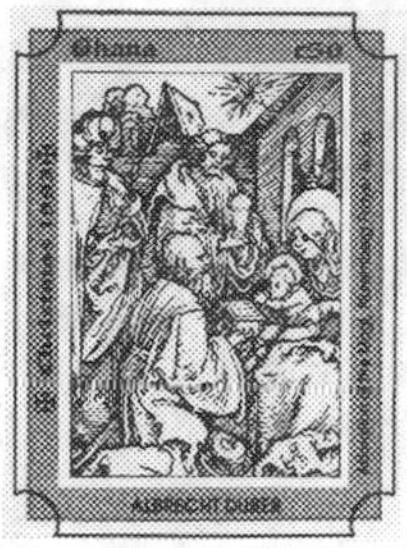

Christmas A279

Paintings and Woodcuts:aintings and Woodcuts: 50ce, Adoration of the Magi. 100ce, The Virgin and Child with Saint John and an Angel, by Botticelli. 150ce, Mary as Queen of Heaven. 200ce, Saint Anne. 250ce, The Madonna of the Magnificat, by Botticelli. 400ce, The Madonna of the Goldfinch, by Tiepolo. 600ce, The Virgin and the Child with the Young St. John the Baptist, by Correggio. 1000ce, Adoration of the Shepherds.

No. 1649, Mystic Nativity (detail), by Botticelli, horiz. No. 1650, Madonna in a Circle, by Durer.

Woodcuts (50ce, 150ce, 200ce, 1000ce) are from Nuremberg Prayer Books, by Durer.

Perf. 13½x14, 14x13½

1993, Dec. 20 Litho.

1641-1648	A279	Set of 8	14.00	14.00

Souvenir Sheets

1649	A279	1000ce multicolored	5.00	5.00
1650	A279	1000ce multicolored	5.00	5.00

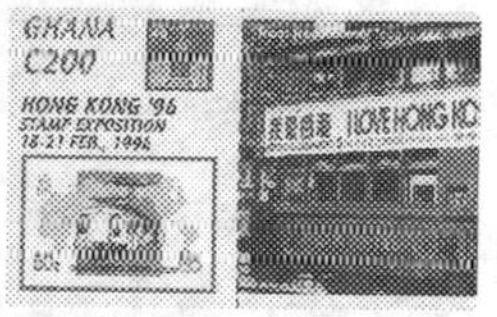

A280

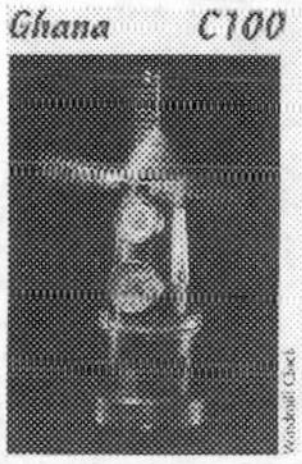

Hong Kong '94 — A281

Stamps, tram from Kennedy Town to Shau Kei: No. 1651, Hong Kong #470, back of tram. No. 1652, Front of tram, #1392.

Imperial Palace clocks: No. 1653a, Windmill. b, Horse. c, Balloon. d, Zodiac. e, Shar-Pei dog. f, Cat.

1994, Feb. 18 Litho. *Perf. 14*

1651	A280	200ce multicolored	1.00	1.00
1652	A280	200ce multicolored	1.00	1.00
a.		Pair, #1651-1652	2.00	2.00

Miniature Sheet

1653	A281	100ce Sheet of 6, #a.-f.	3.00	3.00

Nos. 1651-1652 issued in sheets of 5 pairs. No. 1652a is a continuous design.

New Year 1994 (Year of the Dog) (#1653e).

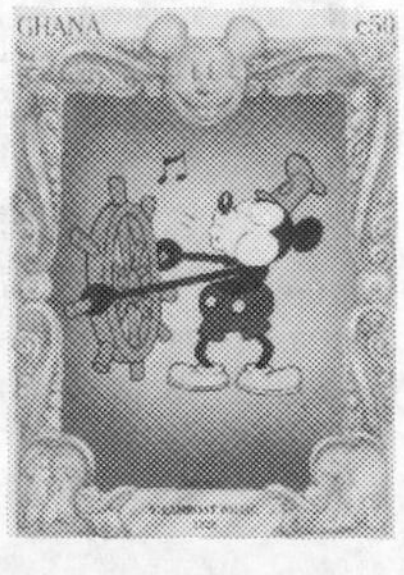

Mickey Mouse, 65th Birthday A282

Mickey's films: 50ce, Steamboat Willie, 1928. 100ce, The Band Concert, 1937. 150ce, Moose Hunters, 1937. 200ce, Brave Little Taylor, 1938. 250ce, Fantasia, 1940. 400ce, The Nifty Nineties, 1941. 600ce, Canne Caddy, 1944. 1000ce, Mickey's Christmas Carol, 1983.

No. 1662, Mickey's Elephant, 1936. No. 1663, Mickey's Amateurs, 1937.

1994   **Litho.**   *Perf. 13¹/₂x14*
1654-1661 A282 Set of 8   8.25 8.25
Souvenir Sheets
1662-1663 A282 1200ce each   3.50 3.50

A283   A284

Hummel Figurines: 50ce, Boy with backpack, walking stick. 100ce, Girl holding basket behind back. 150ce, Boy with rabbits. 200ce, Boy carrying chicks in basket. 250ce, Girl with chicks. 400ce, Girl petting lamb. 600ce, Lamb, girl waving handkerchief. 1000ce, Girl with basket, flowers.

No. 1672a, 500ce, like #1665; b, 150ce, like #1671; c, 1200ce, like #1667.

No. 1673a, 300ce, like #1668; b, 200ce, like #1669; c, 500ce, like #1670; d, 1000ce, like #1666.

1994, Apr. 6   *Perf. 14*
1664-1671 A283 Set of 8   8.25 8.25
Souvenir Sheets
1672 A283 Sheet of 4, #a.-c., #1664 5.75 5.75
1673 A283 Sheet of 4, #a.-d.   6.00 6.00

1994, May 16   **Litho.**   *Perf. 14*
Diana Monkeys: 50ce, Adult, young. 200ce, Sitting in tree. 500ce, Holding food. 800ce, Close-up of face.

1674-1677 A284 Set of 4   4.25 4.25
1677a   Min. sheet, 3 each
      #1674-1677   13.00 13.00

World Wildlife Fund.

Wild Animals
A285

Designs: 100ce, Bushbuck. 150ce, Spotted hyena. 1000ce, Aardvark. No. 1681, Leopard, vert. No. 1682, Waterbuck, vert.

1994, May 16
1678-1680 A285 Set of 3   3.50 3.50
Souvenir Sheets
1681-1682 A285 2000ce each   5.50 5.50

Miniature Sheets of 12

Cats
A286

Designs: No. 1683a, Sorrel Abyssinian. b, Silver classic tabby. c, Chocolate-point Siamese. d, Brown tortie Burmese. e, Exotic shorthair. f, Havana brown. g, Devon rex. h, Black manx. i, British blue shorthair. j, Calico American wirehair. k, Spotted oriental Siamese. l, Red classic tabby.

No. 1684: a, Norwegian forest cat. b, Blue longhair. c, Red self longhair. d, Black longhair. e, Chinchilla. f, Dilut calico longhair. g, Blue tabby-&-white longhair. h, Ruby somali. i, Blue smoke longhair. j, Calico longhair. k, Brown tabby longhair. l, Balinese.

No. 1685, Brown mackeral tabby Scottish fold. No. 1686, Seal-point colorpoint.

1994, June 6   **Litho.**   *Perf. 14*
1683-1684 A286 Set of 2 #a.-l. each 6.50 6.50
Souvenir Sheets
1685-1686 A286 2000ce each   5.50 5.50

Miniature Sheets of 12

Birds
A287

Designs: No. 1687a, Red-bellied paradise flycatcher (b, e). b, Many-colored bush-shrike. c, Broad-tailed paradise whydah (b, e). d, White-crowned robin-chat. e, Violet plantain-eater. f, Village weaver. g, Fire-crowned bishop. h, Shoveler. i, Spur-winged goose (l). j, African crake. k, King reed-hen. l, Tiger bittern.

No. 1688: a, Moho. b, Superb sunbird. c, Blue-breasted kingfisher. d, Blue cuckoo-shrike. e, Blue plantain-eater (d, g). f, Greater flamingo (i). g, Lily-trotter (j). h, Night heron. i, Black-winged stilt (l). j, White-spotted pigmy rail. k, Pigmy goose. k, Angola pitta.

No. 1689, Goliath heron. No. 1690, African spoonbill.

1994, June 13
1687-1688 A287 200ce #a.-l., each 6.50 6.50
Souvenir Sheets
1689-1690 A287 2000ce each   5.50 5.50

4th Republic, 1st Anniv.
A288

Designs: 50ce, Rural water projects. 100ce, Honoring farmers. 200ce, Rural electrification. 600ce, Rural bridge construction. 800ce, Natl. Theater. 1000ce, Lighting Perpetual Flame.

1994, July 11   **Litho.**   *Perf. 14*
1691-1696 A288 Set of 6   7.50 7.50

D-Day, 50th Anniv.
A289

Designs: 60ce, 15-inch Monitor HMS Roberts fires on Houlgate Battery. 100ce, HMS Warspite hits Villerville. 200ce, Flagship USS Augusta. 1500ce, USS Nevada bombards Utah Beach.

1994, July 4   **Litho.**   *Perf. 14*
1697-1699 A289 Set of 3   1.00 1.00
Souvenir Sheet
1700 A289 1500ce multicolored   4.00 4.00

Miniature Sheet of 9

First Manned Moon Landing, 25th Anniv.
A290

German, Japanese, scientist-astronauts: a, Sigmund Jahn. b, Ulf Merbold. c, Hans Wilhelm Schlegal. d, Ulrich Walter. e, Reinhard Furrer. f, Ernst Messerschmid. g, Mamoru Mohri. h, Klaus-Dietrich Flade. i, Chaiki Naito-Mukai.

2000ce, "Frau im Mond."

1994, July 4
1701 A290 300ce #a.-i.   7.25 7.25
Souvenir Sheet
1702 A290 2000ce multicolored   5.50 5.50

Duiker Antelopes
A291

Designs: 50ce, Crowned. 100ce, Red-flanked. 200ce, Yellow-backed. 400ce, Ogilby's. 600ce, Bay. 800ce, Jentink's.

No. 1709, Cephalophus natalensis. No. 1710, Cephalophus niger.

1994, May 16   **Litho.**   *Perf. 14*
1703-1708 A291 Set of 6   5.50 5.50
Souvenir Sheets
1709-1710 A291 2000ce each   5.00 5.00

Intl. Olympic Committee, Cent.
A292   A293

Designs: 300ce, Dieter Modenburg, Germany, high jump, 1984. 400ce, Ruth Fuchs, German Democratic Republic, javelin, 1972, 1976. 1500ce, Jans Weissflog, Germany, large hill ski jump, 1994.

1994, July 4   **Litho.**   *Perf. 14*
1711 A292 300ce multicolored   .75 .75
1712 A292 400ce multicolored   1.00 1.00
Souvenir Sheet
1713 A293 1500ce multicolored   3.75 3.75

PHILAKOREA '94
A294   A295

Designs: 20ce, Ch'unghak-dong village elder in traditional clothes. 150ce, Stone pagoda, Punhwangsa, Korea. 300ce, Traditional country house, Andong region.

Letter pictures, eight-panel screen, Choson Dynasty, 20th cent: Nos. 1717b, f, Birds. c, Rooster. d, Animal with antennae. e, g, Flowers. h, Fish.

1500ce, Temple judges determine final afterlife judgments, horiz.

1994, July 4   *Perf. 14, 13 (#1717)*
1714-1716 A294 Set of 3   1.25 1.25
Miniature Sheet of 8
1717 A295 250ce #a.-h.   5.00 5.00
Souvenir Sheet
1718 A294 1500ce multicolored   3.75 3.75

Miniature Sheet of 6

1994 World Cup Soccer Championships, US — A296

Designs: No. 1719a, Dennis Bergkamp, Netherlands. b, Lothar Matthaus, Germany. c, Giuseppe Signori, Italy. d, Carlos Valderama, Colombia. e, Jorge Campos, Mexico. f, Tony Meola, US.

No. 1720, Citrus Bowl, Orlando, FL, vert. No. 1721, Giants Stadium, Meadowlands, NJ, vert.

1994, July 25   *Perf. 14*
1719 A296 200ce #a.-f.   3.00 3.00
Souvenir Sheets
1720-1721 A296 1200ce each   3.00 3.00

Christmas
A297

Italian art: 100ce, Madonna of the Annunciation, by Simone Martini. 200ce, Madonna and Child, by Niccolo di Pietro Gerini. 250ce, Virgin and Child on the Throne with Angels and Saints, by Raffaello Botticini. 300ce, Madonna and Child with Saints, by Antonio Fiorentino. 400ce, Adoration of the Magi, by Bartolo di Fredi. 500ce, The Annunciation, by Cima da Congeliano. 600ce, Virgin and Child with the Young St. John the Baptist, by Workshop of Botticelli. 1000ce, The Holy Family, by Giorgione.

Details from Adoration of the Kings, by Giorgione: No. 1730, Presenting gifts. No. 1731, Madonna & Child.

1994, Dec. 5   **Litho.**   *Perf. 13¹/₂x14*
1722-1729 A297 Set of 8   7.50 7.50
Souvenir Sheets
1730-1731 A297 2000ce each   4.50 4.50

Intl. Year of the Family — A298

Designs: 50ce, Family. 100ce, Technical training. 200ce, Child care. 400ce, Care for the aged. 600ce, Vocational training. 1000ce, Adult education.

1994, Dec. 20   *Perf. 14*
1732-1737 A298 Set of 6   6.00 6.00

Ghana Civil Aviation Authority, 50th Anniv.
A299

Designs: 100ce, Control tower. 400ce, Insignia, marker light. 1000ce, Airplane leaving runway.

1994, Dec. 20
1738-1740 A299 Set of 3   3.75 3.75
See Nos. 1766-1768.

Red Cross & Red Crescent Societies in Ghana, 75th Anniv.
A300

Designs: 50ce, Transporting victim. 200ce, Aiding mother, children. 600ce, Erecting tents.

1994, Dec. 20   **Litho.**   *Perf. 14*
1741-1743 A300 Set of 3   2.25 2.25
Souvenir Sheet
1744   Sheet of 3, #1741-1742,
      1744a   6.25 6.26
    a. A300 1000ce like #1743   5.00 5.00

Fertility Dolls — A301

Various carvings. Denominations: 50ce, 100ce, 150ce, 200ce, 400ce, 600ce, 800ce, 1000ce.

1994, Dec. 20
1745-1752 A301 Set of 8   5.75 5.75
Souvenir Sheet
1753   Sheet of 4, #1745, 1748-
     1749, 1753a   6.75 6.75
a. A301 250ce like #1752   1.25 1.25

Donald Duck, 60th Birthday (in
1994) — A302

Designs: 40ce, Pluto, Donald, Chip 'n Dale. 50ce, Mickey, pup. 60ce, Daisy. 100ce, Goofy. 150ce, Goofy, diff. 250ce, Donald, Goofy. 400ce, Ludwig Von Drake, Pluto. 500ce, Grandma Duck, pups. 1000ce, Mickey, Minnie. 1500ce, Pluto.
No. 1764, Daisy, Donald, cake, Mickey, vert.
No. 1765, Donald holding fork, spoon, vert.

1995, Feb. 2   **Litho.**   **Perf. 14x13½**
1754-1763 A302 Set of 10   8.50 8.50
Souvenir Sheets
     Perf. 13½x14
1764-1765 A302 2000ce each   4.25 4.25

Civil Aviation Authority Type of 1994 with
ICAO Emblem and New Inscription

Designs: 100ce, like #1738. 400ce, like #1739. 1000ce, like #1740.

1994, Dec. 20   **Litho.**   **Perf. 14**
1766-1768 A299 Set of 3   3.75 3.75
Nos. 1766-1768 are inscribed "50th Anniversary of The International Civil Aviation Organization (ICAO)."

Panafest '94 — A303

Designs: 50ce, Northern region dancer. 100ce, Relics with landmark. 200ce, Chief sitting in state. 400ce, Royalist ceremonial dress. 600ce, Cape Coast Castle. 800ce, Clay figurines of West Africa.

1994   **Litho.**   **Perf. 13½**
1769-1774 A303   Set of 6   4.50 4.50
Pan African Historical Theatre Festival, Dec. 1994.

Forts
A304

Castles
A305

Forts: 50ce, Appolonia, Beyin. 200ce, Patience, Apam. 250ce, Amsterdam, Kormantin. 300ce, St. Jago, Elmina. 400ce, William, Anomabo. 600ce, Kumasi.
Castles: 150ce, Cochem, Germany. 600ce, Hohenzollern, Germany. 800ce, Uwajima, Japan. 100ce, Hohenschwangau, Germany.
Castles: No. 1785a, Windsor, England. b, Osaka, Japan. c, Vaj Dahunyad, Hungary. d, Karlstejn, Czech Republic. e, Kronborg, Denmark. f, Alcazar of Segovia, Spain. g, Chambourd, France. h, Linderhof, Bavaria. i, Red Fort, India.
No. 1786, Elmira Castle. No. 1787, Fort St. Antonio, Axim. No. 1788, Himeji Castle, Japan. No. 1789, Neuschwanstein Castle, Germany.

1995, Apr. 3   **Perf. 14**
1775-1780 A304   Set of 6   3.75 3.75
1781-1784 A305   Set of 4   5.00 5.00
Miniature Sheet of 9
1785 A305   500ce #a.-i.   9.00 9.00
Souvenir Sheets
1786   A304   800ce multi   1.60 1.60
1787   A304   1000ce multi   2.00 2.00
1788-1789 A305 2500ce each   5.00 5.00

Water Birds
A306

Designs: 200ce, Eurasian pochard. 500ce, Mac-coa duck. 800ce, Cape shoveler. 1000ce, Red-crested pochard.
No. 1794: a, African pygmy goose. b, Southern pochard. c, Cape teal. d, Ruddy shelduck. e, Fulvous whistling duck. f, White-faced whistling geese. g, Ferruginous white-eye. h, Hottentot teal. i, African black duck. j, Yellow-billed duck. k, White-checked pintail duck. l, Hartlaub's duck.
No. 1795, Roseate tern. No. 1796, Northern shoveler.

1995, Apr. 28
1790-1793 A306   Set of 4   5.00 5.00
Miniature Sheet of 12
1794   A306   400ce #a.-l.   9.50 9.50
Souvenir Sheets
1795-1796 A306 2500ce each   5.00 5.00
Nos. 1794-1796 have a continuous design. Nos. 1790-1793 have a white border.

1996 Summer Olympics, Atlanta
A307   A308

Athletes: 500ce, Carl Lewis. 800ce, Eric Liddell. 900ce, Runner. 1000ce, Jim Thorpe.
Sports: No. 1801a, Cycling. b, Archery. c, Diving. d, Swimming. e, Gymnastics-Floor Exercise. f, Fencing. g, Boxing. h, Gymnastics-Rings. i, Javelin. j, Tennis. k, Soccer. l, Equestrian.
No. 1802, John Akii Bua. No. 1803, Pierre de Cobertin.

1995, May 2
1797-1800 A307   Set of 4   6.50 6.50
Miniature Sheet of 12
1801   A308   300ce #a.-l.   7.50 7.50
Souvenir Sheets
1802-1803 A308 1200ce each   2.50 2.50

UN, 50th
Anniv. — A309

Secretaries General: No. 1804a, 200ce, Trygve Lie, Norway, 1946-52. b, 300ce, Dag Hammarskjold, Sweden, 1953-61. c, 400ce, U Thant, Burma, 1961-71. d, 500ce, Kurt Waldheim, Austria, 1972-81. e, 600ce, Javier Perez de Cuellar, Peru, 1982-91. f, 800ce, Boutros Boutros-Ghali, Egypt, 1992-.
No. 1805, UN flag, horiz.

1995, July 6   **Litho.**   **Perf. 14**
1804 A309   #a.-f.   5.75 5.75
Souvenir Sheet
1805 A309 1200ce multicolored   2.50 2.50

Miniature Sheets of 6 or 8

End of
World War
II, 50th
Anniv.
A311

Military decorations: No. 1806a, US Navy Cross, US Purple Heart. b, UK Air Force Cross, UK Distinguished Flying Cross. c, US Navy and Marine Corps Medal, US Distinguished Service Cross. d, UK Distinguished Service Medal, UK Distinguished Conduct Medal. e, UK Military Medal, UK Military Cross. f, UK Distinguished Service Cross, UK Distinguished Service Order.
No. 1807: a, Churchill. b, Eisenhower. c, Air Chief Marshall Sir Arthur Tedder. d, Montgomery. c, Bradley. f, de Gaulle. g, French Resistance Organization. h, Patton.
No. 1808, US Medal of Honor. No. 1809, Fuhrer's promise.

1995, July 6   **Litho.**   **Perf. 14**
1806 A310   500ce #a.-f. + label   6.00 6.00
1807 A311   400ce #a.-h. + label   6.50 6.50
Souvenir Sheets
1808-1809 A310 1200ce each   2.50 2.50
No. 1809 contains one 42x56mm stamp.

FAO, 50th
Anniv.
A312

Designs: 200ce, Fish preservation. 300ce, Fishing. 400ce, Ox-drawn plow. 600ce, Harvesting. 800ce, Aforestation.
2000ce, Boat, shoreline, oxen, fruit.

1995, July 6   **Perf. 14**
1810-1814 A312 Set of 5   4.50 4.50
Souvenir Sheet
1815 A312 2000ce multicolored   4.00 4.00

90th Anniversary of Rotary

Rotary Intl.,
90th Anniv.
A313

Designs: 600ce, Natl. flag, Rotary emblem. 1200ce, Rotary emblem on banner, vert.

1995, July 6
1816 A313   600ce multicolored   1.25 1.25
Souvenir Sheet
1817 A313 1200ce multicolored   2.50 2.50

1995 Boy Scout
Jamboree,
Holland — A314

No. 1818: a, 400ce, Two boys. 800ce, Two boys, one wearing glasses. c, 1000ce, Two boys facing left.
1200ce, Boy with bamboo poles.

1995, July 6
1818 A314   Strip of 3, #a.-c.   4.50 4.50
Souvenir Sheet
1819 A314 1200ce multicolored   4.00 4.00
No. 1818 is a continuous design.

Queen Mother,
95th Birthday
A315

No. 1820: a, Drawing. b, Bright green blue hat. c, Formal portrait. d, Coral outfit.
2500ce, Pale blue outfit.

1995, July 6   **Perf. 13½x14**
1820 A315   600ce Strip or block of
     4, #a.-d.   4.75 4.75
Souvenir Sheet
1821 A315 2500ce multicolored   5.00 5.00
No. 1820 was issued in sheets of 8 stamps.

Miniature Sheets of 9

Singapore
'95 — A316

Dinosaurs: No. 1822a, Seismosaurus (d-f). b, Supersaurus (a, d). c, Ultrasaurus (f). d, Saurolophus (e). e, Lambeosaurus (d, g-h). f, Parasaurolophus (e, i). g, Triceratops (h). h, Styracosaurus (e, g i). i, Pachyrhinosaurus (h).
No. 1823a, Peteinosaurus (b, d-e). b, Quetzalcoatlus (a, c, e). c, Eudimorphodon (b). d, Allosaurus (e-f, h-i). e, Daspletosaurus (f). f, Tarbosaurus (i). g, Velociraptor (h-i). h, Herrerasaurus (i). i, Coelophysis.
No. 1824, Albertosaur. No. 1825, Tyrannosaurus rex.

1995, Aug. 8   **Litho.**   **Perf. 14**
1822-1823 A316 400ce #a.-i., each   7.25 7.25
Souvenir Sheet
1824-1825 A316 2500ce each   4.00 4.00

Nobel Prize Recipients — A317

Asantehene, 25th Anniv. — A318

Designs: a, Nelson Mandela, peace, 1993. b, Albert Schweitzer, peace, 1952. c, Wole Soyinka, literature, 1986. d, Emil Fischer, chemistry, 1902. e, Rudolf Mossbauer, physics, 1961. f, Archbishop Desmond Tutu, peace, 1984. g, Max Born, physics, 1954. h, Max Planck, physics, 1918. i, Hermann Hesse, literature, 1946.
1200ce, Paul Ehrlich, medicine, 1908.

1995, Oct. 2   Litho.   Perf. 14
Miniature Sheet of 9
1826 A317   400ce #a.-i.   7.25 7.25
Souvenir Sheet
1827 A317   1200ce multicolored   2.50 2.50

1995   Perf. 13½x13
Designs: 50ce, Emblem. 100ce, Silver casket. 200ce, Golden stool. 400ce, Busummuru sword bearer. 600ce, 800ce, Diff. portraits of Otumfuo Opoku Ware II. 1000ce, Mponponsuo sword bearer.
1828-1834 A318   Set of 7   6.25 6.25

Fauna — A319

Designs: 400ce, Cymothoe beckeri. 500ce, Graphium policene. 1000ce, Urotriorchis macrourus, vert. 2000ce, Xiphias gladius. 3000ce, Monodoctylus sabee. 5000ce, Ardea purpurea, vert.

1995, June 19   Litho.   Perf. 14
1835 A319   400ce multicolored   .80 .80
1836 A319   500ce multicolored   1.00 1.00
1837 A319   1000ce multicolored   2.00 2.00
1838 A319   2000ce multicolored   4.25 4.25
1839 A319   3000ce multicolored   6.25 6.25
1840 A319   5000ce multicolored   10.50 10.50
Nos. 1835-1840 (6)   24.80 24.80

Christmas A320   Ghana   ₵50

Details or entire paintings: 50ce, The Infant Jesus and the Young St. John, by Murillo. 80ce, Rest on Flight to Egypt, by Memling. 300ce, Sacred Family, by Van Dyck. 600ce, The Virgin and the Infant, by Uccello. 800ce, The Virgin and the Infant, by Van Eyck. 1000ce, Head of Christ, by Rembrandt.
No. 1847, Madonna, by Montagna. No. 1848, The Holy Family, by Pulzone.

1995, Dec. 1   Litho.   Perf. 13½x14
1841-1846 A320   Set of 6   4.75 4.75
Souvenir Sheets
1847-1848 A320   2500ce each   4.25 4.25

Miniature Sheet

Motion Pictures, Cent. A321

GHANA ₵400

No. 1849: a, 1903 H. Ernmann camera. b, Charles Chaplin. c, Rudolph Valentino. d, Will Rogers. e, Greta Garbo. f, Jackie Cooper. g, Bette Davis. h, John Barrymore. i, Shirley Temple.
No. 1850, Laurel and Hardy.

1995, Dec. 8
1849 A321   400ce Sheet of 9, #a.-i.   6.00 6.00
Souvenir Sheet
1850 A321   2500ce multicolored   4.25 4.25

A322

John Lennon (1940-80) A323

Designs: Nos. 1852a-1852g, 1852i, various portraits. No. 1852h, like No. 1851.
No. 1853, Lennon playing guitar, water in background.

1995, Dec. 8   Perf. 14
1851 A322   400ce multicolored   .65 .65
Miniature Sheet
Perf. 13½x14
1852 A323   400ce Sheet of 9, #a.-i.   6.50 6.50
Souvenir Sheet
1853 A323   2000ce multicolored   3.50 3.50
No. 1851 was issued in sheets of 16.

Miniature Sheet

Louis Pasteur (1822-95) — A324
GHANA ₵600

Designs: a, In laboratory. b, Discovery of rabies virus and vaccine. c, Pneumococcus discovery, 1880. d, Development of first vaccine with birds. e, Perfection of brewer's yeast culture.

1995, Dec. 13   Perf. 14
1854 A324   600ce Sheet of 5, #a.-e.   6.00 6.00

AIR POST STAMPS
Type of Regular Issue
Designs: 1sh3p, Pennant-winged nightjar. 2sh, Crowned cranes, vert.

Perf. 14½x14, 14x14½
1959, Oct. 5   Photo.   Wmk. 325
C1 A17   1sh3p multicolored   .40 .15
a.   Booklet pane of 4   1.75
C2 A17   2sh multicolored   .55 .45
For surcharges see Nos. C7-C10.

Ships, Tema Harbor and Jet — AP1

Perf. 14x13
1962, Feb. 10   Litho.   Unwmk.
C3 AP1   1sh3p multicolored   .65 .65
C4 AP1   2sh6p multicolored   1.25 1.25
Opening of Tema Harbor, as part of the Volta River Project.

Type of Regular Issue, 1962
1962, Mar. 6   Perf. 13x14
C5 A35   1sh3p multicolored   .50 .35
C6 A35   2sh6p multicolored   1.00 .70

Nos. C1-C2 Surcharged in White or Green with New Value and: "Ghana New Currency / 19th July, 1965"
Perf. 14½x14, 14x14½
1965, July 19   Photo.   Wmk. 325
C7 A17   15pa on 1sh3p multi (W)   .35 .22
C8 A17   24pa on 2sh multi (G)   .70 .35
The two lines of the overprint are diagonal on No. C8.

Nos. C1, C8 Surcharged in White or Red
1967, Feb. 27   Photo.   Wmk. 325
C9 A17   12½np on 1sh3p (W)   1.10 .80
C10 A17   20np on 24pa on 2sh   2.50 1.75

POSTAGE DUE STAMPS
Gold Coast Nos. J2-J6 Overprinted "GHANA" and Bar in Red
Wmk. 4
1958, June 25   Typo.   Perf. 14
J1 D1   1p black   .15 .15
J2 D1   2p black   .15 .15
J3 D1   3p black   .15 .15
J4 D1   6p black   .15 .15
J5 D1   1sh black   .25 .25
Set value   .58 .58

Type of Gold Coast Inscribed "Ghana"
1958, Dec. 1   Perf. 14
J6 D1   1p carmine rose   .15 .15
J7 D1   2p green   .15 .15
J8 D1   3p orange   .15 .15
J9 D1   6p ultramarine   .15 .15
J10 D1   1sh purple   .20 .20
Set value   .46 .46

Nos. J6-J10 Surcharged in Black, Blue or Red with New Value and "Ghana New Currency / 19th July, 1965."
1965, July 19
J11 D1   1pa on 1p car rose   .15 .15
J12 D1   2pa on 2p grn (Bl)   .15 .15
J13 D1   3pa on 3p org (Bl)   .18 .18
J14 D1   6pa on 6p ultra (R)   .35 .35
J15 D1   12pa on 1sh pur (Bl)   .65 .65
Nos. J11-J15 (5)   1.48 1.48

Surcharge diagonal on Nos. J11 and J15.
No. J12 with additional surcharge, "1 ½Np" in red, was reported to have been used at one branch post office (Burma Camp) despite official intention. Four similar added surcharges were prepared: 1np on 1pa, 2½np on 3pa, 5np on 6pa, and 10np on 12pa.

GHANA 1 NP POSTAGE DUE
D2

1970 Unwmk. Litho.   Perf. 14½x14
J16 D2   1np carmine rose   .15 .15
J17 D2   1½np green   .15 .15
J18 D2   2½np orange   .15 .15
J19 D2   5np ultramarine   .15 .15
J20 D2   10np dull purple   .20 .20
Set value   .42 .42

1981   Litho.   Perf. 14½x14
J21 D2   2p red orange   .15 .15
J22 D2   3p brown   .15 .15
Set value   .15 .15

GIBRALTAR
jə-'brȯl-tər

LOCATION — A fortified promontory, including the Rock, extending from Spain's southeast coast at the entrance to the Mediterranean Sea
GOVT. — British Crown Colony
AREA — 2.5 sq. mi.
POP. — 31,183 (1982)
CAPITAL — Gibraltar
   12 Pence = 1 Shilling
   20 Shillings = 1 Pound
   100 Centimos = 1 Peseta (1889-95)
   100 Pence = 1 Pound (1971)

Catalogue values for unused stamps in this country are for Never Hinged items, beginning with Scott 119 in the regular postage section and Scott J1 in the postage due section.

Types of Bermuda Overprinted in Black **GIBRALTAR**

1886, Jan. 1   Wmk. 2   Perf. 14
1 A6   ½p green   7.00 6.00
2 A1   1p rose   22.50 4.50
3 A2   2p violet brown   80.00 55.00
4 A8   2½p ultra   100.00 3.25
5 A7   4p orange brn   95.00 85.00
6 A4   6p violet   200.00 175.00
7 A5   1sh bister brn   425.00 350.00
Nos. 1-7 (7)   929.50 678.75
Forged overprints of No. 7 are plentiful.

Victoria
A6   A7

A8

A9

1886-98   Typo.
8 A6   ½p dull green   2.25 2.25
9 A6   ½p gray grn ('98)   .90 .90
10 A7   1p rose   11.00 2.75
11 A7   1p car rose ('98)   1.75 .35
12 A8   2p brn violet   30.00 16.00
13 A8   2p brn vio & ultra ('98)   7.00 3.50
14 A9   2½p brt ultra ('98)   3.75 .80
a.   2½p ultramarine   45.00 4.00
16 A8   4p orange brn   60.00 60.00
17 A8   4p org brn & grn ('98)   10.00 9.50
18 A8   6p violet   85.00 85.00
19 A8   6p vio & car rose ('98)   27.50 20.00
20 A8   1sh bister   175.00 175.00
21 A8   1sh bis & car rose ('98)   25.00 15.00
Nos. 8-14,16-21 (13)   439.15 391.05

Stamps of 1886 Issue Surcharged in Black   **10 CENTIMOS**

1889, July

22 A6 5c on 1/2p green 8.00 8.00
23 A7 10c on 1p rose 7.00 6.50
24 A8 25c on 2p brn vio 2.25 2.25
a. Small "I" in "CENTIMOS" 225.00 200.00
b. Broken "N" 175.00 165.00
25 A9 25c on 2 1/2p ultra 14.00 2.50
a. Small "I" in "CENTIMOS" 300.00 200.00
b. Broken "N" 300.00 165.00
26 A8 40c on 4p org brn 50.00 50.00
27 A8 50c on 6p violet 50.00 50.00
28 A8 75c on 1sh bister 60.00 60.00
Nos. 22-28 (7) 191.25 179.25

There are two varieties of the figure "5" in the 5c, 25c, 50c and 75c.

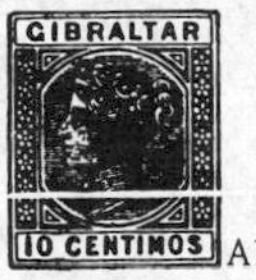
A11

1889-95

29 A11 5c green 1.25 .50
30 A11 10c rose 1.25 .40
a. Value omitted 5,000.
31 A11 20c ol green ('95) 7.00 11.00
31A A11 20c ol grn & brn ('95) 10.00 9.00
32 A11 25c ultra 3.25 .45
33 A11 40c orange brn 1.75 2.25
34 A11 50c violet 2.50 2.25
35 A11 75c olive green 30.00 32.50
36 A11 1p bister 50.00 21.00
36A A11 1p bis & bl ('95) 3.25 3.50
37 A11 2p blk & car rose ('95) 7.00 *16.50*
38 A11 5p steel blue 42.50 60.00
Nos. 29-38 (12) 159.75 159.35

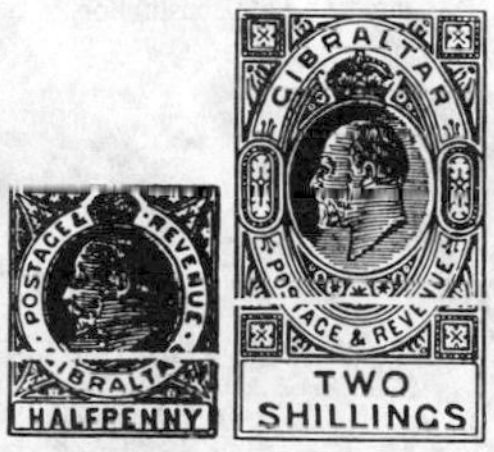
King Edward VII
A12 A13

1903, May 1

39 A12 1/2p grn & bl grn 7.25 4.50
40 A12 1p violet, *red* 25.00 .90
41 A12 2p grn & car rose 12.50 15.00
42 A12 2 1/2p vio & blk, *bl* 2.00 .50
43 A12 6p violet & pur 12.50 15.00
44 A12 1sh blk & car rose 30.00 25.00
45 A13 2sh green & ultra 87.50 90.00
46 A13 4sh vio & green 77.50 90.00
47 A13 8sh vio & blk, *bl* 100.00 110.00
48 A13 £1 vio & blk, *red* 450.00 500.00
Nos. 39-48 (10) 804.25 850.90

1904-12 **Wmk. 3**

Ordinary or Chalky Paper

49 A12 1/2p gray green 4.25 .70
a. 1/2p blue green ('07) 2.00 .15
50 A12 1p violet, *red* 3.00 .25
51 A12 1p car ('07) 1.75 .35
52 A12 2p grn & car rose 4.25 2.00
53 A12 2p gray ('10) 6.00 8.00
54 A12 2 1/2p vio & blk, *bl* 25.00 *65.00*
55 A12 2 1/2p ultra ('07) 3.50 1.00
56 A12 6p vio & pur ('06) 11.00 2.75
a. 6p vio & red violet ('12) 110.00 *185.00*
57 A12 1sh blk & car rose 24.00 9.00
58 A12 1sh blk, *grn* ('10) 19.00 16.00
59 A13 2sh grn & ultra ('05) 55.00 20.00
60 A13 2sh vio & bl, *bl* ('10) 35.00 40.00
61 A13 4sh vio & grn 140.00 52.50
62 A13 4sh blk & red ('10) 72.50 90.00
63 A13 8sh vio & grn ('11) 165.00 190.00
64 A12 £1 vio & blk, *red* 400.00 525.00
Nos. 49-64 (16) 969.25 1,022.

Nos. 49a, 51, 53, 55 are on ordinary paper. Nos. 54, 58, 60-64 are on chalky paper. Others come on both papers.

No. 56a, used, must have a 1912 cancellation. Stamps used later sell for about the same as unused.

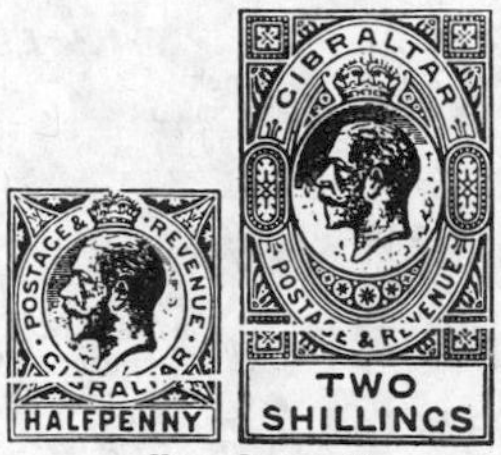
King George V
A14 A15

1912, July 17 **Ordinary Paper**

66 A14 1/2p green 1.40 .40
67 A14 1p scarlet ('16) 2.50 .40
a. 1p carmine 2.00 .40
68 A14 2p gray 2.50 1.25
69 A14 2 1/2p ultra 3.75 1.25

Chalky Paper

70 A14 6p dl vio & red vio 6.50 7.50
71 A14 1sh black, *green* 5.00 3.50
a. 1sh black, *emerald* ('24) 12.00 13.00
b. 1sh black, *blue green*, olive back ('19) 12.00 21.00
c. 1sh black, *emerald*, olive back ('23) 12.00 50.00
72 A15 2sh vio & ultra, *bl* 17.50 2.25
73 A15 4sh black & scar 25.00 50.00
74 A15 8sh vio & green 55.00 60.00
75 A15 £1 vio & blk, *red* 125.00 190.00
Nos. 66-75 (10) 244.15 316.55

1921-32 **Ordinary Paper** **Wmk. 4**

76 A14 1/2p green .25 .20
77 A14 1p rose red .25 .20
78 A14 1 1/2p red brown .45 .20
79 A14 2p gray .55 .50
80 A14 2 1/2p ultra 7.00 7.00
81 A14 3p ultra .70 .65

Chalky Paper

82 A14 6p dl vio & red vio 1.00 1.00
a. 6p gray lilac & red violet 1.75 1.00
83 A14 1sh black, *emer* 8.50 9.00
84 A14 1sh ol grn & blk 5.50 5.75
a. 1sh brn olive & black ('32) 13.00 3.75
85 A15 2sh vio & ultra, *blue* 3.75 *8.50*
86 A15 2sh red brn & black 14.00 15.00
87 A15 2sh6p green & blk 5.75 6.00
88 A15 4sh black & scar 47.50 *57.50*
89 A15 5sh car & black 14.00 17.50
90 A15 8sh vio & green 140.00 170.00
91 A15 10sh ultra & black 21.00 24.00
92 A15 £1 org & black 125.00 190.00
93 A15 £5 dl vio & blk 1,750. *2,750.*
Nos. 76-92 (17) 395.20 513.00

Years issued: 1 1/2p, 1922. 6p, 1923. Nos. 83, 85, 4sh, 8sh, 1924. 2sh6p, 5sh, 10sh, £5, 1925. 1/2p, £1, 1927. Nos. 84, 86, 1929.

Type of 1912 Issue
Inscribed: "THREE PENCE"

1930, Apr. 12 **Ordinary Paper**

94 A14 3p ultramarine 9.50 2.25

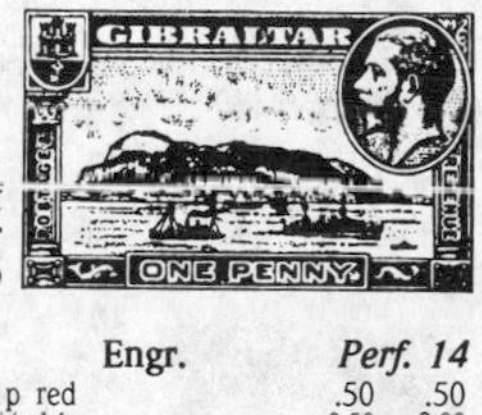
Rock of Gibraltar
A16

1931-33 **Engr.** ***Perf. 14***

96 A16 1p red .50 .50
a. Perf. 13 1/2x14 8.50 2.00
97 A16 1 1/2p red brown .90 .50
a. Perf. 13 1/2x14 3.75 1.25
98 A16 2p gray ('32) 1.75 .80
a. Perf. 13 1/2x14 6.00 1.10
99 A16 3p dk blue ('33) 1.75 1.75
a. Perf. 13 1/2x14 9.00 12.00
Nos. 96-99 (4) 4.90 3.55
Nos. 96a-99a (4) 27.25 16.35

Silver Jubilee Issue
Common Design Type

1935, May 6 ***Perf. 11x12***

100 CD301 2p black & ultra 1.10 1.10
101 CD301 3p ultra & brown 2.25 2.50
102 CD301 6p indigo & green 4.25 5.00
103 CD301 1sh brown vio & ind 7.50 7.50
Nos. 100-103 (4) 15.10 16.10
Set, never hinged 30.00

Coronation Issue
Common Design Type

1937, May 12 ***Perf. 11x11 1/2***

104 CD302 1/2p deep green .20 .15
105 CD302 2p gray black .45 .35
106 CD302 3p deep ultra 1.10 .65
Nos. 104-106 (3) 1.75 1.15
Set, never hinged 3.50

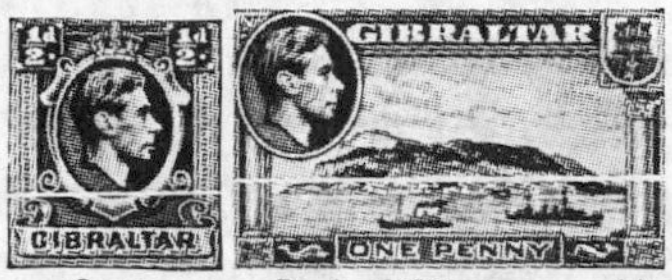
George VI — A17 Rock of Gibraltar — A18

Designs: 2p, Rock from north side. 3p, 5p, Europa Point. 6p, Moorish Castle. 1sh, Southport Gate. 2sh, Eliott Memorial. 5sh, Government House. 10sh, Catalan Bay.

Perf. 13, 13 1/2x14 (1/2p, No. 118), 14 (1 1/2p)

1938-49 **Engr.** **Wmk. 4**

107 A17 1/2p gray green .15 .15
108 A18 1p red brn ('42) .20 .20
a. 1p chestnut, perf. 14 *14.00* .15
b. 1p chestnut, perf. 13 1/2 15.00 1.25
c. Perf. 13 1/2, wmk. sideways ('41) .20 .20
109 A18 1 1/2p carmine rose 25.00 .55
b. Perf. 13 1/2 175.00 25.00
109A A18 1 1/2p gray vio ('43) .15 .15
110 A18 2p dk gray ('42) .50 .50
a. Perf. 14 15.00 .35
c. Perf. 13 1/2 .75 .32
d. Perf. 13 1/2, wmk. sideways ('41) 475.00 35.00
110B A18 2p car rose ('44) .20 .35
111 A18 3p blue ('42) .25 .15
a. Perf. 14 65.00 6.50
b. Perf. 13 1/2 9.00 .40
112 A18 5p red org ('47) .60 .90
113 A18 6p dl vio & car rose 1.25 .80
a. Perf. 14 75.00 1.10
b. Perf. 13 1/2 27.50 2.25
114 A18 1sh grn & blk ('42) 2.25 2.50
a. Perf. 14 25.00 12.00
b. Perf. 13 1/2 35.00 4.50
115 A18 2sh org brn & blk ('42) 2.75 3.25
a. Perf. 14 40.00 20.00
b. Perf. 13 1/2 60.00 25.00
116 A18 5sh dk car & blk ('44) 10.00 15.00
a. Perf 14 ('38) 50.00 *100.00*
b. Perf. 13 1/2 22.50 15.00
117 A18 10sh bl & blk ('43) 30.00 20.00
a. Perf. 14 42.50 75.00
118 A17 £1 orange 27.50 27.50
Nos. 107-118 (14) 100.80 72.00
Set, never hinged 120.00

Nos. 108c and 110d were issued in coils.

No. 108 (1p, perf. 13) exists with watermark both normal and sideways. Nos. 110 and 110B (both 2p, perf. 13) have watermark sideways.

For overprints see Nos. 127-130.

Catalogue values for unused stamps in this section, from this point to the end of the section, are for Never Hinged Items.

Peace Issue
Common Design Type

1946, Oct. 12 ***Perf. 13 1/2x14***

119 CD303 1/2p bright green .15 .15
120 CD303 3p bright ultra .20 .20

Silver Wedding Issue
Common Design Types

1948, Dec. 1 **Photo.** ***Perf. 14x14 1/2***

121 CD304 1/2p dark green .15 .15

Engr.; Name Typo.
Perf. 11 1/2x11

122 CD305 £1 brown orange 70.00 50.00

UPU Issue
Common Design Types

Engr.; Name Typo. on 3p, 6p
Perf. 13 1/2, 11x11 1/2

1949, Oct. 10 **Wmk. 4**

123 CD306 2p rose carmine 1.40 1.25
124 CD307 3p indigo 1.65 1.40
125 CD308 6p rose violet 2.50 2.50
126 CD309 1sh blue green 6.00 6.00
Nos. 123-126 (4) 11.55 11.15

Nos. 110B, 111, 113-114 overprinted in Black or Carmine

NEW CONSTITUTION 1950

1950, Aug. 1 ***Perf. 13x12 1/2***

127 A18 2p carmine rose .50 .50
128 A18 3p blue .55 .55
129 A18 6p dl vio & car rose 1.25 1.25
a. Double overprint 500.00 *600.00*
130 A18 1sh grn & blk (C) 2.00 2.00
Nos. 127-130 (4) 4.30 4.30

Adoption of Constitution of 1950.

Coronation Issue
Common Design Type

1953, June 2 **Engr.** ***Perf. 13 1/2x13***

131 CD312 1/2p olive green & black .25 .18

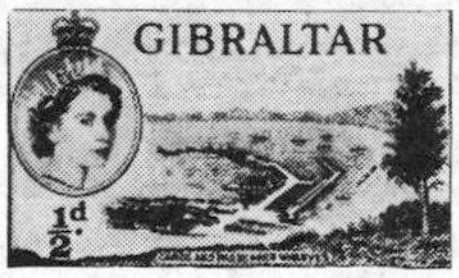
Wharves
A26

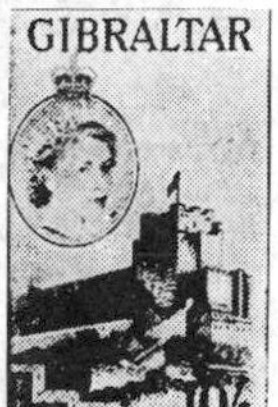
Moorish Castle — A27

Designs: 1p, South view. 1 1/2p, Tunny fishing industry. 2p, Southport Gate. 2 1/2p, Sailing in the bay. 3p, Ocean liner. 4p, Coaling wharf. 5p, Airport. 6p, Europa Point. 1sh, Strait from Buena Vista. 2sh, Rosia Bay. 5sh, Government House. £1, Arms of Gibraltar.

1953, Oct. 19 ***Perf. 12 1/2***

132 A26 1/2p dk grn & ind .15 .15
133 A26 1p blue green .15 .15
134 A26 1 1/2p dark gray .15 .15
135 A26 2p sepia .22 .16
136 A26 2 1/2p car lake .32 .25
137 A26 3p grnsh blue .30 .16
138 A26 4p ultra .38 .30
139 A26 5p deep plum .40 .38
140 A26 6p blue & black .60 .40
141 A26 1sh red brn & bl 1.00 .85
142 A26 2sh vio & org 8.00 3.00
143 A26 5sh dark brown 14.00 6.00
144 A27 10sh ultra & brn 57.50 27.50
145 A27 £1 yellow & red 100.00 35.00
Nos. 132-145 (14) 183.17 74.45
Set, hinged 115.00

Inscribed: "ROYAL VISIT 1954"

1954, May 10

146 A26 3p greenish blue .42 .35

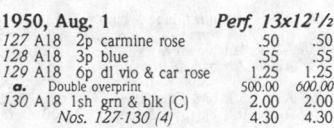

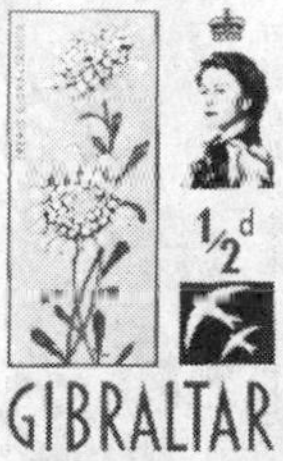
Candytuft
A28

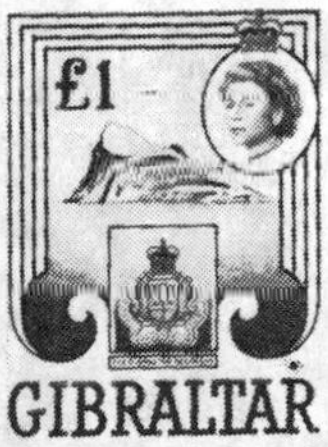
Rock and Badge of Gibraltar Regiment
A30

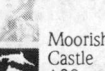

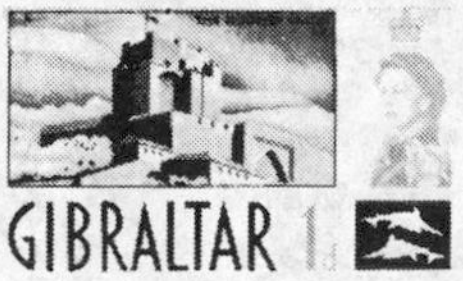
Moorish Castle
A29

Designs: 2p, St. George's Hall and cannons. 2 1/2p, The keys. 3p, Rock by moonlight. 4p, Catalan Bay. 6p, Map. 7p, Air terminal. 9p, American war memorial. 1sh, Barbary ape. 2sh, Barbary partridge. 5sh, Blue rock thrush. 10sh, Narcissus.

Perf. 12 1/2

1960, Oct. 29 **Wmk. 314** **Photo.**

147 A28 1/2p brt green & lil .15 .15
148 A29 1p black & yel grn .15 .15
149 A29 2p org brn & sl .15 .15
150 A28 2 1/2p blue & black .15 .15
151 A29 3p dk blue & ver .16 .15
152 A29 4p choc & grnsh bl .45 .38
a. Wmkd. sideways ('66) .25 .18
153 A28 6p brown & emer .35 .30
154 A28 7p gray & car .48 .40

155 A28 9p grnsh blue & bluish gray .75 .65
156 A29 1sh brown & green .75 .65
157 A29 2sh dark red brn & ultra 3.00 1.90
158 A29 5sh ol & Prus grn 9.25 5.25
159 A28 10sh blue, yel & grn 15.00 18.00

Perf. 14

Engr.

160 A30 £1 org red & slate 30.00 10.50
Nos. 147-160 (14) 60.79 38.78

For overprints see Nos. 165-166.

Freedom from Hunger Issue
Common Design Type

1963, June 4 ***Perf. 14x14½***
161 CD314 9p sepia 15.00 8.50

Red Cross Centenary Issue
Common Design Type

1963, Sept. 2 Litho. ***Perf. 13***
162 CD315 1p black & red .38 .22
163 CD315 9p ultra & red 15.00 12.50

Shakespeare Issue
Common Design Type

1964, Apr. 23 Photo. ***Perf. 14x14½***
164 CD316 7p brown 1.10 1.00

Nos. 151 and 153 Overprinted: "NEW / CONSTITUTION / 1964."

1964, Oct. 16 ***Perf. 12½***
165 A29 3p dk blue & ver .25 .25
166 A28 6p brown & emer .42 .42
a. No period in overprint 15.00 12.50

ITU Issue
Common Design Type

Perf. 11x11½

1965, May 17 Litho. Wmk. 314
167 CD317 4p emerald & yel .75 .40
168 CD317 2sh ap grn & dk bl 25.00 16.00

Intl. Cooperation Year Issue
Common Design Type

1965, Oct. 25 ***Perf. 14½***
169 CD318 ½p lt violet & grn .15 .15
170 CD318 4p blue green & cl 1.75 1.40

Churchill Memorial Issue
Common Design Type

1966, Jan. 24 Photo. ***Perf. 14***

Design in Black, Gold and Carmine Rose

171 CD319 ½p bright blue .15 .15
172 CD319 1p green .15 .15
173 CD319 4p brown .80 .80
174 CD319 9p violet 1.90 1.90
Nos. 171-174 (4) 3.00 3.00

World Cup Soccer Issue
Common Design Type

1966, July 1 Litho. ***Perf. 14***
175 CD321 2½p multicolored .70 .28
176 CD321 6p multicolored 1.50 1.10

Sea Bream A30a

Fish: 7p, Orange scorpionfish. 1sh, Stone bass, vert.

Perf. 14x13½, 13½x14

1966, Aug. 27 Photo. Wmk. 314
177 A30a 4p ultra, rose red & black .15 .15
178 A30a 7p ol, rose red & blk .22 .22
a. Value omitted 625.00
179 A30a 1sh brt grn, brn & blk .35 .35
Nos. 177-179 (3) .72 .72

European Sea Angling Championships, Gibraltar, Aug. 28-Sept. 3.

WHO Headquarters Issue
Common Design Type

1966, Sept. 20 Litho. ***Perf. 14***
180 CD322 6p multicolored 1.40 1.00
181 CD322 9p multicolored 2.75 2.00

"Our Lady of Europa" — A31

Perf. 14x14½

1966, Nov. 15 Photo. Wmk. 314
182 A31 2sh ultra & black 1.50 1.50

Enthronement of the recovered statue of the Madonna in its new shrine, cent.

UNESCO Anniversary Issue
Common Design Type

1966, Dec. 1 Litho. ***Perf. 14***
183 CD323 2p "Education" .22 .15
184 CD323 7p "Science" .65 .35
185 CD323 5sh "Culture" 4.00 3.00
Nos. 183-185 (3) 4.87 3.50

Victory, Nelson's Flagship A32

Ships and Arms of Gibraltar: 1p, S.S. Arab. 2p, H.M.S. Carmania. 2½p, M.V. Mons Calpe. 3p, S.S. Canberra. 4p, H.M.S. Hood. 5p, Cable Ship Mirror. 6p, Xebec, Moorish vessel. 7p, Amerigo Vespucci, Italian training ship (sails). 9p, Raffaello, Italian liner. 1sh, H.M.S. Royal Katherine, 17th century British warship. 2sh, H.M.S. Ark Royal, aircraft carrier. 5sh, H.M.S. Dreadnought, atomic submarine. 10sh, S.S. Neuralia, troopship. £1, Mary Celeste, 19th century mystery ship (sails).

Perf. 14x14½

1967-69 Photo. Wmk. 314

Design in Black, Red and Gold; Background as Indicated

186 A32 ½p deep rose .15 .15
187 A32 1p yellow .15 .15
188 A32 2p ultra .15 .15
189 A32 2½p orange .15 .15
190 A32 3p violet .20 .15
191 A32 4p rose .22 .15
191A A32 5p brn & multi ('69) .80 .60
192 A32 6p gray .32 .22
193 A32 7p yellow grn .40 .25
194 A32 9p green .60 .35
195 A32 1sh rose brown .80 .45
196 A32 2sh brt yellow 2.75 1.65
197 A32 5sh brick red 5.00 4.00
198 A32 10sh emerald 11.50 10.00
199 A32 £1 lt ultra 27.50 22.50
Nos. 186-199 (15) 50.69 40.92

Common Design Types pictured in section before Great Britain.

Cable Car and ITY Emblem — A33

ITY emblem and: 9p, Bull shark, horiz. 1sh, Skin diver, horiz.

Perf. 14½x14, 14x14½

1967, June 15 Photo. Wmk. 314
200 A33 7p red brown, red & blk .22 .18
201 A33 9p brt blue, blk & slate .35 .25
202 A33 1sh emer, black & org brn .45 .38
Nos. 200-202 (3) 1.02 .81

International Tourist Year.

Holy Family — A34

Christmas: 6p, Church window, vert.

1967, Nov. 1 ***Perf. 14½***
203 A34 2p dark red & multi .15 .15
204 A34 6p dark green & multi .20 .20
Set value .30 .30

General Eliott and Map of Europe and Great Britain A35

Designs: 9p, Eliott Memorial and tower. 1sh, Gen. Eliott and map of Gibraltar, vert. 2sh, Gen. Eliott directing rescue operations for enemy sailors during Great Siege 1779-83.

Perf. 14½x14, 14x14½

1967, Dec. 11 Photo. Wmk. 314

Size: 37x21mm, 21x37mm

205 A35 4p multicolored .15 .15
206 A35 9p multicolored .20 .20
207 A35 1sh multicolored .30 .30

Size: 58x21½mm

208 A35 2sh multicolored .60 .60
Nos. 205-208 (4) 1.25 1.25

250th anniv. of the birth of General George Augustus Eliott (1717-1790), Governor of Gibraltar during Great Siege.

Lord Baden-Powell A36

Designs: 7p, Scout flag, Rock of Gibraltar and globe with map of Europe. 9p, Symbolic tents, heads and Scout salute. 1sh, Three Scout badges.

Perf. 14x14½

1968, Mar. 27 Photo. Wmk. 314
209 A36 4p dull yellow & pur .15 .15
210 A36 7p brown org, brn & grn .16 .16
211 A36 9p ultra, black & org .25 .25
212 A36 1sh yellow & emerald .32 .32
Nos. 209-212 (4) .88 .88

60th anniv. of the Gibraltar Scout Assoc.

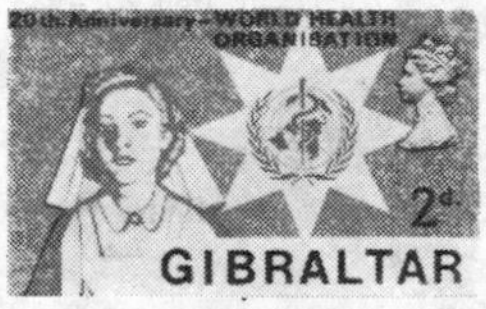

Nurse and WHO Emblem A37

20th anniv. of WHO: 4p, Physician with microscope and WHO emblem.

1968, July 1 Photo. Wmk. 314
213 A37 2p yellow, ultra & blk .15 .15
214 A37 4p pink, black & slate .30 .30

King John Signing Magna Carta — A38

Shepherd, Lamb and Star — A39

Design: 2sh, Rock of Gibraltar, "Freedom" and Human Rights flame.

1968, Aug. 26 ***Perf. 13½x14½***
215 A38 1sh org, gold & dk brn .30 .30
216 A38 2sh brt green & gold .55 .55

International Human Rights Year.

1968, Nov. 1 ***Perf. 14x13½***

Christmas: 9p, Mary, Jesus and lamb.

217 A39 4p lt brown & multi .18 .18
218 A39 9p rose & multi .35 .35

Government House, Gibraltar A40

Designs: 9p, Rock of Gibraltar and Commonwealth Parliamentary Association emblem. 2sh, Big Ben, London, and arms of Gibraltar.

Perf. 14½x14, 14x14½

1969, May 26 Photo. Wmk. 314
219 A40 4p green & gold .15 .15
220 A40 9p brt violet & gold .22 .22
221 A40 2sh lt ultra, gold & red .55 .55
Nos. 219-221 (3) .92 .92

Meeting of the Executive Committee of the General Council of the Commonwealth Parliamentary Assoc., Gibraltar, May 1969.

Rock of Gibraltar A41

1969, July 30 ***Perf. 14½x13½***
222 A41 ½p orange & gold .15 .15
223 A41 5p emerald & silver .15 .15
224 A41 7p brt rose lil & silver .20 .18
225 A41 5sh ultra & gold 1.40 1.30
Nos. 222-225 (4) 1.90 1.78

Gibraltar's new constitution.

Royal Artillery Officer, 1758 — A42

Madonna della Seggiola, by Raphael — A43

Uniforms: 6p, Contemporary soldier of the Royal Anglian Regiment. 9p, Soldier, Royal Engineers, 1786. 2sh, Private of Fox's Marines, 1704.

1969, Nov. 6 Photo. ***Perf. 14***
226 A42 1p gold & multi .15 .15
227 A42 6p silver, gold & multi .70 .70
228 A42 9p silver, gold & multi .95 .95
229 A42 2sh gold & multi 4.00 3.25
Nos. 226-229 (4) 5.80 5.05

Design descriptions are printed on back on top of gum.

See Nos. 234-237, 276-279, 286-289, 299-302, 310-313, 318-321, 330-333.

1969, Dec. 1 ***Perf. 13½x Roulette 9***

Christmas (Paintings): 7p, Madonna and Child, by Luis Morales. 1sh, Virgin of the Rocks, by Leonardo da Vinci.

230 A43 5p gold & multi .30 .30
231 A43 7p gold & multi .50 .50
232 A43 1sh gold & multi .85 .85
a. Triptych, Nos. 230, 232, 231 1.65 1.65

Europa Issue

Europa Point — A44

1970, June 8 ***Perf. 13½***
233 A44 2sh multicolored .85 .75

Uniform Type of 1969

Uniforms: 2p, Royal Scots officer, 1839. 5p, Private of South Wales Borderers. 7p, Private of Queen's Royal Regiment, 1742. 2sh, Piper of Royal Irish Rangers, 1969.

1970, Aug. 28 Photo. *Perf. 14*

234	A42	2p	gold & multi	.25	.25
235	A42	5p	gold & multi	.75	.75
236	A42	7p	gold & multi	1.10	1.10
237	A42	2sh	gold & multi	3.75	3.50
			Nos. 234-237 (4)	5.85	5.60

Design descriptions are printed on back on top of gum.

No. 178a and Rock of Gibraltar A45

Design: 2sh, No. 30a and Moorish Castle.

1970, Sept. 18 *Perf. 13*

238	A45	1sh	red & olive	.30	.28
239	A45	2sh	ultra & rose	.60	.55

Philympia, London Phil. Exhib., Sept. 18-26.

Virgin Mary by Gabriel Loire A46

1970, Dec. 1 Photo. *Perf. 13x14*

240	A46	2sh	multicolored	1.10	.85

Christmas. The design is after a stained glass window in the Church of Our Lady of Perpetual Succour, Glasgow.

Decimal Currency Issue

Battery, Rosia; 20th Century A47

Designs show for each denomination a 19th century print and a contemporary photograph of the same view: 1p, Prince George of Cambridge Quarters, and Trinity Church. 1½p, Wellington Monument, Alameda Gardens. 2p, View from North Bastion. 2½p, Catalan Bay. 3p, Convent, seen from garden. 4p, The Exchange and Spanish Chapel. 5p, Commercial Square, Library and Main Guard. 7p, South Barracks and Rosia Magazine. 8p, Moorish Mosque and Castle. 9p, Europa Pass. 10p, South Barracks, from Rosia Bay. 12½p, Southport Gates. 25p, Guards on Alameda. 50p, Europa Pass Gorge, vert. £1 Prince Edward Gate, vert.

In the listing the 1st number is for the 19th cent. design, the 2nd for the 20th cent. design.

Wmk. 314 Sideways

1971, Feb. 15 Litho. *Perf. 14*

Multicolored and

241	A47	½p	brown red	.15	.15
242	A47	½p	brown red	.15	.15
243	A47	1p	light blue	.18	.15
244	A47	1p	light blue	.18	.15
245	A47	1½p	emerald	.15	.15
246	A47	1½p	emerald	.15	.15
247	A47	2p	dark brown	.45	.45
248	A47	2p	dark brown	.45	.45
249	A47	2½p	vermilion	.15	.15
250	A47	2½p	vermilion	.15	.15
251	A47	3p	pale green	.18	.18
252	A47	3p	pale green	.18	.18
253	A47	4p	gray	1.10	1.10
254	A47	4p	gray	1.10	1.10
255	A47	5p	dark green	.25	.25
256	A47	5p	dark green	.25	.25
257	A47	7p	orange	.38	.38
258	A47	7p	orange	.38	.38
259	A47	8p	dark blue	.45	.45
260	A47	8p	dark blue	.45	.45
261	A47	9p	brick red	.48	.48
262	A47	9p	brick red	.48	.48
263	A47	10p	black	.55	.55
264	A47	10p	black	.55	.55
265	A47	12½p	bister	.65	.65
266	A47	12½p	bister	.65	.65
267	A47	25p	deep purple	1.40	1.40
268	A47	25p	deep purple	1.40	1.40
269	A47	50p	blue	2.25	2.25
270	A47	50p	blue	2.25	2.25
271	A47	£1	sepia	4.75	4.75
272	A47	£1	sepia	4.75	4.75
			Nos. 241-272 (32)	27.04	26.98

The stamps of the same denomination are printed se-tenant both horizontally and vertically in sheets of 100.

1973, Sept. 12 Wmk. 314 Upright

247a	A47	2p	dark brown & multi	.15	.15
248a	A47	2p	dark brown & multi	.15	.15
253a	A47	4p	gray & multi	.30	.30
254a	A47	4p	gray & multi	.30	.30
			Nos. 247a-254a (4)	.90	.90

1975, July 9 Wmk. 373

243a	A47	1p	blue & multi	.15	.15
244a	A47	1p	blue & multi	.15	.15

Elizabeth II — A48

Regimental Coat of Arms — A49

Coil Stamps

Perf. 14½x14

1971, Feb. 15 Photo. Wmk. 314

273	A48	½p	red orange	.15	.15
274	A48	1p	bright blue	.20	.20
275	A48	2p	lt yellow green	.50	.50
a.			Strip of 5 (½p, ½p, 1p, 1p, 2p)	1.40	1.40
			Nos. 273-275 (3)	.85	.85

Uniform Type of 1969

Uniforms: 1p, Soldier, Black Watch, 1845. 2p, Drum Major with antelope mascot, Royal Fusiliers, 1971. 4p, Soldier, Kings Own Royal Border Regiment, 1704. 10p, Soldier, Devonshire and Dorset Regiment, 1801.

1971, Sept. 6 Litho. *Perf. 14*

276	A42	1p	silver & multi	.25	.25
277	A42	2p	gold & multi	.60	.60
278	A42	4p	gold & multi	1.50	1.50
279	A42	10p	sil, gold & multi	4.50	3.75
			Nos. 276-279 (4)	6.85	6.10

Design descriptions are printed on back on top of gum.

1971, Sept. 25 *Perf. 13x12*

280	A49	3p	red, bister & black	.55	.50

Presentation of colors to Gibraltar Regiment, Sept. 25, 1971.

Nativity — A50

Christmas: 5p, Journey to Bethlehem.

1971, Dec. 1 Photo. *Perf. 13x13½*

281	A50	3p	silver & multi	.75	.65
282	A50	5p	gold & multi	1.25	1.10

Artificer, 1773 — A51

"Our Lady of Europa" — A52

Designs: 3p, Tunneler with drill, 1969. 5p, Royal Engineers, 1772 and 1972, and regimental crest, horiz.

1972, Mar. 6 *Perf. 14x13½, 13½x14*

283	A51	1p	dk blue & multi	.30	.25
284	A51	3p	red & multi	1.00	.80
285	A51	5p	green & multi	1.75	1.35
			Nos. 283-285 (3)	3.05	2.40

Bicent. of the Royal Engineers in Gibraltar.

Uniform Type of 1969

Uniforms: 1p, Soldier, Duke of Cornwall's Light Infantry, 1704. 3p, Officer, King's Royal Rifle Corps, 1830. 7p, Officer, 37th North Hampshire Regiment, 1825. 10p, Sailor, Royal Navy, 1972.

1972, July 19 Litho. *Perf. 14*

286	A42	1p	silver & multi	.25	.22
287	A42	3p	slate & multi	.85	.70
288	A42	7p	silver & multi	2.00	1.75
289	A42	10p	gold & multi	3.75	3.25
			Nos. 286-289 (4)	6.85	5.92

Design descriptions printed on back on top of gum.

1972, Oct. 1 *Perf. 14½x14*

290	A52	3p	brown & multi	.22	.22
291	A52	5p	green & multi	.50	.50

Christmas. Design description printed on back.

Silver Wedding Issue, 1972

Common Design Type

Design: Queen Elizabeth II, Prince Philip, keys of Gibraltar and white narcissus.

1972, Nov. 20 Photo. *Perf. 14x14½*

292	CD324	5p	car rose & multi	.35	.35
293	CD324	7p	slate green & multi	.45	.45

Flags of EEC Members and EEC Emblem — A53

Perf. 14½x14

1973, Feb. 22 Litho. Unwmk.

294	A53	5p	red & multi	.52	.45
295	A53	10p	ultra & multi	1.00	.95

Entry into European Economic Community.

Gibraltar Skull — A54

Designs: 6p, Head of Neanderthal man. 10p, Neanderthal family.

1973, May 22 Wmk. 314 *Perf. 13½*

296	A54	4p	lilac rose & multi	.65	.55
297	A54	6p	lt ultra & multi	1.00	.80
298	A54	10p	yel green & multi	1.60	1.30
			Nos. 296-298 (3)	3.25	2.65

125th anniv. of the discovery of the Gibraltar skull.

Uniform Type of 1969

Uniforms: 1p, Fifer, King's Own Scottish Borderers, 1770. 4p, Officer, Royal Welsh Fusiliers, 1800. 6p, Soldier, Royal Northumberland Fusiliers, 1736. 10p, Private, Grenadier Guards, 1898.

1973, Aug. 22 Litho. *Perf. 14*

299	A42	1p	multicolored	.35	.22
300	A42	4p	multicolored	1.65	1.10
301	A42	6p	multicolored	2.50	1.50
302	A42	10p	multicolored	4.25	2.50
			Nos. 299-302 (4)	8.75	5.32

Design descriptions printed on back on top of gum.

Nativity, by Justus Danckerts A55

1973, Oct. 17 Litho. *Perf. 12½x12*

303	A55	4p	brown org & blue	.60	.40
304	A55	6p	green & claret	.85	.60

Christmas.

Princess Anne's Wedding Issue

Common Design Type

1973, Nov. 14 *Perf. 14*

305	CD325	6p	bl grn & multi	.55	.45
306	CD325	14p	brt grn & multi	1.20	1.00

Wedding of Princess Anne and Capt. Mark Phillips, Nov. 14, 1973.

V.R. (Queen Victoria) Pillar Box — A56

Virgin with Green Cushion, Andrea Solario — A57

Pillar Boxes: 6p, G.R. (King George). 14p, E.R. (Queen Elizabeth).

1974, May 2 Litho. *Perf. 14*

307	A56	2p	yel green & multi	.18	.18
308	A56	6p	gray & multi	.55	.55
309	A56	14p	dull yel & multi	1.25	1.25
a.			Souvenir booklet	12.50	
			Nos. 307-309 (3)	1.98	1.98

UPU, cent.

No. 309a contains 2 self-adhesive panes printed on peelable paper backing with multicolored advertising on back. One pane of 6 contains 3 each similar to Nos. 307-308; the other pane of 3 contains one each similar to Nos. 307-309. Stamps are imperf. x roulette.

Uniform Type of 1969

Uniforms: 4p, Officer, East Lancashire Regiment, 1742. 6p, Sergeant, Somerset Light Infantry, 1833. 10p, Company man, Royal Sussex Regiment, 1790. 16p, Officer, Royal Air Force, 1974.

1974, Aug. 21 *Perf. 14*

310	A42	4p	silver & multi	.55	.45
311	A42	6p	silver & multi	.95	.75
312	A42	10p	silver & multi	1.65	1.25
313	A42	16p	silver & multi	2.50	2.75
			Nos. 310-313 (4)	5.65	5.20

Design descriptions are printed on back on top of gum.

1974, Nov. 5 Litho.

Christmas (Painting): 6p, Madonna of the Meadow, by Giovanni Bellini.

314	A57	4p	gold & multi	.60	.42
315	A57	6p	gold & multi	1.10	.70

Churchill, Parliament and Big Ben — A58

Design: 20p, Churchill and King George V-class battleship.

1974, Nov. 30 *Perf. 14x14½*

316	A58	6p	violet & multi	.35	.35
317	A58	20p	multicolored	.90	.90
a.			Souvenir sheet of 2, #316-317	3.00	3.00

Sir Winston Churchill (1874-1965).

Uniform Type of 1969

Uniforms: 4p, Officer, East Surrey Regiment, 1846. 6p, Private, Highland Light Infantry, 1777. 10p, Officer, Coldstream Guards, 1704. 20p, Sergeant, Gibraltar Regiment, 1974.

1975, Mar. 14 Wmk. 373 *Perf. 14*

318	A42	4p	multicolored	.32	.25
319	A42	6p	multicolored	.50	.42
320	A42	10p	multicolored	1.00	.70
321	A42	20p	multicolored	2.00	1.50
			Nos. 318-321 (4)	3.82	2.87

Design descriptions are printed on back on top of gum.

Girl Guides
Emblem
A59

1975, Oct. 10   *Perf. 13¹/₂x13*
322 A59   5p violet, gold & blue   .35   .35
323 A59   7p red brn, gold & blk   .52   .52
324 A59 15p ocher, silver & blk   1.10 1.10
       Nos. 322-324 (3)   1.97 1.97

Girl Guides, 50th anniversary.

Child and   Bruges Madonna, by
Bird — A60   Michelangelo — A61

Designs: b, Angel playing lute. c, Singing boy. d,
Mother and children. e, Praying child. f, Child and
lamb.

1975, Nov. 25   *Perf. 14x14¹/₂*
325   Block of 6   3.00 3.00
  a.-f. A60 6p any single   .48   .48

Christmas. No. 325 printed in sheets of 60 containing 10 blocks of 6 (3x2) stamps with horizontal
and vertical gutters between blocks.

1975, Dec. 17   Litho.   *Perf. 14x13¹/₂*
Sculptures by Michelangelo: 9p, Traddei
Madonna. 15p, Pietà.
326 A61   6p violet blk & multi   .28   .28
327 A61   9p black brn & multi   .45   .45
328 A61 15p dk purple & multi   .75   .75
  a.   Souvenir booklet   5.50
       Nos. 326-328 (3)   1.48 1.48

500th birth anniv. of Michelangelo Buonarroti
(1475-1564), Italian sculptor, painter and architect.
No. 328a contains 2 self-adhesive panes printed
on peelable paper backing with stamp dealer's
advertisements on back. One pane of 6 contains 2
each similar to Nos. 326-328; the other pane of 3
contains one each similar to Nos. 326-328. Stamps
are imperf. x roulette.

American
Bicentennial
Emblem, Arms of   Holy Family — A63
Gibraltar — A62

1976, May 28   *Perf. 14x14¹/₂*
329 A62 25p multicolored   1.00   .90
  a.   Souvenir sheet of 4   4.50 4.50

American Bicentennial. No. 329a is rouletted all
around.

Uniform Type of 1969

Uniforms: 1p, Suffolk Regiment, 1795. 6p,
Northamptonshire Regiment, 1779. 12p, Lanca-
shire Fusiliers, 1793. 25p, Royal Army Ordinance
Corps. 1896.

1976, July 21   *Perf. 14*
330 A42   1p multicolored   .15   .15
331 A42   6p multicolored   .30   .20
332 A42 12p multicolored   .75   .45
333 A42 25p multicolored   1.50 1.10
       Nos. 330-333 (4)   2.70 1.90

Design descriptions printed on back on top of
gum.

1976, Nov. 3   Litho.   Wmk. 373
Stained Glass Windows: 9p, St. Bernard of
Clairvaux. 12p, St. John the Evangelist. 20p, Archangel Michael.
334 A63   6p ultra & multi   .32   .25
335 A63   9p brt green & multi   .40   .32
336 A63 12p orange & multi   .55   .42
337 A63 20p dk carmine & multi   1.25   .75
       Nos. 334-337 (4)   2.52 1.74

Christmas.

Elizabeth II and
Royal Crest — A64

1977, Feb. 7   Litho.   *Perf. 14x13¹/₂*
338 A64   6p multicolored   .30   .30
339 A64 £1 multicolored   3.25 3.25
  a.   Souv. sheet of 2, #338-339, perf. 13 5.50 5.00

25th anniv. of the reign of Queen Elizabeth II.
#338-339 issued in sheets of 9.

Red
Mullet — A65

Designs: ¹/₂p, 3p, 9p, 15p, 25p, Flowers. 1p, 4p,
10p, 50p, Fish. 2p, 5p, 12p, £1, Butterflies. 2¹/₂p,
6p, 20p, £2, Birds. ¹/₂p, 2¹/₂p, 3p, 6p, 9p, 15p,
20p, 25p, £2, £5, vertical.

1977-80   *Perf. 14¹/₂x14, 14x14¹/₂*
340 A65   ¹/₂p Toothed orchid   .15   .15
341 A65   1p shown   .15   .15
342 A65   2p Large blue   .15   .15
343 A65   2¹/₂p Sardinian war-
                  bler   .15   .15
344 A65   3p Giant squill   .15   .15
345 A65   4p Gray wrasse   .15   .15
346 A65   5p Red admiral   .15   .15
347 A65   6p Black kite   .15   .15
348 A65   9p Scorpion vetch   .24   .24
349 A65 10p John Dory   .28   .28
350 A65 12p Clouded yellow   .35   .35
350A A65 15p Winged aspara-
                  gus pea   .35   .35
351 A65 20p Andouin's gull   .55   .55
352 A65 25p Barbary nut   .70   .70
353 A65 50p Swordfish   1.40 1.40
354 A65   £1 Swallowtail   2.75 2.75
355 A65   £2 Hoopoe   2.75 2.75
355A A65   £5 Coat of Arms   12.00 12.00
       Nos. 340-355A (18)   25.32 25.32

¹/₂p also comes inscribed 1982, the 4p, 10p,
12p, 25p & 50p inscribed 1981, 9p inscribed 1978.
Issued: £5, 5/16/79; 15p, 11/12/80; others,
4/1/77.

Gibraltar
No. 182
A66

Designs: 12p, Gibraltar No. 233, vert. 25p,
Gibraltar No. 294, vert.

1977, May 27   Litho.   *Perf. 14*
356 A66   6p multicolored   .20   .20
357 A66 12p multicolored   .42   .42
358 A66 25p multicolored   .90   .90
       Nos. 356-358 (3)   1.52 1.52

Amphilex 77 Intl. Phil. Exhib., Amsterdam, May
26-June 5. Issued in sheets of 6.

Annunciation, by
Rubens — A67

Rubens Paintings: 9p, Nativity. 12p, Adoration of
the Kings, horiz. 15p, Holy Family under Apple
Tree.

                Perf. 14x13¹/₂, 13¹/₂x14
1977, Nov. 2   **Litho.**
359 A67   3p multicolored   .15   .15
360 A67   9p multicolored   .32   .32
361 A67 12p multicolored   .42   .42
362 A67 15p multicolored   .52   .52
  a.   Souvenir sheet of 4, #359-362 2.25 2.25
       Nos. 359-362 (4)   1.41 1.41

Christmas and 400th birth anniv. of Peter Paul
Rubens.

Gibraltar
from Space
A68

Design: 25p, Strait of Gibraltar, aerial view.

1978, May 3   Litho.   *Perf. 13¹/₂*
363 A68 12p multicolored   .52   .45
              Souvenir Sheet
364 A68 25p multicolored   1.10   .95

No. 363 issued in sheets of 10.
No. 364 contains one stamp.

Holyroodhouse — A69

Royal Houses: 9p, St. James Palace. 12p, Sandringham House. 18p, Balmoral.

1978, June 12   Litho.   *Perf. 13¹/₂*
365 A69   6p multicolored   .18   .18
366 A69   9p multicolored   .28   .28
367 A69 12p multicolored   .35   .35
368 A69 18p multicolored   .55   .55
  a.   Souvenir booklet   4.00
       Nos. 365-368 (4)   1.36 1.36

25th anniv. of coronation of Queen Elizabeth II.
No. 368a contains 2 panes printed on peelable
paper backing with pictures of castles. One pane
contains 6 rouletted stamps, 3 each similar to Nos.
367-368; the other pane contains one 25p (Windsor Castle) rouletted stamp.

Sunderland
Seaplane
Landing
A70

Gibraltar and: 9p, Two-tiered Caudron taking off,
1918. 12p, Shackleton, 1953-1966. 16p, Hunter
warplane, 1954-1966. 18p, Nimrod, 1969-1978.

1978, Sept. 6   Litho.   *Perf. 14*
369 A70   3p multicolored   .15   .15
370 A70   9p multicolored   .35   .24
371 A70 12p multicolored   .45   .32
372 A70 16p multicolored   .60   .48
373 A70 18p multicolored   .75   .60
       Nos. 369-373 (5)   2.30 1.79

Royal Air Force, 60th anniversary.

Madonna with
Goldfinch, by
Dürer — A71

Christmas (Paintings by Albrecht Dürer): 5p,
Madonna with Animals. 9p, Nativity. 15p, Adoration of the Kings.

1978, Nov. 1   Litho.   *Perf. 14*
374 A71   5p multicolored   .20   .15
375 A71   9p multicolored   .32   .25
376 A71 12p multicolored   .50   .42
377 A71 15p multicolored   .55   .50
       Nos. 374-377 (4)   1.57 1.32

Rowland
Hill and
Gibraltar
No. 10
A72

Sir Rowland Hill (1795-1879), originator of
penny postage and: 9p, Gibraltar No. 274. 12p,
Parchment scroll with early postal regulations. 25p,
"Barred G" cancellation used on British stamps in
Gibraltar.

1979, Feb. 7   Litho.   *Perf. 13¹/₂*
378 A72   3p multicolored   .15   .15
379 A72   9p multicolored   .30   .28
380 A72 12p yellow grn & black   .45   .38
381 A72 25p yellow & black   .90   .75
       Nos. 378-381 (4)   1.80 1.56

Satellite Earth Station, Post Horn,
Telephone — A73

1979, May 16   *Perf. 13¹/₂x14*
382 A73   3p lt green & green   .22   .15
383 A73   9p lt brown & brown   .70   .25
384 A73 12p gray & ultra   .80   .35
       Nos. 382-384 (3)   1.72   .75

European telecommunications system.

Children, IYC
Emblem,
Nativity — A74

Designs: a, African girl. b, Chinese girl. c, Pacific
islands girl. d, American Indian girl. f, Scandinavian
boy.

         Litho.; Silver Embossed
1979, Nov. 14   *Perf. 14*
385   Block of 6   3.50 3.25
  a.-f. A74 12p any single

Christmas; IYC. No. 385 printed in sheets of 12
containing 2 No. 385 with vertical rouletted gutter
between.

Officers,
Exchange and
Commercial
Library,
1830 — A75

Gibraltar Police Force, 150th anniv.: 6p, Early and modern uniforms, Rock of Gibraltar. 12p, Traffic Officer, ambulance. 37p, Policeman and woman, Police Station, Irish Town.

1980, Feb. 5   Litho.   Wmk. 373
Perf. 14x14½

386	A75	3p multicolored	.15	.15
387	A75	6p multicolored	.20	.18
388	A75	12p multicolored	.40	.35
389	A75	37p multicolored	1.25	1.10
		Nos. 386-389 (4)	2.00	1.78

Archbishop Peter Amigo (1864-1949) — A76

Europa: No. 391, Gustavo Charles Bacarisas (1872-1971), artist. No. 392, John Mackintosh (1865-1940), philanthropist.

1980, May 6   Wmk. 373   Perf. 14½

390	A76	12p multicolored	.50	.40
391	A76	12p multicolored	.50	.40
392	A76	12p multicolored	.50	.40
		Nos. 390-392 (3)	1.50	1.20

Queen Mother Elizabeth Birthday Issue
Common Design Type

1980, Aug. 4   Litho.   Perf. 14

393	CD330	15p multicolored	.38	.38

"Victory" and Rock of Gibraltar, by Monamy Swaine — A77

Paintings: 3p, Lord Nelson, by John Francis Rigaud, 1781, vert. 15p, Lord Nelson, by William Beechey, vert. 40p, Victory Towed into Gibraltar by Clarkson Stanfield.

1980, Aug. 20   Litho.   Perf. 14

394	A77	3p multicolored	.22	.22
395	A77	9p multicolored	.35	.35
396	A77	15p multicolored	.50	.50
a.		Souvenir sheet	1.40	1.40
397	A77	40p multicolored	1.50	1.50
		Nos. 394-397 (4)	2.57	2.57

Horatio Nelson (1758-1805).

Holy Family A78

1980, Nov. 12

398	A78	15p shown	.50	.50
399	A78	15p Three kings	.50	.50
a.		Pair, #398-399	1.00	1.00

Christmas. No. 399a has continuous design.

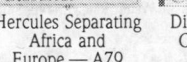

Hercules Separating Africa and Europe — A79

Dining Room, The Convent — A80

Europa: 15p, Hercules standing on Rock of Gibraltar and Morocco.

Perf. 14x13½

1981, Feb. 24   Wmk. 373

400	A79	9p multicolored	.38	.38
401	A79	15p multicolored	.65	.65

1981, May 22   Litho.   Perf. 14½x14

402	A80	4p shown	.15	.15
403	A80	14p King's Chapel	.45	.45
404	A80	15p Aerial view	.50	.50
405	A80	55p Cloister	1.85	1.85
		Nos. 402-405 (4)	2.95	2.95

450th anniv. of The Convent (Governor's residence, originally Franciscan monastery).

Prince Charles and Lady Diana A81

1981, July 27   Litho.   Perf. 14½

406	A81	£1 multicolored	3.25	3.25

Royal wedding. Se-tenant with decorative label.

Queen Elizabeth II — A82

1981, Sept. 29   Perf. 14½

407	A82	1p black	.15	.15
a.		Bklt. pane of 10 + 2 labels (2 #407, 2 #408, 6 #409)	3.00	
b.		Bklt. pane of 5 + label (#407, #408, 3 #409)	1.50	
408	A82	4p dark blue	.15	.15
409	A82	15p green	.40	.40
		Set value	.55	.55

Nos. 407-409 issued in booklets only.

Airmail Service, 50th Anniv. A83

1981, Sept. 29   Perf. 14½

410	A83	14p Paper plane	.45	.45
411	A83	15p Envelopes, aerogram	.50	.50
412	A83	55p Airplane circling globe	1.85	1.85
		Nos. 410-412 (3)	2.80	2.80

Intl. Year of the Disabled — A84

1981, Nov. 19   Litho.   Wmk. 373

413	A84	14p multicolored	.45	.45

Christmas A85

1981, Nov. 19   Perf. 14

414	A85	15p Children singing carols	.50	.50
415	A85	55p Decorated mailbox, vert.	1.85	1.85

Douglas DC-3 — A86

1982, Feb. 10   Litho.   Perf. 14

416	A86	1p shown	.15	.15
417	A86	2p Vickers Viking	.15	.15
a.		Wmk. 384, dated 1986 ('87)	.15	.15
418	A86	3p Airspeed Ambassador	.15	.15
419	A86	4p Vickers Viscount	.15	.15
420	A86	5p Boeing 727	.18	.18
a.		Wmk. 384, dated 1986 ('87)	.18	.18
421	A86	10p Vickers Vanguard	.35	.35
422	A86	14p Short Solent	.45	.45
423	A86	15p Fokker F-27 Friendship	.50	.50

424	A86	17p Boeing 737	.60	.60
425	A86	20p BAC One-eleven	.70	.70
426	A86	25p Lockheed Constellation	.85	.85
427	A86	50p De Havilland Comet 4B	1.75	1.75
428	A86	£1 Saro Windhover	2.50	2.50
429	A86	£2 Hawker Siddeley Trident 2	5.50	5.50
430	A86	£5 DH-89A Dragon Rapide	15.00	15.00
		Nos. 416-430 (15)	28.98	28.98

No. 425 exists with 1985 imprint.

Royal Navy Ship Crests — A87

1982, Apr. 14   Litho.   Perf. 14

431	A87	½p Opossum	.15	.15
432	A87	15½p Norfolk	.45	.45
433	A87	17p Fearless	.55	.55
434	A87	60p Rooke	1.90	1.90
		Nos. 431-434 (4)	3.05	3.05

See Nos. 449-452, 465-468, 474-477, 492-495, 501-504, 528-531, 552-555, 574-577, 587-590.

Europa A88

1982, June 11   Litho.   Perf. 14

435	A88	14p Planes preparing for takeoff	.45	.45
436	A88	17p Generals Eisenhower and Giraud	.60	.60

Operation Torch, 1943.

Chamber of Commerce Centenary — A89

Anniversaries: 15½p, British Forces Postal Service centenary. 60p, Scouting year.

1982, Sept. 22

437	A89	½p multicolored	.15	.15
438	A89	15½p multicolored	.42	.42
439	A89	60p multicolored	1.75	1.75
		Nos. 437-439 (3)	2.32	2.32

Intl. Direct Telephone Dialing System Inauguration — A90

1982, Oct. 1   Perf. 14½

440	A90	17p Map	.60	.60

Christmas A91

Perf. 14x14½

1982, Nov. 18   Litho.   Wmk. 373

441	A91	14p Holly	.45	.45
442	A91	17p Mistletoe	.60	.60

A92

1983, Mar. 14   Litho.   Perf. 14

443	A92	4p Local street	.15	.15
444	A92	14p Scouts on parade	.38	.38
445	A92	17p Flag, vert.	.50	.50
446	A92	60p Queen Elizabeth II, vert.	1.75	1.75
		Nos. 443-446 (4)	2.78	2.78

Commonwealth Day.

Europa A93

1983, May 21   Perf. 14x13½

447	A93	16p St. George's Hall	.48	.48
448	A93	19p Water catchments	.65	.65

Royal Navy Crest Type of 1982

1983, July 1   Litho.   Perf. 14

449	A87	4p Faulknor	.15	.15
450	A87	14p Renown	.38	.38
451	A87	17p Ark Royal	.50	.50
452	A87	60p Sheffield	1.75	1.75
		Nos. 449-452 (4)	2.78	2.78

Fortresses A94

1983, Sept. 13   Perf. 13½x14

453	A94	4p Landport Gate, 1729	.15	.15
454	A94	17p Koehler gun, 1782	.45	.45
455	A94	77p King's Bastion, 1799	2.00	2.00
a.		Souvenir sheet of 3, #453-455	3.00	3.00
		Nos. 453-455 (3)	2.60	2.60

Christmas A95

Raphael Paintings.

1983, Nov. 17   Litho.   Perf. 14

456	A95	4p Adoration of the Magi	.15	.15
457	A95	17p Madonna of Foligno, vert.	.55	.55
458	A95	60p Sistine Madonna, vert.	1.90	1.90
		Nos. 456-458 (3)	2.60	2.60

Europa (1959-1984) — A96

Intl. Postal and Telecommunication Links.

1984, Mar. 6   Litho.   Perf. 14½

459	A96	17p No. 98	.60	.60
460	A96	23p Communications circuit	.75	.75

Field Hockey — A97

1984, May 25　Litho.　Perf. 14
461 A97 20p shown .60 .60
462 A97 21p Basketball .65 .65
463 A97 26p Rowing .75 .75
464 A97 29p Soccer .85 .85
　Nos. 461-464 (4) 2.85 2.85

Royal Navy Crest Type of 1982
1984, Sept. 21　Litho.　Perf. 13½x13
465 A87 20p Active .65 .65
466 A87 21p Foxhound .65 .65
467 A87 26p Valiant .80 .80
468 A87 29p Hood .90 .90
　Nos. 465-468 (4) 3.00 3.00

Christmas
A98

Perf. 14x14½
1984, Nov. 7　Litho.　Wmk. 373
469 A98 20p Parade float .55 .55
470 A98 80p Float, diff. 2.25 2.25

Europa Issue

Musical Symbols — A99

1985, Feb. 26　Photo.　Perf. 12½
Granite Paper
471 A99 20p multi, diff. .60 .60
472 A99 29p shown .85 .85

Save the Children Fund — A100

Designs: Globe and legend in various positions.

1985, May 3　Litho.　Perf. 13x13½
473　Strip of 4 3.00 3.00
a.-d. A100 26p any single .70 .70

Royal Navy Crests Type of 1982
1985, July 3　Litho.　Perf. 14
474 A87 4p Duncan .15 .15
475 A87 9p Fury .20 .20
476 A87 21p Firedrake .52 .52
477 A87 80p Malaya 1.90 1.90
　Nos. 474-477 (4) 2.77 2.77

Intl. Youth Year — A101

1985, Sept. 6　Perf. 14½
478 A101 4p Emblem .15 .15
479 A101 20p Hands, diamond .52 .52
480 A101 80p Girl Guides anniv. emblem 2.00 2.00
　Nos. 478-480 (3) 2.67 2.67

St. Joseph's Parish Church, Cent. — A102　　Creche, Detail — A103

Perf. 13½ x Roulette 7 Between, 13½
1985, Oct. 25　Wmk. 373　Litho.
481 A102 Pair .24 .24
a.　4p Centenary seal .15 .15
b.　4p Church .15 .15
c.　No. 481a, perf. 13½ on 4 sides .15 .15
482 A103 80p multicolored 2.25 2.25

Christmas. Nos. 481a-481b rouletted between. Printed in sheets of 10 pairs with the bottom row containing 5 No. 481c. Strips of 3, Nos. 481a-481c exist.

Europa A104

1986, Feb. 10　Litho.　Perf. 13x13½
483 A104 22p Butterfly, house .65 .65
484 A104 29p Seagull, hotel .85 .85

Postage Stamp Cent. — A105

Elizabeth II, 60th Birthday — A106

1986, Mar. 25　Perf. 13½x13
485 A105 4p No. 18 .15 .15
486 A105 22p No. 42 .68 .68
487 A105 32p No. 67 .95 .95
488 A105 36p No. 118 1.10 1.10

Size: 32x48mm
Perf. 14
489 A105 44p No. 131 1.40 1.40
　Nos. 485-489 (5) 4.28 4.28

Souvenir Sheet
490 A105 29p No. 2 .85 .85

1986, May 22　Litho.　Perf. 14
491 A106 £1 multicolored 3.00 3.00

Royal Naval Crests Type of 1982
1986, Aug. 28　Litho.　Perf. 14
492 A87 22p Lightning .62 .62
493 A87 29p Hermione .82 .82
494 A87 32p Laforey .90 .90
495 A87 44p Nelson 1.25 1.25
　Nos. 492-495 (4) 3.59 3.59

Guns and Artillery — A111

Designs: 1p, 13-inch mortar, 1783. 2p, 6-inch Coast, 1909. 3p, 8-inch Howitzer, 1783. 4p, Bofors L40/70, 1951. 5p, 100-ton RML, 1882. 10p, 5.25 HAA, 1953. 18p, 25-pounder Gun-howitzer, 1943. 19p, 64-pounder RML, 1873. 22p, 12-pounder, 1758. 50p, 10-inch RML, 1870. £1, Russian 24-pounder, 1854. £3, 9.2-inch Coast Mk. 10, 1935. £5, 24-pounder, 1779.

1987, June 1　Wmk. 373　Perf. 12½
508 A111 1p multicolored .15 .15
509 A111 2p multicolored .15 .15
510 A111 3p multicolored .15 .15
511 A111 4p multicolored .15 .15
512 A111 5p multicolored .15 .15

Christmas, Intl. Peace Year — A107

1986, Oct. 14　Litho.　Perf. 14½x14
496 A107 18p St. Mary the Crowned Cathedral .55 .55
497 A107 32p St. Andrew's Church .95 .95

Souvenir Sheet

Wedding of Prince Andrew and Sarah Ferguson — A108

1986, Aug. 28　Litho.　Perf. 15
498 A108 44p multicolored 1.50 1.50

Europa — A109

1987, Feb. 17　Wmk. 384　Perf. 15
499 A109 22p Neptune House .70 .70
500 A109 29p Ocean Heights .90 .90

Royal Navy Crests Type of 1982
1987, Apr. 2　Perf. 13½x13
501 A87 18p Wishart .60 .60
502 A87 22p Charybdis .72 .72
503 A87 32p Antelope 1.05 1.05
504 A87 44p Eagle 1.50 1.50
　Nos. 501-504 (4) 3.87 3.87

Warrant Granted to the Royal Engineers, 200th Anniv. — A110

1987, Apr. 25　Wmk. 373　Perf. 14½
505 A110 18p Victoria Stadium .55 .55
506 A110 32p Casket, Freedom Scroll 1.00 1.00
507 A110 44p Monogram 1.35 1.35
　Nos. 505-507 (3) 2.90 2.90

513 A111 10p multicolored .28 .28
514 A111 18p multicolored .45 .45
515 A111 19p multicolored .52 .52
516 A111 22p multicolored .55 .55
517 A111 50p multicolored 1.40 1.40
518 A111 £1 multicolored 2.75 2.75
519 A111 £3 multicolored 8.00 8.00
520 A111 £5 multicolored 14.00 14.00
　Nos. 508-520 (13) 28.70 28.70

For surcharge see No. 595.

Christmas A112

1987, Nov. 12　Wmk. 384　Perf. 14½
521 A112 4p Three Wise Men .15 .15
522 A112 22p Holy Family .60 .60
523 A112 44p Shepherds 1.25 1.25
　Nos. 521-523 (3) 2.00 2.00

Europa A113

Transport and communication: No. 524, Rock of Gibraltar, Cruise Ship. No. 525, Passenger jet, yacht, dish aerial. No. 526, Bus, buggy. No. 527, Rock of Gibraltar, automobile, telephone.

Perf. 14½x14 on 3 Sides; Rouletted Between
1988, Feb. 16　Litho.　Wmk. 373
524 A113 22p multicolored .85 .85
525 A113 22p multicolored .85 .85
a.　Pair, #524-525 1.75
526 A113 32p multicolored 1.20 1.20
527 A113 32p multicolored 1.20 1.20
a.　Pair, #526-527 2.50
　Nos. 524-527 (4) 4.10 4.10

Nos. 525a, 527a have continuous design.

Royal Navy Crests Type of 1982
Perf. 13½x13
1988, Apr. 7　Wmk. 384
528 A87 18p Clyde .58 .58
529 A87 22p Foresight .72 .72
530 A87 32p Severn 1.05 1.05
531 A87 44p Rodney 1.45 1.45
　Nos. 528-531 (4) 3.80 3.80

Birds — A114

1988, June 15　Wmk. 373　Perf. 14
532 A114 4p Bee eater .15 .15
533 A114 22p Common puffin .85 .85
534 A114 32p Honey buzzard 1.20 1.20
535 A114 44p Blue rock thrush 1.70 1.70
　Nos. 532-535 (4) 3.90 3.90

Operation Raleigh, 1984-88 A115

Designs: 19p, Square-rigger. 22p, Sir Walter Raleigh and expedition emblem. 32p, Maps and modern transport ship Sir Walter Raleigh. 44p, Ship Sir Walter Raleigh.

Perf. 13x13½
1988, Sept. 14　Litho.　Wmk. 373
536 A115 19p multicolored .65 .65
537 A115 22p multicolored .75 .75
538 A115 32p multicolored 1.10 1.10
　Nos. 536-538 (3) 2.50 2.50

Souvenir Sheet
539　Sheet of 2, #537, 539a 2.25 2.25
a. A115 44p multicolored 1.50 1.50

400th anniv. of Sir Walter Raleigh's voyage to the New World to establish the 1st English-speaking colony, in what is now North Carolina.

Christmas — A116

Children's drawings: 4p, Snowman, by Rebecca Falero. 22p, Nativity, by Dennis Penalver. 44p, Santa Claus, by Gavin Key.

1988, Nov. 2   Wmk. 384   Perf. 14
540 A116 4p multicolored .15 .15
541 A116 22p multicolored .80 .80

Size: 25x33mm
542 A116 44p multicolored 1.60 1.60
Nos. 540-542 (3) 2.55 2.55

Europa
A117

Children's toys: 32p, Doll, doll house, puppy, ball, boat.

Perf. 13x13¹/₂
1989, Feb. 15   Wmk. 384
543 A117 25p shown .90 .90
544 A117 32p multicolored 1.15 1.15

Gibraltar Regiment, 50th Anniv. — A118
Intl. Red Cross, 125th Anniv. — A119

Perf. 13¹/₂x13
1989, Apr. 28   Wmk. 373
545 A118 4p The Port Sergeant .16 .16
546 A118 22p Regimental colors, Queen's colors .85 .85
547 A118 32p Drum Major 1.25 1.25
Nos. 545-547 (3) 2.26 2.26

Souvenir Sheet
548 Sheet of 2, Nos. 546, 548a 2.55 2.55
a. A118 44p Regimental arms 1.70 1.70

Perf. 15x14¹/₂
1989, July 7   Wmk. 384
549 A119 25p Mother and child .85 .85
550 A119 32p Malnourished children 1.10 1.10
551 A119 44p Accident victims 1.50 1.50
Nos. 549-551 (3) 3.45 3.45

Royal Navy Crests Type of 1982
1989, Sept. 7   Litho.   Perf. 14
552 A87 22p Blankney .72 .72
553 A87 25p Deptford .80 .80
554 A87 32p Exmoor 1.05 1.05
555 A87 44p Stork 1.40 1.40
Nos. 552-555 (4) 3.97 3.97

Souvenir Sheets

Coins — A120

No. 556: a, 1p Barbary Partridge. b, 2p Lighthouse at Europa Point. c, 10p Tower of Homage. d, 5p Barbary Ape.
No. 557: a, 50p Gibraltar Candytuft. b, £5 Pillars of Hercules. c, £2 Cannon from the Great Siege Period, 1779-1783. d, £1 Natl. coat of arms. e, Common obverse side of coins picturing Maklouf head of Queen Elizabeth II. f, 20p Our Lady of Europa.

1989, Oct. 10   Perf. 14¹/₂x15
556 Sheet of 4 .58 .58
a.-d. A120 4p any single .15 .15
557 Sheet of 6 4.35 4.35
a.-f. A120 22p any single .72 .72

Christmas A121

Perf. 14¹/₂
1989, Oct. 11   Litho.   Wmk. 384
558 A121 4p Santa's sleigh .15 .15
559 A121 22p Shepherds see star .75 .75
560 A121 32p Holy family 1.10 1.10
561 A121 44p Adoration of the Magi 1.50 1.50
Nos. 558-561 (4) 3.50 3.50

Europa 1990 — A122

Post offices: No. 562, G.P.O. exterior. No. 563, Carved crown and "VR" from p.o. archway and G.P.O. interior. No. 564, South District P.O. interior. No. 565, South District P.O. exterior.

Perf. 14¹/₂, Rouletted 9¹/₂ Between
1990, Mar. 6   Litho.   Unwmk.
562 A122 22p multicolored .75 .75
563 A122 22p multicolored .75 .75
a.   Pair, #562-563 1.50 1.50
564 A122 32p multicolored 1.10 1.10
565 A122 32p multicolored 1.10 1.10
a.   Pair, #564-565 2.25 2.25
Nos. 562-565 (4) 3.70 3.70

Pairs are rouletted between.

Early Fire Truck A123

1990, Apr. 2   Perf. 14¹/₂x14
566 A123 4p Early firemen, hose, vert. .15 .15
567 A123 22p shown .68 .68
568 A123 42p Modern truck 1.40 1.40
569 A123 44p Modern fireman, vert. 1.50 1.50
Nos. 566-569 (4) 3.73 3.73

Fire Service, 125th anniv.

Penny Black, 150th Anniv. — A124

Designs: 19p, Henry Corbould, Great Britain No. 1. 22p, 1st Royal Mail coach, Bristol-London. 32p, Sir Rowland Hill, Great Britain No. 1. 44p, Great Britain No. 1, Maltese Cross cancel.

1990, May 3   Perf. 13¹/₂x14
570 A124 19p multicolored .65 .65
571 A124 22p multicolored .75 .75
572 A124 32p multicolored 1.10 1.10
Nos. 570-572 (3) 2.50 2.50

Souvenir Sheet
573 A124 44p multicolored 1.50 1.50

Royal Navy Crest Type of 1982
1990, July 10   Litho.   Perf. 14
574 A87 22p Calpe .75 .75
575 A87 25p Gallant .85 .85
576 A87 32p Wrestler 1.10 1.10
577 A87 44p Greyhound 1.50 1.50
Nos. 574-577 (4) 4.20 4.20

Europort Model A125

1990, Oct. 10   Litho.   Perf. 14¹/₂
578 A125 22p shown .75 .75
579 A125 23p Building components .80 .80
580 A125 25p Land reclamation .88 .88
Nos. 578-580 (3) 2.43 2.43

Christmas A126
Europa A127

1990, Oct. 10   Perf. 13¹/₂
581 A126 4p shown .15 .15
582 A126 22p Santa Claus .75 .75
583 A126 42p Christmas tree 1.50 1.50
584 A126 44p Creche 1.55 1.55
Nos. 581-584 (4) 3.95 3.95

1991, Feb. 26   Litho.   Perf. 13¹/₂
585 A127 25p Spaceplane, satellite .88 .88
586 A127 32p ERS-1 satellite 1.10 1.10

Royal Navy Crest Type of 1982
1991, Apr. 9   Litho.   Perf. 13¹/₂x13
587 A87 4p Hesperus .15 .15
588 A87 21p Forester .75 .75
589 A87 22p Furious .78 .78
590 A87 62p Scylla 2.20 2.20
Nos. 587-590 (4) 3.88 3.88

Birds A128

1991, May 30   Litho.   Perf. 13¹/₂
591 A128 13p Black stork .45 .45
592 A128 13p Egyptian vulture .45 .45
593 A128 13p Barbary partridge .45 .45
594 A128 13p Shag .45 .45
a.   Block of 4, #591-594 1.80 1.80

World Wildlife Fund.

No. 519 Surcharged

≡≡   £1.05

Perf. 12¹/₂
1991, May 30   Litho.   Wmk. 373
595 A111 £1.05 on £3 multi 3.60 3.60

Views of Gibraltar A129

Paintings: 22p, North View of Gibraltar, by Gustavo Bacarisas (1873-1971). 26p, Parson's Lodge, by Elena Mifsud (1906-1989). 32p, Governor's Parade, by Jacobo Azabury, OBE (1890-1980). 42p, Waterport Wharf, by Rudesindo Mannia (1899-1982), vert.

1991, Sept. 10   Litho.   Perf. 15x14
596 A129 22p multicolored .75 .75
597 A129 26p multicolored .90 .90
598 A129 32p multicolored 1.10 1.10

Perf. 14x15
599 A129 42p multicolored 1.45 1.45
Nos. 596-599 (4) 4.20 4.20

Christmas A130

Christmas carols: 4p, Once in Royal David's City. 24p, Silent Night. 25p, Angels We Have Heard on High. 49p, O Come All Ye Faithful.

1991, Oct. 15   Litho.   Perf. 14¹/₂
600 A130 4p multicolored .15 .15
601 A130 24p multicolored .85 .85
602 A130 25p multicolored .88 .88
603 A130 49p multicolored 1.70 1.70
Nos. 600-603 (4) 3.58 3.58

Souvenir Sheet

Phila Nippon '91 — A131

1991, Nov. 15
604 A131 £1.05 Plain tiger 3.75 3.75

Queen Elizabeth II's Accession to the Throne, 40th Anniv.
Common Design Type
Wmk. 373
1992, Feb. 6   Litho.   Perf. 14
605 CD349 4p multicolored .15 .15
606 CD349 20p multicolored .70 .70
607 CD349 24p multicolored .85 .85
608 CD349 44p multicolored 1.55 1.55
609 CD349 54p multicolored 1.90 1.90
Nos. 605-609 (5) 5.15 5.15

Discovery of America, 500th Anniv. — A132

1992, Feb. 6   Unwmk.   Perf. 14¹/₂
610 A132 24p Columbus, Santa Maria .85 .85
611 A132 24p Map, Nina .85 .85
a.   Pair, #610-611 1.70 1.70
612 A132 34p Map, Pinta 1.20 1.20
613 A132 34p Map, sailor 1.20 1.20
a.   Pair, #612-613 2.40 2.40
Nos. 610-613 (4) 4.10 4.10

Europa. Printed in sheets containing 4 pairs.

Around the World Yacht Rally, 1991-92 A133

Compass rose, sail and maps of routes through: 21p, Atlantic Ocean, vert. 24p, Malay Archipelago. 25p, Indian Ocean. 49p, Mediterranean and Red Seas, vert.

1992, Apr. 15   Litho.   Perf. 13¹/₂
614 A133 21p multicolored .75 .75
615 A133 24p multicolored .85 .85
616 A133 25p multicolored .90 .90
Nos. 614-616 (3) 2.50 2.50

Souvenir Sheet

617	A133	Sheet of 2, #614 & 617a	2.45	2.45
a.		A133 49p multicolored	1.70	1.70

Anglican Diocese of Gibraltar, 150th Anniv. A134

Designs: 4p, Holy Trinity Cathedral, vert. 24p, Crest and map. 44p, Construction work on Cathedral during 1800's. 54p, Bishop Tomlinson, first Bishop of Diocese (1842-1863), vert.

1992, Aug. 21   Litho.   Perf. 14

618	A134	4p multicolored	.15	.15
619	A134	24p multicolored	.85	.85
620	A134	44p multicolored	1.55	1.55
621	A134	54p multicolored	1.90	1.90
		Nos. 618-621 (4)	4.45	4.45

Christmas — A135

Designs: 4p, Church of the Sacred Heart of Jesus. 24p, Cathedral of St. Mary the Crowned. 34p, St. Andrew's Church. 49p, St. Joseph's Church.

1992, Nov. 10   Litho.   Perf. 14

622	A135	4p multicolored	.15	.15
623	A135	24p multicolored	.85	.85
624	A135	34p multicolored	1.20	1.20
625	A135	49p multicolored	1.75	1.75
		Nos. 622-625 (4)	3.95	3.95

Contemporary Art — A136

Europa: No. 626, Masks of Comedy and Tragedy, record. No. 627, Painting, dancer, pottery. No. 628, Architecture, sculpture. No. 629, Video camera, 35mm film.

1993, Mar. 2   Litho.   Perf. 14½

626	A136	24p multicolored	.85	.85
627	A136	24p multicolored	.85	.85
a.		Pair, #626-627	1.70	1.70
628	A136	34p multicolored	1.20	1.20
629	A136	34p multicolored	1.20	1.20
a.		Pair, #628-629	2.40	2.40
		Nos. 626-629 (4)	4.10	4.10

Souvenir Sheet

World War II Warships A137

Designs: a, HMS Hood. b, HMS Ark Royal c, HMAS Waterhen. d, USS Gleaves.

1993, Apr. 27   Perf. 14

630	A137	24p Sheet of 4, #a.-d.	3.40	3.40

See Nos. 660, 684.

Architectural Heritage A138

1993-94   Litho.   Perf. 13

631	A138	1p Landport Gate	.15	.15
632	A138	2p St. Mary the Crowned	.15	.15
633	A138	3p Parsons Lodge Battery	.15	.15
634	A138	4p Moorish Castle	.15	.15
635	A138	5p General Post Office	.15	.15
636	A138	10p South Barracks	.30	.30
637	A138	21p American War Memorial	.62	.62
638	A138	24p Garrison Library	.70	.70
639	A138	25p Southport Gates	.72	.72
640	A138	26p Casemates Gate	.75	.75
641	A138	50p Central Police Station	1.45	1.45
642	A138	£1 Prince Edward's Gate	2.90	2.90
643	A138	£3 Lighthouse	8.75	8.75
644	A138	£5 Coat of arms, keys to fortress, vert.	15.00	15.00
		Nos. 631-644 (14)	31.94	31.94

Nos. 631, 635, 637, 639, 642-643 are vert.

Portions of the design on No. 644 were applied by a thermographic process producing a shiny, raised effect.

Issued: £5, 6/6/94; others, 6/28/93.

See Nos. 686-693.

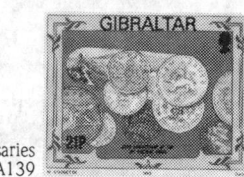

Anniversaries A139

1993, Sept. 21   Litho.   Perf. 13

645	A139	21p Coins	.60	.60
646	A139	24p Jet, biplane fighters	.70	.70
647	A139	34p Garrison Library	1.00	1.00
648	A139	49p Churchill, searchlights	1.40	1.40
		Nos. 645-648 (4)	3.70	3.70

First decimal coins, 25th anniv. Royal Air Force, 75th anniv. Garrison Library, bicent. Churchill's visit to Gibraltar, 50th anniv.

Christmas A140

Mice and: 5p, Christmas tree. 24p, Christmas cracker. 44p, Singing carols. 49p, Snowman.

1993, Nov. 16   Litho.   Perf. 13½

649	A140	5p multicolored	.15	.15
650	A140	24p multicolored	.65	.65
651	A140	44p multicolored	1.25	1.25
652	A140	49p multicolored	1.40	1.40
		Nos. 649-652 (4)	3.45	3.45

European Discoveries — A141

Europa: No. 653, Atoms exploding, Lord Penney (1909-91). No. 654, Chemistry flasks, polonium, radium, Marie Curie. No. 655, Diesel engine, Rudolf Diesel. No. 656, Telescope, Galileo.

1994, Mar. 1   Litho.   Perf. 13½

653	A141	24p multicolored	.70	.70
654	A141	24p multicolored	.70	.70
a.		Pair, #653-654	1.40	1.40
655	A141	34p multicolored	1.00	1.00
656	A141	34p multicolored	1.00	1.00
a.		Pair, #655-656	2.00	2.00
		Nos. 653-656 (4)	3.40	3.40

1994 World Cup Soccer Championships, US — A142

Designs: 26p, FIFA cup, US map, flag. 39p, Players, US map as playing field. 49p, Leg action, vert.

1994, Apr. 19   Litho.   Perf. 13½

657	A142	26p multicolored	.75	.75
658	A142	39p multicolored	1.10	1.10
659	A142	49p multicolored	1.40	1.40
		Nos. 657-659 (3)	3.25	3.25

Souvenir Sheet
World War II Warships Type of 1993

Designs: a, 5p, HMS Penelope. b, 25p, HMS Warspite. c, 44p, USS McLanahan. d, 49p, HNLMS Isaac Sweers.

1994, June 6   Litho.   Perf. 13½x13

660	A137	Sheet of 4, #a.-d.	3.75	3.75

Souvenir Sheet

PHILAKOREA '94 — A143

1994, Aug. 16   Litho.   Perf. 13

661	A143	£1.05 multicolored	3.25	3.25

Marine Life — A144

1994, Sept. 27   Litho.   Perf. 14

662	A144	21p Golden star coral	.65	.65
663	A144	24p Star fish	.75	.75
664	A144	34p Gorgonian sea fan	1.00	1.00
665	A144	49p Turkish wrasse	1.50	1.50
		Nos. 662-665 (4)	3.90	3.90

Intl. Olympic Committee, Cent. A145

1994, Nov. 22   Litho.   Perf. 14

666	A145	49p Discus	1.60	1.60
667	A145	54p Javelin	1.75	1.75

Christmas Songbirds A146

1994, Nov. 22   Perf. 13½

668	A146	5p Great tit, vert.	.16	.16
669	A146	24p Robin	.75	.75
670	A146	34p Blue tit	1.10	1.10
671	A146	54p Goldfinch, vert.	1.75	1.75
		Nos. 668-671 (4)	3.76	3.76

New Members in European Union A147

Flags: 24p, Austria. 26p, Finland. 34p, Sweden. 49p, Sweden, Finland, Austria, emblem of European Union.

1995, Jan. 3   Litho.   Perf. 14

672	A147	24p multicolored	.75	.75
673	A147	26p multicolored	.85	.85
674	A147	34p multicolored	1.10	1.10
675	A147	49p multicolored	1.50	1.50
		Nos. 672-675 (4)	4.20	4.20

Peace & Freedom A148

Europa: No. 676, Cross, barbed wire, text. No. 677, Rainbow, dove, hands. No. 678, Shackles, text. No. 679, Doves, hands.

1995, Feb. 28   Litho.   Perf. 13½

676	A148	24p multicolored	.75	.75
677	A148	24p multicolored	.75	.75
a.		Pair, #676-677	1.50	1.50
678	A148	34p multicolored	1.10	1.10
679	A148	34p multicolored	1.10	1.10
a.		Pair, #678-679	2.25	2.25
		Nos. 676-679 (4)	3.70	3.70

Island Games — A149

1995, May 8   Litho.   Perf. 14x13½

680	A149	24p Sailing	.75	.75
681	A149	44p Running	1.40	1.40
682	A149	49p Swimming	1.75	1.75
		Nos. 680-682 (3)	3.90	3.90
680a		Booklet pane of 3	2.25	
681a		Booklet pane of 3	4.25	
682a		Booklet pane of 3	5.25	
682b		Booklet pane, 1 each #680-682	4.00	
		Commemorative booklet, 1 each #680a-682b	16.00	

Souvenir Sheet

VE Day, 50th Anniv. — A150

Illustration reduced.

1995, May 8

683	A150	£1.05 multicolored	3.50	3.50

World War II Warships Type of 1993
Souvenir Sheet

Designs: a, 5p, HMS Calpe. b, 24p, HMS Victorious. c, 44p, USS Weehawken. d, 49p, FFS Savorgnan de Brazza.

1995, June 6   Litho.   Perf. 13½x14

684	A137	Sheet of 4, #a.-d.	4.00	4.00

Singapore '95 — A151

Orchids: a, 22p, Bee. b, 23p, Brown bee. c, 24p, Pyramidal. d, 25p, Mirror. e, 26p, Sawfly.

1995, Sept. 1   Litho.   Perf. 14x14½

685	A151	Strip of 5, #a.-e.	3.75	3.75

Architectural Heritage Type of 1993

1995, Sept. 1   Litho.   Perf. 13

686	A138	6p House of Assembly	.20	.20
687	A138	7p Bleak House	.20	.20
688	A138	8p Bust of Gen. Eliott	.25	.25
689	A138	9p Supreme Court Bldg.	.30	.30
690	A138	20p Convent	.65	.65
691	A138	30p St. Bernard's Hospital	.95	.95

692	A138	40p City Hall	1.25	1.25
693	A138	£2 Church of Sacred Heart of Jesus	6.25	6.25
		Nos. 686-693 (8)	10.05	10.05

Nos. 686, 688, 691, 693 are vert.

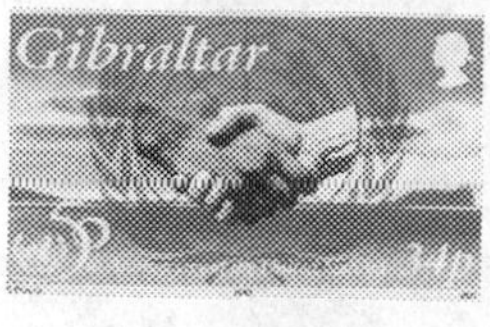

UN, 50th Anniv. A152

1995, Oct. 24 Litho. *Perf. 13½*

694	A152	34p shown	1.10	1.10
695	A152	49p Peace dove	1.50	1.50

Miniature Sheets of 4 + 4 Labels

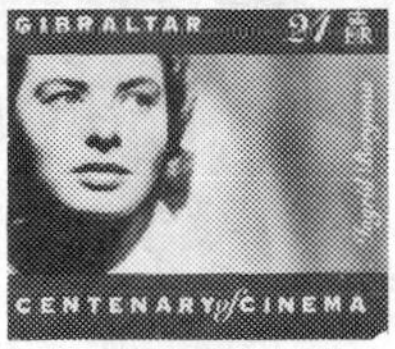

Motion Pictures, Cent. — A153

Designs: No. 696: a, Ingrid Bergman. b, Vittorio De Sica. c, Marlene Dietrich. d, Laurence Olivier.
No. 697: a, 38p, Audrey Hepburn. b, 25p, Romy Schneider. c, 28p, Yves Montand. d, 5p, Marilyn Monroe.

1995, Nov. 13 Litho. *Perf. 14½x14*

696	A153	24p #a.-d.	3.00	3.00
697	A153	#a.-d.	3.00	3.00

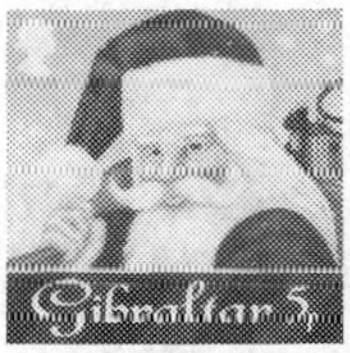

Christmas A154

Designs: 5p, Santa Claus. 24p, Sack of toys. 34p, Reindeer. 54p, Santa with sleigh, reindeer flying over rooftops.

1995, Nov. 27 *Perf. 14*

698	A154	5p multicolored	.15	.15
699	A154	24p multicolored	.75	.75
700	A154	34p multicolored	1.10	1.10
701	A154	54p multicolored	1.75	1.75
		Nos. 698-701 (4)	3.75	3.75

POSTAGE DUE STAMPS

Catalogue values for unused stamps in this section are for Never Hinged items.

D1

1956, Dec. 1 Wmk. 4 Typo. *Perf. 14*

Chalky Paper

J1	D1	1p green	3.25	4.00
J2	D1	2p brown	6.00	6.00
J3	D1	4p ultramarine	7.50	9.25
		Nos. J1-J3 (3)	16.75	19.25

"p" instead of "d"

Perf. 17½x18

1971, Feb. 15 Typo. Wmk. 314

Chalky Paper

J4	D1	½p green	.62	.62
J5	D1	1p dark brown	.62	.62
J6	D1	2p dark blue	1.00	1.00
		Nos. J4-J6 (3)	2.24	2.24

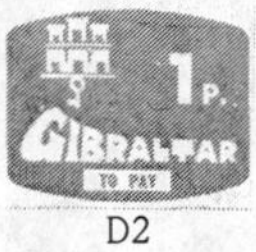

D2

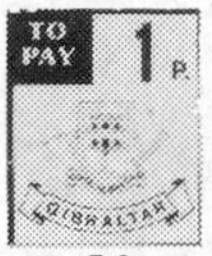

D3

Perf. 14x13½

1976, Oct. 13 Litho. Wmk. 373

J7	D2	1p orange	.15	.15
J8	D2	3p bright ultra	.15	.15
J9	D2	5p vermilion	.15	.18
J10	D2	7p bright red lilac	.25	.25
J11	D2	10p gray	.38	.38
J12	D2	20p green	.75	.75
		Nos. J7-J12 (6)	1.83	1.86

1984, July 2 *Perf. 14½x14*

J13	D3	1p black	.15	.15
J14	D3	3p red	.15	.15
J15	D3	5p blue	.15	.15
J16	D3	10p sky blue	.25	.25
J17	D3	25p lilac	.65	.65
J18	D3	50p orange	1.25	1.25
J19	D3	£1 green	2.50	2.50
		Nos. J13-J19 (7)	5.10	5.10

WAR TAX STAMP

No. 66 Overprinted **WAR TAX**

1918, Apr. Wmk. 3 *Perf. 14*

MR1	A14	½p green	.25	.25
	a.	Double overprint	750.00	

GILBERT AND ELLICE ISLANDS

'gil-bərt ən(d) 'e-ləs 'ī-lənds

LOCATION — Groups of islands in the Pacific Ocean northeast of Australia
GOVT. — British Crown Colony
AREA — 375 sq. mi.
POP. — 57,816 (est. 1973)
CAPITAL — Tarawa

The Gilbert group of which Butaritari, Tarawa and Tamana are the more important, is on the Equator. Ellice Islands, Phoenix Islands, Line Islands (Fanning, Washington and Christmas), and Ocean Island are included in the Colony. The islands were annexed by Great Britain in 1892 and formed into the Gilbert and Ellice Islands Colony in 1915 on request of the native governments.

The colony divided into the Gilbert Islands and Tuvalu, Jan. 1, 1976.

12 Pence = 1 Shilling
20 Shillings = 1 Pound
100 Cents = 1 Dollar (1966)

Catalogue values for unused stamps in this country are for Never Hinged items, beginning with Scott 52.

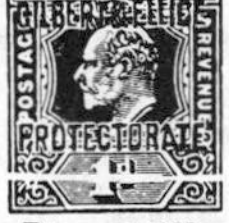

Edward VII A1

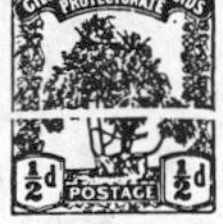

Pandanus A2

Stamps and Type of Fiji Overprinted in Black or Red

1911, Jan. 1 Wmk. 3 *Perf. 14*

Ordinary Paper

1	A1	½p green	10.50	*17.50*
2	A1	1p carmine	32.50	45.00
	a.	Pair, one without overprint		
3	A1	2p gray	7.50	*10.00*
4	A1	2½p ultramarine	16.00	*22.50*

Chalky Paper

5	A1	5p violet & ol grn	21.00	*47.50*
6	A1	6p violet	27.50	42.50
7	A1	1sh black, *green*	21.00	32.50
		Nos. 1-7 (7)	136.00	217.50

1911, Mar. Engr.

Ordinary Paper

8	A2	½p green	3.00	*10.00*
9	A2	1p carmine	1.60	*4.00*
10	A2	2p gray	1.60	*4.00*
11	A2	2½p ultramarine	1.60	*8.00*
		Nos. 8-11 (4)	7.80	*26.00*

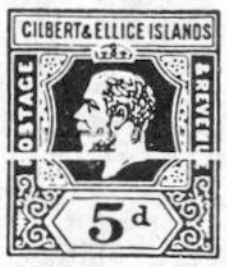

King George V — A3

For description of Dies I and II, see back of this section of the Catalogue.

Die I

1912-24 Typo.

14	A3	½p deep green	.55	*2.50*
15	A3	1p carmine	.80	*2.00*
	a.	1p scarlet	2.75	*5.50*
16	A3	2p gray ('16)	8.00	*15.00*
17	A3	2½p ultra ('16)	2.50	*4.25*

Chalky Paper

18	A3	3p vio, *yel* ('19)	2.25	*4.00*
19	A3	4p blk & red, *yel*	.80	*3.50*
20	A3	5p vio & ol grn	3.00	*11.00*
21	A3	6p vio & red vio	1.90	*5.50*
22	A3	1sh black, *green*	3.75	*6.75*
23	A3	2sh vio & ultra, *bl*	9.50	*20.00*
24	A3	2sh6p blk & red, *bl*	11.00	*17.50*
25	A3	5sh grn & red, *yel*	27.50	*45.00*

Die II

26	A3	£1 vio & blk, *red* ('24)	775.00	*1,600.*
		Nos. 14-25 (12)	71.55	*137.00*

Die II

1921-27 Ordinary Paper Wmk. 4

27	A3	½p green	.30	*1.40*
28	A3	1p deep vio ('27)	.50	*1.75*
29	A3	1½p scarlet ('24)	1.00	*4.25*
30	A3	2p gray	3.75	*8.50*

Chalky Paper

31	A3	10sh green & red, *emer* ('24)	180.00	*325.00*
		Nos. 27-31 (5)	186.45	*340.90*

Silver Jubilee Issue
Common Design Type

1935, May 6 Engr. *Perf. 11x12*

33	CD301	1p black & ultra	1.50	1.75
34	CD301	1½p car & blue	1.10	1.25
35	CD301	3p ultra & brn	3.75	*5.00*
36	CD301	1sh brn vio & ind	10.00	*17.00*
		Nos. 33-36 (4)	16.35	*25.00*

Coronation Issue
Common Design Type

1937, May 12 *Perf. 13½x14*

37	CD302	1p dark purple	.15	.15
38	CD302	1½p carmine	.25	.25
39	CD302	3p bright ultra	.45	.45
		Nos. 37-39 (3)	.85	.85
		Set, never hinged	1.25	

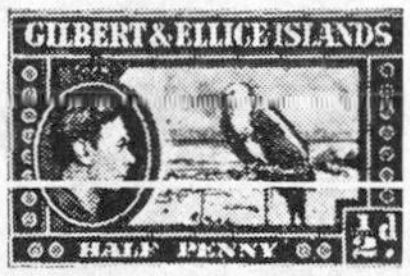

Great Frigate Bird — A4

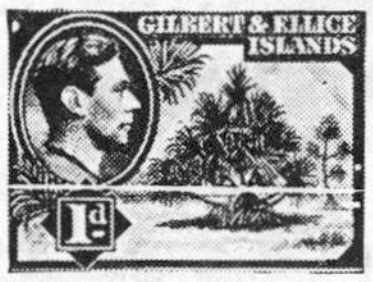

Pandanus — A5

Designs: 1½p, Canoe crossing reef. 2p, Canoe and boat house. 2½p, Islander's house. 3p, Seascape. 5p, Ellice Islands canoe. 6p, Coconut trees. 1sh, Phosphate loading jetty, Ocean Island. 2sh, Cutter "Nimanoa." 2sh6p, Gilbert Islands canoe. 5sh, Coat of arms of colony.

Perf. 11½x11 (Nos. 40, 43, 50), 12½ (Type A5), 13½ (Nos. 42, 44, 45, 48)

1939, Jan. 14 Engr. Wmk. 4

40	A4	½p dk grn & sl bl	.15	.15
41	A5	1p dk vio & brt bl green	.20	.20
42	A4	1½p car & black	.20	.20
43	A4	2p black & brn	.25	.25
44	A4	2½p ol grn & blk	.35	.35
45	A4	3p ultra & black	.25	.25
	a.	Perf. 12 ('55)	.50	.50
46	A5	5p dk brn & ultra	.75	.75
47	A5	6p dl vio & olive	.75	.75
48	A4	1sh gray bl & blk	.52	.52
	a.	Perf. 12 ('51)	3.00	3.00
49	A5	2sh red org & ultra	4.75	4.75
50	A4	2sh6p brt bl grn & bl	4.75	4.75
51	A5	5sh dp blue & red	6.50	6.50
		Nos. 40-51 (12)	19.42	19.42
		Set, never hinged	41.00	

Catalogue values for unused stamps in this section, from this point to the end of the section, are for Never Hinged items.

Peace Issue
Common Design Type

1946, Dec. 16 *Perf. 13½x14*

52	CD303	1p deep magenta	.15	.15
53	CD303	3p deep blue	.25	.25

Common Design Types pictured in section before Great Britain.

Silver Wedding Issue
Common Design Types

1949, Aug. 29 Photo. *Perf. 14x14½*

54	CD304	1p violet	.20	.20

Engraved; Name Typographed

Perf. 11½x11

55	CD305	£1 red	24.00	*47.50*

UPU Issue
Common Design Types

Engr.; Name Typo. on 2p, 3p

1949, Oct. 1 *Perf. 13½, 11x11½*

56	CD306	1p rose violet	.50	.50
57	CD307	2p gray black	1.10	1.10
58	CD308	3p indigo	1.65	1.65
59	CD309	1sh blue	3.75	3.75
		Nos. 56-59 (4)	7.00	7.00

Coronation Issue
Common Design Type

1953, June 2 Engr. *Perf. 13½x13*

60	CD312	2p gray & black	.85	.85

Types of 1939-42 with Portrait of Queen Elizabeth II, and

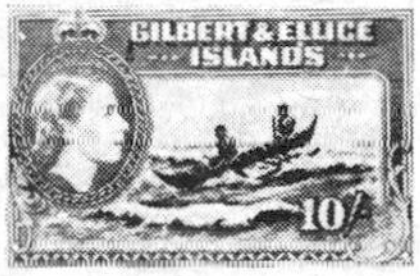

Canoe Crossing Reef — A6

Perf. 11½x11 (Nos. 61, 63, 70), 12½ (Type A5), 12 (Nos. 64-65, 68, 72)

1956, Aug. 1

61	A4	½p brt ultra & blk	.15	.15
62	A5	1p violet & olive	.15	.15
63	A4	2p dull pur & brt green	.20	.15
64	A4	2½p green & black	.25	.15
65	A4	3p dk car & black	.30	.25
66	A5	5p red orange & brt ultra	.70	.50
67	A5	6p dk gray & red brown	.90	.55
68	A4	1sh ol green & blk	1.40	.95
69	A5	2sh dk brown & brt ultra	5.50	3.75
70	A4	2sh6p dp ultra & rose red	6.50	4.25
71	A5	5sh green & blue	12.50	10.00
72	A6	10sh turq blue & blk	26.00	24.00
		Nos. 61-72 (12)	54.55	44.85

See Nos. 84-85.

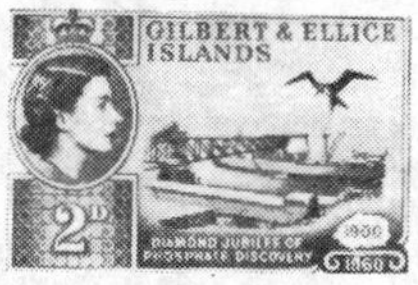

Loading Phosphate on Freighter — A7

Designs: 2½p, Original lump of phosphate. 1sh, Loading phosphate on truck, Ocean Island.

Wmk. 314

1960, May 1 Photo. *Perf. 12*

73	A7	2p rose lilac & green	.40	.30
74	A7	2½p olive & black	.55	.35
75	A7	1sh grnsh blue & blk	1.25	1.10
		Nos. 73-75 (3)	2.20	1.75

60th anniversary of the discovery of phosphate deposits at Ocean Island.

Freedom from Hunger Issue
Common Design Type

1963, June 4 *Perf. 14x14½*

76	CD314	10p ultramarine	4.50	3.50

Red Cross Centenary Issue
Common Design Type

1963, Sept. 2 Litho. *Perf. 13*

77	CD315	2p black & red	1.00	.40
78	CD315	10p ultra & red	5.75	5.25

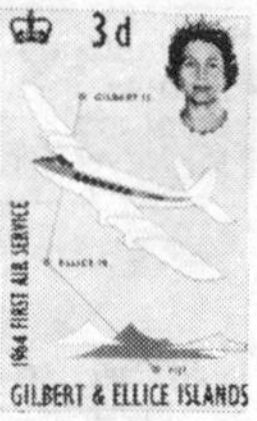

Plane and Fiji-Ellice-Gilbert Route — A8

Designs: 1sh, Eastern reef heron in flight, horiz. 3sh7p, Plane and Tarawa sailboat.

Perf. 11½x11, 11x11½

1964, July 20

79	A8	3p lt blue, bl & blk	.20	.15
80	A8	1sh dk blue, bl & blk	.40	.30
81	A8	3sh7p lt green, grn & blk	1.40	1.25
		Nos. 79-81 (3)	2.00	1.70

Inauguration of air service between Fiji and Gilbert and Ellice Islands.

Queen Types of 1956

Perf. 11½x11, 12½

1964-65 Engr. Wmk. 314

84	A4	2p dull pur & brt green	.95	.95
85	A5	6p dk gray & red brown	2.00	2.00

Issue dates: 2p, Oct. 30. 6p, Apr. 1965.

ITU Issue
Common Design Type

1965, June 4 Litho. *Perf. 11x11½*

87	CD317	3p dp org & turq blue	.20	.20
88	CD317	2sh6p grnsh bl & red lilac	1.75	1.75

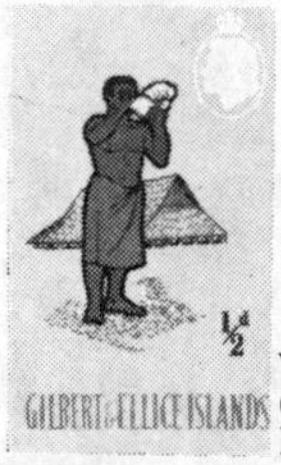

Village Elder Blowing Conch and Meeting House (Maneaba) — A9

Designs: 1p, Ellice Islanders torch fishing. 2p, Gilbertese girl weaving frangipani garland. 3p, Gilbertese woman dancing The Ruoia. 4p, Gilbertese man dancing. 5p, Gilbertese woman drawing water. 6p, Ellice kosu dance. 7p, Fatele taua dance, Ellice men. 1sh, Gilbertese woman harvesting taro roots (babai). 1sh6p, Ellice man and woman dancing fatele toka. 2sh, Ellice Islanders pounding taro roots. 3sh7p, Gilbertese sitting dance, ruoia, horiz. 5sh, Gilbertese boys playing stick game, horiz. 10sh, Ellice men beating box-drum, horiz. £1, Coat of arms, horiz.

Perf. 12x11, 11x12

1965, Aug. 16 Litho. Wmk. 314

89	A9	½p blue grn & multi	.15	.15
90	A9	1p vio bl & multi	.15	.15
91	A9	2p lt olive & multi	.15	.15
92	A9	3p red & multi	.15	.15
93	A9	4p purple & multi	.15	.15
94	A9	5p car rose & multi	.15	.15
95	A9	6p multicolored	.15	.15
96	A9	7p brown & multi	.25	.25
97	A9	1sh bl vio & multi	.40	.40
98	A9	1sh6p yel & multi	.80	.80
99	A9	2sh multicolored	1.10	1.10
100	A9	3sh7p ultra & multi	2.50	2.50
101	A9	5sh multicolored	3.25	3.25
102	A9	10sh green & multi	5.75	5.75
103	A9	£1 blue & multi	9.00	9.00
		Nos. 89-103 (15)	24.10	24.10

See #135-149. For surcharges see #110-124.

Intl. Cooperation Year Issue
Common Design Type

1965, Oct. 25 Litho. *Perf. 14½*

104	CD318	½p blue grn & cl	.15	.15
105	CD318	3sh7p lt violet & grn	1.25	1.25

Churchill Memorial Issue
Common Design Type

1966, Jan. 24 Photo. *Perf. 14*

Design in Black, Gold and Carmine Rose

106	CD319	½p brt blue	.15	.15
107	CD319	3p green	.15	.15
108	CD319	3sh brown	1.40	1.40
109	CD319	3sh7p violet	1.65	1.65
		Nos. 106-109 (4)	3.35	3.35

Nos. 89-103 Surcharged with New Value and Three Bars

Perf. 12x11, 11x12

1966, Feb. 14 Litho.

110	A9	1c on 1p multi	.15	.15
111	A9	2c on 2p multi	.15	.15
112	A9	3c on 3p multi	.15	.15
113	A9	4c on ½p multi	.20	.20
114	A9	5c on 6p multi	.20	.20
115	A9	6c on 4p multi	.30	.30
116	A9	8c on 5p multi	.35	.35
117	A9	10c on 1sh multi	.50	.50
118	A9	15c on 7p multi	.75	.75
119	A9	20c on 1sh6p multi	.95	.95
120	A9	25c on 2sh multi	1.25	1.25
121	A9	35c on 3sh7p multi	1.75	1.75
122	A9	50c on 5sh multi	2.75	2.75
123	A9	$1 on 10sh multi	3.75	3.75
124	A9	$2 on £1 multi	7.75	7.75
		Nos. 110-124 (15)	20.95	20.95

World Cup Soccer Issue
Common Design Type

1966, July 1 Litho. *Perf. 14*

125	CD321	3c multicolored	.15	.15
126	CD321	35c multicolored	1.10	1.10

WHO Headquarters Issue
Common Design Type

1966, Sept. 20 Litho. *Perf. 14*

127	CD322	3c multicolored	.15	.15
128	CD322	12c multicolored	.95	.95

UNESCO Anniversary Issue
Common Design Type

1966, Dec. 1 Litho. *Perf. 14*

129	CD323	5c "Education"	.40	.40
130	CD323	10c "Science"	1.10	1.10
131	CD323	20c "Culture"	2.50	2.50
		Nos. 129-131 (3)	4.00	4.00

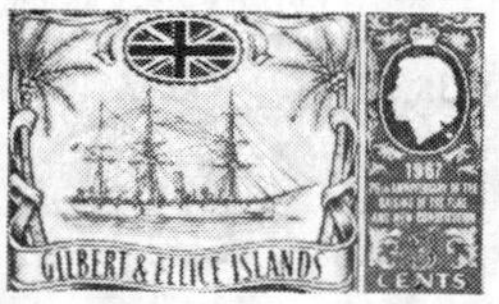

H.M.S. Royalist, 1892, and Union Jack A10

Designs: 10c, Cutter and canoe at trading post. 35c, Family.

Perf. 14½x14

1967, Sept. 1 Photo. Wmk. 314

132	A10	3c green, blue & red	.15	.15
133	A10	10c multicolored	.20	.20
134	A10	35c multicolored	.55	.55
		Nos. 132-134 (3)	.90	.90

75th anniv. as a British Protectorate.

Type of 1965

Perf. 12x11, 11x12

1968, Jan. 1 Litho. Wmk. 314

135	A9	1c like 1p	.15	.15
136	A9	2c like 2p	.15	.15
137	A9	3c like 3p	.15	.15
138	A9	4c like ½p	.15	.15
139	A9	5c like 6p	.20	.15
140	A9	6c like 4p	.22	.18
141	A9	8c like 5p	.25	.25
142	A9	10c like 1sh	.40	.35
143	A9	15c like 7p	.65	.60
144	A9	20c like 1sh6p	.90	.85
145	A9	25c like 2sh	1.40	1.10
146	A9	35c like 3sh7p	1.65	1.45
147	A9	50c like 5sh	2.00	1.65
148	A9	$1 like 10sh	4.25	3.50
149	A9	$2 like £1	8.00	6.75
		Nos. 135-149 (15)	20.52	17.43

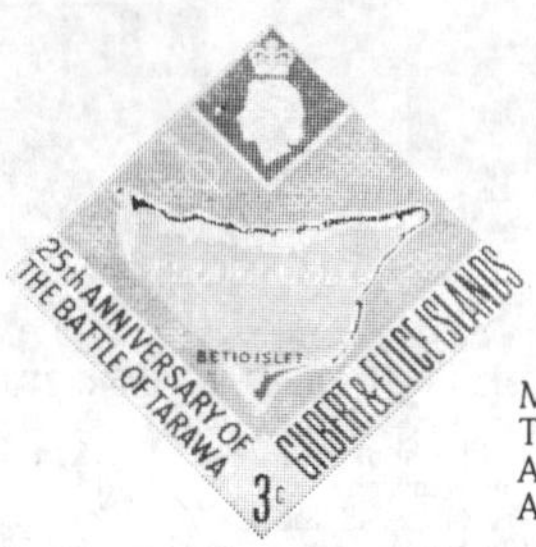

Map of Tarawa Atoll A11

Designs: 10c, US Marines wading ashore at Betio. 15c, Battle scene on Betio. 35c, Raising US and British flags on Betio.

1968, Nov. 21 Photo. *Perf. 14*

150	A11	3c multicolored	.15	.15
151	A11	10c multicolored	.20	.20
152	A11	15c multicolored	.30	.30
153	A11	35c multicolored	.75	.75
		Nos. 150-153 (4)	1.40	1.40

Battle of Tarawa against Japan, 25th anniv.

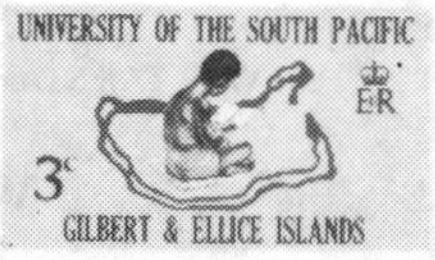

School Boy and Map of Abemama Atoll — A12

Designs: 10c, Secondary school boy and girl on map of Tarawa, with rest of Gilbert and Ellice Islands. 35c, Student in cap and grown on main Fiji island (Viti Levu) and map of South Pacific Islands.

1969, June 2 Litho. *Perf. 12½*

154	A12	3c dull org & multi	.15	.15
155	A12	10c black & multi	.25	.25
156	A12	35c dull grn & multi	.80	.80
		Nos. 154-156 (3)	1.20	1.20

1st anniv. of the University of the South Pacific in Fiji, and to show the progress of education in the area it serves.

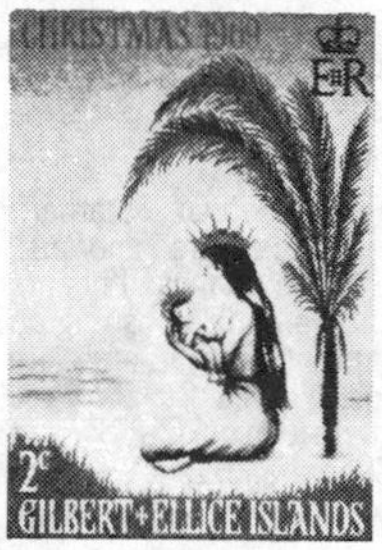

Polynesian Madonna — A13

1969, Oct. 20 *Perf. 11½*

157	A13	2c multicolored	.15	.15
158	A13	10c multicolored	.65	.65

Christmas.

Canceled to Order
The Philatelic Bureau of Gilbert and Ellice Islands began in 1970 to sell canceled sets of new issues. Values in the second ("used") column are for these canceled-to-order stamps.

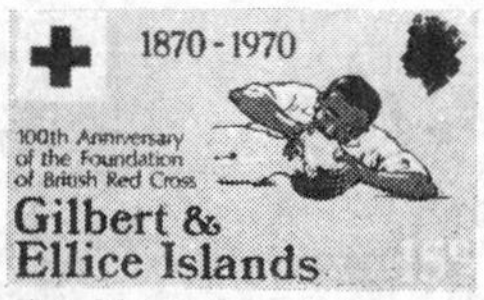

Mouth-to-Mouth Resuscitation — A14

1970, Mar. 9 Litho. *Perf. 14½*

159	A14	10c multi	.20	.15
160	A14	15c multi, diff.	.35	.30
161	A14	35c multi, diff.	1.00	1.00
		Nos. 159-161 (3)	1.55	1.45

Centenary of the British Red Cross.

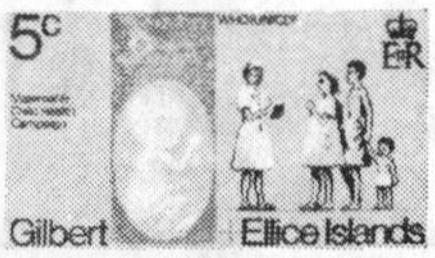

Mother and Child Care — A15

Designs: 10c, Woman physician and laboratory equipment. 15c, Chest X-ray and technician. 35c, Map of Gilbert and Ellice Islands and UN emblem.

Perf. 12½x13

1970, June 26 Litho. Wmk. 314

162	A15	5c lilac & multi	.15	.15
163	A15	10c black, gray & red	.20	.20
164	A15	15c yellow & multi	.35	.35
165	A15	35c blue grn, bl & blk	.80	.80
		Nos. 162-165 (4)	1.50	1.50

25th anniv. of the United Nations.

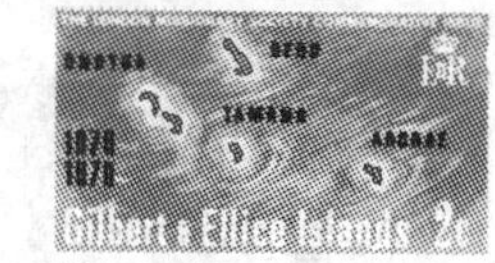

Map of Onotoa, Beru, Tamana and Arorae Islands A16

Designs: 10c, Sailing ship "John Williams III", vert. 25c, Rev. Samuel James Whitmee, vert. 35c, Map of Islands and steamship "John Williams VII."

Perf. 14x14½, 14½x14

1970, Sept. 1 Litho. Wmk. 314

166	A16	2c blue & multi	.15	.15
167	A16	10c brt green & black	.30	.30
168	A16	25c lt ultra & red brn	.70	.70
169	A16	35c ver, blk & lt gray	.95	.95
		Nos. 166-169 (4)	2.10	2.10

Centenary of the landing in the Southern Gilbert Islands by the first missionaries of the London Missionary Society.

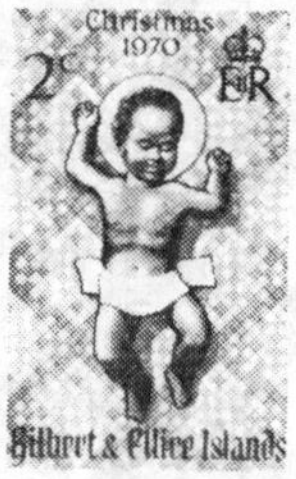

Island Child with Halo on Pandanus Mat — A17

Christmas: 10c, Sanctuary of New Tarawa Cathedral. 35c, Three Gilbertese sailing canoes within Star of Bethlehem.

1970, Oct. 3 *Perf. 14½*

170	A17	2c ocher & multi	.15	.15
171	A17	10c ocher & multi	.25	.25
172	A17	35c pink & multi	.90	.90
		Nos. 170-172 (3)	1.30	1.30

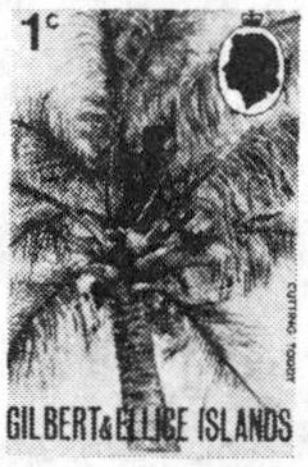

Harvesting Copra — A18

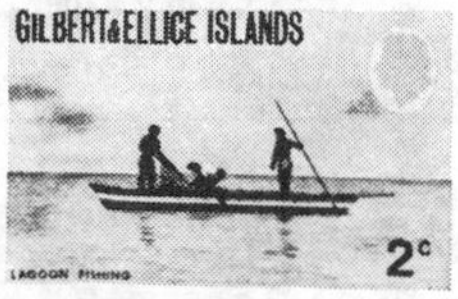

Lagoon Fishing A19

Designs: 3c, Women cleaning pandanus leaves. 4c, Fishermen casting nets. 5c, Gilbertese canoes. 6c, Dehusking coconuts. 8c, Woman weaving pandanus fronds. 10c, Basket weaving. 15c, Tiger shark. 20c, Beating rolled pandanus leaf. 25c, Loading copra. 35c, Night fishing. 50c, Local handicraft. $1, Woman weaving coconut screen. $2, Coat of arms.

Wmk. 314 Upright (A18), Sideways (A19)

1971, May 31   Litho.   Perf. 14

173 A18	1c multicolored	.15	.15
174 A19	2c multicolored	.20	.15
175 A19	3c multicolored	.15	.15
176 A19	4c multicolored	.20	.15
177 A19	5c multicolored	.35	.30
178 A18	6c multicolored	.40	.35
179 A18	8c multicolored	.40	.35
180 A18	10c multicolored	.50	.45
181 A18	15c multicolored	2.00	.95
182 A19	20c multicolored	2.50	1.90
183 A19	25c multicolored	2.00	1.50
184 A19	35c multicolored	2.75	2.00
185 A18	50c multicolored	3.25	2.50
186 A18	$1 multicolored	8.25	5.00
187 A18	$2 multicolored	14.00	10.00
	Nos. 173-187 (15)	37.10	25.90

Wmk. 314 Upright (A19), Sideways (A18)

1972-73

174a A19	2c multicolored	.30	.15
177a A19	5c multicolored	.80	.40
178a A18	6c multicolored	1.00	.52
181a A18	15c multicolored	3.00	1.50
182a A19	20c multicolored	4.00	2.00
	Nos. 174a-182a (5)	9.10	4.57

Issue dates: Sept. 7, 1972, June 13, 1973.

Legislative Council, 1971 (former House of Representatives) — A20

New Constitution: 10c, Meeting House.

1971, Aug. 1   Wmk. 314   Perf. 14

188 A20	3c orange & multi	.15	.15
189 A20	10c green & multi	.60	.60

Nativity Scene — A21

Christmas: 10c, Star of Bethlehem and palm fronds. 35c, Fishermen in outrigger canoe looking at Star.

1971, Oct. 1

190 A21	3c vio blue, blk & yel	.15	.15
191 A21	10c grnsh bl, blk & gold	.30	.30
192 A21	35c car rose, blk & rose	.80	.80
	Nos. 190-192 (3)	1.25	1.25

Children and UNICEF Emblem A22

25th Anniv. of UNICEF: 10c, Seated child. 35c, Child's head.

1971, Dec. 11

193 A22	3c brt pink & multi	.15	.15
194 A22	10c black & multi	.45	.45
195 A22	35c blue & multi	1.25	1.25
	Nos. 193-195 (3)	1.85	1.85

Commission Flag, Map of South Pacific — A23

South Pacific Commission, 25th Anniv.: 10c, Island boats. 35c, Flags of 8 member nations plus Tonga, a non-member.

1972, Feb. 21   Perf. 13½x14

196 A23	3c gray & multi	.15	.15
197 A23	10c tan, ultra & brown	.25	.25
198 A23	35c ultra & multi	.80	.80
	Nos. 196-198 (3)	1.20	1.20

Corals A24

1972, May 26   Perf. 14x14½

199 A24	3c Alveopora	.15	.15
200 A24	10c Euphyllia	.45	.45
201 A24	15c Melithea	.60	.60
202 A24	35c Spongodes	2.25	1.75
	Nos. 199-202 (4)	3.45	2.95

"Peace" on Star of Bethlehem A25

Christmas: 10c, Holy Family, made of shells. 35c, Christ child sleeping in giant clam and covered with dawn cowrie, horiz.

1972, Sept. 15   Perf. 13½

203 A25	3c gold & multi	.20	.15
204 A25	10c gold & multi	.25	.20
205 A25	35c gold & multi	.70	.70
	Nos. 203-205 (3)	1.15	1.05

Silver Wedding Issue, 1972
Common Design Type

Design: Queen Elizabeth II, Prince Philip and kaue floral headdress.

1972, Nov. 20   Photo.   Perf. 14x14½

206 CD324	3c olive & multi	.15	.15
207 CD324	35c rose brown & multi	.70	.70

Funafuti, Land of Bananas A26

Designs: 10c, Butaritari, the smell of the sea. 25c, Tarawa, the center of the world. 35c, Abemama, the land of the moon.

1973, Mar. 5   Litho.   Perf. 14½x14

208 A26	3c yellow & multi	.15	.15
209 A26	10c brt green & multi	.25	.25
210 A26	25c dull blue & multi	.85	.85
211 A26	35c orange & multi	1.10	1.10
	Nos. 208-211 (4)	2.35	2.35

Legends of island names.

Ellice Dancer — A27

Christmas (Within Outline of Nautilus Shell): 10c, Outrigger canoe in lagoon. 35c, Evening on the lagoon. 50c, Map of Christmas Island, Pacific Ocean.

1973, Sept. 24   Perf. 14

212 A27	3c vio blue & multi	.15	.15
213 A27	10c multicolored	.30	.30
214 A27	35c multicolored	.95	.95
215 A27	50c vio blue & multi	1.40	1.40
	Nos. 212-215 (4)	2.80	2.80

Princess Anne's Wedding Issue
Common Design Type

1973, Nov. 14   Perf. 14

216 CD325	3c brt green & multi	.15	.15
217 CD325	35c slate & multi	.70	.70

Meteorological Observation — A28

WMO Emblem and: 10c, Island observation station. 35c, Wind finding radar. 50c, Map of Gilbert and Ellice Islands world weather watch stations.

1973, Nov. 26   Litho.   Perf. 14½

218 A28	3c orange & multi	.20	.20
219 A28	10c dp bister & multi	.75	.75
220 A28	35c gray & multi	2.25	2.25
221 A28	50c dk blue & multi	3.25	3.25
	Nos. 218-221 (4)	6.45	6.45

Cent. of intl. meteorological cooperation.

Te-Mataaua Crest and Canoe — A29

Designs: Various family crests and canoes.

1974, Mar. 4   Litho.   Perf. 13½

222 A29	3c tan & multi	.15	.15
223 A29	10c lt blue & multi	.30	.30
224 A29	35c yellow & multi	1.00	1.00
225 A29	50c pink & multi	1.40	1.40
a.	Souvenir sheet of 4, #222-225	5.25	5.25
	Nos. 222-225 (4)	2.85	2.85

UPU Emblem, "Te Koroba" and No. 26 — A30

UPU cent.: 10c, Sailing ship "Kiakia" and No. 51. 25c, BAC 111 jet and No. 187. 35c, UPU emblem.

1974, June 10   Perf. 14

226 A30	4c blue green & multi	.15	.15
227 A30	10c orange & multi	.25	.25
228 A30	35c dp blue & multi	.65	.65
229 A30	35c red orange & black	.90	.90
	Nos. 226-229 (4)	1.95	1.95

Toy Canoe, Star and Boat — A31

Star of Bethlehem and: 10c, Pinwheel and boat. 25c, Coconut ball (crate) and boat. 35c, Three boats (Wise Men) and stars.

1974, Sept. 23

230 A31	4c yel green & multi	.15	.15
231 A31	10c red brown & multi	.25	.25
232 A31	25c multicolored	.60	.60
233 A31	35c red brown & multi	.90	.90
	Nos. 230-233 (4)	1.90	1.90

Christmas.

Blenheim Palace, Entrance — A32   Churchill Painting — A33

Design: 35c, Churchill Statue, London.

1974, Nov. 30   Litho.   Perf. 14

234 A32	4c multicolored	.15	.15
235 A33	10c ultra & black	.20	.20
236 A33	35c blue, ocher & blk	.70	.70
	Nos. 234-236 (3)	1.05	1.05

Sir Winston Churchill (1874-1965).

Carpilius Maculatus A34

Crabs: 10c, Ranina ranina. 25c, Portunus pelagicus. 35c, Ocypode ceratophthalma.

1975, Jan. 27   Litho.   Perf. 14

237 A34	4c violet & multi	.20	.20
238 A34	10c green & multi	.50	.50
239 A34	25c buff & multi	1.25	1.25
240 A34	35c lt blue & multi	1.90	1.90
	Nos. 237-240 (4)	3.85	3.85

Cypraea Argus — A35

Designs: Living cowries and empty shells.

1975, May 26   Wmk. 314   Perf. 14

241 A35	4c shown	.25	.25
242 A35	10c Cypraea cribraria	.60	.60
243 A35	25c Cypraea talpa	1.50	1.50
244 A35	35c Cypraea mappa	2.25	2.25
a.	Souvenir sheet of 4, #241-244	8.50	8.50
	Nos. 241-244 (4)	4.60	4.60

Map of Beru (The Dud) — A36

Designs: 10c, Map of Onotoa (Six Giants). 25c, Map of Abaiang (Land to the North). 35c, Map of Marakei (Floating fish trap).

Wmk. 314

1975, Aug. 1   Litho.   Perf. 14

245 A36	4c brt green & multi	.15	.15
246 A36	10c brown & multi	.30	.30
247 A36	25c vio blue & multi	.70	.70
248 A36	35c org red & multi	1.00	1.00
	Nos. 245-248 (4)	2.15	2.15

Legends of island names.

Christ Child Within Coconut — A37

Christmas: 10c, Sadd Memorial Chapel (Protestant), Tarawa. 25c, R.C. Church, Ocean Island. 35c, Fishermen in outrigger canoes seeing star.

1975, Sept. 22			Perf. 14	
249	A37	4c brown & multi	.15	.15
250	A37	10c brt blue & multi	.20	.20
251	A37	25c violet & multi	.70	.60
252	A37	35c green & multi	1.00	.90
		Nos. 249-252 (4)	2.05	1.85

POSTAGE DUE STAMPS

D1

1940, Aug. Typo. Wmk. 4 Perf. 12				
J1	D1	1p emerald	1.50	3.00
J2	D1	2p dark red	2.75	5.25
J3	D1	3p chocolate	4.00	7.50
J4	D1	4p deep blue	5.25	11.00
J5	D1	5p deep green	6.50	14.00
J6	D1	6p brt red vio	8.00	17.00
J7	D1	1sh dull violet	13.00	27.50
J8	D1	1sh6p turq green	32.50	65.00
		Nos. J1-J8 (8)	73.50	150.25
		Set, never hinged	125.00	

WAR TAX STAMP

No. 15a Overprinted   **WAR TAX**

1918		Wmk. 3	Perf. 14	
MR1	A3	1p scarlet	.60	.50

GILBERT ISLANDS

'gil–bərt 'ī–lənds

LOCATION — A group of islands in the Pacific Ocean northeast of Australia.
GOVT. — British Crown Colony
AREA — 270 sq. mi.
POP. — 52,000 (1973)
CAPITAL — Tarawa

The Gilbert Islands Colony consists of the Gilbert Islands, Phoenix, Ocean and Line Islands. They were part of the Gilbert and Ellice Islands colony until 1976. See Tuvalu.

> Catalogue values for all unused stamps in this country are for Never Hinged items.

Stamps and Types of Gilbert and Ellice Islands 1971 Overprinted in Red, Black or Gold
THE GILBERT ISLANDS

Wmk. 373; 314 (2c, 4c)

1976, Jan. 2		Litho.	Perf. 14	
253	A18	1c multi (R)	.15	.15
a.		Watermark 314	.15	.15
254	A19	2c multi (R)	.15	.15
a.		Watermark upright	.15	.15
255	A19	3c multi (R)	.15	.15
a.		Watermark 314	22.50	10.00
256	A19	4c multi (R)	.15	.15
257	A19	5c multi (R)	.20	.20
258	A18	6c multi (R)	.20	.20
259	A18	8c multi (R)	.25	.25
260	A18	10c multi (R)	.30	.30
261	A18	15c multi (B)	.65	.60
262	A19	20c multi (R)	1.00	1.00
a.		Watermark 314 sideways	2.00	1.75
b.		Watermark 314 upright	70.00	70.00
263	A19	25c multi (R)	1.40	1.25
a.		Watermark 314	42.50	42.50
264	A19	35c multi (G)	2.00	1.50
265	A18	50c multi (R)	3.75	3.00
266	A18	$1 multi (R)	22.50	19.00
		Nos. 253-266 (14)	32.85	27.90

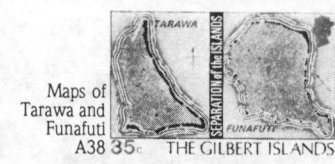

Maps of Tarawa and Funafuti
A38 35c   THE GILBERT ISLANDS

Design: 4c, Charts of Gilbert and Tuvalu Islands.

1976, Jan. 2			Wmk. 373	
267	A38	4c multicolored	.15	.15
268	A38	35c multicolored	2.00	1.50

Separation of the Gilbert and Ellice Islands.

M.V. Teraaka
A39

Designs: 3c, M.V. Tautunu. 4c, Moorish idol. 5c, Hibiscus. 6c, Reef egret. 7c, Roman Catholic Cathedral, Tarawa. 8c, Frangipani. 10c, Maneaba meeting house. 12c, Betio Harbor. 15c, Sunset. 20c, Marakei Atoll. 35c, Chapel, Tangintebu. 40c, Flamboyant tree. 50c, Hypolimnas bolina elliciana (butterfly). $1, Landing craft, Tabakea. $2, Gilbert Islands flag.

1976, July 1		Litho.	Perf. 14	
269	A39	1c multicolored	.15	.15
270	A39	3c multicolored	.15	.15
271	A39	4c multicolored	.15	.15
272	A39	5c multicolored	.15	.15
273	A39	6c multicolored	.20	.20
274	A39	7c multicolored	.20	.20
275	A39	8c multicolored	.25	.25
276	A39	10c multicolored	.25	.25
277	A39	12c multicolored	.30	.30
278	A39	15c multicolored	.40	.40
279	A39	20c multicolored	.45	.45
280	A39	35c multicolored	.65	.65
281	A39	40c multicolored	.90	.90
282	A39	50c multicolored	1.00	1.00
283	A39	$1 multicolored	1.75	1.75
284	A39	$2 multicolored	3.75	3.75
		Nos. 269-284 (16)	10.70	10.70

Church
A40   Gilbert Islands   5c

Children's Drawings: 15c, Feasting (vegetables, fish, pig, chicken), vert. 20c, Communal meeting house, vert. 35c, Children watching dancer.

1976, Sept. 15		Litho.	Perf. 14	
285	A40	5c blue & multi	.20	.20
286	A40	15c green & multi	.40	.40
287	A40	20c rose & multi	.70	.55
288	A40	35c salmon & multi	1.75	1.65
		Nos. 285-288 (4)	3.05	2.80

Christmas.

Porcupine Fish Helmet — A41    Prince Charles, 1970 Visit — A42

Artifacts: 15c, Shark's teeth dagger. 20c, Fighting gauntlet. 35c, Coconut body armor.

1976, Dec. 6		Litho.	Perf. 13½x13	
289	A41	5c multicolored	.25	.22
290	A41	15c multicolored	.40	.40
291	A41	20c multicolored	.70	.55
292	A41	35c multicolored	1.75	1.65
a.		Souvenir sheet of 4, #289-292	12.00	9.50
		Nos. 289-292 (4)	3.10	2.82

1977, Feb. 7			Perf. 14	
Designs: 20c, Prince Philip, 1959 visit. 40c, Queen in coronation robes.				
293	A42	8c multicolored	.15	.15
294	A42	30c multicolored	.30	.30
295	A42	40c multicolored	.85	.60
		Nos. 293-295 (3)	1.30	1.05

Reign of Queen Elizabeth II, 25th anniv.

John Byron and Dolphin, 1765
A43

Explorers: 15c, Edmund Fanning, 1798, and "Betsey." 20c, Fabian Gottlieb von Bellingshausen, 1820, and "Vostok." 35c, Charles Wilkes, 1838-42, and "Vincennes."

1977, June 1		Wmk. 373	Perf. 14	
296	A43	5c multicolored	.68	.60
297	A43	15c multicolored	1.35	1.10
298	A43	20c multicolored	2.25	2.00
299	A43	35c multicolored	4.00	3.75
		Nos. 296-299 (4)	8.28	7.45

Resolution and Discovery off Christmas Island — A44

Designs: 15c, Capt. Cook's logbook entry, 1777, horiz. 20c, Capt. Cook on board ship. 40c, Capt. Cook landing on Christmas Island, horiz.

1977, Sept. 12		Litho.	Perf. 14	
300	A44	8c multicolored	.40	.35
301	A44	15c multicolored	.55	.50
302	A44	20c multicolored	1.00	.80
303	A44	40c multicolored	2.00	1.65
a.		Souvenir sheet of 4, #300-303	9.00	9.00
		Nos. 300-303 (4)	3.95	3.30

Christmas; bicentenary of Capt. Cook's discovery of Christmas Island.

Scout Emblem, Beach Scene — A45   Taurus with Aldebaran — A46

Designs: 15c, Patrol meeting, horiz. 20c, Scout weaving mat, horiz. 40c, Canoeing.

1977, Dec. 5		Litho.	Perf. 13	
304	A45	8c gold & multi	.35	.30
305	A45	15c gold & multi	.45	.40
306	A45	20c gold & multi	.70	.60
307	A45	40c gold & multi	1.50	1.00
		Nos. 304-307 (4)	3.00	2.30

50th anniversary of Gilbert Islands Scouting.

1978, Feb. 20		Litho.	Perf. 14	
Night Sky over Gilbert Islands: 20c, Canis Major with Sirius. 25c, Scorpio with Antares. 45c, Orion with Betelgeuse and Rigel.				
308	A46	10c blue & black	.25	.20
309	A46	20c dp rose & black	.65	.50
310	A46	25c olive grn & black	.75	.65
311	A46	45c orange & black	1.65	1.25
		Nos. 308-311 (4)	3.30	2.60

Elizabeth II Coronation Anniversary
Common Design Types
Souvenir Sheet

1978, Apr. 21			Unwmk.	
312		Sheet of 6	3.00	3.00
a.		CD326 45c Unicorn of Scotland	.40	.40
b.		CD327 45c Elizabeth II	.40	.40
c.		CD328 45c Great frigate bird	.40	.40

Arrows, Tarawa and Abemama Islands, School Insignia
A47

Designs: 10c, Birds inscribed Bikenibeu, Abemama, Bairiki (school locations). 25c, Children greeting each other from maps of Islands. 45c, Abemama and Tarawa school buildings.

Perf. 14x13½

1978, June 5			Wmk. 373	
313	A47	10c multicolored	.30	.20
314	A47	20c multicolored	.50	.35
315	A47	25c multicolored	.70	.50
316	A47	45c multicolored	1.40	1.10
		Nos. 313-316 (4)	2.90	2.15

King George V School, 25th anniversary of return from Abemama to Tarawa.

Garland
A48

Christmas: Various garlands.

1978, Sept. 4		Litho.	Perf. 14	
317	A48	10c multicolored	.25	.22
318	A48	20c multicolored	.30	.30
319	A48	25c multicolored	.55	.50
320	A48	45c multicolored	1.25	1.00
a.		Souvenir sheet of 4, #317-320, perf. 13x13½	5.00	5.00
		Nos. 317-320 (4)	2.35	2.02

Endeavour
A49

Designs: 20c, Green turtle. 25c, Quadrant. 45c, Capt. Cook after Flaxman/Wedgwood medallion.

1979, Jan. 15		Litho.	Perf. 11	
321	A49	10c multicolored	.40	.40
322	A49	20c multicolored	.50	.50
323	A49	25c multicolored	.70	.65

		Litho.; Embossed		
324	A49	45c multicolored	1.00	.85
		Nos. 321-324 (4)	2.60	2.30

Capt. Cook's voyages.
Gilbert Islands stamps were replaced in 1979 by those of Kiribati.

GOLD COAST

'gōld 'kōst

LOCATION — West Africa between Dahomey and Ivory Coast
GOVT. — Former British Crown Colony
AREA — 91,843 sq. mi.
POP. — 3,089,000 (1952)
CAPITAL — Accra

Attached to the colony were Ashanti and Northern Territories (protectorate). Togoland, under British mandate, was also included for administrative purposes. Gold Coast became the independent state of Ghana in 1957.
See Ghana.

12 Pence = 1 Shilling
20 Shillings = 1 Pound

> Catalogue values for unused stamps in this country are for Never Hinged items, beginning with Scott 128.

Queen Victoria
A1 A3

1875, July Typo. Wmk. 1 *Perf. 12½*

1 A1 1p blue 450.00 80.00
2 A1 4p red violet 400.00 100.00
3 A1 6p orange 625.00 75.00

1876-79 *Perf. 14*

4 A1 ½p bister ('79) 30.00 20.00
5 A1 1p blue 13.00 6.50
a. Half used as ½p on cover *2,750.*
6 A1 2p green ('79) 50.00 10.50
a. Half used as 1p on cover *2,500.*
b. Quarter used as ½p on cover *3,500.*
7 A1 4p red violet 150.00 6.75
a. Quarter used as 1p on cover *5,000.*
b. Half used as 2p on cover *4,250.*
8 A1 6p orange 90.00 17.50
a. One sixth used as 1p on cover *5,500.*
b. Half used as 3p on cover *5,000.*
Nos. 4-8 (5) 333.00 61.25

Handstamp Surcharged "1D" in Black

1883, May

9 A1 1p on 4p red violet

Some experts question the status of No. 9.

1883-91 Wmk. 2

10 A1 ½p bister ('83) 145.00 65.00
11 A1 ½p green ('84) .80 .35
12 A1 1p blue ('83) 900.00 65.00
13 A1 1p rose ('84) 1.25 .40
a. Half used as ½p on cover *3,250.*
14 A1 2p gray ('84) 1.60 .50
b. Half used as 1p on cover *3,750.*
15 A1 2½p bl & org ('91) 1.50 .50
16 A1 3p ol green ('89) 3.00 3.00
a. 3p olive bister 4.00 4.00
17 A1 4p dull vio ('84) 2.50 1.00
a. 4p claret 4.50 3.50
b. Half used as 2p on cover —
18 A1 6p orange ('89) 4.00 2.00
a. One sixth used as 1p on cover —
19 A1 1sh purple ('88) 3.25 1.25
a. 1sh violet 25.00 12.50
20 A1 2sh brown ('84) 24.00 12.00
a. 2sh yellow brown 75.00 52.50

ONE PENNY

No. 18 Surcharged in Black

1889, Mar.

21 A1 1p on 6p orange 100.00 50.00

The surcharge exists in two spacings between "PENNY" and bar: 7mm and 8mm.

1889

22 A3 5sh lilac & ultra 50.00 12.00
23 A3 10sh lilac & red 65.00 15.00
24 A3 20sh green & red 3,250.

1894

25 A3 20sh vio & blk, *red* 150.00 37.50

1898-1902

26 A3 ½p lilac & green 1.00 .30
27 A3 1p lil & car rose .50 .30
28 A3 2p lil & red ('02) 25.00 *60.00*
29 A3 2½p lilac & ultra 4.00 3.00
30 A3 3p lilac & yel 3.00 1.40
31 A3 6p lilac & purple 5.00 1.00
32 A3 1sh gray grn & blk 6.00 5.00
33 A3 2sh gray grn & car rose 15.00 15.00
34 A3 5sh grn & lil ('00) 42.50 22.50
35 A3 10sh grn & brn ('00) 110.00 42.50
Nos. 26-35 (10) 212.00 *151.00*

Numerals of 2p, 3p and 6p of type A3 are in color on colorless tablet.

ONE PENNY

Nos. 29 and 31 Surcharged in Black

1901, Oct. 6

36 A3 1p on 2½p lil & ultra 2.00 2.00
37 A3 1p on 6p lilac & pur .90 3.00
a. "ONE" omitted 275.00 *400.00*

Beware of copies offered as No. 37a that have part of "ONE" showing.

King Edward VII
A5 A6

1902 Wmk. 2

38 A5 ½p violet & green .24 .15
39 A5 1p vio & car rose .18 .15
40 A5 2p vio & red org 3.00 2.50
41 A5 2½p vio & ultra 3.00 1.65
42 A5 3p vio & orange 1.75 .75
43 A5 6p violet & pur 3.25 1.00
44 A5 1sh green & blk 3.00 1.25
45 A5 2sh grn & car rose 12.00 7.50
46 A5 5sh green & violet 15.00 18.00
47 A5 10sh green & brn 32.50 *45.00*
48 A5 20sh vio & blk, *red* 110.00 100.00
Nos. 38-48 (11) 183.92 177.95

Numerals of 2p, 3p, 6p and 2sh6p of type A5 are in color on colorless tablet.

1904-07 Wmk. 3

49 A5 ½p vio & grn ('07) 3.25 3.25
50 A5 1p vio & car rose 2.25 .25
51 A5 2p vio & red org 2.50 .40
52 A5 2½p vio & ultra ('06) 27.50 17.50
53 A5 3p vio & org ('05) 9.00 .80
54 A5 6p vio & pur ('06) 25.00 1.50
55 A5 2sh6p grn & yel ('06) 27.50 *65.00*
Nos. 49-55 (7) 98.00 *88.70*

Nos. 49 and 52 are on ordinary paper. Nos. 50, 51, 53 and 54 are on both ordinary and chalky paper. No. 55 is on chalky paper.

1907-13 Ordinary Paper

56 A5 ½p green 1.40 .20
57 A5 1p carmine 2.25 .20
58 A5 2p gray ('09) 1.50 .50
59 A5 2½p ultramarine 2.75 1.25

Chalky Paper

60 A5 3p violet, *yel* ('09) 3.75 .40
61 A5 6p dull violet ('08) 9.50 .40
a. 6p dull violet & red violet 2.75 2.50
62 A5 1sh blk, *grn* ('09) 4.00 1.00
63 A5 2sh violet & bl, *bl* ('10) 7.50 11.00
64 A5 2sh6p blk & red, *blue* ('11) 17.00 *35.00*
65 A5 5sh grn & red, *yel* ('13) 40.00 *70.00*
Nos. 56-65 (10) 89.65 *119.95*

#63 is on both ordinary and chalky paper.

1908, Nov. Ordinary Paper

66 A6 1p carmine .15 .15

King George V
A7 A8

For description of Dies I and II, see back of this section of the Catalogue.

Die I

1913-21 Ordinary Paper

69 A7 ½p green .28 .15
70 A8 1p carmine .15 .15
a. 1p scarlet .35 .15
71 A7 2p gray 2.00 .70
72 A7 2½p ultramarine .85 .55

Chalky Paper

73 A7 3p vio, *yel* ('15) .85 .15
a. Die II ('19) 6.75 5.75
74 A7 6p dull vio & red vio 1.25 1.10
75 A7 1sh black, *green* 1.25 .85
a. 1sh black, *emerald* 2.25 .95
b. 1sh black, *bl grn*, ol back 1.20 .85
c. Die II ('21) 2.25 .95
76 A7 2sh vio & bl, *bl* 6.75 2.00
a. Die II ('21) 200.00 60.00
77 A7 2sh6p blk & red, *bl* 6.75 5.00
a. Die II ('21) 22.50 22.50
78 A7 5sh grn & red, *yel* 11.00 12.50
a. Die II ('21) 19.00 *42.50*
79 A7 10sh grn & red, *grn* ('16) 16.00 21.00
a. 10sh grn & red, *emer* 21.00 21.00
b. 10sh grn & red, *bl grn*, ol back 19.00 21.00
80 A7 20sh vio & blk, *red* ('16) 95.00 55.00
Nos. 69-80 (12) 142.13 99.15

Surface-colored Paper

81 A7 3p violet, *yel* .55 .45
82 A7 5sh grn & red, *yel* 8.50 *17.50*

Numerals of 2p, 3p, 6p and 2sh6p of type A7 are in color on plain tablet.

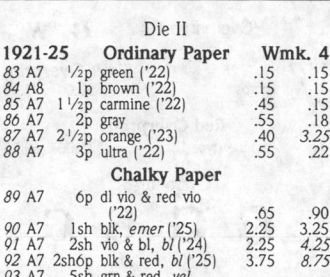

Die II

1921-25 Ordinary Paper Wmk. 4

83 A7 ½p green ('22) .15 .15
84 A8 1p brown ('22) .15 .15
85 A7 1½p carmine ('22) .45 .15
86 A7 2p gray .55 .18
87 A7 2½p orange ('23) .40 *3.25*
88 A7 3p ultra ('22) .55 .22

Chalky Paper

89 A7 6p dl vio & red vio ('22) .65 .90
90 A7 1sh blk, *emer* ('25) 2.25 3.25
91 A7 2sh vio & bl, *bl* ('24) 2.25 *4.25*
92 A7 2sh6p blk & red, *bl* ('25) 3.75 *8.75*
93 A7 5sh grn & red, *yel* ('25) 8.75 *16.00*

Die I

94 A7 15sh dl vio & grn ('21) 130.00 *250.00*
a. Die II ('25) 120.00 *250.00*
95 A7 £2 grn & org 375.00 *625.00*
Nos. 83-94 (12) 149.90 *287.25*

Christiansborg Castle — A9

Perf. 13½x14½

1928, Aug. 1 Photo.

98 A9 ½p green .15 .15
99 A9 1p red brown .15 .15
100 A9 1½p scarlet .30 .20
101 A9 2p slate .15 .15
102 A9 2½p yellow .65 *2.75*
103 A9 3p ultramarine .30 .30
104 A9 6p dull vio & blk .45 .45
105 A9 1sh red org & blk 1.10 1.10
106 A9 2sh purple & black 8.50 8.50
107 A9 5sh ol green & car 25.00 25.00
Nos. 98-107 (10) 36.75 38.75

Silver Jubilee Issue

Common Design Type

1935, May 6 Engr. *Perf. 11x12*

108 CD301 1p black & ultra .25 .18
109 CD301 3p ultra & brown .90 .65
110 CD301 6p indigo & green 3.00 2.75
111 CD301 1sh brown vio & ind 3.25 3.50
Nos. 108-111 (4) 7.40 7.08
Set, never hinged 13.00

Coronation Issue

Common Design Type

1937, May 12 *Perf. 11x11½*

112 CD302 1p brown .15 .15
113 CD302 2p dark gray .15 .15
114 CD302 3p deep ultra .25 .25
Nos. 112-114 (3) .55 .55
Set, never hinged 1.10

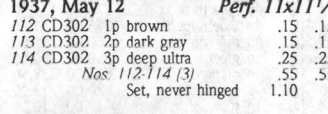

George VI and Christiansborg Castle
A10 A11

1938-41 Wmk. 4 *Perf. 12*

115 A10 ½p green .15 .15
116 A10 1p red brown .15 .15
117 A10 1½p rose red .15 .15
118 A10 2p gray black .24 .15
119 A10 3p ultramarine .15 .15
120 A10 4p rose lilac .15 .15
121 A10 6p rose violet .15 .15
122 A10 9p red orange .30 .30
123 A11 1sh gray grn & blk .30 .18
124 A11 1sh3p turq grn & red brown .28 .25
125 A11 2sh dk vio & dp bl 1.50 .35
126 A11 5sh rose car & ol green 1.50 1.25
127 A11 10sh purple & black 3.00 2.75
Nos. 115-127 (13) 8.02 6.13
Set, never hinged 22.50

Issue dates: 10sh, July, 1940. 1sh3p, Apr. 12, 1941. Others, Apr. 1.

Catalogue values for unused stamps in this section, from this point to the end of the section, are for Never Hinged items.

Peace Issue

Common Design Type

1946, Oct. 14 *Perf. 13½*

128 CD303 2p purple .15 .15
a. Perf. 13½x14 2.25 .75
129 CD303 4p deep red violet .22 .22
a. Perf. 13½x14 4.25 1.50

Mounted Constable — A12

Christiansborg Castle — A13

Designs: 1½p, Emblem of Joint Provincial Council. 2p, Talking Drums. 2½p, Map. 3p, Manganese mine. 4p, Lake Bosumtwi. 6p, Cacao farmer. 1sh, Breaking cacao pods. 2sh, Trooping the colors. 5sh, Surfboats. 10sh, Forest.

1948, July 1 Engr. *Perf. 12*

130 A12 ½p emerald .20 .15
131 A13 1p deep blue .20 .15
132 A13 1½p red .30 .15
133 A12 2p chocolate .40 .15
134 A13 2½p lt brown & red .85 .30
135 A13 3p blue .55 .20
136 A13 4p dk car rose 1.25 .55
137 A12 6p org & black .75 .30
138 A13 1sh red org & blk 1.40 .30
139 A13 2sh rose car & ol brn 4.25 .65
140 A13 5sh gray & red vio 14.00 2.75
141 A12 10sh ol grn & black 17.00 5.50
Nos. 130-141 (12) 41.15 11.15

Silver Wedding Issue

Common Design Types

1948, Dec. 20 Photo. *Perf. 14x14½*

142 CD304 1½p scarlet .15 .15

Engraved; Name Typographed

Perf. 11½x11

143 CD305 10sh dk brown olive 10.00 10.00

Common Design Types pictured in section before Great Britain.

UPU Issue

Common Design Types

Engr.; Name Typo. on 2½p and 3p

1949, Oct. 10 *Perf. 13½, 11x11½*

144 CD306 2p red brown .18 .18
145 CD307 2½p deep orange .28 .28
146 CD308 3p indigo .70 .70
147 CD309 1sh blue green 1.90 1.90
Nos. 144-147 (4) 3.06 3.06

Map of West Africa A14 — Mounted Constable A15

Designs: 1p, Christiansborg Castle. 1½p, Emblem of Joint Provincial Council. 2p, Talking drums. 3p, Manganese mine. 4p, Lake Bosumtwi. 6p, Cacao farmer. 1sh, Breaking cacao pods. 2sh, Trooping the colors. 5sh, Surfboats. 10sh, Forest.

Perf. 11½x12, 12x11½

1952-54 Engr.

148 A14 ½p yel brown & car .15 .15
149 A14 1p deep blue .15 .15
150 A14 1½p green .15 .15
151 A15 2p chocolate .15 .15
152 A15 2½p red .18 .15
153 A14 3p rose .22 .15
154 A14 4p deep blue .25 .15
155 A15 6p orange & black .30 .15
156 A14 1sh red org & black .60 .15
157 A14 2sh rose car & ol brn 1.25 .40

158	A14	5sh	gray & red vio	6.25	.90
159	A15	10sh	olive grn & blk	10.50	2.00
			Nos. 148-159 (12)	20.15	4.65

Nos. 148-149 exist in vertical coils.
Issued: 2½p, 12/19/52; ½p, 1½p, 3p, 4p, 4/1/53; 1p, 2p, 6p, 1sh-10sh, 3/1/54.
For overprints see Ghana #5-13, 25-27.

Coronation Issue
Common Design Type

1953, June 2 ***Perf. 13½x13***

160	CD312	2p dk brown & black	.18	.15

Gold Coast stamps were replaced in 1957 by those of Ghana.

POSTAGE DUE STAMPS

D1

1923-52 **Typo.** **Wmk. 4** ***Perf. 14***

J1	D1	½p	black	20.00	*80.00*
J2	D1	1p	black	.65	.65
J3	D1	2p	black	.65	*2.25*
a.			Wmk. 4a (error)	85.00	
J4	D1	3p	black	.80	*3.25*
a.			Wmk. 4a (error)	85.00	
J5	D1	6p	black ('52)	1.65	*6.00*
a.			Wmk. 4a (error)	125.00	
J6	D1	1sh	black ('52)	3.25	*9.00*
a.			Wmk. 4a (error)	175.00	
			Nos. J1-J6 (6)	27.00	*101.15*

Issue date: 6p, 1sh, Oct. 1.

WAR TAX STAMP

Regular Issue of 1913 Surcharged

WAR TAX

ONE PENNY

1918, June **Wmk. 3** ***Perf. 14***

MR1	A8	1p on 1p scarlet	.15	.15

GRIQUALAND WEST

'gri–kwə–,land 'west

LOCATION — In South Africa west of the Orange Free State and north of the Orange River
GOVT. — Former British Crown Colony
AREA — 15,197 sq. mi.
POP. — 83,375 (1891)
CAPITAL — Kimberley

Originally a territorial division of the Cape of Good Hope Colony, Griqualand West was declared a British Crown Colony in 1873 and together with Griqualand East was annexed to the Cape Colony in 1880.

12 Pence = 1 Shilling

Beware of forgeries.

Stamps of Cape of Good Hope 1864-65 (Type I, 4p, 6p, 1sh) and 1871-76 (Type II, ½p, 1p, 4p, 5sh) Surcharged or Overprinted

Type I - With frame line around stamp.
Type II - Without frame line.

"Hope" — A1

Manuscript Surcharge in Dark Red

1874 **Wmk. 1** ***Perf. 14***

1	A1	1p on 4p blue (type I)	800.00	*1,250.*

Overprinted **G. W.**

1877 **Black Overprint**

2		1p rose	450.00	75.00
a.		Double overprint		*1,350.*

Red Overprint

3		4p blue (type II)	325.00	60.00

Overprinted

G G G G
a b c d

G G G
e f g

In Black on the One Penny, in Red on the Other Values

4	(a)	½p gray black	15.00	13.00
5	(a)	1p rose	15.00	10.00
6	(a)	4p blue (type I)	150.00	20.00
7	(a)	4p blue (type II)	100.00	12.00
8	(a)	6p dull violet	75.00	17.00
9	(a)	1sh green	90.00	14.00
a.		Inverted overprint		325.00
10	(a)	5sh orange	325.00	14.00
11	(b)	½p gray black	30.00	20.00
12	(b)	1p rose	35.00	22.50
13	(b)	4p blue (type I)	325.00	65.00
14	(b)	4p blue (type II)		
15	(b)	6p dull violet	165.00	37.50
16	(b)	1sh green	200.00	30.00
a.		Inverted overprint	—	—
17	(b)	5sh orange	—	50.00
18	(c)	½p gray black	275.00	275.00
19	(c)	1p rose	30.00	25.00
20	(c)	4p blue (type I)	—	400.00
21	(c)	4p blue (type II)	*1,150.*	300.00
22	(c)	6p dull violet	—	350.00
23	(c)	1sh green	—	350.00
24	(c)	5sh orange		22.50
25	(d)	½p gray black	20.00	12.50
26	(d)	1p rose	20.00	15.00
27	(d)	4p blue (type I)	225.00	30.00
28	(d)	4p blue (type II)	165.00	20.00
29	(d)	6p dull violet	100.00	20.00
30	(d)	1sh green	145.00	15.00
31	(d)	5sh orange	450.00	15.00
32	(e)	½p gray black	35.00	30.00
33	(e)	1p rose	35.00	20.00
34	(e)	4p blue (type I)	325.00	80.00
35	(e)	4p blue (type II)	225.00	27.50
36	(e)	6p dull violet	165.00	45.00
37	(e)	1sh green	200.00	27.50
a.		Inverted overprint		
38	(e)	5sh orange		30.00
39	(f)	½p gray black	35.00	30.00
40	(f)	1p rose	40.00	25.00
41	(f)	4p blue (type I)	375.00	125.00
42	(f)	4p blue (type II)	275.00	55.00
43	(f)	6p dull violet	200.00	60.00
44	(f)	1sh green	250.00	30.00
45	(f)	5sh orange	850.00	37.50
46	(g)	½p gray black	20.00	12.00
47	(g)	1p rose	17.00	10.00
48	(g)	4p blue (type I)	175.00	30.00
49	(g)	4p blue (type II)	150.00	20.00
50	(g)	6p dull violet	100.00	22.50
51	(g)	1sh green	125.00	13.00
a.		Inverted overprint		
52	(g)	5sh orange	450.00	13.00

There are minor varieties of types e and f.

Overprinted in Black

G G G G G
i k l m n

G G G G
o p q r

1878

54	(g)	4p blue (type II)	200.00	37.50
55	(g)	6p dull violet	325.00	75.00
56	(i)	1p rose	20.00	11.00
57	(i)	4p blue (type II)	90.00	14.00
58	(i)	6p dull violet	175.00	45.00
59	(k)	1p rose	30.00	12.00
60	(k)	4p blue (type II)	185.00	35.00
61	(k)	6p dull violet	300.00	70.00
62	(l)	1p rose	20.00	15.00
63	(l)	4p blue (type II)	80.00	15.00
64	(l)	6p dull violet	165.00	40.00
65	(m)	1p rose		
66	(m)	4p blue (type II)		
67	(m)	6p dull violet		
68	(n)	1p rose	75.00	
69	(n)	4p blue (type II)	300.00	125.00
70	(n)	6p dull violet	400.00	
71	(o)	1p rose	35.00	27.50
72	(o)	4p blue (type II)	200.00	42.50
73	(o)	6p dull violet	400.00	175.00
74	(p)	1p rose	90.00	40.00
75	(p)	4p blue (type II)	425.00	70.00
76	(p)	6p dull violet	500.00	175.00
77	(q)	1p rose	55.00	50.00
78	(q)	4p blue (type II)	250.00	80.00
79	(q)	6p dull violet	375.00	175.00
80	(r)	1p rose	325.00	250.00
81	(r)	4p blue (type II)	*350.00*	180.00
82	(r)	6p dull violet	*1,350.*	475.00

There are two minor varieties of type i and one of type p.

Overprinted in Red

G G
s t

1878

83	(s)	½p gray black	5.00	6.00
a.		Double overprint	35.00	
b.		Inverted overprint	6.00	6.00
c.		Double overprint, inverted	55.00	
84	(s)	4p blue (type II)	220.00	100.00
a.		Inverted overprint	700.00	100.00
85	(t)	½p gray black	6.00	6.00
a.		Double overprint	55.00	
b.		Inverted overprint	6.00	7.50
86	(t)	4p blue (type II)	275.00	60.00
a.		Inverted overprint	275.00	60.00

Black Overprint

87	(s)	½p gray black	200.00	150.00
a.		Inverted overprint	200.00	*300.00*
b.		With 2nd ovpt. *(s)* in red, invtd.	300.00	
c.		With 2nd ovpt. *(t)* in red, invtd.	110.00	
88	(s)	1p rose	6.00	4.00
a.		Double overprint	125.00	30.00
b.		Inverted overprint	6.00	6.00
c.		Double overprint, inverted	125.00	45.00
d.		With second overprint *(s)* in red, inverted	22.50	25.00
89	(s)	4p blue (type I)		135.00
90	(s)	4p blue (type II)	62.50	14.00
a.		Double overprint		150.00
b.		Inverted overprint	110.00	60.00
c.		Double overprint, inverted		
91	(s)	6p dull violet	75.00	22.50
92	(t)	½p gray black	25.00	30.00
a.		Inverted overprint	25.00	35.00
b.		With 2nd ovpt. inverted	125.00	
93	(t)	1p rose	6.00	5.50
a.		Double overprint		60.00
b.		Inverted overprint	55.00	20.00
c.		Double overprint, inverted		75.00
d.		With 2nd ovpt. *(t)* in red, invtd.	55.00	50.00
94	(t)	4p blue (type I)		130.00
95	(t)	4p blue (type II)	150.00	7.50
a.		Double overprint		150.00
b.		Inverted overprint	200.00	20.00
c.		Double overprint, inverted		
96	(t)	6p dull violet		27.50

Overprinted in Black **G**

97	½p gray black	7.00	5.50
a.	Double overprint	250.00	225.00
98	1p rose	7.00	3.25
a.	Double overprint		125.00
b.	Triple overprint		
c.	Inverted overprint		75.00
99	4p blue (type II)	15.00	3.25
a.	Double overprint		100.00
100	6p brt violet	75.00	6.00
a.	Double overprint	425.00	140.00
b.	Inverted overprint		32.50
101	1sh green	55.00	3.50
a.	Double overprint	200.00	100.00
102	5sh orange	250.00	6.00
a.	Double overprint	350.00	60.00
b.	Triple overprint		275.00

These stamps were declared obsolete in 1880 and the remainders were used in Cape of Good Hope offices as ordinary stamps.

HELIGOLAND

'he–lə–gō–,land

LOCATION — An island in the North Sea near the northern coast of Germany
GOVT. — Former British Possession
AREA — ¼ sq. mi.
POP. — 2,307 (1900)

Great Britain ceded Heligoland to Germany in 1890. It became part of Schleswig-Holstein province. Stamps of Heligoland were superseded by those of the German Empire.

16 Schillings = 1 Mark
100 Pfennig = 1 Mark = 1 Schilling (1875)

Queen Victoria
A1 A2

A3

A4

HALF SCHILLING
A1: Curl below chignon is rounded.
A2: Curl resembles hook or comma.

Typo., Head Embossed

1867-68 **Unwmk.** ***Rouletted***

1	A1	½sch	blue green & rose	400.00	*1,000.*
1A	A2	½sch	blue green & rose	900.00	*1,500.*
2	A1	1sch	rose & deep green	225.00	*225.00*
3	A3	2sch	rose & pale green	15.00	*65.00*
4	A3	6sch	gray green & rose	20.00	*350.00*

Reprints of No. 2 lack the large curl, those of No. 1A are not in blue green, and those of Nos. 3 and 4 are on slightly porous paper and the colors are either too deep or too bright. The 2sch and 6sch perforated exist only as reprints.

Perf. 13½x14½

1869-71 **Thick Soft Paper**

5	A2	½sch	ol grn & car	140.00	*165.00*
a.		½sch	blue green & rose	275.00	*290.00*
b.		½sch	yellow green & rose	400.00	375.00
6	A2	1sch	rose & yel grn	200.00	*250.00*

Reprints are on thinner paper and in too dark colors.

1873 **Thick Quadrille Paper**

7	A4	¼sch	pale rose & pale grn	32.50	*2,000.*
a.		¼sch	deep rose & pale grn	*100.00*	*2,250.*
8	A4	¼sch	yel grn & rose	165.00	*4,000.*
9	A2	½sch	brt grn & rose	140.00	*250.00*
10	A4	¾sch	gray grn & pale rose	40.00	*1,400.*
a.		¾sch	gray green & dp rose	40.00	*1,400.*
11	A2	1sch	rose & pale grn	150.00	*250.00*
12	A4	1½sch	yel grn & rose	75.00	*325.00*

Reprints are never on quadrille paper.

1874 **Thin Wove Paper**

13	A4	¼sch rose & yel grn	24.00	

Originals have the large curl. The early reprints have the small curl. The later reprints are on thin hard paper with smooth white gum and the colors are too bright.

A5

A6

A7

Coat of Arms — A8

1875 **Wove Paper**

14	A5	1pf	dk rose & dk grn	13.00	*650.00*
15	A5	2pf	yel grn & dk rose	13.00	*825.00*
16	A6	5pf	dk rose & dk grn	22.50	*25.00*
17	A6	10pf	blue grn & red	12.00	*32.50*
a.		10pf	yel green & dark rose	100.00	*32.50*
b.		10pf	lt green & pale red	125.00	32.50
18	A7	25pf	rose & dk grn	16.00	*32.50*
a.		25pf	dk rose & dk green	16.00	*32.50*
19	A7	50pf	green & brick red	25.00	*100.00*
a.		50pf	dl grn & dk rose	65.00	*40.00*

The 1pf and 2pf have been reprinted on very white paper with white gum. The colors are too bright and too light.

1876-88 **Typo.**

20	A8	3pf	grn & bright red ('77)	225.00	*1,050.*
a.		3pf	dp grn & dl red	375.00	*1,400.*
21	A8	20pf	ver & brt grn ('88)	12.50	*37.50*
a.		20pf	brown org & green ('87)	425.00	*50.00*
b.		20pf	vio car & yel green ('80)	325.00	150.00
c.		20pf	anil rose & dk green ('85)	425.00	62.50
d.		20pf	lilac rose & dk green	300.00	165.00
e.		20pf	rose red & dk green ('80)	325.00	150.00

The coat-of-arms on Nos. 20, 21 and sub-varieties is printed in three colors: varying shades of yellow, red and green.

The 3pf has been reprinted. The colors are usually too pale, especially the red, which is either orange or orange red.

A9   A10

1879   **Typo.**

22	A9	1m dp green & car	200.00	250.00
a.		1m blue green & salmon	200.00	250.00
b.		1m dark green & vermilion	90.00	
23	A10	5m blue grn & salmon	150.00	1,250.

Perf. 11½

24	A9	1m dp grn & car	1,350.
25	A10	5m bl grn & rose red	1,400.

Nos. 13, 22b, 24 and 25 were never placed in use. Forged cancellations of Nos. 1-23 are plentiful. Heligoland stamps were replaced by those of the German Empire in 1890.

HONG KONG

ˈhäŋ–ˌkäŋ

LOCATION — A peninsula and island in southeast China at the mouth of the Canton River
GOVT. — British Crown Colony
AREA — 426 sq. mi.
POP. — 5,313,000 (est. 1983)
CAPITAL — Victoria

100 Cents = 1 Dollar

Catalogue values for unused stamps in this country are for Never Hinged items, beginning with Scott 174 in the regular postage section, Scott B1 in the semipostal section and Scott J13 in the postage due section.

Watermark

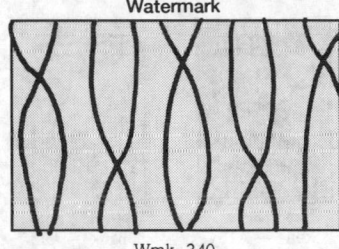

Wmk. 340

Values for unused stamps are for examples with original gum as defined in the catalogue introduction. Very fine examples of Nos. 1-25, 29-48, 61-66d and 69-70a will have perforations touching the design on at least one side due to the narrow spacing of the stamps on the plates. Stamps with perfs clear of the design on all four sides are scarce and will command higher prices.

Queen Victoria — A1

Unwmk.

1862, Dec. 8   **Typo.**   **Perf. 14**

1	A1	2c pale brown	200.00	60.00
a.		2c deep brown	250.00	80.00
2	A1	8c buff	300.00	30.00
3	A1	12c blue	200.00	25.00
4	A1	18c lilac	250.00	30.00
5	A1	24c green	550.00	70.00
6	A1	48c rose	1,750.	200.00
7	A1	96c gray	2,750.	275.00

1863-80   **Wmk. 1**

8	A1	2c brown ('65)	65.00	4.00
9	A1	2c dull rose ('80)	60.00	8.00
10	A1	4c slate	37.50	4.00
11	A1	5c ultra ('80)	140.00	12.00
12	A1	6c lilac	160.00	5.00
a.		6c violet	165.00	5.00

13	A1	8c org buff ('65)	190.00	5.00
a.		8c bright orange	175.00	5.00
b.		8c brownish orange	175.00	6.00
14	A1	10c violet ('80)	225.00	7.50
15	A1	12c light blue	12.00	4.00
a.		12c light greenish blue	225.00	20.00
16	A1	16c yellow ('77)	700.00	30.00
17	A1	18c lilac ('66)	3,000.	225.00
18	A1	24c green ('65)	250.00	8.00
19	A1	30c vermilion	325.00	10.50
20	A1	30c violet ('71)	110.00	4.00
21	A1	48c rose ('65)	400.00	20.00
22	A1	48c brown ('80)	450.00	35.00
23	A1	96c bister ('65)	17,500.	550.00
24	A1	96c gray ('66)	500.00	22.50

Imperfs. are plate proofs.

1874   **Perf. 12½**

25	A1	4c slate	3,750.	225.

See #36-49. For surcharges or overprints on stamps of type A1 see #29-35B, 51-56, 61-66, 69-70.

A2

A3

A4

1874   **Engr.**   **Wmk. 1**   **Perf. 15½x15**

26	A2	$2 sage green	175.00	45.00
27	A3	$3 violet	150.00	25.00
28	A4	$10 rose	4,500.	550.00

Nos. 26-28 are revenues which were used postally. Used values are for postally canceled copies. See Nos. 57-59. For surcharges see Nos. 50, 67. For type surcharged see No. 60.

Nos. 17 and 20 Surcharged in Black:

16 cents.   **28** cents.

1876   **Perf. 14**

29	A1	16c on 18c lilac	1,500.	125.00
30	A1	28c on 30c violet	650.00	32.50

Stamps of 1863-80
Surcharged in Black

5 cents.

1879-80

31	A1	5c on 8c org ('80)	425.00	75.00
a.		Inverted surcharge		7,500.
b.		Double surcharge		
32	A1	5c on 18c lilac	300.00	30.00
33	A1	10c on 12c blue	375.00	35.00
34	A1	10c on 16c yellow	2,000.	100.00
a.		Inverted surcharge		20,000.
35	A1	10c on 24c green ('80)	500.00	30.00

Most copies of No. 31a are damaged.

Nos. 16-17, 35B Surcharged in Black

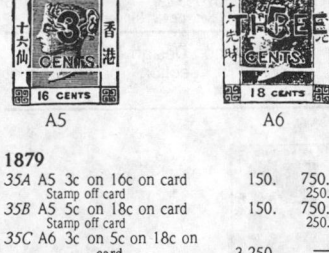

A5   A6

1879

35A	A5	3c on 16c on card	150.	750.
		Stamp off card		250.
35B	A5	5c on 18c on card	150.	750.
		Stamp off card		250.
35C	A6	3c on 5c on 18c on card	3,250.	
		Stamp off card		3,500.

Nos. 35A-35C were sold affixed to postal cards. Most used copies are found off card so values are given for these.

1882-1902   **Wmk. 2**   **Perf. 14**

36	A1	2c rose	7.50	1.00
a.		2c dull rose	7.50	9.50
37	A1	2c green ('00)	8.00	.80
38	A1	4c slate ('96)	6.00	.80
39	A1	4c car rose ('00)	8.00	.80
40	A1	5c ultramarine	8.00	.80
41	A1	5c yellow ('00)	15.00	3.50
42	A1	10c lilac	300.00	7.50
43	A1	10c green	45.00	.30
a.		10c blue green	1,000.	25.00
44	A1	10c vio, red ('91)	7.50	.80
45	A1	10c ultra ('00)	22.00	2.00
46	A1	12c blue ('02)	30.00	35.00
47	A1	30c gray grn ('91)	75.00	5.00
a.		30c yellow green	80.00	19.00
48	A1	30c brown ('01)	20.00	10.00
		Nos. 36-48 (13)	552.00	71.00

No. 47 has fugitive ink. Both colors will turn dull green upon soaking.
The 2c rose, perf 12, is a proof.

No. 28 Surcharged in Black   **12** CENTS.

1880   **Wmk. 1**   **Perf. 15½x15**

50	A4	12c on $10 rose	375.00	225.00

Surcharged in Black   **20** CENTS

1885-91   **Wmk. 2**   **Perf. 14**

51	A1	20c on 30c ver	50.00	4.00
a.		Double surcharge		
52	A1	20c on 30c gray grn ('91)	75.00	80.00
53	A1	50c on 48c brown	175.00	9.00
54	A1	50c on 48c lil ('91)	175.00	175.00
55	A1	$1 on 96c ol gray	400.00	30.00
56	A1	$1 on 96c vio, red ('91)	425.00	175.00

For overprints see Nos. 61-63.

1890-1902   **Wmk. 1**   **Perf. 14**

57	A2	$2 gray green	160.	125.
58	A3	$3 lilac ('02)	200.	200.
59	A4	$10 gray grn ('92)	5,750.	

Fake postmarks are known on No. 59. Beware also of fiscal cancels altered to resemble postal cancels.
For surcharge see No. 68.

Type of 1874
Surcharged in Black

5 DOLLARS

1891, Jan. 1   **Wmk. 2**

60	A4	$5 on $10 vio, red	175.00	90.00

Nos. 52, 54 and 56 Handstamped with Chinese characters

壹   五   壹員
g   h   i

61	A1	(g) 20c on 30c gray green	15.00	2.00
a.		20c on 30c dull green	25.00	3.75
b.		"20 CENTS" double		
62	A1	(h) 50c on 48c lilac	32.50	2.75
63	A1	(i) $1 on 96c vio, red	200.00	12.00

No. 61 may be found with Chinese character 2, 2½ or 3mm high.
The handstamped Chinese surcharges on Nos. 61-63 exist in several varieties including inverted, double, triple, misplaced and omitted.

Nos. 43 and 20 Surcharged **7** cents.

1891

64	A1	7c on 10c green	45.00	5.00
a.		Double surcharge	3,500.	1,500.

Wmk. 1

65	A1	14c on 30c violet	95.00	42.50

Beware of faked varieties.

1841
Hong Kong
JUBILEE
1891

No. 36 Overprinted in Black

1891, Jan. 22   **Wmk. 2**

66	A1	2c rose	225.00	80.00
a.		Double overprint	12,000.	8,500.
b.		"U" of "JUBILEE" shorter	350.00	150.00
c.		"J" of "JUBILEE" shorter	300.00	150.00
d.		Tall "K" in "KONG"	650.00	350.00

50th anniversary of the colony.
Beware of faked varieties.

No. 26 Surcharged (Chinese Handstamped)

壹圓 **ONE DOLLAR**

1897, Sept.   **Wmk. 1**   *Perf. 15½x15*

67	A2	$1 on $2 sage green	110.00	65.00
a.		Without Chinese surcharge	1,000.	900.00

On No. 57
Perf. 14

68	A2	$1 on $2 gray green	160.00	70.00
a.		Without Chinese surcharge	500.00	375.00

拾

Handstamp Surcharged in Black

10 CENTS

1898   **Wmk. 2**

69	A1	10c on 30c gray grn	20.00	25.00
a.		Large Chinese surcharge	600.00	600.00
b.		Without Chinese surcharge	300.00	600.00
70	A1	$1 on 96c black	65.00	65.00
a.		Without Chinese surcharge	1,100.	1,500.

The Chinese surcharge is added separately.
See notes below Nos. 61-63. The small Chinese surcharge is illustrated.

King Edward VII — A10

1903   **Wmk. 2**

71	A10	1c brown & lilac	.90	.15
72	A10	2c gray green	3.00	1.10
73	A10	4c violet, *red*	5.50	.15
74	A10	5c org & gray grn	8.00	8.00
75	A10	8c violet & black	5.00	.85

76	A10	10c ultra & lil, *bl*	25.00	.85
77	A10	12c red vio & gray grn, *yel*	6.50	.85
78	A10	20c org brn & blk	25.00	1.75
79	A10	30c blk & gray grn	27.50	8.50
80	A10	50c red vio & gray green	20.00	18.00
81	A10	$1 olive grn & lil	70.00	12.00
82	A10	$2 scar & black	140.00	150.00
83	A10	$3 dp blue & blk	150.00	200.00
84	A10	$5 blue grn & lil	300.00	250.00
85	A10	$10 org & blk, *bl*	750.00	400.00
		Nos. 71-85 (15)	1,536.	1,052.

1904-11   **Wmk. 3**
Ordinary or Chalky Paper

86	A10	1c brown ('10)	.65	.15
a.		Booklet pane of 4		
87	A10	2c gray green	2.00	.80
88	A10	2c deep green	12.50	1.00
a.		Booklet pane of 4		
b.		Booklet pane of 12		
89	A10	4c violet, *red*	2.00	.15
90	A10	4c carmine	2.50	.25
a.		Booklet pane of 4		
b.		Booklet pane of 12		
91	A10	5c org & gray grn	4.00	3.00
92	A10	6c red vio & org ('07)	8.00	2.00
93	A10	8c vio & blk ('07)	3.00	1.00
94	A10	10c ultra & lil, *bl*	8.50	.25
95	A10	10c ultramarine	5.50	.30
96	A10	12c red vio & gray grn, *yel* ('07)	4.50	4.00
97	A10	20c org brn & blk	10.00	1.00
98	A10	20c ol grn & vio ('11)	27.50	27.50
99	A10	30c blk & gray grn	12.00	5.00
100	A10	30c org & vio ('11)	37.50	12.50
101	A10	50c red vio & gray green	25.00	5.50
102	A10	50c blk, *grn* ('11)	22.50	8.50
103	A10	$1 ol grn & lil	57.50	9.00
104	A10	$2 scar & black	85.00	62.50
105	A10	$2 blk & car ('10)	150.00	125.00
106	A10	$3 dp bl & blk	100.00	125.00
107	A10	$5 bl grn & lil	200.00	200.00
108	A10	$10 org & blk, *bl*	800.00	525.00
		Nos. 86-108 (23)	1,580.	1,119.

Nos. 86, 88, 90, 94 and 95 are on ordinary paper only. Nos. 92, 93, 96, 98, 100, 102, 105, 106 and 107 are on chalky paper and the others of the issue are on both papers.
The 4c, 5c, 8c, 12c 20c, 50c, $2 and $5 denominations of type A10 are expressed in colored letters or numerals and letters on a colorless background.

King George V
A11   A12

A13   A14

A15

1912-14   **Ordinary Paper**

109	A11	1c brown	1.00	.25
a.		Booklet pane of 12		
110	A11	2c deep green	3.00	.25
a.		Booklet pane of 12		
111	A12	4c carmine	2.00	.25
a.		Booklet pane of 12		
b.		Booklet pane of 4		
112	A13	6c orange	2.00	.50
113	A12	8c gray	14.00	3.00
114	A11	10c ultramarine	22.50	.25

Chalky Paper

115	A14	12c vio, *yel*	1.50	3.00
116	A14	20c ol grn & vio	2.25	.50
117	A15	25c red vio & dl violet	8.00	12.00
118	A13	30c org & violet	22.50	3.00
119	A14	50c black, green	5.00	.30
a.		50c black, emerald	13.00	11.00
b.		50c black, *bl grn*, ol back	250.00	15.00
c.		50c black, emer, ol back	14.00	3.00
120	A11	$1 blue & vio, *bl*	15.00	1.00
121	A14	$2 black & red	67.50	22.50
122	A13	$3 vio & green	100.00	40.00
123	A14	$5 red & grn, *grn*	250.00	175.00
a.		$5 red & grn, *bl grn*, ol back	425.00	100.00
124	A13	$10 blk & vio, *red*	225.00	50.00
		Nos. 109-124 (16)	741.25	311.80

For overprints see British Offices in China #1-27.

1914, May   **Surface-colored Paper**

125	A14	12c violet, *yel*	2.50	1.50
126	A14	50c black, *green*	3.00	.60
127	A14	$5 red & grn, *grn*	200.00	115.00
		Nos. 125-127 (3)	205.50	117.10

Stamp of 1912-14 Redrawn

元 instead of 弍 at upper left.

1919, Sept.   **Chalky Paper**

128	A15	25c red vio & dl vio	55.00	30.00

Types of 1912-14 Issue

1921-37   **Wmk. 4**
Ordinary Paper

129	A11	1c brown	.50	.30
130	A11	2c deep green	1.25	.25
131	A12	2c gray ('37)	11.00	4.00
132	A12	3c gray ('31)	3.00	.75
133	A12	4c rose red	2.50	.80
134	A12	5c violet ('31)	2.75	.15
135	A12	8c gray	7.00	35.00
136	A12	8c orange	1.40	.80
137	A11	10c ultramarine	1.75	.15

Chalky Paper

138	A14	12c vio, *yel* ('33)	8.50	.50
139	A14	20c ol grn & dl vio	2.50	.20
140	A15	25c red vio & dl vio, redrawn	2.00	.35
141	A13	30c yel & violet	9.00	1.50
142	A14	50c blk, *emerald*	9.00	.15
143	A11	$1 ultra & vio, *bl*	15.00	.60
144	A14	$2 black & red	57.50	4.75
145	A13	$3 dl vio & grn ('26)	110.00	35.00
146	A14	$5 red & grn, *emer* ('25)	240.00	45.00
		Nos. 129-146 (18)	484.65	130.25

Silver Jubilee Issue
Common Design Type

1935, May 6   **Engr.**   *Perf. 11x12*

147	CD301	3c black & ultra	1.75	1.00
148	CD301	5c indigo & grn	7.00	1.00
149	CD301	10c ultra & brn	17.00	2.75
150	CD301	20c brn vio & ind	20.00	6.00
		Nos. 147-150 (4)	45.75	10.75
		Set, never hinged	100.00	

Coronation Issue
Common Design Type

1937, May 12   *Perf. 11x11½*

151	CD302	4c deep green	1.00	.50
152	CD302	15c dark carmine	2.25	.80
153	CD302	25c deep ultra	4.00	1.75
		Nos. 151-153 (3)	7.25	3.05
		Set, never hinged	18.00	

Common Design Types pictured in section before Great Britain.

King George VI — A16

1938-48   **Typo.**   *Perf. 14*
Ordinary Paper

154	A16	1c brown	.35	.15
155	A16	2c gray	.50	.15
156	A16	4c orange	.60	.15
157	A16	5c green	.30	.15

157B	A16	8c brown red ('41)	.65	.15
c.		Imperf., pair		
158	A16	10c violet	1.50	.15
159	A16	15c carmine	.30	.15
159A	A16	20c gray ('46)	.30	.15
159B	A16	20c rose red ('48)	1.50	.15
160	A16	25c ultramarine	9.25	.15
160A	A16	25c gray ol ('46)	.95	.15
161	A16	30c olive bister	62.50	2.50
161B	A16	30c lt ultra ('46)	1.25	.15
162	A16	50c red violet	1.50	.15

Chalky Paper

162B	A16	80c lilac rose ('48)	1.10	.15
163	A16	$1 lilac & ultra	3.25	.20
163B	A16	$1 dp org & grn ('46)	1.90	.15
164	A16	$2 dp org & grn	30.00	3.50
164A	A16	$2 vio & red ('46)	3.50	.60
165	A16	$5 lilac & red	22.50	1.25
165A	A16	$5 grn & vio ('46)	21.00	.90
166	A16	$10 grn & vio	165.00	30.00
166A	A16	$10 vio & ultra ('46)	40.00	2.50
		Nos. 154-166A (23)	369.70	43.70
		Set, never hinged	675.00	

Coarse Impressions
Ordinary Paper

1941-46   *Perf. 14½x14*

155a	A16	2c gray	3.50	1.25
156a	A16	4c orange ('46)	3.00	1.75
157a	A16	5c green	2.00	2.50
158a	A16	10c violet	1.50	1.50
161a	A16	30c dull olive bister	1.25	1.50
162a	A16	50c red lilac	4.50	1.00
		Nos. 155a-162a (6)	15.75	9.50

A17 FIVE CENTS

1938, Jan. 11   **Wmk. 4**

167	A17	5c green	20.00	25.00
		Never hinged	40.00	

No. 167 is a revenue stamp officially authorized to be sold and used for postal purposes. Used Jan. 11-20, 1938. The used price is for the stamp on cover. CTO covers exist.

Street Scene — A18   Hong Kong Bank — A22

Liner and Junk — A19

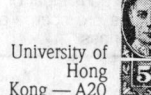

University of Hong Kong — A20

Harbor — A21

China Clipper and Seaplane — A23

Perf. 13½x13, 13x13½

1941, Feb. 26   **Engr.**   **Wmk. 4**

168	A18	2c sepia & org	.50	.30
169	A19	4c rose car & vio	1.25	.75
170	A20	5c yel grn & blk	.60	.20
171	A21	15c red & black	2.25	.75

172 A22 25c dp blue & dk brn 4.25 1.50
173 A23 $1 brn org & brt bl 13.00 4.50
Nos. 168-173 (6) 21.85 8.00
Set, never hinged 70.00

Centenary of British rule.

Catalogue values for unused stamps in this section, from this point to the end of the section, are for Never Hinged items.

Peace Issue

Phoenix Rising from Flames A24

1946, Aug. 29 ***Perf. 13x12½***
174 A24 30c car & dp blue 1.75 1.00
175 A24 $1 car & brown 3.25 2.50

Return to peace after WWII.

Silver Wedding Issue
Common Design Types
Perf. 14x14½

1948, Dec. 22 Photo. Wmk. 4
178 CD304 10c purple .50 .20

Engr.; Name Typo.
Perf. 11½x11
179 CD305 $10 rose car 140.00 40.00
Set, hinged 80.00

UPU Issue
Common Design Types
Engr.; Name Typo. on 20c & 30c

1949, Oct. 10 ***Perf. 13½, 11x11½***
180 CD306 10c violet 6.00 1.10
181 CD307 20c deep carmine 10.50 2.25
182 CD308 30c indigo 14.00 2.25
183 CD309 80c red violet 30.00 7.75
Nos. 180-183 (4) 60.50 13.35

Coronation Issue
Common Design Type

1953, June 2 Engr. ***Perf. 13½x13***
184 CD312 10c purple & black 3.50 .15

Elizabeth II A25

Arms of University A26

1954-60 Typo. ***Perf. 13½x14***
185 A25 5c orange .20 .15
a. Imperf., pair 1,250.
186 A25 10c violet .35 .15
187 A25 15c green .35 .15
188 A25 20c brown .40 .15
189 A25 25c rose red .50 .15
190 A25 30c gray .90 .15
191 A25 40c blue 1.25 .15
192 A25 50c red violet 1.25 .15
193 A25 65c lt gray ('60) 25.00 2.25
194 A25 $1 org & green 2.25 .15
195 A25 $1.30 bl & ver ('60) 25.00 1.50
196 A25 $2 violet & red 12.00 .25
197 A25 $5 green & vio 50.00 .55
198 A25 $10 violet & ultra 90.00 1.50
Nos. 185-198 (14) 209.45 7.40
Set, hinged 90.00

Nos. 185-187 are on ordinary paper; Nos. 188-198 on chalky paper.

Perf. 11½x12

1961, Sept. 11 Photo. Wmk. 314
199 A26 $1 bl, blk, red, grn & gold 6.00 1.50
a. Gold omitted 1,000.

University of Hong Kong, 50th anniv.

Queen Victoria Statue, Victoria Park, Hong Kong — A27

Queen Elizabeth II — A28

1962, May 4 ***Perf. 14***
200 A27 10c car rose & black .22 .15
201 A27 20c blue & black .95 .35
202 A27 50c bister & black 1.90 .75
Nos. 200-202 (3) 3.07 1.25

1st postage stamps of Hong Kong, cent.

Wmk. 314 Upright

1962, Oct. 4 Photo. ***Perf. 14½x14***

Size: 17x21mm

203 A28 5c red orange .20 .15
a. Booklet pane of 4 1.40
204 A28 10c purple .20 .15
a. Booklet pane of 4 2.75
205 A28 15c green 1.00 .15
206 A28 20c red brown 1.10 .15
a. Booklet pane of 4 7.50
207 A28 25c lilac rose 1.50 .15
208 A28 30c dark blue 1.50 .15
209 A28 40c Prus green 1.75 .15
210 A28 50c crimson 1.75 .15
a. Booklet pane of 4 17.00
211 A28 65c ultramarine 9.50 1.50
212 A28 $1 dark brown 9.50 .15

Perf. 14x14½

Size: 25½x30½mm

Portrait in Natural Colors

213 A28 $1.30 sky blue 6.75 .15
a. Ocher (sash) omitted 75.00
b. Yellow omitted 75.00
214 A28 $2 fawn 9.50 .15
a. Yellow and ocher (sash) omitted 100.00
b. Yellow omitted
215 A28 $5 orange 20.00 .75
a. Ocher (sash) omitted 85.00
216 A28 $10 green 42.50 1.00
217 A28 $20 violet blue 95.00 6.00
Nos. 203-217 (15) 201.75 10.90

1966-72 Wmk. 314 Sideways
203b A28 5c ('67) .15 .15
204b A28 10c ('67) .20 .15
205a A28 15c ('67) .30 .15
206b A28 20c .40 .15
207a A28 25c ('67) .55 .15
208a A28 30c ('70) .65 .15
209a A28 40c ('67) .70 .15
210b A28 50c ('67) 1.10 .15
211a A28 65c ('67) 4.75 2.00
212a A28 $1 ('67) 4.75 .20
213c A28 $1.30 ('72) 3.25 .75
214c A28 $2 ('71) 9.50 1.75
215b A28 $5 ('71) 37.50 4.00
217a A28 $20 ('72) 110.00 40.00
Nos. 203b-217a (14) 173.80 49.90

Freedom from Hunger Issue
Common Design Type
Perf. 14x14½

1963, June 4 Photo. Wmk. 314
218 CD314 $1.30 green 40.00 7.50

Red Cross Centenary Issue
Common Design Type

1963, Sept. 2 Litho. ***Perf. 13***
219 CD315 10c black & red .75 .15
220 CD315 $1.30 ultra & red 21.00 3.50

ITU Issue
Common Design Type

1965, May 17 ***Perf. 11x11½***
221 CD317 10c red lil & yel .75 .15
222 CD317 $1.30 apple grn & turq blue 19.00 2.75

Intl. Cooperation Year Issue
Common Design Type

1965, Oct. 25 ***Perf. 14½***
223 CD318 10c blue grn & cl .40 .15
224 CD318 $1.30 lt violet & grn 15.00 2.75

Churchill Memorial Issue
Common Design Type

1966, Jan. 24 Photo. ***Perf. 14***

Design in Black, Gold and Carmine Rose

225 CD319 10c bright blue .75 .15
226 CD319 50c green 4.00 .45
227 CD319 $1.30 brown 12.00 2.75
228 CD319 $2 violet 24.00 3.50
Nos. 225-228 (4) 40.75 6.85

WHO Headquarters Issue
Common Design Type

1966, Sept. 20 Litho. ***Perf. 14***
229 CD322 10c multicolored .15 .15
230 CD322 50c multicolored 5.00 1.00

UNESCO Anniversary Issue
Common Design Type

1966, Dec. 1 Litho. ***Perf. 14***
231 CD323 10c "Education" .85 .15
232 CD323 50c "Science" 4.50 .85
233 CD323 $2 "Culture" 37.50 6.50
Nos. 231-233 (3) 42.85 7.50

Three Rams' Heads A29

Lunar New Year: $1.30, Three rams.

1967, Jan. 17 Photo. ***Perf. 14***
234 A29 10c red, citron & grn 1.25 .15
235 A29 $1.30 red, cit & brt grn 22.50 4.00

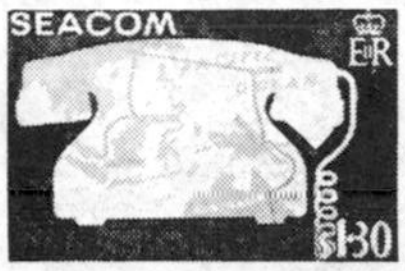

Outline of Telephone with Map of South East Asia and Australia A30

1967, Mar. 30 Photo. ***Perf. 12½***
236 A30 $1.30 dk red & blue 12.00 1.90

Completion of the Hong Kong-Malaysia link of the South East Asia Commonwealth Cable, SEACOM.

Monkeys A31

Lunar New Year: $1.30, Two monkey families.

1968, Jan. 23 Wmk. 314 ***Perf. 14***
237 A31 10c crim, blk & gold 1.00 .15
238 A31 $1.30 crim, blk & gold 19.00 4.00

Liner and New Sea Terminal A32

Seacraft: 20c, Pleasure launch and sailing cruiser. 40c, Vehicle ferry. 50c, Passenger ferry. $1, Sampan. $1.30, Junk.

Perf. 13x12½

1968, Apr. 24 Litho. Unwmk.
239 A32 10c multicolored .70 .15
240 A32 20c sky blue, bis & black 1.75 .25
241 A32 40c org, rose lil & black 4.50 .90
242 A32 50c brt red, emer & black 5.50 .35
243 A32 $1 yel, cop red & black 13.00 1.40
244 A32 $1.30 dk bl, brt pink & black 24.00 2.75
Nos. 239-244 (6) 49.45 5.80

Bauhinia Blakeana — A33

Perf. 14x14½

1968, Sept. 25 Photo. Wmk. 314
245 A33 65c shown 3.00 .30
a. Wmkd. sideways ('72) 7.75 .75
246 A33 $1 Coat of Arms 3.50 .30
a. Wmkd. sideways ('71) 7.25 .60

Human Rights Flame and "Lamp of Life" — A34

1968, Nov. 20 Litho. ***Perf. 13½***
247 A34 10c green, org & blk .65 .15
248 A34 50c magenta, yel & blk 4.50 1.25

International Human Rights Year.

Cock A35

Design: $1.30, Cock, vert.

Perf. 13x13½, 13½x13

1969, Feb. 11 Photo. Unwmk.
249 A35 10c brown, blk, org & red 2.75 .15
a. Red omitted
250 A35 $1.30 ocher, blk, org & red *72.50* 5.00

Lunar New Year, Feb. 17, 1969.

Chinese University Seal — A36

1969, Aug. 26 Unwmk. ***Perf. 13***
251 A36 40c multicolored 4.50 .75

Chinese University of Hong Kong, founded 1963.

Radar, Globe and Satellite A37

Perf. 14x14½

1969, Sept. 24 Photo. Wmk. 314
252 A37 $1 scarlet, blk, sil & bl 6.50 1.75

Opening of the satellite earth station (connected through the Indian Ocean satellite Intelsat III) on Stanley Peninsula, Hong Kong.

Chow — A38

Emblem — A39

Lunar New Year (Year of the Dog): $1.30, Chow, horiz.

1970, Jan. 28 ***Perf. 14***
253 A38 10c black & multi 3.50 .15
254 A38 $1.30 green & multi 67.50 6.00

Perf. 13½x13, 13x13½

1970, Mar. 14 Litho. Wmk. 314

Design: 25c, Emblem and Chinese junks, horiz.

255 A39 15c multicolored .70 .20
256 A39 25c multicolored 1.10 .35

EXPO '70 Intl. Exposition, Osaka, Japan, Mar. 15-Sept. 13.

"A Compassionate Ship on the Bitter Sea" — A40

1970, Apr. 9   Photo.   Perf. 14
257 A40 10c yel green & multi   .40 .15
258 A40 50c scarlet & multi   2.25 1.00

Centenary of the Tung Wah Group of Hospitals (including schools and various charitable organizations).

A.P.Y. Emblem — A41

1970, Aug. 5   Litho.   Wmk. 314
259 A41 10c yellow & multi   1.00 .20

Issued for Asian Productivity Year.

Boar A42

Perf. 13x13¹/₂

1971, Jan. 20   Photo.   Unwmk.
260 A42 10c yel green, gold & black   1.75 .15
261 A42 $1.30 vio, gold & blk   24.00 2.75

Lunar New Year.

Scout Emblem and "60" A43

Perf. 14x14¹/₂

1971, July 23   Litho.   Wmk. 314
262 A43 10c red, yellow & black   .40 .15
263 A43 50c blue, emer & black   2.25 .35
264 A43 $2 vio, lil rose & blk   9.00 2.00
   Nos. 262-264 (3)   11.65 2.50

60th anniversary of Hong Kong Boy Scouts.

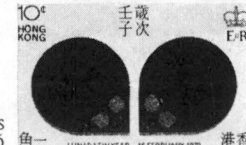

Festival Emblem A44

Symbolic Flower A45

Festival of Hong Kong: 50c, Dancers, horiz.

1971, Nov. 2   Perf. 14
265 A44 10c lilac & orange   .35 .15

Perf. 14¹/₂
266 A45 50c lilac & multi   1.65 .75
267 A45 $1 lilac & multi   3.50 1.50
   Nos. 265-267 (3)   5.50 2.40

Rats A46

1972, Feb. 8   Photo.   Unwmk.
268 A46 10c black, red & gold   1.50 .15
269 A46 $1.30 black, gold & red   25.00 2.00

Lunar New Year.

Cross Harbor Tunnel Entrance — A47

Perf. 14x14¹/₂

1972, Oct. 20   Litho.   Wmk. 314
270 A47 $1 multicolored   4.00 .65

Inauguration of Cross Harbor Tunnel linking Victoria and Kowloon.

Silver Wedding Issue, 1972
Common Design Type

Design: Queen Elizabeth II, Prince Philip, phoenix and dragon.

1972, Nov. 20   Photo.   Perf. 14x14¹/₂
271 CD324 10c citron & multi   .15 .15
272 CD324 50c gray & multi   .85 .40
   Set value   .45

Ox — A48

Lunar New Year: 10c, Ox, vert.

1973, Feb. 3   Perf. 14
273 A48 10c dk brown & red   .90 .15
274 A48 $1.30 dk brn, yel & org   6.00 1.00

Elizabeth II — A49

Wmk. 314 Upright; Sideways (15c, 30c, 40c)
Photo. & Embossed
1973, June 12   Perf. 14¹/₂x14
Size: 20x24mm
275 A49 10c orange   .20 .15
   b. Booklet pane of 4 ('75)   .60
   d. Watermark sideways (coil)   .25 .15
276 A49 15c olive green   .30 .15
   b. Booklet pane of 4 ('75)   1.75
277 A49 20c bright purple   .50 .15
   b. Booklet pane of 4 ('75)   2.50
278 A49 25c deep brown   .60 .15
279 A49 30c ultramarine   .75 .15
280 A49 40c blue green   .75 .20
281 A49 50c red   .95 .15
   b. Booklet pane of 4 ('75)   4.50
282 A49 65c dp bister   2.25 .45
283 A49 $1 dk slate green   2.50 .20

Perf. 14x14¹/₂
Wmk. 314 Sideways
Size: 28x32mm
284 A49 $1.30 dk pur & yel   2.50 .45
285 A49 $2 dp brn & lt grn   2.50 .70
286 A49 $5 dk vio bl & rose   8.00 2.00

Photo. & Embossed
287 A49 $10 dk sl green & pink   15.00 4.50
288 A49 $20 black & rose   30.00 7.50
   Nos. 275-288 (14)   66.80 16.90

1975-78   Wmk. 373   Perf. 14¹/₂x14
Size: 20x24mm
275a A49 10c orange   .20 .15
   c. Booklet pane of 4 ('76)   .30
276a A49 15c olive green   .20 .15
   c. Booklet pane of 4   .55
277a A49 20c bright purple   .20 .15
   c. Booklet pane of 4 ('76)   .70
278a A49 25c deep brown   .35 .15
279a A49 30c ultramarine   .40 .20
280a A49 40c blue green   .55 .30
281a A49 50c red   .65 .30
   c. Booklet pane of 4   2.75
282a A49 65c deep bister   1.00 .40
283a A49 $1 dark slate green   1.50 .15

Perf. 14x14¹/₂
Size: 28x32mm
284a A49 $1.30 dark purple & yel   2.00 .70
285a A49 $2 dp brn & lt grn   3.00 1.10
286a A49 $5 dk vio bl & rose ('78)   7.00 2.75
287a A49 $10 dk sl grn & pink ('78)   14.00 5.50
288a A49 $20 black & rose ('78)   27.50 11.00
   Nos. 275a-288a (14)   58.55 23.30

See Nos. 316-327.

Princess Anne's Wedding Issue
Common Design Type
Wmk. 314

1973, Nov. 14   Litho.   Perf. 14
289 CD325 50c ocher & multi   .40 .20
290 CD325 $2 lilac & multi   2.00 1.00

Chinese Character "Hong" A50

Designs: 50c, "Kong." $1, "Festival."

1973, Nov. 23   Litho.   Perf. 14¹/₂x14
291 A50 10c red & green   .25 .15
292 A50 50c plum & red   1.25 .35
293 A50 $1 emerald & plum   3.25 1.00
   Nos. 291-293 (3)   4.75 1.50

Festival of Hong Kong 1973.

Tiger A51

Lunar New Year: $1.30, Tiger, vert.

Perf. 14¹/₂x14, 14x14¹/₂

1974, Jan. 8   Wmk. 314
294 A51 10c green & multi   .60 .15
295 A51 $1.30 lilac & multi   5.75 .80

Chinese Opera Mask — A52

Designs: Chinese opera masks.

1974, Feb. 1   Photo.   Perf. 12x12¹/₂
296 A52 10c black, red & org   .25 .15
297 A52 $1 multicolored   2.25 .65
298 A52 $2 black, org & gold   5.50 1.50
   a. Souvenir sheet of 3, #296-298, perf. 14x13   35.00 25.00
   Nos. 296-298 (3)   8.00 2.30

Hong Kong Arts Festival.

Carrier Pigeons A53

Cent. of UPU: 50c, Symbolic globe in envelope. $2, Hands holding letters.

1974, Oct. 9   Litho.   Perf. 14
299 A53 10c blue, grn & blk   .15 .15
   a. Unwatermarked   50.00
300 A53 50c magenta & multi   .60 .25
301 A53 $2 violet & multi   2.50 .95
   Nos. 299-301 (3)   3.25 1.35

Rabbit A54

Lunar New Year: $1.30, Two rabbits.

1975, Feb. 5   Wmk. 314   Perf. 14
302 A54 10c silver & red   .30 .15
   a. Unwatermarked   .30 .15
303 A54 $1.30 gold & green   3.75 .90
   a. Unwatermarked   3.75 1.10

Queen Elizabeth II, Prince Philip, Hong Kong Arms — A55

Perf. 13¹/₂

1975, Apr. 30   Litho.   Wmk. 373
304 A55 $1.30 blue & multi   1.50 .40
305 A55 $2 yellow & multi   2.50 .70

Royal Visit 1975.

Mid-Autumn Festival — A56

Brown Laughing Thrush — A57

Abstract Designs: $1, Dragon Boat Festival (boats). $2, Tin Hau Festival (ships with flags).

1975, July 31   Unwmk.   Perf. 14
306 A56 50c rose lilac & multi   2.75 .30
307 A56 $1 brt green & multi   5.50 1.10
308 A56 $2 orange & multi   11.00 2.25
   a. Souvenir sheet of 3, #306-308   70.00 22.50
   Nos. 306-308 (3)   19.25 3.65

Hong Kong Festivals, 1975.

1975, Oct. 29   Litho.   Wmk. 373
Birds: $1.30, Chinese bulbul. $2, Black-capped kingfisher.

309 A57 50c lt blue & multi   1.25 .50
310 A57 $1.30 pink & multi   4.75 1.00
311 A57 $2 yellow & multi   5.00 1.50
   Nos. 309-311 (3)   11.00 3.00

Dragon A58

Lunar New Year: $1.30, like 20c, pattern reversed.

1976, Jan. 21   Litho.   Perf. 14¹/₂
312 A58 20c gold, pur & lilac   .50 .15
313 A58 $1.30 gold, red & grn   5.00 1.00

Queen Elizabeth Type of 1973
Wmk. 373 (#320-323), Unwmkd.
1976-81   Photo.   Perf. 14¹/₂x14
Size: 20x24mm
316 A49 20c bright purple   .85 .15
318 A49 30c ultramarine   1.40 .15
320 A49 60c lt violet ('77)   1.40 .15
321 A49 70c yellow ('77)   1.75 .15
322 A49 80c brt magenta ('77)   2.25 .20
323 A49 90c sepia ('81)   .75 .30

Size: 28x32
Perf. 14x14¹/₂
324 A49 $2 dp brn & lt grn   10.25 .85
325 A49 $5 dk vio bl & rose   24.00 3.50

Photo. & Embossed
326 A49 $10 dk sl grn & pink   65.00 10.50
327 A49 $20 black & rose   175.00 35.00
   Nos. 316-327 (10)   282.65 50.95

Design: $1.30, "60," tents and Girl Guides emblem.

"60" and Girl Guides Emblem A59

1976, Apr. 23   Wmk. 314   Perf. 14½
328	A59	20c silver & multi	.50	.15
329	A59	$1.30 silver & multi	4.00	1.00

60th anniv. of Hong Kong Girl Guides.

"Postal Services" (in Chinese) — A60

Designs: $1.30, General Post Office, 1911-1976. $2, New G.P.O., 1976.

1976, Aug. 11   Litho.   Wmk. 373
330	A60	20c gray, green & black	.45	.15
331	A60	$1.30 gray, red & black	2.00	.60
332	A60	$2 gray, yel & black	3.50	.75
		Nos. 330-332 (3)	5.95	1.50

Opening of new GPO building.

Snake A61

Lunar New Year: $1.30, Snake and branch face left.

1977, Jan. 6   Perf. 13½
333	A61	20c multicolored	.50	.15
334	A61	$1.30 multicolored	3.00	.55

Queen Dotting Eye of Dragon, 1975 Visit A62

Designs: 20c, Presentation of the orb. $2, Orb, vert.

1977, Feb. 7   Litho.
335	A62	20c multicolored	.20	.15
336	A62	$1.30 multicolored	1.25	.45
337	A62	$2 multicolored	2.00	.60
		Nos. 335-337 (3)	3.45	1.20

25th anniv. of the reign of Elizabeth II.

Streetcars — A63

Buttercup Orchid — A64

Designs: 60c, Star ferryboat. $1.30, Funicular railway. $2, Junk and sampan.

Horse and Chinese Character "Ma" — A65

1977, June 30   Wmk. 373   Perf. 13½
338	A63	20c multicolored	.20	.15
339	A63	60c multicolored	.65	.25
340	A63	$1.30 multicolored	1.10	.50
341	A63	$2 multicolored	2.00	.65
		Nos. 338-341 (4)	3.95	1.55

Tourist publicity.

1977, Oct. 12   Litho.   Perf. 14

Designs: $1.30, Lady's-slipper. $2, Susan orchid.
342	A64	20c blue & multi	.30	.15
343	A64	$1.30 yellow & multi	2.50	.65
344	A64	$2 green & multi	4.50	.65
		Nos. 342-344 (3)	7.30	1.45

1978, Jan. 26   Litho.   Perf. 14½
345	A65	20c multicolored	.40	.15
346	A65	$1.30 multicolored	3.00	.55

Lunar New Year.

Elizabeth II   A66

1978, June 2   Litho.   Perf. 14x14½
347	A66	20c carmine & dk blue	.15	.15
348	A66	$1.30 dk blue & carmine	.60	.30

25th anniv. of coronation of Elizabeth II.

Boy and Girl A67

Design: $1.30, Ring-around-a-rosy.

1978, Nov. 8   Wmk. 373   Perf. 14½
349	A67	20c multicolored	.15	.15
350	A67	$1.30 multicolored	.70	.40
		Set value		.47

Centenary of Po Leung Kuk, society for help and education of orphans and poor children.

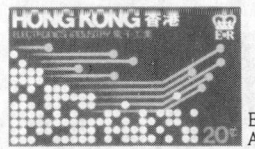

Electronics A68

Industries: $1.30, Toy (bear and drum). $2, Garment (mannequins).

1979, Jan. 9   Litho.   Perf. 14½
351	A68	20c multicolored	.15	.15
352	A68	$1.30 multicolored	.65	.28
353	A68	$2 multicolored	1.10	.55
		Nos. 351-353 (3)	1.90	.98

Precis Orithya — A69

Butterflies: $1, Graphium sarpedon. $1.30, Heliophorus epicles phoenicoparyphus. $2, Danaus genutia.

1979, June 20   Photo.   Unwmk.
354	A69	20c multicolored	.15	.15
355	A69	$1 multicolored	.45	.32
356	A69	$1.30 multicolored	.65	.28
357	A69	$2 multicolored	.80	.55
		Nos. 354-357 (4)	2.05	1.30

Cross Section of Station A70

Mass Transit Railroad: $1.30, Front, rear and side views of train. $2, Map of routes.

1979, Oct. 1   Litho.   Perf. 13½
358	A70	20c multicolored	.15	.15
359	A70	$1.30 multicolored	.35	.20
360	A70	$2 multicolored	1.10	.50
		Nos. 358-360 (3)	1.60	.85

Ching Chung Koon Temple, Tuen Mun — A71

Rural Architecture: 20c, Tsui Shing Lau Pagoda, Sheung Cheung Wai, vert. $1.30, Village house, Sai O.

Perf. 13x13½, 13½x13
1980, May 14   Litho.   Wmk. 373
361	A71	20c multicolored	.15	.15
362	A71	$1.30 multicolored	.60	.32
363	A71	$2 multicolored	.90	.50
		Nos. 361-363 (3)	1.65	.97

Queen Mother Elizabeth Birthday Issue
Common Design Type

1980, Aug. 4   Litho.   Perf. 14
364	CD330	$1.30 multicolored	.55	.30

Botanical Gardens — A72

1980, Nov. 12   Litho.   Perf. 13½
365	A72	20c shown	.15	.15
366	A72	$1 Ocean Park	.40	.26
367	A72	$1.30 Kowloon Park	.55	.32
368	A72	$2 Country Park	.85	.50
		Nos. 365-368 (4)	1.95	1.22

Epinephelus Akaara — A73

1981, Jan. 28   Litho.   Perf. 13½
369	A73	20c shown	.15	.15
370	A73	$1 Nemipterus virgatus	.45	.28
371	A73	$1.30 Choerodon azurio	.60	.35
372	A73	$2 Scarus ghobban	.95	.40
		Nos. 369-372 (4)	2.15	1.18

Royal Wedding Issue
Common Design Type

1981, July 29   Photo.   Perf. 14
373	CD331	20c Bouquet	.15	.15
374	CD331	$1.30 Charles	.45	.28
375	CD331	$5 Couple	1.50	1.10
		Nos. 373-375 (3)	2.10	1.53

Public Housing Development — A74

Designs: Various public housing developments.

1981, Oct. 14   Litho.   Perf. 13½
376	A74	20c multicolored	.15	.15
377	A74	$1 multicolored	.45	.30
378	A74	$1.30 multicolored	.65	.30
379	A74	$2 multicolored	.70	.45
a.		Souvenir sheet of 4, #376-379	3.00	3.00
		Nos. 376-379 (4)	1.95	1.20

Port of Hong Kong A75

Designs: Various views of Port of Hong Kong.

1982, Jan. 12   Litho.   Perf. 14½
380	A75	20c multicolored	.15	.15
381	A75	$1 multicolored	.55	.45
382	A75	$1.30 multicolored	.65	.55
383	A75	$2 multicolored	.80	.65
		Nos. 380-383 (4)	2.15	1.80

Five-banded Civet — A76

1982, May 4   Litho.   Perf. 14½
384	A76	20c shown	.15	.15
385	A76	$1 Pangolin	.35	.32
386	A76	$1.30 Chinese porcupine	.65	.60
387	A76	$5 Barking deer	2.00	1.75
		Nos. 384-387 (4)	3.15	2.82

Queen Elizabeth II
A77   A78

Perf. 14½x14
1982, Aug. 30   Photo.   Wmk. 373
388	A77	10c yellow & dk red	.15	.15
389	A77	20c blue vio & vio	.15	.15
390	A77	30c orange & pur	.15	.15
391	A77	40c lt blue & red	.25	.20
392	A77	50c pale grn & brn	.30	.20
393	A77	60c gray & brt mag	.40	.35
394	A77	70c brt org & dk grn	.50	.35
395	A77	80c gray ol & brn ol	.55	.40
396	A77	90c grnsh bl & grn	.60	.40
397	A77	$1 brt pink & brn org	.60	.40
398	A77	$1.30 rose vio & dk bl	.75	.50
399	A77	$2 buff & blue	.95	.60

Photo. & Embossed
Perf. 14x14½
400	A78	$5 lemon & lake	2.50	1.75
401	A78	$10 brn & blk brn	5.00	3.25
402	A78	$20 lt blue & lake	10.00	6.50
403	A78	$50 gray & lake	22.50	14.00
		Nos. 388-403 (16)	45.40	29.30

Nos. 388 and 397 also issued in coils.

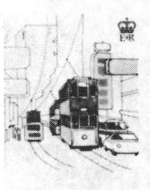 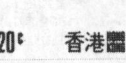

1985-87 **Unwmk.**

388a A77 10c .15 .15
389a A77 20c .40 .30
391a A77 40c .20 .15
392a A77 50c .30 .20
393a A77 60c .35 .25
394a A77 70c .40 .30
395a A77 80c .45 .30
396a A77 90c .50 .35
397a A77 $1 .50 .35
398b A77 $1.30 .55 .40
398A A77 $1.70 brt yel grn & dp bl .30 .20
399a A77 $2 .80 .60
400a A78 $5 2.00 1.50
401a A78 $10 3.75 2.75
402a A78 $20 7.50 5.50
403a A78 $50 17.00 12.00
Nos. 388a-403a (16) 35.15 25.30

Issue dates: $1.30, June 13. $1.70, Sept. 2. 20c, June 1987. Others, Oct. 10, 1985.

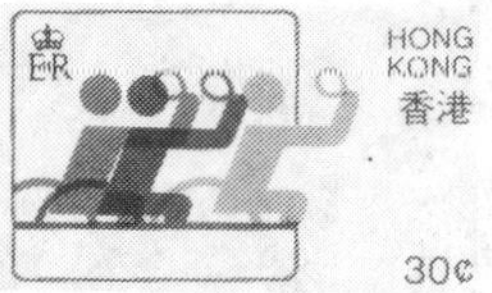

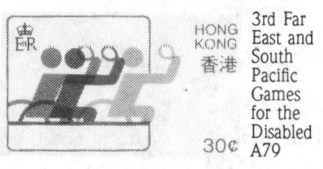

3rd Far East and South Pacific Games for the Disabled A79

Perf. 14x14½

1982, Oct. 31 **Litho.** **Wmk. 373**
404 A79 30c Table tennis .15 .15
405 A79 $1 Racing .60 .42
406 A79 $1.30 Basketball .80 .55
407 A79 $5 Archery 2.50 1.65
Nos. 404-407 (4) 4.05 2.77

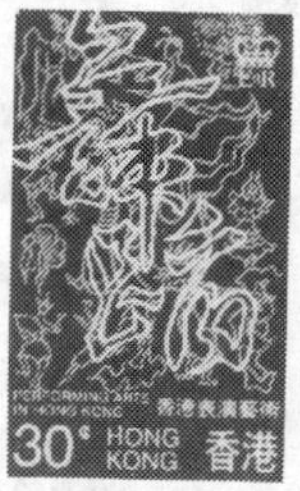

Performing Arts — A80

1983, Jan. 26 **Litho.** ***Perf. 14½x14***
408 A80 30c Dancing .15 .15
409 A80 $1.30 Theater .90 .55
410 A80 $5 Music 2.75 1.65
Nos. 408-410 (3) 3.80 2.35

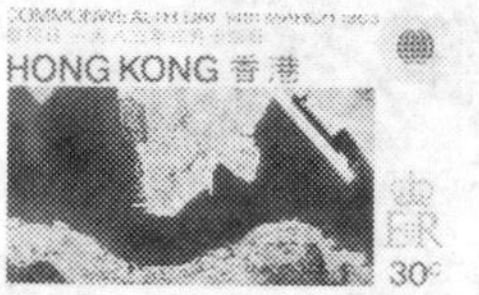

A81

1983, Mar. 14 ***Perf. 14½x13½***
411 A81 30c Aerial view .15 .15
412 A81 $1 Liverpool Bay .60 .45
413 A81 $1.30 Flag .80 .55
414 A81 $5 Queen Elizabeth II 2.50 1.65
Nos. 411-414 (4) 4.05 2.80

Commonwealth Day.

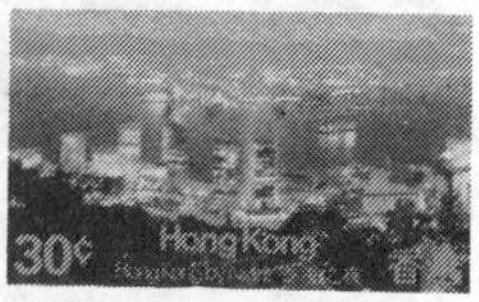

Views by Night A82

1983, Aug. 17 **Litho.** ***Perf. 14½***
415 A82 30c Victoria Harbor .55 .30
416 A82 $1 Space Museum 1.65 .85
417 A82 $1.30 Chinese New Year Fireworks 2.25 1.10
418 A82 $5 Jumbo Restaurant 5.50 2.75
Nos. 415-418 (4) 9.95 5.00

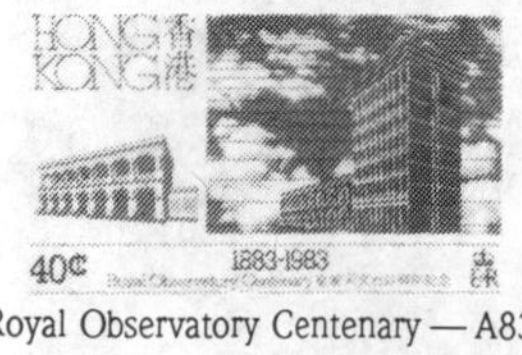

Royal Observatory Centenary — A83

1983, Nov. 23 **Litho.** ***Perf. 14½***
419 A83 40c Technical facilities .30 .20
420 A83 $1 Wind measurement .90 .55
421 A83 $1.30 Temperature measurement 1.10 .70
422 A83 $5 Earthquake measurement 3.00 1.75
Nos. 419-422 (4) 5.30 3.20

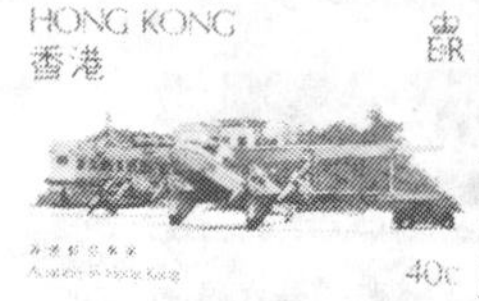

Training Plane, Dorado A84

1984, Mar. 7 **Wmk. 373** ***Perf. 13½***
423 A84 40c shown .30 .20
424 A84 $1 Hong Kong Clipper seaplane .90 .55
425 A84 $1.30 Jumbo jet, Kai Tak Airport 1.10 .70
426 A84 $5 Baldwin Brothers balloon, vert. 3.00 1.75
Nos. 423-426 (4) 5.30 3.20

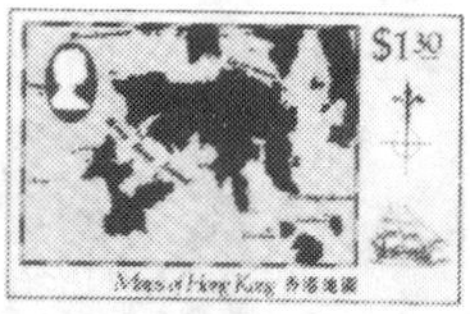

Map of Hong Kong, 19th Cent. A85

Various maps.

1984, June 21 **Litho.** ***Perf. 14***
427 A85 40c multicolored .40 .20
428 A85 $1 multicolored 1.00 .55
429 A85 $1.30 multicolored 1.25 .70
430 A85 $5 multicolored 3.50 1.75
Nos. 427-430 (4) 6.15 3.20

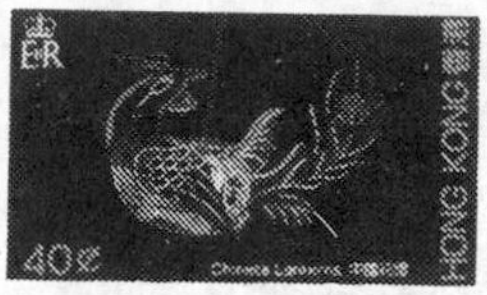

Chinese Lanterns A86

1984, Sept. 6 **Litho.** ***Perf. 13½x13***
431 A86 40c Rooster .40 .20
432 A86 $1 Bull 1.00 .55
433 A86 $1.30 Butterfly 1.25 .70
434 A86 $5 Fish 3.50 1.75
Nos. 431-434 (4) 6.15 3.20

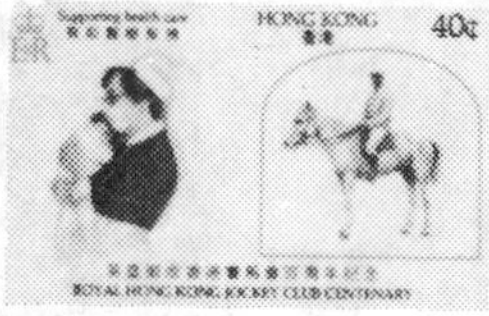

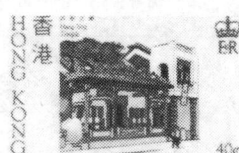

Jockey Club Centenary — A87

1984, Nov. 21 **Litho.** ***Perf. 14½***
435 A87 40c Supporting health care .22 .20
436 A87 $1 Supporting disabled .60 .55
437 A87 $1.30 Supporting the arts .80 .70
438 A87 $5 Supporting Ocean Park 1.90 1.75
a. Souvenir sheet of 4, #435-438 10.00 5.75
Nos. 435-438 (4) 3.52 3.20

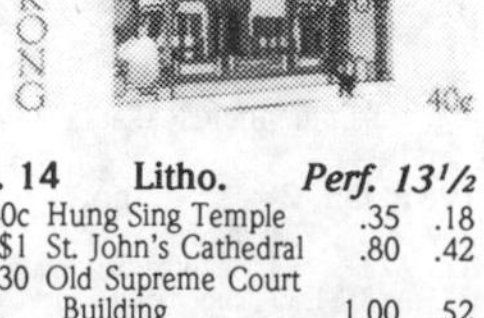

Historic Buildings A88

1985, Mar. 14 **Litho.** ***Perf. 13½***
439 A88 40c Hung Sing Temple .35 .18
440 A88 $1 St. John's Cathedral .80 .42
441 A88 $1.30 Old Supreme Court Building 1.00 .52
442 A88 $5 Wan Chai Post Office 3.00 1.50
Nos. 439-442 (4) 5.15 2.62

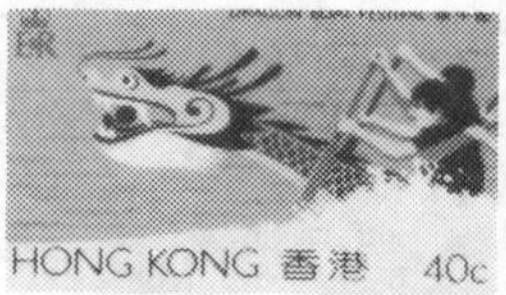

Intl. Dragon Boat Festival A89

1985, June 19 **Litho.** ***Perf. 13½x13***
443 A89 40c multicolored .15 .15
444 A89 $1 multicolored .55 .32
445 A89 $1.30 multicolored .90 .42
446 A89 $5 multicolored 3.00 1.75
b. Souvenir sheet of 4, #443-446, perf. 13x12½ 18.00 10.00
Nos. 443-446 (4) 4.60 2.64

Nos. 443-446 when placed together form a continuous design.

Queen Mother 85th Birthday Issue
Common Design Type

1985, Aug. 7 **Litho.** ***Perf. 14½x14***
447 CD336 40c At Glamis Castle, age 9 .35 .18
448 CD336 $1 On balcony with Princes William and Charles .85 .40
449 CD336 $1.30 Photograph by Cecil Beaton, 1980 .95 .45
450 CD336 $5 Holding Prince Henry 3.00 1.40
Nos. 447-450 (4) 5.15 2.43

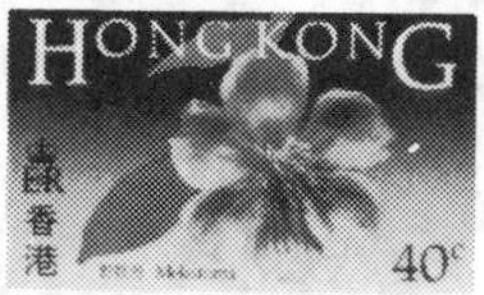

Indigenous Flowers A90

1985, Sept. 25 **Litho.** ***Perf. 13½***
451 A90 40c Melastoma .35 .22
452 A90 50c Chinese lily .50 .28
453 A90 60c Grantham's camellia .50 .32
454 A90 $1.30 Narcissus .85 .52
455 A90 $1.70 Bauhinia 1.10 .60
456 A90 $5 Chinese New Year flower 3.50 2.00
Nos. 451-456 (6) 6.80 3.94

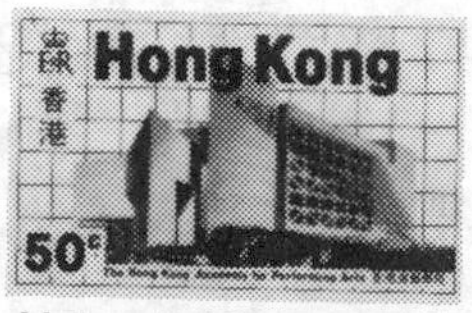

Modern Architecture — A91

1985, Nov. 27 ***Perf. 15***
457 A91 50c Hong Kong Academy for Performing Arts .25 .18
458 A91 $1.30 Exchange Square, vert. .60 .42
459 A91 $1.70 Hong Kong Bank Hdqtrs., vert. .90 .60
460 A91 $5 Hong Kong Coliseum 3.00 1.75
Nos. 457-460 (4) 4.75 2.95

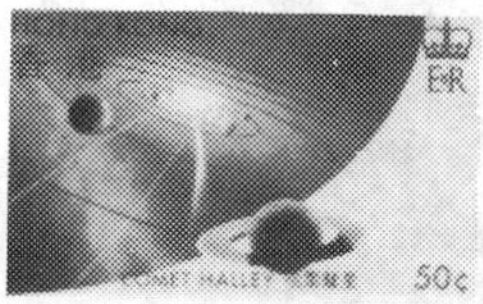

Halley's Comet A92

1986, Feb. 26 **Litho.** ***Perf. 13½x13***
461 A92 50c Comet, solar system .25 .16
462 A92 $1.30 Edmond Halley .70 .42
463 A92 $1.70 Hong Kong, trajectory 1.00 .60
464 A92 $5 Comet, Earth 2.50 1.65
a. Souvenir sheet of 4, #461-464 10.00 6.00
Nos. 461-464 (4) 4.45 2.83

Queen Elizabeth II 60th Birthday
Common Design Type

Designs: 50c, At the wedding of Cecillia Bowes-Lyon, Brompton Parish Church, 1939. $1, Most Noble Order of the Garter, service at St. George's Chapel, Windsor Castle, 1977. $1.30, State visit, 1975. $1.70, Queen Mother's 80th birthday celebration, Royal Lodge, Windsor, 1980. $5, Visiting Crown Agents' offices, 1983.

1986, Apr. 21 ***Perf. 14½***
465 CD337 50c scar, blk & sil .25 .15
466 CD337 $1 ultra & multi .45 .25
467 CD337 $1.30 green & multi .60 .32
468 CD337 $1.70 violet & multi .85 .45
469 CD337 $5 rose vio & multi 3.00 1.50
Nos. 465-469 (5) 5.15 2.67

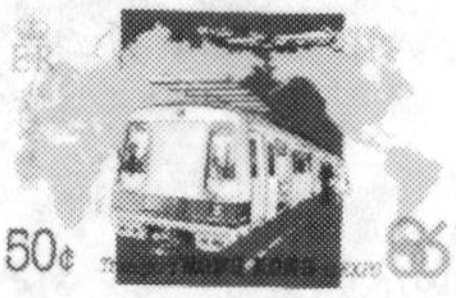

EXPO '86, Vancouver A93

1986, July 18 **Litho.** ***Perf. 13½***
470 A93 50c Transportation .25 .15
471 A93 $1.30 Finance .55 .32
472 A93 $1.70 Trade .75 .42
473 A93 $5 Communications 2.50 1.40
Nos. 470-473 (4) 4.05 2.29

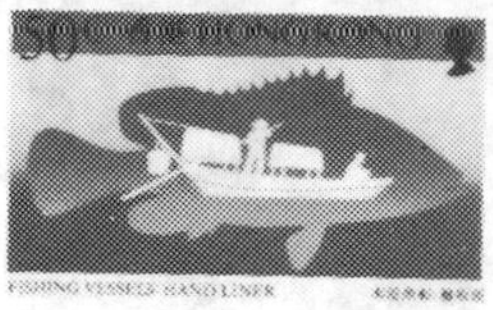
Fishing Vessels A94

1986, Sept. 24 **Litho.**
474 A94 50c Hand-liner sampan .25 .15
475 A94 $1.30 Stern trawler .65 .50
476 A94 $1.70 Long liner junk .80 .65
477 A94 $5 Junk trawler 1.90 1.50
Nos. 474-477 (4) 3.60 2.80

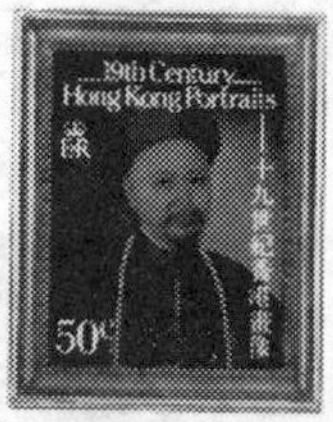

19th Cent. Paintings — A95

Designs: 50c, Possibly, Second puan khequa, by Spoilum. $1.30, Chinese woman, artist unknown. $1.70, Self-portrait at age 52, by Kwan Kiu Chin. $5, Possibly, Wife of a merchant, by George Chinnery.

1986, Dec. 9 **Litho.** ***Perf. 14***
478 A95 50c multicolored .18 .15
479 A95 $1.30 multicolored .60 .50
480 A95 $1.70 multicolored .80 .65
481 A95 $5 multicolored 1.90 1.50
Nos. 478-481 (4) 3.48 2.80

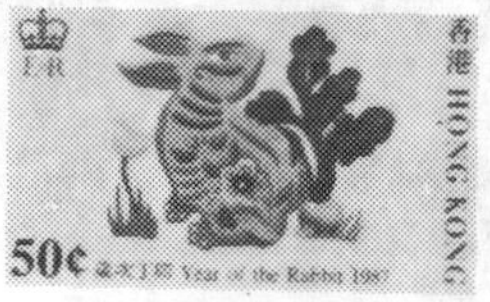

New Year (Year of the Hare) A96

Embroideries of various rabbits.

1987, Jan. 21 **Litho.** ***Perf. 13½x14***
482 A96 50c multicolored .24 .18
483 A96 $1.30 multicolored .65 .48
484 A96 $1.70 multicolored .80 .60
485 A96 $5 multicolored 2.50 1.75
a. Souvenir sheet of 4, #482-485 16.00 10.00
Nos. 482-485 (4) 4.19 3.01

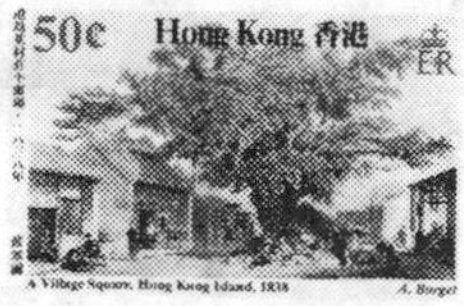

19th Century Paintings in the Hong Kong Museum of Art and Shanghai Banking Corp. — A97

Scenes: 50c, A Village Square, Hong Kong Island, 1838, by Auguste Borget (1809-1877). $1.30, Boat Dwellers in Kowloon Bay, 1838, by Borget. $1.70, Flagstaff House, Lt. Governor D'Aguilar's Residence, 1846, by Murdoch Bruce. $5, A View of Wellington Street, late 19th century, by C. Andrasi.

1987, Apr. 23 Litho. *Perf. 14*

486 A97 50c multicolored .25 .16
487 A97 $1.30 multicolored .65 .45
488 A97 $1.70 multicolored .85 .55
489 A97 $5 multicolored 2.25 1.50
Nos. 486-489 (4) 4.00 2.66

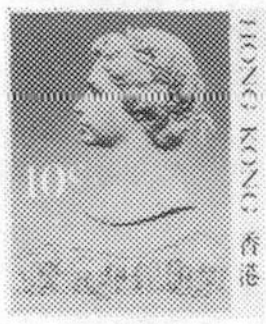

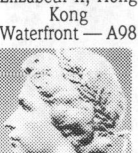

Elizabeth II, Hong Kong Waterfront — A98

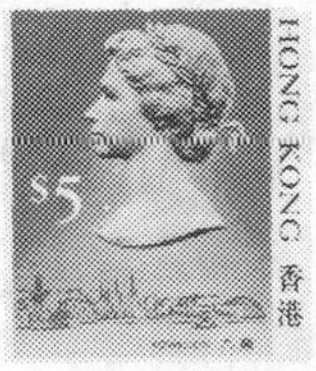

Queen, Natl. Landmarks — A99

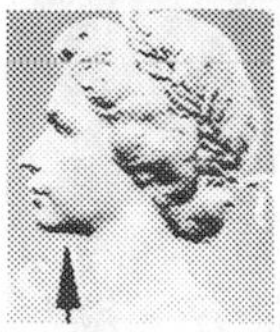

Type I- Darker Shading Under Chin

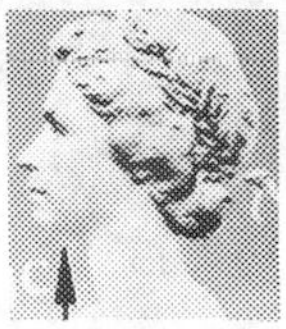

Type II- Lighter Shading Under Chin

Designs: $5, Tsim Shah Tsui, Kowloon. $10, Victoria Harbor. $20, Legislative Council Building. $50, Government House.

1987, July 13 Litho. *Perf. 14½x14*

490 A98 10c yel grn, gray & blk .15 .15
491 A98 40c bluish grn, lt yel & blk .15 .15
492 A98 50c brn org, buff & blk .15 .15
493 A98 60c lt blue, pale rose & blk .15 .15
494 A98 70c vio, pale rose & blk .20 .16
495 A98 80c brt rose lil, lt blue & blk .25 .18
496 A98 90c pink, pale beige & blk .30 .22
497 A98 $1 brt lem & blk .35 .24
498 A98 $1.30 rose claret, brt yel grn & blk .48 .32
499 A98 $1.70 lt blue & blk .60 .40
500 A98 $2 yel grn, cream & blk .70 .45

Perf. 14

501 A99 $5 grn, lt grn & blk 1.90 1.25
502 A99 $10 brn, yel brn & blk 3.50 2.25
503 A99 $20 rose vio, lil & blk 7.50 4.75
504 A99 $50 sep, gray & blk 19.00 12.00
Nos. 490-504 (15) 35.38 22.82

1988, Sept. 1 Type II

490a A98 10c .15 .15
491a A98 40c .18 .15
492a A98 50c .10 .15
493a A98 60c .24 .16
494a A98 70c .28 .18
495a A98 80c .32 .22
496a A98 90c .38 .25
497a A98 $1 .42 .28
498a A98 $1.30 .60 .38
499a A98 $1.70 .70 .48
500a A98 $2 .80 .55
501a A99 $5 2.25 1.50
502a A99 $10 4.25 2.75
b. Souv. sheet of 1, inscribed "1990"
c. As "b," inscribed "1991"
d. As "b," inscribed "1991"
503a A99 $20 8.50 5.75
504a A99 $50 21.00 14.00
Nos. 490a-504a (15) 40.25 26.95

No. 502b for the New Zealand 1990 World Stamp Exhibition. No. 502c for Phila Nippon '91 Intl. Philatelic Exhibition. No. 502d for Hong Kong Post Office sponsorship of 1992 Olympic Games.

Issue dates: No. 502b, Aug. 24. No. 502c, Nov. 16, 1991. No. 502d, Dec. 4, 1991.

Nos. 490a-498a, 500a-504a reissued inscribed "1989," "1990." Nos. 490a, 492a-497a, 499a-504a, "1991."

See Nos. 532-533, 592-593, 629.

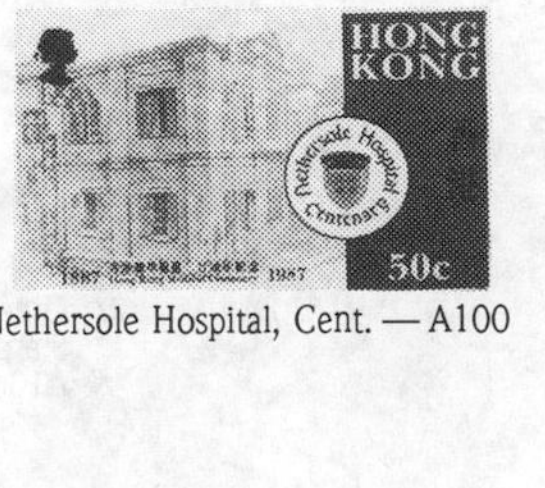

Nethersole Hospital, Cent. — A100

1987, Sept. 8 *Perf. 14½*

505 A100 50c Hospital, 1887 .25 .15
506 A100 $1.30 Patients, staff .60 .38
507 A100 $1.70 Technology, 1987 .75 .48
508 A100 $5 Treatment 2.50 1.40
Nos. 505-508 (4) 4.10 2.41

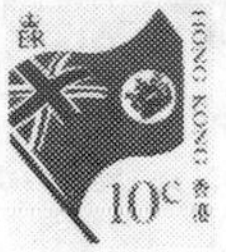

Natl. Flag — A101

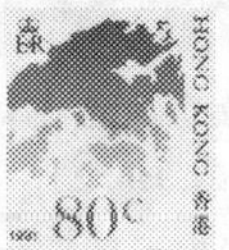

Map of Hong Kong — A101a

Coil Stamps

1987, July 13 *Perf. 15x14*

509 A101 10c shown .20 .20
510 A101a 50c olive green .20 .20

Nos. 509-510 reissued inscribed "1989," No. 509, "1990." See Nos. 611-614.

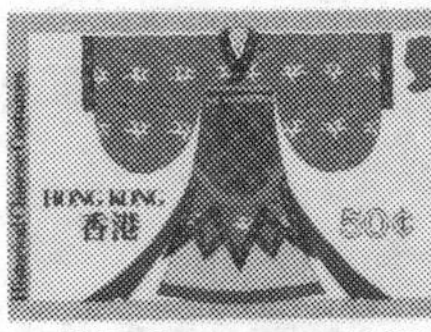

Folk Costumes — A102

1987, Nov. 18 *Perf. 13½*

511 A102 50c multicolored .25 .16
512 A102 $1.30 multi, diff. .60 .42
513 A102 $1.70 multi, diff. .75 .52
514 A102 $5 multi, diff. 2.50 1.65
Nos. 511-514 (4) 4.10 2.75

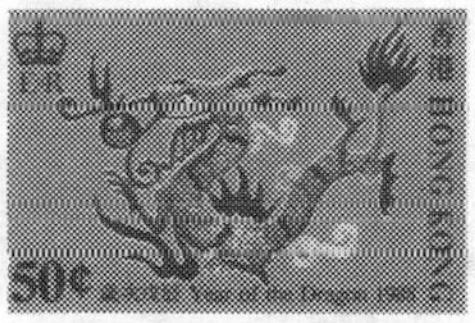

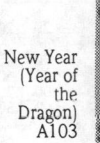

New Year (Year of the Dragon) A103

1988, Jan. 27 Litho. *Perf. 13½*

515 A103 50c multicolored .30 .22
516 A103 $1.30 multi, diff. .80 .60
517 A103 $1.70 multi, diff. 1.00 .80
518 A103 $5 multi, diff. 3.00 2.25
a. Souvenir sheet of 4, #515-518 10.00 5.00
Nos. 515-518 (4) 5.10 3.87

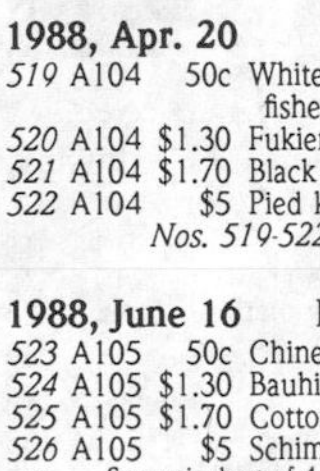

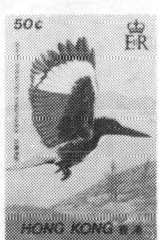

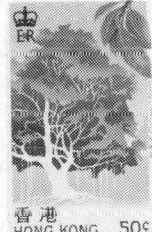

Indigenous Birds — A104

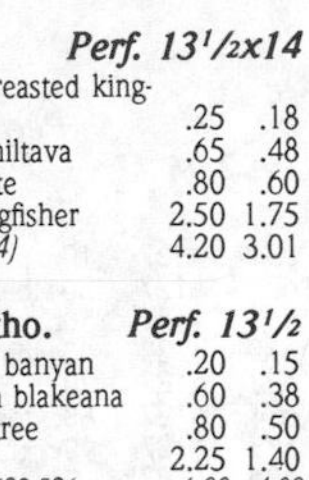

Indigenous Trees — A105

1988, Apr. 20 *Perf. 13½x14*

519 A104 50c White-breasted kingfisher .25 .18
520 A104 $1.30 Fukien niltava .65 .48
521 A104 $1.70 Black kite .80 .60
522 A104 $5 Pied kingfisher 2.50 1.75
Nos. 519-522 (4) 4.20 3.01

1988, June 16 Litho. *Perf. 13½*

523 A105 50c Chinese banyan .20 .15
524 A105 $1.30 Bauhinia blakeana .60 .38
525 A105 $1.70 Cotton tree .80 .50
526 A105 $5 Schima 2.25 1.40
a. Souvenir sheet of 4, #523-526 6.00 4.00
Nos. 523-526 (4) 3.85 2.43

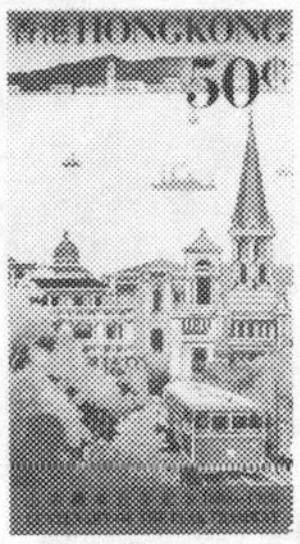

Peak Tramway, Victoria, Cent. — A106

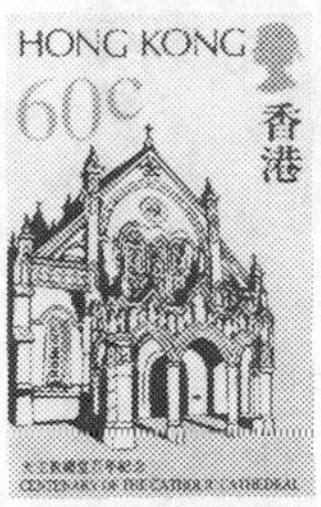

Catholic Cathedral, Caine Road, Cent. — A107

Various views of Hong Kong and the tram line.

1988, Aug. 4 Litho. *Perf. 15*

527 A106 50c multicolored .15 .15
528 A106 $1.30 multi, diff. .35 .35
529 A106 $1.70 multi, diff. .45 .45
530 A106 $5 multi, diff. 1.30 1.30
a. Souvenir sheet of 4, #527-530 7.00 4.50
Nos. 527-530 (4) 2.25 2.25

1988, Sept. 30 Litho. *Perf. 14*

531 A107 60c multicolored 1.00 .15

Queen and Waterfront Type of 1987

Type II

1988, Sept. 1 Litho. *Perf. 14½x14*

532 A98 $1.40 multicolored .75 .35
533 A98 $1.80 multicolored 1.10 .48

Nos. 532-533 reissued inscribed "1990," No. 533, "1991."

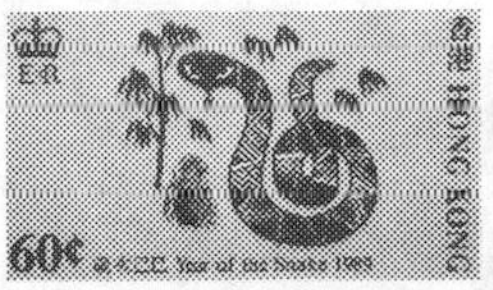

New Year (Year of the Snake) A108

1989, Jan. 18 Litho. *Perf. 13½x14*

534 A108 60c multicolored .35 .18
535 A108 $1.40 multi, diff. .80 .40
536 A108 $1.80 multi, diff. 1.00 .50
a. Bklt. pane, 5 each #534, 536 5.00
537 A108 $5 multi, diff. 3.00 1.40
a. Souvenir sheet of 4, #534-537 5.00 4.00
Nos. 534-537 (4) 5.15 2.48

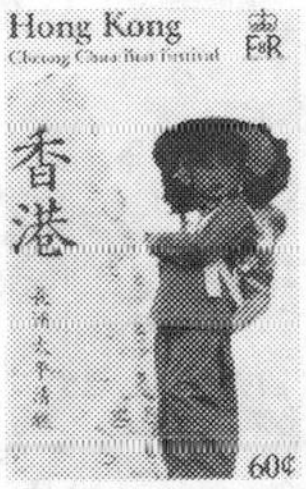

Cheung Chau Bun Festival — A109

1989, May 4 Wmk. *Perf. 13½*

538 A109 60c Girl, doll .30 .18
539 A109 $1.40 Girl .70 .40
540 A109 $1.80 Festival paper god .80 .50
541 A109 $5 Bun tower gate 2.25 1.40
Nos. 538-541 (4) 4.05 2.48

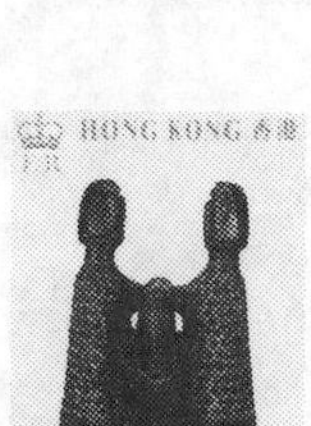

Modern Art — A110

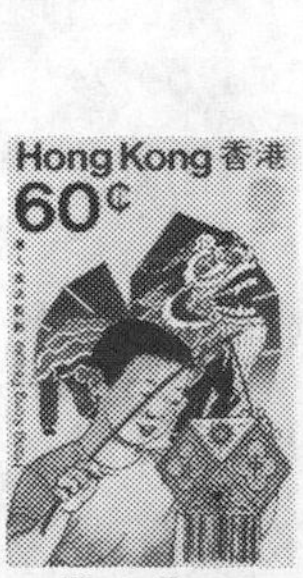

Hong Kong People — A111

Designs: 60c, Twin, sculpture by Cheung Yee (b. 1936). $1.40, Figures, painted by Luis Chan (b. 1905). $1.80, Lotus, sculpture by Van Lau (b. 1933). $5, Zen, painted by Lui Shou-kwan (1919-1975).

Perf. 12x13

1989, July 19 Litho. Unwmk.

542 A110 60c multicolored .25 .16
543 A110 $1.40 multicolored .50 .35
544 A110 $1.80 multicolored .65 .48
545 A110 $5 multicolored 1.75 1.30
Nos. 542-545 (4) 3.15 2.29

Perf. 13x14½

1989, Sept. 6 Litho. Unwmk.

Designs: 60c, Youth holding autumn festival decoration, lunar year festival dragon. $1.40, Shadow boxer, horse racing. $1.80, Office and construction workers. $5, Two women, two men (ethnic multiplicity).

546 A111 60c multicolored .25 .16
547 A111 $1.40 multicolored .45 .35
548 A111 $1.80 multicolored .60 .48
549 A111 $5 multicolored 1.75 1.30
Nos. 546-549 (4) 3.05 2.29

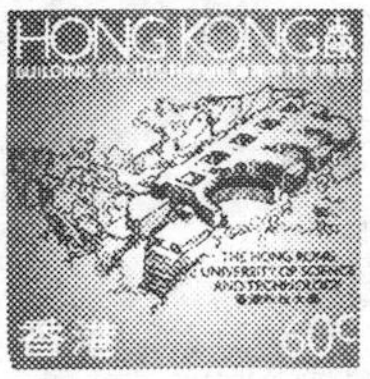

Construction Projects — A112

1989, Oct. 5 Wmk. *Perf. 13*

550 A112 60c University of Science and Technology .25 .16
551 A112 70c Cultural center .30 .18
552 A112 $1.30 Eastern Harbor Crossing .50 .32
553 A112 $1.40 Bank of China .55 .35
554 A112 $1.80 Convention center .80 .45
555 A112 $5 Light rail transit 2.25 1.25
Nos. 550-555 (6) 4.65 2.71

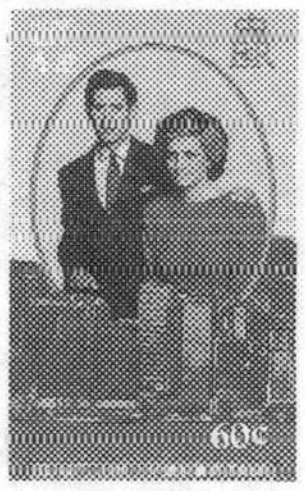

Visit of the Prince and Princess of Wales — A113

Portraits and view of Hong Kong: 60c, Charles and Diana. $1.40, Diana. $1.80, Charles. $5, Couple wearing formal attire.

Perf. 14½

1989, Nov. 8 Litho. Wmk.

556 A113 60c multicolored .25 .16
557 A113 $1.40 multicolored .50 .35
558 A113 $1.80 multicolored .70 .48
559 A113 $5 multicolored 2.00 1.30
a. Souvenir sheet of 1 4.50 3.50
Nos. 556-559 (4) 3.45 2.29

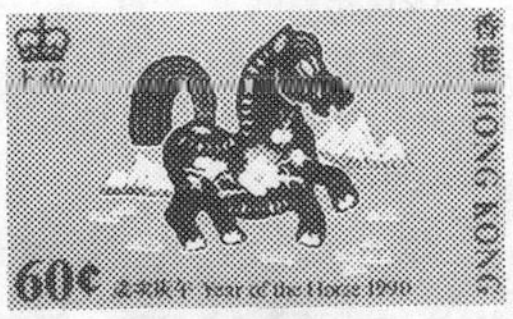

New Year 1990 (Year of the Horse) A114

Perf. 13½x12½

1990, Jan. 23 Wmk.

560 A114 60c multicolored .25 .16
561 A114 $1.40 multi, diff. .60 .35
562 A114 $1.80 multi, diff. .85 .48
a. Bklt. pane, 3 each 60c, $1.80 7.00
563 A114 $5 multi, diff. 2.50 1.30
a. Souvenir sheet of 4, #560-563 8.00
Nos. 560-563 (4) 4.20 2.29

Copies of No. 562a ovptd. with marginal inscription were released on May 3 to publicize Stamp World London '90.

15-Cent Minimum Value
The minimum value for a single stamp is 15 cents. This value reflects the costs of handling inexpensive stamps.

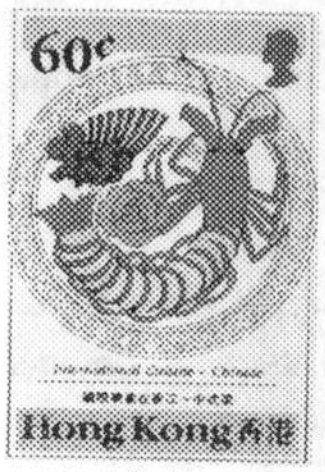

Intl. Cuisine — A115

Pollutants — A116

Perf. 12¹/₂x13

1990, Apr. 26 Litho. Wmk. 340

564 A115 60c Chinese .20 .16
565 A115 70c Indian .28 .20
566 A115 $1.30 Chinese, diff. .48 .35
567 A115 $1.40 Thai .52 .38
568 A115 $1.80 Japanese .68 .50
569 A115 $5 French 1.90 1.35
Nos. 564-569 (6) 4.06 2.94

1990, June 5 Litho. *Perf. 14¹/₂*

570 A116 60c Air .25 .16
571 A116 $1.40 Noise .55 .35
572 A116 $1.80 Water .75 .48
573 A116 $5 Land 2.00 1.25
Nos. 570-573 (4) 3.55 2.24

World Environment Day.

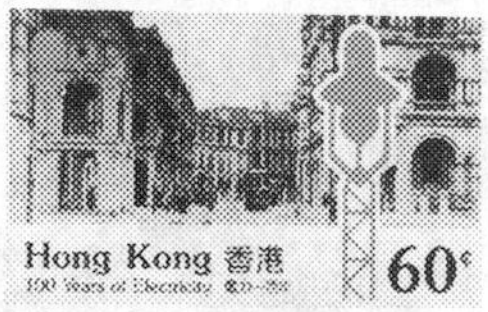

Electrification of Hong Kong, Cent. — A117

Views of Hong Kong and streetlights.

1990, Oct. 2 Litho. *Perf. 14¹/₂*

574 A117 60c 1890 .25 .16
575 A117 $1.40 1940 .55 .35
576 A117 $1.80 1960 .75 .48
577 A117 $5 1980 2.00 1.25
a. Souvenir sheet of 2, #575, 577 5.00 5.00
Nos. 574-577 (4) 3.55 2.24

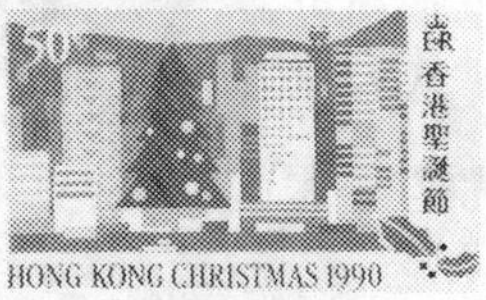

Christmas — A118

1990, Nov. 8

578 A118 50c shown .25 .15
579 A118 60c Dove, holly .30 .16
580 A118 $1.40 Skyline, snowman .60 .35
581 A118 $1.80 Santa Claus' hat, skyscraper .80 .48
582 A118 $2 Children, Santa Claus .90 .50
583 A118 $5 Candy cane, skyline 1.90 1.25
Nos. 578-583 (6) 4.75 2.89

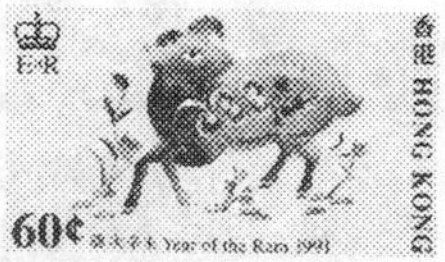

New Year 1991 (Year of the Sheep) A119

Different embroidered rams.

Perf. 13¹/₂x12¹/₂

1991, Jan. 24 Litho.

584 A119 60c multicolored .25 .15
585 A119 $1.40 multicolored .60 .35
586 A119 $1.80 multicolored .75 .45
a. Bklt. pane, 3 each #584, 586 2.50 1.80
587 A119 $5 multicolored 2.00 1.20
a. Souvenir sheet of 4, #584-587 6.00 4.00
Nos. 584-587 (4) 3.60 2.15

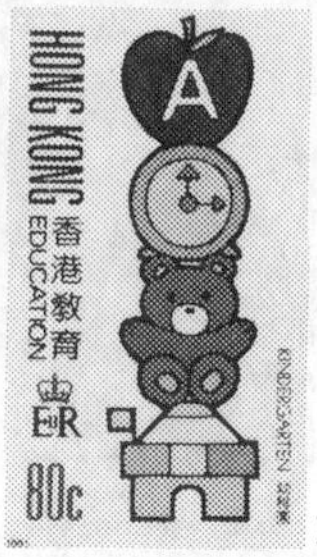

Education — A120

Perf. 13¹/₂x13

1991, Apr. 18 Litho. Unwmk.

588 A120 80c Kindergarten .25 .20
589 A120 $1.80 Primary & secondary .55 .45
590 A120 $2.30 Vocational .70 .60
591 A120 $5 Tertiary 1.50 1.30
Nos. 588-591 (4) 3.00 2.55

Queen and Waterfront Type of 1987
Type II

1991, Apr. 2 Litho. *Perf. 14¹/₂x14*

592 A98 $1.20 multicolored .35 .30
593 A98 $2.30 multicolored .65 .58

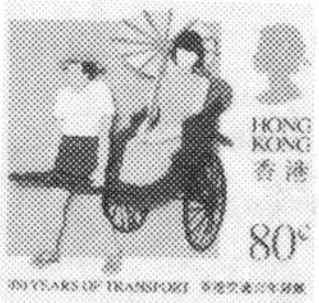

Transportation A121

1991, June 6 Unwmk. *Perf. 14*

594 A121 80c Rickshaw .22 .20
595 A121 90c Bus .25 .22
596 A121 $1.70 Ferry .45 .42
597 A121 $1.80 Tram .50 .45
598 A121 $2.30 Mass transit railway .65 .58
599 A121 $5 Hydrofoil 1.50 1.30
Nos. 594-599 (6) 3.57 3.17

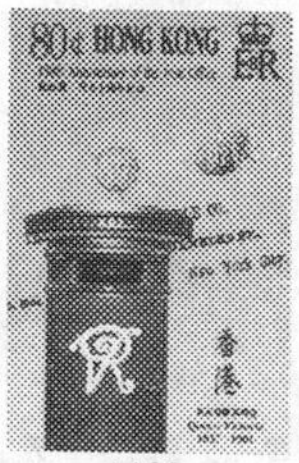

A122

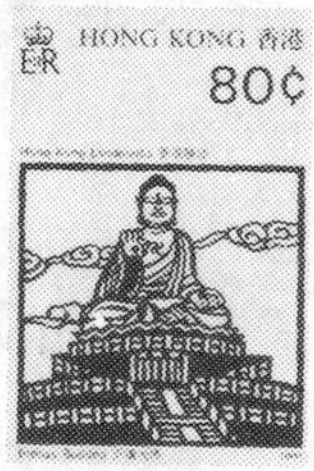

Historic Landmarks — A123

Royal postboxes with contemporary envelopes: 80c, Stamp of Type A1, Queen Victoria. $1.70, Stamps of Type A10, King Edward VII. $1.80, #149, King George V. $2.30, Stamps of Type A16, King George VI. $5, $10, Stamp of Type A98, Queen Elizabeth II.

1991, Aug. 25 Litho. *Perf. 14*

600 A122 80c multicolored .30 .20
601 A122 $1.70 multicolored .65 .42
602 A122 $1.80 multicolored .70 .45
603 A122 $2.30 multicolored .90 .58
604 A122 $5 multicolored 2.00 1.25
Nos. 600-604 (5) 4.55 2.90

Souvenir Sheet

605 A122 $10 multicolored *9.00 6.00*

Hong Kong Post Office, 150th anniv.

1991, Oct. 24

606 A123 80c Bronze Buddha .35 .20
607 A123 $1.70 Peak Pavilion .70 .42
608 A123 $1.80 Clock Tower .75 .45
609 A123 $2.30 Catholic Cathedral 1.00 .58
610 A123 $5 Wong Tai Sin Temple 2.25 1.25
Nos. 606-610 (5) 5.05 2.90

Map of Hong Kong Type

1992, Mar. 26 Photo. *Perf. 14¹/₂x14*

Color of Map

611 A101a 80c red lilac .20 .20
612 A101a 90c blue .22 .22
613 A101a $1.80 brt yel grn .45 .45
614 A101a $2.30 red brown .58 .58
Nos. 611-614 (4) 1.45 1.45

Inscribed 1991.

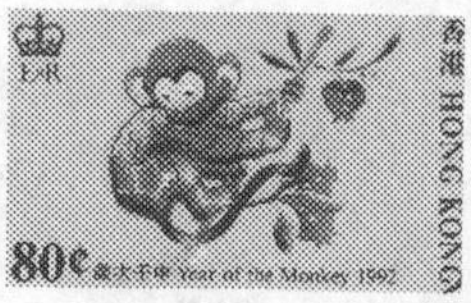

New Year 1992 (Year of the Monkey) A125

Various embroidery designs of monkeys.

1992, Jan. 22 Litho. *Perf. 14¹/₂*

615 A125 80c multicolored .40 .20
616 A125 $1.80 multicolored .80 .45
617 A125 $2.30 multicolored 1.10 .60
a. Bklt. pane, 3 each #615 & #617 2.35
618 A125 $5 multicolored 2.25 1.25
a. Sheet of 4, #615-618 7.00 2.50
Nos. 615-618 (4) 4.55 2.50

Queen Elizabeth II's Accession to the Throne, 40th Anniv.

Common Design Type

Unwmk.

1992, Feb. 11 Litho. *Perf. 14*

619 CD349 80c multicolored .22 .20
620 CD349 $1.70 multicolored .50 .42
621 CD349 $1.80 multicolored .52 .45
622 CD349 $2.30 multicolored .65 .58
623 CD349 $5 multicolored 1.65 1.25
Nos. 619-623 (5) 3.54 2.90

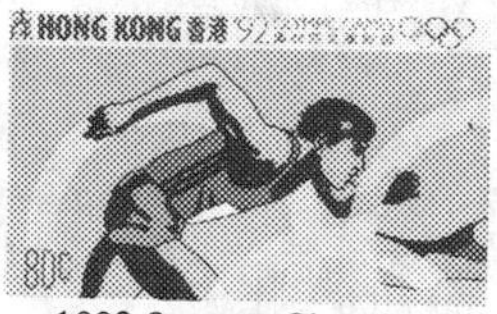

1992 Summer Olympics, Barcelona — A126

1992, Apr. 2 Litho. *Perf. 14¹/₂*

Black Inscription

624 A126 80c Running .30 .20
625 A126 $1.80 Swimming and javelin .70 .45
626 A126 $2.30 Cycling .90 .60
627 A126 $5 High jump 2.00 1.25
Nos. 624-627 (4) 3.90 2.50

Souvenir Sheet

628 Sheet of 4 5.00 2.50
a. A126 80c red inscription .20 .20
b. A126 $1.80 green inscription .45 .45
c. A126 $2.30 blue inscription .60 .60
d. A126 $5 orange yellow inscription 1.25 1.25
e. Sheet of 4 with inscription in margin 4.00 2.50

Issue date: No. 628e, July 25. New inscription on No. 628e sheet margin reads "To Commemorate the Opening of the 1992 Summer Olympic Games 25 July 1992" in English and Chinese.

Queen and Landmarks Type of 1987
Souvenir Sheet

Perf. 14

1992, May 22 Litho. Type II

629 A99 $10 lt violet & black 5.50 3.00

World Columbian Stamp Expo '92.

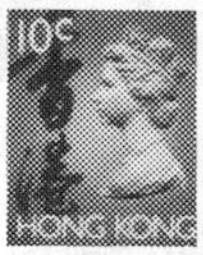

A127

Perf. 15x14

1992-94 Photo. Unwmk.

Background Color

630 A127 10c pink .15 .15
630A A127 20c blue & gray .15 .15
631 A127 50c yellow orange .15 .15
632 A127 60c blue .15 .15
633 A127 70c red lilac .18 .18
634 A127 80c rose .20 .20
635 A127 90c gray green .22 .22
636 A127 $1 orange brown .25 .25
636C A127 $1.10 carmine .28 .28
637 A127 $1.20 violet .30 .30
637A A127 $1.30 orange & dk blue .32 .32
637B A127 $1.50 brown .38 .38
638 A127 $1.70 ultramarine .42 .42
639 A127 $1.80 rose lilac .45 .45
639A A127 $1.90 yellow & green .48 .48
640 A127 $2 blue green .50 .50
640A A127 $2.10 claret .55 .55
641 A127 $2.30 maroon .55 .55
641A A127 $2.40 dark blue & buff .58 .58
641D A127 $2.60 dark brown .70 .70
642 A127 $5 bright green 1.25 1.25
a. Souvenir sheet of 1 1.25 1.25

Size: 25x30mm

Perf. 14¹/₂x14

643 A127 $10 brown 2.50 2.50
a. Souvenir sheet of 1 2.50 2.50
644 A127 $20 orange 5.00 5.00
645 A127 $50 gray 12.50 12.50
Nos. 630-645 (24) 28.21 28.21

Issued: 20c, $1.30, $1.90, $2.40, 11/1/93; #642a, 2/18/94; #643a, 8/16/94; $1.10, $1.50, $2.10, $2.60, 6/1/95; others, 6/16/92.

Nos. 630-631, 635, 637, 639A, 641, 655, 659 also issued in coils. These have numbers on the back of every fifth stamp.

No. 642a issued for Hong Kong '94; No. 643a, for Conference of Commonwealth Postal Administrations.

This is an expanding set. Numbers may change. See Nos. 656, 677-678, 683, 688, 724, 729.

1993-95 Litho. *Perf. 15x14*

636a A127 $1 Litho. .35 .35
b. As "a," bklt. pane of 10 3.50
637c A127 $1.20 Litho. .30 .30
d. As "c," bklt. pane of 10 3.00
Complete booklet, #637d 3.00
639b A127 $1.90 Litho. .65 .65
c. As "b," bklt. pane of 10 6.50
640b A127 $2.10 Litho. .55 .55
c. As "b," bklt. pane of 10 5.50
Complete booklet, #640c 5.50
641b A127 $2.40 Litho. .82 .82
c. As "b," bklt. pane of 10 8.25
641e A127 $2.60 Litho. .70 .70
f. As "e," bklt. pane of 10 7.00
Complete booklet, #641f 7.00
Nos. 636a-641e (6) 3.37 3.37

Chinese characters on Nos. 636a, 637c, 639b, 640b, 641b, 641e are lighter in shade and contrast less with the background color than characters on Nos. 636, 637, 639A, 640A, 641A, 641D.

Issued: #636a, 12/14/93; #639b, 641b, 12/28/93; #637c, 640b, 641e, 6/1/95.

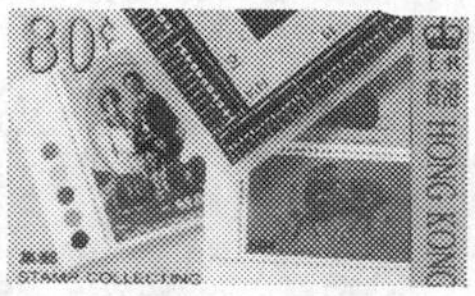

Stamp Collecting A128

Stamps and: 80c, Perforation gauge, #559, 586a. $1.80, Canceler, #66, stamp tongs. $2.30, Magnifying glass, #174, 180, 181. $5, Watermark detector, Type A1.

1992, July 15 Litho. *Perf. 14¹/₂*

652 A128 80c multicolored .20 .20
653 A128 $1.80 multicolored .45 .45
654 A128 $2.30 multicolored .58 .58
655 A128 $5 multicolored 1.25 1.25
Nos. 652-655 (4) 2.48 2.48

Queen Type of 1992
Souvenir Sheet

Perf. 14¹/₂x14

1992, Sept. 1 Photo. Unwmk.

Background Color

656 A127 $10 blue 4.00 2.50

Kuala Lumpur Philatelic Exhibition '92.
Size of stamp: 25x30mm.

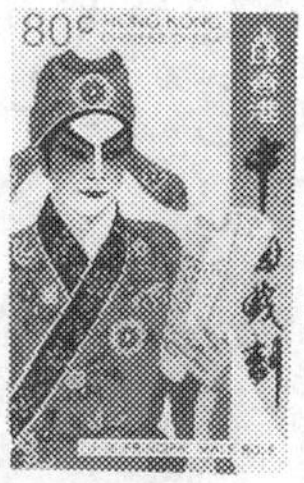

Chinese Opera — A129

1992, Sept. 24 Litho. *Perf. 13¹/₂*

657 A129 80c Principal male role .25 .20
658 A129 $1.80 Martial role .55 .45
659 A129 $2.30 Principal female role .70 .58
660 A129 $5 Comic role 1.50 1.25
Nos. 657-660 (4) 3.00 2.48

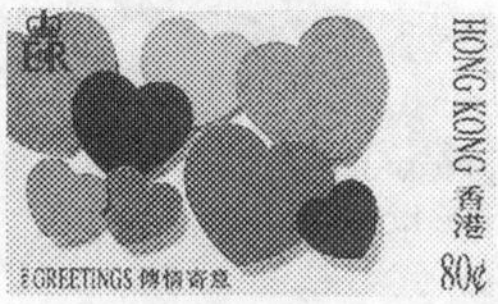

Greetings Stamps A130

1992, Nov. 19	Litho.	Perf. 14¹/₂
661 A130	80c Hearts	.25 .20
662 A130	$1.80 Stars	.55 .45
663 A130	$2.30 Presents	.70 .58
664 A130	$5 Balloons	1.50 1.25
a.	Bklt. pane of 5, #662-664, 3 #661	6.00 3.00
	Nos. 661-664 (4)	3.00 2.48

New Year 1993 (Year of the Rooster) A131

Various embroidery designs of a rooster.

1993, Jan. 7	Litho.	Perf. 13¹/₂
665 A131	80c multicolored	.25 .20
666 A131	$1.80 multicolored	.55 .45
667 A131	$2.30 multicolored	.70 .58
a.	Booklet pane, 3 each #665, #667	4.00
668 A131	$5 multicolored	1.50 1.25
a.	Souvenir sheet of 4, #665-668	4.00 2.50
	Nos. 665-668 (4)	3.00 2.48

Chinese String Instruments — A132

1993, Apr. 14	Litho.	Perf. 14¹/₂
669 A132	80c Pipa	.25 .20
670 A132	$1.80 Erhu	.55 .45
671 A132	$2.30 Ruan	.70 .58
672 A132	$5 Gehu	1.50 1.25
	Nos. 669-672 (4)	3.00 2.48

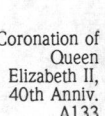

Coronation of Queen Elizabeth II, 40th Anniv. A133

Different views of Hong Kong with portraits of Queen that appear on Types A25, A28, A49 and A127.

1993, June 3	Litho.	Perf. 14
673 A133	80c multicolored	.20 .20
674 A133	$1.80 multicolored	.45 .45
675 A133	$2.30 multicolored	.58 .58
676 A133	$5 multicolored	1.25 1.25
	Nos. 673-676 (4)	2.48 2.48

Queen Type of 1972
Souvenir Sheets

1993, July 6	Litho.	Perf. 14¹/₂x14
Background Color		
677 A127	$10 brown	3.30 2.30

1993, Aug. 12		Background Color
678 A127	$10 bright blue	2.50 2.50

Hong Kong '94 Stamp Exhibition. Nos. 677-678 contain a 25x30mm stamp.

No. 678 exists with gold, silver or red overprints with the Hong Kong Philatelic Society emblem and Chinese characters. These sheets were sold only at various philatelic exhibitions.

Science and Technology — A134

Designs: 80c, Education, Hong Kong University of Science and Technology. $1.80, Public presentation, Hong Kong Science Museum. $2.30, Achievement recognition, Governor's Award. $5, World class telecommunications, telecommunications industry.

1993, Sept. 8		Perf. 14¹/₂
679 A134	80c multicolored	.20 .20
680 A134	$1.80 multicolored	.48 .48
681 A134	$2.30 multicolored	.60 .60
682 A134	$5 multicolored	1.25 1.25
	Nos. 679-682 (4)	2.53 2.53

Queen Type of 1992
Souvenir Sheet

1993, Oct. 5	Litho.	Perf. 14¹/₂x14
Background Color		
683 A127	$10 bright green	3.00 2.50

Bangkok '93 Stamp Exhibition. No. 683 contains a 25x30mm stamp.

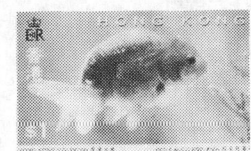

Goldfish A135

1993, Nov. 17	Litho.	Perf. 14¹/₂
684 A135	$1 Red calico egg-fish	.25 .25
685 A135	$1.90 Red cap oranda	.40 .40
686 A135	$2.40 Red & white fringetail	.60 .60
687 A135	$5 Black & gold dragoneye	1.25 1.25
a.	Souvenir sheet of 4, #684-687	3.00 2.50
	Nos. 684-687 (4)	2.50 2.50

Queen Type of 1992

1994, Jan. 27	Photo.	Wmk. 373
		Perf. 15x14
688	Souvenir booklet	10.00 10.00
a.	A127 Sheet of #630, S #640	3.25 3.25
b.	A127 Sheet of #638, S #639	3.25 3.25
c.	A127 Sheet of 5 #636, #642	3.25 3.25

First Hong Kong stamps, 130th anniv. No. 688 sold for $38.

Year of the Dog A136

Various embroidery designs of dogs.

1994, Jan. 27	Litho.	Perf. 14¹/₂
689 A136	$1 multicolored	.30 .25
690 A136	$1.90 multicolored	.60 .48
691 A136	$2.40 multicolored	.70 .60
a.	Booklet pane, 3 each #689, #691	5.00
692 A136	$5 multicolored	1.50 1.25
a.	Souvenir sheet of 4, #689-692	2.50 2.50
	Nos. 689-692 (4)	3.10 2.58

Royal Hong Kong Police Force, 150th Anniv. — A137

Designs: $1, Traffic policeman, woman. $1.20, Marine policeman. $1.90, Male, female officers of 1950. $2, Policeman holding M-16. $2.40, Policemen, 1906, pre-1920. $5, Policemen, 1900.

1994, May 4	Litho.	Perf. 13¹/₂
693 A137	$1 multicolored	.25 .25
694 A137	$1.20 multicolored	.30 .30
695 A137	$1.90 multicolored	.48 .48
696 A137	$2 multicolored	.50 .50
697 A137	$2.40 multicolored	.60 .60
698 A137	$5 multicolored	1.25 1.25
	Nos. 693-698 (6)	3.38 3.38

Traditional Chinese Festivals — A138

Designs: $1, Dragon Boat Festival. $1.90, Lunar New Year. $2.40, Seven Sisters Festival. $5, Mid-Autumn Festival.

1994, June 8	Litho.	Perf. 14
699 A138	$1 multicolored	.25 .25
700 A138	$1.90 multicolored	.48 .48
701 A138	$2.40 multicolored	.60 .60
702 A138	$5 multicolored	1.25 1.25
	Nos. 699-702 (4)	2.58 2.58

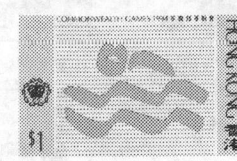

XV Commonwealth Games, Victoria, BC, Canada — A139

Unwmk.

1994, Aug. 25	Litho.	Perf. 14
703 A139	$1 Swimming	.25 .25
704 A139	$1.90 Lawn bowling	.48 .48
705 A139	$2.40 Gymnastics	.60 .60
706 A139	$5 Weight lifting	1.25 1.25
	Nos. 703-706 (4)	2.58 2.58

Dr. James Legge (1815-97), Religious Leader, Translator A140

1994, Oct. 5	Litho.	Perf. 14
707 A140	$1 multicolored	.25 .25

Corals — A141

1994, Nov. 17	Litho.	Perf. 14
708 A141	$1 Alcyonium	.25 .25
709 A141	$1.90 Zoanthus	.50 .50
710 A141	$2.40 Tubastrea	.60 .60
711 A141	$5 Platygyra	1.25 1.25
a.	Souv. sheet of 4, #708-711	2.60 2.60
	Nos. 708-711 (4)	2.60 2.60

New Year 1995 (Year of the Boar) A142

Various embroidery designs of pigs.

1995, Jan 17	Litho.	Perf. 14¹/₂
712 A142	$1 multicolored	.25 .25
713 A142	$1.90 multicolored	.50 .50
714 A142	$2.40 multicolored	.60 .60
715 A142	$5 multicolored	1.25 1.25
a.	Souvenir sheet of 4, #712-715	2.60 2.60
	Nos. 712-715 (4)	2.60 2.60

Intl. Sporting Events A143

Designs: $1, Hong Kong Rugby Sevens. $1.90, China Sea Race. $2.40, Intl. Dragon Boat Races. $5, Hong Kong Intl. Horse Races.

1995, Mar. 22	Litho.	Perf. 14¹/₂
716 A143	$1 multicolored	.25 .25
717 A143	$1.90 multicolored	.50 .50
718 A143	$2.40 multicolored	.60 .60
719 A143	$5 multicolored	1.25 1.25
	Nos. 716-719 (4)	2.60 2.60

Traditional Buildings — A144

	Litho. & Engr.	
1995, May 24		Perf. 13¹/₂
720 A144	$1 Tsui Shing Lau	.25 .25
721 A144	$1.90 Sam Tung UK	.50 .50
722 A144	$2.40 Lo Wai	.60 .60
723 A144	$5 Man Shek Tong	1.25 1.25
	Nos. 720-723 (4)	2.60 2.60

Queen Type of 1992
Souvenir Sheet

1995, Aug. 25	Litho.	Perf. 14
Background Color		
724 A127	$10 carmine	2.50 2.50

Singapore '95 World Stamp Exhibition. No. 724 contains one 25x30mm stamp.

Royal Hong Kong Regiment (1854-1995) — A145

Designs: $1.20, Modern Regimental Badge, vert. $2.10, Current flag. $2.60, Former flag. $5, Royal Hong Kong Defense Force, 1951 soldier's badge, vert.

1995, Aug. 16	Litho.	Perf. 14¹/₂
725 A145	$1.20 multicolored	.30 .30
726 A145	$2.10 multicolored	.55 .55
727 A145	$2.60 multicolored	.65 .65
728 A145	$5 multicolored	1.25 1.25
	Nos. 725-728 (4)	2.75 2.75

Queen Type of 1992
Souvenir Sheet

1995, Oct. 9	Litho.	Perf. 14
Background Color		
729 A127	$10 brown	2.50 2.50

End of World War II, 50th anniv. No. 729 contains one 25x30mm stamp.

Hong Kong Movie Stars A146

1995, Nov. 15	Litho.	Perf. 13¹/₂
730 A146	$1.20 Bruce Lee	.30 .30
731 A146	$2.10 Leung Sing-Por	.55 .55
732 A146	$2.60 Yam Kim-Fai	.70 .70
733 A146	$5 Lin Dai	1.30 1.30
	Nos. 730-733 (4)	2.85 2.85

SEMI-POSTAL STAMPS

Catalogue values for unused stamps in this section are for Never Hinged items.

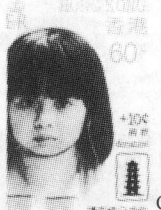

Community Chest of Hong Kong — SP1

HONG KONG (continued)

1988, Nov. 30		**Litho.**	**Perf. 14½**		
B1	SP1	60c +10c Girl		.20	.18
B2	SP1	$1.40 +20c Elderly woman		.45	.40
B3	SP1	$1.80 +30c Blind youth		.65	.55
B4	SP1	$5 +$1 Mother and child		1.90	1.55
		Nos. B1-B4 (4)		3.20	2.68

Surtax for the social welfare organization.

POSTAGE DUE STAMPS

Scales Showing Letter
Overweight — D1

1923, Dec.	**Typo.**	**Wmk. 4**	**Perf. 14**	
J1	D1	1c brown	.75	.35
a.	Chalky paper, wmkd. sideways		.35	.20
J2	D1	2c green	2.25	.70
J3	D1	4c red	3.50	1.00
J4	D1	6c orange	8.75	3.50
J5	D1	10c ultramarine	12.00	1.50
		Nos. J1-J5 (5)	27.25	7.05
		Set, never hinged	60.00	

No. J1a issued Mar. 21, 1956.

1938-47			**Perf. 14**	
J6	D1	2c gray	.35	.35
J7	D1	4c orange yellow	1.10	.45
J8	D1	6c carmine	2.75	1.40
J9	D1	8c fawn ('46)	2.75	1.40
J10	D1	10c violet	1.40	.65
J11	D1	20c black ('46)	2.75	2.00
J12	D1	50c blue ('47)	16.00	11.50
		Nos. J6-J12 (7)	27.10	17.75
		Set, never hinged	55.00	

Nos. J6-J7 and J10 exist on both ordinary and chalky paper.

> Catalogue values for unused stamps in this section, from this point to the end of the section, are for Never Hinged items.

Wmk. 314 Sideways

1965-69			**Perf. 14**	
J13	D1	4c orange yellow	2.50	1.75
J14	D1	5c orange ver ('69)	1.10	.40
a.	5c carmine, wmk. upright ('67)		1.10	.40
J15	D1	10c purple ('67)	2.75	.90
J16	D1	20c black	5.75	2.00
J17	D1	50c dark blue	10.00	3.00
a.	Wmk. upright ('70)		11.00	5.00
		Nos. J13-J17 (5)	22.10	8.05

Size of 5c, 21x18mm.; others, 22x18mm.

Wmk. 314 Upright

1972-74			**Perf. 13½x14**	
J18	D1	5c red brown ('74)	.15	.15
			Perf. 14x14½	
J19	D1	10c lilac	.60	.60
J20	D1	20c black	1.25	1.25
J21	D1	50c dull blue	3.50	3.50
		Nos. J18-J21 (4)	5.50	5.50

Nos. J18-J22 are on glazed paper.

1976, Mar. 19			**Wmk. 373**	
J19a	D1	10c lilac	.25	.15
J20a	D1	20c black	.50	.15
J21a	D1	50c dull blue	1.25	.30
b.	Unwatermarked		1.25	
J22	D1	$1 yellow	2.00	.60
a.	Unwatermarked		2.00	.60
		Nos. J19a-J22 (4)	4.00	1.20

Size of $1, 20½x17mm; others, 22x18mm.
Issue date: No. J21b, J22, Jan. 11, 1986.

D2

			Perf. 14x15	
1986, Mar. 25		**Litho.**	**Unwmk.**	
J23	D2	10c light green	.15	.15
J24	D2	20c dark red brown	.15	.15
J25	D2	50c lilac	.15	.15
J26	D2	$1 light orange	.30	.22
J27	D2	$5 grayish blue	1.40	1.10
J28	D2	$10 rose red	2.75	2.25
		Nos. J23-J28 (6)	4.90	4.02

OCCUPATION STAMPS

Issued under Japanese Occupation

War Factory   Gen. Maresuke
Girl — A144   Nogi — A84

Admiral Heihachiro
Togo — A86

Stamps of Japan,
1942-43 Surcharged in
Black

叁圓 暫定
邮督阗卷杢

		Wmk. 257		
1945, Apr.	**Typo.**		**Perf. 13**	
N1	A144	1½y on 1s org brn	8.25	8.25
N2	A84	3y on 2s ver	5.50	8.25
N3	A86	5y on 5s brn lake	325.00	42.50
		Nos. N1-N3 (3)	338.75	59.00

No. N1 has eleven characters.

INDIA

'in–dē-ə

LOCATION — Southern, central Asia
GOVT. — Republic
AREA — 1,266,732 sq. mi.
POP. — 683,810,051 (1981)
CAPITAL — New Delhi

On August 15, 1947, India was divided into two self-governing dominions: Pakistan and India. India became a republic in 1950.

The stamps of pre-partition India fall into three groups: 1) Issues inscribed simply "India," for use mainly in British India proper, but available and valid throughout the country; 2) Issues as above and overprinted with one of the names of the six states (Chamba, Faridkot, Gwalior, Jind, Nabha and Patiala) which had a postal convention with British India, for use in those states. 3) Issues of the feudatory states, over which the British India government exercised little internal control, valid only within the states issuing them.

12 Pies = 1 Anna
16 Annas = 1 Rupee
100 Naye Paise = 1 Rupee (1957)
100 Paise = 1 Rupee (1964)

> Catalogue values for unused stamps in this country are for Never Hinged items, beginning with Scott 168 in the regular postage section, Scott C7 in the air post section, Scott M44 in the military section, Scott O113 in the official section, Scott RA1 in the postal tax section, Scott 51 in Hyderabad regular issues, Scott O54 in Hyderabad officials, Scott 49 in Jaipur regular issues, Scott O30 in Jaipur officials, Scott 39 in Soruth regular issues and Scott O19 in Soruth official
> All of the values are for Never Hinged for all of the items in the sections for the International Commission in Indo-China, Jasdan, Rajasthan, and Travancore-Cochin.

Watermarks

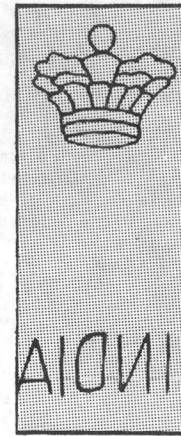

Wmk. 36- Crown
and INDIA

Wmk. 37- Coat of Arms in Sheet.
(Reduced illustration. Watermark covers a
large section of the sheet.)

Wmk. 38-   Wmk. 39- Star
Elephant's Head

Wmk. 40

Wmk. 41- Small   Wmk. 42- Urdu
Umbrella   Characters

Wmk. 43- Shell   Wmk. 196- Multiple
Stars

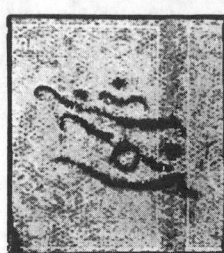

Wmk. 211-
Urdu
Characters

Wmk. 294- Letters and Ornaments in
Sheet (size reduced)

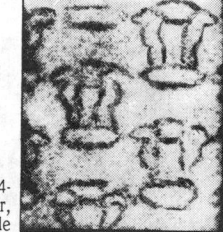

Wmk. 324-
Asoka Pillar,
Multiple

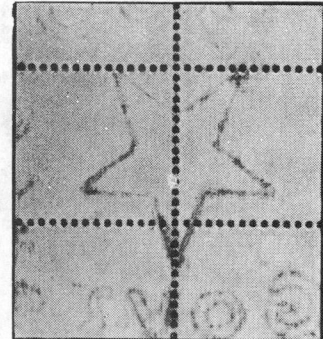

Wmk. 360- Star and GOVT INDIA

SCINDE DISTRICT POST

A1

1852, July 1		**Embossed**	**Imperf.**	
A1	A1	½a white	4,000.	750.
A2	A1	½a blue	9,000.	3,250.
A3	A1	½a red	—	6,750.

Obsolete October, 1854.
Nos. A1-A3 were issued without gum. No. A3 is embossed on red sealing wax. It is usually found with cracks and these examples are worth somewhat less than the value given, depending on the degree of cracking.

GENERAL ISSUES

Unused stamps of India are valued with original gum as defined in the catalogue introduction except for Nos. 1-7 which are valued without gum.

East India Company

Queen Victoria

A1   A2

A3   A4

A5

	Litho.; Typo. (#5)		
1854	**Wmk. 37**		**Imperf.**
1	A1 ½a red	550.00	
2	A2 ½a blue	45.00	65.00
a.	½a deep blue	37.50	9.25
b.	Printed on both sides		5,000.
4	A3 1a red	35.00	30.00
	1a scarlet	35.00	27.50
5	A4 2a green	70.00	17.50
6	A5 4a red & blue	2,800.	275.00
a.	4a deep red & blue	2,000.	325.00
	Cut to shape		14.00
c.	Head inverted		65,000.
	As "c," cut to shape		35,000.
e.	Double impression of head		

No. 1 was not placed in use.

Nos. 2, 4, 5 and 6 are known with unofficial perforation.

There are 3 dies of No. 2, and 2 dies of No. 4, showing slight differences.

There are 4 dies of the head and 2 dies of the frame of No. 6.

 A6

1855

7	A6 1a red	800.00	110.00

No. 7 was printed from a lithographic transfer made from the original die retouched. The lines of the bust at the lower left are nearly straight and meet in a point.

Diadem includes Maltese
Crosses — A7

	1855-64	**Unwmk.**	**Typo.**	**Perf. 14**
	Blue Glazed Paper			
9	A7	4a black	250.00	12.00
a.	Imperf., pair		1,250.	1,250.
b.	Half used as 2a on cover			5,000.
10	A7	8a rose	200.00	9.25
a.	Imperf., pair		1,100.	1,100.
b.	Half used as 4a on cover			

	1855-64			**White Paper**
11	A7	½a blue	16.00	.90
a.	Imperf., pair		365.00	600.00
12	A7	1a brown	7.00	1.25
a.	Imperf., pair		650.00	80.00
b.	Vert. pair, imperf between			
c.	Half used as ½a on cover			6,500.
13	A7	2a dull rose	250.00	15.00
a.	Imperf., pair		600.00	600.00
14	A7	2a yellow green	600.00	
a.	Imperf., pair		1,000.	
15	A7	2a buff	70.00	13.00
a.	2a orange		100.00	13.00
b.	Imperf., pair		650.00	700.00
16	A7	4a black	72.50	5.00
a.	Imperf., pair		600.00	650.00
b.	Diagonal half used as 2a on cover			4,000.
17	A7	4a green ('64)	425.00	24.00
18	A7	8a rose	80.00	8.00
a.	Half used as 4a on cover			6,500.

No. 14 was not regularly issued. See note after No. 25.

Many stamps of types A7-A90 are overprinted "Service" or "On H. M. S." For these, see listings of Official stamps.

Government Issues

Queen Victoria — A8

	1860-64	**Unwmk.**	**Perf. 14**
19	A8 8p lilac	16.00	5.00
a.	Diagonal half used as 4p on cover		8,250.
b.	Imperf., pair	650.00	700.00
19C	A8 8p lilac, bluish	110.00	40.00

	1865-67		**Wmk. 38**
20	A7 ½a blue	3.00	.30
a.	Imperf., pair		350.00
21	A8 8p lilac	5.00	3.00
22	A7 1a brown	2.00	.15
23	A7 2a orange	27.50	1.00
a.	2a yellow	24.00	2.00
b.	Imperf., pair		650.00
24	A7 4a green	200.00	17.00
25	A7 8a rose	650.00	21.50

No. 21 was variously surcharged locally, "NINE" or "NINE PIE," to indicate that it was being sold for 9 pies (the soldier's letter rate had been raised from 8 to 9 pies). These surcharges were made without government authorization.

Stamps of types A7 and A9 overprinted with crown and surcharged with new values were for use in Straits Settlements.

A9   A10

Diadem: Rows of pearls &
diamonds — A11

FOUR ANNAS

Type I - Slanting line at corner of mouth extends downward only. Shading about mouth and chin.

Type II - Line at corner of mouth extends both up and down. Upper lip and chin are defined by a colored line, but there is no shading.

	1866-68			
26	A9	4a green, type I	32.50	.65
26B	A9	4a blue grn, type II	10.00	.35
27	A10	6a8p slate	25.00	17.00
a.	Imperf., pair		850.00	
28	A11	8a rose ('68)	16.00	3.50
	Nos. 26-28 (4)		83.50	21.50

Type A11 is a redrawing of type A7. The main difference is in the diadem.

 A12

SIX ANNAS

Type I - "POSTAGE" 3½mm high
Type II - "POSTAGE" 2½mm high

Blue Glazed Paper
Green Overprint
Perf. 14 Vert.

	1866, June 28		**Wmk. 36**
29	A12 6a violet, type I	625.	110.
a.	Inverted overprint		5,250.
30	A12 6a violet, type II	1,000.	130.

Nos. 29 and 30 were made from revenue stamps with the labels at top and bottom cut off. Most and sometimes all of the watermark was removed with the labels.

These stamps are often found with cracked surface or scuffs. Such examples sell for somewhat less.

A13   A14

A15   A16

	1873-76		**Wmk. 38**	**Perf. 14**
31	A7	½a blue, redrawn	2.50	.22
32	A13	9p lilac ('74)	7.00	7.00
33	A14	6a bister ('76)	4.50	1.25
34	A15	12a red brown ('76)	5.50	4.00
35	A16	1r slate ('74)	24.00	14.00
	Nos. 31-35 (5)		43.50	26.47

In the redrawn ½ anna the lines of the mouth are more deeply cut, making the lips appear fuller and more open, and the nostril is defined by a curved line.

Issues of the Empire

A17   A18

A19   A20

A21   A22

A23   A24

A25   A26

A27

	1882-87		**Wmk. 39**
36	A17	½a green	1.50	.15
a.	Double impression	175.00	
37	A18	9p rose	.60	1.75
38	A19	1a maroon	2.00	.15
a.	1a violet brown	2.00	.15
39	A20	1a6p bister brown	.40	.50
40	A21	2a ultra	2.25	.15
a.	Double impression	425.00	425.00
41	A22	3a brown org	4.00	.20
a.	3a orange	10.00	4.00
42	A23	4a olive green	8.00	.20
43	A24	4a6p green	9.00	4.25
44	A25	8a red violet	12.50	1.50
a.	8a rose lilac	12.50	1.50
45	A26	12a violet, red	5.00	1.50
46	A27	1r gray	10.00	4.00
	Nos. 36-46 (11)		55.25	14.35

A 6a bister and a 12a Venetian red were prepared but not issued.

No. 40a used value is for copy with postal cancellation.

See Nos. 56-58. For surcharges see Nos. 47, 53 and British East Africa No. 59. For overprints see Nos. M2-M4, M6-M9, Gwalior Nos. O1-O5.

No. 43 Surcharged **2½ As.**

1891, Jan. 1

47 A24 2½a on 4a6p green 1.50 1.50

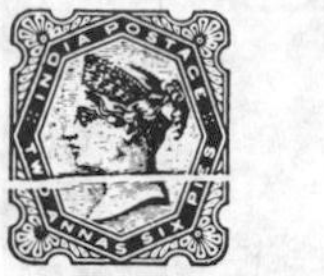
A28

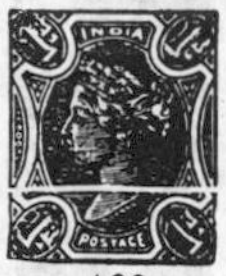
A29

1892

48 A28 2a6p green .50 .35
49 A29 1r car rose & grn 3.25 1.90

See No. 59. For overprints see Nos. M5, M10 and Gwalior No. O6.

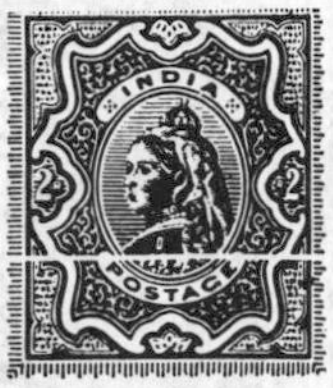
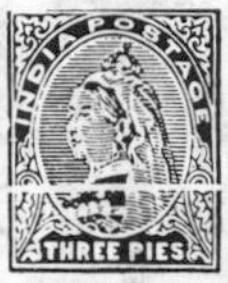
Queen Victoria
A30 A31

1895, Sept. 1

50 A30 2r brown & rose 35.00 10.00
51 A30 3r green & brown 27.50 10.00
52 A30 5r violet & ultra 30.00 21.00
Nos. 50-52 (3) 92.50 41.00

No. 36 Surcharged **1/4**

1898

53 A17 ¼a on ½a green .20 .20
a. Double surcharge 70.00
b. Double impression of stamp 140.00

For #61, 81 with this overprint see #77, 105.

1899

54 A31 3p carmine rose .15 .15

For overprint see No. M1, Gwalior No. O11.

1900

55 A31 3p gray .15 .15
56 A17 ½a light green .40 .15
57 A19 1a carmine rose .40 .15
58 A21 2a violet 2.50 1.25
59 A28 2a6p ultramarine 3.50 3.00
Nos. 55-59 (5) 6.95 4.70

For overprints see Nos. M11, Gwalior O7-O10.

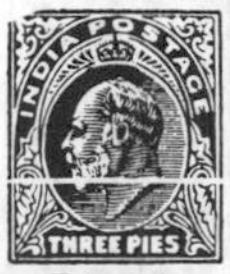
Edward VII — A32

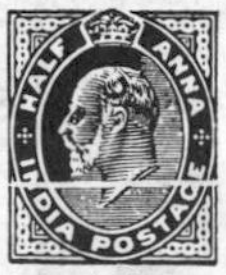
A33

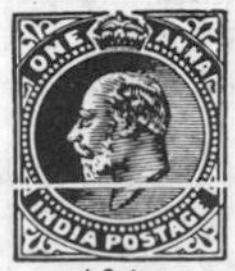
A34

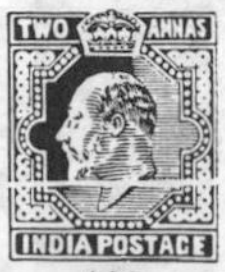
A35

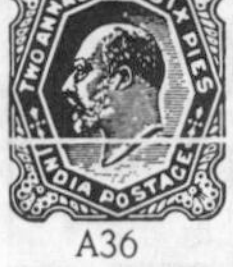
A36

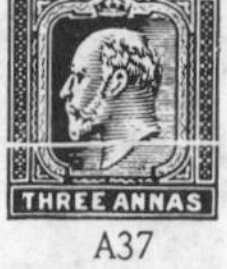
A37

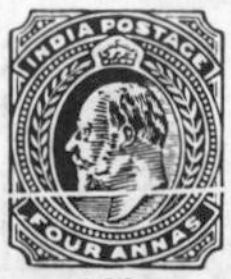
A38

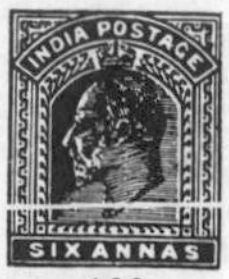
A39

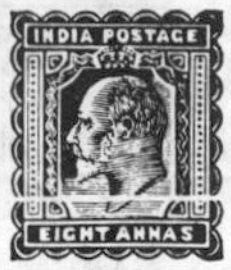
A40

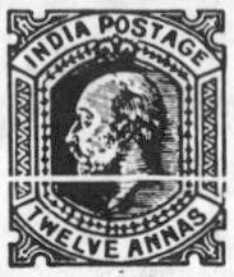
A41

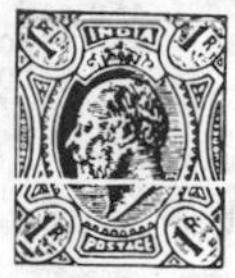
A42

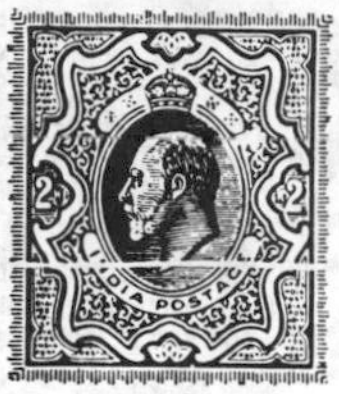
A43

1902-09

60 A32 3p gray .15 .15
61 A33 ½a green .20 .15
a. Booklet pane of 6 ('04) 32.50
62 A34 1a carmine rose .40 .15
a. Booklet pane of 6 ('04) 92.50
63 A35 2a violet 1.25 .15
64 A36 2a6p ultra 3.00 .15
65 A37 3a brown org 3.00 .15
66 A38 4a olive green 2.50 .20
67 A39 6a bister 8.50 1.75
68 A40 8a red violet 6.00 .60
69 A41 12a violet, *red* 6.50 2.00
70 A42 1r car rose & grn 5.75 .45
71 A43 2r brown & rose 26.00 3.25
72 A43 3r green & brn ('04) 18.00 11.50
73 A43 5r violet & ultra ('04) 45.00 32.50
74 A43 10r carmine rose & green ('09) 75.00 22.50
75 A43 15r olive gray & ultra ('09) 115.00 40.00
76 A43 25r ultra & org brown 650.00 700.00
Telegraph cancel 110.00
Nos. 60-75 (16) 316.25 115.65

For overprints see Nos. M12-M20, Gwalior Nos. O12-O18.

No. 61 Surcharged Like No. 53

1905

77 A33 ¼a on ½a green .20 .20
a. Inverted surcharge 600.00

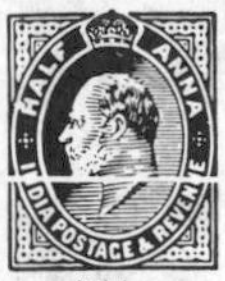
A44

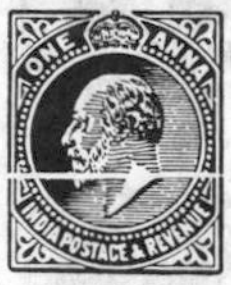
A45

1906

78 A44 ½a green .15 .15
a. Booklet pane of 4 17.50
79 A45 1a carmine rose .18 .15
a. Booklet pane of 4 25.00
Set value .15

For overprints see Gwalior Nos. O19-O20.

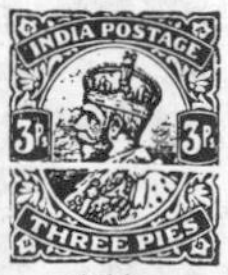
A46

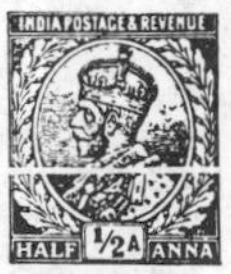
A47

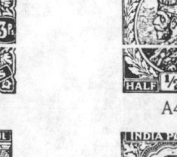

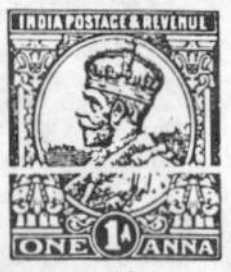
A48

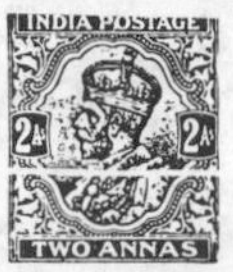
A49

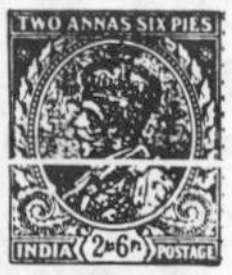
A50

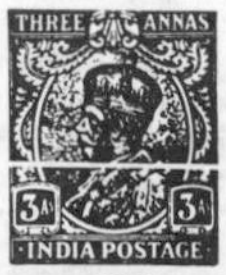
A51

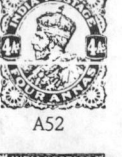

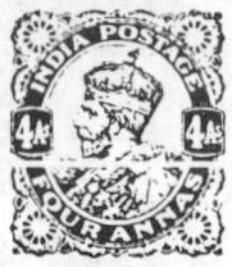
A52

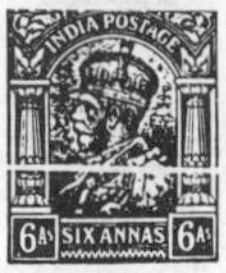
A53

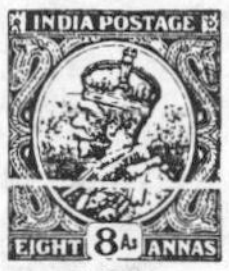
A54

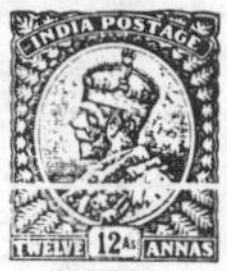
A55

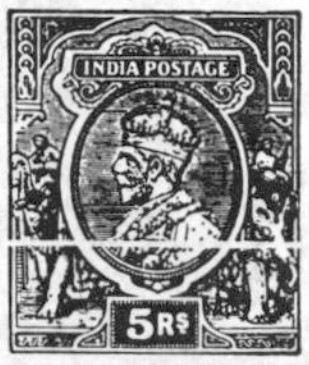
George V — A56

1911-23 **Wmk. 39**

80 A46 3p gray .15 .15
a. Booklet pane of 4 25.00
81 A47 ½a green .15 .15
a. Double impression 175.00
b. Booklet pane of 4 21.00
82 A48 1a carmine rose .20 .15
a. Printed on both sides
b. Booklet pane of 4 35.00
83 A48 1a dk brown ('22) .90 .15
a. Booklet pane of 4 42.50
84 A49 2a dull violet .80 .15
a. Booklet pane of 4 42.50
85 A50 2a6p ultramarine 1.00 .85
86 A51 3a brown org 1.50 .15
87 A51 3a ultra ('23) 5.25 .65
88 A52 4a olive green 2.50 .15
89 A53 6a yel bister 3.00 .70
90 A53 6a bister ('15) 3.00 .80
91 A54 8a red violet 4.00 .35
92 A55 12a claret 5.00 1.00
93 A56 1r grn & red brn 8.50 .60
94 A56 2r brn & car rose 13.00 1.00
95 A56 5r vio & ultra 35.00 4.00
96 A56 10r car rose & grn 55.00 5.50
97 A56 15r ol grn & ultra 85.00 15.00
98 A56 25r ultra & brn org 175.00 25.00
Nos. 80-98 (19) 398.95 56.50

See Nos. 106-125. For type surcharged see No. 104. For overprints see Nos. M23-M25, M27, M29-M37, M39-M43, Gwalior No. O29.

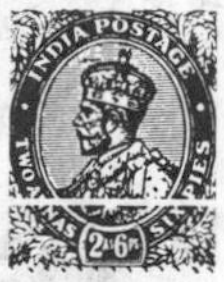
A57

1913-26

99 A57 2a6p ultramarine 1.75 .25
100 A57 2a6p brown org ('26) 8.00 8.00

See #112. For overprints see #M28, M38.

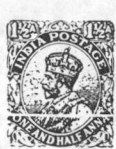

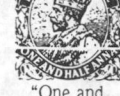

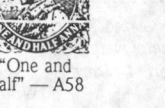

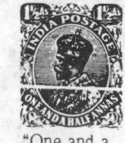

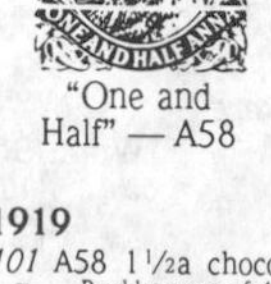
"One and Half" — A58

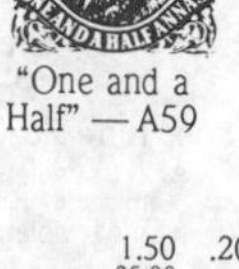
"One and a Half" — A59

1919

101 A58 1½a chocolate 1.50 .20
a. Booklet pane of 4 35.00

For overprint see No. M26.

1921-26

102 A59 1½a chocolate .70 .30
103 A59 1½a rose ('26) .40 .15

See No. 109.

Type of 1911-26 Surcharged **NINE PIES**

1921

104 A48 9p on 1a rose .15 .15
a. Surcharged "NINE-NINE" 30.00 *30.00*
b. Surcharged "PIES-PIES" 30.00 *30.00*
c. Double surcharge 50.00 55.00
e. Booklet pane of 4 27.50

No. 81 Surcharged Like No. 53

1922

105 A47 ¼a on ½a green .15 .15
a. Inverted surcharge 8.00 8.00
b. Pair, one without surcharge 175.00

Types of 1911-26 Issues

1926-36 **Wmk. 196**

106 A46 3p slate .15 .15
107 A47 ½a green .15 .15
108 A48 1a dark brown .18 .15
a. Tete beche pair 1.50 3.00
b. Booklet pane of 4 16.00
109 A59 1½a car rose ('29) .45 .15
110 A49 2a dull violet .75 .20
a. Booklet pane of 4 32.50
111 A49 2a ver ('34) 7.50 .90
a. Small die ('36) 2.50 .60
112 A57 2a6p buff .38 .15
113 A51 3a ultramarine 5.00 1.25
114 A51 3a blue ('30) 5.00 .15
115 A51 3a car rose ('32) .52 .15
116 A52 4a olive green .75 .15
117 A53 6a bister ('35) 8.00 2.00
118 A54 8a red violet 1.90 .15
119 A55 12a claret 2.25 .15
120 A56 1r green & brown 1.65 .15
121 A56 2r brn org & car rose 2.50 .25
122 A56 5r dk vio & ultra 13.00 1.10
123 A56 10r carmine & grn 37.50 2.00
124 A56 15r ol grn & ultra 15.00 15.00
125 A56 25r blue & ocher 90.00 22.50
Nos. 106-125 (20) 192.63 46.85

No. 111 measures 19x22½mm, while the small die, No. 111a, measures 18½x22mm.

For overprints see Gwalior #O30-O39, O44-O45.

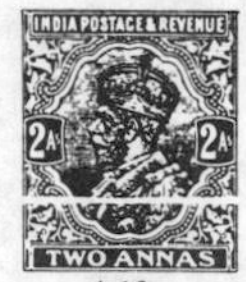
A60

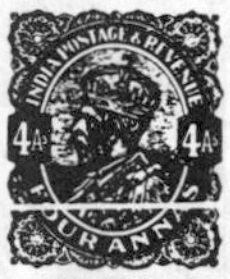
A61

1926-32 **Typo.**

126 A60 2a dull violet .45 .15
a. Tete beche pair 4.50 4.50
b. 2a rose violet .45 .15
c. Booklet pane of 4 19.00
127 A60 2a vermilion ('32) 7.50 2.50
128 A61 4a olive green 1.40 .15
Nos. 126-128 (3) 9.35 2.80

For overprints see Gwalior Nos. O33-O34.

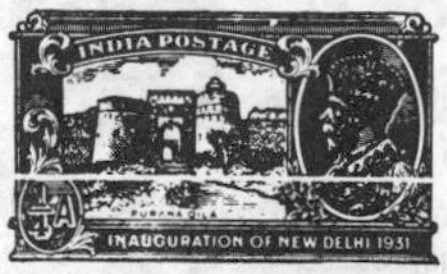
Fortress of Purana Qila — A62

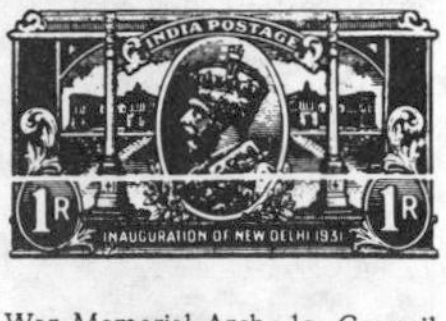
George V Flanked by Dominion Columns A67

Designs: ½a, War Memorial Arch. 1a, Council Building. 2a, Viceroy's House. 3a, Parliament Building.

1931, Feb. 9 **Litho.**

129 A62 ¼a brown & ol grn .85 1.00
130 A62 ½a green & violet .85 .25
131 A62 1a choc & red vio .85 .15
132 A62 2a blue & green 1.00 .85
133 A62 3a car & choc 2.25 1.75
134 A67 1r violet & green 7.50 14.00
Nos. 129-134 (6) 13.30 18.00

Change of the seat of Government from Calcutta to New Delhi.

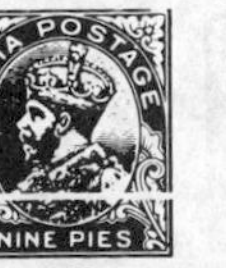

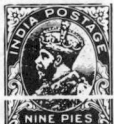

A68

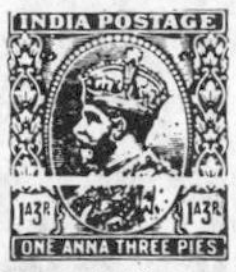

A69

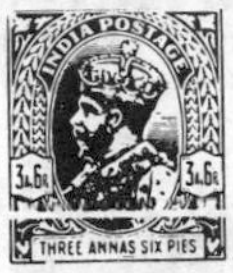

A70

1932, Apr. 22 **Litho.**

135	A68	9p dark green	.28	.15
136	A69	1a3p violet	.25	.15
137	A70	3a6p deep blue	1.25	.18
		Nos. 135-137 (3)	1.78	
		Set value		.28

No. 135 exists both litho. and typo.
For overprints see Gwalior #O41 and O43.

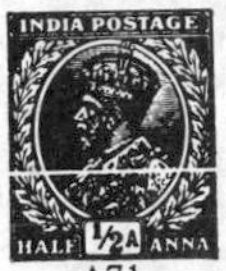

A71

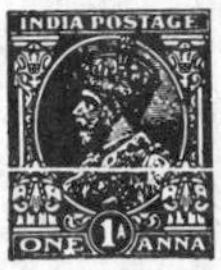

A72

1934 **Typo.**

138	A71	½a green	.80	.15
139	A72	1a dark brown	.80	.15
		Set value		.15

For overprints see Gwalior #O40 and O42.

Silver Jubilee Issue

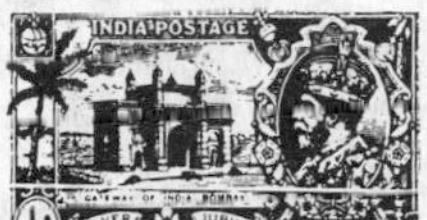

Gateway of India, Bombay A73

Designs: 9p, Victoria Memorial, Calcutta. 1a, Rameswaram Temple, Madras. 1¼a, Jain Temple, Calcutta. 2½a, Taj Mahal, Agra. 3½a, Golden Temple, Amritsar. 8a, Pagoda, Mandalay.

1935 **Litho.** ***Perf. 13½x14***

142	A73	½a lt green & black	.15	.15
143	A73	9p dull green & blk	.15	.15
144	A73	1a brown & black	.15	.15
145	A73	1¼a violet & black	.15	.15
146	A73	2½a brown org & blk	.45	.18
147	A73	3½a blue & black	.75	.48
148	A73	8a rose lilac & blk	1.90	1.00
		Nos. 142-148 (7)	3.70	
		Set value		1.85

25th anniv. of the reign of George V.

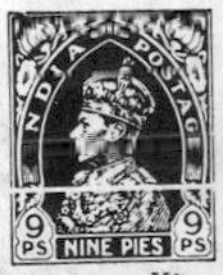

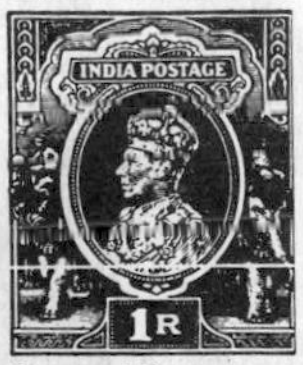

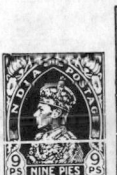

King George VI
A80 A82

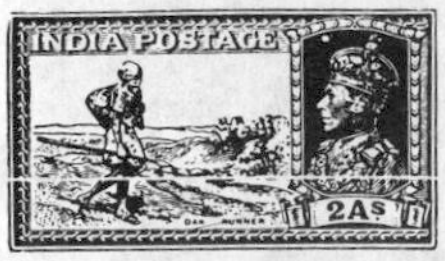

Dak Runner A81

Mail transport: 2a6p, Dak bullock cart. 3a, Dak tonga. 3a6p, Dak camel. 4a, Mail train. 6a, Mail steamer. 8a, Mail truck. 12a, 14a, Mail plane.

1937-40 **Typo.** **Wmk. 196**

150	A80	3p slate	.40	.25
151	A80	½a brown	.40	.25
152	A80	9p green	.65	.25
153	A80	1a carmine	.25	.25
a.		Tete beche pair	.40	.40
b.		Booklet pane of 4	4.25	
154	A81	2a scarlet	.75	.25
155	A81	2a6p purple	.25	.25
156	A81	3a yellow green	.55	.25
157	A81	3a6p ultramarine	.65	.40
158	A81	4a dark brown	.65	.25
159	A81	6a peacock blue	.85	.25
160	A81	8a blue violet	1.10	.25
161	A81	12a car lake	1.50	.70
161A	A81	14a rose vio ('40)	4.25	.25
162	A82	1r brown & slate	.70	.25
163	A82	2r dk brn & dk violet	6.00	.25
164	A82	5r dp ultra & dk green	12.50	.25
165	A82	10r rose car & dk violet	16.00	.90
166	A82	15r dk green & dk brown	85.00	90.00
167	A82	25r dk vio & blue violet	57.50	16.00
		Nos. 150-167 (19)	189.95	111.50

The King's portrait is larger on No. 161A than on other stamps of type A81.
For overprints see Gwalior Nos. O48-O51.

Catalogue values for unused stamps in this section, from this point to the end of the section, are for Never Hinged items.

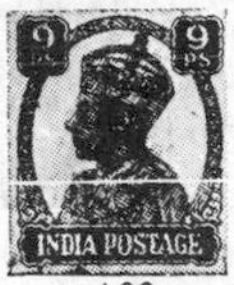

A83

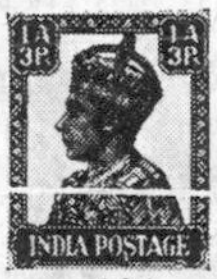

A84

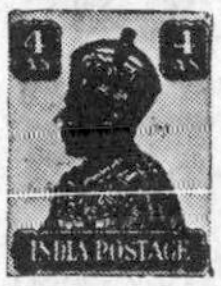

A85

1941-43 **Typo.** **Wmk. 196**

168	A83	3p slate ('42)	.15	.15
169	A83	½a rose vio ('42)	.15	.15
170	A83	9p light green	.18	.15
171	A83	1a car rose ('43)	.18	.15
172	A84	1a3p bister	.90	.15
172A	A84	1½a dark pur ('42)	.20	.15
173	A84	2a scarlet	.30	.15
174	A84	3a violet	.35	.15
175	A84	3½a ultramarine	.52	.15
176	A85	4a chocolate	.52	.15
177	A85	6a peacock blue	.52	.15
178	A85	8a blue violet	.90	.15
179	A85	12a carmine lake	1.40	.20
		Nos. 168-179 (13)	6.27	
		Set value		.80

Early printings of the 1½a and 3a were lithographed.
For surcharge see No. 199.

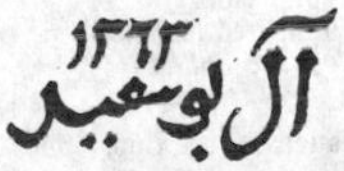

For stamps with this overprint, or a smaller type, see Oman (Muscat).

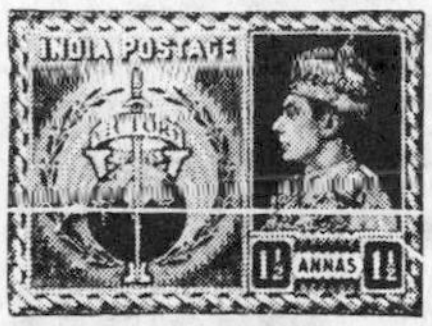

Symbols of Victory A86

1946, Jan. 2 **Litho.** ***Perf. 13***

195	A86	9p green	.15	.15
196	A86	1½a dull purple	.18	.15
197	A86	3½a ultramarine	.22	.22
198	A86	12a brown lake	.60	.60
		Nos. 195-198 (4)	1.15	1.12

Victory of the Allied Nations in WWII.

No. 172 Surcharged With New Value and Bars

1946, Aug. 8 ***Perf. 13½x14***

199	A84	3p on 1a3p bister	.15	.15

Dominion of India

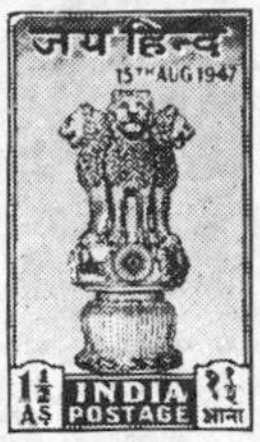

Asoka Pillar — A87

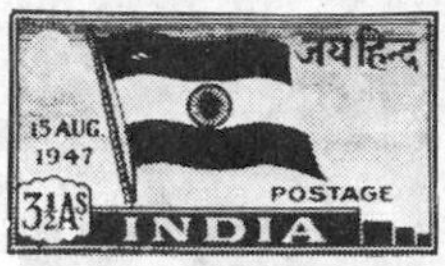

National Flag — A88

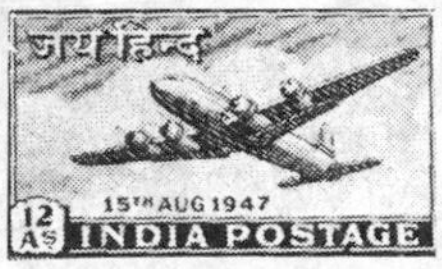

Four-Motor Plane — A89

Perf. 14x13½, 13½x14

1947 **Litho.** **Wmk. 196**

200	A87	1½a greenish gray	.15	.15
201	A88	3½a multicolored	.22	.18
202	A89	12a ultramarine	.90	.45
		Nos. 200-202 (3)	1.27	.78

Elevation to dominion status, Aug. 15, 1947.

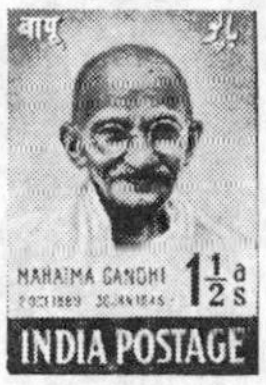

Mahatma Gandhi — A90

Design: 10r, Gandhi profile.

Perf. 11½

1948, Aug. 15 **Unwmk.** **Photo.**

Size: 22x32½mm

203	A90	1½a brown	.15	.15
204	A90	3½a violet	.22	.15
205	A90	12a dark gray green	.90	.18

Size: 22x37mm

206	A90	10r rose brn & brn	60.00	25.00
		Nos. 203-206 (4)	61.27	25.48

Mohandas K. Gandhi, 1869-1948.

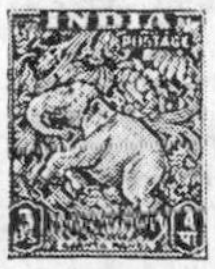

Ajanta Panel — A91

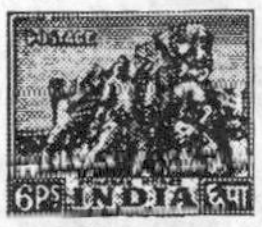

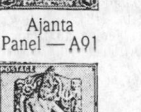

Konarak Horse A92

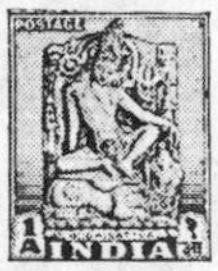

Bodhisattva A93

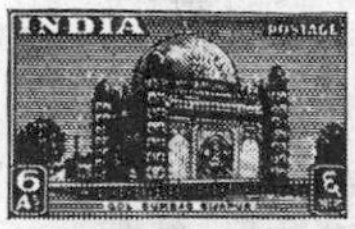

Tomb of Muhammad Adil Shah, Bijapur A95

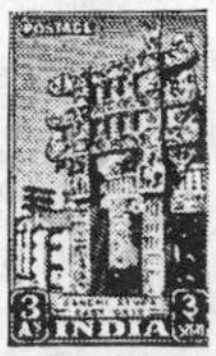

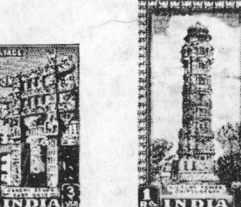

Sanchi Stupa — A94

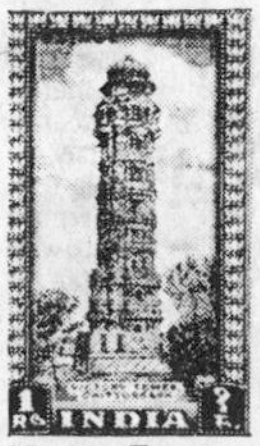

Victory Tower, Chittorgarh — A96

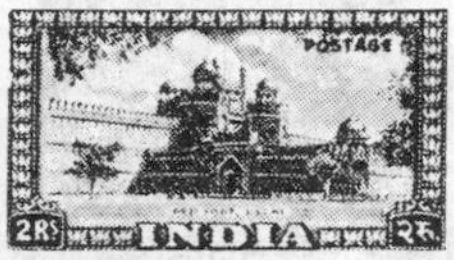

Red Fort, Delhi A97

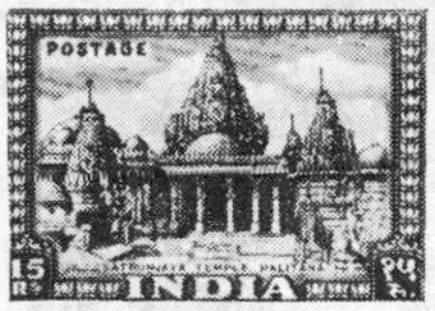

Satrunjaya Temple, Palitana A98

Designs: 9p, Trimurti. 2a, Nataraja. 3½a, Bodh Gaya Temple. 4a, Bhuvanesvara. 8a, Kandarya Mahadeva Temple. 12a, Golden Temple, Amritsar. 5r, Taj Mahal. 10r, Qutb Minar.

Perf. 13½x14, 14x13½

1949, Aug. 15 **Typo.** **Wmk. 196**

207	A91	3p gray violet	.15	.15
208	A92	6p red brown	.15	.15
209	A93	9p green	.15	.15
210	A93	1a turquoise	.15	.15
211	A93	2a carmine	.15	.15
212	A94	3a red orange	.25	.15
213	A94	3½a ultramarine	4.75	2.00
214	A94	4a brown lake	6.25	.15
215	A95	6a purple	2.25	.15
216	A95	8a blue green	2.25	.15
217	A95	12a blue	2.00	.15

Litho.

218	A96	1r dk green & pur	12.50	.15
219	A97	2r pur & rose red	5.25	.15
220	A97	5r brown car & dk green	15.00	.18
221	A96	10r dp bl & brn car	22.50	.75

Perf. 13½x13

222	A98	15r dp car & dk brn	15.00	3.25
		Nos. 207-222 (16)	88.75	
		Set value		6.75

See #231, 235-236. For overprints see #M44-M46, M48-M55 and Intl. Commission in Indo-china issues for Cambodia, #1, 3-5, Laos #1, 3-5 and Vietnam #1, 3-5.

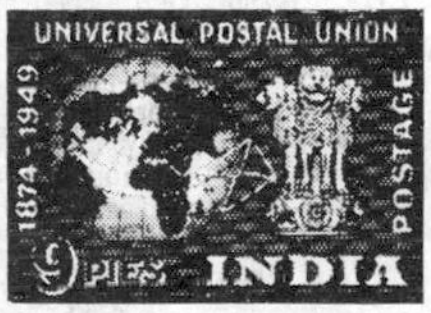

Symbols of UPU and Asoka Pillar — A99

1949, Oct. **Litho.** ***Perf. 13½x13***

223	A99	9p dull green	.25	.18
224	A99	2a carmine rose	.70	.20
225	A99	3½a ultramarine	.85	.45
226	A99	12a red brown	1.75	.60
		Nos. 223-226 (4)	3.55	1.43

75th anniv. of the formation of the UPU.

Republic of India

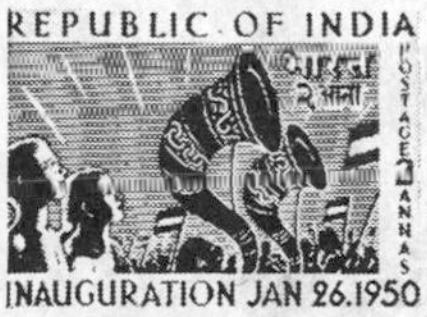

Rejoicing Crowds A100

Designs: 3½a, Quill pen, vert. 4a, Plow and wheat. 12a, Charkha and cloth.

Perf. 13½x13

1950, Jan. 26 **Wmk. 196**

227	A100	2a carmine	.22	.15
228	A100	3½a ultramarine	.70	.30
229	A100	4a purple	.80	.15
230	A100	12a claret	1.40	.42
		Nos. 227-230 (4)	3.12	1.02

Type of 1949 Redrawn

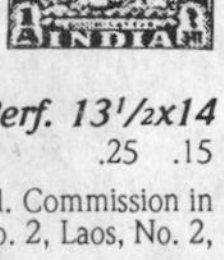

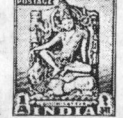

Bodhisattva — A101

1950, July 15 **Typo.** ***Perf. 13½x14***

231	A101	1a turquoise	.25	.15

For overprints see No. M47, Intl. Commission in Indo-china issues for Cambodia, No. 2, Laos, No. 2, and Vietnam, No. 2.

Extinct Stegodon Ganesa A102

1951, Jan. 13   *Perf. 13*
232 A102 2a deep carmine & black   .35 .20
Geological Survey of India, cent.

Torch and Map — A103   Kabir — A104

1951, Mar. 4   *Typo.*
233 A103   2a red vio & red org   .28 .15
234 A103   12a dark brown & ultra   1.00 .35
First Asian Games, New Delhi.

Temple Type of 1949

Designs: 2½a, Bodh Gaya Temple. 4a, Bhuvanesvara.

Perf. 13½x14
1951, Apr. 30   *Wmk. 196*
235 A94 2½a brown lake   .15 .15
236 A94 4a ultramarine   .20 .15
    Set value   .15

1952, Oct. 1   *Photo.*   *Perf. 14x13½*
Portraits: 1a, Tulsidas, poet and saint. 2a, Meera, Rajput princess. 4a, Surdas, blind poet and saint. 4½a, Ghalib, Urdu poet. 12a, Rabindranath Tagore.

237 A104   9p emerald   .15 .15
238 A104   1a crimson   .15 .15
239 A104   2a red orange   .22 .15
240 A104   4a ultramarine   .30 .15
241 A104   4½a red violet   .50 .18
242 A104   12a brown   1.10 .48
    Nos. 237-242 (6)   2.42
    Set value   1.00

First Locomotive and Streamliner A105

1953, Apr. 16   *Perf. 14½x14*
243 A105 2a black   .28 .15
Centenary of India's railroads.

Mt. Everest A106

1953, Oct. 2
244 A106   2a violet   .18 .15
245 A106   14a brown   2.75 .30
Conquest of Mt. Everest, May 29, 1953.

Telegraph Poles of 1851 and 1951 A107

1953, Nov. 1
246 A107   2a blue green   .18 .15
247 A107   12a blue   2.50 .28
    Set value   .35
Centenary of the telegraph in India.

Mail Transport, 1854 A108

Designs: 2a and 14a, Pigeon and plane. 4a, Mail transport, 1954.

1954, Oct. 1
248 A108   1a rose lilac   .15 .15
249 A108   2a rose pink   .15 .15
250 A108   4a yellow brown   1.25 .15
251 A108   14a blue   1.40 .50
    Nos. 248-251 (4)   2.95
    Set value   .76
Centenary of India's postage stamps.

UN Emblem and Lotus Blossom A109

1954, Oct. 24
252 A109 2a Prussian green   .15 .15
United Nations Day.

Forest Research Institute, Dehra Dun — A110

1954, Dec. 11
253 A110 2a ultramarine   .15 .15
4th World Forestry Cong., Dehra Dun.

Tractor A111   Charkha Operator A112

Symbols of Malaria Control A113

Designs: 6p, Power looms. 9p, Bullock irrigation pump. 1a, Damodar Valley dam. 3a, Naga woman at hand loom. 4a, Bullock team. 8a, Chittaranjan Locomotive Works. 10a, Plane over Marine Drive, Bombay. 12a, Hindustan aircraft factory. 14a, Plane over Kashmir valley. 1r, Telephone factory worker. 1r2a, Plane over Cape Comorin. 1r8a, Plane over Kanchenjunga Mountains. 2r, Rare earth factory. 5r, Sindri fertilizer factory. 10r, Steel mill.

Perf. 14x14½, 14½x14
1955, Jan. 26   *Photo.*
254 A111   3p rose lilac   .15 .15
255 A111   6p deep violet   .15 .15
256 A111   9p orange brown   .15 .15
257 A111   1a dp blue green   .15 .15
258 A112   2a blue   .15 .15
259 A112   3a blue green   .15 .15
260 A111   4a rose red   .18 .15
261 A113   6a yellow brown   .18 .15
262 A111   8a deep blue   .50 .15
263 A113   10a aquamarine   .45 .15
264 A111   12a violet blue   .50 .15
265 A113   14a emerald   .50 .15
266 A111   1r greenish black   1.40 .15
267 A113   1r2a gray   3.00 .24
268 A113   1r8a claret   3.25 .25
269 A111   2r carmine rose   2.75 .15
270 A111   5r brown   10.00 .25
271 A111   10r orange   14.00 .90
    Nos. 254-271 (18)   37.61
    Set value   2.40
See Nos. 316-319.

Bodhi Tree — A114

Ornament and Bodhi Tree — A115

1956, May 24   *Wmk. 196*   *Perf. 13*
272 A114   2a brown   .15 .15
273 A115   14a brick red   1.25 .45
2500th anniv. of the birth of Buddha.

Bal Gangadhar Tilak — A116   Map of India — A117

1956, July 23   *Photo.*
274 A116 2a orange brown   .15 .15
Birth cent. of Bal Gangadhar Tilak, independence leader.

1957-58   *Perf. 14x14½*
275 A117   1np blue green   .15 .15
276 A117   2np light brown   .15 .15
277 A117   3np brown   .15 .15
278 A117   5np emerald   3.50 .15
279 A117   6np gray   .15 .15
280 A117   8np brt green ('58)   .35 .25
281 A117   10np dark green   3.50 .15
282 A117   13np brt carmine   .15 .15
283 A117   15np violet ('58)   .25 .15
284 A117   20np bright blue   .30 .15
285 A117   25np ultramarine   .35 .15
286 A117   50np orange   1.50 .15
287 A117   75np plum   1.25 .15
288 A117   90np red lilac ('58)   1.75 .15
    Nos. 275-288 (14)   13.50
    Set value   1.00

Denominations of the 8np, 15np and 90np are inscribed nP.

See #302-315. For overprints see #M60 and Intl. Commission in Indo-china issues for Cambodia, #6-10, Laos, #6-10, and Vietnam, #6-10.

Laxmibai, Rani of Jhansi A118

Banyan Sapling, Arch and Flames — A119

Perf. 14½x14, 13
1957, Aug. 15   *Wmk. 196*
289 A118   15np brown   .18 .15
290 A119   90np bright red violet   .90 .20
    Set value   .28
Centenary of the struggle for independence (Indian Mutiny).

Henri Dunant A120

1957, Oct. 28   *Perf. 13½x13*
291 A120 15np car rose & black   .15 .15
19th Intl. Red Cross Conf., New Delhi.

Boy Eating Banana — A121   Toy Horse — A122

Children's Day: 15np, Girl writing on tablet.

1957, Nov. 14   *Perf. 13½*
292 A121   8np rose lilac   .15 .15
293 A121   15np aquamarine   .15 .15
294 A122   90np lt orange brown   .55 .15
    Nos. 202-204 (3)   .85
    Set value   .27

Madras University — A123

University Centenaries: No. 296, Calcutta. No. 297, Bombay, vert.

1957, Dec. 31   *Photo.*
    Size: 29½x25mm
295 A123   10np light brown   .15 .15
296 A123   10np gray   .15 .15
    Size: 21½x38mm
297 A123   10np violet   .15 .15
    Nos. 295-297 (3)   .45
    Set value   .30

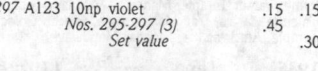

J. N. Tata and Steel Works, Jamshedpur A124

1958, Mar. 1   *Perf. 14½x14*
298 A124 15np red orange   .15 .15
50th anniv. of Indian steel industry.

Dr. Dhondo Keshav Karve — A125

1958, Apr. 18   *Perf. 14x13½*
299 A125 15np orange brown   .15 .15
Cent. of the birth of Karve, educator and pioneer of women's education.

Wapiti and Hunter Planes A126

1958, Apr. 30   *Perf. 14½x14*
300 A126   15np bright blue   .15 .15
301 A126   90np ultramarine   .90 .35
    Set value   .42
25th anniv. of the Indian Air Force.

Map Type of 1957-58 and Industrial Type of 1955

Designs: 1r, Telephone factory worker. 2r, Rare earth factory. 5r, Sindri fertilizer factory. 10r, Steel mill.

Perf. 14x14¹/₂

302	A117	1np blue grn ('60)	.15	.15
a.		Imperf., pair	110.00	
303	A117	2np light brown	.15	.15
304	A117	3np brown	.15	.15
305	A117	5np emerald	.15	.15
306	A117	6np gray ('63)	.15	.15
307	A117	8np bright green	.15	.15
308	A117	10np dark green	.15	.15
309	A117	13np bright car ('63)	.15	.15
310	A117	15np violet ('59)	.15	.15
311	A117	20np bright blue	.15	.15
312	A117	25np ultramarine	.15	.15
313	A117	50np orange ('59)	.55	.15
314	A117	75np plum ('59)	.38	.15
315	A117	90np red lilac ('60)	.50	.15
316	A111	1r dark green ('59)	.70	.15
317	A111	2r lilac rose ('59)	1.65	.15
318	A111	5r brown ('59)	3.75	.20
319	A111	10r orange ('59)	11.00	.48
		Nos. 302-319 (18)	20.18	
		Set value		1.50

For overprints see Nos. M56-M59, M61, Intl. Commission in Indo-china issues for Cambodia, No. 12, Laos, Nos. 12-16, and Vietnam Nos. 11-16.

Bipin Chandra Pal — A128   Nurse and Child — A129

1958, Nov. 7   Perf. 13¹/₂
320 A128 15np dull green   .15 .15
Birth cent. of Pal, early leader of India's freedom movement.

1958, Nov. 30
Portrait: Sir Jagadis Chandra Bose.
321 A128 15np brt greenish blue   .15 .15
Bose, physicist, plant physiologist, birth cent.

1958, Nov. 14   Wmk. 324
322 A129 15np violet   .15 .15
Children's Day, Nov. 14.

Exhibition Gate — A130

1958, Dec. 30   Perf. 14¹/₂x14
323 A130 15np claret   .15 .15
India 1958 Exhibition at Kampur.

Sir Jamsetjee Jeejeebhoy — A131

1959, Apr. 13   Perf. 13¹/₂
324 A131 15np brown   .15 .15
Cent. of the death of Jeejeebhoy, philosopher and philanthropist.

"Triumph of Labor," by D. P. Roy Chowdhary A132

1959, June 15   Perf. 14¹/₂x14
325 A132 15np dull green   .20 .15
40th anniv. of the ILO.

Children Arriving at Institution — A133

Perf. 14x14¹/₂
1959, Nov. 14   Photo.   Wmk. 324
326 A133 15np dull green   .15 .15
a.   Imperf., pair   225.00
Children's Day, Nov. 14.

Farmer Plowing with Bullocks A134

1959, Dec. 30   Perf. 13
327 A134 15np gray   .15 .15
World Agriculture Fair, New Delhi.

Thiruvalluvar Holding Stylus and Palmyra Leaf — A135

1960, Feb. 15   Perf. 14
328 A135 15np rose lilac   .15 .15
Honoring the ancient and saintly Tamil poet, Thiruvalluvar.

Scene from Meghduta — A136

Scene from Sakuntala A137

1960, June 22   Perf. 13
329 A136 15np gray   .15 .15
330 A137 1.03r brown & bister   .30 .15
          Set value   .20
Honoring Kalidasa, 5th cent. poet and dramatist. For surcharge see No. 371.

Subramania Bharati A138   Dr. M. Visvesvaraya A139

1960, Sept. 11 Photo. Perf. 14x13¹/₂
331 A138 15np bright blue   .15 .15
Honoring the poet and statesman Subramania Bharati (1882-1921).

1960, Sept. 15   Perf. 13x13¹/₂
332 A139 15np car rose & brown   .15 .15
Birth cent. of Visvesvaraya, engineer and statesman.

Children Playing and Studying A140

1960, Nov. 14   Perf. 13¹/₂x13
333 A140 15np green   .15 .15
Children's Day, Nov. 14.

Children and UN Emblem A141

1960, Dec. 11   Wmk. 324
334 A141 15np olive gray & org brn .15 .15
UNICEF Day.

Tyagaraja, Indian Musician — A142

1961, Jan. 6   Photo.   Perf. 14
335 A142 15np bright blue   .15 .15
114th anniv. of Tyagaraja's death.

First Airmail Postmark — A143

Boeing 707 Jetliner — A144

Design: 1r, Humber-Sommer biplane.

Perf. 14, 13x13¹/₂
1961, Feb. 18   Wmk. 324
336 A143 5np olive bister   .18 .15
337 A144 15np gray & green   .45 .15
338 A144 1r gray & claret   2.75 .55
     Nos. 336-338 (3)   3.38
          Set value   .70
50th anniv. of the world's 1st airmail. The flight was from Allahabad to Naini, Feb. 18, 1911.

Chatrapati Sivaji Maharaj (1627-1680) — A145

1961, Apr. 17   Perf. 13x13¹/₂
339 A145 15np gray green & brown   .15 .15
Leader of the Marathas in the fight against the Moguls.

Motilal Nehru — A146   Rabindranath Tagore — A147

1961, May 6   Perf. 14x13¹/₂
340 A146 15np orange & ol gray   .15 .15
Cent. of the birth of Motilal Nehru, leader in India's fight for freedom.

1961, May 7   Perf. 13
341 A147 15np blue green & orange   .20 .15
Cent. of the birth of Tagore, poet.

Radio Masts and All India Radio Emblem A148

1961, June 8   Photo.   Wmk. 324
342 A148 15np ultramarine   .15 .15
25th anniv. of All India Radio.

1961, Aug. 2   Perf. 14x13¹/₂
343 A149 15np gray   .15 .15
Cent. of the birth of Ray, scientist.

1961, Sept. 1   Perf. 13
344 A150 15np olive gray   .15 .15
Bhatkhande (1860-1936), musician.

Boy Making Pottery — A151

Gate at Fair — A152

1961, Nov. 14   *Perf. 13½*
345 A151 15np brown   .15 .15
   Children's Day, Nov. 14.

1961, Nov. 14   *Perf. 14x14½*
346 A152 15np blue & carmine   .15 .15
   Indian Industries Fair at New Delhi.

Forest and Himalayas — A153

1961, Nov. 21   *Perf. 13*
347 A153 15np brown & green   .15 .15
   Cent. of the introduction of scientific forestry in India.

Yaksha, God of Fertility — A154

Kalibangan Seal — A155

1961, Dec. 14   Photo.   Perf. 14
348 A154 15np orange brown   .15 .15
349 A155 90np orange brn & olive   .30 .15
   Set value   .18
   Cent. of the Archaeological Survey of India.

Madan Mohan Malaviya — A156

Nunmati Refinery, Gauhati — A157

1961, Dec. 25   *Perf. 14x13½*
350 A156 15np slate   .15 .15
   Cent. of the birth of Malaviya, Pres. of the Indian Natl. Cong. and Vice Chancellor of Benares University.

1962, Jan. 1   Photo.   Perf. 13
351 A157 15np blue   .15 .15
   1st Indian oil refinery at Gauhati.

Bhikaiji Cama — A158

Village Council, Banyan Tree, Parliament and Map — A159

1962, Jan. 26   *Perf. 14*
352 A158 15np rose lilac   .15 .15
   Cent. of the birth of Madame Cama, a leader in India's fight for independence.

1962, Jan. 26   *Perf. 13*
353 A159 15np red lilac   .15 .15
   Panchayati Raj, the system of government by village council.

Dayananda Sarasvati — A160

Ganesh Shankar Vidyarthi — A161

1962, Mar. 4   *Perf. 14*
354 A160 15np brown orange   .15 .15
   135th anniv. of the birth of Sarasvati, reformer of the Vedic religion and founder of the Arya Samaj educational institutions.

1962, Mar. 25
355 A161 15np reddish brown   .15 .15
   Vidyarthi (1890-1931), reformer of community life.

Malaria Eradication Emblem — A162

Dr. Rajendra Prasad — A163

1962, Apr. 7   *Perf. 13*
356 A162 15np dk car rose & yel   .15 .15
   WHO drive to eradicate malaria.

1962, May 13   *Perf. 13*
357 A163 15np bright red lilac   .15 .15
   Prasad, President of India (1950-62).

High Court, Calcutta A164

1962   Photo.   Perf. 13½x14
358 A164 15np green   .15 .15
359 A164 15np Madras   .15 .15
360 A164 15np Bombay   .15 .15
   Nos. 358-360 (3)   .45
   Set value   .18
   Indian High Courts, cent. Issued: No. 358, July 1; No. 359, Aug. 8; No. 360, Aug. 14.

Ramabai Ranade — A165

Indian Rhinoceros — A166

1962, Aug. 15   *Perf. 14*
361 A165 15np brown orange   .15 .15
   Ramabai Ranade (1862-1924), woman social reformer.

1962-63   Wmk. 324   Perf. 14
   Designs: 10np, Gaur. No. 363, Lesser panda, vert. 30np, Elephant, vert. 50np, Tiger. 1r, Lion.
   Size: 30x26mm
361A A166 10np yel org & blk ('63)   .24 .15
362 A166 15np Prus blue & brn   .24 .15
   Perf. 13x13½, 13½x13
   Size: 25x36mm, 36x25mm
363 A166 15np green & red brown
      ('63)   .35 .15
364 A166 30np bister & slate ('63)   .45 .15
365 A166 50np dp grn, ocher &
      brown ('63)   1.10 .25
366 A166 1r brt bl & pale brown
      ('63)   1.50 .60
   Nos. 361A-366 (6)   3.88
   Set value   1.14

Child Reaching for Flag — A167

1962, Nov. 14   *Perf. 13*
367 A167 15np lt bluish grn & ver   .15 .15
   Children's Day.

Eye within Lotus Blossom A168

1962, Dec. 3   Photo.
368 A168 15np olive gray   .15 .15
   16th Intl. Cong. of Ophthalmology, New Delhi, Dec. 1962.

Srinivasa Ramanujan A169

Swami Vivekananda A170

1962, Dec. 22   *Perf. 13½x14*
369 A169 15np olive gray   .15 .15
   75th anniv. of the birth of Ramanujan (1887-1920), mathematician.

1963, Jan. 17   *Perf. 14x14½*
370 A170 15np olive & orange brn   .15 .15
   Cent. of the birth of Vivekananda (1863-1902), philosopher.

No. 330 Surcharged with New Value and Two Bars

1963, Feb. 2   *Perf. 13*
371 A137 1r on 1.03r brown & bis   .30 .15

Hands Reaching for "FAO" Emblem — A171

Henri Dunant and Centenary Emblem — A172

1963, Mar. 21   Photo.
372 A171 15np chalky blue   .15 .15
   UNFAO Freedom from Hunger campaign.

1963, May 8   *Perf. 13*
373 A172 15np gray & red   .15 .15
   Centenary of the International Red Cross.

Field Artillery and Helicopter A173

   Design: 1r, Soldier guarding frontier and plane dropping supplies.

1963, Aug. 15   *Perf. 13½x14*
374 A173 15np dull green   .15 .15
375 A173 1r red brown   .50 .15
   Set value   .18
   Honoring the Armed Forces and the 16th anniv. of independence.

Dadabhoy Naoroji — A174

1963, Sept. 4   *Perf. 13*
376 A174 15np gray green   .15 .15
   Honoring Dadabhoy Naoroji (1825-1917), mathematician and statesman.

Annie Besant — A175

School Lunch — A176

1963, Oct. 1   Photo.   Perf. 14
377 A175 15np blue green   .15 .15
   Besant (1847-1933), an English woman devoted to the cause of India's freedom, theosophist and writer. Stamp gives birth date as 1837.

1963, Nov. 14   Wmk. 324   Perf. 14
378 A176 15np olive bister   .15 .15
   Children's Day.

Eleanor Roosevelt at Spinning Wheel A177

1963, Dec. 10   *Perf. 13*
379 A177 15np rose violet   .15 .15
   Honoring Eleanor Roosevelt on the 15th anniv. of the Universal Declaration of Human Rights.

Gopabandhu Das
(1877-1928)
A178

Lakshmi, Goddess
of Wealth
A179

1964, Jan. 4   **Perf. 13**
380 A178 15np dull purple   .15 .15
Gopabandhu Das, social reformer.

1964, Jan. 4   **Photo.**
381 A179 15np dull violet blue   .15 .15
26th Intl. Cong. of Orientalists, New Delhi, Jan. 4-14.

Purandaradasa Holding
Veena and
Chipala — A180

1964, Jan. 14
382 A180 15np golden brown   .15 .15
400th anniv. of the death of Purandaradasa (1484-1564), musician.

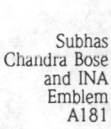

Subhas
Chandra Bose
and INA
Emblem
A181

Design: 55np, Bose addressing troops.

1964, Jan. 23   **Perf. 13**
383 A181 15np olive   .15 .15
384 A181 55np red & black   .25 .18
         Set value   .24
67th anniv. of the birth of Bose, organizer of the Indian Natl. Army.

Sarojini Naidu
(1879-1949)
A182

Kasturba
Gandhi
A183

1964, Feb. 13   **Perf. 14x13½**
385 A182 15np dull lilac & slate grn   .15 .15
Mrs. Sarojini Haidu, poet, politician, governor of United Provinces.

1964, Feb. 22   **Photo.**   **Wmk. 324**
386 A183 15np brown orange   .15 .15
20th anniv. of the death of Kasturba Gandhi (1869-1944), wife of Mahatma Gandhi.

Dr. Waldemar M.
Haffkine (1860-
1930) — A184

1964, Mar. 16   **Perf. 13**
387 A184 15np violet brown, *buff*   .15 .15
Haffkine, bacteriologist, who as director of Haffkine Institute introduced inoculations against cholera and plague.

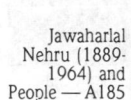

Jawaharlal
Nehru (1889-
1964) and
People — A185

1964, June 12   **Unwmk.**   **Perf. 13**
388 A185 15p grayish blue   .15 .15
Prime Minister Jawaharlal Nehru.

Asutosh
Mookerjee and
High Court,
Calcutta
A186

1964, June 29   **Wmk. 324**
389 A186 15p olive green & brn   .15 .15
Cent. of the birth of Asutosh Mookerjee (1864-1924), educator, lawyer and judge.

Sri Aurobindo Ghose
(1872-1950), Writer
and
Philosopher — A187

1964, Aug. 15   **Photo.**
390 A187 15p violet brown   .15 .15

Raja
Rammohun
Roy — A188

1964, Sept. 27   **Perf. 13**
391 A188 15p reddish brown   .15 .15
Roy (1772-1833), Hindu religious reformer.

Globe, Lotus, and
Calipers — A189

Nehru Medal and
Rose — A190

1964, Nov. 9   **Unwmk.**   **Photo.**
392 A189 15p carmine rose   .15 .15
6th gen. assembly of the Intl. Organization for Standardization.

1964, Nov. 14   **Perf. 13½**
393 A190 15p blue gray   .15 .15
Children's Day. For overprints, see Nos. M62, Intl. Commission in Indo-china issues for Laos and Vietnam, No. 1.

St. Thomas Statue,
Ortona,
Italy — A191

Globe and
Pickax — A192

1964, Dec. 2   **Unwmk.**   **Perf. 13½**
394 A191 15p rose violet   .15 .15
Visit of Pope Paul VI, Nov. 30-Dec. 2.

1964, Dec. 14   **Wmk. 324**
395 A192 15p bright green   .15 .15
22nd Intl. Geological Cong., New Delhi.

Jamsetji N.
Tata — A193

1965, Jan. 7   **Unwmk.**   **Perf. 13**
396 A193 15p dk brown & orange   .15 .15
125th anniv. of the birth of Tata (1839-1904), founder of India's steel industry.

Lala Lajpatrai (1865
1928), a Leader in
India's Fight for
Independence — A194

1965, Jan. 28   **Photo.**   **Perf. 13**
397 A194 15p brown   .15 .15

ICC Emblem
and Globe
A195

1965, Feb. 8   **Litho.**
398 A195 15p dull green & car   .15 .15
20th cong. of the Intl. Chamber of Commerce, New Delhi.

Freighter Jalausha at
Visakhapatnam — A196

1965, Apr. 5   **Photo.**   **Wmk. 324**
399 A196 15p ultramarine   .15 .15
National Maritime Day.

Death Centenary of
Abraham
Lincoln — A197

1965, Apr. 15   **Perf. 13**
400 A197 15p yellow & dk brown   .15 .15

ITU Emblem, Old and New
Communication Equipment — A198

1965, May 17   **Photo.**   **Perf. 14½x14**
401 A198 15p rose violet   .15 .15
Cent. of the ITU.

Torch and
Rose — A199

1965, May 27   **Wmk. 324**   **Perf. 13**
402 A199 15p carmine & blue   .15 .15
1st anniv. of the death of Jawaharlal Nehru.

ICY Emblem
A200

1965, June 26   **Photo.**   **Unwmk.**
403 A200 15p bister & dk green   .15 .15
International Cooperation Year.

Indians Raising Flag
on Everest — A201

1965, Aug. 15   **Unwmk.**   **Perf. 13**
404 A201 15p plum   .15 .15
Success of the Indian Mt. Everest Expedition, May 20, 1965.

Elephant from Konarak Temple, Orissa
A202

Tea Picking
A203

Woman Writing Letter, Chandella Carving, 11th Century — A204

Trombay Atomic Center
A205

Designs: 2p, Vase (bidri ware). 3p, Brass lamp. 4p, Coffee berries. 5p, Family (family planning). 8p, Axis deer (chital). 10p, Electric locomotive, 1961. 20p, Gnat plane. 30p, Male and female figurines. 40p, General Post Office, Calcutta, 1868. 50p, Mangoes. 60p, Somnath Temple. 70p, Stone chariot, Hampi, Mysore. 2r, Dal Lake, Kashmir. 5r, Bhakra Dam, Punjab.

Perf. 14¹⁄₂x14, 14x14¹⁄₂

1965-68   **Photo.**   **Wmk. 324**
405	A202	2p redsh brown ('67)	.15	.15
406	A202	3p olive bis ('67)	.15	.15
407	A203	4p orange brn ('68)	.15	.15
408	A202	5p cerise ('67)	.15	.15
409	A202	6p gray ('66)	.15	.15
410	A202	8p red brown ('67)	.16	.15
411	A203	10p brt blue ('66)	.15	.15
412	A203	15p dk yel green	.15	.15
413	A203	20p plum ('67)	.15	.15
414	A202	30p brown ('67)	.15	.15
415	A203	40p brown vio ('68)	.15	.15
416	A202	50p green ('67)	.15	.15
417	A202	60p dark gray ('67)	.18	.15
418	A203	70p violet ('67)	.60	.15
419	A204	1r deep claret & red brown ('66)	.45	.15
420	A205	2r vio & brt bl ('67)	1.10	.15
421	A205	5r brn & vio ('67)	2.00	.30
422	A205	10r green & gray	5.00	.75
		Nos. 405-422 (18)	11.14	
		Set value		1.85

See Nos. 623, 666-670A, 678, 680, 684-685. For overprints see Nos. RA1-RA2, Intl. Commission in Indo-china issues for Laos and Vietnam, Nos. 2-9.

1975-76   **Wmk. 360**   **Perf. 14¹⁄₂x14**
423	A202	5p cerise	.15	.15

Unwmk.
423A	A202	5p cerise ('76)	.15	.15
		Set value	.15	.15

A206   A207

1965, Sept. 10   **Unwmk.**   **Perf. 13**
424 A206 15p dark green & brown   .15 .15
Govind Ballabh Pant (1887-1961), Home Minister of India.

1965, Oct. 31   **Perf. 14**
425 A207 15p gray   .15 .15
Vallabhbhai Patel (1875-1950), Deputy Prime Minister of India.

Chittaranjan Das (1870-1925)
A208

Vidyapati, 15th Cent. Poet
A209

1965, Nov. 5   **Photo.**   **Perf. 13**
426 A208 15p brown   .15 .15
Das, freedom fighter, pres. of Indian Natl. Cong., mayor of Calcutta.

1965, Nov. 17   **Perf. 14x14¹⁄₂**
427 A209 15p brown   .15 .15

Tomb of Akbar the Great, Sikandra — A210

1966, Jan. 24   **Perf. 14**
428 A210 15p dark gray   .15 .15
Pacific Area Travel Assoc. Conf., New Delhi.

Soldier, Planes and Warships — A211

1966, Jan. 26
429 A211 15p bright violet   .15 .15
Honoring the Indian armed forces.

Lal Bahadur Shastri
A212

Kambar
A213

1966, Jan. 26   **Perf. 13**
430 A212 15p gray   .15 .15
Prime Minister Shastri (1904-66).

1966, Apr. 9   **Perf. 14x14¹⁄₂**
431 A213 15p green   .15 .15
Kambar, 9th century Tamil poet.

B. R. Ambedkar
A214

Kunwar Singh
A215

1966, Apr. 14   **Unwmk.**   **Perf. 14**
432 A214 15p violet brown   .15 .15
10th anniv. of the death of Dr. Bhimrao R. Ambedkar (1891-1956), lawyer and leader in social reform.

1966, Apr. 23   **Photo.**
433 A215 15p orange brown   .15 .15
Kunwar Singh (1777-1858), hero of 1857 War of Independence (1857 Mutiny).

Gopal Krishna Gokhale
A216

1966, May 9   **Unwmk.**   **Perf. 13**
434 A216 15p violet brown & yel   .15 .15
Cent. of the birth of Gokhale (1866-1915), professor of history and political economy and leader of the opposition party.

A. M. P. Dvivedi (1864-1938)
A217

Ranjit Singh (1780-1839)
A218

1966, May 15   **Perf. 14**
435 A217 15p olive gray   .15 .15
Acharya Mahavir Prasad Dvivedi, Hindi writer.

1966, June 28   **Unwmk.**   **Perf. 14**
436 A218 15p plum   .15 .15
Maharaja Ranjit Singh, ruler of Punjab.

Homi Bhabha and Atomic Reactor
A219

1966, Aug. 4   **Perf. 14¹⁄₂x14**
437 A219 15p brown violet   .15 .15
Dr. Homi Bhabha (1909-1966), scientist.

Rama Tirtha — A220

1966, Nov. 11   **Unwmk.**   **Perf. 13**
438 A220 15p greenish blue   .15 .15
60th anniv. of the death of Swami Rama Tirtha (1873-1906).

A221

A222

1966, Nov. 11   **Photo.**   **Perf. 13¹⁄₂**
439 A221 15p dark violet blue   .15 .15
Abdul Kalam Azad (1888-1958), president of the All-India Congress.

1966, Nov. 14   **Perf. 13**
440 A222 15p Child and dove   .15 .15
Children's Day.

Allahabad High Court, Cent.
A223

1966, Nov. 25   **Perf. 14¹⁄₂x14**
441 A223 15p violet brown   .15 .15

Family
A224

1966, Dec. 12   **Perf. 13¹⁄₂x13**
442 A224 15p brown   .15 .15
Intl. Conf. for Marriage Guidance, New Delhi, and Family Planning Week.

Hockey
A225

1966, Dec. 31   **Unwmk.**   **Perf. 13**
443 A225 15p bright blue   .15 .15
Victory of the Indian hockey team at the 5th Asian Games, Bangkok, Dec. 19.

Grain Harvest — A226

1967, Jan. 11   **Perf. 13¹⁄₂**
444 A226 15p yellow green   .15 .15
1st anniv. of the death of Prime Minister Lal Bahadur Shastri, who advocated self-sufficiency in food production.

Voters — A227

Guru Dwara Shrine, Patna — A228

1967, Jan. 13   **Photo.**
445 A227 15p light red brown   .15 .15
General elections, Feb. 1967.

1967, Jan. 17   **Perf. 14**
446 A228 15p violet   .15 .15
300th anniv. of the birth of Gobind Singh (1666-1708), religious leader.

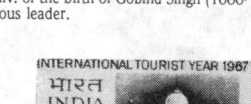

Taj Mahal
A229

1967, Mar. 19   **Perf. 14¹⁄₂x14**
447 A229 15p brown & orange   .15 .15
International Tourist Year.

Nandalal Bose and Garuda — A230

1967, Apr. 16   **Perf. 13¹⁄₂**
448 A230 15p brown   .15 .15
Nandalal Bose (1882-1966), painter.

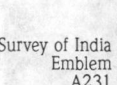

Survey of India Emblem A231

1967, May 1   **Unwmk.**   *Perf. 13*
449 A231 15p lilac   .15   .15
Bicentenary of Survey of India.

Basaveswara, 12th Cent. Statesman and Philosopher, at Work — A232

1967, May 11   *Perf. 13¹/₂x14*
450 A232 15p deep orange   .15   .15

Narsinha Mehta A233

Maharana Pratap A234

1967, May 30   *Perf. 13¹/₂*
451 A233 15p gray brown   .15   .15
Narsina Mehta, 15th cent. musician.

1967, June 11   *Perf. 14x14¹/₂*
452 A234 15p reddish brown   .15   .15
Pratap (1540-1597), Mewar ruler.

Narayana Guru A235

Dr. Sarvepalli Radhakrishnan A236

1967, Aug. 21   **Photo.**   *Perf. 14*
453 A235 15p brown   .15   .15
Narayana Guru (1855-1928), religious reformer.

1967, Sept. 5   **Unwmk.**   *Perf. 13*
454 A236 15p dull claret   .15   .15
Radhakrishnan, Pres. of India 1962-67.

Martyrs' Memorial, Patna A237

1967, Oct. 1   **Photo.**   *Perf. 14¹/₂x14*
455 A237 15p dark carmine   .15   .15
25th anniv. of the "Quit India" revolt led by Gandhi.

Map Showing Indo-European Telegraph — A238

1967, Nov. 9   **Photo.**   *Perf. 13¹/₂*
456 A238 15p blue & black   .15   .15
Cent. of the laying of the Indo-European telegraph line.

Wrestlers — A239

1967, Nov. 12
457 A239 15p ocher & plum   .15   .15
World Wrestling Championships, New Delhi, Nov. 1967.

Nehru and Naga Tribesmen A240

Rashbehari Basu A241

1967, Dec. 4   **Photo.**   *Perf. 13*
458 A240 15p ultramarine   .15   .15

1967, Dec. 26   *Perf. 13¹/₂*
459 A241 15p dull purple   .15   .15
Basu (1886-1945), Bengali leader.

Bugle, Scout Emblem and Scout Sign — A242

1967, Dec. 27   *Perf. 14¹/₂x14*
460 A242 15p orange brown   .15   .15
Boy Scout Movement, 60th anniv.

People Encircling the Globe and Human Rights Flame — A243

1968, Jan. 1   *Perf. 13*
461 A243 15p dark green   .15   .15
Intl. Human Rights Year.

Conference Emblem and Gopuram Temple — A244

1968, Jan. 3   **Photo.**   **Unwmk.**
462 A244 15p purple   .15   .15
2nd Intl. Conf. on Tamil Studies, Madras.

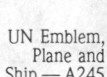

UN Emblem, Plane and Ship — A245

1968, Feb. 1   *Perf. 14¹/₂x14*
463 A245 15p greenish blue   .15   .15
UN Conference on Trade and Development, New Delhi, Feb. 1968.

Symbolic Bow and Quill Pen — A246

1968, Feb. 20   *Perf. 13¹/₂x14*
464 A246 15p ocher & sepia   .15   .15
Cent. of the newspaper Amrit Bazar Patrika, Calcutta.

Maxim Gorky (1868-1936), Russian Writer — A247

1968, Mar. 28   **Photo.**   *Perf. 14*
465 A247 15p brown violet   .15   .15

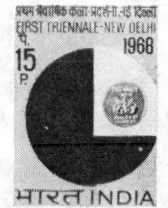

Exhibition Emblem — A248

Symbolic Mail Box — A249

1968, Mar. 31   *Perf. 13*
466 A248 15p dark blue & orange   .15   .15
First Triennial Exhibition, New Delhi.

1968, July 1   **Unwmk.**   *Perf. 13*
467 A249 20p vermilion & blue   .15   .15
Opening of 100,000th Indian post office.

Wheat and Indian Agricultural Research Institute A250

1968, July 15   **Photo.**   *Perf. 13*
468 A250 20p brt green & brown org   .15   .15
India's 1968 bumper wheat crop.

Gaganendranath Tagore (1867-1938), Self-portrait — A251

1968, Sept. 17   **Unwmk.**   *Perf. 13*
469 A251 20p ocher & deep claret   .15   .15

Lakshminath Bezbaruah (1868-1938), Writer — A252

1968, Oct. 5   **Photo.**   *Perf. 13¹/₂*
470 A252 20p sepia   .15   .15

19th Olympic Games, Mexico City — A253

1968, Oct. 12   *Perf. 14¹/₂x14*
471 A253 20p blue gray & red brn   .15   .15
472 A253 1r olive gray & dk brn   .25   .25
Set value   .25   .25

Bhagat Singh (1907-1931), Revolutionary A254

1968, Oct. 19   **Photo.**   *Perf. 13¹/₂x13*
473 A254 20p orange brown   .15   .15

Bose Reading Proclamation A255

Sister Nivedita A256

1968, Oct. 21   *Perf. 14x14¹/₂*
474 A255 20p dark blue   .15   .15
25th anniv. of the establishment of the Azad Hind (Free India) government by Subhas Chandra Bose (1897-1945), independence leader.

1968, Oct. 27
475 A256 20p blue green   .15   .15
Sister Nivedita (Margaret Noble, 1867-1911), Irish-born friend of India.

Marie Curie and Patient Receiving Radiation A257

1968, Nov. 6   *Perf. 14¹/₂x14*
476 A257 20p purple   .15   .15
Marie Sklodowska Curie (1867-1934), discoverer of radium and polonium.

World Map A258

Interior of Cochin Synagogue — A259

1968, Dec. 1   *Perf. 13*
477 A258 20p blue   .15   .15
21st Intl. Geographical Congress.

Perf. 13x13¹/₂
1968, Dec. 15   **Photo.**   **Unwmk.**
478 A259 20p violet blue & car rose   .15   .15
400th anniv. of Cochin Synagogue.

Frigate Nilgiri — A260

1968, Dec. 15   *Perf. 13¹/₂x13*
479 A260 20p dull violet blue   .15   .15
Navy Day. The Nilgiri, launched Oct. 23, 1968, was the 1st Indian warship.

Redbilled Blue Magpie
A261

Birds: 50p, Brown-fronted pied woodpecker. 1r, Slaty-headed scimitar babbler, vert. 2r, Yellow-backed sunbirds.

Perf. 14¹/₂x14, 14x14¹/₂

1968, Dec. 31
480	A261	20p pink & multi	.15	.15
481	A261	50p multicolored	.24	.15
482	A261	1r multicolored	.52	.24
483	A261	2r multicolored	1.00	.52
		Nos. 480-483 (4)	1.91	1.06

Chatterjee (1838-94)
A262

Dr. Bhagavan Das
A263

1969, Jan. 1 *Perf. 13¹/₂*
484 A262 20p ultramarine .15 .15
Bankim Chandra Chatterjee, writer.

1969, Jan. 12 Photo. Perf. 13¹/₂
485 A263 20p red brown .15 .15
Das (1869-1958), philosopher.

Martin Luther King, Jr. (1929-1968), American Civil Rights Leader — A264

1969, Jan. 25
486 A264 20p olive gray .15 .15

Mirza Ghalib
A265

1969, Feb. 17 *Perf. 14¹/₂x14*
487 A265 20p dk gray & salmon .15 .15
Mirza Ghalib (Asad Ullah Beg Khan 1797-1869), poet who modernized the Urdu language.

Osmania University, Hyderabad, 50th Avviv. A266

1969, Mar. 15 Photo. Perf. 14¹/₂x14
488 A266 20p green .15 .15

Rafi Ahmed Kidwai — A267

1969, Apr. 1 *Perf. 13*
489 A267 20p grayish blue .15 .15
Minister of communications and food, introduced around-the-clock airmail service.

ILO Emblems
A268

1969, Apr. 11 *Perf. 14¹/₂x14*
490 A268 20p orange brown .15 .15
50th anniv. of the ILO.

Memorial Monument and Hands Strewing Flowers — A269

1969, Apr. 13 *Perf. 13¹/₂*
491 A269 20p rose carmine .15 .15
50th anniv. of Jallianwala Bagh, Amritsar, massacre.

Nageswara Rao (1867-1938), Journalist and Congressman A270

1969, May 1 Photo. Perf. 13¹/₂x14
492 A270 20p brown .15 .15

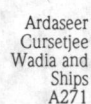 

Ardaseer Cursetjee Wadia and Ships A271

1969, May 27 Photo. Perf. 14¹/₂x14
493 A271 20p blue green .15 .15
Wadia (1808-1877), shipbuilder.

Serampore College, 150th Anniv. — A272

1969, June 7 Photo. Perf. 13¹/₂
494 A272 20p violet brown .15 .15

Dr. Zakir Husain (1897-1969), President of India 1967-1969 — A273

1969, June 11 *Perf. 13*
495 A273 20p olive gray .15 .15

Laxmanrao Kirloskar and Plow — A274

1969, June 20
496 A274 20p gray .15 .15
Kirloskar (1869-1956), industrialist and social reformer, introduced the iron plow to India.

Mahatma Gandhi (1869-1948)
A275

Gandhi on the Dandi March
A276

Designs: 20p, Gandhi and his wife Kasturba, horiz. 5r, Gandhi with spinning wheel, horiz.

1969, Oct. 2 Photo. Unwmk.
Size: 29x25mm
Perf. 13¹/₂
497 A275 20p sepia .15 .15
Size: 28x38mm
Perf. 13
498 A275 75p ol gray, sal & brn .28 .15
Size: 20x38mm
Perf. 14x14¹/₂
499 A276 1r bright blue .45 .20
Size: 35¹/₂x25¹/₂mm
Perf. 13
500 A275 5r orange & sepia 2.00 1.40
Nos. 497-500 (4) 2.88 1.90

Freighter and IMCO Emblem A277

1969, Oct. 14 *Perf. 13*
501 A277 20p ultramarine .15 .15
10th anniv. of the Intergovernmental Maritime Consultative Organization.

Globe and Parliament, New Delhi A278

1969, Oct. 30 Photo. Perf. 14¹/₂x14
502 A278 20p bright blue .15 .15
57th Interparliamentary Conf., New Delhi.

Astronaut on Moon — A279

Nanak Mausoleum, Talwandi, Punjab — A280

1969, Nov. 19 *Perf. 14x14¹/₂*
503 A279 20p olive brown .15 .15
See note after US No. C76.

1969, Nov. 23 Photo. Perf. 13¹/₂
504 A280 20p gray violet .15 .15
500th anniv. of the birth of the Guru Nanak, Sikh leader.

Tiger and Globe A281

1969, Nov. 24 *Perf. 14¹/₂x14*
505 A281 20p olive grn & red brn .15 .15
Intl. Union for the Conservation of Nature and Natural Resources.

T. L. Vaswani
A282

Thakkar Bapa
A283

1969, Nov. 25 *Perf. 14x14¹/₂*
506 A282 20p dark gray .15 .15
T. L. Vaswani (1879-1966), writer and orator.

1969, Nov. 29 *Perf. 13¹/₂*
507 A283 20p dark brown .15 .15
Thakkar Bapa (1869-1951), statesman who worked to help the untouchables.

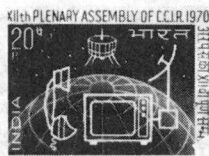

Globe and Telecommunications Symbols — A284

1970, Jan. 21 *Perf. 13*
508 A284 20p Prussian blue .15 .15
12th Plenary Assembly of the Intl. Radio Consultative Committee.

C. N. Annadurai (1909-1969), Journalist — A285

Munshi Newal Kishore and Printing Plant — A286

1970, Feb. 2
509 A285 20p dk blue & magenta .15 .15

1970, Feb. 19 Photo. Perf. 13x13¹/₂
510 A286 20p dark carmine .15 .15
Kishore (1836-1895), publisher.

Cent. of Nalanda College A287

1970, Mar. 27 Photo. Perf. 14¹/₂x14
511 A287 20p light red brown .15 .15

Swami Shraddhanand (1856-1926), Patriot — A288

1970, Mar. 30 *Perf. 13¹/₂*
512 A288 20p orange brown .15 .15

Lenin
A289

1970, Apr. 22   Photo.   Perf. 13
513 A289 20p multicolored   .15 .15

UPU Headquarters, Bern — A290

1970, May 20
514 A290 20p black & green   .15 .15
New UPU Headquarters in Bern.

Sher Shah Suri — A291

1970, May 22   Photo.   Perf. 13
515 A291 20p blue green   .15 .15
Suri, 15th cent. ruler of Delhi and postal service reformer.

Vir D. Savarkar and Prison at Port Blair, Andamans
A292

1970, May 28
516 A292 20p orange brown   .15 .15
V. D. Savarkar (1883-1966), patriot.

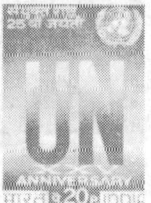

"UN" and UN Emblem — A293

1970, June 26   Photo.   Perf. 13
517 A293 20p blue   .15 .15
25th anniv. of the UN.

Harvest, Crane, Factory and Emblem
A294

1970, Aug. 18   Perf. 14½x14
518 A294 20p violet   .15 .15
Asian Productivity Year.

Dr. Maria Montessori and Education Symbol A295

1970, Aug. 31   Perf. 13½x13
519 A295 20p dull claret   .15 .15
Intl. Education Year and Maria Montessori (1870-1952), Italian educator and physician.

Jatindra Nath Mukherjee A296

1970, Sept. 9   Perf. 14½x14
520 A296 20p dark red brown   .15 .15
Mukherjee (1879-1915), revolutionary leader.

Srinivasa Sastri (1869-1946) A297

Iswar Chandra Vidyasagar A298

1970, Sept. 22   Photo.   Perf. 13
521 A297 20p dk brown & ocher   .15 .15
V. S. Srinivasa Sastri, statesman.

1970, Sept. 26
522 A298 20p rose lilac & brown   .15 .15
Vidyasagar (1820-91), educator and writer.

Maharishi Valmiki (born c. 1400 B.C.), Poet — A299

1970, Oct. 14   Photo.   Perf. 13
523 A299 20p plum   .15 .15

Calcutta Harbor A300

1970, Oct. 17
524 A300 20p blue   .15 .15
Cent. of Calcutta Port Commissioners.

Jamia Millia Islamia University, 50th Anniv. A301

1970, Oct. 29   Perf. 14½x14
525 A301 20p yellow green   .15 .15

Jamnalal Bajaj (1889-1942), Patriot A302

1970, Nov. 4   Wmk. 324   Perf. 13
526 A302 20p sepia   .15 .15

Nurse and Patient A303

Ludwig van Beethoven A305

Sant Namdeo (1270-1350), Holy Man — A304

1970, Nov. 5
527 A303 20p Prussian blue & red   .15 .15
50th anniv. of the Indian Red Cross Soc.

1970, Nov. 9   Photo.
528 A304 20p orange   .15 .15

1970, Dec. 16   Unwmk.   Perf. 13
529 A305 20p dk brown & orange   .15 .15

Children with Stamp Album A306

Design: 1r, Hands holding magnifying glass over Gandhi stamp.

1970, Dec. 23   Photo.   Perf. 13
530 A306 20p dull green & lt brn   .15 .15
531 A306 1r ocher & brown   .25 .15
    Set value   .20
INPEX 1970, Indian Natl. Phil. Exhib., New Delhi, Dec. 23, 1970-Jan. 6, 1971.

Girl Guide and Sign — A307

Hands Shielding Flame — A308

1970, Dec. 27
532 A307 20p dark brown violet   .15 .15
Girl Guides, 60th anniv.

1971, Jan. 11
533 A308 20p bister brn & dp cl   .15 .15
Centenary of Indian Life Insurance.

Kashi Vidyapith, 50th Anniv. A309

1971, Feb. 10   Perf. 14½x14
534 A309 20p black brown   .15 .15
Kashi Vidyapith University, Benares.

Charles Freer Andrews (1871-1940), British Publicist, Friend of Gandhi — A310

1971, Feb. 12   Perf. 13x13½
535 A310 20p orange brown   .15 .15

Ravidas, 15th Cent. Poet and Holy Man — A311

1971, Feb.   Perf. 13
536 A311 20p rose carmine   .15 .15

Acharya Narendra Deo (1889-1956), Educator, Patriot, Statesman — A312

1971, Feb. 18   Photo.   Perf. 13
537 A312 20p olive bister   .15 .15

Cent. of Indian Census A313

1971, Mar. 10
538 A313 20p ultra & sepia   .15 .15

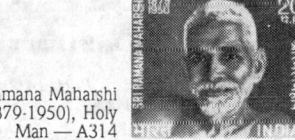

Ramana Maharshi (1879-1950), Holy Man — A314

1971, Apr. 14   Photo.   Perf. 13½x14
539 A314 20p ol gray & orange   .15 .15

Raja Ravi Varma (1848-1906) and His Painting, Damayanti and the Swan — A315

1971, Apr. 29   Perf. 13x13½
540 A315 20p deep yellow green   .15 .15

Dadasaheb Phalke, Movie Camera A316

1971, Apr. 30   Perf. 13½x13
541 A316 20p violet brown   .15 .15
Dadasaheb Phalke (1870-1944), motion picture pioneer.

Abhisarika, by Abanindranath Tagore — A317

Swami Virjanand — A318

1971, Aug. 7 Unwmk. Perf. 14x14½
542 A317 20p dark brown & ocher .15 .15
Tagore (1871-1951), painter.

1971, Sept. 14 Perf. 14x13½
543 A318 20p orange brown .15 .15
Virjanand (1778-1868), scholar and sage.

Scuptures and Stairway, Persepolis Palace A319

1971, Oct. 12 Perf. 13
544 A319 20p sepia .15 .15
2500th anniv. of the founding of the Persian empire by Cyrus the Great.

World Thrift Day — A320

1971, Oct. 31 Perf. 14½x14
545 A320 20p dark violet blue .15 .15

Bodhisatva Padampani, from Ajanta Cave — A321

Girls at Work, by Geeta Gupta — A322

1971, Nov. 4 Perf. 13
546 A321 20p brown .15 .15
25th anniv. of UNESCO.

1971, Nov. 14 Perf. 14x14½
547 A322 20p salmon pink .15 .15
Chidren's Day.

C. V. Raman A323

1971, Nov. 21 Perf. 13
548 A323 20p brown & dp orange .15 .15
Sir Chandrasekhara Venkata Raman (1888-1970), physicist, Nobel Prize winner.

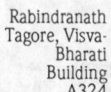 

Rabindranath Tagore, Visva-Bharati Building A324

1971, Dec. 24 Perf. 14½x14
549 A324 20p black brn & org brn .15 .15
50th anniv. of Visva-Bharati, center for Eastern cultural studies.

Indian Cricket Victories A325

1971, Dec. 24
550 A325 20p green .15 .15

Intelsat 3 over Map of Eastern Hemisphere A326

1972, Feb. 26 Photo. Perf. 13½
551 A326 20p dark purple .15 .15
Arvi Satellite Earth Station.

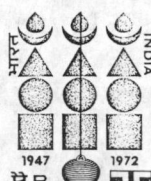 

Plumb Line and Symbols — A327

Signal Panel and Route Diagram — A328

1972, May 29 Photo. Perf. 13
552 A327 20p bluish gray & black .15 .15
India's Bureau of Standards, 25th anniv.

1972, June 30
553 A328 20p black & multi .15 .15
Intl. Railroad Union (UIC), 50th anniv.

Hockey, Olympic Rings — A329

20th Olympic Games, Munich, Aug. 26-Sept. 11: 1.45r, "1972," Olympic rings, symbols for running, wrestling, shooting and hockey.

1972, Aug. 10 Photo. Perf. 13
554 A329 20p dull violet .15 .15
555 A329 1.45r blue green & dk red .32 .20
Set value .25

Marchers with Flag, Parliament A330

1972, Aug. 15
556 A330 20p blue & multi .15 .15
25th anniv. of Independence.

Armed Forces' Emblems — A331

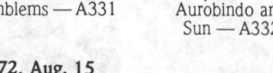

Symbol of Aurobindo and Sun — A332

1972, Aug. 15
557 A331 20p blue & multi .15 .15
Honoring India's defense forces.

1972, Aug. 15 Perf. 14x13½
558 A332 20p yellow & blue .15 .15
Sri Aurobindo Ghose (1872-1950).

V.O. Chidambaram Pillai and Ship — A333

Perf. 13½x13
1972, Sept. 5 Unwmk.
559 A333 20p blue & dk red brown .15 .15
V.O. Chidambaram Pillai (1872-1936), founder of steamship company, trade union leader, resistance fighter.

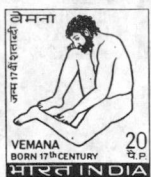 

Vemana, 17th-18th Cent. Poet — A334

Bertrand Russell — A335

1972, Oct. 16 Wmk. 324 Perf. 14
560 A334 20p black .15 .15

1972, Oct. 16 Unwmk.
561 A335 1.45r black .32 .20
British philosopher and pacifist (1872-1970).

Bhai Vir Singh — A336

T. Prakasam — A337

1972, Oct. 16 Perf. 13½
562 A336 20p dull purple .15 .15
Bhai Vir Singh (1872-1957), poet and scholar.

1972, Oct. 16
563 A337 20p yellow brown .15 .15
T. Prakasam (1872-1957), national leader and lawyer.

Hand of Buddha, 9th Century Sculpture — A338

Design: 20p, Stylized Hand of Buddha as Fair emblem.

1972, Nov. 3 Wmk. 324 Perf. 13
564 A338 20p orange & black .15 .15
565 A338 1.45r orange, blk & ind .32 .20
Set value .45
3rd Asian Intl. Trade Fair, ASIA 72, New Delhi.

Vikram Ambalal Sarabhai, Rohini Rocket and Dove — A339

1972, Dec. 30 Unwmk.
566 A339 20p slate green & brown .15 .15
1st anniv. of the death of Dr. Vikram Ambalal Sarabhai (1919-1971), chairman of Natl. Committee for Space Research.

Flag of USSR and Spasski Tower A340

1972, Dec. 30 Perf. 13
567 A340 20p red & yellow .15 .15
50th anniv. of the Soviet Union.

INDIPEX 73 Emblem — A341

Wheel of Asoka, Naga (Serpent) — A342

India Gate, Gnat Planes, India's Colors A343

1973, Jan. 8 Photo. Perf. 13
568 A341 1.45r black, pink & gold .28 .22
Intl. Phil. Exhib., New Delhi, Nov. 14-23, 1973. See Nos. 597-599.

1973, Jan. 26 Perf. 13
569 A342 20p orange & multi .15 .15
Perf. 14½x14
570 A343 1.45r violet & multi .28 .22
Set value .27
Republic Day, 25th year of Independence.

Ramakrishna Paramahamsa (1836-86) — A344

Army Postal Service Corps Emblem — A345

1973, Feb. 18 Photo. Perf. 13
571 A344 20p yellow brown .15 .15
Hindu spiritual leader; Ramakrishna Mission founded by his followers.

1973, Mar. 1
572 A345 20p violet blue & red .15 .15
1st anniv. of establishment of Army Postal Service Corps.

Flower, Flag,
Map — A346

Kumaran
Asan — A347

1973, Apr. 10   Unwmk.   Perf. 13
573 A346 20p blue & multi   .15 .15
1st anniv. of Bangladesh independence.

1973, Apr. 12
574 A347 20p brown   .15 .15
Kumaran Asan (1873-1924), Kerala social reformer and writer.

Flame and Flag of
India — A348

1973, Apr. 13
575 A348 20p deep blue & multi   .15 .15
In honor of the martyrs of the massacre of Jallianwala Bagh, Apr. 13, 1919.

B. R.
Ambedkar
and
Parliament
Building
A349

1973, Apr. 14   Perf. 14½x14
576 A349 20p olive & plum   .15 .15
Bhimrao R. Ambedkar (1891-1956), lawyer, reformer of Hindu law and one of the writers of India's Constitution.

Radha-Kishangarh, by Nihal Chand,
1778 — A350

Indian Miniatures: 50p, Dancing Couple, late 17th century. 1r, Lovers on a Camel, by Nasir-ud-Din, c. 1605. 2r, Chained Elephant, by Zain-al-Abidin, 16th century.

1973, May 5   Photo.   Perf. 13½x13
577 A350 20p gold & multi   .15 .15
578 A350 50p lilac & multi   .15 .15
579 A350 1r ocher & multi   .60 .24
580 A350 2r gold & multi   1.25 .48
    Nos. 577-580 (4)   2.15 1.02

Himalayas
A351

1973, May 15   Perf. 13½x13
581 A351 20p blue   .15 .15
15th anniv. of Indian Mountaineering Foundation.

Air India
Jet — A352

1973, June 8   Photo.   Perf. 13
582 A352 1.45r multicolored   .32 .22
Air India, 25 years of intl. service.

Stone Cross on St.
Thomas's Mount,
Madras — A353

Michael
Madhusudan
Dutt — A354

1973, July 3
583 A353 20p gray ol & blue gray   .15 .15
1900th anniv. of the death of St. Thomas.

1973, July 21   Photo.   Perf. 13
584 A354 20p ocher & olive   .15 .15
Dutt (1824-1873), writer and poet.

Vishnu
Dingambar
Paluskar (1872-
1931),
Musician
A355

1973, July 21
585 A355 30p red brown   .15 .15

Dr. Armauer G.
Hansen,
Microscope,
Petri Dish with
Bacilli — A356

1973, July 21
586 A356 50p deep brown   .23 .15
Cent. of the discovery by Hansen of the Hansen bacillus, the cause of leprosy.

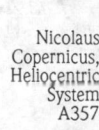

Nicolaus
Copernicus,
Heliocentric
System
A357

1973, July 21
587 A357 1r vio blue & red brown   .45 .25
500th anniv. of the birth of Nicolaus Copernicus (1473-1543), Polish astronomer.

Allan Octavian Hume
ऐलन ऑक्टावीअन ह्यूम (1829-1912) — A358

1973, July 31
588 A358 20p gray   .15 .15
Hume, British civil servant and friend of India, on the 25th anniv. of independence.

Nehru and
Gandhi
A359

1973, Aug. 15   Photo.   Perf. 13
589 A359 20p blue vio & red brown   .15 .15
25th anniv. of India's independence.

Romesh Chunder
Dutt — A360

Ranjit
Sinhji — A361

Vithalbhai Patel (1873-
1933), National
Leader — A362

1973, Sept. 27   Photo.   Perf. 13
590 A360 20p brown   .15 .15
591 A361 30p dark green   .18 .15
592 A362 50p brown   .15 .15
    Set value   .36 .22
Birth anniv.: Dutt (1848-1909), economist and pres. of Natl. Cong. in 1890; Sinhji, Maharaja of Nawanagar (1872-1933), cricketer.

President's Body
Guard — A363

INTERPOL
Emblem — A364

1973, Sept. 30
593 A363 20p multicolored   .20 .15
Bicentenary of President's Body Guard.

1973, Oct. 9   Photo.   Perf. 13
594 A364 20p brown   .15 .15
50th anniv. of Intl. Criminal Police Org.

Syed Ahmad
Khan, Aligarh
University
A365

1973, Oct. 17
595 A365 20p olive gray   .15 .15
Khan (1817-1898), founder of Aligarh Muslim Univ.

Child's Drawing
A366

1973, Nov. 14   Photo.   Perf. 13
596 A366 20p multicolored   .15 .15
Children's Day.

Elephant with Howdah, and No.
200 — A367

1973, Nov. 14
597 A367 20p Emblem   .15 .15
598 A367 1r shown   .38 .15
599 A367 2r Peacock, vert.   .65 .25
  a.   Souvenir sheet of 4   2.00 2.00
    Nos. 597-599 (3)   1.18
    Set value   .42
Intl. Phil. Exhib., INDIPEX 73, New Delhi, Nov. 14-23. No. 599a contains 4 imperf. stamps similar to Nos. 568, 597-599. The imperf. stamps from No. 599a were not valid individually.

NCC Emblem
A368

Rajagopalachari
A369

1973, Nov. 25
600 A368 20p multicolored   .15 .15
National Cadet Corps, 25th anniv.

1973, Dec. 25
601 A369 20p gray olive   .15 .15
Chakravarti Rajagopalachari (1878-1972), statesman, governor general (1948-50).

Sun Mask — A370

Narasimha
Mask — A371

Designs: Masks.

1974, Apr. 15   Photo.   Perf. 13
602 A370 20p shown   .15 .15
603 A370 50p Moon   .15 .15
604 A371 1r shown   .22 .22
605 A371 2r Ravana, horiz.   .45 .45
  a.   Souvenir sheet of 4, #602-605   1.75 1.75
    Nos. 602-605 (4)   .97
    Set value   .78

300th Anniv. of the
Coronation of
Chatrapati Sivaji
Maharaj (1627-1680),
Military Leader of the
Maharattas and
Enlightened
Ruler — A372

1974, June 2   Photo.   Perf. 13
606 A372 25p gold & multi   .15 .15

Maithili Sharan
Gupta — A373

Utkal Gourab
Madhusudan
Das — A374

Kandukuri
Veeresalingam
A375

Tipu Sultan
A376

Designs: No. 608, Jainarain Vyas. 1r, Max
Mueller.

1974		Photo.		Perf. 13	
607	A373	25p red brown		.15	.15
608	A373	25p brown		.15	.15
609	A374	25p olive gray		.15	.15
610	A375	25p red brown		.15	.15
611	A376	50p violet brown		.15	.15
612	A376	1r brown		.30	.15
		Set value		.73	.46

Gupta (1886-1964), poet and patriot; Vyas
(1899-1963), writer and member of parliament;
Das (1848-1934), writer and patriot. Veeresalingam
(1848-1919), reformer; Sultan (1750-99), military
leader and reformer; Mueller (1823-1900), German
scholar of Sanskrit and Indian culture.
Issued: #607-609, July 3; #610-612, July 15.

Kamala Nehru — A377

1974, Aug 1		Photo.	Perf. 14½x14	
613	A377	25p multicolored	.15	.15

Kamala Nehru (1899-1936), champion of India's
freedom, mother of Indira Gandhi.

WPY
Emblem — A378

V. V. Giri — A379

1974, Aug. 14		Unwmk.	Perf. 13½	
614	A378	25p buff & plum	.15	.15

1974, Aug. 24			Perf. 13x13½	
615	A379	25p green & multi	.15	.15

Vaharagiri Venkata Giri, pres. of India, 1969-74.

Type of 1965-68 and

Tiger   Veena
A380   A381

Design: 25p, Axis deer (chital).

1974		Wmk. 324	Perf. 14½x14	
622	A380	15p dk brn (white "15")	.15	.15
623	A202	25p brown	.15	.15
624	A381	1r black & brown	.28	.15
		Set value	.48	.25

Issue dates: 25p, Aug. 20; 15p, 1r, Oct. 1.
See Nos. 671-682.

Madhubani
Folk Design,
UPU Emblem
A384

Designs: 25p, UPU emblem. 2r, Arrows circling
globe, UPU emblem, vert.

1974, Oct. 3		Unwmk.	Perf. 13	
634	A384	25p brt blue & gray	.15	.15
635	A384	1r olive & multi	.50	.15
636	A384	2r ocher & multi	.75	.25
a.		Souvenir sheet of 3, #634-636	2.00	2.00
		Nos. 634-636 (3)	1.40	
		Set value		.43

Cent. of UPU.

Flute   Vidyadhara with
Player — A385   Garland — A386

1974, Oct. 9		Photo.	Perf. 13½	
637	A385	25p vio brown & red brown	.15	.15
638	A386	25p vio brown & red brown	.15	.15
a.		Pair, #637-638	.25	.20

Cent. of Mathura Museum.

Nicholas
Konstantin
Roerich, by
Henry Dropsy
A387

1974, Oct. 9			Perf. 13	
639	A387	1r dark gray & yellow	.22	.15

Roerich (1874-1947), Russian painter and sponsor of Roerich Peace Pact.

Pavapuri
Temple,
Bihar — A388

1974, Nov. 13		Photo.	Perf. 13	
640	A388	25p slate	.15	.15

2500th anniv. of attainment of Nirvana by
Bhagwan Mahavira, leader and preacher of Jainism.

Dancers and
Musician
(Child's
Drawing)
A389

1974, Nov. 14			Perf. 14½x14	
641	A389	25p multicolored	.15	.15

UNICEF in India.

Cat (Child's   Territorial Army
Drawing) — A390   Emblem — A391

1974, Nov. 14			Perf. 13	
642	A390	25p multicolored	.15	.15

Children's Day.

1974, Nov. 16			Perf. 13	
643	A391	25p green, yel & black	.15	.15

Territorial Army, 25th anniv.

Cows, from
Handpainted
Rajasthan
Cloth — A392

1974, Dec. 2			Perf. 14	
644	A392	25p ocher & maroon	.15	.15

19th Intl. Dairy Cong., New Delhi, Dec. 2-6.

Symbol of
Retardates
and
Child — A393

1974, Dec. 8		Photo.	Perf. 13½x13	
645	A393	25p black & vermilion	.15	.15

Help the Retardates!

Guglielmo
Marconi — A394

1974, Dec. 12			Perf. 13x13½	
646	A394	2r slate	.38	.38

Marconi (1874-1937), Italian electrical engineer
and inventor.

St. Francis
Xavier's Tomb
and
Statue — A395

1974, Dec. 24			Perf. 13½x13	
647	A395	25p multicolored	.15	.15

Showing of the body of St. Francis Xavier, Apostle to the Indies.

Saraswati, Goddess of
Language and Learning,
Inscription in
Hindi — A396

1975, Jan. 10		Photo.	Perf. 14x14½	
648	A396	25p dark red & gray	.15	.15

World Hindi Convention, Nagpur, Jan. 10-14.
See No. 654.

Parliament
House — A397

1975, Jan. 26			Perf. 13	
649	A397	25p black, blue & silver	.15	.15

Republic of India, 25th anniv.

Table Tennis
Paddle and
Ball — A398

1975, Feb. 6			Perf. 13½x13	
650	A398	25p black, red & olive	.15	.15

33rd World Table Tennis Championship, Calcutta.

Woman's
Hands
Releasing
Doves
A399

1975, Feb. 16				
651	A399	25p yellow & multi	.15	.15

International Women's Year.

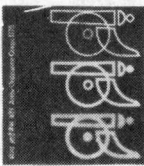

Bicentenary of Army
Ordnance
Corps — A400

1975, Apr. 8		Photo.	Perf. 13x13½	
652	A400	25p black & vermilion	.15	.15

Flame — A401

1975, Apr. 11   *Perf. 13¹/₂x13*
653 A401 25p orange & black   .15   .15

Cent. of the founding of Arya Samaj, a movement dedicated to enlightenment and progress and to a revival of Vedic Law and Aryan culture.

Saraswati Type of 1975

Design: 25p, Saraswati and inscription in Telugu.

1975, Apr. 12   *Perf. 14x14¹/₂*
654 A396 25p dp green & dk gray   .15   .15
World Telugu Conference, Hyderabad, Apr. 12-18.

Aryabhata Satellite A402

1975, Apr. 20   *Perf. 13¹/₂x13*
655 A402 25p multicolored   .15   .15
Launching of 1st Indian satellite, Apr. 19, 1975.

Bluewinged Pitta — A403

Birds: 50p, Black-headed oriole. 1r, Western tragopan, vert. 2r, Himalayan monal pheasant, vert.

Perf. 13¹/₂x13, 13x13¹/₂
1975, Apr. 28
656 A403 25p multicolored   .15   .15
657 A403 50p multicolored   .25   .15
658 A403 1r multicolored   .65   .15
659 A403 2r multicolored   .85   .25
    Nos. 656-659 (4)   1.90
    Set value   .49

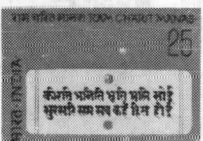

Quotation from Ram Charit Manas A404

1975, May 24   Photo.   *Perf. 13¹/₂x13*
660 A404 25p red, orange & black   .15   .15
Ram Charit Manas, Hindi poem by Goswami Tulsidas (1532-1623).

Women and YWCA Emblem — A405

1975, June 20   Photo.   *Perf. 13x13¹/₂*
661 A405 25p gray & multi   .15   .15
YWCA of India, cent.

Creation of Adam, by Michelangelo
A406   A407

Design: Nos. 664-665, Creation of sun, moon and stars, by Michelangelo.

1975, June 28   *Perf. 14x13¹/₂*
662 A406 50p multicolored   .22   .15
663 A407 50p multicolored   .22   .15
664 A406 50p multicolored   .22   .15
665 A407 50p multicolored   .22   .15
    a.   Block of 4, #662-665   .90   .60
    Set value   .48

Michelangelo Buonarroti (1475-1564), Italian sculptor, painter and architect.

Types of 1965-1974 Without Currency Designation and

Flying Crane — A408

 Jawaharlal Nehru — A409

 Mahatma Gandhi — A410

Himalayas A411

Designs: 2p, Bidri vase. 5p, Family. 10p, Electric locomotive. 15p, Tiger. 20p, Wooden toy horse. 30p, Male and female figurines. 60p, Somnath Temple. 1r, Veena. 5r, Bhakra Dam, Punjab. 10r, Trombay Atomic Center.

Three types of 25p Nehru:
Type I - Size at top, 25mm. Character before NEHRU has 2 lower points.
Type II - Smaller portrait. Size at top, 23mm. Character has 3 points.
Type III - Portrait as in type I. Size at top, 25¹/₂mm. Character has 3 points.

Perf. 14¹/₂x14, 14x14¹/₂; 14 (#674-676); 11¹/₂x12 (#681)
Wmk. 324; 360 (#667, 668, 670)
1975-88   Photo.
666 A202   2(p) redsh brn, wmk.
             324 ('76)   .15   .15
667 A202   2(p) redsh brn, wmk.
             360 ('79)   .15   .15
668 A202   5(p) cerise ('76)   .15   .15
669 A203   10(p) brt blue ('76)   .15   .15
670 A203   10(p) brt blue ('79)   .15   .15
671 A380   15(p) dk brn (brown "15")   .15   .15
672 A408   20(p) green   .15   .15
673 A409   25(p) vio, I ('76)   .15   .15
674 A409   25(p) vio, II ('76)   .15   .15
675 A409   25(p) vio, III ('76)   .15   .15
676 A410   25(p) red brn ('76)   .15   .15
             (23x29mm)
677 A410   25(p) red brn ('78)   .15   .15
             (17x20mm)
678 A202   30(p) brown ('79)   .15   .15
679 A408   50(p) violet blue   .15   .15
680 A202   60(p) dk gray ('76)   .15   .15
681 A410   60(p) black ('88)   .15   .15
682 A381   1r brown & blk   .28   .15
683 A411   2(r) violet & brn   .55   .15
684 A205   5(r) brn & vio ('76)   .70   .20
685 A205   10(r) dl grn & sl ('76)   1.40   .60
          Set value   4.10   1.75

See #841-842, 844-845, 846A-846B, 916.
Size of No. 681, 17x20mm.

 Chhatri at Maheshwar A417

 Bharata Natyam Dance A418

1975, Sept. 4   *Perf. 13x13¹/₂*
691 A417 25p red brown   .15   .15
Queen Ahilyabai Holkar (1725-1795); building shown was place of last rites.

1975, Oct. 20   Photo.   *Perf. 13x13¹/₂*
Designs: Indian traditional dances.
692 A418   25p shown   .15   .15
693 A418   50p Orissi   .18   .15
694 A418   75p Kathak   .20   .15
695 A418   1r Kathakali   .32   .15
696 A418   1.50r Kuchipudi   .50   .18
697 A418   2r Manipuri   .65   .24
      Nos. 692-697 (6)   2.00
      Set value   .75

 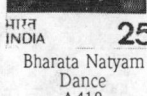

 Krishna Menon — A419

 Ameer Khusrau — A420

Unwmk.
1975, July 28   Photo.   *Perf. 14*
686 A412 25p multicolored   .15   .15
9th Intl. Cong. on Irrigation and Drainage, Moscow, and 25th anniv. of the Intl. Commission on Irrigation and Drainage.

1975, Aug. 1   *Perf. 13x13¹/₂*
687 A413 25p multicolored   .15   .15
Inauguration of the Satellite Instructional Television Experiment (SITE).

Arunagirinathar A414

1975, Aug. 14   Photo.   *Perf. 13¹/₂*
688 A414 50p rose lilac   .22   .15
600th birth anniv. of Arunagirinathar, Advaita philosopher, saint and author of Tiruppugazh, a collection of songs.

A415   A416

1975, Aug. 26   Photo.   *Perf. 13¹/₂*
689 A415 25p rose & black   .15   .15
Namibia Day. See note after UN No. 241.

1975, Sept. 4
690 A416 25p slate green   .15   .15
Mir Anees (1803-1874), Urdu poet.

Design: No. 699, Sardar Vallabhbhai Patel.

1975   *Perf. 13x13¹/₂, 13¹/₂x13*
698 A419 25p olive   .15   .15
699 A420 25p slate   .15   .15
700 A420 50p yellow & brown   .15   .15
701 A421 1r black, brn & buff   .24   .15
      Set value   48   .30

Men of India: V. K. Krishna Menon (1896-1974), founder of India League and member of Parliament; Patel (1875-1950), statesman who unified India, birth cent.; Khusrau (1253-1325), poet; Zafar (1775-1862), last Mogul emperor and poet.
Issue dates: #699, Oct. 31; others Oct. 24.

Poem by Bahadur Shah Zafar — A421

Parliament Annex, New Delhi A422

1975, Oct. 28   *Perf. 14¹/₂x14*
702 A422 2r gray olive   .48   .24
21st Commonwealth Parliamentary Conf., New Delhi, Oct. 28-Nov. 4.

Karmavir Nabin Chandra Bardoloi (1875-1936), Writer and Gandhi Associate — A423

1975, Nov. 3   Photo.   *Perf. 13*
703 A423 25p reddish brown   .15   .15

Cow, Child's Painting A424

1975, Nov. 14
704 A424 25p multicolored   .15   .15
Children's Day.

Security Press Building A425

1975, Dec. 13   Photo.   *Perf. 13*
705 A425 25p multicolored   .15   .15
India Security Press, 50th anniv.

Irrigation Commission Emblem — A412

"Educational Television" — A413

Gurdwara Sisganj, Chandni Chawk — A426

Theosophical Society Emblem — A427

1975, Dec. 16
706 A426 25p multicolored   .15 .15
    300th anniv. of martyrdom of Tegh Bahadur (1621-75), 9th Sikh Guru; building shown was place of beheading.

1975, Dec. 20
707 A427 25p multicolored   .15 .15
    Centenary of Theosophical Society.

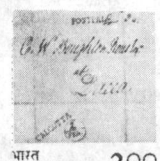

Meteorological Instruments A428

Indian Bishop Mark, 1775 A430

Early Mail Cart — A429

1975, Dec. 24   Photo.   Perf. 13
708 A428 25p blue vio, blk & grn   .15 .15
    Indian Meteorological Dept., cent.

1975, Dec. 25
709 A429 25p brown & black   .15 .15
710 A430 2r reddish brown & black .48 .24
          Set value   .30
    INPEX 75, Indian Natl. Phil. Exhib., Calcutta, Dec. 25-31.

Lalit Narayan Mishra — A431

Tiger — A432

1976, Jan. 3
711 A431 25p sepia   .15 .15
    Mishra (1923-75), Minister of Railroads.

1976, Jan. 24
712 A432 25p multicolored   .15 .15
    Jim Corbett (1875-1955), conservationist.

Painted Storks — A433

1976, Feb. 10   Photo.   Perf. 13
713 A433 25p sky blue & multi   .15 .15
    Keoladeo Ghana, Bharatpur Water Bird Sanctuary.

Tank — A434

1976, Mar. 4   Photo.   Perf. 13
714 A434 25p multicolored   .15 .15
    16th Light Cavalry, senior regiment of Armoured Corps, bicentenary.

Alexander Graham Bell — A435

Muthuswami Dikshitar — A436

1976, Mar. 10 Photo. Perf. 13x13½
715 A435 25p yellow & black   .15 .15
    Cent. of 1st telephone call by Bell, Mar. 10, 1876.

1976, Mar. 18   Perf. 14x13½
716 A436 25p dull violet   .15 .15
    Dikshitar (1775-1835), musician, composer.

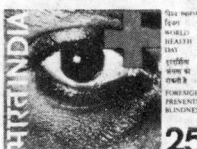

Eye and Red Cross — A437

1976, Apr. 7   Perf. 13½x13
717 A437 25p dark brown & red   .15 .15
World Health Day: "Foresight prevents blindness."

"Industries" — A438

**   Perf. 13x13½**
1976, Apr. 30   Unwmk.
718 A438 25p multicolored   .15 .15
    Industrial development and progress.

WDM 2 Diesel Locomotive, 1963 A439

    Locomotives: 50p, 1 F/I type, Ajmer, 1895. 1r, 1 WP./1, 4-6-2 Pacific type, 1963. 2r, 1 GIP No. 1, 1853.

1976, May 15   Perf. 15x14
719 A439 25p multicolored   .15 .15
720 A439 50p multicolored   .18 .15
721 A439 1r multicolored   .38 .15
722 A439 2r multicolored   .75 .25
          Nos. 719-722 (4)   1.46
          Set value   .49

Kumaraswamy Kamaraj (1903-1975), Independence Fighter — A440

1976, July 15   Photo.   Perf. 13x13½
723 A440 25p sepia   .15 .15

Target, Olympic Rings — A441

Hockey — A442

1976, July 17   Perf. 14
724 A441   25p dk blue & carmine   .15 .15
725 A441   1r "Team handball"   .28 .15
726 A442 1.50r black & brt purple .38 .22
727 A441 2.80r "Running"   .70 .38
         Nos. 724-727 (4)   1.51
         Set value   .80
    21st Olympic Games, Montreal, Canada, July 17-Aug. 1.

Subhadra Kumari Chauhan — A443

Param Vir Chakra Medal — A444

1976, Aug. 6   Photo.   Perf. 13x13½
728 A443 25p grayish blue   .15 .15
    Chauhan (1904-1948), Hindi poetess and member of Legislative Assembly.

1976, Aug. 15
729 A444 25p yellow & multi   .15 .15
    Medal of Honor awarded for bravery to military men.

Women's University, Bombay — A445

1976, Sept. 3   Photo.   Perf. 13½x14
730 A445 25p violet   .15 .15
    Indian Women's Univ., 60th anniv.

Bharatendu Harishchandra A446

Sarat Chandra Chatterji A447

1976, Sept. 9   Perf. 13
731 A446 25p black brown   .15 .15
    Harishchandra (1850-1885), writer, "Father of Modern Hindi."

1976, Sept. 15   Unwmk.
732 A447 25p dull purple   .15 .15
    Chatterji (1876-1938), writer.

Family Planning — A448

1976, Sept. 22 Photo. Perf. 14x14½
733 A448 25p multicolored   .15 .15

Maharaja Agrasen, Coin and Brick Wall -– A449

1976, Sept. 24   Perf. 13½x13
734 A449 25p red brown   .15 .15
    Maharaja Agrasen, legendary ruler of Agra.

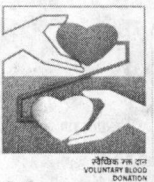

India Blood Donation Day — A450

Wildlife Protection — A451

1976, Oct. 1   Perf. 13x13½
735 A450 25p bister, car & black   .15 .15

1976, Oct. 1   Perf. 14x14½, 14½x14
736 A451 25p Swamp deer   .15 .15
737 A451 50p Lion   .20 .15
738 A451 1r Leopard, horiz.   .32 .15
739 A451 2r Caracal, horiz.   .70 .28
         Nos. 736-739 (4)   1.37
         Set value   .54

Suryakant Tripathi "Nirala" (1896-1961), Hindi Poet — A452

1976, Oct. 15   Perf. 13
740 A452 25p dark violet   .15 .15

Mongoose and Woman — A453

1976, Nov. 14   Unwmk.   *Perf. 14*
741 A453 25p multicolored   .15   .15
Children's Day.

Hiralal Shastri — A454   Hari Singh Gour — A455

1976, Nov. 24   *Perf. 13*
742 A454 25p red brown   .15   .15
Hiralal Shastri (1899-1974), social worker and political leader.

1976, Nov. 26
743 A455 25p plum   .15   .15
Hari Singh Gour (1870-1949), University administrator, member Indian Legislative and Constituent Assemblies.

Airbus A456

1976, Dec. 1   *Perf. 14½x14*
744 A456 2r multicolored   .48   .25
Inauguration of Indian Airlines Airbus.

Hybrid Coconut Palm — A457

1976, Dec. 27   Photo.   *Perf. 13x13½*
745 A457 25p multicolored   .15   .15
75th anniv. of coconut research in India.

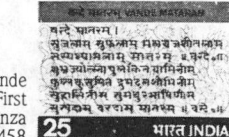

Vande Mataram, First Stanza A458

1976, Dec. 30   *Perf. 13*
746 A458 25p multicolored   .15   .15
Vande Mataram, national song of India, music by Bankim Chandra Chatterjee, 1896, words by Rabindranath Tagore, 1911.

Film and Globe A459

1977, Jan. 3
747 A459 2r multicolored   .48   .25
6th Intl. Film Festival, New Delhi, Jan. 3-16.

Earth's Crust with Fault, Seismograph — A460

1977, Jan. 10
748 A460 2r dull purple   .48   .25
6th World Conference on Earthquake Engineering, New Delhi, Jan. 10-14.

Tarun Ram Phookun — A461   Paramahansa Yogananda — A462

1977, Jan. 22   Photo.   *Perf. 13x13½*
749 A461 25p sepia   .15   .15
Phookun (1877-1939), lawyer, Assam political leader.

1977, Mar. 7   Photo.   *Perf. 13½*
750 A462 25p deep orange   .15   .15
Yogananda (1893-1952), religious leader, founder of Self-realization Society in America.

Red Cross Conference Emblem — A463   Fakhruddin Ali Ahmed (1905-77) — A464

1977, Mar. 9
751 A463 2r multicolored   .30   .20
1st Asian Regional Red Cross Conference, New Delhi, Mar. 9-16.

1977, Mar. 22   Photo.   *Perf. 13½x13*
752 A464 25p multicolored   .15   .15
Ahmed, Pres. of India, 1974-77.

Asian-Oceanic Postal Union Emblem — A465

1977, Apr. 1   *Perf. 13*
753 A465 2r silver & multi   .30   .20
Asian-Oceanic Postal Union, 15th anniv.

"Loyalty" and Morarjee A466

1977, Apr. 2   *Perf. 13½x13*
754 A466 25p blue   .15   .15
Narottam Morarjee (1877-1929), founder of Scindia Steam Ship Navigation Co.

Makhanlal Chaturvedi A467   Mahaprabhu Vallabhacharya A468

1977, Apr. 4   *Perf. 13*
755 A467 25p orange brown   .15   .15
Chaturvedi (1889-1968), Hindi writer.

1977, Apr. 14
756 A468 1r olive brown   .15   .15
Vallabhacharya (1479-1531), philosopher.

Federation Emblem A469

1977, Apr. 23   *Perf. 13½x13*
757 A469 25p ocher & purple   .15   .15
Federation of Indian Chambers of Commerce, 50th anniv.

Protection of Environment A470

1977, June 5   Photo.   *Perf. 13*
758 A470 2r multicolored   .30   .20

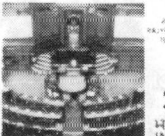

Council of States Chamber A471

1977, June 21
759 A471 25p multicolored   .15   .15
Council of States, Rajya Sabha (Parliament), 25th anniv.

Lotus — A472

50p and 1r are vert.

1977, July 1   *Perf. 15x14, 14x15*
760 A472 25p shown   .15   .15
761 A472 50p Rhododendron   .15   .15
762 A472 1r Kadamba   .20   .15
763 A472 2r Gloriosa lily   .50   .20
       Set value   .85   .42

भारत INDIA

Berliner Gramaphone A473

1977, July 20   *Perf. 13½x13*
764 A473 2r black & brown   .38   .20
Centenary of the phonograph.

Ananda Kentish Coomaraswamy (1877-1947) and Dancing Shiva — A474

1977, Aug. 22   Photo.   *Perf. 13x13½*
765 A474 25p multicolored   .15   .15
Coomaraswamy, art historian and critic.

Ganga Ram (1851-1927) and Hospital, New Delhi A475

1977, Sept. 4   *Perf. 14½x14*
766 A475 25p rose carmine   .15   .15
Ram, social reformer and philanthropist.

Dr. Samuel Hahnemann and Cinchona — A476   19th Century Postman A477

Lion and Palm Tree, East India Co. Essay — A478

1977, Oct. 6   Photo.   *Perf. 13*
767 A476 2r black & green   .30   .20
32nd Intl. Homeopathic Cong., New Delhi.

1977, Oct. 12   *Perf. 13*
768 A477 25p multicolored   .15   .15
       Perf. 13½
769 A478 2r mag & gray, buff   .30   .20
       Set value   .38   .25
INPEX '77 Phil. Exhib., Bangalore, Oct. 12-16.

Ram Manohar Lohia (1910-67), Founder of Congress Socialist Party, Sec. of Foreign Dept. — A479

1977, Oct. 12   *Perf. 13x13½*
770 A479 25p red brown   .15   .15

Red Scinde Dawks, 1852 — A480

Design: 3r, Foreign mail arriving at Ballard Pier, Bombay, 1927.

1977, Oct. 19   *Perf. 13½x13*
771 A480 1r orange & multi   .15   .15
772 A480 3r orange & multi   .45   .32
ASIANA 77, First Asian International Philatelic Exhibition, Bangalore, Oct. 19-23.

Statue of Rani Channamma A481

1977, Oct. 23
773 A481 25p gray green .15 .15
Rani Channamma of Kittue (1778-1829), who fought against British rule.

Mother and Child, Khajuraho Sculpture — A482

1977, Oct. 23 Perf. 13x13½
774 A482 2r gray & sepia .30 .20
15th Intl. Pediatrics Congress.

Sun and National Colors — A483   Stylized Grain — A484

1977, Nov. 8 Photo. Perf. 13
775 A483 25p multicolored .15 .15
Union Public Service Commission, founded 1926.

1977, Nov. 13
776 A484 25p green .15 .15
AGRIEXPO '77, Intl. Agriculture Exhib.

Cats — A485

Design: 1r, Friends. Designs are from children's drawings.

1977, Nov. 14
777 A485 25p multicolored .15 .15
778 A485 1r multicolored .15 .15
Set value .23 .15
Children's Day.

Jotirao Phooley — A486   Senapati Bapat — A487

1977, Nov. 28 Wmk. 324
779 A486 25p gray olive .15 .15
Phooley (1827-1890), social reformer.

1977, Nov. 28
780 A487 25p brown orange .15 .15
Senapati Bapat (Pandurang Mahadev Bapat, 1880-1967), scholar and fighter for India's independence.

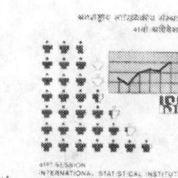

Diagram of Population Growth — A488

1977, Dec. 13 Unwmk.
781 A488 2r carmine & blue grn .30 .20
41st Session of Intl. Statistical Institute, New Delhi, Dec. 5-15.

Perf. 13x13½

Kamta Prasad (1875-1947) and Hindi Grammar — A489

1977, Dec. 25 Wmk. 324 Perf. 14
782 A489 25p sepia .15 .15
Prasad, compiler of Hindi Grammar.

Spasski Tower, Russian Flag — A490

1977, Dec. 30 Unwmk. Perf. 13
783 A490 1r multicolored .15 .15
60th anniv. of Russian October revolution.

Climber Crossing Crevasse — A491

Indian Flag near Summit A492

Perf. 13½x13, 13x13½
1978, Jan. 15 Photo.
784 A491 25p multicolored .15 .15
785 A492 1r multicolored .15 .15
Set value .23 .15
Conquest of Kanchenjunga (Himalayas), by Indian team under Col. N. Kumar, May 31, 1977.

Tourists in Shikara on Dal Lake — A493

1978, Jan. 23 Perf. 13x13½
786 A493 1r multicolored .15 .15
27th Pacific Area Travel Assoc. Conf., New Delhi, Jan. 23-26.

Children in Library, Fair Emblem A494

1978, Feb. 11 Photo. Perf. 13
787 A494 1r rose brown & indigo .15 .15
3rd World Book Fair, New Delhi, Feb. 1978.

Mother of Pondicherry — A495   Wheat, Globe and Genetic Helix — A496

1978, Feb. 21
788 A495 25p dark & light brown .15 .15
Mother of the Sri Aurobindo Ashram, Pondicherry (Mira Richard, 1878-1973, born in Paris).

1978, Feb. 23
789 A496 25p yellow & blue green .15 .15
5th Intl. Wheat Genetics Symposium.

Nanalal Dalpatram Kavi — A497   Surjya Sen (1894-1934), Patriot — A498

Wmk. 324
1978, Mar. 16 Photo. Perf. 13
790 A497 25p rose brown .15 .15
Kavi (1877-1946), Gujarati poet.

1978, Mar. 22
791 A498 25p ver, black & brown .15 .15

Two Vaishnavas (Vishnu Worshippers) by Jaminy Roy — A499

Modern Indian Paintings: 50p, The Mosque, by Sailoz Mookherjea. 1r, Woman's Head, by Rabindranath Tagore. 2r, Hill Women, by Amrita Sher Gil.

Perf. 13½x14
1978, Mar. 23 Unwmk.
792 A499 25p black & multi .15 .15
793 A499 50p black & multi .15 .15
794 A499 1r black & multi .15 .15
795 A499 2r black & multi .30 .20
Set value .61 .40

Rubens, Selfportrait A500

1978, Apr. 4 Photo. Perf. 13½x13
796 A500 2r multicolored .30 .20

"The Little Tramp," Charlie Chaplin — A501   Deendayal Upadhyaya (1916-68) — A502

1978, Apr. 16 Perf. 13
797 A501 25p gold & indigo .15 .15

1978, May 5 Photo. Perf. 13
798 A502 25p multicolored .15 .15
Upadhyaya, social and political reformer.

Syama Prasad Mookerjee (1901-1953) A503   "Airavat," 19th Century Wood Carving A504

Kushan Gold Coin, 1st Century A505

1978, July 6 Photo. Perf. 13
799 A503 25p gray olive .15 .15
Dr. Mookerjee, educator, member of 1st natl. government.

1978, July 27
Designs: 50p, Wish-fulfilling tree, 2nd century B.C. 2r, Dagger and knife.
800 A504 25p multicolored .15 .15
801 A504 50p multicolored .15 .15
802 A505 1r multicolored .15 .15
803 A505 2r multicolored .30 .20
Set value .61 .40
Treasures from Indian museums.

Krishna and Arjuna on Battlefield, Quotation A506

1978, Aug. 25 Unwmk. Perf. 13
804 A506 25p orange red & gold .15 .15
Bhagavad Gita, part of Mahabharata Epic, the Divine Song of the Lord.

Bethune College for Women, Calcutta A507

1978, Sept. 4
805 A507 25p green & brown .15 .15

E. V. Ramasami — A508   Uday Shankar — A509

1978, Sept. 17
806 A508 25p black .15 .15
E. V. Ramasami (1879-1973), founder of Self-respect Movement, fighting caste system and social injustice.

1978, Sept. 26
807 A509 25p buff & violet brown .15 .15
Uday Shankar (1900-77), dancer.

Leo Tolstoi — A510   Vallathol Narayana Menon — A511

1978, Oct. 2
808 A510 1r multicolored .15 .15
Tolstoi, novelist and philosopher.

1978, Oct. 15   Photo.   Perf. 13
809 A511 25p multicolored .15 .15
Menon (1878-1958), poet.

"Two Friends" A512

1978, Nov. 14   Photo.   Perf. 13
810 A512 25p multicolored .15 .15
Children's Day.

Worker at Lathe — A513

1978, Nov. 17   Perf. 13½
811 A513 25p green .15 .15
Small Industries Fair.

Skinner's Horse Soldiers A514   Chakravarti Rajagopalachari A515

1978, Nov. 25   Perf. 13
812 A514 25p multicolored .15 .15
175th anniv. of Skinner's Horse Regiment.

1978, Dec. 10   Photo.   Perf. 13
813 A515 25p maroon .15 .15
Chakravarti Rajagopalachari (1878-1972), first post-independence Governor General.

A516   A517

1978, Dec. 10
814 A516 25p olive green .15 .15
Mohammad Ali Jauhar (1878-1931), writer and patriot.

1978, Dec. 23   Perf. 13x14
815 A517 1r ocher & purple .15 .15
Wright Brothers, Flyer, 75th anniv. of 1st powered flight.

Ravenshaw College, Orissa, Centenary A518

1978, Dec. 24   Perf. 14
816 A518 25p green & maroon .15 .15

Franz Schubert (1797-1828), Austrian Composer — A519

1978, Dec. 25   Perf. 13
817 A519 1r multicolored .15 .15

Punjab Regiment, Uniforms and Crest — A520

1979, Feb. 20   Photo.   Unwmk.
818 A520 25p multicolored .15 .15
Oldest Indian infantry unit.

Bhai Parmanand (1876-1947) A521   Gandhi and Child A522

1979, Feb. 24
819 A521 25p violet blue .15 .15
Parmanand, writer and educator.

1979, Mar. 5   Photo.   Perf. 13
Design: 1r, IYC emblem.
820 A522 25p dk brown & red .15 .15
821 A522 1r dp orange & dk brown .15 .15
  Set value .20 .15

Albert Einstein (1879-1955), Theoretical Physicist A523

1979, Mar. 14
822 A523 1r black .15 .15

Rajarshi Shahu Chhatrapati (1874-1922), Ruler of Kolhapur — A524

1979, May 1   Photo.   Perf. 13x13½
823 A524 25p dull purple .15 .15

Lotus, India '80 Emblem A525

1979, July 2   Photo.   Perf. 13
824 A525 30p deep orange & green .15 .15
India '80 Phil. Exhib., New Delhi, Jan. 25-Feb. 3, 1980.

 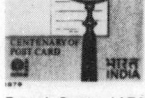 

Postal Cards, 1879 and 1979 — A526   Raja Mahendra Pratap (1886-1979), Patriot — A527

1979, July 2
825 A526 50p multicolored .15 .15

1979, Aug. 15   Photo.   Perf. 13
826 A527 30p olive gray .15 .15

 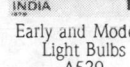

Jatindra Nath Das (1904-1929) A528   Early and Modern Light Bulbs A529

1979, Sept. 13
827 A528 30p dark brown .15 .15
Das, political martyr.

1979, Oct. 21   Photo.   Perf. 13
828 A529 1r rose magenta .15 .15
Centenary of invention of electric light.

Buddhist Text — A530

1979, Oct. 23   Perf. 14½x14
829 A530 30p brown & bister .15 .15
National Archives.

Hirakud Dam — A531

Perf. 13½x13
1979, Oct. 29   Wmk. 324
830 A531 30p brown red & dull grn .15 .15
13th Congress (Golden Jubilee) of the Intl. Commission on Large Dams, New Delhi, 10/29-11/2.

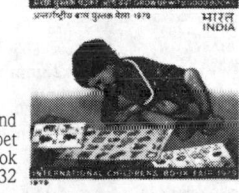

Boy and Alphabet Book A532

1979, Nov. 10   Photo.   Perf. 14½x14
831 A532 30p multicolored .15 .15
Intl. Children's Book Fair, New Delhi, 11/10-19.

Fair Emblem — A533

1979, Nov. 10   Perf. 13
832 A533 1r black & orange .15 .15
India Intl. Trade Fair, New Delhi, 11/10-12/9.

Dove, Agency Emblem A534

1979, Dec. 4   Perf. 13½x13
833 A534 1r multicolored .15 .15
23rd Intl. Atomic Energy Agency Conf., New Delhi, Dec. 4-10.

Hindustan Pushpak Plane, Rohini-1 Glider — A535

1979, Dec. 10   *Perf. 13½x13*

| 834 | A535 | 30p multicolored | .15 | .15 |

Gurdwara Baoli Shrine, Goindwal — A536

1979, Dec. 21   *Perf. 13x13½*

| 835 | A536 | 30p multicolored | .15 | .15 |

Guru Amardas (1469-1574), Sikh spiritual leader.

Types of 1975-79 and

Women in Rice Field A537

Family Planning A537a

Designs: 2p, Adult education. 5p, Fish. 15p, Agricultural technology. 20p, Child nutrition. No. 840, Poultry. No. 840B, Farm, wheat, farmer plowing. 1r, Hybrid cotton. 2r, Weaving. 5r, Rubber tapping.

Perf. 14x14½, 14½x14, 13 (#840B)

1979-85   **Photo.**   **Wmk. 324**

836	A537	2p violet	.15	.15
837	A537	5p blue	.15	.15
838	A537a	15p blue grn ('80)	.15	.15
839	A537a	20p henna brn ('81)	.15	.15
840	A537	25p brown	.15	.15
840B	A537	25p brt green ('85)	.15	.15
841	A409	30p violet ('80)	.15	.15
842	A410	30p red brown ('80)	.15	.15
843	A537	30p yel green	.15	.15
844	A409	35p violet ('80)	.15	.15
845	A410	35p red brown ('80)	.15	.15
846	A537	35p cerise ('80)	.15	.15
846A	A409	50p violet ('83)	.15	.15
846B	A410	50p red brown ('83)	.15	.15

Size: 17x28mm

| 847 | A537a | 1r brown ('80) | .15 | .15 |
| 848 | A537a | 2r rose violet ('80) | .30 | .15 |

Size: 20x37mm

| 849 | A537a | 5r multi ('80) | .45 | .22 |
| | | Set value | 2.00 | 1.10 |

Size: #841-842, 844-845, 846A-846B, 17x20mm. See Nos. 895-900A, 903-917.

1979-83   *Perf. 13*

837a	A537	5p	.15	.15
837b	A537	5p Litho. ('82)	.15	.15
838a	A537a	15p	.15	.15
839a	A537a	20p	.15	.15
840a	A537	25p brown	.15	.15
843a	A537	30p	.15	.15
844a	A409	35p	.15	.15
845a	A410	35p	.15	.15
846c	A537a	35p	.15	.15
846d	A409	50p	.15	.15
846e	A410	50p	.15	.15

Perf. 12½x13

| 847a | A537a | 1r | .20 | .15 |

Perf. 13x13½, 13½x13

848a	A537a	2r ('83)	.50	.25
849a	A537a	5r ('83)	.45	.22
		Set value	1.50	1.00

People Holding Hands, UN Emblem — A538

1980, Jan. 21   **Photo.**   *Perf. 13*

| 851 | A538 | 1r multicolored | .15 | .15 |

UN Industrial Development Org. (INIDO), 3rd Gen. Conf., New Delhi, Jan. 21-Feb. 8.

Field Post Office, Cancels — A539

Money Order Centenary — A540

2-Anna Copper Coins, 1774 A541

Rowland Hill, Birthplace, Kidderminster A542

Wmk. 360, Unwmkd. (1r)

1980, Jan. 25

852	A539	30p gray olive	.15	.15
853	A540	50p brown & citron	.15	.15
854	A541	1r bronze	.15	.15
855	A542	2r dark gray	.25	.15
		Set value	.51	.29

INDIA '80 Intl. Stamp Exhib., New Delhi, Jan. 25-Feb. 3.

India Institution of Engineers, 60th Anniversary A543

Uniforms, 1780 and 1980, Arms and Ribbon A544

Perf. 13x13½

1980, Feb. 17   **Unwmk.**

| 856 | A543 | 30p dark blue & gold | .15 | .15 |

1980, Feb. 26

| 857 | A544 | 30p multicolored | .15 | .15 |

Madras Sappers bicentennial.

2nd Intl. Apiculture Conf., New Delhi — A545

1980, Feb. 29   *Perf. 13½*

| 858 | A545 | 1r multicolored | .15 | .15 |

A546

A547

1980, Feb. 29   **Wmk. 360**

| 859 | A546 | 30p bright blue | .15 | .15 |

4th World Book Fair, New Delhi.

1980, Mar. 18   *Perf. 13x13½*

| 860 | A547 | 30p blue gray | .15 | .15 |

Welthy Fisher (b. 1879), educator, Literacy House, Lucknow.

Darul Uloom Islamic School, Deoband A548

1980, Mar. 21   *Perf. 13½*

| 861 | A548 | 30p gray green | .15 | .15 |

Keshub Chunder Sen — A549

Sivaji, Raigad Fort — A550

Perf. 13x13½

1980, Apr. 15   **Photo.**   **Wmk. 360**

| 862 | A549 | 30p brown | .15 | .15 |

Sen (1838-84), scholar, writer, journalist.

1980, Apr. 21   **Unwmk.**

| 863 | A550 | 30p multicolored | .15 | .15 |

Sivaji (1627-80), Indian patriot.

Narayan Malhar Joshi — A551

Ulloor S. Parameswara Iyer — A552

Perf. 13x13½

1980, June 5   **Wmk. 360**

| 864 | A551 | 30p lilac rose | .15 | .15 |

Joshi (1879-1955), trade union pioneer.

1980, June 6

| 865 | A552 | 30p dull purple | .15 | .15 |

Iyer (1877-1949), poet and scholar.

Syed Mohammad Zamin Ali — A553

Helen Keller (1880-1955) — A554

1980, June 25

| 866 | A553 | 30p dk yellow green | .15 | .15 |

Ali (1880-1955), linguist and educator.

1980, June 27

| 867 | A554 | 30p orange & black | .15 | .15 |

Keller, blind and deaf writer and lecturer.

High Jump, Olympic Rings A555

Prem Chand (1880-1936) A556

1980, July 19   **Photo.**   *Perf. 13½x14*

868	A555	1r shown	.15	.15
869	A555	2.80r Equestrian	.35	.18
		Set value		.24

22nd Summer Olympic Games, Moscow, July 19-Aug. 3.

1980, July 31   *Perf. 13*

| 870 | A556 | 30p red brown | .15 | .15 |

Pen name of Nawab Rai, writer.

Mother Teresa, Nobel Peace Prize Medallion A557

Perf. 13½x13

1980, Aug. 27   **Photo.**   **Wmk. 360**

| 871 | A557 | 30p violet, *grayish* | .15 | .15 |

Mother Teresa, founder of Missionaries of Charity, 70th birthday.

Earl Mountbatten of Burma A558

Asian Table Tennis Championship A559

1980, Aug. 28   *Perf. 13½x13½*

| 872 | A558 | 2.80r multicolored | .35 | .18 |

Mountbatten (1900-79), 1st governor gen. of India.

1980, Sept.   **Photo.**   *Perf. 13x13½*

| 873 | A559 | 30p magenta | .15 | .15 |

Scottish Church College, Calcutta, Sesquicentennial — A560

1980, Sept. 27   **Photo.**   *Perf. 13½*

| 874 | A560 | 35p dull purple | .15 | .15 |

Rajah Annamalai Chettiar (1881-1948), Banker, Founder of Annamalai University — A561

1980, Sept. 30   **Unwmk.**   *Perf. 14x15*

| 875 | A561 | 35p dull purple | .15 | .15 |

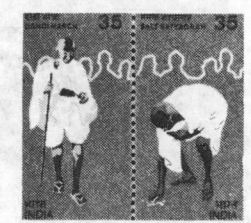

Gandhi on Dandi March — A562   Gandhi Defying Salt Law — A563

1980, Oct. 2   *Perf. 15x14*
876 A562 35p gold & multi .15 .15
877 A563 35p gold & multi .15 .15
   a.   Pair, #876-877 .20 .20

A564   A565

1980, Oct. 8   *Wmk. 360*   *Perf. 14x15*
878 A564 35p red brown .15 .15
   Jayaprakash Narayan (1902-79), writer.

1980, Nov. 1   *Photo.*   *Perf. 13*
879 A565 2.30r Great Indian bustards .30 .15
   Intl. Symposium on Bustards, Jaipur.

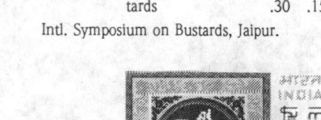

Hegira (Pilgrimage Year) — A566

1980, Nov. 3   *Perf. 13x13½*
880 A566 35p multicolored .15 .15

Children's Day — A567

     Perf. 13½x13
1980, Nov. 14   *Unwmk.*
881 A567 35p multicolored .15 .15

Dhyan Chand — A568   Miner, Molten Gold — A569

1980, Dec. 3   *Wmk. 360*   *Perf. 14x15*
882 A568 35p dark rose brown .15 .15
   Chand (1906-1979), field hockey player.

     Perf. 13x13½
1980, Dec. 20   *Unwmk.*
883 A569 1r multicolored .15 .15
   Kolar gold fields centenary.

Mukhtar Ahmad Ansari (1880-1936), Surgeon — A570

1980, Dec. 25   *Wmk. 360*
884 A570 35p olive gray .15 .15

Government Mint, Bombay, Sesquicentennial — A571

     Perf. 13½x13
1980, Dec. 27   *Unwmk.*
885 A571 35p multicolored .15 .15

Regional Bridal Outfits — A572   Mazharul Haque (1866-1930), Patriot — A573

1980, Dec. 30   *Perf. 13x13½*
886 A572 1r Kashmir .15 .15
887 A572 1r Bengal .15 .15
888 A572 1r Rajasthan .15 .15
889 A572 1r Tamilnada .15 .15
     Set value .48 .24

1981, Jan. 2   *Wmk. 360*   *Perf. 14x15*
890 A573 35p violet .15 .15

St. Stephen's College Centenary — A574

1981, Feb. 1   *Photo.*   *Perf. 14x14½*
891 A574 35p dull red .15 .15

Gommateshwara Statue, Shravanabelgola A575   Ganesh V. Mavalankar (1888-1956) A576

1981, Feb. 9   *Unwmk.*
892 A575 1r multicolored .15 .15

1981, Feb. 27
893 A576 35p light red brown .15 .15
   Mavalankar, 1st speaker of parliament.

Type of 1979
     Perf. 14½x14
1981-86   *Photo.*   *Wmk. 324*
     Size: 19½x37½mm
895   A537 2.25r Cashew .32 .15
   a.   Perf. 14x14½ .32 .15
   b.   Perf. 13 .20 .15

896   A537 2.80r Apples .42 .20
   a.   Perf. 14x14½ .42 .20
897   A537 3.25r Oranges ('83) .48 .24
   a.   Perf. 13½x13 ('85) .30 .15
   b.   Perf. 13 .30 .15
900   A537 10r Trees on hillside ('84) 1.25 .60
   b.   Perf. 13x13½ 1.25 .60

     Perf. 13½x13
     Size: 37½x19½mm
900A A537 50r Windmill ('86) 4.75 2.50
     Nos. 895-900A (5) 7.22 3.69

Homage to Martyrs — A577

1981, Mar. 23   *Unwmk.*   *Perf. 14x15*
901 A577 35p multicolored .15 .15

Heinrich von Stephan and UPU Emblem A578

1981, Apr. 8   *Perf. 15x14*
902 A578 1r red brown & brt blue .15 .15

Types of 1979 and

Telecommunications A578a

Natural Gas A578b

     Perf. 14x14½, 14½x14, 13 (40p, 75p), 13x13½ (20r)
     Wmk. 324, 360 (2p, 5p, 15p)
1981-90   *Photo.*
903 A537 2p violet .15 .15
904 A537 5p blue .15 .15
905 A537 10p Irrigation .15 .15
   a.   Perf. 13 .15 .15
906 A537a 15p blue green .15 .15
912 A578a 40p dull red .15 .15
914 A537 50p Dairy industry .15 .15
   a.   Perf. 13 .15 .15
915 A537a 75p vermilion .15 .15

     Size: 17x20mm
916 A410 1r orange brown .15 .15
917 A578b 20r sepia & dark blue 2.75 1.40
     Set value 3.00 1.65

   Issued: 10p, 50p, 1/25/82; 40p, 10/15/81; 20r, 11/30/88; 75p, 1990; 1r, 1/30/91; others, 3/25/81.

Intl. Year of the Disabled A579

     Perf. 14½x14
1981, Apr. 20   *Photo.*   *Unwmk.*
919 A579 1r blue & black .15 .15

 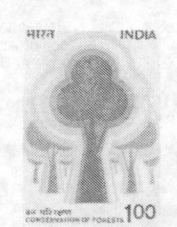

Tribesman — A580   A581

1981, May 30   *Perf. 14x14½*
920 A580 1r Khiamngan Naga .15 .15
921 A580 1r Toda .15 .15
922 A580 1r Bhil .15 .15
923 A580 1r Dandami Maria .15 .15
     Set value .48 .24

1981, June 15
924 A581 1r multicolored .15 .15
   World environment day.

Nilmoni Phukan (1880-1978), Writer — A582   Sanjay Gandhi (1946-1980), Politician — A583

1981, June 22
925 A582 35p red brown .15 .15

1981, June 23   *Perf. 13x13½*
926 A583 35p multicolored .15 .15

SLV-3 Take-off — A584

1981, July 18   *Photo.*   *Perf. 14x15*
927 A584 1r multicolored .15 .15
   Launching of India's 1st satellite, 1st anniv.

Mascot, Field Hockey — A585

1981, July 28   *Perf. 13½x13*
928 A585 1r shown .15 .15
929 A585 1r Emblem .15 .15
     Set value .24 .15
   9th Asian Games, New Delhi, 1982.
   See Nos. 942-943.

Flame of the Forest — A586

   Designs: Flowering trees.

1981, Sept. 1   *Photo.*   *Perf. 13*
930 A586 35p shown .15 .15
931 A586 50p Crateva .15 .15
932 A586 1r Golden shower .15 .15
933 A586 2r Bauhinia .25 .15
     Set value .48 .29

World Food
Day — A587

Cyrestis
Achates — A588

1981, Oct. 16   Photo.   Perf. 14x14¹/₂
934 A587 1r multicolored   .15 .15

1981, Oct. 20   Perf. 13
935 A588 35p Stichophthalma
    camadeva, horiz.   .15 .15
936 A588 50p Cethosia biblis, horiz. .15 .15
937 A588 1r shown   .15 .15
938 A588 2r Treinopalpus imperialis .25 .15
    Set value   .48 .29

Bellary
Raghava
(1880-1946),
Actor
A589

1981, Oct. 31   Perf. 14¹/₂x14
939 A589 35p olive gray   .15 .15

40th Anniv. of
Mahar
Regiment — A590

Children's
Day — A591

1981, Nov. 9   Perf. 13
940 A590 35p multicolored   .15 .15

1981, Nov. 14   Perf. 14x14¹/₂
941 A591 35p multicolored   .15 .15

Asian Games Type of 1981

1981   Perf. 13¹/₂x13
942 A585 1r Rajghat Stadium, domed .15 .15
943 A585 1r Nehru Stadium   .15 .15
    Set value   .24 .15
Issued: No. 942, Nov. 19; No. 943, Dec. 30.

Kashi Prasad Jayaswal
(1881-1937),
Historian — A592

1981, Nov. 27   Perf. 14x14¹/₂
944 A592 35p chalky blue   .15 .15

Intl.
Palestinian
Solidarity
Day — A593

1981, Nov. 29   Perf. 14¹/₂x14
945 A593 1r multicolored   .15 .15

Naval Ship
Taragiri
A594

1981, Dec. 4
946 A594 35p multicolored   .15 .15

Henry Heras
(1888-1955),
Historian
A595

1981, Dec. 14   Photo.   Perf. 14¹/₂x14
947 A595 35p rose violet   .15 .15

Indian Ocean Commonwealth Submarine
Telephone Cable — A596

1981, Dec. 24   Perf. 13¹/₂
948 A596 1r multicolored   .15 .15

5th World Field Hockey Championship,
Bombay — A597

1981, Dec. 29   Perf. 13¹/₂x13
949 A597 1r multicolored   .15 .15

Telephone Service
Centenary — A598

Perf. 13x13¹/₂
1982, Jan. 28   Unwmk.
950 A598 2r multicolored   .25 .15

12th Intl. Soil
Science
Congress, New
Delhi, Feb. 8-
16 — A599

1982, Feb. 8   Perf. 13¹/₂x13
951 A599 1r multicolored   .15 .15

Sir Jamsetjee Jejeebhoy
School of Art,
Bombay — A600

1981, Mar. 2   Photo.   Perf. 14x14¹/₂
952 A600 35p multicolored   .15 .15

Three
Musicians, by
Pablo Picasso
(1881-1973)
A601

1982, Mar. 15   Photo.   Perf. 14
953 A601 2.85r multicolored   .35 .18

Deer, 5th
Cent. Bas
Relief — A602

Radio Telescope,
Ooty — A603

Festival of India, England: No. 955, Krishna, 9th
cent. bronze sculpture.

1982, Mar. 23   Perf. 14x15
954 A602   2r multicolored   .25 .15
955 A602 3.05r multicolored   .38 .18
      Perf. 13
956 A603 3.05r multicolored   .38 .18
    Nos. 954-956 (3)   1.01 .51

TB Bacillus
Centenary
A604

1982, Mar. 24   Perf. 13
957 A604 35p rose violet   .15 .15

Durgabai Deshmukh (1909-1981), Social
Worker — A605

1982, May 9   Photo.   Perf. 14¹/₂x14
958 A605 35p blue   .15 .15

Himalayan
Flowers — A606

1982, May 29   Perf. 14x14¹/₂
959 A606   35p Blue poppies   .15 .15
960 A606   1r Showy inula   .15 .15
961 A606   2r Cobra lily   .25 .15
962 A606 2.85r Brahma kamal   .35 .18
    Set value   .76 .40

Ariana
Passenger
Payload
Experimental
(APPLE)
Satellite, First
Anniv.
A607

1982, June 19   Perf. 13¹/₂x13
963 A607 2r multicolored   .25 .15

Bidhan Chandra Roy (1882-1962),
Physician and Politician — A608

1982, July 1   Perf. 14¹/₂x14
964 A608 50p orange brown   .15 .15

Sagar Samrat
Drilling
Rig — A609

1982, Aug. 14   Photo.   Perf. 13
985 A609 1r multicolored   .15 .15

Bindu (Cosmic
Spirit), by
Raza — A610

Kashmir
Stag — A611

Paintings; 3.05r, Between the Spider and the
Lamp, 1956, by M.F. Husain.

1982, Sept. 17   Perf. 14x14¹/₂
986 A610   2r multicolored   .25 .15
987 A610 3.05r multicolored   .38 .18

1982, Oct. 1   Perf. 13x13¹/₂
988 A611 2.85r multicolored   .35 .18

50th Anniv. of
Indian Air
Force — A612

1982, Oct. 8   Perf. 13¹/₃x13
989 A612 1r Wapiti, MiG 25   .15 .15

50th Anniv. of
Civil Aviation
A613

1982, Oct. 15
990 A613 3.25r J.R.D. Tata and his
      Puss Moth, 1932   .40 .20

Police Memorial Day — A614

1982, Oct. 21
991 A614 50p Beat patrol .15 .15

Post Office Savings Bank Centenary A615

1982, Oct. 23
992 A615 50p brown .15 .15

9th Asian Games — A616

1982 *Perf. 13¹/₂x14*
993 A616 1r Wrestling, by Janaki, 17th cent. .15 .15
993A A616 1r Archery .15 .15
Set value .24 .15

Issue dates: No. 993, Oct. 30, No, 993A, Nov. 6.

India-USSR Troposcatter Communications Link — A617

1982, Nov. 2 *Perf. 13¹/₂x13*
994 A617 3.05r multicolored .38 .18

Children's Day — A618

1982, Nov. 14 *Perf. 14x15*
995 A618 50p multicolored .15 .15

9th Asian Games A619

1982 *Perf. 13*
996 A619 50p Cycling .15 .15
997 A619 2r Yachting .25 .15
998 A619 2r Javelin .25 .15
999 A619 2.85r Rowing .35 .18
1000 A619 2.85r Discus .35 .18
1001 A619 3.25r Soccer .40 .20
Nos. 996-1001 (6) 1.75
Set value .86

Issued: #997, 999, Nov. 25; others Nov. 19.

50th Anniv. of Indian Military Academy, Dehradun A620

1982, Dec. 10 *Perf. 13¹/₂x13*
1002 A620 50p multicolored .15 .15

Purushottamdas Tandon (1882-1962), Politician — A621

1982, Dec. 15 *Perf. 13*
1003 A621 50p bister .15 .15

Darjeeling Himalayan Railway Centenary A622

1982, Dec. 18 *Perf. 13¹/₂x13*
1004 A622 2.85r multicolored .35 .18

Indian Railway Car — A623

Nos. 2 and 201 — A624

1982, Dec. 30 Photo. *Perf. 13, 14*
1005 A623 50p multicolored .15 .15
1006 A624 2r multicolored .25 .15
Set value .18

INPEX '82 Stamp Exhibition.

First Anniv. of Antarctic Expedition A625

1983, Jan. 9 Photo. *Perf. 13¹/₂x13*
1007 A625 1r multicolored .15 .15

Pres. Franklin D. Roosevelt (1882-1945) A626

1983, Jan. 30 *Perf. 13*
1008 A626 3.25r brown .40 .20

Siberian Cranes — A627

1983, Feb. 7 *Perf. 13x13¹/₂*
1009 A627 2.85r multicolored .35 .18

180th Anniv. of Jat Regiment A628

1983, Feb. 16 *Perf. 13¹/₂x13*
1010 A628 50p Soldiers, emblem .15 .15

7th Non-aligned Summit Conference A629

1983, Mar. 7
1011 A629 1r Emblem .15 .15
1012 A629 2r Jawaharlal Nehru .25 .15
Set value .18

Commonwealth Day — A630

1983, Mar. 14 *Perf. 13*
1013 A630 1r Shore Temple, Mahabalipuram .15 .15
1014 A630 2r Mountains, Gomukh .25 .15
Set value .18

86th Session of Intl. Olympic Committee, New Delhi, Mar. 21-28 — A631

1983, Mar. 25 Litho. *Perf. 13¹/₂x13*
1015 A631 1r Acropolis .20 .15

St. Francis of Assisi (1182-1226), by Giovanni Collina.

1983, Apr. 4 Photo. *Perf. 13*
1016 A632 1r brown .20 .15

1983, May 5 Photo. *Perf. 13x12¹/₂*
1017 A633 1r brown .20 .15

Karl Marx (1818-1883).

A632   A633

Charles Darwin (1809-1882) A634

1983, May 18 *Perf. 12¹/₂x13*
1018 A634 2r multicolored .40 .20

50th Anniv. of Kanha Natl. Park — A635

1983, May 30 *Perf. 13¹/₂x13*
1019 A635 1r Barasinga stag .20 .15

World Communications Year — A636

1983, July 18 Photo. *Perf. 13*
1020 A636 1r multicolored .20 .15

Simon Bolivar (1783-1830) A637

1983, July 24
1021 A637 2r multicolored .40 .20

Quit India Resolution, Aug. 8, 1942 — A638

Meera Behn (Madeleine Slade). Disciple of Gandhi, d. 1982 — A639

Design: No. 1024, Mahadev Desai (1892-1942).

1983, Aug. 9 Photo. *Perf. 14*
1022 A638 50p shown .15 .15
Perf. 13¹/₂x13
1023 A639 50p shown .15 .15
1024 A639 50p org. green & brn .15 .15
a. Pair, #1023-1024 .20 .15

See Nos. 1033, 1035, 1042, 1052-1057, 1077, 1093-1094, 1103, 1107, 1109, 1122, 1137-1139, 1144, 1147-1149, 1163, 1167, 1198, 1202-1205, 1229-1231, 1238, 1243, 1257, 1268-1271, 1277.

Ram Nath Chopra (1882-1973), Pharmacologist A640

1983, Aug. 17 *Perf. 13*
1025 A640 50p brown .15 .15

Indian Mountaineering Foundation, 25th Anniv. — A641

1983, Aug. 27 *Perf. 13¹/₂*
1026 A641 2r Nanda Devi, Himalayas .40 .20

Bombay Natural History Soc. — A642

Rock Garden, Chandigarh — A643

1983, Sept. 15 *Perf. 13x13¹/₂*
1027 A642 1r multicolored .20 .15

1983, Sept. 23 *Perf. 13x13¹/₂*
1028 A643 1r multicolored .20 .15

Wildlife A644

1983, Oct. 1 *Perf. 13¹/₂x13*
1029 A644 1r Golden langur .20 .15
1030 A644 2r Lion-tailed macaque .40 .20

World Tourism, 5th General Assembly A645

1983, Oct. 3 *Photo.* *Perf. 14*
1031 A645 2r Ghats of Varanasi .40 .20

Krishna Kanta Handique, Linguist, Sanskritist, Educator and Scholar — A646

1983, Oct. 7 *Litho.* *Perf. 13*
1032 A646 50p deep gray violet .15 .15

Famous Indians Type of 1983
Design: Hemu Kalani, revolutionary patriot.

1983, Oct. 18 *Photo.* *Perf. 13¹/₂x13*
1033 A639 50p org, grn & red brn .15 .15

Children's Day — A648

Painting: Festival, by Kashyap Premswala

1983, Nov. 14 *Photo.* *Perf. 13*
1034 A648 50p multicolored .15 .15

Famous Indians Type of 1983
Design: Acharya Vinoba Bhave (1895-1982), freedom fighter.

1983, Nov. 15 *Photo.* *Perf. 13¹/₂x13*
1035 A639 50p org, grn & dull brn .15 .15

Manned Flight Bicent. — A650

Project Tiger — A651

1983, Nov. 21 *Photo.* *Perf. 13*
1036 A650 1r 1st Indian Balloon .20 .15
1037 A650 2r Montgolfier Balloon .40 .20

1983, Nov. 22 *Photo.* *Perf. 13*
1038 A651 2r multicolored .40 .20

A652

A653

Design: 2r, Goanese Couple, 19th century.

1983, Nov. 23 *Photo.* *Perf. 13*
1039 A652 1r lt brnsh blue & multi .20 .15
1040 A652 2r pink & multi .40 .20

Commonwealth Heads of Government Meeting, New Delhi.

1983, Dec. 5 *Photo.* *Perf. 13*
1041 A653 1r Pratiksha .20 .15

Nanda Lal Bose (1882-1966), artist.

Famous Indians Type of 1983
Design: Surendranath Banerjee, journalist.

1983, Dec. 28 *Photo.* *Perf. 13¹/₂x13*
1042 A639 50p org, green & olive .15 .15

7th Light Cavalry Bicent. — A655

Deccan Horse Regiment, 194th Anniv. — A656

1984, Jan. 7
1043 A655 1r Soldier, banner .20 .15

1984, Jan. 9 *Perf. 13x13¹/₂*
1044 A656 1r multicolored .20 .15

Asiatic Society Bicentenary A657

Design: Society building, Calcutta; founder William Jones.

1984, Jan. 15 *Perf. 13*
1045 A657 1r brt green & dp lilac .20 .15

Postal Life Insurance Centenary — A658

1984, Feb. 1 *Photo.* *Perf. 13x13¹/₂*
1046 A658 1r Emblem .20 .15

Presidential Review of Naval Fleet A659

1984, Feb. 3 *Perf. 13¹/₂x13*
1047 A659 1r Jet .20 .15
1048 A659 1r Aircraft carrier .20 .15
1049 A659 1r Submarine .20 .15
1050 A659 1r Missile destroyer .20 .15
 a. Block of 4, #1047-1050 .80 .40

12th Intl. Leprosy Congress, New Delhi — A660

1984, Feb. 10 *Perf. 13x13¹/₂*
1051 A660 1r Globe, emblem .20 .15

Famous Indians Type of 1983
Designs: No. 1052, Vasudeo Balvant Phadke (d. 1884), freedom fighter. No. 1053, Baba Kanshi Ram. No. 1054, Begum Hazrat Mahal. No. 1055, Mangal Pandey. No. 1056, Nana Sahib. No. 1057, Tatya Tope.

1984 *Perf. 13¹/₂x13*
1052 A639 50p org, grn & dk ol .15 .15
1053 A639 50p org, grn & brn .15 .15
1054 A639 50p org, grn, red org & gray .15 .15
1055 A639 50p org, grn, brn & gray .15 .15
1056 A639 50p org, grn, vio & gray .15 .15
1057 A639 50p org, grn, dk ol & gray .15 .15
 Set value .60 .30

Issue dates: No. 1052, Feb. 23. No. 1053, Apr. 23. Nos. 1054-1057, May 10.

Indian-Russian Space Cooperation — A662

1984, Apr. 3 *Photo.* *Perf. 14*
1058 A662 3r Spacecraft .60 .30

G. D. Birla (1894-1983), Industrialist A663

Design: Birla, Birla Institute of Technology, Pilani.

1984, June 11
1060 A663 50p sepia .15 .15

1984 Summer Olympics A664

Vellore Fort A665

Perf. 13x12¹/₂, 12¹/₂x13
1984, July 28 *Photo.*
1061 A664 50p Basketball .15 .15
1062 A664 1r High jump .20 .15
1063 A664 2r Gymnastics, horiz. .40 .20
1064 A664 2.50r Weight lifting, horiz. .50 .25
 Nos. 1061-1064 (4) 1.25
 Set value .60

1984, Aug. 3 *Perf. 13¹/₂x13, 13x13¹/₂*
1065 A665 50p Gwalior, horiz. .15 .15
1066 A665 1r shown .20 .15
1067 A665 1.50r Simhagad .30 .15
1068 A665 2r Jodhpur, horiz. .40 .20
 Nos. 1065-1068 (4) 1.05
 Set value .50

B.V. Paradkar, Editor — A665a

1984, Sept. 14 *Photo.* *Perf. 13x13¹/₂*
1068A A665a 50p sepia .15 .15

Dr. D.N. Wadia (1883-1969), Geologist A665b

1984, Oct. 23 *Perf. 13*
1068B A665b 1r multicolored .15 .15

Indira Gandhi — A666

1984, Nov. 19 *Photo.* *Perf. 15x14*
1069 A666 50p multicolored .15 .15

Children's Day — A667

12th World Mining Congress — A668

1984, Nov. 14 *Photo.* *Perf. 13*
1070 A667 50p Birds in trees .15 .15

1984, Nov. 20 *Photo.* *Perf. 13*
1071 A668 1r Congress emblem .20 .15

Dr. Rajendra Prasad (1884-1963), 1st, Pres. A669

1984, Dec. 3   Photo.   Perf. 13
1072 A669 50p multicolored   .15   .15

Roses — A670

1984, Dec. 23   Litho.   Perf. 13
1073 A670 1.50r Mrinalini   .18   .15
1074 A670 2r Sugandha   .24   .15
         Set value   .22

Fergusson College Centenary A671

1985, Jan. 2   Photo.   Perf. 13x13½
1076 A671 100p multicolored   .20   .15

Famous Indians Type of 1983
Design: Narhar Vishnu Gadgil (1896-1966), freedom fighter.

1985, Jan. 10   Photo.   Perf. 13½x13
1077 A639 50p orange, green & brn   .15   .15

Artillery Regiment, 50th Anniv. A673

1985, Jan. 15   Perf. 13½x13
1078 A673 1r Gunner, howitzer   .15   .15

Indira Gandhi (1917-1984) — A674

1985, Jan. 31   Perf. 14
1079 A674 2r Addressing UN General
         Assembly   .24   .15
         See Nos. 1098-1099.

Minicoy Lighthouse Cent. — A675

1985, Feb. 2   Perf. 13
1080 A675 1r multicolored   .15   .15

Bengal Medical College, 150th Anniv. — A676

1985, Feb. 20   Perf. 13½x13
1081 A676 1r multicolored   .15   .15

Madras Medical College, 150th Anniv. A677

1985, Mar. 8   Perf. 13½x13
1082 A677 1r multicolored   .15   .15

Assam Rifles, North-East Sentinels, 150th Anniv. A679

1985, Mar. 29
1084 A679 1r multicolored   .16   .15

Potato Research, 50th Anniv. — A680

Baba Jassa Singh Ahluwalia, 1718-1783, Sikh Leader — A681

1985, Apr. 1   Perf. 13
1085 A680 50p brown & pale brown   .15   .15

1985, Apr. 4
1086 A681 50p rose violet   .15   .15

St. Xavier's College, 125th Anniv. A682

1985, Apr. 12
1087 A682 1r multicolored   .16   .15

White-winged Wood Duck A683

Bougainvillea A684

1985, May 18   Perf. 14
1088 A683 2r multicolored   .32   .16

1985, June 5   Perf. 13
1089 A684 50p multicolored   .15   .15
1090 A684 1r multicolored   .16   .15
         Set value   .24   .15

Statue of Didarganj Yakshi, Indian Deity — A685

Yaudheya Tribal Republic Copper Coin, c. 200 B.C. — A686

1985
1091 A685 1r multicolored   .16   .15
1092 A686 2r multicolored   .32   .16
         Set value   .24
Festival of India, festival in France and the US for cultural exchange.
Issue dates: 1r, June 7. 2r, June 13.

Famous Indians Type of 1983
Designs: No. 1093, Jairamdas Doulatram (1891-1979), journalist and politician. No. 1094, Nellie (1909-1973) & Jatindra Mohan (d. 1933) Sengupta, political activists, horiz.

1985   Perf. 13½x13
1093 A639 50p org, grn & dl red brn   .15   .15
         Perf. 13x13½
1094 A639 50p org, green & fawn   .15   .15
         Set value   .16   .15
Issued: No. 1093, July 21. No. 1094, July 22.

Swami Haridas (1478-1573), Philosopher — A689

1985, Sept. 19   Photo.   Perf. 13½x13
1095 A689 1r multicolored   .16   .15

Border Roads Org., 25th Anniv. A690

1985, Oct. 10   Perf. 13x14
1096 A690 2r multicolored   .16   .15

Prime Minister Nehru at Podium A691

1985, Oct. 24   Perf. 13x13½
1097 A691 2r multicolored   .32   .16
         UN, 40th anniv.

Indira Gandhi Memorial Type of 1985
1985   Perf. 14
1098 A674 2r Gandhi addressing
         crowd   .32   .16
1099 A674 3r Portrait   .48   .25
         Issue dates: 2r, Oct. 31. 3r, Nov. 19.

Children's Day — A692

1985, Nov. 14   Perf. 13½x13
1100 A692 50p multicolored   .15   .15

Halley's Comet — A693

1985, Nov. 19   Perf. 13x13½
1101 A693 1r multicolored   .16   .15
Intl. Astronomical Union, 19th General Assembly, New Delhi, Nov. 19-28.

St. Stephen's Hospital, Delhi, Cent. A694

1985, Nov. 25   Perf. 13
1102 A694 1r multicolored   .16   .15

Famous Indians Type of 1983
Design: Kakasaheb Kalelkar (1885-1981), author.

1985, Dec. 2   Perf. 13½x13
1103 A639 50p org, grn & ol brn   .15   .15

Map of South Asia A696

Flags of India, Pakistan, Bangladesh, Nepal, Bhutan, Sri Lanka and the Maldive Islands — A697

1985, Dec. 8   Perf. 13½x13, 14
1104 A696 1r multicolored   .16   .15
1105 A697 3r multicolored   .48   .25
         Set value   .33
South Asian Regional Cooperation, SARC.

Shyama Shastri (1762-1827), Composer — A698

1985, Dec. 21   Perf. 13½x13
1106 A698 1r multicolored   .16   .15

Famous Indians Type of 1983
Design: Master Tara Singh (1885-1967), Sikh leader.

1985, Dec. 23   Perf. 13½x13
1107 A639 50p org, green & blue   .15   .15

Intl. Youth Year — A700

1985, Dec. 24
1108 A700 2r multicolored   .32   .16

Famous Indians Type of 1983

Design: Ravishankar Maharaj (1884-1984), freedom fighter, politician.

1985, Dec. 24 **Perf. 13¹/₂x13**
1109 A639 50p org, green & slate   .15 .15

Handel and Bach — A702

1985, Dec. 27 **Perf. 13x13¹/₂**
1110 A702 5r multicolored   .80 .40

Congress Presidents, 1924-1985 A703

1985, Dec. 28 **Perf. 14**
1111 Block of 4   .64 .64
a.-d. A703 1r any single   .16 .15

Indian Natl. Congress, cent. Withdrawn on day of issue for a period of two weeks.

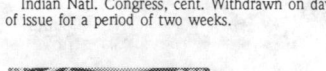

Naval Dockyard, Bombay, 250th Anniv. A704

1986, Jan. 11 Photo. Perf. 13¹/₂
1112 A704 2.50r multicolored   .38 .20

INPEX '86, Jaipur, Feb. 14-19 — A705

Designs: 50p, Hawa Mahal Palace, Jaipur No. 3. 2r, Khar Desert mobile post office.

1986, Feb. 14 **Perf. 13¹/₂x13**
1113 A705 50p multicolored   .15 .15
1114 A705 2r multicolored   .30 .15
    Set value   .38 .20

Vikrant Aircraft Carrier, 25th Anniv. — A706

1986, Feb. 16 **Perf. 13x13¹/₂**
1115 A706 2r multicolored   .32 .16

Inaugural Airmail Flight, 75th Anniv. A707

Perf. 13¹/₂x13, 13x13¹/₂
1986, Feb. 18
1116 A707 50p Biplane   .15 .15

Size: 41x28mm
1117 A707 3r Jet   .48 .24
    Set value   .28

Sixth Triennale of the Arts, Lalit Kala Academy A708

1986, Feb. 22 **Perf. 13x13¹/₂**
1118 A708 1r multicolored   .16 .15

Sri Chaitanya Mahaprabhu A709

1986, Mar. 3 **Perf. 13**
1119 A709 2r multicolored   .28 .15

Mayo College, Ajmer, 111th Anniv. A710

1986, Apr. 12 **Perf. 13¹/₂x13**
1120 A710 1r multicolored   .15 .15

1986 World Cup Soccer Championships, Mexico — A711

1986, May 31 Photo. Perf. 13
1121 A711 5r multicolored   .75 .38

Famous Indians Type of 1983

Design: Bhim Sen Sachar (1894-1978), freedom fighter.

1986, Aug. 14 Photo. Perf. 13¹/₂x13
1122 A639 50p org, green & sepia   .15 .15

Swami Sivananda (1887-1963), Religious Author — A713

10th Asian Games — A714

1986, Sept. 8 Photo. Perf. 13¹/₂x13
1123 A713 2r multicolored   .32 .16

1986, Sept. 16 **Perf. 13x13¹/₂**
1124 A714 1.50r Women's volleyball   .24 .15
1125 A714 3r Hurdling   .48 .24

Madras Post Office, Bicent. A715

1986, Oct. 9 Photo. Perf. 13¹/₂x13
1126 A715 5r black & brown orange   .80 .40

1st Battalion of Parachutists Regiment, 225th Anniv. — A716

Indian Police Force, 125th Anniv. — A717

1986, Oct. 17
1127 A716 3r multicolored   .48 .24

1986, Oct. 21 **Perf. 13¹/₂**
Uniforms, 1861-1986. No. 1129a has a continuous design.
1128 A717 1.50r multicolored   .24 .15
1129 A717 2r multicolored   .32 .16
 a. Pair, #1129, 1128   .56 .35

Intl. Peace Year — A718

1986, Oct. 24
1130 A718 5r sage grn, blue & rose   .80 .40

Children's Day — A719

1986, Nov. 14 Photo. Perf. 13x13¹/₂
1131 A719 50p multicolored   .15 .15

UN, 40th Anniv. A720

1986, Dec. 11 **Perf. 13¹/₂x13**
1132 A720 50p Growth monitoring   .15 .15
1133 A720 5r Immunization   .80 .40
    Set value   .45

Child Survival Campaign.

Miyan Tansen, 17th Cent. Dhrupad Singer, Playing the Surbahar — A721

1986, Dec. 12
1134 A721 1r multicolored   .16 .15

Corbett Natl. Park, 50th Anniv. A722

1986, Dec. 15
1135 A722 1r Elephant   .16 .15
1136 A722 2r Gavial   .32 .16
    Set value   .24

Famous Indians Type of 1983

Designs: No. 1137, Alluri Seetarama Raju (b. 1897), freedom fighter. No. 1138, Sagarmal Gopa (b. 1900), freedom fighter. No. 1139, Veer Surendra Sai (b. 1809), freedom fighter.

1986 **Perf. 13¹/₂x13**
1137 A639 50p red, green & sepia   .15 .15
1138 A639 50p red, green & sl blue   .15 .15
1139 A639 50p red, green & dp red brn   .15 .15
    Set value   .24 .15

Issue dates: No. 1137, Dec. 26, No. 1138, Dec. 29, No. 1139, Dec. 30.

St. Martha's Hospital, Bangalore, Cent. — A724

1986, Dec. 30 **Perf. 13¹/₂**
1140 A724 1r multicolored   .16 .15

Yacht Trishna A725

1987, Jan. 10
1141 A725 6.50r multicolored   1.05 .52

1st Indian Army circumnavigation of the world, Sept. 28, 1985 to 1987.

Africa Fund — A726

1987, Jan. 25 Photo. Perf. 14x14¹/₂
1142 A726 6.50r black   1.05 .52

ICC 29th Congress, New Delhi — A727

1987, Feb. 11 **Perf. 13¹/₂**
1143 A727 5r multicolored   .80 .40

Famous Indians Type of 1983

Design: Hakim Ajmal Khan (1864-1927), physician, politician.

1987, Feb. 13 **Perf. 13¹/₂x13**
1144 A639 60p orange, green & brn   .15 .15

Family Planning
A729   A730

1987, Feb. 27 **Perf. 13, 13x13¹/₂**
1145 A729 35p dark red   .15 .15
1146 A730 60p green & dark red   .15 .15
    Set value   .16 .15

Famous Indians Type of 1983

Designs: No. 1147, Lala Har Dayal (1884-1939). No. 1148, Manabendra Nath Roy (1887-1954). No. 1149, T. Ramaswamy Chowdary (1887-1943).

1987 Photo. Perf. 13½x13
1147 A639 60p org, green & purple .15 .15
1148 A639 60p org, green & red brn .15 .15
1149 A639 60p org, green & brt blue .15 .15
Set value .30 .15
Issue dates: No. 1147, Mar. 18. No. 1148, Mar. 21. Nos. 1149, Apr. 25.

SER Emblem, Blast Furnaces — A732

Electric Train Crossing Bridge — A734

Steam Locomotive No. 691 — A733

Perf. 13x13½, 13½x13
1987, Mar. 28
1150 A733 1r shown .16 .15
1151 A733 1.50r shown .24 .15
1152 A734 2r shown .32 .16
1153 A733 4r Steam locomotive, c. 1890 .65 .32
Nos. 1150-1153 (4) 1.37
Set value .68

Southeastern Railway, cent.

Kalia Bhomora Bridge, Assam A735

1987, Apr. 14 Perf. 13½
1154 A735 2r multicolored .32 .16

Madras Christian College, 150th Anniv. A736

1987, Apr. 16 Perf. 13x13½
1155 A736 1.50r black & rose lake .24 .15

A737 A738

1987, May 1 Perf. 13½
1156 A737 1r dull brown .16 .15

Shree Shree Ma Anandamayee (1896-1982), spiritualist.

1987, May 8 Perf. 14
1157 A738 2r multicolored .32 .16

Rabindranath Tagore (1861-1941), 1913 Nobel Laureate for literature.

A739 A740

1987, May 10 Perf. 13½
1158 A739 1r multicolored .16 .15

Garhwal Rifles and Garhwal Scouts, cent.

1987, May 11
1159 A740 60p black brn & buff .15 .15

J. Krishnamurti (1895-1986), mystic.

7th Battalion, Mechanised Infantry Regiment, Cent. — A741

1987, June 3 Perf. 13½x13
1160 A741 1r multicolored .16 .15

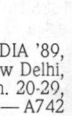

INDIA '89, New Delhi, Jan. 20-29, 1989 — A742

1987, June 15
1161 A742 50p Swan emblem .15 .15
 a. Bklt. pane of 4+inscribed margin ('89) .32
1162 A742 5r Hall of Nations, New Delhi .80 .40
 a. Souv. sheet of 2, #1161-1162 1.25 1.25
 b. Bklt. pane of 4+inscribed margin ('89) 3.25
Set value .45

Inscribed 1986. No. 1162a sold for 8r.

Famous Indians Type of 1983

Design: Kailas Nath Katju (1887-1968), Chief Minister.

1987, June 17 Perf. 13½x13
1163 A639 60p org, green & yel brn .15 .15

Sadyah-Snata, Sanghol Sculpture, c. 2000 B.C. — A744

1987, July 3
1164 A744 6.50r multicolored 1.05 .52

Festival of India in the USSR, July 3, 1987-88.

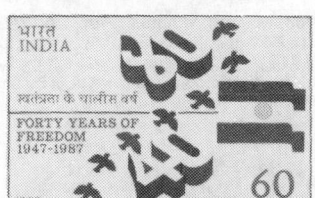

Natl. Independence, 40th Anniv. — A745

1987, Aug. 15 Photo. Perf. 13x13½
1165 A745 60p orange, brt blue & dk green .15 .15

Sant Harchand Singh Longowal (1932-1985), Social Reformer — A746

1987, Aug. 20 Perf. 13½
1166 A746 1r multicolored .16 .15

Famous Indians Type of 1983

Design: S. Satyamurti (1887-1943), political reformer, martyr.

1987, Aug. 22 Perf. 13½x13
1167 A639 60p org, green & brn .15 .15

Guru Ghasidas (1756-1837), Founder of the Saman Sect — A748

Sri Sri Thakur Anukul Chandra (1888-1969), Physician, Guru — A749

1987, Sept. 1
1168 A748 60p henna brown .15 .15

1987, Sept. 2 Perf. 13½
1169 A749 1r multicolored .16 .15

University of Allahabad, Cent. — A750

1987, Sept. 23 Perf. 13½x13
1170 A750 2r multicolored .32 .16

Phoolwalon Ki Sair A751

Maharaja Chhatrasal — A752

1987, Oct. 1 Perf. 13x13½
1171 A751 2r Pankha (embroidered apron) .32 .16

Festival of thanksgiving for fulfilled prayers.

1987, Oct. 2 Perf. 14
1172 A752 60p henna brown .15 .15

Chhatrasal (1649-1731), military commander during the war against the Moguls.

Intl. Year of Shelter for the Homeless A753

1987, Oct. 5 Perf. 13½x13
1173 A753 5r multicolored .80 .40

Asia Regional Conference of Rotary Intl. — A754

1987, Oct. 14
1174 A754 60p shown .15 .15
1175 A754 6.50r Polio immunization 1.05 .52
Set value .56

Service to the Blind, Cent. — A755

1987, Oct. 15
1176 A755 1r shown .16 .15
1177 A755 2r Eye donation .32 .16
Set value .24

World White Cane Day.

INDIA '89 — A756

Designs: 60p, The Iron Pillar, Quwwat-ui-Islam Mosque courtyard, 5th cent., Delhi. 1.50r, The India Gate, New Delhi, war memorial by Luytens, 1921. 5r, The Dewan-E-Khas, Hall of Private Audience, Red Fort, Delhi, c. 1648. 6.50r, Purana Qila, Old Fort, Delhi, c. 1540.

1987, Oct. 17
1178 A756 60p multicolored .15 .15
 a. Bklt. pane of 4 + inscribed margin ('89) .40
1179 A756 1.50r multicolored .24 .15
 a. Bklt. pane of 4 + inscribed margin ('89) 1.00
1180 A756 5r multicolored .80 .40
 a. Bklt. pane of 4 + inscribed margin ('89) 3.25
1181 A756 6.50r multicolored 1.05 .52
 a. Souv. sheet of 4, #1178-1811 2.50 1.25
 b. Bklt. pane of 4 + inscribed margin ('89) 4.25
Nos. 1178-1181 (4) 2.24
Set value 1.08

No. 1181a sold for 15r.

Tyagmurti Goswami Ganeshdutt (1889-1959), Educator, Social Activist — A757

1987, Nov. 2 Perf. 13½
1182 A757 60p terra cotta .15 .15

Children's Day — A758

1987, Nov. 14
1183 A758 60p multicolored .15 .15

Trees — A759

1987, Nov. 19   Photo.   Perf. 13½
1184 A759 60p Chinar, vert.   .15 .15
1185 A759 1.50r Pipal   .24 .15
1186 A759 5r Sal, vert.   .80 .40
1187 A759 6.50r Banyan   1.05 .52
   Nos. 1184-1187 (4)   2.24 1.22

Festival of the USSR in India — A760

Votive coin based on The Worker and the Peasant Woman, by Soviet sculptor Mukhina.

1987, Nov. 21   Perf. 14
1188 A760 5r multicolored   .80 .40

White Tiger — A761

Rameshwari Nehru (1886-1966), Human Rights and World Peace Activist — A762

1987, Nov. 29   Photo.   Perf. 13½
1189 A761 1r shown   .16 .15
1190 A761 5r Snow leopard, horiz.   .80 .40
   Set value   .48

1987, Dec. 10
1191 A762 60p red brown   .15 .15

Execution of Veer Narayan Singh (1795-1857), Sikh Uprising Leader A763

1987, Dec. 10
1192 A763 60p dark brown   .15 .15

Father Kuriakose Elias Chavara (1806-1871), Theologian Beatified by Pope John Paul II Feb. 8, 1986 — A764

1987, Dec. 20
1193 A764 60p dark brown olive   .15 .15

Dr. Rajah Sir M.A. Muthiah Chettiar (1905-1984), Politician, Pro-chancellor of Annamalai University — A765

1987, Dec. 21   Perf. 13
1194 A765 60p chalky blue black   .15 .15

Sri Harmandir Sahib (Gold Temple), Amritsar, 400th Anniv. — A766

1987, Dec. 26   Perf. 13½
1195 A766 60p multicolored   .15 .15

Rukmini Devi (1904-1986), Dancer, Choreographer — A767

1987, Dec. 27
1196 A767 60p dark red   .15 .15

Dr. Hiralal (1867-1934), Historian — A768

1987, Dec. 31
1197 A768 60p dark blue   .15 .15

Famous Indians Type of 1983

Design: Pandit Hriday Nath Kunzru (1887-1978), human rights activist, statesman.

1987, Dec. 31   Perf. 13½x13
1198 A639 60p org, green & red brn   .15 .15

75th Session of the Indian Science Congress Assoc. A770

1988, Jan. 1
1199 A770 4r multicolored   .65 .32

Solar Energy A771

13th Asia Pacific Dental Congress, New Delhi, Jan. 28-Feb.2 A772

Wmk. 324
1988, Jan. 1   Photo.   Perf. 13
1200 A771 5r dp orange & sepia   .80 .40

1988, Jan. 28   Unwmk.   Perf. 13
1201 A772 4r multicolored   .65 .32

Famous Indians Type of 1983

Designs: No. 1202, Mohan Lal Sukhadia (1916-1982). No. 1203, Dr. S.K. Sinha (1887-1961). No. 1204, Chandra Shekhar Azad (1906-1931). No. 1205, Govind Ballabh Pant (1887-1961).

1988   Perf. 13½x13
1202 A639 60p org, green & bluish blk .15 .15
1203 A639 60p org, green & org brn   .15 .15
1204 A639 60p org, green & rose red   .15 .15
1205 A639 60p org, green & purple   .15 .15
   Set value   .40 .20
   Issue dates: Nos. 1202, Feb. 2; No. 1203, Feb. 4; No. 1204, Feb. 27; No. 1205, Mar. 7.

U. Tirot Sing (1800-1833), Patriot — A774

1988, Feb. 3
1206 A774 60p dull brown   .15 .15

Kumaon Regiment 4th Battalion, Bicent. — A775

Balgandharva (1888-1967), Musician — A776

1988, Feb. 19   Perf. 14
1207 A775 1r Uniforms of 1788, 1947, 1988   .16 .15

1988, Feb. 22   Perf. 13x13½
1208 A776 60p brown   .15 .15

Mechanised Infantry Regiment A777

1988, Feb. 24   Perf. 13½x13
1209 A777 1r multicolored   .16 .15

A778

A779

1988, Feb. 26   Perf. 13
1210 A778 60p bluish black   .15 .15
   Sir B.N. Rau (1887-1953), constitutional advisor.

1988, Mar. 14   Photo.   Perf. 13x13½
1211 A779 1r bright rose   .16 .15
   Mohindra College, Patiala, founded in 1875 by Maharaja Mohinder Singh, is now part of Punjabi University.

Dr. D.V. Gundappa (1887-1975), Journalist, and Gikhala Institute of Public Affairs A780

1988, Mar. 17   Perf. 13½x13
1212 A780 60p slate blue   .15 .15

Woman Warrior Riding into Battle — A781

1988, Mar. 20   Perf. 13x13½
1213 A781 60p bright rose   .15 .15
   Rani Avantibai (d. 1858), heroine of the 1857 independence war.

Malayala Manorama Newspaper, Cent. — A782

1988, Mar. 23
1214 A782 1r blue & black   .16 .15
   Malayala Manorama, published in Kottayam, is the largest circulated daily newspaper in India.

Maharshi Dadhichi, Vedic Period Saint Purported to Have Introduced Fire to Man — A783

1988, Mar. 26
1215 A783 60p deep orange   .15 .15

Mohammad Iqbal (1877-1938), Poet — A784

1988, Apr. 21
1216 A784 60p carmine & gold   .15 .15

Samarth Ramdas (1608-1682), Philosopher A785

Swati Tirunal Rama Varma (1813-1846), Carnatic Composer A786

1988, May 1   Perf. 13
1217 A785 60p dk yellow green   .15 .15

1988, May 2   Perf. 13x13½
1218 A786 60p brt violet   .15 .15

1st War of Independence, the "Indian Mutiny of 1857" — A787

Painting: Rani Laxmi Bai transformed from a queen into a warrior fighting for justice, by M.F. Husain.

1988, May 9   Photo.   Perf. 13x13½
1219 A787 60p multicolored   .15 .15

Bhaurao Patil (b. 1887), Educator A788

1988, May 9   Perf. 13½x13
1220 A788 60p red brown   .15 .15

Himalayan Peaks A789

1988, May 19
1221 A789 1.50r Broad Peak   .24 .15
1222 A789 4r Godwin Austin   .65 .32
1223 A789 5r Kanchenjunga   .75 .38
1224 A789 6.50r Nandadevi   1.00 .50
  Nos. 1221-1224 (4)   2.64 1.35

Care for the Elderly — A790

1988, May 24   Perf. 13x13½
1225 A790 60p multicolored   .15 .15

Victoria Terminal, Bombay, Cent. — A791

1988, May 30   Perf. 13½x13
1226 A791 1r multicolored   .16 .15

Lawrence School, Lovedale, 130th Anniv. A792

1988, May 31   Perf. 13
1227 A792 1r dk green & red brown   .16 .15

World Environment Day — A793

1988, June 5   Perf. 14
1228 A793 60p Khejri tree   .15 .15

Famous Indians Type of 1983

Designs: No. 1229, Dr. Anugrah Narain Singh (1887-1957), statesman. No. 1230, Kuladhor Chaliha (1886-1963), political and social reformer. No. 1231, Shivprasad Gupta (1883-1944), freedom fighter.

1988   Perf. 13½x13
1229 A639 60p org, grn & rose vio   .15 .15
1230 A639 60p org, grn & gray blk   .15 .15
1231 A639 60p org, grn & dk vio   .15 .15
  Set value   .30 .15
Issued: #1229, 6/18; #1230, 6/19; #1231, 6/28.

Rani Durgawati (d. 1564), Ruler of Gondwana — A795

1988, June 24
1232 A795 60p red   .15 .15

A796   A797

1988, July 28   Photo.   Perf. 13x13½
1233 A796 60p red brown   .15 .15
Acharya Shanti Dev (687-765), Sanskrit and Pali scholar.

1988, Aug. 4
1234 A797 60p blue violet   .15 .15
Yashwant Singh Parmar (1906-1981), administrator of Himachal Pradesh State.

A798

A798a
Painting by M.F. Husain

1988, Aug. 16   Photo.   Perf. 13x13½
1235 A798 60p multicolored   .15 .15
1236 A798a 60p multicolored   .15 .15
  a.   Pair, #1235-1236   .20 .15
Natl. Independence 40th anniv.

Durgadas Rathore (1638-1718), Guardian of King Ajit Singh — A799

1988, Aug. 26   Litho.
1237 A799 60p dark red brown   .15 .15

Famous Indians Type of 1983
Design: Sarat Chandra Bose (1889-1950), politician, lawyer, publisher.

1988, Sept. 6   Photo.   Perf. 13½x13
1238 A639 60p org, grn & dk blue grn   .15 .15

Gopinath Kaviraj (1887-1976), Scholar — A801

1988, Sept. 7   Perf. 13x13½
1239 A801 60p brown olive   .15 .15

Hindi Language Day, Sept. 14 — A802   Indian Olympic Assoc. Emblem — A803

Glory of Sport, Independence 40th Anniv. — A804

1988, Sept. 14   Photo.   Perf. 13x13½
1240 A802 60p ver & dk olive green   .15 .15

Perf. 13½x13, 13x13½
1988, Sept. 17
1241 A803 60p deep claret   .15 .15
1242 A804 5r multicolored   .80 .40
  Set value   .45

Famous Indians Type of 1983
Design: Baba Kharak (1867-1963), nationalist.

1988, Oct. 6   Perf. 13x13½
1243 A639 60p org, green & org brn   .15 .15

Jerdon's Courser — A806

1988, Oct. 7   Perf. 13½
1244 A806 1r multicolored   .16 .15

The Times of India, Newspaper, 150th Anniv. — A807

1988, Nov. 3   Perf. 13½x14
1245 A807 1.50r black & gold   .25 .15

INDIA '89 — A808

Perf. 13½x13
1988, Oct. 9   Unwmk.   Photo.
1246 A808 4r Bangalore P.O.   .65 .32
  a.   Bklt. pane of 6+inscribed margin ('89)   4.00
1247 A808 5r Bombay P.O.   .70 .35
  a.   Bklt. pane of 6+inscribed margin ('89)   4.25

Portrait of Azad by K.K. Hebbar — A809

1988, Nov. 11
1248 A809 60p multicolored   .15 .15
Maulana Abul Kalam Azad (1888-1958), minister of education, natl. resources and scientific research.

Jawaharlal Nehru — A810

Perf. 13x13½, 13½x13 (1r)
1988, Nov. 14
1249 A810 60p dk gray, dk orange & dk grn   .15 .15
1250 A810 1r Portrait, vert.   .15 .15
  Set value   .24 .15

Birsa, Munda Leader A811

1988, Nov. 15   Perf. 13½x13
1251 A811 60p brown   .15 .15

Bhakra Dam, 25th Anniv. A812

1988, Dec. 15   Perf. 14
1252 A812 60p carmine rose   .15 .15

INDIA '89 — A813

Designs: 60p, Dead-letter cancellations, 1886. 6.50r, Traveling p.o. cancellation, 1864-69.

1988, Dec. 20   *Perf. 13½x13*
1253 A813	60p multicolored	.15	.15
a.	Bklt. pane of 6+inscribed margin ('89)		.48
1254 A813	6.50r multicolored	1.05	.52
a.	Bklt. pane of 6+inscribed margin ('89)		6.30
	Set value		.56

K.M. Munshi (1887-1971), Environmentalist, Statesmen — A814

1988, Dec. 30
1255 A814	60p dark olive green	.15	.15

Mannathu Padmanabhan (1878-1970), Social Reformer — A815

1989, Jan. 2   *Perf. 13½x13*
1256 A815	60p dull brown	.15	.15

Famous Indians Type of 1983

Design: Hare Krushna Mahtab (1899-1987), author.

1989, Jan. 2   *Perf. 13½x13*
1257 A639	60p orange, grn & black	.15	.15

Lok Sabha Secretariat, 60th Anniv. A817

1989, Jan. 10   *Perf. 13½x13*
1258 A817	60p dark olive green	.15	.15

State Museum, Lucknow, 125th Anniv. — A818

1989, Jan. 11   *Perf. 14*
1259 A818	60p Goddess Durga, lion	.15	.15

INDIA '89 — A819

1989, Jan. 20   *Perf. 13½x13*
1260 A819	60p Youth collecting	.15	.15
a.	Bklt. pane of 6 + inscribed margin		.60
1261 A819	1.50r Postal coach & p.o., 1842	.25	.15
a.	Bklt. pane of 6 + inscribed margin		1.50
1262 A819	5r Travancore #2	.80	.40
a.	Bklt. pane of 6 + inscribed margin		4.80
1263 A819	6.50r Philatelic journal mastheads	1.05	.52
a.	Bklt. pane of 6 + inscribed margin		6.30
	Nos. 1260-1263 (4)	2.25	
	Set value		1.09

St. John Bosco (1815-1888), Educonmentalist — A820

1989, Jan. 31   *Perf. 13*
1264 A820	60p carmine rose	.15	.15

3rd Cavalry, 148th Anniv. A821

1989, Feb. 8   *Perf. 13½x13*
1265 A821	60p multicolored	.15	.15

Dargah Sharif Ajmer A822

1989, Feb. 13   Litho.   *Perf. 13½x13*
1266 A822	1r multicolored	.15	.15

President's Review of the Naval Fleet — A823

1989, Feb. 15   *Perf. 14*
1267 A823	6.50r multicolored	1.05	.52

Famous Indians Type of 1983

Designs: No. 1268, Sheikh Mohammad Abdullah. No. 1269, Balasaheb Gangadhar Kher (1888-1957), politician. No. 1270, Saiffuddin Kitchlew (1888-1963), lawyer, diplomat. No. 1271, Rajkumari Amrit Kaur (d. 1964), minister of health and welfare.

1988-89   Photo.   *Perf. 13½x13*
1268 A639	60p org, grn & lil rose	.15	.15
1269 A639	60p org, grn & dk vio	.15	.15
1270 A639	60p org, grn & blk brn	.15	.15
1271 A639	60p org, grn & grnsh blk	.15	.15
	Set value	.40	.20

Issue dates: No. 1268, Dec. 5; No. 1269, Mar. 8, 1989; Nos. 1270-1271, Apr. 13, 1989.

Freedom Fighters — A825

Designs: No. 1272, Baldev Ramji Mirdha (1889-1956). No. 1273, Rao Gopal Singh (1899-1939).

1989   *Perf. 13x13½*
1272 A825	60p slate	.15	.15
1273 A825	60p dark olive	.15	.15
	Set value	.20	.15

Issue dates: #1272, Jan. 17; #1273, Mar. 30.

Freedom Fighters A826

Designs: No. 1274, Shaheed Laxman Nayak (1899-1943), protest leader. No. 1275, Bishu Ram Medhi (1888-1981), politician.

1989   *Perf. 13½x13*
1274 A826	60p org, sage grn & brn	.15	.15

Size: 24x37mm
1275 A826	60p org, sage grn & dp yel grn	.15	.15
	Set value	.20	.15

Issued: No. 1274, Mar. 29; No. 1275, Apr. 24. See Nos. 1292, 1299-1300, 1317, 1429, 1487.

Sydenham College, Bombay A827

1989, Apr. 19   *Perf. 13½*
1276 A827	60p black	.15	.15

Famous Indians Type of 1983

Design: Asaf Ali (1888-1953), patriot.

1989, May 11   Photo.   *Perf. 13½x13*
1277 A639	60p org, green & sepia	.15	.15

N.S. Hardikar (1889-1975), Freedom Fighter — A829

1989, May 13   *Perf. 13x13½*
1278 A829	60p chestnut brown	.15	.15

Sankaracharya (b. 788), Philosopher A830

1989, May 17   *Perf. 14x13½*
1279 A830	60p multicolored	.15	.15

Punjab University, Chandigarh A831

1989, May 19   *Perf. 13½x13*
1280 A831	1r blue green & brown	.15	.15

Film Industry, 75th Anniv. — A832

1989, May 30   Photo.   *Perf. 14*
1281 A832	60p dk olive bister & black	.15	.15

Kirloskar Corporation, Cent. — A833

1989, June 20   Photo.   *Perf. 13½x13*
1282 A833	1r multicolored	.15	.15

DAV Education Movement, Cent. — A834

1989, June 27   Photo.   *Perf. 13½x13*
1283 A834	1r multicolored	.16	.15

Dakshin Gangotri Post Office in the Antarctic, 1988 — A835

1989, July 11   *Perf. 14*
1284 A835	1r multicolored	.16	.15

Allahabad Bank, 125th Anniv. A836

1989, July 19
1285 A836	60p multicolored	.15	.15

Central Reserve Police Force, 50th Anniv. A837

1989, July 27   *Perf. 13½x13*
1286 A837	60p golden brown	.15	.15

Military Farms, Cent. A838

1989, Aug. 18
1287 A838	1r multicolored	.16	.15

Kemal Ataturk (1881-1938), 1st President of Turkey — A839

1989, Aug. 30   *Perf. 13x13½*
1288 A839	5r multicolored	.80	.40

Sarvepalli Radhakrishnan, President of India, 1962-67 — A840

1989, Sept. 11   Photo.   Perf. 13x13½
1289 A840 60p black   .15 .15

P. Subbarayan (1889-1962), Lawyer, Political Reformer — A841

1989, Sept. 30   Perf. 13x13½
1290 A841 60p brown orange   .15 .15

Mohun Bagan Soccer Team, Cent. A842

1989, Sept. 23   Photo.   Perf. 13½x13
1291 A842 1r multicolored   .16 .15

Freedom Fighter Type of 1989

Design: Shyamji Krishna Varma (1857-1930).

1989, Oct. 4   Photo.   Perf. 13½x13
1292 A826 60p org, sage grn & dk red brn   .15 .15

Sayaji Rao Gaekwad III (1863-1939), Maharaja of the Former State of Baroda — A843

1989, Oct. 6   Perf. 13x13½
1293 A843 60p black   .15 .15

Use Pin Code A844

1989, Oct. 14   Perf. 14
1294 A844 60p multicolored   .15 .15

Namakkal Kavignar (1888-1972), Poet Laureate — A845

1989, Oct. 19   Photo.   Perf. 13x13½
1295 A845 60p black   .15 .15

18th Intl. Epilepsy Congress and 14th World Neurology Congress, New Delhi — A846

1989, Oct. 21   Perf. 13½x13
1296 A846 6.50r multicolored   .90 .45

Ramabai and Sharada Sadan School A847

1989, Oct. 26
1297 A847 60p brown   .15 .15

Pandita Ramabai (1858-1920), women's rights activist, founder of mission to help destitute women and children.

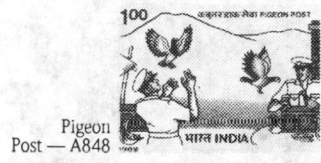

Pigeon Post — A848

1989, Nov. 3
1298 A848 1r brown orange   .15 .15

Freedom Fighter Type of 1989

Designs: No. 1299, Acharya Narendra Deo (1889-1956), democratic socialist movement founder. No. 1300, Acharya Kripalani (1888-1982), politician.

1989   Perf. 13½x13
1299 A826 60p org, sage grn & brn   .15 .15
1300 A826 60p org, sage grn & dp gray   .15 .15
       Set value   .20 .15
Issue dates: #1299, Nov. 6; #1300, Nov. 11.

Jawaharlal Nehru, Birth Cent. — A849

1989, Nov. 14   Perf. 14x15
1301 A849 1r buff, dk red brn & sepia   .15 .15

8th Asian Track and Field Meet, Nov. 14-19, New Delhi — A850

1989, Nov. 19   Perf. 14x14½
1302 A850 1r black, org & dp grn   .15 .15

A851   A852

1989, Nov. 20   Perf. 13x13½
1303 A851 60p deep brown   .15 .15

Gurunath Bewoor (b. 1888), 1st Indian appointed postmaster general.

1989, Dec. 8   Photo.   Perf. 13x13½
1304 A852 60p black   .15 .15

Balkrishna Sharma Navin (1897-1960), litterateur, politician.

Bombay Art Soc., Cent. A853

1989, Dec. 15   Perf. 13½x13
1305 A853 1r multicolored   .16 .15

Likh Florican — A854   Digboi Oil Field, 1889 — A855

1989, Dec. 20   Perf. 13x13½
1306 A854 2r multicolored   .32 .16

1989, Dec. 29   Perf. 14
1307 A855 60p dark red brown   .15 .15

Discovery of oil, Digboi, Assam, cent.

M.G. Ramachandran (1917-1987), Actor, Chief Minister — A856

1990, Jan. 17   Perf. 13x13½
1308 A856 60p dark red brown   .15 .15

Extracting Silt from Sukhna Lake, Chandigarh A857

1990, Jan. 29   Perf. 13x13½
1309 A857 1r multicolored   .16 .15

Sukhna Shramda, society for the preservation of Sukhna Lake.

Presentation of Colors by Pres. Venkataraman to the Bombay Sappers (Corps of Engineers), Feb. 21 — A858

1990, Feb. 21   Photo.   Perf. 15x14x14
1310 A858 60p multicolored   .15 .15

Asian Development Bank — A859

1990, May 2   Photo.   Perf. 14
1311 A859 2r Seashell   .15 .15

Great Britain No. 1, Simulated Cancel of India, Envelope A860

1990, May 6   Perf. 13x13½
1312 A860 6r multicolored   .42 .20

Penny Black, 150th anniv.

Residence and Portrait A861

1990, May 17   Photo.   Perf. 13½x13
1313 A861 2r red brown & green   .15 .15

Ho Chi Minh (1890-1969), Vietnamese Communist Party leader.

A862   A863

1990, May 29
1314 A862 1r orange brown   .15 .15

Prime Minister Chaudhary Charan Singh (1902-1987).

1990, July 30   Photo.   Perf. 13x13½
1315 A863 2r multicolored   .24 .15

Indian peace keeping force in Sri Lanka.

Indian Council of
Agricultural
Research — A864

1990, July 31   *Perf. 14*
1316 A864 2r multicolored   .24 .15

Freedom Fighter Type of 1989
Design: Khudiram Bose (1889-1908), vert.

1990, Aug. 11   **Photo.**   *Perf. 13x13½*
Size: 26x35mm
1317 A826 1r orange, grn & red brn   .15 .15

Russian Child's Drawing of India — A865

Designs: 6.50r, Indian child's drawing of Red
Square.

1990, Aug. 16   **Photo.**   *Perf. 14*
1318 A865 1r multicolored   .15 .15
1319 A865 6.50r multicolored   .78 .40
   a.   Pair, #1318-1319   .90 .50
See Russia Nos. 5925-5926.

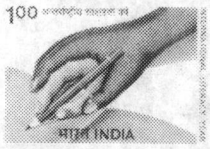

A866   A867

1990, Aug. 24   *Perf. 13*
1320 A866 1r lt red brown   .15 .15
K. Kelappan (1889-1971), social revolutionary.

1990, Sept. 5   *Perf. 13x13½*
1321 A867 1r multicolored   .15 .15
Care for young girls.

Intl. Literacy
Year — A868

1990, Sept. 8   *Perf. 13½x13*
1322 A868 1r blue, brn & tan   .15 .15

A869   A870

1990, Sept. 10   *Perf. 13x14*
1323 A869 4r blue grn & red   .48 .24
Safe drinking water.

1990, Sept. 28   **Photo.**   *Perf. 13x13½*
1324 A870 60p rose lake   .15 .15
Sunder Lal Sharma (1881-1940), social reformer.

A871   A872

1990, Sept. 29
1325 A871 1r Kabbadi   .15 .15
1326 A871 4r Sprinting   .48 .24
1327 A871 4r Cycling   .48 .24
1328 A871 6.50r Archery   .78 .40
   Nos. 1325-1328 (4)   1.89 1.03
11th Asian Games, Beijing.

1990, Oct. 1
1329 A872 1r red brown   .15 .15
A.K. Gopalan (1904-1977), political and social
reformer.

A873   A874

1990, Oct. 1
1330 A873 2r yel brown & dk violet   .24 .15
5th Gurkha Rifles, 3rd and 5th Battalions.

1990, Oct. 19
1331 A874 2r brown & yel brown   .24 .15
Suryamall Mishran (1815-1868), poet.

Children's
Day — A875

       Perf. 13½x13
1990, Nov. 14   **Photo.**   **Unwmk.**
1332 A875 1r multicolored   .15 .15

Border Security
Force, 25th
Anniv.
A876

1990, Nov. 30
1333 A876 5r multicolored   .60 .30

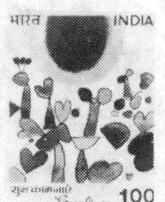

Greetings — A877

Design: 4r, Two elephants carrying riders, horiz.

    Perf. 13x13½, 13½x13
1990, Dec. 17   **Photo.**
1334 A877 1r multicolored   .15 .15
1335 A877 4r multicolored   .48 .24

Cities of
India — A878

1990, Dec. 24   **Photo.**   *Perf. 13½x13*
1336 A878   4r Bikaner   .48 .24
1337 A878   5r Hyderabad   .60 .30
1338 A878   6.50r Cuttack   .72 .36
   Nos. 1336-1338 (3)   1.80 .90

Bhakta Kanakadas
(1488-1578),
Mystic — A879

1990, Dec. 26   *Perf. 14*
1339 A879 1r red orange   .15 .15

A880   A881

1990, Dec. 31   *Perf. 13½x13*
1340 A880 2r org red, red brown &
            blk   .24 .15
Dnyaneshwari, 700th anniv.

Unwmk.
1990, Dec. 28   **Photo.**   *Perf. 14*
Designs: 1r, Shaheed Minar. 6r, Sailing ships on
Ganges River.
1341 A881 1r multicolored   .15 .15
Size: 44x35mm
1342 A881 6r multicolored   .84 .42
Calcutta, 300th anniv.

Pandit Mohan
Malaviya,
Banaras Hindu
University
A882

1991, Jan. 20   *Perf. 13½x13*
1343 A882 1r dk carmine rose   .15 .15
Banaras Hindu University, 75th Anniv.

Intl.
Conference on
Traffic Safety
A883

1991, Jan. 30   *Perf. 13½x13*
1344 A883 6.50r blue, red & black   .78 .40

A884   A885

1991, Feb. 12   **Photo.**   *Perf. 13x13½*
1345 A884 6.50r multicolored   .90 .45
7th Art Triennial.

1991, Feb. 15
1346 A885 2r ultra & henna brn   .28 .15
Jagannath Sunkersett (1803-1865), educator,
reformer.

Tata Memorial
Center, 50th
Anniv.
A886

1991, Feb. 28   *Perf. 13½x13*
1347 A886 2r brown & buff   .28 .15

River Dolphin
A887

1991, Mar. 4
1348 A887   4r shown   .56 .28
1349 A887   6.50r Sea cow   .90 .45

A888   A889

1991, Mar. 5   *Perf. 13x13½*
1350 A888 5r dp violet & red   .70 .35
Fight against drugs.

1991, Mar. 7   **Photo.**   *Perf. 13x13½*
1351 A889 6.50r black & tan   .90 .45
World peace.

Indian
Remote
Sensing
Satellite
1A — A890

1991, Mar. 18   *Perf. 14*
1352 A890 6.50r blue, red brn & blk   .90 .45

Babu Jagjivan Ram
(1908-1976),
Politician — A891

1991, Apr. 5   **Photo.**   *Perf. 13½*
1353 A891 1r yellow & brown   .15 .15

Dr. B.R. Ambedkar (1891-1956), Social Reformer A892

1991, Apr. 14 *Perf. 13¹/₂x13*
1354 A892 1r red brown & blue .15 .15

Tribal Dances A893

1991, Apr. 30 Photo. Perf. 13¹/₂x13
1355 A893 2.50r Valar .35 .18
1356 A893 4r Kayang .55 .28
1357 A893 5r Hozagiri .70 .35
1358 A893 6.50r Velakali .90 .45
Nos. 1355-1358 (4) 2.50 1.26

Ariyakudi Ramanuja Iyengar (1890-1967), Musician A894

1991, May 18
1359 A894 2r green & red brown .28 .15

Karpoori Thakur (1924-1988), Politician — A895

1991, May 30 *Perf. 13x13¹/₂*
1360 A895 1r red brown .15 .15

Antarctic Treaty, 30th Anniv. A896

1991, June 23 Photo. Perf. 13¹/₂x13
1361 A896 5r Penguins .70 .35
1362 A896 6.50r Map, penguins .90 .45
a. Pair, #1361-1362 1.60 .80
No. 1362a printed in continuous design.

New Delhi, 60th Anniv. A897

Views of New Delhi architecture.

1991, June 25
1363 A897 5r multicolored .70 .35
1364 A897 6.50r multicolored .90 .45
a. Pair, #1363-1364 1.60 .80
No. 1364a printed in continuous design.

Sri Ram Sharma Acharya (1911-1990), Social Reformer A898

1991, June 27
1365 A898 1r red & blue green .15 .15

K. Shankar Pillai (1902-1989), Cartoonist A899

1991, July 31 Photo. Perf. 13¹/₂x13
1366 A899 4r shown .55 .28

Perf. 13x13¹/₂
1367 A899 6.50r The Big Show, vert. .90 .45

Sriprakash (1890-1971), Politician A900

1991, Aug. 3 *Perf. 13¹/₂x13*
1368 A900 2r yellow brown .28 .15

Gopinath Bardoloi (1890-1950), Politician — A901

1991, Aug. 5 *Perf. 13x13¹/₂*
1369 A901 1r violet .15 .15

Rajiv Gandhi (1944-1991), Prime Minister — A902

1991, Aug. 20 *Perf. 13*
1370 A902 1r multicolored .15 .15

Jain Muni Mishrimalji (1891-1984), Philospher A903

1991, Aug. 24 Photo. Perf. 13¹/₂
1371 A903 1r brown .15 .15

Mahadevi Verma (1907-1987), Writer and Poet — A904

No. 1373: Jayshankar Prasad (1890-1937), poet and dramatist.

1991, Sept. 16
1372 A904 2r black & blue .28 .15
1373 A904 2r black & blue .28 .15
a. Pair, #1372-1373 .55 .30

37th Commonwealth Parliamentary Conference — A905

1991, Sept. 27 Photo. Perf. 13¹/₂x13
1374 A905 6.50r dk blue & brown .90 .45

Greetings — A906 Orchids — A907

1991, Sept. 30 *Perf. 13x13¹/₂*
1375 A906 1r Frog .15 .15
1376 A906 6.50r Bird .90 .45
a. Pair, #1375-1376 1.05 .52

1991, Oct. 12
1377 A907 1r Cymbidium aloifolium .15 .15
1378 A907 2.50r Paphiopedilum venustum .35 .18
1379 A907 3r Aerides crispum .42 .22
1380 A907 4r Cymbidium bicolour .58 .28
1381 A907 5r Vanda spathulata .70 .35
1382 A907 6.50r Cymbidium devonianum .90 .45
Nos. 1377-1382 (6) 3.10 1.63

2nd Battalion, Third Gurkha Rifles — A908

1991, Oct. 18 *Perf. 13¹/₂x13*
1383 A908 4r multicolored .58 .28

Kamaladevi Chattopadhyaya (1903-1988), Founder of All-India handicrafts Board — A909

1991, Oct. 29 *Perf. 13x13¹/₂*
1384 A909 1r Horsemen .15 .15
1385 A909 6.50r Puppet .90 .45

Chithira Tirunal Bala Rama Varma (1912-1991), Maharaja of Travancore A910

1991, Nov. 7 Photo. Perf. 13¹/₂x13
1386 A910 2r violet .28 .15

Children's Day — A911

1991, Nov. 14 *Perf. 13x13¹/₂*
1387 A911 1r multicolored .15 .15

18th Cavalry, Sesquicentennial (in 1992) — A912

1991, Nov. 14 *Perf. 13¹/₂x13*
1388 A912 6.50r multicolored .90 .45

India Tourism Year — A913

1991, Nov. 15
1389 A913 6.50r multicolored .90 .45

A914 A915

1991, Nov. 18 Photo. Perf. 13x13¹/₂
1390 A914 6.50r multicolored .90 .45

Intl. Conference on Youth Tourism,

1991, Dec. 5
1391 A915 6.50r multicolored .90 .45
Wolfgang Amadeus Mozart, death bicent.

SAARC Year of Shelter A916

1991, Dec. 7 *Perf. 13¹/₂x13*
1392 A916 4r lake & bister .55 .28

Run for Your Heart — A917

1991, Dec. 11
1393 A917 1r black, red & gray .15 .15

Sidhartha with an injured bird. — A918

1991, Dec. 28 *Perf. 13x13¹/₂*
1394 A918 2r multicolored .28 .15
Asit Kumar Haldar (1890-1964), Painter

Yoga Exercises A919

1991, Dec. 30 Photo. Perf. 13¹/₂x13

1395	A919	2r	Bhujangasana	.20	.15
1396	A919	5r	Dhanurasana	.52	.26
1397	A919	6.50r	Ustrasana	.70	.35
1398	A919	10r	Utthita trikonasana	1.05	.52
			Nos. 1395-1398 (4)	2.47	1.28

Intl. Assoc.
for Bridge
and
Structural
Engineering
A920

Designs: No. 1399, Hooghly River Bridge,
Madurai Temple. No. 1400, Sanchi Stupa gates,
Hall of Nations.

1992, Mar. 1 Photo. Perf. 13¹/₂x13

1399	A920	2r sal, brn & blue	.20	.15
1400	A920	2r sal, brn & blue	.20	.15
	a.	Pair, #1399-1400	.40	.20

Fifth Intl.
Conference on
Goats — A921

Natl. Council of
YMCAs, Cent. (in
1991) — A922

1992, Mar. 2 Perf. 13x13¹/₂

| 1401 | A921 | 6r dk blue & brown | .60 | .30 |

1992, Feb. 21

| 1402 | A922 | 1r blue & vermilion | .15 | .15 |

National
Archives
A923

1992, Apr. 20 Photo. Perf. 13¹/₂x13

| 1403 | A923 | 6r multicolored | .60 | .30 |

Krushna Chandra
Gajapathi — A924

Vijay Singh Pathik,
Writer — A925

1992, Apr. 29 Perf. 13x13¹/₂

| 1404 | A924 | 1r violet | .15 | .15 |
| 1405 | A925 | 1r red brown | .15 | .15 |

Adventure
Sports
A926

1992, Apr. 29 Perf. 13¹/₂x13

1406	A926	2r	Hang gliding	.20	.15
1407	A926	4r	Wind surfing	.40	.20
1408	A926	5r	River rafting	.50	.25
1409	A926	11r	Skiing	1.10	.55
			Nos. 1406-1409 (4)	2.20	1.15

Henry Gidney
(1873-1942),
Physician and
Politician
A927

1992, May 9 Perf. 13¹/₂x13

| 1410 | A927 | 1r blue & black | .15 | .15 |

Telecommunication Training Center,
Jabalpur, 50th Anniv. — A928

1992, May 30

| 1411 | A928 | 1r lemon | .15 | .15 |

A929   A930

1992, July 31 Perf. 13x13¹/₂

| 1412 | A929 | 1r black & brown | .15 | .15 |

Sardar Udham Singh (1899-1940), freedom
fighter.

1992, Aug. 8

1413	A930	1r	Discus	.15	.15
1414	A930	6r	Gymnastics	.60	.30
1415	A930	8r	Field hockey	.80	.40
1416	A930	11r	Boxing	1.10	.55
			Nos. 1413-1416 (4)	2.65	1.40

1992 Summer Olympics, Barcelona.

Quit India
Movement,
50th Anniv.
A931

Designs: 1r, Spinning wheel, inscription. 2r,
Mahatma Gandhi, inscription.

1992, Aug. 9 Perf. 13¹/₂x13

1417	A931	1r pink, black & pale pink	.15	.15
1418	A931	2r gray, black & claret	.20	.15
		Set value	.30	.15

60th
Parachute
Field
Ambulance,
50th Anniv.
A932

1992, Aug. 10

| 1419 | A932 | 1r multicolored | .15 | .15 |

Indian Air
Force, 60th
Anniv.
A933

1992, Oct. 8 Photo. Perf. 13¹/₂x13

1420	A933	1r shown	.15	.15
1421	A933	10r Biplane, jet fighter	1.00	.50
	a.	Pair, #1420-1421	1.10	.55

Phad Painting of
Dev
Narayan — A934

1992, Sept. 2 Photo. Perf. 13¹/₂x14

| 1422 | A934 | 5r multicolored | .50 | .25 |

Sisters of Jesus and
Mary, 150th
Anniv. — A935

1992, Nov. 13 Photo. Perf. 13x13¹/₂

| 1423 | A935 | 1r gray & blue | .15 | .15 |

Children's
Day
A936

1992, Nov. 14 Perf. 13¹/₂x13

| 1424 | A936 | 1r multicolored | .15 | .15 |

Shri Yogiji Maharaj,
Religious Leader,
Birth Cent. — A937

1992, Dec. 2 Photo. Perf. 13x13¹/₂

| 1425 | A937 | 1r blue | .15 | .15 |

Army Service
Corps 1760-
1992
A938

1992, Dec. 8 Photo. Perf. 13¹/₂x13

| 1426 | A938 | 1r multicolored | .15 | .15 |

Stephen Smith
(1891-1951),
Rocket Mail
Pioneer
A939

1992, Dec. 19 Photo. Perf. 13¹/₂x13

| 1427 | A939 | 11r multicolored | 1.10 | .55 |

State of
Haryana, 25th
Anniv.
A940

1992, Dec. 20

| 1428 | A940 | 2r green & orange | .20 | .15 |

Freedom Fighter Type of 1989

Design: Madan Lal Dhingra, vert.

1992, Dec. 28 Perf. 13x13¹/₂

| 1429 | A826 | 1r orange, green & brown | .15 | .15 |

Dr. Shri
Shiyali
Ramamrita
Ranganathan
(1892-1972),
Writer and
Librarian
A941

1992, Aug. 30 Photo. Perf. 13¹/₂x13

| 1430 | A941 | 1r blue | .15 | .15 |

Hanuman Prasad
Poddar — A942

Pandit Ravishankar
Shukla — A943

1992, Sept. 19 Photo. Perf. 13x13¹/₂

| 1431 | A942 | 1r green | .15 | .15 |

1992, Dec. 31

| 1432 | A943 | 1r rose lake | .15 | .15 |

Birds — A944

Designs: 2r, Pandion haliaetus. 6r, Falco peregrinus. 8r, Gypaetus barbatus. 11r, Aquila
chrysaetos.

1992, Dec. 30

1433	A944	2r multicolored	.15	.15
1434	A944	6r multicolored	.45	.22
1435	A944	8r multicolored	.60	.30
1436	A944	11r multicolored	.85	.42
		Nos. 1433-1436 (4)	2.05	1.09

William Carey, Baptist Missionary to India,
Bicent. of Appointment — A945

1993, Jan. 9 Photo. Perf. 13¹/₂x13

| 1437 | A945 | 6r multicolored | .48 | .24 |

Fakir Mohan
Senapati,
Writer — A946

Council of
Scientific and
Industrial
Research, 50th
Anniv. — A947

1993, Jan. 14 Perf. 13x13¹/₂

| 1438 | A946 | 1r orange brown | .15 | .15 |

1993, Feb. 28 Perf. 13¹/₂x13

| 1439 | A947 | 1r violet brown | .15 | .15 |

Squadron No. 1, Indian Air Force, 60th Anniv. A948

1993, Apr. 1
1440 A948 1r shown .15 .15
1441 A948 1r Paratroopers, planes, artillery .15 .15
Set value .16 .15
Parachute Field Regiment 9, 50th anniv. (#1441).

Rahul Sankrityayan (1893-1963), Politician A949

1993, Apr. 9
1442 A949 1r multicolored .15 .15

Mountain Locomotives A950

1993, Apr. 16 *Perf. 13¹/₂x13*
1443 A950 1r Neral Matheran .15 .15
1444 A950 6r DHR (Darjeeling) .48 .24
1445 A950 8r Nilgiri Mountain Railway .65 .32
1446 A950 11r Kalka-Simla .90 .45
Nos. 1443-1446 (4) 2.18 1.16

89th Inter-Parliamentary Union Conference, New Delhi — A951

1993, Apr. 11 *Photo.* *Perf. 13¹/₂*
1447 A951 1r indigo .15 .15

Meerut College, Cent. (in 1992) — A952

1993, Apr. 25 *Perf. 14*
1448 A952 1r indigo & red brown .15 .15

P.C. Mahalanobis (b. 1893), Statistician A953

1993, June 29 *Perf. 13x13¹/₂*
1449 A953 1r olive yellow .15 .15

Dadabhai Naoroji's Election to House of Commons, Cent. — A957

1993, Aug. 26 *Photo.* *Perf. 14*
1453 A957 6r blue & red brown .48 .25

Swami Vivekanabda, Chicago Address, Cent. — A958

1993, Sept. 11 *Perf. 13x13¹/₂*
1454 A958 2r gray, red brn & org .16 .15

Trees — A959

Designs: 1r, Lagerstroemia speciosa. 6r, Cochlospermum religiosum. 8r, Erythrina variegata. 11r, Thespesia populnea.

1993, Oct. 9 *Photo.* *Perf. 13x13¹/₂*
1455 A959 1r multicolored .15 .15
1456 A959 6r multicolored .38 .22
1457 A959 8r multicolored .50 .25
1458 A959 11r multicolored .70 .35
Nos. 1455-1458 (4) 1.73 .95

Dr. Dwarkanath Kotnis A960

1993, Dec. 9 *Photo.* *Perf. 13¹/₂x13*
1459 A960 1r black & gray .15 .15

A961   A962

1993, Nov. 14 *Perf. 14*
1460 A961 1r multicolored .15 .15
Children's Day.

1993, Nov. 8 *Perf. 13x13¹/₂*
1461 A962 2r multicolored .28 .28
College of Military Engineering, Pune, 50th anniv.

A963   A964

Design: Dr. Dwarm Venkataswamy Naidu.

1993, Nov. 8
1462 A963 1r orange brown .15 .15

1993, July 31
1463 A964 2r multicolored .28 .15
Bombay Municipal Corporation Building, cent.

India Tea — A965

1993, Dec. 11 *Perf. 13*
1464 A965 6r green & red .40 .20

Papal Seminary, Pune, Cent. — A966

1993, Dec. 16 *Perf. 13¹/₂x13*
1465 A966 6r multicolored .40 .20

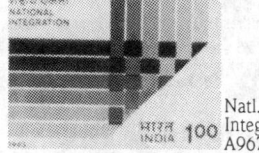

Natl. Integration A967

1993, Aug. 19
1466 A967 1r orange & green .15 .15

Khan Abdul Ghaffar Khan — A968

1993, Aug. 9
1467 A968 1r multicolored .15 .15

Heart Care Festival A969

1993, Dec. 9
1468 A969 6.50r multicolored .42 .22

Inpex '93 — A970

1993
1469 A970 1r shown .15 .15
1470 A970 2r Boats, beach .28 .15
Issued: 1r, Dec. 25; 2r, Dec. 27.

Meghnad Saha (1893-1956), Astrophysicist A971

1993, Dec. 23 *Photo.* *Perf. 13x13¹/₂*
1471 A971 1r dark blue .15 .15

Dinanath Mageshkar, Musician A972

1993, Dec. 29 *Perf. 13¹/₂x13*
1472 A972 1r orange brown .15 .15

Nargis Dutt, Actress and Social Worker — A973

1993, Dec. 30 *Perf. 13*
1473 A973 1r orange brown .15 .15

Indian Natl. Army, 50th Anniv. A974

Design: 1r, Netaji Subhash Bose inspecting soldiers.

1993, Dec. 31 *Perf. 13¹/₂x13*
1474 A974 1r multicolored .15 .15

Satyendra Nath Bose (1894-1974), Mathematician and Physicist — A975

1994, Jan. 1
1475 A975 1r dark rose brown .15 .15

Satyajit Ray (1921-92) A976

Design: 6r, Scene from film, Pather Panchali.

1994, Jan. 11 *Perf. 13*
1476 A976 6r multicolored .38 .20
1477 A976 11r multicolored .70 .35
a. Pair, #1476-1477 1.10 .55
No. 1476 is 68x30mm. No. 1477a is a continuous design.

Dr. Sampurnanand — A977

1994, Jan. 10 *Photo.* *Perf. 13¹/₂x13*
1478 A977 1r multicolored .15 .15

Dr. Shanti Swarup Bhatnagar A978

1994, Feb. 21
1479 A978 1r dark blue .15 .15

Eighth Triennale A979

1994, Mar. 14
1480 A979 6r multicolored .38 .20

Prajapita Brahma (1876-1969), Religious Leader A980

1994, Mar. 7 Photo. Perf. 13¹/₂x13
1481 A980 1r multicolored .15 .15

Sanchi Stupa A981

Wmk. 360
1994, Apr. 4 Photo. Perf. 13
1482 A981 5r blue green & brown .32 .16

ILO, 75th Anniv. A982

1994, May 1 Unwmk. Perf. 13¹/₂x13
1483 A982 6r multicolored .38 .20

United Planters Assoc. of Southern India, Cent. — A983

1994, Mar. 26 Photo. Perf. 13x13¹/₂
1484 A983 2r multicolored .15 .15

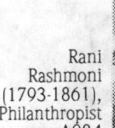

Rani Rashmoni (1793-1861), Philanthropist A984

1994, Apr. 9 Perf. 13¹/₂x13
1485 A984 1r brown .15 .15

Jallianwala Bagh Martyrdom, 75th Anniv. A985

1994, Apr. 13
1486 A985 1r red & black .15 .15

Freedom Fighters Type of 1988

Design: 1r, Chandra Singh Garhwali (1891-1979).

1994, Apr. 23
1487 A826 1r org, sage grn & grn .15 .15

A986

A987

1994, May 25 Perf. 13
1488 A986 2r IPTA .15 .15

1994 Perf. 13x12¹/₂

Small Families: 1r, Family of 3 in front of house.
1489 A987 75c red brown & brown .15 .15
1490 A987 1r green & rose .15 .15
Set value .15 .15

4th Battalion Madras Regiment, Bicent. — A988

1994, Aug. 12
1491 A988 6.50r multicolored .45 .45

Institute of Mental Health, Madras, Bicent. A989

1994, Sept. 23 Photo. Perf. 13¹/₂x13
1492 A989 2r multicolored .15 .15

Mahatma Gandhi (1869-1948) A990

Design: 11r, Flag colors, Gandhi walking and at spinning wheel.

1994, Oct. 2 Perf. 13
1493 A990 6r multicolored .38 .38
1494 A990 11r multicolored .70 .70
a. Pair, #1493-1494 1.10 1.10

No. 1494 is 68x30mm.

16th Intl. Cancer Congress — A991

1994, Oct. 30 Photo. Perf. 13¹/₂
1495 A991 6r multicolored .40 .40

World Conference on Human Resource Development A992

1994, Nov. 8 Perf. 13¹/₂x13
1496 A992 6r multicolored .40 .40

Intl. Year of the Family — A993

1994, Nov. 20 Perf. 13x12¹/₂
1497 A993 2r multicolored .15 .15

Children's Day — A994

1994, Nov. 14 Perf. 13¹/₂x13
1498 A994 1r multicolored .15 .15

J.R.D. Tata (1904-93) — A995

1994 Nov. 29 Perf. 14
1499 A995 2r multicolored .15 .15

Calcutta School for the Blind, Cent. — A996

1994 Nov. 30 Perf. 13¹/₂x13
1500 A996 2r brown & carmine .15 .15

Remount Veterinary Corps, 215th Anniv. — A998

1994, Dec. 14 Photo. Perf. 13x13¹/₂
1505 A998 6r multicolored .40 .40

College of Engineering, Guindy, Madras, Bicent. A999

1994, Dec. 19 Perf. 14
1506 A999 2r multicolored .15 .15

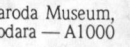

Baroda Museum, Vadodara — A1000

Designs: 6r, Ancient artifact. 11r, Ancient artifact, man standing on pedestal.

1994, Dec. 20 Perf. 14x13¹/₂
1507 A1000 6r black & bister .40 .40
1508 A1000 11r black & bister .75 .75
a. Pair, #1507-1508 1.15 1.15

No. 1508a is a continuous design.

Khuda Bakhsh Oriental Public Library — A1001

1994, Nov. 21 Photo. Perf. 14
1509 A1001 6r multicolored .40 .40

A1002 A1003

1995, Jan. 9 Photo. Perf. 13x13¹/₂
1510 A1002 1r Chhoturam .15 .15

1995, Jan. 7
1511 A1003 6r multicolored .15 .15

India Natl. Science Academy, 30th Anniv.

St. Xavier's College, Bombay, 125th Anniv. A1005

1994, Dec. 4 Photo. Perf. 13¹/₂
1513 A1005 2r multicolored .15 .15

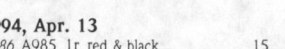

General Post Office, Bombay, Bicent. — A1006

Illustration reduced.

1994, Dec. 28 Litho. Perf. 13¹/₂
1514 A1006 6r multicolored .40 .40

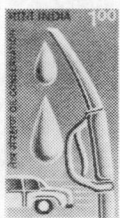

Oil
Conservation
A1008

Rafi Ahmed Kidwai
A1009

1995, Feb. 18   Photo.   Perf. 13
1517 A1008 1r red brown & black   .15 .15

1995, Feb. 18
1518 A1009 1r red brown   .15 .15

K. L. Saigal
A1010

1995, Apr. 4   Photo.   Perf. 13¹/₂x13
1519 A1010 5r black & brown   .32 .32

8th Intl. Conference of
Tamil
Studies — A1011

1995, Jan. 5   Photo.   Perf. 13
1520 A1011 2r King Rajaraja Chola   .15 .15

SAARC Youth
Year — A1012

Prithvi Theater,
50th
Anniv. — A1013

1995, Jan. 12   Photo.   Perf. 13¹/₂x13
1521 A1012 2r multicolored   .15 .15

1995, Jan. 15
1522 A1013 2r multicolored   .15 .15

A1014   A1015

Design: Field Marshall K.M. Cariappa (1900-93).

1995, Jan. 15
1523 A1014 2r multicolored   .15 .15

1995, Jan. 18
1524 A1015 2r multicolored   .15 .15

Tex-Styles India '95, National Textile Fair,
Bombay.

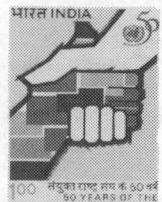

UN, 50th
Anniv. — A1017

Design: 6r, Planting seedling, mother and child,
child reading.

1995, June 6   Photo.   Perf. 13
1526 A1017 1r multicolored   .15 .15
1527 A1017 6r multicolored   .40 .40

R.S. Ruikar
A1018

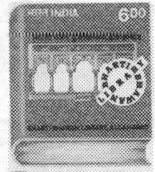

Bharti Bhavan
Library, Allahabad
A1019

1995   Photo.   Perf. 13¹/₂
1528 A1018 1r brown violet   .15 .15

1995, Aug. 30   Perf. 14
1529 A1019 6r multicolored   .35 .35

Headquarters Delhi
Area — A1021

Louis Pasteur (1822-
95) — A1022

1995, Sept. 26   Photo.   Perf. 13
1531 A1021 2r multicolored   .15 .15

1995, Sept. 28
1532 A1022 5r pale yellow & black   .30 .30

La Martiniere
College,
Lucknow,
150th Anniv.
A1023

1995, Oct. 1
1533 A1023 2r multicolored   .15 .15

Mahatma Gandhi (1869-
1948) — A1024

1995, Oct. 2
1534 A1024 1r As young man   .15 .15
1535 A1024 2r As older man   .15 .15
a.   Pair, #1534-1535   .20 .20
b.   Souvenir sheet, #1535a   .20 .20

See South Africa Nos. 918-919.

FAO, 50th
Anniv.
A1025

1995, Oct. 16   Perf. 13¹/₂
1536 A1025 5r multicolored   .30 .30

P.M. Thevar (1908-
63), Politician — A1026

1995, Oct. 30   Perf. 13
1537 A1026 1r carmine   .15 .15

Wilhelm Roentgen
(1845-1923),
Discovery of the X-
Ray, Cent. — A1027

1995, Nov. 8   Photo.   Perf. 13x13¹/₂
1538 A1027 6r multicolored   .40 .40

JAT Regiment,
Bicent.
A1028

1995, Nov. 20   Perf. 13
1539 A1028 5r multicolored   .35 .35

AIR POST STAMPS

De Havilland
Hercules
over
Lake   AP1

1929-30   Typo.   Wmk. 196   Perf. 14
C1 AP1 2a dull green   .55 .28
C2 AP1 3a deep blue   .80 .55
C3 AP1 4a gray olive   2.25 1.10
a.   4a olive green ('30)   2.75 1.10
C4 AP1 6a bister   2.75 .70
C5 AP1 8a red violet   3.25 3.25
C6 AP1 12a brown red   9.75 9.75
Nos. C1-C6 (6)   19.35 15.63

> Catalogue values for unused
> stamps in this section, from this
> point to the end of the section, are
> for Never Hinged items.

Dominion of India

Lockheed
Constellation
AP2

Perf. 13¹/₂x14
1948, May 29   Litho.   Wmk. 196
C7 AP2 12a ultra & slate blk   .55 .28
Bombay-London flight of June 8, 1948.

Republic of India

The Spirit of '76, by
Archibald M.
Willard — AP3

1976, May 29   Perf. 13x13¹/₂
C8 AP3 2.80r multicolored   .75 .55
American Bicentennial.

INDIA '80
Emblem, De
Havilland
Puss Moth
AP4

1979, Oct. 15   Photo.   Perf. 14¹/₂x14
C9 AP4 30p shown   .15 .15
C10 AP4 50p Chetak helicopter   .15 .15
C11 AP4 1r Boeing 737   .15 .15
C12 AP4 2r Boeing 747   .28 .15
Set value   .54 .32

INDIA '80 Intl. Stamp Exhib., New Delhi, Jan.
25-Feb. 3, 1980.

MILITARY STAMPS

China Expeditionary Force

Regular Issues of India,
1882-99, Overprinted   **C. E. F.**

1900   Wmk. 39   Perf. 14
M1 A31 3p carmine rose   .20 .60
M2 A17 ¹/₂a dark green   .50 .70
M3 A19 1a maroon   .60 .75
M4 A21 2a ultra   1.90 4.50
M5 A28 2a6p green   1.50 8.00
M6 A22 3a orange   4.00 12.00
M7 A23 4a olive green   2.50 5.00
M8 A25 8a red violet   2.50 8.00
M9 A26 12a violet, red   4.75 12.00
M10 A29 1r car rose & grn   5.50 10.00
a.   Double overprint
Nos. M1-M10 (10)   23.95 61.55

The 1a6p of this set was overprinted, but not
issued. Value $165.

Overprinted on 1900 Issue of India

1904, Feb. 27
M11 A19 1a carmine rose   22.50 7.00

Overprinted on 1902-09 Issue of India

1904
M12 A32 3p gray   2.00 3.25
M13 A34 1a carmine rose   2.25 .60
M14 A35 2a violet   10.00 1.50
M15 A36 2a6p ultra   1.90 3.50
M16 A37 3a brown org   2.75 3.25
M17 A38 4a olive green   6.50 9.00
M18 A40 8a red violet   5.25 6.75
M19 A41 12a violet, red   7.75 15.00
M20 A42 1r car rose & grn   10.50 21.00
Nos. M12-M20 (9)   48.90 63.85

Overprinted on 1906 Issue of India

1909
M21 A44 ¹/₂a green   1.00 1.00
M22 A45 1a carmine rose   .65 .40

Overprinted on 1911-19 Issues of India

1913-21
M23 A46 3p gray   1.75 10.00
M24 A47 ¹/₂a green   1.40 2.00
M25 A48 1a carmine rose   1.50 1.25
M26 A58 1¹/₂a chocolate   15.00 42.50
M27 A49 2a violet   6.00 30.00
M28 A57 2a6p ultra   6.00 15.00
M29 A51 3a brown org   16.00 100.00
M30 A52 4a olive green   15.00 100.00
M31 A54 8a red violet   13.00 200.00
M32 A55 12a claret   13.00 82.50
M33 A56 1r grn & red brn   42.50 150.00
Nos. M23-M33 (11)   131.15 733.25

Issue dates: No. M23, 1913, others, 1921.

Indian Expeditionary Force

Regular Issues of India,   **I. E. F.**
1911-13, Overprinted

1914 Wmk. 39 *Perf. 14*
M34 A46 3p gray .15 .15
a. Double overprint 17.50 17.50
M35 A47 ½a green .15 .15
M36 A48 1a carmine rose .15 .15
M37 A49 2a violet .30 .25
M38 A57 2a6p ultra .32 .25
M39 A51 3a brown org .60 .60
M40 A52 4a olive green .65 .65
M41 A54 8a red violet 1.00 1.00
M42 A55 12a claret 1.75 1.75
a. Double overprint
M43 A56 1r grn & red brn 3.25 3.50
Nos. M34-M43 (10) 8.32 8.45

Catalogue values for unused stamps in this section, from this point to the end of the section, are for Never Hinged items.

Korea Custodial Unit

Regular Issues of India Overprinted in Black — भारतीय संरक्षा कटक कोरिया

Perf. 13½x14, 14x13½

1953 Wmk. 196
M44 A91 3p gray violet .30 2.25
M45 A92 6p red brown .30 2.25
M46 A91 9p green .30 2.25
M47 A101 1a turquoise .40 2.50
M48 A93 2a carmine .70 2.50
M49 A94 2½a brown lake 1.25 3.00
M50 A94 3a red orange 1.50 3.00
M51 A94 4a ultra 1.75 3.00
M52 A95 6a purple 6.75 7.00
M53 A95 8a blue green 4.75 7.00
M54 A95 12a blue 6.50 14.00
M55 A96 1r dk grn & pur 10.50 14.00
Nos. M44-M55 (12) 35.00 62.75

Hindi overprint reads "Indian Custodial Unit, Korea."

Indian UN Force in Congo

Nos. 302-303, 305, 307, 282 and 313 Overprinted: "U.N. FORCE (INDIA) CONGO"

Wmk. 324, 196 (13np)

1962, Jan. 15 Photo. *Perf. 14x14½*
M56 A117 1np blue green .15 .15
M57 A117 2np light brown .15 .15
M58 A117 5np emerald .15 .15
M59 A117 8np bright green .20 .20
M60 A117 13np brt carmine .35 .35
M61 A117 50np orange .80 .80
Nos. M56-M61 (6) 1.80 1.80

Indian UN Force in Gaza

No. 393 Overprinted in Carmine — UNEF

1965, Jan. 15 Unwmk. *Perf. 13½*
M62 A190 15p blue gray .15 .15

Overprint letters stand for "United Nations Emergency Force."

INTERNATIONAL COMMISSION IN INDO-CHINA

Catalogue values for all unused stamps in this section are for Never Hinged items.

Cambodia

India Nos. 207, 231, 211, 216 and 217 Overprinted in Black — अन्तर्राष्ट्रीय आयोग कम्बोज

Perf. 13½x14

1954, Dec. 1 Wmk. 196
1 A91 3p gray violet .18 .18
2 A101 1a turquoise .25 .25
3 A93 2a carmine .42 .42
4 A95 8a blue green 1.40 1.75
5 A95 12a blue 2.25 2.50
Nos. 1-5 (5) 4.50 5.10

The overprint reads "International Commission Cambodia." Top line is 18mm on Nos. 4-5; 15½mm on Nos. 1-3, 6-12.

Same Overprint on India Nos. 276, 279, 282, 286 and 287

1957, Apr. 1 *Perf. 14x14½*
6 A117 2np light brown .15 .15
7 A117 6np gray .15 .15
8 A117 13np bright carmine .50 .35
9 A117 50np orange 1.25 1.00
10 A117 75np plum 2.50 2.25
Nos. 6-10 (5) 4.55 3.90

Same Overprint on India No. 303

1962 Wmk. 324
12 A117 2np light brown .65 .65

Laos

India Nos. 207, 231, 211, 216 and 217 Overprinted in Black — अन्तर्राष्ट्रीय आयोग लाओस

Perf. 13½x14

1954, Dec. 1 Wmk. 196
1 A91 3p gray violet .18 .18
2 A101 1a turquoise .25 .25
3 A93 2a carmine .42 .42
4 A95 8a blue green 1.40 1.75
5 A95 12a blue 2.25 2.50
Nos. 1-5 (5) 4.50 5.10

The overprint reads "International Commission Laos." Top line is 18mm on Nos. 4-5; 15½mm on Nos. 1-3, 6-16.

Same Overprint on India Nos. 276, 279, 282, 286 and 287

1957, Apr. 1 *Perf. 14x14½*
6 A117 2np light brown .15 .15
7 A117 6np gray .15 .15
8 A117 13np brt carmine .50 .35
9 A117 50np orange 1.25 1.00
10 A117 75np plum 2.50 2.25
Nos. 6-10 (5) 4.55 3.90

Same Overprint on India Nos. 303-305, 313-314

1962-65 Wmk. 324
12 A117 2np light brown .85 1.00
13 A117 3np brown ('63) .18 .18
14 A117 5np emerald ('63) .20 .20
15 A117 50np orange ('65) .65 .75
16 A117 75np plum ('65) 1.40 1.65
Nos. 12-16 (5) 3.28 3.78

Laos and Viet Nam

No. 393 Overprinted in Carmine — ICC

1965, Jan. 15 Unwmk. *Perf. 13½*
1 A190 15p blue gray .32 .32

Overprint letters stand for "International Control Commission."

Nos. 406-408, 411-412, 417 and 419-420 Overprinted in Carmine — अंनिआ ICC

Perf. 14½x14, 14x14½

1968, Oct. 2 Photo. Wmk. 324
2 A202 2p reddish brown .15 .15
3 A202 3p olive bister .15 .15
4 A202 5p cerise .15 .15
5 A203 10p bright blue .15 .15
6 A203 15p green .15 .15
7 A202 60p dark gray .45 .45
8 A204 1r dp cl & red brn .75 .95
9 A205 2r violet & brt blue 1.65 2.25
Nos. 2-9 (8) 3.60 4.40

The arrangement of the lines of the overprint varies on each denomination.

Viet Nam

India Nos. 207, 231, 211, 216 and 217 Overprinted in Black — अन्तर्राष्ट्रीय आयोग वियत नाम

Perf. 13½x14

1954, Dec. 1 Wmk. 196
1 A91 3p gray violet .18 .18
2 A101 1a turquoise .25 .25
3 A93 2a carmine .42 .42
4 A95 8a blue green 1.40 1.75
5 A95 12a blue 2.25 2.50
Nos. 1-5 (5) 4.50 5.10

The overprint reads "International Commission Viet Nam." Top line of overprint is 18mm on Nos. 4-5; 15½mm on Nos. 1-3, 6-16.

Same Overprint on India Nos. 276, 279, 282, 286 and 287

1957, Apr. 1 *Perf. 14x14½*
6 A117 2np light brown .15 .15
7 A117 6np gray .15 .15
8 A117 13np bright carmine .50 .35
9 A117 50np orange 1.25 1.00
10 A117 75np plum 2.50 2.25
Nos. 6-10 (5) 4.55 3.90

Same Overprint on India Nos. 302-305, 313-314

1961-65 Wmk. 324
11 A117 1np blue green .55 .65
12 A117 2np light brown ('62) 1.10 1.10
13 A117 3np brown ('63) .38 .38
14 A117 5np emerald ('63) .22 .32
15 A117 50np orange ('65) .85 1.10
16 A117 75np plum ('65) 1.65 1.90
Nos. 11-16 (6) 4.75 5.45

OFFICIAL STAMPS

Regular Issues Overprinted in Black — Service.

1866, Aug. 1 Unwmk. *Perf. 14*
O1 A7 ½a blue 140.00
a. Inverted overprint
O3 A7 1a brown 90.00
O4 A7 8a rose 8.00 *12.00*

The 8p lilac unwatermarked (No. 19) with "Service" overprint was not officially issued.

Wmk. 38
O5 A7 ½a blue 110.00 15.00
a. Inverted overprint
b. Without period 165.00
O6 A8 8p lilac 15.00 50.00
O7 A7 1a brown 110.00 14.00
a. Inverted overprint
O8 A7 2a yellow 110.00 50.00
a. Imperf.
b. Inverted overprint
O9 A7 4a green 100.00 52.50
a. Inverted overprint
O10 A9 4a green (I) 750.00 200.00

Reprints were made of #O5, O7, O10 (type II).

Revenue Stamps Surcharged or Overprinted

Queen Victoria — O1

Blue Glazed Paper
Black Surcharge

1866 Wmk. 36 *Perf. 14 Vertically*
O11 O1 2a violet 425.00 250.00

The note after No. 30 will apply here also.
No. O10 is often found with cracked surface or scuffs. Such examples sell for somewhat less.

Reprints of No. O11 are surcharged in either black or green, and have the word "SERVICE" 16½x2½mm, instead of 16½x2¾mm and "TWO ANNAS" 18x3mm, instead of 20x3¼mm.

O2

O3

O4

1866

Green Overprint
O12 O2 2a violet 650. 225.
O13 O3 4a violet 1,150. 400.
O14 O4 8a violet 4,000. 2,150.

The note after No. 30 will apply here also.
These stamps are often found with cracked surface or scuffs. Such examples sell for somewhat less.

Reprints of No. O12 have the overprint in sans-serif letters 2¼mm high, instead of Roman letters 2½mm high. On the reprints of No. O13 "SERVICE" measures 16½x2¼mm, instead of 20¼x3mm and "POSTAGE" 18x2¼mm, instead of 22x3mm.

On No. O14 "SERVICE" is 20½mm long, instead of 20mm and "POSTAGE" is 23mm long, instead of 22mm. All three overprints are in a darker green than on the original stamps.

O5

Green Overprint

1866 Wmk. 40 *Perf. 15½x15*

Lilac Paper
O15 O5 ½a violet 350.00 75.00
a. Double overprint 2,100.

Regular Issues Overprinted in Black — Service.

1866-73 Wmk. 38 *Perf. 14*
O16 A7 ½a blue 3.25 .20
O17 A7 ½a bl, re-engraved 125.00 30.00
a. Double overprint
O18 A7 1a brown 17.00 .30
O19 A7 2a orange 4.50 1.50
a. 2a yellow 5.00 1.75
O20 A9 4a green (I) 3.00 1.50
O21 A11 8a rose 3.00 1.25
Nos. O16-O21 (6) 155.75 34.75

The 6a8p with this overprint was not issued. Value $25.

Overprinted in Black — On H. M. S.

1874-82
O22 A7 ½a blue, re-engraved 4.50 .20
a. Blue overprint 250.00 37.50
O23 A7 1a brown 7.00 .15
a. Blue overprint 425.00 85.00
O24 A7 2a orange 15.00 4.00
O25 A9 4a green (I) 6.50 2.50
O26 A11 8a rose 3.00 2.00
Nos. O22-O26 (5) 36.00 8.85

1883-97 Wmk. 39
O27 A17 ½a green .15 .15
a. Pair, one without overprint
b. Double overprint 75.00
O28 A19 1a maroon .15 .15
a. Inverted overprint 75.00 85.00
b. Double overprint 100.00
c. 1a violet brown .15 .15
O29 A21 2a ultramarine .30 .15
O30 A23 4a olive green 2.00 .15
O31 A25 8a red violet .90 .18
O32 A29 1r car rose & grn 3.25 .50
Nos. O27-O32 (6) 6.75
Set value .95

1899
O33 A31 3p carmine rose .50 .15

1900

O34 A17 ½a light green .30 .15
O35 A19 1a carmine rose .90 .15
a. Double overprint 150.00
b. Inverted overprint 100.00
O36 A21 2a violet 2.50 .15
Nos. O34-O36 (3) 3.70
Set value .15

1902-09

O37 A32 3p gray .70 .15
O38 A33 ½a green .90 .15
O39 A34 1a carmine rose .75 .15
O40 A35 2a violet 2.25 .15
O41 A38 4a olive green 4.00 .15
O42 A39 6a bister 2.00 .15
O43 A40 8a red lilac 5.00 .50
O44 A42 1r car rose & green ('05) 4.25 .15
Nos. O37-O44 (8) 19.85
Set value 1.00

1906-07

O45 A44 ½a green .15 .15
O46 A45 1a carmine rose .90 .15
a. Pair, one without overprint
b. Overprint on back
Set value .15

1909

O47 A43 2r brown & rose 7.00 .65
O48 A43 5r violet & ultra 14.00 1.10
O49 A43 10r car rose & grn 18.00 8.00
a. 10r red & green 40.00 5.00
O50 A43 15r ol gray & ultra 50.00 25.00
O51 A43 25r ultra & org brn 140.00 55.00
Nos. O47-O51 (5) 229.00 89.75

For surcharges see Nos. O67-O69.

Regular Issues Overprinted in Black **SERVICE**

1912-22

O52 A46 3p gray .15 .15
O53 A47 ½a green .15 .15
a. Double overprint 90.00
O54 A48 1a carmine rose .15 .15
a. Double overprint 450.00
O55 A48 1a dark brown ('22) .20 .15
a. Imperf., pair 75.00
O56 A49 2a violet .40 .15
O57 A52 4a olive green .80 .15
O58 A53 6a bister 2.50 2.00
O59 A54 8a red violet 1.75 .35

Overprinted in Black **SERVICE**

O60 A56 1r green & red brn 2.25 .55
O61 A56 2r yel brn & car rose 4.00 2.00
O62 A56 5r violet & ultra 15.00 10.00
O63 A56 10r car rose & grn 40.00 27.50
O64 A56 15r ol grn & ultra 72.50 95.00
O65 A56 25r ultra & brn org 165.00 110.00
Nos. O52-O65 (14) 304.85 248.30

For surcharge see No. O69b.

O6

O7

1921 **Black Surcharge**

O66 O6 9p on 1a rose .20 .15

For overprint see Gwalior No. O28.

Official Stamps of 1909 Surcharged **ONE RUPEE**

1925

O67 A43 1r on 15r ol gray & ultra 4.00 2.25
O68 A43 1r on 25r ultra & org brn 21.00 40.00
O69 A43 2r on 10r red & grn 3.75 3.00
a. 2r on 10r car rose & green 175.00 47.50
b. Surcharge on #O63 (error) 700.00

Official Stamps of 1912-13 Surcharged **ONE RUPEE**

O70 A56 1r on 15r ol grn & ultra 21.00 40.00
a. Inverted surcharge
O71 A56 1r on 25r ultra & brn org 5.00 7.25
a. Inverted surcharge 425.00
Nos. O67-O71 (5) 54.75 92.50

1926

O73 O7 1a on 6a bister .50 .40

Regular Issues of 1911-26 Surcharged **SERVICE ONE ANNA**

O74 A48 1a on 1a dk brn (error) 225.00 225.00
O75 A58 1a on 1½a choc .18 .15
O76 A59 1a on 1½a choc .25 .18
b. Double surcharge 30.00
O77 A57 1a on 2a6p ultra .40 .25
Nos. O73-O77 (5) 226.33 225.98

Nos. O74, O75 and O76 have short bars over the numerals in the upper corners.

Regular Issues of 1926-35 Overprinted a **SERVICE**

1926-35 **Wmk. 196**

O78 A46 3p slate ('29) .15 .15
O79 A47 ½a green ('31) .50 .15
O80 A48 1a dark brown 1.25 .15
a. Overprint as on No. O55 35.00 4.75
O81 A49 2a vermilion ('35) 1.00 1.00
a. Small die .85 .15
O82 A60 2a dull violet .15 .15
O83 A60 2a vermilion ('32) .60 .15
O84 A57 2a6p buff ('32) .15 .15
O85 A52 4a olive green ('35) 1.00 .15
O86 A61 4a olive green .24 .15
O87 A53 6a bister('35) 20.00 7.00
O88 A54 8a red violet .35 .15
O89 A55 12a claret .45 .15

Overprinted b **SERVICE**

O90 A56 1r green & brn ('30) 1.25 .50
O91 A56 2r brn org & car rose ('30) 5.25 3.25
O92 A56 10r car & green ('31) 60.00 50.00
Nos. O78-O92 (15) 92.34 63.25

Regular Issues of 1932-34 Overprinted Type "a"

1932-35

O93 A71 ½a green ('35) .30 .15
O94 A68 9p dark green .30 .15
O95 A72 1a dark brown ('35) .30 .15
O96 A69 1a3p violet .15 .15
Nos. O93-O96 (4) 1.05
Set value .25

Regular Issue of 1937 Overprinted Type "a"

1937-39 ***Perf. 13½x14***

O97 A80 ½a brown ('38) 2.00 .15
O98 A80 9p green 4.25 .15
O99 A80 1a carmine .55 .15

Type "b" Overprint

O100 A82 1r brown & slate ('38) .32 .15
O101 A82 2r dk brown & dk vio ('38) 3.50 .20
O102 A82 5r dp ultra & dk green ('38) 4.25 1.65
O103 A82 10r rose car & dark violet ('39) 14.00 3.75
Nos. O97-O103 (7) 28.87 6.20

No. 136 Surcharged in Black **SERVICE 1A**

1939, May **Wmk. 196** ***Perf. 14***

O104 A69 1a on 1a3p violet 1.50 .15

King George VI — O8

1939-43 **Typo.** ***Perf. 13½x14***

O105 O8 3p slate .15 .15
O106 O8 ½a brown .15 .15
O106A O8 ½a dk rose vio ('43) .15 .15
O107 O8 9p green .15 .15
O108 O8 1a car rose .15 .15
O108A O8 1a3p bister ('41) 3.25 .65
O108B O8 1½a dull pur ('43) .15 .15
O109 O8 2a scarlet .15 .15
O110 O8 2½a purple .15 .15
O111 O8 4a dark brown .20 .15
O112 O8 8a blue violet .30 .15
Nos. O105-O112 (11) 4.95
Set value 1.00

For overprints, see Gwalior Nos. O52-O61. Stamps overprinted "Postal Service" or "I. P. N." were not used as postage stamps.

Catalogue values for unused stamps in this section, from this point to the end of the section, are for Never Hinged items.

Nos. 203-206 (Gandhi Issue) Overprinted Type "a"

Perf. 11½

1948, Aug. **Unwmk.** **Photo.**

O112A A90 1½a brown 32.50 25.00
O112B A90 3½a violet 325.00 325.00
O112C A90 12a dk gray green 1,750. 1,750.
O112D A90 10r rose brn & brown 10,000.

Overprint forgeries exist.

Capital of Asoka Pillar
O9 O10

Perf. 13½x14

1950 **Wmk. 196** **Typo.**

O113 O9 3p violet blue .15 .15
O114 O9 6p chocolate .15 .15
O115 O9 9p green .35 .15
O116 O9 1a turquoise .40 .15
O117 O9 2a red .15 .15
O118 O9 3a vermilion .85 .15
O119 O9 4a brown car 3.75 .15
O120 O9 6a purple 3.00 .15
O121 O9 8a orange brn 1.50 .15

Litho.

Perf. 14x13½

O122 O10 1r dark purple 2.00 .15
O123 O10 2r brown red .80 .15
O124 O10 5r dark green 1.50 1.00
O125 O10 10r red brown 4.50 10.00
Nos. O113-O125 (13) 19.10 12.65

Issue dates: 1r-10r, Jan. 2, others, July 1.

1951, Oct. 1 **Typo.**

O126 O9 4a violet blue .15 .15

Type of 1950 Redrawn; Denomination in Naye Paise

Typo. or Litho.

1957-58 ***Perf. 13½x14***

O127 O9 1np slate blue .15 .15
O128 O9 2np blue violet .15 .15
O129 O9 3np chocolate .15 .15
O130 O9 5np yellow green .15 .15
O131 O9 6np turquoise .15 .15
O132 O9 13np red .15 .15
O133 O9 15np dk purple ('58) .15 .15
O134 O9 20np vermilion .15 .15
O135 O9 25np violet blue .20 .15
O136 O9 50np reddish brown .35 .15
Set value 1.10 .50

Issue dates: 15np, June; others, Apr. 1.

Redrawn Type of 1957-58

Typo. or Litho.

1958-71 **Wmk. 324** ***Perf. 13½x14***

O137 O9 1np slate blue ('59) .15 .15
O138 O9 2np blue violet ('59) .15 .15
O139 O9 3np chocolate .15 .15
O140 O9 5np yel green .15 .15
O141 O9 6np turquoise ('59) .15 .15
O142 O9 10np dk green ('63) .15 .15
O142A O9 13np red ('63) .15 .15
O143 O9 15np dk purple .15 .15
O144 O9 20np ver ('59) .15 .15
O145 O9 25np vio blue ('59) .15 .15
O146 O9 50np redsh brown ('59) .15 .15

Litho.

Perf. 14

O147 O10 1r rose vio ('59) .20 .15
O148 O10 2r rose red ('60) .35 .15
a. Watermark sideways ('69) .35 .15
O149 O10 5r green ('59) .90 .28
a. Watermark sideways ('69) .90 .30
O150 O10 10r rose lake ('59) 1.75 .75
a. Watermark sideways ('71) 1.75 .90
Set value 4.00 1.75

Capital of Asoka Pillar
O11 O12

Perf. 14½x14

1967-76 **Photo.** **Wmk. 360**

Without Gum

O151 O11 2p violet black .15 .15
O152 O11 3p dk red brown .15 .15
O153 O11 5p bright green .15 .15
O154 O11 6p Prussian blue .15 .15
O155 O11 10p slate green .15 .15
O156 O11 15p purple .15 .15
O157 O11 20p orange ver .15 .15
O158 O11 25p deep car ('76) .15 .15
O159 O11 30p violet blue .15 .15
O160 O11 50p red brown .16 .15
Set value .70 .40

No. O153 Overprinted **शरणार्थी सहायता REFUGEE RELIEF**

1971, Nov. 15 **Wmk. 360**

Without Gum

O161 O11 5p green .15 .15

No. O153 Overprinted "Refugee / Relief"

O162 O11 5p green .15 .15

No. O162 was used in Maharashtra state.

1971, Dec. 1(?)

Without Gum

O163 O12 5p green .15 .15

Nos. O161-O163 were obligatory on all official mail as a postal tax to benefit refugees from East Pakistan. The tax was paid out of the various governmental departments' budgets.

Type of 1968

1967-74 **Wmk. 324** ***Perf. 14½x14***

O164 O11 2p violet .15 .15
O165 O11 5p brt green ('74) .15 .15
O166 O11 10p slate green ('74) .15 .15
O167 O11 15p purple ('73) .15 .15
O168 O11 20p dp orange ('74) .15 .15
O169 O11 30p ultramarine .15 .15
O170 O11 50p red brown ('73) .16 .15
O171 O11 1r dull purple .32 .15
Set value .75 .40

Without Currency Designation
O13 O14

Perf. 14½x14

1976-80 **Litho.** **Wmk. 360**

Without Gum

O172 O13 2p violet black .15 .15
O173 O13 5p bright green .15 .15
O174 O13 10p slate green .15 .15
O175 O13 15p purple .15 .15
O176 O13 20p brown orange .15 .15
O177 O13 25p carmine rose .15 .15
O178 O13 30p blue ('79) .15 .15
O179 O13 35p violet ('80) .15 .15
O180 O13 50p red brown .15 .15
O181 O13 1r dull purple ('80) .25 .15

Wmk. 324

O182 O13 1r dull purple .20 .15

Perf. 14x13½

O183 O14 2r salmon rose .45 .15
O184 O14 5r deep green 1.10 .35
O185 O14 10r red brown 2.25 .75
Set value 4.75 1.75

O15

Perf. 15x14

1981, Feb. Litho. Wmk. 360

Without Gum

O186 O15 2r orange vermilion .50 .25
O187 O15 5r dark green 1.25 .62
O188 O15 10r dark red brown 2.50 1.25
Nos. O186-O188 (3) 4.25 2.12

Unwmk.

1981, Dec. 10 Litho. *Imperf.*

Cream Paper

O189 O13 5p bright green .15 .15
O190 O13 10p slate green .15 .15
O191 O13 15p purple .15 .15
O192 O13 20p brown orange .15 .15
O193 O13 25p carmine rose .15 .15
O194 O13 35p violet .15 .15
O195 O13 50p brown .15 .15
O196 O13 1r dull purple .25 .15
O197 O15 2r salmon rose .50 .25
O198 O15 5r deep green 1.25 .62
O199 O15 10r red brown 2.50 1.25
Nos. O189-O199 (11) 5.55
Set value 2.50

Perf. 12¹/₂x13

1982, Nov. 22 Photo. Wmk. 360

Without Gum

O200 O13 5p bright green .15 .15
O201 O13 10p slate green .15 .15
O202 O13 15p purple .15 .15
O203 O13 20p fawn .15 .15
O204 O13 25p car rose .15 .15
O205 O13 30p dark blue .15 .15
O206 O13 35p violet .15 .15
O207 O13 50p light brown .15 .15
O208 O13 1r dull purple .25 .15
O209 O15 2r salmon rose .50 .25
O210 O15 5r deep green 1.25 .62
O211 O15 10r red brown 2.50 1.25
Nos. O200-O211 (12) 5.70
Set value 2.60

Perf. 12¹/₂x13

1984, Apr. 16 Photo. Wmk. 324

Without Gum

O212 O13 5p green .15 .15
O213 O13 10p dark green .15 .15
O214 O13 15p rose lake .15 .15
O215 O13 20p fawn .15 .15
O216 O13 25p deep carmine .15 .15
O217 O13 30p blue .15 .15
O218 O13 35p purple .15 .15
O219 O13 40p violet .15 .15
O220 O13 50p brown .15 .15
O221 O13 60p brown .15 .15
O222 O15 1r violet brown .20 .15
O223 O15 2r orange ver .40 .20
O224 O15 5r gray green 1.00 .50
O225 O15 10r red brown 2.00 1.00
Set value 4.25 2.25

Issued: 25p, 1986. 60p, 4/15/88; 40p, 10/15/88; others, 4/16/84.

This is an expanding set. Numbers may change again.

POSTAL TAX STAMPS

Catalogue values for unused stamps in this section are for Never Hinged items.

No. 408 Overprinted शरणार्थी सहायता REFUGEE RELIEF

Perf. 14¹/₂x14

1971, Nov. 15 Photo. Wmk. 324

RA1 A202 5p cerise .15 .15

No. 408 Overprinted "Refugee/Relief"

RA2 A202 5p cerise .15 .15

No. RA2 was used in Maharashtra. In order to make the obligatory tax stamps available immediately throughout India postmasters were authorized to overprint locally No. 408. This resulted in a great variety of mostly handstamped overprints of various types and sizes.

Refugees — PT1

Perf. 14x14¹/₂

1971, Dec. 1 Photo. Wmk. 324

RA3 PT1 5pa cerise .15 .15

Nos. RA1-RA3 were obligatory on all mail. The tax was for refugees from East Pakistan.

See Nos. O161-O163.

CONVENTION STATES OF THE BRITISH EMPIRE IN INDIA

CONVENTION STATES OF THE BRITISH EMPIRE IN INDIA

Stamps of British India overprinted for use in the States of Chamba, Faridkot, Gwalior, Jhind, Nabha and Patiala.

These stamps had franking power throughout all British India.

CHAMBA

'chəm–bə

LOCATION — A State of India located in the north Punjab, south of Kashmir.
AREA — 3,127 sq. mi.
POP. — 168,908 (1941)
CAPITAL — Chamba

The varieties with small letters in the overprint are not listed as the letters are merely broken and not from another font of type.

Indian Stamps Overprinted in Black CHAMBA STATE

1886-95 Wmk. 39 *Perf. 14*

1 A17 ¹/₂a green .16 .20
a. "CHMABA" 100.00 100.00
c. Double overprint
2 A19 1a violet brown .16 .24
a. "CHMABA" 200.00
3 A20 1a6p bis brown ('95) 1.25 2.00
4 A21 2a ultramarine .24 .28
a. "CHMABA" 550.00
5 A28 2a6p green ('95) 16.00 30.00
6 A22 3a brn org .60 .80
a. 3a orange 4.00 8.00
b. Inverted overprint
c. "CHMABA" 1,600.
7 A23 4a olive green .48 1.25
a. "CHMABA" 600.00
8 A25 8a red violet 1.65 3.25
a. "CHMABA" 1,200.
9 A26 12a vio, *red* ('90) 1.25 1.40
a. "CHMABA" 1,600.
b. 1st "T" of "STATE" invtd. 2,400.
10 A27 1r gray 22.00 40.00
a. "CHMABA" 3,000.
11 A29 1r car rose & grn ('95) 1.75 2.75
12 A30 2r brown & rose ('95) 45.00 72.50
13 A30 3r grn & brown ('95) 55.00 80.00
14 A30 5r vio & bl ('95) 65.00 87.50

Wmk. 38

15 A14 6a bister ('90) .65 1.00
Nos. 1-15 (15) 211.19 323.17

1900 Wmk. 39

15B A31 3p carmine rose .15 .15

1902-04

16 A31 3p gray ('04) .15 .15
a. Inverted overprint 45.00
17 A17 ¹/₂a light green .15 .15
18 A19 1a carmine rose .15 .15
19 A21 2a violet ('03) 6.25 7.75
Nos. 16-19 (4) 6.70 8.20

1903-05

20 A32 3p gray .15 .15
21 A33 ¹/₂a green .15 .15
22 A34 1a carmine rose .15 .15
23 A35 2a violet .22 .25
24 A37 3a brown org ('05) .55 .70
25 A38 4a olive green ('04) .60 .75
26 A39 6a bister ('05) .40 .48
27 A40 8a red violet ('04) .52 .60
28 A41 12a violet, *red* .70 .85
29 A42 1r car rose & grn ('05) 2.50 2.75
Nos. 20-29 (10) 5.94 6.83

1907

30 A44 ¹/₂a green .15 .15
31 A45 1a carmine rose .18 .22

1913-24

32 A46 3p gray .15 .15
33 A47 ¹/₂a green .15 .15
34 A48 1a carmine rose .15 .18
35 A48 1a dark brown ('22) .15 .15
36 A49 2a violet .80 .95
37 A51 3a brown orange .80 .95
38 A51 3a ultra ('24) 1.25 2.50
39 A52 4a olive green .25 .32
40 A53 6a bister .32 .38
41 A54 8a red violet .95 1.10
42 A55 12a claret .95 1.10
43 A56 1r green & red brown .80 .95
Nos. 32-43 (12) 6.72 8.88

India No. 104 Overprinted

1921

44 A48 9p on 1a rose .55 .60

India Stamps of 1913-26 Overprinted CHAMBA STATE

1922-27

45 A58 1¹/₂a chocolate 14.00 32.50
46 A59 1¹/₂a chocolate .38 .45
47 A59 1¹/₂a rose .38 .45
48 A57 2a6p ultramarine .60 .80
49 A57 2a6p brown orange .38 .45
Nos. 45-49 (5) 15.74 34.65

India Stamps of 1926 Overprinted CHAMBA STATE

1927-28 Wmk. 196

50 A46 3p slate .15 .15
51 A47 ¹/₂a green .15 .15
52 A48 1a dark brown .15 .15
53 A60 2a dull violet .16 .22
54 A51 3a ultramarine .65 1.25
55 A61 4a olive green .22 .32
57 A54 8a red violet .32 1.25
58 A55 12a claret 1.00 2.00

Overprinted **CHAMBA STATE**

59 A56 1r green & brown 2.00 3.25
Nos. 50-55,57-59 (9) 4.80 8.74

India Stamps of 1926-35 Overprinted CHAMBA STATE

1932-37

60 A71 ¹/₂a green .60 .65
61 A68 9p dark green .22 .26
62 A72 1a dark brown .35 .32
63 A69 1a3p violet .15 .16
64 A59 1¹/₂a carmine rose .16 .22
65 A49 2a vermilion .42 .55
a. Small die 47.50 85.00
66 A57 2a6p buff .20 .22
67 A51 3a carmine rose .65 1.65
68 A52 4a olive green ('36) 3.25 3.50
69 A53 6a bister ('37) 45.00 52.50
Nos. 60-69 (10) 51.00 60.03

Same Overprint on India Stamps of 1937

1938 Wmk. 196 *Perf. 13¹/₂x14*

70 A80 3p slate .60 1.25
71 A80 ¹/₂a brown .28 .32
72 A80 9p green .70 1.90
73 A80 1a carmine .70 .60

Overprinted CHAMBA STATE

74 A81 2a scarlet .38 1.50
75 A81 2a6p purple .28 2.50
76 A81 3a yellow green 3.00 5.50
77 A81 3a6p ultra 1.25 3.00
78 A81 4a dark brown 1.40 2.75
79 A81 6a peacock blue 6.25 10.00
80 A81 8a blue violet 1.25 3.00
81 A81 12a carmine lake 2.50 6.25

Overprinted **CHAMBA STATE**

82 A82 1r brown & slate 6.25 7.75
83 A82 2r dk brn & dk vio 15.00 25.00
84 A82 5r dp ultra & dk green 37.50 45.00
85 A82 10r rose car & dk violet 95.00 95.00
86 A82 15r dk grn & dk brown 140.00 190.00
87 A82 25r dk vio & bl vio 190.00 275.00
Nos. 70-87 (18) 502.34 676.32

India Nos. 151 and 153 Overprinted CHAMBA

1942

87B A80 ¹/₂a brown 3.50 4.25
88 A80 1a carmine 4.25 5.00

Same Overprint on India Stamps of 1941-42

1942-44

89 A83 3p slate .15 .15
90 A83 ¹/₂a rose violet ('43) .15 .15
91 A83 9p lt green ('43) .15 .15
92 A83 1a carmine rose ('43) .15 .15
93 A84 1¹/₂a dk purple ('44) .15 .15
94 A84 2a scarlet ('43) .15 .95
95 A84 3a violet ('43) .22 1.10
96 A84 3¹/₂a ultra ('43) .95 3.25
97 A85 4a chocolate ('43) .65 .95
98 A85 6a pck blue ('43) 1.90 4.75
99 A85 8a blue violet ('43) 2.50 6.50
100 A85 12a car lake ('43) 3.75 9.50
Nos. 89-100 (12) 10.87 27.75

India Nos. 162-167 Overprinted **CHAMBA**

1943 Wmk. 196 *Perf. 13¹/₂x14*

101 A82 1r brown & slate 15.00 15.00
102 A82 2r dk brown & dk vio 19.00 27.50
103 A82 5r dp ultra & dk grn 37.50 45.00
104 A82 10r rose car & dk vio 50.00 77.50
105 A82 15r dk grn & dk brn 140.00 190.00
106 A82 25r dk vio & bl vio 225.00 300.00
Nos. 101-106 (6) 486.50 655.00

India No. 161A Overprinted CHAMBA

1948

107 A81 14a rose violet 6.25 7.75

OFFICIAL STAMPS

SERVICE

Indian Stamps Overprinted in Black CHAMBA STATE

1886-98 Wmk. 39 *Perf. 14*

O1 A17 ¹/₂a green .50 .15
a. "CHMABA" 45.00 45.00
c. "SERV CE" 150.00
O2 A19 1a violet brown .15 .15
a. "CHMABA" 77.50 92.50
c. "SERV CE" 225.00
d. "SERVICE" double 125.00 125.00
O3 A21 2a ultra .22 .26
a. "CHMABA" 350.00 375.00
O4 A22 3a brown orange 1.50 1.25
a. 3a orange 12.50 16.00
b. "CHMABA" 625.00 725.00
O5 A23 4a olive green .65 .55
a. "CHMABA" 375.00 400.00
c. "SERV CE" 925.00
O6 A25 8a red violet .70 .55
a. "CHMABA" 1,100. 1,250.
O7 A26 12a vio, *red* ('90) 5.00 4.00
a. "CHMABA" 1,400.
b. 1st "T" of "STATE" invtd.
O8 A27 1r gray ('90) 5.25 4.50
a. "CHMABA" 1,250.
O9 A29 1r car rose & grn ('98) 5.25 5.25

Wmk. 38

O10 A14 6a bister 1.25 1.10
Nos. O1-O10 (10) 20.47 17.76

1902-04 Wmk. 39

O11 A31 3p gray ('04) .15 .15
O12 A17 ¹/₂a light green .15 .15
O13 A19 1a carmine rose .15 .15
O14 A21 2a violet 3.50 6.25
Nos. O11-O14 (4) 3.95 6.70

1903-05

O15 A32 3p gray .15 .15
O16 A33 ¹/₂a green .15 .15
O17 A34 1a carmine rose .15 .15
O18 A35 2a violet .18 .15
O19 A38 4a olive green ('05) .80 1.10
O20 A40 8a red violet ('05) .80 1.25
O21 A42 1r car rose & grn ('05) .80 1.50
Nos. O15-O21 (7) 3.03 4.45

1907

O22 A44 ¹/₂a green .32 .25
a. Inverted overprint 925.00
O23 A45 1a carmine rose .15 .60

1913

O24 A49 2a violet 7.50
O25 A52 4a olive green 13.00

India No. 63 Overprinted On CHAMBA STATE H. S M.

O26 A35 2a violet 75.00

No. O26 was never placed in use.

India Stamps of 1911-29 Overprinted:

CHAMBA STATE SERVICE
a

CHAMBA STATE SERVICE
b

1913-25

O27	A46 (a)	3p gray	.15	.15
O28	A47 (a)	1/2a green	.15	.15
O29	A48 (a)	1a carmine rose	.15	.15
O30	A48 (a)	1a dk brown ('25)	2.00	.60
O31	A49 (a)	2a violet ('14)	.15	.15
O32	A52 (a)	4a olive green	.18	.18
O33	A54 (a)	8a red violet	.25	.25
O34	A56 (b)	1r grn & red brn	.38	.38
		Nos. O27-O34 (8)	3.41	
		Set value		1.65

India No. O66 Overprinted

1921

O35	O6	9p on 1a rose	.25	.32

India Stamps of 1926-35 Overprinted CHAMBA STATE SERVICE

1927-39 **Wmk. 196**

O36	A46	3p slate	.15	.15
O37	A47	1/2a green	.15	.15
O38	A68	9p dark green ('32)	.28	.28
O39	A48	1a dark brown	.15	.15
O40	A69	1a3p violet ('32)	.22	.15
O41	A60	2a dull violet	.15	.18
O42	A61	4a olive green	.18	.21
O43	A54	8a red violet	.50	.60
O44	A55	12a claret	1.00	.60

Overprinted CHAMBA STATE SERVICE

O45	A56	1r green & brown	1.75	3.50
O45A	A56	2r brn org & car rose ('39)	8.75	
O45B	A56	5r dk vio & ultra ('39)	17.50	
O45C	A56	10r car & grn ('39)	32.50	
		Nos. O36-O45C (13)	63.28	

India Stamps of 1926-35 Overprinted CHAMBA STATE SERVICE

1935-36

O46	A71	1/2a green	.20	.24
O47	A72	1a dark brown	.15	.15
O48	A49	2a vermilion	.24	.24
a.		Small die	.24	.24
O49	A52	4a olive grn ('36)	1.10	1.25
		Nos. O46-O49 (4)	1.69	1.88

Same Overprint on India Stamps of 1937

1938 ***Perf. 13 1/2x14***

O50	A80	9p green	.75	.75
O51	A80	1a carmine	.75	.75

India Stamps of 1937 Overprinted CHAMBA STATE SERVICE

1940-41

O51A	A82	1r brn & sl ('41)	700.00	850.00
O52	A82	2r dk brn & dk vio	30.00	55.00
O53	A82	5r dp ultra & dk grn	55.00	85.00
O54	A82	10r rose car & dk vio	110.00	150.00

India Official Stamps of 1939-43 Overprinted CHAMBA

1941-46 **Wmk. 196**

O55	O8	3p slate ('44)	.20	.20
O56	O8	1/2a brown	3.25	3.00
O57	O8	1/2a dk rose vio ('44)	.20	.20
O58	O8	9p green	.20	.20
O59	O8	1a carmine rose	.20	.20
O60	O8	1a3p bister ('46)	30.00	12.00
O61	O8	1 1/2a dull pur ('46)	.85	.45
O62	O8	2a scarlet ('44)	1.25	1.25
O63	O8	2 1/2a purple ('44)	1.75	3.00
O64	O8	4a dark brown ('44)	3.00	4.75
O65	O8	8a blue vio ('41)	4.25	6.00
		Nos. O55-O65 (11)	45.15	31.25

India Nos. 162-165 Overprinted CHAMBA SERVICE

1944

O66	A82	1r brown & slate	22.50	25.00
O67	A82	2r dk brn & dk vio	30.00	32.50
O68	A82	5r dp ultra & dk grn	75.00	75.00
O69	A82	10r rose car & dk vio	105.00	120.00
		Nos. O66-O69 (4)	232.50	252.50

FARIDKOT

fe-'rēd-ˌkōt

LOCATION — A State of India lying northeast of Nabha in the central Punjab.
AREA — 638 sq. mi.
POP. — 164,364
CAPITAL — Faridkot

Previous stamp issues are listed under Feudatory States. Stamps of Faridkot were superseded by those of India in 1901.

The varieties with small letters in the overprint are not listed as the letters are merely broken and not from another font.

India Stamps Overprinted in Black FARIDKOT STATE

1887-93 **Wmk. 39** ***Perf. 14***

4	A17	1/2a green	.70	1.65
a.		"ARIDKOT"		
5	A19	1a violet brown	.42	.70
6	A21	2a ultramarine	.85	1.65
7	A22	3a orange	.85	1.65
8	A23	4a olive green	1.10	1.90
a.		"ARIDKOT"	250.00	
9	A25	8a red violet	1.50	3.25
a.		"ARIDKOT"	450.00	
10	A27	1r gray	27.50	42.50
a.		"ARIDKOT"	1,050.	
11	A29	1r car rose & grn ('93)	7.50	11.00

Wmk. 38

12	A14	6a bister	1.40	2.75
a.		"ARIDKOT"	250.00	
		Nos. 4-12 (9)	41.82	67.05

1900 **Wmk. Star. (39)**

13	A31	3p car rose	.52	1.10
14	A27	12a violet, *red*	22.50	52.50

OFFICIAL STAMPS

India Stamps Overprinted in Black SERVICE FARIDKOT STATE

1886 **Wmk. 39** ***Perf. 14***

O1	A17	1/2a green	.18	.45
a.		"SERV CE"	250.00	
O2	A19	1a violet brown	.25	.60
a.		"SERV CE"	275.00	
O3	A21	2a ultramarine	1.25	3.00
a.		"SERV CE"	350.00	
O4	A22	3a orange	1.25	3.50
O5	A23	4a olive green	1.75	3.50
a.		"SERV CE"	525.00	
O6	A25	8a red lilac	2.00	3.50
a.		"SERV CE"	600.00	
O7	A27	1r gray	22.50	30.00

Wmk. 38

O8	A14	6a bister	6.00	9.25
a.		"ARIDKOT"	275.00	
b.		"SERVIC"	425.00	
		Nos. O1-O8 (8)	35.18	53.80

1896 **Wmk. 39**

O9	A29	1r car rose & green	32.50	47.50

Obsolete March 31, 1901.

GWALIOR

'gwäl-ē-ˌó(ə)r

LOCATION — One of the Central Provinces of India
AREA — 26,008 sq. mi.
POP. — 4,006,159 (1941)
CAPITAL — Lashkar

The varieties with small letters in the overprint are not listed as the letters are merely broken and not from another font.

India Stamps Overprinted in Black गवालियर GWALIOR

Lines Spaced 16-17mm

1885 **Wmk. 39** ***Perf. 14***

1	A17	1/2a green	12.50	12.50
2	A19	1a violet brown	12.50	15.00
3	A20	1a6p bister brown	12.50	12.50
4	A21	2a ultramarine	12.50	9.25
5	A25	8a red lilac	25.00	
6	A27	1r gray	32.50	

Wmk. 38

7	A9	4a green	22.50	
8	A14	6a bister	22.50	
		Nos. 1-8 (8)	152.50	

The Hindi overprint measures 13 1/2-14x2mm and 15-15 1/2x2 1/2mm.

The two sizes are found in the same sheet in the proportion of one of the smaller to three of the larger.

The 1/2a, 1a, 2a, also exist with lines 13mm apart and the short Hindi overprint.

Reprints of the 1/2a and 1a have the 13mm spacing, the short Hindi overprint and usually carry the overprint "Specimen."

India Stamps Overprinted GWALIOR गवालियर

Red Overprint

1885 **Wmk. 39**

9	A17	1/2a green	.24	.32
10	A21	2a ultramarine	7.50	3.75
11	A27	1r gray	6.25	6.25

Wmk. 38

12	A9	4a green	8.00	8.00
		Nos. 9-12 (4)	21.99	18.32

Nos. 9-12 have been reprinted. They have the short Hindi overprint. Most copies bear the word "Reprint." Those without it cannot be distinguished from the originals.

Black Overprint

1885-91 **Wmk. 39**

13	A17	1/2a green	.15	.15
a.		"GWALICR"	75.00	80.00
b.		Double overprint	200.00	
14	A18	9p rose	24.00	35.00
15	A19	1a violet brown	.22	.15
16	A20	1a6p bister brown	.15	.15
17	A21	2a ultramarine	.30	.15
18	A22	3a orange	.30	.15
19	A23	4a olive green	.45	.30
20	A25	8a red violet	.60	.45
21	A26	12a violet, *red*	.60	.30
22	A27	1r gray	.75	.60

Wmk. 38

23	A14	6a bister	.48	.48
		Nos. 13-23 (11)	28.00	37.88

The Hindi overprint measures 13 1/2-14x2mm and 15-15 1/2x2 1/2mm as in the preceding issue.

1896 **Wmk. 39**

24	A28	2a6p green	3.25	3.50
a.		"GWALICR"	275.00	
25	A29	1r car rose & grn	6.00	6.75
a.		"GWALICR"	325.00	
26	A30	2r bis brn & rose	6.00	3.50
27	A30	3r green & brown	13.00	10.00
28	A30	5r violet & blue	17.50	7.50
		Nos. 24-28 (5)	45.75	31.25

The Hindi inscription varies from 13 to 15 1/2mm long.

1899

29	A31	3p carmine rose	.15	.15
a.		Inverted overprint	200.00	165.00

1901-04

30	A31	3p gray ('04)	4.25	11.00
31	A17	1/2a light green	.15	.15
32	A19	1a carmine rose	.15	.15
33	A21	2a violet	.20	.20
34	A28	2a6p ultra ('03)	.28	.28
		Nos. 30-34 (5)	5.03	11.78

1903-08

35	A32	3p gray	.15	.15
36	A33	1/2a green	.45	.15
37	A34	1a carmine rose	.25	.15
38	A35	2a violet	.55	.15
39	A36	2a6p ultra ('05)	.80	.60
40	A37	3a brown org ('04)	.95	.18
41	A38	4a olive green	.60	.18
42	A39	6a bister ('06)	.32	.32
43	A40	8a red violet	.95	.55
44	A41	12a vio, *red* ('05)	1.40	.60
45	A42	1r car rose & grn ('05)	.80	.60
46	A43	2r brown & rose	5.00	5.00
47	A43	3r grn & brn ('08)	16.00	22.50
48	A43	5r vio & bl ('08)	14.00	17.00
		Nos. 35-48 (14)	42.22	48.13

There are two settings of the overprint on Nos. 35, 37-46. In the first (1903), "GWALIOR" is 14mm long and lines are spaced 1 3/4mm. In the second (1908), "GWALIOR" is 13mm long and lines are 2 3/4mm apart. No. 36 exists only with first overprint, Nos. 47-48 only with second.

1907

49	A44	1/2a green	.95	.15
50	A45	1a carmine rose	.38	.25

No. 49 exists with both settings of overprint. See note below No. 48.

1912-23

51	A46	3p gray	.25	.15
52	A47	1/2a green	.25	.15
a.		Inverted overprint		
53	A48	1a car rose	.15	.15
a.		Double overprint	37.50	
54	A48	1a dk brown ('23)	.15	.15
55	A49	2a violet	.45	.15
56	A51	3a brown orange	.75	.15
57	A52	4a olive grn ('13)	.22	.15
58	A53	6a bister	.22	.18
59	A54	8a red vio ('13)	.80	.60
60	A55	12a claret ('14)	.38	.38
61	A56	1r green & red brn	.70	.70
62	A56	2r brn & car rose	4.75	1.10
63	A56	5r violet & ultra	16.00	3.50
		Nos. 51-63 (13)	25.07	7.51

India No. 104 Overprinted

1921

64	A48	9p on 1a rose	.15	.15
a.		Inverted overprint	50.00	

India Stamps of 1911-26 Overprinted GWALIOR गवालियर

Hindi Overprint 15mm Long

1923-27

66	A59	1 1/2a choc ('25)	.20	.20
67	A59	1 1/2a rose ('27)	.15	.15
a.		Inverted overprint	13.00	13.00
68	A57	2a6p ultra ('25)	.50	.50
69	A57	2a6p brown org ('27)	.20	.24
70	A51	3a ultra ('24)	.20	.20
		Nos. 66-70 (5)	1.25	1.29

Similar Ovpt. on India Stamps of 1926-35
Hindi Overprint 13 1/2mm Long

1928-32 **Wmk. 196**

71	A46	3p slate ('32)	.65	.15
72	A47	1/2a green ('30)	.15	.15
73	A48	1a dark brown	.15	.15
74	A60	2a dull violet	.15	.15
75	A51	3a ultramarine	.18	.15
76	A61	4a olive green	.22	.15
77	A54	8a red violet	.28	.18
78	A55	12a claret	.35	.35

Overprinted GWALIOR गवालियर

79	A56	1r green & brown	.42	.38
80	A56	2r brn org & car rose	1.00	.48
81	A56	5r dk vio & ultra ('29)	13.00	13.00
82	A56	10r car & grn ('30)	24.00	21.00
83	A56	15r olive green & ultra ('30)	47.50	47.50
84	A56	25r bl & ocher ('30)	70.00	77.50
		Nos. 71-84 (14)	157.05	160.29

India Stamps of 1932-35 Overprinted in Black GWALIOR गवालियर

Hindi Overprint 13 1/2mm Long

1933-36

85	A71	1/2a green ('36)	.15	.15
86	A68	9p dk green ('33)	.55	.30
87	A72	1a dk brown ('36)	.15	.15
88	A69	1a3p violet ('36)	.18	.15
89	A49	2a vermilion ('36)	.90	1.10
		Nos. 85-89 (5)	1.93	1.85

Same Ovpt. on India Stamps of 1937

90	A80	3p slate ('40)	1.40	.22
91	A80	1/2a brown	1.40	.15
92	A80	9p green ('40)	24.00	10.00
93	A80	1a carmine	1.75	.15
94	A81	3a yel green ('39)	2.00	2.00
95	A81	4a dark brown	15.00	5.00
96	A81	6a pck blue ('39)	2.00	2.00
		Nos. 90-96 (7)	47.55	19.52

Same Overprinted on India Stamps of 1941-43

100	A83	3p slate ('44)	.15	.15
101	A83	1/2a rose vio ('46)	.20	.15

102 A83 9p light green .15 .15
103 A83 1a car rose ('44) .22 .15
104 A84 1½a dk purple ('44) .45 .15
105 A84 2a scarlet ('44) .20 .15
106 A84 3a violet ('44) .26 .16
108 A85 4a choc ('44) .26 .15
109 A85 6a pck blue ('48) 7.50 7.50
110 A85 8a blue violet 3.25 3.75
111 A85 12a carmine lake 5.50 6.50

GWALIOR

India Nos. 162-167 Overprinted   गवालियर

Perf. 13½x14

112 A82 1r brn & slate ('45) 9.25 .60
113 A82 2r dk brn & dk vio ('49) 6.25 6.25
114 A82 5r dp ultra & dk grn ('49) 30.00 21.00
115 A82 10r rose car & dk vio ('49) 37.50 37.50
116 A82 15r dk grn & dk brn ('48) 87.50 77.50
117 A82 25r dk vio & blue vio ('48) 92.50 87.50
Nos. 100-106,108-117 (17) 281.14 249.31

India Stamps of 1941-43 Overprinted   GWALIOR गवालियर

1949
118 A83 3p slate .35 .35
119 A83 ½a rose violet .48 .48
120 A83 1a carmine rose .55 .55
121 A84 2a scarlet 2.25 2.25
122 A84 3a violet 11.00 7.50
123 A85 4a chocolate 2.25 1.50
124 A85 6a pck blue 19.00 25.00
125 A85 8a blue violet 47.50 45.00
126 A85 12a carmine lake 140.00 95.00
Nos. 118-126 (9) 223.38 177.63

OFFICIAL STAMPS

गवालियर

India Stamps Overprinted in Black   सरविस

1895   Wmk. 39   Perf. 14
O1 A17 ½a green .15 .15
  a. Double overprint 250.00
O2 A19 1a maroon .15 .15
O3 A21 2a ultramarine .16 .15
O4 A23 4a olive green .80 .80
O5 A25 8a red violet .42 .42
O6 A29 1r car rose & grn 2.00 2.00
Nos. O1-O6 (6) 3.68 3.67

Nos. O1 to O6 inclusive are known with the last two characters of the lower word transposed.

1901-04
O7 A31 3p gray ('04) 1.25 1.90
O8 A17 ½a light green .15 .15
O9 A19 1a carmine rose 1.10 .15
O10 A21 2a violet ('03) .60 1.25
Nos. O7-O10 (4) 3.10 3.45

1902
O11 A31 3p carmine rose .25 .25

1903-05
O12 A32 3p gray .15 .15
O13 A33 ½a green .20 .15
O14 A34 1a carmine rose .15 .15
O15 A35 2a violet .18 .15
O16 A38 4a olive grn ('05) .75 .60
O17 A40 8a red violet .50 .30
O18 A42 1r car rose & grn ('05) 1.75 .75
Nos. O12-O18 (7) 3.68
Set value 1.85

1907
O19 A44 ½a green .15 .15
O20 A45 1a carmine rose 1.10 .15
Set value

Two spacings of the overprint lines, 10mm and 8mm, are found on Nos. O12-O20.

1913
O21 A46 3p gray .15 .15
O22 A47 ½a green .15 .15
O23 A48 1a carmine rose .15 .15
  a. Double overprint 57.50
O24 A49 2a violet .15 .15
O25 A52 4a olive green .18 .15
O26 A54 8a red violet .35 .18
O27 A56 1r grn & red brn 3.50 3.50
Nos. O21-O27 (7) 4.63 4.43

India No. O66 Overprinted   गवालियर

1921
O28 O6 9p on 1a rose .15 .15

India No. 83 Overprinted   सरविस

1923
O29 A48 1a dark brown .15 .15

Similar Ovpt. on India Stamps of 1926-35
1927-35   Wmk. 196
O30 A46 3p slate .15 .15
O31 A47 ½a green .15 .15
O32 A48 1a dark brown .15 .15
O33 A60 2a dull violet .15 .15
O34 A61 4a olive green .15 .15
O35 A54 8a red violet .30 .15

गवालियर

Overprinted   सरविस

O36 A56 1r green & brown .40 .35
O37 A56 2r brn org & car rose ('35) 1.25 2.00
O38 A56 5r dk vio & ultra ('32) 12.00 24.00
O39 A56 10r car & grn ('32) 24.00 30.00
Nos. O30-O39 (10) 38.70 57.25

गवालियर

India Stamps of 1926-35 Overprinted   सरविस

1933-37   Perf. 13½x14, 14
O40 A71 ½a green ('36) .35 .25
O41 A68 9p dk green ('35) .15 .25
O42 A72 1a dk brown ('36) .20 .15
O43 A69 1a3p violet ('33) .50 .15
O44 A49 2a ver ('36) .15 .15
  a. Small die ('36) .15 .15
O45 A52 4a olive green ('37) .40 .20
Nos. O40-O45 (6) 1.75
Set value .94

For surcharge see No. O62.

Same Overprint on India Stamps
1938   Perf. 13½x14
O46 A80 ½a brown .75 .22
O47 A80 1a carmine .75 .15

गवालियर

India Nos. 162-165 Overprinted   सरविस

1945-48   Wmk. 196   Perf. 13½x14
O48 A82 1r brown & slate 1.25 1.25
O49 A82 2r dk brn & dk vio 12.00 17.00
O50 A82 5r dp ultra & dk grn ('46) 37.50 62.50
O51 A82 10r rose car & dk vio ('48) 60.00 110.00
Nos. O48-O51 (4) 110.75 190.75

India Official Stamps of 1939-43 Overprinted   गवालियर

1940-44   Wmk. 196   Perf. 13½x14
O52 O8 3p slate .15 .15
O53 O8 ½a brown 2.00 1.40
O54 O8 1½a dk rose vio ('43) .15 .15
O55 O8 9p green ('43) .15 .18
O56 O8 1a dark brown ('41) .15 .15
O57 O8 1a3p bister ('42) 2.50 1.00
O58 O10 1½a dull purple ('43) .70 .15
O59 O8 2a scarlet ('41) .45 .45
O60 O8 4a dark brown ('44) .45 .45
O61 O8 8a blue vio ('44) 1.00 1.00
Nos. O52-O61 (10) 7.40 4.78

Gwalior No. O43 with Additional Surcharge in Black   **1A ———— 1A**

1942
O62 A69 1a on 1a3p violet 6.25 1.90

JIND

'jind

(Jhind)

LOCATION — A State of India in the north Punjab.
AREA — 1,299 sq. mi.
POP. — 361,812 (1941)
CAPITAL — Sangrur

Previous stamp issues are listed under Feudatory States.
The varieties with small letters are not listed as the letters are merely broken and not from another font.

India Stamps Overprinted in Black   [JHIND STATE]

1885   Wmk. 39   Perf. 14
33 A17 ½a green .75 .75
  a. Overprint reading down 52.50 52.50
34 A19 1a violet brown 6.00 7.50
  a. Overprint reading down 275.00
35 A21 2a ultra 4.25 4.25
  a. Overprint reading down 150.00
36 A25 8a red lilac 130.00
  a. Overprint reading down 1,750.
37 A27 1r gray 130.00
  a. Overprint reading down 1,750.

Wmk. 38
38 A9 4a green 19.00 26.00
Nos. 33-38 (6) 290.00 38.50

On the reprints of Nos. 33 to 38 "Jhind" measures 8mm instead of 9mm and "State" 9mm instead of 9½mm.

India Stamps Overprinted in Red or Black   [JEEND STATE]

1885   Wmk. 39
39 A17 ½a green (R) 37.50
40 A19 1a violet brown 37.50
41 A21 2a ultra (R) 42.50
42 A25 8a red lilac 50.00
43 A27 1r gray (R) 57.50

Wmk. 38
44 A9 4a green (R) 45.00
Nos. 39-44 (6) 270.00

India Stamps Overprinted   [JHIND STATE]

Red Overprint
1886   Wmk. 39
45 A17 ½a green 10.50
  a. "JEIND" 225.00
46 A21 2a ultramarine 12.50
  a. "JEIND" 275.00
47 A27 1r gray 27.50
  a. "JEIND" 1,050.

Wmk. 38
48 A9 4a green 14.00
Nos. 45-48 (4) 64.50

Nos. 46, 47 and 48 were not placed in use.

Black Overprint
1886-98   Wmk. 39
49 A17 ½a green ('88) .15 .15
  a. Inverted overprint 150.00
50 A19 1a violet brown .15 .15
  a. "JEIND" 175.00
51 A20 1a6p bister brn ('97) .75 .75
52 A21 2a ultra .30 .24
53 A22 3a orange .24 .20
54 A23 4a olive green .35 .30
55 A25 8a red violet .60 .75
  a. "JEIND" 750.00
56 A26 12a vio, red ('97) .60 .75
57 A27 1r gray ('91) 6.00 8.75
58 A29 2r brn & car green ('98) 4.50 7.50
59 A30 2r brn & rose ('97) 110.00 135.00
60 A30 3r grn & brn ('97) 110.00 135.00
61 A30 5r vio & bl ('97) 180.00 225.00

Wmk. 38
62 A14 6a bister .90 1.00
Nos. 49-62 (14) 414.54 515.54

1900   Wmk. 39
63 A31 3p carmine rose .15 .15

1902-04
64 A31 3p gray ('04) .18 .20
65 A17 ½a light green .26 .30
66 A19 1a carmine rose .30 .35
Nos. 64-66 (3) .74 .85

1903-09
67 A32 3p gray .15 .15
  a. Double overprint
68 A33 ½a green .15 .15
69 A34 1a car rose ('09) .18 .15
  a. Double overprint
70 A35 2a violet ('06) .20 .15
70A A36 2a6p ultra ('09) .30 .35
71 A37 3a brown orange .24 .24
  a. Double overprint 87.50
72 A38 4a olive green .32 .35
73 A39 6a bister ('05) .42 .48
74 A40 8a red violet .42 .48
75 A41 12a vio, red ('05) .60 .75
76 A42 1r car rose & grn ('05) .75 .90
Nos. 67-76 (11) 3.73 4.15

1907
77 A44 ½a green .15 .15
78 A45 1a carmine rose .24 .15
Set value .33 .18

1913
80 A46 3p gray .15 .15
81 A47 ½a green .15 .15
82 A48 1a carmine rose .15 .15
83 A49 2a violet .24 .26
84 A51 3a brown orange .85 1.00
85 A53 6a bister 2.00 2.25
Nos. 80-85 (6) 3.54 3.96

India Stamps of 1911-26 Overprinted   [JIND STATE]

1913-14
88 A46 3p gray .15 .15
89 A47 ½a green .15 .15
90 A48 1a carmine rose .15 .15
91 A49 2a violet .15 .15
92 A51 3a brown orange .15 .15
93 A52 4a olive green .15 .18
94 A53 6a bister .18 .20
95 A54 8a red violet .24 .26
96 A55 12a claret .30 .35
97 A56 1r grn & red brn .48 .48
Set value 1.80 1.90

India No. 104 Overprinted
1921
98 A48 9p on 1a rose 2.00 2.25

India Stamps of 1913-19 Overprinted   [JIND STATE]

1922
99 A58 1½a chocolate .70 .80
100 A57 2a6p ultramarine .38 .45

Same Overprint on India Stamps of 1911-26
1924
101 A48 1a dark brown .15 .15
102 A59 1½a chocolate .38 .45
Set value .50

Same Overprint on India No. 87
1925
103 A51 3a ultramarine .20 .22

Same Overprint on India Stamps of 1911-26
1927
104 A59 1½a rose .15 .18
105 A57 2a6p brown orange .15 .18
106 A56 2r yel brn & car rose 5.25 6.25
107 A56 5r vio & ultra 24.00 27.50
Nos. 104-107 (4) 29.55 34.11

India Stamps of 1926-35 Overprinted   [JIND STATE]

1927-32   Wmk. 196
108 A46 3p slate .15 .15
109 A47 ½a green .15 .15
110 A68 9p dark green ('32) .32 .45
111 A48 1a dark brown .15 .15
112 A69 1a3p violet ('32) .26 .38
113 A59 1½a carmine rose .18 .22
114 A60 2a dull violet .15 .15
115 A57 2a6p buff .15 .15
116 A51 3a ultramarine .32 .38
117 A61 4a olive green .18 .22
118 A54 8a red violet 1.00 1.25
119 A55 12a claret .60 1.50

Overprinted **JIND STATE**

120 A56 1r green & brown .75 *1.90*
121 A56 2r buff & car rose 9.50 11.00
122 A56 5r dk vio & ultra 10.50 14.00
123 A56 10r car rose & grn 21.00 *27.50*
124 A56 15r ol grn & blue 37.50 *82.50*
125 A56 25r blue & ocher 52.50 *110.00*
Nos. 108-125 (18) 135.36 *252.05*

India Stamps of 1926-35 Overprinted **JIND STATE**

1934-37
126 A71 ½a green .15 .15
127 A72 1a dark brown .15 .15
128 A49 2a vermilion .15 .15
129 A51 3a carmine rose .15 .15
130 A70 3a6p deep blue ('37) .15 .15
131 A52 4a olive green .22 .22
132 A53 6a bister ('37) .22 .22
Set value .98 .82

Same Overprint on India Stamps of 1937

1937-38 Wmk. 196 ***Perf. 13½x14***
133 A80 3p slate ('38) .15 .18
134 A80 ½a brown ('38) .18 .22
135 A80 9p green .26 .22
136 A80 1a carmine .15 .15
137 A81 2a scarlet ('38) .15 .15
138 A81 2a6p purple ('38) .15 .15
139 A81 3a yel grn ('38) .18 .15
140 A81 3a6p ultra ('38) .22 .22
141 A81 4a dk brown ('38) .22 .22
142 A81 6a pck blue ('38) .32 .38
143 A81 8a blue vio ('38) .45 *1.10*
144 A81 12a car lake ('38) .65 *1.50*

Overprinted **JIND STATE**

1938
145 A82 1r brown & slate 5.25 5.50
146 A82 2r dk brn & dk violet 9.50 9.50
147 A82 5r dp ultra & dk green 26.00 30.00
148 A82 10r rose car & dk violet 55.00 55.00
149 A82 15r dk grn & dk brown 110.00 *190.00*
150 A82 25r dk vio & bl vio 120.00 *225.00*
Nos. 133-150 (18) 328.83 *519.64*

India Stamps of 1937 Overprinted **JIND**

1942-43 Wmk. 196 ***Perf. 13½x14***
155 A80 3p slate 2.75 2.75
156 A80 ½a brown 2.75 2.75
157 A80 9p green 2.75 2.75
158 A80 1a carmine 2.75 2.75
159 A82 1r brn & slate 3.00 8.25
160 A82 2r dk brn & dk violet 9.25 15.00
161 A82 5r dp ultra & dk green 37.50 62.50
162 A82 10r rose car & dk vio ('43) 62.50 100.00
163 A82 15r dk grn & dk brn ('43) 92.50 140.00
164 A82 25r dk vio & bl vio 140.00 225.00
Nos. 155-164 (10) 355.75 561.75

Same Overprint on India Stamps of 1941-43
165 A83 3p slate .30 .30
166 A83 ½a rose vio ('43) .15 .15
167 A83 9p light green .15 .15
168 A83 1a car rose ('43) .15 .15
169 A84 1a3p bister ('43) .45 .45
170 A84 1½a dark purple 1.90 1.90
171 A84 2a scarlet .18 .15
172 A84 3a violet ('43) 1.10 1.10
173 A84 3½a ultramarine .38 .38
174 A85 4a chocolate .38 .38
175 A85 6a peacock blue .45 .38
176 A85 8a blue violet 1.90 *2.25*
177 A85 12a carmine lake 4.50 *5.25*
Nos. 165-177 (13) 11.99 *12.99*

OFFICIAL STAMPS

India Stamps Overprinted in Black **JHIND STATE SERVICE**

1885 Wmk. 39 ***Perf. 14***
O1 A17 ½a green .15 .15
a. "JHIND STATE" reading down 52.50 32.50
O2 A19 1a violet brown .25 .18
a. "JHIND STATE" reading down 7.00 7.00
O3 A21 2a ultra 17.50 17.50
a. "JHIND STATE" reading down 275.00
Nos. O1-O3 (3) 17.90 17.83

The reprints may be distinguished by the same measurements as the reprints of the corresponding regular issue.

India Stamps Overprinted in Red or Black **SERVICE** **JEEND STATE**

1885
O4 A17 ½a green (R) 35.00
O5 A19 1a violet brown 35.00
O6 A21 2a ultra (R) 42.50
Nos. O4-O6 (3) 112.50

India Stamps Overprinted **SERVICE** **JHIND STATE**

1886

Red Overprint
O7 A17 ½a green 14.00
a. "JEIND" 190.00
b. "ERVICE"
O8 A21 2a ultramarine 14.00
a. "JEIND" 350.00
b. "ERVICE"

No. O8 was not placed in use.

1886-96

Black Overprint
O9 A17 ½a green ('88) .35 .22
O10 A19 1a violet brown 2.25 .22
a. "JEIND" 190.00
b. "ERVICE"
O11 A21 2a ultramarine .28 .22
O12 A23 4a olive green .65 .42
O13 A25 8a red violet 1.90 1.90
O14 A29 1r car rose & grn ('96) 5.50 *10.50*
Nos. O9-O14 (6) 10.93 *13.48*

1902
O15 A17 ½a light green .25 .22

1903-06
O16 A32 3p gray .15 .15
O17 A33 ½a green 1.25 .15
a. "HIND" 175.00
O18 A34 1a carmine rose 1.75 .15
a. "HIND" 175.00
O19 A35 2a violet .28 .15
O20 A38 4a olive green .60 .35
O21 A40 8a red violet 2.50 2.00
O22 A42 1r car rose & grn ('06) 2.75 2.50
Nos. O16-O22 (7) 9.28 5.45

1907
O23 A44 ½a green .20 .15
O24 A45 1a carmine rose .32 .15
Set value .15

Indian Stamps of 1911-26 Overprinted

JIND STATE SERVICE
a

JIND STATE SERVICE
b

1914-27
O25 A46(a) 3p gray .15 .15
O26 A47(a) ½a green .42 .15
O27 A48(a) 1a car rose .42 .15
O28 A49(a) 2a violet .22 .15
O29 A52(a) 4a olive green .22 .15
a. Double overprint
O30 A54(a) 8a red violet .42 .42
O31 A56(b) 1r grn & red brn .65 .42
O32 A56(b) 2r yel brn & car rose ('27) 7.75 *10.50*
O33 A56(b) 5r vio & ultra ('27) 19.00 21.00
Nos. O25-O33 (9) 29.25 33.09

India Nos. 83 and 89 Overprinted Type "a"

1924-27
O34 A48 1a dark brown .15 .15
O35 A53 6a bister ('27) .28 .32
Set value .37

India Stamps of 1926-35 Overprinted

JIND STATE SERVICE
c

1927-32
O36 A46 3p slate .15 .15
O37 A47 ½a green .15 .15
O38 A68 9p dark green ('32) .15 .15
O39 A48 1a dark brown .15 .15
O40 A69 1a3p violet ('32) .20 .22
O41 A60 2a dull violet .15 .15
O42 A61 4a olive green .15 .15
O43 A54 8a red violet .26 .26
O44 A55 12a claret .32 .40

Overprinted **JIND STATE SERVICE**
d

O45 A56 1r green & brown 1.75 1.90
O46 A56 2r buff & car rose 5.75 6.50
O47 A56 5r dk vio & ultra 12.00 13.00
O48 A56 10r car rose & grn 19.00 *26.00*
Nos. O36-O48 (13) 40.18 *49.18*

India Stamps of 1926-35 Overprinted Type "c"

1934-37
O49 A71 ½a green .25 .15
O50 A72 1a dark brown .15 .15
O51 A49 2a vermilion .15 .15
O52 A57 2a6p buff ('37) 1.10 1.10
O53 A52 4a olive green 1.25 1.25
O54 A53 6a bister ('37) 1.25 1.25
Nos. O49-O54 (6) 4.15 4.05

India Nos. 151-153 Overprinted Type "c"

1937-42 ***Perf. 13½x14***
O55 A80 ½a brown ('42) 15.00 .45
O56 A80 9p green .38 .15
O57 A80 1a carmine .42 .15

India Nos. 162-165 Overprinted Type "d"
O58 A82 1r brn & sl ('40) 10.00 11.00
O59 A82 2r dk brn & dk vio ('40) 22.50 *37.50*
O60 A82 5r dp ultra & dk grn ('40) 45.00 *67.50*
O61 A82 10r rose car & dk vio ('40) 67.50 *110.00*
Nos. O55-O61 (7) 160.80 226.75

India Official Stamps of 1939-43 Overprinted **JIND**

1940-43
O62 O8 3p slate .15 .15
O63 O8 ½a brown 2.50 1.25
O64 O8 ½a dk rose vio ('43) .24 .15
O65 O8 9p green .15 .15
O66 O8 1a car rose .15 .15
O67 O8 1½a dull pur ('43) .90 .75
O68 O8 2a scarlet .15 .15
O69 O8 2½a purple .24 .24
O70 O8 4a dark brown .24 .22
O71 O8 8a blue violet .90 .90

India Nos. 162-165 Overprinted **JIND SERVICE**

1942 Wmk. 196 ***Perf. 13½x14***
O72 A82 1r brown & slate 10.50 *12.00*
O73 A82 2r dk brn & dk violet 21.00 *20.00*
O74 A82 5r dp ultra & dk green 45.00 *60.00*
O75 A82 10r rose car & dk violet 75.00 *90.00*
Nos. O62-O75 (14) 157.12 *186.11*

NABHA

'näb–hə

LOCATION — A State of India in the eastern and southeastern Punjab
AREA — 966 sq. mi.
POP. — 340,044 (1941)
CAPITAL — Nabha

The varieties with small letters in the overprint are not listed as the letters are merely broken and not from another font.

Indian Stamps Overprinted in Black **NABHA STATE**

1885 Wmk. 39 ***Perf. 14***
1 A17 ½a green .45 .55
2 A19 1a violet brown 19.00 *30.00*
3 A21 2a ultramarine 9.50 11.00
4 A25 8a red lilac 150.00
5 A27 1r gray 150.00

Wmk. 38
6 A9 4a green 37.50 *45.00*

On the reprints "Nabha" and "State" each measure 9½mm. On the originals they measure 11 and 10mm respectively.

Indian Stamps Overprinted **NABHA STATE**

Red Overprint

1885 Wmk. 39
7 A17 ½a green .50 .52
8 A21 2a ultramarine .80 .85
9 A27 1r gray 60.00 *80.00*

Wmk. 38
10 A9 4a green 17.50 *32.50*

Black Overprint

1885-97 Wmk. 39
11 A17 ½a green .20 .15
12 A18 9p rose ('92) .60 .70
13 A19 1a violet brown .15 .15
14 A20 1a6p bister brn .48 .48
a. "ABHA" 150.00
15 A21 2a ultramarine .48 .40
16 A22 3a orange 1.50 1.50
17 A23 4a olive green .60 .40
18 A25 8a red lilac 1.50 1.50
19 A26 12a vio, *red* ('89) .95 1.25
20 A27 1r gray 10.00 *20.00*
21 A29 1r car rose & grn ('93) 1.75 2.00
a. "N BHA"
22 A30 2r brn & rose ('97) 65.00 *105.00*
23 A30 3r grn & brn ('97) 65.00 *105.00*
24 A30 5r vio & blk ('97) 77.50 *110.00*

Wmk. 38
25 A14 6a bister ('89) 1.75 2.00
Nos. 11-25 (15) 227.46 *350.53*

Nos. 7, 8, 9, 10, 13, and 18 have been reprinted. They usually bear the overprint "Specimen."

1900 Wmk. 39
26 A31 3p carmine rose .15 .15

1903-09
27 A32 3p gray .15 .15
28 A33 ½a green .24 .24
a. "NABH" 165.00
29 A34 1a car rose .42 .35
30 A35 2a violet .42 .42
30A A36 2a6p ultra 27.50 42.50
31 A37 3a brown orange .70 .70
32 A38 4a olive green .70 .70
33 A39 6a bister .90 .90
34 A40 8a red violet .70 .90
35 A41 12a violet, *red* 1.75 1.90
36 A42 1r car rose & grn 1.75 1.90
Nos. 27-36 (11) 35.23 50.66

1907
37 A44 ½a green .15 .15
38 A45 1a carmine rose .22 .15
Set value .32 .21

1913
40 A46 3p gray .15 .15
41 A47 ½a green .15 .15
42 A48 1a carmine rose .15 .15
43 A49 2a violet .15 .15
44 A51 3a brown orange .15 .15
45 A52 4a olive green .30 .30
46 A53 6a bister .18 .22
47 A54 8a red violet .30 .32
48 A55 12a claret .35 .42
49 A56 1r green & red brn 1.50 1.50
Nos. 40-49 (10) 3.38 3.51

1924
50 A48 1a dark brown .15 .15

India Stamps of 1926-35 Overprinted **NABHA STATE**

1927-32 Wmk. 196
51 A46 3p slate ('32) .15 .15
52 A47 ½a green .15 .15
53 A48 1a dark brown .15 .15
54 A60 2a dull violet ('32) .18 .18
55 A57 2a6p buff ('32) .22 .22
56 A51 3a blue ('30) .25 .25
57 A61 4a olive green ('32) .80 .80

Overprinted **NABHA STATE**

58 A56 2r brown org & car rose ('32) 5.75 *7.75*
59 A56 5r dk violet & ultra ('32) 24.00 *27.50*
Nos. 51-59 (9) 31.65 *37.15*

India Stamps of 1926-35 Overprinted **NABHA STATE**

1936-37
63 A71 ½a green .15 .15
64 A68 9p dark green ('37) .15 .15
65 A72 1a dark brown .15 .15
66 A69 1a3p violet ('37) .15 .15
67 A51 3a car rose ('37) .48 .55
68 A52 4a olive green ('37) .52 .60
Nos. 63-68 (6) 1.60 1.75

Same Overprint in Black on 1937 Stamps of India

1938-39 *Perf. 13½x14*
69 A80 3p slate 3.00 1.00
70 A80 ½a brown .42 .48
71 A80 9p green 12.00 8.75
72 A80 1a carmine .22 .25
73 A81 2a scarlet .18 .22
74 A81 2a6p purple .22 .25
75 A81 3a yel green .42 .60
76 A81 3a6p ultramarine .38 .48
77 A81 4a dark brown 1.10 *1.75*
78 A81 6a peacock blue 1.10 *2.50*
79 A81 8a blue violet 2.25 *3.00*
80 A81 12a car lake 2.75 *4.25*

Overprinted **NABHA STATE**

81 A82 1r brown & slate 4.50 *7.25*
82 A82 2r dk brn & dk violet 10.00 *18.00*
83 A82 5r dp ultra & dk green 37.50 *52.50*
84 A82 10r rose car & dk vio ('39) 67.50 *90.00*
85 A82 15r dk grn & dk brn ('39) 100.00 *175.00*
86 A82 25r dk vio & blue vio ('39) 110.00 *200.00*
Nos. 69-86 (18) 353.54 *566.28*

India Stamps of 1937 Overprinted in Black **NABHA**

1942 *Perf. 13½x14*
87 A80 3p slate 22.50 4.00
88 A80 ½a brown 42.50 17.50
89 A80 9p green 17.50 4.50
90 A80 1a carmine 17.50 2.50
Nos. 87-90 (4) 100.00 28.50

Same on India Nos. 168-179

1942-46 **Wmk. 196**
100 A83 3p slate .24 .24
101 A83 ½a rose vio ('43) .38 .38
102 A83 9p lt green ('43) .48 .48
103 A83 1a car rose ('46) .38 .38
104 A84 1a3p bister ('44) .38 .38
105 A84 1½a dark pur ('43) .48 .48
106 A84 2a scarlet ('44) .65 .65
107 A84 3a violet ('44) .95 .95
108 A84 3½a ultramarine 1.40 1.40
109 A85 4a choc ('43) 1.50 1.50
110 A85 6a pck blue ('44) 1.50 1.50
111 A85 8a blue vio ('44) 2.00 2.00
112 A85 12a car lake ('44) 3.75 3.75
Nos. 100-112 (13) 14.09 14.09

OFFICIAL STAMPS

Indian Stamps Overprinted in Black NABHA STATE SERVICE

1885 **Wmk. 39** *Perf. 14*
O1 A17 ½a green .60 .60
O2 A19 1a violet brown .42 .42
O3 A21 2a ultra 37.50 *57.50*
Nos. O1-O3 (3) 38.52 *58.52*

The reprints have the same measurements as the reprints of the regular issue of the same date.

Indian Stamps Overprinted SERVICE NABHA STATE

1885

Red Overprint
O4 A17 ½a green .70 .95
O5 A21 2a ultramarine .52 .55

1885-97

Black Overprint
O6 A17 ½a green .15 .15
a. Period after "SERVICE" 40.00 1.50
O7 A19 1a violet brown .20 .16
a. "NABHA STATE" double *165.00*
b. Period after "SERVICE" 4.50 1.75
O8 A21 2a ultra .40 .40
O9 A22 3a orange 5.00 *8.50*
O10 A23 4a olive green .45 .16
O11 A25 8a red vio ('89) .85 1.00
O12 A26 12a vio, *red* ('89) 4.00 4.25
O13 A27 1r gray ('89) 13.00 *24.00*
O14 A29 1r car rose & grn ('97) 12.00 *15.00*

Wmk. 38
O15 A14 6a bister ('89) 2.50 2.75
Nos. O6-O15 (10) 38.55 *56.37*

Nos. O4, O5, and O7 have been reprinted. They usually bear the overprint "Specimen."

1903-06 **Wmk. 39**
O16 A32 3p gray ('06) .20 .20
O17 A33 ½a green .15 .15
O18 A34 1a carmine rose .15 .15
O19 A35 2a violet .32 .32
O20 A38 4a olive green .32 .22
a. Double overprint
O21 A40 8a red violet .48 .42
O22 A42 1r car rose & grn .80 1.00
Nos. O16-O22 (7) 2.42 2.46

1907
O23 A44 ½a green .15 .15
O24 A45 1a carmine rose .15 .15
Set value .18 .18

1913
O25 A52 4a olive green 17.50
O26 A56 1r grn & red brn 92.50

Indian Stamps of 1911-26 Overprinted:

NABHA STATE SERVICE — a
NABHA STATE SERVICE — b

1913
O27 A46(a) 3p gray .15 .15
O28 A47(a) ½a green .15 .15
O29 A48(a) 1a carmine rose .15 .15
O30 A49(a) 2a violet .15 .15
O31 A52(a) 4a olive green .16 .16
O32 A54(a) 8a red violet .26 .26
O33 A56(b) 1r grn & red brn .52 .52
Set value 1.34 1.27

India Stamps of 1926-35 Overprinted **NABHA STATE SERVICE**

Perf. 13½x14, 14

1932-45 **Wmk. 196**
O34 A46 3p slate .15 .15
O35 A72 1a dark brown ('35) .15 .15
O36 A52 4a olive green ('45) 7.00 1.75
O37 A54 8a red violet ('37) .70 .80
Nos. O34-O37 (4) 8.00 2.85

Same Overprint in Black on India Stamps of 1937

1938
O38 A80 9p green 2.25 2.25
O39 A80 1a carmine .65 .65

Official Stamps of India 1939-43 Overprinted in Black **NABHA**

1942-44 *Perf. 13½x14*
O40 O8 3p slate .20 .20
O41 O8 ½a brown ('43) .20 .20
O42 O8 ½a dk rose vio ('44) 2.25 2.25
O43 O8 9p green ('43) .20 .20
O44 O8 1a car rose ('43) .20 .20
O45 O8 1½a dull purple ('43) .35 .35
O46 O8 2a scarlet ('43) .20 .20
O47 O8 4a dark brown ('43) 1.90 2.75
O48 O8 8a blue violet ('43) 1.90 2.75

India Nos. 162-164 Overprinted in Black **NABHA SERVICE**

O49 A82 1r brown & slate 18.00 *25.00*
O50 A82 2r dk brn & dk vio 50.00 *90.00*
O51 A82 5r dp ultra & dk green 120.00 *185.00*
Nos. O40-O51 (12) 195.40 *309.10*

PATIALA

ˌpət-ē-ˈäl-ə

LOCATION — A State of India in the central Punjab
AREA — 5,942 sq. mi.
POP. — 1,936,259 (1941)
CAPITAL — Patiala

The varieties with small letters in the overprint are not listed as the letters are merely broken and not from another font.

Indian Stamps Overprinted in Red PUTTIALLA STATE

1884 **Wmk. 39** *Perf. 14*
1 A17 ½a green .85 .90
a. Double ovpt., one horiz. 250.00 175.00
2 A19 1a violet brown 14.00 14.00
a. Double overprint
b. Double ovpt., one in black 350.00
c. Pair, one as "b," one without overprint
3 A21 2a ultra 5.25 5.75
4 A25 8a red lilac 125.00 *180.00*
a. Double ovpt., one in black 37.50
c. Overprint reversed
d. Pair like "a," one with overprint reversed
5 A27 1r gray 90.00 100.00

Wmk. 38
6 A9 4a green 14.00 16.00
Nos. 1-6 (6) 249.10 *316.65*

Indian Stamps Overprinted in Red **PUTTIALLA STATE**

1885 **Wmk. 39**
7 A17 ½a green .42 .35
a. "AUTTIALLA" 8.50
c. "STATE" only
8 A21 2a ultra .85 .45
a. "AUTTIALLA" 15.00
9 A27 1r gray 5.00 *10.50*
a. "AUTTIALLA" 170.00

Wmk. 38
10 A9 4a green 1.10 1.10
a. Double overprint, one in black 125.00
b. Pair, one as "a," one with black overprint

Same, Overprinted in Black

Wmk. 39
11 A19 1a violet brown .25 .25
a. "AUTTIALLA" 20.00
c. Double overprint, one in red 4.00
d. Pair, one as "c," one without overprint
12 A25 8a red lilac 4.50 4.50
a. "AUTTIALLA" 200.00
Nos. 7-12 (6) 12.12 *17.15*

Nos. 7-12 have been reprinted. Most of them bear the word "Reprint." The few copies that escaped the overprint cannot be distinguished from the originals.

The error "AUTTIALLA" has been reprinted in entire sheets, in red on the ½, 2, 4a and 1r and in black on the ½, 1, 2, 4, 8a and 1r. "STATE" is 7¾mm long, instead of 8½mm. Most copies are overprinted "Reprint."

Same, Overprinted in Black **PATIALA STATE**

1891-96
13 A17 ½a green .15 .15
14 A18 9p rose .25 .30
15 A19 1a violet brown .18 .15
a. "STATE" only 100.00 100.00
16 A20 1a6p bister brown .35 .40
17 A21 2a ultra .55 .16
18 A22 3a orange .28 .28
19 A23 4a olive grn ('96) .22 .18
a. "STATE" only 160.00 125.00
20 A25 8a red violet ('96) .55 .55
21 A26 12a violet, *red* .45 .55
22 A29 1r car rose & grn ('96) 4.25 *7.00*
23 A30 2r brn & rose ('95) 70.00
24 A30 3r grn & brn ('95) 90.00
25 A30 5r vio & bl ('95) 110.00

Wmk. 38
26 A14 6a bister .35 .30
Nos. 13-26 (14) 277.58

1899 **Wmk. 39**
27 A31 3p carmine rose .15 .15

1902
28 A17 ½a light green .15 .15
29 A19 1a carmine rose .15 .15

1903-06
31 A32 3p gray .15 .15
32 A33 ½a green .15 .15
33 A34 1a carmine rose .15 .15
34 A35 2a violet .16 .15
35 A37 3a brown orange .26 .24
36 A38 4a olive green ('06) .75 .40
37 A39 6a bister ('05) .55 .50
38 A40 8a red violet ('06) .45 .40
39 A41 12a vio, *red* ('06) 1.25 1.25
40 A42 1r car rose & grn ('05) .70 .75
Nos. 31-40 (10) 4.57 4.14

1908
41 A44 ½a green .15 .15
42 A45 1a carmine rose .15 .15
Set value .22 .22

1912-14
43 A46 3p gray .15 .15
44 A47 ½a green .15 .15
45 A48 1a carmine rose .15 .15
46 A49 2a violet .15 .15
47 A51 3a brown orange .26 .26
48 A52 4a olive green .26 .16
49 A53 6a bister .32 .32
50 A54 8a red violet .45 .26
51 A55 12a claret .65 .40
52 A56 1r green & red brn 2.50 2.50
Nos. 43-52 (10) 5.04 4.50

1922-26
53 A48 1a dk brown ('23) .22 .15
54 A58 1½a chocolate .28 .32
55 A51 3a ultra ('26) .22 .22
56 A56 2r yel brn & car rose ('26) 6.75 7.25
57 A56 5r vio & ultra ('26) 14.00 15.00
Nos. 53-57 (5) 21.47 22.94

India Stamps of 1926-35 Overprinted **PATIALA STATE**

1928-34 **Wmk. 196**
60 A46 3p slate .15 .15
61 A47 ½a green .15 .15
62 A68 9p dark green .15 .15
63 A48 1a dark brown .15 .15
64 A69 1a3p violet .15 .15
65 A60 2a dull violet .15 .15
66 A57 2a6p buff 1.50 1.50
67 A51 3a blue .90 .90
68 A61 4a olive green .30 .30
69 A54 8a red violet .40 .40

Overprinted **PATIALA STATE**

70 A56 1r green & brown 1.00 1.25
71 A56 2r buff & car rose 1.75 2.00
Nos. 60-71 (12) 6.75 7.25

India Stamps of 1926-35 Overprinted Like Nos. 60-69

1935-37 *Perf. 14*
75 A71 ½a green ('37) .15 .15
76 A72 1a dk brown ('36) .15 .15
77 A49 2a ver ('36) .15 .15
78 A51 3a car rose ('37) 1.50 1.50
79 A52 4a olive green .50 .50
Nos. 75-79 (5) 2.45 2.45

Same Overprint in Black on Stamps of India, 1937

1937-38 *Perf. 13½x14*
80 A80 3p slate ('38) 19.00 2.50
81 A80 ½a brown ('38) 4.00 .70
82 A80 9p green 2.00 .45
83 A80 1a carmine .32 .25
84 A81 2a scarlet ('38) .22 .25
85 A81 2a6p purple ('38) .25 .25
86 A81 3a yel green ('38) .25 .25
87 A81 3a6p ultra ('38) .38 .38
88 A81 4a dark brown ('38) .32 .32
89 A81 6a pck blue ('38) .40 .45
90 A81 8a blue violet ('38) 1.00 1.10
91 A81 12a car lake ('38) 1.00 1.10

Overprinted Like Nos. 70-71

1938
92 A82 1r brown & slate 8.50 8.50
93 A82 2r dk brn & dk violet 14.00 16.00
94 A82 5r dp ultra & dk green 25.00 *32.50*
95 A82 10r rose car & dk violet 42.50 *70.00*
96 A82 15r dk grn & dk brown 70.00 *130.00*
97 A82 25r dk vio & bl vio 100.00 *175.00*
Nos. 80-97 (18) 289.14 *440.00*

India Nos. 150-153 Overprinted in Black **PATIALA**

1942-43 *Perf. 13½x14*
98 A80 3p slate 12.00 1.50
99 A80 ½a brown ('43) 5.50 1.10
100 A80 9p green ('43) 57.50 3.75
101 A80 1a carmine 9.50 1.50
Nos. 98-101 (4) 84.50 7.85

India Stamps of 1941-43 with same Overprint in Black

1942-47 *Perf. 13½x14*
102 A83 3p slate .15 .15
103 A83 ½a rose violet ('43) .15 .15
104 A83 9p lt green ('43) .15 .15
a. Pair, one without overprint *2,400.*
105 A83 1a car rose ('46) .15 .15
106 A84 1a3p bister ('43) 1.65 1.65
107 A84 1½a dk purple ('43) .16 .15
108 A84 2a scarlet ('46) .24 .15
109 A84 3a violet ('46) .40 .40
110 A84 3½a ultra ('46) 2.75 *4.00*
111 A85 4a choc ('46) .40 .40
112 A85 6a pck blue ('46) .48 .48
113 A85 8a blue vio ('46) 2.50 3.25
114 A85 12a car lake ('45) 5.25 *10.00*

India No. 162 Overprinted in Black **PATIALA**

115 A82 1r brown & slate ('47) 8.00 *14.00*
Nos. 102-115 (14) 22.43 *35.08*

OFFICIAL STAMPS

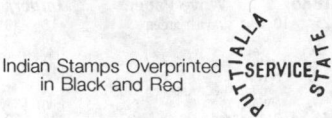

Indian Stamps Overprinted in Black and Red — PUTTIALLA SERVICE STATE

1884 Wmk. 39 *Perf. 14*

O1 A17 ½a green 3.00 .22
O2 A19 1a vio brown .45 .15
a. "SERVICE" double 300.00 175.00
b. "SERVICE" inverted 500.00
c. "PUTTIALLA STATE" double 65.00
d. "PUTTIALLA STATE" inverted 100.00 65.00
O3 A21 2a ultra *2,250.* 200.00

Same, Overprinted in Red or Black:

SERVICE — SERVICE

PUTTIALLA STATE (a) — PUTTIALLA STATE (b)

1885-90

O4 A17(a) ½a green (R & Bk) .55 .15
a. "AUTTIALLA" 45.00 15.00
d. "SERVICE" double 110.00
O5 A17(b) ½a green (Bk) .45 .15
O6 A19(a) 1a vio brn (Bk) .22 .15
a. "AUTTILLA" 150.00 37.50
c. "SERVICE" dble., one invtd. 275.00
d. "SERVICE" double 190.00 190.00
O7 A21(b) 2a ultra (R) .18 .15
c. "SERVICE" dbl., one invtd. 57.50
Nos. O4-O7 (4) 1.40
Set value .42

There are reprints of Nos. O4, O6 and O7. That of No. O4 has "SERVICE" overprinted in red in large letters and that of No. O6 has the same overprint in black. The originals have the word in small black letters. The reprints of No. O7, except those overprinted "Reprint," cannot be distinguished from the originals. These three reprints also exist with the error "AUTTIALLA."

Same, Overprinted in Black — SERVICE PATIALA STATE

1891-1900

O8 A17 ½a green ('95) .15 .15
b. "SERVICE" inverted 67.50
O9 A19 1a vio brown ('00) 2.25 .15
a. "SERVICE" inverted 72.50
O10 A21 2a ultramarine .95 .45
a. "SERVICE" inverted 72.50
O11 A22 3a orange .35 .24
O12 A23 4a olive green .18 .15
O13 A25 8a red violet .30 .22
O14 A26 12a violet, *red* .48 .32
O15 A27 1r gray .55 .32

Wmk. 38

O16 A14 6a bister .45 .38
Nos. O8-O16 (9) 5.66 2.38

1902 Wmk. 39

O17 A19 1a carmine rose .22 .15

1903

O18 A29 1r car rose & green 5.25 5.50

1903-09

O19 A32 3p gray .15 .15
O20 A33 ½a green .15 .15
O21 A34 1a carmine rose .15 .15
O22 A35 2a violet .15 .15
O23 A37 3a brown orange .75 .75
O24 A38 4a olive green ('05) .22 .15
O25 A40 8a red violet .30 .18
O26 A42 1r car rose & grn ('06) .85 .85
Nos. O19-O26 (8) 2.72 2.53

1907

O27 A44 ½a green .15 .15
O28 A45 1a carmine rose .15 .15
Set value .15 .15

India Stamps of 1911-26 Overprinted:

PATIALA STATE — PATIALA STATE

SERVICE (a) — SERVICE (b)

1913-26

O29 A46(a) 3p gray .15 .15
O30 A47(a) ½a green 1.10 .15
O31 A48(a) 1a car rose .15 .15
O32 A49(a) 2a violet .15 .15
O33 A52(a) 4a olive green .18 .15
O34 A54(a) 8a red violet .26 .18
O35 A56(b) 1r grn & red brn .55 .45
O36 A56(b) 2r yel brn & car rose ('26) 5.50 *9.25*
O37 A56(b) 5r vio & ultra ('26) 11.00 *22.50*
Nos. O29-O37 (9) 19.04 *33.13*

Same Overprint on India Nos. 83 and 89

1925-26

O38 A48(a) 1a dark brown .15 .15
O39 A53(a) 6a bister ('26) .22 .18
Set value .26

India Stamps of 1926-35 Overprinted — PATIALA STATE SERVICE

1927-36 Wmk. 196

O40 A46 3p slate .15 .15
O41 A47 ½a green .15 .15
O42 A48 1a dark brown .15 .15
O43 A69 1a3p violet .15 .15
O44 A60 2a dull violet .15 .15
O45 A60 2a vermilion .15 .15
O46 A57 2a6p buff .15 .15
O47 A61 4a olive green .15 .15
O48 A54 8a red violet .24 .24

Overprinted — PATIALA STATE SERVICE

O49 A56 1r green & brown .75 .32
O50 A56 2r brn org & car rose ('36) 3.00 3.25
Set value 4.50 4.25

India Stamps of 1926-34 Overprinted — PATIALA STATE SERVICE

1935-36

O51 A71 ½a green ('36) .15 .15
O52 A72 1a dark brown ('36) .15 .15
O53 A49 2a vermilion .28 .15
a. Small die .22 .15
O54 A52 4a olive green ('36) .30 .15
Set value .78 .28

Same Overprint on India #151-153

1938-39 *Perf. 13½x14*

O55 A80 ½a brown ('39) .60 .15
O56 A80 9p green ('39) 21.00 27.50
O57 A80 1a carmine .60 .15
Nos. O55-O57 (3) 22.20 27.80

India No. 136 Surcharged in Black — PATIALA STATE SERVICE 1A 1A

1939 *Perf. 14*

O58 A69 1a on 1a3p violet 2.00 .70

"SERVICE" measures 9¼mm.

No. 64 Surcharged in Black — 1A SERVICE 1A

1940

O59 A69 1a on 1a3p violet 2.00 1.40

"SERVICE" measures 8½mm.

India Nos. 162-164 Overprinted — PATIALA STATE SERVICE

Perf. 13½x14

O60 A82 1r brown & slate 2.75 2.75
O61 A82 2r dk brn & dk vio 14.00 14.00
O62 A82 5r dp ultra & dk grn 27.50 27.50

India Official Stamps of 1939-43 Overprinted — PATIALA

1940-45

O63 O8 3p slate ('41) .15 .15
O64 O8 ½a brown .15 .15
O65 O8 ½a dk rose vio ('43) .15 .15
O66 O8 9p green .15 .15
O67 O8 1a carmine rose .24 .15
O68 O8 1a3p bister ('41) .15 .15
O69 O8 1½a dull purple ('45) .42 .15
O70 O8 2a scarlet ('41) .15 .15
O71 O8 2½a purple ('41) .15 .15
O72 O8 4a dk brown ('45) .30 .30
O73 O8 8a blue violet ('45) .90 *1.25*

India Nos. 162-164 Overprinted in Black — PATIALA SERVICE

O74 A82 1r brn & slate ('43) 4.50 4.50
O75 A82 2r dk brn & dk vio ('45) 8.50 *12.00*
O76 A82 5r dp ultra & dk grn ('45) 15.00 *18.00*
Nos. O63-O76 (14) 30.91 *37.40*

NATIVE FEUDATORY STATES

NATIVE FEUDATORY STATES

These stamps had franking power solely in the states in which they were issued, except for Cochin and Travancore which had a reciprocal postal agreement.

ALWAR

'əl–wər

LOCATION — A Feudatory State of India, lying southwest of Delhi in the Jaipur Residency.
AREA — 3,158 sq. mi.
POP. — 749,751.
CAPITAL — Alwar

Katar (Indian Dagger) — A1

1877 Unwmk. Litho. *Rouletted*

1 A1 ¼a ultramarine 1.00 .75
a. ¼a blue 1.00 .75
b. Horiz. pair, imperf. vert. 32.50
2 A1 1a brown 1.00 1.00
a. 1a yellow brown 1.00 1.00
b. 1a red brown 1.00 1.00
c. Horiz. pair, imperf. vert. 55.00 55.00

Redrawn

1899-1901 *Pin-perf. 12*

3 A1 ¼a sl blue, wide margins 6.00 3.50
4 A1 ¼a yel grn, narrow margins ('01) 5.25 3.50
a. Horiz. pair, imperf. btwn. 265.00
b. ¼a emer, wide margins ('99) 500.00
c. ¼a emer, narrow margins 5.25 4.75

Nos. 3 and 4b are printed farther apart in the sheet.

On Nos. 3 and 4, the shading of the left border line is missing.

Nos. 1 to 4 occasionally show portions of the papermaker's watermark, W. T. & Co.

Alwar stamps became obsolete in 1902.

BAMRA

'bäm–rə

LOCATION — A Feudatory State in the Eastern States, Orissa States Agency, Bengal.
AREA — 1,988 sq. mi.
POP. — 151,259
CAPITAL — Deogarh

Stamps of Bamra were issued without gum.

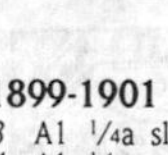

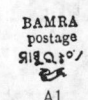

A1

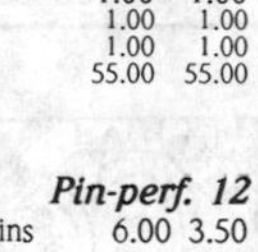

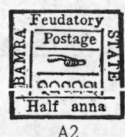

A2

1888 Unwmk. Typeset *Imperf.*

1 A1 ¼a black, *yellow* 80.00
a. "g" inverted *2,000.*
2 A1 ½a black, *rose* 52.50
a. "g" inverted *1,750.*
3 A1 1a black, *blue* 32.50
a. "g" inverted *1,350.*
b. "postge"
4 A1 2a black, *green* 45.00
a. "postge" *1,750.*
5 A1 4a black, *yellow* 32.50
a. "postge" *1,500.*
6 A1 8a black, *rose* 30.00
a. "postge" *1,350.*
Nos. 1-6 (6) 272.50

All values may be found with the scroll inverted, and with the long end of the scroll pointing to the right or left.

Nos. 1 and 2 have been reprinted in blocks of 8 and Nos. 1-6 in blocks of 20. In the reprints the 4th character of the native inscription often has the curved upper line broken at the left, but in many instances comparison with photographic reproductions of the original settings is the only certain test.

1890

7 A2 ¼a black, *rose lilac* 1.00 1.00
a. "Quatrer" 10.00 10.00
b. "e" of "Postage" inverted 10.00 10.00
c. "Eeudatory" 10.00 10.00
8 A2 ½a black, *green* 1.40 1.40
a. "Eeudatory" 16.00 16.00
b. "postage" with small "p" 1.40 1.40
c. First "a" of "anna" inverted 14.00
9 A2 1a black, *yellow* 3.25 3.25
a. "Eeudatory" 35.00 40.00
b. "postage" with small "p" 2.00 2.00
c. "annas" 65.00 65.00
10 A2 2a black, *rose lilac* 4.75 4.75
a. "Eeudatory" 60.00 67.50
11 A2 4a black, *rose lilac* 36.00 36.00
a. "Eeudatory" 150.00 150.00
12 A2 8a black, *rose lilac* 10.00 10.00
a. "BAMBA" 100.00 100.00
b. "Foudatory" & "Postage" 100.00 100.00
c. "postage" with small "p" 10.00 10.00
13 A2 1r black, *rose lilac* 32.50 32.50
a. "BAMBA" 135.00 135.00
b. "Eeudatory" 150.00 150.00
c. "postage" with small "p" 32.50 32.50
Nos. 7-13 (7) 88.90 88.90

1893

14 A2 ¼a black, *rose* .90 .90
a. "postage" with small "p" .90 .90
15 A2 ¼a black, *magenta* .90 .90
a. "postage" with small "p" .90 .90
b. "AM" of "BAMRA" invtd.
c. "M" OF "BAMRA" invtd.
d. "AMRA" of "BAMRA" inverted 22.50
e. "M" and 2nd "A" of "BAMRA" inverted 52.50 52.50
f. First "a" of "anna" inverted 27.50 27.50
16 A2 2a black, *rose* 1.40 1.40
a. "postage" with small "p" 1.40 1.40
17 A2 4a black, *rose* 3.25 3.25
a. "postage" with small "p" 3.25 3.25
b. "BAMBA" 210.00 210.00
18 A2 8a black, *rose* 5.00 5.00
a. "postage" with small "p" 5.00 5.00
19 A2 1r black, *rose* 18.00 20.00
a. "postage" with small "p" 30.00 30.00
Nos. 14-19 (6) 29.45 31.45

The central ornament varies in size and may be found in various positions.

Bamra stamps became obsolete Dec. 31, 1894.

BARWANI

bər–'wän–ē

LOCATION — A Feudatory State of Central India, in the Malwa Agency.
AREA — 1,178 sq. mi.
POP. — 141,110
CAPITAL — Barwani

The stamps of Barwani were all typographed and normally issued in booklets containing panes of four. Exceptions are noted (Nos. 14-15, 20-25). The majority were completely perforated, but some of the earlier printings were perforated only between the stamps, leaving one or two sides imperf. Nos. 1-25 were issued without gum. Many shades exist.

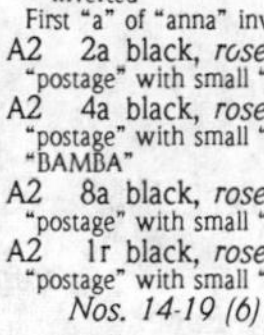

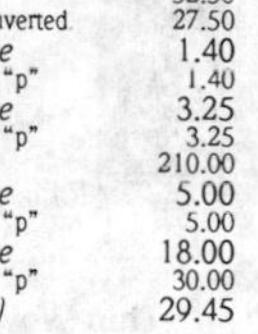

Rana Ranjit Singh
A1 A2

1921, April (?) Unwmk. *Pin-Perf 7*
Toned Medium Wove Paper
Clear Impression

1 A1 ¼a dull Prus green 65.00 *100.00*
2 A1 ½a dull blue 105.00 *150.00*

1921 *Coarse Perf. 7 x Imperf.*
White Thin Wove Paper
Blurred Impression

3 A1 ¼a dull green 12.00 21.00
4 A1 ½a pale blue 12.00 18.00

1921 **Toned Laid Paper** *Imperf.*
5 A1 1/4a light green 7.25
6 A1 1/2a light green 3.00
a. Perf. 11, top or bottom only 5.50

1921 *Coarse Perf. 7, 7 x Imperf.*
Thick Wove Paper
Very Blurred Impression
7 A1 1/4a dull blue 5.00
8 A1 1/2a dull green 13.00

In 1927 #7-8 were printed on thin hard paper.

1922 *Perf. 7 x Imperf.*
Thick Glazed Paper
9 A1 1/4a dull ultra 1.75
Rough Perf. 11 x Imperf.
10 A2 1a vermilion 1.65
11 A2 2a violet 2.00 *4.00*
a. Double impression *200.00*
Nos. 9-11 (3) 5.40

Shades of No. 11 include purple. No. 11 was also printed on thick dark toned paper.

1923-26 *Perf.*
Wove, Laid Paper
12 A1 1/4a grayish ultra, perf. 8 1/2 1.50
13 A1 1/4a black, perf. 7 x imperf. 27.50 *35.00*
14 A1 1/4a dull rose, perf. 11 1/2-12 1.25
15 A1 1/4a dk bl, perf. 11 ('26) 1.50
16 A1 1/2a grn, perf. 11ximperf. 1.10
Nos. 12-16 (5) 32.85

No. 12 was also printed on pale gray thin toned paper.
No. 14 was printed on horizontally laid paper in horizontal sheets of 12 containing three panes of 4.
No. 15 was printed on vertically laid paper in horizontal sheets of 8.

Rana Ranjit Singh — A3

1927-28 *Perf. 7*
Thin Wove Paper
17 A3 4a dull orange 35.00

No. 17 was also printed in light brown on thick paper, pin-perf. 6, and in orange brown on thick paper, rough perf. 7.

1928 *Coarse Perf. 7*
Thick Glazed Paper
18 A1 1/4a bright blue 1.75
19 A1 1/2a bright yel green 1.75

1928, Nov. ***Rough Perf. 10 1/2***
20 A1 1/4a deep ultra 1.25
a. Tête bêche pair 6.50
21 A1 1/2a yellow green 1.75
a. Tête bêche pair 10.00

1929-31 *Perf. 11*
22 A1 1/4a blue .90 1.25
a. 1/4a ultramarine .90 1.25
23 A1 1/2a emerald green .90 1.25
24 A2 1a car pink ('31) 5.00
25 A3 4a salmon 25.00
Nos. 22-25 (4) 31.80

Nos. 20-25 were printed in sheets of 8 (4x2).
No. 22 had five printings in various shades (bright to deep blue) in horizontal or vertical format.
No. 23 also printed in dark myrtle green.

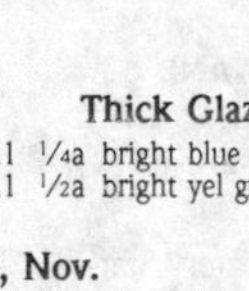
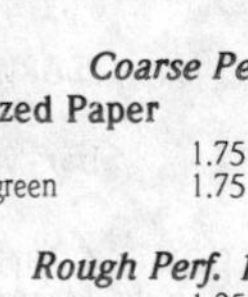
Rana Devi Singh
A4 A5

1932-48 *Perf. 11, 12*
Glazed Paper
26 A4 1/4a dark gray 1.40 4.25
27 A4 1/2a blue green 1.40 1.75
28 A4 1a brown 1.50 3.00
a. 1a chocolate, perf. 8 1/2 ('48) 7.50
29 A4 2a deep red violet 2.75 5.50
a. Perf. 12x11
b. 2a red lilac 12.50
30 A4 4a olive green 8.50 12.50
Nos. 26-30 (5) 15.55 27.00

Types of 1921-27
1934-48 *Perf. 11*
31 A1 1/4a slate gray 1.10 2.75
32 A1 1/2a green 2.25 3.75
33 A2 1a dark brown 2.00 3.75
a. 1a brown, perf. 8 1/2 ('48) 6.00
34 A2 2a brt purple ('38) 42.50
35 A2 2a rose car ('46) 20.00
36 A3 4a olive green 8.50 10.00
Nos. 31-36 (6) 76.35

In the nine printings of Nos. 26-36, several plate settings spaced the cliches from 2 to 9mm apart. Hence the stamps come in different overall sizes. Not all values were in each printing. Values are for the commonest varieties.
No. 36 was also printed in pale sage green.

1938
37 A5 1a dark brown 12.50
a. Booklet pane of 4 50.00

Stamps of type A5 in red are revenues.
Barwani stamps became obsolete July 1, 1948.

BHOPAL

bō-'päl

LOCATION — A Feudatory State of Central India, in the Bhopal Agency.
AREA — 6,924 sq. mi.
POP. — 995,745
CAPITAL — Bhopal

Inscription in Urdu in an octagon embossed on Nos. 1-83, in a circle embossed on Nos. 84-90. On designs A1-A3, A7, A11-A12, A14-A15, A19-A21 the embossing makes up the central part of the design.
The embossing may be found with inverted or sideways.

Expect irregular perfs on the perforated stamps, Nos. 19-77, due to a combination of imperfect perforating methods and the fragility of the papers.
Nos. 1-90 issued without gum.

A1

A2

Double Lined Frame
1876 **Unwmk.** **Litho.** *Imperf.*
1 A1 1/4a black 300.00 300.00
a. "EGAM" 1,750. 1,750.
b. "BFGAM" 1,500. 1,500.
c. "BEGAN" 1,000. 1,000.
2 A1 1/2a red 17.50 17.50
a. "EGAM" 100.00 100.00
b. "BFGAM" 65.00 75.00
c. "BEGAN" 100.00 100.00

Single Lined Frame
1877
3 A2 1/4a black *3,500.*
a. "NWAB"
4 A2 1/2a red 6.75 7.50
a. "NWAB" 30.00 37.50

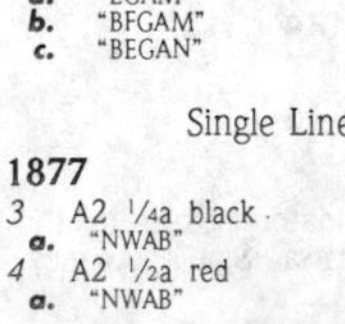
A3
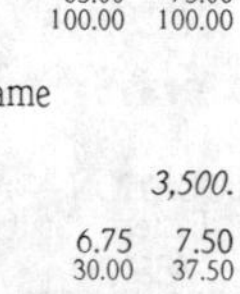
A4

1878
5 A3 1/4a black .42 .42
a. "J" diagonal, plate II .42 .42

All stamps of type A3 are lettered "EEGAM" for "BEGAM."

1878
6 A4 1/2a pale red 2.00 2.00
a. 1/2a brown red 7.25 7.25
b. "NWAB" 10.50 10.50
c. "JAHN" 10.50 10.50
d. "EECAM" 10.50 10.50

A5

A6

1879-80
7 A5 1/4a green 4.00 5.00
8 A5 1/2a red 4.00 13.00
Perf.
9 A5 1/4a green 2.00 2.00
10 A5 1/2a red 2.00 2.00
Nos. 7-10 (4) 12.00 22.00

Nos. 7 and 9 have the value in parenthesis; Nos. 8 and 10 are without parenthesis.

1881 *Imperf.*
11 A6 1/4a green 1.75
a. "NAWA" 12.00
b. "CHAH" 12.00
Perf.
12 A6 1/4a green 2.00 2.00
a. "NAWA" 13.00 13.00
b. "CHAH" 13.00 13.00

A7

1881-89 *Imperf.*
13 A7 1/4a black .35 .90
a. "NWAB" 3.00
14 A7 1/2a red .60 1.40
a. "NWAB" 4.75
15 A7 1a brown .60 1.40
a. "NWAB" 4.75
16 A7 2a blue .75 1.50
a. "NWAB" 5.50
17 A7 4a yellow 4.50 4.75
a. "NWAB" 16.00
Nos. 13-17 (5) 6.80 9.95

A8

A9

1884 *Perf.*
19 A8 1/4a green 110.00 135.00
a. "JAN" 195.00
b. "BEGM" 325.00
c. "NWAB" 550.00
d. "SHAHAN" 550.00
e. "JN" 375.00
f. "JAHA" 250.00
20 A9 1/4a green 2.25
a. "ANAWAB" 16.00

On type A9 there is a dash at the left of "JA" of "JAHAN" instead of a character like a comma as on types A5 and A6.
Imitations of No. 19 were printed about 1904 in black on wove paper and in red on laid paper, both imperf. and pin-perf.

A10

1884 **Laid Paper** *Imperf.*
21 A10 1/4a blue green 25.00 25.00
a. "NWAB" 75.00
b. "NAWAJANAN" 150.00
c. "SAH" 75.00
22 A10 1/2a black .40 .50
a. "NWAB" 2.00
b. "NAWAJANAN" 4.00
c. "SAH" 2.00
Perf.
23 A10 1/4a blue green .28 .32
a. "NWAB" 1.40
b. "NAWAJANAN" 2.75
c. "SAH" 1.40
24 A10 1/2a black .18 .25
a. "NWAB" .80
b. "NAWAJANAN" 1.65
c. "SAH" .80
Nos. 21-24 (4) 25.86 26.07

Type Redrawn
1886 **Wove Paper** *Imperf.*
25 A10 1/4a grayish green .18 .20
a. 1/4a green .18 .20
b. "NWAB" 1.40
c. "NAWA" 1.40
d. "NAWAA" 1.40
e. "NAWABABEGAAM" 2.75
f. "NWABA" 1.40
26 A10 1/2a red .28 .30
a. "SAH" 1.40
b. "NAWABA" 1.40
Perf.
27 A10 1/4a green .18 .32
a. "NWAB" 1.65
b. "NAWA" 1.65
c. "NAWAA" 1.65
d. "NAWABABEGAAM" 2.25
e. "NWABA" 2.25
28 A10 1/2a red 2.50 2.50
a. "SAH" 12.00
b. "NAWABA" 12.00
Nos. 25-28 (4) 3.14 3.32

On Nos. 25-28 the inscriptions are closer to the value than on Nos. 21-24.

A11

A12

1886 *Imperf.*
29 A11 1/2a red .75 1.10
a. "BEGAM" 4.50
b. "NWAB" 4.50
Laid Paper
30 A12 4a yellow 3.25
a. "EEGAM" 16.00
b. Wove paper 6.50
c. As "a," wove paper *500.00*
Perf.
31 A12 4a yellow 1.50
a. "EEGAM" 7.50
Nos. 29-31 (3) 5.50

A13

A14

1889 **Wove Paper** *Imperf.*
32 A13 1/4a green .30 .30
a. "SAH" 3.00
b. "NAWA" 3.00
33 A14 1/4a black 1.10 1.25
a. "EEGAN" 7.25
Perf.
34 A13 1/4a green .32 .32
a. "SAH" 3.25
b. "NAWA" 3.25
c. Imperf. vertically
35 A14 1/4a black .75 .75
a. "EEGAN" 5.00
b. Horiz. pair, imperf. between
Nos. 32-35 (4) 2.47 2.62

Type A13 has smaller letters in the upper corners than Type A10.

A15

A16

1890 *Imperf.*
36 A15 1/4a black .35 .35
37 A15 1a brown .75 .85
a. "EEGAM" 5.75
b. "BBGAM" 5.75
38 A7 2a greenish blue 1.10 .75
a. "BBEGAM" 8.00
b. "NAWAH" 8.00

39 A7 4a yellow 1.10 1.10
40 A16 8a blue 18.00 18.00
a. "HAH" 42.50
b. "JABAN" 42.50
Nos. 36-40 (5) 21.30 21.05

An imperf. imitation of Nos. 36 and 41 was printed about 1904 in black on wove paper.

Perf.

41 A15 1/4a black .75 .75
a. Pair, imperf. between 7.50
42 A15 1a brown .90 1.10
a. "EECAM" 7.50
b. "BBGAM" 7.50
43 A7 2a greenish blue 1.25 1.50
a. "BBEGAM" 12.50
b. "NAWAH" 12.50
44 A7 4a yellow 1.90 1.90
45 A16 8a blue 20.00 20.00
a. "HAH" 47.50
b. "JABAN" 47.50
Nos. 41-45 (5) 24.80 25.25

Nos. 40 and 45 have a frame line around each stamp.

Imperf

46 A12 1/2a red (BECAM) .90 1.10
47 A13 1/2a red (NWAB) .75 .60
a. Inverted "N"
b. "SAH" 7.50

Perf.

48 A12 1/2a red (BECAM) .55 .60
a. Without embossing
49 A13 1/2a red (NWAB) .75 .85
a. Inverted "N"
b. "SAH" 7.50
Nos. 46-49 (4) 2.95 3.15

1891-93 Laid Paper *Imperf.*

50 A16 8a deep green 18.00 18.00
a. "HAH" 42.50 42.50
b. "JABAN" 42.50 42.50

Perf.

51 A16 8a deep green 18.00 18.00
a. "HAH" 42.50 42.50
b. "JABAN" 42.50 42.50

For overprint, see No. 83.

1894 Redrawn *Imperf.*

53 A10 1/4a green .42 .42
a. "NAWAH" 5.00
54 A11 1/2a brick red 2.00 2.25
55 A16 8a blue black 13.00 13.00
a. Laid paper 27.50

Perf.

56 A10 1/4a green .42 .42
a. "NAWAH" 5.00
57 A11 1/2a brick red 2.00 2.25
58 A16 8a blue black 15.00 15.00
Nos. 53-58 (6) 32.84 33.34

The 1/4a redrawn has letters in corners larger; value in very small characters.

The 8a redrawn has no frame to each stamp but a frame to the sheet.

1898 *Imperf.*

60 A16 8a black 18.00 18.00
b. "E" of "BEGAM" inverted 42.50

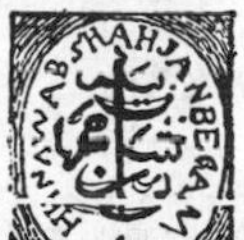
A17

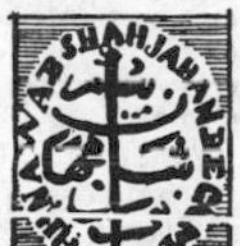
A18

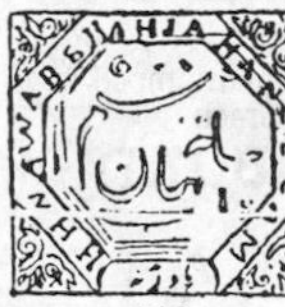
A19

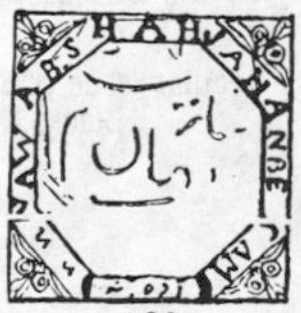
A20

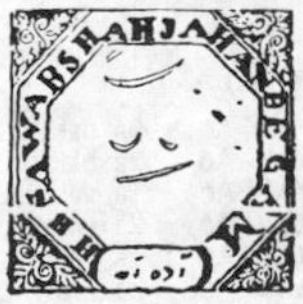
A21

1895

Laid Paper

61 A17 1/4a green 1.50 1.50
62 A18 1/4a red 1.75 1.75
63 A19 1/4a black .75 .75
a. "NAWB" 4.25 4.25
64 A20 1/2a black .75 .75
65 A21 1/2a red .90 1.10

Perf.

66 A17 1/4a green 3.25 3.25
67 A18 1/4a red 1.65 1.65
68 A19 1/4a black 2.50 2.50
a. "NAWB" 18.00
69 A20 1/2a black 1.65 1.65
70 A21 1/2a red
Nos. 61-69 (9) 14.70 14.90

Imperf. imitations of Nos. 65 and 70 were printed about 1904 in deep red on laid paper and in black on wove paper.

Wove Paper

Small Pin-perf.

71 A16 8a blue black

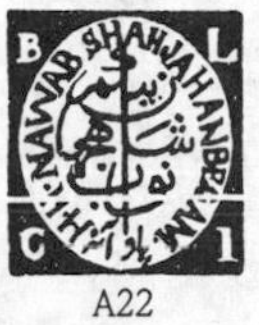
A22

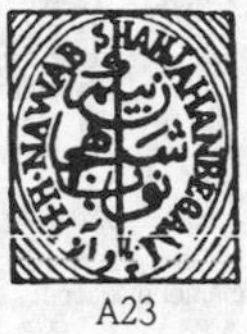
A23

1898 *Imperf.*

72 A22 1/4a black .32 .32
a. "SHAN" 3.25 3.25
73 A22 1/4a green .32 .32
a. "SHAN" 3.25 3.25
74 A23 1/4a black 1.50 .50
Nos. 72-74 (3) 2.14 1.14

1899

75 A13 1/2a black ("NWAB") .60 .60
a. "SHN" 6.00
b. "NWASBAHJAHNJ" 6.00
c. "SIIAN"
d. "SBAH" 6.00
e. "SBAN" 6.00
f. "NWIB" 6.00
g. "BEIAM" 6.00

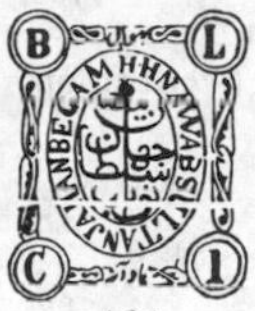
A24

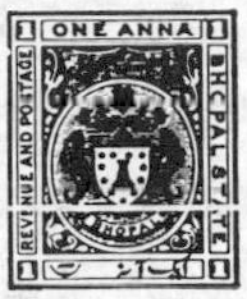
Coat of Arms — A25

1902

76 A24 1/4a red 1.75 1.75
77 A24 1/2a black 2.00 2.00
a. Printed on both sides 365.00
78 A24 1a brown 2.00 2.00
79 A24 2a blue 6.00 7.50
80 A24 4a orange 27.50 32.50
81 A24 8a violet 35.00 45.00
82 A24 1r rose 60.00 75.00
Nos. 76-82 (7) 134.25 165.75

No. 50 Overprinted in Red س

1903

83 A16 8a deep green 20.00 20.00
a. Inverted overprint 47.50 47.50

There are two types of the overprint which is the Arabic S, initial of the Begum.

Inscription in Circle
Embossed on Each Stamp

1903

84 A24 1/4a red .35 .35
85 A24 1/2a black .45 .45
86 A24 1a brown .55 .55
87 A24 2a blue 1.50 1.50
88 A24 4a orange 16.00 16.00
89 A24 8a violet 27.50 35.00
90 A24 1r rose 35.00 47.50
Nos. 84-90 (7) 81.35 101.35

The embossing in a circle, which was first used in 1903, has been applied to many early stamps and impressions from redrawn plates of early issues. So far as is now known, these should be classed as reprints.

1908 Engr. *Perf. 13 1/2*

99 A25 1a yellow green 3.00 .60
a. Printed on both sides 120.00

OFFICIAL STAMPS

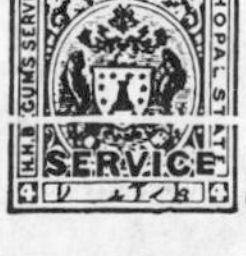
O1

Size: 20 1/2x25mm

Overprinted **SERVICE**

1908 Unwmk. Engr. *Perf. 13 1/2*

O1 O1 1/2a yellow green 1.75 .15
a. Pair, one without ovpt. 120.00
b. Inverted overprint 80.00
c. Double ovpt., one invtd. 80.00
O2 O1 1a carmine 1.75 .15
a. Inverted overprint 60.00
O3 O1 2a blue 10.50 .15
O4 O1 4a red brown 7.50 .15
Nos. O1-O4 (4) 21.50
Set value .27

Overprinted **SERVICE**

O5 O1 1/2a yellow green 2.50 .15
O6 O1 1a carmine 6.00 .90
O7 O1 2a blue 3.00 .20
a. Inverted overprint 35.00
O8 O1 4a red brown 45.00 .20
a. Inverted overprint 27.50
Nos. O5-O8 (4) 56.50 1.45

The difference in the two overprints is in the shape of the letters, most noticeable in the "R."

Type of 1908 Issue
Size: 25 1/2x30 1/2mm

Overprinted **SERVICE**

1930-31 Litho. *Perf. 14*

O9 O1 1/2a gray green ('31) 1.10 .70
O10 O1 1a carmine 1.25 .15
O11 O1 2a blue 1.50 .15
O12 O1 4a brown 1.75 .42
Nos. O9-O12 (4) 5.60 1.42

1/2a, 2a, 4a are inscribed "POSTAGE" on the left side; 1a "POSTAGE AND REVENUE."

Similar to Type O1
Size: 21x25mm
"POSTAGE" at left
"BHOPAL STATE" at right

1932-33 *Perf. 11 1/2, 13, 13 1/2, 14*

O13 O1 1/4a orange yellow 1.65 .15
a. Pair, one without overprint 65.00
b. Perf. 13 1/2 5.25 2.75
c. Perf. 14 8.00 .15

"BHOPAL GOVT." at right

Perf. 13 1/2

O14 O1 1/2a yellow green 1.25 .15
O15 O1 1a brown red 2.00 .15
O16 O1 2a blue 2.25 .15
O17 O1 4a brown 2.75 .50
Nos. O13-O17 (5) 9.90
Set value .86

No. O14, O16-O17 Surcharged in Red, Violet, Black or Blue:

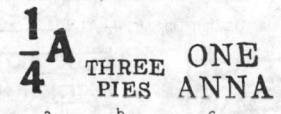

1/4 A (a) THREE PIES (b) ONE ANNA (c)

1935-36 *Perf. 13 1/2*

O18 O1(a) 1/4a on 1/2a (R) 3.50 1.75
a. Inverted surcharge 125.00 60.00
O19 O1(b) 3p on 1/2a (R) .48 .24
O20 O1(a) 1/4a on 2a (R) 3.50 1.75
a. Inverted surcharge 75.00 60.00
O21 O1(b) 3p on 2a (R) .48 .48
a. Inverted surcharge 45.00 35.00
O22 O1(a) 1/4a on 4a (R) 135.00 35.00
O23 O1(a) 1/4a on 4a (Bk) ('36) 14.00 10.50
O24 O1(b) 3p on 4a (R) 35.00 18.00
O25 O1(b) 3p on 4a (Bk) ('36) 1.75 1.10
O26 O1(c) 1a on 1/2a (V) .35 .35
a. Inverted surcharge 40.00 40.00
O27 O1(c) 1a on 2a (R) .35 .28
a. Inverted surcharge 40.00 40.00
O28 O1(c) 1a on 2a (Bk) ('36) .60 .28
O29 O1(c) 1a on 4a (Bl) .40 .28
Nos. O18-O29 (12) 195.41 70.01

Nos. O18-O25 are arranged in composite sheets of 100. The 2 top horizontal rows of each value are surcharged "a" and the next 5 rows as "b." The next 3 rows as "b" but in a narrower setting.

Various errors of spelling or inverted letters are found on Nos. O18-O29.

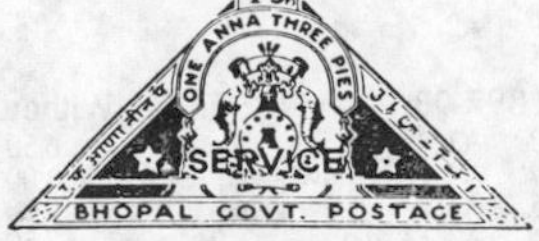
Arms of Bhopal O2

1935 Litho.

O30 O2 1a3p claret & blue .24 .20
a. Overprint omitted 45.00 45.00

Inscribed: "Bhopal State Postage"
Ovptd. "SERVICE" 11mm long

1937 *Perf. 12*

O31 O2 1a6p dk claret & blue .28 .24
a. Overprint omitted 60.00 60.00

See Nos. O42, O45.

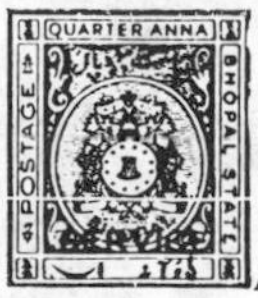
Arms of Bhopal — O3

Brown or Black Overprint

1936-38 Typo.

O32 O3 1/4a orange (B) .60 .15
a. Black overprint 12.00 12.00
c. Inverted overprint 65.00 65.00
d. As "a," inverted 85.00 85.00
O32B O3 1/4a yellow (Br) ('38) 1.25 .15
O33 O3 1a carmine .90 .15
Nos. O32-O34 (4) 2.90
Set value .31

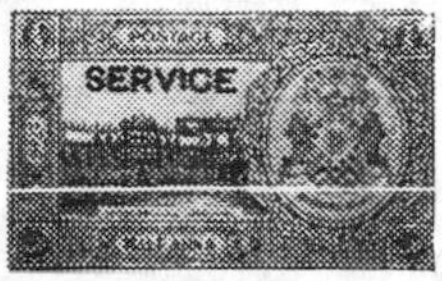
Moti Mahal — O4

Overprinted "SERVICE"

1936 *Perf. 11 1/2*

O34 O4 1/2a green & chocolate .15 .15
a. Double impression of stamp 24.00 9.00

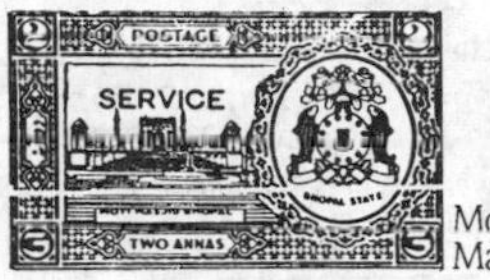
Moti Masjid — O5

Design: 4a, Taj Mahal and Be-Nazir Palaces.

Overprinted "SERVICE"

1937 *Perf. 11 1/2*

O35 O5 2a dk blue & brown .18 .15
a. Inverted overprint 60.00 60.00
O36 O5 4a bister brn & blue .55 .30

Types of 1937
Overprinted "SERVICE" in Black or Brown

1938-44

Designs: 4a, Taj Mahal. 8a, Ahmadabad Palace. 1r, Rait-Ghat.

O37 O4 1/2a dp green & brown .15 .15
O38 O5 2a violet & dp grn .15 .15
O39 O5 4a red brn & brt bl 1.25 .35
O40 O5 8a red vio & blue .75 .35
a. "SERAICE" 120.00 120.00
b. Overprint omitted 65.00 65.00
c. Double overprint 65.00 65.00
O41 O5 1r bl & red vio (Br) 1.25 .60
a. Black overprint ('44) 12.00 9.00
b. "SREVICE" 75.00 85.00
c. Overprint omitted
d. Double overprint 55.00 55.00
Nos. O37-O41 (5) 3.55 1.60

#O39 measures 36 1/2x22 1/2mm, #O40 39x24mm, #O41 45 1/2x27 3/4mm.

Type of 1935

1939 *Perf. 12*

O42 O2 1a6p dark claret .45 .25

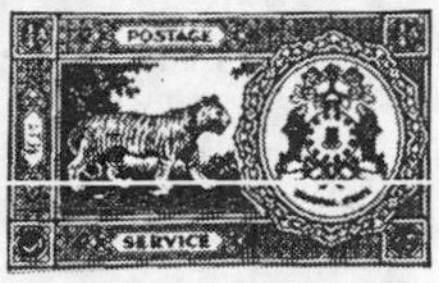
Tiger — O6

Design: 1a, Deer.

1940 Typo. *Perf. 11 1/2*

O43 O6 1/4a ultramarine 1.25 .24
O44 O6 1a red violet 3.25 .48

Type of 1935
Inscribed: "Bhopal State Postage"

1941

O45 O2 1a3p emerald .24 .15

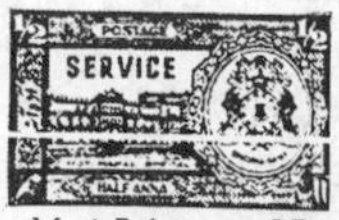

Moti Palace — O7

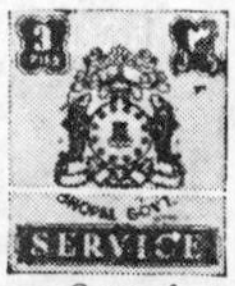

Coat of Arms — O8

Designs: 2a, Moti Mosque. 4a, Be-Nazir Palaces.

Perf. 11 1/2, 12

1944-46 Unwmk. Typo.

O46	O8	3p ultramarine	.15	.15
O47	O7	1/2a light green	.24	.15
O48	O8	9p orange brn ('46)	1.75	.48
a.		Imperf., pair		60.00
O49	O8	1a brt red vio ('45)	.60	.15
O50	O8	1 1/2a deep plum	.24	.15
O51	O7	2a red violet ('45)	.42	.32
O52	O8	3a yellow ('46)	.60	.60
a.		Imperf., pair		60.00
O53	O7	4a brown ('45)	.75	.48
O54	O8	6a brt rose ('46)	4.75	7.50
a.		Imperf., pair		75.00
		Nos. O46-O54 (9)	9.50	9.98

For surcharges, see Nos. O58-O59.

1946-47 Unwmk. *Perf. 11 1/2*

O55	O8	1a violet	.35	.20
O56	O7	2a violet ('47)	1.75	.60
O57	O8	3a deep orange	24.00	24.00
a.		Imperf., pair		
		Nos. O55-O57 (3)	26.10	24.80

No. O50 Surcharged "2 As." and Bars

1949 *Perf. 12*

O58	O8	2a on 1 1/2a dp plum	.75	.60
a.		Inverted surcharge		
b.		Double surcharge		
c.		Imperf., pair	77.50	77.50

Same Surcharged "2 As." and Rosettes

1949 *Perf. 12, Imperf.*

O59	O8	2a on 1 1/2a dp plum	225.00	225.00

Three or more types of "2" in surcharge. Bhopal stamps became obsolete in 1950.

BHOR

'bō(ə)r

LOCATION — A Feudatory State in the Kolhapur Residency and Deccan States Agency.
AREA — 910 sq. mi.
POP. — 141,546
CAPITAL — Bhor

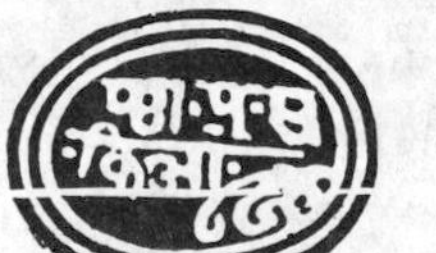

A1

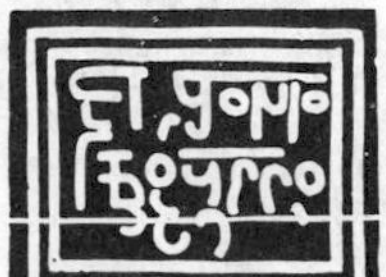

A2

Handstamped

1879 Unwmk. *Imperf.*

Without Gum

1	A1	1/2a carmine	1.75	2.00
2	A2	1a carmine	1.75	2.00

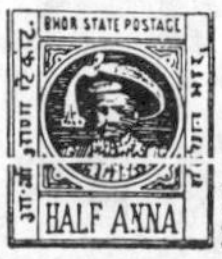

Pant Sachiv Shankarrao — A3

1901 Typo.

Without Gum

3	A3	1/2a red	5.50	*27.50*

BIJAWAR

bi-'jä-wər

LOCATION — A Feudatory State in the Bundelkhand Agency of Central India.
AREA — 973 sq. mi.
POP. — 115,852
CAPITAL — Bijawar

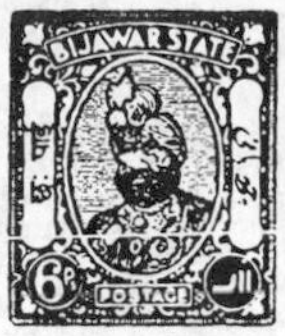

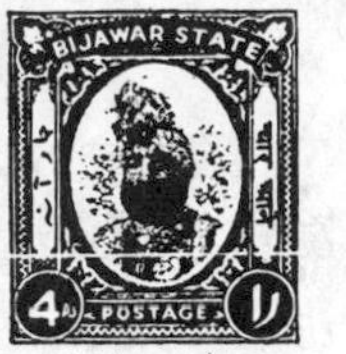

Maharaja Sir Sawant Singh
A1 A2

1935-36 Typo. Unwmk. *Perf. 10 1/2*

1	A1	3p brown	2.50	1.50
a.		Imperf., pair	7.00	
b.		Rouletted 7 ('36)	.95	2.00
2	A1	6p carmine	2.25	1.50
a.		Rouletted 7 ('36)	2.25	2.50
3	A1	9p purple	2.25	1.50
a.		Rouletted 7 ('36)	4.00	4.00
4	A1	1a dark blue	2.75	1.75
a.		Rouletted 7 ('36)	4.25	4.25
5	A1	2a slate green	2.75	2.00
a.		Rouletted 7 ('36)	4.25	7.50

1937 *Perf. 9*

6	A2	4a red orange	4.75	*7.00*
7	A2	6a yellow	4.75	*14.00*
8	A2	8a emerald	5.25	*16.00*
9	A2	12a turquoise blue	5.75	*14.00*
10	A2	1r purple	25.00	*35.00*
a.		"1Rs" instead of "1R"	45.00	*67.50*
		Nos. 1-10 (10)	58.00	*94.25*

Bijawar stamps became obsolete in 1939.

BUNDI

'bün-dē

LOCATION — A Feudatory State in the Rajputana Agency of India.
AREA — 2,220 sq. mi.
POP. — 216,722
CAPITAL — Bundi

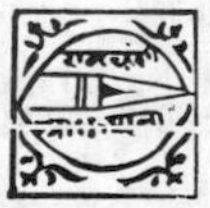

Katar (Indian Dagger) — A1

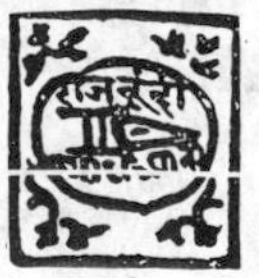

A2

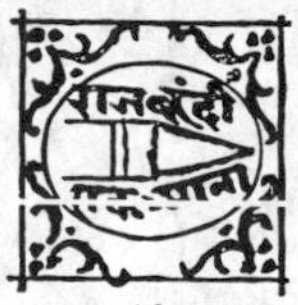

A3

Laid Paper

1894 Unwmk. Litho. *Imperf.*

Without Gum

Gutters between Stamps

1	A1	1/2a slate	2,750.	*2,000.*

Redrawn; Blade Does Not Touch Oval

No Gutters between Stamps

Wove Paper

1A	A1	1/2a slate	15.00	13.00
b.		Value above, name below	180.00	180.00
c.		Top right ornament omitted	500.00	500.00

On No. 1A, the dagger is thinner and its point does not touch the oval inner frame.

1896

Laid Paper

Without Gum

2	A2	1/2a slate	5.00	5.25

1897-98 Without Gum

3	A3	1a red	6.50	6.00
4	A3	2a yellow green	8.00	10.00
5	A3	4a yellow green	17.00	18.00
6	A3	8a red	32.50	40.00
7	A3	1r yellow, *blue*	50.00	52.50
		Nos. 3-7 (5)	114.00	126.50

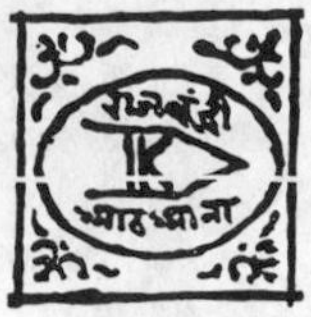

A4

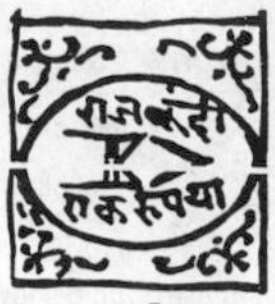

A5

Redrawn; Blade Wider and Diamond-shaped

1898-1900 Without Gum

8	A3	1/2a slate	.40	.40
9	A3	1a red	.75	.60
10	A3	2a emerald	4.50	4.50
a.		1st 2 characters of value omitted	300.00	300.00
11	A3	4a emer (value above)	8.00	8.00
12	A4	8a red	8.00	9.50
13	A5	1r yellow, *blue*	5.00	10.00
a.		Wove paper	8.50	8.50
		Nos. 8-13 (6)	26.65	33.00

On Nos. 9-10, the blade is wider and nearly diamond-shaped.

Point of Dagger to Left

14	A3	4a green	5.00	5.00

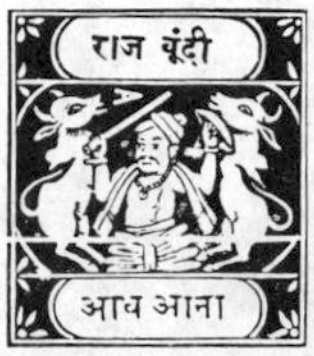

Maharao Rajah with Symbols of Spiritual and Temporal Power — A6

Rouletted 11 to 13 in Color

1915 Typo.

Without Gum

"Bundi" in 3 Characters (word at top right)

15	A6	1/4a blue	.60	.60
a.		Laid paper	7.25	6.25
16	A6	1/2a black	.85	.85
17	A6	1a vermilion	1.10	1.10
a.		Laid paper	9.25	9.25
18	A6	2a emerald	1.25	1.25
19	A6	2 1/2a yellow	3.50	4.25
20	A6	3a brown	2.00	4.25
21	A6	4a yel green	4.25	4.25
23	A6	6a ultramarine	8.50	*21.00*
a.		6a deep blue	8.50	
24	A6	8a orange	6.25	6.25
25	A6	10a olive	7.75	7.75
26	A6	12a dark green	11.50	11.50
27	A6	1r violet	27.50	*35.00*
28	A6	2r car brn & blk	35.00	*42.50*
29	A6	3r blue & brown	85.00	*130.00*
30	A6	4r pale grn & red brown	235.00	*250.00*
31	A6	5r ver & pale grn	250.00	*340.00*

Minor differences in lettering in top and bottom panels may be divided into 8 types, but not all values come in each type. In one sub-type the top appears as one word. Nos. 30-31 have an ornamental frame around the design.
For overprints see Nos. O1-O39.

1941 *Perf. 11*

"Bundi" in 4 Characters (word at top right)

32	A6	1/4a light blue	4.50	4.50
33	A6	1/2a black	37.50	37.50
34	A6	1a carmine	17.50	27.50
35	A6	2a yellow green	32.50	
		Nos. 32-35 (4)	92.00	69.50

The 4-character spelling of "Bundi" is found also on stamps rouletted in color: on 1/2a and 4a in small characters, and on 1/4a, 1/2a, 1a, 4a, 4r and 5r in large characters like those on Nos. 32-35.
For overprints see Nos. O41-O48.

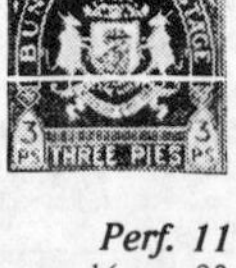

Arms of Bundi — A7

1941-45 Typo. *Perf. 11*

36	A7	3p bright ultra	.16	.30
37	A7	6p indigo	.28	.50
38	A7	1a red orange	.50	*1.00*
39	A7	2a fawn	4.75	*8.00*
a.		2a brown ('45)	4.75	*10.50*
40	A7	4a brt yel green	5.25	*12.00*
41	A7	8a dull green	9.00	*19.00*
42	A7	1r royal blue	11.00	*30.00*
		Nos. 36-42 (7)	30.94	*70.80*

The 1st printing of Nos. 36-42 was gummed. All later printings were without gum. **Values are for copies without gum.**

For overprints see Nos. O49-O55.

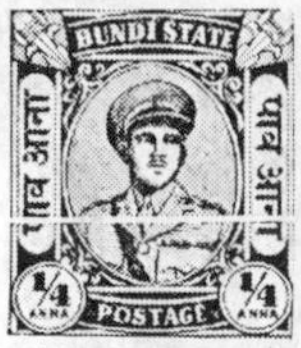

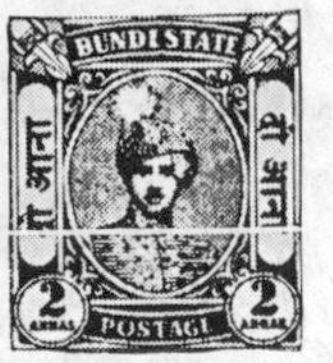

Maj. Maharao Rajah Bahadur Singh
A8 A9

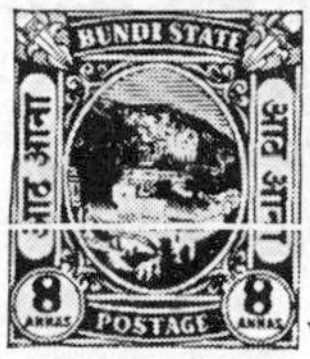

View of Bundi — A10

1947 *Perf. 11*

43	A8	1/4a deep green	.28
44	A8	1/2a purple	.28
45	A8	1a yellow green	.28
46	A9	2a red	.50
47	A9	4a deep orange	1.50
48	A10	8a violet blue	2.50
49	A10	1r chocolate	5.50
		Nos. 43-49 (7)	10.84

For overprints see Rajasthan Nos. 1-14.

OFFICIAL STAMPS

Regular Issue of 1915 Handstamped in Black, Red or Green

बूंदी

a

सरविस

Rouletted 11 to 13 in Color

1918 Unwmk.

Without Gum

O1	A6	1/4a dark blue	.45
O2	A6	1/2a black	2.50
O3	A6	1a vermilion	1.10
O4	A6	2a emerald	2.50
O5	A6	2 1/2a yellow	3.00
O6	A6	3a brown	3.00
O7	A6	4a yel green	6.00
O8	A6	6a blue	4.75
O9	A6	8a orange	9.00
O10	A6	10a olive green	9.00
O11	A6	12a dark green	11.00
O12	A6	1r violet	15.00
O13	A6	2r car brn & blk	90.00
O14	A6	3r blue & brown	150.00
O15	A6	4r pale grn & red brn	275.00
O16	A6	5r ver & pale grn	275.00
		Nos. O1-O16 (16)	857.30

All values come with black handstamp and most exist in red. The overprint is found in various positions, double, inverted, etc.
Several denominations exist in two or more types. See notes following Nos. 31 and 35.

Regular Issue of 1915 Handstamped in Black, Red or Green

BUNDI

b

SERVICE

1919 Without Gum

O17	A6	1/4a dark blue	1.50
O18	A6	1/2a black	3.00
O19	A6	1a vermilion	3.50
O20	A6	2a emerald	6.00
O21	A6	2 1/2a yellow	15.00
O22	A6	3a brown	21.00
O23	A6	4a yel green	15.00
O24	A6	6a blue	15.00
O25	A6	8a orange	30.00
O26	A6	10a olive green	35.00
O27	A6	12a dark green	35.00
O28	A6	1r violet	30.00
O29	A6	2r car brn & blk	105.00
O30	A6	3r blue & brown	160.00
O31	A6	4r pale grn & red brn	325.00
O32	A6	5r ver & pale grn	325.00
		Nos. O17-O32 (16)	1,125.

Note following No. O16 applies to this issue.

Regular Issue of 1915 Handstamped in Carmine or Black

BUNDI

c

SERVICE

1919 *Rouletted in Color*

Without Gum

O33	A6	¼a	blue	5.00	5.00
O34	A6	½a	black	3.50	
O35	A6	1a	vermilion	7.50	
O36	A6	2a	yel green	9.00	
O37	A6	8a	orange	45.00	
O38	A6	10a	olive	45.00	
O39	A6	12a	dark green	75.00	
			Nos. O33-O39 (7)	190.00	

Nos. 33 and 35 Handstamped Type "a" in Black or Carmine

1941 *Perf. 11*

O41	A6	½a	black	55.00
O42	A6	2a	yellow green	55.00

Nos. 32 and 35 Handstamped Type "b" in Black or Carmine

O43	A6	¼a	light blue	47.50
O44	A6	2a	yellow green	80.00

Nos. 32-35 Handstamped Type "c" in Black or Carmine

1941

O45	A6	¼a	light blue	65.00
O46	A6	½a	black	65.00
O47	A6	1a	carmine	75.00
O48	A6	2a	yellow green	27.50
			Nos. O45-O48 (4)	232.50

Nos. 36 to 42 Overprinted in Black or Carmine **SERVICE**

1941 *Perf. 11*

O49	A7	3p	brt ultra (C)	1.25	1.75
O50	A7	6p	indigo (C)	3.00	3.50
O51	A7	1a	red orange	3.50	4.75
O52	A7	2a	fawn	6.00	*9.00*
O53	A7	4a	brt yel green	24.00	*30.00*
O54	A7	8a	dull green	35.00	*45.00*
O55	A7	1r	royal blue (C)	45.00	*60.00*
			Nos. O49-O55 (7)	117.75	*154.00*

BUSSAHIR

'bu̇s-ə-,hi(ə)r

(Bashahr)

LOCATION — A Feudatory State in the Punjab Hill States Agency
AREA — 3,439 sq. mi.
POP. — 100,192
CAPITAL — Bashahr

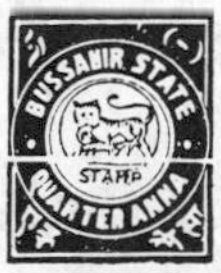
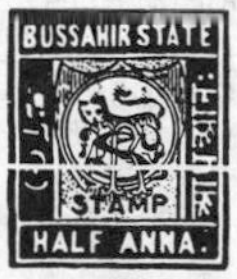

Tiger

A1 A2

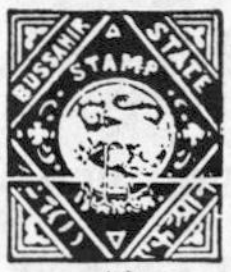
A3

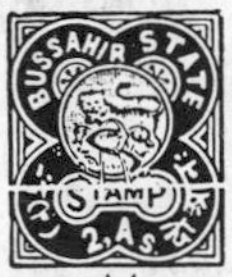
A4

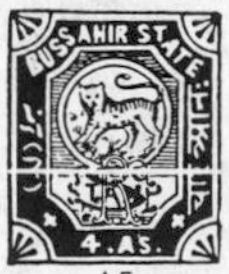
A5

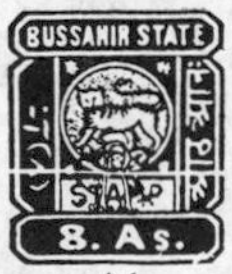
A6

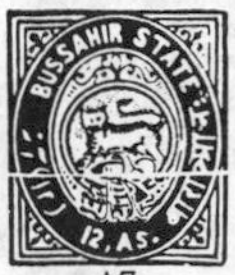
A7

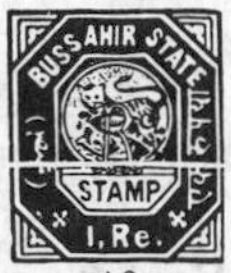
A8

Overprinted "R S" in Violet, Rose, or Blue Green (BG)

Laid Paper

1895 Unwmk. Litho. *Imperf.*

1	A1	¼a	pink (V)	82.50	
2	A2	½a	slate (R)	100.00	
3	A3	1a	red (V)	50.00	
4	A4	2a	yellow (V,R)	10.50	*50.00*
5	A5	4a	violet (V,R)	27.50	
6	A6	8a	brown (V,BG)	27.50	40.00
a.			Without overprint	65.00	
7	A7	12a	green (R)	50.00	
8	A8	1r	ultra (R)	27.50	
			Nos. 1-8 (8)	375.50	

Perf. 7 to 14

9	A1	¼a	pink (V,BG)	20.00	*40.00*
10	A2	½a	slate (R)	13.00	*40.00*
11	A3	1a	red (V)	16.00	*40.00*
a.			Pin-perf.	65.00	*100.00*
12	A4	2a	yel (V,R,BG)	20.00	*50.00*
a.			Pin-perf. (V,R)	25.00	*50.00*
13	A5	4a	violet (V,R,BG)	15.00	*50.00*
a.			Pin-perf. (R)	50.00	
14	A6	8a	brown (V,BG)	14.00	*50.00*
15	A7	12a	green (V,R)	22.50	*47.50*
a.			Pin-perf. (R)	65.00	
b.			Without overprint	47.50	
16	A8	1r	ultra (V,R)	14.00	*40.00*
a.			Pin-perf. (R)	65.00	
			Nos. 9-16 (8)	134.50	*357.50*

"R. S." are the initials of Tika Raghunath Singh, son of the Raja.

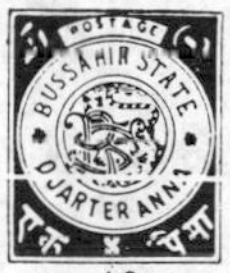
A9

A10

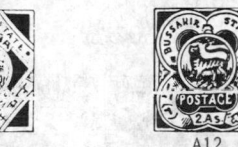

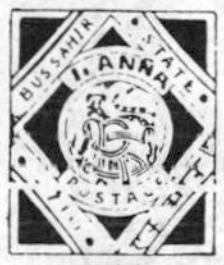
A11

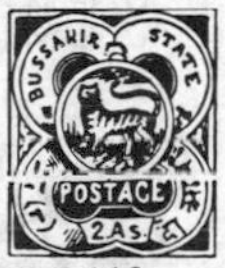
A12

A13

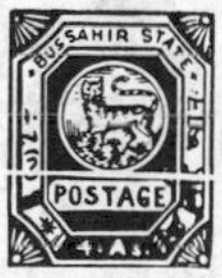
A14

Overprinted "R S" Like Nos. 1-16

Wove Paper

1896 Engr. *Pin-perf.*

17	A9	¼a	dk gray vio (R)	*200.00*	165.00
18	A10	½a	blue gray (R)	325.00	90.00

1900 Litho. *Imperf.*

19	A9	¼a	red (V,BG)	2.25	
20	A9	¼a	violet (V,R)	3.00	
21	A10	½a	blue (V,R)	2.75	
22	A11	1a	olive (R)	9.00	*20.00*
23	A11	1a	red (V,BG)	2.75	
24	A12	2a	yellow (V)	8.50	
a.			2a ocher (R)	8.50	
25	A13	2a	yellow (V)	6.50	
a.			2a ocher (V)	6.50	
26	A14	4a	brn vio (V,R,BG)	17.50	
			Nos. 19-26 (8)	52.25	

Pin-perf.

27	A9	¼a	red (V,BG)	2.75	
28	A9	¼a	violet (V,R)	3.00	
29	A10	½a	blue (V,R)	2.75	
30	A11	1a	olive (V,R)	9.25	
31	A11	1a	red (V)		
32	A11	1a	vermilion (BG)	2.00	
33	A12	2a	yellow (BG)	50.00	*75.00*
34	A13	2a	yellow (V,R)	12.00	
a.			2a ocher (V)	12.00	
35	A14	4a	brn vio (V,R,BG)	22.50	
			Nos. 27-35 (8)	104.25	

Obsolete March 31, 1901.

Stamps overprinted with the monogram above (RNS) or with the monogram "PS" were never issued for postal purposes. They are either reprints or remainders to which this overprint has been applied. Many other varieties have appeared since the stamps became obsolete. It is probable that all or nearly all of them are reprints.

CHARKHARI

chər-'kär-ē

LOCATION — A Feudatory State in the Bundelkhand Agency in Central India.
AREA — 880 sq. mi.
POP. — 120,351
CAPITAL — Maharajnagar

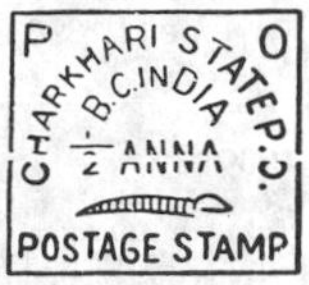

A1

Thin White or Blue Wove Paper

1894 Unwmk. Typo. *Imperf.*

Value in the Plural

Without Gum

1	A1	1a	green	2,250.	2,750.
2	A1	2a	green	2,750.	
3	A1	4a	green	1,850.	

1897

Value in the Singular

Without Gum

3A	A1	¼a	rose	1,500.	1,150.
4	A1	¼a	purple	2.50	2.25
5	A1	½a	purple	2.50	2.25
6	A1	1a	green	5.00	4.50
7	A1	2a	green	7.00	6.25
8	A1	4a	green	7.00	6.25
			Nos. 4-8 (5)	24.00	21.50

In a later printing, the numerals of Nos. 4-8 are smaller or of different shape.

Proofs are known on paper of various colors.

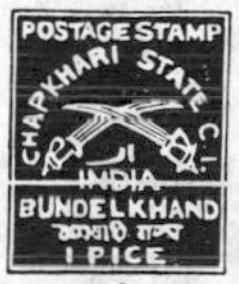

A2

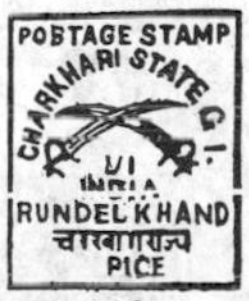

A3

Size: 19½x23mm

1909 Litho. *Perf. 11*

9	A2	1p	red brown	2.25	8.25
10	A2	1p	pale blue	.22	.22
11	A2	½a	scarlet	.55	.55
12	A2	1a	light green	.70	.70
13	A2	2a	ultra	1.10	1.10
14	A2	4a	deep green	1.10	1.10
15	A2	8a	brick red	2.75	*4.50*
16	A2	1r	red brown	6.50	*11.00*
			Nos. 10-16 (7)	12.92	*19.17*

See #22-27, 39-43. For surcharge see #37-38A.

1919 Handstamped *Imperf.*

Without Gum

21	A3	1p	violet	14.00	5.50
c.			Double frameline	27.50	

The 1p black, type A3, is a proof.

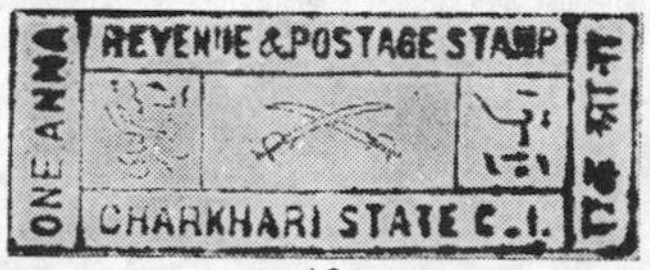

A3a

Wove Paper

1922 Handstamped *Imperf.*

Without Gum

21A	A3a	1a	violet	55.00	55.00
b.			Perf. 11, laid paper	65.00	65.00

Type of 1909 Issue Redrawn

Size: 20x23½mm

1930-40 **Typo.**

Without Gum

22	A2	1p	dark blue	.15	*.65*
23	A2	½a	olive green	.30	*2.00*
23A	A2	½a	cop brown ('40)	.65	
24	A2	1a	light green	.85	*2.00*
25	A2	1a	chocolate	2.00	*3.25*
25A	A2	1a	dull red ('40)	40.00	40.00
26	A2	2a	light blue	.55	*1.25*
a.			Tête bêche pair	4.50	
27	A2	4a	carmine	3.25	*6.50*
a.			Tête bêche pair	10.00	
			Nos. 22-27 (8)	47.75	*55.65*

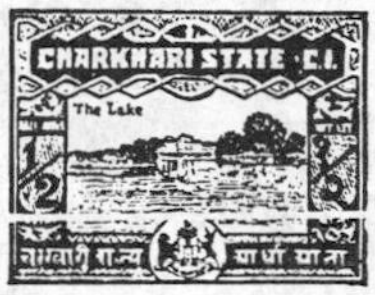

Guesthouse of Raja at Charkhari Reservoir — A4

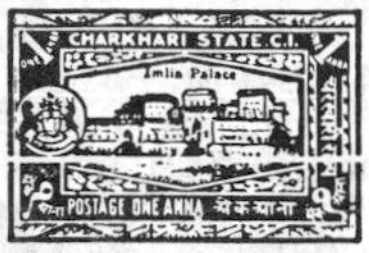

Imlia Palace — A5

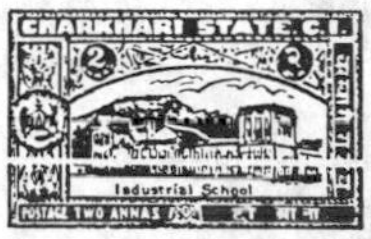

Industrial School — A6

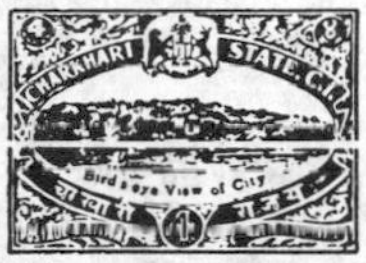

View of City — A7

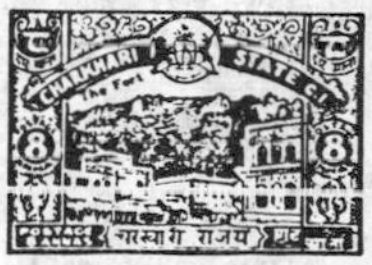

Maharajnagar Fort, Charkhari City — A8

Guesthouse — A9

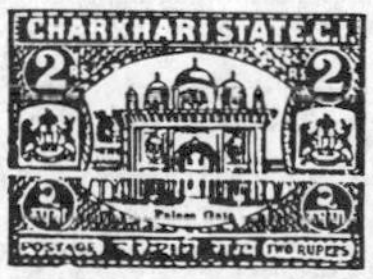

Palace Gate — A10

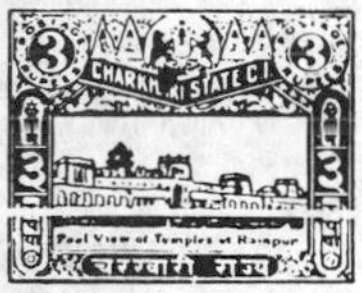
Temples at Rampur — A11

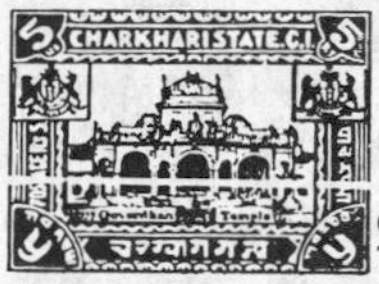

Govordhan Temple — A12

1931 *Perf. 11, 11½, 12*

28	A4	½a	dull green	.15	.15
29	A5	1a	black brown	.15	.15
30	A6	2a	purple	.15	.15
31	A7	4a	olive green	.15	.15
32	A8	8a	magenta	.15	.15
33	A9	1r	rose & green	.20	.15
34	A10	2r	brown & red	.45	.15
35	A11	3r	bl grn & choc	.90	.15
36	A12	5r	violet & blue	.65	.20
			Nos. 28-36 (9)	2.95	
			Set value		.96

Size range of A4-A12: 30-31x19½-24mm.

Many errors of perforation and printing exist. Used values are for canceled to order copies.

Nos. 15-16 Surcharged in Black **½ As.**

1940 *Perf. 11*

37 A2 ½a on 8a brick red 18.00 35.00
a. Surcharge inverted 150.00
b. "1" of "½" inverted 140.00
38 A2 1a on 1r red brown 35.00 60.00
b. Surcharge inverted 240.00
38A A2 "1 ANNA" on 1r red brown 225.00

Type of 1930

1943 Unwmk. Typo. *Imperf.*
Size: 20x23½mm

39 A2 1p violet 9.00 18.00
a. Tête bêche pair 35.00
40 A2 1p apple green 30.00 45.00
41 A2 ½a orange red 7.50 8.50
42 A2 ½a black 35.00 45.00
43 A2 2a grayish green 30.00 32.50
a. Tête bêche pair 75.00
Nos. 39-43 (5) 111.50 149.00

COCHIN

kō-'chin

LOCATION — A Feudatory State in the Madras States Agency in Southern India.
AREA — 1,480 sq. mi.
POP. — 1,422,875 (1941)
CAPITAL — Ernakulam

See the United State of Travancore and Cochin.

6 Puttans = 5 Annas
12 Pies = 1 Anna
16 Annas = 1 Rupee

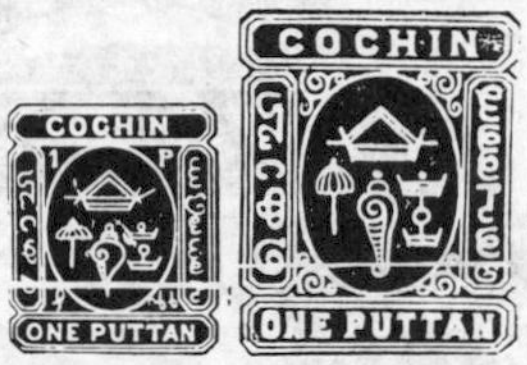

State Seal
A1 A1a

1892 Unwmk. Typo. *Perf. 12*

1 A1 ½p yellow 2.00 .90
a. Imperf., pair 325.00 325.00
b. Laid paper 360.00 360.00
2 A1 1p red violet 2.25 1.65
a. 1p purple (error) 125.00 110.00
3 A1 2p purple 1.00 1.00
a. Imperf.
Nos. 1-3 (3) 5.25 3.55

Nos. 1 to 3 sometimes have watermark large umbrella in the sheet.

Wmk. Coat of Arms and Inscription in Sheet

1896

4 A1a 1p violet 32.50 40.00

Wmk. 43

4A A1a 1p violet 20.00 20.00

Originally intended for revenue use, Nos. 4-4A were later authorized for postal use.

1897 Wmk. 41

Thin Paper

5 A1 ½p orange 1.50 1.50
a. Imperf., pair
6 A1 1p magenta 1.90 1.75
7 A1 2p purple 3.75 3.25
a. Imperf., pair 25.00 25.00
Nos. 5-7 (3) 7.15 6.50

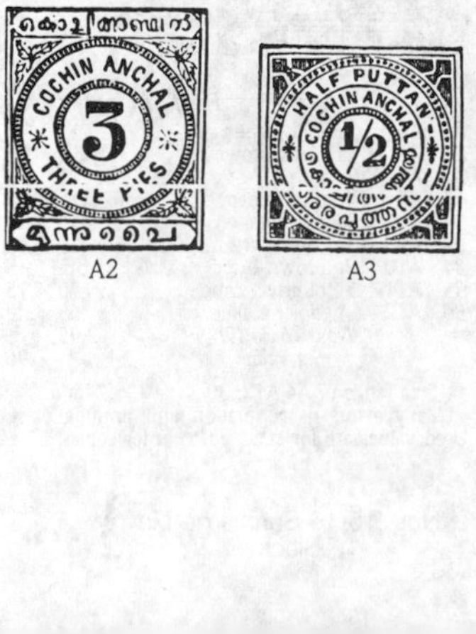

A2 A3

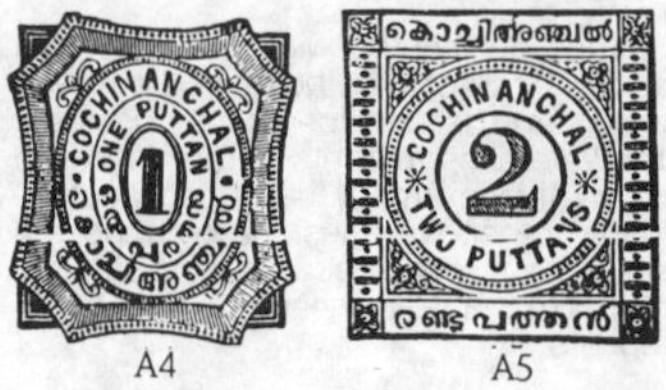

A4 A5

Thin (1898) or Thick (1903) Paper

1898-1903

8 A2 3p ultra .20 .15
9 A3 ½p gray green .55 .15
a. Pair, one sideways 650.00 650.00
10 A4 1p rose 1.35 .25
a. Laid paper 1,750.
b. Tete beche pair 2,250. 2,250.
c. As "a," tete beche pair 6,500.
11 A5 2p purple 2.00 .40
a. Double impression 100.00
Nos. 8-11 (4) 4.10 .95

Type of 1898 Surcharged **2**

1909

13 A2 2p on 3p red violet .35 .30
a. Inverted surcharge 72.50 72.50
b. Pair, stamps tete beche 80.00 80.00
c. Pair, stamps & surch. tete beche 125.00 125.00

The surcharge is also known in a thin "2" measuring 5½x7mm, with curving foot. Value $250.

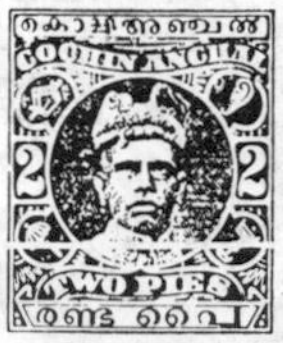

Sri Rama Varma I — A6

1911-14 Engr. *Perf. 14*

14 A6 2p brown .32 .15
a. Imperf., pair
15 A6 3p blue .80 .15
a. Perf. 14x12½ 20.00 9.00
16 A6 4p yel green .55 .15
17 A6 9p car rose .40 .15
18 A6 1a orange buff 1.75 .15
19 A6 1½a lilac 1.75 .15
20 A6 2a gray 9.00 .25
21 A6 3a vermilion 37.50 27.50
Nos. 14-21 (8) 52.07 28.65

For surcharge and overprints see Nos. 34, O2-O9, O23-O24, O27.

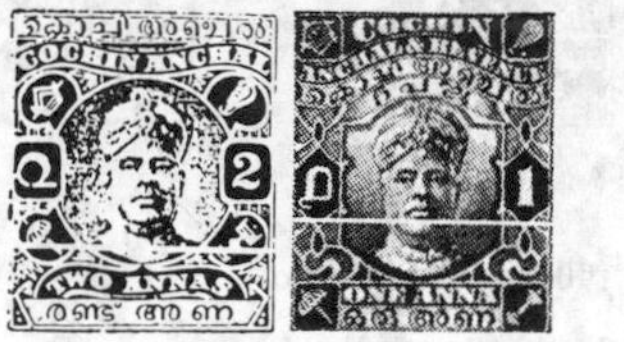

Sri Rama Varma II
A7 A8

1918-23 Engr. *Perf. 14*

23 A7 2p brown .45 .15
24 A7 4p green 1.40 .15
25 A7 6p red brown ('22) 1.50 .15
26 A7 8p black brown ('23) 1.75 .15
27 A7 9p carmine rose 8.00 .42
28 A7 10p deep blue 1.50 .15
29 A8 1a brown orange .90 .15
30 A7 1½a red violet ('21) 5.75 .15
31 A7 2a gray 7.00 .15
32 A7 2¼a yel green ('22) 3.75 .40
33 A7 3a vermilion 7.50 .40
Nos. 23-33 (11) 39.50
Set value 1.78

The 1a is found in two types, the difference lying in the first of the three characters directly above the maharaja's head.

For surcharges and overprints see Nos. 36-40, 52-53, O10-O22, O25-O26, O28-O36, O71A.

2

No. 15 Surcharged

Two pies

Type I - Numeral 8mm high. Curved foot. Top begins with a ball. (As illustrated.)
Type II - Numeral 9mm high. Curved foot. Top begins with a curved line.
Type III - Numeral 6mm high. Straight foot. "Two pies" 15mm wide.
Type IV - "2" as in type III. Capital "P" in "Pies." "Two Pies" 13mm wide.
Type V - Heavy gothic numeral. Capital "P" in "Pies."

1922-29

34 A6 2p on 3p blue (Type I) .40 .15
a. Type II .90 .15
b. Type III .35 .15
c. Type IV .30 .15
d. Type V 35.00 35.00
e. Double surcharge, I 45.00
f. Double surcharge II 45.00

Types II and III exist with a capital "P" in "Pies". It occurs once in each sheet of the second and third settings. There are four settings.

Type V is the first stamp, fourth row, of the fourth setting.

ONE ANNA
ഒരു അണ

No. 32 Surcharged

ANCHAL & REVENUE

1928

36 A7 1a on 2¼a yel green 5.00 9.00
a. Double surcharge 125.00 125.00

Three Pies

Nos. 24, 26 and 28 Surcharged in Black **൩ 3**

മൂന്നു പൈ

1932-33

38 A7 3p on 4p green 1.25 .55
39 A7 3p on 8p black brown 1.25 .55
40 A7 9p on 10p deep blue 3.25 .45
Nos. 38-40 (3) 5.75 1.55

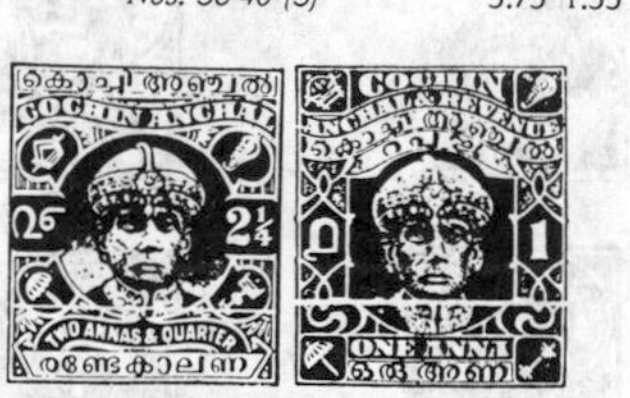

Sri Rama Varma III
A9 A10

1933-38 Engr. *Perf. 13x13½*

41 A9 2p brown ('36) .55 .15
42 A9 4p green 1.40 .15
43 A9 6p red brown .95 .15
44 A10 1a brown org ('34) .48 .15
45 A9 1a8p rose red 5.25 2.25
46 A9 2a gray black ('38) 1.25 .15
47 A9 2¼a yellow green 1.25 .15
48 A9 3a red org ('38) 2.25 .15
49 A9 3a4p violet .95 .15
50 A9 6a8p black brown 3.50 2.25
51 A9 10a deep blue 3.50 2.25
Nos. 41-51 (11) 21.33 7.95

See Nos. 55-58. For overprints and surcharges see Nos. 54, 59-62, 73A-74, 76-77, 89, O37-O57, O70-O71, O72-O77A, O89.

6

Nos. 26 and 28 Surcharged in Red

Six Pies

1934 *Perf. 13½*

52 A7 6p on 8p black brown 2.25 1.25
53 A7 6p on 10p dark blue 2.25 .80

No. 44 Overprinted in Black

a **ANCHAL**

1939 Engr.

54 A10 1a brown orange 1.50 .15

Types of 1933-38

1938-41 Litho. *Perf. 11, 13*

55 A9 2p dull brown .85 .15
56 A9 4p dull green ('41) 2.25 .15
57 A9 6p red brown 2.75 .15
c. Perf. 13 1,500.
57A A10 1a brown orange 35.00 30.00
58 A10 2¼a yellow green 5.50 .15
Nos. 55-58 (5) 46.35 30.60

Type of 1934 Overprinted in Black Type "a" or

b **ANCHAL**

1941-42 *Perf. 11 (#59), 13 (#60)*

59 A10(a) 1a brown orange 47.50 .15
a. Perf. 13 75.00
60 A10(b) 1a brown org ('42) 7.50 .65
a. Perf. 11 2.50 2.50

No. 45 Surcharged in Black

SURCHARGED

c

THREE PIES

1943-44 Engr. *Perf. 13x13½*

61 A9 3p on 1a8p rose red ('44) 4.50 1.75
62 A9 1a3p on 1a8p rose red 1.65 .18

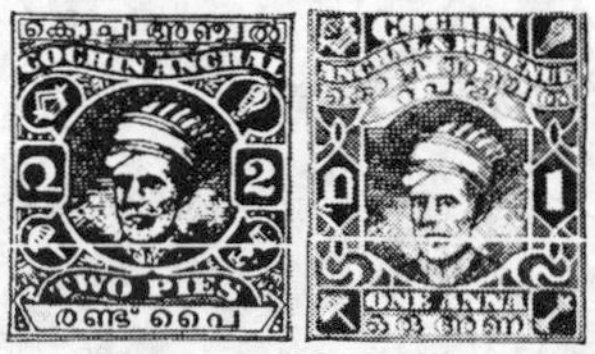

Maharaja Sri Kerala Varma
A11 A12

1943 Litho. Wmk. 294 *Perf. 11, 13*

63 A11 2p dull gray brn, wmk. 41 .65 .15
a. Wmk. 294 22.50 .15
64 A11 4p gray green 3.00 .55
a. Wmk. 41 175.00 125.00
65 A11 6p red brown 1.50 .15
66 A11 9p ultramarine 15.00 1.25
67 A12 1a brown orange 22.50 22.50
a. Wmk. 41 75.00 30.00
68 A11 2¼a lt ol green 12.00 .15
Nos. 63-68 (6) 54.65 24.75

For surcharges and overprints see Nos. 69-73, 75, 78, 78B, O58-O69.

No. 64 Surcharged Type "c"

69 A11 3p on 4p gray green .48 .15
a. Wmk. 41 37.50 5.00

Nos. 64, 64a and 65 Surcharged in Black

d **THREE PIES**

1944-48 Wmk. 294

70 A11 2p on 6p red brown .40 .15
71 A11 3p on 4p gray green .85 .15
72 A11 3p on 6p red brown .35 .15
73 A11 4p on 6p red brown 4.50 2.50
Nos. 70-73 (4) 6.10 2.95

ANCHAL

Nos. 57A, 67a Surcharged in Black

NINE PIES

1944 Litho. Wmk. 41

73A A10 6p on 1a brown org 250.00 12.50
74 A10 9p on 1a brown org 50.00 11.00
75 A12 9p on 1a brown org 5.50 .15
Nos. 73A-75 (3) 305.50 23.65

No. 56 Surcharged Type "c" in Black

76 A9 3p on 4p dull green 6.50 .18

ANCHAL

Nos. 57A, 67a
Surcharged in Black

SURCHARGED NINE PIES

1944

77	A10	9p on 1a brown orange	12.50	.15
78	A12	9p on 1a brown orange	.30	.15
		Set value		.21

No. 67a Surcharged Type "c"

1944 **Wmk. 41**

78B	A12	1a3p on 1a brn org	

Maharaja Ravi Varma
A13   A15

1944-46 **Wmk. 294** **Perf. 13**

79	A13	9p ultra ('46)	4.00	.15
a.		Perf. 11	7.25	1.90
80	A13	1a3p magenta	8.50	.18
81	A13	1a9p ultra ('46)	12.50	1.10
		Nos. 79-81 (3)	25.00	1.43

For overprints and surcharges see Nos. O78-O80,
Travancore 12, 14, O10.

1946-50 **Litho.** **Perf. 13**

82	A15	2p dull brown	.50	.15
a.		Perf. 11	13.00	.75
h.		Perf. 11x13	250.00	80.00
83	A15	3p carmine rose	3.25	.15
83A	A15	4p gray green ('50)	1,500.	27.50
84	A15	6p rd red brown ('47)	12.00	.45
a.		Perf. 11	125.00	.15
85	A15	9p ultramarine	2.25	.15
86	A15	1a dp orange ('47)	6.00	3.50
a.		Perf. 11	375.00	
87	A15	2a gray ('47)	45.00	.15
a.		Perf. 11	95.00	.18
88	A15	3a vermilion	25.00	.24
		Nos. 82-83,84-88 (7)	94.00	4.79

For surcharges and overprints see Nos. 98-99,
O81-O88, Travancore 8, 13, 15-15A, O11.

No. 45 Surcharged Type "d"
Perf. 13x13 1/2

1947-48 **Wmk. 41** **Engr.**

89	A9	6p on 1a8p rose red	2.75	1.40

Maharaja Sri Kerala
Varma II — A16

1948-49 **Wmk. 294** **Perf. 11**

90	A16	2p olive brown	2.00	.15
91	A16	3p car ('49)	1.00	.15
92	A16	4p gray green	3.25	.15
a.		Horiz. pair, imperf. vert.	360.00	
93	A16	6p red brown	3.50	.15
94	A16	9p ultra ('49)	1.65	.15
95	A16	2a black	16.00	.15
96	A16	3a ver ('49)	18.00	.15
97	A16	3a4p violet ('49)	55.00	150.00
		Nos. 90-97 (8)	100.40	151.05

For overprints see Nos. O90-O97, Travancore 9-
11, O8-O9.

No. 86 Surcharged Type "d" in Black
1949

98	A15	6p on 1a dp orange	47.50	47.50
99	A15	9p on 1a dp orange	32.50	32.50

Dutch
Palace — A17

Design: 2a, Chinese fishing net.

1949 **Unwmk.** **Perf. 11**

100	A17	2a gray	.75	.75
a.		Imperf. vert., horiz. pair	425.00	
101	A17	2 1/4a gray green	.75	.75

See Travancore-Cochin for succeeding issues.

OFFICIAL STAMPS

Stamps and Type of 1911-14 Overprinted

ON

h   **C**   **G**

S

1913-14 **Wmk. 41** **Engr.** **Perf. 14**

O2	A6	4p yel green	11.50	.15
a.		Inverted overprint	750.00	350.00
b.		Double inverted overprint		
O3	A6	9p car rose	17.50	.15
O4	A6	1 1/2a red violet	20.00	.15
a.		Double overprint	375.00	
O5	A6	2a gray	15.00	.15
O6	A6	3a vermilion	21.00	.22
O7	A6	6a violet	18.00	1.10
O8	A6	12a blue	30.00	3.25
O9	A6	1 1/2r deep green	22.50	18.00
		Nos. O2-O9 (8)	155.50	23.17

Stamps and Type of 1918-23 with Similar
Overprint

1918-34

O10	A7	4p green	4.75	.15
a.		Double overprint	325.00	
O11	A7	6p red brn ('22)	4.75	.15
a.		Double overprint	325.00	
O12	A7	8p blk brn ('26)	7.50	.15
O13	A7	9p carmine rose	19.00	.15
O14	A7	10p dp blue ('23)	8.00	.15
O16	A7	1 1/2a red vio ('21)	5.00	.15
a.		Double overprint		200.00
O17	A7	2a gray	30.00	.15
O18	A7	2 1/4a yel grn ('22)	7.50	.15
b.		Double overprint		300.00
O19	A7	3a ver ('33)	18.00	.55
a.		Double overprint		325.00
O20	A7	6a violet ('22)	22.50	.85
O21	A7	12a blue ('29)	25.00	4.25
O22	A7	1 1/2r dk green ('34)	27.50	35.00
		Nos. O10-O22 (12)	179.50	41.85

On Nos. O2-O22, width of overprint varies from
14 3/4mm to 16 1/2mm.

No. 15 Overprinted in Red

On

j   **C**   **G**

S

1921

O23	A6	3p blue	52.50	.15

Nos. O3 and O13 Surcharged with New
Values

1923-29

O24	A6	8p on 9p car rose	225.00	.15
O25	A7	8p on 9p car rose	70.00	.15
a.		Double surcharge		300.00
O26	A7	10p on 9p car rose ('25)	70.00	.15
a.		Double surcharge		300.00
O27	A6	10p on 9p car rose ('29)	300.00	13.00
		Nos. O24-O27 (4)	665.00	13.45

Regular Issue of 1918-23 Overprinted

ON

k   **C**   **G**

S

1933-34

O28	A7	4p green	30.00	3.25
O29	A7	6p red brown ('34)	7.25	.15
O30	A7	8p black brown	7.25	.15
O31	A7	10p deep blue	7.25	.15
O32	A7	2a gray ('34)	11.00	.15
O33	A7	3a vermilion	13.00	.15
O34	A7	6a dk violet ('34)	85.00	3.75
		Nos. O28-O34 (7)	160.75	7.75

6

Same with Additional
Surcharge on Type of
Regular Issue of 1918-23
in Red

Six Pies

O35	A7	6p on 8p black brown	1.25	.15
O36	A7	6p on 10p dk blue ('34)	6.00	.15
		Set value, #O35-O36		.16

Regular Issue of 1933 Overprinted Type
"k" in Black as in 1933-34

1933-35 **Perf. 13x13 1/2**

O37	A9	4p green	.90	.15
O38	A9	6p red brown	1.10	.15
O39	A10	1a brown orange	7.50	.15
O40	A9	1a8p rose red	2.50	.15
O41	A9	2a gray	7.50	.15
O42	A9	2 1/4a yellow green	3.50	.15
O43	A9	3a vermilion	15.00	.15
O44	A9	3a4p violet	3.25	.15
O45	A9	6a8p black brown	3.25	.15
O46	A9	10a deep blue	3.25	.22
		Nos. O37-O46 (10)	47.75	
		Set value		.84

Regular Stamps of 1934-38 Overprinted in
Black

ON

m   **C**   **G**

S

1939-41 **Perf. 11, 13x13 1/2**

O47	A10	1a brown orange	90.00	.15
O48	A9	2a gray black	25.00	.22
O49	A9	3a red orange	6.00	.22
		Nos. O47-O49 (3)	121.00	.59

Similar Overprint on Types of 1933-36
Perf. 11, 13x13 1/2

1939-41 **Litho.** **Wmk. 294**

O50	A9	4p dull green ('41)	2.25	.28

Wmk. 41

O51	A9	6p red brown ('41)	1.65	.15
a.		Wmk. 294	32.50	1.10
O52	A10	1a brown orange	1.40	.15
a.		Wmk. 294	2.25	.28
O53	A9	3a orange ('40)	3.50	.15
b.		Wmk. 294	10.00	1.50
		Nos. O50-O53 (4)	8.80	.73

Similar Overprint in Narrow Serifed
Capitals on No. 57

Wmk. 41 **Perf. 11**

O53A	A9	6p red brown	500.00	250.00

Type of 1933-36 Overprinted in Black

ON

o   **C**   **G**

S

Perf. 10 1/2, 11, 13x13 1/2

O54	A9	4p dull green ('41)	7.50	1.10
O55	A9	6p red brown ('41)	5.50	.15
O56	A9	2a gray black	5.50	.15
		Nos. O54-O56 (3)	18.50	1.40

Type of 1934 Overprinted in Black

ON

p   **C**   **G**

S

1941 **Perf. 11**

O57	A10	1a brown orange	165.00	3.75

Stamps and Types of 1944 Overprinted in
Black

ON

q   **C**   **G**

S

Perf. 11, 13x13 1/2

1944-48 **Wmk. 294**

O58	A11	4p gray green	2.75	.15
a.		Perf. 11	50.00	.70
O59	A11	6p red brown	.50	.15
O60	A11	2a gray black	.65	.15
O61	A11	2 1/4a dull yel green	2.00	.55
a.		Additional ovpt. on back		75.00
O62	A11	3a red orange	1.65	.18
		Nos. O58-O62 (5)	7.55	
		Set value		.89

Same Overprint with
Additional Surcharge   **THREE PIES**

O63	A11	3p on 4p gray green	.80	.15
a.		Additional overprint on back		
O64	A12	3p on 1a brown org	3.50	.15
O65	A11	9p on 6p red brown	1.50	.15
O66	A12	1a3p on 1a brown org	3.50	.15
		Nos. O63-O66 (4)	9.30	
		Set value		.24

Same Overprint in Black on Types of 1944
Surcharged Type "c"

O67	A11	3p on 4p gray green	2.75	.32
O68	A11	9p on 6p red brown	.20	.15
O69	A12	1a3p on 1a brown org	3.50	.15
		Nos. O67-O69 (3)	6.45	
		Set value		.46

Nos. O52 and O16 Surcharged Type "d"
Perf. 11, 13x13 1/2, 14

1944 **Wmk. 41**

O70	A10	3p on 1a brown org	1.75	.15
O71	A10	9p on 1a brown org	110.00	1.10

Engr.

O71A	A7	9p on 1 1/2a red vio	150.00	5.50

No. O52 Surcharged Type "c"

O72	A10	1a3p on 1a brn org	110.00	30.00

ON

No. 76 Overprinted in   **C**   **G**
Black

S

Perf. 13

O72A	A9	3p on 4p dull green	90.00	24.00

No. 45 Overprinted Type "k" and
Surcharged Type "d"

1944-48 **Wmk. 41** **Perf. 13x13 1/2**

O73	A9	9p on 1a8p rose red	77.50	11.50
O74	A9	1a9p on 1a8p rose red	1.10	.15

No. 45 Overprinted Type "k" and
Surcharged Type "c"

O75	A9	3p on 1a8p rose red	32.	15
O76	A9	1a9p on 1a8p rose red	.80	.15
		Set value		.18

ON

Type of 1939-41   **C**   **G**
Overprinted in Black

S

1946 **Wmk. 294** **Perf. 11**

O77	A9	2a gray	80.00	1.25
O77A	A9	2 1/4a yellow green	400.00	19.00

Same Overprint in Black on #79-81

1946 **Litho.** **Perf. 13**

O78	A13	9p ultramarine	.25	.15
O79	A13	1a3p magenta	.28	.15
a.		Double overprint	24.00	18.00
O80	A13	1a9p ultramarine	.65	.15
		Nos. O78-O80 (3)	1.18	
		Set value		.25

Types and Stamps of 1946-48 Overprinted
Type "h"

1946-48

O81	A15	3p car rose	.15	.15
O82	A15	4p gray green	18.00	1.65
O83	A15	6p red brown	.75	.15
O84	A15	9p ultra	1.25	.15

O85 A15 1a3p magenta .55 .15
O86 A15 1a9p ultra 1.10 .25
O87 A15 2a gray black 8.00 .15
O88 A15 2¼a olive green 8.50 .15
Nos. O81-O88 (8) 38.30
Set value 2.35

No. 56 Overprinted Type "q" and Surcharged Type "d"

1947 Wmk. 41 Engr. ***Perf. 13x13½***
O89 A9 3p on 4p dull green 8.50 1.40

Stamps and Type of 1948-49 Overprinted Type "o"

1948-49 Wmk. 294 Litho. ***Perf. 11***
O90 A16 3p carmine ('49) .55 .15
O91 A16 4p gray green .55 .15
O92 A16 6p red brown .55 .15
O93 A16 9p ultramarine .70 .15
O94 A16 2a black ('49) .55 .15
O95 A16 2¼a lt ol green ('49) 1.10 .15
O96 A16 3a vermilion ('49) .80 .15
O97 A16 3a4p deep pur ('49) 8.25 8.25
Nos. O90-O97 (8) 13.05 9.30

See Travancore-Cochin for succeeding issues.

DHAR

'där

LOCATION — A Feudatory State in the Malwa Agency in Central India.
AREA — 1,800 sq. mi.
POP. — 243,521
CAPITAL — Dhar

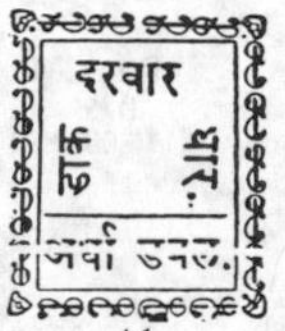
A1

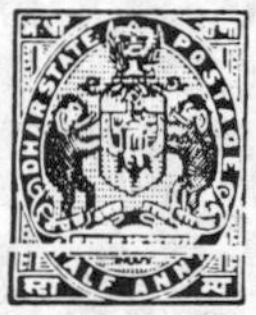
Arms of Dhar — A2

The stamps of type A1 have an oval control mark handstamped in black.

1897-1900 Unwmk. Typeset ***Imperf.***
Without Gum
1 A1 ½p black, *red* .70 .70
a. Characters for "pice" transposed 15.00
b. Five characters in first word .75
c. Without control mark 82.50
2 A1 ¼a black, *org red* ('00) 1.00 .65
a. Without control mark 100.00
3 A1 ½a black, *lil rose* 1.00 .65
4 A1 1a black, *bl grn* 4.50 3.00
5 A1 2a black, *yel* ('00) 17.50 *22.50*
Nos. 1-5 (5) 24.70 *27.50*

1898-1900 Typo. ***Perf. 11½***
6 A2 ½a red .85 .85
7 A2 ½a rose ('00) 1.50 1.50
a. Imperf., pair 35.00
8 A2 1a maroon 1.00 1.00
9 A2 1a violet ('00) 1.25 1.25
10 A2 1a claret ('00) 1.00 1.00
11 A2 2a dark green ('00) 3.25 *5.00*
Nos. 6-11 (6) 8.85 *10.60*

Obsolete Mar. 31, 1901.

DUTTIA

'dət–ē–ə

(Datia)

LOCATION — A Feudatory State in the Bundelkhand Agency in Central India.
AREA — 912 sq. mi.
POP. — 158,834
CAPITAL — Datia

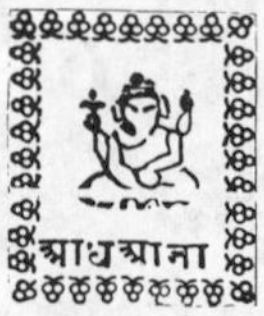
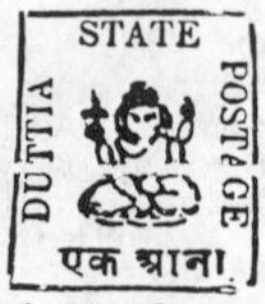

Ganesh, Elephant-headed God
A1 A2

All Duttia stamps have a circular control mark, about 23mm in diameter, handstamped in blue or black. All were issued without gum.

1893 Typeset Unwmk. ***Imperf.***
1 A1 ¼a black, *org red* 1,700.
2 A1 ½a blk, *grysh grn* 2,250.
3 A2 1a black, *red* 1,700.
4 A1 2a black, *yellow* 2,000.
5 A1 4a black, *rose* 1,300.

Type A2 with Frameline around God, Rosettes in Lower Corners

1896 (?)
5A A2 ½ black, *green* *2,750.*
5C A2 2a dk blue, *lemon* *2,000.*

A 1a in this revised type has been reported.

1897
6 A2 ½a black, *green* 12.00 *35.00*
7 A2 1a black 24.00 *45.00*
a. Laid paper 8.50
8 A2 2a black, *yellow* 16.00 *35.00*
9 A2 4a black, *rose* 16.00 *32.50*
Nos. 6-9 (4) 68.00 *147.50*

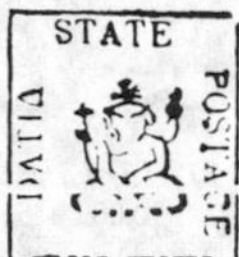

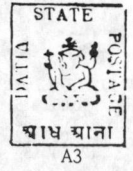

A3

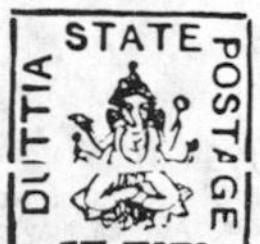

A4

10 A3 ½a black, *green* 55.00
11 A3 1a black 75.00
12 A3 2a black, *yellow* 55.00
13 A3 4a black, *rose* 50.00
Nos. 10-13 (4) 235.00

1899-1900
Rouletted in Colored Lines on 2 or 3 Sides
14 A4 ¼a red (shades) .55
b. Tete beche pair *2,000.*
15 A4 ½a black, *green* .65
16 A4 1a black .55
17 A4 2a black, *yellow* .90
18 A4 4a black, *rose red* 1.25
a. Tete beche pair
Nos. 14-18 (5) 3.90

1904 ***Imperf.***
22 A4 ¼a carmine 1.25
23 A4 ½a black, *green* 7.00
24 A4 1a black 3.00
Nos. 22-24 (3) 11.25

1911 ***Perf. 13½***
25 A4 ¼a carmine 2.25 2.25

1916 ***Imperf.***
26 A4 ¼a dull blue 1.50 *3.25*
27 A4 ½a green 3.00 *6.50*
28 A4 1a violet 3.50 *6.50*
a. Tete beche pair 20.00
29 A4 2a brown 6.50 *13.00*
29A A4 4a brick red 40.00
Nos. 26-29A (5) 54.50

1918
31 A4 ½a ultramarine 3.00
32 A4 1a rose .75
33 A4 2a violet 4.00

Perf. 12
34 A4 ¼a black 4.00
Nos. 31-34 (4) 11.75

1920 ***Rouletted***
35 A4 ¼a blue 1.50 1.50
36 A4 ½a rose 3.00 3.00

Perf. 7
37 A4 ½a dull red 6.00
Nos. 35-37 (3) 10.50

Duttia stamps became obsolete in 1921.

FARIDKOT

fe–'rēd–,kōt

LOCATION — A Feudatory State in the Punjab Agency of India.
AREA — 638 sq. mi.
POP. — 164,364
CAPITAL — Faridkot

4 Folus or Paisas = 1 Anna

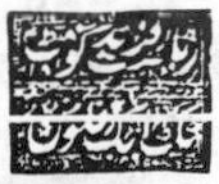
A1

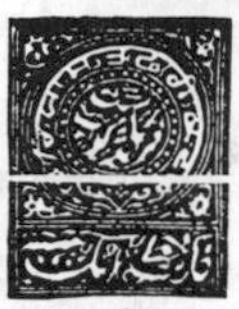
A2

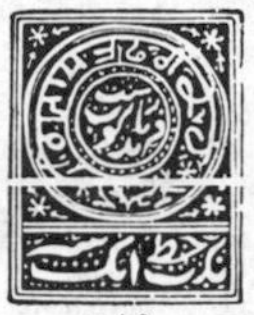
A3

Handstamped

1879-86 Unwmk. ***Imperf.***
Without Gum
1 A1 1f ultramarine .75 .75
a. Laid paper 16.00 16.00
b. Tete beche pair 45.00
2 A2 1p ultramarine .75 .75
a. Laid paper 37.50 37.50
3 A3 1p ultramarine 2.25
a. Tete beche pair 45.00
Nos. 1-3 (3) 3.75

Several other varieties exist, but it is believed that only the stamps listed here were issued for postal use. They became obsolete Dec. 31, 1886. See Faridkot under Convention States for issues of 1887-1900.

HYDERABAD (DECCAN)

'hīd–(ə–)rə–,bad

LOCATION — Central India
AREA — 82,313 sq. mi.
POP. — 16,338,534 (1941)
CAPITAL — Hyderabad

This independent princely state was occupied and annexed by India in 1948.

Catalogue values for unused stamps in this State are for Never Hinged items, beginning with Scott 51 in the regular postage section, and Scott O54 in the officials section.

Expect irregular perfs on the Nos. 1-14 and O1-O20 due to the nature of the paper.

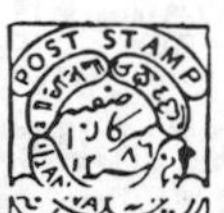

A1

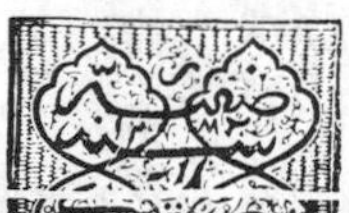
A2

1869-71 Engr. Unwmk. ***Perf. 11½***
1 A1 ½a brown ('71) 5.50 6.00
2 A2 1a olive green 10.00 5.50
a. Imperf. horiz., pair 105.00 85.00
3 A1 2a green ('71) 27.50 24.00
Nos. 1-3 (3) 43.00 35.50

For overprints see Nos. O1-O3, O11-O13.
The reprints are perforated 12½.

A3

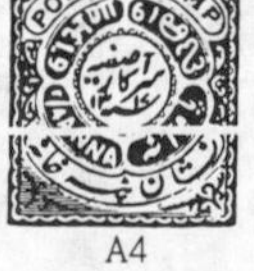

A4

Wove Paper

1871-1909 ***Perf. 12½***
4 A3 ½a orange brown .18 .15
a. ½a red brown .18 .15
b. ½a magenta (error) 25.00 11.00
c. Perf. 11½ 15.00 15.00
d. ½a rose .15 .15
e. ½a bright vermilion .15 .15
5 A3 1a dark brown .50 .38
a. Imperf., pair 25.00
b. Pair, imperf. between 50.00
c. Perf. 11½ 37.50 37.50
6 A3 1a black ('09) .95 .15
7 A3 2a green .15 .15
a. 2a olive green ('09) .18 .15
b. Perf. 11½ 110.00
8 A3 3a yellow brown .30 .18
a. Perf. 11½ 22.50 22.50
9 A3 4a slate .40 .30
a. Imperf. horiz., pair 200.00 200.00
b. Perf. 11½ 50.00 50.00
10 A3 4a deep green .80 .45
a. 4a olive green 2.50 2.25
11 A3 8a bister brown .95 .55
a. Perf. 11½
12 A3 12a blue 1.40 1.40
a. Perf. 11½ 95.00 95.00
b. 12a slate green 1.25 1.25
Nos. 4-12 (9) 5.63 3.71

For overprints see Nos. 13, O4-O10, O14-O20, O25-O26.

Surcharged 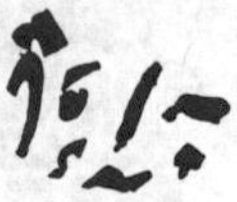

1900
13 A3 ¼a on ½a brt ver 1.00 1.10
a. Inverted surcharge 27.50 19.00

1902
14 A4 ¼a blue 2.00 1.90

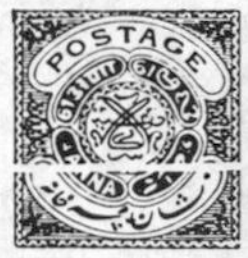

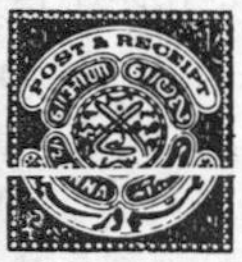

Seal of the Nizam
A5 A6

Engraved by A. G. Wyon

1905 Wmk. 42
17 A5 ¼a blue 2.00 .15
18 A5 ½a red 4.75 .15
19 A5 ½a orange 4.75 .15
Nos. 17-19 (3) 11.50
Set value .26

For overprints see Nos. O21-O23.

Perf. 11, 11½, 12½, 13½ and Compound

1908-11
20 A5 ¼a gray .40 .15
21 A5 ½a green .85 .15
22 A5 1a carmine .50 .15
23 A5 2a lilac .35 .15
24 A5 3a brn orange ('09) .85 .15
25 A5 4a olive green ('09) .85 .22
26 A5 8a violet ('11) .52 .15
27 A5 12a blue green ('11) 6.00 2.75
Nos. 20-27 (8) 10.32
Set value 3.30

For overprints see Nos. O24, O27-O38.

Engr. by Bradbury, Wilkinson & Co.

1912
28 A5 ¼a brown violet .15 .15
29 A5 ½a deep green 2.00 .15
a. Imperf., pair 20.00
Set value .15

The frame of type A5 differs slightly in each denomination.
Nos. 20-21 measure 19½x20½mm.
Nos. 28-29 measure 20x21½mm.
For overprints, see Nos 37, O39-O40, O44.

1915-16
30 A6 ½a green .60 .15
31 A6 1a carmine rose .60 .15
32 A6 1a red 6.00 .15
Nos. 30-32 (3) 7.20
Set value .18

Unless used, imperf. stamps of types A5 and A6 are from plate proof sheets.
See #58. For overprints see #38, O41-O43, O45.

A7

1927 Wmk. 211 Perf. 13½
36 A7 1r yellow 6.00 5.75

Stamps of 1912-16 Surcharged in Red

چارپائی آٹھ پائی

(4 pies) (8 pies)

1930
37 A5 4p on ¼a brown violet .20 .15
a. Perf. 11 130.00
b. Double surcharge
38 A6 8p on ½a green .20 .15
a. Perf. 11 130.00 90.00
Set value .15

For overprints see Nos. O44-O45.

Seal of Nizam — A8

Char Minar — A9

High Court of Justice — A10

Reservoir for City of Hyderabad A11

Bidar College — A13

Entrance to Ajanta Caves — A12

Victory Tower at Daulatabad — A14

Perf. 13½
1931-48 Engr. Wmk. 211
39 A8 4p black .15 .15
a. Laid paper ('47) 5.25 3.25
39B A8 6p car lake ('48) 1.00 .60
40 A8 8p green .15 .15
a. 8p yel grn, laid paper ('47) 5.25 3.25
b. Imperf., pair 47.50
41 A9 1a dark brown .15 .15
42 A10 2a dark violet .22 .15
a. Imperf., pair 100.00
43 A11 4a ultramarine .60 .15
a. Imperf., pair 130.00
44 A12 8a deep orange 1.00 .60
45 A13 12a scarlet 2.00 2.50
46 A14 1r yellow 2.75 2.75
Nos. 39-46 (9) 8.02 7.20

On No. 39B, "POSTAGE" has been moved to ribbon at bottom of design.
Nos. 39a and 40a are printed from worn plates. The background of the design is unshaded.
See #59. For overprints see #O46-O53, O56.

Unani General Hospital A15

Osmania General Hospital A16

Osmania University A17

Osmania Jubilee Hall — A18

Perf. 13½x14
1937, Feb. 13 Litho. Unwmk.
47 A15 4p violet & black .15 .15
48 A16 8p brown & black .15 .15
49 A17 1a dull orange & gray .16 .15
50 A18 2a dull green & gray .52 .52
Set value .85 .71

The Nizam's Silver Jubilee.

Catalogue values for unused stamps in this section, from this point to the end of the section, are for Never Hinged items.

Returning Soldier — A19

1946 Typo. Perf. 13½
51 A19 1a dark blue .15 .15

Wmk. 211
52 A19 1a blue .15 .15

Wmk. Nizam's Seal in Sheet
Laid Paper
53 A19 1a dark blue .50 .35
Set value .53

Victory of the Allied Nations in WW II.

Town Hall, Hyderabad A20

1947, Feb. 17 Litho. Wove Paper
54 A20 1a black .15 .15

Inauguration of the Reformed Legislature, Feb. 17th, 1947.

Power House, Hyderabad A21

Designs: 3a, Kaktyai Arch, Warangal Fort. 6a, Golkunda Fort.

Perf. 13½x14
1947-49 Typo. Wmk. 211
55 A21 1a4p dark green .15 .15
56 A21 3a blue .15 .15
57 A21 6a olive brown 4.00 4.00
a. 6a red brown ('49) 35.00 35.00
b. Imperf., pair 90.00
Nos. 55-57 (3) 4.30 4.30

Seal Type of 1915
1947 Engr. Perf. 13½
58 A6 ½a rose lake .35 .18

For overprint, see No. O54.

Seal Type of 1931
1949 Litho.
59 A8 2p brown 1.25 .18

For overprint, see No. O55.

OFFICIAL STAMPS

Regular Issues of 1869-71 Overprinted سرکاری

1873 Unwmk. Perf. 11½, 12½
Red Overprint
O1 A1 ½a brown 21.00
O2 A2 1a olive green 50.00 25.00
O3 A1 2a green 35.00
O4 A3 ½a red brown 3.50 3.50
O5 A3 1a dark brown 6.50 4.25
O6 A3 2a green 6.50 4.00
O7 A3 3a yel brown 8.50 7.00
O8 A3 4a slate 7.00 6.25
O9 A3 8a bister 8.50 8.50
O10 A3 12a blue 11.00 9.00

Black Overprint
O11 A1 ½a brown 15.00
O12 A2 1a olive green 20.00
O13 A1 2a green 27.50
O14 A3 ½a red brown 3.00 1.75
O15 A3 1a dark brown 2.00 1.75
O16 A3 2a green 2.25 1.75
O17 A3 3a yel brown 2.00 1.00
O18 A3 4a slate 2.75 2.75
O19 A3 8a bister 5.00 5.00
O20 A3 12a blue 8.00 8.00

The above official stamps became obsolete in August, 1878. Since that date the "Official" overprint has been applied to the reprints and probably to original stamps. Two new varieties of the overprint have also appeared, both on the reprints and on the current stamps. These are overprinted in various colors, positions and combinations.

Same Ovpt. On Regular Issues of 1905-11
1908 Wmk. 42
O21 A5 ½a green 2.00 .15
O22 A5 1a carmine 2.00 .15
O23 A5 2a lilac 3.25 .18
Nos. O21-O23 (3) 7.25
Set value .30

Perf. 11, 11½, 12½, 13½ and
Compound
1909-11
O24 A5 ½a red 1.75 .15
O25 A3 1a black 1.00 .15
O26 A3 2a olive green 1.75 .30
O27 A5 3a brown orange 10.00 5.00
O28 A5 4a olive green ('11) 1.50 .30
O29 A5 8a violet ('11) 1.75 .35
O30 A5 12a blue green ('11) 2.50 .35
Nos. O24-O30 (7) 20.25 6.60

Regular Issue of 1908-11 Overprinted سرکاری

1911-12
O31 A5 ¼a gray .18 .15
O32 A5 ½a green .30 .15
O33 A5 1a carmine .15 .15
O34 A5 2a lilac .20 .15
O35 A5 3a brown orange 1.00 .15
O36 A5 4a olive green .75 .15
O37 A5 8a violet 1.00 .18
O38 A5 12a blue green 2.25 .50
Nos. O31-O38 (8) 5.83
Set value 1.05

Same Overprint on Regular Issue of 1912
1912
O39 A5 ¼a brown violet .15 .15
a. ¼a gray violet .15 .15
O40 A5 ½a deep green .20 .15
Set value .15

Same Ovpt. On Regular Issue of 1915-16
1917
O41 A6 ½a green .60 .15
O42 A6 1a carmine rose 1.00 .15
O43 A6 1a red 1.00 .15
Nos. O41-O43 (3) 2.60
Set value .16

Same Overprint on Nos. 37 and 38
1930
O44 A5 4p on ¼a brown violet .80 .15
O45 A6 8p on ½a green .80 .15
Set value .15

Same Overprint on Regular Issue of 1931
1934-47 Wmk. 211 Perf. 13½
O46 A8 4p black .15 .15
a. Laid paper ('47) .30
b. Imperf., pair 50.00
O47 A8 8p green .20 .15
a. 8p yel grn, laid paper ('47) 2.00 .30
b. Inverted overprint 145.00 145.00
O48 A9 1a dark brown .25 .15
O49 A10 2a dark violet .25 .15
O50 A11 4a ultramarine .65 .15
O51 A12 8a deep orange 2.00 .20
O52 A13 12a scarlet 2.00 .25
O53 A14 1r yellow 2.75 .32
Nos. O46-O53 (8) 8.25
Set value 1.00

Catalogue values for unused stamps in this section, from this point to the end of the section, are for Never Hinged items.

Same Overprint on Nos. 58-59, 39B
1947-50 Perf. 13½
O54 A6 ½a rose lake 3.25 1.00
O55 A8 2p brown ('49) 2.50 1.25
O56 A8 6p car lake ('50) 4.00 3.00
Nos. O54-O56 (3) 9.75 5.25

IDAR

'ē–dər

LOCATION — A Feudatory State in the Western India States Agency.
AREA — 1,669 sq. mi.
POP. — 262,660
CAPITAL — Himmatnagar

Stamps of Idar are in booklet panes of four. All stamps have one or two straight edges.

Maharaja Shri Himatsinhji
A1 A2

1939 Unwmk. Typo. Perf. 11
1 A1 ½a light green 2.75 14.00

1941 Same Redrawn
2 A1 ½a green 4.50

The panels containing denomination and name of state are shaded.

1944 Unwmk. Perf. 12
3 A2 ¼a green .75 14.00
4 A2 1a purple .40
5 A2 2a blue .48
a. imperf., pair 135.00
6 A2 4a red 1.40
Nos. 3-6 (4) 3.03

INDORE

in–'dō(ə)r

(Holkar)

LOCATION — A Feudatory State in the Indore Agency in Central India.
AREA — 9,902 sq. mi.
POP. — 1,513,966
CAPITAL — Indore

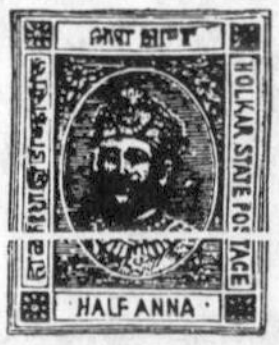
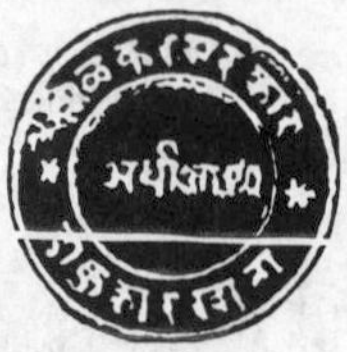

Maharaja Tukoji Rao II — A1 A2

1886 Unwmk. Litho. *Perf. 15*

1	A1	1/2a lilac	2.00	2.00

1889 Handstamped *Imperf.*

3	A2	1/4a black, *rose*	1.75	1.90

No. 3 exists in two types.

The originals of this stamp are printed in water color. The reprints are in oil color and on paper of a deeper shade of rose.

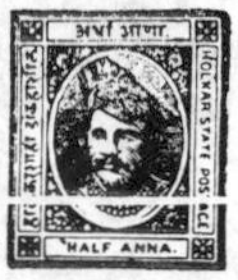

Maharaja Shivaji Rao — A3

1889-92 Engr. *Perf. 15*

4	A3	1/4a orange	.15	.15
5	A3	1/2a brown violet	.18	.18
6	A3	1a green	.50	.50
7	A3	2a vermilion	1.25	.65
		Nos. 4-7 (4)	2.08	1.48

For overprint see No. 14.

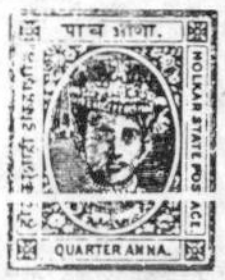
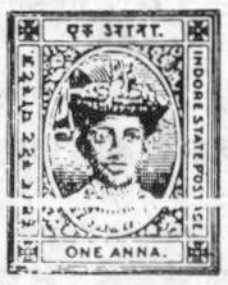

Maharaja Tukoji Rao III
A4 A5

1904-08 *Perf. 13 1/2, 14*

8	A4	1/4a orange	.15	.15
9	A5	1/2a lake ('08)	5.00	.15
a.		Imperf., pair	17.50	
10	A5	1a green ('07)	3.75	.15
a.		Imperf., pair	100.00	
11	A5	2a brown ('05)	2.50	.15
a.		Imperf., pair	62.50	
12	A5	3a violet	2.25	.45
13	A5	4a ultramarine	2.50	.45
		Nos. 8-13 (6)	16.15	
		Set value		1.20

For overprints, see Nos. O1-O7.

No. 5 Surcharged पाव आना.

1905 *Perf. 15*

14	A3	1/4a on 1/2a brown violet	1.75	1.65

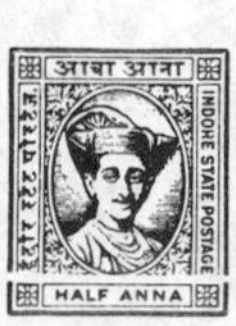
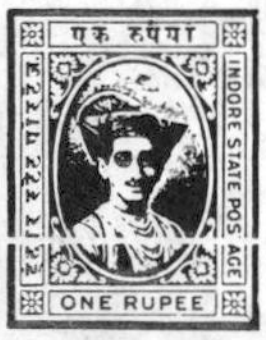

Maharaja Yeshwant Rao II
A6 A7

1928-38 Engr. *Perf. 13 1/2*

15	A6	1/4a orange	.15	.15
16	A6	1/2a claret	.15	.15
17	A6	1a green	.15	.15
18	A6	1 1/4a green ('33)	.38	.15
19	A6	2a dark brown	.90	.65
20	A6	2a Prus blue ('36)	.50	.30
21	A6	3a dull violet	.90	.90
22	A6	3 1/2a dull violet ('34)	1.00	1.00
23	A6	4a ultramarine	1.00	1.00
24	A6	4a bister ('38)	1.75	.50
25	A6	8a gray	2.00	2.00
26	A6	8a red orange ('38)	7.50	3.25
27	A6	12a rose red ('34)	7.00	7.00

Perf. 14

28	A7	1r lt blue & black	11.00	15.00
29	A7	2r car lake & black	22.50	25.00
30	A7	5r org brn & black	30.00	30.00
		Nos. 15-30 (16)	86.88	87.20

Imperforates of types A6 and A7 were used with official sanction at Indore City during a stamp shortage in 1938. They were from sheets placed by the printers (Perkins, Bacon) on top of packets of 100 perforated sheets as identification.

Stamps of 1929-33 Surcharged in Black QUARTER ANNA

1940 *Perf. 13, 14*

31	A7	1/4a on 5r org brn & blk	.65	.15
a.		Dbl. surch., black over green		185.00
32	A7	1/2a on 2r car lake & blk	1.00	.20
33	A6	1a on 1 1/4a green	1.10	.18
a.		Inverted surcharge	75.00	
		Nos. 31-33 (3)	2.75	.53

Stamps with green surcharge only are proofs.

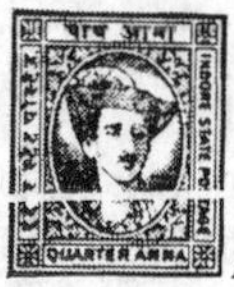

A8

1941-47 Typo. *Perf. 11*

34	A8	1/4a orange	.15	.15
35	A8	1/2a rose lilac	.50	.15
36	A8	1a dk olive green	.65	.15
37	A8	1 1/4a yellow green	.75	.18
a.		Imperf., pair	125.00	
38	A8	2a turquoise blue	6.00	1.75
39	A8	4a bister ('47)	16.00	16.00

Size: 23x28 1/4mm

40	A8	2r car lake & blk ('47)	12.50	25.00
41	A8	5r brn org & blk	14.00	30.00
		Nos. 34-41 (8)	50.55	73.38

OFFICIAL STAMPS

Stamps and Type of 1904-08 Overprinted SERVICE

1904-06 *Perf. 13 1/2, 14*

O1	A5	1/2a lake	.15	.15
a.		Inverted overprint	14.00	
b.		Double overprint	14.00	
c.		Imperf., pair	20.00	
O2	A5	1a green	.15	.15
O3	A5	2a brown ('05)	.15	.15
O4	A5	3a violet ('06)	.75	.75
a.		Imperf., pair	110.00	
O5	A5	4a ultra ('05)	1.25	1.25
		Nos. O1-O5 (5)	2.45	2.45

Same Overprint on No. 8

1907

O6	A4	1/4a orange	.15	.15

No. 9 Overprinted SERVICE

O7	A5	1/2a lake	.15	.15

#O1, O7 differ mainly in the shape of the "R."

JAIPUR

'jī-,pu̇(ə)r

LOCATION — A Feudatory State in the Jaipur Residency of India.
AREA — 15,610 sq. mi.
POP. — 3,040,876
CAPITAL — Jaipur

Catalogue values for unused stamps in this State are for Never Hinged items, beginning with Scott 49 in the regular postage section, and Scott O30 in the officials section.

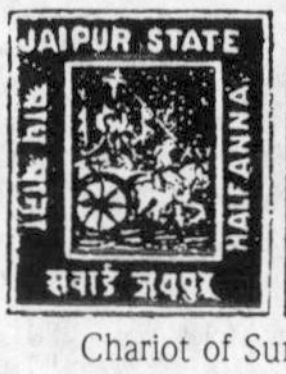
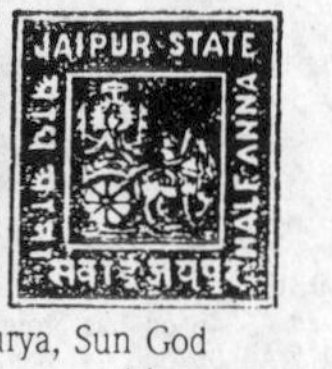

Chariot of Surya, Sun God
A1 A1a

Pin-perf. 14x14 1/2

1904 Typo. Unwmk.

1	A1	1/2a ultramarine	6.25	6.25
a.		1/2a pale blue	16.00	16.00
b.		1/2a gray blue		250.00
c.		As "b," imperf.	325.00	375.00
1D	A1a	1/2a blue	1.75	2.00
e.		1/2a ultramarine	1.75	2.00
f.		Imperf.		
2	A1	1a dull red	1.75	1.90
a.		1a chestnut	12.50	12.50
3	A1	2a pale green	2.75	2.75
a.		2a emerald	4.25	4.50
		Nos. 1-3 (4)	12.50	12.90

No. 1 has 36 varieties (on 2 plates), differing in minor details. Nos. 1b and 1c are from plate II. No. 1D has 24 varieties (one plate).

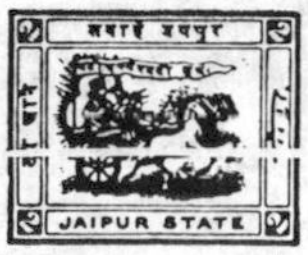

Chariot of Surya — A2

Perf. 12 1/2x12 and 13 1/2

1904-06 Engr.

4	A2	1/4a olive green ('06)	.15	.15
5	A2	1/2a deep blue	.15	.15
6	A2	1a carmine	.38	.32
7	A2	2a dark green	.75	.65
8	A2	4a red brown	3.75	2.00
9	A2	8a violet	2.50	1.90
10	A2	1r yellow	3.75	4.00
		Nos. 4-10 (7)	11.43	9.17

For overprints see Nos. 21-22.

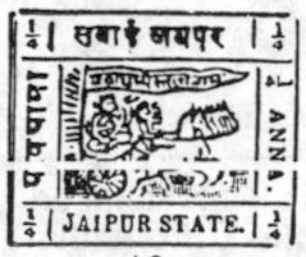
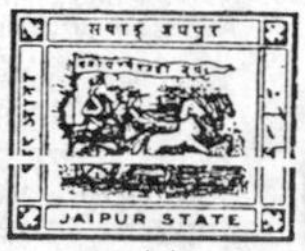

A3 A4

1911 Typo. *Imperf.*
Without Gum

11	A3	1/4a yellow green	1.50	1.75
a.		1/4a olive green	1.50	1.75
b.		"1/4" inverted	2.00	2.00
12	A3	1/4a olive yellow	.20	.20
b.		1/4a blue (error)		
13	A3	1/2a ultramarine	.20	.20
a.		1/2a dull blue	.20	.20
b.		"1/3" for "1/2"	5.00	
14	A3	1a carmine	.30	.30
15	A3	2a deep green	2.50	2.75
a.		2a gray green	2.50	2.75
		Nos. 11-15 (5)	4.70	5.20

There are six types for each value and several settings of the 1/4a and 1/2a in the 1911 issue.

Wmk. "Dorling & Co., London" in Sheet

1913-18 *Perf. 11*

16	A4	1/4a olive bister	.15	.15
a.		Pair, imperf. between	75.00	75.00
17	A4	1/2a ultramarine	.15	.15
18	A4	1a carmine ('18)	.20	.15
a.		1a scarlet	.20	.15
b.		Vertical pair, imperf. between	87.50	87.50
19	A4	2a green ('18)	2.00	2.00
20	A4	4a red brown	.60	.60
		Nos. 16-20 (5)	3.10	3.05

For overprints see Nos. O1-O6, O9-O10.

Stamps of 1904-06 Surcharged ३ आना

1926 Unwmk. Engr. *Perf. 13 1/2*

21	A2	3a on 8a violet	.75	.85
a.		Inverted surcharge	125.00	125.00
22	A2	3a on 1r yellow	.75	.85
a.		Inverted surcharge	125.00	125.00

Wmk. "Overland Bank" in Sheet

1928 Typo. *Perf. 12*

17a	A4	1/2a ultramarine	4.75	4.75
18c	A4	1a rose red	12.50	7.50
18d	A4	1a scarlet	12.50	7.50
19a	A4	2a green	24.00	18.00
20a	A4	4a pale brown		
23	A4	8a violet		
23A	A4	1r red orange	125.00	125.00

Durbar Commemorative Issue

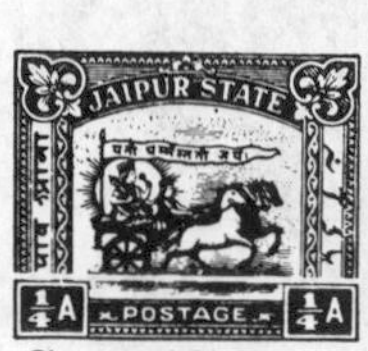
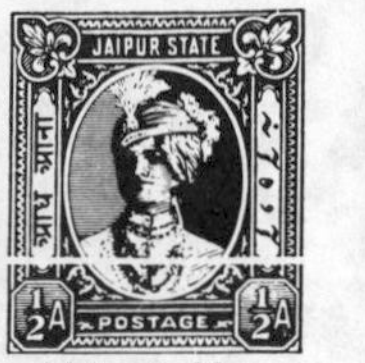

Chariot of Surya, Sun God — A5 Maharaja Man Singh II — A6

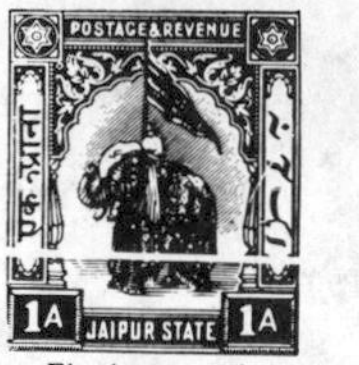
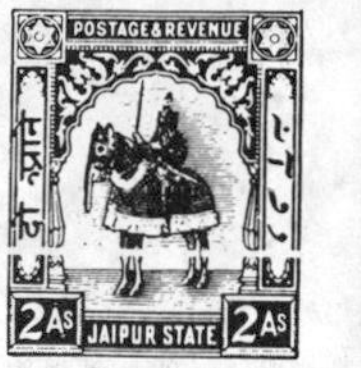

Elephant with Standard — A7 Sowar in Armor — A8

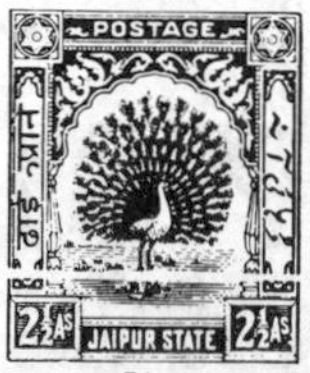
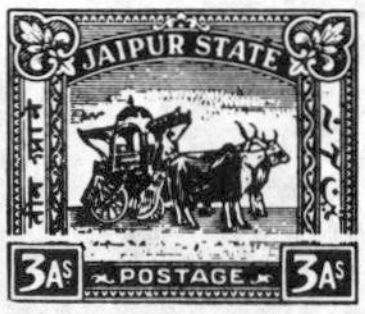

Blue Peafowl — A9 Royal Bullock Carriage — A10

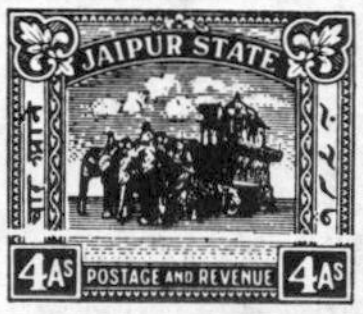

Royal Elephant Carriage — A11

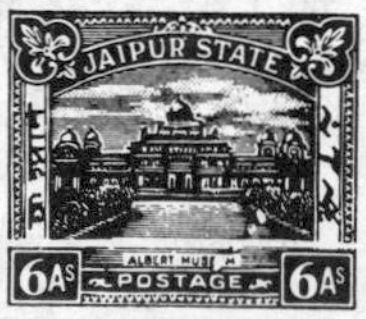

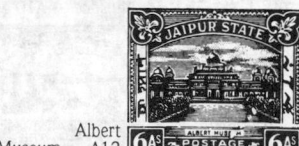

Albert Museum — A12

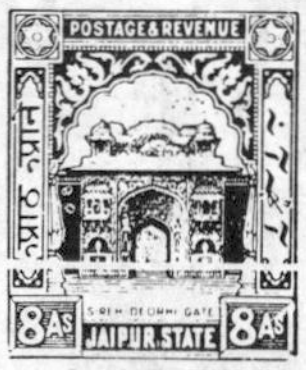
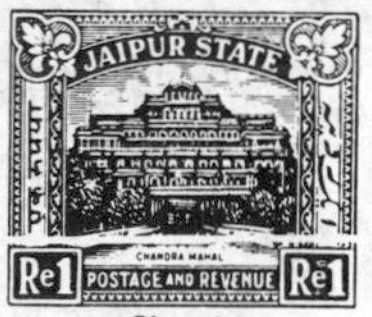

Sireh-Deorhi Gate — A13 Chandra Palace — A14

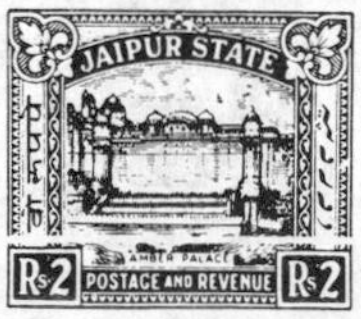

Amber Palace — A15

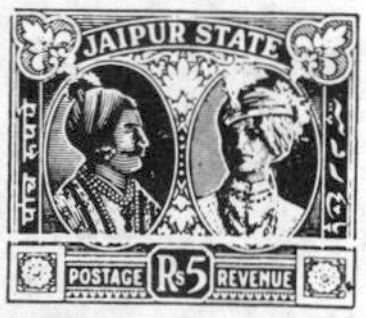

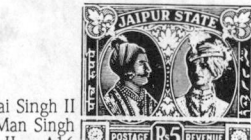

Rajas Jai Singh II and Man Singh II — A16

Perf. 13 1/2x14, 14, 14x13 1/2

1931, Mar. 14 Typo. Unwmk.

24	A5	1/4a red brown & blk	.22	.15
25	A6	1/2a dull vio & blk	.38	.15
26	A7	1a blue & black	1.90	.90
27	A8	2a ocher & black	1.90	.90
28	A9	2 1/2a rose & black	8.50	15.00
29	A10	3a dk green & blk	8.50	14.00
30	A11	4a dull grn & blk	5.50	11.50
31	A12	6a dk blue & blk	5.50	11.50
32	A13	8a brown & black	6.50	14.00
33	A14	1r olive & black	10.00	22.50
34	A15	2r lt green & blk	10.00	27.50
35	A16	5r violet & black	14.00	32.50
		Nos. 24-35 (12)	72.90	150.60

Investiture of the Maharaja Man Singh II with full ruling powers.

Eighteen sets of this issue were overprinted in red "INVESTITURE—MARCH 14, 1931" for presentation to distinguished personages.

For surcharges see Nos. 47, 48, 58. For overprints see Nos. O12-O16, Rajasthan 16.

Man Singh II Type of 1931 and

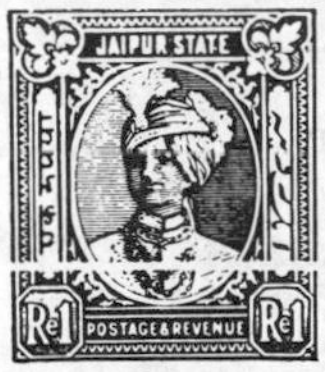

Raja Man Singh II — A18

1932-46 *Perf. 14*

36	A6	1/4a red brown & blk	.15	.15
36A	A6	3/4a brn orange & black ('43)	.15	.15
37	A18	1a blue & black	.15	.15
37A	A6	1a blue & black	.50	.15
38	A18	2a ocher & black	.15	.15
38A	A6	2a ocher & blk ('45)	.75	.15
39	A6	2 1/2a dk car & black	.20	.15
40	A6	3a green & black	.25	.15
41	A18	4a gray grn & black	.75	.75
41A	A6	4a gray green & blk ('45)	1.25	.75
42	A6	6a blue & black	.65	.65
43	A18	8a choc & black	.65	.65
43A	A6	8a choc & blk ('45)	2.00	3.00
44	A18	1r bis & gray blk	7.50	*10.00*
44A	A6	1r bis & gray blk ('46)	7.50	*10.00*
45	A18	2r yel grn & blk	37.50	*50.00*
		Nos. 36-45 (16)	60.10	*77.00*

For overprints see Nos. O17-O30, Rajasthan Nos. 15, 17-25.

Stamps of 1931-32 Surcharged in Red or Black **One Rupee**

1936 *Perf. 14x13 1/2, 13 1/2x14*

46	A18	1r on 2r yel grn & blk (R)	2.25	*3.75*
47	A16	1r on 5r violet & blk	2.00	*3.75*

No. 25 Surcharged in Red **पाव आना**

1938 *Perf. 14x13 1/2*

48	A6	1/4a on 1/2a dull vio & blk	2.25	2.25

Catalogue values for unused stamps in this section, from this point to the end of the section, are for Never Hinged items.

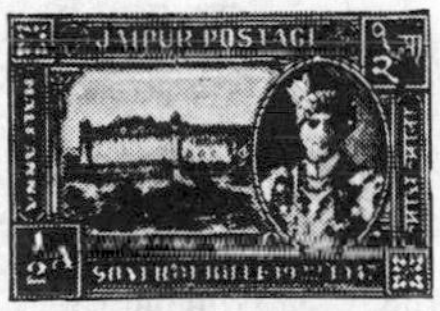

Amber Palace A19

Designs: 1/4a, Palace gate. 3/4a, Map of Jaipur. 1a, Observatory. 2a, Palace of the Winds. 3a, Arms of the Raja. 4a, Gate of Amber Fort. 8a, Chariot of the Sun. 1r, Raja Man Singh II.

1947-48 Unwmk. Engr. *Perf. 14*

49	A19	1/4a dk green & red brn ('48)	.15	.18
50	A19	1/2a blue vio & dp grn	.15	.18
51	A19	3/4a dk car & blk ('48)	.15	.25
52	A19	1a dp ultra & choc	.25	.35
53	A19	2a car & blue vio	.20	.35
54	A19	3a dk gray & grn ('48)	.30	.52
55	A19	4a choc & dp ultra	.40	.70
56	A19	8a dk brown & red	.50	.70
57	A19	1r dk red vio & bl grn ('48)	1.25	2.25
		Nos. 49-57 (9)	3.35	5.48

25th anniv. of the enthronement of Raja Man Singh II.

No. 25 Surcharged in Carmine with New Value and Bars

1947

58	A6	3p on 1/2a	15.00	15.00
a.		"3 PIE"	50.00	50.00
b.		Inverted surcharge	52.50	52.50
c.		Double surch., one inverted	100.00	100.00
d.		As "a", inverted surcharge	225.00	225.00

For overprint, see No. O31.

OFFICIAL STAMPS

Regular Issue of 1913-22 Overprinted in Black or Red **SERVICE**

1929 Unwmk. *Perf. 12 1/2x12, 11*

O1	A4	1/4a olive green	.35	.18
O2	A4	1/2a ultramarine	.35	.15
a.		Inverted overprint		90.00
O3	A4	1/2a ultra (R)	.35	.15
O4	A4	1a red	.50	.15
O5	A4	2a green	.45	.24
O6	A4	4a red brown	2.25	.90
O7	A4	8a purple (R)	18.00	18.00
O8	A4	1r red orange	35.00	35.00
		Nos. O1-O8 (8)	57.25	54.77

The 8a and 1r not issued without overprint.

For overprint see No. O11.

Regular Issue of 1913-22 Overprinted in Black or Red

b **SERVICE**

1931 *Perf. 11, 12 1/2x12*

O9	A4	1/2a ultra	75.00	.15
O10	A4	1/2a ultra (R)	90.00	.15
O10A	A4	8a purple	200.00	200.00
O10B	A4	1r red orange	200.00	200.00
		Nos. O9-O10B (4)	565.00	400.30

No. O5 Surcharged **आध आना**

1932

O11	A4	1/2a on 2a green	120.00	.24

Regular Issue of 1931 Overprinted in Red **SERVICE**

1931-37 *Perf. 13 1/2x14, 14*

O12	A6	1/4a red brn & blk ('36)	.15	.15
O13	A6	1/2a dull vio & blk	.15	.15
O14	A7	1a blue & black	180.00	1.50
O15	A8	2a ocher & blk ('36)	.90	.45
O16	A11	4a dl grn & blk ('37)	7.50	3.00

For overprint see No. O32.

Same on Regular Issue of 1932 in Red

1932-37 *Perf. 14*

O17	A18	1a blue & black	.30	.30
O18	A18	2a ocher & black	.30	.30
O19	A18	4a gray grn & blk ('37)	*175.00*	*115.00*
O20	A18	8a choc & black	2.50	2.50
O21	A18	1r bister & gray blk	9.00	9.00
		Nos. O17-O21 (5)	187.10	127.10

No. 36 Overprinted Type "b" in Black

1939 *Perf. 14*

O22	A6	1/4a red brown & blk	45.00	35.00

Nos. 36A, 38A, 39, 41A, 43A, 44A and Type of 1931 Overprinted in Carmine

SERVICE

1941-46 Unwmk. *Perf. 13 1/2, 14*

O23	A6	3/4a brn org & blk ('43)	.15	.15
O24	A6	1a blue & blk ('41)	.32	.15
O25	A6	2a ocher & black	.45	.15
O26	A6	2 1/2a dk car & blk ('46)	1.20	*4.50*
O27	A6	4a gray grn & blk ('46)	.60	.35
O28	A6	8a choc & black	1.20	.60
O29	A6	1r bis & gray blk	*150.00*	
		Nos. O23-O28 (6)	3.92	*5.90*

Catalogue values for unused stamps in this section, from this point to the end of the section, are for Never Hinged items.

No. O24 Surcharged with New Value and Bars in Carmine

1947 *Perf. 13 1/2*

O30	A6	9p on 1a blue & black	.25	.25

No. 58 Overprinted in Red "SERVICE"

Perf. 14

O31	A6	3p on 1/2a	3.50	5.00
a.		Inverted surcharge	1,200.	1,100.
b.		Double surch., one inverted	65.00	65.00
c.		"3 PIE"	300.00	300.00

No. O13 Surcharged "Three-quarter Anna" in Devanagari, similar to surcharge on No. 48, and Bars in Carmine

1949 *Perf. 14x13 1/2*

O32	A6	3/4a on 1/2a dl vio & blk	10.00	6.00

For later issues see Rajasthan.

JAMMU AND KASHMIR

'jəm-(,)ü and 'kash-,mi(ə)r

LOCATION — A Feudatory State in the Kashmir Residency in the extreme north of India.
AREA — 82,258 sq. mi.
POP. — 4,021,616 (1941)
CAPITAL — Srinagar

All stamps of Jammu and Kashmir were issued without gum.

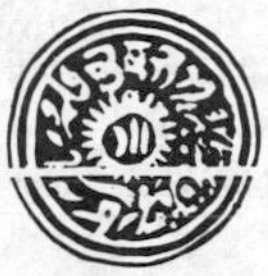

1/2 Anna — A1

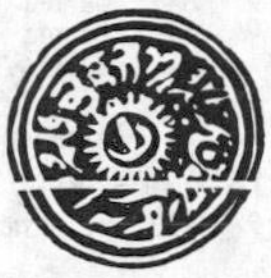

1 Anna — A2

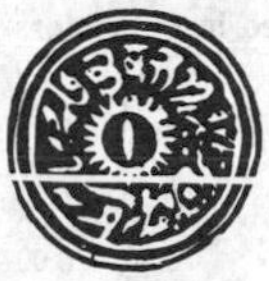

1/4 Rupee — A3

Native Grayish Laid Paper
Handstamped

1866-67 Unwmk. *Imperf.*

Printed in Water Colors

1	A1	1/2a gray black	225.00	115.00
		Cut to shape	25.00	20.00
2	A2	1a dull blue	400.00	110.00
a.		1a ultramarine	400.00	110.00
b.		1a royal blue	450.00	125.00
		Cut to shape	40.00	15.00
3	A2	1a gray black	750.00	750.00
		Cut to shape	75.00	75.00
4	A3	1/4r dull blue	900.00	400.00
a.		1/4r ultramarine	900.00	400.00
b.		1/4r indigo	2,100.	*1,000.*
		Cut to shape	90.00	40.00
5	A3	1/4r gray black	900.00	—
		Cut to shape	90.00	
		Nos. 1-5 (5)	3,175.	1,375.

It has now been proved by the leading authorities on Indian stamps that all stamps of 1/2 anna and 1 anna printed from the so-called Die A are forgeries and that no such die was ever in use.

See Nos. 24-59.

JAMMU

A part of the Feudatory State of Jammu & Kashmir, both being ruled by the same sovereign.

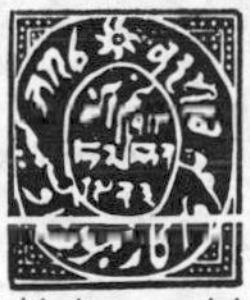

1/2 Anna — A4

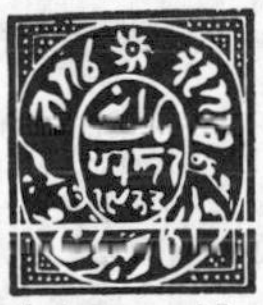

1 Anna — A5

Printed in blocks of four, three types of the 1/2a and one of the 1a.

Native Grayish Laid Paper
Printed in Water Colors

1867-77 Unwmk. *Imperf.*

6	A4	1/2a black	100.00	32.50
7	A4	1/2a indigo	20.00	17.50
a.		1/2a deep ultramarine	27.50	25.00
b.		1/2a deep violet blue	27.50	25.00
8	A4	1/2a red	2.25	1.90
a.		1/2a orange red	32.50	16.00
b.		1/2a orange	47.50	47.50
9	A5	1a black	375.00	250.00
10	A5	1a indigo	55.00	40.00
a.		1a deep ultramarine	55.00	45.00
b.		1a deep violet blue	70.00	45.00
11	A5	1a red	2.75	2.75
a.		1a orange red	16.00	17.50
b.		1a orange		425.00

1876

12	A4	1/2a emerald	275.00	190.00
13	A4	1/2a bright blue		80.00
14	A5	1a emerald	425.00	250.00
15	A5	1a bright blue	80.00	80.00

Native Grayish Laid Paper

1877 Printed in Oil Colors

16	A4	1/2a red	7.00	7.00
a.		1/2a brown red	20.00	16.00
17	A4	1/2a black	275.00	160.00
18	A5	1a red	20.00	20.00
a.		1a brown red	50.00	27.50
19	A5	1a black	*500.00*	*250.00*

The formerly listed 1/2a dark blue, 1/2a dark green, 1a dark blue and 1a dark green are believed to be reprints.

European White Laid Paper

20	A4	1/2a red	*350.00*	*310.00*
a.		Thin laid bâtonné paper		*400.00*
21	A5	1a red	*310.00*	
a.		Thin laid bâtonné paper	*625.00*	

European White Wove Paper

22	A4	1/2a red		*250.00*
23	A5	1a red		*375.00*

RE-ISSUES
For Jammu Only
Native Grayish Laid Paper
Printed in Water Colors

1869-76 *Imperf.*

24	A1	1/2a deep black	4.50	4.50
25	A1	1/2a bright blue	11.00	11.00
26	A1	1/2a orange red	5.75	5.75
a.		1/2a orange	7.00	7.00
b.		1/2a red	7.00	7.00
27	A1	1/2a emerald	32.50	32.50
28	A1	1/2a yellow	62.50	62.50
29	A2	1a deep black	15.00	
30	A2	1a bright blue	11.00	
31	A2	1a orange red	32.50	32.50
b.		1a red	32.50	32.50
32	A2	1a emerald	37.50	37.50
33	A2	1a yellow	55.00	55.00
34	A3	1/4r deep black	30.00	
35	A3	1/4r bright blue	6.75	
a.		1/4r indigo	14.00	
36	A3	1/4r orange red	9.00	
a.		1/4r orange	9.00	
b.		1/4r red	9.00	
37	A3	1/4r emerald	37.50	37.50
38	A3	1/4r yellow	55.00	55.00

Native Grayish Laid Paper

1877 Printed in Oil Colors

39	A1	1/2a red	6.00	4.50
40	A1	1/2a black	3.75	3.75
41	A1	1/2a slate blue	19.00	19.00
42	A1	1/2a sage green	50.00	50.00
43	A2	1a red	20.00	20.00
45	A2	1a slate blue	6.75	6.75
46	A2	1a sage green	62.50	62.50
47	A3	1/4r red	6.00	
50	A3	1/4r sage green	50.00	

European White Laid Paper

51	A1	1/2a red	110.00	110.00
52	A1	1/2a black	4.50	4.50
53	A1	1/2a slate blue	4.50	4.50
54	A1	1/2a yellow	55.00	
56	A2	1a slate blue	22.50	22.50
57	A3	1/4r red	50.00	50.00
58	A3	1/4r sage green	500.00	

European Brownish Wove Paper

59	A1	1/2a red		*190.00*

It is probable that the issues of 1876, 1877 and the re-issues of the circular stamps were made to supply the demands of philatelists more than for postal needs. They were, however, available for postage.

There exist also reprints, printed in a variety of colors, on native and European thin wove paper. Collectors are warned against official imitations, which are very numerous. They are printed on several kinds of paper and in a great variety of colors.

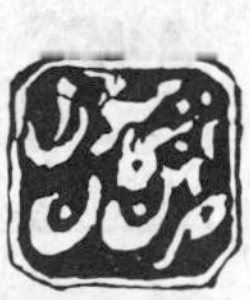

A5a

Handstamped in Oil Color

1877, Nov.

60	A5a (1/2a) red		300.00

This provisional, made with a canceling device, was used only in Nov. 1877, at Jammu city.

KASHMIR

A part of the Feudatory State of Jammu & Kashmir, both being ruled by the same sovereign.

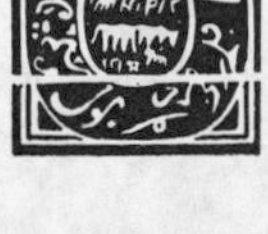

1/2 Anna — A6

Printed in Water Colors
Native Grayish Laid Paper
Printed from a Single Die

1866 **Unwmk.** ***Imperf.***

62	A6	1/2a black	750.00	340.00

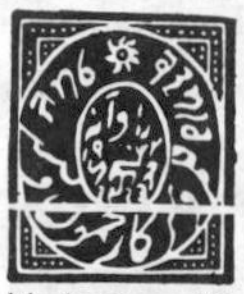

1/4 Anna — A7

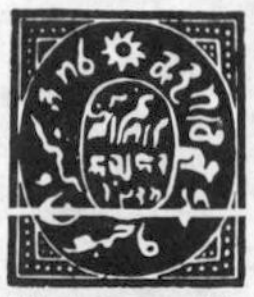

1/2 Anna — A8

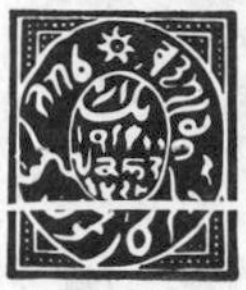

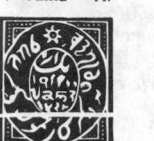

1 Anna — A9

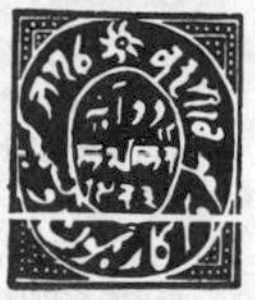

2 Annas — A10

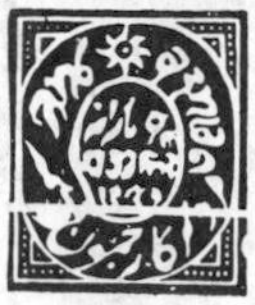

4 Annas — A11

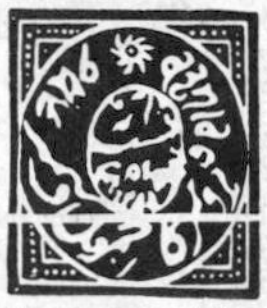

8 Annas — A12

The 1/4a, 1a and 2a are printed in strips of five varieties, the 1/2a in sheets of twenty varieties and the 4a and 8a from single dies.

1866-70

63	A7	1/4a black	.50	.50
64	A8	1/2a black	*350.00*	*140.00*
65	A8	1/2a ultra	1.10	1.10
a.		1/2a blue	1.50	1.50
66	A9	1a black		175.00
67	A9	1a red orange	3.50	3.50
68	A9	1a Venetian red	3.50	3.00
69	A9	1a orange brown	3.50	2.25
70	A9	1a ultra	*2,000.*	750.00
71	A10	2a olive yellow	5.50	4.50
72	A11	4a emerald	8.75	8.75
73	A12	8a red	8.75	8.75

All the stamps printed in oil colors are reprints.
As in Jammu, official imitations are numerous and are found in many colors and on various papers.

JAMMU & KASHMIR

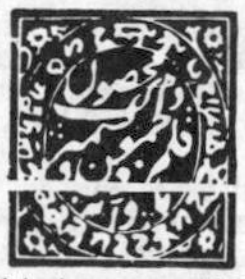

1/4 Anna — A13

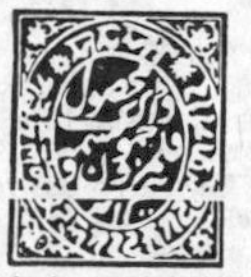

1/2 Anna — A14

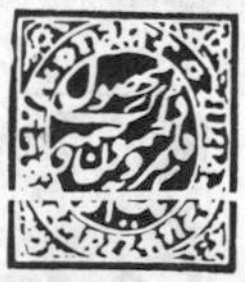

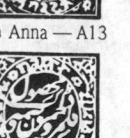

1 Anna — A15

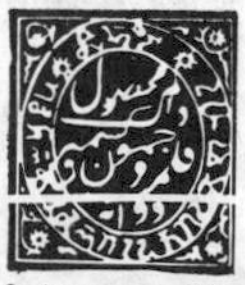

2 Annas — A16

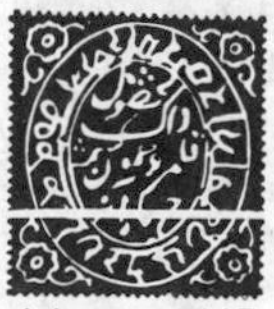

4 Annas — A17

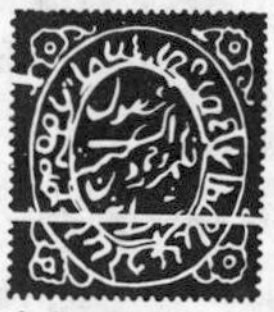

8 Annas — A18

Laid Paper
Printed in Oil Colors

1878 ***Rough Perf. 10-14***

74	A13	1/4a red	*190.00*	*190.00*
75	A14	1/2a red	3.00	3.00
a.		Wove paper		65.00
76	A14	1/2a slate blue	19.50	17.00
77	A15	1a red	225.00	225.00
78	A15	1a bright violet	*300.00*	*300.00*

1878-80 ***Imperf.***

79	A13	1/4a red	7.50	6.00
80	A14	1/2a red	2.25	2.25
81	A14	1/2a slate	7.50	7.50
82	A15	1a red	2.75	2.75
83	A15	1a violet	11.00	11.00
a.		1a dull purple	11.00	11.00
84	A16	2a red	22.50	22.50
85	A16	2a bright violet	11.00	11.00
86	A16	2a dull ultra	*75.00*	
87	A17	4a red	22.50	17.50

Thick Wove Paper

88	A14	1/2a red	11.00	11.00
89	A15	1a red	5.50	5.50
90	A16	2a red	6.00	6.00

Thin Toned Wove Paper

1879-80

91	A13	1/4a red	.50	.50
92	A14	1/2a red	.25	.25
93	A15	1a red	.50	.50
94	A16	2a red	1.00	1.00
95	A17	4a red	1.25	1.25
96	A18	8a red	2.00	2.00
		Nos. 91-96 (6)	5.50	5.50

Thin Laid Bâtonné Paper

1880 **Printed in Water Color**

97	A13	1/4a ultramarine	200.00	175.00

Thin Toned Wove Paper

1881 **Printed in Oil Colors**

98	A13	1/4a orange	3.00	3.00
99	A14	1/2a orange	11.00	11.00
100	A15	1a orange	7.50	7.50
101	A16	2a orange	10.00	10.00
102	A17	4a orange	16.00	16.00
103	A18	8a orange	22.50	22.50
		Nos. 98-103 (6)	70.00	70.00

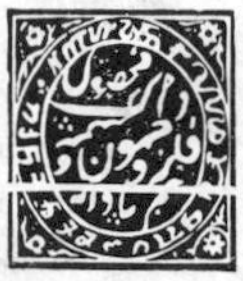

1/8 Anna — A19

Thin White or Yellowish Wove Paper

1883-94

104	A19	1/8a yellow brown	.15	.15
a.		1/8a yellow	.15	.15
105	A13	1/4a brown	.15	.15
a.		Double impression	500.00	
106	A14	1/2a red	.15	.15
a.		1/2a rose	1.10	.50
106B	A19	1/2a bright blue	1.75	1.75
c.		1/2a dull blue	1.75	1.75
107	A15	1a bronze green	.38	.38
108	A15	1a yel green	.15	.15
109	A15	1a blue green	.50	.50
110	A15	1a bister	.38	.38
111	A17	4a green	1.00	1.00
112	A17	4a olive green	4.00	4.00
113	A18	8a deep blue	3.00	3.00
114	A18	8a dark ultra	3.00	3.00
115	A18	8a gray violet	6.00	6.00

Printed in Water Color

116	A18	8a gray blue	11.00	11.00

Printed in Oil Colors
Yellow Pelure Paper

117	A16	2a red	2.25	2.25

Yellow Green Pelure Paper

118	A16	2a red	3.00	3.00

Deep Green Pelure Paper

119	A16	2a red	6.00	6.00

Coarse Yellow Wove Paper

120	A16	2a red	.38	.38
		Nos. 104-120 (18)	43.24	43.24

Thin Creamy Laid Paper

1886-94

121	A19	1/8a yellow	10.00	10.00
122	A13	1/4a brown	3.75	4.00
123	A14	1/2a vermilion	3.75	3.75
124	A14	1/2a rose red	6.00	6.00
125	A15	1a green	75.00	80.00
126	A17	4a green	87.50	87.50

Printed in Water Color

127	A18	8a gray blue	100.00	100.00
		Nos. 121-127 (7)	286.00	291.25

Impressions of types A13 to A19 in colors other than the issued stamps are proofs. Forgeries to defraud the post exist, and some are common.

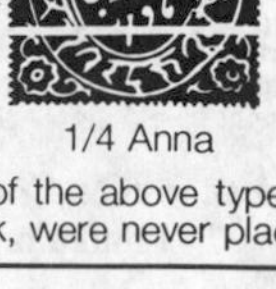

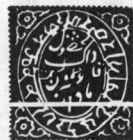

1/4 Anna

Stamps of the above type, printed in red or black, were never placed in use.

OFFICIAL STAMPS

Same Types as Regular Issues
White Laid Paper

1878 **Unwmk.** ***Rough Perf. 10-14***

O1	A14	1/2a black		500.00

Imperf

O3	A14	1/2a black	2.25	2.25
O4	A15	1a black	2.25	2.25
O5	A16	2a black	6.00	3.10
		Nos. O3-O5 (3)	10.50	7.60

Thin White or Yellowish Wove Paper

1880

O6	A13	1/4a black	.15	.15
O7	A14	1/2a black	.15	.15
O8	A15	1a black	.15	.15
O9	A16	2a black	.15	.15
O10	A17	4a black	.38	.38
O11	A18	8a black	.38	.38
		Nos. O6-O11 (6)	1.36	1.36

Thin Creamy Laid Paper

1890-91

O12	A13	1/4a black	3.50	3.50
O13	A14	1/2a black	3.50	3.50
O14	A15	1a black	3.50	3.50
O15	A16	2a black	55.00	55.00
O16	A17	4a black	22.50	15.00
O17	A18	8a black	22.50	15.00
		Nos. O12-O17 (6)	110.50	95.50

Obsolete October 31, 1894.

JASDAN

LOCATION — A Feudatory State in the Kathiawar Agency in Western India.
AREA — 296 sq. mi.
POP. — 34,056 (1931)
CAPITAL — Jasdan

In 1948 Jasdan was incorporated in the United State of Saurashtra (see Soruth).

Catalogue values for all unused stamps in this state are for Never Hinged items.

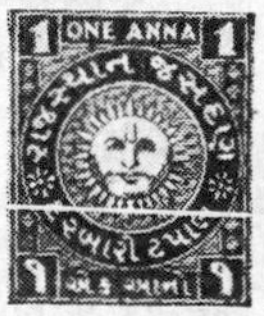

Sun — A1

Perf. 8 1/2 to 10 1/2

1942 **Unwmk.** **Typo.**

1	A1	1a green	2.75

Issued in booklet panes of 4 and 8.
The 1a carmine is a revenue stamp.
Jasdan's stamp became obsolete Feb. 15, 1948.

JHALAWAR

'jäl–ə–,wär

LOCATION — A Feudatory State in the Rajputana Agency of India.
AREA — 813 sq. mi.
POP. — 107,890
CAPITAL — Jhalrapatan

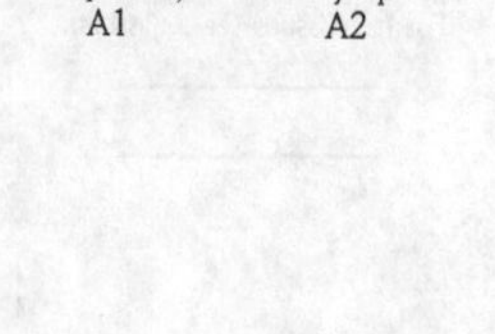

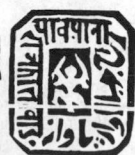

Apsaras, Hindu Nymph
A1 A2

Laid Paper

1887-90 **Unwmk.** ***Imperf.***
Without Gum

1	A1	1p yellow green	2.00	3.25
2	A2	1/4a green	.75	1.25

Obsolete October 31, 1900.

JIND

'jind

(Jhind)

LOCATION — A State of India in the north Punjab.
AREA — 1,299 sq. mi.
POP. — 361,812 (1941)
CAPITAL — Sangrur

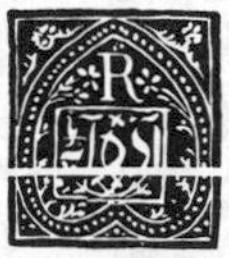

A1

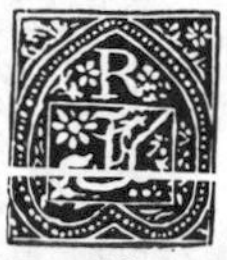

A2

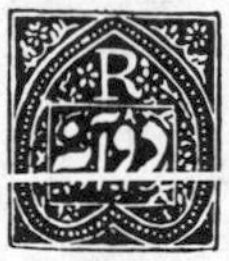

A3

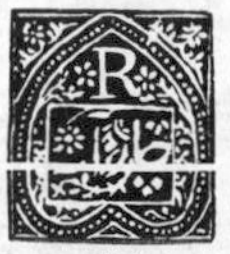

A4

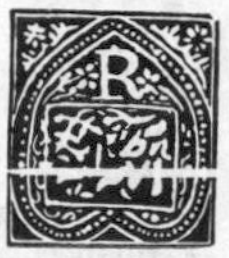

A5

1874 **Unwmk.** **Litho.** ***Imperf.***
Thin White Wove Paper
Without Gum

1	A1	1/2a blue	5.50	3.50
2	A2	1a lilac	7.50	7.50
3	A3	2a yellow	1.25	1.25
4	A4	4a green	27.50	5.50
5	A5	8a dark violet	150.00	40.00
		Nos. 1-5 (5)	191.75	57.75

1875

Thick Blue Laid Paper
Without Gum

6	A1	1/2a blue	.22	.22
7	A2	1a red violet	.50	.50
8	A3	2a brown orange	.75	.75
9	A4	4a green	.85	.85
10	A5	8a purple	4.25	4.25
		Nos. 6-10 (5)	6.57	6.57

1885 **Without Gum** ***Perf. 12***

11	A1	1/2a blue	4.25	4.25

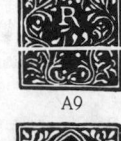

A6

A7

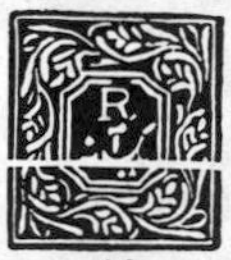

A8

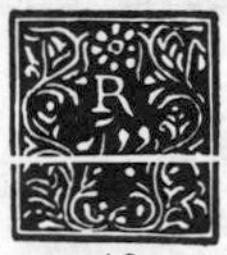

A9

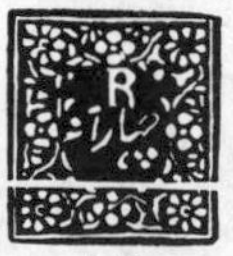

A10

A11

1882-84 **Without Gum** ***Imperf.***
Thin Yellowish Wove Paper

12	A6	1/4a buff	.15	.15
a.		Double impression		
13	A7	1/2a yellow	.55	.55
14	A8	1a brown	1.40	1.40

15	A9	2a blue	.55	.55
16	A10	4a green	.65	.65
17	A11	8a red	2.00	1.40
		Nos. 12-17 (6)	5.30	4.70

Perf. 12

18	A6	¼a buff	.28	.28
19	A7	½a yellow	.38	.38
20	A8	1a brown	.85	.85
21	A9	2a blue	1.50	1.75
22	A10	4a green	2.75	2.75
23	A11	8a red	6.75	6.75
a.		Thick white paper	6.75	6.75
		Nos. 18-23 (6)	12.51	12.76

Laid Paper

Imperf

24	A6	¼a buff	3.50	3.50
25	A7	½a yellow	1.00	1.00
26	A8	1a brown	1.00	1.00
27	A9	2a blue	55.00	55.00
28	A11	8a red	3.75	3.75
		Nos. 24-28 (5)	64.25	64.25

Perf. 12

29	A6	¼a buff	11.00	11.00
30	A7	½a yellow	15.00	11.00
31	A8	1a brown	3.75	3.75
32	A11	8a red	5.00	5.00
		Nos. 29-32 (4)	34.75	30.75

As postage stamps these issues became obsolete in July, 1885, but some possibly remained in use as revenue stamps.

For later issues see Jind under Convention States.

KISHANGARH

'kish–ən–,gär

LOCATION — A Feudatory State in the Jaipur Residency of India.
AREA — 858 sq. mi.
POP. — 85,744
CAPITAL — Kishangarh

Kishangarh was incorporated in Rajasthan in 1947-49.

Stamps were issued without gum except Nos. 27-35.

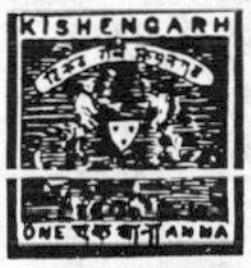

Coat of Arms — A1

1899-1900 Unwmk. Typo. *Imperf.*

Soft Porous Paper

1	A1	1a green	21.00	21.00
2	A1	1a blue ('00)	*450.00*	

Pin-perf

3	A1	1a green	47.50	47.50

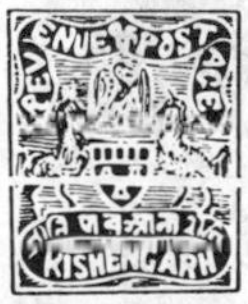

A2

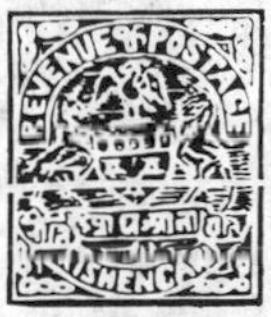

A3

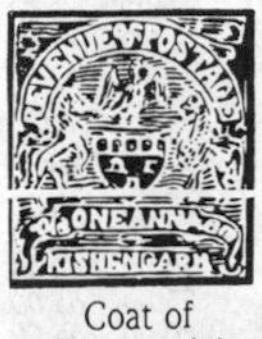

Coat of Arms — A4

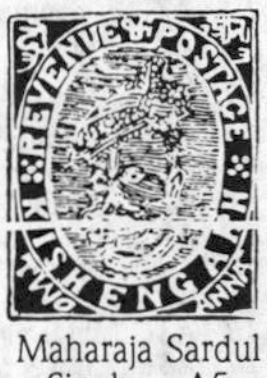

Maharaja Sardul Singh — A5

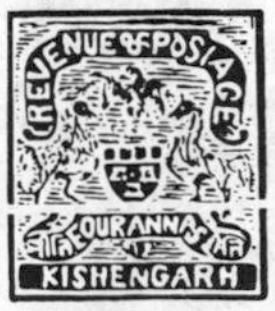

A6

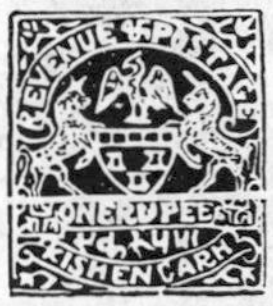

A7

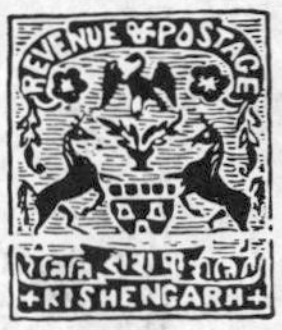

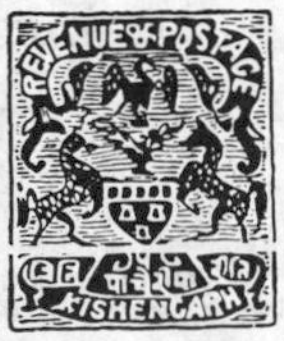

Coat of Arms
A8 A9

Thin Wove Paper

1899-1900 Handstamped *Imperf.*

4	A2	¼a carmine	.45	.45
5	A2	¼a green	125.00	
6	A3	½a blue	.90	.60
7	A3	½a green	13.00	13.00
8	A3	½a carmine	13.00	13.00
9	A3	½a violet	30.00	*35.00*
10	A4	1a gray violet	.60	.45
a.		1a gray	.60	.45
11	A4	1a rose	60.00	65.00
11A	A5	2a orange	4.00	4.00
12	A6	4a chocolate	1.90	1.90
a.		Laid paper	45.00	45.00
13	A7	1r dull green	18.00	
13A	A7	1r light brown	50.00	45.00
14	A8	2r brown red	70.00	
a.		Laid paper	55.00	
15	A9	5r violet	45.00	
a.		Laid paper	75.00	

Pin-perf

16	A2	¼a magenta	.25	.25
a.		¼a rose	.25	
17	A2	¼a green	*150.00*	65.00
a.		Imperf. vertically	250.00	250.00
18	A3	½a blue	.32	.32
a.		½a dark blue	.60	.60
19	A3	½a green	12.00	12.00
a.		Imperf. vert., pair	60.00	60.00
20	A4	1a gray violet	.55	.45
a.		1a gray	.75	.75
b.		1a red lilac		6.00
d.		As "b," laid paper	30.00	22.50
20E	A4	1a rose	40.00	27.50
21	A5	2a orange	7.00	4.50
21B	A6	4a pale red brown	1.50	1.25
c.		4a chocolate	1.50	1.25
22	A7	1r dull green	14.00	19.00
b.		Laid paper	100.00	
23	A8	2r brown red	42.50	42.50
b.		Laid paper	60.00	
24	A9	5r red violet	32.50	
d.		Laid paper	90.00	

Nos. 4-24 exist tête bêche and sell for a slight premium.

For overprints see #O1-O11, Rajasthan #26-28, 30-32.

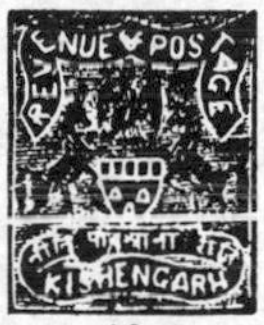

A9a

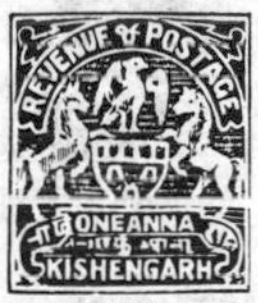

A9b

Soft Porous Paper

1901 Typo.

24A	A9a	½a rose	10.00	10.00
24B	A9b	1a dull violet	18.00	18.00

For overprint see No. O12.

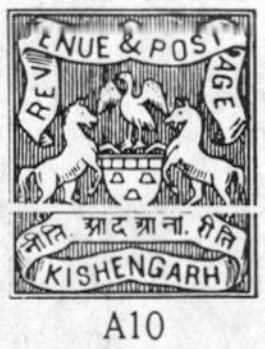

A10

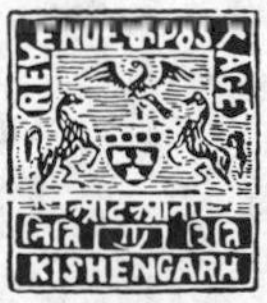

A11

1903 Stout Hard Paper *Imperf.*

25	A10	½a pink	6.50	5.25
a.		Printed on both sides		*1,000.*

1904 Thin Wove Paper *Pin-perf.*

25B	A11	8a gray	6.50	6.50

Exists tête bêche. Slight premium.
For overprints see #O13, O33, Rajasthan #29.

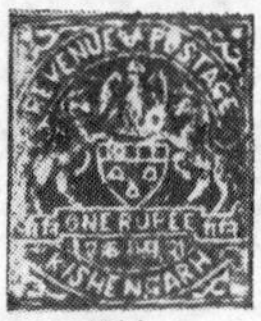

A11a

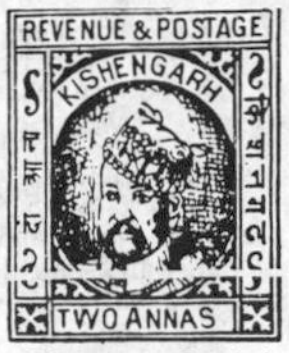

Maharaja Sardul Singh — A12

25D	A11a	1r green	27.50	27.50

For overprint see No. O13A.

1903 *Imperf.*

Stout Hard Paper

26	A12	2a yellow	4.50	4.50

For overprints see Nos. O14, O34.

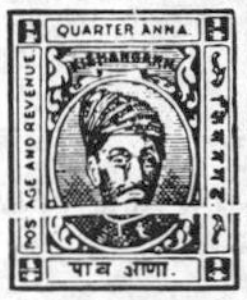

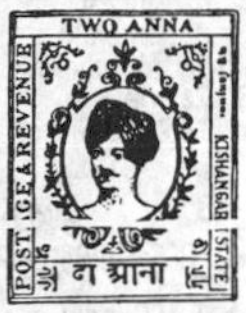

Maharaja Madan Singh
A13 A14

1904-05 Engr. *Perf. 12½, 13½*

27	A13	¼a carmine	.35	.16
28	A13	½a chestnut	.35	.16
29	A13	1a deep blue	1.50	.50
30	A13	2a orange	13.50	13.50
31	A13	4a dark brown	4.00	4.00
32	A13	8a purple ('05)	8.00	8.00
33	A13	1r dark green	11.00	11.00
34	A13	2r lemon yellow	17.00	*27.50*
35	A13	5r purple brown	22.50	*42.50*
		Nos. 27-35 (9)	78.20	*107.32*

For overprints see Nos. O15-O22, O35-O38, Rajasthan Nos. 33-39.

Thin Wove Paper

1913 Typo. *Rouletted 9½*

37	A14	2 "ANNA" violet	2.50	2.50

Exists tete beche. Slight premium.
See #40-50. For overprint see Rajasthan #43.

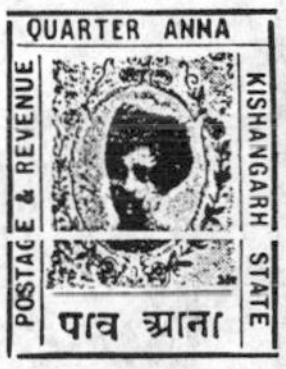

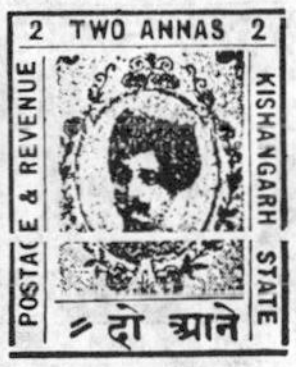

Maharaja Madan Singh
A15 A16

Thick, Chalk-surfaced Paper

1913 *Rouletted 6½, 12*

38	A15	¼a pale blue	.15	.15
a.		"Kishangahr"	3.25	3.25
b.		Imperf., pair	4.50	
39	A16	2a purple	13.00	13.00
a.		"Kishangahr"	85.00	85.00

For overprint see No. O23.

1913-16 *Rouletted 12, 14½*

40	A14	¼a pale blue	.15	.15
41	A14	½a green ('15)	.20	.20
a.		Printed on both sides	200.00	
42	A14	1a carmine	.90	.90
43	A14	2 "ANNAS" purple	2.75	3.50
44	A14	4a ultramarine	5.75	*9.00*
45	A14	8a brown	5.75	*12.00*
46	A14	1r rose lilac	12.00	*24.00*
47	A14	2r dark green	30.00	*35.00*
48	A14	5r brown	45.00	*60.00*
		Nos. 40-48 (9)	102.50	*144.75*

On Nos. 40-48 the halftone screen covers the entire design.

Nos. 41-48 have ornaments on both sides of value in top panel.

For overprints see Nos. O24-O30, O39-O43, Rajasthan Nos. 40-42, 44-48.

Type of 1913-16 Redrawn

1918 *Rouletted*

50	A14	1a rose red	.90	.90

The redrawn stamp is 24¾mm wide instead of 26mm. There is a white oval around the portrait with only traces of the red line. There is less shading outside the wreath.

For overprint see No. O44.

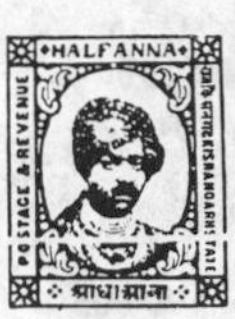

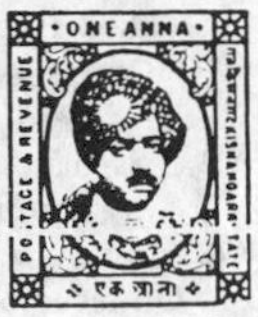

Maharaja Jagjanarajan Singh
A17 A18

Thick Glazed Paper

1928-29 *Pin-perf. 14½ to 16*

52	A17	¼a light blue	.15	.15
53	A17	½a lt yellow green	.28	.28
a.		Imperf., pair	35.00	35.00
54	A18	1a carmine rose	.55	.55
55	A18	2a red violet	2.00	2.00
56	A17	4a yellow brown	1.50	1.50
57	A17	8a purple	4.00	4.00
58	A17	1r green	4.00	4.00
59	A17	2r lemon	15.00	*24.00*
60	A17	5r red brown	30.00	*35.00*
a.		Imperf., pair	105.00	
		Nos. 52-60 (9)	57.48	*71.48*

Thick Soft Unglazed Paper

1945-47

52a	A17	¼a gray blue	1.25	1.25
b.		¼a greenish blue ('47)	1.25	1.25
53b	A17	½a deep green	1.25	1.25
54a	A18	1a dull carmine	2.50	2.50
b.		1a dark violet blue		
55a	A18	2a deep red violet	5.00	5.00
b.		2a violet brown, imperf.	20.00	
56a	A17	4a brown	25.00	25.00
57a	A17	8a violet	32.50	*40.00*
58a	A17	1r deep green	40.00	*55.00*

The 2r and 5r exist on same paper.
For overprints see Rajasthan Nos. 49-58.
For later issues see Rajasthan.

OFFICIAL STAMPS

Used values are for CTO copies.

Regular Issues of 1899-1916 Handstamped

ON
K S
D

Black Handstamp
On Issue of 1899-1900

1918 Unwmk. *Imperf.*

O1	A2	¼a carmine		8.50
O2	A4	1a gray violet	3.50	2.25
O3	A6	4a chocolate	17.00	17.00

Pin-perf

O4	A2	¼a carmine	.50	.50
O4A	A2	¼a green		40.00
O4B	A3	½a blue		27.50
O6	A4	1a gray violet	3.50	1.50
O7	A5	2a orange		
O8	A6	4a chocolate	15.00	15.00
O9	A7	1r dull green	60.00	60.00
O10	A8	2r brown red	105.00	105.00
O11	A9	5r red violet	150.00	150.00

See tete beche note after No. 24.

On Issue of 1901

O12	A9b	1a dull violet		

On Issue of 1904

O13	A11	8a gray	32.50	32.50
O13A	A11a	1r green		

Imperf.

O14	A12	2a yellow	17.00	17.00

On Issue of 1904-05

Perf. 12½, 13

O15	A13	¼a carmine	15.00	12.50
O16	A13	½a chestnut	.60	.50
O17	A13	1a deep blue	9.25	4.00
O18	A13	2a orange		
O19	A13	4a dark brown	15.00	15.00
O20	A13	8a purple	60.00	50.00
O21	A13	1r dark green	195.00	150.00
O22	A13	5r purple brn		

On Issue of 1913

Rouletted

O23	A15	¼a pale blue	8.50	

On Issue of 1913-16

O24	A14	¼a pale blue	.75	.35
O25	A14	½a green	1.35	.60
O26	A14	1a carmine	1.35	.65
O27	A14	2a purple	2.00	2.00
O28	A14	4a ultra	22.50	22.50
O29	A14	8a brown	42.50	42.50
O30	A14	1r rose lilac	85.00	85.00
O31	A14	2r dark green	250.00	
O32	A14	5r brown	340.00	

Red Handstamp
On Issue of 1904
Pin-perf

O33	A11	8a gray	42.50	42.50

Imperf

O34	A12	2a yellow	35.00	35.00

On Issue of 1904-05
Perf. 12½, 13

O35	A13	1a deep blue	12.00	12.00
O36	A13	4a dark brown	15.00	15.00
O37	A13	8a purple	25.00	35.00
O38	A13	1r dark green	45.00	72.50

On Issue of 1913-16
Rouletted

O39	A14	¼a pale blue	8.50	8.50
O40	A14	½a green	8.50	8.50
O41	A14	2a purple	22.50	22.50
O42	A14	4a ultra	42.50	42.50
O43	A14	8a brown	42.50	42.50

On Issue of 1918
Redrawn

O44	A14	1a rose red		

The overprint on Nos. O1 to O44 is hand-stamped and, as usual with that style of overprint, is found inverted, double, etc. In this instance there is evidence that many of the varieties were deliberately made.

LAS BELA

ləs ˈbāl-ə

LOCATION — A Feudatory State in the Baluchistan District.
AREA — 7,132 sq. mi.
POP. — 63,008
CAPITAL — Bela

A1   A2

1897-98   Unwmk. Typo.   Perf. 12

1	A1	½a black, *white*	9.75	9.75
2	A1	½a black, *gray*	2.75	2.50
3	A1	½a black, *blue* ('98)	5.50	5.50
		Nos. 1-3 (3)	18.00	17.75

1901

4	A2	1a black, *red orange*	9.75	9.75

1904   Pin-perf

5	A1	½a black, *lt blue*	6.00	6.00

Granite Paper

6	A1	½a black, *greenish gray*	3.75	3.75

Las Bela stamps became obsolete in Mar. 1907.

MORVI

ˈmȯr-vē

LOCATION — A Feudatory State in the Kathiawar Agency, Western India.
AREA — 822 sq. mi.
POP. — 113,023
CAPITAL — Morvi

In 1948 Morvi was incorporated in the United State of Saurashtra (see Soruth).

Sir Lakhdhirji Waghji The Thakur Sahib of Morvi — A1

1931   Unwmk. Typo.   Perf. 12
Size: 21½x26½mm

1	A1	3p red	.95	1.10
a.		3p deep blue (error)	6.00	

2	A1	½a deep blue	1.50	1.25
3	A1	1a red brown	2.00	2.50
4	A1	2a yellow brown	4.00	4.75
		Nos. 1-4 (4)	8.45	9.60

Nos. 1-4 and 1a were printed in two blocks of four, with stamps 5½mm apart, and perforated on four sides. Nos. 1 and 2 were also printed in blocks of four, with stamps 10mm apart, and perforated on two or three sides.

A2   A3

1932   Size: 21x25½mm   Perf. 11

5	A2	3p rose	.35	.75
6	A2	6p gray green	1.25	1.50
7	A2	6p emerald	1.25	2.50
8	A2	1a ultramarine	1.10	1.65
9	A2	2a violet	7.25	9.00
		Nos. 5-9 (5)	11.20	15.40

1934-48   Perf. 14, Rough Perf. 11

10	A3	3p carmine rose	.24	.28
a.		3p red	.30	.28
11	A3	6p emerald	.28	.60
a.		6p green	.28	.60
12	A3	1a red brown	1.10	1.50
a.		1a brown	1.25	1.75
13	A3	2a violet	1.10	1.50
		Nos. 10-13 (4)	2.72	3.88

The 1934 London printing of Nos. 10-13 is perf. 14; the later Morvi Press printing is rough perf. 11. Morvi stamps became obsolete Feb. 15, 1948.

NANDGAON

ˈnän(d)–ˌgau̇n

LOCATION — A Feudatory State in the Chhattisgarh States Agency in Central India.
AREA — 871 sq. mi.
POP. — 182,380
CAPITAL — Rajnandgaon

A1   A2

White Paper
1892, Feb.   Unwmk. Typo.   Imperf.
Without Gum

1	A1	½a blue	2.50	
2	A1	2a rose	12.00	

Some authorities claim that No. 2 was a revenue stamp.
For overprints see Nos. O1-O2.

1893   Without Gum

4	A2	½a green	9.00	
5	A2	2a rose	10.50	

For overprint see No. O5.

Same Redrawn
1894   Without Gum

6	A2	½a yellow green	13.00	9.50
7	A2	1a rose	30.00	30.00
a.		Laid paper	120.00	

The redrawn stamps have smaller value characters and wavy lines between the stamps.
For overprints see Nos. O3-O4.

OFFICIAL STAMPS

Regular Issues
Handstamped in Violet

1893-94   Unwmk.   Imperf.
Without Gum

O1	A1	½a blue	50.00	
O2	A1	2a red	65.00	
O3	A2	½a yellow green	.55	.55
O4	A2	1a rose	2.00	
a.		Laid paper	6.50	
O5	A2	2a rose	3.00	3.00

Some authorities believe that this handstamp was used as a control mark, rather than to indicate a stamp for official mail.
The 1 anna has been reprinted in brown and in blue.
Nandgaon stamps became obsolete in July, 1895.

NOWANUGGUR

ˌnau̇–ə–ˈnəg–ər

(Navanagar)

LOCATION — A Feudatory State in the Kathiawar Agency, Western India.
AREA — 3,791 sq. mi.
POP. — 402,192
CAPITAL — Navanagar

Stamps of Nowanuggur were superseded by those of India.

6 Dokra = 1 Anna
16 Annas = 1 Rupee

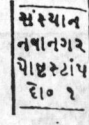

Kandjar (Indian Dagger) — A1   A2

1877   Unwmk. Typo.   Imperf.
Without Gum
Laid Paper

1	A1	1d dull blue	.50	10.00
a.		1d ultramarine	.50	10.00
b.		Tete beche pair	900.00	

Perf. 12½

2	A1	1d slate	65.00	65.00
a.		Tete beche pair	1,650.	
b.		Wove paper		

1877-88   Imperf.
Without Gum
Wove Paper

3	A2	1d black, *red violet*	.45	.90
a.		1d black, *rose*	.45	.90
b.		Characters at beginning of 3rd line read "4102" instead of "418"		
4	A2	2d black, *green*	.60	.90
a.		2d black, *blue green*	.75	1.20
b.		"4102" instead of "418"		
5	A2	3d black, *yellow*	1.10	1.50
a.		3d black, *orange yellow*	1.20	1.75
b.		"4102" instead of "418"		
c.		Laid paper	32.50	
d.		2d black, *yellow* (error in sheet of 3d)	325.00	
		Nos. 3-5 (3)	2.15	3.30

Nos. 3-5 range in width from 14 to 19mm.

Seal of the State — A3

OFFICIAL STAMPS

1893   Thick Paper   Imperf.
Without Gum

6	A3	1d black	60.00	

Perf. 12

7	A3	1d black	7.50	
8	A3	3d orange	4.50	

Imperf
Thin Paper

9	A3	1d black	50.00	
10	A3	2d dark green	50.00	
11	A3	3d orange	42.50	
		Nos. 9-11 (3)	142.50	

Perf. 12

12	A3	1d black	.18	.30
13	A3	2d green	.45	.45
14	A3	3d orange	.60	.60
a.		Imperf. vert., pair		
		Nos. 12-14 (3)	1.23	1.35

Obsolete at end of 1895.

ORCHHA

ˈȯr–chə

(Orcha)

LOCATION — A Feudatory State in the Bundelkhand Agency in Central India.
AREA — 2,080 sq. mi.
POP. — 314,661
CAPITAL — Tikamgarh

Seal of Orchha — A1

1913-17   Unwmk. Litho.   Imperf.
Without Gum

1	A1	¼a ultra ('15)	.18	.22
2	A1	½a emerald ('14)	.20	.28
a.		Background of arms unshaded	20.00	30.00
3	A1	1a carmine ('14)	1.65	2.25
a.		Background of arms unshaded	20.00	
4	A1	2a brown ('17)	4.50	5.50
5	A1	4a orange ('14)	7.50	8.25
		Nos. 1-5 (5)	14.03	16.50

Essays similar to Nos. 2-5 are in different colors.

Maharaja Singh Dev
A2   A3

1939-40   Perf. 13½, 13½x14

6	A2	¼a chocolate	.22	10.00
7	A2	½a yellow green	.22	8.50
8	A2	¾a ultramarine	.22	13.00
9	A2	1a rose red	.22	8.50
10	A2	1¼a deep blue	.22	13.00
11	A2	1½a lilac	.22	12.50
12	A2	2a vermilion	1.25	10.00
13	A2	2½a turq green	1.65	8.50
14	A2	3a dull violet	1.65	12.00
15	A2	4a blue gray	2.50	13.00
16	A2	8a rose lilac	6.00	30.00
17	A3	1r sage green	10.00	40.00
18	A3	2r lt violet ('40)	25.00	65.00
19	A3	5r yel org ('40)	80.00	165.00
20	A3	10r blue	165.00	250.00
		Nos. 6-20 (15)	294.37	659.00

POONCH

ˈpu̇nch

LOCATION — A Feudatory State in the Kashmir Residency in India.
AREA — 1,627 sq. mi.
POP. — 287,000 (estimated)
CAPITAL — Poonch

Poonch was feudatory to Jammu and Kashmir. Cancellations of Jammu and Kashmir are found on Poonch stamps, which

became obsolete in 1894. The stamps are all printed in watercolor and handstamped from single dies. They may be found on various papers, including wove, laid, wove batonne, laid batonne and ribbed, in various colors and tones. Nearly all Poonch stamps exist tete beche and impressed sideways. Issued without gum.

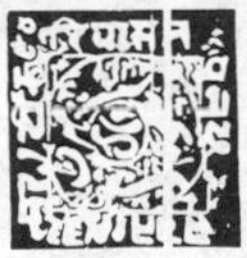
A1

White Paper
Handstamped

1876 Unwmk. *Imperf.*
Size: 22x21mm

1	A1	6p red	105.

1877
Size: 19x17mm

1A	A1	1/2a red	4,500.	*1,250.*

1879
Size: 21x19mm

1B	A1	1/2a red	650.

A2

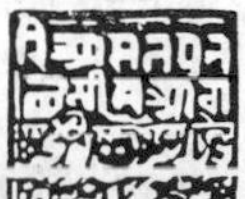
A3

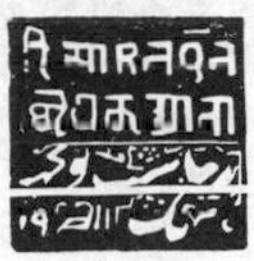
A4

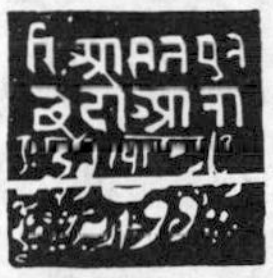
A5

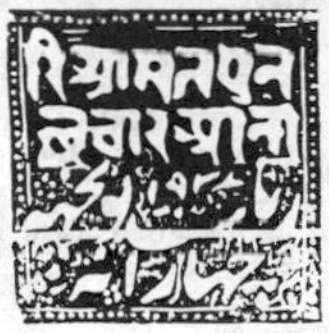
A6

1880-88

White Paper

2	A2	1p red ('84)	12.00	10.50
3	A3	1/2a red	4.75	3.00
4	A4	1a red	4.25	4.25
5	A5	2a red	10.50	10.50
6	A6	4a red	10.50	

Yellow Paper

7	A2	1p red	1.50	1.50
8	A3	1/2a red	1.90	1.50
9	A4	1a red	3.75	3.50
10	A5	2a red	1.90	2.75
11	A6	4a red	1.10	1.10

Blue Paper

12	A2	1p red	7.75	7.75
13	A4	1a red	2.00	2.00

Orange Paper

14	A2	1p red	.30	.30
15	A3	1/2a red	4.75	4.75
16	A5	2a red	10.50	10.50
17	A6	4a red	6.50	6.50

Green Paper

18	A3	1/2a red	5.50	5.50
19	A4	1a red	2.75	2.75
20	A5	2a red	2.50	3.75
21	A6	4a red	10.00	12.00

Lavender Paper

22	A2	1p red	24.00	24.00
23	A4	1a red	12.00	12.00
24	A5	2a red	.90	.90

OFFICIAL STAMPS

White Paper
Handstamped

1888 Unwmk. *Imperf.*

O1	A2	1p black	.35	.60
O2	A3	1/2a black	.50	.75
O3	A4	1a black	.75	.75
O4	A5	2a black	1.00	1.00
O5	A6	4a black	1.50	1.50
		Nos. O1-O5 (5)	4.10	4.60

1890
Yellowish Paper

O6	A2	1p black	1.10	
O7	A3	1/2a black	4.25	4.25
O8	A4	1a black	10.00	7.00
O9	A5	2a black	3.50	3.75
O10	A6	4a black	10.00	
		Nos. O6-O10 (5)	28.85	

Obsolete since 1894.

RAJASTHAN

'rä-jə-,stän

(Greater Rajasthan Union)

LOCATION — India
AREA — 128,424 sq. miles
POP. — 13,085,000

The Rajasthan Union was formed in 1947-49 by 14 Indian States, including the stamp-issuing States of Bundi, Jaipur and Kishangarh.

Catalogue values for all unused stamps in this state are for Never Hinged items.

Bundi Nos. 43 to 49 Overprinted

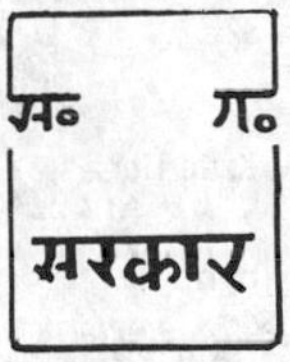
a

1948 Unwmk. *Perf. 11*
Handstamped in Black, Violet or Blue

1	A8	1/4a deep green (Bk, V)	1.10
a.		Blue overprint	12.50
2	A8	1/2a purple (Bk, V)	.55
a.		Blue overprint	7.50
3	A8	1a yel green (Bk)	.40
4	A9	2a red (Bk)	2.75
5	A9	4a dp orange (V)	2.75
a.		Black overprint	6.75
6	A10	8a violet blue (Bk, V)	1.50
7	A10	1r chocolate (Bl)	22.50
a.		Black overprint	
b.		Violet overprint	55.00
		Nos. 1-7 (7)	31.55

Typo. in Black

12	A9	4a deep orange	1.75
13	A10	8a violet blue	16.00
14	A10	1r chocolate	4.00
		Nos. 12-14 (3)	21.75

राजस्थान

Stamps of Jaipur, 1931-47, Overprinted in Blue or Carmine

RAJASTHAN

1949 Center in Black *Perf. 14*

15	A6	1/4a red brown (Bl)	1.25	*2.50*
16	A6	1/2a dull violet	1.25	*2.50*
17	A6	3/4a brown org (Bl)	1.25	*2.50*
18	A6	1a blue	1.50	*3.25*
19	A6	2a ocher	1.50	*3.25*
20	A6	2 1/2a rose (Bl)	1.50	*3.25*
21	A6	3a green	2.00	*4.00*
22	A6	4a gray green	2.50	*4.75*
23	A6	6a blue	3.25	*6.50*
24	A6	8a chocolate	8.00	*20.00*
25	A6	1r bister	12.00	*27.50*
		Nos. 15-25 (11)	36.00	*80.00*

Kishangarh Stamps and Types of 1899-1904 Handstamped Type "a" in Rose

1949 *Pin-perf., Rouletted*

26	A3	1/2a blue (#18)	25.00
27	A4	1a dull lilac (#20)	11.00
28	A6	4a pale red brown (#21B)	15.00
29	A11	8a gray (#25B)	27.50
30	A7	1r dull green (#22)	22.50
31	A8	2r brown red (#23)	25.00
32	A9	5r red violet (#24)	30.00
		Nos. 26-32 (7)	156.00

Kishangarh Nos. 28, 31-36 Handstamped Type "a" in Rose or Green

1949 Engr. *Perf. 13 1/2, 12 1/2*

33	A13	1/2a chestnut (R)	10.50
34	A13	4a dark brown (G)	13.00
35	A13	4a dark brown (R)	13.00
36	A13	8a purple (R)	13.00
37	A13	1r dark green (R)	21.00
38	A13	2r lemon yellow (R)	21.00
39	A13	5r purple brown (R)	25.50
		Nos. 33-39 (7)	117.00

Kishangarh Nos. 40-42, 37, 43, 46-48 Handstamped Type "a" in Rose

1949 Typo. *Rouletted*

40	A14	1/4a pale blue	8.00	8.00
41	A14	1/2a green	8.00	8.00
42	A14	1a carmine	7.50	7.50
43	A14	2 "anna" violet	7.50	7.50
44	A14	2 "annas" purple	7.50	7.50
45	A14	8a brown	7.50	7.50
46	A14	1r rose lilac	9.00	9.00
47	A14	2r dark green	12.00	12.00
48	A14	5r brown	32.50	32.50
		Nos. 40-48 (9)	99.50	99.50

Kishangarh Stamps and Types of 1928-29 Handstamped Type "a" in Rose

1949 *Pin-perf*

49	A17	1/4a greenish blue	13.00	13.00
50	A17	1/2a yel green	6.50	6.50
51	A18	1a car rose	9.00	9.00
52	A18	2a red violet	12.00	12.00
53	A17	4a yel brown	2.50	2.50
54	A17	8a purple	7.25	7.25
55	A17	1r deep green	7.50	7.50
56	A17	2r lemon	24.00	24.00
57	A17	5r red brown	25.00	25.00
		Nos. 49-57 (9)	106.75	106.75

Type of Kishangarh 1928-29, Handstamped Type "a" in Rose

1949 *Pin-perf*

58	A18	1a dark violet blue

No. 58 exists imperf.
Rajasthan stamps became obsolete Apr. 1, 1950.

RAJPEEPLA

räj-'pē-plə

(Rajpipla)

LOCATION — A Feudatory State near Bombay in the Gujarat States Agency in India.
AREA — 1,517 sq. mi.
POP. — 206,086
CAPITAL — Nandod

4 Paisas = 1 Anna

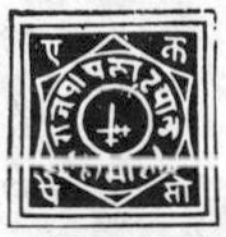
Kandjar (Indian Daggers) — A1

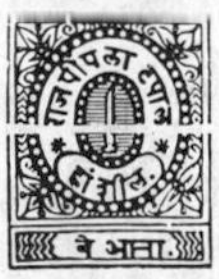
A2

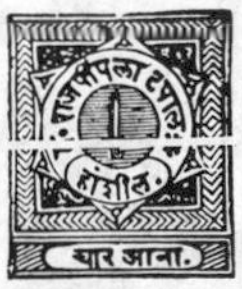
A3

1880 Unwmk. Litho. *Perf. 11, 12 1/2*
Without Gum

1	A1	1pa ultramarine	1.00	4.75
2	A2	2a green	6.25	6.75
a.		Horiz. pair, imperf. btwn.	625.00	625.00
3	A3	4a red	4.50	4.50

The stamps of Rajpeepla have been obsolete since 1886.

SIRMOOR

sir-'mu̇(ə)r

(Sirmur)

LOCATION — A Feudatory State in the Punjab District of India.
AREA — 1,046 sq. mi.
POP. — 148,568
CAPITAL — Nahan

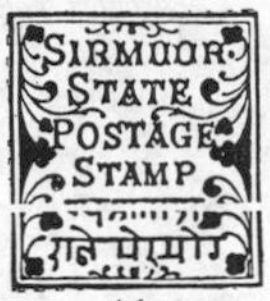
A1

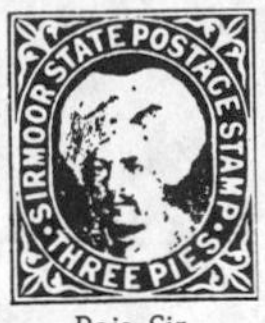
Raja Sir Shamsher Prakash — A2

1879 Unwmk. *Perf. 11 1/2*
Wove Paper

1	A1	1p green	6.00	6.00
a.		Imperf., pair		

Laid Paper

2	A1	1p blue	3.00	*30.00*
a.		Imperf., pair		

1885-88 Litho. *Perf. 14 and 14 1/2.*

3	A2	3p brown	.15	.15
4	A2	3p orange	.15	.15
5	A2	6p green	.60	.60
6	A2	1a blue	.45	.45
7	A2	2a carmine	2.00	2.00
		Nos. 3-7 (5)	3.35	3.35

There are several printings, dies and minor variations of this issue.
For overprints see Nos. O1-O16.

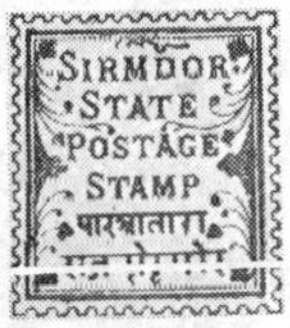
A3

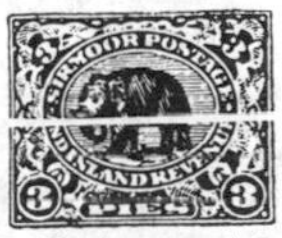
Elephant — A4

1893 *Perf. 11 1/2*

9	A3	1p yellow green	.30	.30
a.		1pa dark blue green	.28	.28
10	A3	1p ultramarine	.48	.48
b.		Imperf., pair	60.00	

Nos. 9 and 10 are re-issues, which were available for postage.
The printed perforation, which is a part of the design, is in addition to the regular perforation.

1895-99 Engr. *Perf. 14*

11	A4	3p orange	.60	.18
12	A4	6p green	.90	.24
13	A4	1a dull blue	1.10	.30
14	A4	2a dull red	1.10	.45
15	A4	3a yellow green	2.00	2.00
16	A4	4a dark green	2.00	2.00
17	A4	8a deep blue	5.50	7.50
18	A4	1r vermilion	7.50	*9.00*
		Nos. 11-18 (8)	20.70	*21.67*

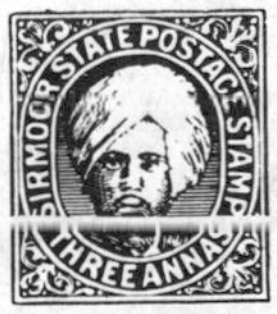
Sir Surendar Bikram Prakash — A5

1899

19	A5	3a yellow green	2.75	*6.00*
20	A5	4a dark green	3.50	*7.25*
21	A5	8a blue	4.00	*7.75*
22	A5	1r vermilion	6.50	*15.00*
		Nos. 19-22 (4)	16.75	*36.00*

OFFICIAL STAMPS

Regular Stamps Overprinted

On
S. S.
S.

Black Overprint

1890-91 Unwmk. *Perf. 14, 14 1/2*

O1	A2	3p orange	1.40	
O2	A2	6p green	1.40	.90
a.		Double overprint		
b.		Double ovpt., one in red	1,050.	
O3	A2	1a blue	12.00	12.00
O4	A2	2a carmine	9.00	9.00
		Nos. O1-O4 (4)	23.80	

1890-92

Red Overprint

O5 A2 6p green		4.50	4.00
O6 A2 1a blue		17.00	9.00

On

S. S.

S.

O7 A2 6p green	2.50	1.60
a. Double overprint		
b. Inverted overprint		
O8 A2 1a blue	6.00	2.00
a. Inverted overprint		200.00
b. Double overprint		200.00

1892

Black Overprint

O9 A2 3p orange	.18	.18
a. Inverted overprint	75.00	
O10 A2 6p green	.75	.75
O11 A2 1a blue	3.25	3.25
a. Double overprint	125.00	
O12 A2 2a carmine	2.50	2.50
a. Inverted overprint	125.00	105.00
Nos. O9-O12 (4)	6.68	6.68

On

S. S.

S.

Black Overprint

O13 A2 3p orange	3.25	1.50
a. Inverted overprint		
O14 A2 6p green	2.75	.48
O15 A2 1a blue	1.90	.75
O16 A2 2a carmine	4.75	4.25
Nos. O13-O16 (4)	12.65	6.98

There are several settings of some of these overprints, differing in the sizes and shapes of the letters, the presence or absence of the periods, etc.

The overprints on Nos. O1-O16 are press printed. In addition, nine varieties of handstamped overprints were applied in 1894-96. Most of the handstamps are very similar to the press printed overprints.

Obsolete Mar. 31, 1901.

SORUTH

(Sorath)

(Junagarh)

(Saurashtra)

LOCATION — A Feudatory State near Bombay in the Western India States Agency in India.

AREA — 3,337 sq. mi.

POP. — 670,719

CAPITAL — Junagarh

The United State of Saurashtra (area 31,885 sq. mi.; population 2,900,000) was formed in 1948 by 217 States, including the stamp-issuing States of Jasdan, Morvi, Nowanuggur and Wadhwan.

Nos. 1-27 were issued without gum.

Catalogue values for unused stamps in this State are for Never Hinged items, beginning with Scott 39 in the regular postage section, and Scott O19 in the officials section.

A1

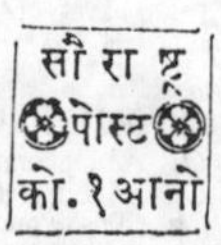

A2

Handstamped in Watercolor

1864 Unwmk. *Imperf.*

Laid Paper

1 A1 (1a) black, *bluish*	360.00	24.00
a. Wove paper		80.00
1B A1 (1a) black, *gray*	360.00	24.00

Wove Paper

2 A1 (1a) black, *cream*		100.00

1868 Typo. *Imperf.*

Wove Paper

3 A2 1a black, *yellowish*		
4 A2 1a red, *green*		1,200.
5 A2 1a red, *blue*		1,200.
6 A2 1a black, *pink*	175.00	42.00
7 A2 2a black, *yellow*		1,750.

Laid Paper

8 A2 1a black, *blue*	25.00	10.00
a. Left character, 3rd line, omitted		
9 A2 1a red	20.00	20.00
a. Left character, 3rd line, omitted		
10 A2 4a black	105.00	*125.00*
a. Left character, 3rd line, omitted		

A 1a black on white laid paper exists in type A2.

In 1890 official imitations of 1a and 4a stamps, type A2, were printed in sheets of 16 and 4. Original sheets have 20 stamps. Four of these imitations are perf. 12, six are imperf.

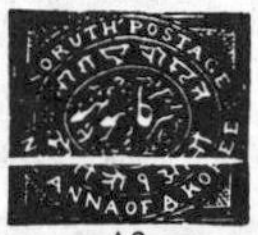

A3

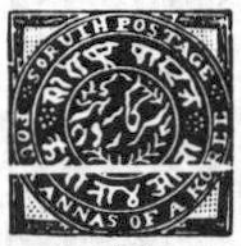

A4

1877-86 Laid Paper *Imperf.*

11 A3 1a green	.15	.15
a. Printed on both sides	210.00	
12 A4 4a vermilion	.75	.75
a. Printed on both sides	210.00	
13 A4 4a scarlet, *bluish*	.90	.90
Nos. 11-13 (3)	1.80	1.80

Perf. 12

14 A3 1a green	.18	.18
a. 1a blue (error)	350.00	350.00
c. Imperf., pair	6.50	6.50
d. Wove paper	.75	.75
e. As "a," wove paper	350.00	350.00
f. As "d," imperf. btwn., pair	10.50	10.50
15 A3 1a green, *bluish*	.80	.80
a. Pair, imperf. btwn.	42.50	42.50
16 A4 4a red	.90	.90
a. 4a carmine	.90	.90
c. Wove paper	1.75	1.75
d. As "c," imperf., pair	12.00	12.00
17 A4 4a scarlet, *bluish*	1.50	1.50
Nos. 14-17 (4)	3.38	3.38

Nos. 14d and 16c Surcharged

Three pies. ત્રણ પાઇ.   One Anna. એક આનો.

1913-14 *Perf. 12*

18 A3 3p on 1a green	.15	.15
a. Laid paper		30.00
b. Inverted surcharge	20.00	
c. Imperf., pair		
19 A4 1a on 4a red	1.00	1.00
a. Laid paper	5.00	5.00
b. Imperf., pair		
c. Double surcharge	175.00	

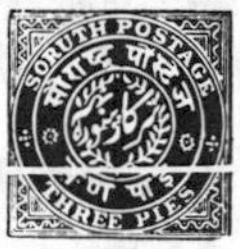

A5

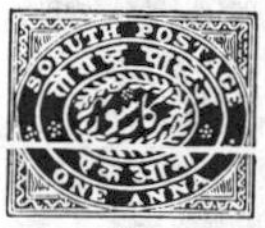

A6

1914 *Perf. 12*

20 A5 3p green	.50	.50
a. Imperf., pair	1.00	1.00
21 A6 1a rose carmine	.50	.60
a. Imperf., pair	4.00	4.00
b. Laid paper	20.00	15.00

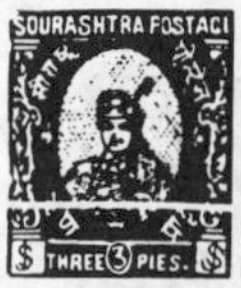

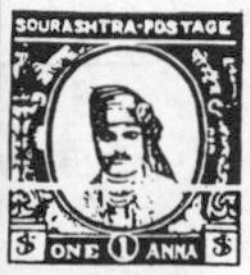

Nawab Mahabat Khan III

A7 A8

1923-29 Wove Paper *Perf. 12*

22 A7 3p violet	.45	.45
a. Imperf.		
b. Laid paper ('29)	.75	.75
c. As "b," imperf. ('29)	1.40	1.40
d. As "b," horiz. pair, imperf. between	30.00	
23 A8 1a red	1.50	1.50
a. Imperf., pair		
b. Laid paper	2.00	2.00

Surcharged with New Value

27 A8 3p on 1a red	1.50	1.50

Two types of surcharge.

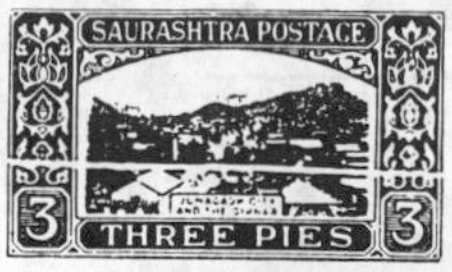

Junagarh City and The Girnar — A9

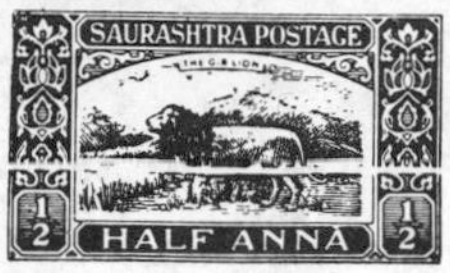

Gir Lion — A10

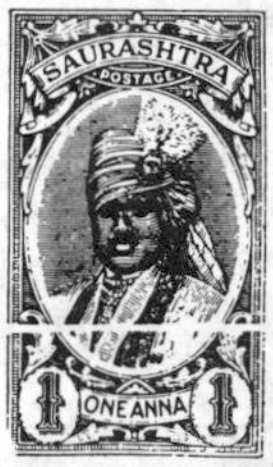

Nawab Mahabat Khan III — A11

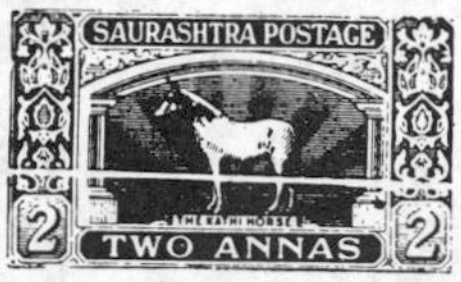

Kathi Horse A12

1929 *Perf. 14*

30 A9 3p dk green & blk	1.00	.16
31 A10 ½a dk blue & blk	3.75	.15
32 A11 1a claret & blk	2.25	.60
33 A12 2a org buff & blk	9.00	.35
34 A9 3a car rose & blk	2.50	.24
35 A10 4a dull vio & blk	10.50	.28
36 A12 8a apple grn & blk	12.00	*8.75*
37 A11 1r dull blue & blk	3.50	*7.00*
Nos. 30-37 (8)	44.50	*17.53*

For surcharges see Nos. 40-42, O20-O25. For overprints see Nos. O1-O14.

Type of 1929

Inscribed "Postage and Revenue"

1937

38 A11 1a claret & black	2.00	.48

For overprint see No. O15.

Catalogue values for unused stamps in this section, from this point to the end of the section, are for Never Hinged items.

United State of Saurashtra

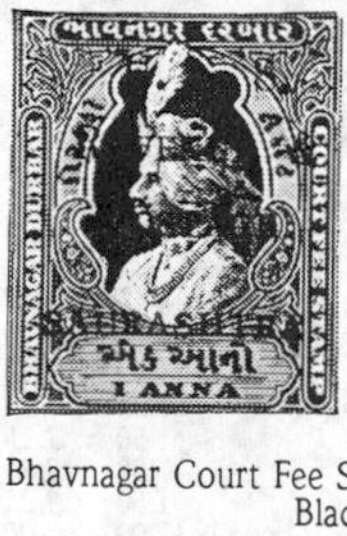

A13

Bhavnagar Court Fee Stamp Overprinted in Black

"U.S.S. Revenue & Postage Saurashtra"

1949 Unwmk. Typo. *Perf. 11*

39 A13 1a deep claret	1.75	1.75
a. "POSTAGE" omitted	100.00	100.00
b. Double overprint	100.00	100.00
c. "REVENUE & POSTAGE" omitted	100.00	100.00

Nos. 30, 31 Surcharged in Black or Carmine "POSTAGE & REVENUE ONE ANNA"

1949-50 *Perf. 14*

40 A9 1a on 3p dk grn & blk (bl) ('50)	10.00	10.00
a. "OSTAGE"	110.00	110.00
41 A10 1a on ½a dk bl & blk (C)	7.00	1.40
a. Double surcharge	100.00	100.00

For overprint see No. O19.

No. 33 Surcharged in Green "Postage & Revenue ONE ANNA"

1949

42 A12 1a on 2a org buff & blk	5.75	2.00

For overprint see No. O26.

OFFICIAL STAMPS

Regular Issue of 1929 Overprinted in Red

a **SARKARI**

1929 Unwmk. *Perf. 14*

O1 A9 3p dk green & black	.15	.15
O2 A10 ½a dk blue & black	.40	.15
O3 A11 1a claret & black	.15	.15
O4 A12 2a org buff & black	.75	.15
O5 A9 3a car rose & black	.40	.15
O6 A10 4a dull violet & blk	.75	.15
O7 A12 8a apple green & blk	1.25	.18
O8 A11 1r dull blue & blk	1.90	2.00
Nos. O1-O8 (8)	5.75	3.08

For surcharges see Nos. O20-O24.

Regular Issue of 1929 Overprinted in Red

b **SARKARI**

1933-49

O9 A9 3p dk grn & black ('49)	145.00	4.25
O10 A10 ½a dk bl & black ('49)	210.00	4.25
O11 A9 3a car rose & blk	9.50	4.50
O12 A10 4a dull vio & blk	22.50	13.00
O13 A12 8a apple grn & blk	22.50	15.00
O14 A11 1r dull blue & blk	25.00	20.00

The 3p is also known with ms. "SARKARI" overprint in carmine.

For surcharge see No. O25.

No. 38 Overprinted Type "a" in Red

1938

O15 A11 1a claret & black	2.50	.50

Catalogue values for unused stamps in this section, from this point to the end of the section, are for Never Hinged items.

United State of Saurashtra

No. 41 with Manuscript "Service" in Carmine

1949

O19 A10 1a on ½a dk bl & blk (C)		27.50

No. 42 is also known with carmine ms. "Service" overprint in English or Gujarati.

Nos. O4-O8 and O14 Surcharged "ONE ANNA" in Blue or Black

1949

Surcharge 2¼mm high

O20 A12 1a on 2a (Bl)	850.00	24.00
O21 A9 1a on 3a	850.00	24.00
O22 A10 1a on 4a	125.00	22.50
O23 A12 1a on 8a	125.00	22.50

Surcharge 4mm High, Handstamped

O24 A11 1a on 1r (#O8)	195.00	15.00
O25 A11 1a on 1r (#O14)	110.00	27.50
Nos. O20-O25 (6)	2,255.	135.50

No. 42 Overprinted Type "b" in Carmine

1949 Unwmk. *Perf. 14*

O26 A12 1a on 2a	20.00	6.75

TRAVANCORE

'trav-ən-,kō(ə)r

LOCATION — A Feudatory State in the Madras States Agency, on the extreme southwest coast of India.

AREA — 7,662 sq. mi.

POP. — 6,070,018 (1941)

CAPITAL — Trivandrum

16 Cash = 1 Chuckram

2 Chuckrams = 1 Anna

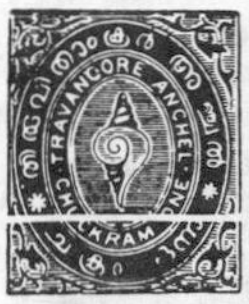
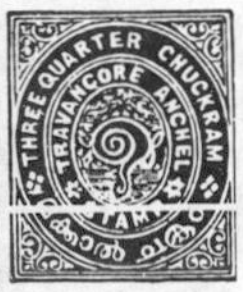

Conch Shell (State Seal)
A1 A2

1888 Unwmk. Typo. *Perf. 12*

Laid Paper

1 A1 1ch ultramarine 6.00 4.50
2 A1 2ch orange red 5.50 4.75
3 A1 4ch green 22.50 22.50
Nos. 1-3 (3) 34.00 31.75

The frame and details of the central medallion differ slightly on each denomination of type A1.
Laid paper printings of Nos. 1-3, 5-7 in completely different colors are essays.

1889-99 Wmk. 43

Wove Paper

4 A1 ½ch violet .15 .15
5 A1 1ch ultramarine .15 .15
a. Vertical pair, imperf. between
6 A1 2ch scarlet .90 .15
a. Horizontal pair, imperf. between 75.00
7 A1 4ch dark green 1.25 .28
Nos. 4-7 (4) 2.45
Set value .48

Shades exist for each denomination.
For surcharges see #10-11. For type surcharged see #20. For overprints see #O1-O2, O4, O6, O18, O24-O25, O27B, O32-O33, O42.

1901-32

8 A2 ¾ch black 1.25 .15
9 A2 ¾ch brt violet ('32) 1.25 .15
a. Horizontal pair, imperf. between
Set value .15

For overprints see Nos. O26-O27, O44, O52.

No. 4 Surcharged **1/4**

1906

10 A1 ¼ch on ½ch violet .45 .15
a. Inverted surcharge 35.00 35.00
11 A1 ⅜ch on ½ch violet .20 .15
a. Pair, one without surcharge
b. Inverted surcharge
c. Double surcharge
Set value .15

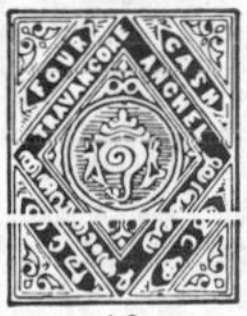
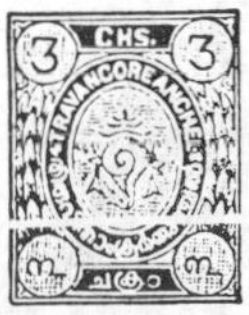

A3 A4

1908-11

12 A3 4ca rose .15 .15
13 A1 6ca red brown ('10) .90 .15
a. Printed on both sides
14 A4 3ch purple ('11) .75 .15
Nos. 12-14 (3) 1.80
Set value .15

For surcharge and overprints see Nos. 19, O3, O5, O8, O13, O15, O20, O22, O30-O31, O53.

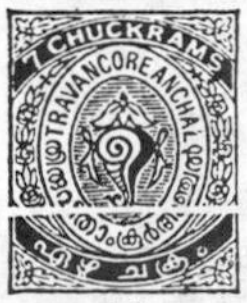
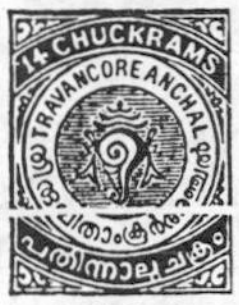

A5 A6

1916

15 A5 7ch red violet 1.90 .28
16 A6 14ch orange 4.00 2.50

For overprints see Nos. O11-O12, O34-O35.

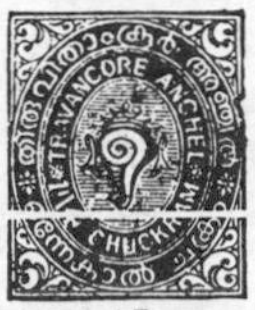
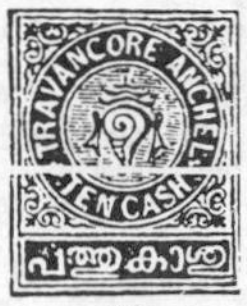

A7 A8

1920-33

17 A7 1¼ch claret 1.25 .15
18 A7 1½ch light red ('33) 1.25 .15
Set value .15

For surcharges see Nos. 27-28. For overprints see Nos. O7, O17, O28-O29, O38, O56.

No. 12 and Type of 1888 Surcharged **1 C**

1921

19 A3 1ca on 4ca rose .15 .15
a. Inverted surcharge 10.50 6.50
20 A1 5ca on 1ch dull bl (R) .15 .15
a. Inverted surcharge 13.00 4.00
b. Double surcharge 18.00 13.00
Set value .20 .15

1921-32

21 A8 5ca bister .15 .15
22 A8 5ca brown ('32) 1.25 .15
23 A8 10ca rose .15 .15
Nos. 21-23 (3) 1.55
Set value .15

For surcharges and overprints see Nos. 29-30, O9-O10, O14, O16, O19, O21, O23, O36-O37.

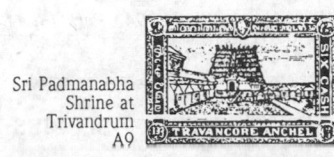

Sri Padmanabha Shrine at Trivandrum
A9

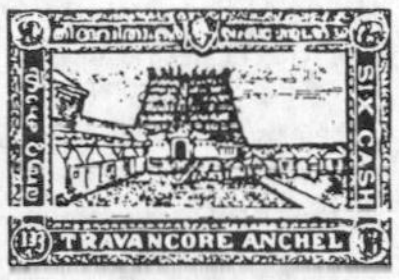

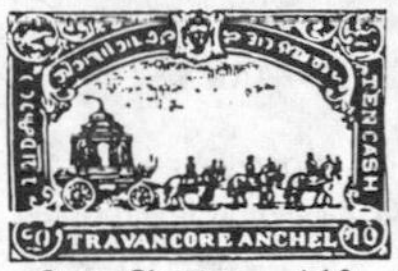
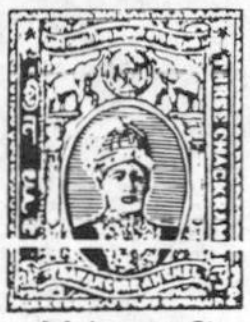

State Chariot — A10 Maharaja Sir Bala Rama Varma — A11

1931, Nov. 6

24 A9 6ca emerald & black .28 .28
25 A10 10ca ultra & black .28 .28
26 A11 3ch violet & black .55 .55
Nos. 24-26 (3) 1.11 1.11

Investiture of Sir Bala Rama Varma with full ruling powers.

No. 17 Surcharged **2 C**

1932, Jan. 14

27 A7 1ca on 1¼ch claret .15 .15
a. Inverted surcharge 5.00 5.00
b. Double surcharge 16.00 16.00
28 A7 2ca on 1¼ch claret .15 .15
a. Inverted surcharge 5.00 5.00
b. Double surcharge 16.00 16.00
c. Pair, one without surcharge 75.00 75.00
Set value .20 .15

Type of 1932 and No. 23 Surcharged like Nos. 19-20

1932, Mar. 5

29 A8 1ca on 5ca vio brown .15 .15
a. Inverted surcharge 13.00 12.00
b. Double surcharge 13.00 13.00
c. Pair, one without surcharge 55.00
30 A8 2ca on 10ca rose .28 .15
a. Inverted surcharge 9.00 9.00
b. Double surcharge 21.00 21.00
Set value .15

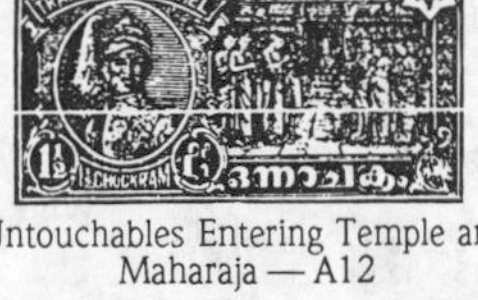

Untouchables Entering Temple and Maharaja — A12

Designs: Different temples and frames.

Perf. 11½, 12½

1937, Mar. 29 Litho.

32 A12 6ca carmine .15 .15
33 A12 12ca ultramarine .15 .15
34 A12 1½ch light green .15 .15
35 A12 3ch purple .32 .15
Nos. 32-35 (4) .77
Set value .40

Temple Entry Bill.

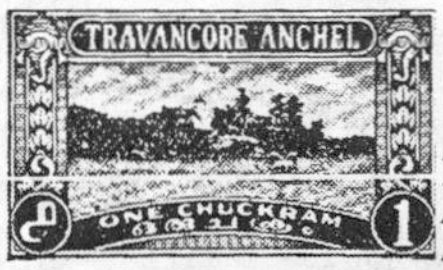

Lake Ashtamudi
A13

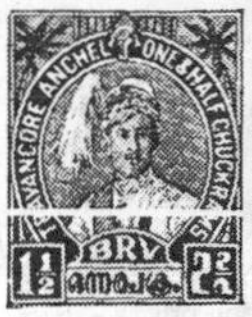
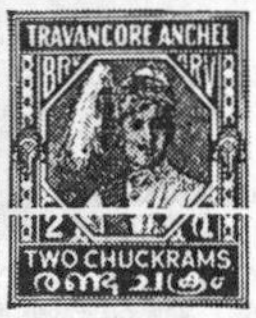

A14 A15

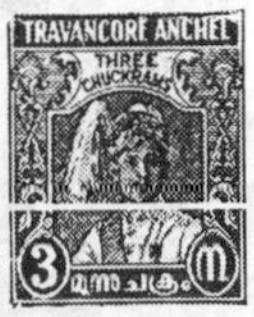

Sir Bala Rama Varma — A16

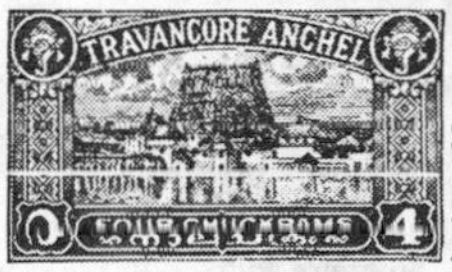

Sri Padmanabha Shrine
A17

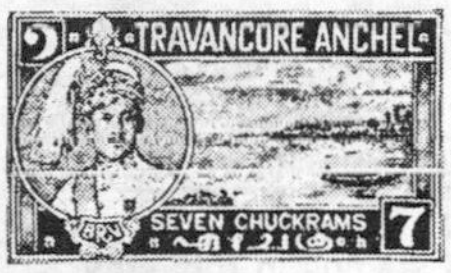

View of Cape Comerin
A18

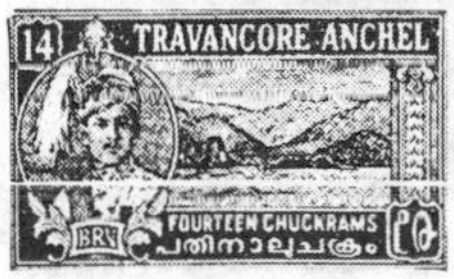

Pachipara Reservoir
A19

Perf. 11, 12, 12½ or Compound

1939, May 9 Litho.

36 A13 1ch yellow green .15 .15
37 A14 1½ch carmine .45 .15
a. Perf. 13½ 18.00 18.00
38 A15 2ch orange .20 .15
39 A16 3ch chocolate .24 .15
40 A17 4ch henna brown .32 .15
41 A18 7ch light blue 1.50 1.10
42 A19 14ch turq green 3.00 2.00
Nos. 36-42 (7) 5.86 3.85

27th birthday of Maharaja Sir Bala Rama Varma.
For surcharges and overprints see Nos. 45, O45-O51, Travancore-Cochin 3-7, O3-O7.

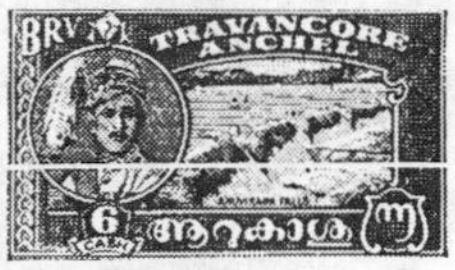

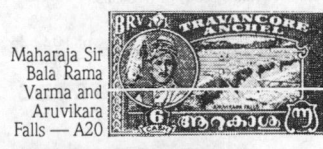

Maharaja Sir Bala Rama Varma and Aruvikara Falls — A20

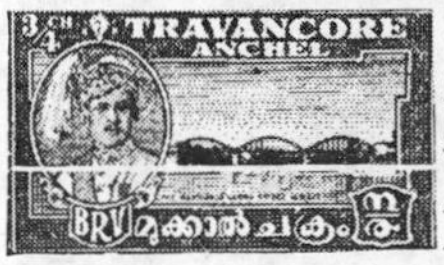

Maharaja and Marthanda Varma Bridge, Alwaye
A21

1941, Oct. 20 Typo.

43 A20 6ca violet black .15 .15
44 A21 ¾ch dull brown .30 .15
Set value .16

29th birthday of the Maharaja, Oct. 20, 1941.
For overprints see Nos. 46-47, 49, O54-O55. For surcharges see Travancore-Cochin Nos. 1, O1.

Stamps and Types of 1939-41 Surcharged in Black **2 CASH**

Perf. 11, 12½

1943, Sept. 17 Wmk. 43

45 A14 2ca on 1½ch carmine .15 .15
46 A21 4ca on ¾ch dull brown .18 .15
47 A20 8ca on 6ca red .45 .15
Nos. 45-47 (3) .78
Set value .26

For overprints see Nos. O57-O59.

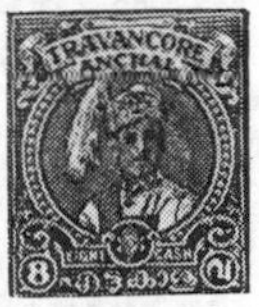

Maharaja Sir Bala Rama Varma — A22

1946, Oct. 24 Typo. *Perf. 11, 12*

48 A22 8ca rose red 1.25 .50

For overprint see No. O60. For surcharges see Travancore-Cochin Nos. 2, O2.

No. O54 Overprinted "SPECIAL" Vertically in Orange

1946 *Perf. 12½*

49 A20 6ca violet black 6.50 6.00

OFFICIAL STAMPS

Nos. O1-O60 were issued without gum.

Regular Issues of 1889-1911 Overprinted in Red or Black **On S S**

Perf. 12, 12½

1911, Aug. 16 Wmk. 43

O1 A1 1ch indigo (R) .38 .15
a. Inverted overprint 8.75 5.50
b. "nO" for "On" 50.00 50.00
c. Double overprint 37.50 37.50
O2 A1 2ch scarlet .50 .15
a. Inverted overprint 11.00 10.00
O3 A4 3ch purple .38 .15
a. Inverted overprint 11.00 10.00
b. Double overprint 40.00 40.00
O4 A1 4ch dark green .50 .15
a. Inverted overprint 12.50 11.00
b. Double overprint 40.00 40.00
Nos. O1-O4 (4) 1.76
Set value .20

Same Ovpt. on Regular Issues of 1889-1920

1918-20

O5 A3 4ca rose .15 .15
a. Imperf., pair 37.50 37.50
b. Inverted overprint 12.50 7.50
c. Double overprint 17.50 5.50
O6 A1 ½ch violet (R) .15 .15
a. Inverted overprint 7.00 3.50
O7 A7 1¼ch claret .30 .15
a. Inverted overprint 12.50 7.50
b. Double overprint 21.00 17.50
Nos. O5-O7 (3) .60
Set value .15

Same Ovpt. on Regular Issues of 1909-21

1921

O8 A1 6ca red brown .25 .15
a. Inverted overprint 8.75 7.50
O9 A8 10ca rose .50 .15
a. Inverted overprint 22.50 12.50
b. Double overprint 27.50 17.50
Set value .20

Same Overprint on Regular Issue of 1921

1922

O10 A8 5ca bister .15 .15
a. Inverted overprint 7.00 3.50

For surcharge see No. O39B.

Same Overprint on Regular Issue of 1916

1925

O11 A5 7ch plum 1.10 .20
O12 A6 14ch orange 1.65 .20

Same Overprint in Blue on Regular Issues of 1889-1921

O13 A3 4ca rose 15.00 1.40
O14 A8 5ca bister
O15 A1 6ca red brown 8.50 1.40
O16 A8 10ca rose 21.00 4.50
O17 A7 1¼ch claret 24.00 6.50
O18 A1 4ch dark green 35.00 9.00

Some authorities question the authenticity of No. O14.

1930

Black Overprint

O19 A8 5ca brown .15 .15

Regular Issues of 1889-1932 Overprinted in Black or Red

On S S

1930-34

O20	A3	4ca rose	8.00	6.00
O21	A8	5ca brown	18.00	13.00
a.		Inverted overprint	90.00	90.00
O22	A1	6ca org brown	.15	.15
O23	A8	10ca rose	1.90	.24
O24	A1	½ch violet ('34)	.35	.15
O25	A1	½ch purple (R)	.18	.15
O26	A2	¾ch black (R) ('32)	.60	.15
O27	A2	¾ch brt vio ('33)	.15	.15
O27B	A1	1ch gray blue (R) ('33)	.75	.15
O28	A7	1¼ch claret	1.50	.45
O29	A7	1½ch dull red ('32)	.30	.15
O30	A4	3ch purple ('33)	1.50	.15
O31	A4	3ch purple (R)	.65	.15
O32	A1	4ch deep green (R)	1.25	.15
O33	A1	4ch deep green	2.75	1.40
O34	A2	7ch maroon	1.75	.15
O35	A6	14ch orange ('31)	2.50	.40
		Nos. O20-O35 (17)	42.28	23.14

The overprint on Nos. O22, O26 and O28 is smaller than the illustration. There are two sizes of the overprint on No. O27.
For surcharges see Nos. O39, O40-O41.

Type of 1921-32 and No. 17 Surcharged and Overprinted

On S S

1932

O36	A8	6ca on 5ca dk brown	.20	.15
O36A	A8	6ca on 5ca bister	.75	.18
O37	A8	12ca on 10a rose	.35	.18
a.		New value inverted	8.50	8.50
O38	A7	1ch8ca on 1¼ch cl	.45	.15
		Nos. O36-O38 (4)	1.75	
		Set value		.52

Nos. O21, O10, O23 and O28 Surcharged in Black

12 c

O39	A8	6ca on 5ca dk brown	.24	.15
a.		New value inverted		
O39B	A8	6ca on 5ca bister	.60	.15
O40	A8	12ca on 10ca rose	.40	.15
a.		New value inverted	8.50	8.50
b.		"On S S" inverted		
c.		Ovpt. & surch. inverted	21.00	21.00
O41	A7	1ch8ca on 1¼ch cl	.60	.15
a.		New value inverted		
		Nos. O39-O41 (4)	1.84	
		Set value		.23

Regular Issue of 1889-94 Overprinted

On S S

1933

O42	A1	½ch violet (Bk)	1.75	1.25

Regular Issue of 1901 Overprinted in Red

On S S

1933

O44	A2	¾ch black	.35	.15

Regular Issue of 1939 Overprinted in Black

a   SERVICE

1939   *Perf. 11, 12, 12½*

O45	A13	1ch yellow green	.18	.15
a.		Inverted overprint	15.00	15.00
b.		Double overprint	15.00	15.00
O46	A14	1½ch carmine	.35	.15
a.		"SESVICE"	20.00	20.00
O47	A15	2ch orange	.45	.15
a.		"SESVICE"	21.00	21.00
O48	A16	3ch chocolate	.35	.15
a.		"SESVICE"	20.00	20.00
O49	A17	4ch henna brown	.75	.24
O50	A18	7ch light blue	1.75	.40
O51	A19	14ch turq green	3.00	.50
		Nos. O45-O51 (7)	6.83	
		Set value		1.40

27th birthday of Maharaja Sir Bala Rama Varma.

No. 9 Overprinted

b   SERVICE

1939   Wmk. 43   *Perf. 12.*

O52	A2	¾ch violet	1.75	.15

No. 13 Overprinted Type "b"

1941

O53	A1	6ca red brown	.50	.15

Nos. 43-44 Overprinted Type "a"

1941   *Perf. 12½*

O54	A20	6ca violet black	.30	.15
O55	A21	¾ch dull brown	.30	.15
		Set value		.16

29th birthday of the Maharaja, Oct. 20, 1941. For overprint see No. 49.

No. 18 Overprinted Type "b"

1945   *Perf. 12*

O56	A7	1½ch light red	.65	.18

Nos. 45-48 Overprinted Type "a"

1945-49   *Perf. 11, 12*

O57	A14	2ca on 1½ch car	.15	.15
O58	A21	4ca on ¾ch dull brn	.35	.15
O59	A20	8ca on 6ca red	.24	.15
O60	A22	8ca rose red ('49)	1.25	.80
a.		Double impression of stamp	30.00	30.00
		Nos. O57-O60 (4)	1.99	
		Set value		1.04

Travancore stamps became obsolete June 30, 1949.

TRAVANCORE-COCHIN

ˈtrav–ən–ˌkō(ə)r kō–ˈchin

LOCATION — Southern India
AREA — 9,155 sq. mi.
POP. — 7,492,000

The United State of Travancore-Cochin was established July 1, 1949.

> **Catalogue values for all unused stamps in this state are for Never Hinged items.**

Travancore Stamps of 1939-47 Surcharged in Red or Black

a   HALF ANNA
അര അണ

Perf. 11, 12, 12½

1949, July 1   Wmk. 43

1	A20	2p on 6ca vio blk (R)	.15	.15
2	A22	4p on 8ca rose red	.15	.15
3	A13	½a on 1ch yel grn	.15	.15
a.		Inverted surcharge	8.00	8.00
b.		"NANA"	32.50	32.50
4	A15	1a on 2ch orange	.15	.15
5	A17	2a on 4ch hn brn	.28	.15
a.		Inverted surcharge	40.00	40.00
6	A18	3a on 7ch lt blue	2.25	.70
7	A19	6a on 14ch turq grn	4.00	2.75
		Nos. 1-7 (7)	7.13	4.20

For overprints see Nos. O1-O7, O12-O17. For types overprinted see Nos. O18-O23.

Cochin Nos. 80, 91 and Types of 1944-46 Surcharged in Black or Carmine

THREE PIES

b

മുന്ന പൈ

1949-50   Wmk. 294   *Perf. 11, 13*

8	A15	3p on 9p ultra	6.75	3.25
9	A16	3p on 9p ultra	1.10	.15
10	A16	3p on 9p ultra (C)	1.40	.15
11	A16	3p on 9p ultra (C)	2.75	.70
12	A13	6p on 1a3p mag ('50)	.95	.15
13	A15	6p on 1a3p magenta	.95	.18

14	A13	1a on 1a9p ultra (C)	2.75	.15
15	A15	1a on 1a9p ultra (C)	5.50	.15
		Nos. 8-15 (8)	22.15	4.88

The surcharge exists with line of Hindi characters varying from 16½ to 23mm wide.
For overprints see Nos. O10-O11, O24.

Cochin No. 86 Overprinted   U. S. T. C.

1949

15A	A15	1a deep orange	7.50	9.25

Conch Shell — A23   View of River — A24

Wmk. 196

1950, Oct.   Litho.   *Perf. 14*

16	A23	2p rose red	.40	.80
17	A24	4p ultramarine	.55	1.40

Cochin No. 86 and Type of 1948-50 Overprinted in Black   T.-C.

1950, Apr. 1   Wmk. 294   *Perf. 13, 11*

18	A15	1a deep orange	3.25	2.75
19	A16	1a deep orange		

The existence of No. 19 has been questioned.

No. 18 Surcharged in Black   SIX PIES

20	A15	6p on 1a deep orange	1.25	1.25
21	A15	9p on 1a deep orange	1.25	1.25

OFFICIAL STAMPS

Travancore Stamps of 1939-46 Surcharged Type "a" in Red or Black and Overprinted

c   SERVICE

1949   Wmk. 43   *Perf. 11, 12, 12½*

O1	A20	2p on 6ca vio blk (R)	.15	.15
O2	A22	4p on 8ca rose red	.20	.15
O3	A13	½a on 1ch yel grn	.20	.15
O4	A15	1a on 2ch orange	6.75	5.50
O5	A17	2a on 4ch hn brn	.45	.25
O6	A18	3a on 7ch lt blue	.55	.28
O7	A19	6a on 14ch turq grn	1.40	.80
		Nos. O1-O7 (7)	9.70	7.28

Cochin Nos. O90-O91 Surcharged Type "b" in Black

1950   Wmk. 294   *Perf. 11*

O8	A16	6p on 3p carmine	.55	.15
a.		Double surcharge	300.00	300.00
O9	A16	9p on 4p gray green	.55	.15
		Set value		.22

No. O9 exists with Hindi characters varying from 18 to 22mm wide.

Travancore-Cochin Nos. 14-15 Overprinted "ON C G S"

Perf. 13

O10	A13	1a on 1a9p ultra	.70	.15
O11	A15	1a on 1a9p ultra	4.00	2.00

Nos. 2-7 Overprinted in Black

d   SERVICE

1949-51   Wmk. 43   *Perf. 11, 12½*

O12	A22	4p on 8ca rose red	.15	.15
O13	A13	½a on 1ch yel green	.28	.15
O14	A15	1a on 2ch orange	.20	.18
O15	A17	2a on 4ch hn brn	.70	.50
O16	A18	3a on 7ch lt blue	.70	.45
O17	A19	6a on 14ch turq grn	2.25	1.50
		Nos. O12-O17 (6)	4.28	2.93

Types of 1949 Overprinted Type "d"

1951   Wmk. 294

O18	A13	½a on 1ch yel green	.18	.15
O19	A15	1a on 2ch orange	.30	.28

Type of 1949 Overprinted Type "c"
Unwmk.

O20	A22	4p on 8ca rose red	1.40	1.10

No. O20 is not from an unwatermarked part of sheet with wmk. 294 but is printed on paper entirely without watermark.

Nos. 1, 3 and 5 Overprinted Type "c"
Wmk. 294

O21	A13	½a on 1ch yel green	.25	.20
O22	A20	2p on 6ca violet black	.15	.15
O23	A17	2a on 4ch henna brown	.32	.15
		Nos. O21-O23 (3)	.72	
		Set value		.34

No. 9 Overprinted in Black   SERVICE

1951

O24	A16	3p on 9p ultra	1.65	.28

WADHWAN

wə–'dwän

LOCATION — A Feudatory State in Kathiawar Agency, Western India.
AREA — 242 sq. mi.
POP. — 44,259
CAPITAL — Wadhwan

Coat of Arms — A1

1888   Litho.   Unwmk.   *Pin-perf.*
Thin Paper

1	A1	½p black		7.50

Perf. 12½

2	A1	½p black		5.00

1889   *Perf. 12 and 12½*
Thick Paper

3	A1	½p black	1.75	
		Nos. 1-3 (3)	14.25	

IONIAN ISLANDS

ī-'ō-nē-ən 'ī-lənds

LOCATION — A group of seven islands, of which six-Corfu, Paxos Lefkas (Santa Maura), Cephalonia, Ithaca and Zante-are in the Ionian Sea west of Greece, and a seventh-Kythera (Cerigo)-is in the Mediterranean south of Greece.
GOVT. — Former British Protectorate
AREA — 752 sq. mi.
POP. — 251,000 (approx.)

These islands were acquired by Great Britain in 1815 but in 1864 were ceded to Greece on request of the inhabitants. Postage stamps issued under Italian and German occupation, 1941-1944, are listed in Vol. 3.

10 Oboli = 1 Penny
12 Pence = 1 Shilling

Watermarks

Wmk. 138- "2"   Wmk. 139- "1"

Queen Victoria — A1

	1859	Unwmk.	Engr.	Imperf.	
1	A1	(½p) orange		60.00	500.00

Wmk. 138

| 2 | A1 | (1p) blue | | 17.50 | 200.00 |

Wmk. 139

| 3 | A1 | (2p) lake | | 17.50 | 200.00 |
| | | Nos. 1-3 (3) | | 95.00 | |

Forged cancellations are plentiful.

IRELAND

'īr-lənd

(Eire)

LOCATION — Comprises the entire island of Ireland, except 5,237 square miles at the extreme north
GOVT. — Republic
AREA — 27,136 sq. mi.
POP. — 3,443,405 (1981)
CAPITAL — Dublin

12 Pence = 1 Shilling
100 Pence = 1 Pound (1971)

Catalogue values for unused stamps in this country are for Never Hinged items, beginning with Scott 99 in the regular postage section, Scott C1 in the air post section, and Scott J5 in the postage due section.

Watermarks

Wmk. 44- SE in Monogram

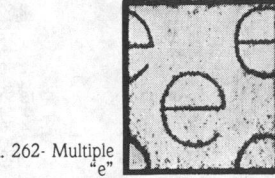

Wmk. 262- Multiple "e"

Overprinted by Dollard, Ltd.
Great Britain Nos. 159-167, 170-172, 179-181 Overprinted

Ríaltar
Sealavač
na
héireann
1922

Overprint measures 15x17½mm

This overprint means "Provisional Government of Ireland."

Black or Gray Black Overprint

	1922, Feb. 17	**Wmk. 33**	**Perf. 15x14**	
1	A82	½p green	.20	.25
		Never hinged	.40	
a.		Inverted overprint	325.00	550.00
2	A83	1p scarlet	.25	.25
		Never hinged	.55	
a.		Inverted overprint	200.00	300.00
3	A86	2½p ultra	.85	3.50
		Never hinged	1.50	
4	A87	3p violet	2.00	4.00
		Never hinged	4.50	
5	A88	4p slate green	2.75	5.00
		Never hinged	6.50	
6	A89	5p yel brown	4.50	8.25
		Never hinged	9.50	
7	A90	9p black brown	12.50	14.00
		Never hinged	30.00	
8	A90	10p light blue	7.50	14.00
		Never hinged	17.50	
		Nos. 1-8 (8)	30.55	49.25

The ½p with red overprint is a proof.

Red or Carmine Overprint

	1922, Apr. - July			
9	A86	2½p ultra	1.25	3.00
		Never hinged	2.50	
10	A88	4p slate green (R)	8.00	11.00
		Never hinged	13.00	
10A	A88	4p slate green (C)	40.00	50.00
		Never hinged	65.00	
11	A90	9p black brown	15.00	14.00
		Never hinged	32.50	
		Nos. 9-11 (4)	64.25	70.00

Overprinted in Black

Ríaltar
Sealavač
na héireann
1922

Overprint measures 21½x14mm

There is a variation that is 21x14mm. The "h" and "é" are 1mm apart. See Nos. 36-38.

	1922, Feb. 17	**Wmk. 34**	**Perf. 11x12**	
12	A91	2sh6p brown	35.00	60.00
		Never hinged	65.00	
13	A91	5sh car rose	60.00	110.00
		Never hinged	100.00	
14	A91	10sh gray blue	150.00	225.00
		Never hinged	250.00	
		Nos. 12-14 (3)	245.00	395.00

Overprinted by Alex. Thom & Co.

Overprinted in Black

Ríaltar
Sealavač
na
héireann
1922.

Overprint measures 14½x16mm

TWO PENCE
Die I - Four horizontal lines above the head. Heavy colored lines above and below the bottom tablet. The inner frame line is closer to the central design than it is to the outer frame line.
Die II - Three lines above the head. Thinner lines above and below the bottom tablet. The inner frame line is midway between the central design and the outer frame line.

	1922, Feb. 17	**Wmk. 33**	**Perf. 15x14**	
15	A84	1½p red brown	1.00	.70
		Never hinged	1.50	
a.		"PENCF"	350.00	350.00
16	A85	2p orange (II)	1.50	.35
		Never hinged	2.50	
a.		Inverted overprint (II)	450.00	625.00
b.		2p orange (I)	1.50	.35
		As "b," never hinged	2.50	
c.		Inverted overprint (I)	165.00	150.00
17	A89	6p red violet	7.50	4.25
		Never hinged	13.00	
18	A90	1sh bister	14.00	9.00
		Never hinged	27.50	
		Nos. 15 18 (4)	24.00	14.30

Important: see Nos. 25-26, 31, 35.

Overprinted by Harrison & Sons
Coil Stamps

Overprinted in Black in Glossy Black Ink

Ríaltar
Sealavač
na
héireann
1922.

Overprint measures 15¼x17mm

	1922, June			
19	A82	½p green	3.50	5.75
		Never hinged	5.50	
20	A83	1p scarlet	1.75	4.00
		Never hinged	3.00	
21	A84	1½p red brown	5.50	11.00
		Never hinged	8.00	
22	A85	2p orange (I)	11.00	15.00
		Never hinged	24.00	
a.		2p orange (II)	15.00	16.00
		Never hinged	25.00	
		Nos. 19-22 (4)	21.75	35.75

* In Harrison overprint, "i" of "Rialtas" extends below the base of the other letters.

The Harrison stamps were issued in coils, either horizontal or vertical. The paper is double where the ends of the strips were overlapped. The perforations are often clipped.

Overprinted by Alex. Thom & Co.
Stamps of Great Britain, 1912-22
Overprinted as Nos. 15 to 18, in Shiny to Dull Blue Black, or Red
Overprint measures 14½x16mm

Note: The blue black overprints can best be distinguished from the black by use of 50-power magnification with a light source behind the stamp.

	1922, July-Nov.		**Perf. 15x14**	
23	A82	½p green	1.40	.90
		Never hinged	2.50	
24	A83	1p scarlet	.45	.35
		Never hinged	.75	
25	A84	1½p red brown	5.50	4.00
		Never hinged	0.75	
26	A85	2p orange (II)	1.75	.60
		Never hinged	3.25	
a.		Inverted overprint (II)	275.00	500.00
b.		2p orange (I)	19.00	2.00
		Never hinged	35.00	
27	A86	2½p ultra (R)	5.50	11.50
		Never hinged	10.00	
28	A87	3p violet	1.40	2.00
		Never hinged	3.50	
29	A88	4p slate green (R)	2.75	4.00
		Never hinged	4.75	
30	A89	5p yellow brown	3.50	7.00
		Never hinged	7.00	
31	A89	6p red violet	5.50	4.00
		Never hinged	10.00	
32	A90	9p black brown (R)	12.00	14.00
		Never hinged	27.50	
33	A90	9p olive green (R)	5.25	13.00
		Never hinged	10.00	
34	A90	10p light blue	26.00	32.50
		Never hinged	50.00	
35	A90	1sh bister	14.00	9.00
		Never hinged	35.00	
		Nos. 23-35 (13)	84.50	102.85

Nos. 23, 24, 28, 34 overprinted in black were not generally issued and may be proofs.

Overprinted as Nos. 12 to 14 in Blue Black (Shiny to Dull)
Overprint measures 21x13½mm

The "h" and "é" are ½mm apart.

	1922	**Wmk. 34**	**Perf. 11x12**	
36	A91	2sh6p gray brown	200.	225.
		Never hinged	325.	
37	A91	5sh car rose	225.	225.
		Never hinged	350.	
38	A91	10sh gray blue	925.	950.
		Never hinged	1,600.	
		Nos. 36-38 (3)	1,350.	1,400.

Ríaltar
Sealavač
na
héireann
1922.

Overprinted in Blue Black

Overprint measures 15 ³/₄x16mm

1922, Dec. Wmk. 33 *Perf. 15x14*

39 A82 ½p green .40 .60
Never hinged 1.40
40 A83 1p scarlet .90 .90
Never hinged 1.90
41 A84 1½p red brown 2.25 6.00
Never hinged 3.25
42 A85 2p orange (II) 9.50 8.50
Never hinged 16.00
43 A90 1sh bister 27.50 37.50
Never hinged 52.50
Nos. 39-43 (5) 40.55 53.50

Stamps of Great Britain, 1912-22, Overprinted in Shiny to Dull Blue Black or Red — **Saorstát Éireann 1922**

This overprint means the "Free State of Ireland."

Overprint measures 15x8 ½mm
"1922" is 6 ¼mm long

The inner loop of the "9" is an upright oval.

The measurement of "1922" is made across the bottom of the numerals and does not include the serif at the top of the "1."

There were 5 plates for printing the overprint on Nos. 44-55. In the impressions from plate I the 12th stamp in the 15th row has no accent on the 2nd "A" of "SAORSTAT." To correct this an accent was inserted by hand, sometimes this was in a reversed position.

On Nos. 56-58 the accent was omitted on the 2nd stamp in the 3rd and 8th rows. Damage to the plate makes the accent look reversed on the 4th stamp in the 7th row. The top of the "t" slants down in a line with the so-called accent.

1922-23 Wmk. 33 *Perf. 15x14*

44 A82 ½p green .20 .20
Never hinged .30
a. Accent omitted 950.00 *800.00*
b. Accent added 125.00 *125.00*
45 A83 1p scarlet .20 .20
Never hinged .40
a. Accent omitted *8,000.* *8,000.*
b. Accent added 125.00 *125.00*
c. Accent and final "t" omitted *8,000.* *7,000.*
d. Accent and final "t" added 200.00 *225.00*
46 A84 1½p red brown 2.50 *7.00*
Never hinged 4.75
47 A85 2p orange (II) 1.50 1.50
Never hinged 2.75
48 A86 2½p ultra (R) 2.50 4.00
Never hinged 4.75
a. Accent omitted 125.00 *150.00*
49 A87 3p violet 6.00 7.00
Never hinged 11.00
a. Accent omitted 250.00 *285.00*
50 A88 4p sl green (R) 2.50 3.00
Never hinged 4.75
a. Accent omitted 140.00 *165.00*
51 A89 5p yel brown 3.25 4.00
Never hinged 6.25
52 A89 6p dull violet 2.50 2.00
Never hinged 4.75
a. Accent added *950.00* *950.00*
53 A90 9p ol green (R) 3.25 4.00
Never hinged 6.25
a. Accent omitted 225.00 *285.00*
54 A90 10p lt blue 15.00 25.00
Never hinged 26.00
55 A90 1sh bister 9.00 10.00
Never hinged 17.00
a. Accent omitted *8,000.* *8,500.*
b. Accent added *875.00* *800.00*

Perf. 11x12
Wmk. 34

56 A91 2sh6p lt brown 32.50 55.00
Never hinged 52.50
a. Accent omitted 325.00 *400.00*
57 A91 5sh car rose 60.00 100.00
Never hinged 92.50
a. Accent omitted 475.00 *575.00*
58 A91 10sh gray blue 140.00 250.00
Never hinged 275.00
a. Accent omitted *2,750.* *3,250.*
Nos. 44-58 (15) 280.90 472.90

See Nos. 77b, 78b and 79b.

Overprinted by Harrison & Sons

Coil Stamps
Same Ovpt. in Black or Blue Black

1923 Wmk. 33 *Perf. 15x14*

59 A82 ½p green 1.50 4.00
Never hinged 3.00
a. Tall "1" 13.00 22.50
Never hinged 18.00
60 A83 1p scarlet 3.00 6.75
Never hinged 6.00
a. Tall "1" 55.00 90.00
Never hinged 80.00
61 A84 1½p red brown 4.25 14.00
Never hinged 8.25
a. Tall "1" 80.00 165.00
Never hinged 125.00
62 A85 2p orange (II) 2.00 5.00
Never hinged 4.00
a. Tall "1" 15.00 27.50
Never hinged 22.50
Nos. 59-62 (4) 10.75 29.75

These stamps were issued in coils, made by joining horizontal or vertical strips of the stamps. In some strips there were two stamps with the "1" of "1922" 2½mm high and with serif at foot.

In this setting the middle "e" of "eireann" is a trifle above the line of the other letters, making the word appear slightly curved. The lower end of the "1" of "1922" is rounded instead of flat.

The inner loop of the "9" is round.

Booklet Panes

For very fine the perforation holes at top or bottom of the pane should be visible, though not necessarily perfect half circles.

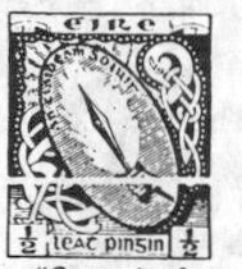

"Sword of Light" — A1

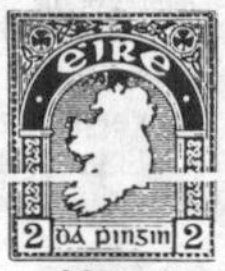

Map of Ireland — A2

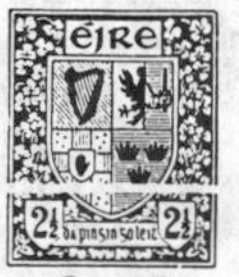

Coat of Arms — A3

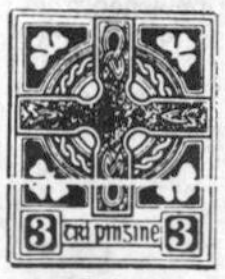

Celtic Cross — A4

The letters "SE" are the initials of "Saorstat Eireann" (Free State Ireland).

1922-23 Typo. Wmk. 44 *Perf. 15x14*

65 A1 ½p emerald .20 .20
Never hinged .55
a. Booklet pane of 6 *300.00*
66 A2 1p car rose .20 .20
Never hinged .65
a. Booklet pane of 6 *275.00*
b. Booklet pane of 3 + 3 labels *400.00*
67 A2 1½p claret 1.50 1.50
Never hinged 4.25
68 A2 2p deep green .20 .20
Never hinged .85
a. Booklet pane of 6 *275.00*
b. Perf. 15 horiz. ('35) *15,000.* *1,700.*

No. 68b is valued in the grade of fine.

69 A3 2½p chocolate 2.50 1.50
Never hinged 4.25
70 A4 3p ultra 1.75 .40
Never hinged 3.50
71 A3 4p slate 2.50 1.40
Never hinged 6.25
72 A1 5p deep violet 12.50 6.00
Never hinged 37.50
73 A1 6p red violet 4.00 2.75
Never hinged 8.00
74 A3 9p violet 12.50 *14.00*
Never hinged 52.50
75 A4 10p brown 8.25 *20.00*
Never hinged 27.50
76 A1 1sh light blue 25.00 6.00
Never hinged 65.00
Nos. 65-76 (12) 71.10 54.15

The 2p was issued in 1922; other denominations in 1923.

No. 68b is a vertical coil stamp.

See Nos. 87, 91-92, 105-117, 137-138, 225-226, 326. For types overprinted see Nos. 118-119.

Overprinted by the Government Printing Office, Dublin Castle and British Board of Inland Revenue at Somerset House, London

Great Britain Nos. 179-181 Ovptd. in Black or Gray Black — **Saorstát Éireann 1922**

"1922" is 5 ½mm long

The measurement of "1922" is made across the bottom of the numerals and does not include the serif at the top of the "1."

1925 Wmk. 34 *Perf. 11x12*

77 A91 2sh6p gray brown 35.00 55.00
Never hinged 55.00
78 A91 5sh rose red 47.50 80.00
Never hinged 77.50
79 A91 10sh gray blue 115.00 200.00
Never hinged 190.00
Nos. 77-79 (3) 197.50 335.00

In 1927 the 2sh6p, 5sh and 10sh stamps were overprinted from a plate in which the Thom and Castle clichés were combined, thus including wide and narrow "1922" in the same setting.

Overprinted by British Board of Inland Revenue at Somerset House, London

Pair with "1922" Wide and Narrow

1927

77a A91 2sh6p 225.
78a A91 5sh 425.
79a A91 10sh 1,000.
Nos. 77a-79a (3) 1,650.

Wide "1922"
"1922" is 6 ¼mm long

1927-28

77b A91 2sh6p 30.00 35.00
78b A91 5sh ('28) 65.00 70.00
79b A91 10sh ('28) 175.00 175.00
Nos. 77b-79b (3) 270.00 280.00

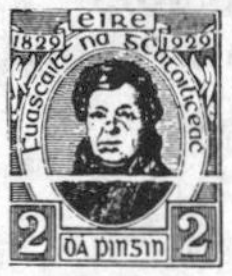

Daniel O'Connell — A5

1929, June 22 Wmk. 44 *Perf. 15x14*

80 A5 2p dark green .35 .30
Never hinged .50
81 A5 3p dark blue 3.75 8.50
Never hinged 10.00
82 A5 9p dark violet 4.00 8.00
Never hinged 12.50
Nos. 80-82 (3) 8.10 16.80

Catholic Emancipation in Ireland, centenary.

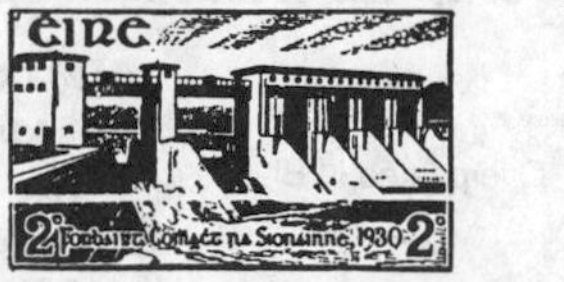

Shannon River Hydroelectric Station — A6

1930, Oct. 15

83 A6 2p black brown .50 .30
Never hinged 2.00

Opening of the hydroelectric development of the River Shannon.

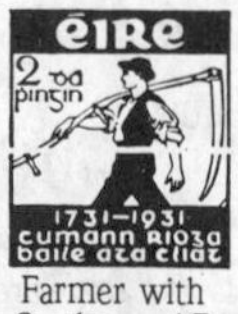

Farmer with Scythe — A7

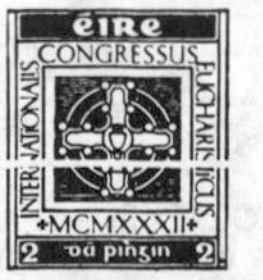

Cross of Cong and Chalice — A8

1931, June 12

84 A7 2p pale blue .80 .25
Never hinged 2.00

Bicentenary of Royal Dublin Society.

1932, May 12

85 A8 2p dark green .80 .25
Never hinged 1.75
86 A8 3p bright blue 2.00 4.50
Never hinged 5.00

International Eucharistic Congress.

Coil Stamp
Type of 1922-23 Issue

1933-34 ***Perf. 15 Horizontally***

87 A2 1p rose ('34) 22.50 35.00
Never hinged 40.00
a. 1p carmine rose 95.00 *175.00*
Never hinged 190.00

No. 87a has a single perforation at each side near the top, while No. 87 is perforated top and bottom only.

See No. 68b.

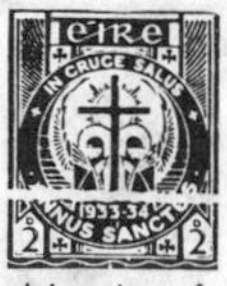

Adoration of the Cross — A9

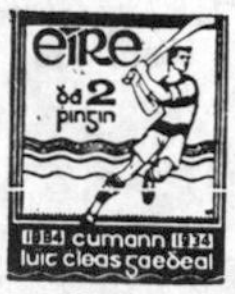

Hurling — A10

1933, Sept. 18 *Perf. 15x14*

88 A9 2p slate green .45 .25
Never hinged .75
89 A9 3p deep blue 2.50 3.75
Never hinged 6.25

Holy Year.

1934, July 27

90 A10 2p green .90 .30
Never hinged 1.65

50th anniv. of the Gaelic Athletic Assoc.

Coil Stamps
Types of 1922-23
Wmk. 44 Sideways

1934 ***Perf. 14 Vertically***

91 A1 ½p green 30.00 40.00
Never hinged 50.00
92 A2 2p gray green 45.00 57.50
Never hinged 110.00

Overprinted by Harrison & Sons and British Board of Inland Revenue at Somerset House, London

Great Britain Nos. 222-224 Overprinted in Black — **Saorstát Éireann 1922**

1935 Wmk. 44 *Perf. 11x12*

93 A91 2sh6p brown 35.00 35.00
Never hinged 60.00
94 A91 5sh carmine 90.00 100.00
Never hinged 175.00
95 A91 10sh dark blue 350.00 *350.00*
Never hinged 625.00
Nos. 93-95 (3) 475.00 *485.00*

Waterlow printing can be distinguished by the crossed lines in the background of portrait. Previous issues have horizontal lines only.

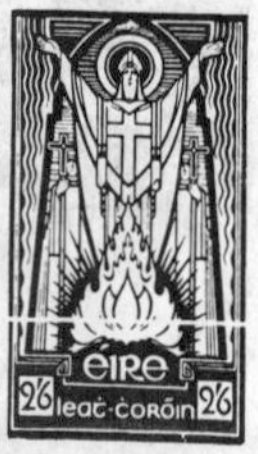

St. Patrick and Paschal Fire — A11

1937, Sept. 8 Wmk. 44 *Perf. 14x15*
96 A11 2sh6p bright green 50.00 67.50
Never hinged 125.00
97 A11 5sh brown violet 55.00 75.00
Never hinged 140.00
98 A11 10sh dark blue 40.00 55.00
Never hinged 125.00
Nos. 96-98 (3) 145.00 197.50

See Nos. 121-123.

Catalogue values for unused stamps in this section, from this point to the end of the section, are for Never Hinged items.

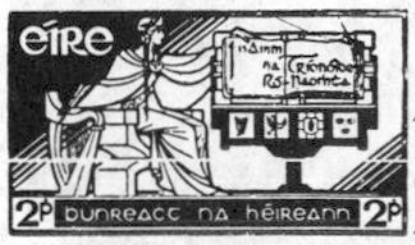
Allegory of Ireland and Constitution A12

1937, Dec. 29 *Perf. 15x14*
99 A12 2p plum 1.25 .25
100 A12 3p deep blue 5.75 2.75

Constitution Day.
See Nos. 169-170.

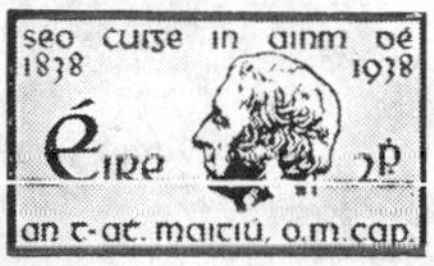
Father Theobald Mathew A13

1938, July 1
101 A13 2p black brown 1.00 .15
102 A13 3p ultramarine 10.50 5.50

Temperance Crusade by Father Mathew, centenary.

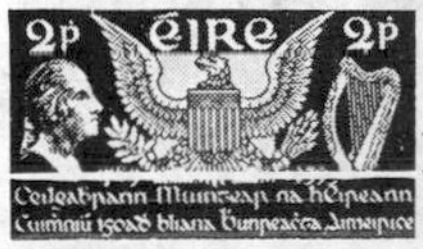
Washington, US Eagle and Harp — A14

1939, Mar. 1
103 A14 2p bright carmine .90 .30
104 A14 3p deep blue 8.50 6.50

US Constitution, 150th anniv.

Coil Stamp
Type of 1922-23

1940-46 Wmk. 262 *Perf. 15 Horiz.*
105 A2 1p car rose ('46) 27.50 20.00
a. Perf. 14 horiz. 50.00 45.00

Types of 1922-23

1940-42 *Perf. 15x14*
Size: 18x22mm
106 A1 ½p emerald ('41) 1.75 .20
a. Booklet pane of 6 350.00
107 A2 1p car rose ('41) .15 .15
a. Booklet pane of 6 5.00
b. Bklt. pane of 3 + 3 labels 1,250.
108 A2 1½p claret ('41) 9.50 .20
a. Booklet pane of 6 140.00
109 A2 2p deep green .22 .15
a. Booklet pane of 6 10.00
110 A3 2½p choc ('41) 6.50 .15
a. Booklet pane of 6 95.00
111 A4 3p dull blue ('41) .30 .15
a. Booklet pane of 6 40.00
112 A3 4p slate .35 .15
a. Booklet pane of 6 65.00
113 A1 5p deep violet .50 .15
114 A1 6p red violet ('42) .60 .15
115 A3 9p violet .70 .20
116 A4 10p olive brown 1.75 .30
117 A1 1sh blue 100.00 7.25
Nos. 106-117 (12) 122.32 9.20

Types of 1922-23 Overprinted in Green or Violet

1941
I gCuimne
Aiséirge
1916

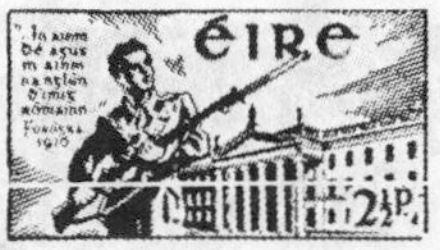
Volunteer Soldier and Dublin Post Office — A15

1941, Apr. 12 *Perf. 15x14*
118 A2 2p yellow orange 2.00 .50
119 A4 3p blue (V) 40.00 16.00

Overprint reads: "In memory of the Rebellion of 1916."

1941, Oct. 27
120 A15 2½p bluish black .90 .30

Nos. 118-120 commemorate the 25th anniv. of the Easter Rebellion.

St. Patrick Type of 1937

1943-45 Wmk. 262 *Perf. 14x15*
121 A11 2sh6p bright green 5.00 .65
122 A11 5sh brown violet 7.75 1.25
123 A11 10sh dark blue ('45) 17.00 3.50
Nos. 121-123 (3) 29.75 5.40

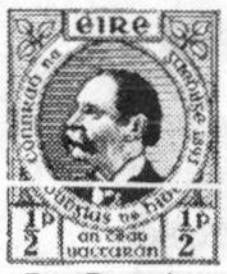
Dr. Douglas Hyde A16

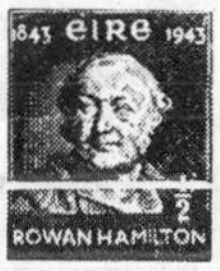
Sir Rowan Hamilton A17

1943, July 31 *Perf. 15x14*
124 A16 ½p green .50 .25
125 A16 2½p red lilac .95 .60

50th anniv. of the Gaelic League.

1943, Nov. 13 Typo. Wmk. 262
126 A17 ½p deep green 1.75 .20
127 A17 2½p dk red brown 1.65 .60

Centenary of discovery of the mathematical formula of Quaternions by William Rowan Hamilton.

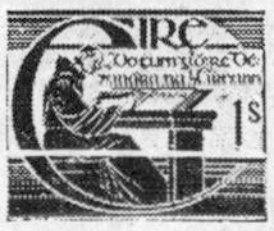
Brother Michael O'Clery — A18

1944, June 30 *Perf. 14x15*
128 A18 ½p emerald .20 .15
a. Booklet pane of 6 20.00
129 A18 1sh reddish brown 1.00 .15
Set value .20

300th anniv. of the death of Michael O'Clery, Irish historian.

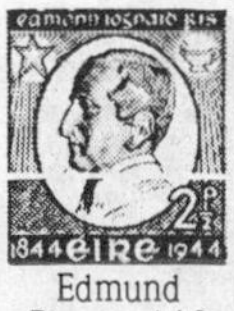
Edmund Rice A19

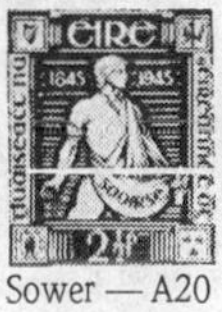
Sower — A20

1944, Aug. 29 *Perf. 15x14*
130 A19 2½p slate .85 .15

Death centenary of Edmund Ignatius Rice, founder of the Christian Brothers of Ireland.

1945, Sept. 15
131 A20 2½p ultramarine 1.50 .15
132 A20 6p red violet 6.75 3.25

Commemorates the work of the Young Irelanders and the death centenary of Thomas Davis, Sept. 16, 1845.

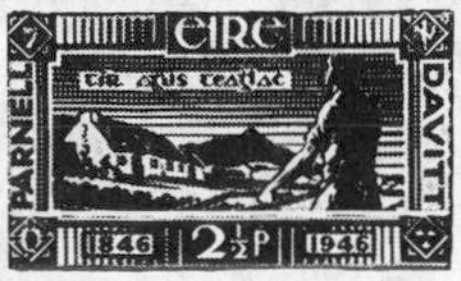
Plowman A21

1946, Sept. 16 **Typo.**
133 A21 2½p red 1.50 .20
134 A21 3p dark blue 4.25 3.25

Birth centenary of Charles Stewart Parnell and Michael Davitt, leaders in the struggle for Irish political independence.

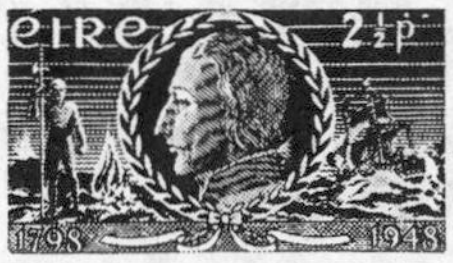
Theobald Wolfe Tone — A22

Perf. 15x14
1948, Nov. 19 Wmk. 262
135 A22 2½p deep plum 1.50 .15
136 A22 3p deep violet 6.75 4.00

Insurrection of 1798, 150th anniversary.

Types of 1922-23

1949
137 A1 8p bright red .75 .25
138 A4 11p carmine rose 1.40 1.00

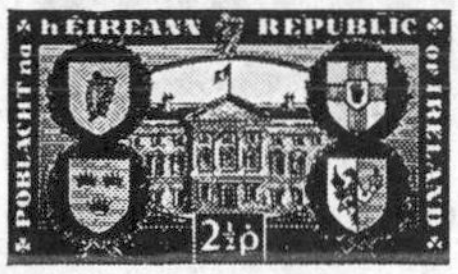
Leinster House, Dublin A23

1949, Nov. 21
139 A23 2½p red brown 1.25 .50
140 A23 3p violet blue 6.25 3.00

International recognition of the Republic, Easter Monday, 1949.

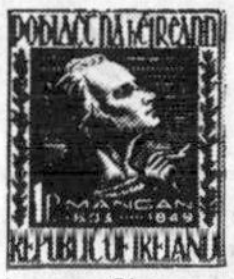
James Clarence Mangan — A24

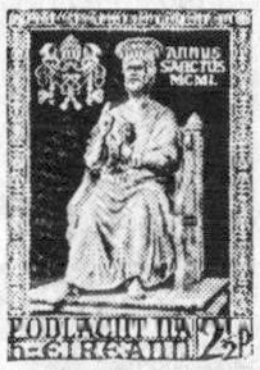
Statue of St. Peter — A25

1949, Dec. 5
141 A24 1p dark green 3.00 .40

Mangan (1803-1849), poet.

Perf. 12½
1950, Sept. 11 Wmk. 262 Engr.
142 A25 2½p violet .60 .15
143 A25 3p blue 11.00 7.25
144 A25 9p brown 12.00 6.00
Nos. 142-144 (3) 23.60 13.40

Holy Year, 1950.

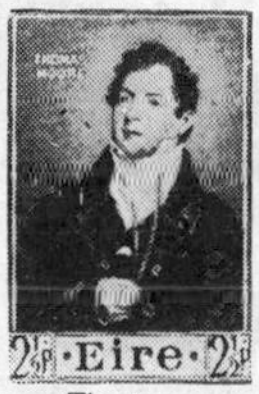
Thomas Moore — A26

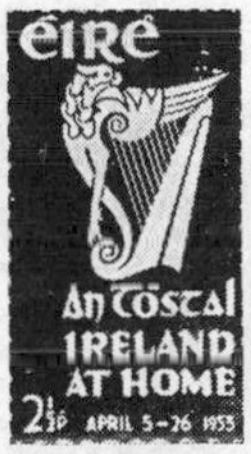
Irish Harp — A27

1952, Nov. 10 *Perf. 13*
145 A26 2½p deep plum .20 .15
146 A26 3½p dk olive green 4.00 2.00

Death centenary of Thomas Moore (1779-1852), poet.

1953, Feb. 9 Typo. *Perf. 14x15*
147 A27 2½p bright green .75 .15
148 A27 1sh4p bright blue 25.00 25.00

Ireland's National festival "An Tostal."

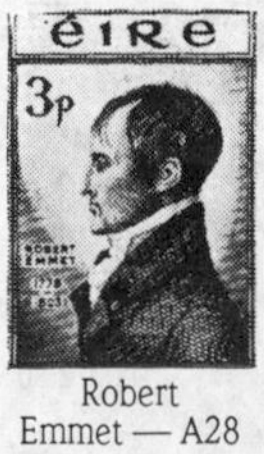
Robert Emmet — A28

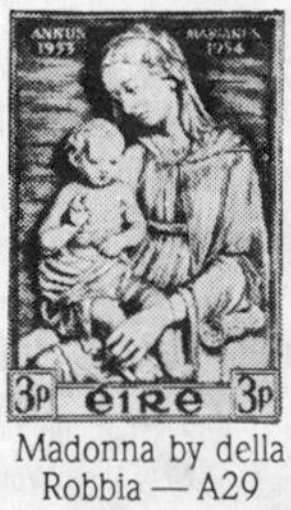
Madonna by della Robbia — A29

1953, Sept. 21 Engr. *Perf. 12½x13*
149 A28 3p deep green 3.00 .40
150 A28 1sh3p carmine rose 47.50 9.50

150th anniv. of the execution of Robert Emmet (1778-1803), Irish nationalist.

1954, May 24 *Perf. 15*
151 A29 3p blue 1.10 .15
152 A29 5p deep green 9.25 4.50

Marian Year, 1953-54.

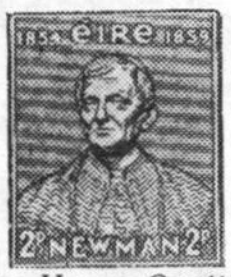
John Henry Cardinal Newman — A30

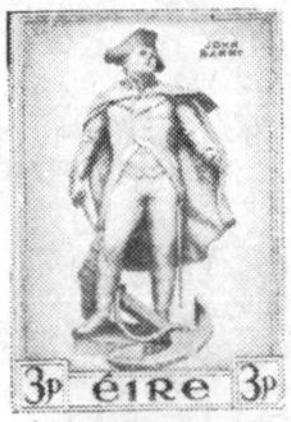
Statue of John Barry — A31

1954, July 19 Typo. *Perf. 15x14*
153 A30 2p rose lilac 2.50 .20
154 A30 1sh3p blue 20.00 9.00

Opening of the Catholic University of Ireland, centenary.

1956, Sept. 16 Engr. *Perf. 15*
155 A31 3p dull purple .75 .15
156 A31 1sh3p blue 10.50 5.50

John Barry (1745-1803), "Father of the American Navy," on the occasion of the unveiling of a statue in Wexford, Ireland, his birthplace.

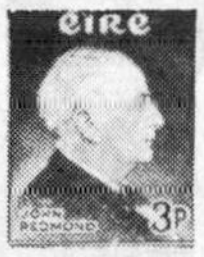
Redmond A32

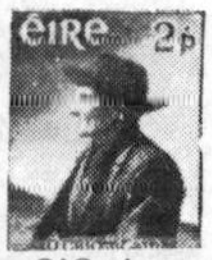
O'Crohan A33

Perf. 14x15
1957, June 11 Wmk. 262
157 A32 3p dark blue 1.00 .15
158 A32 1sh3p rose lake 14.00 8.00

Birth cent. of John Edward Redmond (1856-1918), Irish political leader.

1957, July 1
159 A33 2p dull purple 1.75 .15
160 A33 5p violet 6.00 5.00

Birth cent. of Thomas O'Crohan (Tomas O'Criomhthain) (1856-1937), fisherman and author.

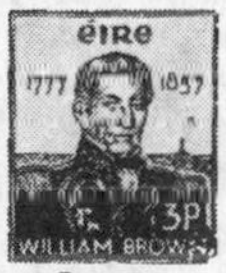
Brown A34

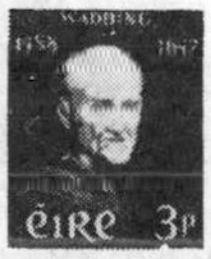
Father Luke Wadding A35

1957, Sept. 23 Typo. *Perf. 15x14*
161 A34 3p blue 2.25 .30
162 A34 1sh3p carmine rose 40.00 12.50

Adm. William (Guillermo) Brown (1777-1857), founder of the Argentine Navy.

1957, Nov. 25 Engr. *Perf. 15*
163 A35 3p dark blue 1.50 .50
164 A35 1sh3p deep claret 20.00 7.00

Luke Wadding (1588-1657), Irish Franciscan friar and historian.

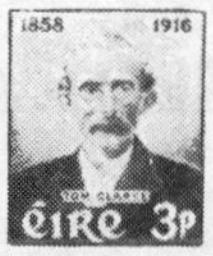
Clarke A36

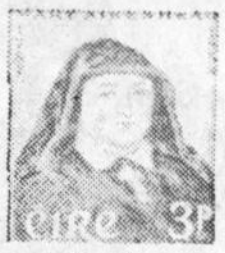
Aikenhead A37

1958, July 28   Wmk. 262
165 A36   3p deep green   .95 .15
166 A36   1sh3p red brown   15.00 5.50
Thomas J. Clarke (1858-1916), patriot.

1958, Oct. 20   Perf. 15x14
167 A37   3p blue   1.25 .15
168 A37   3p carmine   19.00 8.00
Mother Mary Aikenhead (1787-1858), founder of the Irish Sisters of Charity.

Constitution Type of 1937
1958, Dec. 29   Typo.   Wmk. 262
169 A12   3p brown   .55 .20
170 A12   5p bright green   5.00 4.50
21st anniv. of the constitution.

Arthur Guinness — A38

1959, July 20   Engr.   Perf. 15
171 A38   3p rose lake   1.75 .15
172 A38   1sh3p dark blue   17.00 7.50
Bicentenary of Guinness Brewery.

Flight of the Holy Family A39

1960, June 20   Perf. 15
173 A39   3p rose violet   .25 .20
174 A39   1sh3p sepia   1.00 1.65
World Refugee Year, July 1, 1959-June 30, 1960.

Europa Issue

Symbolic Wheel CD3

1960, Sept. 19   Engr.   Perf. 15
175 CD3   6p orange brown   2.25 1.65
176 CD3   1sh3p violet   13.00 11.00
No. 176 has fugitive ink.

De Havilland Dragon, Boeing 707 Jet and Dublin Airport A41

1961, June 26   Perf. 15
177 A41   6p dull blue   1.90 1.40
178 A41   1sh3p green   4.25 3.25
25th anniv. of the founding of Aer Lingus, Irish International Airlines.

St. Patrick — A42

1961, Sept. 25   Perf. 14½
179 A42   3p blue   .60 .25
180 A42   8p pale purple   1.90 2.75
181 A42   1sh3p green   2.00 2.00
    Nos. 179-181 (3)   4.50 5.00
1,500th anniv. of St. Patrick's death.

John O'Donovan and Eugene O'Curry A43

1962, Mar. 26   Perf. 15
182 A43   3p crimson   .40 .15
183 A43   1sh3p purple   4.75 2.75
Death centenaries of John O'Donovan (1806-1861) and Eugene O'Curry (1794-1862), Gaelic scholars and translators.

Europa Issue

19 Leaves on Young Tree — CD5

1962, Sept. 17   Engr.   Wmk. 262
184 CD5   6p pink & dark red   .30 .35
185 CD5   1sh3p bluish grn & dk blue grn   1.25 1.40

Wheat Emblem and Globe — A45

1963, Mar. 21   Wmk. 262
186 A45   4p violet   .20 .15
187 A45   1sh3p red   1.90 1.75
FAO "Freedom from Hunger" campaign.

Common Design Types are pictured in section before Great Britain.

Europa Issue

Stylized Links, Symbolizing Unity — CD6

1963, Sept. 16   Perf. 15
188 CD6   6p rose carmine   .65 .55
189 CD6   1sh3p dark blue   3.75 3.50

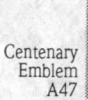 
Centenary Emblem A47

1963, Dec. 2   Photo.   Perf. 14½x14
190 A47   4p gray & red   .20 .15
191 A47   1sh3p brt green, gray & red   1.10 1.40
Centenary of the International Red Cross.

Wolfe Tone — A48

1964, Apr. 13   Engr.   Perf. 15
192 A48   4p black   .70 .20
193 A48   1sh3p dark blue   4.00 3.50
Birth bicentenary of Theobald Wolfe Tone (1763-1798), Irish revolutionist.

Irish Pavilion A49

1964, July 20   Photo.   Perf. 14½x14
194 A49   5p multicolored   .65 .15
195 A49   1sh5p multicolored   4.00 3.50
New York World's Fair, 1964-65.

Europa Issue

CEPT Daisy (22 Petals) — CD7

Perf. 14x14½
1964, Sept. 14   Litho.   Wmk. 262
196 CD7   8p dull grn & ultra   .95 .95
197 CD7   1sh5p red brown & org   4.00 4.00

ITU Emblem, Globe and Communication Waves — A51

1965, May 17   Photo.   Perf. 14½x14
198 A51   3p dp blue & emerald   .30 .20
199 A51   8p black & emerald   1.75 1.90
ITU, cent.

William Butler Yeats — A52

1965, June 14   Perf. 15
200 A52   5p orange brn & blk   .95 .25
201 A52   1sh5p gray green, brn & black   4.75 3.75
Birth centenary of William Butler Yeats (1865-1939), poet and dramatist.

ICY Emblem A53

1965, Aug. 16   Photo.   Perf. 15
202 A53   3p brt blue & vio bl   .75 .20
203 A53   10p redsh brn & dk brn   3.75 5.00
International Cooperation Year.

Europa Issue

Leaves and Fruit — CD8

1965, Sept. 27   Perf. 15
204 CD8   8p brick red & blk   .85 .85
205 CD8   1sh5p lt blue & claret   4.25 3.75

James Connolly A55

Designs: No. 207, Thomas J. Clarke. No. 208, Patrick Henry Pearse. No. 209, Symbolic of lives lost in fight for independence, and of Ireland marching into freedom. No. 210, Eamonn Ceannt. No. 211, Sean MacDiarmada. No. 212, Thomas MacDonagh. No. 213, Joseph Plunkett.

1966, Apr. 12   Wmk. 262   Perf. 15
206 A55   3p blue & black   .75 .35
207 A55   3p olive green   .75 .35
  a.   Pair, #206-207   2.50 2.75
208 A55   5p olive & black   .80 .35
209 A55   5p brt grn, blk & orange   .80 .35
  a.   Pair, #208-209   2.75 3.00

---

210 A55   7p dull org & blk   1.75 1.40
211 A55   7p blue grn & blk   1.75 1.40
  a.   Pair, #210-211   5.00 5.50
212 A55   1sh5p grnsh bl & blk   2.25 1.75
213 A55   1sh5p emerald & blk   2.25 1.75
  a.   Pair, #212-213   8.00 8.75
    Nos. 206-213 (8)   11.10 7.70
50th anniv. of the Easter Week Rebellion, and to honor the signers of the Proclamation of the Irish Republic.

Roger Casement A56

Symbolic Sailboat CD9

1966, Aug. 3   Perf. 15
214 A56   5p black   .20 .15
215 A56   1sh dark red brown   .90 .80
50th death anniv. of Roger Casement (1864-1916), British consular agent and Irish rebel who was executed for treason.

Europa Issue
1966, Sept. 26   Photo.   Perf. 15
216 CD9   7p orange & green   .65 .65
217 CD9   1sh5p gray & green   1.60 1.10

Ballintubber Abbey A58

1966, Nov. 8   Perf. 15
218 A58   5p red brown   .20 .15
219 A58   1sh black   .60 .55
750th anniversary of Ballintubber Abbey.

Cross and Sword Types of 1922
1966-67   Photo.   Perf. 15
Size: 17x20½mm
225 A4   3p blue ('67)   1.25 .25
226 A1   5p brt vio, type II ('68)   2.25 .30
  a.   Booklet pane of 6, No. 226b   19.00
  b.   Type I ('66)   2.25 1.25
Type I has irregularly spaced lines in shading behind sword.

Europa Issue

Cogwheels — CD10

1967, May 2
232 CD10   7p green & gold   .40 .60
233 CD10   1sh5p dk red & gold   1.10 .90

Maple Leaves A60

1967, Aug. 28   Photo.
234 A60   5p multicolored   .15 .15
235 A60   1sh5p multicolored   .55 .60
Centenary of the Canadian Confederation.

Rock of Cashel — A61

1967, Sept. 25 Wmk. 262 *Perf. 15*

236	A61	7p sepia	.20	.30
237	A61	10p Prussian blue	.40	.55

International Tourist Year.

One Cent Fenian Fantasy A62

Swift's Bust and St. Patrick's Cathedral, Dublin A63

Design: 1sh, 24c Fenian fantasy.

1967, Oct. 23 Photo. *Perf. 15*

238	A62	5p lt green & slate grn	.15	.15
239	A62	1sh pale pink & gray	.40	.60

Fenian Rising, centenary. The Fenian fantasy was created by S. Allan Taylor.

1967, Nov. 30 *Perf. 15*

Design: 1sh5p, Gulliver, Lilliputian army.

240	A63	3p gray & sepia	.15	.15
241	A63	1sh5p lt blue & sepia	.40	.50

Birth tercentenary of Jonathan Swift (1667-1745), author of Gulliver's Travels.

Europa Issue

Golden Key with CEPT Emblem CD11

1968, Apr. 29 Photo. Wmk. 262

242	CD11	7p multicolored	.40	.40
243	CD11	1sh5p multicolored	1.00	1.00

St. Mary's Cathedral, Limerick A65

1968, Aug. 26 Engr. *Perf. 15*

244	A65	5p dull blue	.20	.15
245	A65	10p olive	.60	.80

800th anniv. of the founding of St. Mary's Cathedral by Donal Mor O'Brien, last King of Munster.

Countess Markievicz A66

1968, Sept. 23 Photo. Wmk. 262

246	A66	3p black	.15	.15
247	A66	1sh5p dark blue	.45	.65

Birth centenary of Countess Constance Markievicz (1868-1927), champion of Irish Independence and first Minister of Labor.

James Connolly — A67

1968, Sept. 23 *Perf. 15*

248	A67	6p brown, dk brn & blk	.15	.20
249	A67	1sh dull grn, grn & blk	.40	.50

Birth centenary of James Connolly (1868-1916), founder of the Irish Socialist Party, editor of "Workers' Republic" and Commander of the Irish Citizen Army.

Dog from Ancient Brooch, County Kilkenny — A68

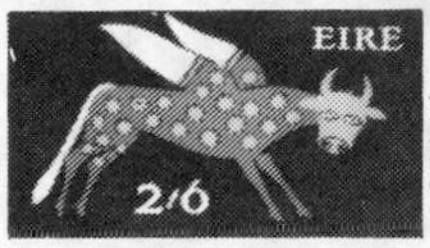

Winged Ox from Lichfield Gospel Book — A69

Designs: ½p, 1p, 2p, 3p, 4p, 5p, 6p, Dog. 7p, 8p, 9p, 10p, 1sh, 1sh9p, Stag from ancient bowl, Kent. 2sh6p, 5sh, Winged ox. 10sh, Eagle, from ancient manuscript.

1968-70 Photo. Wmk. 262 *Perf. 15*

250	A68	½p orange	.15	.15
251	A68	1p yellow green	.15	.15
252	A68	2p ocher	.15	.15
253	A68	3p bright blue	.15	.15
254	A68	4p dark red	.15	.15
255	A68	5p deep green	.18	.15
256	A68	6p brown	.20	.15
a.		Booklet pane of 6 ('70)	25.00	
257	A68	7p yel & brown	.85	.85
258	A68	8p red org & blk	.55	.50
259	A68	9p ol grn & dk bl	.85	.32
260	A68	10p violet & dk brn	.85	.75
261	A68	1sh dk red brn & brown	.85	.32
262	A68	1sh9p grnsh bl & dk brown	1.50	1.75
263	A69	2sh6p red org, bl, ol & dull yel	3.25	.40
264	A69	5sh ol, gray, bis & yel	7.00	.90
265	A69	10sh dk red brn, yel & dp org	14.00	2.75
		Nos. 250-265 (16)	30.83	9.59

Issue dates: 2p, 8p, 2sh6p, 10sh, Oct. 14, 1968. 6p, 9p, 1sh9p, 5sh, Feb. 24, 1969. 4p, 5p, 10p, 1sh, Mar. 31, 1969. ½p, 1p, 3p, 7p, June 9, 1969.
See #290-304, 343-359, 395-402, 466-475.

Coil Stamps

1970 *Perf. 14x15*

251a	A68	1p yellow green	.90	*2.65*
252a	A68	2p ocher	.90	*2.65*
253a	A68	3p bright blue	.90	*2.65*
		Nos. 251a-253a (3)	2.70	*7.95*

Human Rights Flame — A70

1968, Nov. 4 Wmk. 262 *Perf. 15*

266	A70	5p black, ocher & gold	.15	.15
267	A70	7p crimson, ocher & gold	.42	.50

International Human Rights Year.

First Meeting of Irish Parliament A71

1969, Jan. 21 *Perf. 15x14½*

268	A71	6p dark slate green	.15	.15
269	A71	9p dark blue gray	.50	.60

50th anniv. of the first meeting of the Dail Eireann at the Mansion House, Dublin, Jan. 21, 1919.

"EUROPA" and "CEPT" CD12

1969, Apr. 28 Photo. *Perf. 15*

270	CD12	9p ultra, gray & ocher	.60	1.10
271	CD12	1sh9p car, gray & gold	1.75	1.10

Europa and CEPT, 10th anniv.

ILO Emblem — A73

1969, July 14 *Perf. 15*

272	A73	6p gray & black	.15	.15
273	A73	9p yellow & black	.40	.42

ILO, 50th anniv.

Last Supper and Crucifixion, by Evie Hone — A74

Perf. 15x14½

1969, Sept. 1 Photo. Wmk. 262

274	A74	1sh multicolored	.70	1.25

The design is after a stained-glass window by Evie Hone (1894-1955) in the Eton College Chapel.

Mahatma Gandhi A75

1969, Oct. 2 *Perf. 15*

275	A75	6p dk yel green & blk	.15	.15
276	A75	1sh9p yel, green & black	.55	.60

Mohandas K. Gandhi (1869-1948), leader in India's fight for independence.

Stylized Bird, Tree and Shamrock A76

1970, Feb. 23 *Perf. 15*

277	A76	6p olive bister & black	.18	.15
278	A76	9p violet & black	.75	.60

Nature Conservation Year.

Europa Issue

Interwoven Threads CD13

1970, May 4 Photo. *Perf. 15*

279	CD13	6p purple & silver	.30	.15
280	CD13	9p yel brn & silver	1.10	.65
281	CD13	1sh9p dk gray & sil	2.00	1.00
		Nos. 279-281 (3)	3.40	1.80

Sailing Boats, by Peter Monamy (1670-1749) A78

1970, July 13 *Perf. 15*

282	A78	4p gold & multi	.18	.18

250th anniv. of the Royal Cork Yacht Club.

Madonna of Eire, by Mainie Jellett (1896-1943) A79

Tomás MacCurtain A80

1970, Sept. 1 Photo. *Perf. 15*

283	A79	1sh violet blue & multi	.65	.50

1970, Oct. 26 *Perf. 15*

Designs: Nos. 285, 287, Terence MacSwiney.

284	A80	9p violet & black	1.10	.90
285	A80	9p violet & black	1.10	.90
a.		Pair, #284-285	3.00	3.50
286	A80	2sh9p brt blue & blk	3.00	2.25
287	A80	2sh9p brt blue & blk	3.00	2.25
a.		Pair, #286-287	7.50	8.50

50th anniv. of the deaths of Tomás MacCurtain (1884-1920) and Terence MacSwiney (1879-1920), lord mayors of Cork, who died during the Irish war of independence.

Kevin Barry — A81

1970, Nov. 2

288	A81	6p olive green	.20	.15
289	A81	1sh2p violet blue	.65	.60

50th anniv. of the death of Kevin Barry (1902-1920), who was hanged during the Irish war of independence.

Decimal Currency Issue

Types of 1968-69 (Numerals only)

Designs: ½p, 1p, 1½p, 2p, 2½p, 3p, 3½p, 4p, No. 298A, Dog. No. 298, 6p, 7p, 7½p, 9p, Stag. 10p, 12p, 20p, Winged ox. 50p, Eagle.

Two types of 10p:
I - Ox outlined in brown
II - Outlined in dull lilac

1971-75 Wmk. 262 Photo. *Perf. 15*

290	A68	½p yellow green	.15	.15
a.		Booklet pane of 6	32.50	
291	A68	1p bright blue	.62	.15
a.		Booklet pane of 6	2.25	
c.		Bklt. pane of 5 + label ('74)	.75	
292	A68	1½p brown red	.22	.30
293	A68	2p dark green	.22	.15
b.		Booklet pane of 5 + label ('75)	1.25	
294	A68	2½p sepia	.40	.15
a.		Booklet pane of 6	9.50	
295	A68	3p yel orange	.30	.15
296	A68	3½p deep orange	.50	.20
297	A68	4p violet	.22	.15
298	A68	5p ap grn & brn	1.50	.40
298A	A68	5p apple grn ('74)	1.75	.40
c.		Booklet pane of 6 ('74)	10.50	
d.		Bklt. pane of 5 + label ('74)	2.25	
299	A68	6p blue gray & dk brown	2.75	.50
299A	A68	7p ol green & ind ('74)	5.00	3.25
300	A68	7½p rose vio & dk brown	.50	.45
301	A68	9p bl grn & blk	2.50	.62
302	A69	10p lil & multi (I)	8.00	.85
b.		Type II	15.00	3.75
302A	A69	12p multi ('74)	1.00	.30
303	A69	20p slate & multi	4.25	.75
304	A69	50p rose brn & multi	12.50	1.25
		Nos. 290-304 (18)	42.38	10.17

Booklet panes have watermark sideways.
Issued: #298A, 7p, 12p, 1/29/74; others, 2/15/71.
See Nos. 343-359, 395-402, 466-475.

Coil Stamps

1971-74 *Perf. 14x15*

291b	A68	1p bright blue	.90	.45
292a	A68	1½p brown red	.30	.18
293a	A68	2p dark green ('72)	.35	.18
294b	A68	2½p sepia	.30	.15
c.		Strip of 3 (1p, 1½p, 2½p)	1.50	
297a	A68	4p violet ('72)	1.25	.70
b.		Strip of 4 (1½p, 2p, 2½p, 4p) ('72)	2.25	
298b	A68	5p apple green ('74)	1.25	.80
e.		Strip of 4 (2x1½p, 2p, 5p) ('74)	2.25	

Europa Issue, 1971
Common Design Type
Size: 36½x21mm

1971, May 3   Wmk. 262   Perf. 15
305 CD14 4p apple green & blk   .40   .20
306 CD14 6p blue & black   2.50   1.75

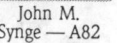

John M. Synge — A82

An Island Man, by Jack B. Yeats — A83

1971, July 19   Photo.   Perf. 15
307 A82 4p gray, black & gold   .28   .16
308 A82 10p org, black & gold   1.10   .90

Birth cent. of John Millington Synge (1871-1909), poet and dramatist.

1971, Aug. 30   Perf. 15
309 A83 6p multicolored   .75   .60

Jack Butler Yeats (1871-1957), painter.

Racial Equality Emblem A84

Madonna, by John Hughes, Loughrea Cathedral A85

Perf. 14x14½
1971, Oct. 18   Litho.   Unwmk.
310 A84 4p red   .25   .16
311 A84 10p black   .95   .80

Intl. Year Against Racial Discrimination.

1971, Nov. 15   Photo.   Perf. 15
312 A85 2½p dp bl grn, gold & slate   .24   .15
313 A85 6p ultra, gold & slate   .75   .90

Christmas.

"Your Heart is your Health" A86

1972, Apr. 7   Photo.   Wmk. 262
314 A86 2½p gold & brown   .55   .22
315 A86 12p silver & black   2.50   2.25

World Health Day.

Europa Issue

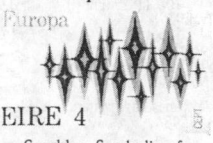

Sparkles, Symbolic of Communications — CD15

1972, May 1   Perf. 15
316 CD15 4p red, black & sil   2.00   .48
317 CD15 6p blue, black & sil   6.25   3.25

Dove Soaring Past Rising Moon — A88

1972, June 1   Photo.
318 A88 4p gray blue, org & dk bl   .22   .24
319 A88 6p olive, yel & dk green   .75   .55

The patriot dead of 1922-23.

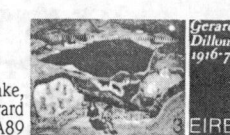

Black Lake, by Gerard Dillon — A89

1972, July 10   Perf. 15
320 A89 3p indigo & multi   .45   .40

Rider from Clonmacnoise Slab and Olympic Rings — A90

1972, Aug. 28   Photo.   Wmk. 262
321 A90 3p yellow, black & gold   .24   .18
322 A90 6p salmon, black & gold   .75   .55

20th Olympic Games, Munich, Aug. 26-Sept. 11, and 50th anniversary of the Olympic Council of Ireland.

Madonna and Child — A91

Ireland No. 68 — A92

1972, Oct. 16   Unwmk.   Perf. 15
323 A91 2½p dk green & multi   .20   .15
324 A91 4p tan & multi   .95   .30
325 A91 12p multicolored   1.25   .85
    Nos. 323-325 (3)   2.40   1.30

Christmas. The design is after a miniature in the Book of Kells, 9th century.

1972, Dec. 6   Photo.
326 A92 6p blue gray & dp grn   .40   .85
  a.   Souvenir sheet of 4   10.00   15.00

50th anniv. of 1st Irish postage stamp.

Recurrent Celtic Head Motif — A93

1973, Jan. 1   Unwmk.
327 A93 6p orange & multi   .45   .30
328 A93 12p green & multi   1.65   1.75

Ireland's entry into the European Community.

Europa Issue

Post Horn of Arrows CD16

1973, Apr. 30
329 CD16 4p bright ultra   .55   .18
330 CD16 6p black   2.50   1.50

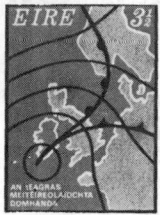

"Berlin Blues I," by William Scott — A95

Perf. 15x14½
1973, Aug. 9   Photo.   Unwmk.
331 A95 5p lt blue, blue & dk brn   .65   .32

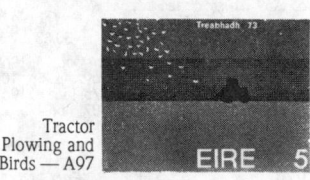

Weather Map of Northwest Europe — A96

1973, Sept. 4   Perf. 14½x15
332 A96 3½p ultra & multi   .24   .20
333 A96 12p lilac & multi   2.00   1.10

Intl. meteorological cooperation, cent.

Tractor Plowing and Birds — A97

1973, Oct. 5   Perf. 15x14½
334 A97 5p emerald & multi   .35   .20
335 A97 7p emerald & multi   1.40   .70

World Plowing Championships, Wellington Bridge, County Wexford, Oct. 1-7.

Flight into Egypt, by Jan de Cock — A98

1973, Nov. 1   Perf. 15
336 A98 3½p black & multi   .22   .15
337 A98 12p gold & multi   1.50   .85

Christmas.

Rescue, by Bernard Gribble A99

Design: Ballycotton lifeboat rescuing crew of Daunt Rock Lightship, 1936.

1974, Mar. 28   Photo.   Wmk. 262
338 A99 5p multicolored   .60   .32

Sesquicentennial of the founding of the Royal National Lifeboat Institution.

Edmund Burke, by John Henry Foley — A100

Oliver Goldsmith, by John Henry Foley — A101

Europa Issue
Perf. 14½x15

1974, Apr. 29   Unwmk.
339 A100 5p lt ultra & black   .70   .15
340 A100 7p lt green & black   2.75   1.25

1974, June 24   Photo.
341 A101 3½p brt citron & blk   .40   .15
342 A101 12p emerald & black   2.00   1.25

Oliver Goldsmith (1728-1774), writer.

Types of 1968-69

Designs: ½p, 1p, 2p, 3p, 3½p, 5p, Nos. 350, 352, Dog. Nos. 349, 351, 8p, 9p, Stag. 10p, 15p, 20p, Winged ox. 50p, £1, Eagle.

1974-78   Unwmk.   Perf. 15
343 A68 ½p yel green ('78)   .15   .15
344 A68 1p brt blue ('75)   .15   .15
345 A68 2p dark green ('76)   .15   .15
346 A68 3p ocher ('75)   .15   .15
347 A68 3½p deep orange   4.00   2.50
348 A68 5p apple green   .30   .16
349 A68 6p bl gray & dk brn   2.75   1.10
350 A68 6p blue gray ('75)   .20   .15
351 A68 7p ol grn & indigo   3.25   .45
352 A68 7p olive green ('75)   .50   .15
  a.   Bklt. pane of 5 + label ('77)   14.00
353 A68 8p brown & dk brn ('75)   .65   .22
354 A68 9p bl grn & black ('75)   .65   .16
355 A68 10p lil & multi ('75)   3.25   .35
356 A69 15p multi ('75)   .48   .16
357 A69 20p slate & multi ('75)   .60   .22
358 A69 50p rose brown & multi ('75)   2.00   .80
359 A69 £1 multi ('75)   3.00   1.65
    Nos. 343-359 (17)   22.23   8.67

Two types of No. 358 differ in clarity of screening, date on tail, etc.

Coil Stamps

1977, Mar. 21   Perf. 14x15
344b A68 1p bright blue   .25   .25
345b A68 2p dark green   .15   .18
348b A68 5p apple green   .65   .55
  c.   Strip of 4 (1p, 2x2p, 5p)   1.10

Kitchen Table, by Norah McGuinness — A102

1974, Aug. 19   Photo.   Perf. 14x15
360 A102 5p multicolored   .60   .18

Rugby — A103

1974, Sept. 2   Engr.   Perf. 15x14
361 A103 3½p slate green   .60   .15
362 A103 12p multicolored   2.50   1.25

Centenary of Irish Rugby Union.

UPU
"Postmark" — A104

Virgin and Child,
by Bellini — A105

1974, Oct. 9   Photo.   Perf. 14½x15
363 A104 5p emerald & black   .40   .20
364 A104 7p ultra & multi   1.25   .55
Centenary of Universal Postal Union.

1974, Nov. 14
365 A105 5p multicolored   .25   .15
366 A105 15p multicolored   1.75   .90
Christmas.

"Peace" — A106

1975, Mar. 25   Photo.   Perf. 14½x15
367 A106 8p dp rose lil & ultra   .30   .22
368 A106 15p ultra & emerald   1.10   .90
International Women's Year.

Europa Issue

Castletown
Hunt (detail),
by Robert
Healy
A107

1975, Apr. 28   Photo.   Perf. 15x14½
369 A107 7p black   .60   .30
370 A107 9p green   1.65 1.10

Chipping
from the
Fringe
A108

1975, June 26   Photo.   Perf. 15x14½
371 A108 6p shown   .40   .15
372 A108 9p Putting   1.40 1.25
9th European Amateur Golf Team Championships, Killarney.

Bird of Prey,
by Oisín
Kelly
A109

1975, July 28
373 A109 15p ocher   .80 1.10

Nano Nagle and
Pupils, Engraving
by Charles
Turner — A110

Clock Tower, St.
Ann's Church,
Shandon — A111

1975, Sept. 1   Photo.   Perf. 14½x15
374 A110 5p light blue & black   .22   .15
375 A110 7p buff & black   .60   .35
Presentation Order of Nuns, bicentenary.

1975, Oct. 6   Photo.   Perf. 12½
Designs: 7p, 9p, Holycross Abbey.
376 A111 5p sepia   .30   .15
377 A111 6p ultra & multi   .60   .80
378 A111 7p sapphire   .75   .32
379 A111 9p multicolored   1.10   .70
    Nos. 376-379 (4)   2.75 1.97
European Architectural Heritage Year.

St. Oliver Plunkett,
by Imogen
Stuart — A112

Madonna and
Child, by Fra
Filippo
Lippi — A113

1975, Oct. 13   Engr.   Perf. 14x14½
380 A112 7p black   .30   .22
381 A112 15p dull red   1.10   .85
Canonization of Oliver Plunkett,
Primate of Ireland.

1975, Nov. 18   Photo.   Perf. 15
382 A113 5p multicolored   .18   .15
383 A113 7p multicolored   .32   .20
384 A113 10p gold & multi   .65   .48
    Nos. 382-384 (3)   1.15   .83
Christmas.

James
Larkin — A114

Bell Making First
Call — A115

1976 Jan. 21   Photo.   Perf. 14½x15
385 A114 7p gray & slate grn   .20   .20
386 A114 11p ocher & brown   1.25   .65
James Larkin (1876-1947), trade union leader.

1976, Mar. 10   Photo.   Perf. 14½x15
387 A115 9p multicolored   .28   .25
388 A115 15p multicolored   1.25   .60
Centenary of first telephone call by Alexander
Graham Bell, March 10, 1876.

13 Stars and
Stripes
A116

Designs: 8p, 50 stars, and stripes. 9p, 15p, Benjamin Franklin on Albany essay of 1847.

1976, May 17   Litho.   Perf. 15x14
389 A116 7p ultra, silver & red   .25   .15
  a.   Silver (inscription) omitted   275.00
390 A116 8p ultra, silver & red   .40   .62
391 A116 9p bl, silver & ocher   .70   .38
392 A116 15p red, silver & blue   .80   .80
  a.   Souvenir sheet of 4, #389-392   7.25 7.50
  b.   Silver (inscription) omitted,
       #392   800.00 900.00
    Nos. 389-392 (4)   2.15 1.95
American Bicentennial. No. 392a exists with silver omitted.

Irish Delft
Spirit Barrel
A117

Europa: 11p, Bowl, Irish Delft. Designs show mark of Henry Delamain's Factory, Dublin, both pieces c. 1756.

1976, July 1   Photo.   Perf. 15x14½
393 A117 9p gray & magenta   .45   .28
394 A117 11p gray & blue   .70   .70
            Types of 1968
Designs: 8p, 9p, No. 399, Dog. No. 398, 11p,
12p, Stag. 17p, Winged ox.

1976-79   Photo.   Unwmk.   Perf. 15
395 A68   8p brown   .35   .15
396 A68   9p blue green   .55   .15
397 A68   9½p red ('79)   .55   .20
398 A68 10p lilac & black   1.50   .32
399 A68 10p purple ('77)   .65   .15
400 A68 11p carmine & black   .90   .22
401 A68 12p emer & black ('77)   .90   .15
402 A69 17p ol, bl & ocher ('77) .80   .16
    Nos. 395-402 (8)   6.20
    Set value   1.25

The Lobster
Pots, by Paul
Henry
A118

1976, Aug. 30   Photo.   Perf. 15
405 A118 15p gold & multi   .75   .50
Paul Henry (1876-1958), birth centenary.

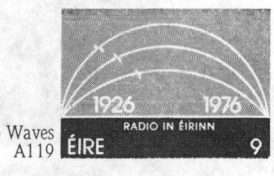

Radio Waves
A119

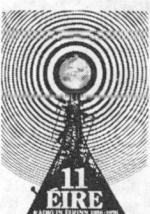

Radio Tower and
Waves, Globe — A120

Perf. 14½x14, 14x14½
1976, Oct. 5   Litho.
406 A119 9p brt blue & black   .18   .15
407 A120 11p black & multi   1.10 1.25
Irish broadcasting, 50th anniversary.

Nativity, by
Lorenzo
Monaco
A121

1976, Nov. 11   Perf. 15x14½
408 A121 7p multicolored   .25   .20
409 A121 9p multicolored   .50   .25
410 A121 15p multicolored   1.00   .60
    Nos. 408-410 (3)   1.75 1.05
Christmas.

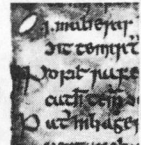

Irish
Manuscript,
16th Century
A122

Stone from
Newgrange
Burial Mound
A123

1977, May 9   Photo.   Perf. 15x14½
411 A122 8p multicolored   .30   .15
412 A123 10p multicolored   .65   .60
Centenaries of National Library (8p) and National Museum (10p).

Europa Issue

View of
Ballynahinch
A124

Lugalla Lake
A125

1977, June 27   Litho.   Perf. 14x14½
413 A124 10p multicolored   .60   .30
414 A125 12p multicolored   1.25 1.00

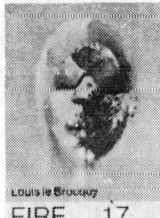

Head, by Louis le
Brocquy,
1973 — A126

1977, Aug. 8   Perf. 14x14½
415 A126 17p multicolored   1.00   .85

Girl Guide and
Tents — A127

Design: 17p, Boy Scout and tents.

1977, Aug. 22   Photo.   Perf. 15x14½
416 A127 8p multicolored   .45   .25
417 A127 17p multicolored   1.00 1.25
European Scout and Guide Conference, Ireland, and 50th anniversary of Catholic Boy Scouts of Ireland.

The Shanachie, by
Jack B. Yeats — A128

Eriugena
A129

Perf. 14x14½, 14½x14
1977, Sept. 12   Litho.
418 A128 10p black   .40 .30
419 A129 12p black   1.10 1.25

Folklore of Ireland Society, 50th anniv. and 1100th death anniv. of Johannes Scottus Eriugena, philosher, poet and mystic.

"Electricity," Mural by Robert Ballagh — A130

Bulls, from Contemporary Coin — A131

Greyhound — A132

Litho. (10p, 17p); Photo. (12p)
Perf. 14½x14; 15x14½ (12p)
1977, Oct. 10
420 A130 10p multicolored   .32 .20
421 A131 12p multicolored   .70 1.10
422 A132 17p multicolored   .55 .70
    Nos. 420-422 (3)   1.57 2.00

50th anniversaries of: Electricity Supply Board (10p); Agricultural Credit Act (12p); introduction of greyhound racing (17p).

Holy Family, by Giorgione — A133

Bremen, Junkers Monoplane — A134

1977, Nov. 3   Photo.   Perf. 14½x15
423 A133 8p multicolored   .35 .20
424 A133 10p multicolored   .55 .30
425 A133 17p multicolored   .95 .48
    Nos. 423-425 (3)   1.85 .98

Christmas.

1978, Apr. 13   Litho.   Perf. 14
426 A134 10p ultra & black   .30 .30
427 A134 17p lt brown & black .80 .60

50th anniversary of first East-West transatlantic flight from Baldonnel, County Dublin, to Greenly Island, Gulf of St. Lawrence.

Spring Gentian — A135

Wild flowers: 10p, Strawberry tree. 11p, Large-flowered butterwort. 17p, St. Daboec's heath.

1978, June 12   Litho.   Perf. 14x14½
428 A135 8p multicolored   .20 .20
429 A135 10p multicolored   .45 .30
430 A135 11p multicolored   .60 .80
431 A135 17p multicolored   .75 .90
    Nos. 428-431 (4)   2.00 2.20

Catherine McAuley — A136

William Orpen, Self-portrait — A138

Vaccination, lithograph by Manigaud A137

1978, Sept. 18   Litho.   Perf. 14
432 A136 10p multicolored   .30 .15
433 A137 11p multicolored   .50 .40
434 A138 17p multicolored   1.00 .80
    Nos. 432-434 (3)   1.80 1.35

Catherine McAuley (1778-1841), founder of Sisters of Mercy (10p); eradication of smallpox (11p); William Orpen (1878-1931), painter (17p).

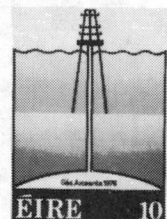

Offshore Oil Well — A139

Virgin and Child, by Guercino — A141

Woodcock on Farthing A140

1978, Oct. 18   Litho.   Perf. 14
435 A139 10p multicolored   .40 .18

First natural gas coming in off the Irish Coast at Kinsale.

1978, Oct. 26   Photo.   Perf. 15x14½

Coins: 10p, Salmon on florin. 11p, Hen and chicks on penny. 17p, Horse on half crown.
436 A140 8p multicolored   .30 .15
437 A140 10p multicolored   .40 .18
438 A140 11p multicolored   .40 .42
439 A140 17p multicolored   .55 .55
    Nos. 436-439 (4)   1.65 1.30

Irish currency, 50th anniversary.

1978, Nov. 16   Photo.   Perf. 14½x15
440 A141 8p multicolored   .30 .15
441 A141 10p multicolored   .35 .15
442 A141 17p multicolored   .65 .60
    Nos. 440-442 (3)   1.30 .90

Christmas.

Conolly Folly, Castletown A142

Europa: 11p, Belvedere on Tower Hill at Dromoland.

1978, Dec. 6   Perf. 15x14½
443 A142 10p brown   .45 .25
444 A142 11p dull green   .65 .40

Cross-country Runners — A143

1979, Aug. 20   Litho.   Perf. 14½x14
445 A143 8p multicolored   .30 .25

7th World Cross-country Championships, Green-park Racecourse, Limerick, March 25.

Rowland Hill, Bronze Statue A144

"European Communities" (7 Languages) A145

1979, Aug. 20   Perf. 14x14½
446 A144 17p multicolored   .50 .55

Sir Rowland Hill (1795-1879), originator of penny postage.

1979, Aug. 20   Photo.   Perf. 14½x15
447 A145 10p lt greenish gray .40 .40
448 A145 11p rose lilac   .45 .45

European Parliament, first direct elections, June 7-10.

Wren A146

Birds: 10p, Great crested grebe. 11p, Greenland white-fronted geese. 17p, Peregrine falcon.

1979, Aug. 30   Litho.   Perf. 14½x14
449 A146 8p multicolored   .30 .15
450 A146 10p multicolored   .40 .35
451 A146 11p multicolored   .45 .45
452 A146 17p multicolored   .85 1.00
    Nos. 449-452 (4)   2.00 1.95

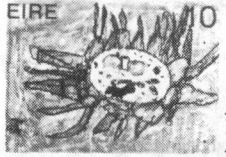

A Happy Flower A147

Children's Drawings: 11p, "Me and my skipping rope," vert. 17p, "Swans on a lake."

Perf. 14½x14, 14x14½
1979, Sept. 13   Litho.
453 A147 10p multicolored   .30 .30
454 A147 11p multicolored   .35 .45
455 A147 17p multicolored   .50 .60
    Nos. 453-455 (3)   1.15 1.35

International Year of the Child.

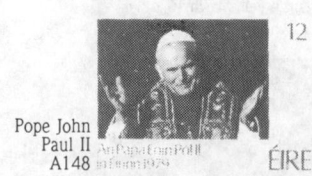

Pope John Paul II A148

1979, Sept. 29   Litho.   Perf. 14½x14
456 A148 12p multicolored   .40 .20

Visit of Pope John Paul II to Ireland.

Hospitaller Brother Teaching Child A149

1979, Oct. 4
457 A149 9½p rose & black   .30 .30

Hospitaller Order of St. John of God, centenary in Ireland.

Windmill and Sun — A150

1979, Oct. 4   Photo.   Perf. 14½x15
458 A150 11p multicolored   .40 .40

Energy conservation.

"Seated Figure," by F.E. McWilliam A151

1979, Oct. 4   Litho.   Perf. 14½x14
459 A151 20p multicolored   .60 .70

Patrick Pearse A152

1979, Nov. 10   Photo.   Perf. 15x14½
460 A152 12p multicolored   .40 .20

Patrick Henry Pearse (1879-1916), Irish writer and leader of Easter Rebellion.

Mother and Child, Panel, Domnach Argid Shrine — A153

1979, Nov. 15   Photo.   Perf. 14½x15
461 A153 9½p multicolored   .30 .20
462 A153 20p multicolored   .60 .35

Christmas.

Europa Issue

Bianconi Long Car, 1836 A154

Laying Transatlantic Cable, Steamer William Cory, 1866 A155

1979, Dec. 6 Litho. Perf. 15x14
463 A154 12p multicolored .25 .20
464 A155 13p multicolored .45 .60

Type of 1968

Designs: 13p, 16p, Stag; others, Dog.

1980-82 Photo. Perf. 15
466 A68 12p green .45 .15
467 A68 13p red brown & dk brn .50 .30
468 A68 15p ultra .45 .15
469 A68 16p olive green & blk .65 .30

Litho.
470 A68 18p dull red brn ('81) .45 .15
471 A68 19p dull blue ('81) .60 .35
472 A68 22p gray blue ('81) .60 .15
473 A68 24p brown olive ('81) .70 .42
474 A68 26p bluish green ('82) .70 .15
475 A68 29p dp rose lilac ('82) 1.00 .55
Nos. 466-475 (10) 6.10 2.67

St. Jean Baptiste de la Salle — A156

1980, Mar. 19 Litho. Perf. 14x15
477 A156 12p multicolored .40 .20

The Brothers of the Christian School (founded by St. Jean Baptiste), centenary in Ireland.

Europa Issue

George Bernard Shaw, by Alick Ritchie A157

Oscar Wilde, by Toulouse Lautrec A158

1980, May 7 Litho. Perf. 14x15
478 A157 12p multicolored .35 .35
479 A158 13p multicolored .45 .45

Irish Ermine — A159

Bodhran Drum and Whistle Players — A160

1980, July 30 Litho. Perf. 14x15
480 A159 12p shown .30 .20
481 A159 15p Irish hare .40 .15
482 A159 16p Fox .40 .30
483 A159 25p Red deer .85 .60
a. Miniature sheet of 4, #480-483 3.00 4.25
Nos. 480-483 (4) 1.95 1.25

1980, Sept. 25 Photo. Perf. 14x15
484 A160 12p shown .35 .25
485 A160 15p Piper, Uilleann pipes .40 .30
486 A160 25p Irish jig .65 .50
Nos. 484-486 (3) 1.40 1.05

Sean O'Casey (1880-1964), Playwright — A161

Gold Painting No. 57, by Patrick Scott — A162

1980, Oct. 23 Litho. Perf. 14x14½
487 A161 12p multicolored .35 .25

1980, Oct. 23 Perf. 14x15
488 A162 25p multicolored .70 .55

A163 A164

1980, Dec. 4 Photo. Perf. 15x14½
489 A163 12p multicolored .30 .15
490 A163 15p multicolored .40 .30
491 A163 25p multicolored .70 .50
Nos. 489-491 (3) 1.40 .95

Christmas.

1981, Mar. 12 Litho. Perf. 14x14½

Scientists and Inventions: 12p, Robert Boyle (1627-1691), and Air Pump, 1659. 15p, Harry Ferguson (1884-1960), hydraulic tractor, 1936. 16p, Charles Parsons (1854-1931), Parsons' turbine, 1884. 25p, John Holland (1841-1914), Holland submarine, 1878.

492 A164 12p multicolored .28 .20
493 A164 15p multicolored .32 .25
494 A164 16p multicolored .35 .35
495 A164 25p multicolored .55 .70
Nos. 492-495 (4) 1.50 1.50

The Cock and the Pot, Rubbing, 1841 — A165

Europa: 19p, The Scales of Judgment, rubbing, 1827.

1981, May 4 Litho. Perf. 14½x15
496 A165 18p multicolored .45 .30
497 A165 19p multicolored .48 .50

Hiking A166

Perf. 14x15, 15x14

1981, June 24 Litho.
498 A166 15p Bicycling, vert. .35 .15
499 A166 18p shown .45 .30
500 A166 19p Mountain climbing .45 .45
501 A166 30p Rock climbing, vert. .75 .60
Nos. 498-501 (4) 2.00 1.50

Youth Hostel Assn., 50th anniv.

Jeremiah O'Donovan Rossa (1831-1915), Journalist — A167

Railway Embankment, by William John Leech (1881-1968) A168

Perf. 14½x15, 15x14½

1981, Aug. 31
502 A167 15p multicolored .35 .30
503 A168 30p multicolored .75 .70

James Hoban (1762-1831), White House Architect A169

1981, Sept. 29 Perf. 15x14
504 A169 18p multicolored .55 .30

Same design used for US Nos. 1935-1936.

Draft Horse King of Diamonds A170

Famous Horses: No. 505, Show-jumper Boomerang. No. 506, Steeplechaser Arkle. 24p, Flat racer Ballymoss. 36p, Connemara pony Coosheen Finn.

1981, Oct. 23 Litho. Perf. 15x14
505 A170 18p multicolored .60 .40
506 A170 18p multicolored .60 .40
a. Pair, #505-506 1.40 1.40
507 A170 22p multicolored .60 .40
508 A170 24p multicolored .60 .80
509 A170 36p multicolored 1.00 1.00
Nos. 505-509 (5) 3.40 3.00

A171 A172

Nativity, by Federico Barocci (Christmas 1981).

1981, Nov. 19 Litho. Perf. 14x15
510 A171 18p multicolored .45 .20
511 A171 22p multicolored .55 .25
512 A171 36p multicolored .90 .60
Nos. 510-512 (3) 1.90 1.05

1981, Dec. 10 Litho. Perf. 14x14½
513 A172 18p multicolored .50 .20

Land Law Act centenary.

250th Anniv. of Royal Dublin Society A173

1981, Dec. 10 Perf. 14½x14
514 A173 22p multicolored .58 .55

50th Anniv. of Killarney Natl. Park A174

1982, Feb. 26 Litho. Perf. 14½x14
515 A174 18p Upper Lake .50 .30
516 A174 36p Eagle's Nest .85 .70

The Stigmatization of St. Francis, by Sassetta — A175

Francis Makemie, Old Presbyterian Church, Ramelton A176

1982, Apr. 2 Perf. 14x15, 15x14
517 A175 22p multicolored .50 .35
518 A176 24p brown .70 .50

800th birth anniv. of St. Francis of Assisi; 300th anniv. of Francis Makemie's ordination (father of American Presbyterianism).

Europa Issue

Great Famine of 1845-50 — A177

Conversion of Ireland to Christianity (St. Patrick and his Followers, by Vincenzo Valdre) A178

1982, May 4
519 A177 26p tan & brown .60 .50
520 A178 29p multicolored .75 .75

Padraic O'Connaire (1882-1928), Writer — A179

Designs: 26p, James Joyce (1882-1941), writer and poet, by Brancusi. 29p, John Field (1782-1837), Composer and pianist, Nocturne score. 44p, Charles Joseph Kickham (1828-1882), journalist and writer. 29p, 44p by Colin Harrison.

1982, June 16 Litho. Perf. 14x15
521 A179 22p blue & black .50 .30
522 A179 26p black & brown .65 .50
523 A179 29p black & blue .75 .75
524 A179 44p gray green & black 1.10 1.10
Nos. 521-524 (4) 3.00 2.65

Porbeagle
Shark
A180

1982, July 29   *Perf. 15x14*
525 A180 22p shown   .60   .40
526 A180 22p Oyster   .60   .40
527 A180 26p Salmon   .85   .35
528 A180 29p Dublin Bay prawn   .95   .95
  Nos. 525-528 (4)   3.00 2.10

Currach
A181

1982, Sept. 21   *Perf. 15x14, 14x15*
529 A181 22p shown   .65   .30
530 A181 22p Galway hooker, vert.   .65   .30
531 A181 26p Asgard II training ship .90   .30
532 A181 29p Howth 17-footer, vert. 1.10 1.10
  Nos. 529-532 (4)   3.30 2.00

The Irish
House of
Commons,
by Francis
Wheatley
A182

1982, Oct. 14   Litho.   *Perf. 14¹⁄₂x14*
533 A182 22p multicolored   .55   .30
  Bicentenary of Grattan's Parliament.

A183   A183a

Eamon de Valera (1882-1975), President, by
Robert Ballagh.

1982, Oct. 14   *Perf. 14x14¹⁄₂*
534 A183 26p multicolored   .70   .30

1982, Nov. 11   Litho.   *Perf. 14¹⁄₂x15*
Madonna and Child, by Andrea della Robbia
(1435-1525)
535 A183a 22p lt violet & multi   .50   .30
536 A183a 26p gray & multi   .70   .40
  Christmas.

A184   A185

Killarney Cathedral,
1855 — A186

Designs: 1p-5p, Central Pavilion, Dublin Botanical Gardens. 6p, 7p, 10p, 12p, Dr. Steeven's Hospital, Dublin. 15p, 20p, 22p, Aughnanure Castle,
Oughterard, 16th cent. 23p, 26p, Cormac's Chapel,
1134. 29p, 30p, St. Mac Dara's Church. 50p,

Casino, Marino. £1, Cahir Castle, 15th century.
£5 Central Bus Station, Dublin, 1953.
  50p, £1, £5 horiz.

1982-90   Litho.   *Perf. 14x15, 15x14*
537 A184 1p dull blue   .15   .15
538 A184 2p gray green   .15   .15
539 A184 3p black   .15   .15
540 A184 4p rose lake   .15   .15
  a.   Perf. 13¹⁄₂ on 3 or 4 sides   .15   .15
541 A184 5p brown   .15   .15
542 A184 6p dull blue   .15   .15
543 A184 7p gray green   .15   .15
544 A184 10p black   .25   .15
545 A184 12p rose lake   .30   .15
546 A185 15p gray green   .40   .20
547 A185 20p rose lake   .50   .30
548 A185 22p dull blue   .55   .30
  a.   Bklt. pane of 7+label (3 4p, 4
         22p) ('88)   3.60
549 A185 23p gray green   .55   .35
550 A185 26p black   .60   .38
  a.   Bklt. pane, 2 each 2p, 22p, 26p   2.25
  b.   Bklt. pane, 4 each 2p, 22p, 26p   4.50
  c.   Bklt. pane, 3 4p, 5 22p, 4 26p
         ('88)   6.00
  d.   Perf. 13¹⁄₂ on 3 sides   .60   .60
551 A184 29p gray green   .70   .40
552 A184 30p black   .70   .45
  a.   Perf. 13¹⁄₂ on 3 or 4 sides   .70   .70

           Perf. 14x15, 15x14
553 A186 44p gray & black   1.10   .70
554 A186 50p gray & dull blue   1.25   .75
555 A186 £1 gray & brown   6.25 2.75
556 A186 £5 gray & rose lake   12.00 7.25
  Nos. 537-556 (20)   26.20 15.18

Stamps from Z#550c imprinted "Booklet Stamp"
in green on reverse side. #550c sold for £2.
Issued: 4p, 6p-7p, 20p, 23p, 30p, 50p, 3/16/83;
1p-3p, 5p, 10p-15p, 7/6/83; #540a, 550d, 552a,
5/3/90; others, 12/15/82.
See Nos. 638-645, 803a, 804b.

Dublin Chamber of
Commerce
Bicentenary — A187

Bank of
Ireland
Bicentenary
A188

1983, Feb. 23   Litho.
557 A187 22p Ouzel Galley goblet   .60   .30
558 A188 26p Bank   .75   .45

Padraig
Siochfhradha
(1883-1964),
Writer — A189

Boys' Brigade
Centenary — A190

1983, Apr. 7   Litho.   *Perf. 14x14¹⁄₂*
559 A189 26p multicolored   .65   .30
560 A190 29p multicolored   .85   .85

Europa
A191

Design: 26p, Newgrange Winter Solstice, Neolithic Pattern Drawing by Louis le Brocquy. 29p,
Quaternion formula, by William Rowan Hamilton
(1805-1865).

1983, May 4   Litho.   *Perf. 14¹⁄₂x14*
561 A191 26p black & gold   3.50   .40
562 A191 29p multicolored   4.50 5.00

Kerry Blue
Terrier
A192

Drawings of dogs by Wendy Walsh.

1983, June 23
563 A192 22p shown   .70   .70
564 A192 26p Irish wolfhound   .80   .80
565 A192 26p Irish water spaniel   .80   .80
566 A192 29p Irish terrier   .95   .95
567 A192 44p Irish setters   1.40 1.40
  a.   Miniature sheet of 5, #563-567 7.00 6.00
                                    4.65 4.65

Sean Mac Diarmada
(1883-1916),
Nationalist — A193

Society for
the
Prevention of
Cruelty to
Animals
A194

Society of St. Vincent
de Paul
Sesquicentennial
A195

Industrial
Credit Co.,
50th Anniv.
A196

US Pres. Andrew
Jackson (1767-
1845) — A197

         Perf. 14x14¹⁄₂, 14¹⁄₂x14
1983, Aug. 11
568 A193 22p multicolored   .85   .85
569 A194 22p multicolored   .85   .85
570 A195 26p multicolored   1.10 1.00
571 A196 26p multicolored   1.10 1.00
572 A197 44p gray   2.00 2.00
  Nos. 568-572 (5)   5.90 5.70

WCY   Handicrafts
A198   A199

1983, Sept. 15   Litho.   *Perf. 14x15*
573 A198 22p Mailman   .50   .35
574 A198 29p Dish antenna   .70   .70

1983, Oct. 13   Litho.   *Perf. 14x15*
575 A199 22p Weaving   .50   .35
576 A199 26p Basketweaving   .60   .40
577 A199 26p Irish crochet   .70   .70
578 A199 44p Harpmaking   1.00 1.00
  Nos. 575-578 (4)   2.80 2.45

La Natividad by Rogier
van der
Weyden — A200

1983, Nov. 30   Litho.   *Perf. 14x14¹⁄₂*
579 A200 22p multicolored   .52   .35
580 A200 26p multicolored   .60   .50
  Christmas.

Irish Railways Sesquicentenary — A201

Locomotives: 23p, Princess, Dublin and Kings-
town Railway. 26p, Macha, Great Southern Railways. 29p, Kestrel, Great Northern Railway. 44p,
Link-Hoffman railcar, Coras Iompair Eireann.

1984, Jan. 30   *Perf. 14¹⁄₂x14*
581 A201 23p multicolored   1.10 1.10
582 A201 26p multicolored   .65   .65
583 A201 29p multicolored   1.25 1.25
584 A201 44p multicolored   2.00 2.00
  a.   Souvenir sheet of 4, #581-584 6.50 5.50
  Nos. 581-584 (4)   5.00 5.00

          Private Overprints
  Nos. 584a, 684a, 708a, 708b, 803a,
804a, 811a, 826a, 847a, 855a, 876b,
and probably others, exist with privately
applied show overprints.

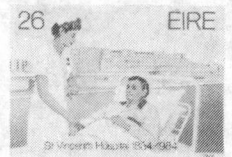

Local
Trees — A202

1984, Mar. 1   Litho.   *Perf. 15x14*
585 A202 22p Irish whitebeam   .85   .55
586 A202 26p Irish yew   1.00   .75
587 A202 29p Irish willow   1.25   .85
588 A202 44p Birch   1.75 1.25
  Nos. 585-588 (4)   4.85 3.40

St. Vincent's Hospital, Dublin,
Sesquicentenary — A203

Royal College
of Surgeons
in Ireland
Bicentenary
A204

1984, Apr. 12   Litho.
589 A203 26p multicolored   .65   .50
590 A204 44p multicolored   1.10 1.00

2nd European Parliament Election A205

1984, May 10   Litho.   Perf. 15x14
591 A205 26p multicolored   .85 .45

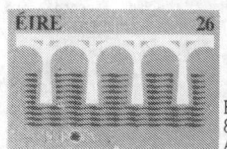

Europa (1959-84) A206

1984, May 10
592 A206 26p multicolored   3.50 1.00
593 A206 29p multicolored   3.50 3.00

John McCormack (1884-1945), Singer — A207

1984, June 6   Litho.   Perf. 14x14½
594 A207 22p multicolored   .55 .35

See US No. 2090.

1984 Summer Olympics A208

1984, June 21   Litho.   Perf. 14½x14
595 A208 22p Hammer throw   .50 .45
596 A208 26p Hurdles   .65 .55
597 A208 29p Running   .70 .70
      Nos. 595-597 (3)   1.85 1.70

Gaelic Athletic Assoc. Centenary A209

1984, Aug. 23   Litho.   Perf. 14x15
598 A209 22p Hurlers   .50 .35
599 A209 26p Soccer, vert.   .65 .45

Mayoral City of Galway, 500th Anniv. — A210

St. Brendan (484-577) A211

1984, Sept. 18   Perf. 14x15, 15x14
600 A210 26p Medal   .75 .65
601 A211 44p Portrait, manuscript 1.25 1.25

Post Office Bicentenary A212

1984, Oct. 19   Perf. 15x14
602 A212 26p Handing sealed letter .70 .35

A213

Virgin And Child by Sassoferrato — A214

Perf. 14½x14, 14x14½
1984, Nov. 26   Litho.
603 A213 17p multicolored   .45 .20
604 A214 22p multicolored   .55 .30
605 A214 26p multicolored   .75 .35
      Nos. 603-605 (3)   1.75 .85

Christmas.

Love A215

A216

1985, Jan. 31   Litho.   Perf. 15x14
606 A215 22p Heart-shaped balloon .50 .30
607 A216 26p Bouquet of hearts   .65 .35

Dunsink Observatory, 200th Anniv. — A217

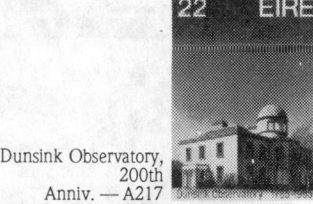

Cork City Charter, 800th Anniv. A218

Royal Irish Academy, 200th Anniv. — A219

1st Manned Flight in Ireland, 200th Anniv. — A220

1985, Mar. 14   Litho.
608 A217 22p black   .50 .45
609 A218 26p multicolored   .65 .50
610 A219 37p multicolored   .85 .85
611 A220 44p multicolored   1.00 1.00
      Nos. 608-611 (4)   3.00 2.80

Butterflies — A221

1985, Apr. 11   Litho.   Perf. 14x15
612 A221 22p Common blue   .90 .85
613 A221 26p Red admiral   1.00 .95
614 A221 28p Brimstone   1.10 1.00
615 A221 44p Marsh fritillary   1.75 1.75
      Nos. 612-615 (4)   4.75 4.55

Europa A222

Design: 26p, Charles Villiers Stanford (1852-1924), composer. 37p, Turlough O'Carolan (1670-1738), Composer.

1985, May 16   Litho.   Perf. 15x14
616 A222 26p multicolored   2.00 1.10
617 A222 37p multicolored   3.00 1.50

European Music Year — A223

Composers: No. 618, Giuseppe Domenico Scarlatti (1685-1757). No. 619, George Frideric Handel (1685-1759). No. 620, Johann Sebastian Bach (1685-1750).

1985, May 16   Litho.   Perf. 14x15
618 A223 22p multicolored   1.50 1.50
619 A223 22p multicolored   1.50 1.50
  a.   Pair, #618-619   3.00 3.00
620 A223 26p multicolored   1.50 1.50
      Nos. 618-620 (3)   4.50 4.50

Irish UN Defense Forces in the Congo, 1960 A224

Thomas Ashe (1885-1917), Patriot and Educator — A225

Bishop George Berkeley (1685-1753), Philosopher and Educator — A226

Perf. 15x14, 14x15
1985, June 20   Litho.
621 A224 22p multicolored   .70 .60
622 A225 26p multicolored   .85 .70
623 A226 44p multicolored   1.40 1.40
      Nos. 621-623 (3)   2.95 2.70

Irish forces as part of the UN Defense Forces, 25th anniv. (22p).

Intl. Youth Year — A227

1985, Aug. 1   Litho.
624 A227 22p multi, horiz.   .85 .65
625 A227 26p multicolored   1.00 .75

Architecture Type of 1982

Designs: 24p, 39p, Aughnanure Castle. 28p, 32p, 37p, St. Mac Dara's Church. 40p, Cahir Castle. £1, Killarney Cathedral. £2, Casino, Marino. 46p, £2, horiz.

Perf. 15x14, 14x15 (A184, No. 644)
1985-88   Litho.
638 A185 24p brown   .45 .30
639 A184 28p rose lake   .50 .30
  a.   Bklt. pane of 12 (4 2p, 2 24p, 1
        4p, 5 28p) ('88)   5.75
  c.   Bklt. pane of 12 (2 22p, 3 4p, 3
        24p, 4 28p) ('88)   6.00
640 A184 32p brown   .65 .40
641 A184 37p dull blue   .75 .45
642 A184 39p rose lake   .80 .50
643 A186 46p gray & gray grn   .95 .60
644 A186 £1   gray & dull bl   1.90 1.10
645 A186 £2   gray & gray grn   6.00 3.00
      Nos. 638-645 (8)   12.00 6.65

Issued: 24p, 28p, 37p, £1, June 27, 1985; 32p, 39p, 46p, May 1, 1986; £2, July 26, 1988.

Industrial Innovations A228

Institution of Engineers, 150th Anniv. A229

1985, Oct. 3   Litho.   Perf. 15x14
646 A228 22p Computer technology   .55 .50
647 A228 26p Peat production   .70 .65
648 A229 44p The Key Man, by
             Sean Keating   1.10 1.10
      Nos. 646-648 (3)   2.35 2.25

Candle, Holly — A230

Virgin and Child in a Landscape, by Adrian van Ijsenbrandt — A231

Christmas: No. 651, The Holy Family, by Murillo. 26p, Adoration of the Shepherds, by Louis Le Nain, horiz.

Perf. 14x15, 15x14

1985, Nov. 26			**Litho.**
649 A230 22p shown		.55	.30
650 A230 22p shown		.55	.30
651 A231 22p multicolored		.55	.30
a.	Pair, #650-651	1.10	.65
652 A231 26p multicolored		.65	.30
	Nos. 649-652 (4)	2.30	1.20

Love — A232

1986, Jan. 30	**Perf. 14x15**	
653 A232 22p shown	.90	.50
654 A232 26p Heart-shaped mailbox	1.10	.55

Ferns — A233   Europa — A234

1986, Mar. 20 Litho. Perf. 14½x15		
655 A233 24p Hart's tongue	.65	.30
656 A233 28p Rusty-back	.75	.40
657 A233 46p Killarney	1.25	1.25
Nos. 655-657 (3)	2.65	1.95

1986, May 1 Perf. 14x15, 15x14		
658 A234 28p Industry and nature	3.00	1.75
659 A234 39p Hedgerows, horiz.	4.00	2.75

Aer Lingus, 50th Anniv. A235

1986, May 27	**Perf. 15x14**	
660 A235 28p Jet, 1986	1.10	.45
661 A235 46p The Eagle, 1936	1.75	1.50

Inland Waterways A236

1986, May 27 Perf. 15x14, 14x15		
662 A236 24p Robertstown Grand Canal	.85	.40
663 A236 28p Fishing, County Mayo, vert.	.95	.50
664 A236 30p Yachting, River Shannon	1.00	.80
Nos. 662-664 (3)	2.80	1.70

British & Irish Steam Packet Co., 150th Anniv. A237

1986, July 10	**Perf. 15x14**	
665 A237 24p Steamer Severn, 1836	.85	.65
666 A237 28p M.V. Leinster, 1986	1.00	.70

Lighthouses — A238

1986, July 10	**Perf. 14½x15**	
667 A238 24p Kish, helicopter	1.25	1.00
668 A238 30p Fastnet	1.75	1.50

Dublin Council of Trade Unions, Cent. — A239

Arthur Griffith (1871-1922), Statesman — A240

Women in Society, Construction Surveyor A241

Intl. Peace Year — A242

Perf. 14½x15, 14x15 (#670, 672), 15x14½, 15x14

1986, Aug. 21		
669 A239 24p multicolored	.75	.65
670 A240 28p multicolored	.85	.70
671 A241 28p multicolored	.85	.70
672 A242 30p multi, vert.	.90	.90
673 A242 46p shown	1.40	1.40
Nos. 669-673 (5)	4.75	4.35

See Nos. 699, 711, 749, 807, 836.

William Mulready (1786-1863), Letter Sheet Designer A243

Carriages by Charles Bianconi (1786-1875) A244

Perf. 15x14, 14x15

1986, Oct. 2		**Litho.**
674 A243 24p multicolored	.70	.50
675 A244 28p multi, vert.	.80	.60
676 A244 39p shown	1.10	1.10
Nos. 674-676 (3)	2.60	2.20

Adoration of the Shepherds, by Francesco Pascucci A245

Adoration of the Magi, by Frans Francken III (1542-1616) — A246

1986, Nov. 20 Perf. 15x14, 14½x15		
677 A245 21p multicolored	.95	.45
678 A246 28p multicolored	1.25	.60

Christmas.

Love A247

Perf. 15x14, 14x15		
1987, Jan. 27		**Litho.**
679 A247 24p Flowers, butterfly	.90	.45
680 A247 28p Postman, vert.	1.10	.55

Trolleys A248

1987, Mar. 4 Litho. Perf. 15x14		
681 A248 24p Cork Electric	.70	.35
682 A248 28p Dublin Standard	.85	.45
683 A248 30p Howth (G.N.R.)	.90	.60
684 A248 46p Galway Horse	1.40	1.25
a.	Miniature sheet of 4, #681-684	5.50	5.50
Nos. 681-684 (4)	3.85	2.65

See note following No. 584.

Waterford Chamber of Commerce, 200th Anniv. A249

Muintir Na Tire, 50th Anniv. A250

Trinity College Botanical Gardens, Dublin, 300th Anniv. — A251

Medical Missionaries of Mary, 50th Anniv. A252

Anniversaries and events: 24p, Three ships, Chamber crest. 28p, Canon Hayes (1887-1957), founder, and symbols of Muintir Na Tire activities. 30p, College crest, Calceolaria burbidgei. 39p, Intl. Missionary Training Hospital, Drogheda, and Mother Mary Martin.

Perf. 15x14, 14x15		
1987, Apr. 9		**Litho.**
685 A249 24p vio blue, blk & dark green	.75	.40
686 A250 28p multicolored	.85	.45
687 A251 30p multicolored	.90	.50
688 A252 39p multicolored	1.20	1.00
Nos. 685-688 (4)	3.70	2.35

Europa A253

Modern architecture, art: 28p, Borda na Mona headquarters, Dublin, and The Turf Cutter, by sculptor John Behan. 39p, St. Mary's Church and ruins of Romanesque monastery at Cong.

1987, May 14	**Perf. 15x14**	
689 A253 28p multicolored	3.75	1.40
690 A253 39p multicolored	5.25	4.00

Cattle A254

1987, July 2		
691 A254 24p Kerry	1.00	.45
692 A254 28p Friesian	1.25	.60
693 A254 30p Hereford	1.25	.70
694 A254 39p Shorthorn	1.50	1.25
Nos. 691-694 (4)	5.00	3.00

Festivals A255

1987, Aug. 27	**Perf. 14x15**	
695 A255 24p Fleadh Nua, Ennis	.70	.35
696 A255 28p Festival Queen, Tralee	.85	.45
697 A255 30p Wexford opera festival	.90	.60
698 A255 46p Ballinasloe horse fair	1.40	1.40
Nos. 695-698 (4)	3.85	2.80

Nos. 695-696 vert.

Statesmen Type of 1986 and

Ewer and Chalice, Company Crest A256

Harp in Shield, Preamble Excerpt A257

Woman Leading Board Meeting — A258

Design: No. 699, Cathal Brugha, vert.

Perf. 14x15, 15x14

1987, Oct. 1   Litho.
699	A240	24p black	.70	.35
700	A256	24p multicolored	.70	.35
701	A257	28p multicolored	.80	.45
702	A258	46p multicolored	1.30	.75
		Nos. 699-702 (4)	3.50	1.90

Company of Goldsmiths of Dublin, 350th anniv. (No. 700); Irish Constitution, 50th anniv. (28p); Women in Society, (46p).

A259

ÉIRE   24   Christmas — A260

Designs: 21p, Twelve Days of Christmas (first three days). 24p, Embroidery (detail), Waterford Vestments, 15th cent. 28p, Neapolitan creche (detail), 1850.

Perf. 15x14, 14x15

1987, Nov. 17   Litho.
703	A259	21p multicolored	.75	.35
704	A260	24p multicolored	.85	.40
705	A260	28p multicolored	.95	.45
		Nos. 703-705 (3)	2.55	1.20

No. 703 issued in discount sheets of 14 + center label; sheet sold for £2.90.

Love — A261

Perf. 15x14½, 14½x15

1988, Jan. 27   Litho.
706	A261	24p shown	.95	.45
707	A261	28p Pillar box, vert.	1.10	.55

Dublin Millennium A262

1988, Mar. 1   Perf. 15x14
708	A262	28p multicolored	.85	.45
a.		Booklet pane of 4, Gaelic	3.50	
b.		Booklet pane of 4, English	3.50	

Nos. 708a, 708b consist of two vert. pairs separated by a history in Gaelic or English. See note following No. 584.

A263

Impact of the Irish Abroad A264

Designs: No. 709, Robert O'Hara Burke (1820-1861), by Sir Sidney Nolan; 19th cent. map of Australia with Burke & Wills expedition route. 46p, Mural (detail) of the Eureka Stockade by Nolan.

1988, Mar. 1
709	A263	24p multicolored	.75	.40
710	A264	46p multicolored	1.40	1.40

Statesmen Type of 1986 and

1988 Summer Olympics, Seoul A265

Order of Malta Ambulance Corps, 50th Anniv. — A266

Barry Fitzgerald (1888-1961), Actor — A267

Designs: 24p, William T. Cosgrave (1880-1965), president of the United Ireland and Fine Gael party. No. 713, Cycling. Nos. 712-713 printed se-tenant.

Perf. 14x15, 15x14

1988, Apr. 7   Litho.
711	A240	24p black	.75	.40
712	A265	28p multicolored	.85	.45
713	A265	28p multicolored	.85	.45
a.		Pair, #712-713	1.75	1.00
714	A266	30p multicolored	.90	.90
715	A267	50p multicolored	1.50	.75
		Nos. 711-715 (5)	4.85	2.95

Nos. 712-713 printed in sheets of 5 each plus two labels.

Historic Transatlantic Crossings A268

Europa A269

Transport and communications: 24p, Sirius sailing from Passage West, County Cork. 28p, Air traffic controllers and A320 Airbus. 39p, Europe on globe, letters. 46p, Maia and Mercury flying boats in Foynes Harbor.

1988, May 12   Litho.   Perf. 15x14
716	A268	24p multicolored	.75	.40
717	A269	28p multicolored	.85	.50
718	A269	39p multicolored	1.10	1.10
719	A268	46p multicolored	1.40	1.40
		Nos. 716-719 (4)	4.10	3.40

1st scheduled transatlantic crossing by steamship, sesquicentennial (24p); 1st east-west transatlantic crossing by seaplane, 50th anniv. (46p).

Conservation of Flora — A270

1988, June 21   Litho.   Perf. 14x15
720	A270	24p Otanthus maritimus	.80	.35
721	A270	28p Saxifraga hartii	.90	.45
722	A270	46p Astragalus danicus	1.40	1.40
		Nos. 720-722 (3)	3.10	2.20

Irish Security Forces A271

1988, Aug. 23   Litho.   Perf. 15x14
723	A271	28p Garda Siochana (police)	.75	.40
724	A271	28p Army	.75	.40
725	A271	28p Navy, air corps	.75	.40
726	A271	28p FCA, Slua Muiri	.75	.40
a.		Block of 4, #723-726	3.00	3.00

Institute of Chartered Accountants, Cent. — A272

Defeat of the Spanish Armada, 400th Anniv. A273

Perf. 14x15, 15x14

1988, Oct. 6   Litho.
727	A272	24p multicolored	.90	.40
728	A273	46p Duquesa Santa Ana off Donegal Coast	1.65	1.65

John F. Kennedy, Portrait by James Wyeth A274

1988, Nov. 24   Litho.   Perf. 15x14
729	A274	28p multicolored	1.00	.50

Christmas
A275   A276

1988, Nov. 24   Perf. 14x15
730	A275	21p St. Kevin's Church, Glendalough	.60	.30
731	A276	24p Adoration of the Magi	.70	.35
732	A276	28p Flight into Egypt	.85	.40
733	A276	46p Holy Family	1.40	1.40
		Nos. 730-733 (4)	3.55	2.45

No. 730 issued only in discount sheets of 14. Sheet sold for £2.90.

Love A277

The Sonnet, by William Mulready (1786-1863) A278

Perf. 15x14, 14x15

1989, Jan. 24   Litho.
734	A277	24p multicolored	.80	.35
735	A278	28p multicolored	.90	.45

Mulready, designer of Rowland Hill's first stamped envelope.

Classic Automobiles — A279

1989, Apr. 11   Litho.   Perf. 15x14
736	A279	24p Silver Stream	.65	.32
737	A279	28p Benz Comfortable	.75	.38
a.		Booklet pane, 2 each 24p, 28p	3.25	
738	A279	39p Thomond Car	1.10	1.00
739	A279	46p Chambers Car	1.25	1.25
a.		Booklet pane of 4, #736-739	4.25	
		Nos. 736-739 (4)	3.75	2.95

Parks and Gardens A280

1989, Apr. 11
740	A280	24p Garinish Is.	.75	.35
741	A280	28p Glenveagh	.85	.45
742	A280	32p Connemara Natl. Park	1.00	.50
743	A280	50p St. Stephen's Green	1.65	1.65
		Nos. 740-743 (4)	4.25	2.95

Europa
A281

ÉIRE 28

1989, May 11
744	A281	28p Ring-a-ring-a-rosie	1.00	.50
745	A281	39p Hopscotch	1.50	1.50

ÉIRE 24

CUMANN
CROISE DEIRGE
NA hÉIREANN
50 BLIAIN

Irish Red Cross
Soc., 50th
Anniv. — A282

1989, May 11   *Perf. 14x15*
746	A282	24p multicolored	.70	.35

ÉIRE 28

European
Parliament 3rd
Elections — A283

1989, May 11
747	A283	28p Stars from flag	.75	.40

ÉIRE 28

Sts. Kilian, Colman and Totnan (d. 689),
Martyred Missionaries, and
Shamrock — A284

1989, June 15   Litho.   *Perf. 13½*
748	A284	28p multicolored	.75	.40
a.		Booklet pane of 4, English	3.00	
b.		Booklet pane of 4, Gaelic	3.00	
c.		Booklet pane of 4, German	3.00	
d.		Booklet pane of 4, Latin	3.00	

See Federal Republic of Germany No. 1580.

Statesmen Type of 1986 and

28 ÉIRE

RIAI
Emblem — A285

Dublin-Cork
Coach,
1789
A286 28

ÉIRE

Singer,
Scene from
La Boheme
EIRE 30   A287

JAWAHARLAL
NEHRU

Nehru — A288   ÉIRE   46

Design: 24p, Sean Thomas O'Kelly (1883-1966),
2nd president.

1989, July 25   *Perf. 14x15, 15x14*   Litho.
749	A240	24p black	.75	.40
750	A285	28p multicolored	.85	.45
751	A286	28p multicolored	.85	.45
752	A287	30p multicolored	.95	.95
753	A288	46p red brown	1.50	1.50
		Nos. 749-753 (5)	4.90	3.75

Royal Institute of Architects, 150th anniv.; Mail
coach in Ireland, bicent.; Margaret Burke Sheridan
(1889-1958), soprano; Jawaharlal Nehru, 1st prime
minister of independent India.

IRELAND   28

Flags and
*Sail Ireland
Yacht
Rounding
Cape Horn*,
by Des
Fallon
A289

1989, Aug. 31   Litho.   *Perf. 15x14*
754	A289	28p multicolored	1.00	.45

Whitbread round of the World Yacht Race 1989-
90.

24   ÉIRE

Wildlife: Game
Birds — A290

1989, Oct. 5   Litho.   *Perf. 13½*
755	A290	24p Lagopus lagopus	.85	.40
756	A290	28p Vanellus vanellus	1.00	.50
757	A290	39p Scolopax rusticola	1.40	1.25
758	A290	46p Phasianus colchicus	1.65	1.65
a.		Miniature sheet of 4, #755-758	6.00	6.00
		Nos. 755-758 (4)	4.90	3.80

NOLLAIG 1989

NOLLAIG 1989

ÉIRE 21   ÉIRE 24

Children and   Miniatures from a
Creche — A291   Flemish Psalter,
                     13th Cent. — A292

1989, Nov. 14   Litho.   *Perf. 14x15*
759	A291	21p multicolored	.65	.35
760	A292	24p Annunciation	.75	.40
761	A292	28p Nativity	.90	.45
762	A292	46p Adoration of the Magi	1.50	1.50
		Nos. 759-762 (4)	3.80	2.70

No. 759 issued only in discount sheets of 14.
Sheet sold for £2.90.

ÉIRE   30

Ireland's Presidency of the European
Communities — A293

ÉIRE   50

European
Tourism
Year
A294

1990, Jan. 9   Litho.   *Perf. 15x14*
763	A293	30p multicolored	.90	.45
764	A294	50p multicolored	1.50	.90

ÉIRE 26   ÉIRE

Love!
30

Love Issue — A295   Love Issue — A296

1990, Jan. 30   Litho.   *Perf. 14x15*
765	A295	26p shown	.95	.50
766	A296	30p "Love!"	1.10	.55

ÉIRE 30

Enamel Latchet
Brooch — A297

ÉIRE £1

Ardagh
Chalice
A298

Art treasures of Ireland: 1p, 2p, Silver Kite
Brooch, vert. 4p, 5p, Dunamase Food Vessel, vert.
10p, Derrinboy Armlets. 20p, Gold Dress Fastener.
26p, 28p, Lismore Crosier, vert. 32p, Brighter Collar. 34p, 37p, 38p, 40p, Gleninsheen Collar, vert.
41p, 44p, 45p, Silver thistle brooch, vert. 50p, 52p,
Brighter boat, vert. £2, Tara Brooch. £5, St. Patrick's Bell Shrine, vert.

1990-92   Litho.   *Perf. 15x14, 14x15*
767	A297	1p blue & blk	.15	.15
768	A297	2p orange & blk	.15	.15
770	A297	4p violet & blk	.15	.15
a.		Perf. 13½x13½	.15	.15
b.		Photo.	.15	.15
771	A297	5p green & blk	.15	.15
774	A297	10p orange & blk	.32	.16
777	A297	20p yellow & blk	.60	.30
779	A297	26p violet & blk	.80	.40
a.		Perf. 13½ on 3 or 4 sides	.80	.80
780	A297	28p orange & blk	.85	.42
a.		Bklt. pane, 3 #770, 4 #780 + label	3.75	
b.		Photo.	.85	.85
782	A297	30p brt blue & blk	.95	.48
a.		Perf. 13½	.95	.48
b.		Bklt. pane, 3 #540a, 1 #550d, 2 #779a, 2 #782a	4.75	
c.		Bklt. pane, 3 #768, 3 #770, #779, 2 #782 + label	3.40	
783	A297	32p green & blk	1.00	.50
a.		Bklt. pane, 2 #770b, #780b, 2 #783d	2.85	1.40
b.		Perf. 13½x13	1.00	1.00
c.		Booklet pane, #770a, 3 #783b	3.25	
d.		Photo.	1.00	1.00
784	A297	34p yellow & blk	1.10	.55
785	A297	37p green & blk	1.10	.55
786	A297	38p purple & blk	1.15	.58
786A	A297	40p blue & black	1.35	.68
787	A297	41p orange & blk	1.30	.65
788	A297	44p orange & blk	1.30	.65
789	A297	45p violet & black	1.50	.75
790	A297	50p yellow & blk	1.60	.80
790A	A297	52p blue & blk	1.50	.75
791	A298	£1 yellow & blk	3.25	1.60
792	A298	£2 green & blk	6.50	3.25
793	A298	£5 blue & blk	15.00	7.50

Self-Adhesive
Die cut perf 11
Size: 27x21mm
794	A297	32p like #783	1.05	.52
		Nos. 779-794 (17)	41.30	20.63

Issue dates: 26p, 30p, 32p, 41p, 50p, £1, Mar.
8. No. 782b, May 3. 1p, 2p, 4p, 10p, 34p, £2, July
26. No. 782c, Nov. 15. 5p, 20p, £5, Jan. 26,
1991. No. 783a, May 14, 1991. 28p, 37p, 38p,
44p, 52p, Apr. 3, 1991. No. 780a, Oct. 17, 1991.
No. 794, Oct. 31, 1991. 40p, 45p, May 14, 1992.
Nos. 770a, 783b, Sept. 24, 1993.

This is an expanding set. Numbers will change if
neccessary.

26   ÉIRE   30

ÉIRE
A299

F.I.F.A. World Cup 1990
A300

1990, Mar. 22   Litho.   *Perf. 14x15*
Booklet Stamps
795	A299	26p Gift boxes	1.25	.55
796	A299	26p Nosegay	1.25	.55
797	A299	30p Horseshoe	1.40	.65
798	A299	30p Balloons	1.40	.65
a.		Bklt. pane of 4, #795-798 English label	5.00	
b.		As "a," Gaelic label	5.00	

Greetings. Available only in discount booklets
containing #798a, 798b. Bklts. sold for £1.98.

1990, Apr. 5   Litho.   *Perf. 14x15*
799	A300	30p Tackle	1.00	.50
800	A300	30p Heading the ball	1.00	.50
a.		Pair, #799-800	2.00	2.00

1990 World Cup Soccer Championships, Italy.
Printed in sheets of 6 plus label.

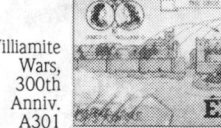

ÉIRE 30

Williamite
Wars,
300th
Anniv.
A301

1990, Apr. 5   Litho.   *Perf. 13½*
801	A301	30p Siege of Limerick	1.00	.50
802	A301	30p Battle of the Boyne	1.00	.50
a.		Pair, #801-802	2.00	2.00

ÉIRE   30

4M
MY5
40   ÉIRE 30

POSTAGE STAMPS 1840-1990

Penny
Black,
150th
Anniv.
A302

1990, May 3   Litho.   *Perf. 15x14*
803	A302	30p #782	1.10	.50
a.		Bklt. pane, #803, 2 each #552a, #782a	4.25	
804	A302	50p #68, 255, 550, 782	1.75	.90
a.		Bklt. pane, 2 ea #803-804	5.25	
b.		Bklt. pane of 4, #552a, #782a, #803-804	4.50	

See note following No. 584.

EUROPA

ÉIRE   30

Europa
1990 — A303

Post offices.

1990, May 3   Litho.   *Perf. 14x15*
805	A303	30p GPO, Dublin	1.10	.50
806	A303	41p Westport P.O., County Mayo	1.50	.80

Printed in sheets of 10+2 labels.

Statesman Type of 1986

1990, June 21   Litho.   *Perf. 14x15*
807	A240	30p Michael Collins	.95	.50

ÉIRE   26

Irish
Missionaries
Irish Missionaries   A304

Design: 50p, Working at water pump.

1990, June 21   *Perf. 15x14*
808 A304 26p multicolored .80 .40
809 A304 50p multicolored 1.60 .80

Garden Flowers — A305

1990, Aug. 30   Litho.   *Perf. 14x15*
810 A305 26p Narcissus .80 .40
811 A305 30p Rosa x hibernica .95 .50
  a.   Bkt. pane, 2 each #810-811 3.60
812 A305 41p Primula 1.30 .65
813 A305 50p Erica erigena 1.60 .80
  a.   Booklet pane of 4, #810-813 4.75
    Nos. 810-813 (4) 4.65 2.35

See note following No. 584.

Theater A306

Designs: No. 814, Playboy of the Western World. No. 815, Juno and the Paycock. No. 816, The Field. No. 817, Waiting for Godot.

1990, Oct. 18   Litho.   *Perf. 13½*
814 A306 30p multicolored 1.10 .55
815 A306 30p multicolored 1.10 .55
816 A306 30p multicolored 1.10 .55
817 A306 30p multicolored 1.10 .55
  a.   Strip of 4, #814-817 4.40 4.40

Christmas
A307   A308

1990, Nov. 15   Litho.   *Perf. 14x15*
818 A307 26p Child praying .90 .45
819 A308 26p Nativity scene .90 .45
820 A308 30p Madonna and Child 1.10 .90
821 A308 50p Adoration of the Magi 1.80 .90
    Nos. 818-821 (4) 4.70 2.35

No. 818 sold only in discount sheets of 12 for £2.86.

Love — A309   Irish Cycles — A310

1991, Jan. 29   Litho.   *Perf. 14x15*
822 A309 26p shown .90 .45
823 A309 30p Boy, girl kissing 1.10 .55

1991, Mar. 5
824 A310 26p Starley rover .90 .45
825 A310 30p Child's horse tricycle 1.10 .55
826 A310 30p Penny farthing 1.80 .90
  a.   Souvenir sheet of 3, #824-826 3.80 1.90
    Nos. 824-826 (3) 3.80 1.90

See note following No. 584.

1916 Rising, 75th Anniv. A311

Design: Statue of Cuchulainn by Oliver Sheppard, 1916 Proclamation.

1991, Apr. 3   Litho.   *Perf. 15x14*
827 A311 32p multicolored 1.00 .50

Dublin, European City of Culture A312

Designs: 28p, La Traviata, performed by Dublin Grand Opera Society. 32p, Dublin City Hall. 44p, St. Patrick's Cathedral, 800th anniv. 52p, Custom House, 200th anniv.

1991, Apr. 11   *Perf. 15x14*
828 A312 28p multicolored .85 .42
829 A312 32p multicolored 1.00 .50
830 A312 44p multicolored 1.30 .65
  a.   Booklet pane of 3, #828-830 3.15

   Size: 41x25mm
   Perf. 13½
831 A312 52p multicolored 1.50 .75
  a.   Booklet pane of 4, #828-831 4.65
    Nos. 828-831 (4) 4.65 2.32

50th anniv. of Dublin Grand Opera Soc. (No. 828).

Europa A313

1991, May 14   Litho.   *Perf. 15x14*
832 A313 32p Giotto probe 1.00 .50
833 A313 44p Hubble telescope 1.30 .65

Williamite Wars, 300th Anniv. A314

1991, May 14
834 A314 28p Siege of Athlone .85 .45
835 A314 28p Treaty of Limerick .85 .45
  a.   Pair, #834-835 1.70 1.70

Statesman Type of 1966 and

Charles Stewart Parnell (1846-1891), Politician — A315

Society of United Irishmen, Bicent. A316

Design: 28p, John A. Costello (1891-1976), politician.

Perf. 14x15, 15x14
1991, July 2   Litho.
836 A240 28p black .85 .40
837 A315 32p multicolored .95 .50
838 A316 52p multicolored 1.50 .75
    Nos. 836-838 (3) 3.30 1.65

Golfing Union of Ireland, Cent. — A317   Irish Sheep — A318

Perf. 15x14, 14x15
1991, Sept. 3   Litho.
839 A317 28p Golfer putting, horiz. .85 .45
840 A317 32p shown .95 .50

Walker Cup Competition, Portmarnock Golf Club (No. 839).

1991, Sept. 3   *Perf. 14x15, 15x14*
841 A318 32p Wicklow Cheviot .95 .50
842 A318 38p Donegal Blackface 1.15 .60
843 A318 52p Galway, horiz. 1.50 .75
    Nos. 841-843 (3) 3.60 1.85

Fishing Fleet A319

1991, Oct. 17   Litho.   *Perf. 15x14*
844 A319 28p Boatyard .85 .40
845 A319 32p Inshore trawler .95 .45
  a.   Bkt. pane of 5, #845, 2 each #768, 783 3.00
  b.   Bkt. pane, 2 each #844, 845 3.60
846 A319 44p Inshore potter 1.30 .65
847 A319 52p Factory ship 1.50 .75
  a.   Booklet pane of 4, #844-847 4.60
    Nos. 844-847 (4) 4.60 2.25

See note following No. 584.

Christmas
A320   A321

1991, Nov. 14   Litho.   *Perf. 14x15*
848 A320 28p Wise men, star .85 .40
849 A321 28p Annunciation .95 .45
850 A321 32p Nativity 1.00 .52
851 A321 52p Adoration of the Magi 1.75 .90
    Nos. 848-851 (4) 4.55 2.27

No. 848 issued only in discount sheets of 13+2 labels which sold for £3.36.

Love A322

Design: 32p, Rainbow over meadow, love etched in stone, vert.

Perf. 15x14, 14x15
1992, Jan. 28   Litho.
852 A322 28p shown .85 .42
853 A322 32p multicolored 1.00 .50

1992 Summer Olympics, Barcelona A323

1992, Feb. 25   Litho.   *Perf. 15x14*
854 A323 32p Boxing 1.00 .50
855 A323 44p Sailing 1.35 .70
  a.   Sheet of 4, 2 each #854-855 4.75 4.75

See note following No. 584.

Healthy Lifestyle — A324

1992, Feb. 25   *Perf. 14x15*
856 A324 28p multicolored .85 .40

Galway Chamber of Commerce and Industry, Bicent. A325

1992, Apr. 2   Litho.   *Perf. 15x14*
857 A325 28p multicolored .90 .45

Intl. Maritime Heritage Year A326

Perf. 15x14, 14x15
1992, Apr. 2   Litho.
858 A326 32p Mari Cog 1.00 .50
859 A326 52p Ovoca, vert. 1.60 .80

Greetings — A327

1992, Apr. 2   *Perf. 14x15*
860 A327 28p Coastline .90 .45
861 A327 28p Mountain .90 .45
862 A327 32p Flowers 1.00 .50
863 A327 32p Pond 1.00 .50
  a.   Bkt. pane of 4, #860-863, 8 English labels 7.50
  b.   Bkt. pane of 4, #860-863, 4 English labels + 4 Gaelic labels 7.50
    Nos. 860-863 (4) 3.80 1.90

#863a contains #860-863 in order. #863b contains #862, 863, 860 and 861 in order.

Discovery of America, 500th Anniv. A328

Europa: 44p, Landing in New World.

1992, May 14   Litho.   *Perf. 15x14*
864 A328 32p multicolored 1.00 .50
865 A328 44p multicolored 1.40 .70

Irish in
the
Americas
A329

Design: No. 867, The White House, bridge, rail-road workers, musicians, workers.

1992, May 14   **Perf. 13½**
866 A329 52p multicolored   1.60   .80
867 A329 52p multicolored   1.60   .80
  a.   Pair, #866-867   3.25 3.25

Pine Marten
A330

1992, July 9   Litho.   Perf. 15x14
868 A330 28p shown   1.00   .50
869 A330 32p In tree   1.10   .55
870 A330 44p With young   1.50   .75
871 A330 52p Holding bird   1.75   .90
   Nos. 868-871 (4)   5.35 2.70

World Wildlife Fund.

Trinity College,
Dublin, 400th
Anniv. — A331

1992, Sept. 2   Litho.   Perf. 13½
872 A331 32p Library   1.05   .50
873 A331 52p Main entrance   1.70   .85

Views of
Dublin by
James
Malton,
Bicent.
A332

1992, Sept. 2   Perf. 15x14
874 A332 28p Rotunda, Assembly
      rooms   .90   .45
875 A332 44p Charlemont House   1.45   .75

Single
European
Market
A333

1992, Oct. 15   Litho.   Perf. 15x14
876 A333 32p multicolored   1.10   .55
  a.   Bklt. pane of 3   3.30
  b.   Bklt. pane of 4   4.40

No. 876b comes with stamps in three formats: four singles, two pairs, and block of four. See note following No. 584.

Food and
Farming — A334

1992, Oct. 15   Perf. 14x15
877 A334 32p Fresh food   1.10   .55
878 A334 32p Cattle   1.10   .55
879 A334 32p Combine harvesting
      grain   1.10   .55
880 A334 32p Growing vegetables   1.10   .55
  a.   Strip of 4, #877-880   4.40 2.20

Christmas

A335   A336

Designs: No. 881, Rural churchyard. No. 882, The Annunciation, manuscript illustration, Chester Beatty Library, Dublin. 32p, Adoration of the Shepherds, by Jocopo da Empoli. 52p, Adoration of the Magi, by Johann Rottenhammer.

1992, Nov. 19
881 A335 28p multicolored   .90   .45
882 A336 28p multicolored   .95   .50
883 A336 32p multicolored   1.10   .55
884 A336 52p multicolored   1.75   .90
   Nos. 881-884 (4)   4.70 2.40

No. 881 issued only in discount sheets of 13+2 labels which sold for £3.36.

Love
A337

Design: 28p, Queen of Hearts, vert.

Perf. 14x15, 15x14
1993, Jan. 26   Litho.
885 A337 28p multicolored   .80   .40
886 A337 32p multicolored   .95   .50

Irish Impressionist Paintings — A338

Designs: 28p, Evening at Tangier, by Sir John Lavery. 32p, The Goose Girl, by William J. Leech. 44p, La Jeune Bretonne, by Roderic O'Conor, vert. 52p, Lustre Jug, by Walter Osborne, vert.

1993, Mar. 4   Perf. 13
887 A338 28p multicolored   .80   .40
888 A338 32p multicolored   .95   .50
  a.   Booklet pane of 2, #887-888   1.75
889 A338 44p multicolored   1.25   .65
890 A338 52p multicolored   1.50   .75
  a.   Booklet pane of 2, #889-890   2.80
  b.   Booklet pane of 4, #887-890   4.55
   Nos. 887-890 (4)   4.50 2.30

No. 890b exists in two formats with different margin inscriptions.

Orchids — A339

1993, Apr. 20   Litho.   Perf. 14x15
891 A339 28p Bee orchid   .85   .45
892 A339 32p O'Kelly's orchid   1.00   .50
893 A339 38p Dark red helleborine   1.10   .60

---

894 A339 52p Irish lady's tresses   1.50   .75
  a.   Souvenir sheet of 4, #891-894 4.50 4.50
  b.   As "a," with blue inscription 4.50 4.50
   Nos. 891-894 (4)   4.45 2.30

No. 894b has a larger top margin than No. 894a. Added inscription includes text and flags of Ireland and Thailand.

Contemporary
Paintings
A340

Europa: 32p, Pears in a Copper Pan, by Hilda van Stockum. 44p, Arrieta Orzola, by Tony O'Malley.

1993, May 18   Litho.   Perf. 13x13½
895 A340 32p multicolored   1.00   .50
896 A340 44p multicolored   1.25   .65

Issued in sheets of 10 + 2 labels.

Gaelic
League,
Cent.
A341

Design: 52p, Illuminated manuscript presented to founder Douglas Hyde, vert.

Perf. 15x14, 14x15
1993, July 8   Litho.
897 A341 32p multicolored   .90   .45
898 A341 52p multicolored   1.40   .70

Irish
Amateur
Swimming
Assoc., Cent.
A342

Designs: No. 899, Swimmer diving into water. No. 900, Woman swimming.

1993, July 8   Perf. 15x14
899 A342 32p multicolored   .90   .45
900 A342 32p multicolored   .90   .45
  a.   Pair, #899-900   1.80   .90

Royal
Hospital
Donnybrook,
250th Anniv.
A343

Ceide Fields,
County
Mayo
A345

Carlow College,   Edward Bunting
Bicent. — A344   (1773-1843),
                         Composer — A346

Perf. 15x14, 14x15, 13½ (52p)
1993, Sept. 2   Litho.
901 A343 28p multicolored   .80   .40
902 A344 32p multicolored   .95   .45
903 A345 44p multicolored   1.25   .65
904 A346 52p multicolored   1.50   .75
   Nos. 901-904 (4)   4.50 2.25

Irish Buses
A347

Designs: 28p, Great Northern Railways Gardner. 32p, CIE Leyland Titan. No. 907, Horse-drawn omnibus. No. 908, Char-a-banc.

1993, Oct. 12   Litho.   Perf. 15x14
905 A347 28p multicolored   .80   .40
906 A347 32p multicolored   .95   .45
  a.   Booklet pane, 2 each #905-906 3.50
907 A347 52p multicolored   1.50   .75
908 A347 52p multicolored   1.50   .75
  a.   Pair, #907-908   3.00 1.50
  b.   Booklet pane of 4, #905-908   4.75
   Nos. 905-908 (4)   4.75 2.35

A348

Christmas
A349

Designs: 32p, Mary placing infant Jesus in manger. 52p, Adoration of the shepherds.

Perf. 14x15, 15x14
1993, Nov. 16   Litho.
909 A348 28p multicolored   .80   .40
910 A349 28p multicolored   .80   .40
911 A349 32p multicolored   .90   .45
912 A349 52p multicolored   1.50   .75
   Nos. 909-912 (4)   4.00 2.00

No. 909 issued only in discount sheets of 13+2 labels which sold for £3.36.

Love
A350

Design: 32p, Man, woman in shape of heart, vert.

Perf. 15x14, 14x15
1994, Jan. 27   Litho.
913 A350 28p multicolored   .80   .40
914 A350 32p multicolored   .95   .45

Greetings
Stamps — A351

1994, Jan. 27   Perf. 14x15
915 A351 32p Face in sun   .95   .45
916 A351 32p Face in flower   .95   .45
917 A351 32p Face in heart   .95   .45
  a.   Souv. sheet of 3, #915-917   3.00 1.40

918 A351 32p Face in rose .95 .45
  a. Booklet pane of 4, #915-918, 4 English + 4 Gaelic labels 4.00
  b. As "a," 8 English labels 4.00
    Nos. 915-918 (4) 3.80 1.80

New Year 1994 (Year of the Dog), Hong Kong '94 (#917a).
#918a contains 915-918 in order. #918b contains 917, 918, 915, 916 in order.

Macra na' Feirme, 50th Anniv.
A352

The Taking of Christ, by Caravaggio
A353

Irish Co-operative Organization Society, Cent.
A354

Irish Congress of Trade Unions, Cent.
A355

1994, Mar. 2   Litho.   *Perf. 15x14*
919 A352 28p blue & gold .80 .40
920 A353 32p multicolored .95 .45
921 A354 38p multicolored 1.10 .75
922 A355 52p blue, blk & lt blue 1.50 .55
    Nos. 919-922 (4) 4.35 2.15

Voyages of St. Brendan (487-577)
A356

Europa: 32p, St. Brendan, Irish monks sailing past volcano. 44p, St. Brendan on island with sheep, monks in boat.

1994, Apr. 18   Litho.   *Perf. 15x14*
923 A356 32p multicolored .95 .45
924 A356 44p multicolored 1.25 .65
  a. Miniature sheet of 2, #923-924 2.25 1.10

See Faroe Islands Nos. 264-265; Iceland Nos. 780-781.

Parliamentary Anniversaries — A357

Designs: No. 925, First meeting of the Dail, 1919. No. 926, Fourth direct elections to European Parliament.

1994, Apr. 27
925 A357 32p multicolored .95 .45
926 A357 32p multicolored .95 .45
  a. Booklet pane, 1 each #925-926 1.90
  b. Booklet pane, 2 each #925-926 3.80

1994 World Cup Soccer Championships, US — A358

Players from: No. 927, Argentina in striped shirt, Ireland in green. No. 928, Ireland, Germany.

1994, May 31   *Perf. 14x15*
927 A358 32p multicolored .95 .45
928 A358 32p multicolored .95 .45
  a. Pair, #927-928 2.00 2.00

Women's Hockey A359

Designs: 32p, 1994 Women's Hockey World Cup, Dublin. 52p, Irish Ladies' Hockey Union, cent.

1994, May 31   *Perf. 13x13¹/₂*
929 A359 32p multicolored .95 .45
930 A359 52p multicolored 1.50 .75

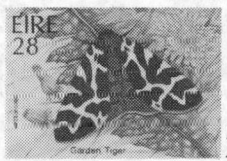

Moths A360

1994, July 12   Litho.   *Perf. 14¹/₂x14*
931 A360 28p Garden tiger .90 .45
932 A360 32p Burren green 1.00 .50
933 A360 38p Emperor 1.25 .60
934 A360 52p Elephant hawkmoth 1.65 .85
  a. Souvenir sheet of 4, #931-934 4.80 4.80
  b. As "a," overprinted 4.75 4.75
    Nos. 931-934 (4) 4.80 2.40

Size: 34x23mm
Self-Adhesive
Die Cut Perf. 11¹/₂
935 A360 32p like #932 1.00 .50
936 A360 32p like #931 1.00 .50
937 A360 32p like #934 1.00 .50
938 A360 32p like #933 1.00 .50
  a. Strip of 4, #935-938 4.00

Overprint on #934b shows PHILAKOREA '94 exhibition emblem and Chinese inscription.

A361

A362   A363

Anniversaries and Events — A364

Designs: 28p, Medieval view of Drogheda. No. 940, Edmund Ignatius Rice (1762-1844), philantropist. No. 941, Edmund Burke (1729-97), political commentator. No. 942, Eamonn Andrews (1922-87), broadcaster. No. 943, Vickers Vimy aircraft.

1994, Sept. 6   Litho.   *Perf. 13¹/₂*
939 A361 28p multicolored .90 .90
    Perf. 14x14¹/₂
940 A362 32p multicolored 1.00 1.00
    Perf. 14x13¹/₂
941 A363 32p multicolored 1.00 1.00
942 A363 52p multicolored 1.65 1.65
    Perf. 15x14
943 A364 52p multicolored 1.65 1.65
    Nos. 939-943 (5) 6.20 6.20

Drogheda, 800th anniv. (#939). First Newfoundland-Ireland transatlantic flight, 75th anniv. (#943).

Nobel Prize Winners A365

Designs: No. 944, George Bernard Shaw (1856-1950), dramatist, essayist. No. 945, Samuel Beckett (1906-89), playwright. 32p, Sean McBride (1904-88), statesman. 52p, William Butler Yeats (1865-1939), poet.

1994, Oct. 18   Litho.   *Perf. 15x14*
944 A365 28p multicolored .90 .90
945 A365 28p multicolored .90 .90
  a. Pair, #944-945 1.80 1.80
946 A365 32p multicolored 1.00 1.00
  a. Booklet pane of 3, #944-946 2.80
  b. Booklet pane of 4, #944-945, 2 #946 3.80
947 A365 52p multicolored 1.65 1.65
  a. Booklet pane, 1 #946, 3 #947 4.30
  b. Booklet pane of 4, #944-947 4.50
    Prestige bklt., #946a-946b, 947a-947b 16.00
    Nos. 944-947 (4) 4.45 4.45

Christmas
A366   A367

Designs: No. 948, Stained glass nativity scene. No. 949, Annunciation, detail, 11th cent. ivory plaque. 32p, Flight Into Egypt, 15th cent. wood carving. 52p, Nativity, detail, 11th cent. ivory plaque.

1994, Nov. 17   Litho.   *Perf. 14x15*
948 A366 28p multicolored .80 .80
949 A367 28p multicolored .90 .90
950 A367 32p multicolored 1.00 1.00
951 A367 52p multicolored 1.65 1.65
    Nos. 948-951 (4) 4.35 4.35

No. 948 issued only in discount sheets of 13+2 labels which sold for £3.36.

Greetings Stamps — A368

1995, Jan. 24   Litho.   *Perf. 14x15*
952 A368 32p Tree of hearts 1.00 .50
Booklet Stamps
953 A368 32p Teddy bear, balloon 1.00 .50
954 A368 32p Clown juggling hearts 1.00 .50
955 A368 32p Bouquet of flowers 1.00 .50
  a. Booklet pane, #952-955 + 4 English, 4 Gaelic labels 4.00
  b. As "a," 8 English labels 4.00
    Complete booklet, #955a-955b 8.00
  c. Souvenir sheet, #952, 954-955 + 3 English, 3 Gaelic labels 3.00 1.50

New Year 1995 (Year of the Boar) (#955c).

No. 955a contains #953-954, 952, 955 in order.
No. 955b contains #952, 955, 953-954 in order.

Narrow Gauge Railways A369

1995, Feb. 28   Litho.   *Perf. 15x14*
956 A369 28p West Clare .90 .45
957 A369 32p Co. Donegal 1.10 .55
958 A369 38p Cork & Muskerry 1.25 .60
959 A369 52p Cavan & Leitrim 1.75 .85
  a. Souvenir sheet of 4, #956-959 5.00 5.00
    Nos. 956-959 (4) 5.00 2.45

No. 959a exists with Singapore '95 overprint in sheet margin.

Peace & Freedom A370

Europa: Nos. 960, 962, Stylized dove, reconstructed city. 44p, No. 963, Stylized dove, map of Europe.

1995, Apr. 6   Litho.   *Perf. 15x14*
960 A370 32p multicolored 1.10 .55
961 A370 44p multicolored 1.40 .70

Size: 34¹/₂x23mm
Self-Adhesive
Die Cut Perf. 11¹/₂
962 A370 32p multicolored 1.10 .55
963 A370 32p multicolored 1.10 .55
    Nos. 960-963 (4) 4.70 2.35

1995 Rugby World Cup A371

1995, Apr. 6   *Perf. 14*
964 A371 32p shown 1.10 .55
965 A371 52p Player being tackled 1.65 .85
Souvenir Sheet
966 A371 £1 like #964 3.25 3.25

No. 966 has a continuous design.

A372   A373

Design: 32p, Irish soldiers, Cross of Fontenoy.

1995, May 15   Photo.   *Perf. 11¹/₂*
967 A372 32p multicolored 1.10 .55

Battle of Fontenoy, 250th Anniv. See Belgium No. 1583.

1995, May 15   Litho.   *Perf. 14x15*

Military uniforms: 28p, Irish Brigade, French Army, 1745. No. 969, Tercio Irlanda, Army of Flanders, 1605. No. 970, Royal Dublin Fusiliers, 1914. 38p, St. Patrick's Battalion, Papal Army, 1860. 52p, The Fighting 69th, Army of Potomac, 1861.

968 A373 28p multicolored .90 .45
969 A373 32p multicolored 1.00 .50
  a. Booklet pane, 2 each #968-969 4.00
970 A373 32p multicolored 1.00 .50
971 A373 38p multicolored 1.25 .60
  a. Bklt. pane of 3, #968-969, #971 3.25
972 A373 52p multicolored 1.75 .85
  a. Bklt. pane of 3, #968-969, 972 3.75
  b. Bklt. pane of 4, #968-969, 971-972 5.00

	Prestige booklet, #969a, 971a, 972a, 972b	16.00	
	Nos. 968-972 (5)	5.90	2.90

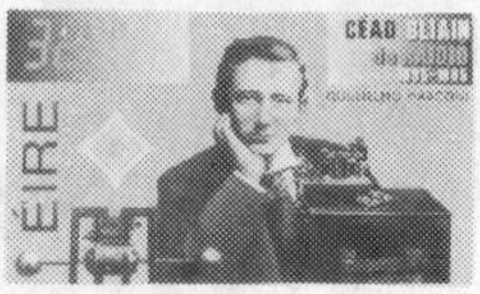
ÉIRE

Radio, Cent. A374

Designs: No. 973, Guglielmo Marconi, transmitting equipment. No. 974, Radio channel dial.

1995, June 8 Litho. *Perf. 13½*

973	A374 32p multicolored	1.10	.55
974	A374 32p multicolored	1.10	.55
a.	Pair, #973-974	2.25	1.10

See Germany #1900, Italy #2038-2039, San Marino #1336-1337, Vatican City #978-979.

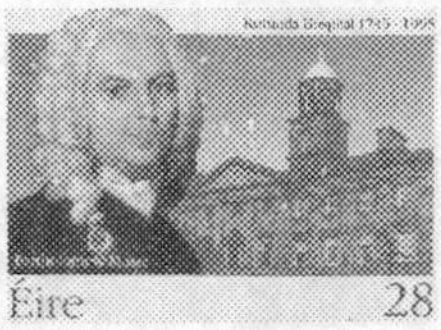

Éire 28 A375

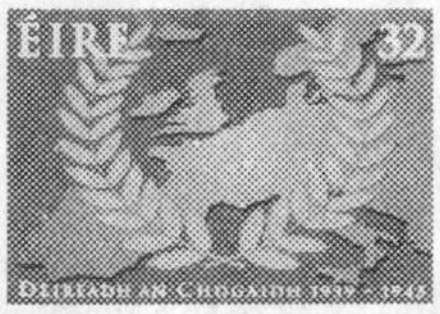
ÉIRE 32

A376

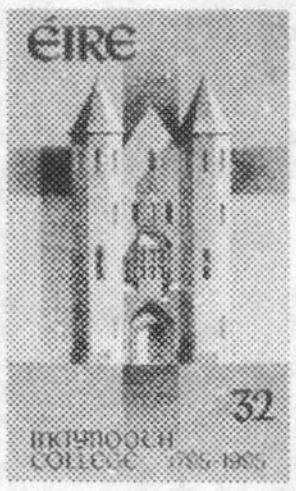
ÉIRE
32

A377

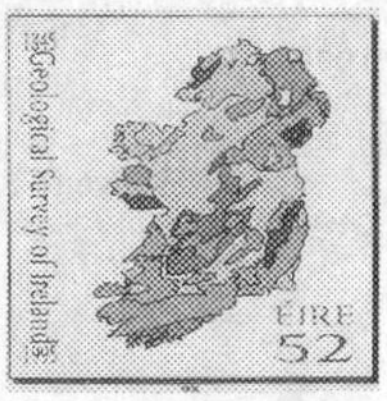
Geological Survey of Ireland
ÉIRE
52

Anniversaries & Events — A378

Designs: 28p, Dr. Bartholomew Mosse, Rotunda Hospital. No. 976, Piper, laurel wreath over map of Europe. No. 977, St. Patrick's College. 52p, Geological map of Ireland.

1995, July 27 Litho. *Perf. 14½x14*

975	A375 28p multicolored	.90	.45
976	A376 32p multicolored	1.00	.50

Perf. 14½

977	A377 32p multicolored	1.00	.50

Perf. 13½

978	A378 52p multicolored	1.65	.80
	Nos. 975-978 (4)	4.55	2.25

Rotunda Hospital, 250th anniv. (#975). End of World War II, 50th anniv. (#976). St. Patrick's College, Maynooth, bicent. (#977). Geological survey of Ireland, 150th anniv. (#978).

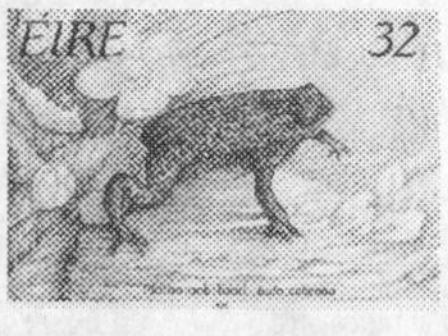
ÉIRE 32

Reptiles & Amphibians A379

1995, Sept. 1 Litho. *Perf. 15x14*

979	A379 32p Natterjack toad	1.00	.50
980	A379 32p Common lizard	1.00	.50
981	A379 32p Smooth newt	1.00	.50
982	A379 32p Common frog	1.00	.50
a.	Strip of 4, #979-982	4.00	2.00
	Nos. 979-982 (4)	4.00	2.00

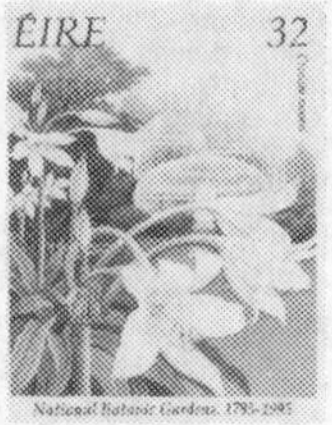
ÉIRE 32

Natl. Botanic Gardens, Bicent. — A380

Designs: 32p, Crinum moorei. 38p, Sarracenia x moorei. 44p, Solanum crispum "glasnevin."

1995, Oct. 9 Litho. *Perf. 14x15*

983	A380 32p multicolored	1.00	.50
984	A380 38p multicolored	1.25	.60
985	A380 44p multicolored	1.40	.70
a.	Booklet pane of 3, #983-985	3.75	
b.	Bklt. pane of 3, #984-985, 2 #983	4.75	
	Complete booklet, #985a-985b	8.50	
	Nos. 983-985 (3)	3.65	1.80

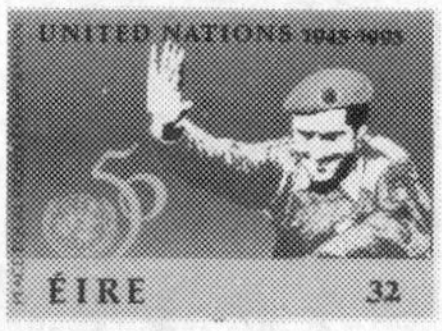
UNITED NATIONS 1945-1995
ÉIRE 32

UN, 50th Anniv. A381

1995, Oct. 19 *Perf. 13x13½*

986	A381 32p shown	1.00	.50
987	A381 52p UN, "50" emblem	1.65	.80

AIR POST STAMPS

Catalogue values for unused stamps in this section are for Never Hinged items.

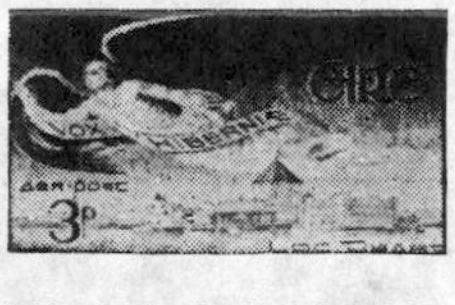
ÉIRE
3P

Angel over Lough Derg — AP1

Designs: 1p, 1sh3p, 1sh5p, Rock of Cashel. 6p, Croagh Patrick. 1sh, Glendalough.

Perf. 15x14

1948-65 Wmk. 262 Engr.

C1	AP1	1p dk brown ('49)	3.75	2.50
C2	AP1	3p blue	6.25	4.00
C3	AP1	6p rose lilac	.65	.15
C4	AP1	8p red brown ('54)	3.25	.28
C5	AP1	1sh green ('49)	1.40	.40
C6	AP1	1sh3p ver ('54)	4.00	.18

Perf. 15

C7	AP1	1sh5p dark blue ('65)	4.00	.70
		Nos. C1-C7 (7)	23.30	8.21

POSTAGE DUE STAMPS

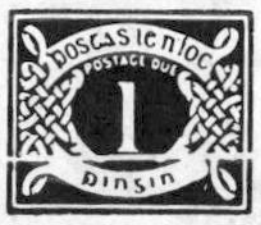
postas le híoc
1
pinsin

D1

1925 Typo. Wmk. 44 *Perf. 14x15*

J1	D1	½p emerald	22.50	17.50
		Never hinged	92.50	
J2	D1	1p carmine	13.00	7.50
		Never hinged	45.00	
J3	D1	2p dark green	25.00	9.00
		Never hinged	80.00	
J4	D1	6p plum	8.25	6.50
		Never hinged	25.00	
		Nos. J1-J4 (4)	68.75	40.50

Catalogue values for unused stamps in this section, from this point to the end of the section, are for Never Hinged items.

1940-70 Wmk. 262

J5	D1	½p emerald ('43)	32.50	22.50
J6	D1	1p brt carmine ('41)	1.10	.50
J7	D1	1½p vermilion ('52)	2.25	5.00
J8	D1	2p dark green	2.25	.55
J9	D1	3p blue ('52)	1.75	1.25
J10	D1	5p royal purple ('43)	3.00	3.50
J11	D1	6p plum ('60)	2.25	1.50
a.		Wmkd. sideways ('67)	2.25	1.65
J12	D1	8p orange ('62)	7.50	5.00
J13	D1	10p red lilac ('65)	7.75	5.00
J14	D1	1sh lt yel grn ('69)	15.00	6.00
a.		Wmkd. sideways ('70)	47.50	11.00
		Nos. J5-J14 (10)	75.35	50.80

1971, Feb. 15 Typo. Wmk. 262

J15	D1	1p sepia	.15	.15
a.		Wmkd. sideways	.60	.60
J16	D1	1½p bright green	.15	.15
J17	D1	3p gray green	.90	.70
J18	D1	4p orange	1.25	.80
J19	D1	5p bright blue	2.25	1.40
J20	D1	7p yellow	.30	.20
J21	D1	8p scarlet	.30	.20
		Nos. J15-J21 (7)	5.30	3.60

1978 Unwmk.

J25	D1	3p gray green	2.50	6.00
J26	D1	4p orange	4.00	*10.50*
J27	D1	5p bright blue	2.50	6.00
		Nos. J25-J27 (3)	9.00	*22.50*

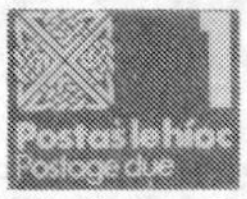
1
Postas le híoc
Postage due

Celtic Knot — D2

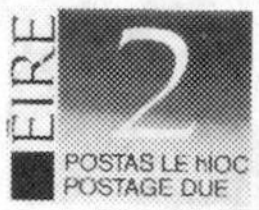
ÉIRE
2
POSTAS LE HÍOC
POSTAGE DUE

D3

1980-85 Photo. *Perf. 15*

J28	D2	1p brt yel green	.15	.15
J29	D2	2p ultramarine	.15	.15
J30	D2	4p dark green	.35	.30
J31	D2	6p yel orange	.50	.45
J32	D2	8p violet blue	.70	.60
J33	D2	18p green	1.50	1.25
J33A	D2	20p org brown ('85)	1.25	1.00
J34	D2	24p emerald	2.00	1.65
J35	D2	30p plum ('85)	1.65	1.40
J36	D2	50p rose pink ('85)	3.00	2.75
		Nos. J28-J36 (10)	11.25	9.70

Issue dates: 1p, 2p, 4p, 6p, 8p, 18p, 24p, June 11. 20p, 30p, 50p, Aug. 22.

1988, Oct. 6 Litho. *Perf. 14x15*

J37	D3	1p blk, dp yel & brt red	.15	.15
J38	D3	2p blk, vio brn & brt red	.15	.15
J39	D3	3p blk, dull vio & brt red	.15	.15
J40	D3	4p blk, vio & brt red	.15	.15
J41	D3	5p blk, vio bl & brt red	.15	.15
J42	D3	17p blk, brt ol grn & brt red	.50	.25
J43	D3	20p blk, bluish gray & brt red	.60	.30
J44	D3	24p blk, bl grn & brt red	.70	.35
J45	D3	30p blk & brt red	.90	.45
J46	D3	50p blk, gray & brt red	1.50	.75
J47	D3	£1 blk, dk ol brn & brt red	3.00	1.50
		Nos. J37-J47 (11)	7.95	4.35

KENYA

'ke–nyə

LOCATION — East Africa, bordering on the Indian Ocean
GOVT. — Republic
AREA — 224,960 sq. mi.
POP. — 18,750,000 (est. 1983)
CAPITAL — Nairobi

Formerly a part of the British colony of Kenya, Uganda, Tanganyika, Kenya gained independence Dec. 12, 1963.

100 Cents = 1 Shilling

Catalogue values for all unused stamps in this country are for Never Hinged items.

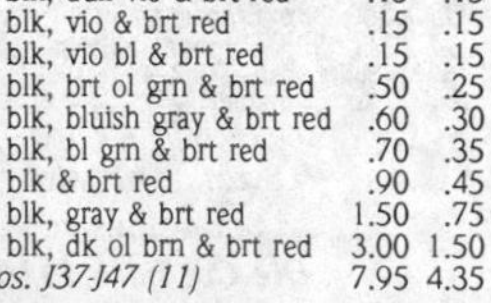
1/30
KENYA
UHURU 1963

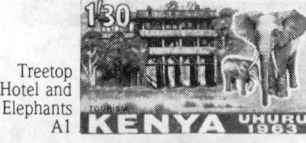

Treetop Hotel and Elephants A1

Designs: 5c, Cattle ranching. 10c, Wood carving. 15c, Riveter. 20c, Timber industry. 30c, Jomo Kenyatta facing Mt. Kenya. 40c, Fishing industry. 50c, Flag and emblem. 65c, Pyrethrum industry (daisies). 1sh, National Assembly bldg. 2sh, Harvesting coffee. 5sh, Harvesting tea. 10sh, Mombasa port. 20sh, Royal College, Nairobi.

Perf. 14x14½

1963, Dec. 12 Photo. Unwmk.

Size: 21x17½mm

1	A1	5c bl, buff & dk brn	.15	.15
2	A1	10c brown	.15	.15
a.		Booklet pane of 4	.30	
3	A1	15c deep magenta	.15	.15
a.		Booklet pane of 4	.30	
4	A1	20c yel grn & dk brn	.15	.15
a.		Booklet pane of 4	.40	
5	A1	30c yel & black	.15	.15
a.		Booklet pane of 4	.55	
6	A1	40c blue & brown	.20	.15
7	A1	50c grn, blk & dp car	.20	.15
a.		Booklet pane of 4	1.25	
8	A1	65c steel blue & yel	.35	.25

Perf. 14½

Size: 41½x25½mm

9	A1	1sh multicolored	.45	.15
10	A1	1.30sh grn, brn & blk	.50	.15
11	A1	2sh multicolored	.70	.20
12	A1	5sh ultra, yel grn & brn	1.40	.40
13	A1	10sh brn & dark brn	3.50	1.25
14	A1	20sh pink & grnsh blk	7.00	2.50
		Nos. 1-14 (14)	15.05	
		Set value		5.00

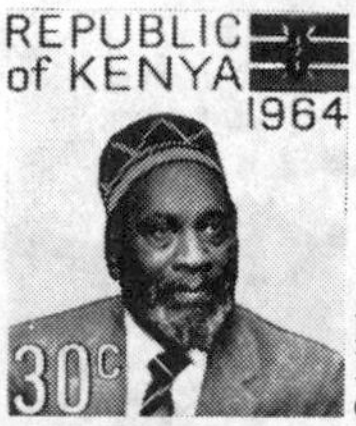
REPUBLIC of KENYA 1964
30c

President Jomo Kenyatta and Flag of Kenya — A2

Flag and: 15c, Cockerel. 50c, African lion. 1.30sh, Hartlaub's touraco. 2.50sh, Nandi flame flower.

1964, Dec. 12 Photo. *Perf. 13x12½*

15	A2	15c lt violet & multi	.20	.15
16	A2	30c dk blue & multi	.40	.15
17	A2	50c dk brown & multi	.60	.35
18	A2	1.30sh multicolored	1.90	.75
19	A2	2.50sh multicolored	4.75	3.75
		Nos. 15-19 (5)	7.85	5.15

Establishment of the Republic of Kenya, Dec. 12, 1964.

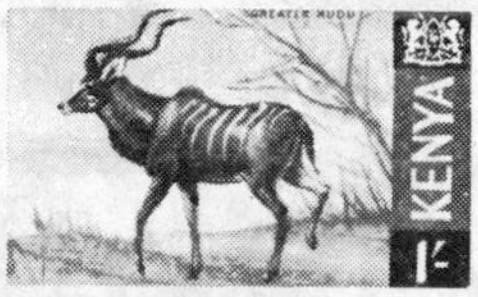
KENYA
1/-

Greater Kudu A3

Animals: 5c, Thomson's gazelle. 10c, Sable antelope. 15c, Aardvark. 20c, Senegal bush baby. 30c, Warthog. 40c, Zebra. 50c, Buffalo. 65c, Black rhinoceros. 70c, Ostrich. 1.30sh, Elephant. 1.50sh, Bat-eared fox. 2.50sh, Cheetah. 5sh, Vervet monkey. 10sh, Giant pangolin. 20sh, Lion.

1966-69 Unwmk. *Perf. 14x14½*

Size: 21x17mm

20	A3	5c gray, black & org	.15	.15
21	A3	10c black & yel green	.15	.15
22	A3	15c dp orange & black	.15	.15
23	A3	20c ultra, lt brn & black	.15	.15
24	A3	30c lt ultra & blk	.15	.15
25	A3	40c ocher & blk	.20	.15
26	A3	50c dp orange & blk	.25	.15
27	A3	65c dp yel green & blk	1.40	.90
28	A3	70c rose lake & black	1.40	.70

Perf. 14½

Size: 41x25mm

29	A3	1sh gray bl, ol & blk	.50	.15
30	A3	1.30sh yel grn & blk	1.40	.15
31	A3	1.50sh brn org, brn & black	1.75	.90
32	A3	2.50sh ol bis, yel & blk	2.50	.45
33	A3	5sh brt grn, ultra & black	2.25	.70
34	A3	10sh red brn, bis & black	4.50	1.40
35	A3	20sh ocher, bis, gold & black	9.00	3.00
		Nos. 20-35 (16)	25.90	9.40

Issued: #28, 31, 9/15/69; others, 12/12/66.

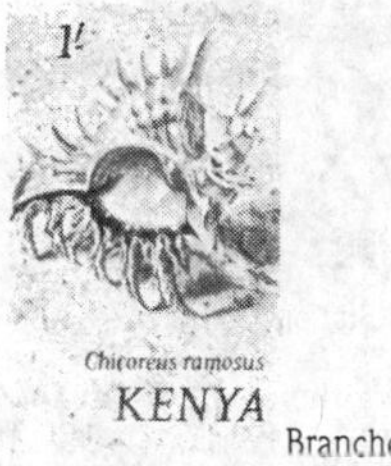

Branched Murex — A4

Sea shells: 5c, Morning pink. 10c, Episcopal miter. 15c, Strawberry-top shell. 20c, Humpback cowrie. 30c, variable abalone. 40c, Flame-top shell. 50c, Violet sailor. 60c, Bull's-mouth helmet. 70c, Pearly nautilus. 1.50sh, Neptune's trumpet. 2.50sh, Mediterranean tulip shell. 5sh, Fluctuating turban. 10sh, Textile cone. 20sh, Scorpion shell.

1971 Dec. 13 Photo. *Perf. 14½x14*

Size: 17x21mm

36 A4 5c bister & multi .15 .15
37 A4 10c dull grn & multi .15 .15
a. Booklet pane of 4 .40
38 A4 15c tan & multi .15 .15
a. Booklet pane of 4 .40
39 A4 20c tan & multi .15 .15
a. Booklet pane of 4 .50
40 A4 30c yellow & multi .20 .15
a. Booklet pane of 4 .80
41 A4 40c gray & multi .20 .15
a. Booklet pane of 4 .80
42 A4 50c buff & multi *(Janthina globosa)* .45 .15
a. Booklet pane of 4 1.80
43 A4 60c lilac & multi .45 .15
44 A4 70c gray grn & multi *(Nautilus pompileus)* .75 .15
a. Booklet pane of 4 2.50

Perf. 14½

Size: 25x41mm

45 A4 1sh ocher & multi .65 .15
46 A4 1.50sh pale grn & multi .90 .15
47 A4 2.50sh vio gray & multi 1.50 .15
48 A4 5sh lemon & multi 3.00 .25
49 A4 10sh multicolored 5.00 .75
50 A4 20sh gray & multi 12.50 1.75
Nos. 36-50 (15) 26.20
Set value 3.70

Used values of Nos. 48-50 are for stamps with printed cancellations.

For surcharges see Nos. 53-55.

Revised Inscription

1974, Jan. 20 *Perf. 14½x14*

51 A4 50c *(Janthina janthina)* 5.00 .30
52 A4 70c *(Nautilus pompilius)* 9.00 1.40

Nos. 46-47, 50 Surcharged with New Value and 2 Bars

1975, Nov. 17 Photo. *Perf. 14½*

53 A4 2sh on 1.50sh multi 2.50 1.60
54 A4 3sh on 2.50sh multi 12.00 15.00
55 A4 40sh on 20sh multi 14.00 14.00
Nos. 53-55 (3) 28.50 30.60

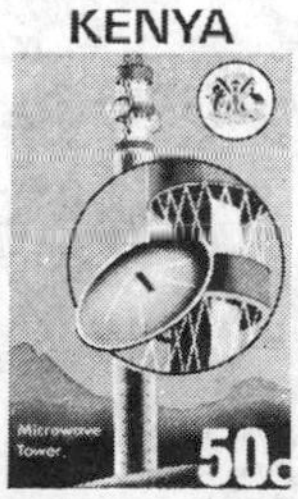

Microwave Tower — A5

Designs: 1sh, Cordless switchboard and operators, horiz. 2sh, Telephones of 1880, 1930 and 1976. 3sh, Message switching center, horiz.

1976, Apr. 15 Litho. *Perf. 14½*

56 A5 50c blue & multi .15 .15
57 A5 1sh red & multi .30 .20
58 A5 2sh yellow & multi .50 .35
59 A5 3sh multicolored .85 .60
a. Souvenir sheet of 4 2.50 2.25
Nos. 56-59 (4) 1.80 1.30

Telecommunication development in East Africa. No. 59a contains 4 stamps similar to Nos. 56-59 with simulated perforations.

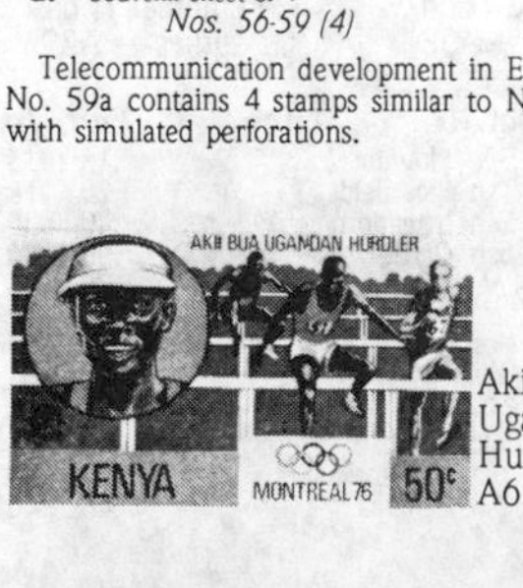

Akii Bua, Ugandan Hurdler A6

Designs: 1sh, Filbert Bayi, Tanzanian runner. 2sh, Steve Muchoki, Kenyan boxer. 3sh, Olympic torch, flags of Kenya, Tanzania and Uganda.

1976, July 5 Litho. *Perf. 14½*

60 A6 50c blue & multi .20 .15
61 A6 1sh red & multi .35 .20
62 A6 2sh yellow & multi .60 .40
63 A6 3sh blue & multi 1.00 .60
a. Souv. sheet of 4, #60-63, perf. 13 6.75 5.75
Nos. 60-63 (4) 2.15 1.35

21st Olympic Games, Montreal, Canada, July 17-Aug. 1.

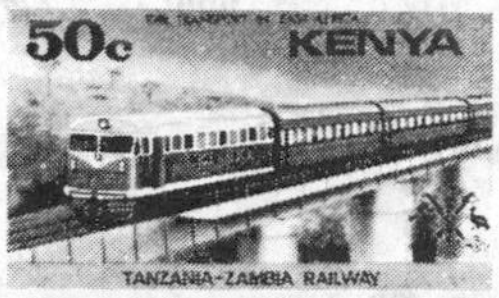

Tanzania-Zambia Railway — A7

Designs: 1sh, Nile Bridge, Uganda. 2sh, Nakuru Station, Kenya. 3sh, Class A locomotive, 1896.

1976, Oct. 4 Litho. *Perf. 14½*

64 A7 50c lilac & multi .35 .15
65 A7 1sh emerald & multi .65 .25
66 A7 2sh brt rose & multi 1.25 .50
67 A7 3sh yellow & multi 2.00 .70
a. Souv. sheet of 4, #64-67, perf. 13 8.00 5.00
Nos. 64-67 (4) 4.25 1.60

Rail transport in East Africa.

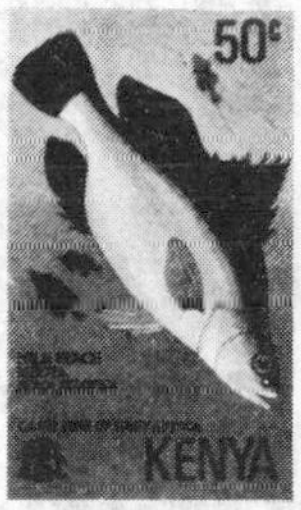

Nile Perch — A8

Game Fish: 1sh, Tilapia. 3sh, Sailfish. 5sh, Black marlin.

1977, Jan. 10 Litho. *Perf. 14½*

68 A8 50c multicolored .20 .15
69 A8 1sh multicolored .40 .20
70 A8 3sh multicolored 1.50 .50
71 A8 5sh multicolored 2.00 1.00
Nos. 68-71 (4) 4.10 1.85
a. Souvenir sheet of 4, #68-71 6.00 5.00

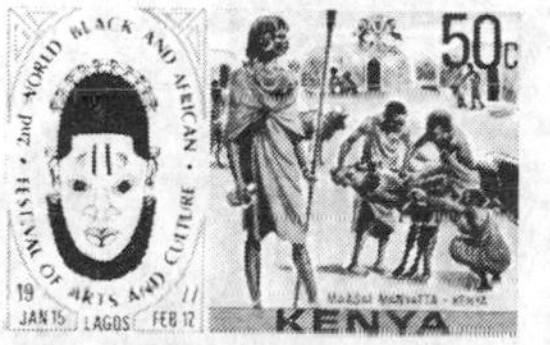

Festival Emblem and Masai Tribesmen Bleeding Cow — A9

Festival Emblem and: 1sh, Dancers from Uganda. 2sh, Makonde sculpture, Tanzania. 3sh, Tribesmen skinning hippopotamus.

1977, Jan. 15 *Perf. 13½x14*

72 A9 50c multicolored .15 .15
73 A9 1sh multicolored .35 .20
74 A9 2sh multicolored 1.25 .40
75 A9 3sh multicolored 1.40 .60
a. Souvenir sheet of 4, #72-75 3.50 2.50
Nos. 72-75 (4) 3.15 1.35

2nd World Black and African Festival, Lagos, Nigeria, Jan. 15-Feb. 12.

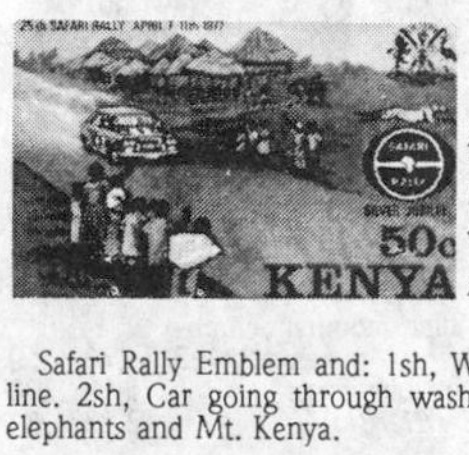

Automobile Passing through Village A10

Safari Rally Emblem and: 1sh, Winner at finish line. 2sh, Car going through washout. 5sh, Car, elephants and Mt. Kenya.

1977, Apr. 5 Litho. *Perf. 14*

76 A10 50c multicolored .20 .15
77 A10 1sh multicolored .35 .25
78 A10 2sh multicolored .70 .50
79 A10 5sh multicolored 1.60 1.25
a. Souvenir sheet of 4, #76-79 5.00 4.00
Nos. 76-79 (4) 2.85 2.15

25th Safari Rally, Apr. 7-11.

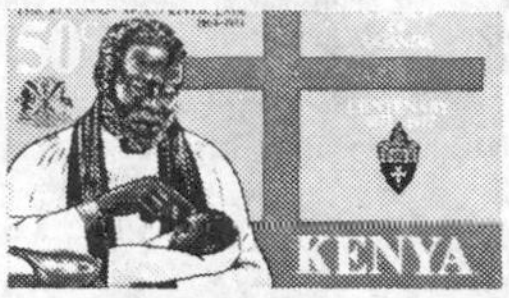

Rev. Canon Apolo Kivebulaya — A11

Designs: 1sh, Uganda Cathedral. 2sh, Early grass-topped Cathedral. 5sh, Early tent congregation, Kigezi.

1977, June 20 Litho. *Perf. 14*

80 A11 50c multicolored .15 .15
81 A11 1sh multicolored .35 .20
82 A11 2sh multicolored .65 .45
83 A11 5sh multicolored 1.50 1.10
a. Souvenir sheet of 4, #80-83 3.00 2.50
Nos. 80-83 (4) 2.65 1.90

Church of Uganda, centenary.

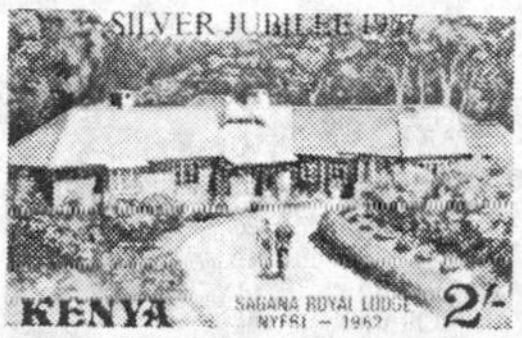

Elizabeth II and Prince Philip at Sagana Lodge — A12

Designs: 5sh, "Treetops" observation hut, Aberdare Forest, and elephants, vert. 10sh, Pres. Jomo Kenyatta, Elizabeth II, crossed spears and shield. 15sh, Elizabeth II and Pres. Kenyatta in open automobile. 50sh, Elizabeth II and Prince Philip at window in Treetops.

1977, July 20 Litho. *Perf. 14*

84 A12 2sh multicolored .40 .35
85 A12 5sh multicolored .60 .75
86 A12 10sh multicolored 2.25 1.75
87 A12 15sh multicolored 2.75 2.25
a. Souvenir sheet of 1 4.50 4.50
Nos. 84-87 (4) 6.00 5.10

Souvenir Sheet

88 A12 50sh multicolored 12.50 10.00

Reign of Queen Elizabeth II, 25th anniv.

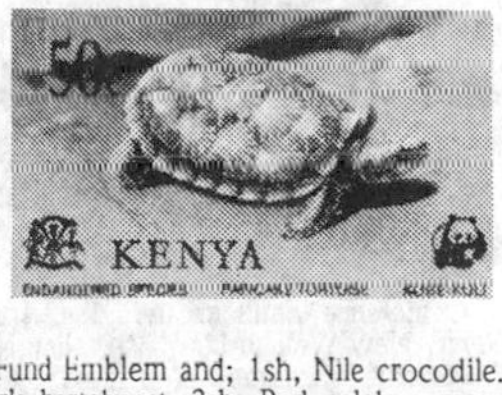

Pancake Tortoise A13

Wildlife Fund Emblem and; 1sh, Nile crocodile. 2sh, Hunter's hartebeest. 3sh, Red colobus monkey. 5sh, Dugong.

1977, Sept. 26 Litho. *Perf. 14x13½*

89 A13 50c multicolored .20 .15
90 A13 1sh multicolored .40 .25
91 A13 2sh multicolored .75 .50
92 A13 3sh multicolored 1.25 .70
93 A13 5sh multicolored 2.00 1.20
a. Souvenir sheet of 4, #90-93 4.00 3.00
Nos. 89-93 (5) 4.60 2.80

Endangered species.

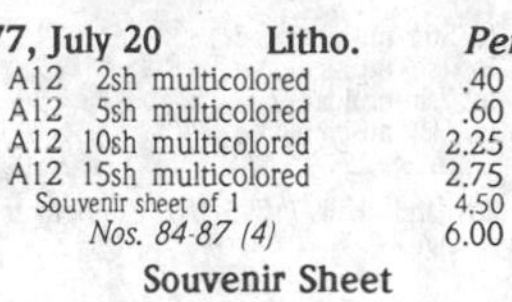

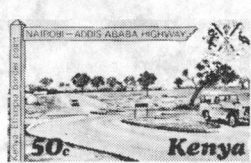

Kenya-Ethiopia Border Point — A14

Designs: 1sh, Station wagon at Archer's Post. 2sh, Thika overpass. 5sh, Marsabit Game Lodge and elephant.

1977, Nov. 10 Litho. *Perf. 14*

94 A14 50c multicolored .20 .15
95 A14 1sh multicolored .25 .20
96 A14 2sh multicolored .55 .25
97 A14 5sh multicolored 1.50 .75
a. Souvenir sheet of 4, #94-97 3.00 2.50
Nos. 94-97 (4) 2.50 1.35

Opening of Nairobi-Addis Ababa highway.

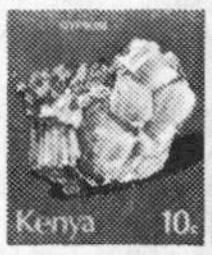

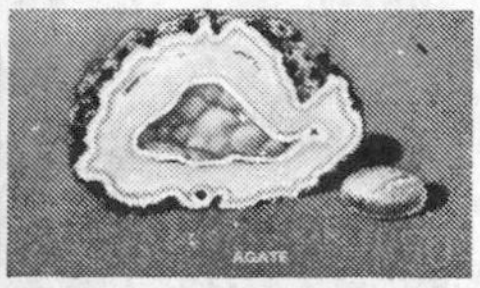

Minerals Found in Kenya
A15 A16

Perf. 14½x14, 14½ (A16)

1977, Dec. 13 Photo.

98 A15 10c Gypsum .15 .15
99 A15 20c Trona .15 .15
100 A15 30c Kyanite .15 .15
101 A15 40c Amazonite .15 .15
102 A15 50c Galena .15 .15
103 A15 70c Silicified wood .25 .15
104 A15 80c Fluorite .30 .15
105 A16 1sh Amethyst .35 .15
106 A16 1.50sh Agate .55 .20
107 A16 2sh Tourmaline .75 .30
108 A16 3sh Aquamarine 1.10 .45
109 A16 5sh Rhodolite garnet 1.90 .75
110 A16 10sh Sapphire 3.75 1.50
111 A16 20sh Ruby 7.50 3.00
112 A16 40sh Green grossular garnet 19.00 6.00
Nos. 98-112 (15) 36.20 13.40

The 10c, 20c, 40c, 50c and 80c were also issued in booklet panes of 4. The 50c was also issued in a booklet pane of 2.

For surcharge see No. 242.

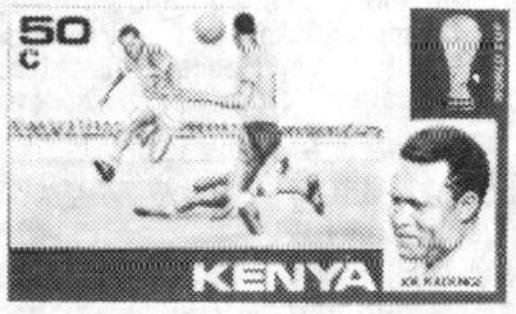

Soccer, Joe Kadenge and World Cup A17

World Cup and: 1sh, Mohammed Chuma receiving trophy, and his portrait. 2sh, Shot on goal and Omari S. Kidevu. 3sh, Backfield defense and Polly Ouma.

1978, Apr. 10 Litho. *Perf. 14x13½*

113 A17 50c green & multi .15 .15
114 A17 1sh lt brown & multi .30 .20
115 A17 2sh lilac & multi .60 .35
116 A17 3sh dk blue & multi 1.00 .55
a. Souvenir sheet of 4, #113-116 2.50 2.10
Nos. 113-116 (4) 2.05 1.25

World Soccer Cup Championships, Argentina 78, June 1-25.

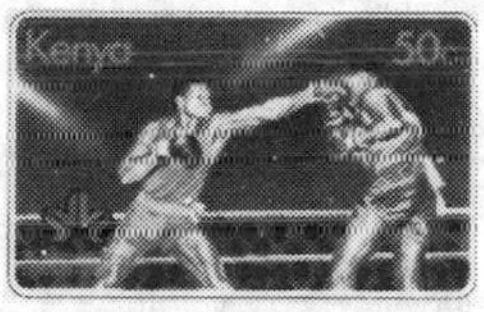

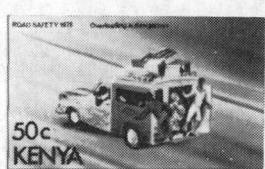

Boxing and Games' Emblem A18

Games Emblem and: 1sh, Pres. Kenyatta welcoming 1968 Olympic team. 3sh, Javelin. 5sh, Pres. Kenyatta, boxing team and trophy.

1978, July 15 Photo. *Perf. 13x14*

117 A18 50c multicolored .15 .15
118 A18 1sh multicolored .25 .15
119 A18 3sh multicolored .75 .40
120 A18 5sh multicolored 1.25 .65
Nos. 117-120 (4) 2.40 1.35

Commonwealth Games, Edmonton, Canada, Aug. 3-12.

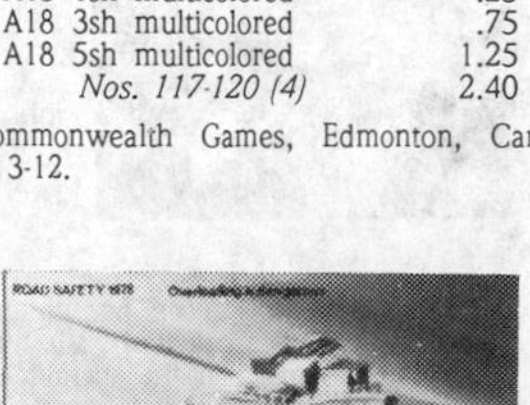

Overloaded Truck — A19

Road Safety: 1sh, Observe speed limit. 1.50sh, Observe traffic lights. 2sh, School crossing. 3sh, Passing. 5sh, Railroad crossing.

1978, Sept. 18 Litho. *Perf. 13½x14*

121 A19 50c multicolored .15 .15
122 A19 1sh multicolored .28 .16
123 A19 1.50sh multicolored .45 .25
124 A19 2sh multicolored .55 .30
125 A19 3sh multicolored .90 .50
126 A19 5sh multicolored 1.40 .75
Nos. 121-126 (6) 3.73 2.11

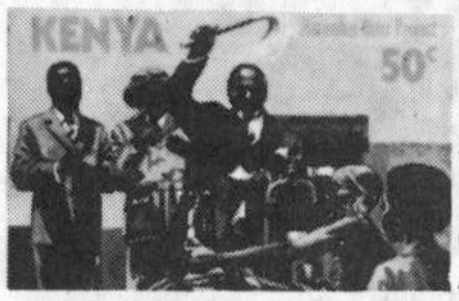

Pres. Kenyatta at Harambee Water Project Opening A20

Kenyatta Day: 1sh, Prince Philip handing over symbol of independence, 1963. 2sh, Pres. Jomo Kenyatta addressing independence rally. 3sh, Stage at 15th independence anniversary celebration. 5sh, Handcuffed Kenyatta led by soldiers, 1952.

1978, Oct. 16 Litho. *Perf. 14*

127 A20 50c multicolored .15 .15
128 A20 1sh multicolored .25 .15
129 A20 2sh multicolored .40 .30
130 A20 3sh multicolored .60 .40
131 A20 5sh multicolored .90 .75
Nos. 127-131 (5) 2.30 1.75

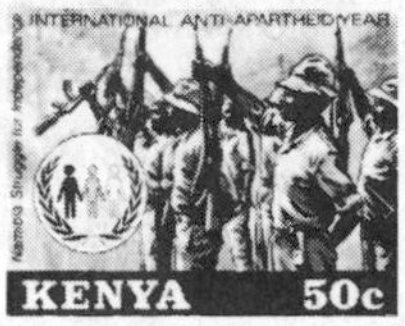

Soldiers and Emblem A21

Anti-Apartheid Emblem and: 1sh, Anti-Apartheid Conference. 2sh, Stephen Biko, South African Anti-Apartheid leader. 3sh, Nelson Mandela, jailed since 1961. 5sh, Bishop Lamont, expelled from Rhodesia in 1977.

1978, Dec. 11 Litho. *Perf. 14x14½*

132 A21 50c multicolored .15 .15
133 A21 1sh multicolored .28 .15
134 A21 2sh multicolored .45 .30
135 A21 3sh multicolored .70 .40
136 A21 5sh multicolored 1.25 .75
Nos. 132-136 (5) 2.83 1.75

Anti-Apartheid Year and Namibia's struggle for independence.

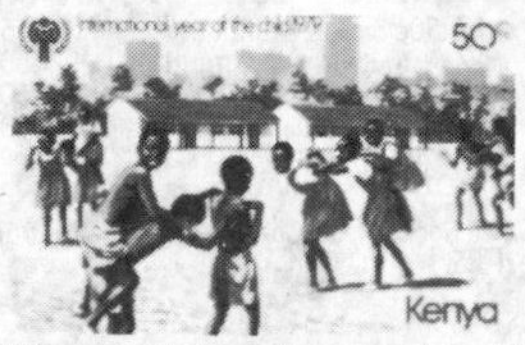

Children on School Playground — A22

Children's Year Emblem and: 2sh, Boy catching fish. 3sh, Children dancing and singing. 5sh, Children and camel caravan.

1979, Feb. 5 Litho. *Perf. 14*

137 A22 50c multicolored .15 .15
138 A22 2sh multicolored .60 .25
139 A22 3sh multicolored .85 .35
140 A22 5sh multicolored 1.50 .60
Nos. 137-140 (4) 3.10 1.35

International Year of the Child.

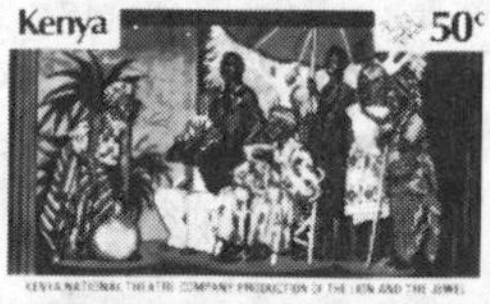

"The Lion and the Jewel" A23

National Theater: 1sh, Dancers and drummers. 2sh, Programs of various productions. 3sh, View of National Theater. 5sh, "Genesis," performed by Nairobi City Players.

1979, Apr. 6 Litho. *Perf. 13½x14*

141 A23 50c multicolored .15 .15
142 A23 1sh multicolored .20 .16
143 A23 2sh multicolored .40 .30
144 A23 3sh multicolored .60 .50
145 A23 5sh multicolored 1.00 .80
Nos. 141-145 (5) 2.35 1.91

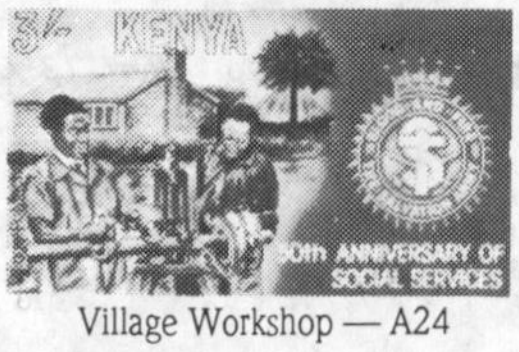

Village Workshop — A24

Salvation Army Emblem and: 50c, Blind telephone operator, vert. 1sh, Care for the aged, vert. 5sh, Vocational training (nurse).

1979, June 4 *Perf. 13½x13, 13x13½*

146 A24 50c multicolored .15 .15
147 A24 1sh multicolored .25 .15
148 A24 3sh multicolored .75 .40
149 A24 5sh multicolored 1.10 .75
Nos. 146-149 (4) 2.25 1.45

Salvation Army Social Services, 50th anniv.

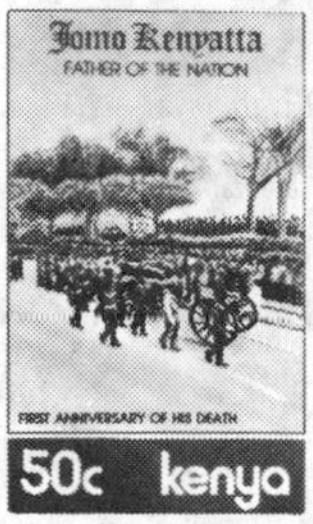

Funeral Procession — A25

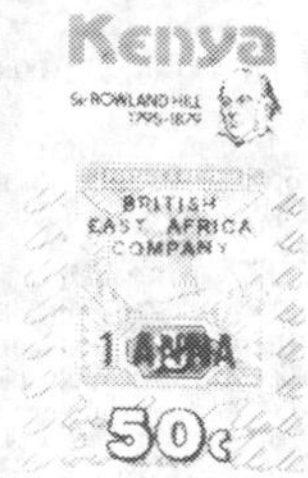

British East Africa No. 2, Hill, Signature — A26

Kenyatta: 1sh, Taking oath of office. 3sh, Addressing crowd. 5sh, As young man with wooden trying plane.

1979, Aug. 22 Litho. *Perf. 13½x14*

150 A25 50c multicolored .16 .15
151 A25 1sh multicolored .26 .16
152 A25 3sh multicolored .70 .45
153 A25 5sh multicolored 1.25 .72
Nos. 150-153 (4) 2.37 1.48

Jomo Kenyatta (1893-1978), first president of Kenya.

1979, Nov. 27 Litho. *Perf. 14*

Hill, Signature and: 1sh, Kenya, Uganda and Tanzania No. 54. 2sh, Penny Black. 5sh, Kenya No. 19.

154 A26 50c multicolored .15 .15
155 A26 1sh multicolored .25 .15
156 A26 2sh multicolored .50 .30
157 A26 5sh multicolored 1.10 .65
Nos. 154-157 (4) 2.00 1.25

Sir Rowland Hill (1795-1879), originator of penny postage.

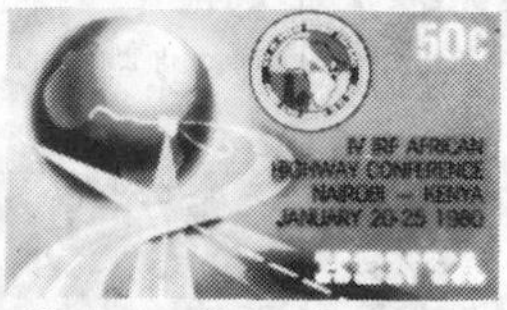

Highways, Globe, Conference Emblem — A27

Conference Emblem and: 1sh, Truck at Athi River, New Weighbridge. 3sh, New Nyali Bridge, Mombasa. 5sh, Jomo Kenyatta Airport Highway.

1980, Jan. 10 Litho. *Perf. 14*

158 A27 50c multicolored .15 .15
159 A27 1sh multicolored .25 .20
160 A27 3sh multicolored .70 .60
161 A27 5sh multicolored 1.25 1.00
Nos. 158-161 (4) 2.35 1.95

4th IRF African Highway Conference, Nairobi, Jan. 20-25.

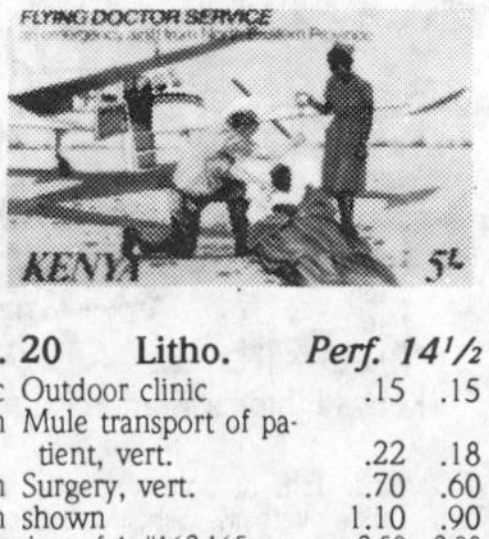

Patient Airlift A28

1980, Mar. 20 Litho. *Perf. 14½*

162 A28 50c Outdoor clinic .15 .15
163 A28 1sh Mule transport of patient, vert. .22 .18
164 A28 3sh Surgery, vert. .70 .60
165 A28 5sh shown 1.10 .90
a. Souvenir sheet of 4, #162-165 2.50 2.00
Nos. 162-165 (4) 2.17 1.83

Flying doctor service.

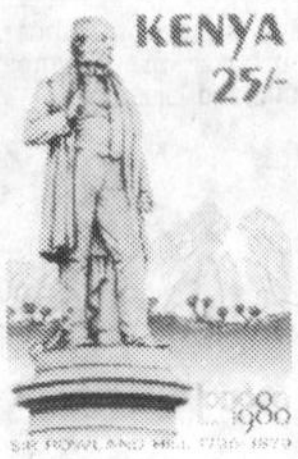

Hill Statue, Kidderminster and Mt. Kenya — A29

1980, May 6 Litho. *Perf. 14*

166 A29 25sh multicolored 5.25 4.00
a. Souvenir sheet 6.00 3.50

London 1980 International Stamp Exhibition, May 6-14.

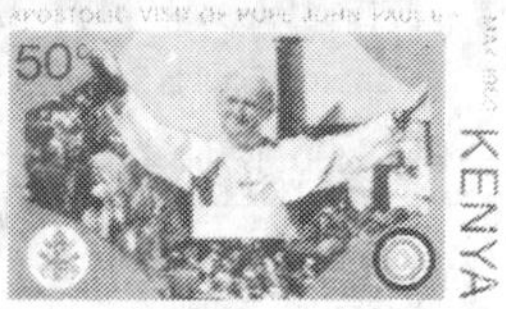

Pope John Paul II and Crowd A30

Visit of Pope John Paul II to Kenya: 1sh, Pope, Nairobi Cathedral, papal flag and arms, vert. 5sh, Pope, papal and Kenya flags, dove, vert. 10sh, Pres. Arap Moi of Kenya, Pope, flag of Kenya on map of Africa.

1980, May 8 *Perf. 13½*

167 A30 50c multicolored .15 .15
168 A30 1sh multicolored .22 .18
169 A30 5sh multicolored 1.10 .90
170 A30 10sh multicolored 2.25 1.75
Nos. 167-170 (4) 3.72 2.98

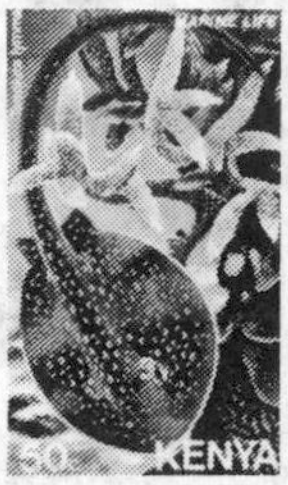

Sting Ray — A31

1980, June 27 Litho. *Perf. 14½*

171 A31 50c shown .15 .15
172 A31 2sh Alkit snapper .48 .40
173 A31 3sh Sea slug .75 .60
174 A31 5sh Hawksbill turtle 1.25 1.00
Nos. 171-174 (4) 2.63 2.15

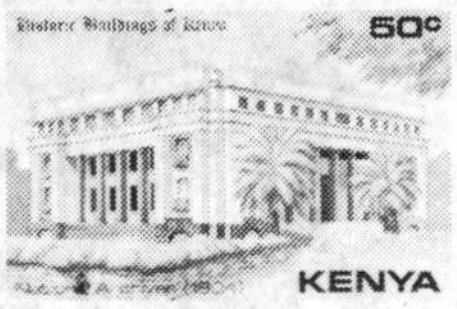

National Archives, 1904 A32

1980, Oct. 9 Litho. *Perf. 14*

175 A32 50c shown .15 .15
176 A32 1sh Commissioner's Office, Nairobi, 1913 .22 .18
177 A32 1.50sh Nairobi House, 1913 .35 .25
178 A32 2sh Norfolk Hotel, 1904 .45 .38
179 A32 3sh McMillan Library, 1929 .70 .60
180 A32 5sh Kipande House, 1913 1.10 1.00
Nos. 175-180 (6) 2.97 2.56

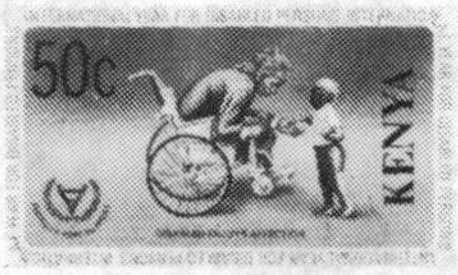

Woman in Wheelchair and Child A33

1981, Feb. 10 Litho. *Perf. 14x13½*

181 A33 50c shown .15 .15
182 A33 1sh Pres. Arap Moi, team captain .22 .18
183 A33 3sh Blind mountain climbers, Mt. Kenya, 1965 .70 .60
184 A33 5sh Disabled artist 1.10 .90
Nos. 181-184 (4) 2.17 1.83

International Year of the Disabled.

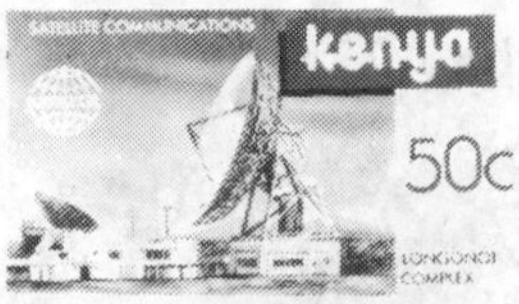

Longonot Earth Station Complex — A34

1981, Apr. 4 Litho. *Perf. 14x14½*

185 A34 50c shown .15 .15
186 A34 2sh Intelsat V .45 .35
187 A34 3sh Longonot I .75 .50
188 A34 5sh Longonot II 1.10 .90
Nos. 185-188 (4) 2.45 1.90

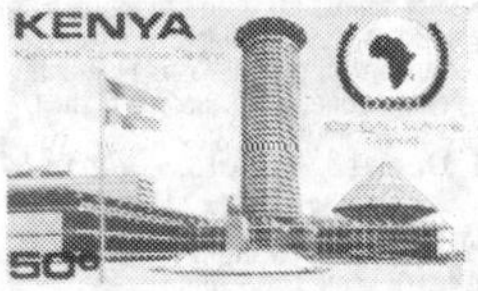

Conference Center, OAU Flag — A35

18th Organization for African Unity Conference, Nairobi: 1sh, Map of Africa showing Panaftel earth stations. 3sh, Parliament Building, Nairobi. 5sh, Jomo Kenyatta Intl. Airport. 10sh, OAU flag.

1981, June 24 Wmk. 373 *Perf. 13½*

189 A35 50c multicolored .15 .15
190 A35 1sh multicolored .20 .16
191 A35 3sh multicolored .60 .50
192 A35 5sh multicolored 1.00 .80
193 A35 10sh multicolored 2.00 1.75
a. Souvenir sheet of 1, perf. 14½ 2.25 2.00
Nos. 189-193 (5) 3.95 3.36

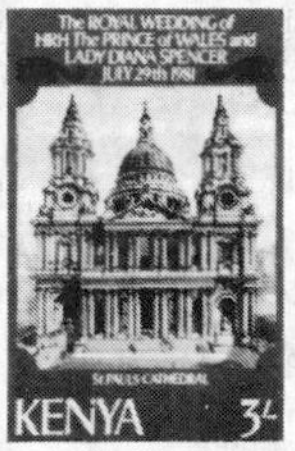

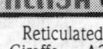

St. Paul's Cathedral — A36

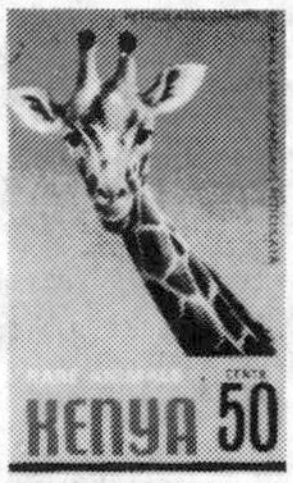

Reticulated Giraffe — A37

1981, July 29 Litho. *Perf. 14*

194 A36 50c Charles, Pres. Arap Moi .15 .15
195 A36 3sh shown .60 .50
196 A36 5sh Britannia 1.00 .80
197 A36 10sh Charles 2.00 1.75
Nos. 194-197 (4) 3.75 3.20

Souvenir Sheet

198 A36 25sh Couple 6.00 5.50

Royal Wedding.

1981, Aug. 31 Litho. *Perf. 14½*

199 A37 50c shown .15 .15
200 A37 2sh Bongo .45 .35
201 A37 5sh Roan antelope 1.10 .90
202 A37 10sh Mangabey 2.25 1.75
Nos. 199-202 (4) 3.95 3.15

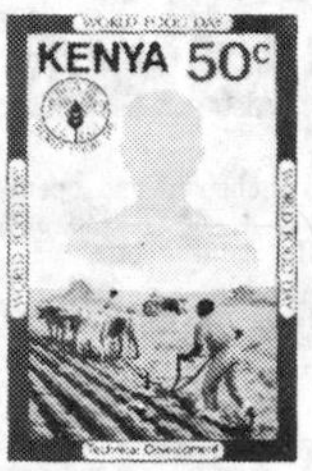

World Food Day — A38

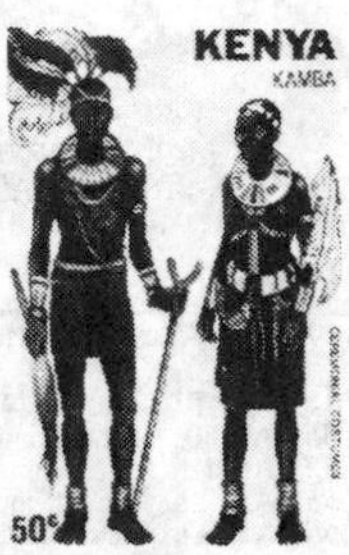

Ceremonial Tribal Costumes — A39

1981, Oct. 16 Litho. *Perf. 14*

203 A38 50c Plowing .15 .15
204 A38 1sh Rice field .20 .18
205 A38 2sh Irrigation .40 .35
206 A38 5sh Cattle 1.00 .80
Nos. 203-206 (4) 1.75 1.48

Perf. 14½x13½

1981, Dec. 18 Litho.

207 A39 50c Kamba .15 .15
208 A39 1sh Turkana .25 .20
209 A39 2sh Giriama .48 .40

210 A39 3sh Masai .70 .60
211 A39 5sh Luo 1.25 1.00
Nos. 207-211 (5) 2.83 2.35

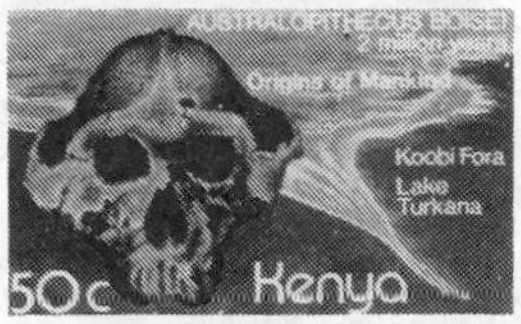

Australopithecus Boisei — A40

1982, Jan. 16 Litho. *Perf. 14*

212 A40 50c shown .18 .15
213 A40 2sh Homo erectus .65 .40
214 A40 3sh Homo habilis 1.00 .60
215 A40 5sh Proconsul africanus 1.65 .90
Nos. 212-215 (4) 3.48 2.05

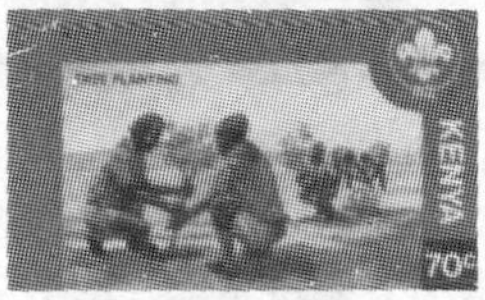

Scouting Year A41

1982, June 2 Litho. *Perf. 14½*

216 A41 70c Tree planting .15 .15
217 A41 70c Paying homage .15 .15
218 A41 3.50sh Be Prepared .60 .50
219 A41 3.50sh Intl. friendship .60 .50
220 A41 5sh Helping disabled .90 .75
221 A41 5sh Community service .90 .75
222 A41 6.50sh Paxtu Cottage 1.10 .90
223 A41 6.50sh Lady Baden-Powell 1.10 .90
Nos. 216-223 (8) 5.50 4.60

Souvenir Sheet

224 Sheet of 4 3.00 2.25
a. A41 70c like #216 .15 .15
b. A41 3.50sh like #218 .60 .45
c. A41 5sh like #220 .90 .70
d. A41 6.50sh like #222 1.25 .85

Stamps of same denomination se-tenant.

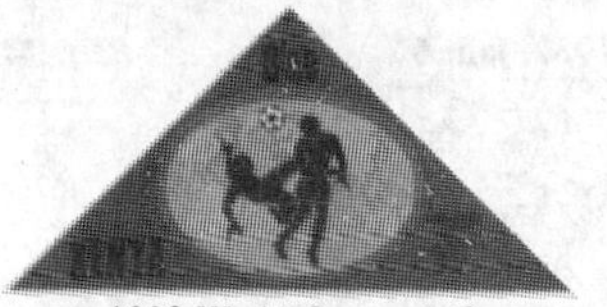

1982 World Cup — A42

Designs: Various soccer players on world map.

1982, July 5 Litho. *Perf. 12½*

225 A42 70c multicolored .15 .15
226 A42 3.50sh multicolored .65 .60
227 A42 5sh multicolored 1.00 .80
228 A42 10sh multicolored 2.00 1.75
Nos. 225-228 (4) 3.80 3.30

Souvenir Sheet

Perf. 13½x14

229 A42 20sh multicolored 4.00 3.50

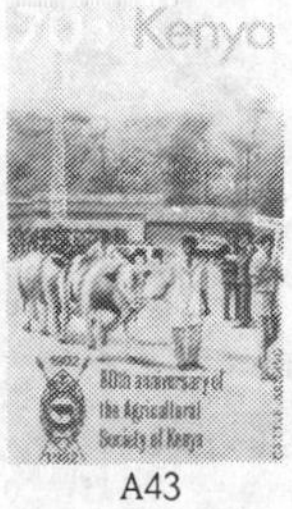

A43

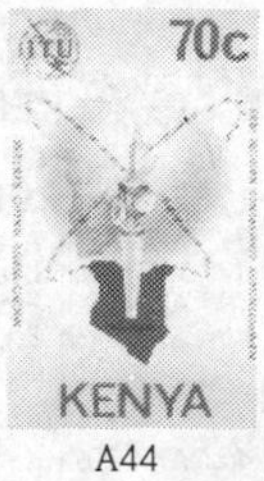

A44

1982, Sept. 28 Litho. *Perf. 14½*

230 A43 70c Cattle judging .15 .15
231 A43 2.50sh Farm machinery .50 .40
232 A43 3.50sh Musical ride .65 .60
233 A43 6.50sh Emblem 1.40 1.25
Nos. 230-233 (4) 2.70 2.40

Agricultural Society, 80th anniv.

1982, Oct. 27 Photo. *Perf. 11½*

Granite Paper

234 A44 70c Microwave radio system .15 .15
235 A44 3.50sh Ship-to-shore communication .60 .50
236 A44 5sh Rural telecommunication .90 .75
237 A44 6.50sh Emblem 1.25 1.00
Nos. 234-237 (4) 2.90 2.40

ITU Plenipotentiaries Conf., Nairobi, Sept.

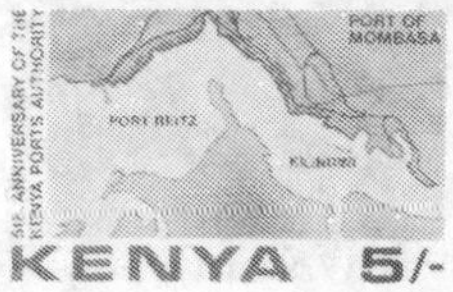

5th Anniv. of Kenya Ports Authority A45

1983, Jan. 20 Litho. *Perf. 14*

238 A45 70c Container cranes .18 .15
239 A45 2sh Cranes, diff. .45 .38
240 A45 3.50sh Cranes, diff. .75 .70
241 A45 5sh Mombasa Harbor map 1.10 .90
a. Souvenir sheet of 4, #238-241 3.50 3.00
Nos. 238-241 (4) 2.48 2.13

No. 104 Surcharged

1983, Jan. Photo. *Perf. 14½x14*

242 A15 70c on 80c multicolored .16 .15

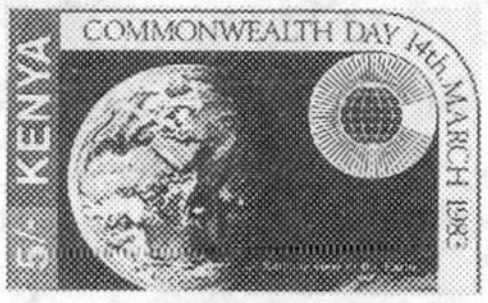

A45a

1983, Mar. 14 Litho. *Perf. 14½*

243 A45a 70c Coffee picking, vert. .15 .15
244 A45a 2sh Pres. Arap Moi, vert. .35 .30
245 A45a 5sh Globe .80 .65
246 A45a 10sh Masai dance 1.60 1.40
Nos. 243-246 (4) 2.90 2.50

Commonwealth Day.

Dichrostachys Cinerea — A46

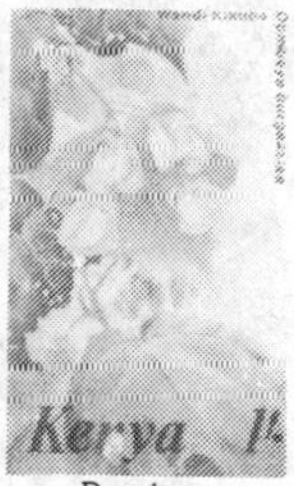

Dombeya Burgessiae — A47

Perf. 14½x14, 14x14½

1983, Feb. 15 Photo.

247 A46 10c shown .15 .15
248 A46 20c Rhamphicarpa montana .15 .15
249 A46 30c Barleria eranthemoides .15 .15
250 A46 40c Commelina .15 .15
251 A46 50c Canarina abyssinica .15 .15
252 A46 70c Aspilia mossambicensis .10 .13
253 A47 1sh Dombeya burgessiae .22 .18
254 A47 1.50sh Lantana trifolia .35 .28
255 A47 2sh Adenium obesum .45 .38
256 A47 2.50sh Terminalia orbicularis .60 .50
257 A47 3.50sh Ceropegia ballyana .75 .70
258 A47 5sh Ruttya fruticosa 1.10 .90
259 A47 10sh Pentanisia ouranogyne 1.75 1.50
260 A47 20sh Brillantaisia nyanzarum 3.00 2.75
261 A47 40sh Crotalaria axillaris 6.00 4.50
Nos. 247-261 (15) 15.15 12.59

See Nos. 350-354.

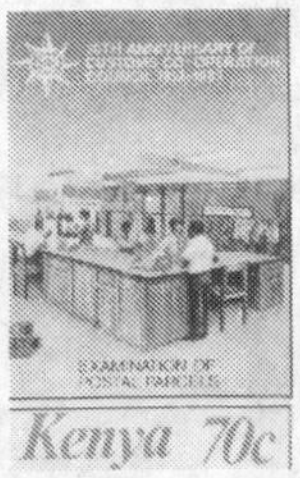

30th Anniv. of Customs Cooperation Council — A48

1983, May 11 Litho. *Perf. 14½*

262 A48 70c Parcel check .15 .15
263 A48 2.50sh Headquarters, Mombasa .50 .40
264 A48 3.50sh Headquarters, Brussels .65 .60
265 A48 10sh Patrol boat 2.00 1.75
Nos. 262-265 (4) 3.30 2.90

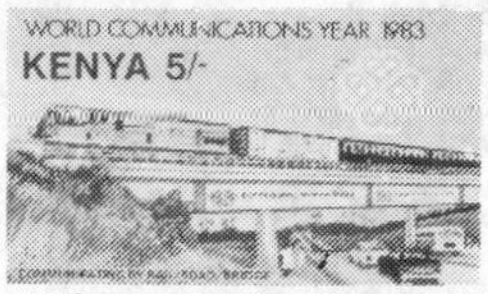

World Communications Year — A49

1983, July 4 Litho. *Perf. 14½*

266 A49 70c Satellite, dish antenna, vert. .15 .15
267 A49 2.50sh Mailbox, birthday card, telephone, vert. .50 .40
268 A49 3.50sh Jet, ship .65 .60
269 A49 5sh Railroad bridge, highway 1.00 .80
Nos. 266-269 (4) 2.30 1.95

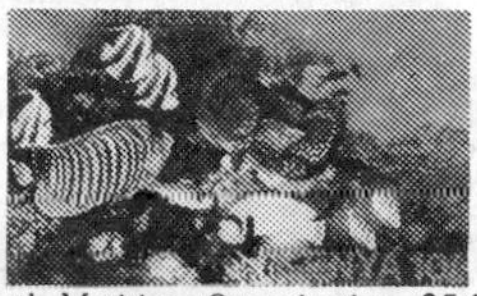

Intl. Maritime Organization, 25th Anniv. — A50

1983, Sept. 22 Litho. *Perf. 14½*

270 A50 70c Kilindini Harbor .15 .15
271 A50 2.50sh Life preserver .38 .30
272 A50 3.50sh Mombasa Container Terminal .52 .40
273 A50 10sh Marine Park 1.50 1.25
Nos. 270-273 (4) 2.55 2.10

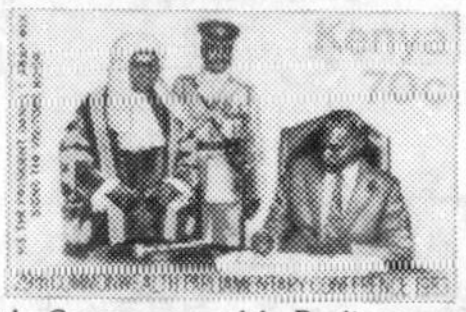

29th Commonwealth Parliamentary Conference — A51

1983, Oct. 31 Litho. *Perf. 14*

274 A51 70c shown .15 .15
275 A51 2.50sh Parliament Bldg., vert. .38 .30
276 A51 5sh State Opening, vert. .75 .60
a. Souv. sheet of 3, #274-276 + label 1.50 1.25
Nos. 274-276 (3) 1.28 1.05

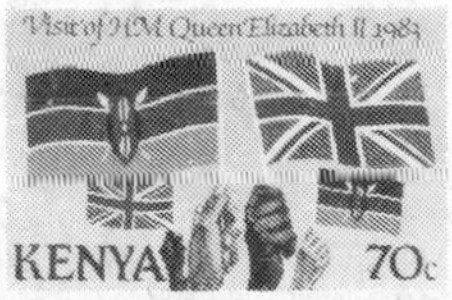

Royal Visit — A52

1983, Nov. 10 Litho. *Perf. 14*

277 A52 70c Flags .15 .15
278 A52 3.50sh Sagana State Lodge .65 .50
279 A52 5sh Tree Tops Hotel .90 .75
280 A52 10sh Elizabeth II and Daniel Arap Moi 1.75 1.50
Nos. 277-280 (4) 3.45 2.90

Souvenir Sheet

281 A52 25sh multicolored 3.75 3.00

No. 281 contains Nos. 277-280 without denominations showing simulated perforations.

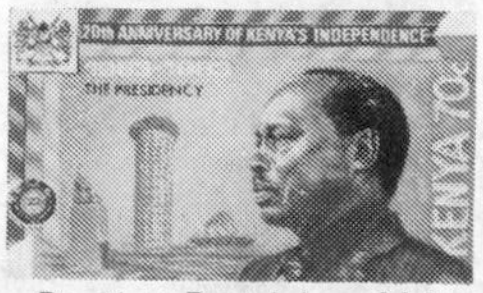

President Daniel Arap Moi, Monument — A53

1983, Dec. 9 Litho. *Perf. 14½*

282 A53 70c shown .15 .15
283 A53 2sh Tree planting .30 .24
284 A53 3.50sh Map, flag, emblem .52 .40
285 A53 5sh School, milk program .75 .60
286 A53 10sh People, flag, banner 1.50 1.20
Nos. 282-286 (5) 3.22 2.59

Souvenir Sheet

Imperf

287 A53 25sh multicolored 3.75 3.00

Independence, 20th Anniv. No. 287 contains Nos. 282-286 without denominations.

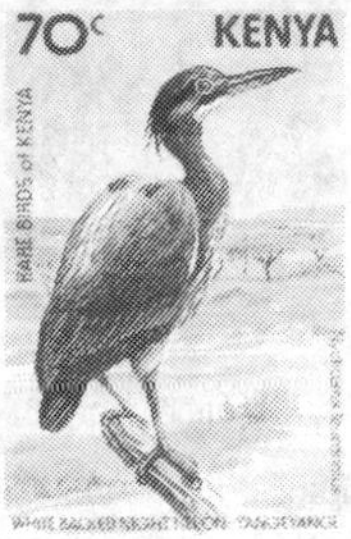

Rare Local Birds — A54

1984, Feb. 6 Litho. *Perf. 14½x13½*

288 A54 70c White-backed night heron .15 .15
289 A54 2.50sh Quail plover .45 .30
290 A54 3.50sh Heller's ground thrush .60 .40
291 A54 5sh Papyrus gonolek .90 .60
292 A54 10sh White-winged Apalis 1.75 1.20
Nos. 288-292 (5) 3.85 2.65

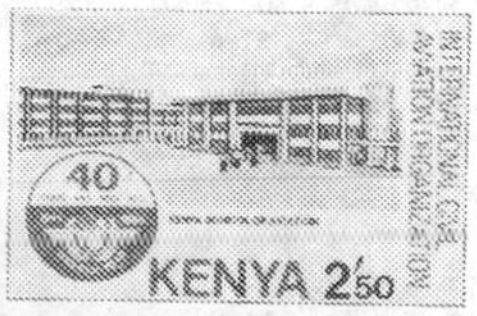

Intl. Civil Aviation Org., 40th Anniv. A55

1984, Apr. 2 Litho. *Perf. 14*

293 A55 70c Radar, vert. .15 .15
294 A55 2.50sh Kenya School of Aviation .38 .30
295 A55 3.50sh Jet, Moi Intl. Airport .52 .40
296 A55 5sh Air traffic control center .75 .60
Nos. 293-296 (4) 1.80 1.45

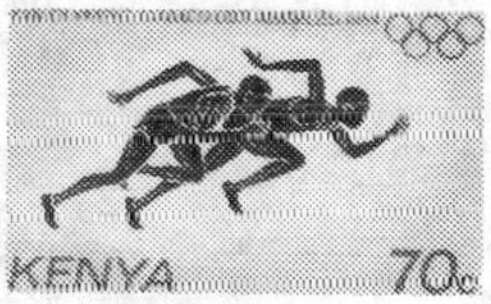

1984 Summer Olympics A56

1984, May 21 *Perf. 14½*

297 A56 70c Running .15 .15
298 A56 2.50sh Hurdles .42 .30
299 A56 5sh Boxing .80 .60
300 A56 10sh Field Hockey 1.65 1.20
Nos. 297-300 (4) 3.02 2.25

Souvenir Sheet

Imperf

301 A56 25sh Torch bearers 3.50 3.50

No. 301 contains designs of Nos. 297-300.

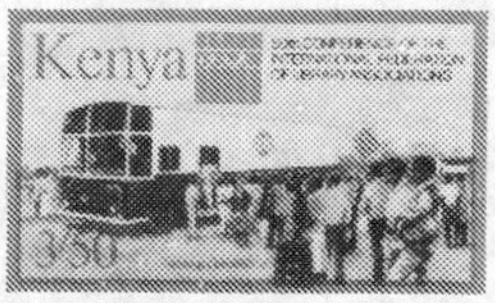

Bookmobile — A57

1984, Aug. 10 Litho. *Perf. 14½*

302 A57 70c Emblem .15 .15
303 A57 3.50sh shown .52 .40
304 A57 5sh Adult library .75 .60
305 A57 10sh Children's library 1.50 1.20
Nos. 302-305 (4) 2.92 2.35

Intl. Fed. of Library Associations, 50th Conf.

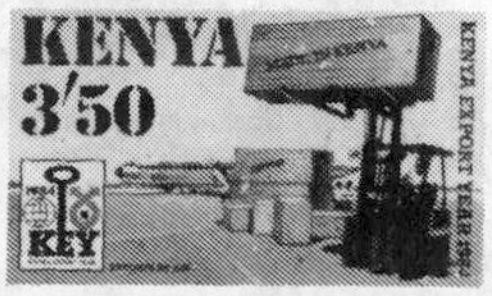

Kenya Export Year (KEY) A58

1984, Oct. 1 Litho. *Perf. 14*

306	A58	70c	Emblem, vert.	.15	.15
307	A58	3.50sh	Airport	.52	.40
308	A58	5sh	Harbor, vert.	.75	.60
309	A58	10sh	Exports	1.50	1.25
			Nos. 306-309 (4)	2.92	2.40

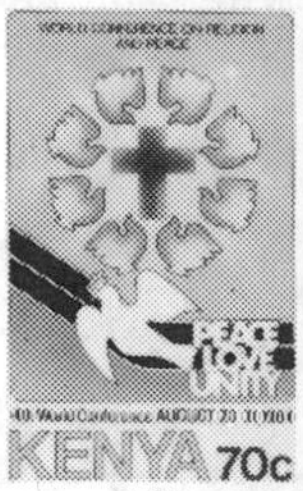

A59

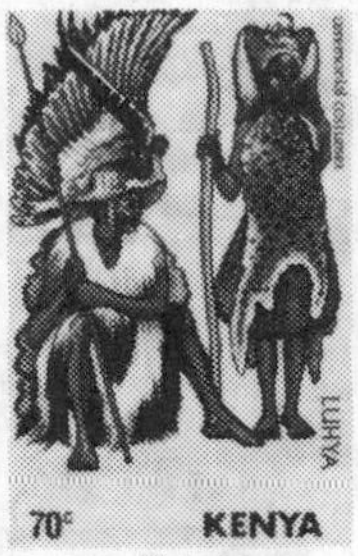

Tribal Costumes — A60

1984, Aug. 23 Litho. *Perf. 14x14½*

310	A59	70c	Doves, cross	.15	.15
311	A59	2.50sh	Doves, Hinduism symbol	.50	.40
312	A59	3.50sh	Doves, Sikhism symbol	.65	.50
313	A59	6.50sh	Doves, Islam symbol	1.40	1.10
			Nos. 310-313 (4)	2.70	2.15

World Conference on Religion and Peace, Nairobi, Aug. 23-31, 1984.

1984, Nov. 5 Litho. *Perf. 14½x13½*

314	A60	70c	Luhya	.15	.15
315	A60	2sh	Kikuyu	.25	.20
316	A60	3.50sh	Pokomo	.45	.35
317	A60	5sh	Nandi	.65	.50
318	A60	10sh	Rendile	1.25	1.10
			Nos. 314-318 (5)	2.75	2.30

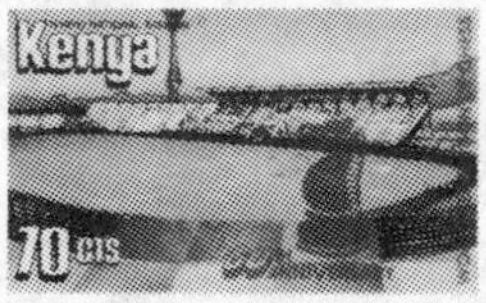

60th Anniv., World Chess Federation — A61

1984, Dec. 21 Litho. *Perf. 14½*

319	A61	70c	Nyayo Stadium, knight	.15	.15
320	A61	2.50sh	Fort Jesus, rook	.35	.28
321	A61	3.50sh	National Monument, bishop	.52	.40
322	A61	5sh	Parliament, queen	.70	.52
323	A61	10sh	Nyayo Fountain, king	1.40	1.00
			Nos. 319-323 (5)	3.12	2.35

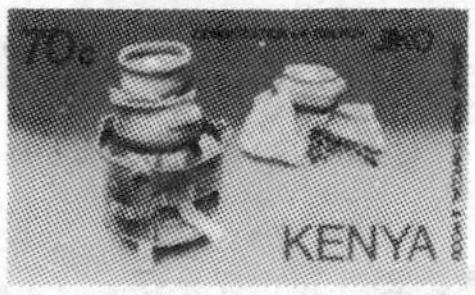

Energy Conservation — A62

1985, Jan. 22 Litho. *Perf. 13½*

324	A62	70c	Stove, fire pit	.15	.15
325	A62	2sh	Solar panel	.30	.24
326	A62	3.50sh	Biogas tank	.52	.40
327	A62	10sh	Plowing field	1.40	1.00

Imperf

328	A62	20sh	Energy conservation	2.75	2.00
			Nos. 324-328 (5)	5.12	3.79

No. 328 contains Nos. 324-327 without denominations.

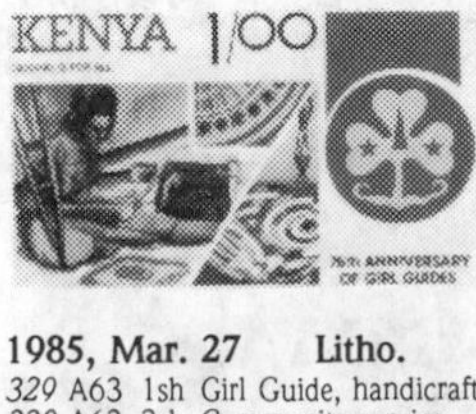

Girl Guides, 75th Anniv. A63

1985, Mar. 27 Litho. *Perf. 13½*

329	A63	1sh	Girl Guide, handicrafts	.15	.15
330	A63	3sh	Community service	.40	.30
331	A63	5sh	Lady Baden-Powell, Kenyan leader	.65	.50
332	A63	7sh	Food project	.90	.68
			Nos. 329-332 (4)	2.10	1.63

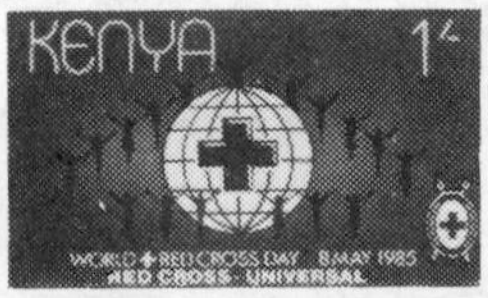

Intl. Red Cross Day A64

1985, May 8 *Perf. 14½*

333	A64	1sh	Emblem	.15	.15
334	A64	4sh	First Aid	.55	.45
335	A64	5sh	Blood donation	.70	.60
336	A64	7sh	Famine relief, cornucopia	1.00	.75
			Nos. 333-336 (4)	2.40	1.95

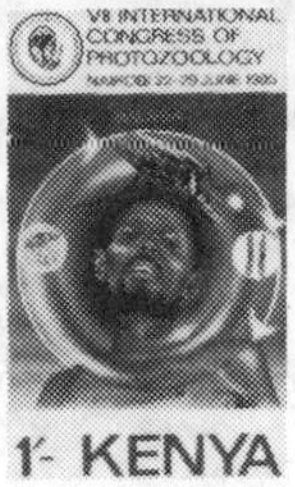

A65

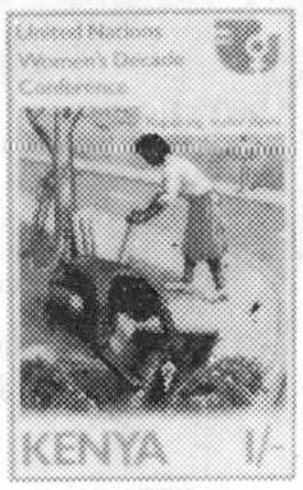

A66

Diseases caused by microorganisms carried by insects.

1985, June 25

337	A65	1sh	Malaria	.15	.15
338	A65	3sh	Leishmaniasis	.45	.32
339	A65	5sh	Trypanosomiasis	.70	.55
340	A65	7sh	Babesiosis	1.00	.75
			Nos. 337-340 (4)	2.30	1.77

7th Intl. Congress on Protozoology, Nairobi, June 22-29.

1985, July 15

341	A66	1sh	Repairing water pipes	.15	.15
342	A66	3sh	Traditional food processing	.40	.30
343	A66	5sh	Basket weaving	.65	.50
344	A66	7sh	Dress making	.90	.68
			Nos. 341-344 (4)	2.10	1.63

UN Decade for Women.

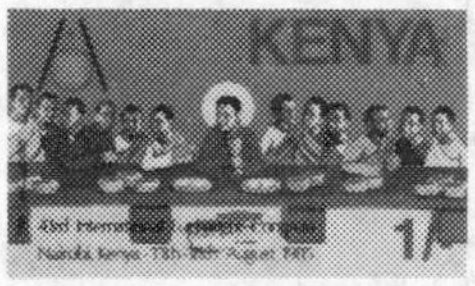

43rd Intl. Eucharistic Congress, Nairobi, Aug. 11-18 A67

1985, Aug. 15 *Perf. 13½*

345	A67	1sh	The Last Supper	.15	.15
346	A67	3sh	Afro-Christian family	.40	.30
347	A67	5sh	Congress altar, Uhuru Park	.65	.50
348	A67	7sh	St. Peter Claver's Church	.90	.68
			Nos. 345-348 (4)	2.10	1.63

Souvenir Sheet

349	A67	25sh	Pope John Paul II	3.25	2.50

Flower Types of 1983

1985 Photo. *Perf. 14½x14, 14½*

350	A46	80c	like #250	.15	.15
351	A46	1sh	Dombeya burgessiae	.15	.15
352	A47	3sh	Calotropis procera	.38	.28
353	A47	4sh	Momordica foetida	.50	.38
354	A47	7sh	Oncoba spinosa	.85	.65
			Nos. 350-354 (5)	2.03	1.61

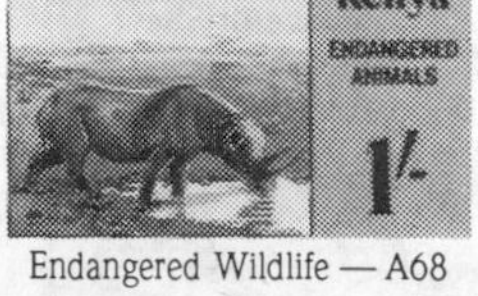

Endangered Wildlife — A68

1985, Dec. 10 Litho. *Perf. 14½*

355	A68	1sh	Diceros bicornis	.20	.18
356	A68	3sh	Acinonyx jubatus	.60	.50
357	A68	5sh	Cercopithecus neglectus	1.10	.75
358	A68	10sh	Equus greyvi	2.25	1.50

Size: 130x122mm

Imperf

359	A68	25sh	Hunter pursuing game	3.00	2.25
			Nos. 355-359 (5)	7.15	5.18

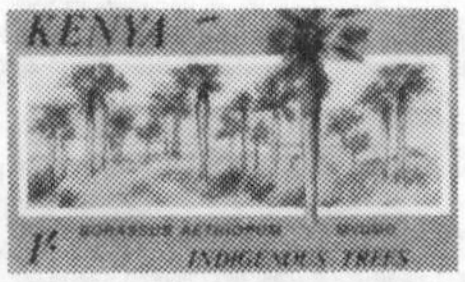

Trees A69

1986, Jan. 24 *Perf. 14½*

360	A69	1sh	Borassus aethiopum	.15	.15
361	A69	3sh	Acacia xanthophloea	.45	.32
362	A69	5sh	Ficus natalensis	.75	.55
363	A69	7sh	Spathodea nilotica	1.00	.75

Size: 117x97mm

Imperf

364	A69	25sh	Glade	3.50	2.75
			Nos. 360-364 (5)	5.85	4.52

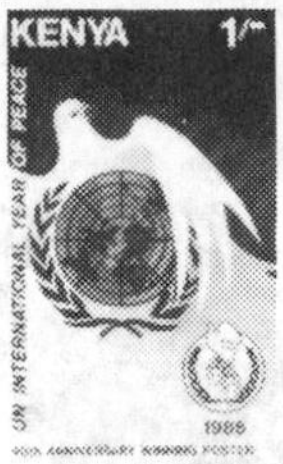

Intl. Peace Year — A70

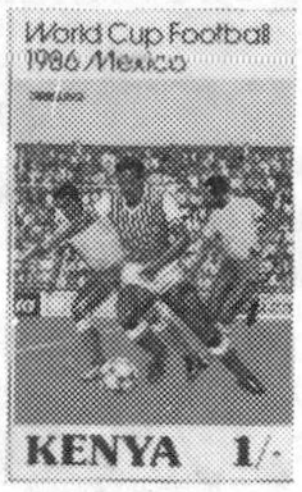

1986 World Cup Soccer Championships, Mexico — A71

1986, Apr. 17 *Perf. 14½*

365	A70	1sh	Dove, UN emblem	.15	.15
366	A70	3sh	UN General Assembly, horiz.	.45	.35
367	A70	7sh	Mushroom cloud	1.00	.75
368	A70	10sh	Isaiah 2:4, horiz.	1.50	1.10
			Nos. 365-368 (4)	3.10	2.35

1986, May 9

369	A71	1sh	Dribbling	.15	.15
370	A71	3sh	Penalty shot	.42	.32
371	A71	5sh	Tackling	.75	.52
372	A71	7sh	Champions	1.00	.70
373	A71	10sh	Heading the ball	1.50	1.25

Size: 110x86mm

Imperf

374	A71	30sh	Harambee Stars	4.25	3.25
			Nos. 369-374 (6)	8.07	6.19

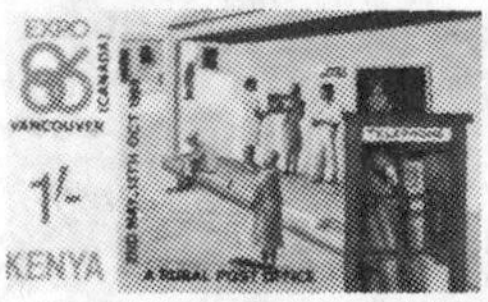

EXPO '86, Vancouver — A72

1986, June 11 *Perf. 13½x13*

375	A72	1sh	Rural post office	.15	.15
376	A72	3sh	Container depot, Embakasi	.45	.32
377	A72	5sh	Plane landing	.75	.50
378	A72	7sh	Shipping exports	1.00	.75
379	A72	10sh	Goods transport	1.40	1.10
			Nos. 375-379 (5)	3.75	2.82

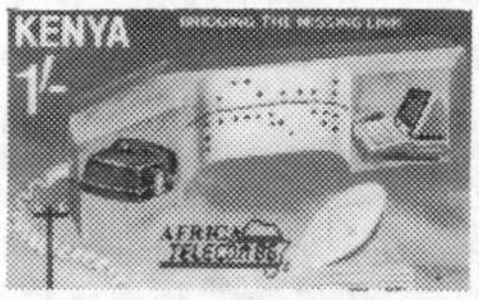

TELECOM '86, Nairobi, Sept. 16-23 — A73

1986, Sept. 16 Litho. *Perf. 14½*

380	A73	1sh	Telephone-computer links	.15	.15
381	A73	3sh	Telephones, 1876-1986	.38	.28
382	A73	5sh	Satellite communications	.62	.45
383	A73	7sh	Switchboards	.85	.65
			Nos. 380-383 (4)	2.00	1.53

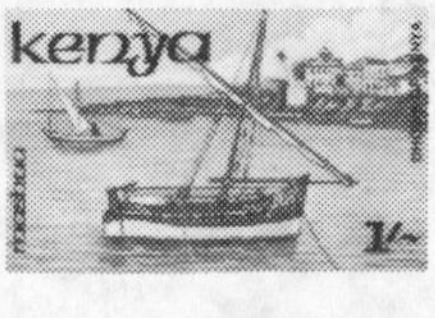

A74

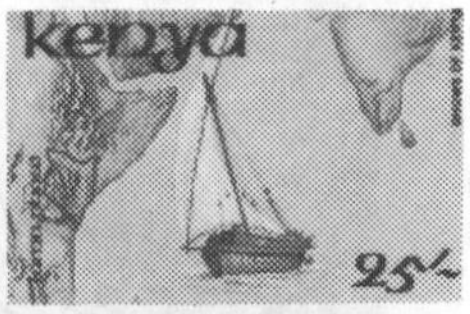

Dhows (Ships) A75

1986, Oct. 30 Litho. *Perf. 14½*

384	A74	1sh	Mashua	.15	.15
385	A74	3sh	Mtepe	.40	.26
386	A74	5sh	Dau La Mwao	.65	.50
387	A74	10sh	Jahazi	1.40	1.00
			Nos. 384-387 (4)	2.60	1.91

Souvenir Sheet

388	A75	25sh	Lamu, map	3.25	2.50

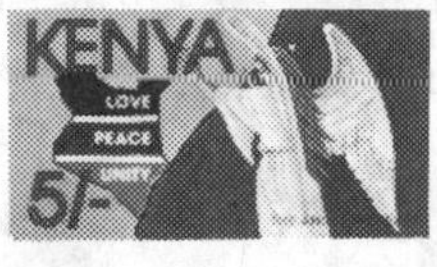

Christmas A76

1986, Dec. 5 *Perf. 12*

389	A76	1sh	Nativity, vert.	.15	.15
390	A76	3sh	Shepherd boy, vert.	.38	.28
391	A76	5sh	Angel, map	.62	.45
392	A76	7sh	Magi	.88	.65
			Nos. 389-392 (4)	2.03	1.53

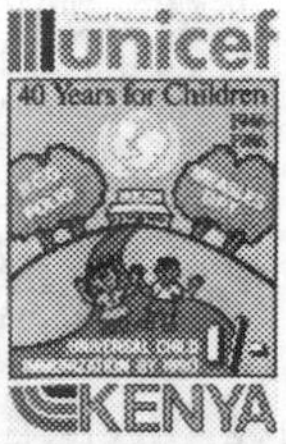

UNICEF, 40th Anniv. — A77

Child Survival Campaign: 1sh, Universal immunization by 1990. 3sh, Food and nutrition. 4sh, Oral rehydration. 5sh, Family planning. 10sh, Literacy of women.

1987, Jan. 6 Litho. *Perf. 14½*

393	A77	1sh	multicolored	.15	.15
394	A77	3sh	multicolored	.38	.28
395	A77	4sh	multicolored	.50	.38
396	A77	5sh	multicolored	.62	.45
397	A77	10sh	multicolored	1.25	.95
			Nos. 393-397 (5)	2.90	2.21

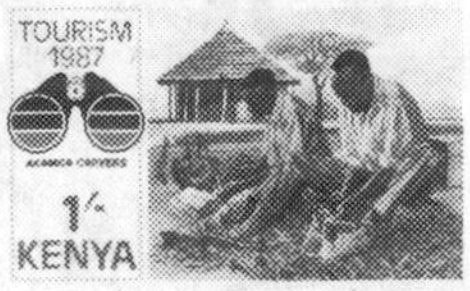

A78

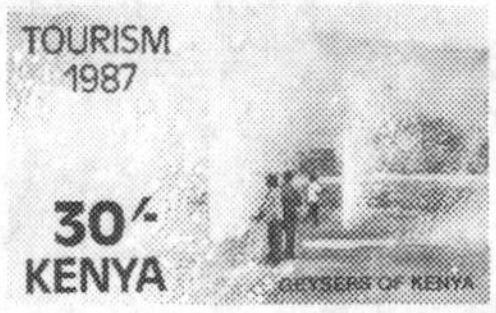

Tourism A79

1987, Mar. 25 Litho. *Perf. 14½*

398	A78	1sh	Akamba carvers	.15	.15
399	A78	3sh	Beach	.38	.28
400	A78	5sh	Escarpment	.65	.45
401	A78	7sh	Pride of lions	.90	.65
			Nos. 398-401 (4)	2.08	1.53

Souvenir Sheet

402	A79	30sh	Kenya geysers	3.75	3.00

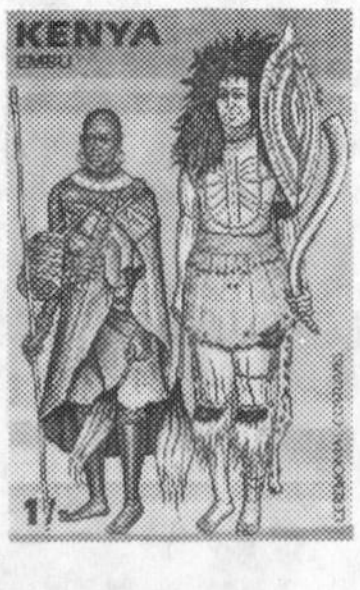

Ceremonial Costumes — A80

1987, May 20 *Perf. 14½x13½*

403 A80 1sh Embu .15 .15
404 A80 3sh Kisii .40 .32
405 A80 5sh Samburu .70 .56
406 A80 7sh Taita 1.00 .80
407 A80 10sh Boran 1.40 1.10
Nos. 403-407 (5) 3.65 2.93

See Nos. 505-509.

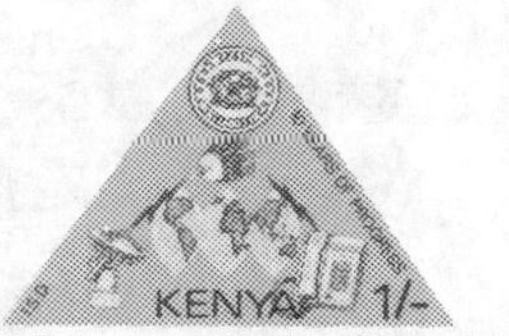

Posts & Telecommunications Corp., 10th Anniv. — A81

1987, July 1 **Litho.** *Perf. 13½*

408 A81 1sh Telecommunications satellite .15 .15
409 A81 3sh Rural post office, Kajiado .35 .28
410 A81 4sh Athletics .48 .36
411 A81 5sh Rural communication .60 .45
412 A81 7sh Speedpost .85 .65
Nos. 408-412 (5) 2.43 1.89

Souvenir Sheet

413 A81 25sh Natl. Flag 3.25 2.50

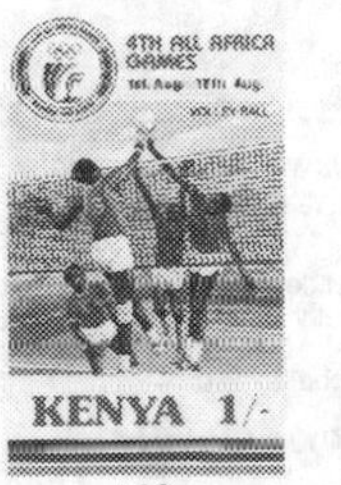

A82

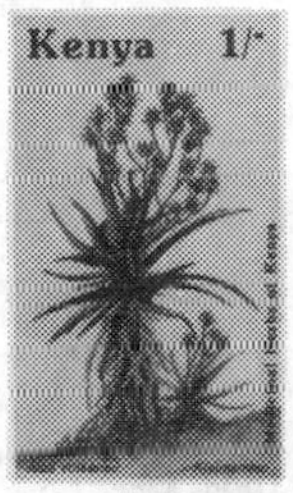

A83

1987, Aug. 5 *Perf. 14½x14*

414 A82 1sh Volleyball .15 .15
415 A82 3sh Cycling .35 .28
416 A82 4sh Boxing .48 .36
417 A82 5sh Swimming .60 .45
418 A82 7sh Steeple chase .85 .65
Nos. 414-418 (5) 2.43 1.89

Souvenir Sheet

Perf. 14x14½

419 A82 30sh Kasarani Sports Complex 3.50 2.75

4th All Africa Games, Nairobi, Aug. 1-12. Nos. 414-418, vert.

1987, Oct. 27 **Litho.** *Perf. 13½x14*

Medicinal herbs.

420 A83 1sh Aloe volkensii .15 .15
421 A83 3sh Cassia didymobotrya .35 .28
422 A83 5sh Erythrina abyssinica .60 .45
423 A83 7sh Adenium obesum .85 .65
424 A83 10sh Herbalist's clinic 1.15 .88
Nos. 420-424 (5) 3.10 2.41

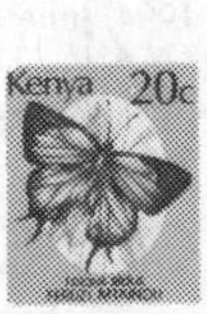

Butterflies — A84

1988-90 **Photo.** *Perf. 15x14*

424A A84 10c Cyrestis camillus .15 .15
425 A84 20c Iolaus sidus .15 .15
426 A84 40c Vanessa cardui .15 .15
427 A84 50c Colotis euippe omphale .15 .15
428 A84 70c Precis westermanni .15 .15
429 A84 80c Colias electo .15 .15
430 A84 1sh Eronia leda .15 .15
430A A84 1.50sh Papilio dardanus planemoides .15 .15

Size: 25x41mm

Perf. 14½

431 A84 2sh Papilio rex .24 .18
432 A84 2.50sh Colotis phisadia .30 .22
433 A84 3sh Papilio desmondi teita .35 .28
434 A84 3.50sh Papilio demodocus .40 .30
435 A84 4sh Papilio phorcas .48 .36
436 A84 5sh Charaxes druceanus teita .58 .45
437 A84 7sh Cymothoe teita .82 .60
438 A84 10sh Charaxes zoolina 1.15 .88
439 A84 20sh Papilio dardanus 2.35 1.75
440 A84 40sh Charaxes cithaeron kennethi 4.65 3.50
Nos. 424A-440 (18) 12.52 9.72

Issue dates: 10c, Sept. 1, 1989. 1.50sh, May 18, 1990. Others, Feb. 14, 1988.

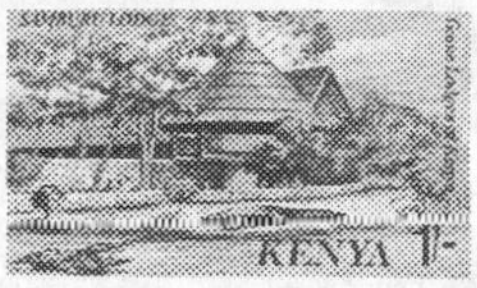

Game Lodges A85

1988, May 31 **Litho.** *Perf. 14½*

441 A85 1sh Samburu .15 .15
442 A85 3sh Naro Moru River .40 .30
443 A85 4sh Mara Serena .52 .40
444 A85 5sh Voi Safari .65 .48
445 A85 7sh Kilimanjaro Buffalo Lodge .90 .68
446 A85 10sh Meru Mulika 1.30 1.00
Nos. 441-446 (6) 3.92 3.01

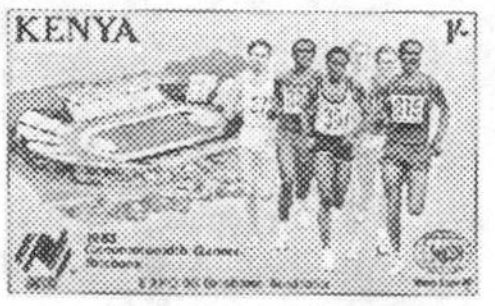

World Expo '88, Brisbane A86

EXPO '88 and Australia bicentennial emblems plus: 1sh, Stadium, site of the 1982 Commonwealth Games, and runners. 3sh, Flying Doctor Service aircraft. 4sh, HMS Sirius, a 19th cent. immigrant ship. 5sh, Ostrich and emu. 7sh, Pres. Daniel Arap Moi, Queen Elizabeth II and Robert Hawke, prime minister of Australia. 30sh, Kenya Pavilion at EXPO '88.

1988, June 10

447 A86 1sh multicolored .15 .15
448 A86 3sh multicolored .40 .30
449 A86 4sh multicolored .52 .40
450 A86 5sh multicolored .65 .48
451 A86 7sh multicolored .90 .68
Nos. 447-451 (5) 2.62 2.01

Souvenir Sheet

452 A86 30sh multicolored 3.25 2.50

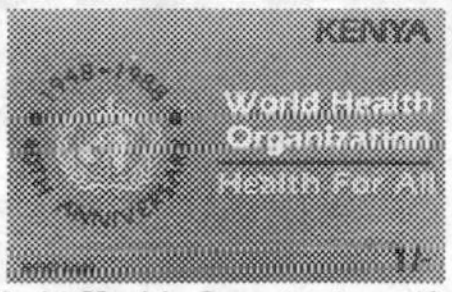

World Health Organization, 40th Anniv. — A87

1988, July 1 **Litho.** *Perf. 14½*

453 A87 1sh shown .15 .15
454 A87 3sh Nutrition .40 .30
455 A87 5sh Immunization .65 .48
456 A87 7sh Water supply .90 .68
Nos. 453-456 (4) 2.10 1.61

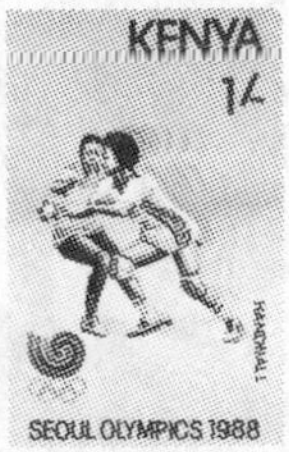

1988 Summer Olympics, Seoul — A88

1988, Aug. 1 **Litho.** *Perf. 14½x14*

457 A88 1sh Handball .15 .15
458 A88 3sh Judo .38 .28
459 A88 5sh Weight lifting .62 .48
460 A88 7sh Javelin .88 .65
461 A88 10sh 400-meter relay 1.25 .95
Nos. 457-461 (5) 3.28 2.51

Souvenir Sheet

462 A88 30sh Tennis 3.75 2.75

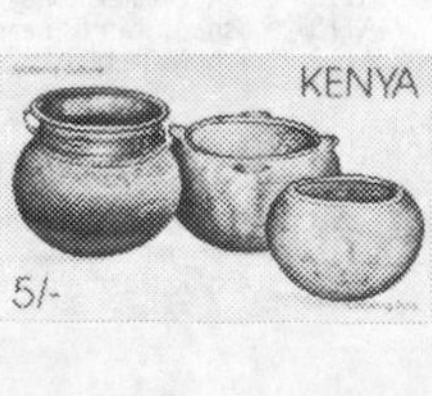

Utensils A89

Perf. 14½x14, 14x14½

1988, Sept. 20 **Litho.**

463 A89 1sh Calabashes, vert. .15 .15
464 A89 3sh Milk gourds, vert. .35 .25
465 A89 5sh Cooking pots .60 .45
466 A89 7sh Winnowing trays .85 .65
467 A89 10sh Reed baskets 1.20 .90
Nos. 463-467 (5) 3.15 2.40

Souvenir Sheet

468 A89 25sh Gourds, calabash, horn 3.25 2.40

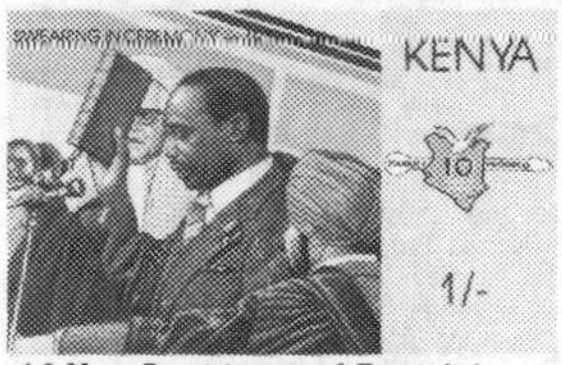

10-Year Presidency of Daniel Arap Moi — A90

Designs: 1sh, Swearing-in ceremony, 1978. 3sh, Promoting soil conservation. 3.50sh, Public transportation (bus), Nairobi. 4sh, Jua Kali artisans at market. 5sh, Moi University, Eldoret, established in 1985. 7sh, Hospital ward expansion. 10sh, British Prime Minister Margaret Thatcher and Pres. Moi inaugurating the Kapsabet Telephone Exchange, Jan. 6, 1988.

Perf. 13½x14½

1988, Oct. 13 **Litho.**

469 A90 1sh multicolored .15 .15
470 A90 3sh multicolored .35 .28
471 A90 3.50sh multicolored .42 .32
472 A90 4sh multicolored .48 .35
473 A90 5sh multicolored .60 .45
474 A90 7sh multicolored .85 .65
475 A90 10sh multicolored 1.20 .90
Nos. 469-475 (7) 4.05 3.10

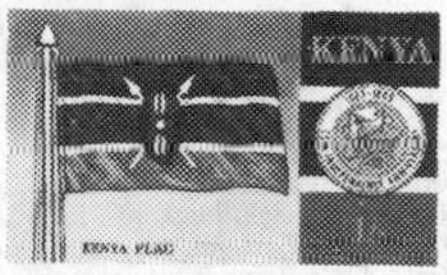

Independence, 25th Anniv. — A91

1988, Dec. 9 **Litho.** *Perf. 11½*

476 A91 1sh Natl. flag .15 .15
477 A91 3sh Coffee picking .35 .28
478 A91 5sh Model of postal hq. .60 .45
479 A91 7sh Harambee Star Airbus A310-300 .85 .65
480 A91 10sh Locomotive 9401 1.20 .90
Nos. 476-480 (5) 3.15 2.43

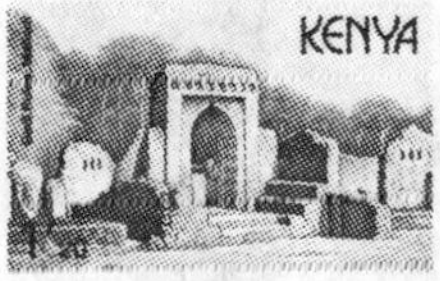

Natl. Monuments A92

1989, Mar. 15 **Litho.** *Perf. 14½*

481 A92 1.20sh Gedi Ruins, Malindi .15 .15
482 A92 3.40sh Vasco Da Gama Pillar, Malindi, vert. .40 .30
483 A92 4.40sh Ishiakani Monument, Kiunga .55 .42
484 A92 5.50sh Ft. Jesus, Mombasa .65 .50
485 A92 7.70sh She Burnan Omwe, Lamu, vert. .92 .70
Nos. 481-485 (5) 2.67 2.07

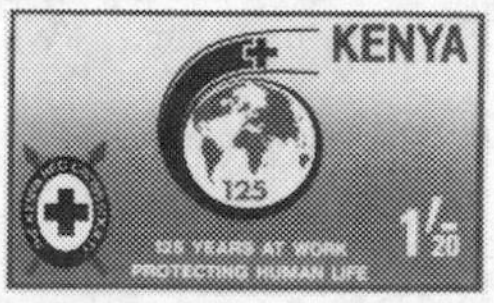

Red Cross, 125th Anniv. A93

1989, May 8 **Litho.** *Perf. 14x13½*

486 A93 1.20sh Anniv. and natl. soc. emblems .15 .15
487 A93 3.40sh First aid .40 .40
488 A93 4.40sh Disaster relief .52 .52
489 A93 5.50sh Jean-Henri Dunant .65 .65
490 A93 7.70sh Blood donation .92 .92
Nos. 486-490 (5) 2.64 2.64

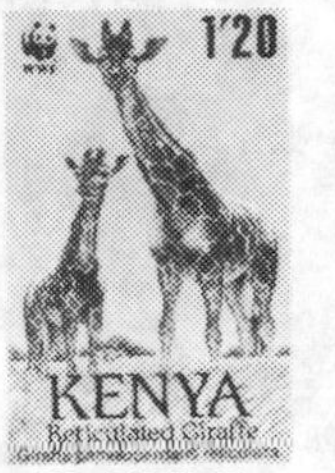

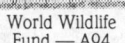

World Wildlife Fund — A94

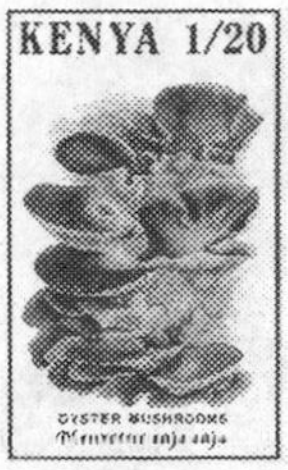

Mushrooms — A95

Giraffes, Giraffa Camelopardalis Reticulata.

1989, July 12 **Litho.** *Perf. 14½*

491 A94 1.20sh multicolored .15 .15
492 A94 3.40sh multicolored .40 .40
493 A94 4.40sh multicolored .52 .52
494 A94 5.50sh multicolored .65 .65

Size: 80x110mm

Imperf

495 A94 30sh multicolored 3.60 3.60
Nos. 491-495 (5) 5.32 5.32

No. 495 contains four labels like Nos. 491-494, perf. 14½, without denominations or WWF emblem.

1989, Sept. 6 **Litho.** *Perf. 14½*

496 A95 1.20sh Oyster .15 .15
497 A95 3.40sh Chestnut .38 .38
498 A95 4.40sh White button .48 .48
499 A95 5.50sh Termite .60 .60
500 A95 7.70sh Shiitake .85 .85
Nos. 496-500 (5) 2.46 2.46

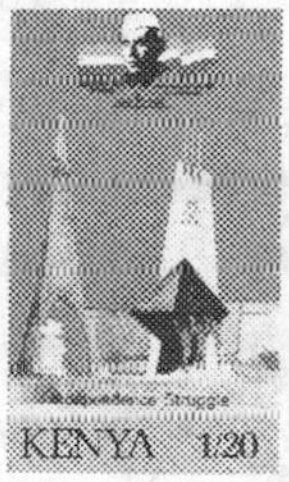

Jawaharlal Nehru, 1st Prime Minister of Independent India — A96

1989, Nov. 9 **Litho.** *Perf. 13½x14*

501 A96 1.20sh Independence struggle .15 .15
502 A96 3.40sh Education .35 .35
503 A96 5.50sh Portrait .58 .58
504 A96 7.70sh Industry .80 .80
Nos. 501-504 (4) 1.88 1.88

Costume Type of 1980

1989, Dec. 8 **Litho.** *Perf. 14½x13½*

505 A80 1.20sh Kipsigis .15 .15
506 A80 3.40sh Rabai .35 .35
507 A80 5.50sh Duruma .60 .60
508 A80 7.70sh Kuria .80 .80
509 A80 10sh Bajuni 1.05 1.05
Nos. 505-509 (5) 2.95 2.95

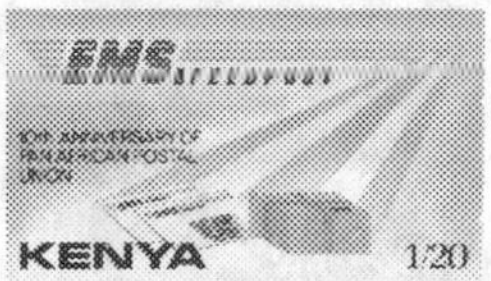

Pan-African Postal Union, 10th Anniv. — A97

Perf. 14x13½, 13½x14

1990, Jan. 31 **Litho.**

510 A97 1.20sh EMS Speedpost .15 .15
511 A97 3.40sh Mail runner .35 .35
512 A97 5.50sh Mandera P.O. .60 .60
513 A97 7.70sh EMS, diff., vert. .80 .80
514 A97 10sh PAPU emblem, vert. 1.05 1.05
Nos. 510-514 (5) 2.95 2.95

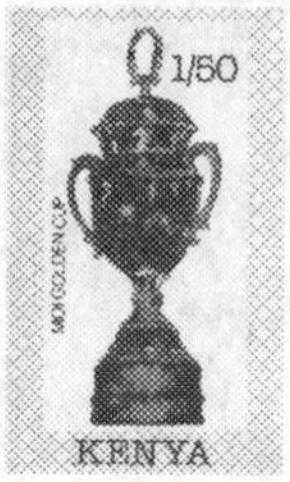

Soccer Trophies — A98

Designs: 1.50sh, Moi Golden Cup. 4.50sh, East and Central Africa Challenge Cup. 6.50sh, East and Central Africa Club Championship Cup. 9sh, World Cup.

1990, May 21 Litho. *Perf. 14½*

515	A98	1.50sh	multicolored	.15	.15
516	A98	4.50sh	multicolored	.45	.45
517	A98	6.50sh	multicolored	.65	.65
518	A98	9sh	multicolored	.90	.90
			Nos. 515-518 (4)	2.15	2.15

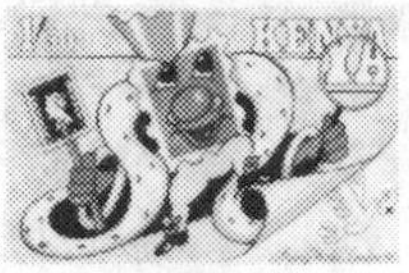

Penny Black 150th Anniv., Stamp World London '90 — A99

1990, Apr. 27 Litho. *Perf. 11½*

519	A99	1.50sh	shown	.15	.15
520	A99	4.50sh	Great Britain No. 1	.48	.48
521	A99	6.50sh	Early British cancellations	.68	.68
522	A99	9sh	Main P.O.	.95	.95
a.			Souvenir sheet of 4, #519-522	3.30	3.30
			Nos. 519-522 (4)	2.26	2.26

No. 522a sold for 30 shillings.

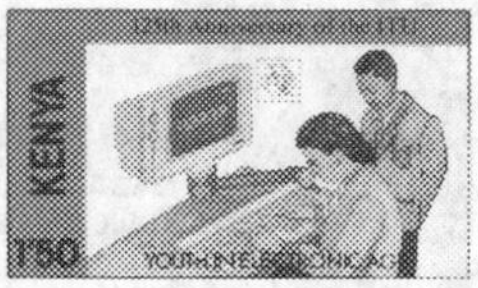

ITU, 125th Anniv. A100

Designs: 4.50sh, Telephone assembly. 6.50sh, ITU Anniversary emblem. 9sh, Telecommunications development.

1990, July 12

523	A100	1.50sh	multicolored	.15	.15
524	A100	4.50sh	multicolored	.45	.45
525	A100	6.50sh	multicolored	.65	.65
526	A100	9sh	multicolored	.90	.90
			Nos. 523-526 (4)	2.15	2.15

Queen Mother, 90th Birthday

Common Design Types

Perf. 14x15

1990, Aug. 4 Litho. Wmk. 384

527	CD343	10sh	Queen Mother	.95	.95

Perf. 14½

528	CD344	40sh	At garden party, 1947	3.75	3.75

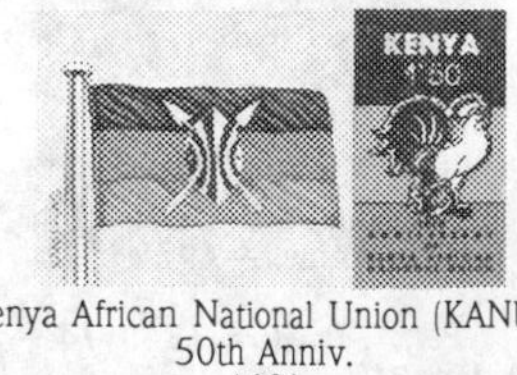

Kenya African National Union (KANU), 50th Anniv. A101

1990, June 11

529	A101	1.50sh	KANU flag	.15	.15
530	A101	2.50sh	Nyayo Monument	.25	.25
531	A101	4.50sh	KICC Party Headquarters	.45	.45
532	A101	5sh	Jomo Kenyatta	.50	.50
533	A101	6.50sh	Daniel T. Arap Moi	.65	.65
534	A101	9sh	KANU mass meeting	.90	.90
535	A101	10sh	Voters	1.00	1.00
			Nos. 529-535 (7)	3.90	3.90

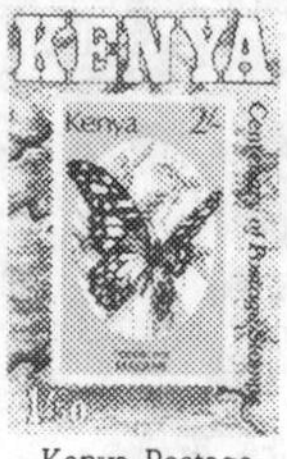

Kenya Postage Stamps, Cent. — A102

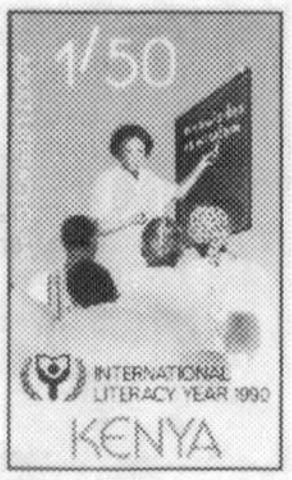

Intl. Literacy Year — A103

Designs: 1.50sh, Kenya #431. 4.50sh, East Africa and Uganda Protectorates #2. 6.50sh, British East Africa #1. 9sh, Kenya and Uganda #25. 20sh, Kenya, Uganda, Tanzania #232.

1990, Sept. 5 Litho. *Perf. 14x14½*

536	A102	1.50sh	multicolored	.15	.15
537	A102	4.50sh	multicolored	.45	.45
538	A102	6.50sh	multicolored	.65	.65
539	A102	9sh	multicolored	.90	.90
540	A102	20sh	multicolored	2.00	2.00
			Nos. 536-540 (5)	4.15	4.15

1990, Nov. 30 Litho. *Perf. 13½x14*

541	A103	1.50sh	Adult literacy class	.15	.15
542	A103	4.50sh	Radio teaching program	.45	.45
543	A103	6.50sh	Technical training	.65	.65
544	A103	9sh	Literacy year emblem	.90	.90
			Nos. 541-544 (4)	2.15	2.15

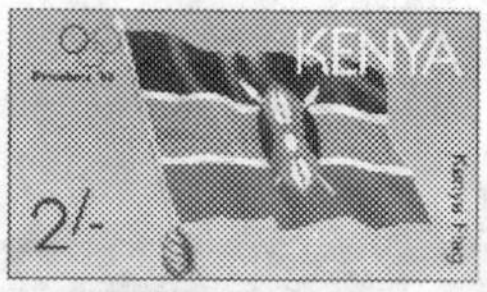

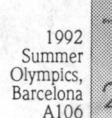

1992 Summer Olympics, Barcelona A106

1991, Nov. 29 Litho. *Perf. 14x13½*

554	A106	2sh	National flag	.15	.15
555	A106	6sh	Basketball	.45	.45
556	A106	7sh	Field hockey	.52	.52
557	A106	8.50sh	Table tennis	.62	.62
558	A106	11sh	Boxing	.82	.82
			Nos. 554-558 (5)	2.56	2.56

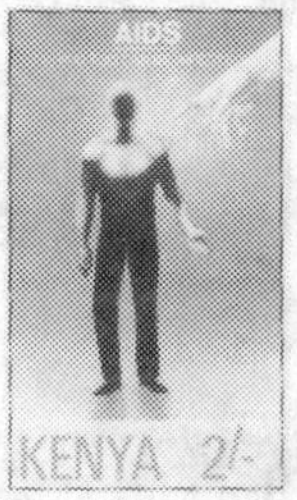

Fight AIDS — A107

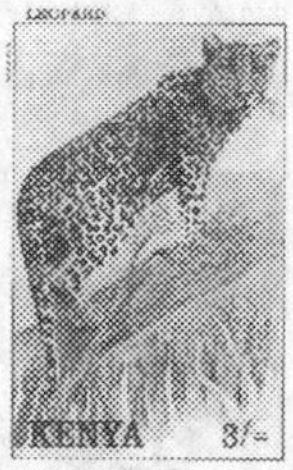

Wildlife — A108

1991, Oct. 31 Litho. *Perf. 13½x14*

559	A107	2sh	You too can be infected	.15	.15
560	A107	6sh	Has no cure	.45	.45
561	A107	8.50sh	Casual sex is unsafe	.62	.62
562	A107	11sh	Sterilize syringe before use	.82	.82
			Nos. 559-562 (4)	2.04	2.04

Queen Elizabeth II's Accession to the Throne, 40th Anniv.

Common Design Type

1992, Feb. 6 Litho. *Perf. 14x13½*

563	CD349	3sh	multicolored	.22	.22
564	CD349	8sh	multicolored	.58	.58
565	CD349	11sh	multicolored	.80	.80
566	CD349	14sh	multicolored	1.00	1.00
567	CD349	40sh	multicolored	2.80	2.80
			Nos. 563-567 (5)	5.40	5.40

1992, May 8 *Perf. 14½*

568	A108	3sh	Leopard	.22	.22
569	A108	8sh	Lion	.58	.58
570	A108	10sh	Elephant	.70	.70
571	A108	11sh	Buffalo	.80	.80
572	A108	14sh	Rhinoceros	1.00	1.00
			Nos. 568-572 (5)	3.30	3.30

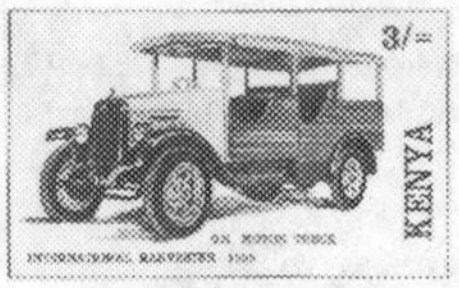

Vintage Cars A109

Designs: 3sh, Intl. Harvester S.S. motor truck, 1926. 8sh, Fiat 509, 1924. 10sh, "R" Hupmobile, 1923. 11sh, Chevrolet Box Body, 1928. 14sh, Bentley Parkward, 1934.

1992, June 24 *Perf. 14½*

573	A109	3sh	multicolored	.22	.22
574	A109	8sh	multicolored	.58	.58
575	A109	10sh	multicolored	.70	.70
576	A109	11sh	multicolored	.80	.80
577	A109	14sh	multicolored	1.00	1.00
			Nos. 573-577 (5)	3.30	3.30

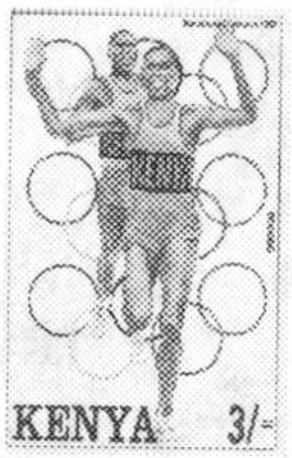

1992 Summer Olympics, Barcelona — A110

1992, July 24 Litho. *Perf. 14½*

578	A110	3sh	Runners	.16	.16
579	A110	8sh	Judo	.45	.45
580	A110	10sh	Women's volleyball	.55	.55
581	A110	11sh	4x100-meter relay	.60	.60
582	A110	14sh	10,000-meter run	.78	.78
			Nos. 578-582 (5)	2.54	2.54

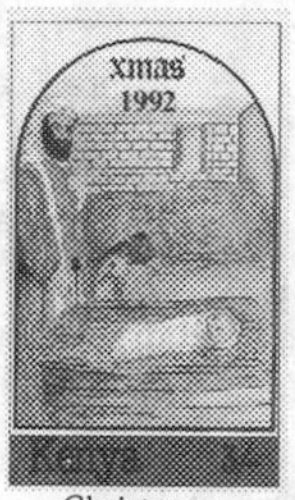

Christmas A111

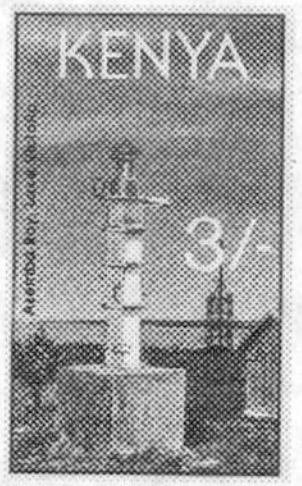

Lighthouses A112

Designs: 3sh, Joseph, Jesus and animals in stable. 8sh, Mary holding Jesus in stable. 11sh, Map of Kenya, Christmas tree. 14sh, Adoration of the Magi.

1992, Dec. 14 Litho. *Perf. 13½x14*

583	A111	3sh	multicolored	.18	.18
584	A111	8sh	multicolored	.50	.50
585	A111	11sh	multicolored	.70	.70
586	A111	14sh	multicolored	.90	.90
			Nos. 583-586 (4)	2.28	2.28

1993, Jan. 25 *Perf. 14½*

Designs: 3sh, Asembo Bay, Lake Victoria. 8sh, Ras Serani, Mombasa. 11sh, Ras Serani, Mombasa, diff. 14sh, Gingira, Lake Victoria.

587	A112	3sh	multicolored	.18	.18
588	A112	8sh	multicolored	.50	.50
589	A112	11sh	multicolored	.70	.70
590	A112	14sh	multicolored	.90	.90
			Nos. 587-590 (4)	2.28	2.28

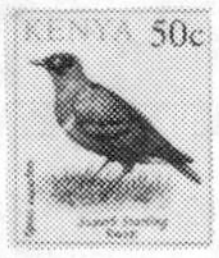

Birds — A113

1993-94 Photo. *Perf. 15x14*

Granite Paper

594	A113	50c	Superb starling	.15	.15
597	A113	1sh	Red & yellow barbet	.15	.15
598	A113	1.50sh	Ross's turaco	.15	.15
600	A113	3sh	Greater honeyguide	.20	.20
601	A113	5sh	African fish eagle	.20	.20
602	A113	7sh	Malachite kingfisher	.45	.45
603	A113	8sh	Speckled pigeon	.50	.50
604	A113	10sh	Cinnamon-chested bee-eater	.65	.65
605	A113	11sh	Scarlet-chested sunbird	.70	.70
606	A113	14sh	Reichenow's weaver	.90	.90

Size: 25x42mm

Perf. 14½

608	A113	50sh	Yellow-billed hornbill	3.25	3.25
609	A113	80sh	Lesser flamingo	5.00	5.00
610	A113	100sh	Hadada ibis	6.45	6.45
			Nos. 594-610 (13)	18.75	18.75

Issued: 1.50sh, 5sh, 2/14/94; others, 2/22/93.
This is an expanding set. Numbers may change.

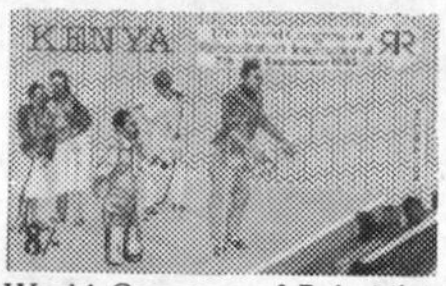

17th World Congress of Rehabilatation Intl. — A114

1993, July 1 Litho. *Perf. 14½*

611	A114	3sh	Health care, vert.	.16	.16
612	A114	8sh	Recreation	.42	.42
613	A114	10sh	Vocational training	.55	.55
614	A114	11sh	Recreation & sports	.58	.58
615	A114	14sh	Emblem, vert.	.75	.75
			Nos. 611-615 (5)	2.46	2.46

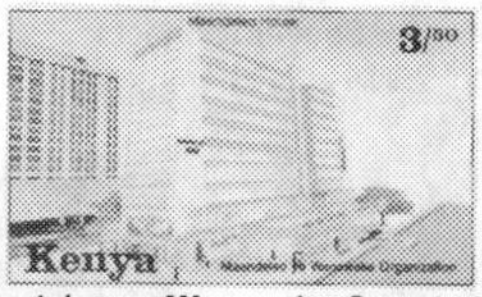

Maendeleo ya Wanawake Organization, 42th Anniv. — A115

Designs: 3.50sh, Maendeleo House. 9sh, Planting trees. 11sh, Rural family planning services, vert. 12.50sh, Water nearer the people. 15.50sh, Maendeleo improved wood cookstove, vert.

Perf. 14x13½, 13½x14

1994, Mar. 17 Litho.

616	A115	3.50sh	multicolored	.18	.18
617	A115	9sh	multicolored	.45	.45
618	A115	11sh	multicolored	.55	.55
619	A115	12.50sh	multicolored	.60	.60
620	A115	15.50sh	multicolored	.80	.80
			Nos. 616-620 (5)	2.58	2.58

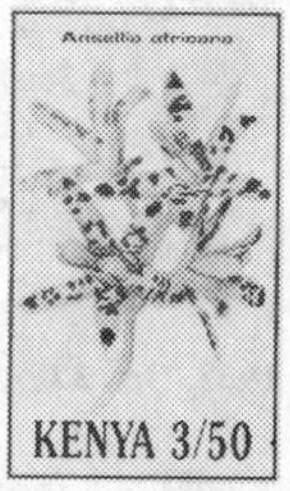

Orchids — A116

Designs: 3.50sh, Ansellia africana. 9sh, Aerangis lutecalba. 12.50sh, Polystachya bella. 15.50sh, Brachycorythis kalbreyeri. 20sh, Eulophia guineensis.

1994, June 27 Litho. *Perf. 13½x14*

621	A116	3.50sh	multicolored	.15	.15
622	A116	9sh	multicolored	.35	.35
623	A116	12.50sh	multicolored	.45	.45
624	A116	15.50sh	multicolored	.55	.55
625	A116	20sh	multicolored	.75	.75
			Nos. 621-625 (5)	2.25	2.25

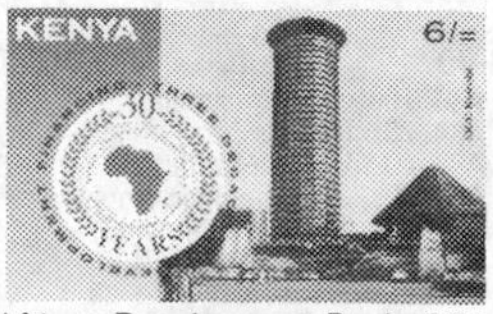

African Development Bank, 30th Anniv. — A117

1994, Nov. 21 Litho. *Perf. 14½*

626	A117	6sh	KICC, Nairobi	.25	.25
627	A117	25sh	Isinya, Kajiado	1.00	1.00

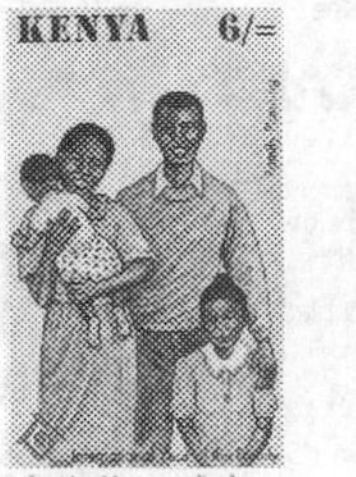

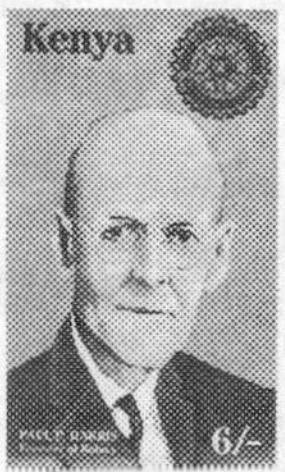

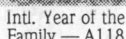

Intl. Year of the Family — A118

Rotary, 50th Anniv. — A119

1994, Dec. 22

628	A118	6sh	Family planning	.25	.25
629	A118	14.50sh	Health	.60	.60
630	A118	20sh	Education, horiz.	.80	.80
631	A118	25sh	Emblem, horiz.	1.00	1.00
			Nos. 628-631 (4)	2.65	2.65

1994, Dec. 29 *Perf. 13½x14*

Designs: 6sh, Paul P. Harris, founder. 14.50sh, Rotary Club of Mombasa. 17.50sh, Polio plus vaccine. 20sh, Water projects. 25sh, Emblem, motto.

632	A119	6sh	multicolored	.25	.25
633	A119	14.50sh	multicolored	.60	.60
634	A119	17.50sh	multicolored	.70	.70
635	A119	20sh	multicolored	.80	.80
636	A119	25sh	multicolored	1.00	1.00
			Nos. 632-636 (5)	3.35	3.35

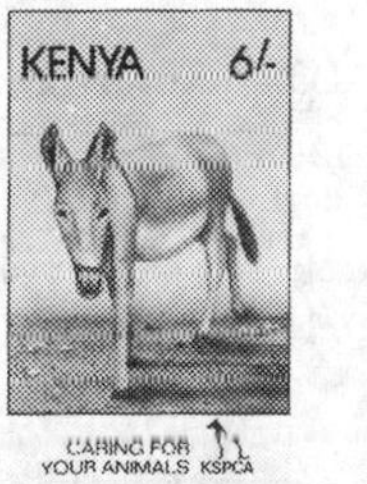

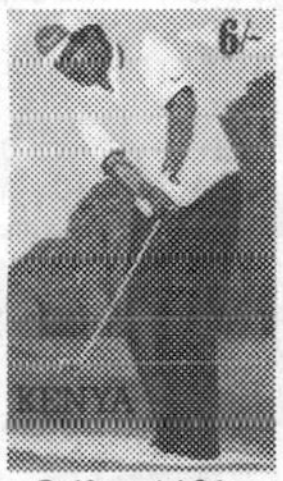

SPCA — A120

Golf — A121

1995, Jan. 13 Litho. *Perf. 14½*

637	A120	6sh	Donkey	.25	.25
638	A120	14.50sh	Cattle	.60	.60
639	A120	17.50sh	Sheep	.70	.70
640	A120	20sh	Dog	.80	.80
641	A120	25sh	Cat	1.00	1.00
			Nos. 637-641 (5)	3.35	3.35

Kenya Society for Prevention of Cruelty to Animals.

1995, Feb. 28 Litho. *Perf. 14½*

642	A121	6sh	Man in vest	.25	.25
643	A121	17.50sh	Woman	.75	.75
644	A121	20sh	Man in red shirt	.90	.90
645	A121	25sh	Golf club	1.10	1.10
			Nos. 642-645 (4)	3.00	3.00

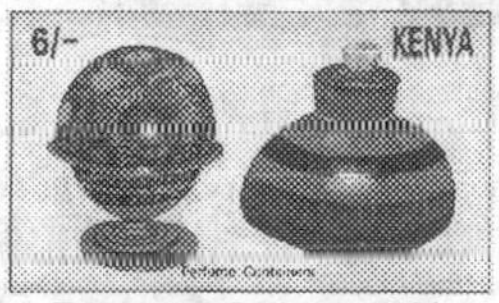

Traditional Crafts — A122

1995, Mar. 24 Litho. *Perf. 14x13½*

646	A122	6sh	Perfume containers	.28	.28
647	A122	14.50sh	Basketry	.65	.65
648	A122	17.50sh	Preservation pots	.80	.80
649	A122	20sh	Gourds	.90	.90
650	A122	25sh	Wooden containers	1.10	1.10
			Nos. 646-650 (5)	3.73	3.73

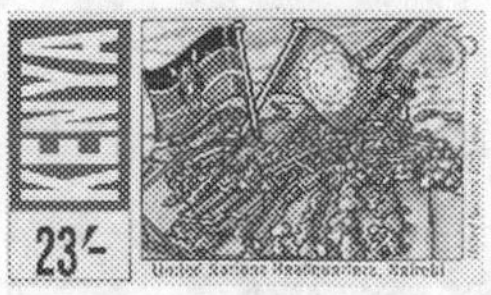

UN, 50th Anniv. A123

Designs: 23sh, UN Headquarters, Nairobi. 26sh, People holding UN emblem. 32sh, UN Peacekeeper's helmet. 40sh, UN emblem.

1995, Oct. 24 Litho. *Perf. 13½*

651	A123	23sh	multicolored	.90	.90
652	A123	26sh	multicolored	1.00	1.00
653	A123	32sh	multicolored	1.30	1.30
654	A123	40sh	multicolored	1.60	1.60
			Nos. 651-654 (4)	4.80	4.80

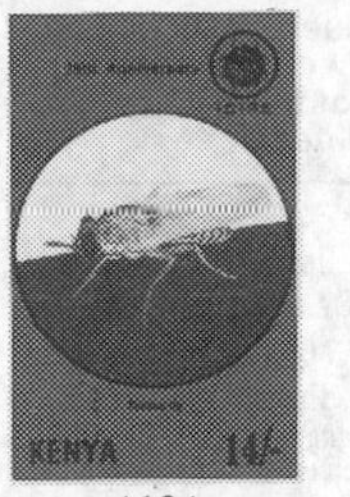

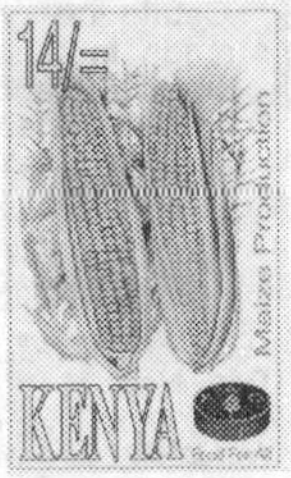

A124

A125

1995, Sept. 29 Litho. *Perf. 13½*

655	A124	14sh	Tse-tse fly	.55	.55
656	A124	26sh	Tick	1.00	1.00
657	A124	32sh	Wild silk moth	1.30	1.30
658	A124	33sh	Maize borer	1.40	1.40
659	A124	40sh	Locust	1.65	1.65
			Nos. 655-659 (5)	5.90	5.90

ICIPE, 25th anniv.

1995, Oct. 16

660	A125	14sh	Maize production	.55	.55
661	A125	28sh	Cattle rearing	1.00	1.00
662	A125	32sh	Poultry keeping	1.30	1.30
663	A125	33sh	Fishing	1.40	1.40
664	A125	40sh	Fruits	1.65	1.65
			Nos. 660-664 (5)	5.90	5.90

FAO, 50th anniv.

POSTAGE DUE STAMPS

D1

Perf. 14x13½

1967-85 Litho. Unwmk.

"POSTAGE DUE" 12½mm long

J1	D1	5c	dark red	.15	.15
J2	D1	10c	green	.15	.15
J3	D1	20c	dark blue	.15	.15
J4	D1	30c	reddish brown	.15	.15
J5	D1	40c	brt red lilac	.16	.15

Perf. 14

J6	D1	80c	brick red	.35	.30

Perf. 15x14

J7	D1	1sh	orange	1.75	*1.90*

Perf. 14½x14

J8	D1	2sh	pale violet	.15	.15
			Set value	1.75	*2.70*

Issued: 80c, 1978. 2sh, 1985; others, Jan. 3, 1967.

See Nos. J9-J14.

1969-70 *Perf. 14*

J1a	D1	5c	.15	.15
J2a	D1	10c	.15	.15
J3a	D1	20c	.15	.15
J4a	D1	30c	.15	.15
J5a	D1	40c	.15	.15
J7a	D1	1sh	1.00	*2.50*
		Nos. J1a-J7a (6)	1.75	*3.25*

Issued: 1sh, 2/18/70; others, 12/16/69.

1971-73 *Perf. 14x15*

J1b	D1	5c	.50	.50
J2b	D1	10c	.50	.50
J3b	D1	20c	.50	.50
J4b	D1	30c	2.00	2.00
J5b	D1	40c	.50	.50
J7b	D1	1sh	1.00	1.25
		Nos. J1b-J7b (6)	5.00	5.25

Issued: 30c, 7/13/71; others, 2/20/73. The 10c, 20c, 1sh on chalky paper were issued 7/13/71.

1973, Dec. 12 *Perf. 15*

J1c	D1	5c	.15	.15
J2c	D1	10c	.15	.15
J3c	D1	20c	.15	.15
J4c	D1	30c	.15	.15
J5c	D1	40c	2.00	2.00
J7c	D1	1sh	1.00	1.25
		Nos. J1c-J7c (6)	3.60	3.85

Nos. J5, J7-J8 Redrawn

1987 Litho. Unwmk. *Perf. 15x14*

J9	D1	40c	bright red lilac	.16	.16
J10	D1	50c	dark green	.15	.15
J11	D1	1sh	light orange	.80	.80
J12	D1	2sh	pale violet	.15	.15
J13	D1	3sh	dark blue	.15	.15
J14	D1	5sh	red brown	.15	.15
			Nos. J9-J14 (6)	1.56	1.56

"KENYA" is 9mm wide and "POSTAGE DUE" is 11½mm wide on Nos. J9, J11. "CENTS" is 4½mm wide and "SHILLING" has cross bar on "G"; both are in a new font.

"KENYA" is 8½mm wide and "POSTAGE DUE" is 11½mm wide on No. J12.

Issued: 40c, 1sh, 1987; others, Dec. 6, 1993.

OFFICIAL STAMPS

Nos. 1-5 and 7 Overprinted **OFFICIAL**

Perf. 14x14½

1964, Oct. 1 Photo. Unwmk.

Size: 21x17½mm

O1	A1	5c	blue, buff & dk brn	.15	.15
O2	A1	10c	brown	.22	.22
O3	A1	15c	dp magenta	.30	.30
O4	A1	20c	yel green & dk brn	.42	.42
O5	A1	30c	yellow & black	.65	.65
O6	A1	50c	green, blk & dp car	1.10	1.10
			Nos. O1-O6 (6)	2.84	2.84

KENYA, UGANDA, TANZANIA

ˈke–nyə, ü–ˈgan–də, ˌtan–zə–ˈnē–ə

LOCATION — East Africa, bordering on the Indian Ocean
GOVT. — States in British Commonwealth
AREA — 679,802 sq. mi.
POP. — 42,760,000 (est. 1977)
CAPITAL — Nairobi (Kenya), Kampala (Uganda), Dar es Salaam (Tanzania)

Kenya became a crown colony in 1906, including the former East Africa Protectorate leased from the Sultan of Zanzibar and known as the Kenya Protectorate. In 1963 the colony became independent. Its stamps are listed under "Kenya."

The inland Uganda Protectorate, lying west of Kenya Colony, was declared a British Protectorate in 1894. Uganda became independent in 1962.

Tanganyika, a trust territory larger than Kenya or Uganda, was grouped with them postally from 1935 under the East African Posts & Telecommunications Administration. Tanganyika became independent in 1961. When it merged with Zanzibar in 1964, "Zanzibar" was added to the inscriptions on stamps issued under the E.A.P. & T. Administration. In 1965 the multiple inscription was changed to "Kenya, Uganda, Tanzania," variously arranged.

Zanzibar withdrew its own stamps in 1968, and K., U. & T. stamps became valid Jan. 1, 1968.

100 Cents = 1 Rupee
100 Cents = 1 Shilling (1922)
20 Shillings = 1 Pound

Catalogue values for unused stamps in this country are for Never Hinged items, beginning with Scott 90.

East Africa and Uganda Protectorates

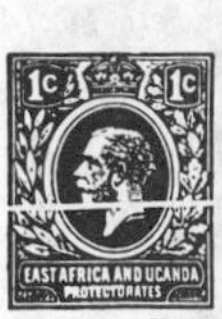

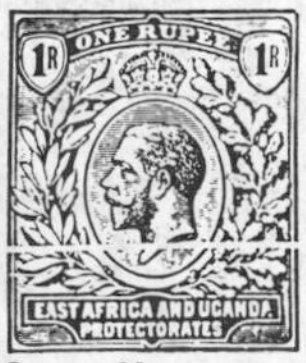

King George V

A1 A2

1921 Typo. Wmk. 4 *Perf. 14*

Ordinary Paper

1	A1	1c	black	.90	.50
2	A1	3c	green	1.25	1.25
3	A1	6c	rose red	2.00	1.50
4	A1	10c	orange	4.25	.20
5	A1	12c	gray	4.25	*12.50*
6	A1	15c	ultramarine	3.25	*10.00*

Chalky Paper

7	A1	50c	gray lilac & blk	9.00	*45.00*
8	A2	2r	blk & red, *blue*	45.00	*95.00*
9	A2	3r	green & violet	70.00	*110.00*
10	A2	5r	gray lil & ultra	75.00	*125.00*
11	A2	50r	gray grn & red	2,100.	*2,500.*
			Nos. 1-10 (10)	214.90	*400.95*

The name of the colony was changed to Kenya in August, 1920, but stamps of the East Africa and Uganda types were continued in use. Stamps of types A1 and A2 watermarked Multiple Crown and C A (3) are listed under East Africa and Uganda Protectorates.

For stamps of Kenya and Uganda overprinted "G. E. A." used in parts of former German East Africa occupied by British forces, see Tanganyika Nos. 1-9.

Kenya and Uganda

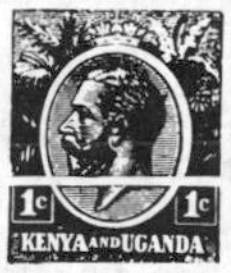

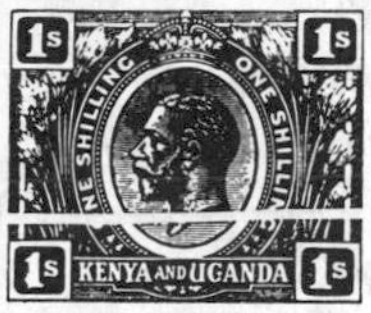

King George V

A3 A4

1922-27 **Wmk. 4**

18	A3	1c	brown	.50	*1.00*
19	A3	5c	violet	1.25	.15
20	A3	5c	green ('27)	1.65	.15
21	A3	10c	green	1.65	.15
22	A3	10c	black ('27)	1.50	.15
23	A3	12c	black	1.50	*18.00*
24	A3	15c	car rose	1.00	.15
25	A3	20c	orange	1.50	.15
26	A3	30c	ultra	1.00	.15
27	A3	50c	gray	2.00	.15
28	A3	75c	ol bister	2.75	*6.25*
29	A4	1sh	green	2.75	1.65
30	A4	2sh	gray lilac	7.00	6.50
31	A4	2sh50c	brown ('25)	18.00	*50.00*
32	A4	3sh	gray black	15.00	6.75
33	A4	4sh	gray ('25)	20.00	*62.50*
34	A4	5sh	carmine	22.50	15.00
35	A4	7sh50c	org ('25)	60.00	*110.00*
36	A4	10sh	ultra	45.00	40.00
37	A4	£1	org & blk	125.00	*165.00*
38	A4	£2	brn vio & grn ('25)	700.00	*1,000.*
39	A4	£3	yel & dl vio ('25)	900.00	*1,250.*
40	A4	£4	rose lil & blk ('25)	1,600.	*2,500.*
41	A4	£5	blue & blk	1,900.	*3,000.*
			Revenue cancel		50.00
41A	A4	£10	grn & blk	*11,000.*	
41B	A4	£20	grn & red ('25)	*12,500.*	
41C	A4	£25	red & blk	*15,000.*	
41D	A4	£50	red & blk	*17,500.*	
41E	A4	£75	red & blk	*37,500.*	
41F	A4	£100	red & blk	*42,500.*	
			Nos. 18-37 (20)	331.55	*483.85*

High face value stamps are known with revenue cancellations removed and forged postal cancellations added.

Kenya, Uganda, Tanganyika
Silver Jubilee Issue
Common Design Type

1935, May Engr. *Perf. 13½x14*

42	CD301	20c	ol grn & lt bl	.30	.15
43	CD301	30c	blue & brown	.75	.70
44	CD301	65c	indigo & green	2.50	2.25
45	CD301	1sh	brt vio & indigo	3.00	2.25
			Nos. 42-45 (4)	6.55	5.35

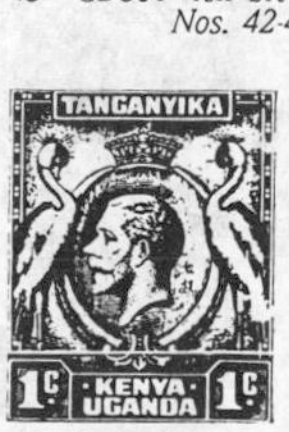

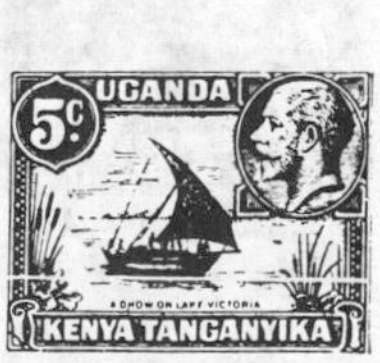

Kavirondo Cranes — A5

Dhow on Lake Victoria — A6

Lion — A7

Mount Kilimanjaro — A8

Jinja Bridge by Ripon Falls — A9

Mount Kenya — A10

Lake Naivasha — A11

FIVE CENTS
Type I - Left rope does not touch sail.
Type II - Left rope touches sail.

Perf. 13, 14, 11½x13, 13x11½

1935, May 1 Engr.; Typo. (10c, £1)

46 A5 1c red brn & blk .15 .15
47 A6 5c grn & blk (I) .15 .15
a. Type II *15.00* 1.50
b. Perf. 13x11½ (I) *1,000.* *250.00*
c. Perf. 13x11½ (II) *375.00* *95.00*
48 A7 10c black & yel .30 .15
49 A8 15c red & black .30 .15
50 A5 20c red org & blk .15 .15
51 A9 30c dk ultra & blk .20 .15
52 A6 50c blk & red vio .50 .15
53 A10 65c yel brn & blk 1.00 1.50
54 A11 1sh grn & black 1.00 .40
a. Perf. 13x11½ ('36) *1,000.* 85.00
55 A8 2sh red vio & rose brn 4.50 2.25
56 A11 3sh blk & ultra 5.00 2.50
a. Perf. 13x11½ *1,500.*
57 A9 5sh car & black 15.00 *22.50*
58 A5 10sh ultra & red vio 37.50 37.50
59 A7 £1 blk & scar 125.00 125.00
Nos. 46-59 (14) 190.75 192.70

Coronation Issue
Common Design Type

1937, May 12 Engr. *Perf. 13½x14*

60 CD302 5c deep green .15 .15
61 CD302 20c deep orange .15 .15
62 CD302 30c brt ultra .25 .25
Set value .45 .45
Set, never hinged 1.40

Kavirondo Cranes — A12

Dhow on Lake Victoria — A13

Lake Naivasha — A14

Jinja Bridge, Ripon Falls — A16

Kenya, Uganda & Tanganyika stamps can be mounted in the Scott British Africa album.

Mt. Kilimanjaro — A15

Lion — A17

FIFTY CENTS:
Type I - Left rope does not touch sail.
Type II - Left rope touches sail.

1938-54 Engr. *Perf. 13*

66 A12 1c red brn & gray blk .40 .20
a. 1c violet brown & black, perf. 13x13½ ('42) .15 .15

Perf. 13x11½

67 A13 5c grn & blk .40 .15
68 A13 5c red org & brn ('49) .30 .15
a. Perf. 13x12½ ('50) .50 .15
69 A14 10c org & brn .50 .15
a. Perf. 14 ('41) 42.50 2.00
70 A14 10c green & black ('49) .25 .15
a. Perf. 13x12½ ('50) .50 .15

Perf. 13x12½

71 A14 10c gray & red brn ('52) .25 .15

Perf. 13½x13, 13x13½

72 A15 15c car & gray blk ('43) .90 .15
a. Booklet pane of 4 4.50
b. Perf. 13 2.50 .15
73 A15 15c green & black ('52) .40 .15
74 A12 20c org & gray blk ('42) 1.25 .15
a. Booklet pane of 4 8.00
b. Imperf., pair
c. Perf. 13 *4.00* .15
d. Perf. 14 ('41) *12.50* 2.75

Perf. 13x12½

75 A13 25c car & black ('52) .60 .30

Perf. 13x13½

76 A16 30c dp bl & gray blk ('42) .35 .15
a. Perf. 14 ('41) *75.00* 10.00
b. Perf. 13 *7.00* .15
77 A16 30c brown & pur ('52) .30 .15
78 A12 40c brt bl & gray blk ('52) .75 .20

Perf. 13x12½

79 A13 50c gray blk & red vio (II) ('49) 1.75 .15
a. Perf. 13x11½ (II) .25 .15
b. Perf. 13x11½ (I) 200.00 100.00
80 A14 1sh yel brn & gray blk ('49) 1.25 .15
a. Perf. 13x11½ .35 .15

Perf. 13½x13

81 A15 2sh red vio & org brn ('44) 3.25 .30
a. Perf. 13 *20.00* 1.00
b. Perf. 14 ('41) *20.00* 3.00

Perf. 13x11½

82 A14 3sh gray blk & ultra 7.50 .50
a. Perf. 13x12½ ('50) 2.00 .60

Perf. 13x13½

83 A16 5sh car rose & gray blk ('44) 7.50 .65
a. Perf. 13 *30.00* 3.50
b. Perf. 14 ('41) *10.00* 1.75
84 A12 10sh ultra & red vio ('44) 10.00 1.75
a. Perf. 13 35.00 6.50
b. Perf. 14 ('41) 27.50 10.00

Typo.
Perf. 14

85 A17 £1 blk & scar ('41) 7.50 4.75
a. Perf. 11½x13 125.00 55.00
b. Perf. 12½ ('54) 8.25 *14.00*
Nos. 66-85 (20) 45.40 10.45
Set, never hinged 75.00

See Nos. 98-99.

South Africa Nos. 48, 57, 60 and 62 Surcharged

5c
KENYA
TANGANYIKA
UGANDA

Basic stamps of Nos. 86-89 are inscribed alternately in English and Afrikaans.

1941-42 Wmk. 201 *Perf. 15x14, 14*

86 A6 5c on 1p car & gray, pair .30 .40
a. Single, English .15 .15
b. Single, Afrikaans .15 .15
87 A17 10c on 3p ultra, pair .40 .40
a. Single, English .15 .15
b. Single, Afrikaans .15 .15
88 A7 20c on 6p org & grn, pair .60 .60
a. Single, English .20 .15
b. Single, Afrikaans .20 .15
89 A11 70c on 1sh lt bl & ol brn, pair .90 .90
a. Single, English .30 .15
b. Single, Afrikaans .30 .15
Nos. 86-89 (4) 2.20 2.30
Set, never hinged 8.50

Issued: #86-88, 7/1/41; #89, 4/20/42.

Catalogue values for unused stamps in this section, from this point to the end of the section, are for Never Hinged items.

Peace Issue
Common Design Type

Perf. 13½x14

1946, Nov. 11 Engr. Wmk. 4

90 CD303 20c red orange .15 .15
91 CD303 30c deep blue .15 .15
Set value .25 .25

Silver Wedding Issue
Common Design Types

1948, Dec. 1 Photo. *Perf. 14x14½*

92 CD304 20c orange .20 .15

Engr.; Name Typo.
Perf. 11½x11

93 CD305 £1 red 27.50 27.50

UPU Issue
Common Design Types

Engr.; Typo. on Nos. 95 and 96

1949, Oct. 10 *Perf. 13, 11x11½*

94 CD306 20c red orange .30 .22
95 CD307 30c indigo .45 .36
96 CD308 50c gray .80 .80
97 CD309 1sh red brown 1.60 1.60
Nos. 94-97 (4) 3.15 2.98

Type of 1949 with Added Inscription: "Royal Visit 1952"

1952, Feb. 1 Engr. *Perf. 13x12½*

98 A14 10c green & black .15 .15
99 A14 1sh yel brown & gray blk .65 .65

Visit of Princess Elizabeth, Duchess of Edinburgh, and the Duke of Edinburgh, 1952.

Coronation Issue
Common Design Type

1953, June 2 *Perf. 13½x13*

101 CD312 20c red orange & blk .15 .15

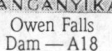

Owen Falls Dam — A18

Giraffe — A19

Elizabeth II — A21

Mt. Kilimanjaro A20

1954, Apr. 28 *Perf. 12½x13*

102 A18 30c dp ultra & black .20 .20

Visit of Queen Elizabeth II and the Duke of Edinburgh, 1954.

1954-59 *Perf. 12½x13, 13x12½*

Designs: 5c, 30c, Owen Falls Dam (without "Royal Visit 1954"). 20c, 40c, 1sh, Lion. 15c, 1.30sh, 5sh, Elephants. 10sh, Royal Lodge, Sagana.

103 A18 5c choc & black .15 .15
a. Booklet pane of 4 .50
b. Dam inverted —
104 A19 10c carmine .15 .15
a. Booklet pane of 4 .60
105 A20 15c lt blue & blk (no period below "c") ('58) .35 .15
a. Booklet pane of 4 2.00
106 A20 15c lt blue & blk (period below "c") ('59) 1.25 .15
a. Booklet pane of 4 6.00
107 A19 20c org & black .20 .15
a. Booklet pane of 4 .80
b. Imperf., pair *800.00*
108 A18 30c ultra & black .20 .15
a. Booklet pane of 4 1.00
109 A19 40c brown ('58) .35 .15
110 A19 50c dp red lilac .45 .15
a. Booklet pane of 4 2.00
111 A20 65c brn car & grn ('55) 1.75 .65
112 A19 1sh dp mag & blk .50 .15
113 A20 1.30sh pur & red org ('55) 1.50 .15
114 A20 2sh dp grn & gray 1.75 .30
115 A20 5sh black & org 5.00 .75
116 A20 10sh ultra & black 10.00 1.40
117 A21 £1 black & ver 15.00 3.25
Nos. 103-117 (15) 38.60 7.85

No. 103b is unique.

For "Official" overprints see Tanganyika Nos. O1-O12.

Map Showing Lakes Victoria and Tanganyika A22

Perf. 12½x13

1958, July 30 Engr. Wmk. 314

118 A22 40c green & blue .30 .30
119 A22 1.30sh violet & green .75 .70

Cent. of the discovery of Lakes Victoria and Tanganyika by Sir Richard F. Burton and Capt. J. H. Speke.

Sisal — A23

A25

Mount Kenya and Giant Plants A24

Designs: 10c, Cotton. 15c, Coffee. 20c, Gnu. 25c, Ostriches. 30c, Thompson's gazelles. 40c, Manta ray. 50c, Zebras. 65c, Cheetah. 1.30sh, Murchison Falls and hippopotamuses. 2sh, Mt. Kilimanjaro and giraffes. 2.50sh, Candelabra tree and black rhinoceroses. 5sh, Crater Lake and Mountains of the Moon. 10sh, Ngorongoro Crater and buffaloes.

Perf. 14½x14

1960, Oct. 1 Photo. Wmk. 314

120 A23 5c dull blue .15 .15
121 A23 10c lt olive green .15 .15
a. Booklet pane of 4 .50
122 A23 15c dull purple .15 .15
a. Booklet pane of 4 .50
123 A23 20c brt lilac rose .15 .15
a. Booklet pane of 4 .70
124 A23 25c olive gray .65 .35
125 A23 30c brt vermilion .20 .20
a. Booklet pane of 4 .90
126 A23 40c bright blue .35 .20
127 A23 50c dull violet .40 .20
a. Booklet pane of 4 1.90
128 A23 65c lemon .95 1.25

Engr.
Perf. 14

129 A24 1sh vio & red lilac .50 .20
130 A24 1.30sh choc & dk car .95 .20
131 A24 2sh dk bl & dull bl 1.25 .35
132 A24 2.50sh ol grn & dull bl 1.65 .75
133 A24 5sh rose red & lilac 3.25 .75
134 A24 10sh sl bl & ol grn 6.50 1.50

Perf. 13½x13

135 A25 20sh lake & bluish violet 13.00 5.00
Nos. 120-135 (16) 30.25 11.55

Booklets issued in 1961.

On Nos. 120-134, positions of "Kenya," "Uganda" and "Tanganyika" are rotated.
For "Official" overprints see Tanganyika Nos. O13-O20.

Agricultural Development — A26

Design: 30c, 1.30sh, Farmer picking corn.

Unwmk.

1963, Mar. 21		**Photo.**	**Perf. 14**
136 A26	15c lt ol green & ultra	.15	.15
137 A26	30c yel & red brown	.20	.15
138 A26	50c dp org & ultra	.30	.16
139 A26	1.30sh lt blue & red brn	.60	.40
Nos. 136-139 (4)		1.25	.86

FAO "Freedom from Hunger" campaign.

Scholars and Open Book A27

1963, June 28	**Unwmk.**	**Perf. 14**	
140 A27	30c multicolored	.15	.15
141 A27	1.30sh multicolored	.35	.35
Set value			.42

Inauguration of University of East Africa.

Red Cross A28

1963, Sept. 2			
142 A28	30c blue & red	.18	.15
143 A28	50c bister brown & red	.60	.30

Centenary of International Red Cross.

Kenya, Uganda, Tanganyika and Zanzibar

Issued by the East African Common Services Organization. Not used in Zanzibar.

Japanese Crest and Olympic Rings — A29

Olympic Rings and Banners A30

Unwmk.

1964, Oct. 25		**Perf. 14**	
144 A29	30c orange & dk purple	.15	.15
145 A29	50c dk purple & org	.15	.15
146 A30	1.30sh blue, grn & org	.32	.32
147 A30	2.50sh blue, vio & lil rose	.60	.60
Nos. 144-147 (4)		1.22	1.22

18th Olympic Games, Tokyo, Oct. 10-25.

Kenya, Uganda, Tanzania

Issued by the East African Common Services Organization.

Safari Rally Emblem and Leopard — A31

Design: 1.30sh, Car on road through national park and emblem of the East African Safari Rally.

1965, Apr. 15	**Unwmk.**	**Perf. 14**	
148 A31	30c blue grn, yel & blk	.15	.15
149 A31	50c brown, yel & blk	.16	.15
150 A31	1.30sh lt ultra, ocher & green	.35	.28
151 A31	2.50sh blue, dk grn & dull red	.65	.65
Nos. 148-151 (4)		1.31	1.23

13th East African Safari Rally, Apr. 15-19, 1965.

ITU Emblem, Old and Modern Communication Equipment — A32

1965, May 17		**Photo.**	
152 A32	30c lilac rose, gold & brn	.15	.15
153 A32	50c gray, gold & brown	.15	.15
154 A32	1.30sh lt vio bl, gold & brn	.35	.30
155 A32	2.50sh brt bl grn, gold & brn	.75	.75
Nos. 152-155 (4)		1.40	1.35

Cent. of the ITU.

ICY Emblem — A33

1965, Aug. 4	**Unwmk.**	**Perf. 14**	
156 A33	30c green & gold	.15	.15
157 A33	50c slate black & gold	.15	.15
158 A33	1.30sh ultra & gold	.35	.30
159 A33	2.50sh car & gold	.70	.70
Nos. 156-159 (4)		1.35	1.30

International Cooperation Year.

Game Park Lodge A34

Tourist Publicity: 50c, Murchison Falls, Uganda. 1.30sh, Lake Nakuru, Kenya. 2.50sh, Deep-sea fishing, Tanzania.

1966, Apr. 4		**Photo.**	**Perf. 14**
160 A34	30c ocher & multi	.15	.15
161 A34	50c green & multi	.15	.15
a.	Blue omitted		
162 A34	1.30sh multicolored	.35	.30
163 A34	2.50sh gray & multi	.75	.75
Nos. 160-163 (4)		1.40	1.35

Javelin Thrower and Games' Emblem A35

1966, Aug. 2	**Unwmk.**	**Perf. 14**	
164 A35	30c multicolored	.15	.15
165 A35	50c multicolored	.15	.15
166 A35	1.30sh multicolored	.35	.30
167 A35	2.50sh multicolored	.75	.75
Nos. 164-167 (4)		1.40	1.35

8th British Commonwealth and Empire Games, Jamaica, Aug. 4-13, 1966.

UNESCO Emblem A36

1966, Oct. 3		**Photo.**	**Perf. 14**
168 A36	30c rose red, brt grn & blk	.15	.15
169 A36	50c lt brn, brt grn & blk	.15	.15
170 A36	1.30sh gray, brt grn & blk	.35	.30
171 A36	2.50sh yel, brt grn & blk	.75	.70
Nos. 168-171 (4)		1.40	1.30

20th anniv. of UNESCO.

Dragon Rapide A37

Planes: 50c, Super VC10. 1.30sh, Comet 4. 2.50sh, F.27 Friendship.

1967, Jan. 23		**Unwmk.**	
172 A37	30c multicolored	.15	.15
173 A37	50c multicolored	.20	.15
174 A37	1.30sh multicolored	.50	.40
175 A37	2.50sh multicolored	1.50	1.50
Nos. 172-175 (4)		2.35	2.20

21st anniversary of East African Airways.

Pillar Tomb, East African Coast — A38

Designs: 50c, Man hunting elephant, petroglyph, Tanzania. 1.30sh, Clay head, Luzira, Uganda. 2.50sh, Proconsul skull, Rusinga Island, Kenya.

1967, May 2		**Photo.**	**Perf. 14**
176 A38	30c rose lake, blk & yel	.15	.15
177 A38	50c gray, black & ver	.15	.15
178 A38	1.30sh green, yel & blk	.35	.30
179 A38	2.50sh cop red, yel & blk	.70	.65
Nos. 176-179 (4)		1.35	1.25

Archaeological relics of East Africa.

Emblems of Kenya, Tanzania and Tanganyika — A39

Photo.; Gold Impressed

1967, Dec. 1		**Perf. 14½x14**	
180 A39	5sh gray, black & gold	1.25	1.25

Establishment of East African Community.

Mount Kenya A40

Designs: 30c Mountain climber. 1.30sh, Mount Kilimanjaro. 2.50sh, Ruwenzori Mountains.

1968, Mar. 4		**Photo.**	**Perf. 14½**
181 A40	30c multicolored	.15	.15
182 A40	50c multicolored	.18	.15
183 A40	1.30sh multicolored	.42	.35
184 A40	2.50sh multicolored	.90	.90
Nos. 181-184 (4)		1.65	1.55

Family and Rural Hospital A41

Family and: 50c, Student nurse. 1.30sh, Microscope. 2.50sh, Mosquito and hand holding hypodermic.

1968, May 13		**Photo.**	**Perf. 13½**
185 A41	30c multicolored	.15	.15
186 A41	50c rose vio, blk & brt pink	.15	.15
187 A41	1.30sh brn org, blk & brt pink	.35	.28
188 A41	2.50sh gray, blk & brt pink	.65	.65
Nos. 185-188 (4)		1.30	1.23

20th anniv. of the WHO.

Stadium A42

Designs: 50c, Diving tower. 1.30sh, Pylons and tracks. 2.50sh, Boxing ring, vert.

Perf. 14½x14, 14x14½

1968, Oct. 14		**Photo.**	
189 A42	30c dull pur & gray grn	.15	.15
190 A42	30c brt grn, blk & gray	.15	.15
191 A42	1.30sh gray grn, blk & dk car	.35	.28
192 A42	2.50sh buff, brn org & brn blk	.65	.65
Nos. 189-192 (4)		1.30	1.23

19th Olympic Games, Mexico City, Oct. 12-27.

Railroad Ferry MV Umoja A43

Water Transport: 50c, Transatlantic liner S.S. Harambee. 1.30sh, Lake motor vessel Victoria. 2.50sh, Ferry St. Michael.

1969, Jan. 20		**Photo.**	**Perf. 14**
193 A43	30c blue, gray & dk bl	.16	.15
194 A43	50c blue, gray & scar	.28	.20
195 A43	1.30sh bl, dk bl & dk green	.70	.60
196 A43	2.50sh bl, dk bl & org	1.60	1.60
Nos. 193-196 (4)		2.74	2.55

Farm Workers and ILO Emblem A44

ILO Emblem and: 50c, Construction. 1.30sh, Industry. 2.50sh, Shipping.

1969, Apr. 14		**Photo.**	**Perf. 14**
197 A44	30c green, blk & yel	.15	.15
198 A44	50c car rose, blk & car	.15	.15
199 A44	1.30sh dp org, blk & org	.30	.25
200 A44	2.50sh grnsh bl, blk & ultra	.60	.60
Nos. 197-200 (4)		1.20	1.15

50th anniv. of the ILO.

Pope Paul VI, Mountains of the Moon, Papal Arms, Crested Crane — A45

Euphorbia Tree in Shape of Africa, Development Bank Emblem — A46

1969, July 31   Photo.   Perf. 14
201 A45	30c dk blue, blk & gold	.15	.15
202 A45	70c plum, blk & gold	.16	.15
203 A45	1.50sh gray bl, blk & gold	.40	.35
204 A45	2.50sh dp vio, blk & gold	.65	.65
	Nos. 201-204 (4)	1.36	1.30

Visit of Pope Paul VI to Uganda, July 31-Aug. 2.

Perf. 14x13½
1969, Dec. 8   Litho.   Unwmk.
205 A46	30c brt grn, dk grn & gold	.15	.15
206 A46	70c plum, dk grn & gold	.16	.15
207 A46	1.50sh grnsh bl, dk grn & gold	.40	.30
208 A46	2.50sh brn org, dk grn & gold	.65	.65
	Nos. 205-208 (4)	1.36	1.25

African Development Bank, 5th anniv.

Amadinda, Uganda A47

Musical Instruments: 30c, Marimba, Tanzania. 1.50sh, Nzomari (trumpet), Kenya. 2.50sh, Adeudeu, Kenya.

1970, Feb. 16   Litho.   Perf. 11x12
209 A47	30c multicolored	.15	.15
210 A47	70c multicolored	.16	.15
211 A47	1.50sh dk rose brn & org	.40	.30
212 A47	2.50sh multicolored	.65	.65
	Nos. 209-212 (4)	1.36	1.25

Satellite Earth Station A48

Designs: 70c, Radar station by day. 1.50sh, Radar station by night. 2.50sh, Satellite transmitting communications to and from earth.

1970, May 18   Litho.   Perf. 14½
213 A48	30c multicolored	.15	.15
214 A48	70c multicolored	.16	.15
215 A48	1.50sh org, blk & vio	.45	.30
216 A48	2.50sh dull bl & multi	.65	.65
	Nos. 213-216 (4)	1.41	1.25

Opening of the East African Satellite Earth Station, Mt. Margaret, Kenya.

Runner — A49

1970, July 16   Litho.   Perf. 14½
217 A49	30c org brn, dk brn & blk	.15	.15
218 A49	70c grn, dk brn & blk	.16	.15
219 A49	1.50sh dull pur, dk brn & blk	.40	.30

220 A49	2.50sh grnsh bl, dk brn & blk	.65	.65
	Nos. 217-220 (4)	1.36	1.25

Issued to publicize the 9th British Commonwealth Games, Edinburgh, July 16-25.

UN Emblem and People A50

1970, Oct. 19   Photo.   Perf. 14½
221 A50	30c org brn, gold & black	.15	.15
222 A50	70c bl grn, gold & black	.16	.15
223 A50	1.50sh dull red brn, gold & blk	.40	.30
224 A50	2.50sh olive, gold & blk	.65	.65
	Nos. 221-224 (4)	1.36	1.25

25th anniversary of the United Nations.

Conversion from Pounds to Kilograms A51

Designs: 70c, Conversion from Fahrenheit to centigrade. 1.50sh, Conversion from gallons to liters. 2.50sh, Conversion from miles to kilometers.

1971, Jan. 4   Photo.   Perf. 14½
225 A51	30c silver & multi	.15	.15
226 A51	70c silver & multi	.16	.15
227 A51	1.50sh silver & multi	.40	.30
228 A51	2.50sh silver & multi	.65	.65
	Nos. 225-228 (4)	1.36	1.25

Conversion to metric system of weights and measures.

Locomotive — A52

Designs: Various locomotives.

1971, Apr. 19   Photo.   Perf. 14½
229 A52	30c gold & multi	.15	.15
230 A52	70c gold & multi	.42	.25
231 A52	1.50sh gold & multi	1.00	1.00
232 A52	2.50sh gold & multi	2.25	2.25
a.	Souvenir sheet of 4, #229-232	10.00	10.00
	Nos. 229-232 (4)	3.82	3.65

70th anniversary of the completion of the Mombasa to Kisumu line.

Bull and Campaign Emblem A53

Designs: 30c, 1.50sh, Campaign emblem and cow. 2.50sh, like 70c.

1971, July 5   Photo.   Perf. 14½
233 A53	30c yel grn, blk & bis	.15	.15
234 A53	70c gray bl, blk & bis	.16	.15
235 A53	1.50sh mag, blk & bis	.40	.30
236 A53	2.50sh red org, blk & bis	.65	.65
	Nos. 233-236 (4)	1.36	1.25

Rinderpest campaign by the Organization for African Unity.

Meeting of Stanley and Livingstone — A54

1971, Oct. 28   Litho.   Perf. 14
237 A54	5sh multicolored	1.50	1.50

Centenary of the meeting at Ujiji of Dr. David Livingstone, missionary, and Henry M. Stanley, journalist, who had been sent to find Livingstone.

Modern Farming Village A55

Designs: 30c, Pres. Julius K. Nyerere carried in triumph, 1961, vert. 1.50sh, University of Dar es Salaam. 2.50sh, Kilimanjaro International Airport.

1971, Dec. 9   Perf. 14
238 A55	30c bister & multi	.15	.15
239 A55	70c lt blue & multi	.16	.15
240 A55	1.50sh lt green & multi	.40	.30
241 A55	2.50sh yel & multi	.85	.85
	Nos. 238-241 (4)	1.56	1.45

10th anniv. of independence of Tanzania.

Flags of African Nations and Fair Emblem A56

1972, Feb. 23   Perf. 13½x14
242 A56	30c lt bl & multi	.15	.15
243 A56	70c gray & multi	.16	.15
244 A56	1.50sh yel & multi	.40	.30
245 A56	2.50sh multicolored	.65	.65
	Nos. 242-245 (4)	1.36	1.25

First All-Africa Trade Fair, Nairobi, Kenya, Feb. 23-Mar. 5.

Child Drinking Milk, UNICEF Emblem A57

25th Anniv. (in 1971) of UNICEF: 70c, Children playing ball. 1.50sh, Child writing on blackboard. 2.50sh, Boy playing with tractor.

1972, Apr. 24   Litho.   Perf. 14½x14
246 A57	30c brn org & multi	.15	.15
247 A57	70c lt ultra & multi	.25	.15
248 A57	1.50sh yel & multi	.55	.45
249 A57	2.50sh green & multi	1.00	1.00
	Nos. 246-249 (4)	1.95	1.75

Hurdles, Olympic and Motion Emblems A58

1972, Aug. 28
250 A58	40c shown	.15	.15
251 A58	70c Running	.22	.15
252 A58	1.50sh Boxing	.38	.30
253 A58	2.50sh Hockey	.75	.75
a.	Souvenir sheet of 4, #250-253	5.00	5.00
	Nos. 250-253 (4)	1.50	1.35

20th Olympic Games, Munich, Aug. 26-Sept. 11.

Uganda Kob, Semliki Game Reserve A59

1972, Oct. 9   Litho.   Perf. 14
254 A59	40c shown	.18	.15
255 A59	70c Intl. Conf. Center	.30	.18
256 A59	1.50sh Makarere Univ., Kampala	.70	.55
257 A59	2.50sh Uganda arms	1.90	1.90
a.	Souvenir sheet of 4, #254-257, perf. 13x14	5.00	5.00
	Nos. 254-257 (4)	3.08	2.78

Uganda's independence, 10th anniv. #256 also for 50th anniv. of Makarere University, Kampala.

Flag of East Africa — A60

1972, Dec. 1   Litho.   Perf. 14½x14
258 A60	5sh multicolored	2.50	2.50

5th anniv. of the East African Community.

Anemometer, Lake Victoria Station — A61

WMO Emblem and: 70c, Release of weather balloon, vert. 1.50sh, Hail suppression by meteorological rocket. 2.50sh, Meteorological satellite receiving antenna.

1973, Mar. 5   Litho.   Perf. 14
259 A61	40c multicolored	.15	.15
260 A61	70c ultra & multi	.25	.15
261 A61	1.50sh emer & multi	.55	.45
262 A61	2.50sh multicolored	1.00	1.00
	Nos. 259-262 (4)	1.95	1.75

Cent. of intl. meteorological cooperation.

Scouts Laying Bricks — A62

Designs: 70c, Baden-Powell's gravestone, Nyeri, Kenya. 1.50sh, World Scout emblem. 2.50sh, Lord Baden-Powell.

1973, July 16   Litho.   Perf. 14
263 A62	40c ocher & multi	.25	.15
264 A62	70c multicolored	.40	.30
265 A62	1.50sh multicolored	.90	.75
266 A62	2.50sh grn & ultra	2.25	1.50
	Nos. 263-266 (4)	3.80	2.70

24th Boy Scout World Conference (1st in Africa), Nairobi, Kenya, July 16-21.

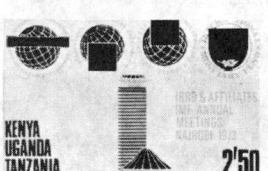

International Bank for Reconstruction and Development and Affiliates' Emblems — A63

Designs: 40c, Arrows dividing 4 bank affiliate emblems. 70c, Vert. lines dividing 4 emblems. 1.50sh, Kenyatta Conference Center, Nairobi, vert.

1973, Sept. 24   Litho.   Perf. 14x13½
267 A63	40c gray, blk & grn	.20	.15
268 A63	70c brn, gray & blk	.32	.20
269 A63	1.50sh lem, gray & blk	.75	.60
270 A63	2.50sh blk, org & gray	1.40	1.40
a.	Souvenir sheet of 4	2.50	2.50
	Nos. 267-270 (4)	2.67	2.35

Intl. Bank for Reconstruction and Development and Affiliate Intl. Monetary Fund Meetings, Nairobi.
No. 270a contains stamps similar to Nos. 267-270 with simulated perforations.

INTERPOL Emblem, Policeman and Dog — A64

Designs: 70c, East African policemen and emblem. 1.50sh, INTERPOL emblem. 2.50sh, INTERPOL Headquarters, St. Cloud, France.

1973-74   Litho.   Perf. 14x14½

271	A64	40c yellow & multi	.22	.15
272	A64	70c multicolored	.38	.22
273	A64	1.50sh violet & multi	.80	.70
274	A64	2.50sh lemon & multi (St. Clans)	1.90	1.90
275	A64	2.50sh lemon & multi (St. Cloud) ('74)	1.90	1.90
		Nos. 271-275 (5)	5.20	4.87

50th anniv. of Intl. Criminal Police Org. Issued: Nos. 271-274, Oct. 24, 1973.

Tea Factory, Nandi Hills A65

1973, Dec. 12   Photo.   Perf. 13x14

276	A65	40c shown	.15	.15
277	A65	70c Kenyatta Hospital	.25	.15
278	A65	1.50sh Nairobi Airport	.55	.45
279	A65	2.50sh Kindaruma hydroelectric plant	1.00	1.00
		Nos. 276-279 (4)	1.95	1.75

10th anniversary of independence.

Afro-Shirazi Party Headquarters — A66

Designs: 70c, Michenzani housing development. 1.50sh, Map of East Africa and television screen with flower. 2.50sh, Amaan Stadium.

1974, Jan. 12   Perf. 13½x14

280	A66	40c multicolored	.15	.15
281	A66	70c multicolored	.25	.15
282	A66	1.50sh black & multi	.55	.45
283	A66	2.50sh black & multi	1.00	1.00
		Nos. 280-283 (4)	1.95	1.75

10th anniversary of Zanzibar revolution.

Symbol of Union A67

Designs: 70c, Map of Tanganyika and Zanzibar, and handshake. 1.50sh, Map of Tanganyika and Zanzibar, and communications symbols. 2.50sh, Flags of Tanu, Tanzania and Afro-Shirazi Party.

1974, Apr. 24   Litho.   Perf. 14½

284	A67	40c sepia & multi	.15	.15
285	A67	70c blue grn & multi	.25	.15
286	A67	1.50sh ultra & multi	.65	.50
287	A67	2.50sh multicolored	1.50	1.50
		Nos. 284-287 (4)	2.55	2.30

Union of Tanganyika and Zanzibar, 10th anniv.

Family and Home A68

Designs: 70c, Drummer at dawn. 1.50sh, Family hoeing, and livestock. 2.50sh, Telephonist, train, plane, telegraph lines.

1974, July 15   Litho.   Perf. 14½

288	A68	40c multicolored	.15	.15
289	A68	70c multicolored	.25	.15
290	A68	1.50sh multicolored	.65	.50
291	A68	2.50sh multicolored	1.20	1.20
		Nos. 288-291 (4)	2.25	2.00

17th Intl. Conf. on Social Welfare, July 14-20.

Post and Telegraph Headquarters, Kampala — A69

Cent. of the UPU: 70c, Mail train and truck. 1.50sh, UPU Headquarters, Bern. 2.50sh, Loading mail on East African Airways VC-10.

1974, Oct. 9   Litho.   Perf. 14

292	A69	40c lt green & multi	.15	.15
293	A69	70c gray & multi	.25	.15
294	A69	1.50sh yel & multi	.65	.50
295	A69	2.50sh lt blue & multi	1.20	1.20
		Nos. 292-295 (4)	2.25	2.00

Family Planning Clinic A70

World Population Year: 70c, "Tug of War." 1.50sh, Scales and world population figures. 2.50sh, World Population Year emblem.

1974, Dec. 16   Litho.   Perf. 14½

296	A70	40c multicolored	.15	.15
297	A70	70c purple & multi	.25	.15
298	A70	1.50sh multicolored	.65	.50
299	A70	2.50sh blue blk & multi	1.20	1.20
		Nos. 296-299 (4)	2.25	2.00

Seronera Wild Life Lodge, Tanzania A71

Game lodges of East Africa: 70c, Mweya Safari Lodge, Uganda. 1.50sh, Ark-Aberdare Forest Lodge, Kenya. 2.50sh, Paraa Safari Lodge, Uganda.

1975, Feb. 24   Perf. 14½

300	A71	40c multicolored	.20	.15
301	A71	70c multicolored	.32	.20
302	A71	1.50sh multicolored	.90	.65
303	A71	2.50sh multicolored	1.60	1.60
		Nos. 300-303 (4)	3.02	2.60

Wooden Comb, Bajun, Kenya — A72

African Artifacts: 1sh, Earring, Chaga, Tanzania. 2sh, Armlet, Acholi, Uganda. 3sh, Kamba gourd, Kenya.

1975, May 5   Litho.   Perf. 13½

304	A72	50c gray & multi	.18	.15
305	A72	1sh gray & multi	.35	.30
306	A72	2sh multicolored	.75	.60
307	A72	3sh multicolored	1.20	1.20
		Nos. 304-307 (4)	2.48	2.25

Map Showing OAU Members, Ugandan Flag — A73

Elephant, Kenya — A74

OAU Emblem and: 50c, Entebbe Airport, horiz. 2sh, Nile Hotel, Kampala, horiz. 3sh, Ugandan Martyrs' Shrine, Namugongo.

Perf. 11½x11, 11x11½

1975, July 28   Litho.

308	A73	50c multicolored	.18	.15
309	A73	1sh multicolored	.35	.30
310	A73	2sh multicolored	.75	.60
311	A73	3sh multicolored	1.20	1.20
		Nos. 308-311 (4)	2.48	2.25

Organization for African Unity (OAU), Summit Conf., Kampala, July 28 - Aug. 1.

1975, Sept. 11   Litho.   Perf. 11x11½

Protected animals: 1sh, Albino buffalo, Uganda. 2sh, Elephant, exhibit in National Museum, Kenya. 3sh, Abbott's duiker, Tanzania.

312	A74	50c multicolored	.40	.30
313	A74	1sh brown & multi	.70	.60
314	A74	2sh yel green & multi	1.50	1.25
315	A74	3sh blue grn & multi	2.50	2.50
		Nos. 312-315 (4)	5.10	4.65

Masai Villagers Bleeding Cow, Masai, Kenya — A75

Festival Emblem and: 1sh, Ugandan dancers. 2sh, Family, Makonde sculpture, Tanzania. 3sh, Skinning hippopotamus, East Africa.

1975, Nov. 3   Litho.   Perf. 13½x14

316	A75	50c org brown & multi	.18	.15
317	A75	1sh brt green & multi	.35	.30
318	A75	2sh dk blue & multi	.75	.60
319	A75	3sh lilac & multi	1.20	1.20
		Nos. 316-319 (4)	2.48	2.25

2nd World Black and African Festival of Arts and Culture, Lagos, Nigeria, Jan. 5 - Feb. 12.

Fokker Friendship, Nairobi Airport — A76

East African Airways, 30th anniv.: 1sh, DC-9 Kilimanjaro Airport. 2sh, Super VC10, Entebbe Airport. 3sh, East African Airways emblem.

1976, Jan. 2   Litho.   Perf. 11½

320	A76	50c ultra & multi	.25	.25
321	A76	1sh rose & multi	.40	.40
322	A76	2sh orange & multi	1.00	1.00
323	A76	3sh black & multi	1.60	1.60
		Nos. 320-323 (4)	3.25	3.25

POSTAGE DUE STAMPS

Kenya and Uganda

D1

D2

Perf. 14½x14

1928-33   Typo.   Wmk. 4

J1	D1	5c deep violet	1.00	1.25
J2	D1	10c orange red	1.00	1.25
J3	D1	20c yel green	1.00	1.65
J4	D1	30c ol brn ('31)	9.00	7.00
J5	D1	40c dull blue	4.50	9.00
J6	D1	1sh grnsh gray ('33)	35.00	125.00
		Nos. J1-J6 (6)	51.50	145.15

Kenya, Uganda, Tanganyika

1935, May 1   Perf. 13½x14

J7	D2	5c violet	.20	.25
J8	D2	10c red	.20	.20
J9	D2	20c green	.35	.30
J10	D2	30c brown	.55	.90
J11	D2	40c ultramarine	3.50	6.00
J12	D2	1sh gray	10.00	14.00
		Nos. J7-J12 (6)	14.80	21.65

OFFICIAL STAMPS

The 1959-60 "OFFICIAL" overprints on Nos. 103-104, 106-108, 110, 112-117, 120-123, 125, 127, 129, 133 are listed under Tanganyika, as they were used by the Tanganyika government.

KIRIBATI

'kir-ə-ˌbas

LOCATION — A group of islands in the Pacific Ocean northeast of Australia
GOVT. — Republic
AREA — 264 sq. mi.
POP. — 60,302 (1982)
CAPITAL — Tarawa

Kiribati, former Gilbert Islands, consists of the Gilbert, Phoenix, Ocean and Line Islands.

Catalogue values for all unused stamps in this country are for Never Hinged items.

Watermark

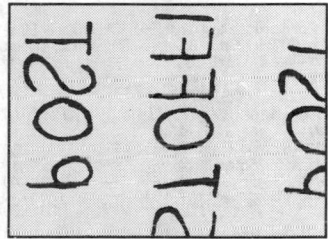

Wmk. 380- "POST OFFICE"

Kiribati Flag — A50

Parliament, London, Assembly, Tarawa A51

Wmk. 373

1979, July 12   Litho.   Perf. 14

325	A50	10c multicolored	.15	.15
326	A51	45c multicolored	.70	.70

Independence.

Training Ship Teraaka A52

Designs: 3c, Passenger launch Tautunu. 5c, Hibiscus. 7c, Cathedral, Tarawa. 10c, House of Assembly, Bikenibeu Island. 12c, Betio harbor. 15c,

Reef egret. 20c, Flamboyant tree. 25c, Moorish idol (fish). 30c, Frangipani blossoms. 35c, Chapel, Tangintebu Island. 50c, Hypolimnas bolina elliciana (butterfly). $1, Tarawa Lagoon ferry, Tabakea. $2, Sunset over lagoon. $5, Natl. flag.

1979-80 Wmk. 373

327	A52	1c multicolored	.15	.15
328	A52	3c multicolored	.15	.15
329	A52	5c multicolored	.15	.15
330	A52	7c multicolored	.15	.15
331	A52	10c multicolored	.15	.15
332	A52	12c multicolored	.15	.15
333	A52	15c multicolored	.25	.20
334	A52	20c multicolored	.35	.30
335	A52	25c multicolored	.35	.35
336	A52	30c multicolored	.40	.40
337	A52	35c multicolored	.40	.40
338	A52	50c multicolored	.70	.70
339	A52	$1 multicolored	1.25	.85
340	A52	$2 multicolored	2.25	1.75
340A	A52	$5 multicolored	5.00	5.25
		Nos. 327-340A (15)	11.85	11.10

Issued: $5, Aug. 27, 1980. Others, July 12, 1979.

1980-81 Unwmk.

327a	A52	1c multi ('81)	.15	.15
328a	A52	3c multi ('81)	.15	.15
329a	A52	5c multi	.15	.15
330a	A52	7c multi	.15	.15
331a	A52	10c multi	.15	.15
332a	A52	12c multi	.20	.15
333a	A52	15c multi	.25	.20
334a	A52	20c multi ('81)	.30	.30
335a	A52	25c multi	.30	.30
336a	A52	30c multi ('81)	.40	.40
337a	A52	35c multi ('81)	.40	.50
338a	A52	50c multi ('81)	.65	.65
339a	A52	$1 multi	1.10	1.25
340b	A52	$2 multi	2.75	2.75
340c	A52	$5 multi ('80)	4.00	4.00
		Nos. 327a-340c (15)	11.10	11.25

For overprints see Nos. O1-O15.

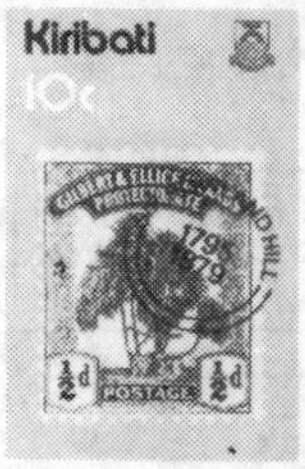

Gilbert and Ellice Islands No. 1 — A53

Simulated Cancel and: 20c, Gilbert and Ellice No. 70. 25c, Great Britain No. 139. 45c, Gilbert and Ellice No. 31.

Wmk. 373

1979, Sept. 27 Litho. *Perf. 14*

341	A53	10c multicolored	.15	.15
342	A53	20c multicolored	.30	.30
343	A53	25c multicolored	.35	.35
344	A53	45c multicolored	.40	.40
a.		Souvenir sheet of 4, #341-344	1.40	1.40
		Nos. 341-344 (4)	1.20	1.20

Sir Rowland Hill (1795-1879), originator of penny postage.

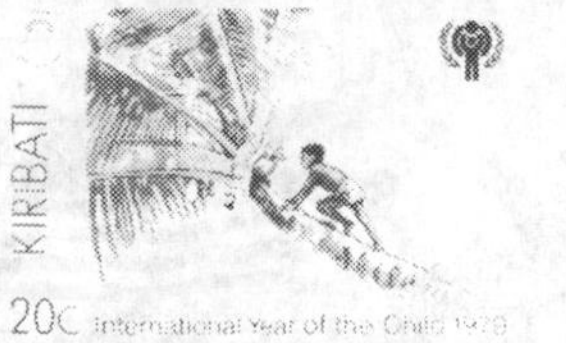

Boy Climbing Coconut Palm, IYC Emblem — A54

IYC Emblem, Coat of Arms and: 10c, Boy and giant clam shell. 45c, Girl reading book. $1, Boy wearing garlands. All vert.

Perf. 14x13½, 13½x14

1979, Nov. 28 Litho.

345	A54	10c multicolored	.15	.15
346	A54	20c multicolored	.30	.30
347	A54	45c multicolored	.35	.35
348	A54	$1 multicolored	.85	.85
		Nos. 345-348 (4)	1.65	1.65

International Year of the Child.

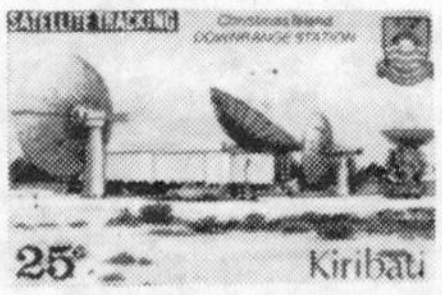

Downrange Station A55

National Space Development Agency of Japan (NASDA) Satellite Tracking: 45c, Experimental satellite trajectory (map). $1, Rocket launch, Tanegashima, Japan, vert.

1980, Feb. 20 Litho. *Perf. 14½*

349	A55	25c multicolored	.20	.20
350	A55	45c multicolored	.45	.45
351	A55	$1 multicolored	.90	.90
		Nos. 349-351 (3)	1.55	1.55

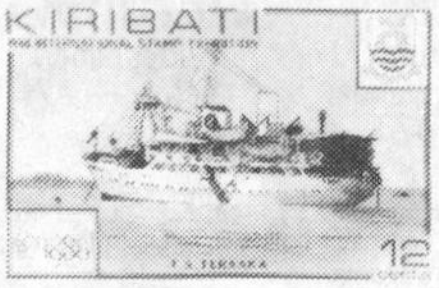

T.S. Teraaka, London 1980 Emblem A56

1980, Apr. 30 Litho. Unwmk.

352	A56	12c shown	.15	.15
353	A56	25c Air Tungaru plane, Bonriki Airport	.15	.15
354	A56	30c Radio operator	.25	.25
355	A56	$1 Bairiki post office	.90	.90
a.		Souvenir sheet of 4, #352-355	1.75	1.75
		Nos. 352-355 (4)	1.45	1.45

London 1980 Intl. Stamp Exhib., May 6-14.

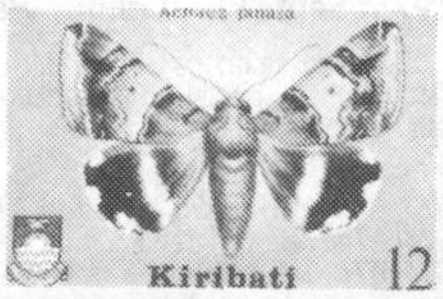

Achaea Janata A57

1980, Aug. 27 Litho. *Perf. 14*

356	A57	12c shown	.15	.15
357	A57	25c Ethmia nigroapicella	.25	.25
358	A57	30c Utetheisa pulchelloides	.35	.35
359	A57	50c Anua coronata	.65	.65
		Nos. 356-359 (4)	1.40	1.40

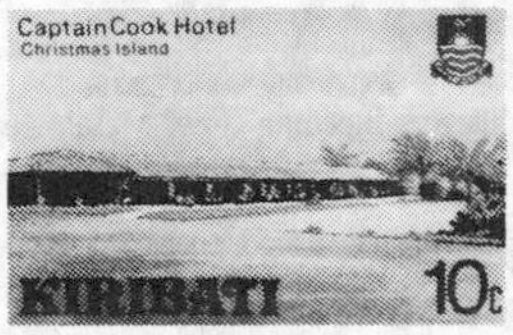

Capt. Cook Hotel A58

1980, Nov. 19 Wmk. 373 *Perf. 13½*

360	A58	10c shown	.15	.15
361	A58	20c Stadium	.20	.20
362	A58	25c Intl. Airport, Bonriki	.25	.25
363	A58	35c National Library	.40	.40
364	A58	$1 Otintai Hotel	1.00	1.00
		Nos. 360-364 (5)	2.00	2.00

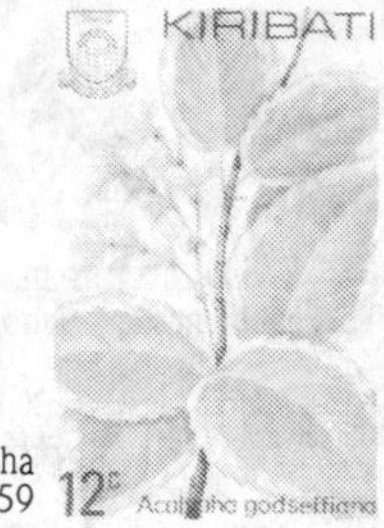

Acalypha Godseffiana — A59

Perf. 14x13½

1981, Feb. 18 Litho. Wmk. 373

365	A59	12c shown	.15	.15
366	A59	30c Hibiscus schizopetalus	.35	.35
367	A59	35c Calotropis gigantea	.40	.40
368	A59	50c Euphorbia pulcherrima	.60	.60
		Nos. 365-368 (4)	1.50	1.50

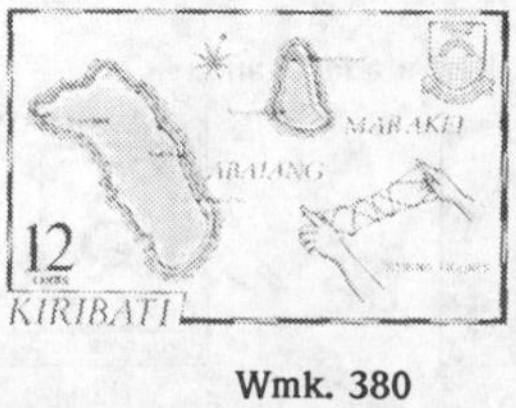

Abaiang and Marakei Islands, String Figures A60

Wmk. 380

1981, May 6 Litho. *Perf. 14*

369	A60	12c shown	.20	.20
370	A60	30c Butaritari, Little Makin, house	.35	.35
371	A60	35c Maiana, Coral Road	.50	.50
372	A60	$1 Christmas Isld., Resolution	1.00	1.00
		Nos. 369-372 (4)	2.05	2.05

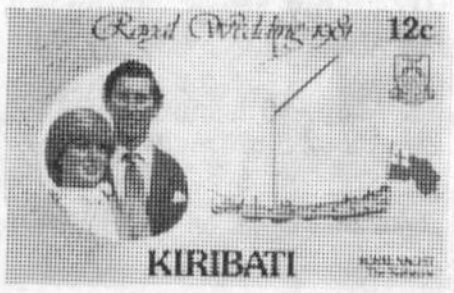

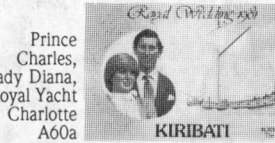

Prince Charles, Lady Diana, Royal Yacht Charlotte A60a

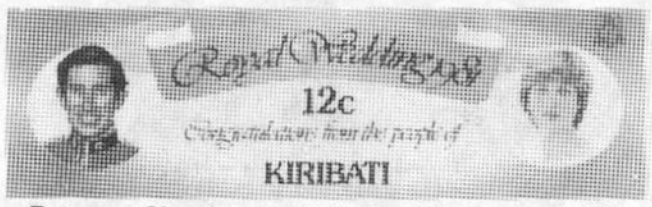

Prince Charles and Lady Diana — A60b

Illustration A60b is greatly reduced.

Wmk. 380

1981, July 29 Litho. *Perf. 14*

373	A60a	12c Couple, The Katherine	.15	.15
a.		Bklt. pane of 4, perf. 12, unwmkd.	.65	
374	A60b	12c Couple	.20	.20
375	A60a	50c The Osborne	.65	.65
376	A60b	50c like #374	.65	.65
a.		Bklt. pane of 2, perf. 12, unwmkd.	1.40	
377	A60a	$2 Britannia	2.50	2.50
378	A60b	$2 like #374	2.50	2.50
		Nos. 373-378 (6)	6.65	6.65

Souvenir Sheet

Perf. 12

379	A60b	$1.20 like #374	2.75	2.75

Royal wedding.

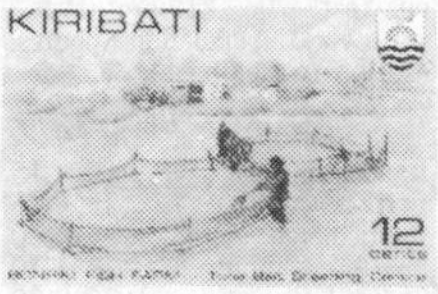

Bonriki Tuna Fish Bait Breeding Center A61

1981, Nov. 19

380	A61	12c shown	.15	.15
381	A61	30c Fishing boat	.40	.40
382	A61	35c Cold storage, Betio	.45	.45
383	A61	50c Nei Manganibuka	.70	.70
a.		Souvenir sheet of 4, #380-383	1.75	1.75
		Nos. 380-383 (4)	1.70	1.70

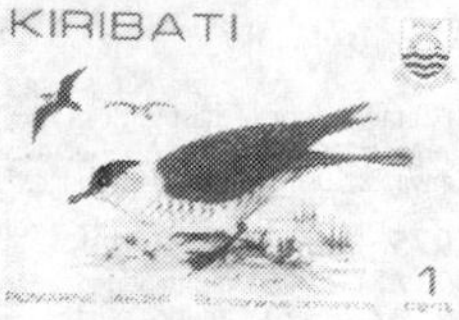

Pomarine Jaegers A62

1982-85 Litho. *Perf. 14*

384	A62	1c shown	.15	.15
385	A62	2c Mallards	.15	.15
386	A62	4c Collared petrels	.15	.15
387	A62	5c Blue-faced boobies	.15	.15
388	A62	7c Friendly quail dove	.15	.15
389	A62	8c Shovelers	.15	.15
390	A62	12c Christmas Isld. warblers	.25	.25
391	A62	15c Pacific plovers	.30	.30
392	A62	20c Reef herons	.40	.40
392A	A62	25c Brown noddies ('83)	.45	.45
393	A62	30c Brown boobies	.55	.55
394	A62	35c Audubon's shearwaters	.65	.65
395	A62	40c White-throated storm petrels, vert.	.70	.70
396	A62	50c Bristle-thighed curlews, vert.	.95	.95
396A	A62	55c Fairy tern ('85)	.55	.55
397	A62	$1 Scarlet-breasted lorikeets, vert.	2.00	2.00
398	A62	$2 Long-tailed cuckoo, vert.	2.50	2.50
399	A62	$5 Great frigate birds, vert.	7.25	7.25
		Nos. 384-399 (18)	17.45	17.45

Issue dates: 25c, Jan. 31, 1983; 55c, Nov. 19, 1985; others, Feb. 18, 1982.
For overprints see Nos. O16-O20.

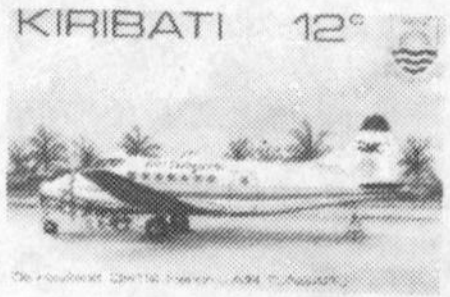

Air Tungaru A63

1982, Feb. 18 Wmk. 380

400	A63	12c De Havilland DH114 Heron	.15	.15
401	A63	30c Britten-Norman Trislander	.45	.45
402	A63	35c Casa 212 Aviocar	.55	.55
403	A63	50c Boeing 727	.80	.80
		Nos. 400-403 (4)	1.95	1.95

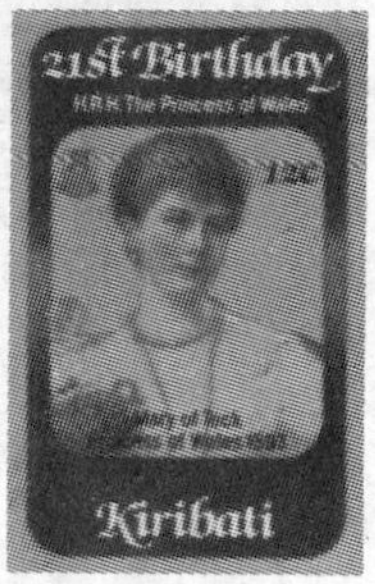

21st Birthday of Princess Diana, July 1 — A64

1982, May 19

404	A64	12c Mary of Teck, 1893	.15	.15
405	A64	50c Teck arms	.60	.60
406	A64	$1 Diana	1.25	1.25
		Nos. 404-406 (3)	2.00	2.00

Nos. 404-406 Overprinted: "ROYAL BABY"

1982, July 14

407	A64	12c multicolored	.15	.15
408	A64	50c multicolored	.60	.60
409	A64	$1 multicolored	1.25	1.25
		Nos. 407-409 (3)	2.00	2.00

Birth of Prince William of Wales, June 21.

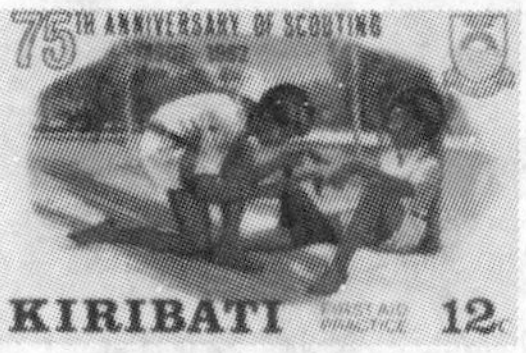

Scouting Year — A65

1982, Aug. 12

410	A65	12c First aid	.15	.15
411	A65	25c Repairing boat	.30	.30
412	A65	30c Saluting	.35	.35
413	A65	50c Gilbert Islds. #304	.65	.65
		Nos. 410-413 (4)	1.45	1.45

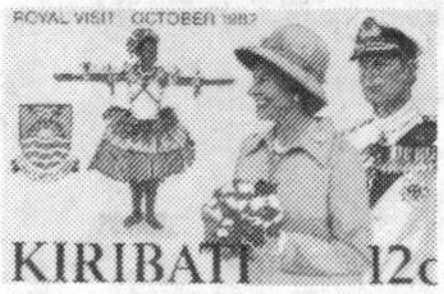

Visit of Queen Elizabeth II and Prince Philip A66

Wmk. 380

1982, Oct. 23 Litho. *Perf. 14*

414	A66	12c Couple, dancer	.20	.20
415	A66	25c Couple, boat	.40	.40
416	A66	35c Philatelic Bureau	.60	.60
		Nos. 414-416 (3)	1.20	1.20

Souvenir Sheet

417	A66	50c Queen Elizabeth II, vert.	.85	.85

Nos. 414-416 also issued in sheets of 6.

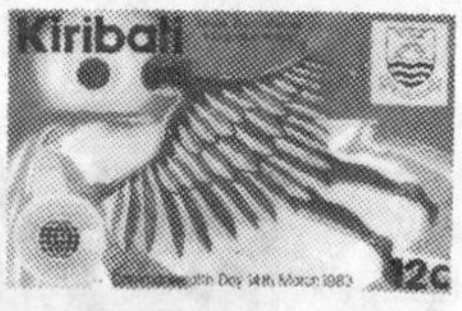

A67

1983, Mar. 14 Wmk. 380 *Perf. 14*

418	A67	12c Obaia the Feathered legend	.15	.15
419	A67	30c Robert Louis Stevenson Hotel, Abemama	.40	.40

420 A67 50c Betio Harbor .70 .70
421 A67 $1 Map 1.40 1.40
Nos. 418-421 (4) 2.65 2.65

Commonwealth day.

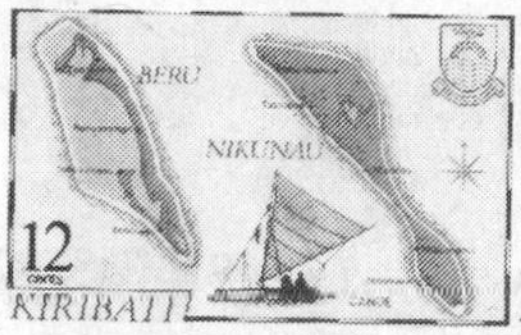

Map of Beru and Nikunau Islds., Canoe A68

1983, May 19 Litho. *Perf. 14*
422 A68 12c shown .15 .15
423 A68 25c Abemama, Kuria, Aranuka .30 .30
424 A68 35c Nonouti, vert. .45 .45
425 A68 50c Tarawa, vert. .65 .65
Nos. 422-425 (4) 1.55 1.55

See #436-439, 456-459, 475-479, 487-490.

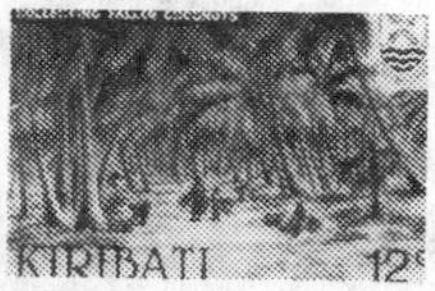

Copra Industry A69

Designs: 12c, Collecting fallen Coconuts. 25c, Selecting Coconuts for Copra. 30c, Removing Husk from Coconuts. 35c, Drying Copra in the Sun. 50c, Loading Copra, Betio Harbor.

1983, Aug. 8 Litho. *Perf. 14*
426 A69 12c multicolored .20 .20
427 A69 25c multicolored .40 .40
428 A69 30c multicolored .50 .50
429 A69 35c multicolored .60 .60
430 A69 50c multicolored .85 .85
Nos. 426-430 (5) 2.55 2.55

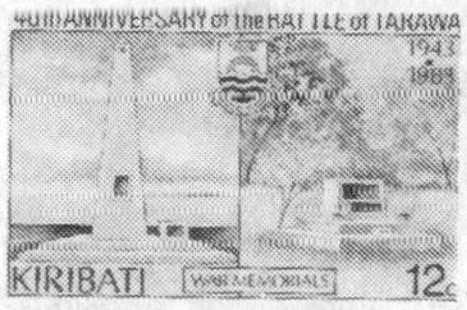

Battle of Tarawa, 40th Anniv. A70

1983, Nov. 17 Litho. Wmk. 380
431 A70 12c War memorials .15 .15
432 A70 30c Battle map .45 .45
433 A70 35c Defense gun .50 .50
434 A70 50c Scenes, 1943, 1983 .75 .75
435 A70 $1 Aircraft carrier 1.50 1.50
Nos. 431-435 (5) 3.35 3.35

Map Type of 1983

1984, Feb. 14 Wmk. 380 *Perf. 14*
436 A68 12c Teraina .20 .20
437 A68 30c Nikumaroro .50 .50
438 A68 35c Kanton .60 .60
439 A68 50c Banaba .85 .85
Nos. 436-439 (4) 2.15 2.15

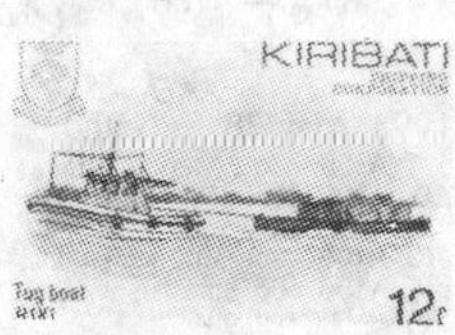

Local Ships A71

1984, May 9 Litho. Wmk. 380
440 A71 12c Tug boat .20 .20
441 A71 35c Ferry landing craft .60 .60
442 A71 50c Ferry .85 .85
443 A71 $1 Cargo and passanger boat 1.75 1.75
a. Souvenir sheet of 4, #440-443, perf. 13½ 4.00 4.00
Nos. 440-443 (4) 3.40 3.40

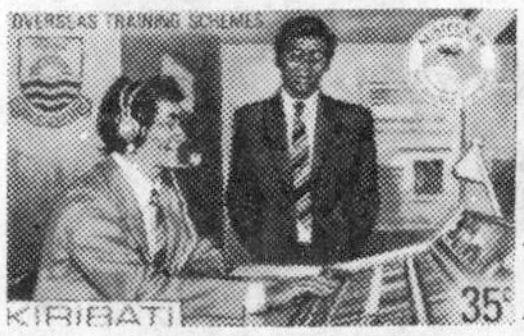

Ausipex '84 A72

1984, Aug. 21 Litho. *Perf. 14*
444 A72 12c South Tarawa sewer & water system .20 .20
445 A72 30c Fishing boat Nouamake .50 .50
446 A72 35c Overseas communications training .60 .60
447 A72 50c Intl. telecommunications link .85 .85
Nos. 444-447 (4) 2.15 2.15

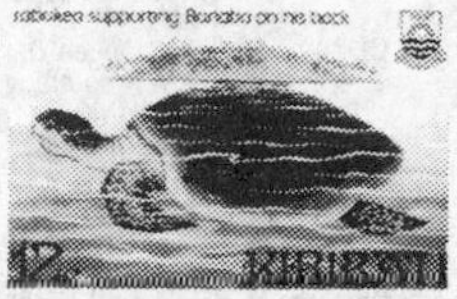

Legends A73

Designs: 12c, Tabakea supporting Banaba on his back. 30c, Nakaa, Judge of the Dead. 35c, Naareau and Tiku-Tiku-Tamoamoa. 50c, Whistling Ghosts.

1984, Nov. 21 Wmk. 380 *Perf. 14*
448 A73 12c multicolored .20 .20
449 A73 30c multicolored .50 .50
450 A73 35c multicolored .60 .60
451 A73 50c multicolored .85 .85
Nos. 448-451 (4) 2.15 2.15

See Nos. 464-467.

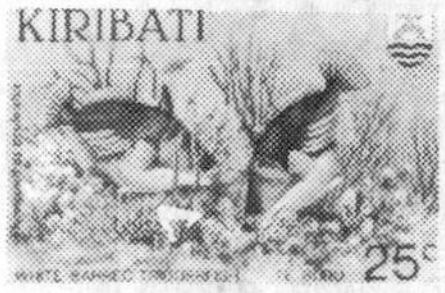

Reef Fish — A74

1985, Feb. 19 Litho. *Perf. 14*
452 A74 12c Tang .15 .15
453 A74 25c White-barred triggerfish .30 .30
454 A74 35c Surgeon fish .50 .50
455 A74 80c Squirrel fish 1.10 1.10
a. Souvenir sheet of 4, #452-455 2.50 2.50
Nos. 452-455 (4) 2.05 2.05

See Nos. 480-483, 491-494, 540-554, 567.

Map Type of 1983

1985, May 9 Litho. *Perf. 13½*
456 A68 12c Tabuaeran, frigate bird .20 .20
457 A68 35c Rawaki, coconuts .50 .50
458 A68 50c Arorae, xanthid crab .70 .70
459 A68 $1 Tamana, fish hook 1.40 1.40
Nos. 456-459 (4) 2.80 2.80

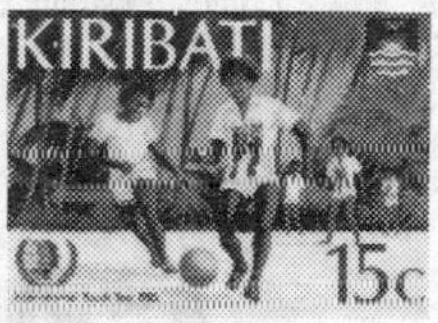

Intl. Youth Year — A76

1985, Aug. 5
460 A76 15c Boys playing soccer .20 .20
461 A76 35c Emblems .50 .50
462 A76 40c Girl processing fruit, vert. .55 .55
463 A76 55c Intl. youth exchange .75 .75
Nos. 460-463 (4) 2.00 2.00

Legends Type of 1984

Designs: 15c, Nang Kineia and the Tickling Ghosts. 35c, Myth of Auriaria and Tituabine. 40c, First Coming of Babai at Arorae. 55c, Riiki and the Milky Way.

1985, Nov. 19 Wmk. 380 *Perf. 14*
464 A73 15c multicolored .25 .25
465 A73 35c multicolored .55 .55
466 A73 40c multicolored .60 .60
467 A73 55c multicolored .85 .85
Nos. 464-467 (4) 2.25 2.25

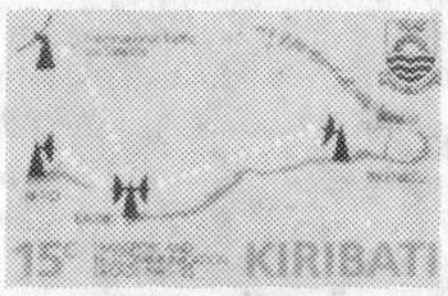

Transport and Telecommunications Decade 1985-95 — A77

1985, Dec. 9 Litho. *Perf. 14*
468 A77 15c Satellite network .25 .25
469 A77 40c Tarawa-Suva feeder service .55 .55

Queen Elizabeth II 60th Birthday
Common Design Type

Designs: 15c, Review of Girl Guides, Windsor Castle, 1938. 35c, Birthday parade, Buckingham Palace, 1980. 40c, With Prince Philip during royal tour, 1982. 55c, Banquet, Austrian embassy in London, 1966. $1, Visiting Crown Agents' offices, 1983.

1986, Apr. 21 *Perf. 14½x14*
470 CD337 15c scar, black & sil .20 .20
471 CD337 35c ultra & multi .45 .45
472 CD337 40c green & multi .55 .55
473 CD337 55c violet & multi .70 .70
474 CD337 $1 rose vio & multi 1.40 1.40
Nos. 470-474 (5) 3.30 3.30

For overprints see Nos. 495-499.

Map Type of 1983

1986, June 17 Wmk. 380 *Perf. 14*
475 A68 15c Manra .20 .20
476 A68 30c Birnie, McKean .40 .40
477 A68 35c Orona .50 .50
478 A68 40c Malden .55 .55
479 A68 55c Vostok, Caroline, Flint .75 .75
Nos. 475-479 (5) 2.40 2.40

Fish Type of 1985

1986, Aug. 26 Unwmk. *Perf. 14*
480 A74 15c Lepidodactylus lugubris .20 .20
481 A74 35c Gehyra mutilata .45 .45
482 A74 40c Hemidactylus frenatus .50 .50
483 A74 55c Gehyra oceanica .70 .70
Nos. 480-483 (4) 1.85 1.85

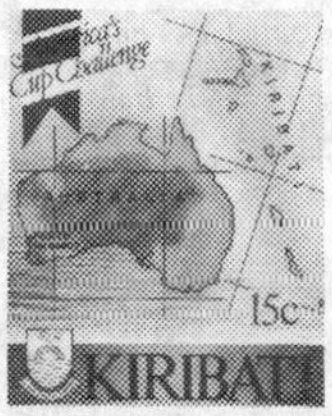

America's Cup — A80

Perf. 14x14½

1986, Dec. 29 Unwmk.
484 Strip of 3 2.75 2.75
a. A80 15c Map of Australia .20 .20
b. A80 55c Course, trophy .65 .65
c. A80 $1.50 Australia II 1.75 1.75

No. 484 has a continuous design.

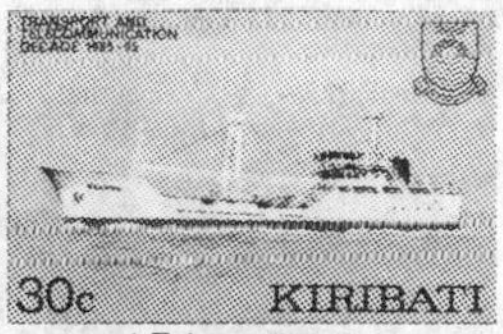

Transport and Telecommunications Decade (1985-1995) — A81

Designs: 30c, Nei Moamoa, flagship of Kiribati overseas shipping line. 55c, Manual and electronic telephone switching systems.

1987, Mar. 31 Litho. *Perf. 14*
485 A81 30c multicolored .40 .40
486 A81 55c multicolored .70 .70

Map Type of 1983

1987, Sept. 22 Litho. Unwmk.
487 A68 15c Starbuck, red-tailed tropicbird .20 .20
488 A68 30c Enderbury, white tern .40 .40
489 A68 55c Tabiteuea, pandanus .70 .70
490 A68 $1 Onotoa, Okai house 1.25 1.25
Nos. 487-490 (4) 2.55 2.55

Nos. 487-490 vert.

Fish Type of 1985

Lizards.

1987, Oct. 27 *Perf. 15*
491 A74 15c Emoia nigra .20 .20
492 A74 35c Cryptoblepharus .45 .45
493 A74 40c Emoia cyanura .50 .50
494 A74 $1 Lipinia noctua 1.25 1.25
a. Souvenir sheet of 4, #491-494 2.50 2.50
Nos. 491-494 (4) 2.40 2.40

Nos. 470-474 Overprinted "40TH WEDDING ANNIVERSARY" in Silver

Perf. 14½x14

1987, Nov. 30 Litho. Unwmk.
495 CD337 15c scar, black & sil .25 .25
496 CD337 35c ultra & multi .50 .50
497 CD337 40c green & multi .55 .55
498 CD337 55c violet & multi .75 .75
499 CD337 $1 rose vio & multi 1.40 1.40
Nos. 495-499 (5) 3.45 3.45

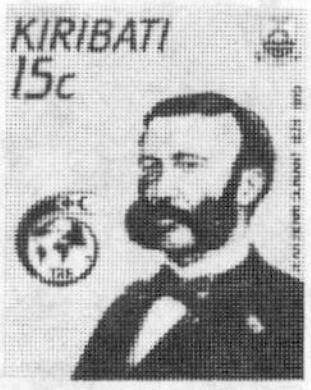

Intl. Red Cross and Red Crescent Organizations, 125th Annivs. — A83

Designs: 15c, Jean Henri Dunant (1828-1910), founder. 35c, Red Cross volunteers on parade. 40c, Stretcher bearers. 55c, Gilbert and Ellice Islands No. 159.

Perf. 14½x14

1988, May 8 Litho. Unwmk.
500 A83 15c multicolored .25 .25
501 A83 35c multicolored .55 .55
502 A83 40c multicolored .65 .65
503 A83 55c multicolored .85 .85
Nos. 500-503 (4) 2.30 2.30

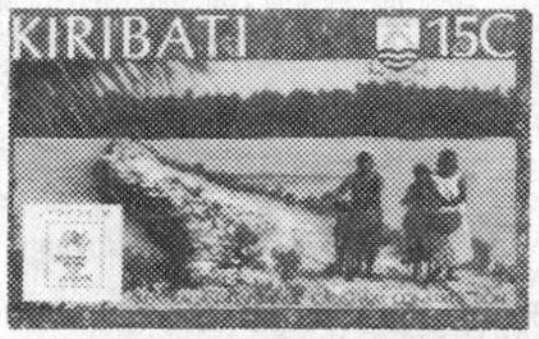

A84

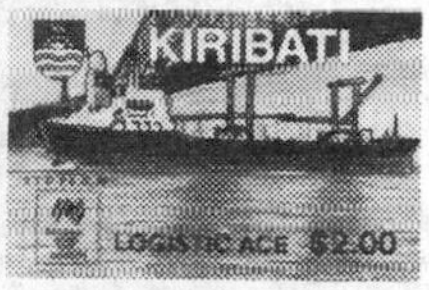

SYDPEX '88, Australia Bicentennial A85

Emblem and: 15c, Australia-assisted causeway construction. 35c, Capt. Cook, map of Australia and Kiribati. No. 506, Australia bicentennial banknote obverse. No. 507, Bank note reverse. $2, "Logistic Ace."

1988, July 30 Litho. *Perf. 14½*
504 A84 15c multicolored .25 .25
505 A84 35c multicolored .60 .60
506 A84 $1 multicolored 1.65 1.65
507 A84 $1 multicolored 1.65 1.65
a. Pair, #506-507 3.50 3.50
Nos. 504-507 (4) 4.15 4.15

Souvenir Sheet

Perf. 13½x14

508 A85 $2 multicolored 3.00 3.00

Robert F. Stockton, 1st propeller-driven steamship, 150th anniv.

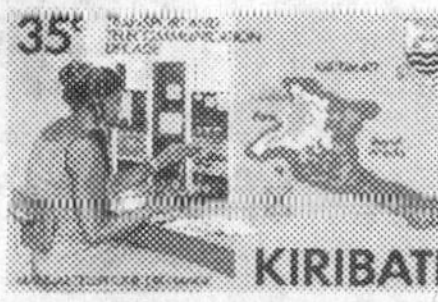

Transport and Telecommunications Decade (1985-1995) — A86

Wmk. 373

1988, Dec. 28 Litho. *Perf. 14*
509 A86 35c Telephone operator, map .65 .65
510 A86 45c Betio-Bairiki Causeway .80 .80

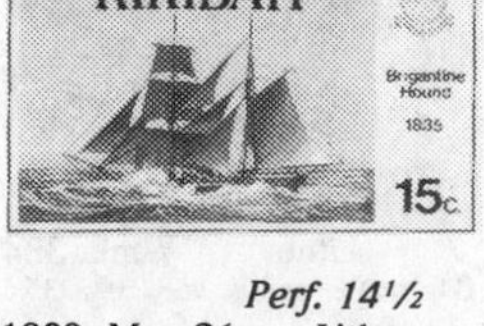

Ships A87

Perf. 14½

1989, May 26 Litho. Wmk. 384
511 A87 15c Brigantine Hound, 1835 .25 .25
512 A87 30c Brig Phantom, 1854 .50 .50
513 A87 40c HMS Alacrity, 1873 .65 .65
514 A87 $1 Whaler Charles W. Morgan, 1851 1.60 1.60
Nos. 511-514 (4) 3.00 3.00

See Nos. 557-561.

A88   Birds — A89

Perf. 13½x14
1989, July 12   Litho.   Wmk. 384
515 A88 15c House of Assembly   .25 .25
516 A88 $1 Constitution   1.60 1.60
Natl. Independence, 10th anniv.

Moon Landing, 20th Anniv.
Common Design Type

Apollo 10: 20c, Service and command modules, launch escape system. 50c, Eugene A. Cernan, Thomas P. Stafford and John W. Young. 60c, Mission emblem. 75c, Splashdown, Honolulu. $2.50, Apollo 11 command module in space.

1989, July 20   Perf. 14
Size of Nos. 518-519: 29x29mm
517 CD342 20c multicolored   .35 .35
518 CD342 50c multicolored   .80 .80
519 CD342 60c multicolored   .95 .95
520 CD342 75c multicolored   1.10 1.10
Nos. 517-520 (4)   3.20 3.20

Souvenir Sheet
521 CD342 $2.50 multicolored   4.00 4.00

Perf. 14½x14
1989, June 28   Litho.   Wmk. 384
522 A89 15c Eastern reef heron   .25 .25
523 A89 15c Brood in nest   .25 .25
a.   Pair, #522-523   .50 .50
524 A89 $1 White-tailed tropicbird
    in flight   1.55 1.55
525 A89 $1 Seated tropicbird   1.55 1.55
a.   Pair, #524-525   3.10 3.10
Nos. 522-525 (4)   3.60 3.60

Nos. 523a, 525a have continuous designs.
For overprints see Nos. 534-535.

Souvenir Sheets

PHILEXFRANCE '89
A90

A91

Perf. 14x13½
1989, Aug. 7   Litho.   Wmk. 384
526 A90 $2 Gilbert & Ellice Isls. #58   3.25 3.25

Perf. 14x13½
1989, Sept. 25   Litho.   Unwmk.
Workmen renovating the Statue of Liberty: a, Torch. b, Drilling copper sheeting. c, Glancing at a sketch of the statue.
527   Sheet of 3   1.65 1.65
a.-c.   A91 35c any single   .55 .55

World Stamp Expo '89, Washington, DC, PHILEXFRANCE '89, Paris. No. 526 margin pictures #435, France #634 and US #2224.

Transport and Telecommunications
Decade, 1985-95 — A92

1989, Oct. 16   Wmk. 384   Perf. 14
528 A92 30c shown   .50 .50
529 A92 75c MV Mataburo   1.20 1.20

Christmas — A93

Paintings: 10c, Adoration of the Holy Child (detail), by Denys Calvert. 15c, Adoration of the Holy Child (entire painting). 55c, The Holy Family and St. Elizabeth, by Rubens. $1, Madonna with Child and Mary Magdalene, School of Corregio.

1989, Dec. 1
530 A93 10c multicolored   .20 .20
531 A93 15c multicolored   .25 .25
532 A93 55c multicolored   .90 .90
533 A93 $1 multicolored   1.60 1.60
Nos. 530-533 (4)   2.95 2.95

Nos. 524-525 Ovptd.

1989, Oct. 21   Litho.   Perf. 14½x14
534 A89 $1 on No. 524   1.55 1.55
535 A89 $1 on No. 525   1.55 1.55
a.   Pair, #534-535   3.10 3.10
STAMPSHOW '89, Melbourne.

Penny Black 150th Anniv., Stamp World London '90 — A94

Stamps on stamps: 15c, Gilbert & Ellice #15, Great Britain #2. 50c, Gilbert & Ellice #8, Great Britain #1 canceled. 60c, Kiribati #384, Great Britain #58. $1, Gilbert Islands #269, Great Britain #3.

1990, May 1   Litho.   Perf. 14
536 A94 15c multicolored   .25 .25
537 A94 50c multicolored   .80 .80
538 A94 60c multicolored   .95 .95
539 A94 $1 multicolored   1.50 1.50
Nos. 536-539 (4)   3.50 3.50

Fish Type of 1985
Fish: 1c, Blue-barred orange parrotfish. 5c, Honeycomb rock cod. 10c, Bluefin jack. 15c, Paddle tail snapper. 20c, Variegated emperor. 25c, Rainbow runner. 30c, Black saddled coral trout. 35c, Great barracuda. 40c, Convict surgeonfish. 50c, Violet squirrelfish. 60c, Freckled hawkfish. 75c, Pennant coral fish. $1, Yellow and blue sea perch. $2, Pacific sailfish. $5, Whitetip reef shark.

Wmk. 373
1990, July 12   Litho.   Perf. 14
540 A74 1c multicolored   .15 .15
541 A74 5c multicolored   .15 .15
542 A74 10c multicolored   .15 .15
543 A74 15c multicolored   .20 .20
544 A74 20c multicolored   .25 .25
545 A74 25c multicolored   .35 .35
546 A74 30c multicolored   .40 .40
547 A74 35c multicolored   .45 .45
548 A74 40c multicolored   .55 .55
549 A74 50c multicolored   .65 .65
550 A74 60c multicolored   .80 .80
551 A74 75c multicolored   1.00 1.00
552 A74 $1 multicolored   1.25 1.25
553 A74 $2 multicolored   2.50 2.50
554 A74 $5 multicolored   6.50 6.50
Nos. 540-554 (15)   15.35 15.35

Dated 1990. See No. 567. For overprints see Nos. 587-590.

Queen Mother 90th Birthday
Common Design Types

1990, Aug. 4   Wmk. 384   Perf. 14x15
555 CD343 75c Queen Mother   1.15 1.15

Perf. 14½
556 CD344 $2 King, Queen &
    WWII bombing vic-
    tim, 1940   3.05 3.05

Ships Type of 1989

1990, Nov. 5   Litho.   Perf. 14½
557 A87 15c Whaling ship Herald,
    1851   .25 .25
558 A87 50c Bark Belle, 1849   .85 .85
559 A87 60c Schooner Supply, 1851   1.00 1.00
560 A87 75c Whaling ship Triton,
    1848   1.25 1.25
Nos. 557-560 (4)   3.35 3.35

Souvenir Sheet
561 A87 $2 Convict transport Char-
    lotte, 1789   3.25 3.25

Manta Ray — A95

1991, Jan. 17   Wmk. 373   Perf. 14
562 A95 15c shown   .25 .25
563 A95 20c Manta ray, diff.   .30 .30
564 A95 30c Whale shark   .45 .45
565 A95 35c Whale shark, diff.   .55 .55
Nos. 562-565 (4)   1.55 1.55

World Wildlife Fund.

Fish Type of 1985
Design: 23c, Bennett's pufferfish.

1991, Apr. 30   Wmk. 384
567 A74 23c multicolored   .35 .35

For overprint see No. 587.

Elizabeth & Philip, Birthdays
Common Design Types

1991, June 17   Perf. 14½
571 CD345 65c multicolored   1.00 1.00
572 CD346 70c multicolored   1.05 1.05
a.   Pair, #571-572 + label   2.05 2.05

Phila Nippon '91 A96

Opening of new Tungaru Central Hospital: 23c, Aerial view. 50c, Traditional dancers. 60c, Main entrance. 75c, Foundation stone, plaque. $5, Ambulance, nursing staff.

1991, Nov. 16   Perf. 13½x14
573 A96 23c multicolored   .35 .35
574 A96 50c multicolored   .80 .80
575 A96 60c multicolored   .95 .95
576 A96 75c multicolored   1.20 1.20
Nos. 573-576 (4)   3.30 3.30

Souvenir Sheet
577 A96 $5 multicolored   7.50 7.50

Christmas A97

Designs: 23c, Island mother and child. 50c, Family in island hut. 60c, Nativity Scene. 75c, Adoration of the Shepherds.

1991, Dec. 2   Wmk. 373
578 A97 23c multicolored   .35 .35
579 A97 50c multicolored   .80 .80
580 A97 60c multicolored   .95 .95
581 A97 75c multicolored   1.20 1.20
Nos. 578-581 (4)   3.30 3.30

Queen Elizabeth II's Accession to the Throne, 40th Anniv.
Common Design Type
Wmk. 373
1992, Feb. 6   Litho.   Perf. 14
582 CD349 23c multicolored   .35 .35
583 CD349 30c multicolored   .45 .45
584 CD349 50c multicolored   .75 .75
585 CD349 60c multicolored   .90 .90
586 CD349 75c multicolored   1.15 1.15
Nos. 582-586 (5)   3.60 3.60

Nos. 550-551, 553, & 567
Ovptd.

Wmk. 384, 373
1992, June 1   Litho.   Perf. 14
587 A74 23c on No. 567   .35 .35
588 A74 60c on No. 550   .90 .90
589 A74 75c on No. 551   1.15 1.15
590 A74 $2 on No. 553   3.00 3.00
Nos. 587-590 (4)   5.40 5.40

Marine Training Center, 25th Anniv.
A98

1992, Aug. 28   Perf. 14
591 A98 23c Entrance   .35 .35
592 A98 50c Cadets at morning
    parade   .75 .75
593 A98 60c Fire school   .90 .90
594 A98 75c Lifeboat training   1.15 1.15
Nos. 591-594 (4)   3.15 3.15

FAO, WHO
A99

Wmk. 373
1992, Dec. 1   Litho.   Perf. 14
595 A99 23c Children running   .35 .35
596 A99 50c Night fishing   .75 .75
597 A99 60c Fruit   .90 .90
598 A99 75c Ship   1.15 1.15
Nos. 595-598 (4)   3.15 3.15

Water Birds — A100

Perf. 14½
1993, May 28   Litho.   Wmk. 373
599 A100 23c Phoenix petrel   .32 .32
600 A100 23c Cooks petrel   .32 .32
a.   Pair, #599-600   .65 .65
601 A100 60c Northern pintail   .85 .85
602 A100 60c Eurasian widgeon   .85 .85
a.   Pair, #601-602   1.70 1.70
603 A100 75c Spectacled tern   1.05 1.05
604 A100 75c Black naped tern   1.05 1.05
a.   Pair, #603-604   2.10 2.20
605 A100 $1 Stilt wader   1.40 1.40
606 A100 $1 Wandering tattler   1.40 1.40
a.   Pair, #605-606   2.80 2.80
Nos. 599-606 (8)   7.24 7.24

Insects — A101

Perf. 14½x14
1993, Aug. 23   Litho.   Wmk. 373
607 A101 23c Chilocorus nigritus   .30 .30
608 A101 60c Rodolia pumila   .85 .85
609 A101 75c Rodolia cardinalis   1.05 1.05

610 A101 $1 Cryptolaemus mon-
                trouzleri   1.40 1.40
        Nos. 607-610 (4)   3.60 3.60

Liberation of
Kiribati, 50th
Anniv.
A102

Designs: No. 611a, Air reconnaissance of Tarawa
Atoll. b, USS Nautilus surveys Tarawa. c, USS Indi-
anapolis. d, USS Pursuit leads seaborne assault. e,
Kingfisher spotter plane. f, Destroyers USS Ringgold
and USS Dashiell. g, Sherman tank on seabed. h,
Fighter plane in lagoon. i, Naval gun on seabed. j,
First US aircraft to land on Betio Island.
No. 612a, Transports disembark landing craft. b,
Marines assault Betio Island. c, Sea and air assault
of Betio. d, Marines pinned down in surf. e, USS
Maryland firing broadside. f, Betio from the air. g,
Memorial to US Navy dead. h, Memorial to expatri-
ates. i, Memorial to Japanese dead. j, Battle map of
Betio.

Wmk. 373
1993, Nov. 1   Litho.   Perf. 14
Sheets of 10
611 A102 23c #a.-j. + label   3.50 3.50
612 A102 75c #a.-j. + label   10.50 10.50

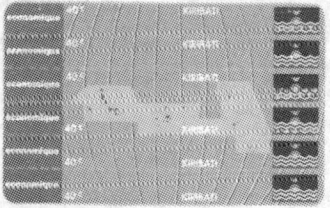

Christmas — A103

Perf. 13¹/₂x14
1993, Dec. 1   Litho.   Wmk. 373
613 A103 23c Shepherds   .30 .30
614 A103 40c Three kings   .55 .55
615 A103 60c Holy Family   .80 .80
616 A103 75c Mother, children   1.00 1.00
        Nos. 613-616 (4)   2.65 2.65

Souvenir Sheet
617 A103 $3 Madonna and Child   4.00 4.00

Stampcards — A104

Illustration reduced.

Rouletted 6 on 2 or 3 Sides
1993, Nov. 1   Litho.
Self-Adhesive
Cards of 6 + 6 labels
618 A104 40c #a.-f.   2.75 2.75
619 A104 $1 #a.-f.   6.75 6.75
620 A104 $1.20 #a.-f.   8.25 8.25
621 A104 $1.60 #a.-f.   11.00 11.00
        Nos. 618-621 (4)   28.75 28.75

Nos. 619-621 are airmail. Individual stamps measure 70x9mm and have a card backing. Se-tenant
labels on No. 618 inscribed "economique." Se-tenant labels on Nos. 619-621 inscribed "prioritaire
AIR MAIL."

Souvenir Sheet

New Year 1994 (Year of the Dog) — A105

Wmk. 373
1994, Feb. 18   Litho.   Perf. 14
622 A105 $3 multicolored   4.00 4.00

Hong Kong '94.

Whales
A106

Designs: 23c, Bryde's whale. 40c, Blue whale.
60c, Humpback whale. 75c, Killer whale.

1994, May 2
623 A106 23c multicolored   .30 .30
624 A106 23c multicolored   .30 .30
  a.   Pair, #623-624   .65 .65
625 A106 40c multicolored   .55 .55
626 A106 40c multicolored   .55 .55
  a.   Pair, #625-626   1.10 1.10
627 A106 60c multicolored   .85 .85
628 A106 60c multicolored   .85 .85
  a.   Pair, #627-628   1.70 1.70
629 A106 75c multicolored   1.10 1.10
630 A106 75c multicolored   1.10 1.10
  a.   Pair #629-630   2.20 2.20
        Nos. 623-630 (8)   5.60 5.60

Value at UL on Nos. 623, 625, 627, 629; at UR
on others.
Nos. 624a-630a have continuous designs.

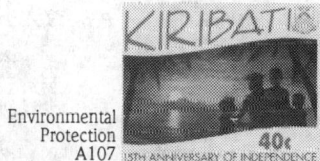

Environmental
Protection
A107

Designs: 40c, Family on beach at sunset. 60c,
Fish. 75c, Frigate birds.

1994, July 12
631 A107 40c multicolored   .55 .55
632 A107 60c multicolored   .85 .85
633 A107 75c multicolored   1.10 1.10
        Nos. 631-633 (3)   2.50 2.50

Independence, 15th anniv.

Butterflies — A108   Flowers — A109

Designs: 1c, Diaphania indica. 5c,
Herpetogamma licarsisalis. 10c, Parotis suralis. 12c,
Sufetula sunidesalis. 20c, Aedia serices. 23c,
Anomis vitiensis. 30c, Anticarsia irrorata. 35c,
Spodoptera litura. 40c, Mocis frugalis. 45c, Agrius
convolvuli. 50c, Cephonodes picus. 55c, Gnathoth-
libus erotus. 60c, Macroglossum hirundo. 75c,
Badamia exclamationis. $1, Precis villida. $2,
Danaus plexippus. $3, Hypolimnas bolina (male).
$5, Hypolimnas bolina (female).

1994, Aug. 19
634 A108 1c multicolored   .15 .15
635 A108 5c multicolored   .15 .15
636 A108 10c multicolored   .15 .15
637 A108 12c multicolored   .20 .20
638 A108 20c multicolored   .30 .30
639 A108 23c multicolored   .35 .35
640 A108 30c multicolored   .45 .45
641 A108 35c multicolored   .55 .55
642 A108 40c multicolored   .60 .60
643 A108 45c multicolored   .65 .65
644 A108 50c multicolored   .75 .75
645 A108 55c multicolored   .80 .80
646 A108 60c multicolored   .90 .90
647 A108 75c multicolored   1.10 1.10
648 A108 $1 multicolored   1.50 1.50
649 A108 $2 multicolored   3.00 3.00
650 A108 $3 multicolored   4.50 4.50
651 A108 $5 multicolored   7.50 7.50
        Nos. 634-651 (18)   23.60 23.60

1994, Oct. 31
652 A109 23c Nerium oleander   .35 .35
653 A109 60c Catharanthus roseus   .90 .90
654 A109 75c Ipomea pes-caprae   1.10 1.10
655 A109 $1 Calophyllum mophyl-
               lum   1.50 1.50
        Nos. 652-655 (4)   3.85 3.85

A110   A111

Constellations.

1995, Jan. 31
656 A110 50c Gemini   .75 .75
657 A110 60c Cancer   .90 .90
658 A110 75c Cassiopeia   1.10 1.10
659 A110 $1 Southern cross   1.50 1.50
        Nos. 656-659 (4)   4.25 4.25

Perf. 14¹/₂
1995, Apr. 3   Litho.   Wmk. 384
Scenes of Kiribati: No. 660a, Architecture. b,
Men, canoe, sailboat. c, Gun emplacement,
Tarawa. d, Children, shells. e, Outdoor sports.
No. 661a, Women traditionally attired. b, Wind-
surfing. c, Filleting fish. d, Snorkeling, scuba diving.
e, Weaving.

660 A111 30c Strip of 5, #a.-e.   2.25 2.25
661 A111 40c Strip of 5, #a.-e.   3.00 3.00
  f.   Booklet pane, #660, #661 + 5 labels 6.75
        Complete booklet, #661f   6.75

Visit South Pacific Year.

End of World War II, 50th Anniv.
Common Design Type

Designs: 23c, Grumman TBM-3E Avenger. 40c,
Curtiss SOC. 3-1 seagull. 50c, Consolidated B-24J
Liberator. 60c, Grumman Goose. 75c, Martin B-26
Marauder. $1, Northrop P-61B Black Widow. $2,
Reverse of War Medal 1939-45.

Perf. 14x13¹/₂
1995, May 8   Wmk. 373
662 CD351 23c multicolored   .35 .35
663 CD351 40c multicolored   .60 .60
664 CD351 50c multicolored   .75 .75
665 CD351 60c multicolored   .90 .90
666 CD351 75c multicolored   1.10 1.10
667 CD351 $1 multicolored   1.50 1.50
        Nos. 662-667 (6)   5.20 5.20

Souvenir Sheet
Perf. 14
668 CD352 $2 multicolored   3.00 3.00

Souvenir Sheet of 4

Environmental Protection — A112

Marine life: a, Electus parrot, great frigate bird,
coconut crab. b, Red-tailed tropic bird, common
dolphin, pantropical spotted dolphin. c, Yellow &
blue sea perch, green turtle, blue-barred orange parrot fish. d, Pennant coral fish, red-banded wrasse,
violet squirrel fish.

Wmk. 373
1995, July 12   Litho.   Perf. 14
669 A112 60c #a.-d. + 4 labels   3.50 3.50

For overprint see No. 672.

Souvenir Sheet

New Year 1995 (Year of the Boar) — A113

Design: $2, Sow, piglets. Illustration reduced.

1995, Sept. 1   Litho.   Perf. 13
670 A113 $2 multicolored   3.00 3.00

Singapore '95.

Souvenir Sheet

Beijing '95 — A114

Design: $2, like #670, with sheet margin as
shown in reduced Illustration.

1995, Sept. 14
671 A114 $2 multicolored   3.00 3.00

No. 669 Overprinted

Wmk. 373
1995, Aug. 19   Litho.   **Perf. 14**
672 A112 60c #a.-d. + 4 labels   3.50 3.50

Police Maritime
Unit — A115

Patrol boat RKS Teanoai: No. 673, In harbor. No. 674, Under way.

Wmk. 373
1995, Nov. 30   Litho.   **Perf. 13**
673 A115 75c multicolored   1.10 1.10
674 A115 75c multicolored   1.10 1.10
   a.   Pair, #673-674   2.25 2.25

Dolphins
A116

Designs: 23c, Pantropical spotted. 60c, Spinner. 75c, Fraser's. $1, Rough-toothed.

Wmk. 384
1996, Jan. 15   Litho.   **Perf. 14**
675 A116 23c multicolored   .35 .35
676 A116 60c multicolored   .90 .90
677 A116 75c multicolored   1.10 1.10
678 A116 $1 multicolored   1.50 1.50
   Nos. 675-678 (4)   3.85 3.85

POSTAGE DUE STAMPS

Natl. Arms — D1

1981, Aug. 27   Litho.   **Perf. 14**
J1 D1 1c brt pink & black   .15 .15
J2 D1 2c greenish blue & blk   .15 .15
J3 D1 5c brt yel grn & black   .15 .15
J4 D1 10c lt red brown & blk   .20 .20
J5 D1 20c ultra & black   .30 .30
J6 D1 30c yel bister & black   .45 .45
J7 D1 40c brt pur & black   .60 .60
J8 D1 50c green & black   .80 .80
J9 D1 $1 red orange & blk   1.50 1.50
   Nos. J1-J9 (9)   4.30 4.30

OFFICIAL STAMPS

Nos. 327a-340c Overprinted "O.K.G.S."

1981, May   Litho.   Unwmk.   **Perf. 14**
O1 A52 1c multicolored   .15 .15
O2 A52 3c multicolored   .15 .15
O3 A52 5c multicolored   .15 .15
O4 A52 7c multicolored   .15 .15
O5 A52 10c multicolored   .15 .15
O6 A52 12c multicolored   .20 .20
O7 A52 15c multicolored   .25 .25
O8 A52 20c multicolored   .30 .30
O9 A52 25c multicolored   .40 .40
O10 A52 30c multicolored   .45 .45
O11 A52 35c multicolored   .50 .50
O12 A52 50c multicolored   .75 .75
O13 A52 $1 multicolored   1.50 1.50
O14 A52 $2 multicolored   3.00 3.00
O15 A52 $5 multicolored   7.50 7.50
   Nos. O1-O15 (15)   15.60 15.60

Nos. O1-O15 have thick overprint. The 1c, 10c, 12c, 15c, 20c, 30c, 50c, $1, $2, $5 exist watermarked with thick overprint, all but the $5 watermarked but with thin overprint.

Nos. 390, 393-394, 396, 398 Overprinted "O.K.G.S."

1983, June 28   Litho.   **Perf. 14**
O16 A62 12c multicolored   .20 .20
O17 A62 30c multicolored   .45 .45
O18 A62 35c multicolored   .50 .50

O19 A62 50c multicolored   .75 .75
O20 A62 $2 multicolored   3.25 3.25
   Nos. O16-O20 (5)   5.15 5.15

This overprint has shorter, thinner letters than the one used for Nos. O1-O15. It also exists on Nos. 327, 331-334, 336-340. These have been questioned.

KUWAIT

kù-'wāt

LOCATION — Northwestern coast of the Persian Gulf
GOVT. — Sheikdom
AREA — 7,000 sq. mi.
POP. — 1,910,856 (est. 1985)
CAPITAL — Kuwait

Kuwait was under British protection until June 19, 1961, when it became a fully independent state.

16 Annas = 1 Rupee
100 Naye Paise = 1 Rupee (1957)
1000 Fils = 1 Kuwaiti Dinar (1961)

> Catalogue values for unused stamps in this country are for Never Hinged items, beginning with Scott 72 in the regular postage section, Scott C5 in the air post section, and Scott J1 in the postage due section.

There was a first or trial setting of the overprint with the word "Koweit." Twenty-four sets of regular and official stamps were printed with this spelling.

> Catalogue values for Nos. 1-71 used, are for postally used examples. Stamps with telegraph cancellations are worth less.

Stamps of India, 1911-23, Overprinted

KUWAIT   **KUWAIT**
a   b

1923-24   Wmk. 39   **Perf. 14**
1 A47(a) ½a green   .55 2.50
2 A48(a) 1a dk brown   .55 1.25
3 A58(a) 1½a chocolate   .85 3.25
4 A49(a) 2a violet   .40 .80
5 A57(a) 2a6p ultra   .90 6.50
6 A51(a) 3a brown org   2.25 14.00
   a.   Inverted overprint
7 A51(a) 3a ultra ('24)   2.50 1.65
8 A52(a) 4a ol green   2.00 19.00
9 A53(a) 6a bister   2.50 10.50
10 A54(a) 8a red violet   4.00 21.00
11 A55(a) 12a claret   4.25 22.50
12 A56(b) 1r grn & red brown   8.00 12.00
13 A56(b) 2r brn & car rose   27.50 72.50
14 A56(b) 5r vio & ultra   70.00 165.00
15 A56(b) 10r car & green   165.00 350.00
   Nos. 1-15 (15)   291.25 702.45

Overprint "a" on India No. 102 is generally considered unofficial.
For overprints see Nos. O1-O13.

Stamps of India, 1926-35, Overprinted
type "a"

1929-37   Wmk. 196
17 A47 ½a green   .70 .25
18 A71 ½a green ('34)   .95 .30
19 A48 1a dark brown   4.00 .40
20 A72 1a dk brown ('34)   1.75 1.00
21 A60 2a dk violet   .40 .30
22 A60 2a vermilion   24.00 37.50
23 A49 2a ver ('34)   15.00 5.25
   a.   Small die   3.50 1.25
24 A51 3a ultramarine   3.25 1.00
25 A51 3a car rose ('34)   5.00 4.00
26 A61 4a olive green   24.00 30.00
27 A52 4a ol green ('34)   5.75 6.75
28 A53 6a bister ('37)   18.00 19.00
29 A54 8a red violet   8.00 7.25
30 A55 12a claret   18.00 22.50

Overprinted

KUWAIT

c

31 A56 1r green & brown   10.00 10.00
32 A56 2r buff & car rose   15.00 13.00
33 A56 5r dk vio & ultra ('37)   70.00 125.00
34 A56 10r car & grn ('34)   165.00 250.00
35 A56 15r ol grn & ultra ('37)   500.00 850.00
   Nos. 17-35 (19)   888.80 1,383.

For overprints see Nos. O15-O25.

Stamps of India, 1937, Overprinted type "a" (A80, A81) or "c" (A82)

1939   Wmk. 196   **Perf. 13½x14**
45 A80 ½a brown   .45 1.00
46 A80 1a carmine   .45 1.00
47 A81 2a scarlet   .85 1.50
48 A81 3a yel green   1.25 1.75
49 A81 4a dark brown   2.00 10.00
50 A81 6a peacock blue   2.00 6.00
51 A81 8a blue violet   3.50 25.00
52 A81 12a car lake   4.00 25.00
53 A82 1r brown & slate   1.50 2.00
54 A82 2r dk brown & dk violet   8.50 8.00
55 A82 5r dp ultra & dk green   11.00 15.00
56 A82 10r rose car & dk violet   47.50 60.00
   a.   Double overprint   350.00 350.00
57 A82 15r dk green & dk brown   60.00 125.00
   Nos. 45-57 (13)   143.00 281.25
   Set, never hinged   250.00

Stamps of India 1940-43, Overprinted in Black   **KUWAIT**

1945   Wmk. 196   **Perf. 13½x14**
59 A83 3p slate   .50 .70
60 A83 ½a rose violet   .20 .20
61 A83 9p lt green   .25 .30
62 A83 1a car rose   .25 .20
63 A84 1½a dark purple   .45 .65
64 A84 2a scarlet   .40 .65
65 A84 3a violet   .60 .80
66 A84 3½a ultramarine   1.00 1.40
67 A85 4a chocolate   .45 .40
68 A85 6a peacock blue   7.50 9.00
69 A85 8a blue violet   1.00 .90
70 A85 12a car lake   1.25 1.25
71 A81 14a rose violet   6.00 12.50
   Nos. 59-71 (13)   19.85 28.95
   Set, never hinged   37.50

> Catalogue values for unused stamps in this section, from this point to the end of the section, are for Never Hinged items.

British Postal Administration

See Oman (Muscat) for similar stamps with surcharge of new value only.

KUWAIT

Great Britain Nos. 258 to 263, 243 and 248 Surcharged in Black

½
ANNA

1948-49   Wmk. 251   **Perf. 14½x14**
72 A101 ½a on ½p grn   .25 .15
73 A101 1a on 1p ver   .25 .15
74 A101 1½a on 1½p lt red brown   .15 .15
75 A101 2a on 2p lt org   .15 .15
76 A101 2½a on 2½p ultra   .15 .15
77 A101 3a on 3p violet   .15 .15
   a.   Pair, one without surcharge
78 A102 6a on 6p rose lil   .25 .15
79 A103 1r on 1sh brown   .55 .40

Great Britain
Nos. 249A, 250
and 251A
Surcharged in
Black

2 RUPEES

Wmk. 259   **Perf. 14**
80 A104 2r on 2sh6p yel grn   1.90 3.00
81 A104 5r on 5sh dull red   6.00 3.75
81A A105 10r on 10sh ultra   32.50 17.50
   Nos. 72-81A (11)   42.30 25.70

Issued: #72-81, Apr., 1948; 10r, July 4, 1949.
Bars of surcharge at bottom on No. 81A.

Silver Wedding Issue

Great Britain Nos. 267 and 268 Surcharged in Black   **KUWAIT 2½ ANNAS**

Perf. 14½x14, 14x14½
1948   Wmk. 251
82 A109 2½a on 2½p brt ultra   .15 .15
83 A110 15r on £1 deep chalky blue   32.50 45.00

Three bars obliterate the original denomination on No. 83.

Olympic Games Issue

Great Britain Nos. 271 to 274 Surcharged "KUWAIT" and New Value in Black

1948   **Perf. 14½x14**
84 A113 2½a on 2½p brt ultra   .20 .20
85 A114 3a on 3p dp violet   .35 .35
86 A115 6a on 6p red violet   .60 .60
87 A116 1r on 1sh dk brown   1.00 1.00
   Nos. 84-87 (4)   2.15 2.15

A square of dots obliterates the original denomination on No. 87.

UPU Issue

Great Britain Nos. 276 to 279 Surcharged "KUWAIT", New Value and Square of Dots in Black

1949, Oct. 10   **Photo.**
89 A117 2½a on 2½p brt ultra   .25 .25
90 A118 3a on 3p brt vio   .50 .50
91 A119 6a on 6p red vio   .90 .90
92 A120 1r on 1sh brown   1.65 1.65
   Nos. 89-92 (4)   3.30 3.30

Great Britain Nos. 280-285 Surcharged Like Nos. 72-79 in Black

1950-51   Wmk. 251   **Perf. 14½x14**
93 A101 ½a on ½p lt org   .50 1.00
94 A101 1a on 1p ultra   .50 .50
95 A101 1½a on 1½p green   .50 2.00
96 A101 2a on 2p lt red brown   .50 .50
97 A101 2½a on 2½p org vio   .50 1.00
98 A102 4a on 4p ultra ('50)   .50 .40

═ **KUWAIT**

Great Britain Nos. 286-288 Surcharged in Black

2 RUPEES

Wmk. 259   **Perf. 11x12**
99 A121 2r on 2sh6p green   12.00 4.00
100 A121 5r on 5sh dl red   15.00 5.00
101 A122 10r on 10sh ultra   26.00 8.00
   Nos. 93-101 (9)   56.00 22.40

Longer bars, at lower right, on No. 101.
Issued: 4a, Oct. 2, 1950; others, May 3, 1951.

Stamps of Great Britain, 1952-54 Surcharged "KUWAIT" and New Value in Black or Dark Blue

1952-54   Wmk. 298   **Perf. 14½x14**
102 A126 ½a on ½p red org ('53)   .15 .15
103 A126 1a on 1p ultra ('53)   .15 .15
104 A126 1½a on 1½p green ('53)   .15 .15
105 A126 2a on 2p red brn ('53)   .15 .15
106 A127 2½a on 2½p scarlet ('53)   .15 .15
107 A127 3a on 3p dk pur (Dk Bl) ('54)   .15 .15
108 A128 4a on 4p ultra ('53)   .60 .15
109 A129 6a on 6p lilac rose ('54)   .90 .15
111 A132 12a on 1sh6p dk green ('53)   3.00 .75
112 A131 1r on 1sh6p dk blue ('53)   3.50 .65
   Nos. 102-112 (10)   8.90
   Set value   2.00

Coronation Issue

Great Britain Nos. 313-316 Surcharged "KUWAIT" and New Value in Black

1953, June 3
113 A134 2½a on 2½p scarlet   .70 .50
114 A135 4a on 4p brt ultra   .95 .50
115 A136 12a on 1sh3p dk grn   2.25 1.10
116 A137 1r on 1sh6p dk blue   3.00 1.75
   Nos. 113-116 (4)   6.90 3.85

Squares of dots obliterate the original denominations on Nos. 115 and 116.

Great Britain Stamps of 1955-56 Surcharged "KUWAIT" and New Value in Black

1955 Wmk. 308 Engr. *Perf. 11x12*

117	A133	2r on 2sh6p dk brown	2.00	1.00
118	A133	5r on 5sh crimson	6.50	2.75
119	A133	10r on 10sh dp ultra	11.00	6.50
		Nos. 117-119 (3)	19.50	10.25

The surcharge on #117-119 exists in two types.

1956 Photo. *Perf. 14½x14*

120	A126	½a on ½p red org	.30	.25
121	A126	1a on 1p ultra	.15	.15
122	A126	1½a on 1½p green	.15	.15
123	A126	2a on 2p red brown	.15	.15
124	A127	2½a on 2½p scar	.35	.15
125	A128	4a on 4p ultra	1.75	.65
126	A129	6a on 6p lil rose	.45	.20
127	A132	12a on 1sh3p dk grn	4.50	1.10
128	A131	1r on 1sh6p dk bl	1.10	.45
		Nos. 120-128 (9)	8.90	3.25

Great Britain Nos. 317-325, 328 and 332 Surcharged "KUWAIT" and New Value in Black

1957-58 Wmk. 308 *Perf. 14½x14*

129	A129	1np on 5p lt brown	.15	.15
130	A126	3np on ½p red org	.15	.15
131	A126	6np on 1p ultra	.15	.15
132	A126	9np on 1½p green	.15	.15
133	A126	12np on 2p red brn	.30	.30
134	A127	15np on 2½p scar, type I	.35	.35
a.		Type II ('58)	30.00	30.00
135	A127	20np on 3p dk pur	.35	.25
136	A128	25np on 4p ultra	1.00	.60
137	A129	40np on 6p lilac rose	.60	.55
138	A130	50np on 9p dp ol grn	2.50	1.50
139	A132	75np on 1sh3p dk grn	3.00	1.75
		Nos. 129-139 (11)	8.70	5.90

The arrangement of the surcharge varies on different values; there are three bars through value on No. 138.

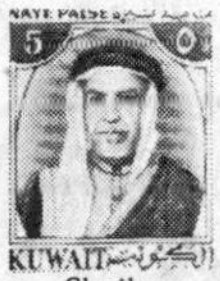

Sheik Abdullah A1

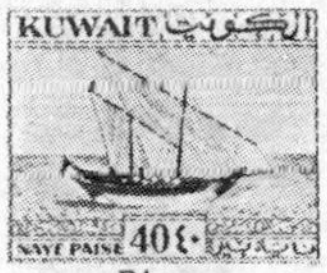

Dhow A2

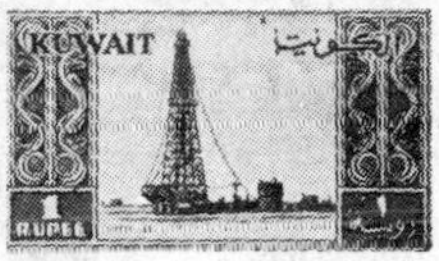

Oil Derrick A3

Designs: 50np, Pipe lines. 75np, Main square, Kuwait. 2r, Dhow, derrick and Sheik. 5r, Mosque and Sheik. 10r, Oil plant at Burgan and Sheik.

Perf. 12½

1959, Feb. 1 Unwmk. Engr.

140	A1	5np green	.15	.15
141	A1	10np rose brown	.15	.15
142	A1	15np yellow brown	.40	.30
143	A1	20np gray violet	.25	.15
144	A1	25np vermilion	.25	.15
145	A1	40np rose claret	2.25	1.10

Perf. 13½x13

146	A2	40np dark blue	.35	.30
147	A2	50np carmine	.35	.30
148	A2	75np olive green	.60	.45

Perf. 14x13½

149	A3	1r claret	.70	.55
150	A3	2r red brn & dp bl	1.65	1.00
151	A3	5r green	4.00	2.25
152	A3	10r purple	13.00	6.50
		Nos. 140-152 (13)	24.10	13.35

No. 140-141 and 145 were issued in 1958 for local use. They became valid for international mail on Feb. 1, 1959, but No. 145 was withdrawn after two weeks.

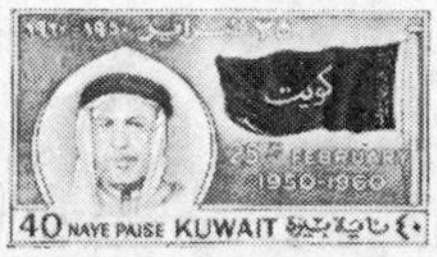

Sheik Abdullah and Flag — A4

1960, Feb. 25 Engr. *Perf. 14*

153	A4	40np olive grn & red	.30	.15
154	A4	60np blue & red	.55	.30

10th anniv. of the accession of Sheik Sir Abdullah As-Salim As-Sabah.

Types of 1959, Redrawn

Designs: 20f, 3d, Mosque and Sheik. 25f, 100f, Vickers Viscount. 30f, 75f, Dhow, derrick and Sheik. 35f, 90f, Shuwaikh secondary school. 45f, 1d, Wara Hill, Burgan oil field.

1961 *Perf. 12½*

155	A1	1f green	.15	.15
156	A1	2f rose brown	.15	.15
157	A1	4f yellow brown	.15	.15
158	A1	5f gray violet	.15	.15
159	A1	8f salmon pink	.15	.15
160	A1	15f rose claret	.15	.15

Perf. 14x13½, 13½ (40f, 250f)

161	A3	20f green	.15	.15
162	A3	25f blue	.15	.15
163	A3	30f red brn & dp bl	.20	.15
164	A3	35f ver & black	.40	.30
165	A2	40f dark blue	.20	.20
166	A3	45f violet brown	.20	.20
167	A3	75f green & sepia	.30	.20
168	A3	90f ultra & brown	.45	.30
169	A3	100f rose red	.45	.30
170	A2	250f olive grn	2.25	.70
171	A3	1d orange	7.25	3.75
172	A3	3d brick red	30.00	22.50
		Nos. 155-172 (18)	42.90	29.80

Nos. 165 and 170 are 32x22mm.
Issued: 75f, 90f, 4/27; 35f, 5/8; others, 4/1.

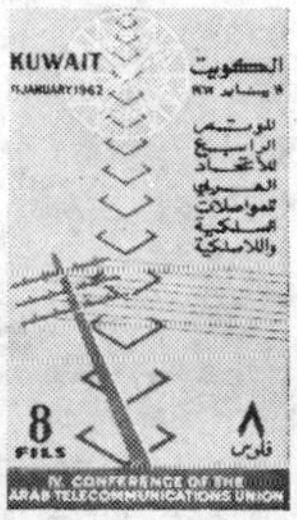

Symbols of Telecommunications A5

Perf. 11½

1962, Jan. 11 Unwmk. Photo. Granite Paper

173	A5	8f blue & black	.20	.15
174	A5	20f rose & black	.50	.25

4th Arab Telecommunications Union Conference.

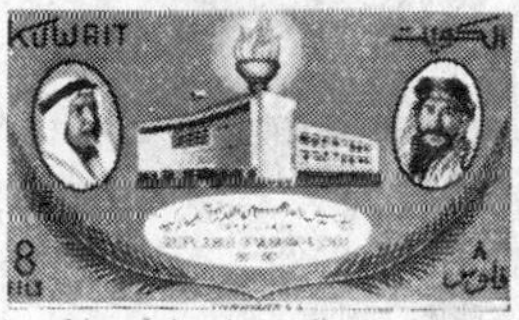

Mubarakiya School and Sheiks Abdullah and Mubarak — A6

1962, Apr. 15 Unwmk. *Perf. 11½*

175	A6	8f gldn brn, blk, org & gold	.20	.15
176	A6	20f lt blue, blk, org & gold	.55	.30

50th anniversary of Mubarakiya School.

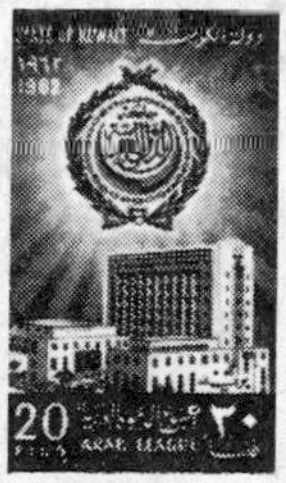

Arab League Building, Cairo, and Emblem — A7

1962, Apr. 23 *Perf. 13½x13*

177	A7	20f purple	.15	.15
178	A7	45f brown	.55	.30

Arab Publicity Week, Mar. 22-28.

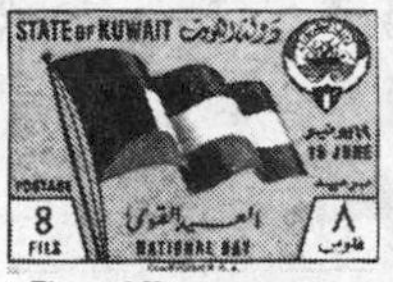

Flag of Kuwait — A8

Malaria Eradication Emblem — A9

1962, June 19 *Perf. 11½*
Flag in Green, Black & Red

179	A8	8f black & tan	.20	.15
180	A8	20f black & yellow	.35	.30
181	A8	45f black & lt blue	.55	.45
182	A8	90f black & lilac	1.50	.90
		Nos. 179-182 (4)	2.60	1.80

Issued for National Day, June 19.

1962, Aug. 1 *Perf. 13½x13*

183	A9	4f slate green & yel grn	.15	.15
184	A9	25f green & gray	.50	.30

WHO drive to eradicate malaria.
No. 184 has laurel leaves added and inscription rearranged.

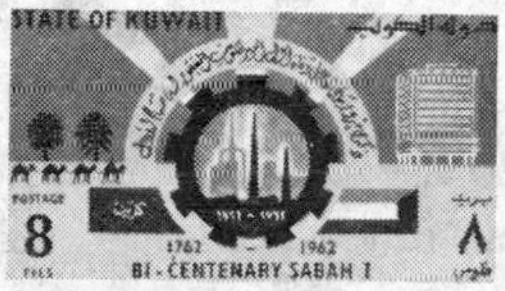

Cogwheel, Oil Wells, Camels and Modern Building — A10

Perf. 11x13

1962, Dec. 8 Unwmk. Litho.

185	A10	8f multicolored	.20	.15
186	A10	20f multicolored	.24	.15
187	A10	45f multicolored	.50	.24
188	A10	75f multicolored	1.00	.45
		Nos. 185-188 (4)	1.94	.99

Bicentenary of the Sabah dynasty.

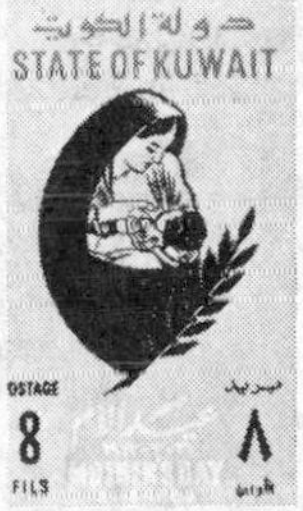

Mother and Child — A11

1963, Mar. 21 Photo. *Perf. 14½x14*

189	A11	8f yel, red, blk & green	.15	.15
190	A11	20f blue, red, blk & grn	.30	.22
191	A11	45f lt ol, red, blk & grn	.60	.42
192	A11	75f gray, red, blk & green	.70	.70
		Nos. 189-192 (4)	1.75	1.49

Issued for Mother's Day, Mar. 21, 1963.

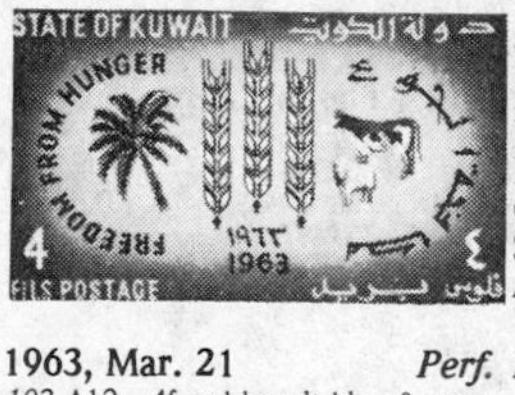

Wheat Emblem, Date Palm, Cow and Sheep A12

1963, Mar. 21 *Perf. 14x14½*

193	A12	4f red brn, lt blue & grn	.22	.15
194	A12	8f brown, yel & green	.38	.15
195	A12	20f red brn, pale vio & green	.55	.32
196	A12	45f red brn, rose & green	1.10	.65
		Nos. 193-196 (4)	2.25	1.27

FAO "Freedom from Hunger" campaign.

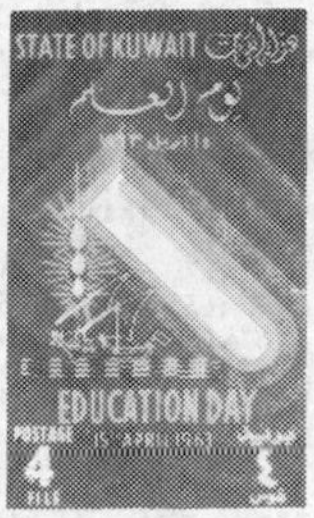

Test Tube, Oil Drops and Ship — A13

1963, Apr. 15 Photo. *Perf. 14½x14*

197	A13	4f brown, yel & blue	.15	.15
198	A13	20f green, yel & blue	.38	.24
199	A13	45f brt mag, yel & blue	.70	.50
		Nos. 197-199 (3)	1.23	.89

Issued for Education Day.

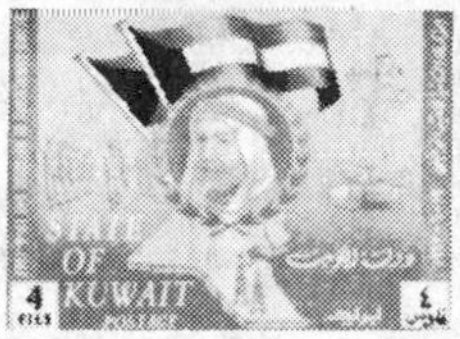

Sheik Abdullah, Flags and Map of Kuwait A14

1963, June 19 *Perf. 14x13*
Flags in Black, Bright Green & Red; Denominations in Black

200	A14	4f ultramarine	.95	.60
201	A14	5f ocher	1.25	.75
202	A14	20f bright lilac	4.75	2.75
203	A14	50f olive	8.00	5.00
		Nos. 200-203 (4)	14.95	9.10

Second anniversary of National Day.

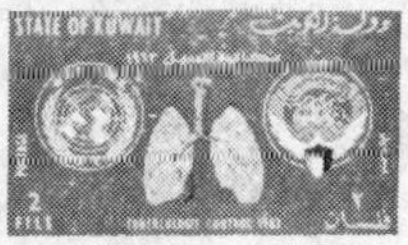

Lungs and Emblems of World Health Organization and Kuwait Tuberculosis Society — A15

1963, July 27 *Perf. 13x13½*
Design in Yellow, Black, Emerald & Red

204	A15	2f ocher	.15	.15
205	A15	4f dark green	.24	.15
206	A15	8f lt violet blue	.32	.15
207	A15	20f rose brown	.55	.24
		Nos. 204-207 (4)	1.26	
		Sct value		.52

Issued to publicize tuberculosis control.

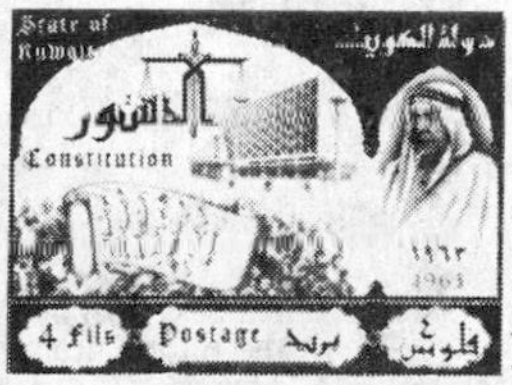

Sheik Abdullah, Scroll and Scales of Justice A16

1963, Oct. 29 Photo. *Perf. 11x13*
Center in Gray

208	A16	4f dp red & red brn	.15	.15
209	A16	8f dk green & red brn	.15	.15
210	A16	20f vio brown & red brn	.50	.25
211	A16	45f brown org & red brn	.75	.40
212	A16	75f purple & red brown	1.25	.75
213	A16	90f ultra & red brown	1.50	.90
		Nos. 208-213 (6)	4.30	2.60

Promulgation of the constitution.

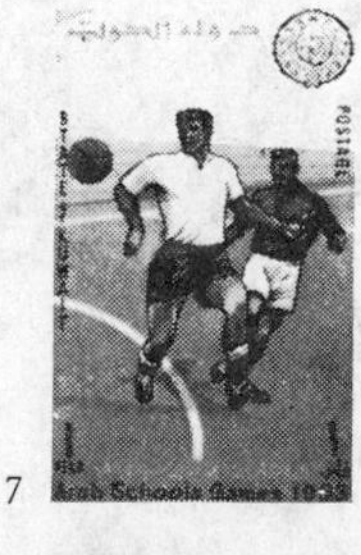

Soccer — A17

Sports: 4f, Basketball. 5f, Swimming, horiz. 8f, Track. 15f, Javelin, horiz. 20f, Pole vault, horiz. 35f, Gymnast on rings, horiz. 45f, Gymnast on parallel bars.

1963, Nov. 8 Unwmk. *Perf. 14½x14*

214	A17	1f multicolored	.15	.15
215	A17	4f multicolored	.15	.15
216	A17	5f multicolored	.15	.15
217	A17	8f multicolored	.25	.15
218	A17	15f multicolored	.30	.15
219	A17	20f multicolored	.50	.30
220	A17	35f multicolored	1.00	.40
221	A17	45f multicolored	2.00	.60
		Nos. 214-221 (8)	4.50	2.05

Arab School Games of 1963.

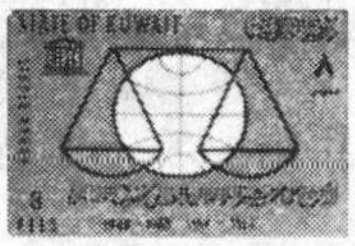

UNESCO Emblem, Scales and Globe — A18

1963, Dec. 10 Litho. *Perf. 13x12½*

222	A18	8f violet, blk & pale grn	.20	.15
223	A18	20f gray, black & yel	.30	.15
224	A18	25f blue, black & tan	.50	.18
		Nos. 222-224 (3)	1.00	
		Set value		.40

15th anniv. of the Universal Declaration of Human Rights.

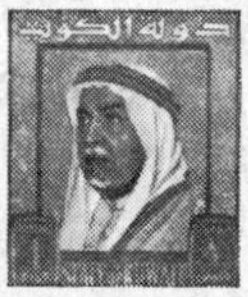

Sheik Abdullah — A19

Perf. 12½x13

1964, Feb. 1 Unwmk. Photo.

Portrait in Natural Colors

225	A19	1f gray & silver	.15	.15
a.		Booklet pane of 6 ('66)	1.50	
226	A19	2f brt blue & silver	.15	.15
227	A19	4f ocher & silver	.15	.15
a.		Booklet pane of 6 ('66)	1.65	
228	A19	5f fawn & silver	.15	.15
229	A19	8f dk brown & sil	.15	.15
230	A19	10f citron & sil	.15	.15
a.		Booklet pane of 6 ('66)	1.75	
231	A19	15f brt green & sil	.75	.75
a.		Booklet pane of 6 ('66)	1.10	
232	A19	20f blue gray & sil	.35	.15
a.		Booklet pane of 6 ('66)	2.25	
233	A19	25f green & silver	.45	.25
234	A19	30f gray grn & sil	.50	.30
235	A19	40f brt vio & sil	.70	.35
236	A19	45f violet & silver	.75	.35
237	A19	50f olive & silver	.90	.45
238	A19	70f red lilac & sil	1.50	.50
239	A19	75f rose red & sil	1.75	.60
240	A19	90f ultra & silver	2.00	.75
241	A19	100f pale lilac & sil	2.50	.80

Perf. 14x14½

Size: 25x30mm

242	A19	250f brown & sil	5.25	1.90
243	A19	1d brown vio & sil	21.00	8.00
		Nos. 225-243 (19)	39.30	16.05

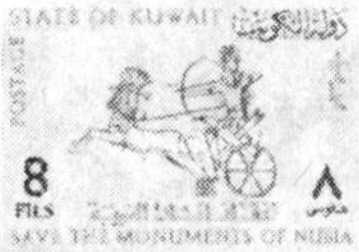

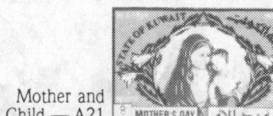

Ramses II Battling the Hittites (from Abu Simbel) — A20

Perf. 13x12½

1964, Mar. 8 Engr. & Litho.

244	A20	8f buff, ind & maroon	.16	.15
245	A20	20f lt blue, indigo & vio	.40	.30
246	A20	30f bluish grn, ind & vio	.70	.48
		Nos. 244-246 (3)	1.26	.93

UNESCO world campaign to save historic monuments in Nubia.

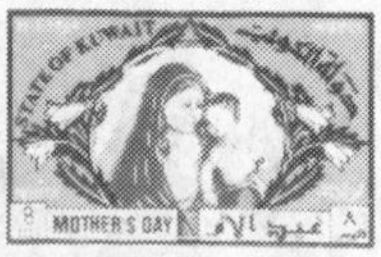

Mother and Child — A21

1964, Mar. 21 Litho. *Perf. 14x13*

247	A21	8f green, gray & vio blk	.16	.15
248	A21	20f green, red & vio blk	.22	.15
249	A21	30f green, ol bis & vio blk	.32	.20
250	A21	45f green, saph & vio blk	.55	.40
		Nos. 247-250 (4)	1.25	.90

Issued for Mother's Day, Mar. 21.

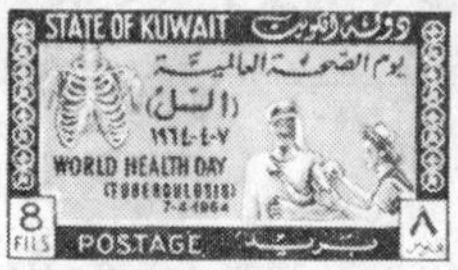

Nurse Giving TB Test, and Thorax A22

Perf. 13x13½

1964, Apr. 7 Photo. Unwmk.

251	A22	8f brown & green	.35	.22
252	A22	20f green & rose red	1.10	.40

Issued for World Health Day (fight against tuberculosis), Apr. 7, 1964.

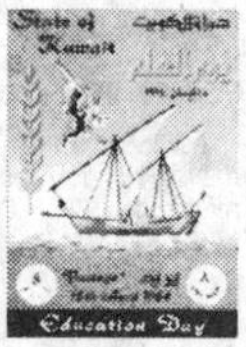

Microscope and Dhow — A23

1964, Apr. 15 *Perf. 12½x13*

253	A23	8f multicolored	.22	.15
254	A23	15f multicolored	.24	.15
255	A23	20f multicolored	.32	.15
256	A23	30f multicolored	.50	.38
		Nos. 253-256 (4)	1.28	
		Set value		.70

Issued for Education Day.

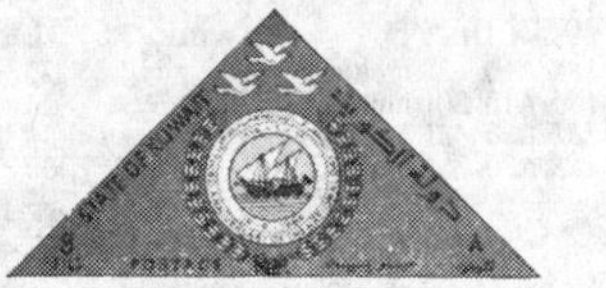

Doves and State Seal — A24

1964, June 19 Litho. *Perf. 13½*

Seal in Blue, Brown, Black, Red & Green

257	A24	8f black & bister brn	.30	.15
258	A24	20f black & green	.45	.22
259	A24	30f black & gray	.75	.38
260	A24	45f black & blue	1.00	.65
		Nos. 257-260 (4)	2.50	1.40

Third anniversary of National Day.

Arab Postal Union Emblem — A25

1964, Nov. 21 Photo. *Perf. 11x11½*

261	A25	8f lt blue & brown	.20	.15
262	A25	20f yellow & ultra	.55	.30
263	A25	45f olive & brown	1.00	.65
		Nos. 261-263 (3)	1.75	1.10

Permanent Office of the APU, 10th anniv.

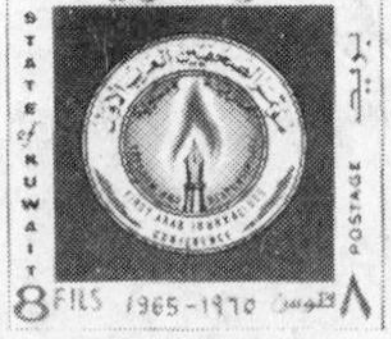

Conference Emblem — A26

1965, Feb. 8 Litho. *Perf. 14*

264	A26	8f black, org brn & yel	.45	.16
265	A26	20f multicolored	.90	.25

First Arab Journalists' Conference.

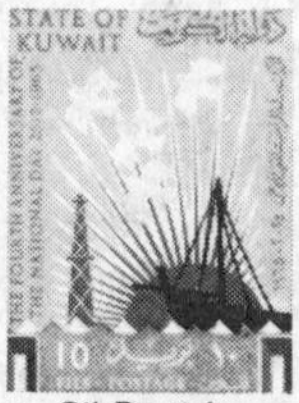

Oil Derrick, Dhow, Sun and Doves A27

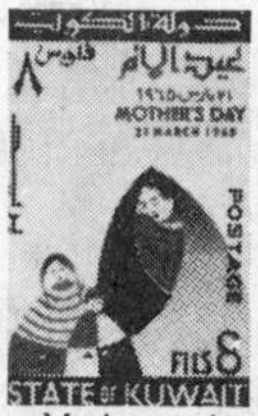

Mother and Children A28

1965, Feb. 25 *Perf. 13½*

266	A27	10f lt green & multi	.20	.15
267	A27	15f pink & multi	.35	.15
268	A27	20f gray & multi	.65	.25
		Nos. 266-268 (3)	1.20	
		Set value		.48

Fourth anniversary of National Day.

1965, Mar. 21 Unwmk. *Perf. 13½*

269	A28	8f multicolored	.22	.15
270	A28	15f multicolored	.40	.15
271	A28	20f multicolored	.50	.24
		Nos. 269-271 (3)	1.12	.54

Mother's Day, Mar. 21.

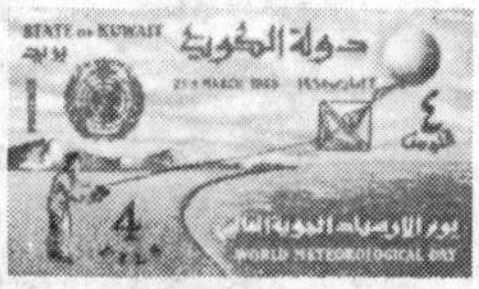

Weather Balloon A29

1965, Mar. 23 Photo. *Perf. 11½x11*

272	A29	4f deep ultra & yellow	.40	.15
273	A29	5f blue & dp orange	.75	.15
274	A29	20f dk blue & emerald	.95	.15
		Nos. 272-274 (3)	2.10	
		Set value		.38

Fifth World Meteorological Day.

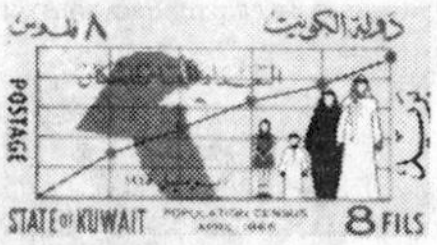

Census Chart, Map and Family A30

1965, Mar. 28 Litho. *Perf. 13½*

275	A30	8f multicolored	.30	.15
276	A30	20f multicolored	.90	.40
277	A30	50f multicolored	1.75	1.00
		Nos. 275-277 (3)	2.95	1.55

Issued to publicize the 1965 census.

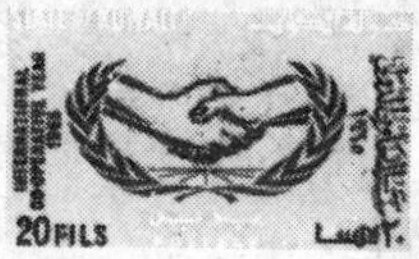

ICY Emblem A31

1965, Mar. 7 Engr.

278	A31	8f red & black	.15	.15
279	A31	20f lt ultra & black	.65	.40
280	A31	30f emerald & black	1.20	.65
		Nos. 278-280 (3)	2.00	1.20

International Cooperation Year.

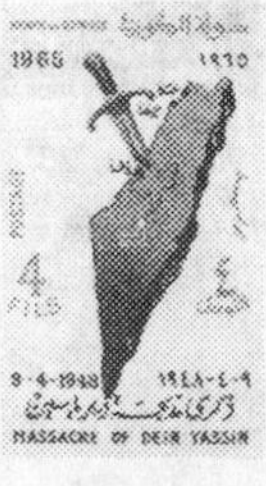

Dagger in Map of Palestine — A31a

Perf. 11x11½

1965, Apr. 9 Photo. Unwmk.

281	A31a	4f red & ultra	.52	.32
282	A31a	45f red & emerald	1.50	.70

Deir Yassin massacre, Apr. 9, 1948. See Iraq Nos. 372-373.

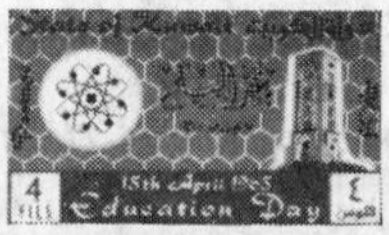

Tower of Shuwaikh School and Atom Symbol — A32

1965, Apr. 15 Litho. *Perf. 14x13*

283	A32	4f multicolored	.20	.15
284	A32	20f multicolored	.45	.20
285	A32	45f multicolored	.80	.40
		Nos. 283-285 (3)	1.45	.75

Issued for Education Day.

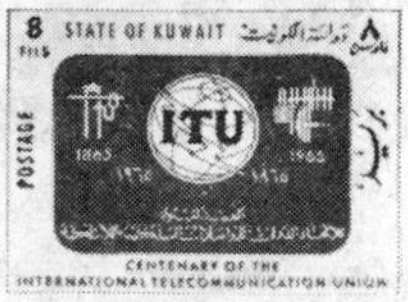

ITU Emblem, Old and New Communication Equipment A33

1965, May 17 *Perf. 13½x14*

286	A33	8f dk blue, lt bl & red	.60	.35
287	A33	20f green, lt grn & red	1.25	.60
288	A33	45f red, pink & blue	2.00	1.00
		Nos. 286-288 (3)	3.85	1.95

ITU, centenary.

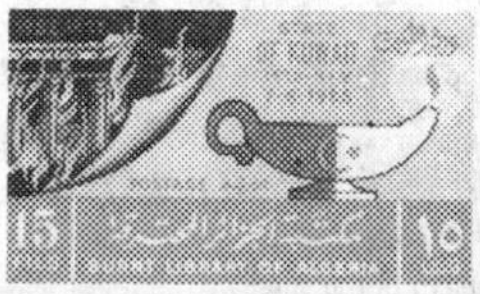

Library Aflame and Lamp A33a

1965, June 7 Photo. *Perf. 11*

289	A33a	8f black, green & red	.65	.20
290	A33a	15f black, red & green	1.00	.20

Burning of Library of Algiers, June 2, 1962.

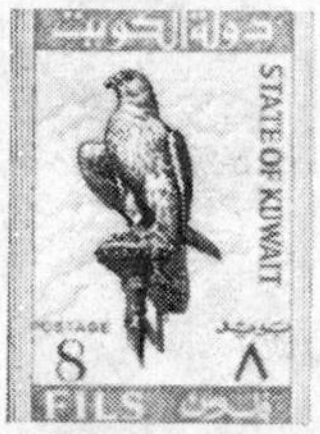

Falcon — A34

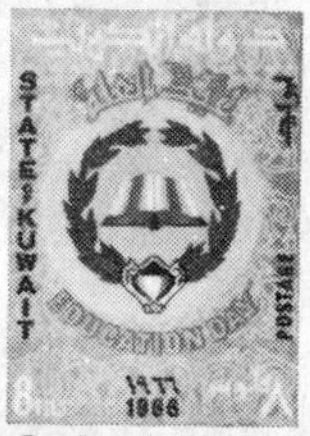

Book and Wreath Emblem — A35

1965, Dec. 1 Engr. *Perf. 13*

Center in Sepia

291	A34	8f red lilac	.70	.20
292	A34	15f olive green	.50	.22
293	A34	20f dark blue	.85	.35
294	A34	25f orange	1.10	.50
295	A34	30f emerald	1.00	.55
296	A34	45f blue	1.75	.85
297	A34	50f claret	2.25	1.00
298	A34	90f carmine	4.25	2.00
		Nos. 291-298 (8)	12.40	5.67

1966, Jan. 10 Photo. *Perf. 14x15*

299	A35	8f lt violet & multi	.35	.15
300	A35	20f brown red & multi	.60	.15
301	A35	30f blue & multi	.65	.28
		Nos. 299-301 (3)	1.60	
		Set value		.50

Issued for Education Day.

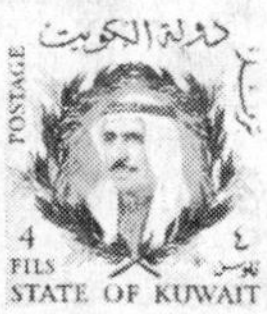

Sheik Sabah as-Salim as-Sabah — A36

1966, Feb. 1 Photo. *Perf. 14x13*

302	A36	4f lt blue & multi	.22	.15
303	A36	5f pale rose & multi	.22	.15
304	A36	20f multicolored	.70	.22
305	A36	30f lt violet & multi	.75	.35
306	A36	40f salmon & multi	1.10	.50
307	A36	45f lt gray & multi	1.25	.60
308	A36	70f yellow & multi	1.90	.85
309	A36	90f pale green & multi	2.50	1.10
		Nos. 302-309 (8)	8.64	3.92

Wheat and Fish — A37

1966, Feb. 15   *Perf. 11x11½*
310 A37 20f multicolored   1.40   .75
311 A37 45f multicolored   2.50 1.40
"Freedom from Hunger" campaign

Eagle, Banner, Scales and Emblems A38

1966, Feb. 25   Litho.   Perf. 12½x13
312 A38 20f tan & multi   1.10   .42
313 A38 25f lt green & multi   1.50   .45
314 A38 45f gray & multi   2.00   .85
  Nos. 312-314 (3)   4.60 1.72
Fifth anniversary of National Day.

Wheel of Industry and Map of Arab Countries A39

1966, Mar. 1   *Perf. 14x13½*
315 A39 20f brt blue, brt grn & blk   .48   .25
316 A39 50f lt red brn, brt grn &
             black   1.00   .65
Issued to publicize the conference on industrial development in Arab countries.

Mother and Children — A40

1966, Mar. 21   *Perf. 11½x11*
317 A40 20f pink & multi   .70   .20
318 A40 45f multicolored   1.50   .40
Mother's Day, Mar. 21.

Medical Conference Emblem — A41   Composite View of a City — A42

1966, Apr. 1   Photo.   Perf. 14½x14
319 A41 15f blue & red   .38   .18
320 A41 30f red & blue   .90   .60
Fifth Arab Medical Conference, Kuwait.

1966, Apr. 7   Litho.   Perf. 12½x13
321 A42 8f multicolored   .60   .18
322 A42 10f multicolored   1.50   .28
Issued for World Health Day, Apr. 7.

Inauguration of WHO Headquarters, Geneva A43

Traffic Signal at Night A44   "Blood Transfusion" A45

1966, May 3   Litho.   Perf. 11x11½
323 A43 5f dull sal, ol grn & vio bl   .65   .15
324 A43 10f lt grn, ol grn & vio blue   .80   .18
  Set value   .15

1966, May 4
325 A44 10f green, red & black   .85   .15
326 A44 15f green, red & black   1.25   .32
Issued for Traffic Day.

1966, May 5   *Perf. 13½*
327 A45 4f multicolored   .60   .15
328 A45 8f multicolored   .70   .15
  Set value   .22
Blood Bank Day, May 5.

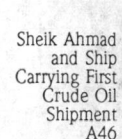

Sheik Ahmad and Ship Carrying First Crude Oil Shipment A46

1966, June 30   *Perf. 13½*
329 A46 20f multicolored   .65   .22
330 A46 45f multicolored   1.25   .35
20th anniv. of the first crude oil shipment, June 30, 1946.

Ministry of Guidance and Information — A47

1966, July 25   Photo.   Perf. 11½x11
331 A47 4f rose & brown   .22   .15
332 A47 5f yel brown & brt green .28   .15
333 A47 8f brt green & purple   .32   .15
334 A47 20f salmon & ultra   .38   .15
  Nos. 331-334 (4)   1.20
  Set value   .40
Opening of Ministry of Guidance and Information Building.

Fishing Boat, Lobster, Fish, Crab and FAO Emblem A48

1966, Oct. 10   Litho.   Perf. 13½
335 A48 4f buff & multi   1.25   .15
336 A48 20f lt lilac & multi   1.65   .28
  Set value   .38
Fisheries' Conference of Near East Countries under the sponsorship of the FAO, Oct. 1966.

United Nations Flag — A49   UNESCO Emblem — A50

1966, Oct. 24   *Perf. 13x14*
337 A49 20f dk blue & pink   1.40   .40
338 A49 45f blue, dk bl & pale grn   2.25   .75
Issued for United Nations Day.

1966, Nov. 4   Litho.   Perf. 12½x13
339 A50 20f multicolored   1.75   .90
340 A50 45f multicolored   1.90 1.75
20th anniversary of UNESCO.

 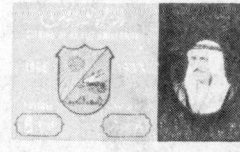

Kuwait University Emblem A51

1966, Nov. 27   Photo.   Perf. 14½
Emblem in Yellow, Bright Blue, Green and Gold
341 A51 8f lt ultra, vio & gold   .35   .18
342 A51 10f red, brown & gold   .80   .20
343 A51 8f yel grn, slate & gold .95   .38
344 A51 45f buff, green & gold   1.75 1.00
  Nos. 341-344 (4)   3.85 1.76
Opening of Kuwait University.

Jabir al-Ahmad al-Jabir and Sheik Sabah A52

1966, Dec. 11   *Perf. 14x13*
345 A52 8f yel green & multi   .65   .15
346 A52 20f yellow & multi   .85   .42
347 A52 45f pink & multi   1.65 1.00
  Nos. 345-347 (3)   3.15 1.57
Appointment of the heir apparent, Jabir al-Ahmad al-Jabir.

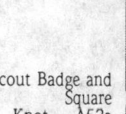

Scout Badge and Square Knot — A52a

1966, Dec. 21   Litho.   Perf. 14x13
347A A52a 4f lt ol green & fawn   .50   .15
347B A52a 20f yel brn & blue grn 2.25   .40
Kuwait Boy Scouts, 30th anniversary.

"Symbols of Science and Peace" — A53

1967, Jan. 15   Litho.   Perf. 13x14
348 A53 10f multicolored   .35   .16
349 A53 45f multicolored   1.10   .52
Issued for Education Day.

Fertilizer Plant — A54

1967, Feb. 19   Unwmk.   Perf. 13
350 A54 8f lt blue & multi   .60   .18
351 A54 20f cream & multi   1.40   .42
Opening of Chemical Fertilizer Plant.

Sun, Dove and Olive Branch — A55

1967, Feb. 25   Litho.   Perf. 13
352 A55 8f salmon & multi   .40   .16
353 A55 10f yellow & multi   1.10   .40
Sixth anniversary of National Day.

Map of Arab States and Municipal Building A56

1967, Mar. 11   *Perf. 14½x13*
354 A56 20f gray & multi   1.50   .35
355 A56 30f lt brown & multi   2.50   .55
1st conf. of the Arab Cities Org., Kuwait.

Family — A57   Arab League Emblem — A58

1967, Mar. 21   Litho.   Perf. 13x13½
356 A57 20f pale rose & multi   1.10   .35
357 A57 45f pale green & multi   2.75   .70
Issued for Family Day, Mar. 21.

1967, Mar. 27   *Perf. 13x14*
358 A58 8f gray & dk blue   .80   .15
359 A58 10f bister & green   1.00   .22
Issued for Arab Publicity Week.

Sabah Hospital and Physicians at Work — A59

1967, Apr. 7   *Perf. 14x13*
360 A59 8f dull rose & multi   1.25   .22
361 A59 20f gray & multi   1.50   .60
Issued for World Health Day.

Two Heads of Ramses II — A60

1967, Apr. 17   *Perf. 13½*
362 A60 15f citron, green & brn   .90   .30
363 A60 20f chalky blue, grn & pur 1.40   .35
Arab Week to Save the Nubian Monuments.

Traffic Policeman A61

1967, May 4 Litho. Perf. 14x13
364 A61 8f lt green & multi 1.90 .35
365 A61 20f rose lilac & multi 2.00 .95
Issued for Traffic Day.

ITY
Emblem — A62

1967, June 4 Photo. Perf. 13
366 A62 20f Prus blue, lt bl & blk 1.00 .60
367 A62 45f rose lilac, lt bl & blk 2.00 1.25
International Tourist Year.

Arab League
Emblem and
Hands Reaching
for
Knowledge — A63

Map of
Palestine and
UN
Emblem — A64

1967, Sept. 8 Litho. Perf. 13x14
368 A63 8f blue & multi 1.10 .15
369 A63 20f dull rose & multi 1.40 .32
Issued to publicize the literacy campaign.

1967, Oct. 24 Litho. Perf. 13
370 A64 20f blue & pink .70 .30
371 A64 45f orange & pink 1.65 .65
Issued for United Nations Day.

Factory and Cogwheels — A65

1967, Nov. 25 Photo. Perf. 13
372 A65 20f crimson & yellow 1.00 .30
373 A65 45f gray & yellow 2.25 .65
3rd Conf. of Arab Labor Ministers, Kuwait.

Flag and Open
Book — A66

Map of Kuwait and
Oil Derrick — A67

1968, Jan. 15 Litho. Perf. 14
374 A66 20f brt blue & multi .90 .42
375 A66 45f yel orange & multi 1.90 .90
Issued for Education Day.

1968, Feb. 23 Litho. Perf. 12
376 A67 10f multicolored 1.00 .55
377 A67 20f multicolored 2.00 1.00
30th anniv. of the discovery of oil in the Greater
Burgan Field.

Sheik Sabah
and
Sun — A68

1968, Feb. 25 Litho. Perf. 14x15
378 A68 8f red lilac & multi .28 .18
379 A68 10f lt blue & multi .38 .28
380 A68 15f violet & multi .60 .38
381 A68 20f vermilion & multi .70 .48
Nos. 378-381 (4) 1.96 1.32
Seventh anniversary of National Day.

Open Book and
Emblem — A69

1968, Mar. 2 Perf. 14
382 A69 8f yellow & multi .32 .15
383 A69 20f lilac rose & multi .42 .20
384 A69 45f orange & multi .80 .40
Nos. 382-384 (3) 1.54 .75
Issued for Teachers' Day.

Family
Picnic — A70

1968, Mar. 21 Perf. 13½x13
385 A70 8f blue & multi .30 .15
386 A70 10f red & multi .32 .15
387 A70 15f lilac & multi .42 .15
388 A70 20f dk brown & multi .50 .15
Nos. 385-388 (4) 1.54
Set value .50
Issued for Family Day.

Sheik Sabah, Arms of WHO and
Kuwait — A71

1968, Apr. 7 Photo. Perf. 12
389 A71 20f brt lilac & multi .80 .80
390 A71 45f multicolored 1.65 1.65
20th anniv. of WHO.

Dagger in Map of Palestine — A72

1968, Apr. 9 Litho. Perf. 14
391 A72 20f lt blue & vermilion .65 .28
392 A72 45f lilac & vermilion 1.40 .50
Deir Yassin massacre, 20th anniv.

Street
Crossing
A74

1968, May 4 Photo. Perf. 14x14½
395 A74 10f dk brown & multi 1.25 .90
396 A74 15f brt violet & multi 1.50 1.25
397 A74 20f green & multi 2.50 1.50
Nos. 395-397 (3) 5.25 3.65
Issued for Traffic Day.

Map of Palestine and
Torch — A75

Perf. 13½x12½
1968, May 15 Litho.
398 A75 10f lt ultra & multi .22 .15
399 A75 20f yellow & multi 1.10 .28
400 A75 45f aqua & multi 2.25 .55
Nos. 398-400 (3) 3.57 .98
Issued for Palestine Day.

Palestinian Refugees — A76

1968, June 5 Litho. Perf. 13x13½
401 A76 20f pink & multi .38 .15
402 A76 30f ultra & multi .55 .15
403 A76 45f green & multi .70 .18
404 A76 90f lilac & multi 1.25 .38
Nos. 401-404 (4) 2.88 .86
International Human Rights Year.

Museum of
Kuwait — A77

Perf. 12½
1968, Aug. 25 Unwmk. Engr.
405 A77 1f dk brown & brt grn .15 .15
406 A77 2f dp claret & grn .15 .15
407 A77 5f black & orange .15 .15
408 A77 8f dk brown & grn .15 .15
409 A77 10f Prus blue & cl .15 .15
410 A77 20f org brown & blue .32 .15
411 A77 25f dk blue & orange .42 .20
412 A77 30f Prus blue & yel grn .50 .24
413 A77 45f plum & vio black .65 .32
414 A77 50f green & carmine .80 .42
Set value 3.00 1.65

Man Reading
Book, Arab
League, UN
and UNESCO
Emblems
A78

1968, Sept. 8 Litho. Perf. 12½x13
415 A78 15f blue gray & multi .60 .15
416 A78 20f pink & multi .80 .15
Set value .22
Issued for International Literacy Day.

Map of
Palestine on
UN Building
and Children
with
Tent — A79

1968, Oct. 25 Litho. Perf. 13
417 A79 10f multicolored .35 .15
418 A79 30f gray & multi .70 .20
419 A79 45f salmon pink & multi .85 .28
Nos. 417-419 (3) 1.90 .63
Issued for United Nations Day.

Kuwait
Chamber of
Commerce
A80

1968, Nov. 6 Litho. Perf. 13½x12½
420 A80 10f dp orange & dk brn .20 .15
421 A80 15f rose claret & vio bl .42 .20
422 A80 20f brown org & dk green .60 .25
Nos. 420-422 (3) 1.22 .60
Opening of the Kuwait Chamber of Commerce
Building.

Conference Emblem — A81

1968, Nov. 10 Litho. Perf. 13
Emblem in Ocher, Blue, Red and Black
423 A81 10f dk brown & blue .32 .15
424 A81 15f dk brown & orange .45 .20
425 A81 20f dk brown & vio blue .60 .25
426 A81 30f dk brown & org brn .95 .40
Nos. 423-426 (4) 2.32 1.00
14th Conference of the Arab Chambers of Commerce, Industry and Agriculture.

Shuaiba Refinery — A82

1968, Nov. 18 Perf. 13½
Emblem in Red, Black and Blue
427 A82 10f black & lt blue grn .50 .20
428 A82 20f black & gray 1.10 .40
429 A82 30f black & salmon 1.25 .65
430 A82 45f black & emerald 2.25 .85
Nos. 427-430 (4) 5.10 2.10
Opening of Shuaiba Refinery.

Koran,
Scales and
People
A83

1968, Dec. 19 Photo. Perf. 14x14½
431 A83 5f multicolored .42 .22
432 A83 20f multicolored 1.00 .60
433 A83 30f multicolored 1.40 .85
434 A83 45f multicolored 2.00 1.25
Nos. 431-434 (4) 4.82 2.92
The 1400th anniversary of the Koran.

Boeing
707
A84

1969, Jan. 1 Litho. Perf. 13½x14
435 A84 10f brt yellow & multi .60 .20
436 A84 20f green & multi 1.10 .50
437 A84 25f multicolored 1.25 .60
438 A84 45f lilac & multi 2.00 1.10
Nos. 435-438 (4) 4.95 2.40

Introduction of Boeing 707 service by Kuwait Airways.

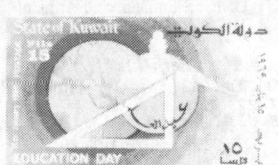

Globe, Retort and Triangle — A85

1969, Jan. 15 Perf. 13
439 A85 15f gray & multi .65 .32
440 A85 20f multicolored 1.00 .38

Issued for Education Day.

Kuwait Hilton Hotel — A86

1969, Feb. 15 Litho. Perf. 14x12½
441 A86 10f brt blue & multi .28 .15
442 A86 20f pink & multi .65 .15
Set value .25

Opening of the Kuwait Hilton Hotel.

Teachers' Society Emblem, Father and Children — A87

1969, Feb. 15 Perf. 13
443 A87 10f violet & multi .32 .18
444 A87 20f rose & multi .80 .42

Issued for Education week.

Wreath, Flags and Dove — A88

Emblem, Teacher and Students — A89

1969, Feb. 25 Photo. Perf. 14½x14
445 A88 15f lilac & multi .42 .25
446 A88 20f blue & multi .70 .30
447 A88 30f ocher & multi .90 .55
Nos. 445-447 (3) 2.02 1.10

Eighth anniversary of National Day.

1969, Mar. 8 Litho. Perf. 13x12½
448 A89 10f multicolored .32 .15
449 A89 20f deep red & multi .65 .20

Issued for Teachers' Day.

Family A90

1969, Mar. 21 Perf. 13½
450 A90 10f dark blue & multi .65 .15
451 A90 20f deep car & multi 1.10 .30

Issued for Family Day.

Avicenna, WHO Emblem, Patient and Microscope — A91

1969, Apr. 7 Litho. Perf. 13½
452 A91 15f red brown & multi .60 .15
453 A91 20f lt green & multi 1.40 .15
Set value .24

Issued for World Health Day, Apr. 7.

Motorized Traffic Police — A92

1969, May 4 Litho. Perf. 12½x13
454 A92 10f multicolored .75 .25
455 A92 20f multicolored 3.25 .60

Issued for Traffic Day.

ILO Emblem — A93

1969, June 1 Perf. 11½
456 A93 10f red, black & gold .35 .15
457 A93 20f lt blue grn, blk & gold .80 .15
Set value .15

50th anniv. of the ILO.

S.S. Al Sabahiah A94

1969, June 10 Litho. Perf. 13½
458 A94 20f multicolored 1.00 .25
459 A94 45f multicolored 2.50 .80

4th anniversary of Kuwait Shipping Co.

UNESCO Emblem, Woman, Globe and Book — A95

1969, Sept. 8 Litho. Perf. 13½
460 A95 10f blue & multi .20 .15
461 A95 20f rose red & multi .42 .15
Set value .15

International Literacy Day, Sept. 8.

Sheik Sabah — A96

UN Emblem and Scroll — A97

1969-74 Litho. Perf. 14
462 A96 8f lt blue & multi .15 .15
463 A96 10f pink & multi .16 .16
464 A96 15f gray & multi .30 .15
465 A96 20f yellow & multi .38 .20
466 A96 25f violet & multi .45 .30
467 A96 30f sal & multi .58 .38
468 A96 45f tan & multi .80 .50
469 A96 50f yel grn & multi 1.00 .58
470 A96 70f multicolored 1.25 .75
471 A96 75f ultra & multi 1.50 .80
472 A96 90f rose & multi 1.90 1.00
473 A96 250f lilac & multi 6.75 3.00
473A A96 500f gray green & multi 13.00 9.50
473B A96 1d lilac rose & multi 27.50 15.00
Nos. 462-473B (14) 55.72 32.47

Nos. 473A-473B issued Jan. 12, 1974; others Oct. 5, 1969.

1969, Oct. 24 Litho. Perf. 13
474 A97 10f emer & multi .15 .15
475 A97 20f bister & multi .32 .18
476 A97 45f rose red & multi .65 .38
Nos. 474-476 (3) 1.12 .71

Issued for United Nations Day.

Radar, Satellite Earth Station, Kuwait A98

Design: 45f, Globe and radar, vert.

1969, Dec. 15 Photo. Perf. 14½
477 A98 20f silver & multi .65 .28
478 A98 45f silver & multi 1.65 .60

Inauguration of the Kuwait Earth Station for Satellite Communications.

Globe with Science Symbols, and Education Year Emblem A99

1970, Jan. 15 Photo. Perf. 13½x13
479 A99 20f brt lilac & multi .80 .30
480 A99 45f blue & multi 1.25 .85

International Education Year.

Shoue A100

Old Kuwaiti Vessels: 10f, Sambook. 15f, Baghla. 20f, Batteel. 25f, Boom. 45f, Bakkara. 50f, Shipbuilding.

1970, Feb. 1 Perf. 14½x14
481 A100 8f multicolored .45 .15
482 A100 10f multicolored .65 .15
483 A100 15f multicolored .75 .30
484 A100 20f multicolored 1.00 .24
485 A100 25f multicolored 1.50 .30
486 A100 45f multicolored 2.25 .70
487 A100 50f multicolored 3.25 .70
Nos. 481-487 (7) 9.85 2.54

Refugee Father and Children A101

Kuwait Flag, Emblem and Sheik Sabah A102

1970 Photo. Perf. 14x12½
488 A101 20f red brown & multi 2.00 .65
489 A101 45f olive & multi 4.25 1.75

Issued for Universal Palestinian Refugees Week, Dec. 16-22, 1969.

1970, Feb. 25 Perf. 13½x13
490 A102 15f silver & multi .55 .15
491 A102 20f gold & multi .80 .20

Ninth anniversary of National Day.

Dome of the Rock, Jerusalem, and Boy Commando — A103

Designs: 20f, Dome and man commando. 45f, Dome and woman commando.

1970, Mar. 4 Litho. Perf. 13
492 A103 10f pale violet & multi .95 .20
493 A103 20f lt blue & multi 1.90 .60
494 A103 45f multicolored 4.00 1.25
Nos. 492-494 (3) 6.85 2.05

Honoring Palestinian commandos.

Parents and Children A104

1970, Mar. 21 Perf. 14
495 A104 20f multicolored .50 .17
496 A104 30f pink & multi .75 .32

Issued for Family Day.

Map of Arab League Countries, Flag and Emblem A104a

1970, Mar. 22 Perf. 11½x11
497 A104a 20f lt blue, grn & lt brn .50 .25
498 A104a 45f salmon, grn & dk pur 1.40 .60

25th anniversary of the Arab League.

Census Graph and Kuwait Arms A105

1970, Apr. 1 Litho. Perf. 13½x13
499 A105 15f dull orange & multi .28 .15
500 A105 20f yellow & multi .35 .15
501 A105 30f pink & multi .60 .28
Nos. 499-501 (3) 1.23 .58

Issued to publicize the 1970 census.

"Fight Cancer,"
Kuwait Arms, WHO
Emblem — A106

1970, Apr. 7   *Perf. 13¹/₂x13*
502 A106 20f blue, vio bl & rose lil   .42   .15
503 A106 30f dl yel, vio bl & lil rose   .55   .24
World Health Organization Day, Apr. 7, and to
publicize the fight against cancer.

Traffic
Signs — A107

1970, May 4   **Photo.**   *Perf. 13¹/₂*
504 A107 20f multicolored   1.65   .65
505 A107 30f multicolored   2.75   1.00
Issued for Traffic Day.

Red
Crescent
A108

1970, May 8   **Litho.**   *Perf. 12¹/₂x13¹/₂*
506 A108 10f yellow & multi   .65   .16
507 A108 15f emerald & multi   1.10   .25
508 A108 30f tan & multi   2.25   .70
   Nos. 506-508 (3)   4.00   1.11
Intl. Red Crescent and Red Cross Day.

Opening of
UPU
Headquarters,
Bern — A109

1970, May 25   **Photo.**   *Perf. 12x11¹/₂*
509 A109 20f multicolored   .85   .32
510 A109 30f multicolored   1.10   .50

Sheik
Sabah — A110

1970, June 15   **Photo.**   *Perf. 14*
511 A110 20f silver & multi   1.00   .20
512 A110 45f gold & multi   2.25   .50
  a.   Miniature sheet of 2   5.00   1.75
Nos. 511-512 have circular perforation around
vignette set within a white square of paper, perforated on 4 sides. #512a contains 2 imperf. stamps
similar to #511-512.

UN Emblem, Symbols
of Peace, Progress,
Justice — A111

1970, July 1   **Litho.**   *Perf. 13¹/₂x12¹/₂*
513 A111 20f lt green & multi   .52   .18
514 A111 45f multicolored   .95   .42
25th anniversary of the United Nations.

Tanker
Loading
Crude Oil
from Sea
Island
A112

1970, Aug. 1   *Perf. 13¹/₂x13*
515 A112 20f multicolored   1.10   .35
516 A112 45f multicolored   2.75   .85
Issued to publicize the artificial "Sea Island" loading facilities in Kuwait.

"Writing,"
Kuwait and
UN Emblems
A113

1970, Sept. 8   **Photo.**   *Perf. 13¹/₂*
517 A113 10f brt blue & multi   .85   .15
518 A113 15f brt green & multi   1.40   .15
   Set value   .17
International Literacy Day, Sept. 8.

National
Guard and
Emblem
A114

1970, Oct. 20   **Photo.**   *Perf. 13x13¹/₂*
519 A114 10f gold & multi   .80   .15
520 A114 20f silver & multi   1.65   .26
First National Guard graduation.

Flag of Kuwait,
Symbols of
Development
A115

1971, Feb. 25   **Litho.**   *Perf. 12*
521 A115 20f gray & multi   1.00   .40
522 A115 30f multicolored   1.40   .65
Tenth anniversary of National Day.

Charles H.
Best,
Frederick G.
Banting
A116

1971, Apr. 7   **Litho.**   *Perf. 14*
523 A116 20f multicolored   .55   .20
524 A116 45f multicolored   1.25   .55
World Health Day; discoverers of insulin.

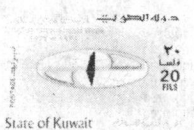

Globe with Map
of Palestine
A117

1971, May 3   **Litho.**   *Perf. 12¹/₂x13*
525 A117 20f yel green & multi   1.50   1.10
526 A117 45f lilac & multi   3.00   2.25
International Palestine Week.

ITU Emblem
and Waves
A118

1971, May 17   **Photo.**   *Perf. 13x13¹/₂*
527 A118 20f silver, dk red & blk   1.25   .32
528 A118 45f gold, dk red & blk   2.50   .85
3rd World Telecommunications Day.

Men of 3
Races — A119

1971, June 5   **Litho.**   *Perf. 11¹/₂x11*
529 A119 15f red brown & multi   .80   .30
530 A119 30f ultra & multi   1.25   .70
Intl. Year against Racial Discrimination.

Arab Postal
Union Emblem
A120

1971, Aug. 30   *Perf. 13x12¹/₂*
531 A120 20f brown & multi   .65   .38
532 A120 45f blue & multi   1.40   .55
25th anniv. of the Conf. of Sofar, Lebanon, establishing the Arab Postal Union.

Symbols of Learning,
UNESCO and
Kuwait
Emblems — A121

1971, Sept. 8   *Perf. 12*
533 A121 25f dull yellow & multi   .90   .25
534 A121 60f lt blue & multi   2.00   .90
International Literacy Day, Sept. 8.

Soccer
A122

Design: 30f, Soccer, different.

1971, Dec. 10   *Perf. 13*
535 A122 20f green & multi   1.25   .50
536 A122 30f ultra & multi   1.75   .70
Regional Sports Tournament, Kuwait, Dec.

UNICEF Emblem and Arms of
Kuwait — A123

    Perf. 11x11¹/₂
1971, Dec. 11   **Litho. & Engr.**
537 A123 25f gold & multi   .60   .28
538 A123 60f silver & multi   1.25   .70
25th anniv. of UNICEF.

Book Year
Emblem
A124

1972, Jan. 2   **Litho.**   *Perf. 14x13*
539 A124 20f black & buff   .80   .40
540 A124 45f black & lt blue grn   1.65   .90
International Book Year.

Kuwait
Emblem with
11 Rays,
Olive Branch
A125

1972, Feb. 25   **Litho.**   *Perf. 13x13¹/₂*
541 A125 20f pink, gold & multi   1.25   .70
542 A125 45f lt blue, gold & multi   1.90   1.25
11th anniversary of National Day.

Telecommunications Center — A126

1972, Feb. 28   *Perf. 13¹/₂*
543 A126 20f lt blue & multi   1.50   .60
544 A126 45f multicolored   3.75   1.50
Opening of Kuwait Telecommunications Center.

"Your Heart is
your
Health" — A127

Nurse and
Child — A128

1972, Apr. 7   **Photo.**   *Perf. 14¹/₂x14*
545 A127 20f red & multi   1.65   .60
546 A127 45f red & multi   4.00   1.40
World Health Day.

1972, May 8   **Litho.**   *Perf. 12¹/₂x13*
547 A128 8f vio blue, red & emer   1.10   .15
548 A128 40f pink & multi   3.50   1.00
Red Cross and Red Crescent Day.

Soccer, Olympic Emblems A129

1972, Sept. 2   Litho.   Perf. 14½
549 A129   2f shown   .15   .15
550 A129   4f Running   .15   .15
551 A129   5f Swimming   .15   .15
552 A129   8f Gymnastics   .15   .15
553 A129   10f Discus   .20   .16
554 A129   15f Equestrian   .75   .75
555 A129   20f Basketball   .85   .30
556 A129   25f Volleyball   1.10   .35
Nos. 549-556 (8)   3.50   1.66

20th Olympic Games, Munich, Aug. 26-Sept. 11.

FAO Emblem, Vegetables, Fish and Ship — A130

1972, Sept. 9   Litho.   Perf. 14x13½
557 A130   5f blue & multi   .40   .40
558 A130   10f emerald & multi   1.50   1.10
559 A130   20f orange & multi   3.00   2.00
Nos. 557-559 (3)   4.90   3.50

11th FAO Regional Conference in the Near East, Kuwait, Sept.

National Bank Emblem A131

1972, Nov. 15   Photo.   Perf. 13x14
560 A131   10f green & multi   .45   .25
561 A131   35f dull red & multi   1.50   1.00

20th anniversary of Kuwait National Bank.

Capitals — A132

Relics of Failaka: 5f, View of excavations. 10f, Acanthus leaf capital. 15f, Excavations.

1972, Dec. 4   Litho.   Perf. 12
562 A132   2f lilac rose & multi   .18   .15
563 A132   5f bister & multi   .18   .15
564 A132   10f lt blue & multi   .95   .22
565 A132   15f green & multi   1.40   .32
Nos. 562-565 (4)   2.71   .84

Flower and Kuwait Emblem — A133

INTERPOL Emblem — A134

1973, Feb. 25   Litho.   Perf. 13½x13
566 A133   10f lt olive & multi   .45   .25
567 A133   20f multicolored   .95   .65
568 A133   30f yellow & multi   1.40   .95
Nos. 566-568 (3)   2.80   1.85

12th anniversary of National Day.

1973, June 3   Litho.   Perf. 12
569 A134   10f emerald & multi   .75   .70
570 A134   15f red orange & multi   1.40   .95
571 A134   20f blue & multi   2.25   1.40
Nos. 569-571 (3)   4.40   3.05

50th anniv. of Intl. Criminal Police Org. (INTERPOL).

I.C.M.S. Emblem and Flag of Kuwait — A135

Kuwait Airways Building — A136

1973, June 24   Perf. 13
572 A135   30f gray & multi   .95   .55
573 A135   40f brown & multi   1.50   .75

Intl. Council of Military Sports, 25th anniv.

1973, July 1   Litho.   Perf. 12½x14
574 A136   10f lt green & multi   .50   .18
575 A136   15f lilac & multi   .70   .32
576 A136   20f lt ultra & multi   1.00   .40
Nos. 574-576 (3)   2.20   .90

Opening of Kuwait Airways Corporation Building.

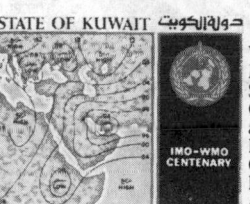

Weather Map of Suez Canal and Persian Gulf Region A137

1973, Sept. 4   Photo.   Perf. 14
577 A137   5f red & multi   .40   .16
578 A137   10f green & multi   .75   .16
579 A137   15f multicolored   1.25   .24
Nos. 577-579 (3)   2.40   .56

Intl. meteorological cooperation, cent.

Sheiks Ahmad and Sabah — A138

1973, Nov. 12   Photo.   Perf. 14
580 A138   10f lt green & multi   .50   .22
581 A138   20f yel orange & multi   1.00   .35
582 A138   70f lt blue & multi   3.50   1.40
Nos. 580-582 (3)   5.00   1.97

Stamps overprinted "Kuwait," 50th anniv.

Mourning Dove, Eurasian Hoopoe, Rock Dove, Stone Curlew — A139

Designs: Birds and traps.

1973, Dec. 1   Litho.   Perf. 14
Size (single stamp): 32x32mm
583 A139   Block of 4   2.75   1.40
a.   5f Mourning dove   .65   .30
b.   5f Eurasian hoopoe   .65   .30
c.   5f Rock dove   .65   .30
d.   5f Stone curlew   .65   .30
584 A139   Block of 4   3.50   1.75
a.   8f Great gray shrike   .80   .40
b.   8f Red-backed shrike   .80   .40
c.   8f Rufous-backed shrike   .80   .40
d.   8f Black-naped oriole   .80   .40
585 A139   Block of 4   4.25   2.50
a.   10f Willow warbler   1.00   .55
b.   10f Great reed warbler   1.00   .55
c.   10f Blackcap   1.00   .55
d.   10f Common (barn) swallow   1.00   .55
586 A139   Block of 4   7.00   4.25
a.   15f Common rock thrush   1.75   .90
b.   15f European redstart   1.75   .90
c.   15f Wheatear   1.75   .90
d.   15f Bluethroat   1.75   .90
587 A139   Block of 4   8.50   4.50
a.   20f Houbara bustard   2.00   1.00
b.   20f Pin-tailed sandgrouse   2.00   1.00
c.   20f Ypecaha wood rail   2.00   1.00
d.   20f Spotted crake   2.00   1.00

Size (single stamp): 35x35mm
588 A139   Block of 4   9.00   5.75
a.   25f American sparrow hawk   2.25   1.25
b.   25f Great black-backed gull   2.25   1.25
c.   25f Purple heron   2.25   1.25
d.   25f Wryneck   2.25   1.25
589 A139   Block of 4   13.00   7.00
a.   30f European bee-eater   4.00   1.65
b.   30f Goshawk   4.00   1.65
c.   30f Gray wagtail   4.00   1.65
d.   30f Pied wagtail   4.00   1.65
590 A139   Block of 4   18.00   10.00
a.   45f Crossbows   4.25   2.25
b.   45f Tent-shaped net   4.25   2.25
c.   45f Hand net   4.25   2.25
d.   45f Rooftop trap   4.25   2.25
Nos. 583-590 (8)   66.00   37.15

Human Rights Flame — A141

1973, Dec. 10   Litho.   Perf. 12
594 A141   10f red & multi   .60   .15
595 A141   40f lt green & multi   1.65   .52
596 A141   75f lilac & multi   2.25   .85
Nos. 594-596 (3)   4.50   1.52

25th anniv. of the Universal Declaration of Human Rights.

Promoting Animal Resources — A142

Stylized Wheat and Kuwaiti Flag — A143

1974, Feb. 16   Litho.   Perf. 12½
597 A142   30f violet blue & multi   .85   .30
598 A142   40f rose & multi   1.25   .42

4th Congress of the Arab Veterinary Union, Kuwait.

1974, Feb. 25   Perf. 13½x13
599 A143   20f lemon & multi   .28   .22
600 A143   30f bister brn & multi   1.00   .38
601 A143   70f silver & multi   1.90   .90
Nos. 599-601 (3)   3.18   1.50

13th anniversary of National Day.

Conference Emblem and Sheik Sabah A144

1974, Mar. 8   Perf. 12½
602 A144   30f multicolored   1.90   .70
603 A144   40f yellow & multi   3.00   .90

12th Conf. of the Arab Medical Union and 1st Conf. of the Kuwait Medical Soc.

Tournament Emblem — A145

1974, Mar. 15
604 A145   25f multicolored   1.25   .50
605 A145   45f multicolored   2.25   .75

Third Soccer Tournament for the Arabian Gulf Trophy, Kuwait, Mar. 1974.

Scientific Research Institute — A146

1974, Apr. 3   Photo.   Perf. 12½
606 A146   15f magenta & multi   1.00   .28
607 A146   20f green & multi   1.90   .32

Opening of Kuwait Scientific Research Institute.

Arab Postal Union, Kuwait and UPU Emblems A147

1974, May 1   Perf. 13x14
608 A147   20f gold & multi   .25   .18
609 A147   30f gold & multi   .40   .25
610 A147   60f gold & multi   .75   .52
Nos. 608-610 (3)   1.40   .95

Centenary of Universal Postal Union.

Telephone Dial with Communications Symbols and Globe — A148

1974, May 17   Perf. 14x13½
611 A148   20f lt blue & multi   .40   .18
612 A148   30f multicolored   1.25   .58
613 A148   40f black & multi   1.65   .80
Nos. 611-613 (3)   3.30   1.56

World Telecommunications Day, May 17.

Emblem of Unity Council and Flags of Member States — A149

1974, June 25   Litho.   Perf. 13½
614 A149   20f red, black & green   .90   .40
615 A149   30f green, black & red   1.00   .55

17th anniversary of the signing of the Arab Economic Unity Agreement.

WPY Emblem, Embryo, "Growth" A150

1974, Aug. 19   Litho.   Perf. 14x14½
616 A150 30f black & multi   1.25   .40
617 A150 70f violet blue & multi 2.00   .90
World Population Year.

Development Building and Emblem — A151

1974, Oct. 30   Litho.   Perf. 13x13½
618 A151 10f pink & multi   .65   .15
619 A151 20f ultra & multi   1.10   .28
Kuwait Fund for Arab Economic Development.

Emblem of Shuaiba Industrial Area — A152

1974, Dec. 17   Litho.   Perf. 12½x12
620 A152 10f lt blue & multi   .60   .20
621 A152 20f salmon & multi   1.50   .42
622 A152 30f lt green & multi   1.90   .80
        Nos. 620-622 (3)   4.00 1.40
Shuaiba Industrial Area, 10th anniversary.

Arms of Kuwait and "14" — A153

1975, Feb. 25   Litho.   Perf. 13x13½
623 A153 20f multicolored   .50   .30
624 A153 70f yel green & multi 1.75   .85
625 A153 75f rose & multi   2.00 1.00
        Nos. 623-625 (3)   4.25 2.15
14th anniversary of National Day.

Male and Female Symbols — A154

1975, Apr. 14   Photo.   Perf. 11½x12
626 A154   8f lt green & multi   .25   .15
627 A154 20f rose & multi   .35   .25
628 A154 30f blue & multi   .60   .42
629 A154 70f yellow & multi   1.65   .85
630 A154 100f black & multi   2.50 1.40
        Nos. 626-630 (5)   5.35 3.07
Kuwaiti census 1975.

IWY and Kuwaiti Women's Union Emblems — A155

1975, June 10   Litho.   Perf. 14½
631 A155 15f brown org & multi   .65   .25
632 A155 20f olive & multi   .85   .40
633 A155 30f violet & multi   1.25   .65
        Nos. 631-633 (3)   2.75 1.30
International Women's Year.

Classroom and UNESCO Emblem A156

1975, Sept. 8   Litho.   Perf. 12½x12
634 A156 20f green & multi   .75   .24
635 A156 30f multicolored   1.25   .65
International Literacy Day.

Symbols of Measurements A157

UN Flag, Rifle and Olive Branch A158

1975, Oct. 14   Photo.   Perf. 14x13
636 A157 10f green & multi   .40   .18
637 A157 20f purple & multi   .80   .40
World Standards Day.

1975, Oct. 24   Litho.   Perf. 12x12½
638 A158 20f multicolored   .70   .25
639 A158 45f orange & multi   1.50   .70
United Nations, 30th anniversary.

Sheik Sabah — A159

1975, Dec. 22   Litho.   Perf. 12½x12
640 A159   8f yellow & multi   .45   .22
641 A159 20f lilac & multi   .75   .28
642 A159 30f buff & multi   .95   .40
643 A159 50f salmon & multi   1.65   .70
644 A159 90f lt blue & multi   3.25 1.25
645 A159 100f multicolored   3.75 1.50
        Nos. 640-645 (6)   10.80 4.35

"Progress" A160

1976, Feb. 25   Litho.   Perf. 12
646 A160 10f multicolored   .45   .15
647 A160 20f multicolored   .95   .20
15th anniversary of National Day.

Medical Equipment, Emblem and Surgery — A161

Telephones, 1876 and 1976 — A162

1976, Mar. 1   Litho.   Perf. 14½
648 A161   5f dull green & multi .15   .15
649 A161 10f blue & multi   .95   .30
650 A161 30f gray & multi   2.75   .80
        Nos. 648-650 (3)   3.85 1.25
Kuwait Medical Assoc., 2nd annual conference.

1976, Mar. 10   Litho.   Perf. 12
651 A162   5f orange & black   .25   .15
652 A162 15f lt blue & black   .95   .20
        Set value   .25
Centenary of first telephone call by Alexander Graham Bell, Mar. 10, 1876.

Human Eye — A163

Photo. & Engr.
1976, Apr. 7   Perf. 11½
653 A163 10f multicolored   .35   .15
654 A163 20f black & multi   .65   .30
655 A163 30f multicolored   1.00   .45
        Nos. 653-655 (3)   2.00   .90
World Health Day: "Foresight prevents blindness."

Red Crescent Emblem A164

1976, May 8   Litho.   Perf. 12x11½
656 A164 20f brt green, blk & red   .60   .35
657 A164 30f vio blue, blk & red   1.25   .45
658 A164 45f yellow, blk & red   1.40   .80
659 A164 75f lilac rose, blk & red 2.50 1.25
        Nos. 656-659 (4)   5.75 2.85
Kuwait Red Crescent Society, 10th anniv.

Modern Suburb of Kuwait A165

1976, June 1   Photo.   Perf. 13x13½
660 A165 10f light green & multi .50   .15
661 A165 20f salmon & multi   .95   .25
Habitat, UN Conference on Human Settlements, Vancouver, Canada, May 31-June 11.

Basketball, Kuwait Olympic Emblem — A166

Various Races, Map of Sri Lanka — A167

Designs: 8f, Running. 10f, Judo. 15f, Fieldball. 20f, Gymnastics. 30f, Water polo. 45f, Soccer. 70f, Swimmers at start.

1976, July 17   Litho.   Perf. 14½
662 A166   4f black & multi   .15   .15
663 A166   8f red & multi   .15   .15
664 A166 10f green & multi   .20   .15
665 A166 15f lemon & multi   .30   .16
666 A166 20f blue & multi   .45   .20
667 A166 30f lilac & multi   .65   .40
668 A166 45f multicolored   .95   .55
669 A166 70f brown & multi   1.65   .85
        Nos. 662-669 (8)   4.50 2.61
21st Olympic Games, Montreal, Canada, July 17-Aug. 1.

1976, Aug. 16   Photo.   Perf. 14
670 A167 20f dk blue & multi   .50   .15
671 A167 30f purple & multi   .75   .45
672 A167 45f green & multi   1.25   .65
        Nos. 670-672 (3)   2.50 1.25
5th Summit Conf. of Non-aligned Countries, Colombo, Sri Lanka, Aug. 9-19.

"UNESCO," Torch and Kuwait Arms A168

1976, Nov. 4   Litho.   Perf. 12x11½
673 A168 20f yel green & multi   .65   .15
674 A168 45f scarlet & multi   1.50   .70
30th anniversary of UNESCO.

Blindman's Buff — A169

Popular games. 5f, 15f, 30f, vertical.

Perf. 14½x14, 14x14½
1977, Jan. 10   Litho.
675 A169   5f Pot throwing   .20   .20
676 A169   5f Kite flying   .20   .20
677 A169   5f Balancing sticks   .20   .20
678 A169   5f Spinning tops   .20   .20
679 A169 10f shown   .25   .20
680 A169 10f Rowing   .25   .20
681 A169 10f Hoops   .25   .20
682 A169 10f Ropes   .25   .20
683 A169 15f Rope skipping   .55   .35
684 A169 15f Marbles   .55   .35
685 A169 15f Cart steering   .55   .35
686 A169 15f Teetotum   .55   .25
687 A169 20f Halma   .75   .55
688 A169 20f Model boats   .75   .55
689 A169 20f Pot and candle   .75   .55
690 A169 20f Hide and seek   .75   .55
691 A169 30f Throwing bones   1.00   .75
692 A169 30f Mystery gifts   1.00   .75
693 A169 30f Hopscotch   1.00   .75
694 A169 30f Catch as catch can 1.00   .75
695 A169 40f Bowls   1.65 1.00
696 A169 40f Sword fighting   1.65 1.00
697 A169 40f Mother and child   1.65 1.00
698 A169 40f Fivestones   1.65 1.00
699 A169 60f Hiding a cake   2.50 1.75
700 A169 60f Chess   2.50 1.75
701 A169 60f Dancing   2.50 1.75
702 A169 60f Treasure hunt   2.50 1.75
703 A169 70f Hobby-horses   2.75 1.90
704 A169 70f Hide and seek   2.75 1.90
705 A169 70f Catch   2.75 1.90
706 A169 70f Storytelling   2.75 1.90
        Nos. 675-706 (32)   38.60 26.70
Stamps of same denomination printed se-tenant in blocks of 4, sheets of 100.

Diseased Knee — A170

1977, Feb. 15   Perf. 13x13½
707 A170 20f yellow & multi   .50   .25
708 A170 30f multicolored   .90   .45
709 A170 45f red & multi   1.25   .70
710 A170 75f black & multi   2.25 1.25
        Nos. 707-710 (4)   4.90 2.65
World Rheumatism Year.

Sheik Sabah A171

1977, Feb. 25 Photo. Perf. 13½x13

711	A171	10f multicolored	.20 .20
712	A171	15f multicolored	.30 .22
713	A171	30f multicolored	.50 .30
714	A171	80f multicolored	1.25 .80
		Nos. 711-714 (4)	2.25 1.52

16th National Day.

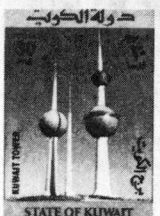

Kuwait Tower — A172
APU Emblem — A173

1977, Feb. 26 Perf. 14x13½

715	A172	30f multicolored	.65 .25
716	A172	80f multicolored	1.65 .70

Inauguration of Kuwait Tower.

1977, Apr. 12 Litho. Perf. 13½x14

717	A173	5f yellow & multi	.30 .15
718	A173	15f pink & multi	.30 .15
719	A173	30f lt blue & multi	.60 .30
720	A173	80f lilac & multi	1.50 .90
		Nos. 717-720 (4)	2.70 1.50

Arab Postal Union, 25th anniversary.

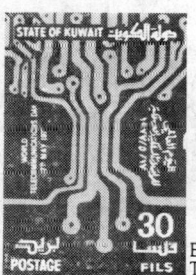

Electronic Tree — A174

1977, May 17 Litho. Perf. 12x12½

721	A174	30f brown & red	.95 .40
722	A174	80f green & red	2.25 1.00

World Telecommunications Day.

Sheik Sabah — A175
Games Emblem — A176

1977, June 1 Photo. Perf. 11½x12

723	A175	15f blue & multi	.40 .50
724	A175	25f yellow & multi	.80 .50
725	A175	30f red & multi	1.00 .70
726	A175	80f violet & multi	3.25 1.75
727	A175	100f dp org & multi	3.50 2.00
728	A175	150f ultra & multi	5.50 3.25
729	A175	200f olive & multi	7.25 4.50
		Nos. 723-729 (7)	21.70 13.20

1977, Oct. 1 Litho. Perf. 12

730	A176	30f multicolored	.75 .75
731	A176	80f multicolored	1.90 1.50

4th Asian Basketball Youth Championship, Oct. 1-15.

Dome of the Rock, Bishop Capucci, Fatima Bernawi, Sheik Abu Tair
A177

1977, Nov. 1 Perf. 14

732	A177	30f multicolored	1.90 1.00
733	A177	80f multicolored	4.00 2.25

Struggle for the liberation of Palestine.

Children and Houses A178

Children's Paintings: No. 735, Women musicians. No. 736, Boats. No. 737, Women preparing food, vert. No. 738, Women and children, vert. No. 739, Seated woman, vert.

1977, Nov. Photo. Perf. 13½x13

734	A178	15f lt green & multi	.45 .30
735	A178	15f yellow & multi	.45 .30
736	A178	30f brt yellow & multi	.85 .60
737	A178	30f lt violet & multi	.85 .60
738	A178	80f black & multi	2.00 1.65
739	A178	80f rose & multi	2.00 1.65
		Nos. 734-739 (6)	6.60 5.10

Dentist Treating Patient — A179

1977, Dec. 3

740	A179	30f green & multi	.85 .85
741	A179	80f violet & multi	2.50 1.65

10th Arab Dental Union Congress, Kuwait, Dec. 3-6.

Ships Unloading Water A180

Water resources in Kuwait. 30f, 80f, 100f, vertical.

Perf. 14x13½, 13½x14

1978, Jan. 25 Litho.

742		Block of 4	.70 .40
a.		5f shown	.15 .15
b.		5f Home delivery by camel	.15 .15
c.		5f Man with water bags	.15 .15
d.		5f Man with wheelbarrow	.15 .15
743		Block of 4	1.10 .60
a.		10f Well	.25 .15
b.		10f Trough	.25 .15
c.		10f Water hole	.25 .15
d.		10f Irrigation	.25 .15
744		Block of 4	1.65 .70
a.		15f Sheep drinking	.35 .15
b.		15f Laundresses	.35 .15
c.		15f Sheep and camels drinking	.35 .15
d.		15f Water stored in skins	.35 .15
745		Block of 4	1.75 .90
a.		20f Animals at well	.40 .15
b.		20f Water in home	.40 .15
c.		20f Water pot	.40 .15
d.		20f Communal fountain	.40 .15
746		Block of 4	2.25 1.25
a.		25f Distillation plant	.50 .30
b.		25f Motorized delivery	.50 .30
c.		25f Water trucks	.50 .30
d.		25f Water towers	.50 .30
747		Block of 4	2.50 1.40
a.		30f Shower bath	.60 .30
b.		30f Water tower	.60 .30
c.		30f Gathering rain water	.60 .30
d.		30f 2 water towers	.60 .30
748		Block of 4	7.50 4.00
a.		80f Donkey with water bags	1.90 .90
b.		80f Woman with water can	1.90 .90
c.		80f Woman with water skin	1.90 .90
d.		80f Loading tank car	1.90 .90
749		Block of 4	8.75 4.75
a.		100f Truck delivering water	2.25 1.10
b.		100f Barnyard water supply	2.25 1.10
c.		100f Children at water basin	2.25 1.10
d.		100f Well in courtyard	2.25 1.10
		Nos. 742-749 (8)	26.20 13.90

Radar, Torch, Minarets A181

1978, Feb. 25 Litho. Perf. 14x14½

750	A181	30f multicolored	.50 .35
751	A181	80f multicolored	1.50 1.00

17th National Day.

Man with Smallpox, Target — A182

1978, Apr. 17 Litho. Perf. 12½

752	A182	30f violet & multi	.60 .42
753	A182	80f green & multi	1.75 1.10

Global eradication of smallpox.

Antenna and ITU Emblem A183

1978, May 17 Perf. 14

754	A183	30f silver & multi	.52 .38
755	A183	80f silver & multi	1.65 1.00

10th World Telecommunications Day.

Sheik Sabah — A184

1978, June 28 Litho. Perf. 13x14
Portrait in Brown
Size: 21½x27mm

756	A184	15f green & gold	.20 .20
757	A184	30f orange & gold	.45 .45
758	A184	80f rose lilac & gold	1.10 1.10
759	A184	100f lt green & gold	1.25 1.25
760	A184	130f lt brown & gold	1.75 1.75
761	A184	180f violet & gold	2.75 2.75

Size: 23½x29mm

762	A184	1d red & gold	14.00 13.00
763	A184	4d blue & gold	60.00 60.00
		Nos. 756-763 (8)	81.50 80.50

Mt. Arafat, Pilgrims, Holy Kaaba A185

1978, Nov. 9 Photo. Perf. 11½

764	A185	30f multicolored	.75 .60
765	A185	80f multicolored	2.00 1.50

Pilgrimage to Mecca.

UN and Anti-Apartheid Emblems A186

1978, Nov. 27 Litho. Perf. 12

766	A186	30f multicolored	.50 .40
767	A186	80f multicolored	1.10 1.00
768	A186	180f multicolored	3.25 2.25
		Nos. 766-768 (3)	4.85 3.65

Anti-Apartheid Year.

Refugees, Human Rights Emblems A187

1978, Dec. 10 Photo. Perf. 13x13½

769	A187	30f multicolored	.60 .45
770	A187	80f multicolored	1.75 1.10
771	A187	100f multicolored	2.50 1.40
		Nos. 769-771 (3)	4.85 2.95

Declaration of Human Rights, 30th anniv.

Information Center A188

1978, Dec. 26 Photo. Perf. 13

772	A188	5f multicolored	.15 .15
773	A188	15f multicolored	.22 .16
774	A188	30f multicolored	.52 .35
775	A188	80f multicolored	1.25 .85
		Nos. 772-775 (4)	2.14 1.51

New Kuwait Information Center.

Kindergarten A189

1979, Jan. 24 Photo. Perf. 13½x14

776	A189	30f multicolored	.60 .48
777	A189	80f multicolored	1.50 1.25

International Year of the Child.

Flag and Peace Doves — A190

1979, Feb. 25 Perf. 14½x14

778	A190	30f multicolored	.60 .45
779	A190	80f multicolored	1.40 1.10

18th National Day.

Modern Agriculture in Kuwait A191

1979, Mar. 13 Photo. Perf. 14

780	A191	30f multicolored	.55 .42
781	A191	80f multicolored	1.40 1.10

4th Congress of Arab Agriculture Ministers of the Gulf and Arabian Peninsula.

World Map, Book, Symbols of Learning A192

1979, Mar. 22

782	A192	30f multicolored	.55 .42
783	A192	80f multicolored	1.40 1.10

Cultural achievements of the Arabs.

Children with
Balloons — A193

Children's Paintings: No. 785, Boys flying kites.
No. 786, Girl and doves. No. 787, Children and
houses, horiz. No. 788, Four children, horiz. No.
789, Children sitting in circle, horiz.

1979, Apr. 18   Photo.   Perf. 14
784 A193 30f yellow & multi   .55 .45
785 A193 30f buff & multi   .55 .45
786 A193 30f pale yel & multi   .55 .45
787 A193 80f lt blue & multi   1.50 1.25
788 A193 80f yel green & multi   1.50 1.25
789 A193 80f lilac & multi   1.50 1.25
        Nos. 784-789 (6)   6.15 5.10

Cables, ITU
Emblem,
People
A194

1979, May 17
790 A194 30f multicolored   .50 .40
791 A194 80f multicolored   1.40 1.25

World Telecommunications Day.

Military Sports Council
Emblem — A195

1979, June 1   Photo.   Perf. 14
792 A195 30f multicolored   .50 .40
793 A195 80f multicolored   1.40 1.25

29th Intl. Military Soccer Championship.

Child, Industrial Landscape, Environmental
Emblems — A196

1979, June 5   Perf. 12x11¹⁄₂
794 A196 30f multicolored   .75 .60
795 A196 80f multicolored   2.00 1.65

World Environment Day, June 5.

Children Holding
Globe, UNESCO
Emblem — A197

1979, July 25   Litho.   Perf. 11¹⁄₂x12
796 A197   30f multicolored   .50 .40
797 A197   80f multicolored   1.25 1.10
798 A197 130f multicolored   2.00 1.75
        Nos. 796-798 (3)   3.75 3.25

Intl. Bureau of Education, Geneva, 50th anniv.

Kuwait
Kindergartens,
25th Anniversary
A198

Children's Drawings: 80f, Children waving flags.

1979, Sept. 15   Litho.   Perf. 12¹⁄₂
799 A198 30f multicolored   .60 .40
800 A198 80f multicolored   1.50 1.10

Pilgrims at
Holy Ka'aba,
Mecca
Mosque
A199

1979, Oct. 29   Perf. 14x14¹⁄₂
801 A199 30f multicolored   .60 .45
802 A199 80f multicolored   2.00 1.25

Hegira (Pilgrimage Year).

International
Palestinian
Solidarity
Day — A200

1979, Nov. 29   Photo.   Perf. 11¹⁄₂x12
803 A200 30f multicolored   1.90 .95
804 A200 80f multicolored   4.50 1.90

Kuwait
Airways 25th
Anniversary
A201

1979, Dec. 24   Photo.   Perf. 13x13¹⁄₂
805 A201 30f multicolored   .80 .60
806 A201 80f multicolored   2.25 1.75

19th National
Day — A202

1980, Feb. 25   Litho.   Perf. 14x14¹⁄₂
807 A202 30f multicolored   .55 .40
808 A202 80f multicolored   1.40 1.10

1980
Population
Census
A203

1980, Mar. 18   Perf. 13¹⁄₂x14
809 A203 30f multicolored   .50 .35
810 A203 80f multicolored   1.65 .85

World
Health
Day — A204

1980, Apr. 7
811 A204 30f multicolored   .85 .55
812 A204 80f multicolored   2.50 1.65

Kuwait Municipality,
50th
Anniversary — A205

1980, May 1   Photo.   Perf. 14
813 A205 15f multicolored   .28 .18
814 A205 30f multicolored   .60 .40
815 A205 80f multicolored   1.75 1.10
        Nos. 813-815 (3)   2.63 1.68

Citizens of
Kuwait
A206

Future Kuwait (Children's Drawings): 80f, Super
highway.

1980, May 14   Litho.   Perf. 14x14¹⁄₂
816 A206 30f multicolored   .70 .45
817 A206 80f multicolored   2.25 1.40

World
Environment
Day — A207

1980, June 5   Litho.   Perf. 12x11¹⁄₂
818 A207 30f multicolored   .45 .30
819 A207 80f multicolored   1.40 .85

Swimming, Moscow
'80 and Kuwait
Olympic Committee
Emblems — A208

1980, July 19   Litho.   Perf. 12x12¹⁄₂
820 A208 15f Volleyball   .18 .15
821 A208 15f Tennis   .18 .15
822 A208 30f shown   .42 .32
823 A208 30f Weight lifting   .42 .32
824 A208 30f Basketball   .42 .32
825 A208 30f Judo   .42 .32
826 A208 80f Gymnast   1.40 .90
827 A208 80f Badminton   1.40 .90
828 A208 80f Fencing   1.40 .90
829 A208 80f Soccer   1.40 .90
        Nos. 820-829 (10)   7.64 5.18

22nd Summer Olympic Games, Moscow, July
19-Aug. 3. Stamps of same denomination se-tenant.

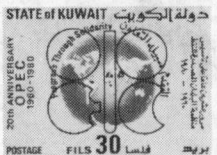

20th
Anniversary of
OPEC
A209

1980, Sept. 16   Litho.   Perf. 14x14¹⁄₂
830 A209 30f multicolored   .75 .50
831 A209 80f multicolored   2.25 .80

Hegira
(Pilgrimage
Year)
A210

1980, Nov. 9   Photo.   Perf. 12x11¹⁄₂
832 A210 15f multicolored   .32 .20
833 A210 30f multicolored   .70 .45
834 A210 80f multicolored   2.00 1.25
        Nos. 832-834 (3)   3.02 1.90

Dome of the
Rock,
Jerusalem
A211

1980, Nov. 29   Perf. 12x11¹⁄₂
835 A211 30f multicolored   1.50 .60
836 A211 80f multicolored   3.75 1.65

International Palestinian Solidarity Day.

Avicenna (980-
1037), Philosopher
and
Physician — A212

Conference
Emblem — A213

1980, Dec. 7   Perf. 12x12¹⁄₂
837 A212 30f multicolored   .85 .35
838 A212 80f multicolored   1.75 .95

1981, Jan. 12   Photo.   Perf. 13¹⁄₂x13
839 A213 30f multicolored   .65 .45
840 A213 80f multicolored   2.00 1.25

First Islamic Medical Conference.

Girl in
Wheelchair
A214

International Year of the Disabled: 30f, Man in
wheelchair playing billiards, vert.

Perf. 13¹⁄₂x13, 13x13¹⁄₂
1981, Jan. 26   Photo.
841 A214 30f multicolored   .65 .45
842 A214 80f multicolored   2.00 1.25

20th National
Day — A215

1981, Feb. 25   Litho.   Perf. 13x13¹⁄₂
843 A215 30f multicolored   .65 .45
844 A215 80f multicolored   2.00 1.25

First Kuwait Dental
Association
Conference
A216

1981, Mar. 14   Perf. 11½x12
845 A216 30f multicolored   1.25   .85
846 A216 80f multicolored   3.75 2.25

A217

A218

1981, May 8   Photo.   Perf. 14
847 A217 30f multicolored   1.25   .80
848 A217 80f multicolored   3.75 2.25

Intl. Red Cross day.

1981, May 17   Litho.   Perf. 14½x14
849 A218 30f multicolored   1.10   .75
850 A218 80f multicolored   3.25 2.00

13th World Telecommunications day.

World
Environment
Day — A219

1981, June 5   Photo.   Perf. 12
851 A219 30f multicolored   1.10   .70
852 A219 80f multicolored   3.25 1.90

Sief
Palace — A220

A221

1981, Sept. 16   Litho.   Perf. 12
853 A220   5f multicolored   .15   .15
854 A220   10f multicolored   .15   .15
855 A220   15f multicolored   .15   .15
856 A220   25f multicolored   .22   .22
857 A220   30f multicolored   .28   .22
858 A220   40f multicolored   .32   .22
859 A220   60f multicolored   .50   .28
860 A220   80f multicolored   .65   .46
861 A220 100f multicolored   .85   .65
862 A220 115f multicolored   1.00   .80
863 A220 130f multicolored   1.10 1.00
864 A220 150f multicolored   1.40 1.00
865 A220 180f multicolored   1.65 1.10
866 A220 250f multicolored   2.25 1.25
867 A220 500f multicolored   4.50 1.65
868 A221   1d multicolored   8.25 2.25
869 A221   2d multicolored   17.00 3.25
870 A221   3d multicolored   25.00 10.00
871 A221   4d multicolored   32.50 12.50
  Nos. 853-871 (19)   97.92 37.29

Islamic
Pilgrimage
A222

World Food
Day — A223

1981, Oct. 7   Photo.   Perf. 13x13½
872 A222 30f multicolored   .85   .70
873 A222 80f multicolored   3.00 1.75

1981, Oct. 16   Litho.   Perf. 13
874 A223 30f multicolored   .95   .65
875 A223 80f multicolored   3.00 1.75

A224

A225

1981, Dec. 30   Photo.   Perf. 14
876 A224 30f multicolored   1.00   .65
877 A224 80f multicolored   3.00 1.75

20th anniv. of national television.

1982, Jan. 16   Photo.   Perf. 14
878 A225 30f multicolored   .95 1.25
879 A225 80f multicolored   3.00 1.75

First Intl. Pharmacology of Human Blood Vessels
Symposium, Jan. 16-18.

21st Natl.
Day — A226

1982, Feb. 25   Perf. 13½x13
880 A226 30f multicolored   .70   .45
881 A226 80f multicolored   2.00 1.25

Scouting
Year — A227

1982, Mar. 22   Photo.   Perf. 12x11½
882 A227 30f multicolored   .90   .55
883 A227 80f multicolored   3.50 1.50

Arab Pharmacists' Day — A228

1982, Apr. 2   Litho.   Perf. 12x11½
884 A228 30f lt green & multi   1.25   .90
885 A228 80f pink & multi   4.00 2.50

World Health
Day — A229

Arab Postal
Union, 30th
Anniv. — A230

1982, Apr. 7   Litho.   Perf. 13½x13
886 A229 30f multicolored   1.50   .95
887 A229 80f multicolored   4.50 2.50

1982, Apr. 12   Photo.   Perf. 13½x13
888 A230 30f multicolored   1.25   .85
889 A230 80f multicolored   4.00 2.25

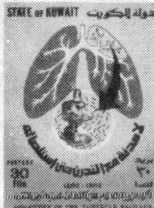

TB Bacillus
Centenary — A231

1982, May 24   Litho.   Perf. 11½x12
890 A231 30f multicolored   1.40   .90
891 A231 80f multicolored   4.25 2.50

1982 World
Cup
A232

1982, June 17   Photo.   Perf. 14
892 A232 30f multicolored   .95   .65
893 A232 80f multicolored   3.00 1.75

10th Anniv. of
Science and Natural
History
Museum — A233

1982, July 14   Perf. 14
894 A233 30f multicolored   2.25 1.50
895 A233 80f multicolored   6.75 4.50

6th Anniv. of
United Arab
Shipping
Co. — A234

Designs: Freighters.

1982, Sept. 1   Perf. 13
896 A234 30f multicolored   .85   .40
897 A234 80f multicolored   2.00 1.10

Arab Day of the
Palm Tree — A235

1982, Sept. 15   Perf. 14
898 A235 30f multicolored   .75   .45
899 A235 80f multicolored   2.25 1.25

Islamic
Pilgrimage
A236

1982, Sept. 26   Litho.
900 A236 15f multicolored   .45   .28
901 A236 30f multicolored   1.00   .65
902 A236 80f multicolored   2.75 1.75
  Nos. 900-902 (3)   4.20 2.68

Desert Flowers &
Plants — A237

1983, Jan. 25   Litho.   Perf. 12
903   Strip of 10   1.10   .90
  a.-j. A237 10f any single   .15   .15
904   Strip of 10   1.40 1.10
  a.-j. A237 15f any single   .15   .15
905   Strip of 10   2.75 2.25
  a.-j. A237 30f any single   .25   .22
906   Strip of 10   3.25 2.75
  a.-j   A237 40f any single, horiz. .32 .25
907   Strip of 10   6.75 5.75
  a.-j. A237 80f any single, horiz. .65 .55
  Nos. 903-907 (5)   15.25 12.75

22nd Natl.
Day — A238

1983, Feb. 25   Litho.   Perf. 12½
908 A238 30f multicolored   .80   .50
909 A238 80f multicolored   2.25 1.40

25th Anniv.
of Intl.
Maritime
Org.
A239

1983, Mar. 17   Photo.   Perf. 14
910 A239 30f multicolored   .50   .30
911 A239 80f multicolored   1.40   .85

Map of
Middle East
and Africa,
Conference
Emblem
A240

1983, Mar. 19   Perf. 13
912 A240 15f multicolored   .32   .22
913 A240 30f multicolored   .75   .50
914 A240 80f multicolored   2.25 1.40
  Nos. 912-914 (3)   3.32 2.12

3rd Intl. Conference on the Impact of Viral Diseases on the Development of the Middle East and
Africa, Mar. 19-27.

World
Health
Day — A241

1983, Apr. 7   *Perf. 12x11½*
915 A241 15f multicolored   .48   .30
916 A241 30f multicolored   .95   .70
917 A241 80f multicolored   2.75   1.90
     Nos. 915-917 (3)   4.18   2.90

World Communications Year — A242

1983, May 17   Photo.   *Perf. 13x13½*
918 A242 15f multicolored   .48   .30
919 A242 30f multicolored   .95   .70
920 A242 80f multicolored   2.75   1.90
     Nos. 918-920 (3)   4.18   2.90

World Environment Day — A243

1983, June 5   Litho.   *Perf. 12½*
921 A243 15f multicolored   .48   .30
922 A243 30f multicolored   .95   .70
923 A243 80f multicolored   2.75   1.90
     Nos. 921-923 (3)   4.18   2.90

Wall of Old Jerusalem A244

1983, July 25   Litho.   *Perf. 12*
924 A244 15f multicolored   .40   .25
925 A244 30f multicolored   1.00   .55
926 A244 80f multicolored   2.75   1.65
     Nos. 924-926 (3)   4.15   2.45

World Heritage Year.

Islamic Pilgrimage A245

1983, Sept. 15   Photo.   *Perf. 11½*
927 A245 15f multicolored   .40   .25
928 A245 30f multicolored   1.00   .55
929 A245 80f multicolored   2.75   1.65
     Nos. 927-929 (3)   4.15   2.45

Intl. Palestinian Solidarity Day — A246

1983, Nov. 29   Photo.   *Perf. 14*
930 A246 15f multicolored   .40   .25
931 A246 30f multicolored   1.00   .55
932 A246 80f multicolored   2.75   1.65
     Nos. 930-932 (3)   4.15   2.45

21st Pan Arab Medical Congress, Jan. 30-Feb. 2 — A247

1984, Jan. 30   Litho.   *Perf. 14½x14*
933 A247 15f purple & multi   .40   .25
934 A247 30f blue grn & multi   1.00   .55
935 A247 80f pink & multi   2.75   1.65
     Nos. 933-935 (3)   4.15   2.45

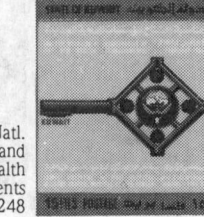

Key, Natl. Emblem, and Health Establishments Emblem — A248

1984, Feb. 20   Photo.   *Perf. 13x13½*
936 A248 15f multicolored   .40   .25
937 A248 30f multicolored   1.00   .55
938 A248 80f multicolored   2.75   1.65
     Nos. 936-938 (3)   4.15   2.45

Inauguration of Amiri and Al-Razi Hospitals, Allergy Center and Medical Stores Center.

23rd National Day — A249

1984, Feb. 25   Litho.   *Perf. 13½*
939 A249 15f multicolored   .40   .25
940 A249 30f multicolored   1.00   .55
941 A249 80f multicolored   2.75   1.65
     Nos. 939-941 (3)   4.15   2.45

2nd Kuwait Intl. Medical Science Conf., Mar. 4-8 — A250

1984, Mar. 4   Photo.   *Perf. 12*
Granite Paper
942 A250 15f multicolored   .40   .25
943 A250 30f multicolored   1.00   .55
944 A250 80f multicolored   2.75   1.65
     Nos. 942-944 (3)   4.15   2.45

30th Anniv. of Kuwait Airways Corp. — A251

1984, Mar. 15   *Perf. 13½*
946 A251 30f multicolored   .95   .90
947 A251 80f multicolored   2.50   1.65

Al-Arabi Magazine, 25th Anniv. — A252

1984, Mar. 20   *Perf. 14½x14*
948 A252 15f multicolored   .35   .24
949 A252 30f multicolored   .85   .52
950 A252 80f multicolored   2.25   1.50
     Nos. 948-950 (3)   3.45   2.26

World Health Day — A253

1984, Apr. 7   *Perf. 12*
951 A253 15f multicolored   .40   .25
952 A253 30f multicolored   1.00   .55
953 A253 80f multicolored   2.75   1.65
     Nos. 951-953 (3)   4.15   2.45

Hanan Kuwaiti Orphan Village, Sudan — A254

1984, May 15   Litho.   *Perf. 12*
954 A254 15f multicolored   .40   .25
955 A254 30f multicolored   1.00   .55
956 A254 80f multicolored   2.75   1.65
     Nos. 954-956 (3)   4.15   2.45

Intl. Civil Aviation Org., 40th Anniv. A255

1984, June 12
957 A255 15f multicolored   .40   .25
958 A255 30f multicolored   1.00   .55
959 A255 80f multicolored   2.75   1.65
     Nos. 957-959 (3)   4.15   2.45

Arab Youth Day — A256

1984, July 5   *Perf. 13½*
960 A256 30f multicolored   1.00   .55
961 A256 80f multicolored   2.75   1.65

1984 Summer Olympics A257

1984, July 28   *Perf. 15x14*
962 A257 30f Swimming   .42   .32
963 A257 30f Hurdles   .42   .32
   a.   Pair, #962-96   .85   .85
964 A257 80f Judo   1.10   .90
965 A257 80f Equestrian   1.10   .90
   a.   Pair, #964-965   2.25   2.25
     Nos. 962-965 (4)   3.04   2.44

10th Anniv. of the Science Club A258

1984, Aug. 11   Photo.   *Perf. 13½x13*
966 A258 15f multicolored   .40   .25
967 A258 30f multicolored   1.00   .55
968 A258 80f multicolored   2.50   1.65
     Nos. 966-968 (3)   3.90   2.45

Islamic Pilgrimage A259

1984, Sept. 4   Photo.   *Perf. 12x11½*
969 A259 30f multicolored   1.00   .55
970 A259 80f multicolored   2.50   1.65

INTELSAT '84, 20th Anniv. — A260

1984, Oct. 1   Litho.   *Perf. 13½x14*
971 A260 30f multicolored   1.00   .55
972 A260 80f multicolored   2.50   1.65

G.C.C. Supreme Council, 5th Session A261

1984, Nov. 24   Litho.   *Perf. 15x14*
973 A261 30f multicolored   1.00   .55
974 A261 80f multicolored   2.50   1.65

Map of Israel, Fists, Shattered Star of David — A262

1984, Nov. 29   Photo.   *Perf. 12*
975 A262 30f multicolored   1.00   .55
976 A262 80f multicolored   2.50   1.65

Intl. Palestinian Solidarity Day.

Globe, Emblem — A263

1984, Dec. 24   *Perf. 12x11½*
Granite Paper
977 A263 30f multicolored   1.00   .25
978 A263 80f multicolored   2.75   1.10

Kuwait Oil Co., 50th anniv.

Intl. Youth Year — A264   24th Natl. Day — A265

1985, Jan. 15   *Perf. 13½*
979 A264 30f multicolored   .55   .25
980 A264 80f multicolored   1.65   1.10

1985, Feb. 25   Litho.   *Perf. 14x15*
981 A265 30f multicolored   .80   .42
982 A265 80f multicolored   2.50   1.65

Intl. Program for
the Development
of
Communications
A266

1985, Mar. 4   Photo.   Perf. 11½
Granite Paper
983 A266 30f multicolored   1.00   .55
984 A266 80f multicolored   2.50 1.65

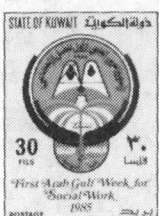

1st Arab Gulf Week
for Social
Work — A267

1985, Mar. 13   Photo.   Perf. 13½x13
985 A267 30f multicolored   1.00   .55
986 A267 80f multicolored   2.50 1.65

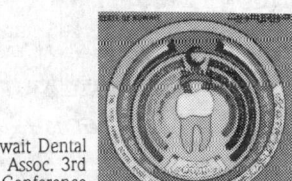

Kuwait Dental
Assoc. 3rd
Conference
A268

1985, Mar. 23   Litho.   Perf. 13½
987 A268 30f multicolored   1.00   .55
988 A268 80f multicolored   2.50 1.65

1985
Census — A269

World Health
Day — A270

1985, Apr. 1   Perf. 14x13½
989 A269 30f multicolored   1.25   .55
990 A269 80f multicolored   2.75 1.65

1985, Apr. 7   Photo.   Perf. 13½x13
991 A270 30f multicolored   1.25   .55
992 A270 80f multicolored   2.75 1.65

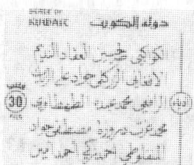

Names of Books,
Authors and
Poets in
Arabic — A271

1985, May 20   Perf. 12
Granite Paper
993   Block of 4   2.75 1.75
a.-d. A271 30f any single   .65   .42
994   Block of 4   7.25 5.00
a.-d. A271 80f any single   1.75 1.10
Central Library, 50th anniv.

World
Environment
Day — A272

1985, June 5   Perf. 11½
995 A272 30f multicolored   1.25   .55
996 A272 80f multicolored   2.75 1.65

Org. of
Petroleum
Exporting
Countries,
25th Anniv.
A273

1985, Sept. 1   Perf. 13x13½
997 A273 30f multicolored   1.25   .55
998 A273 80f multicolored   2.75 1.65

Inauguration
of Civil
Information
System
A274

1985, Oct. 1   Photo.   Perf. 12x11½
999 A274 30f multicolored   1.25   .55
1000 A274 80f multicolored   2.75 1.65

Intl. Day of
Solidarity with
Palestinian
People — A275

1985, Nov. 29   Photo.   Perf. 12
1001 A275 15f multicolored   1.10   .45
1002 A275 30f multicolored   2.00   .90
1003 A275 80f multicolored   3.75 2.25
  Nos. 1001-1003 (3)   6.85 3.60

25th Natl.
Day — A276

1986, Feb. 25   Litho.   Perf. 15x14
1004 A276 20f multicolored   .32   .22
1005 A276 30f multicolored   .95   .50
1006 A276 80f multicolored   2.25 1.25
  Nos. 1004-1006 (3)   3.52 1.97

Natl. Red
Crescent Soc.,
20th
Anniv. — A277

1986, Mar. 26   Photo.   Perf. 13½
1007 A277 20f multicolored   .80   .65
1008 A277 25f multicolored   1.25 1.00
1009 A277 70f multicolored   3.75 2.75
  Nos. 1007-1009 (3)   5.80 4.40

World Health
Day — A278

1986, Apr. 7   Perf. 13½x13
1010 A278 20f multicolored   .80   .65
1011 A278 25f multicolored   1.25 1.00
1012 A278 70f multicolored   3.75 2.75
  Nos. 1010-1012 (3)   5.80 4.40

Intl. Peace
Year — A279

1986, June 5   Litho.   Perf. 13½
1013 A279 20f multicolored   .60   .45
1014 A279 25f multicolored   1.10   .70
1015 A279 70f multicolored   3.00 2.00
  Nos. 1013-1015 (3)   4.70 3.15

United Arab
Shipping Co.,
10th Anniv.
A280

1986, July 1   Photo.   Perf. 12x11½
1016 A280 20f Al Mirqab   .80   .65
1017 A280 70f Al Mubarakiah   3.75 2.75

Gulf Bank,
25th Anniv.
A281

1986, Oct. 1   Photo.   Perf. 12½
1018 A281 20f multicolored   .70   .50
1019 A281 25f multicolored   1.25   .70
1020 A281 70f multicolored   3.50 2.25
  Nos. 1018-1020 (3)   5.45 3.45

Sadu
Art — A282

Various tapestry weavings.

1986, Nov. 5   Photo.   Perf. 12x11½
Granite Paper
1021 A282 20f multicolored   .50   .35
1022 A282 70f multicolored   2.00 1.40
1023 A282 200f multicolored   5.50 4.00
  Nos. 1021-1023 (3)   8.00 5.75

Intl. Day of
Solidarity
with the
Palestinian
People
A283

1986, Nov. 29   Perf. 14
1024 A283 20f multicolored   1.10   .75
1025 A283 25f multicolored   1.50 1.00
1026 A283 70f multicolored   4.25 3.00
  Nos. 1024-1026 (3)   6.85 4.75

5th Islamic Summit Conference — A284

1987, Jan. 26   Litho.   Perf. 14½
1027 A284 25f multicolored   .70   .45
1028 A284 50f multicolored   1.40 1.00
1029 A284 150f multicolored   4.50 3.00
  Nos. 1027-1029 (3)   6.60 4.45

26th Natl.
Day
A285

1987, Feb. 25   Perf. 13½x14
1030 A285 50f multicolored   1.50 1.00
1031 A285 150f multicolored   4.75 3.25

Natl. Health
Sciences
Center
A286

1987, Mar. 15   Photo.   Perf. 12x11½
Granite Paper
1032 A286 25f multicolored   .50   .35
1033 A286 150f multicolored   3.25 2.25
3rd Kuwait Intl. Medical Sciences Conference on
Infectious Diseases in Developing Countries.

World Health
Day — A287

1987, Apr. 7   Photo.   Perf. 13x13½
1034 A287 25f multicolored   .65   .45
1035 A287 50f multicolored   1.40   .90
1036 A287 150f multicolored   4.25 2.50
  Nos. 1034-1036 (3)   6.30 3.85

Day of
Ghods
(Jerusalem)
A288

1987, June 7   Photo.   Perf. 12x11½
1037 A288 25f multicolored   .35   .22
1038 A288 50f multicolored   .80   .60
1039 A288 150f multicolored   2.75 1.75
  Nos. 1037-1039 (3)   3.90 2.57

Islamic
Pilgrimage
to Miqat
Wadi
Mihrim
A289

1987, Aug.   Photo.   Perf. 13½x14½
1040 A289 25f multicolored   .50   .50
1041 A289 50f multicolored   1.00   .80
1042 A289 150f multicolored   3.25 2.00
  Nos. 1040-1042 (3)   4.75 3.30

Arab Telecommunications Day — A290

1987, Sept. 9   Litho.   Perf. 14x13½
1043 A290 25f multicolored   .50   .30
1044 A290 50f multicolored   1.00   .75
1045 A290 150f multicolored   3.25 1.25
  Nos. 1043-1045 (3)   4.75 2.35

World
Maritime
Day
A291

1987, Sept. 24   *Perf. 12x11¹/₂*
Granite Paper
1046 A291 25f multicolored   .50   .30
1047 A291 50f multicolored   1.00   .80
1048 A291 150f multicolored   3.25 2.00
   Nos. 1046-1048 (3)   4.75 3.10

Al Qurain Housing
Project — A292

1987, Oct. 5   *Perf. 13x13¹/₂*
1049 A292 25f multicolored   .50   .30
1050 A292 50f multicolored   1.00   .80
1051 A292 150f multicolored   3.25 2.00
   Nos. 1049-1051 (3)   4.75 3.10

Port
Authority,
10th
Anniv.
A293

1987, Nov. 16   **Litho.**   *Perf. 14¹/₂*
1052 A293 25f multicolored   .40   .20
1053 A293 50f multicolored   .85   .50
1054 A293 150f multicolored   2.75 1.75
   Nos. 1052-1054 (3)   4.00 2.45

A294   A295

1987, Nov. 29   *Perf. 14x13¹/₂*
1055 A294 25f multicolored   .45   .30
1056 A294 50f multicolored   .90   .60
1057 A294 150f multicolored   2.50 2.00
   Nos. 1055-1057 (3)   3.85 2.90

Intl. Day of Solidarity with the Palestinian People

1988, Feb. 3   **Photo.**   *Perf. 14*
1058 A295 25f multicolored   .45   .30
1059 A295 50f multicolored   .90   .50
1060 A295 150f multicolored   2.50 1.50
   Nos. 1058-1060 (3)   3.85 2.30

Women's Cultural and Social Soc., 25th anniv.

A296   A297

1988, Feb. 25
1061 A296 25f multicolored   .45   .30
1062 A296 50f multicolored   .90   .50
1063 A296 150f multicolored   2.50 1.50
   Nos. 1061-1063 (3)   3.85 2.30

National Day, 27th anniv.

1988, Apr. 7   **Litho.**   *Perf. 14x15*
1064 A297 25f multicolored   .45   .20
1065 A297 50f multicolored   .90   .45
1066 A297 150f multicolored   2.50 1.40
   Nos. 1064-1066 (3)   3.85 2.05

World Health Day, WHO 40th anniv.

A298   A299

1988, Apr. 24   **Photo.**   *Perf. 12*
Granite Paper
1067 A298 35f multicolored   .60   .35
1068 A298 50f multicolored   .90   .55
1069 A298 150f multicolored   2.75 1.75
   Nos. 1067-1069 (3)   4.25 2.65

Regional Marine Environment Day. Kuwait
Regional Convention on the Marine Environment,
10th anniv. See Iraq Nos. 1333-1336.

1988, July 10   **Photo.**   *Perf. 14*
1070 A299 25f multicolored   .45   .20
1071 A299 50f multicolored   .90   .55
1072 A299 150f multicolored   2.75 1.75
   Nos. 1070-1072 (3)   4.10 2.50

Kuwait Teachers Soc., 25th anniv.

Pilgrimage to
Mecca
A300

1988, Sept. 12   **Litho.**   *Perf. 13¹/₂x14*
1073 A300 25f multicolored   .45   .20
1074 A300 50f multicolored   .90   .55
1075 A300 150f multicolored   2.75 1.75
   Nos. 1073-1075 (3)   4.10 2.50

Palestinian
"Children of
Stone" Fighting
Israelis — A301

1988, Sept. 15   **Photo.**   *Perf. 13x13¹/₂*
1076 A301 50f multicolored   1.25   .70
1077 A301 150f multicolored   4.50 2.50

Palestinian Uprising. Dated 1987.

Arab Housing
Day — A302

1988, Oct. 3
1078 A302 50f multicolored   .85   .60
1079 A302 100f multicolored   1.75 1.10
1080 A302 150f multicolored   2.75 1.75
   Nos. 1078-1080 (3)   5.35 3.45

Intl. Day for
Solidarity with
the Palestinian
People — A303

1988, Nov. 29   **Litho.**   *Perf. 14x13*
1081 A303 50f multicolored   .85   .60
1082 A303 100f multicolored   1.75 1.10
1083 A303 150f multicolored   2.75 1.75
   Nos. 1081-1083 (3)   5.35 3.45

A304   A305

1988, Dec. 5   *Perf. 13x14*
1084 A304 50f multicolored   .75   .50
1085 A304 100f multicolored   1.65 1.00
1086 A304 150f multicolored   2.75 1.50
   Nos. 1084-1086 (3)   5.15 3.00

Intl. Volunteers Day.

1989, Feb. 18   **Litho.**   *Perf. 14x13¹/₂*
1087 A305 50f multicolored   .45   .28
1088 A305 100f multicolored   .90   .55
1089 A305 150f multicolored   1.75   .90
   Nos. 1087-1089 (3)   3.10 1.73

18th Arab Engineering Conference.

28th Natl.
Day — A306

1989, Feb. 25   *Perf. 13x13¹/₂*
1090 A306 50f multicolored   .45   .28
1091 A306 100f multicolored   .90   .55
1092 A306 150f multicolored   1.75   .90
   Nos. 1090-1092 (3)   3.10 1.73

5th Natl. Dental
Assoc.
Conference — A307

1989, Mar. 30   **Litho.**   *Perf. 13¹/₂x13*
1093 A307 50f multicolored   .52   .32
1094 A307 150f multicolored   1.50 1.00
1095 A307 250f multicolored   2.50 1.65
   Nos. 1093-1095 (3)   4.52 2.97

World Health
Day — A308

1989, Apr. 7   *Perf. 13x13¹/₂*
1096 A308 50f multicolored   .52   .32
1097 A308 150f multicolored   1.50 1.00
1098 A308 250f multicolored   2.50 1.65
   Nos. 1096-1098 (3)   4.52 2.97

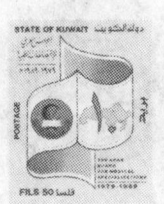   

A309   A310

1989, May 10   *Perf. 13x14*
1099 A309 50f multicolored   .52   .24
1100 A309 150f multicolored   1.50   .75
1101 A309 250f multicolored   2.50 1.25
   Nos. 1099-1101 (3)   4.52 2.24

Arab Board for Medical Specializations, 10th
anniv.

1989, June 10   **Litho.**   *Perf. 14x15*
1102 A310 50f multicolored   .58   .38
1103 A310 200f multicolored   2.25 1.50
1104 A310 250f multicolored   3.00 2.00
   Nos. 1102-1104 (3)   5.83 3.88

Natl. Journalists Assoc., 25th anniv.

Al-Taneem
Mosque
A311

1989, July 9   **Litho.**   *Perf. 13¹/₂x14¹/₂*
1105 A311 50f multicolored   .52   .32
1106 A311 165f multicolored   1.65   .52
1107 A311 200f multicolored   2.00 1.40
   Nos. 1105-1107 (3)   4.17 2.24

Pilgrimage to Mecca.

Arab Housing
Day — A312

1989, Oct. 2   *Perf. 13¹/₂*
1108 A312 25f multicolored   .28   .15
1109 A312 50f multicolored   .60   .20
1110 A312 150f multicolored   1.90   .60
   Nos. 1108-1110 (3)   2.78   .95

Annual Greenery
Week   Dhow — A314
Celebration — A313

1989, Oct. 15   *Perf. 13¹/₂x13*
1111 A313 25f multicolored   .28   .15
1112 A313 50f multicolored   .60   .20
1113 A313 150f multicolored   1.90   .60
   Nos. 1111-1113 (3)   2.78   .95

**Numbers in Black, Moon and Dhow in
Gold**
1989, Nov. 1   *Perf. 14x15*

Coil Stamps
1114 A314 50f brt apple grn   .90   .90
1115 A314 100f brt blue   1.75 1.75
1116 A314 200f vermilion   3.75 3.75
   Nos. 1114-1116 (3)   6.40 6.40

Nos. 1114-1116 available only at two post office
locations, where they were dispensed from
machines. Printed in rolls of 3000 consecutively
numbered stamps.

Gulf Investment Corp., 5th Anniv. — A315

1989, Nov. 4   *Perf. 15x14*
1117 A315   25f multicolored   .32 .16
1118 A315   50f multicolored   .65 .18
1119 A315 150f multicolored   2.00 .65
    Nos. 1117-1119 (3)   2.97 .99

Declaration of Palestinian State, 1st Anniv. — A316   Zakat House, Orphan Sponsorship Program — A317

1989, Nov. 15   Litho.   *Perf. 14x15*
1120 A316   50f multicolored   .85 .25
1121 A316 150f multicolored   2.50 .85
1122 A316 200f multicolored   3.50 1.10
    Nos. 1120-1122 (3)   6.85 2.20

1989, Dec. 10   *Perf. 13½x13*
1123 A317   25f multicolored   .35 .20
1124 A317   50f multicolored   .75 .22
1125 A317 150f multicolored   2.25 .75
    Nos. 1123-1125 (3)   3.35 1.17

Kuwait Police, 50th Anniv. — A318

1989, Dec. 30   Litho.   *Perf. 15x14*
1126 A318   25f gray & multi   .32 .16
1127 A318   50f lt ultra & multi   .65 .18
1128 A318 150f lt violet & multi   2.00 .65
    Nos. 1126-1128 (3)   2.97 .99

National Day, 29th Anniv. — A319

1990, Feb. 25   *Perf. 14x13½*
1129 A319   25f multicolored   .32 .16
1130 A319   50f multicolored   .65 .18
1131 A319 150f multicolored   2.00 .65
    Nos. 1129-1131 (3)   2.97 .99

World Meteorological Day — A320

1990, Mar. 23   Litho.   *Perf. 13½x14*
1132 A320   50f multicolored   .80 .30
1133 A320 100f multicolored   1.75 .55
1134 A320 150f multicolored   2.50 .80
    Nos. 1132-1134 (3)   5.05 1.65

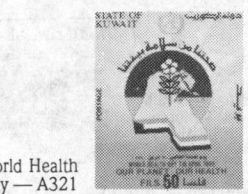

World Health Day — A321

1990, Apr. 7   *Perf. 14x15*
1135 A321   50f multicolored   1.00 .25
1136 A321 100f multicolored   2.00 .60
1137 A321 150f multicolored   2.75 1.00
    Nos. 1135-1137 (3)   5.75 1.85

Warning
There are reports that a number of pre-war issues have gone back on sale at the post office. Nos. 1138-1140 have been specifically mentioned.

Hawk — A322   Liberation of Kuwait — A323

1990, July 7   Litho.   *Perf. 14½*
1138 A322   50f blue & gold
1139 A322 100f maroon & gold
1140 A322 150f green & gold
    Nos. 1138-1140 (3)   35.00

1991   Litho.   *Perf. 14½*
1141 A323   25f multicolored   .75
1142 A323   50f multicolored   1.50
1143 A323 150f multicolored   4.50
    Nos. 1141-1143 (3)   6.75

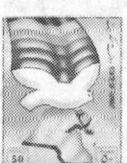

Peace — A324   Reconstruction — A325

1991, May   *Perf. 13½x14*
1144 A324   50f multicolored   1.20
1145 A324 100f multicolored   2.40
1146 A324 150f multicolored   3.60
    Nos. 1144-1146 (3)   7.20

1991, May
1147 A325   50f multicolored   1.20
1148 A325 150f multicolored   3.60
1149 A325 200f multicolored   4.80
    Nos. 1147-1149 (3)   9.60

Liberation of Kuwait — A326

Flags of forces joining international coalition for liberation of Kuwait: Sweden, USSR, US, Kuwait, Saudi Arabia, UN, Singapore, France, Italy, Egypt, Morocco, UK, Philippines, UAE, Syria, Poland, Australia, Japan, Hungary, Netherlands, Denmark, New Zealand, Czechoslovakia, Bahrain, Honduras, Turkey, Greece, Oman, Qatar, Belgium, Sierra Leone, Argentina, Norway, Canada, Germany, South Korea, Bangladesh, Bulgaria, Senegal, Spain, Niger, and Pakistan. No. 1151, all forces of coalition.

1991, July 25   Litho.   *Perf. 14½*
1150 A326   50f Sheet of 42   24.00

Size: 87x134mm
Imperf
1151 A326   1d multicolored   15.00
    Individual stamps from No. 1150 are not given minor letters due to size of sheet. Each stamp can be identified by country name.

Invasion of Kuwait, 1st Anniv. — A327

1991, Aug. 2   *Perf. 14½*
1152 A327   50f Human terror   1.25
1153 A327 100f Invasion of Kuwait   3.00
1154 A327 150f Environmental terrorism, horiz.   4.50

Size: 90x65mm
Imperf
1155 A327 250f Desert Storm   7.00
    Nos. 1152-1155 (4)   15.75

12th Gulf Cooperation Council Summit A328

Design: 150f, Tree of flags.

1991, Dec. 23   Litho.   *Perf. 14½*
1156 A328   25f multicolored   .30
  a.   see footnote   .30
1157 A328 150f multicolored   1.75
  a.   Sheet of 4, 2 each #1156-1157   6.25
  b.   Sheet of 4, 2 each #1156a, 1157   6.25

No. 1156a has tree with inscriptions (country names in Arabic) in colors of flags shown on No. 1157.

Intl. Literacy Year — A329   OPEC, 30th Anniv. (in 1990) — A330

1992, Feb. 12   Litho.   *Perf. 13½x13*
1158 A329   50f dark blue & buff   1.00
1159 A329 100f dark blue & citron   2.00
1160 A329 150f dk blue & pale lil   3.00
    Nos. 1158-1160 (3)   6.00

Dated 1990.

1992, Oct. 29   *Perf. 14½x13½*
1161 A330   25f red & multi   .25
1162 A330   50f yellow & multi   .50
1163 A330 150f green & multi   1.50
    Nos. 1161-1163 (3)   2.25

31st Natl. Day A331

1992   *Perf. 14½*
1164 A331   50f Flag, doves   .50
1165 A331 150f Flags   1.50
  a.   Miniature sheet 2 each #1164-1165   4.00
Liberation Day (No. 1165). Issue dates, 50f, Feb. 25; 150f, Feb. 26.

Don't Forget Our P.O.W.'s — A332

1991, Nov. 16
1166 A332   50f Flag, chains   1.00
1167 A332 150f Cell bars, chains   3.00
  a.   Min. sheet, 2 each #1166-1167   9.00
Dated 1991. Issued: 50f, Feb, 25. 150f, Feb. 26.

Camels A333

1991, Nov. 16   *Perf. 12½*
1168 A333   25f pink & multi   .25
1169 A333   50f beige & multi   .50
1170 A333 150f lt violet & multi   1.50
1171 A333 200f blue & multi   2.00
1172 A333 350f orange & multi   3.50
    Nos. 1168-1172 (5)   7.75

Environmental Terrorism, by Jafar Islah — A334

Designs: No. 1174, Snake, flag, map. No. 1175, Skull, dead fish. No. 1176, Dying camel.

1992, June   *Perf. 14½*
1173 A334 150f multicolored   2.25
1174 A334 150f multicolored   2.25
1175 A334 150f multicolored   2.25
1176 A334 150f multicolored   2.25
  a.   Block of 4, #1173-1176   9.00
  b.   Miniature sheet of 4, #1173-1176   11.50
Earth Summit, Rio De Janeiro. No. 1176a printed in continuous design.

EXPO '92, Seville A335

Designs: No. 1177, Kuwaiti Pavilion, La Giralda Tower, Seville. No. 1178, Dhows. No. 1179, Dhow. No. 1180, Pavilion, dhow.
    Flags of Spain or Kuwait and: No. 1181, Pavilion. No. 1182, La Giralda Tower. No. 1183, La Giralda Tower, dhow. No. 1184, Pavilion, dhow.

1992, June 19
1177 A335   50f multicolored   .40
1178 A335   50f multicolored   .40
1179 A335   50f multicolored   .40
1180 A335   50f multicolored   .40
  a.   Block of 4, #1177-1180   1.60
1181 A335 150f multicolored   1.20
1182 A335 150f multicolored   1.20
1183 A335 150f multicolored   1.20

1184 A335 150f multicolored 1.20
  a. Block of 4, #1181-1184 4.80
  b. Miniature sheet of 8, #1177-1184 6.40
    Nos. 1177-1184 (8) 6.40

Nos. 1180a, 1184a have continuous designs.

Palace of
Justice
A336

1992, July 4   *Perf. 12½*
1185 A336 25f lilac & multi .20
1186 A336 50f lilac rose & multi .40
1187 A336 100f yel green & multi 1.20
1188 A336 150f yel orange & multi 1.25
1189 A336 250f blue green & multi 2.00
    Nos. 1185-1189 (5) 5.05

1992 Summer
Olympics,
Barcelona — A337

Olympic flag, Fahed Al Ahmed Al Sabah, member of the Intl. Olympic committee and: 50f, Swimmer, soccer player. 100f, Runner, basketball player. 150f, Judo, equestrian.

1992, July 25   *Perf. 14½*
1190 A337 50f multicolored .90
1191 A337 100f multicolored 1.75
1192 A337 150f multicolored 2.75
    Nos. 1190-1192 (3) 5.40

Invasion by Iraq, 2nd Anniv. — A338

Children's paintings: No. 1193, Tanks, people holding signs, two people being tortured. No. 1194, Truck, Iraqi soldiers looting. No. 1195, Iraqi soldiers killing civilians, tanks. No. 1196, Houses ablaze. No. 1197, Tanks, civilians, soldiers. No. 1198, Planes bombing in attack on fort. No. 1199, Tank, civilians holding flags, signs. No. 1200, Battlefield.

1992, Aug. 2   **Litho.**   *Perf. 14x14½*
1193 A338 50f multicolored .40
1194 A338 50f multicolored .40
1195 A338 50f multicolored .40
1196 A338 50f multicolored .40
  a. Block of 4, #1193-1196 1.60
1197 A338 150f multicolored 1.25
1198 A338 150f multicolored 1.25
1199 A338 150f multicolored 1.25
1200 A338 150f multicolored 1.25
  a. Block of 4, #1197-1200 5.00
  b. Min. sheet of 8, #1193-1200 7.00
    Nos. 1193-1200 (8) 6.60

Extinguishing of Oil Well Fires, 1st
Anniv. — A339

Various scenes showing oil well fire being extinguished.

1992   **Litho.**   *Perf. 14½*
1201 A339 25f multi, vert. .18 .18
1202 A339 50f multi, vert. .38 .38
1203 A339 150f multi, vert. 1.10 1.10
1204 A339 250f multicolored 1.85 1.85
    Nos. 1201-1204 (4) 3.51 3.51

 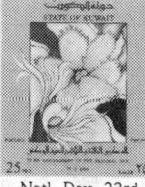

Kuwait
Tower — A340   A341

1993, Jan. 16   **Litho.**   *Perf. 14x15*
Background Color
1205 A340 25f lilac .18 .18
1206 A340 100f blue .75 .75
1207 A340 150f salmon 1.10 1.10
    Nos. 1205-1207 (3) 2.03 2.03

1993, Feb. 25   **Litho.**   *Perf. 13½x14*
1208 A341 25f green & multi .18 .18
1209 A341 50f blue & multi .36 .36
1210 A341 150f pink & multi 1.10 1.10
    Nos. 1208-1210 (3) 1.64 1.64

National Day, 32nd anniv.

Liberation Day,
2nd
Anniv. — A342

1993, Feb. 26   *Perf. 15x14*
1211 A342 25f orange yel & multi .25 .25
1212 A342 50f green & multi .55 .55
1213 A342 150f red lilac & multi 1.65 1.65
    Nos. 1211-1213 (3) 2.45 2.45

Remembering
Prisoners of
War — A343

Designs: 50f, Prisoner shackled in cell, vert. 150f, Shackled hand pointing to cell window, bird. 200f, Cell, prisoner's face, vert.

     Perf. 13½x14, 14x13½
1993, May 15   **Litho.**
1214 A343 50f multicolored .60 .60
1215 A343 150f multicolored 1.65 1.65
1216 A343 200f multicolored 2.25 2.25
    Nos. 1214-1216 (3) 4.50 4.50

A344   A345

1993, Apr. 20   **Litho.**   *Perf. 11½x12*
Granite Paper
1217 A344 25f gray & multi .18 .18
1218 A344 50f green & multi .38 .38
1219 A344 150f yellow & multi 1.15 1.15
1220 A344 150f rose & multi 2.65 2.65
    Nos. 1217-1220 (4) 4.36 4.36

18th Deaf Child Week.

1993, Aug. 2   **Litho.**   *Perf. 13½x14*
1221 A345 50f green & multi .40 .40
1222 A345 150f orange & multi 1.25 1.25

Invasion by Iraq, 3rd anniv.

Kuwait
Airforce,
40th Anniv.
A346

1993, Dec. 9   **Litho.**   *Perf. 13x13½*
1223 A346 50f blue & multi .38 .38
1224 A346 150f green & multi 1.10 1.10

Natl. Day, 33rd   Liberation Day, 3rd
Anniv. — A347   Anniv. — A348

1994, Feb. 25   **Litho.**   *Perf. 13½x14*
1225 A347 25f salmon & multi .18 .18
1226 A347 50f yellow & multi .38 .38
1227 A347 150f green & multi 1.10 1.10
    Nos. 1225-1227 (3) 1.66 1.66

1994, Feb. 26
1228 A348 25f yellow & multi .18 .18
1229 A348 50f blue & multi .38 .38
1230 A348 150f gray green & multi 1.10 1.10
    Nos. 1228-1230 (3) 1.66 1.66

Central Bank of
Kuwait, 25th
Anniv. — A349

1994, Apr. 20   **Litho.**   *Perf. 13½x13*
1231 A349 25f salmon & multi .20 .20
1232 A349 50f green & multi .40 .40
1233 A349 150f blue violet & multi 1.25 1.25
    Nos. 1231-1233 (3) 1.85 1.85

A350   A351

Intl. Year of
the Family
A352

1994, May 15   **Litho.**   *Perf. 13*
1234 A350 50f multicolored .38 .38
1235 A351 150f multicolored 1.10 1.10
1236 A352 200f multicolored 1.50 1.50
    Nos. 1234-1236 (3) 2.98 2.98

A353   A354

1994, June 5   **Litho.**   *Perf. 14*
1237 A353 50f yellow & multi .38 .38
1238 A353 100f blue & multi .75 .75
1239 A353 150f green & multi 1.10 1.10
    Nos. 1237-1239 (3) 2.23 2.23

Industrial Bank of Kuwait, 20th anniv.

1994, June 15   **Litho.**   *Perf. 13*
1240 A354 50f Whirlpool .38 .38
1241 A354 100f Shifting sands .75 .75
1242 A354 150f Finger print 1.10 1.10
1243 A354 250f Clouds 1.90 1.90
  a. Miniature sheet of 4, #1240-1243 4.25 4.25
    Nos. 1240-1243 (4) 4.13 4.13

Martyr's Day.

A355   A356

1994, June 25   **Litho.**   *Perf. 14*
1244 A355 50f vio & multi .38 .38
1245 A355 150f pink & multi 1.10 1.10
1246 A355 350f blue & multi 2.75 2.75
    Nos. 1244-1246 (3) 4.23 4.23

ILO, 75th anniv.

1994, Aug. 2   **Litho.**   *Perf. 12½x13½*
1247 A356 50f green blue & multi .38 .38
1248 A356 150f blue & multi 1.10 1.10
1249 A356 350f lilac & multi 2.75 2.75
    Nos. 1247-1249 (3) 4.23 4.23

Invasion by Iraq, 4th anniv.

Port   Science Club, 20th
Authority — A357   Anniv. — A358

1994, Aug. 31   **Litho.**   *Perf. 12½x14*
1250 A357 50f pink & multi .38 .38
1251 A357 150f blue & multi 1.10 1.10
1252 A357 350f green & multi 2.75 2.75
    Nos. 1250-1252 (3) 4.23 4.23

1994, Sept. 11   *Perf. 14*
1253 A358 50f blue & multi .38 .38
1254 A358 100f green & multi .75 .75
1255 A358 150f red & multi 1.10 1.10
    Nos. 1253-1255 (3) 2.23 2.23

A359   A360

Designs showing emblem and: 50f, Map of Arab countries, building. 100f, Windows, building. 150f, Doors below portico.

1994, Nov. 12   *Perf. 11½*
1256 A359 50f multicolored .38 .38
1257 A359 100f multicolored .75 .75
1258 A359 150f multicolored 1.10 1.10
    Nos. 1256-1258 (3) 2.23 2.23

Arab Towns Organization, opening of headquarters.

1994, Dec. 7 — Perf. 14½

Designs: 100f, Emblems, sailing ship. 150f, Emblems, co-operation, co-ordination. 350f, Emblem, airplane in flight.

1259	A360	100f silver, gold & multi	.75	.75
1260	A360	150f silver, gold & multi	1.10	1.10
1261	A360	350f gold & multi	2.75	2.75
		Nos. 1259-1261 (3)	4.60	4.60

ICAO, 50th anniv.

A361   A362

1994, Dec. 20 — Perf. 13x14

1262	A361	50f lake & multi	.38	.38
1263	A361	100f green & multi	.75	.75
1264	A361	150f slate & multi	1.10	1.10
		Nos. 1262-1264 (3)	2.23	2.23

Kuwait Airways, 40th anniv.

1995, Feb. 6 — Litho. — Perf. 14

1265	A362	50f yellow & multi	.38	.38
1266	A362	100f green & multi	.75	.75
1267	A362	150f brown & multi	1.10	1.10
		Nos. 1265-1267 (3)	2.23	2.23

1995 Census.

National Day, 34th Anniv. — A363   Liberation Day, 4th Anniv. — A364

1995, Feb. 25 — Perf. 13

1268	A363	25f blue & multi	.18	.18
1269	A363	50f yellow & multi	.38	.38
1270	A363	150f lilac & multi	1.10	1.10
		Nos. 1268-1270 (3)	1.66	1.66

1995, Feb. 26

1271	A364	25f blue & multi	.18	.18
1272	A364	50f green & multi	.38	.38
1273	A364	150f rose lilac & multi	1.10	1.10
		Nos. 1271-1273 (3)	1.66	1.66

Medical Research A365

1995, Mar. 20 — Perf. 14

1274	A365	50f Medical building	.38	.38
1275	A365	100f Classroom instruction	.75	.75
1276	A365	150f Map of Kuwait	1.10	1.10
		Nos. 1274-1276 (3)	2.23	2.23

Arab League, 50th Anniv. A366

Designs: 50f, Kuwaiti, league flags over emblems, map, vert. 100f, Flags over "50," 150f, Flags as clasping hands, vert.

1995, Mar. 22 — Perf. 13

1277	A366	50f multicolored	.38	.38
1278	A366	100f multicolored	.75	.75
1279	A366	150f multicolored	1.10	1.10
		Nos. 1277-1279 (3)	2.23	2.23

A367   A368

1995, Apr. 7 — Litho. — Perf. 13½x13

1280	A367	50f blue & multi	.40	.40
1281	A367	150f pink & multi	1.10	1.10
1282	A367	200f yellow & multi	1.50	1.50
		Nos. 1280-1282 (3)	3.00	3.00

World Health Day.

1995, June 5 — Litho. — Perf. 14

Designs: 50f, One gold ball. 100f, Gold "1," one gold ball. 150f, "1," both balls in gold.

1283	A368	50f shown	.35	.35
1284	A368	100f multicolored	.65	.65
1285	A368	150f multicolored	1.00	1.00
		Nos. 1283-1285 (3)	2.00	2.00

Volleyball, cent.

Invasion by Iraq, 5th Anniv. — A369

1995, Aug. 2 — Litho. — Perf. 13

1286	A369	50f purple & multi	.40	.40
1287	A369	100f red & multi	.75	.75
1288	A369	150f green & multi	1.10	1.10
		Nos. 1286-1288 (3)	2.25	2.25

UN, 50th Anniv. A370

1995, Aug. 12 — Perf. 13x13½

1289	A370	25f multi	.20	.20
1290	A370	50f orange & multi	.40	.40
1291	A370	150f blue green & multi	1.10	1.10
		Nos. 1289-1291 (3)	1.70	1.70

FAO, 50th Anniv. — A371

People in traditional dress with: 50f, Cattle, camels, sheep. 100f, Fish, boat. 150f, Poultry, fruits, vegetables.

1995, Sept. 21 — Perf. 13½x13

1292	A371	50f multicolored	.40	.40
1293	A371	100f multicolored	.75	.75
1294	A371	150f multicolored	1.10	1.10
a.		Min. sheet of 3, #1292-1294	2.25	2.25
		Nos. 1292-1294 (3)	2.25	2.25

A372

World Standards Day — A373

1995, Oct. 14 — Perf. 13

1295	A372	50f multicolored	.40	.40
1296	A373	100f green & multi	.75	.75
1297	A373	150f violet & multi	1.10	1.10
		Nos. 1295-1297 (3)	2.25	2.25

AIR POST STAMPS

Air Post Stamps of India, 1929-30, Overprinted type "c"

1933-34 — Wmk. 196 — Perf. 14

C1	AP1	2a dull green	8.00	11.00
C2	AP1	3a deep blue	1.75	1.65
C3	AP1	4a gray olive	110.00	150.00
C4	AP1	6a bister ('34)	4.50	4.00
		Nos. C1-C4 (4)	124.25	166.65

Counterfeits of Nos. C1-C4 exist.

> Catalogue values for unused stamps in this section, from this point to the end of the section, are for Never Hinged items.

Dakota and Comet Planes — AP1

Perf. 11x11½

1964, Nov. 29 — Litho. — Unwmk.

C5	AP1	20f multicolored	.20	.30
C6	AP1	25f multicolored	.75	.40
C7	AP1	30f multicolored	1.00	.40
C8	AP1	45f multicolored	1.25	.60
		Nos. C5-C8 (4)	3.20	1.70

10th anniversary of Kuwait Airways.

POSTAGE DUE STAMPS

> Catalogue values for unused stamps in this section are for Never Hinged items.

D1

Perf. 14x15

1963, Oct. 19 — Unwmk. — Litho.
Inscriptions in Black

J1	D1	1f ocher	.40	.15
J2	D1	2f lilac	.45	.15
J3	D1	5f blue	.60	.25
J4	D1	8f pale green	.65	.30
J5	D1	10f yellow	.70	.40
J6	D1	25f brick red	1.40	.65
		Nos. J1-J6 (6)	4.20	1.90

D2

1965, Apr. 1 — Perf. 13

J7	D2	4f rose & yellow	.25	.20
J8	D2	15f dp rose & blue	.50	.45
J9	D2	40f blue & brt yel grn	1.40	1.00
J10	D2	50f green & pink	1.90	1.25
J11	D2	100f dk blue & yel	3.50	2.50
		Nos. J7-J11 (5)	7.55	5.40

OFFICIAL STAMPS

Stamps of India, 1911-23, Overprinted

KUWAIT

KUWAIT

SERVICE	SERVICE
Nos. O1-O9	Nos. O10-O14

1923-24 — Wmk. 39 — Perf. 14

O1	A47	½a green	.40	5.00
O2	A48	1a brown	.50	4.00
O3	A58	1½a chocolate	1.25	10.00
O4	A49	2a violet	2.75	12.50
O5	A57	2a6p ultra	2.00	17.50
O6	A51	3a brown org	3.50	27.50
O7	A51	3a ultra ('24)	3.75	22.50
O8	A52	4a olive grn	2.00	27.50
O9	A54	8a red violet	4.25	30.00
O10	A56	1r grn & brn	10.00	55.00
O11	A56	2r brn & car rose	15.00	90.00
O12	A56	5r vio & ultra	62.50	200.00
O13	A56	10r car & grn	95.00	225.00
O14	A56	15r ol grn & ultra	160.00	375.00
		Nos. O1-O14 (14)	362.90	

Stamps of India, 1926-30, Overprinted

KUWAIT

KUWAIT

SERVICE	SERVICE
Nos. O15-O20	Nos. O21-O25

1929-33 — Wmk. 196

O15	A48	1a dk brown	2.00	7.50
O16	A60	2a violet	50.00	60.00
O17	A51	3a blue	2.00	8.00
O18	A61	4a ol green	4.00	5.00
O19	A54	8a red violet	3.00	7.00
O20	A55	12a claret	18.00	25.00
O21	A56	1r green & brn	4.75	15.00
O22	A56	2r buff & car rose	7.00	30.00
O23	A56	5r dk vio & ultra	25.00	100.00
O24	A56	10r car & green	50.00	140.00
O25	A56	15r olive grn & ultra	125.00	325.00
		Nos. O15-O25 (11)	290.75	

LABUAN

lə-ˈbü-ən

LOCATION — An island in the East Indies, about six miles off the northwest coast of Borneo

GOVT. — A British possession, administered as a part of the North Borneo Colony

AREA — 35 sq. mi.

POP. 8,963 (estimated)

CAPITAL — Victoria

The stamps of Labuan were replaced by those of Straits Settlements in 1906.

100 Cents = 1 Dollar

Watermark

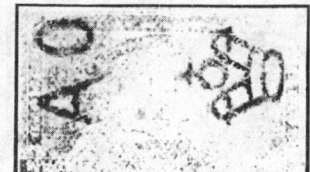

Wmk. 46- C A over Crown

Queen Victoria — A1

On Nos. 1, 2, 3, 4 and 11 the watermark is 32mm high. It is always placed sideways and extends over two stamps.

1879, May Engr. Wmk. 46 *Perf. 14*

1	A1	2c green	575.00	575.00
2	A1	6c orange	140.00	125.00
3	A1	12c carmine	850.00	375.00
4	A1	16c blue	35.00	*65.00*
		Nos. 1-4 (4)	1,600.	1,140.

See Nos. 5-10, 16-24, 33-39, 42-48. For surcharges see Nos. 12-15, 25, 31, 40-41.

1880-82 Wmk. 1

5	A1	2c green	10.00	12.50
6	A1	6c orange	60.00	65.00
7	A1	8c carmine ('82)	60.00	70.00
8	A1	10c yel brown	60.00	75.00
9	A1	12c carmine	160.00	150.00
10	A1	16c blue ('81)	50.00	60.00
		Nos. 5-10 (6)	400.00	432.50

A2

A3

A3a

A4

1880 Wmk. 46

11	A2	6c on 16c blue (with additional "6" across original value) (R)	1,050.	625.00

1880-83 Wmk. 1

12	A2	8c on 12c car ('80)	500.00	425.00
a.		Original value not obliterated	700.00	600.00
b.		Additional surcharge "8" across original value	600.00	500.00
c.		"8" inverted	600.00	500.00
13	A3	8c on 12c car ('81)	275.00	200.00
14	A3a	8c on 12c car ('81)	70.00	75.00
a.		"Eighr"	*6,000.*	
b.		Inverted surcharge	5,500.	
c.		Double surcharge	650.00	650.00
15	A4	$1 on 16c blue (R) ('83)	*2,250.*	

On No. 12 the original value is obliterated by a pen mark in either black or red.

1883-86 Wmk. 2

16	A1	2c green	10.00	15.00
a.		Horiz. pair, imperf. btwn.	3,750.	
17	A1	2c rose red ('85)	1.65	4.00
18	A1	8c carmine	125.00	70.00
19	A1	8c dk violet ('85)	11.00	7.00
20	A1	10c yellow brn	19.00	25.00
21	A1	10c black brn ('86)	6.00	15.00
22	A1	16c blue	60.00	*90.00*
23	A1	16c gray blue ('86)	70.00	90.00
24	A1	40c ocher	8.50	*35.00*
		Nos. 16-24 (9)	311.15	351.00

Nos. 1-10, 16-24 are in sheets of 10.
For surcharges see Nos. 26-30, 32.

A5

A6

A7

A8

1885 Wmk. 1

25	A5	2c on 16c blue	675.00	650.00

Wmk. 2

26	A5	2c on 8c car	85.00	47.50
a.		Double surcharge		
27	A6	2c on 16c blue	75.00	*130.00*
a.		Double surcharge		*2,000.*
28	A7	2c on 8c car	40.00	*70.00*

1891

Black or Red Surcharge

29	A8	6c on 8c violet	4.00	2.00
a.		6c on 8c dark violet	40.00	35.00
b.		Double surcharge	200.00	200.00
c.		"Cents" omitted	250.00	250.00
d.		Inverted surcharge	70.00	65.00
e.		Dbl. surch., one inverted	300.00	300.00
f.		Dbl. surch., both inverted	—	—
g.		"6" omitted	—	
30	A8	6c on 8c dk vio (R)	400.00	200.00
a.		Inverted surcharge	500.00	300.00

Wmk. 46

31	A8	6c on 16c blue	1,400.	1,400.
a.		Inverted surcharge	2,750.	2,250.

Wmk. 2

32	A8	6c on 40c ocher	3,500.	2,250.
a.		Inverted surcharge	2,750.	2,750.

From Jan. 1, 1890, to Jan. 1, 1906, Labuan was administered by the British North Borneo Co. During that period Nos. 33-39, 42-83, 53a, 63a, 64a, 65a, 66a, 68a, 85-86, 96-118, 103a, 107a, J1-J9, J3a and J6a were canceled to order by bars forming an oval. Values for these stamps used are for those with this form of cancellation. These stamps with dated town cancellation sell for 4 to 20 times as much as those with with bar cancellation. Nos. 63b, 64b, 65b, J6a, and possibly others, only exist c.t.o.

1892 Engr. Unwmk.

33	A1	2c rose	1.50	.30
34	A1	6c yellow green	4.00	.30
35	A1	8c violet	2.00	.30
36	A1	10c brown	4.00	.30
37	A1	12c deep ultra	3.00	.30
38	A1	16c gray	3.00	.30
39	A1	40c ocher	15.00	.30
		Nos. 33-39 (7)	32.50	2.10

The 2c, 8c and 10c are in sheets of 30; others in sheets of 10.

Nos. 39 and 38 Surcharged **Two Cents**

1893

40	A1	2c on 40c ocher	125.00	75.00
a.		Inverted surcharge	200.00	*300.00*
41	A1	6c on 16c gray	200.00	125.00
a.		Inverted surcharge	225.00	175.00
b.		Surcharge sideways	—	—
c.		"Six" omitted		
d.		"Cents" omitted		

Surcharges on Nos. 40-41 each exist in 10 types. Counterfeits exist.

1894, Apr. Litho.

42	A1	2c bright rose	.90	.15
43	A1	6c yellow green	4.50	.30
a.		Horiz. pair, imperf. btwn.	*2,500.*	
44	A1	8c bright violet	4.00	.30
45	A1	10c brown	13.00	.30
46	A1	12c light ultra	12.00	.30
47	A1	16c gray	14.00	.30
48	A1	40c orange	20.00	.50
		Nos. 42-48 (7)	68.40	2.15

Counterfeits exist.

Dyak Chieftain — A9

Malayan Sambar — A10

Sago Palm — A11

Argus Pheasant — A12

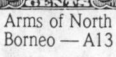

Arms of North Borneo — A13

Dhow — A14

Saltwater Crocodile — A15

Mt. Kinabalu — A16

Arms of North Borneo — A17

1894 Engr.

49	A9	1c lilac & black	1.10	.30
a.		Vert. pair, imperf. between	400.00	250.00
50	A10	2c blue & black	2.75	.30
a.		Imperf., pair	375.00	
51	A11	3c bister & black	3.25	.30
52	A12	5c green & black	15.00	.30
53	A13	6c brown red & blk	2.50	.30
a.		Imperf., pair	400.00	250.00
54	A14	8c red & black	8.00	.30
55	A15	12c orange & black	15.00	.30
56	A16	18c ol bister & blk	20.00	.30
57	A17	24c lilac & blue	13.00	.30
		Nos. 49-57 (9)	80.60	2.70

For overprints see Nos. 66-71.

A18

A19

A20

A21

1895, June Litho.

58	A18	4c on $1 red	1.00	.35
59	A18	10c on $1 red	1.50	.35
60	A18	20c on $1 red	11.00	.35
61	A18	30c on $1 red	14.00	.35
62	A18	40c on $1 red	12.00	.35
		Nos. 58-62 (5)	39.50	1.75

1896

63	A19	25c blue green	15.00	.80
a.		Without overprint	11.00	2.00
b.		As "a," imperf., pair		30.00
64	A20	50c claret	17.50	.80
a.		Without overprint	10.00	2.00
b.		As "a," imperf., pair		30.00
65	A21	$1 dark blue	30.00	.80
a.		Without overprint	15.00	2.00
b.		As "a," imperf., pair		30.00
		Nos. 63-65 (3)	62.50	2.40

For surcharges and overprint see #93-95, 116-118, 120.

Nos. 49-54 Overprinted 1846 JUBILEE 1896

1896

66	A9	1c lilac & black	14.00	.70
a.		Orange overprint	160.00	20.00
b.		Double overprint	190.00	190.00
c.		"JEBILEE"		250.00
67	A10	2c blue & black	18.00	.70
a.		Vert. pair, imperf. btwn.	350.00	
b.		"JEBILEE"	500.00	
68	A11	3c bister & black	20.00	.70
a.		Double overprint	200.00	125.00
b.		Triple overprint	800.00	
c.		"JEBILEE"		600.00
69	A12	5c green & black	32.50	.70
a.		Double overprint	225.00	225.00
70	A13	6c brown red & blk	17.00	.70
a.		Double overprint	275.00	275.00
71	A14	8c rose & black	22.50	.70
		Nos. 66-71 (6)	124.00	4.20

Cession of Labuan to Great Britain, 50th anniv.

Dyak Chieftain — A22

Malayan Sambar — A23

Sago Palm — A24

Argus Pheasant — A25

A26

Dhow — A27

Saltwater Crocodile — A28

Mt. Kinabalu "Postal Revenue" — A29

Coat of Arms — A30

1897-1900 Engr.

72	A22	1c lilac & black	2.00	.20
72A	A22	1c red brn & black	5.00	.20
73	A23	2c blue & black	6.00	.20
74	A23	2c green & blk ('00)	3.50	.20
75	A24	3c bister & black	5.00	.20
76	A25	5c green & black	15.00	.30
77	A25	5c lt bl & blk ('00)	13.00	.20
78	A26	6c brown red & blk	5.00	.30
79	A27	8c red & black	18.00	.35
80	A28	12c red & black	25.00	.50
81	A29	18c ol bister & black	18.00	.50
82	A30	24c gray lilac & blue	11.00	.50
		Nos. 72-82 (12)	126.50	3.65

The 2c, 3c 6c and 18c exist in pairs, imperf. between.
For surcharges see Nos. 87-89, 110-112.

"Postage & Revenue" — A31

"Postage & Revenue" — A32

1897

83	A31	18c bister & black	60.00	5.00
84	A32	24c brn lilac & blue	15.00	*30.00*

For surcharges see Nos. 92, 115.

"Postage & Revenue" — A33

"Postage & Revenue" — A34

1898

85	A33	12c red & black	27.50	1.50
86	A34	18c bister & black	20.00	1.50

For surcharges see Nos. 90-91, 113-114.

Regular Issue Surcharged in Black

4
CENTS

1899

87	A25	4c on 5c grn & blk	17.50	25.00
88	A26	4c on 6c brn red & blk	14.00	15.00
89	A27	4c on 8c red & blk	27.50	30.00
90	A33	4c on 12c red & blk	24.00	25.00
91	A34	4c on 18c bis & blk	15.00	15.00
a.		Double surcharge	250.00	*275.00*
92	A32	4c on 24c lil & bl	15.00	20.00
93	A19	4c on 25c blue grn	5.50	7.50
94	A20	4c on 50c claret	5.50	7.50
95	A21	4c on $1 dk blue	5.50	7.50
		Nos. 87-95 (9)	129.50	152.50

Orangutan A35

Sun Bear A36

Railroad Train — A37

Crown — A38

1899-1901

96	A35	4c yel brown & blk	4.00	.20
a.		Vert. pair, imperf. btwn.	350.00	
97	A35	4c car & blk ('00)	7.50	.25
98	A36	10c gray vio & dk brn ('01)	30.00	.35
99	A37	16c org brn & grn (G) ('01)	40.00	.35
		Nos. 96-99 (4)	81.50	1.15

Perf. 12½ to 16 and Compound

1902-03 **Engr.**

99A	A38	1c vio & black	2.50	.25
100	A38	2c green & blk	2.50	.25
100A	A38	3c sepia & blk	2.50	.25
101	A38	4c car & black	2.50	.25
102	A38	8c org & black	3.00	.25
103	A38	10c sl blue & brn	2.50	.25
a.		Vert. pair, imperf. between		400.00
104	A38	12c yel & black	3.00	.25
105	A38	16c org brn & grn	3.00	.25
106	A38	18c bis brn & blk	3.00	.25
107	A38	25c grnsh bl & grn	4.00	.25
a.		25c greenish blue & black		200.00
108	A38	50c gray lil & vio	8.50	.35
109	A38	$1 org & red brn	6.00	.40
		Nos. 99A-109 (12)	43.00	3.25

Part perforate examples exist of 12c (vert. strip of 3 imperf. between) and 16c (vert. pair, imperf. between).

Regular Issue of 1896-97 Surcharged in Black

4
cents

1904

110	A25	4c on 5c green & blk	17.00	.90
111	A26	4c on 6c brown red & black	11.00	.90
112	A27	4c on 8c red & blk	15.00	.90
113	A33	4c on 12c red & blk	18.00	.90
114	A34	4c on 18c bis & blk	15.00	.90
115	A32	4c on 24c brn lil & bl	13.00	.90
116	A19	4c on 25c blue green	7.00	.90
117	A20	4c on 50c claret	7.00	.90
a.		Double surcharge	200.00	
118	A21	4c on $1 dark blue	7.00	.90
		Nos. 110-118 (9)	110.00	8.10

Stamps of North Borneo, 1893, and Labuan No. 65a Overprinted in Black:

LABUAN a

LABUAN b

c LABUAN

1905

119	A30(a)	25c slate blue	900.	425.
120	A21(c)	$1 blue		425.
121	A33(b)	$2 gray green	2,400.	950.
122	A34(c)	$5 red violet	3,750.	850.
123	A35(c)	$10 brown	—	*3,750.*

POSTAGE DUE STAMPS

Regular Issues Overprinted

POSTAGE DUE

1901 **Unwmk.** ***Perf. 14***

J1	A23	2c green & black	9.00	.25
a.		Double overprint	140.00	
J2	A24	3c bister & black	14.00	.25
J3	A35	4c car & black	16.00	.25
a.		Double overprint		200.00
J4	A25	5c lt blue & black	20.00	.25
J5	A26	6c brown red & blk	22.50	.35
J6	A27	8c red & black	25.00	.25
a.		Center inverted, ovpt. reading down		*5,500.*
J7	A33	12c red & black	42.50	1.25
J8	A34	18c ol bister & blk	17.00	.35
J9	A32	24c brown lil & bl	32.50	.50
		Nos. J1-J9 (9)	198.50	3.70

See note after No. 32.

The stamps of Labuan were superseded by those of Straits Settlements in 1907.

LAGOS

'lā-,gās

LOCATION — West Africa, bordering on the former Southern Nigeria Colony
GOVT. — Former British Crown Colony and Protectorate
AREA — 3,460 sq. mi. (approx.)
POP. — 1,500,000 (1901)
CAPITAL — Lagos

This territory was purchased by the British in 1861 and placed under the Governor of Sierra Leone. In 1874 it was detached and formed part of the Gold Coast Colony until 1886 when the Protectorate of Lagos was established. It was chartered to the Royal Niger Company until 1899 when all territories of this Company were surrendered to the Crown of Great Britain and formed into the Northern and Southern Nigeria Protectorates. In 1906 Lagos and Southern Nigeria were united to form the Colony and Protectorate of Southern Nigeria.

12 Pence = 1 Shilling

Queen Victoria — A1

1874-75 **Typo.** **Wmk. 1** ***Perf. 12½***

1	A1	1p lilac	45.00	27.50
2	A1	2p blue	45.00	25.00
3	A1	3p red brown ('75)	77.50	35.00
a.		Value in chestnut	77.50	45.00
4	A1	4p rose	60.00	37.50
5	A1	6p blue green	65.00	10.00
a.		Value in yellow green	65.00	10.00
6	A1	1sh orange ('75)	200.00	50.00
a.		Value 15½mm instead of 16½mm long	275.00	140.00
		Nos. 1-6 (6)	492.50	185.00

1876 ***Perf. 14***

7	A1	1p lilac	30.00	15.00
8	A1	2p blue	30.00	10.00
9	A1	3p red brown	77.50	16.00
10	A1	4p rose	140.00	10.00
11	A1	6p green	75.00	5.00
12	A1	1sh orange	475.00	65.00
		Nos. 7-12 (6)	827.50	121.00

The 4p exists with watermark sideways.

1882-1902 **Wmk. 2**

13	A1	½p green ('86)	.30	.30
14	A1	1p lilac	15.00	7.50
15	A1	1p car rose	.35	.28
16	A1	2p blue	100.00	7.50
17	A1	2p gray	35.00	4.50
18	A1	2p lil & bl ('87)	1.10	.65
19	A1	2½p ultra ('91)	.60	.38
a.		2½p blue	75.00	40.00
20	A1	3p orange brn	10.00	5.00
21	A1	3p lilac & brn orange ('91)	1.50	1.65
22	A1	4p rose	90.00	11.00
23	A1	4p violet	70.00	5.25
24	A1	4p lil & blk ('87)	1.50	1.50
25	A1	5p lil & grn ('94)	3.00	*10.00*
26	A1	6p olive green	4.50	*6.25*
27	A1	6p lilac & red violet ('87)	4.00	2.50
28	A1	6p lilac & car rose ('02)	4.00	*15.00*
29	A1	7½p lilac & car rose ('94)	1.90	*7.50*
30	A1	10p lil & yel ('94)	2.25	*6.25*
31	A1	1sh orange ('85)	5.00	*7.50*
32	A1	1sh green & blk ('87)	3.00	*5.00*
33	A1	2sh6p ol brn ('86)	375.00	300.00
34	A1	2sh6p green & car rose ('87)	20.00	*27.50*
35	A1	5sh blue ('86)	700.00	350.00
36	A1	5sh green & ultra ('87)	30.00	*42.50*
37	A1	10sh brn vio ('86)	1,000.	825.00
38	A1	10sh grn & brn ('87)	55.00	*95.00*

Excellent forgeries exist of Nos. 33, 35 and 37 on paper with genuine watermark.

No. 24 Surcharged in Black

HALF PENNY

1893

39	A1	½p on 4p lilac & blk	2.50	2.00
a.		Double surcharge	60.00	60.00
b.		Triple surcharge	95.00	
c.		½p on 2p lilac & blue (#18)		

Four settings of surcharge.

King Edward VII — A3

1904, Jan. 22

40	A3	½p grn & bl grn	2.25	*4.50*
41	A3	1p vio & blk, *red*	.60	.18
42	A3	2p violet & ultra	6.25	*9.25*
43	A3	2½p vio & ultra, *bl*	1.90	*2.75*
44	A3	3p vio & org brn	1.40	2.50
45	A3	6p vio & red vio	11.00	4.50
46	A3	1sh green & blk	27.50	25.00
47	A3	2sh6p grn & car rose	82.50	*175.00*
48	A3	5sh grn & ultra	150.00	*225.00*
49	A3	10sh green & brn	325.00	*775.00*
		Nos. 40-49 (10)	608.40	*1,223.*

1904-05 **Wmk. 3**

50	A3	½p grn & bl grn	5.00	1.50
51	A3	1p vio & blk, *red*	.80	.15
52	A3	2p violet & ultra	1.50	.70
53	A3	2½p vio & ultra, *bl*	1.40	*13.00*
54	A3	3p vio & org brn	2.50	.75
55	A3	6p vio & red vio	3.25	1.10
56	A3	1sh green & blk	5.00	2.00
57	A3	2sh6p grn & car rose	10.00	*20.00*
58	A3	5sh grn & ultra	17.50	*60.00*
59	A3	10sh green & brn	42.50	*110.00*
		Nos. 50-59 (10)	89.45	*209.20*

The 2½p is on chalky paper, the other values are on both ordinary and chalky.

The stamps of Lagos were superseded by those of Southern Nigeria.

LESOTHO

lə-'sō-(,)tō

LOCATION — An enclave within the Republic of South Africa
GOVT. — Independent state in British Commonwealth
AREA — 11,720 sq. mi.
POP. — 1,470,000 (est. 1984)
CAPITAL — Maseru

Basutoland, the British Crown Colony, became independent, October 4, 1966, taking the name Lesotho.

100 Cents = 1 Rand
100 Lisente (s) = 1 Maloti (1979)

Catalogue values for all unused stamps in this country are for Never Hinged items.

Watermark

Wmk. 362- Basotho Hat Multiple

Moshoeshoe I and II — A1

Perf. 12½x13

1966, Oct. 4 **Photo.** **Unwmk.**

1	A1	2½c red brn, blk & red	.15	.15
2	A1	5c red brn, blk & brt bl	.15	.15
3	A1	10c red brn, blk & brt green	.25	.25
4	A1	20c red brn, blk & red lilac	.45	.45
		Nos. 1-4 (4)	1.00	1.00

Lesotho's independence, Oct. 4, 1966.

Basutoland Nos. 72-74, **LESOTHO** 76-82 Overprinted

Perf. 13½

1966, Nov. 1 **Wmk. 4** **Engr.**

5	A7	½c dk brown & gray	.15	.15
6	A7	1c dp grn & gray blk	.15	.15
7	A7	2c orange & dp blue	.15	.15
8	A7	3½c dp blue & indigo	.15	.15
9	A7	5c dk grn & org brn	.16	.16
10	A7	10c rose vio & dk ol	.32	.32
11	A7	12½c aqua & brown	.40	.40
12	A7	25c lil rose & dp ultra	.80	.80
13	A7	50c dp car & black	1.60	1.60

Perf. 11½

14	A8	1r dp claret & blk	4.40	4.40
a.		"Lseotho"	100.00	
		Nos. 5-14 (10)	8.28	8.28

Same Overprint on Nos. 87-91 and Type of 1954

Wmk. 314 ***Perf. 13½***

15	A7	1c green & gray blk	.15	.15
16	A7	2½c car & ol green	.15	.15
17	A7	5c dk grn & org brn	.20	.20
18	A7	12½c aqua & brown	.40	.40
19	A7	50c dp car & black	1.40	1.40

Perf. 11½

20	A8	1r dp claret & blk	2.75	2.75
a.		"Lseotho"	50.00	
		Nos. 15-20 (6)	5.05	5.05

UNESCO Emblem, Microscope, Book, Violin and Retort — A2

Unwmk.

1966, Dec. 1 **Litho.** ***Perf. 14***

21	A2	2½c green & ocher	.15	.15
22	A2	5c olive & brt green	.15	.15
23	A2	12½c ver & lt blue	.40	.40
24	A2	25c dull blue & orange	.65	.65
		Nos. 21-24 (4)	1.35	1.35

20th anniv. of UNESCO.

King Moshoeshoe II and Corn — A3

King Moshoeshoe II — A4

Designs: 1c, Bull. 2c, Aloes. 2½c, Basotho hat. 3½c, Merino sheep. 5c, Basotho pony. 10c, Wheat. 12½c, Angora goat. 25c, Maletsunyane Falls. 50c, Diamonds. 1r, Coat of Arms.

Perf. 13½x14½

1967, Apr. 1 Photo. Unwmk.

25	A3	½c violet & green	.15	.15
26	A3	1c dk red & brown	.15	.15
27	A3	2c green & yellow	.15	.15
28	A3	2½c yel bister & blk	.15	.15
29	A3	3½c yellow & black	.15	.15
30	A3	5c brt blue & yel bis	.18	.15
31	A3	10c gray & ocher	.30	.20
32	A3	12½c orange & blk	.35	.30
33	A3	25c ultra & blk	.75	.75
34	A3	50c Prus green & blk	1.75	1.75
35	A3	1r gray & multi	2.75	2.75

Perf. 14½x13½

36	A4	2r mag, blk & gold	6.00	6.00
		Nos. 25-36 (12)	12.83	12.65

See Nos. 47-59.

University Buildings and Graduates A4a

1967, Apr. 7 *Perf. 14x14½*

37	A4a	1c yel, sep & dp blue	.15	.15
38	A4a	2½c blue, sep & dp bl	.15	.15
39	A4a	12½c dl rose, sep & dp bl	.25	.25
40	A4a	25c lt vio, sep & dp bl	.45	.45
		Set value	.80	.80

1st conferment of degrees by the Univ. of Botswana, Lesotho and Swaziland at Roma, Lesotho.

Statue of Moshoeshoe I — A5

1st Anniv. of Independence: 12½c, Flag of Lesotho. 25c, Crocodile.

1967, Oct. 4 Photo. *Perf. 14*

41	A5	2½c apple green & black	.15	.15
42	A5	12½c multicolored	.35	.35
43	A5	25c tan, blk & dp green	.65	.65
		Nos. 41-43 (3)	1.15	1.15

Boy Scout and Lord Baden-Powell — A6

1967, Nov. 1 Unwmk. *Perf. 14x14½*

44	A6	15c lt ol grn, dk grn & brn	.50	.50

60th anniversary of the Boy Scouts.

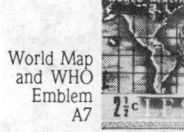

World Map and WHO Emblem A7

20th anniv. of WHO: 25c, Nurse and child, arms of Lesotho and WHO emblem.

1968, Apr. 8 Photo. *Perf. 14x14½*

45	A7	2½c dp bl, car rose & gold	.15	.15
46	A7	25c gold, gray grn & redsh brown	.45	.40
		Set value	.51	.45

Types of 1967

Design: 3c, Sorghum. Others as before.

Perf. 13½x14½

1968-69 Photo. Wmk. 362

47	A3	½c violet & green	.15	.15
48	A3	1c dk red & brown	.15	.15
49	A3	2c green & yellow	.15	.15
50	A3	2½c yel bister & blk	.15	.15
51	A3	3c lt brn, dk brn & green	.18	.18
52	A3	3½c yellow & black	.18	.18
53	A3	5c brt bl & yel bis	.22	.18
54	A3	10c gray & ocher	.55	.45
55	A3	12½c org & blk ('69)	.90	.75
56	A3	25c ultra & blk ('69)	1.60	1.25
57	A3	50c Prussian grn & black ('69)	3.50	2.75
58	A3	1r gray & multi	6.00	5.50

Perf. 14½x13½

59	A4	2r magenta, blk & gold ('69)	15.00	11.50
		Nos. 47-59 (13)	28.73	23.34

Hunters, Rock Painting — A8

Rock Paintings: 3½c, Baboons. 5c, Javelin thrower, vert. 10c, Archers. 15c, Cranes, vert. 20c, Eland. 25c, Hunting scene.

Perf. 14½x14, 14x14½

1968, Nov. 1 Photo. Wmk. 362

60	A8	3c dk & lt green & brn	.15	.15
61	A8	3½c dk brown & yel	.15	.15
62	A8	5c sepia, yel & red brn	.20	.20
63	A8	10c black, brt rose & org	.45	.45
64	A8	15c olive brn & buff	.75	.75
65	A8	20c black, yel & lt grn	1.00	1.00
66	A8	25c dk brown, yel & org	1.25	1.25
		Nos. 60-66 (7)	3.95	3.95

Protection for Lesotho's rock paintings.

Queen Elizabeth II Hospital A9

Designs: 10c, Radio Lesotho. 12½c, Leabua Jonathan Airport. 25c, Royal Palace.

1969, Mar. 11 Litho. *Perf. 14x13½*

67	A9	2½c multicolored	.15	.15
68	A9	10c multicolored	.25	.25
69	A9	12½c multicolored	.28	.28
70	A9	25c multicolored	.65	.65
		Nos. 67-70 (4)	1.33	1.33

Centenary of Maseru, capital of Lesotho.

Mosotho Horseman and Car A10

Designs: 12½c, Car on mountain pass. 15c, View from Sani Pass and signal flags. 20c, Map of Lesotho and Independence Trophy.

1969, Sept. 26 Photo. *Perf. 14½x14*

71	A10	2½c brown & multi	.15	.15
72	A10	12½c multicolored	.28	.28
73	A10	15c multicolored	.35	.35
74	A10	20c yellow & multi	.50	.50
		Nos. 71-74 (4)	1.28	1.28

Roof of Africa Auto Rally, Sept. 19-20.

Plateosauravus and Footprints — A11

Prehistoric Reptile Footprints, Moyeni: 3c, Dinosaur. 5c, Gryponyx. 15c, Tritylodon. 25c, Massospondylus.

Perf. 14½x14

1970, Jan. 5 Wmk. 362

Size: 60x23mm

75	A11	3c brown, yel & black	.15	.15

Perf. 15x14

Size: 40x23mm

76	A11	5c maroon, blk & pink	.32	.32
77	A11	10c sepia, blk & yel	.65	.65
78	A11	15c slate grn, blk & yel	1.10	1.10
79	A11	25c gray blue, blk & bl	1.50	1.50
		Nos. 75-79 (5)	3.72	3.72

Moshoeshoe I — A12

Design: 25c, Moshoeshoe I with top hat.

Perf. 14x13½

1970, Mar. 11 Litho. Wmk. 362

80	A12	2½c brt grn & car rose	.15	.15
81	A12	25c lt blue & org brn	.65	.65

Cent. of the death of Moshoeshoe I, chief of the Bakoena clan of the Basothos.

UN Headquarters, New York — A13

Designs: 2½c, UN emblem. 12½c, UN emblem and people. 25c, UN emblem and peace dove.

1973, June 26 Litho. *Perf. 14½x14*

82	A13	2½c pink, red brn & bl	.15	.15
83	A13	10c blue & multi	.25	.20
84	A13	12½c olive, ver & lt blue	.25	.22
85	A13	25c tan & multi	.60	.50
		Nos. 82-85 (4)	1.25	1.07

25th anniversary of the United Nations.

Basotho Hat Gift Shop, Maseru A14

Tourism: 5c, Trout fishing. 10c, Horseback riding. 12½c, Skiing, Maluti Mountains. 20c, Holiday Inn, Maseru.

1970, Oct. 27 *Perf. 14x14½*

86	A14	2½c multicolored	.15	.15
87	A14	5c multicolored	.20	.20
88	A14	10c multicolored	.45	.45
89	A14	12½c multicolored	.45	.45
90	A14	20c multicolored	.65	.65
		Nos. 86-90 (5)	1.90	1.90

Corn — A15

Designs: 1c, Bull. 2c, Aloes. 2½c, Basotho hat. 3c, Sorghum. 3½c, Merino sheep. 4c, National flag. 5c, Basotho pony. 10c, Wheat. 12½c, Angora goat. 25c, Maletsunyane Falls. 50c, Diamonds. 1r, Coat of Arms. 2r, Statue of King Moshoeshoe I in Maseru, vert.

1971 Litho. Wmk. 362 *Perf. 14*

91	A15	½c lilac & green	.15	.15
92	A15	1c brn red & brn	.15	.15
93	A15	2c yel brn & yel	.15	.15
94	A15	2½c dull yel & blk	.15	.15
95	A15	3c bis, brn & grn	.15	.15
96	A15	3½c yellow & black	.15	.15
97	A15	4c ver & multi	.15	.15
98	A15	5c blue & brown	.15	.15
99	A15	10c gray & ocher	.28	.28
100	A15	12½c orange & brn	.32	.32
101	A15	25c ultra & black	.70	.70
102	A15	50c lt bl grn & blk	1.75	1.75
103	A15	1r gray & multi	2.25	2.25
104	A15	2r ultra & brown	5.75	5.75
a.		Unwmkd. ('80)	5.25	5.25
		Nos. 91-104 (14)	12.25	12.25

Issue dates: 4c, Apr. 1; others, Jan. 4.

For overprints and surcharges see #132-135, 245, 312.

Lammergeier — A16

Birds: 5c, Bald ibis. 10c, Rufous rock jumper. 12½c, Blue korhaan (bustard). 15c, Painted snipe. 20c, Golden-breasted bunting. 25c, Ground woodpecker.

1971, Mar. 1 *Perf. 14*

105	A16	2½c multicolored	.50	.22
106	A16	5c multicolored	1.00	.50
107	A16	10c multicolored	1.65	1.25
108	A16	12½c multicolored	2.50	1.50
109	A16	15c multicolored	3.00	2.00
110	A16	20c multicolored	4.00	2.50
111	A16	25c multicolored	4.50	3.50
		Nos. 105-111 (7)	17.15	11.47

Lionel Collett Dam A17

Designs: 10c, Contour farming. 15c, Earth dams. 25c, Beaver dams.

1971, July 15 Litho. Wmk. 362

112	A17	4c multicolored	.15	.15
113	A17	10c multicolored	.32	.32
114	A17	15c multicolored	.45	.45
115	A17	25c multicolored	.75	.75
		Nos. 112-115 (4)	1.67	1.67

Soil conservation and erosion control.

Diamond Mining A18

Designs: 10c, Potter. 15c, Woman weaver at loom. 20c, Construction worker and new buildings.

1971, Oct. 4

116	A18	4c olive & multi	.15	.15
117	A18	10c ocher & multi	.28	.28
118	A18	15c red & multi	.45	.45
119	A18	20c dk brown & multi	.60	.60
		Nos. 116-119 (4)	1.48	1.48

Mail Cart, 19th Century A19

Designs: 10c, Postal bus. 15c, Cape of Good Hope No. 17, vert. 20c, Maseru Post Office.

1972, Jan. 3

120	A19	5c pink & black	.15	.15
121	A19	10c lt blue & multi	.35	.35
122	A19	15c gray, black & blue	.50	.50
123	A19	20c yellow & multi	.90	.90
		Nos. 120-123 (4)	1.90	1.90

Centenary of mail service between Maseru and Aliwal North in Cape Colony.

Runner and Olympic Rings — A20

1972, Sept. 1

124 A20	4c shown	.15	.15
125 A20	10c Shot put	.25	.25
126 A20	15c Hurdles	.35	.35
127 A20	25c Broad jump	.75	.75
	Nos. 124-127 (4)	1.50	1.50

20th Olympic Games, Munich, Aug. 26-Sept. 11.

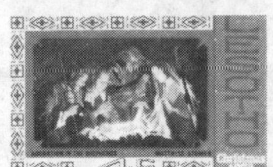

Adoration of the Shepherds, by Matthias Stomer — A21

1972, Dec. 1   Litho.   Perf. 14

128 A21	4c blue & multi	.15	.15
129 A21	10c red & multi	.35	.35
130 A21	25c emerald & multi	.90	.90
	Nos. 128-130 (3)	1.40	1.40

Christmas.

WHO Emblem A22

1973, Apr. 7   Litho.   Perf. 13½

131 A22	20c blue & yellow	.50	.50

WHO, 25th anniversary.

Nos. 94, 97-99 overprinted:
"O.A.U. / 10th Anniversary / Freedom in Unity"

1973, May 25   Wmk. 362   Perf. 14

132 A15	2½c dull yellow & black	.15	.15
133 A15	4c vermilion & multi	.20	.20
134 A15	5c blue & brown	.25	.25
135 A15	10c gray & ocher	.50	.50
	Nos. 132-135 (4)	1.10	1.10

Basotho Hat, WFP/FAO Emblem — A23

Designs: 15c, School lunch. 20c, Child drinking milk and cow. 25c, Map of mountain roads and farm workers.

1973, June 1   Perf. 13½

136 A23	4c ultra & multi	.15	.15
137 A23	15c buff & multi	.30	.30
138 A23	20c yellow & multi	.40	.40
139 A23	25c violet & multi	.60	.60
	Nos. 136-139 (4)	1.45	1.45

World Food Program, 10th anniversary.

Christmas Butterfly A24

Designs: Butterflies of Lesotho.

1973, Sept. 3   Perf. 14x14½

140 A24	4c Mountain Beauty	.30	.30
141 A24	5c shown	.45	.45
142 A24	10c Painted lady	.90	.90
143 A24	15c Yellow pansy	1.25	1.25
144 A24	20c Blue pansy	1.75	1.75
145 A24	25c African monarch	2.50	2.50
146 A24	30c Orange tip	3.50	3.50
	Nos. 140-146 (7)	10.65	10.65

Map of Northern Lesotho and Location of Diamond Mines — A25

Designs: 15c, Kimberlite (diamond-bearing) rocks. 20c, Diagram of Kimberlite volcano, vert. 30c, Diamond prospector, vert.

Perf. 13½x14, 14x13½

1973, Oct. 1   Litho.   Wmk. 362

147 A25	10c gray & multi	.75	.50
148 A25	15c multicolored	1.00	.75
149 A25	20c multicolored	1.25	1.00
150 A25	30c multicolored	2.50	1.50
	Nos. 147-150 (4)	5.50	3.75

International Kimberlite Conference.

Nurses' Training and Medical Care A26

Designs: 10c, Classroom, student with microscope. 20c, Farmers with tractor and bullock team and crop instruction. 25c, Potter and engineers with lathe. 30c, Boy scouts and young bricklayers.

1974, Feb. 18   Litho.   Perf. 13½x14

151 A26	4c lt blue & multi	.15	.15
152 A26	10c ocher & multi	.20	.20
153 A26	20c multicolored	.40	.40
154 A26	25c bister & multi	.60	.60
155 A26	30c multicolored	.75	.75
	Nos. 151-155 (5)	2.10	2.10

Youth and development.

Open Book and Wreath — A27

Designs: 15c, Flags of Botswana, Lesotho and Swaziland; cap and diploma. 20c, Map of Africa and location of Botswana, Lesotho and Swaziland. 25c, King Moshoeshoe II, Chancellor of UBLS, capping graduate.

1974, Apr. 7   Litho.   Perf. 14

156 A27	10c multicolored	.30	.30
157 A27	15c multicolored	.50	.50
158 A27	20c multicolored	.60	.60
159 A27	25c multicolored	.75	.75
	Nos. 156-159 (4)	2.15	2.15

10th anniversary of the University of Botswana, Lesotho and Swaziland.

Senqunyane River Bridge, Marakabei — A28

Designs: 5c, Tsoelike River Bridge. 10c, Makhaleng River Bridge. 15c, Seaka Bridge, Orange/Senqu River. 20c, Masianokeng Bridge, Phuthiatsana River. 25c, Mahobong Bridge, Hlotse River.

1974, June 26   Wmk. 362   Perf. 14

160 A28	4c multicolored	.15	.15
161 A28	5c multicolored	.15	.15
162 A28	10c multicolored	.25	.25
163 A28	15c multicolored	.50	.40
164 A28	20c multicolored	.65	.50
165 A28	25c multicolored	.80	.60
	Nos. 160-165 (6)	2.50	2.05

Bridges and rivers of Lesotho.

UPU Emblem — A29

1974, Sept. 6   Litho.   Perf. 14x13

166 A29	4c shown	.15	.15
167 A29	10c Map of Lesotho	.25	.25
168 A29	15c GPO, Maseru	.40	.40
169 A29	20c Rural mail delivery	.60	.60
	Nos. 166-169 (4)	1.40	1.40

Centenary of Universal Postal Union.

Siege of Thaba-Bosiu — A30

King Moshoeshoe I — A31

Designs: 5c, King Moshoeshoe II laying wreath at grave of Moshoeshoe I. 20c, Makoanyane, warrior hero.

Perf. 12½x12, 12x12½

1974, Nov. 25

170 A30	4c multicolored	.15	.15
171 A30	5c multicolored	.18	.18
172 A31	10c multicolored	.35	.35
173 A31	20c multicolored	.85	.85
	Nos. 170-173 (4)	1.53	1.53

Sesquicentennial of Thaba-Bosiu becoming the capital of Basutoland and Lesotho.

Mamokhorong A32

Musical Instruments of the Basotho: 10c, Lesiba. 15c, Setolotolo. 20c, Meropa (drums).

Perf. 14x14½

1975, Jan. 25   Wmk. 362

174 A32	4c multicolored	.15	.15
175 A32	10c multicolored	.40	.40
176 A32	15c multicolored	.60	.60
177 A32	20c multicolored	.80	.80
a.	Souvenir sheet of 4, #174-177	2.50	2.50
	Nos. 174-177 (4)	1.95	1.95

View, Sehlabathebe National Park — A33

Designs: 5c, Natural arch. 15c, Mountain stream. 20c, Lake and mountains. 25c, Waterfall.

1975, Apr. 8   Litho.   Perf. 14

178 A33	4c multicolored	.15	.15
179 A33	5c multicolored	.20	.20
180 A33	15c multicolored	.60	.60
181 A33	20c multicolored	.80	.80
182 A33	25c multicolored	1.00	1.00
	Nos. 178-182 (5)	2.75	2.75

Sehlabathebe National Park.

Moshoeshoe I (1824-1870) A34

Mofumahali Mantsebo Seeiso (1940-1960) A35

Leaders of Lesotho: 4c, Moshoeshoe II. 5c, Letsie I (1870-1891). 6c, Lerotholi (1891-1905). 10c, Letsie II (1905-1913). 15c, Griffith (1913-1939). 20c, Seeiso Griffith Lerotholi (1939-1940).

1975, Sept. 10   Litho.   Wmk. 362

183 A34	3c dull blue & black	.15	.15
184 A34	4c lilac rose & black	.15	.15
185 A34	5c pink & black	.15	.15
186 A34	6c brown & black	.15	.15
187 A34	10c rose car & black	.25	.25
188 A34	15c orange & black	.35	.35
189 A34	20c olive & black	.45	.45
190 A35	25c lt blue & black	.60	.60
	Nos. 183-190 (8)	2.25	2.25

No. 190 issued for Intl. Women's Year.

Mokhibo, Women's Dance — A36

Traditional Dances: 10c, Ndlamo, men's dance. 15c, Raleseli, men and women. 20c, Mohobelo, men's dance.

1975, Dec. 17   Perf. 14x14½

191 A36	4c blue & multi	.15	.15
192 A36	10c black & multi	.35	.35
193 A36	15c black & multi	.50	.50
194 A36	20c blue & multi	.75	.75
a.	Souvenir sheet of 4, #191-194	3.00	3.00
	Nos. 191-194 (4)	1.75	1.75

Enrollment in Junior Red Cross A37

Designs: 10c, First aid team and truck. 15c, Red Cross nurse on horseback in rural area. 25c, Supplies arriving by plane.

1976, Feb. 20   Litho.   Perf. 14

195 A37	4c red & multi	.15	.15
196 A37	10c red & multi	.35	.35
197 A37	15c red & multi	.50	.50
198 A37	25c red & multi	.80	.80
	Nos. 195-198 (4)	1.80	1.80

Lesotho Red Cross, 25th anniversary.

Mosotho Horseman A38

King Moshoeshoe II — A39

Designs: 2c, Tapestry (weavers and citation). 4c, Map of Lesotho. 5c, Hand holding Lesotho brown diamond. 10c, Lesotho Bank. 15c, Flags of Lesotho and Organization of African Unity. 25c, Sehlabathebe National Park. 40c, Pottery. 50c, Prehistoric rock painting.

1976, June 2 *Perf. 14*

199 A38	2c multicolored	.15	.15
200 A38	3c multicolored	.15	.15
201 A38	4c multicolored	.15	.15
202 A38	5c multicolored	.15	.15
203 A38	10c multicolored	.30	.30
204 A38	15c multicolored	.45	.45
205 A38	25c multicolored	.75	.75
206 A38	40c multicolored	1.20	1.20
207 A38	50c multicolored	1.50	1.50
208 A39	1r multicolored	2.00	2.00
	Nos. 199-208 (10)	6.80	6.80

For surcharges see Nos. 302-311.

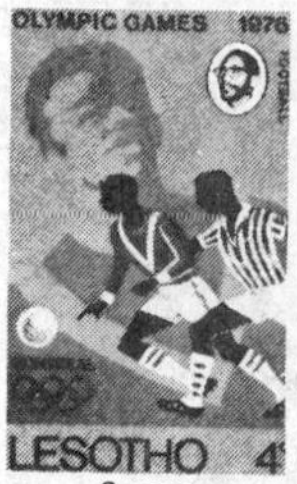

Soccer A40

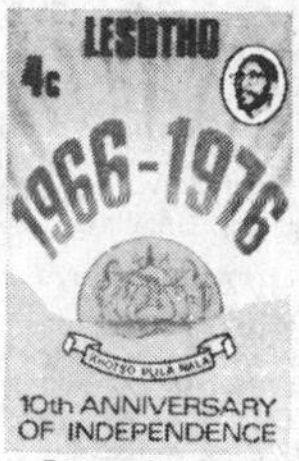

Rising Sun of Independence A41

Olympic Rings and: 10c, Weight lifting. 15c, Boxing. 25c, Discus.

1976, Aug. 9 **Litho.** **Wmk. 362**

209 A40	4c citron & multi	.15	.15
210 A40	10c lilac & multi	.28	.25
211 A40	15c salmon & multi	.40	.35
212 A40	25c blue & multi	.80	.65
	Nos. 209-212 (4)	1.63	1.40

21st Olympic Games, Montreal, Canada, July 17-Aug. 1.

1976, Oct. 4 *Perf. 14*

Designs: 10c, Opening gates. 15c, Broken chain. 25c, Plane over Molimo Restaurant.

213 A41	4c yellow & multi	.15	.15
214 A41	10c pink & multi	.30	.30
215 A41	15c blue & multi	.45	.45
216 A41	25c dull blue & multi	.75	.75
	Nos. 213-216 (4)	1.65	1.65

Lesotho's independence, 10th anniversary.

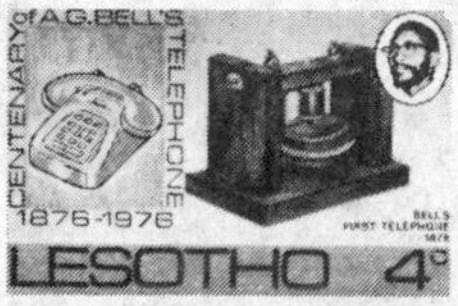

Telephones, 1876 and 1976 A42

Designs: 10c, Woman using telephone, and 1895 telephone. 15c, Telephone operators and wall telephone. 25c, A.G. Bell and 1905 telephone.

Perf. 13x13½

1976, Dec. 6 **Wmk. 362**

217 A42	4c multicolored	.15	.15
218 A42	10c multicolored	.22	.22
219 A42	15c multicolored	.35	.35
220 A42	25c multicolored	.60	.60
	Nos. 217-220 (4)	1.32	1.32

Centenary of first telephone call by Alexander Graham Bell, Mar. 10, 1876.

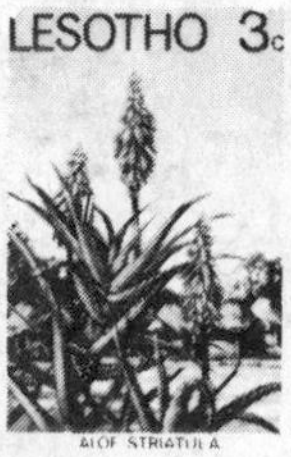

Aloe Striatula — A43

Aloes and Succulents: 4c, Aloe aristata. 5c, Kniphofia caulescens. 10c, Euphorbia pulvinata. 15c, Aloe saponaria. 20c, Caralluma lutea. 25c, Aloe polyphylla.

1977, Feb. 14 **Litho.** *Perf. 14*

221 A43	3c multicolored	.18	.15
222 A43	4c multicolored	.22	.15
223 A43	5c multicolored	.25	.20
224 A43	10c multicolored	.50	.40
225 A43	15c multicolored	.90	.50
226 A43	20c multicolored	1.10	.75
227 A43	25c multicolored	1.25	1.00
	Nos. 221-227 (7)	4.40	3.15

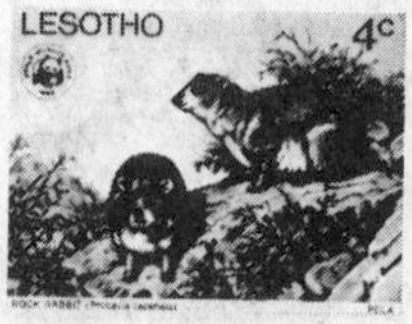

Rock Rabbits — A44

Perf. 14x14½

1977, Apr. 25 **Wmk. 362**

228 A44	4c shown	.20	.15
229 A44	5c Porcupine	.25	.20
230 A44	10c Polecat	.50	.40
231 A44	15c Klipspringers	.80	.60
232 A44	25c Baboons	1.50	1.00
	Nos. 228-232 (5)	3.25	2.35

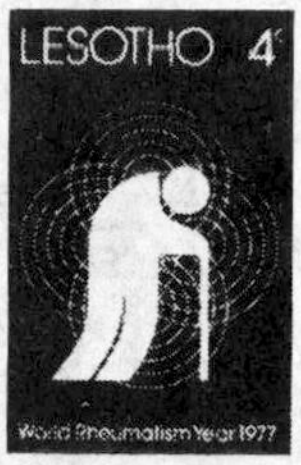

Man with Cane, Concentric Circles — A45

Man with Cane: 10c, Surrounded by flames of pain. 15c, Surrounded by chain. 25c, Man and globe.

1977, July 4 **Litho.** *Perf. 14*

233 A45	4c red & yellow	.15	.15
234 A45	10c dk blue & lt blue	.28	.15
235 A45	15c blue green & yellow	.48	.35
236 A45	25c black & orange	.80	.60
	Nos. 233-236 (4)	1.71	1.25

World Rheumatism Year.

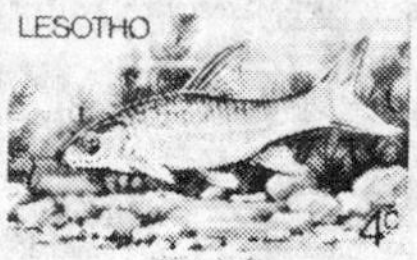

Small-mouthed Yellow-fish A46

Fresh-water Fish: 10c, Orange River mud fish. 15c, Rainbow trout. 25c, Oreodaimon quathlambae.

1977, Sept. 28 **Wmk. 362** *Perf. 14*

237 A46	4c multicolored	.15	.15
238 A46	10c multicolored	.32	.25
239 A46	15c multicolored	.48	.35
240 A46	25c multicolored	.80	.60
	Nos. 237-240 (4)	1.75	1.35

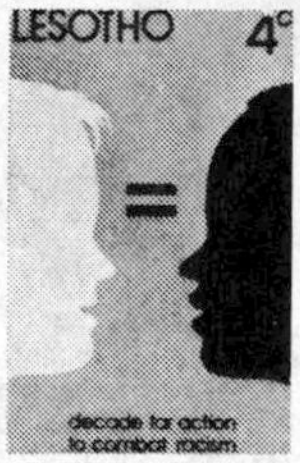

White and Black Equal — A47

Designs: 10c, Black and white jigsaw puzzle. 15c, White and black cogwheels. 25c, Black and white handshake.

1977, Dec. 12 **Litho.** *Perf. 14*

241 A47	4c lilac rose & black	.15	.15
242 A47	10c brt blue & black	.22	.22
243 A47	15c orange & black	.35	.35
244 A47	25c lt green & black	.60	.60
	Nos. 241-244 (4)	1.32	1.32

Action to Combat Racism Decade.

No. 99 Surcharged

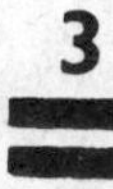

1977, Dec. 7

245 A15	3c on 10c gray & ocher	1.60	1.40

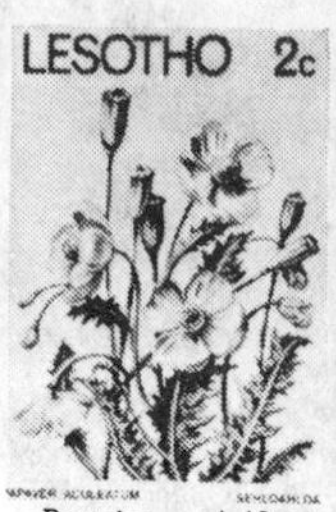

Poppies — A48

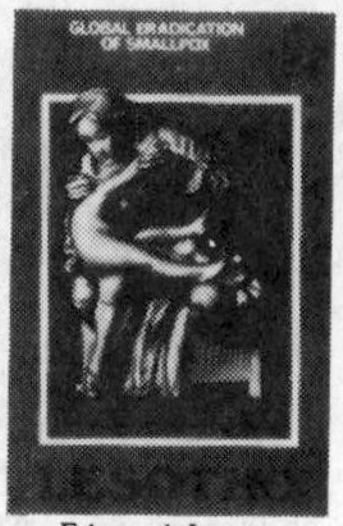

Edward Jenner Vaccinating Child — A49

Flowers of Lesotho: 3c, Diascia integerrima. 4c, Helichrysum trilineatum. 5c, Zaluzianskya maritima. 10c, Gladioli. 15c, Chironia krebsii. 25c, Wahlenbergia undulata. 40c, Brunsvigia radulosa.

1978, Feb. 13 **Litho.** **Wmk. 362**

246 A48	2c multicolored	.15	.15
247 A48	3c multicolored	.15	.15
248 A48	4c multicolored	.15	.15
249 A48	5c multicolored	.15	.15
250 A48	10c multicolored	.25	.25
251 A48	15c multicolored	.40	.40
252 A48	25c multicolored	.65	.65
253 A48	40c multicolored	1.00	1.00
	Nos. 246-253 (8)	2.90	2.90

1978, May 8 **Litho.** *Perf. 13½x13*

Global Eradication of Smallpox: 25c, Child's head and WHO emblem.

254 A49	5c multicolored	.15	.15
255 A49	25c multicolored	.75	.75

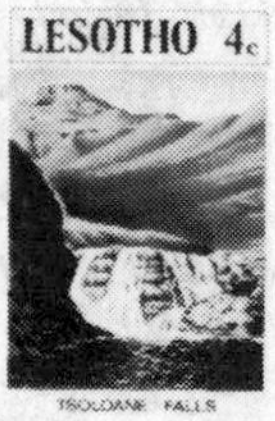

Tsoloane Falls — A50

Lesotho Waterfalls: 10c, Qiloane Falls. 15c, Tsoelikana Falls. 25c, Maletsunyane Falls.

1978, July 28 **Litho.** *Perf. 14*

256 A50	4c multicolored	.15	.15
257 A50	10c multicolored	.32	.32
258 A50	15c multicolored	.50	.50
259 A50	25c multicolored	.80	.80
	Nos. 256-259 (4)	1.77	1.77

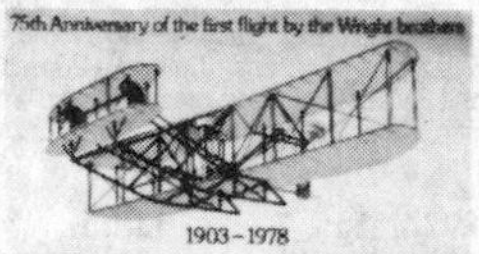

Flyer 1 A51 5c LESOTHO

Design: 25c, Orville and Wilbur Wright, Flyer 1.

1978, Oct. 9 **Wmk. 362** *Perf. 14½*

260 A51	5c multicolored	.15	.15
261 A51	25c multicolored	.50	.50

75th anniversary of 1st powered flight.

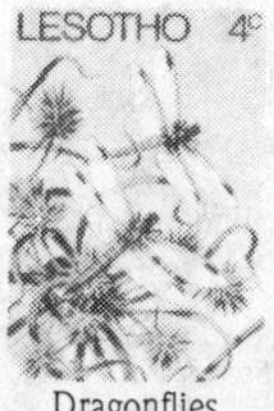

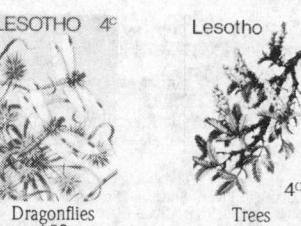

Dragonflies A52

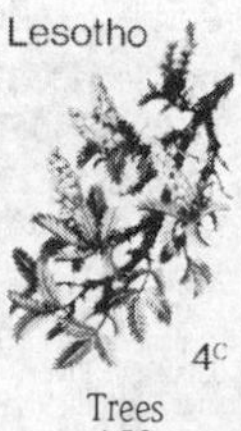

Trees A53

Insects: 10c, Winged grasshopper. 15c, Wasps. 25c, Praying mantis.

1978, Dec. 18 **Litho.** *Perf. 14*

262 A52	4c multicolored	.15	.15
263 A52	10c multicolored	.30	.30
264 A52	15c multicolored	.45	.45
265 A52	25c multicolored	.75	.75
	Nos. 262-265 (4)	1.65	1.65

1979, Mar. 26 **Litho.** *Perf. 14*

266 A53	4c Leucosidea Sericea	.15	.15
267 A53	10c Wild olive	.30	.30
268 A53	15c Blinkblaar	.45	.45
269 A53	25c Cape holly	.75	.75
	Nos. 266-269 (4)	1.65	1.65

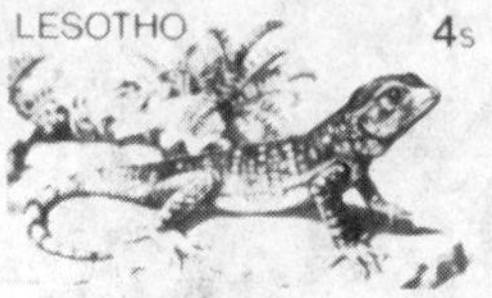

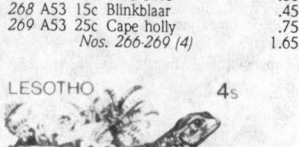

Reptiles A54

1979, June 4 **Wmk. 362** *Perf. 14*

270 A54	4s Agama Lizard	.15	.15
271 A54	10s Berg adder	.30	.30
272 A54	15s Rock lizard	.45	.45
273 A54	25s Spitting snake	.75	.75
	Nos. 270-273 (4)	1.65	1.65

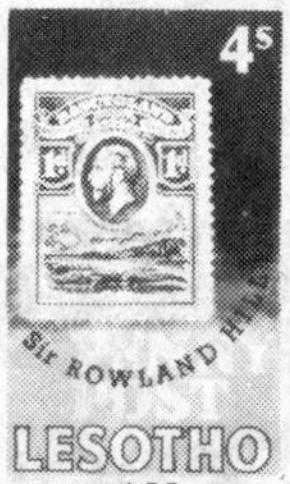

A55

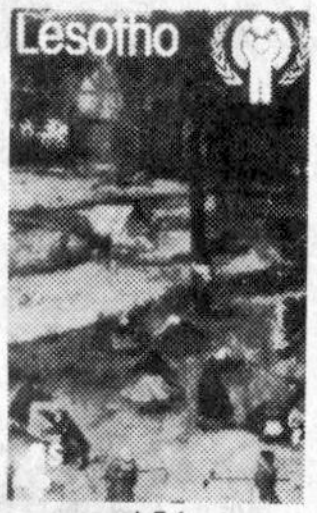

A56

1979, Oct. 22 **Litho.** *Perf. 14½*

274 A55	4s Basutoland No. 2	.15	.15
275 A55	15s Basutoland No. 72	.30	.30
276 A55	25s Penny Black	.50	.50
	Nos. 274-276 (3)	.95	.95

Souvenir Sheet

277 A55	50s Lesotho No. 122	1.25	1.25

Sir Rowland Hill (1795-1879), originator of penny postage.

Children's Games, by Brueghel the Elder, and IYC emblem: 4s, Children Climbing Tree. 10s, Follow the leader. 15s, Three cup montie. 25s, Entire painting.

1979, Dec. 10 **Wmk. 362** *Perf. 14½*

278 A56	4s multicolored	.15	.15
279 A56	10s multicolored	.22	.22
280 A56	15s multicolored	.35	.35
	Nos. 278-280 (3)	.72	.72

Souvenir Sheet

281 A56	25s multicolored	.60	.60

International Year of the Child.

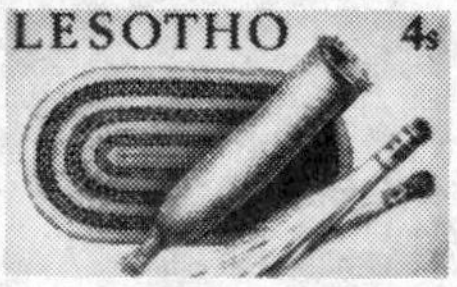

Beer Strainer, Brooms and Mat A57

1980, Feb. 18 **Litho.** *Perf. 14½*

282 A57	4s shown	.15	.15
283 A57	10s Winnowing basket	.20	.20
284 A57	15s Basotho hat	.30	.30
285 A57	25s Grain storage pots	.50	.50
	Nos. 282-285 (4)	1.15	1.15

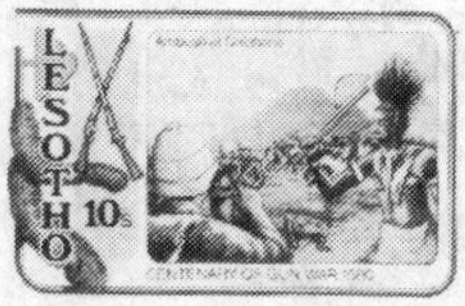

Qalabane Ambush A58

Gun War Centenary: 4s, Praise poet, text. 5s, Basotho army commander Lerotholi. 15s, Snider and Martini-Henry rifles. 25s, Map of Basutoland showing battle sites.

1980, May 6 **Litho.** *Perf. 14*

286 A58	4s multicolored	.15	.15
287 A58	5s multicolored	.15	.15
288 A58	10s multicolored	.25	.25
289 A58	15s multicolored	.35	.35
290 A58	25s multicolored	.60	.60
	Nos. 286-290 (5)	1.50	1.50

St. Basil's, Moscow, Olympic Torch A59

1980, Sept. 20   Litho.   Perf. 14½
291	A59	25s shown	.55	.55
292	A59	25s Torch and flags	.55	.55
293	A59	25s Soccer	.55	.55
294	A59	25s Running	.55	.55
295	A59	25s Misha and stadium	.55	.55
a.		Strip of 5, #291-295	2.75	2.75
		Nos. 291-295 (5)	2.75	2.75

Souvenir Sheet
296	A59	1.40m Classic and modern torch bearers	3.25	3.25

22nd Summer Olympic Games, Moscow, July 19-Aug. 3.

Beer Mug and Man Drinking A60

Prince Philip — A61

Wmk. 362
1980, Oct. 1   Litho.   Perf. 14
297	A60	4s shown	.15	.15
298	A60	10s Beer brewing pot	.22	.22
299	A60	15s Water pot	.35	.35
300	A60	25s Pots and jugs	.60	.60
		Nos. 297-300 (4)	1.32	1.32

Souvenir Sheet
Perf. 14x14½
301		Sheet of 4	3.50	2.25
a.	A61	40s shown	.70	.50
b.	A61	40s Queen Elizabeth	.70	.50
c.	A61	40s Prince Charles	.70	.50
d.	A61	40s Princess Anne	.70	.50

Traditional pottery; 250th birth anniversary of Josiah Wedgwood, potter.

Nos. 104, 199-208 Surcharged
Wmk. 362
1980, Oct. 20   Litho.   Perf. 14
302	A38	2s on 2c multi	.15	.15
303	A38	3s on 3c multi	.15	.15
304	A38	5s on 5c multi	.15	.15
a.		5s on 6s on 5c multi	.15	.15
305	A38	4s on 4c multi	.15	.15
306	A38	10s on 10c multi	.18	.18
307	A38	25s on 25c multi	.40	.40
308	A38	40s on 40c multi	.65	.65
309	A38	50s on 50c multi	.90	.90
310	A38	75s on 15c multi	2.25	2.25
311	A39	1m on 1r multi	2.75	2.75
312	A15	2m on 2r multi	5.00	5.00
		Nos. 302-312 (11)	12.73	12.73

Souvenir Sheet

Queen Mother Elizabeth and Prince Charles — A62

Basutoland No. 36, Flags of Lesotho and Britain — A63

1980, Dec. 1   Perf. 14½
313		Sheet of 9	5.00	5.00
a.	A62	5s shown	.15	.15
b.	A62	10s Portrait	.20	.20
c.	A63	1m shown	2.00	2.00

Queen Mother Elizabeth, 80th birthday. No. 313 contains 3 each Nos. 313a-313c.

St. Agnes' Anglican Church, Teyateyaneng — A63a

Nativity A64

1980, Dec. 8   Perf. 14x14½
314	A63a	4s Lesotho Evangelical Church, Morija	.15	.15
315	A63a	15s shown	.35	.35
316	A63a	25s Our Lady's Victory Cathedral, Maseru	.60	.60
317	A63a	75s University Chapel, Roma	1.75	1.75
		Nos. 314-317 (4)	2.85	2.85

Souvenir Sheet
318	A64	1.50m shown	3.25	2.00

Christmas.

Voyager Satellite and Saturn A65

1981, Mar. 15   Litho.   Perf. 14
319		Strip of 5	2.75	2.75
a.	A65	25s Voyager, planet	.55	.55
b.	A65	25s shown	.55	.55
c.	A65	25s Voyager, Saturn's rings	.55	.55
d.	A65	25s Columbia space shuttle	.55	.55
e.	A65	25s Columbia, diff.	.55	.55

Souvenir Sheet
320	A65	1.40m Saturn	3.25	3.25

Voyager expedition to Saturn and flight of Columbia space shuttle.

Rock Pigeons A66

1981, Apr. 20   Perf. 14½
321	A66	1s Greater kestrel, vert.	.15	.15
322	A66	2s shown	.15	.15
323	A66	3s Crowned cranes, vert.	.15	.15
324	A66	5s Bokmakierie, vert.	.15	.15
325	A66	6s Cape robins, vert.	.15	.15
326	A66	7s Yellow canary, vert.	.18	.18
327	A66	10s Red-billed teal	.25	.25
328	A66	25s Malachite kingfisher, vert.	.60	.60
329	A66	40s Malachite sunbirds	1.00	1.00
330	A66	60s Orange-throated long-claw	1.50	1.50
331	A66	75s African hoopoe	1.75	1.75

332	A66	1m Red bishops	2.50	2.50
333	A66	2m Egyptian goose	4.75	4.75
334	A66	5m Lilac-breasted rollers	10.00	10.00
		Nos. 321-334 (14)	23.28	23.28

For surcharges see Nos. 558A, 561-563, 598A, 599, 600B, 600C.

1981   Litho.   Perf. 13
321a	A66	1s		
322a	A66	2s		
324a	A66	5s		
327a	A66	10s		

Perf. 14½
1982, June 14   Litho.   Wmk. 373
321b	A66	1s		
322b	A66	2s		
323a	A66	3s		
324b	A66	5s		
325a	A66	6s		
326a	A66	7s		
327b	A66	10s		
328a	A66	25s		
329a	A66	40s		
330a	A66	60s		
331a	A66	75s		
332a	A66	1m		
333a	A66	2m		
334a	A66	5m		

Royal Wedding Issue
Common Design Type and

Royal Wedding — A66a

Illustration reduced.

1981, July 22   Litho.   Perf. 14
335	CD331	25s Bouquet	.40	.40
a.		Booklet pane of 3 + label	1.25	
336	CD331	50s Charles	.75	.75
a.		Booklet pane of 3 + label	2.50	
337	CD331	75s Couple	1.10	1.10
b.		Booklet pane of 3 + label	3.50	
c.		Bklt. pane of 2, #335-337 + label	2.75	
		Nos. 335-337 (3)	2.25	2.25

1981   Litho.   Perf. 14½
337A	A66a	1.50m Couple	3.00	3.00

Nos. 335-337A exist imperf.

Tree Planting A67

1981, Oct. 30   Litho.   Perf. 14½
338	A67	6s Duke of Edinburgh	.15	.15
339	A67	7s shown	.15	.22
340	A67	25s Digging	.50	.50
341	A67	40s Mountain climbing	.80	.80
342	A67	75s Emblem	1.50	1.50
		Nos. 338-342 (5)	3.10	3.17

Souvenir Sheet
343	A67	1.40m Duke of Edinburgh, diff.	2.75	2.75

Duke of Edinburgh's Awards, 25th anniv. #343 contains 1 45x29mm stamp, perf. 13½.

Santa Claus at Globe, by Norman Rockwell A68

The Mystic Nativity, by Botticelli — A69

Christmas: Saturday Evening Post covers by Norman Rockwell.

1981, Oct. 5   Perf. 13½x14
344	A68	6s multicolored	.15	.15
345	A68	10s multicolored	.20	.20
346	A68	15s multicolored	.30	.30
347	A68	20s multicolored	.40	.40
348	A68	25s multicolored	.50	.50
349	A68	75s multicolored	1.25	1.25
		Nos. 344-349 (6)	2.80	2.80

Souvenir Sheet
350	A69	1.25m multicolored	2.50	2.50

Chacma Baboons A70

Perf. 14x13½, 14½ (20s, 40s, 50s)
1982, Jan. 15   Litho.
351	A70	6s African wild cat	.15	.15
352	A70	20s shown	.40	.40
353	A70	25s Cape eland	.50	.50
354	A70	40s Porcupine	.80	.80
355	A70	50s Oribi	1.00	1.00
		Nos. 351-355 (5)	2.85	2.85

Souvenir Sheet
Perf. 14
356	A70	1.50m Black-backed jackal	3.00	3.00

6s, 25s; 50x37mm. No. 356 contains one stamp 48x31mm.

Scouting Year — A71

1982, Mar. 5   Litho.   Perf. 14x13½
357	A71	6s Bugle call	.15	.15
358	A71	30s Hiking	.60	.60
359	A71	40s Drawing	.80	.80
360	A71	50s Holding flag	1.00	1.00
361	A71	75s Salute	1.50	1.50
a.		Booklet pane of 10 + sheet	12.50	
		Nos. 357-361 (5)	4.05	4.05

Souvenir Sheet
362	A71	1.50m Baden-Powell	2.75	2.75

No. 361a contains 2 each Nos. 357-361 with gutter and No. 362.
#357-361 issued in sheets of 8 with gutter.

1982 World Cup Soccer A72

Championships, 1930-1978: a, Uruguay, 1930. b, Italy, 1934. c, France, 1938. d, Brazil, 1950. e, Switzerland, 1954. f, Sweden, 1958. g, Chile, 1962. h, England, 1966. i, Mexico, 1970. j, Germany, 1974. k, Argentina, 1978. l, World Cup.

1982, Apr. 14   Perf. 14½
363		Sheet of 12	3.25	3.25
a.-l.		A72 15s any single	.25	.25

Souvenir Sheet
364	A72	1.25m Stadium	2.50	2.50

Nos. 363b, 363c, 363f, 363g, 363j, 363k exist se-tenant in sheets of 72.

George Washington's Birth Bicentenary — A73

Designs: Paintings.

1982, June 7
365	A73	6s	Portrait	.15	.15
366	A73	7s	With children	.15	.15
367	A73	10s	Indian Chief's Prophecy	.20	.20
368	A73	25s	With troops	.50	.50
369	A73	40s	Arriving at New York	.80	.80
370	A73	1m	Entry into New York	2.00	2.00
		Nos. 365-370 (6)		3.80	3.80

Souvenir Sheet
371 A73 1.25m Crossing Delaware 2.50 2.50

Princess Diana Issue
Common Design Type
Wmk. 373

1982, July 1   Litho.   Perf. 14
372	CD333	30s	Arms	.45	.45
373	CD333	50s	Diana	.75	.75
374	CD333	75s	Wedding	1.10	1.10
375	CD333	1m	Portrait	1.50	1.50
		Nos. 372-375 (4)		3.80	3.80

Sesotho Bible Centenary — A74   Birth of Prince William of Wales, June 21 — A75

1982, Aug. 20   Litho.   Perf. 14½
376 A74 6s Man reading bible .15 .15
377 A74 15s Angels, bible .25 .25

Size: 59½x40½mm
378 A74 1m Bible, Maseru Cathedral 1.75 1.75
    Nos. 376-378 (3) 2.15 2.15

Issued in sheets of 9 (3 each Nos. 376-378).

1982, Sept. 30
379 A75 6s Congratulation .15 .15
380 A75 60s Diana, William 1.10 1.10

Issued in sheets of 6 (No. 379, 5 No. 380).

Christmas — A76

Designs: Scenes from Walt Disney's The Twelve Days of Christmas. Stamps of same denomination se-tenant.

1982, Dec. 1   Litho.   Perf. 11
381	A76	2s	multicolored	.15	.15
382	A76	2s	multicolored	.15	.15
383	A76	3s	multicolored	.15	.15
384	A76	3s	multicolored	.15	.15
385	A76	4s	multicolored	.15	.15
386	A76	4s	multicolored	.15	.15
387	A76	75s	multicolored	1.50	1.50
388	A76	75s	multicolored	1.50	1.50
		Nos. 381-388 (8)		3.90	3.90

Souvenir Sheet
Perf. 14x13½
389 A76 1.50m multicolored 3.25 3.25

Local Mushrooms — A77

1983, Jan. 11   Perf. 14½
390 A77 10s Lepista caffrorum .20 .20
391 A77 30s Broomexia congregate .60 .60
a.   Booklet pane of 2, #390, 391 .85

392 A77 50s Afroboletus luteolus 1.00 1.00
393 A77 75s Lentinus tuberregium 1.50 1.50
a.   Booklet pane of 4, #390-393 3.50
    Nos. 390-393 (4) 3.30 3.30

Commonwealth Day — A78

1983, Mar. 14   Litho.   Perf. 14½
394 A78 5s Ba-Leseli dance .15 .15
395 A78 30s Tapestry weaving .50 .50
396 A78 60s Elizabeth II 1.00 1.00
397 A78 75s Moshoeshoe II 1.10 1.10
    Nos. 394-397 (4) 2.75 2.75

Trance Dancers A79

Hunters — A79a

Rock Paintings: 25s, Baboons, Sehonghong Thaba Tseka. 60s, Hunter attacking mountain reedbuck, Makhetha Berera. 75s, Eland, Leribe.

1983, May 20   Litho.   Perf. 14½
398 A79 6s multicolored .15 .15
399 A79 25s multicolored .50 .50
400 A79 60s multicolored 1.25 1.25
401 A79 75s multicolored 1.50 1.50
    Nos. 398-401 (4) 3.40 3.40

Souvenir Sheet
402   Sheet of 5, #398-401, 402a 3.75 3.75
a.   A79a 10s multicolored .20 .20

Manned Flight Bicentenary A80

1983, July 11   Litho.   Perf. 14½
403 A80 7s Montgolfier, 1783 .15 .15
404 A80 30s Wright brothers .40 .40
405 A80 60s 1st airmail plane 1.20 1.20
406 A80 1m Concorde 2.00 2.00
    Nos. 403-406 (4) 3.75 3.75

Souvenir Sheet
407   Sheet of 5 4.00 4.00
a.   A80 6s Dornier 228 .15 .15

No. 407 contains Nos. 403-406, 407a (60x60mm).

Sesquicentennial of French Missionaries' Arrival — A81

1983, Sept. 5   Litho.   Perf. 13½x14
408 A81 6s Rev. Eugene Casalis, flags .15 .15
409 A81 25s Morija, 1833 .50 .50

410 A81 40s Baptism of Libe .80 .80
411 A81 75s Map of Basutoland, 1834 1.50 1.50
    Nos. 408-411 (4) 2.95 2.95

Christmas — A82

Scenes from Disney's Old Christmas, from Washington Irving's Sketch Book.

1983, Dec.   Litho.   Perf. 14
412	A82	1s	shown	.15	.15
413	A82	2s	Christmas eve, diff.	.15	.15
414	A82	3s	Christmas day	.15	.15
415	A82	4s	Christmas day, diff.	.15	.15
416	A82	5s	Christmas dinner	.15	.15
417	A82	6s	Christmas dinner, diff.	.15	.15
418	A82	75s	Christmas games	1.50	1.50
419	A82	1m	Christmas dancers	2.00	2.00
		Nos. 412-419 (8)		4.40	4.40

Souvenir Sheet
420 A82 1.75m Christmas eve 3.50 3.50

African Monarch A83

Butterflies.

1984, Jan. 20   Litho.
421	A83	1s	shown	.15	.15
422	A83	2s	Mountain Beauty	.15	.15
423	A83	3s	Orange Tip	.15	.15
424	A83	4s	Blue Pansy	.15	.15
425	A83	5s	Yellow Pansy	.15	.15
426	A83	6s	African Migrant	.15	.15
427	A83	7s	African Leopard	.15	.15
428	A83	10s	Suffused Acraea	.20	.20
429	A83	15s	Painted Lady	.30	.30
430	A83	20s	Lemon Traveller	.40	.40
431	A83	30s	Foxy Charaxes	.60	.60
432	A83	50s	Broad-Bordered Grass Yellow	1.00	1.00
433	A83	60s	Meadow White	1.25	1.25
434	A83	75s	Queen Purple Tip	1.50	1.50
435	A83	1m	Diadem	2.00	2.00
436	A83	5m	Christmas Butterfly	10.00	10.00
		Nos. 421-436 (16)		18.30	18.30

For surcharges see Nos. 559-560, 561A, 564-566, 600, 600A, 600D, 617A-617B.

Easter A84

Designs: Nos. 437a-437j, The Ten Commandments. 1.50m, Moses holding tablets.

1984, Mar. 30   Litho.   Perf. 14
437   Sheet of 10 + 2 labels 3.50 3.50
a.-j.   A84 20s any single .35 .35

Souvenir Sheet
438 A84 1.50m multicolored 2.50 2.50

No. 438 contains one stamp 45x29mm.

1984 Summer Olympics — A85

1984, May 5   Litho.   Perf. 13½
439 A85 10s Torch bearer .15 .15
440 A85 30s Equestrian .45 .45
441 A85 50s Swimming .75 .75
442 A85 75s Basketball 1.25 1.25
443 A85 1m Running 1.50 1.50
    Nos. 439-443 (5) 4.10 4.10

Souvenir Sheet
444 A85 1.50m Flags, flame, stadium 2.50 2.50

Prehistoric Footprints — A86

1984, July 2   Litho.   Perf. 13½
445 A86 10s Sauropodomorph .18 .18
446 A86 30s Lesothosaurus .50 .50
447 A86 50s Carnivorous dinosaur .90 .90
    Nos. 445-447 (3) 1.58 1.58

Mail Coach Bicentenary and Ausipex '84 — A87

Designs: 6s, Wells Fargo, 1852. 7s, Basotho mail cart, 1900. 10s, Bath mail coach, 1784. 30s, Cobb coach, 1853. 50s, Exhibition buildings. 1.75m, Penny Black, Basutoland #O4, Western Australia #3.

1984, Sept. 5   Litho.   Perf. 14
448 A87 6s multicolored .15 .15
449 A87 7s multicolored .15 .15
450 A87 10s multicolored .18 .18
451 A87 30s multicolored .55 .55

Size: 82x26mm
451A A87 50s multicolored .90 .90
    Nos. 448-451A (5) 1.93 1.93

Souvenir Sheet
452 A87 1.75m multicolored 3.00 3.00

No. 452 contains one stamp 82x26mm.

Trains A88

1984, Nov. 5   Litho.   Perf. 13½
453 A88 6s Orient Express, 1900 .15 .15
454 A88 15s 05.001, Class 5, 1935 .20 .20
455 A88 30s Cardean, Caledonian, 1906 .40 .40
456 A88 60s Santa Fe, Super Chief, 1940 .75 .75
457 A88 1m Flying Scotsman, 1934 1.40 1.40
    Nos. 453-457 (5) 2.90 2.90

Souvenir Sheet
Perf. 14x13½
458 A88 2m The Blue Train, 1972 3.00 3.00

Indigenous Young Animals A89

1984, Dec. 20   Perf. 14½
459 A89 15s Cape Eland calf .22 .22
460 A89 20s Chacma baboons .26 .26
461 A89 30s Oribo calf .38 .38
462 A89 75s Red rock hares .95 .95

Size: 47x28mm
Perf. 13½
463 A89 1m Black-backed jackals 1.40 1.40
    Nos. 459-463 (5) 3.21 3.21

King Moshoeshoe II — A90

1985, Jan. 30   Litho.   Perf. 15
464 A90 6s Royal crown, 1974   .15 .15
465 A90 30s Moshoeshoe II, 1966   .45 .45
466 A90 75s In Basotho dress   1.10 1.10
467 A90 1m In military uniform   1.50 1.50
   Nos. 464-467 (4)   3.20 3.20
     25th anniversary of reign.

Miniature Sheet

Easter — A91

Stations of the Cross: a, Condemned to death. b, Bearing cross. c, Falls the first time. d, Meets his mother. e, Cyrenean helps carry cross. f, Veronica wipes His face. g, Second fall. h, Consoles women of Jerusalem. i, Third fall. j, Stripped. k, Nailed to cross. l, Dies on cross. m, Taken down from cross. n, Laid in sepulchre. No. 469, The Crucifixion, detail, by Mathias Grunewald (c. 1460-1528).

1985, Mar. 8   Perf. 11
468   Sheet of 14 + label   4.25
a.-n. A91 20s any single   .30 .30

Souvenir Sheet
Perf. 14
469 A91 2m multicolored   3.00 3.00

Queen Mother, 85th Birthday A92

Photographs: 10s, Queen Mother, Princess Elizabeth, 1931. 30s, 75th birthday portrait. 60s With Queen Elizabeth II and Princess Margaret, 80th birthday. No. 473, With Queen Elizabeth II, Princess Diana, Princes Henry and Charles, christening of Prince Henry. No. 474, like No. 473, with Prince William.

1985, May 30   Perf. 13½x14
470 A92 10s multicolored   .16 .16
471 A92 30s multicolored   .50 .50
472 A92 60s multicolored   1.25 1.25
473 A92 2m multicolored   3.00 3.00
   Nos. 470-473 (4)   4.91 4.91

Souvenir Sheet
474 A92 2m multicolored   3.00 3.00
No. 474 contains one stamp 38x51mm.

Automobile Centenary — A93

Luxury cars.

1985, June 10   Perf. 14
475 A93 6s BMW 732i   .15 .15
476 A93 10s Ford LTD Crown Victoria   .18 .18
477 A93 30s Mercedes-Benz 500SE   .55 .55
478 A93 90s Cadillac Eldorado Biarritz 1.50 1.50
479 A93 2m Rolls Royce Silver Spirit 3.50 3.50
   Nos. 475-479 (5)   5.88 5.88

Souvenir Sheet
480 A93 2m 1907 Rolls Royce Silver
       Ghost Tourer, vert.   3.75 3.75
   No. 480 contains one stamp 38x51mm.

Audubon Birth Bicentenary A94

Illustrations of North American bird species by artist and naturalist John J. Audubon.

1985, Aug. 5   Perf. 14½
481 A94 5s Cliff swallow, vert.   .15 .15
482 A94 6s Great crested grebe   .15 .15
483 A94 10s Vesper sparrow   .15 .15
484 A94 30s Greenshank   .45 .45
485 A94 60s Stilt sandpiper   .90 .90
486 A94 2m Glossy ibis   3.00 3.00
   Nos. 481-486 (6)   4.80 4.80
Nos. 481-486 printed in sheets of 5 with labels picturing various birds.

Intl. Youth Year, Girl Guides 75th Anniv. — A95

1985, Sept. 26   Perf. 15
487 A95 10s Mountain climbing   .15 .15
488 A95 30s Medical research   .45 .45
489 A95 75s Guides on parade   1.10 1.10
490 A95 2m Guide saluting   3.00 3.00
   Nos. 487-490 (4)   4.70 4.70

Souvenir Sheet
491 A95 2m Lady Baden-Powell,
       World Chief Guide   3.00 3.00

UN, 40th Anniv. A96   Wildflowers A97

Designs: 10s, UN No. 1, flag, horiz. 30s, Dish satellite, Ha Sofonia Earth Satellite Station, ITU emblem. 50s, Aircraft, Maseru Airport, ICAO emblem, horiz. 2m, Maimonides (1135-1204), medieval Jewish scholar, WHO emblem.

1985, Oct. 15   Litho.   Perf. 15
492 A96 10s multicolored   .15 .15
493 A96 30s multicolored   .42 .42
494 A96 50s multicolored   .80 .80
495 A96 2m multicolored   3.00 3.00
   Nos. 492-495 (4)   4.37 4.37

1985, Nov. 11   Perf. 11
496 A97 6s Cosmos   .15 .15
497 A97 10s Small agapanthus   .15 .15
498 A97 30s Pink witchweed   .42 .42
499 A97 60s Small iris   .90 .90
500 A97 90s Wild geranium   1.25 1.25
501 A97 1m Large spotted orchid   1.50 1.50
   Nos. 496-501 (6)   4.37 4.37

Mark Twain, Author, Jacob and Wilhelm Grimm, Fabulists A98

Disney characters acting out Mark Twain quotes or portraying characters from The Wishing Table, by the Grimm Brothers.

1985, Dec. 2   Perf. 11
502 A98 6s multicolored   .15 .15
503 A98 10s multicolored   .15 .15
504 A98 50s multicolored   .80 .80
505 A98 60s multicolored   1.00 1.00
506 A98 75s multicolored   1.25 1.25
507 A98 90s multicolored   1.40 1.40
508 A98 1m multicolored   1.65 1.65
509 A98 1.50m multicolored   2.75 2.75
   Nos. 502-509 (8)   9.15 9.15

Souvenir Sheets
Perf. 14
510 A98 1.25m multicolored   2.00 2.00
511 A98 1.50m multicolored   2.75 2.75
Christmas. #505, 507 printed in sheets of 8.

World Wildlife Fund — A99   Flora and Fauna — A100

Lammergeier vulture.

1986, Jan. 20   Perf. 15
512 A99 7s Male   .15 .15
513 A99 15s Male, female   .22 .22
514 A99 50s Male in flight   .75 .75
515 A99 1m Adult, young   1.50 1.50
   Nos. 512-515 (4)   2.62 2.62

1986, Jan. 20
516 A100 9s Prickly pear   .15 .15
517 A100 12s Stapelia   .18 .18
518 A100 35s Pig's ears   .52 .52
519 A100 2m Columnar cereus   3.25 3.25
   Nos. 516-519 (4)   4.10 4.10

Souvenir Sheet
520 A100 2m Black eagle   3.25 3.25

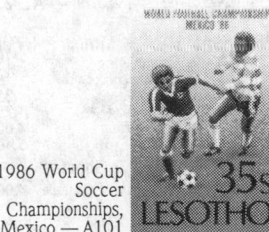

1986 World Cup Soccer Championships, Mexico — A101

Various soccer plays.

1986, Mar. 17   Perf. 14
521 A101 35s multicolored   .55 .55
522 A101 50s multicolored   .75 .75
523 A101 1m multicolored   1.50 1.50
524 A101 2m multicolored   3.00 3.00
   Nos. 521-524 (4)   5.80 5.80

Souvenir Sheet
525 A101 3m multicolored   5.00 5.00

HALLEY'S COMET 1985-6 A102

Halley's Comet A103

Designs: 9s, Hale Telescope, Mt. Palomar, Galileo. 15s, Venus 2 probe, 1985 sighting. 70s, 684 sighting illustration, Nuremberg Chronicles. 3m, 1066 sighting, Norman conquest of England. 4m, Comet over Lesotho.

1986, Apr. 5
526 A102 9s multicolored   .15 .15
527 A102 15s multicolored   .15 .15
528 A102 70s multicolored   .70 .70
529 A102 3m multicolored   3.00 3.00
   Nos. 526-529 (4)   4.00 4.00

Souvenir Sheet
530 A103 4m multicolored   4.00 4.00

Queen Elizabeth II, 60th Birthday
Common Design Type

Designs: 90s, In pantomime during youth. 1m, At Windsor Horse Show, 1971. 2m, At Royal Festival Hall, 1971. 4m, Age 8.

1986, Apr. 21
531 CD339 90s lt yel bis & black   .90 .90
532 CD339 1m pale grn & multi   1.00 1.00
533 CD339 2m dull vio & multi   2.00 2.00
   Nos. 531-533 (3)   3.90 3.90

Souvenir Sheet
534 CD339 4m tan & black   4.00 4.00
For overprints see Nos. 636-639.

Statue of Liberty, Cent. A104

Statue and famous emigrants: 15s, Bela Bartok (1881-1945), composer. 35s, Felix Adler (1857-1933), philosopher. 1m, Victor Herbert (1859-1924), composer. No. 538, David Niven (1910-1983), actor. No. 539, Statue, vert.

1986, May 1
535 A104 15s multicolored   .15 .15
536 A104 35s multicolored   .35 .35
537 A104 1m multicolored   1.00 1.00
538 A104 3m multicolored   3.00 3.00
   Nos. 535-538 (4)   4.50 4.50

Souvenir Sheet
539 A104 3m multicolored   3.00 3.00

AMERIPEX '86 — A105

Walt Disney characters.

1986, May 22   Perf. 11
540 A105 15s Goofy, Mickey   .15 .15
541 A105 35s Mickey, Pluto   .40 .40
542 A105 1m Goofy   1.10 1.10
543 A105 2m Donald, Pete   2.25 2.25
   Nos. 540-543 (4)   3.90 3.90

Souvenir Sheet
Perf. 14
544 A105 4m Goofy, Chip'n'Dale   4.50 4.50

Royal Wedding Issue, 1986
Common Design Type

Designs: 50s, Prince Andrew and Sarah Ferguson. 1m, Andrew. 3m, Andrew at helicopter controls. 4m, Couple, diff.

1986, July 23   Perf. 14
545 CD340 50s multicolored   .50 .50
546 CD340 1m multicolored   1.00 1.00
547 CD340 3m multicolored   3.00 3.00
   Nos. 545-547 (3)   4.50 4.50

Souvenir Sheet
548 CD340 4m multicolored   4.00 4.00

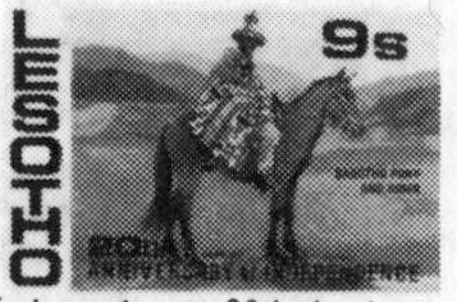

Natl. Independence, 20th Anniv. — A106

1986, Oct. 20 Litho. *Perf. 15*

549 A106 9s Basotho pony, rider .15 .15
550 A106 15s Mohair spinning .15 .15
551 A106 35s River crossing .35 .35
552 A106 3m Thaba Tseka P.O. 3.00 3.00
Nos. 549-552 (4) 3.65 3.65

Souvenir Sheet

553 A106 4m Moshoeshoe I 4.00 4.00

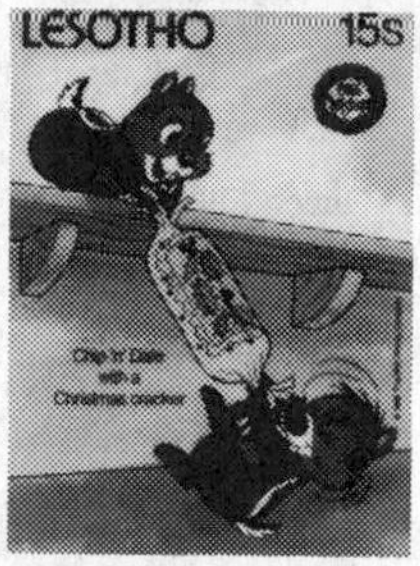

Christmas
A107

Walt Disney characters.

1986, Nov. 4 Litho. *Perf. 11*

554 A107 15s Chip'n'Dale .15 .15
555 A107 35s Mickey, Minnie .35 .35
556 A107 1m Pluto 1.00 1.00
557 A107 2m Aunt Matilda 2.00 2.00
Nos. 554-557 (4) 3.50 3.50

Souvenir Sheet

Perf. 14

558 A107 5m Huey and Dewey 5.00 5.00

Butterfly and Bird Type of 1981-84 Surcharged

1986 Litho. *Perf. 14, 14½*

558A A66 9s on 10s #327b
b. 9s on 10s #327
559 A83 9s on 30s No. 431 .15 .15
a. 9s on 30s #431 (surcharge smaller & sans serif)
560 A83 9s on 60s No. 433 .15 .15
561 A66 15s on 1s No. 321 .15 .15
b. 15s on 1s #321a
c. 15s on 1s #321b
561A A83 15s on 1s No. 421 2.00 2.00
562 A66 15s on 2s No. 322 .15 .15
563 A66 15s on 60s No. 330 .15 .15
a. 15s on 60s #330a
564 A83 15s on 2s No. 422 .15 .15
565 A83 15s on 3s No. 423 .15 .15
566 A83 35s on 75s No. 434 .35 .35
a. 35s on 75s #434, small "s"

Issued: Nos. 559-560, July 1. Nos. 561-563, Aug. 22. Nos. 561A, 564-566, June 25.
See Nos. 617A-617B.

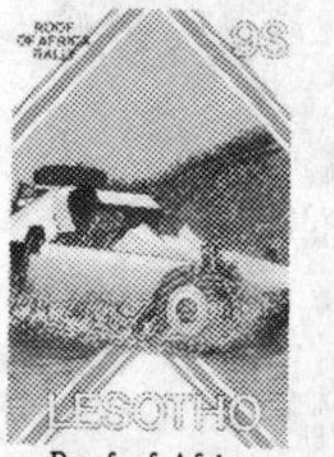

Roof of Africa Rally — A108

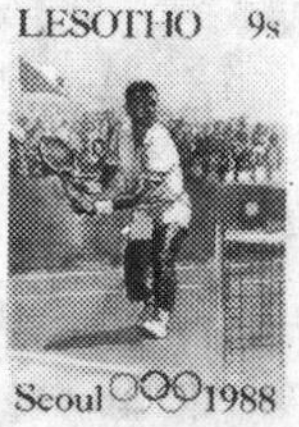

1988 Summer Olympics, Seoul — A109

1987, Apr. 28 Litho. *Perf. 14*

567 A108 9s White car .15 .15
568 A108 15s Motorcycle #26 .15 .15
569 A108 35s Motorcycle #25 .35 .35
570 A108 4m Red car 4.00 4.00
Nos. 567-570 (4) 4.65 4.65

1987, May 29 *Perf. 14*

571 A109 9s Tennis .15 .15
572 A109 15s Judo .15 .15
573 A109 20s Running .20 .20
574 A109 35s Boxing .35 .35
575 A109 1m Diving 1.00 1.00
576 A109 3m Bowling 3.00 3.00
Nos. 571-576 (6) 4.85 4.85

Souvenir Sheet

577 A109 2m Tennis, diff. 2.00 2.00
577A A109 4m Soccer 4.00 4.00

See Nos. 606-611.
No. 577A shows green at lower left diagonal half of the flag.

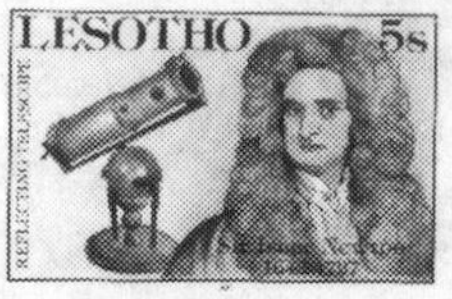

Inventors and Innovators
A110

Designs: 5s, Sir Isaac Newton, reflecting telescope. 9s, Alexander Graham Bell, telephone. 75s, Robert H. Goddard, liquid fuel rocket. 4m, Chuck Yeager (b. 1923), test pilot. No. 582, Mariner 10 spacecraft.

1987, June 30 *Perf. 15*

578 A110 5s multicolored .15 .15
579 A110 9s multicolored .15 .15
580 A110 75s multicolored .75 .75
581 A110 4m multicolored 4.00 4.00
Nos. 578-581 (4) 5.05 5.05

Souvenir Sheet

582 A110 4m multicolored 4.00 4.00

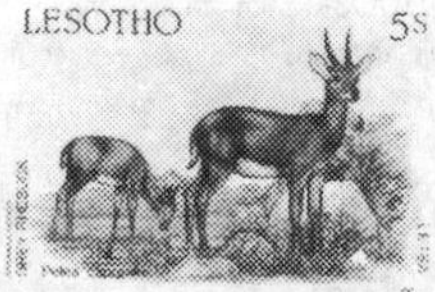

Fauna and Flora
A111

1987, Aug. 14

583 A111 5s Gray rhebuck .15 .15
584 A111 9s Cape clawless otter .15 .15
585 A111 15s Cape gray mongoose .15 .15
586 A111 20s Free state daisy .20 .20
587 A111 35s River bells .35 .35
588 A111 1m Turkey flower 1.00 1.00
589 A111 2m Sweet briar 2.00 2.00
590 A111 3m Mountain reedbuck 3.00 3.00
Nos. 583-590 (8) 7.00 7.00

Souvenir Sheet

591 A111 2m Pig-lily 2.00 2.00
592 A111 4m Cape wildebeest 4.00 4.00

Nos. 586-589 and 591 vert.

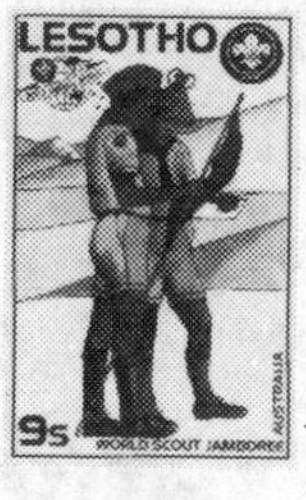

16th World Scout Jamboree, Australia, 1987-88 — A112

1987, Sept. 10 Litho. *Perf. 14*

593 A112 9s Orienteering .15 .15
594 A112 15s Playing soccer .15 .15
595 A112 35s Kangaroos .35 .35
596 A112 75s Salute, flag .75 .75
597 A112 4m Windsurfing 4.00 4.00
Nos. 593-597 (5) 5.40 5.40

Souvenir Sheet

598 A112 4m Map, flag of Australia 4.00 4.00

Nos. 324, 425, 424, 328 and 427 Surcharged

15s
═══

1987 Litho. *Perf. 14½, 14*

598A A66 9s on 5s No. 324 .15 .15
599 A66 15s on 5s No. 324 .15 .15
600 A83 15s on 5s No. 425 .15 .15
600A A83 20s on 4s No. 424 .20 .20
600B A66 35s on 25s No. 328 .35 .35
e. 35s on 25s #328, small "s"
f. 35s on 25s #328a
g. 35s on 25s #328a, small "s"
600C A66 35s on 75s #331
h. 35s on 75s #331, small "s"
600D A83 40s on 7s No. 427 .40 .40

Issue dates: Nos. 599-600, Nov. 16. No. 600B, Dec. 15. No. 598A, 600A and 600D, Dec. 30.

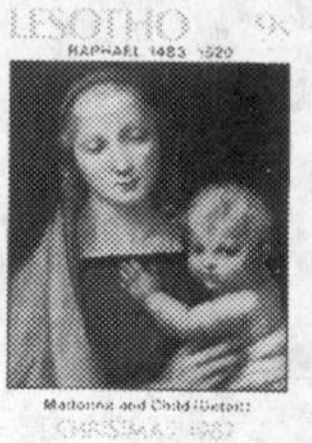

A113

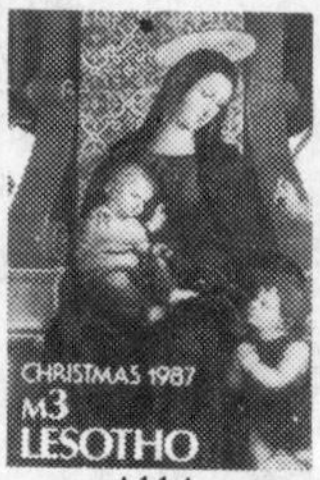

A114

Religious paintings (details) by Raphael: 9s, Madonna and Child. 15s, Marriage of the Virgin. 35s, Coronation of the Virgin. 90s, Madonna of the Chair. 3m, Madonna and Child Enthroned with Five Saints.

1987, Dec. 21 *Perf. 14*

601 A113 9s multicolored .15 .15
602 A113 15s multicolored .18 .18
603 A113 35s multicolored .40 .40
604 A113 90s multicolored 1.05 1.05
Nos. 601-604 (4) 1.78 1.78

Souvenir Sheet

605 A114 3m multicolored 3.25 3.25

Christmas.

Summer Olympics Type of 1987

1987, Nov. 30 Litho. *Perf. 14*

606 A109 5s like 9s .15 .15
607 A109 10s like 15s .15 .15
608 A109 25s like 20s .25 .25
609 A109 40s like 35s .40 .40
610 A109 50s like 1m .50 .50
611 A109 3.50m like 3m 3.50 3.50
Nos. 606-611 (6) 4.95 4.95

Souvenir Sheet

612 A109 4m Soccer 4.00 4.00

No. 612 shows green at lower right diagonal half of the flag.

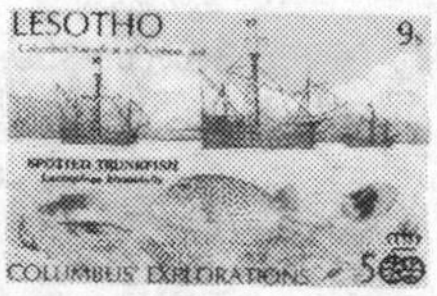

Discovery of America, 500th Anniv. (in 1992)
A115

Columbus's fleet and marine life: 9s, Spotted trunkfish. 15s, Green sea turtle. 35s, Common dolphin. 5m, White-tailed tropicbird. 4m, Ship.

1987, Dec. 14 Litho. *Perf. 14*

613 A115 9s multicolored .15 .15
614 A115 15s multicolored .15 .15
615 A115 35s multicolored .35 .35
616 A115 5m multicolored 5.00 5.00
Nos. 613-616 (4) 5.65 5.65

Souvenir Sheet

617 A115 4m multicolored 4.00 4.00

No. 559 Surcharged

1988, Feb. 2 Litho. *Perf. 14*

617A A83 3s on 9s on 30s
617B A83 7s on 9s on 30s

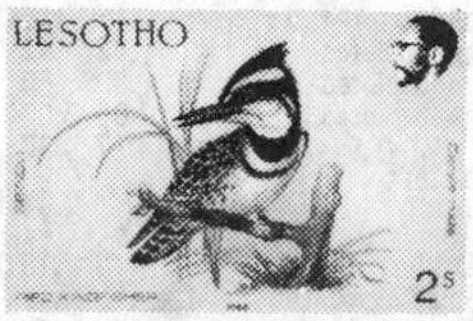

Birds
A116

1988, Apr. 5 Litho. *Perf. 15*

618 A116 2s Pied kingfisher .15 .15
619 A116 3s Three-banded plover .15 .15
620 A116 5s Spurwing goose .15 .15
621 A116 10s Clapper lark .15 .15
622 A116 12s Red-eyed bulbul .15 .15
623 A116 16s Cape weaver .16 .16
624 A116 20s Red-headed finch .20 .20
625 A116 30s Mountain chat .30 .30
626 A116 40s Stone chat .40 .40
627 A116 55s Pied barbet .55 .55
628 A116 60s Cape glossy starling .60 .60
629 A116 75s Cape sparrow .75 .75
630 A116 1m Cattle egret 1.00 1.00
631 A116 3m Giant kingfisher 3.00 3.00
632 A116 10m Crowned guinea fowl 10.00 10.00
Nos. 618-632 (15) 17.71 17.71

For surcharges see Nos. 755, 805-806.

1989, Sept. 18 *Perf. 14*

620a A116 5s multicolored .15 .15
622a A116 12s multicolored .15 .15
623a A116 16s multicolored .15 .15
624a A116 20s multicolored .16 .16
630a A116 1m multicolored .80 .80
631a A116 3m multicolored 2.40 2.40
632a A116 10m multicolored 8.00 8.00
Nos. 620a-632a (7) 11.81 11.81

Dated 1989.

1990 *Perf. 12½x12*

620b A116 5s multicolored .15 .15
622b A116 12s multicolored .15 .15
623b A116 16s multicolored .15 .15
624b A116 20s multicolored .16 .16
630b A116 1m multicolored .80 .80
631b A116 3m multicolored 2.40 2.40
632b A116 10m multicolored 8.00 8.00
Nos. 620b-632b (7) 11.81 11.81

Dated 1989.

1991 (?) *Perf. 11½x13*

620c A116 5s multicolored .15 .15
622c A116 12s multicolored .15 .15
623c A116 16s multicolored .15 .15
624c A116 20s multicolored .16 .16
630c A116 1m multicolored .80 .80
631c A116 3m multicolored 2.40 2.40
632c A116 10m multicolored 8.00 8.00
Nos. 620c-632c (7) 11.81 11.81

Dated 1989.

Nos. 531-534 Overprinted "40th WEDDING ANNIVERSARY / H.M. QUEEN ELIZABETH II / H.R.H. THE DUKE OF EDINBURGH" in Silver

1988, May 3 *Perf. 14*

636 CD339 90s lt yel bis & blk .90 .90
637 CD339 1m pale grn & multi 1.00 1.00
638 CD339 2m dull vio & multi 2.00 2.00
Nos. 636-638 (3) 3.90 3.90

Souvenir Sheet

639 CD339 4m tan & black 4.00 4.00

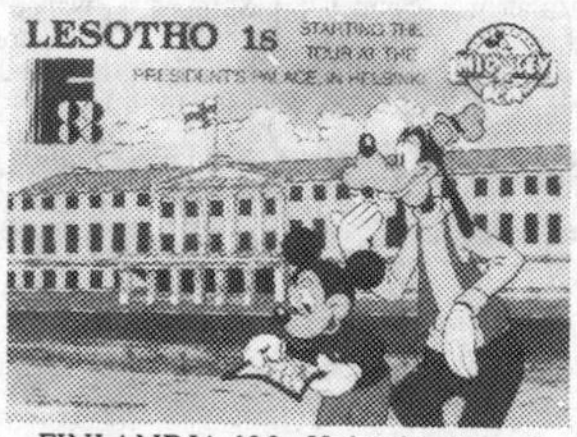

FINLANDIA '88, Helsinki, June 1-12 — A117

Disney animated characters and Helsinki sights.

1988, June 2 Litho. *Perf. 14x13½*

640 A117 1s Touring President's Palace .15 .15
641 A117 2s Sauna .15 .15
642 A117 3s Lake Country fishing .15 .15
643 A117 4s Finlandia Hall .15 .15
644 A117 5s Photographing Sibelius Monument .15 .15
645 A117 10s Pony trek, youth hostel .15 .15
646 A117 3m Olympic Stadium 2.25 2.25
647 A117 5m Santa Claus, Arctic Circle 3.50 3.50
Nos. 640-647 (8) 6.65 6.65

Souvenir Sheets

Perf. 14x13½, 13½x14

648 A117 4m Market Square 3.00 3.00
649 A117 4m Lapp encampment, vert. 3.00 3.00

Mickey Mouse, 60th anniv.

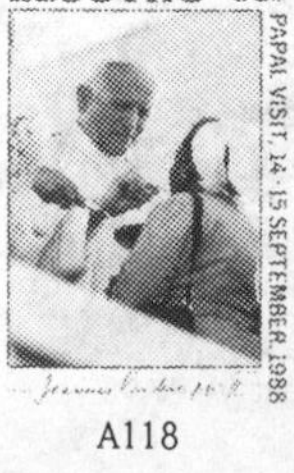

A118

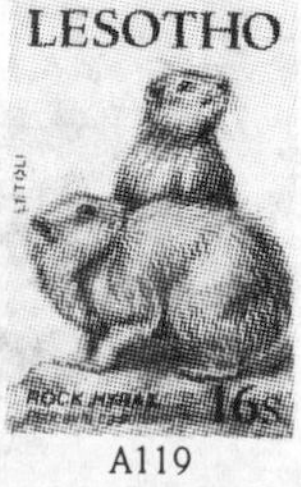

A119

1988, Sept. 1 Litho. *Perf. 14*

650 A118 55s Pope giving communion .55 .55
651 A118 2m Leading procession 2.00 2.00
652 A118 3m Walking in garden 3.00 3.00
653 A118 4m Wearing scullcap 4.00 4.00
Nos. 650-653 (4) 9.55 9.55

Souvenir Sheet

654 A118 5m Pope, Archbishop
Morapeli of Lesotho,
horiz. 5.00 5.00
Visit of Pope John Paul II, Sept. 14-16.

1988, Oct. 13   Litho.   Perf. 14
Small indigenous mammals.

655 A119 16s Rock hyrax .16 .16
656 A119 40s Honey badger .40 .40
657 A119 75s Genet .75 .75
658 A119 3m Yellow mongoose 3.00 3.00
Nos. 655-658 (4) 4.31 4.31

Souvenir Sheet

659 A119 4m Meerkat 4.00 4.00

Birth of Venus,
1480, by
Botticelli
A120 LESOTHO 15s

Paintings: 25s, View of Toledo, 1608, by El
Greco. 40s, Maids of Honor, 1656, by Diego Velazquez. 50s, The Fifer, 1866, by Manet. 55s, The
Starry Night, 1889, by Van Gogh. 75s, Prima Ballerina, 1876, by Degas. 2m, Bridge over Water Lilies,
1899, by Monet. 3m, Guernica, 1937, by Picasso.
No. 668, The Presentation of the Virgin in the
Temple, c. 1534, by Titian. No. 669, The Miracle of
the Newborn Infant, 1511, by Titian.

1988, Oct. 17   Litho.   Perf. 13¹/₂x14

660 A120 15s multicolored .15 .15
661 A120 25s multicolored .25 .25
662 A120 40s multicolored .40 .40
663 A120 50s multicolored .50 .50
664 A120 55s multicolored .55 .55
665 A120 75s multicolored .75 .75
666 A120 2m multicolored 2.00 2.00
667 A120 3m multicolored 3.00 3.00
Nos. 660-667 (8) 7.60 7.60

Souvenir Sheets

668 A120 4m multicolored 4.00 4.00
669 A120 4m multicolored 4.00 4.00

1988 Summer   Intl. Tennis
Olympics,   Federation, 75th
Seoul — A121   Anniv. — A122

1988, Nov. 11   Litho.   Perf. 14

670 A121 12s Wrestling, horiz. .15 .15
671 A121 16s Equestrian .16 .16
672 A121 55s Shooting, horiz. .55 .55
673 A121 3.50m like 16s 3.50 3.50
Nos. 670-673 (4) 4.36 4.36

Souvenir Sheet

674 A121 4m Eternal flame 4.00 4.00

1988, Nov. 18
Tennis champions, views of cities or landmarks:
12s, Yannick Noah, Eiffel Tower, horiz. 20s, Rod
Laver, Sydney Opera House and Harbor Bridge,
horiz. 30s, Ivan Lendl, Prague, horiz. 65s, Jimmy
Connors, Tokyo. 1m, Arthur Ashe, Barcelona.
1.55m, Althea Gibson, NYC. 2m, Chris Evert,
Vienna. 2.40m, Boris Becker, London. 3m, Martina
Navratilova, Golden Gate Bridge, horiz. 4m, Steffi
Graf, Berlin, West Germany.

675 A122 12s multi .15 .15
676 A122 20s multi .20 .20
677 A122 30s multi .30 .30
678 A122 65s multi .65 .65
679 A122 1m multi 1.00 1.00
680 A122 1.55m multi 1.55 1.55
681 A122 2m multi 2.00 2.00

682 A122 2.40m multi 2.40 2.40
683 A122 3m multi 3.00 3.00
Nos. 675-683 (9) 11.25 11.25

Souvenir Sheet

684 A122 4m multi 4.00 4.00
No. 676 has "Sidney" instead of "Sydney." No.
679 has "Ash" instead of "Ashe".

LESOTHO   Paintings by
12s Titian — A123

Designs: 12s, The Averoldi Polyptych. 20s, Christ
and the Adulteress (Christ). 35s, Christ and the
Adulteress (adultress). 45s, Angel of the Annunciation. 65s, Saint Dominic. 1m, The Vendramin Family. 2m, Mary Magdalen. 3m, The Tribute Money.
No. 693, Christ and the Woman Taken in Adultery.
No. 694, The Mater Dolorosa.

1988, Dec. 1   Perf. 14x13¹/₂

685 A123 12s multicolored .15 .15
686 A123 20s multicolored .20 .20
687 A123 35s multicolored .35 .35
688 A123 45s multicolored .45 .45
689 A123 65s multicolored .65 .65
690 A123 1m multicolored 1.00 1.00
691 A123 2m multicolored 2.00 2.00
692 A123 3m multicolored 3.00 3.00
Nos. 685-692 (8) 7.80 7.80

Souvenir Sheets

693 A123 5m multicolored 5.00 5.00
694 A123 5m multicolored 5.00 5.00
Birth of Titian, 500th anniv. Nos. 685-693
inscribed "Christmas 1988."

Intl. Red
Cross, 125th
Anniv.
A124

Anniv. emblem, supply and ambulance planes:
12s, Pilatus PC 6 Turbo Porter. 20s, Cessna Caravan. 55s, De Havilland DHC-6 Otter. 3m, Douglas
DC-3 in thunderstorm. 4m, Douglas DC-3, diff.

1989, Jan. 30   Litho.   Perf. 14

695 A124 12s multicolored .15 .15
696 A124 20s multicolored .20 .20
697 A124 55s multicolored .55 .55
698 A124 3m multicolored 3.00 3.00
Nos. 695-698 (4) 3.90 3.90

Souvenir Sheet

699 A124 4m multi, vert. 4.00 4.00

Landscapes by Hiroshige — A125

Designs: 12s, Dawn Mist at Mishima. 16s, Night
Snow at Kambara. 20s, Wayside Inn at Mariko Sta-
tion. 35s, Shower at Shono. 55s, Snowfall on the
Kisokaido Near Oi. 1m, Autumn Moon at Seba.
3.20m, Evening Moon at Ryogaku Bridge. 5m,
Cherry Blossoms, Arashiyama. No. 709, Listening
to the Singing Insects at Dokanyama. No. 709,
Moonlight, Nagakubo.

1989, June 19   Litho.   Perf. 14x13¹/₂

700 A125 12s multi .15 .15
701 A125 16s multi .15 .15
702 A125 20s multi .16 .16
703 A125 35s multi .28 .28
704 A125 55s multi .45 .45
705 A125 1m multi .80 .80
706 A125 3.20m multi 2.50 2.50
707 A125 5m multi 4.00 4.00
Nos. 700-707 (8) 8.49 8.49

Souvenir Sheets

708 A125 4m multi 3.60 3.60
709 A125 4m multi 3.60 3.60
Hirohito (1901-1989) and enthronement of Akihito as emperor of Japan.

PHILEXFRANCE '89, French Revolution
Bicent. — A126

Disney characters wearing insurgent uniforms.

Perf. 13¹/₂x14, 14x13¹/₂

1989, July 10

710 A126 1s General .15 .15
711 A126 2s Infantry .15 .15
712 A126 3s Grenadier .15 .15
713 A126 4s Cavalry .15 .15
714 A126 5s Hussar .15 .15
715 A126 10s Marine .15 .15
716 A126 3m Natl. guard 2.40 2.40
717 A126 5m Admiral 4.00 4.00
Nos. 710-717 (8) 7.30 7.30

Souvenir Sheets

718 A126 4m Natl. guard, royal family, horiz. 3.60 3.60
719 A126 4m La Marseillaise 3.60 3.60

LESOTHO   LESOTHO
MALOTI MOUNTAINS   12s

A127   A128

Maloti Mountains: a, Sotho thatched dwellings.
b, Two trees, cliff edge. c, Waterfall. d, Tribesman.

1989, Sept.   Litho.   Perf. 14

720 Strip of 4 3.20 3.20
a.-d. A127 1m any single .80 .80

Souvenir Sheet

721 A127 4m Flora 4.00 4.00

1989, Sept. 8   Litho.   Perf. 14
Mushrooms.

722 A128 12s Paxillus involutus .15 .15
723 A128 16s Ganoderma ap-
planatum .15 .15
723A A128 55s Suillus granulatus .44 .44
724 A128 5m Stereum hirsutum 4.00 4.00
Nos. 722-724 (4) 4.74 4.74

Souvenir Sheet

725 A128 4m Scleroderma
flavidum 3.20 3.20

MARSH SANDPIPER   Lesotho

Birds
12s   A129

1989, Oct. 23   Litho.   Perf. 14

726 A129 12s Marsh sandpipers .15 .15
727 A129 65s Little stints .52 .52
728 A129 1m Ringed plovers .80 .80
729 A129 4m Curlew sandpipers 3.20 3.20
Nos. 726-729 (4) 4.67 4.67

Souvenir Sheet

730 A129 5m Ruff, vert. 4.00 4.00

1st Moon
Landing,
20th
Anniv.
A130

Highlights of the Apollo 11 mission.

1989, Nov. 6   Perf. 14

731 A130 12s Liftoff .15 .15
732 A130 16s Eagle landing .15 .15
733 A130 40s Astronaut on ladder .32 .32
734 A130 55s Buzz Aldrin .45 .45
735 A130 1m Solar wind experiment .80 .80
736 A130 2m Eagle lifting off 1.60 1.60
737 A130 3m Columbia in orbit 2.40 2.40
738 A130 4m Splashdown 3.20 3.20
Nos. 731-738 (8) 9.07 9.07

Souvenir Sheet

739 A130 5m Astronaut, Eagle 4.00 4.00
Nos. 731, 733, 738-739 vert.

Lesotho   Postal
Marking,
England,
1680
75s   A131

Cathedral Church of Sts. Peter and Paul,
Washington, DC — A132

Designs (No. 740): b, Wax seal and feather, Germany, 1807. c, Crete #1. d, Perot postmaster's
provisional, Bermuda, 1848. e, Pony Express handstamp, US, 1860. f, Finland #1 g, Fiji #1. h, Swedish newspaper handstamp, 1823. i, Bhor #1.

1989, Nov. 17   Litho.   Perf. 14

740 Sheet of 9 3.80 3.80
a.-i. A131 75s any single .42 .42

Souvenir Sheet

741 A132 4m shown 3.00 3.00
World Stamp Expo '89.

CHRISTMAS 1989

Christmas — A133
12s
LESOTHO

Religious paintings by Velazquez: 12s, The
Immaculate Conception. 20s, St. Anthony Abbot
and St. Paul the Hermit. 35s, St. Thomas the Apostle. 55s, Christ in the House of Martha and Mary.
1m, St. John Writing the Apocalypse on Patmos.
3m, The Virgin Presenting the Chasuble to St.
Ildephonsus. 4m, The Adoration of the Magi. 5m,
The Coronation of the Virgin.

1989, Dec. 18

742 A133 12s multicolored .15 .15
743 A133 20s multicolored .16 .16
744 A133 35s multicolored .28 .28
745 A133 55s multicolored .45 .45
746 A133 1m multicolored .75 .75
747 A133 3m multicolored 2.25 2.25
748 A133 4m multicolored 3.00 3.00
Nos. 742-748 (7) 7.04 7.04

Souvenir Sheet

749 A133 5m multicolored 3.75 3.75

1990 World Cup Soccer Championships,
Italy — A134

Various athletes, emblem and name of previous
championship host nations.

1989, Dec. 27
750 A134 12s England, 1966   .15   .15
751 A134 16s Mexico, 1970   .15   .15
752 A134 55s West Germany, 1974   .45   .45
753 A134 5m Spain, 1982   3.75 3.75
    Nos. 750-753 (4)   4.50 4.50

Souvenir Sheet
754 A134 4m Diego Maradona, Ar-
          gentina   3.00 3.00

No. 622a Surcharged

1990   **Litho.**   **Perf. 14**
755 A116 16s on 12s multi   .15   .15

Orchids
A135

1990, Mar. 12   Litho.   Perf. 14
756 A135 12s Satyrium
          princeps   .15   .15
757 A135 16s Huttonaea pul-
          chra   .15   .15
758 A135 55s Herschelia
          graminifolia   .45   .45
759 A135 1m Ansellia gigantea   .80   .80
760 A135 1.55m Polystachya
          pubescens   1.25 1.25
761 A135 2.40m Penthea filicornis 1.90 1.90
762 A135 3m Disperis capensis   2.40 2.40
763 A135 4m Disa uniflora   3.20 3.20
    Nos. 756-763 (8)   10.30 10.30

Souvenir Sheet
764 A135 5m Stenoglottis
          longifolia   4.00 4.00

Expo '90.

Butterflies — A136

1990, Feb. 26   Litho.   Perf. 14
765 A136 12s Pseudo ergolid   .15   .15
766 A136 16s Painted lady   .15   .15
767 A136 55s Ringed pansy   .50   .50
768 A136 65s False acraea   .58   .58
769 A136 1m Eyed pansy   .90   .90
770 A136 2m Golden pansy   1.80 1.80
771 A136 3m African monarch   2.70 2.70
772 A136 4m African giant swal-
          lowtail   3.60 3.60
    Nos. 765-772 (8)   10.38 10.38

Souvenir Sheet
773 A136 5m Citrus swallowtail   4.50 4.50

Queen Mother, 90th Birthday
A137   A138

1990, July 5   Litho.   Perf. 14
774 A137 1.50m shown   1.20 1.20
775 A138 1.50m shown   1.20 1.20
776 A137 1.50m Young woman, diff. 1.20 1.20
    Nos. 774-776 (3)   3.60 3.60

Souvenir Sheet
777 A138 5m Like No. 775   4.00 4.00

A139   A140

Designs: 12s, King Moshoeshoe II, Prince
Mohato wearing blankets. 16s, Prince Mohato in
Seana-Marena blanket. 1m, Pope John Paul II in
Seana-Marena blanket. 3m, Basotho men on horses.
5m, Pope with blanket and hat.

1990, Aug. 17   Litho.   Perf. 14
778 A139 12s multicolored   .15   .15
779 A139 16s multicolored   .15   .15
780 A139 1m multicolored   .75   .75
781 A139 3m multicolored   2.30 2.30
    Nos. 778-781 (4)   3.35 3.35

Souvenir Sheet
782 A139 5m multi, horiz.   4.00 4.00

1990, Aug. 24
Highland Water Project: 16s, Moving gravel. 20s,
Fuel truck. 55s, Piers for bridge construction. 2m,
Road construction. 5m, Drilling blasting holes.
783 A140 16s multicolored   .15   .15
784 A140 20s multicolored   .18   .18
785 A140 55s multicolored   .48   .48
786 A140 2m multicolored   1.50 1.50
    Nos. 783-786 (4)   2.31 2.31

Souvenir Sheet
787 A140 5m multicolored   4.00 4.00

A141   A142

1990, Sept. 26   Litho.   Perf. 14
788 A141 12s Breastfeeding   .15   .15
789 A141 55s Oral rehydration   .48   .48
790 A141 1m Baby being weighed   .75   .75
    Nos. 788-790 (3)   1.38 1.38

UNICEF Save the Children campaign.

1990, Oct. 5
791 A142 16s Triple jump   .15   .15
792 A142 55s 200-meter race   .48   .48
793 A142 1m 5000-meter race   .75   .75
794 A142 4m Equestrian show jump-
          ing   3.00 3.00
    Nos. 791-794 (4)   4.38 4.38

Souvenir Sheet
795 A142 5m Lighting Olympic
          flame   3.75 3.75

1992 Summer Olympics, Barcelona.

Christmas
A143

Different details from paintings by Rubens: 12s,
1m, 3m, Virgin and Child. 16s, 80s, 2m, 4m, Adoration of the Magi. 55s, Head of One of the Three
Kings, diff. 5m, Assumption of the Virgin.

1990, Dec. 5   Litho.   Perf. 13½x14
796 A143 12s multicolored   .15   .15
797 A143 16s multicolored   .15   .15
798 A143 55s multicolored   .40   .40
799 A143 80s multicolored   .60   .60
800 A143 1m multicolored   .75   .75
801 A143 2m multicolored   1.50 1.50
802 A143 3m multicolored   2.25 2.25
803 A143 4m multicolored   3.00 3.00
    Nos. 796-803 (8)   8.80 8.80

Souvenir Sheet
804 A143 5m multicolored   3.75 3.75

Nos. 625-626 Surcharged   **16 s**

1991, Jan. 18   Litho.   Perf. 15
805 A116 16s on 30s #625   .15   .15
806 A116 16s on 40s #626   .15   .15
    Set value   .24   .24

Phila Nippon '91 — A144

Walt Disney characters visit Japan: 20s, Mickey
at Nagasaki Peace Park. 30s, Mickey at Kamakura
Beach. 40s, Mickey, Donald entertain at Bunraku
Puppet Theater. 50s, Mickey, Donald eat soba at
noodle shop. 75s, Minnie, Mickey at tea house.
1m, Mickey, Bullet Train. 3m, Mickey, deer at
Todaiji Temple. 4m, Mickey, Minnie before Imperial Palace. No. 815, Mickey skiing at Happo-One,
Nagano. No. 816, Mickey, Minnie at Suizenji Park.

1991, June 10   Litho.   Perf. 14x13½
807 A144 20s multicolored   .16   .16
808 A144 30s multicolored   .24   .24
809 A144 40s multicolored   .32   .32
810 A144 50s multicolored   .40   .40
811 A144 75s multicolored   .60   .60
812 A144 1m multicolored   .80   .80
813 A144 3m multicolored   2.40 2.40
814 A144 4m multicolored   3.20 3.20
    Nos. 807-814 (8)   8.12 8.12

Souvenir Sheets
815 A144 6m multicolored   3.50 3.50
816 A144 6m multicolored   3.50 3.50

Entertainers in Films
About Africa — A145

Designs: 12s, Stewart Granger, King Solomon's
Mines. 16s, Johnny Weissmuller, Tarzan, the Ape
Man. 30s, Clark Gable, Grace Kelly, Mogambo.
55s, Sigourney Weaver, Gorillas in the Mist. 70s,
Humphrey Bogart, Katharine Hepburn, The African
Queen. 1m, John Wayne, Hatari. 2m, Meryl Streep,
Out of Africa. 4m, Eddie Murphy, Arsenio Hall,
Coming to America. 5m, Elsa, Born Free.

1991, June 20   Litho.   Perf. 14
817 A145 12s multicolored   .15   .15
818 A145 16s multicolored   .15   .15
819 A145 30s multicolored   .24   .24
820 A145 55s multicolored   .45   .45
821 A145 70s multicolored   .55   .55
822 A145 1m multicolored   .80   .80
823 A145 2m multicolored   1.60 1.60
824 A145 4m multicolored   3.20 3.20
    Nos. 817-824 (8)   7.14 7.14

Souvenir Sheet
825 A145 5m multicolored   4.00 4.00

Butterflies
A146

1991, Aug. 1   Litho.   Perf. 13½
827 A146 2s Satyrus aello   .15   .15
828 A146 3s Erebia medusa   .15   .15
829 A146 5s Melanargia
          galathea   .15   .15
830 A146 10s Erebia aethiops   .15   .15
831 A146 20s Coenonympha
          pamphilus   .16   .16
832 A146 25s Pyrameis atalanta   .20   .20
833 A146 30s Charaxes jasius   .24   .24
834 A146 40s Colias palaeno   .32   .32
835 A146 50s Colias cliopatra   .40   .40
836 A146 60s Colias philodice   .48   .48
837 A146 70s Rhumni gonepter-
          ix   .56   .56
838 A146 1m Colias caesonia   .80   .80
839 A146 2m Pyrameis cardui   1.60 1.60
840 A146 3m Danaus chrysip-
          pus   2.40 2.40
840A A146 10m Apatura iris   8.00 8.00
    Nos. 827-840A (15)   15.76 15.76

Exist dated 1992.

SADCC,
10th Anniv.
A147

Tourism: 12s, Wattled cranes. 16s, Butterfly,
flowers in national parks. 25s, Tourist bus and
Mukurub, the Finger of God. 3m, People in traditional dress.

1991, Oct. 10   Litho.   Perf. 14x13½
841 A147 12s multicolored   .15   .15
842 A147 16s multicolored   .15   .15
843 A147 25s multicolored   .20   .20
    Nos. 841-843 (3)   .50   .50

Souvenir Sheet
844 A147 3m multicolored   2.40 2.40

Say No to
Drugs
A148

1991, Oct. 10
845 A148 16s multicolored   .15   .15

Charles de Gaulle,
Birth Cent. — A149

DeGaulle: 40s, Wearing brigadier general's kepi.
50s, Facing left. 60s, Facing right. 4m, In later
years.

1991, Dec. 6   Litho.   Perf. 14
846 A149 20s black & brown   .16   .16
847 A149 40s black & violet   .32   .32
848 A149 50s black & olilve   .40   .40
849 A149 60s black & dk blue   .48   .48
850 A149 4m black & brn org   3.15 3.15
    Nos. 846-850 (5)   4.51 4.51

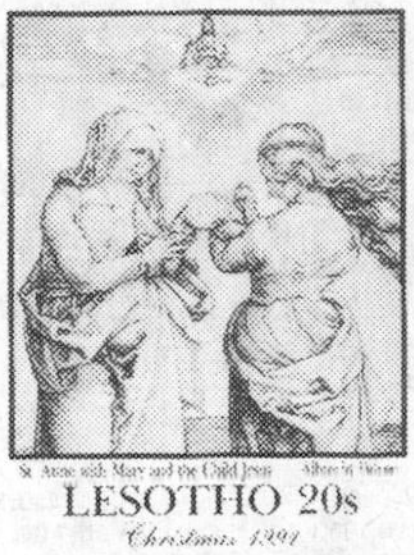
LESOTHO 20s
Christmas 1991

Christmas A150

Engravings by Albrecht Durer: 20s, St. Anne with Mary and the Child Jesus. 30s, Mary on the Grass Bench. 50s, Mary with the Crown of Stars. 60s, Mary with Child beside a Tree. 70s, Mary with Child beside the Wall. 1m, Mary in a Halo on the Crescent Moon. 2m, Mary Breastfeeding Her Child. 4m, Mary with the Infant in Swaddling Clothes. No. 859, Holy Family with the Dragonfly. No. 860, The Birth of Christ.

1991, Dec. 13 Litho. *Perf. 12*

851	A150	20s rose & black	.16	.16
852	A150	30s blue & black	.24	.24
853	A150	50s green & black	.40	.40
854	A150	60s red & black	.48	.48
855	A150	70s yellow & black	.55	.55
856	A150	1m yel org & black	.80	.80
857	A150	2m violet & black	1.60	1.60
858	A150	4m dk blue & black	3.20	3.20
		Nos. 851-858 (8)	7.43	7.43

Souvenir Sheets

Perf. 14½

859	A150	5m blue & black	4.00	4.00
860	A150	5m pink & black	4.00	4.00

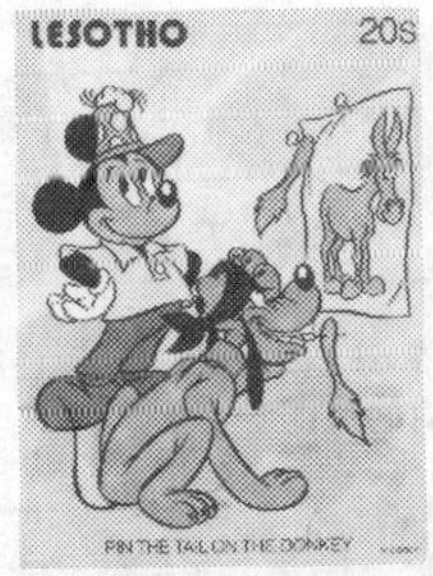
LESOTHO 20s
PIN THE TAIL ON THE DONKEY

Games A151

Walt Disney characters playing games: 20s, Mickey, Pluto playing pin the tail on the donkey. 30s, Mickey enjoying board game, Mancala. 40s, Mickey hoop rolling. 50s, Minnie with hula hoops. 70s, Mickey throwing Frisbee to Pluto. 1m, Donald trying to play Diabolo. 2m, Huey, Dewey and Louie playing marbles. 3m, Donald frustrated by Rubik's cube. No. 869, Donald and Mickey's nephews in tug-of-war. No. 870, Mickey, Donald stick fighting.

1991, Dec. 16 *Perf. 13½x14*

861	A151	20s multicolored	.16	.16
862	A151	30s multicolored	.24	.24
863	A151	40s multicolored	.32	.32
864	A151	50s multicolored	.40	.40
865	A151	70s multicolored	.55	.55
866	A151	1m multicolored	.80	.80
867	A151	2m multicolored	1.60	1.60
868	A151	3m multicolored	2.40	2.40
		Nos. 861-868 (8)	6.47	6.47

Souvenir Sheets

869	A151	5m multicolored	4.00	4.00
870	A151	5m multicolored	4.00	4.00

Royal Family Birthday, Anniversary

Common Design Type

1991, Dec. 9 Litho. *Perf. 14*

871	CD347	50s multicolored	.40	.40
872	CD347	70s multicolored	.55	.55
873	CD347	1m multicolored	.80	.80
874	CD347	3m multicolored	2.40	2.40
		Nos. 871-874 (4)	4.15	4.15

Souvenir Sheet

875	CD347	4m Charles, Diana, sons	3.20	3.20

Charles and Diana, 10th wedding anniversary. Numbers have been reserved for additional values in this set.

Queen Elizabeth II's Accession to the Throne, 40th Anniv.

Common Design Type

1992, Feb. 6 Litho. *Perf. 14*

881	CD348	20s multicolored	.16	.16
882	CD348	30s multicolored	.24	.24
883	CD348	1m multicolored	.80	.80
884	CD348	4m multicolored	3.20	3.20
		Nos. 881-884 (4)	4.40	4.40

Souvenir Sheet

885	CD348	5m multicolored	4.00	4.00

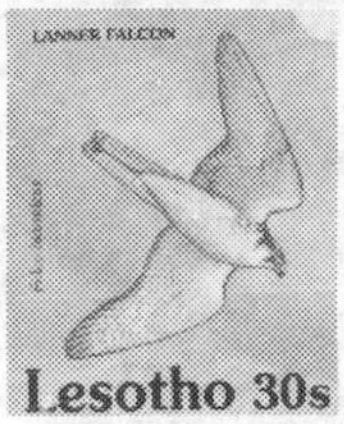
LANNER FALCON
Lesotho 30s

Birds — A152

Designs: a, Lanner falcon. b, Bataleur. c, Red-headed finch. d, Lesser-striped swallow. e, Alpine swift. f, Diederik cuckoo. g, Malachite sunbird. h, Crimson-breasted shrike. i, Pin-tailed whydah. j, Lilac-breasted roller. k, Black korhaan. l, Black-collared barbet. m, Secretary bird. n, Red-billed quelea. o, Red bishop. p, Ring-necked dove. q, Yellow canary. r, Orange-throated longclaw. s, Blue waxbill. t, Golden bishop.

1992, Feb. 10 *Perf. 14½*

886	A152	30s Sheet of 20, #a.-t.	4.80	4.80

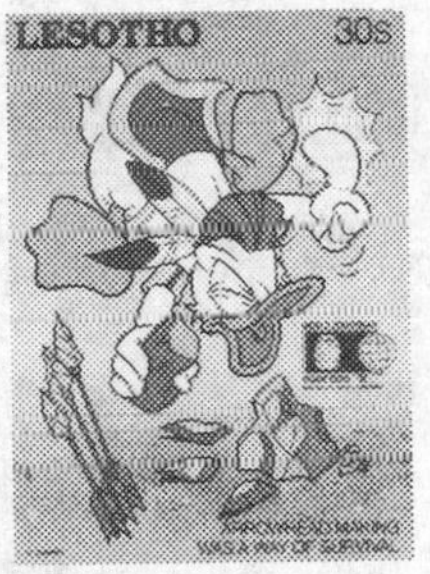
LESOTHO 30s

World Columbian Stamp Expo '92, Chicago A153

Walt Disney characters depicting native Americans: 30s, Donald Duck making arrowheads. 40s, Goofy playing lacrosse. 1m, Mickey, Donald planting corn. 3m, Minnie Mouse mastering art of beading. No. 891, Mickey as "Blackhawk" hunting for moose.

1992, Apr. Litho. *Perf. 13½x14*

887	A153	30s multicolored	.25	.25
888	A153	40s multicolored	.32	.32
889	A153	1m multicolored	.78	.78
890	A153	3m multicolored	2.35	2.35
		Nos. 887-890 (4)	3.70	3.70

Souvenir Sheet

891	A153	5m multicolored	3.90	3.90

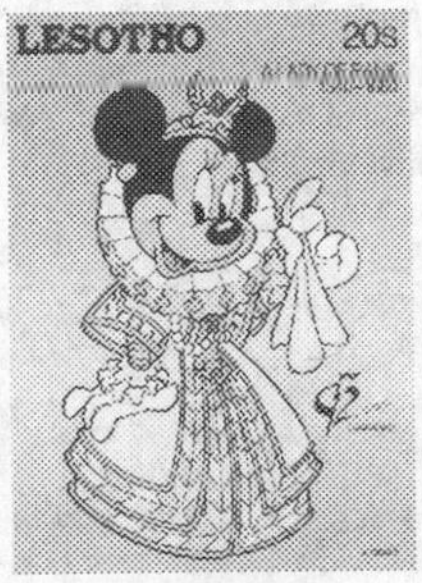
LESOTHO 20s

Granada '92 — A154

Walt Disney characters in Spanish costumes: 20s, Minnie Mouse as Lady of Rank, 1540-1660. 50s, Mickey as conqueror of Lepanto, 1571. 70s, Donald Duck from Galicia, 1880. 2m, Daisy Duck from Aragon, 1880. No. 901, Goofy as bullfighter.

1992, Apr. 13 Litho. *Perf. 13½x14*

897	A154	20s multicolored	.15	.15
898	A154	50s multicolored	.40	.40
899	A154	70s multicolored	.55	.55
900	A154	2m multicolored	1.60	1.60
		Nos. 897-900 (4)	2.70	2.70

Souvenir Sheet

901	A154	5m multicolored	3.90	3.90

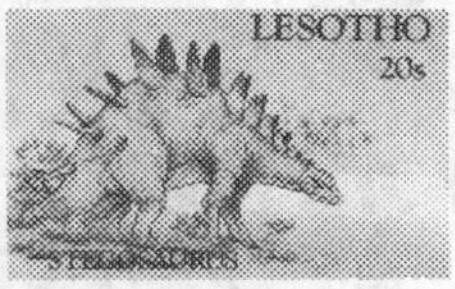
LESOTHO
20s

Dinosaurs A155

1992, June 9 *Perf. 14*

907	A155	20s Stegosaurus	.15	.15
908	A155	30s Ceratosaurus	.25	.25
909	A155	40s Procompsognathus	.32	.32
910	A155	50s Lesothosaurus	.40	.40
911	A155	70s Plateosaurus	.55	.55
912	A155	1m Gasosaurus	.80	.80
913	A155	2m Massospondylus	1.60	1.60
914	A155	3m Archaeopteryx	2.40	2.40
		Nos. 907-914 (8)	6.47	6.47

Souvenir Sheet

915	A155	5m Archaeopteryx, diff.	4.00	4.00
916	A155	5m Lesothosaurus, diff.	4.00	4.00

No. 915 printed in continuous design.

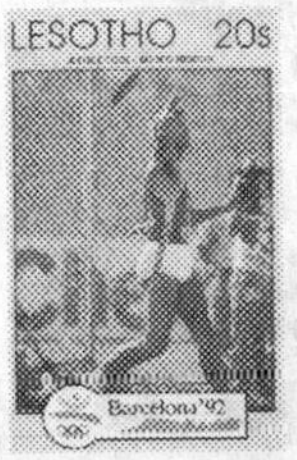
LESOTHO 20s
Barcelona '92

1992 Olympics, Barcelona and Albertville — A156

Designs: 20s, Discus. 30s, Long jump. 40s, Women's 4x100-meter relay. 70s, Women's 100-meter dash. 1m, Parallel bars. 2m, Two-man luge, horiz. 3m, Women's cross-country skiing, horiz. 4m, Biathlon. No. 925, Ice hockey, horiz. No. 926, Women's figure skating.

1992, Aug. 5 Litho. *Perf. 14*

917	A156	20s multicolored	.15	.15
918	A156	30s multicolored	.25	.25
919	A156	40s multicolored	.32	.32
920	A156	70s multicolored	.55	.55
921	A156	1m multicolored	.78	.78
922	A156	2m multicolored	1.55	1.55
923	A156	3m multicolored	2.40	2.40
924	A156	4m multicolored	3.20	3.20
		Nos. 917-924 (8)	9.20	9.20

Souvenir Sheet

925	A156	5m multicolored	4.00	4.00
926	A156	5m multicolored	4.00	4.00

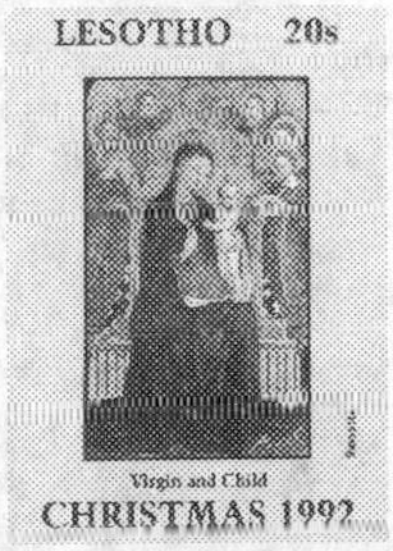
LESOTHO 20s
Virgin and Child
CHRISTMAS 1992

Christmas A158

Details or entire paintings: 20s, Virgin and Child, by Sassetta. 30s, Coronation of the Virgin, by Master of Bonastre. 40s, Virgin and Child, by Master of Saints Cosmas and Damian. 70s, The Virgin of Great Panagia, by Russian School, 12th cent. 1m, Madonna and Child, by Vincenzo Foppa. 2m, Madonna and Child, by School of Lippo Memmi. 3m, Virgin and Child, by Barnaba da Modena. 4m, Virgin and Child, by Simone Dei Crocifissi. No. 935, Virgin & Child Enthroned & Surrounded by Angels, by Cimabue. No. 936, Virgin and Child with Saints (entire triptych), by Dei Crocifissi.

1992, Nov. 2 Litho. *Perf. 13½x14*

927	A158	20s multicolored	.15	.15
928	A158	30s multicolored	.24	.24
929	A158	40s multicolored	.32	.32
930	A158	70s multicolored	.55	.55
931	A158	1m multicolored	.80	.80
932	A158	2m multicolored	1.60	1.60
933	A158	3m multicolored	2.40	2.40
934	A158	4m multicolored	3.20	3.20
		Nos. 927-934 (8)	9.26	9.26

Souvenir Sheets

935	A158	5m multicolored	4.00	4.00
936	A158	5m multicolored	4.00	4.00

Souvenir Sheet

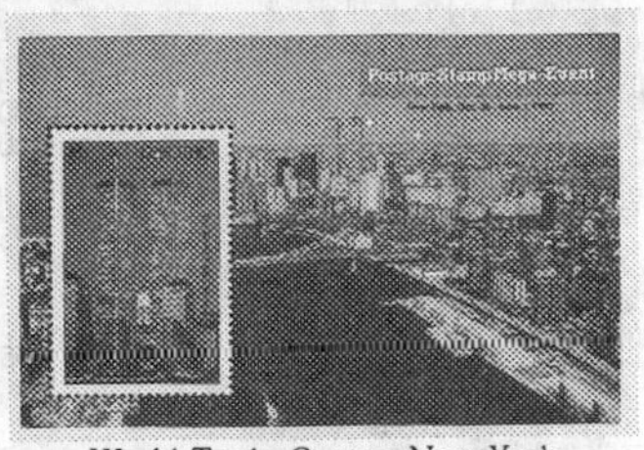

World Trade Center, New York City — A159

1992, Oct. 28 Litho. *Perf. 14*

937	A159	5m multicolored	4.00	4.00

Postage Stamp Mega Event '92, New York City.

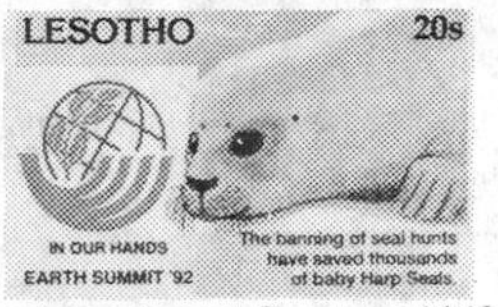
LESOTHO 20s
IN OUR HANDS
EARTH SUMMIT '92
The banning of seal hunts have saved thousands of baby Harp Seals.

Anniversaries and Events — A160

Designs: 20s, Baby harp seal. 30s, Giant panda. 40s, Graf Zeppelin, globe. 70s, Woman grinding corn. 4m, Zeppelin shot down over Cuffley, UK by Lt. Leefe Robinson flying BE 2c, WWI. No. 943, Valentina Tereshkova, first woman in space. No. 944, West African crowned cranes. No. 945, Dr. Ronald McNair.

1993, Jan. Litho. *Perf. 14*

938	A160	20s multicolored	.20	.20
939	A160	30s multicolored	.24	.24
940	A160	40s multicolored	.32	.32
941	A160	70s multicolored	.55	.55
942	A160	4m multicolored	3.20	3.20
943	A160	5m multicolored	4.00	4.00
		Nos. 938-943 (6)	8.51	8.51

Souvenir Sheets

944	A160	5m multicolored	4.00	4.00
945	A160	5m multicolored	4.00	4.00

Earth Summit, Rio de Janeiro (#938-939, 944). Count Zeppelin, 75th death anniv. (#940, 942). Intl. Conference on Nutrition, Rome (#941). Intl. Space Year (#943, 945).

A number has been reserved for an additional value in this set.

Miniature Sheet of 8

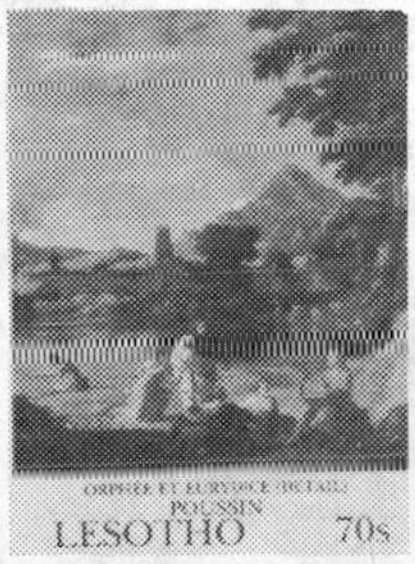
LESOTHO 70s

Louvre Museum, Bicent. A161

Details or entire paintings, by Nicolas Poussin: No. 947a, Orpheus and Eurydice. b-c, Rape of the Sabine Women (left, right). d-e, The Death of Sapphira (left, right). f-g, Echo and Narcissus (left, right). h, Self-portrait.

No. 948, The Moneychanger and His Wife, by Quentin Metsys.

1993, Mar. 19 Litho. *Perf. 12*

947	A161	70s #a.-h. + label	4.50	4.50

Souvenir Sheet

Perf. 14½

948	A161	5m multicolored	4.00	4.00

No. 948 contains one 55x88mm stamp.

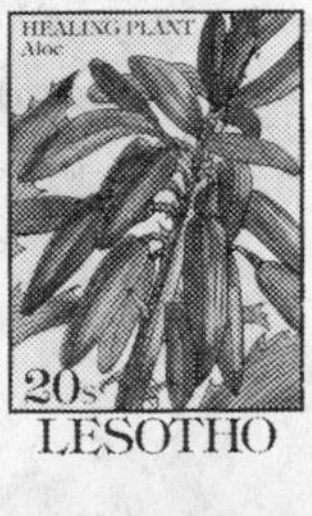
HEALING PLANT
Aloe
20s
LESOTHO

Flowers — A162

1993, June **Litho.** ***Perf. 14***

949 A162 20s Healing plant .15 .15
950 A162 30s Calla lily .25 .25
951 A162 40s Bird of Paradise .32 .32
952 A162 70s Belladonna .58 .58
953 A162 1m African lily .80 .80
954 A162 2m Veldt lily 1.60 1.60
955 A162 4m Watsonia 3.25 3.25
956 A162 5m Gazania 4.00 4.00
Nos. 949-956 (8) 10.95 10.95

Souvenir Sheets

957 A162 7m Leadwort 5.75 5.75
958 A162 7m Desert rose 5.75 5.75

Miniature Sheet

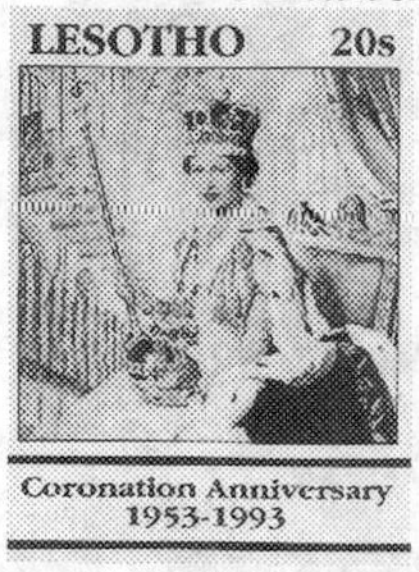

Coronation of Queen Elizabeth II, 40th Anniv. — A163

Designs: a, 20s, Official coronation photograph. b, 40s, St. Edward's Crown, Scepter with the Cross. c, 1m, Queen Mother. d, 5m, Queen, family.
7m, Conversation Piece at Royal Lodge, Windsor, by Sir James Gunn, 1950.

1993, June 2 **Litho.** ***Perf. 13¹/₂x14***

959 A163 Sheet, 2 each, #a.-d. 10.50 10.50

Souvenir Sheet

Perf. 14

960 A163 7m multicolored 5.50 5.50

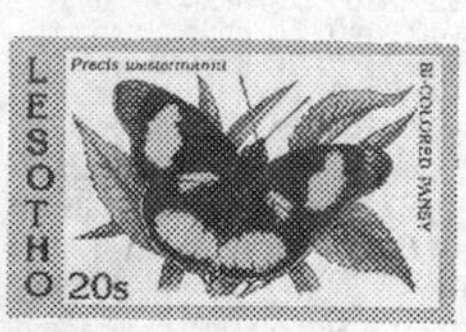

Butterflies A164

1993, June 30 **Litho.** ***Perf. 14***

961 A164 20s Bi-colored pansy .16 .16
962 A164 40s Golden pansy .35 .35
963 A164 70s Yellow pansy .55 .55
964 A164 1m Pseudo ergolid .80 .80
965 A164 2m African giant swallowtail 1.65 1.65
966 A164 5m False acraea 4.00 4.00
Nos. 961-966 (6) 7.51 7.51

Souvenir Sheets

967 A164 7m Seasonal pansy 5.75 5.75
968 A164 7m Ringed pansy 5.75 5.75

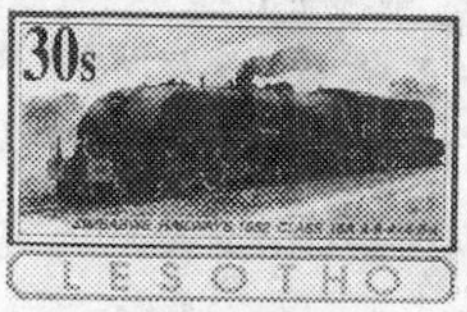

African Trains A165

Designs: 20s, East African Railways Vulcan 2-8-2, 1929. 30s, Zimbabwe Railways Class 15A, 1952. 40s, South African Railways Class 25 4-8-4, 1953. 70s, East African Railways A58 Class Garratt. 1m, South Africa Class 9E Electric. 2m, East African Railways Class 87, 1971. 3m, East African Railways Class 92, 1971. 5m, South Africa Class 26 2-D-2, 1982. No. 977, Algeria 231-132BT Class, 1937. No. 978, South African Railway Class 6E Bo-Bo, 1969.

1993, Sept. 24 **Litho.** ***Perf. 14***

969 A165 20s multicolored .15 .15
970 A165 30s multicolored .25 .25
971 A165 40s multicolored .32 .32
972 A165 70s multicolored .58 .58
973 A165 1m multicolored .80 .80
974 A165 2m multicolored 1.65 1.65
975 A165 3m multicolored 2.50 2.50
976 A165 5m multicolored 4.00 4.00
Nos. 969-976 (8) 10.25 10.25

Souvenir Sheets

977 A165 7m multicolored 5.75 5.75
978 A165 7m multicolored 5.75 5.75

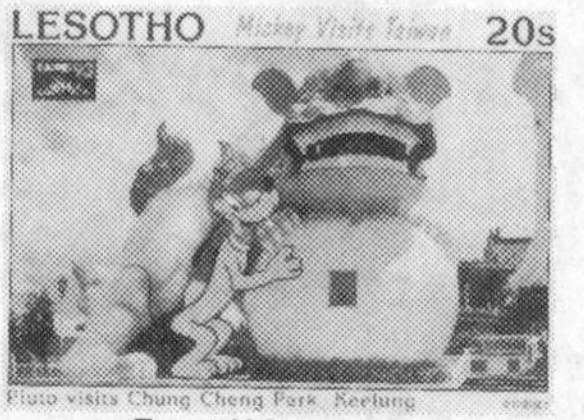

Taipei '93 — A166

Disney characters in Taiwan: 20s, Chung Cheng Park, Keelung. 30s, Chiao-Tienkung Temple Festival. 40s, Procession. 70s, Temple Festival. 1m, Queen's Head Rock Formation, Yehliu, vert. 1.20m, Natl. Concert Hall, Taiwan, vert. 2m, C.K.S. Memorial Hall, Taiwan, vert. 2.50m, Grand Hotel, Taipei.
#987, 6m, Natl. Palace Museum, Taipei. #988, 6m, Presidential Palace Museum, Taipei, vert.

1993 **Litho.** ***Perf. 14x13¹/₂, 13¹/₂x14***

979-986 A166 Set of 10 6.00 6.00

Souvenir Sheets

987-988 A166 6m Set of 2 7.00 7.00

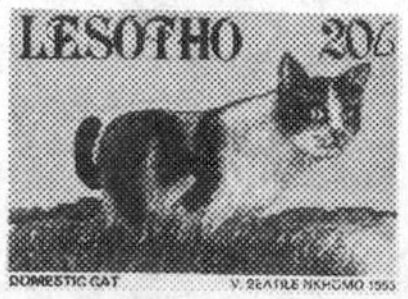

Domestic Cats — A167

Various cats: 20s, 30s, 70s, 5m.
No. 992A, Brown cat eating mouse, vert.

1993, Oct. 29 **Litho.** ***Perf. 14***

989-992 A167 Set of 4 4.75 4.75

Souvenir Sheet

992A A167 5m multicolored 3.50 3.50

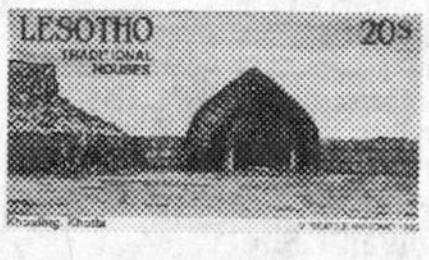

Traditional Houses A168

Designs: 20s, Khoaling, Khotla. 30s, Lelapa le seotloana morao ho, 1833. 70s, Thakaneng, Baroetsana. 4m, Mohlongoafatse pele ho, 1833.
No. 996A, Lelapa litema le mekhabiso.

1993, Sept. 24

993-996 A168 Set of 4 4.25 4.25

Souvenir Sheet

996A A168 4m multicolored 2.75 2.75

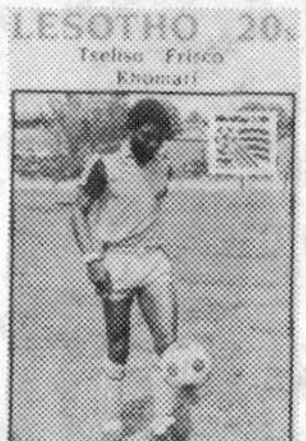

A169

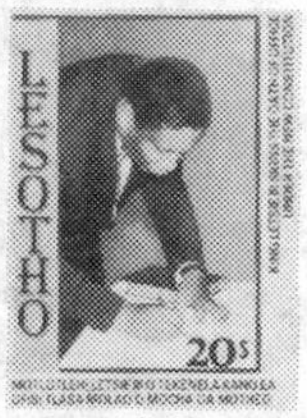

A170

Players, country: 20s, Khomari, Lesotho. 30s, Mohale, Lesotho. 40s, Davor, Yugoslavia; Rincon, Colombia. 50s, Lekhotla, Lesotho. 70s, Khali, Lesotho. 1m, Milla, Cameroun. 1.20m, Platt, England. 2m, Rummenigge, Germany; Lerby, Denmark.
No. 1005, Stejskal & Hasek, Czechoslovakia; Baresi, Italy, horiz. No. 1006, Lindenberger, Czechoslovakia; Schillaci, Italy.

1993 **Litho.** ***Perf. 13¹/₂x14***

997-1004 A169 Set of 8 5.00 5.00

Souvenir Sheets

Perf. 13

1005-1006 A169 6m Set of 2 10.00 10.00

1994 World Cup Soccer Championships, US.

1994, Apr. 2 **Litho.** ***Perf. 14***

New Democratic Government: 20s, King Letsie III signs oath of office under new constitution. 30s, Parliament building. 50s, Dr. Ntsu Mokhehle sworn in as prime minister. 70s, Transfer of power from Major Gen. P. Ramaema to Dr. Mokhehle.

30s, 50s, 70s are horizontal.

1007 A170 20s multicolored .15 .15
1008 A170 30s multicolored .25 .25
1009 A170 50s multicolored .40 .40
1010 A170 70s multicolored .58 .58
Nos. 1007-1010 (4) 1.38 1.38

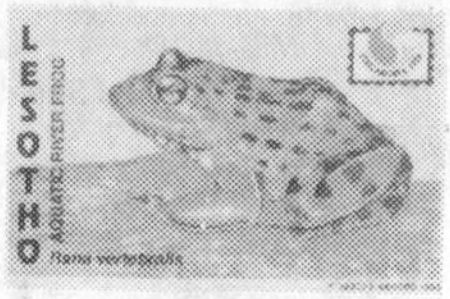

A171

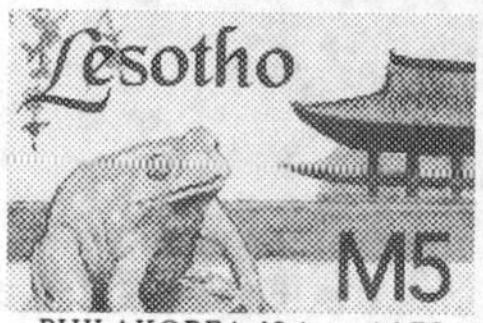

PHILAKOREA '94 — A172

Frogs: 35c, Aquatic river. 50c, Bubbling kassina. $1, Guttural toad. $1.50, Common river.
No. 1015, Green frog statue. No. 1016, Black spotted frog, oriental white-eye bird, vert.

1994, Aug. 16 **Litho.** ***Perf. 14***

1011-1014 A171 Set of 4 2.50 2.50

Souvenir Sheets

1015-1016 A172 5m each 3.50 3.50

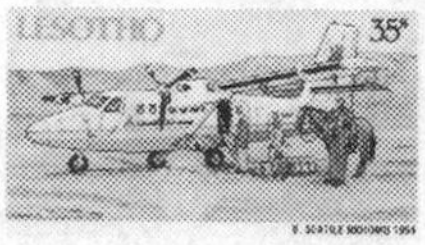

ICAO, 50th Anniv. A173

Designs: 35s, Airplane, passengers on ground. 50s, Airplane, control tower. 1m, Airplane banking, terminal, control tower. 1.50m, Airplane ascending.

1994 **Litho.** ***Perf. 14***

1017 A173 35s multicolored .20 .20
1018 A173 50s multicolored .30 .30
1019 A173 1m multicolored .60 .60
1020 A173 1.50m multicolored .90 .90
Nos. 1017-1020 (4) 2.00 2.00

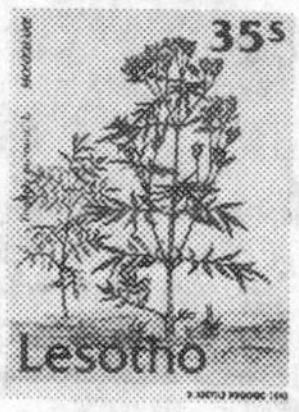

Medicinal Plants — A174

Designs: 35s, Tagetes minuta. 50s, Plantago lanceolata. 1m, Amaranthus spinosus. 1.50m, Taraxacum officinale.
5m, Datura stramonium.

1995, May 22 **Litho.** ***Perf. 14***

1021-1024 A174 Set of 4 2.00 2.00

Souvenir Sheet

1025 A174 5m multicolored 3.00 3.00

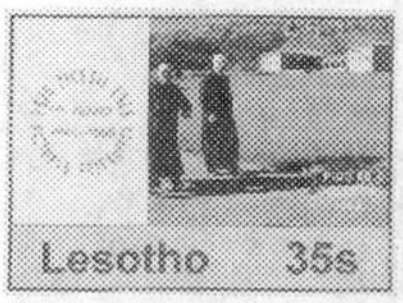

Pius XII Natl. University, 50th Anniv. — A175

Designs: 35s, Pius XII College, 1962. 50s, Univ. of Basutoland, Bechuanaland Protectorate & Swaziland, 1965. 70s, Univ. of Botswana, Lesotho & Swaziland, 1970. 1m, Univ. of Bostswana, Lesotho & Swaziland, 1975. 1.50m, Natl. Univ. of Lesotho, 1988. 2m, Natl. Univ. of Lesotho, procession of vice-chancellors at celebration.

1995, July 26 **Litho.** ***Perf. 14***

1026-1031 A175 Set of 6 3.75 3.75

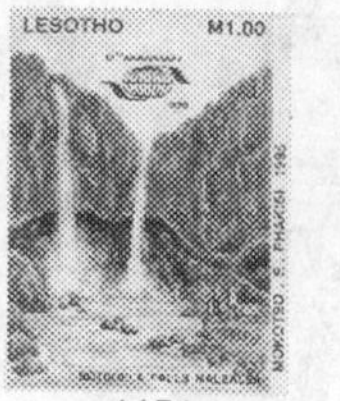

A176

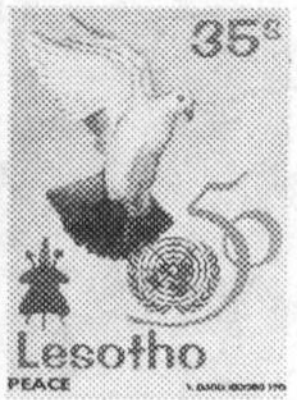

A177

Designs: 35s, Qiloane Pinnacle, Thaba-Bosiu, horiz. 50s, Rock Formation, Ha Mohalenyane, horiz. 1m, Botsoela Falls, Malealea. 1.50m, Backpacking, Makhaleng River Gorge, horiz.
4m, Red hot porkers.

1995, Aug. 28 **Litho.** ***Perf. 14***

1032-1035 A176 Set of 4 2.00 2.00

Souvenir Sheet

1036 A176 4m multicolored 2.50 2.50

No. 1036 contains one 38x58mm stamp.
World Tourism Organization, 20th anniv.

1995, Sept. 26

UN emblem and: 35s, Peace dove. 50s, Scales of justice. 1.50m, Handshake of reconciliation, horiz.

1037-1039 A177 Set of 3 1.40 1.40

UN, 50th anniv.

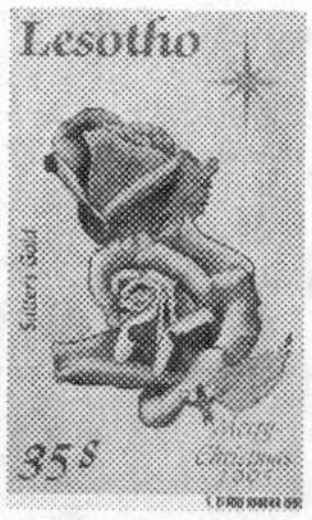

Christmas — A178

Roses: 35s, Sutter's Gold. 50s, Michele Meilland. 1m, J. Otto Thilow. 2m, Papa Meilland.

1995, Nov. 1 **Litho.** ***Perf. 14***

1040-1043 A178 Set of 4 2.30 2.30

POSTAGE DUE STAMPS

Basutoland Nos. J9-J10 Overprinted: "LESOTHO"

Wmk. 314

1966, Nov. 1 **Typo.** ***Perf. 14***

J1 D2 1c carmine .20 .25
  a. "Lseotho" 50.00
J2 D2 5c dark purple .75 .60
  a. "Lseotho" 85.00

D1

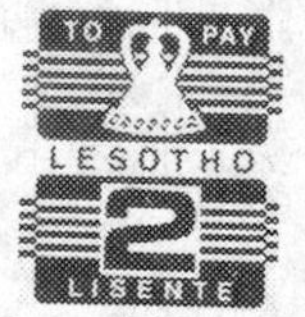

D2

Perf. 13¹/₂

1967, Apr. 1 **Unwmk.** **Litho.**

J3 D1 1c dark blue .15 .15
J4 D1 2c dull rose .24 .28
J5 D1 5c emerald .60 .70
Nos. J3-J5 (3) .99 1.13

1976, Nov. 30 **Wmk. 362**

J7 D1 2c dull rose .15 .15
J8 D1 5c emerald .20 .20
Set value .30 .30

1986 **Litho.** ***Perf. 13x13¹/₂***

J9 D2 2s green .15 .15
J10 D2 5s blue .15 .15
J11 D2 25s purple .20 .20
Set value .28 .28

This is an expanding set. Numbers will change if necessary.

MADAGASCAR

ˌma–də–ˈgas–kər

British Consular Mail

Postage stamps issued by the British Consulate in Madagascar were in use for a short period until the British relinquished all claims to this territory in favor of France in return for which France recognized Great Britain's claims in Zanzibar.

12 Pence = 1 Shilling

> British Consular Mail stamps of Madagascar were gummed only in one corner. Unused values are for stamps without gum. Examples having the original corner gum will command higher prices. Most used examples of these stamps have small faults and values are for stamps in this condition. Used stamps without faults are scarce and are worth more. Used stamps are valued with the commonly used crayon or pen cancellations.

"B C M" and Arms — A1

Handstamped "British Vice-Consulate"

1884　Unwmk.　Typo.　Rouletted
Black Seal Handstamped

1	A1	1p violet	425.	325.
b.		Seal omitted	3,000.	2,500.
2	A1	2p violet	275.	225.
3	A1	3p violet	275.	225.
4	A1	4p violet 1 oz.	2,250.	1,900.
a.		"1 oz." corrected to "4 oz." in mss.	650.	575.
b.		Seal omitted	3,000.	2,500.
5	A1	6p violet	450.	400.
6	A1	1sh violet	400.	400.
7	A1	1sh6p violet	400.	400.
8	A1	2sh violet	600.	600.
9	A1	1p on 1sh vio		
10	A1	4½ on 1sh vio		
11	A1	6p red	550.	425.

1886
Violet Seal Handstamped

12	A1	4p violet	1,200.	—
13	A1	6p violet	1,600.	—

Handstamped "British Consular Mail" as on A3
Black Seal Handstamped

14	A1	4p violet	1,750.	1,750.

Violet Seal Handstamped

15	A1	4p violet	2,750.	2,750.

The 1, 2, 3 and 4 pence are inscribed "POSTAL PACKET," the other values of the series are inscribed "LETTER."

> *Madagascar stamps can be mounted in the Scott British Africa album.*

"British Vice-Consulate" — A2

Three types of A2 and A3:
I - "POSTAGE" 29½mm. Periods after "POSTAGE" and value.
II - "POSTAGE" 29½mm. No periods.
III - "POSTAGE" 24½mm. Period after value.

1886
Violet Seal Handstamped

16	A2	1p rose, I	275.	250.
a.		Type II	950.	
17	A2	1½p rose, I	750.	750.
a.		Type II	1,400.	—
18	A2	2p rose, I	300.	275.
19	A2	3p rose, I	400.	325.
a.		Type II	1,100.	—
20	A2	4p rose, III	450.	
21	A2	4½p rose, I	425.	300.
a.		Type II	1,250.	—
22	A2	6p rose, II	1,000.	
23	A2	8p rose, I	1,100.	1,000.
a.		Type III	550.	300.
24	A2	9p rose	1,000.	1,000.
24A	A2	1sh rose, III	—	
24B	A2	1sh6p rose, III	2,750.	—
25	A2	2sh rose, III	1,750.	

Black Seal Handstamped
Type I

26	A2	1p rose	110.	110.
27	A2	1½p rose	1,000.	900.
28	A2	2p rose	140.	150.
29	A2	3p rose	1,000.	800.
30	A2	4½p rose	900.	450.
31	A2	8p rose	1,600.	1,600.
32	A2	9p rose	2,750.	2,750.
32A	A2	2sh rose, III		

"British Consular Mail" A3

1886
Violet Seal Handstamped

33	A3	1p rose, II	100.	—
34	A3	1½p rose, II	110.	—
35	A3	2p rose, II	150.	—
36	A3	3p rose, III	140.	—
37	A3	4p rose, III	300.	—
38	A3	4½p rose, II	140.	—
39	A3	6p rose, II	250.	—
40	A3	8p rose, III	500.	—
a.		Type I	1,300.	1,300.
41	A3	9p rose, III	275.	—
42	A3	1sh rose, III	1,100.	—
43	A3	1sh6p rose, III	1,300.	—
44	A3	2sh rose, III	1,500.	—

Black Seal Handstamped

45	A3	1p rose, I	75.	60.
a.		Type II	80.	100.
46	A3	1½p rose, I	75.	60.
a.		Type II	75.	80.
47	A3	2p rose, I	90.	80.
a.		Type II	75.	80.
48	A3	3p rose, I	90.	100.
a.		Type II	80.	85.
49	A3	4p rose, III	200.	175.
50	A3	4½p rose, I	90.	100.
a.		Type II	80.	85.
51	A3	6p rose, II	80.	85.
52	A3	8p rose, I	110.	110.
a.		Type III	500.	500.
53	A3	9p rose, I	100.	125.
54	A3	1sh rose, III	425.	—
55	A3	1sh6p rose, III	425.	—
56	A3	2sh rose, III	600.	—

Seal Omitted

45b	A3	1p rose, III	1,400.	
46b	A3	1½p rose, II	1,400.	
48b	A3	3p rose, III	1,600.	
49a	A3	4p rose, III	1,750.	
50b	A3	4½p rose, II	1,750.	
51a	A3	6p rose, III	1,800.	
52b	A3	8p rose, III	1,800.	
53a	A3	9p rose, I	2,250.	
54a	A3	1sh rose, III	1,800.	
55a	A3	1sh6p rose, III	2,750.	
56a	A3	2sh rose, III	2,750.	

Some students of these issues doubt that the 1886 "seal omitted" varieties were regularly issued.

Red Seal Handstamped

57	A3	3p rose, I		3,250.
58	A3	4½p rose, I		2,250.

MALAWI

mə–ˈlä–wē

LOCATION — Southeast Africa
GOVT. — Republic in British Commonwealth
AREA — 36,100 sq. mi.
POP. — 5,530,000 (est. 1977)
CAPITAL — Lilongwe

The British Protectorate of Nyasaland became the independent state of Malawi on July 6, 1964, and a republic on July 6, 1966.

12 Pence = 1 Shilling
20 Shillings = 1 Pound
100 Tambalas = 1 Kwacha (1970)

> Catalogue values for all unused stamps in this country are for Never Hinged items.

Watermark

Wmk. 357- Multiple Cockerel

Dr. H. Kamuzu Banda and Independence Monument — A1

Prime Minister Banda and: 6p, Sun rising from lake. 1sh3p, National flag. 2sh6p, Coat of Arms.

Perf. 14½

1964, July 6　Unwmk.　Photo.

1	A1	3p dk gray & lt ol green	.15	.15
2	A1	6p car rose, red, gold & bl	.15	.15
3	A1	1sh3p dull vio, blk, red & grn	.18	.18
4	A1	2sh6p multicolored	.40	.40
		Set value	.70	.70

Malawi's independence, July 6, 1964.

MALAWI Mother and Child — A2

Designs: 1p, Chambo fish. 2p, Zebu bull. 3p, Peanuts. 4p, Fishermen in boat. 6p, Harvesting tea. 9p, Tung nut, flower and leaves. 1sh, Lumber and tropical pine branch. 1sh3p, Tobacco drying and Turkish tobacco plant. 2sh6p, Cotton industry. 5sh,

Monkey Bay, Lake Nyasa. 10sh, Afzelia tree (pod mahogany). £1, Nyala antelope, vert.

1964, July 6
Size: 23x19mm

5	A2	½p lilac	.15	.15
6	A2	1p green & black	.15	.15
7	A2	2p red brown	.15	.15
8	A2	3p pale brn, brn red & grn	.15	.15
9	A2	4p org yel & indigo	.15	.15

Size: 41½x25, 25x41½mm

10	A2	6p bl, vio bl & brt yel grn	.25	.15
11	A2	9p grn, yel & brn	.30	.25
12	A2	1sh yel, brn & dk green	.35	.25
13	A2	1sh3p red brn & olive	.45	.30
14	A2	2sh6p blue & brown	.75	.60
15	A2	5sh "Monkey Bay-Lake Nyasa"	2.75	2.25
16	A2	10sh org brn, grn & gray	3.00	2.50
17	A2	£1 yel & dk brn	6.75	4.75
		Nos. 5-17 (13)	15.35	11.80

See #26, 41-51. For surcharges see #27-28.

Star of Bethlehem over World — A3

1964, Dec. 1　Photo.　Perf. 14½

18	A3	3p brt green & gold	.15	.15
19	A3	6p lilac rose & gold	.15	.15
20	A3	1sh3p lilac & gold	.35	.35
21	A3	2sh6p ultra & gold	.65	.65
a.		Souvenir sheet of 4	2.25	2.00
		Nos. 18-21 (4)	1.30	1.30

Christmas. No. 21a contains Nos. 18-21 with simulated perforations.

Sixpence, Shilling, Florin and Half-Crown Coins — A4

1965, Mar. 1　Unwmk.　Perf. 13x13½
Coins in Silver and Black

22	A4	3p green	.15	.15
23	A4	9p rose	.18	.18
a.		Silver omitted		
24	A4	1sh6p rose violet	.35	.35
25	A4	3sh dark blue	.65	.65
a.		Souvenir sheet of 4	1.50	1.40
		Nos. 22-25 (4)	1.33	1.33

First coinage of Malawi. No. 25a contains Nos. 22-25 with simulated perforations. Sold for 6sh.

Type of 1964 Redrawn

1965, June 1　Photo.　Perf. 14½

26	A2	5sh "Monkey Bay-Lake Malawi"	1.75	1.75

Nos. 13-14 Surcharged with New Value and Two Bars

1965, June 14

27	A2	1sh6p on 1sh3p	.35	.35
28	A2	3sh on 2sh6p	.65	.65

John Chilembwe, Rebels and Church at Mbwombwe — A5

1965, Aug. 20　Photo.　Perf. 14½

29	A5	3p yel grn & purple	.15	.15
30	A5	9p red org & olive	.15	.15
31	A5	1sh6p dk blue & red brn	.30	.30

32 A5 3sh dull bl & green .60 .60
a. Souvenir sheet of 4, #29-32 6.25 5.25
Nos. 29-32 (4) 1.20 1.20

50th anniversary of the revolution of Jan. 23, 1915, led by John Chilembwe (1871-1915), missionary.

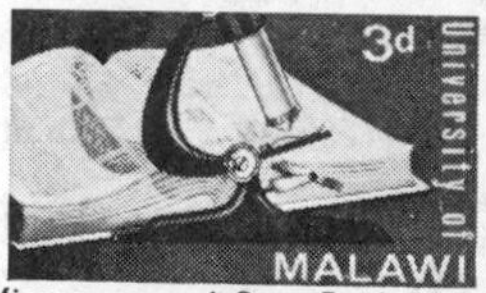

Microscope and Open Book — A6

1965, Oct. 6 ***Perf. 14***
33 A6 3p emer & slate .15 .15
34 A6 9p brt rose & slate .15 .15
35 A6 1sh6p purple & slate .35 .25
36 A6 3sh ultra & slate .60 .40
a. Souvenir sheet of 4, #33-36 6.25 5.75
Nos. 33-36 (4) 1.25
Set value .77

Opening of the University of Malawi in temporary quarters in Chichiri secondary school, Blantyre. The University will be located in Zomba.

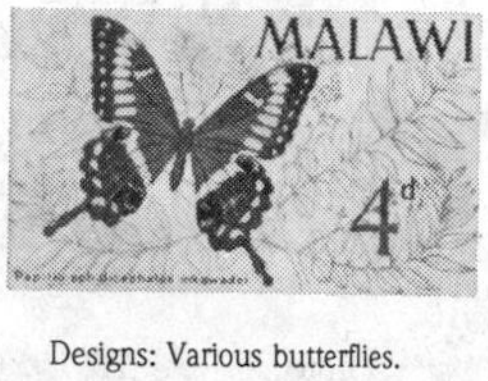

African Danaine A7

Designs: Various butterflies.

Perf. 13x13½
1966, Feb. 15 **Unwmk.**
37 A7 4p multicolored .30 .18
38 A7 9p multicolored .70 .60
39 A7 1sh6p lil, blk & blue 1.50 1.25
40 A7 3sh blue, dk brn & bis 3.00 2.50
a. Souvenir sheet of 4, #37-40 14.00 12.50
Nos. 37-40 (4) 5.50 4.53

See No. 51.

Type of 1964

Designs: 1sh6p, Curing tobacco and Burley tobacco plant. £2, Cyrestis camillus sublineatus (butterfly). Other designs as in 1964.

Perf. 14½
1966-67 **Photo.** **Wmk. 357**
Size: 23x19mm
41 A2 ½p lilac .15 .15
42 A2 1p green & black .15 .15
43 A2 2p red brown ('67) .15 .15
44 A2 3p multi ('67) .18 .15
Size: 41½x25mm
45 A2 6p blue, vio bl & brt yel grn ('67) .45 .15
46 A2 9p grn, yel & brn ('67) .52 .25
47 A2 1sh yel, brn & dk green .58 .28
48 A2 1sh6p choc & emer .95 .58
49 A2 5sh multi ('67) 6.50 2.25
50 A2 10sh org brn, grn & gray ('67) 10.50 5.25
51 A2 £2 dl vio, yel & blk 29.00 22.00
Nos. 41-51 (11) 49.13 31.36

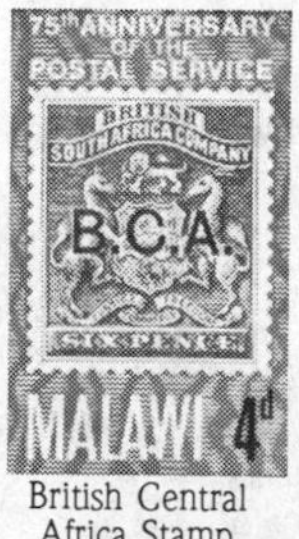

British Central Africa Stamp 1891 — A8

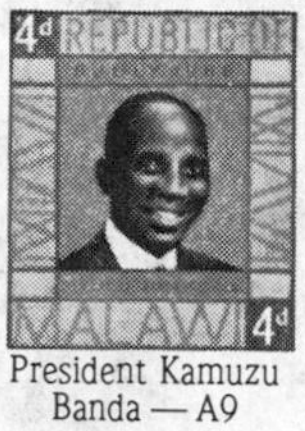

President Kamuzu Banda — A9

1966, May 4 ***Perf. 14½***
54 A8 4p yel grn & sl blue .15 .15
55 A8 9p dull rose & sl blue .20 .20
56 A8 1sh6p lil & slate blue .35 .35
57 A8 3sh blue & slate blue .65 .65
a. Souvenir sheet of 4, #54-57 4.00 3.00
Nos. 54-57 (4) 1.35 1.35

Postal service, 75th anniv.

Perf. 14x14½
1966, July 6 **Wmk. 357**
58 A9 4p green, sil & brn .15 .15
59 A9 9p magenta, sil & brn .15 .15
60 A9 1sh6p violet, sil & brn .25 .25
61 A9 3sh blue, sil & brn .50 .50
a. Souvenir sheet of 4, #58-61 2.50 1.75
Nos. 58-61 (4) 1.05 1.05

Republic Day, July 6, 1966; 2nd anniv. of Independence.

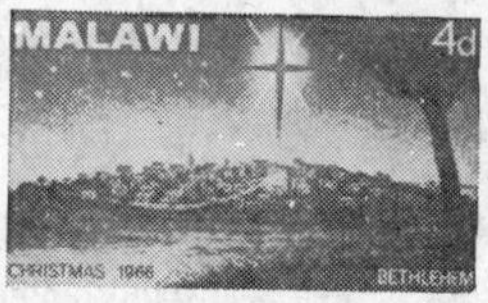

Star over Bethlehem A10

1966, Oct. 12 **Photo.** ***Perf. 14½x14***
63 A10 4p deep green & gold .15 .15
64 A10 9p plum & gold .25 .25
65 A10 1sh6p orange & gold .50 .50
66 A10 3sh deep blue & gold 1.00 1.00
Nos. 63-66 (4) 1.90 1.90

Christmas.

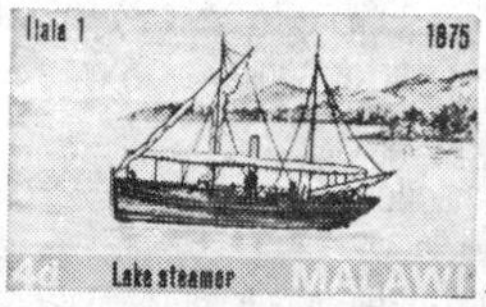

Ilala I, 1875 A11

Steamers on Lake Malawi: 9p, Dove, 1892. 1sh6p, Chauncey Maples, 1901. 3sh, Guendolen, 1899.

1967, Jan. 4 ***Perf. 14½x14***
67 A11 4p emer, black & yel .15 .15
a. Yellow omitted
68 A11 9p car rose, blk & yellow .28 .25
69 A11 1sh6p lt vio, blk & red .60 .50
70 A11 3sh ultra, black & red 1.50 1.00
Nos. 67-70 (4) 2.53 1.90

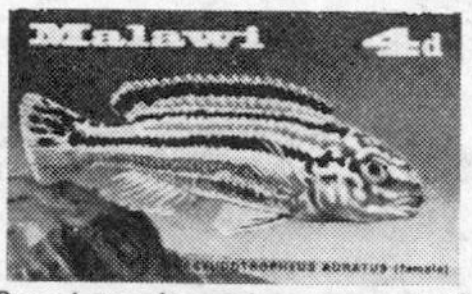

Pseudotropheus Auratus — A12

Fish of Lake Malawi: 9p, Labeotropheus trewavasae. 1sh6p, Pseudotropheus zebra. 3sh, Pseudotropheus tropheops.

1967, May 3 **Photo.** ***Perf. 12½x12***
71 A12 4p green & multi .18 .15
72 A12 9p ocher & multi .40 .35
73 A12 1sh6p multicolored .85 .75
74 A12 3sh ultra & multi 1.75 1.50
Nos. 71-74 (4) 3.18 2.75

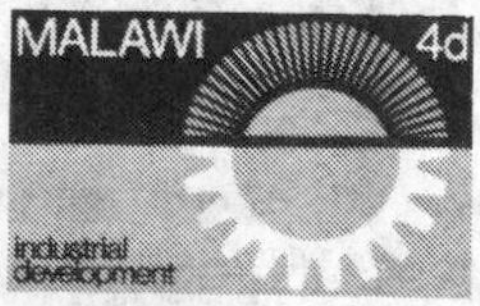

Rising Sun and Cogwheel A13

Perf. 13½x13
1967, July 5 **Litho.** **Unwmk.**
75 A13 4p black & brt grn .15 .15
76 A13 9p black & car rose .15 .15
77 A13 1sh6p black & brt pur .30 .30
78 A13 3sh black & brt ultra .60 .60
a. Souvenir sheet of 4, #75-78 1.75 1.75
Nos. 75-78 (4) 1.20 1.20

Malawi industrial development.

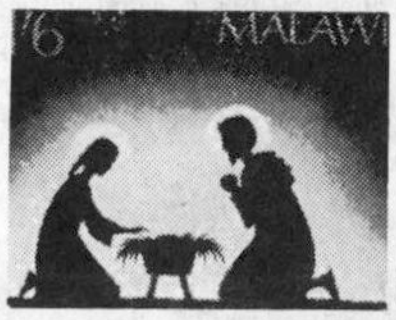

Nativity — A14

Perf. 14x14½
1967, Oct. 12 **Photo.** **Wmk. 357**
79 A14 4p vio blue & green .15 .15
80 A14 9p vio blue & red .15 .15
81 A14 1sh6p vio blue & yel .30 .30
82 A14 3sh bright blue .60 .60
a. Souvenir sheet of 4, #79-82, perf. 14x13½ 3.00 2.50
Nos. 79-82 (4) 1.20 1.20

Christmas.

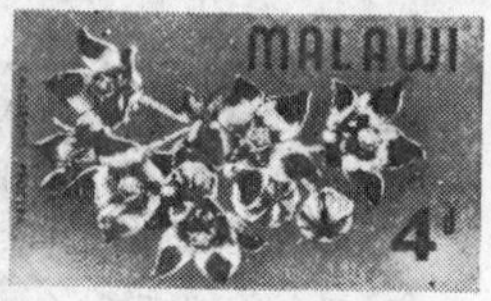

Calotropis Procera A15

Wild Flowers: 9p, Borreria dibrachiata. 1sh6p, Hibiscus rhodanthus. 3sh, Bidens pinnatipartita.

1968, Apr. 24 **Litho.** ***Perf. 13½x13***
83 A15 4p green & multi .15 .15
84 A15 9p pale green & multi .28 .28
85 A15 1sh6p lt green & multi .55 .55
86 A15 3sh brt blue & multi 1.10 1.10
a. Souvenir sheet of 4, #83-86 3.75 3.50
Nos. 83-86 (4) 2.08 2.08

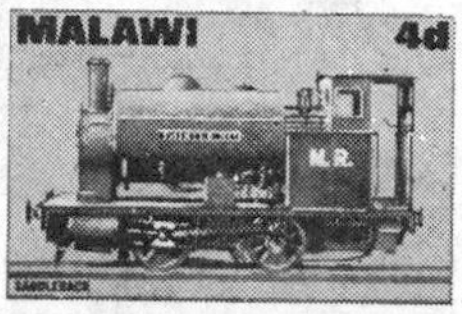

Thistle No. 1, 1902 A16

Locomotives: 9p, G-class steam engine, 1954. 1sh6p, "Zambesi" diesel locomotive No. 202, 1963. 3sh, Diesel rail car No. 1, 1955.

1968, July 24 **Photo.** ***Perf. 14x14½***
87 A16 4p gray grn & multi .22 .22
88 A16 9p red & multi .55 .55
89 A16 1sh6p cream & multi 1.10 1.10
90 A16 3sh lt ultra & multi 2.25 2.25
a. Souv. sheet of 4, #87-90, perf. 14 5.50 5.00
Nos. 87-90 (4) 4.12 4.12

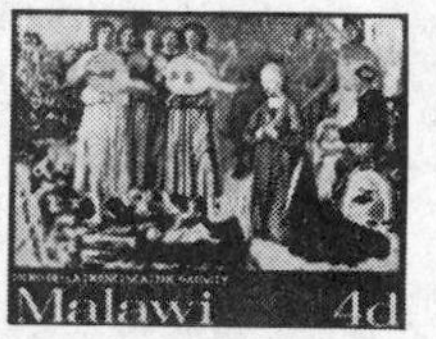

Nativity, by Piero della Francesca A17

Paintings: 9p, Adoration of the Shepherds, by Murillo. 1sh6p, Adoration of the Shepherds, by Guido Reni. 3sh, Nativity with God the Father and the Holy Ghost, by Giovanni Batista Pittoni.

1968, Nov. 6 **Photo.** **Wmk. 357**
91 A17 4p black & multi .15 .15
92 A17 9p multicolored .20 .20
93 A17 1sh6p multicolored .40 .40
94 A17 3sh blue & multi .90 .90
a. Souvenir sheet of 4, #91-94, perf. 14x13½ 2.75 2.50
Nos. 91-94 (4) 1.65 1.65

Christmas.

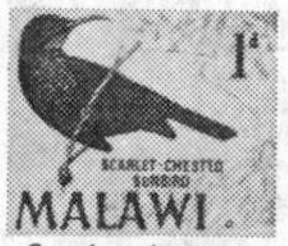

Scarlet-chested Sunbird A18

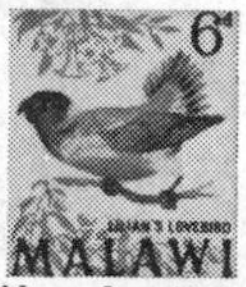

Nyasa Lovebird A19

Birds: 2p, Violet-backed starling. 3p, White-browed robin-chat. 4p, Red-billed firefinch. 9p, Yellow bishop. 1sh, Southern carmine bee-eater. 1sh6p, Grayheaded bush shrike. 2sh, Paradise whydah. 3sh, African paradise flycatcher. 5sh, Bateleur. 10sh, Saddlebill. £1, Purple heron. £2, Livingstone's lorie.

1968, Nov. 13 ***Perf. 14½***
Size: 23x19, 19x23mm
95 A18 1p multicolored .15 .15
96 A18 2p multicolored .20 .15
97 A18 3p multicolored .25 .15
98 A18 4p multicolored .38 .15
99 A19 6p multicolored .60 .22
100 A19 9p multicolored .75 .30
Perf. 14
Size: 42x25, 25x42mm
101 A18 1sh multicolored .90 .50
102 A18 1sh6p multicolored 1.75 .80
103 A18 2sh multicolored 2.75 1.25
104 A19 3sh multicolored 3.75 2.25
105 A19 5sh multicolored 5.00 3.50
106 A19 10sh multicolored 8.25 5.75
107 A19 £1 multicolored 16.50 12.00
109 A18 £2 multicolored 27.50 25.00
Nos. 95-109 (14) 68.73 52.17

No. 104 was surcharged "30t Special United Kingdom Delivery Service" in 5 lines and issued Feb. 8, 1971, during the British postal strike. The 30t was to pay a private postal service.

See Nos. 136-137. For overprint see No. 131.

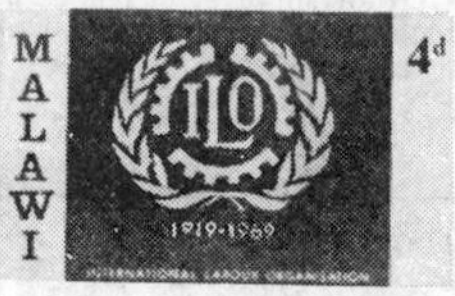

ILO Emblem A20

Photo., Gold Impressed (Emblem)
Perf. 14x14½
1969, Feb. 5 **Wmk. 357**
110 A20 4p deep green .15 .15
111 A20 9p dk rose brown .15 .15
112 A20 1sh6p dark gray .30 .30
113 A20 3sh dark blue .60 .60
a. Souvenir sheet of 4, #110-113 7.00 7.00
Nos. 110-113 (4) 1.20 1.20

ILO, 50th anniversary.

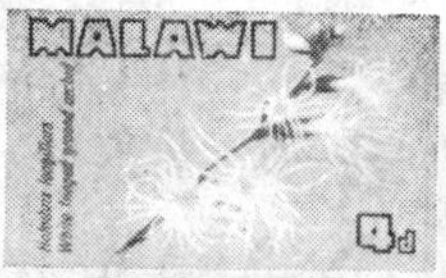

White Fringed Ground Orchid A21

Malawi Orchids: 9p, Red ground orchid. 1sh6p, Leopard tree orchid. 3sh, Blue ground orchid.

1969, July 9 **Litho.** ***Perf. 13½***
114 A21 4p gray & multi .20 .15
115 A21 9p gray & multi .45 .35
116 A21 1sh6p gray & multi .90 .75
117 A21 3sh gray & multi 2.00 1.50
a. Souvenir sheet of 4, #114-117 3.75 3.00
Nos. 114-117 (4) 3.55 2.75

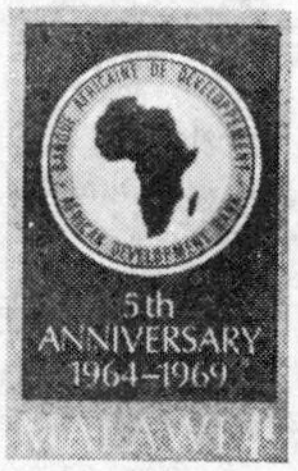

African Development Bank Emblem — A22

1969, Sept. 10 ***Perf. 14***
118 A22 4p multicolored .15 .15
119 A22 9p multicolored .15 .15
120 A22 1sh6p multicolored .30 .30
121 A22 3sh multicolored .60 .60
a. Souvenir sheet of 4, #118-121 1.75 1.75
Nos. 118-121 (4) 1.20 1.20

African Development Bank, 5th anniv.

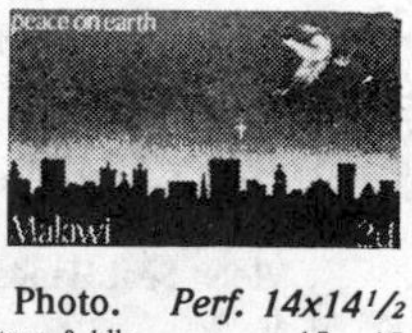

"Peace on Earth" — A23

1969, Nov. 5 **Photo.** ***Perf. 14x14½***
122 A23 2p citron & blk .15 .15
123 A23 4p Prus blue & blk .15 .15
124 A23 9p scarlet & blk .25 .25
125 A23 1sh6p purple & blk .45 .45
126 A23 3sh ultra & blk .90 .90
a. Souvenir sheet of 5, #122-126 2.75 2.75
Nos. 122-126 (5) 1.90 1.90

Christmas.

Elegant
Grasshopper
A24

Runner
A25

Insects: 9p, Bean blister beetle. 1sh6p, Pumpkin ladybird. 3sh, Praying mantis.

1970, Feb. 4   Litho.   Perf. 14x14½
127 A24 4p multicolored   .15 .15
128 A24 9p multicolored   .25 .25
129 A24 1sh6p multicolored   .50 .50
130 A24 3sh multicolored   1.00 1.00
  a. Souvenir sheet of 4, #127-130 2.75 2.75
      Nos. 127-130 (4)   1.90 1.90

No. 102 Overprinted:
"Rand Easter Show / 1970"

1970, Mar. 18   Photo.   Perf. 14
131 A18 1sh6p multicolored   .50 .50

75th Anniversary Rand Easter Show, Johannesburg, South Africa, Mar. 24-Apr. 6.

1970, June 3   Litho.   Perf. 13
132 A25 4p green & dk blue   .15 .15
133 A25 9p rose & dk bl   .18 .18
134 A25 1sh6p dull yel & dk bl   .35 .35
135 A25 3sh blue & dk blue   .65 .65
  a. Souvenir sheet of 4, #132-135 1.75 1.75
      Nos. 132-135 (4)   1.33 1.33

9th Commonwealth Games, Edinburgh, Scotland, July 16-25.

Dual Currency Issue
Bird Type of 1968 with Denominations in Tambalas

Designs: 10t/1sh, Southern carmine bee-eater. 20t/2sh, Paradise whydah.

1970, Sept. 2   Photo.   Perf. 14½
Size: 42x25mm
136 A18 10t/1sh multicolored   .35 .35
137 A18 20t/2sh multicolored   .75 .75

Aegocera
Trimenii
A26

Moths of Malawi: 9p, Epiphora bauhiniae. 1sh6p, Parasa karschi. 3sh, Teracotona euprepia.

Perf. 11x11½
1970, Sept. 30   Wmk. 357
138 A26 4p multicolored   .16 .15
139 A26 9p multicolored   .35 .30
140 A26 1sh6p lt vio & multi   .70 .65
141 A26 3sh multicolored   1.75 1.25
  a. Souvenir sheet of 4, #138-141 4.50 4.50
      Nos. 138-141 (4)   2.96 2.35

Mother
and Child
A27

1970, Nov. 4   Litho.   Perf. 14½
142 A27 2p black & yel   .15 .15
143 A27 4p black & emer   .15 .15
144 A27 9p black & dp org   .25 .25
145 A27 1sh6p black & red lil   .50 .50
146 A27 3sh black & ultra   1.00 1.00
  a. Souv. sheet of 5, #142-146 + label 2.50 2.50
      Nos. 142-146 (5)   2.05 2.05

Christmas.

Decimal Currency

Greater
Kudu — A28

Eland — A29

Antelopes: 2t, Nyala. 3t, Reedbuck. 5t, Puku. 8t, Impala. 15t, Klipspringer. 20t, Livingstone's suni. 30t, Roan antelope. 50t, Waterbuck. 1k, Bushbuck. 2k, Red duiker. 4k, Gray bush duiker.

Perf. 13½x14 (A28), 14x14½ (A29)
1971, Feb. 15   Litho.   Wmk. 357
148 A28 1t dull vio & multi   .15 .15
  a. Perf. 14½x14, coil   .15 .15
  b. Perf. 14 ('74)   .16 .15
149 A28 2t dp yel & multi   .15 .15
150 A28 3t ap grn & multi   .15 .15
  a. Perf. 14 ('74)   .28 .22
151 A28 5t multicolored   .16 .15
  a. Perf. 14 ('74)   .38 .32
152 A28 8t org red & multi   .28 .22
153 A29 10t green & multi   .32 .28
154 A29 15t brt pur & multi   .55 .55
155 A29 20t bl gray & multi   .70 .70
156 A29 30t dull blue & multi   1.10 1.10
157 A29 50t multicolored   1.90 1.90
158 A29 1k multicolored   2.75 2.75
159 A29 2k gray & multi   5.50 5.50
160 A29 4k multicolored   13.50 12.00
      Nos. 148-160 (13)   27.21 25.60

Decimal
Coins
A30

1971, Feb. 15   Perf. 14½
161 A30 3t multicolored   .15 .15
162 A30 8t dull red & multi   .18 .18
163 A30 15t purple & multi   .35 .35
164 A30 30t brt blue & multi   .65 .65
  a. Souvenir sheet of 4, #161-164 1.75 1.75
      Nos. 161-164 (4)   1.33 1.33

Introduction of decimal currency and coinage.

Christ on the Cross,
by Dürer — A31

Design: Nos. 166, 168, 170, 172, The Resurrection, by Albrecht Dürer.

1971, Apr. 7   Litho.   Perf. 14x13½
165 A31 3t emerald & black   .15 .15
166 A31 3t emerald & black   .15 .15
167 A31 8t orange & black   .18 .18
168 A31 8t orange & black   .18 .18
169 A31 15t red lilac & black   .35 .35
170 A31 15t red lilac & black   .35 .35
171 A31 30t blue & black   .65 .65
  a. Souv. sheet of 4, #165, 167, 169,
      171   1.75 1.75
172 A31 30t blue & black   .65 .65
  a. Souv. sheet of 4, #166, 168, 170,
      172   1.75 1.75
      Nos. 165-172 (8)   2.66 2.66

Easter. The 2 designs of each denomination are printed se-tenant, arranged checkerwise, in sheets of 25.

Holarrhena
Febrifuga — A32

Drum
Major — A33

Flowering Shrubs and Trees: 8t, Brachystegia spiciformis. 15t, Securidaca longepedunculata. 30t, Pterocarpus rotundifolius.

1971, July 14   Litho.   Wmk. 357
173 A32 3t gray & multi   .15 .15
174 A32 8t gray & multi   .18 .18
175 A32 15t gray & multi   .35 .35
176 A32 30t gray & multi   .65 .65
  a. Souvenir sheet of 4, #173-176 2.25 2.25
      Nos. 173-176 (4)   1.33 1.33

1971, Oct. 5   Perf. 14x14½
177 A33 30t lt blue & multi   .90 .90

50th anniversary of Malawi Police Force.

Madonna and Child, by
William Dyce — A34

Paintings of Holy Family by: 8t, Martin Schongauer. 15t, Raphael. 30t, Bronzino.

1971, Nov. 10   Perf. 14½
178 A34 3t green & multi   .15 .15
179 A34 8t carmine & multi   .20 .20
180 A34 15t dp claret & multi   .40 .40
181 A34 30t dull blue & multi   .90 .90
  a. Souvenir sheet of 4, #178-181 2.75 2.75
      Nos. 178-181 (4)   1.65 1.65

Christmas.

Vickers Viscount — A35

Airplanes: 8t, Hawker Siddeley 748. 15t, Britten Norman Islander. 30t, B.A.C. One Eleven.

1972, Feb. 9   Litho.   Perf. 13½x14
182 A35 3t brt grn, blk & red   .15 .15
183 A35 8t red org & black   .25 .25
184 A35 15t dp rose lil, red & black .50 .50
185 A35 30t vio blue & multi   1.00 1.00
  a. Souvenir sheet of 4, #182-185 4.00 4.00
      Nos. 182-185 (4)   1.90 1.90

Publicity for Air Malawi.

Figures,
Chencherere
Hill — A36

Rock Paintings: 8t, Lizard and cat, Chencherere Hill. 15t, Symbols, Diwa Hill. 30t, Sun behind rain, Mikolongwe Hill.

1972, May 10   Perf. 13½
186 A36 3t black & yel grn   .15 .15
187 A36 8t black & dp car   .20 .20
188 A36 15t black, vio & car   .40 .40
189 A36 30t black, blue & yel   .90 .90
  a. Souv. sheet of 4, #186-189, perf. 15 2.25 2.25
      Nos. 186-189 (4)   1.65 1.65

Athlete and
Olympic
Rings — A37

1972, Aug. 9   Perf. 14x14½
190 A37 3t gray, black & green   .15 .15
191 A37 8t gray, black & scar   .18 .18
192 A37 15t gray, black & lilac   .32 .32
193 A37 30t gray, black & blue   .65 .65
  a. Souvenir sheet of 4, #190-193 2.00 2.00
      Nos. 190-193 (4)   1.30 1.30

20th Olympic Games, Munich, Aug. 26-Sept. 10.

Malawi Coat of
Arms — A38

1972, Oct. 20   Litho.   Perf. 13½x14
194 A38 15t blue & multi   .50 .50

18th Commonwealth Parliamentary Conference, Malawi, Oct. 1972.

Adoration of the
Kings, by
Orcagna — A39

Paintings of the Florentine School: 8t, Madonna and Child Enthroned, anonymous. 15t, Madonna and Child with Sts. Bonaventura and Louis of Toulouse, by Carlo Crivelli. 30t, Madonna and Child with St. Anne, by Jean de Bruges.

Perf. 14½x14
1972, Nov. 8   Wmk. 357
195 A39 3t lt olive & multi   .15 .15
196 A39 8t carmine & multi   .20 .20
197 A39 15t purple & multi   .40 .40
198 A39 30t blue & multi   .90 .90
  a. Souvenir sheet of 4, #195-198 2.50 2.50
      Nos. 195-198 (4)   1.65 1.65

Christmas.

Charaxes Bohemani — A40

1973   Perf. 13½x14
199 A40 3t shown   .20 .16
200 A40 8t Uranothauma craw-
         shayi   .60 .50
201 A40 15t Charaxes acuminatus 1.25 1.00
202 A40 30t "Euphaedra zaddachi" 3.25 2.00
  a. Souvenir sheet of 4, #199-202 9.00 2.50
203 A40 30t Amauris ansorgei   2.75 2.00
      Nos. 199-203 (5)   8.05 5.66

Issued: #199-202, Feb. 7; #203, Apr. 5.

Dr. Livingstone and Map of West
Africa — A41

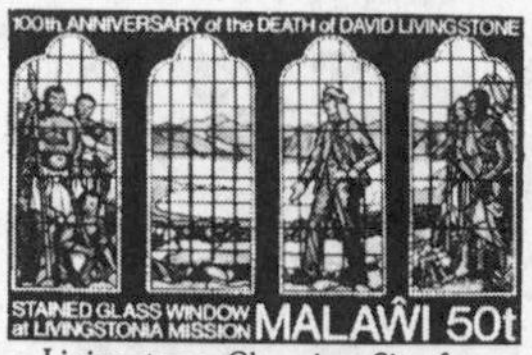

Livingstone Choosing Site for Mission — A42

1973 Litho. *Perf. 13½x14*

204 A41 3t apple grn & multi .15 .15
205 A41 8t red orange & multi .30 .30
206 A41 15t multicolored .60 .60
207 A41 30t blue & multi 1.25 1.25
a. Souvenir sheet of 4, #204-207 2.25 2.25
208 A42 50t black & multi 1.25 1.25
a. Souvenir sheet of 1 2.00 2.00
Nos. 204-208 (5) 3.55 3.55

Dr. David Livingstone (1813-73), medical missionary and explorer.
Issued: #204-207, 207a, 5/1; #208, 208a, 12/12.

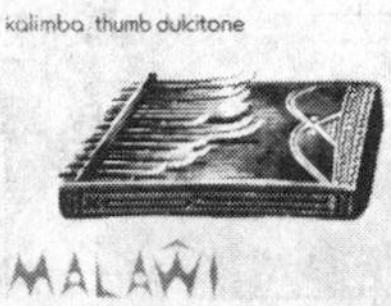

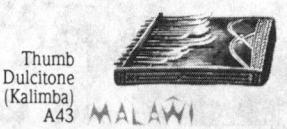

Thumb Dulcitone (Kalimba) A43

African Musical Instruments: 8t, Hand zither (bangwe; vert.). 15t, Hand drum (ng'oma; vert.). 30t, One-stringed fiddle (kaligo).

1973, Aug. 8 Wmk. 357 *Perf. 14*

209 A43 3t brt green & multi .15 .15
210 A43 8t red & multi .25 .25
211 A43 15t violet & multi .48 .48
212 A43 30t blue & multi 1.00 1.00
a. Souvenir sheet of 4, #209-212 2.25 2.25
Nos. 209-212 (4) 1.88 1.88

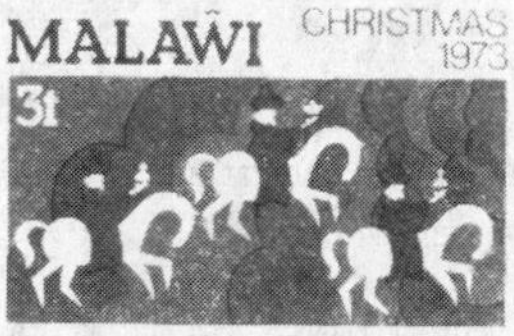

The Three Kings A44

1973, Nov. 8 *Perf. 13½x14*

213 A44 3t blue & multi .15 .15
214 A44 8t ver & multi .20 .20
215 A44 15t multicolored .40 .40
216 A44 30t orange & multi .80 .80
a. Souvenir sheet of 4, #213-216 2.00 2.00
Nos. 213-216 (4) 1.55 1.55

Christmas.

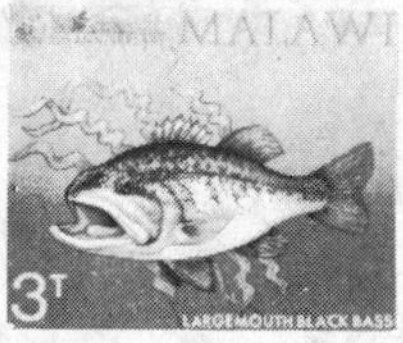

Largemouth Black Bass — A45

Designs: Game fish.

1974, Feb. 20 Litho. *Perf. 14x14½*

217 A45 3t shown .15 .15
218 A45 8t Rainbow trout .40 .40
219 A45 15t Lake salmon .90 .90
220 A45 30t Triggerfish 1.60 1.60
a. Souvenir sheet of 4, #217-220 3.00 3.00
Nos. 217-220 (4) 3.05 3.05

30th anniv. of Angling Society of Malawi.

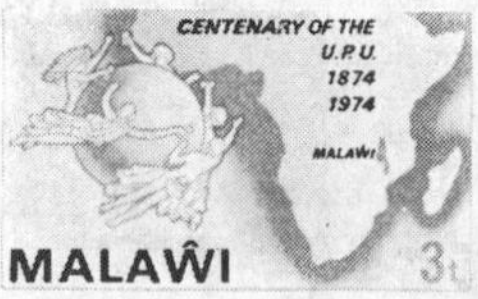

UPU Emblem, Map of Africa with Malawi A46

1974, Apr. 24 *Perf. 13½*

221 A46 3t green & bister .15 .15
222 A46 8t ver & bister .20 .20
223 A46 15t lilac & bister .40 .40
224 A46 30t gray & bister .85 .85
a. Souvenir sheet of 4, #221-224 2.25 2.00
Nos. 221-224 (4) 1.60 1.60

Centenary of Universal Postal Union.

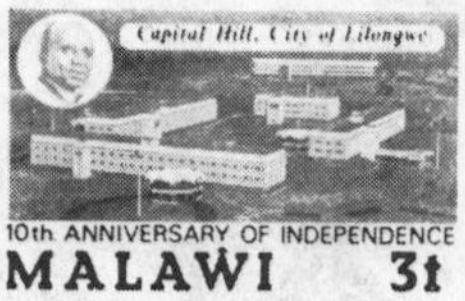

Capital Hill, Lilongwe and Pres. Kamuzu Banda A47

1974, July 3 Litho. *Perf. 14*

225 A47 3t emerald & multi .15 .15
226 A47 8t red & multi .22 .22
227 A47 15t lilac & multi .45 .45
228 A47 30t vio blue & multi .90 .90
a. Souvenir sheet of 4, #225-228 1.40 1.40
Nos. 225-228 (4) 1.72 1.72

10th anniversary of independence.

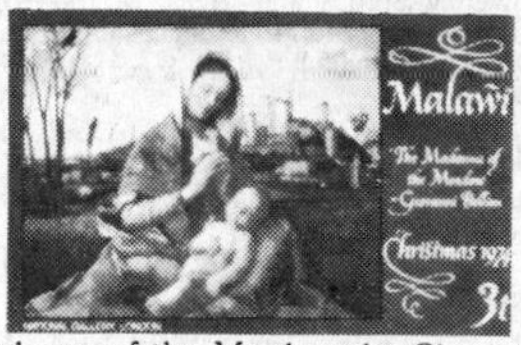

Madonna of the Meadow, by Giovanni Bellini — A48

Paintings: 8t, Holy Family, by Jacob Jordaens. 15t, Nativity, by Peter F. de Grebber. 30t, Adoration of the Shepherds, by Lorenzo di Credi.

1974, Dec. 4 Litho. *Perf. 13½x14*

229 A48 3t dk green & multi .15 .15
230 A48 8t multicolored .20 .20
231 A48 15t purple & multi .40 .40
232 A48 30t dk blue & multi .85 .85
a. Souvenir sheet of 4, #229-232 1.75 1.75
Nos. 229-232 (4) 1.60 1.60

Christmas.

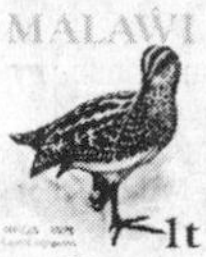

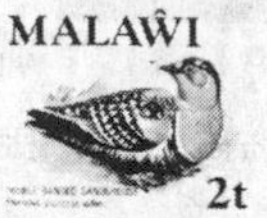

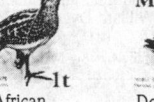

African Snipe — A49 Double-banded Sandgrouse — A50

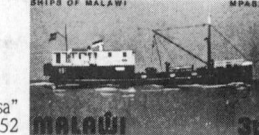

Malawi Coat of Arms — A51

Birds: 3t, Blue quail. 5t, Red-necked francolin. 8t, Harlequin quail. 10t, Spurwing goose. 15t, Denham's bustard. 20t, Knob-billed duck. 30t, Helmeted guinea fowl. 50t, Pigmy goose. 1k, Garganey. 2k, White-faced tree duck. 4k, Green pigeon.

Wmk. 357

1975, Feb. 19 Litho. *Perf. 14*

Size: 17x21, 21x17mm

233 A49 1t multicolored .15 .15
234 A50 2t multicolored .15 .15
235 A50 3t multicolored .18 .15
236 A49 5t multicolored .22 .15
237 A50 8t multicolored .35 .22

Perf. 14½

Size: 25x41, 41x25mm

238 A49 10t multicolored .60 .38
239 A49 15t multicolored .82 .55
240 A49 20t multicolored 1.00 .65
241 A49 30t multicolored 1.55 1.00
242 A50 50t multicolored 2.50 .55
243 A50 1k multicolored 4.75 3.25
244 A49 2k multicolored 9.50 7.00
245 A50 4k multicolored 15.50 11.00
Nos. 233-245 (13) 37.27 25.20

See #270-279. For overprints see #263, 294.

Coil Stamps

1975-85 *Perf. 14½x14*

246 A51 1t dark violet blue .15 .15
247 A51 5t red ('85) .15 .15
Set value .15 .15

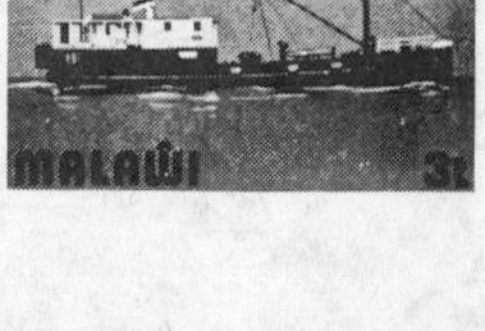

"Mpasa" A52

Designs: Lake Malawi ships.

1975, Mar. 12 Wmk. 357 *Perf. 13½*

251 A52 3t shown .15 .15
252 A52 8t "Ilala II" .30 .30
253 A52 15t "Chauncy Maples" .60 .60
254 A52 30t "Nkwazi" 1.25 1.25
a. Souvenir sheet of 4, #251-254, perf. 14½ 2.75 2.75
Nos. 251-254 (4) 2.30 2.30

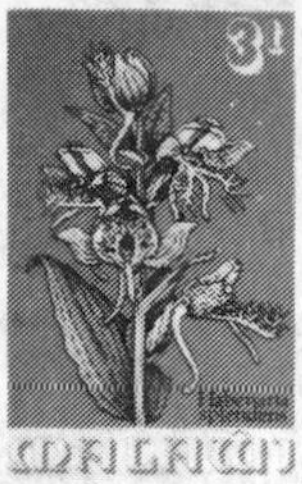

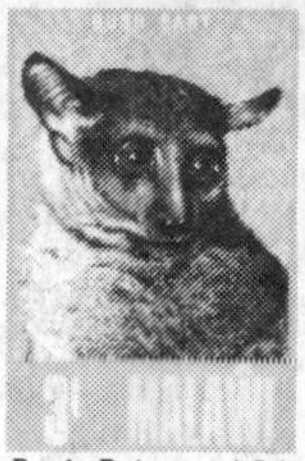

Habenaria Splendens — A53 Bush Baby — A54

Orchids of Malawi: 10t, Eulophia cucullata. 20t, Disa welwitschii. 40t, Angraecum conchiferum.

1975, June 6 Litho. *Perf. 14½*

255 A53 3t lt green & multi .15 .15
256 A53 10t red orange & multi .42 .42
257 A53 20t dull vio & multi .90 .90
258 A53 40t multicolored 1.75 1.75
a. Souvenir sheet of 4, #255-258 2.75 2.75
Nos. 255-258 (4) 3.22 3.22

1975, Sept. 3 Litho. *Perf. 14*

259 A54 3t shown .15 .15
260 A54 10t Leopard .42 .42
261 A54 20t Roan antelope .90 .90
262 A54 40t Burchell's zebra 1.75 1.75
a. Souvenir sheet of 4, #259-262 4.25 4.25
Nos. 259-262 (4) 3.22 3.22

Animals of Malawi.

No. 242 Overprinted: "10th ACP / Ministerial / Conference / 1975"

1975, Dec. 9 Litho. *Perf. 14½*

263 A50 50t multicolored 1.25 1.25

10th African, Caribbean and Pacific Ministerial Conference.

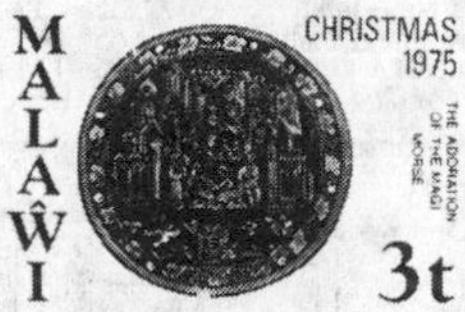

Adoration of the Kings, French A55

Christmas: 10t, Nativity, 16th century, Spanish. 20t, Nativity, by Pierre Raymond, 16th century. 40t, Angel Appearing to the Shepherds, 14th century, English.

1975, Dec. 12 *Perf. 13x13½*

264 A55 3t multicolored .15 .15
265 A55 10t multicolored .25 .25
266 A55 20t purple & multi .50 .50
267 A55 40t blue & multi 1.00 1.00
a. Souv. sheet of 4, #264-267, perf. 14 1.90 1.90
Nos. 264-267 (4) 1.90 1.90

Bird Types of 1975

1975 Litho. Unwmk. *Perf. 14*

Size: 21x17mm

270 A50 3t multicolored .15 .15

Perf. 14½

Size: 25x41mm

273 A49 10t multicolored .32 .32
274 A49 15t multicolored .70 .70
279 A49 2k multicolored 11.00 7.00
Nos. 270-279 (4) 12.17 8.17

For overprint see No. 293.

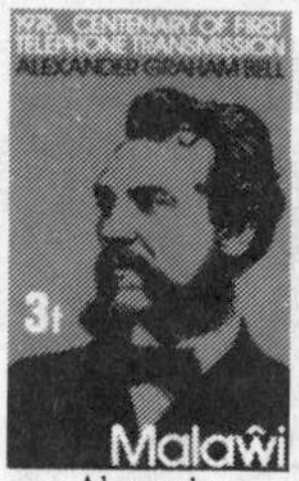

Alexander Graham Bell — A56

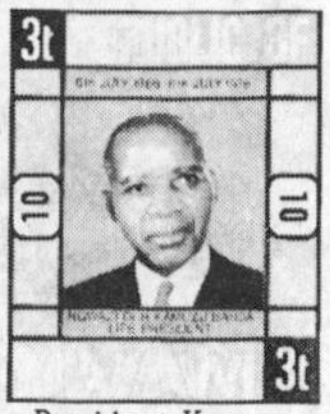

President Kamuzu Banda — A57

Perf. 14x14½

1976, Mar. 24 Litho. Wmk. 357

281 A56 3t green & black .15 .15
282 A56 10t dp lilac rose & blk .22 .22
283 A56 20t brt purple & blk .45 .45
284 A56 40t brt blue & blk .90 .90
a. Souvenir sheet of 4, #281-284 1.90 1.90
Nos. 281-284 (4) 1.72 1.72

Centenary of first telephone call by Alexander Graham Bell, Mar. 10, 1876.

1976, July 1 Photo. *Perf. 13*

285 A57 3t brt green & multi .15 .15
286 A57 10t multicolored .16 .16
287 A57 20t violet & multi .35 .35
288 A57 40t dull blue & multi .65 .65
a. Souvenir sheet of 4, #285-288 2.00 2.00
Nos. 285-288 (4) 1.31 1.31

10th anniversary of the Republic.

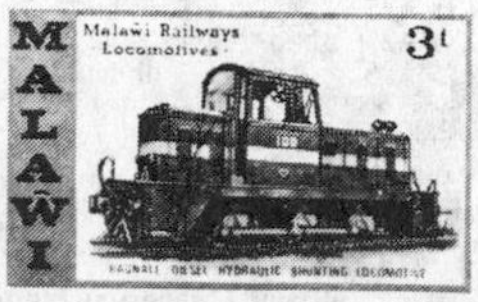

Bagnall Diesel No. 100 A58

Diesel Locomotives: 10t, Shire class No. 503. 20t, Nippon Sharyo No. 301. 40t, Hunslet No. 110.

1976, Oct. 1 Litho. *Perf. 14½*

289 A58 3t emerald & multi .15 .15
290 A58 10t red & multi .45 .28
291 A58 20t lilac & multi .90 .60
292 A58 40t blue & multi 1.90 1.10
a. Souvenir sheet of 4, #289-292 4.50 4.00
Nos. 289-292 (4) 3.40 2.13

Malawi Railways.

Nos. 274 and 241 Overprinted: **Blantyre Mission Centenary 1876-1976**

1976, Oct. 22 Litho. Unwmk.

293 A49 15t multicolored .45 .45

Wmk. 357

294 A49 30t multicolored .90 .90

Blantyre Mission centenary.

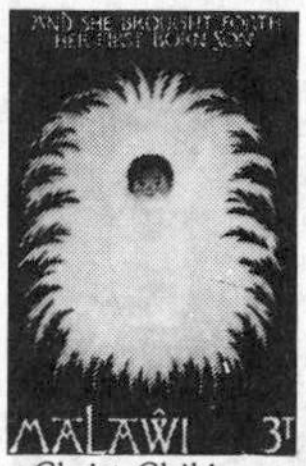

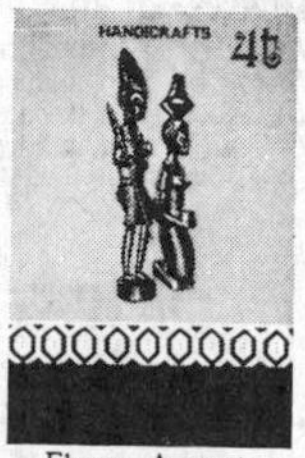

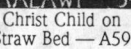

Christ Child on Straw Bed — A59 Ebony Ancestor Figures — A60

1976, Dec. 6 Wmk. 357 *Perf. 14*

295 A59 3t green & multi .15 .15
296 A59 10t magenta & multi .22 .22
297 A59 20t purple & multi .45 .45
298 A59 40t dk blue & multi .90 .90
a. Souvenir sheet of 4, #295-298 1.75 1.75
Nos. 295-298 (4) 1.72 1.72

Christmas.

1977, Apr. 1 Litho. Wmk. 357

Handicrafts: 10t, Ebony elephant, horiz. 20t, Ebony rhinoceros, horiz. 40t, Wooden antelope.

299 A60 4t yellow & multi .15 .15
300 A60 10t black & multi .20 .20
301 A60 20t ocher & multi .40 .40

302 A60 40t ver & multi .85 .85
a. Souvenir sheet of 4, #299-302 2.25 2.25
Nos. 299-302 (4) 1.60 1.60

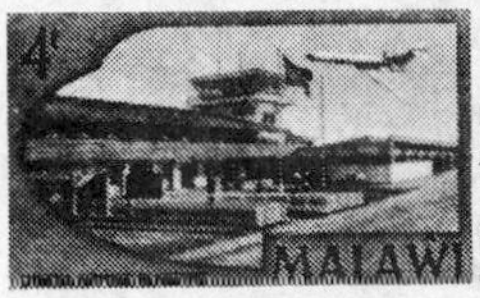

Chileka Airport, Blantyre, and VC10
A61

Transportation in Malawi: 10t, Leyland bus on Blantyre-Lilongwe Road. 20t, Ilala II on Lake Malawi. 40t, Freight train of Blantyre-Nacala line on overpass.

1977, July 12 Litho. *Perf. 14½*

303 A61 4t multicolored .15 .15
304 A61 10t multicolored .20 .20
305 A61 20t multicolored .40 .40
306 A61 40t multicolored .85 .85
a. Souvenir sheet of 4, #303-306 2.75 2.75
Nos. 303-306 (4) 1.60 1.60

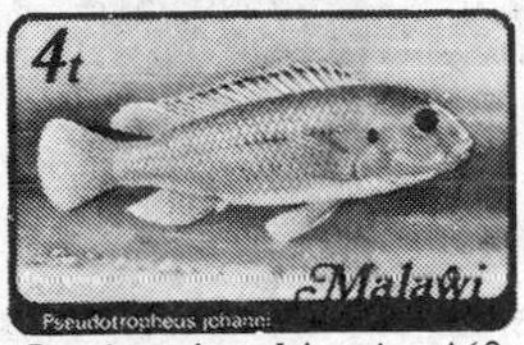

Pseudotropheus Johanni — A62

Lake Malawi Fish: 10t, Pseudotropheus livingstoni. 20t, Pseudotropheus zebra. 40t, Genyochromis mento.

Wmk. 357, Unwmkd.

1977, Oct. 4 Litho. *Perf. 13½x14*

307 A62 4t multicolored .15 .15
308 A62 10t multicolored .25 .25
309 A62 20t multicolored .50 .50
310 A62 40t multicolored 1.00 1.00
a. Souvenir sheet of 4, #307-310 2.00 2.00
Nos. 307-310 (4) 1.90 1.90

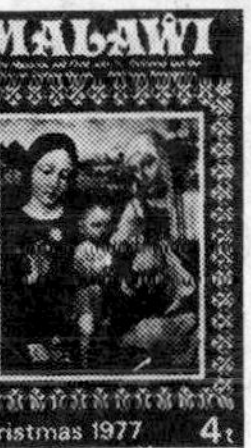

Virgin and Child, by Bergognone
A63

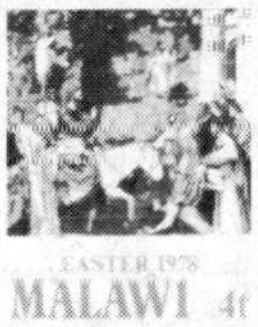

Entry into Jerusalem, by Giotto
A64

Virgin and Child: 10t, with God the Father and Angels, by Ambrogio Bergognone. 20t, detail from Bottigella altarpiece, by Vincenzo Foppa. 40t, with the fountain, by Jan Van Eyck.

Perf. 14x13½

1977, Nov. 21 Unwmk.

311 A63 4t multicolored .15 .15
312 A63 10t red & multi .20 .20
313 A63 20t lilac & multi .40 .40
314 A63 40t vio blue & multi .85 .85
a. Souvenir sheet of 4, #311-314 2.00 2.00
Nos. 311-314 (4) 1.60 1.60

Christmas.

1978, Mar. 1 Litho. *Perf. 12x12½*

Giotto Paintings: 10t, Crucifixion. 20t, Descent from the Cross. 40t, Jesus Appearing to Mary.

315 A64 4t multicolored .15 .15
316 A64 10t multicolored .20 .20
317 A64 20t multicolored .40 .40
318 A64 40t multicolored .85 .85
a. Souvenir sheet of 4, #315-318 2.75 1.75
Nos. 315-318 (4) 1.60 1.60

Easter.

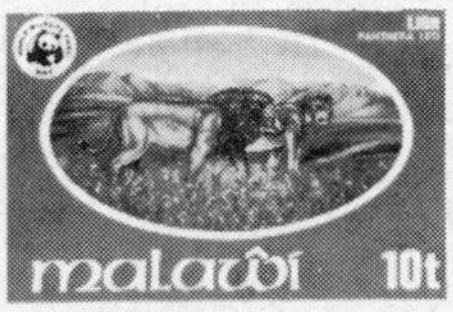

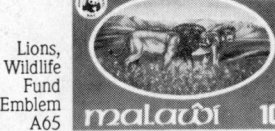

Lions, Wildlife Fund Emblem
A65

Animals and Wildlife Fund Emblem: 4t, Nyala, vert. 20t, Burchell's zebras. 40t, Reedbuck, vert.

1978, June 1 Unwmk. *Perf. 13x13½*

319 A65 4t multicolored .18 .18
320 A65 10t multicolored .60 .60
321 A65 20t multicolored 1.25 1.25
322 A65 40t multicolored 2.50 2.50
a. Souvenir sheet of 4, #319-322, perf. 13½ 5.00 5.00
Nos. 319-322 (4) 4.53 4.53

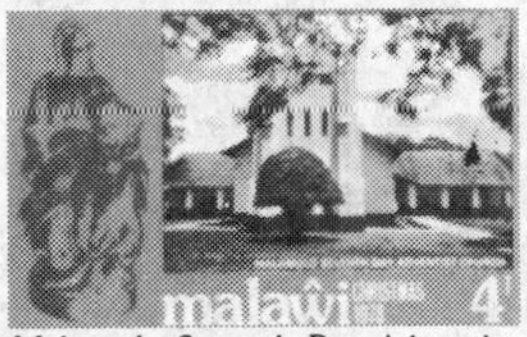

Malamulo Seventh Day Adventist Church — A66

Virgin and Child and: 10t, Likoma Cathedral. 20t, St. Michael's and All Angel's, Blantyre. 40t, Zomba Catholic Cathedral.

1978, Nov. 15 Wmk. 357 *Perf. 14*

323 A66 4t multicolored .15 .15
324 A66 10t multicolored .22 .22
325 A66 20t multicolored .45 .45
326 A66 40t multicolored .90 .90
a. Souvenir sheet of 4, #323-326 1.75 1.75
Nos. 323-326 (4) 1.72 1.72

Christmas.

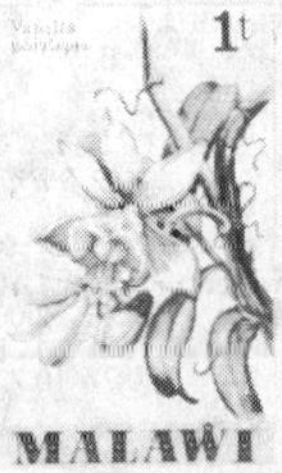

Vanilla Polylepis — A67

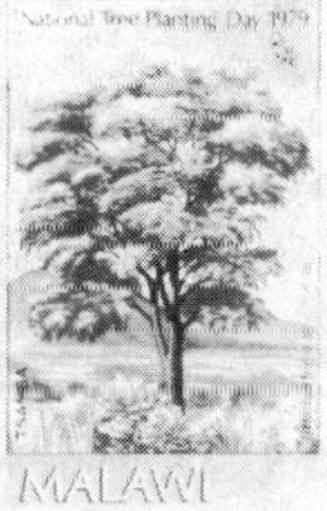

Brachystegia Spiciformis — A68

Orchids of Malawi: 2t, Cirrhopetalum umbellatum. 5t, Calanthe natalensis. 7t, Ansellia gigantea. 8t, Tridactyle bicaudata. 10t, Acampe pachyglossa. 15t, Eulophia quartiniana. 20t, Cyrtorchis arcuata. 30t, Eulophia tricristata. 50t, Disa hamatopetala. 75t, Cynorchis glandulosa. 1k, Aerangis kotschyana. 1.50k, Polystachya dendrobiiflora. 2k, Disa ornithantha. 4k, Cytorchis praetermissa.

1979, Jan. 2 Litho. *Perf. 13½*

327 A67 1t multicolored .15 .15
328 A67 2t multicolored .15 .15
329 A67 5t multicolored .15 .15
330 A67 7t multicolored .15 .15
331 A67 8t multicolored .15 .15
332 A67 10t multicolored .18 .18
333 A67 15t multicolored .28 .28
334 A67 20t multicolored .35 .35
335 A67 30t multicolored .50 .50
336 A67 50t multicolored .90 .90
337 A67 75t multicolored 1.40 1.40
338 A67 1k multicolored 1.75 1.75
339 A67 1.50k multicolored 2.50 2.50
340 A67 2k multicolored 3.25 3.25
341 A67 4k multicolored 7.50 7.50
Nos. 327-341 (15) 19.36 19.36

1979, Jan. 21 *Perf. 14x13½*

Trees: 10t, Widdringtonia nodiflora. 20t, Sandalwood. 40t, African mahogany.

342 A68 5t multicolored .15 .15
343 A68 10t multicolored .22 .22
344 A68 20t multicolored .45 .45
345 A68 40t multicolored .90 .90
a. Souvenir sheet of 4, #342-345 1.75 1.75
Nos. 342-345 (4) 1.72 1.72

National Tree Planting Day.

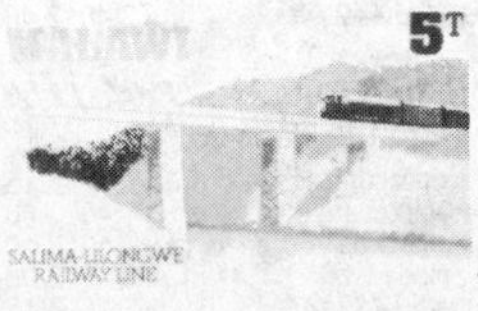

Railroad Bridge
A69

Designs: 10t, Station and train. 20t, 40t, Train passing through man-made pass, diff.

1979, Feb. 17 Litho. *Perf. 14½*

346 A69 5t multicolored .15 .15
347 A69 10t multicolored .25 .25
348 A69 20t multicolored .52 .52
349 A69 40t multicolored 1.05 1.05
a. Souvenir sheet of 4, #346-349 1.75 1.75
Nos. 346-349 (4) 1.97 1.97

Inauguration of Salima-Lilongwe Railroad.

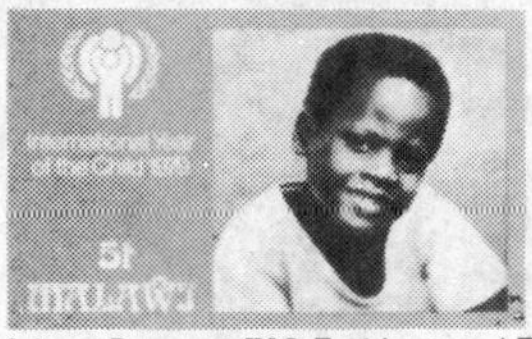

Malawi Boy and IYC Emblem — A70

Designs: Malawi children and IYC emblem.

1979, July 10 Wmk. 357 *Perf. 14*

350 A70 5t multicolored .15 .15
351 A70 10t multicolored .18 .18
352 A70 20t multicolored .35 .35
353 A70 40t multicolored .75 .75
Nos. 350-353 (4) 1.43 1.43

International Year of the Child.

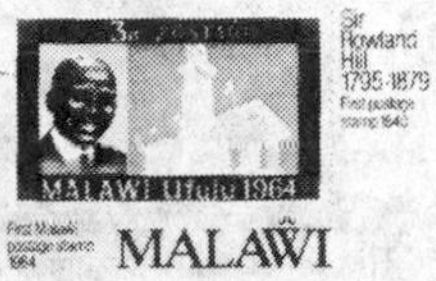

Malawi No. 1 — A71

Stamps of Malawi: 10t, #2. 20t, #3. 40t, #4.

1979, Sept. 17 Litho. *Perf. 13½x14*

354 A71 5t multicolored .15 .15
355 A71 10t multicolored .20 .20
356 A71 20t multicolored .35 .35
357 A71 40t multicolored .65 .65
a. Souvenir sheet of 4, #354-357 2.25 2.25
Nos. 354-357 (4) 1.35 1.35

Sir Rowland Hill (1795-1879), originator of penny postage.

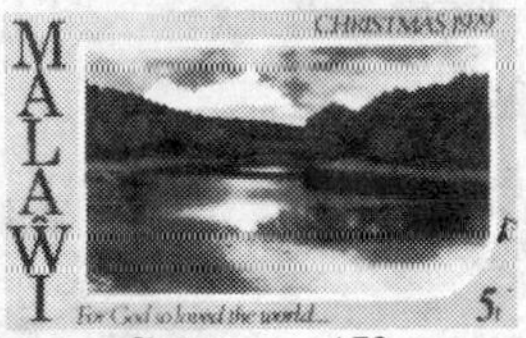

Christmas — A72

Designs: Landscapes.

1979, Nov. 15 Litho. *Perf. 13½x14*

358 A72 5t multicolored .15 .15
359 A72 10t multicolored .18 .18
360 A72 20t multicolored .35 .35
361 A72 40t multicolored .65 .65
Nos. 358-361 (4) 1.33 1.33

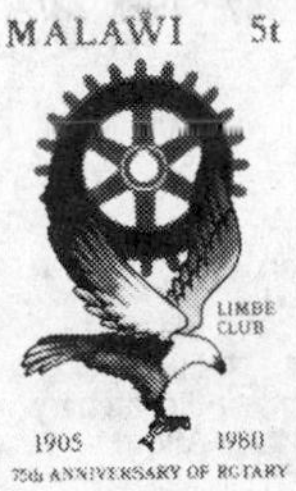

Limbe Rotary Club Emblem — A73

Malawi Rotary Club Emblems: 10t, Blantyre. 20t, Lilongwe. 40t, Rotary International.

1980, Feb. 23 Litho. *Perf. 13½*

362 A73 5t multicolored .15 .15
363 A73 10t multicolored .18 .18
364 A73 20t multicolored .35 .35
365 A73 40t multicolored .65 .65
a. Souvenir sheet of 4, #362-365 1.50 1.50
Nos. 362-365 (4) 1.33 1.33

Rotary International, 75th anniversary.

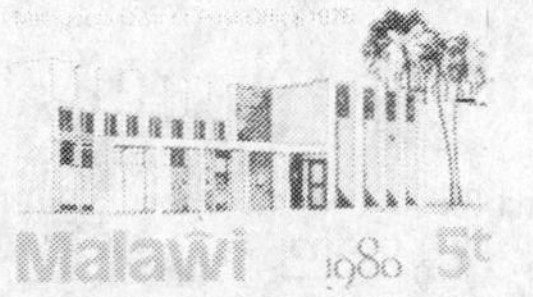

Mangochi District Post Office, 1976, London 1980 Emblem
A74

London 1980 Emblem and: 10t, New Blantyre sorting office, 1979. 20t, Mail transfer hut, Walala. 1k, Nyasaland Post Office, Chiromo, 1891.

1980, May 6 Wmk. 357 *Perf. 14½*

366 A74 5t blue green & blk .15 .15
367 A74 10t red & black .15 .15
368 A74 20t dp violet & black .30 .30
369 A74 1k dk blue & black 1.40 1.40
a. Souvenir sheet of 4, #366-369 2.50 2.50
Nos. 366-369 (4) 2.00 2.00

London 1980 International Stamp Exhibition, May 6-14.

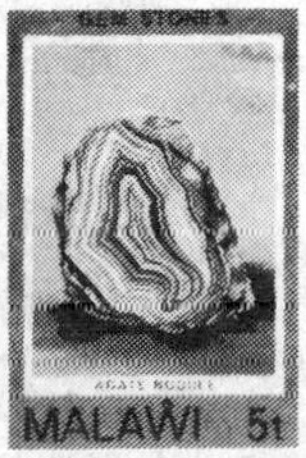

Agate Nodule — A75

1980, Aug. 20 Litho. *Perf. 13½*

370 A75 5t shown .22 .22
371 A75 10t Sunstone .40 .40
372 A75 20t Smoky Quartz .75 .75
373 A75 1k Kyanite crystal 3.75 3.75
Nos. 370-373 (4) 5.12 5.12

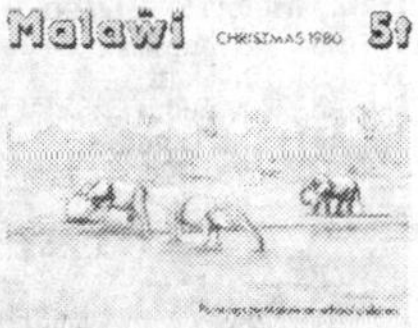

Elephants Drinking (Christmas)
A76

1980, Nov. 10 Litho. *Perf. 13*

374 A76 5t shown .15 .15
375 A76 10t Flowers .16 .16
376 A76 20t Train .35 .35
377 A76 1k Bird 1.75 1.75
Nos. 374-377 (4) 2.41 2.41

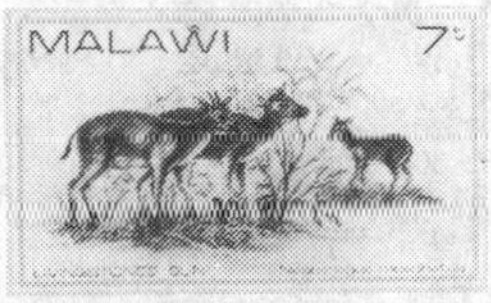

Livingstone's Suni — A77

1981, Feb. 4 Litho. *Perf. 14½*

378 A77 7t shown .15 .15
379 A77 10t Blue duikers .18 .18
380 A77 20t African buffalo .40 .40
381 A77 1k Lichtenstein's hartebeests 1.90 1.90
Nos. 378-381 (4) 2.63 2.63

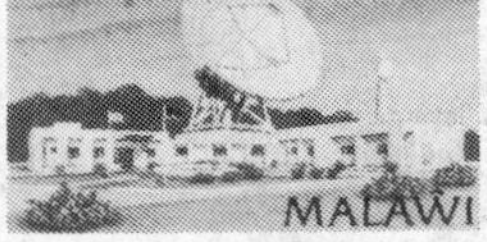

Standard A Earth Station
A78

1981, Apr. 24 Litho. *Perf. 14½*

382 A78 7t shown .15 .15
383 A78 10t Blantyre International Gateway Exchange .16 .16
384 A78 20t Standard B Earth Station .35 .35
385 A78 1k Satellite and earth 1.75 1.75
a. Souvenir sheet of 4, #382-385 2.50 2.50
Nos. 382-385 (4) 2.41 2.41

International communications.

World Food
Day
A79

1981, Sept. 11   Litho.   Perf. 14

386	A79	7t Corn	.15	.15
387	A79	10t Rice	.16	.16
388	A79	20t Finger millet	.35	.35
389	A79	1k Wheat	1.75	1.75
		Nos. 386-389 (4)	2.41	2.41

Holy Family,
by Lippi
A80

Christmas: 7t, Adoration of the Shepherds, by Murillo, vert. 20t, Adoration of the Shepherds, by Louis Le Nain. 1k, Virgin and Child, St. John the Baptist and Angel, by Paolo Morando, vert.

Perf. 13¹/₂x13, 13x13¹/₂

1981, Nov. 26   Litho.

390	A80	7t multicolored	.15	.15
391	A80	10t multicolored	.16	.16
392	A80	20t multicolored	.35	.35
393	A80	1k multicolored	1.75	1.75
		Nos. 390-393 (4)	2.41	2.41

Wildlife in
Natl. Parks
A81

1982, Mar. 15   Litho.   Perf. 14¹/₂x14

394	A81	7t Impalas	.15	.15
395	A81	10t Lions	.16	.16
396	A81	20t Kudus	.35	.35
397	A81	1k Flamingos	1.75	1.75
		Nos. 394-397 (4)	2.41	2.41

Kamuzu
Academy
A82

Designs: Academy views.

1982, July 1   Litho.   Perf. 14¹/₂

398	A82	7t multicolored	.15	.15
399	A82	20t multicolored	.28	.28
400	A82	30t multicolored	.40	.40
401	A82	1k multicolored	1.40	1.40
		Nos. 398-401 (4)	2.23	2.23

1982 World
Cup — A83

1982, Sept.   Perf. 14x14¹/₂

402	A83	7t Players	.15	.15
403	A83	20t World Cup	.40	.40
404	A83	30t Stadium	.55	.55
		Nos. 402-404 (3)	1.10	1.10

Souvenir Sheet

405	A83	1k Emblem on field	2.00	2.00

Remembrance Day — A84

Designs: War Memorials.

1982, Nov. 5   Perf. 14¹/₂

406	A84	7t Blantyre	.15	.15
407	A84	20t Zomba	.35	.35
408	A84	30t Chichiri, badges	.50	.50
409	A84	1k Lilongwe	1.75	1.75
		Nos. 406-409 (4)	2.75	2.75

A85

1983, Mar. 14   Wmk. 357   Perf. 14

410	A85	7t Kwacha Intl. Conf. Ctr.	.15	.15
411	A85	20t Tea picking, Mulanje	.35	.35
412	A85	30t Map	.50	.50
413	A85	1k Pres. Banda, flag	1.75	1.75
		Nos. 410-413 (4)	2.75	2.75

Commonwealth Day.

The Miraculous Draught of Fishes, by
Raphael (1483-1517) — A86

Designs: 7t, 20t, 30t, Details. 1k, Entire painting. 7t, 20t vert.

1983, Apr. 4   Litho.   Wmk. 357

414	A86	7t multicolored	.15	.15
415	A86	20t multicolored	.35	.35
416	A86	30t multicolored	.50	.50
		Nos. 414-416 (3)	1.00	1.00

Souvenir Sheet

417	A86	1k multicolored	1.50	1.50

Fish Eagles — A87

Designs: a, Lakeside sentinel. b, Gull-like, far-carrying call. c, Diving on its fish prey. d, Prey captured. e, Feeding on its catch. Nos. 418a-418e in continuous design.

1983, July 11   Wmk. 357   Perf. 14¹/₂

418		Strip of 5	4.50	4.50
a.-e.		A87 30t multicolored	.75	.75

Manned
Flight
Bicentenary
A88

Kamuzu Intl. Airport.

1983, Aug. 31   Litho.   Perf. 14

419	A88	7t multicolored	.15	.15
420	A88	20t multi, diff.	.35	.35
421	A88	30t multi, diff.	.50	.50
422	A88	1k multi, diff.	1.75	1.75
a.		Souvenir sheet of 4, #419-422	2.75	2.75
		Nos. 419-422 (4)	2.75	2.75

Christmas — A89

Local flowers.

1983, Nov. 1   Wmk. 357   Perf. 14

423	A89	7t Clerodendium myri-coides	.15	.15
424	A89	20t Gloriosa superba	.35	.35
425	A89	30t Gladiolus laxiflorus	.50	.50
426	A89	1k Aframomum angustifoli-um	1.75	1.75
		Nos. 423-426 (4)	2.75	2.75

Aquarium
Species, Lake
Malawi — A90

Perf. 14¹/₂x14

1984, Feb. 2   Wmk. 373

427	A90	1t Melanochromis auratus	.15	.15
428	A90	2t Haplochromis compressiceps	.15	.15
429	A90	5t Labeotropheus fuelleborni	.15	.15
430	A90	7t Pseudotropheus lombardoi	.15	.15
431	A90	8t Gold pseudotropheus zebra	.15	.15
432	A90	10t Trematocranus jacob-freibergi	.15	.15
433	A90	15t Melanochromis crabro	.16	.16
434	A90	20t Marbled pseado-tropheus	.22	.22
435	A90	30t Labidochromis caeruleus	.32	.32
436	A90	40t Haplochromis venustus	.42	.42
437	A90	50t Aulonacara of Thumbi	.55	.55
438	A90	75t Melanochromis vermivorus	.85	.85
439	A90	1k Pseudotropheus zebra	1.10	1.10
440	A90	2k Trematocranus spp.	2.00	2.00
441	A90	4k Aulonacara of Mbenje	4.25	4.25
		Nos. 427-441 (15)	10.77	10.77

Nos. 427, 430-436 exist inscribed "1986."

Nyika Red
Hare
A91

1984, Feb. 2   Wmk. 357   Perf. 14

442	A91	7t shown	.15	.15
443	A91	20t Sun squirrel	.38	.38
444	A91	30t Hedgehog	.55	.55
445	A91	1k Genet	1.75	1.75
		Nos. 442-445 (4)	2.83	2.83

1984 Summer
Olympics
A92

Local Butterflies
A93

1984, June 1   Litho.   Perf. 14

446	A92	7t Running	.15	.15
447	A92	20t Boxing	.30	.30
448	A92	30t Bicycling	.45	.45
449	A92	1k Long jump	1.50	1.50
a.		Souvenir sheet of 4, #446-449	2.50	2.50
		Nos. 446-449 (4)	2.40	2.40

1984, Aug. 1   Photo.   Perf. 11¹/₂
Granite Paper

450	A93	7t Euphaedra neophron	.15	.15
451	A93	20t Papilio dardanus	.40	.40
452	A93	30t Antanartia schaeneia	.60	.60
453	A93	1k Spindasis	2.00	2.00
		Nos. 450-453 (4)	3.15	3.15

CHRISTMAS 1984 Christmas — A94

Virgin and Child Paintings.

Perf. 14¹/₂

1984, Oct. 15   Litho.   Wmk. 357

454	A94	7t Duccio	.15	.15
455	A94	20t Raphael	.40	.40
456	A94	30t Lippi	.60	.60
457	A94	1k Wilton diptych	2.00	2.00
		Nos. 454-457 (4)	3.15	3.15

Fungi
A94a

1985, Jan. 23   Perf. 14¹/₂x14

458	A94a	7t Leucopaxillus gracil-limus	.15	.15
459	A94a	20t Limacella guttata	.38	.38
460	A94a	30t Termitomyces eurhizles	.60	.60
461	A94a	1k Xerulina asprata	1.90	1.90
		Nos. 458-461 (4)	3.03	3.03

Southern African Development
Coordination Conference — A95

1985, Apr. 1   Litho.   Perf. 14

462	A95	7t Forestry	.15	.15
463	A95	15t Communications	.18	.18
464	A95	20t Transportation	.24	.24
465	A95	1k Fishing	1.20	1.20
		Nos. 462-465 (4)	1.77	1.77

Ships on
Lake Malawi
A96

1985, June 3   Perf. 13¹/₂x13

466	A96	7t Ufulu	.15	.15
467	A96	15t Chauncy Maples	.28	.28
468	A96	20t Mtendere	.35	.35
469	A96	1k Ilala	1.90	1.90
a.		Souvenir sheet of 4, #466-469, perf. 13x12	2.75	2.75
		Nos. 466-469 (4)	2.68	2.68

Audubon Birth
Bicent. — A97

1985, Aug. 1   Litho.   Perf. 14

470	A97	7t Stierling's woodpecker	.20	.20
471	A97	15t Lesser seed-cracker	.42	.42
472	A97	20t Gunning's akalat	.55	.55
473	A97	1k Boehm's bee-eater	2.75	2.75
a.		Souvenir sheet of 4, #470-473	4.50	4.50
		Nos. 470-473 (4)	3.92	3.92

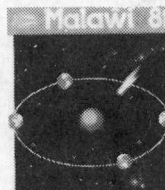

Christmas — A98

Halley's
Comet — A99

Paintings: 7t, The Virgin of Humility, by Jaime Serra. 15t, Adoration of the Magi, by Stefano da Zevio. 20t, Madonna and Child, by Gerard van Honthorst. 1k, Virgin of Zbraslav, by a Master of Vissi Brod.

Perf. 11¹/₂x12

1985, Oct. 14		Unwmk.	
474 A98	7t multicolored	.15	.15
475 A98	15t multicolored	.30	.30
476 A98	20t multicolored	.35	.35
477 A98	1k multicolored	2.00	2.00
	Nos. 474-477 (4)	2.80	2.80

1986, Feb. 10	Wmk. 357	Perf. 14¹/₂	
478 A99	8t Earth, comet and Giotto trajectories	.15	.15
479 A99	15t Comet over Earth	.18	.18
480 A99	20t Over Malawi	.24	.24
481 A99	1k Giotto probe	1.20	1.20
	Nos. 478-481 (4)	1.77	1.77

1986 World Cup Soccer Championships, Mexico — A100

Various soccer plays.

Perf. 12x11¹/₂

1986, May 26		Unwmk.	
	Granite Paper		
482 A100	8t multicolored	.15	.15
483 A100	15t multicolored	.28	.28
484 A100	20t multicolored	.35	.35
485 A100	1k multicolored	1.75	1.75
a.	Souvenir sheet of 4, #482-485	2.75	2.75
	Nos. 482-485 (4)	2.53	2.53

Natl. Independence, 20th Anniv. A101

Christmas A102

1986, June 30	Litho.	Perf. 14	
486 A101	8t Pres. Banda	.15	.15
487 A101	15t Natl. flag	.18	.18
488 A101	20t Natl. crest	.24	.24
489 A101	1k Natl. airline	1.20	1.20
	Nos. 486-489 (4)	1.77	1.77

1986, Dec. 15   Litho.   Perf. 11¹/₂

Paintings: 8t, Virgin and Child, by Botticelli (1445-1510). 15t, Adoration of the Shepherds, by Guido Reni (1575-1642). 20t, Madonna of the Veil, by Carlo Dolci (1616-86). 1k, Adoration of the Magi, by Jean Bourdichon.

490 A102	8t multicolored	.15	.15
491 A102	15t multicolored	.20	.20
492 A102	20t multicolored	.25	.25
493 A102	1k multicolored	1.25	1.25
	Nos. 490-493 (4)	1.85	1.85

World Wildlife Fund — A103

Bugeranus carunculatus.

1987, Jan. 30	Wmk. 357	Perf. 14¹/₂	
494 A103	8t Wattled crane	.20	.20
495 A103	15t Two cranes	.40	.40
496 A103	20t Nesting	.55	.55
497 A103	75t Crane in water	2.00	2.00
	Nos. 494-497 (4)	3.15	3.15

1988, Oct.		Wmk. 373	
494a A103	8t	.15	.15
495a A103	15t	.15	.15
496a A103	20t	.15	.15
497a A103	75t	.58	.58
	Nos. 494a-497a (4)	1.03	1.03

British Steam Locomotives A104

1987, May 25	Litho.	Perf. 14x13¹/₂	
498 A104	10t Shamrock No. 2, 1902	.15	.15
499 A104	25t D Class No. 8, 1914	.35	.35
500 A104	30t Thistle No. 1, 1902	.45	.45
501 A104	1k Kitson No. 6, 1903	1.40	1.40
	Nos. 498-501 (4)	2.35	2.35

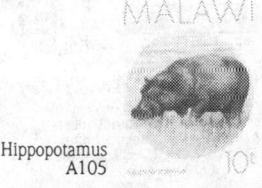

Hippopotamus A105

1987, Aug. 24	Photo.	Perf. 12¹/₂	
	Granite Paper		
502 A105	10t Feeding	.18	.18
503 A105	25t Swimming, roaring	.28	.28
504 A105	30t Mother and young swimming	.35	.35
505 A105	1k At rest, egret	1.25	1.25
a.	Souvenir sheet of 4, #502-505	2.00	2.00
	Nos. 502-505 (4)	2.06	2.06

Wild Flowers — A106

Locally Carved and Staunton Chessmen — A107

1987, Oct. 19	Litho.	Perf. 14	
	Unwmk.		
506 A106	10t Stathmostelma spectabile	.15	.15
507 A106	25t Pentanisia schweinfurthii	.30	.30
508 A106	30t Chironia krebsii	.38	.38
509 A106	1k Ochna macrocalyx	1.25	1.25
	Nos. 506-509 (4)	2.08	2.08

1988, Feb. 8	Wmk. 384	Perf. 14¹/₂	
510 A107	15t Knights	.15	.15
511 A107	35t Bishops	.35	.35
512 A107	50t Rooks	.50	.50
513 A107	2k Queens	2.00	2.00
	Nos. 510-513 (4)	3.00	3.00

Angling Soc. of Malawi, 50th Anniv. A111

1989, Apr. 11			
542 A111	15t Tsungwa	.15	.15
543 A111	35t Mpasa	.25	.25
544 A111	50t Yellow fish	.38	.38
545 A111	2k Tiger fish	1.50	1.50
	Nos. 542-545 (4)	2.28	2.28

1988 Summer Olympics, Seoul — A108

Birds — A109

1988, June 13	Unwmk.	Perf. 14	
514 A108	15t High jump	.15	.15
515 A108	35t Javelin	.35	.35
516 A108	50t Women's tennis	.48	.48
517 A108	2k Shot put	1.90	1.90
a.	Souvenir sheet of 4, #514-517	2.90	2.90
	Nos. 514-517 (4)	2.88	2.88

1988	Photo.	Perf. 14x14¹/₂	
	Granite Paper (1t-4k)		
518 A109	1t Eastern forest scrub-warbler	.15	.15
519 A109	2t Yellow-throated warbler	.15	.15
520 A109	5t Moustached green tinkerbird	.15	.15
521 A109	7t Waller's chestnut-wing starling	.15	.15
522 A109	8t Oriole finch	.15	.15
523 A109	10t Starred robin	.15	.15
524 A109	15t Bar-tailed trogon	.15	.15
525 A109	20t Green twinspot	.15	.15
526 A109	30t Gray cuckoo shrike	.20	.20
527 A109	40t Black-fronted bush shrike	.28	.28
528 A109	50t White-tailed crested flycatcher	.35	.35
529 A109	75t Green barbet	.52	.52
530 A109	1k Cinnamon dove	.70	.70
531 A109	2k Silvery-cheeked hornbill	1.40	1.40
532 A109	4k Crowned eagle	2.75	2.75
533 A109	10k Red-and-blue sun-bird	7.00	7.00
	Nos. 518-533 (16)	14.40	14.40

Issue dates: 10k, Oct. 3, others, July 25.

Lloyds of London, 300th Anniv.
Common Design Type

Designs: 15t, Royal Exchange, 1844. 35t, Opening of the Nkula Falls hydroelectric power station, horiz. 50t, Air Malawi passenger jet, horiz. 2k, Cruise ship Queen Elizabeth (Seawise University) on fire, Hong Kong, 1972.

		Wmk. 373	
1988, Oct. 24		Litho.	Perf. 14
534 CD341	15t multicolored	.15	.15
535 CD341	35t multicolored	.28	.28
536 CD341	50t multicolored	.38	.38
537 CD341	2k multicolored	1.50	1.50
	Nos. 534-537 (4)	2.31	2.31

Christmas — A110

Paintings: 15t, Madonna in the Church, by Jan Van Eyck (d. 1441). 35t, Virgin, Infant Jesus and St. Anne, by Leonardo da Vinci. 50t, Virgin and Angels, by Cimabue (c. 1240-1302). 2k, Virgin and Child, by Alesso Baldovinetti (c. 1425-1499).

1988, Nov. 28	Unwmk.	Perf. 14	
538 A110	15t multicolored	.15	.15
539 A110	35t multicolored	.25	.25
540 A110	50t multicolored	.38	.38
541 A110	2k multicolored	1.50	1.50
	Nos. 538-541 (4)	2.28	2.28

Natl. Independence, 25th Anniv. — A112

1989, June 26			
546 A112	15t Independence Arch	.15	.15
547 A112	35t Grain silos	.25	.25
548 A112	50t Capital Hill	.35	.35
549 A112	2k Reserve Bank Head-quarters	1.45	1.45
	Nos. 546-549 (4)	2.20	2.20

African Development Bank, 25th Anniv. — A113

1989, Oct. 30			
550 A113	15t Blantyre Digital Telex Exchange	.15	.15
551 A113	40t Dzalanyama steer	.30	.30
552 A113	50t Mikolongwe heifer	.38	.38
553 A113	2k Zebu bull	1.50	1.50
	Nos. 550-553 (4)	2.33	2.33

Cooperation with the UN, 25th Anniv. — A114

1989, Dec. 1		Perf. 14	
554 A114	15t shown	.15	.15
555 A114	40t House, diff.	.30	.30
556 A114	50t Thatched dwelling, house	.38	.38
557 A114	2k Tea Plantation	1.50	1.50
	Nos. 554-557 (4)	2.33	2.33

Rural Housing Program.

Christmas A115

Designs: 15t, St. Michael and All Angels Church. 40t, Limbe Cathedral. 50t, Nkhoma CCAP Church. 2k, Likoma Is. Cathedral.

1989, Dec. 15			
558 A115	15t multicolored	.15	.15
559 A115	40t multicolored	.30	.30
560 A115	50t multicolored	.38	.38
561 A115	2k multicolored	1.50	1.50
	Nos. 558-561 (4)	2.33	2.33

Classic Cars A116

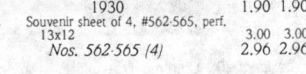

		Perf. 14x13¹/₂	
1990, Apr. 2	Litho.		Unwmk.
562 A116	15t Ford Sedan, 1915	.18	.18
563 A116	40t Two-seater Ford, 1915	.38	.38
564 A116	50t Ford, 1915	.50	.50
565 A116	2k Chevrolet Luxury Bus, 1930	1.90	1.90
a.	Souvenir sheet of 4, #562-565, perf. 13x12	3.00	3.00
	Nos. 562-565 (4)	2.96	2.96

World Cup Soccer Championships, Italy — A117

1990, June 14 Litho. *Perf. 14*

566 A117 15t shown .15 .15
567 A117 40t Two players .28 .28
568 A117 50t Shot on goal .35 .35
569 A117 2k World Cup Trophy 1.40 1.40
a. Souvenir sheet of 4, #566-569 2.25 2.25
Nos. 566-569 (4) 2.18 2.18

SADCC, 10th Anniv. A118

1990, Aug. 24 Litho. *Perf. 14*

570 A118 15t Map .15 .15
571 A118 40t Chambo .28 .28
572 A118 50t Cedar trees .35 .35
573 A118 2k Nyala 1.40 1.40
a. Souvenir sheet of 4, #570-573 2.25 2.25
Nos. 570-573 (4) 2.18 2.18

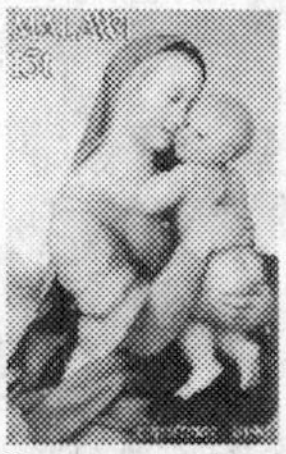

Christmas — A119

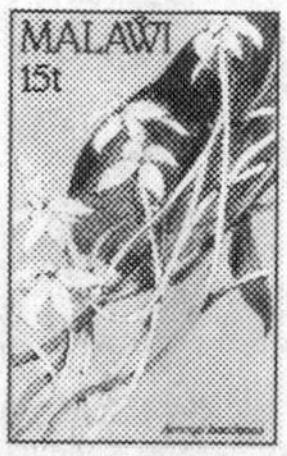

Orchids — A120

Paintings by Raphael: 15t, Virgin and Child. 40t, The Transfiguration, detail. 50t, St. Catherine of Alexandrie. 2k, The Transfiguration.

1990, Dec. *Perf. 13½x14*

574 A119 15t multicolored .15 .15
575 A119 40t multicolored .28 .28
576 A119 50t multicolored .35 .35
577 A119 2k multicolored 1.40 1.40
a. Souvenir sheet of 4, #574-577, perf. 12x13 2.25 2.25
Nos. 574-577 (4) 2.18 2.18

1990, Dec.

578 A120 15t Aerangis kotschyana .20 .20
579 A120 40t Angraecum eburneum .35 .35
580 A120 50t Aerangis luteo alba .50 .50
581 A120 2k Cyrtorchis arcuata 1.90 1.90
a. Souvenir sheet of 4, #578-581, perf. 12x13 3.00 3.00
Nos. 578-581 (4) 2.95 2.95

Wild Animals A121

1991, Apr. 23 Litho. *Perf. 14x13½*

582 A121 20t Buffalo .15 .15
583 A121 60t Cheetah .45 .45
584 A121 75t Greater kudu .55 .55
585 A121 2k Black rhinoceros 1.50 1.50
a. Souvenir sheet of 4, #582-585, perf. 13x12 2.65 2.65
Nos. 582-585 (4) 2.65 2.65

Malawi Postal Services, Cent. A122

Designs: 20t, Chiromo Post Office, 1891. 60t, Mail exchange hut, Walala. 75t, Mangochi Post Office. 2k, Standard A Earth station, 1981.

1991, July 2 *Perf. 14x13½*

586 A122 20t multicolored .15 .15
587 A122 60t multicolored .45 .45
588 A122 75t multicolored .55 .55
589 A122 2k multicolored 1.50 1.50
a. Souvenir sheet of 4, #586-589, perf. 13x12 2.65 2.65
Nos. 586-589 (4) 2.65 2.65

Insects — A123

Christmas — A124

1991, Sept. 21 *Perf. 13½x14*

590 A123 20t Red locust .15 .15
591 A123 60t Weevil .45 .45
592 A123 75t Cotton stainer bug .55 .55
593 A123 2k Pollen beetle 1.50 1.50
Nos. 590-593 (4) 2.65 2.65

1991, Nov. 26 Litho. *Perf. 13½x14*

594 A124 20t Christ Child in manger .15 .15
595 A124 60t Adoration of the Magi .45 .45
596 A124 75t Nativity .55 .55
597 A124 2k Virgin and Child 1.50 1.50
Nos. 594-597 (4) 2.65 2.65

Birds A125

Designs: a, Red bishop. b, Lesser striped swallow. c, Long-crested eagle. d, Lilac-breasted roller. e, African paradise flycatcher. f, White-fronted bee-eater. g, White-winged black tern. h, Brown-backed fire-finch. i, White-browed robin-chat. j, African fish eagle. k, Malachite kingfisher. l, Cabani's masked weaver. m, African barn owl. n, Yellow-bellied sunbird. o, Lesser flamingo. p, Crowned crane. q, African pitta. r, African darter. s, White-faced tree duck. t, African pied wagtail.

1992, Apr. 7 Litho. *Perf. 14*

598 A125 75t Sheet of 20, #a.-t. 11.00 11.00

A number has been reserved for an additional value in this set.

1992 Summer Olympics, Barcelona A126

1992, July 28 Litho. *Perf. 13½*

600 A126 20t Long jump .15 .15
601 A126 60t High jump .45 .45
602 A126 75t Javelin .55 .55
603 A126 2k Running 1.50 1.50
a. Souvenir sheet of 4, #600-603 2.65 2.65
Nos. 600-603 (4) 2.65 2.65

Christmas — A127

Details from paintings: 20t, Angel from The Annunciation, by Philippe de Champaigne. 75t, Virgin and Child, by Bernardino Luini. 95t, Virgin and Child, by Sassoferrato. 2k, Mary from The Annunciation, by Champaigne.

1992, Nov. 9 Litho. *Perf. 14*

604 A127 20t multicolored .15 .15
605 A127 75t multicolored .38 .38
606 A127 95t multicolored .48 .48
607 A127 2k multicolored 1.05 1.05
Nos. 604-607 (4) 2.06 2.06

Intl. Space Year — A128

Designs: 20t, Voyager II, Saturn. 75t, Center of a galaxy. 95t, Kanjedza II ground station. 2k, Communication satellite.

1992, Dec. 7 Litho. *Perf. 13½*

608 A128 20t multicolored .15 .15
609 A128 75t multicolored .38 .38
610 A128 95t multicolored .48 .48
611 A128 2k multicolored 1.00 1.00
Nos. 608-611 (4) 2.01 2.01

Fruit — A129

Butterflies — A130

1993, Mar. 21 Litho. *Perf. 13½x14*

612 A129 20t Strychnos spinosa .15 .15
613 A129 75t Adansonia digitata .35 .35
614 A129 95t Ximenia caffra .42 .42
615 A129 2k Uapaca kirkiana .90 .90
Nos. 612-615 (4) 1.82 1.82

1993, June 28 Litho. *Perf. 13*

616 A130 20t Apaturopsis cleocharis .15 .15
617 A130 75t Euryphura achlys .35 .35
618 A130 95t Cooksonia aliciae .42 .42
619 A130 2k Charaxes protoclea azota .90 .90
Nos. 616-619 (4) 1.82 1.82

A131

Dinosaurs A132

Designs: No. 623a, Tyrannosaurus Rex. b, Dilophosaurus. c, Brachiosaurus. d, Gallimimus. e, Triceratops. f, Velociraptor.

1993, Dec. 30 Litho. *Perf. 13*

620 A131 20t Kentrosaurus .15 .15
621 A131 75t Stegosaurus .35 .35
622 A131 95t Sauropod .42 .42
Nos. 620-622 (3) .92 .92

Miniature Sheet

623 A132 2k Sheet of 6, #a.-f. 5.50 5.50

Christmas — A133

1993, Nov. 30 Photo. *Perf. 11½*

Granite Paper

624 A133 20t Holy family .15 .15
625 A133 75t Shepherds .35 .35
626 A133 95t Wise men .42 .42
627 A133 2k Adoration of the magi .90 .90
Nos. 624-627 (4) 1.82 1.82

Fish of Lake Malawi A134

Designs: 20t, Pseudotropheus socolofi. 75t, Melanochromis auratus. 95t, Pseudotropheus lombardoi. 1k, Labeotropheus trewavasae. 2k, Pseudotropheus zebra. 4k, Pseudotropheus elongatus.

1994, Mar. 21 Litho. *Perf. 14x15*

628 A134 20t multicolored .15 .15
629 A134 75t multicolored .35 .35
630 A134 95t multicolored .42 .42
631 A134 1k multicolored .45 .45
632 A134 2k multicolored .90 .90
633 A134 4k multicolored 1.75 1.75
Nos. 628-633 (6) 4.02 4.02

Ships of Lake Malawi A135

1994, Oct. 19 Litho. *Perf. 13x13½*

634 A135 20t Ilala .15 .15
635 A135 75t MV Ufulu .15 .15
636 A135 95t The Pioneer .16 .16
637 A135 2k Dove .35 .35
Set value .68 .68

Souvenir Sheet

638 A135 5k Monteith .90 .90

Christmas — A136

Details or entire paintings: 20t, Virgin and Child, by Durer, vert. 75t, Magi Present Gifts to Infant Jesus, Franco-Flemish Book of Hours, vert. 95t, The Nativity, by Fra Filippo Lippi. 2k, Nativity with Magi, by Rogier van der Weyden.

1994, Nov. 30 Litho. *Perf. 14½*

639 A136 20t multicolored .15 .15
640 A136 75t multicolored .15 .15
641 A136 95t multicolored .16 .16
642 A136 2k multicolored .35 .35
Set value .68 .68

Pres. Bakili Muluzi — A137

1995, Apr. 10 Litho. *Perf. 11½x12*

643 A137 40t red & multi .15 .15
644 A137 1.40k green & multi .20 .20
645 A137 1.80k blue & multi .20 .20
646 A137 2k brn org & multi .25 .25
Nos. 643-646 (4) .80 .80

Establishment of COMESA (Common Market for Eastern & Southern African States).

Christmas
A138

1995, Nov. 13   Litho.   Perf. 11½
Granite Paper

647	A138	40t Pre-schoolers	.15	.15
648	A138	1.40k Dispensing medicine	.20	.20
649	A138	1.80k Water supply	.25	.25
650	A138	2k Voluntary return	.30	.30
		Nos. 647-650 (4)	.90	.90

POSTAGE DUE STAMPS

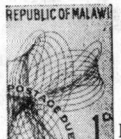
D1

Perf. 11½
1967, Sept. 1   Litho.   Wmk. 357

J1	D1	1p deep lilac rose	.15	.15
J2	D1	2p sepia	.22	.22
J3	D1	4p lilac	.45	.45
J4	D1	6p dark blue	.55	.55
J5	D1	8p emerald	.90	.90
J6	D1	1sh black	1.10	1.10
		Nos. J1-J6 (6)	3.37	3.37

Values in Decimal Currency

1971, Feb. 15
Size: 18x23mm

J7	D1	2t sepia	.15	.15
J8	D1	4t lilac	.20	.20
J9	D1	6t dark blue	.30	.30
J10	D1	8t green	.40	.40
J11	D1	10t black	.50	.50
		Nos. J7-J11 (5)	1.55	1.55

Type of 1971 Redrawn

1975   Wmk. 357   Perf. 14
Size: 17x21mm

J12	D1	2t brown	.20	.20

No. J12 has accent mark over "W."

1977-78   Litho.   Unwmk.   Perf. 14
Size: 18x21mm

J13	D1	2t sepia	.15	.15
J14	D1	4t rose lilac	.30	.30
J15	D1	8t brt green ('78)	.60	.60
J16	D1	10t black	.75	.75
		Nos. J13-J16 (4)	1.80	1.80

1982   Wmk. 357, Sideways

J13a	D1	2t	.15	.15
J14a	D1	4t	.15	.15
J16a	D1	10t	.25	.25
		Nos. J13a-J16a (3)	.55	.55

MALAYA

mə-'lā-ə

Federated Malay States

LOCATION — Malay peninsula
GOVT. — Former British Protectorate
AREA — 27,585 sq. mi.
CAPITAL — Kuala Lumpur

The Federated Malay States consisted of the sultanates of Negri Sembilan, Pahang, Perak and Selangor.
Stamps of the Federated Malay States replaced those of the individual states and were used until 1935, when individual issues were resumed.

100 Cents = 1 Dollar

> Catalogue values for unused stamps in this country are for Never Hinged items, beginning with Scott 80 in the regular postage section, Scott J20 in the postage due section, Scott 128 in Johore, Scott 55 in Kedah, Scott 44 in Kelantan, Scott 1 in Malacca, Scott 36 in Negri Sembilan, Scott 44 in Pahang, Scott 1 in Penang, Scott 99 in Perak, Scott 1 in Perlis, Scott 74 in Selangor, and Scott 47 in Trengganu.

Watermarks

Wmk. 47 - Multiple Rosettes

Wmk. 71 - Rosette

Wmk. 338 - PTM Multiple

(PTM stands for Persekutuan Tanah Melayu, or Federation of Malaya.)

Stamps of Straits Settlements overprinted "BMA MALAYA" are listed in Straits Settlements.

Stamps and Type of Negri Sembilan Overprinted in Black — **FEDERATED MALAY STATES**

1900   Wmk. 2   Perf. 14

1	A2	1c lilac & green	1.75	2.75
2	A2	2c lilac & brown	22.50	45.00
3	A2	3c lilac & black	2.25	3.50
4	A2	5c lilac & olive	60.00	110.00
5	A2	10c lilac & org	3.00	12.50
6	A2	20c green & olive	50.00	70.00
7	A2	25c grn & car rose	150.00	200.00
8	A2	50c green & black	60.00	85.00
		Nos. 1-8 (8)	349.50	528.75

Overprinted on Perak Nos. 51, 53, 57-58, 60-61

1900

9	A9	5c lilac & olive	10.00	45.00
10	A9	10c lilac & org	55.00	55.00

Wmk. 1

11	A10	$1 green & lt grn	100.00	125.00
12	A10	$2 green & car rose	85.00	120.00
13	A10	$5 green & ultra	175.00	300.00
13A	A10	$25 green & org	4,250.	
		Revenue cancel		200.00
		Nos. 9-13 (5)	425.00	645.00

No. 10 with bar omitted is an essay.

Elephants and Howdah — A3

Tiger — A4

Stamps of type A4 are watermarked sideways.

1900   Typo.

14	A3	$1 green & lt green	60.00	65.00
15	A3	$2 grn & car rose	70.00	75.00
16	A3	$5 green & ultra	125.00	130.00
17	A3	$25 grn & orange	1,050.	675.00
		Nos. 14-17 (4)	1,305.	945.00

High values with revenue cancellations are plentiful and inexpensive.

1901   Wmk. 2

18	A4	1c blue grn & blk	1.00	.30
19	A4	3c brown & gray	2.50	.20
20	A4	4c rose & black	4.00	.40
21	A4	5c scar & grn, yel	2.00	1.50
22	A4	8c ultra & blk	25.00	3.00
23	A4	10c violet & blk	35.00	3.75
24	A4	25c black & gray vio	22.50	6.00
25	A4	50c brn org & black	57.50	25.00
		Nos. 18-25 (8)	149.50	40.15

1904-10   Wmk. 3

26	A4	1c green & black	17.50	.60
27	A4	3c brown & gray	17.50	.30
28	A4	4c rose & black	4.00	.25
29	A4	5c scar & grn, yel	4.50	1.25
30	A4	8c ultra & black ('05)	6.25	3.00
31	A4	10c violet & black	12.50	.35
32	A4	20c blk & gray vio ('05)	3.00	.35
33	A4	50c brn org & blk ('05)	25.00	4.00

The 1c and 4c are on ordinary paper, the other values on both ordinary and chalky papers.

Chalky Paper

34	A3	$1 green & lt green ('07)	40.00	25.00
35	A3	$2 green & car rose ('06)	60.00	85.00
36	A3	$5 grn & ultra ('06)	85.00	90.00
37	A3	$25 grn & org ('10)	950.00	475.00
		Nos. 26-36 (11)	275.25	210.10

High values with revenue cancellations are plentiful and inexpensive.

1906-22   Ordinary Paper

Two dies for Nos. 38 and 44·
I - Thick line under "Malay."
II - Thin line under "Malay."

38	A4	1c dull grn, die II	1.90	.20
b.		Die I	5.00	.40
39	A4	1c brown ('19)	2.00	1.10
40	A4	2c green ('19)	.65	.30
41	A4	3c brown	4.50	.15
42	A4	3c carmine ('09)	2.25	.15
43	A4	3c dp gray ('19)	1.10	.15
44	A4	3c scar, die I ('19)	1.75	2.00
b.		Die II	1.10	.30
45	A4	6c orange ('19)	1.90	1.25
46	A4	8c ultra ('09)	12.00	.80
47	A4	10c ultra ('19)	5.50	.80
48	A4	35c red, yellow	6.00	11.00
		Nos. 38-48 (11)	39.55	17.90

1922-32   Wmk. 4

Ordinary Paper

49	A4	1c brown ('22)	1.75	1.75
50	A4	1c black ('23)	.45	.15
51	A4	2c dk brown ('25)	3.75	1.75
52	A4	2c green ('26)	.60	.15
53	A4	3c dp gray ('23)	2.75	4.25
54	A4	3c green ('24)	2.25	1.75
55	A4	3c brown ('27)	.60	.30
56	A4	4c scar (II) ('23)	2.25	.40
57	A4	4c orange ('26)	.50	.15
c.		Unwatermarked	200.00	95.00
58	A4	5c vio, yel ('22)	.75	.15
59	A4	5c dk brown ('32)	1.50	.15
60	A4	6c orange ('22)	.50	.35
61	A4	6c scarlet ('26)	.75	.15
62	A4	10c ultra ('23)	1.25	5.00
63	A4	10c ultra & blk ('23)	1.75	.50
64	A4	10c vio, yel ('31)	5.75	.35
65	A4	12c ultra ('22)	1.25	.15
66	A4	20c blk & vio ('23)	4.50	.25

Chalky Paper

67	A4	25c red vio & ol vio ('29)	2.25	.75
68	A4	30c yel & dl vio ('29)	3.00	1.50
69	A4	35c red, yel ('28)	5.75	12.50
70	A4	35c dk vio & car ('31)	12.00	10.50
71	A4	50c org & blk ('24)	12.00	3.75
72	A4	50c blk, bl grn ('31)	4.00	1.25
73	A3	$1 gray grn & yel grn ('26)	12.00	27.50
a.		$1 green & blue green	17.50	50.00
74	A3	$2 grn & car ('26)	12.00	50.00
75	A3	$5 grn & ultra ('25)	60.00	90.00
76	A3	$25 grn & org ('28)	700.00	350.00
		Nos. 49-75 (27)	155.90	215.45

#64 is on chalky paper; #66 exists on both ordinary and chalky paper; #69 is on ordinary paper.

1931-34

77	A4	$1 red & blk, blue	11.00	2.50
78	A4	$2 car & green, yel ('34)	27.50	26.00
79	A4	$5 car & green, emer ('34)	115.00	125.00
		Nos. 77-79 (3)	153.50	153.50

FEDERATION OF MALAYA

GOVT. — Sovereign state in British Commonwealth of Nations
AREA — 50,700 sq. mi.
POP. — 7,139,000 (est. 1961)
CAPITAL — Kuala Lumpur

The Federation comprised the nine states of Johore, Pahang, Negri Sembilan, Selangor, Perak, Kedah, Perlis, Kelantan and Trengganu and the settlements of Penang and Malacca.
Malaya joined the Federation of Malaysia in 1963.

100 Sen (Cents) = 1 Dollar (1957)

> Catalogue values for unused stamps in this section are for Never Hinged items.

The Peace Issue of 1946 8c stamp inscribed "MALAYAN UNION" was not issued.

Rubber Tapping
A5

Map of Federation
A6

Designs: 12c, Federation coat of arms. 25c, Tin dredge and flag.

Perf. 13x12½, 12½
Engr., Litho.

1957, May 5   Wmk. 314

80	A5	6c blue, red & yel	.15	.15
a.		Yellow omitted	40.00	

81	A5	12c car & multi	.15	.15
82	A5	25c multicolored	.24	.15
83	A6	30c dp claret & red org	.38	.15
		Set value		.92	.22

Chief Minister
Tunku Abdul
Rahman and
People of
Various
Races — A7

Perf. 12½
1957, Aug. 31   Wmk. 4   Engr.

| 84 | A7 | 10c brown | .15 | .15 |

Independence Day, Aug. 31.

United Nations
Emblem — A8

Design: 30c, UN emblem, vert.

Perf. 13½, 12½
1958, Mar. 5   Wmk. 314

| 85 | A8 | 12c rose red | .38 | .24 |
| 86 | A8 | 30c plum | .42 | .28 |

Conf. of the Economic Commission for Asia and the Far East (ECAFE), Kuala Lumpur, Mar. 5-15.

Merdeka Stadium
and Flag — A9

Tuanku Abdul
Rahman,
Paramount Ruler
of Malaya — A10

Perf. 13½x14½, 14½x13½
1958, Aug. 31   Photo.   Wmk. 314

87	A9	10c multicolored	.15	.15
88	A10	30c multicolored	.42	.28
		Set value		.34

1st anniv. of the Independence of the Federation of Malaya.

Torch of Freedom and Broken Chain
A11   A12

Perf. 12½x13, 13x12½
1958, Dec. 10   Litho.   Wmk. 314

| 89 | A11 | 10c multicolored | .15 | .15 |

Photo.

| 90 | A12 | 30c green | .52 | .35 |
| | | Set value | | .42 |

10th anniv. of the signing of the Universal Declaration of Human Rights.

Mace and
People — A13

WRY Emblem — A14

Perf. 12½x13½
1959, Sept. 12   Photo.   Unwmk.

91	A13	4c rose red	.15	.15
92	A13	10c violet	.16	.15
93	A13	25c yellow green	.38	.32
		Nos. 91-93 (3)	.69	
		Set value		.48

1st Federal Parliament of Malaya, inauguration.

Perf. 13½, 13
1960, Apr. 7   Engr.   Wmk. 314

Design: 30c, Similar to 12c, vert.

| 94 | A14 | 12c lilac | .28 | .24 |
| 95 | A14 | 30c dark green | .30 | .20 |

World Refugee Year, July 1, 1959-June 30, 1960.

Rubber Tree Seedling on
Map of Malaya — A15

Tuanku Syed
Putra — A16

Perf. 13x13½
1960, Sept. 19   Litho.   Unwmk.

96	A15	6s red brown, grn & blk	.15	.15
97	A15	30s ultra, yel grn & blk	.55	.38
		Set value		.45

15th meeting of the Intl. Rubber Study Group and the Natural Rubber Research Conference, Kuala Lumpur, Sept. 26-Oct. 1.

Perf. 13½x14½
1961, Jan. 4   Photo.   Wmk. 314

| 98 | A16 | 10s blue & black | .15 | .15 |

Installation of Tuanku Syed Putra of Perlis as Paramount Ruler (Yang di-Pertuan Agong.)

Colombo Plan
Emblem — A17

Malaria
Eradication
Emblem — A18

1961, Oct. 30   Unwmk.   Perf. 13½

99	A17	12s rose pink & black	.32	.22
100	A17	25s brt yellow & black	.42	.30
101	A17	30s brt blue & black	.52	.22
		Nos. 99-101 (3)	1.26	.74

13th meeting of the Consultative Committee for Technical Co-operation in South and South East Asia, Kuala Lumpur, Oct. 30-Nov. 18.

Wmk. PTM Multiple (338)
1962, Apr. 7   Perf. 14x14½

102	A18	25s orange brown	.26	.15
103	A18	30s dull violet	.30	.16
104	A18	50s ultramarine	.48	.35
		Nos. 102-104 (3)	1.04	.66

WHO drive to eradicate malaria.

Palmyra
Leaf — A19

1962, July 21   Photo.   Perf. 13½

105	A19	10s violet & gldn brown	.15	.15
106	A19	20s bluish grn & gldn brn	.20	.15
107	A19	35s car rose & gldn brown	.42	.32
		Nos. 105-107 (3)	.77	
		Set value		.50

National Language Month. Watermark inverted on alternating stamps.

Children and their
Future
Shadows — A20

1962, Oct. 1   Wmk. 338   Perf. 13½

108	A20	10s bright rose lilac	.15	.15
109	A20	25s ocher	.35	.30
110	A20	30s bright green	.40	.26
		Nos. 108-110 (3)	.90	
		Set value		.60

Free primary education introduced Jan. 1962.

Forms of Food
Production and
Ears of
Wheat — A21

**1963, Mar. 21   Unwmk.   Perf. 11½
Granite Paper**

111	A21	25s lt ol grn & lilac rose	.32	.24
112	A21	35s dk car & lilac rose	.42	.18
113	A21	50s ultra & lilac rose	.52	.28
		Nos. 111-113 (3)	1.26	.70

FAO "Freedom from Hunger" campaign.

Cameron
Highlands Dam
and
Pylon — A22

1963, June 26   Wmk. 338   Perf. 14

| 114 | A22 | 20s purple & brt green | .45 | .30 |
| 115 | A22 | 30s ultra & brt green | .65 | .45 |

Opening of the Cameron Highlands hydroelectric plant.

Check listings for individual states for additional stamps inscribed "Malaya."

POSTAGE DUE STAMPS

D1   D2

Perf. 14½x14
1924-26   Typo.   Wmk. 4

J1	D1	1c violet	2.25	2.25
J2	D1	2c black	1.40	1.75
J3	D1	4c green ('26)	5.50	9.50
J4	D1	8c red	5.00	11.00
J5	D1	10c orange	5.50	11.00
J6	D1	12c ultramarine	8.50	18.00
		Nos. J1-J6 (6)	28.15	53.50

1936-38   Perf. 14½x14

J7	D2	1c dk violet ('38)	2.50	.50
J8	D2	4c yellow green	4.25	1.00
J9	D2	8c scarlet	3.00	4.25
J10	D2	10c yel orange	3.00	.45
J11	D2	12c blue violet	4.00	5.00
J12	D2	50c black ('38)	13.00	12.50
		Nos. J7-J12 (6)	29.75	23.70

#J7-J12 were also used in Straits Settlements. For overprints see #NJ1-NJ20, Malacca #NJ1-NJ6.

1945-49

J13	D2	1c reddish violet	2.50	1.50
J14	D2	3c yel green	7.25	10.00
J15	D2	5c org scarlet	10.00	12.00
J16	D2	8c yel org ('49)	20.00	10.00
J17	D2	9c yel orange	45.00	35.00

J18	D2	15c blue vio	80.00	35.00
J19	D2	20c dk blue ('48)	10.00	12.00
		Nos. J13-J19 (7)	174.75	115.50

For surcharge see No. J34.

> Catalogue values for unused stamps in this section, from this point to the end of the section, are for Never Hinged items.

1951-62   Wmk. 4   Perf. 14

J20	D2	1c dull violet ('52)	.30	.35
J21	D2	2c dk gray ('53)	.35	.50
J22	D2	3c green ('52)	12.50	10.00
J23	D2	4c dk brown ('53)	.40	2.50
J24	D2	5c vermilion	27.50	10.00
J25	D2	8c yel orange	2.00	2.50
J26	D2	12c magenta ('54)	1.00	2.50
J27	D2	20c deep blue	5.00	6.00
		Nos. J20-J27 (8)	49.05	34.35

Nos. J13-J27 were used throughout the Federation and in Singapore, later in Malaysia.

1957-62   Perf. 12½

J21a	D2	2c ('60)	.30	7.50
J23a	D2	4c ('60)	.65	7.00
J26a	D2	12c ('62)	1.50	12.50
J27a	D2	20c	5.00	25.00
		Nos. J21a-J27a (4)	7.45	52.00

1965   Wmk. 314   Perf. 12

J28	D2	1c plum	.20	2.00
J29	D2	2c bluish black	.25	5.00
J30	D2	4c brown	.30	7.50
J31	D2	8c yel orange	4.50	10.00
J32	D2	12c magenta	2.50	20.00
J33	D2	20c dark blue	3.50	27.50
		Nos. J28-J33 (6)	11.25	72.00

Nos. J28-J33 were used in Malaysia.

1964, Apr. 14   Perf. 12½

J28a	D2	1c	.20	2.00
J29a	D2	2c	.30	7.50
J30a	D2	4c	.65	7.00
J32a	D2	12c	1.50	12.50
J33a	D2	20c	5.00	25.00
		Nos. J28a-J33a (5)	7.65	54.00

10 cents

No. J16 Surcharged

1965, Jan.   Wmk. 4

| J34 | D2 | 10c on 8c yel orange | .50 | 1.00 |

OCCUPATION STAMPS

Issued Under Japanese Occupation

Malayan Fruit and
Fronds
OS1

Tin Dredging
OS2

Monument to
Japanese War Dead
OS3

Malayan
Plowman
OS4

1943   Unwmk.   Litho.   Perf. 12½

N30	OS1	2c emerald	.25	.25
a.		Rouletted	1.25	1.00
b.		Imperf., pair	3.75	3.75
N31	OS2	4c rose red	.25	.25
a.		Rouletted	1.25	1.25
N32	OS3	8c dull blue	.25	.25
		Nos. N30-N32 (3)	.75	.75

1943, Sept. 1

| N33 | OS4 | 8c violet | 8.50 | 3.50 |
| N34 | OS4 | 15c carmine red | 8.50 | 3.50 |

Publicity for Postal Savings which had reached a $10,000,000 total in Malaya.

Rubber Tapping — OS5   Seaside Houses — OS6

Japanese Shrine, Singapore — OS7   Sago Palms — OS8

Johore Bahru and Strait of Johore — OS9   Malay Mosque, Kuala Lumpur — OS10

1943, Oct. 1

N35	OS5	1c gray green	.50	.40
N36	OS5	3c olive gray	.50	.40
N37	OS6	10c red brown	.50	.40
N38	OS7	15c violet	.65	.65
N39	OS8	30c olive green	.65	.65
N40	OS9	50c blue	1.25	1.25
N41	OS10	70c dull blue	15.00	16.00
		Nos. N35-N41 (7)	19.05	19.75

Rice Planting and Map of Malaysia — OS11

1944, Feb. 15

N42	OS11	8c carmine	7.50	3.50
N43	OS11	15c violet	4.50	3.50

Issued on the anniversary of the fall of Singapore to commemorate the "Birth of New Malaya".

OCCUPATION POSTAGE DUE STAMPS

Stamps and Type of Postage Due Stamps of 1936-38 Handstamped in Black, Red or Brown

1942	**Wmk. 4**	**Perf. 14½x14**		
NJ1	D2	1c violet	12.50	15.00
NJ2	D2	3c yellow green	25.00	17.50
NJ3	D2	4c yellow green	20.00	20.00
NJ4	D2	8c red	30.00	35.00
NJ5	D2	10c yellow orange	22.50	25.00
NJ6	D2	12c blue violet	22.50	25.00
NJ7	D2	50c black	50.00	50.00
		Nos. NJ1-NJ7 (7)	182.50	187.50

DAI NIPPON

Overprinted in Black   **2602**

MALAYA

1942				
NJ8	D2	1c violet	2.50	2.50
NJ9	D2	3c yel green	3.50	3.75
NJ10	D2	4c yel green	6.00	6.50
NJ11	D2	8c red	7.50	12.00
NJ12	D2	10c yel orange	3.25	4.00
NJ13	D2	12c blue violet	3.25	4.00
		Nos. NJ8-NJ13 (6)	26.00	32.75

The 9c and 15c with this overprint were not regularly issued.

大日本郵便

Postage Due Stamps of 1936-45 Overprinted

1943				
NJ14	D2	1c reddish vio	1.00	1.75
NJ15	D2	3c yel green	1.00	1.75
NJ15A	D2	4c yel green	50.00	45.00
NJ16	D2	5c scarlet	1.00	2.50
NJ17	D2	9c yel orange	1.50	1.75
NJ18	D2	10c yel orange	1.50	1.75
NJ19	D2	12c blue violet	1.50	1.75
NJ20	D2	15c blue violet	1.50	1.75
		Nos. NJ14-NJ20 (8)	59.00	58.00

#NJ15A is said to have been extensively forged.

ISSUED UNDER THAI OCCUPATION

For use in Kedah, Kelantan, Perlis and Trengganu

War Memorial — OS1

		Perf. 12½		
1943, Dec.		**Unwmk.**		**Litho.**
2N1	OS1	1c pale yellow	10.00	10.00
2N2	OS1	2c buff	6.00	6.00
2N3	OS1	3c pale green	7.50	10.00
a.		Imperf., pair	175.00	
2N4	OS1	4c dull lilac	7.50	15.00
2N5	OS1	8c rose	7.50	10.00
2N6	OS1	15c lt blue	20.00	35.00
		Nos. 2N1-2N6 (6)	58.50	86.00

These stamps, in cent denominations, were for use only in the four Malayan states ceded to Thailand by the Japanese. The states reverted to British rule in September, 1945.

JOHORE

jə-'hōr

LOCATION — At the extreme south of the Malay Peninsula.
AREA — 7,330 sq. mi.
POP. — 1,009,649 (1960)
CAPITAL — Johore Bahru

Stamps of the Straits Settlements Overprinted in Black

Overprinted   **JOHORE.**

1876		**Wmk. 1**		**Perf. 14**
1	A2	2c brown	6,500.	3,000.

Overprinted   **JOHORE.**

Overprint 13 to 14mm Wide

1884-86		**Wmk. 2**		
1A	A2	2c rose	75.00	80.00

Without Period

Overprint 16 to 17x2mm

2	A2	2c rose	375.00	175.00
a.		Double overprint		1,200.

Overprinted   **JOHORE**

Overprint 11x2½mm

3	A2	2c rose	37.50	52.50

Overprinted   **JOHORE**

Overprint 17½x2¾mm

4	A2	2c rose	1,250.	1,000.

Overprinted   **JOHOR**

Overprint 12½ to 15x2¾mm

5	A2	2c rose	6.00	8.50

Overprinted   **JOHOR**

Overprint 9x2½mm

6	A2	2c brown		
7	A2	2c rose	25.00	25.00

Overprinted   **JOHOR**

Overprint 9x3mm

8	A2	2c rose	22.50	22.50

Overprinted   **JOHOR**

Overprint 14 to 15x3mm

9	A2	2c rose	4.00	4.00
		Tall "J" 3½mm high		
10	A2	2c rose	110.00	125.00

Overprinted   **JOHOR**

Overprint 15 to 15½x3mm

11	A2	2c rose	27.50	27.50

Overprinted   **JOHOR**

1891				
		Overprint 12½ to 13x2½mm		
12	A2	2c rose	9.00	6.50
		Overprint 12x2¾mm		
13	A2	2c rose		4,750.

Surcharged in Black:

JOHOR Two CENTS	JOHOR *Two* CENTS
a	b
JOHOR *Two* CENTS	**JOHOR** *Two* CENTS
c	d

1891				
14	A3(a)	2c on 24c green	30.00	45.00
15	A3(b)	2c on 24c green	70.00	70.00
16	A3(c)	2c on 24c green	20.00	30.00
a.		"CENST"	475.00	225.00
17	A3(d)	2c on 24c green	70.00	70.00
		Nos. 14-17 (4)	190.00	215.00

Sultan Abubakar — A5

1892-94		**Typo.**		**Unwmk.**
18	A5	1c lilac & vio ('94)	.35	.50
19	A5	2c lilac & yellow	.60	1.25
20	A5	3c lilac & car rose ('94)	.95	.55
21	A5	4c lilac & black	3.75	6.00
22	A5	5c lilac & green	9.00	17.50
23	A5	6c lilac & blue	11.00	15.00
24	A5	$1 green & car rose	37.50	87.50
		Nos. 18-24 (7)	63.15	128.30

For surcharges and overprints see #26-36.

Stamps of 1892-94 Surcharged in Black   **3 cents.**

1894				
26	A5	3c on 4c lilac & blk	.95	.50
a.		No period after "Cents"	35.00	35.00
27	A5	3c on 5c lilac & grn	.95	1.50
a.		No period after "Cents"	42.50	50.00
28	A5	3c on 6c lilac & bl	.95	1.75
a.		No period after "Cents"	45.00	50.00
29	A5	3c on $1 green & car	8.00	30.00
a.		No period after "Cents"	150.00	275.00
		Nos. 26-29 (4)	10.85	33.75

Coronation Issue
Stamps of 1892-94 Overprinted "KEMAHKOTAAN"

1896				
30	A5	1c lilac & violet	.45	.70
31	A5	2c lilac & yellow	.40	.70
32	A5	3c lilac & car rose	1.10	1.40
33	A5	4c lilac & black	.90	1.10
34	A5	5c lilac & green	3.50	5.75
35	A5	6c lilac & blue	1.50	5.00
36	A5	$1 green & car rose	35.00	55.00
		Nos. 30-36 (7)	42.85	69.65

Overprinted "KETAHKOTAAN"

30a	A5	1c	2.75	3.50
31a	A5	2c	3.00	3.00
32a	A5	3c	3.50	6.00
33a	A5	4c	2.25	4.50
34a	A5	5c	3.25	5.00
35a	A5	6c	3.50	4.50
36a	A5	$1	27.50	70.00
		Nos. 30a-36a (7)	45.75	97.00

Coronation of Sultan Ibrahim.

Sultan Ibrahim — A7

1896-99		**Typo.**		**Wmk. 71**
37	A7	1c green	.25	.30
38	A7	2c green & blue	.25	.25
39	A7	3c green & vio	.45	.60
40	A7	4c green & car rose	.30	.30
41	A7	4c yel & red ('99)	.30	.40
42	A7	5c green & brn	.40	1.10
43	A7	6c green & yel	.55	1.40
44	A7	10c green & black	7.50	30.00
45	A7	25c green & vio	7.50	25.00
46	A7	50c grn & car rose	15.00	27.50
47	A7	$1 lilac & green	22.50	45.00
48	A7	$2 lilac & car rose	22.50	45.00
49	A7	$3 lilac & blue	27.50	65.00
50	A7	$4 lilac & brn	30.00	52.50
51	A7	$5 lilac & green	65.00	90.00
		Nos. 37-51 (15)	200.00	384.35

On Nos. 44-46 the numerals are on white tablets. Numerals of Nos. 48-51 are on tablets of solid color.

Stamps of 1896-1926 with revenue cancellations sell for a fraction of those used postally. For surcharges see Nos. 52-58.

Nos. 40-41 Surcharged in Black   **3 cents.**

1903				
52	A7	3c on 4c yel & red	.75	.75
a.		Without bars	4.50	4.25
53	A7	10c on 4c grn & car rose	2.25	3.00
a.		Without bars	22.50	35.00

Bars on Nos. 52-53 were handruled with pen and ink.

Surcharged   **50 Cents.**

54	A7	50c on $3 lilac & blue	19.00	55.00

Surcharged   **One Dollar**

55	A7	$1 on $2 lilac & car rose	47.50	80.00
a.		Inverted "e" in "one"		1,250.

Surcharged   **10 CENTS**

1904				
56	A7	10c on 4c yel & red	22.50	32.50
a.		Double surcharge		7,500.
57	A7	10c on 4c grn & car rose	8.00	30.00
58	A7	50c on $5 lil & org	50.00	90.00
		Nos. 56-58 (3)	80.50	152.50

Sultan Ibrahim — A8

The 10c, 21c, 25c, 50c, and $10 to $500 denominations of type A8 show the numerals on white tablets. The numerals of the 8c, 30c, 40c, and $2 to $5 denominations are shown on tablets of solid colors.

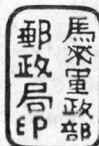

1904-08 Typo. Wmk. 71

59	A8	1c violet & green	.50	.20
60	A8	2c violet & brn org	1.00	1.50
61	A8	3c violet & black	1.00	.25
62	A8	4c violet & red	6.00	1.00
63	A8	5c violet & ol grn	.70	2.00
64	A8	8c violet & blue	2.00	4.00
65	A8	10c violet & black	25.00	7.00
66	A8	25c violet & green	2.50	15.00
67	A8	50c violet & red	25.00	11.00
68	A8	$1 green & vio	12.00	45.00
69	A8	$2 green & car	17.00	40.00
70	A8	$3 green & blue	21.00	55.00
71	A8	$4 green & brn	22.50	75.00
72	A8	$5 green & org	30.00	65.00
73	A8	$10 green & blk	42.50	100.00
74	A8	$50 green & blue	140.00	200.00
75	A8	$100 green & scar	275.00	400.00
		Revenue cancel		30.00
		Nos. 59-73 (15)	208.70	421.95

The 1c, 2c and 10c also exist on chalky paper.

Nos. 74 and 75 were theoretically available for postage but were mostly used for revenue purposes.

For surcharge see No. 86.

1910-18 Wmk. 47

Chalky Paper

76	A8	1c violet & green	.25	.15
77	A8	2c violet & orange	3.50	.50
78	A8	3c violet & black	2.50	.50
79	A8	4c violet & red	2.00	.60
80	A8	5c violet & ol grn	1.75	.50
81	A8	8c violet & blue	3.25	3.50
82	A8	10c violet & black	18.00	2.00
83	A8	25c violet & green	3.50	17.00
84	A8	50c violet & red	45.00	60.00
85	A8	$1 green & vio	50.00	55.00
		Nos. 76-85 (10)	129.75	139.75

#78-79, 82 exist with horizontal watermark.

No. 64 Surcharged **3 CENTS.**

1912 Wmk. 71

86	A8	3c on 8c vio & blue	1.50	3.00
a.		"T" of "CENTS" omitted	400.00	

1918-19 Typo. Wmk. 3

Chalky Paper

87	A8	2c violet & orange	.60	1.25
88	A8	2c violet & grn ('19)	.40	.55
89	A8	4c violet & red	.45	.15
90	A8	5c vio & olive grn ('19)	1.25	1.75
91	A8	10c violet & blue	1.25	1.25
92	A8	21c violet & orange	2.25	3.50
93	A8	25c vio & grn ('19)	6.50	12.00
94	A8	50c vio & red ('19)	15.00	25.00
95	A8	$1 grn & red vio	8.75	35.00
96	A8	$2 green & scar	18.00	35.00
97	A8	$3 green & blue	22.50	60.00
98	A8	$4 green & brn	35.00	75.00
99	A8	$5 green & org	45.00	85.00
100	A8	$10 green & blk	100.00	150.00
		Nos. 87-100 (14)	256.95	485.45

1921-40 Wmk. 4

101	A8	1c violet & black	.15	.15
102	A8	2c violet & brn	.55	1.10
103	A8	2c green & dk grn ('28)	.15	.15
104	A8	3c green ('25)	1.40	2.75
105	A8	3c dull vio & brn ('28)	.90	1.00
106	A8	4c vio & red	1.40	.15
107	A8	5c vio & ol grn	.30	.15
108	A8	6c vio & red brown	.25	.15
109	A8	10c vio & blue	14.00	24.00
110	A8	10c vio & yel ('22)	.30	.15
111	A8	12c vio & blue	1.00	1.25
111A	A8	12c ultra ('40)	22.50	5.00
112	A8	21c dull vio & org ('28)	2.25	2.25
113	A8	25c vio & green	1.25	.75
114	A8	30c dull vio & org ('36)	2.25	2.00
115	A8	40c dull vio & brn ('36)	2.25	3.25
116	A8	50c violet & red	2.25	1.00
117	A8	$1 grn & red violet	2.25	.70
118	A8	$2 grn & red	5.00	3.50
119	A8	$3 grn & blue	27.50	45.00
120	A8	$4 grn & brn ('26)	50.00	90.00
121	A8	$5 grn & org	37.50	45.00
122	A8	$10 grn & blk	110.00	150.00
123	A8	$50 grn & ultra	500.00	
124	A8	$100 grn & red	1,200.	
125	A8	$500 ultra & org brn ('26)	17,000.	
		Revenue cancel		140.00
		Nos. 101-122 (23)	285.40	379.45

Nos. 123, 124 and 125 were available for postage but were probably used only fiscally.

A9

A10

1935, May 15 Engr. *Perf. 12½*

126	A9	8c Sultan Ibrahim, Sultana	1.75	.55

1940, Feb. *Perf. 13½*

127	A10	8c Sultan Ibrahim	7.00	.25

Catalogue values for unused stamps in this section, from this point to the end of the section, are for Never Hinged items.

Silver Wedding Issue

Common Design Types

Inscribed: "Malaya Johore"

Perf. 14x14½

1948, Dec. 1 Wmk. 4 Photo.

128	CD304	10c purple	.20	.20

Perf. 11½x11

Engr.; Name Typo.

129	CD305	$5 green	24.00	24.00

Sultan Ibrahim — A11

1949-55 Wmk. 4 Typo. *Perf. 18*

130	A11	1c black	.25	.15
131	A11	2c orange	.25	.15
132	A11	3c green	.75	.35
133	A11	4c chocolate	.25	.15
134	A11	5c rose vio ('52)	.35	.15
135	A11	6c gray	.45	.20
a.		Wmk. 4a (error)	425.00	
136	A11	8c rose red	1.40	.90
137	A11	8c green ('52)	.75	1.00
138	A11	10c plum	.45	.15
a.		Imperf., pair	850.00	
139	A11	12c rose red ('52)	.90	1.75
140	A11	15c ultra	1.40	.45
141	A11	20c dk grn & blk	1.40	.60
142	A11	20c ultra ('52)	.95	.25
143	A11	25c org & rose lil	1.10	.20
144	A11	30c plum & rose red ('55)	2.75	1.50
145	A11	35c dk vio & rose red ('52)	2.25	1.40
146	A11	40c dk vio & rose red	2.75	4.50
147	A11	50c ultra & blk	2.00	.25
148	A11	$1 vio brn & ultra	3.75	1.25
149	A11	$2 rose red & emer	14.00	4.00
150	A11	$5 choc & emer	27.50	8.50
		Nos. 130-150 (21)	65.65	27.85

UPU Issue

Common Design Types

Inscribed: "Malaya-Johore"

Engr.; Name Typo. on 15c, 25c

1949, Oct. 10 *Perf. 13½, 11x11½*

151	CD306	10c rose violet	.30	.20
152	CD307	15c indigo	.50	.80
153	CD308	25c orange	.60	1.10
154	CD309	50c slate	1.25	1.75
		Nos. 151-154 (4)	2.65	3.85

Coronation Issue

Common Design Type

1953, June 2 Engr. *Perf. 13½x13*

155	CD312	10c magenta & black	.26	.15

Sultan Ibrahim — A12

1955, Nov. 1 Wmk. 4 *Perf. 14*

156	A12	10c carmine lake	.26	.15

Sultan Ibrahim's Diamond Jubilee.

Sultan Ismail and Johore State Crest Seal — A13

Perf. 11½

1960, Feb. 10 Unwmk. Photo.

Granite Paper

157	A13	10c multicolored	.26	.15

Coronation of Sultan Ismail.

Types of Kedah 1957 with Portrait of Sultan Ismail

1960 Wmk. 314 Engr. *Perf. 13*

158	A8	1c black	.15	.15
159	A8	2c red orange	.15	.15
160	A8	4c dark brown	.15	.15
161	A8	5c dk car rose	.15	.15
162	A8	8c dark green	.75	.28
163	A7	10c violet brown	.18	.15
164	A7	20c blue	.28	.15
165	A7	50c ultra & black	.70	.15
166	A8	$1 plum & ultra	1.40	.55
167	A8	$2 red & green	2.75	2.00
168	A8	$5 ol, grn & brn	11.00	8.50
		Nos. 158-168 (11)	17.66	12.38

Starting in 1965, issues of Johore are listed with Malaysia.

POSTAGE DUE STAMPS

D1

Perf. 12½

1938, Jan. 1 Typo. Wmk. 4

J1	D1	1c rose red	7.50	25.00
J2	D1	4c green	17.50	32.50
J3	D1	8c dull yellow	35.00	110.00
J4	D1	10c bister brown	35.00	40.00
J5	D1	12c rose violet	45.00	100.00
		Nos. J1-J5 (5)	140.00	307.50

OCCUPATION POSTAGE DUE STAMPS

Issued under Japanese Occupation

Johore Nos. J1-J5 Overprinted in Black, Brown or Red

馬來軍政部
郵政局
EP

1942 Wmk. 4 *Perf. 12½*

NJ1	D1	1c rose red	42.50	70.00
NJ2	D1	4c green	55.00	70.00
NJ3	D1	8c dull yellow	65.00	80.00
NJ4	D1	10c bister brown	15.00	45.00
NJ5	D1	12c rose violet	25.00	45.00
		Nos. NJ1-NJ5 (5)	202.50	310.00

Johore Nos. J1-J5 Overprinted in Black

大日本郵便

1943

NJ6	D1	1c rose red	2.00	10.00
NJ7	D1	4c green	2.00	10.00
NJ8	D1	8c dull yellow	7.00	12.50
NJ9	D1	10c bister brown	5.00	15.00
NJ10	D1	12c rose violet	5.00	20.00
		Nos. NJ6-NJ10 (5)	21.00	67.50

Nos. NJ6-NJ10 exist with second character sideways.

KEDAH

'ke–də

LOCATION — On the west coast of the Malay Peninsula.
AREA — 3,660 sq. mi.
POP. — 752,706 (1960)
CAPITAL — Alor Star

Sheaf of Rice — A1

Native Plowing — A2

Council Chamber — A3

1912-21 Engr. Wmk. 3 *Perf. 14*

1	A1	1c green & black	.25	.25
2	A1	1c brown ('19)	.35	.40
3	A1	2c green ('19)	.50	.25
4	A1	3c car & black	2.00	.25
5	A1	3c dk violet ('19)	.50	.45
6	A1	4c slate & car	7.50	.25
7	A1	4c scarlet ('19)	1.50	.20
8	A1	5c org brown & grn	1.75	2.50
9	A1	8c ultra & blk	1.25	2.00
10	A2	10c black brn & bl	1.50	.75
11	A2	20c yel grn & blk	2.50	3.50
12	A2	21c red vio & vio ('19)	5.00	30.00
13	A2	25c red vio & bl ('21)	1.65	17.50
14	A2	30c car & black	1.65	8.00
15	A2	40c lilac & blk	2.75	10.00
16	A2	50c dull bl & brn	7.50	10.00
17	A3	$1 scar & blk, *yel*	11.00	15.00
18	A3	$2 dk brn & dk grn	12.50	50.00
19	A3	$3 dk bl & blk, *bl*	45.00	100.00
20	A3	$5 car & black	50.00	90.00
		Nos. 1-20 (20)	156.65	341.30

There are two types of No. 7, one printed from separate plates for frame and center, the other printed from a single plate.

Overprints are listed after No. 45.

Stamps of 1912 Surcharged **FIFTY CENTS**

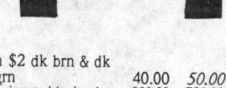

1919

21	A3	50c on $2 dk brn & dk grn	40.00	50.00
a.		"C" of ovpt. inserted by hand	900.00	725.00
22	A3	$1 on $3 dk bl & blk, *blue*	25.00	70.00

1921-36 Wmk. 4

Two types of 1c:

I - The 1's have rounded corners, small top serif. Small letters "c."

II - The 1's have square-cut corners, large top serif. Large letters "c."

Two types of 2c:

I - The 2's have oval drops. Letters "c" are fairly thick and rounded.

II - The 2's have round drops. Letters "c" thin and slightly larger.

23	A1	1c brown	.15	.15
24	A1	1c blk (I) ('22)	.15	.15
a.		1c black (II) ('39)	10.50	6.75
25	A1	2c green (I)	.15	.15
a.		2c green (II) ('40)	55.00	10.00
26	A1	3c dk violet	.55	.35
27	A1	3c green ('22)	.80	.20
28	A1	4c carmine	2.50	.15
29	A1	4c dull vio ('26)	.25	.15
30	A1	5c yellow ('22)	1.00	.35
31	A1	6c scarlet ('26)	.25	.20
32	A1	8c gray ('36)	5.00	.50
33	A2	10c blk brn & bl	1.00	.35
34	A2	12c dk ultra & blk ('26)	1.00	3.75
35	A2	20c green & blk	1.00	.60
36	A2	21c red vio & vio	2.50	7.75
37	A2	25c red vio & bl	1.10	2.00
38	A2	30c red & blk ('22)	2.00	1.50
39	A2	35c claret ('26)	5.00	10.00
40	A2	40c red vio & blk	2.00	7.25
41	A2	50c dp blue & brn	.85	3.00
42	A3	$1 scar & blk, *yel* ('22)	5.00	6.00
43	A3	$2 brn & green	10.00	55.00

44 A3 $3 dk bl & blk, *bl* 25.00 *47.50*
45 A3 $5 car & black 37.50 *90.00*
Nos. 23-45 (23) 104.75 *237.05*

For overprints see Nos. N1-N6.

Stamps of 1912-21 Overprinted in Black: "MALAYA-BORNEO EXHIBITION." in Three Lines

1922 Wmk. 3

3a A1 2c green 5.75 *17.00*
12a A2 21c red vio & vio 20.00 *67.50*
13a A2 25c red vio & blue 20.00 *82.50*
b. Inverted overprint 750.00
16a A2 50c dull blue & brn 22.50 *85.00*

Wmk. 4

23a A1 1c brown 2.00 *14.00*
26a A1 3c dark violet 3.00 *25.00*
28a A1 4c carmine 3.00 *25.00*
33a A2 10c blk brn & blue 5.75 *35.00*
Nos. 3a-33a (8) 82.00 *351.00*

Industrial fair at Singapore, Mar. 31-Apr. 15, 1922.

On Nos. 12a, 13a and 16a, "BORNEO" exists both 14mm and 15mm wide.

Sultan of Kedah, Sir Abdul Hamid Halim Shah — A4

1937, July Wmk. 4 *Perf. 12½*

46 A4 10c sepia & ultra 2.00 .35
47 A4 12c gray vio & blk 17.00 *9.00*
48 A4 25c brn vio & ultra 5.50 *3.25*
49 A4 30c dp car & yel grn 6.25 *7.00*
50 A4 40c brn vio & blk 2.00 *10.00*
51 A4 50c dp blue & sepia 3.00 *3.25*
52 A4 $1 dk green & blk 2.25 *7.50*
53 A4 $2 dk brn & yel grn 75.00 60.00
54 A4 $5 dp car & black 25.00 *62.50*
Nos. 46-54 (9) 138.00 *162.85*

For overprints see Nos. N7-N15.

Catalogue values for unused stamps in this section, from this point to the end of the section, are for Never Hinged items.

Silver Wedding Issue
Common Design Types
Inscribed: "Malaya Kedah"

1948, Dec. 1 Photo. *Perf. 14x14½*

55 CD304 10c purple .20 .20

Perf. 11½x11
Engraved; Name Typographed

56 CD305 $5 rose car 25.00 25.00

UPU Issue
Common Design Types
Inscribed: "Malaya-Kedah"
Engr.; Name Typo. on 15c, 25c

1949, Oct. 10 *Perf. 13½, 11x11½*

57 CD306 10c rose violet .18 .18
58 CD307 15c indigo .42 .42
59 CD308 25c orange .70 .70
60 CD309 50c slate 1.50 1.50
Nos. 57-60 (4) 2.80 2.80

Sheaf of Rice — A5

Sultan Tungku Badlishah — A6

1950-55 Wmk. 4 Typo. *Perf. 18*

61 A5 1c black .15 .15
62 A5 2c orange .15 .15
63 A5 3c green .30 .32
64 A5 4c chocolate .15 *.20*
65 A5 5c rose vio ('52) .15 .15
66 A5 6c gray .16 .15
67 A5 8c rose red .45 *1.25*
68 A5 8c green ('52) .30 *1.25*
69 A5 10c plum .15 .15
70 A5 12c rose red ('52) .24 *2.50*
71 A5 15c ultramarine .90 *.85*
72 A5 20c dk green & blk .90 *2.50*
73 A5 20c ultra ('52) .38 .25
74 A6 25c org & rose lilac .50 .45
75 A6 30c plum & rose red ('55) 2.00 *.85*
76 A6 35c dk vio & rose red ('52) .60 *1.65*
77 A6 40c dk vio & rose red 1.25 *5.50*
78 A6 50c ultra & black .65 .20
79 A6 $1 yel brown & ultra 4.50 1.65
80 A6 $2 rose red & emer 17.00 *21.00*
81 A6 $5 choc & emerald 22.50 *27.50*
Nos. 61-81 (21) 53.38 *68.67*

Coronation Issue
Common Design Type

1953, June 2 Engr. *Perf. 13½x13*

82 CD312 10c magenta & black .28 .15

Fishing Craft — A7

Weaving and Sultan — A8

Portrait of Sultan Tungku Badlishah and: 1c, Copra. 2c, Pineapples. 4c, Rice field. 5c, Mosque. 8c, East Coast Railway. 10c, Tiger. 50c, Aborigines with blowpipes. $1, Government offices. $2, Bersilat.

Perf. 13x12½, 12½x13

1957 Engr. Wmk. 314

83 A8 1c black .15 .15
84 A8 2c red orange .15 .15
85 A8 4c dark brown .15 .15
86 A8 5c dk car rose .15 .15
87 A8 8c dark green 2.50 2.00
88 A7 10c chocolate .25 .15
89 A7 20c blue .65 .20

Perf. 12½, 13½ ($1)

90 A7 50c ultra & black 1.25 .50
91 A8 $1 plum & ultra 2.25 .80
92 A8 $2 red & green 11.00 3.75
Revenue cancel .15
93 A8 $5 ol grn & brown 16.00 5.75
Revenue cancel .30
Nos. 83-93 (11) 34.50 13.75

See Nos. 95-105.

Sultan Abdul Halim — A9

Perf. 14x14½

1959, Feb. 20 Photo. Wmk. 314

94 A9 10c ultra, red & yellow .18 .15

Installation of the Sultan of Kedah, Abdul Halim.

Types of 1957

Designs as before with portrait of Sultan Abdul Halim.

Perf. 13x12½, 12½x13, 12½, 13½

1959-62 Engr. Wmk. 314

95 A8 1c black .15 .15
96 A8 2c red orange .15 .15
97 A8 4c dark brown .15 .15
98 A8 5c dk car rose .15 .15
99 A8 8c dark green .15 .15
100 A8 10c chocolate .45 .15
101 A7 20c blue .40 .15
102 A7 50c ultra & blk, perf. 12½x13 ('60) .75 .15
a. Perf. 12½ .65 .28
103 A8 $1 plum & ultra 2.25 .60
104 A8 $2 red & green 5.50 2.25
105 A8 $5 ol grn & brn, perf. 13x12½ ('62) 12.00 3.75
a. Perf. 12½ 8.25 3.75
Nos. 95-105 (11) 22.10 7.80

Starting in 1965, issues of Kedah are listed with Malaysia.

OCCUPATION STAMPS

Issued Under Japanese Occupation

Stamps of Kedah 1922-36, Overprinted in Red or Black

DAI NIPPON
2602

1942, May 13 Wmk. 4 *Perf. 14*

N1 A1 1c black (R) 1.75 2.00
N2 A1 2c green (R) 30.00 30.00
N3 A1 4c dull violet (R) 2.50 3.00
N4 A1 5c yellow (R) 2.25 3.00
a. Black overprint 120.00 120.00
N5 A1 6c scarlet (Bk) 1.75 3.50
N6 A1 8c gray (R) 2.75 2.75

Nos. 46 to 54 Overprinted in Red

DAI NIPPON
2602

Perf. 12½

N7 A4 10c sepia & ultra 5.00 5.50
N8 A4 12c gray vio & blk 13.00 15.00
N9 A4 25c brn vio & ultra 6.50 8.00
a. Black overprint 100.00 100.00
N10 A4 30c dp car & yel grn 60.00 65.00
N11 A4 40c brn vio & blk 22.50 25.00
N12 A4 50c dp blue & sep 25.00 25.00
N13 A4 $1 dk grn & blk 125.00 125.00
a. Inverted overprint 250.00 250.00
N14 A4 $2 dk brn & yel green 200.00 140.00
N15 A4 $5 dp car & blk 75.00 65.00
a. Black overprint 210.00 225.00
Nos. N1-N15 (15) 573.00 517.75

KELANTAN

kə-ˈlan-ˌtan

LOCATION — On the eastern coast of the Malay Peninsula.
AREA — 5,750 sq. mi.
POP. — 545,620 (1960)
CAPITAL — Kota Bharu

Symbols of Government — A1

1911-15 Typo. Wmk. 3 *Perf. 14*
Ordinary Paper

1 A1 1c gray green 1.00 .25
a. 1c green .15 .15
2 A1 3c rose red .25 .15
3 A1 4c black & red .30 .15
4 A1 5c grn & red, *yel* .90 .15
5 A1 8c ultramarine 3.25 1.10
6 A1 10c black & violet 4.00 .30

Chalky Paper

7 A1 30c violet & red 6.00 .45
8 A1 50c black & org 3.75 2.75
9 A1 $1 green & emer 42.50 45.00
10 A1 $1 grn & brn ('15) 25.00 3.00
11 A1 $2 grn & car rose 1.50 *4.00*
12 A1 $5 green & ultra 11.50 *9.00*
13 A1 $25 green & org 45.00 *72.50*
Nos. 1-13 (13) 144.95 *138.80*

For overprints see listings after No. 26. For surcharges see Nos. N20-N22.

1921-28 Wmk. 4
Ordinary Paper

14 A1 1c green 3.00 1.10
15 A1 1c black ('23) .20 .15
16 A1 2c brown 3.00 *3.50*
17 A1 2c green ('26) .30 .15
18 A1 3c brown ('27) 1.25 1.40
19 A1 4c black & red .20 .15
20 A1 5c grn & red, *yel* .25 .15
21 A1 6c claret 2.25 *3.50*
22 A1 6c rose red ('28) 4.00 4.75
23 A1 10c black & violet 1.25 .20

Chalky Paper

24 A1 30c dull vio & red ('26) 2.50 *4.75*
25 A1 50c black & orange 4.50 *16.00*
26 A1 $1 green & brown 22.50 *42.50*
Nos. 14-26 (13) 45.20 *78.30*

Stamps of 1911-21 Overprinted in Black: "MALAYA BORNEO EXHIBITION" in Three Lines

1922 Wmk. 3

3a A1 4c black & red 2.75 *25.00*
4a A1 5c green & red, *yel* 4.25 *27.50*
7a A1 30c violet & red 5.50 *50.00*
8a A1 50c black & orange 7.00 *55.00*
10a A1 $1 green & brown 22.50 *75.00*
11a A1 $2 green & car rose 55.00 *140.00*
12a A1 $5 green & ultra 140.00 *325.00*

Wmk. 4

14a A1 1c green 2.00 *25.00*
23a A1 10c black & violet 4.75 *45.00*
Nos. 3a-23a (9) 243.75

Industrial fair at Singapore, Mar. 31-Apr. 15, 1922.

Sultan Ismail
A2 A2a

1928-33 Engr. *Perf. 12*
Size: 21½x30mm

27 A2 $1 ultramarine 14.00 *35.00*

Perf. 14

28 A2 $1 blue ('33) 50.00 *47.50*

1937-40 *Perf. 12*
Size: 22½x34½mm

29 A2a 1c yel & ol green .20 .30
30 A2a 2c deep green .20 .15
31 A2a 4c brick red .45 .40
32 A2a 5c red brown .90 .15
33 A2a 6c car lake 2.25 2.25
34 A2a 8c gray green 1.25 .15
35 A2a 10c dark violet 3.25 2.50
36 A2a 12c deep blue 1.25 *1.25*
37 A2a 25c vio & red org 2.75 *2.50*
38 A2a 30c scar & dk vio 15.00 *16.00*
39 A2a 40c blue grn & org 4.50 *15.00*
40 A2a 50c org & ol grn 13.00 *8.50*
41 A2a $1 dp grn & dk violet 5.25 *10.00*
42 A2a $2 red & red brn ('40) 150.00 *200.00*
43 A2a $5 rose lake & org ('40) 250.00 *250.00*
Nos. 29-43 (15) 450.25 *509.15*

For overprints see Nos. N1-N19.

Catalogue values for unused stamps in this section, from this point to the end of the section, are for Never Hinged items

Silver Wedding Issue
Common Design Types
Inscribed: "Malaya Kelantan"

Perf. 14x14½

1948, Dec. 1 Wmk. 4 Photo.

44 CD304 10c purple .20 .20

Perf. 11½x11
Engraved; Name Typographed

45 CD305 $5 rose car 24.00 *25.00*

UPU Issue
Common Design Types
Inscribed: "Malaya-Kelantan"
Engr.; Name Typo. on 15c, 25c

1949, Oct. 10 *Perf. 13½, 11x11½*

46 CD306 10c rose violet .30 .30
47 CD307 15c indigo .60 .60
48 CD308 25c orange .85 .85
49 CD309 50c slate 1.50 1.50
Nos. 46-49 (4) 3.25 3.25

Sultan Ibrahim — A3

Wmk. 4

1951, July 11 Typo. *Perf. 18*

50 A3 1c black .15 .25
51 A3 2c orange .20 .25
52 A3 3c green 2.00 1.00
53 A3 4c chocolate .20 .15
54 A3 6c gray .20 .15
55 A3 8c rose red .50 *2.50*
56 A3 10c plum .30 .15
57 A3 15c ultramarine 1.50 .50
58 A3 20c dk green & blk .50 3.50
59 A3 25c orange & plum .50 .50
60 A3 40c vio brn & rose red 2.75 7.50
61 A3 50c dp ultra & blk .70 .30
62 A3 $1 vio brown & ultra 4.00 3.00
63 A3 $2 rose red & emer 15.00 17.00
64 A3 $5 choc & emer 45.00 35.00

1952-55

65 A3 5c rose violet .30 .30
66 A3 8c green .70 *1.50*
67 A3 12c rose red .70 *2.00*
68 A3 20c ultramarine .70 *.20*

69 A3 30c plum & rose red ('55) 1.00 1.50
70 A3 35c dk vio & rose red .80 *1.25*
Nos. 50-70 (21) 77.70 78.50

Compare with Pahang A8, Perak A16, Selangor A15, Trengganu A5.

Coronation Issue
Common Design Type

1953, June 2 Engr. ***Perf. 13½x13***
71 CD312 10c magenta & black .25 .20

Fishing Craft — A4

Government Offices and Sultan — A5

Portrait of Sultan Ibrahim and: 1c, Copra. 2c, Pineapples. 4c, Rice field. 5c, Mosque. 8c, East Coast Railway. 10c, Tiger. 50c, Aborigines with blowpipes. $2, Bersilat. $5, Weaving.

Perf. 13x12½, 12½x13, 13½ ($1)
1957-63 Engr. Wmk. 314
72 A5 1c black .15 .20
73 A5 2c red orange .40 .30
74 A5 4c dark brown .15 .15
75 A5 5c dk car rose .15 .15
76 A5 8c dark green .50 1.75
77 A4 10c chocolate .40 .15
78 A4 20c blue .25 .20
79 A4 50c ultra & blk ('60) .90 .20
a. Perf 12½ .50 .40
80 A5 $1 plum & ultra 2.50 1.10
81 A5 $2 red & grn ('63) 5.00 *11.00*
a. Perf. 12½ 4.75 *5.00*
82 A5 $5 ol grn & brn ('63) 12.00 *12.00*
a. Perf. 12½ 11.00 *18.00*
Nos. 72-82 (11) 22.40 *27.20*

Common Design Types pictured in section before Great Britain.

Sultan Yahya Petra — A6

1961, July 17 Photo. ***Perf. 14½x14***
83 A6 10s multicolored .30 .20

Installation of Sultan Yahya Petra.

Types of 1957 with Portrait of Sultan Yahya Petra

Designs as before.

Perf. 13x12½, 12½x13
1961-62 Engr. Wmk. 338
84 A5 1c black .15 .15
85 A5 2c red orange .15 .15
86 A5 4c dark brown .15 .15
87 A5 5c dk car rose .15 .15
88 A5 8c dark green .70 .70
89 A4 10c violet brown ('61) .15 .15
90 A4 20c blue .28 .25
Nos. 84-90 (7) 1.73
Set value 1.20

Starting in 1965, issues of Kelantan are listed with Malaysia.

OCCUPATION STAMPS

Issued Under Japanese Occupation

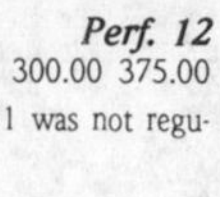

Kelantan No. 35 Handstamped in Black

1942 Wmk. 4 ***Perf. 12***
N1 A2a 10c dark violet 300.00 375.00

Some authorities believe No. N1 was not regularly issued.

Kelantan Nos. 29-40 Surcharged in Black or Red and Handstamped with Oval Seal "a" in Red

1 Cents

Sunakawa — a

Handa — b

1942
N2 1c on 50c org & ol green 150.00 150.00
a. With "b" seal 47.50 47.50
N3 2c on 40c bl grn & orange 250.00 250.00
a. With "b" seal 40.00 47.50
N4 5c on 12c dp bl (R) 150.00 150.00
N5 8c on 5c red brn (R) 170.00 125.00
a. With "b" seal (R) 120.00 140.00
N6 10c on 6c car lake 70.00 110.00
a. With "b" seal 70.00 110.00
N7 12c on 8c gray green (R) 45.00 100.00
N8 30c on 4c brick red 800.00 900.00
N9 40c on 2c dp grn (R) 45.00 75.00
N10 50c on 1c yel & ol green 850.00 800.00

Kelantan Nos. 29-40, 19-20, 22 Surcharged in Black or Red and Handstamped with Oval Seal "a" in Red

2 CENTS **$1.00**

N10A 1c on 50c org & ol green 95.00 80.00
N11 2c on 40c bl grn & orange 95.00 90.00
N11A 4c on 30c scar & dark vio 850.00 900.00
N12 5c on 12c dp bl (R) 150.00 150.00
N13 6c on 25c vio & red org 150.00 150.00
N14 8c on 5c red brown (R) 85.00 65.00
N15 10c on 6c car lake 85.00 90.00
N16 12c on 8c gray grn (R) 165.00 175.00
a. With "b" seal (R) 55.00 75.00
N17 25c on 10c dk vio 875.00 *925.00*
N17A 30c on 4c brick red 1,200. *1,300.*
N18 40c on 2c dp grn (R) 45.00 75.00
N19 50c on 1c yel & ol green *850.00* 800.00

Perf. 14
N20 $1 on 4c blk & red (R) 47.50 65.00
N21 $2 on 5c grn & red, *yel* 47.50 65.00
N22 $5 on 6c rose red 47.50 65.00

Examples of Nos. N2-N22 without handstamped seal are from the remainder stocks sent to Singapore after Kelantan was ceded to Thailand. Some authorities believe stamps without seals were used before June 1942.

ISSUED UNDER THAI OCCUPATION

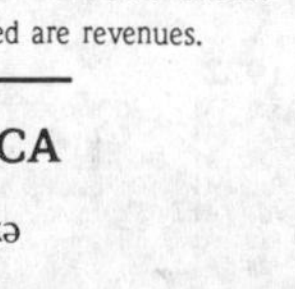
OS1

1943, Nov. 15 ***Perf. 11***
2N1 OS1 1c violet & black *125.00 150.00*
2N2 OS1 2c violet & black *140.00 150.00*
2N3 OS1 4c violet & black *140.00 175.00*
2N4 OS1 8c violet & black *125.00 150.00*
2N5 OS1 10c violet & black *175.00 200.00*
Nos. 2N1-2N5 (5) *705.00 825.00*

Stamps with centers in red are revenues.

MALACCA

mə-ˈla-kə

Melaka

LOCATION — On the west coast of the Malay peninsula.
AREA — 640 sq. mi.
POP. — 318,110 (1960)
CAPITAL — Malacca

Catalogue values for unused stamps in this section are for Never Hinged items.

Silver Wedding Issue
Common Design Types
Inscribed: "Malaya Malacca"

Perf. 14x14½
1948, Dec. 1 Wmk. 4 Photo.
1 CD304 10c purple .25 .25

Engraved; Name Typographed
Perf. 11½x11
2 CD305 $5 lt brown 24.00 25.00

Type of Straits Settlements, 1937-41, Inscribed "Malacca"

Wmk. 4
1949, Mar. 1 Typo. ***Perf. 18***
3 A29 1c black .15 .60
4 A29 2c orange .30 .35
5 A29 3c green .30 *1.25*
6 A29 4c chocolate .20 .20
7 A29 6c gray .20 .25
8 A29 8c rose red .30 *3.50*
9 A29 10c plum .30 .15
10 A29 15c ultramarine .30 .50
11 A29 20c dk green & blk .30 *3.50*
12 A29 25c org & rose lil .30 .75
13 A29 40c dk vio & rose red 1.00 *8.00*
14 A29 50c ultra & black .40 .15
15 A29 $1 vio brn & ultra 4.75 *11.00*
16 A29 $2 rose red & emer 15.00 *16.00*
17 A29 $5 choc & emer 35.00 *35.00*
Nos. 3-17 (15) 58.80 *81.20*

See Nos. 22-26.

UPU Issue
Common Design Types
Inscribed: "Malaya-Malacca"

Engr.; Name Typo. on 15c, 25c
Perf. 13½, 11x11½
1949, Oct. 10 Wmk. 4
18 CD306 10c rose violet .25 .40
19 CD307 15c indigo .55 *1.50*
20 CD308 25c orange .75 *3.00*
21 CD309 50c slate 1.25 *3.75*
Nos. 18-21 (4) 2.80 *8.65*

Type of Straits Settlements, 1937-41, Inscribed "Malacca"

1952, Sept. 1 Wmk. 4 ***Perf. 18***
22 A29 5c rose violet .35 *1.00*
23 A29 8c green .75 *3.00*
24 A29 12c rose red .85 *3.00*
25 A29 20c ultramarine 1.00 1.75
26 A29 35c dk vio & rose red 1.00 *2.00*
Nos. 22-26 (5) 3.95 *10.75*

Coronation Issue
Common Design Type

1953, June 2 Engr. ***Perf. 13½x13***
27 CD312 10c magenta & black .45 .15

Queen Elizabeth II — A1

1954-55 Wmk. 4 Typo. ***Perf. 18***
29 A1 1c black .15 .15
30 A1 2c orange .15 .15
31 A1 4c chocolate .15 .15
32 A1 5c rose violet .15 .15
33 A1 6c gray .20 .15
34 A1 8c green .40 .30
35 A1 10c plum .25 .15
36 A1 12c rose red .40 .25
37 A1 20c ultramarine .65 .45
38 A1 25c orange & plum .60 .20
39 A1 30c plum & rose red ('55) .85 .40
40 A1 35c vio brn & rose red .95 .55
41 A1 50c ultra & black 1.10 .45
42 A1 $1 vio brn & ultra 2.00 1.10
43 A1 $2 rose red & grn 6.00 3.50
44 A1 $5 choc & emerald 17.00 8.50
Nos. 29-44 (16) 31.00 16.60

Types of Kedah with Portrait of Queen Elizabeth II

Perf. 13x12½, 12½x13
1957 Engr. Wmk. 314
45 A8 1c black .15 .15
46 A8 2c red orange .15 .15
47 A8 4c dark brown .15 .15
48 A8 5c dark car rose .15 .15
49 A8 8c dark green .50 .25
50 A7 10c chocolate .35 .15
51 A7 20c blue .55 .15

Perf. 12½, 13½ ($1)
52 A7 50c ultra & black .80 .20
53 A8 $1 plum & ultra 1.65 1.00
54 A8 $2 red & green 5.25 3.00
55 A8 $5 olive grn & brn 11.00 6.00
Nos. 45-55 (11) 20.70 11.35

Types of Kedah, 1957, With Melaka Tree and Mouse Deer Replacing Portrait of Queen Elizabeth II

Perf. 13x12½, 12½x13, 13½ ($1)
1960, Mar. 15 Engr. Wmk. 314
56 A8 1c black .15 .15
57 A8 2c red orange .15 .15
58 A8 4c dark brown .15 .15
59 A8 5c dark car rose .15 .15
60 A8 8c dark green .45 .20
61 A7 10c violet brown .20 .15
62 A7 20c blue .40 .15
63 A7 50c ultra & black .90 .20
64 A8 $1 plum & ultra 1.50 .65
65 A8 $2 red & green 3.50 1.50
66 A8 $5 ol grn & brn 9.00 2.75
Nos. 56-66 (11) 16.55 6.20

Starting in 1965, issues of Malacca (Melaka) are listed with Malaysia.

OCCUPATION STAMPS

Issued Under Japanese Occupation
Stamps of Straits Settlements, 1937-41 Handstamped in Carmine

The handstamp covers four stamps. Values are for single stamps. Blocks of four showing complete handstamp sell for six times the price of singles.

1942 Wmk. 4 ***Perf. 14***
N1 A29 1c black 100.00 60.00
N2 A29 2c brown orange 90.00 60.00
N3 A29 3c green 100.00 60.00
N4 A29 5c brown 90.00 100.00
N5 A29 8c gray 125.00 150.00
N6 A29 10c dull violet 100.00 70.00
N7 A29 12c ultramarine 80.00 85.00
N8 A29 15c ultramarine 60.00 65.00
N9 A29 30c org & vio *1,900. 1,900.*
N10 A29 40c dk vio & rose red 800.00 600.00
N11 A29 50c blk, *emerald* 950.00 700.00
N12 A29 $1 red & blk, *bl* 1,000. 900.00
N13 A29 $2 rose red & gray grn *1,500. 1,250.*
N14 A29 $5 grn & red, *grn* *1,750. 2,100.*

Some authorities believe Nos. N9, N13, and N14 were not regularly issued.

OCCUPATION POSTAGE DUE STAMPS

Malaya Postage Due Stamps and Type of 1936-38, Handstamped Like Nos. N1-N14 in Carmine

1942 Wmk. 4 ***Perf. 14½x14***
NJ1 D2 1c violet *200.00 140.00*
NJ2 D2 4c yel green *200.00 200.00*
NJ3 D2 8c red *1,250. 1,250.*
NJ4 D2 10c yel orange *200.00 200.00*
NJ5 D2 12c blue violet *500.00 300.00*
NJ6 D2 50c black *1,250. 900.00*
Nos. NJ1-NJ6 (6) *3,600. 2,990.*

Pricing note above No. N1 also applies to Nos. NJ1-NJ6.

NEGRI SEMBILAN

ˈne-grē səm-ˈbē-lən

LOCATION — South of Selangor on the west coast of the Malay Peninsula, bordering on Pahang on the east and Johore on the south.
AREA — 2,580 sq. mi.
POP. — 401,742 (1960)
CAPITAL — Seremban

Stamps of the Straits Settlements Overprinted in Black **Negri Sembilan**

1891 Wmk. 2 Perf. 14
Overprint 14½ to 15mm Wide
1 A2 2c rose 2.00 4.00

Tiger — A1

Tiger Head — A2

1891-94 Typo.
2 A1 1c green ('93) 2.50 1.10
3 A1 2c rose 3.50 3.50
4 A1 5c blue ('94) 20.00 25.00
Nos. 2-4 (3) 26.00 29.60

For surcharges see Nos. 17-18.

1895-99
5 A2 1c lilac & green 4.50 2.00
6 A2 2c lilac & brown 24.00 70.00
7 A2 3c lilac & car rose 3.00 .65
8 A2 5c lilac & olive 5.00 4.00
9 A2 8c lilac & blue 20.00 12.00
10 A2 10c lilac & orange 25.00 11.00
11 A2 15c green & vio 27.50 55.00
12 A2 20c grn & ol ('99) 30.00 30.00
13 A2 25c grn & car rose 60.00 70.00
14 A2 50c green & black 47.50 55.00
Nos. 5-14 (10) 246.50 309.65

For surcharges see Nos. 15-16, 19-20.

Stamps of 1891-99 Surcharged **Four cents.**

1899 Green Surcharge
15 A2 4c on 8c lil & blue 2.00 3.50
a. Double surcharge 1,250. 1,250.
b. Pair, one without surcharge — 2,000.
c. Double surcharge, 1 green, 1 red 750.00 750.00

Black Surcharge
16 A2 4c on 8c lil & blue 800.00 850.00
Same Surcharge and Bar in Black
17 A2 4c on 1c green 1.00 10.00
18 A1 4c on 5c blue 1.00 10.00
19 A2 4c on 3c lil & car rose 2.75 11.00
a. Double surcharge 900.00 800.00
b. Pair, one without surcharge 2,000. 2,250.
d. Bar double 600.00

Bar at bottom on #17-18, at top on #19.

No. 11 Surcharged in Black **One cent.**

1900
20 A2 1c on 15c grn & vio 80.00 140.00
a. Inverted period 275.00 450.00

Arms of Negri Sembilan
A4 A5

1935-41 Typo. Wmk. 4
21 A4 1c black ('36) .75 .15
22 A4 2c dp green ('36) .50 .15
22A A4 2c brown org ('41) .15 27.50
22B A4 3c green ('41) .15 4.00
23 A4 4c brown orange .50 .15
24 A4 5c chocolate .50 .15
25 A4 6c rose red 2.75 .90
25A A4 6c gray ('41) 1.90 50.00
26 A4 8c gray 1.25 .25
27 A4 10c dull vio ('36) 1.25 .20
28 A4 12c ultra ('36) 1.50 .45
28A A4 15c ultra ('41) 2.00 35.00
29 A4 25c rose red & dull vio ('36) 1.50 1.50
30 A4 30c org & dull vio ('36) 2.00 2.75

31 A4 40c dull vio & car .90 3.50
32 A4 50c blk, emer ('36) 3.75 .90
33 A4 $1 red & blk, bl ('36) 1.50 2.00
34 A4 $2 rose red & grn ('36) 20.00 26.00
35 A4 $5 brn red & grn, emer ('36) 15.00 35.00
Nos. 21-35 (19) 57.85 190.55

For overprints see Nos. N1-N31.

Catalogue values for unused stamps in this section, from this point to the end of the section, are for Never Hinged items.

Silver Wedding Issue
Common Design Types
Inscribed: "Malaya Negri Sembilan"
1948, Dec. 1 Photo. Perf. 14x14½
36 CD304 10c purple .20 .20
Perf. 11½x11
Engraved; Name Typographed
37 CD305 $5 green 22.50 25.00

1949-55 Wmk. 4 Typo. Perf. 18
38 A5 1c black .15 .15
39 A5 2c orange .15 .15
40 A5 3c green .35 .30
41 A5 4c chocolate .15 .15
42 A5 5c rose violet .20 .15
43 A5 6c gray .30 .15
44 A5 8c rose red .55 .60
45 A5 8c green 2.00 2.00
46 A5 10c plum .30 .15
47 A5 12c rose red 2.00 2.00
48 A5 15c ultramarine 1.50 .40
49 A5 20c dk green & blk .80 .85
50 A5 20c ultramarine 1.00 .30
51 A5 25c org & rose lilac .45 .25
52 A5 30c plum & rose red ('55) 2.50 1.50
53 A5 35c dk vio & rose red 1.00 2.00
54 A5 40c dk vio & rose red 1.10 4.00
55 A5 50c ultra & black 1.10 .40
56 A5 $1 vio brn & ultra 2.50 1.00
57 A5 $2 rose red & emer 10.00 8.00
58 A5 $5 choc & emerald 45.00 30.00
Nos. 38-58 (21) 73.10 54.50

UPU Issue
Common Design Types
Inscribed: "Malaya-Negri Sembilan"
Engr.; Name Typo. on 15c, 25c
1949, Oct. 10 Perf. 13½, 11x11½
59 CD306 10c rose violet .20 .20
60 CD307 15c indigo .40 .40
61 CD308 25c orange .75 .75
62 CD309 50c slate 1.50 2.25
Nos. 59-62 (4) 2.85 3.60

Coronation Issue
Common Design Type
1953, June 2 Engr. Perf. 13½x13
63 CD312 10c magenta & black .35 .15

Types of Kedah with Arms of Negri Sembilan
Perf. 13x12½, 12½x13, 13½ ($1)
1957-63 Engr. Wmk. 314
64 A8 1c black .15 .15
65 A8 2c red orange .15 .15
66 A8 4c dark brown .15 .15
67 A8 5c dk car rose .15 .15
68 A8 8c dark green .25 1.00
69 A7 10c chocolate .40 .15
70 A7 20c blue .25 .15
71 A7 50c ultra & blk ('60) .65 .20
a. Perf. 12½ .65 .20
72 A8 $1 plum & ultra 1.50 .50
73 A8 $2 red & grn ('63) 4.00 6.00
a. Perf. 12½ 3.50 4.25
74 A8 $5 ol grn & brn ('62) 10.00 10.00
a. Perf. 12½ 3.50 5.75
Nos. 64-74 (11) 17.65 18.60

Negri Sembilan State Crest and Tuanku Munawir — A6

1961, Apr. 17 Unwmk. Perf. 14x13
75 A6 10s blue & multi .18 .15
Installation of Tuanku Munawir as ruler (Yang di-Pertuan Besar) of Negri Sembilan.
Starting in 1965, issues of Negri (Negeri) Sembilan are listed with Malaysia.

OCCUPATION STAMPS

Issued under Japanese Occupation

Stamps and Type of Negri Sembilan, 1935-41, Handstamped in Red, Black, Brown or Violet

1942 Wmk. 4 Perf. 14
N1 A4 1c black 18.00 12.00
N2 A4 2c brown org 12.00 13.00
N3 A4 3c green 16.00 16.00
N4 A4 5c chocolate 21.00 20.00
N5 A4 6c rose red 450.00 450.00
N6 A4 6c gray 110.00 110.00
N7 A4 8c gray 65.00 65.00
N8 A4 8c rose red 40.00 35.00
N9 A4 10c dark violet 80.00 80.00
N10 A4 12c ultramarine 650.00 650.00
N11 A4 15c ultramarine 15.00 8.00
N12 A4 25c rose red & dk vio 25.00 30.00
N13 A4 30c org & dk vio 125.00 140.00
N14 A4 40c dk vio & car 550.00 550.00
N15 A4 $1 red & blk, bl 100.00 100.00
N16 A4 $5 brn red & grn, emerald 325.00 350.00

The 8c rose red is not known to have been issued without overprint.
Some authorities believe Nos. N5 and N7 were not regularly issued.

DAI NIPPON
2602
MALAYA

Stamps of Negri Sembilan, 1935-41, Overprinted in Black

N17 A4 1c black 1.00 1.00
a. Inverted overprint 12.50 20.00
b. Dbl. ovpt., one invtd. 35.00 50.00
N18 A4 2c brown orange 1.25 1.00
N19 A4 3c green 1.00 .75
N20 A4 5c chocolate .65 .65
N21 A4 6c gray 1.50 1.50
a. Inverted overprint 750.00
N22 A4 8c rose red 2.00 2.00
N23 A4 10c dk violet 4.00 4.00
N24 A4 15c ultramarine 6.00 3.50
N25 A4 25c rose red & dk vio 1.50 5.00
N26 A4 30c org & dk vio 3.00 3.75
N27 A4 $1 red & blk, bl 100.00 125.00
Nos. N17-N27 (11) 121.90 148.15

The 8c rose red is not known to have been issued without overprint.

Negri Sembilan, Nos. 21, 24 and 29, Overprinted or Surcharged in Black:

a b c
2 cts. **6 cts.**

1943
N28 A4 1c black .50 .50
a. Inverted overprint 12.50 17.50
N29 A4 2c on 5c choc .40 .50
N30 A4 6c on 5c choc .50 .65
a. "6 cts." inverted 250.00 300.00
N31 A4 25c rose red & dk violet 1.50 2.00
Nos. N28-N31 (4) 2.90 3.65

The Japanese characters read: "Japanese Postal Service."

PAHANG

pə-'haŋ

LOCATION — On the east coast of the Malay Peninsula.
AREA — 13,820 sq. mi.
POP. — 338,210 (1960)
CAPITAL — Kuala Lipis

Stamps of the Straits Settlements Overprinted in Black

Overprinted **PAHANG**

Overprint 16x2¾mm
1889 Wmk. 2 Perf. 14
1 A2 2c rose 70.00 40.00
2 A3 8c orange 1,600. 1,100.
3 A7 10c slate 250.00 250.00

Overprinted **PAHANG**
Overprint 12½x2mm
4 A2 2c rose 3.00 6.00

Overprinted **PAHANG**
1890 Overprint 15x2½mm
5 A2 2c rose — 850.00

Overprinted **PAHANG**
Overprint 16x2¾mm
6 A2 2c rose 55.00 14.00

Surcharged in Black:

PAHANG Two CENTS | **PAHANG Two CENTS**
a | b
PAHANG Two CENTS | **PAHANG Two CENTS**
c | d

1891
7 A3 (a) 2c on 24c green 175.00 175.00
8 A3 (b) 2c on 24c green 175.00 175.00
9 A3 (c) 2c on 24c green 70.00 80.00
10 A3 (d) 2c on 24c green 60.00 65.00
Nos. 7-10 (4) 480.00 495.00

A5 A6

1892-95 Typo.
11 A5 1c green 4.75 4.50
12 A5 2c rose 1.25 1.65
13 A5 5c blue 6.00 15.00
Nos. 11-13 (3) 12.00 21.15

For surcharges see Nos. 21-22.

1895-99
14 A6 3c lilac & car rose 2.00 .85
14A A6 4c lil & car rose ('99) 5.50 2.50
15 A6 4c lilac & olive 18.00 12.00
Nos. 14-15 (3) 25.50 15.35

For surcharge see No. 28.

Stamps of Perak, 1895-99, Overprinted **Pahang.**

1898-99
16 A9 10c lilac & orange 15.00 15.00
17 A9 25c green & car rose 60.00 85.00
18 A9 50c green & black 110.00 95.00
18A A9 50c lilac & black 140.00 125.00

Overprinted **Pahang.**
Wmk. 1
19 A10 $1 green & lt grn 140.00 150.00
20 A10 $5 green & ultra 525.00 600.00
Nos. 16-20 (6) 990.00 1,070.

No. 13 Cut in Half and Surcharged With New Value and Initials in ms.

1897 Wmk. 2
Red Surcharge
21 A5 2c on half of 5c blue 850. 300.
a. Black surcharge 4,000. 2,000.
22 A5 3c on half of 5c blue 850. 300.
a. Black surcharge 4,000. 2,000.

Perak No. 52 Surcharged

Pahang
Four cents

1899
25 A9 4c on 8c lilac & blue 3.00 *5.00*
b. Inverted surcharge 1,000. 800.00

Same Surcharge on pieces of White Paper
1898 Without Gum *Imperf.*
26 4c black 1,000.
27 5c black 850.00

Pahang No. 15 Surcharged

Four cents.

1899 ***Perf. 14***
28 A6 4c on 5c lilac & olive 8.50 *25.00*

Sultan Abu Bakar
A7 A8

1935-41 Typo. Wmk. 4 *Perf. 14*
29 A7 1c black ('36) .15 .15
30 A7 2c dp green ('36) .90 .15
30A A7 3c green ('41) .20 *3.25*
31 A7 4c brown orange .50 .15
32 A7 5c chocolate .60 .15
33 A7 6c rose red ('36) 2.25 *6.00*
34 A7 8c gray 1.50 .15
34A A7 8c rose red ('41) .50 *16.00*
35 A7 10c dk violet ('36) .50 .15
36 A7 12c ultra ('36) 2.00 1.90
36A A7 15c ultra ('41) 1.25 *20.00*
37 A7 25c rose red & pale vio ('36) 1.50 .65
38 A7 30c org & dk vio ('36) .90 1.00
39 A7 40c dk vio & car 1.25 1.50
40 A7 50c black, *emer* ('36) 5.00 1.40
41 A7 $1 red & blk, *blue* ('36) 2.75 3.75
42 A7 $2 rose red & green ('36) 24.00 *45.00*
43 A7 $5 brn red & grn, *emer* ('36) 8.75 *45.00*
Nos. 29-43 (18) 54.50 *146.35*

The 3c was printed on both ordinary and chalky paper; the 15c only on ordinary paper; other values only on chalky paper.

A 2c brown orange and 6c gray, type A7, exist, but are not known to have been regularly issued.

For overprints see Nos. N1-N21.

Catalogue values for unused stamps in this section, from this point to the end of the section, are for Never Hinged items.

Silver Wedding Issue
Common Design Types
Inscribed: "Malaya Pahang"
Perf. 14x14¹/₂
1948, Dec. 1 Photo. Wmk. 4
44 CD304 10c purple .20 .20
Perf. 11¹/₂x11
Engraved; Name Typopgraphed
45 CD305 $5 green 24.00 35.00

UPU Issue
Common Design Types
Inscribed: "Malaya-Pahang"
Engr.; Name Typo. on 15c, 25c
1949, Oct. 10 *Perf. 13¹/₂, 11x11¹/₂*
46 CD306 10c rose violet .20 .20
47 CD307 15c indigo .28 .28
48 CD308 25c orange .80 .80
49 CD309 50c slate 1.40 1.40
Nos. 46-49 (4) 2.68 2.68

1950, June 1 Wmk. 4 Typo. *Perf. 18*
50 A8 1c black .15 .15
51 A8 2c orange .15 .15
52 A8 3c green .20 .30
53 A8 4c chocolate .15 .15
54 A8 6c gray .15 .15
55 A8 8c rose red .35 *1.50*
56 A8 10c plum .15 .15
57 A8 15c ultramarine .30 .15
58 A8 20c dk green & blk .30 *1.65*
59 A8 25c org & rose lilac .35 .15
60 A8 40c dk vio & rose red .70 *5.50*
61 A8 50c dp ultra & black .30 .15
62 A8 $1 vio brn & ultra 1.75 1.50
63 A8 $2 rose red & emer 10.00 15.00
64 A8 $5 choc & emer 42.50 *32.50*

1952-55
65 A8 5c rose violet .20 .15
66 A8 8c green .20 .65
67 A8 12c rose red .75 1.00
68 A8 20c ultramarine .50 .15
69 A8 30c plum & rose red ('55) .95 .30
70 A8 35c dk vio & rose red .50 .25
Nos. 50-70 (21) 60.60 *61.65*

Coronation Issue
Common Design Type
1953, June 2 Engr. *Perf. 13¹/₂x13*
71 CD312 10c magenta & black .25 .22

Types of Kedah with Portrait of Sultan Abu Bakar
Perf. 13x12¹/₂, 12¹/₂x13, 13¹/₂ ($1)
1957-62 Engr. Wmk. 314
72 A8 1c black .15 .15
73 A8 2c red orange .15 .15
74 A8 4c dark brown .15 .15
75 A8 5c dark car rose .15 .15
76 A8 8c dark green .26 .18
77 A7 10c chocolate .18 .15
78 A7 20c blue .40 .15
79 A7 50c ultra & blk ('60) .65 .26
a. Perf. 12¹/₂ .65 .26
80 A8 $1 plum & ultra 1.50 .65
81 A8 $2 red & green ('62) 3.50 2.00
a. Perf. 12¹/₂ 3.50 2.00
82 A8 $5 ol grn & brn ('60) 8.75 5.00
a. Perf. 12¹/₂ 8.75 5.00
Nos. 72-82 (11) 15.84 8.99

Starting in 1965, issues of Pahang are listed with Malaysia.

OCCUPATION STAMPS

Issued under Japanese Occupation

Stamps of Pahang, 1935-41, Handstamped in Black, Red, Brown or Violet

1942 Wmk. 4 *Perf. 14*
N1 A7 1c black 25.00 30.00
N1A A7 3c green 90.00 100.00
N2 A7 5c chocolate 11.00 7.00
N3 A7 8c rose red 19.00 8.00
N3A A7 8c gray 175.00 175.00
N4 A7 10c dk violet 45.00 45.00
N5 A7 12c ultramarine 900.00 900.00
N6 A7 15c ultramarine 65.00 65.00
N7 A7 25c rose red & pale vio 16.00 27.50
N8 A7 30c org & dk vio 12.50 24.00
N9 A7 40c dk vio & car 13.00 25.00
N10 A7 50c blk, *emerald* 225.00 250.00
N11 A7 $1 red & blk, *bl* 75.00 90.00
N12 A7 $5 brown red & grn, *emer* 475.00 550.00

Some authorities claim the 2c green, 4c brown orange, 6c rose red and $2 rose red and green were not regularly issued with this overprint.

Stamps of Pahang, 1935-41, Overprinted in Black

DAI NIPPON
2602
MALAYA

N13 A7 1c black 1.50 .80
N14 A7 5c chocolate 1.50 1.50
N15 A7 8c rose red 26.00 2.75
N16 A7 10c violet brown 15.00 6.75
N17 A7 12c ultramarine 1.50 2.25
N18 A7 25c rose red & pale vio 5.50 *7.75*
N19 A7 30c org & dk vio 2.00 *4.00*
Nos. N13-N19 (7) 53.00 *25.80*

Pahang No. 32 Overprinted and Surcharged in Black

大日本郵便
6 cts.
e

大日本郵便
6 cts.
f

1943
N20 A7(e) 6c on 5c chocolate 1.00 1.00
N21 A7(f) 6c on 5c chocolate 1.50 1.10

The Japanese characters read: "Japanese Postal Service."

PENANG

pə-naŋ

LOCATION — An island off the west coast of the Malay Peninsula, plus a coastal strip called Province Wellesley.
AREA — 400 sq. mi.
POP. — 616,254 (1960)
CAPITAL — Georgetown

Catalogue values for unused stamps in this section are for Never Hinged items.

Silver Wedding Issue
Common Design Types
Inscribed: "Malaya Penang"
Perf. 14x14¹/₂
1948, Dec. 1 Wmk. 4 Photo.
1 CD304 10c purple .20 .20
Perf. 11¹/₂x11
Engraved; Name Typographed
2 CD305 $5 lt brown 27.50 24.00

Type of Straits Settlements, 1937-41, Inscribed "Penang"
1949-52 *Perf. 18*
3 A29 1c black .15 .15
4 A29 2c orange .15 .15
5 A29 3c green .15 .25
6 A29 4c chocolate .15 .15
7 A29 5c rose vio ('52) .30 1.00
8 A29 6c gray .45 .15
9 A29 8c rose red .60 *2.50*
10 A29 8c green ('52) .60 .90
11 A29 10c plum .90 .15
12 A29 12c rose red ('52) .90 .60
13 A29 15c ultramarine 1.00 *2.00*
14 A29 20c dk grn & blk 1.10 1.00
15 A29 20c ultra ('52) .90 .35
16 A29 25c org & rose lilac .75 .15
17 A29 35c dk vio & rose red ('52) 1.50 .80
18 A29 40c dk vio & rose red 2.25 *6.00*
19 A29 50c ultra & black 2.00 .15
20 A29 $1 vio brn & ultra 3.75 .85
21 A29 $2 rose red & emer 8.00 .90
22 A29 $5 choc & emerald 32.50 1.25
Nos. 3-22 (20) 58.10 *19.45*

UPU Issue
Common Design Types
Inscribed: "Malaya-Penang"
Engr.; Name Typo. on 15c, 25c
1949, Oct. 10 *Perf. 13¹/₂, 11x11¹/₂*
23 CD306 10c rose violet .20 .15
24 CD307 15c indigo .40 .45
25 CD308 25c orange .70 .70
26 CD309 50c slate 1.40 1.40
Nos. 23-26 (4) 2.70 2.70

Coronation Issue
Common Design Type
1953, June 2 Engr. *Perf. 13¹/₂x13*
27 CD312 10c magenta & black .40 .15

Type of Malacca, 1954
1954-55 Wmk. 4 Typo. *Perf. 18*
29 A1 1c black .15 .25
30 A1 2c orange .40 .25
31 A1 4c chocolate .65 .15
32 A1 5c rose violet 2.00 1.50
33 A1 6c gray .20 .15
34 A1 8c green .20 *1.50*
35 A1 10c plum .20 .15
36 A1 12c rose red .30 2.00
37 A1 20c ultramarine .50 .15
38 A1 25c orange & plum .40 .15
39 A1 30c plum & rose red ('55) 1.00 .50
40 A1 35c vio brn & rose red .85 .50
41 A1 50c ultra & black .85 .35
42 A1 $1 vio brn & ultra 2.25 .35
43 A1 $2 rose red & grn 4.25 1.40
44 A1 $5 choc & emerald 19.00 3.25
Nos. 29-44 (16) 33.20 12.60

Types of Kedah with Portrait of Queen Elizabeth II
Perf. 13x12¹/₂, 12¹/₂x13
1957 Engr. Wmk. 314
45 A8 1c black .15 .20
46 A8 2c red orange .15 .25
47 A8 4c dark brown .15 .15
48 A8 5c dk car rose .15 .15
49 A8 8c dark green .80 1.00
50 A7 10c chocolate .25 .15
51 A7 20c blue .55 .15
Perf. 12¹/₂, 13¹/₂ ($1)
52 A7 50c ultra & black .95 .20
53 A8 $1 plum & ultra 1.40 .25
54 A8 $2 red & green 6.00 5.00
55 A8 $5 ol green & brown 12.00 6.00
Nos. 45-55 (11) 22.55 13.50

Types of Kedah, 1957 with Penang State Crest and Areca-nut Palm Replacing Portrait of Elizabeth II
Perf. 13x12¹/₂, 12¹/₂x13, 13¹/₂ ($1)
1960, Mar. 15 Engr. Wmk. 314
56 A8 1c black .15 .15
57 A8 2c red orange .15 .15
58 A8 4c dark brown .15 .15
59 A8 5c dk car rose .15 .15
60 A8 8c dark green .60 .40
61 A7 10c violet brown .15 .15
62 A7 20c blue .20 .15
63 A7 50c ultra & black .50 .15
64 A8 $1 plum & ultra 1.00 .30
65 A8 $2 red & green 2.50 .70
Revenue cancel .20
66 A8 $5 ol green & brown 7.00 1.25
Nos. 56-66 (11) 12.55
Set value 3.00

Starting in 1965, issues of Penang (Pulau Pinang) are listed with Malaysia.

OCCUPATION STAMPS

Issued under Japanese Occupation

Stamps of Straits Settlements, 1937-41, Overprinted in Red or Black

DAI NIPPON
2602
PENANG

1942 Wmk. 4 *Perf. 14*
N1 A29 1c black (R) 1.25 1.25
N2 A29 2c brown orange 6.50 3.25
N3 A29 3c green (R) 1.25 1.25
N4 A29 5c brown (R) 1.25 1.25
N5 A29 8c gray (R) 3.25 1.25
N6 A29 10c dull vio (R) 2.00 2.00
N7 A29 12c ultra (R) 2.75 *5.00*
N8 A29 15c ultra (R) 2.00 2.00
N9 A29 40c dk vio & rose red 3.25 *5.25*
N10 A29 50c black, *emer* (R) 5.25 *12.50*
N11 A29 $1 red & blk, *bl* 14.00 *17.50*
N12 A29 $2 rose red & gray grn 35.00 *50.00*
N13 A29 $5 grn & red, *grn* 475.00 450.00
Nos. N1-N13 (13) 552.75 552.50

Stamps of Straits Settlements Handstamped in Red

Okugawa Seal

1942 Wmk. 4 *Perf. 14*
N14 A29 1c black 14.00 12.50
N15 A29 2c brown orange 22.50 20.00
N16 A29 3c green 20.00 22.50
N17 A29 5c brown 35.00 25.00
N18 A29 8c gray 25.00 25.00
N19 A29 10c dull violet 40.00 40.00
N20 A29 12c ultramarine 35.00 25.00
N21 A29 15c ultramarine 25.00 30.00
N22 A29 40c dk vio & rose red 125.00 90.00
N23 A29 50c blk, *emerald* 125.00 140.00
N24 A29 $1 red & blk, *bl* 150.00 175.00
N25 A29 $2 rose red & gray grn 325.00 350.00
N26 A29 $5 grn & red, *grn* 900.00 950.00
Nos. N14-N26 (13) 1,841. 1,905.

Handstamped in Red

Uchibori Seal

N14a A29 1c 80.00 70.00
N15a A29 2c 85.00 70.00
N16a A29 3c 60.00 70.00
N17a A29 5c 600.00 600.00
N18a A29 8c 45.00 50.00
N19a A29 10c 45.00 55.00
N20a A29 12c 45.00 55.00
N21a A29 15c 45.00 55.00
Nos. N14a-N21a (8) 1,005. 1,025.

PERAK

'per-ə-,ak

LOCATION — On the west coast of the Malay Peninsula.
AREA — 7,980 sq. mi.
POP. — 1,327,120 (1960)
CAPITAL — Taiping

Straits Settlements No. 10
Handstamped in Black

1878		**Wmk. 1**	**Perf. 14**	
1	A2	2c brown	1,400.	1,000.

Overprinted **PERAK**

Overprint 17x3½mm Wide

1880				
2	A2	2c brown	22.50	35.00

Overprinted **PERAK**

Overprint 10 to 14½mm Wide

3	A2	2c brown	70.00	75.00

Same Overprint on Straits Settlements Nos. 40, 41a

1883			**Wmk. 2**	
4	A2	2c brown	17.00	22.50
5	A2	2c rose	10.00	18.00

Overprinted **PERAK**

Overprint 14 to 15½mm Wide

6	A2	2c rose	1.00	.90
a.	Inverted overprint		250.00	225.00
b.	Double overprint		575.00	

Overprinted **PERAK**

Overprint 12¾ to 14mm Wide

1886-90				
7	A2	2c rose	1.10	4.00
a.	"FERAK" corrected by pen		165.00	175.00

Overprinted **PERAK**

Overprint 10x1¾mm

8	A2	2c rose	10.00	15.00

Overprinted **PERAK**

Overprint 13x2¾mm

10	A2	2c rose	2.75	1.00

Overprinted **PERAK**

Overprint 10¾x2½mm

11	A2	2c rose	50.00	32.50

Straits Settlements Nos. 42, 41a
Surcharged in Black or Blue

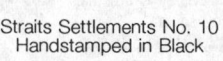

2 CENTS PERAK
q

ONE CENT PERAK.
r

ONE CENT PERAK
s

PERAK ONE CENT
t

12	A2(q)	2c on 4c rose	500.00	250.00
13	A2(t)	1c on 2c rose	37.50	28.00
14	A2(r)	1c on 2c rose	32.50	40.00
a.	Without period after "PERAK"		350.00	
15	A2(s)	1c on 2c rose (Bl)	20.00	27.50
15A	A2(s)	1c on 2c rose (Bk)	1,000.	925.00

In type "r" PERAK is 11½ to 14mm wide.

Surcharged in Black **1 CENT PERAK**

16	A2	1c on 2c rose	50.00	60.00
a.	Double surcharge			

Surcharged **I CENT PERAK**

17	A2	1c on 2c rose		

Some authorities question the status of No. 17.

Surcharged **1 CENT PERAK**

18	A2	1c on 2c rose	900.00	900.00
b.	Double surcharge, one inverted			
c.	"PREAK"			

Surcharged **I CENT PERAK**

18A	A2	1c on 2c rose	325.00	325.00

Surcharged **One CENT PERAK**

19	A2	1c on 2c rose	.75	2.50
a.	Double surcharge, one inverted			
b.	Inverted surcharge			
c.	"One" inverted		575.00	
d.	Double surcharge			

Straits Settlements No. 41a Surcharged

One CENT PERAK — u
One CENT PERAK — v
One CENT PERAK — w
One CENT PERAK — x
One CENT PERAK — y
One CENT PERAK — z
One CENT PERAK — h

1889-90				
20	A2(u)	1c on 2c rose	.50	.85
a.	Italic Roman "K" in "PERAK"		60.00	75.00
b.	Double surcharge			
21	A2(v)	1c on 2c rose	350.00	350.00
23	A2(w)	1c on 2c rose	7.00	15.00
a.	"PREAK"		200.00	250.00
24	A2(x)	1c on 2c rose	35.00	45.00
25	A2(y)	1c on 2c rose	4.25	5.00
26	A2(z)	1c on 2c rose	3.00	7.50
27	A2(h)	1c on 2c rose	11.00	11.00

Straits Settlements Nos. 41a, 48, 54
Surcharged in Black:

PERAK One CENT — a
PERAK Two CENTS — b
PERAK One CENT — c
PERAK One CENT — d
PERAK One CENT — e
PERAK One CENT — f

PERAK One CENT
g

1891			**Wmk. 2**	
28	A2(a)	1c on 2c rose	.70	2.25
a.	Bar omitted		100.00	
29	A2(a)	1c on 6c violet	30.00	25.00
30	A3(b)	1c on 24c green	8.00	8.00
31	A2(c)	1c on 2c rose	1.65	1.75
a.	Bar omitted		325.00	
32	A2(d)	1c on 2c rose	.38	.45
a.	Bar omitted		150.00	
33	A2(d)	1c on 6c violet	60.00	60.00
34	A3(d)	1c on 24c green	30.00	25.00
35	A2(e)	1c on 2c rose	5.00	11.00
a.	Bar omitted		325.00	
36	A2(e)	1c on 6c violet	110.00	115.00
37	A3(e)	2c on 24c green	75.00	50.00
38	A2(f)	1c on 6c violet	95.00	50.00
39	A3(f)	2c on 24c green	75.00	60.00
40	A2(g)	1c on 6c violet	100.00	105.00
41	A3(g)	2c on 24c green	75.00	60.00
		Nos. 28-41 (14)	665.73	573.45

A7

1892-95		**Typo.**	**Perf. 14**	
42	A7	1c green	1.75	.45
43	A7	2c rose	1.00	.45
44	A7	2c orange ('95)	.55	3.25
45	A7	5c blue	3.25	3.00
		Nos. 42-45 (4)	6.55	7.15

For overprint see No. O10.

Common Design Types
Pictured in section before Great Britain.

Type of 1892 Surcharged **3 CENTS** in Black

1895				
46	A7	3c on 5c rose	.50	2.25

A9 (1c) / A10

1895-99		**Wmk. 2**	**Perf. 14**	
47	A9	1c lilac & green	.75	.35
48	A9	2c lilac & brown	.60	.35
49	A9	3c lilac & car rose	1.90	.25
50	A9	4c lil & car rose ('99)	5.00	4.25
51	A9	5c lilac & olive	2.25	.50
52	A9	8c lilac & blue	22.50	.50
53	A9	10c lilac & orange	7.50	.40
54	A9	25c grn & car rose ('96)	90.00	10.00
55	A9	50c lilac & black	27.50	27.50
56	A9	50c grn & blk ('99)	90.00	90.00
			Wmk. 1	
57	A10	$1 green & lt grn	75.00	75.00
58	A10	$2 grn & car rose ('96)	110.00	110.00
59	A10	$3 green & ol ('96)	125.00	140.00
60	A10	$5 green & ultra	300.00	275.00
61	A10	$25 grn & org ('96)	4,000.	1,250.
		Nos. 47-57 (11)	323.00	209.10

For surcharges and overprint see #62-68, O11, Malaya 9-13A.

Stamps of 1895-99 Surcharged in Black:

One Cent. — i
ONE CENT. — k
Three Cent. — m

1900			**Wmk. 2**	
62	A9(i)	1c on 2c lilac & brown	.45	1.00
63	A9(k)	1c on 4c lilac & car rose	.45	1.40
64	A9(i)	1c on 5c lilac & ol	.50	1.65
65	A9(i)	3c on 8c lilac & blue	2.00	2.00
a.	No period after "Cent"		75.00	100.00
b.	Double surcharge		275.00	275.00
66	A9(i)	3c on 50c green & black	.90	1.65
a.	No period after "Cent"		70.00	110.00
			Wmk. 1	
67	A10(m)	3c on $1 grn & lt green	50.00	110.00
68	A10(m)	3c on $2 grn & car rose	25.00	60.00
		Nos. 62-68 (7)	79.30	177.70

Sultan Iskandar
A14   A15

1935-37		**Typo.**	**Wmk. 4**	
		Chalky Paper		
69	A14	1c black ('36)	.15	.15
70	A14	2c dp grn ('36)	.15	.15
71	A14	4c brn orange	.20	.15
72	A14	5c chocolate	.15	.15
73	A14	6c rose red ('37)	2.25	1.75
74	A14	8c gray	1.50	.30
75	A14	10c dk vio ('36)	.45	.15
76	A14	12c ultra ('36)	2.00	.85
77	A14	25c rose red & pale vio ('36)	1.00	.95
78	A14	30c org & dark vio ('36)	1.00	1.50
79	A14	40c dk vio & car	3.25	3.25
80	A14	50c blk, emerald ('36)	2.00	1.40
81	A14	$1 red & blk, bl ('36)	1.50	1.50
82	A14	$2 rose red & green ('36)	12.50	8.50
83	A14	$5 brn red & grn, emer ('36)	25.00	20.00
		Nos. 69-83 (15)	53.10	40.75

1938-41				
84	A15	1c black ('39)	1.75	.15
85	A15	2c dp green ('39)	1.25	.15
85A	A15	2c brn org ('41)	.45	1.25
85B	A15	3c green ('41)	.75	.30
86	A15	4c brn org ('39)	12.50	.15
87	A15	5c choc ('39)	1.25	.15
88	A15	6c rose red ('39)	12.50	.15
89	A15	8c gray	12.50	.15
89A	A15	8c rose red ('41)	.50	4.00
90	A15	10c dk violet ('39)	12.50	.15
91	A15	12c ultramarine	12.50	1.90
91A	A15	15c ultra ('41)	1.10	11.00
92	A15	25c rose red & pale vio ('39)	45.00	2.50
93	A15	30c org & dk vio	6.50	1.65
94	A15	40c dk vio & rose red	30.00	1.65
95	A15	50c blk, emerald	15.00	.40
96	A15	$1 red & blk, bl ('40)	70.00	13.00
97	A15	$2 rose red & grn ('40)	70.00	50.00
98	A15	$5 red, emer ('40)	125.00	200.00
		Nos. 84-98 (19)	431.05	288.70

For overprints see Nos. N1-N40.

Catalogue values for unused stamps in this section, from this point to the end of the section, are for Never Hinged items.

Silver Wedding Issue
Common Design Types
Inscribed: "Malaya Perak"

1948, Dec. 1	**Photo.**	**Perf. 14x14½**		
99	CD304	10c purple	.15	.15

Perf. 11½x11
Engraved; Name Typographed

100	CD305	$5 green	24.00	24.00

UPU Issue
Common Design Types
Inscribed: "Malaya-Perak"
Engr.; Name Typo. on 15c, 25c
Perf. 13½, 11x11½

1949, Oct. 10			**Wmk. 4**	
101	CD306	10c rose violet	.20	.20
102	CD307	15c indigo	.45	.40
103	CD308	25c orange	.65	.80
104	CD309	50c slate	1.50	1.75
		Nos. 101-104 (4)	2.80	3.15

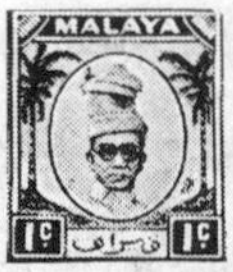
Sultan Yussuf Izuddin Shah — A16

1950, Aug. 17 Typo. *Perf. 18*
105 A16 1c black .15 .15
106 A16 2c orange .15 .15
107 A16 3c green .95 .50
108 A16 4c chocolate .25 .15
109 A16 6c gray .35 .15
110 A16 8c rose red .55 .40
111 A16 10c plum .35 .15
112 A16 15c ultramarine .80 .25
113 A16 20c dk grn & blk 1.00 .45
114 A16 25c org & plum .70 .15
115 A16 40c vio brn & rose red 1.90 2.50
116 A16 50c dp ultra & blk 1.10 .15
117 A16 $1 vio brn & ultra 3.00 .40
118 A16 $2 rose red & emer 9.00 2.50
119 A16 $5 choc & emerald 30.00 10.00

1952-55
120 A16 5c rose violet .30 .15
121 A16 8c green .75 .50
122 A16 12c rose red .70 1.25
123 A16 20c ultramarine .70 .15
124 A16 30c plum & rose red ('55) 1.40 .20
125 A16 35c dk vio & rose red 1.25 .25
Nos. 105-125 (21) 55.35 20.55

Coronation Issue
Common Design Type
1953 Engr. *Perf. 13½x13*
126 CD312 10c magenta & black .25 .15

Types of Kedah with Portrait of Sultan Yussuf Izuddin Shah
Perf. 13x12½, 12½x13, 13½ ($1)
1957-61 Engr. Wmk. 314
127 A8 1c black .15 .15
128 A8 2c red orange .15 .15
129 A8 4c dark brown .15 .15
130 A8 5c dk car rose .15 .15
131 A8 8c dark green .90 .22
132 A7 10c chocolate .15 .15
133 A7 20c blue .22 .15
134 A7 50c ultra & blk ('60) .52 .16
a. Perf. 12½ .52 .16
135 A8 $1 plum & ultra 1.10 .22
136 A8 $2 red & grn ('61) 2.75 .65
a. Perf. 12½ 2.75 .90
137 A8 $5 ol grn & brn ('60) 9.00 2.00
a. Perf. 12½ 9.00 2.75
Nos. 127-137 (11) 15.24 4.15

Starting with 1963, issues of Perak are listed with Malaysia.

OFFICIAL STAMPS

Stamps and Types of Straits Settlements Overprinted in Black **P.G.S.**

1890 Wmk. 1 *Perf. 14*
O1 A3 12c blue 125.00 150.00
O2 A3 24c green 375.00 *400.00*

Wmk. 2
O3 A2 2c rose 2.25 2.75
a. No period after "S" 40.00 40.00
b. Double overprint 1,100. 1,100.
O4 A2 4c brown 5.00 12.00
a. No period after "S" 72.50 *100.00*
O5 A2 6c violet 16.00 25.00
O6 A3 8c orange 20.00 55.00
O7 A7 10c slate 55.00 55.00
O8 A3 12c vio brown 140.00 170.00
O9 A3 24c green 90.00 *110.00*

P.G.S. stands for Perak Government Service.

Perak No. 45 Overprinted **Service.**

1894
O10 A7 5c blue 25.00 .75
a. Inverted overprint 550.00 400.00

Same Overprint on No. 51

1897
O11 A9 5c lilac & olive 1.25 .30
a. Double overprint 325.00 350.00

OCCUPATION STAMPS

Issued under Japanese Occupation

Stamps of Perak, 1938-41, Handstamped in Black, Red, Brown or Violet

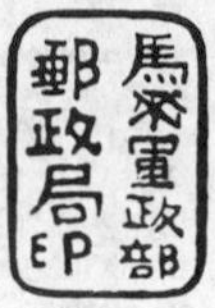

1942 Wmk. 4 *Perf. 14*
N1 A15 1c black 35.00 25.00
N2 A15 2c brn orange 25.00 16.00
N3 A15 3c green 25.00 27.50
N4 A15 5c chocolate 8.50 8.00
N5 A15 8c gray 40.00 27.50
N6 A15 8c rose red 18.00 25.00
N7 A15 10c dk violet 17.00 20.00
N8 A15 12c ultramarine 110.00 110.00
N9 A15 15c ultramarine 22.50 25.00
N10 A15 25c rose red & pale vio 20.00 22.00
N11 A15 30c org & dk vio 25.00 30.00
N12 A15 40c dk vio & rose red 125.00 140.00
N13 A15 50c blk, *emerald* 42.50 *45.00*
N14 A15 $1 red & blk, *bl* 200.00 225.00
N15 A15 $2 rose red & grn *1,100.* *1,100.*
N16 A15 $5 red, *emerald* 450.00 450.00

Some authorities claim No. N6 was not regularly issued. This overprint also exists on No. 85

Stamps of Perak, 1938-41, Overprinted in Black **DAI NIPPON 2602 MALAYA**

N16A A15 1c black 30.00 30.00
N17 A15 2c brown orange 1.25 1.25
a. Inverted overprint 20.00 21.00
N18 A15 3c green .95 1.00
a. Inverted overprint 20.00 22.50
N18B A15 5c chocolate 30.00
N19 A15 8c rose red .95 .50
a. Inverted overprint 7.50 7.50
b. Dbl. ovpt., one invtd. 175.00 200.00
c. Pair, one without ovpt. 350.00 350.00
N20 A15 10c dk violet 6.25 7.00
N21 A15 15c ultramarine 4.50 5.00
N21A A15 30c org & dk vio 25.00 25.00
N22 A15 50c blk, *emerald* 3.00 4.50
N23 A15 $1 red & blk, *bl* 250.00 *275.00*
N24 A15 $5 red, *emerald* 45.00 50.00
a. Inverted overprint 250.00 *300.00*

Some authorities claim Nos. N16A, N18B and N21A were not regularly issued.

Overprinted on Perak No. 87 and Surcharged in Black "2 Cents"
N25 A15 2c on 5c chocolate 1.50 1.00

Perak Nos. 84 and 89A Overprinted in Black **DAI NIPPON YUBIN**

N26 A15 1c black 2.50 3.00
a. Inverted overprint 25.00 30.00
N27 A15 8c rose red 2.50 1.50
a. Inverted overprint 15.00 17.50

Overprinted on Perak No. 87 and Surcharged in Black "2 Cents"
N28 A15 2c on 5c chocolate 3.75 3.75
a. Inverted overprint 25.00 35.00
b. As "a," "2 Cents" omitted 37.50 42.50

Stamps of Perak, 1938-41, Overprinted or Surcharged in Black:

大日本郵便 — n
大日本郵便 2 Cents — No. N31
大日本郵便 2 cts. — No. N32

1943
N29 A15 1c black .50 .50
N30 A15 2c brn orange 26.00 26.00
N31 A15 2c on 5c choc .75 .75
a. "2 Cents" inverted 25.00 30.00
b. Entire surcharge inverted 25.00 30.00
N32 A15 2c on 5c choc 1.00 1.00
a. Vertical characters invtd. 25.00 30.00
b. Entire surcharge inverted 25.00 30.00
N33 A15 3c green 27.50 27.50
N34 A15 5c chocolate .75 .75
a. Inverted overprint 37.50 45.00
N35 A15 8c gray 25.00 25.00
N36 A15 8c rose red .75 .75
a. Inverted overprint 25.00 30.00
N37 A15 10c dk violet .90 .90
N38 A15 30c org & dk vio 2.00 3.00
N39 A15 50c blk, *emerald* 4.00 7.00
N40 A15 $5 red, *emerald* 55.00 62.50
Nos. N29-N40 (12) 144.15 155.65

No. N34 was also used in the Shan States of Burma. The Japanese characters read: "Japanese Postal Service."

Some authorities claim Nos. N30, N33 and N35 were not regularly issued.

PERLIS

'per–ləs

LOCATION — On the west coast of the Malay peninsula, adjoining Siam and Kedah.
AREA — 310 sq. mi.
POP. — 97,645 (1960)
CAPITAL — Kangar

Catalogue values for unused stamps in this section are for Never Hinged items.

Silver Wedding Issue
Common Design Types
Inscribed: "Malaya Perlis"
Perf. 14x14½
1948, Dec. 1 Photo. Wmk. 4
1 CD304 10c purple .20 .20

Engraved; Name Typographed
Perf. 11½x11
2 CD305 $5 lt brown 25.00 27.50

UPU Issue
Common Design Types
Inscribed: "Malaya-Perlis"
Engr.; Name Typo. on 15c, 25c
1949, Oct. 10 *Perf. 13½, 11x11½*
3 CD306 10c rose violet .25 .25
4 CD307 15c indigo .50 .50
5 CD308 25c orange .85 .85
6 CD309 50c slate 1.90 1.90
Nos. 3-6 (4) 3.50 3.50

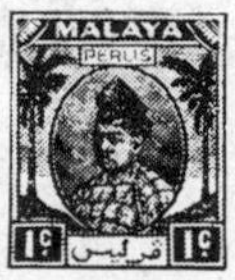
Raja Syed Putra — A1

Wmk. 4
1951, Mar. 26 Typo. *Perf. 18*
7 A1 1c black .15 *.15*
8 A1 2c orange .15 *.15*
9 A1 3c green .85 *2.00*
10 A1 4c chocolate .20 .25
11 A1 6c gray .22 .30
12 A1 8c rose red .65 2.00
13 A1 10c plum .35 .15
14 A1 15c ultramarine 1.00 3.00
15 A1 20c dk green & blk 2.00 3.50
16 A1 25c org & rose lilac .85 .85
17 A1 40c dk vio & rose red 2.00 *4.00*
18 A1 50c ultra & black 1.65 1.15
19 A1 $1 vio brn & ultra 5.25 4.25
20 A1 $2 rose red & emer 7.50 *15.00*
21 A1 $5 choc & emerald 35.00 *47.50*

1952-55
22 A1 5c rose violet .16 .30
23 A1 8c green .42 *2.00*
24 A1 12c rose red .42 *2.50*
25 A1 20c ultramarine .60 .75
26 A1 30c plum & rose red ('55) 3.25 *5.00*
27 A1 35c dk vio & rose red 1.00 *3.00*
Nos. 7-27 (21) 63.67 *97.80*

Coronation Issue
Common Design Type
1953, June 2 Engr. *Perf. 13½x13*
28 CD312 10c magenta & black .35 .35

Types of Kedah with Portrait of Raja Syed Putra
Perf. 13x12½, 12½x13, 12½ ($2, $5), 13½ ($1)
1957-62 Engr. Wmk. 314
29 A8 1c black .15 .15
30 A8 2c red orange .15 *.15*
31 A8 4c dark brown .15 .15
32 A8 5c dk car rose .15 .15
33 A8 8c dark green 1.00 .35
34 A7 10c chocolate .15 .15
35 A7 20c blue .16 .15
36 A7 50c ultra & blk ('62) .60 .50
a. Perf. 12½ .48 .40
37 A8 $1 plum & ultra 1.25 *1.50*
38 A8 $2 red & green 3.00 *2.50*
39 A8 $5 ol green & brown 10.00 *5.50*
Nos. 29-39 (11) 16.76 *11.25*

Starting in 1965, issues of Perlis are listed with Malaysia.

SELANGOR

sə–'laŋ–ər

LOCATION — South of Perak on the west coast of the Malay Peninsula.
AREA — 3,160 sq. mi.
POP. — 1,012,891 (1960)
CAPITAL — Kuala Lumpur

Stamps of the Straits Settlements Overprinted

Handstamped in Black or Red

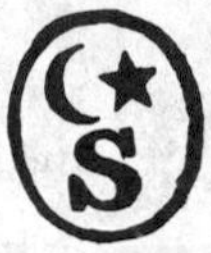

1878 Wmk. 1 *Perf. 14*
1 A2 2c brown (Bk)
2 A2 2c brown (R)

The authenticity of Nos. 1-2 and the 2c brown, watermarked Crown and CA, is questioned.

Overprinted in Black **S.**

1882 Wmk. 2
3 A2 2c brown 1,400.
4 A2 2c rose

Overprinted **SELANGOR**

Overprint 16 to 16¾mm Wide
1881 Wmk. 1
5 A2 2c brown 40.00 50.00
a. Double overprint

Overprint 16 to 17mm Wide
1882-83 Wmk. 2
6 A2 2c brown 75.00 65.00
7 A2 2c rose 75.00 65.00

Overprinted **SELANGOR**

Overprint 14¼x3mm
8 A2 2c rose 4.00 4.50
a. Double overprint

Overprinted **SELANGOR**

Overprint 14½ to 15½mm Wide
1886-89
9 A2 2c rose 15.00 15.00

Overprinted **SELANGOR**

Overprint 16½x1¾mm
9A A2 2c rose 35.00 32.50

Overprinted **SELANGOR**

Overprint 15½ to 17mm Wide
With Period
10 A2 2c rose 22.50 22.50
Without Period
11 A2 2c rose 4.00 2.00
Same Overprint, but Vertically
12 A2 2c rose 12.50 12.50

Overprinted **SELANGOR**

12A A2 2c rose 32.50 2.25

Overprinted ***Selangor***

Overprint 17mm Wide
13 A2 2c rose 675.00 *725.00*

Overprinted **SELANGOR**

14 A2 2c rose 250.00 150.00

Overprinted
Vertically **SELANGOR**

1889
15 A2 2c rose   82.50 16.00

Overprinted
Vertically *SELANGOR*

Overprint 19 to 20¾mm Wide
16 A2 2c rose   60.00 30.00
Similar Overprint, but Diagonally
17 A2 2c rose   1,100.

Overprinted Vertically **SELANGOR**

18 A2 2c rose   35.00 5.25
Same Overprint Horizontally
18A A2 2c rose   3,250.

Surcharged in Black:

SELANGOR | *SELANGOR*
Two | *Two*
CENTS | CENTS
a | b

SELANGOR | SELANGOR
Two | Two
CENTS | CENTS
c | d

SELANGOR
Two
CENTS
e

1891
19 A3 (a) 2c on 24c green   12.50 13.00
20 A3 (b) 2c on 24c green   80.00
21 A3 (c) 2c on 24c green   80.00
22 A3 (d) 2c on 24c green   50.00
23 A3 (e) 2c on 24c green   85.00
  Nos. 19-23 (5)   307.50

A6

1891-95   Typo.   Wmk. 2
24 A6 1c green   1.25 .20
25 A6 2c rose   2.25 .35
26 A6 2c orange ('95)   .90 .35
27 A6 5c blue   8.50 2.50
  Nos. 24-27 (4)   12.90 3.40

Type of 1891 Surcharged **3 CENTS**

1894
28 A6 3c on 5c rose   1.25 .40

A8   A9

1895-99   Wmk. 2   Perf. 14
29 A8 3c lilac & car rose   2.00 .15
30 A8 5c lilac & olive   .45 .25
31 A8 8c lilac & blue   32.50 5.00
32 A8 10c lilac & orange   6.50 .50
33 A8 25c grn & car rose   40.00 17.50
34 A8 50c lilac & black   27.50 12.50
35 A8 50c green & black   125.00 37.50
  Wmk. 1
36 A9 $1 green & lt grn   42.50 55.00
37 A9 $2 grn & car rose   90.00 90.00
38 A9 $3 green & olive   200.00 125.00
39 A9 $5 green & ultra   125.00 125.00
40 A9 $10 grn & brn vio   325.00 250.00
41 A9 $25 green & org   1,400.

High values with revenue cancellations are plentiful and inexpensive.

Surcharged in Black:

One cent. | **Three cents.**

1900   Wmk. 2
42 A8 1c on 5c lilac & olive   50.00 75.00
43 A8 1c on 50c grn & blk   1.00 1.25
  a. Double surcharge   1,200.
44 A8 3c on 50c grn & blk   6.50 9.50
  Nos. 42-44 (3)   57.50 85.75

Mosque at Klang A12 | Sultan Sulaiman A13

1935-41   Typo.   Wmk. 4   Perf. 14
45 A12 1c black ('36)   .15 .15
46 A12 2c dp green ('36)   .15 .15
46A A12 2c org brn ('41)   .15 1.00
46B A12 3c green ('41)   .15 1.25
47 A12 4c orange brown   .30 .15
48 A12 5c chocolate   .20 .15
49 A12 6c rose red   4.00 .15
50 A12 8c gray   .35 .15
51 A12 10c dk violet ('36)   .35 .15
52 A12 12c ultra ('36)   1.40 .15
52A A12 15c ultra ('41)   5.00 20.00
53 A12 25c rose red & pale vio ('36) .50 .55
54 A12 30c org & dk vio ('36)   .75 .80
55 A12 40c dk vio & car ('36)   1.25 1.00
56 A12 50c blk, emer ('36)   1.50 .45
57 A13 $1 red & black, blue ('36) 4.75 .65
58 A13 $2 rose red & green ('36) 16.00 4.25
59 A13 $5 brn red & grn, emer ('36) 40.00 26.00
  Nos. 45-59 (18)   76.95 57.15

Nos. 46A-46B were printed on both ordinary and chalky paper; 15c only on ordinary paper; other values only on chalky paper.
An 8c rose red was prepared but not issued.
For overprints see #N1-N15, N18A-N24, N26-N39.

Sultan Hisam-ud-Din Alam Shah
A14   A15

1941
72 A14 $1 red & blk, blue   6.50 3.25
73 A14 $2 car & green   40.00 20.00

A $5 stamp of type A14, issued during the Japanese occupation with different overprints (Nos. N18, N25A, N42), also exists without overprint. The unoverprinted stamp was not issued before or after the occupation.
For overprints see #N16-N17, N24A, N25, N40-N41.

> Catalogue values for unused stamps in this section, from this point to the end of the section, are for Never Hinged items.

Silver Wedding Issue
Common Design Types
Inscribed: "Malaya Selangor"
Perf. 14x14½
1948, Dec. 1   Photo.   Wmk. 4
74 CD304 10c purple   .20 .20
Perf. 11½x11
Engraved; Name Typographed
75 CD305 $5 green   25.00 24.00

UPU Issue
Common Design Types
Inscribed: "Malaya-Selangor"
Engr.; Name Typo. on Nos. 77 & 78
1949, Oct. 10   Perf. 13½, 11x11½
76 CD306 10c rose violet   .32 .32
77 CD307 15c indigo   .38 .38
78 CD308 25c orange   .65 .65
79 CD309 50c slate   1.25 1.25
  Nos. 76-79 (4)   2.60 2.60

1949, Sept. 12   Typo.   Perf. 18
80 A15 1c black   .15 .15
81 A15 2c orange   .15 .15
82 A15 3c green   .30 .70
83 A15 4c chocolate   .20 .15
84 A15 6c gray   .25 .15
85 A15 8c rose red   .30 .70
86 A15 10c plum   .20 .15
87 A15 15c ultramarine   .80 .15
88 A15 20c dk grn & black   1.40 .40
89 A15 25c orange & rose lil   .75 .15
90 A15 40c dk vio & rose red   1.75 3.00
91 A15 50c ultra & black   .50 .15
92 A15 $1 vio brn & ultra   2.00 .18
93 A15 $2 rose red & emer   6.00 .75
94 A15 $5 choc & emerald   42.50 1.50

1952-55
95 A15 5c rose violet   .20 .15
96 A15 8c green   .25 .15
97 A15 12c rose red   .50 .30
98 A15 20c ultramarine   1.00 .15
99 A15 30c plum & rose red ('55) 1.40 .30
100 A15 35c dk vio & rose red   .80 .40
  Nos. 80-100 (21)   61.40 9.88

Coronation Issue
Common Design Type
1953, June 2   Engr.   Perf. 13½x13
101 CD312 10c magenta & black   .25 .15

Sultan Hisam-ud-Din Alam Shah
A16   A17

Designs as in Kelantan, 1957.

Perf. 13x12½, 12½x13, 13½ ($1)
1957-60   Engr.   Wmk. 314
102 A17 1c black   .15 .15
103 A17 2c red orange   .15 .15
104 A17 4c dark brown   .15 .15
105 A17 5c dark car rose   .15 .15
106 A17 8c dark green   1.00 .25
107 A16 10c chocolate   .15 .15
108 A16 20c blue   .22 .15
109 A16 50c ultra & blk ('60)   .55 .15
  a. Perf. 12½   .55 .18
110 A17 $1 plum & ultra   1.10 .30
111 A17 $2 red & grn ('60)   3.00 1.00
  a. Perf. 12½   3.00 1.25
112 A17 $5 ol grn & brn ('60)   6.25 2.00
  a. Perf. 12½   8.00 2.75
  Nos. 102-112 (11)   12.87
  Set value   3.95
See Nos. 114-120.

Sultan Salahuddin Abdul Aziz Shah — A18

1961, June 28   Photo.   Perf. 14½x14
113 A18 10s multicolored   .18 .15
Sultan Salahuddin Abdul Aziz Shah, installation.

Types of 1957 with Portrait of Sultan Salahuddin Abdul Aziz Shah
Designs as before.
Perf. 13x12½, 12½x13
1961-62   Engr.   Wmk. 338
114 A17 1c black   .15 .15
115 A17 2c red orange   .15 .15
116 A17 4c dark brown   .15 .15
117 A17 5c dark car rose   .15 .15
118 A17 8c dark green   .38 .38

119 A16 10c vio brown ('61)   .30 .15
120 A16 20c blue   .45 .18
  Set value   1.50 .94
Starting in 1965, issues of Selangor are listed with Malaysia.

OCCUPATION STAMPS

Issued under Japanese Occupation

Stamps of Selangor 1935-41 Handstamped Vertically or Horizontally in Black, Red, Brown or Violet

1942, Apr. 3   Wmk. 4   Perf. 14
N1 A12 1c black   11.00 16.00
N2 A12 2c deep green   450.00 450.00
N3 A12 2c orange brown   40.00 40.00
N4 A12 3c green   25.00 12.50
N5 A12 5c chocolate   7.50 7.50
N6 A12 6c rose red   150.00 150.00
N7 A12 8c gray   20.00 20.00
N8 A12 10c dark violet   17.00 20.00
N9 A12 12c ultramarine   35.00 35.00
N10 A12 15c ultramarine   12.50 15.00
N11 A12 25c rose red & pale vio 60.00 70.00
N12 A12 30c org & dk vio   11.00 22.50
N13 A12 40c dk vio & car   75.00 100.00
N14 A12 50c blk, emerald   30.00 35.00
N15 A13 $5 brn red & grn, emer 200.00 200.00

Some authorities believe No. N15 was not issued regularly.

Handstamped Vertically on Stamps and Type of Selangor 1941 in Black or Red
N16 A14 $1 red & blk, bl   45.00 60.00
N17 A14 $2 car & green   60.00 85.00
N18 A14 $5 brn red & grn, emer 80.00 80.00

Stamps and Type of Selangor, 1935-41, Overprinted in Black

1942, May
N18A A12 1c black   80.00 80.00
N19 A12 3c green   .75 .75
N19A A12 5c chocolate   80.00 80.00
N20 A12 10c dark violet   25.00 25.00
N21 A12 12c ultramarine   2.00 3.75
N22 A12 15c ultramarine   4.00 3.00
N23 A12 30c org & dk vio   25.00 25.00
N24 A12 40c dk vio & car   3.00 3.00
N24A A12 $1 red & blk, bl   25.00 25.00
N25 A14 $2 car & green   17.50 22.50
N25A A14 $5 red & grn, emer   40.00 40.00
  Nos. N18A-N25A (11)   302.25 308.00

Overprint is horizontal on $1, $2, $5.
On Nos. N18A and N19 the overprint is known reading up, instead of down.
Some authorities claim Nos. N18A, N19A, N20, N23, N24A and N25A were not regularly issued.

Selangor No. 46B Overprinted in Black

1942, Dec.
N26 A12 3c green   300.00 300.00

Stamps and Type of Selangor, 1935-41, Overprinted or Surcharged in Black or Red:

i | k
l | m
6 cts. | **6 cts.**

1943
N27 A12(i) 1c black   1.00 1.00
N28 A12(k) 1c black (R)   .65 .65
N29 A12(l) 2c on 5c choc (R)   .65 .65
N30 A12(i) 3c green   .75 .75
N31 A12(l) 3c on 5c choc   .50 .75
N32 A12(k) 5c choc (R)   .50 .75

N33	A12(l)	6c on 5c choc	.25	.65
N34	A12(m)	6c on 5c choc	.25	.75
N35	A12(i)	12c ultra	1.00	1.25
N36	A12(i)	15c ultra	5.00	7.50
N37	A12(k)	15c ultra	10.00	10.00
N38	A12(i)	$1 on 10c dk vio	.38	1.00
N39	A12(m)	$1.50 on 30c org & dk vio	.38	1.00
N40	A14(i)	$1 red & blk, blue	5.00	6.25
N41	A14(i)	$2 car & grn	17.50	17.50
N42	A14(i)	$5 brn red & grn, emer	37.50	40.00
	Nos. N27-N42 (16)		81.31	90.45

The "i" overprint is vertical on Nos. N40-N42 and is also found reading in the opposite direction on Nos. N30, N35 and N36.
The overprint reads: "Japanese Postal Service."

Singapore is listed following Sierra Leone.

SUNGEI UJONG

ˈsu̇ŋə ü–ˌju̇ŋ

Formerly a nonfederated native state on the Malay Peninsula, which in 1895 was consolidated with the Federated State of Negri Sembilan.

Stamps of the Straits Settlements Overprinted in Black

Overprinted

1878		**Wmk. 1**	**Perf. 14**
2	A2 2c brown		2,500. 2,250.

Overprinted **SUNGEI UJONG**

4	A2 2c brown	90.00
5	A4 4c rose	800.00

No. 5 is no longer recognized by some experts.

Overprinted **S.U.**

1882-83		**Wmk. 2**
6	A2 2c brown	125. 125.
7	A4 4c rose	1,600. 1,800.

This overprint on the 2c brown, wmk. 1, is probably a trial printing.

Overprinted **SU**

11	A2 2c brown	125.00 175.00

Overprinted **SUNGEI UJONG**

1881-84			
14	A2 2c brown	165.00	150.00
15	A2 2c rose	80.00	90.00
	a. "Ujong" printed sideways		
	b. "Sungei" printed twice		
16	A2 4c brown	72.50	72.50
17	A3 8c orange	825.00	550.00
18	A7 10c slate	500.00	400.00

Overprinted **SUNGEI UJONG.**

19	A2 2c brown	30.00 70.00

Overprinted **SUNGEI UJONG**

1885-90		
	Without Period	
20	A2 2c rose	16.00 17.00
	With Period	
21	A2 2c rose	45.00 50.00
	a. "UNJOG"	2,100. 2,100.

Overprinted *Sungei Ujong*

22	A2 2c rose	35.00	37.50
	a. Double overprint	400.00	400.00

Overprinted **SUNGEI UJONG**

23	A2 2c rose	35.00 37.50

Overprinted **SUNGEI UJONG**

24	A2 2c rose	9.00	25.00
	a. Double overprint		

Overprinted **SUNGEI UJONG**

25	A2 2c rose	27.50 30.00

Overprinted **SUNGEI UJONG**

26	A2 2c rose	45.00	47.50
	c. Double overprint		

Overprinted **SUNGEI UJONG**

Overprint 14-16x3mm

26A	A2 2c rose	4.50 6.00

Overprinted **SUNGEI UJONG**

26B	A2 2c rose	25.00 12.50

Stamp of 1883-91 Surcharged:

SUNGEI UJONG Two CENTS   **SUNGEI UJONG Two CENTS**
a   b

SUNGEI UJONG Two CENTS   **SUNGEI UJONG Two CENTS**
c   d

1891			
27	A3 (a) 2c on 24c green	85.00	110.00
28	A3 (b) 2c on 24c green	325.00	350.00
29	A3 (c) 2c on 24c green	110.00	120.00
30	A3 (d) 2c on 24c green	225.00	275.00
	Nos. 27-30 (4)	745.00	855.00

On Nos. 27-28, SUNGEI is 14½mm, UJONG 12¾x2½mm.

A3   A4

1891-94	**Typo.**	**Perf. 14**	
31	A3 2c rose	22.50	27.50
32	A3 2c orange ('94)	1.75	4.50
33	A3 5c blue ('93)	4.00	5.50
	Nos. 31-33 (3)	28.25	37.50

Type of 1891 Surcharged in Black **1 CENT**

1894			
34	A3 1c on 5c green	1.50	1.50
35	A3 3c on 5c rose	2.75	2.50

1895			
36	A4 3c lilac & car rose	4.00	3.00

Stamps of Sungei Ujong were superseded by those of Negri Sembilan in 1895.

TRENGGANU

tre-ˈgä-(ˌ)nü

LOCATION — On the eastern coast of the Malay Peninsula.
AREA — 5,050 sq. mi.
POP. — 302,171 (1960)
CAPITAL — Kuala Trengganu

Sultan Zenalabidin
A1   A2

1910-19	**Typo.**	**Wmk. 3**	**Perf. 14**	
		Ordinary Paper		
1	A1	1c gray green	.40	.75
2	A1	2c red vio & brn ('15)	.55	.65
3	A1	3c rose red	1.25	1.50
4	A1	4c brn orange	2.50	4.50
5	A1	4c grn & org brn ('15)	1.65	4.25
6	A1	4c scarlet ('19)	.50	1.50
7	A1	5c gray	.70	2.50
8	A1	5c choc & gray ('15)	1.65	2.25
9	A1	8c ultramarine	.70	5.00
10	A1	10c red & grn, yel ('15)	1.65	2.25
		Chalky Paper		
11	A1	10c violet, yel	1.10	2.00
12	A1	20c red vio & vio	2.00	3.00
13	A1	25c dl vio & grn ('15)	3.50	17.50
14	A1	30c blk & dl vio ('15)	4.50	30.00
15	A1	50c blk & sep, grn	3.50	5.00
16	A1	$1 red & blk, blue	10.00	17.00
17	A1	$3 red & grn ('15)	65.00	150.00
18	A2	$5 lil & blue grn	90.00	275.00
19	A2	$25 green & car	675.00	
		Revenue Cancel		200.00
	Nos. 1-18 (18)		191.15	524.65

On No. 19 the numerals and Arabic inscriptions at top, left and right are in color on a colorless background.
Overprints are listed after No. 41. For surcharges see Nos. B1-B4.

Sultan Badaru'l-alam
A3   A4

1921-38		**Wmk. 4**	**Perf. 14**	
		Chalky Paper		
20	A3	1c black ('25)	.30	.15
21	A3	2c deep green	.15	.15
22	A3	3c dp grn ('25)	.60	.60
23	A3	3c lt brn ('38)	4.50	4.50
24	A3	4c rose red	.24	.15
25	A3	5c choc & gray	1.50	.60
26	A3	5c vio, red ('25)	.95	.50
27	A3	6c orange ('24)	2.50	.60
28	A3	8c gray ('38)	4.50	.75
29	A3	10c ultramarine	1.40	.60
30	A3	12c ultra ('25)	4.50	4.50
31	A3	20c org & dl vio	1.50	.60
32	A3	25c dk vio & grn	2.00	2.50
33	A3	30c blk & dl vio	3.00	.60
34	A3	35c red, yel ('25)	3.50	6.00
35	A3	50c car & green	4.50	.75
36	A3	$1 ultra & vio, bl ('29)	14.00	4.50
37	A3	$3 red & green, emer ('25)	47.50	47.50
38	A4	$5 red & grn, yel ('38)	200.00	600.00
39	A4	$25 blue & lil	500.00	700.00
40	A4	$50 org & green	1,000.	1,600.
41	A4	$100 red & green	3,500.	
	Nos. 20-37 (18)		97.14	75.20

On Nos. 39 to 41 the numerals and Arabic inscriptions at top, left and right are in color on a colorless background.
A 2c orange, 6c gray, 8c rose red and 15c ultramarine, type A3, exist, but are not known to have been regularly issued.
For surcharges and overprints see Nos. 45-46, N1-N60.

Stamps of 1910-21 Overprinted in Black: "MALAYA BORNEO EXHIBITION" in THREE LINES

1922, Mar.			**Wmk. 3**	
8a	A1	5c chocolate & gray	2.50	20.00
10a	A1	10c red & green, yel	2.50	20.00
12a	A1	20c red vio & violet	1.40	25.00
13a	A1	25c dull vio & green	1.65	25.00
14a	A1	30c black & dull vio	2.00	25.00
15a	A1	50c blk & sepia, grn	2.25	25.00
16a	A1	$1 red & blk, blue	12.50	50.00
17a	A1	$3 red & grn, green	95.00	300.00
18a	A2	$5 lil & blue green	200.00	400.00
			Wmk. 4	
21a	A3	2c deep green	.70	24.00
24a	A3	4c rose red	3.00	24.00
	Nos. 8a-24a (11)		323.50	938.00

Industrial fair at Singapore, Mar. 31-Apr. 15.

1921		**Wmk. 3**		
		Chalky Paper		
42	A3	$1 ultra & vio, bl	12.00	15.00
43	A3	$3 red & grn, emer	55.00	70.00
44	A4	$5 red & green, yel	60.00	65.00
	Nos. 42-44 (3)		127.00	150.00

Types of 1921-25 Surcharged in Black **8 CENTS**

1941, May 1	**Wmk. 4**	**Perf. 13½x14**	
45	A3 2c on 5c magenta, yel	5.00	4.00
46	A3 8c on 10c lt ultra	8.00	4.00

For overprints see #N30-N33, N46-N47, N59-N60.

Catalogue values for unused stamps in this section, from this point to the end of the section, are for Never Hinged items.

Silver Wedding Issue
Common Design Types
Inscribed: "Malaya Trengganu"

1948, Dec. 1	**Photo.**	**Perf. 14x14½**	
47	CD304 10c purple	.20	.20
	Engraved; Name Typographed		
	Perf. 11½x11		
48	CD305 $5 rose car	24.00	30.00

UPU Issue
Common Design Types
Inscribed: "Malaya-Trengganu"
Engr.; Name Typo. on 15c, 25c
Perf. 13½, 11x11½

1949, Oct. 10			**Wmk. 4**	
49	CD306	10c rose violet	.35	.35
50	CD307	15c indigo	.45	1.25
51	CD308	25c orange	.75	2.00
52	CD309	50c slate	1.25	2.00
	Nos. 49-52 (4)		2.80	5.60

Sultan Ismail Nasiruddin Shah — A5

1949, Dec. 27		**Typo.**	**Perf. 18**	
53	A5	1c black	.20	.15
54	A5	2c orange	.20	.15
55	A5	3c green	.55	.45
56	A5	4c chocolate	.25	.15
57	A5	6c gray	.55	.35
58	A5	8c rose red	.75	.60
59	A5	10c plum	.30	.15
60	A5	15c ultramarine	.45	.15
61	A5	20c dk grn & black	1.10	1.50
62	A5	25c org & rose lilac	.95	1.00
63	A5	40c dk vio & rose red	2.00	8.00
64	A5	50c dp ultra & black	1.25	.80
65	A5	$1 vio brn & ultra	2.50	3.00
66	A5	$2 rose red & emer	12.50	7.50
67	A5	$5 choc & emerald	37.50	20.00

1952-55				
68	A5	5c rose violet	.20	.15
69	A5	8c green	.75	1.00
70	A5	12c rose red	.75	2.00
71	A5	20c ultramarine	.75	.45
72	A5	30c plum & rose red ('55)	1.50	2.00
73	A5	35c dk vio & rose red	1.65	2.00
	Nos. 53-73 (21)		67.00	51.90

Coronation Issue
Common Design Type

1953, June 2	**Engr.**	**Perf. 13½x13**	
74	CD312 10c magenta & blk	.28	.18

Types of Kedah with Portrait of Sultan Ismail

Perf. 13x12½, 12½x13, 13½ ($1), 12½ ($2)

1957-63 Engr. Wmk. 314

75	A8	1c black	.15	.15
76	A8	2c red orange	.50	.20
77	A8	4c dark brown	.15	.15
78	A8	5c dark car rose	.15	.15
79	A8	8c dark green	3.50	.20
80	A7	10c chocolate	.30	.15
81	A7	20c blue	.30	.25
82	A7	50c ultra & blk ('62)	.70	.60
a.		Perf. 12½	.70	.60
83	A8	$1 plum & ultra	3.50	2.50
84	A8	$2 red & green	6.50	3.00
85	A8	$5 ol grn & brn ('63)	11.00	8.00
a.		Perf. 12½	9.50	6.25
		Nos. 75-85 (11)	26.75	15.35

Starting in 1965, issues of Trengganu are listed with Malaysia.

SEMI-POSTAL STAMPS

RED CROSS

Nos. 3, 4 and 9 Surcharged

2c.

1917, Oct. Wmk. 3 *Perf. 14*

B1	A1	3c + 2c rose red	.35	*2.25*
a.		"CSOSS"	40.00	*65.00*
b.		Comma after "2c"	2.50	*6.50*
c.		Pair, one without surcharge	1,750.	1,750.
B2	A1	4c + 2c brn org	.55	*3.25*
a.		"CSOSS"	165.00	*165.00*
b.		Comma after "2c"	10.00	*26.00*
B3	A1	8c + 2c ultra	.90	*6.50*
a.		"CSOSS"	110.00	*125.00*
b.		Comma after "2c"	0.25	*32.50*
		Nos. B1-B3 (3)	1.80	*12.00*

Same Surcharge on No. 5

1918

B4	A1	4c + 2c grn & org brn	1.25	*6.50*
a.		Pair, one without surcharge	*1,400.*	

POSTAGE DUE STAMPS

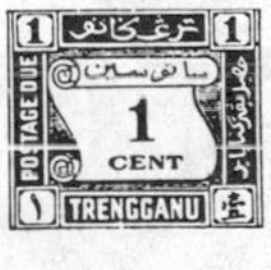

D1

Wmk. 4

1937, Aug. 10 Typo. *Perf. 14*

J1	D1	1c rose red	8.50	*40.00*
J2	D1	4c green	8.50	*40.00*
J3	D1	8c lemon	50.00	*200.00*
J4	D1	10c light brown	75.00	*75.00*
		Nos. J1-J4 (4)	142.00	*355.00*

For overprints see Nos. NJ1-NJ4.

OCCUPATION STAMPS

Issued under Japanese Occupation

Stamps of Trengganu, 1921-38, Handstamped in Black or Brown

馬來軍政部 郵政局 EP

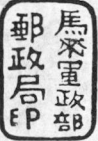

1942 Wmk. 4 *Perf. 14*

N1	A3	1c black	85.00	80.00
N2	A3	2c deep green	140.00	200.00
N3	A3	3c lt brown	100.00	80.00
N4	A3	4c rose red	200.00	140.00
N5	A3	5c violet, *yel*	13.00	14.00
N6	A3	6c orange	10.00	15.00
N7	A3	8c gray	13.00	18.00
N8	A3	10c ultramarine	10.00	20.00
N9	A3	12c ultramarine	11.00	18.00
N10	A3	20c org & dl vio	11.00	17.00
N11	A3	25c dk vio & grn	10.00	20.00
N12	A3	30c blk & dl vio	10.00	18.00
N13	A3	35c red, *yel*	17.00	20.00
N14	A3	50c car & grn	85.00	70.00
N15	A3	$1 ultra & vio, *blue*	1,200.	1,300.
N16	A3	$3 red & grn, *emerald*	90.00	100.00
N17	A4	$5 red & grn, *yellow*	175.00	175.00
N17A	A4	$25 blue & lil	1,100.	
N17B	A4	$50 org & grn	*6,500.*	
N17C	A4	$100 red & grn	600.00	

Handstamped in Red

N18	A3	1c black	200.00	160.00
N19	A3	2c dp green	100.00	125.00
N20	A3	5c violet, *yel*	25.00	15.00
N21	A3	6c orange	15.00	15.00
N22	A3	8c gray	200.00	175.00
N23	A3	10c ultramarine	200.00	200.00
N24	A3	12c ultramarine	40.00	40.00
N25	A3	20c org & dl vio	25.00	25.00
N26	A3	25c dk vio & grn	30.00	30.00
N27	A3	30c blk & dl vio	25.00	25.00
N28	A3	35c red, *yellow*	25.00	15.00
N29	A3	$3 red & grn, *emerald*	75.00	30.00
N29A	A3	$25 blue & lil	500.00	500.00

Handstamped on Nos. 45 and 46 in Black or Red

N30	A3	2c on 5c (Bk)	100.00	100.00
N31	A3	2c on 5c (R)	75.00	75.00
N32	A3	8c on 10c (Bk)	18.00	25.00
N33	A3	8c on 10c (R)	35.00	40.00

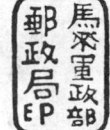

Stamps of Trengganu, 1921-38, Overprinted in Black

馬來軍政部 郵政局 EP

1942

N34	A3	1c black	11.00	12.50
N35	A3	2c deep green	75.00	*100.00*
N36	A3	3c light brown	12.00	21.00
N37	A3	4c rose red	11.00	15.00
N38	A3	5c violet, *yel*	7.50	15.00
N39	A3	6c orange	7.50	12.50
N40	A3	8c gray	50.00	15.00
N41	A3	12c ultramarine	7.50	10.00
N42	A3	20c org & dl vio	10.00	18.00
N43	A3	25c dk vio & grn	10.00	12.50
N44	A3	30c blk & dl vio	10.00	15.00
N45	A3	$3 red & grn, *emer*	75.00	100.00

Overprinted on Nos. 45 and 46 in Black

N46	A3	2c on 5c mag, *yel*	10.00	12.50
N47	A3	8c on 10c lt ultra	8.50	15.00
		Nos. N34-N47 (14)	305.00	*374.00*

Stamps of Trengganu, 1921-38, Overprinted in Black

大日本郵便

1943

N48	A3	1c black	10.00	14.00
N49	A3	2c deep green	10.00	20.00
N50	A3	5c violet, *yel*	8.50	20.00
N51	A3	6c orange	11.00	20.00
N52	A3	8c gray	70.00	50.00
N53	A3	10c ultramarine	75.00	125.00
N54	A3	12c ultramarine	14.00	*25.00*
N55	A3	20c org & dl vio	15.00	*25.00*
N56	A3	25c dl vio & grn	14.00	*25.00*
N57	A3	30c blk & dl vio	15.00	*25.00*
N58	A3	35c red, *yellow*	15.00	*30.00*

Overprinted on Nos. 45 and 46 in Black

N59	A3	2c on 5c mag, *yel*	8.00	*25.00*
N60	A3	8c on 10c lt ultra	20.00	*25.00*
		Nos. N48-N60 (13)	285.50	*429.00*

The Japanese characters read: "Japanese Postal Service."

OCCUPATION POSTAGE DUE STAMPS

Trengganu Nos. J1-J4 Handstamped in Black or Brown

DAI NIPPON
2602
MALAYA

1942 Wmk. 4 *Perf. 14*

NJ1	D1	1c rose red	50.00	*70.00*
NJ2	D1	4c green	90.00	*90.00*
NJ3	D1	8c lemon	18.00	*50.00*
NJ4	D1	10c light brown	18.00	*50.00*
		Nos. NJ1-NJ4 (4)	176.00	*260.00*

The handstamp reads: "Seal of Post Office of Malayan Military Department."

MALAYSIA

mə-'lā-zh(ē-)ə

LOCATION — Malay peninsula and northwestern Borneo
GOVT. — Federation within the British Commonwealth
AREA — 128,328 sq. mi.
POP. — 15,070,000 (est. 1984)
CAPITAL — Kuala Lumpur

The Federation of Malaysia was formed Sept. 16, 1963, by a merger of the former Federation of Malaya, Singapore, Sarawak, and North Borneo (renamed Sabah), totaling 14 states. Singapore withdrew in 1965.

Sabah and Sarawak, having different rates than mainland Malaysia, continued to issue their own stamps after joining the federation. The system of individual state issues was extended to Perak in Oct. 1963, and to the 10 other members in Nov. 1965.

100 Cents (Sen) = 1 Dollar (Ringgit)

Catalogue values for all unused stamps in this country are for Never Hinged items.

Watermarks

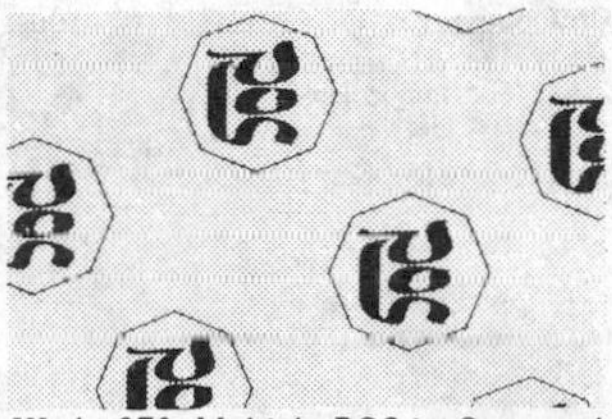

Wmk. 378- Multiple POS in Octagonal Frame

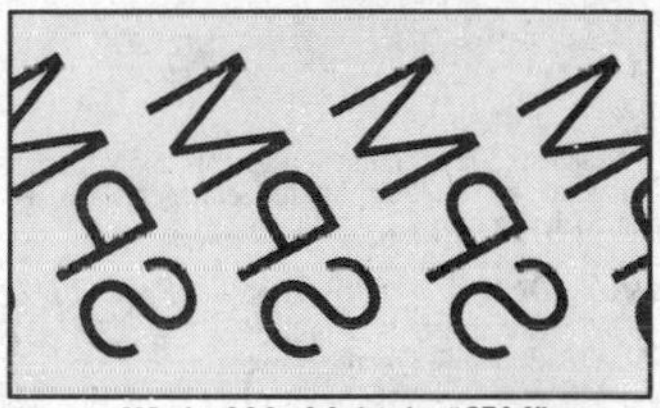

Wmk. 388- Multiple "SPM"

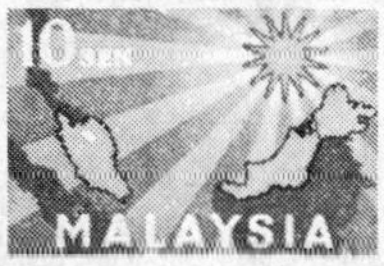

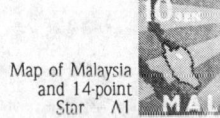

Map of Malaysia and 14-point Star — A1

Wmk. PTM Multiple (338)

1963, Sept. 16 Photo *Perf. 14*

1	A1	10s violet & yellow	.15	.15
a.		Yellow omitted	100.00	
2	A1	12s green & yellow	.40	.28
3	A1	50s dk red brown & yel	.55	.28
		Nos. 1-3 (3)	1.10	
		Set value		.60

Formation of the Federation of Malaysia.

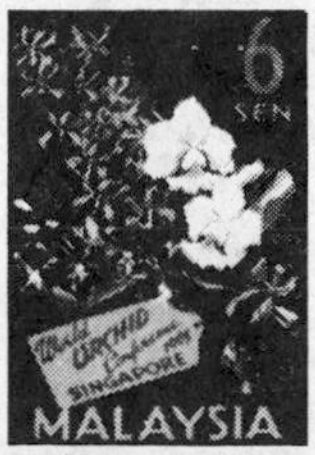

Orchids — A2

1963, Oct. 3 Unwmk. *Perf. 13x14*

4	A2	6s red & multi	.26	.15
5	A2	25s black & multi	1.40	.40
		Set value		.47

4th World Orchid Conf., Singapore, Oct. 8-11.

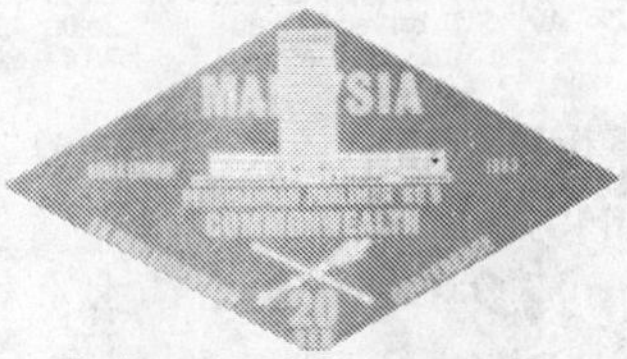

Parliament and Commonwealth Parliamentary Association Emblem — A4

1963, Nov. 4 *Perf. 13½*

7	A4	20s dk car rose & gold	.25	.16
8	A4	30s dk green & gold	.50	.25

9th Commonwealth Parliamentary Assoc. Conf.

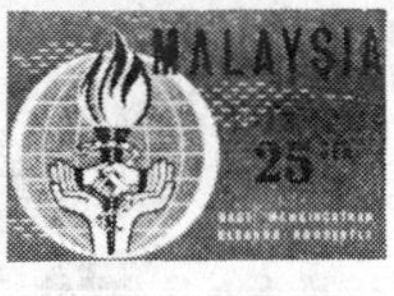

Globe, Torch, Snake and Hands — A5

1964, Oct. 10 Photo. *Perf. 14x13*

9	A5	25s Prus green, red & black	.15	.15
10	A5	30s lt violet, red & blk	.26	.15
11	A5	50s dull yellow, red & blk	.50	.22
		Nos. 9-11 (3)	.91	
		Set value		.42

Eleanor Roosevelt, 1884-1962.

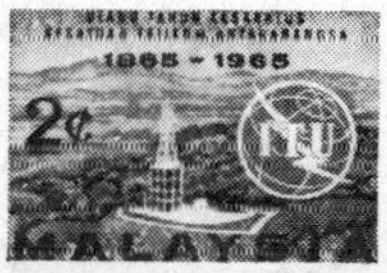

ITU Emblem and Radar Tower — A6

1965, May 17 Photo. *Perf. 11½*

Granite Paper

12	A6	2c violet, blk & org	.15	.15
13	A6	25c brown, blk & org	.42	.20
14	A6	50c emerald, blk & brn	1.00	.30
		Nos. 12-14 (3)	1.57	
		Set value		.55

Cent. of the ITU.

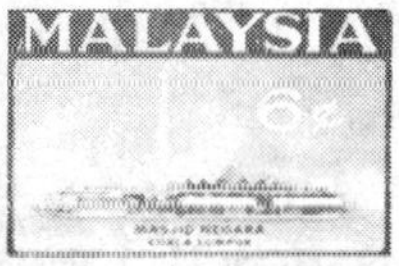

National Mosque, Kuala Lumpur — A7

1965, Aug. 27 Wmk. 338 *Perf. 14½*

15	A7	6c dark car rose	.15	.15
16	A7	15c dark red brown	.16	.15
17	A7	20c Prussian green	.24	.16
		Nos. 15-17 (3)	.55	
		Set value		.32

Natl. Mosque at Kuala Lumpur, opening.

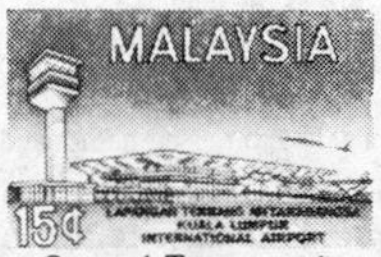

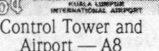

Control Tower and Airport — A8

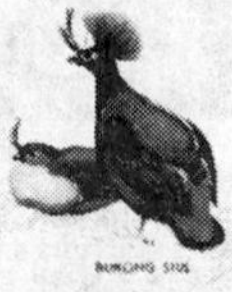

Crested Wood Partridge — A9

1965, Aug. 30 *Perf. 14½x14*

18	A8	15c blue, blk & grn	.15	.15
a.		Green omitted	18.00	
19	A8	30c brt pink, blk & grn	.32	.15
		Set value		.21

Intl. Airport at Kuala Lumpur, opening.

1965, Sept. 9 Photo. *Perf. 14½*

Birds: 30c, Fairy bluebird. 50c, Blacknaped oriole. 75c, Rhinoceros hornbill. $1, Zebra dove. $2, Argus pheasant. $5, Indian paradise flycatcher. $10, Banded pitta.

20	A9	25c orange & multi	.35	.15
21	A9	30c tan & multi	.42	.15
a.		Blue omitted	87.50	
22	A9	50c rose & multi	.65	.15
a.		Rose omitted	42.50	
23	A9	75c yel green & multi	1.25	.15
24	A9	$1 ultra & multi	1.75	.15
25	A9	$2 maroon & multi	5.25	.42

26	A9	$5 dk green & multi	13.00	1.25
27	A9	$10 brt red & multi	26.00	4.25
		Nos. 20-27 (8)	48.67	6.67

Soccer and Sepak Raga (Ball Game) — A10

National Monument, Kuala Lumpur — A11

1965, Dec. 14 Unwmk. Perf. 13

28	A10	25c shown	.22	.18
29	A10	30c Runner	.45	.22
30	A10	50c Diver	.80	.55
		Nos. 28-30 (3)	1.47	.95

3rd South East Asia Peninsular Games, Kuala Lumpur, Dec. 14-21.

1966, Feb. 8 Wmk. 338 Perf. 13½

31	A11	10c yellow & multi	.15	.15
a.		Blue omitted	52.50	
32	A11	20c ultra & multi	.50	.35
		Set value		.40

The National Monument by US sculptor Felix W. de Weldon commemorates the struggle of the people of Malaysia for peace and for freedom from communism.

Tuanku Ismail Nasiruddin A12

Penang Free School A13

1966, Apr. 11 Unwmk. Perf. 13½

33	A12	15c yellow & black	.16	.15
34	A12	50c blue & black	.55	.42
		Set value		.50

Installation of Tuanku Ismail Nasiruddin of Trengganu as Paramount Ruler (Yang di-Pertuan Agong).

Perf. 13x12½
1966, Oct. 21 Photo. Wmk. 338

Design: 50c, like 20c with Malayan inscription and school crest added.

35	A13	20c multicolored	.22	.15
36	A13	50c multicolored	.65	.42

Penang Free School, 150th anniversary.

Mechanized Plowing and Palms — A14

Designs: No. 38, Rural health nurse, mother and child, dispensary. No. 39, Communication: train, plane, ship, cars and radio tower. No. 40, School children. No. 41, Dam and rice fields.

1966, Dec. 1 Unwmk. Perf. 13

37	A14	15c bister brn & multi	.42	.16
38	A14	15c blue & multi	.42	.16
39	A14	15c crimson & multi	.42	.16
40	A14	15c ol green & multi	.42	.16
41	A14	15c yellow & multi	.42	.16
		Nos. 37-41 (5)	2.10	.80

Malaysia's First Development Plan.

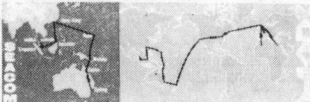

Maps Showing International and South East Asia Telephone Links — A15

1967, Mar. 30 Photo. Perf. 13

42	A15	30c multicolored	.45	.24
43	A15	75c multicolored	2.00	.90

Completion of the Hong Kong-Malaysia link of the South East Asia Commonwealth Cable, SEACOM.

Hibiscus and Rulers of Independent Malaysia — A16

1967, Aug. 31 Wmk. 338 Perf. 14

44	A16	15c yellow & multi	.15	.15
45	A16	50c blue & multi	.60	.35
		Set value		.44

10th anniversary of independence.

Arms of Sarawak and Council Mace — A17

1967, Sept. 8 Photo.

46	A17	15c yel green & multi	.15	.15
47	A17	50c multicolored	.45	.35
		Set value		.42

Representative Council of Sarawak, cent.

Straits Settlements No. 13 and Malaysia No. 20 A18

Designs: 30c, Straits Settlements No. 15 and Malaysia No. 21. 50c, Straits Settlements No. 17 and Malaysia No. 22.

1967, Dec. 2 Unwmk. Perf. 11½

48	A18	25c brt blue & multi	.50	.32
49	A18	30c dull green & multi	.55	.32
50	A18	50c yellow & multi	1.10	.75
		Nos. 48-50 (3)	2.15	1.39

Cent. of the Malaysian (Straits Settlements) postage stamps.

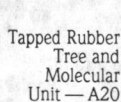 

Tapped Rubber Tree and Molecular Unit — A20

Tapped Rubber Tree and: 30c, Rubber packed for shipment. 50c, Rubber tires for Vickers VC 10 plane.

Wmk. 338
1968, Aug. 29 Litho. Perf. 12

53	A20	25c brick red, blk & org	.26	.18
54	A20	30c yellow, black & org	.40	.22
55	A20	50c ultra, black & org	.65	.48
		Nos. 53-55 (3)	1.31	.88

Natural Rubber Conference, Kuala Lumpur.

Olympic Rings, Mexican Hat and Cloth — A21

Tunku Abdul Rahman Putra Al-Haj — A22

Designs: 75c, Olympic rings and Malaysian batik cloth.

1968, Oct. 12 Wmk. 338 Perf. 12

56	A21	30c rose red & multi	.32	.20
57	A21	75c ocher & multi	.80	.60

19th Olympic Games, Mexico City, Oct. 12-27.

Perf. 13½
1969, Feb. 8 Photo. Unwmk.

Designs: Various portraits of Prime Minister Tunku Abdul Rahman Putra Al-Haj with woven pandanus patterns as background. 50c is horiz.

58	A22	15c gold & multi	.18	.15
59	A22	20c gold & multi	.24	.15
60	A22	50c gold & multi	.60	.45
		Nos. 58-60 (3)	1.02	.75

Issued for Solidarity Week, 1969.

Malaysian Girl Holding Sheaves of Rice — A23

1969, Dec. 8 Wmk. 338 Perf. 13½

61	A23	15c silver & multi	.20	.15
62	A23	75c gold & multi	1.00	.80

International Rice Year.

Kuantan Radar Station A24

Intelsat III Orbiting Earth A25

Perf. 14x13
1970, Apr. 6 Photo. Unwmk.

63	A24	25c multicolored	.38	.15
64	A25	30c multicolored	.75	.55
65	A25	30c gold & multi	.65	.30
		Nos. 63-65 (3)	1.78	1.00

Satellite Communications Earth Station at Kuantan, Pahang, Malaysia.

No. 63 was printed tete beche (50 pairs) in sheet of 100 (10x10).

Blue-branded King Crow — A26

ILO Emblem — A27

Butterflies: 30c, Saturn. 50c, Common Nawab. 75c, Great Mormon. $1, Orange albatross. $2, Raja Brooke's birdwing. $5, Centaur oakblue. $10, Royal Assyrian.

1970, Aug. 31 Litho. Perf. 13x13½

66	A26	25c multicolored	.32	.15
67	A26	30c multicolored	.42	.15
68	A26	50c multicolored	.60	.15
69	A26	75c multicolored	1.00	.15
70	A26	$1 multicolored	1.25	.15
71	A26	$2 multicolored	2.50	.50
72	A26	$5 multicolored	5.75	1.40
73	A26	$10 multicolored	12.50	4.00
		Nos. 66-73 (8)	24.34	6.65

1970, Sept. 7 Perf. 14½x13½

74	A27	30c gray & blue	.40	.24
75	A27	75c rose & blue	1.00	.80

50th anniv. of the ILO.

UN Emblem and Doves — A28

Sultan Abdul Halim — A29

Designs: 25c, Doves in elliptical arrangement. 30c, Doves arranged diagonally.

1970, Oct. 24 Litho. Perf. 13x12½

76	A28	25c lt brown, blk & yel	.28	.20
77	A28	30c lt blue, yel & black	.35	.24
78	A28	50c lt ol green & black	.60	.52
		Nos. 76-78 (3)	1.23	.96

25th anniversary of the United Nations.

Perf. 14½x14
1971, Feb. 20 Photo. Unwmk.

79	A29	10c yellow, blk & gold	.15	.15
80	A29	15c purple, blk & gold	.24	.18
81	A29	50c blue, blk & gold	.85	.80
		Nos. 79-81 (3)	1.24	1.13

Installation of Sultan Abdul Halim of Kedah as Paramount Ruler.

Bank Building and Crescent — A30

1971, May 15 Photo. Perf. 14

82	A30	25c silver & black	.65	.52
83	A30	50c gold & brown	1.25	1.25

Opening of Main office of the Negara Malaysia Bank. Nos. 82-83 have circular perforations around vignette set within a white square of paper, perf. on 4 sides.

Malaysian Parliament — A31

Malaysian Parliament, Kuala Lumpur — A32

1971, Sept. 13 Litho. Perf. 13½

84	A31	25c multicolored	.52	.26

Perf. 12½x13

85	A32	75c multicolored	1.25	.95

17th Commonwealth Parliamentary Conference, Kuala Lumpur.

Malaysian Festival — A33

1971, Sept. 18 Perf. 14½

86	A33	Strip of 3	1.90	1.90
a.		30c Dancing couple	.60	.50
b.		30c Dragon	.60	.50
c.		30c Flags and stage horse	.60	.50

Visit ASEAN (Association of South East Asian Nations) Year.

Elephant and Tiger — A34

Children's Drawings: No. 88, Cat and kittens. No. 89, Sun, flower and chick. No. 90, Monkey, elephant and lion in jungle. No. 91, Butterfly and flowers.

1971, Oct. 2   **Perf. 12½**
Size: 35x28mm
87 A34 15c pale yellow & multi   .45 .30
88 A34 15c pale yellow & multi   .45 .30
Size: 21x28mm
89 A34 15c pale yellow & multi   .45 .30
Size: 35x28mm
90 A34 15c pale yellow & multi   .45 .30
91 A34 15c pale yellow & multi   .45 .30
a.   Strip of 5, #87-91   2.50 2.50
25th anniv. of UNICEF.

Track and Field — A35

Designs: 30c, Sepak Raga (a ball game). 50c, Hockey.

1971, Dec. 11   **Perf. 14½**
92 A35 25c orange & multi   .52 .45
93 A35 30c violet & multi   .65 .60
94 A35 50c green & multi   1.25 1.12
   Nos. 93-94 (3)   2.42 2.17
6th South East Asia Peninsular Games. Kuala Lumpur, Dec. 11-18.

South East Asian Tourist Attractions — A36

Designs include stylized map.

1972, Jan. 31   **Litho.**   **Perf. 14½**
95 A36   Strip of 3   2.50 2.50
a.   30c Flag at left   .80 .50
b.   30c High rise building   .80 .50
c.   30c Horse & rider   .80 .50
Pacific Area Tourist Assoc. Conference.

BANDARAYA KUALA LUMPUR 1972
Secretariat Building — A37

Design: 50c, Kuala Lumpur Secretariat Building by night.

1972, Feb. 1   **Perf. 14½x14**
96 A37 25c lt blue & multi   .52 .38
97 A37 50c black & multi   1.10 .80
Achievement of city status by Kuala Lumpur.

Social Security Emblem A38   WHO Emblem A39

1973, July 2   **Litho.**   **Perf. 14½x13½**
98 A38 10c orange & multi   .18 .15
99 A38 15c yellow & multi   .30 .15
100 A38 50c gray & multi   1.00 .75
   Nos. 98-100 (3)   1.48 1.05
Introduction of Social Security System.

1973, Aug. 1   **Perf. 13x12½, 12½x13**
Design: 30c, WHO emblem, horiz.
101 A39 30c green & multi   .38 .35
102 A39 75c blue & multi   1.10 1.10
25th anniv. of World Health Org.

Flag of Malaysia, Fireworks, Hibiscus — A40

1973, Aug. 31   **Litho.**   **Perf. 14½**
103 A40 10c olive & multi   .18 .15
104 A40 15c brown & multi   .20 .18
105 A40 50c gray & multi   1.00 1.00
   Nos. 103-105 (3)   1.38 1.33
10th anniversary of independence.

INTERPOL and Malaysian Police Emblems A41

Design: 75c, "50" with INTERPOL and Malaysian police emblems.

1973, Sept. 15   **Perf. 12½**
106 A41 25c brown org & multi   .65 .42
107 A41 75c deep violet & multi   1.90 1.50
50th anniv. of the Intl. Criminal Police Organization (INTERPOL).

MAS Emblem and Plane — A42

1973, Oct. 1   **Litho.**   **Perf. 14½**
108 A42 15c green & multi   .20 .15
109 A42 30c blue & multi   .48 .42
110 A42 50c brown & multi   .80 .80
   Nos. 108-110 (3)   1.48 1.37
Inauguration of Malaysian Airline System.

View of Kuala Lumpur — A43

1974, Feb. 1   **Litho.**   **Perf. 12½x13**
111 A43 25c multicolored   .60 .52
112 A43 50c multicolored   1.25 1.25
Establishment of Kuala Lumpur as a Federal Territory.

Development Bank Emblem and Projects — A44

1974, Apr. 25   **Litho.**   **Perf. 13½**
113 A44 30c gray & multi   .75 .60
114 A44 75c bister & multi   2.00 2.00
7th annual meeting of the Board of Governors of the Asian Development Bank.

Map of Malaysia and Scout Emblem — A45

Scout Saluting, Malaysian and Scout Flags — A46

Design: 50c, Malaysian Scout emblem.

Perf. 14x13½, 13x13½ (15c)
1974, Aug. 1   **Litho.**
115 A45 10c multicolored   .20 .15
116 A46 15c multicolored   .42 .20
117 A45 50c multicolored   2.00 .95
   Nos. 115-117 (3)   2.62 1.30
Malaysian Boy Scout Jamboree.

Power Installations, NEB Emblem — A47

National Electricity Board Building A48

Perf. 14x14½, 13½x14½
1974, Sept. 1   **Litho.**
118 A47 30c multicolored   .50 .40
119 A48 75c multicolored   1.25 1.25
National Electricity Board, 25th anniversary.

"100," UPU and P.O. Emblems A49

1974, Oct. 9   **Litho.**   **Perf. 14½x13½**
120 A49 25c olive, red & yel   .30 .25
121 A49 30c blue, red & yel   .38 .32
122 A49 75c ocher, red & yel   1.00 1.00
   Nos. 120-122 (3)   1.68 1.57
Centenary of Universal Postal Union.

Gravel Pump Tin Mine — A50

Designs: 20c, Open cast mine. 50c, Silver tin ingot and tin dredge.

1974, Oct. 31   **Litho.**   **Perf. 14**
123 A50 15c silver & multi   .22 .16
124 A50 20c silver & multi   .35 .30
125 A50 50c silver & multi   1.25 .85
   Nos. 123-125 (3)   1.82 1.31
4th World Tin Conference, Kuala Lumpur.

Hockey, Cup and Emblem A51

1975, Mar. 1   **Litho.**   **Perf. 14**
126 A51 30c yellow & multi   .48 .38
127 A51 75c blue & multi   1.65 1.25
Third World Cup Hockey Tournament, Kuala Lumpur, Mar. 1-15.

Trade Union Emblem and Workers — A52

1975, May 1   **Litho.**   **Perf. 14x14½**
128 A52 20c orange & multi   .35 .30
129 A52 25c lt green & multi   .45 .35
130 A52 30c ultra & multi   .52 .52
   Nos. 128-130 (3)   1.32 1.17
Malaysian Trade Union Cong., 25th anniv.

National Women's Organization Emblem and Heads — A53

1975, Aug. 25   **Litho.**   **Perf. 14**
131 A53 10c emerald & multi   .15 .15
132 A53 15c lilac rose & multi   .25 .15
133 A53 50c blue & multi   1.00 .75
   Nos. 131-133 (3)   1.40 1.05
International Women's Year.

Ubudiah Mosque, Perak — A54

Designs: b, Zahir Mosque, Kedah. c, National Mosque, Kuala Lumpur. d, Sultan Abu Bakar Mosque, Johore. e, Kuching State Mosque, Sarawak.

1975, Sept. 23   **Litho.**   **Perf. 14½x14**
134   Strip of 5   2.00 2.00
a.-e.   A54 15c single stamp   .40 .24
Koran reading competition 1975, Malaysia.

Rubber Plantation and Emblem A55

Designs: 30c, "50" in form of latex cup and tire with emblem. 75c, Six test tubes showing various aspects of natural rubber.

1975, Oct. 22   **Litho.**   **Perf. 14x14½**
135 A55 10c gold & multi   .18 .15
136 A55 30c gold & multi   .45 .45
137 A55 75c gold & multi   1.10 1.10
   Nos. 135-137 (3)   1.73 1.70
Rubber Research Institute of Malaysia, 50th anniversary.

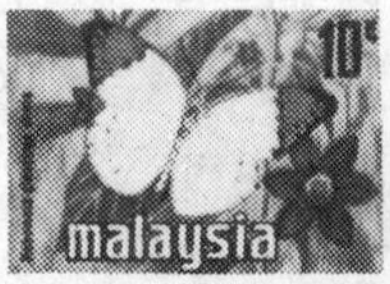

Butterflies A55a

Coil Stamps

1976, Feb. 6 *Perf. 14*

137A A55a 10c Hebomoia glaucippe aturia	.22	.22
137B A55a 15c Precis orithya wallacei	.28	.28

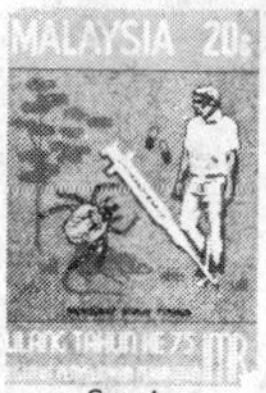

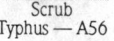

Scrub Typhus — A56

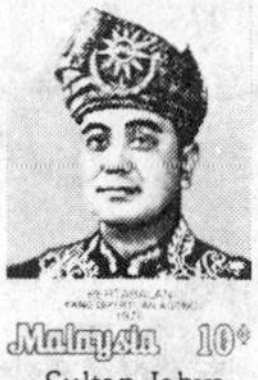

Sultan Jahya Petra — A57

Designs: 25c, Malaria (microscope, blood cells, slides). $1, Beri-beri (grain and men).

1976, Feb. 6 **Litho.** *Perf. 14*

138 A56 20c red orange & multi	.20	.20
139 A56 25c ultra & multi	.24	.24
140 A56 $1 yellow & multi	1.40	1.00
Nos. 138-140 (3)	1.84	1.44

Institute for Medical Research, Kuala Lumpur, 75th anniversary.

Perf. 14½x13½

1976, Feb. 28 **Photo.**

141 A57 10c yel, black & bis	.25	.15
142 A57 15c lilac, black & bis	.32	.18
143 A57 50c blue, black & bis	1.90	.95
Nos. 141-143 (3)	2.47	1.28

Installation of Sultan Jahya Petra of Kelantan as Paramount Ruler (Yang di-Pertuan Agong).

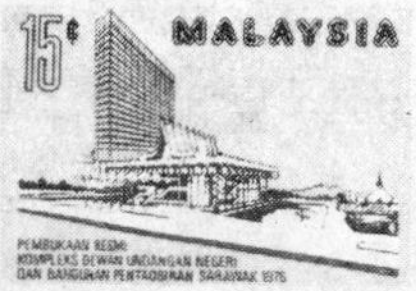

Council and Administrative Buildings A58

1976, Aug. 17 **Litho.** *Perf. 12½*

144 A58 15c orange & black	.26	.22
145 A58 20c brt red lilac & black	.32	.26
146 A58 50c blue & black	.80	.80
Nos. 144-146 (3)	1.38	1.28

Opening of the State Council Complex and Administrative Building, Sarawak.

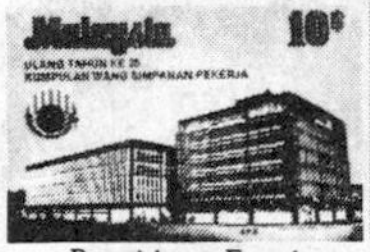

Provident Fund Building — A59

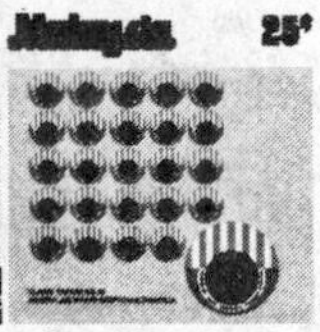

Provident Fund Emblems — A60

Design: 50c, Provident Fund Building at night.

Perf. 13½x14½, 14½ (A60)

1976, Oct. 18 **Litho.**

147 A59 10c blue & multi	.15	.15
148 A60 25c gray & multi	.26	.22
149 A59 50c violet & multi	.60	.60
Nos. 147-149 (3)	1.01	.97

Employees' Provident Fund, 25th anniv.

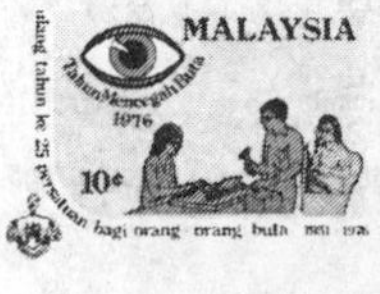

Rehabilitation of the Blind — A61

Design: 75c, Blind man casting large shadow.

1976, Nov. 20 *Perf. 13½x14½*

150 A61 10c multicolored	.18	.15
151 A61 75c multicolored	1.50	1.25

25th anniv. of the Malaysian Assoc. for the Blind.

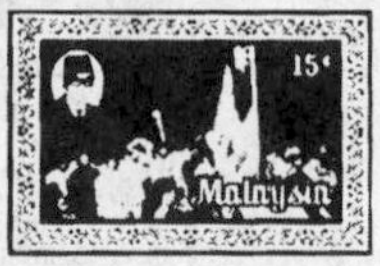

Abdul Razak and Crowd — A62

Designs: b, Abdul Razak in cap and gown at lectern. c, Abdul Razak pointing to new roads and bridges on map. d, New constitution. e, Abdul Razak addressing Association of Southeast Asian Countries.

1977, Jan. 14 **Photo.** *Perf. 14x14½*

152 Strip of 5	1.75	1.75
a.-e. A62 15c single stamp	.26	.26

Prime Minister Tun Haji Abdul Razak bi Dato Hussein (1922-1976).

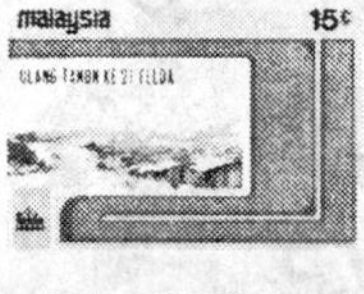

FELDA Housing Development A63

Design: 30c, View of oil palm settlement area and FELDA emblem.

1977, July 7 **Litho.** *Perf. 13½x14½*

153 A63 15c multicolored	.22	.16
154 A63 30c multicolored	.55	.32

Federal Land Development Authority (FELDA), 21st anniversary.

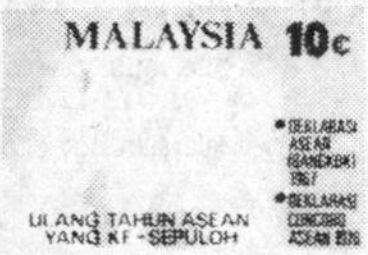

"10" — A64

ASEAN, 10th anniv.: 75c, Flags of ASEAN members: Malaysia, Philippines, Singapore, Thailand and Indonesia.

1977, Aug. 8 **Litho.** *Perf. 13½x14½*

155 A64 10c multicolored	.15	.15
156 A64 75c multicolored	1.10	.80

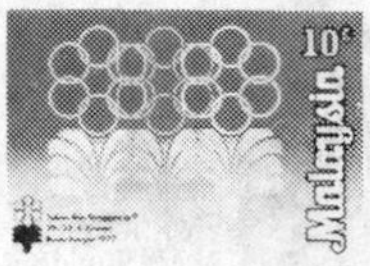

SEA Games Emblems — A65

Designs: 20c, Ball, symbolic of 9 participating nations. 75c, Running.

Perf. 13½x14½

1977, Nov. 19 **Litho.**

157 A65 10c multicolored	.15	.15
158 A65 20c multicolored	.25	.20
159 A65 75c multicolored	1.25	.75
Nos. 157-159 (3)	1.65	1.10

9th South East Asia Games, Kuala Lumpur.

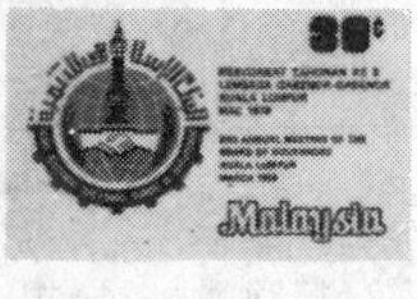

Bank Emblem A66

1978, Mar. 15 **Litho.** *Perf. 14*

160 A66 30c multicolored	.30	.30
161 A66 75c multicolored	1.00	.75

2nd annual meeting of Islamic Development Bank Governors, Kuala Lumpur, Mar. 1978.

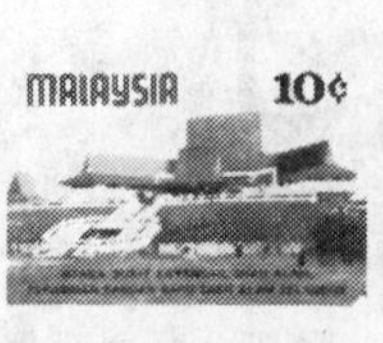

Government Building — A67

Designs: Views of Shah Alam.

1978, Dec. 7 **Litho.** *Perf. 13½x14½*

162 A67 10c multicolored	.15	.15
163 A67 30c multicolored	.25	.25
164 A67 75c multicolored	.70	.70
Nos. 162-164 (3)	1.10	1.10

Inauguration of Shah Alam as state capital of Selangor.

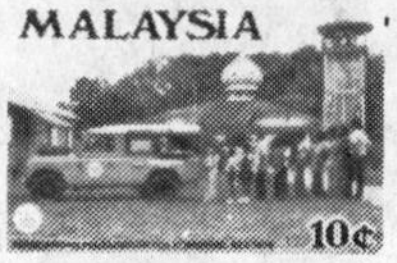

Mobile Post Office in Village — A68

Designs: 25c, General Post Office, Kuala Lumpur. 50c, Motorcyclist, rural mail delivery.

1978, July 10 *Perf. 13*

165 A68 10c multicolored	.15	.15
166 A68 25c multicolored	.35	.35
167 A68 50c multicolored	.70	.70
Nos. 165-167 (3)	1.20	1.20

4th Conf. of Commonwealth Postal Administrators.

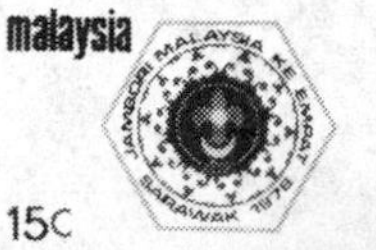

Jamboree Emblem — A69

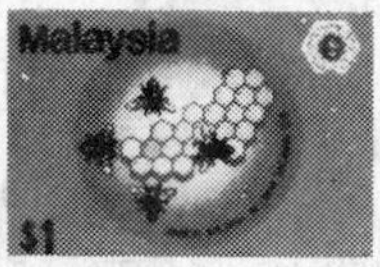

Bees and Honeycomb A70

1978, July 26 **Litho.** *Perf. 13½*

168 A69 15c multicolored	.18	.18
169 A70 $1 multicolored	1.25	1.25

4th Boy Scout Jamboree, Sarawak.

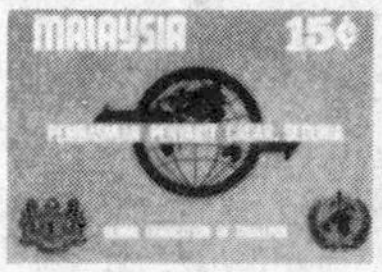

Globe, Crest and WHO Emblem — A71

1978, Sept. 30 *Perf. 13½x14½*

170 A71 15c blue, red & black	.18	.18
171 A71 30c green, red & black	.35	.35
172 A71 50c pink, red & black	.60	.60
Nos. 170-172 (3)	1.13	1.13

Global eradication of smallpox.

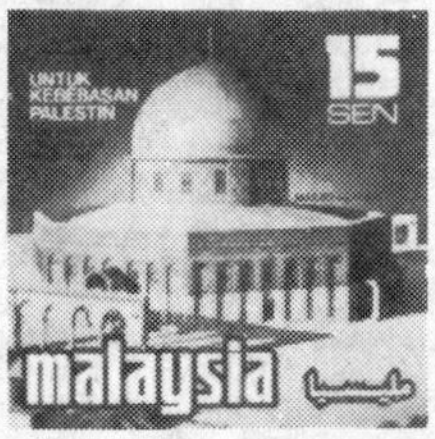

Dome of the Rock — A72

1978, Aug. 21 **Litho.** *Perf. 12½*

173 A72 15c red & multi	.32	.26
174 A72 30c blue & multi	.85	.52

For Palestinian fighters and their families.

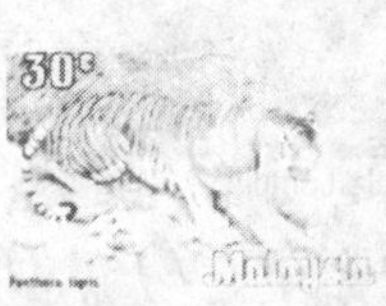

Tiger — A73

Designs: 40c, Cobego. 50c, Chevrotain. 75c, Pangolin. $1, Leatherback turtle. $2, Tapir. $5, Gaur. $10, Orangutan, vert.

Perf. 15x14½, 14½x15

1979, Jan. 4 **Litho.** **Wmk. 378**

175 A73 30c multicolored	.22	.22
176 A73 40c multicolored	.28	.28
177 A73 50c multicolored	.35	.35
178 A73 75c multicolored	.55	.55
179 A73 $1 multicolored	.75	.75
180 A73 $2 multicolored	1.40	1.40
181 A73 $5 multicolored	3.50	3.50
182 A73 $10 multicolored	7.25	7.25
Nos. 175-182 (8)	14.30	14.30

1983-87

Unwmk.

175a A73 30c ('84)	.72	.72
176a A73 40c ('84)	.98	.98
177a A73 50c ('84)	1.20	1.20
178a A73 75c ('87)	1.80	1.80
179a A73 $1	2.40	2.40
180a A73 $2	4.75	4.75
181a A73 $5 ('85)	12.00	12.00
182a A73 $10 ('86)	25.00	25.00
Nos. 175a-182a (8)	48.85	48.85

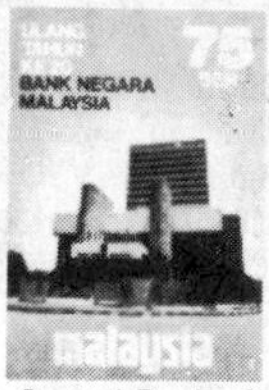

Central Bank of Malaysia — A74

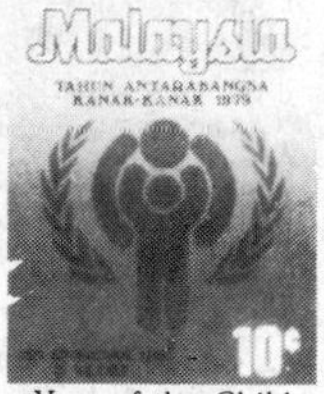

Year of the Child Emblem — A75

Design: 10c, Central Bank of Malaysia and emblem, horiz.

Perf. 13½

1979, Jan. 26 **Litho.** **Unwmk.**

183 A74 10c multicolored	.15	.15
184 A74 75c multicolored	.85	.85

Central Bank of Malaysia, 30th anniv.

1979, Feb. 24 *Perf. 14*

Intl. Year of the Child: 15c, Children of the world, globe and ICY emblem. $1, Children at play, ICY emblem.

185 A75 10c multicolored	.15	.15
186 A75 15c multicolored	.18	.15
187 A75 $1 multicolored	1.50	1.10
Nos. 185-187 (3)	1.83	1.40

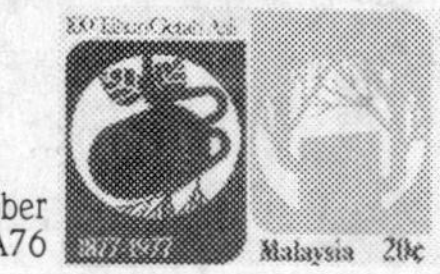

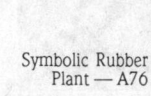

Symbolic Rubber Plant — A76

Designs: 10c, Symbolic palm. 75c, Symbolic rubber products.

1979, Apr. 30 **Litho.** *Perf. 13*

188 A76 10c brt green & gold	.15	.15
189 A76 20c multicolored	.20	.15
190 A76 75c brt green & gold	.75	.75
Nos. 188-190 (3)	1.10	1.05

Centenary of rubber production (in 1977).

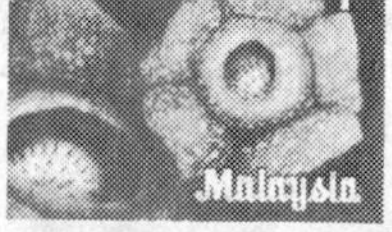

Rafflesia Hasseltii — A77

Flowers: 2c, Pterocarpus indicus. 5c, Lagerstroemia speciosa. 10c, Durio zibethinus. 15c, Hibiscus. 20c, Rhododendron scortechinii. 25c, Phaeomeria speciosa.

Perf. 15x14½

1979, Apr. 30 **Wmk. 378**

191 A77 1c multicolored	.15	.15
192 A77 2c multicolored	.15	.15
193 A77 5c multicolored	.15	.15
a. Unwmkd. ('84)		
194 A77 10c multicolored	.15	.15
a. White flowers, unwmkd. ('84)	.15	.15
195 A77 15c multicolored	.15	.15
a. 15c yellow & multi, unwmkd. ('83)	.15	.15
196 A77 20c multicolored	.18	.15
a. 20c greenish & multi, unwmkd. ('83)	.18	.15
197 A77 25c multicolored	.24	.15
a. Unwmkd. ('85)	5.00	
Set value	.80	.45

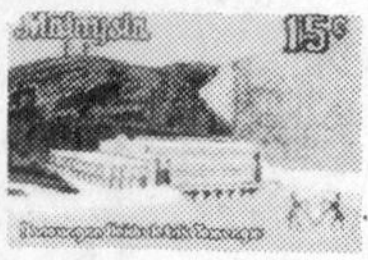

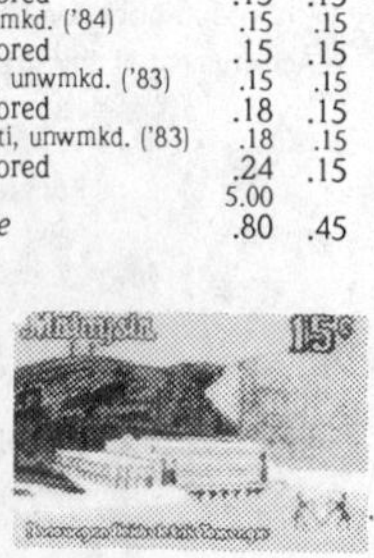

Temengor Hydroelectric Dam — A78

Designs: 25c, 50c, Dam and river, diff.

1979, Sept. 19   **Perf. 13½x14½**
Litho.
198 A78	15c multicolored	.15	.15
199 A78	25c multicolored	.24	.15
200 A78	50c multicolored	.48	.24
	Nos. 198-200 (3)	.87	
	Set value		.44

"TELECOM 79" — A79

Telecom Emblem and: 15c, Telephone receiver and globes. 50c, Modes of communication.

1979, Sept. 20   **Perf. 13½**
Size: 34x25mm
201 A79	10c multicolored	.15	.15
202 A79	15c multicolored	.16	.15

Perf. 14
Size: 29x28mm
203 A79	50c multicolored	.55	.28
	Nos. 201-203 (3)	.86	
	Set value		.40

3rd World Telecommunications Exhibition, Geneva, Sept. 20-26.

Haji Ahmad Shah — A80

1980, July 10   **Litho.**   **Perf. 14½**
204 A80	10c multicolored	.15	.15
205 A80	15c multicolored	.16	.15
206 A80	50c multicolored	.55	.28
	Nos. 204-206 (3)	.86	
	Set value		.40

Installation of Sultan Haji Ahmad Shah of Pahang as Paramount Ruler (Yang di-Pertuan Agong).

Pahang-Sarawak Cable — A81

Designs: 15c, Dial with views of Kuantan and Kuching. 50c, Telephone and maps.

1980, Aug. 31   **Litho.**   **Perf. 13½**
207 A81	10c shown	.15	.15
208 A81	15c multicolored	.16	.15
209 A81	50c multicolored	.52	.22
	Nos. 207-209 (3)	.83	
	Set value		.32

National University of Malaysia, 10th Anniversary A82

Designs: 15c, Jalan Pantai Baru campus. 75c, Great Hall and Tun Haji Abdul Razak (1st chancellor).

1980, Sept. 2   **Litho.**   **Perf. 13½**
210 A82	10c shown	.15	.15
211 A82	15c multicolored	.15	.15
212 A82	75c multicolored	.70	.35
	Nos. 210-212 (3)	1.00	
	Set value		.45

Hegira (Pilgrimage Year) — A83

1980, Nov. 9
213 A83	15c multicolored	.20	.15
214 A83	50c multicolored	.70	.35
	Set value		.41

A84   Emblem — A85

1981, Feb. 14   **Litho.**   **Perf. 13½**
215 A84	10c Child learning to walk	.15	.15
216 A84	15c Seamstress	.15	.15
217 A84	80c Athlete	.80	.40
	Nos. 215-217 (3)	1.10	
	Set value		.50

International Year of the Disabled.

1981, Mar. 21   **Litho.**   **Perf. 14½**
218 A85	10c multicolored	.15	.15
219 A85	15c multicolored	.18	.15
220 A85	50c multicolored	.60	.30
	Nos. 218-220 (3)	.93	
	Set value		.40

Installation of Sultan Mahmud of Trengganu.

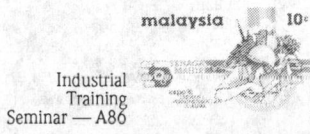

Industrial Training Seminar — A86

Designs: Various workers.

1981, May 2   **Litho.**   **Perf. 13½**
221 A86	10c multicolored	.15	.15
222 A86	15c multicolored	.15	.15
223 A86	30c multicolored	.20	.15
224 A06	75c multicolored	.50	.35
	Nos. 221-224 (4)	1.00	
	Set value		.45

Sources of Energy — A87

1981, June 17   **Litho.**   **Perf. 13½**
225 A87	10c "25"	.15	.15
226 A87	15c shown	.16	.15
227 A87	75c Non-renewable energy	.80	.40
	Nos. 225-227 (3)	1.11	
	Set value		.53

World Energy Conference, 25th anniv.

Centenary of Sabah — A88

1981, Aug. 31   **Litho.**   **Perf. 12**
228 A88	15c Views, 1881 and 1981	.15	.15
229 A88	80c Traditional and modern farming	.80	.40
	Set value		.45

Rain Tree — A89

1981, Dec. 16   **Litho.**   **Perf. 14**
230 A89	15c shown	.15	.15
231 A89	50c Simber tree, vert.	.52	.26
232 A89	80c Borneo camphor-wood, vert.	1.00	.50
	Nos. 230-232 (3)	1.67	.91

Scouting Year and Jamboree, Apr. 9-16 A90

1982, Apr. 10   **Litho.**   **Perf. 13½x13**
233 A90	15c Jamboree emblem	.15	.15
234 A90	50c Flag, emblem	.42	.22
235 A90	80c Emblems, knot	.70	.35
	Nos. 233-235 (3)	1.27	.72

15th Anniv. of Assoc. of South East Asian Nations (ASEAN) A91

1982, Aug. 8   **Litho.**   **Perf. 14**
236 A91	15c Meeting Center	.16	.15
237 A91	$1 Flags	1.10	.55

Dome of the Rock, Jerusalem A92

1982, Aug. 21   **Perf. 13½**
238 A92	15c multicolored	.16	.15
239 A92	$1 multicolored	1.10	.55

For the freedom of Palestine.

25th Anniv. of Independence A93

1982, Aug. 31   **Litho.**   **Perf. 14**
240 A93	10c Kuala Lumpur	.15	.15
241 A93	15c Independence celebration	.15	.15
242 A93	50c Parade	.52	.26
243 A93	80c Independence ceremony	.70	.35
a.	Souvenir sheet of 4, #240-243	1.50	.75
	Nos. 240-243 (4)	1.52	
	Set value		.72

Traditional Games — A94

1982, Oct. 30   **Perf. 13½**
244 A94	10c Shadow play	.15	.15
245 A94	15c Cross top	.15	.15
246 A94	75c Kite flying	.75	.38
	Nos. 244-246 (3)	1.05	
	Set value		.50

Handicrafts — A95

1982, Nov. 26   **Litho.**   **Perf. 13x13½**
247 A95	10c Sabah hats	.15	.15
248 A95	15c Gold-threaded cloth	.15	.15
249 A95	75c Sarawak pottery	.70	.35
	Nos. 247-249 (3)	1.00	
	Set value		.46

Commonwealth Day — A96

1983, Mar. 14   **Litho.**   **Perf. 14**
250 A96	15c Flag	.15	.15
251 A96	20c Seri Paduka Baginda	.15	.15
252 A96	40c Oil palm refinery	.30	.15
253 A96	$1 Globe	.75	.38
	Nos. 250-253 (4)	1.35	
	Set value		.65

First Shipment of Natural Gas, Bintulu, Sarawak A97

1983, Jan. 22   **Litho.**   **Perf. 13½**
254 A97	15c Bintulu Port Authority emblem	.15	.15
255 A97	20c Freighter Tenaga Satu	.16	.15
256 A97	$1 Gas plant	.85	.42
	Nos. 254-256 (3)	1.16	
	Set value		.56

Freshwater Fish — A98

1983, June 15   **Perf. 12x12½**
257	Pair	.38	.18
a.	A98 20c Tilapia nilotica	.18	.15
b.	A98 20c Cyprinus carpio	.18	.15
258	Pair	.75	.38
a.	A98 40c Puntius gonionotus	.35	.18
b.	A98 40c Ctenopharyngodon idellus	.35	.18
c.	As #258, perf. 13½x14	2.25	1.10

Opening of East-West Highway — A99

1983, July 1   **Perf. 14x13½**
259 A99	15c Lower Sungei Pergau Bridge	.15	.15
260 A99	20c Sungei Perak Reservoir Bridge	.16	.15
261 A99	$1 Map	.85	.42
	Nos. 259-261 (3)	1.16	
	Set value		.56

Armed Forces, 50th Anniv. A100

Designs: 15c, Royal Malaysian Aircraft. 20c, Navy vessel firing missile. 40c, Battle at Pasir Panjang. 80c, Trooping of the Royal colors.

1983, Sept. 16   **Litho.**   **Perf. 13½**
262 A100	15c multicolored	.15	.15
263 A100	20c multicolored	.18	.15
264 A100	40c multicolored	.35	.18
265 A100	80c multicolored	.75	.38
a.	Souvenir sheet of 4, #262-265	1.50	.75
	Nos. 262-265 (4)	1.43	
	Set value		.72

Helmeted Hornbill — A101

Various hornbills.

1983, Oct. 26 Litho. *Perf. 13½*

266 A101 15c shown .15 .15
267 A101 20c Wrinkled .18 .15
268 A101 50c White crested .45 .22
269 A101 $1 Rhinoceros hornbill .90 .45
Nos. 266-269 (4) 1.68
Set value .82

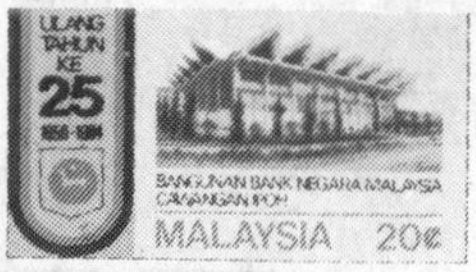

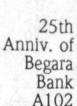

25th Anniv. of Begara Bank A102

Branch offices.

1984, Jan. 26 Litho. *Perf. 13½x14*

270 A102 20c Ipoh .16 .15
271 A102 $1 Alor Setar .85 .42
Set value .50

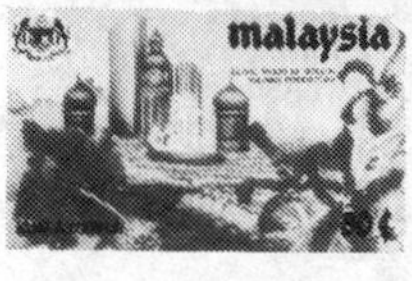

10th Anniv. of Federal Territory A103

Views of Kuala Lumpur. 20c, 40c vert.

Perf. 14x13½, 13½x14

1984, Feb. 1 Litho.

272 A103 20c multicolored .16 .15
273 A103 40c multicolored .32 .16
274 A103 80c multicolored .70 .35
Nos. 272-274 (3) 1.18 .66

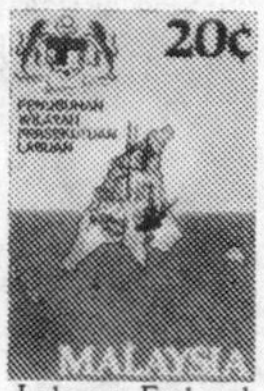

Labuan Federal Territory A104

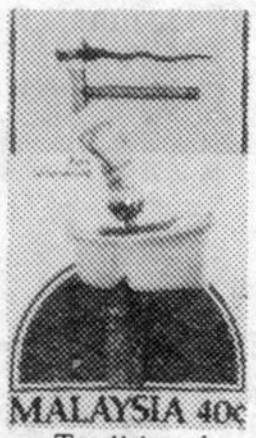

Traditional Weapons A105

1984, Apr. 16 Litho. *Perf. 13½x14*

275 A104 20c Development symbols, map, arms .16 .15
276 A104 $1 Flag, map .85 .42
Set value .50

1984, May 30 *Perf. 13x14*

277 A105 40c Keris Semenanjung .35 .18
278 A105 40c Keris Pekakak .35 .18
279 A105 40c Keris Jawa .35 .18
280 A105 40c Tumbuk Lada .35 .18
a. Block of 4, #277-280 1.50 .75

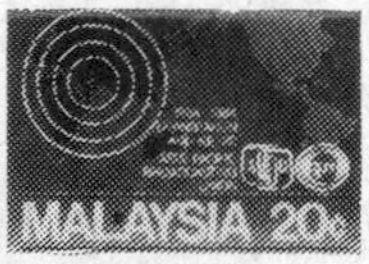

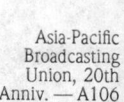

Asia-Pacific Broadcasting Union, 20th Anniv. — A106

1984, June 23 *Perf. 14x14½*

281 A106 20c Map, waves .16 .15
282 A106 $1 "20" .75 .38
Set value .46

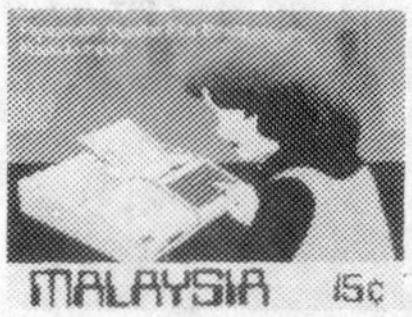

Kuala Lumpur Post Office Opening A107

1984, Oct. 29 *Perf. 12x11½*

283 A107 15c Facsimile transmission .15 .15
284 A107 20c Building .20 .15
285 A107 $1 Mail bag conveyor 1.00 .50
Nos. 283-285 (3) 1.35
Set value .67

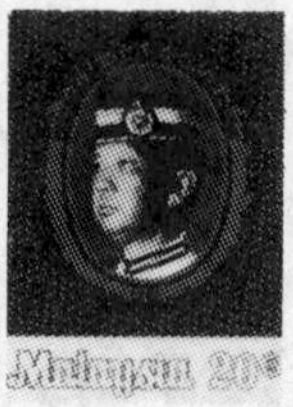

Installation of Sultan of Johore as 8th Paramount Ruler of Malaysia — A108

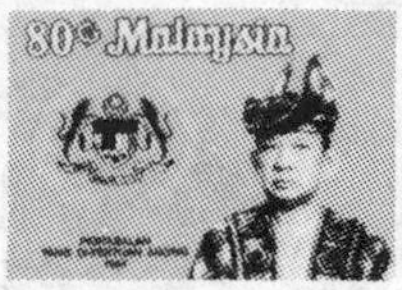

Sultan Mahmood, Arms — A109

1984, Nov. 15 Litho. *Perf. 12*

286 A108 15c multicolored .15 .15
287 A108 20c multicolored .16 .15
288 A109 40c multicolored .32 .16
289 A109 80c multicolored .64 .32
Nos. 286-289 (4) 1.27
Set value .62

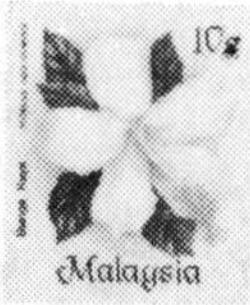

A110

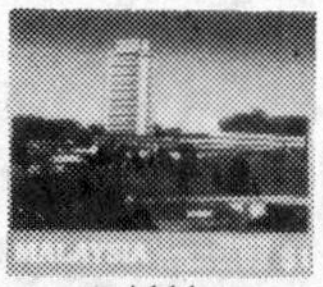
A111

Malaysian hibiscus.

1984, Dec. 12 Litho. *Perf. 13½*

290 A110 10c White hibiscus .15 .15
291 A110 20c Red hibiscus .16 .15
292 A110 40c Pink hibiscus .32 .16
293 A110 $1 Orange hibiscus .80 .40
Nos. 290-293 (4) 1.43
Set value .68

Perf. 13½x14, 14x13½

1985, Mar. 30 Litho.

294 A111 20c Badge, vert. .16 .15
295 A111 $1 Parliament, Kuala Lumpur .75 .38
Set value .46

Parliament, 25th anniv.

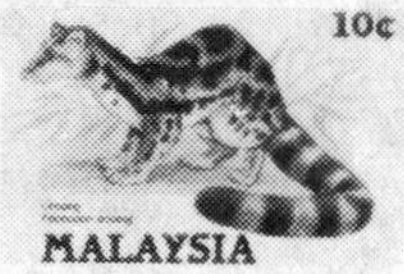

Protected Wildlife A112

1985, Apr. 25 *Perf. 14*

296 A112 10c Prionodon linsang .15 .15
297 A112 40c Nycticebus coucang, vert. .32 .16
298 A112 $1 Petaurista elegans, vert. .80 .40
Nos. 296-298 (3) 1.27
Set value .60

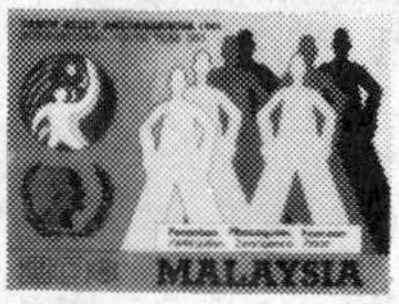

Intl. Youth Year — A113

1985, May 15 *Perf. 13*

299 A113 20c Youth solidarity .16 .15
300 A113 $1 Participation in natl. development .80 .40

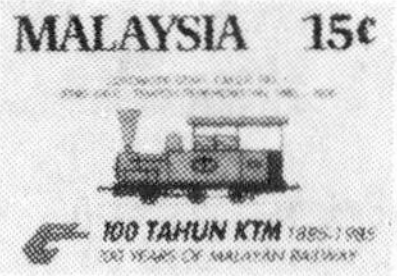

Malaya Railways Centenary A114

Locomotives.

1985, June 1 *Perf. 13*

301 A114 15c Steam engine, 1885 .15 .15
302 A114 20c Diesel-electric, 1957 .18 .15
303 A114 $1 Diesel, 1963 .85 .42
Nos. 301-303 (3) 1.18
Set value .57

Souvenir Sheet

Perf. 14x13

304 A114 80c Train leaving Kuala Lumpur Station, 1938 .80 .40

No. 304 contains one stamp 48x32mm.

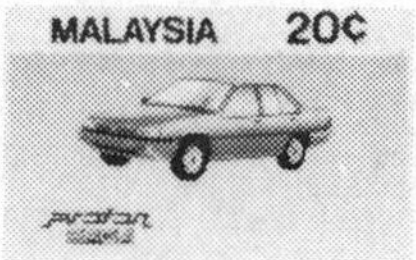

Proton Saga — A115

1985, July 9 *Perf. 14*

305 A115 20c multicolored .16 .15
306 A115 40c multicolored .32 .16
307 A115 $1 multicolored .80 .40
Nos. 305-307 (3) 1.28 .71

Inauguration of natl. automotive industry.

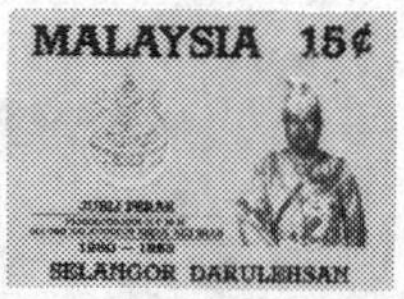

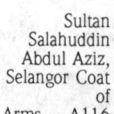

Sultan Salahuddin Abdul Aziz, Selangor Coat of Arms — A116

1985, Sept. 5 *Perf. 13*

308 A116 15c multicolored .15 .15
309 A116 20c multicolored .16 .15
310 A116 $1 multicolored .80 .40
Nos. 308-310 (3) 1.11
Set value .54

25th anniv. of coronation.

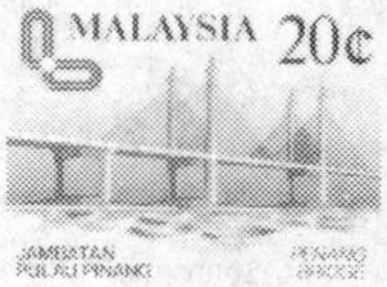

Penang Bridge Opening A117

1985, Sept. 15 Litho. *Perf. 13½x13*

311 A117 20c shown .16 .15
312 A117 40c Bridge, map .35 .18

Size: 44x28mm

Perf. 12½

313 A117 $1 Map .85 .42
Nos. 311-313 (3) 1.36
Set value .68

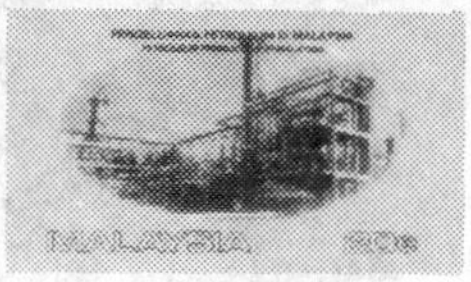

Natl. Oil Industry A118

1985, Nov. 4 *Perf. 12½*

314 A118 15c Offshore rig, vert. .15 .15
315 A118 20c 1st refinery .18 .15
316 A118 $1 Map of oil and gas fields .90 .45
Nos. 314-316 (3) 1.23
Set value .60

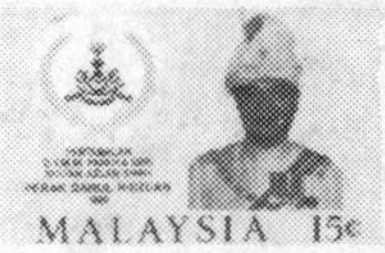

Coronation of Paduka Seri, Sultan of Perak — A119

1985, Dec. 9 *Perf. 14*

317 A119 15c lt blue & multi .15 .15
318 A119 20c lilac & multi .16 .15
319 A119 $1 gold & multi .80 .40
Nos. 317-319 (3) 1.11
Set value .54

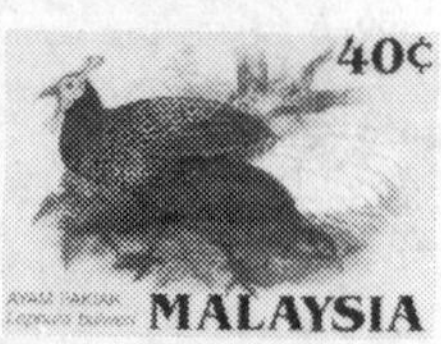

Birds A120

1986, Mar. 11 Litho. *Perf. 13½*

320 A120 20c Lophura ignita, vert. .18 .15
321 A120 20c Pavo malacense, vert. .18 .15
a. Pair, #320-321 .36 .20
322 A120 40c Lophura bulweri .35 .18
323 A120 40c Argusianus argus .35 .18
a. Pair, #322-323 .70 .36
Nos. 320-323 (4) 1.06
Set value .54

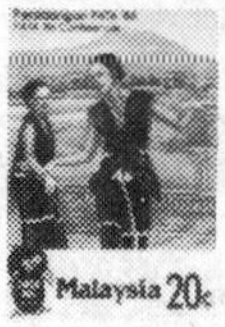

PATA '86, Pacific Area Travel Assoc. Conference, Persidangan — A121

Designs: No. 324a, Two women dancing. No. 324b, Woman in red. No. 324c, Man and woman. No. 325a, Woman in gold. No. 325b, Woman holding fan. No. 325c, Woman in violet.

1986, Apr. 14 Litho. *Perf. 15x14½*

324 Strip of 3 .45 .22
a.-c. A121 20c any single .15 .15
325 Strip of 3 .90 .45
a.-c. A121 40c any single .30 .15

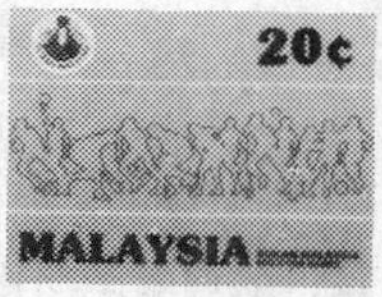

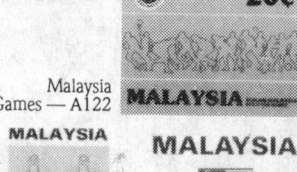

Malaysia Games — A122

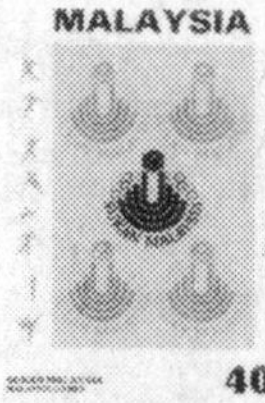

Games Emblem — A123

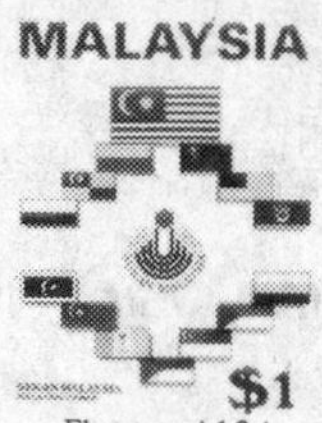

Flags — A124

1986, Apr. 14 Litho. *Perf. 12*

326 A122 20c multicolored .15 .15
327 A123 40c multicolored .28 .15
328 A124 $1 multicolored .75 .38
Nos. 326-328 (3) 1.18
Set value .58

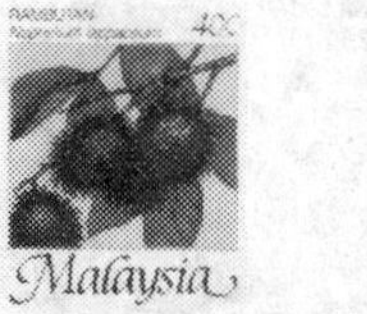

Nephelium Lappaceum A125

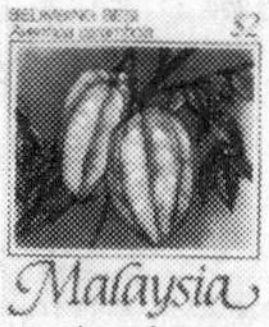

Averrhoa Carambola A126

1986, June 5

329 A125 40c shown .25 .15
330 A125 50c Ananas comosus .30 .15
331 A125 80c Durio zibethinus .50 .25
332 A125 $1 Garcinia mangostana .60 .30

Perf. 13½

333 A126 $2 shown 1.25 .60
334 A126 $5 Musa sapientum 3.00 1.50
335 A126 $10 Mangifera odorata 6.00 3.00
336 A126 $20 Carica papaya 12.00 6.00
Nos. 329-336 (8) 23.90 11.95

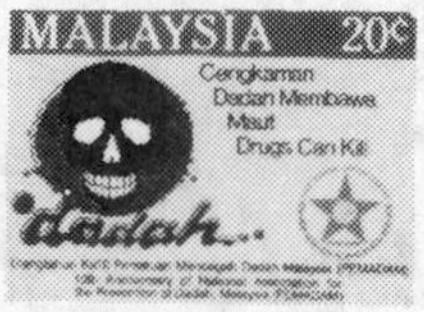

Natl. Assoc. for the Prevention of Drug Abuse, 10th Anniv. A127

1986, June 26 — Perf. 13

337	A127	20c Skull	.15	.15
338	A127	40c Dove	.28	.15
339	A127	$1 Addict, vert.	.75	.38
		Nos. 337-339 (3)	1.18	.68

Malaysian Airlines Kuala Lumpur-Los Angeles Inaugural Flight — A128

1986, July 31 — Perf. 14x13½

340	A128	20c Flight routes map	.15	.15
341	A128	40c MAS emblem, new route	.28	.15
342	A128	$1 Emblem, stops	.75	.38
		Nos. 340-342 (3)	1.18	.68

Industrial Productivity — A129

1986, Nov. 3 — Litho. — Perf. 14

343	A129	20c Construction, vert.	.15	.15
344	A129	40c Industry	.28	.15
345	A129	$1 Automobile factory	.75	.38
		Nos. 343-345 (3)	1.18	.68

Historic Buildings A130

Designs: 15c, Istana Lama Seri Menanti, Negri Sembilan. 20c, Istana Kenangan, Perak. 40c, Bangunan Stadthuys, Malacca. $1, Istana Kuching, Sarawak.

1986, Dec. 20 — Perf. 13

346	A130	15c multicolored	.15	.15
347	A130	20c multicolored	.15	.15
348	A130	40c multicolored	.30	.15
349	A130	$1 multicolored	.75	.38
		Nos. 346-349 (4)	1.35	
		Set value		.70

Folk Music Instruments — A131

1987, Mar. 7 — Litho. — Perf. 12

350	A131	15c Sompotan	.15	.15
351	A131	20c Sapih	.16	.15
352	A131	50c Serunai, vert.	.40	.20
353	A131	80c Kebab, vert.	.65	.32
		Nos. 350-353 (4)	1.36	
		Set value		.66

Intl. Year of Shelter for the Homeless A132

1987, Apr. 6 — Litho. — Perf. 12

354	A132	20c Model village	.16	.15
355	A132	$1 Symbols of family, shelter	.85	.42

UN Anti-Drug Campaign and Congress, Vienna — A133

1987, June 8 — Litho. — Perf. 13½x13

356	A133	20c Health boy, family, rainbow	.16	.15
357	A133	20c Holding drugs	.16	.15
a.		Pair, #356-357	.32	.20
358	A133	40c Child warding off drugs	.32	.16
359	A133	40c Drugs, damaged body in capsule	.32	.16
a.		Pair, #358-359	.65	.32
		Nos. 356-359 (4)	.96	
		Set value		.48

Nos. 357a, 359a have continuous designs.

Kenyir Hydroelectric Power Station Inauguration — A134

1987, July 13 — Perf. 12

360	A134	20c Power facility, dam	.16	.15
361	A134	$1 Side view	.85	.42

33rd Commonwealth Parliamentary Conference — A135

1987, Sept. 1 — Litho. — Perf. 12

362	A135	20c Maces, parliament	.16	.15
363	A135	$1 Parliament, maces, diff.	.85	.42

Transportation and Communications Decade in Asia and the Pacific (1985-94) — A136

Designs: 15c, Satellites, Earth, satellite dish. 20c, Car, diesel train, Kuala Lumpur Station. 40c, MISC container ship. $1, Malaysia Airlines jet, Kuala Lumpur Airport.

1987, Oct. 26 — Perf. 13½x13

364	A136	15c multicolored	.15	.15
365	A136	20c multicolored	.16	.15
366	A136	40c multicolored	.35	.18
367	A136	$1 multicolored	.85	.42
		Nos. 364-367 (4)	1.51	
		Set value		.74

Protected Wildcats A137

1987, Nov. 14

368	A137	15c Felis temminckii	.15	.15
369	A137	20c Felis planiceps	.16	.15
370	A137	40c Felis marmorata	.35	.18
371	A137	$1 Neofelis nebulosa	.85	.42
		Nos. 368-371 (4)	1.51	
		Set value		.74

ASEAN, 20th Anniv. A138

1987, Dec. 14 — Litho. — Perf. 13

372	A138	20c "20," flags	.15	.15
373	A138	$1 Flags, Earth	.85	.42

Opening of Sultan Salahuddin Abdul Aziz Shah Mosque, Selangor A139

Dome, minarets and: 15c, Arches. 20c, Sultan Abdul Aziz Shah, Selangor crest. $1, Interior, vert.

1988, Mar. 11 — Litho. — Perf. 12

374	A139	15c multicolored	.15	.15
375	A139	20c multicolored	.16	.15
376	A139	$1 multicolored	.80	.40
		Nos. 374-376 (3)	1.11	
		Set value		.54

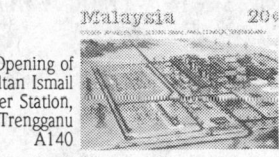

Opening of Sultan Ismail Power Station, Trengganu A140

1988, Apr. 4 — Perf. 13

377	A140	20c shown	.16	.15
378	A140	$1 Station, diff.	.80	.40

Wildlife Protection — A141

Birds.

1988, June 30 — Litho. — Perf. 13

379	A141	20c Hypothymis azurea	.16	.15
380	A141	20c Dicaeum cruentatum	.16	.15
a.		Pair, #379-380	.32	.18
381	A141	50c Aethopyga siparaja	.40	.20
382	A141	50c Cymbirhynchus macrorhynchos	.40	.20
a.		Pair, #381-382	.80	.40
		Nos. 379-382 (4)	1.12	
		Set value		.56

Independence of Sabah and Sarawak, 25th Anniv.

A142   A143

1988, Aug. 31 — Litho. — Perf. 13x13½

383	A142	20c Sabah	.16	.15
384	A142	20c Sarawak	.16	.15
a.		Pair, #383-384	.35	.20
385	A143	$1 State and natl. symbols	.80	.40
		Nos. 383-385 (3)	1.12	
		Set value		.56

A144   Malaysia 20c

Marine Life — A145

Nudibranchs: No. 386a, Glossodoris atromarginata. No. 386b, Phyllidia ocellata. No. 386c, Chromodoris annae. No. 386d, Flabellina macasarana. No. 386e, Fryeria ruppelli.

1988, Dec. 17 — Litho. — Perf. 12

386		Strip of 5	.80	.40
a.-e.		A144 20c any single	.16	.15

Souvenir Sheet
Perf. 14

387	A145	$1 Pomacanthus annularis	.80	.40

No. 387 contains one stamp 50x40mm.

Historic Buildings, Malacca A146

Designs: No. 388, Perisytiharan Kemerdekaan Memorial. No. 389, Istana Kesultanan. $1, Porta da Santiago, vert.

Perf. 13½x13, 13x13½

1989, Apr. 15 — Litho.

388	A146	20c multicolored	.16	.15
389	A146	20c multicolored	.16	.15
390	A146	$1 multicolored	.80	.40
		Nos. 388-390 (3)	1.12	
		Set value		.56

Crustaceans A147

Wmk. 388

1989, June 29 — Litho. — Perf. 12

391	A147	20c Tetralia nigrolineata	.16	.15
392	A147	20c Neopetrolisthes maculatus	.16	.15
a.		Pair, #391-392	.32	.18
393	A147	40c Periclimenes holthuisi	.32	.16
394	A147	40c Synalpheus neomeris	.32	.16
a.		Pair, #393-394	.65	.32
		Nos. 391-394 (4)	.96	
		Set value		.48

7th Natl. Scout Jamboree A148

1989, July 26 — Perf. 13x13½

395	A148	10c Map, badges	.15	.15
396	A148	20c Scout salute, natl. flag	.16	.15
397	A148	80c Camping out	.65	.32
		Nos. 395-397 (3)	.96	
		Set value		.45

Nos. 395-396 vert.

15th SEA Games, Kuala Lumpur — A149

Installation of Sultan Azlan as Supreme Ruler — A150

Designs: 10c, Cycling, horiz. 20c, Track events, horiz. 50c, Swimming. $1, Torch-bearer, stadium and flags.

Perf. 13½x13, 13x13½

1989, Aug. 20   Litho.   Wmk. 388
398	A149	10c multicolored	.15	.15
399	A149	20c multicolored	.16	.15
400	A149	50c multicolored	.40	.20
401	A149	$1 multicolored	.80	.40
		Nos. 398-401 (4)	1.51	
		Set value		.72

1989, Sept. 18   Perf. 13x13½
402	A150	20c multicolored	.16	.15
403	A150	40c multicolored	.32	.16
404	A150	$1 multicolored	.80	.40
		Nos. 402-404 (3)	1.28	.71

Commonwealth Heads of Government Meeting A151

Perf. 13½x13, 13x13½

1989, Oct. 18
405	A151	20c Conference center	.16	.15
406	A151	50c Folk dancers, vert.	.40	.20
407	A151	$1 Map, flag	.80	.40
		Nos. 405-407 (3)	1.36	.75

Malaysia Airlines Inaugural Non-stop Flight to London, Dec. 2 A152

Designs: No. 408, Passenger jet, Malaysian clock tower, Big Ben. No. 409, Passenger jet, Malaysian skyscraper, Westminster Palace. $1, Map, passenger jet.

Wmk. 388

1989, Dec. 2   Litho.   Perf. 13
408	A152	20c shown	.16	.15
409	A152	20c multicolored	.16	.15
a.		Pair, #408-409	.32	.16
410	A152	$1 multicolored	.80	.40
		Nos. 408-410 (3)	1.12	
		Set value		.56

National Park, 50th Anniv. — A153

1989, Dec. 28   Perf. 13x13½
411	A153	20c Map, sloth	.16	.15
412	A153	$1 Crested arguses	.80	.40

Visit Malaysia.

Visit Malaysia Year — A154

1990, Jan. 11   Perf. 12
413	A154	20c Map	.16	.15
414	A154	50c Drummers	.40	.20
415	A154	$1 Yachts, scuba divers	.80	.40
		Nos. 413-415 (3)	1.36	.75

Wildflowers — A155

1990, Mar. 12
416	A155	15c Dillenia suffruticosa	.15	.15
417	A155	20c Mimosa pudica	.16	.15
418	A155	50c Ipomoea carnea	.40	.20
419	A155	$1 Nymphaea pubescens	.80	.40
		Nos. 415-419 (5)	2.31	
		Set value		.74

Kuala Lumpur A156

Wmk. 388

1990, May 14   Litho.   Perf. 12
420	A156	20c Flag, rainbow, vert.	.16	.15
421	A156	40c shown	.32	.16
422	A156	$1 Cityscape	.80	.40
		Nos. 420-422 (3)	1.28	.71

South-South Consultation and Cooperation Conference — A157

1990, June 1   Perf. 13
423	A157	20c shown	.16	.15
424	A157	80c Emblem	.64	.32

Alor Setar, 250th Anniv. — A158

1990, June 2   Perf. 12
425	A158	20c shown	.16	.15
426	A158	40c Musicians, vert.	.32	.16
427	A158	$1 Government bldg., vert.	.80	.40
		Nos. 425-427 (3)	1.28	.71

Intl. Literacy Year — A159

1990, Sept. 8
428	A159	20c Letters, sign language	.16	.15
429	A159	40c People reading	.32	.16
430	A159	$1 Globe, pen nib, vert.	.80	.40
		Nos. 428-430 (3)	1.28	.71

Turtles A160

1990, Nov. 17
431	A160	15c Dermochelys coriacea	.15	.15
432	A160	20c Chelonia mydas	.15	.15
433	A160	40c Eretmochelys imbricata	.30	.16
434	A160	$1 Lepidochelys olivacea	.75	.38
		Nos. 431-434 (4)	1.35	
		Set value		.68

MARA (Council of Indigenous People), 25th Anniv. A161

1991, Apr. 25
435	A161	20c Construction	.15	.15
436	A161	40c Education	.30	.16
437	A161	$1 Banking & industry	.75	.38
		Nos. 435-437 (3)	1.20	.69

Wasps — A162

Designs: 15c, Eustenogaster calyptodoma. 20c, Vespa affinis indonensis. 50c, Sceliphron javanum. $1, Ampulex compressa.

1991, July 29
438	A162	15c multicolored	.15	.15
439	A162	20c multicolored	.15	.15
440	A162	50c multicolored	.38	.18
441	A162	$1 multicolored	.75	.38
a.		Souvenir sheet of 4, #438-441, perf. 14½x14	1.40	
		Nos. 438-441 (4)	1.43	
		Set value		.70

Prime Ministers — A163

Designs: No. 442, Tunku Abdul Rahman Putra Al-Haj (1903-1990). No. 443, Tun Hussein Onn (1922-1990). No. 444, Tun Abdul Razak Hussein (1922-1976).

1991, Aug. 30
442	A163	$1 multicolored	.75	.38
443	A163	$1 multicolored	.75	.38
444	A163	$1 multicolored	.75	.38
		Nos. 442-444 (3)	2.25	1.14

Historic Buildings A164

Designs: 15c, Istana Maziah, Trengganu. 20c, Istana Besar, Johore. 40c, Istana Bandar, Kuala Langat, Selangor. $1, Istana Jahar, Kelantan.

1991, Nov. 7
445	A164	15c multicolored	.15	.15
446	A164	20c multicolored	.15	.15
447	A164	40c multicolored	.30	.15
448	A164	$1 multicolored	.75	.38
		Nos. 445-448 (4)	1.35	
		Set value		.68

Sarawak Museum, Cent. — A165

Museum buildings, fabric pattern and: 30c, Brass lamp. $1, Vase.

1991, Dec. 21
449	A165	30c multicolored	.22	.15
450	A165	$1 multicolored	.75	.38

Malaysian Postal Service — A166

Designs: No. 451a, Postman on bicycle. b, Postman on motorcycle. c, Mail truck. d, Mail truck, diff., oil tank. e, Globe, airplane.

1992, Jan. 1
451	A166	30c Strip of 5, #a.-e.	1.15	.58

Malaysian Tropical Forests — A167

Designs: 20c, Hill Dipterocarp Forest, Dyera costulata. 50c, Mangrove Swamp Forest, Rhizophora apiculata. $1, Lowland Dipterocarp Forest, Neobalanocarpus heimii.

1992, Mar. 23
452	A167	20c multicolored	.15	.15
453	A167	50c multicolored	.38	.20
454	A167	$1 multicolored	.75	.38
		Nos. 452-454 (3)	1.28	.73

Installation of Yang di-Pertuan Besar of Negri Sembilan, Silver Jubilee — A168

1992, Apr. 18
455	A168	30c Portrait, arms	.22	.15
456	A168	$1 Building	.75	.38

1992 Thomas Cup Champions in Badminton — A169

1992, July 25   Perf. 12
457	A169	$1 Cup, flag	.75	.38
458	A169	$1 Players	.75	.38

Souvenir Sheet
459	A169	$2 multicolored	1.50	.75

No. 459 contains one 75x28mm stamp.

ASEAN, 25th Anniv. A170

1992, Aug. 8
460	A170	30c shown	.22	.15
461	A170	50c Flora	.38	.18
462	A170	$1 Architecture	.75	.38
		Nos. 460-462 (3)	1.35	.71

Postage Stamps in Malaysia, 125th Annv. — A171

Designs: No. 463, Straits Settlements #1, Malaya #84. No. 464, Straits Settlements #2, Malaysia #2. No. 465, Straits Settlements #11, Malaysia #421. No. 466, Straits Settlements #14, Malaysia #467. No. 467, Flag, simulated stamp.

1992, Sept. 1
463	A171	30c multicolored	.22	.15
464	A171	30c multicolored	.22	.15
a.		Pair #463-464	.45	.22
465	A171	50c multicolored	.38	.20
466	A171	50c multicolored	.38	.20
a.		Pair #465-466	.75	.40
		Nos. 463-466 (4)	1.20	
		Set value		.62

Souvenir Sheet
467	A171	$2 multicolored	1.50	.75

Kuala Lumpur '92.

Malaysia 30¢ A173

MALAYSIA $2

Coral
A174

No. 471: a, Acropora. b, Dendronephthya. c, Dendrophyllia. d, Sinularia. e, Melithaea.
No. 472, Subergorgia.

1992, Dec. 21
471 A173 30c Strip of 5, #a.-e.   1.20   .60

Souvenir Sheet
472 A174 $2 multicolored   1.60   .80

16th Asian-Pacific Dental Congress
A175

Children from various countries: No. 473, Four girls. No. 474, Four girls, one holding koala.
Dentists, flags of: No. 475, Japan, Malaysia, South Korea. No. 476, New Zealand, Thailand, People's Republic of China, Indonesia.

1993, Apr. 24
473 A175 30c multicolored   .24   .15
474 A175 30c multicolored   .24   .15
a.   Pair, #473-474   .48   .24
475 A175 50c multicolored   .38   .20
476 A175 $1 multicolored   .78   .40
a.   Pair, #475-476   1.20   .60
Nos. 473-476 (4)   1.64   .90

MALAYSIA RM1   MALAYSIA 20c

A176   A177

1993, June 24
477 A176 30c Fairway, vert.   .24   .15
478 A176 50c Old, new club houses, vert.   .40   .20
479 A176 $1 Sand trap   .78   .40
Nos. 477-479 (3)   1.42   .75

Royal Selangor Golf Club, cent.

1993, Aug. 2
Wildflowers.
480 A177 20c Alpinia rafflesiana   .16   .15
481 A177 30c Achasma megalocheilos   .24   .15
482 A177 50c Zingiber spectabile   .40   .20
483 A177 $1 Costus speciosus   .80   .40
Nos. 480-483 (4)   1.60   .90

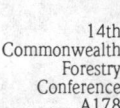 

14th Commonwealth Forestry Conference
A178

1993, Sept. 13
484 A178 30c Globe, forest   .25   .15
485 A178 50c Hand holding trees   .40   .20
486 A178 $1 Trees under dome, vert.   .80   .40
Nos. 484-486 (3)   1.45   .75

Kingfishers — A179

1993, Oct. 23
487 A179 30c Halcyon smyrnensis   .25   .15
488 A179 30c Alcedo meninting   .25   .15
a.   Pair, #487-488   .50   .30
489 A179 50c Halcyon concreta   .40   .20
490 A179 50c Ceyx erithacus   .40   .20
a.   Pair, #489-490   .80   .40
Nos. 487-490 (4)   1.30   .70

Langkawi Intl. Maritime and Aerospace Exhibition (LIMA '93) — A180

1993, Dec. 7
491 A180 30c SME MD3-160 airplane   .22   .15
492 A180 50c Eagle X-TS airplane   .38   .18
493 A180 $1 Patrol boat KD Kasturi   .75   .38
Nos. 491-493 (3)   1.35   .71

Souvenir Sheet
494 A180 $2 Map of Malaysia   1.50   .75

Visit Malaysia Year — A181

1994, Jan. 1
495 A181 20c Jeriau Waterfalls   .15   .15
496 A181 30c Flowers   .22   .15
497 A181 50c Marine life   .38   .18
498 A181 $1 Wildlife   .75   .38
Nos. 495-498 (4)   1.50   .86

Kuala Lumpur Natl. Planetarium
A182

Designs: 30c, Exterior. 50c, Interior displays. $1, Theater auditorium.

1994, Feb. 7
499 A182 30c multicolored   .22   .15
500 A182 50c multicolored   .38   .18
501 A182 $1 multicolored   .75   .38
Nos. 499-501 (3)   1.35   .71

Orchids — A183

Designs: 20c, Spathoglottis aurea. 30c, Paphiopedilum barbatum. 50c, Bulbophyllum lobbii. $1, Aerides odorata. $2, Grammatophyllum speciosum.

1994, Feb. 17
502 A183 20c multicolored   .16   .15
503 A183 30c multicolored   .25   .15
504 A183 50c multicolored   .40   .20
505 A183 $1 multicolored   .80   .40
Nos. 502-505 (4)   1.61   .90

Souvenir Sheet
506 A183 $2 multicolored   1.65   1.65

Hong Kong '94 (#506).

A184   A185

1994, June 17
507 A184 20c Decorative bowl   .16   .15
508 A184 30c Celestial sphere   .25   .15
509 A184 50c Dinar coins   .40   .20
510 A184 $1 Decorative tile   .80   .40
Nos. 507-510 (4)   1.61   .90

World Islamic Civilization Festival '94.
See Nos. 528-531.

1994, July 26
511 A185 30c shown   .25   .15
512 A185 50c Meat processing   .40   .20
513 A185 $1 Cattle, laboratory   .80   .40
Nos. 511-513 (3)   1.45   .75

Veterinary Services, cent.

Electrification, Cent. — A186

1994, Sept. 3
514 A186 30c Laying cable   .25   .15
515 A186 30c Lighted city   .25   .15
a.   Pair, #514-515   .50   .25
516 A186 $1 Futuristic city   .80   .40
Nos. 514-516 (3)   1.30   .70

North-South Expressway
A187

1994, Sept. 8
517 A187 30c shown   .25   .15
518 A187 50c Interchange   .40   .20
519 A187 $1 Bridge   .80   .40
Nos. 517-519 (3)   1.45   .75

A188   A189

1994, Sept. 22
520 A188 30c pink & multi   .25   .15
521 A188 50c yellow & multi   .40   .20
522 A188 $1 green & multi   .80   .40
Nos. 520-522 (3)   1.45   .75

Installation of 10th Yang Di-Pertuan Agong (Head of State).

Wmk. 388
1994, Oct. 29   **Litho.**   *Perf. 12*
523 A189 $1 shown   .80   .40
524 A189 $1 Mascot   .80   .40
a.   Pair, #523-524   1.60   .80

1998 Commonwealth Games, Kuala Lumpur.

Official Opening of Natl. Library Building
A190

1994, Dec. 16
525 A190 30c Library building   .25   .15
526 A190 50c Computer terminal   .40   .20
527 A190 $1 Manuscript   .80   .40
Nos. 525-527 (3)   1.45   .75

Nos. 507-510 with Added Inscription

1994   **Litho.**   **Wmk. 388**   *Perf. 12*
528 A184 20c multicolored   .16   .15
529 A184 30c multicolored   .25   .15
530 A184 50c multicolored   .40   .20
531 A184 $1 multicolored   .80   .40
Nos. 528-531 (4)   1.61   .90

Memorial to Tunku Abdul Rahman Putra Al-Haj (1903-1990), Former Prime Minister
A191

1994, Nov. 10   **Unwmk.**   *Perf. 14½*
532 A191 30c shown   .25   .15
533 A191 $1 Building complex   .80   .40

Fungi — A192

1995, Jan. 18   *Perf. 14½x14*
534 A192 20c Bracket fungus   .16   .15
535 A192 30c Cup fungus   .25   .15
536 A192 50c Veil fungus   .40   .20
537 A192 $1 Coral fungus   .80   .40
Nos. 534-537 (4)   1.61   .90

Neofelis Nebulosa
A193

1995, Apr. 18   **Wmk. 373**   *Perf. 13½*
538 A193 20c shown   .16   .15
539 A193 30c With young   .25   .15
540 A193 50c With mouth open   .40   .20
541 A193 $1 Lying on rock   .80   .40
a.   Strip of 4, #538-541   1.65   .80

Nos. 538-541 were issued in sheets of 4 #541a.
World Wildlife Fund.

Marine Life — A194

1995   **Litho.**   **Wmk. 388**   *Perf. 12*
542 A194 20c Feather stars   .16   .15
543 A194 20c Sea fans   .16   .15
a.   Pair, #542-543   .32   .16
544 A194 30c Soft coral   .22   .15
545 A194 30c Cup coral   .22   .15
a.   Pair, #544-545   .45   .22
Nos. 542-545 (4)   .76   .60

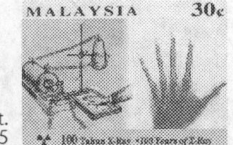

X-Ray, Cent.
A195

Designs: No. 546, Early machine x-raying hand. No. 547, CAT scan machine. No. $1, Chest x-ray.

1995, May 29
546 A195 30c multicolored .22 .15
547 A195 30c multicolored .22 .15
a. Pair, #546-547 .45 .22
548 A195 $1 multicolored .75 .38
Nos. 546-548 (3) 1.19 .68

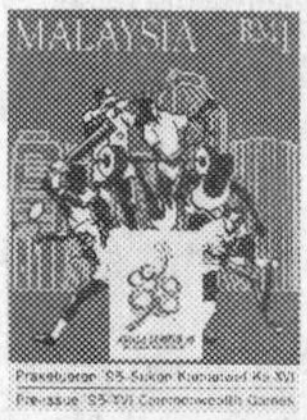

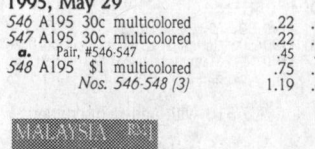

1998 Commonwealth Games, Kuala Lumpur — A196

Various sporting events: No. 549, Badminton, cricket, shooting, tennis, weight lifting, hurdles, field hockey. No. 550, Cycling, lawn bowling, boxing, basketball, rugby, gynmastics.

Wmk. 388

1995, Sept. 10 Litho. *Perf. 14*
549 A196 $1 multicolored .80 .40
550 A196 $1 multicolored .80 .40

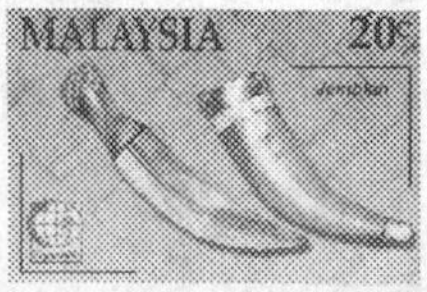

Traditional Weapons A197

1995, Sept. 1 Litho. *Perf. 14*
551 A197 20c Jemblah .15 .15
552 A197 30c Keris panjang .25 .25
553 A197 50c Kerambit .40 .40
554 A197 $1 Keris sundang .80 .80
Nos. 551-554 (4) 1.60 1.60

Souvenir Sheet
555 A197 $2 Lading terus 1.65 1.65

Singapore '95.

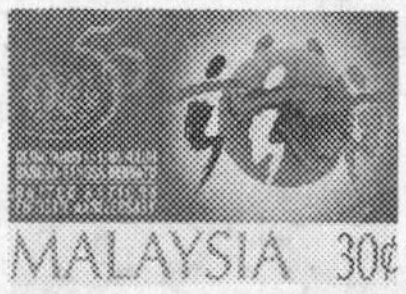

UN, 50th Anniv. A198

1995, Oct. 24 *Perf. 13¹/₂*
556 A198 30c shown .25 .15
557 A198 $1 UN emblem .80 .40

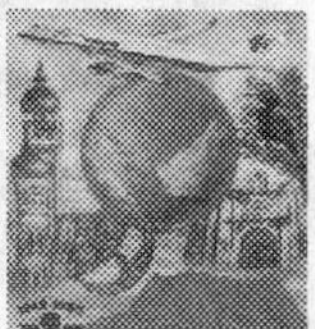

Intl. Assoc. of Travel Agents (IATA), 50th Anniv. — A199

Jet, globe and: No. 558, Historic buildings. No. 559, Sydney Opera House, Great Wall of China. No. 560, Eiffel Tower, Tower Bridge. No. 561, Hollywood Walk of Fame, Latin American pyramid.

1995, Oct. 30 *Perf. 14*
558 A199 30c multicolored .25 .25
559 A199 30c multicolored .25 .25
a. Pair, #558-559 .50 .50
560 A199 50c multicolored .40 .40
561 A199 50c multicolored .40 .40
a. Pair, #560-561 .80 .80

POSTAGE DUE STAMPS

Until 1966 Malaysia used postage due stamps of the Malayan Postal Union. See listings under Malaya.

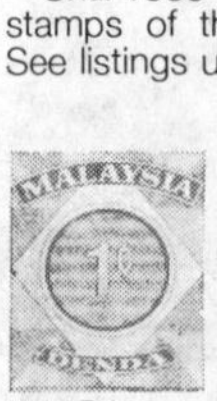

D1

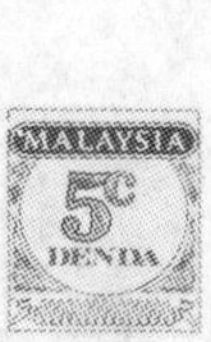

D2

Wmk. 338 Upright

1966, Aug. 15 Litho. *Perf. 14¹/₂x14*
J1 D1 1c pink .15 .15
J2 D1 2c slate .15 .15
J3 D1 4c lt yellow green .15 .15
J4 D1 8c bright green .18 .18
J5 D1 10c ultramarine .18 .18
J6 D1 12c purple .15 .15
J7 D1 20c brown .45 .45
J8 D1 50c olive bister 1.25 1.25
Set value 2.30 2.30

1972 Wmk. 338 Sideways
J4a D1 8c bright green .50 .50
J5a D1 10c ultramarine .75 .75
J7a D1 20c brown 1.00 1.00
J8a D1 50c olive bister 2.50 2.50
Nos. J4a-J8a (4) 4.75 4.75

1981-84 Litho. Unwmk. *Perf. 15x14*
J9 D1 2c slate .15 .15
J10 D1 8c bright green .15 .15
J11 D1 10c blue .15 .15
J11A D1 12c maroon ('84)
J12 D1 20c brown .20 .15
J13 D1 50c olive bister .50 .30
Set value, Nos. J9-J11, J12-J13 .95 .55

1988, Sept. 15 Litho. *Perf. 12*
J14 D2 5c brt rose & lil rose .15 .15
J15 D2 10c black & gray .15 .15
J16 D2 20c deep org & yel org .16 .16
J17 D2 50c blue grn & lt bl grn .40 .40
J18 D2 $1 brt blue & lt ultra .80 .80
Nos. J14-J18 (5) 1.66 1.66

JOHORE

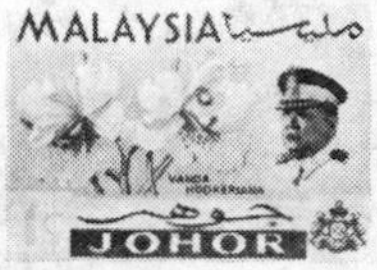

Vanda Hookeriana and Sultan Ismail — A14

Orchids: 2c, Arundina graminifolia. 5c, Paphiopedilum niveum. 6c, Spathoglottis plicata. 10c, Arachnis flosaeris. 15c, Rhyncostylis retusa. 20c, Phalaenopsis violacea.

Perf. 14¹/₂

1965, Nov. 15 Photo. Wmk. 338

Flowers in Natural Colors
169 A14 1c blk & lt grnsh bl .15 .15
a. Black omitted 50.00
b. Watermark sideways ('70) .15 .15
170 A14 2c black, red & gray .15 .15
171 A14 5c black & Prus bl .20 .15
a. Yellow omitted 24.00
172 A14 6c black & lt lil .24 .15
173 A14 10c black & lt ultra .35 .15
a. Watermark sideways ('70) .65 .55
174 A14 15c blk, lil rose & grn .48 .28
175 A14 20c black & brown .75 .48
Nos. 169-175 (7) 2.32
Set value 1.00

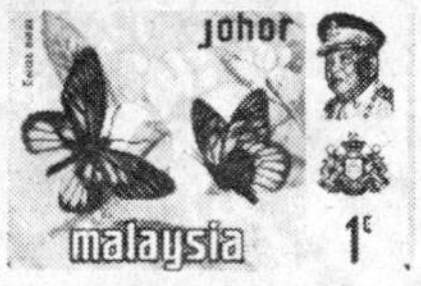

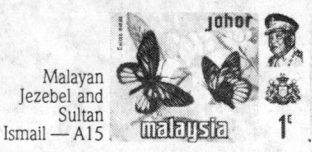

Malayan Jezebel and Sultan Ismail — A15

Butterflies: 2c, Black-veined tiger. 5c, Clipper. 6c, Lime butterfly. 10c, Great orange tip. 15c, Blue pansy. 20c, Wanderer.

Perf. 13¹/₂x13

1971, Feb. 1 Litho. Unwmk.
176 A15 1c multicolored .15 .15
177 A15 2c multicolored .15 .15
178 A15 5c multicolored .15 .15
179 A15 6c multicolored .25 .15
180 A15 10c multicolored .38 .15
181 A15 15c multicolored .60 .18
182 A15 20c multicolored .80 .30
Nos. 176-182 (7) 2.48
Set value .88

1977 Photo.
176a A15 1c .38 .18
177a A15 2c .38 .18
178a A15 5c .38 .18
180a A15 10c .55 .28
181a A15 15c 1.25 .45
182a A15 20c 1.50 .55
Nos. 176a-182a (6) 4.44 1.82

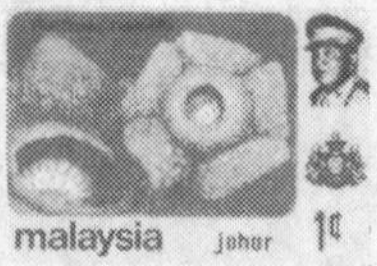

Rafflesia Hasseltii and Sultan Ismail — A16

Flowers: 2c, Pterocarpus indicus. 5c, Lagerstroemia speciosa. 10c, Durio zibethinus. 15c, Hibiscus. 20c, Rhododendron scortechinii. 25c, Phaeomeria speciosa.

Perf. 14¹/₂

1979, Apr. 30 Litho. Wmk. 378
183 A16 1c multicolored .15 .15
184 A16 2c multicolored .15 .15
185 A16 5c multicolored .15 .15
186 A16 10c multicolored .16 .15
187 A16 15c multicolored .25 .15
188 A16 20c multicolored .32 .15
189 A16 25c multicolored .40 .15
Set value 1.37 .45

1984

"Johor" in round type
185a A16 5c .15 .15
186a A16 10c .16 .15
187a A16 15c .25 .15
188a A16 20c .32 .15
Nos. 185a-188a (4) .88 .60

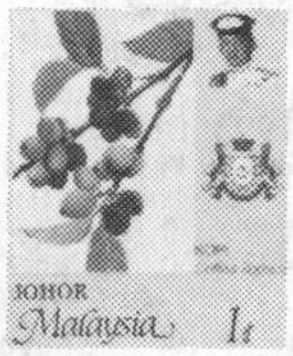

Agriculture, State Arms and Sultan Mahmood Iskandar Al-Haj, Regent — A19

Wmk. 388

1986, Oct. 25 Litho. *Perf. 12*
190 A19 1c Coffea liberica .15 .15
191 A19 2c Cocos nucifera .15 .15
192 A19 5c Theobroma cacao .15 .15
193 A19 10c Piper nigrum .15 .15
194 A19 15c Hevea brasiliensis .15 .15
195 A19 20c Elaeis guineensis .16 .15
196 A19 30c Oryza sativa .24 .15
Set value .75 .45

KEDAH

Orchid Type of Johore, 1965, with Portrait of Sultan Abdul Halim

Perf. 14¹/₂

1965, Nov. 15 Photo. Wmk. 338

Flowers in Natural Colors
106 A14 1c blk & lt grnsh bl .15 .15
a. Black omitted 50.00
b. Watermark sideways ('70) .75 .75
107 A14 2c black, red & gray .15 .15
108 A14 5c black & Prus bl .15 .15
109 A14 6c black & lt lil .15 .15
110 A14 10c black & lt ultra .22 .15
a. Watermark sideways ('70) 3.25 2.50
111 A14 15c blk, lil rose & grn .28 .18
112 A14 20c black & brown .42 .28
Set value 1.30 .70

Butterfly Type of Johore, 1971, with Portrait of Sultan Abdul Halim

Perf. 13¹/₂x13

1971, Feb. 1 Litho. Unwmk.
113 A15 1c multicolored .15 .15
114 A15 2c multicolored .15 .15
115 A15 5c multicolored .20 .15
116 A15 6c multicolored .24 .15
117 A15 10c multicolored .35 .15
118 A15 15c multicolored .60 .18
119 A15 20c multicolored .75 .20
Nos. 113-119 (7) 2.44
Set value .70

1977 Photo. Same Designs
114a A15 2c *2.50 1.00*
115a A15 5c .18 .15
117a A15 10c .30 .15
118a A15 15c .60 .30
119a A15 20c .85 .40
Nos. 114a-119a (5) *4.43 2.00*

Flower Type of Johore, 1979, with Portrait of Sultan Abdul Halim

Perf. 14¹/₂

1979, Apr. 30 Litho. Wmk. 378
120 A16 1c multicolored .15 .15
121 A16 2c multicolored .15 .15
122 A16 5c multicolored .15 .15
123 A16 10c multicolored .15 .15
a. Unwmkd. ('85)
124 A16 15c multicolored .20 .15
a. Unwmkd. ('84) 3.25
125 A16 20c multicolored .26 .15
a. Pale yellow flowers ('84) .26 .15
126 A16 25c multicolored .32 .16
Set value 1.08 .60

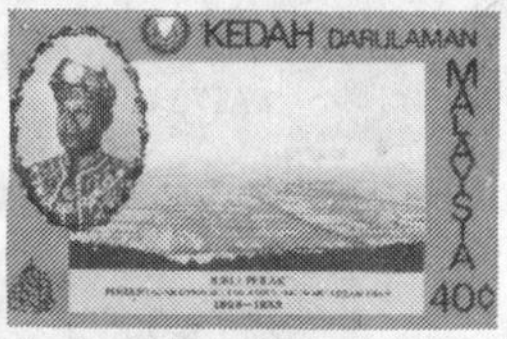

25th Anniv. of Installation of Sultan Abdul Halim — A10

1983, July 15 Litho. *Perf. 13¹/₂*
127 A10 20c Portrait, vert. .24 .15
128 A10 40c View from Mt. Gunung Jerai .50 .25
129 A10 50c Rice fields, Mt. Gunung Jerai .60 .30
Nos. 127-129 (3) 1.34 .70

Agriculture and State Arms Type of Johore with Sultan Abdul Halim

Wmk. 388

1986, Oct. 25 Litho. *Perf. 12*
130 A19 1c multicolored .15 .15
131 A19 2c multicolored .15 .15
132 A19 5c multicolored .15 .15
133 A19 10c multicolored .15 .15
134 A19 15c multicolored .15 .15
135 A19 20c multicolored .16 .15
136 A19 30c multicolored .24 .15
Set value .75 .45

KELANTAN

Orchid Type of Johore, 1965, with Portrait of Sultan Yahya Petra

Perf. 14¹/₂

1965, Nov. 15 Photo. Wmk. 338

Flowers in Natural Colors
91 A14 1c blk & lt grnsh bl .15 .15
a. Watermark sideways ('70) .32 .32
92 A14 2c black, red & gray .15 .15
93 A14 5c black & Prus bl .22 .15
94 A14 6c black & lt lil .28 .15
95 A14 10c black & lt ultra .40 .18
a. Watermark sideways ('70) 1.40 1.10
96 A14 15c blk, lil rose & grn .55 .35
97 A14 20c black & brown .85 .60
Nos. 91-97 (7) 2.60 1.73

Butterfly Type of Johore, 1971, with Portrait of Sultan Yahya Petra

Perf. 13¹/₂x13

1971, Feb. 1 Litho. Unwmk.
98 A15 1c multicolored .15 .15
99 A15 2c multicolored .15 .15
100 A15 5c multicolored .20 .15
101 A15 6c multicolored .24 .15
102 A15 10c multicolored .35 .18
103 A15 15c multicolored .60 .30
104 A15 20c multicolored .75 .38
Nos. 98-104 (7) 2.44
Set value 1.18

1977 Photo.
98a A15 1c .60 .30
100a A15 5c .60 .30
102a A15 10c 1.25 .45
103a A15 15c 3.00 1.00
Nos. 98a-103a (4) 5.45 2.05

Flower Type of Johore, 1979, with Portrait of Sultan Yahya Petra

Perf. 14¹/₂

1979, Apr. 30 Litho. Wmk. 378
105 A16 1c multicolored .15 .15
106 A16 2c multicolored .15 .15
107 A16 5c multicolored .15 .15
a. Unwmkd. ('86) 1.05
108 A16 10c multicolored .15 .15
a. White flowers ('84) .15 .15
109 A16 15c multicolored .18 .15
110 A16 20c multicolored .24 .15
a. Pale yellow flowers ('84) .24 .15
111 A16 25c multicolored .30 .15
Set value 1.00 .55

ANNOUNCING A SPECTACULAR SERIES OF
MAJOR AUCTIONS

IN YOUR HOME!

Sandafayre Limited
Knutsford
Cheshire
WA16 8XN
England

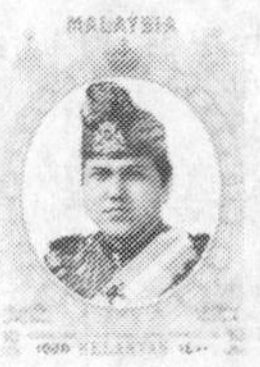

Sultan Tengku Ismail Petra, Installation — A7

1980, Mar. 30 Litho. *Perf. 14½*

112 A7	10c multicolored	.15	.15
113 A7	15c multicolored	.15	.15
114 A7	50c multicolored	.42	.22
	Set value	.62	.32

Agriculture and State Arms Type of Johore with Sultan Ismail Petra

Wmk. 388

1986, Oct. 25 Litho. *Perf. 12*

115 A19	1c multicolored	.15	.15
116 A19	2c multicolored	.15	.15
117 A19	5c multicolored	.15	.15
118 A19	10c multicolored	.15	.15
119 A19	15c multicolored	.15	.15
120 A19	20c multicolored	.16	.15
121 A19	30c multicolored	.24	.15
	Set value	.75	.45

MALACCA

(Melaka)

Orchid Type of Johore, 1965, with State Crest

Perf. 14½

1965, Nov. 15 Photo. Wmk. 338

Flowers in Natural Colors

67 A14	1c blk & lt grnsh blue	.15	.15
a.	Watermark sideways ('70)	.24	.24
68 A14	2c blk, red & gray	.15	.15
69 A14	5c black & Prus bl	.25	.15
70 A14	6c black & lt lilac	.32	.15
71 A14	10c black & lt ultra	.48	.15
a.	Watermark sideways ('70)	1.00	.80
72 A14	15c blk, lil rose & grn	.65	.26
73 A14	20c black & brown	.95	.45
	Nos. 67-73 (7)	2.95	
	Set value		1.05

Butterfly Type of Johore, 1971, with State Crest

Perf. 13½x13

1971, Feb. 1 Litho. Unwmk.

74 A15	1c multicolored	.15	.15
75 A15	2c multicolored	.15	.15
76 A15	5c multicolored	.18	.15
77 A15	6c multicolored	.25	.15
78 A15	10c multicolored	.38	.18
79 A15	15c multicolored	.60	.32
80 A15	20c multicolored	.75	.35
	Nos. 74-80 (7)	2.46	
	Set value		1.15

1977 Photo.

74a	A15	1c	.60	.32
76a	A15	5c	.48	.28
78a	A15	10c	.80	.50
79a	A15	15c	1.65	.85
80a	A15	20c	2.00	1.10
		Nos. 74a-80a (5)	5.53	3.05

Flower Type of Johore, 1979, with State Crest

Perf. 14½

1979, Apr. 30 Litho. Wmk. 378

81 A16	1c multicolored	.15	.15
82 A16	2c multicolored	.15	.15
83 A16	5c multicolored	.15	.15
84 A16	10c multicolored	.15	.15
85 A16	15c multicolored	.18	.15
86 A16	20c multicolored	.24	.15
87 A16	25c multicolored	.30	.15
	Set value	1.00	.55

1983-86 Unwmk.

84a	A16	10c ('85)	2.15
85a	A16	15c ('86)	3.25
86a	A16	20c	4.25
		Nos. 84a-86a (3)	9.65

Agriculture and State Arms Type of Johore

Wmk. 388

1986, Oct. 25 Litho. *Perf. 12*

88 A19	1c multicolored	.15	.15
89 A19	2c multicolored	.15	.15
90 A19	5c multicolored	.15	.15
91 A19	10c multicolored	.15	.15
92 A19	15c multicolored	.15	.15
93 A19	20c multicolored	.16	.15
94 A19	30c multicolored	.24	.15
	Set value	.75	.45

NEGRI SEMBILAN

(Negeri Sembilan)

Orchid Type of Johore, 1965, with State Crest

Perf. 14½

1965, Nov. 15 Photo. Wmk. 338

Flowers in Natural Colors

76 A14	1c blk & lt grnsh blue	.15	.15
a.	Watermark sideways ('70)	.55	.55
77 A14	2c black, red & gray	.15	.15
78 A14	5c black & Prus blue	.22	.15
79 A14	6c black & lt lilac	.28	.15
80 A14	10c black & lt ultra	.42	.15
81 A14	15c blk, lil rose & grn	.55	.16
82 A14	20c black & brown	.85	.28
	Nos. 76-82 (7)	2.62	
	Set value		.72

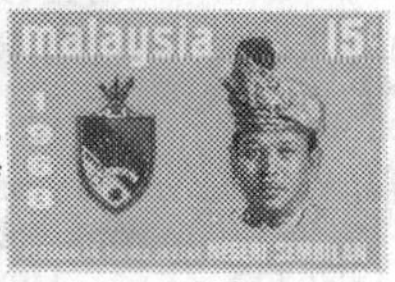

Tuanku Ja'afar and Crest of Negri Sembilan — A7

1968, Apr. 8 Photo. *Perf. 13½*

83 A7	15c brt blue & multi	.15	.15
84 A7	50c yellow & multi	.50	.50

Installation of Tuanku Ja'afar ibni Al-Marhum as ruler (Yang di-Pertuan Besar) of Negri Sembilan.

Butterfly Type of Johore, 1971, with State Crest

Perf. 13½x13

1971, Feb. 1 Litho. Unwmk.

85 A15	1c multicolored	.15	.15
86 A15	2c multicolored	.15	.15
87 A15	5c multicolored	.20	.15
88 A15	6c multicolored	.26	.15
89 A15	10c multicolored	.40	.15
90 A15	15c multicolored	.65	.22
91 A15	20c multicolored	.80	.25
	Nos. 85-91 (7)	2.61	
	Set value		.85

1977 Photo.

86a	A15	2c	.52	.22
87a	A15	5c	.52	.22
89a	A15	10c	1.00	.44
90a	A15	15c	1.90	.75
91a	A15	20c	2.50	1.10
		Nos. 86a-91a (5)	6.44	2.73

Flower Type of Johore, 1979, with State Crest

Perf. 14½

1979, Apr. 30 Litho. Wmk. 378

92 A16	1c multicolored	.15	.15
93 A16	2c multicolored	.15	.15
94 A16	5c multicolored	.15	.15
a.	Unwmkd. ('85)	1.05	
95 A16	10c multicolored	.15	.15
a.	White flowers ('84)	.15	.15
96 A16	15c multicolored	.18	.15
a.	Unwmkd. ('84)	3.25	
97 A16	20c multicolored	.24	.15
a.	Pale yellow flowers ('84)	.24	.15
98 A16	25c multicolored	.30	.15
	Set value	1.00	.55

Agriculture and State Arms Type of Johore

Wmk. 388

1986, Oct. 25 Litho. *Perf. 12*

99 A19	1c multicolored	.15	.15
100 A19	2c multicolored	.15	.15
101 A19	5c multicolored	.15	.15
102 A19	10c multicolored	.15	.15
103 A19	15c multicolored	.15	.15
104 A19	20c multicolored	.16	.15
105 A19	30c multicolored	.24	.15
	Set value	.75	.45

PAHANG

Orchid Type of Johore, 1965, with Portrait of Sultan Abu Bakar

Perf. 14½

1965, Nov. 15 Photo. Wmk. 338

Flowers in Natural Colors

83 A14	1c blk & lt grnsh bl	.15	.15
a.	Watermark sideways ('70)	.15	.15
84 A14	2c black, red & gray	.15	.15
a.	Unwmkd. ('85)		
85 A14	5c black & Prus bl	.16	.15
86 A14	6c black & lt lil	.20	.15
87 A14	10c black & lt ultra	.30	.15
a.	Watermark sideways ('70)	.62	.50
88 A14	15c blk, lil rose & grn	.40	.16
89 A14	20c black & brown	.60	.26
	Nos. 83-89 (7)	1.96	
	Set value		.74

Butterfly Type of Johore, 1971, Portrait of Sultan Abu Bakar

Perf. 13½x13

1971, Feb. 1 Litho. Unwmk.

90 A15	1c multicolored	.15	.15
91 A15	2c multicolored	.15	.15
92 A15	5c multicolored	.15	.15
a.	Booklet pane of 4 ('73)	.60	
93 A15	6c multicolored	.20	.15
94 A15	10c multicolored	.32	.15
a.	Booklet pane of 4 ('73)	1.30	
95 A15	15c multicolored	.52	.20
a.	Booklet pane of 4 ('73)	2.25	
96 A15	20c multicolored	.65	.22
	Nos. 90-96 (7)	2.14	
	Set value		.75

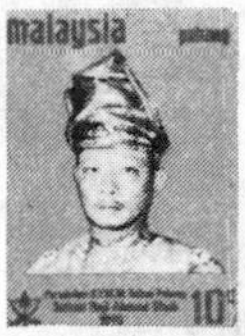

Sultan Haji Ahmad Shah — A9

1975, May 8 Litho. *Perf. 14x14½*

97 A9	10c lilac, gold & black	.15	.15
98 A9	15c yellow, green & black	.22	.18
99 A9	50c ultra, dk blue & black	.65	.65
	Nos. 97-99 (3)	1.02	.98

Installation of Sultan Haji Ahmad Shah as ruler of Pahang.

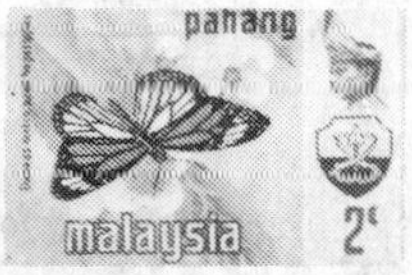

A18

1977-78

100 A18	2c multi ('78)	22.50	22.50
101 A18	5c multicolored	.24	.24
102 A18	10c multi ('78)	.35	.35
103 A18	15c multi ('78)	.70	.70
104 A18	20c multi ('78)	1.25	1.25
	Nos. 100-104 (5)	25.04	25.04

Flower Type of Johore, 1979, with Portrait of Sultan Haji Ahmad Shah

Perf. 14½

1979, Apr. 30 Litho. Wmk. 378

105 A16	1c multicolored	.15	.15
106 A16	2c multicolored	.15	.15
107 A16	5c multicolored	.15	.15
a.	5c brt rose pink & yel flowers ('84)	.15	.15
108 A16	10c multicolored	.15	.15
a.	Unwmkd. ('85)	2.15	
109 A16	15c multicolored	.18	.15
110 A16	20c multicolored	.25	.15
a.	Unwmkd. ('84)	.40	.15
111 A16	25c multicolored	.32	.16
	Set value	1.00	.55

Agriculture and State Arms Type of Johore with Sultan Haji Ahmad Shah

Wmk. 388

1986, Oct. 25 Litho. *Perf. 12*

112 A19	1c multicolored	.15	.15
113 A19	2c multicolored	.15	.15
114 A19	5c multicolored	.15	.15
115 A19	10c multicolored	.15	.15
116 A19	15c multicolored	.15	.15
117 A19	20c multicolored	.16	.15
118 A19	30c multicolored	.24	.15
	Set value	.75	.45

PENANG

(Pulau Pinang)

Orchid Type of Johore, 1965, with State Crest

Perf. 14½

1965, Nov. 15 Photo. Wmk. 338

Orchids in Natural Colors

67 A14	1c black & lt grnsh bl	.15	.15
a.	Watermark sideways ('70)	.32	.32
68 A14	2c black, red & gray	.15	.15
69 A14	5c black & Prus blue	.15	.15
a.	Prussian blue omitted		
b.	Yellow omitted		
70 A14	6c black & lt lilac	.15	.15
71 A14	10c black & lt ultra	.22	.15
a.	Watermark sideways ('70)	1.40	1.10
72 A14	15c black, lil rose & grn	.28	.15
73 A14	20c black & brown	.42	.20
	Set value	1.28	.55

Butterfly Type of Johore, 1971, with State Crest

Perf. 13½x13

1971, Feb. 1 Litho. Unwmk.

74 A15	1c multicolored	.15	.15
75 A15	2c multicolored	.15	.15
76 A15	5c multicolored	.20	.15
77 A15	6c multicolored	.24	.15
78 A15	10c multicolored	.35	.15
79 A15	15c multicolored	.60	.18
80 A15	20c multicolored	.75	.22
	Nos. 74-80 (7)	2.44	
	Set value		.75

1977 Photo.

74a	A15	1c	3.25	1.25
76a	A15	5c	.28	.15
78a	A15	10c	.40	.15
79a	A15	15c	1.10	.40
80a	A15	20c	1.40	.50
		Nos. 74a-80a (5)	6.43	2.45

Flower Type of Johore, 1979, with State Crest

Perf. 14½

1979, Apr. 30 Litho. Wmk. 378

81 A16	1c multicolored	.15	.15
82 A16	2c multicolored	.15	.15
83 A16	5c multicolored	.15	.15
84 A16	10c multicolored	.15	.15
85 A16	15c multicolored	.18	.15
86 A16	20c multicolored	.24	.15
87 A16	25c multicolored	.30	.15
	Set value	1.00	.55

1984-85 Unwmk.

83a	A16	5c	.40	.15
84a	A16	10c ('85)		
85a	A16	15c	3.25	
86a	A16	20c	.40	.15

The State arms are larger on Nos. 83a-86a.

Agriculture and State Arms Type of Johore

Wmk. 388

1986, Oct. 25 Litho. *Perf. 12*

88 A19	1c multicolored	.15	.15
89 A19	2c multicolored	.15	.15
90 A19	5c multicolored	.15	.15
91 A19	10c multicolored	.15	.15
92 A19	15c multicolored	.15	.15
93 A19	20c multicolored	.16	.15
94 A19	30c multicolored	.24	.15
	Set value	.75	.45

PERAK

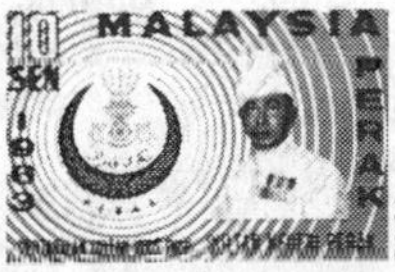

Sultan Idris Shah — A17

Wmk. 338

1963, Oct. 26 Photo. *Perf. 14*

138 A17	10c yel, blk, blue & brn	.18	.15

Installation of Idris Shah as Sultan of Perak.

Orchid Type of Johore, 1965, with Portrait of Sultan Idris Shah

1965, Nov. 15 Wmk. 338 *Perf. 14½*

Flowers in Natural Colors

139 A14	1c blk & lt grnsh bl	.15	.15
a.	Watermark sideways ('70)	.25	.25
140 A14	2c black, red & gray	.15	.15
141 A14	5c black & Prus blue	.20	.15
a.	Yellow omitted	20.00	
142 A14	6c black & lt lilac	.25	.15
143 A14	10c black & lt ultra	.38	.15
a.	Watermark sideways ('70)	1.00	.95
144 A14	15c blk, lil rose & grn	.50	.15
a.	Lilac rose omitted	80.00	
145 A14	20c black & brown	.75	.25
	Nos. 139-145 (7)	2.38	
	Set value		.65

Butterfly Type of Johore, 1971, with Portrait of Sultan Idris Shah

Perf. 13½x13

1971, Feb. 1 Litho. Unwmk.

146 A15	1c multicolored	.15	.15
147 A15	2c multicolored	.15	.15
148 A15	5c multicolored	.25	.15
a.	Booklet pane of 4 ('73)	.20	
149 A15	6c multicolored	.30	.15
150 A15	10c multicolored	.45	.15
a.	Booklet pane of 4 ('73)	.50	

151 A15 15c multicolored .75 .22
a. Booklet pane of 4 ('73) .80
152 A15 20c multicolored .95 .26
Nos. 146-152 (7) 3.00
Set value .90

1977 **Photo.**
146a A15 1c .42 .15
148b A15 5c .65 .18
150b A15 10c .75 .22
151b A15 15c 1.75 .50
152a A15 20c 2.25 .60
Nos. 146a-152a (5) 5.82 1.65

Flower Type of Johore, 1979, with Portrait of Sultan Idris Shah

Perf. 14½

1979, Apr. 30 Litho. Wmk. 378
153 A16 1c multicolored .15 .15
154 A16 2c multicolored .15 .15
155 A16 5c multicolored .15 .15
a. Brt rose pink & yel flowers ('84) .15 .15
156 A16 10c multicolored .15 .15
a. White flowers ('84) .15 .15
157 A16 15c multicolored .18 .15
a. Unwmkd. ('85) 3.25
158 A16 20c multicolored .24 .15
a. Unwmkd. ('84) .30 .15
159 A16 25c multicolored .30 .15
Set value 1.00 .55

Agriculture and State Arms Type of Johore with Tun Azlan Shah, Raja

Wmk. 388

1986, Oct. 25 Litho. *Perf. 12*
160 A19 1c multicolored .15 .15
161 A19 2c multicolored .15 .15
162 A19 5c multicolored .15 .15
163 A19 10c multicolored .15 .15
164 A19 15c multicolored .15 .15
165 A19 20c multicolored .16 .15
166 A19 30c multicolored .24 .15
Set value .75 .45

PERLIS

Orchid Type of Johore, 1965, with Portrait of Regent Yang Teramat Mulia

Perf. 14½

1965, Nov. 15 Photo. Wmk. 338

Flowers in Natural Colors
40 A14 1c black & lt grnsh bl .15 .15
41 A14 2c black, red & gray .15 .15
42 A14 5c black & Prus blue .16 .15
43 A14 6c black & lt lilac .20 .16
44 A14 10c black & ultra .30 .24
45 A14 15c blk, lil rose & grn .50 .50
46 A14 20c black & brown .80 .80
Nos. 40-46 (7) 2.26 2.15

Butterfly Type of Johore, 1971, with Portrait of Sultan Syed Putra

Perf. 13½x13

1971, Feb. 1 Litho. Unwmk.
47 A15 1c multicolored .15 .15
48 A15 2c multicolored .15 .15
49 A15 5c multicolored .18 .15
a. Booklet pane of 4 ('73) .75
50 A15 6c multicolored .25 .18
51 A15 10c multicolored .38 .22
a. Booklet pane of 4 ('73) 1.65
52 A15 15c multicolored .65 .40
a. Booklet pane of 4 ('73) 2.75
53 A15 20c multicolored .75 .55
Nos. 47-53 (7) 2.51 1.80

1977 **Photo.**
51b A15 10c 10.00 10.00
52b A15 15c 1.90 1.50
53a A15 20c 8.50 8.50
Nos. 51b-53a (3) 20.40 20.00

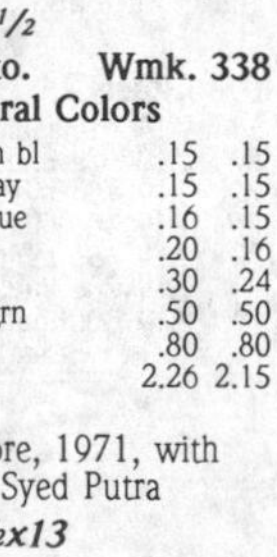

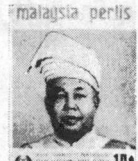

Sultan Syed Putra — A2

1971, Mar. 28 Litho. *Perf. 13½x13*
54 A2 10c silver, yel & black .18 .18
55 A2 15c silver, blue & blk .35 .35
56 A2 50c silver, lt vio & blk 1.10 1.10
Nos. 54-56 (3) 1.63 1.63

25th anniversary of the installation of Syed Putra as Raja of Perlis. Sold throughout Malaysia on Mar. 28, then only in Perlis.

Flower Type of Johore, 1979, with Portrait of Sultan Syed Putra

Perf. 14½

1979, Apr. 30 Litho. Wmk. 378
57 A16 1c multicolored .15 .15
58 A16 2c multicolored .15 .15
59 A16 5c multicolored .15 .15
60 A16 10c multicolored .15 .15
61 A16 15c multicolored .18 .15
62 A16 20c multicolored .24 .15
a. Unwmk. ('85) 4.25
63 A16 25c multicolored .30 .15
Set value 1.00 .55

Agriculture and State Arms Type of Johore with Tuanku Syed Putra, Raja

Wmk. 388

1986, Oct. 25 Litho. *Perf. 12*
64 A19 1c multicolored .15 .15
65 A19 2c multicolored .15 .15
66 A19 5c multicolored .15 .15
67 A19 10c multicolored .15 .15
68 A19 15c multicolored .15 .15
69 A19 20c multicolored .16 .15
70 A19 30c multicolored .24 .15
Set value .75 .45

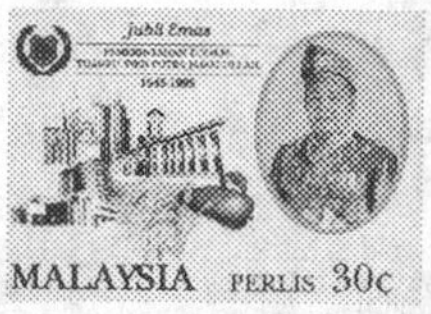

Reign of Tuanku Syed Putra Jamalullail, Raja of Perlis, 50th Anniv. — A3

Portrait and: 30c, Industry and produce. $1, Palace.

Wmk. 388

1995, Dec. 4 Litho. *Perf. 14*
71 A3 30c green & multi .25 .25
72 A3 $1 blue & multi .80 .80

SABAH

North Borneo Nos. 280-295 Overprinted:

SABAH On 1c-75c — **SABAH** On $1-$10

Perf. 13x12½, 12½x13

1964, July 1 Engr. Wmk. 314
1 A92 1c lt red brn & grn .15 .15
2 A92 4c orange & olive .15 .15
3 A92 5c violet & sepia .15 .15
4 A92 6c bluish grn & sl .15 .15
5 A92 10c rose red & lt grn .15 .15
6 A92 12c dull green & brn .15 .15
7 A92 20c ultra & blue grn .15 .15
8 A92 25c rose red & gray .32 .25
9 A92 30c gray ol & sepia .40 .32
10 A92 35c redsh brn & stl bl .50 .40
11 A92 50c brn org & blue grn .65 .50
12 A92 75c red vio & sl blue 1.00 .70
13 A93 $1 yel green & brn 1.50 1.00
14 A93 $2 slate & brown 3.00 2.75
15 A93 $5 brown vio & grn 8.00 6.50
16 A93 $10 blue & carmine 16.00 13.00
Nos. 1-16 (16) 32.42 26.47

Orchid Type of Johore, 1965, with State Crest

Perf. 14½

1965, Nov. 15 Wmk. 338 Photo.

Flowers in Natural Colors
17 A14 1c black & lt grnsh bl .15 .15
18 A14 2c black, red & gray .15 .15
19 A14 5c black & Prus bl .15 .15
20 A14 6c black & lt lilac .15 .15
21 A14 10c black & lt ultra .25 .18
a. Watermark sideways ('70) .50 .50
22 A14 15c black, lil rose & grn .40 .20
23 A14 20c black & brown .60 .45
Set value 1.62 1.09

Butterfly Type of Johore, 1971, with State Crest

Perf. 13½x13

1971, Feb. 1 Litho. Unwmk.
24 A15 1c multicolored .15 .15
25 A15 2c multicolored .15 .15
26 A15 5c multicolored .15 .15
a. Booklet pane of 4 ('73) .25
27 A15 6c multicolored .15 .15
28 A15 10c multicolored .15 .15
a. Booklet pane of 4 ('73) .65
29 A15 15c multicolored .20 .18
a. Booklet pane of 4 ('73) 1.00
30 A15 20c multicolored .35 .25
Set value .92 .74

1977 **Photo.**
24a A15 1c .15 .15
25a A15 2c .15 .15
26b A15 5c .15 .15
28b A15 10c .15 .15
29b A15 15c .30 .30
Nos. 24a-29b (5) .90 .90

Flower Type of Johore, 1979, with State Crest

Perf. 14½

1979, Apr. 30 Wmk. 378 Litho.
32 A16 1c multicolored .15 .15
33 A16 2c multicolored .15 .15
34 A16 5c multicolored .15 .15
35 A16 10c multicolored .15 .15
a. Unwmkd. ('85) 7.50
36 A16 15c multicolored .18 .15
a. Unwmkd. ('83) 6.00
37 A16 20c multicolored .24 .15
a. Unwmkd. ('83)
38 A16 25c multicolored .30 .15
Set value .95 .44

1983-85 **Unwmk.**
35a A16 10c ('85) 7.50
36a A16 15c 6.00
37a A16 20c

Agriculture and State Arms Type of Johore

Wmk. 388

1986, Oct. 25 Litho. *Perf. 12*
39 A19 1c multicolored .15 .15
40 A19 2c multicolored .15 .15
41 A19 5c multicolored .15 .15
42 A19 10c multicolored .15 .15
43 A19 15c multicolored .15 .15
44 A19 20c multicolored .16 .15
45 A19 30c multicolored .24 .15
Set value .75 .45

Sarawak

Stamps of types A14, A16 and A19 issued for Sarawak are listed in the "S" section.

SELANGOR

Orchid Type of Johore, 1965, with Portrait of Sultan Salahuddin Abdul Aziz Shah

Perf. 14½

1965, Nov. 15 Photo. Wmk. 338

Flowers in Natural Colors
121 A14 1c blk & lt grnsh bl .15 .15
a. Watermark sideways ('70) .18 .15
122 A14 2c black, red & gray .15 .15
a. Rose carmine omitted
123 A14 5c black & Prus blue .20 .15
124 A14 6c black & lt lilac .25 .15
125 A14 10c black & lt ultra .38 .15
a. Watermark sideways ('70) .60 .42
126 A14 15c blk, lil rose & grn .50 .15
127 A14 20c black & brown .80 .25
a. Watermark sideways ('70) .95 .60
Nos. 121-127 (7) 2.43
Set value .55

Butterfly Type of Johore, 1971, with Portrait of Sultan Salahuddin

Perf. 13½x13

1971, Feb. 1 Litho. Unwmk.
128 A15 1c multicolored .15 .15
129 A15 2c multicolored .15 .15
130 A15 5c multicolored .18 .15
a. Booklet pane of 4 ('73) .75
131 A15 6c multicolored .25 .15
132 A15 10c multicolored .38 .15
a. Booklet pane of 4 ('73) 1.65
133 A15 15c multicolored .65 .16
a. Booklet pane of 4 ('73) 2.75
134 A15 20c multicolored .75 .20
Nos. 128-134 (7) 2.51
Set value .70

1977 **Photo.**
128a A15 1c .42 .15
130b A15 5c .60 .20
132b A15 10c .75 .22
133b A15 15c 1.65 .50
134a A15 20c 2.00 .65
Nos. 128a-134a (5) 5.42 1.72

Flower Type of Johore, 1979, with Portrait of Sultan Salahuddin Abdul Aziz Shah

Perf. 14½

1979, Apr. 30 Litho. Wmk. 378
135 A16 1c multicolored .15 .15
136 A16 2c multicolored .15 .15
137 A16 5c multicolored .15 .15
a. brt rose pink & yel flowers ('84) .15 .15
138 A16 10c multicolored .15 .15
a. Unwmkd. ('85) 2.15
139 A16 15c multicolored .20 .15
a. Unwmkd. ('84) 3.25
140 A16 20c multicolored .26 .15
a. pale yellow flowers ('84) .26 .15
141 A16 25c multicolored .32 .16
Set value 1.05 .58

Agriculture and State Arms Type of Johore with Sultan Salahuddin Abdul Aziz Shah

Wmk. 388

1986, Oct. 25 Litho. *Perf. 12*
142 A19 1c multicolored .15 .15
143 A19 2c multicolored .15 .15
144 A19 5c multicolored .15 .15
145 A19 10c multicolored .15 .15
146 A19 15c multicolored .15 .15
147 A19 20c multicolored .16 .15
148 A19 30c multicolored .24 .15
Set value .75 .45

TRENGGANU

Orchid Type of Johore, 1965, with Portrait of Sultan Ismail

Perf. 14½

1965, Nov. 15 Photo. Wmk. 338

Flowers in Natural Colors
86 A14 1c black & lt grnsh bl .15 .15
87 A14 2c black, red & gray .15 .15
88 A14 5c black & Prus blue .20 .15
89 A14 6c black & lt lilac .25 .15
90 A14 10c black & lt ultra .35 .15
91 A14 15c blk, lil rose & grn .50 .18
92 A14 20c black & brown .75 .30
Nos. 86-92 (7) 2.35
Set value .75

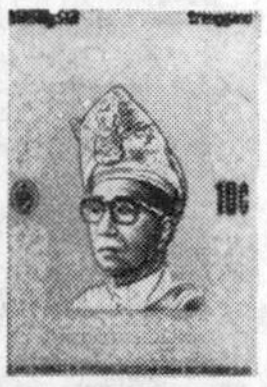

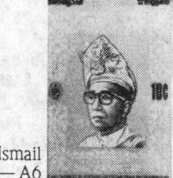

Tuanku Ismail Nasiruddin — A6

Perf. 14½x13½

1970, Dec. 16 Photo. Unwmk.
93 A6 10c multicolored .20 .20
94 A6 15c brt yellow multi .35 .35
95 A6 50c dp plum & multi 1.10 1.10
Nos. 93-95 (3) 1.65 1.65

Installation of Tuanku Ismail Nasiruddin Shah as Sultan of Trengganu, 25th anniv.

Butterfly Type of Johore, 1971, with Portrait of Sultan Ismail Nasiruddin

Perf. 13½x13

1971, Feb. 1 Litho. Unwmk.
96 A15 1c multicolored .15 .15
97 A15 2c multicolored .15 .15
98 A15 5c multicolored .20 .15
a. Booklet pane of 4 ('73) .80
99 A15 6c multicolored .28 .18
100 A15 10c multicolored .40 .22
a. Booklet pane of 4 ('73) 1.65
101 A15 15c multicolored .70 .38
a. Booklet pane of 4 ('73) 3.00
102 A15 20c multicolored .85 .42
Nos. 96-102 (7) 2.73 1.65

1977 **Photo.**
98b A15 5c 5.00 5.00
100b A15 10c 1.25 1.25
101b A15 15c 1.25 1.25
Nos. 98b-101b (3) 7.50 7.50

Flower Type of Johore, 1979, with Portrait of Sultan Ismail Nasiruddin

Perf. 14½

1979, Apr. 30 Litho. Wmk. 378
103 A16 1c multicolored .15 .15
104 A16 2c multicolored .15 .15
105 A16 5c multicolored .15 .15
106 A16 10c multicolored .15 .15
107 A16 15c multicolored .18 .15
108 A16 20c multicolored .24 .15
109 A16 25c multicolored .30 .15
Set value 1.00 .55

1983-86 **Unwmk.**
106a A16 10c ('86) .42 .15
107a A16 15c ('85) .75
108a A16 20c 1.65
109a A16 25c Pale salmon flowers .30 .15
Nos. 106a-109a (4) 3.12

The portrait and State arms are smaller.

Agriculture and State Arms Type of Johore with Sultan Mahmud Al Marhum

Wmk. 388

1986, Oct. 25 Litho. *Perf. 12*
110 A19 1c multicolored .15 .15
111 A19 2c multicolored .15 .15
112 A19 5c multicolored .15 .15
113 A19 10c multicolored .15 .15
114 A19 15c multicolored .15 .15

115 A19 20c multicolored .16 .15
116 A19 30c multicolored .24 .15
Set value .75 .45

WILAYAH PERSEKUTUAN

Agriculture and State Arms Type of Johore

Wmk. 388

1986, Oct. 25 Litho. *Perf. 12*

1 A19 1c multicolored .15 .15
2 A19 2c multicolored .15 .15
3 A19 5c multicolored .15 .15
4 A19 10c multicolored .15 .15
5 A19 15c multicolored .15 .15
6 A19 20c multicolored .16 .15
7 A19 30c multicolored .24 .15
Set value .75 .45

MALDIVE ISLANDS

'mȯl-ˌdīv 'ī-lənds

LOCATION — A group of 2,000 islands in the Indian Ocean about 400 miles southwest of Ceylon.
GOVT. — Republic
AREA — 115 sq. mi.
POP. — 168,000 (est. 1983)
CAPITAL — Male

Maldive Islands was a British Protectorate, first as a dependency of Ceylon, then from 1948 as an independent sultanate, except for a year (1953) as a republic. The islands became completely independent on July 26, 1965, and became a republic again on November 11, 1968.

100 Cents = 1 Rupee
100 Larees = 1 Rafiyaa (1951)

Catalogue values for unused stamps in this country are for Never Hinged items, beginning with Scott 20.

Watermarks

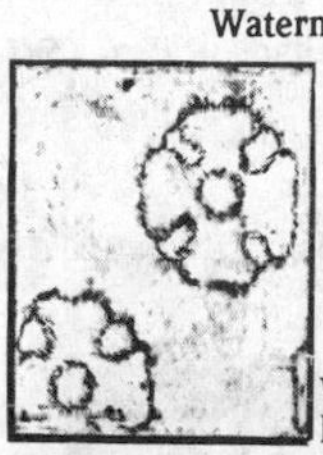

Wmk. 47- Multiple Rosette

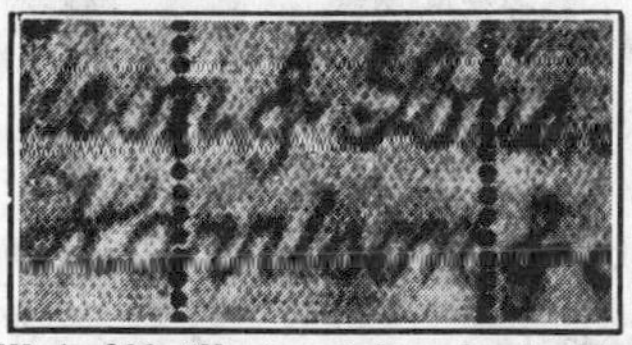

Wmk. 233- "Harrison & Sons, London" in Script

Stamps of Ceylon, 1904-05, Overprinted **MALDIVES**

1906, Sept. 9 Wmk. 3 *Perf. 14*

1 A36 2c orange brown 11.00 *15.00*
2 A37 3c green 12.50 *17.50*
3 A37 4c yellow & blue 30.00 *42.50*
4 A38 5c dull lilac 5.00 *6.00*
5 A40 15c ultramarine 52.50 *75.00*
6 A40 25c bister 62.50 *85.00*
Nos. 1-6 (6) 173.50 *241.00*

Minaret of Juma Mosque, near Male — A1

1909 Engr. Wmk. 47

7 A1 2c orange brown 1.50 .75
8 A1 3c green .50 .60
9 A1 5c red violet .50 .30
10 A1 10c carmine 1.50 .75
Nos. 7-10 (4) 4.00 2.40

Type of 1909 Issue Redrawn

Perf. 14½x14

1933 Photo. Wmk. 233

11 A1 2c gray 1.50 1.50
12 A1 3c yellow brown 1.00 1.10
13 A1 5c brown lake 5.00 7.50
14 A1 6c brown red 3.25 3.75
15 A1 10c green .80 1.00
16 A1 15c gray black 3.75 4.00
17 A1 25c red brown 3.75 4.00
18 A1 50c red violet 3.75 4.00
19 A1 1r blue black 5.00 3.75
Nos. 11-19 (9) 27.80 30.60

On the 6c, 15c, 25c and 50c, the right hand panel carries only the word "CENTS."

Nos. 11-19 exist with watermark vert. or horiz. The 5c with vert. watermark sells for twice the price of the horiz. watermark.

Catalogue values for unused stamps in this section, from this point to the end of the section, are for Never Hinged items.

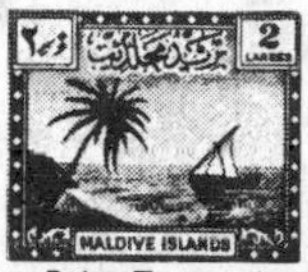

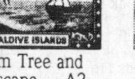

Palm Tree and Seascape — A2

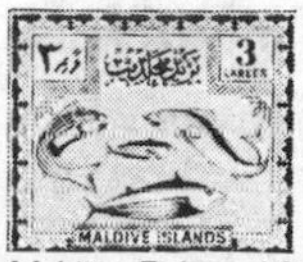

Maldive Fish — A3

Unwmk.

1950, Dec. 24 Engr. *Perf. 13*

20 A2 2 l olive green .90 .90
21 A2 3 l deep blue 3.75 2.25
22 A2 5 l dp blue green 3.75 2.50
23 A2 6 l red brown .60 .60
24 A2 10 l red .60 .60
25 A2 15 l orange .70 .70
26 A2 25 l rose violet .75 .75
27 A2 50 l violet blue 1.50 1.50
28 A2 1r dark brown 6.75 6.75
Nos. 20-28 (9) 19.30 16.55

1952

29 A3 3 l shown .30 .30
30 A3 5 l Urns .20 .20

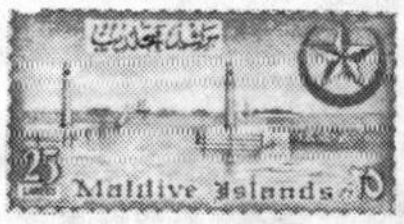

Harbor of Male — A4

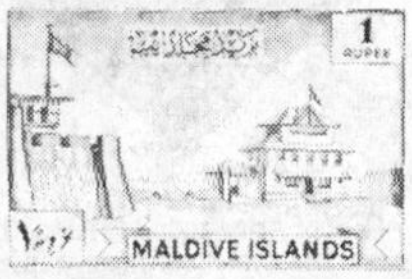

Fort and Governor's Palace — A5

Perf. 13½ (A4), 11½x11 (A5)

1956 Engr. Unwmk.

31 A4 2 l lilac .15 .15
32 A4 3 l gray green .15 .15
33 A4 5 l reddish brown .15 .15
34 A4 6 l blue violet .15 .15
35 A4 10 l light green .15 .15
36 A4 15 l brown .15 .15
37 A4 25 l rose red .15 .15
38 A4 50 l orange .20 .20
39 A5 1r light green .40 .40
40 A5 5r ultramarine 1.50 1.50
41 A5 10r magenta 2.50 2.50
Set value 5.00 5.00

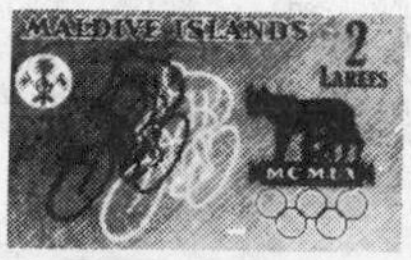

Bicyclists and Olympic Emblem — A6

Design: 25 l, 50 l, 1r, Basketball, vert.

Perf. 11½x11, 11x11½

1960, Aug. 20 Engr.

42 A6 2 l rose violet & green .15 .15
43 A6 3 l grnsh gray & plum .15 .15
44 A6 5 l vio brn & dk blue .15 .15
45 A6 10 l brt green & brn .15 .15
46 A6 15 l brown & blue .15 .15
47 A6 25 l rose red & olive .20 .20
48 A6 50 l orange & dk vio .30 .30
49 A6 1r brt green & plum .50 .50
Set value 1.30 1.30

17th Olympic Games, Rome, Aug. 25-Sept. 11.

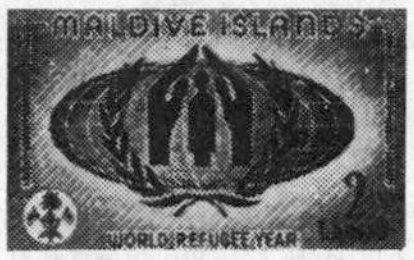

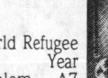

World Refugee Year Emblem — A7

1960, Oct. 15 *Perf. 11½x11*

50 A7 2 l orange, vio & grn .15 .15
51 A7 3 l green, brn & red .15 .15
52 A7 5 l sepia, grn & red .15 .15
53 A7 10 l dull pur, grn & red .15 .15
54 A7 15 l gray grn, pur & red .15 .15
55 A7 25 l redsh brn, ultra & olive .15 .15
56 A7 50 l rose, olive & blue .20 .20
57 A7 1r gray, car rose & vio .35 .35
Set value 1.00 1.00

WRY, July 1, 1959-June 30, 1960.

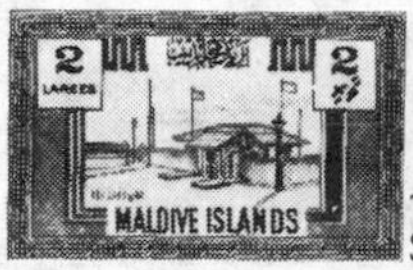

Tomb of Sultan — A8

Designs: 3 l, Custom house. 5 l, Cowry shells. 6 l, Old royal palace. 10 l, Road to Minaret, Juma Mosque, Male. 15 l, Council house. 25 l, Government secretariat. 50 l, Prime minister's office. 1r, Tomb and sailboats. 5r, Tomb by the sea. 10r, Port.

1960, Oct. 15 *Perf. 11½x11*

Various Frames

58 A8 2 l lilac .15 .15
59 A8 3 l green .15 .15
60 A8 5 l brown orange .15 .15
61 A8 6 l bright blue .15 .15
62 A8 10 l carmine rose .15 .15
63 A8 15 l sepia .15 .15
64 A8 25 l dull violet .15 .15
65 A8 50 l slate .20 .20
66 A8 1r orange .35 .35
67 A8 5r dark blue 1.60 1.60
68 A8 10r dull green 3.50 3.50
Nos. 58-68 (11) 6.70 6.70

Stamps in 25r, 50r and 100r denominations were also issued, but primarily for revenue purposes.

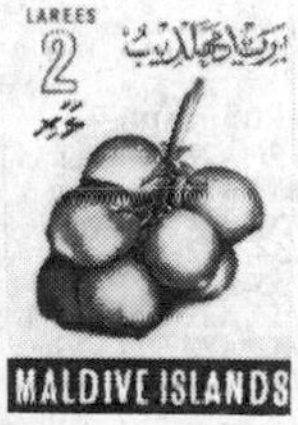

Coconuts — A9

Map of Male Showing Population Distribution A10

Perf. 14x14½, 14½x14

1961, Apr. 20 Photo. Unwmk.

Coconuts in Ocher

69 A9 2 l green .15 .15
70 A9 3 l ultramarine .15 .15
71 A9 5 l lilac rose .15 .15
72 A9 10 l red orange .15 .15
73 A9 15 l black .15 .15
74 A10 25 l multicolored .15 .15
75 A10 50 l multicolored .25 .25
76 A10 1r multicolored .45 .45
Set value 1.10 1.10

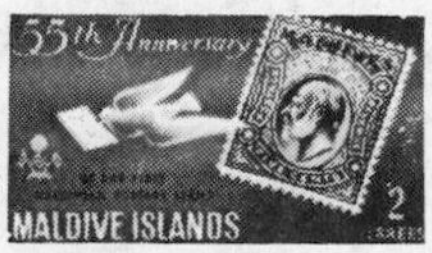

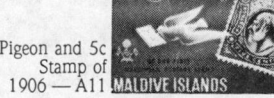

Pigeon and 5c Stamp of 1906 — A11

Designs: 10 l, 15 l, 20 l, Post horn and 3c stamp of 1906. 25 l, 50 l, 1r, Laurel branch and 2c stamp of 1906.

1961, Sept. 9 *Perf. 14½x14*

77 A11 2 l violet blue & mar .15 .15
78 A11 3 l violet blue & mar .15 .15
79 A11 5 l violet blue & mar .15 .15
80 A11 6 l violet blue & mar .15 .15
81 A11 10 l maroon & green .15 .15
82 A11 15 l maroon & green .15 .15
83 A11 20 l maroon & green .15 .15
84 A11 25 l green, mar & blk .15 .15
85 A11 50 l green, mar & blk .20 .20
86 A11 1r green, mar & blk .35 .35
a. Souvenir sheet of 4 1.80 1.80
Set value 1.00 1.00

55th anniv. of the 1st postage stamps of the Maldive Islands.

No. 86a contains 4 No. 86, with simulated perforations.

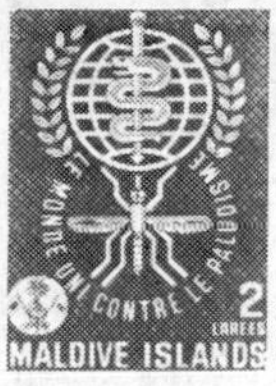

Malaria Eradication Emblem — A12

1962, Apr. 7 Engr. *Perf. 13½x13*

87 A12 2 l orange brown .15 .15
88 A12 3 l green .15 .15
89 A12 5 l blue .15 .15
90 A12 10 l vermilion .15 .15
91 A12 15 l black .15 .15
92 A12 25 l dark blue .15 .15
93 A12 50 l green .25 .25
94 A12 1r purple .45 .45
Set value 1.15 1.15

WHO drive to eradicate malaria.

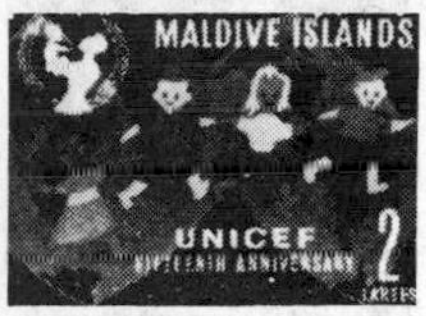

Children and Map of Far East and Americas A13

UNICEF, 15th Anniv.: 25 l, 50 l, 1r, 5r, Children and Map of Africa, Europe and Asia.

Perf. 14½x14

1962, Sept. 9 Photo. Unwmk.

Children in Multicolor

95 A13 2 l sepia .15 .15
96 A13 6 l violet .15 .15
97 A13 10 l dark green .15 .15
98 A13 15 l ultramarine .15 .15
99 A13 25 l blue .15 .15
100 A13 50 l bright green .15 .15
101 A13 1r rose claret .28 .28
102 A13 5r emerald 1.40 1.40
Set value 2.00 2.00

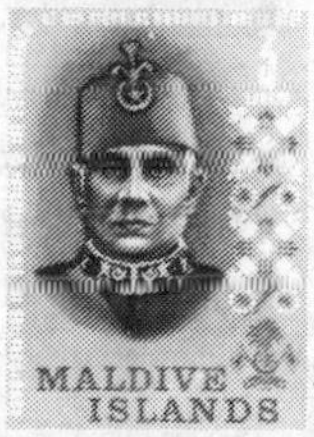

Sultan Mohamed Farid Didi — A14

1962, Nov. 29 *Perf. 14x14½*

Portrait in Orange Brown and Sepia

103 A14 3 l bluish green .15 .15
104 A14 5 l slate .15 .15
105 A14 10 l blue .15 .15
106 A14 20 l olive .15 .15
107 A14 50 l dk carmine rose .20 .20
108 A14 1r dark purple .40 .40
Set value .80 .80

9th anniv. of the enthronement of Sultan Mohamed Farid Didi.

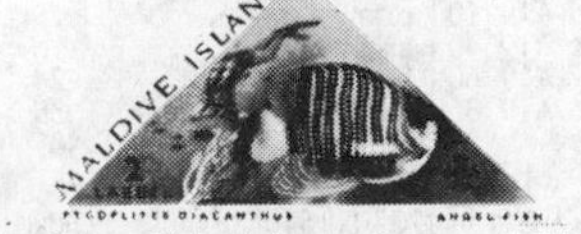

Regal Angelfish, Sultan's Crest and Skin Diver — A15

Tropical Fish: 10 l, 25 l, Moorish idol. 50 l, Diadem squirrelfish. 1r, Surgeonfish. 5r, Orange butterflyfish.

1963, Feb. 2 *Perf. 13½*

109	A15	2 l multicolored	.15	.15
110	A15	3 l multicolored	.15	.15
111	A15	5 l multicolored	.15	.15
112	A15	10 l multicolored	.15	.15
113	A15	25 l multicolored	.28	.28
114	A15	50 l multicolored	.55	.55
115	A15	1r multicolored	1.10	1.10
116	A15	5r multicolored	5.75	5.75
		Nos. 109-116 (8)	8.28	8.28

Fish in Net — A16

Design: 5 l, 10 l, 50 l, Wheat emblem and hand holding rice, vert.

1963, Mar. 21 **Photo.** *Perf. 12*

117	A16	2 l green & lt brown	.15	.15
118	A16	5 l dull rose & lt brn	.15	.15
119	A16	7 l grnsh blue & lt brn	.15	.15
120	A16	10 l blue & lt brown	.15	.15
121	A16	25 l brn red & lt brn	.50	.50
122	A16	50 l violet & lt brown	1.00	1.00
123	A16	1r rose cl & lt brn	2.00	2.00
		Nos. 117-123 (7)	4.10	4.10

FAO "Freedom from Hunger" campaign.

Centenary Emblem A17

1963, Oct. **Unwmk.** *Perf. 14x14½*

124	A17	2 l dull purple & red	.15	.15
125	A17	15 l slate green & red	.15	.15
126	A17	50 l brown & red	.25	.25
127	A17	1r dk blue & red	.50	.50
128	A17	4r dk ol grn & red	1.75	1.75
		Nos. 124-128 (5)	2.80	2.80

Centenary of the International Red Cross.

Scout Emblem and Knot — A18

1963, Dec. 7 **Unwmk.** *Perf. 13½*

129	A18	2 l purple & dp green	.15	.15
130	A18	3 l brown & dp green	.15	.15
131	A18	25 l dk blue & dp green	.15	.15
132	A18	1r dp car & dp grn	.40	.40
		Set value	.60	.60

11th Boy Scout Jamboree, Marathon, Aug. 1963. Printed in sheets of 12 (3x4) with ornamental borders and inscriptions.

Mosque at Male — A19

Perf. 11½

1964, Aug. 10 **Engr.** **Wmk. 314**

133	A19	2 l rose violet	.15	.15
134	A19	3 l green	.15	.15
135	A19	10 l carmine rose	.15	.15
136	A19	40 l black brown	.16	.16
137	A19	60 l blue	.24	.24
138	A19	85 l orange brown	.35	.35
		Set value	.85	.85

Conversion of the Maldive Islanders to Mohammedanism in 1733 (1153 by Islamic calendar).

Shot Put and Maldive Arms — A20

Design: 15 l, 25 l, 50 l, 1r, Runner and Maldive arms.

Perf. 14x13½

1964, Oct. 6 **Litho.** **Wmk. 314**

139	A20	2 l grnsh bl & dull vio	.15	.15
140	A20	3 l red brn & maroon	.15	.15
141	A20	5 l dk green & gray	.15	.15
142	A20	10 l plum & indigo	.15	.15
143	A20	15 l bis brn & dk brn	.15	.15
144	A20	25 l dk bl & bluish blk	.16	.16
145	A20	50 l olive & black	.32	.32
146	A20	1r gray & dk purple	.60	.60
a.		Souvenir sheet of 3	2.00	2.00
		Set value	1.40	1.40

18th Olympic Games, Tokyo, Oct. 10-25. #146a contains 3 imperf. stamps similar to #144-146.

General Electric Observation Communication Satellite — A21

Perf. 14½

1965, July 1 **Photo.** **Unwmk.**

147	A21	5 l dark blue	.15	.15
148	A21	10 l brown	.18	.18
149	A21	25 l green	.45	.45
150	A21	1r magenta	1.75	1.75
		Nos. 147-150 (4)	2.53	2.53

Quiet Sun Year, 1964-65. Printed in sheets of 9 (3x3) with ornamental borders and inscriptions.

Queen Nefertari Holding Sistrum and Papyrus — A22

Designs: 3 l, 10 l, 25 l, 1r, Ramses II.

1965, Sept. 1 **Litho.** **Wmk. 314**

151	A22	2 l dull bl grn & mar	.15	.15
152	A22	3 l lake & green	.15	.15
153	A22	5 l green & lake	.15	.15
154	A22	10 l dk blue & ocher	.15	.15
155	A22	15 l redsh brn & ind	.15	.15
156	A22	25 l dull lil & indigo	.15	.15
157	A22	50 l green & brown	.30	.30
158	A22	1r brown & green	.60	.60
		Set value	1.35	1.35

UNESCO world campaign to save historic monuments in Nubia.

John F. Kennedy and Doves — A23

Design: 1r, 2r, President Kennedy and hands holding olive branches.

Unwmk.

1965, Oct. 1 **Photo.** *Perf. 12*

159	A23	2 l slate & brt pink	.15	.15
160	A23	5 l brown & brt pink	.15	.15
161	A23	25 l blue blk & brt pink	.15	.15
162	A23	1r red lil, yel & grn	.28	.28
163	A23	2r sl green, yel & grn	.55	.55
a.		Souvenir sheet of 4	3.75	3.75
		Set value	1.00	1.00

#163a contains 4 imperf. stamps similar to #163.

UN Flag — A24

1965, Nov. 24 **Photo.** *Perf. 12*

Flag in Aquamarine

164	A24	3 l red brown	.15	.15
165	A24	10 l violet	.15	.15
166	A24	1r dark olive brown	.50	.50
		Set value	.60	.60

20th anniversary of the United Nations.

ICY Emblem A25

1965, Dec. 20 **Photo.** *Perf. 12*

167	A25	5 l bister & dk brn	.15	.15
168	A25	15 l dull vio & dk brn	.15	.15
169	A25	50 l olive & dk brn	.22	.22
170	A25	1r orange & dk brn	.45	.45
171	A25	2r blue & dk brn	.90	.90
a.		Souvenir sheet of 3	2.25	2.25
		Nos. 167-171 (5)	1.87	1.87

Intl. Cooperation Year. No. 171a contains three imperf. stamps with simulated perforation similar to Nos. 169-171.

Sea Shells — A26

A27

Coat of Arms and: 2 l, 10 l, 30 l, No. 181, Conus alicus and cymatium maldiviensis (shells). 5 l, 10r, Conus litteratus and distorsia reticulata (shells). 7 l, No. 182, 2r, India-rubber vine flowers. 15 l, 50 l, 5r, Crab plover and gull. 3 l, 20 l, 1.50r, Reinwardtia trigynia.

1966, June 1 **Unwmk.** *Perf. 12*

172	A26	2 l multicolored	.15	.15
173	A27	3 l multicolored	.15	.15
174	A26	5 l multicolored	.15	.15
175	A27	7 l multicolored	.15	.15
176	A26	10 l multicolored	.15	.15
177	A26	15 l multicolored	.15	.15
178	A27	20 l multicolored	.16	.16
179	A26	30 l multicolored	.22	.22
180	A26	50 l multicolored	.40	.40
181	A26	1r multicolored	.80	.80
182	A27	1r multicolored	.80	.80
183	A27	1.50r multicolored	1.20	1.20
184	A27	2r multicolored	1.60	1.60
185	A26	5r multicolored	4.00	4.00
186	A26	10r multicolored	8.00	8.00
		Nos. 172-186 (15)	18.08	18.08

Flag A28

1966, July 26 *Perf. 14x14½*

187	A28	10 l grnsh blue, red & grn	.15	.15
188	A28	1r ocher, brn, red & grn	.50	.50
		Set value	.55	.55

1st anniv. of full independence from Great Britain.

Luna 9 on Moon — A29

Designs: 25 l, 1r, 5r, Gemini 6 and 7, rendezvous in space. 2r, Gemini spaceship as seen from second Gemini spaceship.

1966, Nov. 1 **Litho.** *Perf. 15x14*

189	A29	10 l gray bl, lt brn & ultramarine	.15	.15
190	A29	25 l car rose & green	.15	.15
191	A29	50 l green & dp org	.20	.20
192	A29	1r org brn & grnsh bl	.45	.45
193	A29	2r violet & green	.90	.90
194	A29	5r Prus blue & pink	2.25	2.25
a.		Souvenir sheet of 3	4.25	4.25
		Nos. 189-194 (6)	4.10	4.10

Rendezvous in space of Gemini 6 and 7 (US), Dec. 4, 1965, and the soft landing on Moon by Luna 9 (USSR), Feb. 3, 1966. No. 194a contains 3 imperf. stamps similar to Nos. 192-194 with simulated perforations.

UNESCO Emblem, Owl and Book — A30

20th anniv. of UNESCO: 3 l, 1r, Microscope, globe and communication waves. 5 l, 5r, Palette, violin and mask.

1966, Nov. 15 **Litho.** *Perf. 15x14*

195	A30	2 l green & multi	.15	.15
196	A30	3 l lt violet & multi	.15	.15
197	A30	5 l orange & multi	.15	.15
198	A30	50 l rose & multi	.30	.30
199	A30	1r citron & multi	.60	.60
200	A30	5r multicolored	3.00	3.00
		Nos. 195-200 (6)	4.35	4.35

Winston Churchill and Coffin on Gun Carriage — A31

Designs: 10 l, 25 l, 1r, Churchill and catafalque.

1967, Jan. 1 *Perf. 14½x13½*

201	A31	2 l ol grn, red & dk blue	.15	.15
202	A31	10 l Prus grn, red & dk blue	.15	.15
203	A31	15 l grn, red & dk bl	.15	.15
204	A31	25 l vio, red & dk bl	.25	.25
205	A31	1r brn, red & dk bl	1.00	1.00
206	A31	2.50r brn lake, red & dk blue	2.50	2.50
		Nos. 201-206 (6)	4.20	4.20

Sir Winston Spencer Churchill (1874-1965), statesman and World War II leader.

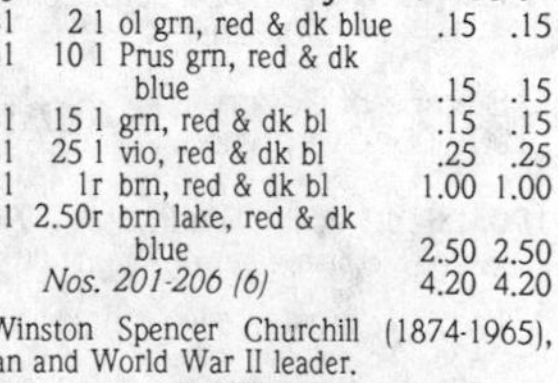

Soccer and Jules Rimet Cup A32

Designs: 3 l, 5 l, 25 l, 50 l, 1r, Various scenes from soccer and Jules Rimet Cup. 2r, British flag, Games' emblem and Big Ben Tower, London.

Perf. 14x13½

1967, Mar. 22 Photo. Unwmk.

207	A32	2 l ver & multi	.15	.15
208	A32	3 l olive & multi	.15	.15
209	A32	5 l brt purple & multi	.15	.15
210	A32	25 l brt green & multi	.18	.18
211	A32	50 l orange & multi	.40	.40
212	A32	1r brt blue & multi	.75	.75
213	A32	2r brown & multi	1.50	1.50
a.		Souvenir sheet of 3	2.50	2.50
		Nos. 207-213 (7)	3.28	3.28

England's victory in the World Soccer Cup Championship. No. 213a contains 3 imperf. stamps similar to Nos. 211-213.

Clown Butterflyfish — A33

Tropical Fish: 3 l, 1r, Four-saddled puffer. 5 l, Indo-Pacific blue trunkfish. 6 l, Striped triggerfish. 50 l, 2r, Blue angelfish.

1967, May 1 Photo. *Perf. 14*

214	A33	2 l brt violet & multi	.15	.15
215	A33	3 l emerald & multi	.15	.15
216	A33	5 l org brn & multi	.15	.15
217	A33	6 l brt blue & multi	.15	.15
218	A33	50 l olive & multi	.25	.25
219	A33	1r rose red & multi	.50	.50
220	A33	2r orange & multi	1.00	1.00
		Set value	1.90	1.90

Plane at Hulule Airport — A34

Designs: 5 l, 15 l, 50 l, 10r, Plane over administration building, Hulule Airport.

1967, July 26 *Perf. 14x13½*

221	A34	2 l citron & lil	.15	.15
222	A34	5 l violet & green	.15	.15
223	A34	10 l lt green & lilac	.15	.15
224	A34	15 l yel bister & grn	.15	.15
225	A34	30 l sky blue & vio bl	.15	.15
226	A34	50 l brt pink & brn	.20	.20
227	A34	5r org & vio blue	1.75	1.75
228	A34	10r lt ultra & dp brn	3.50	3.50
		Nos. 221-228 (8)	6.20	6.20

For overprints see Nos. 235-242.

Man and Music Pavilion and EXPO '67 Emblem — A35

Designs: 5 l, 50 l, 2r, Man and his Community Pavilion and EXPO '67 emblem.

Perf. 14x13½

1967, Oct. 1 Photo. Unwmk.

EXPO '67 Emblem in Gold

229	A35	2 l ol gray, ol & brt rose	.15	.15
230	A35	5 l ultra, grnsh blue & brn	.15	.15
231	A35	10 l brn red, lt grn & red org	.15	.15
232	A35	50 l brn, grnsh blue & org	.20	.20
233	A35	1r vio, grn & rose lil	.40	.40
234	A35	2r dk grn, emer & red brn	.80	.80
a.		Souvenir sheet of 2	1.50	1.50
		Set value	1.50	1.50

EXPO '67 Intl. Exhibition, Montreal, Apr. 28-Oct. 27. No. 234a contains 2 imperf. stamps similar to Nos. 233-234 with simulated perforations.

Nos. 221-228 Overprinted in Gold: "International Tourist Year 1967"

1967, Dec. 1 Photo. *Perf. 14x13½*

235	A34	2 l citron & lilac	.15	.15
236	A34	5 l violet & green	.15	.15
237	A34	10 l lt green & lilac	.15	.15
238	A34	15 l yel bister & grn	.15	.15
239	A34	30 l sky blue & vio bl	.15	.15
240	A34	50 l brt pink & brn	.20	.20
241	A34	5r org & vio blue	1.75	1.75
242	A34	10r lt ultra & dp brn	3.50	3.50
		Nos. 235-242 (8)	6.20	6.20

The overprint is in 3 lines on the 2 l, 10 l, 30 l, 5r; one line on the 5 l, 15 l, 50 l, 10r.

Lord Baden-Powell, Wolf Cubs, Campfire and Flag Signals — A36

Boy Scouts: 3 l, 1r, Lord Baden-Powell, Boy Scout saluting and drummer.

1968, Jan. 1 Litho. *Perf. 14x14½*

243	A36	2 l yel, brown & green	.15	.15
244	A36	3 l lt bl, ultra & rose car	.15	.15
245	A36	25 l dp org, red brn & vio blue	.22	.22
246	A36	1r yel grn, grn & red brn	.90	.90
		Nos. 243-246 (4)	1.42	1.42

Sheets of 12 (4x3) with decorative border.
For overprints see Nos. 278-281.

French Satellites D-1 and A-1 — A37

Designs: 3 l, 25 l, Luna 10, USSR. 7 l, 1r, Orbiter and Mariner, USA. 10 l, 2r, Edward White, Virgil Grissom and Roger Chaffee, USA. 5r, Astronaut V. M. Komarov, USSR.

1968, Jan. 27 Photo. *Perf. 14*

247	A37	2 l dp ultra & brt pink	.15	.15
248	A37	3 l dk ol bis & vio	.15	.15
249	A37	7 l rose car & ol	.15	.15
250	A37	10 l blk, gray & dk bl	.15	.15
251	A37	25 l purple & brt grn	.15	.15
252	A37	50 l brown org & blue	.20	.20
253	A37	1r dk sl grn & vio brn	.40	.40
254	A37	2r blk, bl & dk brn	.80	.80
a.		Souvenir sheet of 2	1.75	1.75
255	A37	5r blk, tan & lil rose	2.00	2.00
		Nos. 247-255 (9)	4.15	4.15

International achievements in space and to honor American and Russian astronauts, who gave their lives during space explorations in 1967. No. 254a contains 2 imperf. stamps similar to Nos. 253-254.

Shot Put — A38

Design: 6 l, 15 l, 2.50r, Discus.

1968, Feb. Litho. *Perf. 14½*

256	A38	2 l emerald & multi	.15	.15
257	A38	6 l dull yel & multi	.15	.15
258	A38	10 l multicolored	.15	.15
259	A38	15 l orange & multi	.15	.15
260	A38	1r blue & multi	.80	.80
261	A38	2.50r rose & multi	2.00	2.00
		Nos. 256-261 (6)	3.40	3.40

19th Olympic Games, Mexico City, Oct. 12-27.

On the Adria, by Charles P. Bonington — A39

Seascapes: 1r, Ulysses Deriding Polyphemus (detail), by Joseph M. W. Turner. 2r, Sailboat at Argenteuil, by Claude Monet. 5r, Fishing Boats at Saintes-Maries, by Vincent Van Gogh.

1968, Apr. 1 Photo. *Perf. 14*

262	A39	50 l ultra & multi	.25	.25
263	A39	1r dk green & multi	.55	.55
264	A39	2r multicolored	1.10	1.10
265	A39	5r multicolored	2.75	2.75
		Nos. 262-265 (4)	4.65	4.65

Montgolfier Balloon, 1783, and Zeppelin LZ-130, 1928 — A40

History of Aviation: 3 l, 1r, Douglas DC-3, 1933, and Boeing 707, 1958. 5 l, 50 l, Lilienthal's glider, 1892, and Wright brothers' plane, 1905. 7 l, 2r, British-French Concorde and Supersonic Boeing 733, 1968.

1968, June 1 Photo. *Perf. 14x13*

266	A40	2 l yel grn, ultra & bis brn	.15	.15
267	A40	3 l org brn, greenish bl & lil	.15	.15
268	A40	5 l grnsh bl, sl grn & lilac	.15	.15
269	A40	7 l org, cl & ultra	.15	.15
270	A40	10 l rose lil, bl & brn	.15	.15
271	A40	50 l ol, sl grn & mag	.25	.25
272	A40	1r ver, blue & emer	.50	.50
273	A40	2r ultra, ol & brn vio	1.50	1.00
		Set value	2.50	2.00

Issued in sheets of 12.

WHO Headquarters, Geneva — A41

1968, July 15 Litho. *Perf. 14½x13*

274	A41	10 l grnsh bl, bl grn & vio	.15	.15
275	A41	25 l org, ocher & green	.15	.15
276	A41	1r emer, brt grn & brown	.50	.50
277	A41	2r rose lil, dp rose lil & dk blue	1.00	1.00
		Nos. 274-277 (4)	1.80	1.80

20th anniv. of WHO.

Nos. 243-246 Overprinted: "International / Boy Scout Jamboree, / Farragut Park, Idaho, / U.S.A. / August 1-9, 1967"

1968, Aug. 1 *Perf. 14x14½*

278	A36	2 l multicolored	.15	.15
279	A36	3 l multicolored	.15	.15
280	A36	25 l multicolored	.25	.25
281	A36	1r multicolored	1.00	1.00
		Nos. 278-281 (4)	1.55	1.55

1st anniv. of the Intl. Boy Scout Jamboree in Farragut State Park, ID.

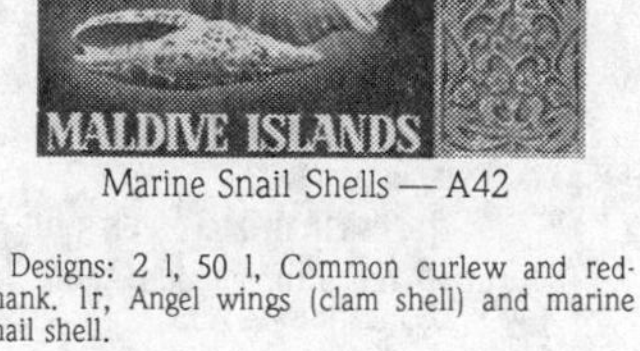

Marine Snail Shells — A42

Designs: 2 l, 50 l, Common curlew and redshank. 1r, Angel wings (clam shell) and marine snail shell.

1968, Sept. 24 Photo. *Perf. 14x13*

282	A42	2 l ultra & multi	.15	.15
283	A42	10 l brown & multi	.15	.15
284	A42	25 l multicolored	.20	.15
285	A42	50 l multicolored	.40	.30
286	A42	1r multicolored	.75	.60
287	A42	2r multicolored	1.50	1.20
		Nos. 282-287 (6)	3.15	2.55

Discus A43

Designs: 50 l, Runner. 1r, Bicycling. 2r, Basketball.

1968, Oct. 12 *Perf. 14*

288	A43	10 l ultra & multi	.15	.15
289	A43	50 l multicolored	.40	.40
290	A43	1r plum & multi	.80	.80
291	A43	2r violet & multi	1.60	1.60
		Nos. 288-291 (4)	2.95	2.95

19th Olympic Games, Mexico City, Oct. 12-27.
For overprints see Nos. 302-303.

Republic

Dhow A44

Republic Day: 1r, Coat of arms, map and flag of Maldive Islands.

Perf. 14x14½

1968, Nov. 11 Unwmk.

292	A44	10 l yel grn, ultra & dk brn	.15	.15
293	A44	1r ultra, red & emerald	1.10	.75

The Thinker, by Auguste Rodin — A45

Rodin Sculptures and UNESCO Emblem: 10 l, Hands. 1.50r, Sister and Brother. 2.50r, The Prodigal Son.

1969, Apr. 10 Photo. *Perf. 13½*

294	A45	6 l emerald & multi	.15	.15
295	A45	10 l multicolored	.15	.15
296	A45	1.50r brt blue & multi	.50	.50
297	A45	2.50r multicolored	.85	.85
a.		Souvenir sheet of 2	2.50	2.50
		Set value	1.40	1.40

Intl. Human Rights Year and honoring UNESCO.
No. 297a contains 2 imperf. stamps similar to Nos. 296-297.

Astronaut Gathering Rock Samples on Moon — A46

Designs: 6 l, Lunar landing module. 1.50r, Astronaut on steps of module. 2.50r, Astronaut with television camera.

1969, Sept. 25 Litho. *Perf. 14*

298	A46	6 l multicolored	.15	.15
299	A46	10 l multicolored	.15	.15
300	A46	1.50r multicolored	1.00	1.00
301	A46	2.50r multicolored	1.60	1.60
a.		Souvenir sheet of 4	2.25	2.25
		Nos. 298-301 (4)	2.90	2.90

Man's 1st moon landing. See note after US #C76.
Exist imperf.
No. 301a contains stamps similar to Nos. 298-301, with designs transposed on 10 l and 2.50r. Simulated perfs.
For overprints see Nos. 343-345.

Nos. 289-290 Overprinted: "REPUBLIC OF MALDIVES" and Commemorative Inscriptions

Designs: 50 l, overprinted "Gold Medal Winner / Mohamed Gammoudi / 5000m. run / Tunisia". 1r, overprinted "Gold Medal Winner / P. Trentin—Cycling / France."

1969, Dec. 10   Photo.   Perf. 14

302	A43	50 l multicolored	.30	.30
303	A43	1r multicolored	.60	.60

Columbia Daumon Victoria, 1899 — A47

Automobiles (pre-1908): 5 l, 50 l, Duryea Phaeton, 1902. 7 l, 1r, Packard S.24, 1906. 10 l, 2r, Autocar Runabout, 1907. 25 l, like 2 l.

1970, Feb. 1   Litho.   Perf. 12

304	A47	2 l multicolored	.15	.15
305	A47	5 l brt pink & multi	.15	.15
306	A47	7 l ultra & multi	.15	.15
307	A47	10 l ver & multi	.15	.15
308	A47	25 l ocher & multi	.15	.15
309	A47	50 l olive & multi	.30	.25
310	A47	1r orange & multi	.62	.50
311	A47	2r multicolored	1.25	1.00
a.		Souvenir sheet of 2, #310-311, perf. 11½	2.50	2.00
		Set value	2.50	2.00

Exist imperf.

Orange Butterflyfish — A48

Fish: 5 l, Spotted triggerfish. 25 l, Spotfin turkeyfish. 50 l, Forceps fish. 1r, Imperial angelfish. 2r, Regal angelfish.

1970, Mar. 1   Litho.   Perf. 10½

312	A48	2 l blue & multi	.15	.15
313	A48	5 l orange & multi	.15	.15
314	A48	25 l emerald & multi	.15	.15
315	A48	50 l brt pink & multi	.30	.25
316	A48	1r lt vio bl & multi	.62	.50
317	A48	2r olive & multi	1.25	1.00
		Nos. 312-317 (6)	2.62	2.20

UN Headquarters, New York and UN Emblem — A49

25th anniv. of the UN: 10 l, Surgeons, nurse and WHO emblem. 25 l, Student, performer, musician and UNESCO emblem. 50 l, Children reading and playing, and UNICEF emblem. 1r, Lamb, cock, fish, grain and FAO emblem. 2r, Miner and ILO emblem.

1970, June 26   Litho.   Perf. 13½

318	A49	2 l multicolored	.15	.15
319	A49	10 l multicolored	.15	.15
320	A49	25 l multicolored	.15	.15
321	A49	50 l multicolored	.25	.25
322	A49	1r multicolored	.55	.55
323	A49	2r multicolored	1.10	1.10
		Nos. 318-323 (6)	2.35	2.35

IMCO Emblem, Buoy and Ship — A50   EXPO Emblem and Australian Pavilion — A51

Design: 1r, Lighthouse and ship.

1970, July 26   Litho.   Perf. 13½

324	A50	50 l multicolored	.25	.20
325	A50	1r multicolored	.50	.40

10th anniv. of the Intergovernmental Maritime Consultative Organization (IMCO).

1970, Aug. 1   Perf. 13½x14

EXPO Emblem and: 3 l, West German pavilion. 10 l, US pavilion. 25 l, British pavilion. 50 l, Russian pavilion. 1r, Japanese pavilion.

326	A51	2 l green & multi	.15	.15
327	A51	3 l violet & multi	.15	.15
328	A51	10 l brown & multi	.15	.15
329	A51	25 l multicolored	.15	.15
330	A51	50 l claret & multi	.30	.30
331	A51	1r ultra & multi	.60	.60
		Set value	1.20	1.20

EXPO '70 International Exhibition, Osaka, Japan, Mar. 15-Sept. 13, 1970.

Guitar Player, by Watteau — A52

Paintings: 7 l, Guitar Player in Spanish Costume, by Edouard Manet. 50 l, Guitar-playing Clown, by Antoine Watteau. 1r, Mandolin Player and Singers, by Lorenzo Costa (inscribed Ercole Roberti). 2.50r, Guitar Player and Lady, by Watteau. 5r, Mandolin Player, by Frans Hals.

1970, Aug. 1   Litho.   Perf. 14

332	A52	3 l gray & multi	.15	.15
333	A52	7 l yellow & multi	.15	.15
334	A52	50 l multicolored	.20	.20
335	A52	1r multicolored	.40	.40
336	A52	2.50r multicolored	1.00	1.00
337	A52	5r multicolored	2.00	2.00
a.		Souvenir sheet of 2	4.25	4.25
		Nos. 332-337 (6)	3.90	3.90

No. 337a contains 2 stamps similar to Nos. 336-337 but rouletted 13 and printed se-tenant.

Education Year Emblem and Adult Education — A53

Education Year Emblem and: 10 l, Teacher training. 25 l, Geography class. 50 l, Classroom. 1r, Instruction by television.

1970, Sept. 7   Litho.   Perf. 14

338	A53	5 l multicolored	.15	.15
339	A53	10 l multicolored	.15	.15
340	A53	25 l multicolored	.15	.15
341	A53	50 l multicolored	.30	.30
342	A53	1r multicolored	.62	.62
		Set value	1.15	1.15

Issued for International Education Year.

Nos. 299-301 Overprinted in Silver: "Philympia / London 1970"

1970, Sept. 18

343	A46	10 l multicolored	.15	.15
344	A46	1.50r multicolored	.75	.75
345	A46	2.50r multicolored	1.25	1.25
		Nos. 343-345 (3)	2.15	2.15

Issued to commemorate Philympia 1970, London Philatelic Exhibition, Sept. 18-26.

This overprint was also applied to No. 301a. Value $2.25.

Soccer Play, Rimet Cup — A54   Boy Holding UNICEF Flag — A55

Designs: Various Soccer Scenes, and Rimet Cup.

1970   Litho.   Perf. 13½

346	A54	3 l emerald & multi	.15	.15
347	A54	6 l rose lilac & multi	.15	.15
348	A54	7 l dp orange & multi	.15	.15
349	A54	25 l blue & multi	.15	.15
350	A54	1r olive & multi	.60	.60
		Set value	.90	.90

Jules Rimet 9th World Soccer Championships, Mexico City, May 30-June 21.

1971, Apr. 1   Litho.   Perf. 12

UNICEF, 25th. Anniv.: 10 l, 2r, Girl holding balloon with UNICEF emblem.

351	A55	5 l pink & multi	.15	.15
352	A55	10 l lt blue & multi	.15	.15
353	A55	1r yellow & multi	.50	.50
354	A55	2r pale lilac & multi	1.00	1.00
		Nos. 351-354 (4)	1.80	1.80

 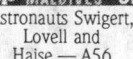 

Astronauts Swigert, Lovell and Haise — A56   Flowers Symbolizing Races and World — A57

Safe return of Apollo 13: 20 l, Spacecraft and landing module. 1r, Capsule and boat in Pacific Ocean.

1971, Apr. 27   Perf. 14

355	A56	5 l dull purple & multi	.15	.15
356	A56	20 l multicolored	.20	.20
357	A56	1r brt blue & multi	1.00	1.00
		Nos. 355-357 (3)	1.35	1.35

1971, May 3

358	A57	10 l multicolored	.15	.15
359	A57	25 l gray & multi	.15	.15
		Set value	.21	.21

Intl. year against racial discrimination.

Mother and Child, by Auguste Renoir — A58

Mother and Child Paintings by: 7 l, Rembrandt. 10 l, Titian. 20 l, Degas. 25 l, Berthe Morisot. 1r, Rubens. 3r, Renoir.

1971, Sept.   Litho.   Perf. 12

360	A58	5 l multicolored	.15	.15
361	A58	7 l multicolored	.15	.15
362	A58	10 l multicolored	.15	.15
363	A58	20 l multicolored	.15	.15
364	A58	25 l multicolored	.15	.15
365	A58	1r multicolored	.50	.50
366	A58	3r multicolored	1.50	1.50
		Set value	2.40	2.40

Capt. Alan B. Shepard, Jr. — A59

Designs: 10 l, Maj. Stuart A. Roosa. 1.50r, Com. Edgar D. Mitchell. 5r, Apollo 14 shoulder patch.

1971, Nov. 11   Photo.   Perf. 12½

367	A59	6 l dp green & multi	.15	.15
368	A59	10 l claret & multi	.15	.15
369	A59	1.50r ultra & multi	.90	.90
370	A59	5r multicolored	3.00	3.00
		Nos. 367-370 (4)	4.20	4.20

Apollo 14 US moon landing mission, 1/31-2/9.

Ballerina, by Degas — A60

Paintings: 10 l, Dancing Couple, by Auguste Renoir. 2r, Spanish Dancer, by Edouard Manet. 5r, Ballerinas, by Degas. 10r, Moulin Rouge, by Henri Toulouse-Lautrec.

1971, Nov. 19   Litho.   Perf. 14

371	A60	5 l plum & multi	.15	.15
372	A60	10 l green & multi	.15	.15
373	A60	2r org brown & multi	1.10	1.10
374	A60	5r dk blue & multi	2.75	2.75
375	A60	10r multicolored	5.50	5.50
		Nos. 371-375 (5)	9.65	9.65

Nos. 371-375 Overprinted Vertically: "ROYAL VISIT 1972"

1972, Mar. 13   Litho.   Perf. 14

376	A60	5 l plum & multi	.15	.15
377	A60	10 l green & multi	.15	.15
378	A60	2r org brown & multi	1.10	1.10
379	A60	5r dk blue & multi	2.75	2.75
380	A60	10r multicolored	5.50	5.50
		Nos. 376-380 (5)	9.65	9.65

Visit of Elizabeth II and Prince Philip.

Book Year Emblem — A61

1972, May 1   Perf. 13x13½

381	A61	25 l orange & multi	.15	.15
382	A61	5r multicolored	2.75	2.75

International Book Year.

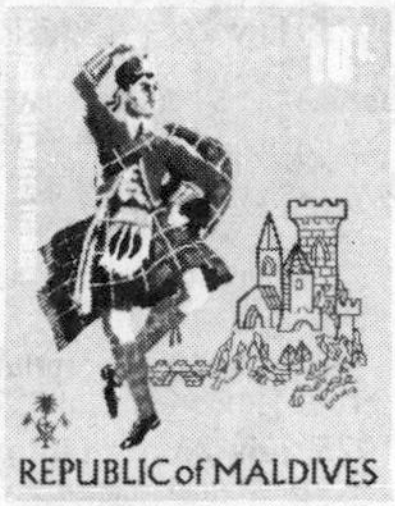
REPUBLIC of MALDIVES
National Costume of Scotland A62

National Costumes: 15 l, Netherlands. 25 l, Norway. 50 l, Hungary. 1r, Austria. 2r, Spain.

1972, May 15 *Perf. 12*

383 A62	10 l gray & multi	.15	.15
384 A62	15 l lt brown & multi	.15	.15
385 A62	25 l multicolored	.15	.15
386 A62	50 l lt brown & multi	.25	.25
387 A62	1r gray & multi	.50	.50
388 A62	2r lt olive & multi	1.00	1.00
	Nos. 383-388 (6)	2.20	2.20

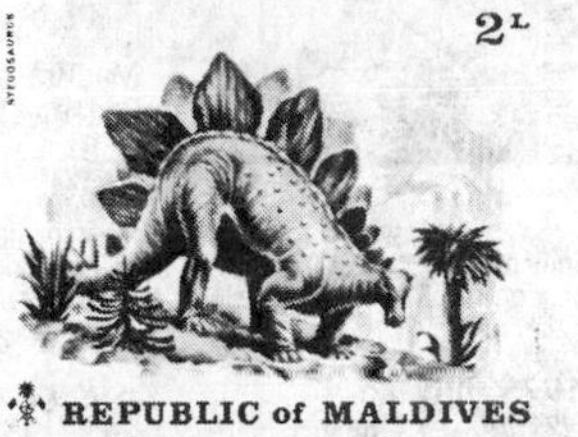
2L
REPUBLIC of MALDIVES
Stegosaurus — A63

Designs: Prehistoric reptiles.

1972, May 31 *Perf. 14*

389 A63	2 l shown	.15	.15
390 A63	7 l Edaphosaurus	.15	.15
391 A63	25 l Diplodocus	.15	.15
392 A63	50 l Triceratops	.30	.30
393 A63	2r Pteranodon	1.20	1.20
394 A63	5r Tyrannosaurus	3.00	3.00
	Nos. 389-394 (6)	4.95	4.95

A souvenir sheet has five stamps similar to Nos. 389-394 with simulated perforations. It was not regularly issued.

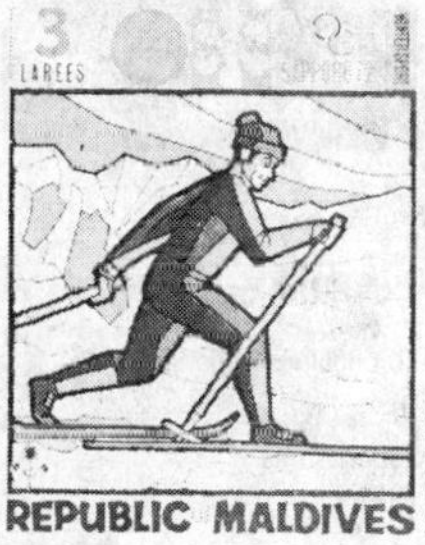
3
LAREES
REPUBLIC MALDIVES
Sapporo '72 Emblem, Cross Country Skiing — A64

1972, June **Litho.** *Perf. 14*

395 A64	3 l shown	.15	.15
396 A64	6 l Bobsledding	.15	.15
397 A64	15 l Speed skating	.15	.15
398 A64	50 l Ski jump	.30	.30
399 A64	1r Figure skating	.60	.60
400 A64	2.50r Ice hockey	1.50	1.50
	Nos. 395-400 (6)	2.85	2.85

11th Winter Olympic Games, Sapporo, Japan, Feb. 3-13.

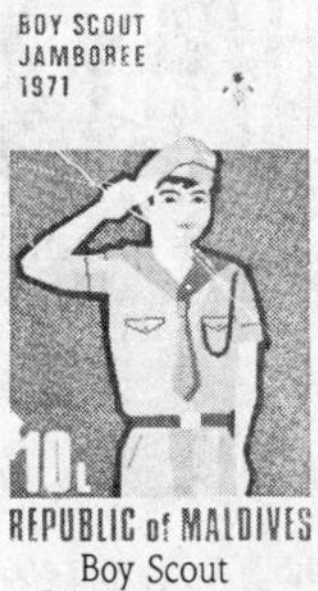
BOY SCOUT
JAMBOREE
1971
10L
REPUBLIC of MALDIVES
Boy Scout Saluting — A65

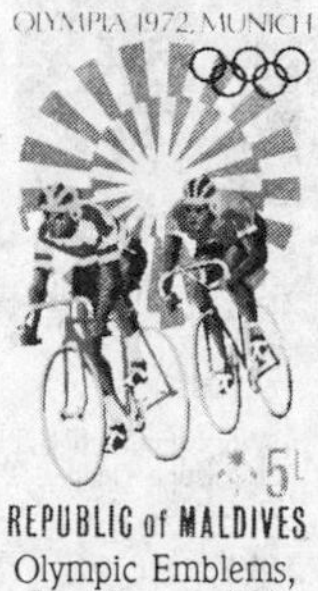
OLYMPIA 1972 MUNICH
5L
REPUBLIC of MALDIVES
Olympic Emblems, Bicycling — A66

Scout: 15 l, with signal flags. 50 l, Bugler. 1r, Drummer.

1972, Aug. 1

401 A65	10 l Prus green & multi	.15	.15
402 A65	15 l dk red & multi	.15	.15
403 A65	50 l dp green & multi	.38	.30
404 A65	1r purple & multi	.80	.62
	Nos. 401-404 (4)	1.48	1.22

13th International Boy Scout Jamboree, Asagiri Plain, Japan, Aug. 2-11, 1971.

1972, Oct. **Litho.** *Perf. 14½x14*

405 A66	5 l shown	.15	.15
406 A66	10 l Running	.15	.15
407 A66	25 l Wrestling	.15	.15
408 A66	50 l Hurdles, women's	.25	.25
409 A66	2r Boxing	1.00	1.00
410 A66	5r Volleyball	2.50	2.50
	Nos. 405-410 (6)	4.20	4.20

Souvenir Sheet

Perf. 15

411	Sheet of 2	4.00	4.00
a.	A66 3r like 50 l	1.50	1.50
b.	A66 4r like 10 l	1.90	1.90

20th Olympic Games, Munich, Aug. 26-Sept. 11.
For overprints see Nos. 417-419.

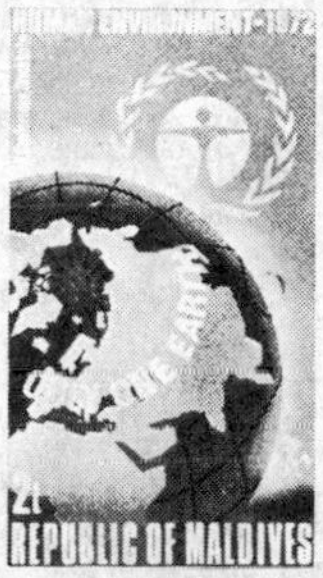
HUMAN ENVIRONMENT 1972
REPUBLIC OF MALDIVES
Globe, Environment Emblem — A67

1972, Nov. 15 **Litho.** *Perf. 14½*

412 A67	2 l violet & multi	.15	.15
413 A67	3 l brown & multi	.15	.15
414 A67	15 l blue & multi	.15	.15
415 A67	50 l red & multi	.30	.30
416 A67	2.50r green & multi	1.50	1.50
	Nos. 412-416 (5)	2.25	2.25

UN Conference on Human Environment, Stockholm, June 5-16.

Nos. 409-411 Overprinted in Violet Blue:
a. LEMECHEV / MIDDLE-WEIGHT /GOLD MEDALLIST
b. JAPAN / GOLD MEDAL / WINNER
c. EHRHARDT / 100 METER / HURDLES / GOLD MEDALLIST
d. SHORTER / MARATHON / GOLD MEDALLIST

1973, Feb. **Litho.** *Perf. 14½x14*

417 A66(a)	2r multicolored	1.00	1.00
418 A66(b)	5r multicolored	2.50	2.50

Souvenir Sheet

419	Sheet of 2	4.00	4.00
a.	A66(c) 3r multicolored	1.50	1.50
b.	A66(d) 4r multicolored	1.90	1.90

Gold medal winners in 20th Olympic Games: Viatschesiav Lemechev, USSR, middleweight boxing, Japanese team, volleyball. Annelie Ehrhardt, Germany, 100m. hurdles; Frank Shorter, US, marathon.

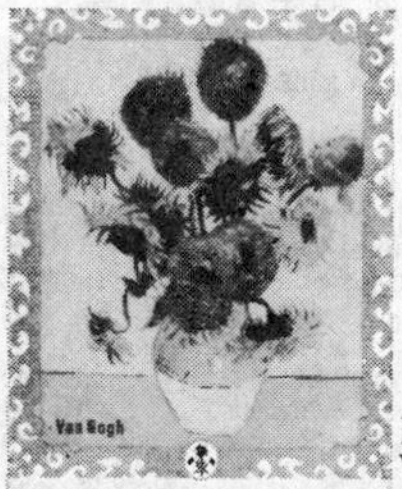
Van Gogh
REPUBLIC of MALDIVES
Flowers, by Vincent Van Gogh — A68

Paintings of Flowers by: 2 l, 3 l, 1r, 3r, 5r, Auguste Renoir (each different). 50 l, 5 l, Ambrosius Bosschaert.

1973, Feb. *Perf. 13½*

420 A68	1 l blue & multi	.15	.15
421 A68	2 l tan & multi	.15	.15
422 A68	3 l lilac & multi	.15	.15
423 A68	50 l ultra & multi	.25	.25
424 A68	1r emerald & multi	.50	.50
425 A68	5r magenta & multi	2.50	2.50
	Nos. 420-425 (6)	3.70	3.70

Souvenir Sheet

Perf. 15

426	Sheet of 2	3.25	3.25
a.	A68 2r black & multi	1.25	1.25
b.	A68 3r black & multi	1.75	1.75

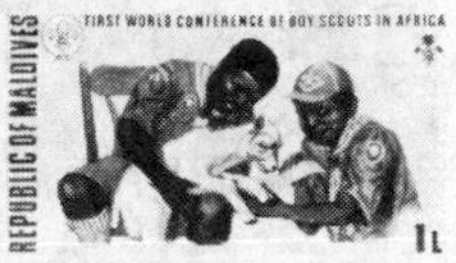
FIRST WORLD CONFERENCE OF BOY SCOUTS IN AFRICA
REPUBLIC OF MALDIVES
1L
Scouts Treating Injured Lamb A69

Designs: 2 l, 1r, Lifesaving. 3 l, 5r, Agricultural training. 4 l, 2r, Carpentry. 5 l, Leapfrog.

1973, Aug. **Litho.** *Perf. 14½*

427 A69	1 l black & multi	.15	.15
428 A69	2 l black & multi	.15	.15
429 A69	3 l black & multi	.15	.15
430 A69	4 l black & multi	.15	.15
431 A69	5 l black & multi	.15	.15
432 A69	1r black & multi	.50	.50
433 A69	2r black & multi	1.00	1.00
434 A69	3r black & multi	1.50	1.50
	Set value	3.25	3.25

Souvenir Sheet

435 A69	5r black & multi	3.50	3.50

24th Boy Scout World Conference (1st in Africa), Nairobi, Kenya, July 16-21.
For overprints see Nos. 571-574.

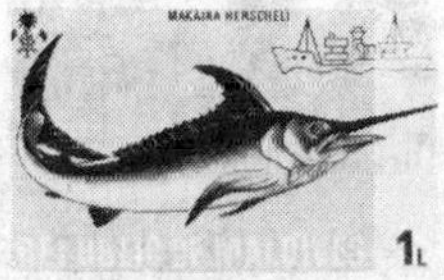
MAKAIRA HERSCHELI
1L
Herschel's Marlin A70

Fish and Ships: 2 l, 4r, Skipjack tuna. 3 l, Bluefin tuna. 5 l, 2.50r, Dolphinfish. 60 l, 75 l, Red snapper. 1.50r, Yellow crescent tail. 3r, Plectropoma maculatum. 5r, Like 1 l. 10r, Spanish mackerel.

1973, Aug. *Perf. 14½*

Size: 38½x24mm

436 A70	1 l lt green & multi	.15	.15
437 A70	2 l dull org & multi	.15	.15
438 A70	3 l brt red & multi	.15	.15
439 A70	5 l multicolored	.15	.15

Size: 28x22mm

440 A70	60 l yellow & multi	.38	.38
441 A70	75 l purple & multi	.45	.45

Size: 38½x24mm

442 A70	1.50r violet & multi	.90	.90
443 A70	2.50r blue & multi	1.50	1.50
444 A70	3r multicolored	1.90	1.90
445 A70	10r orange & multi	6.25	6.25
	Nos. 436-445 (10)	11.98	11.98

Souvenir Sheet

Perf. 15

446	Sheet of 2	5.25	5.25
a.	A70 4r carmine & multi	2.00	2.00
b.	A70 5r bright green & multi	3.00	3.00

Nos. 436-445 exist imperf.

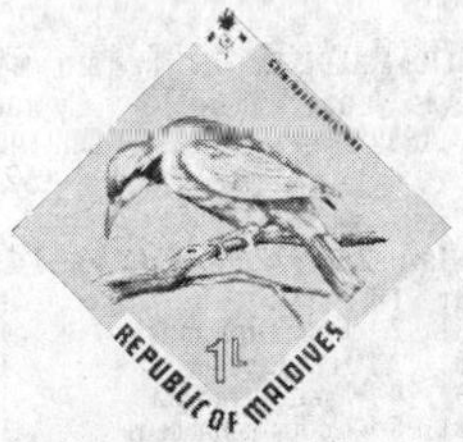
1L
REPUBLIC OF MALDIVES
Goldenfronted Leafbird — A71

Designs: 2 l, 3r, Fruit bat. 3 l, 50 l, Indian starred tortoise. 4 l, 5r, Kallima inachus (butterfly).

1973, Oct. **Litho.** *Perf. 14½*

447 A71	1 l brt pink & multi	.15	.15
448 A71	2 l brt blue & multi	.15	.15
449 A71	3 l ver & multi	.15	.15
450 A71	4 l citron & multi	.15	.15
451 A71	50 l emerald & multi	.30	.30
452 A71	2r lt violet & multi	1.20	1.20
453 A71	3r multicolored	1.75	1.75
	Nos. 447-453 (7)	3.85	3.85

Souvenir Sheet

454 A71	5r yellow & multi	3.25	3.25

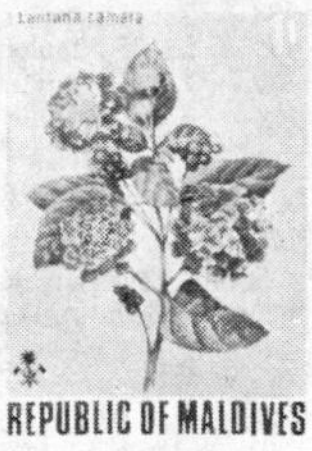
REPUBLIC OF MALDIVES
Lantana Camara — A72

Native Flowers: 2 l, Nerium oleander. 3 l, 2r, Rosa polyantha. 4 l, Hibiscus manihot. 5 l, Bougainvillea glabra. 10 l, 3r, Plumera alba. 50 l, Poinsettia pulcherrima. 5r, Ononis natrix.

1973, Dec. 19 **Litho.** *Perf. 14*

455 A72	1 l ultra & multi	.15	.15
456 A72	2 l dp orange & multi	.15	.15
457 A72	3 l emerald & multi	.15	.15
458 A72	4 l blue grn & multi	.15	.15
459 A72	5 l lemon & multi	.15	.15
460 A72	10 l lilac & multi	.15	.15
461 A72	50 l yel grn & multi	.20	.20
462 A72	5r red & multi	2.25	2.25
	Set value	2.70	2.70

Souvenir Sheet

463	Sheet of 2	3.25	3.25
a.	A72 2r lilac & multi	1.10	1.10
b.	A72 3r blue & multi	1.90	1.90

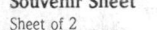

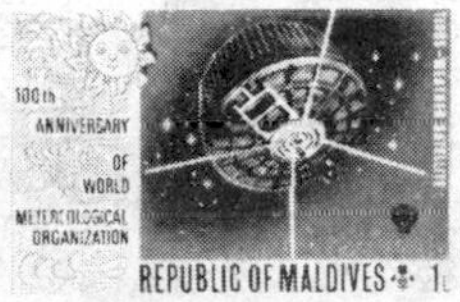
100th
ANNIVERSARY
OF
WORLD
METEROLOGICAL
ORGANIZATION
REPUBLIC OF MALDIVES
1L
Tiros Weather Satellite A73

Designs: 2 l, 10r, Nimbus satellite. 3 l, 3r, Nomad weather ("weater") station. 4 l, A.P.T. instant weather picture (radar). 5 l, Richard's electrical wind speed recorder. 2r, like 1 l.

1974, Jan. 10 *Perf. 14½*

464 A73	1 l olive & multi	.15	.15
465 A73	2 l multicolored	.15	.15
466 A73	3 l brt blue & multi	.15	.15
467 A73	4 l ocher & multi	.15	.15
468 A73	5 l ocher & multi	.15	.15
469 A73	2r ultra & multi	1.00	1.00
470 A73	3r orange & multi	1.50	1.50
	Set value	2.70	2.70

Souvenir Sheet

471 A73	10r lilac & multi	5.50	5.50

World Meteorological Cooperation, cent.

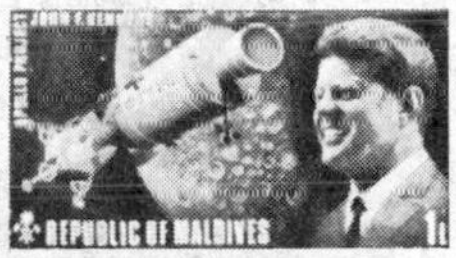
REPUBLIC OF MALDIVES
1L
Apollo Spacecraft, John F. Kennedy A74

Designs: 2 l, 3r, Mercury spacecraft and John Glenn. 3 l, Vostok 1 and Yuri Gagarin. 4 l, Vostok 6 and Valentina Tereshkova. 5 l, Soyuz 11 and Salyut spacecrafts. 2r, Skylab. 10r, Like 1 l.

1974, Feb. 1 **Litho.** *Perf. 14½*

472 A74	1 l multicolored	.15	.15
473 A74	2 l multicolored	.15	.15
474 A74	3 l multicolored	.15	.15
475 A74	4 l multicolored	.15	.15
476 A74	5 l multicolored	.15	.15
477 A74	2r multicolored	1.25	1.25
478 A74	3r multicolored	1.90	1.90
	Set value	3.35	3.35

Souvenir Sheet

479 A74	10r multicolored	6.25	6.25

Space explorations of US and USSR.

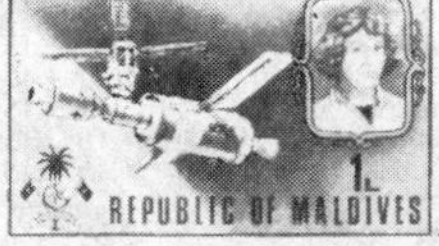
1L
REPUBLIC OF MALDIVES
Skylab and Copernicus A75

Copernicus, Various Portraits and: 2 l, 1.50r, Futuristic orbiting station. 3 l, 5r, Futuristic flight station. 4 l, Mariner 2 on flight to Venus. 5 l, Mariner 4 on flight to Mars. 25 l, like 1 l. 10r, Copernicus Orbiting Observatory.

1974, Apr. 10 **Litho.** *Perf. 14½*

480 A75	1 l multicolored	.15	.15
481 A75	2 l multicolored	.15	.15
482 A75	3 l multicolored	.15	.15
483 A75	4 l multicolored	.15	.15

484	A75	5 l	multicolored	.15	.15
485	A75	25 l	multicolored	.15	.15
486	A75	1.50r	multicolored	.70	.70
487	A75	5r	multicolored	2.40	2.40
			Set value	3.40	3.40

Souvenir Sheet

488	A75	10r	multicolored	6.25	6.25

500th anniversary of the birth of Nicolaus Copernicus (1473-1543), Polish astronomer.

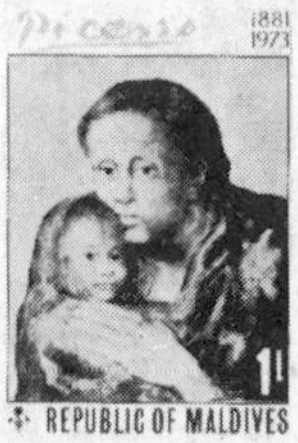

"Motherhood," by Picasso — A76

Picasso Paintings: 2 l, Harlequin and his Companion. 3 l, Pierrot Sitting. 20 l, 2r, Three Musicians. 75 l, L'Aficionada. 3r, 5r, Still life.

1974, May *Perf. 14*

489	A76	1 l	multicolored	.15	.15
490	A76	2 l	multicolored	.15	.15
491	A76	3 l	multicolored	.15	.15
492	A76	20 l	multicolored	.15	.15
493	A76	75 l	multicolored	.45	.45
494	A76	5r	multicolored	3.00	3.00
			Nos. 489-494 (6)	4.05	4.05

Souvenir Sheet

495			Sheet of 2	4.00	4.00
a.	A76	2r	multicolored	1.10	1.10
b.	A76	3r	multicolored	1.75	1.75

Pablo Picasso (1881-1973), painter.

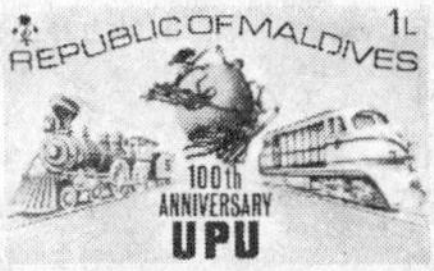

UPU Emblem, Old and New Trains A77

UPU Emblem and: 2 l, 2.50r, Old and new ships. 3 l, Zeppelin and jet. 1.50r, Mail coach and truck. 4r, 5r, Like 1 l.

1974, May **Litho.** *Perf. 14½, 13½*

496	A77	1 l	lt green & multi	.15	.15
497	A77	2 l	yellow & multi	.15	.15
498	A77	3 l	rose & multi	.15	.15
499	A77	1.50r	yel green & multi	1.00	.75
500	A77	2.50r	blue & multi	1.40	1.25
501	A77	5r	ocher & multi	2.75	2.25
			Nos. 496-501 (6)	5.60	4.70

Souvenir Sheet

502	A77	4r	ver & multi	*9.50*	

UPU cent. No. 502 exists imperf.

Nos. 496-501 were printed in sheets of 50, perf. 14½, and also in sheets of 5 plus label, perf. 13½. The label shows UPU emblem, post horn, globe and carrier pigeon.

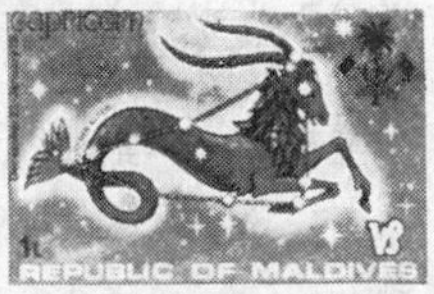

Capricorn A78

Designs: Zodiac signs and constellations.

1974, July 3

503	A78	1 l	shown	.15	.15
504	A78	2 l	Aquarius	.15	.15
505	A78	3 l	Pisces	.15	.15
506	A78	4 l	Aries	.15	.15
507	A78	5 l	Taurus	.15	.15
508	A78	6 l	Gemini	.15	.15
509	A78	7 l	Cancer	.15	.15
510	A78	10 l	Leo	.15	.15
511	A78	15 l	Virgo	.15	.15
512	A78	20 l	Libra	.15	.15
513	A78	25 l	Scorpio	.15	.15
514	A78	5r	Sagittarius	2.75	1.40
			Set value	3.50	1.80

Souvenir Sheet

515	A78	10r	Sun	5.50	5.50

Stamp size of 10r: 50x37mm.

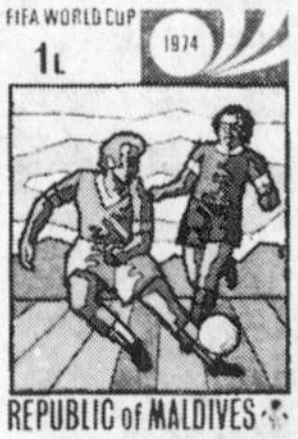

Soccer and Games' Emblem — A79

Designs: Various soccer scenes and games' emblem.

1974, July 31 **Litho.** *Perf. 14½*

516	A79	1 l	brown & multi	.15	.15
517	A79	2 l	green & multi	.15	.15
518	A79	3 l	ultra & multi	.15	.15
519	A79	4 l	red & multi	.15	.15
520	A79	75 l	lt blue & multi	.35	.35
521	A79	4r	olive & multi	2.00	2.00
522	A79	5r	lilac & multi	2.50	2.50
			Nos. 516-522 (7)	5.45	5.45

Souvenir Sheet

523	A79	10r	rose & multi	5.50	5.50

World Cup Soccer Championship, Munich, June 13-July 7.

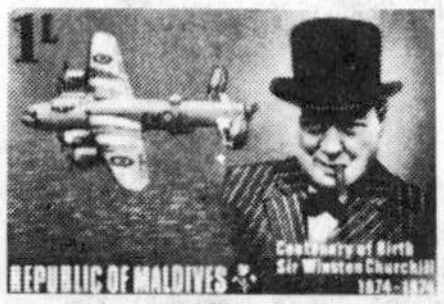

Churchill and WWII Plane A80

Churchill: 2 l, As pilot. 3 l, First Lord of the Admiralty and battleship. 4 l, Aircraft carrier. 5 l, RAF fighters. 60 l, Anti-aircraft unit. 75 l, Tank. 5r, Seaplane.

Design: 10r, Like 4 l.

1974, Nov. 30 **Litho.** *Perf. 14½*

524	A80	1 l	multicolored	.15	.15
525	A80	2 l	multicolored	.15	.15
526	A80	3 l	multicolored	.15	.15
527	A80	4 l	multicolored	.15	.15
528	A80	5 l	multicolored	.15	.15
529	A80	60 l	multicolored	.30	.30
530	A80	75 l	multicolored	.35	.35
531	A80	5r	multicolored	2.50	2.50
			Set value	3.35	3.35

Souvenir Sheet

532	A80	10r	multicolored	5.00	5.00

Sir Winston Churchill (1874-1965), birth centenary.

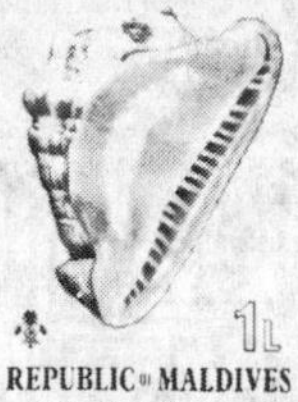

Cassis Nana A81

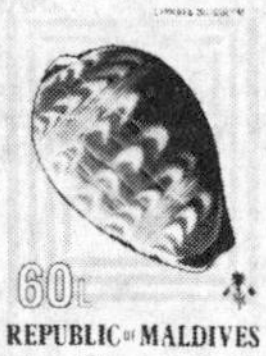

Cypraea Diliculum A82

1975, Jan. 25 *Perf. 14½, 14 (A82)*

533	A81	1 l	shown	.15	.15
534	A81	2 l	Murex triremus	.15	.15
535	A81	3 l	Harpa major	.15	.15
536	A81	4 l	Lambis chiragra	.15	.15
537	A81	5 l	Conus pennaceus	.15	.15
538	A82	60 l	shown	.30	.30
539	A82	75 l	Clanculus pharaonis	.40	.40
540	A81	5r	Chicoreus ramosus	3.00	3.00
			Nos. 533-540 (8)	4.45	4.45

Souvenir Sheet

Perf. 13½

541			Sheet of 2	2.75	2.75
a.	A81	2r	like 3 l	.80	.80
b.	A81	3r	like 2 l	1.20	1.20

Sea shells, including cowries.

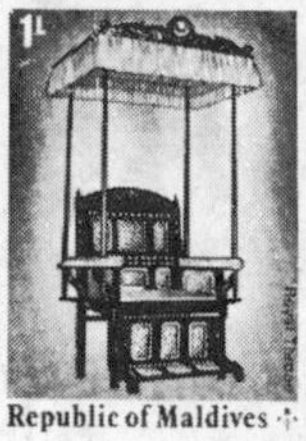

Throne — A83

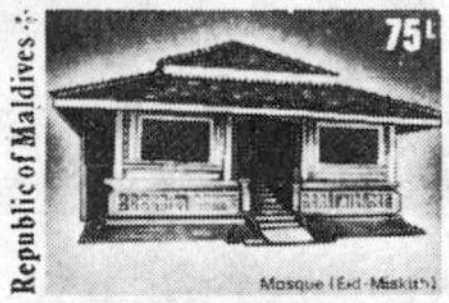

Eid-Miskith Mosque A84

Designs: 10 l, Ornamental candlesticks (dullisa). 25 l, Tree-shaped lamp. 60 l, Royal umbrellas. 3r, Tomb of Al-Hafiz Abu-al Barakath al-Barubari.

1975, Feb. 22 **Litho.** *Perf. 14*

542	A83	1 l	multicolored	.15	.15
543	A83	10 l	multicolored	.15	.15
544	A83	25 l	multicolored	.15	.15
545	A83	60 l	multicolored	.30	.30
546	A84	75 l	multicolored	.40	.40
547	A84	3r	multicolored	1.60	1.60
			Nos. 542-547 (6)	2.75	2.75

Historic relics and monuments.

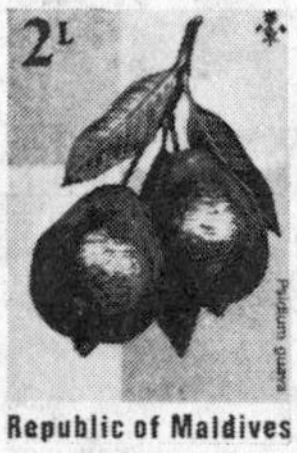

Tropical Fruit — A85

1975, Mar. **Litho.** *Perf. 14½*

548	A85	2 l	Guava	.15	.15
549	A85	4 l	Maldive mulberry	.15	.15
550	A85	5 l	Mountain apples	.15	.15
551	A85	10 l	Bananas	.15	.15
552	A85	20 l	Mangoes	.15	.15
553	A85	50 l	Papaya	.28	.28
554	A85	1r	Pomegranates	.52	.52
555	A85	5r	Coconut	2.75	2.75
			Nos. 548-555 (8)	4.30	4.30

Souvenir Sheet

Perf. 13½

556			Sheet of 2	3.50	3.50
a.	A85	2r	like 10 l	1.25	1.25
b.	A85	3r	like 2 l	1.75	1.75

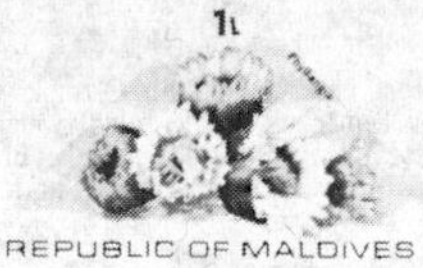

Phyllangia — A86

Designs: Corals, sea urchins and starfish.

1975, June 6 **Litho.** *Perf. 14½*

557	A86	1 l	shown	.15	.15
558	A86	2 l	Madrepora oculata	.15	.15
559	A86	3 l	Acropora gravida	.15	.15
560	A86	4 l	Stylotella	.15	.15
561	A86	5 l	Acropora cervicornis	.15	.15
562	A86	60 l	Strongylocentrotus pupuratus	.30	.30
563	A86	75 l	Pisaster ochraceus	.40	.40
564	A86	5r	Marthasterias glacialis	2.50	2.50
			Set value	3.40	3.40

Souvenir Sheet

Imperf

565	A86	4r	shown	3.25	3.25

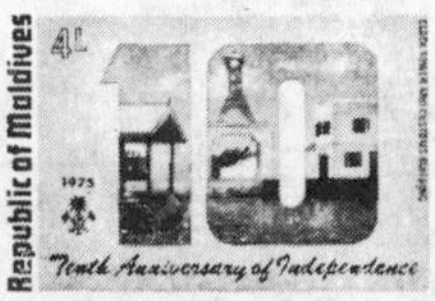

"10," Clock Tower and Customs House A87

"10" and: 5 l, Government offices. 7 l, North Eastern waterfront, Male. 15 l, Mosque and Minaret. 10r, Sultan Park and Museum.

1975, July 26 **Litho.** *Perf. 14½*

566	A87	4 l	salmon & multi	.15	.15
567	A87	5 l	lt blue & multi	.15	.15
568	A87	7 l	bister & multi	.15	.15
569	A87	15 l	lilac & multi	.15	.15
570	A87	10r	lt green & multi	6.00	6.00
			Nos. 566-570 (5)	6.60	6.60

10th anniversary of independence.

Nos. 432-435 Overprinted: "14th Boy Scout Jamboree / July 29-Aug. 7, 1975"

1975, July 26 **Litho.** *Perf. 14½*

571	A69	1r	multicolored	.50	.50
572	A69	2r	multicolored	1.20	1.20
573	A69	3r	multicolored	1.80	1.80
			Nos. 571-573 (3)	3.50	3.50

Souvenir Sheet

574	A69	5r	multicolored	3.00	3.00

Nordjamb 75, 14th World Boy Scout Jamboree, Lillehammer, Norway, July 29-Aug. 7.

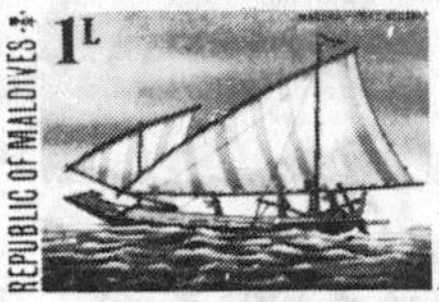

Madura-Prau Bedang A88

Sailing ships, except 5r: 2 l, Ganges patile. 3 l, Indian palla, vert. 4 l, "Odhi," vert. 5 l, Maldivian schooner. 25 l, Cutty Sark. 1r, 10r, Maldivian baggala, vert. 5r, Freighter Maldive Courage.

1975, July 26 *Perf. 14½*

575	A88	1 l	multicolored	.15	.15
576	A88	2 l	multicolored	.15	.15
577	A88	3 l	multicolored	.15	.15
578	A88	4 l	multicolored	.15	.15
579	A88	5 l	multicolored	.15	.15
580	A88	25 l	multicolored	.15	.15
581	A88	1r	multicolored	.60	.60
582	A88	5r	multicolored	3.00	3.00
			Nos. 575-582 (8)	4.50	4.50

Souvenir Sheet

Perf. 13½

583	A88	10r	multicolored	6.00	6.00

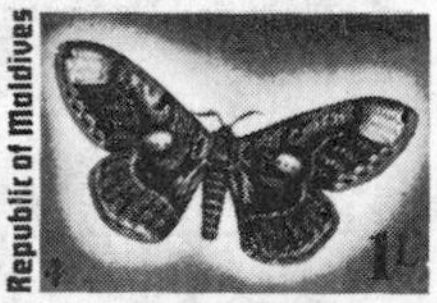

Brahmaea Wallichii A89

Designs: Butterflies.

1975, Sept. 7 **Litho.** *Perf. 14½*

584	A89	1 l	shown	.15	.15
585	A89	2 l	Teoinopalpus imperialis	.15	.15
586	A89	3 l	Cethosia biblis	.15	.15
587	A89	4 l	Hestia jasonia	.15	.15
588	A89	5 l	Apatura	.15	.15
589	A89	25 l	Kallima horsfieldi	.16	.15
590	A89	1.50r	Hebomoia leucippe	1.25	.70
591	A89	5r	Papilio memnon	3.00	2.50
			Nos. 584-591 (8)	5.16	4.10

Souvenir Sheet

Perf. 13½

592	A89	10r	like 25 l	6.25	6.25

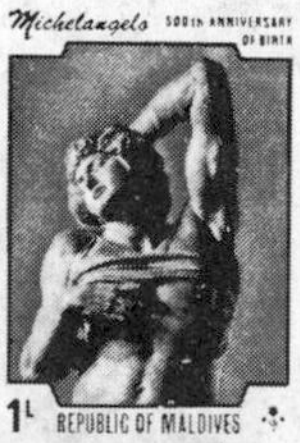

Dying Slave by Michelangelo A90

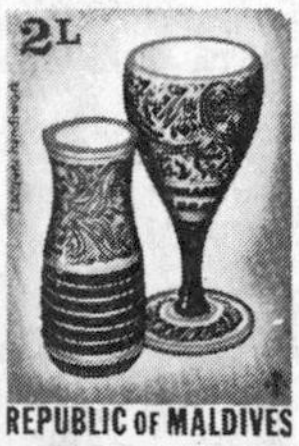

Cup and Vase A91

Works by Michelangelo: 2 l, 4 l, 1r, 5r, paintings from Sistine Chapel. 3 l, Apollo. 5 l, Bacchus. 2r, 10r, David.

1975, Oct. 9 **Litho.** *Perf. 14½*

593	A90	1 l	blue & multi	.15	.15
594	A90	2 l	multicolored	.15	.15
595	A90	3 l	red & multi	.15	.15
596	A90	4 l	multicolored	.15	.15
597	A90	5 l	emerald & multi	.15	.15
598	A90	1r	multicolored	.60	.60

599 A90 2r red & multi 1.25 1.25
600 A90 5r multicolored 3.25 3.25
Nos. 593-600 (8) 5.85 5.85

Souvenir Sheet

Perf. 13½

601 A90 10r multicolored 6.00 6.00

Michelangelo Buonarotti (1475-1564), Italian sculptor, painter and architect.

1975, Dec. Litho. *Perf. 14*

Designs: 4 l, Boxes. 50 l, Vase with lid. 75 l, Bowls with covers. 1r, Worker finishing vases.

602 A91 2 l ultra & multi .15 .15
603 A91 4 l rose & multi .15 .15
604 A91 50 l multicolored .30 .30
605 A91 75 l blue & multi .45 .45
606 A91 1r multicolored .55 .55
Set value 1.40 1.40

Maldivian lacquer ware.

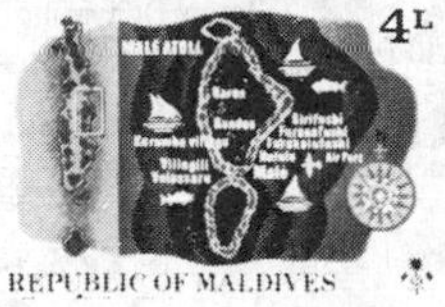

Map of Islands and Atolls A92

Designs: 5 l, Yacht at anchor. 7 l, Sailboats. 15 l, Deep-sea divers and corals. 3r, Hulule Airport. 10r, Cruising yachts.

1975, Dec. 25 Litho. *Perf. 14*

607 A92 4 l multicolored .15 .15
608 A92 5 l multicolored .15 .15
609 A92 7 l multicolored .15 .15
610 A92 15 l multicolored .15 .15
611 A92 3r multicolored 1.75 1.75
612 A92 10r multicolored 5.50 5.50
Nos. 607-612 (6) 7.85 7.85

Tourist publicity.

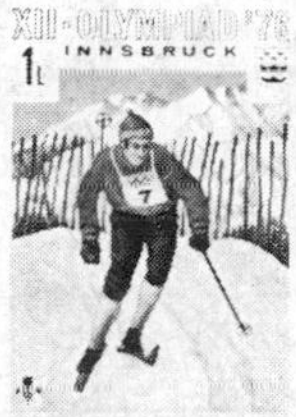

Cross-country Skiing — A93

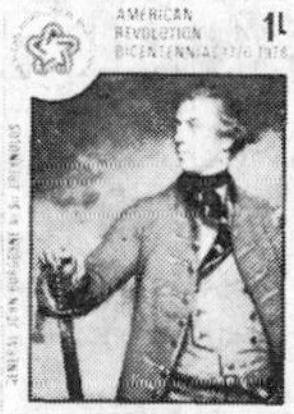

Gen. Burgoyne, by Joshua Reynolds — A94

Winter Olympic Games' Emblem and: 2 l, Speed skating. 3 l, Figure skating, pair. 4 l, Bobsled. 5 l, Ski jump. 25 l, Figure skating, woman. 1.15r, Slalom. 4r, Ice hockey. 10r, Skiing.

1976, Jan. 10 Litho. *Perf. 14½*

613 A93 1 l multicolored .15 .15
614 A93 2 l multicolored .15 .15
615 A93 3 l multicolored .15 .15
616 A93 4 l multicolored .15 .15
617 A93 5 l multicolored .15 .15
618 A93 25 l multicolored .15 .15
619 A93 1.15r multicolored .65 .65
620 A93 4r multicolored 2.25 2.25
Set value 3.20 3.20

Souvenir Sheet

Perf. 13½

621 A93 10r multicolored 6.25 6.25

12th Winter Olympic Games, Innsbruck, Austria, Feb. 4-15.

1976, Feb. 15 *Perf. 14½*

Paintings: 2 l, John Hancock, by John S. Copley. 3 l, Death of Gen. Montgomery, by John Trumbull, horiz. 4 l, Paul Revere, by Copley. 5 l, Battle of Bunker Hill, by Trumbull, horiz. 2r, Crossing of the Delaware, by Thomas Sully, horiz. 3r, Samuel Adams, by Copley. 5r, Surrender of Cornwallis, by Trumbull, horiz. 10r, Washington at Dorchester Heights, by Gilbert Stuart.

622 A94 1 l multicolored .15 .15
623 A94 2 l multicolored .15 .15
624 A94 3 l multicolored .15 .15
625 A94 4 l multicolored .15 .15
626 A94 5 l multicolored .15 .15
627 A94 2r multicolored 1.25 1.25
628 A94 3r multicolored 1.75 1.75
629 A94 5r multicolored 3.00 3.00
Nos. 622-629 (8) 6.75 6.75

Souvenir Sheet

Perf. 13½

630 A94 10r multicolored 6.25 6.25

American Bicentennial.
For overprints see Nos. 639-642.

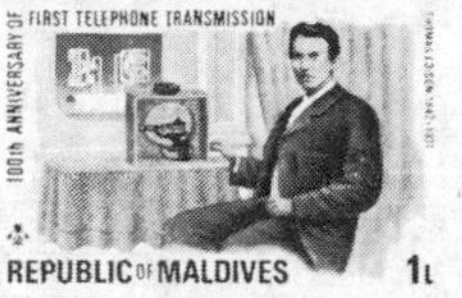

Thomas Alva Edison A95

Designs: 2 l, Alexander Graham Bell and his telephone. 3 l, Telephones of 1919, 1937 and 1972. 10 l, Cable tunnel. 20 l, Equalizer circuit assembly. 1r, Ships laying underwater cable. 4r, Telephones of 1876, 1890 and 1879 Edison telephone. 10r, Intelsat IV-A over earth station.

1976, Mar. 10 Litho. *Perf. 14½*

631 A95 1 l multicolored .15 .15
632 A95 2 l multicolored .15 .15
633 A95 3 l multicolored .15 .15
634 A95 10 l multicolored .15 .15
635 A95 20 l multicolored .15 .15
636 A95 1r multicolored .60 .60
637 A95 10r multicolored 6.00 6.00
Nos. 631-637 (7) 7.35 7.35

Souvenir Sheet

Perf. 13½

638 A95 4r multicolored 2.50 2.50

Centenary of first telephone call by Alexander Graham Bell, Mar. 10, 1876.

Nos. 627-630 Overprinted in Silver or Black: MAY 29TH-JUNE 6TH "INTERPHIL" 1976

1976, May 29 Litho. *Perf. 14½*

639 A94 2r multicolored (S) 1.20 1.20
640 A94 3r multicolored (S) 1.80 1.80
641 A94 5r multicolored (B) 3.00 3.00
Nos. 639-641 (3) 6.00 6.00

Souvenir Sheet

Perf. 13½

642 A94 10r multicolored (S) 6.25 6.25

Interphil 76 Intl. Philatelic Exhibition, Philadelphia, Pa., May 29-June 6. Overprint on 3r and 10r vertical. Same overprint in one horizontal silver line in margin of No. 642.

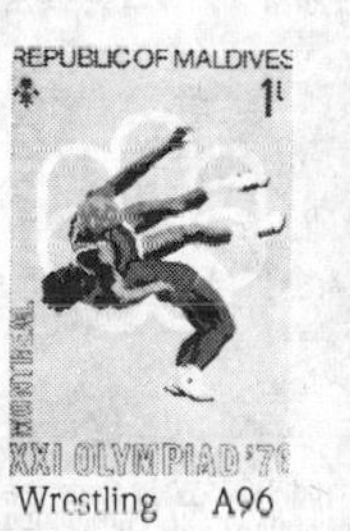

Wrestling A96

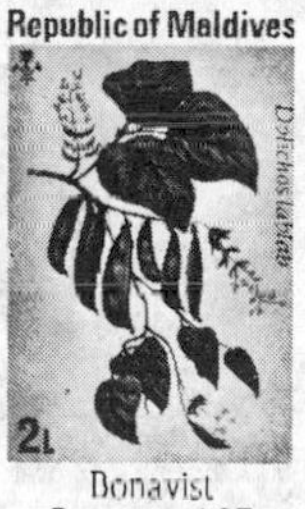

Bonavist Beans — A97

Olympic Rings and: 2 l, Shot put. 3 l, Hurdles. 4 l, Hockey. 5 l, Women running. 6 l, Javelin. 1.50r, Discus. 5r, Team handball. 10r, Hammer throw.

1976, June 1 *Perf. 14½*

643 A96 1 l multicolored .15 .15
644 A96 2 l multicolored .15 .15
645 A96 3 l salmon & multi .15 .15
646 A96 4 l multicolored .15 .15
647 A96 5 l pink & multi .15 .15
648 A96 6 l multicolored .15 .15
649 A96 1.50r bister & multi .90 .90
650 A96 5r lilac & multi 3.00 3.00
Nos. 643-650 (8) 4.80 4.80

Souvenir Sheet

Perf. 13½

651 A96 10r lemon & multi 6.25 6.25

21st Olympic Games, Montreal, Canada, July 17-Aug. 1.

1976-77 Litho. *Perf. 14*

Designs: 4 l, 20 l, Beans. 10 l, Eggplant. 50 l, Cucumber. 75 l, 2r, Snake gourd. 1r, Balsam pear.

652 A97 2 l green & multi .15 .15
653 A97 4 l lt blue & multi .15 .15
654 A97 10 l ocher & multi .15 .15
655 A97 20 l blue & multi ('77) .15 .15
656 A97 50 l multicolored .25 .25
657 A97 75 l bister & multi .32 .32
658 A97 1r lilac & multi .45 .45
659 A97 2r bis & multi ('77) .90 .90
Set value 2.15 2.15

1976 stamps issued July 26.

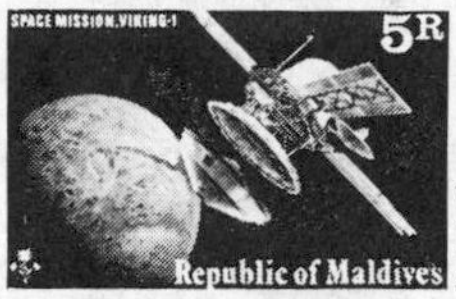

Viking I and Mars A98

Design: 20r, Landing craft on Mars.

1976, Dec. 2 Litho. *Perf. 14*

660 A98 5r multicolored 3.00 3.00

Souvenir Sheet

661 A98 20r multicolored 12.00 12.00

Viking I US Mars Mission.

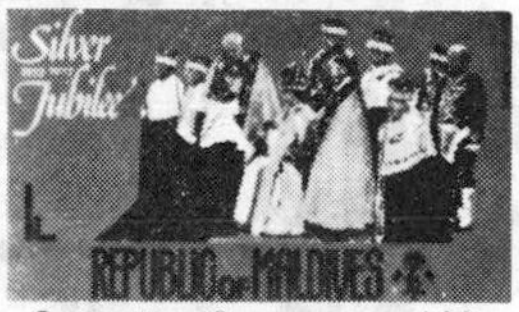

Coronation Ceremony — A99

Designs: 2 l, Elizabeth II and Prince Philip. 3 l, Queen, Prince Philip, Princes Edward and Andrew. 1.15r, Queen in procession. 3r, State coach. 4r, Queen, Prince Philip, Princess Anne and Prince Charles. 10r, Queen and Prince Charles.

1977, Feb. 6 *Perf. 14x13½, 12*

662 A99 1 l multicolored .15 .15
663 A99 2 l multicolored .15 .15
664 A99 3 l multicolored .15 .15
665 A99 1.15r multicolored .80 .80
666 A99 3r multicolored 1.40 1.40
667 A99 4r multicolored 2.00 2.00
Nos. 662-667 (6) 4.65 4.65

Souvenir Sheet

668 A99 10r multicolored 5.00 5.00

25th anniv. of the reign of Elizabeth II.
Nos. 662-667 were printed in sheets of 40 (4x10), perf. 14x13½, and sheets of 5 plus label, perf. 12, in changed colors.

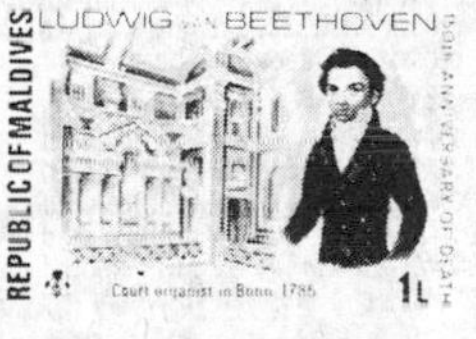

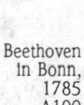

Beethoven in Bonn, 1785 A100

Designs: 2 l, Moonlight Sonata and portrait, 1801. 3 l, Goethe and Beethoven, Teplitz, 1811. 4 l, Beethoven, 1815, and his string instruments. 5 l, Beethoven House, Heiligenstadt, 1817. 25 l, Composer's hands, gold medal. 2r, Missa Solemnis, portrait, 1823. 4r, Piano, room where Beethoven died, death mask. 5r, Portrait, 1825, hearing aids.

1977, Mar. 26 Litho. *Perf. 14*

669 A100 1 l multicolored .15 .15
670 A100 2 l multicolored .15 .15
671 A100 3 l multicolored .15 .15
672 A100 4 l multicolored .15 .15
673 A100 5 l multicolored .15 .15
674 A100 25 l multicolored .15 .15
675 A100 2r multicolored 1.10 1.10
676 A100 5r multicolored 2.75 2.75
Set value 4.10 4.10

Souvenir Sheet

677 A100 4r multicolored 2.10 2.10

Ludwig van Beethoven (1770-1827), composer, 150th death anniversary.

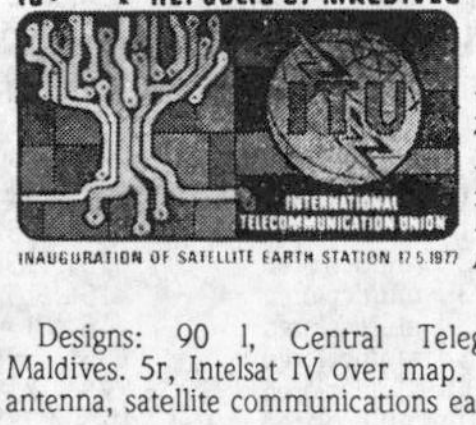

Electronic Tree and ITU Emblem A101

Designs: 90 l, Central Telegraph Office, Maldives. 5r, Intelsat IV over map. 10r, Parabolic antenna, satellite communications earth station.

1977, May 17 Litho. *Perf. 14*

678 A101 10 l multicolored .15 .15
679 A101 90 l multicolored .45 .45
680 A101 10r multicolored 5.50 5.50
Nos. 678-680 (3) 6.10 6.10

Souvenir Sheet

681 A101 5r multicolored 2.50 2.50

Inauguration of Satellite Earth Station and for World Telecommunications Day.

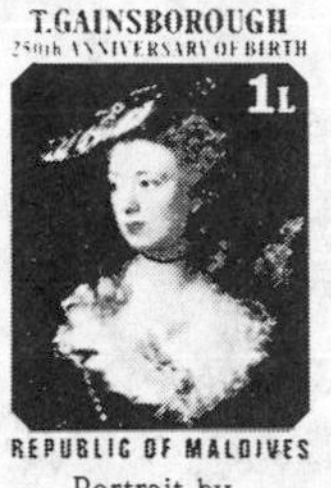

Portrait by Gainsborough A102

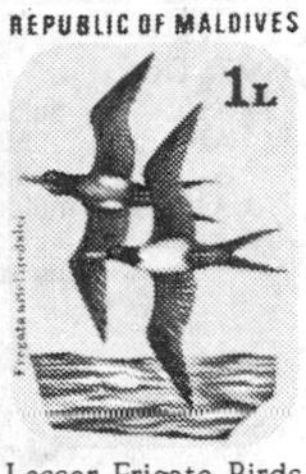

Lesser Frigate Birds A103

Paintings: 2 l, 5 l, 10r, Rubens. 3 l, 95 l, 5r, Titian. 4 l, 1r, Gainsborough.

1977, May 20

682 A102 1 l multicolored .15 .15
683 A102 2 l multicolored .15 .15
684 A102 3 l multicolored .15 .15
685 A102 4 l multicolored .15 .15
686 A102 5 l multicolored .15 .15
687 A102 95 l multicolored .45 .45
688 A102 1r multicolored .50 .50
689 A102 10r multicolored 5.00 5.00
Nos. 682-689 (8) 6.70 6.70

Souvenir Sheet

690 A102 5r multicolored 2.50 2.50

Birth annivs. of Thomas Gainsborough; Peter Paul Rubens; Titian.

1977, July 26 Litho. *Perf. 14½*

Birds: 2 l, Crab plovers. 3 l, Long-tailed tropic bird. 4 l, Wedge-tailed shearwater. 5 l, Gray heron. 20 l, White tern. 95 l, Cattle egret. 1.25r, Blacknaped terns. 5r, Pheasant coucals. 10r, Striated herons.

691 A103 1 l multicolored .15 .15
692 A103 2 l multicolored .15 .15
693 A103 3 l multicolored .15 .15
694 A103 4 l multicolored .15 .15
695 A103 5 l multicolored .15 .15
696 A103 20 l multicolored .15 .15
697 A103 95 l multicolored .62 .50
698 A103 1.25r multicolored .90 .62
699 A103 5r multicolored 3.75 2.50
Nos. 691-699 (9) 6.17 4.52

Souvenir Sheet

700 A103 10r multicolored 5.00 5.00

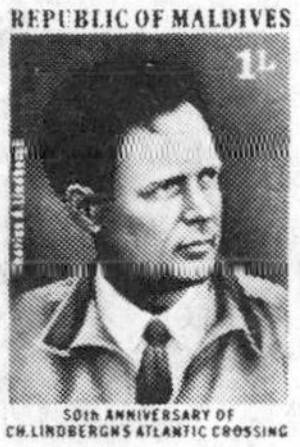

Charles A. Lindbergh — A104

Designs: 2 l, Lindbergh and Spirit of St. Louis. 3 l, Mohawk plane, horiz. 4 l, Lebaudy I airship, 1902, horiz. 5 l, Count Ferdinand von Zeppelin, and Zeppelin in Pernambuco. 1r, Los Angeles, U. S. Navy airship, 1924, horiz. 3r, Henry Ford and Lindbergh, 1942. 5r, Spirit of St. Louis, Statue of Liberty and Eiffel Tower, horiz. 7.50r, German naval airship over battleship, horiz. 10r, Vickers airship, 1917.

Perf. 13x13½, 13½x13

1977, Oct. 31 Litho.

701 A104 1 l multicolored .15 .15
702 A104 2 l multicolored .15 .15
703 A104 3 l multicolored .15 .15
704 A104 4 l multicolored .15 .15
705 A104 5 l multicolored .15 .15
706 A104 1r multicolored .48 .48
707 A104 3r multicolored 1.50 1.50
708 A104 10r multicolored 4.75 4.75
Nos. 701-708 (8) 7.48 7.48

Souvenir Sheet

709 Sheet of 2 6.75 6.75
a. A104 5r multicolored 2.50 2.50
b. A104 7.50r multicolored 3.75 3.75

Charles A. Lindbergh's solo transatlantic flight from New York to Paris, 50th anniv., and 75th anniv. of first navigable airship.

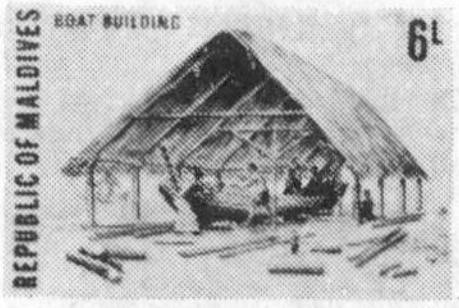

Boat Building
A105

Maldivian Occupations: 15 l, High sea fishing. 20 l, Cadjan weaving. 90 l, Mat weaving. 2r, Lacemaking, vert.

1977, Dec. 12

710	A105	6 l multicolored	.15	.15
711	A105	15 l multicolored	.15	.15
712	A105	20 l multicolored	.15	.15
713	A105	90 l multicolored	.45	.45
714	A105	2r multicolored	1.00	1.00
		Set value	1.65	1.65

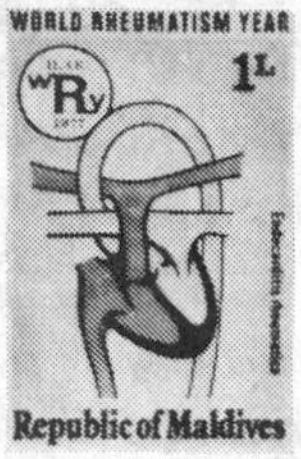

Rheumatic Heart — A106

X-Ray Pictures: 50 l, Shoulder. 2r, Hand. 3r, Knee.

1978, Feb. 9 *Perf. 14*

715	A106	1 l multicolored	.15	.15
716	A106	50 l multicolored	.30	.30
717	A106	2r multicolored	1.25	1.25
718	A106	3r multicolored	1.75	1.75
		Nos. 715-718 (4)	3.45	3.45

World Rheumatism Year.

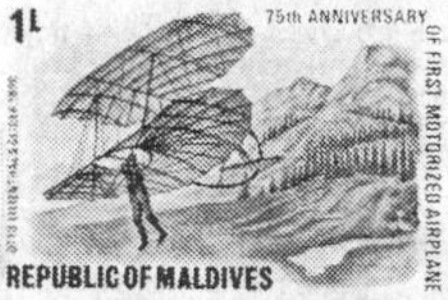

Otto Lilienthal's Glider, 1890
A107

Designs: 2 l, Chanute's glider, 1896. 3 l, Wright brothers testing glider, 1900. 4 l, A. V. Roe's plane with paper-covered wings, 1908. 5 l, Wilbur Wright showing his plane to King Alfonso of Spain, 1909. 10 l, Roe's second biplane. 20 l, Alexander Graham Bell and Wright brothers in Washington D.C., 1910. 95 l, Clifton Hadley's triplane, 1910. 5r, British B.E.2 planes, Upavon Field, 1914. 10r, Wilbur Wright flying first motorized plane, 1903.

1978, Feb. 27 Litho. *Perf. 13x13½*

719	A107	1 l multicolored	.15	.15
720	A107	2 l multicolored	.15	.15
721	A107	3 l multicolored	.15	.15
722	A107	4 l multicolored	.15	.15
723	A107	5 l multicolored	.15	.15
724	A107	10 l multicolored	.15	.15
725	A107	20 l multicolored	.15	.15
726	A107	95 l multicolored	.45	.45
727	A107	5r multicolored	2.50	2.50
		Set value	3.25	3.25

Souvenir Sheet

Perf. 14

728	A107	10r multicolored	4.50	4.50

75th anniversary of first motorized airplane.

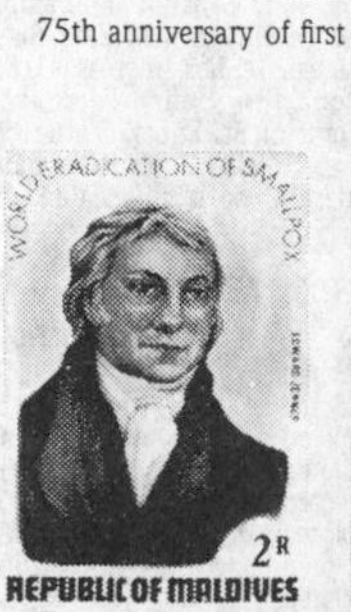

Edward Jenner, Vaccination Discoverer — A108

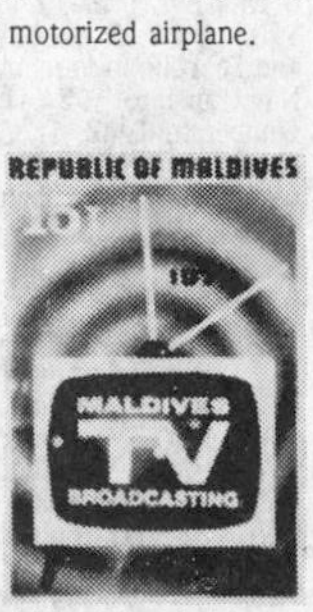

TV with Maldives Broadcasting Symbol — A109

Designs: 15 l, Foundling Hospital, London, where children were first inoculated, 1743, horiz. 50 l, Newgate Prison, London, where first experiments were carried out, 1721.

1978, Mar. 15 *Perf. 14*

729	A108	15 l multicolored	.15	.15
730	A108	50 l multicolored	.20	.20
731	A108	2r multicolored	.80	.80
		Nos. 729-731 (3)	1.15	1.15

World eradication of smallpox.

1978, Mar. 29

Designs: 25 l, Circuit pattern. 1.50r, Station control panel, horiz.

732	A109	15 l multicolored	.15	.15
733	A109	25 l multicolored	.16	.16
734	A109	1.50r multicolored	1.00	1.00
		Nos. 732-734 (3)	1.31	1.31

Inauguration of Maldive Islands television.

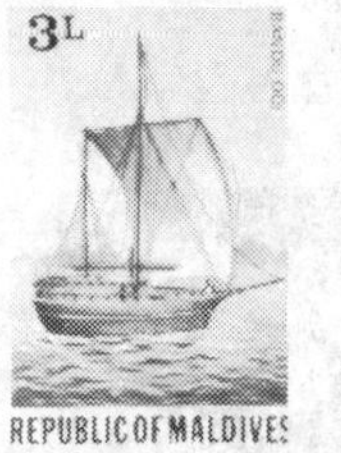

Sailing Ship — A110

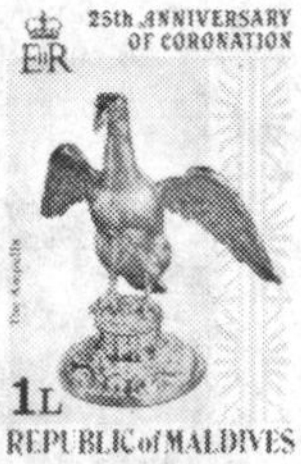

The Ampulla — A111

Ships: 1 l, Phoenician. 2 l, Two-master. 5 l, Freighter Maldive Trader. 1r, Trading schooner. 1.25r, 4r, Sailing boat. 3r, Barque Bangala. (1 l, 2 l, 5 l, 1.25r, 4r, horiz.)

1978, Apr. 27 Litho. *Perf. 14½*

735	A110	1 l multicolored	.15	.15
736	A110	2 l multicolored	.15	.15
737	A110	3 l multicolored	.15	.15
738	A110	5 l multicolored	.15	.15
739	A110	1r multicolored	.40	.40
740	A110	1.25r multicolored	.50	.50
741	A110	3r multicolored	1.20	1.20
742	A110	4r multicolored	1.60	1.60
a.		Souvenir sheet of 2	2.20	2.20
		Nos. 735-742 (8)	4.30	4.30

No. 742a contains No. 742 and a 1r stamp in the design of No. 736.

1978, May 15 *Perf. 14*

Designs: 2 l, Scepter with dove. 3 l, Orb with cross. 1.15r, St. Edward's crown. 2r, Scepter with cross. 5r, Queen Elizabeth II. 10r, Anointing spoon.

743	A111	1 l multicolored	.15	.15
744	A111	2 l multicolored	.15	.15
745	A111	3 l multicolored	.15	.15
746	A111	1.15r multicolored	.55	.55
747	A111	2r multicolored	1.00	1.00
748	A111	5r multicolored	2.50	2.50
		Nos. 743-748 (6)	4.50	4.50

Souvenir Sheet

749	A111	10r multicolored	4.75	4.75

Coronation of Elizabeth II, 25th anniv.

#743-748 were printed in sheets of 40 and in sheets of 3 + label, in changed colors. Labels show coronation regalia.

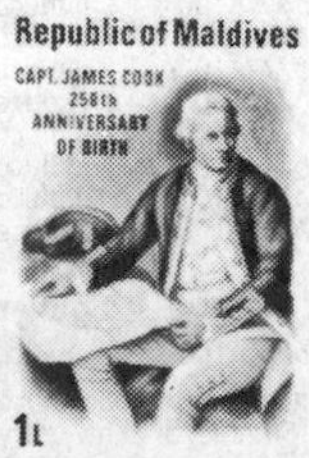

Capt. James Cook — A112

Designs: 2 l, Kamehameha I statue, Honolulu. 3 l, "Endeavour" and boat. 25 l, Capt. Cook and route of his 3rd voyage. 75 l, "Discovery" and "Resolution," map of Hawaiian Islands, horiz. 1.50r, Capt. Cook's first meeting with Hawaiians, horiz. 5r, "Endeavour." 10r, Capt. Cook's death, horiz.

1978, July 15 Litho. *Perf. 14½*

750	A112	1 l multicolored	.15	.15
751	A112	2 l multicolored	.15	.15
752	A112	3 l multicolored	.15	.15
753	A112	25 l multicolored	.15	.15
754	A112	75 l multicolored	.35	.35
755	A112	1.50r multicolored	.75	.75
756	A112	10r multicolored	4.75	4.75
		Nos. 750-756 (7)	6.45	6.45

Souvenir Sheet

757	A112	5r multicolored	2.25	2.25

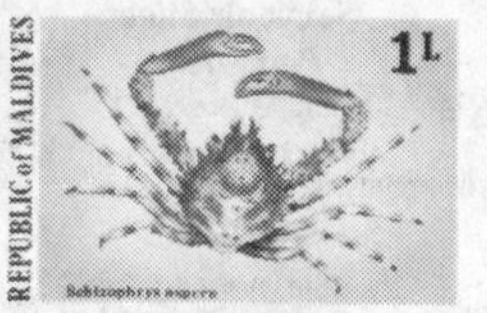

Schizophrys Aspera — A113

Maldivian Crabs and Lobster: 2 l, Atergatis floridus. 3 l, Percnon planissimum. 90 l, Portunus granulatus. 1r, Carpilius maculatus. No. 763, Huenia proteus. No. 765, Panulirus longipes, vert. 25r, Etisus laevimanus.

1978, Aug. 30 Litho. *Perf. 14*

758	A113	1 l multicolored	.15	.15
759	A113	2 l multicolored	.15	.15
760	A113	3 l multicolored	.15	.15
761	A113	90 l multicolored	.48	.48
762	A113	1r multicolored	.55	.55
763	A113	2r multicolored	1.10	1.10
764	A113	25r multicolored	12.50	12.50
		Nos. 758-764 (7)	15.08	15.08

Souvenir Sheet

765	A113	2r multicolored	1.00	1.00

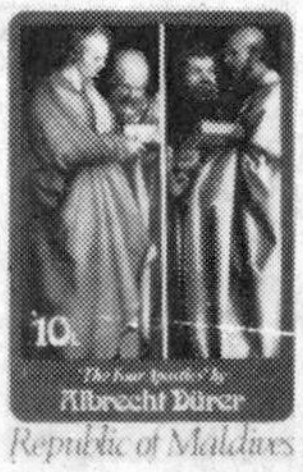

Four Apostles, by Dürer — A114

Paintings by Albrecht Dürer (1471-1528): 20 l, Self-portrait, age 27. 55 l, Virgin and Child with Pear. 1r, Rhinoceros, horiz. 1.80r, Hare. 3r, The Great Piece of Turf. 10r, Columbine.

1978, Oct. 28 Litho. *Perf. 14*

766	A114	10 l multicolored	.15	.15
767	A114	20 l multicolored	.15	.15
768	A114	55 l multicolored	.30	.30
769	A114	1r multicolored	.52	.52
770	A114	1.80r multicolored	1.00	1.00
771	A114	3r multicolored	1.60	1.60
		Nos. 766-771 (6)	3.72	3.72

Souvenir Sheet

772	A114	10r multicolored	4.75	4.75

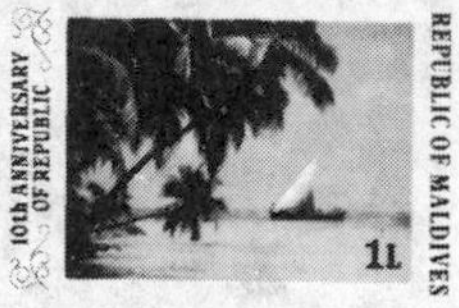

Palms and Fishing Boat
A115

Designs: 5 l, Montessori School. 10 l, TV tower and ITU emblem, vert. 25 l, Island with beach. 50 l, Boeing 737 over island. 95 l, Walk along the beach. 1.25r, Fishing boat at dawn. 2r, Presidential residence. 3r, Fishermen preparing nets. 5r, Afeefuddin Mosque.

1978, Nov. 11 Litho. *Perf. 14½*

773	A115	1 l multicolored	.15	.15
774	A115	5 l multicolored	.15	.15
775	A115	10 l multicolored	.15	.15
776	A115	25 l multicolored	.15	.15
777	A115	50 l multicolored	.25	.25
778	A115	95 l multicolored	.45	.45
779	A115	1.25r multicolored	.62	.62
780	A115	2r multicolored	1.00	1.00
781	A115	5r multicolored	2.50	2.50
		Nos. 773-781 (9)	5.42	5.42

Souvenir Sheet

782	A115	3r multicolored	1.75	1.75

10th anniversary of Republic.

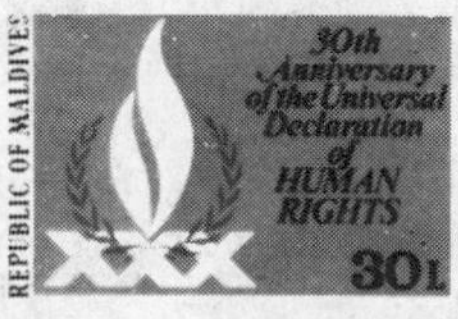

Human Rights Emblem
A116

1978, Dec. 10 *Perf. 14*

783	A116	30 l multicolored	.15	.15
784	A116	90 l multicolored	.45	.45
785	A116	1.80r multicolored	.90	.90
		Nos. 783-785 (3)	1.50	1.50

Universal Declaration of Human Rights, 30th anniversary.

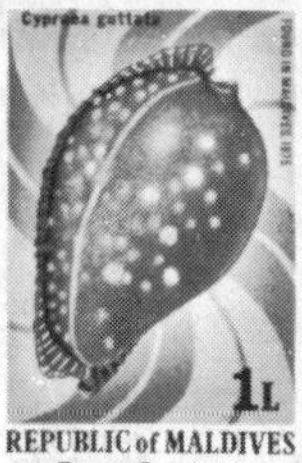

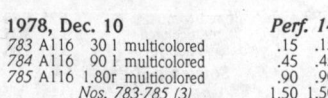

Rare Spotted Cowrie — A117

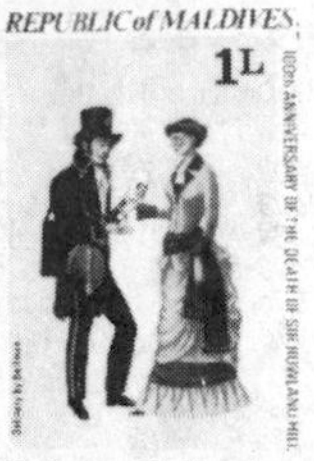

Bellman Delivering Mail — A118

Sea Shells: 2 l, Imperial cone. 3 l, Green turban. 10 l, Giant spider conch. 1r, Leucodon cowrie. 1.80r, Fig cone. 3r, Glory of the sea. 5r, Top vase.

1979, Jan. Litho. *Perf. 14*

786	A117	1 l multicolored	.15	.15
787	A117	2 l multicolored	.15	.15
788	A117	3 l multicolored	.15	.15
789	A117	10 l multicolored	.15	.15
790	A117	1r multicolored	.48	.48
791	A117	1.80r multicolored	.90	.90
792	A117	3r multicolored	1.40	1.40
		Nos. 786-792 (7)	3.38	3.38

Souvenir Sheet

793	A117	5r multicolored	3.00	3.00

1979, Feb. 28 Litho. *Perf. 14*

Designs: 2 l, Royal mail coach, 1840, horiz. 3 l, First London letter box, 1855. 1.55r, Great Britain No. 1 and post horn. 5r, Maldive Islands No. 5 and carrier pigeon. 10r, Rowland Hill.

794	A118	1 l multicolored	.15	.15
795	A118	2 l multicolored	.15	.15
796	A118	3 l multicolored	.15	.15
797	A118	1.55r multicolored	.78	.60
798	A118	5r multicolored	2.50	2.00
		Nos. 794-798 (5)	3.73	3.05

Souvenir Sheet

799	A118	10r multicolored	4.75	4.75

Sir Rowland Hill (1795-1879), originator of penny postage.

For overprints, see Nos. 853-855.

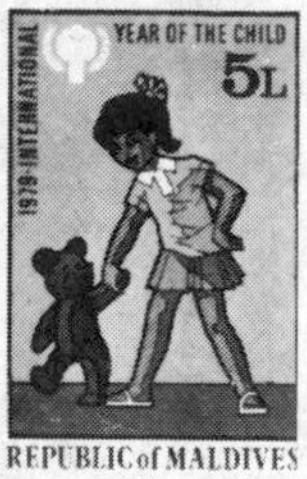

Girl with Teddy Bear — A119

IYC Emblem, Boy and: 1.25r, Model boat. 2r, Rocket launcher. 3r, Blimp. 5r, Train.

1979, May 10 Litho. *Perf. 14*

800	A119	5 l multicolored	.15	.15
801	A119	1.25r multicolored	.62	.62
802	A119	2r multicolored	1.00	1.00
803	A119	3r multicolored	1.50	1.50
		Nos. 800-803 (4)	3.27	3.27

Souvenir Sheet

804	A119	5r multicolored	2.50	2.50

International Year of the Child.

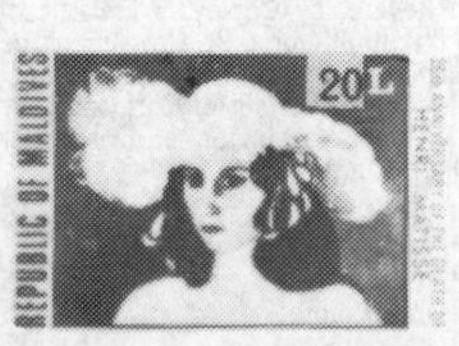

White Feathers, by Matisse
A120

Paintings by Henri Matisse (1869-1954): 25 l, Joy of Life. 30 l, Eggplants. 1.50r, Harmony in Red. 4r, Water Pitcher. 5r, Still-life.

1979, Aug. 20 Litho. *Perf. 14*

805	A120	20 l multicolored	.15	.15
806	A120	25 l multicolored	.15	.15
807	A120	30 l multicolored	.15	.15

808 A120	1.50r	multicolored	.75	.75
809 A120	5r	multicolored	2.50	2.50
		Nos. 805-809 (5)	3.70	3.70

Souvenir Sheet

810 A120	4r	multicolored	2.25	2.25

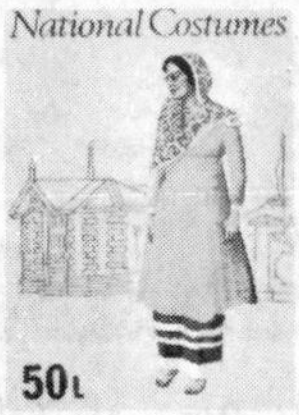

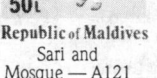

Sari and Mosque — A121

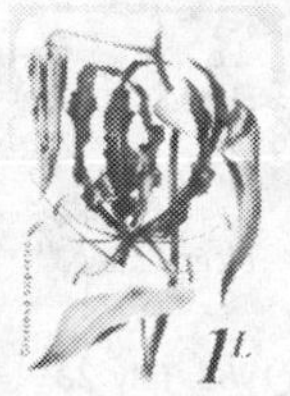

Gloriosa Superba — A122

National Costumes: 75 l, Sashed apron dress. Male Harbor. 90 l, Serape with necklace, radar station. 95 l, Flowered dress, mosque and minaret.

1979, Aug. 22 — Litho. — Perf. 14

811 A121	50 l	multicolored	.25	.25
812 A121	75 l	multicolored	.38	.38
813 A121	90 l	multicolored	.45	.45
814 A121	95 l	multicolored	.48	.48
		Nos. 811-814 (4)	1.56	1.56

1979, Oct. 29 — Litho. — Perf. 14

815 A122	1 l	shown	.15	.15
816 A122	3 l	Hibiscus	.15	.15
817 A122	50 l	Barringtonia asiatica	.25	.25
818 A122	1r	Abutilon indicum	.50	.50
819 A122	5r	Guettarda speciosa	2.50	2.50
		Nos. 815-819 (5)	3.55	3.55

Souvenir Sheet

820 A122	4r	Pandanus odoratissimus	2.00	2.00

Maldive wildflowers.

Handicraft Exhibition A123

1979, Nov. 11

821 A123	5 l	shown	.15	.15
822 A123	10 l	Jar and cup	.15	.15
823 A123	1.30r	Tortoise-shell jewelry	.65	.65
824 A123	2r	Wooden boxes	1.00	1.00
		Nos. 821-824 (4)	1.95	1.95

Souvenir Sheet

825 A123	5r	Bracelets, necklace	2.25	2.25

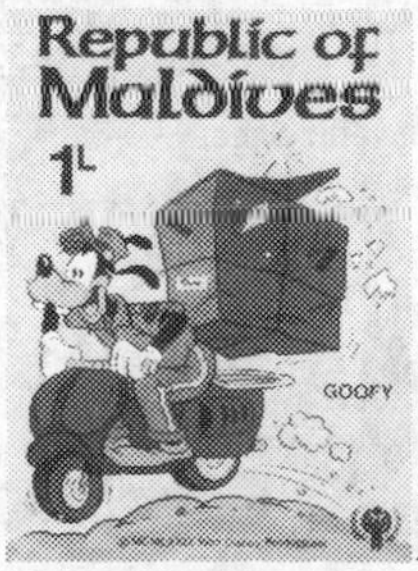

Postal Scenes A123a

1 l, Goofy delivering package. 2 l, Mickey at mailbox. 3 l, Goofy buried in letters. 4 l, Minnie Mouse, Pluto. 5 l, Mickey Mouse on skates. 10 l, Donald Duck at mailbox. 15 l, Chip and Dale carrying letter. 1.50r, Donald Duck on unicycle. 4r, Pluto at mailbox. 5r, Donald Duck wheeling crate.

1979, Dec. — Litho. — Perf. 11

826 A123a	1 l	multicolored	.15	.15
827 A123a	2 l	multicolored	.15	.15
828 A123a	3 l	multicolored	.15	.15
829 A123a	4 l	multicolored	.15	.15
830 A123a	5 l	multicolored	.15	.15
831 A123a	10 l	multicolored	.15	.15
832 A123a	15 l	multicolored	.15	.15
833 A123a	1.50r	multicolored	.90	.90
834 A123a	5r	multicolored	3.00	3.00
		Set value	4.25	4.25

Souvenir Sheet

Imperf

835 A123a	4r	multicolored	14.00	14.00

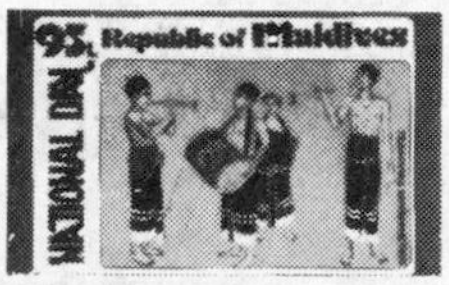

Post Ramadan Dancing A124

Designs: 15 l, Festival of Eeduu. 95 l, Sultan's ceremonial band. 2r, Music festival.

1980, Jan. 19 — Litho. — Perf. 14

836 A124	5 l	multicolored	.15	.15
837 A124	15 l	multicolored	.15	.15
838 A124	95 l	multicolored	.48	.48
839 A124	2r	multicolored	1.00	1.00
		Nos. 836-839 (4)	1.78	1.78

Souvenir Sheet

840 A124	5r	multicolored	3.00	3.00

National Day.

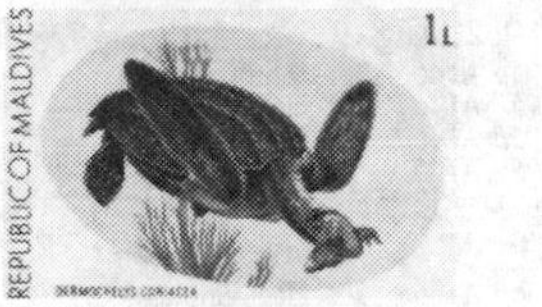

Leatherback Turtle — A125

1980, Feb. 17 — Litho. — Perf. 14

841 A125	1 l	shown	.15	.15
842 A125	2 l	Flatback turtle	.15	.15
843 A125	5 l	Hawksbill turtle	.15	.15
844 A125	10 l	Loggerhead turtle	.15	.15
845 A125	75 l	Olive ridley	.38	.38
846 A125	10r	Atlantic ridley	5.00	5.00
		Nos. 841-846 (6)	5.98	5.98

Souvenir Sheet

847 A125	4r	Green turtle	2.00	2.00

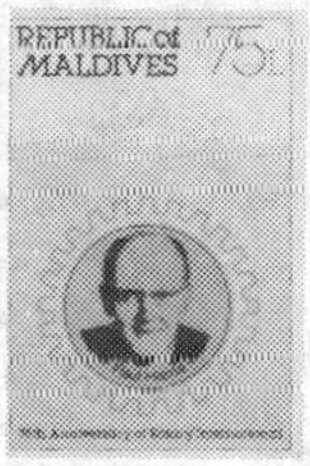

Paul Harris in Rotary Emblem — A126

1980, Mar. — Litho. — Perf. 14

848 A126	75 l	shown	.38	.38
849 A126	90 l	Family	.45	.45
850 A126	1r	Grain	.50	.50
851 A126	10r	Caduceus	5.00	5.00
		Nos. 848-851 (4)	6.33	6.33

Souvenir Sheet

852 A126	5r	Anniversary emblem	2.50	2.50

Rotary International, 75th anniversary.

Nos. 797-799 Overprinted "LONDON 1980"

1980, May 6 — Litho. — Perf. 14

853 A118	1.55r	multicolored	.78	.78
854 A118	5r	multicolored	2.50	2.50

Souvenir Sheet

855 A118	10r	multicolored	5.00	5.00

London 1980 International Stamp Exhibition, May 6-14. Sheet margin overprinted "Earls Court—London 6-14 May 1980."

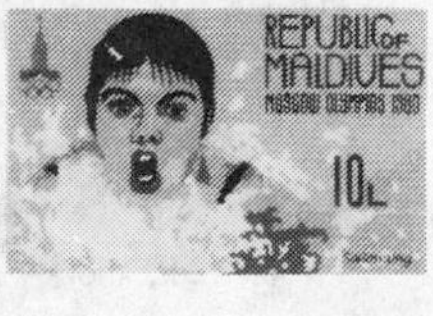

Swimming, Moscow '80 Emblem A127

1980, June 4 — Litho. — Perf. 14

856 A127	10 l	shown	.15	.15
857 A127	50 l	Sprinting	.25	.25
858 A127	3r	Shot put	1.50	1.50
859 A127	4r	High jump	2.00	2.00
		Nos. 856-859 (4)	3.90	3.90

Souvenir Sheet

860 A127	5r	Weight lifting	2.50	2.50

22nd Summer Olympic Games, Moscow, July 19-Aug. 3.

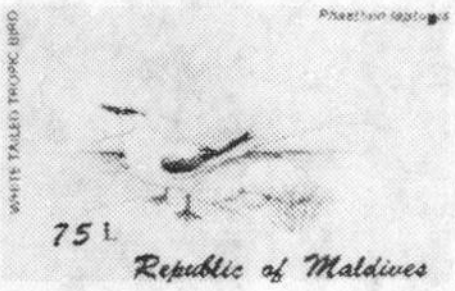

White-tailed Tropic Bird A128

1980, July 10 — Litho. — Perf. 14

861 A128	75 l	shown	.38	.38
862 A128	95 l	Sooty tern	.48	.48
863 A128	1r	Brown noddy	.50	.50
864 A128	1.55r	Eurasian curlew	.78	.78
865 A128	2r	Wilson's petrel	1.00	1.00
866 A128	4r	Caspian tern	2.00	2.00
		Nos. 861-866 (6)	5.14	5.14

Souvenir Sheet

867 A128	5r	Red-footed & brown boobies	2.50	2.50

Seal of Sultan Ibrahim II (1720-1750) A129

Sultans' Seals: 2 l, Mohamed Imadudeen II (1704-1720). 5 l, Mohamed Bin Haji Ali (1692-1701). 1r, Kuda Mohamed Rasgefaanu (1687-1691). 2r, Ibrahim Iskander I (1648-1687). 3r, Ibrahim Iskander, second seal.

1980, July 26

868 A129	1 l	violet brn & blk	.15	.15
869 A129	2 l	violet brn & blk	.15	.15
870 A129	5 l	violet brn & blk	.15	.15
871 A129	1r	violet brn & blk	.50	.50
872 A129	2r	violet brn & blk	1.00	1.00
		Set value	1.60	1.60

Souvenir Sheet

873 A129	3r	violet brn & blk	1.50	1.50

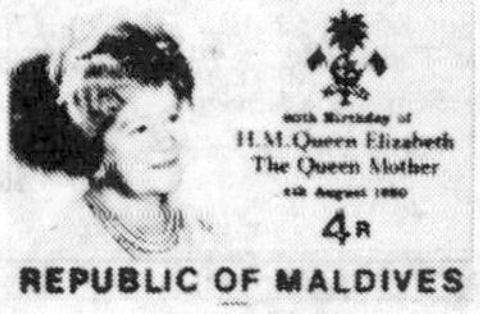

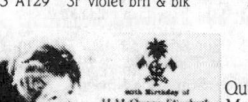

Queen Mother Elizabeth, 80th Birthday A130

1980, Sept. 29 — Perf. 14

874 A130	4r	multicolored	2.00	2.00

Souvenir Sheet

Perf. 12

875 A130	5r	multicolored	2.50	2.50

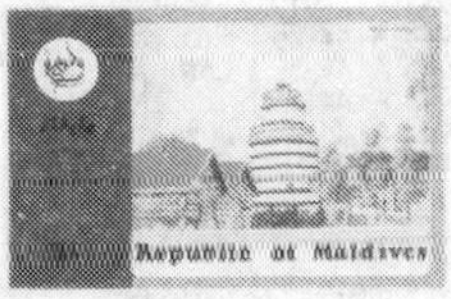

Munnaaru Tower A131

1980, Nov. 9 — Litho. — Perf. 15

876 A131	5 l	shown	.15	.15
877 A131	10 l	Hukuru Miskiiy Mosque	.15	.15
878 A131	30 l	Medhuziyaaraiy Shrine	.15	.15
879 A131	55 l	Koran verses on wooden tablets	.28	.28
880 A131	90 l	Mother teaching son	.45	.45
		Set value	.95	.95

Souvenir Sheet

881 A131	2r	Map and arms of Maldives	1.00	1.00

Hegira (Pilgrimage Year).

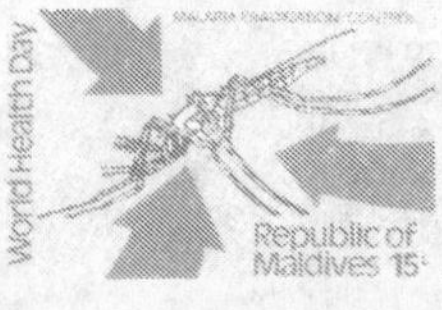

Malaria Eradication Control A132

1980, Nov. 30 — Perf. 14

882 A132	15 l	shown	.15	.15
883 A132	25 l	Balanced diet	.15	.15
884 A132	1.50r	Oral hygiene	.75	.75
885 A132	5r	Clinic visit	2.50	2.50
		Nos. 882-885 (4)	3.55	3.55

Souvenir Sheet

886 A132	4r	like #885	2.00	2.00

World Health Day. No. 886 shows design of No. 885 in changed colors.

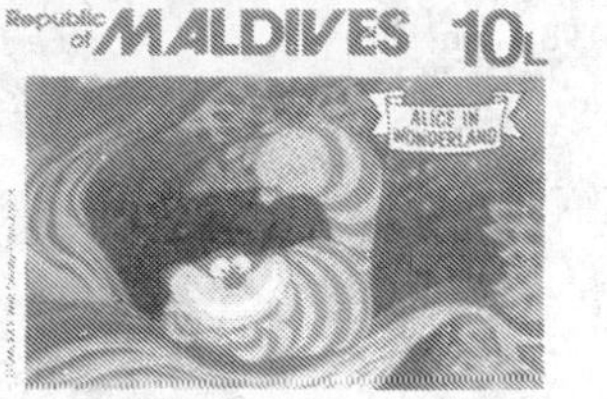

The Cheshire Cat — A133

Designs: Scenes from Walt Disney's Alice in Wonderland. 5r, vert.

1980, Dec. 22 — Perf. 11

887 A133	1 l	multicolored	.15	.15
888 A133	2 l	multicolored	.15	.15
889 A133	3 l	multicolored	.15	.15
890 A133	4 l	multicolored	.15	.15
891 A133	5 l	multicolored	.15	.15
892 A133	10 l	multicolored	.15	.15
893 A133	15 l	multicolored	.15	.15
894 A133	2.50r	multicolored	1.25	1.25
895 A133	4r	multicolored	2.00	2.00
		Set value	3.60	3.60

Souvenir Sheet

896 A133	5r	multicolored	3.50	3.50

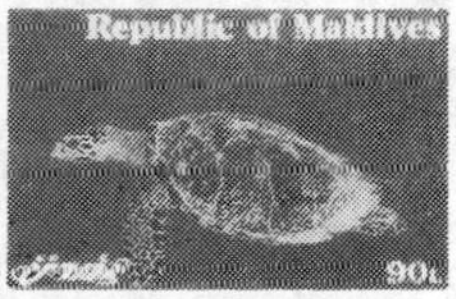

Ridley Turtle A134

1980, Dec. 29 — Litho. — Perf. 14

897 A134	90 l	shown	.45	.45
898 A134	1.25r	Angel flake fish	.62	.62
899 A134	2r	Spiny lobster	1.00	1.00
		Nos. 897-899 (3)	2.07	2.07

Souvenir Sheet

900 A134	4r	Fish	2.00	2.00

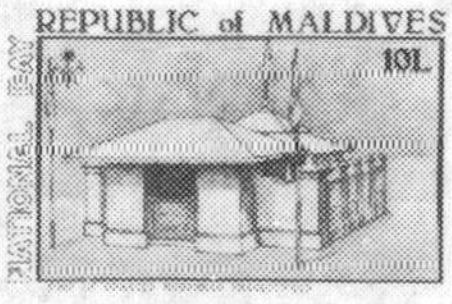

Tomb of Ghaazee Muhammad Thakurufaan — A135

National Day (Furniture and Palace of Muhammad Thakurufaan): 20 l, Hanging lamp, 16th century, vert. 30 l, Chair, vert. 95 l, Utheem Palace. 10r, Couch, vert.

1981, Jan. 7 — Perf. 15

901 A135	10 l	multicolored	.15	.15
902 A135	20 l	multicolored	.15	.15
903 A135	30 l	multicolored	.15	.15
904 A135	95 l	multicolored	.48	.48
905 A135	10r	multicolored	5.00	5.00
		Nos. 901-905 (5)	5.93	5.93

Royal Wedding Issue

Common Design Type

1981, June 22 — Litho. — Perf. 14

906 CD331	1r	Couple	.50	.50
907 CD331	2r	Buckingham Palace	1.00	1.00
908 CD331	5r	Charles	2.50	2.50
		Nos. 906-908 (3)	4.00	4.00

Souvenir Sheet

909 CD331	10r	Royal state coach	5.00	5.00

Nos. 906-908 also printed in sheets of 5 plus label, perf. 12, in changed colors.

Majlis Chamber, 1932 A136

50th Anniv. of Citizens' Majlis (Grievance Rights); 1r, Sultan Muhammed Shamsuddin III (instituted system, 1932), vert. 4r, Constitution, 1932.

1981, June 27   *Perf. 15*
910 A136 95 l multicolored   .35 .35
911 A136 1r multicolored   .40 .40

Souvenir Sheet
912 A136 4r multicolored   2.00 2.00

Self-portrait with Palette, by Picasso (1881-1973) — A137

Child Holding a Dove A138

1981, Aug. 26   **Litho.**   *Perf. 14*
913 A137 5 l shown   .15 .15
914 A137 10 l Woman in Blue   .15 .15
915 A137 25 l Boy with a Pipe   .15 .15
916 A137 30 l Card Player   .15 .15
917 A137 90 l Sailor   .22 .22
918 A137 3r Self-portrait   .75 .75
919 A137 5r Harlequin   1.25 1.25

Imperf
920 A138 10r shown   4.75 4.75
Nos. 913-920 (8)   7.57 7.57

No. 5 on Airmail Cover — A139

1981, Sept. 9   **Litho.**   *Perf. 14*
921 A139 25 l multicolored   .15 .15
922 A139 75 l multicolored   .36 .36
923 A139 5r multicolored   2.50 2.50
Nos. 921-923 (3)   3.01 3.01

Postal service, 75th anniv.

Hulule Intl. Airport Opening A140

1981, Nov. 11
924 A140 5 l Jet taking off   .15 .15
925 A140 20 l Passengers leaving jet   .15 .15
926 A140 1.80r Refueling   .90 .90
927 A140 4r shown   2.00 2.00
Nos. 924-927 (4)   3.20 3.20

Souvenir Sheet
928 A140 5r Terminal   2.00 2.00

Intl. Year of the Disabled — A141   Decade for Women — A142

1981, Nov. 18   **Litho.**   *Perf. 14½*
929 A141 2 l Homer   .15 .15
930 A141 5 l Cervantes   .15 .15
931 A141 1r Beethoven   .50 .50
932 A141 5r Van Gogh   2.50 2.50
Nos. 929-932 (4)   3.30 3.30

Souvenir Sheet
933 A141 4r Helen Keller, Anne Sullivan   2.00 2.00

1981, Nov. 25   *Perf. 14*
934 A142 20 l Preparing fish   .15 .15
935 A142 90 l 16th cent. woman   .45 .45
936 A142 1r Tending yam crop   .50 .50
937 A142 2r Making coir rope   1.00 1.00
Nos. 934-937 (4)   2.10 2.10

Fishermen's Day — A143

1981, Dec. 10
938 A143 5 l Collecting bait   .15 .15
939 A143 15 l Fishing boats   .15 .15
940 A143 90 l Fisherman holding catch   .45 .45
941 A143 1.30r Sorting fish   .70 .70
Nos. 938-941 (4)   1.45 1.45

Souvenir Sheet
942 A143 3r Loading fish for export   1.50 1.50

World Food Day — A144

1981, Dec. 30   **Litho.**   *Perf. 14*
943 A144 10 l Breadfruit   .15 .15
944 A144 25 l Hen, chicks   .15 .15
945 A144 30 l Corn   .15 .15
946 A144 75 l Skipjack tuna   .38 .38
947 A144 1r Pumpkins   .50 .50
948 A144 2r Coconuts   1.00 1.00
Nos. 943-948 (6)   2.33 2.33

Souvenir Sheet
949 A144 5r Eggplants   2.25 2.25

50th Anniv. of Walt Disney's Pluto (1980) A145

1982, Mar. 29   **Litho.**   *Perf. 13½x14*
950 A145 4r Scene from Chain Gang, 1930   2.50 2.50

Souvenir Sheet
951 A145 6r The Pointer, 1939   4.00 4.00

Princess Diana Issue
Common Design Type
1982, July 15   **Litho.**   *Perf. 14½x14*
952 CD332 95 l Balmoral   .50 .50
953 CD332 3r Honeymoon   1.50 1.50
954 CD332 5r Diana   2.50 2.50
Nos. 952-954 (3)   4.50 4.50

Souvenir Sheet
955 CD332 8r Diana, diff.   3.50 3.50

#952-954 also issued in sheetlets of 5 plus label. For overprints and surcharges see Nos. 966-969, 1050, 1052, 1054, 1056.

Scouting Year A146

1982, Aug. 9   **Litho.**   *Perf. 14*
956 A146 1.30r Saluting   .65 .65
957 A146 1.80r Fire building   .90 .90
958 A146 4r Lifesaving   2.00 2.00
959 A146 5r Map reading   2.50 2.50
Nos. 956-959 (4)   6.05 6.05

Souvenir Sheet
960 A146 10r Flag, emblem   4.75 4.75

1982 World Cup — A147   TB Bacillus Cent. — A148

Various soccer players.

1982, Oct. 4   **Litho.**   *Perf. 14*
961 A147 90 l multicolored   .45 .45
962 A147 1.50r multicolored   .75 .75
963 A147 3r multicolored   1.50 1.50
964 A147 5r multicolored   2.50 2.50
Nos. 961-964 (4)   5.20 5.20

Souvenir Sheet
965 A147 10r multicolored   5.00 5.00

Nos. 952-955 Overprinted: "ROYAL BABY/21.6.82"

1982, Oct. 18   *Perf. 14½x14*
966 CD332 95 l multicolored   .50 .50
967 CD332 3r multicolored   1.50 1.50
968 CD332 5r multicolored   2.50 2.50
Nos. 966-968 (3)   4.50 4.50

Souvenir Sheet
969 CD332 8r multicolored   4.00 4.00

Birth of Prince William of Wales, June 21. #966-968 also issued in sheetlets of 5 + label. For surcharges see #1051, 1053, 1055, 1057.

1982, Nov. 22   *Perf. 14½*
970 A148 5 l Koch isolating bacillus   .15 .15
971 A148 15 l Slide, microscope   .15 .15
972 A148 95 l Koch, 1905   .75 .75
973 A148 3r Koch, book illus. plates   2.25 2.25
Nos. 970-973 (4)   3.30 3.30

Souvenir Sheet
974 A148 5r Koch in lab   2.25 2.25

Natl. Education — A149

Designs: 90 l, Basic education scheme, 1980-85. 95 l, Formal primary education. 1.30r, Teacher training. 2.50r, Educational materials production. 6r, Thanna typewrite.

1982, Nov. 15
975 A149 90 l multicolored   .35 .35
976 A149 95 l multicolored   .38 .38
977 A149 1.30r multicolored   .55 .55
978 A149 2.50r multicolored   .90 .90
Nos. 975-978 (4)   2.18 2.18

Souvenir Sheet
979 A149 6r multicolored   2.75 2.75

Manned Flight Bicentenary A150

1983, July 28   **Litho.**   *Perf. 14*
980 A150 90 l Blohm & Voss Ha-139   .45 .45
981 A150 1.45r Macchi Castoldi MC-72   .72 .72
982 A150 4r Boeing F4B-3   2.00 2.00
983 A150 5r Le France   2.50 2.50
Nos. 980-983 (4)   5.67 5.67

Souvenir Sheet
984 A150 10r Nadar's Le Geant   4.75 4.75

For overprints see Nos. 1020-1022.

Roughtooth Dolphin A151

1983, Sept. 6   **Litho.**   *Perf. 14*
985 A151 30 l shown   .15 .15
986 A151 40 l Indopacific humpback dolphin   .20 .20
987 A151 4r Finless porpoise   2.00 2.00
988 A151 6r Pygmy sperm whale   3.00 3.00
Nos. 985-988 (4)   5.35 5.35

Souvenir Sheet
989 A151 5r Striped dolphins   2.50 2.50

Classic Cars A152

1983, Aug. 15   **Litho.**   *Perf. 14½x15*
990 A152 5 l Curved Dash Olds-mobile, 1902   .15 .15
991 A152 30 l Aston Martin Tourer, 1932   .15 .15
992 A152 40 l Lamborghini Miura, 1966   .20 .20
993 A152 1r Mercedes-Benz 300sl, 1954   .50 .50
994 A152 1.45r Stutz Bearcat, 1913   .72 .72
995 A152 5r Lotus Elite, 1958   2.50 2.50
Nos. 990-995 (6)   4.22 4.22

Souvenir Sheet
996 A152 10r Grand Prix Sunbeam, 1924   4.75 4.75

World Communications Year — A153

Designs: 50 l, Dish antenna. 1r, Mail transport. 2r, Ship-to-shore communications. 10r, Land-air communications. 20r, Telephone calls.

1983, Oct. 9   *Perf. 14*
997 A153 50 l multicolored   .25 .25
998 A153 1r multicolored   .50 .50
999 A153 2r multicolored   1.00 1.00
1000 A153 10r multicolored   5.00 5.00
Nos. 997-1000 (4)   6.75 6.75

Souvenir Sheet
1001 A153 20r multicolored   9.50 9.50

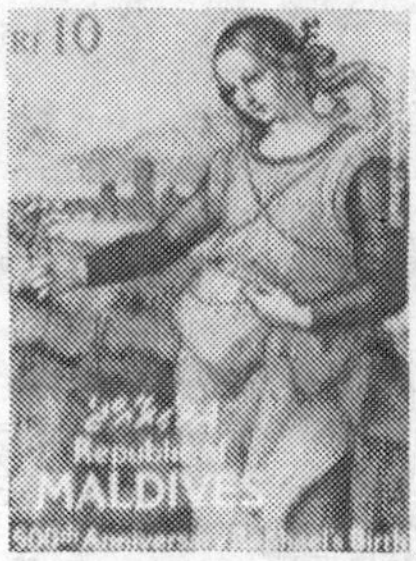

Raphael, 500th Birth Anniv. A154

1983, Oct. 25 Litho. *Perf. 13½x14*

1002 A154	90 l	La Donna Gravida	.45	.45
1003 A154	3r	Jean of Aragon	1.50	1.50
1004 A154	4r	The Woman with the Unicorn	2.00	2.00
1005 A154	6r	La Muta	3.00	3.00
		Nos. 1002-1005 (4)	6.95	6.95

Souvenir Sheet

1006 A154	10r	The Knights Dream	4.75	4.75

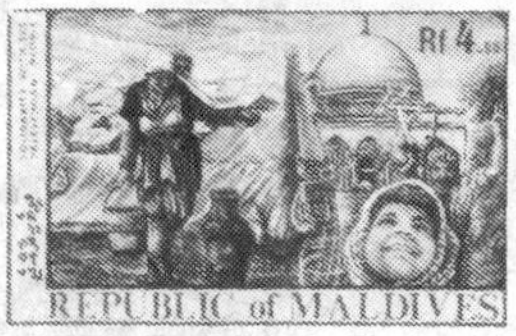

Intl. Palestinian Solidarity Day — A155

Various refugees, mosque.

1983, Nov. 29 Litho. *Perf. 14*

1007 A155	4r	multicolored	2.00	2.00
1008 A155	5r	multicolored	2.50	2.50
1009 A155	6r	multicolored	3.00	3.00
		Nos. 1007-1009 (3)	7.50	7.50

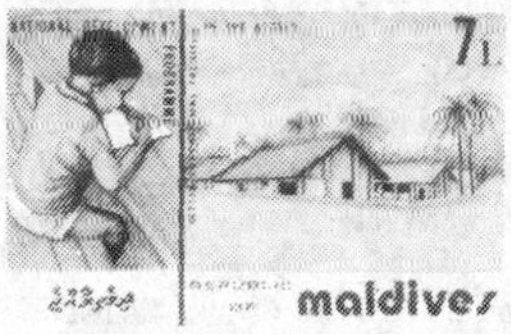

Natl. Development Programs — A156

1983, Dec. 10 Litho. *Perf. 13½x14*

1010 A156	7 l	Education	.15	.15
1011 A156	10 l	Health care	.15	.15
1012 A156	5r	Food production	2.50	2.50
1013 A156	6r	Fishing industry	3.00	3.00
		Nos. 1010-1013 (4)	5.80	5.80

Souvenir Sheet

1014 A156	10r	Inter-atoll transportation	4.75	4.75

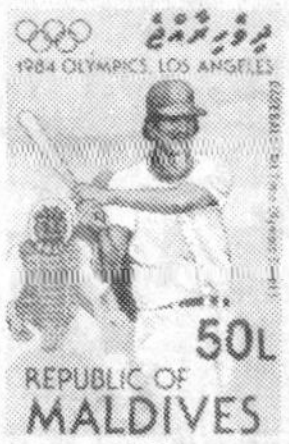

A157

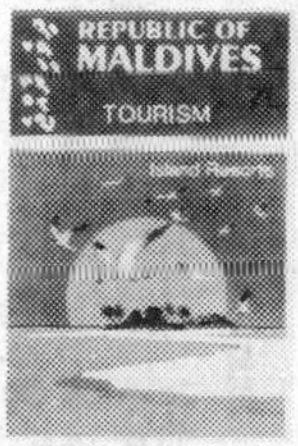

Tourism — A158

1984, Feb. *Perf. 14*

1015 A157	50 l	Baseball	.25	.25
1016 A157	1.55r	Swimming	.80	.80
1017 A157	3r	Judo	1.50	1.50
1018 A157	4r	Shot put	2.00	2.00
		Nos. 1015-1018 (4)	4.55	4.55

Souvenir Sheet

1019 A157	10r	Handball	4.75	4.75

23rd Olympic Games, Los Angeles, 7/28-8/12. For overprints see Nos. 1090-1094.

Nos. 982-984 Overprinted: "19th UPU/CONGRESS HAMBURG"

1984 Litho. *Perf. 14*

1020 A150	4r	multicolored	2.00	2.00
1021 A150	5r	multicolored	2.50	2.50

Souvenir Sheet

1022 A150	10r	multicolored	4.75	4.75

1984, Sept. 21 Litho. *Perf. 14½*

1023 A158	7 l	Island resorts	.15	.15
1024 A158	15 l	Cruising	.15	.15
1025 A158	20 l	Snorkelling	.15	.15
1026 A158	2r	Wind surfing	.55	.55
1027 A158	4r	Scuba diving	1.10	1.10
1028 A158	6r	Night fishing	1.75	1.75
1029 A158	8r	Big game fishing	2.25	2.25
1030 A158	10r	Nature (turtle)	2.75	2.75
		Nos. 1023-1030 (8)	8.85	8.85

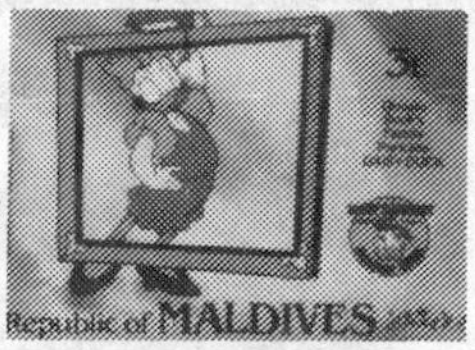

50th Anniv. of Donald Duck A160

Scenes from various cartoons and movies.

1984, Nov. Litho. *Perf. 14*

1040 A160	3 l	multi	.15	.15
1041 A160	4 l	multi	.15	.15
1042 A160	5 l	multi	.15	.15
1043 A160	10 l	multi	.15	.15
1044 A160	15 l	multi	.15	.15
1045 A160	25 l	multi	.15	.15
1045A A160	5r	multi, perf. 12x12½	1.75	1.75
1046 A160	8r	multi	2.75	2.75
1047 A160	10r	multi	3.50	3.50
		Nos. 1040-1047 (9)	8.90	8.90

Souvenir Sheets

1048 A160	15r	multi	5.00	5.00
1049 A160	15r	multi	5.00	5.00

Nos. 952-955, 966-969 Surcharged

1984, July Litho. *Perf. 14½x14*

1050 CD332	1.45r on 95 l #952	*2.50*	*2.00*
1051 CD332	1.45r on 95 l #966	*2.50*	*2.00*
1052 CD332	1.45r on 3r #953	*2.50*	*2.00*
1053 CD332	1.45r on 3r #967	*2.50*	*2.00*
1054 CD332	1.45r on 5r #954	*2.50*	*2.00*
1055 CD332	1.45r on 5r #968	*2.50*	*2.00*
	Nos. 1050-1055 (6)	*15.00*	*12.00*

Souvenir Sheet

1056 CD332	1.45r on 8r #955	*10.00*	*8.00*
1057 CD332	1.45r on 8r #969	*10.00*	*8.00*

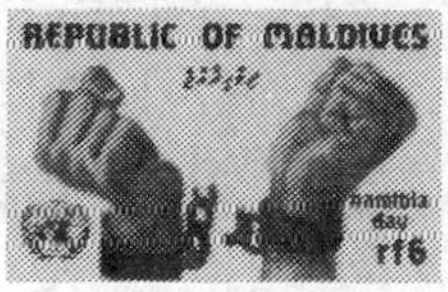

Namibia Day A161

1984, Aug. 26 *Perf. 15*

1058 A161	6r	Breaking chain	1.75	1.75
1059 A161	8r	Family, rising sun	2.25	2.25

Souvenir Sheet

1060 A161	10r	Map, sun	2.75	2.75

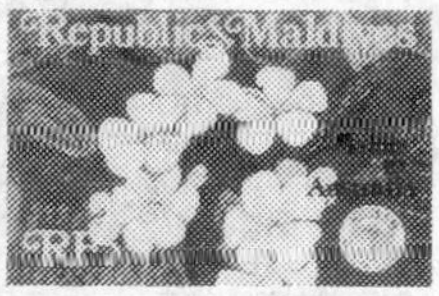

Ausipex '84 — A162

1984, Sept. 21

1061 A162	5r	Frangipani	2.00	2.00
1062 A162	10r	Cooktown orchid	4.00	4.00

Souvenir Sheet

1063 A162	15r	Sun orchids	6.00	6.00

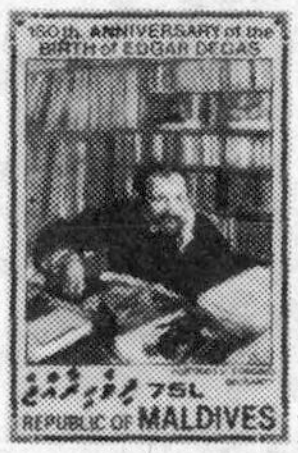

150th Birth Anniv. of Edgar Degas — A163

1984, Oct. Litho. *Perf. 14*

1064 A163	75 l	Portrait of Edmond Iduranty	.20	.20
1065 A163	2r	Portrait of James Tissot	.55	.55
1066 A163	5r	Portrait of Achille Degas	1.40	1.40
1067 A163	10r	Lady with Chrysanthemums	2.75	2.75
		Nos. 1064-1067 (4)	4.90	4.90

Souvenir Sheet

1068 A163	15r	Self-Portrait	4.00	4.00

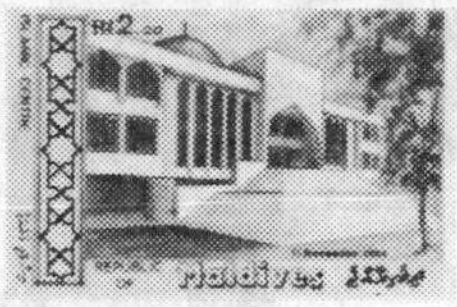

Opening of Islamic Center A164

1984, Nov. 11 Litho. *Perf. 15*

1069 A164	2r	Mosque	.50	.50
1070 A164	5r	Mosque, minaret, vert.	1.25	1.25

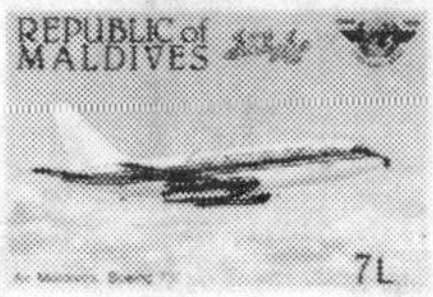

40th Anniv., International Civil Aviation Organization A165

1984, Nov. 19 Litho. *Perf. 14*

1071 A165	7 l	Boeing 737	.15	.15
1072 A165	4r	Lockheed L-1011	1.10	1.10
1073 A165	6r	McDonnell Douglas DC-10	1.75	1.75
1074 A165	8r	Lockheed L-1011	2.25	2.25
		Nos. 1071-1074 (4)	5.25	5.25

Souvenir Sheet

1075 A165	15r	Shorts SC7 Skyvan	4.00	4.00

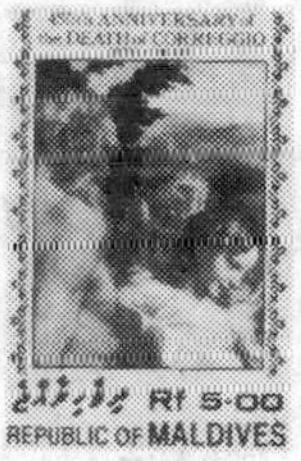

450th Anniv. of the Death of Correggio — A166

1984, Dec. 10 Litho. *Perf. 14*

1076 A166	5r	Detail from The Day	1.40	1.40
1077 A166	10r	Detail from The Night	2.75	2.75

Souvenir Sheet

1078 A166	15r	Portrait of a Man	4.00	4.00

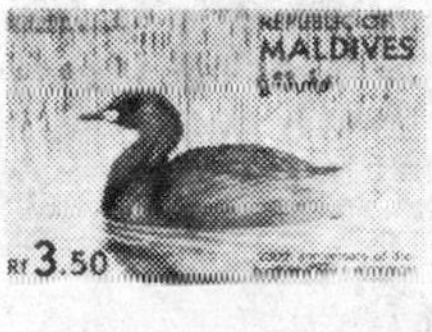

John J. Audubon A167

Illustrations from Audubon's Birds of America.

1985, Mar. 9 Litho. *Perf. 14*

1079 A167	3r	Flesh-footed shearwater, vert.	.90	.90
1080 A167	3.50r	Little grebe	1.00	1.00
1081 A167	4r	Great cormorant, vert.	1.10	1.10
1082 A167	4.50r	White-faced storm petrel	1.25	1.25
		Nos. 1079-1082 (4)	4.25	4.25

Souvenir Sheet

1083 A167	15r	Red-necked phalarope	4.00	4.00

See Nos. 1195-1204.

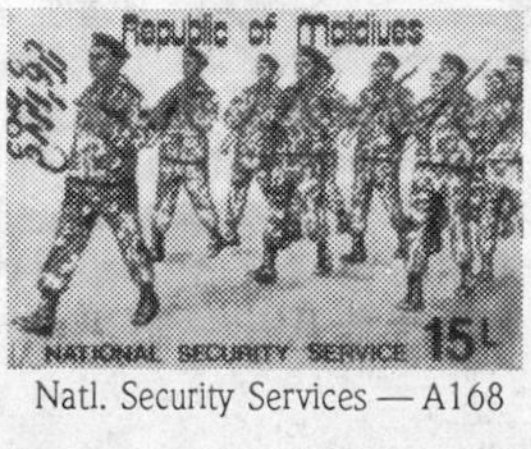

Natl. Security Services — A168

1985, June 6 Litho. *Perf. 14*

1084 A168	15 l	Drill	.15	.15
1085 A168	20 l	Combat training	.15	.15
1086 A168	1r	Fire fighting	.30	.30
1087 A168	2r	Coast guard	.60	.60
1088 A168	10r	Parade, vert.	3.00	3.00
		Nos. 1084-1088 (5)	4.20	4.20

Souvenir Sheet

1089 A168	10r	Badge, cannon	3.00	3.00

Nos. 1015-1019 Ovptd. with Country or "Gold Medalist," Winner and Nation in 3 Lines

1985, July 17

1090 A157	50 l	Japan	.15	.15
1091 A157	1.55r	Theresa Andrews	.45	.45
1092 A157	3r	Frank Wieneke	.90	.90
1093 A157	4r	Claudia Loch	1.25	1.25
		Nos. 1090-1093 (4)	2.75	2.75

Souvenir Sheet

1094 A157	10r	US	3.00	3.00

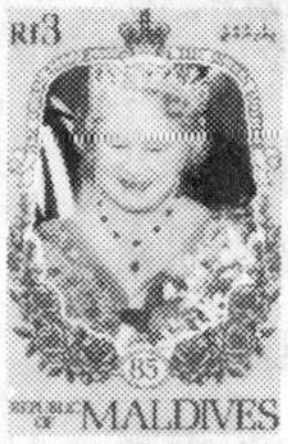

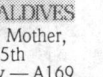

Queen Mother, 85th Birthday — A169

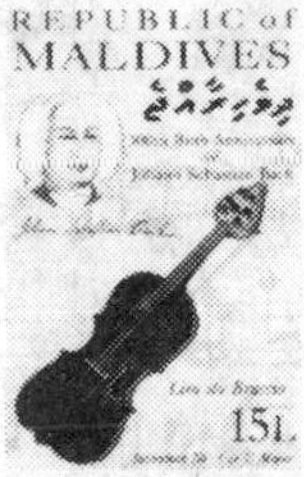

Johann Sebastian Bach, Composer — A170

1985-86 *Perf. 14, 12 (1r, 4r, 10r)*

1095 A169	1r	Wearing tiara	.22	.22
1096 A169	3r	like 1r	.70	.70
1097 A169	4r	At Middlesex Hospital, horiz.	.90	.90
1098 A169	5r	like 4r	1.10	1.10
1099 A169	7r	Wearing fur stole	1.50	1.50
1100 A169	10r	like 7r	2.25	2.25
		Nos. 1095-1100 (6)	6.67	6.67

Souvenir Sheet

1101 A169	15r	With Prince of Wales	4.25	4.25

Issued: 1r, 4r, 10r, 1/4/86; 3r, 5r, 7r, 15r, 8/20/85. #1095, 1097, 1100 printed in sheets of 5 + label.

1985, Sept. 3 *Perf. 14*

Portrait, Invention No. 1 in C Major and: 15 l, Lira da Braccio. 2r, Tenor oboe. 4r, Serpent. 10r, Table organ.

1102 A170	15 l	multi	.15	.15
1103 A170	2r	multi	.60	.60
1104 A170	4r	multi	1.25	1.25
1105 A170	10r	multi	3.00	3.00
		Nos. 1102-1105 (4)	5.00	5.00

Souvenir Sheet

1106 A170	15r	Portrait	4.25	4.25

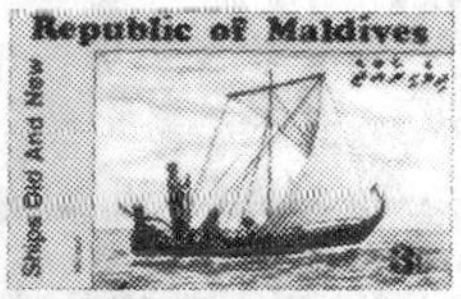

Ships A171

1985, Sept. 23

1107 A171	3 l	Masodi	.15	.15
1108 A171	5 l	Naalu Baththeli	.15	.15
1109 A171	10 l	Addu Odi	.15	.15
1110 A171	2.60r	Masdhoni, 2nd generation	.78	.78
1111 A171	2.70r	Masdhoni	.80	.80
1112 A171	3r	Baththeli Dhoni	.90	.90
1113 A171	5r	Inter 1	1.50	1.50
1114 A171	10r	Yacht Dhoni	3.00	3.00
		Nos. 1107-1114 (8)	7.43	7.43

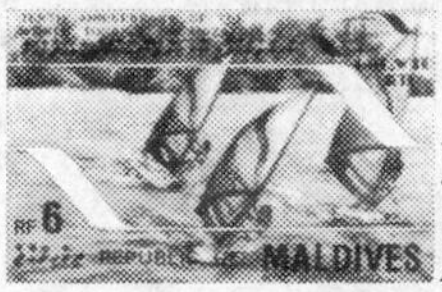

World Tourism Org., 10th Anniv. A172

1985, Oct. 2

1115 A172	6r	Wind surfing	1.75	1.75
1116 A172	8r	Scuba diving	2.50	2.50

Souvenir Sheet

1117 A172	15r	Kuda Hithi Resort	4.25	4.25

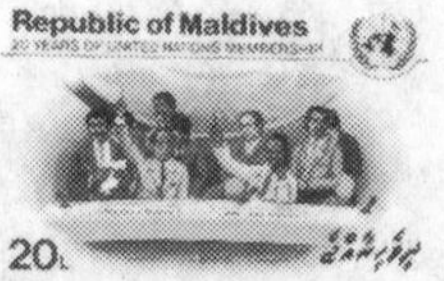

Maldives Admission to UN, 20th Anniv. A173

1985, Oct. 24

1118 A173 20 l shown .15 .15
1119 A173 15r Flags, UN building 4.25 4.25

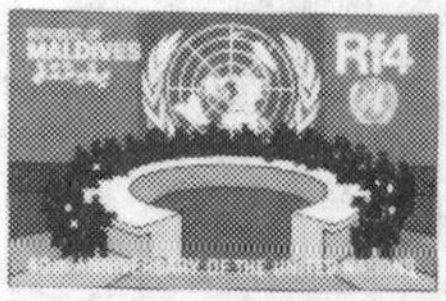

UN 40th Anniv., Intl. Peace Year A174

1985, Oct. 24 **Litho.** ***Perf. 14***

1120 A174 15 l UN Building .15 .15
1121 A174 2r IPY emblem .60 .60
1122 A174 4r Security Council 1.20 1.20
1123 A174 10r Lion, lamb 3.00 3.00
Nos. 1120-1123 (4) 4.95 4.95

Souvenir Sheet

1124 A174 15r UN Building, diff. 4.50 4.50

Nos. 1120-1121, 1123-1124, vert.

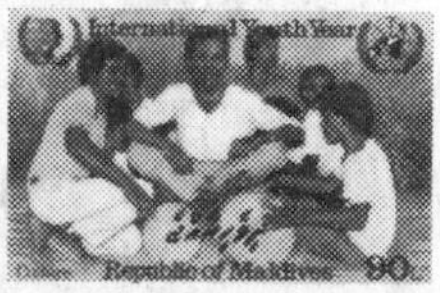

Intl. Youth Year — A175

1985, Nov. 20 ***Perf. 15***

1125 A175 90 l Culture .28 .28
1126 A175 6r Games 1.75 1.75
1127 A175 10r Community service, vert. 3.00 3.00
Nos. 1125-1127 (3) 5.03 5.03

Souvenir Sheet

1128 A175 15r Youth camp, vert. 4.25 4.25

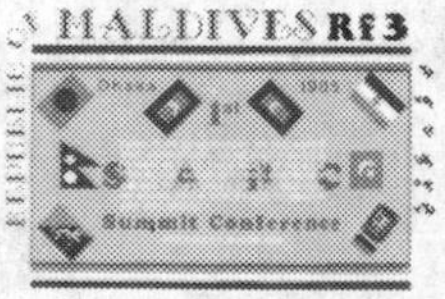

Summit Nations Flags, Dedication by Pres. Maumoon A176

1985, Dec. 8 ***Perf. 14***

1129 A176 3r multicolored .90 .90

South Asian Regional Cooperation, SARC, 1st Summit, Dec. 7-8, 1985.

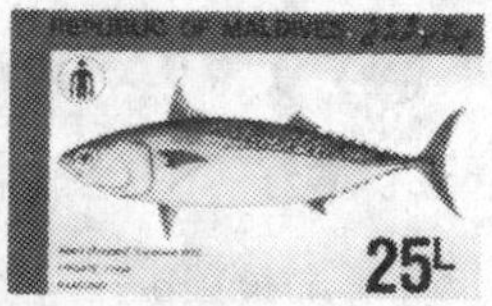

Tuna A177

1985, Dec. 10

1130 A177 25 l Frigate .15 .15
1131 A177 75 l Little tuna .22 .22
1132 A177 3r Dogtooth .90 .90
1133 A177 5r Yellowfin 1.50 1.50
Nos. 1130-1133 (4) 2.77 2.77

Souvenir Sheet

1134 A177 15r Skipjack 4.25 4.25

Fisherman's Day.

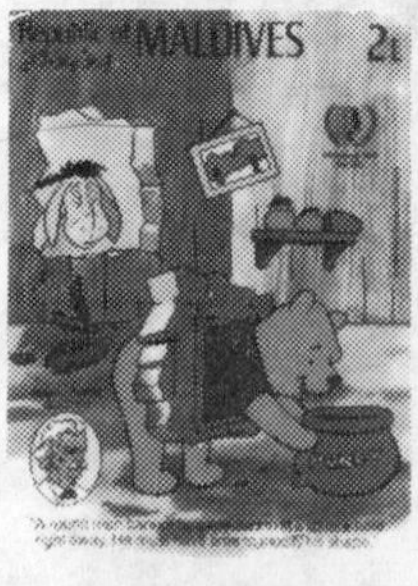

Mark Twain, American Novelist A178

Disney characters and Twain quotes.

1985, Dec. 21

1135 A178 2 l multicolored .15 .15
1136 A178 3 l multicolored .15 .15
1137 A178 4 l multicolored .15 .15
1138 A178 20 l multicolored .15 .15
1139 A178 4r multicolored 1.25 1.25
1140 A178 13r multicolored 4.00 4.00
Nos. 1135-1140 (6) 5.85 5.85

Souvenir Sheet

1141 A178 15r multicolored 4.50 4.50

Intl. Youth Year. 4r issued in sheet of 8.

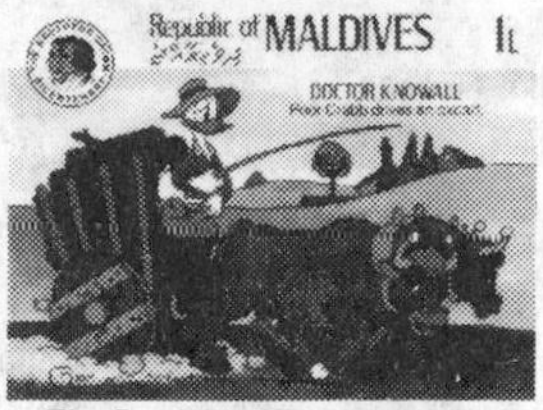

The Brothers Grimm — A179

Disney characters in Doctor Knowall.

1985, Dec. 21

1142 A179 1 l multicolored .15 .15
1143 A179 5 l multicolored .15 .15
1144 A179 10 l multicolored .15 .15
1145 A179 15 l multicolored .15 .15
1146 A179 3r multicolored .90 .90
1147 A179 14r multicolored 4.25 4.25
Nos. 1142-1147 (6) 5.75 5.75

Souvenir Sheet

1148 A179 15r multicolored 4.50 4.50

3r issued in sheets of 8.

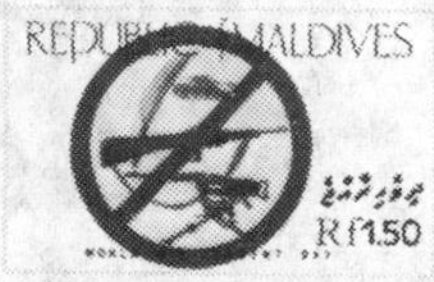

World Disarmament Day — A180

1986, Feb. 10 ***Perf. 14½x14***

1149 A180 1.50r shown .45 .45
1150 A180 10r Dove 3.00 3.00

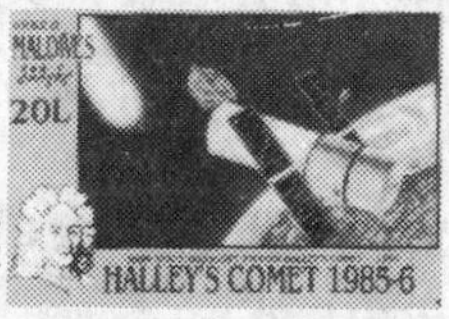

Halley's Comet A181

Designs: 20 l, NASA space telescope. 1.50r, Giotto space probe. 2r, Plant-A probe, Japan. 4r, Edmond Halley, Stonehenge. 5r, Vega probe, USSR. 15r, Comet over Male.

1986, Apr. 29

1151 A181 20 l multicolored .15 .15
1152 A181 1.50r multicolored .45 .45
1153 A181 2r multicolored .60 .60
1154 A181 4r multicolored 1.20 1.20
1155 A181 5r multicolored 1.50 1.50
Nos. 1151-1155 (5) 3.90 3.90

Souvenir Sheet

1156 A181 15r multicolored 4.50 4.50

See Nos. 1210-1215.

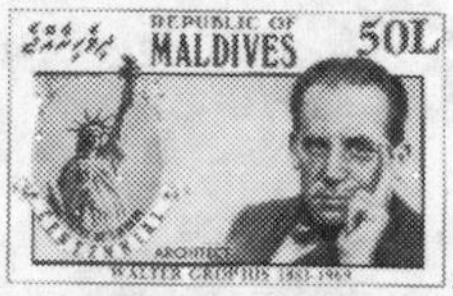

Statue of Liberty, Cent. A182

Detail of statue and: 50 l, Walter Gropius (1883-1969), architect. 70 l, John Lennon (1940-1980), musician. 1r, George Balanchine (1904-1983), choreographer. 10r, Franz Werfel (1890-1945), writer. 15r, Close-up of statue, vert.

1986, May 5

1157 A182 50 l multicolored .15 .15
1158 A182 70 l multicolored .20 .20
1159 A182 1r multicolored .30 .30
1160 A182 10r multicolored 3.00 3.00
Nos. 1157-1160 (4) 3.65 3.65

Souvenir Sheet

1161 A182 15r multicolored 4.50 4.50

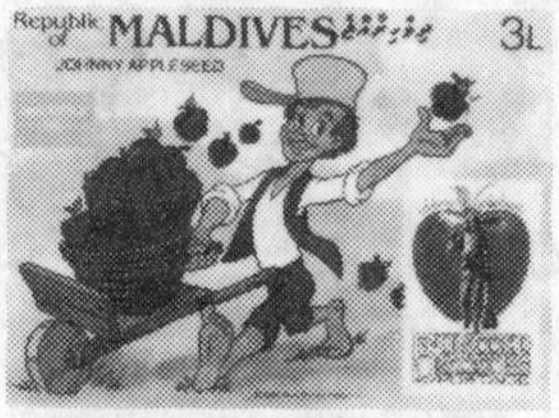

AMERIPEX '86 — A183

US stamps and Disney portrayals of American legends: 3 l, No. 1317, Johnny Appleseed. 4 l, No. 1122, Paul Bunyan. 5 l, No. 1381, Casey at the Bat. 10 l, No. 1548, Tales of Sleepy Hollow. 15 l, No. 922, John Henry. 20 l, No. 1061, Windwagon Smith. 13r, No. 1409, Mike Fink. 14r, No. 993, Casey Jones. No. 1170, Remember the Alamo, No. 1330. No. 1171, Pocahontas, Nos. 328-330.

1986, May 22 ***Perf. 11***

1162 A183 3 l multicolored .15 .15
1163 A183 4 l multicolored .15 .15
1164 A183 5 l multicolored .15 .15
1165 A183 10 l multicolored .15 .15
1166 A183 15 l multicolored .15 .15
1167 A183 20 l multicolored .15 .15
1168 A183 13r multicolored 3.75 3.75
1169 A183 14r multicolored 4.00 4.00
Nos. 1162-1169 (8) 8.65 8.65

Souvenir Sheets

Perf. 14

1170 A183 15r multicolored 4.50 4.50
1171 A183 15r multicolored 4.50 4.50

Queen Elizabeth II, 60th Birthday
Common Design Type

1986, May 29 ***Perf. 14***

1172 CD339 1r Girl Guides' rally, 1938 .30 .30
1173 CD339 2r Canada visit, 1985 .60 .60
1174 CD339 12r At Sandringham, 1970 3.60 3.60
Nos. 1172-1174 (3) 4.50 4.50

Souvenir Sheet

1175 CD339 15r Royal Lodge, 1940 4.50 4.50

For overprints see Nos. 1288-1291.

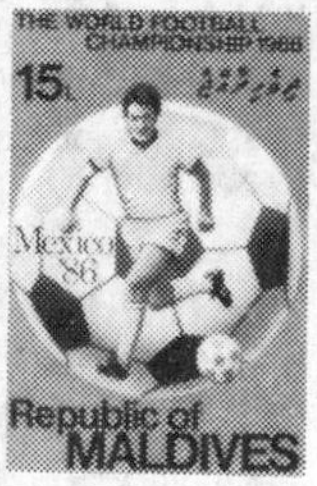

1986 World Cup Soccer Championships, Mexico — A184

Various soccer plays.

1986, June 18 **Litho.** ***Perf. 14***

1176 A184 15 l multicolored .15 .15
1177 A184 2r multicolored .60 .60
1178 A184 4r multicolored 1.20 1.20
1179 A184 10r multicolored 3.00 3.00
Nos. 1176-1179 (4) 4.95 4.95

Souvenir Sheet

1180 A184 15r multicolored 4.50 4.50

For overprints see Nos. 1205-1209.

Royal Wedding Issue, 1986
Common Design Type

Designs: 10 l, Prince Andrew and Sarah Ferguson. 2r, Andrew. 12r, Andrew on ship's deck in uniform. 15r, Couple, diff.

1986, July 23

1181 CD340 10 l multi .15 .15
1182 CD340 2r multi .60 .60
1183 CD340 12r multi 3.60 3.60
Nos. 1181-1183 (3) 4.35 4.35

Souvenir Sheet

1184 CD340 15r multi 4.50 4.50

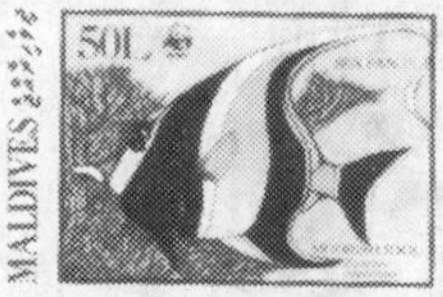

Marine Life — A185

1986, Sept. 22 **Litho.** ***Perf. 15***

1185 A185 50 l Sea fan, moorish idol .15 .15
1186 A185 90 l Regal angelfish .28 .28
1187 A185 1r Anemone fish .30 .30
1188 A185 2r Stinging coral, tiger cowrie .60 .60
1189 A185 3r Emperor angelfish, staghorn coral .90 .90
1190 A185 4r Black-naped tern 1.20 1.20
1191 A185 5r Fiddler crab, staghorn coral 1.50 1.50
1192 A185 10r Hawksbill turtle 3.00 3.00
Nos. 1185-1192 (8) 7.93 7.93

Souvenir Sheets

1193 A185 15r Trumpet fish 4.50 4.50
1194 A185 15r Long-nosed butterflyfish 4.50 4.50

Nos. 1185-1187, 1189 and 1193 show the World Wildlife Fund emblem.

Audubon Type of 1985

1986, Oct. 9 **Litho.** ***Perf. 14***

1195 A167 3 l Little blue heron .15 .15
1196 A167 4 l White-tailed kite, vert. .15 .15
1197 A167 5 l Greater shearwater .15 .15
1198 A167 10 l Magnificent frigatebird, vert. .15 .15
1199 A167 15 l Eared grebe, vert. .15 .15
1200 A167 20 l Common merganser, vert. .15 .15
1201 A167 13r Great-footed hawk 4.00 4.00
1202 A167 14r Greater prairie chicken 4.25 4.25
Nos. 1195-1202 (8) 9.15 9.15

Souvenir Sheets

1203 A167 15r White-fronted goose 4.50 4.50
1204 A167 15r Northern fulmar, vert. 4.50 4.50

Nos. 1197, 1199-1201 printed se-tenant with labels picturing a horned puffin, gray kingbird, downy woodpecker and water pipit, respectively.

Nos. 1176-1180 Ovptd. "WINNERS / Argentina 3 / W. Germany 2" in Gold

1986, Oct. 25

1205 A184 15 l multicolored .15 .15
1206 A184 2r multicolored .60 .60
1207 A184 4r multicolored 1.20 1.20
1208 A184 10r multicolored 3.00 3.00
Nos. 1205-1208 (4) 4.95 4.95

Souvenir Sheet

1209 A184 15r multicolored 4.50 4.50

Nos. 1151-1156 Printed with Halley's Comet Symbol in Silver

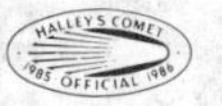

1986, Oct. 30

1210 A181 20 l multicolored .15 .15
1211 A181 1.50r multicolored .45 .45
1212 A181 2r multicolored .60 .60
1213 A181 4r multicolored 1.20 1.20
1214 A181 5r multicolored 1.50 1.50
Nos. 1210-1214 (5) 3.90 3.90

Souvenir Sheet

1215 A181 15r multicolored 4.50 4.50

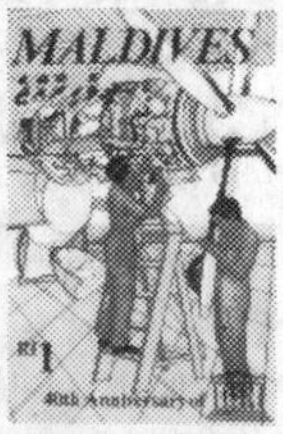

UNESCO, 40th Anniv. — A186

1986, Nov. 4 ***Perf. 15***

1216 A186 1r Aviation .30 .30
1217 A186 2r Boat-building .60 .60
1218 A186 3r Education .90 .90
1219 A186 5r Research 1.50 1.50
Nos. 1216-1219 (4) 3.30 3.30

Souvenir Sheet

1220 A186 15r Ocean exploration 4.50 4.50

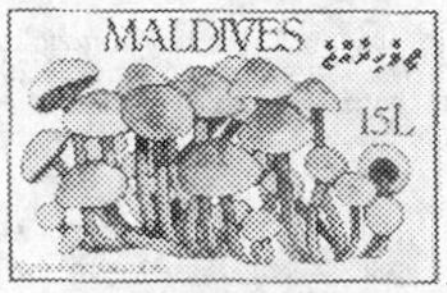
Mushrooms A187

1986, Dec. 31 Litho. *Perf. 15*

1221 A187 15 l Hypholoma fascicu-lare .15 .15
1222 A187 50 l Kuehneromyces mutabilis .15 .15
1223 A187 1r Amanita muscaria .30 .30
1224 A187 2r Agaricus campestris .60 .60
1225 A187 3r Amanita pantherina .90 .90
1226 A187 4r Coprinus comatus 1.20 1.20
1227 A187 5r Pholiota spectabilis 1.50 1.50
1228 A187 10r Pluteus cervinus 3.00 3.00
Nos. 1221-1228 (8) 7.80 7.80

Souvenir Sheets

1229 A187 15r Armillaria mellea 4.50 4.50
1230 A187 15r Stropharia aerugi-nosa 4.50 4.50

Nos. 1222-1223, 1225-1226 vert.

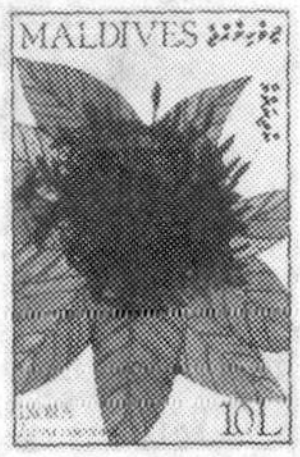
Flowers — A188

1987, Jan. 29 Litho. *Perf. 15*

1231 A188 10 l Ixora .15 .15
1232 A188 20 l Frangipani .15 .15
1233 A188 50 l Crinum .15 .15
1235 A188 2r Pink rose .60 .60
1236 A188 4r Flamboyant 1.20 1.20
1238 A188 10r Ground orchid 3.00 3.00
Nos. 1231-1238 (6) 5.25 5.25

Souvenir Sheet

1239 A188 15r Gardenia 4.50 4.50
1240 A188 15r Oleander 4.50 4.50

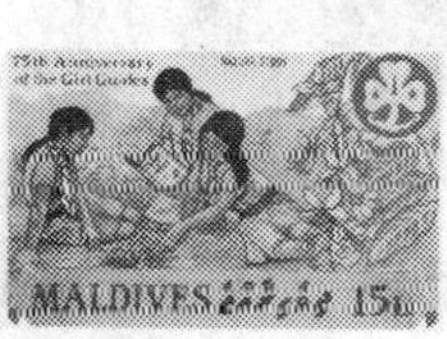
Girl Guides, 75th Anniv. (in 1985) A189

1987, Apr. 4 Litho. *Perf. 15*

1241 A189 15 l Nature study .15 .15
1242 A189 2r Guides, rabbits .60 .60
1243 A189 4r Bird-watching 1.20 1.20
1244 A189 12r Lady Baden-Powell, flag 3.50 3.50
Nos. 1241-1244 (4) 5.45 5.45

Souvenir Sheet

1245 A189 15r Sailing 4.50 4.50

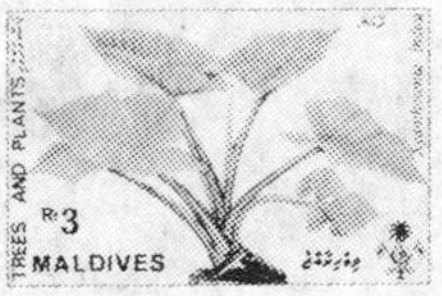
Indigenous Trees and Plants A190

1987, Apr. 22 Litho. *Perf. 14*

1246 A190 50 l Thespesia populnea, vert. .15 .15
1247 A190 1r Cocos nucifera, vert. .30 .30
1248 A190 2r Calophyllum mophyllum, vert. .60 .60
1249 A190 3r Xyanthosoma indica .90 .90
1250 A190 5r Ipomoea batatas 1.50 1.50
1251 A190 7r Artocarpus altilis, vert. 2.00 2.00
Nos. 1246-1251 (6) 5.45 5.45

Souvenir Sheet

1252 A190 15r Cocos nucifera, diff., vert. 4.50 4.50

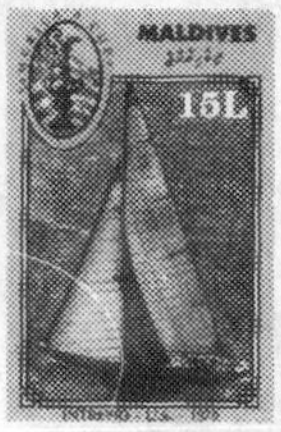
A191

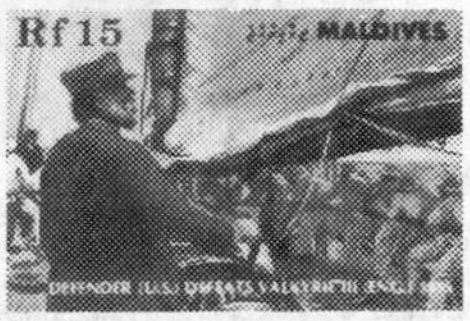
America's Cup A192

1987, May 4 Litho. *Perf. 15*

1253 A191 15 l Intrepid, 1970 .15 .15
1254 A191 1r France II, 1974 .30 .30
1255 A191 2r Gretel, 1962 .60 .60
1256 A191 12r Volunteer, 1887 3.50 3.50
Nos. 1253-1256 (4) 4.55 4.55

Souvenir Sheet

1257 A192 15r Defender Vs. Valkyrie III, 1895 4.50 4.50

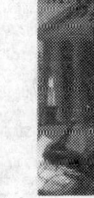

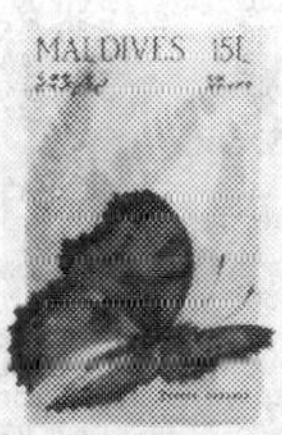
Butterflies — A193

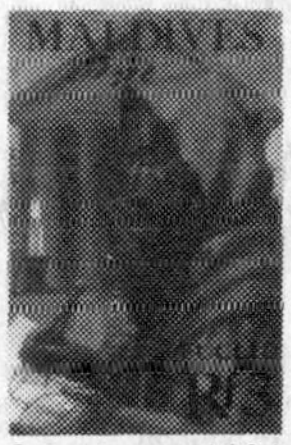
Scientists — A194

1987, Dec. 16 Litho. *Perf. 15*

1258 A193 15 l Precis octavia .15 .15
1259 A193 20 l Pachliopta hector .15 .15
1260 A193 50 l Teinopalpus imperialis .15 .15
1261 A193 1r Kallima horsfieldi .30 .30
1262 A193 2r Cethosia biblis .60 .60
1263 A193 4r Hestia jasonia 1.20 1.20
1264 A193 7r Papilio memnon 2.10 2.10
1265 A193 10r Meneris tulbaghia 3.00 3.00
Nos. 1258-1265 (8) 7.65 7.65

Souvenir Sheets

1266 A193 15r Acraea violae ac-raeinae 4.50 4.50
1267 A193 15r Hebomoia leucippe 4.50 4.50

1988, Jan. 10 *Perf. 14*

Designs: 1.50r, Sir Isaac Newton using prism to demonstrate his Theory of Light, horiz. 3r, Euclid (c. 300 B.C.), mathematician. 4r, Gregor Johann Mendel (1822-1884), botanist; father of genetics. 5r, Galileo, 1st man to observe 4 moons of Jupiter, horiz. 15r, Apollo spacecraft orbiting the moon.

1268 A194 1.50r multicolored .45 .45
1269 A194 3r multicolored .90 .90
1270 A194 4r multicolored 1.15 1.15
1271 A194 5r multicolored 1.50 1.50
Nos. 1268-1271 (4) 4.00 4.00

Souvenir Sheet

1272 A194 15r multicolored 4.50 4.50

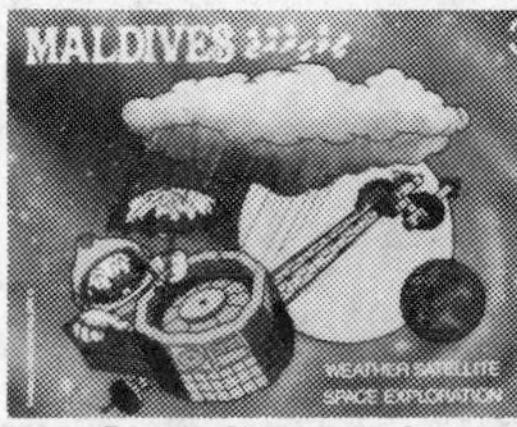
Disney Characters, Space Exploration — A195

1988, Feb. 15

1273 A195 3 l Weather satellite .15 .15
1274 A195 4 l Navigation satellite .15 .15
1275 A195 5 l Communication satellite .15 .15
1276 A195 10 l Moon rover .15 .15
1277 A195 20 l Space shuttle .15 .15
1278 A195 13r Space docking 3.50 3.50
1279 A195 14r Voyager 2 3.75 3.75
Nos. 1273-1279 (7) 8.00 8.00

Souvenir Sheets

1280 A195 15r 1st Man on Moon 4.00 4.00
1281 A195 15r Space station colony 4.00 4.00

Nos. 1276-1278 and 1281 vert.

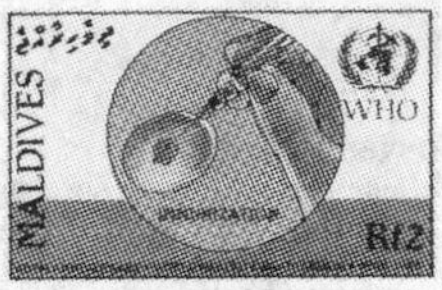
WHO, 40th Anniv. A196

1988, Apr. 7 Litho. *Perf. 14*

1282 A196 2r Immunization .58 .58
1283 A196 4r Clean water 1.15 1.15

For overprints see Nos. 1307-1308.

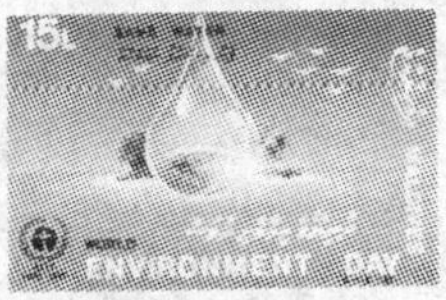
World Environment Day — A197

1988, May 9 *Perf. 15*

1284 A197 15 l Save water .15 .15
1285 A197 75 l Protect the reef .22 .22
1286 A197 2r Conserve nature .58 .58
Nos. 1284-1286 (3) .95 .95

Souvenir Sheet

1287 A197 15r Banyan tree, vert. 4.25 4.25

Nos. 1172-1175 Ovptd. "40th WEDDING ANNIVERSARY/ H.M. QUEEN ELIZABETH II/ H.R.H. THE DUKE OF EDINBURGH" in Gold

1988, July 7 Litho. *Perf. 14*

1288 CD339 1r multicolored .30 .30
1289 CD339 2r multicolored .58 .58
1290 CD339 12r multicolored 3.40 3.40
Nos. 1288-1290 (3) 4.28 4.28

Souvenir Sheet

1291 CD339 15r multicolored 4.25 4.25

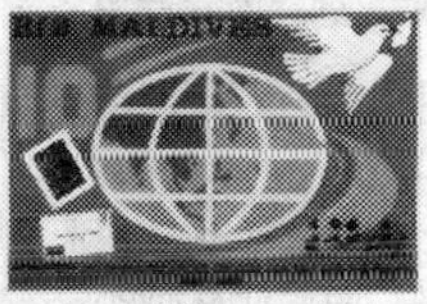
Transportation and Communication Decade for Asia and the Pacific — A198

Globe and: 2r, Postal communications. 3r, Earth satellite telecommunications technology. 5r, Space telecommunications technology. 10r, Automobile, aircraft and ship.

1988, May 31 Litho. *Perf. 14*

1292 A198 2r multicolored .58 .58
1293 A198 3r multicolored .85 .85
1294 A198 5r multicolored 1.45 1.45
1295 A198 10r multicolored 2.85 2.85
Nos. 1292-1295 (4) 5.73 5.73

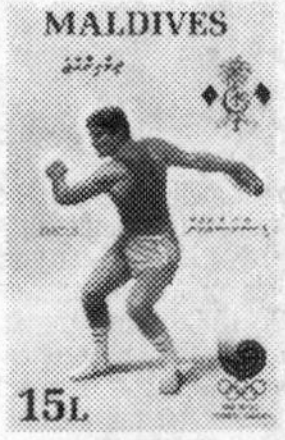
1988 Summer Olympics, Seoul — A199

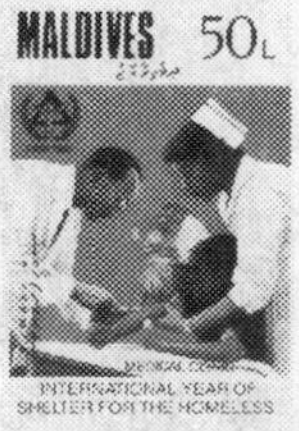
Intl. Year of Shelter for the Homeless — A200

1988, July 16

1296 A199 15 l Discus .15 .15
1297 A199 2r 100-Meter sprint .58 .58
1298 A199 4r Gymnastics, horiz. 1.15 1.15
1299 A199 12r Steeplechase, horiz. 3.45 3.45
Nos. 1296-1299 (4) 5.33 5.33

Souvenir Sheet

1300 A199 20r Tennis, horiz. 5.25 5.25

For overprints see Nos. 1311-1315.

1988, July 20

1301 A200 50 l Medical clinic .15 .15
1302 A200 3r Prefab housing .90 .90

Souvenir Sheet

1303 A200 15r Construction site 4.25 4.25

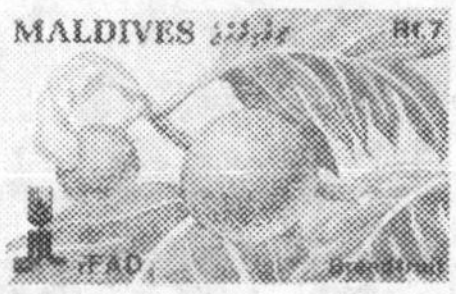
Intl. Fund for Agricultural Development (IFAD), 10th Anniv. — A201

1988, July 30

1304 A201 7r Breadfruit 2.00 2.00
1305 A201 10r Mango, vert. 2.75 2.75

Souvenir Sheet

1306 A201 15r Coconut palm, yellowtail tuna 4.25 4.25

Nos. 1282-1283 Ovptd.

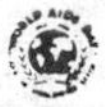

1988, Dec. 1 Litho. *Perf. 14*

1307 A196 2r multicolored .58 .58
1308 A196 4r multicolored 1.15 1.15

Intl. Day for the Fight Against Aids.

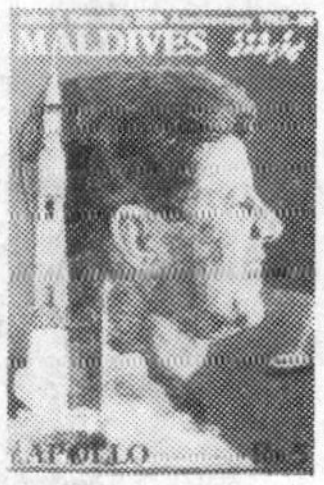
John F. Kennedy (1917-1963), 35th US President — A202

Space achievements: a, Apollo launch. b, 1st Man on the Moon. c, Earth and astronaut driving moon rover. d, Space module and Kennedy. 15r, Kennedy addressing the nation.

1989, Feb. 19

1309 Strip of 4 5.80 5.80
a.-d. A202 5r any single 1.45 1.45

Souvenir Sheet

1310 A202 15r multicolored 4.25 4.25

Nos. 1296-1300 Overprinted for Olympic Winners

1989, Apr. 29 Litho. *Perf. 14*

1311 A199 15 l "J. SCHULT / DDR" .15 .15
1312 A199 2r "C. LEWIS / USA" .58 .58
1313 A199 4r "MEN'S ALL AROUND / V. ARTEMOV USSR" 1.15 1.15
1314 A199 12r "TEAM SHOW JUMPING / W. GERMANY" 3.45 3.45
Nos. 1311-1314 (4) 5.33 5.33

Souvenir Sheet

1315 A199 20r multi 5.25 5.25

No. 1315 has marginal ovpt. "OLYMPIC WINNERS / MEN'S SINGLES / GOLD M. MECIR / CZECH. / SILVER T. MAYOTTE / USA / BRONZE B. GILBERT / USA."

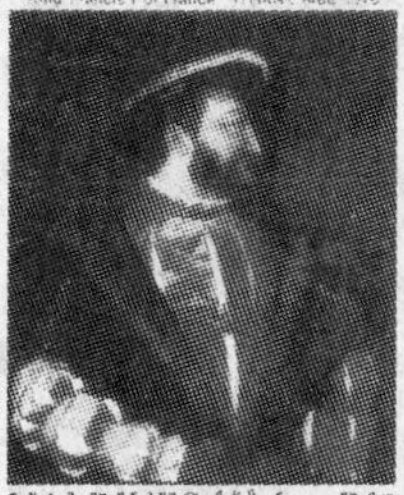
Paintings by Titian (b. 1489) A203

Designs: 15 l, Portrait of Benedetto Varchi, c. 1540. 1r, Portrait of a Young Man in a Fur, 1515. 2r, King Francis I of France, 1538. 5r, Portrait of Pietro Aretino, 1545. 15r, The Bravo, c. 1520. 20r, The Concert, 1512. No. 1322, An Allegory of Prudence, c. 1565. No. 1323, Portrait of Francesco Maria Della Rovere.

1989, May 15 Litho. *Perf. 13½x14*

1316	A203	15 l multicolored	.15	.15
1317	A203	1r multicolored	.25	.25
1318	A203	2r multicolored	.50	.50
1319	A203	5r multicolored	1.25	1.25
1320	A203	15r multicolored	3.75	3.75
1321	A203	20r multicolored	5.00	5.00
		Nos. 1316-1321 (6)	10.90	10.90

Souvenir Sheets

1322	A203	20r multicolored	5.00	5.00
1323	A203	20r multicolored	5.00	5.00

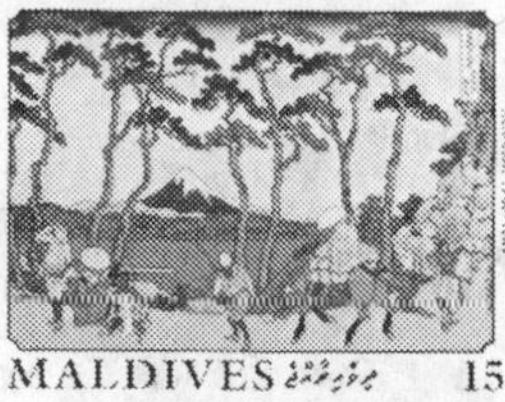

"Thirty-six Views of Mt. Fuji" — A204

Prints by Hokusai (1760-1849): 15 l, Fuji from Hodogaya. 50 l, Fuji from Lake Kawaguchi. 1r, Fuji from Owari. 2r, Fuji from Tsukudajima in Edo. 4r, Fuji from a Teahouse at Yoshida. 6r, Fuji from Tagonoura. 10r, Fuji from Mishima-goe. 12r, Fuji from the Sumida River in Edo. No. 1332, Fuji from Fukagawa in Edo. No. 1333, Fuji from Inume Pass.

1989 *Perf. 14*

1324	A204	15 l multicolored	.15	.15
1325	A204	50 l multicolored	.15	.15
1326	A204	1r multicolored	.25	.25
1327	A204	2r multicolored	.50	.50
1328	A204	4r multicolored	1.00	1.00
1329	A204	6r multicolored	1.50	1.50
1330	A204	10r multicolored	2.50	2.50
1331	A204	12r multicolored	3.00	3.00
		Nos. 1324-1331 (8)	9.05	9.05

Souvenir Sheets

1332	A204	20r multicolored	5.00	5.00
1333	A204	20r multicolored	5.00	5.00

Hirohito (1901-1989) and enthronement of Akihito as emperor of Japan.
Issue dates: #1332, Oct. 16, others, Sept. 2.

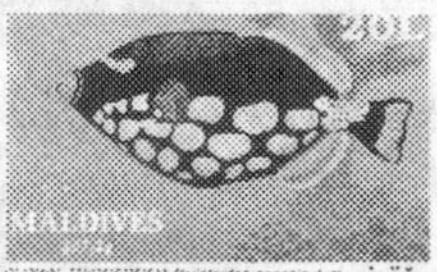

Tropical Fish — A205

1989, Oct. 16 Litho. *Perf. 14*

1334	A205	20 l Clown triggerfish	.15	.15
1335	A205	50 l Blue surgeonfish	.15	.15
1336	A205	1r Bluestripe snapper	.25	.25
1337	A205	2r Oriental sweetlips	.50	.50
1338	A205	3r Wrasse	.75	.75
1339	A205	8r Treadfin butterflyfish	2.00	2.00
1340	A205	10r Bicolor parrotfish	2.50	2.50
1341	A205	12r Saber squirrelfish	3.00	3.00
		Nos. 1334-1341 (8)	9.30	9.30

Souvenir Sheet

1342	A205	15r Butterfly perch	3.75	3.75
1343	A205	15r Semicircle angelfish	3.75	3.75

Nos. 1293-1294 Ovptd. "ASIA-PACIFIC / TELECOMMUNITY / 10 YEARS" in Silver

1989, July 5 Litho. *Perf. 14*

1344	A198	3r multicolored	.75	.75
1345	A198	5r multicolored	1.25	1.25

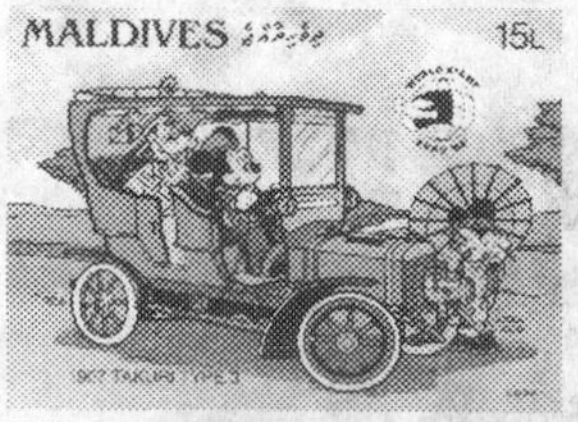

World Stamp Expo '89 Emblem, Disney Characters and Japanese Automobiles — A206

Designs: 15 l, 1907 Takuri Type 3. 50 l, 1917 Mitsubishi Model A. 1r, 1935 Datsun Roadstar. 2r, 1940 Mazda. 4r, 1959 Nissan Bluebird 310. 6r, 1958 Subaru 360. 10r, 1966 Honda 5800. 12r, 1966 Daihatsu Fellow. No. 1354, 1981 Isuzu Trooper II. No. 1355, 1985 Toyota Supra.

1989, Nov. 17 Litho. *Perf. 14x13½*

1346	A206	15 l multicolored	.15	.15
1347	A206	50 l multicolored	.15	.15
1348	A206	1r multicolored	.22	.22
1349	A206	2r multicolored	.45	.45
1350	A206	4r multicolored	.90	.90
1351	A206	6r multicolored	1.35	1.35
1352	A206	10r multicolored	2.25	2.25
1353	A206	12r multicolored	2.75	2.75
		Nos. 1346-1353 (8)	8.22	8.22

Souvenir Sheets

1354	A206	20r multicolored	4.50	4.50
1355	A206	20r multicolored	4.50	4.50

Souvenir Sheet

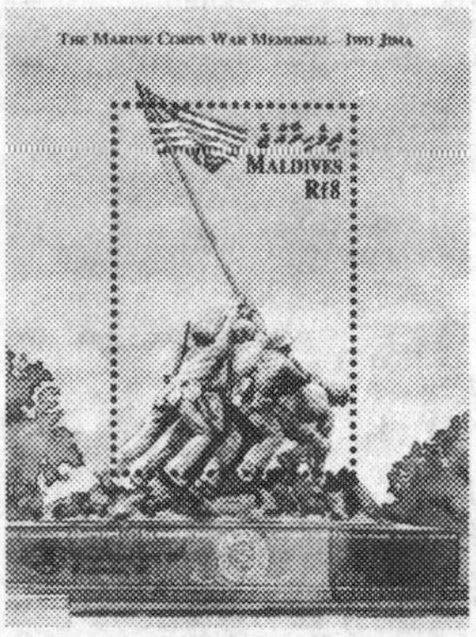

The Marine Corps War Memorial, Arlington, VA — A207

1989, Nov. 17 Litho. *Perf. 14*

1356	A207	8r multicolored	2.00	2.00

World Stamp Expo '89.

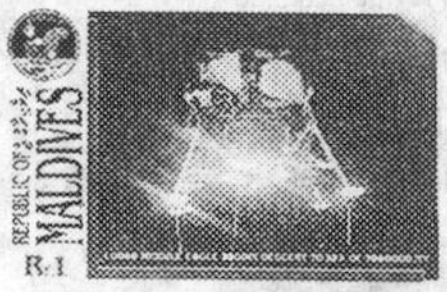

1st Moon Landing, 20th Anniv. A208

1989, Nov. 24 *Perf. 14*

1357	A208	1r *Eagle* lunar module	.25	.25
1358	A208	2r Aldrin taking soil samples	.50	.50
1359	A208	6r Solar wind experiment	1.50	1.50
1360	A208	10r Nixon, astronauts	2.50	2.50
		Nos. 1357-1360 (4)	4.75	4.75

Souvenir Sheet

1361	A208	18r Armstrong descending ladder	4.50	4.50

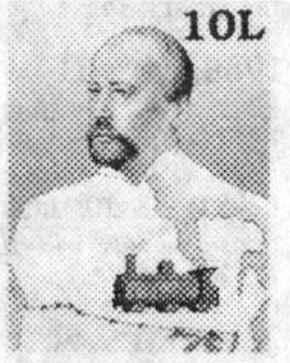

Railway Pioneers — A209

Designs: 10 l, Sir William Cornelius Van Horne (1843-1915), chairman of Canadian Pacific Railway, map and locomotive, 1894. 25 l, Matthew Murray, built rack locomotives for Middleton Colliery. 50 l, Louis Favre (1826-1879), built the St. Gotthard (spiral) Tunnel, 1881. 2r, George Stephenson (1781-1848), locomotive, 1825. 6r, Richard Trevithick (1771-1833), builder of 1st rail locomotive, 1804. 8r, George Nagelmackers, Orient Express dining car, 1869. 10r, William Jessop, Surrey horse-drawn cart on rails, 1770. 12r, Isambard Kingdom Brunel (1806-1859), chief engineer of Great Western Railway, introduced broad gauge, 1830's. No. 1370, George Pullman (1831-1897), *Pioneer* passenger car. No. 1371, Rudolf Diesel (1858-1913), inventor of the diesel engine, 1892, and diesel train.

1989, Dec. 26 Litho. *Perf. 14*

1362	A209	10 l multicolored	.15	.15
1363	A209	25 l multicolored	.15	.15
1364	A209	50 l multicolored	.15	.15
1365	A209	2r multicolored	.48	.48
1366	A209	6r multicolored	1.45	1.45
1367	A209	8r multicolored	1.90	1.90
1368	A209	10r multicolored	2.40	2.40
1369	A209	12r multicolored	2.85	2.85
		Nos. 1362-1369 (8)	9.53	9.53

Souvenir Sheets

1370	A209	18r multicolored	4.50	4.50
1371	A209	18r multicolored	4.50	4.50

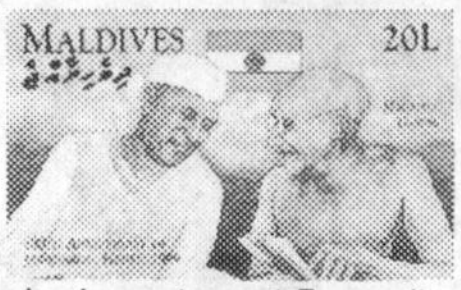

Anniversaries and Events (in 1989) — A210

Designs: 20 l, Flag of India, Jawaharlal Nehru, Mahatma Gandhi. 50 l, Syringe, opium poppies, vert. 1r, William Shakespeare, birthplace, Stratford-on-Avon. 2r, Flag of France, storming of the Bastille, Paris, 1789, vert. 3r, Concorde jet, flags of France, Britain. 8r, George Washington, Mount Vernon estate, Virginia. 10r, Capt. William Bligh, the *Bounty*. 12r, Ships in port. No. 1380, 1st Televised baseball game, 1939, vert. No. 1381, Franz von Taxis (1458-1517), vert.

1990, Feb. 15 Litho. *Perf. 14*

1372	A210	20 l multicolored	.15	.15
1373	A210	50 l multicolored	.15	.15
1374	A210	1r multicolored	.25	.25
1375	A210	2r multicolored	.50	.50
1376	A210	3r multicolored	.75	.75
1377	A210	8r multicolored	2.00	2.00
1378	A210	10r multicolored	2.50	2.50
1379	A210	12r multicolored	3.00	3.00
		Nos. 1372-1379 (8)	9.30	9.30

Souvenir Sheets

1380	A210	18r multicolored	4.50	4.50
1381	A210	18r multicolored	4.50	4.50

Birth cent. of Nehru (20 l); SAARC Year for Combatting Drug Abuse (50 l); 425th birth anniv. of Shakespeare (1r); French Revolution, bicent. (2r); first test flight of the Concorde supersonic jet, 20th anniv. (3r); American presidency, bicent. (8r); Mutiny on the *Bounty*, bicent. (10r); Hamburg, 800th anniv. (12r); 1st televised baseball game, 50th anniv. (No. 1380); and European postal communications, 500th anniv. (No. 1381).

Johann von Taxis was the first postmaster of Thurn & Taxis in 1489, not Franz, who is credited on No. 1381.

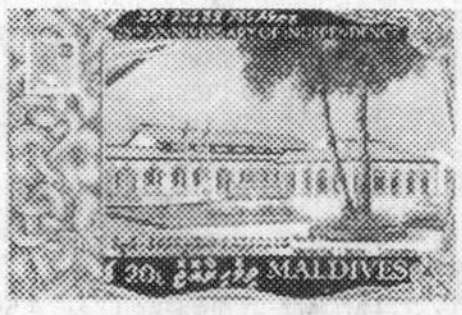

Natl. Independence, 25th Anniv. — A211

Designs: 20 l, Bodu Thakurufaanu Memorial Center, Utheemu. 25 l, Islamic Center, Male. 50 l, Natl. flag, UN, Islamic Conf., Commonwealth and SAARC emblems. 2r, Muleeaage, Male. 5r, Natl. Security Service, Maldives. 10r, Natl. crest, emblem of the Citizens' Majlis (parliament).

1990, Jan. 1 Litho. *Perf. 14*

1382	A211	20 l multicolored	.15	.15
1383	A211	25 l multicolored	.15	.15
1384	A211	50 l multicolored	.15	.15
1385	A211	2r multicolored	.50	.50
1386	A211	5r multicolored	1.25	1.25
		Nos. 1382-1386 (5)	2.20	2.20

Souvenir Sheet

1387	A211	10r multicolored	2.50	2.50

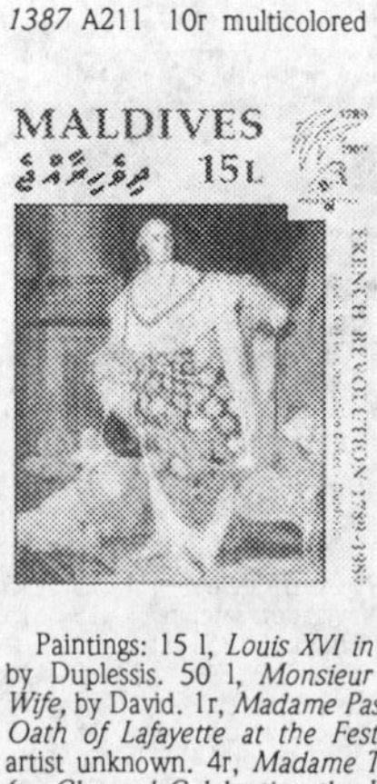

French Revolution, Bicent. (in 1989) — A212

Paintings: 15 l, *Louis XVI in Coronation Robes*, by Duplessis. 50 l, *Monsieur Lavoisier and His Wife*, by David. 1r, *Madame Pastoret*, by David. 2r, *Oath of Lafayette at the Festival of Federation*, artist unknown. 4r, *Madame Trudaine*, by David. 6r, *Chenard Celebrating the Liberation of Savoy*, by Boilly. 10r, *An Officer Swears Allegiance to the Constitution*, artist unknown. 12r, *Self-portrait*, by David. No. 1396, *The Tennis Court Oath, June 20, 1789*, by David, horiz. No. 1397, *Jean-Jacques Rousseau and the Symbols of the Revolution*, by Jeaurat.

1990, Jan. 11 Litho. *Perf. 14*

1388	A212	15 l multicolored	.15	.15
1389	A212	50 l multicolored	.15	.15
1390	A212	1r multicolored	.24	.24
1391	A212	2r multicolored	.48	.48
1392	A212	4r multicolored	.95	.95
1393	A212	6r multicolored	1.45	1.45
1394	A212	10r multicolored	2.40	2.40
1395	A212	12r multicolored	2.85	2.85
		Nos. 1388-1395 (8)	8.67	8.67

Souvenir Sheets

1396	A212	20r multicolored	4.75	4.75
1397	A212	20r multicolored	4.75	4.75

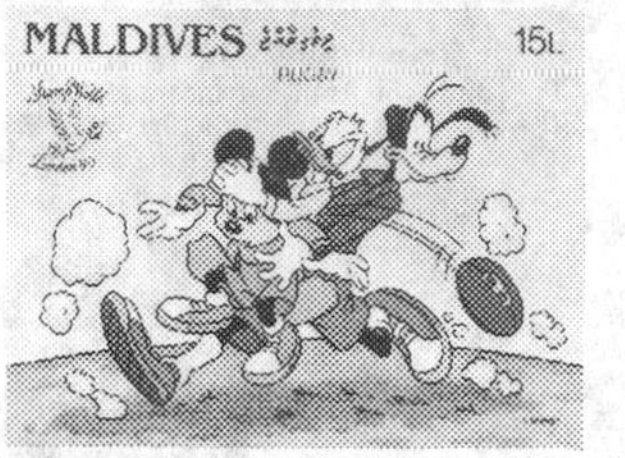

Stamp World London '90 — A213

Walt Disney characters demonstrating sports popular in Britain.

1990 Litho. *Perf. 14x13½*

1398	A213	15 l Rugby	.15	.15
1399	A213	50 l Curling	.15	.15
1400	A213	1r Polo	.24	.24
1401	A213	2r Soccer	.48	.48
1402	A213	4r Cricket	.95	.95
1403	A213	6r Horse racing, Ascot	1.45	1.45
1404	A213	10r Tennis	2.40	2.40
1405	A213	12r Lawn bowling	2.85	2.85
		Nos. 1398-1405 (8)	8.67	8.67

Souvenir Sheets

1406	A213	20r Fox hunting	4.75	4.75
1407	A213	20r Golf, St. Andrews, Scotland	4.75	4.75

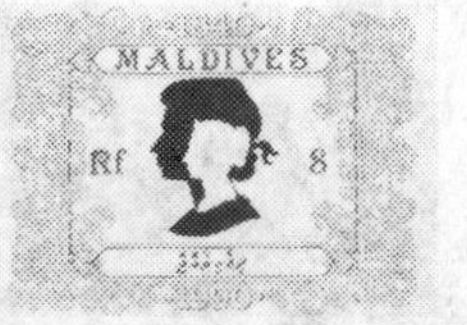

Penny Black, 150th Anniv. A214

1990, May 3 Litho. *Perf. 15x14*

1408	A214	8r Silhouettes	2.00	2.00
1409	A214	12r Silhouettes, diff.	3.00	3.00

Souvenir Sheet

1410	A214	18r Penny Black	4.50	4.50

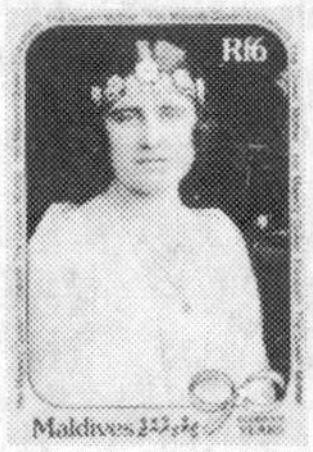

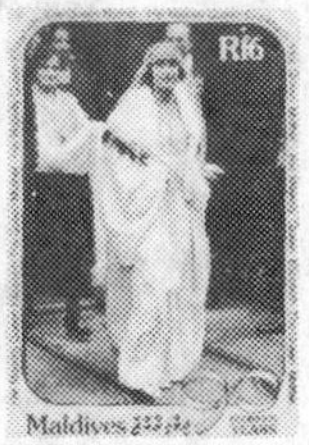

Queen Mother 90th Birthday
A215 A216

1990, July 8 *Perf. 14*

1411	A215	6r shown	1.50	1.50
1412	A216	6r shown	1.50	1.50
1413	A215	6r As Lady Bowes-Lyon, diff.	1.50	1.50
		Nos. 1411-1413 (3)	4.50	4.50

Souvenir Sheet

1414	A216	18r On Wedding Day, diff.	4.50	4.50

Nos. 1411-1413 printed in sheets of 9.

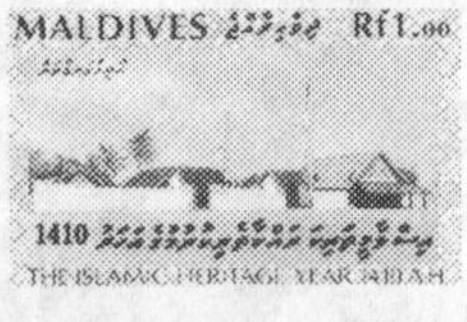

A217

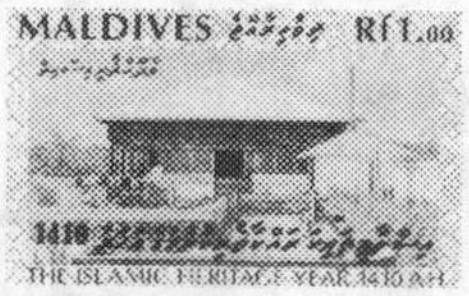

A218

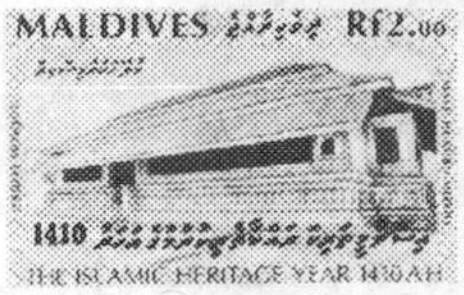

A219

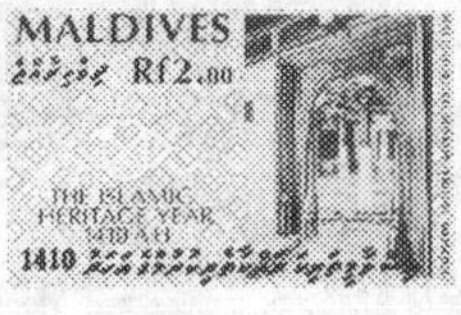

Islamic Heritage Year
A220

1990, July 22 Litho. *Perf. 14*

1415 A217 1r blue & black .25 .25
1416 A218 1r blue & black .25 .25
1417 A218 1r Building, diff. .25 .25
1418 A219 2r blue & black .50 .50
1419 A220 2r blue & black .50 .50
1420 A219 2r Building, diff. .50 .50
a. Block of 6, #1415-1420 2.25 2.25

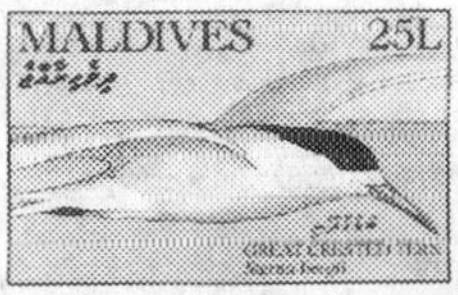

Great Crested Tern
A221

1990, Aug. 9 Litho. *Perf. 14*

1421 A221 25 l shown .15 .15
1422 A221 50 l Koel .15 .15
1423 A221 1r White tern .25 .25
1424 A221 3.50r Cinnamon bittern .88 .88
1425 A221 6r Sooty tern 1.50 1.50
1426 A221 8r Audubon's shearwater 2.00 2.00
1427 A221 12r Brown noddy 3.00 3.00
1428 A221 15r Lesser frigatebird 3.75 3.75
Nos. 1421-1428 (8) 11.68 11.68

Souvenir Sheets

1429 A221 18r White-tailed tropicbird 4.50 4.50
1430 A221 18r Grey heron 4.50 4.50

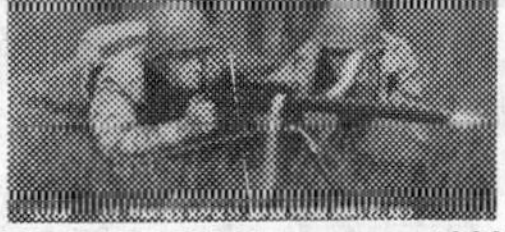

World War II Milestones — A222

Designs: 15 l, US Marines repulse Japanese invasion of Wake Island, Dec. 11, 1941. 25 l, Gen. Stilwell begins offensive in Burma, Mar. 4, 1944. 50 l, US begins offensive in Normandy, July 3, 1944. 1r, US forces secure Saipan, July 9, 1944. 2.50r, D-Day, June 6, 1944. 3.50r, Allied forces land in Norway, Apr. 14, 1940. 4r, Adm. Mountbatten named Chief of Combined Operations, Mar. 18, 1942. 6r, Gen. MacArthur accepts Japanese surrender, Sept. 2, 1945. 10r, Potsdam Conference, July 16, 1945. 12r, Allied invade Sicily, July 10, 1943. 18r, Atlantic convoys.

1990, Aug. 9 Litho. *Perf. 14*

1431 A222 15 l multicolored .15 .15
1432 A222 25 l multicolored .15 .15
1433 A222 50 l multicolored .15 .15
1434 A222 1r multicolored .25 .25
1435 A222 2.50r multicolored .62 .62
1436 A222 3.50r multicolored .88 .88
1437 A222 4r multicolored 1.00 1.00
1438 A222 6r multicolored 1.50 1.50
1439 A222 10r multicolored 2.50 2.50
1440 A222 12r multicolored 3.00 3.00
Nos. 1431-1440 (10) 10.20 10.20

Souvenir Sheet

1441 A222 18r multicolored 4.50 4.50

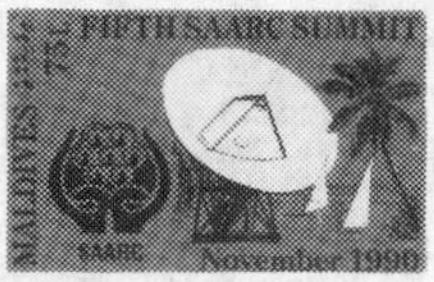

A223

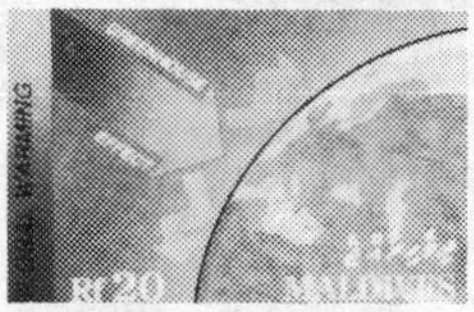
5th SAARC Summit
A224

1990, Nov. 21 Litho. *Perf. 14*

1442 A223 75 l Satellite communications .18 .18
1443 A223 3.50r Flags .88 .88

Souvenir Sheet

1444 A224 20r Map 5.00 5.00

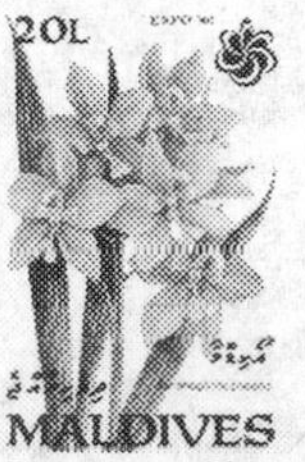

Flowers — A225

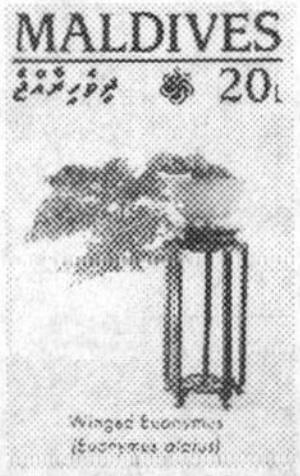

Bonsai — A226

1990, Dec. 9 Litho. *Perf. 14*

1445 A225 20 l Spathoglottis plicata .15 .15
1446 A225 75 l Hippeastrum puniceum .18 .18
1447 A225 2r Tecoma stans .50 .50
1448 A225 3.50r Catharanthus roseus .88 .88
1449 A225 10r Ixora coccinea 2.50 2.50
1450 A225 12r Clitoria ternatea 3.00 3.00
1451 A225 15r Caesalpinia pulcherrima 3.75 3.75
Nos. 1445-1451 (7) 10.96 10.96

Souvenir Sheets

1452 A225 20r Rosa sp. 5.00 5.00
1453 A225 20r Plumeria obtusa 5.00 5.00
1454 A225 20r Jasminum grandiflorum 5.00 5.00
1455 A225 20r Hibiscus tiliaceous 5.00 5.00

Expo '90, Intl. Garden and Greenery Exposition, Osaka, Japan.
2r, 3.50r, 10r, 12r are horiz.

1990-91

1456 A226 20 l Winged Euonymus .15 .15
1457 A226 50 l Japanese black pine .15 .15
1458 A226 1r Japanese five needle pine .25 .25
1459 A226 3.50r Flowering quince .88 .88
1460 A226 5r Chinese elm 1.25 1.25
1461 A226 8r Japanese persimmon 2.00 2.00
1462 A226 10r Japanese wisteria 2.50 2.50
1463 A226 12r Satsuki azalea 3.00 3.00
Nos. 1456-1463 (8) 10.18 10.18

Souvenir Sheets

1464 A226 20r Sargent juniper 5.00 5.00
1465 A226 20r Trident maple 5.00 5.00

Expo '90, Intl. Garden and Greenery Exposition, Osaka, Japan.
Issued: 50 l, 1r, 8r, 10r, #1464, 12/9/90; 20 l, 3.50r, 5r, 12r, #1465, 1/29/91.

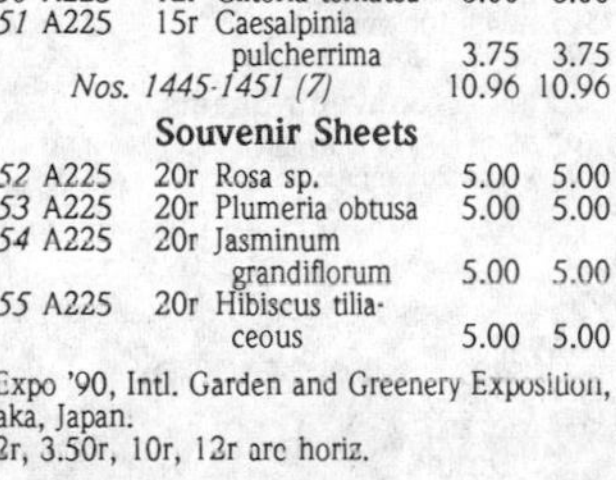

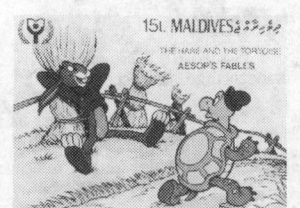

Aesop's Fables — A227

Walt Disney characters: 15 l, Tortoise and the Hare. 50 l, Town Mouse and Country Mouse. 1r, Fox and the Crow. 3.50r, Travellers and the Bear. 4r, Fox and the Lion. 6r, Mice and the Cat. 10r, Fox and the Goat. 12r, Dog in the Manger. No. 1474, Miller, his Son and the Ass, vert. No. 1475, Miser's Gold, vert.

1990, Dec. 11 Litho. *Perf. 14*

1466 A227 15 l multicolored .15 .15
1467 A227 50 l multicolored .15 .15
1468 A227 1r multicolored .25 .25
1469 A227 3.50r multicolored .88 .88
1470 A227 4r multicolored 1.00 1.00
1471 A227 6r multicolored 1.50 1.50
1472 A227 10r multicolored 2.50 2.50
1473 A227 12r multicolored 3.00 3.00
Nos. 1466-1473 (8) 9.43 9.43

Souvenir Sheets

1474 A227 20r multicolored 5.00 5.00
1475 A227 20r multicolored 5.00 5.00

Intl. Literacy Year.

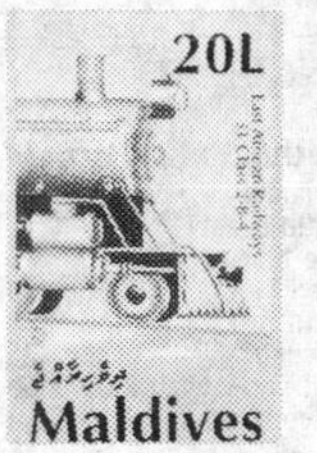

A228

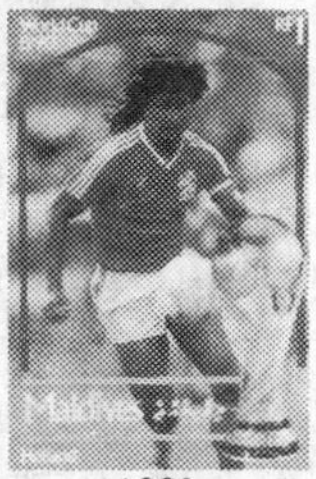
A229

Steam Locomotives: 20 l, "31" Class, East African Railways. 50 l, Mikado, Sudan Railways. 1r, Beyer-Garratt GM Class, South African Railways. 3r, "7th" Class, Rhodesia Railways. 5r, Central Pacific 229. 8r, Reading 415. 10r, Porter Narrow-guage. 12r, Great Northern 515. No. 1484, American Standard 315. No. 1485, East African Railways 5950.

1990, Dec. 15

1476 A228 20 l multicolored .15 .15
1477 A228 50 l multicolored .15 .15
1478 A228 1r multicolored .25 .25
1479 A228 3r multicolored .75 .75
1480 A228 5r multicolored 1.25 1.25
1481 A228 8r multicolored 2.00 2.00
1482 A228 10r multicolored 2.50 2.50
1483 A228 12r multicolored 3.00 3.00
Nos. 1476-1483 (8) 10.05 10.05

Souvenir Sheets

1484 A228 20r multicolored 5.00 5.00
1485 A228 20r multicolored 5.00 5.00

1990, Dec. 27

Various players from participating countries.

1486 A229 1r Holland .25 .25
1487 A229 2.50r England .62 .62
1488 A229 5r Brazil 1.25 1.25
1489 A229 10r Russia 2.50 2.50
Nos. 1486-1489 (4) 4.62 4.62

Souvenir Sheets

1490 A229 18r Austria 4.50 4.50
1491 A229 18r South Korea 4.50 4.50
1492 A229 20r Italy (dk blue shirt) 5.00 5.00
1493 A229 20r Argentina (blue & white shirt) 5.00 5.00

World Cup Soccer Championships, Italy.

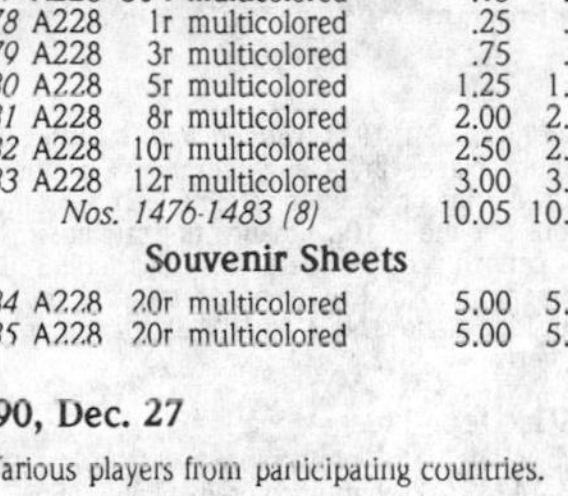

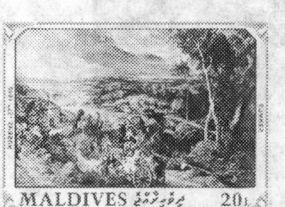

Peter Paul Rubens (1577-1640), Painter — A230

Entire works or details from paintings by Rubens: 20 l, Summer. 50 l, Landscape with Rainbow. 1r, Wreckage of Aeneas. 2.50r, Chateau de Steen. 3.50r, Landscape with Herd of Cows. 7r, Ruins of Palantine. 10r, Landscape with Peasants and Cows. 12r, Wagon Fording a Stream. No. 1502, Landscape with a Sunset. No. 1503, Peasants with Cattle by a Stream in a Woody Landscape. No. 1504, Shepherd with his Flock in a Wooded Landscape. No. 1505, Stuck Wagon.

1991, Feb. 7 Litho. *Perf. 14x13½*

1494 A230 20 l multicolored .15 .15
1495 A230 50 l multicolored .15 .15
1496 A230 1r multicolored .25 .25
1497 A230 2.50r multicolored .62 .62
1498 A230 3.50r multicolored .88 .88
1499 A230 7r multicolored 1.75 1.75
1500 A230 10r multicolored 2.50 2.50
1501 A230 12r multicolored 3.00 3.00
Nos. 1494-1501 (8) 9.30 9.30

Souvenir Sheets

1502-1505 A230 20r each 5.00 5.00

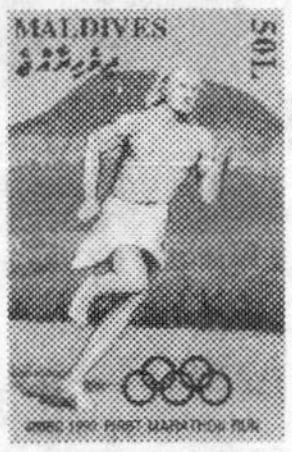

First Marathon Run, 490 B.C. — A231

Events and anniversaries (in 1990): 1r, Anthony Fokker (1890-1939), aircraft builder. 3.50r, Launch of first commercial satellite, 25th anniv. 7r, East, West German foreign ministers sign re-unification documents, Oct. 3, 1990, horiz. 8r, Magna Carta, 775th anniv. 10r, Dwight D. Eisenhower. 12r, Winston Churchill. 15r, Pres. Reagan destroying Berlin Wall, horiz. No. 1514, Brandenburg Gate, horiz. No. 1515, Battle of Britain, 50th anniv., horiz.

1991, Mar. 11 *Perf. 14*

1506 A231 50 l multicolored .15 .15
1507 A231 1r multicolored .25 .25
1508 A231 3.50r multicolored .88 .88
1509 A231 7r multicolored 1.75 1.75
1510 A231 8r multicolored 2.00 2.00
1511 A231 10r multicolored 2.50 2.50
1512 A231 12r multicolored 3.00 3.00
1513 A231 15r multicolored 3.75 3.75
Nos. 1506-1513 (8) 14.28 14.28

Souvenir Sheets

1514 A231 20r multicolored 5.00 5.00
1515 A231 20r multicolored 5.00 5.00

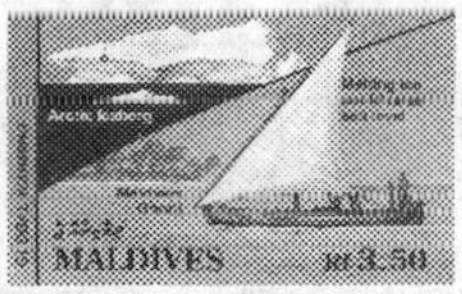

Global Warming
A232

1991, Apr. 10

1516 A232 3.50r Dhoni .88 .88
1517 A232 7r Freighter 1.75 1.75

Souvenir Sheet

1517A A232 20r Greenhouse effect 5.00 5.00

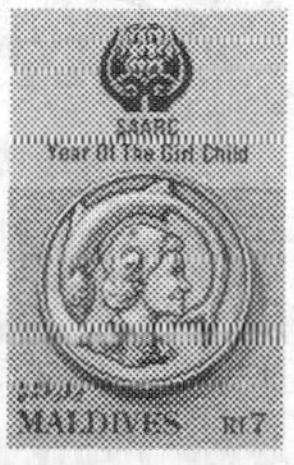

Year of the Girl Child — A233

1991, Apr. 14

1518 A233 7r multicolored 1.75 1.75

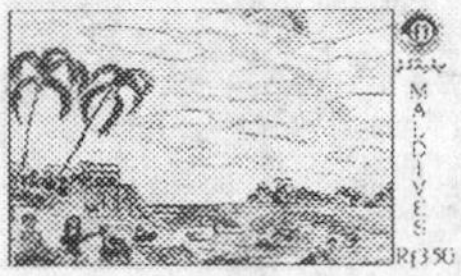

Year of the Child
A234

Children's drawings: 3.50r, Beach scene. 5r, City scene. 10r, Visualizing fruit. 25r, Scuba diver.

1991, May 10

1519 A234 3.50r multicolored .88 .88
1520 A234 5r multicolored 1.25 1.25
1521 A234 10r multicolored 2.50 2.50
1522 A234 25r multicolored 6.25 6.25
Nos. 1519-1522 (4) 10.88 10.88

VINCENT'S BEDROOM IN ARLES
VINCENT VAN GOGH 1853-1890
MALDIVES ދިވެހިރާއްޖެ RF2

Paintings by Vincent Van Gogh — A235

Designs: 15 l, Japanese Vase with Roses and Anemones, vert. 20 l, Still Life: Red Poppies and Daisies, vert. 2r, Vincent's Bedroom in Arles. 3.50r, The Mulberry Tree. 7r, Blossoming Chestnut Branches. 10r, Morning: Peasant Couple Going to Work. 12r, Still Life: Pink Roses. 15r, Child with Orange, vert. No. 1531, Courtyard of the Hospital at Arles. No. 1532, Houses in Auvers, vert.

1991, June 6		Litho.	Perf. 13½	
1523	A235	15 l multicolored	.15	.15
1524	A235	20 l multicolored	.15	.15
1525	A235	2r multicolored	.50	.50
1526	A235	3.50r multicolored	.88	.88
1527	A235	7r multicolored	1.75	1.75
1528	A235	10r multicolored	2.50	2.50
1529	A235	12r multicolored	3.00	3.00
1530	A235	15r multicolored	3.75	3.75
		Nos. 1523-1530 (8)	12.68	12.68

Sizes: 100x75mm, 75x100mm

Imperf

1531	A235	25r multicolored	6.25	6.25
1532	A235	25r multicolored	6.25	6.25

Royal Family Birthday, Anniversary
Common Design Type

1991, July 4		Litho.	Perf. 14	
1533	CD347	1r multi	.25	.25
1534	CD347	2r multi	.50	.50
1535	CD347	3.50r multi	.88	.88
1536	CD347	5r multi	1.25	1.25
1537	CD347	7r multi	1.75	1.75
1538	CD347	8r multi	2.00	2.00
1539	CD347	12r multi	3.00	3.00
1540	CD347	15r multi	3.75	3.75
		Nos. 1533-1540 (8)	13.38	13.38

Souvenir Sheets

1541	CD347	25r Elizabeth, Philip	6.25	6.25
1542	CD347	25r Charles, Diana, sons	6.25	6.25

1r, 3.50r, 7r, 15r, No. 1542, Charles and Diana, 10th wedding anniversary. Others, Queen Elizabeth II, 65th birthday.

ދިވެހިރާއްޖެ 10l
MALDIVES

Hummel Figurines — A236

M.J.Hummel

Designs: 10 l, No. 1552a, Child painting. 25 l, No. 1552b, Boy reading at table. 50 l, No. 1552c, Boy with back pack. 2r, No. 1551a, School Girl. 3.50r, No. 1551b, The Bookworm (boy sitting and reading). 8r, No. 1551c, Little Brother's Lesson. 10r, No. 1551d, School Girls. 25r, No. 1552d, Three school boys.

1991, July 25		Litho.	Perf. 14	
1543	A236	10 l multicolored	.15	.15
1544	A236	25 l multicolored	.15	.15
1545	A236	50 l multicolored	.15	.15
1546	A236	2r multicolored	.50	.50
1547	A236	3.50r multicolored	.88	.88
1548	A236	8r multicolored	2.00	2.00
1549	A236	10r multicolored	2.50	2.50
1550	A236	25r multicolored	6.25	6.25
		Nos. 1543-1550 (8)	12.58	12.58

Souvenir Sheets

1551	A236	5r Sheet of 4, #a.-d.	5.00	5.00
1552	A236	8r Sheet of 4, #a.-d.	8.00	8.00

MALDIVES ދިވެހިރާއްޖެ

Japanese Steam Locomotives — A237

1991, Aug. 25		Litho.	Perf. 14	
1553	A237	15 l C 57, vert.	.15	.15
1554	A237	25 l Series 6250	.15	.15
1555	A237	1r D 51, vert.	.25	.25
1556	A237	3.50r Series 8620	.88	.88
1557	A237	5r Class 10	1.25	1.25
1558	A237	7r C 61, vert.	1.75	1.75
1559	A237	10r Series 9600	2.50	2.50
1560	A237	12r D 52	3.00	3.00
		Nos. 1553-1560 (8)	9.93	9.93

Souvenir Sheets

1561	A237	20r Class 1080	5.00	5.00
1562	A237	20r C 56	5.00	5.00

Phila Nippon '91.

Sasakia sonorsa   Panda caerulea

BLUE SALAMIS

MALDIVES ދިވެހިރާއްޖެ 10L
Butterflies A238

1991, Dec. 2		Litho.	Perf. 14	
1563	A238	10 l Blue salamis	.15	.15
1564	A238	25 l Mountain beauty	.15	.15
1565	A238	50 l Lucerne blue	.15	.15
1566	A238	2r Monarch	.50	.50
1567	A238	3.50r Common rose	.88	.88
1568	A238	5r Black witch	1.25	1.25
1569	A238	8r Oriental swallowtail	2.00	2.00
1570	A238	10r Gaudy commodore	2.50	2.50
		Nos. 1563-1570 (8)	7.58	7.58

Souvenir Sheets

1571	A238	20r Pearl crescent	5.00	5.00
1572	A238	20r Friar	5.00	5.00

No. 1570 inscribed "guady."

MALDIVES ދިވެހިރާއްޖެ

Japanese Space Program A239

NASDA 20l

Designs: 15 l, H-11 Launch Vehicle. 20 l, H-II Orbiting plane. 2r, Geosynchronous satellite 5. 3.50r, Marine observation satellite-1. 7r, Communications satellite 3. 10r, Broadcasting satellite-2. 12r, H-1 Launch Vehicle, vert. 15r, Space flier unit, space shuttle. No. 1581, Katsura tracking and data acquisition station. No. 1582, M-3S II Launch vehicle, vert.

1991, Dec. 11				
1573	A239	15 l multicolored	.15	.15
1574	A239	20 l multicolored	.15	.15
1575	A239	2r multicolored	.50	.50
1576	A239	3.50r multicolored	.88	.88
1577	A239	7r multicolored	1.75	1.75
1578	A239	10r multicolored	2.50	2.50
1579	A239	12r multicolored	3.00	3.00
1580	A239	15r multicolored	3.75	3.75
		Nos. 1573-1580 (8)	12.68	12.68

Souvenir Sheets

1581	A239	20r multicolored	5.00	5.00
1582	A239	20r multicolored	5.00	5.00

Miniature Sheet

MALDIVES Rf 3.50 ދިވެހިރާއްޖެ

World War II Leaders of the Pacific Theater A240

Designs: a, Franklin D. Roosevelt. b, Douglas MacArthur. c, Chester Nimitz. d, Jonathan Wainwright. e, Ernest King. f, Claire Chennault. g, William Halsey. h, Marc Mitscher. i, James Doolittle. j, Raymond Spruance.

1991, Dec. 30		Litho.	Perf. 14½x15	
1583	A240	3.50r Sheet of 10, #a.-j.	8.80	8.80

MALDIVES ދިވެހިރާއްޖެ 20L

Grand Prix Race Cars A241

WILLIAMS FW-07

Designs: 20 l, Williams FW-07. 50 l, Brabham BT50 BMW Turbo. 1r, Williams FW-11 Honda. 3.50r, Ferrari 312 T3. 5r, Lotus Honda 99T. 7r, Benetton Ford B188. 10r, Tyrrell P34 Six-wheeler.

21r, Renault RE-30B Turbo. No. 1592, Ferrari F189. No. 1593, Brabham BT50 BMW Turbo, diff.

1991, Dec. 28		Litho.	Perf. 14	
1584	A241	20 l multicolored	.15	.15
1585	A241	50 l multicolored	.15	.15
1586	A241	1r multicolored	.25	.25
1587	A241	3.50r multicolored	.88	.88
1588	A241	5r multicolored	1.25	1.25
1589	A241	7r multicolored	1.75	1.75
1590	A241	10r multicolored	2.50	2.50
1591	A241	21r multicolored	5.25	5.25
		Nos. 1584-1591 (8)	12.18	12.18

Souvenir Sheets

1592	A241	25r multicolored	6.25	6.25
1593	A241	25r multicolored	6.25	6.25

Miniature Sheet

MALDIVES Rf 5 ދިވެހިރާއްޖެ

Enzo Ferrari (1898-1988) — A242

Race cars: a, 1957 Testa Rossa. b, 1966 275GTB. c, 1951 "Aspirarta." d, Testarossa. f, 1958 Dino 246. g, 1952 Type 375. h, Mansell's Formula One. i, 1975 312T.

1991, Dec. 28				
1594	A242	5r Sheet of 9, #a.-i.	11.25	11.25

Rf.10 MALDIVES ދިވެހިރާއްޖެ

17th World Scout Jamboree A243

Boy Scouts exploring coral reef off Maldive Islands
17th WORLD SCOUT JAMBOREE KOREA· 1991

Designs: 10r, Scouts diving on reef. 11r, Hand making scout sign, emblem, vert. 18r, Lord Robert Baden-Powell, emblem, vert. 20r, Czechoslovakian scout (local) stamp, vert.

1991, Dec. 30				
1595	A243	10r multicolored	2.00	2.00
1596	A243	11r multicolored	2.20	2.20

Souvenir Sheets

1597	A243	18r multicolored	4.50	4.50
1598	A243	20r multicolored	5.00	5.00

MALDIVES ދިވެހިރާއްޖެ 50L

Wolfgang Amadeus Mozart, Death Bicent. A244

Die Schwarzenberg Palast
WOLFGANG AMADEUS MOZART 1756-1791

Portrait of Mozart and: 50 l, Schwarzenberg Palace. 1r, Spa at Baden. 2r, Royal Palace, Berlin. 5r, Viennese Masonic seal. 7r, St. Marx. No. 1604, Josepsplatz, Vienna.

1991, Dec. 30				
1599	A244	50 l multicolored	.15	.15
1600	A244	1r multicolored	.25	.25
1601	A244	2r multicolored	.50	.50
1602	A244	5r multicolored	1.25	1.25
1603	A244	7r multicolored	1.75	1.75
1604	A244	20r multicolored	5.00	5.00
		Nos. 1599-1604 (6)	8.90	8.90

Souvenir Sheet

1605	A244	20r Bust of Mozart, vert.	5.00	5.00

MALDIVES ދިވެހިރާއްޖެ 20.l

200th ANNIVERSARY OF BRANDENBURG GATE

Brandenburg Gate, Bicent. — A245

Designs: 20 l, Flag. 1.75 l, Man embracing child, Berlin wall. 4r, Soldiers behind barricade, demonstrator. 15r, World War I Iron Cross. No. 1610, Helmet. No. 1611, 1939 helmet. No. 1612, Studded helmet.

1991, Dec. 30				
1606	A245	20 l multicolored	.15	.15
1607	A245	1.75r multicolored	.45	.45
1608	A245	4r multicolored	1.00	1.00
1609	A245	15r multicolored	3.75	3.75
		Nos. 1606-1609 (4)	5.35	5.35

Souvenir Sheets

1610	A245	18r multicolored	4.50	4.50
1611	A245	18r multicolored	4.50	4.50
1612	A245	18r multicolored	4.50	4.50

Rf.6 MALDIVES ދިވެހިރާއްޖެ

Flugzeug Nr.16.
OTTO LILIENTHAL First of the successful gliding pioneers

Anniversaries and Events — A246

Designs: No. 1613, Otto Lilienthal, glider No. 16. No. 1614, "D-Day," Normandy 1944, Charles de Gaulle. 7r, Front of locomotive, vert. 8r, Kurt Schwitters, artist and Landesmuseum. 9r, Map, man in Swiss costume. 10r, Charles de Gaulle in Madagascar, 1958. 12r, Steam locomotive. 15r, Portrait of Charles de Gaulle, vert. 20r, Locomotive and coal car.

1991, Dec. 30		Litho.	Perf. 14	
1613	A246	6r multicolored	1.50	1.50
1614	A246	6r multicolored	1.50	1.50
1615	A246	7r multicolored	1.75	1.75
1616	A246	8r multicolored	2.00	2.00
1617	A246	9r multicolored	2.25	2.25
1618	A246	10r multicolored	2.50	2.50
1619	A246	12r multicolored	3.00	3.00
		Nos. 1613-1619 (7)	14.50	14.50

Souvenir Sheets

1620	A246	15r multicolored	3.75	3.75
1621	A246	20r multicolored	5.00	5.00

First glider flight, cent. (#1613). Charles de Gaulle, birth cent. in 1990 (#1614, #1618, & #1620). Trans-Siberian Railway, cent. (#1615, #1619 & #1621). Hanover, 750th anniv. (#1616). Swiss Confederation, 700th anniv. (#1617). No. 1621 contains one 58x43mm stamp.

MALDIVES ދިވެހިރާއްޖެ 10l

Birds — A247

Perf. 14½, 13 (6.50r+50 l, 30r, 40r)
1992-94

1624	A247	10 l Numenius phaeopus	.15	.15
1625	A247	25 l Egretta alba	.15	.15
1626	A247	50 l Ardea cinerea	.15	.15
1627	A247	2r Phalacro- corax aristotelis	.50	.50
1628	A247	3.50r Sterna dougallii	.90	.90
1629	A247	5r Tringa nebularia	1.25	1.25
1630	A247	6.50r +50 l Neophron percnopterus	1.40	1.40
1631	A247	8r Upupa epops	2.00	2.00
1632	A247	10r Elanus caeruleus	2.50	2.50
1633	A247	25r Eudocimus ruber	6.25	6.25
1634	A247	30r Falco peregrinus	6.00	6.00
1635	A247	40r Milvus migrans	8.00	8.00
1636	A247	50r Pluvialis squatarola	10.00	10.00
		Nos. 1624-1636 (13)	39.25	39.25

Issued: 10 l, 25 l, 50 l, 2r, 3.50r, 5r, 8r, 10r, 25r, 2/17/92; 6.50r+50 l, 30r, 11/93; 40r, 1994(?).

Queen Elizabeth II's Accession to the Throne, 40th Anniv.
Common Design Type

1992, Feb. 6			Perf. 14	
1637	CD348	1r multicolored	.25	.25
1638	CD348	3.50r multicolored	.90	.90
1639	CD348	7r multicolored	1.75	1.75
1640	CD348	10r multicolored	2.50	2.50
		Nos. 1637-1640 (4)	5.40	5.40

Souvenir Sheets

1641	CD348	18r Queen, palm trees	4.50	4.50
1642	CD348	18r Queen, boat	4.50	4.50

This set differs from the common design in that the Queen's portrait and local view are separated by a curved line rather than with a cypher outline.

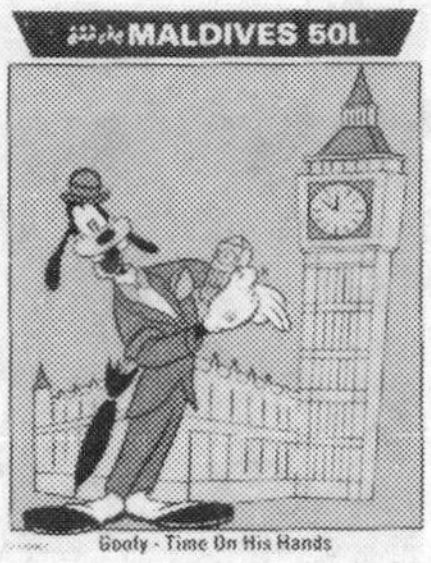

Disney Characters on World Tour — A248

Designs: 25 l, Mickey on Flying Carpet Airways. 50 l, Goofy at Big Ben, London. 1r, Mickey in Holland. 2r, Pluto eating pasta, Italy. 3r, Mickey, Donald do sombero stomp in Mexico. 3.50r, Mickey, Goofy, and Donald form Miki Tiki, Polynesia. 5r, Goofy's Alpine antics, Austria. 7r, Mickey Maus, Germany. 10r, Donald as Samurai Duck. 12r, Mickey in Russia. 15r, Mickey's Oom-pah Band in Germany. 25r, Mickey, globe. No. 1651, Donald in Ireland chasing leprechaun with pot of gold at end of rainbow, horiz. No. 1655A, Pluto, kangaroo with joey, Australia.

1992, Feb. 4 *Perf. 13x13½*

1643 A248 25 l multi .15 .15
1644 A248 50 l multi .15 .15
1645 A248 1r multi .25 .25
1646 A248 2r multi .50 .50
1647 A248 3r multi .75 .75
1648 A248 3.50r multi .70 .70
1649 A248 5r multi 1.00 1.00
1650 A248 7r multi 1.40 1.40
1651 A248 10r multi 2.00 2.00
1652 A248 12r multi 2.50 2.50
1653 A248 15r multi 3.75 3.75
Nos. 1643-1653 (11) 13.15 13.15

Souvenir Sheets

1654 A248 25r multi 6.25 6.25
1655 A248 25r multi 5.00 5.00
1655A A248 25r multi 5.00 5.00

While the rest of the set has the same issue date as Nos. 1644-1645, 1647, 1653-1654, their dollar value was lower when they were released.

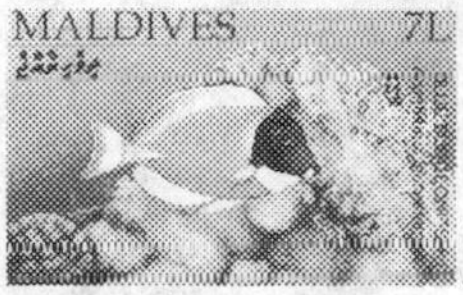

Fish A249

1992, Mar. 23 **Litho.** *Perf. 14*

1656 A249 7 l Blue surgeonfish .15 .15
1657 A249 20 l Bigeye .15 .15
1658 A249 50 l Yellowfin tuna .15 .15
1659 A249 1r Two-spot red snapper .20 .20
1660 A249 3.50r Sabre squirrelfish .70 .70
1661 A249 5r Picasso triggerfish 1.00 1.00
1662 A249 8r Bennet's butterfly fish 1.60 1.60
1663 A249 10r Parrotfish 2.00 2.00
1664 A249 12r Grouper 2.50 2.50
1665 A249 15r Skipjack tuna 3.00 3.00
Nos. 1656-1665 (10) 11.45 11.45

Souvenir Sheets

1666 A249 20r Clownfish 4.00 4.00
1667 A249 20r Sweetlips 4.00 4.00
1667A A249 20r Threadfin butterflyfish 4.00 4.00
1667B A249 20r Clown triggerfish 4.00 4.00

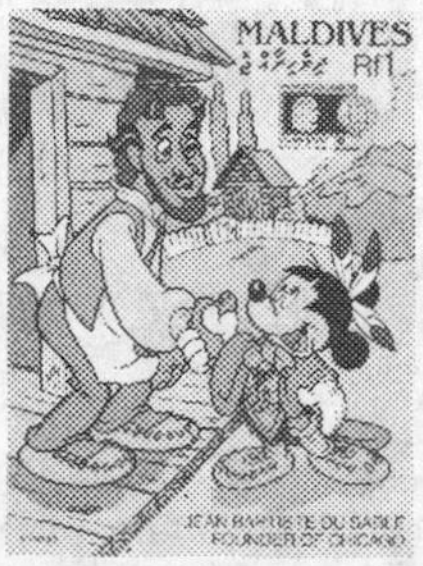

World Columbian Stamp Expo '92, Chicago A250

Walt Disney characters in Chicago: 1r, Mickey as Indian with Jean Baptiste Pointe du Sable, founder of Chicago. 3.50r, Donald at old Chicago post office, 1831. 7r, Donald in old Fort Dearborn. 15r, Goofy, mastodon at Museum of Science and Industry. 25r, Minnie and Mickey at Ferris wheel midway, Columbian Exposition, 1893, horiz.

1992, Apr. 15 *Perf. 13½x14*

1668 A250 1r multicolored .20 .20
1669 A250 3.50r multicolored .70 .70
1670 A250 7r multicolored 1.40 1.40
1671 A250 15r multicolored 3.00 3.00
Nos. 1668-1671 (4) 5.30 5.30

Souvenir Sheet

Perf. 14x13½

1672 A250 25r multicolored 5.00 5.00

No. 1671 identifies Field Museum as Museum of Science and Industry.

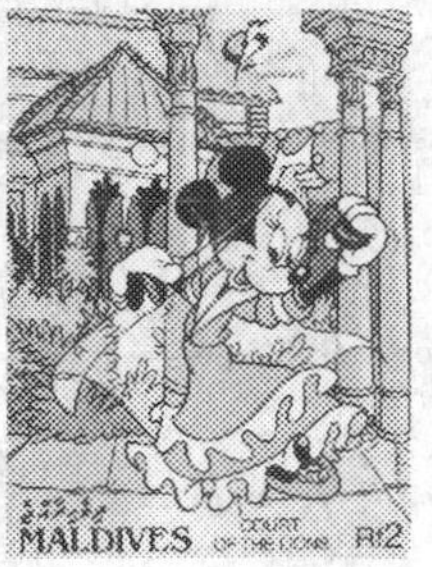

Granada '92 — A251

Disney characters in old Alhambra, Granada: 2r, Minnie in Court of Lions. 5r, Goofy bathing in Lions Fountain. 8r, Mickey walking near Gate of Justice. 12r, Donald Duck serenading Daisy in Vermilion Towers. No. 1682, Goofy and Mickey outside Towers of the Alhambra.

1992, Apr. 15 *Perf. 13½x14*

1678 A251 2r multicolored .40 .40
1679 A251 5r multicolored 1.00 1.00
1680 A251 8r multicolored 1.60 1.60
1681 A251 12r multicolored 2.50 2.50
Nos. 1678-1681 (4) 5.50 5.50

Souvenir Sheet

1682 A251 25r multicolored 5.00 5.00

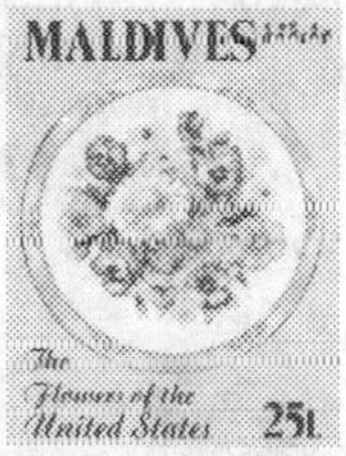

A252

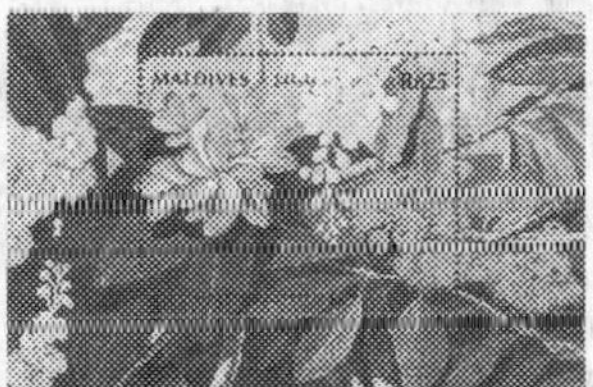

Flowers of the World — A253

1992, Apr. 26 **Litho.** *Perf. 14½*

1688 A252 25 l United States .15 .15
1689 A252 50 l Australia .15 .15
1690 A252 2r England .40 .40
1691 A252 3.50r Brazil .70 .70
1692 A252 5r Holland 1.00 1.00
1693 A252 8r France 1.60 1.60
1694 A252 10r Japan 2.00 2.00
1695 A252 15r Africa 3.00 3.00
Nos. 1688-1695 (8) 9.00 9.00

Souvenir Sheets

Perf. 14

1696 A253 25r org, yel & red vio flowers 5.00 5.00
1696A A253 25r Red, pink & yellow flowers 5.00 5.00

No. 1696 contains one 57x43mm stamp. No. 1696A contains one 57x34mm stamp.

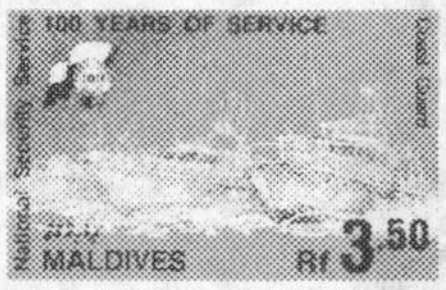

Natl. Security Service, Cent. A254

1992, Apr. 21 *Perf. 14*

1697 A254 3.50r Coast Guard .70 .70
1698 A254 5r Infantry 1.00 1.00
1699 A254 10r Aakoatey 2.00 2.00
1700 A254 15r Fire department 3.00 3.00
Nos. 1697-1700 (4) 6.70 6.70

Souvenir Sheet

1701 A254 20r Sultan in procession 4.00 4.00

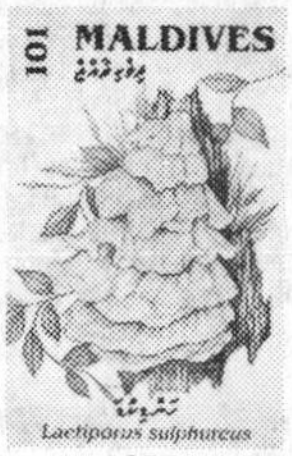

A255

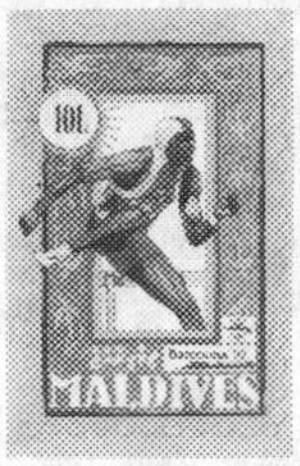

A256

Mushrooms: 10 l, Laetiporus sulphureus. 25 l, Coprinus atramentarius. 50 l, Gandoderma lucidum. 3.50r, Russula aurata. 5r, Polyporus umbellatus. 8r, Suillus grevillei. 10r, Clavaria zollingeri. No. 1709, Boletus edulis. No. 1710, Trametes cinnabarina. No. 1711, Marasmius oreades.

1992, May 14 **Litho.** *Perf. 14*

1702 A255 10 l multicolored .15 .15
1703 A255 25 l multicolored .15 .15
1704 A255 50 l multicolored .15 .15
1705 A255 3.50r multicolored .70 .70
1706 A255 5r multicolored 1.00 1.00
1707 A255 8r multicolored 1.60 1.60
1708 A255 10r multicolored 2.00 2.00
1709 A255 25r multicolored 5.00 5.00
Nos. 1702-1709 (8) 10.75 10.75

Souvenir Sheets

1710 A255 25r multicolored 5.00 5.00
1711 A255 25r multicolored 5.00 5.00

1992, June 1

1712 A256 10 l Hurdles .15 .15
1713 A256 1r Boxing .20 .20
1714 A256 3.50r Women's running .70 .70
1715 A256 5r Discus 1.00 1.00
1716 A256 7r Basketball 1.40 1.40
1717 A256 10r Running 2.00 2.00
1718 A256 12r Rhythmic gymnastics 2.50 2.50
1719 A256 20r Fencing 4.00 4.00
Nos. 1712-1719 (8) 11.95 11.95

Souvenir Sheets

1720 A256 25r Torch 5.00 5.00
1721 A256 25r Olympic rings, flags 5.00 5.00

1992 Summer Olympics, Barcelona.

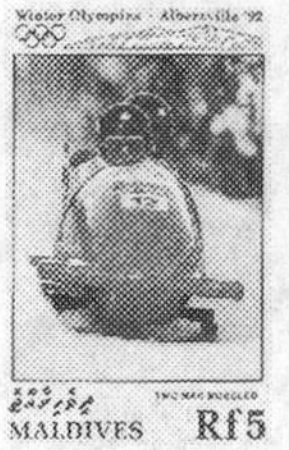

A256a

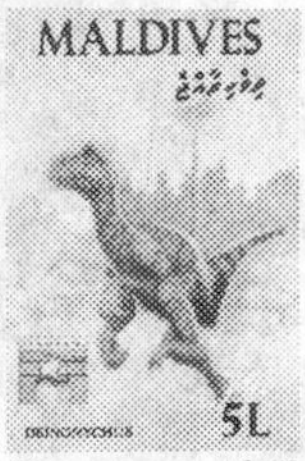

Dinosaurs — A257

1992 Winter Olympics, Albertville: 5r, Two-man bobsled. 8r, Free-style ski jump. 10r, Women's cross-country skiing. No. 1725, Women's slalom skiing, horiz. No. 1726, Men's figure skating.

1992, June 1 **Litho.** *Perf. 14*

1722 A256a 5r multicolored 1.00 1.00
1723 A256a 8r multicolored 1.60 1.60
1724 A256a 10r multicolored 2.00 2.00
Nos. 1722-1724 (3) 4.60 4.60

Souvenir Sheets

1725 A256a 25r multicolored 5.00 5.00
1726 A256a 25r multicolored 5.00 5.00

1992, Sept. 15 **Litho.** *Perf. 14*

1727 A257 5 l Deinonychus .15 .15
1728 A257 10 l Styracosaurus .15 .15
1729 A257 25 l Mamenchisaurus .15 .15
1730 A257 50 l Stenonychosaurus .15 .15
1731 A257 1r Parasaurolophus .20 .20
1732 A257 1.25r Scelidosaurus .25 .25
1733 A257 1.75r Tyrannosaurus .35 .35
1734 A257 2r Stegosaurus .40 .40
1735 A257 3.50r Iguanodon .70 .70
1736 A257 4r Anatosaurus .80 .80
1737 A257 5r Monoclonius 1.00 1.00
1738 A257 7r Tenontosaurus 1.40 1.40
1739 A257 8r Brachiosaurus 1.60 1.60
1740 A257 10r Euoplocephalus 2.00 2.00
1741 A257 25r Triceratops 5.00 5.00
1742 A257 50r Apatosaurus 10.00 10.00
Nos. 1727-1742 (16) 24.30 24.30

Souvenir Sheets

1743 A257 25r Iguanodon, allosaurus 5.00 5.00
1744 A257 25r Hadrosaur 5.00 5.00
1745 A257 25r Tyrannosaurus, triceratops 5.00 5.00
1746 A257 25r Brachiosaurus, iguanodons 5.00 5.00

Genoa '92.

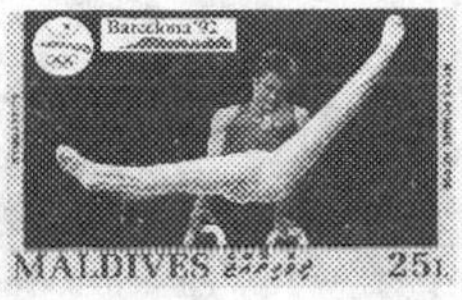

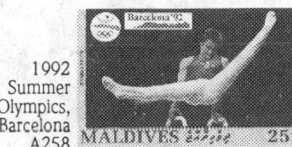

1992 Summer Olympics, Barcelona A258

1992, June 1 **Litho.** *Perf. 14*

1747 A258 10 l Pole vault, vert. .15 .15
1748 A258 25 l Pommel horse .15 .15
1749 A258 50 l Shot put, vert. .15 .15
1750 A258 1r Horizontal bar .20 .20
1751 A258 2r Triple jump .40 .40
1752 A258 3.50r Table tennis, vert. .70 .70
1753 A258 7r Wrestling 1.40 1.40
1754 A258 9r Baseball, vert. 1.80 1.80
1755 A258 12r Swimming 2.40 2.40
Nos. 1747-1755 (9) 7.35 7.35

Souvenir Sheet

1756 A258 25r Decathlon (high jump) 5.00 5.00

Souvenir Sheets

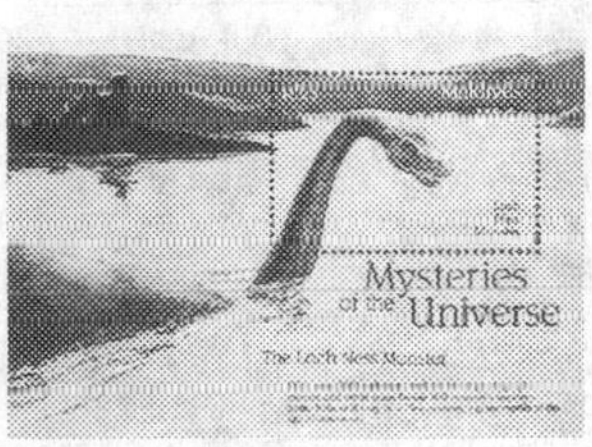

Mysteries of the Universe — A259

Designs: No. 1757, Loch Ness monster. No. 1758, Explosion of the Hindenburg. No. 1759, Crystal skulls. No. 1760, Black holes. No. 1761, UFO over Washington State. No. 1762, UFO near Columbus, Ohio. No. 1763, Explosion at Chernobyl, 1986. No. 1764, Crop circles of Great Britain. No. 1765, Ghosts of English castles and mansions. No. 1766, Drawings of Plain of Nasca, Peru, vert. No. 1767, Stonehenge, England, vert. No. 1768, Bust of Plato, the disappearance of Atlantis. No. 1769, Footprint of Yeti (abominable snowman), vert. No. 1770, Pyramids of Giza. No. 1771, Bermuda Triangle. No. 1772, The Marie Celeste, vert.

1992, Oct. 28

1757-1772 A259 25r each 5.00 5.00

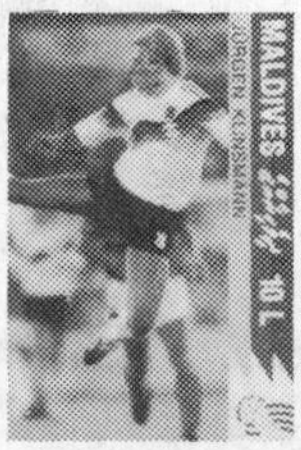

1994 World Cup Soccer Championships, US — A260

Players of 1990 German team: 10 l, Jurgen Klinsmann. 25 l, Pierre Littbarski. 50 l, Lothar Matthaus. 1r, Rudi Voller. 2r, Thomas Hassler. 3.50r, Thomas Berthold. 4r, Jurgen Kohler. 5r, Berti Vogts, trainer. 6r, Bodo Illgner. 7r, Klaus Augenthaler. 8r, Franz Beckenbauer, coach. 10r, Andreas Brehme. 12r, Guido Buchwald.

No. 1786, Team members, horiz. No. 1787, Unidentified player in action, horiz.

1992, Aug. 10 Litho. *Perf. 14*

1773	A260	10 l	multicolored	.15	.15
1774	A260	25 l	multicolored	.15	.15
1775	A260	50 l	multicolored	.15	.15
1776	A260	1r	multicolored	.20	.20
1777	A260	2r	multicolored	.40	.40
1778	A260	3.50r	multicolored	.70	.70
1779	A260	4r	multicolored	.80	.80
1780	A260	5r	multicolored	1.00	1.00
1781	A260	6r	multicolored	1.20	1.20
1782	A260	7r	multicolored	1.40	1.40
1783	A260	8r	multicolored	1.60	1.60
1784	A260	10r	multicolored	2.00	2.00
1785	A260	12r	multicolored	2.40	2.40
			Nos. 1773-1785 (13)	12.15	12.15

Souvenir Sheets

1786	A260	35r	multicolored	7.00	7.00
1787	A260	35r	multicolored	7.00	7.00

Souvenir Sheet

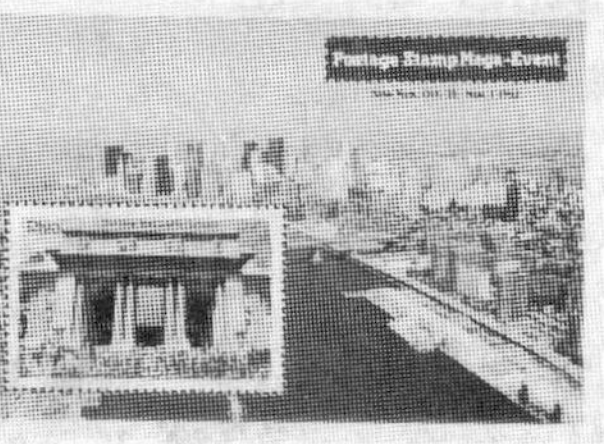
Postage Stamp Mega-Event

New York Public Library — A261

1992, Oct. 28 Litho. *Perf. 14*

1788	A261	20r	multicolored	4.00	4.00

Postage Stamp Mega Event '92, New York City.

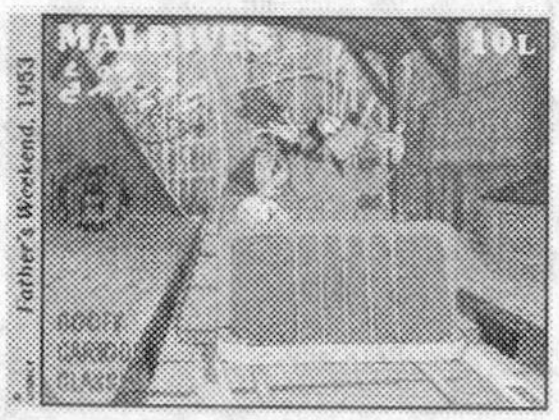
MALDIVES
10L
Father's Weekend 1953

Walt Disney's Goofy, 60th Anniv. — A262

Scenes from Disney cartoon films: 10 l, Father's Weekend, 1953. 50 l, Symphony Hour, 1942. 75 l, Frank Duck Brings 'Em Back Alive, 1946. 1r, Crazy with the Heat, 1947. 2r, The Big Wash, 1948. 3.50r, How to Ride a Horse, 1950. 5r, Two Gun Goofy, 1952. 8r, Saludos Amigos, 1943, vert. 10r, How to Be a Detective, 1952. 12r, For Whom the Bulls Toil, 1953. 15r, Double Dribble, 1946, vert.

No. 1801, Mickey and the Beanstalk, 1947. No. 1802, Double Dribble, 1946, vert., diff. No. 1803, The Goofy Success Story, 1955.

Perf. 14x13½, 13½x14

1992, Dec. 7 Litho.

1789	A262	10 l	multicolored	.15	.15
1791	A262	50 l	multicolored	.15	.15
1792	A262	75 l	multicolored	.15	.15
1793	A262	1r	multicolored	.20	.20
1794	A262	2r	multicolored	.40	.40
1795	A262	3.50r	multicolored	.70	.70
1796	A262	5r	multicolored	1.00	1.00
1797	A262	8r	multicolored	1.60	1.60
1798	A262	10r	multicolored	2.00	2.00
1799	A262	12r	multicolored	2.40	2.40
1800	A262	15r	multicolored	3.00	3.00
			Nos. 1789-1800 (11)	11.75	11.75

Souvenir Sheets

1801	A262	20r	multicolored	4.00	4.00
1802	A262	20r	multicolored	4.00	4.00
1803	A262	20r	multicolored	4.00	4.00

A number has been reserved for an additional value in this set.

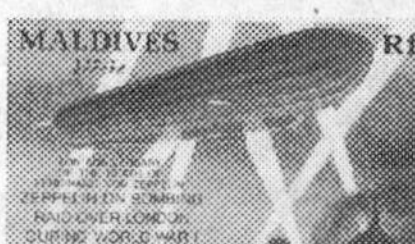
MALDIVES
Rf1

A263

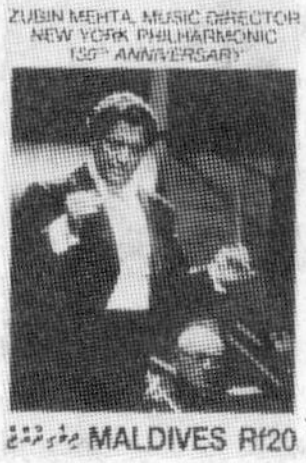
ZUBIN MEHTA, MUSIC DIRECTOR
NEW YORK PHILHARMONIC
150TH ANNIVERSARY
MALDIVES Rf20

Anniversaries and Events — A264

Designs: 1r, Zeppelin on bombing raid over London during World War I. No. 1805, German, French flags, Konrad Adenauer, Charles de Gaulle. No. 1806, Radio telescope. No. 1807, Columbus studying globe. No. 1808, Indian rhinoceros. 7r, WHO, ICN, and FAO emblems. 8r, Green sea turtle. No. 1822, Scarlet macaw. No. 1811, Lion's Intl. emblem and Melvin Jones, founder. No. 1812, Yacht America, first America's Cup winner, 1851. 12r, Columbus claiming San Salvador for Spain. No. 1814, Voyager 1 approaching Saturn. No. 1815, NATO flag, airplanes, Adenauer. 20r, Graf Zeppelin over New York City. No. 1817, Landsat satellite. No. 1818, Count Zeppelin. No. 1819, Santa Maria. No. 1820, Konrad Adenauer. No. 1821, Zubin Mehta, music director, NY Philharmonic, vert. No. 1823, Friedrich Schmiedl (b. 1902), rocket mail pioneer.

1992-93 Litho. *Perf. 14*

1804	A263	1r	multicolored	.20	.20
1805	A263	3.50r	multicolored	.70	.70
1806	A263	3.50r	multicolored	.70	.70
1807	A263	6r	multicolored	1.20	1.20
1808	A263	6r	multicolored	1.20	1.20
1809	A263	7r	multicolored	1.40	1.40
1810	A263	8r	multicolored	1.60	1.60
1811	A263	10r	multicolored	2.00	2.00
1812	A263	10r	multicolored	2.00	2.00
1813	A263	12r	multicolored	2.40	2.40
1814	A263	15r	multicolored	3.00	3.00
1815	A263	15r	multicolored	3.00	3.00
1816	A263	20r	multicolored	4.00	4.00
			Nos. 1804-1816 (13)	23.40	23.40

Souvenir Sheets

1817	A263	20r	multicolored	4.00	4.00
1818	A263	20r	multicolored	4.00	4.00
1819	A263	20r	multicolored	4.00	4.00
1820	A263	20r	multicolored	4.00	4.00
1821	A264	20r	multicolored	4.00	4.00
1822	A263	20r	multicolored	4.00	4.00
1823	A263	25r	multicolored	5.00	5.00
			Nos. 1817-1823 (7)	29.00	29.00

Count Zeppelin, 75th anniv. of death (#1804, 1816, 1818). Konrad Adenauer, 25th anniv. of death (#1805, 1815, 1820). Intl. Space Year (#1806, 1814, 1817). Columbus' discovery of America, 500th anniversary (#1807, 1813, 1819). Earth Summit, Rio de Janeiro (#1808, 1810, 1822). Intl. Conference on Nutrition, Rome (#1809). Lions Intl., 75th anniversary (#1811). America's Cup yacht race (#1812). New York Philharmonic, 150th anniv. (#1821).

No. 1823 contains one 27x35mm stamp.

Issue dates: Nos. 1805, 1808, 1810, 1815, 1820, 1822, Jan. 1993. Others, Nov. 1992.

Miniature Sheet

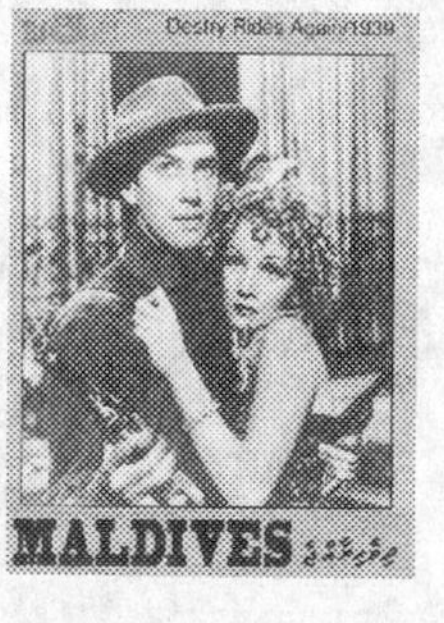
Destry Rides Again 1939
MALDIVES

Western Films A265

Actors and film: No. 1824a, Jimmy Stewart and Marlene Dietrich, Destry Rides Again, 1939. b, Gary Cooper, The Westerner, 1940. c, Henry Fonda, My Darling Clementine, 1940. d, Alan Ladd, Shane, 1953. e, Kirk Douglas and Burt Lancaster, Gunfight at the O.K. Coral, 1957. f, Steve McQueen, The Magnificent Seven, 1960. g, Robert Redford and Paul Newman, Butch Cassidy & The Sundance Kid, 1969. h, Jack Nicholson and Randy Quaid, The Missouri Breaks, 1976.

No. 1825, Clint Eastwood, Pale Rider. No. 1826, John Wayne, The Searchers, 1956.

1992 Litho. *Perf. 13½x14*

1824	A265	5r	Sheet of 8, #a.-h.	8.00	8.00

Souvenir Sheets

1825	A265	20r	multicolored	4.00	4.00
1826	A265	20r	multicolored	4.00	4.00

Issued: #1824-1825, 1992; #1825, Jan. 1993.

Miniature Sheet

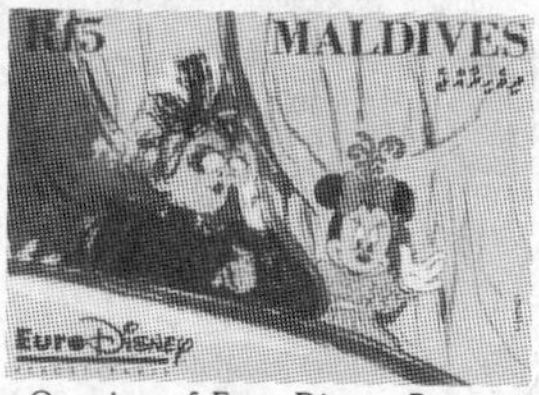
Rf5
MALDIVES
EuroDisney

Opening of Euro Disney Resort, Paris — A266

Disney characters in paintings by French impressionists: No. 1827a, Minnie on theater balcony. b, Goofy playing cards. c, Mickey and Minnie walking by outdoor cafe. d, Mickey fishing. e, Goofy dancing to music of harp player. f, Mickey and Minnie in boat. g, Minnie on dance floor. h, Mickey strolling through country. i, Minnie standing behind Polynesian woman.

1992, Dec. *Perf. 14x13½*

1827	A266	5r	Sheet of 9, #a.-i.	6.30	6.30

Souvenir Sheets

1828	A266	20r	Goofy	4.00	4.00
1829	A266	20r	Minnie	4.00	4.00
1830	A266	20r	Mickey	4.00	4.00

Perf. 13½x14

1831	A266	20r	Doinald Duck, vert.	4.00	4.00

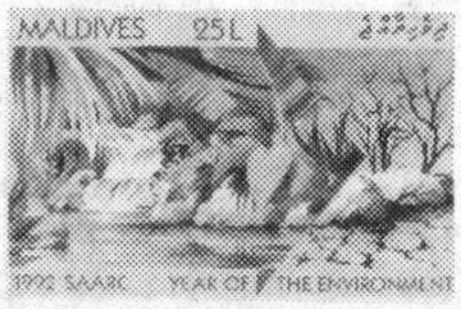
MALDIVES 25L
1992 SAARC YEAR OF THE ENVIRONMENT

SAARC Year of the Environment — A267

Designs: 25 l, Waterfall, drought area. 50 l, Clean, polluted beaches. 5r, Clean, polluted ocean. 10r, Clean island with vegetation, island polluted with trees dying.

1992, Dec. Litho. *Perf. 14*

1832	A267	25 l	multicolored	.15	.15
1833	A267	50 l	multicolored	.15	.15
1834	A267	5r	multicolored	1.00	1.00
1835	A267	10r	multicolored	2.00	2.00
			Nos. 1832-1835 (4)	3.30	3.30

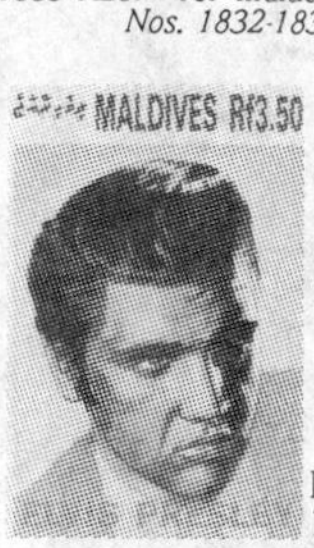
MALDIVES Rf3.50
ELVIS PRESLEY

Elvis Presley (1935-1977) — A268

Designs: a, Portrait. b, With guitar. c, With microphone.

1993

1836	A268	3.50r	Strip of 3, #a.-c.	2.10	2.10

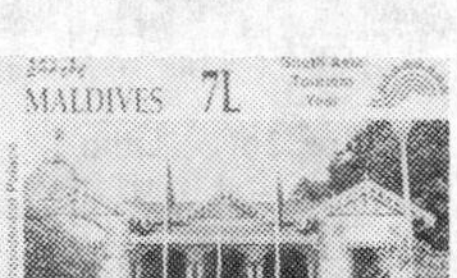
MALDIVES 7L

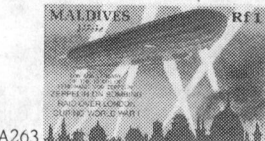

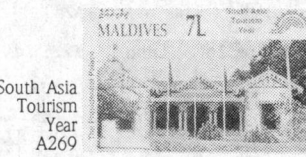

South Asia Tourism Year A269

Designs: 7 l, Presidential Palace. 50 l, Fish. 3.50r, Beach Cafe (Bodufinolhu). 10r, Fun Island (Bodufinolhu).

1993, Apr. Litho. *Perf. 14*

1837	A269	7 l	multicolored	.15	.15
1838	A269	50 l	multicolored	.15	.15
1839	A269	3.50r	multicolored	.70	.70
1840	A269	10r	multicolored	2.00	2.00
			Nos. 1837-1840 (4)	3.00	3.00

Miniature Sheets

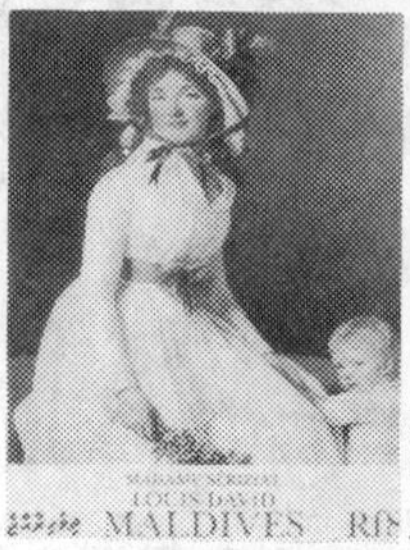
LOUIS DAVID
MALDIVES

Louvre Museum, Bicent. A270

Details or entire paintings, by Jacques-Louis David: No. 1841a, Madame Seriziat. b, Pierre Seriziat. c, Madame de Verninac. d, Madame Recamier. e, Self-portrait. f, General Bonaparte. g-h, The Lictors Returning to Brutus the Bodies of his Sons (left, right).

No. 1842a, Self-portrait. b, The Woman in Blue. c, The Jeweled Woman. d, Young Girl in her Dressing Room. e, Haydee. f, Chartres Cathedral. g, The Belfry at Douai. h, The Bridge at Mantes.

Paintings by Jean-Honore Fragonard (1732-1806): No. 1843a, The Study. b, Denis Diderot. c, Marie-Madeleine Guimard. d, The Inspiration. e, Tivoli Cascades. f, The Music Lesson. g, The Bolt. h, Blindman's Buff.

No. 1844, The Gardens of the Villa D'Este, Tivoli, by Jean-Baptiste-Camille Corot, horiz.

No. 1845, Young Tiger Playing with its Mother, by Delacroix.

1993, Jan. 7 Litho. *Perf. 12*

1841	A270	8r	Sheet of 8, #a.-h. + label	13.00	13.00
1842	A270	8r	Sheet of 8, #a.-h. + label	13.00	13.00
1843	A270	8r	Sheet of 8, #a.-h. + label	13.00	13.00

Souvenir Sheets

Perf. 14½

1844	A270	20r	multicolored	4.00	4.00
1845	A270	20r	multicolored	4.00	4.00

Nos. 1844-1845 contains one 88x55mm stamp.

Miniature Sheet

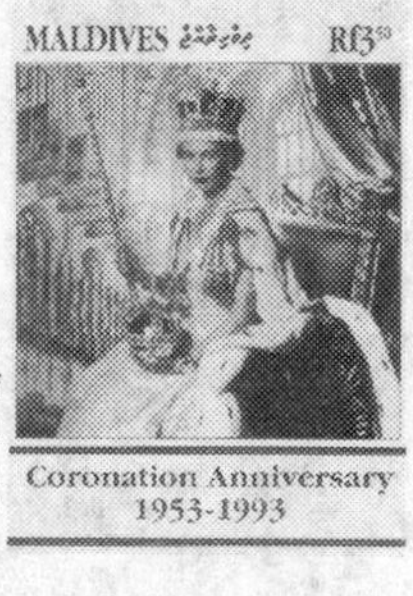
MALDIVES
Rf3.50
Coronation Anniversary
1953-1993

Coronation of Queen Elizabeth II, 40th Anniv. — A271

Designs: a, 3.50r, Official coronation photograph. b, 5r, St. Edward's crown. c, 10r, Dignataries viewing ceremony. d, 10r, Queen, Prince Philip examining banknote.

1993, June 2 *Perf. 13½x14*

1846	A271		Sheet, 2 each #a.-d.	13.50	13.50

A number has been reserved for an additional value in this set.

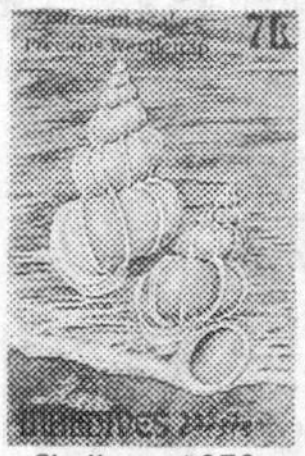
7L

Shells — A272

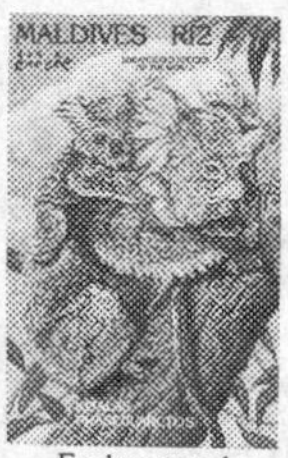
MALDIVES Rf2

Endangered Animals — A273

1993, July 15 Litho. *Perf. 14*

1848	A272	7 l	Precious wentletrap	.15	.15
1849	A272	15 l	Purple sea snail	.15	.15
1850	A272	50 l	Arabian cowrie	.15	.15
1850A	A272	3.50r	Major harp	.70	.70
1850B	A272	4r	Royal paper bubble	.80	.80
1851	A272	5r	Sieve cowrie	1.00	1.00
1852	A272	6r	Episcopal miter	1.20	1.20

1852A	A272	7r	Camp pitar-venus	1.40	1.40
1853	A272	8r	Eyed auger	1.60	1.60
1854	A272	10r	Onyx cowrie	2.00	2.00
1854A	A272	12r	Map cowrie	2.40	2.40
1855	A272	20r	Caltrop murex	4.00	4.00
	Nos. 1848-1855 (12)			15.55	15.55

Souvenir Sheets

1856	A272	25r	Scorpion spider conch	5.00	5.00
1857	A272	25r	Black striped triton	5.00	5.00
1857A	A272	25r	Bull's-mouth helmet	5.00	5.00

1993, July 20 Litho. *Perf. 14*

1857B	A273	7 l	Sifaka lemur	.15	.15
1858	A273	10 l	Snow leopard	.15	.15
1859	A273	15 l	Numbat	.15	.15
1859A	A273	25 l	Gorilla	.15	.15
1860	A273	2r	Koalas	.40	.40
1860A	A273	3.50r	Cheetah	.70	.70
1861	A273	5r	Yellow-footed rock wallaby	1.00	1.00
1862	A273	7r	Orangutan	1.40	1.40
1863	A273	8r	Black lemur	1.60	1.60
1864	A273	10r	Black rhinoceros	2.00	2.00
1865	A273	15r	Humpback whale	3.00	3.00
1865A	A273	20r	Mauritius parakeet	4.00	4.00
	Nos. 1857B-1865A (12)			14.70	14.70

Souvenir Sheets

1866	A273	25r	Asian elephant	5.00	5.00
1867	A273	25r	Tiger	5.00	5.00
1867A	A273	25r	Giant panda	5.00	5.00

Miniature Sheets

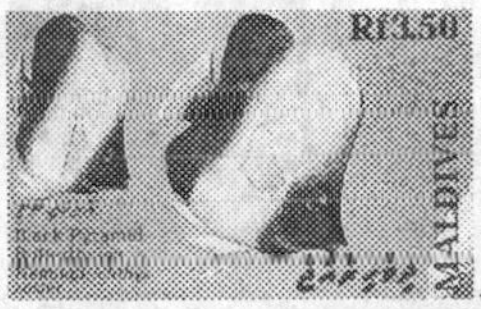

Fish
A274

Designs: No. 1868b, Black pyramid butterflyfish. c, Bird wrasse. d, Checkerboard wrasse. e, Blue face angelfish. f, Bannerfish. g, Threadfin butterflyfish. h, Picasso triggerfish. i, Pennantfish. j, Grouper. k, Black back butterflyfish. l, Redfin triggerfish. m, Redfin butterflyfish.

No. 1868n, Yellow goatfish. o, Emperor angelfish. p, Madagascar butterflyfish. q, Empress angelfish. r, Longnose butterfly. s, Racoon butterflyfish. t, Harlequin filefish. u, Wedgetailed triggerfish. v, Clark's anemonefish. w, Clown triggerfish. x, Zebra lionfish. y, Maldive clownfish.

No. 1869, Goldbelly anemone, vert. No. 1869A, Klein's butterflyfish, vert.

1993, June 30 *Perf. 14x13½*

Sheets of 12

1868	A274	3.50r	#b.-m.	8.40	8.40
1868A	A274	3.50r	#n.-y.	8.50	8.50

Souvenir Sheets

Perf. 12x13

1869	A274	25r	multicolored	5.00	5.00
1869A	A274	25r	multicolored	5.00	5.00

Miniature Sheets

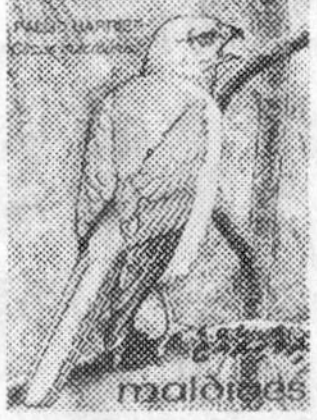

Birds — A275

Designs: No. 1870a, Pallid harrier. b, Cattle egret. c, Koel (b). d, Tree pipit. e, Short-ear owl. f, European kestrel. g, Yellow wagtail. h, Common heron. i, Black bittern. j, Common snipe. k, Little egret. l, Little stint.

No. 1871a, Gull-billed tern. b, Long-tailed tropicbird (a). c, Frigate bird. d, Wilson's petrel. e, White tern. f, Brown booby. g, Marsh harrier. h, Common noddy. i, Little heron. j, Turnstone. k, Curlew. l, Crab plover.

No. 1872, Caspian tern, horiz. No. 1873, Audubon's shearwater, horiz.

1993, July 5 *Perf. 13½x14*

1870	A275	3.50r Sheet of 12, #a.-l.	8.40	8.40
1871	A275	3.50r Sheet of 12, #a.-l.	8.50	8.50

Souvenir Sheet

Perf. 13x12

1872	A275	25r multicolored	5.00	5.00
1873	A275	25r multicolored	5.00	5.00

No. 1871 is horiz.

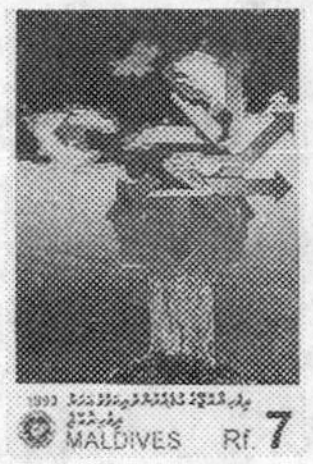

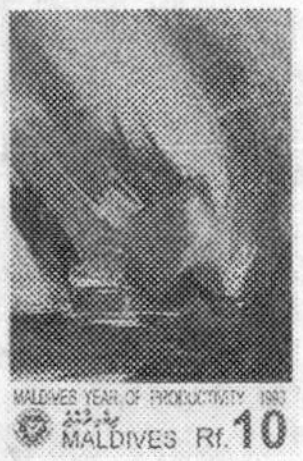

Year of Productivity
A276 A277

1993, July 25 *Perf. 14*

1874	A276	7r multicolored	1.40	1.40
1875	A277	10r multicolored	2.00	2.00

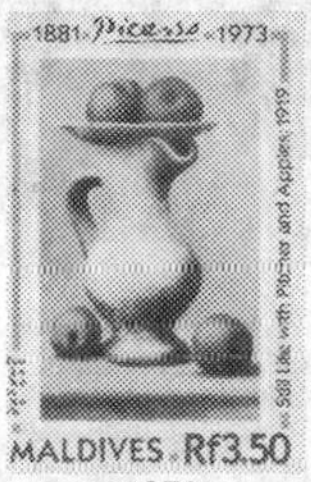

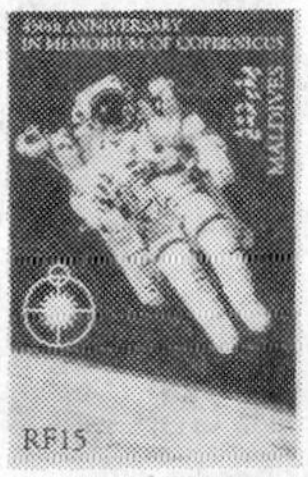

A278 A279

Picasso (1881-1973): 3.50r, Still Life with Pitcher and Apples, 1919. 5r, Bowls and Jug, 1908. 10r, Bowls of Fruit and Loaves, 1908. 20r, Green Still Life, 1914, horiz.

1993, Oct. 11 Litho. *Perf. 14*

1876	A278	3.50r multicolored	.70	.70
1877	A278	5r multicolored	1.00	1.00
1878	A278	10r multicolored	2.00	2.00
	Nos. 1876-1878 (3)		3.70	3.70

Souvenir Sheet

1879	A278	20r multicolored	4.00	4.00

1993, Oct. 11

Copernicus (1473-1543): 3.50r, Early astronomical instrument. 15r, Astronaut wearing Manned Maneuvering Unit. 20r, Copernicus.

1880	A279	3.50r multicolored	.70	.70
1881	A279	15r multicolored	3.00	3.00

Souvenir Sheet

1882	A279	20r multicolored	4.00	4.00

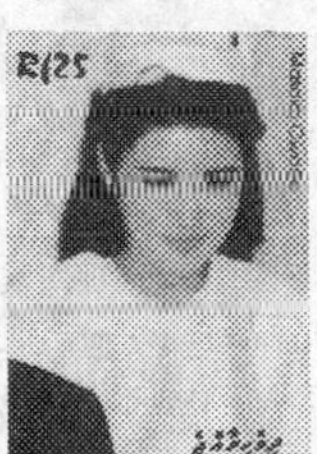

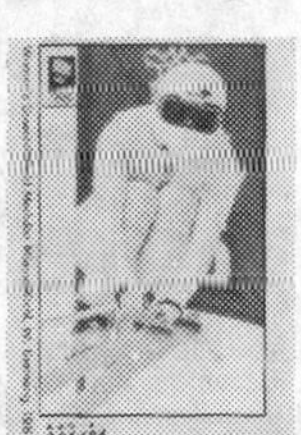

A280 A281

Royal Wedding of Crown Prince Naruhito, Princess Masako: 3.50r, Princess Masako. 10r, Crown Prince Naruhito. 25r, Princess Masako, horiz.

1993, Oct. 11

1883	A280	3.50r multicolored	.70	.70
1884	A280	10r multicolored	2.00	2.00

Souvenir Sheet

1885	A280	25r multicolored	5.00	5.00

1993, Oct. 11

1994 Winter Olympics, Lillehammer, Norway: 8r, Marina Kiehl, gold medalist, women's downhill, 1988. 15r, Vegard Ulvang, gold medalist, cross-country skiing, 1992. 25r, Soviet ice hockey goalie, 1980.

1886	A281	8r multicolored	1.65	1.65
1887	A281	15r multicolored	3.00	3.00

Souvenir Sheet

1888	A281	25r multicolored	5.00	5.00

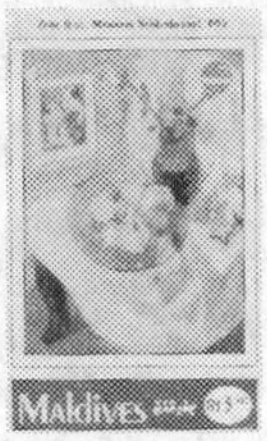

Polska '93 — A282

Fine arts: 3.50r, Zolte Roze, by Menasze Seidenbeurel, 1932. 5r, Cracow Historical Museum. 18r, Apples and Curtain, by Waclaw Borowski. 25r, Seascape, by Roman Sielski, 1931, horiz.

1993, Oct. 11 Litho. *Perf. 14*

1889	A282	3.50r multicolored	.70	.70
1890	A282	5r multicolored	1.00	1.00
1891	A282	8r multicolored	1.65	1.65
	Nos. 1889-1891 (3)		3.35	3.35

Souvenir Sheet

1892	A282	25r multicolored	5.00	5.00

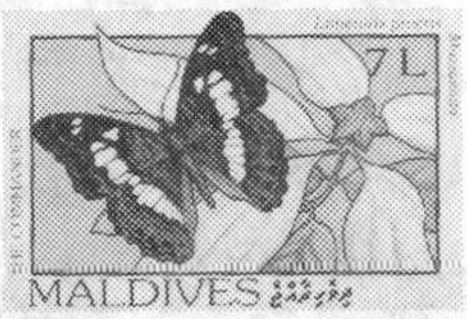

Butterflies
A283

1993, Oct. 25

1893	A283	7 l	Commander	.15	.15
1894	A283	20 l	Blue tiger	.15	.15
1895	A283	25 l	Centaur oakblue	.15	.15
1896	A283	50 l	Common banded peacock	.15	.15
1897	A283	5r	Glad-eye bushbrown	1.00	1.00
1898	A283	6.50r	+ 50 l Common tree nymph	1.40	1.40
1899	A283	7r	Lemon emigrant	1.40	1.40
1900	A283	10r	Blue pansy	2.00	2.00
1901	A283	12r	Painted lady	2.50	2.50
1902	A283	15r	Blue mormon	3.00	3.00
1903	A283	18r	Tamil yeoman	3.50	3.50
1904	A283	20r	Crimson rose	4.00	4.00
	Nos. 1893-1904 (12)			19.40	19.40

Souvenir Sheets

1905	A283	25r Common imperial	5.00	5.00
1906	A283	25r Great orange tip	5.00	5.00
1907	A283	25r Black prince	5.00	5.00

Nos. 1905-1907 are vert.

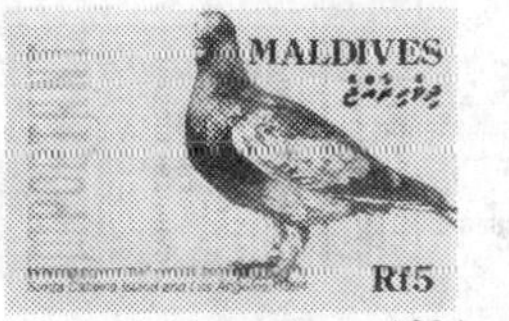

Aviation Anniversaries A284

Designs: 3.50r, Zeppelin on bombing raid caught in British search lights, vert. 5r, Homing pigeon. 10r, Dr. Hugo Eckener, vert. 15r, Airmail service medal, Jim Edgerton's Jenny, mail truck. 20r, USS Macon approaching mooring mast, vert.

Souvenir Sheets: No. 1913, 25r, Blanchard's balloon, 1793, vert. No. 1914, 25r, Santos-Dumont's flight around Eiffel Tower, 1901, vert.

1993, Nov. 22 Litho. *Perf. 14*

1908-1912	A284	Set of 5	11.00	11.00

Souvenir Sheets

1913-1914	A284	25r each	5.00	5.00

Dr. Hugo Eckener, 125th birth anniv. (3.50r, 10r, 20r, No. 1913).

Miniature Sheets

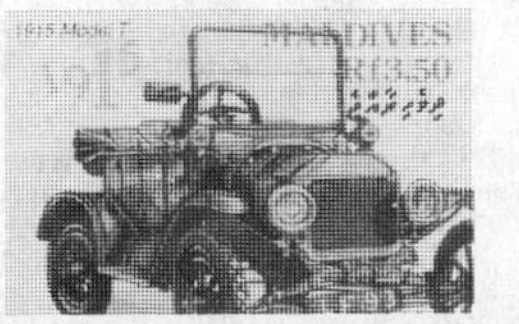

First Ford Engine, First Benz Four-Wheeled Car, Cent. — A285

Designs: No. 1915a, 1915 Model T (b, d-e). b, Henry Ford (e). c, Drawing of first Ford engine (b, e-f). d, 1993 Ford Probe GT (e). e, 1947 Ford Sportsman, front (f). f, 1947 Ford Sportsman, rear (e). g, 1915 Ford advertisement (j). h, 1955 Ford Thunderbird (g, i). i, Ford emblem (f, h). j, 1958 Edsel Citation. k, 1941 Ford half-ton pickup. l, Model T.

No. 1916a, 1937 Daimler-Benz Straight 8 (b). b, Karl Benz (e). c, Mercedes-Benz advertisement (f). d, 1929 Mercedes 38-250SS (e). e, 1893 Benz Viktoria (f, h). f, Mercedes star emblem (i). g, WWI Mercedes engine. h, 1957 Mercedes-Benz 300SL Gullwing (g). i, 1993 Mercedes Benz SL coupe/roadster (h). j, 1906 Benz 4-cylinder car (k). k, Early Benz advertisement. l, Benz Viktoria, 1893.

1993, Nov. 22

1915	A285	3.50r Sheet of 12, #a.-l.	8.50	8.50
1916	A285	3.50r Sheet of 12, #a.-l.	8.50	8.50

Souvenir Sheets

1917	A285	25r 1933 Ford Model Y	5.00	5.00
1918	A285	25r 1955 Mercedes 300S	5.00	5.00

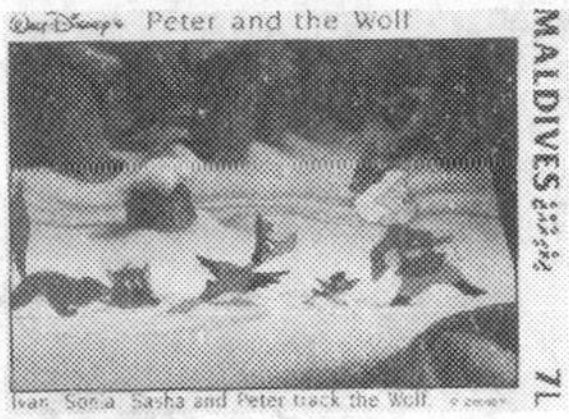

Peter and the Wolf — A286

Characters and scenes from Disney animated film: 7 l, 15 l, 20 l, 25 l, 50 l, 1r.

Nos. 1925a-1925i: Part 1.

Nos. 1926a-1926i: Part 2.

1993, Dec. 20

1919-1924	A286	Set of 6	.32	.32

Miniature Sheet

1925	A286	3.50r Sheet of 9, #a.-i.	6.25	6.25
1926	A286	3.50r Sheet of 9, #a.-i.	6.25	6.25

Souvenir Sheets

1927	A286	25r Sonya	5.00	5.00
1928	A286	25r Ivan	5.00	5.00

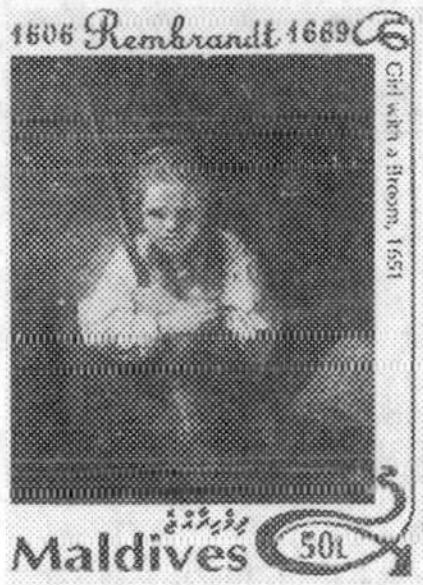

Fine
Art — A287

Paintings by Rembrandt: 50 l, Girl with a Broom. No. 1931, 3.50r, Young Girl at half-open Door. 5r, The Prophetess Hannah (Rembrandt's Mother). 7r, Woman with a Pink Flower. 12r, Lucretia. No. 1939, 15r, Lady with an Ostich Feather Fan.

Paintings by Matisse: 2r, Girl with Tulips (Jeanne Vaderin). No. 1932, 3.50r. Portrait of Greta Moll. 6.50r, The Idol. 9r, Mme. Matisse in Japanese Robe. 10r, Portrait of MMe Matisse (The Green Line). No. 1940, 15r, The Woman with the Hat.

No. 1941, Married Couple with 3 Children (A Family Group), by Rembrandt, horiz. No. 1942, The Painter's Family, by Matisse. No. 1942A: The Music Makers, by Rembrandt.

1994, Jan. 11 Litho. *Perf. 13*

1929-1940	A287	Set of 12	17.50	17.50

Souvenir Sheets

1941-1942A	A287	25r each	7.50	7.50

No. 1942A issued Feb. 2.

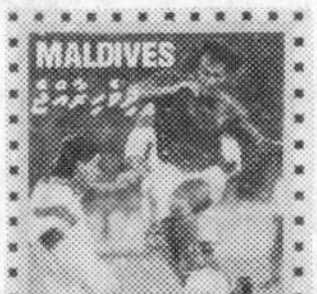

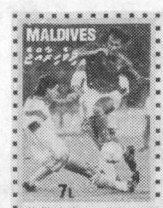

1994 World Cup
Soccer US — A288

Players, country: 7 l, Windischmann, US; Giannini, Italy. 20 l, Carnevale, Gascoigne. 25 l, Platt & teammates, England. 3.50r, Koeman, Holland; Klinsmann, Germany. 5r, Quinn, Ireland; Maldini, Italy. 7r, Lineker, England. 15r, Hassam, Egypt; Moran, Ireland. 18r, Canniggia, Argentina.

No. 1951, Conejo, Costa Rica; Mozer, Brazil, horiz. No. 1952, Armstrong & Barboa, US; Orgis, Austria.

1994, Jan. 11　　　　　　Perf. 14
1943-1950 A288　　Set of 8　　10.00 10.00
Souvenir Sheets
1951-1952 A288 25r each　　5.00 5.00

Hong Kong
'94 — A290

Stamps, Moon-Lantern Festival, Hong Kong: No. 1953, Hong Kong #416, girls, lanterns. No. 1954, Lanterns, #660.
Cloisonne Enamel, Qing Dynasty: No. 1955a, Vase. b, Flower holder. c, Elephant with vase on back. d, Pot (Tibetan-style lama's milk-tea pot. e, Fo-dog. f, Pot with swing handle.

1994, Feb. 18　Litho.　　Perf. 14
1953 A289 4r multicolored　　.80 .80
1954 A289 4r multicolored　　.80 .80
　a.　Pair, #1953-1954　　1.65 1.65
Miniature Sheet
1955 A290 2r Sheet of 6, #a.-f.　　2.50 2.50
　Nos. 1953-1954 issued in sheets of 5 pairs. No. 1954a is a continuous design.
New Year 1994 (Year of the Dog) (#1955e).

Miniature Sheets of 6 or 8

Sierra Club,
Cent.
A290a

Various animals: No. 1956a-1956b, Prairie dog. c.-e, Woodland caribou. f, Galapagos penguin.
No. 1957, vert: a, Humpback whale. b.-c, Ocelot. d, Snow monkey. e, Prairie dog. f, Golden lion tamarin.
No. 1958: a.-b, Golden lion tamarin. c.-d, Humpback whale. e, Bengal tiger. f, Ocelot. g.-h, Snow monkey.
No. 1959, vert: a.-b, Galapagos penguin. c.-d, Bengal tiger. e.-g, Philippine tarsier. h, Sierra Club centennial emblem.

1994, May 20　Litho.　　Perf. 14
1956-1957 A290a 6.50r #a.-f, each　　7.25 7.25
1958-1959 A290a 6.50r #a.-h, each　　9.50 9.50

Dome of the Rock,
Jerusalem — A291

1994, June 10　　　　Perf. 13½
1960 A291 8r multicolored　　1.50 1.50

Elasmosaurus A292

Designs: 25 l, Elasmosaurus. 50 l, Dilophosaurus. 1r, Avimimus. 5r, Chasmosaurus. 8r, Edmontonia. 10r, Anatosaurus. 15r, Velociraptor. 20r, Spinosaurus.
No. 1969: a, Dimorphodon. b, Megalosaurus. c, Kuehneosaurus. d, Dryosaurus. e, Kentrosaurus. f, Baraposaurus (c). g, Tenontosaurus. h, Elaphrosaurus (i). i, Maiasaura. j, Huayangosaurus. k, Rutiodon. l, Pianitzkysaurus.
No. 1970: a, Quetzalcoatlus. b, Daspletosaurus. c, Pleurocoelus. d, Baryonyx. e, Pentaceratops. f, Kritosaurus. g, Microvenator (h). h, Nodosaurus. i, Montanaceratops. j, Dromiceiomimus. k, Dryptosaurus. l, Parkosaurus.
No. 1971, Gallimimus. No. 1972, Plateosaurus, vert.

1994, June 20　　　　Perf. 14
1961-1968 A292　　Set of 8　　11.00 11.00
Miniature Sheets of 12
1969-1970 A292 3r #a.-l, each　　6.50 6.50
Souvenir Sheets
1971-1972 A292 25r each　　4.50 4.50
　Nos. 1969-1970 are continuous design.

Locomotives　　　Domestic Cats
A293　　　　　　A294

Designs: 25 l, 2-6-6-0 Mallet, Indonesia, horiz. 50 l, C62, Japan, horiz. 1r, D51, Japan. 5r, 4-6-0 Steam, India. 8r, Class 485 electric, Japan, horiz. 10r, Class WP Pacific, India. 15r, "People" class RM 4-6-2, China. 20r, C57, Japan, horiz.
No. 1981: a, W Class 0-6-2, India. b, C53 Class, Indonesia. c, C-10, Japan. d, Hanomag 4-8-0, India. e, Hakari bullet train, Japan. f, C-55, Japan.
No. 1982, 4-4-0, Indonesia. No. 1983, Series 8620, Japan.

1994, July 4
1973-1980 A293　　Set of 8　　11.00 11.00
Miniature Sheet of 6
1981 A293 6.50r +50 l, #a.-f.　　7.50 7.50
Souvenir Sheets
1982-1983 A293 25r each　　4.50 4.50

1994, July 11
Designs: 7 l, Japanese bobtail, horiz. 20 l, Siamese. 25 l, Persian longhair, horiz. 50 l, Somali. 3.50r, Oriental shorthair, horiz. 5r, Burmese, horiz. 7r, Bombay, horiz. 10r, Turkish van. 12r, Javanese. 15r, Singapura, horiz. 18r, Turkish angora. 20r, Egyptian mau.
　#1996, Birman. #1997, Korat. #1998, Abyssinian.
1984-1995 A294　　Set of 12　　17.00 17.00
Souvenir Sheets
1996-1998 A294 25r each　　4.50 4.50

Miniature Sheets of 6

1994 World Cup Soccer Championships,
US — A295

Designs: No. 1999a, 10 l, Franco Baresi, Italy, Stuart McCall, Scotland. b, 25 l, McCarthy, Great Britain, Lineker, Ireland. c, 50 l, J. Helt, Denmark, R. Gordillo, Spain. d, 5r, Martin Vasquez, Spain, Enzo Scifo, Belgium. e, 10r, Emblem. f, 12f, Tomas Brolin, Sweden, Gordon Durie, Scotland.
No. 2000a, Bebeto, Brazil. b, Lothar Matthaus, Great Britain. c, Diego Maradona, Argentina. d, Stephane Chapuasti, Switzerland. e, George Hagi, Romania. f, Carlos Valderama, Colombia.
No. 2001, Hossam Hassan, 2nd Egyptian player.

1994, Aug. 4　Litho.　　Perf. 14
1999 A295　　#a.-f.　　5.00 5.00
2000 A295 6.50r #a.-f, vert.　　7.00 7.00
Souvenir Sheet
2001 A295　　10r multicolored　　1.75 1.75

D-Day,
50th
Anniv.
A296

Designs: 2r, Amphibious DUKW approaches Utah Beach. 4r, Landing craft tank, Sword Beach. 18r, Landing craft infantry damaged at Omaha Beach.
No. 2006, Canadian commandos, Juno Beach.

1994, Aug. 8
2003-2005 A296　　Set of 3　　4.50 4.50
Souvenir Sheet
2006 A296 25r multicolored　　4.50 4.50

Intl. Olympic Committee, Cent.
A297　　　　　　A298

Designs: 7r, Linford Christie, Great Britain, track 1988. 12r, Koji Gushiken, Japan, gymnastics, 1984. 25r, George Hackl, Germany, single luge, 1994.

1994, Aug. 8
2007 A297　7r multicolored　　1.25 1.25
2008 A297　12r multicolored　　2.25 2.25
Souvenir Sheet
2009 A298 25r multicolored　　4.50 4.50

A299

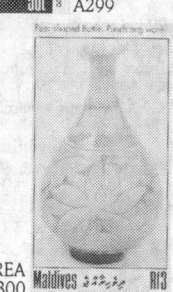

PHILAKOREA
'94 — A300

Designs: 50 l, Suwan Folk Village duck pond. 3.50r, Youngduson Park. 20r, Ploughing, Hahoe Village, Andong region.
　Ceramics, Choson & Koryo Dynasties: No. 2013a, Pear-shaped bottle. b, Vase. c, Vase with repaired lip. d, Labed vase, stoneware. e, Vase, celadon-glazed. f, Vase, unglazed stone. g, Ritual water sprinkler. h, Celadon-glazed vase.
　25r, Hunting (detail from eight-panel screen, Choson Dynasty), vert.

1994, Aug. 8　Perf. 14, 13½ (#2013)
2010-2012 A299　　Set of 3　　4.25 4.25
Miniature Sheet of 8
2013 A300　3r #a.-h.　　4.25 4.25
Souvenir Sheet
2014 A299 25r multicolored　　4.50 4.50

Miniature Sheets of 6

First
Manned
Moon
Landing,
25th Anniv.
A301

No. 2015: a, Apollo 11 crew. b, Apollo 11 patch, signatures of crew. c, "Buzz" Aldrin, lunar module, Eagle. d, Apollo 12 crew. e, Apollo 12 patch, signatures of crew. f, Alan Bean transporting ALSEP.

No. 2016: a, Apollo 16 crew. b, Apollo 16 patch, signatures of crew. c, John Young gives a "Navy salute." d, Apollo 17 crew. e, Apollo 17 patch, signatures of crew. f, Night launch of Apollo 17. 25r, Launch at Baikonur.

1994, Aug. 8　　　　Perf. 14
2015-2016 A301 5r #a.-f, each　　5.50 5.50
Souvenir Sheet
2017 A301 25r multicolored　　4.50 4.50

UN Development Plan — A302

Designs: 1r, Woman, baby, undernourished man, city on island. 8r, Island native, case worker, island, ship.

1994　　　Litho.　　Perf. 14
2018 A302　1r multicolored　　.18 .18
2019 A302　8r multicolored　　1.40 1.40

Miniature Sheet of 12

Space Exploration
A304

Designs: No. 2020a, Voyager 2. b, Sputnik. c, Apollo-Soyuz. d, Apollo 10 descent. e, Apollo 11 mission insignia. f, Hubble space telescope. g, Buzz Aldrin. h, RCA lunar cam. i, Lunar rover. j, Jim Irwin. k, Apollo 12 lunar module. l, Lunar soil extraction.
No. 2021, David Scott in open hatch of Apollo 9 command module. No. 2022, Alan Shepard, Jr. waving salute from moon, Apollo 14, horiz.

1994, Aug. 8　Litho.　　Perf. 14
2020 A304 5r #a.-l.　　11.00 11.00
Souvenir Sheets
2021-2022 A304 25r each　　4.50 4.50

Aminiya
School, 50th
Anniv.
A305

Designs: 15 l, Discipline. 50 l, Arts. 1r, Emblem, hand holding book, vert. 8r, Girls carrying books, vert. 10r, Sports. 11r, Girls cheering, vert. 13r, Science.

1994, Nov. 28
2023-2029 A305　Set of 7　　7.75 7.75

ICAO,
50th
Anniv.
A306

Designs: 50 l, Boeing 747. 1r, De Havilland Comet 4. 2r, Male Intl. Airport, Maldives. 3r, Lockheed 1649 Super Star. 8r, European Airbus. 10r, Dornier Do228. 25r, Concorde.

1994, Dec. 31
2030-2035 A306　Set of 6　　4.50 4.50
Souvenir Sheet
2036 A306 25r multicolored　　4.50 4.50

Miniature Sheets of 9

Water Birds A307

Designs: No. 2037a, Northern pintail (b, d). b, Comb duck (c). c, Ruddy duck. d, Garganey (a, e, g, h). e, Lesser whistling duck (b, c, f). f, Green winged teal. g, Fulvous whistling duck. h, Northern shoveler (e). i, Cotton pygmy goose (h).

No. 2038, Northern vert.: a, Pochard (b). b, Mallard (c, e, f). c, Wigeon. d, Northern shoveler (e, g). e, Northern pintail (h). f, Garganey (e, i). g, Tufted duck. h, Ferruginous duck (i). i, Red-crested pochard.

No. 2039, Cotton pygmy goose, vert. No. 2040, Garganey, diff.

1995, Feb. 27   Litho.   *Perf. 14*
2037 A307   5r #a.-i.   8.25   8.25
2038 A307   6.50r + 50 l #a.-i.   11.50   11.50

Souvenir Sheets
2039-2040 A307 25r each   4.50   4.50

Monuments of the World A308

Designs: 7 l, Taj Mahal. 10 l, Washington Monument. 15 l, Mt. Rushmore Memorial. 25 l, Arc de Triomphe, vert. 50 l, Sphinx, vert. 5r, El Castillo Monument of the Toltec, Chichen Itza, Yucatan, Mexico. 8r, Toltec monument, Tula, Mexico, vert. 12r, Victory Column, Berlin, vert.

No. 2049, Moai statues, Easter Island. No. 2050, Stonehenge.

1995, Feb. 28
2041-2048 A308   Set of 8   4.75   4.75

Souvenir Sheets
2049-2050 A308 25r each   4.50   4.50
No. 2049 contains one 43x57mm stamp, No. 2050 one 85x28mm stamp.

Donald Duck, 50th Birthday (in 1994) — A309

Scenes from "Donald and the Wheel:" 3 l, Racing chariot. 4 l, Standing on log. 5 l, Operating steam locomotive. 10 l, Looking at cave drawing, vert. 20 l, Sitting in "junked" car, vert. 25 l, Listening to phonograph. 5r, Climbing on mammoth. 20r, Pushing old car.

Disney Duck family orchestra, vert: No. 2059a, Donald Duck, saxophone. b, Moby Duck, violin. c, Feathry Duck, banjo. d, Daisy Duck, harp. e, Gladstone Gander, clarinet. f, Dewey, Louie, Huey, oboe. g, Gus Goose, flute. h, Ludwig von Drake, trombone.

Donald Duck family portraits, vert: No. 2060a, Daisy. b, Donald. c, Grandma. d, Gus Goose. e, Gyro Gearloose, f, Huey, Dewey, Louie. g, Ludwig von Drake. h, Scrooge McDuck.

No. 2061, Dixieland band, vert. No. 2062, Donald conducting symphony orchestra. No. 2063, Donald being photographed, vert. No. 2064, Huey, Dewey, Louie in family portrait.

Perf. 13¹/₂x13, 13x13¹/₂
1995, Mar. 22   Litho.
2051-2058 A309   Set of 8   4.75   4.75

Miniature Sheets of 8
2059-2060 A309   5r #a.-h., each   7.25   7.25

Souvenir Sheets
2061-2064 A309 25r each   4.50   4.50

EID Greetings — A310

Designs: 1r, Mosque. 1r, Rose. 8r, Hibiscus. 10r, Orchids.

1995, May 1   Litho.   *Perf. 14*
2065-2068 A310 Set of 4   3.75   3.75

Whales, Dolphins, & Porpoises A311

Nos. 2079-2072: 1r, Killer whale. 2r, Bottlenose dolphin. 8r, Humpback whale. 10r, Common dolphin.

No. 2073: a, Hourglass dolphin. b, Bottlenose dolphin. c, Dusky dolphin. d, Spectacled porpoise. c, Fraser's dolphin. f, Cameron's dolphin. g, Spinner dolphin. h, Dalls dolphin. i, Spotted dolphin. j, Indus river dolphin. k, Hector's dolphin. l, Amazon river dolphin.

No. 2074: a, Right whale (d). b, Killer whale (a). c, Humpback whale (f). d, Beluga. e, Narwhale. f, Blue whale (c, g). g, Bowhead whale (h, k). h, Fin whale (d, e, g). i, Pilot whale. j, Grey whale. k, Sperm whale (l). l, Goosebeaked whale.

No. 2075, Hourglass dolphin. No. 2076, Sperm whale.

1995, May 16
2069-2072 A311   Set of 4   3.75   3.75

Miniature Sheets of 12
2073-2074 A311   3r #a.-l., each   6.50   6.50

Souvenir Sheets
2075-2076 A311 25r each   4.50   4.50

Singapore '95.

UN, 50th Anniv. A311a

Designs: 30 l, Emblem, security of small states. 8r, Women in development. 11r, Peace keeping, peace making operations. 13r, Disarmament.

1995, July 6   Litho.   *Perf. 14*
2076A-2076D A311a   Set of 3   5.75   5.75

UN, 50th Anniv. — A312

No. 2077: a, 6.50r+50 l, Child, dove flying left. b, 8r, Earth from space. c, 10r, Child, Dove flying right.
25r, UN emblem, dove.

1995, July 6   Litho.   *Perf. 14*
2077 A312   Strip of 3, #a.-c.   4.50   4.50

Souvenir Sheet
2078 A312 25r multicolored   4.50   4.50
No. 2077 is a continuous design.

FAO, 50th Anniv. — A312a

1995   Litho.   *Perf. 14*
2078A A312a   7r Food for all   1.25   1.25
2078B A312a   8r Dolphin-friendly fishing   1.40   1.40

FAO, 50th Anniv. — A313

No. 2079: a, 6.50r+50 l, Child eating. b, 8r, FAO emblem, 10r, Mother, child.
25r, Food emblem, child, horiz.

1995, July 6
2079 A313   Strip of 3, #a.-c.   4.50   4.50

Souvenir Sheet
2080 A313 25r multicolored   4.50   4.50

1995 Boy Scout Jamboree, Holland A314

No. 2081: a, 10r, Natl. flag, scouts, tents. b, 12r, Scout cooking. c, 15r, Scouts sitting before tents. 25r, Scout playing flute, camp at night, vert.

1995, July 6
2081 A314   Strip of 3, #a.-c.   6.75   6.75

Souvenir Sheet
2082 A314 25r multicolored   4.50   4.50
No. 2081 is a continuous design.

Queen Mother, 95th Birthday A315

No. 2083: a, Drawing. b, Blue print dress, pearls. c, Formal portrait. d, Blue outfit.
25r, Pale violet hat, violet & blue dress.

1995, July 6   *Perf. 13¹/₂x14*
2083 A315   5r Block or strip of 4, #a.-d.   1.75   1.75

Souvenir Sheet
2084 A315 25r multicolored   4.50   4.50
No. 2083 was issued in sheets of 2.

Natl. Library, 50th Anniv. A316

Designs: 2r, Boys seated at library table. 8r, Two people standing, two at table. 10r, Library entrance.

1995, July 12   *Perf. 14*
2085 A316   2r multicolored   .35   .35
2086 A316   8r multicolored   1.40   1.40
   Size: 100x70mm
   Imperf
2087 A316   10r multicolored   1.75   1.75

Miniature Sheets of 6 or 8

End of World War II, 50th Anniv. A317

No. 2088: a, 203mm Red Army howitzer. b, Ruins of Hitler's residence, Berchtesgaden. c, Operation Manna, Allies drop food to starving Dutch. d, Soviet IL-1 fighter. e, Inmates, British troops burn last hut at Belsen. f, Last V1 Buzz Bomb launched against London. g, US 3rd Armored Division passes through ruins of Cologne. h, Gutted Reichstag, May 7, 1946.

No. 2089: a, Grumman F6F-3 Hellcat. b, F4-U1 attacking with rockets. c, Douglas Dauntless. d, Guadalcanal, Aug. 7, 1942. e, US Marines in Alligator landing craft. f, US Infantry landing craft.

No. 2090, Allied soldiers with smiling faces. No. 2091, Corsair fighters.

1995, July 6   Litho.   *Perf. 14*
2088 A317   5r #a.-h. + label   7.25   7.25
2089 A317   6.50r +50 l #a.-f. + label   7.50   7.50

Souvenir Sheets
2090-2091 A317 25r each   4.50   4.50

Turtles A318

Hawksbill turtle: No. 2092a, Crawling. b, Two in water. c, One crawling out of water. d, Swimming.

No. 2093: a, Spur-thighed tortoise. b, Aldabra turtle. c, Loggerhead turtle. d, Olive ridley. e, Leatherback turtle. f, Green turtle. g, Atlantic ridley. h, Hawsbill turtle.
25r, Chelonia mydas.

1995, Aug. 22
2092 A318   10r Strip of 4, #a.-d.   7.25   7.25

Miniature Sheet of 8
2093 A318   3r #a.-h.   4.25   4.25

Souvenir Sheet
2094 A318 25r multicolored   4.50   4.50
World Wildlife Fund (#2092). No. 2092 was printed in sheets of 12 stamps.

Miniature Sheets

Singapore '95 A319

Mushrooms, butterflies: No. 2095a, Russula aurata, papilio demodocus. b, Kallimoides rumia, lepista saeva. c, Lapista nuda, hypolimnas salmacis. d, Precis octavia, boletus subtomentosus.

No. 2096: a, 5r, Gyroporus castaneus, hypolimnas salmacis. b, 8r, Papilio dardanus, Gomphidius glutinosus. c, 10r, Russula olivacea, precis octavia. d, 12r, Prepona praeneste, boletus edulis.

No. 2097: a, Hypolimnas salmacis, boletus rhodoxanthus, vert. No. 2098, Amanita musearia, kallimoides rumia, vert.

1995, Oct. 18   Litho.   *Perf. 14*
2095 A319   2r Sheet of 4, #a.-d.   1.40   1.40
2096 A319   Sheet of 4, #a.-d.   6.25   6.25

Souvenir Sheets
2097-2098 A319 25r each   5.00   5.00

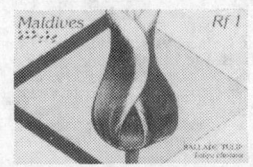

Flowers A320

Designs: 1r, Ballade tulip. 3r, White mallow. 5r, Regale trumpet lily. 7r, Lilactime dahlia. 8r, Blue ideal iris. 10r, Red crown imperial.

No. 2105, a, Dendrobium waipahu beauty. b, Brassocattleya Jean Murray "Allan Christenson." c, Cymbidium Fort George "Lewes." d, Paphiopedilum malipoense. e, Cycnoches chlorochilon. f, Rhyncholaelia digbgana. g, Lycaste deppei. h, Masdevallia constricta. i, Paphiopedilum Clair de Lune "Edgard Van Belle."

No. 2106, Psychopsis krameriana. No. 2107, Cockleshell orchid.

1995, Dec. 4 Litho. *Perf. 14*
2099-2104 A320 Set of 6 6.25 6.25

Miniature Sheet
2105 A320 5r Sheet of 9, #a.-i. 8.25 8.25

Souvenir Sheets
2106-2107 A320 25r each 4.50 4.50

Miniature Sheet

Elvis Presley (1935-77) A321

Various portraits.

1995, Dec. 8 *Perf. 13½x14*
2108 A321 5r Sheet of 9, #a.-i. 8.00 8.00

Souvenir Sheet
Perf. 14x13½
2109 A321 25r multi, horiz. 4.50 4.50

Miniature Sheets

John Lennon (1940-80), Entertainer — A322

No. 2110, Various portraits.

No. 2111: a, 10r, As young man. b, 8r, Younger man with glasses. c, 3r, With beard. d, 2r, Older picture without beard.

No. 2112, Standing at microphone.

1995, Dec. 8
2110 A322 5r Sheet of 6, #a.-f. 5.50 5.50
2111 A322 Sheet of 4, #a.-d. 4.25 4.25

Souvenir Sheet
2112 A322 25r multicolored 4.50 4.50

Miniature Sheets of 9

Nobel Prize Fund Established, Cent. — A323

Recipients: No. 2113a, Bernardo A. Houssay, medicine, 1947. b, Paul H. Müller, medicine, 1948. c, Walter R. Hess, medicine, 1949. d, Sir MacFarlane Burnet, medicine, 1960. e, Baruch S. Blumberg, medicine, 1976. f, Daniel Nathans, medicine, 1978. g, Glenn T. Seaborg, chemistry, 1951. h, Ilya Prigogine, chemistry, 1977. i, Kenichi Fukui, chemistry, 1981.

No. 2114: a, Johannes Van Der Waals, physics, 1910. b, Charles Édouard Guillaume, physics, 1920. c, Sir James Chadwick, physics, 1935. d, Willem Einthoven, medicine, 1924. e, Henrik Dam, medicine, 1943. f, Sir Alexander Fleming, medicine, 1945. g, Hermann J. Muller, medicine, 1946. h, Rodney R. Porter, medicine, 1972. i, Werner Arber, medicine, 1978.

No. 2115: a, Dag Hammarskjold, peace, 1961. b, Alva R. Myrdal, peace, 1982. c, Archbishop Desmond M. Tutu, peace, 1984. d, Rudolf C. Eucken, literature, 1908. e, Aleksandr Solzhenitsyn, literature, 1970. f, Gabriel Garcia Márquez, literature, 1982. g, Chen N. Yang, physics, 1957. h, Karl A. Müller, physics, 1987. i, Melvin Schwartz, physics, 1988.

No. 2116: a, Niels Bohr, physics, 1922. b, Ben R. Mottelson, physics, 1975. c, Patrick White, literature, 1973. d, Elias Canetti, literature, 1981. e, Theodor Kocher, medicine, 1909. f, August Krogh, medicine, 1920. g, William P. Murphy, medicine, 1934. h, John H. Northrop, chemistry, 1946. i, Luis F. Leloir, chemistry, 1970.

No. 2117: a, Carl Spitteler, literatue, 1919. b, Henri Bergson, literature, 1927. c, Johannes V. Jensen, literature, 1944. d, Antoine-Henri Becquerel, physics, 1903. e, Sir William H. Bragg, physics, 1915. f, Sir William L. Bragg, physics, 1915. g, Fredrik Bajer, peace, 1908. h, Léon Bourgeois, peace, 1920. i, Karl Branting, peace, 1921.

No. 2118: a, Robert A. Millikan, physics, 1923. b, Louis V. de Broglie, physics, 1929. c, Ernest Walton, physics, 1951. d, Richard Willstätter, chemistry, 1915. e, Lars Onsager, chemistry, 1968. f, Gerhard Herzberg, chemistry, 1971. g, William B. Yeats, literature, 1923. h, George B. Shaw, literature, 1925. i, Eugene O'Neill, literature, 1936.

No. 2119, Eisaku Sato, peace, 1974. No. 2120, Robert Koch, medicine, 1905. No. 2121, Otto Wallach, chemistry, 1910. No. 2122, Konrad Bloch, medicine, 1964. No. 2123, Samuel Beckett, literature, 1969. No. 2124, Hideki Yukawa, physics, 1949.

1995, Dec. 28 Litho. *Perf. 14*
2113-2118 A323 5r #a.-i., each 8.00 8.00

Souvenir Sheets
2119-2124 A323 25r each 4.50 4.50

MALTA

'mȯl–tə

LOCATION — A group of islands in the Mediterranean Sea off the coast of Sicily
GOVT. — Republic within the British Commonwealth
AREA — 122 sq. mi.
POP. — 329,189 (1983)
CAPITAL — Valletta

The former colony includes the islands of Malta, Gozo, and Comino. It became a republic Dec. 13, 1974.

4 Farthings = 1 Penny
12 Pence = 1 Shilling
20 Shillings = 1 Pound
10 Mils = 1 Cent (1972)
100 Cents = 1 Pound (1972)

Catalogue values for unused stamps in this country are for Never Hinged items, beginning with Scott 206 in the regular postage section, Scott B1 in the semi-postal section, Scott C2 in the air post section, and Scott J21 in the postage due section.

Watermark

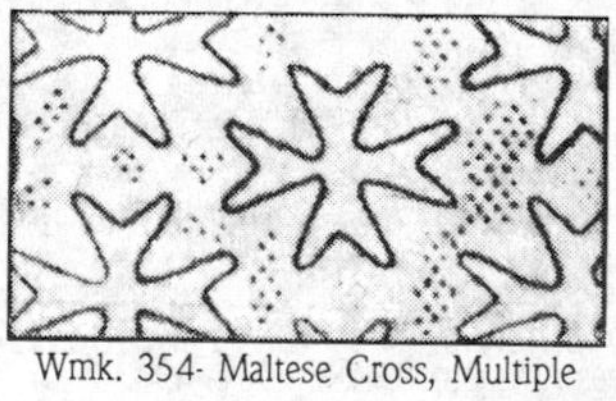

Wmk. 354- Maltese Cross, Multiple

Values for unused stamps are for examples with original gum as defined in the catalogue introduction. Very fine examples of Nos. 1-7 will have perforations touching the frameline on one or more sides due to the narrow spacing of the stamps on the plate. Stamps with perfs clear of the frameline are scarce and will command higher prices.

Queen Victoria
A1 A2

A3 A4

1860-61 Unwmk. Typo. *Perf. 14*
1 A1 ½p buff ('61) 525.00 300.00
2 A1 ½p buff, *bluish* 950.00 700.00
a. Imperf. *11,000.*

1863-80 Wmk. 1
3 A1 ½p orange yel ('80) 50.00 14.00
a. ½p buff 70.00 50.00
b. ½p brown orange 200.00 75.00
c. ½p yellow buff 60.00 40.00
4 A1 ½p golden yel ('74) 225.00 200.00

1865 *Perf. 12½*
5 A1 ½p buff 70.00 45.00
a. ½p yellow buff 235.00 225.00

1878 *Perf. 14x12½*
6 A1 ½p buff 110.00 85.00
a. Perf. 12½x14

1882 Wmk. 2 *Perf. 14*
7 A1 ½p orange 15.00 11.50

1885, Jan. 1
8 A1 ½p green 1.00 .30
9 A2 1p car rose 1.40 .25
a. 1p rose 60.00 15.00
10 A3 2p gray 3.00 1.40
11 A4 2½p ultramarine 25.00 .50
a. 2½p bright ultramarine 25.00 .50
b. 2½p dull blue 27.50 .50
12 A3 4p brown 7.00 2.50
a. Imperf., pair 5,000. *4,750.*
13 A3 1sh violet 25.00 5.50
Nos. 8-13 (6) 62.40 10.45

For surcharge see No. 20.

Queen Victoria within Maltese Cross — A5

1886 Wmk. 1
14 A5 5sh rose 110.00 80.00

Gozo Fishing Boat — A6 Ancient Galley — A7

1899, Feb. 4 Engr. Wmk. 2
15 A6 4½p black brown 10.00 7.50
16 A7 5p brown red 20.00 10.00

See Nos. 42-45.

"Malta" — A8 St. Paul after Shipwreck — A9

1899 Wmk. 1
17 A8 2sh6p olive gray 27.50 11.50
18 A9 10sh blue black 65.00 47.50

See No. 64. For overprint see No. 85.

Valletta Harbor — A10

1901, Jan. 1 Wmk. 2
19 A10 1f red brown .55 .65

See Nos. 28-29.

No. 11 Surcharged in Black **One Penny**

1902, July 4
20 A4 1p on 2½p ultra .45 .45
a. "Pnney" 22.50 *27.50*
b. Double surcharge 4,000. 4,000.

King Edward VII — A12

1903-04 Typo.
21 A12 ½p dark green 3.00 .20
22 A12 1p car & black 7.50 .15
23 A12 2p gray & red vio 12.50 5.00
24 A12 2½p ultra & brn vio 11.00 1.50
25 A12 3p red vio & gray .60 .35
26 A12 4p brown & blk ('04) 20.00 11.00
27 A12 1sh violet & gray 11.00 5.00
Nos. 21-27 (7) 65.60 23.20

1904-11 Wmk. 3
28 A10 1f red brown ('05) .50 .20
29 A10 1f dk brown ('10) .50 .25
30 A12 ½p green 1.25 .15
31 A12 1p car & blk ('05) 4.00 .25
32 A12 1p carmine ('07) .70 .25
33 A12 2p gray & red vio ('05) 3.75 .50
34 A12 2p gray ('11) 1.50 3.00
35 A12 2½p ultra & brn vio 8.00 .60
36 A12 2½p ultra ('11) 3.00 1.00
37 A12 4p brn & blk ('06) 5.75 5.50
38 A12 4p scar & blk, *yel* ('11) 2.50 3.50
39 A12 1sh violet & gray 40.00 3.00
40 A12 1sh blk, *grn* ('11) 4.75 3.00
41 A12 5sh scar & grn, *yel* ('11) 42.50 60.00

Engr.
42 A6 4½p black brn ('05) 14.00 5.50
43 A6 4½p orange ('11) 2.75 3.00
44 A7 5p red ('04) 14.00 5.25
45 A7 5p ol green ('10) 2.50 3.50
Nos. 28-45 (18) 151.95 98.45

A13 A15

King George V — A16

1914-21 Typo.

Ordinary Paper
49 A13 ¼p brown .25 .15
50 A13 ½p green .35 .15
51 A13 1p scarlet ('15) .60 .15
a. 1p carmine ('14) .60 .15
52 A13 2p gray ('15) 4.00 2.50
53 A13 2½p ultramarine .55 .30

Chalky Paper
54 A15 3p vio, *yel* 3.25 4.25
58 A13 6p dull vio & red vio 6.00 10.00
59 A15 1sh black, *green* 7.00 15.00
a. 1sh black, *bl grn*, ol back 12.50 12.50
b. 1sh black, *emerald* ('21) 7.50 15.00
c. As "b," olive back 8.00 15.00
60 A16 2sh ultra & dl vio, *bl* 42.50 65.00
61 A16 5sh scar & grn, *yel* 62.50 70.00

Surface-colored Paper
62 A15 1sh blk, *grn* ('15) 9.00 12.00
Nos. 49-54,58-62 (11) 136.00 179.50

See Nos. 66-68, 70-72. For overprints see Nos. 77-82, 84.

Valletta Harbor — A17

1915   **Engr.**
Ordinary Paper
63 A17 4p black   10.00 6.00

St. Paul
A18

George V
A19

1919
64 A8 2sh6p olive green   40.00 45.00
65 A18 10sh black   3,250. 3,700.
    Revenue cancel   70.00
For overprint see No. 83.

1921-22   **Typo.**   **Wmk. 4**
Ordinary Paper
66 A13 ¼p brown   .20 .25
67 A13 ½p green   1.25 12.00
68 A13 1p rose red   .20 .15
69 A19 2p gray   2.00 .50
70 A13 2½p ultramarine   2.50 15.00
Chalky Paper
71 A13 6p dull vio & red vio   22.50 45.00
72 A16 2sh ultra & dull vio, bl   55.00 150.00
Engr.
Ordinary Paper
73 A18 10sh black   275.00 425.00
   Nos. 66-73 (8)   358.65 647.90
For overprints and surcharge see Nos. 86-93, 97.

Stamps of 1914-19
Overprinted in Red or
Black

SELF-GOVERNMENT

1922   **Wmk. 3**
Ordinary Paper
Overprint 21mm
77 A13 ½p green   .15 .15
78 A13 2½p ultra   4.00 15.00
Chalky Paper
79 A15 3p violet, yel   1.00 8.00
80 A13 6p dull lil & red vio   1.00 8.00
81 A15 1sh black, emer   2.00 8.00
Overprint 28mm
82 A16 2sh ultra & dull vio,
         bl (R)   200.00 275.00
83 A8 2sh6p olive grn   16.00 25.00
Chalky Paper
84 A16 5sh scar & grn, yel   45.00 70.00
   Nos. 77-84 (8)   269.15 409.15

Wmk. 1
Ordinary Paper
85 A9 10sh blue black (R)   160.00 190.00

Same Overprint on Stamps of 1921
1922   **Ordinary Paper**   **Wmk. 4**
Overprint 21mm
86 A13 ¼p brown   .70 .20
87 A13 ½p green   .65 3.00
88 A13 1p rose red   .20 .20
89 A19 2p gray   .55 .85
90 A13 2½p ultramarine   .45 .45
Chalky Paper
91 A13 6p dull vio & red vio   5.00 15.00
Overprint 28mm
92 A16 2sh ultra & dull vio, bl
         (R)   30.00 65.00
Ordinary Paper
93 A18 10sh black (R)   100.00 125.00
   Nos. 86-93 (8)   137.55 209.70

No. 69 Surcharged   **One Farthing**

1922, Apr. 15
97 A19 1f on 2p gray   .15 .15

"Malta" — A20

Britannia and
Malta — A21

1922-26   **Typo.**
Chalky Paper
98 A20 ¼p brown   .60 .20
99 A20 ½p green   .70 .20
100 A20 1p buff & plum   .70 .20
101 A20 1p violet ('24)   .90 .20
102 A20 1½p org brn ('23)   1.40 .20
103 A20 2p ol brn & turq   .90 .20
104 A20 2½p ultra ('26)   .90 .45
105 A20 3p ultramarine   1.75 1.40
   a.   3p blue   1.75 1.40
106 A20 3p blk, yel ('26)   1.00 5.00
107 A20 4p yel & ultra   1.00 1.40
108 A20 6p ol grn & vio   1.75 1.00
109 A21 1sh ol brn & blue   3.00 2.00
110 A21 2sh ultra & ol brn   5.00 8.00
111 A21 2sh6p blk & red vio   7.00 8.00
112 A21 5sh ultra & org   12.50 25.00
113 A21 10sh ol brn & gray   45.00 80.00
Engr.
Ordinary Paper
114 A20 £1 car red & blk
       ('25)   95.00 175.00
   a.   £1 rose car & blk ('22)   95.00 175.00
   Nos. 98-114 (17)   179.10 308.45
No. 114a has watermark sideways.
For overprints and surcharges see Nos. 115-129.

No. 105 Surcharged   **Two pence halfpenny**

1925, Dec.
115 A20 2½p on 3p ultramarine   .50 .65

Stamps of 1922-26
Overprinted   **POSTAGE**

1926
116 A20 ¼p brown   .20 .20
117 A20 ½p green   .20 .20
118 A20 1p violet   .20 .20
119 A20 1½p orange brown   .25 .20
120 A20 2p ol brn & turq   .35 .35
121 A20 2½p ultramarine   .35 .25
122 A20 3p black, yel   .40 .40
   a.   Inverted overprint   175.00 425.00
123 A20 4p yel & ultra   3.00 7.00
124 A20 6p ol grn & vio   1.25 1.25
125 A21 1sh ol brn & bl   4.00 6.00
126 A21 2sh ultra & ol brown   35.00 90.00
127 A21 2sh6p blk & red vio   8.50 22.50
128 A21 5sh ultra & org   7.50 25.00
129 A21 10sh ol brn & gray   5.50 12.00
   Nos. 116-129 (14)   66.70 165.55

George
V — A22

Valletta
Harbor — A23

St.
Publius — A24

Notabile
(Mdina) — A25

Gozo Fishing
Boat — A26

Statue of
Neptune — A27

Ruins at
Mnaidra — A28

St. Paul — A29

1926-27   **Typo.**   **Perf. 14½x14**
131 A22 ¼p brown   .25 .15
132 A22 ½p green   1.25 .15
133 A22 1p red   1.65 .20
134 A22 1½p orange brn   1.65 .20
135 A22 2p gray   2.00 2.75
136 A22 2½p blue   1.90 .50
137 A22 3p dark violet   1.90 2.25
138 A22 4p org red & blk   3.00 3.25
139 A22 4½p yel buff & vio   3.00 2.50
140 A22 6p red & violet   3.25 2.50
Engr.   **Perf. 12½**
Inscribed: "Postage"
141 A23 1sh black   3.25 3.25
142 A24 1sh6p green & blk   4.50 8.00
143 A25 2sh dp vio & blk   6.75 12.00
144 A26 2sh6p ver & black   11.00 27.50
145 A27 3sh blue & blk   9.75 25.00
146 A28 5sh green & blk   17.50 40.00
147 A29 10sh car & blk   37.50 90.00
   Nos. 131-147 (17)   110.10 220.20
See #167-183. For overprints see #148-166.

POSTAGE
Stamps and Type of 1926-   **AND**
27 Overprinted in Black   **REVENUE**

1928   **Perf. 14½x14**
148 A22 ¼p brown   .50 .15
149 A22 ½p green   .50 .15
150 A22 1p red   1.10 .35
151 A22 1p orange brown   1.75 1.40
152 A22 1½p yel brown   1.25 .35
153 A22 1½p red   2.75 .15
154 A22 2p gray   2.50 7.00
155 A22 2½p blue   .90 .30
156 A22 3p dark violet   .90 .40
157 A22 4p org red & blk   .90 1.00
158 A22 4½p yel & violet   1.65 1.00
159 A22 6p red & violet   1.65 1.60

POSTAGE
Overprinted in Red   **AND**
         REVENUE.

       Perf. 12½
160 A23 1sh black   1.65 1.90
161 A24 1sh6p green & blk   3.75 8.00
162 A25 2sh dp vio & blk   14.00 30.00
163 A26 2sh6p ver & black   9.50 20.00
164 A27 3sh ultra & blk   13.00 27.50
165 A28 5sh yel grn & blk   19.00 27.50
166 A29 10sh car rose & black   40.00 80.00
   Nos. 148-166 (19)   117.25 208.75
Issued: Nos. 151, 153, Dec. 5; others, Oct. 1.

Types of 1926-27 Issue
1930, Oct. 20   **Typo.**   **Perf. 14½x14**
Inscribed: "Postage & Revenue"
167 A22 ¼p brown   .40 .15
168 A22 ½p green   .40 .15
169 A22 1p yel brown   .45 .15
170 A22 1½p red   .55 .15
171 A22 2p gray   .80 .50
172 A22 2½p blue   1.50 .25
173 A22 3p dark violet   1.25 .30
174 A22 4p org red & blk   1.00 2.50
175 A22 4½p yel & violet   2.00 1.40
176 A22 6p red & violet   1.50 .70
Engr.   **Perf. 12½**
177 A23 1sh black   4.75 8.00
178 A24 1sh6p green & blk   4.25 11.00
179 A25 2sh dp vio & blk   6.00 14.00
180 A26 2sh6p ver & black   10.50 35.00
181 A27 3sh ultra & blk   17.50 45.00
182 A28 5sh yel grn & blk   21.00 50.00
183 A29 10sh car rose & blk   52.50 95.00
   Nos. 167-183 (17)   126.35 264.25

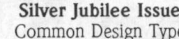

Silver Jubilee Issue
Common Design Type
1935, May 6   **Perf. 11x12**
184 CD301 ½p green & blk   .20 .20
185 CD301 2½p ultra & brn   1.25 1.00
186 CD301 6p ol grn & lt bl   4.50 5.25
187 CD301 1sh brn vio & ind   7.50 10.50
   Nos. 184-187 (4)   13.45 16.95
   Set, never hinged   27.50

Coronation Issue
Common Design Type
   Perf. 13½x14
1937, May 12   **Wmk. 4**
188 CD302 ½p deep green   .15 .15
189 CD302 1½p carmine   .15 .15
190 CD302 2½p bright ultra   .50 .50
   Set value   .65 .65
   Set, never hinged   .75

Valletta
Harbor — A30

Fort St.
Angelo — A31

Verdala Palace — A32

Neolithic
Ruins — A33

Victoria and Citadel,
Gozo — A34

De l'Isle Adam
Entering Mdina
A35

St. John's Co-
Cathedral
A36

Mnaidra
Temple — A37

Statue of Antonio
Manoel de
Vilhena — A38

Woman in
Faldetta — A39

St. Publius — A40

Mdina
Cathedral — A41

Palace
Square — A43

Statue of Neptune — A42 St. Paul — A44

1938-43 Wmk. 4 *Perf. 12½*

191	A30	1f brown	.15	.15
192	A31	½p green	.40	.15
192A	A31	½p chnt ('43)	.15	.15
193	A32	1p chestnut	2.50	.20
193A	A32	1p grn ('43)	.15	.15
194	A33	1½p rose red	.25	.15
194A	A33	1½p dk gray ('43)	.20	.15
195	A34	2p dark gray	.90	.75
195A	A34	2p rose red ('43)	.40	.25
196	A35	2½p blue	.90	.60
196A	A35	2½p violet ('43)	.35	.35
197	A36	3p violet	.75	.55
197A	A36	3p blue ('43)	.40	.20
198	A37	4½p ocher & ol green	.30	.30
199	A38	6p rose red & ol green	.60	.30
200	A39	1sh black	.60	.55
201	A40	1sh6p sage grn & black	4.50	1.00
202	A41	2sh dk bl & lt grn	1.10	1.10
203	A42	2sh6p rose red & black	3.00	3.00
204	A43	5sh bl grn & blk	3.75	3.75
205	A44	10sh dp rose & blk	8.75	8.75
		Nos. 191-205 (21)	30.10	22.55
		Never hinged	40.00	

See #236a. For overprints see #208-222.

Catalogue values for unused stamps in this section, from this point to the end of the section, are for Never Hinged items.

Peace Issue
Common Design Type
Inscribed: "Malta" and Crosses
Perf. 13½x14

1946, June 8 Engr. Wmk. 4

206	CD303	1p bright green	.15	.15
207	CD303	3p dark ultra	.20	.20
		Set value	.30	.30

Stamps of 1938-43 Overprinted in Black or Carmine

a SELF-GOVERNMENT 1947

1948, Nov. 25 *Perf. 12½*

208	A30	1f brown	.20	.20
209	A31	½p chestnut	.20	.20
210	A32	1p green	.65	.20
211	A33	1½p dk gray (C)	.50	.20
212	A34	2p rose red	.70	.30
213	A35	2½p violet (C)	.70	.30
214	A36	3p blue (C)	.75	.30
215	A37	4½p ocher & ol grn	1.90	.90
216	A38	6p rose red & ol green	.60	.45
217	A39	1sh black	1.90	.65
218	A40	1sh6p sage grn & blk	2.50	1.10
219	A41	2sh dk bl & lt grn (C)	3.00	1.75
220	A42	2sh6p rose red & blk	6.00	3.50
221	A43	5sh bl grn & blk (C)	11.00	8.00
222	A44	10sh dp rose & blk	24.00	20.00
		Nos. 208-222 (15)	54.60	38.05

The overprint is smaller on No. 208. It reads from lower left to upper right on Nos. 209 and 221.
See Nos. 235-240.

Silver Wedding Issue
Common Design Types
Inscribed: "Malta" and Crosses

1949, Jan. 4 Photo. *Perf. 14x14½*

223	CD304	1p dark green	.20	.20

Perf. 11½x11
Engr.

224	CD305	£1 dark blue	40.00	30.00

Malta stamps can be mounted in the Scott British Europe album.

UPU Issue
Common Design Types
Inscribed: "Malta" and Crosses
Perf. 13½, 11x11½

1949, Oct. 10 Engr. Wmk. 4

225	CD306	2½p violet	.25	.25
226	CD307	3p indigo	.60	.60
227	CD308	6p dp carmine	1.10	1.10
228	CD309	1sh slate	2.25	2.25
		Nos. 225-228 (4)	4.20	4.20

Princess Elizabeth — A45 Madonna and Child — A46

1950, Dec. 1 Engr. *Perf. 12x11½*

229	A45	1p emerald	.15	.15
230	A45	3p bright blue	.35	.35
231	A45	1sh gray black	.70	.70
		Nos. 229-231 (3)	1.20	1.20

Visit of Princess Elizabeth.

1951, July 12

232	A46	1p green	.15	.15
233	A46	3p purple	.25	.20
234	A46	1sh slate black	.80	.80
		Nos. 232-234 (3)	1.20	1.15

700th anniv. of the presentation of the scapular to St. Simon Stock.

Types of 1938-43 Overprinted Type "a" in Red or Black

1953, Jan. 8 Wmk. 4 *Perf. 12½*

235	A32	1p gray (R)	.15	.15
236	A33	1½p green	.20	.15
	a.	Overprint omitted		*8,000.*
237	A34	2p ocher	.30	.25
238	A35	2½p rose red	.50	.35
239	A36	3p violet (R)	.35	.15
240	A37	4½p ultra & ol grn (R)	.75	.60
		Nos. 235-240 (6)	2.25	1.65

Coronation Issue
Common Design Type
Inscribed: "Malta" and Crosses

1953, June 3 Engr. *Perf. 13½x13*

241	CD312	1½p dk green black	.20	.15

Type of 1938-43 with Portrait of Queen Elizabeth II Inscribed: "Royal Visit 1954."

1954, May 3 *Perf. 12½*

242	A36	3p violet	.20	.15

Visit of Elizabeth II and the Duke of Edinburgh, 1954.

Central Altarpiece, Collegiate Parish Church, Cospicua — A47

Perf. 14½x13½

1954, Sept. 8 Photo. Wmk. 4

243	A47	1½p bright green	.15	.15
244	A47	3p ultramarine	.20	.15
245	A47	1sh gray black	.70	.70
		Nos. 243-245 (3)	1.05	1.00

Cent. of the promulgation of the Dogma of the Immaculate Conception.

Monument of the Great Siege, 1565 — A48 Auberge de Castille — A49

Designs: ½p, Wignacourt Aqueduct Horsetrough. 1p, Victory Church. 1½p, War Memorial. 2p, Mosta Dome. 3p, King's Scroll. 4½p, Roosevelt's Scroll. 6p, Neolithic Temples at Tarxien. 8p, Vedette. 1sh, Mdina Gate. 1sh6p, Les Gavroches. 2sh, Monument of Christ the King. 2sh6p, Monument of Nicolas Cottoner. 5sh, Raymond Perellos Monument. 10sh, St. Paul. £1, Baptism of Christ.

1956-57 Engr. *Perf. 11½*

246	A48	¼p violet	.15	.15
247	A48	½p yel orange	.15	.15
248	A48	1p black	.15	.15
249	A48	1½p brt green	.15	.15
250	A48	2p brown	.15	.15
251	A49	2½p orange brown	.25	.15
252	A48	3p rose red	.15	.15
253	A48	4½p blue	.15	.15
254	A49	6p slate blue	.15	.15
255	A48	8p olive bister	.30	*.95*
256	A48	1sh purple	.50	.38
257	A48	1sh6p Prus green	.90	.60
258	A48	2sh olive green	1.65	.95

Perf. 13½x13

259	A48	2sh6p cop brown	3.50	1.25
260	A48	5sh emerald	7.00	4.00
261	A48	10sh dk carmine	32.50	17.50
262	A48	£1 yel brn ('57)	37.50	27.50
		Nos. 246-262 (17)	85.30	54.48

See Nos. 296-297.

First George Cross Issue

Symbol of Malta's War Effort — A50 Searchlights over Malta — A51

Design: 1sh, Bombed houses.

Perf. 14x14½, 14½x14

1957, Apr. 15 Photo.

Cross in Silver

263	A50	1½p green	.15	.15
264	A51	3p bright red	.15	.15
265	A50	1sh dark red brown	.38	.38
		Set value	.58	.57

Award of the George Cross to Malta for its war effort.
See Nos. 269-274.

Symbols of Architecture A52

Designs: 3p, Symbols of Industry, vert. 1sh, Symbols of electronics and chemistry and Technical School, Paola.

Perf. 14½x14, 14x14½

1958, Feb. 15 Wmk. 314

266	A52	1½p dp green & blk	.15	.15
267	A52	3p rose red, blk & gray	.15	.15
268	A52	1sh gray, blk & lilac	.50	.50
		Set value	.70	.65

Technical education on Malta.

Second George Cross issue
Types of 1957

Designs: 1½p, Bombed-out family and searchlights. 3p, Convoy entering harbor. 1sh, Searchlight battery.

Perf. 14½x14, 14x14½

1958, Apr. 15

Cross in Silver

269	A51	1½p black & brt green	.15	.15
270	A50	3p black & vermilion	.15	.15
271	A51	1sh black & brt lilac	.55	.55
		Nos. 269-271 (3)	.85	
		Set value		.72

Third George Cross Issue
Types of 1957

Designs: 1½p, Air Raid Precautions Organization helping wounded. 3p, Allegory of Malta. 1sh, Mother and child during air raid.

Perf. 14x14½, 14½x14

1959, Apr. 15

272	A50	1½p gold, green & black	.15	.15
273	A51	3p gold, lilac & black	.15	.15
274	A50	1sh gold, gray & black	.65	.65
		Nos. 272-274 (3)	.95	
		Set value		.80

St. Paul's Shipwreck, Painting in St. Paul's Church, Valletta — A53

Statue of St. Paul, St. Paul's Grotto, Rabat A54

Designs: 3p, Consecration of St. Publius. 6p, St. Paul leaving Malta; painting, St. Paul's Church, Valletta. 1sh, Angel holding tablet with quotations from Acts of the Apostles. 2sh6p, St. Paul and St. Paul's Bay islets.

Wmk. 314

1960, Feb. 9 Photo. *Perf. 13*

275	A53	1½p bister, brt bl & gold	.16	.15
	a.	Gold dates & crosses omitted	*75.00*	*57.50*
276	A53	3p lt blue, red lil & gold	.18	.16
277	A53	6p car, gray & gold	.40	.28

Perf. 14x14½

278	A54	8p black & gold	.65	.50
279	A54	1sh brt cl & gold	.85	.65
280	A54	2sh6p brt grnsh bl & gold	4.00	3.00
	a.	Gold omitted	*375.00*	
		Nos. 275-280 (6)	6.24	4.74

19th centenary of St. Paul's shipwreck on Malta.

Stamp of 1860 — A55

Perf. 13x13½

1960, Dec. 1 Engr. Wmk. 314

281	A55	1½p multi	.15	.15
282	A55	3p multi	.15	.15
283	A55	6p multi	.60	.60
		Nos. 281-283 (3)	.90	.90

Centenary of Malta's first postage stamp.

Fourth George Cross Issue

George Cross A56

Background designs: 3p, Sun and water. 1sh, Maltese crosses.

1961, Apr. 15 Photo. *Perf. 14½x14*

284	A56	1½p gray, bister & buff	.15	.15
285	A56	3p ol gray, lt & dk grnsh blue	.15	.15
286	A56	1sh ol green, vio & lil	1.10	1.10
		Nos. 284-286 (3)	1.40	1.40

19th anniv. of the award of the George Cross to Malta.

Madonna Damascena — A57

David Bruce and Themistocles Zammit — A58

Designs: 3p, Great Siege Monument by Antonio Sciortino. 6p, Grand Master La Valette (1557-1568). 1sh, Assault on Fort Elmo (old map).

Perf. 12½x12

1962, Sept. 7 **Wmk. 314**

287 A57 2p ultramarine .15 .15
288 A57 3p dark red .15 .15
289 A57 6p olive green .24 .24
290 A57 1sh rose lake .60 .60
Nos. 287-290 (4) 1.14 1.14

Great Siege of 1565 in which the knights of the Order of St. John and the Maltese Christians defeated the Turks.

Freedom from Hunger Issue
Common Design Type

1963, June 4 *Perf. 14x14½*

291 CD314 1sh6p sepia 4.00 3.25

Red Cross Centenary Issue
Common Design Type

1963, Sept. 2 **Litho.** *Perf. 13*

292 CD315 2p black & red .28 .15
293 CD315 1sh6p ultra & red 3.50 3.00

Type of 1956

Designs as before.

1963-64 **Engr.** *Perf. 11½*

296 A48 1p black .50 .42
297 A48 2p brown ('64) .85 .75

Perf. 14x13½

1964, Apr. 14 **Photo.** **Wmk. 314**

Design: 1sh6p, Goat and laboratory equipment.

298 A58 2p dl grn, blk & brn .15 .15
a. Black omitted
299 A58 1sh6p rose lake & blk 1.25 1.00

Anti-Brucellosis (Malta fever) Congress of the UN FAO, Valletta, June 8-13.

Nicola Cottoner Attending Sick Man and Congress Emblem — A59

Designs: 6p, Statue of St. Luke and St. Luke's Hospital. 1sh6p, Sacra Infermeria, Valletta.

Perf. 13½x14

1964, Sept. 5 **Wmk. 354**

300 A59 2p multicolored .15 .15
301 A59 6p multicolored .52 .45
302 A59 1sh6p multicolored 1.75 1.65
Nos. 300-302 (3) 2.42 2.25

1st European Cong. of Catholic Physicians, Malta, Sept. 6-10.

Independent State

Dove, Maltese Cross and British Crown — A60

Nativity — A61

Dove, Maltese Cross and: 3p, 1sh6p, Pope's tiara. 6p, 2sh6p, UN Emblem.

Perf. 14½x13½

1964, Sept. 21 **Photo.**

Gold and

303 A60 2p gray ol & red .16 .15
304 A60 3p dk red brn & red .22 .18
305 A60 6p sl blue & red .70 .35
306 A60 1sh ultra & red 1.50 .55
307 A60 1sh6p bl blk & red 4.50 2.50
308 A60 2sh6p vio bl & red 6.00 4.00
Nos. 303-308 (6) 13.08 7.73

Malta's independence.

Perf. 13x13½

1964, Nov. 3 **Wmk. 354**

309 A61 2p magenta & gold .15 .15
310 A61 4p ultra & gold .32 .28
311 A61 8p dp green & gold 1.40 1.25
Nos. 309-311 (3) 1.87 1.68

Cippus, Phoenician and Greek Inscriptions — A62

British Arms, Armory, Valletta A63

Designs (History of Malta): ½p, Neolithic (sculpture of sleeping woman). 1½p, Roman (sculpture). 2p, Proto-Christian (lamp, Roman temple, Chrismon). 2½p, Saracen (tomb, 12th cent.). 3p, Siculo Norman (arch, Palazzo Gatto-Murina, Notabile). 4p, Knights of Malta (lamp base, cross, and armor of knights). 4½p, Maltese navy (16th cent. galleons). 5p, Fortifications. 6p, French occupation (Cathedral of Notabile, cap, fasces). 10p, Naval Arsenal.

1sh, Maltese Corps of the British Army (insignia). 1sh3p, International Eucharistic Congress, 1913 (angels adoring Eucharist and map of Malta). 1sh6p, Self Government, 1921 (Knights of Malta Hall, present assembly seat). 2sh, Civic Council, Gozo (Statue of Livia, Gozo City Hall). 2sh6p, State of Malta (seated woman and George Cross). 3sh, Independence (doves, UN emblem, British crown, and Pope's tiara).

5sh, "HAFMED," (headquarters and insigne of Allied Forces, Mediterranean). 10sh, Map of Mediterranean. £1, Catholicism (Sts. Paul, Publius and Agatha).

Perf. 14x14½, 14½ (A63)

1965-70 **Photo.** **Wmk. 354**

312 A62 ½p violet & yel .15 .15
313 A62 1p multi .15 .15
a. Booklet pane of 6 ('70) .35
314 A62 1½p multi .15 .15
315 A62 2p multi .15 .15
a. Gold omitted 25.00
b. Booklet pane of 6 ('70) .40
316 A62 2½p multi .15 .15
a. Gold ("SARACENIC") omitted 55.00
317 A62 3p multi .15 .15
a. Imperf., pair 250.00
b. Gold (windows) omitted 37.50
318 A62 4p multi .15 .15
a. Black (arms shading) omitted 47.50
b. Silver omitted 45.00
319 A62 4½p multi .15 .15
319A A62 5p multi ('70) .25 .15
b. Booklet pane of 6 ('71) 1.75
320 A62 6p multi .15 .15
a. Black omitted 60.00
b. Silver ("MALTA") omitted 60.00
321 A63 8p multi .18 .15
321A A63 10p multi ('70) .35 .22
322 A63 1sh multi .35 .16
323 A63 1sh3p multi .75 .45
324 A63 1sh6p multi .60 .25
a. Queen's head omitted 225.00
325 A63 2sh multi .75 .45
326 A63 2sh6p multi .90 .50
327 A63 3sh multi 1.10 .60
328 A63 5sh multi 1.90 1.00
329 A63 10sh multi 3.75 2.50
330 A63 £1 multi 7.25 4.50
a. Pink (shading on figures) omitted 30.00
Nos. 312-330 (21) 19.48 12.28

Issued: 5p, 10p, 8/1/70; others 1/7/65.
For surcharges see Nos. 447-449, 521.

Dante, by Raphael — A64

1965, July 7 **Unwmk.** *Perf. 14*

331 A64 2p dark blue .15 .15
332 A64 6p olive green .28 .22
333 A64 2sh chocolate 1.00 .85
Nos. 331-333 (3) 1.43 1.22

700th birth anniv. of Dante Alighieri.

Turkish Encampment and Fort St. Michael A65

Blockading Turkish Armada A66

Designs: 3p, Knights and Turks in battle. 8p, Arrival of relief force. 1sh, Trophy, arms of Grandmaster Jean de La Valette. 1sh6p, Allegory of Victory, mural by Calabrese from St. John's Co-Cathedral. 2sh6p, Great Siege victory medal; Jean de La Valette on obverse, David slaying Goliath on reverse.

Perf. 14½x14, 13

1965, Sept. 1 **Photo.** **Wmk. 354**

334 A65 2p ol grn, red & blk .15 .15
335 A65 3p lt gray, red, blk & ol grn .18 .15
336 A66 6p ol grn, red org, cl, blk & gold .40 .30
a. Black omitted 140.00
b. Gold omitted 165.00
337 A65 8p dk bl, red & gold .55 .48
338 A66 1sh bluish blk, red & gold 1.40 1.10
339 A65 1sh6p blk, yel brn & red 1.75 1.50
340 A65 2sh6p ol grn, blk, dk brn & red 4.50 4.00
Nos. 334-340 (7) 8.93 7.68

Great Siege (Turks against Malta), 4th cent.

The Three Wise Men — A67

Perf. 11x11½

1965, Oct. 7 **Photo.** **Wmk. 354**

341 A67 1p dk purple & red .15 .15
342 A67 4p dk pur & blue 1.00 .85
343 A67 1sh3p dk pur & dp mag 1.10 1.00
Nos. 341-343 (3) 2.25 2.00

Winston Churchill, Map and Cross of Malta — A68

Winston Churchill: 3p, 1sh6p, Warships in Valletta Harbor and George Cross.

1966, Jan. 24 *Perf. 14½x14*

344 A68 2p black, gold & red .15 .15
345 A68 3p dk grn, gold & black .15 .15
346 A68 1sh dp cl, gold & red .38 .38
a. Gold omitted 225.00
347 A68 1sh6p dk bl, gold & vio .60 .50
Nos. 344-347 (4) 1.28 1.18

Grand Master Jean Parisot de la Valette — A69

Designs: 3p, Pope St. Pius V. 6p, Map of Valletta. 1sh, Francesco Laparelli, Italian architect. 2sh6p, Girolamo Cassar, Maltese architect.

1966, Mar. 28 **Unwmk.** *Perf. 12*

348 A69 2p gold & multi .15 .15
349 A69 3p gold & multi .15 .15
350 A69 6p gold & multi .15 .15
351 A69 1sh gold & multi .24 .18
352 A69 2sh6p gold & multi .75 .75
Nos. 348-352 (5) 1.44
Set value 1.20

400th anniversary of Valletta.

Kennedy — A70

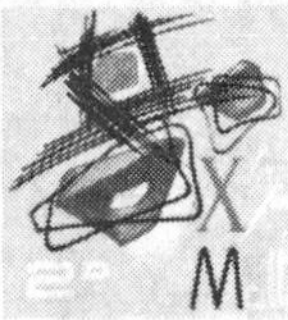
Trade Fair — A71

Perf. 15x14

1966, May 28 **Photo.** **Wmk. 354**

353 A70 3p ol gray, blk & gold .15 .15
354 A70 1sh6p dull bl, blk & gold .45 .45

President John F. Kennedy (1917-1963).

1966, June 16 *Perf. 13x13½*

355 A71 2p multicolored .15 .15
356 A71 8p gray & multi .32 .32
357 A71 2sh6p tan & multi .90 .90
Nos. 355-357 (3) 1.37 1.37

The 10th Malta Trade Fair.

Nativity — A72

George Cross — A73

1966, Oct. 7 **Photo.** **Wmk. 354**

358 A72 1p multicolored .15 .15
359 A72 4p multicolored .13 .13
360 A72 1sh3p multicolored .30 .28
Set value .48 .42

1967, Mar. 1 *Perf. 14½x14*

361 A73 2p multicolored .15 .15
362 A73 4p multicolored .15 .15
363 A73 3sh slate & multi .40 .40
Set value .56 .53

25th anniv. of the award of the George Cross to Malta and Gozo for the war effort.

Crucifixion of St. Peter — A74

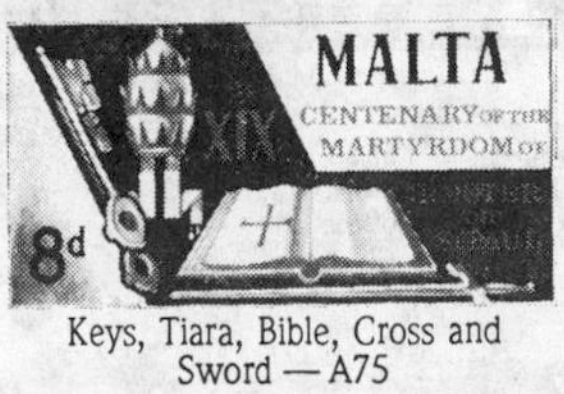
Keys, Tiara, Bible, Cross and Sword — A75

Design: 3sh, Beheading of St. Paul.

Perf. 14¹/₂, 13¹/₂x14
1967, June 28   Photo.   Wmk. 354
364 A74 2p black & brn orange .15 .15
365 A75 8p blk, gold & lt ol grn .15 .15
366 A74 3sh black & brt blue .50 .45
　　Nos. 364-366 (3) .80
　　Set value .63
1900th anniv. of the martyrdom of the Apostles Peter and Paul.

St. Catherine of Siena by Melchior Gafá — A76

Sculptures by Gafá: 4p, St. Thomas from Villanova. 1sh6p, Christ's baptism. 2sh6p, St. John the Baptist.

1967, Aug. 1   Perf. 13¹/₂
367 A76 2p black, gold, buff & ultra .15 .15
368 A76 4p gold, buff, blk & grn .15 .15
369 A76 1sh6p gold, buff, blk & org brown .24 .24
370 A76 2sh6p black, gold, buff & dp car .45 .45
　　Set value .85 .83
Melchior Gafá (1635-67), Maltese sculptor.

Ruins of Megalithic Temples, Tarxien — A77

Designs: 6p, Facade of Palazzo Falzon, Notabile. 1sh, Facade of Old Parish Church, Birkirkara. 3sh, Entrance to Auberge de Castille.

1967, Sept. 12   Photo.   Perf. 14¹/₂
371 A77 2p gold, Prus bl & blk .15 .15
372 A77 6p org brn, blk, gray & gold .15 .15
373 A77 1sh gold, ol, ind & blk .22 .22
374 A77 3sh dk car, rose, blk, gray & gold .42 .42
　　Set value .80 .78
Issued to publicize the 15th Congress of the History of Architecture, Malta, Sept. 12-16.

Nativity
A78   A79

Design: 1sh4p, Angels facing left.

1967, Oct. 20   Perf. 13¹/₂x12¹/₂
375 A78 1p slate, gold & red .15 .15
a.　Red omitted (stars) 50.00
376 A79 8p slate, gold & red .15 .15
377 A78 1sh4p slate, gold & red .28 .28
a.　Triptych, #375-377 .52 .50
　　Set value .44 .42
Sheets of Nos. 375-377 were arranged in 2 ways: sheets containing 60 stamps of the same denomination arranged tête bêche, and sheets containing 20 triptychs.

Arms of Malta — A80

Designs: 4p, Queen Elizabeth II in the robes of the Order of St. Michael and St. George, vert. 3sh, Queen and arms of Malta.

Human Rights Flame and People A81

1967, Nov. 13   Photo.   Wmk. 354
378 A80 2p slate & multi .15 .15
379 A80 4p dp claret, blk & gold .15 .15
380 A80 3sh black & gold .35 .35
　　Set value .51 .49
Visit of Queen Elizabeth II, Nov. 14-17.

1968, May 2   Photo.   Perf. 14¹/₂
Size: 40x19mm
381 A81 2p sepia, dp car, blk & gold .15 .15
Perf. 12x12¹/₂
Size: 24x24mm
382 A81 6p gray, dk blue, blk & gold .15 .15
Perf. 14¹/₂
Size: 40x19mm
383 A81 2sh gray, grnsh blue, blk & gold .32 .28
　　Set value .52 .44
International Human Rights Year.

Fair Emblem — A82

Perf. 14x14¹/₂
1968, June 1   Photo.   Wmk. 354
384 A82 4p black & multi .15 .15
385 A82 8p Prus blue & multi .15 .15
386 A82 3sh dp claret & multi .50 .50
　　Nos. 384-386 (3) .80
　　Set value .68
12th Malta Intl. Trade Fair, July 1-15.

La Valette in Battle Dress — A83

La Valette's Tomb, Church of St. John, Valletta — A84

Designs: 1p, Arms of Order of St. John of Jerusalem and La Valette's arms, horiz. 2sh6p, Putti bearing shield with date of La Valette's death, and map of Malta.

Perf. 13x14, 14x13
1968, Aug. 1   Photo.   Wmk. 354
387 A83 1p black & multi .15 .15
388 A83 8p dull blue & multi .15 .15
389 A84 1sh6p blue grn & multi .22 .22
390 A83 2sh6p dp claret & multi .45 .45
　　Set value .85 .85
400th anniv. of the death of Grand Master Jean de La Valette (1494-1568).

Star of Bethlehem, Shepherds and Angel — A85

Designs: 8p, Nativity. 1sh4p, The Three Wise Men.

Perf. 14¹/₂x14
1968, Oct. 3   Wmk. 354
391 A85 1p multicolored .15 .15
392 A85 8p gray & multi .15 .15
393 A85 1sh4p tan & multi .32 .32
　　Set value .50 .50
Christmas. Printed in sheets of 60 with alternate rows inverted.

"Agriculture" A86

Mahatma Gandhi A87

Designs: 1sh, Greek medal and FAO emblem. 2sh6p, Woman symbolizing soil care.

1968, Oct. 21   Photo.   Perf. 12¹/₂x12
394 A86 4p ultra & multi .15 .15
395 A86 1sh gray & multi .18 .18
396 A86 2sh6p multicolored .60 .60
　　Nos. 394-396 (3) .93 .93
6th Regional Congress for Europe of the FAO, Malta, Oct. 28-31.

Perf. 12x12¹/₂
1969, Mar. 24   Photo.   Wmk. 354
397 A87 1sh6p gold, blk & sepia .35 .32
Birth cent. of Mohandas K. Gandhi (1869-1948), leader in India's struggle for independence.

ILO Emblem — A88

1969, May 26   Perf. 13¹/₂x14¹/₂
398 A88 2p indigo, blue grn & gold .15 .15
399 A88 6p brn blk, red brn & gold .18 .18
　　Set value .24 .24
50th anniv. of the ILO.

Sea Bed, UN Emblem and Dove A89

Designs: 2p, Robert Samut, bar of music and coat of arms. 10p, Map of Malta and homing birds. 2sh, Grand Master Pinto and arms of Malta University.

1969, July 26   Photo.   Perf. 13¹/₂
400 A89 2p vio blk, blk, gold & red .15 .15
401 A89 5p gray, Prus blue, gold & blk .15 .15
402 A89 10p olive, blk & gold .18 .18
403 A89 2sh dk olive, blk, red & gold .40 .40
　　Nos. 400-403 (4) .88 .88
Cent. of the birth of Robert Samut, composer of Natl. Anthem (2p); UN resolution on peaceful uses of the sea bed (5p); convention of Maltese emigrants (10p), Aug. 3-16; bicent. of the founding of Malta University (2sh).

June 17, 1919, Uprising Monument A90

"Tourism" A91

Designs: 5p, Maltese flag and 5 doves, horiz. 1sh6p, Dove and emblems of Malta, UN and Council of Euorpe. 2sh6p, Dove and symbols of trade and industry.

Perf. 13x12¹/₂
1969, Sept. 20   Photo.   Wmk. 354
404 A90 2p black, gray, buff & gold .15 .15
405 A91 5p gray, blk, red & gold .15 .15

406 A91 10p gold, Prus blue, gray & blk .15 .15
407 A91 1sh6p gold, olive & multi .32 .32
408 A91 2sh6p gold, brn ol, gray & blk .55 .55
　　Set value 1.14 1.14
Fifth anniversary of independence.

St. John the Baptist in Robe of Knight of Malta A92

Mortar and Jars from Infirmary — A93

Designs: 1p, The Beheading of St. John By Caravaggio. 5p, Interior of St. John's Co-Cathedral. 6p, Allegory depicting functions of the Order. 8p, St. Jerome, by Caravaggio. 1sh6p, St. Gerard Receiving Godfrey de Bouillon, 1093, by Antoine de Favray. 2sh, Sacred vestments.

Perf. 14x13 (1p, 8p); 13¹/₂x14 (2p, 6p, 1sh6p); 13¹/₂ (5p) 12x12¹/₂ (10p, 2sh)
1970, Mar. 21   Photo.   Wmk. 354
409 A92 1p black & multi .15 .15
410 A92 2p black & multi .15 .15
411 A92 5p black & multi .15 .15
412 A92 6p black & multi .15 .15
413 A92 8p black & multi .20 .20
414 A92 10p black & multi .25 .25
415 A93 1sh6p black & multi .40 .40
416 A93 2sh black & multi .55 .55
　　Nos. 409-416 (8) 2.00 2.00
13th Council of Europe Art Exhibition in honor of the Order of St. John in Malta, Apr. 2-July 1.
Sizes: 1p, 8p, 54x38mm; 2p, 6p, 44x30mm; 5p, 37x37mm; 10p, 2sh, 60x19mm; 1sh6p, 44x33mm.

EXPO '70 Emblem — A94

1970, May 29   Perf. 15
417 A94 2p gold & multi .15 .15
418 A94 5p gold & multi .15 .15
419 A94 3sh gold & multi .65 .65
　　Set value .80 .80
Issued to publicize EXPO '70 International Exhibition, Osaka, Japan, Mar. 15-Sept. 13.

UN Emblem, Dove, Scales and Symbolic Figure — A95

Perf. 14x14¹/₂
1970, Sept. 30   Litho.   Wmk. 354
420 A95 2p brown & multi .15 .15
421 A95 5p purple & multi .15 .15
422 A95 2sh6p vio blue & multi .65 .65
　　Nos. 420-422 (3) .95 .95
25th anniversary of the United Nations.

Books and Quill — A96

Dun Karm, Books and Pens — A97

Perf. 13x14

1971, Mar. 20 Litho. Wmk. 354

423 A96 1sh6p multicolored .28 .28
424 A97 2sh black & multi .40 .40

No. 423 issued in memory of Canon Gian Pietro Francesco Agius Sultana (De Soldanis; 1712-1770), historian and writer; No. 424 for the centenary of the birth of Mgr. Karm Psaila (Dun Karm, 1871-1961), Maltese poet.

Europa Issue, 1971
Common Design Type

1971, May 3 *Perf. 13½x14½*

Size: 32x22mm

425 CD14 2p olive, org & black .15 .15
426 CD14 5p ver, org & black .15 .15
427 CD14 1sh6p gray, org & black .55 .55
Set value .73 .73

St. Joseph, by Giuseppe Cali — A98

Design: 5p, 1sh6p, Statue of Our Lady of Victory. 10p, Like 2p.

Perf. 13x13½

1971, July 24 Litho. Wmk. 354

428 A98 2p dk blue & multi .15 .15
429 A98 5p gray & multi .15 .15
430 A98 10p multicolored .38 .38
431 A98 1sh6p multicolored .60 .60
Nos. 428-431 (4) 1.28 1.28

Centenary (in 1970) of the proclamation of St. Joseph as patron of the Universal Church (2p, 10p), and 50th anniversary of the coronation of the statue of Our Lady of Victory in Senglea, Malta.

Blue Rock Thrush A99

Design: 2p, 1sh6p, Thistle, vert.

Perf. 14x14½, 14½x14

1971, Sept. 18

432 A99 2p multicolored .15 .15
433 A99 5p bister & multi .15 .15
434 A99 10p orange & multi .32 .32
435 A99 1sh6p bister & multi .60 .60
Nos. 432-435 (4) 1.22 1.22

Heart and WHO Emblem A100

1972, Mar. 20 *Perf. 14*

436 A100 2p yel green & multi .15 .15
437 A100 10p lilac & multi .20 .20
438 A100 2sh6p lt blue & multi .70 .70
Nos. 436-438 (3) 1.05 1.05

World Health Day, Apr. 7.

Coin Showing Mnara (Lampstand) A101

Sparkles, Symbolic of Communications CD15

Decimal Currency Coins: 2m, Maltese Cross. 3m, Bee and honeycomb. 1c, George Cross. 2c, Penthesilea. 5c, Altar, Megalithic Period. 10c, Grandmaster's Barge, 18th century. 50c, Great Siege Monument, by Antonio Sciortino.

Perf. 14 (16x21mm), 2m, 3m, 2c; Perf. 14½x14 (21x26mm), 5m, 1c, 5c

1972, May 16

439 A101 2m rose red & multi .15 .15
440 A101 3m pink & multi .15 .15
441 A101 5m lilac & multi .15 .15
442 A101 1c multicolored .15 .15
443 A101 2c orange & multi .15 .15
444 A101 5c multicolored .22 .22

Perf. 13½

Size: 27x35mm

445 A101 10c yellow & multi .50 .50
446 A101 50c multicolored 2.50 2.50
Nos. 439-446 (8) 3.97 3.97

Coins to mark introduction of decimal currency.

Nos. 319A, 321 and 323 Surcharged with New Value and 2 Bars

Perf. 14x14½, 14½

1972, Sept. 30 Photo. Wmk. 354

447 A62 1c3m on 5p multi .15 .15
448 A63 3c on 8p multi .15 .15
449 A63 5c on 1sh3p multi .30 .30
Nos. 447-449 (3) .60 .60

Europa Issue 1972

1972, Nov. 11 Litho. *Perf. 13x13½*

450 CD15 1c3m yellow & multi .15 .15
451 CD15 3c multicolored .20 .20
452 CD15 5c pink & multi .32 .32
453 CD15 7c5m multicolored .45 .45
Nos. 450-453 (4) 1.12 1.12

Issued in sheets of 10 plus 2 labels (4x3). Labels are in top row.

Archaeology A103

Woman with Grain, FAO Emblem A104

1973, Mar. 31 Litho. *Perf. 13½*

Size: 22x24mm

454 A103 2m shown .15 .15
455 A103 4m History (knights) .15 .15
456 A103 5m Folklore .15 .15
457 A103 8m Industry .15 .15
458 A103 1c Fishing .15 .15
459 A103 1c3m Pottery .15 .15
460 A103 2c Agriculture .15 .15
461 A103 3c Sport .15 .15
462 A103 4c Marina .15 .15
463 A103 5c Fiesta .16 .16
464 A103 7c5m Regatta .25 .25
465 A103 10c Charity (St. Martin) .35 .35
466 A103 50c Education 1.40 1.40
467 A103 £1 Religion 3.00 3.00

Perf. 13½x14

Size: 32x27mm

468 A103 £2 Arms of Malta 12.00 12.00
Nos. 454-468 (15) 18.51 18.51

Europa Issue 1973
Common Design Type

1973, June 2 Unwmk. *Perf. 14*

Size: 36½x19½mm

469 CD16 3c multicolored .22 .22
470 CD16 5c multicolored .40 .40
471 CD16 7c5m dk bl & multi .70 .70
Nos. 469-471 (3) 1.32 1.32

1973, Oct. 6 Wmk. 354 *Perf. 13½*

Designs: 7c5m, Mother and child, WHO emblem. 10c, Two heads, Human Rights flame.

472 A104 1c3m yel grn, blk & gold .15 .15
473 A104 7c5m ultra, blk & gold .45 .45
474 A104 10c claret, blk & gold .60 .60
Nos. 472-474 (3) 1.20 1.20

World Food Program, 10th anniv.; WHO, 25th anniv.; Universal Declaration of Human Rights, 25th anniv.

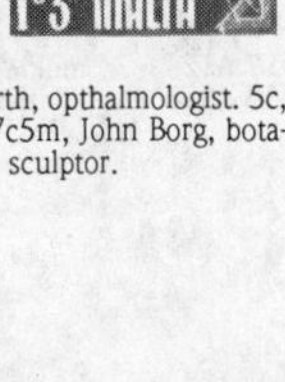

Girolamo Cassar, Architect — A105

Portraits: 3c, Giuseppe Barth, opthalmologist. 5c, Nicolo' Isouard, composer. 7c5m, John Borg, botanist. 10c, Antonio Sciortino, sculptor.

1974, Jan. 12 Litho. *Perf. 14*

475 A105 1c3m slate green & gold .15 .15
476 A105 3c indigo & gold .15 .15
477 A105 5c olive gray & gold .22 .22
478 A105 7c5m slate blue & gold .32 .32
479 A105 10c brn vio & gold .55 .55
Nos. 475-479 (5) 1.39 1.39

Prominent Maltese.

Statue of Goddess, 3rd Millenium B.C. A106

Europa (CEPT Emblem and): 3c, Carved door, Cathedral, Mdina, 11th cent, vert. 5c, Silver monstrance, 1689. 7c5m, "Vettina" (statue of nude woman), by Antonio Sciortino (1879-1947), vert.

Perf. 13½x14, 14x13½

1974, July 13

480 A106 1c3m gray blue, blk & gold .15 .15
481 A106 3c ol brn, blk & gold .28 .28
482 A106 5c lilac, blk & gold .45 .45
483 A106 7c5m dull grn, blk & gold .90 .90
Nos. 480-483 (4) 1.78 1.78

Heinrich von Stephan, Coach and Train, UPU Emblem A107

UPU Emblem, von Stephan and: 5c, Paddle steamer and ocean liner. 7c5m, Balloon and jet. 50c, UPU Congress Building, Lausanne, and UPU Headquarters, Bern.

Perf. 13½

1974, Sept. Litho. Wmk. 354

484 A107 1c3m multicolored .15 .15
485 A107 5c multicolored .22 .22
486 A107 7c5m multicolored .35 .35
487 A107 50c multicolored 2.25 2.25
a. Souvenir sheet of 4, #484-487 3.25 3.25
Nos. 484-487 (4) 2.97 2.97

Centenary of Universal Postal Union.

President, Prime Minister, Minister of Justice at Microphone — A108

Designs: 1c3m, President, Prime Minister, Speaker at Swearing-in ceremony. 5c, Flag of Malta.

1975, Mar. 31 *Perf. 14*

488 A108 1c3m red & multi .15 .15
489 A108 5c gray, red & black .40 .40
490 A108 25c red & multi 1.75 1.75
Nos. 488-490 (3) 2.30 2.30

Proclamation of the Republic, Dec. 13, 1974.

IWY Emblem, Mother and Child — A109

Designs: 3c, 20c, Secretary (woman in public life), IWY emblem. 5c, Like 1c3m.

Wmk. 354

1975, May 30 Litho. *Perf. 13*

491 A109 1c3m violet & gold .15 .15
492 A109 3c blue gray & gold .70 .32
493 A109 5c olive & gold 1.40 .90
494 A109 20c red brown & gold 6.50 4.50
Nos. 491-494 (4) 8.75 5.87

International Women's Year.

Allegory of Malta, by Francesco de Mura — A110

Europa: 15c, Judith and Holofernes, by Valentin de Boulogne.

1975, July 15 Litho. *Perf. 14*

495 A110 5c multicolored .28 .28
496 A110 15c multicolored .95 .95

Floor Plan of Ggantija Complex, 3000 B.C. — A111

Designs: 3c, View of Mdina. 5c, Typical Maltese town. 25c, Fort St. Angelo.

1975, Sept. 16 *Perf. 14*

497 A111 1c3m black & org .15 .15
498 A111 3c org, pur & black .35 .30
499 A111 5c gray, black & org .60 .50
500 A111 25c org, tan & black 4.00 2.50
Nos. 497-500 (4) 5.10 3.45

European Architectural Heritage Year.

"Right to Work" — A112

Designs: 5c, Protection of the Environment (Landscape). 25c, Maltese flags.

1975, Dec. 12 Litho. Wmk. 354

501 A112 1c3m multicolored .15 .15
502 A112 5c multicolored .42 .24
503 A112 25c multicolored 1.75 1.10
Nos. 501-503 (3) 2.32 1.49

First anniversary of Malta Republic.

Republic Coat of Arms — A113

Perf. 13½x14

1976, Jan. 28 Litho. Wmk. 354

504 A113 £2 black & multi 9.50 9.50

Feast of Sts. Peter and Paul — A114

Designs: 1c3m, "Festa" (flags and fireworks; vert.). 7c5m, Carnival. 10c, Good Friday (Christ carrying cross; vert.).

1976, Feb. 26 Litho. *Perf. 14*

505 A114 1c3m multicolored .15 .15
506 A114 5c multicolored .38 .30
507 A114 7c5m multicolored .55 .40
508 A114 10c multicolored 1.90 1.25
Nos. 505-508 (4) 2.98 2.10

Maltese folk festivals.

Water Polo, Olympic Rings — A115

Olympic Rings and: 5c, Yachting. 30c, Running.

1976, Apr. 28 Litho. *Perf. 13½x14*

509 A115 1c7m sl green & red .15 .15
510 A115 5c dp blue & red .38 .22
511 A115 30c sepia & red 2.50 1.90
Nos. 509-511 (3) 3.03 2.27

21st Olympic Games, Montreal, Canada, July 17-Aug. 1.

Europa
A116

1976, July 8   Litho.   Wmk. 354
512 A116 7c Lace-making   .35 .35
513 A116 15c Stone carving   .90 .80

Grandmaster Nicola Cotoner,
Founder — A117

Designs: 5c, Dissected arm and hand. 7c, Dr. Fra
Giuseppe Zammit, first professor. 11c, School and
balustrade.

1976, Sept. 14   Litho.   Perf. 13½
514 A117 2c multicolored   .15 .15
515 A117 5c multicolored   .18 .15
516 A117 7c multicolored   .28 .22
517 A117 11c multicolored   .90 .75
     Nos. 514-517 (4)   1.51 1.27

School of Anatomy and Surgery, Valletta, 300th
anniversary.

Armor of Grand Master Jean
de La Valette — A118

Suits of Armor: 7c, Grand Master Aloph de
Wignacourt. 11c, Grand Commander Jean Jacques
de Verdelin.

1977, Jan. 20   Litho.   Wmk. 354
518 A118 2c green & multi   .15 .15
519 A118 7c brown & multi   .42 .35
520 A118 11c ultra & multi   .75 .60
     Nos. 518-520 (3)   1.32 1.10

No. 318 Surcharged with New Value and
Bar
1977, Mar. 24 Photo. Perf. 14x14½
521 A62 1c7m on 4p multicolored .35 .16

Annunciation, Tapestry after
Rubens — A119

Nativity
A120

Tapestries after Designs by Rubens: 7c, The Four
Evangelists. 20c, Adoration of the Kings. Flemish
tapestries commissioned for St. John's Co-Cathedral, Valletta.

Wmk. 354
1977, Mar. 30   Litho.   Perf. 14
522 A119 2c multicolored   .15 .15
523 A119 7c multicolored   .35 .30
524 A120 11c multicolored   .65 .60
525 A120 20c multicolored   1.25 1.25

1978, Jan. 26
Flemish Tapestries: 2c, Jesus' Entry into Jerusalem, by unknown painter. 7c, Last Supper, by

---

Nicholas Poussin. 11c, Crucifixion, by Rubens. 25c,
Resurrection, by Rubens.

526 A120 2c multicolored   .15 .15
527 A120 7c multicolored   .30 .30
528 A120 11c multicolored   .50 .50
529 A120 25c multicolored   1.25 1.25

1979, Jan. 24
Tapestries after Designs by Rubens (Triumph of):
2c, Catholic Church. 7c, Charity. 11c, Faith. 25c,
Truth.

530 A119 2c multicolored   .15 .15
531 A119 7c multicolored   .30 .30
532 A119 11c multicolored   .45 .45
533 A119 25c multicolored   1.10 1.10
     Nos. 522-533 (12)   6.60 6.50

Consecration of St. John's Co-Cathedral, Valletta,
400th anniv. (#522-533). Peter Paul Rubens (1577-
1640; #522-525).
See Nos. 567-569.

Malta Map, Telecommunication — A121

Designs: 1c, 6c, Map of Italy, Sicily, Malta and
North Africa, telecommunication tower and waves,
vert. 17c, like 8c.

Perf. 14x13½, 13½x14
1977, May 17   Litho.   Wmk. 354
535 A121 1c green, red & blk   .15 .15
536 A121 6c multicolored   .22 .22
537 A121 8c multicolored   .35 .35
538 A121 17c purple, red & blk .85 .85
     Nos. 535-538 (4)   1.57 1.57

World Telecommunication Day.

View of Ta' L-Isperanza — A122

Europa: 20c, Harbor, Is-Salini.

1977, July   Litho.   Perf. 13½
539 A122 7c multicolored   .42 .42
540 A122 20c multicolored   .95 .95

     Issued in sheets of 10.

MALTA Help Given Handicapped
Worker — A123

Designs: 7c, Stonemason and shipbuilder. 20c,
Mother holding dead son, and Service to the Repub-
lic order, horiz. Sculptures from Workers'
Monument.

1977, Oct. 12   Litho.   Wmk. 354
541 A123 2c red brown & brn   .15 .15
542 A123 7c brown & dk brn   .32 .32
543 A123 20c multicolored   1.00 1.00
     Nos. 541-543 (3)   1.47 1.47

     Tribute to Maltese workers.

Lady on Horseback   Grand Master
and Soldier, by   Nicola Cotoner
Dürer   Monument
A124   A125

Dürer Engravings: 8c, Bagpiper. 17c, Madonna
with Long-tailed Monkey.

1978, Mar. 7   Perf. 14
544 A124 1c7m dk blue, blk & red .15 .15
545 A124 8c gray, blk & red   .35 .35
546 A124 17c dk grn, blk & red .80 .80
     Nos. 544-546 (3)   1.30 1.30

Albrecht Dürer (1471-1528), German painter
and engraver.

1978, Apr. 26   Perf. 14x13½
Europa: 25c, Grand Master Ramon Perellos monument, by Giusepe Mazzuoli. The monument on 7c
is believed to be the work of Giovanni Batista
Foggini.

547 A125 7c multicolored   .35 .35
548 A125 25c multicolored   1.25 1.25

Goalkeeper — A126

Argentina '78 Emblem and: 11c, 15c, different
soccer scenes.

1978, June 6   Litho.   Wmk. 354
549 A126 2c multicolored   .15 .15
550 A126 11c multicolored   .50 .50
551 A126 15c multicolored   .80 .80
  a. Souvenir sheet of 3, #549-551 1.75 1.75
     Nos. 549-551 (3)   1.45 1.45

11th World Cup Soccer Championship, Argentina, June 1-25.

Fishing   Maltese Speronara and
Boat — A127   AirMalta
                     Fuselage — A128

Designs: 5c, 17c Changing of colors. 7c, 20c,
British soldier and oranges. 8c, like 2c.

1979, Mar. 31   Perf. 14
552 A127 2c claret & multi   .15 .15
553 A127 5c claret & multi   .25 .25
554 A127 7c claret & multi   .32 .32
555 A127 8c dk blue & multi   .40 .40
556 A127 17c dk blue & multi   .75 .75
557 A127 20c dk blue & multi   .90 .90
     Nos. 552-557 (6)   2.77 2.77

End of military agreement between Malta and
Great Britain.

1979, May 9

Europa: 25c, Coastal watch tower and radio link
tower.

558 A128 7c multicolored   .32 .32
559 A128 25c multicolored   1.25 1.25

Children and
Globe — A129

Designs: 7c, Children flying kites. 11c, Children
in a circle holding hands.

1979, June 13   Perf. 14x13½, 14
          Size: 20x38mm
560 A129 2c multicolored   .15 .15
          Size: 27x33mm
561 A129 7c multicolored   .40 .40
562 A129 11c multicolored   .70 .70
     Nos. 560-562 (3)   1.25 1.25

International Year of the Child.

Loggerhead
Turtle — A130

Marine Life: 2c, Gibbula nivosa. 7c, Dolphinfish.
25c, Noble pen shell.

1979, Oct. 10   Litho.   Perf. 13½
563 A130 2c multicolored   .15 .15
564 A130 5c multicolored   .24 .24
565 A130 7c multicolored   .30 .30
566 A130 25c multicolored   1.25 1.25
     Nos. 563-566 (4)   1.94 1.94

Tapestry Type of 1977-79

Tapestries after Designs by Rubens: 2c, The Institution of Corpus Domini. 8c, The Destruction of
Idolatry. 50c, Portrait of Grand Master Perellos,
vert.

1980, Jan. 30   Wmk. 354   Perf. 14
567 A120 2c multicolored   .15 .15
568 A120 8c multicolored   .32 .32
          Souvenir Sheet
569 A119 50c multicolored   1.75 1.75

Victoria
Citadel,
Gozo
A131

Monument Restoration (UNESCO Emblem and):
2c5m, Hal Saflieni Catacombs, Paola, 2500 B.C.,
vert. 6c, Vilhena Palace, Mdina, 18th century, vert.
12c, St. Elmo Fort, Valletta, 16th century.

1980, Feb. 15
570 A131 2c5m multicolored   .15 .15
571 A131 6c multicolored   .30 .30
572 A131 8c multicolored   .38 .38
573 A131 12c multicolored   .60 .60
     Nos. 570-573 (4)   1.43 1.43

Don Gorg Preca (1880-
1962), Founder of Soc. of
Christian Doctrine — A132

1980, Apr. 12   Litho.   Perf. 14x13½
574 A132 2c5m gray violet   .15 .15

Ruzar Briffa (1906-1963), Poet, by Vincent
Apap — A133

Europa (Vincent Apap Sculpture): 30c, Mikiel Anton Vassalli (1764-1829), freedom fighter and scholar.

1980, Apr. 29   *Perf. 13¹/₂x14*
575 A133 8c slate green & dp bis   .32 .32
576 A133 30c brown red & olive   1.40 1.40

Chess Pieces — A134

Designs: Chess pieces. 30c, vert.

1980, Nov.   Litho.   Perf. 14
577 A134 2c5m multicolored   .15 .15
578 A134 8c multicolored   .40 .40
579 A134 30c multicolored   1.50 1.50
  Nos. 577-579 (3)   2.05 2.05

Chess Olympiad, Valletta, Nov. 20-Dec. 8.

Barn Owl — A135

1981, Jan. 20   Wmk. 354   Perf. 13¹/₂
580 A135 3c shown   .16 .16
581 A135 8c Sardinian warbler .45 .45
582 A135 12c Woodchat shrike   .70 .70
583 A135 23c Stormy petrel   1.25 1.25
  Nos. 580-583 (4)   2.56 2.56

Europa Issue 1981

Climbing the Gostra (Greasy Pole) — A136

1981, Apr. 28   Litho.   Perf. 14
584 A136 8c Horse race   .38 .38
585 A136 30c shown   1.40 1.40

25th Intl. Fair of Malta, Naxxar, July 1-15 — A137

1981, June 12   Perf. 13¹/₂
586 A137 4c multicolored   .18 .18
587 A137 25c multicolored   1.25 1.25

Disabled Artist — A138   World Food Day — A139

1981, July 17   Litho.   Perf. 13¹/₂
588 A138 3c shown   .15 .15
589 A138 35c Boy on crutches 1.65 1.65
  Intl. Year of the Disabled.

1981, Oct. 16   Litho.   Perf. 14
590 A139 8c multicolored   .40 .40
591 A139 23c multicolored   1.10 1.10

Men Hauling Building Stone — A140

1981, Oct. 31   Wmk. 354   Perf. 14
592 A140 5m shown   .15 .15
593 A140 1c Growing cotton   .15 .15
594 A140 2c Ship building   .15 .15

595 A140 3c Minting coins   .15 .15
596 A140 5c Artistic achieve-
                 ments   .20 .20
597 A140 6c Fishing   .22 .22
598 A140 7c Farming   .25 .25
599 A140 8c Quarrying   .30 .30
600 A140 10c Grape pressing   .35 .35
601 A140 12c Ship repairing   .42 .42
602 A140 15c Energy   .52 .52
603 A140 20c Communications   .70 .70
604 A140 25c Factories   .85 .85
605 A140 50c Water drilling   1.65 1.65
606 A140 £1 Sea transport   3.25 3.25
607 A140 £3 Air transport   9.50 9.50
  Nos. 592-607 (16)   18.81 18.81

Shipbuilding and Repairing, Tarznar Shipyards — A141

1982, Jan. 29   Litho.   Perf. 13¹/₂x14
608 A141 3c Assembly sheds   .15 .15
609 A141 8c Ships in dry dock   .35 .35
610 A141 13c Tanker   .60 .60
611 A141 27c Tanker, diff.   1.25 1.25
  Nos. 608-611 (4)   2.35 2.35

Man and Home for the Elderly A142

1982, Mar. 16   Litho.   Perf. 14
612 A142 8c shown   .35 .35
613 A142 30c Woman, hospital   1.50 1.50

Europa Issue 1982

Redemption of the Islands, 1428 — A143

1982, Apr. 29   Litho.   Perf. 14
614 A143 8c shown   .35 .35
615 A143 30c Declaration of Rights,
                 1802   1.50 1.50

1982 World Cup — A144

Designs: Various soccer players.

1982, June 11   Litho.   Perf. 14
616 A144 3c multicolored   .18 .18
617 A144 12c multicolored   .72 .72
618 A144 15c multicolored   .90 .90
  a. Souvenir sheet of 3, #616-618 2.25 2.25
  Nos. 616-618 (3)   1.80 1.80

Brigantine — A145

1982, Nov. 13   Litho.
619 A145 3c shown   .15 .15
619A A145 8c Tartana   .45 .45
619B A145 12c Xebec   .60 .60
619C A145 20c Speronara   1.10 1.10
  Nos. 619-619C (4)   2.30 2.30

See #637-640, 670-673, 686-689, 703-706.

Malta Railway Centenary — A146

1983, Jan. 21   Wmk. 354   Perf. 14
620 A146 3c Manning Wardle,
                 1883   .18 .18
621 A146 13c Black Hawthorn, 1884 .75 .75
622 A146 27c Beyer Peacock, 1895 1.50 1.50
  Nos. 620-622 (3)   2.43 2.43

Commonwealth Day — A147

1983, Mar. 14
623 A147 8c Map   .35 .35
624 A147 12c Transportation   .55 .55
625 A147 15c Beach, vert.   .65 .65
626 A147 23c Industry, vert.   1.10 1.10
  Nos. 623-626 (4)   2.65 2.65

Europa Issue 1983

Megalithic Temples, Ggantija — A148

1983, May 5   Wmk. 354   Perf. 14
627 A148 8c shown   .40 .40
628 A148 30c Fort St. Angelo   1.50 1.50

World Communications Year — A149

Perf. 13¹/₂x14
1983, July 14   Litho.   Wmk. 354
629 A149 3c Dish antennas   .15 .15
630 A149 7c Ships   .32 .32
631 A149 13c Trucks   .65 .65
632 A149 20c Games emblem   1.00 1.00
  Nos. 629-632 (4)   2.12 2.12

25th anniv. of Intl. Maritime Org. (7c); 30th anniv. of Customs Cooperation Council (13c); 9th Mediterranean Games, Casablanca, 9/3-17 (20c).

Monsignor Giuseppe De Piro (1877-1933), Founder of Missionary Society of St. Paul — A150

1983, Sept. 1   Litho.   Perf. 14
633 A150 3c multicolored   .15 .15

40th Anniv. of General Workers' Union A151

1983, Oct. 5   Litho.   Perf. 14x13¹/₂
634 A151 3c Founding rally   .15 .15
635 A151 8c Family, workers   .38 .38
636 A151 27c Headquarters   1.25 1.25
  Nos. 634-636 (3)   1.78 1.78

Maltese Ship Type of 1982
1983, Nov. 17   Litho.   Perf. 14x13¹/₂
637 A145 2c Strangler, 1813   .15 .15
638 A145 12c Tigre 1839   .60 .60
639 A145 13c La Speranza, 1844   .65 .65
640 A145 20c Wignacourt 1844   1.00 1.00
  Nos. 637-640 (4)   2.40 2.40

Europa (1959-1984) — A152

1984, Apr. 27   Wmk. 354   Perf. 14
641 A152 8c multicolored   .42 .42
642 A152 30c multicolored   1.50 1.50

Police Force, 170th Anniv. — A153   1984 Summer Olympics — A154

1984, June 14   Litho.   Perf. 14x13¹/₂
643 A153 3c Officer, 1880   .15 .15
644 A153 8c Mounted policeman   .36 .36
645 A153 11c Officer on motorcycle .50 .50
646 A153 25c Traffic duty, firemen 1.15 1.15
  Nos. 643-646 (4)   2.16 2.16

1984, July 26   Litho.   Perf. 13¹/₂x14
647 A154 7c Running   .35 .35
648 A154 12c Gymnastics   .55 .55
649 A154 23c Swimming   1.10 1.10
  Nos. 647-649 (3)   2.00 2.00

10th Anniv. of Republic — A155   Malta Post Office Cent. — A156

1984, Dec. 12   Litho.   Wmk. 354
650 A155 3c Dove on map   .15 .15
651 A155 8c Fortress   .38 .38
652 A155 30c Hands, flag   1.40 1.40
  Nos. 650-652 (3)   1.93 1.93

1985, Jan. 2   Litho.   Perf. 14
653 A156 3c No. 8   .16 .16
654 A156 8c No. 9   .40 .40
655 A156 12c No. 11   .60 .60
656 A156 20c No. 12   1.00 1.00
  a. Souvenir sheet of 4, #653-656 2.25 2.25
  Nos. 653-656 (4)   2.16 2.16

International Youth Year — A157

1985, Mar. 7   Perf. 14x13¹/₂, 13¹/₂x14
657 A157 2c shown   .15 .15
658 A157 13c Three youths, vert. .54 .54
659 A157 27c Female holding flame 1.10 1.10
  Nos. 657-659 (3)   1.79 1.79

Composers — A158

Europa: 8c, Nicolo Baldacchino (1895-1971).
30c, Francesco Azopardi (1748-1809).

1985, Apr. 25   Litho.   Perf. 14
660 A158 8c multicolored   .38   .38
661 A158 30c multicolored   1.50 1.50

Guzeppi
Bajada and
Manwel
Attard,
Martyrs
A159

Designs: 7c, Karmnu Abela and Wenzu Dyer.
35c, June 7 Uprising Memorial Monument, vert.

1985, June 7   Perf. 14x14¹/₂, 14¹/₄x14
662 A159 3c multicolored   .15   .15
663 A159 7c multicolored   .28   .28
664 A159 35c multicolored   1.40 1.40
       Nos. 662-664 (3)   1.83 1.83

June 7 Uprising, 66th anniv.

UN, 40th
Anniv.
A160

1985, July 26   Perf. 13¹/₂x14
665 A160 4c Stylized birds   .16   .16
666 A160 11c Arrows   .45   .45
667 A160 31c Human figures   1.25 1.25
       Nos. 665-667 (3)   1.86 1.86

Famous Men — A161

Portraits: 8c, George Mitrovich (1794-1885), politician and author, novel frontispiece, The Cause of
the People of Malta Now Before Parliament. 12c,
Pietru Caxaru (1438-1485), scholar, manuscript.

1985, Oct. 3   Perf. 14
668 A161 8c multicolored   .32   .32
669 A161 12c multicolored   .48   .48

Ships Type of 1982

1985, Nov. 27
670 A145 3c Scotia paddle steamer,
              1844   .15   .15
671 A145 7c Tagliaferro, 1882   .28   .28
672 A145 15c Gleneagles, 1885   .60   .60
673 A145 23c L'Isle Adam, 1886   .90   .90
       Nos. 670-673 (4)   1.93 1.93

Intl. Peace
Year
A162

Perf. 14x14¹/₂, 13¹/₂x14 (#675)
1986, Jan. 28   Litho.   Wmk. 354
674 A162 8c John XXIII Peace Lab-
              oratory   .30   .30
675 A162 11c Unity   .40   .40
676 A162 27c Peaceful coexistence 1.00 1.00
       Nos. 674-676 (3)   1.70 1.70

Size of No. 675: 43x27mm.

Europa Issue 1986

malta 8c   Butterflies — A163

1986, Apr. 3   Perf. 14¹/₂x14
677 A163 8c shown   .32   .32
678 A163 35c Earth, air, fire and
              water   1.40 1.40

1986 World Cup
Soccer
Championships,
Mexico — A164

1986, May 30   Wmk. 354   Perf. 14
679 A164 3c Heading the ball   .15   .15
680 A164 7c Goalie catching ball   .28   .28
681 A164 23c Dribbling   .92   .92
  a. Souvenir sheet of 3, #679-681 1.35 1.35
       Nos. 679-681 (3)   1.35 1.35

Philanthropists
A165

Designs: 2c, Fra Diegu (1831-1902). 3c, Adelaide Cini (1838-1885). 8c, Alfonso Maria Galea
(1861-1941). 27c, Vincenzo Bugeja (1820-1890).

1986, Aug. 28   Perf. 14¹/₂x14
682 A165 2c multicolored   .15   .15
683 A165 3c multicolored   .15   .15
684 A165 8c multicolored   .32   .32
685 A165 27c multicolored   1.10 1.10
       Nos. 682-685 (4)   1.72 1.72

Ships Type of 1982

1986, Nov. 19   Wmk. 354   Perf. 14
686 A145 7c San Paul   .38   .38
687 A145 10c Knight of Malta   .52   .52
688 A145 12c Valetta City   .65   .65
689 A145 20c Saver   1.05 1.05
       Nos. 686-689 (4)   2.60 2.60

Malta Ornithological Society, 25th
Anniv. — A166

1987, Jan. 26   Litho.   Perf. 14
690 A166 3c Erithacus rubecula   .18   .18
691 A166 8c Falco peregrinus   .45   .45
692 A166 13c Upupa epops   .70   .70
693 A166 23c Calonectris diomedea 1.50 1.50
       Nos. 690-693 (4)   2.83 2.83

Nos. 691-692 vert.

Europa Issue 1987

Limestone
Buildings — A167   **MALTA 8c**

1987, Apr. 15   Litho.   Perf. 14¹/₂x14
694 A167 8c Aquasun Lido   .42   .42
695 A167 35c St. Joseph's Church,
              Manikata   1.85 1.85

MALTA 3c Military
Uniforms — A168

Uniforms of the Order of St. John of Jerusalem
(1530-1798).

1987, June 10   Wmk. 354   Perf. 14
696 A168 3c Soldier, 16th cent.   .16   .16
697 A168 7c Officer, 16th cent.   .38   .38
698 A168 10c Flag bearer, 18th cent. .52 .52
699 A168 27c General of the galleys,
              18th cent   1.40 1.40
       Nos. 696-699 (4)   2.46 2.46

See #723-726, 739-742, 764-767, 774-777.

MALTA 5c
European Environment Year — A169

Anniversaries and events: 8c, Esperanto movement, cent. 23s, Intl. Year of Shelter for the
Homeless.

Perf. 14¹/₂x14
1987, Aug. 18   Wmk. 354
700 A169 5c shown   .25   .25
701 A169 8c multicolored   .38   .38
702 A169 23c multicolored   1.10 1.10
       Nos. 700-702 (3)   1.73 1.73

Ships Type of 1982

1987, Oct. 16   Litho.   Perf. 14
703 A145 2c Medina, 1969   .15   .15
704 A145 11c Rabat, 1974   .60   .60
705 A145 13c Ghawdex, 1979   .70   .70
706 A145 20c Pinto, 1987   1.10 1.10
       Nos. 703-706 (4)   2.55 2.55

MALTA

A170

Designs: 8c, Dr. Arvid Pardo, representative to
UN from Malta who proposed the resolution. 12c,
UN emblem.

Perf. 14¹/₂
1987, Dec. 18   Litho.   Wmk. 354
707 A170 8c multicolored   .42   .42
708 A170 12c multicolored   .65   .65

Souvenir Sheet
Perf. 13x13¹/₂
709   Sheet of 2   1.10 1.10
  a. A170 8c multicolored   .42   .42
  b. A170 12c multicolored   .65   .65

UN resolution for peaceful use of marine
resources, 20th anniv. Nos. 709a-709b printed in a
continuous design.

Nazju Falzon (1813-
1865),
Clergyman — A171

Famous men: 3c, Monsignor Sidor Formosa
(1851-1931), benefactor of the poor. 4c, Sir Luigi
Preziosi (1888-1965), opthalmologist who developed an operation for the treatment of glaucoma.
10c, Father Anastasju Cuschieri (1876-1962), theologian, poet. 25c, Monsignor Pietru Pawl Saydon
(1895-1971), translator, commentator on scripture.

1988, Jan. 23   Perf. 14¹/₂x14
                           Wmk. 354
710 A171 2c shown   .15   .15
711 A171 3c multicolored   .16   .16
712 A171 4c multicolored   .22   .22
713 A171 10c multicolored   .52   .52
714 A171 25c multicolored   1.30 1.30
       Nos. 710-714 (5)   2.35 2.35

Anniversaries and
Events — A172

Designs: 10c, Statue of youth and St. John Bosco
in the chapel at St. Patrick's School, Sliema. 12c,
Assumption of Our Lady, main altarpiece at Ta'
Pinu Sanctuary, Gozo, completed in 1619 by
Amodeo Bartolomeo Perugino. 14c, Christ the King
monument at the Mall, Floriana, by Antonio Sciortino (1879-1947).

1988, Mar. 5   Litho.   Perf. 14
715 A172 10c multicolored   .52   .52
716 A172 12c multicolored   .62   .62
717 A172 14c multicolored   .72   .72
       Nos. 715-717 (3)   1.86 1.86

St. John Bosco (1815-88), educator (10c); Marian Year (12c); Intl. Eucharistic Congress, Malta,
Apr. 24-28, 1913, 75th anniv. (14c).

Land, Sea and Air
10c   MALTA Transportation — A173

Europa (Transport and communication): 35c,
Telecommunications.

1988, Apr. 9   Perf. 14
718 A173 10c multicolored   .52   .52
719 A173 35c multicolored   1.80 1.80

Intl.
Anniversaries
and
Events — A174

Globe picturing hemispheres and: 4c, Red Cross,
Red Crescent emblems. 18c, Symbolic design dividing world into north and south regions. 19c, Caduceus, EKG readout.

1988, May 25 Litho. *Perf. 14*

720 A174 4c multicolored .25 .25
721 A174 18c multicolored 1.10 1.10
722 A174 19c multicolored 1.20 1.20
Nos. 720-722 (3) 2.55 2.55

Intl. Red Cross and Red Crescent Organizations, 125th annivs. (4c); European Public Campaign on North-South Interdependence and Solidarity (18c); WHO, 40th anniv. (19c).

Military Uniforms Type of 1987

Designs: 3c, Light Infantry private, 1800. 4c, Coast Artillery gunner, 1802. 10c, lst Maltese Provincial Battalion field officer, 1805. 25c, Royal Malta Regiment subaltern, 1809.

1988, July 23 Litho. Wmk. 354

723 A168 3c multicolored .20 .20
724 A168 4c multicolored .25 .25
725 A168 10c multicolored .62 .62
726 A168 25c multicolored 1.55 1.55
Nos. 723-726 (4) 2.62 2.62

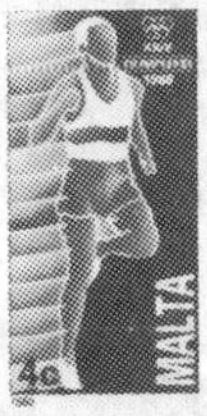
A175

A176

Perf. 14x13½

1988, Sept. 17 Wmk. 354

727 A175 4c Running .25 .25
728 A175 10c Women's diving .58 .58
729 A175 35c Basketball 2.00 2.00
Nos. 727-729 (3) 2.83 2.83

1988 Summer Olympics, Seoul.

1989, Jan. 28 Litho. *Perf. 13½*

730 A176 2c Commonwealth .15 .15
731 A176 3c Council of Europe .20 .20
732 A176 4c United Nations .25 .25
733 A176 10c Labor .62 .62
734 A176 12c Justice .75 .75

Size: 41x32mm

Perf. 14

735 A176 25c Liberty 1.60 1.60
Nos. 730-735 (6) 3.57 3.57

Natl. independence, 25th anniv.

New Natl. Emblem A177

1989, Mar. 25 *Perf. 14*

736 A177 £1 multicolored 5.90 5.90

Children's Toys — A178

Europa.

1989, May 6

737 A178 10c Kite .60 .60
738 A178 35c Dolls 2.10 2.10

Military Uniforms Type of 1987

Designs: 3c, Officer of the Maltese Veterans, 1815. 4c, Subaltern of the Royal Malta Fencibles, 1839. 10c, Militia private, 1856. 25c, Royal Malta Fencibles Artillery colonel, 1875.

1989, June 24 Litho. Wmk. 354

739 A168 3c multicolored .18 .18
740 A168 4c multicolored .24 .24
741 A168 10c multicolored .60 .60
742 A168 25c multicolored 1.50 1.50
Nos. 739-742 (4) 2.52 2.52

Anniversaries and Events — A179

1989, Oct. 17 Litho. Wmk. 354

743 A179 3c multicolored .18 .18
744 A179 4c multi, diff. .24 .24
745 A179 10c multi, diff. .60 .60
746 A179 14c multi, diff. .82 .82
747 A179 25c multi, diff. 1.45 1.45
Nos. 743-747 (5) 3.29 3.29

UN Declaration on Social Progress and Development, 20th anniv. (3c); signing of the European Social Charter by Malta (4c); Council of Europe, 40th anniv. (10c); Natl. Teachers' Union, 70th anniv. (14c); assembly of the Knights of the Sovereign Military Order of Malta (25c).

Pres. Bush, Map and Gen.-Sec. Gorbachev — A180

1989, Dec. 2 Litho. Wmk. 354

748 A180 10c chalky blue, org & brn .60 .60

US-Soviet summit, Malta, Dec. 2-3.

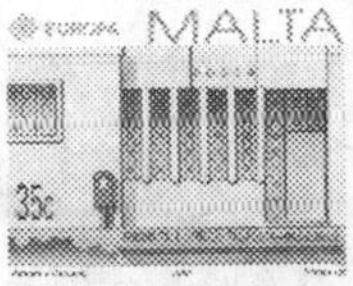
Europa 1990 — A181

Post offices: 10c, Auberge d'Italie, Valletta, 1574, vert. 35c, Branch P.O., Zebbug, 1987.

1990, Feb. 9

749 A181 10c multicolored .58 .58
750 A181 35c multicolored 2.00 2.00

Anniversaries & Events — A182

1990, Apr. 7

751 A182 3c multi, vert. .18 .18
752 A182 4c shown .24 .24
753 A182 19c multicolored 1.15 1.15
754 A182 20c multi, vert. 1.20 1.20
Nos. 751-754 (4) 2.77 2.77

UNESCO World Literacy Year (3c); subjection of Malta to Count Roger the Norman and subsequent rulers of Sicily, 900th anniv. (4c); 25th anniv. of Malta's membership in the ITU (19c); and 20th Congress of the Union of European Soccer Associations, Malta (20c).

British Poets and Novelists — A183

1990, May 3 *Perf. 13½*

755 A183 4c Samuel Taylor Coleridge .24 .24
756 A183 10c Lord Byron .60 .60
757 A183 12c Sir Walter Scott .72 .72
758 A183 25c William Makepeace Thackeray 1.50 1.50
Nos. 755-758 (4) 3.06 3.06

Visit of Pope John Paul II, May 25-27 — A184

1990, May 25 *Perf. 14*

759 A184 4c St. Paul .25 .25
760 A184 25c Pope John Paul II 1.50 1.50
a. Pair, #759-760 1.75 1.75

World Cup Soccer Championships, Italy — A185

Soccer ball and: 5c, flags. 10c, hands and goal net.

1990, June 8 Wmk. 354

761 A185 5c multicolored .30 .30
762 A185 10c multicolored .60 .60
763 A185 14c multicolored .85 .85
a. Souvenir sheet of 3, #761-763 1.80 1.80
Nos. 761-763 (3) 1.75 1.75

Military Uniforms Type of 1987

Designs: 3c, Captain, Royal Malta Militia, 1889. 4c, Field Officer, Royal Malta Artillery, 1905. 10c, Laborer, Malta Labor Corps, 1915. 25c, Lieutenant, King's Own Malta Regiment of Militia, 1910.

1990, Aug. 25 *Perf. 14*

764 A168 3c multicolored .18 .18
765 A168 4c multicolored .25 .25
766 A168 10c multicolored .60 .60
767 A168 25c multicolored 1.50 1.50
Nos. 764-767 (4) 2.53 2.53

Maltese Philatelic Society, 25th Anniv. A186

1991, Mar. 6 Litho. Wmk. 354

768 A186 10c multicolored .65 .65

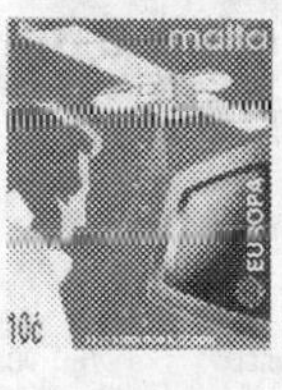
Europa — A187

1991, Mar. 16

769 A187 10c Eurostar .65 .65
770 A187 35c Ariane 4, space plane 2.30 2.30

St. Ignatius of Loyola (1491-1556), Founder of Jesuit Order — A188

Designs: 4c, Marie Therese Pisani (1806-1865), Benedictine Nun, vert. 30c, St. John of the Cross (1542-1591), Christian mystic.

1991, Apr. 29 Litho. *Perf. 14*

771 A188 3c multicolored .18 .18
772 A188 4c multicolored .24 .24
773 A188 30c multicoloed 1.80 1.80
Nos. 771-773 (3) 2.22 2.22

Military Uniforms Type of 1987

Colors Officers: 3c, Royal Malta Fencibles, 1860. 10c, Royal Malta Regiment of Militia, 1903. 19c, King's Own Malta Regiment, 1968. 25c, Armed Forces of Malta, 1991.

Wmk. 354

1991, Sept. 23 Litho. *Perf. 14*

774 A168 3c multicolored .18 .18
775 A168 10c multicolored .60 .60
776 A168 19c multicolored 1.15 1.15
777 A168 25c multicolored 1.50 1.50
Nos. 774-777 (4) 3.43 3.43

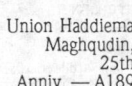

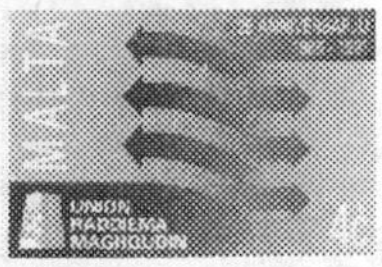
Union Haddiema Maghqudin, 25th Anniv. — A189

1991, Sept. 23 *Perf. 14x13½*

778 A189 4c multicolored .24 .24

Birds of Prey — A190

1991, Oct. 3 *Perf. 14*

779 A190 4c Pernis apivorus .25 .25
780 A190 4c Circus aeruginosus .25 .25
781 A190 10c Falco eleonorae .60 .60
782 A190 10c Falco naumanni .60 .60
a. Strip of 4, #779-782 1.70 1.70

World Wildlife Fund.

Tourism A191

Designs: 1c, Ta' Hagrat neolithic temples, Mgarr. 2c, Cottoner Gate. 3c, St. Michael's Bastion, Valletta. 4c, Spinola Palace, St. Julian's. 5c, Old church, Birkirkara. 10c, Wind surfing, Mellieha Bay. 12c, Boat anchored at Wied iz-Zurrieq. 14c, Mgarr Harbor, Gozo. 20c, Yacht Marina. 50c, Gozo Channel. £1, Statue of Arab Horses, by Sciortino. £2, Independence Monument, by Bonnici, vert.

1991, Dec. 9 *Perf. 13½*

783 A191 1c multicolored .15 .15
784 A191 2c multicolored .15 .15
785 A191 3c multicolored .18 .18
786 A191 4c multicolored .25 .25
787 A191 5c multicolored .32 .32
788 A191 10c multicolored .65 .65
789 A191 12c multicolored .75 .75
790 A191 14c multicolored .85 .85
791 A191 20c multicolored 1.25 1.25
792 A191 50c multicolored 3.25 3.25
793 A191 £1 multicolored 6.25 6.25
794 A191 £2 multicolored 12.50 12.50
Nos. 783-794 (12) 26.55 26.55

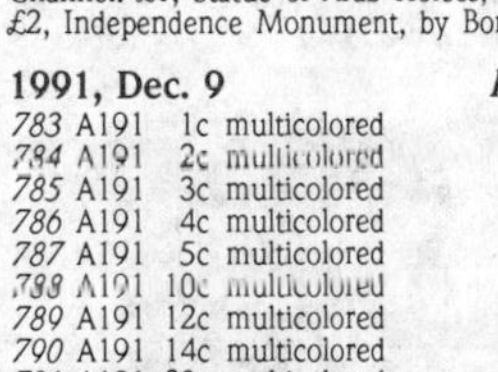
Malta Intl. Airport A192

1992, Feb. 8 *Perf. 14*

795 A192 4c shown .25 .25
796 A192 10c Flags, airport .60 .60

Discovery of America, 500th Anniv. A193

1992, Feb. 20   Perf. 14x14½
797 A193 10c Columbus' fleet   .65   .65
798 A193 35c Columbus, map   2.15 2.15
                         Europa.

George Cross,
1942 — A194

George Cross and: 4c, Royal Malta Artillery. 10c,
Siege Bell. 50c, Santa Maria convoy entering Grand
Harbor.

1992, Apr. 15   Perf. 14
799 A194 4c multicolored   .25   .25
800 A194 10c multicolored   .60   .60
801 A194 50c multicolored   3.00 3.00
      Nos. 799-801 (3)   3.85 3.85

1992
Summer
Olympics,
Barcelona
A195

1992, June 24
802 A195 3c Runners   .18   .18
803 A195 10c High jump   .65   .65
804 A195 30c Swimmer   1.95 1.95
      Nos. 802-804 (3)   2.78 2.78

Historic
Buildings
A196

Designs: 3c, Church of the Flight of the Holy
Family into Egypt, vert. 4c, St. John's Co-Cathedral.
19c, Church of the Madonna del Pilar. 25c,
Auberge de Provence, vert.

1992, July 5
805 A196 3c blk, gray & buff   .20   .20
806 A196 4c blk, salmon & buff   .28   .28
807 A196 19c blk, green & buff   1.25 1.25
808 A196 25c blk, pink & buff   1.65 1.65
      Nos. 805-808 (4)   3.38 3.38

University of Malta, 400th Anniv. — A197

1992, Nov. 11
809 A197 4c Early building, vert.   .24   .24
810 A197 30c Modern complex   1.80 1.80

Lions Intl., 75th
Anniv. — A198

1993, Feb. 4
811 A198 4c We serve   .20   .20
812 A198 50c Sight first campaign   2.55 2.55

Europa
A199

Contemporary paintings by: 10c, Pawl Carbo-
naro, vert. 35c, Alfred Chircop.

1993, Apr. 7
813 A199 10c multicolored   .52   .52
814 A199 35c multicolored   1.85 1.85

5th Games
of Small
States of
Europe
A200

1993, May 4   Perf. 13½x14
815 A200 3c Torchbearer   .16   .16
816 A200 4c Cycling   .22   .22
817 A200 10c Tennis   .55   .55
818 A200 35c Sailing   1.90 1.90
  a. Souvenir sheet of 4, #815-818 2.80 2.80
      Nos. 815-818 (4)   2.83 2.83

Boy Scouts and Girl
Guides of
Malta — A201

1993, July 21   Perf. 14
819 A201 3c Leader bandaging girl   .15   .15
820 A201 4c Bronze Cross   .20   .20
821 A201 10c Scout at camp fire   .50   .50
822 A201 35c Scout recieving Bronze
             Cross   1.75 1.75
      Nos. 819-822 (4)   2.60 2.60
Girl Guides in Malta, 70th anniv. (#819). Award
of Bronze Cross for Gallantry to Boy Scouts of
Malta, 50th anniv. (#820-822).

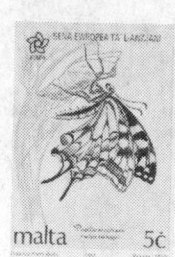

A202   A203

1993, Sept. 23   Perf. 14½x14
823 A202 5c Papilio machaon   .25   .25
824 A202 35c Vanessa atalanta   1.90 1.90

1993, Oct. 5   Perf. 13½
825 A203 4c multicolored   .20   .20
General Worker's Union, 50th anniv.

Souvenir Sheet

Local Councils — A204

Designs showing various local flags with denominations at: a, UL. b, UR. c, LL. d, LR.

1993, Nov. 20   Perf. 14½
826   Sheet of 4   1.00 1.00
  a.-d. A204 5c any single   .25   .25

Dental Assoc. of
Malta, 50th
Anniv. — A205

Design: 44c, Dental instrument, teeth.

1994, Feb. 12
827 A205 5c multicolored   .25   .25
828 A205 44c multicolored   2.00 2.00

Europa — A206

Designs: 14c, Sir Themistocles Zammit (1864-
1935), discoverer of micro-organism causing undu-
lant fever. 30c, Marble candelabrum, 2nd cent.
B.C., Natl. Museum of Archaeology, Valletta.

1994, Mar. 29   Perf. 14
829 A206 14c multicolored   .70   .70
830 A206 30c multicolored   1.50 1.50

Anniversaries and
Events — A207

1994, May 10
831 A207 5c shown   .25   .25
832 A207 9c Crosses   .45   .45
833 A207 14c Farm animals   .70   .70
834 A207 20c Factory worker   1.00 1.00
835 A207 25c Cathedral, vert.   1.25 1.25
      Nos. 831-835 (5)   3.65 3.65
Intl. Year of the Family (#831). Malta Red Cross
Society, 3rd anniv. (#832). Agrarian Society, 150th
anniv. (#833). ILO, 75th anniv. (#834). St. Paul's
Anglican Cathedral, 150th anniv. (#835).

1994 World Cup
Soccer
Championships,
US — A208

1994, June 9
836 A208 5c shown   .25   .25
837 A208 14c Ball, net, map   .70   .70
838 A208 30c Ball, field, map   1.50 1.50
  a. Souvenir sheet of 3, #836-838 2.50 2.50
      Nos. 836-838 (3)   2.45 2.45

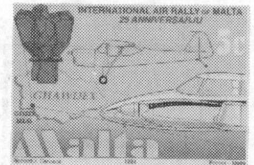

Aviation Anniversaries & Events — A209

Aircraft, related objects: 5c, Trophy, map, Twin
Comanche. 14c, Airshow emblem, Phantom jet,
demonstration team in silhouette, Alouette helicopter, flag. 20c, Emblem, Avro York, old terminal
building, DeHavilland Dove. 25c, Emblem,
DeHavilland Comet, new terminal, Airbus 320.

1994, July 2
839 A209 5c multicolored   .25   .25
840 A209 14c multicolored   .75   .75
841 A209 20c multicolored   1.00 1.00
842 A209 25c multicolored   1.25 1.25
      Nos. 839-842 (4)   3.25 3.25
Intl. Air Rally of Malta, 25th anniv. (#839).
Malta Intl. Airshow (#840). ICAO, 50th anniv.
(#841-842).

First Manned Moon
Landing, 25th
Anniv. — A210

1994, July 20
843 A210 14c multicolored   .75   .75

Christmas — A211

1994, Oct. 26
844 A211 5c shown   .28   .28
          Size: 28x40mm
845 A211 9c +2c Angel in pink   .60   .60
846 A211 14c +3c Madonna & child   .95   .95
847 A211 20c +3c Angel in green   1.25 1.25
      Nos. 844-847 (4)   3.08 3.08

Antique Maltese
Silver — A212

Designs: 5c, Ewer, Vilhena period. 14c, Balsamina, Pinto period. 20c, Coffee pot, Pinto period.
25c, Sugar box, Pinto period.

                     Wmk. 354
1994, Dec. 12   Litho.   Perf. 14
848 A212 5c multicolored   .28   .28
849 A212 14c multicolored   .75   .75
850 A212 20c multicolored   1.10 1.10
851 A212 25c multicolored   1.40 1.40
      Nos. 848-851 (4)   3.53 3.53

Anniversaries &
Events — A213

1995, Feb. 27
852 A213 2c multicolored   .15   .15
853 A213 5c multicolored   .28   .28
854 A213 14c multicolored   .75   .75
855 A213 20c multicolored   1.10 1.10
856 A213 25c multicolored   1.40 1.40
      Nos. 852-856 (5)   3.68 3.68
Natl. Assoc. of Pensioners, 25th anniv. (#852).
Natl. Youth Council of Malta, 10th anniv. (#853).
4th World Conf. on Women, Beijing (#854). Malta
Memorial District Nursing Assoc., 50th anniv.
(#855). Louis Pasteur (1822-95) (#856).

Europa: 14c, Hand with olive twig, rainbow,
vert. 30c, Doves.

Peace &
Freedom
A214

1995, Mar. 29

857	A214	14c multicolored	.75	.75
858	A214	30c multicolored	1.65	1.65

50th Anniversaries — A215

Designs: 5c, End of World War II, ships, planes.
14c, Formation of UN, people joining hands. 35c,
FAO, hands holding bowl of wheat, FAO emblem.

1995, Apr. 21

859	A215	5c multicolored	.28	.28
860	A215	14c multicolored	.80	.80
861	A215	35c multi, vert.	2.00	2.00
		Nos. 859-861 (3)	3.08	3.08

Telecommunications &
Electricity — A216

1995, June 15

862	A216	2c Light bulb	.15	.15
863	A216	5c Cable, binary numbers	.30	.30
864	A216	9c Satellite dish	.50	.50
865	A216	14c Sun's rays, trees	.80	.80
866	A216	20c Telephone, satellite	1.15	1.15
		Nos. 862-866 (5)	2.90	2.90

European Nature Conservation
Year — A217

1995, July

867	A217	5c Ruins, Girna	.30	.30
868	A217	14c Podarcis filfolensis	.75	.75
869	A217	44c Pina halepensis	2.50	2.50
		Nos. 867-869 (3)	3.55	3.55

Antique
Clocks — A218

Designs: 1c, Pinto's turret clock. 5c, Michelangelo Sapiano, long case & smaller clock. 14c, Arlogg
tal-lira (case) clock. 25c, Maltese sundials.

1995, Oct. 5

870	A218	1c multicolored	.15	.15
871	A218	5c multicolored	.30	.30
872	A218	14c multicolored	.80	.80
873	A218	25c multicolored	1.40	1.40
		Nos. 870-873 (4)	2.65	2.65

Christmas — A219

Designs: 5c, Christmas Eve children's procession.
5c+2c, Children carrying manger. 14c+3c, Boy carrying manger, boy with lamp. 25c+3c, Boy with
lamp, balcony.
Illustration reduced.

Wmk. 354

1995, Nov. 15   Litho.   Perf. 14

874	A219	5c multi	.30	.30

Size: 26x32mm

875	A219	5c +2c multi	.40	.40
876	A219	14c +3c multi	1.00	1.00
877	A219	25c +3c multi	1.65	1.65
		Nos. 874-877 (4)	3.35	3.35

Surtax for child welfare organizations.

SEMI-POSTAL STAMPS

All semi-postal issues are for
Christmas unless otherwise noted.

Catalogue values for unused
stamps in this section are for Never
Hinged items.

Angels with
Trumpet and
Harp, Star of
Bethlehem and
Mdina
Cathedral
SP1

Star of Bethlehem and: 1p+1p, Two peasants
with tambourine and bagpipe. 1sh6p+3p, Choir
boys singing Christmas carols. The background of
the 3 stamps together shows the Cathedral of
Mdina, Malta, and surrounding countryside.

1969, Nov. 8   Wmk. 354   Perf. 12½

B1	SP1	1p +1p multi	.15	.15
B2	SP1	5p +1p multi	.15	.15
B3	SP1	1sh6p +3p multi	.35	.35
a.		Triptych, #B1-B3	.55	.55
		Set value	.50	.50

Nos. B1-B3 were printed singly in sheets of 60
and in sheets containing 20 triptychs.

Christmas Eve
Procession — SP2

Designs: 10p+2p, Nativity and Cathedral.
1sh6p+3p, Adoration of the Shepherds and Mdina
Cathedral.

1970, Nov. 7   Photo.   Perf. 14x13½

B4	SP2	1p +½p multi	.15	.15
B5	SP2	10p +2p multi	.24	.24
B6	SP2	1sh6p +3p multi	.60	.60
		Nos. B4-B6 (3)	.99	.99

Surtax for child welfare organizations.

Angel — SP3

Designs: 10p+2p, Madonna and Child.
1sh6p+3p, Shepherd.

1971, Nov. 8   Perf. 14

B7	SP3	1p +½p multi	.15	.15
B8	SP3	10p +2p multi	.28	.28
B9	SP3	1sh6p +3p multi	.55	.55
a.		Souv. sheet of 3, #B7-B9, perf. 15	1.25	1.25
		Nos. B7-B9 (3)	.98	.98

1972, Dec.   Litho.   Perf. 13½

Designs: 3c+1c, Angel playing tambourine.
7c5m+1c5m, Angel singing.

B10	SP3	8m +2m dk gray & gold	.15	.15
B11	SP3	3c +1c dk purple & gold	.22	.22
B12	SP3	7c5m +1c5m slate & gold	.60	.60
a.		Souvenir sheet of 3, #B10-B12	1.25	1.25
		Nos. B10-B12 (3)	.97	.97

1973, Nov. 10   Litho.   Perf. 13½

Designs: 8m+2m, Singers and organ pipes.
3c+1c, Virgin and Child with star. 7c5m+1c5m,
Star, candles, buildings, tambourine.

B13	SP3	8m +2m multi	.15	.15
B14	SP3	3c +1c multi	.40	.40
B15	SP3	7c5m +1c5m multi	1.00	1.00
a.		Souvenir sheet of 3, #B13-B15	2.00	2.00
		Nos. B13-B15 (3)	1.55	1.55
		Nos. B7-B15 (9)	3.50	3.50

Star and Holy
Family — SP4

Designs: 3c+1c, Star and two shepherds. 5c+1c,
Star and three shepherds. 7c5m+1c5m, Star and
Three Kings.

1974, Nov. 22   Litho.   Perf. 14

B16	SP4	8m +2m multi	.15	.15
B17	SP4	3c +1c multi	.20	.20
B18	SP4	5c +1c multi	.45	.45
B19	SP4	7c5m +1c5m multi	.70	.70
		Nos. B16-B19 (4)	1.50	1.50

Nativity, by Maestro Alberto — SP5

Designs: 8m+2m, Shepherds. 7c5m+1c5m,
Three Kings.

1975, Nov. 4   Perf. 13½
Size: 24x23mm (#B20, B22);
49x23mm (#B21)

B20	SP5	8m +2m multi	.15	.15
B21	SP5	3c +1c multi	.75	.55
B22	SP5	7c5m +1c5m multi	4.50	3.50
a.		Triptych, #B20-B22	6.50	6.50
		Nos. B20-B22 (3)	5.40	4.20

Printed singly and as triptychs. Surtax for child
welfare.

SP6   Madonna and Saints, by
             Domenico di
             Michelino — SP7

Designs (Details of Painting): 5c+1c, Virgin and
Child. 7c+1c5m, St. Christopher and Bishop.

1976, Nov. 23   Litho.   Perf. 13½

B23	SP6	1c +5m multi	.18	.15
B24	SP6	5c +1c multi	.50	.38
B25	SP6	7c +1c5m multi	.90	.85

Perf. 13½x14

B26	SP7	10c +2c multi	2.00	1.10
		Nos. B23-B26 (4)	3.58	2.48

Nativity
SP8

Crèche Figurines: 1c+5m, Annunciation to the
Shepherds. 11c+1c5m, Shepherds.

Christmas Decorations,
People and
Church — SP9

Perf. 13½x14
1977, Nov. 16   Wmk. 354

B27	SP8	1c +5m multi	.15	.15
B28	SP8	7c +1c multi	.30	.30
B29	SP8	11c +1c5m multi	1.00	1.00
a.		Triptych, #B27-B29	1.50	1.50
		Nos. B27-B29 (3)	1.45	1.45

Nos. B27-B29 printed singly and as triptychs.
Surtax was for child welfare.

Designs: 5c+1c, Decorations and angels.
7c+1c5m, Decorations and carolers. 11c+3c, Combined designs of #B30-B32.

1978, Nov. 9   Litho.   Perf. 14
Size: 24x30mm

B30	SP9	1c +5m multi	.15	.15
B31	SP9	5c +1c multi	.25	.25
B32	SP9	7c +1c5m multi	.35	.35

Perf. 13½
Size: 58x22½mm

B33	SP9	11c +3c multi	.65	.65
		Nos. B30-B33 (4)	1.40	1.40

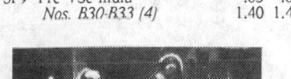 

Nativity, by Giuseppe Cali — SP10

Designs (Cali Paintings): 5c+1c, 11c+3c, Flight
into Egypt. 7c+1c5m, Nativity.

1979, Nov. 14   Litho.   Perf. 14x13½

B34	SP10	1c +5m multi	.15	.15
B35	SP10	5c +1c multi	.32	.32
B36	SP10	7c +1c5m multi	.42	.42
B37	SP10	11c +3c multi	.80	.80
		Nos. B34-B37 (4)	1.69	1.69

Nativity, by Anton Inglott (1915-
1945) — SP11

Designs (Details of Painting): 2c+5m, Annunciation. 6c+1c, Angel. 8c+1c5m, Holy Family.

1980, Oct. 7   Litho.   Perf. 14x13½
Size: 20x47mm

B38	SP11	2c +5m multi	.15	.15
B39	SP11	6c +1c multi	.28	.28
B40	SP11	8c +1c5m multi	.35	.35

Perf. 14½x14
Size: 47x39mm

B41	SP11	12c +3c shown	.55	.55
		Nos. B38-B41 (4)	1.33	1.33

SP12

1981, Nov. 18   Wmk. 354   Perf. 14

B42	SP12	2c +1c Children, vert.	.15	.15
B43	SP12	8c +2c Procession	.42	.42
B44	SP12	20c +3c Service, vert.	1.10	1.10
		Nos. B42-B44 (3)	1.67	1.67

SP13

Three Kings Following Star: 2c+1c, Star. 8c+2c, Three Kings, 20c+3c, Entire design.

1982, Oct. 8   Litho.   Perf. 13½
B45 SP13 2c +1c multi   .15   .15
B46 SP13 8c +2c multi   .55   .55

Perf. 14
Size: 45x36mm
B47 SP13 20c +3c multi   1.25 1.25
   Nos. B45-B47 (3)   1.95 1.95

SP14

Illuminated Manuscripts, Book of Hours, 15th Cent.: 2c+1c, Annunciation. 8c+2c, Nativity. 20c+3c, Three Kings bearing gifts. Surtax was for child welfare.

1983, Sept. 6   Litho.   Perf. 14
B48 SP14 2c +1c multi   .15   .15
B49 SP14 8c +2c multi   .55   .55
B50 SP14 20c +3c multi   1.30 1.30
   Nos. B48-B50 (3)   2.00 2.00

SP15

Paintings by Peter-Paul Caruana, Church of Our Lady of Porto Salvo, Valletta, 1850: 2c+1c, Visitation, vert. 8c+2c, Epiphany. 20c+3c, Jesus Among the Doctors.

1984, Oct. 5   Litho.   Perf. 14
B51 SP15 2c +1c multi   .15   .15
B52 SP15 8c +2c multi   .45   .45
B53 SP15 20c +3c multi   1.10 1.10
   Nos. B51-B53 (3)   1.70 1.70

SP16

1985, Oct. 10   Litho.   Perf. 14
B54 SP16 2c +1c Adoration of the
            Magi   .15   .15
B55 SP16 8c +2c Nativity   .40   .40
B56 SP16 20c +3c Trumpeter Angels .90   .90
   Nos. B54-B56 (3)   1.45 1.45

Surtax for child welfare organizations.

SP17

Paintings by Giuseppe D'Arena (1633-1719).

1986, Oct. 10   Wmk. 354   Perf. 14½
B57 SP17 2c +1c The Nativity   .15   .15
B58 SP17 8c +2c The Nativity, de-
            tail, vert.   .40   .40
B59 SP17 20c +3c The Epiphany .92   .92
   Nos. B57-B59 (3)   1.47 1.47

Surtax for child welfare organizations.

2c+1c SP18

Illuminated text from choral books of the Veneranda Assemblea of St. John's Conventual Church, Valletta.

1987, Nov. 6   Litho.   Perf. 14
B60 SP18 2c +1c Mary's Visit to
            Elizabeth   .18   .18
B61 SP18 8c +2c Nativity   .55   .55
B62 SP18 20c +3c Adoration of the
            Magi   1.25 1.25
   Nos. B60-B62 (3)   1.98 1.98

Surtax for child welfare organizations and the handicapped.

SP19 MALTA 3c+1c

1988, Nov. 5   Litho.   Perf. 14½x14
B63 SP19 3c +1c Shepherd   .25   .25
B64 SP19 10c +2c Nativity   .70   .70
B65 SP19 25c +3c Magi   1.65 1.65
   Nos. B63-B65 (3)   2.60 2.60

Surtax for child welfare organizations and the handicapped.

3c + 1c SP20

Various angels from frescoes by Mattia Preti in the vault of St. John's Co-Cathedral, Valletta, 1666.

1989, Nov. 11   Perf. 14
B66 SP20 3c +1c multi   .22   .22
B67 SP20 10c +2c multi   .70   .70
B68 SP20 20c +3c multi   1.30 1.30
   Nos. B66-B68 (3)   2.22 2.22

Surtax for child welfare organizations and the handicapped.

SP21    SP22

Creche figures.

1990, Nov. 10
Size: #B70, 41x27mm
B69 SP21 3c +1c Carrying water .25   .25
B70 SP21 10c +2c Nativity   .78   .78
B71 SP21 25c +3c Shepherd   1.80 1.80
   Nos. B69-B71 (3)   2.83 2.83

Surtax for child welfare organizations.

1991, Nov. 6
B72 SP22 3c +1c Wise men   .24   .24
B73 SP22 10c +2c Mary, Joseph,
            Jesus   .72   .72
B74 SP22 25c +3c Shepherds   1.70 1.70
   Nos. B72-B74 (3)   2.66 2.66

Surtax for child welfare organizations.

SP23

Paintings from dome spandrels of Mosta Parish Church by Giuseppe Cali (1846-1930): 3c+1c, Nativity scene. 10c+2c, Adoration of the Magi. 25c+3c, Christ among the Elders in the Temple.

1992, Oct. 22
B75 SP23 3c +1c multi   .25   .25
B76 SP23 10c +2c multi   .75   .75
B77 SP23 25c +3c multi   1.75 1.75
   Nos. B75-B77 (3)   2.75 2.75

Surtax for child welfare organizations.

SP24

Designs: 3c+1c, Christ Child in manger. 10c+2c, Christmas tree. 25c+3c, Star.

1993, Nov. 20
B78 SP24 3c +1c multi   .20   .20
B79 SP24 10c +2c multi   .60   .60
B80 SP24 25c +3c multi   1.40 1.40
   Nos. B78-B80 (3)   2.20 2.20

AIR POST STAMPS

No. 140 Overprinted   **AIR MAIL**

Perf. 14½x14
1928, Apr. 1   Typo.   Wmk. 4
C1 A22 6p red & violet   5.50 6.75

> Catalogue values for unused stamps in this section, from this point to the end of the section, are for Never Hinged items.

Jet over Valletta — AP1

Designs: 3c, 5c, 20c, 35c, Winged emblem. 7c5m, 25c, like 4c.

Perf. 13½
1974, Mar.   Litho.   Wmk. 354
Cross Emblem in Red and Blue
C2 AP1 3c ol brown & gold   .15   .15
C3 AP1 4c dk blue & gold   .16   .16
C4 AP1 5c dk vio bl & gold   .22   .22
C5 AP1 7c5m sl green & gold   .32   .32
C6 AP1 20c vio brn & gold   .85   .85
C7 AP1 25c slate & gold   1.10 1.10
C8 AP1 35c brown & gold   1.65 1.65
   Nos. C2-C8 (7)   4.45 4.45

Jet and Megalithic Temple — AP2

Designs: 7c, 20c, Air Malta Boeing 720B approaching Malta. 11c, 75c, Jumbo jet landing at Luqa Airport. 17c, like AP2.

1978, Oct. 3   Litho.   Perf. 13½
C9 AP2 5c multicolored   .20   .20
C10 AP2 7c multicolored   .28   .28
C11 AP2 11c multicolored   .45   .45

C12 AP2 17c multicolored   .70   .70
C13 AP2 20c multicolored   .90   .90
C14 AP2 75c multicolored   3.00 3.00
   Nos. C9-C14 (6)   5.53 5.53

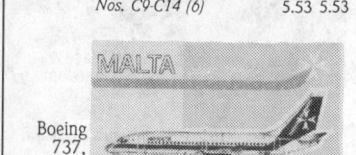

Boeing 737, 1984 AP3

1984, Jan. 26   Wmk. 354   Perf. 14
C15 AP3 7c shown   .32   .32
C16 AP3 8c Boeing 720B, 1974   .36   .36
C17 AP3 16c Vickers Vanguard, 1964 .72   .72
C18 AP3 23c Vickers Viscount, 1958 1.05 1.05
C19 AP3 27c Douglas DC3 Dakota,
            1948   1.25 1.25
C20 AP3 38c AW Atlanta, 1936 1.75 1.75
C21 AP3 75c Dornier Wal, 1929 3.40 3.40
   Nos. C15-C21 (7)   8.85 8.85

POSTAGE DUE STAMPS

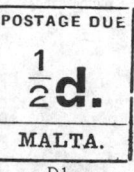

D1   Maltese
              Cross — D2

1925   Typeset   Unwmk.   Imperf.
J1 D1 ½p black, white   1.00 1.40
J2 D1 1p black, white   1.00 1.90
J3 D1 1½p black, white   2.00 2.50
J4 D1 2p black, white   2.00 2.75
J5 D1 2½p black, white   2.25 3.25
   a. "2" of "½" omitted   1,200. 1,350.
J6 D1 3p black, gray   2.25 4.25
J7 D1 4p black, orange   3.00 4.25
J8 D1 6p black, orange   4.00 5.50
J9 D1 1sh black, orange   7.00 13.00
J10 D1 1sh6p black, orange   16.00 22.00
   Nos. J1-J10 (10)   40.50 60.80

These stamps were typeset in groups of 42. In each sheet there were four impressions of a group, two of them being inverted and making tete beche pairs.

Forged examples of No. J5a are known.

Wmk. 4 Sideways
1925   Typo.   Perf. 12
J11 D2 ½p blue green   .65   .65
J12 D2 1p violet   .65   .35
J13 D2 1½p yellow brown   .90   .90
J14 D2 2p gray   10.50 10.50
J15 D2 2½p orange   3.00 2.00
J16 D2 3p dark blue   1.75 1.75
J17 D2 4p olive green   9.50 9.50
J18 D2 6p claret   4.00 4.00
J19 D2 1sh gray black   2.50 4.25
J20 D2 1sh6p deep rose   5.50 7.75
   Nos. J11-J20 (10)   38.95 41.65

In 1953-57 six values (½p-2p, 3p, 4p) were reissued on chalky paper in slightly different colors.

> Catalogue values for unused stamps in this section, from this point to the end of the section, are for Never Hinged items.

1966   Wmk. 314   Perf. 12
J21 D2 2p sepia   32.50 32.50

1968 Wmk. 354 Sideways Perf. 12½
J22 D2 ½p green   .15   .15
J23 D2 1p rose violet   .18   .18
J24 D2 1½p bister brn   .30   .30
J25 D2 2p brown black   .55   .55
J26 D2 2½p orange   .65   .65
J27 D2 3p Prus blue   .75   .75
J28 D2 4p olive   1.10 1.10
J29 D2 6p purple   1.90 1.90
J30 D2 1sh black   2.00 2.00
J31 D2 1sh6p rose car   4.50 4.50
   Nos. J22-J31 (10)   12.08 12.08

1967, Nov. 9   Perf. 12
J22a D2 ½p   4.00 4.00
J23a D2 1p   5.50 5.50
J25a D2 2p   8.00 8.00
J28a D2 4p   100.00 140.00
   Nos. J22a-J28a (4)   117.50 157.50

Numeral — D3

Scroll — D4

Perf. 13x13½

1973, Apr. 28 Litho. Wmk. 354

J32	D3	2m brown	.15	.15
J33	D3	3m brown orange	.15	.15
J34	D3	5m carmine	.15	.15
J35	D3	1c deep green	.15	.15
J36	D3	2c black	.15	.15
J37	D3	3c olive	.15	.15
J38	D3	5c violet blue	.25	.25
J39	D3	10c deep magenta	.52	.52
		Set value	1.20	1.20

Wmk. 354

1993, Jan. 4 Litho. *Perf. 14*

J40	D4	1c brt pink & lt pink	.15	.15
J41	D4	2c brt blue & lt blue	.15	.15
J42	D4	5c brt grn & lt grn	.28	.28
J43	D4	10c org yel & brt yel	.52	.52
		Nos. J40-J43 (4)	1.10	1.10

WAR TAX STAMPS

Nos. 50, 25 Overprinted **WAR TAX**

1918 Wmk. 3 *Perf. 14*

MR1	A13	½p green	.30	.30

Wmk. 2

MR2	A12	3p red violet & gray	3.00	4.00

MAURITIUS

mȯ-ˈri-sh(ē-)əs

LOCATION — Island in the Indian Ocean about 550 miles east of Madagascar
GOVT. — Republic
AREA — 720 sq. mi.
POP. — 969,191 (est. 1983)
CAPITAL — Port Louis

12 Pence = 1 Shilling
100 Cents = 1 Rupee (1878)

The British Crown Colony of Mauritius was granted self-government in 1967 and became an independent state on March 12, 1968.

Nos. 1-6, 14-17 unused are valued without gum.

Nos. 3a-8, 14-15 are printed on fragile paper with natural irregularities which might be mistaken for faults.

Catalogue values for unused stamps in this country are for Never Hinged items, beginning with Scott 220 in the regular postage section, Scott J1 in the postage due section.

Queen Victoria
A1 A2

1847 Unwmk. Engr. *Imperf.*

1	A1	1p orange	*1,100,000.*	*500,000.*
2	A1	2p dark blue		*500,000.*

Nos. 1 and 2 were engraved and printed in Port Louis. There is but one type of each value. The initials "J. B." on the bust are those of the engraver, J. Barnard.

All unused copies of the 2p are in museums. There is one unused copy of the 1p in private hands.

1848

Earliest Impressions
Thick Yellowish Paper

3	A2	1p orange	*32,500.*	*12,500.*
4	A2	2p dark blue	*30,000.*	*13,500.*
d.		"PENOE"	*40,000.*	*21,000.*

Early Impressions
Yellowish White Paper

3a	A2	1p orange	*14,000.*	*5,250.*
4a	A2	2p blue	*16,000.*	*5,750.*
e.		"PENOE"	*22,500.*	*9,000.*

Bluish Paper

5	A2	1p orange	*15,000.*	*5,250.*
6	A2	2p blue	*16,500.*	*5,750.*
c.		"PENOE"	*22,500.*	*9,000.*

Intermediate Impressions
Yellowish White Paper

3b	A2	1p red orange	*6,750.*	2,000.
4b	A2	2p blue	*6,000.*	2,000.
f.		"PENOE"	*12,500.*	*4,500.*

Bluish Paper

5a	A2	1p red orange	*6,750.*	1,800.
6a	A2	2p blue	*6,500.*	2,000.
d.		"PENOE"	*12,500.*	*4,500.*
f.		Double impression		—

Worn Impressions
Yellowish White Paper

3c	A2	1p orange red	2,000.	375.
d.		1p brownish red	2,000.	375.
4c	A2	2p blue	2,000.	750.
g.		"PENOE"	*3,000.*	1,350.

Bluish Paper

5b	A2	1p orange red	1,450.	350.
c.		1p brownish red	1,450.	350.
d.		Pair, double impression		
6b	A2	2p blue	2,000.	675.
e.		"PENOE"	2,750.	1,350.

Latest Impressions
Yellowish or Grayish Paper

3e	A2	1p orange red	1,250.	350.
f.		1p brownish red	1,200.	350.
4h	A2	2p blue	1,600.	450.
i.		"PENOE"	*2,750.*	900.

Bluish Paper

5c	A2	1p orange red	1,200.	325.
f.		1p brownish red	1,150.	325.
6g	A2	2p blue	1,500.	425.
h.		"PENOE"	2,600.	900.

These stamps were printed in sheets of twelve, four rows of three, and each position differs in details. The "PENOE" error is the most pronounced variety on the plates and is from position 7.

The stamps were in use until 1859. Earliest impressions, Nos. 3-4, show the full background of diagonal and vertical lines with the diagonal lines predominant. Early impresions, Nos. 3a-4a, 5-6, show the full background with the vertical lines predominating. As the plate became worn the vertical lines disappeared, giving the intermediate impressions, Nos. 3b-4b, 5a-6a.

Worn impressions, Nos. 3c-4c, 5b-6b, have little background remaining, and latest impressions, Nos. 3e-4h, 5e-6g, have also lost details of the frame and head. The paper of the early impressions is usually rather thick, that of the worn impressions rather thin. Expect fibrous inclusions in the paper of all impressions.

"Britannia"
A3 A4

1849-58

7	A3	red brown, *blue*	6.00	
8	A3	blue ('58)	3.00	

Nos. 7-8 were never placed in use.

1858-59

9	A3	(4p) green, *bluish*	400.00	190.00
10	A3	(6p) red	20.00	*30.00*
11	A3	(9p) mag ('59)	450.00	200.00

No. 11 was re-issued in Nov. 1862, as a 1p stamp. When used as such it is always canceled "B53." Same value as No. 11 used.

1858 Black Surcharge

12	A4	4p green, *bluish*	675.00	350.00

Queen Victoria — A5

Early Impressions

1859, Mar.

14	A5	2p blue, *grayish*	3,250.	1,500.
a.		2p deep blue, *grayish*	4,500.	1,750.
14B	A5	2p blue, *bluish*	3,250.	1,500.
c.		Worn impression	1,000.	400.

Type A5 was engraved by Lapirot, in Port Louis, and was printed locally. There were twelve varieties in the sheet.

A6

A7

1859, Oct.

15	A6	2p blue, *bluish*	*100,000.*	4,000.

No. 15 was printed from the plate of the 1848 issue after it had been entirely re-engraved by Sherwin. It is commonly known as the "fillet head." The plate of the 1p, 1848, was also re-engraved but was never put in use.

1859, Dec. Litho.

Laid Paper

16	A7	1p red	4,250.	650.
a.		1p deep red	5,000.	1,350.
17	A7	2p blue	3,000.	400.
a.		2p slate blue	6,000.	625.

Lithographed locally by Dardenne.

"Britannia" A8

1859 Wove Paper Engr. *Imperf.*

18	A8	6p blue	450.00	27.50
19	A8	1sh vermilion	1,900.	50.00

1861

20	A8	6p gray violet	16.00	22.50
21	A8	1sh green	275.00	60.00

1862 *Perf. 14 to 16*

22	A8	6p slate	13.50	25.00
23	A8	1sh deep green	1,600.	300.00

Very Fine examples of Nos. 22-23 will have perforations touching the design on one or more sides. Examples with perfs clear on four sides are scarce and will sell for more. Inferior examples will sell for much reduced prices.

A9

A10

1860-63 Typo. *Perf. 14*

24	A9	1p brown lilac	80.00	14.00
25	A9	2p blue	110.00	22.50
26	A9	4p rose	110.00	17.00
27	A9	6p green ('62)	450.00	90.00
28	A9	6p lilac ('63)	110.00	60.00
29	A9	9p dull lilac	60.00	25.00
30	A9	1sh buff ('62)	150.00	45.00
31	A9	1sh green ('63)	450.00	110.00

For surcharges see Nos. 43-45.

1863-72 Wmk. 1

32	A9	1p lilac brown	30.00	6.00
a.		1p bister brown	40.00	4.50
33	A9	2p blue	50.00	4.50
a.		Imperf., pair	1,100.	1,500.
34	A9	3p vermilion	30.00	7.50
35	A9	4p rose	65.00	1.75
36	A9	6p lilac ('64)	90.00	20.00
37	A9	6p blue grn ('65)	75.00	3.25
a.		6p yellow green ('65)	90.00	10.00
38	A9	9p green ('72)	95.00	*100.00*
39	A9	1sh yellow ('64)	100.00	10.00
a.		1sh orange yellow	100.00	10.00
40	A9	1sh blue ('70)	110.00	15.00
41	A9	5sh red violet	110.00	32.50
a.		5sh bright violet	125.00	32.50
		Nos. 32-41 (10)	755.00	200.50

For surcharges see Nos. 48-49, 51-58, 87.

1872

42	A10	10p claret	110.00	22.50

For surcharges see Nos. 46-47.

No. 29 Surcharged in Black or Red:

HALF PENNY
a

½ d
HALF PENNY
b

1876 Unwmk.

43	A9(a)	½p on 9p	3.50	*6.00*
a.		Inverted surcharge	500.00	
b.		Double surcharge		—
44	A9(b)	½p on 9p	*1,250.*	
45	A9(b)	½p on 9p (R)	*800.00*	

Nos. 44 and 45 were never placed in use. No. 45 is valued with perfs cutting into the design.

Stamps of 1863-72 Surcharged in Black:

HALF PENNY
c

One Penny
d

1876-77 Wmk. 1

46	A10(a)	½p on 10p claret	1.75	*11.00*
47	A10(c)	½p on 10p cl ('77)	3.50	*20.00*
48	A9(d)	1p on 4p rose ('77)	6.00	10.00
49	A9(d)	1sh on 5sh red vio ('77)	150.00	70.00
a.		1sh on 5sh violet ('77)	175.00	85.00

A16

Black Surcharge

1878

50	A16	2c claret	4.50	3.50

Stamps and Type of 1863-72 Surcharged in Black

4 CENTS
e

51	A9	4c on 1p bister brn	6.50	3.00
52	A9	8c on 2p blue	55.00	1.25
53	A9	13c on 3p org red	6.00	17.00
54	A9	17c on 4p rose	85.00	2.00
55	A9	25c on 6p sl blue	110.00	4.00
56	A9	38c on 9p violet	17.00	*35.00*
57	A9	50c on 1sh green	70.00	2.50
58	A9	2r50c on 5sh violet	11.50	8.00
		Nos. 50-58 (9)	365.50	76.25

For surcharge see No. 87.

A18

A19

A20

A21

A22

A23

A24

A25

A26

1879-80 **Wmk. 1**
59 A18 2c red brown ('80) 25.00 9.00
60 A19 4c orange 45.00 2.50
61 A20 8c blue ('80) 11.00 1.25
62 A21 13c slate ('80) 100.00 120.00
63 A22 17c rose ('80) 35.00 4.00
64 A23 25c bister 150.00 7.00
65 A24 38c violet ('80) 125.00 150.00
66 A25 50c green ('80) 3.00 2.00
67 A26 2r50c brn vio ('80) 22.50 *42.50*
Nos. 59-67 (9) 516.50 338.25

Nos. 59-67 are known imperforate.
For surcharges & overprints see #76-78, 83-86, 122-123.

1882-93 **Wmk. 2**
68 A18 1c violet ('93) .45 .35
69 A18 2c red brown 19.00 3.50
70 A18 2c green ('85) 1.00 .30
71 A19 4c orange 47.50 2.00
72 A19 4c rose ('85) 1.25 .25
73 A20 8c blue ('91) .90 .60
74 A23 25c bister ('83) 3.00 1.40
75 A25 50c dp orange ('87) 25.00 7.00
Nos. 68-75 (8) 98.10 15.40

For surcharges and overprint see #88-89, 121.

Nos. 63 and Type of 1882 Surcharged in Black:

16 CENTS
f

SIXTEEN CENTS
g

1883 **Wmk. 1**

Surcharge Measures 14x3 1/2mm
76 A22(f) 16c on 17c rose 90.00 40.00
a. Double surcharge

Surcharge Measures 15 1/2x3 1/2mm
77 A22(f) 16c on 17c rose 95.00 40.00

Surcharge Measures 15 1/2x2 3/4mm
78 A22(f) 16c on 17c rose *150.00* *90.00*

Wmk. 2
79 A22(g) 16c on 17c rose 40.00 1.50
Nos. 76-79 (4) *375.00* *171.50*

Queen Victoria — A29

1885-94
80 A29 15c orange brown ('92) 1.25 .40
81 A29 15c blue ('94) 3.50 .25
82 A29 16c orange brown 3.50 .25
Nos. 80-82 (3) 8.25 .90

For surcharges see Nos. 90, 116.

Various Stamps Surcharged in Black or Red:

2 CENTS
h

2 CENTS
j

1885-87 **Wmk. 1**
83 A24(h) 2c on 38c violet 70.00 30.00
a. Inverted surcharge 350.00 350.00
b. Double surcharge 400.00
c. Without bar 55.00
84 A21(j) 2c on 13c sl (R) ('87) 25.00 *42.50*
a. Inverted surcharge 100.00 *125.00*
b. Double surcharge 375.00
c. As "b," one on back *425.00*

TWO CENTS
k

TWO CENTS
l

1891
85 A22(k) 2c on 17c rose 60.00 60.00
a. Inverted surcharge 175.00 175.00
b. Double surcharge 300.00 300.00
86 A24(k) 2c on 38c vio 2.00 4.00
a. Double surcharge 75.00 75.00
b. Dbl. surch., one invtd. 75.00 75.00
c. Inverted surcharge 300.00 300.00
87 A9(e+l) 2c on 38c on 9p vio 1.25 3.25
a. Double surcharge 375.00 375.00
b. Inverted surcharge 125.00 125.00
c. Dbl. surch., one invtd. 75.00 75.00

Wmk. 2
88 A19(k) 2c on 4c rose .50 .30
a. Double surcharge 65.00 65.00
b. Inverted surcharge 65.00 65.00
c. Dbl. surch., one invtd. 70.00 70.00
Nos. 85-88 (4) 63.75 67.55

ONE CENT
m

ONE CENT
n

1893, Jan.
89 A18(m) 1c on 2c violet .50 *5.00*
90 A29(n) 1c on 16c org brown .50 *1.00*

Coat of Arms — A38

1895-1904 **Wmk. 2**
91 A38 1c lilac & ultra .25 .35
92 A38 1c gray blk & black .30 .25
93 A38 2c lilac & orange 1.50 .30
94 A38 2c dull lil & vio 1.50 .20
95 A38 3c lilac .85 .40
96 A38 3c grn & scar, *yel* 1.75 .30
97 A38 4c lilac & green 1.10 .20
98 A38 4c dull lil & car, *yel* 1.40 .25
99 A38 4c gray green & pur 3.00 .55
100 A38 4c black & car, *blue* 2.50 .25
101 A38 5c lilac & vio, *buff* 3.00 *35.00*
102 A38 5c lilac & blk, *buff* 1.35 1.35
103 A38 6c grn & rose 2.50 2.25
104 A38 6c violet & scar, *red* 1.35 .65
105 A38 8c gray grn & blk, *buff* .55 .85
106 A38 12c black & car rose 1.50 1.50
107 A38 15c grn & org 5.75 *5.00*
108 A38 15c blk & ultra, *blue* 30.00 1.00
109 A38 18c gray grn & ultra 5.50 4.00
110 A38 25c grn & car, *grn* 4.25 *9.00*
111 A38 50c green, *yel* 8.50 *17.00*
Nos. 91-111 (21) 78.40 *80.65*

The 25c is on both ordinary and chalky paper.
Ornaments in lower panel omitted on #106-111.
Year of issue: #103, 107, 1899; #92, 94, 98, 1900; #96, 99, 101-102, 104-106, 110-111, 1902; #100, 108, 1904; others, 1895.
See #128-135. For surcharges and overprints see #113, 114, 117-120.

Diamond Jubilee Issue

Arms — A39

1898, May 23 **Wmk. 46**
112 A39 36c brown org & ultra 8.50 12.00

60th year of Queen Victoria's reign.
For surcharge see No. 127.

No. 109 Surcharged in Red

6
CENTS

1899 **Wmk. 2**
113 A38 6c on 18c .50 .50
a. Inverted surcharge 175.00 150.00

No. 112 Surcharged in Blue

15
CENTS

Wmk. 46
114 A39 15c on 36c 2.00 1.50
a. Without bar 140.00

Admiral Mahe de La Bourdonnais — A40

1899, Dec. **Engr.** **Wmk. 1**
115 A40 15c ultra 8.00 2.00

Birth bicent. of Admiral Mahe de La Bourdonnais, governor of Mauritius, 1734-46.

No. 82 Surcharged in Black

4
Cents

1900 **Wmk. 2**
116 A29 4c on 16c orange brown 1.00 3.00

No. 109 Surcharged in Black

12
CENTS
r

1902
117 A38 12c on 18c grn & ultra 1.40 *4.00*

Preceding Issues Overprinted in Black

Postage & Revenue.

1902
118 A38 4c lilac & car, *yel* .70 .35
119 A38 6c green & rose .60 *2.00*
120 A38 15c green & orange .60 .40
121 A23 25c bister .95 2.00

Wmk. 1
122 A25 50c green 3.00 1.25
123 A26 2r50c brown violet 45.00 60.00
Nos. 118-123 (6) 50.85 66.00

Coat of Arms — A41

1902 **Wmk. 1**
124 A41 1r blk & car rose 35.00 25.00

Wmk. 2 Sideways
125 A41 2r50c grn & blk, *bl* 12.00 *50.00*
126 A41 5r blk & car, *red* 45.00 *75.00*
Nos. 124-126 (3) 92.00 *150.00*

No. 112 Surcharged type "r" but with longer bar

1902 **Wmk. 46**
127 A39 12c on 36c 1.25 2.00
a. Inverted surcharge 350.00 250.00

Arms Type of 1895-1904

1904-07 **Wmk. 3**

Chalky Paper
128 A38 1c gray blk & black ('07) 6.00 1.75
129 A38 2c dl lil & vio ('05) 9.50 .45
130 A38 3c grn & scar, *yel* 16.00 4.25
131 A38 4c blk & car, *blue* 1.90 .15
132 A38 6c vio & scar, *red* ('06) 1.25 .15
133 A38 15c blk & ultra, *bl* 3.00 .80
135 A38 50c green, *yel* .90 2.00
136 A41 1r black & car rose ('07) 14.00 *27.50*
Nos. 128-136 (8) 52.55 *37.05*

The 2c, 4c, 6c also exist on ordinary paper.
Ornaments in lower panel omitted on 15c and 50c.

Arms — A42

Edward VII — A43

1910 **Wmk. 3**

Ordinary Paper
137 A42 1c black 1.00 .15
138 A42 2c brown 1.50 .15
139 A42 3c green 1.25 .15
140 A42 4c ol grn & rose 1.25 .15
141 A43 5c gray & rose 1.00 *1.50*
142 A42 6c carmine 1.00 .15
143 A42 8c brown orange 1.50 *1.00*
144 A43 12c gray .75 .90
145 A42 15c ultramarine 6.00 .15

Chalky Paper
146 A43 25c blk & scar, *yel* 1.40 *6.00*
147 A43 50c dull vio & blk 1.40 *10.00*
148 A43 1r blk, *green* 2.75 *5.50*
149 A43 2r50c blk & car, *bl* 5.50 *32.50*
150 A43 5r grn & car, *yel* 19.00 *52.50*
151 A43 10r grn & car, *grn* 60.00 *110.00*
Nos. 137-151 (15) 105.30 *220.80*

Numerals of 12c, 25c and 10r of type A43 are in color on plain tablet.
See Nos. 161-178.

King George V — A44

Die I

For description of dies I and II see back of this section of the Catalogue.
Numeral tablet of 5c, 50c, 1r, 2.50r and 5r of type A44 has lined background with colorless denomination.

1912-22 **Wmk. 3**

Ordinary Paper
152 A44 5c gray & rose 1.00 1.10
153 A44 12c gray 1.75 .35

Chalky Paper
154 A44 25c blk & red, *yel* .50 .90
a. 25c gray black & red, *yellow*, Die II .75 *8.00*
155 A44 50c dull vio & blk 15.00 *26.00*
156 A44 1r blk, *bl grn*, olive back 1.25 *7.50*
a. 1r black, *emerald*, olive back ('21) 4.75 *25.00*
b. Die II, black, *emerald* 1.50 4.00
157 A44 2r50c blk & red, *bl* 10.00 *22.50*
158 A44 5r grn & red, *yel* 30.00 *47.50*
a. Die II ('22) 24.00 *57.50*
159 A44 10r grn & red, *grn* 30.00 *57.50*
a. 10r green & red, *bl grn*, olive back 550.00
b. 10r green & red, *emer* 17.50 *27.50*
c. 10r grn & red, *emer*, olive back 17.50 *27.50*
d. Die II, black, *emer* ('21) 17.00 *37.50*

Surface-colored Paper
160 A44 25c blk & red, *yel* ('16) 1.50 3.00
Nos. 152-160 (9) 91.00 *166.35*

1921-26 **Wmk. 4**

Ordinary Paper
161 A42 1c black .50 .70
162 A42 2c brown .50 .15
163 A42 2c violet, *yel* ('25) .45 .60
164 A42 3c green ('25) 1.65 .50
165 A42 4c ol grn & rose 1.25 *1.50*
166 A42 4c green .65 .15
167 A42 4c brown ('25) .20 .50
168 A42 6c rose red 6.50 4.00
169 A42 6c violet .35 .15
170 A42 8c brown org ('25) 1.50 7.50
171 A42 10c gray ('22) 1.75 3.00
172 A42 10c rose red ('25) 1.65 .65
173 A42 12c rose red .90 .30
174 A42 12c gray ('25) .50 1.25
175 A42 15c ultramarine 3.50 2.50
176 A42 15c dull blue ('25) .45 .30
177 A42 20c ultra ('22) 1.75 .40
178 A42 20c dull vio ('25) 5.00 6.50
Nos. 161-178 (18) 29.05 30.65

Ornaments in lower panel omitted on #171-178.
For surcharges see Nos. 201-203.

Die II

1922-34

Ordinary Paper
179 A44 1c black .60 .35
180 A44 2c brown .40 .15
181 A44 3c green .45 .20
182 A44 4c olive grn & red ('27) .30 .15
a. Die I ('32) 4.50 *20.00*
183 A44 4c green, die I ('33) 2.25 *.30*
184 A44 5c gray & car .60 .15
a. Die I ('32) 2.50 1.65
185 A44 6c olive brn ('28) .50 .50
186 A44 8c orange .45 *5.50*
187 A44 10c rose red ('26) .80 .15
a. Die I ('32) 3.25 3.75
188 A44 12c gray, small "c" ('22) .25 .30
189 A44 12c gray, "c" larger & thinner ('34) .50 *6.50*
190 A44 12c rose red .35 2.00
191 A44 15c dk blue ('28) .60 .50
192 A44 20c dull vio .45 .55
193 A44 20c dk blue ('34) 7.50 .75
a. Die I ('27) 8.50 .30

194 A44 25c black & red, *yel* .25 .15
a. Die I ('32) 2.25 *17.00*

Chalky Paper

195 A44 50c dull vio & blk 6.00 2.75
196 A44 1r blk, *emerald* 1.00 .20
a. Die I ('32) 6.50 *14.00*
197 A44 2r50c blk & red, *bl* 12.00 5.00
198 A44 5r green & red, *yel* 18.00 *47.50*
199 A44 10r green & red, *emer* ('28) 40.00 *80.00*
Nos. 179-199 (21) 93.25 *153.65*

A45

1924

200 A45 50r lilac & green 750.00 *1,350.*

Nos. 166, 173, 177 Surcharged

10 Cents

1925

201 A42 3c on 4c green 1.00 1.50
202 A42 10c on 12c rose red .25 .70
203 A42 15c on 20c ultra .25 .70
Nos. 201-203 (3) 1.50 2.90

Silver Jubilee Issue
Common Design Type

1935, May 6 Engr. ***Perf. 13½x14***

204 CD301 5c gray black & ultra .25 .15
205 CD301 12c indigo & green .60 .60
206 CD301 20c blue & brown 2.25 1.75
207 CD301 1r brt vio & indigo 22.50 22.50
Nos. 204-207 (4) 25.60 25.00

Coronation Issue
Common Design Type
Perf. 13½x14

1937, May 12 Wmk. 4

208 CD302 5c dark purple .15 .15
209 CD302 12c carmine .15 .15
210 CD302 20c bright ultra .25 .25
Nos. 208-210 (3) .55 .55

King George VI — A46

1938-43 Typo. ***Perf. 14***

211 A46 2c gray .15 .15
a. Perf. 15x14 ('43) .50 .15
212 A46 3c rose vio & car 1.00 .40
213 A46 4c green 1.25 .40
214 A46 5c violet 2.25 .25
a. Perf. 15x14 ('43) 14.00 .15
215 A46 10c carmine 1.25 .15
a. Perf. 15x14 ('43) 12.00 .50
216 A46 12c salmon pink .50 .15
a. Perf. 15x14 ('43) 25.00 .50
217 A46 20c blue .50 .15
218 A46 25c maroon 1.50 .15
219 A46 1r brown black 5.00 .40
220 A46 2.50r pale violet 11.00 3.50
221 A46 5r olive green 13.00 10.00
222 A46 10r rose violet 5.75 8.00
Nos. 211-222 (12) 43.15 23.70

Catalogue values for unused stamps in this section, from this point to the end of the section, are for Never Hinged items.

Peace Issue
Common Design Type
Perf. 13½x14

1946, Nov. 20 Engr. Wmk. 4

223 CD303 5c lilac .15 .15
224 CD303 20c deep blue .15 .15
Set value .25 .25

"Post Office" Stamp of 1847 — A47

1948, Mar. 22 ***Perf. 11½***

225 A47 5c red vio & orange .15 .15
226 A47 12c green & orange .15 .15
227 A47 20c blue & dp blue .16 .16
228 A47 1r lt red brn & dp blue .60 .60
Nos. 225-228 (4) 1.06 1.06

Cent. of the 1st Mauritius postage stamps.

Silver Wedding Issue
Common Design Types

1948, Oct. 25 Photo. ***Perf. 14x14½***

229 CD304 5c violet .15 .15

Perf. 11½x11

Engraved; Name Typographed

230 CD305 10r lilac rose 9.00 15.50

UPU Issue
Common Design Types
Engr.; Name Typo. on 20c, 35c
Perf. 13½, 11x11½

1949, Oct. 10 Wmk. 4

231 CD306 12c rose carmine .38 .38
232 CD307 20c indigo .42 .42
233 CD308 35c rose violet .50 .50
234 CD309 1r sepia .85 .75
Nos. 231-234 (4) 2.15 2.05

Sugar Factory — A48

Aloe Plant — A49

Designs: 2c, Grand Port. 4c, Tamarind Falls. 5c, Rempart Mountain. 10c, Transporting cane. 12c, Map and dodo. 20c, "Paul et Virginie." 25c, Statue of Mahe La Bourdonnais. 35c, Government House. 50c, Pieter Both Mountain. 1r, Sambar. 2.50r, Port Louis. 5r, Beach scene. 10r, Arms.

Perf. 13½x14½, 14½x13½

1950, July 1 Photo.

235 A48 1c red violet .15 .15
236 A48 2c cerise .15 .15
237 A49 3c yel green .15 .15
238 A49 4c green .15 .15
239 A48 5c greenish blue .15 .15
240 A48 10c red .22 .15
241 A48 12c olive green .15 .15
242 A49 20c brt ultra .22 .18
243 A49 25c vio brown .45 .35
244 A48 35c rose violet .40 .25
245 A49 50c emerald .65 .45
246 A48 1r sepia 1.90 1.25
247 A48 2.50r orange 3.25 2.25
248 A48 5r red brown 5.00 4.00
249 A48 10r gray blue 17.50 7.50
Nos. 235-249 (15) 30.49 17.28

Coronation Issue
Common Design Type

1953, June 2 Engr. ***Perf. 13½x13***

250 CD312 10c dk green & black .25 .18

Sugar Factory — A50

Tamarind Falls — A51

Designs: 2c, Grand Port. 3c, Aloe plant. 5c, Rempart Mountain. 15c, Museum, Mahebourg. 20c, Statue of Mahe La Bourdonnais. 25c, "Paul et Virginie." 35c, Government House. 50c, Pieter Both Mountain. 60c, Map and dodo. 1r, Sambar. 2.50r, Port Louis. 5r, Beach scene. 10r, Arms.

Perf. 13½x14½, 14½x13½

1953-54 Photo. Wmk. 4

251 A50 2c rose car ('54) .15 .15
252 A51 3c yel green ('54) .15 .15
253 A50 4c red violet .15 .15
254 A50 5c grnsh blue ('54) .15 .15
255 A51 10c dk green .18 .15
256 A50 15c scarlet .18 .15
257 A51 20c violet brown .25 .15
a. Imperf., pair
258 A51 25c brt ultra .40 .15
259 A50 35c rose vio ('54) .40 .15
260 A51 50c emerald .70 .20
261 A50 60c gray grn ('54) 1.75 .50
262 A50 1r sepia 1.00 .40
a. Imperf., pair
263 A50 2.50r orange ('54) 4.00 2.00
264 A50 5r red brn ('54) 6.50 2.75
265 A50 10r gray blue ('54) 10.00 3.75
Nos. 251-265 (15) 25.96 10.95

See Nos. 273-275.

King George III and Queen Elizabeth II — A52

Perf. 13½

1961, Jan. 11 Wmk. 314 Litho.

266 A52 10c dk red & dk brown .15 .15
267 A52 20c lt blue & dk blue .18 .18
268 A52 35c org yel & brown .35 .35
269 A52 1r yel green & dk brn .75 .75
Nos. 266-269 (4) 1.43 1.43

Sesquicentenary of postal service under British administration.

Freedom from Hunger Issue
Common Design Type

1963, June 4 Photo. ***Perf. 14x14½***

270 CD314 60c lilac .40 .40

Red Cross Centenary Issue
Common Design Type

1963, Sept. 2 Litho. ***Perf. 13***

271 CD315 10c black & red .15 .15
272 CD315 60c ultra & red .50 .50

Types of 1953-54
Perf. 14½x13½, 13½x14½

1963-64 Photo. Wmk. 314

273 A51 10c dark green ('64) .15 .15
274 A50 60c gray green ('64) .65 .40
275 A50 2.50r orange 2.00 2.00
Nos. 273-275 (3) 2.80 2.55

Gray White-Eye A53

Birds of Mauritius: 3c, Rodriguez fody. 4c, Olive white-eye. 5c, Mauritius paradise flycatcher. 10c, Mauritius fody. 15c, Rose-ringed parakeet. 20c, Cuckoo shrike. 25c, Mauritian kestrel. 35c, Pink pigeon. 50c, Mauritius olivaceous bulbul. 60c, Mauritius blue pigeon. 1r, Dodo. 2.50r, Rodriguez solitaire. 5r, Van den Broeck's red rail. 10r, Broad-billed Mauritian parrot.

Perf. 14½

1965, Mar. 16 Photo. Wmk. 314
Birds in Natural Colors

276 A53 2c brt yel & brn .15 .15
a. Gray (leg, etc.) omitted 50.00
277 A53 3c brn & dk brn .15 .15
a. Black (eye, beak) omitted 45.00
278 A53 4c dl rose lil & blk .15 .15
a. Rose lilac omitted 30.00
279 A53 5c gray & ultra 1.25 .15
a. Wmkd. sideways ('66) .15 .15
280 A53 10c dl grn & dk brn .15 .15
281 A53 15c lt gray & dk brn 1.10 .15
a. Carmine (beak) omitted 45.00
282 A53 20c pale yel & dk brown 1.10 .15
283 A53 25c gray & brown 1.75 .15
284 A53 35c vio bl & blk 1.50 .15
a. Wmkd. sideways ('67) .30 .30
285 A53 50c pale yel & blk .40 .15
286 A53 60c pale cit & brn .20 .15
287 A53 1r lt yel grn & blk 1.75 .20
a. Pale gray (ground) omitted 80.00
b. Pale orange omitted 80.00
288 A53 2.50r pale grn & brn 3.50 5.00
289 A53 5r pale blue & blk 11.00 5.50
290 A53 10r pale grn & ultra 20.00 9.00
Nos. 276-290 (15) 44.15 21.35

On No. 278 the background was printed in two colors. The rose lilac tint is omitted on No. 278a.
See #327-332. For overprints see #306-320.

ITU Issue
Common Design Type
Perf. 11x11½

1965, May 17 Litho. Wmk. 314

291 CD317 10c dp org & apple grn .15 .15
292 CD317 60c yellow & violet .45 .35

Intl. Cooperation Year Issue
Common Design Type

1965, Oct. 25 ***Perf. 14½***

293 CD318 10c lt green & claret .15 .15
294 CD318 60c lt violet & green .35 .35
Set value .43 .43

Churchill Memorial Issue
Common Design Type

1966, Jan. 24 Photo. ***Perf. 14***
Design in Black, Gold and Carmine Rose

295 CD319 2c brt blue .15 .15
296 CD319 10c green .15 .15
297 CD319 60c brown .50 .50
298 CD319 1r violet 1.10 1.10
Nos. 295-298 (4) 1.90 1.90

UNESCO Anniversary Issue
Common Design Type

1966, Dec. 1 Litho. ***Perf. 14***

299 CD323 5c "Education" .15 .15
300 CD323 10c "Science" .20 .15
301 CD323 60c "Culture" .75 .60
Nos. 299-301 (3) 1.10 .90

Red-Tailed Tropic Bird A54

Birds of Mauritius: 10c, Rodriguez bush warbler. 60c, Newton's parakeet. 1r, Mauritius swiftlet.

1967, Sept. 1 Photo. ***Perf. 14½***

302 A54 2c lt ultra & multi .15 .15
303 A54 10c emerald & multi .15 .15
304 A54 60c salmon & multi .40 .40
305 A54 1r yellow & multi .75 .75
Nos. 302-305 (4) 1.45 1.45

Attainment of self-government, Sept. 1, 1967.

Bird Issue of 1965-67 and Type Overprinted: "SELF GOVERNMENT 1967"

1967, Dec. 1 Photo. Wmk. 314

306 A53 2c multicolored .15 .15
307 A53 3c multicolored .15 .15
308 A53 4c multicolored .15 .15
309 A53 5c multicolored .15 .15
310 A53 10c multicolored .15 .15
311 A53 15c multicolored .15 .15
312 A53 20c multicolored .15 .15
313 A53 25c multicolored .15 .15
314 A53 35c multicolored .15 .15
315 A53 50c multicolored .25 .20
316 A53 60c multicolored .30 .20
317 A53 1r multicolored .45 .35
318 A53 2.50r multicolored 1.25 1.25
319 A53 5r multicolored 2.50 2.50
320 A53 10r multicolored 5.00 5.00
Nos. 306-320 (15) 11.10 10.05

5c, 10c, 35c watermarked sideways.

Independent State

Flag of Mauritius A55

Designs: 3c, 20c, 1r, Dodo emerging from egg and coat of arms.

Perf. 13½x13

1968, Mar. 12 Litho. Unwmk.

321 A55 2c brt violet & multi .15 .15
322 A55 3c red brown & multi .15 .15
323 A55 15c brown & multi .15 .15
324 A55 20c multicolored .15 .15
325 A55 60c dk green & multi .40 .40
326 A55 1r brt violet & multi .65 .65
Set value 1.35 1.35

Independence of Mauritius.

Bird Type of 1965 in Changed Background Colors

Perf. 14½

1968, July 12 Photo. Wmk. 314

Birds in Natural Colors

327	A53	2c	lemon & brown	.15	.15
328	A53	3c	ultra & dk brown	.15	.15
329	A53	15c	tan & dk brown	.30	.15
330	A53	20c	dull yel & dk brn	.42	.20
331	A53	60c	pink & black	1.10	.50
332	A53	1r	rose lilac & black	1.90	.90
			Nos. 327-332 (6)	4.02	2.05

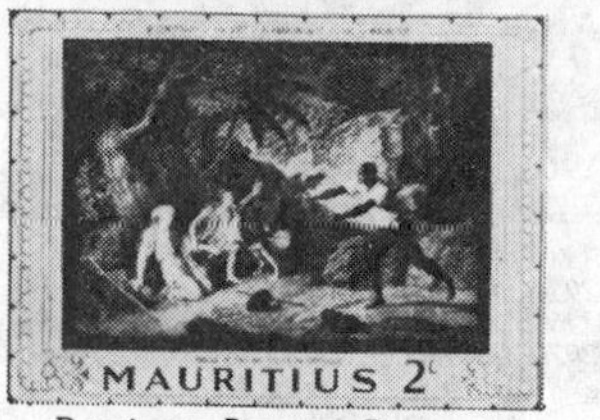

Domingue Rescuing Paul and Virginie — A56

Designs: 15c, Paul and Virginie crossing river, vert. 50c, La Bourdonnais visiting Madame de la Tour. 60c, Paul and Virginie, vert. 1r, Departure of Virginie for Europe. 2.50r, Bernardin de St. Pierre, vert. The designs are from old prints illustrating "Paul et Virginie."

Perf. 13½

1968, Dec. 2 Unwmk. Litho.

333	A56	2c	multicolored	.15	.15
334	A56	15c	multicolored	.15	.15
335	A56	50c	multicolored	.25	.25
336	A56	60c	multicolored	.30	.30
337	A56	1r	multicolored	.50	.50
338	A56	2.50r	multicolored	1.35	1.35
			Nos. 333-338 (6)	2.70	2.70

Bicent. of the visit of Bernardin de St. Pierre (1737-1814), author of "Paul et Virginie."

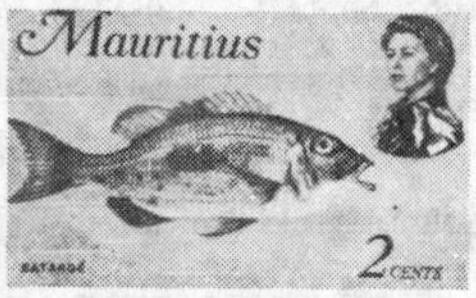

Batardé Fish A57

Marine Life: 3c, Red reef crab. 4c, Episcopal miter shell. 5c, Bourse fish. 10c, Starfish. 15c, Sea urchin. 20c, Fiddler crab. 25c, Spiny shrimp. 30c, Single and double harp shells. 35c, Argonaut shell. 40c, Nudibranch (sea-slug). 50c, Violet and orange spider shells. 60c, Blue marlin. 75c, Conus clytospira. 1r, Dorad. 2.50r, Spiny lobster. 5r, Sacré chien rouge fish. 10r, Moonfish.

Wmk. 314 Sideways (#339-344, 351-352), others Upright

1969, Mar. 12 Photo. *Perf. 14*

339	A57	2c	pink & multi	.15	.15
340	A57	3c	yellow & multi	.15	.15
341	A57	4c	multicolored	.15	.15
342	A57	5c	lt blue & multi	.15	.15
343	A57	10c	salmon & multi	.15	.15
344	A57	15c	pale blue & multi	.15	.15
345	A57	20c	pale gray & multi	.15	.15
346	A57	25c	multicolored	.15	.15
347	A57	30c	multicolored	.18	.18
348	A57	35c	multicolored	.20	.20
349	A57	40c	tan & multi	.25	.22
350	A57	50c	lt vio & multi	.30	.28
351	A57	60c	ultra & multi	.38	.30
352	A57	75c	lemon & multi	.48	.38
353	A57	1r	cream & multi	.55	.50
354	A57	2.50r	lt vio & multi	2.50	2.50
355	A57	5r	multicolored	4.50	4.50
356	A57	10r	multicolored	8.00	8.00
			Nos. 339-356 (18)	18.54	18.26

For overprints see Nos. 368-369.

Wmk. 314 Upright (#339a-344a, 351a-352a), others Sideways

1972-74

339a	A57	2c	multi ('74)	.15	.15
340a	A57	3c	multi ('74)	.15	.15
341a	A57	4c	multi ('74)	.15	.15
342a	A57	5c	multi ('74)	.15	.15
343a	A57	10c	multicolored	.15	.15
344a	A57	15c	multi ('74)	.15	.15
345a	A57	20c	multicolored	.15	.15
346a	A57	25c	multi ('73)	.15	.15
347a	A57	30c	multicolored	.22	.18
348a	A57	35c	multicolored	.28	.22
349a	A57	40c	multicolored	.30	.30
350a	A57	50c	multi ('73)	.30	.30
351a	A57	60c	multi ('74)	.38	.32
352a	A57	75c	multicolored	.52	.42
353a	A57	1r	multicolored	.60	.52
354a	A57	2.50r	multi ('73)	1.50	1.40
355a	A57	5r	multi ('73)	3.00	2.50
356a	A57	10r	multicolored	5.75	5.00
			Nos. 339a-356a (18)	14.05	12.36

1975-77 Wmk. 373

339b	A57	2c	multi ('77)	.15	.15
340b	A57	3c	multi ('77)	.15	.15
341b	A57	4c	multi ('77)	.15	.15
342b	A57	5c	multicolored	.15	.15
344b	A57	15c	multicolored	.18	.15
345b	A57	20c	multi ('76)	.20	.18
346b	A57	25c	multicolored	.26	.20
347b	A57	30c	multicolored	.30	.26
348b	A57	35c	multi ('76)	.30	.26
349b	A57	40c	multi ('76)	.32	.30
350b	A57	50c	multi ('76)	.40	.32
351b	A57	60c	multi ('77)	.52	.42
352b	A57	75c	multi ('77)	.52	.48
353b	A57	1r	multi ('76)	.80	.75
354b	A57	2.50r	multi ('77)	3.25	2.00
355b	A57	5r	multicolored	5.50	4.25
356b	A57	10r	multicolored	13.00	8.75
			Nos. 339b-356b (17)	26.15	18.92

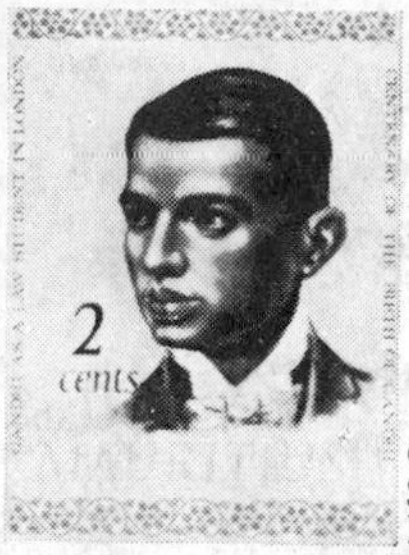

Gandhi as Law Student in London — A58

Portraits of Gandhi: 15c, as stretcher bearer during Zulu rebellion. 50c, as member of non-violent movement in South Africa (Satyagrahi). 60c, wearing Indian garment at No. 10 Downing Street, London. 1r, wearing turban in Mauritius, 1901. 2.50r, as old man.

1969, July 1 Litho. *Perf. 13½*

357	A58	2c	dull org & multi	.15	.15
358	A58	15c	brt blue & multi	.15	.15
359	A58	50c	multicolored	.18	.18
360	A58	60c	brick red & multi	.25	.25
361	A58	1r	multicolored	.50	.50
362	A58	2.50r	olive & multi	1.25	1.25
a.			Souvenir sheet of 6, #357-362	5.25	5.25
			Nos. 357-362 (6)	2.48	2.48

Mohandas K. Gandhi (1869-1948), leader in India's struggle for independence.

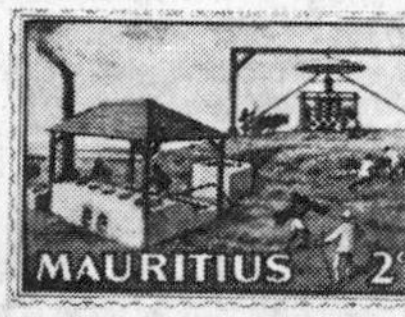

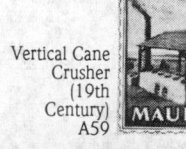

Vertical Cane Crusher (19th Century) A59

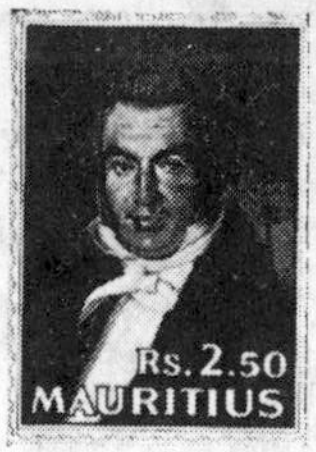

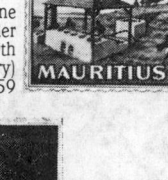

Dr. Charles Telfair (1778-1833) — A60

Designs: 15c, The Frangourinier, 18th century cane crusher. 60c, Beau Rivage sugar factory, 1867, painting by Numa Desjardin. 1r, Mon Desert-Alma sugar factory, 1969.

Perf. 11x11½, 11½x11

1969, Dec. 22 Photo. Wmk. 314

363	A59	2c	multicolored	.15	.15
364	A59	15c	multicolored	.15	.15
365	A59	60c	multicolored	.25	.25
366	A59	1r	multicolored	.38	.38
367	A60	2.50r	multicolored	.90	.90
a.			Souvenir sheet of 5	2.00	2.00
			Nos. 363-367 (5)	1.83	1.83

150th anniv. of Telfair's improvements of the sugar industry.

No. 367a contains one each of Nos. 363-367. The 2.50r in the sheet is imperf., the others are perf. 11x11½.

Nos. 351 and 353 Overprinted: "EXPO '70 / OSAKA"

1970, Apr. 7 *Perf. 14*

368	A57	60c	ultra & multi	.25	.25
369	A57	1r	cream & multi	.38	.38

EXPO '70 Intl. Exhib., Osaka, Japan, Mar. 15-Sept. 13.

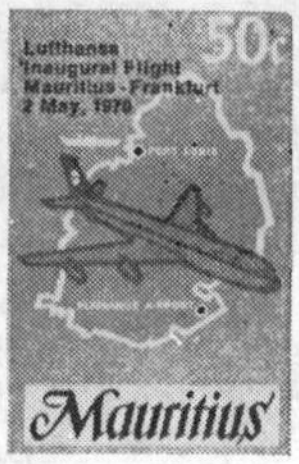

Lufthansa Plane over Mauritius — A61

Design: 25c, Brabant Hotel, Morne Beach, horiz.

1970, May 2 Litho. *Perf. 14*

370	A61	25c	multicolored	.15	.15
371	A61	50c	multicolored	.25	.25

Lufthansa's inaugural flight from Mauritius to Frankfurt, Germany, May 2, 1970.

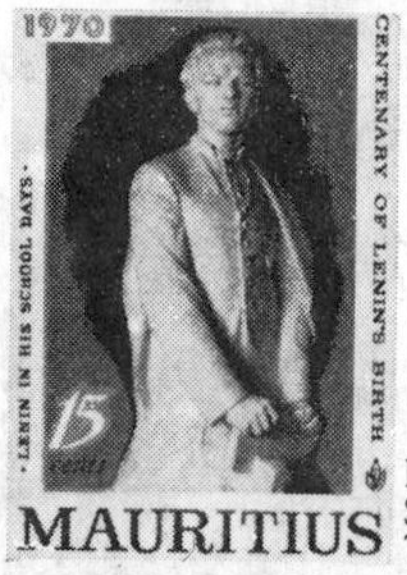

Lenin as Student, by V. Tsigal — A62

Design: 75c, Bust of Lenin.

1970, May 15 Photo. *Perf. 12x11½*

372	A62	15c	dk slate blue & sil	.15	.15
373	A62	75c	dk brown & gold	.45	.45
			Set value	.50	.50

Birth cent. of Lenin (1870-1924), Russian communist leader.

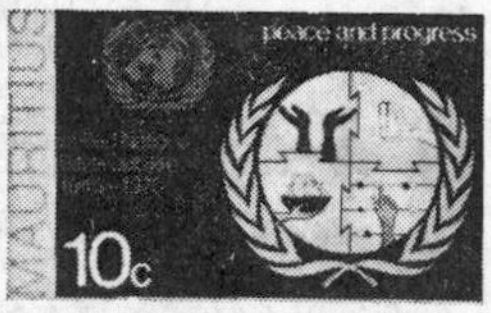

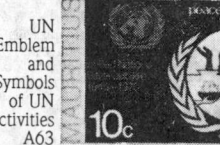

UN Emblem and Symbols of UN Activities A63

1970, Oct. 24 Litho. *Perf. 14*

374	A63	10c	blue black & multi	.15	.15
375	A63	60c	blue black & multi	.28	.28
			Set value	.34	.34

25th anniversary of the United Nations.

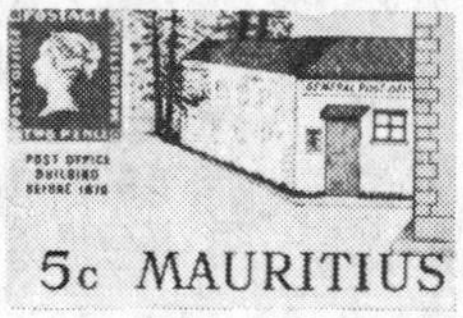

Mauritius No. 2, and Post Office before 1870 A64

Designs: 15c, General Post Office Building, 1870-1970. 50c, Mauritius mail coach, 1870. 75c, Port Louis harbor, 1970. 2.50r, Arrival of Pierre André de Suffren de St. Tropez in Port Louis harbor, 1783.

1970, Oct. 15 Litho. *Perf. 14*

376	A64	5c	multicolored	.15	.15
377	A64	15c	multicolored	.15	.15
378	A64	50c	multicolored	.20	.20
379	A64	75c	multicolored	.30	.30
380	A64	2.50r	multicolored	1.00	1.00
a.			Souvenir sheet of 5	2.00	2.00
			Nos. 376-380 (5)	1.80	1.80

Centenary of the General Post Office and to show the improvements of Port Louis harbor. No. 380a contains one each of Nos. 376-380 and a label showing map of Mauritius.

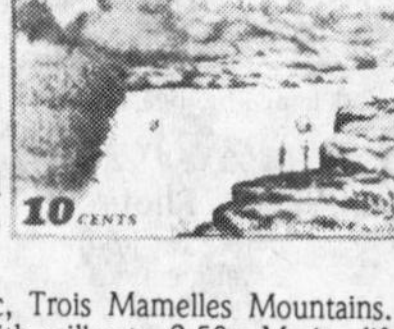

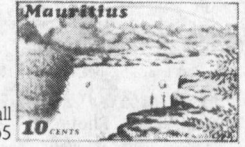

Waterfall A65

Designs: 15c, Trois Mamelles Mountains. 60c, Beach scene with sailboats. 2.50r, Marine life.

1971, Apr. 12 Litho. *Perf. 14*

381	A65	10c	multicolored	.15	.15
382	A65	15c	multicolored	.15	.15
383	A65	60c	multicolored	.25	.25
384	A65	2.50r	multicolored	1.25	1.25
			Nos. 381-384 (4)	1.80	1.80

Tourist publicity. Each stamp has a different 6-line message printed in black on back.

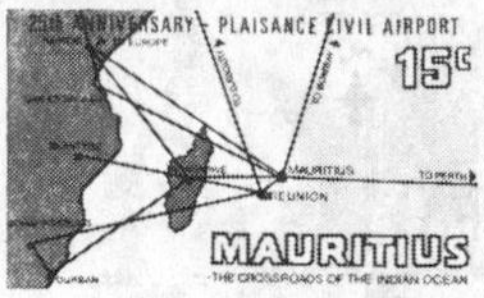

Mauritius at Crossroads of Indian Ocean A66

Designs: 60c, Plane at Plaisance Airport. 1r, Stewardesses on plane ramp. 2.50r, Roland Garros' airplane, Choisy Airfield, 1937.

1971, Oct. 23 Wmk. 314 *Perf. 14½*

385	A66	15c	multicolored	.15	.15
386	A66	60c	multicolored	.25	.25
387	A66	1r	multicolored	.35	.35
388	A66	2.50r	multicolored	1.25	1.25
			Nos. 385-388 (4)	2.00	2.00

25th anniversary of Plaisance Civil Airport.

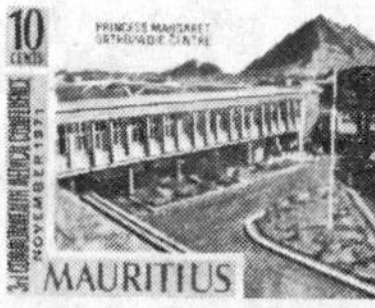

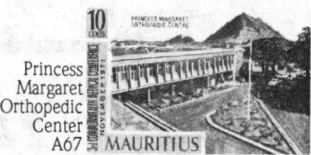

Princess Margaret Orthopedic Center A67

Design: 75c, Operating room, National Hospital.

1971, Nov. 2 *Perf. 14x14½*

389	A67	10c	multicolored	.15	.15
390	A67	75c	multicolored	.30	.30
			Set value	.35	.35

3rd Commonwealth Medical Conf., Nov. 1971.

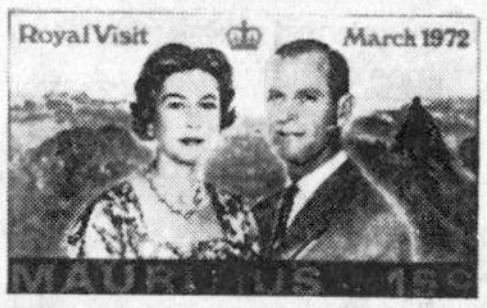

Elizabeth II and Prince Philip A68

Design: 2.50r, Queen Elizabeth II, vert.

1972, Mar. Litho. *Perf. 14½*

391	A68	15c	brown & multi	.15	.15
392	A68	2.50r	ultra & multi	1.75	1.75

Visit of Elizabeth II and Prince Philip.

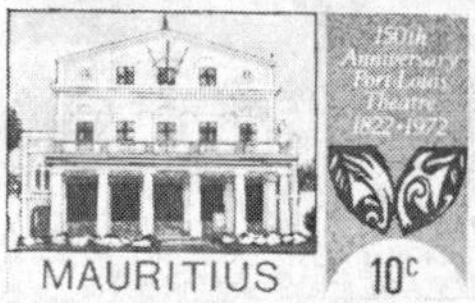

Port Louis Theater and Masks A69

Design: 1r, Interior view and masks of Comedy and Tragedy.

1972, June 26

393	A69	10c	brown & multi	.15	.15
394	A69	1r	multicolored	.30	.30
			Set value	.35	.35

Sesquicentennial of Port Louis Theater.

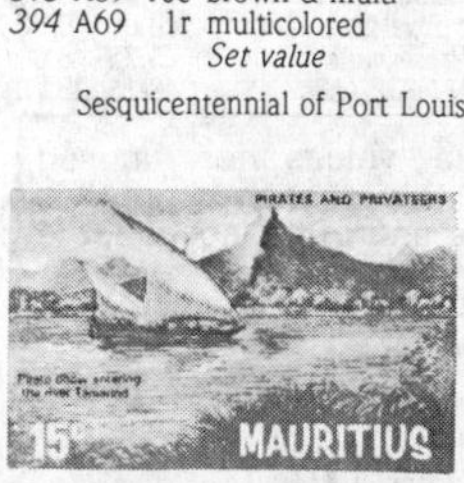

Pirate Dhow Entering Tamarind River A70

Perf. 14x14½, 14½x14

1972, Nov. 17 Litho.

395	A70	15c	shown	.15	.15
396	A70	60c	Treasure chest, vert.	.20	.20
397	A70	1r	Lememe and brig Hirondelle, vert.	.40	.40
398	A70	2.50r	Robert Surcouf	1.75	1.75
			Nos. 395-398 (4)	2.50	2.50

Pirates and privateers.

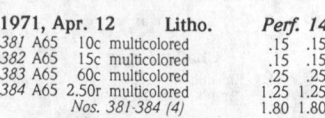

Mauritius University A71 15c

Designs: 60c, Tea development plant. 1r, Bank of Mauritius.

1973, Apr. 10   **Perf. 14¹/₂**
399 A71 15c green & multi   .15   .15
400 A71 60c yellow & multi   .20   .20
401 A71 1r red & multi   .30   .30
         Set value   .55   .55
5th anniversary of independence.

OCAM Emblem A72 10c

Design: 2.50r, Handshake, map of Africa; inscriptions in French, vert.

1973, Apr. 25
402 A72 10c multicolored   .15   .15
403 A72 2.50r lt blue & multi   .90   .90

Conference of the Organisation Commune Africaine, Malgache et Mauricienne (OCAM), Mauritius, Apr. 25-May 6.

WHO Emblem A73

Perf. 14¹/₂x14
1973, Nov. 20   **Wmk. 314**
404 A73 1r green & multi   .35   .35
25th anniv. of WHO.

Meteorological Station, Vacoas — A74

1973, Nov. 27
405 A74 75c multicolored   .25   .25
Cent. of intl. meteorological cooperation.

Surcouf and Capture of the "Kent" A75

1974, Mar. 21 Litho.   Perf. 14¹/₂x14
406 A75 60c sepia & multi   .38   .38
Bicentenary of the birth of Robert Surcouf (1773-1827), French privateer.

Philibert Commerson and Bougainvillaea — A76

1974, Apr. 18   **Perf. 14**
407 A76 2.50r slate green & multi   .90   .90
Philibert Commerson (1727-1773), French physician and naturalist.

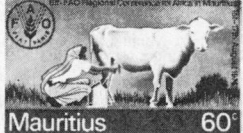

FAO Emblem, Woman Milking Cow A77

1974, Oct. 23   **Perf. 14¹/₂**
408 A77 60c multicolored   .25   .25
8th FAO Regional Conference, Aug. 1-17.

Mail Train and UPU Emblem A78

Design: 1r, New General Post Office Building, Port Louis, and UPU emblem.

1974, Dec. 4   Litho.   Perf. 14¹/₂
409 A78 15c multicolored   .15   .15
410 A78 1r multicolored   .40   .40
         Set value   .46   .46
Centenary of Universal Postal Union.

Cottage Life, by F. Leroy A79

Paintings: 60c, Milk Seller, by A. Richard, vert. 1r, Entrance to Port Louis Market, by Thuillier. 2.50r, Washerwomen, by Max Boullé, vert.

1975, Mar. 6   **Wmk. 373**
411 A79 15c multicolored   .15   .15
412 A79 60c multicolored   .25   .25
413 A79 1r multicolored   .40   .40
414 A79 2.50r multicolored   1.00 1.00
         Nos. 411-414 (4)   1.80 1.80
Artistic views of life on Mauritius.

Mace, Map and Arms of Mauritius, Association Emblem — A80

1975, Nov. 21 Litho.   Wmk. 373
415 A80 75c multicolored   .25   .25
Conference of the French-speaking Parliamentary Association.

Woman and Aladdin's Lamp A81

1975, Dec. 5   **Perf. 14¹/₂**
416 A81 2.50r multicolored   .90   .90
International Women's Year.

Parched Land A82

Drought in Africa: 60c, Map of Africa, carcass and desert, vert.

1976, Feb. 26 Litho.   Wmk. 373
417 A82 50c vermilion & multi   .18   .18
418 A82 60c blue & multi   .24   .24

Pierre Loti, 1953-1970 A83

Mail Carriers: 15c, Secunder, 1907. 50c, Hindoostan, 1842. 60c, St. Geran, 1740. 2.50r, Maen, 1638.

1976, July 2   Litho.   Wmk. 373
419 A83 10c multicolored   .15   .15
420 A83 15c multicolored   .15   .15
421 A83 50c multicolored   .25   .25
422 A83 60c multicolored   .30   .30
423 A83 2.50r multicolored   1.50 1.50
a. Souvenir sheet of 5, #419-423   2.25 2.25
         Nos. 419-423 (5)   2.35 2.35

Flame, and "Hindi Carried Across the Sea" A84

Designs: 75c, like 10c. 1.20r, Flame and tablet with Hindi inscription.

1976, Aug. 28   **Perf. 14¹/₂x14**
424 A84 10c multicolored   .15   .15
425 A84 75c lt blue & multi   .20   .20
426 A84 1.20r multicolored   .35   .35
         Set value   .60   .60
2nd World Hindi Convention.

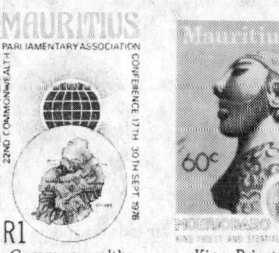

Commonwealth Emblem, Map of Mauritius — A85

King Priest and Steatite Pectoral — A86

Design: 2.50r, Commonwealth emblem twice.

1976, Sept. 22 Litho.   Perf. 14x14¹/₂
427 A85 1r multicolored   .30   .30
428 A85 2.50r multicolored   .75   .75
22nd Commonwealth Parliamentary Association Conference, Mauritius, Sept. 17-30.

1976, Dec. 15 Wmk. 373   Perf. 14
Designs: 1r, House with well, and goblet. 2.50r, Terracotta goddess and necklace.
429 A86 60c multicolored   .15   .15
430 A86 1r multicolored   .30   .30
431 A86 2.50r multicolored   .75   .75
         Nos. 429-431 (3)   1.20 1.20
UNESCO campaign to save Mohenjo-Daro excavations.

Sega Dance A87

1977, Jan. 20   Litho.   Perf. 13
432 A87 1r multicolored   .25   .25
2nd World Black and African Festival, Lagos, Nigeria, Jan. 15-Feb. 12.

Elizabeth II at Mauritius Legislative Assembly — A88

Designs: 75c, Queen holding scepter and orb. 5r, Presentation of scepter and orb.

1977, Feb. 7   **Perf. 14¹/₂x14**
433 A88 50c multicolored   .15   .15
434 A88 75c multicolored   .18   .18
435 A88 5r multicolored   1.10 1.10
         Nos. 433-435 (3)   1.43 1.43
25th anniv. of the reign of Elizabeth II.

Hugonia Tomentosa A89

Flowers: 1r, Oehna mauritiana, vert. 1.50r, Dombeya acuntangula. 5r, Trochetia blackburniana, vert.

1977, Sept. 22   Wmk. 373   Perf. 14
436 A89 20c multicolored   .15   .15
437 A89 1r multicolored   .32   .32
438 A89 1.50r multicolored   .50   .50
439 A89 5r multicolored   1.50 1.50
a. Souvenir sheet of 4, #436-439   2.50 2.50
         Nos. 436-439 (4)   2.47 2.47

Twin Otter of Air Mauritius A90

Designs: 50c, Air Mauritius emblem (red-tailed tropic bird) and Twin Otter. 75c, Piper Navajo and Boeing 747. 5r, Air Mauritius Boeing 707 in flight.

1977, Oct. 31   Litho.   Perf. 14¹/₂
440 A90 25c multicolored   .15   .15
441 A90 50c multicolored   .15   .15
442 A90 75c multicolored   .18   .18
443 A90 5r multicolored   1.25 1.25
a. Souvenir sheet of 4, #440-443   1.90 1.90
         Nos. 440-443 (4)   1.73 1.73
Air Mauritius International Inaugural Flight.

Mauritius, Portuguese Map, 1519 — A91

Dutch Occupation, 1638-1710 — A92

Designs: 20c, Mauritius, map by Van Keulen, c. 1700. 25c, 1st settlement of Rodrigues, 1708. 35c, Proclamation, arrival of French settlers, 1715. 50c, Construction of Port Louis, c. 1736. 60c, Pierre Poivre and nutmeg tree. 70c, Map by Belin, 1763. 75c, First coin minted in Mauritius, 1810. 90c, Naval battle of Grand Port, 1810. 1r, Landing of the British, Nov. 1810. 1.20r, Government House, c. 1840. 1.25r, Invitation with No. 1 and ball of Lady Gomm, 1847. 1.50r, Indian immigration in Mauritius, 1835. 2r, Champ de Mars race course, c. 1870. 3r, Place D'Armes, c. 1880. 5r, Postal card commemorating visit of Prince and Princess of Wales, 1901. 10r, Curepipe College, 1914. 15r,

Raising flag of Mauritius, 1968. 25r, Raman Osman, first Governor General and Seewoosagur Ramgoolan, first Prime Minister.

1978, Mar. 12 Wmk. 373 *Perf. 13½*

444 A91 10c multicolored .15 .15
445 A92 15c multicolored .15 .15
446 A92 20c multicolored .15 .15
447 A91 25c multicolored .15 .15
448 A91 35c multicolored .15 .15
b. Perf. 14½, "1986" .15 .15
449 A92 50c multicolored .15 .15
450 A91 60c multicolored .15 .15
451 A92 70c multicolored .15 .15
452 A91 75c multicolored .15 .15
453 A92 90c multicolored .18 .18
454 A92 1r multicolored .20 .20
455 A92 1.20r multicolored .25 .25
456 A91 1.25r multicolored .25 .25
457 A92 1.50r multicolored .30 .30
458 A92 2r multicolored .40 .40
459 A92 3r multicolored .60 .60
460 A92 5r multicolored 1.00 1.00
461 A92 10r multicolored 2.00 2.00
462 A91 15r multicolored 3.00 3.00
463 A92 25r multicolored 5.00 5.00
Nos. 444-463 (20) 14.53 14.53

Nos. 448, 452, 456, 458 reprinted inscribed 1983; Nos. 444, 447-449, 452, 454, 456, 460 reprinted inscribed 1985.

1985-89 Wmk. 384 *Perf. 14½*

446a A92 20c "1987" .15 .15
447a A91 25c "1987" .15 .15
448a A91 35c ('85) .15 .15
449a A92 50c ('85) .15 .15
452a A91 75c ('85) .15 .15
458a A92 2r "1987" .15 .15
459a A92 3r "1989" .42 .42
460a A92 5r "1989" .70 .70
463a A92 25r "1989" 3.45 3.45
Nos. 446a-463a (9) 5.47 5.47

Issue dates: 20c, 25c, 2r, Jan. 11, 1987. 3r-25r, Jan. 19, 1989.

Elizabeth II Coronation Anniv. Issue
Common Design Types
Souvenir Sheet

1978, Apr. 21 Unwmk. *Perf. 15*

464 Sheet of 6 3.25
a. CD326 3r Antelope of Bohun .55 .55
b. CD327 3r Elizabeth II .55 .55
c. CD328 3r Dodo .55 .55

No. 464 contains 2 se-tenant strips of Nos. 464a-464c, separated by horizontal gutter with commemorative and descriptive inscriptions and showing central part of coronation procession with coach.

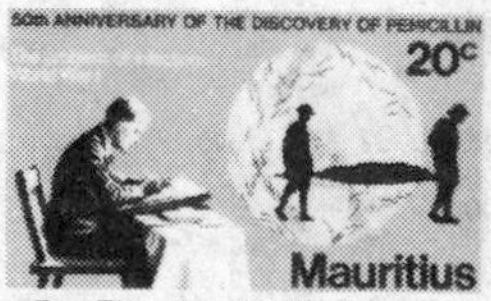

Dr. Fleming, WWI Casualty, Bacteria — A93

Designs: 1r, Microscope and 1st mold growth, 1928. 1.50r, Penicillium notatum, close-up. 5r, Alexander Fleming and nurse administering penicillin.

Perf. 13½

1978, Aug. 3 Wmk. 373 Litho.

465 A93 20c multicolored .15 .15
466 A93 1r multicolored .20 .20
467 A93 1.50r multicolored .30 .30
468 A93 5r multicolored 1.75 1.75
a. Souvenir sheet of 4, #465-468 2.75 2.75
Nos. 465-468 (4) 2.40 2.40

Discovery of penicillin by Dr. Alexander Fleming, 50th anniversary.

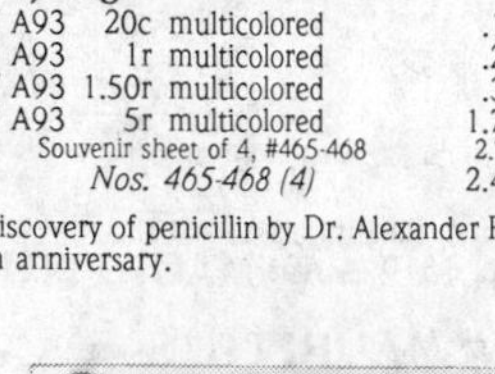

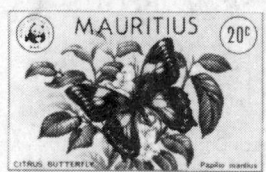

Citrus Butterfly — A94

Wildlife Protection (Wildlife Fund Emblem and): 1r, Geckos. 1.50r, Flying foxes. 5r, Mauritius kestrels.

1978, Sept. 21 *Perf. 13½x14*

469 A94 20c multicolored .20 .20
470 A94 1r multicolored .52 .52
471 A94 1.50r multicolored .80 .80
472 A94 5r multicolored 2.50 2.50
a. Souvenir sheet of 4, #469-472 5.00 5.00
Nos. 469-472 (4) 4.02 4.02

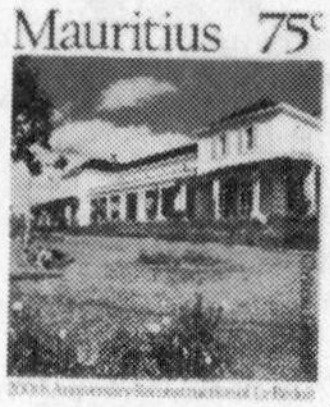

Le Reduit — A95

Designs: 15c, Ornate table. 3r, Reduit gardens.

1978, Dec. 21 *Perf. 14½x14*

473 A95 15c multicolored .15 .15
474 A95 75c multicolored .30 .30
475 A95 3r multicolored 1.00 1.00
Nos. 473-475 (3) 1.45 1.45

Reconstruction of Chateau Le Reduit, 200th anniversary.

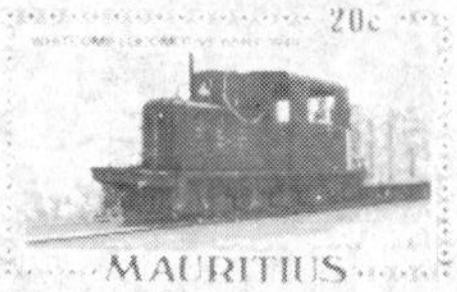

Whitcomb, 1949 A96

Locomotives: 1r, Sir William, 1922. 1.50r, Kitson, 1930. 2r, Garratt, 1927.

1979, Feb. 1 *Perf. 14½*

476 A96 20c multicolored .15 .15
477 A96 1r multicolored .40 .40
478 A96 1.50r multicolored .60 .60
479 A96 2r multicolored .80 .80
a. Souvenir sheet of 4, #476-479 2.00 2.00
Nos. 476-479 (4) 1.95 1.95

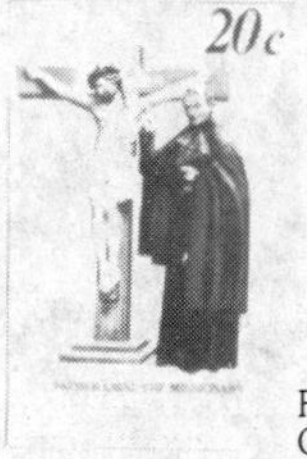

Father Laval and Crucifix — A97

Designs: 1.50r, Jacques Desire Laval. 5r, Father Laval's sarcophagus, horiz.

1979, Apr. 30 Wmk. 373 *Perf. 14*

480 A97 20c multicolored .15 .15
481 A97 1.50r multicolored .30 .30
482 A97 5r multicolored 1.00 1.00
a. Souvenir sheet of 3, #480-482 1.50 1.50
Nos. 480-482 (3) 1.45 1.45

Beatification of Father Laval (1803-1864), physician and missionary.

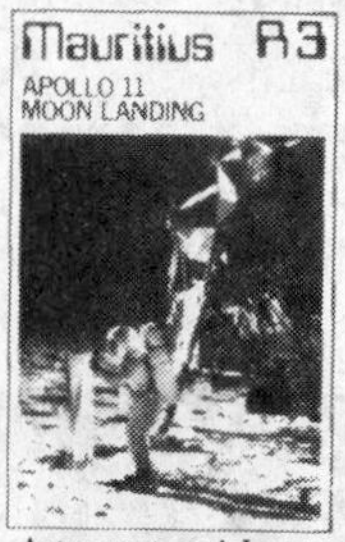

Astronaut and Lunar Module — A98

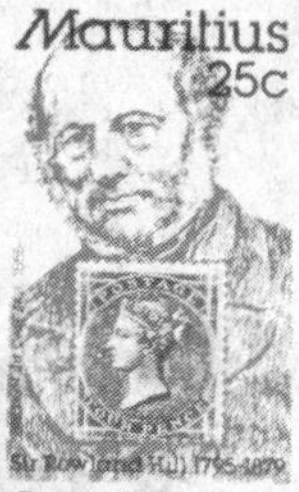

Rowland Hill and Great Britain No. 23 — A99

Designs: 20c, Neil Armstrong on moon. 5r, Astronaut walking on moon.

Imperf. x Roulette 5

1979, July 20 Litho.

Self-adhesive

483 A98 Souvenir booklet 5.50
a. Bklt. pane of 3 (20c, 5r, 3r) 2.50
b. Bklt. pane of 6 (3 each 20c, 3r) 2.75

10th anniv. of Apollo 11 moon landing. No. 483 contains 2 panes printed on peelable paper backing showing (a) map of moon and (b) details of uniform and spacecraft.

1979, Aug. 29 *Perf. 14½*

Rowland Hill and: 2r, Mauritius No. 261. 3r, Mauritius No. 2. 5r, Mauritius No. 1.

484 A99 25c multicolored .15 .15
485 A99 2r multicolored .40 .40
486 A99 5r multicolored 1.00 1.00
Nos. 484-486 (3) 1.55 1.55

Souvenir Sheet
Imperf

487 A99 3r multicolored .75 .75

Sir Rowland Hill (1795-1879), originator of penny postage. No. 487 contains one stamp.

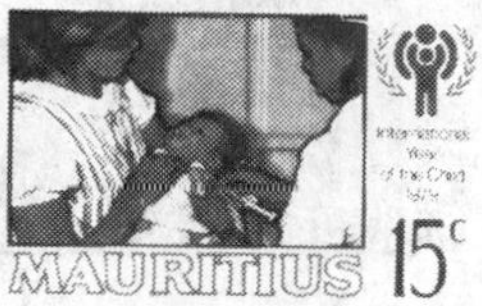

Infant Vaccination — A100

IYC Emblem and: 25c, Children playing. 1r, Coat of arms, vert. 1.50r, Children in laboratory. 3r, Teacher and student working lathe.

Wmk. 373

1979, Oct. 11 Litho. *Perf. 14*

488 A100 15c multicolored .15 .15
489 A100 25c multicolored .15 .15
490 A100 1r multicolored .20 .20
491 A100 1.50r multicolored .30 .30
492 A100 3r multicolored .60 .60
Set value 1.20 1.20

International Year of the Child.

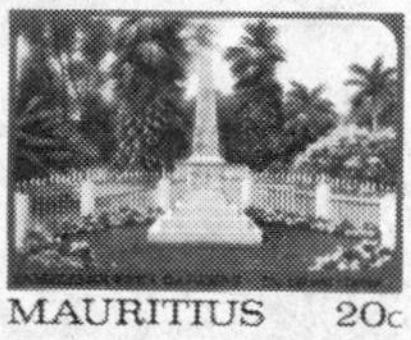

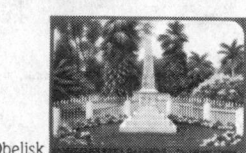

Lienard Obelisk A101

Designs: 25c, Poivre Avenue, 1r, Pandanus. 2r, Giant water lilies, 5r, Mon Plaisir.

1980, Jan. 24 *Perf. 14x14½*

493 A101 20c multicolored .15 .15
494 A101 25c multicolored .15 .15
495 A101 1r multicolored .20 .20
496 A101 2r multicolored .40 .40
497 A101 5r multicolored 1.00 1.00
a. Souvenir sheet of 5, #493-497 1.75 1.75
Nos. 493-497 (5) 1.90 1.90

Pamplemousses Botanical Gardens.

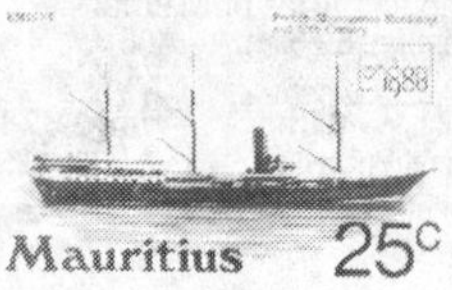

"Emirne," 19th Century, London 1980 Emblem A102

1980, May 6 Litho. *Perf. 14½*

498 A102 25c shown .15 .15
499 A102 1r Boissevain, 1930's .20 .20
500 A102 2r La Boudeuse, 18th cent. .40 .40
501 A102 5r Sea Breeze, 19th cent. 1.00 1.00
Nos. 498-501 (4) 1.75 1.75

London 80 Intl. Stamp Exhib., May 6-14.

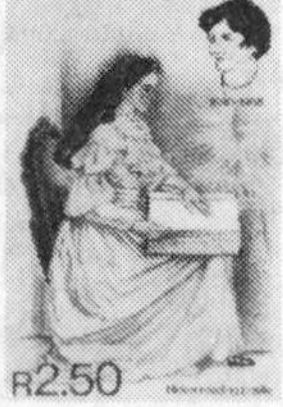

Helen Keller Reading Braille — A103

1980, June 27 Litho. *Perf. 14½*

502 A103 25c Blind men weaving baskets .15 .15
503 A103 1r Teacher and deaf girl .25 .25
504 A103 2.50r shown .50 .50
505 A103 5r Keller graduating college 1.00 1.00
Nos. 502-505 (4) 1.90 1.90

Helen Keller (1880-1968), blind and deaf writer and lecturer.

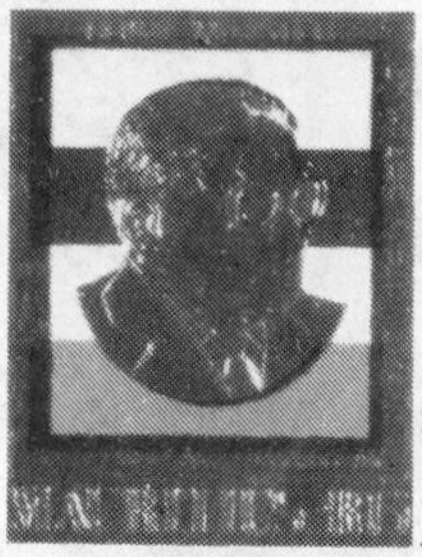

Prime Minister Seewoosagur Ramgoolan, 80th Birthday A104

Litho.; Gold Embossed

1980, Sept. 18 *Perf. 13½*

506 A104 15r multicolored 2.00 2.00

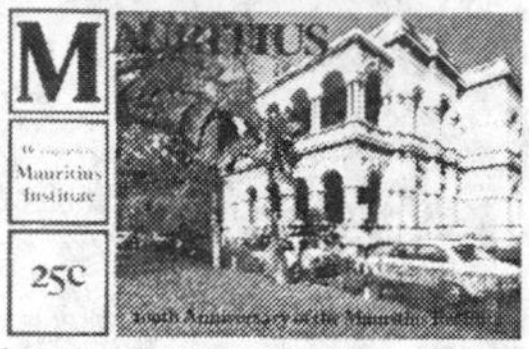

Mauritius Institute, Centenary — A105

1980, Oct. 1 Litho. *Perf. 13*

507 A105 25c shown .15 .15
508 A105 2r Rare Veda copy .40 .40
509 A105 2.50r Rare cone .50 .50
510 A105 5r Landscape, by Henri Harpignies 1.00 1.00
Nos. 507-510 (4) 2.05 2.05

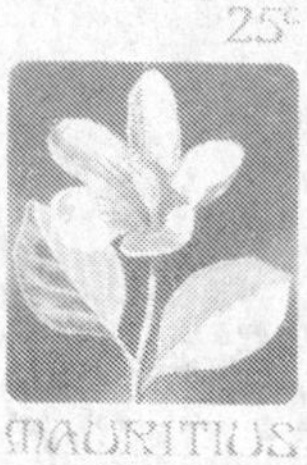

Hibiscus Liliiflorus — A106

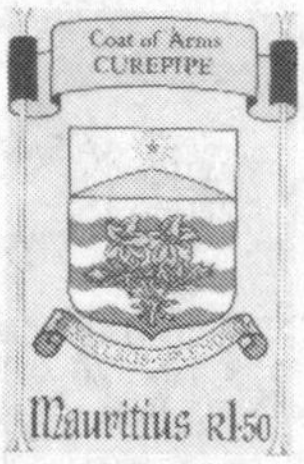

Arms of Curepipe — A107

1981, Jan. 15 Litho. *Perf. 14*

511 A106 25c shown .15 .15
512 A106 2r Erythrospermum monticolum .45 .45
513 A106 2.50r Chasalia boryana .55 .55
514 A106 5r Hibiscus columnaris 1.10 1.10
Nos. 511-514 (4) 2.25 2.25

Perf. 13½x13

1981, Apr. 10 Litho. Wmk. 373

Designs: City coats of arms.

515 A107 25c Beau-Bassin / Rose Hill .15 .15
516 A107 1.50r shown .30 .30
517 A107 2r Quatre-Bornes .40 .40
518 A107 2.50r Vacoas/Phoenix .50 .50
519 A107 5r Port Louis 1.00 1.00
a. Souv. sheet of 5, #515-519, perf. 14 2.25 2.25
Nos. 515-519 (5) 2.35 2.35

Royal Wedding Issue
Common Design Type

1981, July 22 Litho. *Perf. 14*

520 CD331 25c Bouquet .15 .15
521 CD331 2.50r Charles .50 .50
522 CD331 10r Couple 2.00 2.00
Nos. 520-522 (3) 2.65 2.65

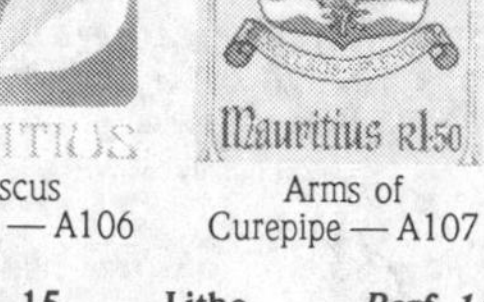

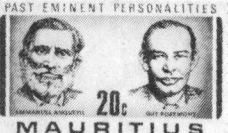

Emmanuel Anquetil and Guy Rozemont A108

Famous Men: 25c, Remy Ollier, Sookdeo Bissoondoyal. 1.25r, Maurice Cure, Barthelemy Ohsan. 1.50r, Guy Forget, Renganaden Seeneevassen. 2r, Abdul Razak Mohamed, Jules Koenig. 2.50r, Abdoollatiff Mahomed Osman, Dazzi Rama. 5r, Thomas Lewis.

1981, Aug. 13 *Perf. 14½*

523 A108 20c black & red .15 .15
524 A108 25c black & yellow .15 .15
525 A108 1.25r black & green .25 .25
526 A108 1.50r black & vermilion .30 .30
527 A108 2r black & ultra .40 .40

528 A108 2.50r black & red brn .50 .50
529 A108 5r black & blue grn 1.00 1.00
Nos. 523-529 (7) 2.75 2.75

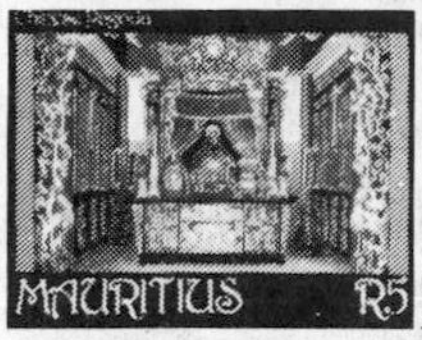

Chinese Pagoda A109

1981, Sept. 16 *Perf. 13½*
530 A109 20c Tamil Women .15 .15
531 A109 2r Swami Sivananda, vert. .40 .40
532 A109 5r shown 1.00 1.00
Nos. 530-532 (3) 1.55 1.55

World Tamil (Hindu sect) Culture Conference, 1980 (20c).

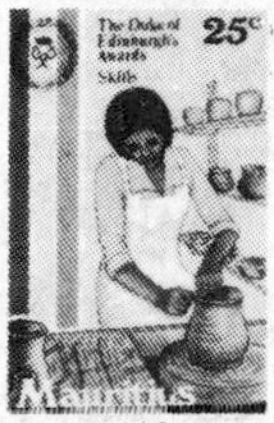

A110

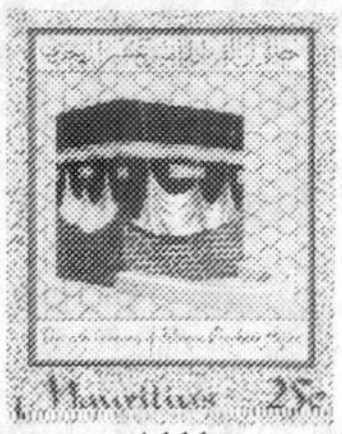

A111

1981, Oct. 26 Litho. *Perf. 14*
533 A110 25c Pottery making .15 .15
534 A110 1.25r Dog grooming .18 .18
535 A110 5r Hiking .75 .75
536 A110 10r Duke of Edinburgh 1.50 1.50
Nos. 533-536 (4) 2.58 2.58

Duke of Edinburgh's Awards, 25th anniv.

1981, Nov. 26 Wmk. 373 *Perf. 14½*
537 A111 25c Holy Ka'aba, Mecca .15 .15
538 A111 2r Prophet's Mosque .40 .40
539 A111 5r Holy Ka'aba, Prophet's Mosque 1.00 1.00
Nos. 537-539 (3) 1.55 1.55

Hegira, 1,500th anniv.

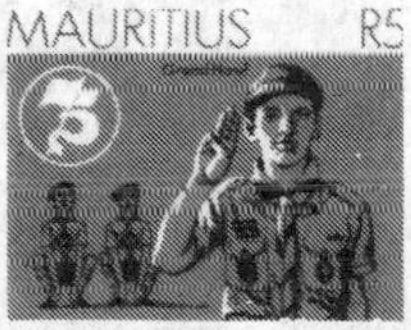

Scouting Year — A112

1982, Feb. 25 Litho. *Perf. 14x14½*
540 A112 25c Emblem .15 .15
541 A112 2r Baden-Powell .35 .35
542 A112 5r Grand howl, sign .85 .85
543 A112 10r Scouts, mountain 1.75 1.75
Nos. 540-543 (4) 3.10 3.10

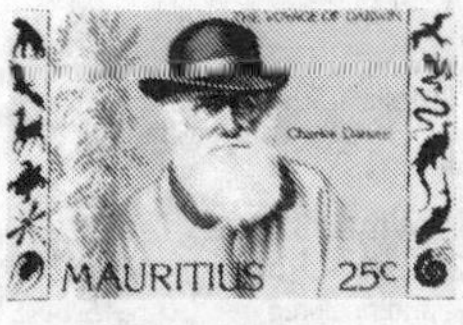

Darwin Death Centenary A113

1982, Apr. 19 Litho. *Perf. 14*
544 A113 25c Portrait .15 .15
545 A113 2r Telescope .40 .40
546 A113 2.50r Riding elephant .50 .50
547 A113 10r The Beagle 2.00 2.00
Nos. 544-547 (4) 3.05 3.05

Princess Diana Issue
Common Design Type

1982, July 1 Litho. *Perf. 13*
548 CD333 25c Arms .15 .15
549 CD333 2.50r Diana .50 .50
550 CD333 5r Wedding 1.00 1.00
551 CD333 10r Portrait 2.00 2.00
Nos. 548-551 (4) 3.65 3.65

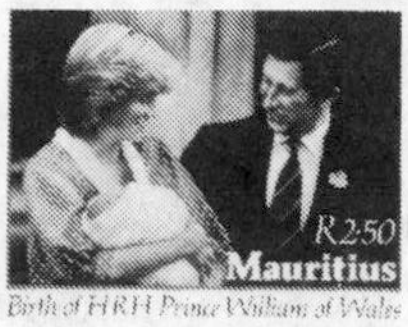

Birth of Prince William of Wales, June 21 — A114

1982, Sept. 22 Litho. *Perf. 14½*
552 A114 2.50r multicolored .60 .60

Issued in sheets of 9.

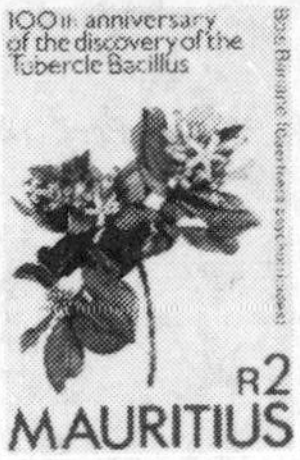

TB Bacillus Centenary — A115

1982, Dec. 15 *Perf. 14*
553 A115 25c Aphloia theiformis .15 .15
554 A115 1.25r Central Market, Port Louis .24 .24
555 A115 2r Gaertnera psychotrioides .38 .38
556 A115 5r Selaginella deliquescens .85 .85
557 A115 10r Koch 1.90 1.90
Nos. 553-557 (5) 3.52 3.52

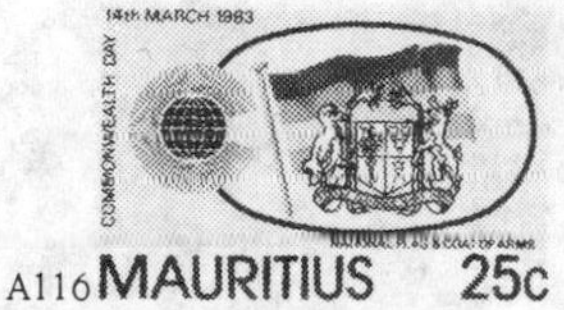

A116

1983, Mar. 14 *Perf. 13x13½*
558 A116 25c Flag, arms .15 .15
559 A116 2.50r Satellite view .42 .42
560 A116 5r Sugar cane harvest .85 .85
561 A116 10r Port Louis Harbor 1.75 1.75
Nos. 558-561 (4) 3.17 3.17

Commonwealth Day.

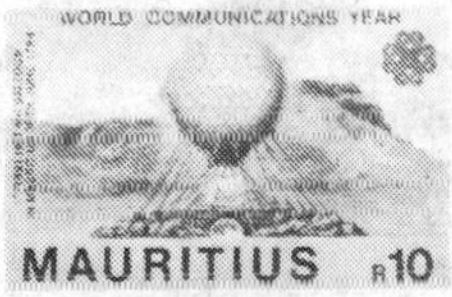

World Communications Year — A117

1983, June 24 Wmk. 373 *Perf. 14*
562 A117 25c Antique telephone, vert. .15 .15
563 A117 1.25r Early telegraph apparatus .28 .28
564 A117 2r Earth satellite station, vert. .45 .45
565 A117 10r 1st hot air balloon in Mauritius, 1784 2.25 2.25
Nos. 562-565 (4) 3.13 3.13

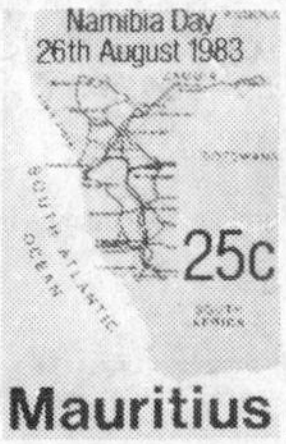

Namibia Day — A118

1983, Aug. 26
566 A118 25c Map .15 .15
567 A118 2.50r Breaking chains .50 .50
568 A118 5r Family, village 1.00 1.00
569 A118 10r Diamond mining 2.00 2.00
Nos. 566-569 (4) 3.65 3.65

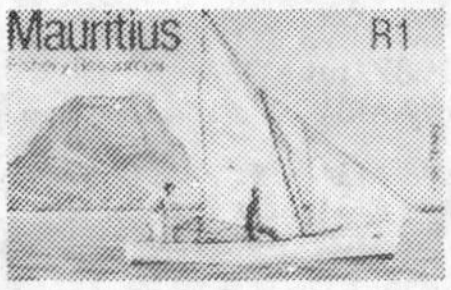

Fishery Resources A119

1983, Oct. 7
570 A119 25c Fish trap, vert. .15 .15
571 A119 1r Fishermen in boat .16 .16
572 A119 5r Game fishing, vert. .80 .80
573 A119 10r Octopus drying 1.75 1.75
Nos. 570-573 (4) 2.86 2.86

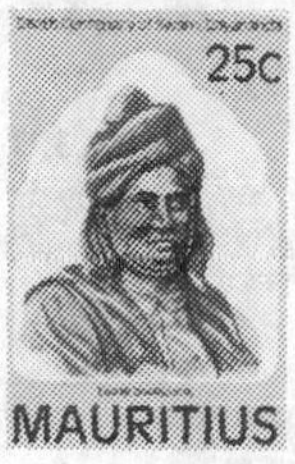

Swami Dayananda, Death Centenary — A120

1983, Nov. 3 Litho. Wmk. 373
574 A120 25c shown .15 .15
575 A120 35c Last meeting with father .15 .15
576 A120 2r Receiving instruction .32 .32
577 A120 5r Demonstrating strength .80 .80
578 A120 10r Religious gathering 1.75 1.75
Nos. 574-578 (5) 3.17 3.17

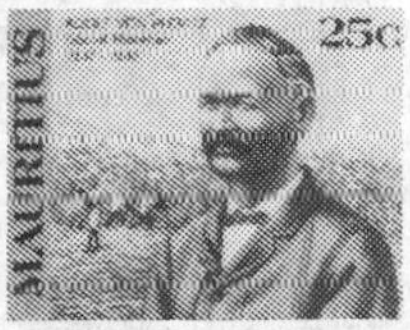

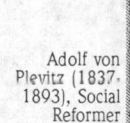

Adolf von Plevitz (1837-1893), Social Reformer A121

1983, Dec. 8
579 A121 25c shown .15 .15
580 A121 1.25r Government school .42 .42
581 A121 5r Addressing Commission of Enquiry .70 .70
582 A121 10r Indian field workers 1.50 1.50
Nos. 579-582 (4) 2.77 2.77

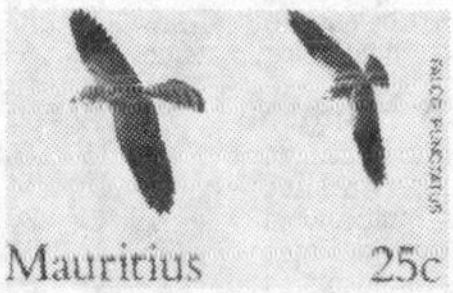

Mauritius Kestrels A122

1984, Mar. 26 Wmk. 373 *Perf. 14*
583 A122 25c Courtship chase .15 .15
584 A122 2r Side view, vert. .42 .42
585 A122 2.50r Fledgling .52 .52
586 A122 10r Bird, diff., vert. 2.25 2.25
Nos. 583-586 (4) 3.34 3.34

Lloyd's List Issue
Common Design Type

1984, May 23 Litho. *Perf. 14½x14*
587 CD335 25c Tayeb, Port Lewis .15 .15
588 CD335 1r Taher .15 .15
589 CD335 5r East Indiaman Triton .70 .70
590 CD335 10r Astor 1.65 1.65
Nos. 587-590 (4) 2.65 2.65

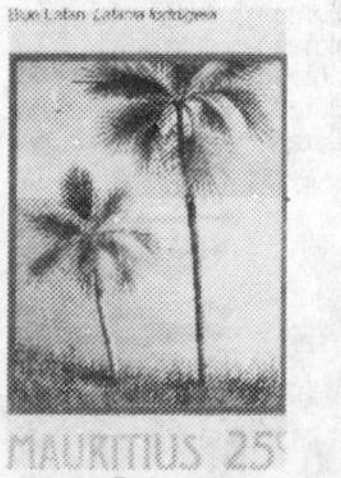

Palm Trees — A123

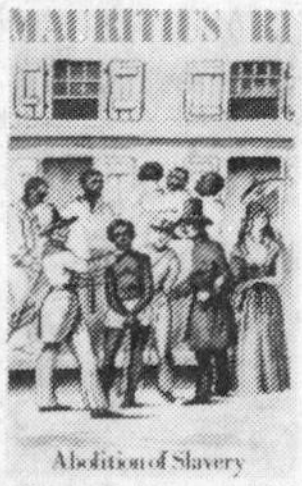

Slave Sale — A124

1984, July 23 Litho. *Perf. 14*
591 A123 25c Blue latan .15 .15
592 A123 50c Hyophorbe vaughanii .15 .15
593 A123 2.50r Tectiphiala ferox .40 .40
594 A123 5r Round Isld. bottle-palm .80 .80
595 A123 10r Hyophorbe amaricaulis 1.75 1.75
Nos. 591-595 (5) 3.25 3.25

1984, Aug. *Perf. 14½*
596 A124 25c Woman .15 .15
597 A124 1r shown .16 .16
598 A124 2r Family, horiz. .32 .32
599 A124 10r Immigrant arrival, horiz. 1.75 1.75
Nos. 596-599 (4) 2.38 2.38

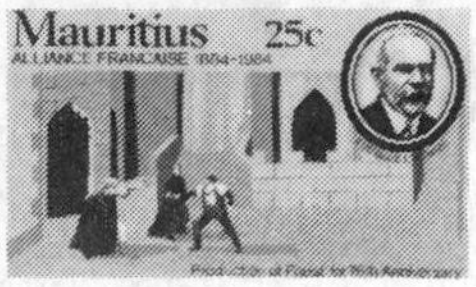

Alliance Francaise Centenary A125

1984, Sept. 10 *Perf. 14½*
600 A125 25c Production of Faust, 1959 .15 .15
601 A125 1.25r Award ceremony .20 .20
602 A125 5r Headquarters .70 .70
603 A125 10r Lion Mountain 1.50 1.50
Nos. 600-603 (4) 2.55 2.55

Queen Mother 85th Birthday
Common Design Type
Perf. 14½x14

1985, June 7 Wmk. 384
604 CD336 25c Portrait, 1926 .15 .15
605 CD336 2r With Princess Margaret .35 .35
606 CD336 5r On Clarence House balcony .90 .90
607 CD336 10r Holding Prince Henry 1.75 1.75
Nos. 604-607 (4) 3.15 3.15

Souvenir Sheet
608 CD336 15r On Royal Barge, reopening Stratford Canal, 1964 2.75 2.75

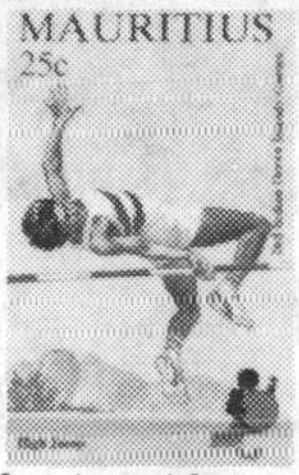

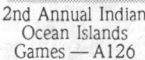

2nd Annual Indian Ocean Islands Games — A126

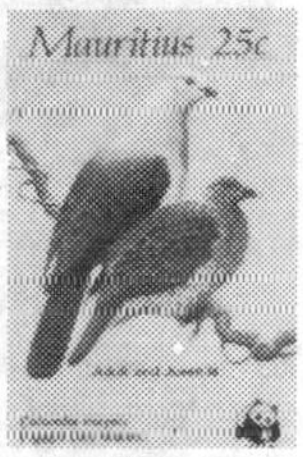

Pink Pigeon — A127

1985, Aug. 24 Wmk. 373 *Perf. 14½*
609 A126 25c High jump .15 .15
610 A126 50c Javelin .15 .15
611 A126 1.25r Cycling .22 .22
612 A126 10r Wind surfing 1.75 1.75
Nos. 609-612 (4) 2.27 2.27

1985, Sept. 2 Wmk. 384 *Perf. 14*
613 A127 25c Adult and young .15 .15
614 A127 2r Nest site display .65 .65
615 A127 2.50r Nesting .80 .80
616 A127 5r Preening 1.65 1.65
Nos. 613-616 (4) 3.25 3.25

World Wildlife Fund.

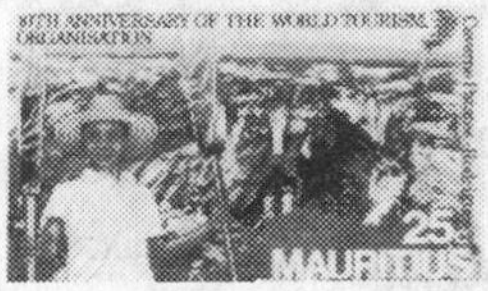

World Tourism Org., 10th Anniv. A128

1985, Sept. 20 *Perf. 14½*
617 A128 25c Patates Caverns .15 .15
618 A128 35c Colored Earth, Chamarel .15 .15
619 A128 5r Serpent Island .80 .80
620 A128 10r Coin de Mire Is. 1.75 1.75
Nos. 617-620 (4) 2.85 2.85

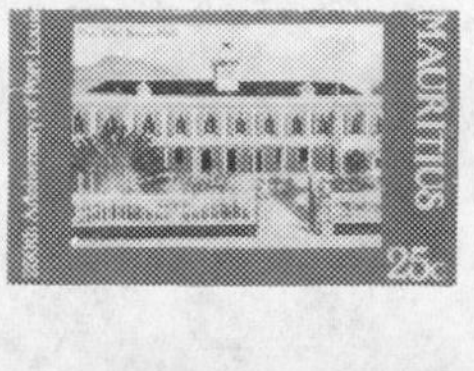

Port Louis, 250th Anniv. A129

1985, Nov. 22 — *Perf. 13½*
621 A129 25c Old Town Hall .15 .15
622 A129 1r Al-Aqsa Mosque .16 .16
623 A129 2.50r Tamil-speaking Indians, settlement .40 .40
624 A129 10r Port Louis Harbor 1.65 1.65
Nos. 621-624 (4) 2.36 2.36

Halley's Comet
A130

1986, Feb. 21 — **Wmk. 384** — *Perf. 14*
625 A130 25c Halley, map .15 .15
626 A130 1.25r Newton's telescope, 1682 sighting .16 .16
627 A130 3r Mauritius from space .40 .40
628 A130 10r Giotto space probe 1.40 1.40
Nos. 625-628 (4) 2.11 2.11

Queen Elizabeth II 60th Birthday
Common Design Type

Designs: 25c, In uniform, Grenadier Guards, 1942. 75c, Investiture of the Prince of Wales, 1969. 2r, State visit with Prince Philip. 3r, State visit to Germany, 1978. 15r, Visiting Crown Agents' offices, 1983.

1986, Apr. 21 — **Litho.** — *Perf. 14½x14*
629 CD337 25c scar, black & sil .15 .15
630 CD337 75c ultra & multi .15 .15
631 CD337 2r green & multi .30 .30
632 CD337 3r violet & multi .45 .45
633 CD337 15r rose vio & multi 2.15 2.15
Nos. 629-633 (5) 3.20 3.20

Intl. Events — A131

Orchids — A132

Designs: 25c, World Food Day. 1r, African Regional Industrial Property Organization, 10th anniv. 1.25r, Intl. Peace Year. 10r, 1986 World Cup Soccer Championships.

1986, July 25 — **Litho.** — *Perf. 14*
634 A131 25c FAO emblem, corn .15 .15
635 A131 1r ARIPO emblem .15 .15
636 A131 1.25r IPY emblem .20 .20
637 A131 10r Athlete, MFA 1.50 1.50
Nos. 634-637 (4) 2.00 2.00

1986, Oct. 3 — **Litho.** — *Perf. 14½*
638 A132 25c Cryptopus elatus .15 .15
639 A132 2r Jumellea recta .42 .42
640 A132 2.50r Angraecum mauritianum .55 .55
641 A132 10r Bulbophyllum longiflorum 2.25 2.25
Nos. 638-641 (4) 3.37 3.37

Bridges A133

1987, May 22 — **Wmk. 373**
642 A133 25c Hesketh Bell .15 .15
643 A133 50c Sir Colville Deverell .15 .15
644 A133 2.50r Cavendish .35 .35
645 A133 5r Tamarin .70 .70
646 A133 10r Grand River North West 1.40 1.40
Nos. 642-646 (5) 2.75 2.75

The Bar, Bicent. A134

1987, June 2 — **Wmk. 384**
647 A134 25c Port Louis Supreme Court .15 .15
648 A134 1r Flacq District Court .15 .15
649 A134 1.25r Statue of Justice .18 .18
650 A134 10r Barristers, 1787-1987 1.40 1.40
Nos. 647-650 (4) 1.88 1.88

Intl. Festival of the Sea — A135

1987, Sept. 5 — **Wmk. 373**
651 A135 25c Dodo mascot, vert. .15 .15
652 A135 1.50r Sailboats .22 .22
653 A135 3r Water-skier .42 .42
654 A135 5r Tall ship Svanen, vert. .70 .70
Nos. 651-654 (4) 1.49 1.49

Industrialization — A136

1987, Oct. 30 — *Perf. 14*
655 A136 20c Toy .15 .15
656 A136 35c Spinning .15 .15
657 A136 50c Rattan .15 .15
658 A136 2.50r Optical .38 .38
659 A136 10r Stone carving 1.40 1.40
Nos. 655-659 (5) 2.23 2.23

Art & Architecture A137

Designs: 25c, Maison Ouvriere, Intl. Year of Shelter for the Homeless emblem. 1r, Paul et Virginie, a lithograph. 1.25r, Chateau Rosney. 2r, Old Farmhouse, Boulle. 5r, Three Peaks, watercolor.

1988, June 29 — **Wmk. 384** — *Perf. 14½*
660 A137 25c multicolored .15 .15
661 A137 1r gray & black .16 .16
662 A137 1.25r multicolored .20 .20
663 A137 2r multicolored .32 .32
664 A137 5r multicolored .80 .80
Nos. 660-664 (5) 1.63 1.63

Natl. Independence, 20th Anniv. A138

Designs: 25c, University of Mauritius. 75c, Calisthenics at sunset in stadium. 2.50r, Runners, Sir Maurice Rault Stadium. 5r, Air Mauritius jet at gate, Sir Seewoosagur Ramgoolam Intl. Airport. 10r, Gov.-Gen. Veerasamy Ringadoo and Prime Minister Aneerood Jugnauth.

1988, Mar. 11 — **Wmk. 373** — *Perf. 14*
665 A138 25c multicolored .15 .15
666 A138 75c multicolored .15 .15
667 A138 2.50r multicolored .40 .40
668 A138 5r multicolored .80 .80
669 A138 10r multicolored 1.60 1.60
Nos. 665-669 (5) 3.10 3.10

WHO, 40th Anniv. — A139

1988, July 1 — **Wmk. 373** — *Perf. 13½*
670 A139 20c Breast-feeding .15 .15
671 A139 2r Immunization .32 .32
672 A139 3r Nutrition .48 .48
673 A139 10r Emblem 1.55 1.55
Nos. 670-673 (4) 2.50 2.50

Mauritius Commercial Bank, Ltd., 150th Anniv. A140

1988, Sept. 1 — **Wmk. 373** — *Perf. 14*
674 A140 25c Bank, 1981, vert. .15 .15
675 A140 1r Bank, 1897 .15 .15
676 A140 1.25r Coat of arms, vert. .18 .18
677 A140 25r 15-Dollar bank note, 1838 3.65 3.65
Nos. 674-677 (4) 4.13 4.13

1988 Summer Olympics, Seoul — A141

1988, Oct. 1
678 A141 25c shown .15 .15
679 A141 35c Wrestling .15 .15
680 A141 1.50r Running .25 .25
681 A141 10r Swimming 1.55 1.55
Nos. 678-681 (4) 2.10 2.10

Environmental Protection — A142

Wmk. 384 (20c, 40c, 50c, 1r, 10r), 373 (Others)

1989-91 — **Litho.** — *Perf. 14*
682 A142 15c Tropical reef .15 .15
683 A142 30c Greenshank .15 .15
684 A142 40c shown .15 .15
a. Wmk. 373 .15 .15
685 A142 50c Round Island, vert. .15 .15
686 A142 75c Bassin Blanc .15 .15
688 A142 1r Mangrove, vert. .15 .15
690 A142 1.50r Whimbrel .20 .20
691 A142 2r Le Morne .22 .22
692 A142 3r Fish .45 .45
693 A142 4r Fern tree, vert. .58 .58
694 A142 5r Riviere du Poste Estuary .58 .58
695 A142 6r Ecological scenery, vert. .88 .88
699 A142 10r Phelsuma ornata,vert. 1.45 1.45
700 A142 15r Benares surf 1.75 1.75
701 A142 25r Migratory birds, vert. 3.50 3.50
Nos. 682-701 (15) 10.51 10.51

Issue dates: 40c, 3r-10r, Mar. 11, 1989. No. 684a, Feb. 19, 1991. 50c, 75c, 2r, 5r, 15r, Oct. 4, 1991. Others, Nov. 22, 1990.
Nos. 682, 684a, 693 exist inscribed "1994."
For surcharge see No. 781.
This is an expanding set. Numbers will change if necessary.

A143   A144

French Revolution, Bicent.: 30c, La Tour Sumeire, Place Du Theatre Municipal. 1r, Salle De Spectacle Du Jardin. 8r, Le Comte De Malartic. 15r, Anniv. emblem.

1989, July 14 — **Wmk. 373**
702 A143 30c multicolored .15 .15
703 A143 1r multicolored .15 .15
704 A143 8r multicolored 1.10 1.10
705 A143 15r multicolored 2.00 2.00
Nos. 702-705 (4) 3.40 3.40

1989, Oct. 13 — *Perf. 14x13½*
Visit of Pope John Paul II: 30c, Cardinal Jean Margeot. 40c, Pope welcoming Prime Minister Aneerood Jugnauth to the Vatican, 1988. 3r, Mother Mary Magdalene of the Cross (1810-1889) and Filles des Marie Chapel, Port Louis, 1864. 6r, St. Francis of Assisi Church, 1756, Pamplemousses. 10r, Pope John Paul II.
706 A144 30c multicolored .15 .15
707 A144 40c multicolored .15 .15
708 A144 3r multicolored .40 .40
709 A144 6r multicolored .80 .80
710 A144 10r multicolored 1.35 1.35
Nos. 706-710 (5) 2.85 2.85

Jawaharlal Nehru, 1st Prime Minister of India A145

Designs: 1.50r, Nehru and Indira, Rajiv and Sanjay Gandhi. 3r, With Mahatma Gandhi. 4r, With Nasser and Tito. 10r, With children.

1989, Oct. 13 — **Wmk. 384** — *Perf. 14*
711 A145 40c shown .15 .15
712 A145 1.50r multicolored .20 .20
713 A145 3r multicolored .40 .40
714 A145 4r multicolored .55 .55
715 A145 10r multicolored 1.35 1.35
Nos. 711-715 (5) 2.65 2.65

Sugar Cane Industry, 350th Anniv. A146

1990, Jan. 10 — *Perf. 13½x14* — **Litho.** — **Wmk. 384**
716 A146 30c Cutting cane .15 .15
717 A146 40c Refinery, 1867 .15 .15
718 A146 1r Mechanically loading cane .15 .15
719 A146 25r Modern refinery 3.35 3.35
Nos. 716-719 (4) 3.80 3.80

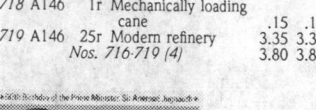

Prime Minister Jugnauth's 60th Birthday A147

Jugnauth: 35c, And symbols of the industrial estate. 40c, At his desk. 1.50r, And stock exchange emblem. 4r, And Gov.-Gen. Ramgoolam. 10r, And Pope John Paul II, map.

Wmk. 373
1990, Mar. 29 — **Litho.** — *Perf. 14*
720 A147 35c multicolored .15 .15
721 A147 40c multicolored .15 .15
722 A147 1.50r multicolored .22 .22
723 A147 4r multicolored .55 .55
724 A147 10r multicolored 1.40 1.40
Nos. 720-724 (5) 2.47 2.47

Mauritian Television, 25th Anniv. A148

Anniversaries and Events: 30c, Death of Desjardins, naturalist, 150th anniversary, vert. 6r, Line barracks, 250th anniversary, vert. 8r, Municipality of Curepipe, centenary.

1990, July 5

725	A148	30c lt orange & multi	.15	.15
726	A148	35c pink & multi	.15	.15
727	A148	6r lt blue & multi	.85	.85
728	A148	8r lt green & multi	1.10	1.10
		Nos. 725-728 (4)	2.25	2.25

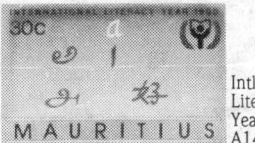

Intl. Literacy Year A149

Wmk. 373
1990, Sept. 28   Litho.   Perf. 14

729	A149	30c shown	.15	.15
730	A149	1r Blind girl printing braille	.15	.15
731	A149	3r Globe, open book	.42	.42
732	A149	10r Open book, world map	1.40	1.40
		Nos. 729-732 (4)	2.12	2.12

Elizabeth & Philip, Birthdays
Common Design Types
Perf. 14½
1991, June 17   Litho.   Wmk. 384

733	CD345	8r multicolored	.92	.92
734	CD346	8r multicolored	.92	.92
a.		Pair, #733-734 + label	1.84	1.84

Port Louis, City Incorporation, 25th Anniv. — A150

Anniversaries and Events: 4r, Col. Draper, 150th death anniv., vert. 6r, Joseph Barnard, engraver of first Mauritius stamps, 175th birth anniv., vert. 10r, Spitfire, Mauritius' contribution to Allied war effort, 1939-1945.

Wmk. 373
1991, Aug. 18   Litho.   Perf. 14

735	A150	40c multicolored	.15	.15
736	A150	4r multicolored	.45	.45
737	A150	6r multicolored	.70	.70
738	A150	10r multicolored	1.15	1.15
		Nos. 735-738 (4)	2.45	2.45

Phila Nippon '91 — A151

Butterflies: 40c, Euploea euphon. 3r, Hypolimnas misippus, female. 8r, Papilio manlius. 10r, Hypolimnas misippus, male.

Perf. 14x14½
1991, Nov. 15   Litho.   Wmk. 373

739	A151	40c multicolored	.15	.15
740	A151	3r multicolored	.35	.35
741	A151	8r multicolored	.95	.95
742	A151	10r multicolored	1.15	1.15
		Nos. 739-742 (4)	2.60	2.60

Flora and Fauna From Island States of Mauritius A152

Designs: 40c, Chelonia mydas, Tromelin. 1r, Ibis, Agalega. 2r, Takamaka flowers, Chagos Archipelago. 15r, Lambis violacea, St. Brandon.

1991, Dec. 13   Perf. 14

743	A152	40c multicolored	.15	.15
744	A152	1r multicolored	.15	.15
745	A152	2r multicolored	.22	.22
746	A152	15r multicolored	1.70	1.70
		Nos. 743-746 (4)	2.22	2.22

Republic

Proclamation of the Republic of Mauritius — A153

1992, Mar. 12

747	A153	40c President	.15	.15
748	A153	4r Prime Minister	.45	.45
749	A153	8r Mauritian children	.95	.95
750	A153	10r President's flag	1.15	1.15
		Nos. 747-750 (4)	2.70	2.70

8th African Track and Field Championships A154

Designs: 40c, Games mascot, Tricolo. 4r, Sir Anerood Jugnauth Stadium, horiz. 5r, High jumper, horiz. 6r, Torch, emblem of games.

1992, June 25   Perf. 13½

751	A154	40c multicolored	.15	.15
752	A154	4r multicolored	.45	.45
753	A154	5r multicolored	.58	.58
754	A154	6r multicolored	.70	.70
		Nos. 751-754 (4)	1.00	1.00

Anniversaries and Events — A155

Designs: 40c, Flower, vert. 1r, Swami Krishnanandji Maharaj, vert. 2r, Boy and dog. 3r, Building, flags. 15r, Radio telescope antenna.

1992, Aug. 13

755	A155	40c multicolored	.15	.15
756	A155	1r multicolored	.15	.15
757	A155	2r multicolored	.28	.28
758	A155	3r multicolored	.40	.40
759	A155	15r multicolored	2.00	2.00
		Nos. 755-759 (5)	2.98	2.98

Fleurir Maurice, 25th anniv. (#755). 25th anniv. of Swami Maharaj's arrival (#756). Humane education (#757). Indian Ocean Commission, 10th anniv. (#758). Inauguration of radio telescope project (#759).

Bank of Mauritius, Silver Jubilee A156

Designs: 40c, Bank of Mauritius building, vert. 4r, Dodo gold bullion coin. 8r, First bank note issues. 15r, Foreign exchange reserves 1967-1992.

Perf. 14½x14, 14x14½
1992, Oct. 29   Litho.   Wmk. 373

760	A156	40c multicolored	.15	.15
761	A156	4r multicolored	.52	.52
762	A156	8r multicolored	1.10	1.10
763	A156	15r multicolored	2.00	2.00
		Nos. 760-763 (4)	3.77	3.77

National Day, 25th Anniv. — A157

Designs: 30c, Housing development. 40c, Computer showing gross domestic product. 3r, Flag in shape of map of Mauritius. 4r, Ballot box. 15r, Medal for Grand Commander of the Order of the Star and Key of the Indian Ocean.

1993, Mar. 12   Perf. 15x14

764	A157	30c multicolored	.15	.15
765	A157	40c multicolored	.15	.15
766	A157	3r multicolored	.35	.35
767	A157	4r multicolored	.48	.48
768	A157	15r multicolored	1.75	1.75
		Nos. 764-768 (5)	2.88	2.88

Air Mauritius Ltd., 25th Anniv. A158

Designs: 40c, Bell 206B Jet Ranger. 3r, Boeing 747SP. 4r, ATR 42. 10r, Boeing 767-200ER.

1993, June 14   Perf. 14

769	A158	40c multicolored	.15	.15
770	A158	3r multicolored	.35	.35
771	A158	4r multicolored	.45	.45
772	A158	10r multicolored	1.15	1.15
a.		Souvenir sheet of 4, #769-772	2.10	2.10
		Nos. 769-772 (4)	2.10	2.10

5th Francophone Summit — A159

Designs: 1r, 1715 Act of French Seizure of Mauritius, 1810 Act of Surrender. 5r, Signs. 6r, Page from Napoleonic Code. 7r, French publications.

1993, Oct. 16

773	A159	1r multicolored	.15	.15
774	A159	5r multicolored	.60	.60
775	A159	6r multicolored	.70	.70
776	A159	7r multicolored	.80	.80
		Nos. 773-776 (4)	2.25	2.25

Telecommunications — A160

Designs: 40c, SS Scotia, cable laying. 3r, Morse code, Morse key. 4r, Signal mountain station. 8r, Communications satellite.

1993, Nov. 25   Perf. 13

777	A160	40c multicolored	.15	.15
778	A160	3r multicolored	.35	.35
779	A160	4r multicolored	.48	.48
780	A160	8r multicolored	1.00	1.00
		Nos. 777-780 (4)	1.98	1.98

No. 686 Surcharged

40cs
═══

1993, Sept. 15   Litho.   Perf. 14

781	A142	40c on 75c multi	.15	.15

Mammals A161

Perf. 14½
1994, Mar. 9   Litho.   Wmk. 384

782	A161	40c Mongoose	.15	.15
783	A161	2r Hare	.22	.22
784	A161	8r Monkey	.90	.90
785	A161	10r Tenrec	1.10	1.10
		Nos. 782-785 (4)	2.37	2.37

Anniversaries and Events — A162

Designs: 40c, Dr. E. Brown-Sequard (1817-94). 4r, Silhouettes of family. 8r, World Cup trophy, US map. 10r, Control Tower, SSR Intl. Airport.

Wmk. 373
1994, June 16   Litho.   Perf. 14

786	A162	40c multicolored	.15	.15
787	A162	4r multicolored	.45	.45
788	A162	8r multicolored	.90	.90
789	A162	10r multicolored	1.10	1.10
		Nos. 786-789 (4)	2.60	2.60

Intl. Year of the Family (#787). 1994 World Cup Soccer Championships, US (#788). ICAO, 50th anniv. (#789).

Wreck of the St. Geran, 250th Anniv. A163

Wmk. 384
1994, Aug. 18   Perf. 14

790	A163	40c Leaving L'Orient	.15	.15
791	A163	5r In rough seas	.55	.55
792	A163	6r Ship's bell	.65	.65
793	A163	10r Relics from ship	1.10	1.10
		Nos. 790-793 (4)	2.45	2.45

Souvenir Sheet

794	A163	15r St. Geran, vert.	1.65	1.65

Children's Paintings of Leisure Activities A164

Designs: 30c, "Ring Around the Rosey." 40c, Playing with balls, jump rope. 8r, Water sports. 10r, "Blindman's Buff."

Perf. 13½
1994, Oct. 25   Litho.   Wmk. 373

795	A164	30c multicolored	.15	.15
796	A164	40c multicolored	.15	.15
797	A164	8r multicolored	.90	.90
798	A164	10r multicolored	1.10	1.10
		Nos. 795-798 (4)	2.30	2.30

Spices — A165

Perf. 13x14

1995, Mar. 10 Litho. Wmk. 373

799	A165	40c Nutmeg	.15	.15
800	A165	4r Coriander	.45	.45
801	A165	5r Cloves	.55	.55
802	A165	10r Cardamon	1.10	1.10
		Nos. 799-802 (4)	2.25	2.25

End of World War II

Common Design Type

Designs: No. 803, HMS Mauritius. No. 304, Mauritian servicemen, map of North Africa. No. 305, Catalina, Tombeau Bay.

Wmk. 373

1995, May 8 Litho. *Perf. 14*

Size: 35x28mm

803	CD351	5r multicolored	.55	.55
804	CD351	5r multicolored	.55	.55
805	CD351	5r multicolored	.55	.55
		Nos. 803-805 (3)	1.65	1.65

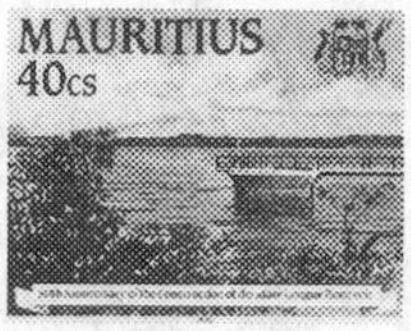

Anniversaries & Events A166

1995, May 8

806	A166	40c multicolored	.15	.15
807	A166	4r multicolored	.45	.45
808	A166	10r multicolored	1.10	1.10
		Nos. 806-808 (3)	1.70	1.70

Construction of Mare Longue Reservoir, 50th anniv. (#806). Construction of Mahebourg-Curepipe Road, bicent. (#807). Great fire of Port Louis, cent. (#808).

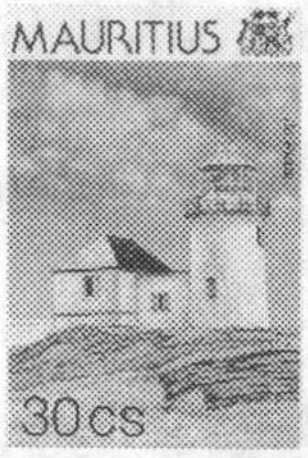

Lighthouses — A167

Perf. 13x14

1995, Aug. 28 Litho. Wmk. 373

809	A167	30c Ile Plate	.15	.15
810	A167	40c Pointe aux Caves	.15	.15
811	A167	8r Ile aux Fouquets	.90	.90
812	A167	10r Pointe aux Canonniers	1.10	1.10
a.		Souvenir sheet of 4, #809-812	2.25	2.25
		Nos. 809-812 (4)	2.30	2.30

UN, 50th Anniv.

Common Design Type

Designs: 40c, Silhouettes of children under UNICEF umbrella. 4r, ILO contruction site. 8r, WMO satellite view of hurricane. 10r, Bread, grain representing FAO.

Wmk. 373

1995, Oct. 24 Litho. *Perf. 14*

813	CD353	40c multicolored	.15	.15
814	CD353	4r multicolored	.45	.45
815	CD353	8r multicolored	.90	.90
816	CD353	10r multicolored	1.10	1.10
		Nos. 813-816 (4)	2.60	2.60

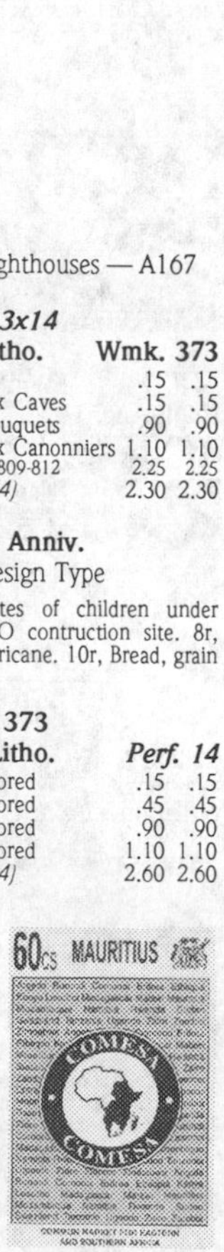

Common Market for Eastern and Southern Africa (COMESA) — A168

1995, Dec. 8 Litho. *Perf. 13*

817	A168	60c pink & multi	.15	.15
818	A168	4r blue & multi	.45	.45
819	A168	8r yellow & multi	.90	.90
820	A168	10r green & multi	1.10	1.10
		Nos. 817-820 (4)	2.60	2.60

SPECIAL DELIVERY STAMPS

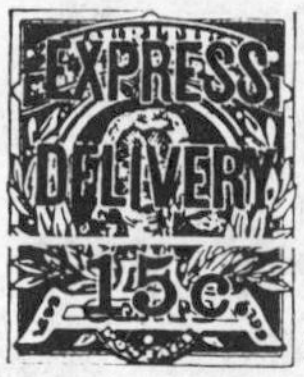

SD1

1903 Wmk. 1 *Perf. 14*

Red Surcharge

E1	SD1	15c on 15c ultra	9.00	10.00

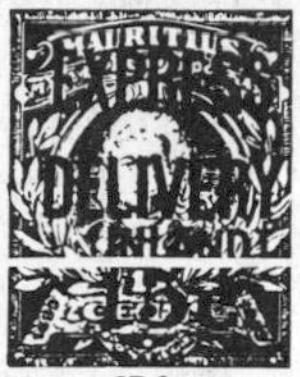

SD2

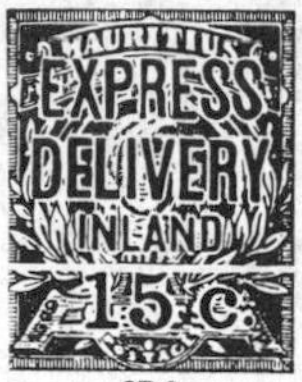

SD3

1904

E2	SD2	15c on 15c ultra	15.00	14.00
a.		"INLAND" inverted	175.00	175.00
b.		Inverted "A" in "INLAND"	250.00	250.00
E3	SD3	15c on 15c ultra	8.00	2.00
a.		Double surcharge	175.00	
b.		Inverted surcharge		*175.00*
c.		No period after "c"	150.00	150.00

To make No. E2 the word "INLAND" was printed on No. E1. For No. E3 a new setting of the surcharge was made with different spacing between the words.

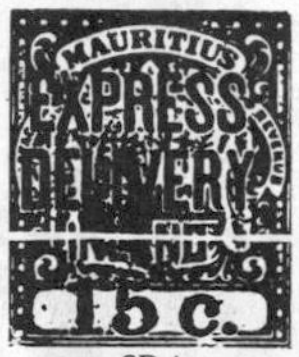

SD4

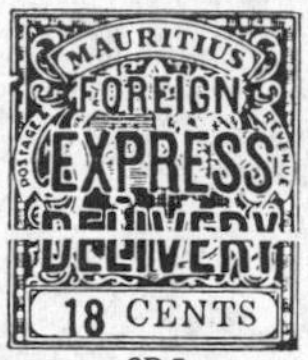

SD5

E4	SD4	15c green & red	5.00	2.50
a.		Double surcharge	150.00	150.00
b.		Inverted surcharge	100.00	100.00
c.		"LNIAND."	125.00	125.00
d.		As "c," double surcharge	*450.00*	
E5	SD5	18c green & black	3.50	5.00
a.		Exclamation point (!) instead of "I" in "FOREIGN"	200.00	

POSTAGE DUE STAMPS

Catalogue values for unused stamps in this section are for Never Hinged items.

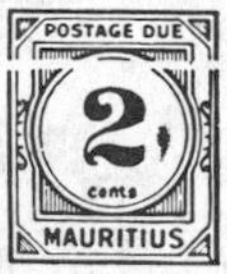

Numeral — D1

Perf. 14 1/2x14

1933-54 Typo. Wmk. 4

J1	D1	2c black	.15	.15
J2	D1	4c violet	.15	.15
J3	D1	6c red	.20	*.70*
J4	D1	10c green	.30	*.60*
J5	D1	20c ultramarine	.45	*1.50*
J6	D1	50c dp red lilac ('54)	.90	*2.25*
J7	D1	1r orange ('54)	.90	*3.75*
		Nos. J1-J7 (7)	3.05	*9.10*

1966-68 Wmk. 314 *Perf. 14*

J8	D1	2c black ('67)	.15	.15

Perf. 14 1/2 14

J9	D1	4c rose violet ('68)	.15	.15
J10	D1	6c dp orange ('68)	.15	.15
J11	D1	10c yel green ('67)	.15	.15
J12	D1	20c ultramarine	.25	.20
J13	D1	50c dp red lilac ('68)	.65	.35
		Nos. J8-J13 (6)	1.50	1.15

Nos. 445-446, 450, 455, 457, 462 Surcharged "POSTAGE/ DUE" and New Value

Perf. 13 1/2

1982, Oct. 25 Litho. Wmk. 373

J14	A92	10c on 15c multi	.15	.15
J15	A92	20c on 20c multi	.15	.15
J16	A91	50c on 60c multi	.15	.15
J17	A92	1r on 1.20r multi	.20	.20
J18	A92	1.50r on 1.50r multi	.25	.25
J19	A91	5r on 15r multi	.75	.75
		Nos. J14-J19 (6)	1.65	1.65

MESOPOTAMIA

ˌme–s(ə–)pə–ˈtā–mē–ə

LOCATION — In Western Asia, bounded on the north by Syria and Turkey, on the east by Persia, on the south by Saudi Arabia and on the west by Trans-Jordan.
GOVT. — A former Turkish Province
AREA — 143,250 (1918) sq. mi.
POP. — 2,849,282 (1920)
CAPITAL — Baghdad

During World War I this territory was occupied by Great Britain. It was recognized as an independent state and placed under British Mandate but in 1932 the Mandate was terminated and the country admitted to membership in the League of Nations as the Kingdom of Iraq. Postage stamps of Iraq are now in use.

16 Annas = 1 Rupee

Watermark

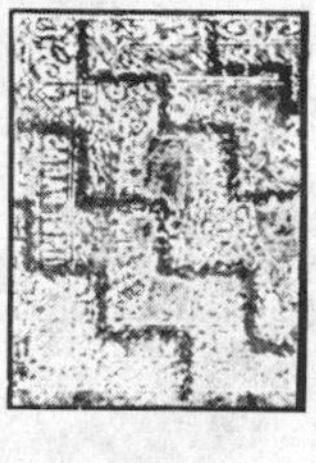

Wmk. 48 - Diagonal Zigzag Lines

Issued under British Occupation

Baghdad Issue

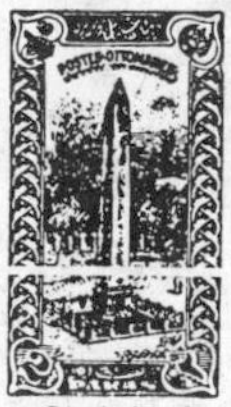

Obelisk of Theodosius, Constantinople A24

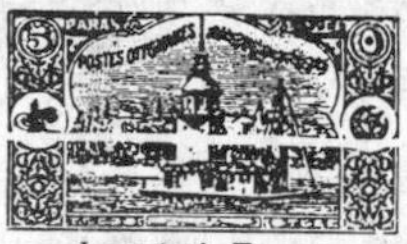

Leander's Tower A26

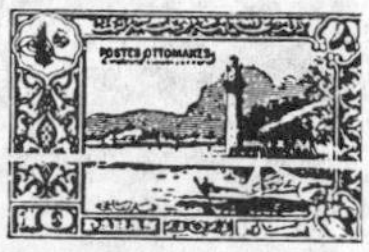

Fenerbahç e (Garden Lighthouse) A28

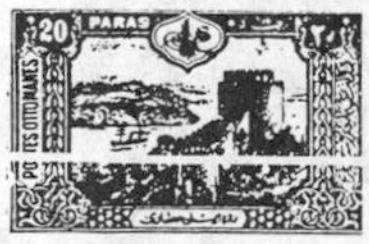

Castle of Europe on Bosporus — A29

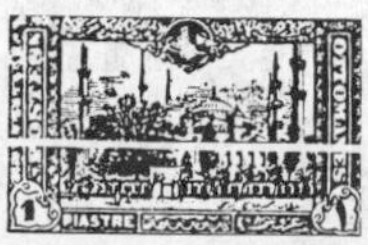

Mosque of Sultan Ahmed — A30

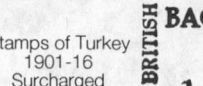

Stamps of Turkey 1901-16 Surcharged

IN BRITISH
BAGHDAD
OCCUPATION
1/2 An

The surcharges were printed from slugs which were arranged to fit the various shapes of the stamps.

1917 Unwmk. *Perf. 12, 13 1/2*

On Turkey Nos. 254, 256, 258-260

N1	A24	1/4a on 2pa red lil	90.00	105.00
a.		"IN BRITISH" omitted	*4,250.*	
N2	A26	1/4a on 5pa vio brown	75.00	82.50
a.		"1/4 An" omitted	*3,750.*	
N3	A28	1/2a on 10pa green	525.00	525.00
N4	A29	1a on 20pa red	450.00	400.00
N5	A30	2a on 1pi blue	140.00	165.00
		Nos. N1-N5 (5)	1,280.	1,277.

General Post Office, Constantinople — A22

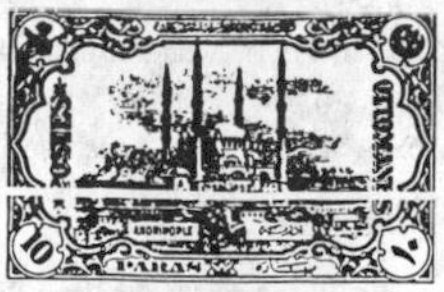

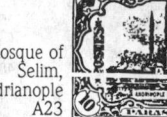

Mosque of Selim, Adrianople A23

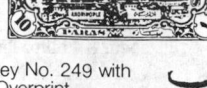

On Turkey No. 249 with Overprint ب

N6	A22	2a on 1pi ultra	250.	250.

On Turkey No. 251

N7	A23	1/2a on 10pa green	950.	900.

On Turkey Nos. 272-273 with Overprint ★

N8	A29	1a on 20pa red	250.	250.
a.		"OCCUPATION" omitted	*3,000.*	
N9	A30	2a on 1pi blue	4,000.	4,000.

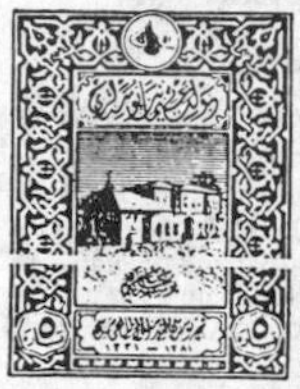

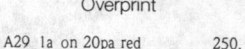

Old General Post Office, Constantinople — A41

On Turkey Nos. 346-348

N10	A41	1/2a on 10pa car	225.00	225.00
N11	A41	1a on 20pa ultra	900.00	750.00
a.		"1 An" omitted	*4,250.*	
N12	A41	2a on 1pi vio & black	57.50	57.50
a.		"BAGHDAD" omitted	*2,500.*	

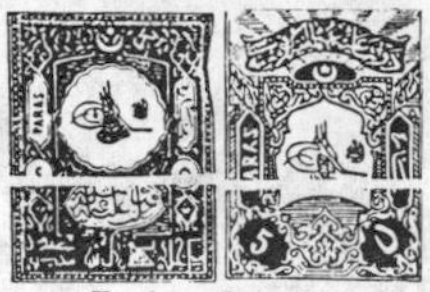

Tughra, Sultan's Monogram

A17 A18

On Various Issues with Overprint

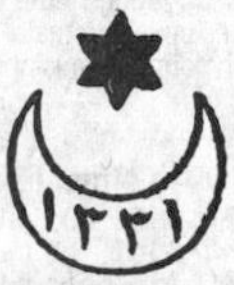

On Turkey Nos. 297, 300

N13	A17	1/4a on 5pa purple	*2,500.*	
N14	A17	2a on 1pi blue	120.00	120.00

On Turkey No. 306

N15	A18	1a on 20pa car	300.00	250.00

On Turkey Nos. 329-331

N16	A22	1/2a on 10pa bl grn	60.00	60.00
N17	A22	1a on 20pa car rose	265.00	265.00
a.		"1 An" omitted	*2,500.*	*2,500.*
N18	A22	2a on 1pi ultra	110.00	110.00

On Turkey No. 337 With Overprint ب

N19	A22	1a on 20pa car rose	*4,000.*	*4,000.*

On Turkey No. P125 with Overprint

and Overprint

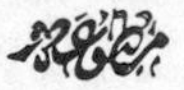

N20 A17 1a on 20pa car *2,500. 2,600.*

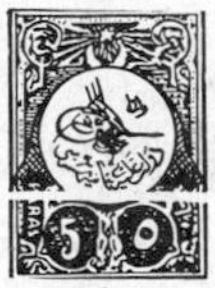
A21

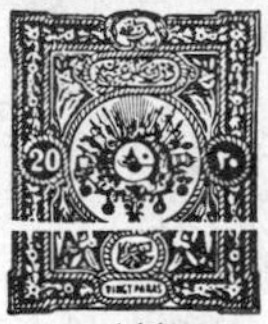
A11

On Turkey Nos. B1, B8 with Overprint

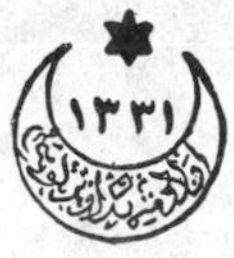

Inscription in crescent is obliterated by another crescent handstamped in violet black on Nos. N21-N27.

N21 A18 1/2a on 10pa dull grn 70.00 62.50
a. "OCCUPATION" omitted *3,250.*
N22 A21 1a on 20pa car rose 275.00 200.00

On Semi-Postal Stamps of 1916 with Overprint

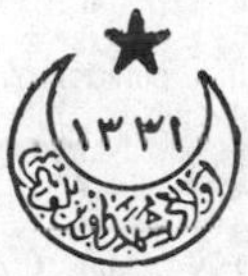

On Turkey No. B29

N23 A21 2a on 1pi ultra 900.00 900.00

On Turkey Nos. B33-B34

N24 A22 1a on 20pa car rose 85.00 85.00
N25 A22 2a on 1pi ultra 140.00 125.00
a. "OCCUPATION" omitted *3,250.*
b. "BAGHDAD" omitted *3,250.*

On Turkey No. B42

N26 A41 1/2a on 10pa car 140.00 140.00
a. "BAGHDAD" double *2,000.*

On Turkey No. B38 with Surcharge

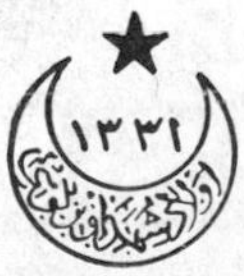

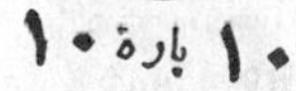

N27 A11 1a on 10pa on 20pa vio brn 190.00 200.00

Iraq Issue

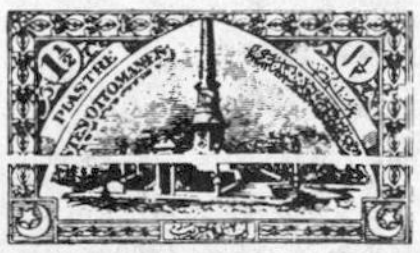
Monument to the Martyrs of Liberty — A31

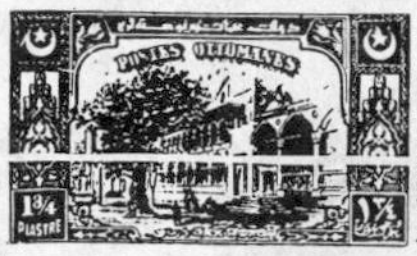
Fountains of Suleiman A32

Cruiser "Hamidie" A33

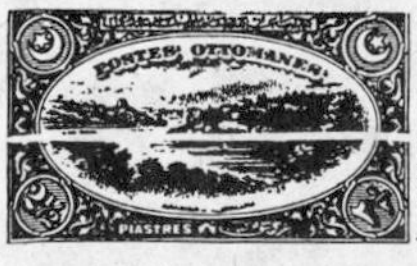
Kandili on the Bosporus A34

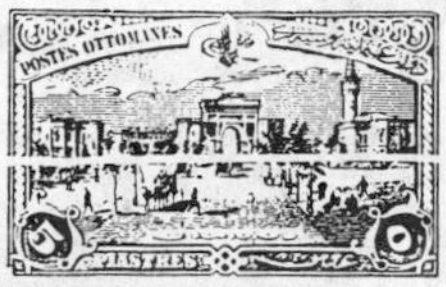
War Ministry A35

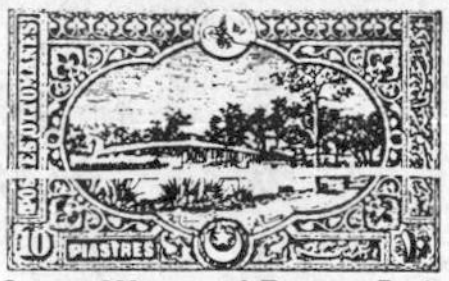
Sweet Waters of Europe Park, Constantinople — A36

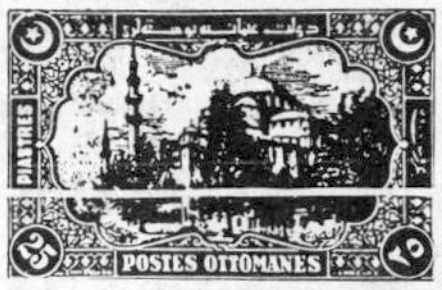
Mosque of Suleiman A37

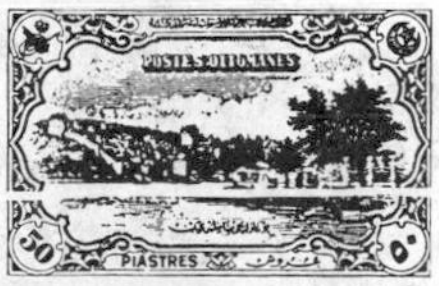
The Bosporus A38

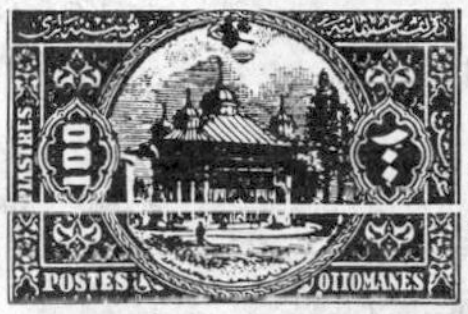
Sultan Ahmed's Fountain A39

Turkey Nos. 256, 258-269 Surcharged

IRAQ
IN BRITISH OCCUPATION
1An.

1918-20 *Perf. 12*

N28 A26 1/4a on 5pa vio brn .15 .15
N29 A28 1/2a on 10pa grn .15 .15
N30 A29 1a on 20pa red .15 .15
N31 A26 1 1/2a on 5pa vio brn .15 .15
N32 A30 2 1/2a on 1pi blue .15 .15
a. Inverted surcharge *3,250.*
N33 A31 3a on 1 1/2pi car & black .15 .15
a. Double surcharge, red & blk *1,750.*
N34 A32 4a on 1 3/4pi slate & red brn .15 .15
a. Center inverted *10,000.*
N35 A33 6a on 2pi grn & black .30 .25
N36 A34 8a on 2 1/2pi org & ol grn .25 .18
N37 A35 12a on 5pi dl vio 1.25 .50
N38 A36 1r on 10pi red brown 1.25 .45
N39 A37 2r on 25pi ol grn 3.50 2.00
N40 A38 5r on 50pi car 18.00 8.75
N41 A39 10r on 100pi dp blue 27.50 7.50
Nos. N28-N41 (14) 55.10 20.68

See #N50-N53. For overprints see #NO1-NO21.

Mosul Issue

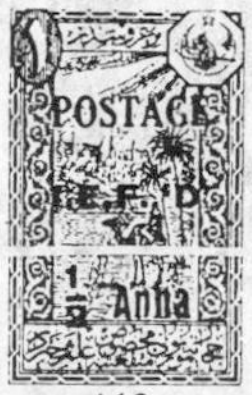
A13

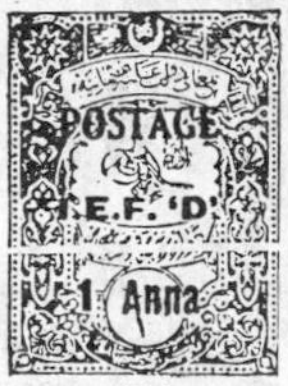
A14

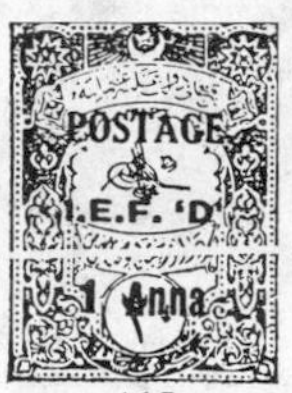
A15

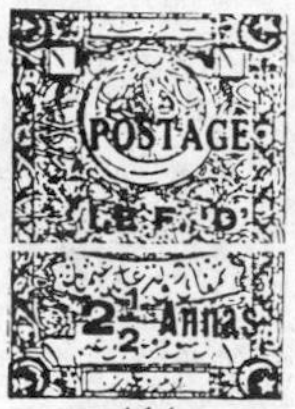
A16

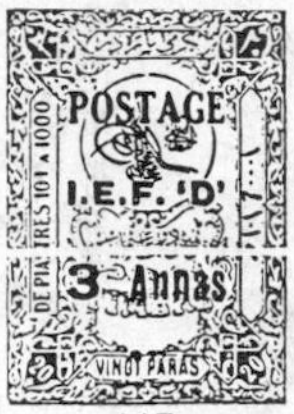
A17

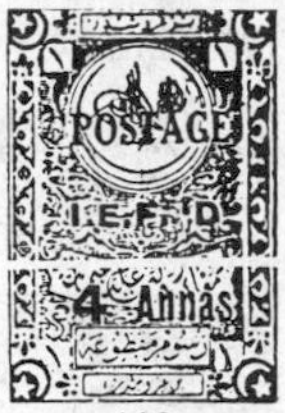
A18

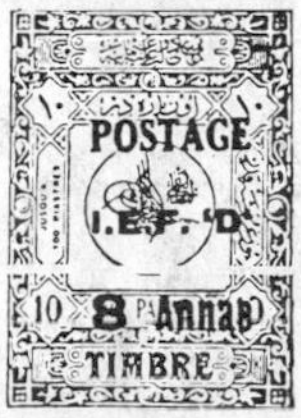
A19

1919 Unwmk. *Perf. 11 1/2, 12*

N42 A13 1/2a on 1pi grn & brn red .85 .50
N43 A14 1a on 20pa *rose* .85 .50
a. "POSTAGE" omitted
N44 A15 1a on 20pa *rose* 3.75 3.75
a. Double surcharge

Turkish word at right of tughra ("reshad") is large on No. N43, small on No. N44.

Wmk. Turkish Characters
Perf. 12 1/2

N45 A16 2 1/2a on 1pi vio & yel .38 .30
N46 A17 3a on 20pa grn & yel 25.00 25.00

Wmk. 48

N47 A17 3a on 20pa green 1.00 .50
N48 A18 4a on 1pi dull vio 2.00 1.40
a. Double surcharge
b. "4" omitted 1,650.
c. As "b," double surcharge
N49 A19 8a on 10pa claret 2.50 2.00
a. Double surcharge *500.00*
b. Inverted surcharge *500.00*
c. 8a on 1pi dull violet *1,100.*
Nos. N42-N49 (8) 36.33 33.95

Value for No. 49c is for copies with the perfs cutting into the design.

Iraq Issue
Types of 1918-20 Issue

1921 Wmk. 4 *Perf. 12*

N50 A28 1/2a on 10pa green .50 .25
N51 A26 1 1/2a on 5pa dp brn .50 .25
N52 A37 2r on 25pi ol grn 11.00 10.00
Nos. N50-N52 (3) 12.00 10.50

Type of 1918-20 without "Reshad"

1922 Unwmk.

N53 A36 1r on 10pi red brn 110.00 12.50

"Reshad" is the small Turkish word at right of the tughra in circle at top center.
For overprint, see No. NO22.

OFFICIAL STAMPS

Nos. N29-N41 Overprinted:

ON STATE SERVICE

1920 Unwmk. *Perf. 12*

NO1 A28 1/2a on 10pa green .18 .15
NO2 A29 1a on 20pa red .25 .15
NO3 A26 1 1/2a on 5pa vio brown 1.10 .35
NO4 A30 2 1/2a on 1pi blue 1.10 .60
NO5 A31 3a on 1 1/2pi car & black 1.10 .38
NO6 A32 4a on 1 3/4pi sl & red brn 1.65 .50
NO7 A33 6a on 2pi grn & black 1.10 .38
NO8 A34 8a on 2 1/2pi org & ol grn 1.10 .50
NO9 A35 12a on 5pi dull violet 2.75 1.65
NO10 A36 1r on 10pi red brown 2.75 1.10
NO11 A37 2r on 25pi ol green 7.25 8.00
NO12 A38 5r on 50pi car 30.00 15.00
NO13 A39 10r on 100pi dp blue 45.00 19.00
Nos. NO1-NO13 (13) 95.33 47.76

Same Overprint on Types of Regular Issue of 1918-20

1921-22 Wmk. 4

NO14 A28 1/2a on 10pa green .15 .15
NO15 A29 1a on 20pa red .15 .15
NO16 A26 1 1/2a on 5pa dp brn .28 .28
NO17 A32 4a on 1 3/4pi gray & red brn .28 .28
NO18 A33 6a on 2pi grn & black 3.75 3.25
NO19 A34 8a on 2 1/2pi org & yel grn .80 .55
NO20 A35 12a on 5pi dl vio 2.75 2.75
NO21 A37 2r on 25pi ol grn 20.00 14.00
Nos. NO14-NO21 (8) 28.16 21.41

Same Overprint on No. N53

1922 Unwmk.

NO22 A36 1r on 10pi red brn 12.00 5.00

NAMIBIA

nə-'mi-bē-ə

LOCATION — In southwestern Africa between Angola and South Africa, bordering on the Atlantic Ocean
GOVT. — Republic
AREA — 318,261 sq. mi.
POP. — 1,372,475 (1989)
CAPITAL — Windhoek

Formerly South West Africa.

100 Cents = 1 Rand
100 Cents = 1 Dollar (1993)

Catalogue values for unused stamps in this country are for Never Hinged items.

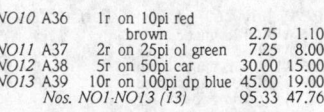

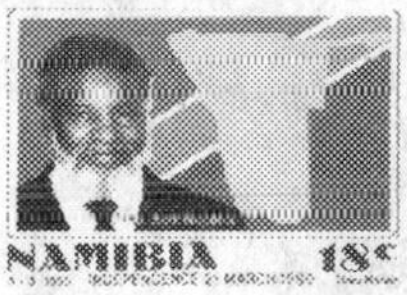
Pres. Sam Nujoma, Map and Natl. Flag — A137

Perf. 14 1/2x14, 14x14 1/2

1990, Mar. 21 Litho. Unwmk.

659 A137 18c shown .15 .15
660 A137 45c Dove, map, hands unchained, vert. .35 .35
661 A137 60c Flag, map .50 .50
Nos. 659-661 (3) 1.00 1.00

Independence from South Africa.

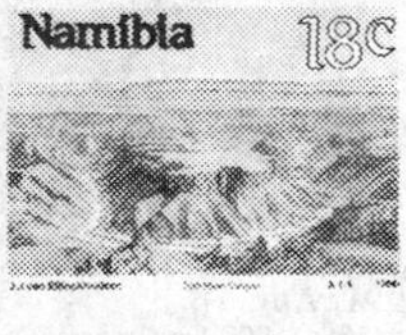
Sights of Namibia A138

1990, Apr. 26 *Perf. 14 1/2x14*

662 A138 18c Fish River Canyon .15 .15
663 A138 35c Quiver-tree Forest .30 .30
664 A138 45c Tsaris Mountains .35 .35
665 A138 60c Dolerite Hills .50 .50
a. Souvenir sheet of 1 1.25 1.25
Nos. 662-665 (4) 1.30 1.30

No. 665a publicizies the 150th anniv. of the Penny Black. Sold for 1.50r.

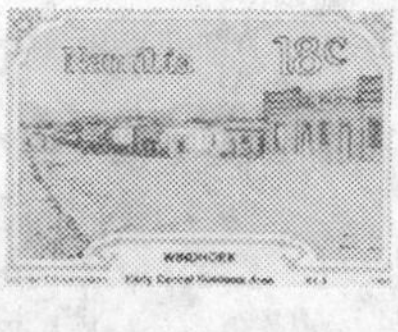
Architectural Development of Windhoek A139

Designs: 18c, Early central business area. 35c, Modern central business area. 45c, First municipal building. 60c, Current municipal building.

1990, July 26 *Perf. 14½x14*

666	A139	18c	multicolored	.15	.15
667	A139	35c	multicolored	.30	.30
668	A139	45c	multicolored	.35	.35
669	A139	60c	multicolored	.50	.50
			Nos. 666-669 (4)	1.30	1.30

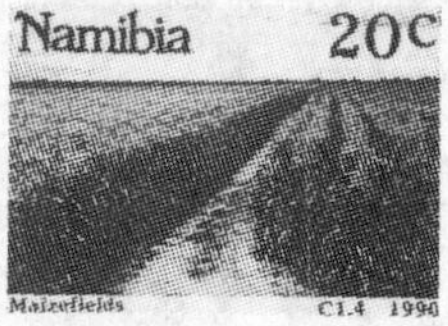

Farming and Ranching A140

1990, Oct. 11 *Perf. 14½x14*

670	A140	20c	Cornfields	.15	.15
671	A140	35c	Sanga cattle	.30	.30
672	A140	50c	Damara sheep	.40	.40
673	A140	65c	Irrigation	.50	.50
			Nos. 670-673 (4)	1.35	1.35

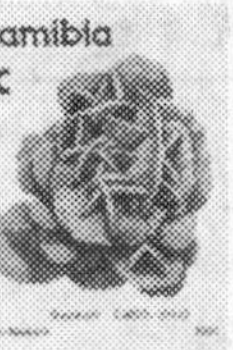

Gypsum A141

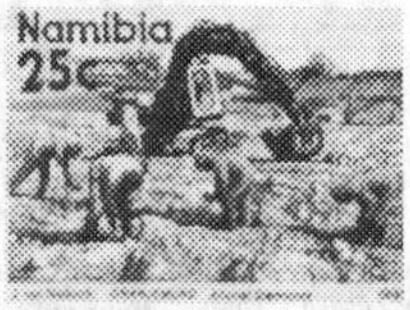

Oranjemund Alluvial Diamond Mine A142

1991, Jan. 2 *Perf. 14½x14*

674	A141	1c	shown	.15	.15
675	A141	2c	Flourite	.15	.15
676	A141	5c	Mimetite	.15	.15
677	A141	10c	Azurite	.15	.15
679	A141	20c	Dioptase	.15	.15
680	A142	25c	shown	.20	.20
681	A142	30c	Tsumeb mine	.20	.20
682	A142	35c	Rosh Pinah mine	.25	.25
683	A141	40c	Diamond	.30	.30
684	A142	50c	Uis mine	.40	.40
685	A141	65c	Boltwoodite	.50	.50
686	A142	1r	Rossing mine	.75	.75
687	A141	1.50r	Wolfenite	1.10	1.10
688	A141	2r	Gold	1.50	1.50
689	A141	5r	Willemite	3.75	3.75
			Nos. 674-689 (15)	9.70	9.70

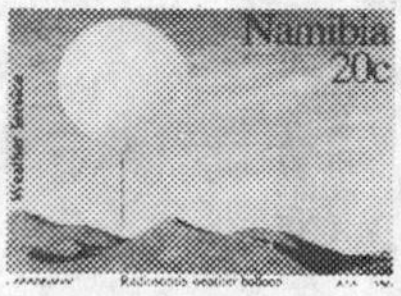

Namibian Weather Service, Cent. — A143

1991, Feb. 2 *Perf. 14½x14*

690	A143	20c	Weather balloon	.15	.15
691	A143	35c	Sunshine recorder	.30	.30
692	A143	50c	Measuring equipment	.40	.40
693	A143	65c	Gobabeb weather station	.50	.50
			Nos. 690-693 (4)	1.35	1.35

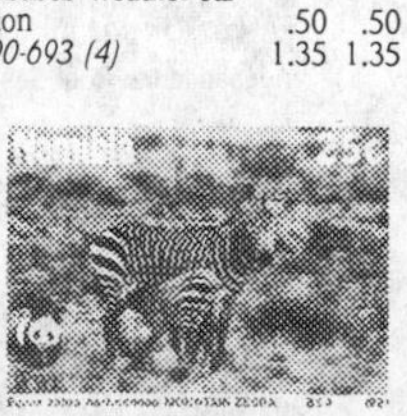

Mountain Zebra — A144

1991, Apr. 18 *Perf. 14½x14*

694	A144	20c	Four zebras	.15	.15
695	A144	25c	Mother suckling foal	.20	.20
696	A144	45c	Three zebras	.35	.35
697	A144	60c	Two zebras	.50	.50
			Nos. 694-697 (4)	1.20	1.20

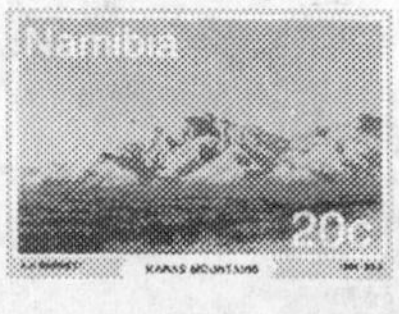

Mountains A145

1991, July 18 *Perf. 14½x14*

698	A145	20c	Karas	.15	.15
699	A145	25c	Gamsberg	.20	.20
700	A145	45c	Brukkaros	.35	.35
701	A145	60c	Erongo	.50	.50
			Nos. 698-701 (4)	1.20	1.20

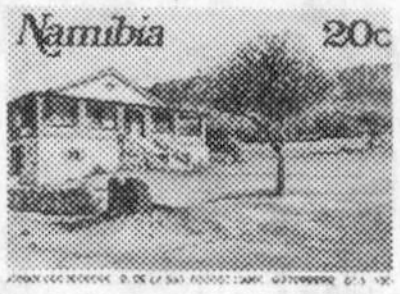

Tourist Camps — A146

Designs: 20c, Bernabe De la Bat Tourist Camp, Waterberg. 25c, Von Bach Recreation Resort. 45c, Gross Barmen Hot Springs. 60c, Namutoni Rest Camp.

1991, Oct. 24 *Perf. 14½x14*

702	A146	20c	multicolored	.15	.15
703	A146	25c	multicolored	.20	.20
704	A146	45c	multicolored	.35	.35
705	A146	60c	multicolored	.50	.50
			Nos. 702-705 (4)	1.20	1.20

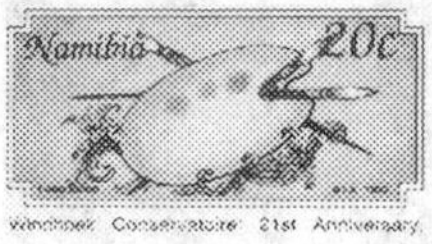

Windhoek Conservatoir, 21st Anniv. A147

Designs: 20c, Artist's palette, brushes. 25c, French horn, neck of violin. 45c, Pan pipes, masks of Comedy and Tragedy, lyre. 60c, Ballet pas de deux.

1992, Jan. 30 *Perf. 14x14½*

706	A147	20c	multicolored	.15	.15
707	A147	25c	multicolored	.20	.20
708	A147	45c	multicolored	.35	.35
709	A147	60c	multicolored	.50	.50
			Nos. 706-709 (4)	1.20	1.20

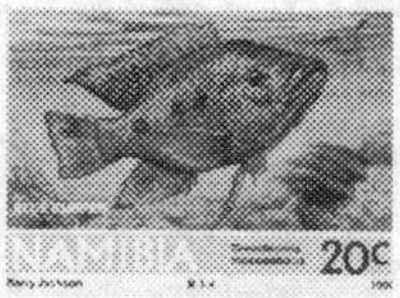

Freshwater Fish — A148

1992, Apr. 16 *Perf. 14½x14*

710	A148	20c	Blue kurper	.15	.15
711	A148	25c	Yellow fish	.20	.20
712	A148	45c	Carp	.35	.35
713	A148	60c	Catfish	.50	.50
			Nos. 710-713 (4)	1.20	1.20

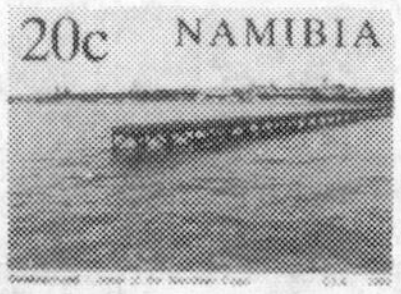

Views of Swakopmund A149

1992, July 2 *Perf. 14½x14*

714	A149	20c	Jetty	.15	.15
715	A149	25c	Swimming pool	.20	.20
716	A149	45c	State House, lighthouse	.35	.35
717	A149	60c	Palm beach	.50	.50
a.			Souvenir sheet of 4, #714-717	1.25	1.25
			Nos. 714-717 (4)	1.20	1.20

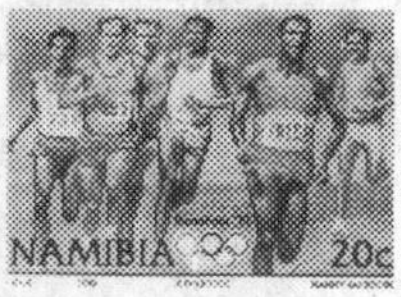

1992 Summer Olympics, Barcelona A150

1992, July 24 *Perf. 14½x14*

718	A150	20c	Runners	.15	.15
719	A150	25c	Flag, emblem	.20	.20
720	A150	45c	Swimmers	.35	.35
721	A150	60c	Olympic stadium	.50	.50
a.			Souvenir sheet of 4, #718-721	1.60	1.60
			Nos. 718-721 (4)	1.20	1.20

No. 721a sold for 2r.

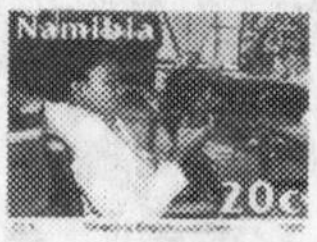

Disabled Workers — A151

Designs: 20c, Wrapping cucumbers. 25c, Finishing a woven mat. 45c, At a spinning wheel. 60c, Cleaning potted plants.

1992, Sept. 10 *Perf. 14x14½*

722	A151	20c	multicolored	.15	.15
723	A151	25c	multicolored	.20	.20
724	A151	45c	multicolored	.35	.35
725	A151	60c	multicolored	.50	.50
			Nos. 722-725 (4)	1.20	1.20

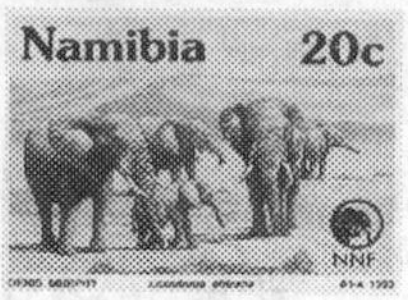

Endangered Animals A152

1993, Feb. 25 *Perf. 14½x14*

726	A152	20c	Loxodonta africana	.15	.15
727	A152	25c	Tragelaphus spekei	.20	.20
728	A152	45c	Diceros bicornis	.32	.32
729	A152	60c	Lycaon pictus	.40	.40
a.			Souvenir sheet of 4, #726-729	1.25	1.25
			Nos. 726-729 (4)	1.07	1.07

Namibia Nature Foundation. No. 729a sold for 2.10r.

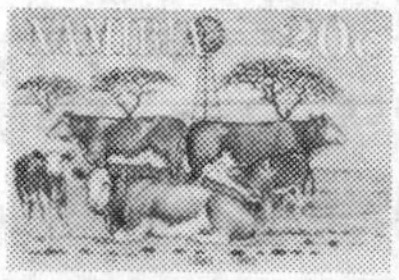

Arrival of Simmentaler Cattle in Namibia, Cent. — A153

1993, Apr. 16 *Perf. 14½x14*

730	A153	20c	Cows and calves	.15	.15
731	A153	25c	Cow and calf	.20	.20
732	A153	45c	Head of stud bull	.30	.30
733	A153	60c	Arrival on boat, 1893	.40	.40
			Nos. 730-733 (4)	1.05	1.05

A souvenir sheet of one No. 732 has inscription for National Philatelic Exhibition. Sold for 3r.

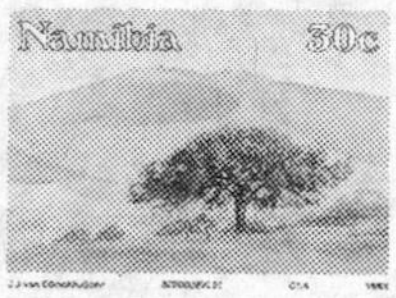

Namib Desert — A154

1993, June 4 *Perf. 14½x14*

734	A154	30c	Sossusvlei	.20	.20
735	A154	40c	Blutkuppe	.30	.30
736	A154	65c	Homeb	.45	.45
737	A154	85c	Moon landscape	.60	.60
			Nos. 734-737 (4)	1.55	1.55

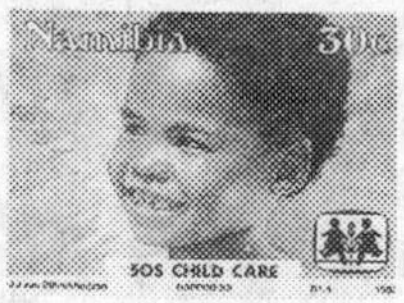

SOS Children's Village — A155

1993, Aug. 6 **Litho.** *Perf. 14*

738	A155	30c	Happiness	.20	.20
739	A155	40c	A loving family	.30	.30
740	A155	65c	Home sweet home	.45	.45
741	A155	85c	My village	.60	.60
			Nos. 738-741 (4)	1.55	1.55

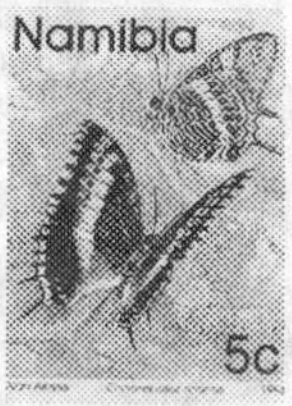

Butterflies — A156

Designs: 5c, Charaxes jasius saturnus. 10c, Acraea anemosa. 20c, Papilio nireus lyaeus. 30c, Junonia octavia sesamus. (35c), Graphium antheus. 40c, Hypolimnas misippus. 50c, Physcaeneura panda. 65c, Charaxes candiope. 85c, Junonia hierta cebrene. 90c, Colotis celimene pholoe. $1, Cacyreus dicksoni. $2, Charaxes bohemani. $2.50, Stugeta bowkeri tearei. $5, Byblia anvatara acheloia.

1993-94 *Perf. 14x14½*

742	A156	5c	multicolored	.15	.15
743	A156	10c	multicolored	.15	.15
744	A156	20c	multicolored	.15	.15
745	A156	30c	multicolored	.20	.20
745A	A156	(35c)	multicolored	2.25	2.25
746	A156	40c	multicolored	.30	.30
747	A156	50c	multicolored	.35	.35
748	A156	65c	multicolored	.45	.45
749	A156	85c	multicolored	.60	.60
750	A156	90c	multicolored	.65	.65
751	A156	$1	multicolored	.70	.70
752	A156	$2	multicolored	1.40	1.40
753	A156	$2.50	multicolored	1.75	1.75
754	A156	$5	multicolored	3.50	3.50
			Nos. 742-754 (14)	12.60	12.60

No. 745A is inscribed "STANDARDISED MAIL" and sold for 35c when issued.

Issued: No. 745A, 4/8/94; others, 10/1/93.

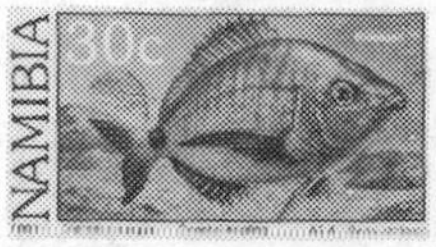

Coastal Angling A157

1994, Feb. 4 **Litho.** *Perf. 14*

755	A157	30c	Blacktail	.20	.20
756	A157	40c	Kob	.25	.25
757	A157	65c	Steenbras	.40	.40
758	A157	85c	Galjoen	.55	.55
a.			Souvenir sheet of 4, #755-758	1.40	1.40
			Nos. 755-758 (4)	1.40	1.40

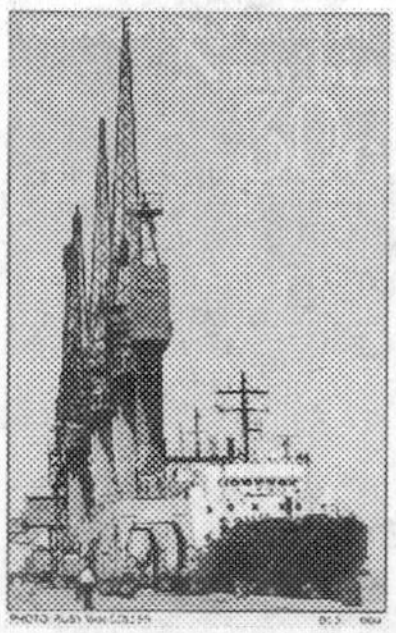

Incorporation of Walvis Bay into Namibia A158

1994, Mar. 1

759	A158	30c	Quay	.20	.20
760	A158	65c	Aerial view	.40	.40
761	A158	85c	Map of Namibia	.55	.55
			Nos. 759-761 (3)	1.15	1.15

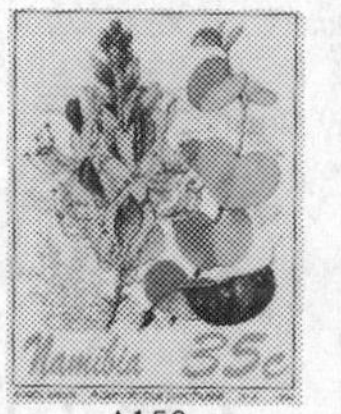

A159

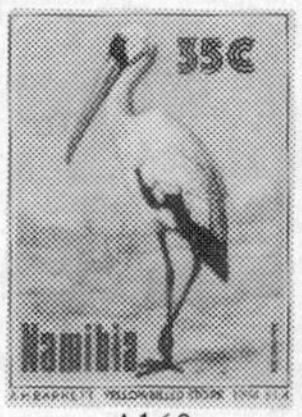

A160

Flowers: 35c, Adenolobus pechuelii. 40c, Hibiscus elliottiae. 65c, Pelargonium cortusifolium. 85c, Hoodia macrantha.

1994, Apr. 8 **Litho.** *Perf. 14*

762	A159	35c	multicolored	.20	.20
763	A159	40c	multicolored	.20	.20
764	A159	65c	multicolored	.40	.40
765	A159	85c	multicolored	.50	.50
			Nos. 762-765 (4)	1.30	1.30

1994, June 3 **Litho.** *Perf. 14*

Storks of Etosha.

766	A160	35c	Yellowbilled	.20	.20
767	A160	40c	Abdim's	.20	.20
768	A160	80c	Openbilled	.45	.45
769	A160	$1.10	White	.65	.65
			Nos. 766-769 (4)	1.50	1.50

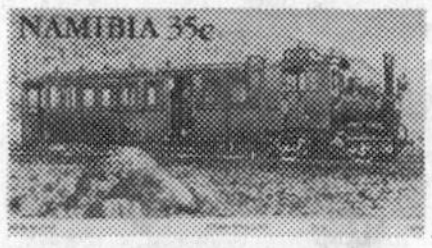

Trains A161

1994, Aug. 5 **Litho.** *Perf. 13½x14*

770	A161	35c	Steam railcar	.20	.20
771	A161	70c	Class Krauss	.40	.40
772	A161	80c	Class 24	.45	.45
773	A161	$1.10	Class 7C	.65	.65
			Nos. 770-773 (4)	1.70	1.70

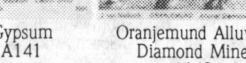

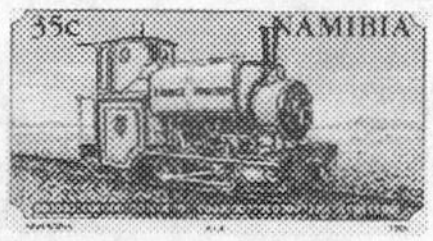

Railways in Namibia, Cent. A162

Locomotives: 35c, Prince Edward, 1st in service. 70c, Ex-German SWA 2-8-0 tank. 80c, Class 8. $1.10, Class 33 400 diesel electric.

1995, Mar. 8 Litho. *Perf. 14*

774	A162	35c multicolored	.20	.20
775	A162	70c multicolored	.40	.40
776	A162	80c multicolored	.50	.50
777	A162	$1.10 multicolored	.65	.65
a.		Souvenir sheet of 4, #774-777	2.00	2.00
		Nos. 774-777 (4)	1.75	1.75

No. 777a sold for $3.50.

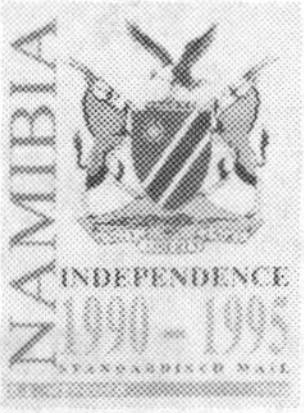

A163

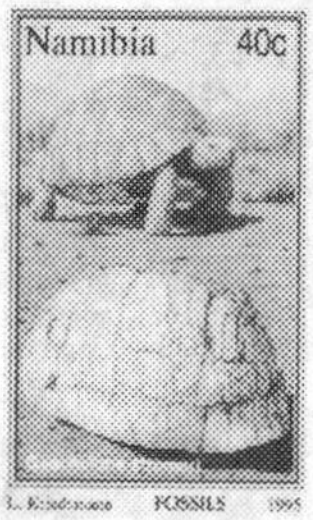

A164

1995, Mar. 21 Litho. *Perf. 14*

778	A163	(35c) multicolored	.20	.20

Independence, 5th anniv. No. 778 is inscribed "STANDARDISED MAIL" and sold for 35c on day of issue.

1995, May 24 Litho. *Perf. 14*

Fossils: 40c, Geochelone stromeri. 80c, Diamantornis wardi. 90c, Prohyrax hendeyi. $1.20, Crocodylus lloydi.

779	A164	40c multicolored	.20	.20
780	A164	80c multicolored	.45	.45
a.		Souvenir sheet of 1	.45	.45
781	A164	90c multicolored	.50	.50
782	A164	$1.20 multicolored	.65	.65
		Nos. 779-782 (4)	1.80	1.80

No. 780a is a continuous design.

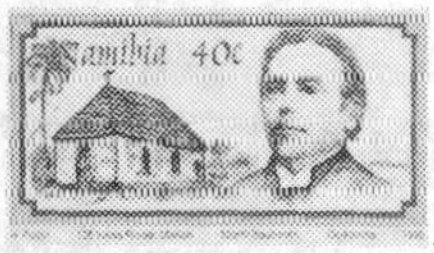

Finnish Mission, 125th Anniv. A165

Designs: 40c, Mission church, Martti Rautanen (1845-1926). 80c, Albin Savola (1867-1934), Oniipa printing press. 90c, Oxwagon, Karl Emanuel August Weikkolin (1842-91). $1.20, Dr. Selma Raino (1873-1939), Onandjokwe Hospital.

1995, July 10 Litho. *Perf. 14*

783	A165	40c multicolored	.20	.20
784	A165	80c multicolored	.45	.45
785	A165	90c multicolored	.50	.50
786	A165	$1.20 multicolored	.65	.65
		Nos. 783-786 (4)	1.80	1.80

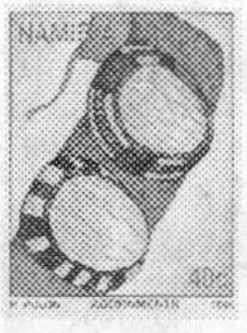

Traditional Adornments — A166

1995, Aug. 16 Litho. *Perf. 14½x14*

787	A166	40c Ivory buttons	.25	.25
788	A166	80c Conus shell	.50	.50
789	A166	90c Cowrie shells	.55	.55
790	A166	$1.20 Shell button	.75	.75
		Nos. 787-790 (4)	2.05	2.05

Souvenir Sheet

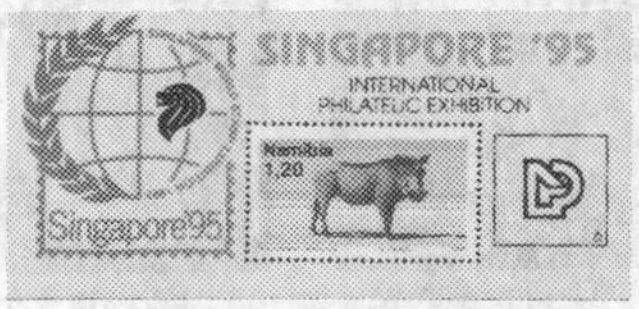

Singapore '95 — A167

Illustration reduced.

1995, Sept. 10 Litho. *Perf. 14*

791	A167	$1.20 Phacochoerus aethiopicus	.75	.75

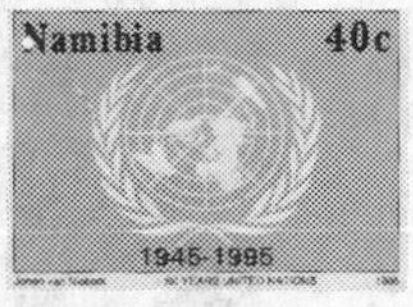

UN, 50th Anniv. — A168

1995, Oct. 24

792	A168	40c blue & black	.25	.25

NATAL

nə-'tal

LOCATION — Southern coast of Africa, bordering on the Indian Ocean
GOVT. — Former British Crown Colony
AREA — 35,284 sq. mi.
POP. — 1,206,386 (1908)
CAPITAL — Pietermaritzburg

Natal united with Cape of Good Hope, Orange Free State and the Transvaal in 1910 to form the Union of South Africa.

12 Pence = 1 Shilling
20 Shillings = 1 Pound

Values for Nos. 1-7 are for examples with complete margins and free from damage. Unused values for No. 8 on are for stamps with original gum as defined in the catalogue introduction. Very fine examples of Nos. 8-49, 61-63 and 79 will have perforations touching the design on one or more sides due to the narrow spacing of the stamps on the plates. Stamps with perfs clear of the design on all four sides are scarce and will command higher prices.

Watermark

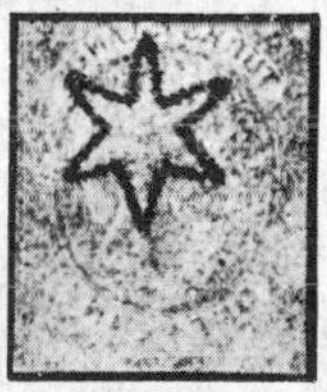

Wmk. 5 - Small Star

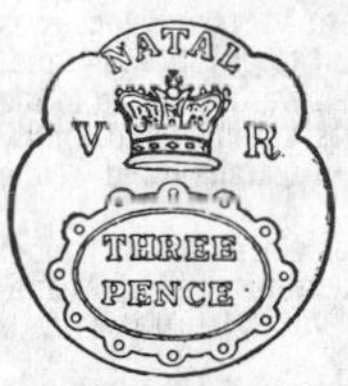

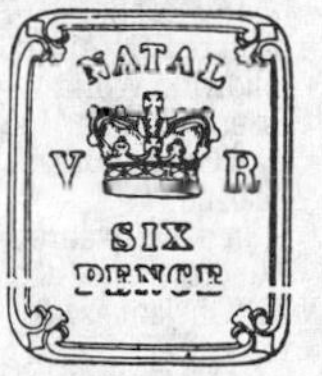

Crown and V R (Victoria Regina) A2

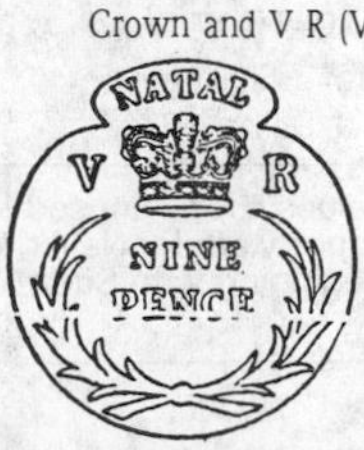

Crown and Laurel — A3

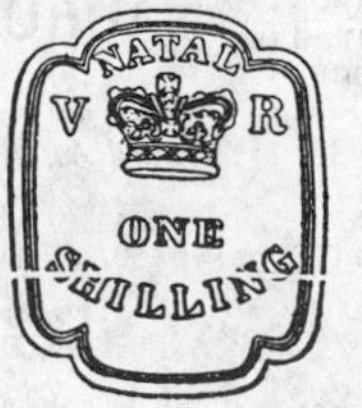

A4

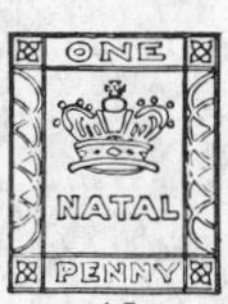

A5

Colorless Embossing

1857 Unwmk. *Imperf.*

1	A1	3p *rose*	550.
a.		Tete beche pair	*15,000.*
2	A2	6p *green*	1,200.
a.		Diagonal half used as 3p on cover	*10,000.*
3	A3	9p *blue*	*10,000.*
4	A4	1sh *buff*	*8,500.*

1858

5	A5	1p *blue*	1,200.
6	A5	1p *rose*	1,850.
a.		No. 1 embossed over No. 6	—
7	A5	1p *buff*	1,000.

Reprints: The paper is slightly glazed, the embossing sharper and the colors as follows: 1p pale blue, deep blue, carmine rose or yellow; 3p pale rose or carmine rose; 6p bright green or yellow green; 1sh pale buff or pale yellow. Bogus cancellations are found on the reprints.

The stamps printed on surface-colored paper are revenue stamps with trimmed perforations.

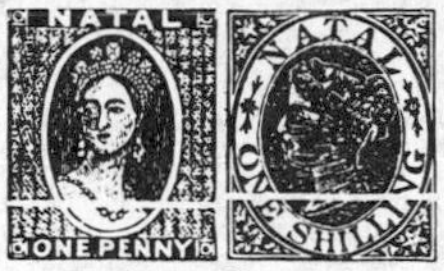

Queen Victoria
A6 A7

1860 Engr. *Perf. 14*

8	A6	1p rose	135.00	70.00
9	A6	3p blue	125.00	40.00

1863 *Perf. 13*

10	A6	1p carmine lake	75.00	25.00

1861 *Clean-cut Perf. 14 to 16*

11	A6	3p blue	175.00	65.00

1862 *Rough Perf. 14 to 16*

12	A6	3p blue	90.00	27.50
a.		Imperf., pair		*1,750.*
b.		Imperf. horiz. or vert., pair	*2,250.*	
13	A6	6p gray	135.00	47.50

1862 Wmk. 5

14	A6	1p rose	120.00	50.00

Imperforate copies of the 1p and 3p on paper watermarked small star are proofs.

1864 Wmk. 1 *Perf. 12½*

15	A6	1p carmine red	75.00	30.00
a.		1p brown red	110.00	32.50
b.		Imperf.		
16	A6	6p violet	37.50	15.00
a.		6p dull violet	55.00	25.00

1867 Typo. *Perf. 14*

17	A7	1sh green	130.00	25.00

For types A6 and A7 overprinted or surcharged see Nos. 18-50, 61-63, 76, 79.

Stamps of 1860-67 Overprinted: **Postage.**

1869

Overprint 12¾mm

18	A6	1p rose red (#15)	250.00	60.00
a.		Double overprint		500.00
19	A6	3p blue (#12)	360.00	82.50
19A	A6	3p blue (#9)		475.00
19B	A6	3p blue (#11)	500.00	200.00
20	A6	6p violet (#16)	425.00	60.00
21	A7	1sh green (#17)		550.00

Same Overprint 13¾mm

22	A6	1p rose red (#15)	450.00	150.00
23	A6	3p blue (#12)	1,000.	235.00
a.		Inverted overprint		
23B	A6	3p blue (#9)		
23C	A6	3p blue (#11)		
24	A6	6p violet (#16)	900.00	120.00
25	A7	1sh green (#17)		*1,250.*

Same Overprint 14½ to 15½mm

26	A6	1p rose red (#15)	450.00	150.00
27	A6	3p blue (#12)		200.00
27A	A6	3p blue (#11)		250.00
27B	A6	3p blue (#9)		
28	A6	6p violet (#16)	900.00	75.00
29	A7	1sh green (#17)		*1,350.*

Overprinted **POSTAGE.**

30	A6	1p rose red (#15)	70.00	25.00
a.		1p carmine red	120.00	25.00
b.		Inverted overprint		
31	A6	3p blue (#12)	125.00	40.00
a.		Double overprint		550.00
31B	A6	3p blue (#11)	100.00	27.50
31C	A6	3p blue (#9)	225.00	40.00
32	A6	6p violet (#16)	100.00	42.50
33	A7	1sh green (#17)	150.00	55.00

Overprinted POSTAGE

34	A6	1p rose red (#15)	225.00	50.00
35	A6	3p blue (#12)	350.00	75.00
35A	A6	3p blue (#11)	400.00	190.00
35B	A6	3p blue (#9)		
36	A6	6p violet (#16)	325.00	50.00
a.		Inverted overprint		
37	A7	1sh green (#17)		*1,000.*

Overprinted in Black or Red POSTAGE POSTAGE

1870-73 Wmk. 1 *Perf. 12½*

38	A6	1p red	60.00	12.00
39	A6	3p ultra (R) ('72)	60.00	12.00
40	A6	6p lilac ('73)	120.00	24.00
		Nos. 38-40 (3)	240.00	48.00

Overprinted in Red, Black or Green

g POSTAGE

1870 *Perf. 14*

41	A7	1sh green (R)	*3,000.*	
42	A7	1sh green (Bk)	*2,000.*	*1,000.*
a.		Double overprint	*3,000.*	*1,250.*
43	A7	1sh green (G)	45.00	10.00

See No. 76.

Type of 1867 Overprinted POSTAGE

1873

44	A7	1sh brown lilac	110.00	17.50

No. 44 without overprint is a revenue.

Type of 1864 Overprinted POSTAGE POSTAGE

1874 *Perf. 12½*

45	A6	1p rose red	140.00	50.00
a.		Double overprint		

Overprinted POSTAGE

1875

46	A6	1p carmine	75.00	7.50
a.		1p rose red	75.00	27.50
b.		Double overprint	400.00	275.00

Overprinted **POSTAGE**

Overprint 14½mm

1875 *Perf. 12½*

47	A6	1p yellow	70.00	70.00
48	A6	1p rose red	70.00	45.00
a.		Inverted overprint	500.00	400.00
49	A6	6p violet	50.00	5.00
a.		Inverted overprint	600.00	175.00
b.		Double overprint		525.00

Perf. 14

50	A7	1sh green	80.00	5.00
a.		Double overprint		300.00
		Nos. 47-50 (4)	270.00	125.00

The 1p yellow without overprint is a revenue.

A8

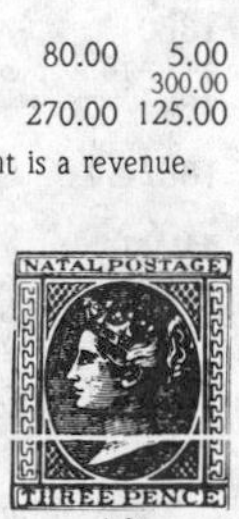

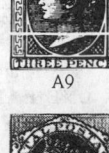

A9

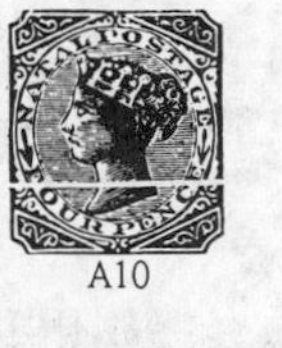

A10

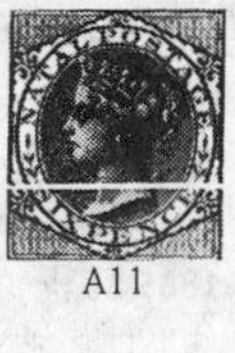

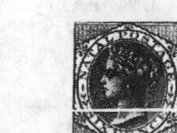

A11

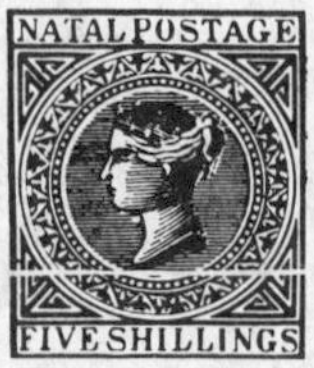

Queen Victoria — A12

1874-78 Typo. Wmk. 1 *Perf. 14*

51 A8 1p rose 20.00 1.90
52 A9 3p ultramarine 75.00 13.00
a. Perf. 14x12½ 1,400. 900.00
53 A10 4p brown ('78) 85.00 10.00
54 A11 6p violet 30.00 5.00

Perf. 15½x15

55 A12 5sh claret 125.00 35.00

Perf. 14

56 A12 5sh claret ('78) 110.00 25.00
57 A12 5sh rose ('78) 60.00 25.00

Perf. 12½

58 A10 4p brown ('78) 325.00 60.00

See Nos. 65-71. For types A8-A10 surcharged see Nos. 59-60, 72-73, 77, 80.

Surcharged in Black:

POSTAGE

HALF ½ — n

Half-penny ½ — No. 60

o

1877 *Perf. 14*

59 A8(n) ½p on 1p rose 20.00 60.00
a. Double surcharge "1/2"
60 A8(n) ½p on 1p rose 40.00 80.00

The "1/2" only of No. 60 is illustrated. Surcharge "n" exists in 3 or more types each of the large "1/2" (No. 59) and the small "1/2" (No. 60).

"HALF" and "½" were overprinted separately; "½" may be above, below or overlapping.

Perf. 12½

61 A6(o) ½p on 1p yel 8.00 10.00
a. Double surcharge 250.00 175.00
b. Inverted surcharge 250.00 175.00
c. Pair, one without surcharge 1,000. 900.00
d. "POTAGE" 200.00 175.00
e. "POSAGE" 200.00 175.00
f. "POSTAGE" omitted 1,100.
62 A6(o) 1p on 6p vio 40.00 8.00
a. "POSTAGE" omitted
b. "POTAGE" 275.00 150.00
63 A6(o) 1p on 6p rose 80.00 25.00
a. Inverted surcharge 275.00
b. Double surcharge 225.00
c. Dbl. surch., one inverted 250.00 190.00
d. Triple surch., one invtd.
e. Quadruple surcharge 350.00 190.00
f. "POTAGE" 350.00
Nos. 61-63 (3) 128.00 43.00

No. 63 without overprint is a revenue.

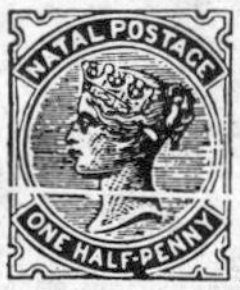

A14

1880 Typo. *Perf. 14*

64 A14 ½p blue green 9.00 10.00
a. Vertical pair, imperf. between

1882-89 Wmk. Crown and CA (2)

65 A14 ½p blue green ('84) 85.00 15.00
66 A14 ½p gray green ('84) .75 .25
67 A8 1p rose ('84) .85 .15
68 A9 3p ultra ('84) 90.00 15.00
69 A9 3p gray ('89) 2.00 1.00
70 A10 4p brown 2.50 .50
71 A11 6p violet 3.00 .75
Nos. 65-71 (7) 184.10 32.65

Surcharged in Black:

ONE HALF-PENNY.

p

TWO PENCE

q

1885-86

72 A8(p) ½p on 1p rose 15.00 11.00
73 A9(q) 2p on 3p gray ('86) 18.00 6.00

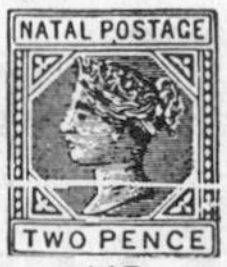

A17

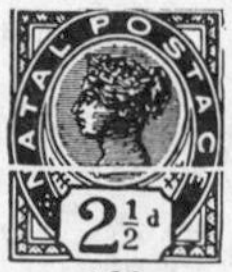

A20

1887

74 A17 2p olive green, die B 1.00 .50
a. Die A 15.00 1.50

For explanation of dies A and B see back of this section of the Catalogue.

Type of 1867 Overprinted Type "g" in Red

1888

76 A7 1sh orange 1.25 .50
a. Double overprint

Surcharged in Black — TWOPENCE HALFPENNY

1891

77 A10 2½p on 4p brown 5.25 5.00
a. "PENGE" 40.00 32.50
b. "PENN" 325.00 110.00
c. Double surcharge 175.00 100.00
d. Inverted surcharge 185.00 110.00

1891, June

78 A20 2½p ultramarine 2.00 1.00

Surcharged in Red or Black:

POSTAGE.

Half-Penny

No. 79

HALF

No. 80

1895, Mar. Wmk. 1 *Perf. 12½*

79 A6 ½p on 6p vio (R) .45 2.50
a. "Ealf" 12.50 20.00
b. "Penny" 10.00 16.00
c. Double surcharge, one vertical 325.00

Stamps with fancy "P," "T" or "A" in surcharge sell for twice as much.

Wmk. 2 *Perf. 14*

80 A8 ½p on 1p rose (Bk) .50 .75
a. Pair, one without and the other with double surcharge

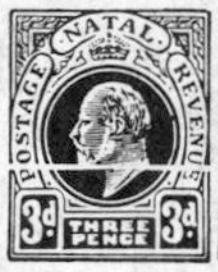

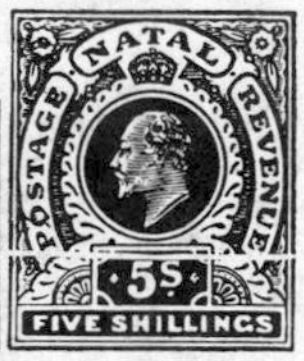

King Edward VII
A23 A24

1902-03 Typo. Wmk. 2 *Perf. 14*

81 A23 ½p blue green .60 .15
82 A23 1p rose 1.10 .15
83 A23 1½p blk & blue grn 1.10 .85
84 A23 2p ol grn & scar .70 .20
85 A23 2½p ultramarine .90 2.50
86 A23 3p gray & red vio .70 .35
87 A23 4p brown & scar 2.50 7.50
88 A23 5p org & black 1.10 2.50
89 A23 6p mar & bl grn 1.10 .90
90 A23 1sh pale bl & dp rose 3.00 1.00
91 A23 2sh vio & bl grn 42.50 8.00
92 A23 2sh6p red violet 30.00 9.50
93 A23 4sh yel & dp rose 52.50 47.50

Wmk. 1

94 A24 5sh car lake & dk blue 18.00 7.50
95 A24 10sh brn & dp rose 45.00 25.00
96 A24 £1 ultra & blk 125.00 40.00
97 A24 £1 10sh vio & bl green 225.00 65.00
Revenue cancel 1.65
98 A24 £5 black & vio *1,750.* *325.00*
Revenue cancel 11.00
99 A24 £10 org & green *7,000.*
Revenue cancel 82.50
100 A24 £20 green & car *11,500.*
Revenue cancel 140.00
Nos. 81-96 (16) 325.80 153.60

1904-08 Wmk. 3

101 A23 ½p blue green 2.00 .15
102 A23 1p rose 2.00 .15
a. Booklet pane of 6
b. Booklet pane of 5 + 1 label
103 A23 2p ol green & scar 2.75 2.75
104 A23 4p brn & scar 1.75 .80
105 A23 5p org & blk ('08) 2.00 2.75
106 A23 1sh pale bl & dp rose 45.00 4.50
107 A23 2sh vio & bl grn 37.50 20.00
108 A23 2sh6p red violet 32.50 21.00
109 A24 £1 10sh vio & org brn, chalky paper 1,000.
Revenue cancel 18.00
Nos. 101-108 (8) 125.50 52.10

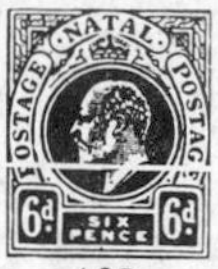

A25

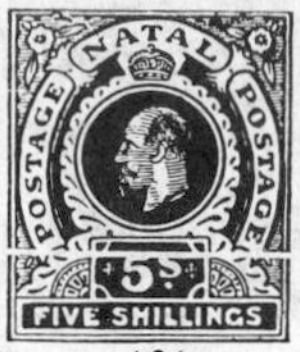

A26

1908-09

110 A25 6p red violet 4.50 1.75
111 A25 1sh black, *green* 5.00 1.75
112 A25 2sh bl & vio, *bl* 17.50 3.25
113 A25 2sh6p red & blk, *bl* 27.50 2.75
114 A26 5sh red & grn, *yellow* 17.50 10.50
115 A26 10sh red & grn, *green* 50.00 50.00
116 A26 £1 blk & vio, *red* 300.00 165.00
Nos. 110-115 (6) 122.00 70.00

OFFICIAL STAMPS

Nos. 101-103, 106 and Type A23 Overprinted — OFFICIAL

1904 Wmk. 3 *Perf. 14*

O1 A23 ½p blue green 3.00 .60
O2 A23 1p rose 1.50 .60
O3 A23 2p ol grn & scar 14.00 8.00
O4 A23 3p gray & red vio 7.00 5.00
O5 A23 6p mar & bl grn 30.00 30.00
O6 A23 1sh pale bl & dp rose 75.00 125.00
Nos. O1-O6 (6) 130.50 169.20

Stamps of Natal were replaced by those of the Union of South Africa.

NAURU

nä-'ü-(,)rü

LOCATION — An island on the Equator in the west central Pacific Ocean, midway between the Marshall and Solomon Islands.

GOVT. — Republic

AREA — 8½ sq. mi.

POP. — 8,421 (est. 1983)

CAPITAL — None. Parliament House is in Yaren District.

The island, a German possession, was captured by Australian forces in 1914 and, following World War I, was mandated to the British Empire. It was administered jointly by Great Britain, Australia and New Zealand.

In 1947 Nauru was placed under United Nations trusteeship, administered by Australia. On January 31, 1968, Nauru became a republic.

See North West Pacific Islands.

12 Pence = 1 Shilling
100 Cents = 1 Dollar (1966)

Catalogue values for unused stamps in this country are for Never Hinged items, beginning with Scott 39.

Great Britain Stamps of 1912-13 Overprinted at Bottom of Stamp — NAURU

1916-23 Wmk. 33 *Perf. 14½x14*

1 A82 ½p green .35 1.00
2 A83 1p scarlet .45 1.10
3 A84 1½p red brn ('23) 67.50 90.00
4 A85 2p org (die I) .80 1.65
a. 2p deep orange (die II) ('23) 55.00 80.00
6 A86 2½p ultra 1.65 3.50
7 A87 3p violet 2.25 4.25
8 A88 4p slate green 2.25 6.00
a. Double overprint
9 A89 5p yel brown 3.25 8.00
10 A89 6p dull violet 4.00 9.50
11 A90 9p black brown 8.00 17.50
12 A90 1sh bister 9.50 17.50
Nos. 1-12 (11) 100.00 160.00

Overprinted — NAURU

Wmk. 34 *Perf. 11x12*

13 A91 2sh6p light brown 70.00 100.00
a. 2sh6p black brown 550.00 600.00
14 A91 5sh carmine 175.00 185.00
a. 5sh rose carmine 2,500. 2,500.
15 A91 10sh lt blue (R) 375.00 425.00
a. 10sh indigo blue 6,500. 6,000.

Same Ovpt. on Great Britain No. 179

1920

16 A91 2sh6p gray brown 90.00 150.00
Nos. 13-16 (4) 710.00 860.00
Nos. 1-16 (15) 810.00 1,020.

Overprint Centered

1923

1a A82 ½p 4.00 50.00
2a A83 1p 22.50 40.00
3a A84 1½p 30.00 50.00
4b A85 2p As No. 4a 42.50 75.00
Nos. 1a-4b (4) 99.00 215.00

On Nos. 1-12 "NAURU" is usually 12¾mm wide and at the foot of the stamp. In 1923 four values were overprinted with the word 13½mm wide and across the middle of the stamp.

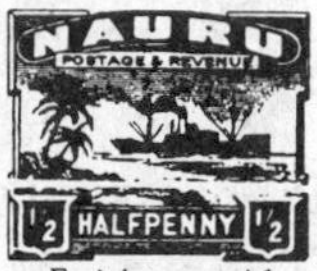

Freighter — A1

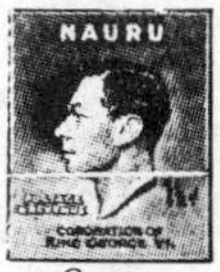

George VI — A2

1924-47 Unwmk. Engr. *Perf. 11*

17 A1 ½p orange brown 1.00 1.90
a. Perf. 14 ('47) 1.10 4.75
18 A1 1p green 1.40 1.90
19 A1 1½p red 1.00 1.00
20 A1 2p orange 1.65 5.25
21 A1 2½p blue .90 2.50
a. Horiz. pair, imperf. between
22 A1 3p grnsh gray ('37) 2.00 5.50
a. 3p pale blue 2.75 6.25
23 A1 4p olive green 3.50 5.75
24 A1 5p dk brown 2.25 2.75
25 A1 6p dark violet 3.00 2.50
26 A1 9p brown olive 4.50 13.00
27 A1 1sh brown red 4.50 1.90
28 A1 2sh6p slate green 25.00 20.00
29 A1 5sh claret 35.00 35.00
30 A1 10sh yellow 80.00 65.00
Nos. 17-30 (14) 165.70 163.95

In 1937 new printings of Nos. 17-30 were made on glazed-surface paper in slighly different shades.

Stamps of Type A1 Overprinted in Black — HIS MAJESTY'S JUBILEE. 1910-1935

1935, July 12 Glazed Paper *Perf. 11*

31 A1 1½p red .55 .65
32 A1 2p orange 1.25 1.50
33 A1 2½p blue 2.50 2.75
34 A1 1sh brown red 7.00 8.25
Set, never hinged 18.00
Nos. 31-34 (4) 11.30 13.15

25th anniv. of the reign of George V.

1937, May 10 Engr.

35 A2 1½p salmon rose .20 .20
36 A2 2p dull orange .20 .30
37 A2 2½p blue .20 .20
38 A2 1sh brown violet .45 .45
Nos. 35-38 (4) 1.05 1.15
Set, never hinged 1.90

Coronation of George VI & Elizabeth.

Catalogue values for unused stamps in this section, from this point to the end of the section, are for Never Hinged items.

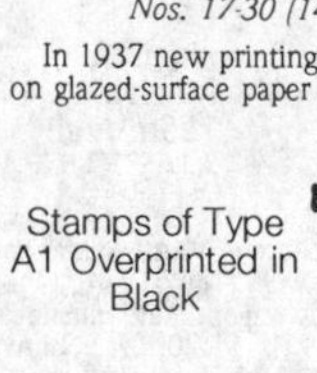

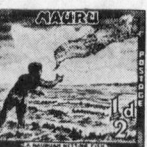

Casting Throw-net — A3

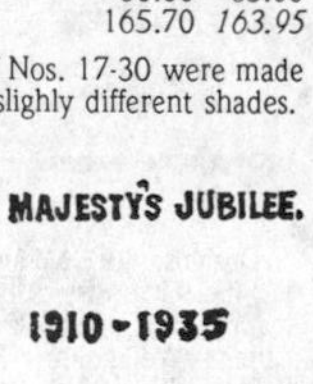

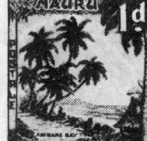

Anibare Bay — A4

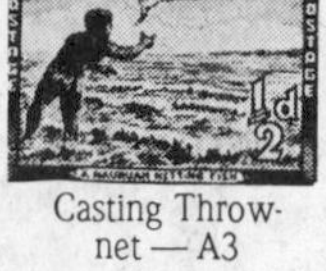

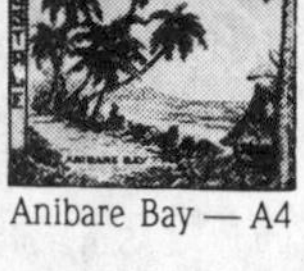

Designs: 3½p, Loading phosphate. 4p, Frigate bird. 6p, Nauruan canoe. 9p, Meeting house (domaneab). 1sh, Palms. 2sh6p, Buada lagoon. 5sh, Map.

1954, Feb. 6 ***Perf. 14½x14, 14x14½***

39	A3	½p purple	.15	.15
40	A4	1p green	.22	.15
41	A3	3½p red	.50	.28
42	A3	4p deep blue	.60	.35
43	A3	6p orange	.70	.38
44	A3	9p brown lake	1.25	.70
45	A4	1sh dk rose violet	1.40	.90
46	A3	2sh6p dk gray green	6.75	4.00
47	A4	5sh lilac rose	14.00	7.50
		Nos. 39-47 (9)	25.57	14.41

See Nos. 58-71.

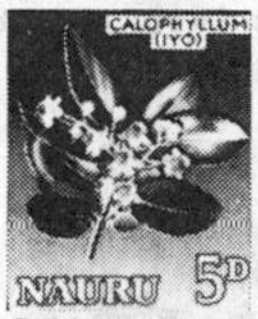

Balsam — A5

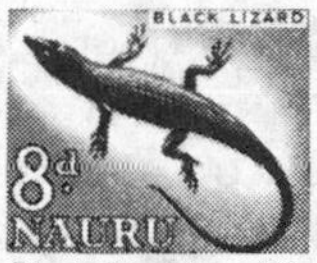

Black Lizard — A6

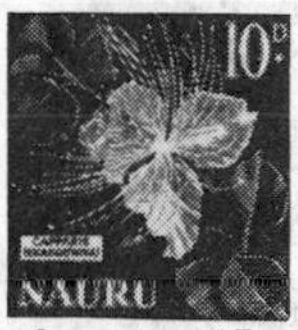

Capparis — A7

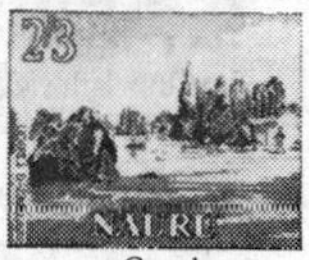

Coral Pinnacles — A8

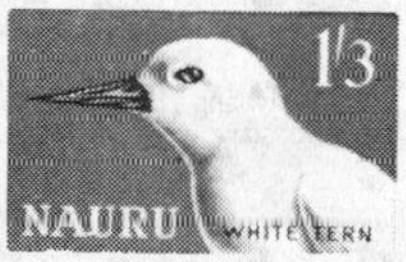

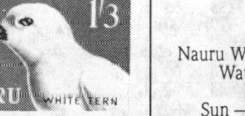

White Tern — A9

Designs: 2p, Micronesian pigeon, vert. 3p, Poison nut flower. 3sh3p, Nightingale reed warbler.

Perf. 13½, Perf. 14½x13½ (10p), Perf. 14½ (2sh3p)

Photo.; Engraved (10p, 2sh3p)

1963-65 **Unwmk.**

49	A9	2p multi ('65)	.20	.15
50	A6	3p red org, sl grn & yel ('64)	.30	.24
51	A5	5p gray, bl grn & yellow	.75	.52
52	A6	8p green & black	1.50	.65
53	A7	10p black ('64)	2.00	1.10
54	A9	1sh3p ap grn, blk & Prus bl ('65)	3.00	2.00
55	A8	2sh3p vio blue ('64)	3.75	2.50
56	A6	3sh3p lt yel, bl, brn & blk ('65)	7.50	5.00
		Nos. 49-56 (8)	19.00	12.16

Issue dates: 5p, Apr. 22. 8p, July 1. 3p, 10p, 2sh3p, Apr. 16. 2p, 1sh3p, 3sh3p, May 3.

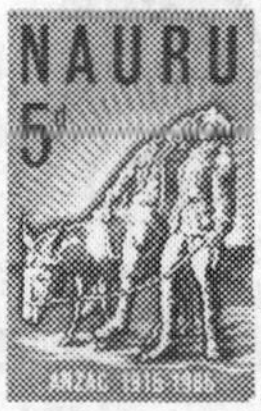

"Simpson and His Donkey" by Wallace Anderson — A9a

Perf. 13½x13

1965, Apr. 14 **Photo.** **Unwmk.**

57	A9a	5p brt green, sepia & blk	.75	.75

See note after Australia No. 387.

Types of 1954-65
Values in Cents and Dollars

Designs: 1c, Anibare Bay. 2c, Casting throw-net. 3c, Loading phosphate. 4c, Balsam. 5c, Palms. 7c, Black lizard. 8c, Capparis. 10c, Frigate bird. 15c, White tern. 25c, Coral pinnacles. 30c, Poison nut flower. 35c, Reed warbler. 50c, Micronesian pigeon, vert. $1, Map.

Engr.; Photo. (4c, 7c, 15c, 30c-50c)

1966 ***Perf. 14½x14, 14x14½***

58	A4	1c dark blue	.15	.15
59	A3	2c claret	.15	.15
60	A3	3c green	.15	.15
61	A5	4c lilac, grn & yel	.18	.15
62	A4	5c violet blue	.25	.20
63	A6	7c fawn & black	.28	.25
64	A7	8c olive green	.32	.28
65	A3	10c dark red	.42	.32
66	A9	15c ap grn, blk & Prus blue	.52	.45
67	A3	25c sepia	1.00	.80
68	A6	30c brick red, sl grn, & yellow	1.25	1.00
69	A6	35c lt yel, bl, brn & black	2.00	1.65
70	A9	50c yel, bluish blk & brown	2.50	2.50
71	A4	$1 claret	5.25	4.25
		Nos. 58-71 (14)	14.42	12.30

The engraved stamps are luminescent.

Issued: 2c, 3c, 5c, 15c, 25c, 35c, 5/25; others, 2/14.

Republic

Nos. 58-71 Overprinted in Red, Black or Orange "REPUBLIC / OF / NAURU"

1968

72	A4	1c dark blue (R)	.15	.15
73	A3	2c claret	.15	.15
74	A3	3c green	.15	.15
75	A5	4c lilac, grn & yel	.15	.15
76	A4	5c violet blue (O)	.15	.15
77	A6	7c fawn & blk (R)	.20	.20
78	A7	8c olive green (R)	.25	.25
79	A3	10c dark red	.30	.30
80	A9	15c ap grn, blk & Prus blue	3.25	3.25
81	A3	25c sepia (R)	.90	.90
82	A6	30c brick red, sl grn & yellow	1.50	1.10
83	A6	35c multicolored	2.00	1.50
84	A9	50c yel, bluish blk & brown	2.50	2.50
85	A4	$1 claret	4.50	4.50
		Nos. 72-85 (14)	16.15	15.25

Issued: 4c, 7c, 30c, 35c, May 15; others, Jan 31.

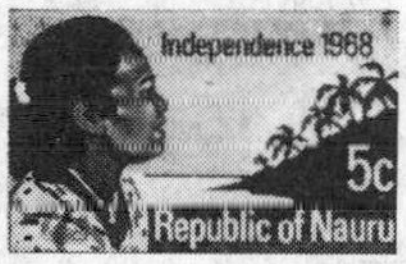

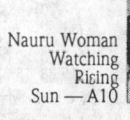

Nauru Woman Watching Rising Sun — A10

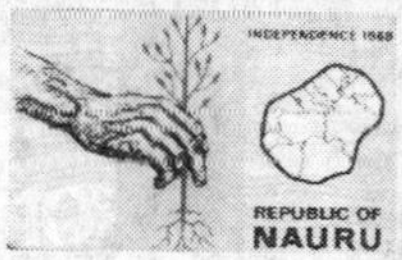

Planting Seedling and Map of Nauru — A11

Perf. 13x13½

1968, Sept. 11 **Photo.** **Unwmk.**

86	A10	5c multicolored	.16	.16
87	A11	10c brt blue, blk & green	.32	.32

Independence of Nauru.

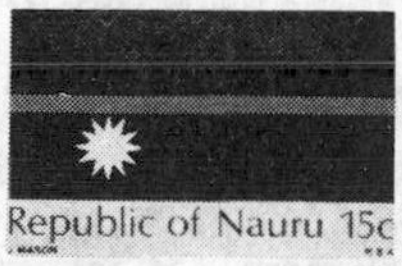

Flag of Nauru — A12

1969, Jan. 31 **Litho.** ***Perf. 13½***

88	A12	15c dk vio blue, yel & org	.42	.40

For overprint see No. 90.

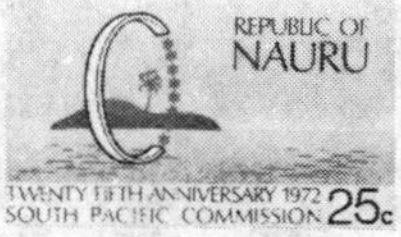

Commission Emblem and Nauru — A13

1972, Feb. 7 **Litho.** ***Perf. 14½x14***

89	A13	25c blue, yellow & black	.85	.85

South Pacific Commission, 25th anniv.

No. 88 Overprinted in Gold:

Independence 1968-1973

1973, Jan. 31 ***Perf. 13½***

90	A12	15c multicolored	.70	.70

Fifth anniversary of independence.

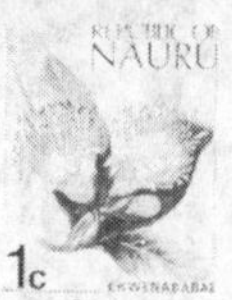

Lotus (Ekwenababae) A14

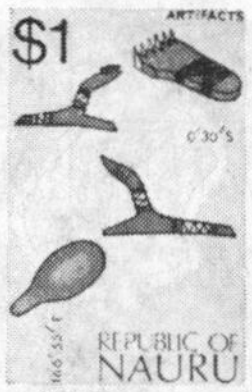

Map of Nauru, Artifacts A15

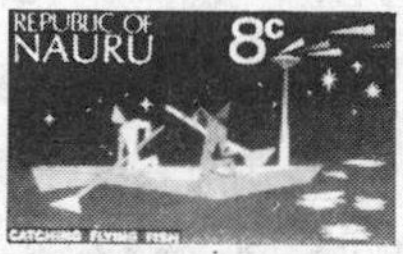

Catching Flyingfish A16

Designs: 2c, Kauwe iud. 3c, Rimone. 4c, Denea. 5c, Beach morning-glory. 7c, Golden butterflyfish. 10c, Nauruan ball game (itsibweb). 15c, Nauruan wrestling. 20c, Snaring frigate birds. 25c, Nauruan girl with flower garland. 30c, Men catching noddies. 50c, Frigate birds.

1973 **Litho.** ***Perf. 13½x14***

91	A14	1c pale yellow & multi	.15	.15
92	A14	2c pale ocher & multi	.15	.15
93	A14	3c pale violet & multi	.15	.15
94	A14	4c pale green & multi	.15	.15
95	A14	5c pale blue & multi	.16	.16

Perf. 14½x14, 14x14½

96	A16	7c blue & multi	.22	.22
97	A16	8c black & multi	.28	.28
98	A16	10c multicolored	.35	.35
99	A15	15c green & multi	.38	.38
100	A15	20c blue & multi	.45	.45
101	A15	25c yellow & multi	.55	.55
102	A16	30c multicolored	.70	.70
103	A16	50c multicolored	1.40	1.40
104	A15	$1 blue & multi	2.75	2.75
		Nos. 91-104 (14)	7.84	7.84

Issue dates: Nos. 97-100, May 23; Nos. 96, 101-103, July 25; others Mar. 28, 1973.

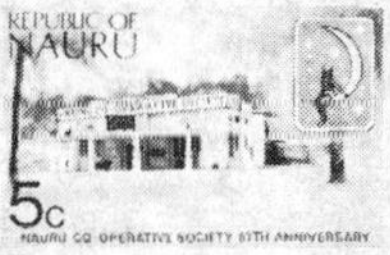

Cooperative Store — A17

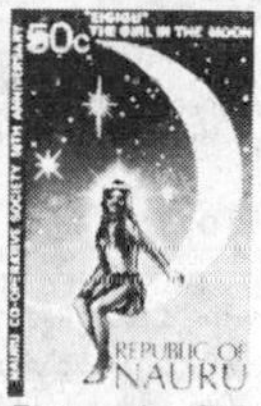

Eigigu, the Girl in the Moon — A18

Design: 25c, Timothy Detudamo and cooperative store emblem.

1973, Dec. 20 **Litho.** ***Perf. 14½x14***

105	A17	5c multicolored	.42	.30
106	A17	25c multicolored	1.50	1.10
107	A18	50c multicolored	3.25	3.00
		Nos. 105-107 (3)	5.17	4.40

50th anniversary of Nauru Cooperative Society, founded by Timothy Detudamo.

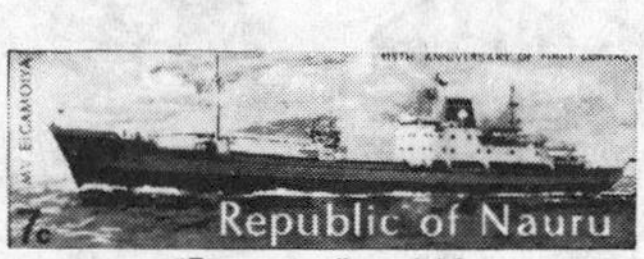

"Eigamoiya" — A19

Designs: 10c, Phosphate mining. 15c, "Nauru Chief" plane over Nauru. 25c, Nauru chieftain with frigate-bird headdress. 35c, Capt. J. Fearn, sailing ship "Hunter" and map of Nauru. 50c, "Hunter" off Nauru.

Perf. 13x13½, 13½x13

1974, May 21 **Litho.**

Sizes: 70x22mm (7c, 35c, 50c); 33x20mm (10c, 15c, 25c)

108	A19	7c multicolored	.32	.15
109	A19	10c multicolored	.45	.18
110	A19	15c multicolored	.80	.35
111	A19	25c multicolored	2.25	.90
112	A19	35c multicolored	8.00	3.50
113	A19	50c multicolored	7.50	3.00
		Nos. 108-113 (6)	19.32	8.08

175th anniversary of Nauru's first contact with the outside world.

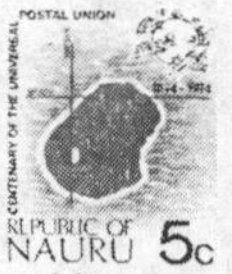

Map of Nauru — A20

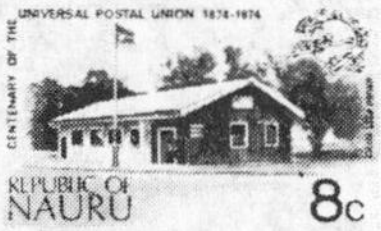

Post Office — A21

UPU Emblem and: 20c, Mailman on motorcycle. $1, Flag of Nauru and UPU Building, Bern, vert.

1974, July 23 **Litho.** ***Perf. 14***

114	A20	5c multicolored	.15	.16

Perf. 13½x13, 13x13½

115	A21	8c multicolored	.18	.18
116	A21	20c multicolored	.70	.52
117	A21	$1 multicolored	4.00	3.75
a.		Souv. sheet of 4, #114-117, imperf.	9.00	8.00
		Nos. 114-117 (4)	5.03	4.61

Cent. of the UPU.

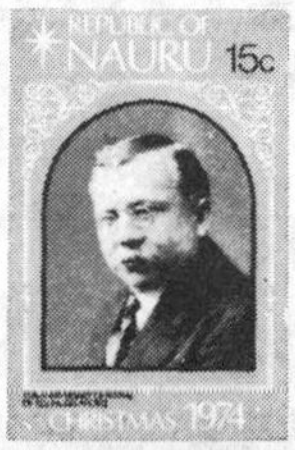

Rev. P. A. Delaporte — A22

1974, Dec. 10 **Litho.** ***Perf. 14½***

118	A22	15c brt pink & multi	.70	.48
119	A22	20c blue & multi	1.25	1.10

Christmas 1974. Delaporte, a German-born American missionary, took Christianity to Nauru and translated the New Testament into Nauruan.

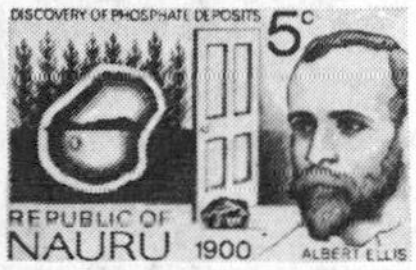

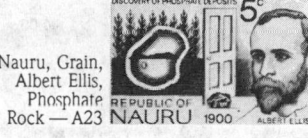

Nauru, Grain, Albert Ellis, Phosphate Rock — A23

Designs: 7c, Phosphate mining and coolie carrying load. 15c, Electric freight train, tugs and ship. 25c, Excavator, cantilever and truck.

1975, July 23 **Litho.** ***Perf. 14½x14***

120	A23	5c multicolored	.15	.15
121	A23	7c multicolored	.20	.18
122	A23	15c multicolored	.95	.75
123	A23	25c multicolored	1.50	1.10
		Nos. 120-123 (4)	2.80	2.18

75th anniv. of discovery of phosphate (5c); 70th anniv. of Pacific Phosphate Co. Mining Agreement (7c); 50th anniv. of British Phosphate Commissioners (15c); 5th anniv. of Nauru Phosphate Corp. (25c).

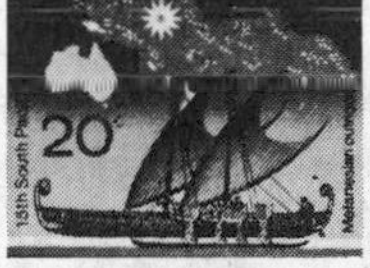

Melanesian Outrigger and Map of SPC's Area — A24

1975, Sept. 1 **Litho.** ***Perf. 14x14½***

124	A24	20c Micronesian outrigger	.70	.52
125	A24	20c Polynesian double hull	.70	.52
126	A24	20c shown	.70	.52
127	A24	20c Polynesian outrigger	.70	.52
a.		Block of 4, #124-127	3.00	3.00
		Nos. 124-127 (4)	2.80	2.08

South Pacific Commission Conference, Nauru, Sept. 29-Oct. 10.

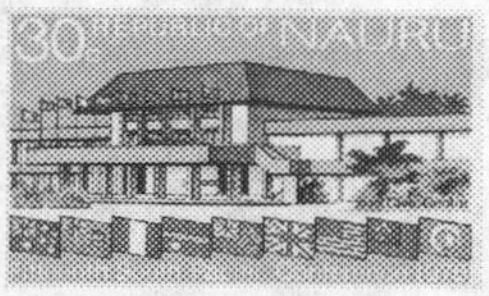

New Civic Center A25

Design: 50c, "Domaneab" (meeting house) and flags of participating nations.

1975, Sept. 29 Litho. Perf. 14½
128 A25 30c multicolored .70 .70
129 A25 50c multicolored 1.25 1.25

South Pacific Commission Conference, Nauru, Sept. 29-Oct. 10.

 Virgin Mary, Stained-glass Window — A26

Christmas: 7c, 15c, "Suffer little children to come unto me," stained-glass window, Orro Protestant Church. 25c, like 5c, Yaren Catholic Church.

1975, Nov. 7 Litho. Perf. 14½
130 A26 5c gray blue & multi .15 .15
131 A26 7c green & multi .22 .18
132 A26 15c brown & multi .52 .42
133 A26 25c lilac & multi .90 .70
Nos. 130-133 (4) 1.79 1.45

 Frangipani Forming Lei Around Nauru A27

Designs: 14c, Hand crowning Nauru with lei. 25c, Reed warbler, birds flying from Truk to Nauru. 40c, Reunion of islanders in Boar Harbor.

1976, Jan. 31 Litho. Perf. 14½
134 A27 10c green & multi .18 .16
135 A27 14c violet & multi .28 .25
136 A27 25c red & multi .52 .42
137 A27 40c blue & multi 1.00 .80
Nos. 134-137 (4) 1.98 1.63

30th anniversary of the return of the islanders from Japanese internment on Truk.

 Nauru Nos. 7 and 11 A28

Designs: 15c, Nauru Nos. 10 and 12. 25c, Nauru No. 13. 50c, Nauru No. 14, "Specimen."

1976, May 6 Litho. Perf. 13½x14
138 A28 10c multicolored .20 .16
139 A28 15c multicolored .32 .25
140 A28 25c multicolored .50 .42
141 A28 50c multicolored 1.00 .90
Nos. 138-141 (4) 2.02 1.73

60th anniv. of Nauru's 1st postage stamps.

 Nauru Shipping and Pandanus — A29

Designs: 20c, Air Nauru Boeing 737 and Fokker F28, and tournefortia argentea. 30c, Earth satellite station and thespesia populnea. 40c, Area produce and cordia subcordata.

1976, July 26 Litho. Perf. 13½x14
142 A29 10c multicolored .20 .15
143 A29 20c multicolored .38 .30
144 A29 30c multicolored .55 .45
145 A29 40c multicolored .85 .55
Nos. 142-145 (4) 1.98 1.45

7th South Pacific Forum, Nauru, July 1976.

 Nauruan Children's Choir
A30   A31

Designs: 20c, Angels. Designs after children's paintings.

1976, Nov. Litho. Perf. 14x13½
146 A30 15c multicolored .42 .40
147 A31 15c multicolored .42 .40
a. Pair, #146-147 .85 .80
148 A30 20c multicolored .55 .52
149 A31 20c multicolored .55 .52
a. Pair, #148-149 1.10 1.10
Nos. 146-149 (4) 1.94 1.84

Christmas.

 Nauru House, Melbourne, and Coral Pinnacles — A32 / Cable-laying Ship Anglia, 1902 — A33

Design: 30c, Nauru House and Melbourne skyline.

1977, Apr. 14 Photo. Perf. 14½
150 A32 15c multicolored .55 .50
151 A32 30c multicolored 1.10 1.00

Opening of Nauru House in Melbourne, Australia. For surcharges see Nos. 161-164.

1977, Sept. 7 Photo. Perf. 14½
Designs: 15c, Nauru radar station. 20c, Stern of Anglia. 25c, Radar antenna.
152 A33 7c multicolored .15 .15
153 A33 15c multicolored .28 .24
154 A33 40c multicolored .40 .32
155 A33 25c multicolored .48 .38
Nos. 152-155 (4) 1.31 1.09

1st transpacific cable, 75th anniv., and 1st artificial earth satellite, 20th anniv.

 Catholic Church, Yaren, and Father Kayser — A34  Coat of Arms of Nauru — A35

Designs: 25c, Congregational Church, Orro. 30c, Catholic Church, Arubo.

1977, Oct. Photo. Perf. 14½
156 A34 15c multicolored .28 .28
157 A34 25c multicolored .48 .48
158 A34 30c multicolored .55 .55
Nos. 156-158 (3) 1.31 1.31

Christmas, and 55th anniversary of first Roman Catholic Church on Nauru.

1978, Jan. 31 Litho. Perf. 14½
159 A35 15c blue & multi .30 .28
160 A35 60c emerald & multi 1.25 1.10

10th anniversary of independence.

Nos. 150-151 Surcharged with New Value and Two Bars
1978, Apr. Photo. Perf. 14½
161 A32 4c on 15c multi 4.50 4.50
162 A32 5c on 15c multi 4.50 4.50
163 A32 8c on 30c multi 4.50 4.50
164 A32 10c on 30c multi 4.50 4.50
Nos. 161-164 (4) 18.00 18.00

 Girls Catching Fish in Buada Lagoon A36

Designs: 1c, Fisherman and family collecting shellfish. 2c, Pigs foraging near coral reef. 3c, Gnarled tree and birds. 4c, Girl catching fish with hands. 5c, Bird catching fish. 10c, Ijuw Lagoon. 15c, Young girl and coral formation. 20c, Reef pinnacles, Anibare Bay. 25c, Pinnacles, Meneng shore. 30c, Frigate bird. 32c, Coconut palm and noddies. 40c, Iwiyi, wading bird. 50c, Frigate birds. $1, Pinnacles, Topside. $2, Newly uncovered pinnacles, Topside. $5, Old pinnacles, Topside.

1978-79 Photo. Perf. 14½
165 A36 1c multicolored .15 .15
166 A36 2c multicolored .15 .15
167 A36 3c multicolored .15 .15
168 A36 4c multicolored .15 .15
169 A36 5c multicolored .15 .15
170 A36 7c multicolored .15 .15
171 A36 10c multicolored .15 .15
172 A36 15c multicolored .22 .22
173 A36 20c multicolored .28 .28
174 A36 25c multicolored .35 .35
175 A36 30c multicolored .45 .45
176 A36 32c multicolored .48 .48
177 A36 40c multicolored .55 .55
178 A36 50c multicolored .70 .70
179 A36 $1 multicolored 1.40 1.40
180 A36 $2 multicolored 2.75 2.75
181 A36 $5 multicolored 7.00 7.00
Nos. 165-181 (17) 15.23 15.23

Issued: #166-169, June 6, 1979; others, May 1978.

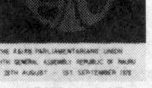 "APU" — A37  Mother and Child — A38

1978, Aug. 28 Litho. Perf. 13½
182 A37 15c multicolored 1.00 .90
183 A37 20c gold, blk & dk blue 1.25 1.10

14th General Assembly of Asian Parliamentary Union, Nauru, Aug. 28-Sept. 1. On sale during conference only.

1978, Nov. 1 Litho. Perf. 14
Christmas: 15c, 20c, Angel over the Pacific, horiz. 30c, like 7c.
184 A38 7c multicolored .15 .15
185 A38 15c multicolored .25 .25
186 A38 20c multicolored .35 .35
187 A38 30c multicolored .52 .52
Nos. 184-187 (4) 1.27 1.27

 Lord Baden-Powell and Cub Scout — A39

Lord Baden-Powell and: 30c, Boy Scout. 50c, Explorer.

1978, Dec. 1 Litho. Perf. 14
188 A39 20c multicolored .32 .32
189 A39 30c multicolored .42 .42
190 A39 50c multicolored .70 .70
Nos. 188-190 (3) 1.44 1.44

70th anniversary of 1st Scout Troop.

NAURU 10
 Flyer A over Nauru Airfield A40

Designs: No. 192, "Southern Cross" and Boeing 727. No. 193, "Southern Cross" and Boeing 737. 30c, Wright Flyer over Nauru.

1979, Jan. Litho. Perf. 14½
191 A40 10c multicolored .20 .20
192 A40 15c multicolored .28 .28
193 A40 15c multicolored .28 .28
a. Pair, #192-193 .60 .60
194 A40 30c multicolored .60 .60
Nos. 191-194 (4) 1.36 1.36

1st powered flight, 75th anniv. and Kingsford Smith's US-Australia and Australia-New Zealand flights, 50th anniv.
Nos. 192-193 printed checkerwise.

 Rowland Hill, Marshall Islands No. 15 with Nauru Cancel A41

1979, Feb. 27 Litho. Perf. 14½
195 A41 5c shown .15 .15
196 A41 15c Nauru No. 15 .22 .22
197 A41 60c Nauru No. 160 .90 .90
a. Souvenir sheet of 3, #195-197 1.25 1.25
Nos. 195-197 (3) 1.27 1.27

Sir Rowland Hill (1795-1879), originator of penny postage.

 Dish Antenna, Earth Station, ITU Emblem A42

ITU Emblem and: 32c, Woman operating Telex machine. 40c, Radio beacon operator.

1979, Aug. Litho. Perf. 14½
198 A42 7c multicolored .15 .15
199 A42 32c multicolored .40 .40
200 A42 40c multicolored .50 .50
Nos. 198-200 (3) 1.05 1.05

Intl. Radio Consultative Committee (CCIR) of the ITU, 50th anniv.

 Nauruan Girl — A43

IYC Emblem, Nauruan Children: 15c, Boy. 25c, 32c, 50c, Girls, diff.

1979, Oct. 3 Litho. Perf. 14½
201 A43 8c multicolored .15 .15
202 A43 15c multicolored .15 .15
203 A43 25c multicolored .25 .25
204 A43 32c multicolored .30 .30
205 A43 50c multicolored .48 .48
a. Strip of 5, #201-205 1.25 1.25

International Year of the Child.

 Star, Scroll, Ekwenababa Flower — A44

Star and Flowers: 15c, Milos. 20c, Denea. 30c, Morning glories.

1979, Nov. 14 Litho. Perf. 14½

206	A44	7c multicolored	.15	.15
207	A44	15c multicolored	.22	.22
208	A44	20c multicolored	.26	.26
209	A44	30c multicolored	.42	.42
		Nos. 206-209 (4)	1.05	1.05

Christmas.

Nauruan Plane over Melbourne — A45

Air Nauru, 10th Anniversary (Plane Over): 20c, Tarawa. 25c, Hong Kong. 30c, Auckland.

1980, Feb. 28 Litho. Perf. 14½

210	A45	15c multicolored	.24	.24
211	A45	20c multicolored	.32	.32
212	A45	25c multicolored	.40	.40
213	A45	30c multicolored	.50	.50
		Nos. 210-213 (4)	1.46	1.46

Early Steam Locomotive A46

1980, May 6 Litho. Perf. 15

214	A46	8c shown	.15	.15
215	A46	40c Electric locomotive	.40	.40
216	A46	60c Clyde diesel-hydraulic locomotive	.75	.75
a.		Souvenir sheet of 3, #214-216	1.75	1.75
		Nos. 214-216 (3)	1.30	1.30

Nauru Phosphate Corp., 10th anniv. No. 216a also for London 1980 Intl. Stamp Exhibition, May 6-14; Penny Black, 140th anniv.

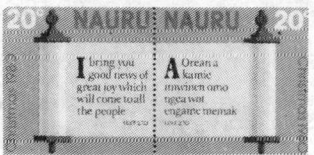

Christmas 1980
A47   A48

Designs: 30c, "Glory to God in the Highest . . ." in English and Nauruan.

1980, Sept. 24 Litho. Perf. 15

217	A47	20c multicolored	.25	.25
218	A48	20c multicolored	.25	.25
a.		Pair, #217-218	.50	.50
219	A47	30c multicolored	.35	.35
220	A48	30c multicolored	.35	.35
a.		Pair, #219-220	.75	.75
		Nos. 217-220 (4)	1.20	1.20

See Nos. 236-239.

Flags of Nauru, Australia, Gt. Britain and New Zealand, UN Emblem — A49

1980, Dec. 20 Litho. Perf. 14½

221	A49	25c shown	.32	.32

Size: 72x22mm
Perf. 14

222	A49	30c UN Trusteeship Council	.38	.38
223	A49	50c 1968 independence ceremony	.55	.55
		Nos. 221-223 (3)	1.25	1.25

UN de-colonization declaration, 20th anniv. No. 222 printed se-tenant with label showing flags of UN and Nauru, issued Feb. 11, 1981.

Timothy Detudamo (Former Head Chief), Domaneab (Meeting House) — A50

1981, Feb. Litho. Perf. 14½

224	A50	20c shown	.25	.25
225	A50	30c Raymond Gadabu	.35	.35
226	A50	50c Hammer DeRoburt	.65	.65
		Nos. 224-226 (3)	1.25	1.25

Legislative Council, 30th anniversary.

Casting Net by Hand A51

1981 Litho. Perf. 12

227	A51	8c shown	.15	.15
228	A51	20c Ancient canoe	.28	.28
229	A51	32c Powered boat	.45	.45
230	A51	40c Fishing vessel	.65	.65
a.		Souvenir sheet of 4, #230	2.00	2.00
		Nos. 227-230 (4)	1.53	1.53

Bank of Nauru, 5th Anniv. A52

1981, July 21 Litho. Perf. 14x14½

231	A52	$1 multicolored	1.25	1.25

ESCAP Secy. Maramis Delivering Inaugural Speech — A53

1981, Oct. 24 Litho. Perf. 14½

232	A53	15c shown	.25	.25
233	A53	20c Maramis, Pres. de Roburt	.35	.35
234	A53	25c Plaque	.45	.45
235	A53	30c Raising UN flag	.52	.52
		Nos. 232-235 (4)	1.57	1.57

UN Day and first anniv. of Economic and Social Commission for Asia and Pacific (ESCAP) liason office in Nauru.

Christmas Type of 1980

Christmas (Biblical Scriptures in English and Nauruan): 20c, "His Name Shall Be Called Emmanuel." 30c, "To You is Born This Day . . ."

1981, Nov. 14 Litho. Perf. 14½

236	A47	20c multicolored	.30	.30
237	A48	20c multicolored	.30	.30
a.		Pair, #236-237	.60	.60
238	A47	30c multicolored	.45	.45
239	A48	30c multicolored	.45	.45
a.		Pair, #238-239	.95	.95
		Nos. 236-239 (4)	1.50	1.50

10th Anniv. of South Pacific Forum A54

1981, Dec. 9 Litho. Perf. 13½x14

240	A54	10c Globe, dish antenna	.15	.15
241	A54	20c Ship	.30	.30
242	A54	30c Jet	.45	.45
243	A54	40c Produce	.60	.60
		Nos. 240-243 (4)	1.50	1.50

Scouting Year — A55

1982, Feb. 23 Litho. Perf. 14

244	A55	7c Carrying packages	.15	.15
245	A55	8c Scouts, life preserver, vert.	.15	.15
246	A55	15c Pottery making, vert.	.22	.22
247	A55	20c Inspection	.30	.30
248	A55	25c Scout, cub	.38	.38
249	A55	40c Troop	.60	.60
a.		Souv. sheet of 6, #244-249, imperf.	2.00	2.00
		Nos. 244-249 (6)	1.80	1.80

A56

Ocean Thermal Energy Conversion — A57

Designs: No. 250, Plant under construction. No. 251, Completed plant.

1982, June 10 Litho. Perf. 13½

250		Pair	.90	.90
a.-b.	A56	25c any single	.45	.45
251		Pair	1.40	1.40
a.-b.	A56	40c any single	.70	.70

75th Anniv. of Phosphate Industry A58

1982, Oct. 11 Litho. Perf. 14

252	A58	5c Freighter Fido, 1907	.15	.15
253	A58	10c Locomotive Nellie, 1907	.18	.18
254	A58	30c Modern Clyde diesel train, 1982	.50	.50
255	A58	60c Flagship Eigamoiya, 1969	1.00	1.00
		Nos. 252-255 (4)	1.83	1.83

Souvenir Sheet

256	A58	$1 Freighters	2.00	2.00

ANPEX '82 Natl. Stamp Exhibition, Brisbane, Australia, Nos. 252-255 se-tenant with labels describing stamp. No. 256 contains one 68x27mm stamp.

Visit of Queen Elizabeth II and Prince Philip A59

1982, Oct. 21 Perf. 14½

257	A59	20c Elizabeth, vert.	.28	.28
258	A59	50c Philip, vert.	.70	.70
259	A59	$1 Couple	1.40	1.40
		Nos. 257-259 (3)	2.38	2.38

Christmas A60

Clergymen: 20c, Father Bernard Lahn, Catholic Mission Church. 30c, Rev. Itubwa Amram, Orro Central Church. 40c, Pastor James Aingimea, Tsiminita Memorial Church, Denigomodu. 50c, Bishop Paul Mea, Diocese of Tarawa-Nauru-Tuvalu.

1982, Nov. 17

260	A60	20c multicolored	.28	.28
261	A60	30c multicolored	.42	.42
262	A60	40c multicolored	.55	.55
263	A60	50c multicolored	.70	.70
		Nos. 260-263 (4)	1.95	1.95

15th Anniv. of Independence — A61

1983, Mar. 23 Wmk. 373 Perf. 14½

264	A61	15c Speaker of Parliament, vert.	.25	.25
265	A61	20c People's Court, vert.	.35	.35
266	A61	30c Law Courts	.50	.50
267	A61	50c Parliament	.85	.85
		Nos. 264-267 (4)	1.95	1.95

World Communications Year — A62

1983, May 11 Litho. Perf. 14

268	A62	5c Earth Satellite Staion NZ	.15	.15
269	A62	10c Omni-directional Range Installation	.15	.15
270	A62	20c Fixed-station ambulance driver	.30	.30
271	A62	25c Radio Nauru broadcaster	.38	.38
272	A62	40c Air mail service	.60	.60
		Nos. 268-272 (5)	1.58	1.58

Angam Day (Homecoming) — A63

Perf. 14x13½
1983, Sept. 14 Litho. Wmk. 373

273	A63	15c MV Trinza arriving	.22	.22

Size: 25x40mm
Perf. 14

274	A63	20c Elsie Agio in exile	.30	.30
275	A63	30c Baby on scale	.45	.45
276	A63	40c Children	.60	.60
		Nos. 273-276 (4)	1.57	1.57

Christmas A64

Designs: 5c, The Holy Virgin, the Holy Child and St. John, School of Raphael. 15c, The Mystical Betrothal of St. Catherine with Jesus, School of Paolo Veronese. 50c, Madonna on the Throne Surrounded by Angels, School of Seville.

Perf. 14½x14, 14x14½
1983, Nov. 16 Litho. Wmk. 373

277	A64	5c multi, vert.	.15	.15
278	A64	15c multi, vert.	.25	.25
279	A64	40c multicolored	.85	.85
		Nos. 277-279 (3)	1.25	1.25

Lloyd's List Issue
Common Design Type

1984, May 23 Litho. Perf. 14½x14

280	CD335	20c Ocean Queen	.38	.38
281	CD335	25c Enna G.	.48	.48
282	CD335	30c Baron Minto loading phosphate	.60	.60
283	CD335	40c Triadic, 1940	.75	.75
		Nos. 280-283 (4)	2.21	2.21

1984 UPU
Congress — A65

1984, June 4   Wmk. 373   Perf. 14
284 A65 $1 No. 117   1.50 1.50

Coastal
Scene
A66

Perf. 13¹/₂x14, 14x13¹/₂
1984, Sept. 21
285 A66   1c shown   .15   .15
286 A66   3c Woman, vert.   .15   .15
287 A66   5c Fishing vessel   .15   .15
288 A66 10c Golfer   .18   .18
289 A66 15c Phosphate excava-
                tion, vert.   .25   .25
290 A66 20c Surveyor, vert.   .35   .35
291 A66 25c Air Nauru jet   .45   .45
292 A66 30c Elderly man, vert.   .52   .52
293 A66 40c Social service   .70   .70
294 A66 50c Fishing, vert.   .85   .85
295 A66 $1 Tennis, vert.   1.75 1.75
296 A66 $2 Lagoon Anabar   3.50 3.50
       Nos. 285-296 (12)   9.00 9.00

For surcharges see Nos. 425-427.

Local
Butterflies
A67

1984, July 24   Perf. 14
297 A67 25c Common eggfly (fe-
               male)   .50   .50
298 A67 30c Common eggfly (male)   .60   .60
299 A67 50c Wanderer (female)   1.00 1.00
       Nos. 297-299 (3)   2.10 2.10

Christmas
A68

1984, Nov. 14
300 A68 30c Buada Chapel, vert.   .55   .55
301 A68 40c Detudamo Memorial
               Church, vert.   .70   .70
302 A68 50c Candle-light service   .90   .90
       Nos. 300-302 (3)   2.15 2.15

Air Nauru,
15th Anniv.
A69

1985, Feb. 26   Wmk. 373   Perf. 14
303 A69 20c Jet   .35   .35
304 A69 30c Crew, vert.   .55   .55
305 A69 40c Fokker F28 over Nauru   .70   .70
306 A69 50c Cargo handling, vert.   .90   .90
       Nos. 303-306 (4)   2.50 2.50

Nauru
Phosphate
Corp., 15th
Anniv.
A70

1985, July 31
307 A70 20c Open-cut mining   .38   .38
308 A70 25c Rail transport   .48   .48
309 A70 30c Phosphate drying plant   .55   .55
310 A70 30c Early steam engine   .90   .90
       Nos. 307-310 (4)   2.31 2.31

Christmas — A71

1985, Oct.
311 A71 50c Canoe   .95   .95
312 A71 50c Mother and child   .95   .95
 a.   Pair, #311-312   2.00 2.00

No. 312a has a continuous design.

Audubon Birth
Bicentenary
A72

Illustrations of the brown noddy by John J.
Audubon.

1985, Dec. 31
313 A72 10c Adult and young   .18   .18
314 A72 20c Flying   .35   .35
315 A72 30c Two adults   .52   .52
316 A72 50c Adult   .90   .90
       Nos. 313-316 (4)   1.95 1.95

Early Transportation — A73

1986, Mar. 5   Wmk. 384
317 A73 15c Douglas motorcycle   .28   .28
318 A73 20c Truck   .35   .35
319 A73 30c German steam locomo-
               tive, 1910   .55   .55
320 A73 40c Baby Austin   .75   .75
       Nos. 317-320 (4)   1.93 1.93

Bank of
Nauru, 10th
Anniv.
A74

Winning drawings of children's competition.

1986, July 21   Litho.   Perf. 14
321 A74 20c multicolored   .38   .38
322 A74 25c multicolored   .48   .48
323 A74 30c multicolored   .55   .55
324 A74 40c multicolored   .75   .75
       Nos. 321-324 (4)   2.16 2.16

Flowers — A75

1986, Sept. 30   Wmk. 384
325 A75 20c Plumeria rubra   .38   .38
326 A75 25c Tristellateia australis   .48   .48
327 A75 30c Bougainvillea cultivar   .55   .55
328 A75 40c Delonix regia   .75   .75
       Nos. 325-328 (4)   2.16 2.16

Christmas
A76

1986, Dec. 8   Wmk. 373
329 A76 20c Men caroling   .35   .35
330 A76 $1 Carolers, invalid   1.75 1.75

Tribal
Dances — A77

1987, Jan. 31
331 A77 20c Girls   .35   .35
332 A77 30c Men and women   .52   .52
333 A77 50c Boy, vert.   .90   .90
       Nos. 331-333 (3)   1.77 1.77

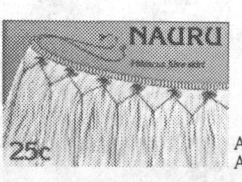

Artifacts
A78

1987, July 30   Perf. 14
334 A78 25c Hibiscus-fiber skirt   .35   .35
335 A78 40c Headband, necklaces   .42   .42
336 A78 45c Necklaces   .65   .65
337 A78 60c Pandanus-leaf fan   .85   .85
       Nos. 334-337 (4)   2.27 2.27

World Post
Day — A79

Perf. 14¹/₂x14
1987, Oct. 9   Litho.   Wmk. 384
338 A79 40c UPU emblem, airmail
               label   .70   .70

Souvenir Sheet

1987, Oct. 20   Imperf.
339 A79 $1 Emblem, vert.   1.90 1.90

Nauru Congregational
Church, Cent. — A80

Perf. 13x13¹/₂
1987, Nov. 5   Wmk. 373
340 A80 40c multicolored   .75   .75

Island
Christmas
Celebration
A81

1987, Nov. 27   Wmk. 384   Perf. 14
341 A81 20c shown   .32   .32
342 A81 $1 Sign on building   1.65 1.65

Natl.
Independence,
20th
Anniv. — A83

Heraldic elements independent of or as part of
the natl. arms: 25c, Phosphate mining and shipping.
40c, Tomano flower, vert. 55c, Frigate bird, vert.
$1, Natl. arms.

Perf. 13¹/₂x14, 14x13¹/₂
1988, May 16   Unwmk.
343 A82 25c multicolored   .40   .40
344 A82 40c multicolored   .65   .65
345 A82 55c multicolored   .85   .85

Perf. 13
346 A83 $1 multicolored   1.50 1.50
       Nos. 343-346 (4)   3.40 3.40

Nauru
Post
Office,
80th
Anniv.
A84

Designs: 30c, Nauru highlighted on German map
of the Marshall Islands, and canceled Marshall
Islands No. 25. 50c, Letter mailed from Nauru to
Dresden and post office, 1908. 70c, Post office,
1988, and Nauru No. 348 canceled on airmail
cover.

1988, July 14   Wmk. 384   Perf. 14
347 A84 30c multicolored   .50   .50
348 A84 50c multicolored   .82   .82
349 A84 70c multicolored   1.15 1.15
       Nos. 347-349 (3)   2.47 2.47

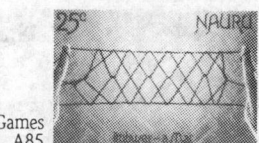

String Games
A85

1988, Aug. 1 Unwmk. Perf. 13¹/₂x14
350 A85 25c Mat   .32   .32
351 A85 40c The Pursuer   .50   .50
352 A85 55c Holding Up the Sky   .75   .75
353 A85 80c Manujie's Sword   1.10 1.10
       Nos. 350-353 (4)   2.67 2.67

UPU,
Cent. — A86

1988, Oct. 1   Perf. 13¹/₂x14
354 A86 $1 multicolored   1.65 1.65

Hark! The
Herald Angels
Sing, by
Charles Wesley
(1703-91)
A87

1988, Nov. 28   Perf. 13¹/₂
355 A87 20c "Hark..."   .35   .35
356 A87 60c "Glory to..."   1.00 1.00
357 A87 $1 "Peace on Earth"   1.75 1.75
       Nos. 355-357 (3)   3.10 3.10

A88 — Christmas — A89

1989, Nov. 19   **Perf. 14x15**
358 A88 15c NIC emblem   .24   .24
359 A88 50c APT, ITU emblems   .78   .78
360 A88 $1 Mounted photograph   1.55   1.55
361 A88 $2 UPU emblem, US Capitol   3.15   3.15
    Nos. 358-361 (4)   5.72   5.72

Annivs. and events: Nauru Insurance Corp., 15th Anniv. (15c). World Telecommunications Day and 10th anniv of the Asia-Pacific Telecommunity (50c); Photography 150th anniv. ($1); and 20th UPU Congress, Washington, DC ($2).

1989, Dec. 15   **Litho.**   **Perf. 14x15**
362 A89 20c shown   .32   .32
363 A89 $1 Children opening gifts   1.40   1.40

A90 — A91

Legend of Eigigu, The Girl in the Moon: 25c, Eigigu works while sisters play, rocket lift-off. 30c, Eigigu climbing tree, capsule in lunar orbit. 50c, Eigigu stealing from blind woman, lunar module on moon. $1, Eigigu with husband, Maramen (the moon), astronaut stepping on moon.

1989, Dec. 22   **Litho.**   **Perf. 14x15**
364 A90 25c multicolored   .90   .90
365 A90 30c multicolored   1.10   1.10
366 A90 50c multicolored   1.90   1.90
367 A90 $1 multicolored   3.75   3.75
    Nos. 364-367 (4)   7.65   7.65

Limited supplies of Nos. 364-367 were available through agent.

1990, July 3   **Litho.**   **Perf. 14x15**
368 A91 50c Mining by hand   .80   .80
369 A91 $1 Mechanized extraction   1.60   1.60

Nauru Phosphate Corp., 20th anniv.

Christmas — A92 — A93

1990, Nov. 26   **Litho.**   **Perf. 14**
370 A92 25c Children   .38   .38
371 A92 25c Telling Christmas story   .38   .38
   a.   Pair, #370-371   .76   .76

1990, Dec. 24   **Litho.**   **Perf. 14x15**
372 A93 25c Woman with baby   .38   .38
373 A93 30c Weaving flowers   .45   .45
374 A93 50c Listening to storm   .75   .75
375 A93 $1 Couple   1.50   1.50
    Nos. 372-375 (4)   3.08   3.08

Legend of Eoiyepiang, Daughter of Thunder and Lightning.

NAURU   15c   Flowers — A94

1991, July 15   **Litho.**   **Perf. 14½**
380 A94 15c Oleander   .24   .24
381 A94 20c Lily   .30   .30
382 A94 25c Passion Flower   .38   .38
383 A94 30c Lily, diff.   .45   .45
384 A94 35c Caesalpinia   .55   .55
385 A94 40c Clerodendron   .62   .62
387 A94 45c Bauhina pinnata   .70   .70
388 A94 50c Hibiscus, vert.   .78   .78
389 A94 75c Apocynaceae   1.15   1.15
390 A94 $1 Bindweed, vert.   1.55   1.55
391 A94 $2 Tristellateia, vert.   3.10   3.10
392 A94 $3 Impala lily, vert.   4.65   4.65
    Nos. 380-392 (12)   14.47   14.47

This is an expanding set. Numbers will change if necessary.

Souvenir Sheet

Christmas — A95

1991, Dec. 12   **Litho.**   **Perf. 14**
395 A95 $2 Stained glass window   3.10   3.10

Asian Development Bank, 25th Meeting — A96

1992, May 4   **Litho.**   **Perf. 14x14½**
396 A96 $1.50 multicolored   2.35   2.35

Christmas — A97

Children's drawings: 45c, Christmas trees, flags and balloons. 60c, Santa in sleigh, reindeer on flag.

1992, Nov. 23   **Litho.**   **Perf. 14½x14**
397 A97 45c multicolored   .60   .60
398 A97 60c multicolored   .80   .80

Hammer DeRoburt (1922-1992) — A98

1993, Jan. 31   **Litho.**   **Perf. 14x14½**
399 A98 $1 multicolored   1.35   1.35

Independence, 25th anniv.

Constitution Day, 15th Anniv. — A99

24th South Pacific Forum — A100

1993, May 17   **Litho.**   **Perf. 14x14½**
400 A99 70c Runners   1.00   1.00
401 A99 80c Declaration of Republic   1.10   1.10

1993, Aug. 9   **Litho.**   **Perf. 14½x14**
402 A100 60c Seabirds   .80   .80
403 A100 60c Birds, dolphin   .80   .80
404 A100 60c Coral, fish   .80   .80
405 A100 60c Fish, coral, diff.   .80   .80
   a.   Block of 4, #402-405   3.25   3.25
   b.   Souvenir sheet of 4, #402-405   6.00   6.00

No. 405a is a continuous design.

Christmas — A101

Designs: 55c, "Peace on earth..." 65c, "Hark the Herald Angels Sing."

1993, Nov. 29   **Litho.**   **Perf. 14½x14**
406 A101 55c multicolored   .75   .75
407 A101 65c multicolored   .90   .90

Child's Best Friend — A102

1994, Feb. 10   **Litho.**   **Perf. 14**
408 A102 $1 Girls, dogs   1.40   1.40
409 A102 $1 Boys, dogs   1.40   1.40
   a.   Pair, #408-409   2.75   2.75
   b.   Souvenir sheet of 2, #408-409   2.75   2.75
   c.   As "b," ovptd. in sheet margin   2.75   2.75
   d.   As "b," ovptd. in sheet margin   3.75   3.75

No. 409c ovptd. with Hong Kong '94 emblem.
No. 409d ovptd. with SINGPEX '94 emblem in gold.
Issued: #409c, 2/18/94; #409d, 8/31/94.

15th Commonwealth Games, Victoria — A103

1994, Sept. 8   **Litho.**   **Perf. 14x14½**
410 A103 $1.50 Weight lifting   2.25   2.25

ICAO, 50th Anniv. — A104

Designs: 55c, Emblems. 65c, Nauru Intl. Airport. 80c, DVOR navigational aid. $1, Airport fire engines.

1994, Dec. 14
411 A104 55c multicolored   .80   .80
412 A104 65c multicolored   1.00   1.00
413 A104 80c multicolored   1.25   1.25

414 A104 $1 multicolored   1.50   1.50
   a.   Souvenir sheet of 4, #411-414   4.50   4.50
    Nos. 411-414 (4)   4.55   4.55

United Nations, 50th Anniv. — A105

1995, Jan. 1   **Perf. 14x14½**
415 A105 75c Natl. flag   1.10   1.10
416 A105 75c Natl. coat of arms   1.10   1.10
417 A105 75c Canoe, UN emblem   1.10   1.10
418 A105 75c Jet, ship, UN emblem   1.10   1.10
   a.   Block of 4, #415-418   4.50   4.50
   b.   Souvenir sheet of 4, #415-418   4.50   4.50

Nos. 417-418 are a continuous design.

Christmas — A106

1994, Nov. 20   **Litho.**   **Perf. 14½x14**
419 A106 65c shown   1.00   1.00
420 A106 75c Star over Bethlehem   1.10   1.10

Membership in Intl. Olympic Committee — A107

1994, Dec. 27   **Perf. 14x14½**
421 A107 50c multicolored   .75   .75

Nauru Phosphate Corporation, 25th Anniv. — A108

Designs: No. 422, Signing of Phosphate Agreement, June 15, 1967. No. 423, Nauru Pres. Bernard Dowiyogo, Australian Prime Minister Paul Keating at signing Nauru Australia Compact of Settlement. $2, Mining phosphate.

1995, July 1   **Litho.**   **Perf. 14x15**
422 A108 60c multicolored   .90   .90
423 A108 60c multicolored   .90   .90
   a.   Pair, #422-423   1.80   1.80

Souvenir Sheet

424 A108 $2 multicolored   3.00   3.00

No. 291 Surcharged

at Beijing

50c

1995   **Litho.**   **Perf. 13½x14**
    Overprinted:
425 A66 50c on 25c "at Beijing"   .75   .75
426 A66 $1 on 25c "at Singapore"   1.50   1.50
427 A66 $1 on 25c "at Jakarta"   1.50   1.50
   a.   Strip of 3, #425-427   3.75   3.75

SEMI-POSTAL STAMP

Miniature Sheet of 4

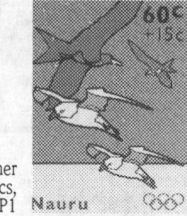

1996 Summer
Olympics,
Atlanta — SP1

Designs: a, Birds, denomination UR. b. Birds,
denomination UL. c, 4 dolphins. d, 2 dolphins.

1995, Sept. 1　　Litho.　　Perf. 12
B1　SP1　60c +15c, #a.-d.　4.50　4.50

Surcharge for sports development in Nauru.

NEPAL

nə-'pòl

LOCATION — In the Himalaya Mountains
between India and Tibet
GOVT. — Kingdom
AREA — 56,136 sq. mi.
POP. — 16,100,000 (est. 1982)
CAPITAL — Kathmandu

Although an independent state, Nepal's
close political and economic ties with India
make it advisable to include its stamps in
this section. The stamps were valid only in
Nepal and India until April 1959, when they
became valid to all parts of the world.

4 Pice = 1 Anna
64 Pice = 16 Annas = 1 Rupee
100 Paisa = 1 Rupee (1958)

> Catalogue values for unused
> stamps in this country are for Never
> Hinged items, beginning with Scott
> 103 in the regular postage section,
> Scott C1 in the air post section and
> Scott O1 in the officials section.

Nos. 1-24, 29A were issued without
gum.

Sripech and Crossed　　Siva's Bow and Two
Khukris — A1　　　　Khukris — A2

1881　　Typo.　　Unwmk.　　Pin-perf.
European Wove Paper
1　A1　1a ultramarine　175.00　300.00
2　A1　2a purple　250.00　200.00
3　A1　4a green　250.00　300.00
　a.　Tete beche pair
Imperf
4　A1　1a blue　105.00　110.00
5　A1　2a purple　130.00　130.00
　a.　Tete beche pair
6　A1　4a green　165.00　60.00

1886　　Native Wove Paper　　Imperf.
7　A1　1a ultramarine　15.00　8.00
　a.　Tete beche pair　125.00　175.00
8　A1　2a violet　17.50　10.00
　a.　Tete beche pair　150.00　200.00
9　A1　4a green　45.00　12.00
　a.　Tete beche pair　200.00　250.00
　　　Nos. 7-9 (3)　77.50　30.00

1899-1903　　　　　　　　Imperf.
Native Wove Paper
10　A2　½a black　11.00
　a.　Tete beche pair　200.00

11　A2　½a red orange ('03)　1,000.
　a.　Tete beche pair
Pin-perf.
12　A2　½a black　20.00
　a.　Tete beche pair　150.00

No. 11 probably was used only on tele-
graph/telephone forms.

Type of 1881
1898-1904　　　　　　　　Imperf.
13　A1　1a pale blue　12.50　6.00
　a.　1a bluish green　50.00　60.00
　b.　Tete beche pair　150.00　150.00
14　A1　2a gray violet　25.00　10.00
　a.　Tete beche pair　250.00　300.00
15　A1　2a claret　30.00　12.00
　a.　Tete beche pair　275.00　325.00
16　A1　2a brown　10.00
　a.　Tete beche pair　25.00
17　A1　4a dull green　10.00　15.00
　a.　Tete beche pair　70.00　400.00
　b.　Cliche of 1a in plate of 4a ('04)　300.00
　　　Nos. 13-17 (5)　87.50　43.00

#17b has the recut frame of the 1904 issue.
#17b probably was used only on tele-
graph/telephone forms.

Pin-perf.
18　A1　1a pale blue　17.50　10.00
　a.　Tete beche pair　100.00　150.00
19　A1　2a gray violet　25.00　12.00
　a.　Tete beche pair　200.00　225.00
20　A1　2a claret　8.75　6.00
　a.　Tete beche pair　45.00
21　A1　2a brown　7.50
　a.　Tete beche pair　45.00
22　A1　4a dull green　50.00　18.00
　a.　Tete beche pair　400.00　450.00

Frame Recut on All Cliches, Fewer Lines
1903-04　　Native Wove Paper　　Imperf.
23　A1　1a bright blue　10.00
　a.　Tete beche pair　50.00
Pin-perf.
24　A1　1a bright blue　15.00
　a.　Tete beche pair　100.00

No. 23 exists on European wove paper.

Siva　　　　　　　A4
Mahadeva — A3

1907　　Engr.　　Perf. 13½
European Wove Paper
26　A3　2p brown　.90　.60
27　A3　4p green　1.50　.95
28　A3　8p carmine　6.25　.95
29　A3　16p violet　10.50　1.50
　　　Nos. 26-29 (4)　19.15　4.00

Type A3 has five characters in bottom panel,
reading "Gurkha Sirkar." Date divided in lower corners is "1964." Outer side panels carry denomination (also on A5).

1917-18　　　　　　　　Imperf.
29A　A4　1a indigo　20.00　1.00
　b.　1a bright blue　10.00　1.00
　c.　Pin-perf.

During 1917-18, due to a shortage of current
stamps, remainder stocks and further printings of
types A1 and A4 were used provisionally on official
mail and to prepay telegrams. The usual telegraph
cancellation is crescent-shaped.

Type of 1907 Redrawn

 A5

Nine characters in bottom panel
reading "Nepal Sirkar"
1929　　　　　　　Perf. 14, 14½
Size: 24¾x18¾mm
30　A5　2p dark brown　.55　.30
31　A5　4p green　.85　.30
32　A5　8p deep red　.95　.35
33　A5　16p dark red vio　1.65　.65
34　A5　24p orange yellow　2.50　1.25
35　A5　32p dark ultra　2.75　1.50
Size: 26x19½mm
36　A5　1r orange red　4.25　3.75

Size: 28x21mm
37　A5　5r brown & black　17.00　22.50
　　　Nos. 30-37 (8)　30.50　30.60

On Nos. 30-37 the date divided in lower corners
is "1986."

Type of 1929 Redrawn

Date characters in Lower Corners read
"1992"
1935　　Unwmk.　　Engr.　　Perf. 14
38　A5　2p dark brown　2.50　.45
39　A5　4p green　3.50　.35
40　A5　8p bright red　35.00　6.50
41　A5　16p dk red violet　7.25　.95
42　A5　24p orange yellow　8.25　1.00
43　A5　32p dark ultra　18.00　3.25
　　　Nos. 38-43 (6)　74.50　12.50

Redrawn Type of 1935
Perf. 11, 11x11½, 12x11½
1941-46　　　　　　　Typo.
44　A5　2p black brown　.65　.40
　a.　2p green (error)　1.00
45　A5　4p bright green　.65　.48
46　A5　8p rose red　.90　.20
47　A5　16p chocolate ('42)　2.75　2.25
48　A5　24p orange ('46)　3.25　2.75
49　A5　32p deep blue ('46)　7.25　6.25
Size: 29x19½mm
50　A5　1r henna brown ('46)　15.00　12.50
　　　Nos. 44-50 (7)　30.45　24.83

Exist imperf. vert. or horiz.

Swayambhunath
Stupa — A6

Temple of　　　　View of
Krishna — A7　　Kathmandu — A8

Pashupati (Siva
Mahadeva)
A9

Designs: 4p, Temple of Pashupati. 6p, Tri-Chun-
dra College. 8p, Mahabuddha Temple. 24p, Gues-
wori Temple, Patan. 32p, The 22 Fountains, Balaju.

Perf. 13½x14, 13½, 14
1949, Oct. 1　　Litho.　　Unwmk.
51　A6　2p brown
52　A6　4p green
53　A6　6p rose pink
54　A6　8p vermilion
55　A7　16p rose lake
56　A8　20p blue
57　A8　24p carmine
58　A8　32p ultramarine
59　A9　1r red orange
　　　Nos. 51-59 (9)　30.00　20.00

King Tribhuvana Bir
Bikram — A10

1954, Apr. 15　　Unwmk.　　Perf. 14
Size: 18x22mm
60　A10　2p chocolate　.15　.15
61　A10　4p green　.15　.18
62　A10　6p rose　.16　.22
63　A10　8p violet　.18　.22
64　A10　12p red orange　.28　.40
Size: 25½x29½mm
65　A10　16p red brown　.35　.60
66　A10　20p car rose　.42　.70
67　A10　24p rose lake　.70　1.10

68　A10　32p ultramarine　.85　1.40
69　A10　50p rose pink　1.10　2.00
70　A10　1r vermilion　1.75　4.00
71　A10　2r orange　4.00　8.00
　　　Nos. 60-71 (12)　10.09　18.97

Map of
Nepal — A11

1954, Apr. 15
Size: 29½x17½mm
72　A11　2p chocolate　.22　.15
73　A11　4p green　.25　.15
74　A11　6p rose　.42　.15
75　A11　8p violet　.50　.18
76　A11　12p red orange　.85　.28
Size: 38x21½mm
77　A11　16p red brown　1.10　.50
78　A11　20p car rose　1.25　.55
79　A11　24p rose lake　1.25　.55
80　A11　32p ultramarine　1.65　.80
81　A11　50p rose pink　2.50　1.10
82　A11　1r vermilion　5.00　4.00
83　A11　2r orange　10.00　11.00
　　　Nos. 72-83 (12)　24.99　19.41

Planting　　　　Throne — A13
Rice — A12

Hanuman　　King Mahendra Bir
Gate — A14　　Bikram and Queen
　　　　　　　Ratna — A15

Design: 8p, Ceremonial arch and elephant.

Perf. 13½x14, 11½, 13½, 14
Litho., Photo. (6p)
1956　　Granite Paper　　Unwmk.
84　A12　4p green　.15　.35
85　A13　6p crimson & org　.15　.35
86　A12　8p light violet　.15　.55
87　A14　24p carmine rose　.32　1.40
88　A15　1r brown red　27.50　72.50
　　　Nos. 84-88 (5)　28.27　75.15

Coronation of King Mahendra Bir Bikram and
Queen Ratna Rajya Lakshmi.

Mountain
Village and UN
Emblem
A16

1956, Dec. 14　　Litho.　　Perf. 13½
89　A16　12p ultra & orange　1.00　.70

1st anniv. of Nepal's admission to the UN.

Crown of　　　　Lumbini
Nepal — A17　　Temple — A18

Perf. 13½x14
1957, June 22　　　　　Unwmk.
Size: 18x22mm
90　A17　2p dull red brown　.18　.55
91　A17　4p light green　.18　.55
92　A17　6p pink　.20　.60
93　A17　8p light violet　.28　1.10

94 A17 12p orange vermilion .35 *1.00*

Size: 25½x30mm

95 A17 16p red brown .42 .30
96 A17 20p deep pink .55 .35
97 A17 24p brt car rose .70 .45
98 A17 32p ultramarine .85 .60
99 A17 50p rose red 1.40 1.10
100 A17 1r brown orange 2.50 *4.25*
101 A17 2r orange 5.00 *9.00*
Nos. 90-101 (12) 12.61 *19.85*

1958, Dec. 10 Typo. *Perf. 11*
Without Gum

102 A18 6p yellow .15 .15

10th anniversary of Universal Declaration of Human Rights. Exists imperf.

Catalogue values for unused stamps in this section, from this point to the end of the section, are for Never Hinged items.

Map and Flag — A19

1959, Feb. 18 Engr. *Perf. 14½*

103 A19 6p carmine & light green .15 .15

First general elections in Nepal.

Statue of Vishnu, Changu Narayan — A20
Krishna Conquering Black Serpent — A21

Designs: 4p, Nepalese glacier. 6p, Golden Gate, Bhaktapur. 8p, Nepalese musk deer. 12p, Rhinoceros. 16p, 20p, 24p, 32p, 50p, Nyatapola Temple, Bhatgaon. 1r, 2r, Himalayan impeyan pheasant. 5r, Satyr tragopan.

Perf. 13½x14, 14x13½
1959-60 Litho. Unwmk.
Size: 18x22mm

104 A20 1p chocolate .15 .15
105 A21 2p gray violet .15 .15
106 A20 4p light ultra .15 .15
107 A20 6p vermilion .15 .15
108 A21 8p sepia .15 .15
109 A21 12p greenish gray .15 .15

Size: 25½x30mm

110 A20 16p brown & lt vio .15 .15
111 A20 20p blue & dull rose .28 .15
112 A20 24p green & pink .18 .15
113 A20 32p brt vio & ultra .28 .16
114 A20 50p rose red & grn .55 .20
115 A20 1r redsh brn & bl 6.50 3.25
116 A20 2r rose lil & ultra 1.90 .90
117 A20 5r vio & rose red ('60) 22.50 10.00
Nos. 104-117 (14) 33.24 14.86

Nepal's admission to the UPU.

Spinning Wheel — A22
King Mahendra — A23

1959, Apr. 10 Typo. *Perf. 11*

118 A22 2p dark red brown .15 .15

Issued to promote development of cottage industries. Exists imperf.

1959, Apr. 14

119 A23 12p bluish black .15 .15

Nepal's admission to UPU. Exists imperf. and ungummed.

King Mahendra Opening Parliament — A24

1959, July 1 Unwmk. *Perf. 10½*

120 A24 6p deep carmine .15 .15

First session of Parliament. Exists imperf.

Sri Pashupati Nath — A25
King Mahendra — A26

1959, Nov. 19 *Perf. 11*
Size: 18x24½mm

121 A25 4p dp yellow green .15 .15

Size: 20½x28mm

122 A25 8p carmine .18 .15

Size: 24½x33mm

123 A25 1r light blue .70 .32
Nos. 121-123 (3) 1.03
Set value .42

Renovation of Sri Pashupati Temple. The 4p exists imperf.

1960, June 11 Photo. *Perf. 14*
Size: 25x30mm

124 A26 1r red lilac .70 .28

King Mahendra's 40th birthday. See Nos. 147-151A. For overprint, see No. O15.

Children, Temple and Mt. Everest — A27
Mount Everest — A28

1960 Typo. *Perf. 11*

125 A27 6p dark blue 5.00 3.50

1st Children's Day, Mar. 1, 1960. Printed in sheets of four. Exists imperf.; value $25 unused.

1960-61 Photo. *Perf. 14*

Himalaya mountain peaks: 5p, Machha Puchhre. 40p, Mansalu.

126 A28 5p claret & brown ('61) .15 .15
127 A28 10p ultra & rose lilac .15 .15
128 A28 40p violet & red brn ('61) .24 .20
Set value .39 .32

King Tribhuvana A29
King Mahendra A30

1961, Feb. 18 *Perf. 13x13½*

129 A29 10p red brown & orange .15 .15

Tenth Democracy Day.

1961, June 11 *Perf. 14x14½*

130 A30 6p emerald .15 .15
131 A30 12p ultramarine .15 .15
132 A30 50p carmine rose .18 .15
133 A30 1r brown .42 .35
Set value .72 .60

King Mahendra's 41st birthday.

Prince Gyanendra Canceling Stamps — A31
Malaria Eradication Emblem and Temple — A32

1961 Typo. *Perf. 11*

134 A31 12p orange 20.00 8.75

Issued for Children's Day, Mar. 1, 1961.

1962, Apr. 7 Litho. *Perf. 13x13½*

Design: 1r, Emblem and Nepalese flag.

135 A32 12p blue & lt blue .15 .15
136 A32 1r magenta & orange .35 .35
Set value .42 .40

WHO drive to eradicate malaria.

King Mahendra A33

1962, June 11 Unwmk. *Perf. 13*

137 A33 10p slate blue .15 .15
138 A33 15p brown .15 .15
139 A33 45p dull red brown .28 .18
140 A33 1r olive gray .55 .38
Nos. 137-140 (4) 1.13
Set value .68

King Mahendra's 42nd birthday.

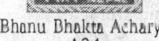

Bhanu Bhakta Acharya A34
King Mahendra A35

Portraits: 10p, Moti Ram Bhatta. 40p, Shambu Prasad.

1962 Photo. *Perf. 14x14*

141 A34 5p orange brown .15 .15
142 A34 10p deep aqua .15 .15
143 A34 40p olive bister .15 .15
Set value .22 .22

Issued to honor Nepalese poets.

Mahendra Type of 1960 and Type A35

1962-66 *Perf. 14½x14*

144 A35 1p car rose .15 .15
145 A35 2p brt blue .15 .15
145A A35 3p gray ('66) .15 .15
146 A35 5p golden brown .15 .15

Perf. 14x14½
Size: 21½x38mm

147 A26 10p rose claret .15 .15
148 A26 40p brown .15 .15
149 A26 75p blue green 2.50 2.50

Perf. 14
Size: 25x30mm

150 A26 2r red orange .70 .45
151 A26 5r gray green 2.00 1.00
151A A26 10r violet ('66) 3.75 3.50
Nos. 144-151A (10) 9.85 8.35

See No. 199. For overprints, see Nos. O12-O14.

Blackboard, Book and UN Emblem A36

1963, Jan. 6 *Perf. 14½x14*

152 A36 10p dark gray .15 .15
153 A36 15p brown .15 .15
154 A36 50p violet blue .28 .20
Set value .43 .33

UNESCO "Education for All" campaign.

Five-pointed Star and Hands Holding Lamps — A37
Man, Tractor and Wheat — A38

Unwmk.
1963, Feb. 19 Photo. *Perf. 13*

155 A37 5p blue .15 .15
156 A37 10p reddish brown .15 .15
157 A37 50p rose lilac .18 .15
158 A37 1r blue green .35 .20
Set value .65 .40

Panchayat System and National Day.

1963, Mar. 21 *Perf. 14x14½*

159 A38 10p orange .15 .15
160 A38 15p dark ultra .15 .15
161 A38 50p green .15 .15
162 A38 1r brown .18 .18
Set value .37 .37

FAO "Freedom from Hunger" campaign.

Map of Nepal and Hand — A39

1963, Apr. 14 Unwmk. *Perf. 13*

163 A39 10p green .15 .15
164 A39 15p claret .15 .15
165 A39 50p slate .18 .15
166 A39 1r violet blue .35 .18
Set value .64 .36

Rastriya Panchayat system.

King Mahendra — A40

1963, June 11 *Perf. 13*

167 A40 5p violet .15 .15
168 A40 10p brown orange .15 .15
169 A40 15p dull green .15 .15
Set value .20 .20

King Mahendra's 43rd birthday.

East-West Highway on Map of Nepal and King Mahendra A41

1964, Feb. 19   Photo.   *Perf. 13*
170 A41 10p blue & dp orange   .15   .15
171 A41 15p dk blue & dp orange   .15   .15
172 A41 50p dk green & redsh
                    brown   .18   .18
          Set value   .28   .28
Issued to publicize the East-West Highway as "The Prosperity of the Country."

King Mahendra Speaking Before Microphone A42

Crown Prince Birendra A43

1964, June 11   *Perf. 14*
173 A42 1p brown olive   .15   .15
174 A42 2p gray   .15   .15
175 A42 2r golden brown   .75   .55
          Set value   .87   .67
King Mahendra's 44th birthday.

Perf. 14x14¹/₂
1964, Dec. 28   Photo.   Unwmk.
176 A43 10p dark green   .15   .15
177 A43 15p brown   .24   .15
          Set value   .17
19th birthday (coming of age) of Crown Prince Birendra Bir Bikram Shah Deva.

Nepalese Flag and Swords, Olympic Emblem A44

1964, Dec. 31   Litho.   *Perf. 13x13¹/₂*
178 A44 10p red & ultra   .15   .15
18th Olympic Games, Tokyo, Oct. 10-25.

Farmer Plowing — A45

Family — A46

Designs: 5p, Grain. 10p, Chemical plant.

1965   Photo.   *Perf. 13¹/₂*
179 A45 2p brt green & black   .15   .15
180 A45 5p pale yel green & brn .15   .15
181 A45 10p gray & purple   .15   .15
182 A46 15p yellow & brown   .15   .15
          Set value   .34   .24
Issued to publicize land reform. The 2p also exists on light green paper. Issue dates: 15p, Feb. 10; others, Dec. 16.

Mail Circling Globe — A47

1965, Apr. 13   *Perf. 14¹/₂x14*
183 A47 15p rose lilac   .15   .15
Issued for Nepalese New Year.

King Mahendra — A48

Perf. 14x14¹/₂
1965, June 11   Photo.   Unwmk.
184 A48 50p rose violet   .30   .15
King Mahendra's 45th birthday.

Victims of Revolution, 1939-40 A49

1965, June 11   *Perf. 13*
185 A49 15p bright green   .15   .15
The men executed by the Rana Government 1939-40 were: Shukra Raj Shastri, Dasharath Chand, Dharma Bhakta and Ganga Lal Shresta.

ITU Emblem A50

Devkota A51

1965, Sept. 15   Photo.   *Perf. 13*
186 A50 15p deep plum & black   .15   .15
Cent. of the ITU.

1965, Oct. 14   *Perf. 14x14¹/₂*
187 A51 15p red brown   .15   .15
Lakshmi Prasad Devkota (1908-1959), poet.

ICY Emblem — A52

Engr. and Litho.
1965, Oct. 24   *Perf. 11¹/₂x12*
188 A52 1r multicolored   .45   .25
International Cooperation Year.

Nepalese Flag and King — A53

1966, Feb. 18   Photo.   *Perf. 14¹/₂x14*
189 A53 15p deep blue & red   .15   .15
Issued for Democracy Day.

Siva, Parvati and Pashupati Temple — A54

1966, Feb. 18   *Perf. 14*
190 A54 15p violet   .15   .15
Hindu festival Maha Sivaratri.

Emblem — A55

Perf. 14¹/₂x14
1966, June 10   Photo.   Unwmk.
191 A55 15p dk green & orange   .15   .15
National Philatelic Exhib., June 10-16.

King Mahendra A56

Kanti Rajya Lakshmi A57

1966, June 11   *Perf. 13x13¹/₂*
192 A56 15p yellow & vio brown   .15   .15
Issued for King Mahendra's 46th birthday.

1966, July 5   Photo.   *Perf. 14x14¹/₂*
193 A57 15p golden brown   .15   .15
60th birthday of Queen Mother Kanti Rajya Lakshmi.

Queen Ratna Rajya Lakshmi Devi Shah — A58

1966, Aug. 19   Photo.   *Perf. 13*
194 A58 15p yellow & brown   .15   .15
Issued for Children's Day.

Krishna with Consort Radha and Flute — A59

1966, Sept. 7
195 A59 15p dk purple & yellow   .15   .15
Krishnastami 2023, the birthday of Krishna.

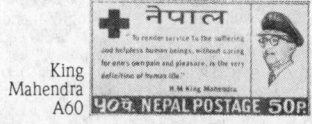

King Mahendra A60

1966, Oct. 1   Photo.   *Perf. 14¹/₂x14*
196 A60 50p slate green & dp car   .45   .20
Issued to commemorate the official recognition of the Nepalese Red Cross.

Opening of WHO Headquarters Building, Geneva — A61

Lekhnath Paudyal — A62

1966, Nov. 11   Photo.   *Perf. 14*
197 A61 1r purple   .60   .30

1966, Dec. 29   Photo.   *Perf. 14*
198 A62 15p dull violet blue   .15   .15
Lekhnath Paudyal (1884-1966), poet.

King Type of 1962
1967, Feb. 10   Photo.   *Perf. 14¹/₂x14*
199 A35 75p blue green   .28   .24

Rama and Sita — A63

Buddha — A64

1967, Apr. 18   Litho.   *Perf. 14*
200 A63 15p brown & yellow   .15   .15
Rama Navami 2024, the birthday of Rama.

1967, May 23   Photo.   *Perf. 13¹/₂x13*
201 A64 75p orange & purple   .30   .30
2,511th birthday of Buddha.

King Mahendra Addressing Crowd and Himalayas — A65

1967, June 11   *Perf. 13*
202 A65 15p dk brown & lt blue   .15   .15
King Mahendra's 47th birthday.

Queen Ratna among Children — A66

1967, Aug. 20   Photo.   *Perf. 13*
203 A66 15p pale yel & dp brown   .15   .15
Issued for Children's Day on the birthday of Queen Ratna Rajya Lakshmi Devi Shah.

Durbar Square, Bhaktapur A67

Design: 5p, Ama Dablam Mountain and ITY emblem.

1967, Oct. 24   *Perf. 13¹/₂x14*
                  Size: 29¹/₂x21mm
204 A67 5p violet   .15   .15

Perf. 14¹/₂x14
                  Size: 37¹/₂x19¹/₂mm
205 A67 65p brown   .30   .30
          Set value   .35   .35
Intl. Tourist Year, 1967. See No. C2.

Official
Reading
Proclamation
A68

1967, Dec. 16   Litho.   *Perf. 13*
206 A68 15p multicolored   .15 .15
"Back to the Villages" campaign.

Crown Prince Birendra, Boy Scouts and
Scout Emblem
A69

1967, Dec. 29   Photo.   *Perf. 14½x14*
207 A69 15p ultramarine   .15 .15
60th anniv. of Boy Scouts.

Prithvi
Narayan
A70

Arms of Nepal
A71

1960, Jan. 11   *Perf. 14x14½*
208 A70 15p blue & rose   .15 .15
Rajah Prithvi Narayan (1779-1839), founder of
modern Nepal.

1968, Feb. 19 Photo.   *Perf. 14x14½*
209 A71 15p crimson & dk blue   .20 .15
Issued for National Day.

WHO Emblem
and Flag of
Nepal — A72

1968, Mar. 25   *Perf. 13*
210 A72 1.20r dull yel, red & ultra .60 .32
World Health Day (UN WHO).

Goddess Sita
and Shrine
A73

1968, May 6   Photo.   *Perf. 14½x14*
211 A73 15p violet & org brown   .15 .15

King Mahendra,
Pheasant and
Himalayas
A74

1968, June 11 Photo.   *Perf. 13½*
212 A74 15p multicolored   .15 .15
King Mahendra's 48th birthday.

Flag, Children and
Queen Ratna — A75

1968, Aug. 19 Litho.   *Perf. 13x13½*
213 A75 5p blue grn, yel & ver   .15 .15
Fourth National Children's Day.

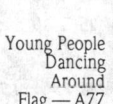

Buddha and
Human Rights
Flame — A76

1968, Dec. 10 Photo.   *Perf. 14½x14*
214 A76 1r dk green & red   .45 .20
International Human Rights Year.

Young People
Dancing
Around
Flag — A77

1968, Dec. 28 Photo.   *Perf. 14½x14*
215 A77 25p violet blue   .15 .15
23rd birthday of Crown Prince Birendra, which
is celebrated as Youth Festival.

UN Building, Nepalese
and UN Flags — A78

Amsu
Varma — A79

1969, Jan. 1   *Perf. 13½x13*
216 A78 1r multicolored   .45 .20
Issued to commemorate Nepal's admission to the
UN Security Council for 1969-1970.

1969, Apr. 13 Photo.   *Perf. 14x14½*
Portraits: 25p, Ram Shah. 50p, Bhimsen Thapa.
217 A79 15p green & purple   .15 .15
218 A79 25p blue green   .15 .15
219 A79 50p orange brown   .30 .18
    Nos. 217-219 (3)   .60
    Set value   .32
Amsu Varma, 7th cent. ruler and reformer; Ram
Shah, 17th cent. ruler and reformer, and Bhimsen
Thapa, 18-19th cent. administrator and reformer.

ILO Emblem
A80

1969, May 1   Photo.   *Perf. 14½x14*
220 A80 1r car rose, blk & lt brown .60 .35
50th anniv. of the ILO.

King
Mahendra — A81

1969, June 20   *Perf. 13½x13*
221 A81 25p gold & multi   .15 .15
King Mahendra's 49th birthday (50th by Oriental
count). Issuance delayed from June 11 to 20.

King
Tribhuvana
and Wives
A82

1969, July 1   *Perf. 14½x14*
222 A82 25p yellow & ol gray   .15 .15
64th anniv. of the birth of King Tribhuvana.

Queen Ratna &
Child
Playing — A83

Rhododendron &
Himalayas — A84

1969, Aug. 20 Photo.   *Perf. 14x14½*
223 A83 25p gray & rose car   .15 .15
Issued for the 5th National Children's Day and to
commemorate the 41st birthday of Queen Ratna
Rajya Lakshmi Devi Shah.

1969, Sept. 17 Photo. *Perf. 13½*
Flowers: No. 225, Narcissus. No. 226, Marigold.
No. 227, Poinsettia.
224 A84 25p lt blue & multi   .28 .24
225 A84 25p brown red & multi   .28 .24
226 A84 25p black & multi   .28 .24
227 A84 25p multicolored   .28 .24
  a.   Block of 4, #224-227   1.15 1.15

Durga,
Goddess of
Victory — A85

Crown Prince Birendra
and Princess
Aishwarya — A86

1969, Oct. 17 Photo.   *Perf. 14x14½*
228 A85 15p black & orange   .15 .15
229 A85 50p black, bis brn & vio .20 .15
    Set value   .29 .15
Issued to celebrate the Dasain Festival.

1970, Feb. 27 Photo.   *Perf. 13½*
230 A86 25p multicolored   .15 .15
Wedding of Crown Prince Birendra Bir Bikram
Shah Deva and Crown Princess Aishwarya Rajya
Lakshmi Devi Rana, Feb. 27-28.

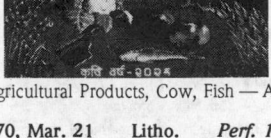

Agricultural Products, Cow, Fish — A87

1970, Mar. 21 Litho.   *Perf. 12½*
231 A87 25p multicolored   .15 .15
Issued to publicize the Agricultural Year.

Bal Bhadra
Kunwar
A88

1970, Apr. 13 Photo.   *Perf. 14½x14*
232 A88 1r ol bister & red lilac .30 .24
Bal Bhadra Kunwar, leader in the 1814 battle of
Kalanga against British forces.

King Mahendra, Mountain Peak and
Crown — A89

1970, June 11 Litho.   *Perf. 11½*
233 A89 50p gold & multi   .15 .15
King Mahendra's 50th birthday.

Gosainkund
A90

Lakes: 25p, Phewa Tal. 1r, Rara Daha.

1970, June 11 Photo.   *Perf. 13½*
234 A90 5p dull yellow & multi   .15 .15
235 A90 25p gray & multi   .15 .15
236 A90 1r pink & multi   .30 .28
    Set value   .44 .40

A.P.Y.
Emblem
A91

1970, July 1   *Perf. 14½x14*
237 A91 1r dark blue & blue   .30 .24
Asian Productivity Year 1970.

Bal Mandir
Building and
Queen Ratna
A92

1970, Aug. 20 Photo.   *Perf. 14½x14*
238 A92 25p gray & bister brn   .15 .15
Issued for Children's Day. The Bal Mandir Building in Taulihawa is the headquarters of the National
Children's Organization.

New UPU
Headquarters,
Bern — A93

1970, Oct. 9   Photo.   *Perf. 14½x14*
239 A93 2.50r ocher & sepia   .60 .60

UN Flag—A94

1970, Oct. 24 Photo. Perf. 14¹/₂x14
240 A94 25p blue & brown .15 .15
25th anniversary of the United Nations.

Royal Palace and Square, Patan A95

Designs: 25p, Bodhnath stupa, near Kathmandu, vert. 1r, Gauri Shankar, holy mountain.

Perf. 11x11¹/₂, 11¹/₂x11
1970, Dec. 28 Litho.
241 A95 15p multicolored .15 .15
242 A95 25p multicolored .15 .15
243 A95 1r multicolored .35 .28
Set value .50 .40
Crown Prince Birendra's 25th birthday.

Statue of Harihar (Vishnu-Siva)—A96

1971, Jan. 26 Photo. Perf. 14x14¹/₂
244 A96 25p bister brn & black .15 .15

Torch and Target — A97

1971, Mar. 21 Photo. Perf. 13¹/₂x13
245 A97 1r bluish gray & dp orange .35 .24
Intl. year against racial discrimination.

King Mahendra and Subjects A98

1971, June 11 Photo. Perf. 14¹/₂x14
246 A98 25p dull purple & blue .15 .15
King Mahendra's 51st birthday.

Sweta Bhairab (Siva) — A99

Sculptures of Siva: 25p, Manhankal Bhairab. 50p, Kal Bhairab.

1971, July 11 Perf. 13x13¹/₂
247 A99 15p orange brown & black .15 .15
248 A99 25p lt green & black .15 .15
249 A99 50p blue & black .24 .15
Set value .43 .27

Queen Ratna Receiving Garland A100

1971, Aug. 20 Photo. Perf. 11¹/₂
Granite Paper
250 A100 25p gray & multi .15 .15
Children's Day, Queen Ratna's birthday.

Map and Flag of Iran, Flag of Nepal A101

1971, Oct. 14
Granite Paper
251 A101 1r pink & multi .45 .28
2500th anniversary of the founding of the Persian empire by Cyrus the Great.

UNICEF Emblem, Mother and Child A102

1971, Dec. 11 Perf. 14¹/₂x14
252 A102 1r gray blue .45 .28
25th anniversary of UNICEF.

Everest A103

Himalayan Peaks: 1r, Kangchenjunga. 1.80r, Annapurna I.

1971, Dec. 28 Perf. 13¹/₂x13
253 A103 25p blue & brown .15 .15
254 A103 1r dp blue & brown .30 .20
255 A103 1.80r blue & yel brown .60 .45
Nos. 253-255 (3) 1.05
Set value
"Visit Nepal."

Royal Standard — A104

Araniko and White Dagoba, Peking — A105

1972, Feb. 19 Photo. Perf. 13
256 A104 25p dark red & black .15 .15
National Day.

1972, Apr. 13 Litho. Perf. 13
257 A105 15p lt blue & ol gray .15 .15
Araniko, a 14th century Nepalese architect, who built the White Dagoba at the Miaoying Monastery, Peking, 1348.

Book Year Emblem, Ancient Book A106

1972, Sept. 8 Photo. Perf. 14¹/₂x14
258 A106 2p ocher & brown .15 .15
259 A106 5p tan & black .15 .15
260 A106 1r blue & black .30 .24
Set value .40 .34
International Book Year.

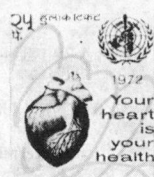

Heart and WHO Emblem—A107

1972, Nov. 6 Photo. Perf. 13x13¹/₂
261 A107 25p dull grn & claret .15 .15
"Your heart is your health," World Health Month.

King Mahendra (1920-1972) — A108

1972, Dec. 15 Photo. Perf. 13¹/₂x13
262 A108 25p brown & black .15 .15

King Birendra — A109

Northern Border Costume — A110

1972, Dec. 28 Photo. Perf. 13x13¹/₂
263 A109 50p ocher & purple .18 .15
King Birendra's 27th birthday.

1973, Feb. 18 Photo. Perf. 13
Nepalese Costumes: 50p, Hill dwellers. 75p, Kathmandu Valley couple. 1r, Inner Terai couple.
264 A110 25p dull lilac & multi .15 .15
265 A110 50p lemon & multi .15 .15
266 A110 75p multicolored .18 .15
267 A110 1r multicolored .24 .18
a. Block of 4, #264-267 .65 .60
Set value .60 .44
National Day.

Babu Ram Acharya (1888-1972), Historian — A111

1973, Mar. 12 Photo. Perf. 13
268 A111 25p olive gray & car .15 .15

Nepalese Family and Home A112

1973, Apr. 7 Photo. Perf. 14¹/₂x14
269 A112 1r Prus blue & ocher .50 .30
25th anniv. of the WHO.

Lumbini Garden, Birthplace of Buddha — A113

1973, May 17 Photo. Perf. 13x13¹/₂
270 A113 25p shown .15 .15
271 A113 75p Mt. Makalu .20 .15
272 A113 1r Gorkha Village .30 .20
Nos. 270-272 (3) .65
Set value .40

FAO Emblem, Women Farmers A114

1973, June 29 Photo. Perf. 14¹/₂x14
273 A114 10p dark gray & violet .15 .15
World food program, 10th anniversary.

INTERPOL Headquarters and Emblem A115

1973, Sept. 3
274 A115 25p bister & blue .15 .15
50th anniversary of the International Criminal Police Organization (INTERPOL).

Shom Nath Sigdyal (1884-1972), Scholar — A116

1973, Oct. 5 Photo. Perf. 13x13¹/₂
275 A116 1.25r violet blue .32 .24

Cow — A117

1973, Oct. 25 Photo. Perf. 13¹/₂x13
276 A117 2p shown .15 .15
277 A117 3.25r Yak .75 .75
Set value .80 .80
Festival of Lights (Tihar).

King Birendra — A118

Perf. 13, 13¹/₂x14, 15x14¹/₂
1973-74 Photo.
278 A118 5p dark brown .15 .15
279 A118 15p ol brn & dk brn ('74) .15 .15
280 A118 1r reddish brn & dk brn ('74) .30 .24
Set value .47 .38
King Birendra's 28th birthday.

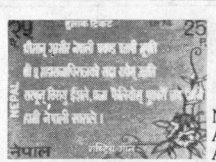

National
Anthem
A119

Natl. Day: 1r, Score of national anthem.

1974, Feb. 18 Photo. Perf. 13¹/₂x13
281 A119 25p rose carmine   .15   .15
282 A119 1r deep green   .24   .24
        Set value   .29   .29

King Janak on
Throne — A120

1974, Apr. 14 Litho. Perf. 13¹/₂
283 A120 2.50r multicolored   .75   .60

Children's Village and SOS
Emblem — A121

1974, May 20 Litho. Perf. 13¹/₂x13
284 A121 25p ultra & red   .15   .15
25th anniv. of SOS Children's Village Intl.

Baghchal — A122

1974, July 1 Litho. Perf. 13
285 A122 2p Soccer   .15   .15
286 A122 2.75r shown   .75   .60
        Set value   .80   .65
Popular Nepalese games.

WPY
Emblem — A123

UPU Monument,
Bern — A124

1974, Aug. 19 Litho. Perf. 13
287 A123 5p ocher & blue   .15   .15
World Population Year.

1974, Oct. 9 Litho. Perf. 13
288 A124 1r olive & black   .24   .18
Centenary of Universal Postal Union.

Butterfly — A125

Designs: Nepalese butterflies.

1974, Oct. 16
289 A125 10p lt brown & multi   .15   .15
290 A125 15p lt blue & multi   .15   .15
291 A125 1.25r multicolored   .35   .28
292 A125 1.75r buff & multi   .60   .45
        Set value   1.00   .82

King Birendra
A126

Muktinath
A127

Peacock
Window
A128

1974, Dec. 28 Litho. Perf. 13¹/₂x13
293 A126 25p gray green & black   .15   .15
King Birendra's 29th birthday.

Perf. 13x13¹/₂, 13¹/₂x13
1974, Dec. 31
294 A127 25p multicolored   .15   .15
295 A128 1r multicolored   .30   .18
        Set value   .36   .23
Tourist publicity.

Guheswari
Temple — A129

Pashupati
Temple — A131

Rara — A130

Tourist Year
Emblem
A133

Swayambhunath Stupa,
Kathmandu — A134

Perf. 12¹/₂x13¹/₂, 13¹/₂x12¹/₂
1975, May 25 Litho.
302 A133 2p yellow & multi   .15   .15
303 A134 25p violet & black   .15   .15
        Set value   .15   .15
South Asia Tourism Year.

Tiger
A135

1975, July 17 Litho. Perf. 13
304 A135 2p shown   .15   .15
305 A135 5p Deer, vert.   .15   .15
306 A135 1r Panda   .28   .18
        Set value   .38   .28
Wildlife conservation.

Queen Aishwarya and IWY
Emblem — A136

1975, Nov. 8 Litho. Perf. 13
307 A136 1r lt blue & multi   .30   .18
International Women's Year.

Ganesh Peak — A137

Rupse
Falls — A138

Kumari, Living Goddess
of Nepal — A139

1975, Dec. 16 Litho. Perf. 13¹/₂
308 A137 2p multicolored   .15   .15
309 A138 5p multicolored   .15   .15
310 A139 50p multicolored   .24   .15
        Set value   .40   .26
Tourist publicity.

King Birendra — A140

1975, Dec. 28 Photo. Perf. 13
311 A140 25p rose lilac & red lilac .15 .15
King Birendra's 30th birthday.

Flag and Map
of
Nepal — A141

1976, Feb. 19 Litho. Perf. 13
312 A141 2.50r dark blue & red   .45   .45
National or Democracy Day.

Rice Cultivation — A142

1976, Apr. 11 Litho. Perf. 13
313 A142 25p multicolored   .15   .15
Agricultural development.

Flags of Nepal and
Colombo
Plan — A143

Runner — A144

1976, July 1 Photo. Perf. 13x13¹/₂
314 A143 1r multicolored   .24   .18
Colombo Plan, 25th anniversary.

1976, July 31 Photo. Perf. 13x13¹/₂
315 A144 3.25r black & ultra   .45   .45
21st Olympic Games, Montreal, Canada, July 17-
Aug. 1.

Dove and Map of
South East
Asia — A145

1976, Aug. 17 Litho. Perf. 13¹/₂
316 A145 5r bister, black & ultra .75   .75
5th Summit Conference of Non-aligned Countries, Colombo, Sri Lanka, Aug. 9-19.

Folk Dances
A146

1976, Sept. 27 Litho. Perf. 13¹/₂x13
317 A146 10p Lakha mask   .15   .15
318 A146 15p Maruni   .15   .15
319 A146 30p Jhangad   .15   .15
320 A146 1r Sebru   .30   .20
        Set value   .48   .35

King Birendra and Queen
Aishwarya — A132

Designs: 1r, Throne. 1.25r, Royal Palace.

1975, Feb. 24 Litho. Perf. 13x13¹/₂
296 A129 25p multicolored   .15   .15

Photo.
Perf. 14¹/₂x14
297 A130 50p multicolored   .15   .15

Granite Paper
Perf. 11¹/₂, 11 (A131)
298 A132 1r olive & multi   .24   .18
299 A132 1.25r multicolored   .30   .22
300 A131 1.75r multicolored   .35   .30
301 A132 2.75r gold & multi   .60   .50
  a. Souvenir sheet of 3   1.25   1.25
    Nos. 296-301 (6)   1.79   1.50

Coronation of King Birendra, Feb. 24, 1975. No.
301a contains 3 imperf. stamps similar to Nos. 298-
299, 301 and label with commemorative
inscription.

Nepalese Lily — A147

King Birendra — A148

Flowers: No. 322, Meconopsis grandis. No. 323, Cardiocrinum giganteum, horiz. No. 324, Megacodon stylophorus, horiz.

1976-77   Litho.   Perf. 13
321 A147 30p lt ultra & multi   .15 .15
322 A147 30p brown & multi ('77)   .15 .15
323 A147 30p violet & multi ('77)   .15 .15
324 A147 30p green & multi ('77)   .15 .15
           Set value   .24 .20
Issue dates: Nov. 7, 1976, Jan. 24, 1977.

1976, Dec. 28   Photo.   Perf. 14
325 A148 5p green   .15 .15
326 A148 30p multicolored   .15 .15
           Set value   .15 .15
King Birendra's 31st birthday.

Bell and American Bicentennial Emblem A149

1976, Dec. 31   Litho.   Perf. 13½
327 A149 10r multicolored   1.75 1.75
American Bicentennial.

Warrior Kazi Amar Singh Thapa, Natl. Hero — A150

1977, Feb. 18   Photo.   Perf. 13x13½
328 A150 10p multicolored   .15 .15

Terracotta Figurine, Kapilavastu Excavations A151

Asoka Pillar, Lumbini A152

1977, May 3   Photo.   Perf. 14½x14
329 A151 30p dark violet   .15 .15
330 A152 5r green & brown   .90 .90
Tourist publicity.

Cheer Pheasant A153

Birds of Nepal: 5p, Great pied hornbill, vert. 1r, Green magpie. 2.30r, Nepalese laughing thrush, vert.

1977, Sept. 17   Photo.   Perf. 13
331 A153 5p multicolored   .15 .15
332 A153 15p multicolored   .15 .15
333 A153 1r multicolored   .18 .18
334 A153 2.30r multicolored   .40 .40
           Set value   .68 .68

Tukuche Peak, Nepalese Police Flag — A154

1977, Oct. 2
335 A154 1.25r multicolored   .22 .22
Ascent of Tukuche, Himalaya Mountains, by Nepalese police team, first anniversary.

Scout Emblem, Map of Nepal — A155

1977, Nov. 7   Litho.   Perf. 13½
336 A155 3.50r multicolored   .65 .65
Boy Scouts of Nepal, 25th anniversary.

Dhanwantari, Health Goddess — A156

1977, Nov. 9   Photo.   Perf. 13
337 A156 30p bluish green   .15 .15
Health Day.

Flags, Map of Nepal — A157

King Birendra — A158

1977, Dec. 5   Photo.   Perf. 13½
338 A157 1r multicolored   .18 .18
Colombo Plan, 26th Consultative Meeting, Kathmandu, Nov. 29-Dec. 7.

1977, Dec. 28
339 A158 5p olive   .15 .15
340 A158 1r red brown   .18 .18
           Set value   .22 .22
King Birendra's 32nd birthday.

Post Office Seal, New Post Office A159

Design: 75p, Post Office date stamp and new Post Office.

1978, Apr. 14   Photo.   Perf. 14½x14
341 A159 25p orange brown & black .15 .15
342 A159 75p bister & black   .15 .15
           Set value   .18 .18
Centenary of Nepalese postal service.

Mt. Everest A160

Design: 4r, Mt. Everest, different view.

1978, May 29   Photo.   Perf. 13½x13
343 A160 2.30r red brown & slate   .40 .40
344 A160 4r green & violet blue   .70 .70
1st ascent of Mt. Everest, 25th anniv.

Mountains, Trees, Environmental Emblem A161

1978, June 5
345 A161 1r blue green & orange   .18 .18
World Environment Day, June 5.

Queen Mother Ratna — A162

1978, Aug. 20   Photo.   Perf. 14
346 A162 2.30r olive gray   .40 .40
Queen Mother Ratna, 50th birthday.

Trisula River Rapids — A163

Tourist Publicity: 50p, Nepalese window. 1r, Dancer, Mahakali dance, vert.

1978, Sept. 15   Litho.   Perf. 14
347 A163 10p multicolored   .15 .15
348 A163 50p multicolored   .15 .15
349 A163 1r multicolored   .18 .18
           Set value   .32 .32

Human Rights Emblem — A164

1978, Oct. 10   Litho.   Perf. 13½
350 A164 25p red brown & red   .15 .15
351 A164 1r dark blue & red   .18 .18
           Set value   .26 .26
Universal Declaration of Human Rights, 30th anniversary.

Choerospondias Axillaris — A165

Designs: 1r, Castanopsis indica, vert. 1.25r, Elaeocarpus sphaericus.

1978, Oct. 31   Photo.   Perf. 13
352 A165 5p multicolored   .15 .15
353 A165 1r multicolored   .18 .18
354 A165 1.25r multicolored   .22 .22
           Set value   .45 .45

King Birendra — A166

1978, Dec. 17   Perf. 13½x14
355 A166 30p brown & indigo   .15 .15
356 A166 2r violet & black   .35 .35
           Set value   .40 .40
King Birendra's 33rd birthday.

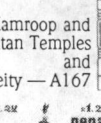  

Kamroop and Patan Temples and Deity — A167

Red Machhindra Chariot — A168

Perf. 14½x14, 13½
1979   Photo., Litho.
357 A167 75p claret & olive   .15 .15
358 A168 1.25r multicolored   .22 .22
Red Machhindra Nath Festival, Lalitpur (Patan). Issue dates: 75p, Apr. 27; 1.25r, July 25.

Bas-relief — A169

Tree Planting — A170

1979, May 12   Photo.   Perf. 13
359 A169 1r yellow & brown   .18 .18
Lumbini Year.

1979, June 29   Photo.   Perf. 13x13½
360 A170 2.30r multicolored   .40 .40
Afforestation campaign.

Children with Flag, IYC Emblem — A172

1979, Aug. 20   Perf. 13½
362 A172 1r light brown   .18 .18
Intl. Year of the Child; Natl. Children's Day.

Mount Pabil — A173

Tourism: 50p, Swargadwari Temple. 1.25r, Altar with statues of Shiva and Parbati.

1979, Sept. 26   Photo.   Perf. 13½x13
363 A173 30p dk blue green   .15 .15
364 A173 50p multicolored   .15 .15
365 A173 1.25r multicolored   .22 .22
           Set value   .37 .37

Northern
Shrike — A174

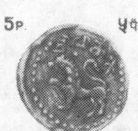

Coin, Lichhavi
Period,
Obverse — A175

Malla Period,
Obverse — A175a

Shaw Period,
Obverse — A175b

Perf. 14¹/₂x13¹/₂

1979, Nov. 22 **Photo.**
366 A174 10p shown   .15 .15
367 A174 10r Aethopyga ignicauda 2.00 2.00

Intl. World Pheasant Assoc. Symposium, Kathmandu, Nov. 21-23. See No. C7.

1979, Dec. 16 **Photo.** **Perf. 15**
Ancient Coins: No. 369, Lichhavi Period, reverse. No. 371, Malla Period, reverse. No. 373, Shah Period, reverse.

368 A175 5p brown & brown org .15 .15
369 A175 5p brown & brown org .15 .15
a.   Pair, #368-369   .15 .15
370 A175a 15p dark blue   .15 .15
371 A175a 15p dark blue   .15 .15
a.   Pair, #370-371   .15 .15
372 A175b 1r slate blue   .18 .18
373 A175b 1r slate blue   .18 .18
a.   Pair, #372-373   .36 .36
        Set value   .50 .50

King Birendra
A176

Ban-Ganga Dam
A177

1979, Dec. 28 **Litho.** **Perf. 14**
374 A176 25p multicolored   .15 .15
375 A177 2.30r multicolored   .42 .42
        Set value   .46 .46

King Birendra's 34th birthday.

Samyak
Pooja
Festival
A178

1980, Jan. 15 **Perf. 13¹/₂**
376 A178 30p violet brown & gray .15 .15

Holy Basil — A179

1980, Mar. 24 **Photo.** **Perf. 14x14¹/₂**
377 A179 5p shown   .15 .15
378 A179 30p Himalayan valerian .15 .15
379 A179 1r Nepalese pepper   .18 .18
380 A179 2.30r Himalayan rhubarb .42 .42
        Set value   .70 .70

Gyandil
Das — A180

Nepalese Writers: 30p, Shddhi Das Amatya. 1r, Pahal Man Singh Snwar. 2.30r, Jay Prithibi Bahadur Singh.

1980, Apr. 13 **Perf. 13¹/₂x13**
381 A180 5p bister & rose lilac .15 .15
382 A180 30p vio brn & lt red brn .15 .15
383 A180 1r blue & olive gray .18 .18
384 A180 2.30r ol green & dk blue .42 .42
        Set value   .70 .70

Jwalaji Dailekh
(Temple), Holy
Flame — A181

Temple
Statue — A182

1980, Sept. 14 **Litho.** **Perf. 14¹/₂**
385 A181 10p shown   .15 .15
386 A181 1r Godavari Pond   .18 .18
387 A181 5r Mt. Dhaulagiri   .90 .90
        Nos. 385-387 (3)   1.23 1.23

1980, Oct. 29 **Perf. 14x13¹/₂**
388 A182 25r multicolored   4.50 4.50

World Tourism Conf., Manila, Sept. 27.

King Birendra's 35th
Birthday — A183

1980, Dec. 28 **Litho.** **Perf. 14**
389 A183 1r multicolored   .18 .18

International
Year of the
Disabled
A184

1981, Jan. 1
390 A184 5r multicolored   .90 .90

Nepal Rastra
Bank, 25th
Anniv. — A185

1981, Apr. 26 **Litho.** **Perf. 14**
391 A185 1.75r multicolored   .32 .32

A186   A187

1981, July 16
392 A186 10p No. 1   .15 .15
393 A186 40p No. 2   .15 .15
394 A186 3.40r No. 3   .60 .60
a.   Souvenir sheet of 3, #392-394 .75 .75
        Set value   .72 .72

Nepalese stamp cent.

1981, Oct. 30 **Litho.** **Perf. 14**
395 A187 1.75r multicolored   .32 .32

Intl. Hotel Assoc., 70th council meeting, Kathmandu.

Stamp
Centenary
A188

King Birendra's
36th Birthday
A189

1981, Dec. 27 **Litho.** **Perf. 14**
396 A188 40p multicolored   .15 .15

Nepal '81 Stamp Exhibition, Kathmandu, Dec. 27-31.

1981, Dec. 28
397 A189 1r multicolored   .18 .18

Hrishikesh, Buddhist
Stone Carving,
Ridi — A190

1981, Dec. 30
398 A190 5p shown   .15 .15
399 A190 25p Tripurasundari Pavilion, Baitadi .15 .15
400 A190 2r Mt. Langtang Lirung .35 .35
        Set value   .45 .45

Royal Nepal Academy,
25th Anniv. — A191

Balakrishna
Sama — A192

1982, June 23 **Litho.** **Perf. 14**
401 A191 40p multicolored   .15 .15

1982, July 21 **Perf. 13¹/₂**
402 A192 1r multicolored   .18 .18

Dish Antenna,
Satellite — A193

Mt.
Nuptse — A194

1982, Nov. 7 **Litho.** **Perf. 14**
403 A193 5r multicolored   .90 .90

1982, Nov. 18 **Perf. 13¹/₂**
Intl. Union of Alpinists Assoc., 50th Anniv. (Himalaya Peaks): b, Mt. Lhotse (31x31mm). c, Mt. Everest (40x31mm). Se-tenant in continuous design.

404   Strip of 3   1.00 1.00
a.   A194 25p multicolored   .15 .15
b.   A194 2r multicolored   .35 .35
c.   A194 3r multicolored   .55 .55

9th Asian
Games — A195

1982, Nov. 19 **Perf. 14**
405 A195 3.40r multicolored   .65 .65

Kulekhani Hydro-
electric
Plant — A196

1982, Dec. 2 **Perf. 13¹/₂**
406 A196 2r Lake, dam   .35 .35

A197   A198

1982, Dec. 28 **Perf. 12¹/₂**
407 A197 5p multicolored   .15 .15

King Birendra's 37th birthday.

1983, June 15 **Litho.** **Perf. 14**
408 A198 50p multicolored   .15 .15

25th anniv. of Nepal Industrial Development Co.

25th Anniv. of
Royal Nepal
Airlines — A199

1983, Aug. 1 **Perf. 13¹/₂**
409 A199 1r multicolored   .15 .15

World
Communications
Year — A200

1983, Oct. 30 **Litho.** **Perf. 12**
410 A200 10p multicolored   .15 .15

A201   A202

Musical instruments.

1983, Nov. 3
411 A201 5p Sarangi   .15 .15
412 A201 10p Kwota   .15 .15
413 A201 50p Narashinga   .15 .15
414 A201 1r Murchunga   .15 .15
        Set value   .20 .20

1983, Dec. 20
415 A202 4.50r multicolored   .38 .38

Chakrapani Chalise (1883-1957), national anthem composer and poet.

King Birendra's
38th
Birthday — A203

1983, Dec. 28   *Perf. 14*
416 A203 5r multicolored   .42 .42

Temple,
Barahkshetra
A204

1983, Dec. 30   *Perf. 14*
417 A204 1r shown   .15 .15
418 A204 2.20r Triveni pilgrimage
     site   .20 .20
419 A204 6r Mt. Cho-oyu   .50 .50
    Nos. 417-419 (3)   .85 .85

Auditor General,
25th
Anniv. — A204a

1984, June 28   Litho.   *Perf. 14*
419A A204a 25p Open ledger   .15 .15

A205   A206

1984, July 1   Litho.   *Perf. 14*
420 A205 5r Transmission tower   .42 .42
Asia-Pacific Broadcasting Union, 20th anniv.

1984, July 8
421 A206 50p University emblem   .15 .15
Tribhuvan University, 25th anniv.

A207   A208

1984, Aug. 5
422 A207 10r Boxing   .85 .85
1984 Summer Olympic Games, Los Angeles.

1984, Sept. 18
423 A208 1r multicolored   .15 .15
Family Planning Assoc., 25th anniv.

Social Services
Day — A209

1984, Sept. 24
424 A209 5p multicolored   .15 .15

Wildlife — A210

1984, Nov. 30
425 A210 10p Gavialis gangeticus   .15 .15
426 A210 25p Panthera uncia   .15 .15
427 A210 50p Antilope cervicapra   .15 .15
    Set value   .15 .15

Chhinna Masta
Bhagvati Temple
and Goddess
Sakhandeshwari
Devi,
Statue — A211

Designs: 10p, Lord Vishu the Giant, Yajna Ceremony on Bali, bas-relief, A. D. 467, vert. 5r, Mt.
Api, Himalayas, vert.

1984, Dec. 21
428 A211 10p multicolored   .15 .15
429 A211 1r multicolored   .15 .15
430 A211 5r multicolored   .42 .42
    Set value   .56 .56

King Birendra,
39th
Birthday — A212

1984, Dec. 28
431 A212 1r multicolored   .15 .15

Sagarmatha
Natl.
Park — A213

1985, May 6
432 A213 10r Mt. Everest, wildlife   .85 .85
King Mahendra Trust Congress for Nature Conservation, May 6-11.

Illustration from Shiva
Dharma Purana, 13th
Cent. Book — A214

Design: Maheshware, Lord Shiva, with brahma
and vishnu.

1985, May 30
433   Strip of 5   .24 .24
a.-e. A214 50p any single   .15 .15

#433 has a continuous design. #433 also exists
imperf. between stamps. Sizes: #433a, 433e,
26x22mm; #433b, 433d, 24x22mm; #433c,
17x22mm.

UN, 40th
Anniv. — A215

1985, Oct. 24   Litho.   *Perf. 13¹⁄₂x14*
434 A215 5r multicolored   .30 .30

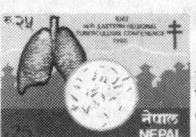

14th Eastern
Regional
Tuberculosis
Conference
A216

1985, Nov. 25
435 A216 25r multicolored   1.50 1.50

First South
Asian
Regional
Cooperation
Summit
A217

1985, Dec. 8   *Perf. 14*
436 A217 5r Flags   .30 .30

Temple of
Jaleshwar,
Mohottary
Underwater
Project
A218

1985, Dec. 15   Litho.   *Perf. 14x13¹⁄₂*
437 A218 10p shown   .15 .15
438 A218 1r Temple of
     Shaileshwari, Doti   .15 .15
439 A218 2r Lake Phoksundo,
     Dolpa   .15 .15
    Set value   .22 .22

Intl. Youth
Year — A219   Devi Ghat Hydro-
electric Dam
Project — A220

1985, Dec. 21   *Perf. 14*
440 A219 1r multicolored   .15 .15

1985, Dec. 28   Litho.   *Perf. 14*
441 A220 2r multicolored   .15 .15

King Birendra,
40th Birthday
A221   Panchayat System, 25th
Anniv.
A222

1985, Dec. 28
442 A221 50p Portrait   .15 .15

1986, Apr. 10   *Perf. 13¹⁄₂*
443 A222 4r multicolored   .24 .24

Pharping
Hydroelectric
Station, 75th
Anniv.
A223

1986, Oct. 9   Litho.   *Perf. 14x13¹⁄₂*
444 A223 15p multicolored   .15 .15

Architecture,
Artifacts — A224

1986, Oct. 9   Photo.   *Perf. 13x13¹⁄₂*
445 A224 5p Pashupati Temple   .15 .15
446 A224 10p Lumbini Fort   .15 .15
446A A224 50p like 5p ('87)   .15 .15
447 A224 1r Crown of Nepal   .15 .15
    Set value   .20 .20

No. 446A issued Apr. 14.

Asian
Productivity
Org., 25th
Anniv. — A225

1986, Oct. 26   Litho.   *Perf. 13¹⁄₂x14*
448 A225 1r multicolored   .15 .15

Reclining
Buddha,
Kathmandu
Valley
A226

Mt. Pumori,
Khumbu
Range — A227

Perf. 14, 13¹⁄₂x13
1986, Oct. 26   Litho.
449 A226 60p multicolored   .15 .15
450 A227 8r multicolored   .48 .48
    Set value   .52 .52

King Birendra, 41st
Birthday — A228   Intl. Peace
Year — A229

1986, Dec. 28   Litho.   *Perf. 13x13¹⁄₂*
451 A228 1r multicolored   .15 .15

1986, Dec. 28   *Perf. 14*
452 A229 10r multicolored   .75 .75

Social Service Natl. Coordination Council,
10th Anniv. — A230

1987, Sept. 22   Litho.   *Perf. 13¹⁄₂*
453 A230 1r Natl. flag, emblem   .15 .15

Birth of
Buddha
A231

Design: Asoka Pillar, enlargement of commemorative text and bas-relief of birth.

1987, Oct. 28   *Perf. 14*
454 A231 4r multicolored   .45 .45

First Natl.
Boy Scout
Jamboree,
Kathmandu
A232

1987, Oct. 28   Litho.   *Perf. 14*
455 A232 1r multicolored   .15 .15

A233   A234

1987, Nov. 2
456 A233 60p gold & lake   .15   .15
3rd SAARC (Southeast Asian Assoc. for Regional Cooperation) Summit Conference, Kathmandu.

1987, Nov. 10
457 A234 4r multicolored   .45   .45
Rastriya Samachar Samiti nNatl. news agency), 25th anniv.

Intl. Year of Shelter for the Homeless
A235

1987, Dec. 21   Litho.   Perf. 14
458 A235 5r multicolored   .85   .85

Kashthamandap Temple, Kathmandu
A236

Surya Bikram Gyawali (b. 1898), Historian
A237

1987, Dec. 21   Photo.   Perf. 13½x13
459 A236 25p multicolored   .15   .15

1987, Dec. 21   Perf. 13x13½
460 A237 60p multicolored   .15   .15

King Birendra, 42nd Birthday — A238

Perf. 14½x13½
1987, Dec. 28   Litho.
461 A238 25p multicolored   .15   .15

Mount Kanjiroba
A239

1987, Dec. 30   Perf. 14
462 A239 10r multicolored   1.70 1.70

Crown Prince Dipendra's 18th Birthday — A240

Nepal Bank, Ltd., 50th Anniv. — A241

1988, Mar. 28   Litho.   Perf. 14
463 A240 1r multicolored   .20   .20

1988, Apr. 8
464 A241 2r multicolored   .38   .38

Kanti Childrens' Hospital, 25th Anniv.
A242

1988, Apr. 8
465 A242 60p multicolored   .15   .15

Royal Shuklaphanta Wildlife Reserve — A243

1988, Apr. 8
466 A243 60p Swamp deer   .15   .15

A244   A245

1988, Aug. 20   Litho.   Perf. 14x13½
467 A244 5r multicolored   .95   .95
Queen Mother Ratna Rajya Laxmi Devi Shah, 60th birthday.

1988, Sept. 12   Litho.   Perf. 14x13½
468 A245 1r dull tawn & dark red   .18   .18
Nepal Red Cross, 25th anniv.

Bindhyabasini, Pokhara — A246

1988, Oct. 16   Litho.   Perf. 14½
469 A246 15p multicolored   .15   .15

A247   A248

1988, Dec. 28   Litho.   Perf. 14
470 A247 4r multicolored   .72   .72
King Birendra, 43rd birthday.

1989, Mar. 3   Litho.   Perf. 13½x14
471 A248 1r Temple   .18   .18
Pashupati Area Development Trust.

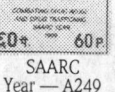 

SAARC Year — A249   A250

1989, Dec. 8   Perf. 13x13½
472 A249 60p multicolored   .15   .15
Combating Drug Abuse & Trafficking.

1989, Oct. 5   Perf. 14
473 A250 4r violet, brt green & blk   .52   .52
Asia-Pacific Telecommunity, 10th anniv.

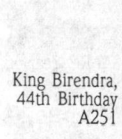

King Birendra, 44th Birthday
A251

Perf. 13½x14½
1989, Dec. 28   Litho.
474 A251 2r multicolored   .28   .28

Child Survival — A252

Design: Oral rehydration therapy, immunization, breast-feeding and growth monitoring.

1989, Dec. 28   Perf. 13½
475 A252 1r multicolored   .18   .18

Rara Natl. Park — A253

1989, Dec. 31   Perf. 14½x15
476 A253 4r multicolored   .50   .50

Mt. Ama Dablam — A254

1989, Dec. 31   Perf. 14
477 A254 5r multicolored   .62   .62

A255   A257

Temple of the Goddess Manakamana, Gorkha — A256

1990, Jan. 3
478 A255 1r multicolored   .15   .15
Crown Prince Dipendra investiture, Jan. 3.

1990, Apr. 12   Litho.   Perf. 14½
479 A256 60p deep blue & black   .15   .15

1990, Aug. 20   Litho.   Perf. 14
480 A257 1r multicolored   .15   .15
Nepal Children's Organization, 25th anniv.

A258   A259

1990, Sept. 13   Litho.   Perf. 14x13½
481 A258 60p orange, blue & red   .15   .15
Bir Hospital, cent.

1990, Oct. 9   Perf. 14½
482 A259 4r multicolored   .55   .55
Asian-Pacific Postal Training Center, 20th anniv.

SAARC Year of the Girl Child — A260

1990, Dec. 24   Litho.   Perf. 14½
483 A260 4.60r multicolored   .65   .65

Bageshwori Temple, Nepalganj
A261

Mt. Saipal — A262

1990, Dec. 24   *Perf. 13½*
484 A261 1r multicolored .15 .15
485 A262 5r multicolored .70 .70

B.P. Koirala (1914-82) — A263   King Birendra, 45th Birthday — A264

1990, Dec. 31   *Perf. 14*
486 A263 60p red, orange brn & blk .15 .15

1990, Dec. 28
487 A264 2r multicolored .22 .22

Royal Chitwan Natl. Park — A265

1991, Feb. 10   Litho.   *Perf. 14½*
488 A265 4r multicolored .45 .45

Restoration of Multiparty Democracy, 1st Anniv. — A266   Natl. Census — A267

1991, Apr. 9   Litho.   *Perf. 14*
489 A266 1r multicolored .15 .15

1991, May 3   *Perf. 14x13½*
490 A267 60p multicolored .15 .15

A268   A269

1991, Aug. 15   *Perf. 14½x13½*
491 A268 3r multicolored .30 .30
Federation of Nepalese Chambers of Commerce and Industry, 25th anniv.

1991, Sept. 4   Litho.   *Perf. 14*
492 A269 60p gray & red .15 .15
Nepal Junior Red Cross, 25th anniv.

Re-establishment of Parliament, 1st Session — A270

1991, Sept. 10   *Perf. 14½*
493 A270 1r multicolored .16 .16

Constitution Day — A271

1991, Nov. 9   Litho.   *Perf. 15x14*
494 A271 50p multicolored .15 .15

Mt. Kumbhakarna A272

1991, Oct.   Litho.   *Perf. 13½x14*
495 A272 4.60r multicolored .55 .55

Vivaha Mandap — A274   SAARC Year of Shelter — A275

1991, Dec. 11   *Perf. 11½*
497 A274 1r multicolored .18 .18

1991, Dec. 28   *Perf. 13½x14*
498 A275 9r multicolored .95 .95

King Birendra, 46th Birthday — A276

1991, Dec. 28   *Perf. 14x13½*
499 A276 8r multicolored .90 .90

Nepal Philatelic Society, 25th Anniv. — A277

1992, July 11   Litho.   *Perf. 13*
500 A277 4r multicolored .38 .38

Protect the Environment A278

1992, Oct. 24   Litho.   *Perf. 12½x13*
501 A278 60p multicolored .15 .15

Rights of the Child — A279

1992, Oct. 24   *Perf. 13½x13*
502 A279 1r multicolored .18 .18

A280   A281

Temples: 75p, Thakurdwara. 1r, Namo Buddha. 2r, Narijhowa. 11r, Dantakali.

1992, Nov. 10   *Perf. 14*
503 A280 75p multicolored .15 .15
504 A280 1r multicolored .18 .18
505 A280 2r multicolored .38 .38
506 A280 11r multicolored 2.00 2.00
    Nos. 503-506 (4) 2.71 2.71
No. 506 is airmail.

1992, Dec. 20   Photo.   *Perf. 13x13½*
507 A281 40p brown & green .15 .15
Agricultural Development Bank, 25th anniv.

Birds — A282

Designs: 1r, Pin-tailed green pigeon. 3r, Bohemian waxwing. 25r, Rufous-tailed finch lark.

1992, Dec. 20   Litho.   *Perf. 11½*
508 A282 1r multicolored .18 .18
509 A282 3r multicolored .55 .55
510 A282 25r multicolored 4.50 4.50
    Nos. 508-510 (3) 5.23 5.23

King Birendra, 47th Birthday A283

1992, Dec. 28   *Perf. 12½x13*
511 A283 7r multicolored 1.25 1.25

Poets A284   1992 Summer Olympics, Barcelona A285

Designs: No. 512, Pandit Kulchandra Gautam. No. 513, Chittadhar Hridaya. No. 514, Vidyapati. No. 515, Teongsi Sirijunga.

1992, Dec. 31   *Perf. 11½*
512 A284 1r blue & multi .18 .18
513 A284 1r brown & multi .18 .18
514 A284 1r tan & multi .18 .18
515 A284 1r gray & multi .18 .18
    Nos. 512-515 (4) .72 .72

1992, Dec. 31
516 A285 25r multicolored 4.50 4.50

Fish — A286

Designs: 25p, Tor putitora. 1r, Schizothorax plagiostomus. 5r, Anguilla bengalensis, temple of Chhabdi Barahi. 10r, Psilorhynchus pseudecheneis.

1993, Aug. 6   Litho.   *Perf. 11½*
      Granite Paper
517 A286 25p multicolored .15 .15
518 A286 1r multicolored .15 .15
519 A286 5r multicolored .35 .35
520 A286 10r multicolored .75 .75
   a.   Souvenir sheet of 4, #517-520 1.20 1.20
      Set value 1.20 1.20

World AIDS Day — A287

1993, Dec. 1   Litho.   *Perf. 13½x14½*
521 A287 1r multicolored .15 .15

Tanka Prasad Acharga — A288

1993, Dec. 2   *Perf. 13½*
522 A288 25p shown .15 .15
523 A288 1r Sungdare Sherpa .15 .15
524 A288 7r Siddhi Charan Shrestha .50 .50
525 A288 15r Falgunand 1.10 1.10
    Set value 1.65 1.65

Holy Places — A289

Designs: 1.50r, Halesi Mahadev, Khotang. 5r, Devghat, Tanahun. 8r, Bagh Bhairab, Kirtipur.

      Perf. 13½x14½
1993, Dec. 28   Litho.
526 A289 1.50r multicolored .15 .15
527 A289 5r multicolored .35 .35
528 A289 8r multicolored .60 .60
    Nos. 526-528 (3) 1.10 1.10

Tourism A290

Designs: 5r, Tushahiti Sundari Chowk, Patan. 8r, White water rafting.

1993, Dec. 28
529 A290 5r multicolored .35 .35
530 A290 8r multicolored .60 .60

King Birendra, 48th
Birthday — A291

1993, Dec. 28   *Perf. 14*
531 A291 10r multicolored   .70 .70

Large Building,
Courtyard
A293

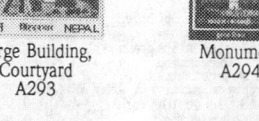

Monument
A294

Arms — A295

Fort — A296

Mt. Everest — A299

Map of
Nepal — A301

Design: 50p, Pagoda, vert.

1994-95   Litho.   *Perf. 14½*
533 A293 10p green   .15 .15
534 A294 20p violet brown   .15 .15
535 A295 25p carmine   .15 .15
536 A296 30p slate   .15 .15
537 A293 50p dark blue   .15 .15
539 A299 1r multicolored   .15 .15

Perf. 14½x13½
540 A301 5r multicolored   .35 .35
    Set value   .75 .75

Issued: 20p, 25p, 30p, 5/17/94. 1r, 7/6/94. 5r, 9/22/94; 10p, 50p, 1995. This is an expanding set. Numbers may change.

Pasang Lhamu
Sherpa (1960-
1993)
A304

1994, Sept 2   Litho.   *Perf. 14*
544 A304 10r multicolored   .70 .70

Stop Smoking
Campaign
A305

1994, Sept. 26   *Perf. 13½x14*
545 A305 1r multicolored   .15 .15

Methods of Transporting
Mail — A306

1994, Oct. 9   *Perf. 13x13½*
546 A306 1.50r multicolored   .15 .15

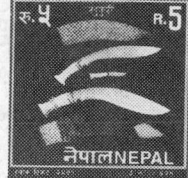

Traditional
Weapons
A307

Designs: No. 547a, Daggers, scabbards. b, Yataghans. c, Sabers, shield. d, Carved stone daggers.

1994, Oct. 9   *Perf. 14*
547 A307 5r Block of 4, #a.-d.   1.50 1.50

ILO,
75th
Anniv.
A308

1994, Oct. 9   *Perf. 13*
548 A308 15r blue & bister   1.10 1.10

World Food Day — A309

1994, Oct. 23   *Perf. 14*
549 A309 25r multicolored   1.75 1.75

Orchids — A310

Designs: a, Dendrobium densiflorum. b, Coelogyne flaccida. c, Cymbidium devonianum. d, Coelogyne corymbosa.

1994, Nov. 7   *Perf. 14x13½*
550 A310 10r Block of 4, #a.-d.   3.00 3.00

Intl. Year of the
Family — A311

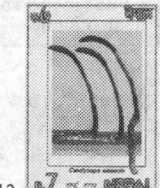

ICAO, 50th
Anniv. — A312

1994, Dec. 5   *Perf. 12½x13*
551 A311 9r green & red   .70 .70

1994, Dec. 7
552 A312 11r blue & bister   .80 .80

Mushrooms — A313

1994, Dec. 20   *Perf. 14*
553 A313 7r Cordyceps sinensis   .60 .60
554 A313 7r Morchella conica   .60 .60
555 A313 7r Amanita caesarea   .60 .60
556 A313 7r Russula nepalensis   .60 .60
   Nos. 553-556 (4)   2.40 2.40

Famous
Men — A314

Designs: 1r, Dharanidhar Koirala, poet. 2r, Narayan Gopal Guruwacharya, singer. 6r, Bahadur Shah, military leader, vert. 7r, Balaguru Shadananda, religious leader.

Perf. 13½x14, 14x13½
1994, Dec. 23
557 A314 1r multicolored   .15 .15
558 A314 2r multicolored   .15 .15
559 A314 6r multicolored   .45 .45
560 A314 7r multicolored   .50 .50
   Nos. 557-560 (4)   1.25 1.25

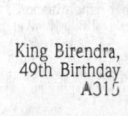

King Birendra,
49th Birthday
A315

1994, Dec. 28   *Perf. 14*
561 A315 9r multicolored   .70 .70

Tilicho Lake,
Manang
A316

Design: 11r, Taleju Temple, Katmandou, vert.

Perf. 13½x14, 14x13½
1994, Dec. 28
562 A316 9r multicolored   .70 .70
563 A316 11r multicolored   .80 .80

Care of
Children — A317

Designs: No. 564a, Vaccination. b, Education. c, Playground activities. d, Stamp collecting.

1994, Dec. 30   *Perf. 14*
564 A317 1r Block of 4, #a.-d.   .32 .32

Fight Against
Cancer — A318

Famous
People — A319

1995, June   Litho.   *Perf. 14x13½*
565 A318 2r red & black   .15 .15

1995, July   *Perf. 14*
Designs: a, Bhim Nidhi Tiwari, writer. b, Yuddha Prasad Mishra, writer. c, Chandra Man Singh Maskey, artist. d, Parijat, writer.

566 A319 3r Block of 4, #a.-d.   .85 .85

Famous Men — A320

Designs: 15p, Bhakti Thapa, warrior. 1r, Madan Bhandari, politician. 4r, Prakash Raj Kaphley, human rights activist.

1995, Aug.   Litho.   *Perf. 14x13½*
567 A320 15p multicolored   .15 .15
568 A320 1r multicolored   .15 .15
569 A320 4r multicolored   .30 .30
    Set value   .40 .40

Animals
A321

Designs: a, Bos gaurus. b, Felis lynx. c, Macaca assamensis. d, Hyaena hyaena.

1995, Aug.   Litho.   *Perf. 12*
570 A321 10p Block of 4, #a.-d.   2.75 2.75

Tourism
A322

Designs: 1r, Bhimeshwor Temple, Dolakha, vert. 5r, Ugra Tara Temple, Dadeldhura. 7r, Mt. Nampa. 18r, Thanka art, Nrity Aswora, vert.

Perf. 14x13½, 13½x14
1995, Sept.   Litho.
574 A322 1r multicolored   .15 .15
575 A322 5r multicolored   .35 .35
576 A322 7r multicolored   .50 .50

Size: 26x39mm
577 A322 18r multicolored   1.25 1.25
   Nos. 574-577 (4)   2.25 2.25

FAO, 50th
Anniv. — A323

1995, Oct.   Litho.   *Perf. 13½x14*
578 A323 7r multicolored   .45 .45

UN, 50th Anniv. A324

1995, Oct. Litho. *Perf. 11½*
Granite Paper

579 A324 50r multicolored 3.25 3.25

AIR POST STAMPS

Catalogue values for unused stamps in this section are for Never Hinged items.

Bird over Kathmandu — AP1

Rough Perf 11½
1958, Oct. 16 Typo. Unwmk.
Without Gum

C1 AP1 10p dark blue .15 .15

Plane over Kathmandu AP2

1967, Oct. 24 Photo. *Perf. 13½x13*

C2 AP2 1.80r multicolored .75 .60

International Tourist Year.

God Akash Bhairab and Nepal Airlines Emblem AP3

Map of Nepal with Airlines Network AP4

Design: 2.50r, Plane over Himalayas.

Perf. 14½x14, 13 (65p)
1968, July 1 Photo.

C3 AP3 15p blue & bis brn .15 .15
C4 AP4 65p violet blue .18 .15
C5 AP3 2.50r dp blue & scar .60 .45
Set value .82 .65

10th anniv. of the Royal Nepal Airlines Corp.

Flyer and Jet — AP5

1978, Dec. 12 Photo. *Perf. 13*

C6 AP5 2.30r blue & ocher .42 .42

75th anniversary of 1st powered flight.

Pheasant Type of 1979

1979, Nov. 22 Photo. *Perf. 14½x14*

C7 A174 3.50r Impeyan pheasant, horiz. 2.00 1.00

OFFICIAL STAMPS

Catalogue values for unused stamps in this section are for Never Hinged items.

Soldiers and Arms of Nepal — O1

Perf. 13½
1959, Nov. 1 Litho. Unwmk.
Size: 29x17½mm

O1 O1 2p reddish brown .15 .15
O2 O1 4p yel green .15 .15
O3 O1 6p salmon pink .15 .15
O4 O1 8p brt violet .15 .15
O5 O1 12p red orange .18 .15

Size: 37½x21½mm

O6 O1 16p red brown .24 .15
O7 O1 24p carmine .30 .15
O8 O1 32p rose car .45 .15
O9 O1 50p ultramarine .60 .15
O10 O1 1r rose red 1.25 .18
O11 O1 2r orange 2.75 .30
Nos. O1-O11 (11) 6.37
Set value 1.00

Nos. 144-146 and 124 Overprinted in Black **काज सरकारी**

1960-62 Photo. *Perf. 14½x14*
Overprint 12½mm Long

O12 A35 1p carmine rose ('62) .15 .15
O13 A35 2p bright blue ('62) .15 .15
O14 A35 5p golden brown ('62) .15 .15
Set value .27 .27

Perf. 14
Overprint 14½mm Long

O15 A26 1r red lilac .18

The overprint, "Kaj Sarkari" in Devanagari characters means "Service." Five other denominations, 10p, 40p, 75p, 2r and 5r, were similarly overprinted but not issued.

In 1983 substantial quantities of the set of nine values were sold as remainders by the Post Office at face value (under $1 for the set).

NEW BRITAIN

'nü 'bri-tᵊn

LOCATION — South Pacific Ocean, northeast of New Guinea
GOVT. — Australian military government
AREA — 13,000 sq. mi. (approx.)
POP. — 50,600 (approx.)
CAPITAL — Rabaul

The island Neu-Pommern, a part of former German New Guinea, was captured during World War I by Australian troops and named New Britain. Following the war it was mandated to Australia and designated a part of the Mandated Territory of New Guinea. See German New Guinea, North West Pacific Islands and New Guinea.

12 Pence = 1 Shilling

Kaiser's Yacht "The Hohenzollern"
A3 A4

Stamps of German New Guinea, 1900, Surcharged

First Setting

Surcharge lines spaced 6mm on 1p-8p, 4mm on 1sh-5sh.

Perf. 14, 14½
1914, Oct. 17 Unwmk.

1 A3 1p on 3pf brown 225.00 225.00
2 A3 1p on 5pf green 25.00 35.00
3 A3 2p on 10pf car *50.00* *75.00*
4 A3 2p on 20pf ultra 25.00 40.00
  a. "2d." dbl., "G.R.I." omitted 1,600.
  b. Inverted surcharge —
5 A3 2½p on 10pf car 65.00 *125.00*
6 A3 2½p on 20pf ultra 67.50 *125.00*
  a. Inverted surcharge
7 A3 3p on 25pf org & blk, *yel* 155.00 165.00
8 A3 3p on 30pf org & blk, *sal* 175.00 190.00
  a. Double surcharge *3,250.* *3,000.*
  b. Triple surcharge
9 A3 4p on 40pf lake & black 200.00 *250.00*
  a. Double surcharge 850.00 1,250.
  b. Inverted surcharge *3,000.*
  c. "4d." omitted
10 A3 5p on 50pf pur & blk, *sal* 375.00 500.00
  a. Double surcharge *3,250.*
11 A3 8p on 80pf lake & blk, *rose* 500.00 700.00
  a. No period after "8d" *1,500.*
12 A4 1sh on 1m car 1,250. *1,450.*
13 A4 2sh on 2m blue 1,250. *1,750.*
14 A4 3sh on 3m blk vio 3,750. 3,750.
15 A4 5sh on 5m slate & car 4,500. *5,500.*
  a. No period after "I" — —

"G.R.I." stands for Georgius Rex Imperator.

Second Setting

Surcharge lines spaced 5mm on 1p-8p, 5½mm on 1sh-5sh.

1914, Dec. 16

16 A3 1p on 3pf brown 40.00 40.00
  a. Double surcharge 300.00 *425.00*
  b. "1" omitted 315.00
  c. As "b," double surcharge
  d. Inverted surcharge 700.00 *1,250.*
  e. "4" for "1" —
  f. Small "1" 200.00
17 A3 1p on 5pf green 13.00 20.00
  a. Double surcharge 700.00
  b. "G. I. R." 2,750. *3,250.*
  c. "d" inverted 750.00
  d. No periods after "G R I" —
  e. Small "1" 90.00 125.00
  f. "1d" double —
  g. No period after "1d"
  h. Triple surcharge
18 A3 2p on 10pf car 20.00 25.00
  a. Double surcharge 3,250. —
  b. Dbl. surch., one inverted 1,750.
  c. Surcharged "G. I. R., 3d" *4,150.*
  d. Surcharged "1d" 2,250. 1,750.
  e. Period before "G" *2,000.*
  f. No period after "2d" 100.00 150.00
  g. Inverted surcharge
  h. "2d" double, one inverted
  i. "1d" on "2d"
  j. Pair, #18, 20 —
19 A3 2p on 20pf ultra 22.50 30.00
  a. Double surcharge 775.00 *1,400.*
  b. Double surch., one inverted 1,000. *1,300.*
  c. "R" inverted *1,500.*
  d. Surcharged "1d" 3,000. 3,000.
  f. Inverted surcharge 1,750. *2,500.*
  g. "1d" on "2d" *8,750.*
  h. Pair, one without surcharge
  i. Pair, #19, 21 — —
20 A3 2½p on 10pf car 125.00 275.00
21 A3 2½p on 20pf ultra 1,000. 1,300.
  a. Double surcharge, one invtd.
  b. "2½" triple
  c. Surcharged "3d"
22 A3 3p on 25pf org & blk, *yel* 85.00 110.00
  a. Double surcharge 2,000. *2,750.*
  b. Inverted surcharge 2,000 *2,750.*
  c. "G. R. I." only
  d. "G. I. R." 1,100. 1,100.
  e. Pair, one without surcharge —
  f. Surcharged "G. I. R., 5d"
23 A3 3p on 30pf org & blk, *sal* 70.00 90.00
  a. Double surcharge 850.00 *1,250.*
  b. Double surcharge, one invtd. 1,000. *1,400.*
  c. "d" inverted 550.00
  d. Surcharged "1d" 2,750. —
  e. Triple surcharge
  g. Double inverted surcharge 2,250. *3,000.*
  h. Pair, one without surcharge *3,000.*
24 A3 4p on 40pf lake & blk 85.00 110.00
  a. Double surcharge 700.00 700.00
  b. Double surcharge, one invtd. 1,250. 1,250.
  e. Surcharged "1d" 1,500.
  f. "1" on "4"
25 A3 5p on 50pf pur & blk, *sal* 145.00 150.00
  a. Double surcharge 1,000.
  b. Double surcharge, one invtd. 1,500. *3,000.*
  c. "5" omitted 550.00
  d. Inverted surcharge 1,500.
  e. Double inverted surcharge 2,000. *3,000.*
  f. "G. I. R."
26 A3 8p on 80pf lake & blk, *rose* 425.00 375.00
  a. Double surcharge 1,400. *1,500.*
  b. Double surcharge, one invtd. 1,400. *1,500.*
  c. Triple surcharge 1,400. *1,750.*
  d. No period after "8d"
  e. Inverted surcharge 2,250. *3,000.*
  f. Surcharged "3d" 3,500.
27 A4 1sh on 1m car 1,500. *2,000.*
28 A4 2sh on 2m bl 2,000. *3,000.*
  a. Surcharged "5s"
  b. Double surcharge
29 A4 3sh on 3m blk vio 2,750. *4,500.*
  a. No periods after "R I"
  b. "G.R.I." double —
29C A4 5sh on 5m sl & car 10,000. *12,500.*
  d. No periods after "R I"
  e. Surcharged "1s"

Same Surcharge on Stamps of Marshall Islands

1914

30 A3 1p on 3pf brown 35.00 45.00
  a. Inverted surcharge 1,350.
31 A3 1p on 5pf green 40.00 45.00
  a. Double surcharge 750.00 *1,500.*
  b. No period after "d"
  c. Inverted surcharge 900.00
32 A3 2p on 10pf car 13.50 24.00
  a. Double surcharge 700.00 *1,250.*
  b. Double surcharge, one invtd. 850.00 *1,250.*
  c. Surcharge sideways 2,500.
  d. No period after "2d"
  e. No period after "G" 450.00
33 A3 2p on 20 pf ultra 15.00 24.00
  a. No period after "d" 35.00 *75.00*
  b. Double surcharge 750.00 —
  c. Double surcharge, one invtd. 1,450. —
  d. Inverted surcharge — —
  e. "I" omitted
34 A3 3p on 25pf org & blk, *yel* 325.00 325.00
  a. Double surcharge 975.00 *1,400.*
  b. Double surcharge, one invtd. 1,100.
  c. No period after "d" 550.00 600.00
  d. Inverted surcharge 2,000.
35 A3 3p on 30pf org & blk, *sal* 350.00 350.00
  a. No period after "d" 550.00 600.00
  b. Inverted surcharge — —
  c. Double surcharge 1,500.
  d. Double surcharge, one invtd.
36 A3 4p on 40pf lake & blk 85.00 100.00
  a. No period after "d" 225.00 *325.00*
  b. Double surcharge 1,250. *1,750.*
  c. "4d" omitted
  d. "1d" on "4d"
  e. No period after "R"
  f. Inverted surcharge 1,400.
  g. Surcharged "1d" 3,000.
37 A3 5p on 50pf pur & blk, *sal* 110.00 140.00
  a. "d" omitted 950.00
  b. Double surcharge 1,750.
  c. "5d" double 475.00
38 A3 8p on 80pf lake & blk, *rose* 400.00 425.00
  a. Inverted surcharge —
  b. Double surcharge 1,750.
  c. Double surcharge, one invtd.
  d. Triple surcharge —
39 A4 1sh on 1m car 1,400. *2,250.*
  a. Double surchage —
  b. Dbl. surch., one with "s1" for "1s"
  c. No period after "I" 2,250.
40 A4 2sh on 2m blue 1,250. 1,450.
  a. Double surcharge, one invtd. — *6,000.*
  b. Double surchage —
  c. Large "S"
  d. No period after "I" 1,750. *2,500.*
41 A4 3sh on 3m blk vio 2,500. *3,250.*
  a. Double surcharge — —
  b. No period after "I" 3,250.
  c. No period after "R I" 2,900.
  d. Inverted surcharge
42 A4 5sh on 5m sl & car *7,000.* 5,500.
  a. Double surcharge, one invtd. *10,000.*

See Nos. 44-45.

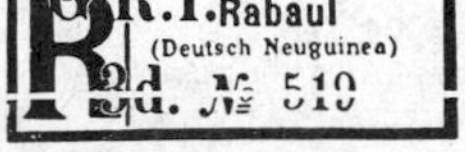

A5

Surcharged in Black on Registration Label

1914 *Perf. 12*

43 A5 3p black & red (Rabaul) 100.00 *150.00*
  a. "Friedrich Wilhelmshaven" 150.00 *275.00*
  b. "Herbertshohe" 165.00 *325.00*
  c. "Kawieng" 225.00 *275.00*
  d. "Kieta" 375.00 *450.00*
  e. "Manus" 200.00 *375.00*
  f. Double surcharge (Rabaul) 900.00 *1,250.*
  g. As "c," double surcharge *1,000.*
  h. As "e," double surcharge *1,500.*

Nos. 43a, 43c and 43e exist with town name in letters with serifs. The varieties Deutsch-Neuguinea, Deutsch Neu-Guinea, etc., are known.

Nos. 32-33 Surcharged with Large "1"

1915

44 A3 1p on 2p on 10pf 175. 150.
  a. "1" double —
  b. "1" inverted — —

45	A3	1p on 2p on 20pf	3,000.	1,900.
a.		"1" inverted	—	
b.		No period after "d"	—	

The stamps of Marshall Islands surcharged "G. R. I." and new values in British currency were all used in New Britain and are therefore listed here.

OFFICIAL STAMPS

O1

German New Guinea Nos. 7-8 Surcharged

1915 Unwmk. *Perf. 14*

O1	O1	1p on 3pf brown	25.00	60.00
a.		Double surcharge	1,400.	
O2	O1	1p on 5pf green	75.00	125.00

NEW GUINEA

'nü 'gi–nē

LOCATION — On an island of the same name in the South Pacific Ocean, north of Australia.
GOVT. — Mandate administered by Australia
AREA — 93,000 sq. mi.
POP. — 675,369 (1940)
CAPITAL — Rabaul

The territory occupies the northeastern part of the island and includes New Britain and other nearby islands. It was formerly a German possession and should not be confused with British New Guinea (Papua) which is in the southeastern part of the same island, nor Netherlands New Guinea (Vol. 4). For previous issues see German New Guinea, New Britain, North West Pacific Islands. Issues for 1952 and later are listed under Papua.

12 Pence = 1 Shilling
20 Shillings = 1 Pound

Native Huts — A1

Bird of Paradise — A2

1925-28 Engr. *Perf. 11*

1	A1	½p	orange	1.00	2.00
2	A1	1p	yellow green	1.10	2.25
3	A1	1½p	vermilion ('26)	1.90	1.75
4	A1	2p	claret	2.75	1.65
5	A1	3p	deep blue	4.50	3.25
6	A1	4p	olive green	10.00	14.00
7	A1	6p	yel bister ('28)	6.50	40.00
a.			6p light brown	18.00	40.00
b.			6p olive bister ('27)	8.00	35.00
8	A1	9p	deep violet	13.00	35.00
9	A1	1sh	gray green	13.00	20.00
10	A1	2sh	red brown	22.50	35.00
11	A1	5sh	olive bister	30.00	60.00
12	A1	10sh	dull rose	95.00	90.00
13	A1	£1	grnsh gray	200.00	250.00
			Nos. 1-13 (13)	401.25	554.90

For overprints see Nos. C1-C13, O1-O9.

1931, Aug. 2

18	A2	1p	light green	.65	2.00
19	A2	1½p	red	2.50	4.00
20	A2	2p	violet brown	1.40	3.00
21	A2	3p	deep blue	1.40	7.50
22	A2	4p	olive green	3.00	5.00
23	A2	5p	slate green	3.00	8.00
24	A2	6p	bister	3.00	9.00
25	A2	9p	dull violet	3.75	12.50
26	A2	1sh	bluish gray	4.00	12.50
27	A2	2sh	red brown	7.50	22.50
28	A2	5sh	olive brown	30.00	42.50
29	A2	10sh	rose red	72.50	85.00
30	A2	£1	gray	110.00	140.00
			Nos. 18-30 (13)	242.70	353.50

10th anniversary of Australian Mandate.
For overprints see #C14-C27, O12-O22.

Type of 1931 without date scrolls

1932-34 *Perf. 11*

31	A2	1p	light green	.45	.25
32	A2	1½p	violet brown	.90	4.50
33	A2	2p	red	.50	.45
34	A2	2½p	dp green ('34)	4.25	10.00
35	A2	3p	gray blue	.90	.75
36	A2	3½p	magenta ('34)	9.00	10.50
37	A2	4p	olive green	.90	2.00
38	A2	5p	slate green	.90	.75
39	A2	6p	bister	1.00	2.50
40	A2	9p	dull violet	6.50	12.50
41	A2	1sh	bluish gray	4.25	7.50
42	A2	2sh	red brown	4.25	10.00
43	A2	5sh	olive brown	22.50	37.50
44	A2	10sh	rose red	70.00	80.00
45	A2	£1	gray	95.00	100.00
			Nos. 31-45 (15)	221.30	279.20

For overprints see #46-47, C28-C43, O23-O35.

Silver Jubilee Issue

Stamps of 1932-34 Overprinted

HIS MAJESTY'S JUBILEE. 1910 — 1935

1935, June 27

Glazed Paper

46	A2	1p	light green	.75	.75
47	A2	2p	red	1.00	.75

King George VI — A3

1937, May 18 Engr.

48	A3	2p	salmon rose	.20	.20
49	A3	3p	blue	.20	.20
50	A3	5p	green	.35	.30
51	A3	1sh	brown violet	.60	.50
			Nos. 48-51 (4)	1.35	1.20

Coronation of George VI and Queen Elizabeth.

AIR POST STAMPS

Regular Issues of 1925-28 Overprinted

AIR MAIL

1931, June *Perf. 11*

C1	A1	½p	orange	.35	.95
C2	A1	1p	yellow green	.45	1.25
C3	A1	1½p	vermilion	.85	2.75
C4	A1	2p	claret	1.75	4.00
C5	A1	3p	deep blue	2.75	3.00
C6	A1	4p	olive green	3.75	4.00
C7	A1	6p	light brown	3.75	4.00
C8	A1	9p	deep violet	5.25	5.50
C9	A1	1sh	gray green	6.50	7.00
C10	A1	2sh	red brown	11.50	12.00
C11	A1	5sh	ol bister	26.00	35.00
C12	A1	10sh	light red	55.00	72.50
C13	A1	£1	grnsh gray	135.00	150.00
			Nos. C1-C13 (13)	252.90	301.95

Type of Regular Issue of 1931 and Nos. 18-30 Overprinted

AIR MAIL

1931, Aug.

C14	A2	½p	orange	.35	.35
C15	A2	1p	light green	.55	.55
C16	A2	1½p	red	1.90	1.90
C17	A2	2p	violet brown	1.90	2.00
C18	A2	3p	deep blue	2.25	2.25
C19	A2	4p	olive green	2.75	2.75
C20	A2	5p	slate green	3.00	3.00
C21	A2	6p	bister	4.00	4.50
C22	A2	9p	dull violet	4.50	4.50
C23	A2	1sh	bluish gray	5.00	5.00
C24	A2	2sh	red brown	8.00	5.50
C25	A2	5sh	olive brown	25.00	17.50
C26	A2	10sh	rose red	65.00	75.00
C27	A2	£1	gray	140.00	175.00
			Nos. C14-C27 (14)	264.20	299.80

10th anniversary of Australian Mandate.

Same Overprint on Type of Regular Issue of 1932-34 and Nos. 31-45

1932-34 *Perf. 11*

C28	A2	½p	orange	.25	.30
C29	A2	1p	light green	.25	.30
C30	A2	1½p	violet brown	.50	.65
C31	A2	2p	red	1.00	1.25
C32	A2	2½p	dp green ('34)	2.00	2.50
C33	A2	3p	gray blue	1.50	2.00
C34	A2	3½p	magenta ('34)	2.00	2.50
C35	A2	4p	olive green	2.25	2.75
C36	A2	5p	slate green	3.75	5.00
C37	A2	6p	bister	3.75	5.50
C38	A2	9p	dull violet	4.25	6.00
C39	A2	1sh	bluish gray	2.50	3.50
C40	A2	2sh	red brown	8.00	13.00
C41	A2	5sh	olive brown	19.00	25.00
C42	A2	10sh	rose red	87.50	100.00
C43	A2	£1	gray	87.50	67.50
			Nos. C28-C43 (16)	206.00	237.75

No. C28 exists without overprint, but is believed not to have been issued in this condition.

Plane over Bulolo Goldfield AP1

1935, May 1 Engr. Unwmk.

C44	AP1	£2	violet	175.00	150.00
C45	AP1	£5	green	650.00	300.00

AP2

1939, Mar. 1

C46	AP2	½p	orange	.25	.65
C47	AP2	1p	green	.25	.55
C48	AP2	1½p	vio brown	.70	1.65
C49	AP2	2p	red orange	1.25	2.25
C50	AP2	3p	dark blue	2.25	5.25
C51	AP2	4p	ol bister	1.75	5.25
C52	AP2	5p	slate grn	1.65	2.25
C53	AP2	6p	bister brn	2.25	5.25
C54	AP2	9p	dl violet	3.00	6.50
C55	AP2	1sh	sage green	3.50	8.50
C56	AP2	2sh	car lake	17.50	26.00
C57	AP2	5sh	ol brown	35.00	52.50
C58	AP2	10sh	rose red	100.00	110.00
C59	AP2	£1	grnsh gray	55.00	75.00
			Nos. C46-C59 (14)	224.35	301.60

OFFICIAL STAMPS

Regular Issue of 1925 Overprinted

O S

1925-29 Unwmk. *Perf. 11*

O1	A1	1p	yellow green	.60	3.50
O2	A1	1½p	vermilion ('29)	6.50	15.00
O3	A1	2p	claret	.90	3.25
O4	A1	3p	deep blue	2.25	5.50
O5	A1	4p	olive green	2.75	7.50
O6	A1	6p	yel bister ('29)	5.75	35.00
a.			6p olive bister	5.75	35.00
O7	A1	9p	deep violet	7.50	35.00
O8	A1	1sh	gray green	11.00	35.00
O9	A1	2sh	red brown	21.00	70.00
			Nos. O1-O9 (9)	58.25	209.75

Nos. 18-28 Overprinted

O S

1931, Aug. 2

O12	A2	1p	light green	1.10	2.75
O13	A2	1½p	red	1.50	4.50
O14	A2	2p	violet brown	2.75	4.50
O15	A2	3p	deep blue	3.25	6.50
O16	A2	4p	olive green	4.50	8.25
O17	A2	5p	slate green	4.50	10.00
O18	A2	6p	bister	5.50	11.00
O19	A2	9p	dull violet	6.50	16.00
O20	A2	1sh	bluish gray	8.50	17.50
O21	A2	2sh	red brown	22.50	45.00
O22	A2	5sh	olive brown	100.00	150.00
			Nos. O12-O22 (11)	160.60	276.00

10th anniversary of Australian Mandate.

Same Overprint on Nos. 31-43

1932-34

O23	A2	1p	light green	.50	1.00
O24	A2	1½p	violet brown	.85	1.90
O25	A2	2p	red	1.90	3.00
O26	A2	2½p	dp green ('34)	3.25	5.50
O27	A2	3p	gray blue	3.75	7.00
O28	A2	3½p	magenta ('34)	3.75	8.50
O29	A2	4p	olive green	3.25	3.75
O30	A2	5p	slate green	3.75	5.00
O31	A2	6p	bister	5.00	8.00
O32	A2	9p	dull violet	8.50	15.00
O33	A2	1sh	bluish gray	12.00	19.00
O34	A2	2sh	red brown	30.00	57.50
O35	A2	5sh	olive brown	90.00	140.00
			Nos. O23-O35 (13)	166.50	275.15

NEW HEBRIDES

'nü 'he–brə–ˌdēz

LOCATION — A group of islands in the South Pacific Ocean northeast of New Caledonia
GOVT. — Condominium under the joint administration of Great Britain and France
AREA — 5,790 sq. mi.
POP. — 100,000 (est. 1976)
CAPITAL — Vila (Port-Vila)

Stamps were issued by both Great Britain and France. In 1911 a joint issue bore the coats of arms of both countries. The British stamps bore the arms of Great Britain and the value in British currency on the right and the French arms and value at the left. On the French stamps the positions were reversed. After World War II when the franc dropped in value, both series were sold for their value in francs.

New Hebrides became the independent state of Vanuatu in 1980.

12 Pence = 1 Shilling
100 Centimes = 1 Franc
100 Centimes = 1 Hebrides Franc (FNH) (1977)

See Volume 4 for French Issues ("Nouvelles Hebrides").

Catalogue values for unused stamps in this country are for Never Hinged items, beginning with Scott 62 in the regular postage section, Scott J11 in the postage due section.

British Issues

Stamps of Fiji, 1903-06, Overprinted

NEW HEBRIDES
CONDOMINIUM.

1908-09 Wmk. 2 *Perf. 14*

Colored Bar Covers "FIJI" on #2-6, 9

1	A22	½p	gray green ('09)	47.50	47.50
2	A22	2p	vio & orange	1.25	1.25
3	A22	2½p	vio & ultra, *bl*	1.25	1.25
4	A22	5p	vio & green	3.25	3.25
5	A22	6p	vio & car rose	3.25	3.25
6	A22	1sh	grn & car rose	150.00	200.00
			Nos. 1-6 (6)	206.50	256.50

Wmk. Multiple Crown and CA (3)

7	A22	½p	gray green	.75	5.00
8	A22	1p	carmine	.50	1.00
a.			Pair, one without overprint	4,750.	
9	A22	1sh	grn & car rose ('09)	15.00	14.00
			Nos. 7-9 (3)	16.25	20.00

Nos. 2-6, 9 are on chalk-surfaced paper.

Stamps of Fiji, 1904- 11, Overprinted in Black or Red

NEW HEBRIDES
CONDOMINIUM

1910, Dec. 15

10	A22	½p	green	3.50	15.00
11	A22	1p	carmine	6.00	7.50
12	A22	2p	gray	1.00	1.75
13	A22	2½p	ultra	1.25	2.00
14	A22	5p	violet & ol grn	1.65	3.50
15	A22	6p	violet	2.50	5.00
16	A22	1sh	black, *grn* (R)	3.50	6.50
			Nos. 10-16 (7)	19.40	41.25

Nos. 14-16 are on chalk-surfaced paper.

Native Idols — A1

1911, July 25 Engr. Wmk. 3

17	A1	½p pale green	.55	1.00
18	A1	1p red	1.50	.80
19	A1	2p gray	3.00	2.75
20	A1	2½p ultramarine	2.00	2.75
21	A1	5p olive green	1.65	2.00
22	A1	6p claret	2.50	2.25
23	A1	1sh black, *green*	2.75	6.50
24	A1	2sh violet, *blue*	12.00	15.00
25	A1	5sh green, *yel*	24.00	40.00
		Nos. 17-25 (9)	49.95	73.05

See Nos. 33-37. For surcharges see Nos. 26-29, 38-39, French Issues No. 36.

Surcharged **1d.**

1920-21

26	A1	1p on 5p ol green ('21)	14.00	32.50
a.		Inverted surcharge	1,400.	
27	A1	1p on 1sh black, *grn*	4.00	9.00
28	A1	1p on 2sh violet, *blue*	2.50	9.00
29	A1	1p on 5sh green, *yel*	2.50	9.00

On French Issue No. 16

30	A2	2p on 40c red, *yel* ('21)	2.25	9.00
		Nos. 26-30 (5)	25.25	68.50

On French Issue No. 27

Wmk. R F in Sheet

31	A2	2p on 40c red, *yel* ('21)	165.00	225.00

The letters "R.F." are the initials of "Republique Francaise." They are large double-lined Roman capitals, about 120mm high. About one-fourth of the stamps in each sheet show portions of the watermark, the other stamps are without watermark.

No. 26a is considered by some to be printers' waste.

Type of 1911 Issue

1921, Oct. Wmk. 4

33	A1	1p rose red	3.00	8.00
34	A1	2p gray	4.00	10.00
37	A1	6p claret	9.25	25.00
		Nos. 33-37 (3)	16.25	43.00

For surcharge see No. 40.

Stamps of 1911-21 Surcharged with New Values as in 1920-21

1924, May 1 Wmk. 3

38	A1	1p on ½p pale green	1.50	6.00
39	A1	5p on 2½p ultra	3.75	5.00
a.		Inverted surcharge	1,200.	

Wmk. 4

40	A1	3p on 1p rose red	3.25	9.00
		Nos. 38-40 (3)	8.50	20.00

No. 39a is considered by some to be printers' waste.

A3

The values at the lower right denote the currency and amount for which the stamps were to be sold. The English stamps could be bought at the French post office in French money.

1925 Engr.

41	A3	½p (5c) black	.50	2.00
42	A3	1p (10c) green	.60	2.00
43	A3	2p (20c) grnsh gray	.65	1.75
44	A3	2½p (25c) brown	1.00	2.00
45	A3	5p (50c) ultra	2.00	3.00
46	A3	6p (60c) claret	2.50	7.50
47	A3	1sh (1.25fr) black, *grn*	2.50	9.00
48	A3	2sh (2.50fr) vio, *bl*	6.50	12.50
49	A3	5sh (6.25fr) grn, *yel*	8.00	17.50
		Nos. 41-49 (9)	24.25	57.25

Beach Scene — A5

1938, June 1 Wmk. 4 *Perf. 12*

50	A5	5c green	1.00	.50
51	A5	10c dark orange	.75	.65
52	A5	15c violet	1.00	.65
53	A5	20c rose red	.90	.80
54	A5	25c brown	.90	.80
55	A5	30c dark blue	1.00	1.00
56	A5	40c olive green	3.00	1.40
57	A5	50c brown vio	1.40	1.40
58	A5	1fr car, *emerald*	3.50	3.50
59	A5	2fr dk blue, *emer*	17.50	7.25
60	A5	5fr red, *yellow*	45.00	27.50
61	A5	10fr violet, *blue*	80.00	47.50
		Nos. 50-61 (12)	155.95	92.95

Catalogue values for unused stamps in this section, from this point to the end of the section, are for Never Hinged items.

UPU Issue

Common Design Type

1949, Oct. 10 Engr. *Perf. 13½*

62	CD309	10c red orange	.40	.40
63	CD309	15c violet	.40	.40
64	CD309	30c violet blue	.75	.50
65	CD309	50c rose violet	1.25	1.00
		Nos. 62-65 (4)	2.80	2.30

Outrigger Canoes with Sails — A6

Designs: 25c, 30c, 40c and 50c, Native Carving. 1fr, 2fr and 5fr, Island couple.

1953, Apr. 30 *Perf. 12½*

66	A6	5c green	.20	.20
67	A6	10c red	.20	.15
68	A6	15c yellow	.30	.20
69	A6	20c ultramarine	.32	.30
70	A6	25c olive	.50	.40
71	A6	30c light brown	.60	.50
72	A6	40c black brown	.90	.80
73	A6	50c violet	1.00	.90
74	A6	1fr deep orange	2.00	1.75
75	A6	2fr red violet	6.00	10.00
76	A6	5fr scarlet	15.00	18.00
		Nos. 66-76 (11)	27.02	33.20

Coronation Issue

Common Design Type

1953, June 2 *Perf. 13½x13*

77	CD312	10c car & black	.75	.75

Discovery of New Hebrides, 1606 — A7

Designs: 20c, 50c, Britannia, Marianne, Flags and Mask.

Perf. 14½x14

1956, Oct. 20 Photo. Wmk. 4

78	A7	5c emerald	.15	.15
79	A7	10c crimson	.15	.15
80	A7	20c ultramarine	.25	.25
81	A7	50c purple	.65	.65
		Nos. 78-81 (4)	1.20	1.20

50th anniv. of the establishment of the Anglo-French Condominium.

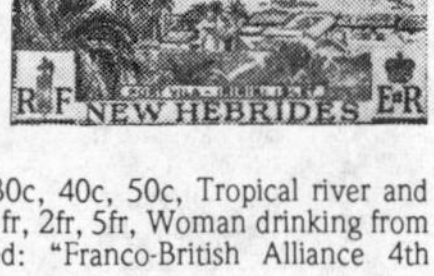

Port Vila and Iririki Islet — A8

Designs: 25c, 30c, 40c, 50c, Tropical river and spear fisherman. 1fr, 2fr, 5fr, Woman drinking from coconut (inscribed: "Franco-British Alliance 4th March 1947").

1957, Sept. 3 Engr. *Perf. 13½x13*

82	A8	5c green	.15	.15
83	A8	10c red	.15	.15
84	A8	15c orange yellow	.25	.15
85	A8	20c ultramarine	.30	.20
86	A8	25c olive	.35	.25
87	A8	30c light brown	.45	.40
88	A8	40c sepia	.70	.50
89	A8	50c violet	.95	.65
90	A8	1fr orange	1.90	1.25
91	A8	2fr rose lilac	5.50	2.50
92	A8	5fr black	12.00	5.50
		Nos. 82-92 (11)	22.70	11.70

Freedom from Hunger Issue

Common Design Type

Perf. 14x14½

1963, Sept. 2 Photo. Wmk. 314

93	CD314	60c green	1.00	.70

Red Cross Centenary Issue

Common Design Type with Royal Cipher and "RF" Replacing Queen's Portrait

1963, Sept. 2 Litho. *Perf. 13*

94	CD315	15c black & red	.35	.20
95	CD315	45c ultra & red	.90	.70

Copra Industry — A9

Designs: 5c, Manganese loading, Forari Wharf. 10c, Cacao. 20c, Map of New Hebrides, tuna, marlin, ships. 25c, Striped triggerfish. 30c, Pearly nautilus (mollusk). 40c, 60c, Turkeyfish. 50c, Lined tang (fish). 1fr, Cardinal honey-eater and hibiscus. 2fr, Buff-bellied flycatcher. 3fr, Thicket warbler. 5fr, White-collared kingfisher.

Wmk. 314 (10c, 20c, 40c, 60c, 3fr); Unwmkd. (others)

Perf. 12½ (10c, 20c, 40c, 60c); 14 (3fr); 13 (others)

Photo. (10c, 20c, 40c, 60c, 3fr); Engraved (others)

1963-67

96	A9	5c Prus bl & cl ('66)	.20	.15
97	A9	10c brt grn, org brn & dk brn ('65)	.20	.15
98	A9	15c dk pur, yel & brn	.25	.25
99	A9	20c brt blue, gray & cit ('65)	.30	.25
100	A9	25c vio, rose lil & org brn ('66)	.55	.50
101	A9	30c lilac, brn & cit	.80	.75
102	A9	40c dk bl & ver ('65)	1.10	1.10
103	A9	50c Prus bl, yel & green	.90	.80
103A	A9	60c dk bl & ver ('67)	1.50	1.25
104	A9	1fr blue grn, blk & red ('66)	2.25	2.25
105	A9	2fr ol, blk & brn	3.25	3.00
106	A9	3fr org grn, brt grn & blk ('65)	8.50	7.50
107	A9	5fr indigo, dp bl & gray ('67)	16.00	15.00
		Nos. 96-107 (13)	35.80	32.95

For surcharge see No. 141.

ITU Emblem CD317

Perf. 11x11½

1965, May 17 Litho. Wmk. 314

108	CD317	15c ver & ol bister	.20	.15
109	CD317	60c ultra & ver	.80	.60

Cent. of the ITU.

Intl. Cooperation Year Issue

Common Design Type with Royal Cipher and "RF" Replacing Queen's Portrait

1965, Sept. 24 *Perf. 14½*

110	CD318	5c blue grn & claret	.15	.15
111	CD318	55c lt violet & green	.65	.65

Churchill Memorial Issue

Common Design Type with Royal Cipher and "RF" Replacing Queen's Portrait

1966, Jan. 24 Photo. *Perf. 14*

112	CD319	5c multicolored	.15	.15
113	CD319	15c multicolored	.30	.20
114	CD319	25c multicolored	.65	.35
115	CD319	30c multicolored	.95	.65
		Nos. 112-115 (4)	2.05	1.35

World Cup Soccer Issue

Common Design Type with Royal Cipher and "RF" Replacing Queen's Portrait

1966, July 1 Litho. *Perf. 14*

116	CD321	20c multicolored	.30	.30
117	CD321	40c multicolored	.70	.70

WHO Headquarters Issue

Common Design Type with Royal Cipher and "RF" Replacing Queen's Portrait

1966, Sept. 20 Litho. *Perf. 14*

118	CD322	25c multicolored	.25	.25
119	CD322	60c multicolored	.65	.65

UNESCO Anniversary Issue

Common Design Type with Royal Cipher and "RF" Replacing Queen's Portrait

1966, Dec. 1 Litho. *Perf. 14*

120	CD323	15c "Education"	.25	.25
121	CD323	30c "Science"	.50	.50
122	CD323	45c "Culture"	.80	.80
		Nos. 120-122 (3)	1.55	1.55

Coast Watchers — A11

Designs: 25c, Map of South Pacific war zone, US Marine and Australian soldier. 60c, Australian cruiser Canberra. 1fr, Flying fortress taking off from Bauer Field, and view of Vila.

Perf. 14x13

1967, Sept. 26 Photo. Wmk. 314

123	A11	15c lt blue & multi	.15	.15
124	A11	25c yellow & multi	.35	.35
125	A11	60c multicolored	.80	.80
126	A11	1fr pale salmon & multi	1.40	1.40
		Nos. 123-126 (4)	2.70	2.70

25th anniv. of the Allied Forces' campaign in the South Pacific War Zone.

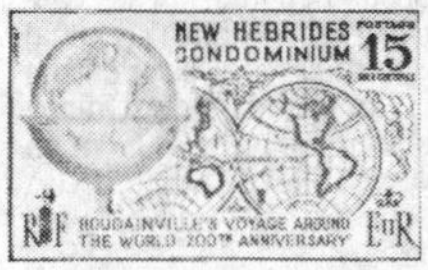

Globe and World Map — A12

Designs: 25c, Ships La Boudeuse and L'Etoile and map of Bougainville Strait. 60c, Louis Antoine de Bougainville, ship's figurehead and bougainvillaea.

1968, May 23 Engr. *Perf. 13*

127	A12	15c ver, emer & dull vio	.15	.15
128	A12	25c ultra, olive & brn	.30	.30
129	A12	60c magenta, grn & brn	.55	.55
		Nos. 127-129 (3)	1.00	1.00

200th anniv. of Louis Antoine de Bougainville's (1729-1811) voyage around the world.

Concorde Airliner A13

Design: 60c, Concorde, sideview.

1968, Oct. 9 Litho. *Perf. 14x13½*

130	A13	25c vio bl, red & lt bl	1.10	.75
131	A13	60c red, ultra & black	1.90	1.25

Development of the Concorde supersonic airliner, a joint Anglo-French project to produce a high speed plane.

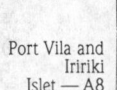

Kauri Pine — A14

Perf. 14x14½
1969, June 30   **Wmk. 314**
132 A14 20c brown & multi   .25 .25

Issued to publicize the New Hebrides timber industry. Issued in sheets of 9 (3x3) on simulated wood grain background.

Relay Race, French and British Flags — A15

Design: 1fr, Runner at right.

Perf. 12½x13
1969, Aug. 13   **Photo.**   **Unwmk.**
133 A15 25c ultra, car, brn & gold   .24 .24
134 A15 1fr brn, car, ultra & gold   .95 .95

3rd South Pacific Games, Port Moresby, Papua and New Guinea, Aug. 13-23.

Land Diver, Pentecost Island A16

Designs: 15c, Diver in starting position on tower. 1fr, Diver nearing ground.

Perf. 12½
1969, Oct. 15   **Wmk. 314**   **Litho.**
135 A16 15c yellow & multi   .16 .16
136 A16 25c pink & multi   .30 .30
137 A16 1fr gray & multi   1.10 1.10
    Nos. 135-137 (3)   1.56 1.56

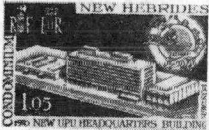

UPU Headquarters and Monument, Bern — A17

Unwmk.
1970, May 20   **Engr.**   **Perf. 13**
138 A17 1.05fr org, lilac & slate   .95 .95

Opening of the new UPU Headquarters, Bern.

Charles de Gaulle — A18

1970, July 20   **Photo.**   **Perf. 13**
139 A18 65c brown & multi   .65 .65
140 A18 1.10fr dp blue & multi   1.40 1.40

30th anniv. of the rallying to the Free French. For overprints see Nos. 144-145.

No. 99 Surcharged

1970, Oct. 15   **Wmk. 314**   **Perf. 12½**
141 A9 35c on 20c multi   .60 .60

Virgin and Child, by Giovanni Bellini — A19

Christmas: 50c, Virgin and Child, by Giovanni Cima.

Perf. 14½x14
1970, Nov. 30   **Litho.**   **Wmk. 314**
142 A19 15c tan & multi   .16 .16
143 A19 50c lt green & multi   .48 .48

Nos. 139-140 Overprinted with 2 Black Vertical Bars and Gold Inscription: "1890-1970 / IN MEMORIAM / 9-11-70"

Unwmk.
1971, Jan. 19   **Photo.**   **Perf. 13**
144 A18 65c brown & multi   .60 .60
145 A18 1.10fr dp blue & multi   1.10 1.10

In memory of Gen. Charles de Gaulle (1890-1970), President of France.

Soccer A20

Design: 65c, Basketball, vert.

1971, July 13   **Photo.**   **Perf. 12½**
146 A20 20c multicolored   .24 .24
147 A20 65c multicolored   .65 .65

4th South Pacific Games, Papeete, French Polynesia, Sept. 8-19.

Kauri Pine, Cone and Arms of Royal Society — A21

Perf. 14½x14
1971, Sept. 7   **Litho.**   **Wmk. 314**
148 A21 65c multicolored   .75 .75

Royal Society of London for the Advancement of Science expedition to study vegetation and fauna, July 1-October.

Adoration of the Shepherds, by Louis Le Nain — A22

Design: 50c, Adoration of the Shepherds, by Jacopo Tintoretto.

1971, Nov. 23   **Perf. 14x13½**
149 A22 25c lt green & multi   .28 .28
150 A22 50c lt blue & multi   .60 .60

Christmas. See Nos. 167-168.

Drover Mk III
NEW HEBRIDES Condominium A23

Airplanes: 25c, Sandringham seaplane. 30c, Dragon Rapide. 65c, Caravelle.

Perf. 13½x13
1972, Feb. 29   **Photo.**   **Unwmk.**
151 A23 20c lt green & multi   .32 .32
152 A23 25c ultra & multi   .40 .40
153 A23 30c orange & multi   .60 .60
154 A23 65c dk blue & multi   1.40 1.40
    Nos. 151-154 (4)   2.72 2.72

Headdress, South Malekula — A24   Baker's Pigeon — A25

Artifacts: 15c, Slit gong and carved figure, North Ambrym. 1fr, Carved figures, North Ambrym. 3fr, Ceremonial headdress, South Malekula.
Birds: 20c, Red-headed parrot-finch. 35c, Chestnut-bellied kingfisher. 2fr, Green palm lorikeet.
Sea shells: 25c, Cribraria fischeri. 30c, Oliva rubrolabiata. 65c, Strombus plicatus. 5fr, Turbo marmoratus.

1972, July 24   **Photo.**   **Perf. 12½x13**
155 A24 5c plum & multi   .15 .15
156 A25 10c blue & multi   .15 .20
157 A24 15c red & multi   .30 .35
158 A25 20c org brown & multi   .40 .45
159 A24 25c dp blue & multi   .55 .70
160 A24 30c dk green & multi   .70 .75
161 A25 35c gray bl & multi   .80 .90
162 A24 65c dk green & multi   1.40 3.00
163 A24 1fr orange & multi   2.25 2.50
164 A25 2fr multicolored   4.00 3.75
165 A24 3fr yellow & multi   6.00 5.50
166 A24 5fr pink & multi   10.00 11.00
    Nos. 155-166 (12)   26.70 29.25

For overprints and surcharges see #181-182, 217-228.

Christmas Type of 1971

Designs: 25c, Adoration of the Magi (detail), by Bartholomaeus Spranger. 70c, Virgin and Child, by Jan Provoost.

Perf. 14x13½
1972, Sept. 25   **Litho.**   **Wmk. 314**
167 A22 25c lt green & multi   .20 .20
168 A22 70c lt blue & multi   .60 .60

Silver Wedding Issue, 1972
Common Design Type

Design: Elizabeth II and Prince Philip.

1972, Nov. 20   **Photo.**   **Perf. 14x14½**
169 CD324 35c vio black & multi   .20 .20
170 CD324 65c olive & multi   .40 .40

Dendrobium Teretefolium A26   New Wharf, Vila A27

Orchids: 30c, Ephemerantha comata. 35c, Spathoglottis petri. 65c, Dendrobium mohlianum.

1973, Feb. 26   **Litho.**   **Perf. 14**
171 A26 25c blue vio & multi   .45 .35
172 A26 30c multicolored   .55 .45
173 A26 35c violet & multi   .65 .55
174 A26 65c dk green & multi   1.40 1.10
    Nos. 171-174 (4)   3.05 2.45

1973, May 14   **Wmk. 314**

Design: 70c, New wharf, horiz.
175 A27 25c multicolored   .15 .15
176 A27 70c multicolored   .55 .55

New wharf at Vila, finished Nov. 1972.

Wild Horses, Tanna Island — A28

Perf. 13x12½
1973, Aug. 13   **Photo.**   **Unwmk.**
177 A28 35c shown   .45 .45
178 A28 70c Yasur Volcano, Tanna   1.50 1.25

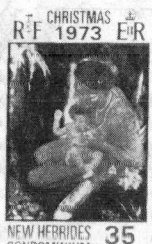

Mother and Child, by Marcel Moutouh — A29

Christmas: 70c, Star over Lagoon, by Tatin d'Avesnieres.

Perf. 14x13½
1973, Nov. 19   **Litho.**   **Wmk. 314**
179 A29 35c tan & multi   .28 .28
180 A29 70c lilac rose & multi   .70 .70

Nos. 161 and 164 Overprinted in Red or Black: "ROYAL VISIT / 1974"

Perf. 12½x13
1974, Feb. 11   **Photo.**   **Unwmk.**
181 A25 35c multicolored (R)   .22 .22
182 A25 2fr multicolored (B)   1.25 1.25

Visit of British Royal Family, Feb. 11-12.

Pacific Dove — A30

Designs: 35c, Night swallowtail. 70c, Green sea turtle. 1.15fr, Flying fox.

1974, Feb. 11   **Perf. 13x12½**
183 A30 25c gray & multi   .85 .60
184 A30 35c gray & multi   1.25 .85
185 A30 70c gray & multi   2.25 1.65
186 A30 1.15fr gray & multi   2.50 2.25
    Nos. 183-186 (4)   6.85 5.35

    Nature conservation.

Old Post Office, Vila — A31

Design: 70c, New Post Office.

1974, May 6   **Unwmk.**   **Perf. 12**
187 A31 35c blue & multi   .40 .40
188 A31 70c red & multi   .80 .80
   a.   Pair, #187-188   1.25 1.25

Opening of New Post Office, May, 1974.

Capt. Cook and Tanna Island A32

Designs: No. 190, William Wales, and boat landing on island. No. 191, William Hodges painting islanders and landscape. 1.15fr, Capt. Cook, "Resolution" and map of New Hebrides.

Wmk. 314

1974, Aug. 1   Litho.   Perf. 13

Size: 40x25mm

189	A32	35c multicolored	1.65	.75
190	A32	35c multicolored	1.65	.75
191	A32	35c multicolored	1.65	.75
a.		Strip of 3, #189-191	5.00	3.00

Perf. 11

Size: 58x34mm

192	A32	1.15fr lilac & multi	3.50	3.00
		Nos. 189-192 (4)	8.45	5.25

Bicentenary of the discovery of the New Hebrides by Capt. Cook. No. 191a has continuous design.

Exchange of Letters, UPU Emblem A33

Perf. 13x12½

1974, Oct. 9   Photo.   Unwmk.

193	A33	70c multicolored	.50	.50

Centenary of Universal Postal Union.

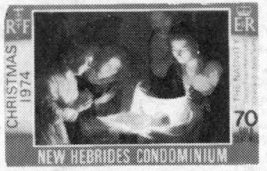

Nativity, by Gerard van Honthorst — A34

Christmas: 35c, Adoration of the Kings, by Velazquez, vert.

Perf. 13½

1974, Nov. 14   Litho.   Wmk. 314

194	A34	35c multicolored	.30	.30
195	A34	70c multicolored	.60	.60

Charolais Bull — A35

1975, Apr. 29   Engr.   Perf. 13

196	A35	10fr multicolored	10.00	12.00

For surcharge see No. 229.

A36   A37

1975, Aug. 5   Litho.   Perf. 14x13½

197	A36	25c Kayak race	.28	.28
198	A36	35c Camp cooks	.35	.35
199	A36	1fr Map makers	1.00	1.00
200	A36	5fr Fishermen	8.00	6.50
		Nos. 197-200 (4)	9.63	8.13

Nordjamb 75, 14th Boy Scout Jamboree, Lillehammer, Norway, July 29-Aug. 7.

Perf. 14½x14

1975, Nov. 11   Litho.   Wmk. 373

Christmas (After Michelangelo): 35c, Pitti Madonna. 70c, Bruges Madonna. 2.50fr, Taddei Madonna.

201	A37	35c ol green & multi	.22	.22
202	A37	70c brown & multi	.45	.45
203	A37	2.50fr blue & multi	1.50	1.50
		Nos. 201-203 (3)	2.17	2.17

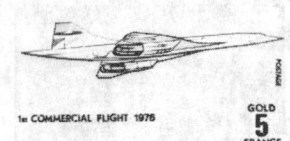

Concorde, British Airways Colors and Emblem — A38

Unwmk.

1976, Jan. 30   Typo.   Perf. 13

204	A38	5fr blue & multi	11.00	8.50

First commercial flight of supersonic jet Concorde from London to Bahrain, Jan. 21.

Telephones, 1876 and 1976 — A39

Designs: 70c, Alexander Graham Bell. 1.15fr, Nouméa earth station and satellite.

1976, Mar. 31   Photo.   Perf. 13

205	A39	25c black, car & blue	.16	.16
206	A39	70c black & multi	.40	.40
207	A39	1.15fr black, org & vio bl	.75	.75
		Nos. 205-207 (3)	1.31	1.31

Centenary of first telephone call by Alexander Graham Bell, Mar. 10, 1876.

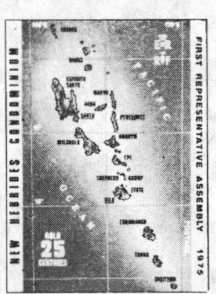

Map of New Hebrides A40

View of Santo — A41

Design: 2fr, View of Vila.

1976, June 29   Photo.   Perf. 13

208	A40	25c blue & multi	.15	.15
209	A41	1fr multicolored	.55	.55
210	A41	2fr multicolored	1.25	1.25
		Nos. 208-210 (3)	1.95	1.95

Opening of First Representative Assembly, June 29 (25c); first Santo Municipal Council (1fr); first Vila Municipal Council (2fr).

Flight into Egypt, by Francisco Vieira Lusitano — A42

Christmas (Portuguese 16th Cent. Paintings): 70c, Adoration of the Shepherds. 2.50fr, Adoration of the Kings.

Wmk. 373

1976, Nov. 8   Litho.   Perf. 14

211	A42	35c purple & multi	.20	.20
212	A42	70c blue & multi	.40	.40
213	A42	2.50fr lt green & multi	1.40	1.40
		Nos. 211-213 (3)	2.00	2.00

Queen's Visit, 1974 — A43

Designs: 70c, Imperial state crown. 2fr, The blessing.

1977, Feb. 7   Perf. 14x13½

214	A43	35c lt green & multi	.15	.15
215	A43	70c blue & multi	.30	.30
216	A43	2fr pink & multi	.80	.80
		Nos. 214-216 (3)	1.25	1.25

25th anniv. of the reign of Elizabeth II.

Nos. 155-166, 196 Surcharged with New Value, "FNH" and Bars

Perf. 12½x13

1977, July 1   Photo.   Unwmk.

217	A24	5fr on 5c multi	.15	.15
218	A25	10fr on 10c multi	.28	.28
219	A24	15fr on 15c multi	.40	.40
220	A25	20fr on 20c multi	.50	.50
221	A24	25fr on 25c multi	.65	.65
222	A24	30fr on 30c multi	.80	.80
223	A25	35fr on 35c multi	1.00	1.00
224	A24	40fr on 65c multi	1.10	1.10
225	A24	50fr on 1fr multi	2.00	2.00
226	A25	70fr on 2fr multi	3.50	3.50
227	A24	100fr on 3fr multi	5.00	5.00
228	A24	200fr on 5fr multi	6.50	6.50

Wmk. 314

Engr.   Perf. 13

229	A35	500fr on 10fr multi	14.00	14.00
		Nos. 217-229 (13)	35.88	35.88

Nos. 217-229 were surcharged in Paris. Eleven denominations were surcharged later in Vila with slightly larger, different letters and different bars; nine were sold at post offices.

Erromango and Kaori Tree — A44   Tempi Madonna, by Raphael — A45

Designs: 10fr, Archipelago and man making copra. 15fr, Espiritu Santo Island and cattle. 20fr, Efate Island and Post Office, Vila. 25fr, Malakula Island and headdresses. 30fr, Aoba and Maewo Islands and pig tusks. 35fr, Pentecost Island and land diving. 40fr, Tanna Island and Prophet John Frum's Red Cross. 50fr, Shepherd Island and canoe with sail. 70fr, Banks Island and dancers. 100fr, Ambrym Island and carvings. 200fr, Aneityum

---

Island and decorated baskets. 500fr, Torres Islands and fishing with bow and arrow.

1977-78   Wmk. 373   Litho.   Perf. 14

238	A44	5fr multicolored	.15	.15
239	A44	10fr multicolored	.15	.15
240	A44	15fr multicolored	.20	.20
241	A44	20fr multicolored	.28	.28
242	A44	25fr multicolored	.35	.35
243	A44	30fr multicolored	.45	.45
244	A44	35fr multicolored	.55	.55
245	A44	40fr multicolored	.60	.60
246	A44	50fr multicolored	.70	.70
247	A44	70fr multicolored	1.00	1.00
248	A44	100fr multicolored	1.50	1.50
249	A44	200fr multicolored	3.25	3.25
250	A44	500fr multicolored	7.00	7.00
		Nos. 238-250 (13)	16.18	16.18

Issue dates: 5fr, 20fr, 50fr, 100fr, 200fr, Sept. 7; 15fr, 25fr, 30fr, 40fr, Nov. 23, 1977; 10fr, 35fr, 70fr, 500fr, May 9, 1978.

1977, Dec. 8   Litho.   Perf. 12

Christmas: 15fr, Virgin and Child, by Gerard David. 30fr, Virgin and Child, by Pompeo Batoni.

251	A45	10fr multicolored	.18	.18
252	A45	15fr multicolored	.25	.25
253	A45	30fr multicolored	.55	.55
		Nos. 251-253 (3)	.98	.98

British Airways Concorde over New York City — A46

Designs: 20fr, British Airways Concorde over London. 30fr, Air France Concorde over Washington. 40fr, Air France Concorde over Paris.

1978, May 9   Wmk. 373   Perf. 14

254	A46	10fr multicolored	.40	.20
255	A46	20fr multicolored	.65	.40
256	A46	30fr multicolored	1.00	.60
257	A46	40fr multicolored	1.25	.80
		Nos. 254-257 (4)	3.30	2.00

Concorde, 1st commercial flight, Paris to NYC.

Elizabeth II Coronation Anniversary Issue

Common Design Types

Souvenir Sheet

1978, June 2   Unwmk.   Perf. 15

258		Sheet of 6	4.50	4.50
a.	CD326	40fr White horse of Hanover	.70	.70
b.	CD327	40fr Elizabeth II	.70	.70
c.	CD328	40fr Gallic cock	.70	.70

No. 258 contains 2 se-tenant strips of Nos. 258a-258c, separated by horizontal gutter with commemorative and descriptive inscriptions and showing central part of coronation procession with coach.

Virgin and Child, by Dürer — A47

Dürer Paintings: 15fr, Virgin and Child with St. Anne. 30fr, Virgin and Child with Goldfinch. 40fr, Virgin and Child with Pear.

Perf. 14x13½

1978, Dec. 1   Litho.   Wmk. 373

259	A47	10fr multicolored	.18	.18
260	A47	15fr multicolored	.25	.25
261	A47	30fr multicolored	.52	.52
262	A47	40fr multicolored	.80	.80
		Nos. 259-262 (4)	1.75	1.75

Christmas and 450th death anniv. of Albrecht Dürer (1471-1528), German painter.

Type of 1976 Surcharged with New Value, Bars over Denomination and Inscription at Right. Longitude changed to "166E."

1979, Jan. 11 Photo. *Perf. 13*

263	A40	10fr on 25c bl & multi	.20	.20
264	A40	40fr on 25c lt grn & multi	.80	.80

1st anniv. of Internal Self-Government.

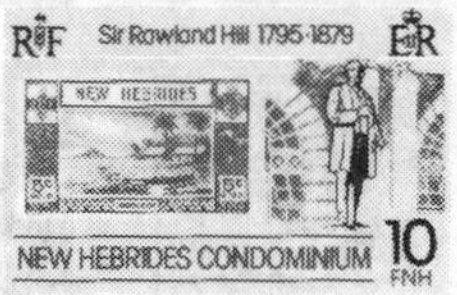

New Hebrides No. 50 — A48

Rowland Hill and New Hebrides Stamps: 20fr, No. 136. 40fr, No. 43.

1979, Sept. 10 Litho. *Perf. 14*

265	A48	10fr multicolored	.15	.15
266	A48	20fr multicolored	.28	.28
a.		Souvenir sheet of 2	.60	.60
267	A48	40fr multicolored	.60	.60
		Nos. 265-267 (3)	1.03	1.03

Sir Rowland Hill (1795-1879), originator of penny postage. No. 266a contains New Hebrides, British, No. 266, and French, No. 286; margin shows Mulready envelope.

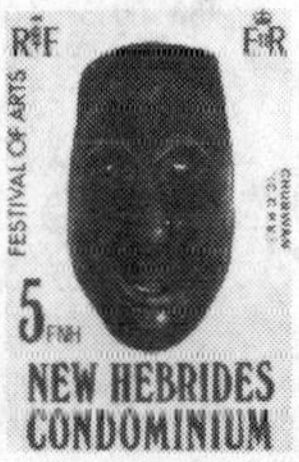

Arts Festival — A49

Designs: 10fr, Clubs and spears. 20fr, Ritual puppet. 40fr, Headdress.

1979, Nov. 16 Wmk. 373 *Perf. 14*

268	A49	5fr multicolored	.15	.15
269	A49	10fr multicolored	.15	.15
270	A49	20fr multicolored	.28	.28
271	A49	40fr multicolored	.52	.52
		Nos. 268-271 (4)	1.10	1.10

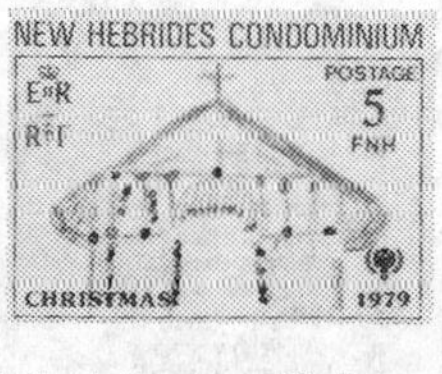

Church, IYC Emblem A50

IYC Emblem, Children's Drawings: 10fr, Father Christmas. 20fr, Cross and Bible, vert. 40fr, Stars, candle and Santa Claus, vert.

1979, Dec. 4 *Perf. 13x13½*

272	A50	5fr multicolored	.15	.15
273	A50	10fr multicolored	.15	.15
274	A50	20fr multicolored	.30	.30
275	A50	40fr multicolored	.48	.48
		Nos. 272-275 (4)	1.08	1.08

Christmas; Intl. Year of the Child.

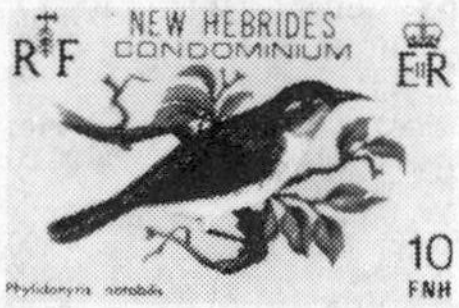

White-bellied Honeyeater — A51

1980, Feb. 27 Litho. *Perf. 14*

276	A51	10fr shown	.35	.18
277	A51	20fr Scarlet robins	.50	.40
278	A51	30fr Yellow white-eyes	.80	.55
279	A51	40fr Fan-tailed brush cuckoo	1.00	.75
		Nos. 276-279 (4)	2.65	1.88

New Hebrides stamps were replaced in 1980 by these of Vanuatu.

POSTAGE DUE STAMPS

British Issues

Type of 1925 Overprinted **POSTAGE DUE.**

1925, June Engr. Wmk. 4 *Perf. 14*

J1	A3	1p (10c) green	37.50	1.50
J2	A3	2p (10c) gray	45.00	1.75
J3	A3	3p (30c) carmine	50.00	1.75
J4	A3	5p (50c) ultra	55.00	4.00
J5	A3	10p (1fr) car, *blue*	67.50	5.00
		Nos. J1-J5 (5)	255.00	14.00

Values for Nos. J1-J5 are for toned copies.

Regular Stamps of 1938 Overprinted in Black **POSTAGE DUE**

1938, June 1 *Perf. 12*

J6	A5	5c green	9.50	20.00
J7	A5	10c dark orange	10.00	20.00
J8	A5	20c rose red	11.00	25.00
J9	A5	40c olive green	15.00	32.50
J10	A5	1fr car, *emerald*	30.00	45.00
		Nos. J6-J10 (5)	75.50	142.50

Catalogue values for unused stamps in this section, from this point to the end of the section, are for Never Hinged items.

Regular Stamps of 1953 Overprinted in Black **POSTAGE DUE**

1953, Apr. 30 *Perf. 12½*

J11	A6	5c green	.95	*2.00*
J12	A6	10c red	1.10	*2.75*
J13	A6	20c ultramarine	3.00	*6.50*
J14	A6	40c black brown	6.50	*15.00*
J15	A6	1fr deep orange	7.50	*17.50*
		Nos. J11-J15 (5)	19.05	*43.75*

Same on Nos. 82-83, 85, 88 and 90

1957, Sept. 3 *Perf. 13½x13*

J16	A8	5c green	.20	*.50*
J17	A8	10c red	.35	*.90*
J18	A8	20c ultramarine	.80	*1.25*
J19	A8	40c sepia	2.25	*2.75*
J20	A8	1fr orange	4.25	*6.50*
		Nos. J16-J20 (5)	7.85	*11.90*

NEW REPUBLIC

'nü ri–'pə–blik

LOCATION — In South Africa, located in the northern part of the present province of Natal
GOVT. — A former Republic
CAPITAL — Vryheid

New Republic was created in 1884 by Boer adventurers from Transvaal who proclaimed Dinizulu king of Zululand and claimed as their reward a large tract of country as their own, which they called New Republic. This area was excepted when Great Britain annexed Zululand in 1887, but New Republic became a part of Transvaal in 1888 and was included in the Union of South Africa.

12 Pence = 1 Shilling
20 Shillings = 1 Pound

New Republic stamps were individually handstamped on gummed and perforated sheets of paper. Naturally many of the impressions are misaligned and touch or intersect the perforations. Values are for stamps with good color and, for Nos. 37-64, sharp embossing. The alignment does not materially alter the value of the stamp.

New Republic stamps can be mounted in the Scott British Africa album.

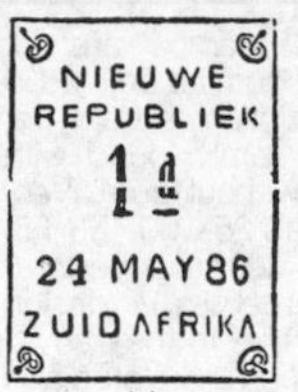

A1

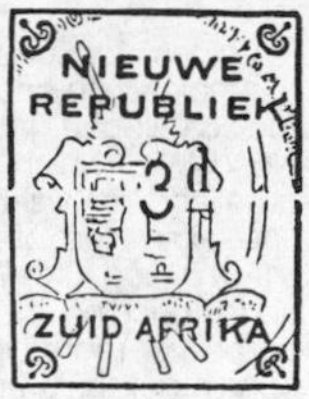

A2

Handstamped

1886 Unwmk. *Perf. 11½*

1	A1	1p violet, *yel*	9.00	11.00
1A	A1	1p black, *yel*		*3,250.*
2	A1	2p violet, *yel*	9.00	12.50
a.		Without date		
b.		Tête bêche pair		
3	A1	3p violet, *yel*	22.50	
a.		Double impression		
4	A1	4p violet, *yel*	32.50	
a.		Without date		
5	A1	6p violet, *yel*	30.00	
a.		Double impression		
6	A1	9p violet, *yel*	27.50	
7	A1	1sh violet, *yel*	75.00	
a.		"1/S"	475.00	
8	A1	1/6 violet, *yel*	75.00	
a.		Without date		
b.		"1shóp"	475.00	
9	A1	2sh violet, *yel*	35.00	
a.		Tête bêche pair	550.00	
10	A1	2sh6p violet, *yel*	95.00	
a.		Without date		
b.		"2/6"	135.00	
11	A1	4sh violet, *yel*	425.00	
12	A1	5sh violet, *yel*	30.00	30.00
a.		Without date		
13	A1	5/6 violet, *yel*	35.00	35.00
a.		"5shóp"	150.00	
14	A1	7sh6p violet, *yel*	90.00	
a.		"7/6"	150.00	
15	A1	10sh violet, *yel*	90.00	90.00
16	A1	10sh6p violet, *yel*	175.00	
16A	A1	13sh violet, *yel*	400.00	
17	A1	£1 violet, *yel*	125.00	
18	A1	30sh violet, *yel*	90.00	
a.		Tête bêche pair	550.00	

Granite Paper

19	A1	1p violet, *gray*	12.00	13.00
20	A1	2p violet, *gray*	12.00	13.00
a.		Without "ZUID AFRIKA"		
21	A1	3p violet, *gray*	15.00	17.50
a.		Tête bêche pair	275.00	
22	A1	4p violet, *gray*	12.50	17.50
23	A1	6p violet, *gray*	25.00	22.50
24	A1	9p violet, *gray*	30.00	
25	A1	1sh violet, *gray*	27.50	27.50
a.		Tête bêche pair	700.00	
26	A1	1shóp violet, *gray*	40.00	
a.		Tête bêche pair	600.00	
b.		"1/6"	140.00	
27	A1	2sh violet, *gray*	110.00	
28	A1	2shóp violet, *gray*	150.00	
a.		"2/6"	175.00	
29	A1	4sh violet, *gray*	200.00	
30	A1	5shóp violet, *gray*	165.00	
a.		"5/6"	190.00	
31	A1	7shóp violet, *gray*	190.00	
32	A1	10sh violet, *gray*	190.00	225.00
a.		Tête bêche pair	500.00	
32B	A1	10sh 6p vio, *gray*	185.00	
c.		Without date		
33	A1	12sh violet, *gray*	275.00	
34	A1	13sh violet, *gray*	400.00	
35	A1	£1 violet, *gray*	250.00	
36	A1	30sh violet, *gray*	250.00	

Same with Embossed Arms

37	A1	1p violet, *yel*	13.00	14.00
a.		Arms inverted	25.00	25.00
b.		Arms tête bêche, pair	105.00	125.00
38	A1	2p violet, *yel*	13.00	14.00
a.		Arms inverted	25.00	27.50
39	A1	4p violet, *yel*	18.00	18.00
a.		Arms inverted	100.00	75.00
b.		Arms tête bêche, pair	275.00	
40	A1	6p violet, *yel*	35.00	

Granite Paper

41	A1	1p violet, *gray*	13.00	15.00
a.		Imperf. vert., pair		
b.		Arms inverted	30.00	35.00
c.		Arms tête bêche, pair		
42	A1	2p violet, *gray*	13.00	15.00
a.		Imperf. horiz., pair		
b.		Arms inverted	45.00	
c.		Arms tête bêche, pair		

There were several printings of the above stamps and the date upon them varies from "JAN 86" and "7 JAN 86" to "20 JAN 87."

Nos. 7, 8, 10, 13, 14, 26, 28 and 30 have the denomination expressed in two ways. Example: "1s 6d" or "1/6."

1887 Arms Embossed

43	A2	3p violet, *yel*	13.00	13.00
a.		Arms inverted	24.00	24.00
b.		Tête bêche pair	360.00	
c.		Imperf. vert., pair		
d.		Arms omitted		
e.		Arms tête bêche, pair		
44	A2	4p violet, *yel*	12.50	12.50
a.		Arms inverted	27.50	27.50
45	A2	6p violet, *yel*	11.00	11.00
a.		Arms inverted	52.50	52.50
b.		Arms omitted	200.00	
c.		Arms tête bêche, pair	315.00	
46	A2	9p violet, *yel*	11.00	11.00
47	A2	1sh violet, *yel*	13.00	13.00
a.		Arms inverted	65.00	
b.		Arms omitted	55.00	
48	A2	1shóp violet, *yel*	16.00	12.00
49	A2	2sh violet, *yel*	24.00	24.00
a.		Arms inverted	75.00	
b.		Arms omitted	100.00	100.00
50	A2	2shóp violet, *yel*	21.00	21.00
a.		Arms inverted	24.00	24.00
50B	A2	3sh violet, *yel*	42.50	42.50
c.		Arms inverted	47.50	47.50
51	A2	4sh violet, *yel*	12.00	12.00
a.		Arms omitted		
52	A2	5sh violet, *yel*	12.00	12.00
a.		Imperf. vert., pair		
b.		Arms inverted	90.00	
53	A2	5shóp violet, *yel*	12.00	12.00
54	A2	7shóp violet, *yel*	18.00	18.00
a.		Arms inverted	80.00	
b.		Arms tête bêche, pair		
55	A2	10sh violet, *yel*	12.00	12.00
a.		Arms inverted	21.00	21.00
b.		Arms omitted	75.00	75.00
c.		Imperf. vert., pair		
d.		Arms tête bêche, pair	210.00	
56	A2	10shóp violet, *yel*	20.00	20.00
a.		Imperf. vert., pair		
b.		Arms inverted		
c.		Arms omitted		
57	A2	£1 violet, *yel*	50.00	50.00
a.		Arms inverted	52.50	
b.		Tête bêche pair	475.00	475.00
58	A2	30sh violet, *yel*	100.00	100.00

Granite Paper

59	A2	1p violet, *gray*	12.50	12.50
a.		Arms omitted	110.00	110.00
b.		Arms inverted	21.00	21.00
c.		Imperf. vert., pair		
d.		Tête bêche pair	300.00	
60	A2	2p violet, *gray*	8.00	8.00
a.		Arms omitted	100.00	100.00
b.		Arms inverted	22.50	22.50
c.		Tête bêche pair	450.00	
61	A2	3p violet, *gray*	12.00	12.00
a.		Arms inverted	65.00	65.00
b.		Tête bêche pair	465.00	
62	A2	4p violet, *gray*	12.00	12.00
a.		Arms inverted	85.00	85.00
b.		Tête bêche pair	450.00	
63	A2	6p violet, *gray*	12.00	12.00
a.		Arms inverted	100.00	100.00
64	A2	1shóp violet, *gray*	13.00	13.00
a.		Arms inverted		

These stamps were valid only in New Republic.

All these stamps may have been valid for postage but bona-fide canceled specimens of any but the 1p and 2p stamps are quite rare.

NEW SOUTH WALES

'nü saúth 'wā(ə)lz

LOCATION — Southeast coast of Australia in the South Pacific Ocean
GOVT. — A former British Crown Colony
AREA — 309,432 sq. mi.
POP. — 1,500,000 (estimated, 1900)
CAPITAL — Sydney

In 1901 New South Wales united with five other British colonies to form the Commonwealth of Australia. Stamps of Australia are now used.

12 Pence = 1 Shilling
20 Shillings = 1 Pound

Watermarks

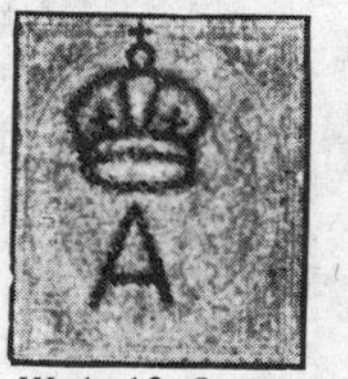

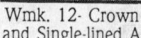

Wmk. 12- Crown and Single-lined A

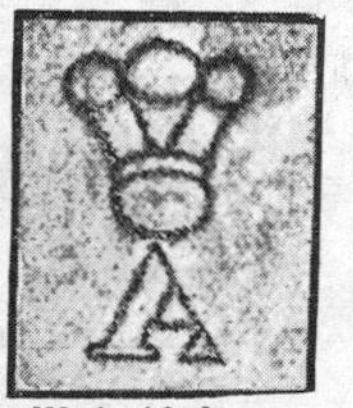

Wmk. 13- Large Crown and Double-lined A

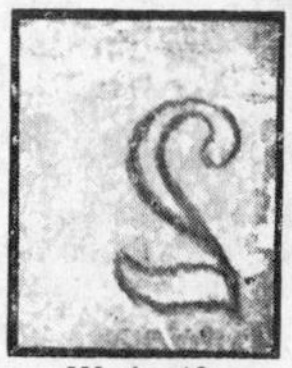

Wmk. 49- Double-lined Numerals Corresponding with the Value

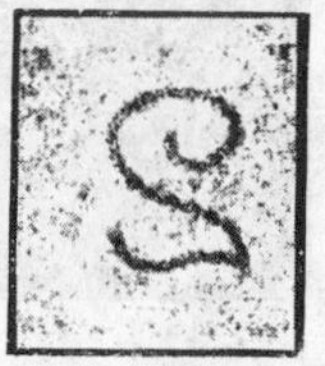

Wmk. 50- Single-lined Numeral

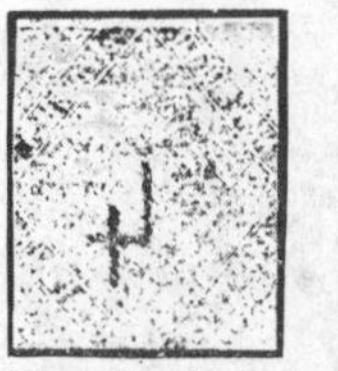
Wmk. 51- Single-lined Numeral

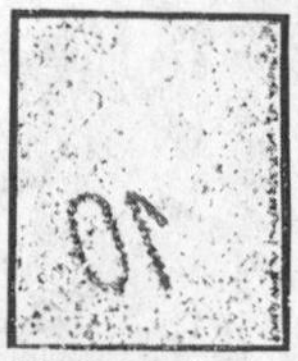
Wmk. 52- Single-lined Numeral

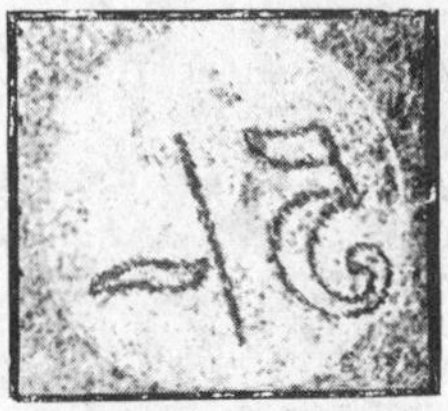
Wmk. 53- 5/-

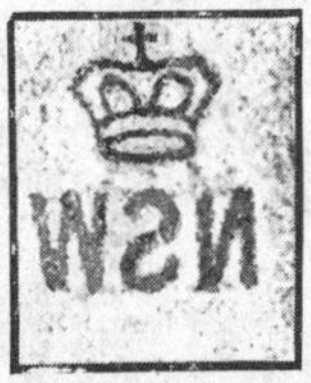
Wmk. 54- Small Crown and NSW

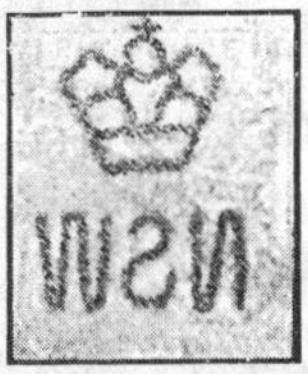
Wmk. 55- Large Crown and NSW

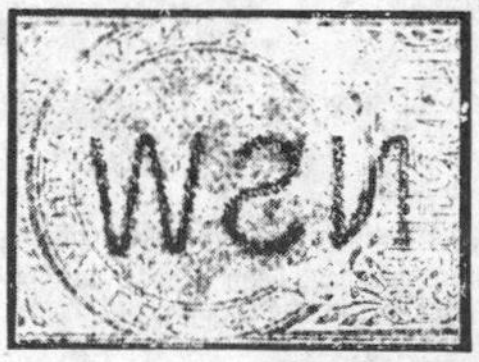
Wmk. 56- NSW

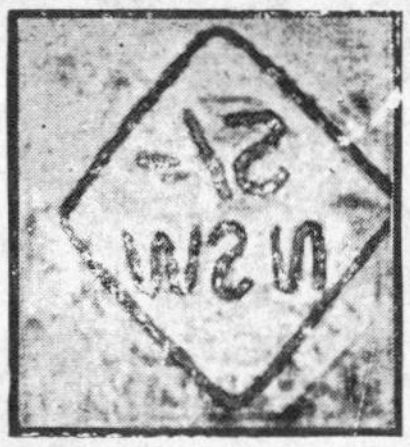
Wmk. 57- 5/- NSW in Diamond

Wmk. 58- 20/- NSW in Circle

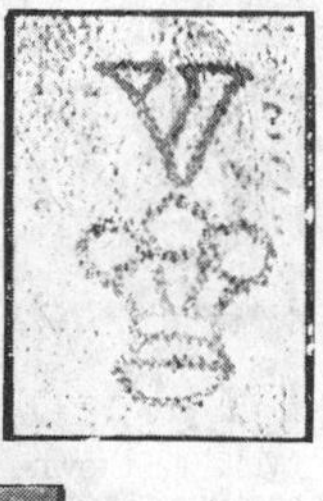
Wmk. 70- V and Crown

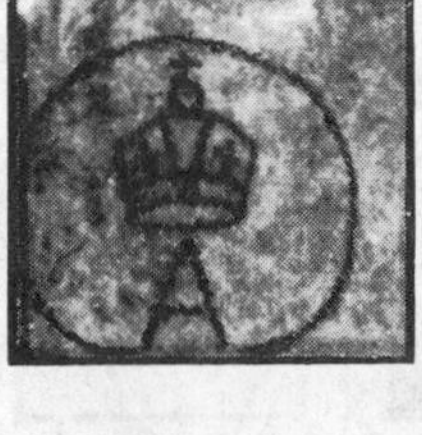
Wmk. 199- Crown and A in Circle

Values for unused stamps are for examples with original gum as defined in the catalogue introduction except for Nos. 1-20 which are rarely found with gum and are valued without gum. Very fine examples of Nos. 35-100, F3-F5, J1-J10 and O1-O40 will have perforations touching the framelines or design on one or more sides due to the narrow spacing of the stamps on the plates and imperfect perforation methods. Stamps with perfs clear of the design on all four sides are scarce and will command higher prices.

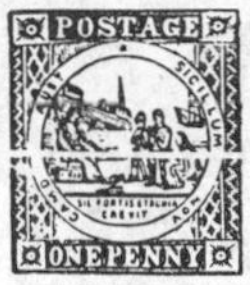

Seal of the Colony
A1 A2

A1 has no clouds. A2 has clouds added to the design, except in pos. 15.

1850 Unwmk. Engr. *Imperf.*

1	A1 1p red, *yelsh wove*	4,000.	400.
b.	1p red, *bluish wove*	4,000.	350.
2	A2 1p red, *yelsh wove*	2,500.	275.
b.	1p red, *yellowish laid*	4,000.	275.
c.	1p red, *bluish wove*	2,500.	275.
e.	1p red, *bluish laid*	4,000.	275.
f.	Hill unshaded	4,000.	275.
g.	No clouds	4,000.	275.
h.	No trees	4,000.	275.

Twenty-five varieties.

Stamps from early impressions of the plate sell at considerably higher prices.

No. 1 was reproduced by the collotype process in a souvenir sheet distributed at the London International Stamp Exhibition 1950. The paper is white.

Plate I — A3

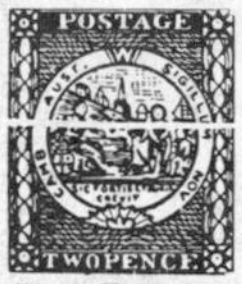
Plate II — A4

Plate I: Vertically lined background.

Plate I re-touched: Lines above and below "POSTAGE" and "TWO PENCE" deepened. Outlines of circular band around picture also deepened.

Plate II (First re-engraving of Plate I): Horizontally lined background; the bale on the left side is dated and there is a dot in the star in each corner.

Plate II retouched: Dots and dashes added in lower spandrels.

Plate I
Late (worn plate) Impressions

3	A3 2p blue, *yelsh wove*	1,000.	150.
a.	Early impressions	4,500.	350.

Twenty-four varieties.

Plate I, Retouched

4	A3 2p blue, *yelsh wove*	2,750.	250.

Twelve varieties.

Plate II
Late (worn plate) Impressions

5	A4 2p blue, *yelsh wove*	1,150.	175.
a.	2p blue, *bluish wove*		175.
b.	2p blue, *grayish wove*		175.
c.	"CREVIT" omitted	2,750.	350.
d.	Pick and shovel omitted	2,750.	375.
e.	No whip	1,800.	250.
h.	Early impressions	4,000.	225.

Plate II, Retouched

5F	A4 2p blue, *bluish wove*	1,800.	200.
g.	No whip	3,250.	275.
i.	"CREVIT" omitted		275.

Twelve varieties.

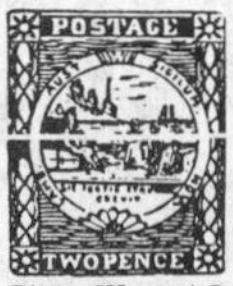
Plate III — A5

Plate IV — A6

Plate III (Second re-engraving of Plate I): The bale is not dated and, with the exception of Nos. 7, 10 and 12, it is single-lined. There are no dots in the stars.

Plate IV (Third re-engraving of Plate I): The bale is double-lined and there is a circle in the center of each star.

1850-51

6	A5 2p blue, *grayish wove*	1,400.	175.
a.	Fan with 6 segments	2,500.	300.
b.	Double-lined bale	2,300.	250.
c.	No whip	2,500.	250.
7	A6 2p blue, *bluish wove* ('51)	1,650.	150.
a.	2p blue, *white laid*	2,500.	150.
b.	2p blue, *grayish wove*	1,650.	150.
c.	Fan with 6 segments	2,500.	200.
d.	No clouds	2,500.	200.

Twenty-four varieties.

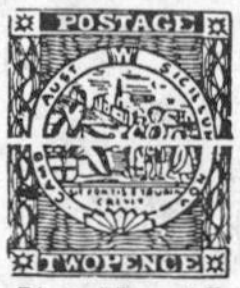
Plate V — A7

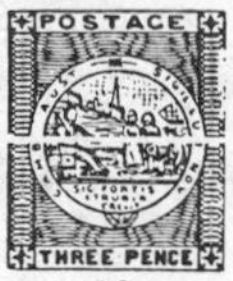
A8

Plate V (Fourth re-engraving of Plate I): There is a pearl in the fan-shaped ornament below the central design.

1850-51

8	A7 2p blue, *grayish wove* ('51)	1,650.	165.
a.	2p blue, *white laid*	3,250.	275.
b.	Fan with 6 segments	2,500.	225.
c.	Pick and shovel omitted	2,500.	200.
9	A8 3p green, *bluish wove*	2,150.	200.
a.	3p green, *yellowish wove*	3,750.	225.
b.	3p green, *yellowish laid*	4,250.	400.
c.	3p green, *bluish laid*	4,250.	400.
d.	No whip	2,500.	300.

Twenty-four varieties.

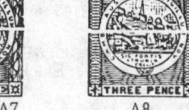

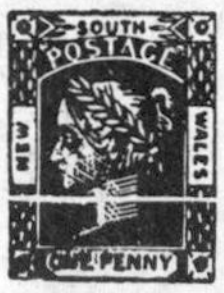
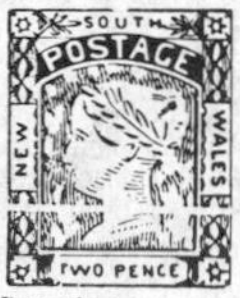
Queen Victoria
A9 A10

TWO PENCE
Plate I - Background of wavy lines.
Plate II - Stars in corners.
Plate III (Plate I re-engraved) - Background of crossed lines.

SIX PENCE
Plate I - Background of fine lines.
Plate II (Plate I re-engraved) - Background of coarse lines.

1851 Yellowish Wove Paper

10	A9 1p carmine	1,650.	250.00
b.	No leaves to right of "SOUTH"	*3,250.*	365.00
c.	Two leaves to right of "SOUTH"	*3,250.*	365.00
d.	"WALE"	*3,250.*	365.00
11	A9 2p ultra, Plate I	650.00	90.00

1852 Bluish Laid Paper

12	A9 1p carmine	3,000.	400.
a.	No leaves to right of "SOUTH"		500.
b.	Two leaves to right of "SOUTH"		500.
c.	"WALE"		500.

1852-55
Bluish or Grayish Wove Paper

13	A9 1p red	750.00	125.00
a.	1p carmine	1,000.	140.00
b.	No leaves to right of "SOUTH"		200.00
c.	Two leaves to right of "SOUTH"		250.00
d.	"WALE"		200.00
14	A9 2p blue, Plate I	300.00	27.50
a.	2p ultramarine	325.00	27.50
b.	2p slate	425.00	27.50
15	A10 2p blue, Plate II ('53)	900.00	87.50
a.	"WAEES"	*2,300.*	450.00
16	A9 2p blue, Plate III ('55)	425.00	55.00
17	A9 3p green	900.00	140.00
a.	3p emerald	1,300.	100.00
b.	"WACES"	2,300.	325.00
18	A9 6p brown, Plate I	2,000.	250.00
a.	6p black brown	2,000.	225.00
b.	"WALLS"	4,250.	425.00
19	A9 6p brown, Plate II	2,000.	250.00
a.	6p bister brown	2,000.	225.00
20	A9 8p yellow ('53)	3,600.	475.00
a.	8p orange	3,600.	550.00
b.	No leaves to right of "SOUTH"		900.00

The plates of the 1, 2, 3 and 8p each contained 50 varieties and those of the 6p 25 varieties.

The 2p, plate II, 6p, plate II, and 8p have been reprinted on grayish blue wove paper. The reprints of the 2p have the spandrels and background much worn. Most of the reprints of the 6p have no floreate ornaments to the right and left of "South." On all the values the wreath has been retouched.

Type of 1851 and:

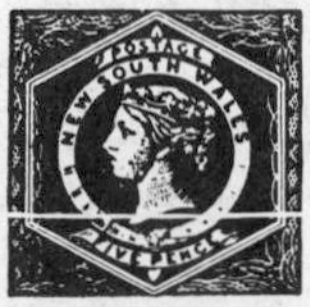
A11

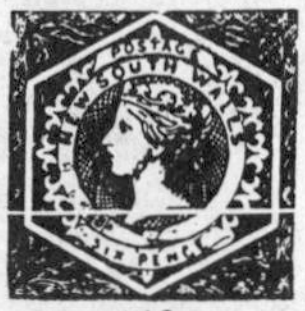
A12

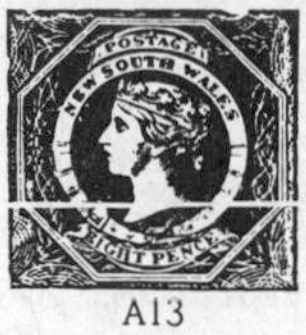
A13

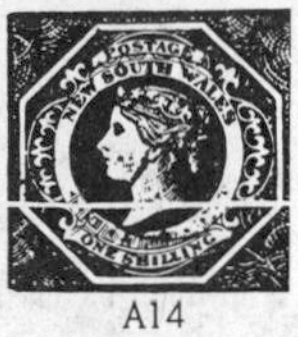
A14

1854-55 Wmk. 49

23	A9 1p orange	125.00	13.00
a.	No leaves to right of "SOUTH"	275.00	60.00
b.	Two leaves to right of "SOUTH"	400.00	100.00
c.	"WALE"	400.00	110.00
24	A9 2p blue	100.00	8.50
a.	2p ultramarine	100.00	10.00
25	A9 3p green	150.00	22.50
a.	"WACES"		80.00
b.	Watermarked "2"		500.00

Value for No. 25b is for copy with the design cut into.

26	A11 5p green	800.00	375.00
27	A12 6p sage green	425.00	32.50
28	A12 6p brown	450.00	30.00
a.	Watermarked "8"	1,650.	85.00
29	A12 6p gray	325.00	30.00
a.	Watermarked "8"	1,650.	80.00
30	A13 8p orange ('55)	4,750.	825.00
a.	8p yellow	4,750.	825.00
31	A14 1sh pale red brown	650.00	75.00
a.	1sh red	650.00	75.00
b.	Watermarked "8"	2,000.	150.00

See Nos. 38-42, 56, 58, 65, 67.

Nos. 38-42 exist with wide margins. Copies with perforations trimmed are often offered as Nos. 26, 30, and 30a.

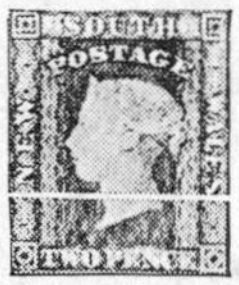
A15

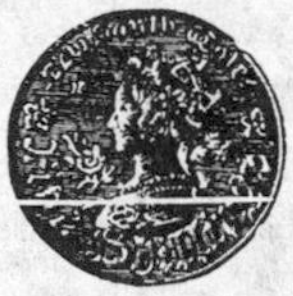
A16

1856

32	A15 1p red	90.00	16.00
a.	1p orange	90.00	16.00
b.	Printed on both sides		*2,250.*
33	A15 2p blue	110.00	5.00
a.	Watermarked "1"		5,000.
b.	Watermarked "5"	550.00	25.00
c.	Watermarked "8"		125.00
34	A15 3p green	750.00	60.00
a.	3p yellow green	725.00	75.00
b.	Watermarked "2"		*4,000.*
	Nos. 32-34 (3)	950.00	81.00

The 1p has been reprinted in orange on paper watermarked Small Crown and NSW, and the 2p in deep blue on paper watermarked single lined "2." These reprints are usually overprinted "SPECIMEN."

See Nos. 34C-37, 54, 63, 90.

1859 Litho.

34C	A15 2p light blue		625.00

1860-63 Engr. Wmk. 49 *Perf. 13*

35	A15 1p red	55.00	7.25
a.	1p orange	100.00	7.25
b.	Perf. 12x13		2,000.
c.	Perf. 12	90.00	15.00
36	A15 2p blue, perf. 12	100.00	9.00
a.	Watermarked "1"		3,500.
c.	Perf. 12x13	2,600.	250.00
37	A15 3p blue green	45.00	7.25
a.	3p yellow green	50.00	7.00
b.	3p deep green	25.00	7.50
c.	Watermarked "6"	60.00	10.50
d.	Perf. 12	600.00	45.00
38	A11 5p dark green	32.50	12.50
a.	5p yellow green	50.00	21.00
b.	Perf. 12	165.00	42.50
39	A12 6p brown, perf. 12	275.00	45.00
a.	6p gray, perf. 12	275.00	45.00
40	A12 6p violet	55.00	3.00
a.	6p aniline lilac	950.00	150.00
b.	Watermarked "5"	360.00	30.00
c.	Watermarked "12"	240.00	20.00
e.	Perf. 12	275.00	25.00
41	A13 8p yellow	125.00	35.00
a.	8p orange	150.00	35.00
b.	Perf. 12	2,100.	550.00
42	A14 1sh rose	65.00	8.00
a.	1sh carmine	55.00	5.75
c.	Perf. 12	400.00	50.00
	Nos. 35-42 (8)	752.50	127.00

1864 Wmk. 50 *Perf. 13*

43	A15 1p red	30.00	15.00

1861-80 Wmk. 53 Perf. 13

44 A16 5sh dull violet	250.00	40.00
a. 5sh purple	225.00	30.00
b. 5sh dull violet, perf. 12	1,650.	400.00
c. 5sh purple, perf. 12	250.00	50.00
d. 5sh purple, perf. 10	250.00	42.50
e. 5sh purple, perf. 12x10	450.00	65.00

See No. 101. For overprint see No. O11.
Reprints are perf. 10 and overprinted "REPRINT" in black.

A17   A18

1862-65 Typo. Unwmk. Perf. 13

45 A17 1p red ('65)	72.50	20.00
a. Perf. 14	72.50	55.00
46 A18 2p blue	30.00	2.50
a. Perf. 14	60.00	17.50

1863-64 Wmk. 50 Perf. 13

47 A17 1p red	21.00	.90
a. Watermarked "2"	95.00	10.50
48 A18 2p blue	10.00	.35
a. Watermarked "1"	135.00	5.00

1862 Wmk. 49 Perf. 13

49 A18 2p blue	50.00	8.50
a. Watermarked "5"	135.00	18.00
b. Perf. 12x13	600.00	
c. Perf. 12	165.00	16.00

See Nos. 52-53, 61-62, 70-76.

A19   A20

1867, Sept. Wmk. 51, 52 Perf. 13

50 A19 4p red brown	30.00	3.25
a. Imperf.		
51 A20 10p lilac	11.00	3.50
a. Imperf.		
b. Horiz. pair, imperf. between	600.00	

See Nos. 55, 64, 91, 97, 117, 129.

A21   A22

A23

Typo.; Engr. (3p, 5p, 8p)
1871-84 Wmk. 54 Perf. 13

52 A17 1p red	4.50	.15
a. Perf. 10	400.00	15.00
b. Perf. 13x10	15.00	.18
c. Horiz. pair imperf. between		
53 A18 2p blue	7.00	.18
a. Imperf.		
b. Horiz. pair, imperf. vert.		800.00
c. Perf. 10	400.00	21.00
d. Perf. 13x10	4.50	.18
e. Perf. 12x11		
f. Perf. 11x12		30.00
54 A15 3p green ('74)	21.00	1.75
a. Perf. 11	225.00	150.00
b. Perf. 10	500.00	250.00
c. Perf. 10x12	175.00	35.00
d. Perf. 12x11	135.00	50.00
e. Perf. 10	70.00	4.50
f. Perf. 10x11	135.00	13.00
55 A19 4p red brown ('77)	40.00	5.00
a. Perf. 10	300.00	50.00
b. Perf. 13x10	75.00	2.50
56 A11 5p dk grn, perf. 10 ('84)	15.00	7.50
a. Imperf.		
b. Perf. 12	325.00	135.00
c. Perf. 10x12	24.00	9.00
d. Perf. 13x10		
57 A21 6p lilac ('72)	35.00	.75
a. Imperf.		
b. Perf. 13x10	50.00	1.75
c. Perf. 10	325.00	9.00
58 A13 8p yellow ('77)	90.00	16.00
a. Imperf.		
b. Perf. 10	325.00	21.00
c. Perf. 13x10	225.00	18.00

59 A22 9p on 10p red brown, perf. 12 (Bk)	14.00	3.00
a. Double surcharge, blk & bl	195.00	
b. Perf. 10x12	375.00	300.00
c. Perf. 10	12.00	3.25
d. Perf. 12x11	18.00	5.75
e. Perf. 11x12	18.00	5.75
f. Perf. 13	24.00	2.75
g. Perf. 11	40.00	7.25
h. Perf. 10x11	50.00	12.00
60 A23 1sh black ('76)	75.00	1.50
a. Imperf.		
b. Perf. 13x10	275.00	3.25
c. Perf. 10	550.00	12.00
d. Perf. 11		
Nos. 52-60 (9)	301.50	35.83

The surcharge on #59 measures 15mm.
See #66, 68. For overprints see #O1-O10.

Typo.; Engr. (3p, 5p, 8p)
1882-91 Wmk. 55 Perf. 11x12

61 A17 1p red	5.00	.15
a. Perf. 10	9.00	.15
b. Perf. 10x13	120.00	5.00
c. Perf. 10x12	325.00	85.00
d. Perf. 12x11		150.00
e. Perf. 10x11	600.00	150.00
f. Perf. 11		200.00
g. Perf. 13		135.00
62 A18 2p blue	5.00	.20
a. Perf. 10	12.00	.20
b. Perf. 13x10	90.00	2.50
c. Perf. 13		135.00
d. Perf. 12x10	325.00	70.00
e. Perf. 11		135.00
f. Perf. 12x11		135.00
g. Perf. 11x10	600.00	135.00
h. Perf. 12		275.00
63 A15 3p green	4.75	.35
a. Imperf., pair	200.00	
b. Vert. pair, imperf. btwn.	225.00	
c. Imperf. vert., pair		
d. Double impression		
e. Perf. 10	7.25	.35
f. Perf. 11	7.25	.35
g. Perf. 12	8.00	.35
h. Perf. 12x11	8.00	.40
i. Perf. 10x12	210.00	12.50
m. Perf. 10x11	20.00	1.25
n. Perf. 10x13	100.00	3.50
64 A19 4p red brown	27.50	1.40
a. Perf. 10	27.50	1.65
b. Perf. 10x12		150.00
c. Perf. 12		40.00
65 A11 5p dk blue green	7.25	.70
a. Imperf., pair	225.00	
b. Perf. 11	13.00	.75
c. Perf. 10	13.00	.80
d. Perf. 12	13.00	.80
e. Perf. 10x12		
f. 5p green, perf. 12x11	7.50	.75
g. 5p green, perf. 11x10	42.50	2.00
h. 5p green, perf. 12x10	75.00	3.25
i. 5p green, perf. 10x11	35.00	3.75
j. 5p green, perf. 11		3.75
66 A21 6p lilac, perf. 10	30.00	.75
a. Horiz. pair, imperf. between	825.00	
b. Perf. 10x12	30.00	.75
c. Perf. 11x12	32.50	1.25
d. Perf. 12	95.00	2.75
e. Perf. 11x10	60.00	.75
f. Perf. 11	95.00	6.00
g. Perf. 10x13	325.00	
67 A13 8p yellow, perf. 10	100.00	15.00
a. Perf. 11	90.00	13.00
b. Perf. 12	120.00	18.00
c. Perf. 10x12	100.00	20.00
68 A23 1sh black	60.00	.75
a. Perf. 10x13		12.00
b. Perf. 10	55.00	.75
c. Perf. 11	225.00	12.00
d. Perf. 10x12		
Nos. 61-68 (8)	239.50	19.30

Nos. 63 and 65 exist with two types of watermark 55 - spacings of 1mm or 2mm between crown and NSW.
See No. 90. For surcharges and overprints see Nos. 92-94, O12-O19.
The 1, 2, 4, 6, 8p and 1sh have been reprinted on paper watermarked Large Crown and NSW. The 1, 2, 4p and 1sh are perforated 11x12, the 6p is perforated 10 and the 8p 11. All are overprinted "REPRINT," the 1sh in red and the others in black.

1886-87 Typo. Wmk. 56 Perf. 11x12
Bluish Revenue Stamp Paper

70 A17 1p scarlet	11.00	2.50
a. Perf. 10	18.00	4.50
71 A18 2p dark blue	15.00	4.50
a. Perf. 10	65.00	9.00

For overprint, see No. O20.

A24

Perf. 12 (#73-75), 12x10 (#72, 75A) and Compound
1885-86
"POSTAGE" in Black

72 A24 5sh green & vio	450.00	65.00
a. Perf. 10		
73 A24 10sh rose & vio	1,250.	240.00
74 A24 £1 rose & vio	2,750.	1,000.
a. Perf. 13		2,100.

"POSTAGE" in Blue
Bluish Paper

75 A24 10sh rose & vio	175.00	35.00
b. Perf. 10	750.00	165.00
c. Perf. 12x11	375.00	150.00

White Paper

75A A24 £1 rose & vio	3,750.	1,750.

For overprints, see Nos. O21-O23.
The 5sh with black overprint and the £1 with blue overprint have been reprinted on paper watermarked NSW. They are perforated 12x10 and are overprinted "REPRINT" in black.

1894 White Paper
"POSTAGE" in Blue

76 A24 10sh rose & violet	175.00	30.00
a. Double overprint		

See No. 108B.

View of Sydney — A25   Emu — A26

Captain Cook — A27   Victoria and Coat of Arms — A28

Lyrebird A29   Kangaroo A30

1888-89 Wmk. 55 Perf. 11x12

77 A25 1p violet	3.50	.15
a. Perf. 12	4.50	.15
b. Perf. 12x11½	16.00	.15
78 A26 2p blue	3.00	.15
a. Imperf., pair	125.00	
b. Perf. 12	7.50	.15
c. Perf. 12x11½	13.00	.15
79 A27 4p brown	9.00	.75
a. Perf. 12x11½	15.00	.75
b. Perf. 12	15.00	.75
c. Perf. 11	450.00	135.00
d. Imperf.		
80 A28 6p carmine rose	22.50	1.25
a. Perf. 12	15.00	1.25
b. Perf. 12x11½	35.00	1.75
81 A29 8p red violet	11.00	.75
a. Perf. 12	9.00	1.50
b. Perf. 12x11½	12.00	1.50
82 A30 1sh vio brown ('89)	14.00	.75
a. Imperf., pair	725.00	
b. Perf. 12x11½	16.00	.75
c. Perf. 12	24.00	.75
Nos. 77-82 (6)	63.00	3.80

First British settlement in Australia, cent.
For overprints see Nos. O24-O29.

1888 Wmk. 56 Perf. 11x12

83 A25 1p violet	11.00	1.40
84 A26 2p blue	65.00	6.75

See #104B-106C, 113-115, 118, 125-127, 130.

Map of Australia — A31   Governors Capt. Arthur Phillip (above) and Lord Carrington — A32

1888-89 Wmk. 53 *Perf. 10*
85 A31 5sh violet ('89) 240.00 55.00
86 A32 20sh ultra 375.00 175.00

See #88, 120. For overprints see #O30-O31.

1890 Wmk. 57 *Perf. 10*
87 A31 5sh violet 200.00 17.50
a. Perf. 11 200.00 22.50
b. Perf. 10x11 225.00 17.50
c. Perf. 12 360.00 25.00

Perf. 11x12
Wmk. 58
88 A32 20sh ultra 225.00 75.00
a. Perf. 11 250.00 57.50
b. Perf. 10 250.00 77.50
c. Perf. 12 350.00 135.00

For overprints see Nos. O32-O33.

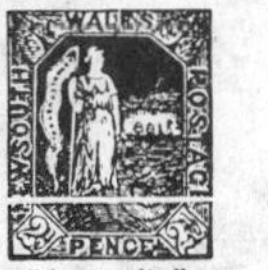
"Australia"
A33

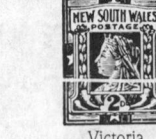

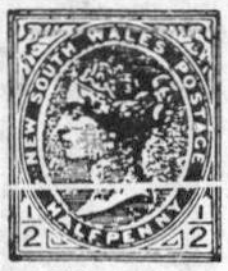
Victoria
A37

1890, Dec. 22 Wmk. 55 *Perf. 11x12*
89 A33 2½p ultra 2.00 .38
a. Perf. 12 11.50 .38
b. Perf. 12x11½ 67.50 *50.00*

For overprint see No. O35.

Type of 1856
1891 Engr. Wmk. 52 *Perf. 10*
90 A15 3p green 10.00 15.00
a. Double impression

Type of 1867
1893 Typo. *Perf. 11*
91 A20 10p lilac 15.00 6.00
a. Perf. 10 16.00 7.50
b. Perf. 11x10 or 10x11 24.00 12.00
c. Perf. 12x11 175.00 24.00

Types of 1862-84 Surcharged in Black:
SEVEN-PENCE
Halfpenny
a
HALFPENNY
b

1891, Jan. 5 Wmk. 55 *Perf. 11x12*
92 A17(a) ½p on 1p gray 1.25 1.25
a. Imperf.
b. Surcharge omitted
c. Double surcharge
93 A21(b) 7½p on 6p brown 3.50 1.65
a. Perf. 10 3.50 1.25
b. Perf. 11 3.50 1.25
c. Perf. 12 4.25 1.75
d. Perf. 10x12 4.25 1.75
94 A23(b) 12½p on 1sh red 7.00 4.00
a. Perf. 12x11½ 4.75 4.00
b. Perf. 10 7.00 4.00
c. Perf. 11 4.75 4.00
d. Perf. 12 5.50 4.00
Nos. 92-94 (3) 11.75 6.90

For overprints see Nos. O34, O36-O37.

1892
95 A37 ½p slate 1.25 .15
a. Perf. 12x11½ 1.25 .15
b. Perf. 12 1.25 .15
c. Perf. 10 27.50 .90
d. Perf. 10x12 150.00 10.50
e. Perf. 11 165.00 9.00

See #102, 109, 121. For overprint see #O38.

Types of 1867-71
1897 *Perf. 11x12*
96 A22 9p on 10p red brn (Bk) 8.00 3.25
a. 9p on 10p org brn (Bk) 8.00 3.25
b. Surcharge omitted 125.00
c. Double surcharge 125.00 100.00
d. Perf. 11 11.00 7.50
e. Perf. 12 9.00 7.50
97 A20 10p violet 12.00 5.50
a. Perf. 12x11½ 12.00 5.50
b. Perf. 11 13.00 6.00
c. Perf. 12 13.00 6.00

The surcharge on No. 96 measures 13½mm.
For overprints see Nos. O39-O40.

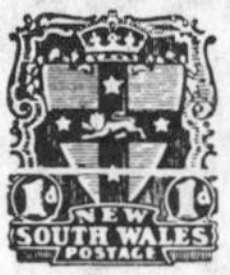
Seal
A38

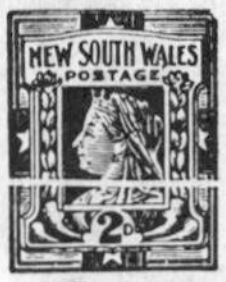
Victoria
A39

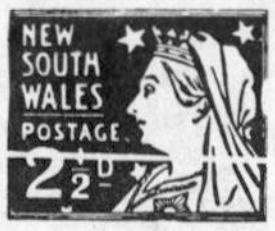
A40

ONE PENNY:
Die I - The first pearl in the crown at the left is merged into the arch, the shading under the fleur-de-lis is indistinct, and the "s" of "WALES" is open.
Die II - The first pearl is circular, the vertical shading under the fleur-de-lis is clear, and the "s" of "WALES" not so open.

2½ PENCE:
Die I - There are 12 radiating lines in the star on the Queen's breast.
Die II - There are 16 radiating lines in the star. The eye is nearly full of color.

1897 *Perf. 12*
98 A38 1p rose red (II) 2.50 .15
a. Die I, perf. 11x12 3.00 .15
b. Imperf., pair 75.00
c. Imperf. horiz., pair 600.00
d. Die I, perf. 12x11½ 4.50 .15
e. Die I, perf. 12 7.50 .60
f. Die II, perf. 12x11½ 2.00 .15
g. Die II, perf. 11x12 3.00 .15
99 A39 2p deep blue 2.25 .15
a. Perf. 11x12 2.75 .15
b. Perf. 12x11½ 2.75 .15
100 A40 2½p dp purple (II) 4.25 1.10
a. Die I, perf. 12x11 6.50 1.10
b. Die I, perf. 11 7.50 1.90
c. Die I, perf. 11½x12 10.50 1.10
d. Die II, perf. 11x12 4.25 1.10
e. Die II, perf. 11½x12 8.00 1.10
Nos. 98-100 (3) 9.00 1.40

Sixtieth year of Queen Victoria's reign.
See Nos. 103-104, 110-112, 122-124.

Type of 1861
1897 Engr. Wmk. 53 *Perf. 11*
101 A16 5sh red violet 75.00 15.00
a. Horiz. pair, imperf. btwn. *3,000.*
b. Perf. 11x12 or 12x11 75.00 17.00
c. Perf. 12 90.00 15.00

Perf. 12x11½, 11½x12
1899, Oct. Typo. Wmk. 55
HALF PENNY:
Die I - Narrow "H" in "HALF."
102 A37 ½p blue green (I) 1.00 .15
a. Imperf., pair 60.00 45.00
103 A39 2p ultra 1.25 .15
a. Imperf., pair 55.00
104 A40 2½p dk blue (II) 2.50 .38
a. Imperf., pair 90.00
104B A27 4p org brown 9.00 .50
c. Imperf. pair 300.00
105 A28 6p emerald 37.50 3.25
a. Imperf., pair 235.00
106 A28 6p orange 11.00 .75
a. 6p yellow 14.00 .75
b. Imperf., pair 195.00
106C A29 8p magenta 9.00 2.00
Nos. 102-106C (7) 71.25 7.18

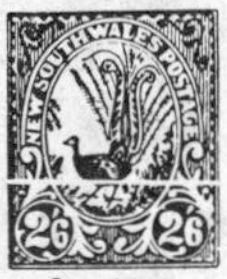
Lyrebird
A41

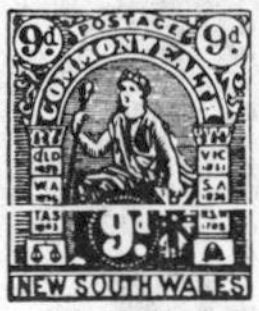
"Australia"
A42

1903 *Perf. 12x11½*
107 A41 2sh6p blue green 42.50 14.00

See Nos. 119, 131.

1903 Wmk. 70 *Perf. 12½*
108 A42 9p org brn & ultra 10.00 2.75
a. Perf. 11 750.00 425.00

See No. 128.

Type of 1885-86
1904 Wmk. 56 *Perf. 11*
Chalky Paper
"POSTAGE" in Blue
108B A24 10sh brt rose & violet 175.00 25.00
c. Perf. 12x11 140.00 25.00
d. Perf. 12 140.00 25.00

The watermark (NSW) of No. 108B is 20x7mm, with rounded angles in "N" and "W." On No. 75, the watermark is 21x7mm, with sharp angles in the "N" and "W."

HALF PENNY:
Die II - Wide "H" in "HALF."

Perf. 11, 11x12½, 12x11½ and Compound
1905-06 Wmk. 12
109 A37 ½p blue grn (II) 1.25 .40
a. ½p blue green (I) 2.75 .40
b. Booklet pane of 12
110 A38 1p car rose (II) 1.25 .15
a. Booklet pane of 6
b. Booklet pane of 12
111 A39 2p deep ultra 1.50 .15
112 A40 2½p dk blue (II) 2.50 .40
113 A27 4p org brown 8.25 .75
114 A28 6p orange 10.00 .75
a. 6p yellow 8.50 .75
b. Perf. 11 250.00
115 A29 8p magenta 11.00 1.50
117 A20 10p violet 12.50 2.25
118 A30 1sh vio brown 11.00 .75
119 A41 2sh6p blue green 27.50 12.00

Wmk. 199
120 A32 20sh ultra 200.00 75.00
Nos. 109-115,117-120 (11) 286.75 94.10

1906 Wmk. 13
121 A37 ½p green (I) 4.00 .50
122 A38 1p rose (II) 2.75 .32
123 A39 2p ultra 2.75 .32
124 A40 2½p blue (II) 70.00
125 A27 4p org brown 8.75 3.25
126 A28 6p orange 22.50 8.25
127 A29 8p red violet 27.50 9.25
128 A42 9p org brn & ultra, perf. 12x12½ 8.00 1.65
a. Perf. 11 65.00 55.00
129 A20 10p violet 52.50
130 A30 1sh vio brown 27.50 6.50
131 A41 2sh6p blue green 50.00 32.50
Nos. 121-131 (11) 276.25
Nos. 121-123,125-128,130-131 (9) 62.54

Portions of some of the sheets on which the above are printed show the watermark "COMMONWEALTH OF AUSTRALIA." Stamps may also be found from portions of the sheet without watermark.

SEMI-POSTAL STAMPS

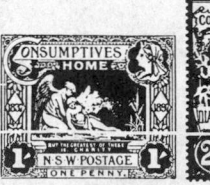

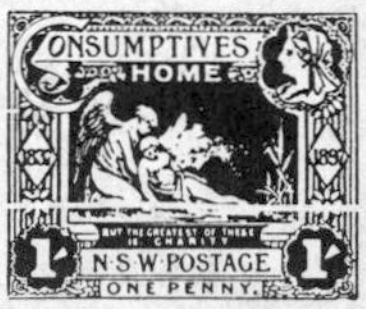
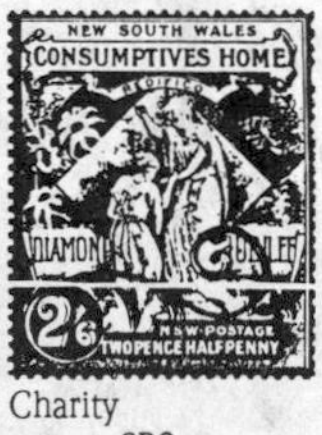
Allegory of Charity
SP1 SP2

1897, June Wmk. 55 *Perf. 11*
B1 SP1 1p (1sh) green & brown 35.00 25.00
B2 SP2 2½p (2sh6p) rose, bl & gold 225.00 250.00

Diamond Jubilee of Queen Victoria.
The difference between the postal and face values of these stamps was donated to a fund for a home for consumptives.

REGISTRATION STAMPS

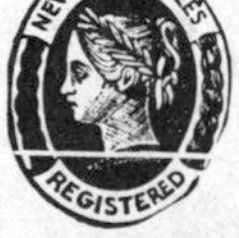
Queen Victoria — R1

1856, Jan. 1 Unwmk. Engr. *Imperf.*
F1 R1 (6p) orange & blue 600.00 75.00
F2 R1 (6p) red & blue 575.00 75.00
a. Frame printed on back *2,750.* *1,350.*

1860 *Perf. 12, 13*
F3 R1 (6p) orange & blue 280.00 30.00
F4 R1 (6p) red & blue 265.00 30.00

Nos. F1 to F4 exist also on paper with papermaker's watermark in sheet.

1863 Wmk. 49
F5 R1 (6p) red & blue 75.00 15.00

Fifty varieties.
Nos. F1-F2 were reprinted on thin white wove unwatermarked paper and on thick yellowish wove unwatermarked paper; the former are usually overprinted "SPECIMEN." No. F4 was reprinted on thin white wove unwatermarked paper; perf. 10 and overprinted "REPRINT" in black.

POSTAGE DUE STAMPS

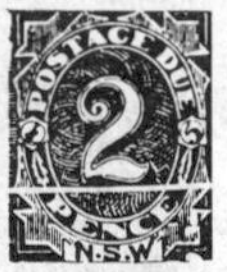
D1

Perf. 10, 11, 11½, 12 and Compound
1891-92 Typo. Wmk. 55
J1 D1 ½p green, perf 10 3.25 1.50
J2 D1 1p green 4.00 .75
a. Perf. 12 20.00 3.75
J3 D1 2p green 5.00 .75
a. Perf. 10x12 17.00 4.00
J4 D1 3p green 10.00 2.50
J5 D1 4p green 10.00 .75
J6 D1 6p green, perf 10 15.00 2.25
J7 D1 8p green, perf 10 70.00 10.00
J8 D1 5sh green, perf 10 150.00 25.00
a. Perf. 11 225.00 85.00
J9 D1 10sh green, perf 12x10 200.00 50.00
a. Perf. 10 365.00
J10 D1 20sh green, perf 12x10 300.00
a. Perf. 10 350.00 70.00
b. Perf. 12 350.00
Nos. J1-J10 (10) 767.25 93.50

Nos. J1-J5 exist on both ordinary and chalky paper.
Used values for Nos. J8-J10 are for c-t-o copies.

OFFICIAL STAMPS

Regular Issues Overprinted in Black or Red O S

Perf. 10, 11, 12, 13 and Compound
1879-80 Wmk. 54
O1 A17 1p red 9.25 1.50
a. Perf. 10 325.00 40.00
b. Perf. 10x13 22.50 4.00
O2 A18 2p blue *15.00* 2.50
a. Perf. 11x12 250.00
b. Perf. 10 250.00 40.00
O3 A15 3p green (R) 300.00
O4 A15 3p green 225.00 65.00
a. Watermarked "6" 500.00
b. Double overprint
O5 A19 4p red brown 225.00 11.50
a. Perf. 10x13 300.00 14.00
O6 A11 5p dark green 24.00 13.00
O7 A21 6p lilac 300.00 10.00
a. Perf. 10 65.00
b. Perf. 10x13
O8 A13 8p yellow (R) *1,000.* 200.00
O9 A13 8p yellow 22.50
a. Perf. 10 375.00 115.00
O10 A23 1sh black (R) 300.00 11.00
a. Perf. 10 16.00
b. Perf. 10x13 30.00

1880 Wmk. 53
O11 A16 5sh lilac, perf. 11 265.00 75.00
a. Double overprint
b. Perf. 10 375.00 150.00
c. Perf. 12x10 325.00 130.00
d. Perf. 13 465.00 82.50
e. Perf. 10x12

1881 Wmk. 55
O12 A17 1p red 6.00 .75
a. Perf. 10x13 225.00
O13 A18 2p blue 6.50 1.00
a. Perf. 10x13 360.00 100.00
O14 A15 3p green 6.00 1.65
a. Double overprint
b. Perf. 12 240.00 130.00
c. Perf. 11
O15 A19 4p red brown 11.00 2.25
a. Perf. 10x12 90.00
b. Perf. 12 360.00 225.00
O16 A11 5p dark green 12.00 5.00
a. Perf. 12 100.00
b. Perf. 10x12 400.00 130.00
O17 A21 6p lilac 22.50 4.00
a. Perf. 12 60.00
b. Perf. 11x12 72.50 16.00
O18 A13 8p yellow 27.50 9.50
a. Double overprint
b. Perf. 12 240.00 50.00
O19 A23 1sh black (R) 27.50 *3.25*
a. Double overprint
b. Perf. 10x13 70.00
c. Perf. 11
Nos. O12-O19 (8) 119.00 27.40

Beware of other red overprints on watermark 55 stamps.

1881 Wmk. 56
O20 A17 1p red 32.50 10.00

1887-90
O21 A24 10sh on #75 *350.00*
O22 A24 £1 on #75A *3,250.* *3,250.*

No. 75 Overprinted O S

1889

O23	A24	10sh rose & vio	1,950.	600.00
a.		Perf. 10	3,500.	2,250.

Overprinted **O S**

1888-89   **Wmk. 55**

O24	A25	1p violet	1.50	.15
a.		Overprinted "O" only		
O25	A26	2p blue	1.50	.15
O26	A27	4p red brown	6.00	1.50
O27	A28	6p carmine	8.00	2.00
O28	A29	8p red lilac	14.00	4.00
O29	A30	1sh vio brown	14.00	2.00
a.		Double overprint		
		Nos. O24-O29 (6)	45.00	9.80

Wmk. 53

O30	A31	5sh violet (R)	700.00	450.00
O31	A32	20sh ultra	1,250.	

1890   **Wmk. 57**

O32	A31	5sh violet	150.00	60.00
a.		Perf. 12	625.00	

Wmk. 58

O33	A32	20sh ultra	2,000.	

Centenary of the founding of the Colony (Nos. O24-O33).

1891   **Wmk. 55**

O34	A17(a)	½p on 1p gray & black	47.50	14.00
a.		Double overprint		
O35	A33	2½p ultra	7.00	3.25
O36	A21(b)	7½p on 6p brn & black	35.00	12.00
O37	A23(b)	12½p on 1sh red & black	60.00	32.50
		Nos. O34-O37 (4)	149.50	61.75

1892

O38	A37	½p gray	5.50	4.00

1894   **Wmk. 54**

O39	A22	9p on 10p red brn	300.00	350.00

Wmk. 52

O40	A20	10p lilac, perf. 10	225.00	200.00
a.		Perf. 11x10	350.00	325.00

The official stamps became obsolete on Dec. 31, 1894. In Aug., 1895, sets of 32 varieties of "O.S." stamps, together with some envelopes and postal cards, were placed on sale at the Sydney post office at £2 per set. These sets contained most of the varieties listed above and a few which are not known in the original issues. An obliteration consisting of the letters G.P.O. or N.S.W. in three concentric ovals was lightly applied to the center of each block of four stamps. It is understood that the earlier stamps and many of the overprints were reprinted to make up these sets.

NEW ZEALAND

'nū 'zē-lənd

LOCATION — Group of islands in the south Pacific Ocean, southeast of Australia
GOVT. — Self-governing dominion of the British Commonwealth
AREA — 107,241 sq. mi.
POP. — 3,230,000 (est. 1983)
CAPITAL — Wellington

12 Pence = 1 Shilling
20 Shillings = 1 Pound
100 Cents = 1 Dollar (1967)

Catalogue values for unused stamps in this country are for Never Hinged items, beginning with Scott 246 in the regular postage section, Scott AR99 in the postal-fiscal section, Scott B9 in the semi-postal section, Scott J21 in the postage due section, Scott O92 in the officials section, Scott OY29 in the Life Insurance Department section, and Scott L1 in Ross Dependency.

Watermarks

Wmk. 6- Large Star   Wmk. 59- N Z

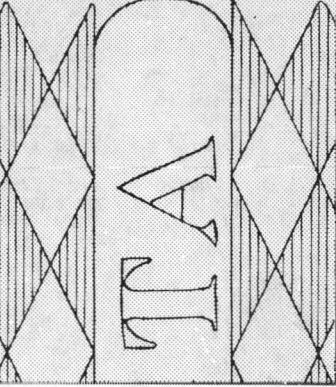

Wmk. 60- Lozenges

This watermark includes the vertical word "INVICTA" once in each quarter of the sheet.

Wmk. 61- N Z and Star Close Together   Wmk. 62- N Z and Star Wide Apart

On watermark 61 the margins of the sheets are watermarked "NEW ZEALAND POSTAGE" and parts of the double-lined letters of these words are frequently found on the stamps. It occasionally happens that a stamp shows no watermark whatever.

Wmk. 63- Double-lined N Z and Star   Wmk. 64- Large Star

Wmk. 253- Multiple N Z and Star

Values for unused stamps are for examples with original gum as defined in the catalogue introduction.

Very fine examples of the perforated issues between Nos. 7a-69, AR1-AR30, J1-J11, OY1-OY9 and P1-P4 will have perforations touching the framelines or design on one or more sides due to the narrow spacing of the stamps on the plates and imperfect perforating methods.

The rouletted and serrate rouletted stamps of the same period rarely have complete roulettes and are valued as sound and showing partial roulettes. Stamps with complete roulettes range from very scarce to very rare, are seldom traded, and command great premiums.

Victoria — A1

London Print
1855, July 18 Engr. Wmk. 6 *Imperf.*
White Paper

1	A1	1p dull carmine	27,500.	8,500.

Blued Paper

2	A1	2p deep blue	12,500.	500.
3	A1	1sh yellow green	22,500.	4,500.
a.		Half used as 6p on cover		18,000.

The blueing was caused by chemical action in the printing process. "White" paper varieties are believed to be those where the blueing has later disappeared.

Auckland Print

1855-58	**Blue Paper**	**Unwmk.**		
4	A1	1p orange red	5,500.	1,000.
5	A1	2p blue ('56)	2,000.	250.
6	A1	1sh green ('58)	20,000.	2,500.
a.		Half used as 6p on cover		12,500.

Nos. 4-6 may be found with parts of the papermaker's name in double-lined letters.

1857-61		**Unwmk.**		
Thin Hard or Thick Soft White Paper				
7	A1	1p orange ('58)	1,200.	350.
e.		Wmk. 6 ('57)		16,000.
8	A1	2p blue ('58)	650.	175.
9	A1	6p brown ('59)	900.	300.
e.		6p bister brown ('59)	1,800.	450.
f.		6p chestnut ('59)	2,250.	500.
10	A1	1sh blue green ('61)	6,000.	1,100.
e.		1sh emerald	6,000.	1,100.

No. 7e is identical to a shade of No. 11. The only currently known examples are a pair on a cover front. To qualify as No. 7e, a stamp must have a cancellation prior to 1862.

1859		***Pin Rouletted 9-10***	
7a	A1	1p dull orange	4,250.
8a	A1	2p blue	3,000.
9a	A1	6p brown	3,500.
10a	A1	1sh greenish blue	5,000.

1859		***Serrate Rouletted 16, 18***	
7b	A1	1p dull orange	3,500.
8b	A1	2p blue	2,500.
9b	A1	6p brown	2,500.
g.		6p chestnut	5,250.
10b	A1	1sh greenish blue	4,500.

Value for No. 10b is for a damaged stamp.

1859		***Rouletted 7***		
7c	A1	1p dull orange	5,000.	3,000.
f.		Pair, imperf between		
8c	A1	2p blue	6,500.	2,500.
9c	A1	6p brown	4,250.	2,500.
10c	A1	1sh greenish blue	7,500.	4,000.

1862		***Perf. 13***		
7d	A1	1p orange vermilion	—	—
8d	A1	2p blue	3,500.	2,000.
9d	A1	6p brown		6,000.

1862-63		**Wmk. 6**	***Imperf.***	
11	A1	1p orange ver	375.00	140.00
d.		1p carmine vermilion ('63)	375.00	140.00
e.		1p vermilion	375.00	140.00
12	A1	2p blue	250.00	62.50
d.		2p slate blue	1,250.	215.00
13	A1	3p brown lilac ('63)	375.00	85.00
14	A1	6p red brown ('63)	450.00	65.00
d.		6p black brown	700.00	85.00
e.		6p brown ('63)	700.00	90.00
15	A1	1sh yellow green	800.00	150.00
d.		1sh deep green	850.00	150.00

See No. 7e.

1862 *Pin Rouletted 9-10*

12a	A1	2p deep blue		
14a	A1	6p black brown		2,000.

1862 *Serrate Rouletted 16, 18*

11b	A1	1p orange vermilion		1,250.
12b	A1	2p blue		1,150.
13b	A1	3p lilac brown		1,600.
14b	A1	6p black brown		2,000.
15b	A1	1sh yellow green		2,500.

1862 *Rouletted 7*

11c	A1	1p vermilion	2,000.	500.
12c	A1	2p blue	1,400.	400.
13c	A1	3p brown lilac	1,600.	600.
14c	A1	6p red brown	1,600.	350.
15c	A1	1sh yellow green	2,500.	500.

The 1p, 2p, 6p and 1sh come in two or more shades.

1863 *Perf. 13*

16	A1	1p carmine ver	450.00	150.00
17	A1	2p blue	225.00	40.00
18	A1	3p brown lilac	500.00	140.00
19	A1	6p red brown	500.00	45.00
20	A1	1sh yellow green	600.00	150.00

The 1p, 2p, 6p and 1sh come in two or more shades.

1862 **Unwmk.** *Imperf.*

Pelure Paper

21	A1	1p vermilion	4,250.	1,100.
b.		Rouletted 7		2,750.
22	A1	2p pale dull ultra	2,500.	600.
c.		2p gray blue	2,500.	600.
23	A1	3p brown lilac	*25,000.*	
24	A1	6p black brown	1,000.	250.
b.		Rouletted 7	2,000.	350.
c.		Serrate perf. 15		3,250.
25	A1	1sh deep yel green	4,750.	700.
b.		1sh deep green	4,750.	400.
c.		Rouletted 7	4,250.	1,000.

No. 23 was never placed in use.

1863 *Perf. 13*

21a	A1	1p vermilion	7,500.	3,750.
22a	A1	2p gray blue	3,500.	400.
b.		2p pale dull ultramarine	3,500.	400.
24a	A1	6p black brown	3,000.	225.
25a	A1	1sh deep green	4,500.	1,000.

1863 **Unwmk.** *Imperf.*

Thick White Paper

26	A1	2p dull dark blue	2,000.	650.
a.		Perf. 13	1,400.	400.

Nos. 26 and 26a differ from 8 and 8d by a white patch of wear at right of head.

1864 **Wmk. 59** *Imperf.*

27	A1	1p carmine ver	750.	175.
28	A1	2p blue	700.	150.
29	A1	6p red brown	1,750.	425.
30	A1	1sh green	850.	200.

1864 *Rouletted 7*

27a	A1	1p carmine vermilion		3,000.
28a	A1	2p blue		800.
29a	A1	6p deep red brown		3,000.
30a	A1	1sh green		850.

1864 *Perf. 12½*

27B	A1	1p carmine ver		2,750.
28B	A1	2p blue	200.00	40.00
29B	A1	6p red brown	225.00	30.00
30B	A1	1sh dp yel green		2,000.

1864 *Perf. 13*

27C	A1	1p carmine ver	5,500.	3,500.
28C	A1	2p blue	575.	225.
30C	A1	1sh yellow green	1,400.	500.
d.		Horiz. pair, imperf. btwn.	8,000.	

1864-71 **Wmk. 6** *Perf. 12½*

31	A1	1p vermilion	65.00	20.00
a.		1p orange ('71)	125.00	40.00
32	A1	2p blue	85.00	15.00
a.		2p blue, worn plate	70.00	15.00
b.		Horiz. pair, imperf. btwn. (#32)		*1,500.*
c.		Perf. 10x12½		5,000.
d.		Imperf., pair (#32)	1,150.	1,150.
33	A1	3p lilac	55.00	22.50
a.		3p mauve	200.00	37.50
b.		Imperf., pair (#33)	1,500.	950.00
c.		As "a", imperf., pair	1,250.	1,000.
d.		3p brown lilac		
34	A1	4p deep rose ('65)	1,750.	250.00
35	A1	4p yellow ('65)	80.00	40.00
a.		4p orange yellow	*1,100.*	900.00
36	A1	6p red brown	75.00	15.00
a.		6p brown	90.00	15.00
b.		Horiz. pair, imperf. btwn.		
37	A1	1sh pale yel green	90.00	45.00
a.		1sh yellow green	90.00	45.00
b.		1sh green	400.00	125.00

The 1p, 2p and 6p come in two or more shades.

Imperforate examples of the 1p pale orange, worn plate; 2p dull blue and 6p dull chocolate brown are reprints. Value, each $100.

1871 **Wmk. 6** *Perf. 10*

38	A1	1p deep brown	375.00	60.00

1871 *Perf. 12½*

39	A1	1p brown	90.00	22.50
a.		Imperf.		1,000.
40	A1	2p orange	65.00	20.00
a.		2p vermilion	80.00	25.00
b.		Imperf., pair		1,250.
41	A1	6p blue	70.00	25.00
		Nos. 39-41 (3)	225.00	67.50

Shades exist.

1871 *Perf. 10x12½*

42	A1	1p brown	90.00	25.00
43	A1	2p orange	90.00	22.50
44	A1	6p blue	600.00	200.00
		Nos. 42-44 (3)	780.00	247.50

The 6p usually has only one side perf. 10, the 1p and 2p more rarely so.

Shades exist.

1872 **Wmk. 59** *Perf. 12½*

45	A1	1p brown		2,500.
46	A1	2p vermilion	300.00	90.00

1872 **Unwmk.** *Perf. 12½*

47	A1	1p brown	275.00	45.00
48	A1	2p vermilion	55.00	30.00
49	A1	4p yellow orange	125.00	*400.00*

The watermark "T.H. SAUNDERS" in double-line capitals falls on 16 of the 240 stamps in a sheet. The 1p and 2p are also known with script "WT & CO" watermark.

1872 **Wmk. 60**

50	A1	2p vermilion	*4,000.*	600.

A2 A3 A4

A5 A6 A7

Perf. 10x12½, 11½, 12, 12½

1874 **Typo.** **Wmk. 62**

51	A2	1p violet	50.00	2.00
a.		Bluish paper	75.00	25.00
b.		Imperf.	475.00	
52	A3	2p rose	40.00	1.25
a.		Bluish paper	250.00	50.00
53	A4	3p brown	70.00	35.00
a.		Bluish paper	200.00	60.00
54	A5	4p claret	200.00	55.00
a.		Bluish paper	400.00	105.00
55	A6	6p blue	140.00	9.00
a.		Bluish paper	275.00	75.00
56	A7	1sh green	400.00	22.50
a.		Bluish paper	800.00	150.00
		Nos. 51-56 (6)	900.00	124.75

1875 **Wmk. 6** *Perf. 12½*

57	A2	1p violet	625.00	175.00
58	A3	2p rose	325.00	45.00

A8

1878 **Wmk. 62** *Perf. 12x11½*

59	A8	2sh deep rose	300.00	350.00
60	A8	5sh gray	325.00	230.00

No. 60 has numeral "5" in each of the four spandrels.

A9 A10 A11

A12

A13

A14

A15

Perf. 10, 11, 11½, 12, 12½ and Compound

1882

61	A9	1p rose	6.75	3.50
a.		Vert. pair, imperf. horiz.	*475.00*	
b.		Perf. 12x11½	30.00	7.00
c.		Perf. 12½	200.00	110.00
62	A10	2p violet	8.75	3.00
a.		Vert. pair, imperf. btwn.	*450.00*	
b.		Perf. 12½	200.00	110.00
63	A11	3p orange	27.50	3.50
a.		3p yellow	27.50	3.50
64	A12	4p blue green	37.50	3.50
a.		Perf. 10x11	52.50	7.00
65	A13	6p brown	45.00	3.50
66	A14	8p blue	77.50	35.00
67	A15	1sh red brown	82.50	10.00
		Nos. 61-67 (7)	285.50	62.00

See #87. For overprints see #O1-O2, O5, O7-O8.

A15a A16 A17

1891-95

67A	A15a	½p black ('95)	3.00	.25
b.		Perf. 12x11½	14.00	14.00
68	A16	2½p ultramarine	45.00	9.00
a.		Perf. 12½	275.00	110.00
69	A17	5p olive gray	35.00	7.00
		Nos. 67A-69 (3)	83.00	16.25

In 1893 advertisements were printed on the backs of Nos. 61-67, 68-69.

See #86C. For overprints see #O3-O4, O9.

Mt. Cook — A18

Lake Taupo — A19

Pembroke Peak — A20

Mt. Earnslaw, Lake Wakatipu — A21

Mt. Earnslaw, Lake Wakatipu — A22

Huia, Sacred Birds — A23

White Terrace, Rotomahana A24

Otira Gorge and Mt. Ruapehu A25

Kiwi — A26

Maori Canoe — A27

Pink Terrace, Rotomahana — A28

Kea & Kaka (Hawk-billed Parrots) — A29

Milford Sound — A30

Mt. Cook — A31

Perf. 12 to 16

1898, Apr. 5 **Engr.** **Unwmk.**

70	A18	½p lilac gray	3.50	.40
a.		Horiz. or vert. pair, imperf. btwn.	650.00	600.00
71	A19	1p yel brn & bl	2.50	.25
a.		Horiz. pair, imperf. btwn.	550.00	550.00
72	A20	2p rose brown	21.00	.15
a.		Horiz. pair, imperf. vert.	550.00	550.00
73	A21	2½p bl *(Wakitipu)*	6.50	*15.00*
74	A22	2½p bl *(Wakatipu)*	13.00	2.50
a.		Vert. pair, imperf. horiz.		
75	A23	3p orange brn	20.00	7.00
76	A24	4p rose	11.00	10.00
77	A25	5p red brown	26.00	10.00
a.		5p violet brown	45.00	*100.00*
78	A26	6p green	45.00	20.00
79	A27	8p dull blue	35.00	20.00
80	A28	9p lilac	30.00	20.00
81	A29	1sh dull red	50.00	16.00
82	A30	2sh blue green	85.00	70.00
a.		Vert. pair, imperf. btwn.	1,000.	

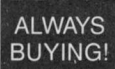

83	A31	5sh vermilion	200.00	180.00
		Revenue cancel		25.00
		Nos. 70-83 (14)	548.50	371.30

See Nos. 84, 88-89, 91-98, 99B, 102, 104, 106-107, 111-112, 114-121, 126-128. For overprint see No. O10.

The 5sh stamps are often found with revenue cancellations that are embossed or show a crown on the top of a circle. These are worth much less.

A32 A33 A34

1900 Wmk. 63 *Perf. 11*

Thick Soft Wove Paper

84	A18	½p green	5.00	.40
85	A32	1p carmine rose	6.00	.15
a.		1p lake	10.00	2.50
86	A33	2p red violet	6.50	.35
a.		Vert. pair, imperf. horiz.	550.00	550.00
b.		Horiz. pair, imperf. vert.		
		Nos. 84-86 (3)	17.50	.90

Nos. 84 and 86 are re-engravings of Nos. 70 and 72 and are slightly smaller.

See No. 110.

1899-1900 Wmk. 63

86C	A15a	½p black ('00)	8.00	5.00
87	A10	2p violet ('00)	17.00	3.50

Unwmk.

88	A22	2½p blue	12.50	2.00
a.		Vert. pair, imperf. horiz.	550.00	550.00
89	A23	3p org brown	22.50	2.00
a.		Horiz. pair, imperf. vert.	450.00	450.00
b.		Horiz. pair, imperf. btwn.	450.00	450.00
90	A34	4p yel brn & bl ('00)	8.00	2.50
a.		Imperf.		
b.		Double impression of center		
91	A25	5p red brown	17.00	4.00
a.		5p violet brown	16.00	1.75
92	A26	6p green	50.00	50.00
a.		Imperf.		
93	A26	6p rose ('00)	35.00	4.00
a.		6p carmine	25.00	4.00
b.		Double impression	475.00	475.00
c.		Imperf., pair	165.00	165.00
d.		Horiz. pair, imperf. vert.	300.00	300.00
94	A27	8p dark blue	17.50	11.00
95	A28	9p red lilac	25.00	11.00
96	A29	1sh red	45.00	8.00
97	A30	2sh blue green	75.00	30.00
98	A31	5sh vermilion	175.00	165.00
		Nos. 86C-98 (13)	507.50	298.00

See #113. For overprints see #O11-O15.

The 5sh stamps are often found with revenue cancellations that are embossed or show a crown on the top of a circle. These are worth much less.

"Commerce" — A35

1901, Jan. 1 Unwmk. *Perf. 12 to 16*

99	A35	1p carmine	8.00	3.00

Universal Penny Postage.

See Nos. 100, 103, 105, 108, 129. For overprint see No. O16. Compare design A35 with A42.

Boer War Contingent A36

Perf. 14, 11x14, 14x11

1901 Wmk. 63

Thick Soft Paper

99B	A18	½p green	10.00	3.00

Perf. 11, 14 and Compound

100	A35	1p carmine	6.50	.50
a.		Horiz. pair, imperf. vert.	300.00	300.00
101	A36	1½p brown org	8.00	4.50
a.		Vert. pair, imperf. horiz.	525.00	525.00
b.		Imperf., pair	650.00	650.00
		Nos. 99B-101 (3)	24.50	8.00

No. 101 was issued to honor the New Zealand forces in the South African War.

See No. 109.

Thin Hard Paper

102	A18	½p green	25.00	16.00
103	A35	1p carmine	19.00	6.25
a.		Horiz. pair, imperf. vert.	300.00	

1902 Unwmk.

104	A18	½p green	10.00	3.00
105	A35	1p carmine	15.00	2.00

1902 *Perf. 11*

Thin White Wove Paper

106	A26	6p rose red	32.50	4.00
a.		Watermarked letters	65.00	45.00

The sheets of No. 106 are watermarked with the words "LISBON SUPERFINE" in two lines, covering ten stamps.

Perf. 11, 14, 11x14, 14x13, 14x14½

1902-07 Wmk. 61

107	A18	½p green	3.00	.15
a.		Horiz. pair, imperf. vert.	250.00	250.00
108	A35	1p carmine	12.00	.25
a.		1p rose carmine	12.00	.25
b.		Imperf., pair	250.00	250.00
c.		Imperf. x serrate perf.	175.00	175.00
d.		Imperf. horiz. or vert. pair	250.00	250.00
f.		Booklet pane of 6	165.00	
109	A36	1½p brown org ('07)	13.00	*35.00*
110	A33	2p dull vio ('03)	5.50	.25
a.		Horiz. pair, imperf. vert.	315.00	315.00
b.		Vert. pair, imperf. horiz.	315.00	315.00
111	A22	2½p blue	8.50	1.65
112	A23	3p org brown	16.00	1.00
113	A34	4p yel brn & bl	7.00	1.25
a.		Horiz. pair, imperf. vert.	285.00	285.00
b.		Center inverted		
114	A25	5p red brown	16.00	4.00
a.		5p violet brown	15.00	3.50
115	A26	6p rose red	30.00	4.00
a.		6p rose	30.00	4.00
b.		6p pink	30.00	4.00
c.		6p brick red	30.00	4.00
d.		Horiz. pair, imperf. vert.	315.00	315.00
116	A27	8p deep blue	22.50	5.00
117	A28	9p red violet	22.50	5.00
118	A29	1sh orange red	12.00	1.75
a.		1sh scarlet	10.50	1.50
b.		1sh brown red	13.00	1.50
119	A30	2sh blue green	45.00	16.00
120	A31	5sh vermilion	175.00	150.00
		Nos. 107-120 (14)	388.00	225.30

Wmk. 61 is normally sideways on 3p, 5p, 6p, 8p and 1sh.

See No. 129. For overprints see Nos. O17-O22.

The 5sh stamps are often found with revenue cancellations that are embossed or show a crown on the top of a circle. These are worth much less.

In 1908 a quantity of the 1p carmine was overprinted "King Edward VII Land" and taken on a Shackleton expedition to the Antarctic. Because of the weather Shackleton landed at Victoria Land instead. The stamp was never sold to the public at face value. See No. 121a.

Similar conditions prevailed for the 1909-12 ½p green and 1p carmine overprinted "VICTORIA LAND." See Nos. 130d-131d.

1903 Unwmk. *Perf. 11*

Laid Paper

121	A30	2sh blue green	350.00	175.00

No. 108a Overprinted in Black:
"King Edward VII Land"
in Two Lines Reading Up

1908, Jan. 15 *Perf. 14*

121a	A35	1p rose carmine	350.00	40.00

See note after No. 120.

Christchurch Exhibition Issue

Arrival of the Maoris A37

Maori Art — A38

Landing of Capt. Cook — A39

Annexation of New Zealand A40

1906, Nov. Wmk. 61 Typo. *Perf. 14*

122	A37	½p emerald	10.00	*15.00*
123	A38	1p vermilion	10.00	10.00
a.		1p claret	*6,000.*	*10,000.*
124	A39	3p blue & brown	50.00	75.00
125	A40	6p gray grn & rose	125.00	125.00
		Nos. 122-125 (4)	195.00	225.00

Value for No. 123a is for a fine copy.

Designs of 1902-07 Issue, but smaller

Perf. 14, 14x13, 14x14½

1907-08 Engr.

126	A23	3p orange brown	*30.00*	5.50
127	A26	6p carmine rose	*32.50*	2.75
128	A29	1sh orange red	*110.00*	14.00
		Nos. 126-128 (3)	*172.50*	22.25

The small stamps are about 21mm high, those of 1898-1902 about 23mm.

Type of 1902 Redrawn

1908 Typo. *Perf. 14x14½*

129	A35	1p carmine	20.00	1.00

REDRAWN, 1p: The lines of shading in the globe are diagonal and the other lines of the design are generally thicker than on No. 108.

Edward VII A41

"Commerce" A42

1909-12 *Perf. 14x14½*

130	A41	½p yellow green	2.75	.15
a.		Booklet pane of 6	*225.00*	
b.		Booklet pane 5 + label	*650.00*	
c.		Imperf., pair	225.00	
131	A42	1p carmine	.50	.15
a.		Imperf., pair	250.00	250.00
b.		Booklet pane of 6	100.00	

Perf. 14x14½, 14x13½, 14

Engr.

Various Frames

132	A41	2p mauve	14.00	1.25
133	A41	3p orange brown	17.00	.35
134	A41	4p red orange	14.00	16.00
135	A41	4p yellow ('12)	12.50	3.50
136	A41	5p red brown	10.00	1.25
137	A41	6p carmine rose	17.00	.32
138	A41	8p deep blue	15.00	.40
139	A41	1sh vermilion	27.50	2.00
		Nos. 130-139 (10)	130.25	25.37

Nos. 133, 136-138 exist in vert. pairs with perf. 14x13½ on top and perf. 14x14½ on the bottom. These sell for a premium.

See #177. For overprint see Cook Islands #49.

Nos. 130-131 Overprinted in Black:
"VICTORIA LAND" in Two Lines

1911-13

130d	A41	½p yellow green	*500.00*	*500.00*
131d	A42	1p carmine	60.00	60.00

See note after No. 120.

Issue dates: 1p, Feb. 9; ½p, Jan. 10, 1913.

Stamps of 1909 Overprinted in Black:
"AUCKLAND EXHIBITION, 1913," in
Three Lines

1913

130e	A41	½p yellow green	26.00	*27.50*
131e	A42	1p carmine	16.00	*21.00*
133e	A41	3p orange brown	135.00	*160.00*
137e	A41	6p carmine rose	150.00	*210.00*
		Nos. 130e-137e (4)	327.00	*418.50*

This issue was valid only within New Zealand and to Australia from Dec. 1, 1913, to Feb. 28, 1914. The Auckland Stamp Collectors Club inspired this issue.

King George V — A43

1915 Typo. *Perf. 14x15*

144	A43	½p yellow green	.85	.15
b.		Booklet pane of 6	*140.00*	

See Nos. 163-164, 176, 178. For overprints see No. MR1, Cook Islands No. 40.

A44

A45

Perf. 14x14½, 14x13½

1915-22 Engr.

145	A44	1½p gray	1.25	.65
146	A45	2p purple	9.00	13.00
147	A45	2p org yel ('16)	7.50	6.50
148	A44	2½p dull blue	4.25	1.90
149	A45	3p violet brown	5.50	.25
150	A45	4p orange yellow	6.50	*15.00*
151	A45	4p purple ('16)	7.50	.15
a.		Imperf., pair	*1,500.*	
b.		Horiz. pair, imperf. vert.		
152	A44	4½p dark green	14.00	10.50
153	A45	5p light blue ('21)	7.00	.70
a.		Imperf., pair	150.00	
154	A45	6p carmine rose	5.50	.25
a.		Horiz. pair, imperf. vert.		
155	A44	7½p red brown	16.00	16.00
156	A45	8p blue ('21)	15.00	15.00
157	A45	8p red brown ('22)	21.00	2.00
158	A45	9p olive green	13.00	2.25
a.		Imperf., pair	*825.00*	
159	A45	1sh vermilion	15.00	1.25
a.		Imperf., pair	400.00	
		Nos. 145-159 (15)	148.00	85.40

Nos. 145-156, 158-159 exist in vert. pairs with perf 14x13½ on top and perf 14x14½ on the bottom. These sell for a premium. No. 157 only comes perf 14x13½.

For overprints see Cook Islands Nos. 53-60.

A46

A47

1916-19 Typo. *Perf. 14x15, 14*

160	A46	1½p gray black	10.00	.35
161	A47	1½p gray black	9.00	.15
162	A47	1½p brown orange ('18)	3.25	.15
163	A43	2p yellow	2.00	.15
164	A43	3p chocolate ('19)	6.00	.80
		Nos. 160-164 (5)	30.25	1.60

The engr. stamps have a background of geometric lathe-work; the typo. stamps have a background of crossed dotted lines.

Type A43 has three diamonds at each side of the crown, type A46 has two, and type A47 has one.

In 1916 the 1½, 2, 3 and 6p of the 1915 16 issue and the 8p of the 1909 issue were printed on paper intended for the long rectangular stamps of the 1902-07 issue. In this paper the watermarks are set wide apart, so that the smaller stamps often show only a small part of the watermark or miss it altogether.

For overprints see Cook Islands #50-52.

Victory Issue

"Peace" and British Lion — A48

Peace and Lion — A49

Maori Chief — A50

British Lion A51

"Victory" A52

King George V, Lion and Maori Fern at Sides — A53

1920, Jan. 27 *Perf. 14*

165	A48	½p yellow green	1.25	1.00
166	A49	1p carmine	4.00	.25
167	A50	1½p brown orange	3.00	.20
168	A51	3p black brown	12.50	10.00
169	A52	6p purple	11.00	*12.50*
170	A53	1sh vermilion	22.50	*32.50*
		Nos. 165-170 (6)	54.25	*56.45*

No. 165 Surcharged in Red

2d. 2d.

TWOPENCE

1922, Mar.

174	A48	2p on ½p yellow green	2.00	.40

Map of New Zealand — A54

1923 Typo. *Perf. 14x15*

175	A54	1p carmine rose	1.25	.15

Restoration of Penny Postage. The paper varies from thin to thick.

Types of 1909-15

N Z and Star printed on back in blue

1925 Unwmk. *Perf. 14x14½*

176	A43	½p yellow green	1.65	1.00
177	A42	1p carmine	2.25	.90
178	A43	2p yellow	15.00	*25.00*
		Nos. 176-178 (3)	18.90	*26.90*

Exhibition Buildings A55

1925, Nov. 17 Wmk. 61

Surface Tinted Paper

179	A55	½p yel green, *grnsh*	2.50	*8.25*
180	A55	1p car rose, *pink*	2.50	*5.75*
181	A55	4p red violet, *lilac*	32.50	*52.50*
		Nos. 179-181 (3)	37.50	*66.50*

Dunedin Exhibition.

George V in Admiral's Uniform A56

In Field Marshal's Uniform A57

1926 *Perf. 14, 14½x14*

182	A56	2sh blue	37.50	14.00
a.		2sh dark blue	45.00	19.00
183	A56	3sh violet	90.00	70.00
a.		3sh deep violet	90.00	70.00

Perf. 14, 14x14½

184	A57	1p rose red	.60	.15
a.		Booklet pane of 6	75.00	
b.		Imperf., pair	75.00	
		Nos. 182-184 (3)	128.10	84.15

For overprints see Cook Islands Nos. 74-75.

Pied Fantail and Clematis — A58

Kiwi and Cabbage Palm — A59

Maori Woman Cooking in Boiling Spring — A60

Maori Council House (Whare) — A61

Mt. Cook and Mountain Lilies — A62

Maori Girl Wearing Tiki — A63

Mitre Peak — A64

Striped Marlin A65

Harvesting — A66

Tuatara Lizard — A67

Maori Panel from Door — A68

Tui or Parson Bird — A69

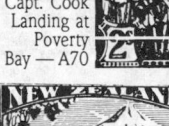

Capt. Cook Landing at Poverty Bay — A70

Mt. Egmont, North Island — A71

Perf. 14x14½, 14x13½, 13½x14, 13½

1935, May 1 Engr. Wmk. 61

185	A58	½p bright green	.40	.15
186	A59	1p copper red	.40	.15
186A	A59	1p copper red, re-engraved	13.00	3.75
b.		Booklet pane of 6 + ad labels	*80.00*	
187	A60	1½p red brown	1.25	1.90
188	A61	2p red orange	2.00	.15
189	A62	2½p dk gray & dk brown	4.00	1.90
190	A63	3p chocolate	4.50	.40
191	A64	4p black brn & blk	1.25	.65
192	A65	5p violet blue	7.00	2.25
193	A66	6p red	8.50	1.75
194	A67	8p dark brown	4.50	3.25

Litho.

Size: 18x21¼mm

195	A68	9p black & scarlet	10.00	3.50

Engr.

196	A69	1sh dk sl green	7.50	1.40
197	A70	2sh olive green	30.00	2.50
198	A71	3sh yel brn & brn black	18.00	9.50
		Nos. 185-198 (15)	112.30	33.20
		Set, never hinged	190.00	

On No. 186A, the horizontal lines in the sky are much darker.

The 2½p, 5p, 2sh and 3sh are perf. 13½ vertically; perf. 14 horizontally with alternate rows mixed perf. 14 and 13.

See Nos. 203-216, 244-245.

Silver Jubilee Issue

Queen Mary and King George V A72

1935, May 7 *Perf. 11x11½*

199	A72	½p blue green	.25	.15
200	A72	1p dark car rose	.20	.15
201	A72	6p vermilion	16.00	*25.00*
		Nos. 199-201 (3)	16.45	*25.30*
		Set, never hinged	25.00	

25th anniv. of the reign of King George V.

Types of 1935

Perf. 12½ to 15 and Compound

1936-41 Wmk. 253

203	A58	½p bright green	.25	.15
204	A59	1p copper red	.45	.15
205	A60	1½p red brown	1.90	1.65
206	A61	2p red orange	.15	.15
a.		Perf. 14	1.00	.35
b.		Perf. 14x15	1.25	.35
207	A62	2½p dk gray & dk brn	1.00	1.25
208	A63	3p chocolate	7.00	.60
209	A64	4p black brn & blk	1.25	.20
210	A65	5p violet blue	1.40	.60
211	A66	6p red	.45	.20
212	A67	8p dark brown	1.40	.15

Litho.

Size: 18x21½mm

213	A68	9p gray & scarlet	13.00	7.00
a.		9p black & scarlet	15.00	1.75

Engr.

214	A69	1sh dark slate grn	1.75	.25
215	A70	2sh olive green	7.75	.55
a.		Perf. 13½x14	27.50	.80
216	A71	3sh yel brn & blk brn	8.50	.70
a.		Perf. 12½ ('41)	9.00	2.25
		Nos. 203-216 (14)	46.25	13.60
		Set, never hinged	85.00	

Wool Industry A73

Butter Industry A74

Sheep Farming A75

Apple Industry A76

Shipping A77

1936, Oct. 1 Wmk. 61 *Perf. 11*

218	A73	½p deep green	.15	.15
219	A74	1p red	.15	.15
220	A75	2½p deep blue	1.65	2.75
221	A76	4p dark purple	1.25	1.90
222	A77	6p red brown	1.40	1.65
		Nos. 218-222 (5)	4.60	6.60
		Set, never hinged	5.00	

Congress of the Chambers of Commerce of the British Empire held in New Zealand.

Queen Elizabeth and King George VI A78

Perf. 13½x13

1937, May 13 Wmk. 253

223	A78	1p rose carmine	.15	.15
224	A78	2½p dark blue	.20	.50
225	A78	6p vermilion	.65	.75
		Nos. 223-225 (3)	1.00	1.40
		Set, never hinged	2.25	

Coronation of George VI and Elizabeth.

A79

A80

1938-44 Engr. *Perf. 13½*

226	A79	½p emerald	.45	.15
226B	A79	½p brown org ('41)	.15	.15
227	A79	1p rose red	.60	.15
227A	A79	1p lt blue grn ('41)	.15	.15
228	A80	1½p violet brown	7.75	1.65
228B	A80	1½p red ('44)	.15	.15
228C	A80	3p blue ('41)	.15	.15
		Nos. 226-228C (7)	9.40	2.55
		Set, never hinged	18.00	

See Nos. 258-264. For surcharges see Nos. 242-243, 279, 285.

Landing of the Maoris in 1350 — A81

Captain Cook, His Map of New Zealand, 1769, H.M.S. Endeavour A82

Victoria, Edward VII, George V, Edward VIII and George VI — A83

Abel Tasman, Ship, and Chart of West Coast of New Zealand A84

Treaty of Waitangi, 1840 — A85

Pioneer Settlers Landing on Petone Beach, 1840 — A86

The Progress of Transport A87

H.M.S. "Britomart" at Akaroa — A88

Route of Ship Carrying First Shipment of Frozen Mutton to England — A89

Maori Council A90

Gold Mining in 1861 and Modern Gold Dredge A91

Giant Kauri — A92

Perf. 13½x13, 13x13½, 14x13½

1940, Jan. 2   Engr.   Wmk. 253

229	A81	½p dk blue green	.15 .15
230	A82	1p scarlet & sepia	.20 .15
231	A83	1½p brt vio & ultra	.35 .15
232	A84	2p black brown & Prussian green	.25 .15
233	A85	2½p dk bl & myr grn	.35 .35
234	A86	3p dp plum & dk violet	1.90 .30
235	A87	4p dk red vio & vio brn	1.90 1.00
236	A88	5p brown & lt bl	2.25 1.75
237	A89	6p vio & brt grn	2.25 .65
238	A90	7p org red & black	2.00 4.00
239	A90	8p org red & black	3.25 1.65
240	A91	9p dp org & olive	5.50 2.50
241	A92	1sh dk sl grn & ol	5.75 4.50
		Nos. 229-241 (13)	26.10 17.30
		Set, never hinged	32.50

Centenary of British sovereignty established by the treaty of Waitangi.
For surcharge see No. 246.

Stamps of 1938 Surcharged with New Values in Black

1941   Wmk. 253   Perf. 13½

242	A79	1p on ½p emerald	.20 .15
243	A80	2p on 1½p violet brn	.15 .15
		Set value	.15
		Set, never hinged	.75

Type of 1935 Redrawn

**1941 Typo. Wmk. 61 Perf. 14x15
Size: 17¼x20¼mm**

244	A68	9p int black & scarlet	52.50 15.00

Wmk. 253

245	A68	9p int black & scarlet	4.00 3.50
		Set, never hinged	95.00

> Catalogue values for unused stamps in this section, from this point to the end of the section, are for Never Hinged items.

No 231 Surcharged in Black

✚ **TENPENCE** ✚

1944   Perf. 13½x13

246	A83	10p on 1½p brt vio & ultra	.45 .45

Peace Issue

Lake Matheson A93

Parliament House, Wellington — A94

St. Paul's Cathedral, London — A95

The Royal Family — A96

Badge of Royal New Zealand Air Force — A97

New Zealand Army Overseas Badge — A98

Badge of Royal Navy — A99

New Zealand Coat of Arms — A100

Knight, Window of Wellington Boys' College — A101

Natl. Memorial Campanile, Wellington — A103

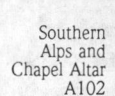

Southern Alps and Chapel Altar A102

Engr.; Photo. (1½p, 1sh)
Perf. 13x13½, 13½x13

1946, Apr. 1   Wmk. 253

247	A93	½p choc & dk bl grn	.15 .15
248	A94	1p emerald	.15 .15
249	A95	1½p scarlet	.15 .15
250	A96	2p rose violet	.15 .15
251	A97	3p dk grn & ultra	.15 .15
252	A98	4p brn org & ol grn	.18 .15
253	A99	5p ultra & blue grn	.15 .15
254	A100	6p org red & red brn	.20 .15
255	A101	8p brown lake & blk	.22 .18

256	A102	9p black & brt bl	.22 .26
257	A103	1sh gray black	.50 .26
		Set value	1.75 1.34

Return to peace at the close of WWII.

George VI Type of 1938 and

King George VI — A104

1947   Engr.   Perf. 13½

258	A80	2p orange	.15 .15
260	A80	4p rose lilac	.38 .30
261	A80	5p gray	.80 .15
262	A80	6p rose carmine	.45 .15
263	A80	8p deep violet	1.10 .15
264	A80	9p chocolate	1.50 .15

Perf. 14

265	A104	1sh dk car rose & chnt	1.40 .15
266	A104	1sh3p ultra & chnt	1.75 .15
267	A104	2sh dk grn & brn org	3.25 .25
268	A104	3sh gray blk & chnt	4.25 1.65
		Nos. 258-268 (10)	15.03 3.25

Nos. 265-267 have watermark either upright or sideways. On No. 268 watermark is always sideways.

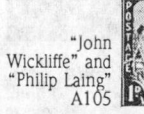

"John Wickliffe" and "Philip Laing" A105

Cromwell, Otago A106

First Church, Dunedin — A107

University of Otago A108

1948, Feb. 23   Perf. 13½

269	A105	1p green & blue	.15 .15
270	A106	2p brown & green	.15 .15
271	A107	3p violet	.15 .15
272	A108	6p lilac rose & gray blk	.15 .16
		Set value	.35 .40

Otago Province settlement, cent.

> A Royal Visit set of four was prepared but not issued. Copies of the 3p have appeared on the stamp market.

A109

Cathedral at Christchurch — A110

"They Passed this Way" — A111

Wmk. 253

**1950, July 28   Typo.   Perf. 14
Black Surcharge**

273	A109	1½p rose red	.15 .15
		See No. 367.	

1950, Nov. 20   Engr.   Perf. 13x13½

Designs: 3p, John Robert Godley. 6p, Canterbury University College. 1sh, View of Timaru.

274	A110	1p blue grn & blue	.15 .15
275	A111	2p car & red org	.15 .15
276	A110	3p indigo & blue	.15 .15
277	A111	6p brown & blue	.20 .20
278	A111	1sh claret & blue	.65 .65
		Set value	1.12 1.10

Centenary of the founding of Canterbury Provincial District.

No. 227A Surcharged in Black

1952, Dec.   Perf. 13½

279	A79	3p on 1p lt blue green	.15 .15

Coronation Issue

Buckingham Palace and Elizabeth II A112

Queen Elizabeth II — A113

Westminster Abbey — A114

Designs: 4p, Queen Elizabeth and state coach. 1sh6p, Crown and royal scepter.

Perf. 13x12½, 14x14½ (3p, 8p)
Engr., Photo. (3p, 8p)

1953, May 25

280	A112	2p ultramarine	.15 .15
281	A113	3p brown	.20 .15
282	A112	4p carmine	.60 .35
283	A114	8p slate black	.80 .70
284	A112	1sh6p vio blue & pur	1.50 1.50
		Nos. 280-284 (5)	3.25 2.85

No. 226B Surcharged in Black

1953, Sept.   Perf. 13½

285	A79	1p on ½p brown orange	.15 .15

Queen Elizabeth II — A115

Queen Elizabeth II and Duke of Edinburgh A116

Perf. 12½x13½, 13½x13

1953, Dec. 9   Engr.

286	A115	3p lilac	.15 .15
287	A116	4p deep blue	.20 .20
		Set value	.30 .24

Visit of Queen Elizabeth II and the Duke of Edinburgh.

A117

A118

A119

1953-57 *Perf. 13½*

288	A117	½p gray	.15	.15
289	A117	1p orange	.15	.15
290	A117	1½p rose brown	.20	.15
291	A117	2p blue green	.15	.15
292	A117	3p red	.15	.15
293	A117	4p blue	.20	.15
294	A117	6p rose violet	.45	.15
295	A117	8p rose car	.40	.15
296	A118	9p emerald & org brn	.50	.15
297	A118	1sh car & blk	1.25	.15
298	A118	1sh6p blue & blk	1.25	.15
298A	A118	1sh9p org & blk	3.75	.55
298B	A119	2sh6p redsh brn	30.00	4.75
299	A119	3sh blue green	10.50	.55
300	A119	5sh rose car	17.50	3.00
301	A119	10sh vio blue	30.00	22.50
		Nos. 288-301 (16)	96.60	33.00

The 1½p was issued in 1953; 1sh9p and 2sh6p in 1957; all others in 1954.

No. 298A exists on both ordinary and chalky paper.

Two dies of the 1sh differ in shading on the sleeve.

See #306-312. For surcharge see #320.

Maori Mailman
A120

Queen Elizabeth II
A121

Douglas DC-3
A122

Perf. 13½ (2p), 14 (3p), 13 (4p)

1955, July 18 **Wmk. 253**

302 A120	2p deep green & brown	.15	.15
303 A121	3p claret	.15	.15
304 A122	4p ultra & black	.45	.45
	Nos. 302-304 (3)	.75	
	Set value		.50

Cent. of New Zealand's 1st postage stamps.

Type of 1953-54 Redrawn

1955-59 **Wmk. 253** *Perf. 13½*

306 A117	1p orange ('56)	.15	.15
307 A117	1½p rose brown	.50	.15
308 A117	2p blue green ('56)	.20	.15
309 A117	3p vermilion ('56)	1.00	.15
310 A117	4p blue ('58)	3.50	.45
311 A117	6p violet	3.50	.45
312 A117	8p brown red ('59)	8.50	8.50
	Nos. 306-312 (7)	17.35	10.00

The numeral has been enlarged and the ornament in the lower right corner omitted.

Nos. 306, 308-310 exist on both ordinary and chalky paper.

For surcharges see Nos. 319, 354.

Whalers of Foveaux Strait
A123

"Agriculture" with Cow and Sheep
A124

Notornis (Takahe) — A125

1956, Jan. *Perf. 13x12½, 13 (8p)*

313 A123	2p deep green	.15	.15
314 A124	3p sepia	.15	.15
315 A125	8p car & blue vio	1.50	1.25
	Nos. 313-315 (3)	1.80	1.55

Southland centennial.

Lamb and Map of New Zealand — A126

Lamb, S. S. "Dunedin" and Refrigeration Ship — A127

Perf. 14x14½, 14½x14

1957, Feb. 15 **Photo.**

316 A126	4p bright blue	1.00	.70
317 A127	8p brick red	1.75	1.50

New Zealand Meat Export Trade, 75th anniv.

Sir Truby King — A128

Nelson Diocese Seal — A129a

Sir Charles Kingsford-Smith and "Southern Cross" — A129

1957, May 14 **Engr.** *Perf. 13*

318 A128	3p rose red	.20	.15

Plunket Society, 50th anniversary.

Nos. 307, 290 Surcharged **2d**

1958, Jan. 15 *Perf. 13½*

319 A117	2p on 1½p (#307)	.20	.15
a.	Small surcharge	.20	.15
320 A117	2p on 1½p (#290)	140.00	*200.00*

Surcharge measures 9½mm vert. on Nos. 319-320; 9mm on No. 319a. Diameter of dot 4½mm on Nos. 319-320; 3¾mm on No. 319a.

The small surcharge exists on No. 290.

Counterfeits exist.

Perf. 14x14½

1958, Aug. 27 **Engr.** **Wmk. 253**

321 A129	6p brt violet blue	.35	.35

1st air crossing of the Tasman Sea, 30th anniv. See Australia No. 310.

1958, Sept. 29 *Perf. 13*

322 A129a	3p carmine rose	.20	.15

Centenary of Nelson City.

Statue of "Pania," Napier — A130

Gannet Sanctuary, Cape Kidnappers A131

Design: 8p, Maori shearing sheep.

Perf. 13½x14½, 14½x14

1958, Nov. 3 **Photo.** **Wmk. 253**

323 A130	2p yellow green	.15	.15
324 A131	3p ultramarine	.15	.15
325 A130	8p red brown	2.25	1.50
	Nos. 323-325 (3)	2.55	1.80

Centenary of Hawkes Bay province.

Jamboree Kiwi Badge — A132

1959, Jan. 5 **Engr.** *Perf. 13*

326 A132	3p car rose & brown	.25	.15

Pan-Pacific Scout Jamboree, Auckland, Jan. 3-10.

"Endeavour" at Ship Cove A133

Designs: 3p, Shipping wool at Wairau bar, 1857. 8p, Salt Industry, Grassmere.

1959, Mar. 2 **Photo.** *Perf. 14½x14*

327 A133	2p green	.15	.15
328 A133	3p dark blue	.15	.15
329 A133	8p brown	2.50	2.50
	Nos. 327-329 (3)	2.80	2.80

Centenary of Marlborough Province.

The Explorer — A134

Westland Centennial: 3p, The Gold Digger. 8p, The Pioneer Woman.

1960, May 16 *Perf. 14x14½*

330 A134	2p green	.15	.15
331 A134	3p orange	.15	.15
332 A134	8p gray	2.25	1.75
	Nos. 330-332 (3)	2.55	2.05

Kaka Beak Flower — A135

Timber Industry — A136

Tiki — A137

Maori Rock Drawing — A138

Butter Making A139

Designs: ½p, Manuka flower. 1p, Karaka flower. 2½p, Titoki flower. 3p, Kowhai flower. 4p, Hibiscus. 5p, Mountain daisy. 6p, Clematis. 7p, Koromiko flower. 8p, Rata flower. 9p, Flag. 1sh3p, Rainbow trout. 1sh9p, Plane spraying farmland. 3sh, Ngauruhoe Volcano, Tongariro National Park. 5sh, Sutherland Falls. 10sh, Tasman Glacier, Mount Cook. £1, Pohutu Geyser.

Perf. 14½x14, 14x14½

1960-66 **Photo.** **Wmk. 253**

333	A135	½p dp car, grn & pale bl	.15	.15
b.		Green omitted	70.00	
c.		Pale blue omitted	55.00	
334	A135	1p brn, org & grn	.15	.15
b.		Orange omitted	150.00	
c.		Perf. 14½x13, wmkd. sideways	1.75	1.75
335	A135	2p grn, rose car, blk & yel	.15	.15
b.		Black omitted	200.00	
c.		Yellow omitted	225.00	
336	A135	2½p blk, grn, red & brn	.25	.15
a.		Brown omitted	50.00	
b.		Green & red omitted	160.00	
c.		Green omitted	75.00	
d.		Red omitted	90.00	
337	A135	3p Prus bl, yel, brn & grn	.15	.15
b.		Yellow omitted	45.00	
c.		Brown omitted	45.00	
d.		Green omitted	45.00	
e.		Perf. 14½x13, wmkd. sideways	2.00	2.00
338	A135	4p bl, grn, yel & lilac	.20	.15
a.		Yellow omitted	100.00	
b.		Lilac omitted	45.00	
339	A135	5p pur, blk, yel & grn	.25	.15
a.		Yellow omitted	125.00	
340	A135	6p dp grn, lt grn & lil	.25	.15
a.		Light green omitted	60.00	
b.		Lilac omitted	70.00	
340C	A135	7p pink, red, grn & yel	.40	.60
341	A135	8p gray, grn, pink & yel	.40	.15
342	A136	9p ultra & car	.60	.16
a.		Carmine omitted	150.00	
343	A136	1sh green & brn	.45	.15
344	A137	1sh3p bl, brn & carmine	.85	.15
a.		Carmine omitted	150.00	
345	A137	1sh6p org brn & olive grn	.95	.18
346	A136	1sh9p pale brown	5.75	.40
347	A138	2sh buff & blk	1.65	.16
348	A139	2sh6p red brn & yellow	3.25	.42
a.		Yellow omitted	275.00	
349	A139	3sh gray brown	28.00	1.40
350	A138	5sh dark green	7.50	.65
351	A139	10sh blue	6.50	3.50
352	A138	£1 magenta	14.00	9.25
		Nos. 333-352 (21)	71.85	18.37

Nos. 334c and 337e were issued in coils.

Only on chalky paper: 2½p, 5p, 7p. On ordinary and chalky paper: 1p, 3p, 4p, 6p, 1sh9p, 2sh, 3sh, 5sh, 10sh. Others on ordinary paper only.

Issued: 2p, 4p, 1sh, 1sh3p, 1sh6p, 1sh9p, 2sh, 2sh6p, 3sh, 5sh, 10sh, £1, 7/11/60; ½p, 1p, 3p, 6p, 8p, 9p, 9/1/60; 2½p, 11/1/61; 5p, 5/14/62; 7p, 3/16/66; #334c, 11/63; #337e, 10/3/63.

See Nos. 360-361, 382-404.

Adoration of the Shepherds, by Rembrandt
A140

Perf. 11½x12

1960, Nov. 1 **Wmk. 253**

353 A140	2p dp brown & red, *cream*	1.00	.15
a.	Red omitted	*450.00*	*250.00*

Christmas. See No. 355.

No. 309 Surcharged with New Value and Bars

Two types of surcharge:
Type I - "2½d" is 5½mm wide.
Type II - "2½d" is 5mm wide.

1961, Sept. 1 **Engr.** *Perf. 13½*

354 A117	2½p on 3p vermilion, I	.25	.15
a.	Type II	.25	.15

Type of 1960

Christmas: 2½p, Adoration of the Magi, by Dürer.

1961, Oct. 16   Photo.   Perf. 14½x14
Size: 30x34mm
355 A140 2½p multicolored   .90 .20

Morse Key and Port Hills, Lyttelton, 1862 A141

Design: 8p, Teleprinter and tape, 1962.

1962, June 1   Wmk. 253
356 A141 3p dk brown & green   .15 .15
   a. Green omitted
357 A141 8p dk red & gray   1.90 1.90
   a. Imperf., pair   900.00
   b. Gray omitted   300.00
Centenary of the New Zealand telegraph.

Madonna in Prayer by Sassoferrato — A142

1962, Oct. 15   Perf. 14½x14
358 A142 2½p multicolored   .60 .15
Christmas.

Holy Family by Titian — A143

1963, Oct. 14   Photo.   Perf. 12½
359 A143 2½p multicolored   .18 .15
   a. Imperf., pair   225.00
   b. Yellow omitted   400.00
Christmas.

Types of 1960-62

Designs: 1sh9p, Plane spraying farmland. 3sh, Ngauruhoe volcano, Tongariro National Park.

1963-64   Perf. 14½x14
360 A136 1sh9p brt blue, grn & yel   2.75 .55
361 A139 3sh blue, green & bister   5.00 1.10
Issued: 1sh9p, 11/4/63; 3sh, 4/1/64.

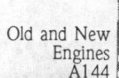 
Old and New Engines A144

Design: 1sh9p, Express train and Mt. Ruapehu.

1963, Nov. 25   Perf. 14
362 A144 3p multicolored   .15 .15
   a. Blue (sky) omitted   300.00
363 A144 1sh9p bl, blk, yel & carmine   3.50 3.50
   a. Carmine (value) omitted   750.00
Centenary of New Zealand Railways.

Cable Around World and Under Sea — A144a

1963, Dec. 3   Unwmk.   Perf. 13½
364 A144a 8p yel, car, blk & bl   1.90 1.90
Opening of the Commonwealth Pacific (telephone) cable service (COMPAC).
See Australia No. 381.

Map of New Zealand and Steering Wheel A145

Perf. 14½x14
1964, May 1   Wmk. 253
365 A145 3p multicolored   .18 .15
National Road Safety Campaign.

Rev. Samuel Marsden Conducting First Christian Service, Rangihoua Bay, Christmas 1814 A146

1964, Oct. 12   Perf. 14x13½
366 A146 2½p multicolored   .22 .15
Christmas.

Postal-Fiscal Type of 1950

1964, Dec. 14   Typo.   Perf. 14
Black Surcharge
367 A109 7p rose red   .38 .52

ANZAC Issue

Anzac Cove, Gallipoli A147

Design: 5p, Anzac Cove and poppy.

Perf. 12½
1965, Apr. 14   Unwmk.   Photo.
368 A147 4p light brown   .15 .15
369 A147 5p green & red   .35 .35
   Set value   .41
50th anniv. of the landing of the Australian and New Zealand Army Corps, ANZAC, at Gallipoli, Turkey, Apr. 25, 1915.

ITU Emblem, Old and New Communication Equipment — A148

Perf. 14½x14
1965, May 17   Photo.   Wmk. 253
370 A148 9p lt brown & dk blue   .60 .60
Centenary of the ITU.

Sir Winston Spencer Churchill (1874-1965) — A148a

1965, May 24   Unwmk.   Perf. 13½
371 A148a 7p lt blue, gray & blk   .48 .48
See Australia No. 389.

Provincial Council Building, Wellington A149

Perf. 14½x14
1965, July 26   Photo.   Wmk. 253
372 A149 4p multicolored   .25 .15
Centenary of the establishment of Wellington as seat of government. The design is from a water color by L. B. Temple, 1867.

ICY Emblem A150

1965, Sept. 28   Litho.   Perf. 14
373 A150 4p ol bister & dk red   .22 .15
International Cooperation Year.

"The Two Trinities" by Murillo — A151

1965, Oct. 11   Photo.   Perf. 13½x14
374 A151 3p multicolored   .22 .15
   a. Gold omitted   900.00
Christmas.

Parliament House, Wellington and Commonwealth Parliamentary Association Emblem — A152

Designs: 4p, Arms of New Zealand and Queen Elizabeth II. 2sh, Wellington from Mt. Victoria.

1965, Nov. 30   Unwmk.   Perf. 14
375 A152 4p multicolored   .28 .15
   a. Blue omitted   500.00
376 A152 9p multicolored   .95 1.00
377 A152 2sh multicolored   5.50 5.00
   Nos. 375-377 (3)   6.73 6.15
11th Commonwealth Parliamentary Assoc. Conf.

Scout Emblem, Maori Pattern — A153

Virgin with Child, by Carlo Maratta — A154

Perf. 14x14½
1966, Jan. 5   Photo.   Wmk. 253
378 A153 4p green & gold   .22 .15
   a. Gold omitted   500.00
4th National Scout Jamboree, Trentham.

1966, Oct. 3   Wmk. 253   Perf. 14
379 A154 3p multicolored   .25 .15
Christmas.

Queens Victoria and Elizabeth II — A155

New Zealand PO Savings Bank cent.: 9p, Reverse of half sovereign, 1867, and 1967 dollar.

Perf. 14x14½
1967, Feb. 3   Photo.   Wmk. 253
380 A155 4p plum, gold & black   .15 .15
381 A155 9p dk grn, bl, blk, sil & gold   .45 .45

Decimal Currency
Types of 1960-62

Designs: ½c, Manuka flower. 1c, Karaka flower. 2c, Kaka beak flower. 2½c, Kowhai flower. 3c, Hibiscus. 4c, Mountain daisy. 5c, Clematis. 6c, Koromiko flower. 7c, Rata flower. 7½c, Brown trout. 8c, Flag. 10c, Timber industry. 15c, Tiki. 20c, Maori rock drawing. 25c, Butter making. 28c, Fox Glacier, Westland National Park. 30c, Ngauruhoe Volcano, Tongarino National Park. 50c, Sutherland Falls. $1, Tasman Glacier, Mount Cook. $2, Pohutu Geyser.

Wmk. 253, Unwmkd. (#400)

1967-70   Photo.   Various Perfs.
382 A135 ½c multicolored   .24 .18
383 A135 1c multicolored   .15 .15
   a. Booklet pane of 5 + label   2.25
384 A135 2c multicolored   .24 .15
385 A135 2½c multicolored   .15 .16
386 A135 3c multicolored   .15 .15
387 A135 4c multicolored   .32 .25
388 A135 5c multicolored   .28 .15
389 A135 6c multicolored   .38 .15
390 A135 7c multicolored   .55 .42
391 A137 7½c multicolored   .70 .45
392 A136 8c ultra & car   .38 .18
393 A136 10c green & brown   .55 .30
394 A137 15c org brn & slate grn   .85 .38
395 A137 15c grn, sl grn & red ('68)   .85 .55
396 A138 20c buff & black   1.65 .22
397 A139 25c brown & yel   2.25 1.40
398 A138 28c multi ('68)   1.75 .42
399 A139 30c multicolored   3.75 .65
400 A139 30c multi ('70)   11.00 4.25
401 A138 50c dark green   3.50 .55
402 A139 $1 blue   21.00 4.25
403 A138 $2 magenta   18.00 20.00
404 A138 $2 multi ('68)   32.50 21.00
   Nos. 382-404 (23)   101.19 56.36

Perf. 13½x14: ½c to 3c, 5c, 7c. Perf. 14½x14: 4c, 6c, 8c, 10c, 25c, 30c, $1. Perf. 13½: 7½c. Perf. 14x14½: 15c, 20c, 28c, $2.
Issued: 7½c, 8/29/67; #395, 3/19/68; 28c, 7/30/68; #404, 12/10/68; #400, 1970; others, 7/10/67.
The 7½c was issued to commemorate the centenary of the brown trout's introduction to New Zealand, and retained as part of the regular series.
No. 395 has been redrawn. The "c" on No. 395 lacks serif; No. 394 has serif.

Adoration of the Shepherds, by Poussin — A156

Sir James Hector — A157

Perf. 13½x14
1967, Oct. 3   Photo.   Wmk. 253
405 A156 2½c multicolored   .18 .15
Christmas.

1967, Oct. 10   Litho.   Perf. 14
Design: 4c, Mt. Aspiring, aurora australis and Southern Cross.
406 A157 4c multicolored   .20 .15
407 A157 8c multicolored   .50 .48
Centenary of the Royal Society of New Zealand to Promote Science.

Maori Bible — A158

1968, Apr. 23   Litho.   Perf. 13½
408 A158 3c multicolored   .25 .18
   a. Gold omitted   100.00
Publication of the Bible in Maori, cent.

Soldiers of Two Eras and Tank — A159

Designs: 10c, Airmen of two eras, insigne and plane. 28c, Sailors of two eras, insigne and battleships.

1968, May 7 *Perf. 14x13½*

409 A159 4c multicolored .15 .15
410 A159 10c multicolored .40 .40
411 A159 28c multicolored 2.50 2.50
Nos. 409-411 (3) 3.05 3.05

Issued to honor the Armed Services.

"Universal Suffrage" — A160 Human Rights Flame — A161

Perf. 13½

1968, Sept. 19 Photo. Unwmk.

412 A160 3c ol grn, lt bl & grn .15 .15
413 A161 10c dp grn, yel & red .60 .60

75th anniv. of universal suffrage in New Zealand; Intl. Human Rights Year.

Adoration of the Holy Child, by Gerard van Honthorst A162

Perf. 14x14½

1968, Oct. 1 Wmk. 253

414 A162 2½c multicolored .25 .15

Christmas.

Romney Marsh Sheep and Woolmark on Carpet A163

Designs: 7c, Trawler and catch. 8c, Apples and orchard. 10c, Radiata pines and stacked lumber. 20c, Cargo hoist and grazing cattle. 25c, Dairy farm in Taranaki, Mt. Egmont and crated dairy products.

Wmk. 253 (10c, 18c, 25c); others Unwmkd.

Perf. 13½; 14½x14 (10c, 25c)

1968-69 Litho.; Photo. (10c, 25c)

415 A163 7c multi ('69) 1.00 .95
416 A163 8c multi ('69) 1.10 1.10
417 A163 10c multicolored 1.10 .28
418 A163 18c multi ('69) 2.50 .45
419 A163 20c multi ('69) 2.00 .30
420 A163 25c multicolored 4.50 1.00
Nos. 415-420 (6) 12.20 4.08

ILO Emblem A164

Perf. 14½x14

1969, Feb. 11 Photo. Wmk. 253

421 A164 7c scarlet & black .75 .75

50th anniv. of the ILO.

Law Society Coat of Arms A165 Otago University A166

Designs: 3c, Supreme Court Building, Auckland, horiz. 18c, "Justice" from memorial window of the University of Canterbury Hall, Christchurch.

1969, Apr. 8 Litho. *Perf. 13½*

422 A165 3c multicolored .15 .15
423 A165 10c multicolored .60 .55
424 A165 18c multicolored 1.25 2.00
Nos. 422-424 (3) 2.00 2.70

Centenary of New Zealand Law Society.

1969, June 3

Design: 10c, Conferring degree and arms of the University, horiz.

425 A166 3c multicolored .15 .15
426 A166 10c multicolored 1.00 .90

Centenary of the University of Otago.

Oldest House in New Zealand, Kerikeri A167

Design: 6c, Bay of Islands.

1969, Aug. 18 Litho. Wmk. 253

427 A167 4c multicolored .50 .50
428 A167 6c multicolored 1.10 1.10

Early European settlements in New Zealand on the 150th anniv. of the founding of Kerikeri, the oldest existing European settlement.

Nativity, by Federico Fiori — A168

Perf. 13½x14

1969, Oct. 1 Photo. Wmk. 253

429 A168 2½c multicolored .22 .15

Unwmk.

430 A168 2½c multicolored .22 .16

Christmas.

Capt. Cook, Transit of Venus and Octant A169

Designs: 6c, Joseph Banks and bark Endeavour. 18c, Dr. Daniel Solander and matata branch (rhabdothamnus solandri). 28c, Queen Elizabeth II and map showing Cook's chart of 1769.

1969, Oct. 9 *Perf. 14½x14*

431 A169 4c dk bl, blk & brt rose .30 .32
432 A169 6c sl grn & choc 1.25 1.40
433 A169 18c choc, sl grn & black 2.50 2.50
434 A169 28c dk ultra, blk & brt rose 5.00 7.00
a. Souvenir sheet of 4, #431-434 26.00 26.00
Nos. 431-434 (4) 9.05 11.22

Cook's landing in New Zealand, bicent.

Child Drinking Milk, and Cattle A170

Design: 7c, Wheat and child with empty bowl.

1969, Nov. 18 Photo. *Perf. 13*

435 A170 7c multicolored 1.50 1.40
436 A170 8c multicolored 1.50 1.40

25th anniv. of CORSO (Council of Organizations for Relief Services Overseas).

Cardigan Bay — A171

1970, Jan. 28 Unwmk. *Perf. 11½*

Granite Paper

437 A171 10c multicolored .65 .50

Return to New Zealand from the US of Cardigan Bay, 1st standard bred light-harness race horse to win a million dollars in stake money.

Glade Copper Butterfly — A172 Scarlet Parrotfish — A173

New Zealand Coat of Arms and Queen Elizabeth II — A174

Maori Fishhook A175

Egmont National Park — A176

Hauraki Gulf Maritime Park — A177

Designs: 1c, Red admiral butterfly. 2c, Tussock butterfly. 2½c, Magpie moth. 3c, Lichen moth. 4c, Puriri moth. 6c, Sea horses. 7c, Leatherjackets (fish). 7½c, Garfish. 8c, John dory (fish). 18c, Maori club. 20c, Maori tattoo pattern. 30c, Mt. Cook National Park (chamois). 50c, Abel Tasman National Park. $1, Geothermal power plant. $2, Helicopter over field, molecule (agricultural technology).

1970-71 Wmk. 253 *Perf. 13½x13*

438 A172 ½c ultra & multi .30 .16
439 A172 1c dp bis & multi .18 .15
a. Bklt. pane of 3 + 3 labels ('71) 1.75
440 A172 2c ol grn & multi .20 .15
441 A172 2½c yellow & multi .20 .15
442 A172 3c brown & multi .25 .15
443 A172 4c dk brown & multi .20 .15
444 A173 5c dk green & multi .38 .15
445 A173 6c dp car & multi .38 .15
446 A173 7c brn red & multi .42 .16
447 A173 7½c dk vio & multi .95 1.00
448 A173 8c blue grn & multi .55 .15

Perf. 14½x14

449 A174 10c dk bl, sil, red & ultra .42 .18

Perf. 14x13, 13x14

450 A175 15c brick red, sal & blk ('71) 1.65 .25
451 A177 18c yel grn, blk & red brn ('71) 2.00 .25
452 A175 20c yel brn & blk ('71) 3.00 .22

Perf. 13½x12½

Unwmk.

453 A176 23c bl, grn & blk ('71) .52 .52

Litho.

Perf. 13½

454 A177 25c gray & multi ('71) 2.25 .22
a. Perf. 14 ('76) .75 .25
455 A177 30c tan & multi ('71) .50 .50
a. Perf. 14 ('76) .90 .38

Photo.

Perf. 13½x12½

456 A176 50c sl grn & multi ('71) .65 .25

Perf. 11½

Granite Paper

457 A175 $1 light ultra & multi ('71) 1.40 .50
458 A175 $2 ol & multi ('71) 3.25 1.50
Nos. 438-458 (21) 19.65 6.91

The 10c for the visit of Queen Elizabeth II, Prince Philip and Princess Anne.

Issued: 10c, 3/12/70; ½c-4c, 9/2/70; 5c-8c, 11/4/70; 15c-20c, 1/20/71; 25c-50c, 9/1/71; $1-$2, 4/14/71; 23c, 12/1/71.

See #533-546. For surcharge see #480.

EXPO '70 Emblem, Geyser Restaurant A178

Designs: 8c, EXPO '70 emblem and New Zealand Pavilion. 18c, EXPO '70 emblem and bush walk (part of N.Z. exhibit).

Perf. 13x13½

1970, Apr. 8 Photo. Unwmk.

459 A178 7c multicolored 1.10 1.10
460 A178 8c multicolored 1.10 1.10
461 A178 18c multicolored 2.00 2.00
Nos. 459-461 (3) 4.20 4.20

EXPO '70 Intl. Expo., Osaka, Japan.

UN Headquarters, New York — A179

UN, 25th anniv.: 10c, Plowing toward the sun and "25" with laurel.

1970, June 24 Litho. *Perf. 13½*

462 A179 3c multicolored .15 .15
463 A179 10c yellow & red .75 .75

Adoration, by Correggio — A180

Tower, Catholic Church, Sockburn A181

Christmas: 3c, Holy Family, stained glass window, First Presbyterian Church, Invercargill.

1970, Oct. 1 Unwmk. *Perf. 12½*

464 A180 2½c multicolored .15 .15
465 A180 3c multicolored .15 .22
a. Green omitted 200.00
466 A181 10c silver, org & blk .95 .95
Nos. 464-466 (3) 1.25 1.32

Chatham
Islands
Mollymawk
A182

1970, Dec. 2   Photo.   Perf. 13x13½
467 A182 1c Chatham Islands lily   .15   .15
468 A182 2c shown   .28   .28

G Clef,
Emblem and
Spinning
Wheel
A183

Rotary
Emblem and
Map of New
Zealand
A184

1971, Feb. 10   Photo.   Perf. 13x13½
469 A183 4c multicolored   .22   .22
470 A184 10c lemon, dk blue & gold   .60   .60

50th anniv. of Country Women's Inst. (4c) and Rotary Intl. in New Zealand (10c).

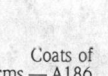

Ocean Racer
A185

Design: 8c, One Ton Cup and blueprint of racing yacht.

1971, Mar. 3   Litho.   Perf. 13½x13
471 A185 5c blue, blk & red   .35   .35
472 A185 8c ultra & black   .85 1.00

First challenge in New Zealand waters for the One Ton Cup ocean race.

Coats of
Arms — A186

1971, May 12   Photo.   Perf. 13x13½
473 A186 3c Palmerston North   .15   .15
474 A186 4c Auckland   .28   .28
475 A186 5c Invercargill   .48   .48
   Nos. 473-475 (3)   .91   .91

Centenary of New Zealand cities.

Map of
Antarctica
A187

1971, June 9   Photo.   Perf. 13x13½
476 A187 6c dk blue, pur & grn   2.00 2.00

10th anniv. of the Antarctic Treaty pledging peaceful uses of and scientific cooperation in Antarctica.

Child on Swing — A188

1971, June 9   Perf. 13½x13
477 188 7c yellow & multi   1.10 1.50

25th anniv. of UNICEF.

Opening of New Zealand's 1st Satellite
Earth Station near Warkworth — A189

1971, July 14   Perf. 11½
478 A189 8c Radar Station   .95 1.10
479 A189 10c Satellite   .95 1.50

4c

No. 441 Surcharged

=

1971   Wmk. 253   Perf. 13½x13
480 A172 4c on 2½c multi   .38   .15
   a.   Narrow bars   .25   .16

Surcharge typographed on No. 480, photogravure or typographed on No. 480a.

Holy
Night,
by Carlo
Maratta
A190

The Three
Kings
A191

World Rose
Convention
A192

Christmas: 4c, Annunciation, stained glass window, St. Luke's Anglican Church, Havelock North.

Perf. 13x13½
1971, Oct. 6   Photo.   Unwmk.
481 A190 3c orange & multi   .15   .15
482 A191 4c multicolored   .15   .15
483 A191 10c dk blue & multi   .95   .95
   Nos. 481-483 (3)   1.25 1.25

1971, Nov. 3   Perf. 11½
484 A192 2c Tiffany rose   .15   .15
485 A192 7c Peace rose   .38   .30
486 A192 8c Chrysler Imperial rose   .70   .70
   Nos. 484-486 (3)   1.23 1.15

Rutherford and
Alpha Particles
Passing Atomic
Nucleus
A193

Design: 7c, Lord Rutherford, by Sir Oswald Birley, and formula of disintegration of nitrogen atom.

1971, Dec. 1   Litho.   Perf. 13½x13
487 A193 1c gray & multi   .15   .15
488 A193 7c multicolored   .90   .90

Centenary of the birth of Ernest Lord Rutherford (1871-1937), physicist.

Benz,
1895 — A194

Vintage Cars: 4c, Oldsmobile, 1904. 5c, Model T Ford, 1914. 6c, Cadillac service car, 1915. 8c, Chrysler, 1924. 10c, Austin 7, 1923.

1972, Feb. 2   Perf. 14x14½
489 A194 3c brn, car & multi   .16   .16
490 A194 4c brt lilac & multi   .16   .16
491 A194 5c lilac rose & multi   .35   .50
492 A194 6c gray grn & multi   .65   .90
493 A194 8c vio blue & multi   1.00 1.00
494 A194 10c sepia & multi   1.65 1.65
   Nos. 489-494 (6)   3.97 4.37

13th International Vintage Car Rally, New Zealand, Feb. 1972.

Asian-Oceanic
Postal Union
A195

Designs: 3c, Wanganui City arms and Drurie Hill tower, vert. 5c, De Havilland DH89 and Boeing 737 planes, vert. 8c, French frigate and Maori palisade at Moturua, vert. 10c, Stone cairn at Kaeo (site of first Methodist mission).

1972, Apr. 5   Perf. 13x14, 14x13
495 A195 3c violet & multi   .15   .15
496 A195 4c brn org, blk & brn   .16   .16
497 A195 5c blue & multi   .25   .25
498 A195 8c green & multi   1.75 2.00
499 A195 10c olive, yel & blk   2.10 2.50
   Nos. 495-499 (5)   4.41 5.06

Cent. of Council government at Wanganui (3c); 10th anniv. of Asian-Oceanic Postal Union (4c); 25th anniv. of Nat. Airways Corp. (5c); bicent. of the landing by Marion du Fresne at the Bay of Islands (8c); 150th anniv. of the Methodist Church in New Zealand (10c).

Black Scree
Cotula — A196

Madonna and Child, by
Murillo — A197

Alpine Plants: 6c, North Is. edelweiss. 8c, Haast's buttercup. 10c, Brown mountain daisy.

1972, June 7   Litho.   Perf. 13x14
500 A196 4c orange & multi   .32   .22
501 A196 6c dp blue & multi   .90 1.00
502 A196 8c rose lilac & multi   1.10 1.50
503 A196 10c yel green & multi   3.25 3.25
   Nos. 500-503 (4)   5.57 5.97

1972, Oct. 4   Photo.   Perf. 11½

Christmas: 5c, Resurrection, stained-glass window, St. John's Methodist Church, Levin. 10c, Pohutukawa (New Zealand's Christmas flower).

504 A197 3c gray & multi   .15   .15
505 A197 5c gray & multi   .20   .20
506 A197 10c gray & multi   1.10 1.10
   Nos. 504-506 (3)   1.45 1.45

New Zealand
Lakes — A198

1972, Dec. 6   Photo.   Unwmk.
507 A198 6c Waikaremoana   1.10 1.10
508 A198 8c Hayes   1.50 2.00
509 A198 18c Wakatipu   3.75 3.75
510 A198 23c Rotomahana   4.00 5.00
   Nos. 507-510 (4)   10.35 11.85

Old Pollen
Street
A199

Coal Mining
and
Landscape
A200

Cloister,
University of
Canterbury
A201

Forest, Birds
and
Lake — A202

Rowing and
Olympic
Emblems
A203

Progress
Chart
A204

1973, Feb. 7   Litho.   Perf. 13½x13
511 A199 3c ocher & multi   .15   .15
512 A200 4c blue & multi   .20   .15
513 A201 5c multicolored   .32   .30
514 A202 6c blue & multi   1.00 1.10
515 A203 8c multicolored   1.25 1.25
516 A204 10c blue & multi   1.65 1.50
   Nos. 511-516 (6)   4.57 4.45

Centenaries of Thames and Westport Boroughs (3c, 4c); centenary of the Univ. of Canterbury, Christchurch (5c); 50th anniv. of Royal Forest and Bird Protection Soc. (6c); success of New Zealand rowing team at 20th Olympic Games (8c); 25th anniv. of the Economic Commission for Asia and the Far East (ECAFE, 10c).

Class W Locomotive, 1889 — A205

New Zealand Steam Locomotives: 4c, Class X, 1908. 5c, "Passchendale" Ab Class. 10c, Ja Class, last steam locomotive.

1973, Apr. 4   Litho.   Perf. 14½
517 A205 3c lt green & multi   .45   .15
518 A205 4c lil rose & multi   .60   .25
519 A205 5c lt blue & multi   .80   .60
520 A205 10c cream & multi   2.50 3.00
   Nos. 517-520 (4)   4.35 4.00

Maori Woman and
Child, by Hodgkins
A206

Christmas in
New Zealand
A207

Paintings by Frances Hodgkins: 8c, The Hill Top. 10c, Barn in Picardy. 18c, Self-portrait, Still Life.

1973, June 6   Photo.   Perf. 12x11½
521 A206 5c multicolored   .35   .35
522 A206 8c multicolored   1.25 1.25
523 A206 10c multicolored   1.40 1.40
524 A206 18c multicolored   2.00 2.00
   Nos. 521-524 (4)   5.00 5.00

1973, Oct. 3   Photo.   Perf. 12½x13½

Christmas: 3c, Tempi Madonna, by Raphael. 5c, Three Kings, stained-glass window, St. Theresa's R.C. Church, Auckland.

525 A207 3c gold & multi   .15   .15
526 A207 5c gold & multi   .25   .15
527 A207 10c gold & multi   .95   .95
   Nos. 525-527 (3)   1.35 1.25

Mitre Peak — A208

Hurdles and Games' Emblem — A209

Perf. 13x13½, 13½x13

1973, Dec. 5 **Photo.**

528	A208	6c shown	.65	.60
529	A208	8c Mt. Ngauruhoe	1.10	1.50
530	A208	18c Mt. Sefton, horiz.	1.75	2.00
531	A208	23c Burnett Range, horiz.	2.75	2.75
		Nos. 528-531 (4)	6.25	6.85

Types of 1970-71

Designs as before.

Perf. 13½x13

1973-76 **Photo.** **Unwmk.**

533	A172	1c multi ('74)	.40	.15
534	A172	2c multicolored	.35	.20
536	A172	3c multi ('75)	.45	.20
537	A172	4c multicolored	.35	.15
538	A173	5c multi ('75)	.70	.25
539	A173	6c multi ('74)	.70	.30
540	A173	7c multi ('75)	3.75	.95
542	A173	8c multi ('75)	4.50	.65
		Perf. 14x13½		
543	A174	10c multicolored	.60	.15
		Perf. 13x14, 14x13		
544	A175	15c multi ('76)	.70	.15
545	A177	18c multi ('75)	.70	.30
546	A175	20c yel brn & blk ('75)	.70	.25
		Nos. 533-546 (12)	13.90	3.70

Issued: 2c, 10c, 6/73; 1c, 4c, 6c, 9/7/73; 5c, 1973; 3c, 7c, 8c, 18c, 20c, 1974; 15c, 8/2/76.

For surcharges see Nos. 630-631.

1974, Jan. 9 **Litho.** ***Perf. 13x13½***

Designs: 5c, Paraplegic ballplayer. 10c, Bicycling. 18c, Rifle shooting. 23c, Lawn bowling. 4c, 10c, 18c and 23c stamps also show Commonwealth Games' emblem.

547	A209	4c yellow & multi	.15	.15
548	A209	5c violet & black	.18	.18
549	A209	10c brt red & multi	.40	.40
550	A209	18c brown & multi	.80	.80
551	A209	23c yel green & multi	1.10	1.10
		Nos. 547-551 (5)	2.63	2.63

10th British Commonwealth Games, Christchurch, Jan. 24-Feb. 2. No. 548 publicizes the 4th Paraplegic Games, Dunedin, Jan. 10-20.

Souvenir Sheet

New Zealand Day — A210

Illustration reduced.

1974, Feb. 6 **Litho.** ***Perf. 13***

552	A210	Sheet of 5	2.00	2.00
a.		4c Treaty House, Waitangi	.25	.25
b.		4c Parliament extension buildings	.25	.25
c.		4c Signing Treaty of Waitangi	.25	.25
d.		4c Queen Elizabeth II	.25	.25
e.		4c Integrated school	.25	.25

New Zealand Day (Waitangi Day). No. 552 has marginal inscription and imprint.

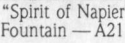

"Spirit of Napier" Fountain — A211

Clock Tower, Bern — A212

Design: 8c, UPU emblem.

1974, Apr. 3 **Photo.** ***Perf. 11½***

553	A211	4c blue green & multi	.15	.15
554	A212	5c brown & multi	.18	.18
555	A212	8c lemon & multi	1.10	1.10
		Nos. 553-555 (3)	1.43	1.43

Centenaries of Napier (4c); UPU (5c, 8c).

Boeing Seaplane, 1919 A213

Designs: 4c, Lockheed Electra, 1937. 5c, Bristol freighter, 1958. 23c, Empire S30 flying boat, 1940.

1974, June 5 **Litho.** ***Perf. 14x13***

556	A213	3c multicolored	.22	.15
557	A213	4c multicolored	.20	.15
558	A213	5c multicolored	.35	.40
559	A213	23c multicolored	2.50	2.50
		Nos. 556-559 (4)	3.27	3.20

Development of New Zealand's air transport.

Adoration of the Kings, by Conrad Witz — A214

Christmas: 5c, Angels, stained glass window, St. Paul's Church, Wellington. 10c, Christmas lily (lilium candidum).

1974, Oct. 2 **Photo.** ***Perf. 11½***

Granite Paper

560	A214	3c olive & multi	.15	.15
561	A214	5c lilac & multi	.22	.22
562	A214	10c orange & multi	1.00	.60
		Nos. 560-562 (3)	1.37	.97

Offshore Islands — A215

1974, Dec. 4 **Photo.** ***Perf. 13½x13***

563	A215	6c Great Barrier	.28	.28
564	A215	8c Stewart	.75	.75
565	A215	18c White	1.25	1.25
566	A215	23c The Brothers	1.90	1.90
		Nos. 563-566 (4)	4.18	4.18

Child Using Walker A216

Farm Woman and Children A217

IWY Symbol A218

Otago Medical School A219

1975, Feb. 5 **Litho.** ***Perf. 13½x13***

567	A216	3c orange & multi	.15	.15
568	A217	5c green & multi	.20	.16
569	A218	10c blue & multi	.60	.50
570	A219	18c multicolored	1.00	.80
		Nos. 567-570 (4)	1.95	1.61

New Zealand Crippled Children's Soc., 40th anniv. (3c); Women's Division Federated Farmers of N. Z., 50th anniv. (5c); IWY (10c); Otago Medical School cent. (18c).

Scow "Lake Erie," 1873 A220

Historic Sailing Ships: 5c, Schooner "Herald," 1826. 8c, Brigantine "New Zealander," 1828. 10c, Topsail schooner "Jessie Kelly," 1866. 18c, Barque "Tory," 1834. 23c, Clipper "Rangitiki," 1863.

1975, Apr. 2 **Litho.** ***Perf. 13½x13***

571	A220	4c vermilion & blk	.15	.15
572	A220	5c grnsh blue & blk	.20	.15
573	A220	8c yellow & black	.50	.50
574	A220	10c yellow grn & blk	.50	.60
575	A220	18c brown & black	1.25	.95
576	A220	23c dull lilac & blk	1.50	1.25
		Nos. 571-576 (6)	4.10	3.60

State Forest Parks — A221

1975, June 4 **Photo.** ***Perf. 13½x13***

577	A221	6c Lake Sumner	.40	.40
578	A221	8c North West Nelson	.75	1.00
579	A221	18c Kaweka	1.50	1.40
580	A221	23c Coromandel	2.00	1.75
		Nos. 577-580 (4)	4.65	4.55

Virgin and Child, by Zanobi Machiavelli (1418-1479) — A222

Stained Glass Window, Greendale Methodist/Presbyterian Church — A223

Christmas: 10c, Medieval ships and doves.

Perf. 13½x14, 14x13½

1975, Oct. 1 **Photo.**

581	A222	3c multicolored	.16	.15
582	A223	5c multicolored	.22	.16
583	A223	10c multicolored	.95	.65
		Nos. 581-583 (3)	1.33	.96

Sterling Silver — A224

Roses: 2c, Lilli Marlene. 3c, Queen Elizabeth. 4c, Super star. 5c, Diamond jubilee. 6c, Cresset. 7c, Michele Meilland. 8c, Josephine Bruce. 9c, Iceberg.

1975, Nov. 26 **Photo.** ***Perf. 14½x14***

584	A224	1c multicolored	.15	.15
585	A224	2c orange & multi	.15	.15
586	A224	3c ultra & multi	.15	.15
a.		Perf. 14½ ('79)	.15	.15
587	A224	4c purple & multi	.15	.15
588	A224	5c brown & multi	.15	.15
589	A224	6c multicolored ('76)	.15	.15
a.		Perf. 14½	.35	.22
590	A224	7c multicolored ('76)	.15	.15
a.		Perf. 14½	1.40	.90
591	A224	8c yellow & multi ('76)	.18	.15
a.		Perf. 14½	1.10	.22
592	A224	9c blue & multi	.15	.15
		Set value	.90	.80

For surcharges see Nos. 693, 695, 718.

Family and Mothers' League Emblem A225

Designs: 7c, "Weight, measure, temperature and capacity." 8c, 1st emigrant ship "William Bryan" and Mt. Egmont. 10c, Maori and Caucasian women and YWCA emblem. 25c, Telecommunications network on Goode's equal area projection.

1976, Feb. 4 **Litho.** ***Perf. 14***

593	A225	6c olive & multi	.18	.15
594	A225	7c lilac & multi	.20	.18
595	A225	8c red & multi	.25	.20
596	A225	10c yellow & multi	.32	.30
597	A225	25c tan & multi	.80	.80
		Nos. 593-597 (5)	1.75	1.63

League of Mothers of New Zealand, 50th anniv. (6c); Metric conversion, 1976 (7c); cent. of New Plymouth (8c); YWCA in New Zealand, 50th anniv. (10c); cent. of link into intl. telecommunications network (25c).

Gig — A226

Farm Vehicles: 7c, Thornycroft truck. 8c, Scandi wagon. 9c, Traction engine. 10c, Wool wagon. 25c, One-horse cart.

1976, Apr. 7 **Litho.** ***Perf. 14x13½***

598	A226	6c dk olive & multi	.16	.16
599	A226	7c gray & multi	.20	.15
600	A226	8c dk blue & multi	.50	.30
601	A226	9c maroon & multi	.40	.45
602	A226	10c brown & multi	.42	.50
603	A226	25c multicolored	1.40	1.25
		Nos. 598-603 (6)	3.08	2.81

Purakaunui Falls — A227

Nativity, Carved Ivory, Spain, 16th Century — A228

Waterfalls: 14c, Marakopa Falls. 15c, Bridal Veil Falls. 16c, Papakorito Falls.

1976, June 2 **Photo.** ***Perf. 11½***

604	A227	10c blue & multi	.35	.16
605	A227	14c lilac & multi	.75	.80
606	A227	15c ocher & multi	.75	.80
607	A227	16c multicolored	.95	.85
		Nos. 604-607 (4)	2.80	2.61

Perf. 14x14½, 14½x14

1976, Oct. 6 **Photo.**

Christmas: 11c, Risen Christ, St. Joseph's Church, Grey Lynn, Auckland, horiz. 18c, "Hark the Herald Angels Sing," horiz.

608	A228	7c ocher & multi	.15	.15
609	A228	11c ocher & multi	.40	.50
610	A228	18c ocher & multi	1.00	.80
		Nos. 608-610 (3)	1.55	1.45

Maripi (Carved Wooden Knife) — A229

Maori Artifacts: 12c, Putorino, carved flute. 13c, Wahaika, hardwood club. 14c, Kotiate, violin-shaped weapon.

1976, Nov. 24 **Photo.** ***Perf. 11½***

Granite Paper

611	A229	11c multicolored	.20	.15
612	A229	12c multicolored	.20	.15
613	A229	13c multicolored	.22	.15
614	A229	14c multicolored	.24	.15
		Nos. 611-614 (4)	.86	.60

Arms of Hamilton A230

Automobile Assoc. Emblem A231

Designs: No. 616, Arms of Gisborne. No. 617, Arms of Masterton. No. 619, Emblem of Royal Australasian College of Surgeons.

1977, Jan. 19 Litho. *Perf. 13x13½*

615 A230	8c multicolored	.32	.20
616 A230	8c multicolored	.32	.20
617 A230	8c multicolored	.32	.20
a.	Strip of 3, #615-617	1.00	1.00
618 A231	10c multicolored	.42	.32
619 A230	10c multicolored	.42	.32
a.	Pair, #618-619	.90	.75
	Nos. 615-619 (5)	1.80	1.24

Centenaries of Hamilton, Gisborne and Masterton (cities); 75th anniv. of the New Zealand Automobile Assoc. and 50th anniv. of the Royal Australasian College of Surgeons.

Souvenir Sheet

Queen Elizabeth II, 1976 — A232

Designs: Various portraits.

1977, Feb. Photo. *Perf. 14x14½*

620	Sheet of 5	1.40	1.40
a.-e.	A232 8c single stamp	.15	.15
f.	Sheet imperf.		

25th anniv. of the reign of Elizabeth II.

Physical Education, Maori Culture — A233

Education Dept., Geography, Science — A234

Designs: No. 623, Special school for the deaf; kindergarten. No. 624, Language class. No. 625, Home economics, correspondence school, teacher training.

1977, Apr. 6 Litho. *Perf. 13x13½*

621 A233	8c multicolored	.50	.50
622 A234	8c multicolored	.50	.50
623 A233	8c multicolored	.50	.50
624 A234	8c multicolored	.50	.50
625 A233	8c multicolored	.50	.50
a.	Strip of 5, #621-625	3.50	3.50
	Nos. 621-625 (5)	2.50	2.50

Cent. of Education Act, establishing Dept. of Education.

Karitane Beach — A235

Seascapes and beach scenes: 16c, Ocean Beach, Mount Maunganui. 18c, Piha Beach. 30c, Kaikoura Coast.

1977, June 1 Photo. *Perf. 14½*

626 A235	10c multicolored	.15	.22
627 A235	16c multicolored	.32	.32
628 A235	18c multicolored	.40	.60
629 A235	30c multicolored	.65	.35
	Nos. 626-629 (4)	1.52	1.49

Nos. 536-537 Surcharged with New Value and Heavy Bar

1977 Unwmk. *Perf. 13½x13*

630 A172	7c on 3c multicolored	.38	.38
631 A172	8c on 4c multicolored	.38	.38

Holy Family, by Correggio A236

Window, St. Michael's and All Angels Church — A237

Partridge in a Pear Tree — A238

1977, Oct. 5 Photo. *Perf. 11½*

632 A236	7c multicolored	.16	.16
633 A237	16c multicolored	.45	.35
634 A238	23c multicolored	.70	.52
	Nos. 632-634 (3)	1.31	1.03

Christmas.

Merryweather Manual Pump, 1860 — A239

Fire Fighting Equipment: 11c, 2-wheel hose reel and ladder, 1880. 12c, Shand Mason Steam Fire Engine, 1873. 23c, Chemical fire engine, 1888.

1977, Dec. 7 Litho. *Perf. 14x13½*

635 A239	10c multicolored	.16	.16
636 A239	11c multicolored	.28	.28
637 A239	12c multicolored	.35	.30
638 A239	23c multicolored	.55	.55
	Nos. 635-638 (4)	1.34	1.29

A240

A240a

Parliament Building, Wellington — A241

A242

1977-82 Photo. *Perf. 14½*

648 A240	10c ultra & multi	.15	.15
a.	Perf. 14½x14	.80	.32

Perf. 14½x14

649 A240a	24c blue & lt green	.30	.16
a.	Perf. 13x12½	.45	.16

Perf. 13

650 A241	$5 multicolored	5.00	5.00
	Nos. 648-650 (3)	5.45	5.31

Issued: #648, 2/79; #648b, 12/7/77; $5, 12/2/81; #649, 4/1/82; #649a, 12/13/82.

For surcharge see #694.

Coil Stamps

1978 Photo. *Perf. 13½x13*

651 A242	1c red lilac	.15	.15
652 A242	2c orange	.15	.15
653 A242	5c brown	.15	.15

Perf. 14½x14

654 A242	10c ultramarine	.20	.15
	Set value	.40	.35

Issue dates: 10c, May 3. Others, June 9.

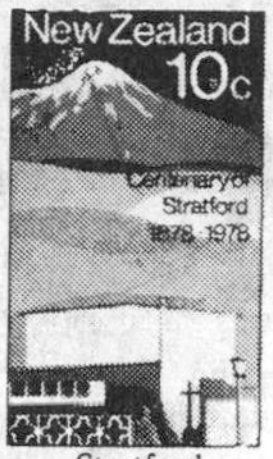

Ashburton A244

Stratford A245

Old Telephone — A246

Bay of Islands A247

1978, Feb. 1 Litho. *Perf. 14*

656 A244	10c multicolored	.20	.16
657 A245	10c multicolored	.20	.16
a.	Pair, #656-657	.45	.45
658 A246	12c multicolored	.28	.28
659 A247	20c multicolored	.45	.35
	Nos. 656-659 (4)	1.13	.95

Cent. of the cities of Ashburton, Stratford, the NZ Telephone Co. and Bay of Islands County.

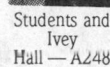

Students and Ivey Hall — A248

Maui Gas Drilling Platform — A249

Designs: 12c, Grazing sheep. 15c, Mechanical fertilization. 16c, Furrow, plow and tractor. 20c, Combine harvester. 30c, Grazing cattle.

1978, Apr. 26 *Perf. 14½*

660 A248	10c multicolored	.24	.24
661 A248	12c multicolored	.28	.28
662 A248	15c multicolored	.30	.30
663 A248	16c multicolored	.30	.30
664 A248	20c multicolored	.42	.42
665 A248	30c multicolored	.65	.65
	Nos. 660-665 (6)	2.19	2.19

Cent. of Lincoln Univ. College of Agriculture.

1978, June 7 Litho. *Perf. 13½x14*

The sea and its resources: 15c, Fishing boat. 20c, Map of New Zealand and 200-mile limit. 23c, Whale and bottle-nosed dolphins. 35c, Kingfish, snapper, grouper and squid.

666 A249	12c multicolored	.24	.18
667 A249	15c multicolored	.28	.24
668 A249	20c multicolored	.32	.28
669 A249	23c multicolored	.40	.32
670 A249	35c multicolored	.70	.50
	Nos. 666-670 (5)	1.94	1.52

All Saints Church, Howick A250

Christmas: 7c, Holy Family, by El Greco, vert. 23c, Beach scene.

1978, Oct. 4 Photo. *Perf. 11½*

671 A250	7c gold & multi	.18	.18
672 A250	16c gold & multi	.45	.45
673 A250	23c gold & multi	.60	.60
	Nos. 671-673 (3)	1.23	1.23

Paua (Haliotis Iris) — A251

Julius Vogel — A252

Sea Shells: 30c, Toheroa (paphies ventricosa). 40c, Coarse dosinia (dosinia anus). 50c, Spiny murex (poirieria zelandica).

1978, Nov. 29 Photo. *Perf. 13x12½*

674 A251	20c multicolored	.30	.20
675 A251	30c multicolored	.45	.30
676 A251	40c multicolored	.55	.45
677 A251	50c multicolored	.70	.55
	Nos. 674-677 (4)	2.00	1.50

See Nos. 696-697.

1979, Feb. 7 Litho. *Perf. 13x13½*

Portraits: No. 679, George Grey. No. 680, Richard John Seddon.

678 A252	10c light & dark brown	.38	.30
679 A252	10c light & dark brown	.38	.30
680 A252	10c light & dark brown	.38	.30
a.	Strip of 3, #678-680	1.25	1.25

19th cent. NZ statesmen.

Riverlands Cottage, Blenheim A253

Early NZ Architecture: 12c, Mission House, Waimate North, 1831-32. 15c, The Elms, Anglican Church Mission, Tauranga, 1847. 20c, Provincial Council Buildings, Christchurch, 1859.

1979, Apr. 4 *Perf. 13½x13*

681 A253	10c multicolored	.15	.15
682 A253	12c multicolored	.20	.30
683 A253	15c black & gray	.25	.35
684 A253	20c multicolored	.32	.40
	Nos. 681-684 (4)	.92	1.20

Whangaroa Harbor — A254

Small Harbors: 20c, Kawau Island. 23c, Akaroa Harbor, vert. 35c, Picton Harbor, vert.

Perf. 13x13½, 13½x13

1979, June 6 Photo.

685 A254	15c multicolored	.22	.22
686 A254	20c multicolored	.30	.30
687 A254	23c multicolored	.32	.32
688 A254	35c multicolored	.52	.30
	Nos. 685-688 (4)	1.36	1.14

IYC — A255

1979, June 6 Litho. *Perf. 14*

689 A255	10c Children playing	.25	.20

Virgin and Child, by Lorenzo Ghiberti — A256

Christmas: 25c, Christ Church, Russell, 1835. 35c, Pohutukawa ("Christmas") tree.

1979, Oct. 3 Photo. *Perf. 11½*

690 A256 10c multicolored	.15	.15
691 A256 25c multicolored	.35	.30
692 A256 35c multicolored	.45	.42
Nos. 690-692 (3)	.95	.87

Nos. 591a, 648 and 589a Surcharged

Perf. 14½, 14½x14 (14c)

1979, Sept.

693 A224 4c on 8c multi	.15	.15
694 A240 14c on 10c multi	.20	.15
695 A224 17c on 6c multi	.25	.15
Nos. 693-695 (3)	.60	
Set value		.32

Shell Type of 1978

Sea Shells: $1, Scallop (pecten novaezelandiae). $2, Circular saw (astraea heliotropium).

1979, Nov. 26 Photo. *Perf. 13x12½*

696 A251 $1 multicolored	1.50	.15
697 A251 $2 multicolored	3.00	1.00

Debating Chamber, House of Parliament — A257

1979, Nov. 26 Litho. *Perf. 14x13½*

698 A257 14c shown	.18	.18
699 A257 20c Mace, black rod	.45	.50
700 A257 30c Wall hanging	.75	.60
Nos. 698-700 (3)	1.38	1.28

25th Commonwealth Parliamentary Conference, Wellington, Nov. 26-Dec. 2.

NZ No. 1 A258

1980, Feb. 7 Litho. *Perf. 14x13½*

701 A258 14c shown	.35	.35
702 A258 14c No. 2	.35	.35
703 A258 14c No. 3	.35	.35
a. Souvenir sheet of 3, #701-703	2.75	2.75
b. Strip of 3, #701-703	1.10	1.10

NZ postage stamps, 125th anniv. No. 703a publicizes Zeapex '80 Intl. Stamp Exhib., Auckland, Aug. 23-31; it sold for 52c, of which 10c went to exhib. fund.

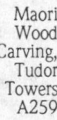

Maori Wood Carving, Tudor Towers A259

Earina Autumnalis and Thelymitra Venosa A260

Tractor Plowing, Golden Plow Trophy A261

1980, Feb. 7 *Perf. 14½*

704 A259 17c multicolored	.24	.24
705 A260 25c multicolored	.35	.35
706 A261 30c multicolored	.45	.45
Nos. 704-706 (3)	1.04	1.04

Rotorua cent.; Intl. Orchid Conf., Auckland, Oct.; World Plowing Championship, Christchurch, May.

Ewelme Cottage, Parnell, 1864 A262

Early NZ Architecture: 17c, Broadgreen, Nelson, 1855. 25c, Courthouse, Oamaru, 1822, 30c, Government Buildings, Wellington, 1877.

1980, Apr. 2 Litho. *Perf. 13½x13*

707 A262 14c multicolored	.18	.18
708 A262 17c multicolored	.22	.22
709 A262 25c green & black	.32	.32
710 A262 30c multicolored	.45	.50
Nos. 707-710 (4)	1.17	1.22

Harbors — A263

1980, June 4 Photo. *Perf. 13x13½*

711 A263 25c Auckland	.30	.40
712 A263 30c Wellington	.35	.35
713 A263 35c Lyttelton	.40	.40
714 A263 50c Port Chalmers	.60	.60
Nos. 711-714 (4)	1.65	1.75

Madonna and Child with Cherubim, by Andrea della Robbia — A264

1980, Oct. 1 Photo. *Perf. 12*

715 A264 10c shown	.15	.15
716 A264 25c St. Mary's Church, New Plymouth	.32	.32
717 A264 35c Picnic	.45	.45
Nos. 715-717 (3)	.92	.92

Christmas.

No. 590 Surcharged

1980, Sept. 29 Photo. *Perf. 14½x14*

718 A224 20c on 7c multicolored	.80	.16

Te Heu Heu Tukino IV, Ngati Tuwharetoa Tribal Chief — A265

Maori Leaders: 25c, Te Hau-Takiri Wharepapa. 35c, Princess Te Puea Herangi. 45, Apirana Ngata. 60c, Hakopa Te Ata-o-tu.

1980, Nov. 26 *Perf. 13*

719 A265 15c multicolored	.20	.20
720 A265 25c multicolored	.32	.32
721 A265 35c multicolored	.45	.45
722 A265 45c multicolored	.50	.50
723 A265 60c multicolored	.85	.85
Nos. 719-723 (5)	2.32	2.32

Henry A. Feilding, Borough Emblem A266

1981, Feb. 4 Litho. *Perf. 14½*

724 A266 20c multicolored	.28	.28

Borough of Feilding centenary.

IYD A267

1981, Feb. 4

725 A267 25c orange & black	.35	.35

Family and Dog — A268

1981, Apr. 1 Litho. *Perf. 13*

726 A268 20c shown	.25	.15
727 A268 25c Grandparents	.32	.32
728 A268 30c Parents reading to children	.40	.30
729 A268 35c Family outing	.45	.45
Nos. 726-729 (4)	1.42	1.22

Shotover River — A269

1981, June 3 Photo. *Perf. 13½*

730 A269 30c Kaiauai River, vert.	.40	.30
731 A269 35c Mangahao River, vert.	.45	.55
732 A269 40c shown	.52	.52
733 A269 60c Cleddau River	.85	.50
Nos. 730-733 (4)	2.22	1.87

Prince Charles and Lady Diana A270

1981, July 29 Litho. *Perf. 14½*

734 A270 20c shown	.40	.40
735 A270 20c St. Paul's Cathedral	.40	.40
a. Pair, #734-735	.80	.80

Royal Wedding.

Golden Tainui — A271

Christmas: 14c, Madonna and Child, by Marco d'Oggiono, 15th cent. 30c, St. John's Church, Wakefield.

1981, Oct. Photo. *Perf. 11½*

Granite Paper

736 A271 14c multicolored	.18	.18
737 A271 30c multicolored	.40	.40
738 A271 40c multicolored	.52	.52
Nos. 736-738 (3)	1.10	1.10

SPCA Centenary A272

Intl. Science Year A273

Centenaries: No. 739, Tauranga. No. 740, Hawera. 30c, Frozen meat exports.

1982, Feb. 3 Litho. *Perf. 14½*

739 A272 20c multicolored	.28	.16
740 A272 20c multicolored	.28	.16
a. Pair, #739-740	.60	.40
741 A272 25c multicolored	.35	.35
742 A272 30c multicolored	.45	.45
743 A273 35c multicolored	.50	.50
Nos. 739-743 (5)	1.86	1.62

Alberton Farmhouse, Auckland, 1867 A274

1982, Apr. 7 Litho.

744 A274 20c shown	.24	.24
745 A274 25c Caccia Birch, Palmerston North, 1893	.30	.30
746 A274 30c Dunedin Railway Station, 1904	.50	.50
747 A274 35c PO, Ophir, 1886	.80	.50
Nos. 744-747 (4)	1.84	1.54

Summer, Kaiteriteri A275

1982, June 2 Photo. *Perf. 13½*

748 A275 35c shown	.50	.50
749 A275 40c Autumn, Queenstown	.55	.55
750 A275 45c Winter, Mt. Ngauruhoe	.60	.60
751 A275 70c Spring, Wairarapa	1.00	1.00
Nos. 748-751 (4)	2.65	2.65

Madonna with Child and Two Angels, by Piero di Cosimo — A276

Christmas: 35c, Rangiatea Maori Church, Otaki. 45c, Surf life-saving patrol.

1982, Oct. 6 Photo. *Perf. 14*

752 A276 18c multicolored	.20	.20
753 A276 35c multicolored	.65	.42
754 A276 45c multicolored	.75	.70
Nos. 752-754 (3)	1.60	1.32

Nephrite A277

Fruit Export A278

Native Birds — A279

1982-83 Litho.

755 A277 1c shown	.15	.15
a. Perf 13x12½	.80	
756 A277 2c Agate	.15	.15
a. Perf 13x12½	1.50	
757 A277 3c Iron pyrites	.15	.15
758 A277 4c Amethyst	.15	.15
759 A277 5c Carnelian	.15	.15
760 A277 9c Native sulphur	.20	.20
761 A278 10c Grapes	.15	.15
762 A278 20c Citrus fruit	.25	.25
763 A278 30c Nectarines	.40	.30
764 A278 40c Apples	.50	.40
765 A278 50c Kiwifruit	.65	.15
Set value	2.40	1.60

Issue dates: A277, Dec. 1; A278, Dec. 7, 1983.

1985-89 — Perf. 14½

766	A279	30c Kakapo	.50	.15
767	A279	45c Falcon	.95	.50
768	A279	$1 Kokako	1.25	.15
769	A279	$2 Black Robin	2.75	1.10
a.		Souvenir sheet of one	4.50	4.50
770	A279	$3 Stitchbird	3.00	1.50
770A	A279	$4 Saddleback	4.00	2.00
		Nos. 766-770A (6)	12.45	5.40

No. 769a for PHILEXFRANCE '89 and has margin picturing progressive proofs of No. 769. No. 769a sold for $3.50.

Issued: $1, $2, Apr. 24; $3, $4, Apr. 23, 1986; 30c, 45c, May 1, 1986; No. 769a, July 7, 1989.
See Nos. 830-835, 918C-935C.

Salvation Army in NZ Cent. — A280

Univ. of Auckland Cent. — A281

NZ-Australia Closer Economic Relationship Agreement — A282

Introduction of Rainbow Trout Cent. — A283

WCY — A284

Perf. 14, 14x13½ (35c)
1983, Feb. 2 — Litho.

771	A280	24c multicolored	.30	.15
772	A281	30c multicolored	.35	.35
773	A282	35c multicolored	.42	.42
774	A283	40c multicolored	.48	.48
775	A284	45c multicolored	.55	.55
		Nos. 771-775 (5)	2.10	1.95

A285

Commonwealth Day 14 March 1983

1983, Mar. 14 — Litho. — Perf. 14

776	A285	24c Queen Elizabeth II	.30	.30
777	A285	35c Maori rock painting	.42	.42
778	A285	40c Wool industry logos	.48	.48
779	A285	45c Arms	.55	.55
		Nos. 776-779 (4)	1.75	1.75

Commonwealth Day.

Island Bay, by Rita Angus (1908-1970) — A286

Landscapes.

1983, Apr. 6 — Litho. — Perf. 14½

780	A286	24c shown	.32	.32
781	A286	30c Central Otago	.40	.40
782	A286	35c Wanaka	.45	.45
783	A286	45c Tree, Greymouth	.60	.60
		Nos. 780-783 (4)	1.77	1.77

Lake Matheson A287

Perf. 13½x13, 13x13½
1983, June 1 — Photo.

784	A287	35c Mt. Egmont, vert.	.45	.45
785	A287	40c Cooks Bay, vert.	.52	.52
786	A287	45c shown	.60	.60
787	A287	70c Lake Alexandrina	.90	.90
		Nos. 784-787 (4)	2.47	2.47

Christmas 1983 — A288

1983, Oct. 5 — Photo. — Perf. 12

788	A288	18c Holy Family of the Oak Tree, by Raphael	.22	.22
789	A288	35c St. Patrick's Church, Greymouth	.42	.42
790	A288	45c Star, poinsettias	.55	.55
		Nos. 788-790 (3)	1.19	1.19

Antarctic Research A289

1984, Feb. 1 — Litho. — Perf. 13½x13

791	A289	24c Geology	.32	.16
792	A289	40c Biology	.52	.52
793	A289	58c Glaciology	.75	.75
794	A289	70c Meteorology	.90	.90
a.		Souvenir sheet of 4, #791-794	3.00	
		Nos. 791-794 (4)	2.49	2.33

Ferry Mountaineer, Lake Wakatipu, 1879 — A290

1984, Apr. 4 — Litho. — Perf. 13½

795	A290	24c shown	.32	.16
796	A290	40c Waikana, Otago Harbor, 1909	.52	.52
797	A290	58c Britannia, Waitemata Harbor, 1885	.75	.75
798	A290	70c Wakatere, Firth of Thames, 1896	1.00	.90
		Nos. 795-798 (4)	2.59	2.33

Skier, Mount Hutt — A291

1984, June 6 — Litho. — Perf. 13½x13

799	A291	35c shown	.38	.16
800	A291	40c Coronet Peak	.42	.42
801	A291	45c Turoa	.50	.50
802	A291	70c Whakapapa	.75	.60
		Nos. 799-802 (4)	2.05	1.68

Hamilton's Frog A292

1984, July 11 — Perf. 13½

803	A292	24c shown	.28	.28
804	A292	24c Great barrier skink	.28	.28
a.		Pair, #803-804	.60	.60
805	A292	30c Harlequin gecko	.35	.35
806	A292	58c Otago skink	.60	.60
807	A292	70c Gold-striped gecko	.75	1.00
		Nos. 803-807 (5)	2.26	2.51

No. 804a has continuous design.

Christmas — A293

Designs: 18c, Adoration of the Shepherds, by Lorenzo Di Credi. 35c, Old St. Paul's Church, Wellington, vert. 45c, Bell, vert.

Perf. 13½x14, 14x13½
1984, Sept. 26 — Photo.

808	A293	18c multicolored	.24	.24
809	A293	35c multicolored	.46	.46
810	A293	45c multicolored	.60	.60
		Nos. 808-810 (3)	1.30	1.30

Military History A294

1984, Nov. 7 — Litho. — Perf. 15x14

811	A294	24c South Africa, 1901	.32	.32
812	A294	40c France, 1917	.52	.52
813	A294	58c North Africa, 1942	.78	.78
814	A294	70c Korea & Southeast Asia, 1950-72	.95	.95
a.		Souvenir sheet of 4, #811-814	2.75	2.75
		Nos. 811-814 (4)	2.57	2.57

St. John Ambulance Assoc. Cent. in NZ — A295

1985, Jan. 16 — Litho. — Perf. 14

815	A295	24c multicolored	.32	.16
816	A295	30c multicolored	.40	.40
817	A295	40c multicolored	.52	.52
		Nos. 815-817 (3)	1.24	1.08

Early Transportation — A296

1985, Mar. 6 — Litho. — Perf. 13½

818	A296	24c Nelson Horse Tram, 1862	.32	.32
819	A296	30c Graham's Town-Steam, 1871	.40	.40
820	A296	35c Dunedin Cable Car, 1881	.45	.45
821	A296	40c Auckland Electric, 1902	.52	.52
822	A296	45c Wellington Electric, 1904	.60	.60
823	A296	58c Christchurch Electric, 1905	.75	1.00
		Nos. 818-823 (6)	3.04	3.29

Bridges A297

1985, June 12 — Photo. — Perf. 11½

824	A297	35c Shotover	.32	.32
825	A297	40c Alexandra	.38	.38
826	A297	45c So. Rangitikei	.42	.42
827	A297	70c Twin Bridges	1.00	.65
		Nos. 824-827 (4)	2.12	1.77

Bird Type of 1985 and

Elizabeth II — A298

1985-89 — Litho. — Perf. 14½x14

828	A298	25c multicolored	.50	.15
829	A298	35c multicolored	.60	.45

Perf. 14½

830	A279	40c Blue duck	.60	.20
831	A279	60c Brown teal	.65	.65
832	A279	70c Paradise shelduck	.75	.95
a.		Souvenir sheet of 1	7.00	7.00
835	A279	$5 Takahe	6.00	3.75
		Nos. 828-835 (6)	9.10	6.15

Size of 70c, 22x27mm.
No. 832a for World Stamp Expo '89. Sold for $1.50.
Issued: 25c, 35c, 7/1/85; 40c, 60c, 2/2/87; 70c, 6/7/88; $5, 4/20/88; #832a, 11/17/89.

Christmas — A301

Carol "Silent Night, Holy Night," by Joseph Mohr (1792-1848), Austrian clergyman.

Perf. 13½x12½
1985, Sept. 18 — Litho.

836	A301	18c Stable	.18	.18
837	A301	40c Shepherds	.40	.40
838	A301	50c Angels	.50	.50
		Nos. 836-838 (3)	1.08	1.08

Navy Ships A302

1985, Nov. 6 — Litho. — Perf. 13½

839	A302	25c Philomel, 1914-1947	.35	.25
840	A302	45c Achilles, 1936-1946	.75	.65
841	A302	60c Rotoiti, 1949-1965	1.10	.95
842	A302	75c Canterbury, 1971-	1.25	1.10
a.		Souvenir sheet of 4, #839-842	4.50	4.50
		Nos. 839-842 (4)	3.45	2.95

Police Force Act, Cent. — A303

Designs: a, Radio operators, 1940-1985. b, Mounted policeman, 1890, forensic specialist in mobile lab, 1985. c, Police station, 1895, policewoman and badge, 1985. d, 1920 motorcycle, 1940s car, modern patrol cars and graphologist. e, Original Mt. Cook Training Center and modern Police College, Poriria.

1986, Jan. 15 — Perf. 14½x14

843		Strip of 5	1.40	1.40
a.-e.		A303 25c any single	.28	.28

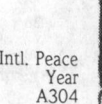

Intl. Peace
Year
A304

1986, Mar. 5   *Perf. 13¹/₂x13*
844 A304 25c Tree   .28   .28
845 A304 25c Dove   .28   .28
   a.   Pair, #844-845   .60   .60

Motorcycles
A305

1986, Mar. 5
846 A305 35c 1920 Indian Power
     Plus   .38   .38
847 A305 45c 1927 Norton CS1   .50   .50
848 A305 60c 1930 BSA Sloper   1.00   .80
849 A305 75c 1915 Triumph Model
     H   1.00   1.00
   Nos. 846-849 (4)   2.88   2.68

Knight's
Point — A306

1986, June 11   *Litho.*   *Perf. 14*
850 A306 55c shown   .65   .65
851 A306 60c Beck's Bay   .70   .70
852 A306 65c Doubtless Bay   .75   .75
853 A306 80c Wainui Bay   .90   .90
   a.   Miniature sheet of one   1.50   1.50
   Nos. 850-853 (4)   3.00   3.00

No. 853a sold for $1.20. Surtax benefited the "NZ 1990" executive committee.
No. 853a exists with Stockholmia '86 emblem.

The Twelve Days of
Christmas — A307

1986, Sept. 17   *Photo.*   *Perf. 14¹/₂*
854 A307 25c First day   .30   .16
855 A307 55c Second   .65   .65
856 A307 65c Third   .80   .80
   Nos. 854-856 (3)   1.75   1.61

Music — A308   Tourism — A309

1986, Nov. 5   *Litho.*   *Perf. 14¹/₂x14*
857 A308 30c Conductor   .28   .28
858 A308 60c Brass band   .55   .55
859 A308 80c Highland pipe band   .75   .75
860 A308 $1 Country music   .90   .90
   Nos. 857-860 (4)   2.48   2.48

1987, Jan. 14   *Perf. 14¹/₂x14*
861 A309 60c Boating   .55   .55
862 A309 70c Aviation   .65   .65
863 A309 80c Camping   .70   .70
864 A309 80c Windsurfing   .75   .75
865 A309 $1.05 Mountain climbing   1.10   1.10
866 A309 $1.30 White water rafting   1.25   1.25
   Nos. 861-866 (6)   5.00   5.00

Blue Water
Classics
A310

1987, Feb. 2   *Perf. 14x14¹/₂*
867 A310 40c Southern Cross Cup   .45   .45
868 A310 80c Admiral's Cup   .90   .90
869 A310 $1.05 Kenwood Cup   1.20   1.20
870 A310 $1.30 America's Cup   1.45   1.45
   Nos. 867-870 (4)   4.00   4.00

Vesting
Day
A311

Designs: a, Motor vehicles, plane. b, Train, bicycle.

1987, Apr. 1   *Litho.*   *Perf. 13¹/₂*
871   Pair   1.00   1.00
   a.-b.   A311 40c any single   .48   .48

Establishment of NZ Post Ltd., Apr. 1, replacing the NZ PO.

Royal NZ Air
Force, 50th
Anniv.
A312

Designs: 40c, Avro 626, Wigram Airfield, c. 1937. 70c, P-40 Kittyhawks. 80c, Sunderland seaplane. 85c, A4 Skyhawks.

1987, Apr. 15   *Perf. 14x14¹/₂*
872 A312 40c multicolored   .48   .48
873 A312 70c multicolored   .82   .82
874 A312 80c multicolored   .95   .95
875 A312 85c multicolored   1.00   1.00
   a.   Souvenir sheet of 4, #872-875   3.25   3.25
   Nos. 872-875 (4)   3.25   3.25

No. 875a with Capex '87 overprint in sheet margin was sold only at the New Zealand P. O. booth at the show.

Natl. Parks System,
Cent. — A313

1987, June 17   *Litho.*   *Perf. 14¹/₂*
876 A313 70c Urewera   .85   .45
877 A313 80c Mt. Cook   .95   .55
878 A313 85c Fiordland   1.00   .65
879 A313 $1.30 Tongariro   1.50   .70
   a.   Souvenir sheet of one   2.00   2.00
   Nos. 876-879 (4)   4.30   2.35

No. 879a sold for $1.70 to benefit the NZ 1990 World Phil. Exhib., Auckland.

Christmas   Maori Fiber
Carols — A314   Art — A315

1987, Sept. 16   *Litho.*   *Perf. 14x14¹/₂*
880 A314 35c Hark! The Herald An-
     gels Sing   .45   .45
881 A314 70c Away in a Manger   .85   .85
882 A314 85c We Three Kings of
     Orient Are   1.05   1.05
   Nos. 880-882 (3)   2.35   2.35

1987, Nov. 4   *Litho.*   *Perf. 12*
883 A315 40c Knot   .45   .45
884 A315 60c Binding   .65   .65
885 A315 80c Plait   .90   .90
886 A315 85c Flax fiber   .95   .95
   Nos. 883-886 (4)   2.95   2.95

Royal Phil.
Soc. of NZ,
Cent.
A316

Portrait of Queen
Victoria by
Chalon — A317

Queen Elizabeth II and: No. 887, No. 61 (blue background). No. 888, No. 62 (red background).

1988, Jan. 13   *Perf. 14x14¹/₂*
887 A316 40c multicolored   .45   .45
888 A316 40c multicolored   .45   .45
   a.   Pair, #887-888   .90   .90

Souvenir Sheet

889 A317 $1 multicolored   1.10   1.10

No. 889 exists overprinted in the margin with the SYDPEX 88 emblem.

NZ Electrification, Cent. — A318

1988, Jan. 13   *Perf. 14x14¹/₂*
890 A318 40c Geothermal   .48   .48
891 A318 60c Thermal   .55   .55
892 A318 70c Gas   .60   .60
893 A318 80c Hydroelectric   .95   .95
   Nos. 890-893 (4)   2.58   2.58

Maori Rafter
Paintings — A319

1988, Mar. 2   *Litho.*   *Perf. 14¹/₂*
894 A319 40c Mangopare   .48   .48
895 A319 40c Koru   .48   .48
896 A319 40c Raupunga   .48   .48
897 A319 60c Koiri   .70   .70
   Nos. 894-897 (4)   2.14   2.14

Greetings   Landscapes — A321
Messages — A320

1988, May 18   *Litho.*   *Perf. 13¹/₂x13*
Booklet Stamps
898 A320 40c Good luck   .55   .55
899 A320 40c Keeping in touch   .55   .55
900 A320 40c Happy birthday   .55   .55

     Size: 41x27mm

901 A320 40c Congratulations   .55   .55
902 A320 40c Get well soon   .55   .55
   a.   Bklt. pane of 5, #898-902   2.75

1988, June 8   *Perf. 14¹/₂*
903 A321 70c Milford Track   .60   .60
904 A321 80c Heaphy Track   .75   .75
905 A321 85c Copland Track   .85   .85
906 A321 $1.30 Routeburn Track   1.40   .90
   a.   Miniature sheet of one   2.00   2.00
   Nos. 903-906 (4)   3.60   3.10

No. 906a sold for $1.70 to benefit the exhibition.

NEW ZEALAND 1990
Souvenir Sheets
Four souvenir sheets were sold by the New Zealand post to benefit NEW ZEALAND 1990 World Stamp Exhibition. They each contain three $1 and one $2 "stamps" picturing antarctic scenes. They are not valid for postage.

Australia
Bicentennial
A322

Caricature: Kiwi and koala around campfire.

1988, June 21
907 A322 40c multicolored   .55   .52

See Australia No. 1086.

Christmas
Carols — A323

Illuminated manuscripts: 35c, O, Come All Ye Faithful, by John Francis Wade, 1742. 70c, Hark! the Herald Angels Sing. 80c, Ding Dong! Merrily on High. 85c, The First Noel, first published in Davies & Gilbert's Some Ancient Christmas Carols, 1832.

1988, Sept. 14   *Litho.*   *Perf. 14¹/₂*
908 A323 35c multicolored   .42   .42
909 A323 70c multicolored   .85   .85
910 A323 80c multicolored   .95   .95
911 A323 85c multicolored   1.00   .70
   Nos. 908-911 (4)   3.22   2.92

New
Zealand
Heritage
A324

The Land. Paintings by 19th cent. artists: 40c, Lake Pukaki, 1862, by John Gully. 60c, On the Grass Plain Below Lake Arthur, 1846, by William Fox. 70c, View of Auckland, 1873, by John Hoyte. 80c, Mt. Egmont from the Southward, 1840, by Charles Heaphy. $1.05, Anakiwa, Queen Charlotte Sound, 1871, by John Kinder. $1.30, White Terraces, Lake Rotomahana, 1880, by Charles Barraud.

1988, Oct. 5   *Litho.*   *Perf. 14x14¹/₂*
912 A324 40c multicolored   .45   .45
913 A324 60c multicolored   .65   .65
914 A324 70c multicolored   .80   .80
915 A324 80c multicolored   .90   .90
916 A324 $1.05 multicolored   1.10   1.10
917 A324 $1.30 multicolored   1.40   1.40
   Nos. 912-917 (6)   5.30   5.30

Treaty of Waitangi, 150th anniv.

Kiwi — A325

1988, Oct. 19 Engr. *Perf. 14½*
918 A325 $1 green 3.00 2.50
a. Booklet pane of 6 14.00
b. Litho. 1.25 1.25

Value is for copy with surrounding selvage. No. 918 issued in booklets only.
No. 918b is from No. 1161a.
See Nos. 1027, 1161.

Bird Type of 1985

1988-95 Litho. *Perf. 14½x14*
Sizes: $10, 26x31½mm, Others, 22x27mm
918C A279 5c Spotless crake .15 .15
919 A279 10c Banded dotterel .15 .15
920 A279 20c Yellowhead .25 .20
921 A279 30c Silvereye .40 .25
922 A279 40c Brown kiwi .52 .30
922A A279 45c Rock wren .52 .25
b. Booklet pane of 10 5.20
923 A279 50c Kingfisher .65 .35
924 A279 60c Spotted shag .78 .78
a. Sheet of 8, #918C, 919-922, 922A, 923-924 3.00 3.00
925 A279 80c Fiordland crested penguin 1.05 1.05
925A A279 80c New Zealand falcon .85 .85
b. Booklet pane of 10 8.50
c. Perf. 12 on 3 sides 1.00 1.00
d. As "c," booklet pane of 10 10.00
Complete booklet, #925d 10.00
926 A279 90c South Is. robin 1.20 1.20
935 A279 $10 Little spotted kiwi 12.00 6.00
d. Souv. sheet of 1 12.50 12.50

Self-Adhesive

Die Cut Perf 11½
935A A279 40c like #922 .48 .48
935B A279 45c like #922A .52 .52

Die Cut Perf 10½x11
935C A279 45c like #922A .45 .45
Nos. 918C-935C (15) 19.97 12.98

No. 935C has a darker blue background than No. 935B and has perf "teeth" at the corners while No. 935B does not. Perf "teeth" on the top and left side are staggered to line up with perf "holes" on the bottom and right on No. 935C. "Teeth" line up with "teeth" on No. 935B.
PHILAKOREA '94 (#924a). POST'X 95 Postal Exhibition (#935d).
No. 925A comes in booklets only.
Issued: $10, 4/19/89; #935A, 4/17/91; 5c, #922A, 935B, 7/1/91; #935C, 1991; #925A, 3/31/93; #924a, 8/16/94; #935d, 2/3/95; others, 11/2/88.
This is an expanding set. Numbers will change if necessary.

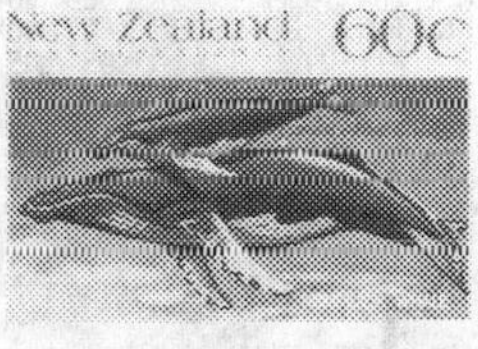
New Zealand 60C
Whales of the Southern Oceans A326

1988, Nov. 2 Litho. *Perf. 13½*
936 A326 60c Humpback .80 .70
937 A326 70c Killer 1.00 1.00
938 A326 80c Southern right 1.25 1.25
939 A326 85c Blue 1.25 1.25
940 A326 $1.05 Southern bottlenose 2.00 1.50
941 A326 $1.30 Sperm 2.25 1.90
Nos. 936-941 (6) 8.55 7.60

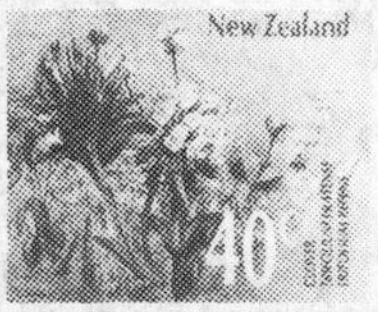
New Zealand
40c
Wildflowers A327

1989, Jan. 18 Litho. *Perf. 14½*
942 A327 40c Clover .55 .55
943 A327 60c Lotus .82 .82
944 A327 70c Montbretia .95 .95
945 A327 80c Wild ginger 1.10 1.10
Nos. 942-945 (4) 3.42 3.42

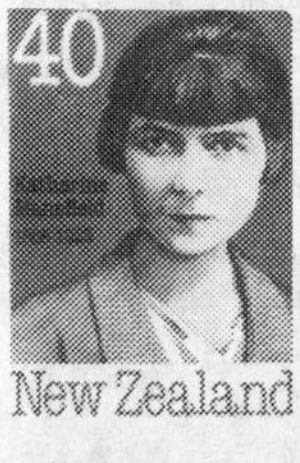
40
New Zealand
Authors — A328

Portraits: 40c, Katherine Mansfield (1888-1923). 60c, James K. Baxter (1926-1972). 70c, Bruce Mason (1921-1982). 80c, Ngaio Marsh (1899-1982).

1989, Mar. 1 Litho. *Perf. 12½*
946 A328 40c multicolored .52 .52
947 A328 60c multicolored .78 .78
948 A328 70c multicolored .90 .90
949 A328 80c multicolored 1.05 1.05
Nos. 946-949 (4) 3.25 3.25

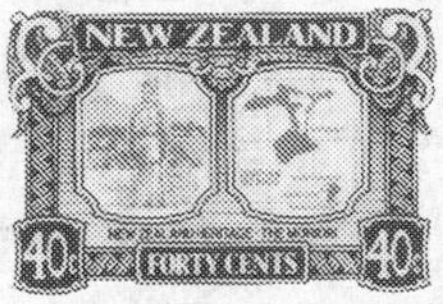
NEW ZEALAND
40c
FORTY CENTS
40c
New Zealand Heritage A329

The people.

1989, May 17 *Perf. 14x14½*
950 A329 40c Moriori .52 .52
951 A329 60c Prospectors .78 .78
952 A329 70c Land settlers .92 .92
953 A329 80c Whalers 1.05 1.05
954 A329 $1.05 Missionaries 1.40 1.40
955 A329 $1.30 Maori 1.70 1.70
Nos. 950-955 (6) 6.37 6.37

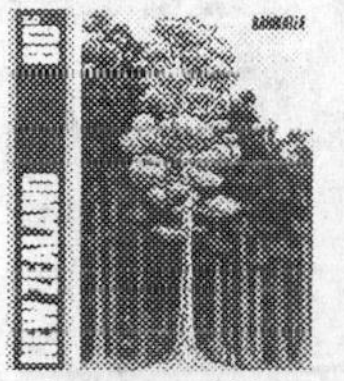
NEW ZEALAND
Trees — A330

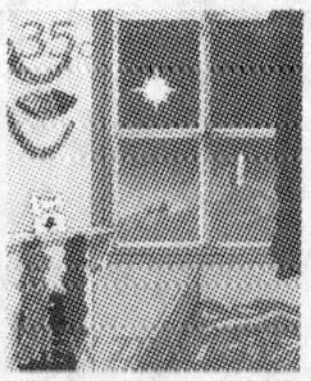
Christmas — A331

1989, June 7
956 A330 80c Kahikatea 1.05 1.05
957 A330 85c Rimu 1.10 1.10
958 A330 $1.05 Totara 1.40 1.40
959 A330 $1.30 Kauri 1.70 1.70
a. Miniature sheet of one 2.35 2.35
Nos. 956-959 (4) 5.25 5.25

No. 959a sold for $1.80. Surtax benefited the "NZ 1990" executive committee.

1989, Sept. 13 Litho. *Perf. 14½*

Star of Bethlehem illuminating settings: 35c, View of One Tree Hill from a bedroom window. 65c, A shepherd overlooking snow-capped mountains. 80c, Boats in harbor. $1, Earth.

960 A331 35c multicolored .42 .42
a. Booklet pane of 10 4.25
961 A331 65c multicolored .80 .80
962 A331 80c multicolored .98 .98
963 A331 $1 multicolored 1.20 1.20
Nos. 960-963 (4) 3.40 3.40

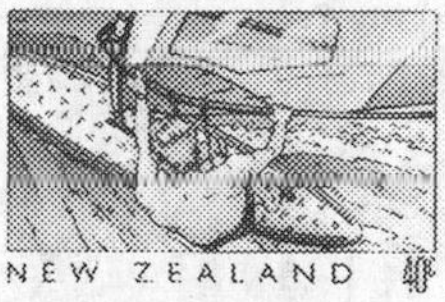
NEW ZEALAND
New Zealand Heritage A332

The sea.

1989, Oct. 11 Litho. *Perf. 14x14½*
964 A332 40c Windsurfing .48 .48
965 A332 60c Fishing .72 .72
966 A332 65c Swordfish .78 .78
967 A332 80c Harbor .95 .95
968 A332 $1 Gulls over coast 1.20 1.20
969 A332 $1.50 Container ship 1.80 1.80
Nos. 964-969 (6) 5.93 5.93

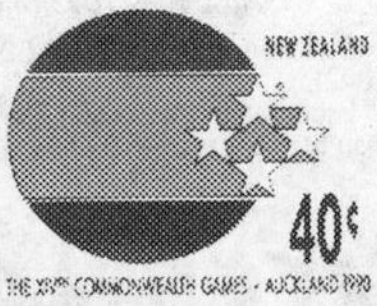
NEW ZEALAND
40c
14th Commonwealth Games, Auckland, Jan. 24-Feb. 3, 1990 — A333

1989, Nov. 8 *Perf. 14½*
970 A333 40c Emblem .50 .50
971 A333 40c Goldie character trademark .50 .50
a. Souvenir sheet of 2, #970-971, sailboats ('90) 1.00 1.00
b. As "a," stadium ('90) 1.00 1.00
972 A333 40c Gymnastics .50 .50
973 A333 50c Weight lifting .60 .60
974 A333 65c Swimming .80 .80
975 A333 80c Cycling .95 .95
976 A333 $1 Lawn bowling 1.25 1.25
977 A333 $1.80 Hurdles 2.25 2.25
Nos. 970-977 (8) 7.35 7.35

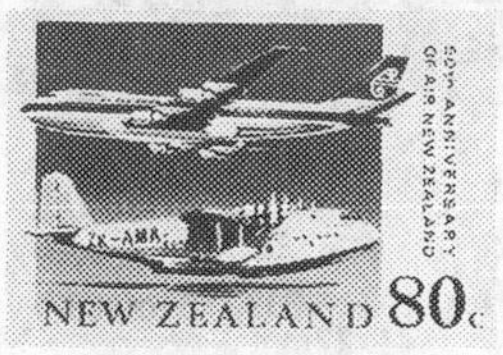
NEW ZEALAND 80c
Air New Zealand, 50th Anniv. A334

1990, Jan. 17 *Perf. 13½x14½*
978 A334 80c multicolored .95 .95

Souvenir Sheet

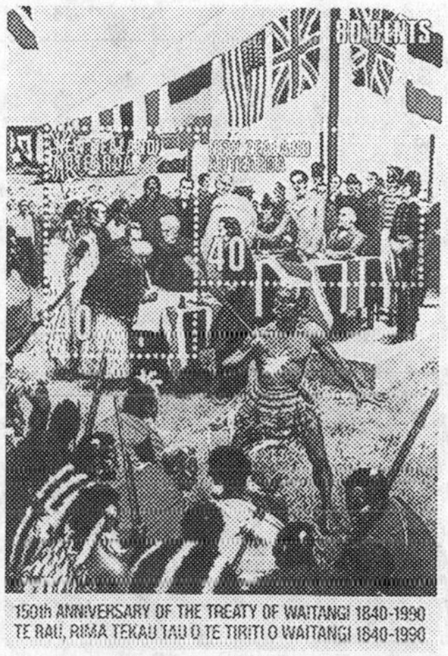
150th ANNIVERSARY OF THE TREATY OF WAITANGI 1840-1990
TE RAU, RIMA TEKAU TAU O TE TIRITI O WAITANGI 1840-1990
Treaty of Waitangi, 150th Anniv. — A335

Painting by Leonard Mitchell: a, Maori chief signing the treaty. b, Chief Hone Heke shaking hand of Lt.-Gov. William Hobson.

1990, Jan. 17 *Perf. 13½*
979 A335 Sheet of 2 1.10 1.10
a.-b. 40c any single .55 .55

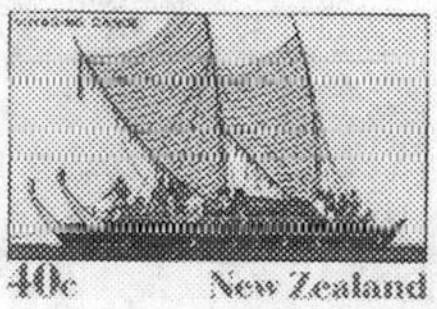
40c New Zealand
New Zealand Heritage A336

The Ships.

1990, Mar. 7 Litho. *Perf. 14x14½*
980 A336 40c Polynesian double-hulled canoe, c. 1000 .48 .48
981 A336 50c *Endeavour* .60 .60
a. Souvenir sheet of 1 *8.75 8.75*
982 A336 60c *Tory* .70 .70
983 A336 80c *Crusader* .95 .95
984 A336 $1 *Edwin Fox* 1.20 1.20
985 A336 $1.50 *Arawa* 1.75 1.75
Nos. 980-985 (6) 5.68 5.68

No. 981a for Stamp World London '90. Sold for $1.30. Issued May 3.

Miniature Sheet

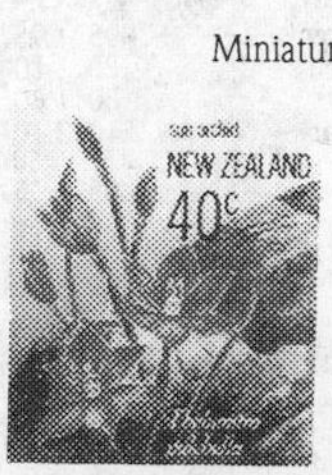
NEW ZEALAND
40c
Orchids — A337

Designs: a, Sun. b, Spider. c, Winika. d, Greenhood. e, Odd-leaved orchid.

1990, Apr. 18 Litho. *Perf. 14½*
986 Sheet of 5 2.90 2.90
a.-d. A337 40c any single .48 .48
e. A337 80c multicolored .95 .95

No. 986 sold for $4.90. Surcharge for the intl. stamp exhibition, Auckland, Aug. 24-Sept 2. Imperf. sheets were available only in season tickets which were sold for $25.

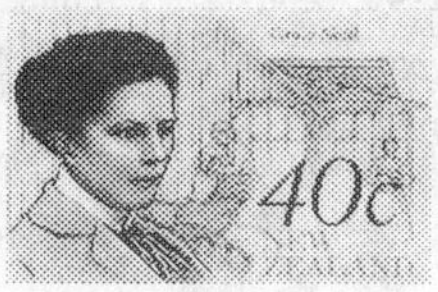
40c
NEW ZEALAND
New Zealand Heritage A338

The Achievers: 40c, Grace Neill (1846-1926), nurse, journalist. 50c, Jean Batten (1909-1982), aviator. 60c, Katherine Sheppard (1848-1934), social worker. 80c, Richard Pearse (1877-1953), inventor. $1, Gov.-Gen. Bernard Freyberg (1889-1963). $1.50, Peter Buck (1877-1951), cabinet minister.

1990, May 16 Litho. *Perf. 14x14½*
987 A338 40c multicolored .48 .48
988 A338 50c multicolored .60 .60
989 A338 60c multicolored .70 .70
990 A338 80c multicolored .95 .95
991 A338 $1 multicolored 1.20 1.20
992 A338 $1.50 multicolored 1.75 1.75
Nos. 987-992 (6) 5.68 5.68

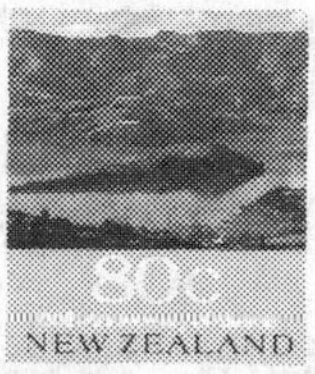
80c
NEW ZEALAND
Akaroa Harbor — A339

Early Settlements: $1, Durie Hill, Wanganui River. $1.50, Mt. Victoria, Wellington. $1.80, Rangitoto Island, Takapuna Beach, Auckland.

1990, June 13 Litho. *Perf. 14½*
993 A339 80c multicolored .95 .95
994 A339 $1 multicolored 1.15 1.15
995 A339 $1.50 multicolored 1.75 1.75
996 A339 $1.80 multicolored 2.10 2.10
a. Souvenir sheet of 1 2.75 2.75
Nos. 993-996 (4) 5.95 5.95

No. 996a sold for $2.30. Surtax for world philatelic expo, New Zealand '90.

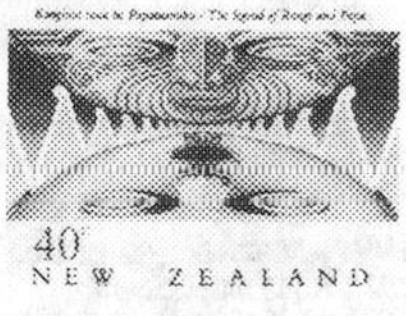
40c NEW ZEALAND
New Zealand Heritage A340

The Maori: 40c, Legend of Rangi and Papa. 50c, Maori feather cloak. 60c, Song. 80c, Maori tattoo. $1, War canoe prow. $1.50, Maori war dance.

1990, Aug. 24 Litho. *Perf. 14*
997 A340 40c multi .45 .45
998 A340 50c multi .60 .60
999 A340 60c multi .70 .70
1000 A340 80c multi .95 .95
1001 A340 $1 multi 1.20 1.20
1002 A340 $1.50 multi 1.75 1.75
Nos. 997-1002 (6) 5.65 5.65

Souvenir Sheet

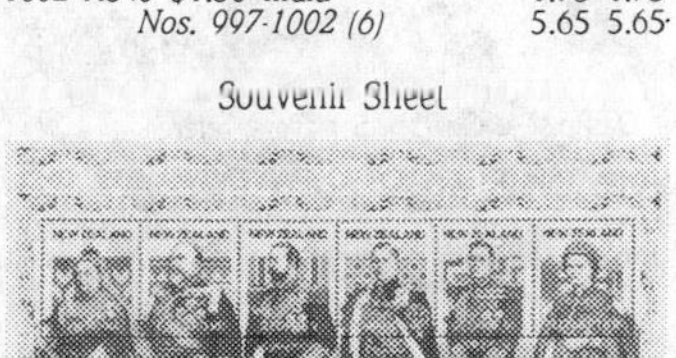
First Postage Stamps, 150th Anniv. — A341

Designs: a, Victoria. b, Edward VII. c, George V. d, Edward VIII. e, George VI. f, Elizabeth II.

1990, Aug. 29 Engr. *Perf. 14½x14*
1003 Sheet of 6 2.80 2.80
a.-f. A341 40p any single .45 .45

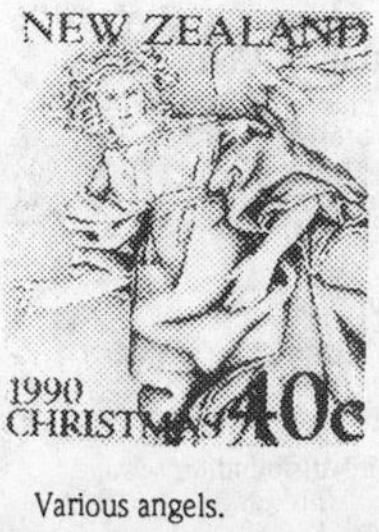
NEW ZEALAND
1990 CHRISTMAS
40c
Christmas A342

Various angels.

1990, Sept. 12 Litho. *Perf. 14*

1004 A342 40c multicolored .45 .45
1005 A342 $1 multicolored 1.15 1.15
1006 A342 $1.50 multicolored 1.75 1.75
1007 A342 $1.80 multicolored 2.10 2.10
Nos. 1004-1007 (4) 5.45 5.45

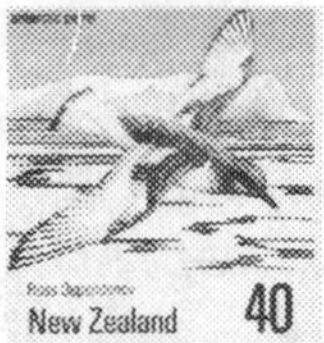

Antarctic Petrel — A343

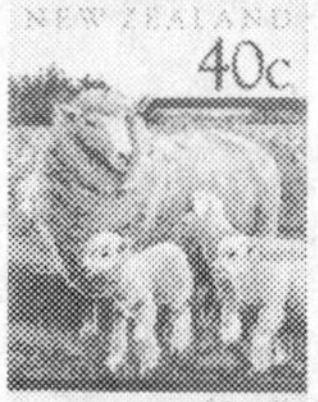

Sheep — A344

1990, Nov. 7 *Perf. 13¹/2x13*

1008 A343 40c shown .45 .45
1009 A343 50c Wilson's storm petrel .58 .58
1010 A343 60c Snow petrel .70 .70
1011 A343 80c Antarctic fulmar .92 .92
1012 A343 100c Chinstrap penguin 1.20 1.20
1013 A343 150c Emperor penguin 1.75 1.75
Nos. 1008-1013 (6) 5.60 5.60

1991, Jan. 23 Litho. *Perf. 14¹/2*

1014 A344 40c Coopworth .48 .48
1015 A344 60c Perendale .75 .75
1016 A344 80c Corriedale 1.00 1.00
1017 A344 $1 Drysdale 1.25 1.25
1018 A344 $1.50 South Suffolk 1.85 1.85
1019 A344 $1.80 Romney 2.25 2.25
Nos. 1014-1019 (6) 7.58 7.58

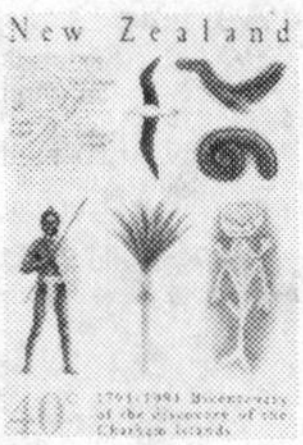

Map, Royal Albatross, Designs from Moriori House, Moriori Man, Nikau Palm, Tree Carving — A345

Design: 80c, Map, sailing ship, carving, petroglyph, Moriori house, Tommy Solomon, last full-blooded Moriori.

1991, Mar. 6 Litho. *Perf. 13¹/2*

1020 A345 40c shown .48 .48
1021 A345 80c multicolored 1.00 1.00

Discovery of the Chatham Islands, Bicent.

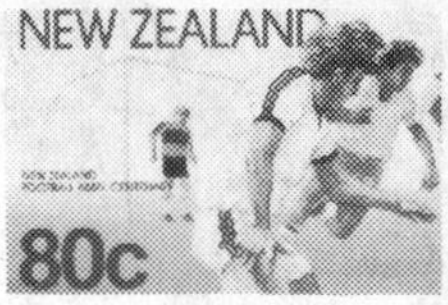

New Zealand Football (Soccer) Assoc., Cent. A346

Designs: a, Goal. b, 5 players, referee.

1991, Mar. 6

1022 Pair 2.00 2.00
a.-b. A346 80c any single 1.00 1.00

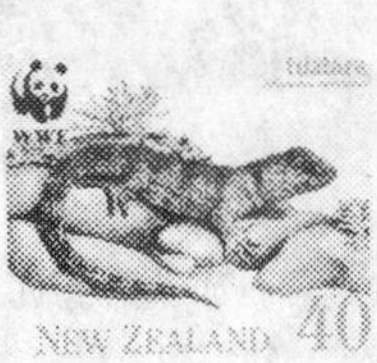

Tuatara — A347

Designs: No. 1023, Juvenile. No. 1024, In burrow. No. 1025, Female. No. 1026, Male.

1991, Apr. 17 Litho. *Perf. 14¹/2*
Denomination Color

1023 A347 40c gray blue .48 .48
1024 A347 40c dark brown .48 .48
1025 A347 40c olive green .48 .48
1026 A347 40c orange brown .48 .48
Nos. 1023-1026 (4) 1.92 1.92

Kiwi Type of 1988

1991, Apr. 17 Engr. *Perf. 14¹/2*

1027 A325 $1 red 1.20 1.20
a. Litho. 1.25 1.25

Value is for copy with surrounding selvage. No. 1027a is from No. 1161a.

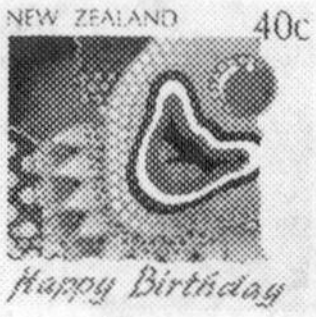

Happy Birthday — A348

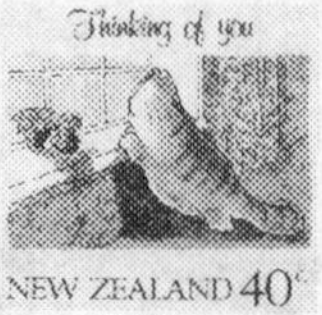

Thinking of You — A349

1991, May 15 Litho. *Perf. 14x13¹/2*
Size of Nos. 1031-1032, 1036-1037: 41x27mm

1028 A348 40c Clown face .48 .48
1029 A348 40c Balloons .48 .48
1030 A348 40c Birthday hat .48 .48
1031 A348 40c Present .48 .48
1032 A348 40c Cake & candles .48 .48
a. Bklt. pane of 5, #1028-1032 2.40
1033 A349 40c shown .48 .48
1034 A349 40c Cat, slippers .48 .48
1035 A349 40c Cat, alarm clock .48 .48
1036 A349 40c Cat looking out window .48 .48
1037 A349 40c Cat walking by door .48 .48
a. Bklt. pane of 5, #1033-1037 2.40

See Nos. 1044-1953.

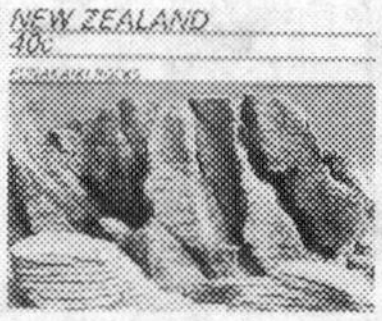

Rock Formations A350

1991, June 12 Litho. *Perf. 14¹/2*

1038 A350 40c Punakaiki Rocks .45 .45
1039 A350 50c Moeraki Boulders .55 .55
1040 A350 80c Organ Pipes .85 .85
1041 A350 $1 Castle Hill 1.10 1.10
1042 A350 $1.50 Te Kaukau Point 1.60 1.60
1043 A350 $1.80 Ahuriri River Clay Cliffs 2.00 2.00
Nos. 1038-1043 (6) 6.55 6.55

Greetings Types

1991, July 1 Litho. *Perf. 14x13¹/2*
Size of Nos. 1047-1048, 1052-1053: 41x27mm

1044 A348 45c like #1028 .52 .52
1045 A348 45c like #1029 .52 .52
1046 A348 45c like #1030 .52 .52
1047 A348 45c like #1031 .52 .52
1048 A348 45c like #1032 .52 .52
a. Bklt. pane of 5, #1044-1048 2.60
1049 A349 45c like #1033 .52 .52
1050 A349 45c like #1034 .52 .52
1051 A349 45c like #1035 .52 .52
1052 A349 45c like #1036 .52 .52
1053 A349 45c like #1037 .52 .52
a. Bklt. pane of 5, #1049-1053 2.60

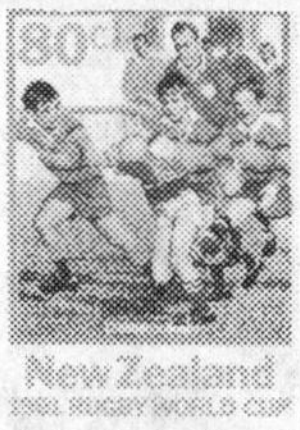

1991 Rugby World Cup — A351

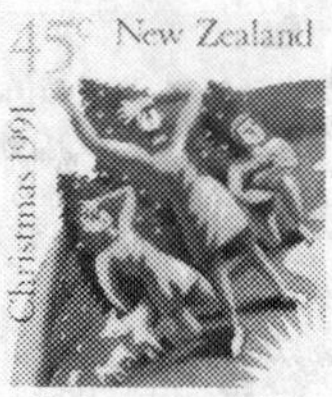

Christmas — A352

1991, Aug. 21 Litho. *Perf. 14¹/2x14*

1054 A351 80c Children's .95 .95
1055 A351 $1 Women's 1.20 1.20
1056 A351 $1.50 Senior 1.80 1.80
1057 A351 $1.80 All Blacks 2.10 2.10
a. Souvenir sheet of 1 2.50 2.50
Nos. 1054-1057 (4) 6.05 6.05

No. 1057a sold for $2.40 to benefit philatelic trust for hobby support.

1991, Sept. 18 Litho. *Perf. 13¹/2x14*

1058 A352 45c Shepherds .52 .52
1059 A352 45c Wise men, camels .52 .52
1060 A352 45c Mary, Baby Jesus .52 .52
1061 A352 45c Wise man, gift .52 .52
a. Block of 4, #1058-1061 2.10 2.10
1062 A352 65c Star .75 .75
1063 A352 $1 Crown 1.15 1.15
1064 A352 $1.50 Angel 1.75 1.75
Nos. 1058-1064 (7) 5.73 5.73

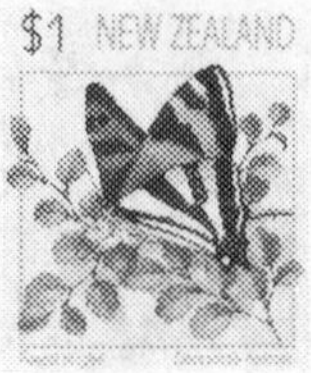

Butterflies — A354

1991-95 Litho. *Perf. 14¹/2*

1075 A354 $1 Forest ringlet 1.15 1.15
a. Perf. 14x14¹/2 1.30 1.30
b. Booklet pane of 5 + 5 labels 6.50
Complete booklet, #1075b 6.50
1076 A354 $2 Southern blue 2.30 2.30
1077 A354 $3 Yellow admiral 3.50 3.50
a. Souvenir sheet of 1 3.50 3.50
1078 A354 $4 Common copper 5.00 5.00
1079 A354 $5 Red admiral 6.25 6.25
Nos. 1075-1079 (5) 18.20 18.20

No. 1077a issued later for Phila Nippon '91.
Issued: $1-$3, 11/6/91; $4-$5, 1/25/95; #1075b, 9/1/95.
This is an expanding set. Numbers will change if necessary.

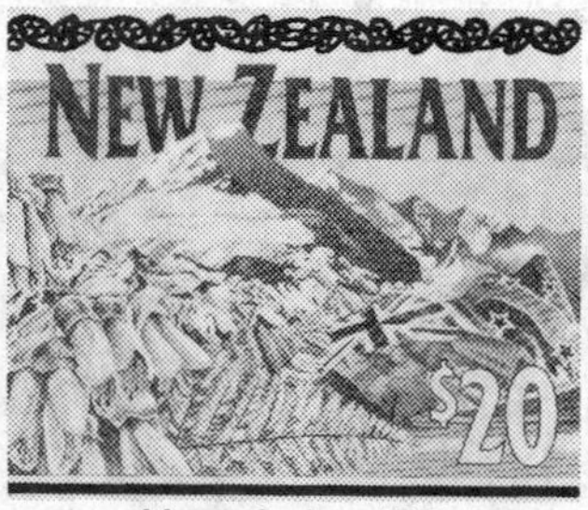

Mount Cook — A356

Die Stamped & Engr.
1994 Wmk. 387 *Perf. 14¹/2x15*

1084 A356 $20 gold & blue 22.50 22.50

Issued: $20, Feb. 18, 1994. This is an expanding set. Number may change.

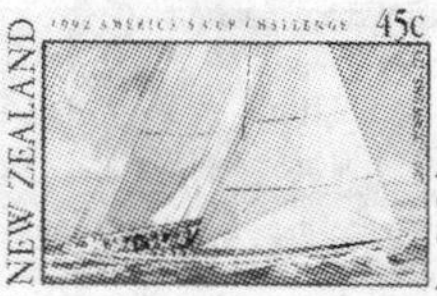

1992 America's Cup Competition A357

1992, Jan. 22 Litho. *Perf. 14x14¹/2*

1085 A357 45c KZ7 Kiwi Magic, 1987 .52 .52
1086 A357 80c KZ1 New Zealand, 1988 .95 .95
1087 A357 $1 America, 1851 1.15 1.15
1088 A357 $1.50 New Zealand, 1992 1.75 1.75
Nos. 1085-1088 (4) 4.37 4.37

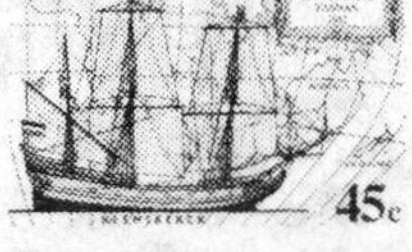

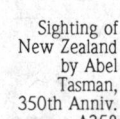

Sighting of New Zealand by Abel Tasman, 350th Anniv. A358

1992, Mar. 12 *Perf. 13¹/2x14¹/2*

1089 A358 45c Heemskerck .52 .45
1090 A358 80c Zeehaen .95 .95
1091 A358 $1 Santa Maria 1.15 1.15
1092 A358 $1.50 Pinta and Nina 1.75 1.75
a. Souvenir sheet of 2, #1091-1092, Perf. 14x14¹/2 4.00 4.00
Nos. 1089-1092 (4) 4.37 4.30

Discovery of America, 500th anniv. (#1091-1092).
Issue date: No. 1092a, May 22. World Columbian Stamp Expo (#1092a).

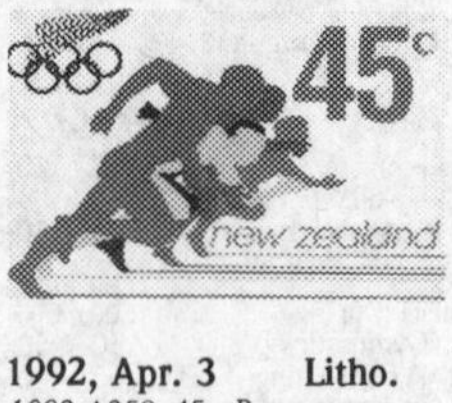

1992 Summer Olympics, Barcelona A359

1992, Apr. 3 Litho. *Perf. 13¹/2*

1093 A359 45c Runners .52 .45

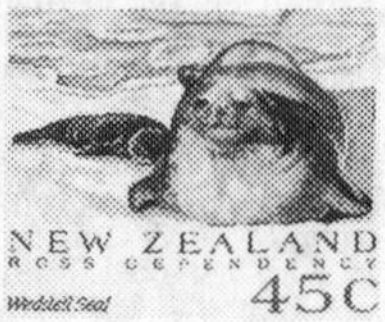

Antarctic Seals — A360

1992, Apr. 8 *Perf. 14x13¹/2*

1094 A360 45c Weddell seal .52 .52
1095 A360 50c Crabeater seal .58 .58
1096 A360 65c Leopard seal .75 .75
1097 A360 80c Ross seal .95 .95
1098 A360 $1 Southern elephant seal 1.15 1.15
1099 A360 $1.80 Hooker's sea lion 2.10 2.10
Nos. 1094-1099 (6) 6.05 6.05

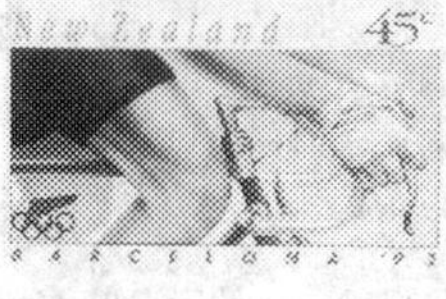

1992 Summer Olympics, Barcelona A361

1992, May 13 Litho. *Perf. 13¹/2*

1100 A361 45c Cycling .45 .45
1101 A361 80c Archery .80 .80
1102 A361 $1 Equestrian 1.00 1.00
1103 A361 $1.50 Board sailing 1.50 1.50
a. Souvenir sheet of 4, #1100-1103, perf 14x14¹/2 3.50 3.50
b. No. 1103a overprinted 3.50 3.50
Nos. 1100-1103 (4) 3.75 3.75

No. 1103b overprint consists of World Columbian Stamp Expo emblem in sheet margin. Issue date: No. 1103b, May 22.

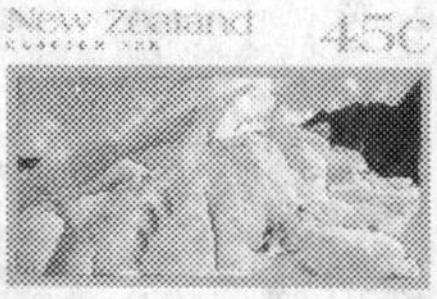

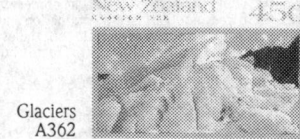

Glaciers A362

1992, June 12

1104 A362 45c Glacier ice .45 .45
1105 A362 50c Tasman glacier .50 .50
1106 A362 80c Snowball glacier .80 .80
1107 A362 $1 Brewster glacier 1.00 1.00
1108 A362 $1.50 Fox glacier 1.50 1.50
1109 A362 $1.80 Franz Josef glacier 1.80 1.80
Nos. 1104-1109 (6) 6.05 6.05

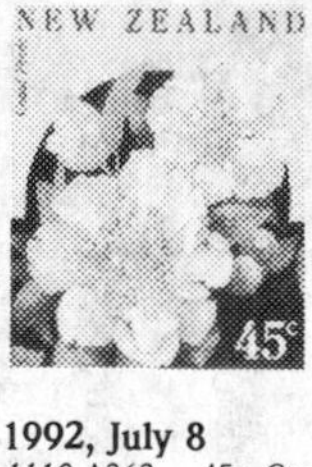

Camellias — A363

1992, July 8 *Perf. 14¹/2*

1110 A363 45c Grand finale .45 .45
1111 A363 50c Showa-no-sakae .50 .50
1112 A363 80c Sugar dream .80 .80
1113 A363 $1 Night rider 1.00 1.00
1114 A363 $1.50 E.G. Waterhouse 1.50 1.50
1115 A363 $1.80 Dr. Clifford Parks 1.80 1.80
Nos. 1110-1115 (6) 6.05 6.05

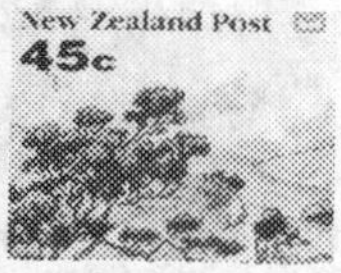

Scenic Views of New Zealand — A364

1992, Sept. 1 Litho. *Perf. 14x14¹/2*
Booklet Stamps

1116 A364 45c Tree, hills .45 .45
1117 A364 45c Hills, stream .45 .45
1118 A364 45c Hills, mountain tops .45 .45
1119 A364 45c Glacier .45 .45
1120 A364 45c Trees, green hills .45 .45
1121 A364 45c Tree branch, rapids .45 .45
1122 A364 45c Rocky shoreline .45 .45
1123 A364 45c Fjord .45 .45
1124 A364 45c Glacial runoff .45 .45
1125 A364 45c Vegetation, stream .45 .45
a. Bklt. pane of 10, #1116-1125 4.50

No. 1125a has continous design.

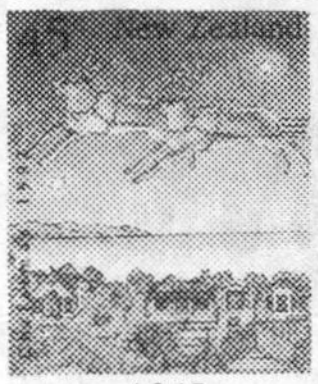
A365

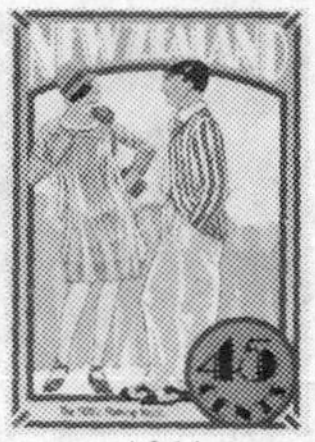
A366

Christmas: No. 1126, Two reindeer over village. No. 1127, Two reindeer pulling Santa's sleigh. No. 1128, Christmas tree in window. No. 1129, Two children looking out window. 65c, Fireplace, stockings. $1, Church. $1.50, People beneath pohutukawa tree at beach.

1992, Sept. 16 *Perf. 14½*

1126	A365	45c multicolored	.45	.45
1127	A365	45c multicolored	.45	.45
1128	A365	45c multicolored	.45	.45
1129	A365	45c multicolored	.45	.45
a.		Block of 4, #1126-1129	1.80	1.80
1130	A365	65c multicolored	.65	.65
1131	A365	$1 multicolored	1.00	1.00
1132	A365	$1.50 multicolored	1.50	1.50
		Nos. 1126-1132 (7)	4.95	4.95

No. 1129a has continous design.

1992, Nov. 4 **Litho.** *Perf. 13½*

The Emerging Years: The 1920s: 45c, Flaming youth. 50c, Birth of broadcasting. 80c, All Blacks rugby player. $1, The swaggie. $1.50, Motorcar brings freedom. $1.80, Arrival of the air age.

1133	A366	45c multicolored	.45	.45
1134	A366	50c multicolored	.50	.50
1135	A366	80c multicolored	.80	.80
1136	A366	$1 multicolored	1.00	1.00
1137	A366	$1.50 multicolored	1.50	1.50
1138	A366	$1.80 multicolored	1.80	1.80
		Nos. 1133-1138 (6)	6.05	6.05

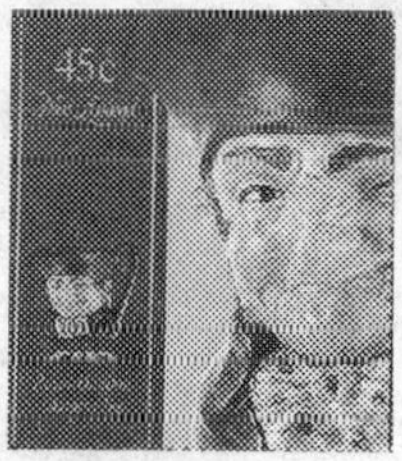
Royal Doulton Ceramics A367

Designs: 45c, Character jug, "Old Charley." 50c, Plate from "Bunnykins" series. 80c, Maori art tea ware. $1, Hand painted "Ophelia" plate. $1.50, Burslem figurine of St. George. $1.80, Salt glazed vase.

1993, Jan. 20 **Litho.** *Perf. 13*

1139	A367	45c multicolored	.45	.45
1140	A367	50c multicolored	.50	.50
1141	A367	80c multicolored	.80	.80
1142	A367	$1 multicolored	1.00	1.00
1143	A367	$1.50 multicolored	1.50	1.50
1144	A367	$1.80 multicolored	1.80	1.80
a.		Souvenir sheet of 1	1.80	1.80
		Nos. 1139-1144 (6)	6.05	6.05

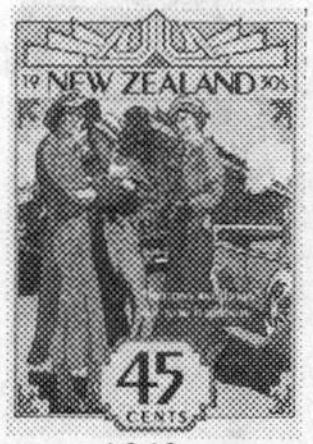
A368

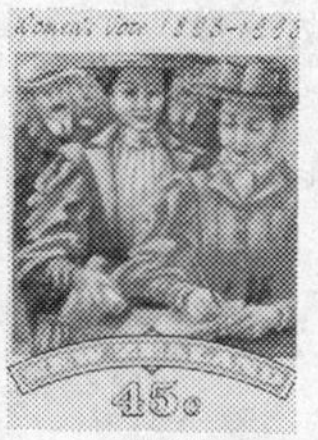
A369

The Emerging Years: The 1930's: 45c, Buttons and bows, the new femininity. 50c, The Great Depression. 80c, Race horse, Phar Lap. $1, State housing. $1.50, Free milk for schools. $1.80, The talkies.

1993, Feb. 17 **Litho.** *Perf. 14½x14*

1145	A368	45c multicolored	.45	.45
1146	A368	50c multicolored	.50	.50
1147	A368	80c multicolored	.80	.80
1148	A368	$1 multicolored	1.00	1.00
1149	A368	$1.50 multicolored	1.50	1.50
1150	A368	$1.80 multicolored	1.80	1.80
		Nos. 1145-1150 (6)	6.05	6.05

1993, Mar. 31 **Litho.** *Perf. 13½*

1151	A369	45c First vote	.45	.45
1152	A369	80c War work	.80	.80
1153	A369	$1 Child care	1.00	1.00
1154	A369	$1.50 Contemporary women	1.50	1.50
		Nos. 1151-1154 (4)	3.75	3.75

Woman Suffrage, cent.

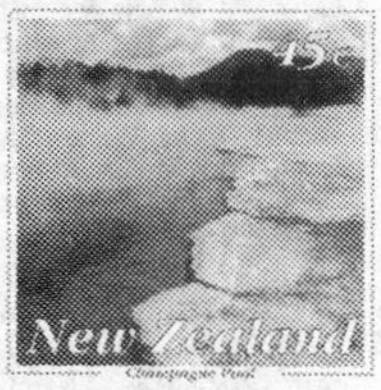
Thermal Wonders A370

Designs: 45c, Champagne Pool. 50c, Boiling mud, Rotorua. 80c, Emerald Pool. $1, Hakereteke Falls. $1.50, Warbrick Terrace. $1.80, Pohutu Geyser.

1993, May 5 **Litho.** *Perf. 12*

1155	A370	45c multicolored	.48	.48
1156	A370	50c multicolored	.55	.55
1157	A370	80c multicolored	.85	.85
1158	A370	$1 multicolored	1.10	1.10
1159	A370	$1.50 multicolored	1.60	1.60
1160	A370	$1.80 multicolored	1.95	1.95
a.		Souvenir sheet of 1	2.00	2.00
		Nos. 1155-1160 (6)	6.53	6.53

No. 1160a inscribed with Bangkok '93 emblem in sheet margin. Issue date: No. 1160a, Oct. 1.

Kiwi Type of 1988

1993, June 9 **Engr.** *Perf. 14½*

1161	A325	$1 blue	1.10	1.10
a.		Souv. sheet of 3, #916b, 1027a, 1161	6.50	6.50
b.		Litho.	1.25	1.25
c.		Souv. sheet of 3, #918b, 1027a, 1161b	3.50	3.50

Taipei '93, Asian Intl. Stamp Exhibition (#1164a), Hong Kong '94 (#1161c).

Value is for copy with surrounding selvage.

Issued: #1161a, 8/14/93; #1161c, 2/18/94.

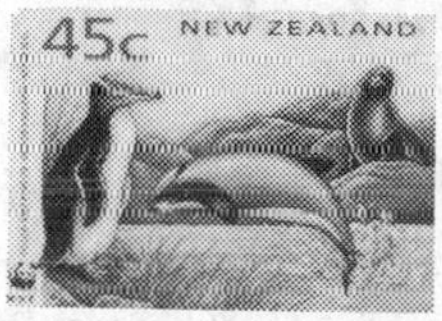
Species Unique to New Zealand A371

Designs: No. 1162a, Yellow-eyed penguin, Hector's dolphin, New Zealand fur seal. b, Taiko, Mt. Cook lily, blue duck. c, Giant snail, rock wren, Hamilton's frog. d, Kaka, Chatham Island pigeon, giant weta.

No. 1163, Tusked weta.

1993, June 9 **Litho.** *Perf. 14x14½*

1162	A371	45c Block of 4, #a.-d.	1.95	1.95

Perf. 13½

1163	A371	45c multicolored	.48	.48

World Wildlife Fund.

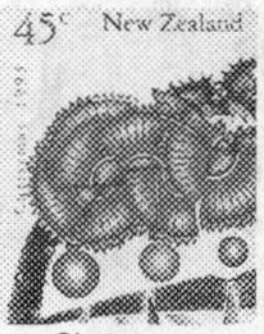
Christmas A372

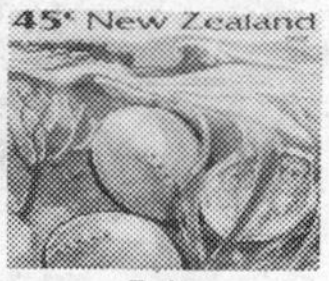
Fish A373

Christmas designs: No. 1164, Flowers from pohutukawa tree, denomination at UL. No. 1165, Like #1164, denomination at UR. No. 1166, Present with yellow ribbon, denomination at LL. No. 1167, Present with red ribbon, denomination at LR. $1.00, Ornaments, cracker, sailboats. $1.50, Wreath, sailboats, present.

1993, Sept. 1 **Litho.** *Perf. 14½x14*

1164	A372	45c multicolored	.48	.48
1165	A372	45c multicolored	.48	.48
1166	A372	45c multicolored	.48	.48
1167	A372	45c multicolored	.48	.48
a.		Block of 4, #1165-1167	2.00	2.00
1168	A372	$1 multicolored	1.10	1.10
1169	A372	$1.50 multicolored	1.65	1.65
		Nos. 1164-1169 (6)	4.67	4.67

Booklet Stamps

Perf. 12

1164a	A372	45c multicolored	.48	.48
1165a	A372	45c multicolored	.48	.48
1166a	A372	45c multicolored	.48	.48
1167b	A372	45c multicolored	.48	.48
c.		Booklet pane, 3 each #1164a-1165a, 2 each #1166a, 1167b	5.00	

At least one edge of No. 1167c is guillotined.

1993, Sept. 1 *Perf. 13½*

Designs: No. 1170, Paua (#1175). No. 1171, Greenshell mussels. No. 1172, Terakihi (#1171). No. 1173, Salmon (#1172). No. 1174, Southern bluefin tuna, albacore tuna, kahawai (#1173). No. 1175, Rock lobster (#1171). No. 1176, Snapper (#1177). No. 1177, Groper (#1178). No. 1178, Orange roughy (#1179). No. 1179, Squid, hoki, oreo dory (#1173, #1174, #1178).

Booklet Stamps

1170	A373	45c multicolored	.48	.48
1171	A373	45c multicolored	.48	.48
1172	A373	45c multicolored	.48	.48
1173	A373	45c multicolored	.48	.48
1174	A373	45c multicolored	.48	.48
1175	A373	45c multicolored	.48	.48
1176	A373	45c multicolored	.48	.48
1177	A373	45c multicolored	.48	.48
1178	A373	45c multicolored	.48	.48
1179	A373	45c multicolored	.48	.48
a.		Booklet pane of 10, #1170-1179 + 2 labels	5.00	

Nos. 1179a has continuous design.

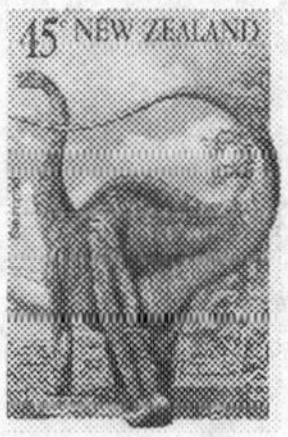
Dinosaurs — A374

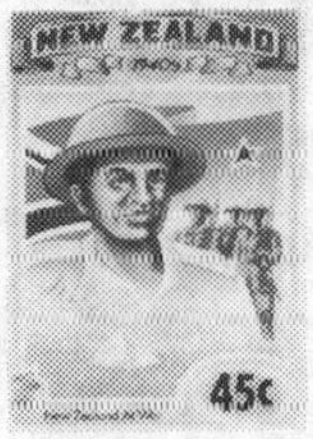
The 1940s — A375

1993, Oct. 1

1180	A374	45c Sauropod	.48	.48
1181	A374	80c Pterosaur	.90	.90
1182	A374	$1 Ankylosaur	1.10	1.10
1183	A374	$1.20 Mauisaurus	1.25	1.25
1184	A374	$1.50 Carnosaur	1.65	1.65
a.		Souvenir sheet of 1, perf. 14½x14	1.65	1.65
b.		As "a," inscribed with Bangkok '93 emblem	1.65	1.65
		Nos. 1180-1184 (5)	5.38	5.38

Booklet Stamp

Size: 25½x23½mm

Perf. 12

1185	A374	45c Carnosaur, sauropod	.48	.48
a.		Booklet pane of 10 + 2 labels	4.75	4.75

1993, Nov. 3 **Litho.** *Perf. 14*

Designs: 45c, New Zealand at war. 50c, Crop dusting. 80c, State produces hydroelectricity. $1, New Zealand Marching Assoc. $1.50, The American invasion. $1.80, Victory.

1186	A375	45c multicolored	.50	.50
1187	A375	50c multicolored	.55	.55
1188	A375	80c multicolored	.90	.90
1189	A375	$1 multicolored	1.10	1.10
1190	A375	$1.50 multicolored	1.65	1.65
1191	A375	$1.80 multicolored	2.00	2.00
		Nos. 1186-1191 (6)	6.70	6.70

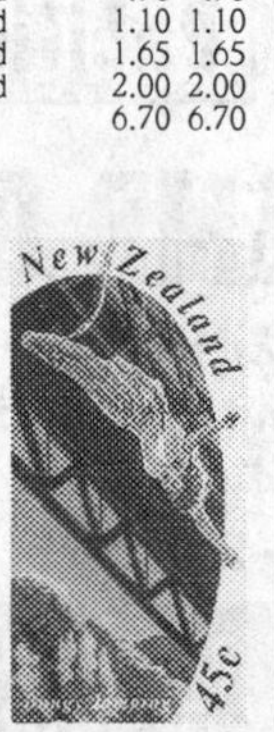
Outdoor Adventure Sports — A376

1994, Jan. 19 **Litho.** *Perf. 12*

1192	A376	45c Bungy jumping	.50	.50
1193	A376	80c Trout fishing	.90	.90
1194	A376	$1 Jet boating, horiz.	1.10	1.10
1195	A376	$1.50 Tramping	1.65	1.65
1196	A376	$1.80 Heli-skiing	2.00	2.00
a.		Souvenir sheet of 1	2.00	2.00
		Nos. 1192-1196 (5)	6.15	6.15

No. 1196a inscribed in sheet margin with Hong Kong '94 emblem and text in English and Chinese. Issue date: No. 1196a, Feb. 18.

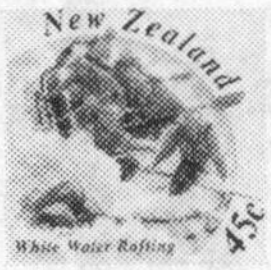
White Water Rafting — A377

1994, Jan. 19 **Litho.** *Perf. 12*

Booklet Stamp

1197	A377	45c multicolored	.52	.52
a.		Booklet pane of 10 + 4 labels	5.25	

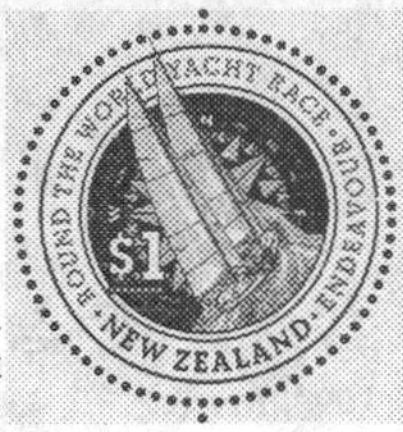
Whitbread Trans-Global Yacht Race — A378

1994, Jan. 19 *Perf. 15*

1198	A378	$1 Endeavour	1.10	1.10

Used value is for stamp with complete selvage.

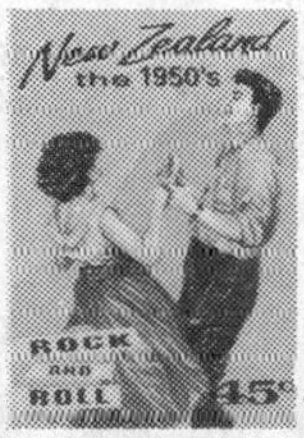
The 1050's — A379

Designs: 45c, Rock and roll. 80c, Conquest of Mt. Everest. $1, Aunt Daisy, "Good Morning Everybody." $1.20, Royal visit, 1953. $1.50, Opo, the Friendly Dolphin. $1.80, The Coat Hanger (Auckland Harbor Bridge.)

1994, Mar. 24 **Litho.** *Perf. 14*

1199	A379	45c multicolored	.50	.50
1200	A379	80c multicolored	.90	.90
1201	A379	$1 multicolored	1.10	1.10
1202	A379	$1.20 multicolored	1.40	1.40
1203	A379	$1.50 multicolored	1.65	1.65
1204	A379	$1.80 multicolored	2.00	2.00
		Nos. 1199-1204 (6)	7.55	7.55

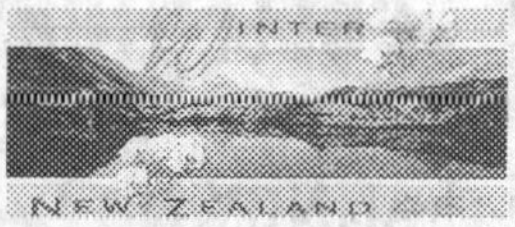
Scenic Views of the Four Seasons A380

Designs: 45c, Winter, Mt. Cook, Mt. Cook lily. 70c, Spring, Lake Hawea, kowhai flower. $1.50, Summer, Opononi, pohutukawa flower. $1.80, Autumn, Mt. Cook, Lake Pukaki, puriri flower.

1994, Apr. 27 *Perf. 12*

1205	A380	45c multicolored	.50	.50
1206	A380	70c multicolored	.80	.80
1207	A380	$1.50 multicolored	1.65	1.65
1208	A380	$1.80 multicolored	2.00	2.00
a.		Strip of 4, #1205-1208	5.00	5.00

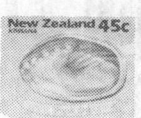

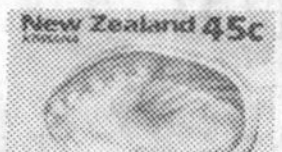
Paua Shell — A381

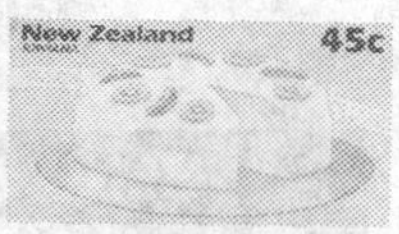
Pavlova Dessert A382

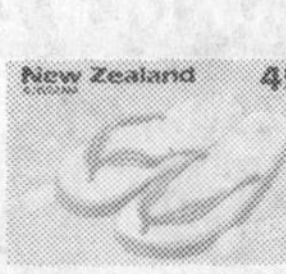
Jandals — A383

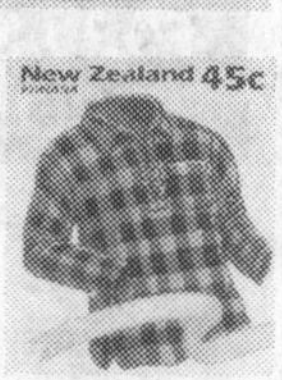
Bush Shirt — A384

Buzzy Bee
Toy — A385

Kiwi Fruit — A386

Kiwiana: No. 1211, Hokey pokey ice cream. No. 1212, Fish and chips. No. 1216, Black singlet, gumboots. No. 1217, Rugby shoes, ball.

1994, Apr. 27　　Litho.　　Perf. 12
Booklet Stamps

1209 A381 45c multicolored	.52	.52
1210 A382 45c multicolored	.52	.52
1211 A381 45c multicolored	.52	.52
1212 A382 45c multicolored	.52	.52
1213 A383 45c multicolored	.52	.52
1214 A384 45c multicolored	.52	.52
1215 A385 45c multicolored	.52	.52
1216 A384 45c multicolored	.52	.52
1217 A385 45c multicolored	.52	.52
1218 A386 45c multicolored	.52	.52
a. Booklet pane of 10, #1209-1218	5.25	

Maori
Myths — A387

Designs: 45c, Maui pulls up Te Ika (the fish). 80c, Rona is snatched up by Marama (moon). $1, Maui attacks Tuna (eel). $1.20, Tane separates Rangi (sky) and Papa (earth). $1.50, Matakauri slays Giant of Wakatipu. $1.80, Panenehu shows Koura (crayfish) to Tangaroa.

1994, June 8　　　　　　Perf. 13

1219 A387 45c multicolored	.50	.50
1220 A387 80c multicolored	.95	.95
1221 A387 $1 multicolored	1.10	1.10
1222 A387 $1.20 multicolored	1.40	1.40
1223 A387 $1.50 multicolored	1.75	1.75
1224 A387 $1.80 multicolored	2.00	2.00
Nos. 1219-1224 (6)	7.70	7.70

First Manned Moon
Landing, 25th
Anniv. — A388

1994, July 20　　Litho.　　Perf. 12

1225 A388 $1.50 multicolored	1.65	1.65

No. 1225 has a holographic image. Soaking in water may affect the hologram.

People Reaching
People — A389

Die Cut Perf. 11
1994, July 20
Self-Adhesive　　　　　　Photo.

1226 A389 45c multicolored	.50	.50
See No. 1311.		

Wild Animals
A390

1994, Aug. 16　　Litho.　　Perf. 14

1227 A390 45c Hippopotamus	.50	.50
1228 A390 45c Spider monkey	.50	.50
1229 A390 45c Giant panda	.50	.50
1230 A390 45c Polar bear	.50	.50
1231 A390 45c African elephant	.50	.50
1232 A390 45c White rhinoceros	.50	.50
1233 A390 45c African lion	.50	.50
1234 A390 45c Plains zebra	.50	.50
1235 A390 45c Giraffe	.50	.50
1236 A390 45c Siberian tiger	.50	.50
b. Block of 10, #1227-1236	5.00	5.00
Souvenir sheet of 6, #1229-1231, 1233, 1235-1236	3.00	3.00

PHILAKOREA '94 (#1236b). Nos. 1227-1236 printed in sheets of 100. Because of the design of these sheets, blocks or strips of Nos. 1227-1236 exist in 10 different arrangements. Value assigned to No. 1236a applies to all arrangements.

Christmas
A391

Designs: No. 1237, Children, Nativity scene. 70c, Magi, father, child. 80c, Carolers, stained glass window. $1, Carolers, Christmas tree. $1.50, Children, candles. $1.80, Father, mother, infant. No. 1243, Children, Christmas tree, Santa.

1994, Sept. 21　　Litho.　　Perf. 14

1237 A391 45c multicolored	.55	.55
1238 A391 70c multicolored	.85	.85
1239 A391 80c multicolored	1.00	1.00
1240 A391 $1 multicolored	1.25	1.25
a. Souvenir sheet, 1 each #1237-1240	3.75	3.75
1241 A391 $1.50 multicolored	1.90	1.90
1242 A391 $1.80 multicolored	2.25	2.25
Nos. 1237-1242 (6)	7.80	7.80

Booklet Stamp
Size: 30x25mm

1243 A391 45c multicolored	.55	.55
a. Booklet pane of 10	5.50	

Cricket in New
Zealand,
Cent. — A392

Beach Cricket — A393

1994, Nov. 2　　　　　Perf. 13½

1244 A392 45c Batting	.55	.55
1245 A392 80c Bowling	1.00	1.00
1246 A392 $1 Wicketkeeping	1.25	1.25
1247 A392 $1.80 Fielding	2.25	2.25
Nos. 1244-1247 (4)	5.05	5.05
Perf. 12		
1248 A393 45c Bklt. pane of 10	5.50	5.50
a.-j. Any single	.55	.55

New
Zealand at
Night
A394

1995, Feb. 22　　Litho.　　Perf. 12

1249 A394 45c Auckland	.55	.55
1250 A394 80c Wellington	1.00	1.00
1251 A394 $1 Christchurch	1.25	1.25
1252 A394 $1.20 Dunedin	1.50	1.50
1253 A394 $1.50 Rotorua	1.90	1.90
1254 A394 $1.80 Queenstown	2.25	2.25
a. Souvenir sheet of 6, #1249-1254	9.00	9.00
Nos. 1249-1254 (6)	8.45	8.45

Singapore '95, Jakarta '95 (#1254a). Issued: No. 1254a, 9/1/95.

Golf courses — A395

1995, Mar. 22　　Litho.　　Perf. 14

1255 A395 45c Waitangi	.58	.58
1256 A395 80c New Plymouth	1.00	1.00
1257 A395 $1.20 Rotorua	1.50	1.50
1258 A395 $1.80 Queenstown	2.25	2.25
Nos. 1255-1258 (4)	5.33	5.33

Environmental
Protection — A396

Designs: No. 1259, Native fauna, flora. No. 1260, Plant native trees, shrubs. No. 1261, Protect marine mammals. No. 1262, Conserve power, water. No. 1263, Enjoy natural environment. No. 1264, Control animal pests. No. 1265, Eliminate noxious plants. No. 1266, Return undersized catches. No. 1267, Control air, water quality. No. 1268, Dispose of trash properly.

1995, Mar. 22

1259 A396 45c multicolored	.58	.58
1260 A396 45c multicolored	.58	.58
1261 A396 45c multicolored	.58	.58
1262 A396 45c multicolored	.58	.58
1263 A396 45c multicolored	.58	.58
1264 A396 45c multicolored	.58	.58
1265 A396 45c multicolored	.58	.58
1266 A396 45c multicolored	.58	.58
1267 A396 45c multicolored	.58	.58
1268 A396 45c multicolored	.58	.58
a. Booklet pane, #1259-1268	5.80	
Complete booklet, #1268a	5.80	

Maori
Language — A397

Designs: 45c, Treasured Language Nest. 70c, Sing to awaken the spirit. 80c, Acquire knowledge through stories. $1, The welcoming call. $1.50, Recite the genealogies that link people. $1.80, Tell the lore of the people.

1995, May 3　　Litho.　　Perf. 13½

1269 A397 45c multicolored	.60	.60
1270 A397 70c multicolored	.95	.95
1271 A397 80c multicolored	1.10	1.10
1272 A397 $1 multicolored	1.40	1.40
1273 A397 $1.50 multicolored	2.00	2.00
1274 A397 $1.80 multicolored	2.50	2.50
Nos. 1269-1274 (6)	8.55	8.55

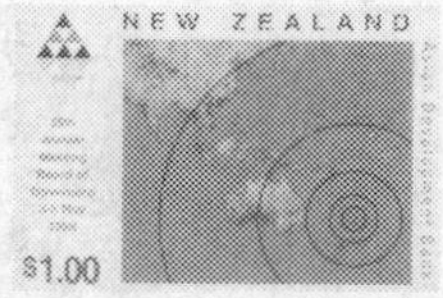

Asian Development Bank, 28th Meeting of the Board of Governors, Auckland
A398

Design: $1.50, Pacific Basin Economic Council, 28th Intl. Meeting, Auckland.

1995, May 3

1275	A398	$1	Map shown	1.40	1.40
1276	A398	$1.50	Map of Pacific	2.00	2.00

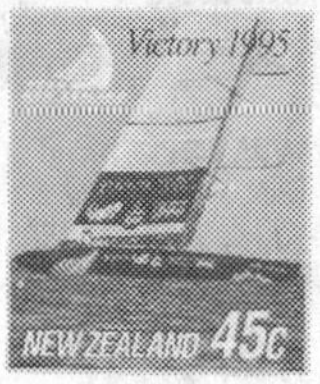

Team New Zealand, 1995 America's Cup Winner — A399

1995, May 16 *Perf. 12*

1277	A399	45c	Black Magic yacht	.60	.60

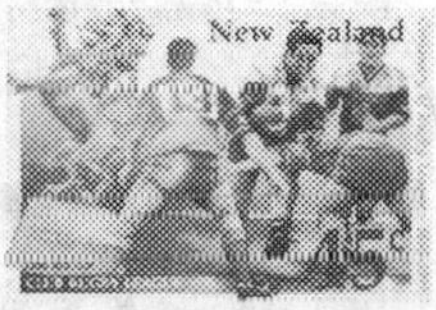

Rugby League, Cent.
A400

Designs: No. 1278, Club Rugby League, Lion Red Cup. No. 1282, Trans Tasman. $1.00, Mini League. $1.50, George Smith, Albert Baskerville, Early Rugby League. $1.80, Intl. Rugby League, Courtney Intl. Goodwill Trophy.

1995, July 26 Litho. *Perf. 14*

1278	A400	45c	multicolored	.60	.60
1279	A400	$1	multicolored	1.40	1.40
1280	A400	$1.50	multicolored	2.00	2.00
1281	A400	$1.80	multicolored	2.50	2.50
a.			Souvenir sheet of 1	2.50	2.50
			Nos. 1278-1281 (4)	6.50	6.50

Booklet Stamp
Perf. 12 on 3 Sides

1282	A400	45c	multicolored	.60	.60
a.			Booklet pane of 10	6.00	6.00
			Complete booklet, #1282a	6.00	

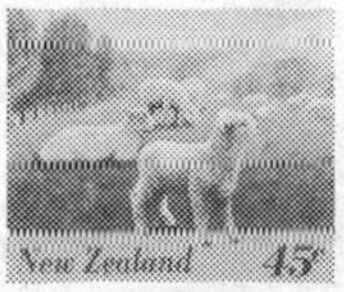

Farm Animals — A401

1995 Litho. *Perf. 14x14½*
Booklet Stamps

1283	A401	40c	Sheep	.55	.55
1284	A401	40c	Deer	.55	.55
1285	A401	40c	Horses	.55	.55
1286	A401	40c	Cattle	.55	.55
1287	A401	40c	Goats	.55	.55
1288	A401	40c	Turkey	.55	.55
1289	A401	40c	Ducks	.55	.55
1290	A401	40c	Chickens	.55	.55
1291	A401	40c	Pigs	.55	.55
1292	A401	40c	Border collie	.55	.55
a.			Booklet pane of 10, #1283-1292	5.50	
			Complete booklet	5.50	
1293	A401	45c	Sheep	.60	.60
1294	A401	45c	Deer	.60	.60
1295	A401	45c	Horses	.60	.60
1296	A401	45c	Cattle	.60	.60
1297	A401	45c	Goats	.60	.60
1298	A401	45c	Turkey	.60	.60
1299	A401	45c	Ducks	.60	.60
1300	A401	45c	Chickens	.60	.60
1301	A401	45c	Pigs	.60	.60
1302	A401	45c	Border collie	.60	.60
a.			Booklet pane of 10, #1293-1302	6.00	
			Complete booklet, #1302a	6.00	
b.			Souvenir sheet of 5, #1298-1302, perf. 12	3.00	3.00
			Nos. 1283-1302 (20)	11.50	11.50

Singapore '95 (#1302b).
Issued: #1302a, 9/1/95; #1292a, 10/2/95.

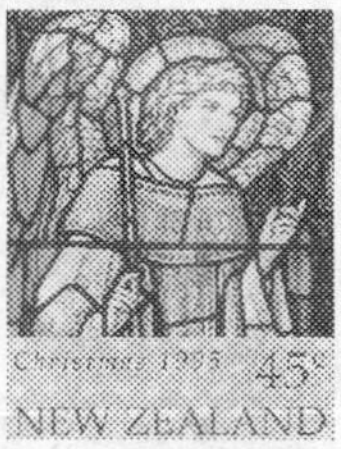

Christmas — A402

Stained glass windows: 40c, 45c, Archangel Gabriel. No. 1309A, Angel with trumpet. 70c, Mary. 80c, Shepherds. $1, Madonna and Child. $1.50, Two wise men. $1.80, One wise man.

1995 *Perf. 12*

1303	A402	40c	multicolored	.55	.55
1304	A402	45c	multicolored	.60	.60
1305	A402	70c	multicolored	.90	.90
1306	A402	80c	multicolored	1.00	1.00
1307	A402	$1	multicolored	1.30	1.30
1308	A402	$1.50	multicolored	2.00	2.00
1309	A402	$1.80	multicolored	2.40	2.40

Booklet Stamp
Size: 25x30mm
Perf. 14½x14

1309A	A402	40c	multicolored	.55	.55
b.			Booklet pane of 10	5.50	
			Complete booklet, #1309b	5.50	
			Nos. 1303-1309A (8)	9.30	9.30

Issued: 45c-$1.80, 9/1; #1303, 10/2; #1309A, 11/9.

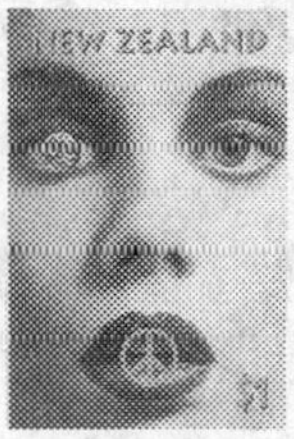

Nuclear Disarmament — A403

1995, Sept. 1 Litho. *Perf. 13½*

1310	A403	$1	multicolored	1.40	1.40

People Reaching People Type of 1994

1995, Oct. 2 Photo. ***Die Cut Perf. 11***
Self-Adhesive

1311	A389	40c	multicolored	.55	.55

Mitre Peak — A404

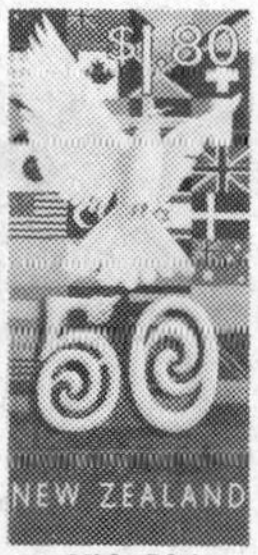

UN, 50th Anniv. — A405

1995, Oct. 2 Litho. *Perf. 13½*

1312	A404	40c	multicolored	.55	.55

1995, Oct. 4 *Perf. 14½*

1313	A405	$1.80	multicolored	2.40	2.40

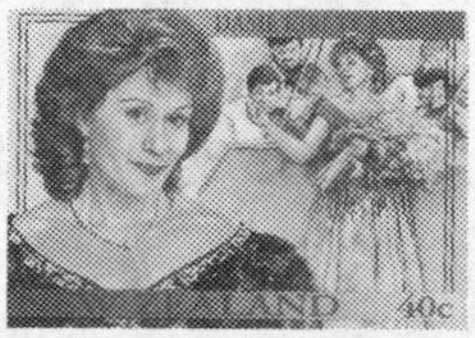

Famous Living New Zealanders — A406

Person, career field: 40c, Dame Kiri Te Kanawa, performing arts. 80c, Charles Upham, service, business, development. $1, Barry Crump, fine arts, literature. $1.20, Sir Brian Barratt-Boyes, science, medicine, education. $1.50, Dame Whina Cooper, community leader, social campaigner. $1.80, Sir Richard Hadlee, sports.

1995, Oct. 4 *Perf. 12*

1314	A406	40c	multicolored	.55	.55
1315	A406	80c	multicolored	1.10	1.10
1316	A406	$1	multicolored	1.40	1.40
1317	A406	$1.20	multicolored	1.65	1.65
1318	A406	$1.50	multicolored	2.00	2.00
1319	A406	$1.80	multicolored	2.40	2.40
			Nos. 1314-1319 (6)	9.10	9.10

Nos. 1314-1319 issued with se-tenant tab inscribed "STAMP / MONTH / OCTOBER / 1995."

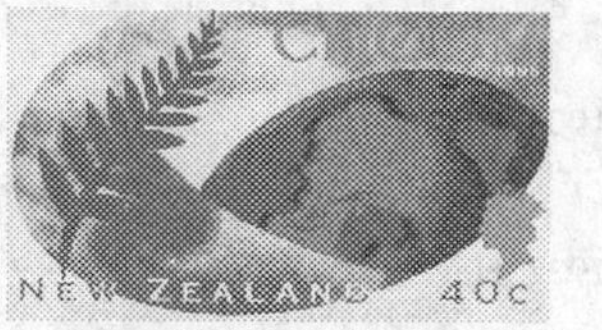

Commonwealth Heads of Government Meeting, Auckland — A407

Designs: 40c, Fern, sky, globe, $1.80, Fern, sea, national flag.

1995, Nov. 9 Litho. *Perf. 14*

1320	A407	40c	multicolored	.55	.55
1321	A407	$1.80	multicolored	2.40	2.40

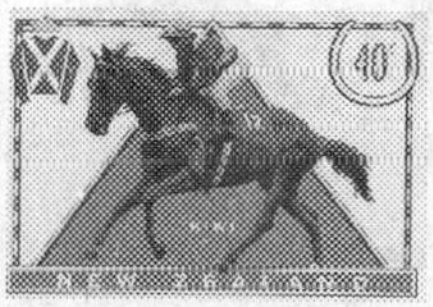

Racehorses
A408

1996, Jan. 24 Litho. *Perf. 13½x14*

1322	A408	40c	Kiwi	.55	.55
1323	A408	80c	Rough Habit	1.10	1.10
1324	A408	$1	Blossom Lady	1.30	1.30
1325	A408	$1.20	Il Vicolo	1.60	1.60
1326	A408	$1.50	Horlicks	2.00	2.00
1327	A408	$1.80	Bonecrusher	2.40	2.40
			Nos. 1322-1327 (6)	8.95	8.95

Booklet

1328	A408	Souvenir bklt.	18.00

#1328 contains one booklet pane of #1322-1327 and individual panes of 1 each #1322-1327.

POSTAL-FISCAL

In 1881 fiscal stamps of New Zealand of denominations over one shilling were made acceptable for postal duty. Values for canceled stamps are for postal cancellations. Denominations above £5 appear to have been used primarily for fiscal purposes.

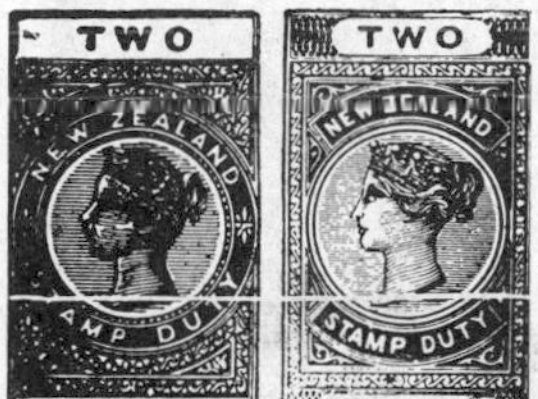

Queen Victoria
PF1 PF2

Perf. 11, 12, 12½

1882 Typo. Wmk. 62

AR1	PF1	2sh	blue	60.00	3.50
AR2	PF1	2sh6p	dk brown	80.00	4.25
AR3	PF1	3sh	violet	125.00	5.00
AR4	PF1	4sh	brown vio	165.00	8.00
AR5	PF1	4sh	red brown	165.00	11.00
AR6	PF1	5sh	green	90.00	11.00
AR7	PF1	6sh	rose	165.00	25.00
AR8	PF1	7sh	ultra	180.00	37.50
AR9	PF1	7sh6p	ol gray	275.00	42.50
AR10	PF1	8sh	dull blue	225.00	37.50
AR11	PF1	9sh	org red	275.00	45.00
AR12	PF1	10sh	red brown	250.00	14.00

1882-90

AR13	PF2	15sh	dk grn	475.00	25.00
AR15	PF2	£1	rose	400.00	40.00
AR16	PF2	25sh	blue		50.00
AR17	PF2	30sh	brown		35.00
AR18	PF2 £1	15sh	yellow		165.00
AR19	PF2	£2	purple		55.00

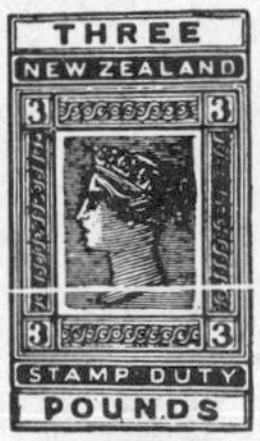

PF3

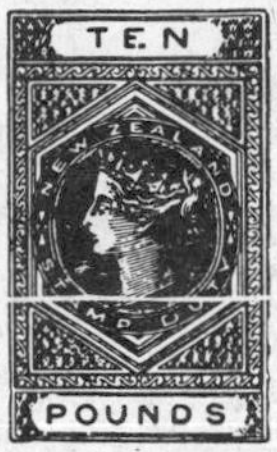

PF4

AR20	PF3 £2	10sh	red brown		75.00
AR21	PF3	£3	yel green		50.00
AR22	PF3 £3	10sh	rose		210.00
AR23	PF3	£4	ultramarine		175.00
AR24	PF3 £4	10sh	olive brown		210.00
AR25	PF3	£5	dark blue		25.00
AR26	PF4	£6	orange red		100.00
AR27	PF4	£7	brown red		100.00
AR28	PF4	£8	green		100.00
AR29	PF4	£9	rose		165.00
AR30	PF4	£10	blue		65.00

With "COUNTERPART" at Bottom

1901

AR31	PF1	2sh6p	brown	250.00	175.00

Perf. 11, 14, 14½x14

1903-15 Wmk. 61

AR32	PF1	2sh	blue ('07)	40.00	4.50
AR33	PF1	2sh6p	brown	40.00	4.50
AR34	PF1	3sh	violet	70.00	5.00
AR35	PF1	4sh	brown red	75.00	7.00
AR36	PF1	5sh	green ('06)	70.00	7.00
AR37	PF1	6sh	rose	140.00	14.00
AR38	PF1	7sh	dull blue	150.00	17.00
AR39	PF1	7sh6p	ol gray ('06)	300.00	55.00
AR40	PF1	8sh	dark blue	150.00	25.00
AR41	PF1	9sh	dl org ('06)	185.00	42.50
AR42	PF1	10sh	dp claret	215.00	12.00
AR43	PF2	15sh	blue grn	275.00	32.50
AR44	PF2	£1	rose	350.00	35.00

Perf 14½

AR45	PF2	£2	deep vio ('25)	500.00	57.50
a.			Perf. 14	525.00	57.50
			Nos. AR32-AR45 (14)	2,560.	318.50

For overprints see Cook Islands Nos. 67-71.

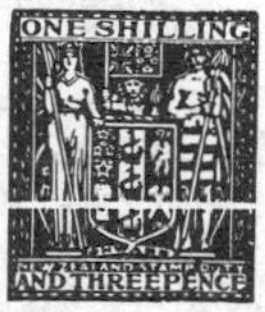

Coat of Arms — PF5

1931-39 *Perf. 14*

Type PF5

AR46	1sh3p	lemon	10.00	5.75
AR47	1sh3p	orange ('32)	3.25	.75
AR48	2sh6p	brown	8.00	.80
AR49	4sh	dull red ('32)	10.00	.95
AR50	5sh	green	15.00	2.25
AR51	6sh	brt rose ('32)	17.50	7.00
AR52	7sh	gray blue	22.50	5.00
AR53	7sh6p	olive gray ('32)	42.50	40.00
AR54	8sh	dark blue	15.00	9.00
AR55	9sh	brn org	30.00	25.00
AR56	10sh	dark car	12.00	4.00
AR57	12sh6p	brn vio ('35)	140.00	140.00
AR58	15sh	ol grn ('32)	50.00	16.00
AR59	£1	pink ('32)	50.00	12.50
AR60	25sh	turq bl ('38)	200.00	225.00
AR61	30sh	dk brn ('36)	250.00	125.00
AR62	35sh	yellow ('37)	1,600.	1,600.
AR63	£2	violet ('33)	250.00	47.50
AR64	£2 10sh	dark red ('36)	200.00	200.00
AR65	£3	light grn ('32)	275.00	80.00
AR66	£3 10sh	rose ('39)	1,000.	750.00
AR67	£4	light blue	275.00	75.00
AR68	£4 10sh	dk ol gray ('39)	1,250.	1,000.
AR69	£5	dk blue ('32)	400.00	125.00

For overprints see Cook Islands Nos. 80-83.

No. AR62 Surcharged in Black **35/-**

1939 *Perf. 14*

AR70	PF5	35sh on 35sh	yel	300.00	250.00

Type PF5 Surcharged in Black

1940 Wmk. 61

AR71	3sh6p on 3sh6p dl green	10.00	4.00
AR72	5sh6p on 5sh6p rose lilac	17.50	12.00
AR73	11sh on 11sh pale yellow	80.00	55.00
AR74	22sh on 22sh scarlet	125.00	100.00
	Nos. AR71-AR74 (4)	232.50	171.00

Type of 1931

1940-58   Wmk. 253   Perf. 14
Type PF5

AR75	1sh3p orange	1.90	.35
AR76	2sh6p brown	5.50	.20
AR77	4sh dull red	6.50	.50
AR78	5sh green	8.50	.75
AR79	6sh brt rose	13.00	2.00
AR80	7sh gray bl	16.00	4.50
AR81	7sh6p ol gray ('50)	42.50	65.00
AR82	8sh dk blue	30.00	6.00
AR83	9sh orange ('46)	20.00	6.00
AR84	10sh dk carmine	16.00	1.25
AR85	15sh olive ('45)	27.50	10.50
AR86	£1 pink ('45)	25.00	3.50
a.	Perf. 14x13½ ('58)	27.50	15.00
AR87	25sh blue ('46)	200.00	200.00
AR88	30sh choc ('46)	165.00	65.00
AR89	£2 violet ('46)	57.50	18.00
AR90	£2 10sh dk red ('51)	190.00	150.00
AR91	£3 lt grn ('46)	60.00	27.50
AR92	£3 10sh rose ('48)	1,250.	900.00
AR93	£4 lt blue ('52)	125.00	35.00
AR94	£5 dk blue ('40)	125.00	40.00

Type PF5 Surcharged in Black

1942-45   Wmk. 253

AR95	3sh6p on 3sh6p grn	7.75	6.50
AR96	5sh6p on 5sh6p rose lil ('44)	11.00	7.00
AR97	11sh on 11sh yel	30.00	24.00
AR98	22sh on 22sh car ('45)	135.00	125.00
	Nos. AR95-AR98 (4)	183.75	162.50

> Catalogue values for unused stamps in this section, from this point to the end of the section, are for Never Hinged items.

Type of 1931 Redrawn Surcharged in Black

1953   Typo.

AR99	PF5 3sh6p on 3sh6p green	35.00	35.00

Denomination of basic stamp is in small, sans-serif capitals without period after "sixpence."

Type of 1931

1955   Wmk. 253   Perf. 14
Denomination in Black

AR100	PF5 1sh3p orange	2.25	.40

1956   Denomination in Blue

AR101	PF5 1sh3p orange yel	12.50	10.00

1967, July 10   Perf. 14

AR102	PF5 $4 purple	5.00	2.50
AR103	PF5 $6 green	7.50	5.00
AR104	PF5 $8 light blue	10.00	8.00
AR105	PF5 $10 dark blue	12.50	10.00
	Nos. AR102-AR105 (4)	35.00	25.50

1987   Unwmk.

AR103a	PF5 $6 green	7.25	7.25
AR104a	PF5 $8 light blue	9.50	9.50
AR105a	PF5 $10 dark blue	12.00	12.00
	Nos. AR103a-AR105a (3)	28.75	28.75

SEMI-POSTAL STAMPS

Nurse
SP1   SP2

Inscribed: "Help Stamp out Tuberculosis, 1929"

Wmk. 61

1929, Dec. 11   Typo.   Perf. 14

B1	SP1 1p + 1p scarlet	10.00	12.50

Inscribed: "Help Promote Health, 1930"

1930, Oct. 29

B2	SP2 1p + 1p scarlet	20.00	20.00

Boy — SP3   Hygeia, Goddess of Health — SP4

1931, Oct. 31   Perf. 14½x14

B3	SP3 1p + 1p scarlet	75.00	75.00
B4	SP3 2p + 1p dark blue	75.00	70.00

1932, Nov. 18   Engr.   Perf. 14

B5	SP4 1p + 1p carmine	25.00	25.00
	Never hinged	40.00	

Road to Health — SP5   Crusader — SP6

1933, Nov. 8

B6	SP5 1p + 1p carmine	10.00	11.00
	Never hinged	19.00	

1934, Oct. 25   Perf. 14x13½

B7	SP6 1p + 1p dark carmine	8.00	8.00
	Never hinged	12.00	

Child at Bathing Beach — SP7    Anzac — SP8

1935, Sept. 30   Perf. 11

B8	SP7 1p + 1p scarlet	1.90	2.00
	Never hinged	3.75	

> Catalogue values for unused stamps in this section, from this point to the end of the section, are for Never Hinged items.

1936, Apr. 27

B9	SP8 ½p + ½p green	.50	.50
B10	SP8 1p + 1p red	.50	.50

21st anniv. of Anzac landing at Gallipoli.

"Health" SP9

1936, Nov. 2

B11	SP9 1p + 1p red	2.00	1.50

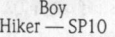 

Boy Hiker — SP10   Children at Play — SP11

1937, Oct. 1

B12	SP10 1p + 1p red	2.50	2.25

Perf. 14x13½

1938, Oct. 1   Wmk. 253

B13	SP11 1p + 1p red	2.00	1.25

Children at Play — SP12   Children in Swing — SP13

1939, Oct. 16   Wmk. 61   Perf. 11½
Black Surcharge

B14	SP12 1p on ½p + ½p grn	2.75	2.75
B15	SP12 2p on 1p + 1p scar	2.75	2.75

1940, Oct. 1

B16	SP12 1p + ½p green	3.50	3.50
B17	SP12 2p + 1p org brown	4.00	4.00

The surtax was used to help maintain children's health camps.

Semi-Postal Stamps of 1940, Overprinted in Black "1941"

1941, Oct. 4   Perf. 11½

B18	SP12 1p + ½p green	.90	.90
B19	SP12 2p + 1p org brown	1.20	1.20

1942, Oct. 1   Engr.

B20	SP13 1p + ½p green	.50	.50
B21	SP13 2p + 1p dp org brown	.60	.60

Princess Margaret Rose — SP14

Design: 2p+1p, Princess Elizabeth.

1943, Oct. 1   Wmk. 253   Perf. 12

B22	SP14 1p + ½p dark green	.15	.15
a.	Vert. pair, imperf. between		
B23	SP14 2p + 1p red brown	.20	.20
a.	Vert. pair, imperf. between		

Princesses Margaret Rose and Elizabeth SP16

1944, Oct. 9   Perf. 13½

B24	SP16 1p + ½p blue green	.15	.15
B25	SP16 2p + 1p chalky blue	.18	.18
	Set value	.28	.28

Peter Pan Statue, London SP17   Statue of Eros, London SP19

Soldier Helping Child over Stile — SP18

1945, Oct. 1

B26	SP17 1p + ½p gray green & bister brown	.15	.15
B27	SP17 2p + 1p car & olive bis	.15	.15
	Set value	.25	.25

1946, Oct. 24   Perf. 13½x13

B28	SP18 1p + ½p dk grn & org brn	.15	.15
B29	SP18 2p + 1p dk brn & org brn	.15	.15
	Set value	.22	.22

1947, Oct. 1   Engr.   Perf. 13x13½

B30	SP19 1p + ½p deep green	.15	.15
B31	SP19 2p + 1p deep carmine	.15	.15
	Set value	.22	.22

Children's Health Camp SP20

1948, Oct. 1   Perf. 13½x13

B32	SP20 1p + ½p blue grn & ultra	.15	.15
B33	SP20 2p + 1p red & dk brown	.15	.15
	Set value	.22	.20

Nurse and Child — SP21   Princess Elizabeth and Prince Charles — SP22

1949, Oct. 3   Photo.   Perf. 14x14½

B34	SP21 1p + ½p deep green	.15	.15
B35	SP21 2p + 1p ultramarine	.15	.15
	Set value	.25	.22

1950, Oct. 2

B36	SP22 1p + ½p green	.15	.15
B37	SP22 2p + 1p violet brown	.15	.15
	Set value	.25	.22

Racing Yachts SP23

Perf. 13½x13

1951, Nov. 1   Engr.   Wmk. 253

B38	SP23 1½p + ½p red & yellow	.15	.15
B39	SP23 2p + 1p dp green & yel	.15	.15
	Set value	.24	.24

Princess Anne — SP24

Prince Charles — SP25

Perf. 14x14½

1952, Oct. 1   Wmk. 253   Photo.
B40 SP24 1½p + ½p crimson   .15 .15
B41 SP25 2p + 1p brown   .20 .15

Girl Guides Marching SP26

Boy Scouts at Camp SP27

1953, Oct. 7
B42 SP26 1½p + ½p bright blue   .15 .15
B43 SP27 2p + 1p deep green   .24 .15

The border of No. B43 consists of Morse code reading "Health" at top and bottom and "New Zealand" on each side. On No. B42 the top border line is replaced by "Health" in Morse code.

Young Mountain Climber Studying Map — SP28

1954, Oct. 4   Engr.   Perf. 13½
B44 SP28 1½p + ½p pur & brown   .16 .15
B45 SP28 2p + 1p vio gray & brn   .20 .16

Child's Head SP29

Children Picking Apples SP30

1955, Oct. 3   Wmk. 253   Perf. 13
B46 SP29 1½p + ½p brn org & sep   .15 .15
B47 SP29 2p + 1p grn & org brn   .18 .15
B48 SP29 3p + 1p car & sepia   .22 .20
  Nos. B46-B48 (3)   .55
    Set value   .40

1956, Sept. 24
B49 SP30 1½p + ½p chocolate   .15 .15
B50 SP30 2p + 1p blue green   .16 .15
B51 SP30 3p + 1p dark carmine   .18 .16
  Nos. B49-B51 (3)   .49
    Set value   .34

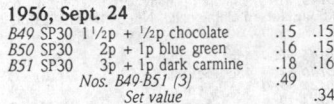

Life-Saving Team — SP31

Design: 3p+1p, Children playing and boy in canoe.

1957, Sept. 25   Perf. 13½
B52 SP31 2p + 1p emer & blk   .22 .18
  a. Miniature sheet of 6   5.75 5.75
B53 SP31 3p + 1p car & ultra   .22 .18
  a. Miniature sheet of 6   5.75 5.75

The watermark is sideways on Nos. B52a and B53a. In a second printing, the watermark is upright; values double.

Girls' Life Brigade Cadet — SP32

Design: 3p+1p, Bugler, Boys' Brigade.

1958, Aug. 20   Photo.   Perf. 14x14½
B54 SP32 2p + 1p green   .15 .15
  a. Miniature sheet of 6   5.75 5.75
B55 SP32 3p + 1p ultramarine   .15 .15
  a. Miniature sheet of 6   5.75 5.75

75th anniv. of the founding of the Boys' Brigade. The surtax on this and other preceding semi-postals was for the maintenance of children's health camps.

Globes and Red Cross Flag — SP33

1959, June 3   Perf. 14½x14
B56 SP33 3p + 1p ultra & car   .25 .15
  a. Red Cross omitted   1,200.

The surtax was for the Red Cross.

Gray Teal (Tete) — SP34

Sacred Kingfisher (Kotare) — SP35

Design: 3p+1p, Pied stilt (Poaka).

1959, Sept. 16   Perf. 14x14½
B57 SP34 2p + 1p pink, black, yellow & gray   .16 .15
  a. Miniature sheet of 6   6.50 6.50
B58 SP34 3p + 1p blue, black & pink   .16 .15
  a. Miniature sheet of 6   6.50 6.50
  b. Pink omitted   150.00 50.00

1960, Aug. 10   Engr.   Perf. 13x13½

Design: 3p+1p, NZ pigeon (Kereru).

B59 SP35 2p + 1p grnsh blue & sepia   .30 .25
  a. Min. sheet of 6, perf. 11½x11   12.00 12.00
B60 SP35 3p + 1p org & sepia   .38 .30
  a. Min. sheet of 6, perf. 11½x11   12.00 12.00

Type of 1959

Birds: 2p+1p, Great white egret (kotuku). 3p+1p, NZ falcon (karearea).

1961, Aug. 2   Wmk. 253
B61 SP34 2p + 1p pale lil & blk   .24 .20
  a. Miniature sheet of 6   9.00 9.00
B62 SP34 3p + 1p yellow green & black brown   .30 .28
  a. Miniature sheet of 6   9.00 9.00

Type of 1959

Birds: 2½p+1p, Red-fronted parakeet (kakariki). 3p+1p, Saddleback (tieke).

1962, Oct. 3   Photo.   Perf. 15x14
B63 SP34 2½p + 1p lt bl, blk, grn & org   .22 .20
  a. Miniature sheet of 6   10.00 10.00
B64 SP34 3p + 1p salmon, blk, grn & org   .25 .22
  a. Miniature sheet of 6   10.00 10.00
  b. Orange omitted

Prince Andrew SP36

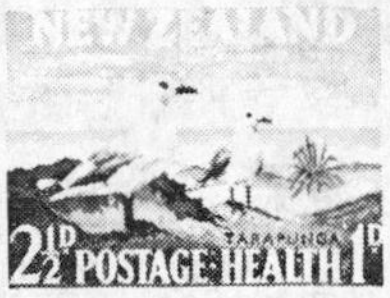

Red-billed Gull (Tarapunga) SP37

Design: 3p+1p, Prince without book.

1963, Aug. 7   Engr.   Perf. 14
B65 SP36 2½p + 1p ultramarine   .18 .15
  a. Miniature sheet of 6   8.50 8.50
B66 SP36 3p + 1p rose car   .22 .15
  a. Miniature sheet of 6   8.50 8.50

1964, Aug. 5   Photo.   Perf. 14

Design: 3p+1p, Blue penguin (korora).

B67 SP37 2½p + 1p lt bl, pale yel, red & blk   .28 .18
  a. Miniature sheet of 8   20.00 20.00
  b. Red omitted
  c. Yellow omitted
B68 SP37 3p + 1p blue, yellow & black   .32 .28
  a. Miniature sheet of 8   20.00 20.00

Kaka — SP38

Bellbird & Bough of Kowhai Tree — SP39

Design: 4p+1p, Fantail (piwakawaka).

1965, Aug. 4   Perf. 14x14½
B69 SP38 3p + 1p gray, red, brn & yellow   .22 .18
  a. Miniature sheet of 6   11.50 11.50
B70 SP38 4p + 1p yel, blk, emerald & brown   .25 .22
  a. Miniature sheet of 6   11.50 11.50

1966, Aug. 3   Photo.   Wmk. 253

Design: 4p+1p, Flightless rail (weka) and fern.

B71 SP39 3p + 1p lt bl & multi   .18 .15
  a. Miniature sheet of 6   7.50 7.50
B73 SP39 4p + 1p lt grn & multi   .24 .20
  a. Miniature sheet of 6   7.50 7.50
  b. Brown omitted

National Team Rugby Player and Boy — SP40

Design: 3c+1c, Man and boy placing ball for place kick, horiz.

1967, Aug. 2   Perf. 14½x14, 14x14½
B73 SP40 2½c + 1c multicolored   .18 .15
  a. Miniature sheet of 6   7.75 7.75
B74 SP40 3c + 1c multicolored   .20 .18
  a. Miniature sheet of 6   7.75 7.75

Boy Running and Olympic Rings — SP41

Design: 3c+1c, Girl swimming and Olympic rings.

1968, Aug. 7   Perf. 14½x14
B75 SP41 2½c + 1c multicolored   .15 .15
  a. Miniature sheet of 6   7.50 7.50
B76 SP41 3c + 1c multicolored   .18 .15
  a. Miniature sheet of 6   7.50 7.50

Boys Playing Cricket — SP42

Dr. Elizabeth Gunn — SP43

Design: 3c+1c, playing cricket.

Perf. 13½x13, 13x13½
1969, Aug. 6   Litho.   Unwmk.
B77 SP42 2½c + 1c multicolored   .15 .15
  a. Miniature sheet of 6   8.00 8.00
B78 SP42 3c + 1c multicolored   .18 .15
  a. Miniature sheet of 6   8.00 8.00
B79 SP43 4c + 1c multicolored   2.00 2.00
  a. Miniature sheet of 6   8.00 8.00
  Nos. B77-B79 (3)   2.33

50th anniv. of Children's Health Camps, founded by Dr. Elizabeth Gunn.

Boys Playing Soccer SP44

Design: 2½c+1c, Girls playing basketball, vert.

1970, Aug. 5   Unwmk.   Perf. 13½
B80 SP44 2½c + 1c multicolored   .20 .18
  a. Miniature sheet of 6   7.75 7.75
B81 SP44 3c + 1c multicolored   .22 .20
  a. Miniature sheet of 6   7.75 7.75

Hygienist and Child SP45

Designs: 3c+1c, Girls playing hockey. 4c+1c, Boys playing hockey.

1971, Aug. 4   Litho.   Perf. 13½
B82 SP45 3c + 1c multicolored   .25 .22
  a. Miniature sheet of 6   8.00 8.00
B83 SP45 4c + 1c multicolored   .30 .25
  a. Miniature sheet of 6   8.00 8.00
B84 SP45 5c + 1c multicolored   .65 .65
  a. Miniature sheet of 6   8.00 8.00
  Nos. B82-B84 (3)   1.20

50th anniv. of School Dental Service (No. B84).

Boy Playing Tennis — SP46

Prince Edward — SP47

Design: 4c+1c, Girl playing tennis.

1972, Aug. 2   Litho.   Perf. 13x13½
B85 SP46 3c + 1c gray & lt brn   .24 .20
  a. Miniature sheet of 6   9.25 9.25
B86 SP46 4c + 1c brown, yellow & gray   .24 .20
  a. Miniature sheet of 6   9.25 9.25

1973, Aug. 1   Photo.
B87 SP47 3c + 1c green & brown   .24 .20
  a. Miniature sheet of 6   8.25 8.25
B88 SP47 4c + 1c dk red & blk   .24 .20
  a. Miniature sheet of 6   8.25 8.25

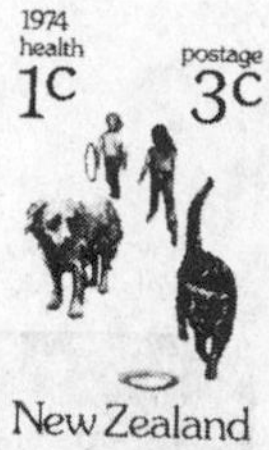

Children with Cat and Dog — SP48

Designs: 4c+1c, Girl with dogs and cat. 5c+1c, Children and dogs.

1974, Aug. 7 Litho. *Perf. 13½x14*

B89 SP48 3c + 1c multicolored .20 .16
B90 SP48 4c + 1c multicolored .28 .24
a. Miniature sheet of 10 22.50 22.50
B91 SP48 5c + 1c multicolored .90 .90
Nos. B89-B91 (3) 1.38 1.30

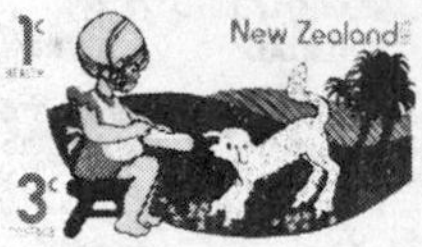

Girl Feeding Lamb SP49

Designs: 4c+1c, Boy with hen and chicks. 5c+1c, Boy with duck and duckling.

1975, Aug. 6 Litho. *Perf. 14x13½*

B92 SP49 3c + 1c multicolored .20 .16
B93 SP49 4c + 1c multicolored .24 .20
a. Miniature sheet of 10 18.00 18.00
B94 SP49 5c + 1c multicolored .60 .60
Nos. B92-B94 (3) 1.04 .96

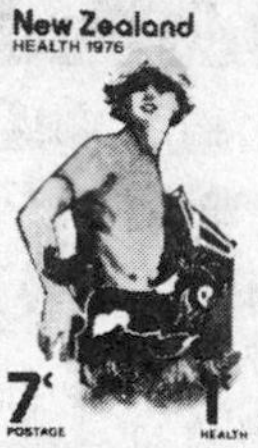

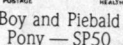

Boy and Piebald Pony — SP50

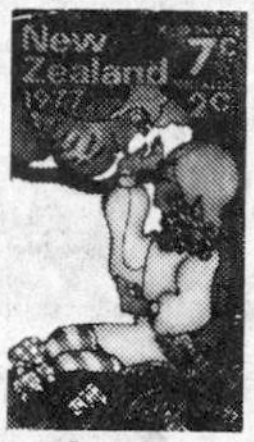

Girl and Bluebird — SP51

Designs: 8c+1c, Farm girl and calf. 10c+1c, 2 girls watching nest-bound thrush.

1976, Aug. 4 Litho. *Perf. 13½x14*

B95 SP50 7c + 1c multicolored .25 .25
B96 SP50 8c + 1c multicolored .30 .30
B97 SP50 10c + 1c multicolored .52 .52
a. Miniature sheet, 2 each #B95-B97 7.25 7.25
Nos. B95-B97 (3) 1.07 1.07

1977, Aug. 3 Litho. *Perf. 13½x14*

Designs: 8c+2c, Boy and frog. 10c+2c, Girl and butterfly.

B98 SP51 7c + 2c multi .20 .15
B99 SP51 8c + 2c multi .24 .20
B100 SP51 10c + 2c multi .30 .30
a. Miniature sheet of 6 4.25 4.25
Nos. B98-B100 (3) .74 .65

No. B100a contains 2 each of Nos. B98-B100 in 2 strips of continuous design.

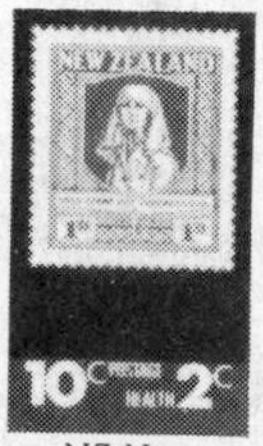

NZ No. B1 — SP52

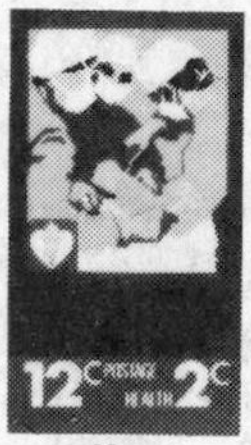

Heart Surgery — SP53

1978, Aug. 2 Litho. *Perf. 13½x14*

B101 SP52 10c + 2c multi .32 .32
B102 SP53 12c + 2c multi .35 .35
a. Min. sheet, 3 each #B101-B102 4.50 4.50

50th Health Stamp issue (No. B101) and National Heart Foundation (No. B102).

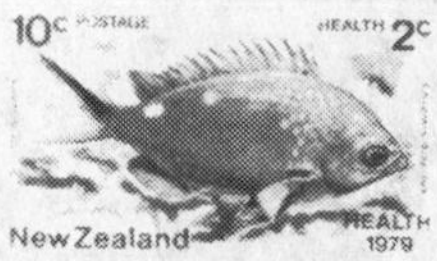

Demoiselle Fish — SP54

Designs: No. B104, Sea urchin. 12c+2c, Underwater photographer and red mullet, vert.

Perf. 13½x13, 13x13½

1979, July 25

B103 SP54 10c + 2c multi .20 .16
B104 SP54 10c + 2c multi .20 .16
a. Pair, #B103-B104 .40 .40
B105 SP54 12c + 2c multi .28 .28
a. Min. sheet, 2 each #B103-B105 3.50 3.50
Nos. B103-B105 (3) .68 .60

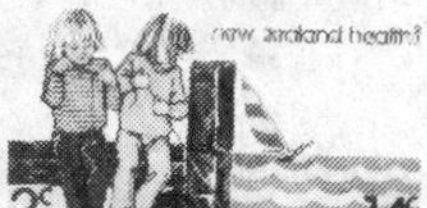

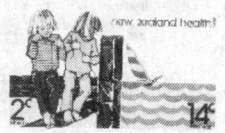

Children Wharf Fishing SP55

1980, Aug. 6 Litho. *Perf. 13½x13*

B106 SP55 14c + 2c shown .22 .22
B107 SP55 14c + 2c Surfcasting .22 .22
a. Pair, #B106-B107 .45 .45
B108 SP55 17c + 2c Underwater fishing .28 .28
a. Min. sheet, 2 each #B106-B108 2.10 2.10
Nos. B106-B108 (3) .72 .72

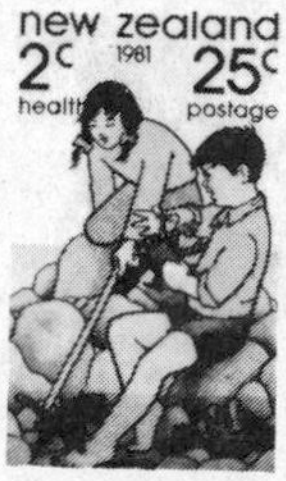

Boy and Girl at Rock Pool — SP56

1981, Aug. 5 Litho. *Perf. 14½*

B109 SP56 20c + 2c Girl, starfish .35 .35
B110 SP56 20c + 2c Boy fishing .35 .35
a. Pair, #B109-B110 .70 .70
B111 SP56 25c + 2c shown .40 .40
a. Min. sheet, 2 each #B109-B111 2.00 2.00
Nos. B109-B111 (3) 1.10 1.10

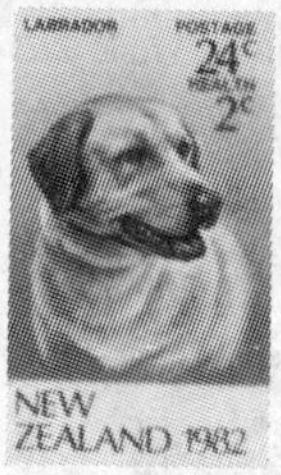

Labrador — SP57

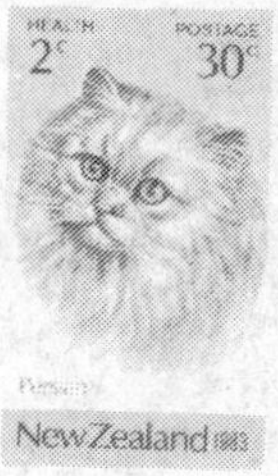

Persian Cat — SP58

1982, Aug. 4 Litho. *Perf. 13x13½*

B112 SP57 24c + 2c shown .35 .35
B113 SP57 24c + 2c Border collie .35 .35
a. Pair, #B112-B113 .70 .70
B114 SP57 30c + 2c Cocker spaniel .45 .45
a. Min. sheet, 2 each #B112-B114, perf. 14x13½ 2.50 2.50
Nos. B112-B114 (3) 1.15 1.15

1983, Aug. 3 Litho. *Perf. 14½*

B115 SP58 24 + 2c Tabby .35 .35
B116 SP58 24 + 2c Siamese .35 .35
a. Pair, #B115-B116 .70 .70
B117 SP58 30 + 2c shown .45 .45
a. Min. sheet, 2 each #B115-B117 2.50 2.50
Nos. B115-B117 (3) 1.15 1.15

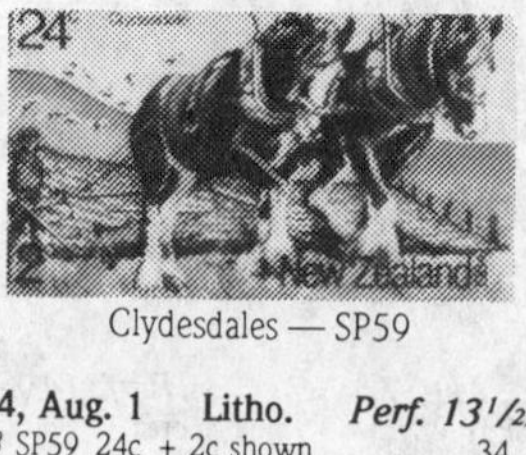

Clydesdales — SP59

1984, Aug. 1 Litho. *Perf. 13½x13*

B118 SP59 24c + 2c shown .34 .34
B119 SP59 24c + 2c Shetlands .34 .34
a. Pair, #B118-B119 .70 .70
B120 SP59 30c + 2c Thoroughbreds .42 .42
a. Min. sheet, 2 each #B118-B120 2.25 2.25
Nos. B118-B120 (3) 1.10 1.10

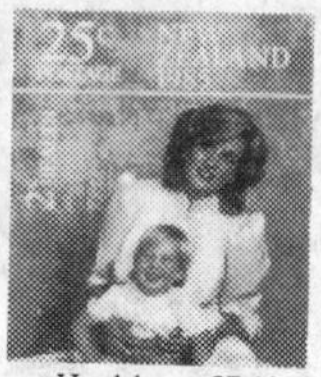

Health — SP60

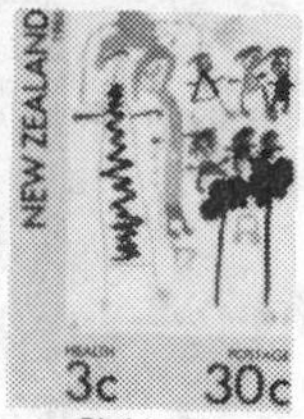

Children's Drawings — SP61

Princess Diana and: No. B121, Prince William. No. B122, Prince Henry. No. B123, Princes Charles, William and Henry.

1985, July 31 Litho. *Perf. 13½*

B121 SP60 25c + 2c multi .28 .28
B122 SP60 25c + 2c multi .28 .28
a. Pair, #B121-B122 .60 .60
B123 SP60 35c + 2c multi .38 .38
a. Min. sheet, 2 each #B121-B123 2.00 2.00
Nos. B121-B123 (3) .94 .94

Surtax for children's health camps.

1986, July 30 Litho. *Perf. 14½x14*

B124 SP61 30c + 3c shown .38 .38
B125 SP61 30c + 3c Children playing .38 .38
a. Pair, #B124-B125 .80 .80
B126 SP61 45c + 3c Skipping rope, horiz. .55 .55
a. Min. sheet, 2 each #B124-B126 2.75 2.75
Nos. B124-B126 (3) 1.31 1.31

Surtax for children's health camps.
No. B126a exists with Stockholmia '86 emblem.

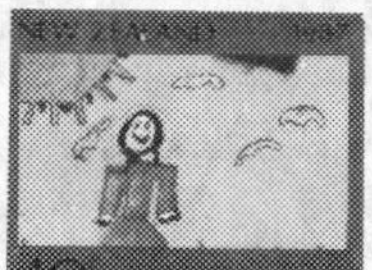

Children's Drawings SP62

1987, July 29 Litho. *Perf. 14½*

B127 SP62 40c + 3c shown .52 .52
B128 SP62 40c + 3c Swimming .52 .52
a. Pair, #B127-B128 1.10 1.10
B129 SP62 60c + 3c Riding horse, vert. .75 .75
a. Min. sheet, 2 each #B127-B129 3.75 3.75
Nos. B127-B129 (3) 1.79 1.79

Surtax benefited children's health camps.

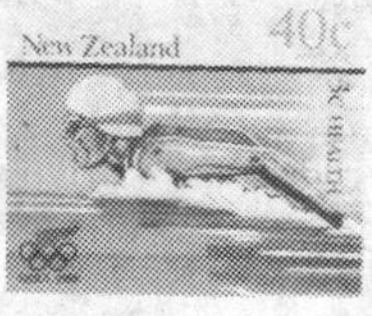

1988 Summer Olympics, Seoul — SP63

1988, July 27 Litho. *Perf. 14½*

B130 SP63 40c + 3c Swimming .60 .60
B131 SP63 60c + 3c Running .88 .88
B132 SP63 70c + 3c Rowing 1.00 1.00
B133 SP63 80c + 3c Equestrian 1.15 1.15
a. Souvenir sheet of 4, #B130-B133 3.75 3.75
Nos. B130-B133 (4) 3.63 3.63

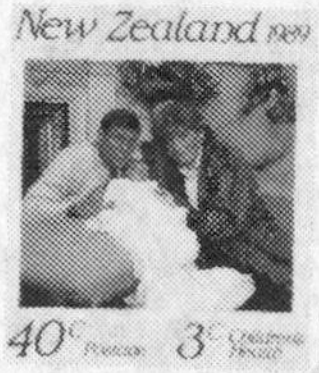

Children's Health — SP64

Designs: No. B134, Duke and Duchess of York, Princess Beatrice. No. B135, Duchess, princess. No. B136, Princess.

1989, July 23

B134 SP64 40c + 3c multi .55 .55
B135 SP64 40c + 3c multi .55 .55
a. Pair, #B134-B135 1.25 1.25
B136 SP64 80c + 3c multi 1.05 1.05
a. Min. sheet, 2 each #B134-B136 4.30 4.30
Nos. B134-B136 (3) 2.15 2.15

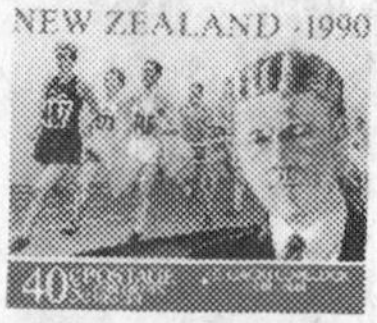

Athletes — SP65

Designs: 40c+5c, Jack Lovelock (1910-1949), runner. 80c+5c, George Nepia (1905-1986), rugby player.

1990, July 25 Litho. *Perf. 14½x14*

B137 SP65 40c +5c multi .50 .50
B138 SP65 80c +5c multi 1.00 1.00
a. Min. sheet, 2 each #B137-B138 3.00 3.00

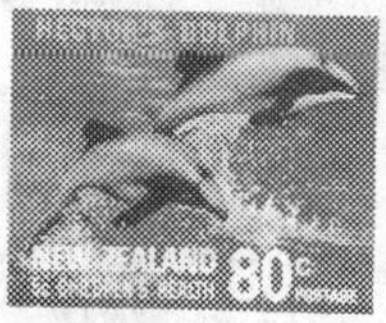

Hector's Dolphin — SP66

1991, July 24 Litho. *Perf. 14½*

B139 SP66 45c +5c 3 swimming .55 .55
B140 SP66 80c +5c 2 jumping .90 .90
a. Souvenir sheet, 2 each #B139-B140 2.90 2.90

Surtax benefited children's health camps.

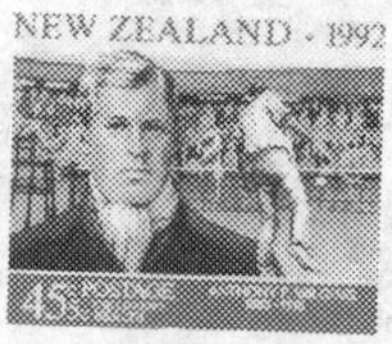

Anthony F. Wilding (1883-1915), Tennis Player — SP67

Design: No. B142, C.S. "Stewie" Dempster (1903-1974), cricket player.

1992, Aug. 12 Litho. *Perf. 14x13½*

B141 SP67 45c +5c multi .50 .50
B142 SP67 80c +5c multi .85 .85
a. Souv. sheet, 2 each #B141-B142, perf. 14½ 2.70 2.70

Surtax for children's health camps.

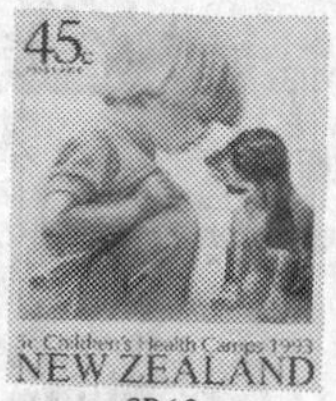

SP68

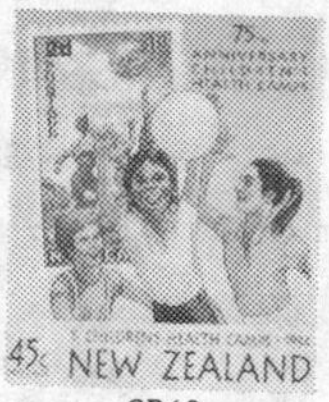

SP69

1993, July 21 Litho. *Perf. 13½x14*

B143 SP68 45c +5c Boy, puppy .55 .55
B144 SP68 80c +5c Girl, kitten .95 .95
a. Souvenir sheet, 2 each #B143-B144, perf. 14½ 3.00 3.00
b. As "a," inscribed in sheet margin 3.00 3.00

Surtax for children's health camps.
No. B144b inscribed with "TAIPEI '93" emblem.
Issue date: No. B144b, Aug. 14.

1994, July 20 Litho. *Perf. 14*

Children's Health Camps, 75th Anniv.: No. B145, #B15, Children playing with ball. No. B146, #B34, Nurse holding child. No. B147, #B79, Children reading. 80c+5c, #B4, Boy.

B145 SP69 45c +5c multi .60 .60
B146 SP69 45c +5c multi .60 .60
B147 SP69 45c +5c multi .60 .60
B148 SP69 80c +5c multi 1.00 1.00
a. Souvenir sheet of 4, #B145-B148 2.80 2.80
Nos. B145-B148 (4) 2.80 2.80

Surtax for children's health camps.

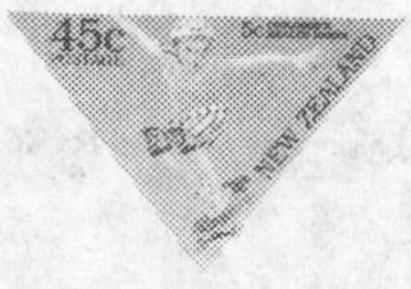

Children's Health Camps SP70

Designs: 45c+5c, Boy on skateboard. 80c+5c, Child on bicycle.

1995, June 21 Litho. *Perf. 14½*

B149 SP70 45c +5c multi .65 .65
B150 SP70 80c +5c multi 1.25 1.25
a. Souvenir sheet, 2 each #B149-B150 3.75 3.75
b. As "a," with added inscription 3.75 3.75

No. B150b inscribed with Stampex '95 emblem in sheet margin.
Surtax for children's health camps.

AIR POST STAMPS

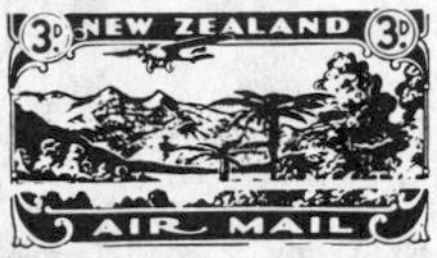

Plane over Lake Manapouri
AP1

Perf. 14x14½

1931, Nov. 10 Typo. Wmk. 61

C1 AP1 3p chocolate 17.50 12.50
a. Perf. 14x15 200.00 *425.00*
C2 AP1 4p dark violet 20.00 24.00
C3 AP1 7p orange 24.00 15.00
Nos. C1-C3 (3) 61.50 51.50

Most copies of No. C1a are poorly centered.

Type of 1931 Surcharged in Red **FIVE PENCE**

1931, Dec. 18 *Perf. 14x14½*

C4 AP1 5p on 3p yel green 10.00 8.00

Type of 1931 Overprinted in Dark Blue

TRANS-TASMAN AIR MAIL "FAITH IN AUSTRALIA."

1934, Feb. 17

C5 AP1 7p bright blue 24.00 24.00

1st official air mail flight between NZ and Australia.

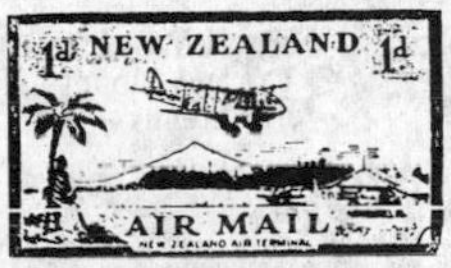

Airplane over Landing Field — AP2

1935, May 4 Engr. *Perf. 14*

C6 AP2 1p rose carmine .55 .28
C7 AP2 3p dark violet 1.40 1.25
C8 AP2 6p gray blue 2.25 1.80
Nos. C6-C8 (3) 4.20 3.33
Set, never hinged 11.00

SPECIAL DELIVERY STAMPS

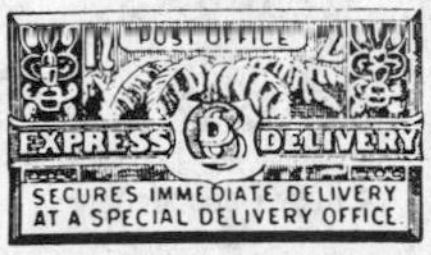

SD1

1903-26 Typo. Wmk. 61 *Perf. 14x15*

E1 SD1 6p purple & red ('26) 30.00 20.00
a. 6p violet & red, perf. 11 32.50 17.50

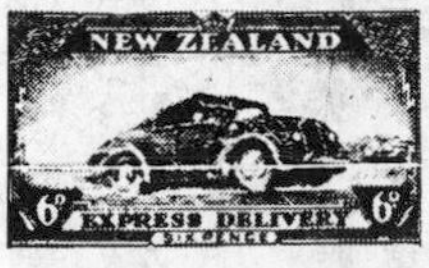

Mail Car — SD2

1939, Aug. 16 Engr. *Perf. 14*

E2 SD2 6p violet 1.50 2.25
Never hinged 2.00

POSTAGE DUE STAMPS

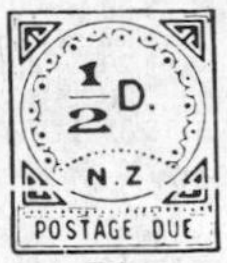

D1

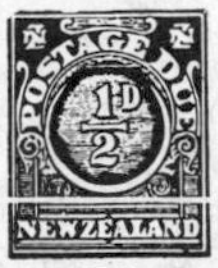

D2

Wmk. 62

1899, Dec. 1 Typo. *Perf. 11*

J1 D1 ½p green & red 4.50 7.00
a. No period after "D" 37.50 37.50
J2 D1 1p green & red 8.00 2.00
J3 D1 2p green & red 16.00 2.50
J4 D1 3p green & red 14.00 2.75
J5 D1 4p green & red 15.00 6.50
J6 D1 5p green & red 19.00 19.00
J7 D1 6p green & red 27.50 22.50
J8 D1 8p green & red 72.50 110.00
J9 D1 10p green & red 77.50 65.00
J10 D1 1sh green & red 72.50 55.00
J11 D1 2sh green & red 125.00 110.00
Nos. J1-J11 (11) 451.50 402.25

Nos. J1-J11 may be found with N. Z. and D. varying in size.

1902, Feb. 28 Unwmk.

J12 D2 ½p gray grn & red 2.50 3.50

Wmk. 61

J13 D2 ½p gray grn & red 1.40 1.25
J14 D2 1p gray grn & red 8.25 3.75
J15 D2 2p gray grn & red 160.00 160.00

1904-28 *Perf. 14, 14x14½*

J16 D2 ½p green & car 2.25 1.75
J17 D2 1p green & car 1.25 .40
J18 D2 2p green & car 4.50 .80
J19 D2 3p grn & rose ('28) 18.00 19.00
Nos. J16-J19 (4) 26.00 21.95

N Z and Star printed on the back in Blue

1925 Unwmk. *Perf. 14x14½, 14x15*

J20 D2 ½p green & rose 2.50 *12.50*
J21 D2 2p green & rose 4.00 *9.50*

Catalogue values for unused stamps in this section, from this point to the end of the section, are for Never Hinged items.

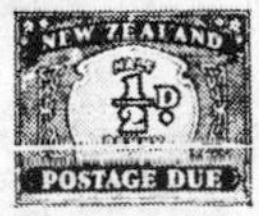

D3

1939 Wmk. 61 Typo. *Perf. 15x14*

J22 D3 ½p turquoise green 5.00 *3.00*
J23 D3 1p rose pink .70 .35
J24 D3 2p ultramarine 6.50 2.00
J25 D3 3p brown orange 16.00 6.50
Nos. J22-J25 (4) 28.20 11.85

1945-49 Wmk. 253

J27 D3 1p rose pink ('49) 1.00 1.00
J28 D3 2p ultramarine ('47) 2.00 2.00
J29 D3 3p brown orange 11.00 7.00
Nos. J27-J29 (3) 14.00 10.00

The use of postage due stamps was discontinued in Sept., 1951.

WAR TAX STAMP

No. 144 Overprinted in Black **★ ★ WAR STAMP**

Perf. 14x14½

1915, Sept. 24 Wmk. 61

MR1 A43 ½p green .50 .15

OFFICIAL STAMPS

Regular Issues Ovptd. "O. P. S. O." Handstamped on Stamps of 1882-92

1892 Wmk. 62 *Perf as Before*

Rose or Magenta Handstamp

O1 A9 1p rose *325.*
O2 A10 2p violet *475.*
O3 A16 2½p ultramarine *275.*
O4 A17 5p olive gray *475.*
O5 A13 6p brown *550.*

Violet Handstamp

O6 N1 ½p rose *625.*
O7 A9 1p rose *210.*
O8 A10 2p violet

Handstamped on No. 67A in Rose

1899 *Perf. 10, 10x11, 11*

O9 A15a ½p black *210.*

Handstamped on No. 79 in Violet

Unwmk. *Perf. 14, 15*

O10 A27 8p dull blue *550.*

Handstamped on Stamps of 1899-1900 in Violet

1902 *Perf. 11*

O11 A22 2½p blue *500.*
O12 A23 3p org brown *500.*
O13 A25 5p red brown *400.*
O14 A27 8p dark blue *385.*

Green Handstamp

O15 A25 5p red brown *385.*

Handstamped on Stamp of 1901 in Violet

Wmk. 63 *Perf. 11, 14*

O16 A35 1p carmine *250.*

Handstamped on Stamps of 1902-07 in Violet or Magenta

1905-07 Wmk. 61

O17 A18 ½p green *250.*
O18 A35 1p carmine *250.*
O19 A22 2½p blue *300.*
O20 A25 5p red brown
O21 A27 8p deep blue
O22 A30 2sh blue green *1,000.*

The "O. P. S. O." handstamp is usually struck diagonally, reading up, but on No. O19 it also occurs horizontally. The letters stand for "On Public Service Only."

Overprinted in Black **OFFICIAL.**

On Stamps of 1902-07

1907 *Perf. 14, 14x13, 14x14½*

O23 A18 ½p green 7.50 .65
O24 A35 1p carmine 8.00 .40
a. Booklet pane of 6 60.00
O25 A33 2p violet 7.50 1.10
O26 A23 3p orange brn 35.00 2.50
O27 A26 6p carmine rose 105.00 14.00
a. Horiz. pair, imperf. vert. *1,000.*
O28 A29 1sh brown red 80.00 18.00
O29 A30 2sh blue green 70.00 30.00
a. Horiz. pair, imperf. vert. *1,500.*
O30 A31 5sh vermilion 175.00 150.00
Nos. O23-O30 (8) 488.00 214.65

On No. 127

Perf. 14x13, 14x14½

O31 A26 6p carmine rose 175.00 35.00

On No. 129

1909 *Perf. 14x14½*

O32 A35 1p car (redrawn) 57.50 .60

On Nos. 130-131, 133, 137, 139

1910 *Perf. 14, 14x13½, 14x14½*

O33 A41 ½p yellow green 1.90 .15
O34 A42 1p carmine 1.10 .15
O35 A41 3p orange brown 10.00 1.75
O36 A41 6p carmine rose 15.00 2.75
O37 A41 1sh vermilion 25.00 8.25
Nos. O33-O37 (5) 53.00 13.05

On Postal-Fiscal Stamps No. AR32, AR36, AR44

1911-14

O38 PF1 2sh blue ('14) 18.00 20.00
O39 PF1 5sh green ('13) 65.00 52.50
O40 PF2 £1 rose 525.00 450.00
Nos. O38-O40 (3) 608.00 522.50

On Stamps of 1909-19

Perf. 14x13½, 14x14½

1915-19 Typo.

O41 A43 ½p green .95 .15
O42 A46 1½p gray black ('16) 8.50 1.00
O43 A47 1½p gray black ('16) 3.75 .20
O44 A47 1½p brown org ('19) 3.00 .15
O45 A43 2p yellow ('17) 1.10 .15
O46 A43 3p chocolate ('19) 4.75 .15

Engr.

O47 A45 3p vio brn ('16) 2.00 .85
O48 A45 6p car rose ('16) 1.50 .32
O49 A41 8p dp bl (R) ('16) 12.00 *20.00*
O50 A45 1sh vermilion ('16) 7.75 2.75
a. 1sh orange 7.75 2.75
Nos. O41-O50 (10) 45.30 *25.72*

On No. 157

1922

O51 A45 8p red brown 100.00 90.00

On Nos. 151, 158

1925

O52 A45 4p purple 15.00 1.00
O53 A45 9p olive green 25.00 17.00

On No. 177

1925 *Perf. 14x14½*

O54 A42 1p carmine 3.25 5.00

On Nos. 184, 182

1927-28 Wmk. 61 *Perf. 14, 14½x14*

O55 A57 1p rose red 1.25 .15
O56 A56 2sh blue 60.00 35.00

On No. AR50

1933 *Perf. 14*

O57 PF5 5sh green 275.00 275.00

Nos. 186, 187, 196 Overprinted in Black ***Official***

1936 *Perf. 14x13½, 13½x14, 14*

O58 A59 1p copper red 1.75 .15
O59 A60 1½p red brown 9.50 11.00
O60 A69 1sh dark slate grn 5.50 7.50
Nos. O58-O60 (3) 16.75 18.65

Same Overprint Horizontally in Black or Green on Stamps of 1936

Perf. 12½, 13½, 13x13½, 14x13½, 13½x14, 14

1936-42 Wmk. 253

O61 A58 ½p brt grn ('37) 2.75 1.75
O62 A59 1p copper red 2.00 .15
O63 A60 1½p red brown 2.75 2.50
O64 A61 2p red org ('38) .65 .15
a. Perf. 12½ ('42) 27.50 11.00
O65 A62 2½p dk gray & dk brown 3.50 3.00
O66 A63 3p choc ('38) 20.00 1.75
O67 A64 4p blk brn & blk 2.00 .22
O68 A66 6p red ('37) 2.25 .32
O68B A67 8p dp brn ('42) 2.75 2.25
O69 A68 9p black & scar (G) ('38) 14.00 14.00
O70 A69 1sh dk slate grn 4.00 .50

Overprint Vertical

O71 A70 2sh ol grn ('37) 11.00 2.75
Nos. O61-O71 (12) 67.65 29.34

Same Overprint Horizontally in Black on Nos. 226, 227, 228

1938

O72 A79 ½p emerald 6.00 1.65
O73 A79 1p rose red 8.00 .30
O74 A80 1½p violet brn 40.00 10.00
Nos. O72-O74 (3) 54.00 11.95

Same Overprint on No. AR50

1938 Wmk. 61 *Perf. 14*

O75 PF5 5sh green 17.00 16.00

Nos. 229-235, 237, 239-241 Overprinted in Red or Black ***Official***

Perf. 13½x13, 13x13½, 14x13½

1940 Wmk. 253

O76 A81 ½p dk bl grn (R) .20 .25
a. "ff" joined 20.00 18.00
O77 A82 1p scar & sepia .50 .15
a. "ff" joined 20.00 18.00
O78 A83 1½p brt vio & ultra .50 .38
O79 A84 2p black brn & Prus green .80 .15
a. "ff" joined 20.00 18.00
O80 A85 2½p dk bl & myr grn 1.50 3.50
a. "ff" joined 20.00 18.00
O81 A86 3p deep plum & dark vio (R) 2.50 .50
a. "ff" joined 20.00 18.00
O82 A87 4p dark red vio & violet brn 3.00 1.25
a. "ff" joined 24.00 24.00

O83	A89	6p vio & brt grn	7.50	1.25
a.		"ff" joined	30.00	24.00
O84	A90	8p org red & blk	10.00	7.00
a.		"ff" joined	30.00	24.00
O85	A91	9p dp org & olive	3.00	4.00
O86	A92	1sh dk sl grn & ol	17.50	4.00
		Nos. O76-O86 (11)	47.00	22.43

Nos. 227A, 228C Overprinted in Black — *Official*

1941 Wmk. 253 *Perf. 13½*

O88	A79	1p light blue green	.20	.15
O89	A80	3p blue	.35	.15
		Set value		.18

Same Overprint on No. 245

1944 *Perf. 14x15*

Size: 17¼x20¼mm

O90	A68	9p int black & scar	12.00	18.00

Same Overprint on No. AR78

Perf. 14

O91	PF5	5sh green	7.75	5.00

Catalogue values for unused stamps in this section, from this point to the end of the section, are for Never Hinged items.

Same Ovpt. on Stamps of 1941-47

1946-51 *Perf. 13½, 14*

O92	A79	½p brn org ('46)	1.75	.55
O92B	A80	1½p red	4.50	.65
O93	A80	2p orange	.85	.15
O94	A80	4p rose lilac	4.00	.70
O95	A80	6p rose carmine	7.00	.60
O96	A80	8p deep violet	8.50	3.50
O97	A80	9p chocolate	13.00	6.50
O98	A104	1sh dk car rose & chestnut	12.00	.70
O99	A104	2sh dk green & brown org	9.00	11.00
		Nos. O92-O99 (9)	60.60	24.35

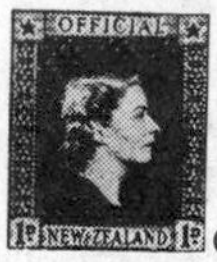

Queen Elizabeth II — O1

Perf. 13½x13

1954, Mar. 1 Engr. Wmk. 253

O100	O1	½p orange	.20	.15
O101	O1	1½p rose brown	1.25	1.25
O102	O1	2p green	.60	.15
O103	O1	3p red	.40	.15
O104	O1	4p blue	.65	.15
O105	O1	9p rose carmine	1.40	.20
O106	O1	1sh rose violet	2.25	.45
		Nos. O100-O106 (7)	6.75	2.50

Nos. O102, O101 Surcharged with New Value and Dots

1959-61

O107	O1	2½p on 2p green ('61)	1.00	.60
O108	O1	6p on 1½p rose brn	1.50	.85

1963, Mar. 1

O109	O1	2½p dark olive	2.00	1.00
O111	O1	3sh slate	32.50	32.50

LIFE INSURANCE

Lighthouses
LI1 LI2

Perf. 10, 11, 10x11, 12x11½

1891, Jan. 2 Typo. Wmk. 62

OY1	LI1	½p purple	65.00	2.00
OY2	LI1	1p blue	60.00	.45
OY3	LI1	2p red brown	65.00	1.50
OY4	LI1	3p chocolate	275.00	22.50
OY5	LI1	6p green	375.00	55.00
OY6	LI1	1sh rose pink	725.00	140.00
		Nos. OY1-OY6 (6)	1,565.	221.45

Stamps from outside rows of the sheets sometimes lack watermark.

Perf. 11, 14x11, 14

1903-04 Wmk. 61

OY7	LI1	½p purple	42.50	2.25
OY8	LI1	1p blue	67.50	.85
OY9	LI1	2p red brown	65.00	25.00
		Nos. OY7-OY9 (3)	175.00	28.10

1905-32 *Perf. 11, 14, 14x14½*

OY10	LI2	½p yel grn ('13)	2.00	.50
OY11	LI2	½p green ('32)	1.75	1.40
OY12	LI2	1p blue	200.00	25.00
OY13	LI2	1p dp rose ('13)	11.00	.50
OY14	LI2	1p scarlet ('31)	5.00	.50
OY15	LI2	1½p gray ('17)	25.00	3.00
OY16	LI2	1½p brn org ('19)	1.50	1.00
OY17	LI2	2p red brown	1,800.	125.00
OY18	LI2	2p violet ('13)	25.00	12.50
OY19	LI2	2p yellow ('21)	4.50	2.00
OY20	LI2	3p ocher ('13)	22.50	15.00
OY21	LI2	3p choc ('31)	11.00	8.00
OY22	LI2	6p carmine rose ('13)	19.00	17.50
OY23	LI2	6p pink ('31)	15.00	15.00
		Nos. OY10-OY23 (14)	2,143.	226.90

#OY15, OY16 have "POSTAGE" at each side.

Stamps from outside rows of the sheets sometimes lack watermark.

1946-47 Wmk. 253 *Perf. 14x15*

OY24	LI2	½p yel grn ('47)	1.90	1.90
OY25	LI2	1p scarlet	2.00	1.40
OY26	LI2	2p yellow	2.25	1.40
OY27	LI2	3p chocolate	11.00	13.00
OY28	LI2	6p pink ('47)	6.50	10.00
		Nos. OY24-OY28 (5)	23.65	27.70
		Set, never hinged	30.00	

Catalogue values for unused stamps in this section, from this point to the end of the section, are for Never Hinged items.

New Zealand Lighthouses

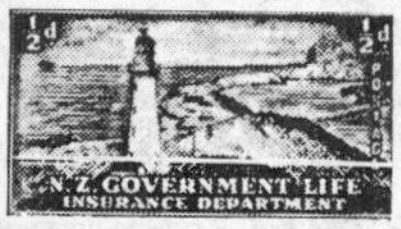

Castlepoint
LI3

Taiaroa — LI4

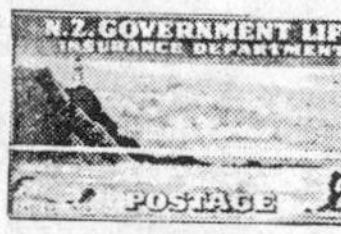

Cape Palliser
LI5

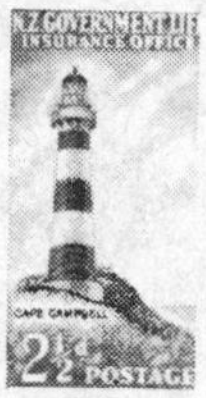

Cape Campbell
LI6

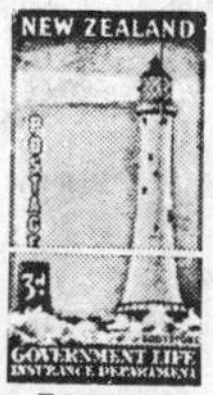

Eddystone (England)
LI7

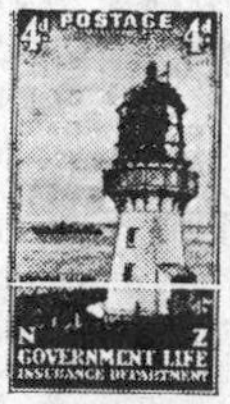

Stephens Island
LI8

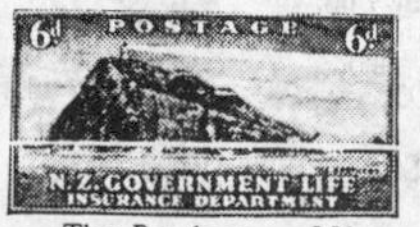

The Brothers — LI9

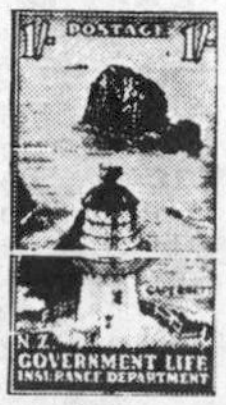

Cape Brett — LI10

Perf. 13½x13, 13x13½

1947-65 Engr. Wmk. 253

OY29	LI3	½p dk grn & red orange	2.50	1.75
OY30	LI4	1p dk ol grn & blue	.30	.35
OY31	LI5	2p int bl & gray	.35	.20
OY32	LI6	2½p ultra & blk ('63)	7.50	5.50
OY33	LI7	3p red vio & bl	1.00	.22
OY34	LI8	4p dk brn & org	3.00	.90
a.		Wmkd. sideways ('65)	9.00	7.00
OY35	LI9	6p dk brn & bl	2.20	1.40
OY36	LI10	1sh red brn & bl	2.00	1.40
		Nos. OY29-OY36 (8)	18.85	11.72

Set first issued Aug. 1, 1947.

Nos. OY30, OY32-OY33, OY34a, OY35-OY36 and Types Surcharged

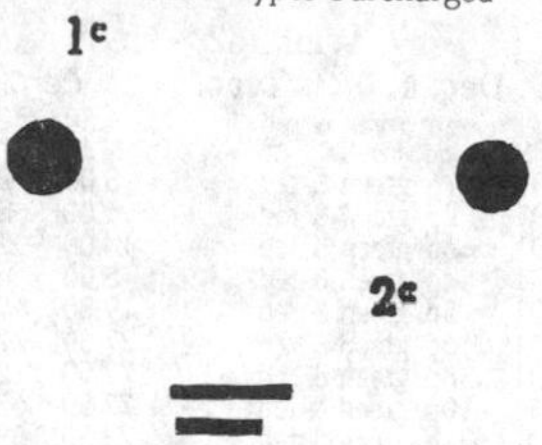

Perf. 13½x13, 13x13½

1967-68 Engr. Wmk. 253

OY37	LI4	1c on 1p dk ol grn & lt bl	1.75	1.65
a.		Wmkd. upright ('68)	2.00	1.40
OY38	LI6	2c on 2½p ultra & black	6.00	5.00
OY39	LI7	2½c on 3p, wmkd. sideways ('68)	3.00	3.25
a.		Watermarked upright	2.75	1.90
OY40	LI8	3c on 4p dk brn & orange	4.00	3.50
OY41	LI9	5c on 6p dk brn & blue	3.50	4.00
OY42	LI10	10c on 1sh red brn & bl, wmkd. sideways	2.50	3.25
a.		Watermarked upright	7.00	7.00
		Nos. OY37-OY42 (6)	20.75	20.65

The surcharge is different on each stamp and is adjusted to obliterate old denomination. One dot only on 2½c.

Set first issued July 10, 1967.

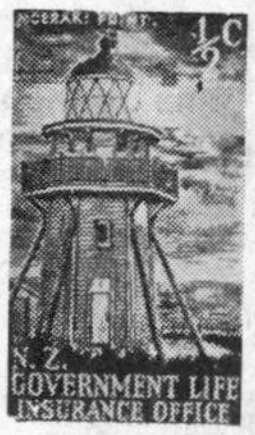

Moeraki Point Lighthouse — LI11

Lighthouses: 2½c, Puysegur Point, horiz. 3c, Baring Head. 4c, Cape Egmont, horiz. 8c, East Cape. 10c, Farewell Spit. 15c, Dog Island.

Perf. 13x13½, 13½x13, 14 (8c, 10c)

1969-76 Litho. Unwmk.

OY43	LI11	½c pur, bl & yel	1.75	1.75
OY44	LI11	2½c yel, ultra & grn	1.10	.50
OY45	LI11	3c yellow & brown	.15	.20
OY46	LI11	4c lt ultra & ocher	.15	.20
OY47	LI11	8c multicolored	.25	.40
OY48	LI11	10c multicolored	.30	.30
OY49	LI11	15c multicolored	2.75	1.40
a.		Perf. 14 ('78)	.42	.45
		Nos. OY43-OY49 (7)	6.45	4.75

Cent. of Government Life Insurance Office.

Issued: #OY47-OY48, 11/17/76; others 3/27/69.

No. OY44 Surcharged with New Value and 4 Diagonal Bars

Perf. 13½x13

1978, Mar. 8 Litho. Wmk. 253

OY50	LI11	25c on 2½c multi	.75	.75

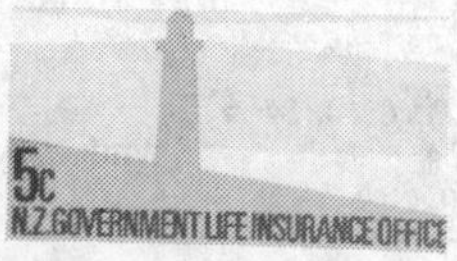

Lighthouse LI12

1981, June 3 Litho. *Perf. 14½*

OY51	LI12	5c multicolored	.15	.15
OY52	LI12	10c multicolored	.15	.15
OY53	LI12	20c multicolored	.25	.25
OY54	LI12	30c multicolored	.40	.40
OY55	LI12	40c multicolored	.52	.52
OY56	LI12	50c multicolored	.65	.65
		Nos. OY51-OY56 (6)	2.12	2.12

Government Life Insurance Stamps have been discontinued.

NEWSPAPER STAMPS

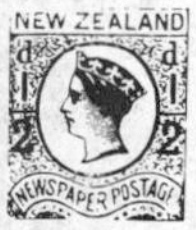

Queen Victoria — N1

Wmk. 59

1873, Jan. 1 Typo. *Perf. 10*

P1	N1	½p rose	40.00	12.50
a.		Perf. 12½x10	125.00	62.50
b.		Perf. 12½	125.00	47.50

The "N Z" watermark (illustrated over No. 27) is widely spaced and intended for larger stamps. About a third of the stamps in each sheet are unwatermarked. They are worth a slight premium.

For overprint, see No. O6.

1875, Jan. Wmk. 64 *Perf. 12½*

P3	N1	½p rose	7.50	.65
a.		Pair, imperf. between	750.00	375.00
b.		Perf. 12	50.00	4.50

1892 Wmk. 62 *Perf. 12½*

P4	N1	½p bright rose	2.00	.25
a.		Unwatermarked	10.00	4.50

ROSS DEPENDENCY

Catalogue values for unused stamps in this section are for Never Hinged items.

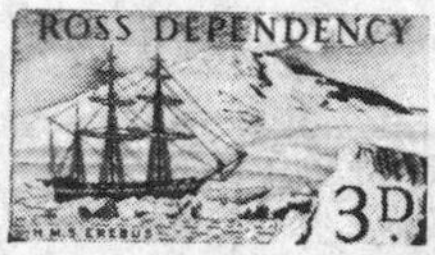

H.M.S. Erebus and Mount Erebus — A1

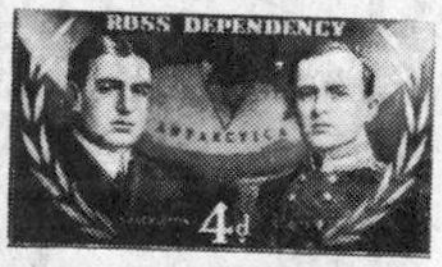

Ernest H. Shackleton and Robert F. Scott — A2

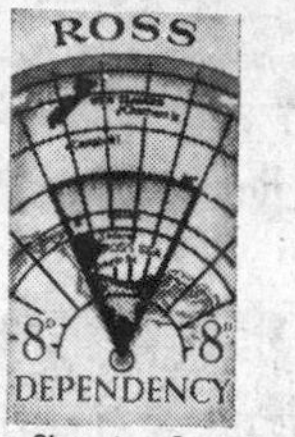

Map Showing Location of Ross Dependency
A3

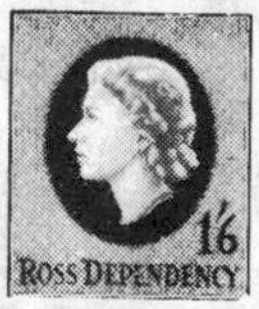

Queen Elizabeth II
A4

Perf. 14, 13 (A4)

1957, Jan. 11 Engr. Wmk. 253

L1	A1	3p dark blue	1.75	1.75
L2	A2	4p dark carmine	2.00	1.90
L3	A3	8p ultra & car rose	2.50	1.90
L4	A4	1sh6p dull violet	4.50	3.50
		Nos. L1-L4 (4)	10.75	9.05

1967, July 10

L5	A1	2c dark blue	6.50	4.50
L6	A2	3c dark carmine	6.50	4.50
L7	A3	7c ultra & car rose	7.75	5.25
L8	A4	15c dull violet	16.00	10.50
		Nos. L5-L8 (4)	36.75	24.75

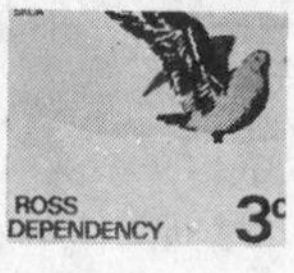

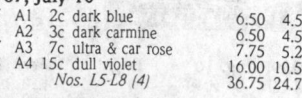

Skua — A5

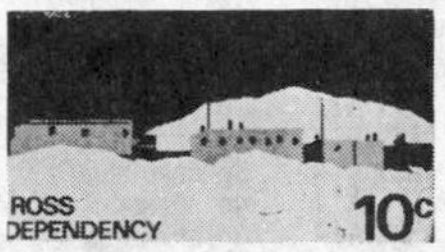

Scott Base — A6

Designs: 4c, Hercules plane unloading at Williams Field. 5c, Shackleton's hut, Cape Royds. 8c, Naval supply ship Endeavour unloading. 18c, Tabular ice floe.

Perf. 13x13½

1972, Jan. 18	Litho.	Unwmk.	
L9 A5	3c lt bl, blk & gray	.55	.50
L10 A5	4c black & violet	.45	.42
L11 A5	5c rose lil, blk & gray	.50	.45
L12 A5	8c blk, dk gray & brn	.80	.75

Perf. 14x13½

L13 A6	10c slate grn, brt grn & blk ('79)	.65	.60
a.	Perf. 14½x14	.45	.45
L14 A6	18c pur & black ('79)	1.25	1.10
a.	Perf. 14½x14	1.10	1.10
	Nos. L9-L14 (6)	4.20	3.82

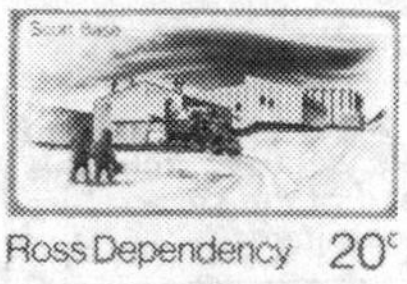

25th Anniv. of Scott Base — A7

1982, Jan. 20	Litho.	*Perf. 15½*	
L15 A7	5c Adelie penguins	.15	.15
L16 A7	10c Tracked vehicles	.15	.15
L17 A7	20c shown	.18	.16
L18 A7	30c Field party, Upper Taylor Valley	.45	.40
L19 A7	40c Vanda Station	.75	.70
L20 A7	50c Scott's hut, Cape Evans, 1911	.90	.85
	Nos. L15-L20 (6)	2.58	2.41

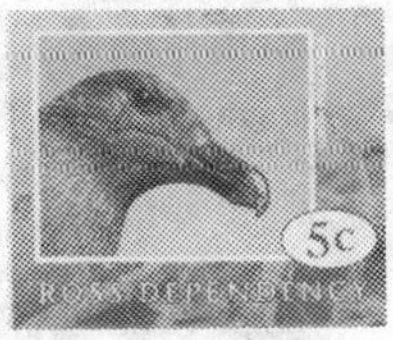

Wildlife — A8

1994-95	Litho.	*Perf. 13½*	
L21 A8	5c South polar skua	.15	.15
L22 A8	10c Snow petrel chick	.15	.15
L23 A8	20c Black-browed albatross	.25	.25
L23A A8	40c like No. 24	.55	.55
L24 A8	45c Emperor penguins	.55	.55
L25 A8	50c Chinstrap penguins	.60	.60
L26 A8	70c Adelie penguins	.85	.85
L27 A8	80c Elephant seals	1.00	1.00
L28 A8	$1 Leopard seal	1.25	1.25
L29 A8	$2 Weddell seal	2.50	2.50
L30 A8	$3 Crabeater seal pup	3.75	3.75
	Nos. L21-L30 (11)	11.60	11.60

Issued: 40c, 10/2/95; others, 11/2/94.

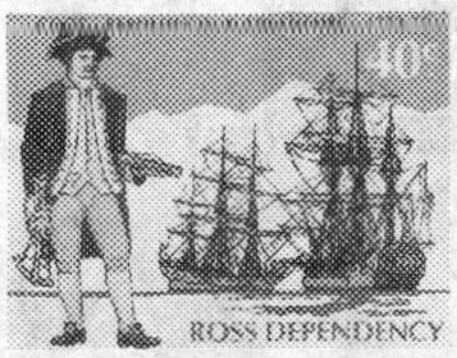

Antarctic Explorers A9

Explorer, ships: 40c, James Cook, Resolution & Adventure. 80c, James Clark Ross, Erebus & Terror. $1, Roald Amundsen, Fram. $1.20, Robert Falcon Scott, Terra Nova. $1.50, Ernest Henry Shackleton, Endurance. $1.80, Richard Evelyn Byrd, Floyd Bennett (airplane).

1995, Nov. 9	Litho.	*Perf. 14½*	
L31 A9	40c multicolored	.55	.55
L32 A9	80c multicolored	1.10	1.10
L33 A9	$1 multicolored	1.40	1.40
L34 A9	$1.20 multicolored	1.65	1.65
L35 A9	$1.50 multicolored	2.00	2.00
L36 A9	$1.80 multicolored	2.40	2.40
	Nos. L31-L36 (6)	9.10	9.10

NIGER COAST PROTECTORATE

'nī–jər 'kōst prə–'tek–t(ə–)rət

(Oil Rivers Protectorate)

LOCATION — West coast of Africa on Gulf of Guinea
GOVT. — British Protectorate

This territory was originally known as the Oil Rivers Protectorate, and its affairs were conducted by the British Royal Niger Company. The Company surrendered its charter to the Crown in 1899. In 1900 all of the territories formerly controlled by the Royal Niger Company were incorporated into the two protectorates of Northern and Southern Nigeria, the latter absorbing the area formerly known as Niger Coast Protectorate. In 1914 Northern and Southern Nigeria joined to form the Crown Colony of Nigeria. (See Nigeria, Northern Nigeria, Southern Nigeria and Lagos.)

12 Pence = 1 Shilling

Stamps of Great Britain, 1881-87, Overprinted in Black

BRITISH
PROTECTORATE

OIL RIVERS

1892	Wmk. 30	*Perf. 14*	
1 A54	½p vermilion	7.25	3.50
2 A40	1p lilac	6.50	2.50
a.	"OIL RIVERS" at top	4,500.	
b.	Half used as ½p on cover		3,000.
3 A56	2p green & car	7.25	3.50
a.	Half used as 1p on cover		—
4 A57	2½p violet, *bl*	3.50	2.00
5 A61	5p lilac & blue	5.00	4.00
6 A65	1sh green	45.00	50.00
	Nos. 1-6 (6)	74.50	65.50

For surcharges see Nos. 7-36, 50.

No. 2 Surcharged in Red or Violet

½d
½d

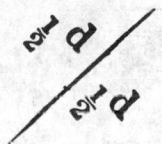

1893			
7 A40	½p on half of 1p (R)	150.	140.
c.	Unsevered pair	400.	400.
d.	"½" omitted		
7A A40	½p on half of 1p (V)	5,500.	4,750.
b.	Surcharge double	9,000.	

Nos. 3-6 Handstamp Surcharged in Violet, Red, Carmine, Bluish Black, Deep Blue, Green or Black

Half
Penny

1893	Wmk. 30	*Perf. 14*	
8 A56	½p on 2p (V)	250.	250.
9 A57	½p on 2½p (V)	3,000.	
10 A57	½p on 2½p (R)	190.	130.
11 A57	½p on 2½p (C)	7,250.	6,500.
12 A57	½p on 2½p (B)	7,250.	6,500.
13 A57	½p on 2½p (G)	375.	375.

HALF
PENNY.

14 A56	½p on 2p (V)	250.	250.
15 A56	½p on 2p (Bl)	1,000.	500.
16 A57	½p on 2½p (V)	2,750.	
17 A57	½p on 2½p (R)	350.	350.
18 A57	½p on 2½p (Bl)	275.	275.
19 A57	½p on 2½p (G)	300.	300.

HALF
PENNY

20 A56	½p on 2p (V)	500.	300.
21 A57	½p on 2½p (R)	300.	300.
22 A57	½p on 2½p (C)	200.	200.
23 A57	½p on 2½p (Bl Bk)	2,500.	
24 A57	½p on 2½p (Bl)	250.	250.
25 A57	½p on 2½p (G)	190.	190.
26 A57	½p on 2½p (Bk)	2,250.	

HALF
PENNY

27 A57	½p on 2½p (R)	3,750.	
28 A57	½p on 2½p (G)	325.	325.

One
Shilling

29 A56	1sh on 2p (V)	450.	450.
30 A56	1sh on 2p (R)	375.	475.
31 A56	1sh on 2p (Bk)	5,500.	

5/–

32 A56	5sh on 2d (V)	5,750.	5,750.
33 A61	10sh on 5p (R)	6,000.	6,000.
34 A65	20sh on 1sh (V)	62,500.	
35 A65	20sh on 1sh (R)	85,000.	
36 A65	20sh on 1sh (Bk)	85,000.	

The handstamped 1893 surcharges are known inverted, vertical, etc.

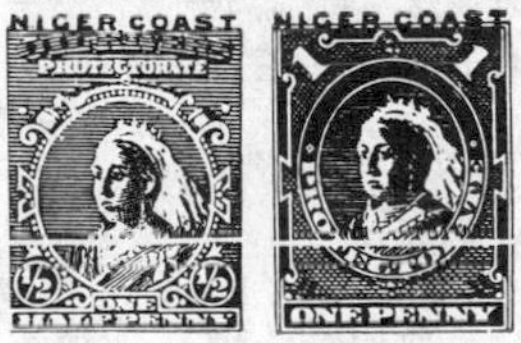

Queen Victoria
A8 A9

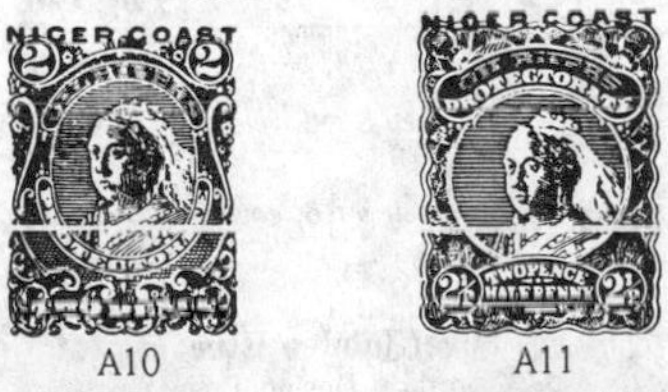

A10 A11

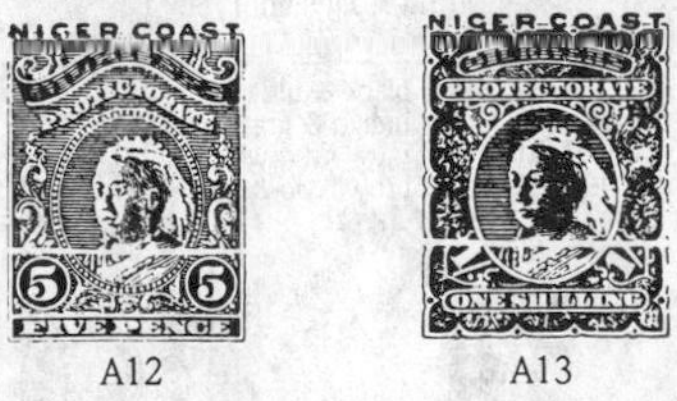

A12 A13

1893	Unwmk.	*Perf. 12 to 15*	
37 A8	½p vermilion	4.00	3.50
38 A9	1p light blue	4.50	3.50
a.	Half used as ½p on cover		600.00
39 A10	2p green	17.00	14.00
a.	Half used as 1p on cover		800.00
b.	Horiz. pair, imperf. between		4,000.
40 A11	2½p car lake	3.75	3.00
41 A12	5p gray lilac	12.00	8.50
a.	5p lilac	11.00	12.50
42 A13	1sh black	15.00	12.00
	Nos. 37-42 (6)	56.25	44.50

For surcharge see No. 49.

Niger Coast Protectorate stamps can be mounted in the Scott British Africa album.

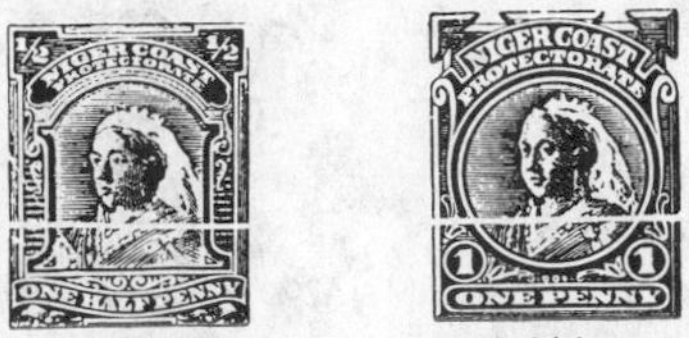

A15 A16

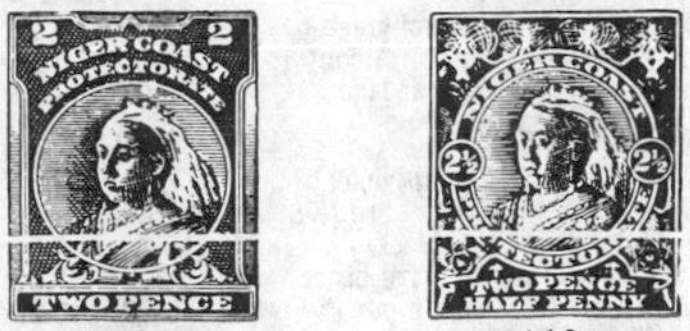

A17 A18

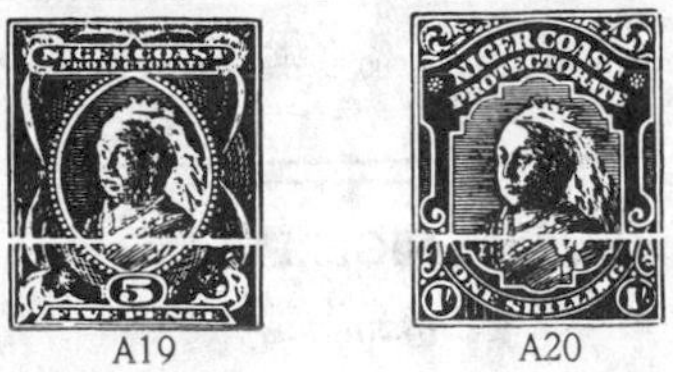

A19 A20

1894		Engr.	
43 A15	½p yel green	1.50	2.50
44 A16	1p vermilion	7.50	3.00
a.	1p orange vermilion	9.00	7.00
b.	Diagonal half, used as ½p on cover		600.00
45 A17	2p car lake	12.00	5.00
a.	Half used as 1p on cover		
46 A18	2½p blue	10.00	3.50
47 A19	5p dp violet	5.00	5.00
48 A20	1sh black	16.00	11.00
	Nos. 43-48 (6)	52.00	30.00

See #55-59, 61. For surcharges see #51-54.

Halves of Nos. 38, 3 and 44 Surcharged in Red, Blue, Violet or Black:

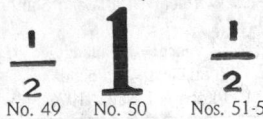

1/2 (No. 49) 1 (No. 50) 1/2 (Nos. 51-53)

1894			
49 A9	½p on half of 1p (R)	1,100.	250.00
a.	Inverted surcharge	5,250.	

Perf. 14
Wmk. 30

50 A56	1p on half of 2p (R)	600.	300.
a.	Double surcharge	1,250.	1,100.
b.	Inverted surcharge		1,100.

Perf. 12 to 15
Unwmk.

51 A16	½p on half of 1p (Bl)	1,400.	250.
a.	Double surcharge		
52 A16	½p on half of 1p (V)	1,300.	400.
53 A16	½p on half of 1p (Bk)	1,750.	500.

This surcharge is found on both vertical and diagonal halves of the 1p.

No. 46 Surcharged in Black

ONE
HALF PENNY

1894			
54 A18	½p on 2½p blue	300.	200.
a.	Double surcharge	1,750.	1,750.

The surcharge is found in eight types. The "OIE" variety is broken type.

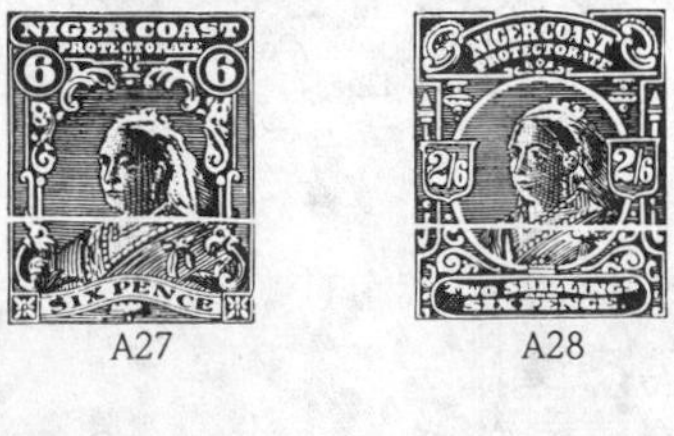

A27 A28

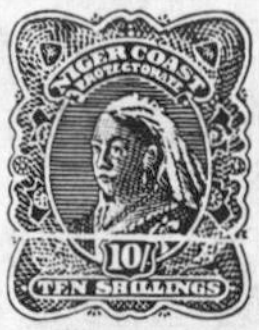
A29

1897-98 **Wmk. 2**

55	A15	½p yel green	2.00	1.25
56	A16	1p vermilion	2.50	1.25
57	A17	2p car lake	2.00	1.25
58	A18	2½p blue	3.00	2.00
a.		2½p slate blue	3.00	1.65
59	A19	5p dp violet	8.00	50.00
60	A27	6p yel brn ('98)	7.00	6.00
61	A20	1sh black	15.00	15.00
62	A28	2sh6p olive bister	30.00	35.00
63	A29	10sh dp pur ('98)	80.00	140.00
a.		10sh bright purple	85.00	140.00
		Nos. 55-63 (9)	149.50	251.75

The stamps of Niger Coast Protectorate were superseded in Jan. 1900, by those of Northern and Southern Nigeria.

NIGERIA

nī-'jir-ē-ə

LOCATION — West coast of Africa, bordering on the Gulf of Guinea
GOVT. — Republic
AREA — 356,669 sq. mi.
POP. — 82,390,000 (est. 1983)
CAPITAL — Lagos

The colony and protectorate were formed in 1914 by the union of Northern and Southern Nigeria. The mandated territory of Cameroons (British) was also attached for administrative purposes. The Federation of Nigeria was formed in 1960. It became a republic in 1963. See Niger Coast Protectorate, Lagos, Northern Nigeria and Southern Nigeria.

12 Pence = 1 Shilling
20 Shillings = 1 Pound
100 Kobo = 1 Naira (1973)

Catalogue values for unused stamps in this country are for Never Hinged items, beginning with Scott 71 in the regular postage section, Scott B1 in the semi-postal section and Scott J1 in the postage due section.

Watermarks

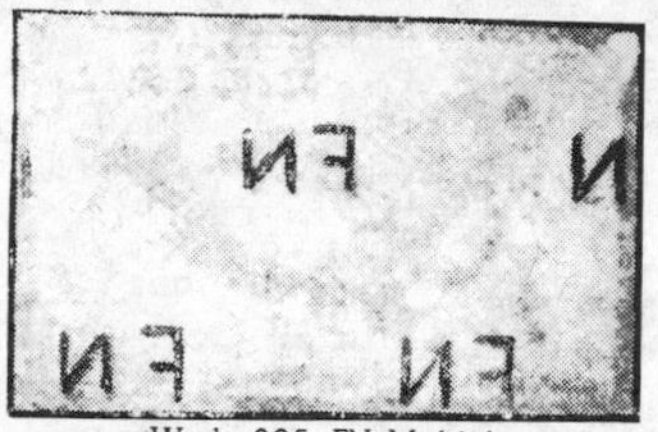
Wmk. 335- FN Multiple

Wmk. 379- NIGERIA in Continuous Wavy Lines

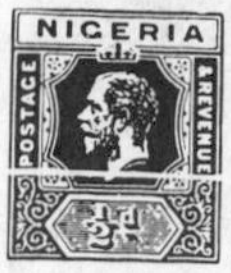
King George V — A1

Numerals of 3p, 4p, 6p, 5sh and £1 of type A1 are in color on plain tablet.

Dies I and II are described at back of this volume.

Wmk. Multiple Crown and CA (3)

1914-27 **Typo.** ***Perf. 14***

Die I

Ordinary Paper

1	A1	½p green	1.00	.30
a.		Booklet pane of 6		
2	A1	1p carmine	2.00	.15
a.		Booklet pane of 6		
b.		1p scarlet	2.50	.15
3	A1	2p gray	2.00	1.00
4	A1	2½p ultramarine	1.50	1.00

Chalky Paper

5	A1	3p violet, *yel*	1.50	1.50
6	A1	4p black & red, *yel*	1.10	*3.00*
7	A1	6p dull vio & red vio	3.00	3.00
8	A1	1sh black, *green*	1.00	*5.00*
a.		1sh black, *emerald*	1.10	*8.00*
b.		1sh black, *bl grn*, ol back	13.00	15.00
c.		As "a," olive back	4.00	*18.00*
9	A1	2sh6p blk & red, *bl*	7.00	3.00
10	A1	5sh grn & red, *yel*	7.50	*22.50*
11	A1	10sh grn & red, *grn*	37.50	*85.00*
a.		10sh grn & red, *emer*	30.00	*70.00*
b.		10sh green & red, *blue grn*, olive back	650.00	*1,050.*
c.		As "a," olive back	75.00	95.00
12	A1	£1 vio & blk, *red*	150.00	*175.00*
a.		Die II ('27)	175.00	*200.00*
		Nos. 1-12 (12)	215.10	*300.45*

Surface-colored Paper

13	A1	3p violet, *yel*	3.50	5.00
14	A1	4p black & red, *yel*	1.25	*5.00*
15	A1	1sh black, *green*	1.00	*6.00*
a.		1sh black, *emerald*		
16	A1	5sh grn & red, *yel*	12.00	*20.00*
17	A1	10sh grn & red, *grn*	47.50	*100.00*
		Nos. 13-17 (5)	65.25	*136.00*

1921-33 **Wmk. 4**

Die II

Ordinary Paper

18	A1	½p green	1.50	.75
a.		Die I	.70	.35
19	A1	1p carmine	.90	.45
a.		Booklet pane of 6	25.00	
b.		Die I	.20	.15
c.		Booklet pane of 6, Die I	25.00	
20	A1	1½p orange ('31)	2.00	.15
21	A1	2p gray	3.25	.30
a.		Die I	1.65	2.00
b.		Booklet pane of 6, Die I	50.00	
22	A1	2p red brown ('27)	2.00	.90
a.		Booklet pane of 6	50.00	
23	A1	2p dk brown ('28)	.75	.15
a.		Booklet pane of 6	25.00	
b.		Die I ('32)	4.50	.50
24	A1	2½p ultra (die I)	.75	2.25
25	A1	3p dp violet	6.00	1.25
a.		Die I ('24)	3.50	3.00
26	A1	3p ultra ('31)	2.50	2.00

Chalky Paper

27	A1	4p blk & red, *yel*	.55	.50
a.		Die I ('32)	5.00	7.00
28	A1	6p dull vio & red vio	5.00	5.00
a.		Die I	5.50	7.00
29	A1	1sh black, *emerald*	.90	.90
30	A1	2sh6p blk & red, *bl*	5.50	15.00
a.		Die I ('32)	30.00	35.00
31	A1	5sh green & red, *yel* ('26)	12.50	*45.00*
a.		Die I ('32)	45.00	*90.00*
32	A1	10sh green & red, *emer*	45.00	120.00
a.		Die I ('32)	80.00	*175.00*
		Nos. 18-32 (15)	89.10	194.60

Silver Jubilee Issue

Common Design Type

1935, May 6 **Engr.** ***Perf. 11x12***

34	CD301	1½p black & ultra	.50	*.40*
35	CD301	2p indigo & green	1.25	*.50*
36	CD301	3p ultra & brown	2.50	*6.00*
37	CD301	1sh brown vio & ind	2.50	*12.50*
		Nos. 34-37 (4)	6.75	*19.40*

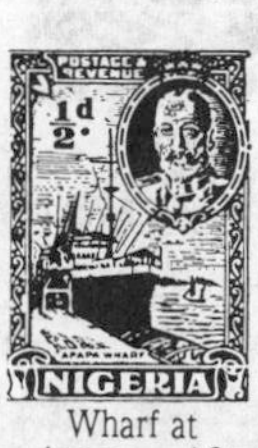
Wharf at Apapa — A2

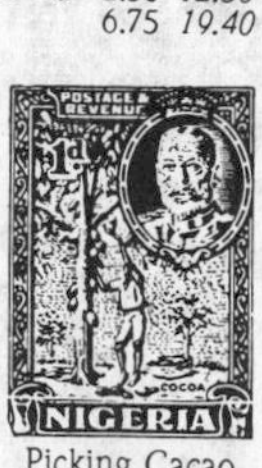
Picking Cacao Pods — A3

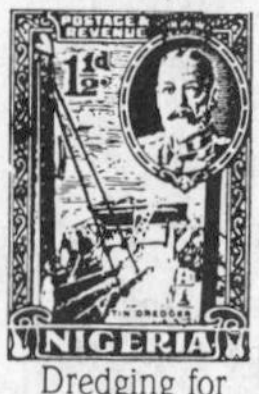
Dredging for Tin — A4

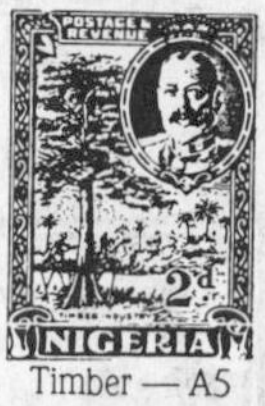
Timber — A5

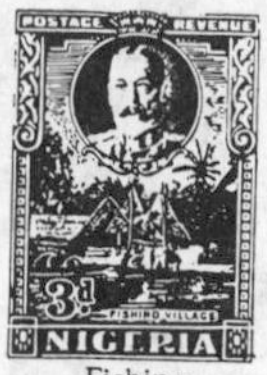
Fishing Village — A6

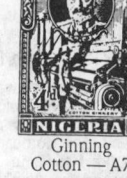

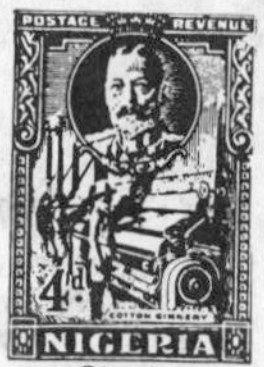
Ginning Cotton — A7

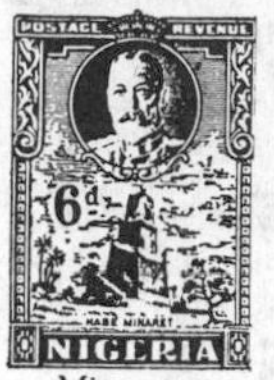
Minaret at Habe — A8

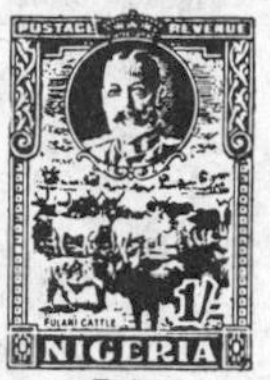
Fulani Cattle — A9

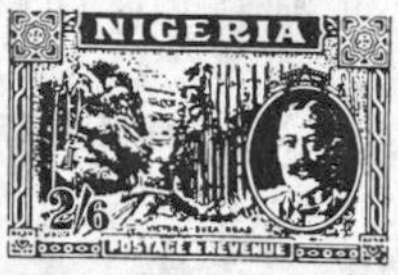
Victoria-Buea Road — A10

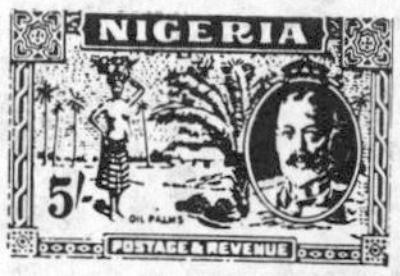
Oil Palms — A11

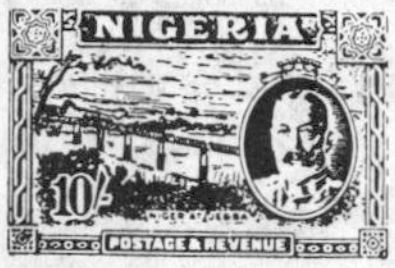
View of Niger at Jebba — A12

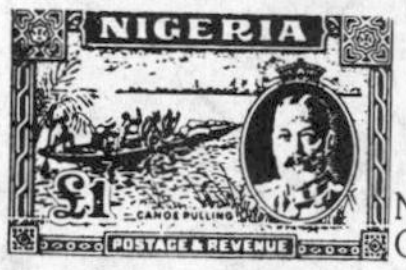
Nigerian Canoe — A13

1936, Feb. 1 ***Perf. 11½x13***

38	A2	½p green	.40	.40
39	A3	1p rose carmine	.30	.30
40	A4	1½p brown	.30	.30
a.		Perf. 12½x13½	25.00	2.00
41	A5	2p black	.50	.50
42	A6	3p dark blue	.70	.60
a.		Perf. 12½x13½	70.00	20.00
43	A7	4p red brown	1.10	1.10
44	A8	6p dull violet	.70	.55
45	A9	1sh olive green	3.00	*12.50*

Perf. 14

46	A10	2sh6p ultra & blk	7.50	*12.50*
47	A11	5sh ol grn & blk	15.00	*17.50*
48	A12	10sh slate & blk	37.50	*50.00*
49	A13	£1 orange & blk	75.00	*110.00*
		Nos. 38-49 (12)	142.00	*206.25*

Coronation Issue

Common Design Type

1937, May 12 ***Perf. 11x11½***

50	CD302	1p dark carmine	.15	.15
51	CD302	1½p dark brown	.15	.15
52	CD302	3p deep ultra	.15	.15
		Set value	.30	.30

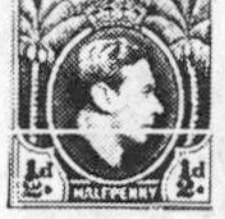
George VI — A14

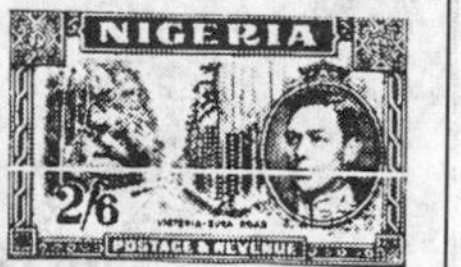
Victoria-Buea Road — A15

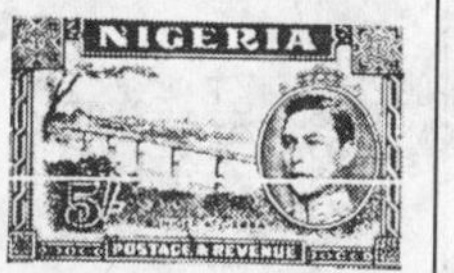
Niger at Jebba — A16

1938-51 **Wmk. 4** ***Perf. 12***

53	A14	½p deep green	.15	.15
a.		Perf. 11½ ('50)	.15	.15
54	A14	1p dk carmine	.15	.15
55	A14	1½p red brown	.15	.15
a.		Perf. 11½ ('50)	.15	.15
56	A14	2p black	.20	.15
57	A14	2½p orange ('41)	.15	.20
58	A14	3p deep blue	.15	.15
59	A14	4p orange	17.50	4.25
60	A14	6p brown violet	.15	.15
a.		Perf. 11½ ('51)	.20	.15
61	A14	1sh olive green	.25	.15
a.		Perf. 11½ ('50)	.25	.15
62	A14	1sh3p turq blue ('40)	.35	.20
a.		Perf. 11½ ('50)	.35	.20
63	A15	2sh6p ultra & blk ('51)	3.25	2.75
a.		Perf. 13½ ('42)	1.25	.70
b.		Perf. 14 ('42)	1.25	.70
c.		Perf. 13x11½	11.00	6.00
64	A16	5sh org & blk, perf. 13½ ('42)	2.25	1.10
a.		Perf. 12 ('49)	3.50	1.10
b.		Perf. 14 ('48)	2.25	1.10
c.		Perf. 13x11½	22.50	3.50

1944, Dec. 1 ***Perf. 12***

65	A14	1p red violet	.15	.15
a.		Perf. 11½ ('50)	.15	.15
66	A14	2p deep red	.15	.15
a.		Perf. 11½ ('50)	.15	.15
67	A14	3p black	.15	.15
68	A14	4p dark blue	.15	.15
		Nos. 53-68 (16)	25.30	10.15

Issue date: Nos. 65a, 66a, Feb. 15.

Catalogue values for unused stamps in this section, from this point to the end of the section, are for Never Hinged items.

Peace Issue

Common Design Type

1946, Oct. 21 **Engr.** ***Perf. 13½x14***

71	CD303	1½p brown	.15	.15
72	CD303	4p deep blue	.20	.20

Silver Wedding Issue

Common Design Types

1948, Dec. 20 **Photo.** ***Perf. 14x14½***

73	CD304	1p brt red violet	.20	.20

Perf. 11½x11

Engraved; Name Typographed

74	CD305	5sh brown orange	7.50	*10.00*

UPU Issue

Common Design Types

Engr.; Name Typo. on 3p, 6p

Perf. 13½, 11x11½

1949, Oct. 10 **Wmk. 4**

75	CD306	1p red violet	.20	.15
76	CD307	3p indigo	.40	.30
77	CD308	6p rose violet	1.20	.90
78	CD309	1sh olive	2.00	1.50
		Nos. 75-78 (4)	3.80	2.85

Coronation Issue

Common Design Type

1953, June 2 **Engr.** ***Perf. 13½x13***

79	CD312	1½p brt green & black	.30	.15

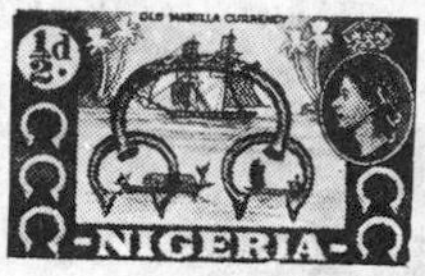
Manilla (Bracelet) Currency A17

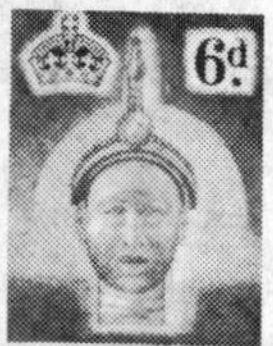
Olokun Head, Ife — A18

Designs: 1p, Bornu horsemen. 1½p, Peanuts, Kano City. 2p, Mining tin. 3p, Jebba Bridge over Niger River. 4p, Cocoa industry. 1sh, Logging. 2sh6p, Victoria harbor. 5sh, Loading palm oil. 10sh, Goats and Fulani cattle. £1, Lagos waterfront, 19th and 20th centuries.

1953, Sept. 1 ***Perf. 13½, 14***

Size: 35½x22½mm

80	A17	½p red orange & blk	.15	.15
a.		Booklet pane of 4 ('57)	.50	
81	A17	1p olive gray & blk	.15	.15
a.		Booklet pane of 4 ('57)	.50	
82	A17	1½p blue green	.40	.15
83	A17	2p bister & blk	3.25	.15
84	A17	3p purple & blk	.45	.15
a.		Booklet pane of 4 ('57)		

85	A17	4p ultra & black	2.00	.15
86	A18	6p blk & org brn	.25	.15
87	A17	1sh brn vio & blk	.30	.15
a.		Booklet pane of 4 ('57)		

Size: 40½x24½mm

88	A17	2sh6p green & black	4.00	.30
89	A17	5sh ver & black	2.75	.65
90	A17	10sh red brown & blk	7.00	1.50

Size: 42x31½mm

91	A17	£1 violet & black	12.00	5.00
			32.70	8.65

See No. 93.

No. 83 Overprinted in   **ROYAL VISIT**
Black   **1956**

1956, Jan. 28   Wmk. 4   Perf. 13½

92	A17	2p bister & black	.15	.15

Visit of Queen Elizabeth II to Nigeria, Jan.-Feb., 1956.

Mining Tin Type of 1953

Two types:
I - Broken row of dots between "G" and miner's head.
II - Complete row of dots.

1956-57

93	A17	2p bluish gray (shades) (I)	.15	.15
a.		Booklet pane of 4 (II) ('57)	.65	
b.		2p gray (shades) (II)	.15	.15

Ambas Bay, Victoria Harbor A19

Perf. 13½

1958, Dec. 1   Wmk. 314   Engr.

94	A19	3p purple & black	.15	.15

Cent. of the founding of Victoria, Southern Cameroons.

1959, Mar. 14

Designs: 3p, Lugard Hall, Kaduna. 1sh, Kano Mosque.

95	A19	3p purple & black	.15	.15
96	A19	1sh green & black	.35	.30

Attainment of self-government by the Northern Region, Mar. 15, 1959.

Federation of Nigeria

Man Paddling Canoe — A20

Designs: 1p, Federal Legislature. 6p, Federal Supreme Court. 1sh3p, Map of Africa, dove and torch.

Perf. 13½

1960, Oct. 1   Photo.   Wmk. 335

Size: 35x22mm

97	A20	1p carmine & black	.15	.15
98	A20	3p blue & black	.15	.15
99	A20	6p dk red brn & emer	.15	.15

Size: 39½x23½mm

100	A20	1sh3p ultra & yellow	.30	.25
		Set value	.55	.50

Nigeria's independence, Oct. 1, 1960.

Peanuts — A21

Central Bank, Lagos A22

Designs: 1p, Coal miner. 1½p, Adult education. 2p, Potter. 3p, Oyo carver. 4p, Weaver. 6p, Benin mask. 1sh, Yellow-casqued hornbill. 1sh3p, Camel

---

train and map. 5sh, Nigeria museum and sculpture. 10sh, Kano airport. £1, Lagos terminal.

Perf. 14½x14

1961, Jan. 1   Wmk. 335

101	A21	½p emerald	.15	.15
102	A21	1p purple	.15	.15
a.		Booklet pane of 6	.45	
103	A21	1½p rose red	.15	.15
104	A21	2p ultra	.15	.15
105	A21	3p dark green	.15	.15
a.		Booklet pane of 6	.50	
106	A21	4p blue	.15	.15
107	A21	6p black & yel	.20	.15
a.		Booklet pane of 6	1.00	
b.		Yellow omitted		375.00
108	A21	1sh yellow green	.30	.15
109	A21	1sh3p orange	.50	.15
a.		Booklet pane of 6	3.25	
110	A22	2sh6p yellow & blk	1.00	.20
111	A22	5sh emerald & blk	2.00	.40
112	A22	10sh dp ultra & blk	3.25	1.00
113	A22	£1 dp car & blk	5.00	3.00
		Nos. 101-113 (13)	13.15	
		Set value		5.50

For overprint see No. 198.

Globe and Train A23

1961, July 25   Wmk. 335

114	A23	1p shown	.15	.15
115	A23	3p Truck	.15	.15
116	A23	1sh3p Plane	.30	.30
117	A23	2sh6p Ship	.65	.65
		Nos. 114-117 (4)	1.25	1.25

Nigeria's admission to the UPU.

Coat of Arms — A24

Map and Natural Resources A25

Designs: 6p, Eagle carrying banner. 1sh3p, Flying eagles forming flag. 2sh6p, Young couple looking at flag and government building.

Perf. 14½x14, 14x14½

1961, Oct. 1   Photo.   Wmk. 335

118	A24	3p multicolored	.15	.15
119	A25	4p org, yel grn & dk red	.20	.20
120	A25	6p emerald	.20	.15
121	A25	1sh3p ultra, emer & gray	.25	.20
122	A25	2sh6p blue, emer & sep	.50	.50
		Nos. 118-122 (5)	1.30	1.20

First anniversary of independence.

Map of Africa and Staff of Aesculapius — A26

Map of Africa and: 3p, Lyre, book and scroll. 6p, Cogwheel. 1sh, Radio beacon. 1sh3p, Hands holding globe.

1962, Jan. 25   Perf. 14x14½

123	A26	1p bister	.15	.15
124	A26	3p deep magenta	.15	.15
125	A26	6p blue green	.20	.15

126	A26	1sh chestnut	.30	.20
127	A26	1sh3p bright blue	.40	.35
		Set value	1.00	.80

Issued to honor the conference of heads of state of African and Malagasy Governments.

Malaria Eradication Emblem and Larvae — A27

Emblem and: 6p, Man with spray gun. 1sh3p, Plane spraying insecticide. 2sh6p, Microscope, retort and patient.

1962, Apr. 7   Perf. 14½

128	A27	3p emerald, brn & ver	.15	.15
129	A27	6p lilac rose & dk blue	.20	.15
130	A27	1sh3p dk blue & lil rose	.25	.20
131	A27	2sh6p yel brown & blue	.55	.55
		Nos. 128-131 (4)	1.15	
		Set value		.90

WHO drive to eradicate malaria.

National Monument, Lagos — A28

Ife Bronze Head and Flag — A29

Perf. 14½x14, 14x14½

1962, Oct. 1   Wmk. 335   Photo.

132	A28	3p lt ultra & emerald	.15	.15
a.		Emerald omitted		
133	A29	5sh vio, emer & org red	1.75	1.75

Second anniversary of independence.

Fair Emblem — A30

Globe and Arrows — A31

Designs (horizontal): 6p, "Wheels of Industry." 1sh, Cornucopia, goods and trucks. 2sh6p, Oil derricks and tanker.

1962, Oct. 27   Wmk. 335

134	A30	1p brown olive & org	.15	.15
135	A30	6p crimson & blk	.15	.15
136	A30	1sh dp orange & blk	.25	.20
137	A30	2sh6p dk ultra, yel & blk	.55	.50
		Nos. 134-137 (4)	1.10	
		Set value		.85

Lagos Intl. Trade Fair, Oct. 27-Nov. 8.

1962, Nov. 5

Designs: 4p, National Hall and Commonwealth emblem, horiz. 1sh3p, Palm tree, emblem and doves.

138	A31	2½p sky blue	.15	.15
139	A31	4p dp rose & slate bl	.15	.15
140	A31	1sh3p gray & yellow	.45	.45
		Nos. 138-140 (3)	.75	
		Set value		.65

8th Commonwealth Parliamentary Conf., Lagos.

Herdsman with Cattle — A32

US Mercury Capsule over Kano Tracking Station — A33

Design: 6p, Tractor and corn, horiz.

1963, Mar. 21   Photo.   Perf. 14½

141	A32	3p olive green	.15	.15
142	A32	6p brt lilac rose	.30	.25
		Set value		.35

FAO "Freedom from Hunger" campaign.

1963, June 21   Perf. 14½

Design: 1sh3p, Syncom II satellite and US tracking ship "Kingsport," Lagos harbor.

143	A33	6p dk blue & yellow grn	.20	.15
144	A33	1sh3p black & dp green	.40	.40

Peaceful uses of outer space.
Printed in sheets of 12 (4x3) with ornamental borders and inscriptions.

Nigerian and Greek Scouts Shaking Hands and Jamboree Emblem — A34

Design: 1sh, Scouts dancing around campfire.

1963, Aug. 1   Photo.   Perf. 14

145	A34	3p gray olive & red	.15	.15
146	A34	1sh red & black	.40	.40
a.		Souvenir sheet of 2, #145-146	1.10	1.10

11th Boy Scout Jamboree, Marathon, Greece, Aug. 1963.

Republic

First Aid — A35

Designs: 6p, Blood donors and ambulances. 1sh3p, Helping the needy.

1963, Sept. 1   Wmk. 335   Perf. 14½

147	A35	3p dk blue & red	.15	.15
148	A35	6p dk green & red	.20	.20
149	A35	1sh3p black & red	.55	.55
a.		Souvenir sheet of 4, #149	1.75	1.75
		Nos. 147-149 (3)	.90	.90

Cent. of the Intl. Red Cross.

Pres. Nnamdi Azikiwe and State House — A36

"Freedom of Worship" — A37

Designs: 1sh3p, President and Federal Supreme Court. 2sh6p, President and Parliament Building.

1963, Oct. 1   Unwmk.   Perf. 14x13

150	A36	3p dull green & yel grn	.15	.15
151	A36	1sh3p brown & bister	.25	.20
a.		Bister (head) omitted		
152	A36	2sh6p vio bl & brt grnsh bl	.50	.50
		Nos. 150-152 (3)	.90	.85

Independence Day, Oct. 1, 1963.

1963, Dec. 10 Wmk. 335 *Perf. 13*

Designs: 3p, Charter and broken whip, horiz. 1sh3p, "Freedom from Want." 2sh6p, "Freedom of Speech."

153 A37 3p vermilion .15 .15
154 A37 6p green .15 .15
155 A37 1sh3p deep ultra .20 .20
156 A37 2sh6p red lilac .35 .35
Set value .65 .65

15th anniv. of the Universal Declaration of Human Rights.

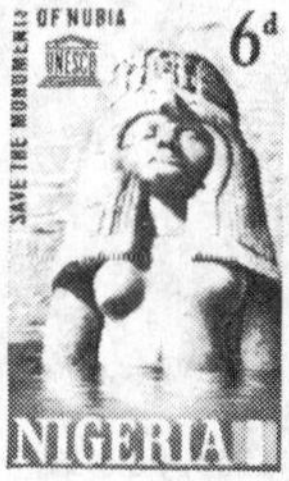

Queen Nefertari — A38

1964, Mar. 8 Photo. *Perf. 14*
157 A38 6p shown .20 .20
158 A38 2sh6p Ramses II .90 .90

UNESCO world campaign to save historic monuments in Nubia.

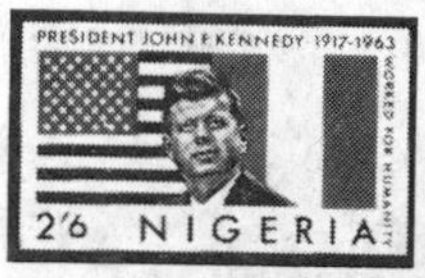

John F. Kennedy, US and Nigerian Flags — A39

Designs: 1sh3p, Kennedy bust and laurel. 5sh, Kennedy coin (US), flags of US and Nigeria at half-mast.

1964, Aug. 20 Unwmk. *Perf. 13x14*
159 A39 1sh3p black & lt vio .25 .25
160 A39 2sh6p multicolored .55 .55
161 A39 5sh multicolored 1.10 1.10
a. Souvenir sheet of 4 5.25 5.25
Nos. 159-161 (3) 1.90 1.90

Issued in memory of President John F. Kennedy (1917-1963). No. 161a contains 4 imperf. stamps similar to No. 161 with simulated perforations.

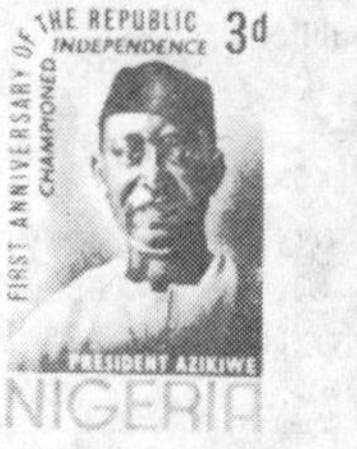

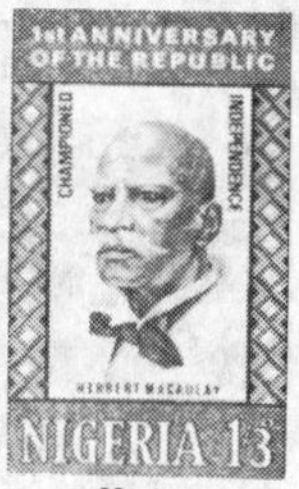

Pres. Nnamdi Azikiwe — A40 Herbert Macaulay — A41

Design: 2sh6p, King Jaja of Opobo.

Perf. 14x13, 14
1964, Oct. 1 Photo. Unwmk.
162 A40 3p red brown .15 .15
163 A41 1sh3p green .25 .25
164 A41 2sh6p slate green .55 .55
Nos. 162-164 (3) .95 .95

First anniversary of the Republic.

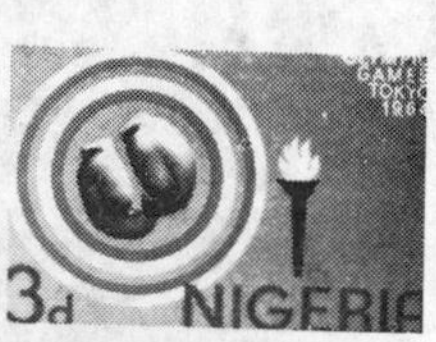

Boxing Gloves and Torch — A42

Hurdling — A43

Designs: 6p, High jump. 1sh3p, Woman runner, vert.

1964, Oct. *Perf. 14½*
165 A42 3p olive grn & sepia .15 .15
166 A42 6p dk blue & emer .15 .15
167 A42 1sh3p olive & brown .30 .30

Perf. 14
168 A43 2sh6p orange red & brn .50 .50
a. Souvenir sheet of 4 3.25 3.25
Nos. 165-168 (4) 1.10 1.10

18th Olympic Games, Tokyo, Oct. 10-25.
No. 168a contains 4 imperf. stamps similar to No. 168 with simulated perforations.

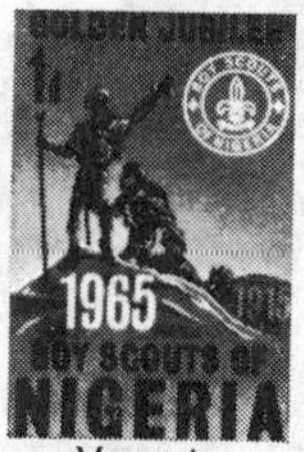

Mountain Climbing Scouts — A44

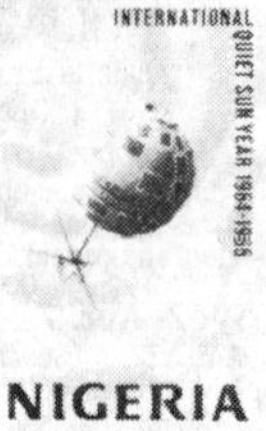

IQSY Emblem and Telstar, Map of Africa — A45

Designs: 3p, Golden Jubilee emblem. 6p, Nigeria's Scout emblem and merit badges. 1sh3p, Lord Baden-Powell and Nigerian Boy Scout.

1965, Jan. Photo. *Perf. 14½*
169 A44 1p brown .15 .15
170 A44 3p emer, blk & red .15 .15
171 A44 6p yel grn, red & blk .20 .20
172 A44 1sh3p sep, yel & dk grn .55 .55
a. Souvenir sheet of 4 3.00 3.00
Nos. 169-172 (4) 1.05 1.05

50th anniv. of the founding of the Nigerian Boy Scouts.
No. 172a contains four imperf. stamps similar to No. 172 with simulated perforation.

1965, Apr. 1 Unwmk. *Perf. 14x13*
Design: 1sh3p, Explorer XII over map of Africa.
173 A45 6p grnsh bl & vio .18 .18
174 A45 1sh3p lilac & green .42 .42

Intl. Quiet Sun Year, 1964-65. Printed in sheets of 12 (4x3) with ornamental borders and inscriptions.

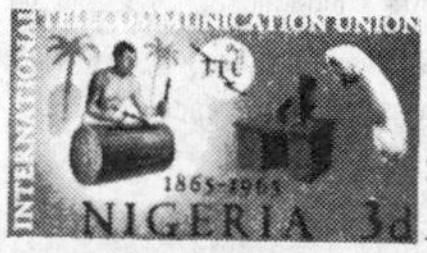

ITU Emblem, Drummer, Man at Desk and Telephone A46

Cent. of the ITU: 1sh3p, ITU emblem and telecommunication tower, vert. 5sh, ITU emblem, Relay satellite and map of Africa showing Nigeria.

Perf. 11x11½, 11½x11
1965, Aug. 2 Photo. Unwmk.
175 A46 3p ocher, red & blk .15 .15
176 A46 1sh3p ultra, grn & blk .65 .65
177 A46 5sh multicolored 2.75 2.75
Nos. 175-177 (3) 3.55 3.55

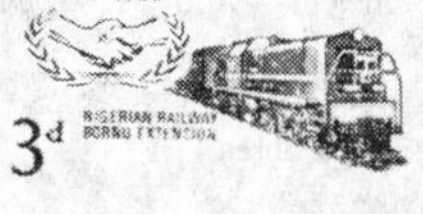

ICY Emblem, Diesel Locomotive and Camel Caravan A47

ICY Emblem and: 1sh, Students and hospital, Lagos. 2sh6p, Kainji Dam, Niger River.

1965, Sept. 1 Wmk. 335 *Perf. 14x15*
178 A47 3p orange, grn & car .22 .15
179 A47 1sh ultra, blk & yel .50 .35
180 A47 2sh6p ultra, yel & grn 2.50 1.10
Nos. 178-180 (3) 3.22 1.60

Intl. Cooperation Year and 20th anniv. of the UN.

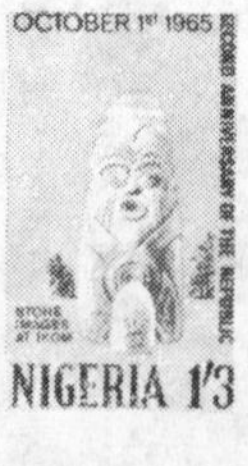

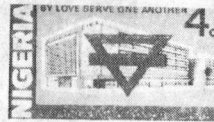

Stone Images, Ikom — A48

Designs: 3p, Carved frieze, horiz. 5sh, Seated man, Taba bronze.

Perf. 14x15, 15x14
1965, Oct. 1 Photo. Unwmk.
181 A48 3p ocher, black & red .15 .15
182 A48 1sh3p lt ultra, grn & reddish brn .40 .40
183 A48 5sh emer, dk brn & reddish brn 1.75 1.75
Nos. 181-183 (3) 2.30 2.30

Second anniversary of the Republic.

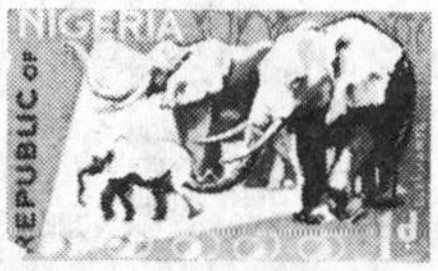

Elephants A49

Designs: ½p, Lioness and cubs, vert. 1½p, Splendid sunbird. 2p, Weaverbirds. 3p, Cheetah. 4p, Leopard and cubs. 6p, Saddle-billed storks, vert. 9p, Gray parrots. 1sh, Kingfishers. 1sh3p, Crowned cranes. 2sh6p, Buffon's kobs (antelopes). 5sh, Giraffes. 10sh, Hippopotami, vert. £1, Buffalos.

"MAURICE FIEVET" below Design.*

Perf. 12x12½, 12½x12, 14x13½ (1p, 2p, 3p, 4p, 9p)

1965-66 Photo.
Size: 23x38mm, 38x23mm
184 A49 ½p multicolored .15 .15
185 A49 1p red & multi .15 .15
186 A49 1½p lt blue & multi .16 .15
187 A49 2p brt red & multi .16 .15
a. White "2d" ('70) 7.00 2.00
188 A49 3p brt grn, yel & dl brn 1.00 .65
189 A49 4p lilac & multi .32 .15
a. Perf 12½x12 .55 .15
b. "4" 5mm wide ('71) 3.75 1.00
190 A49 6p violet & multi .40 .15
191 A49 9p blue & orange 1.25 .65

Perf. 12½
Size: 45x26mm, 26x45mm
192 A49 1sh gray & multi .80 .15
a. Red omitted
193 A49 1sh3p brt bl & multi .85 .15
194 A49 2sh6p dk brn, yel & ocher 1.65 .32
195 A49 5sh brn, yel & red brown 3.25 .80
196 A49 10sh grnsh bl & multi 4.50 3.25
197 A49 £1 brt green & multi 11.00 6.50
Nos. 184-197 (14) 25.64 13.37

* The designer's name, Maurice Fievet, appears at right or left, in small or large capitals. Nos. 187a and 189b have "MAURICE FIEVET" at right, 5mm wide. No. 187a has "2d" in white instead of yellow. No. 189b has "REPUBLIC" and "4d" larger, bolder.
Issued: ½p, 1p, 11/1/65; 2p, 4/1/66; 1½p, #189a, 6p, 1sh, 1sh3p, 2sh6p, 5sh, 10sh, 1£, 5/2/66; 3p, 9p, 10/17/66; 4p, 1966.
9 values were overprinted "F. G. N./ F. G. N." (Federal Government of Nigeria) in 1969. They were not issued, but some were irregularly sold. Later the Nigerian Philatelic Service sold copies, stating they were not postally valid.
See Nos. 258-267.

No. 110 Overprinted in Red: "COMMONWEALTH / P.M. MEETING / 11. Jan. 1966"

Perf. 14½x14
1966, Jan. 11 Photo. Wmk. 335
198 A22 2sh6p yellow & black .52 .52

Conf. of British Commonwealth Prime Ministers, Lagos.

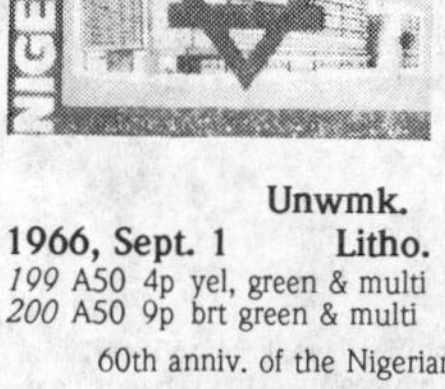

YWCA Building, Lagos — A50

Unwmk.
1966, Sept. 1 Litho. *Perf. 14*
199 A50 4p yel, green & multi .15 .15
200 A50 9p brt green & multi .32 .32

60th anniv. of the Nigerian YWCA.

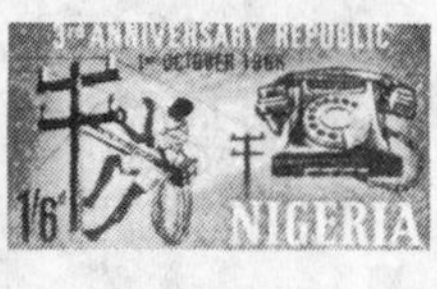

Lineman and Telephone A51

Designs: 4p, Flag and letter carrying pigeon, vert. 2sh6p, Niger Bridge.

Perf. 14½x14, 14x14½
1966, Oct. 1 Photo. Wmk. 335
201 A51 4p green .15 .15
202 A51 1sh6p lilac, blk & sep .60 .60
203 A51 2sh6p multicolored 1.00 1.00
Nos. 201-203 (3) 1.75 1.75

Third anniversary of the Republic.

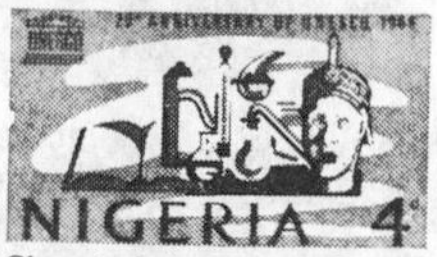

Book, Chemical Apparatus, Carved Head and UNESCO Emblem A52

1966, Nov. 4 *Perf. 14½x14*
204 A52 4p dl org, mar & blk .40 .15
205 A52 1sh6p bl grn, plum & black 1.25 .80
206 A52 2sh6p pink, plum & blk 2.50 2.50
Nos. 204-206 (3) 4.15 3.45

20th anniv. of UNESCO.

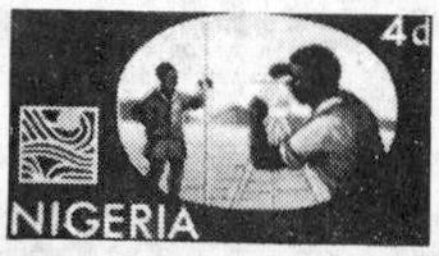

Surveyors and Hydrological Decade Emblem A53

Design: 2sh6p, Water depth gauge on dam and Hydrological Decade emblem, vert.

Perf. 14½x14, 14x14½
1967, Feb. 1 Photo. Wmk. 335
207 A53 4p multicolored .15 .15
208 A53 2sh6p multicolored 1.25 1.25

Hydrological Decade (UNESCO), 1965-74.

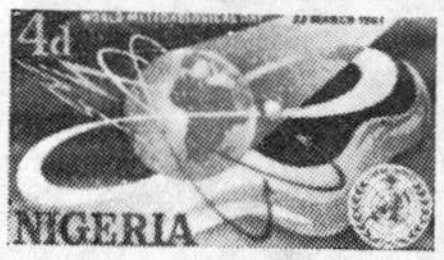

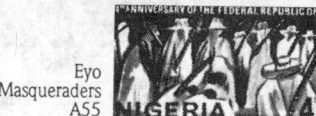

Weather Satellite Orbiting Earth — A54

Design: 1sh6p, Storm over land and sea and World Meteorological Organization emblem.

1967, Mar. 23 Photo. *Perf. 14½x14*
209 A54 4p dp ultra & brt rose .15 .15
210 A54 1sh6p ultra & yellow .75 .75

World Meteorological Day, March 23.

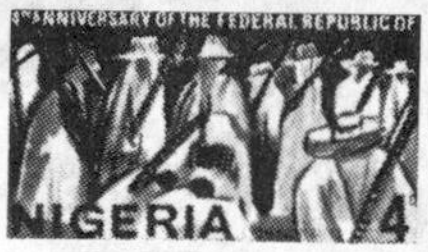

Eyo Masqueraders A55

Designs: 1sh6p, Acrobat. 2sh6p, Stilt dancer, vert.

Perf. 11x11½, 11½x11
1967, Oct. 1 Photo. Unwmk.
211 A55 4p multicolored .15 .15
212 A55 1sh6p turq bl & multi 1.25 1.25
213 A55 2sh6p pale grn & multi 2.00 1.50
Nos. 211-213 (3) 3.40 2.90

4th anniversary of the Federal Republic.

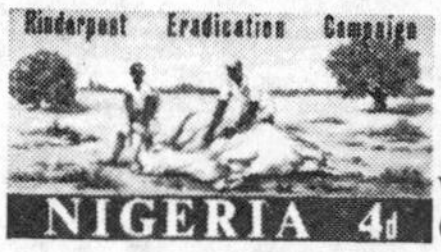

Vaccination of Cattle — A56

1967, Dec. 1 *Perf. 14½x14*
214 A56 4p maroon & multi .16 .15
215 A56 1sh6p ultra & multi .95 .95

Campaign to eradicate cattle plague.

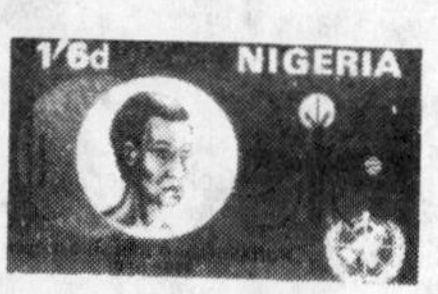

Anopheles Mosquito and Sick Man — A57

20th anniv. of the WHO: 4p, WHO emblem and vaccination.

1968, Apr. 7   Litho.   Perf. 14
216 A57   4p dp lilac rose & blk   .15   .15
217 A57   1sh6p orange yel & black   .80   .80

Shackled Hands, Map of Nigeria and Human Rights Flame — A58

Design: 1sh6p, Flag of Nigeria and human rights flame, vert.

1968, July 1   Photo.   Perf. 14
218 A58   4p dp blue, yel & blk   .15   .15
219 A58   1sh6p green, blk & red   .55   .55

International Human Rights Year.

Hand and Doves — A59

1968, Oct. 1   Unwmk.   Perf. 14
220 A59   4p brt blue & multi   .15   .15
221 A59   1sh6p black & multi   .50   .50
         Set value   .56

5th anniversary of the Federal Republic.

Olympic Rings, Nigerian Flag and Athletes A60

Design: 4p, Map of Nigeria and Olympic rings.

1968, Oct. 14   Photo.   Perf. 14
222 A60   4p red, black & emer   .15   .15
223 A60   1sh6p multicolored   .50   .50
         Set value   .56

19th Olympic Games, Mexico City, Oct. 12-27.

G.P.O., Lagos — A61

1969, Apr. 11   Unwmk.   Perf. 14
224 A61   4p emerald & black   .15   .15
225 A61   1sh6p dk blue & black   .48   .48
         Set value   .55   .54

Opening of the Nigerian Philatelic Service of the GPO, Lagos.

Gen. Yakubu Gowon and Victoria Zakari A62

**   Perf. 13x13½**
1969, Sept. 20   Litho.   Unwmk.
226 A62   4p emerald & choc   .15   .15
227 A62   1sh6p emerald & black   .48   .48
         Set value   .55   .54

Wedding of Yakubu Gowon, head of state of Nigeria, and Miss Victoria Zakari, Apr. 19, 1969.

Development Bank Emblem and "5" — A63

Design: 1sh6p, Emblem and rays.

1969, Oct. 18   Litho.   Perf. 14
228 A63   4p dk bl, blk & org   .15   .15
229 A63   1sh6p dk pur, yel & blk   .55   .55

African Development Bank, 5th anniv.

ILO Emblem A64

50th anniv. of the ILO: 1sh6p, ILO emblem and world map.

1969, Nov. 15   Photo.
230 A64   4p purple & black   .15   .15
231 A64   1sh6p green & black   .55   .55

Tourist Year Emblem and Musicians A65

12-Spoke Wheel and Arms of Nigeria A66

Designs: 4p, Olumo Rock and Tourist Year emblem, horiz. 1sh6p, Assob Falls.

1969, Dec. 30   Photo.   Perf. 14
232 A65   4p blue & multi   .15   .15
233 A65   1sh emerald & black   .36   .36
234 A65   1sh6p multicolored   .55   .55
         Nos. 232-234 (3)   1.06 1.06

International Year of African Tourism.

**   Perf. 11½x11, 11x11½**
1970, May 28   Photo.   Unwmk.

Designs: 4p, Map of Nigeria and tree with 12 fruits representing 12 tribes. 1sh6p, People bound by common destiny and map of Nigeria. 2sh, Torch with 12 flames and map of Africa, horiz.

235 A66   4p gold, blue & blk   .15   .15
236 A66   1sh gold & multi   .38   .38
237 A66   1sh6p green & black   .55   .55
238 A66   2sh bl, org, gold & black   .75   .75
         Nos. 235-238 (4)   1.83 1.83

Establishment of a 12-state administrative structure in Nigeria.

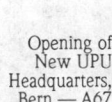 

Opening of New UPU Headquarters, Bern — A67

1970, June 29   Unwmk.   Perf. 14
239 A67   4p purple & yellow   .15   .15
240 A67   1sh6p blue & vio blue   .50   .50

UN Emblem and Charter — A68

Student — A69

25th anniv. of the UN: 1sh6p, UN emblem and headquarters, New York.

1970, Sept. 1   Photo.   Perf. 14
241 A68   4p brn org, buff & blk   .15   .15
242 A68   1sh6p dk bl, gold & bis brn .48   .48
         Set value   .56   .54

1970, Sept. 30   Litho.   Perf. 14x13½

Designs: 2p, Oil drilling platform. 6p, Durbar horsemen. 9p, Soldier and sailors raising flag. 1sh, Soccer player. 1sh6p, Parliament Building. 2sh, Kainji Dam. 2sh6p, Export products: Timber, rubber, peanuts, cocoa and palm produce.

243 A69   2p blue & multi   .15   .15
244 A69   4p blue & multi   .15   .15
245 A69   6p blue & multi   .15   .15
246 A69   9p blue & multi   .25   .25
247 A69   1sh blue & multi   .35   .35
248 A69   1sh6p blue & multi   .65   .65
249 A69   2sh blue & multi   .85   .85
250 A69   2sh6p blue & multi   1.10 1.10
         Nos. 243-250 (8)   3.65 3.65

Ten years of independence.

Black and White Men Uprooting Racism — A70

Ibibio Mask, c. 1900 — A71

Designs: 4p, Black and white school children and globe, horiz. 1sh6p, World map with black and white stripes. 2sh, Black and white men, shoulder to shoulder, horiz.

**   Perf. 13½x14, 14x13½**
1971, Mar. 22   Photo.   Unwmk.
251 A70   4p multicolored   .15   .15
252 A70   1sh yellow & multi   .20   .20
253 A70   1sh6p blue, yel & blk   .38   .38
254 A70   2sh multicolored   .60   .60
         Nos. 251-254 (4)   1.33 1.33

Intl. year against racial discrimination.

1971, Sept. 30   Perf 13½x14

Nigerian Antiquities: 1sh3p, Bronze mask of a King of Benin, c. 1700. 1sh9p, Bronze figure of a King of Ife.

255 A71   4p lt blue & black   .15   .15
256 A71   1sh3p yellow bis & blk   .44   .44
257 A71   1sh9p apple grn, dp grn & blk .60 .60
         Nos. 255-257 (3)   1.19 1.19

Type of 1965-66 Redrawn
Imprint: "N.S.P. & M. Co. Ltd."
Added to "MAURICE FIEVET"
Perf. 13x13½; 14x13½ (6p)
1969-72   Photo.

Size: 38x23mm
258 A49   1p red & multi   .15   .15
259 A49   2p brt red & multi   .20   .15
260 A49   3p multi ('71)   .20   .15
261 A49   4p lilac & multi   .32   .15
262 A49   6p brt vio & multi ('71)   .80   .24
263 A49   9p dl bl & dp org ('70)   .80   .32

Size: 45x26mm
264 A49   1sh multi ('71)   .90   .40
265 A49   1sh3p multi ('71)   1.25   .48
266 A49   2sh6p multi ('72)   4.75 2.00
267 A49   5sh multi ('72)   6.50 3.25
         Nos. 258-267 (10)   15.87 7.29

UNICEF Emblem and Children A72

Satellite Earth Station A73

UNICEF 25th anniv.: 1sh3p, Mother and child. 1sh9p, African mother carrying child on back.

1971, Dec. 11   Photo.   Perf. 14
270 A72   4p purple & yellow   .15   .15
271 A72   1sh3p org, pur & plum   .45   .45
272 A72   1sh9p blue & dk blue   .65   .65
         Nos. 270-272 (3)   1.25 1.25

1971, Dec. 30   Photo.   Perf. 14

Designs: Various views of satellite communications earth station, Lanlate, Nigeria. All horizontal.

273 A73   4p multicolored   .15   .15
274 A73   1sh3p blue, blk & grn   .65   .65
275 A73   1sh9p orange & blk   .95   .95
276 A73   3sh brt pink & blk   1.50 1.50
         Nos. 273-276 (4)   3.25 3.25

Satellite communications earth station, Lanlate, Nigeria.

Fair Emblem — A74

Fair Emblem and: 1sh3p, Map of Africa, horiz. 1sh9p, Globe with map of Africa.

**   Perf. 13½x13, 13x13½**
1972, Feb. 23   Litho.
277 A74   4p multicolored   .15   .15
278 A74   1sh3p dull pur, yel & gold   .48   .48
279 A74   1sh9p orange, yel & blk   .70   .70
         Nos. 277-279 (3)   1.33 1.33

First All-Africa Trade Fair, Nairobi, Kenya, Feb. 23-Mar. 5.

Traffic — A75

Designs: 1sh3p, Traffic flow at circle. 1sh9p, Car and truck on road. 3sh, Intersection with lights and pedestrians.

1972, June 23   Photo.   Perf. 13x13½
280 A75   4p orange & blk   .15   .15
281 A75   1sh3p lt blue & multi   .90   .90
282 A75   1sh9p emerald & multi   1.35 1.35
283 A75   3sh yellow & multi   2.00 2.00
         Nos. 280-283 (4)   4.40 4.40

Introduction of right-hand driving in Nigeria, Apr. 2, 1972.

Nok Style Terra-cotta Head, Katsina Ala — A76

Designs: 1sh3p, Roped bronze vessel, Igbo Ukwu. 1sh9p, Bone harpoon, Daima, horiz.

Perf. 13½x13, 13x13½

1972, Sept. 1   Litho.
284 A76 4p dk blue & multi   .15 .15
285 A76 1sh3p gold & multi   .65 .65
286 A76 1sh9p dp blue & multi   .85 .85
Nos. 284-286 (3)   1.65 1.65

All-Nigeria Festival of the Arts, Kaduna, Dec. 9.

Games Emblem and Soccer — A77

Designs: 5k, Running. 18k, Table tennis. 25k, Stadium, vert.

1973, Jan. 8   Litho.   **Perf. 13x13½**
287 A77 5k lilac, blue & blk   .20 .20
288 A77 12k multicolored   .45 .45
289 A77 18k yellow & multi   .70 .70
290 A77 25k brown & multi   1.00 1.00
Nos. 287-290 (4)   2.35 2.35

2nd All-Africa Games, Lagos, Jan. 7-18.

Hides and Skins — A78

Designs: 2k, Natural gas tanks. 3k, Cement works. 5k, Cattle ranching. 7k, Lumbermill. 8k, Oil refinery. 10k, Leopards, Yankari Game Reserve. 12k, New civic building. 15k, Sugar cane harvesting. 18k, Palm oil production, vert. 20k, Vaccine production. 25k, Modern docks. 30k, Argungu Fishing Festival, vert. 35k, Textile industry. 50k, Pottery, vert. 1n, Eko Bridge. 2n, Teaching Hospital, Lagos.

Imprint at left: "N S P & M Co Ltd" 6mm on Litho. Stamps, 5¼ mm on Photo. Stamps

1973-74   Litho.; Photo. (50k)   **Perf. 14**
291 A78 1k multi, buff imprint   .22 .22
292 A78 2k multi ('74)   .35 .32
293 A78 3k multi ('74)   .15 .15
294 A78 5k grn & multi ('74)   .45 .32
295 A78 7k multicolored   .22 .16
296 A78 8k multicolored   .25 .18
297 A78 10k multicolored   .55 .35
298 A78 12k multicolored   .40 .25
299 A78 15k multicolored   .45 .35
300 A78 18k multicolored   .60 .40
301 A78 20k multicolored   .65 .45
302 A78 25k multicolored   .75 .55
303 A78 30k multicolored   .85 .65
304 A78 35k multicolored   1.00 .70
305 A78 50k black background   4.50 2.75
306 A78 1n multicolored   3.00 2.25
307 A78 2n multicolored   4.50 5.25
Nos. 291-307 (17)   18.89 15.30

Imprint on 35k has periods.

Imprint at left: "N. S. P. & M. Co. Ltd."
1973   Photo., Imprint 5¼mm
291a A78 1k multi, dk grn foliage   .15 .15
291b A78 1k multi, brt grn foliage   .15 .15
292a A78 2k multicolored   .15 .15
294a A78 5k multi, emer fields   .65 .45
294b A78 5k multi, yel grn fields   .35 .22
297a A78 10k multicolored   .45 .25
298a A78 12k multicolored   1.10 1.00
300a A78 18k multicolored   1.50 1.25
301a A78 20k multicolored   2.75 2.50
303a A78 30k multicolored   3.00 2.50
305a A78 50k dk brn background   2.25 1.75
306a A78 1n multicolored   9.00 8.00
Nos. 291a-306a (12)   21.50 18.37

1975-79   Wmk. 379
291c A78 1k multi, dk grn foliage   .15 .15
292b A78 2k multi ('75)   .15 .15
293a A78 3k multi ('75)   .15 .15
294c A78 5k emerald fields ('76)   .18 .15
296a A78 8k multi ('76)   .22 .15
297b A78 10k multi ('76)   .35 .18
299a A78 15k multicolored   .45 .35
301b A78 20k multi, pale pink table, door, windows ('79)   .65 .45
302a A78 25k multi, pur barges   .70 .70
302b A78 25k multi, brn barges   .70 .70
305b A78 50k dk brn background, gm imprint   1.50 1.25
307a A78 2n multicolored   5.50 5.25
Nos. 291c-307a (12)   10.70 9.63

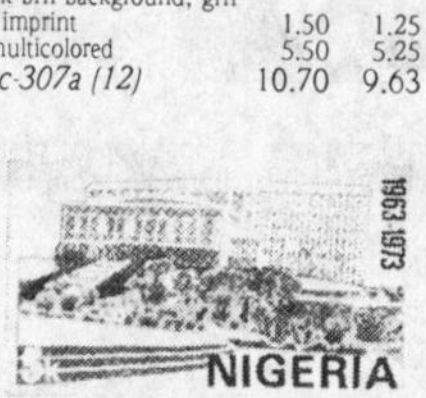

OAU Headquarters A79

Designs: 18k, OAU flag, vert. 30k, Stairs leading to OAU emblem, vert.

1973, May 25   Litho.   **Perf. 14**
308 A79 5k blue & multi   .16 .16
309 A79 18k olive grn & multi   .65 .65
310 A79 30k lilac & multi   1.10 1.10
Nos. 308-310 (3)   1.91 1.91

Org. for African Unity, 10th anniv.

WMO Emblem, Weather Vane — A80

1973, Sept. 4   Litho.   **Perf. 13**
311 A80 5k multicolored   .18 .18
312 A80 30k multicolored   1.40 1.40

Cent. of intl. meteorological cooperation.

View of Ibadan University A81

Designs: 12k, Campus, crest and graph showing growth, vert. 18k, Campus, students and crest. 30k, Teaching hospital.

1973, Nov. 17   **Perf. 14**
313 A81 5k lt blue & multi   .20 .20
314 A81 12k lilac & multi   .50 .50
315 A81 18k orange & multi   .75 .75
316 A81 30k blue, org & blk   1.25 1.25
Nos. 313-316 (4)   2.70 2.70

University of Ibadan, 25th anniversary.

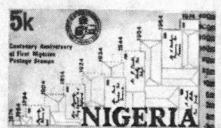

Growth of Mail, 1874-1974 A82

Designs: 12k, Nigerian Post emblem and Northern Nigeria No. 18A. 18k, Postal emblem and Lagos No. 1. 30k, Map of Nigeria and means of transportation.

1974, June 10   Litho.   **Perf. 14**
317 A82 5k green, black & org   .20 .20
318 A82 12k green & multi   .48 .48
319 A82 18k green, lilac & blk   1.25 1.25
320 A82 30k black & multi   1.65 1.65
Nos. 317-320 (4)   3.58 3.58

Centenary of first Nigerian postage stamps.

Globe and UPU Emblem A83

UPU cent.: 18k, World map and means of transportation. 30k, Letters.

1974, Oct. 9
321 A83 5k blue & multi   .28 .28
322 A83 18k orange & multi   1.00 1.00
323 A83 30k brown & multi   1.65 1.65
Nos. 321-323 (3)   2.93 2.93

Hungry and Well-fed Children — A84

Designs: 12k, Chicken farm, horiz. 30k, Irrigation project.

1974, Nov. 25   Litho.   **Perf. 14**
324 A84 5k orange, blk & grn   .24 .24
325 A84 12k multicolored   .55 .55
326 A84 30k multicolored   1.40 1.40
Nos. 324-326 (3)   2.19 2.19

Freedom from Hunger.

A85   Map of Nigeria with Telex Network, Teleprinter — A86

1975, July 3   Litho.   **Perf. 14**
327 A85 5k multicolored   .20 .20
328 A85 12k multicolored   .50 .50
329 A86 18k multicolored   .75 .75
330 A86 30k multicolored   1.25 1.25
Nos. 327-330 (4)   2.70 2.70

Inauguration of Nigeria Telex Network.

Queen Amina of Zaria (1536-1566) A87   Alexander Graham Bell A88

1975, Aug. 18   Litho.   **Perf. 14**
331 A87 5k multicolored   .25 .25
332 A87 18k multicolored   .90 .90
333 A87 30k multicolored   1.50 1.50
Nos. 331-333 (3)   2.65 2.65

International Women's Year.

1976, Mar. 10   Wmk. 379

Designs: 18k, Hands beating gong, modern telephone operator, horiz. 25k, Telephones, 1876, 1976.

334 A88 5k pink, black & ocher   .22 .22
335 A88 18k deep lilac & multi   .80 .80
336 A88 25k lt bl, vio bl & blk   1.10 1.10
Nos. 334-336 (3)   2.12 2.12

Centenary of first telephone call by Alexander Graham Bell, Mar. 10, 1876.

Children Going to School — A89

Designs: 5k, Child learning to write, horiz. 25k, Classroom.

1976, Sept. 20   Litho.   **Perf. 14**
337 A89 5k multicolored   .22 .22
338 A89 18k multicolored   .80 .80
339 A89 25k multicolored   1.10 1.10
Nos. 337-339 (3)   2.12 2.12

Launching of universal primary education in 1976.

Traditional Musical Instruments A90

Designs: 5k, Carved mask (festival emblem). 10k, National Arts Theater, Lagos. 12k, Nigerian and African women's hair styles. 30k, Nigerian carvings.

1976-77   Wmk. 379
340 A90 5k black, gold & grn   .18 .18
341 A90 10k multicolored   .35 .35
342 A90 12k multicolored   .45 .45

---

343 A90 18k brown, ocher & blk   .65 .65
344 A90 30k multicolored   1.10 1.10
Nos. 340-344 (5)   2.73 2.73

2nd World Black and African Festival of Arts and Culture, Lagos, Jan. 15-Feb. 12, 1977. Issue dates: 5k, 18k, Nov. 1, 1976; others Jan. 15, 1977.

Gen. Muhammed Broadcasting and Map of Nigeria A91

Designs: 18k, Gen. Muhammed as Commander in Chief, vert. 30k, in battle dress, vert.

1977, Feb. 13   Litho.   **Perf. 14**
345 A91 5k multicolored   .16 .16
346 A91 18k multicolored   .60 .60
347 A91 30k multicolored   1.00 1.00
Nos. 345-347 (3)   1.76 1.76

Gen. Murtala Ramat Muhammed, Head of State and Commander in Chief, 1st death anniversary.

Scouts Clearing Street — A92

Designs: 5k, Senior and Junior Boy Scouts saluting, vert. 25k, Scouts working on farm. 30k, African Scout Jamboree emblem, map of Africa.

1977, Apr. 1   Wmk. 379
348 A92 5k multicolored   .22 .22
349 A92 18k multicolored   .65 .65
350 A92 25k multicolored   .95 .95
351 A92 30k multicolored   1.30 1.30
Nos. 348-351 (4)   3.12 3.12

First All-Africa Boy Scout Jamboree, Sherehills, Jos, Nigeria, Apr. 2-8, 1977.

Trade Fair Emblem A93

Emblem and: 5k, View of Fair grounds. 30k, Weaver and potter.

1977, Nov. 27   Litho.   **Perf. 13**
352 A93 5k multicolored   .16 .16
353 A93 18k multicolored   .55 .55
354 A93 30k multicolored   .95 .95
Nos. 352-354 (3)   1.66 1.66

1st Lagos Intl. Trade Fair, Nov. 27-Dec. 11.

Nigeria's 13 Universities A94

Designs: 12k, Map of West African highways and telecommunications network. 18k, Training of technicians, and cogwheel. 30k, World map and map of Argentina with Buenos Aires.

1978, Apr. 28   Wmk. 379
355 A94 5k multicolored   .15 .15
356 A94 12k multicolored   .32 .32
357 A94 18k multicolored   .48 .48
358 A94 30k multicolored   .80 .80
Nos. 355-358 (4)   1.75 1.75

Global Conf. on Technical Cooperation among Developing Countries, Buenos Aires.

Antenna and ITU Emblem A95

1978, May 17   Litho.   **Perf. 14**
359 A95 30k multicolored   1.00 1.00

10th World Telecommunications Day.

Students on Cassava Plantation A96

"Operation Feed the Nation": 18k, Woman working in backyard vegetable garden. 30k, Plantain harvest, vert.

1978, July 7   Litho.   Perf. 14
360 A96   5k multicolored   .15   .15
361 A96 18k multicolored   .42   .42
362 A96 30k multicolored   .65   .65
   Nos. 360-362 (3)   1.22 1.22

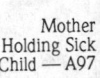

Mother Holding Sick Child — A97

Designs: 12k, Sick boy at health station. 18k, Vaccination of children. 30k, Syringe and WHO emblem, vert.

1978, Aug. 31   Wmk. 379
363 A97   5k multicolored   .15   .15
364 A97 12k multicolored   .34   .34
365 A97 18k multicolored   .48   .48
366 A97 30k multicolored   .75   .75
   Nos. 363-366 (4)   1.72 1.72

Global eradication of smallpox.

Bronze Horseman from Benin — A98   Anti-Apartheid Emblem — A99

Nigerian antiquities: 5k, Nok terracotta figure from Bwari. 12k, Bronze snail and animal from Igbo-Ukwu, horiz. 18k, Bronze statue of a king of Ife.

1978, Oct. 27   Litho.   Perf. 14
367 A98   5k multicolored   .15   .15
368 A98 12k multicolored   .32   .32
369 A98 18k multicolored   .48   .48
370 A98 30k multicolored   .70   .70
   Nos. 367-370 (4)   1.65 1.65

1978, Dec. 10   Perf. 14
371 A99 18k red, yellow & black   .45   .45

Anti-Apartheid Year.

Wright Brothers, Flyer A A100

Design: 18k, Nigerian Air Force fighters flying in formation.

1978, Dec. 28
372 A100   5k multicolored   .15   .15
373 A100 18k multicolored   .48   .48

75th anniversary of powered flight.

Murtala Muhammed Airport A101

1979, Mar. 15   Litho.   Perf. 14
374 A101 5k bright blue & black   .15   .15

Inauguration of Murtala Muhammed Airport.

Young Stamp Collector A102

1979, Apr. 11
375 A102 5k multicolored   .15   .15

Philatelic Week and 10th anniversary of National Philatelic Service.

Mother Nursing Child, IYC Emblem A103

Designs: 18k, Children at study. 25k, Children at play, vert.

1979, June 28   Wmk. 379   Perf. 14
376 A103   5k multicolored   .15   .15
377 A103 18k multicolored   .38   .38
378 A103 25k multicolored   .48   .48
   Nos. 376-378 (3)   1.01 1.01

International Year of the Child.

A104   A105

Design: 10k, Preparation of audio-visual material. 30k, Adult education class.

1979, July 25   Photo. & Engr.
379 A104 10k multicolored   .18   .18
380 A104 30k multicolored   .55   .55

Intl. Bureau of Education, Geneva, 50th anniv.

1979, Sept. 20   Litho.   Perf. 13½x14
381 A105 10k Necom house, Lagos   .30   .30

Intl. Radio Consultative Committee (CCIR) of the ITU, 50th anniv.

Trainees and Survey Equipment A106

1979, Dec. 12   Photo.   Perf. 14
382 A106 10k multicolored   .30   .30

Economic Commission for Africa, 21st anniv.

Soccer Cup and Ball on Map of Nigeria A107

1980, Mar. 8
383 A107 10k shown   .15   .15
384 A107 30k Player, vert.   .45   .45

12th African Cup of Nations Soccer Championship, Lagos and Ibadan, Mar.

Swimming, Moscow '80 Emblem A108

1980, July 19   Litho. & Engr.   Perf. 14
385 A108 10k Wrestling, vert.   .22   .22
386 A108 20k Long jump, vert.   .42   .42
387 A108 30k shown   .65   .65

388 A108 45k Women's basketball, vert.   1.00 1.00
   Nos. 385-388 (4)   2.29 2.29

22nd Summer Olympic Games, Moscow, July 19-Aug. 3.

Men Holding OPEC Emblem A109

1980, Sept. 15   Litho. & Engr.
389 A109 10k shown   .18   .18
390 A109 45k Anniversary emblem, vert.   .80   .80

OPEC, 20th anniversary.

First Steam Locomotive in Nigeria A110

1980, Oct. 2   Wmk. 379   Perf. 14
391 A110 10k shown   .22   .22
392 A110 20k Unloading freight car   .42   .42
393 A110 30k Freight train   .65   .65
   Nos. 391-393 (3)   1.29 1.29

Nigerian Railway Corp., 75th anniv.

Technician Performing Quality Control Test — A111

1980, Oct. 14
394 A111 10k Scale, ruler, vert.   .18   .18
395 A111 30k shown   .55   .55

World Standards Day.

Map of West Africa showing ECOWAS Members, Modes of Communication — A112

1980, Nov. 5   Litho. & Engr.
396 A112 10k shown   .20   .20
396A A112 25k Transportation   .48   .48
397 A112 30k Map, cow, cocoa   .60   .60
398 A112 45k Map, industrial symbols   .85   .85
   Nos. 396-398 (4)   2.13 2.13

Woman with Cane Sweeping — A113

Wmk. 379
1981, June 25   Litho.   Perf. 14
399 A113 10k shown   .16   .16
400 A113 30k Amputee photographer   .50   .50

Intl. Year of the Disabled.

World Food Day — A114

1981, Oct. 16   Litho. & Engr.
401 A114 10k Pres. Shenu Shagari   .20   .20
402 A114 25k Produce, vert.   .50   .50
403 A114 30k Tomato crop, vert.   .60   .60
404 A114 45k Pig farm   .90   .90
   Nos. 401-404 (4)   2.20 2.20

Anti-apartheid Year — A115

1981, Dec. 10   Litho.
405 A115 30k Soweto riot   .55   .55
406 A115 45k Police hitting man, vert.   .80   .80

Scouting Year — A116

1982, Feb. 22   Litho.   Perf. 14
407 A116 30k Animal first aid   .50   .50
408 A116 45k Baden-Powell, scouts   .75   .75

TB Bacillus Centenary A117

1982, Mar. 24   Litho.   Perf. 14
409 A117 10k Inoculation   .16   .16
410 A117 30k Research   .48   .48
411 A117 45k Patient being x-rayed, vert.   .70   .70
   Nos. 409-411 (3)   1.34 1.34

10th Anniv. of UN Conference on Human Environment A118

1982, June 10   Litho.
412 A118 10k Keep your environment clean   .15   .15
413 A118 20k Check air pollution   .30   .30
414 A118 30k Preserve natural environment   .48   .48
415 A118 45k Reafforestation concerns all   .70   .70
   Nos. 412-415 (4)   1.63 1.63

Salamis Parnassus A119

1982, Sept. 15   Litho.
416 A119 10k shown   .20   .20
417 A119 20k Papilio zalmoxis   .38   .38
418 A119 30k Pachylophus beckeri   .60   .60
419 A119 45k Papilio hesperus   .85   .85
   Nos. 416-419 (4)   2.03 2.03

25th Anniv. of Natl. Museum A120

1982, Nov. 18   Wmk. 379
420 A120 10k Statuettes, vert.   .16   .16
421 A120 20k Bronze leopard   .30   .30
422 A120 30k Soapstone seated figure, vert.   .48   .48
423 A120 45k Wooden helmet mask   .70   .70
   Nos. 420-423 (4)   1.64 1.64

Family Day — A121   Commonwealth Day — A122

1983, Mar. 8 Litho. Perf. 14
424 A121 10k Extended family, house, horiz. .25 .25
425 A121 30k Family .75 .75

1983, Mar. 14
426 A122 10k Satellite view, horiz. .22 .22
427 A122 25k Natl. Assembly buildings, horiz. .55 .55
428 A122 30k Oil exploration .70 .70
429 A122 45k Runners 1.00 1.00
Nos. 426-429 (4) 2.47 2.47

10th Anniv. of Natl. Youth Service Corps A123

1983, May 25 Litho. Perf. 14
430 A123 10k Construction .25 .25
431 A123 25k Climbing wall, vert. .55 .55
432 A123 30k Marching, vert. .75 .75
Nos. 430-432 (3) 1.55 1.55

World Communications Year — A124

Wmk. 379
1983, July 22 Litho. Perf. 14
433 A124 10k Mailman, vert. .20 .20
434 A124 25k Newspaper stand .52 .52
435 A124 30k Traditional horn messenger .65 .65
436 A124 45k TV news broadcast .95 .95
Nos. 433-436 (4) 2.32 2.32

World Fishery A125

1983, Sept. 22 Litho. Wmk. 379
437 A125 10k Pink shrimp .20 .20
438 A125 25k Long neck groaker .50 .50
439 A125 30k Barracuda .60 .60
440 A125 45k Fishing technique .90 .90
Nos. 437-440 (4) 2.20 2.20

Boys' Brigade, 75th Anniv. A126

1983, Oct. 14 Perf. 14
441 A126 10k Boys, emblem, vert. .22 .22
442 A126 30k Food production .55 .55
443 A126 45k Skill training 1.00 1.00
Nos. 441-443 (3) 1.77 1.77

Fight Against Polio Campaign A127

1984, Feb. 29 Litho. Perf. 14
444 A127 10k Crippled boy, vert. .20 .20
445 A127 25k Vaccination .50 .50
446 A127 30k Healthy child, vert. .65 .65
Nos. 444-446 (3) 1.35 1.35

Hartebeests A128

1984, May 25 Wmk. 379 Perf. 14
447 A128 10k Waterbuck, vert. .20 .20
448 A128 25k shown .50 .50
449 A128 30k Buffalo .65 .65
450 A128 45k African golden monkey, vert. .95 .95
Nos. 447-450 (4) 2.30 2.30

Central Bank of Nigeria, 25th Anniv. A129

1984, July 2 Wmk. 379
451 A129 10k £1 note, 1968 .22 .22
452 A129 25k Bank .55 .55
453 A129 30k £5 note, 1959 .70 .70
Nos. 451-453 (3) 1.47 1.47

1984 Summer Olympics, Los Angeles A130

African Development Bank, 20th Anniv. A131

Wmk. 379
1984, Aug. 9 Litho. Perf. 14
454 A130 10k Boxing .18 .18
455 A130 25k Discus .42 .42
456 A130 30k Weight lifting .50 .50
457 A130 45k Bicycling .75 .75
Nos. 454-457 (4) 1.85 1.85

1984, Sept. 10
Designs: 10k, Irrigation project, Lesotho. 25k, Bomi Hills roadway, Liberia. 30k, Education development, Seychelles. 45k, Coal mining and transportation, Niger. Nos. 459-461 horiz.

458 A131 10k multicolored .18 .18
459 A131 25k multicolored .45 .45
460 A131 30k multicolored .52 .52
461 A131 45k multicolored .80 .80
Nos. 458-461 (4) 1.95 1.95

Rare Bird Species — A132

1984, Oct. 24
462 A132 10k Pin-tailed whydah .20 .20
463 A132 25k Spur-winged plover .50 .50
464 A132 30k Red bishop .60 .60
465 A132 45k Francolin .90 .90
Nos. 462-465 (4) 2.20 2.20

Inscriptions, including country name, denomination and descriptions vary widely in size and style.

Intl. Civil Aviation Organization, 40th Anniv. A132a

1984, Dec. 7 Litho. Perf. 14
465A A132a 10k shown .28 .28
465B A132a 45k Jet circling Earth 1.25 1.25

Fight Against Indiscipline A133

1985, Feb. 27
466 A133 20k Encourage punctuality .38 .38
467 A133 50k Discourage bribery .95 .95

Intl. Youth Year — A134

OPEC, 25th Anniv. — A135

1985, June 5
468 A134 20k Sports, horiz. .25 .25
469 A134 50k Nationalism .65 .65
470 A134 55k Service organizations .75 .75
Nos. 468-470 (3) 1.65 1.65

1985, Sept. 15
471 A135 20k shown .38 .38
472 A135 50k World map, horiz. .95 .95

Natl. Independence, 25th Anniv. A136

1985, Sept. 25
473 A136 20k Oil refinery .35 .35
474 A136 50k Map of states .85 .85
475 A136 55k Monument .90 .90
476 A136 60k Eleme Oil Refinery 1.00 1.00
a. Souvenir sheet of 4, #473-476 7.50
Nos. 473-476 (4) 3.10 3.10

 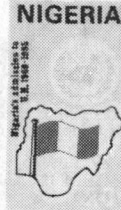

World Tourism Day — A137

UN, 40th Anniv. — A138

1985, Sept. 27
477 A137 20k Waterfalls .24 .24
478 A137 50k Crafts, horiz. .60 .60
479 A137 55k Carved calabashes, flag .65 .65
480 A137 60k Leather goods, rug .75 .75
Nos. 477-480 (4) 2.24 2.24

1985, Oct. 7
481 A138 20k Emblem, map, flag .40 .40
482 A138 50k UN building, horiz. 1.00 1.00
483 A138 55k Emblem, horiz. 1.10 1.10
Nos. 481-483 (3) 2.50 2.50

Admission of Nigeria to UN, 25th anniv.

African Reptiles A139

1986, Apr. 15 Wmk. 379 Perf. 14
484 A139 10k Python .20 .20
485 A139 20k Crocodile .40 .40
486 A139 25k Gopher tortoise .50 .50
487 A139 30k Chameleon .60 .60
Nos. 484-487 (4) 1.70 1.70

Volkswagen Automobile Assembly Factory A140

Designs: 1k, Social worker with children, vert. 5k, Modern housing development. 10k, Modern method of harvesting coconuts, vert. 15k, Port activities. 20k, Tecoma stans, flower, vert. 25k, Medical care. 30k, Birom folk dancers. 35k, Telephone operators. 40k, Nkpokiti dancers, vert. 45k, Hibiscus. 50k, Modern p.o. 1n, Stone quarry. 2n, Technical education.

1986, June 16 Wmk. 379 Perf. 14
488 A140 1k multicolored .15 .15
489 A140 2k multicolored .15 .15
490 A140 5k multicolored .15 .15
491 A140 10k multicolored .15 .15
492 A140 15k multicolored .15 .15
493 A140 20k multicolored .15 .15
494 A140 25k multicolored .15 .15
494A A140 30k multicolored .15 .15
495 A140 35k multicolored .18 .18
496 A140 40k multicolored .20 .20
497 A140 45k multicolored .22 .22
498 A140 50k multicolored .25 .25
499 A140 1n multicolored .50 .50
500 A140 2n multicolored 1.00 1.00
Set value 2.85 2.85

Use of some denominations began as early as 1984. Date of issue of the 30k is not definite.

Intl. Peace Year — A141

1986, June 20 Litho. Perf. 14
501 A141 10k Emblem .16 .16
502 A141 20k Hands touching globe .34 .34

Insects A142

1986, July 14
503 A142 10k Goliath beetle .20 .20
504 A142 20k Wasp .40 .40
505 A142 25k Cricket .50 .50
506 A142 30k Carpet beetle .60 .60
a. Souvenir sheet of 4, #503-506 1.75 1.75
Nos. 503-506 (4) 1.70 1.70

UNICEF, 40th Anniv. — A143

Institute of Intl. Affairs, 25th Anniv. — A144

1986, Nov. 11
507 A143 10k Oral rehydration .15 .15
508 A143 20k Immunization .22 .22
509 A143 25k Breast-feeding .28 .28
510 A143 30k Mother playing with child .34 .34
Nos. 507-510 (4) .99 .99

UN Child Survival Campaign.

1986, Dec. 13
511 A144 20k Intl. understanding, horiz. .15 .15
512 A144 30k shown .22 .22

Seashells A145

1987, Mar. 31
513 A145 10k Freshwater clam .15 .15
514 A145 15k Periwinkle .15 .15
515 A145 25k Bloddy cockle .16 .16
516 A145 30k Mangrove oyster .20 .20
Set value .54 .54

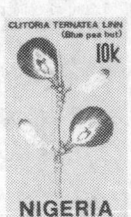

A146

A147

1987, May 28
517	A146	10k Blue pea but	.15 .15
518	A146	20k Hibiscus	.15 .15
519	A147	25k Acanthus montanus	.18 .18
520	A147	30k Combretum	
		racemosum	.20 .20
		Nos. 517-520 (4)	.68 .68

Hair Styles
A148

Intl. Year of Shelter for the Homeless
A149

1987, Sept. 15   Wmk. 379   Perf. 14
521	A148	10k Doka	.15 .15
522	A148	20k Eting	.15 .15
523	A148	25k Agogo	.15 .15
524	A148	30k Goto	.15 .15
		Set value	.42 .42

1987, Dec. 10   Litho.
525	A149	20k Homeless family	.15 .15
526	A149	30k Moving to new home	.15 .15
		Set value	.25 .25

A150

A152

1988, Feb. 17   Litho.   Perf. 14
527	A150	20k Help the Needy	.15 .15
528	A150	30k Care for the sick	.15 .15
		Set value	.25 .25

Intl. Red Cross and Red Crescent Organizations, 125th annivs.

1988, Apr. 7   Wmk. 379   Perf. 14
529	A151	10k Immunization	.15 .15
530	A151	20k Map, globe, emblem	.15 .15
531	A151	30k Mobile hospital	.15 .15
		Set value	.30 .30

WHO, 40th anniv.

1988, May 25
532	A152	10k shown	.15 .15
533	A152	20k Emblem, map, 4 men	.15 .15
		Set value	.25 .25

Organization of African Unity, 25th anniv.

Shrimp
A153

1988, June 2
534	A153	10k Pink shrimp	.15 .15
535	A153	20k Tiger shrimp	.15 .15
536	A153	25k Deepwater roseshrimp	.15 .15
537	A153	30k Estuarine prawn	.15 .15
a.		Miniature sheet of 4, #534-537	.65 .65
		Set value	.42 .42

1988 Summer Olympics, Seoul
A154

1988, Sept. 6   Wmk. 379   Perf. 14
538	A154	10k Weight lifting	.15 .15
539	A154	20k Boxing	.15 .15
540	A154	30k Running, vert.	.15 .15
		Set value	.30 .30

A155

A156

Nigerian Security Printing and Minting Co., Ltd., 25th Anniv.
A157

1988, Oct. 28
541	A155	10k Bank note production	.15 .15
542	A155	20k Coin production	.15 .15
543	A156	25k Products	.15 .15
544	A157	30k Anniv. emblem	.15 .15
		Set value	.42 .42

Traditional Musical Instruments
A158

Wmk. 379

1989, June 29   Litho.   Perf. 14
545	A158	10k Tambari	.15 .15
546	A158	20k Kundung	.15 .15
547	A158	25k Ibid	.15 .15
548	A158	30k Dundun	.15 .15
		Set value	.25 .25

African Development Bank, 25th Anniv. — A159

Nigerian Girl Guides Assoc., 70th Anniv. — A160

1989, Sept. 10
549	A159	10k Reservoir, Mali	.15 .15
550	A159	20k Irrigation project,	
		Gambia	.15 .15

551	A159	25k Bank headquarters	.15 .15
552	A159	30k shown	.15 .15
		Set value	.25 .25
		Nos. 549-551 horiz.	

1989, Sept. 16
553	A160	10k Campfire, horiz.	.15 .15
554	A160	20k shown	.15 .15
		Set value	.15 .15

A161

A162

Traditional costumes.

1989, Oct. 26
555	A161	10k Etubom	.15 .15
556	A161	20k Fulfulde	.15 .15
557	A161	25k Aso-ofi	.15 .15
558	A161	30k Fuska Kura	.15 .15
		Set value	.25 .25

1990, Jan. 18
559	A162	10k shown	.15 .15
560	A162	20k Map, delivery	.15 .15
		Set value	.15 .15

Pan-African Postal Union, 10th anniv.

Ancient Wall, Kano
A162a

1990, May 23   Litho.   Perf. 14
560A A162a 20n multicolored

Three additional stamps are known to exist with this set. The editors would like to see them.

Pottery
A163

1990, May 24
561	A163	10k Oil lamp	.15 .15
562	A163	20k Water pot	.15 .15
563	A163	25k Musical pots	.15 .15
564	A163	30k Water jug	.15 .15
a.		Sheet of 4 + 4 labels	2.50 2.50
		Set value	.26 .26

Inscriptions, including country name, denomination and descriptions vary widely in size and style.

Intl. Literacy Year — A164

1990, Aug. 8
565	A164	20k multicolored	.15 .15
566	A164	30k multicolored	.15 .15
		Set value	.15 .15

A165

A166

A167

1990, Sept. 14
567	A165	10k shown	.15 .15
568	A166	20k Flags	.15 .15
569	A165	25k Globe	.15 .15
570	A166	30k shown	.15 .15
		Set value	.26 .26

Organization of Petroleum Exporting Countries (OPEC), 30th anniv.

1990, Nov. 8
571	A167	20k Grey parrot	.15 .15
572	A167	30k Roan antelope	.15 .15
573	A167	1.50n Grey-necked rock	
		fowl	.38 .38
574	A167	2.50n Mountain gorilla	.65 .65
		Nos. 571-574 (4)	1.33 1.33

Inscriptions vary widely in size and style.

A168

A170

A169

1991, Mar. 20
575	A168	10k Eradication	.15 .15
576	A169	20k shown	.15 .15
577	A168	30k Prevention	.15 .15

Natl. Guineaworm Eradication Day.

1991, May 26
578	A170	20k Progress	.15 .15
579	A170	25k Unity	.15 .15
580	A170	50k Freedom	.15 .15
		Set value	.15 .15

OAU Heads of State Meeting, Abiya.

ECOWAS Summit, Abuja
A171

1991, July 4
581	A171	20k Flags	.15 .15
582	A171	50k Map of West Africa	.15 .15
		Set value	.15 .15

Economic Community of West African States.

Fish — A172

1991, July 10
583	A172	10k Electric catfish	.15 .15
584	A172	20k Niger perch	.15 .15
585	A172	30k Talapia	.15 .15
586	A172	50k African catfish	.15 .15
		Set value	.18 .18

Telecom '91 — A173

1991, Oct. 7
587 A173 20k shown .15 .15
588 A173 50k multi, vert. .15 .15
　　　　Set value .15 .15

Sixth World Forum and Exposition on Telecommunications, Geneva, Switzerland.

1992 Summer Olympics, Barcelona A174

1992, Jan. 24 Unwmk.
589 A174 50k Boxing .15 .15
590 A174 1n Running .15 .15
591 A174 1.50n Table tennis .22 .22
　　　　Wmk. 379
592 A174 2n Taekwondo .28 .28
　　　Nos. 589-592 (4) .80 .80

1992 Summer Olympics, Barcelona A175

World Health Day A176

1992, Apr. 3 Litho. Perf. 14
593 A175 1.50n multicolored .38 .38

1992, Apr. 7 Unwmk.

Designs: 50k, Heart and blood pressure gauge. 1n, Globe and blood pressure gauge. 1.50n, Heart in rib cage. 2n, Cross-section of heart.

594 A176 50k multicolored .15 .15
595 A176 1n multicolored .25 .25
596 A176 1.50n multicolored .38 .38
597 A176 2n multicolored .50 .50
　　　Nos. 594-597 (4) 1.28 1.28

Intl. Institute of Tropical Agriculture, 25th Anniv. A177

Designs: 50k, Plantain, vert. 1n, Food products. 1.50n, Harvesting cassava tubers, vert. 2n, Yam barn, vert.

1992, July 17
598 A177 50k multicolored .15 .15
599 A177 1n multicolored .25 .25
600 A177 1.50n grn, blk & brown .38 .38
601 A177 2n multicolored .50 .50
　　　Nos. 598-601 (4) 1.28 1.28

Olymphilex '92 — A178

Design: 1.50n, Stamp under magnifying glass, Olympic rings.

　　　　Wmk. 379
1992, July 3 Litho. Perf. 14
602 A178 50k multicolored .15 .15
603 A178 1.50n multicolored .18 .18
　a.　Souvenir sheet of 2, #602-603 + 4 labels, unwmkd. .24 .24
　　　　Set value .24 .24

Maryam Babangida, Natl. Center for Women's Development
A179　　　A180

A180a

Designs: 50k, Emblem of Better Life Program. 1n, Women harvesting corn. 1.50n, Natl. Center, horiz. 2n, Woman using loom.

1992, Oct. 16
604 A179 50k multicolored .15 .15
605 A180 1n multicolored .25 .25
606 A180 1.50n multicolored .38 .38
607 A180a 2n multicolored .50 .50
　　　Nos. 604-607 (4) 1.28 1.28

Traditional Dances — A181

　　　　Unwmk.
1992, Dec. 15 Litho. Perf. 14
608 A181 50k Sabada .15 .15
609 A181 1n Sato .25 .25
610 A181 1.50n Asian Ubo Ikpa .38 .38
611 A181 2n Dundun .50 .50
　　　Nos. 608-611 (4) 1.28 1.28

Intl. Conference on Nutrition, Rome A182

1992, Dec. 1 Litho. Perf. 14
612 A182 50k Vegetables .15 .15
613 A182 1n Child eating .25 .25
614 A182 1.50n Fruits, vert. .35 .35
615 A182 2n Vegetables, diff. .50 .50
　　　Nos. 612-615 (4) 1.25 1.25

Animals A182a

Leki Beach A182b

1992-93 Litho. Perf. 14
615A A182a 1.50n African elephant
615B A182a 5n Stanley crane, vert.
615C A182b 10n multicolored
615D A182a 20n Roan antelope
615E A182a 30n Lion

World Environment Day — A183

Designs: 1n, Clean environment ensures good health. 1.50n, Check water pollution. 5n, Preserve your environment. 10n, Environment and nature.

1993, June 4 Litho. Perf. 14
616 A183 1n multicolored .15 .15
617 A183 1.50n multicolored .15 .15
618 A183 5n multicolored .40 .40
619 A183 10n multicolored .80 .80
　　　Nos. 616-619 (4) 1.50 1.50

Natl. Commission for Museums and Monuments, 50th Anniv. A184

1993, July 28 Litho. Perf. 14
620 A184 1n Oni figure, vert. .15 .15
621 A184 1.50n Queen Mother head, vert. .15 .15
622 A184 5n Pendant .40 .40
623 A184 10n Nok head, vert. .80 .80
　　　Nos. 620-623 (4) 1.50 1.50

Orchids — A185

1993, Oct. 28 Litho. Perf. 14
624 A185 1n Bulbophyllum distans .15 .15
625 A185 1.50n Eulophia cristata .15 .15
626 A185 5n Eulophia horsfalli .40 .40
627 A185 10n Eulophia quartiniana .80 .80
　a.　Souv. sheet of 4, #624-627 4.50 4.50
　　　Nos. 624-627 (4) 1.50 1.50

No. 627a exists with perforations through either the bottom or top margins.

Intl. Year of the Family A186

Designs: 1.50n, Child abuse, classroom scene. 10n, Fending for the family, market scene.

1994, Mar. 30 Litho. Perf. 14
628 A186 1.50n multicolored .15 .15
629 A186 10n multicolored .90 .90

Nigerian Philatelic Service, 25th Anniv. A187

Designs: 1n, #224. 1.50n, Bureau building. 5n, Map made of stamps. 10n, Counter staff, customers.

1994, Apr. 11
630 A187 1n multicolored .15 .15
631 A187 1.50n multicolored .15 .15
632 A187 5n multicolored .45 .45
633 A187 10n multicolored .90 .90
　　　Nos. 630-633 (4) 1.65 1.65

First Nigerian Postage Stamps, 120th Anniv. — A188

Designs: 1n, "I love stamps." 1.50n, "I collect stamps." 5n, Methods of transporting mail. 10n, Lagos type A1 on airmail envelope.

1994, June 10 Litho. Perf. 14
634 A188 1n multicolored .15 .15
635 A188 1.50n multicolored .15 .15
636 A188 5n multicolored .45 .45
637 A188 10n multicolored .90 .90
　　　Nos. 634-637 (4) 1.65 1.65

PHILAKOREA '94 — A189

1994, Aug. 16 Litho. Perf. 14
638 A189 30n multicolored 2.75 2.75

Crabs A190

1994, Aug. 12 Litho. Perf. 14
639 A190 1n Geryon quinquedens .15 .15
640 A190 1.50n Spider crab .15 .15
641 A190 5n Red spider .45 .45
642 A190 10n Geryon maritae .90 .90
　　　Nos. 639-642 (4) 1.65 1.65

African Development Bank, 30th Anniv. — A191

1994, Sept. 16
643 A191 1.50n Water treatment plant .15 .15
644 A191 30n Emblem, field 2.75 2.75

NIPOST/NITEL, 10th Anniv. — A192

Designs: 1n, Putting letter into mailbox, vert. 1.50n, Airmail letter. 5n, NIPOST, NITEL logos. 10n, Telephones, vert.

1995, Jan. 1 Litho. Perf. 14
645 A192 1n multicolored .15 .15
646 A192 1.50n multicolored .15 .15
647 A192 5n multicolored .45 .45
648 A192 10n multicolored .90 .90
　　　Nos. 645-648 (4) 1.65 1.65

Family Support Program A194

Designs: 1n, Feed the family. 1.50n, Monitoring child education. 5n, Caring for the family. 10n, Support agriculture.

1995, July 20 Litho. Perf. 14
653 A194 1n multicolored .15 .15
654 A194 1.50n multicolored .15 .15
655 A194 5n multicolored .45 .45
656 A194 10n multicolored .90 .90
　　　Nos. 653-656 (4) 1.65 1.65

First Telephone in Nigeria, Cent. — A195

Designs: 1.50n, Dial telephone, c. 1919. 10n, Crank telephone, c. 1885.

1995, Oct. 9 **Litho.** *Perf. 14*

657 A195	1.50n	multicolored	.15	.15
658 A195	10n	multicolored	.90	.90

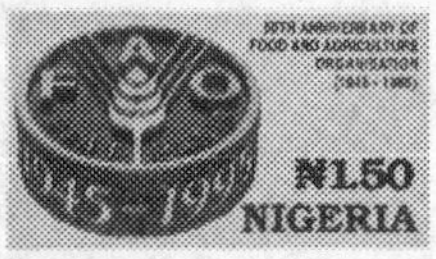

FAO, 50th Anniv. A196

1995, Oct. 16

659 A196	1.50n	shown	.15	.15
660 A196	30n	Fishing boats	2.75	2.75

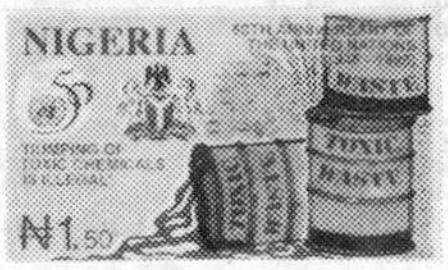

UN, 50th Anniv. A197

Designs: 1n, Emblem of justice, vert. 1.50n, Against illegal dumping of toxic chemicals. 5n, Tourism. 10n, Peace-keeping soldiers.

1995, Oct. 24

661 A197	1n	multicolored	.15	.15
662 A197	1.50n	multicolored	.15	.15
663 A197	5n	multicolored	.45	.45
664 A197	10n	multicolored	.90	.90
		Nos. 661-664 (4)	1.65	1.65

SEMI-POSTAL STAMPS

Catalogue values for unused stamps in this section are for Never Hinged items.

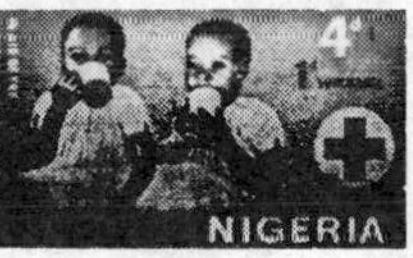

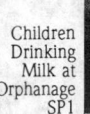

Children Drinking Milk at Orphanage SP1

Designs: 1sh6p+3p, Civilian first aid, vert. 2sh6p+3p, Military first aid.

1966, Dec. 1 **Photo.** *Perf. 14½x14*

B1 SP1	4p + 1p	pur, blk & red	.28	.28
B2 SP1	1sh6p + 3p	multi	1.00	1.00
B3 SP1	2sh6p + 3p	multi	1.75	1.75
		Nos. B1-B3 (3)	3.03	3.03

The surtax was for the Nigerian Red Cross.

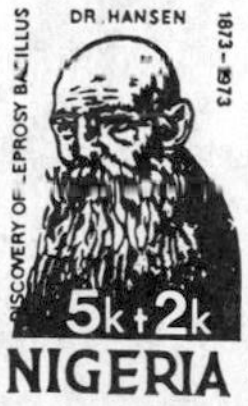

Dr. Armauer G. Hansen — SP2

1973, July 30 **Litho.** *Perf. 14*

B4 SP2	5k + 2k	blk, brn & buff	.40	.40

Centenary of the discovery of the Hansen bacillus, the cause of leprosy. The surtax was for the Nigerian Anti-Leprosy Association.

POSTAGE DUE STAMPS

Catalogue values for unused stamps in this section are for Never Hinged items.

D1

D2

Perf. 14½x14

1959, Jan. 4 **Wmk. 4** **Litho.**

J1 D1	1p	orange	.15	.15
J2 D1	2p	orange	.15	.15
J3 D1	3p	orange	.15	.15
J4 D1	6p	orange	1.00	*1.00*
J5 D1	1sh	black	2.25	*2.25*
		Nos. J1-J5 (5)	3.70	*3.70*

1961, Aug. 1 **Wmk. 335**

J6 D1	1p	red	.15	.15
J7 D1	2p	blue	.15	.15
J8 D1	3p	emerald	.18	.18
J9 D1	6p	yellow	.40	.40
J10 D1	1sh	dark blue	1.25	*1.25*
		Nos. J6-J10 (5)	2.13	*2.13*

Perf. 12½x13½

1973, May 3 **Litho.** **Unwmk.**

J11 D2	2k	red	.15	.15
J12 D2	3k	blue	.15	.15
J13 D2	5k	orange	.20	.20
J14 D2	10k	yellow green	.35	.35
		Nos. J11-J14 (4)	.85	.85

NIUE

nē-'ü-(,)ā

LOCATION — Island in the south Pacific Ocean, northeast of New Zealand
GOVT. — Self-government, in free association with New Zealand
AREA — 100 sq. mi.
POP. — 3,019 (est. 1984)
CAPITAL — Alofi

Niue, also known as Savage Island, was annexed to New Zealand in 1901 with the Cook Islands. Niue achieved internal self-government in 1974.

12 Pence = 1 Shilling
20 Shillings = 1 Pound
100 Cents = 1 Dollar (1967)

Catalogue values for unused stamps in this country are for Never Hinged items, beginning with Scott 90 in the regular postage section, Scott B1 in the semi-postal section, Scott C1 in the air post section, and Scott O1 in the officials section.

Watermarks

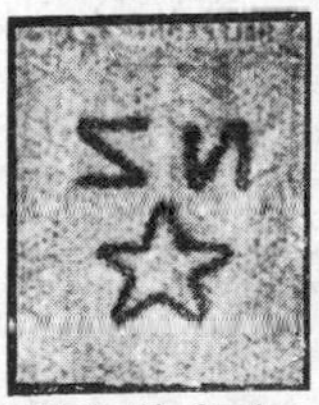

Wmk. 61- Single-lined NZ and Star Close Together

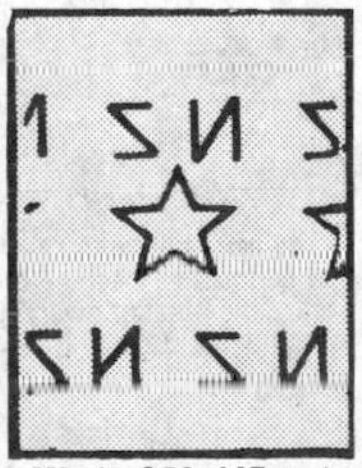

Wmk. 253- NZ and Star

New Zealand No. 100 Handstamped in Green **NIUE**

1902 **Wmk. 63** *Perf. 11*

Thick Soft Paper

1 A35	1p	carmine	375.00	375.00

Stamps of New Zealand Surcharged in Carmine, Vermilion or Blue:

NIUE. ½ PENI. — 1/2p
NIUE. TAHA PENI. — 1p
NIUE. 2½ PENI — 2 1/2p

Perf. 14

Thin Hard Paper

3 A18	½p	green (C)	1.50	*3.00*
a.		Inverted surcharge	300.00	*400.00*
4 A35	1p	carmine (Bl)	8.00	10.00
a.		No period after "PENI"	140.00	150.00
b.		Perf. 11x14	1.25	1.10
c.		As "a," perf. 11x14	11.00	12.50

Perf. 14

Wmk. 61

6 A18	½p	green (V)	.60	.85
7 A35	1p	carmine (Bl)	.85	1.10
a.		No period after "PENI"	9.00	*16.00*
b.		Double surcharge	*725.00*	

Perf. 11

Unwmk.

8 A22	2½p	blue (C)	4.00	4.50
a.		No period after "PENI"	45.00	47.50
9 A22	2½p	blue (V)	1.75	2.00
a.		No period after "PENI"	20.00	25.00

The surcharge on the ½ & 1p stamps is printed in blocks of 60. Two stamps in each block have a space between the "U" and "E" of "NIUE" and one of the 1p stamps has a broken "E" like an "F."

Blue Surcharge on Stamps of New Zealand, Types of 1898:

NIUE. Tolu e Pene. — e
NIUE Ono e Pene. — f
NIUE. Taha e Sileni. — g
NIUE. Tahae Sileni. — h

1903 **Wmk. 61** *Perf. 11*

10 A23(e)	3p	yellow brown	5.00	4.50
11 A26(f)	6p	rose	6.50	10.00
13 A29(g)	1sh	brown red	22.50	22.50
a.		1sh scarlet	22.50	22.50
b.		1sh orange red	35.00	35.00
c.		As "b," surcharge "h" (error)	800.00	*1,100.*
		Nos. 10-13 (3)	34.00	37.00

Surcharged in Carmine or Blue on Stamps of New Zealand

NIUE. ½ PENI. — i

1911-12 *Perf. 14, 14x14½*

14 A41(i)	½p	yellow grn (C)	.60	.70
15 A41(f)	6p	car rose (Bl)	2.50	*6.00*
16 A41(g)	1sh	vermilion (Bl)	8.00	*35.00*
		Nos. 14-16 (3)	11.10	*41.70*

1915 *Perf. 14*

18 A22(d)	2½p	dark blue (C)	9.00	17.50

Surcharged in Brown or Dark Blue on Stamps of New Zealand

1917 *Perf. 14x13½, 14x14½*

19 A42	1p	carmine (Br)	5.00	5.50
a.		No period after "PENI"	140.00	150.00
20 A45(e)	3p	violet brn (Bl)	50.00	75.00
a.		No period after "Pene"	650.00	700.00

New Zealand Stamps of 1909-19 Overprinted in Dark Blue or Red

NIUE. — k

1917-20 **Typo.**

21 A43	½p	yellow grn (R)	.40	.75
22 A42	1p	carmine (Bl)	3.00	3.50
23 A47	1½p	gray black (R)	.16	.90
24 A47	1½p	brown org (R)	1.00	3.00
25 A43	3p	chocolate (Bl)	1.60	5.25

Engr.

26 A44	2½p	dull blue (R)	1.00	3.00
27 A45	3p	violet brown (Bl)	1.40	1.50
28 A45	6p	car rose (Bl)	4.50	15.00
29 A45	1sh	vermilion (Bl)	4.50	15.00
		Nos. 21-29 (9)	17.56	47.90

Same Overprint On Postal-Fiscal Stamps of New Zealand, 1906-15

Perf. 14, 14½ and Compound

1918-23

30 PF1	2sh	blue (R)	14.00	30.00
31 PF1	2sh6p	brown (Bl) ('23)	16.00	40.00
32 PF1	5sh	green (R)	18.00	*45.00*
33 PF1	10sh	red brn (Bl) ('23)	72.50	80.00
34 PF2	£1	rose (Bl) ('23)	125.00	140.00
		Nos. 30-34 (5)	245.50	335.00

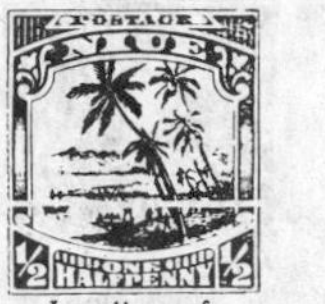

Landing of Captain Cook A16

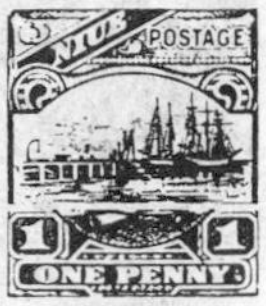

Avarua Waterfront A17

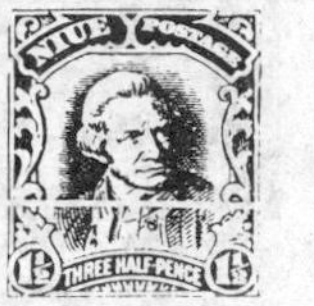

Capt. James Cook — A18

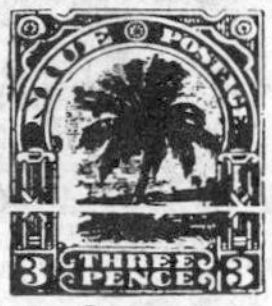

Coconut Palm — A19

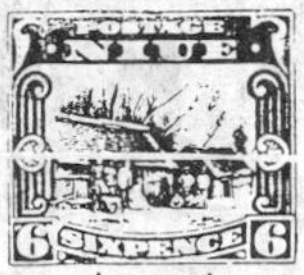

Arorangi Village — A20

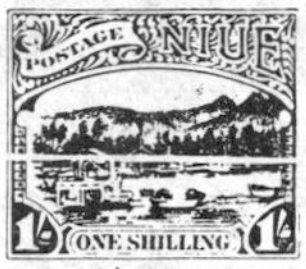

Avarua Harbor — A21

Unwmk.

1920, Aug. 23 **Engr.** *Perf. 14*

35 A16	½p	yellow grn & blk	3.00	*3.00*
36 A17	1p	car & black	1.50	1.00
37 A18	1½p	red & black	2.00	3.50
38 A19	3p	pale blue & blk	1.00	*6.00*
39 A20	6p	dp grn & red brn	1.25	*11.00*
a.		Center inverted	*500.00*	
40 A21	1sh	blk brn & blk	2.50	*10.00*
		Nos. 35-40 (6)	11.25	*34.50*

See Nos. 41-42. For surcharge see No. 48.

Types of 1920 Issue and

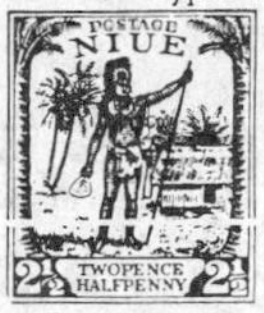

Rarotongan Chief (Te Po) — A22

Avarua Harbor — A23

1925-27 **Wmk. 61**

41 A16	½p	yel grn & blk ('26)	.30	.40
42 A17	1p	car & black	.30	.40
43 A22	2½p	dk blue & blk ('27)	3.00	5.50
44 A23	4p	dull vio & blk ('27)	3.00	6.00
		Nos. 41-44 (4)	6.60	12.30

New Zealand No. 182 Overprinted Type "k" in Red

1927

47 A56	2sh	blue	16.00	30.00
a.		2sh dark blue	16.00	30.00

No. 37 Surcharged **TWO PENCE**

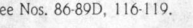

1931 **Unwmk.** *Perf. 14*

48 A18	2p on 1½p	red & blk	1.10	1.10

New Zealand Postal-Fiscal Stamps of 1931-32 Overprinted Type "k" in Blue or Red

1931, Nov. 12 **Wmk. 61**

49 PF5	2sh6p	deep brown	8.00	13.00
50 PF5	5sh	green (R)	17.00	27.50
51 PF5	10sh	dark carmine	32.50	45.00
52 PF5	£1	pink ('32)	50.00	72.50
		Nos. 49-52 (4)	107.50	158.00

See Nos. 86-89D, 116-119.

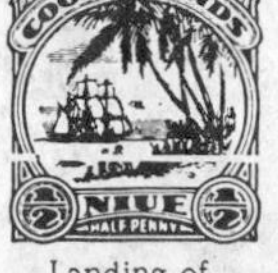

Landing of Captain Cook — A24

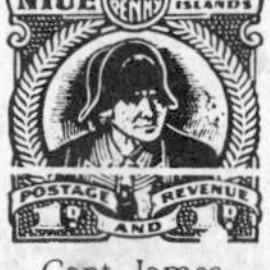

Capt. James Cook — A25

Polynesian Migratory Canoe — A26

Islanders Unloading Ship — A27

View of Avarua Harbor — A28

R.M.S. Monowai — A29

King George V — A30

Perf. 13, 14 (4p, 1sh)

1932, Mar. 16   Engr.   Unwmk.

53	A24	½p yel grn & blk	3.75	7.00
a.		Perf. 14x13	85.00	100.00
54	A25	1p dp red & blk	.55	.15
55	A26	2p org brn & blk	.55	1.65
56	A27	2½p indigo & blk	4.00	21.00
57	A28	4p Prus blue & blk	5.00	17.00
a.		Perf. 13	5.00	17.00
58	A29	6p dp org & blk	1.25	1.00
59	A30	1sh dull vio & blk	1.10	2.75
		Nos. 53-59 (7)	16.20	50.55

For types overprinted see Nos. 67-69.

1933-36   Wmk. 61   Perf. 14

60	A24	½p yel grn & blk	.40	.80
61	A25	1p deep red & blk	.40	.30
62	A26	2p brown & blk ('36)	.40	.65
63	A27	2½p indigo & blk	.40	2.00
64	A28	4p Prus blue & blk	1.10	1.10
65	A29	6p org & blk ('36)	.55	.90
66	A30	1sh dk vio & blk ('36)	5.00	12.00
		Nos. 60-66 (7)	8.25	17.75

See Nos. 77-82.

Silver Jubilee Issue

Types of 1932 Overprinted in Black or Red

SILVER JUBILEE OF KING GEORGE V. 1910 - 1935.

1935, May 7   Perf. 14

67	A25	1p car & brown red	.70	1.25
68	A27	2½p indigo & bl (R)	3.00	3.00
a.		Vert. pair, imperf. horiz.	275.00	
69	A29	6p dull org & grn	3.00	5.00
		Nos. 67-69 (3)	6.70	9.25

The vertical spacing of the overprint is wider on No. 69.
No. 68a is from proof sheets.

Coronation Issue

New Zealand Stamps of 1937 **NIUE** Overprinted in Black

Perf. 13½x13

1937, May 13   Wmk. 253

70	A78	1p rose carmine	.15	.15
71	A78	2½p dark blue	.15	.15
72	A78	6p vermilion	.28	.28
		Nos. 70-72 (3)	.58	.58

George VI — A31

Village Scene — A32

Coastal Scene with Canoe — A33

Mt. Ikurangi behind Avarua — A34

1938, May 2   Wmk. 61   Perf. 14

73	A31	1sh dp violet & blk	2.50	2.00
74	A32	2sh dk red brown & blk	6.00	4.25
75	A33	3sh yel green & blue	9.00	7.00
		Nos. 73-75 (3)	17.50	13.25

See Nos. 83-85.

Perf. 13½x14

1940, Sept. 2   Engr.   Wmk. 253

76	A34	3p on 1½p rose vio & blk	.15	.15

Types of 1932-38

1944-46   Wmk. 253   Perf. 14

77	A24	½p yel grn & blk	.40	1.00
78	A25	1p dp red & blk ('45)	.40	.65
79	A26	2p org brn & blk ('46)	3.75	3.50
80	A27	2½p dk bl & blk ('45)	.50	1.00
81	A28	4p Prus blue & blk	1.10	.90
82	A29	6p dp orange & blk	.60	1.00
83	A31	1sh dp vio & blk	1.40	1.00
84	A32	2sh dk red brn car & blk ('45)	7.00	2.75
85	A33	3sh yel grn & bl ('45)	10.00	7.00
		Nos. 77-85 (9)	25.15	18.80

New Zealand Postal-Fiscal Stamps

Overprinted Type "k" (narrow "E") in Blue or Red

1941-45   Wmk. 61   Perf. 14

86	PF5	2sh6p brown	16.00	19.00
87	PF5	5sh green (R)	135.00	150.00
88	PF5	10sh rose	92.50	115.00
89	PF5	£1 pink	135.00	150.00
		Nos. 86-89 (4)	378.50	434.00

Wmk. 253

89A	PF5	2sh6p brown	2.75	5.00
89B	PF5	5sh green (R)	4.50	7.50
e.		5sh light yellow green, wmkd. sideways ('67)	45.00	70.00
89C	PF5	10sh rose	35.00	40.00
89D	PF5	£1 pink	30.00	35.00
		Nos. 89A-89D (4)	72.25	87.50

No. 89e exists in both line and comb perf.

> Catalogue values for unused stamps in this section, from this point to the end of the section, are for Never Hinged items.

Peace Issue

New Zealand Nos. 248, 250, 254 and 255 Overprinted in Black or Blue:

NIUE p   **NIUE** q   **NIUE**

1946, June 4   Perf. 13x13½, 13½x13

90	A94 (p)	1p emerald	.15	.15
91	A96 (q)	2p rose violet (Bl)	.15	.15
92	A100 (p)	6p org red & red brn	.20	.20
93	A101 (p)	8p brn lake & blk (Bl)	.25	.25
		Nos. 90-93 (4)	.75	.75

Map of Niue — A35

H.M.S. Resolution — A36

Designs: 2p, Alofi landing. 3p, Thatched Dwelling. 4p, Arch at Hikutavake. 6p, Alofi bay. 9p, Fisherman. 1sh, Cave at Makefu. 2sh, Gathering bananas. 3sh, Matapa Chasm.

Perf. 14x13½, 13½x14

1950, July 3   Engr.   Wmk. 253

94	A35	½p red orange & bl	.15	.15
95	A36	1p green & brown	.15	.15
96	A36	2p rose car & blk	.15	.15
97	A36	3p blue vio & blue	.25	.20
98	A36	4p brn vio & ol grn	.40	.30
99	A36	6p brn org & bl grn	.55	.50
100	A35	9p dk brn & brn org	.85	.75
101	A36	1sh black & purple	1.00	.85
102	A35	2sh dp grn & brn org	1.35	1.20
103	A35	3sh black & dp blue	2.75	2.00
		Nos. 94-103 (10)	7.60	6.25

For surcharges see Nos. 106-115.

Coronation Issue

Queen Elizabeth II — A36a

Westminster Abbey — A36b

1953, May 24   Photo.   Perf. 14x14½

104	A36a	3p brown	.50	.50
105	A36b	6p slate black	1.00	1.00

Nos. 94-103 Surcharged **1c**

Perf. 14x13½, 13½x14

1967, July 10   Engr.   Wmk. 253

106	A35	½c on ½p red org & blue	.15	.15
107	A36	1c on 1p green & brn	.30	.15
108	A36	2c on 2p rose car & black	.15	.15
109	A36	2½c on 3p bl vio & bl	.15	.15
110	A36	3c on 4p brn vio & ol grn		
111	A36	5c on 6p brn org & green	.15	.15
112	A35	8c on 9p dk brn & brn org	.25	.25
113	A36	10c on 1sh blk & pur	.40	.40
114	A35	20c on 2sh dp grn & brown org	.95	.95
115	A35	30c on 3sh blk & dp bl	1.25	1.25
			1.50	1.50
		Nos. 106-115 (10)	5.25	5.10

The position of the numeral varies on each denomination. The surcharge on the ½c, 2½c, 8c, 10c and 20c contains one dot only.

New Zealand Arms — A37

Wmk. 253

1967, July 10   Typo.   Perf. 14
Black Surcharge

116	A37	25c yellow brown	1.10	.65
117	A37	50c green	1.65	1.25
118	A37	$1 cerise	1.25	2.50
119	A37	$2 pale pink	1.75	4.25
		Nos. 116-119 (4)	5.75	8.65

1967   Perf. 11

116a	A37	25c	8.50	13.00
117a	A37	50c	9.00	15.00
118a	A37	$1	12.00	15.00
119a	A37	$2	16.00	20.00
		Nos. 116a-119a (4)	45.50	63.00

The perf. 11 stamps were produced when a normal perforating machine broke down and 2,500 of each denomination were perforated on a treadle machine first used by the N.Z. Post Office in 1899.

Christmas Issues

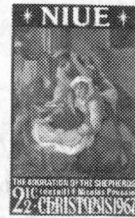
Adoration of the Shepherds, by Poussin — A37a

Nativity, by Federico Fiori — A37b

Perf. 13½x14

1967, Oct. 3   Photo.   Wmk. 253

120	A37a	2½c multicolored	.25	.25

1969, Oct. 1   Photo.   Wmk. 253

121	A37b	2½c multicolored	.25	.25

Pua — A38

Flowers (except 20c): 1c, Golden shower. 2c, Flamboyant. 2½c, Frangipani. 3c, Niue crocus. 5c, Hibiscus. 8c, Passion fruit. 10c, Kamapui. 20c, Queen Elizabeth II. 30c, Tapeu orchid.

Perf. 12½x13

1969, Nov. 27   Litho.   Unwmk.

122	A38	½c green & multi	.15	.15
123	A38	1c orange & multi	.15	.15
124	A38	2c gray & multi	.15	.15
125	A38	2½c bister & multi	.15	.15
126	A38	3c blue & multi	.20	.15
127	A38	5c ver & multi	.32	.22
128	A38	8c violet & multi	.55	.40
129	A38	10c yellow & multi	.65	.50
130	A38	20c dk blue & multi	1.10	.90
131	A38	30c olive grn & multi	1.65	1.50
		Nos. 122-131 (10)	5.07	4.27

Edible Crab — A39

Perf. 13½x12½

1969, Aug. 19   Litho.

132	A39	3c Kalahimu	.15	.15
133	A39	5c Kalavi	.22	.22
134	A39	30c Unga	1.10	1.10
		Nos. 132-134 (3)	1.47	1.47

Christmas Issue

Adoration, by Correggio — A39a

1970, Oct. 1   Litho.   Perf. 12½

135	A39a	2½c multicolored	.20	.20

Plane over Outrigger Canoe — A40

Designs: 5c, Plane over ships in harbor. 8c, Civair plane over island.

1970, Dec. 9   Litho.   Perf. 13½

136	A40	3c multicolored	.15	.15
137	A40	5c multicolored	.25	.25
138	A40	8c multicolored	.40	.40
		Nos. 136-138 (3)	.80	.80

Opening of Niue Airport.

Polynesian Triller (Heahea) — A41

Birds: 10c, Crimson-crowned fruit pigeon (kulukulu). 20c, Blue-crowned lory (henga).

1971, June 23   Litho.   Perf. 13½x13

139	A41	5c multicolored	.25	.25
140	A41	10c multicolored	.50	.50
141	A41	20c multicolored	1.00	1.00
		Nos. 139-141 (3)	1.75	1.75

Christmas Issue

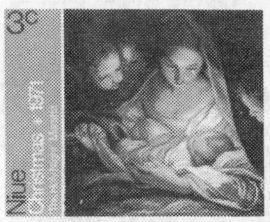

Holy Night, by Carlo Maratta A41a

1971, Oct. 6   Photo.   Perf. 13x13½
142 A41a 3c orange & multi .20 .20

People of Niue A42

Octopus Lure and Octopus A43

1971, Nov. 17
143 A42 4c Boy .15 .15
144 A42 6c Girl .24 .24
145 A42 9c Man .32 .32
146 A42 14c Woman .55 .55
    Nos. 143-146 (4) 1.26 1.26

1972, May 3   Litho.   Perf. 13x13½

Designs: 5c, Warrior and weapons. 10c, Sika (spear) throwing, horiz. 25c, Vivi dance, horiz.

147 A43 3c blue & multi .15 .15
148 A43 5c rose & multi .15 .15
149 A43 10c blue & multi .25 .25
150 A43 25c yellow & multi .65 .65
    Nos. 147-150 (4) 1.20 1.20

So. Pacific Festival of Arts, Fiji, May 6-20.

Alofi Wharf A44

South Pacific Commission Emblem and: 5c, Health service. 6c, School children. 18c, Cattle and dwarf palms.

1972, Sept. 6   Litho.   Perf. 13½x14
151 A44 4c blue & multi .15 .15
152 A44 5c blue & multi .15 .15
153 A44 6c blue & multi .18 .18
154 A44 18c blue & multi .55 .55
    Nos. 151-154 (4) 1.03 1.03

So. Pacific Commission, 25th anniv.

Christmas Issue, 1972

Madonna and Child, by Murillo — A44a

1972, Oct. 4   Photo.   Perf. 11½
155 A44a 3c gray & multi .15 .15

Pempheris Oualensis A45

Designs: Various fish.

Perf. 13½x13
1973, June 27   Litho.   Unwmk.
156 A45 8c shown .30 .30
157 A45 10c Cephalopholis .40 .40
158 A45 15c Variola louti .55 .55
159 A45 20c Etelis carbunculus .75 .75
    Nos. 156-159 (4) 2.00 2.00

Flowers, by Jan Breughel — A46

Paintings of Flowers: 5c, by Hans Bollongier. 10c, by Rachel Ruysch.

1973, Nov. 21   Litho.   Perf. 13½x13
160 A46 4c bister & multi .15 .15
161 A46 5c orange brn & multi .15 .15
162 A46 10c emerald & multi .40 .40
    Nos. 160-162 (3) .70 .70

Christmas.

Capt. Cook and "Resolution" A47

Capt. Cook and: 3c, Cook's landing place and ship. 8c, Map of Niue. 20c, Administration Building and flag of 1774.

1974, June 20   Litho.   Perf. 13½x14
163 A47 2c multicolored .15 .15
164 A47 3c multicolored .16 .16
165 A47 8c multicolored .40 .40
166 A47 20c multicolored 1.00 1.00
    Nos. 163-166 (4) 1.71 1.71

Bicentenary of Cook's landing on Niue.

King Fataaiki — A48

Annexation Day, Oct. 19, 1900 — A49

Village Meeting A50

Design: 10c, Legislative Assembly Building.

Perf. 14x13½, 13½x14
1974, Oct. 19   Litho.
167 A48 4c multicolored .15 .15
168 A49 8c multicolored .25 .25
169 A50 10c multicolored .35 .35
170 A50 20c multicolored .65 .65
    Nos. 167-170 (4) 1.40 1.40

Referendum for Self-government, Sept. 3, 1974.

Decorated Bicycle — A51

Christmas: 10c, Decorated motorcycle. 20c, Going to church by truck.

1974, Nov. 13   Litho.   Perf. 12½
171 A51 3c green & multi .15 .15
172 A51 10c dull blue & multi .22 .22
173 A51 20c brown & multi .50 .50
    Nos. 171-173 (3) .87 .87

Children Going to Church — A52

Children's Drawings: 5c, Child on bicycle trailing balloons. 10c, Balloons and gifts hanging from tree.

1975, Oct. 29   Litho.   Perf. 14½
174 A52 4c multicolored .15 .15
175 A52 5c multicolored .20 .20
176 A52 10c multicolored .40 .40
    Nos. 174-176 (3) .75 .75

Christmas.

Opening of Tourist Hotel — A53

Design: 20c, Hotel, building and floor plan.

1975, Nov. 19   Litho.   Perf. 14x13½
177 A53 8c multicolored .20 .20
178 A53 20c multicolored .50 .50

Preparing Ground for Taro — A54

Designs: 2c, Planting taro (root vegetable). 3c, Banana harvest. 4c, Bush plantation. 5c, Shellfish gathering. 10c, Reef fishing. 20c, Luku (fern) harvest. 50c, Canoe fishing. $1, Husking coconuts. $2, Hunting uga (land crab).

1976, Mar. 3   Litho.   Perf. 13½x14
179 A54 1c multicolored .15 .15
180 A54 2c blue & multi .15 .15
181 A54 3c lilac & multi .15 .15
182 A54 4c red & multi .15 .15
183 A54 5c green & multi .15 .15
184 A54 10c ocher & multi .18 .18
185 A54 20c multicolored .42 .42
186 A54 50c yellow & multi .85 .85
187 A54 $1 multicolored 1.50 1.50
188 A54 $2 multicolored 3.25 3.25
    Nos. 179-188 (10) 6.95 6.95

See #222-231. For surcharges see #203-210.

Water Tower, Girl Drawing Water — A55

Designs: 15c, Teleprinter and Niue radio station. 20c, Instrument panel, generator and power station.

1976, July 7   Litho.   Perf. 14x14½
189 A55 10c multicolored .18 .18
190 A55 15c multicolored .25 .25
191 A55 20c multicolored .35 .35
    Nos. 189-191 (3) .78 .78

Technical achievements.

Christmas Tree (Flamboyant) and Administration Building — A56

Christmas: 15c, Avatele Church, interior.

1976, Sept. 15   Litho.   Perf. 14½
192 A56 9c orange & multi .20 .20
193 A56 15c orange & multi .35 .35

Elizabeth II, Coronation Portrait, and Westminster Abbey — A57

Design: $2, Coronation regalia.

1977, June 7   Photo.   Perf. 13½
194 A57 $1 multicolored 1.40 1.25
195 A57 $2 multicolored 4.25 3.75
  a. Souvenir sheet of 2, #194-195 5.75 5.75

25th anniv. of reign of Elizabeth II. Nos. 194-195 each printed in sheets of 5 stamps and label showing Niue flag and Union Jack.
For surcharge see No. 213.

Mothers and Infants — A58

Designs: 15c, Mobile school dental clinic. 20c, Elderly couple and home.

1977, June 29   Litho.   Perf. 14½
196 A58 10c multicolored .18 .18
197 A58 15c multicolored .22 .22
198 A58 20c multicolored .30 .30
    Nos. 196-198 (3) .70 .70

Personal (social) services.
For surcharges see Nos. 211-212.

Annunciation, by Rubens — A59

Rubens Paintings (details, Virgin and Child): 12c, Adoration of the Kings. 20c, Virgin with Garland. 35c, Holy Family.

1977, Nov. 15   Photo.   Perf. 13x13½
199 A59 10c multicolored .15 .15
200 A59 12c multicolored .15 .15
201 A59 20c multicolored .25 .25
202 A59 35c multicolored .45 .45
  a. Souvenir sheet of 4, #199-202 1.25 1.25
    Nos. 199-202 (4) 1.00 1.00

Christmas and 400th birth anniversary of Peter Paul Rubens (1577-1640). Nos. 199-202 each printed in sheets of 6 stamps.

Stamps of 1976-77 Surcharged with New Value and 4 Bars in Black or Gold Printing and Perforations as Before

1977, Nov. 15
203 A54 12c on 1c (#179) .18 .18
204 A54 16c on 2c (#180) .22 .22
205 A54 30c on 3c (#181) .40 .40
206 A54 35c on 4c (#182) .48 .48
207 A54 40c on 5c (#183) .60 .60
208 A54 60c on 20c (#185) .80 .80
209 A54 70c on $1 (#187) .90 .90
210 A54 85c on $2 (#188) 1.25 1.25
211 A58 $1.10 on 10c (#196) 1.40 1.40
212 A58 $2.60 on 20c (#198) 3.25 3.25
213 A57 $3.20 on $2 (#195, G) 8.00 8.00
    Nos. 203-213 (11) 17.48 17.48

"An Inland View in Atooi," by John Webber A60

Scenes in Hawaii, by John Webber: 16c, A View of Karakooa in Owyhee. 20c, An Offering Before Capt. Cook in the Sandwich Islands. 30c, Tereoboo, King of Owyhee, bringing presents (boats). 35c, Masked rowers in boat.

1978, Jan. 18 Photo. *Perf. 13½*

214	A60 12c gold & multi	.25	.20
215	A60 16c gold & multi	.32	.28
216	A60 20c gold & multi	.40	.35
217	A60 30c gold & multi	.65	.55
218	A60 35c gold & multi	.75	.65
a.	Souv. sheet of 5, #214-218 + label	3.00	2.50
	Nos. 214-218 (5)	2.37	2.03

Bicentenary of Capt. Cook's arrival in Hawaii. Nos. 214-218 printed in sheets of 5 stamps and one label showing flags of Hawaii and Niue.

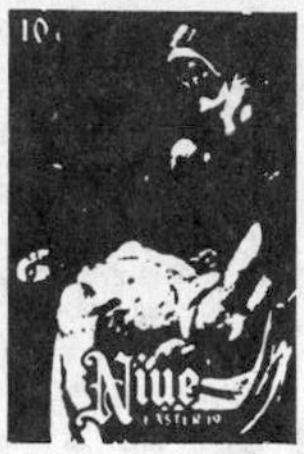

Descent from the Cross, by Caravaggio — A61

Easter: 20c, Burial of Christ, by Bellini.

1978, Mar. 15 Photo. *Perf. 13x13½*

219	A61 10c multicolored	.18	.18
220	A61 20c multicolored	.38	.38
a.	Souv. sheet of 2, #219-220, perf. 13½	.75	.75

Nos. 219-220 issued in sheets of 8.
See Nos. B1-B2.

Souvenir Sheet

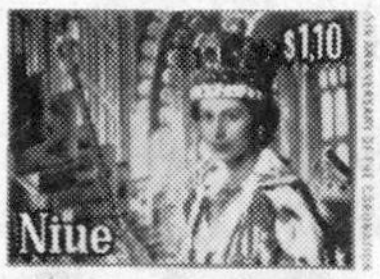

Elizabeth II — A62

1978, June 26 Photo. *Perf. 13*

221	Sheet of 6	8.00	8.00
a.	A62 $1.10 Niue and UK flags	1.10	1.10
b.	A62 $1.10 shown	1.10	1.10
c.	A62 $1.10 Queen's New Zealand flag	1.10	1.10
d.	Souvenir sheet of 3	5.50	5.50

25th anniv. of coronation of Elizabeth II. No. 221 contains 2 horizontal se-tenant strips of Nos. 221a-221c, separated by horizontal gutter showing coronation coach. No. 221d contains a vertical se-tenant strip of Nos. 221a-221c.

Type of 1977

Designs: 12c, Preparing ground for taro. 16c, Planting taro. 30c, Banana harvest. 35c, Bush plantation. 40c, Shellfish gathering. 60c, Reef fishing. 75c, Luku (fern) harvest. $1.10, Canoe fishing. $3.20, Husking coconuts. $4.20, Hunting uga (land crab).

1978, Oct. 27 Litho. *Perf. 14*

222	A54 12c silver & multi	.22	.22
223	A54 16c silver & multi	.28	.28
224	A54 30c silver & multi	.55	.55
225	A54 35c silver & multi	.60	.60
226	A54 40c silver & multi	.65	.65
227	A54 60c silver & multi	1.00	1.00
228	A54 75c silver & multi	1.40	1.40
229	A54 $1.10 silver & multi	2.00	2.00
230	A54 $3.20 silver & multi	4.75	4.75
231	A54 $4.20 silver & multi	5.75	5.75
	Nos. 222-231 (10)	17.20	17.20

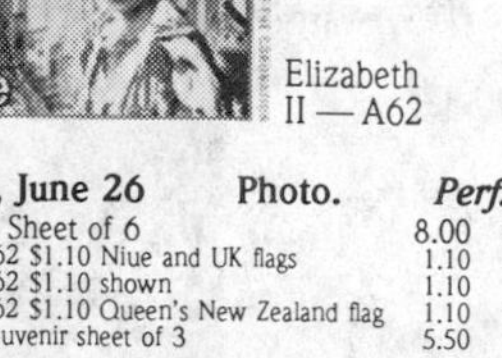

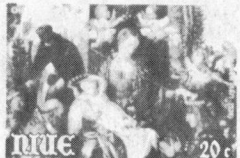

Celebration of the Rosary, by Dürer — A63

Designs: 30c, Nativity, by Dürer. 35c, Adoration of the Kings, by Dürer.

1978, Nov. 30 Photo. *Perf. 13*

232	A63 20c multicolored	.28	.28
233	A63 30c multicolored	.45	.45
234	A63 35c multicolored	.50	.50
a.	Souv. sheet of 3, #232-234 + label	1.50	1.50
	Nos. 232-234 (3)	1.23	1.23

Christmas and 450th death anniversary of Albrecht Dürer (1471-1528). Nos. 232-234 each printed in sheets of 5 stamps and descriptive label.
See Nos. B3-B5.

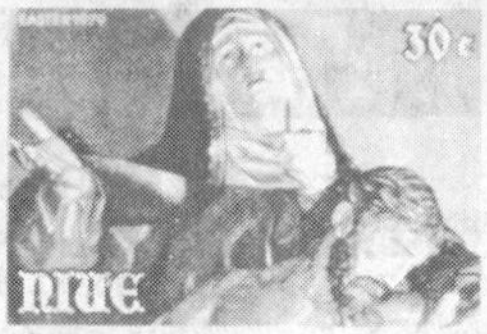

Pietà, by Gregorio Fernandez A64

Easter: 35c, Burial of Christ, by Pedro Roldan.

1979, Apr. 2

235	A64 30c multicolored	.45	.45
236	A64 35c multicolored	.55	.55
a.	Souvenir sheet of 2, #235-236	1.10	1.10

See Nos. B6-B7.

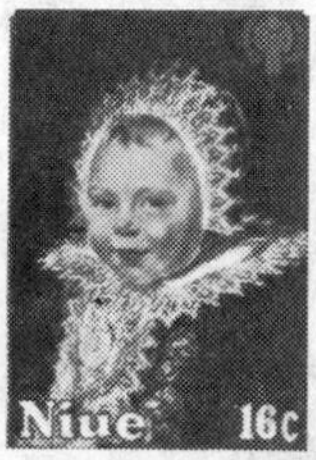

Child, by Franz Hals — A65

IYC (Emblem and Details from Paintings): 16c, Nurse and Child. 20c, Child of the Duke of Osuna, by Goya. 30c, Daughter of Robert Strozzi, by Titian. 35c, Children Eating Fruit, by Murillo.

1979, May 31 Photo. *Perf. 14*

237	A65 16c multicolored	.22	.22
238	A65 20c multicolored	.28	.28
239	A65 30c multicolored	.42	.42
240	A65 35c multicolored	.50	.50
a.	Souvenir sheet of 4, #237-240	1.75	1.75
	Nos. 237-240 (4)	1.42	1.42

See Nos. B8-B11.

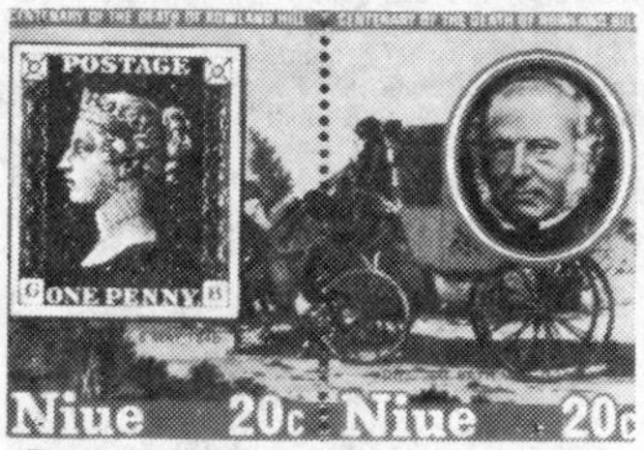

Penny Black, Bath Mail Coach, Rowland Hill — A66

Designs: 30c, Basel No. 3L1 and Alpine village coach. 35c, US No. 1 and 1st US transatlantic mail ship. 50c, France No. 3 and French railroad mail car, 1849. 60c, Bavaria No. 1 and Bavarian mail coach.

1979, July 3 Photo. *Perf. 14*

241	A66 20c pair	.40	.40
242	A66 30c pair	.60	.60
243	A66 35c pair	.70	.70
244	A66 50c pair	1.05	1.05
245	A66 60c pair	1.25	1.25
a.	Souv. sheet of 10, #241-245 + 2 labels	4.50	4.50
	Nos. 241-245 (5)	4.00	4.00

Sir Rowland Hill (1795-1879), originator of penny postage.
For overprints and surcharges see Nos. 281-285, B16, B21, B26, B30, B33, B41.

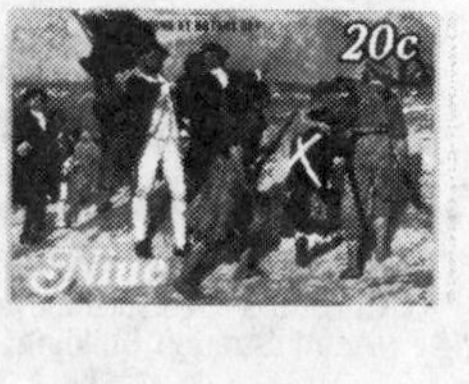

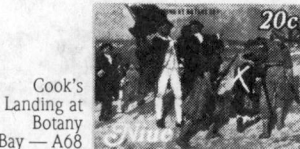

Cook's Landing at Botany Bay — A68

18th Century Paintings: 30c, Cook's Men during a Landing on Erromanga. 35c, Resolution and Discovery in Queen Charlotte's Sound. 75c, Death of Capt. Cook on Hawaii, by Johann Zoffany.

1979, July 30 Photo. *Perf. 14*

251	A68 20c multicolored	.28	.28
252	A68 30c multicolored	.42	.42
253	A68 35c multicolored	.50	.50
254	A68 75c multicolored	1.10	1.10
a.	Souv. sheet of 4, #251-254, perf. 13½	2.75	2.75
	Nos. 251-254 (4)	2.30	2.30

200th death anniv. of Capt. James Cook.
For surcharges see Nos. B18, B23, B28, B36.

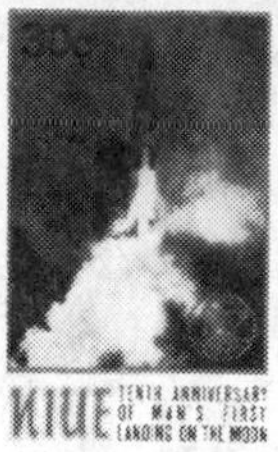

Apollo 11 Lift-off — A69

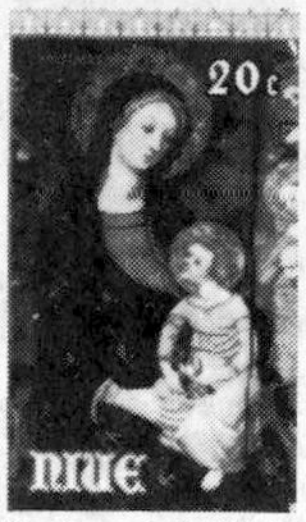

Virgin and Child, by P. Serra — A70

1979, Sept. 27 Photo. *Perf. 13½*

255	A69 30c shown	.35	.35
256	A69 35c Lunar module	.42	.42
257	A69 60c Splashdown	.80	.80
a.	Souvenir sheet of 3	2.00	2.00
	Nos. 255-257 (3)	1.57	1.57

Apollo 11 moon landing, 10th anniversary. No. 257a contains Nos. 255-257 in changed colors.
For surcharges see Nos. B24, B29, B35.

1979, Nov. 29 Photo. *Perf. 13*

Virgin and Child by: 25c, R. di Mur. 30c, S. diG. Sasseta. 50c, J. Huguet.

258	A70 20c multicolored	.28	.28
259	A70 25c multicolored	.35	.35
260	A70 30c multicolored	.42	.42
261	A70 50c multicolored	.70	.70
a.	Souvenir sheet of 4, #258-261	2.25	2.25
	Nos. 258-261 (4)	1.75	1.75

Christmas. See Nos. B12-B15. For surcharges see Nos. B19-B20, B25, B32.

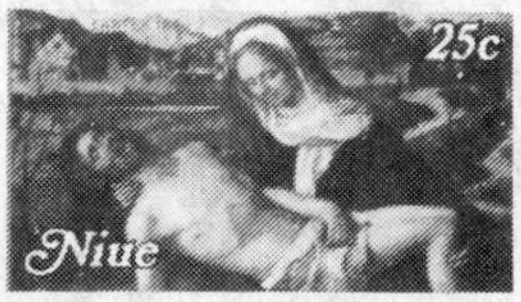

Pietà, by Giovanni Bellini — A71

Easter (Pietà, Paintings by): 30c, Botticelli. 35c, Anthony Van Dyck.

1980, Apr. 2 Photo. *Perf. 13*

262	A71 25c multicolored	.25	.25
263	A71 30c multicolored	.30	.30
264	A71 35c multicolored	.35	.35
	Nos. 262-264 (3)	.90	.90

See Nos. B37-B40.

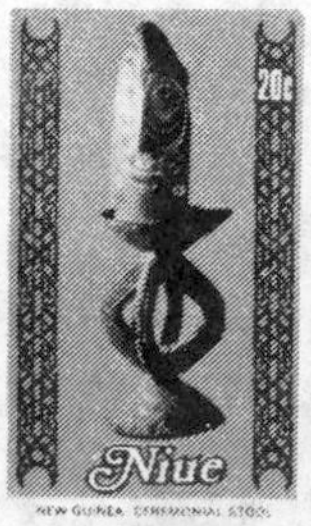

Ceremonial Stool, New Guinea — A72

1980, July 30 Photo. *Perf. 13*

265	A72 20c shown	.20	.20
266	A72 20c Ku-Tagwa plaque	.20	.20
267	A72 20c Suspension hook	.20	.20
268	A72 20c Ancestral board	.20	.20
269	A72 25c Platform post	.25	.25
270	A72 25c Canoe ornament	.25	.25
271	A72 25c Carved figure	.25	.25
272	A72 25c Woman and child	.25	.25
273	A72 30c God A'a, statue	.30	.30
274	A72 30c Tangaroa, statue	.30	.30
275	A72 30c Ivory pendant	.30	.30
276	A72 30c Tapa cloth	.30	.30
277	A72 35c Maori feather box	.35	.35
a.	Sheet of 4 (#265, 269, 273, 277)	1.50	1.50
278	A72 35c Hei-tiki	.35	.35
a.	Sheet of 4 (#266, 270, 274, 278)	1.50	1.50
279	A72 35c House post	.35	.35
a.	Sheet of 4 (#267, 271, 275, 279)	1.50	1.50
280	A72 35c God Ku, feather image	.35	.35
a.	Sheet of 4 (#268, 272, 276, 280)	1.50	1.50
	Nos. 265-280 (16)	4.40	4.40

3rd South Pacific Festival of Arts, Port Moresby, Papua New Guinea, June 30-July 12. Stamps of same denomination se-tenant horizontally in sheets of 24. Souvenir sheet stamps have 2c surcharge.
For surcharges see Nos. 626-641.

Nos. 241-250, Overprinted in Black on Silver

ZEAPEX'80 AUCKLAND
NEW ZEALAND STAMP EXHIBITION

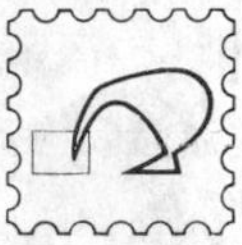

1980, Aug. 22 *Perf. 14*

281	A66 20c pair	.50	.50
282	A66 30c pair	.70	.70
283	A66 35c pair	.80	.80
284	A66 50c pair	1.10	1.10
285	A66 60c pair	1.40	1.40
	Nos. 281-285 (5)	4.50	4.50

ZEAPEX '80, New Zealand International Stamp Exhibition, Auckland, Aug. 23-31.

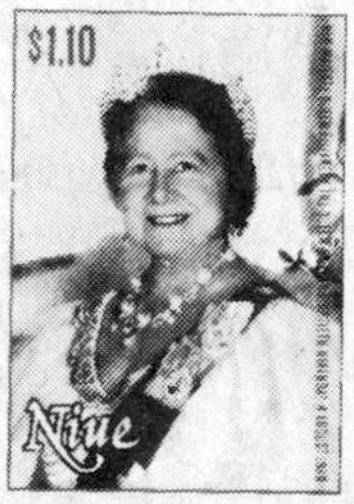

Queen Mother Elizabeth, 80th Birthday — A73

1980, Sept. 15 Photo. *Perf. 13x13½*

291	A73 $1.10 multicolored	1.75	1.75

Souvenir Sheet

292	A73 $3 multicolored	4.00	4.00

No. 291 issued in sheets of 5 and label showing coad of arms.

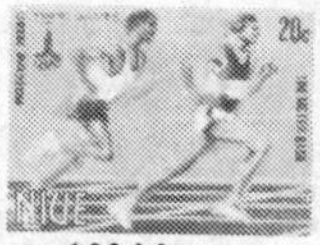

100-Meter Dash — A74

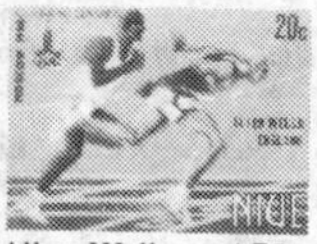

Allen Wells — A75

Designs: Nos. 295-296, 400-Meter freestyle. Nos. 297-298, Soling class yachting. Nos. 299-300, Soccer. Stamps of same denomination se-tenant in sheets of 32.

1980, Oct. 30 Photo. *Perf. 14*

293	A74 20c multicolored	.28	.28
294	A75 20c multicolored	.28	.28
295	A74 25c multicolored	.35	.35
296	A75 25c multicolored	.35	.35
297	A74 30c multicolored	.40	.40
298	A75 30c multicolored	.40	.40
299	A74 35c multicolored	.45	.45
300	A75 35c multicolored	.45	.45
	Nos. 293-300 (8)	2.96	2.96

22nd Summer Olympic Games, Moscow, July 19-Aug. 3.
See No. B42.

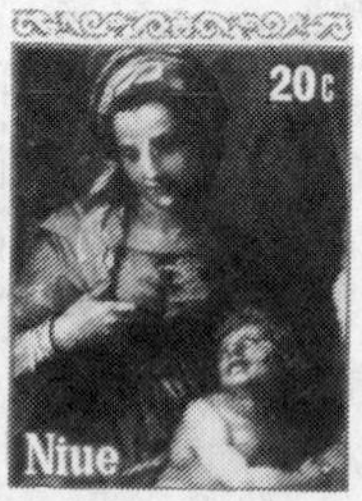

Virgin and Child, by del Sarto — A76

Designs: Paintings of Virgin and Child, by Andrea del Sarto.

1980, Nov. 28 Photo. *Perf. 13x13½*

301 A76 20c multicolored .25 .25
302 A76 25c multicolored .30 .30
303 A76 30c multicolored .35 .35
304 A76 35c multicolored .45 .45
a. Souvenir sheet of 4, #301-304 1.65 1.65
Nos. 301-304 (4) 1.35 1.35

Christmas and 450th death anniversary of Andrea del Sarto.
See Nos. B43-B46.

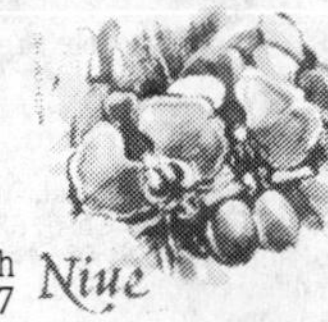

Moth Orchid — A77

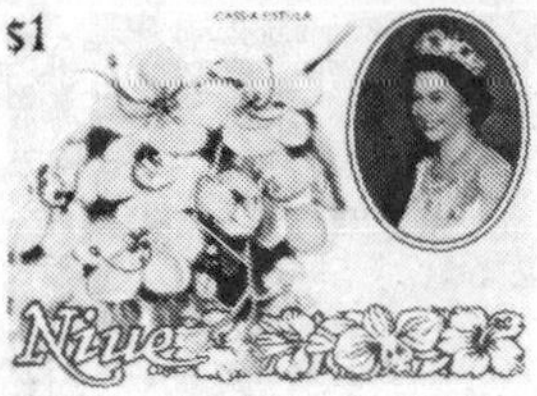

Golden Shower Tree — A77a

1981 Photo. *Perf. 13x13½*

305 A77 2c Phalaenopsis sp. .15 .15
306 A77 2c shown .15 .15
307 A77 5c Euphorbia pulcherrima .15 .15
308 A77 5c Poinsettia .15 .15
309 A77 10c Thunbergia alata .15 .15
310 A77 10c Black-eyed Susan .15 .15
311 A77 15c Cochlospermum hibiscoides .18 .18
312 A77 15c Buttercup tree .18 .18
313 A77 20c Begonia sp. .25 .25
314 A77 20c Begonia .25 .25
315 A77 25c Plumeria sp. .32 .32
316 A77 25c Frangipani .32 .32
317 A77 30c Sterlitzia reginae .35 .35
318 A77 30c Bird of paradise .35 .35
319 A77 35c Hibiscus syriacus .40 .40
320 A77 35c Rose of Sharon .40 .40
321 A77 40c Nymphaea sp. .45 .45
322 A77 40c Water lily .45 .45
323 A77 50c Tibouchina sp. .60 .60
324 A77 50c Princess flower .60 .60
325 A77 60c Nelumbo sp. .70 .70
326 A77 60c Lotus .70 .70
327 A77 80c Hybrid hibiscus 1.00 1.00
328 A77 80c Yellow hibiscus 1.00 1.00

Perf. 13½

329 A77a $1 shown 1.25 1.25
330 A77a $2 Orchid var. 2.50 2.50
331 A77a $3 Orchid sp. 3.50 3.50
332 A77a $4 Poinsettia 5.00 5.00
333 A77a $6 Hybrid hibiscus 7.25 7.25
334 A77a $10 Hibiscus rosa-sinensis 12.50 12.50
Nos. 305-334 (30) 41.40 41.40

Issue dates: 2c, 5c, 10c, 15c, 20c, 25c, Apr. 2, 30c, 35c, 40c, 50c, 60c, 80c, May 26. $1, $2, $3, Dec. 9, 1981; $4, $6, $10, Jan. 15, 1982.
Stamps of same denomination se-tenant.
For surcharges and overprints see Nos. 406-413, 413E, 594-595, O14, O16, O19.

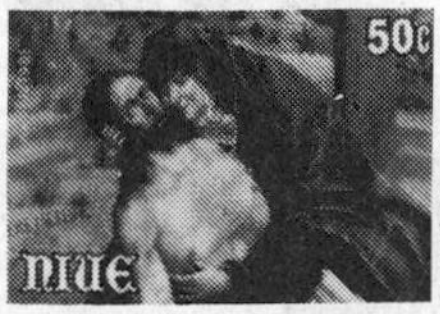

Jesus Defiled, by El Greco — A78

Easter (Paintings): 50c, Pieta, by Fernando Gallego. 60c, The Supper of Emaus, by Jacopo da Pontormo.

1981, Apr. 10 *Perf. 14*

337 A78 35c multicolored .48 .48
338 A78 50c multicolored .65 .65
339 A78 60c multicolored .80 .80
Nos. 337-339 (3) 1.93 1.93

See Nos. B47-B50.

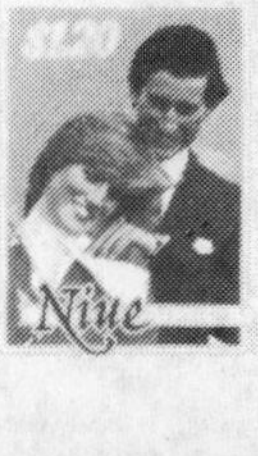

Prince Charles and Lady Diana — A79

1981, June 26 Photo. *Perf. 14*

340 A79 75c Charles .80 .80
341 A79 95c Lady Diana 1.00 1.00
342 A79 $1.20 shown 1.40 1.40
a. Souvenir sheet of 3, #340-342 4.00 4.00
Nos. 340-342 (3) 3.20 3.20

Royal Wedding. Nos. 340-342 each printed in sheets of 5 plus label showing St. Paul's Cathedral.
For overprints and surcharges see Nos. 357-359, 413A, 413C, 455, 596-598, B52-B55.

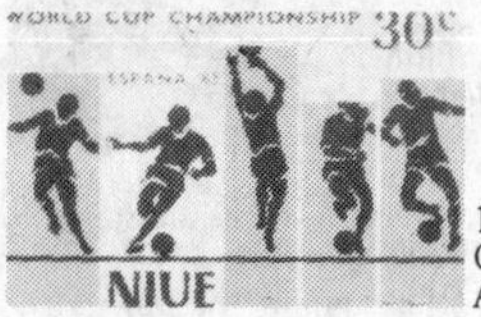

1982 World Cup Soccer A80

1981, Oct. 16 Photo. *Perf. 13*

343 Strip of 3 1.10 1.10
a. A80 30c any single .35 .35
344 Strip of 3 1.40 1.40
a. A80 35c any single .45 .45
345 Strip of 3 1.50 1.50
a. A80 40c any single .50 .50
Nos. 343-345 (3) 4.00 4.00

See No. B51.

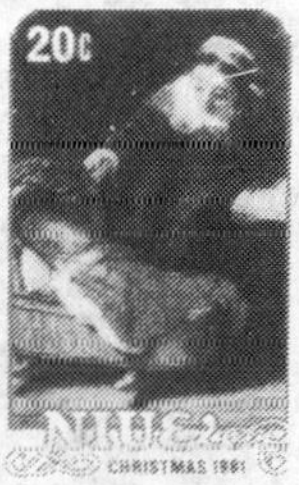

Christmas 1981 — A81

Rembrandt Paintings: 20c, Holy Family with Angels, 1645. 35c, Presentation in the Temple, 1631. 50c, Virgin and Child in Temple, 1629. 60c, Holy Family, 1640.

1981-82 Photo. *Perf. 14x13*

346 A81 20c multicolored .25 .25
347 A81 35c multicolored .45 .45
348 A81 50c multicolored .60 .60
349 A81 60c multicolored .75 .75
a. Souvenir sheet of 4, #346-349 2.50 2.50
Nos. 346-349 (4) 2.05 2.05

Souvenir Sheets

350 A81 80c + 5c like #346 1.10 1.10
351 A81 80c + 5c like #347 1.10 1.10
352 A81 80c + 5c like #348 1.10 1.10
353 A81 80c + 5c like #349 1.10 1.10

Surtax was for school children. Issue dates: Nos. 346-349a, Dec. 11; others, Jan. 22, 1982.

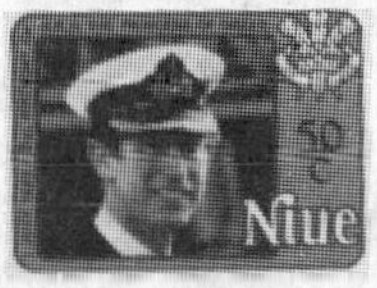

21st Birthday of Princess Diana — A82

1982, July 1 *Perf. 14*

354 A82 50c Charles .50 .50
355 A82 $1.25 Wedding 1.25 1.25
356 A82 $2.50 Diana 2.50 2.50
a. Souvenir sheet of 3, #354-356 5.25 5.25
Nos. 354-356 (3) 4.25 4.25

Nos. 354-356 each printed in sheets of 5 plus label showing wedding day picture.
For overprints and surcharges see Nos. 359B-359D, 413B, 413D, 456.

Nos. 340-342a Overprinted: "COMMEMORATING THE ROYAL BIRTH 21 JUNE 1982" or "BIRTH OF PRINCE WILLIAM OF WALES 21 JUNE 1982"

1982, July 23 *Perf. 14*

357 A79 75c multicolored 1.25 1.25
358 A79 95c multicolored 1.50 1.50
359 A79 $1.20 multicolored 2.00 2.00
a. Souvenir sheet of 3 5.00 5.00
Nos. 357-359 (3) 4.75 4.75

Birthday Stamps of 1982 Inscribed "COMMEMORATING THE BIRTH OF PRINCE WILLIAM OF WALES—21 JUNE 1982."

1982 Photo. *Perf. 14*

359B A82 50c like #354 .55 .55
359C A82 $1.25 like #355 1.40 1.40
359D A82 $2.50 like #356 2.75 2.75
e. Souvenir sheet of 3 4.75 4.75
Nos. 359B-359D (3) 4.70 4.70

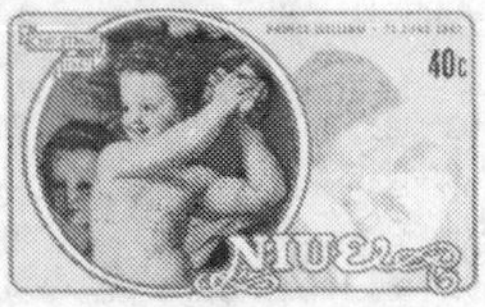

Christmas — A83

Princess Diana Holding Prince William and Paintings of Infants by: 40c, Bronzino (1502-1572). 52c, Murillo (1617-1682). 83c, Boucher (1703-1770). Singles in No. 363a: 34x30mm, showing paintings only.

Perf. 13½x14½

1982, Dec. 3 Photo.

360 A83 40c multicolored .55 .55
361 A83 52c multicolored .65 .65
362 A83 83c multicolored 1.10 1.10
363 A83 $1.05 multicolored 1.40 1.40
a. Souvenir sheet of 4, #364-367 3.75 3.75
Nos. 360-363 (4) 3.70 3.70

Souvenir Sheets

364 A83 80c + 5c like #360 1.10 1.10
365 A83 80c + 5c like #361 1.10 1.10
366 A83 80c + 5c like #362 1.10 1.10
367 A83 80c + 5c like #363 1.10 1.10

Nos. 364-367 each contain one 30x42mm stamp showing Royal family. Surtax was for children's funds.

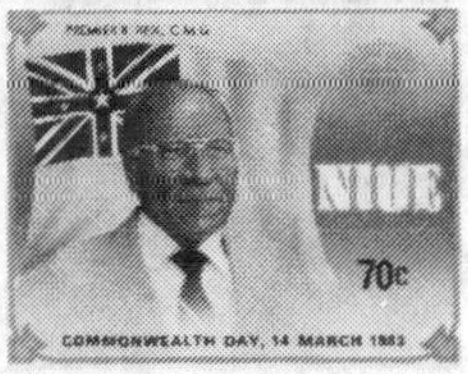

Commonwealth Day — A84

1983, Mar. 14 Photo. *Perf. 13*

368 A84 70c Flag, Premier Robert R. Rex .85 .85
369 A84 70c Resolution, Adventurer .85 .85
370 A84 70c Passion flower .85 .85
371 A84 70c Lime branch .85 .85
a. Block of 4, #368-371 3.40 3.40

For overprints see Nos. 484-487.

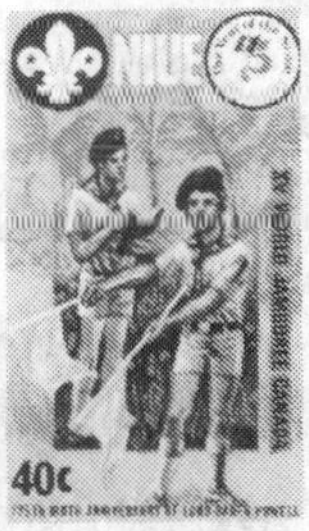

Scouting Year — A85

1983, Apr. 28 Photo. *Perf. 13*

372 A85 40c Flag signals .55 .55
373 A85 50c Tree planting .65 .65
374 A85 83c Map reading 1.20 1.20
Nos. 372-374 (3) 2.40 2.40

Souvenir Sheet

375 Sheet of 3 2.50 2.50
a. A85 40c + 3c like 40c .60 .60
b. A85 50c + 3c like 50c .65 .65
c. A85 83c + 3c like 83c 1.10 1.10

Nos. 372-375 Overprinted in Black on Silver: "XV WORLD JAMBOREE CANADA"

1983, July 14 Photo.

376 A85 40c multicolored .55 .55
377 A85 50c multicolored .65 .65
378 A85 83c multicolored 1.10 1.10
Nos. 376-378 (3) 2.30 2.30

Souvenir Sheet

379 Sheet of 3 2.50 2.50
a. A85 40c + 3c multicolored .60 .60
b. A85 50c + 3c multicolored .65 .65
c. A85 83c + 3c multicolored 1.25 1.25

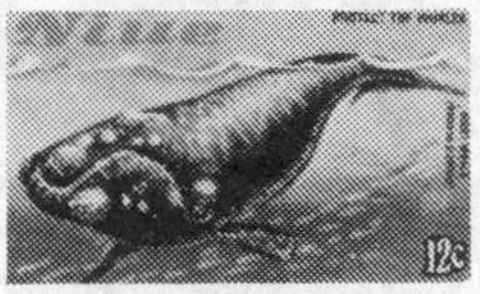

Save the Whales Campaign A86

1983, Aug. 15 *Perf. 13x14*

380 A86 12c Right whale .16 .16
381 A86 25c Fin whale .35 .35
382 A86 35c Sei whale .45 .45
383 A86 40c Blue whale .55 .55
384 A86 58c Bowhead whale .80 .80
385 A86 70c Sperm whale 1.00 1.00
386 A86 83c Humpback whale 1.20 1.20
387 A86 $1.05 Lesser rorqual 1.40 1.40
388 A86 $2.50 Gray whale 3.50 3.50
Nos. 380-388 (9) 9.41 9.41

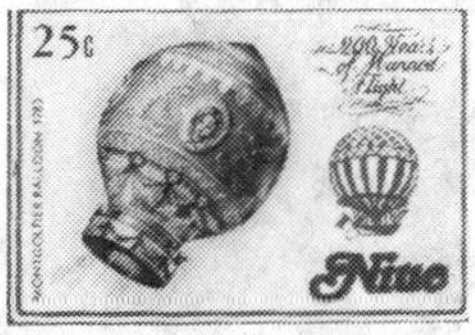

Manned Flight Bicentenary A87

1983, Oct. 14 Photo. *Perf. 14*

389 A87 25c Montgolfier, 1783 .30 .30
390 A87 40c Wright Bros. Flyer, 1903 .45 .45
391 A87 58c Graf Zeppelin, 1928 .65 .65
392 A87 70c Boeing 247, 1933 .85 .85
393 A87 83c Apollo VIII, 1968 .95 .95
394 A87 $1.05 Columbia space shuttle 1.25 1.25
a. Souvenir sheet of 6 4.50 4.50
Nos. 389-394 (6) 4.45 4.45

No. 394a contains Nos. 389-394 inscribed "AIRMAIL."

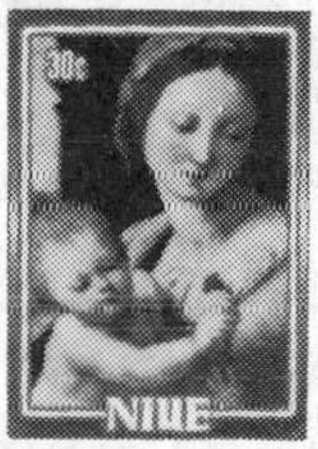

Christmas — A87a

Paintings by Raphael (1483-1520): 30c, Garvagh Madonna, National Gallery, London. 40c, Granduca Madonna, Pitti Gallery, Florence. 58c, Goldfinch Madonna, Uffizi Gallery, Florence. 70c, Holy Family of Francis I, Louvre, Paris. 83c, Holy Family with Saints, Alte Pinakothek, Munich.

1983 Photo. *Perf. 14*

395 A87a 30c multicolored .32 .32
396 A87a 40c multicolored .40 .40
397 A87a 58c multicolored .58 .58
398 A87a 70c multicolored .70 .70
399 A87a 83c multicolored .85 .85
Nos. 395-399 (5) 2.85 2.85

Souvenir Sheets

Perf. 13½

400 Sheet of 5 3.00 3.00
a. A87a 30c + 3c like #395 .32 .32
b. A87a 40c + 3c like #396 .42 .42
c. A87a 58c + 3c like #397 .60 .60
d. A87a 70c + 3c like #398 .70 .70
e. A87a 83c + 3c like #399 .85 .85
401 A87a 85c + 5c like #395 1.00 1.00
402 A87a 85c + 5c like #396 1.00 1.00
403 A87a 85c + 5c like #397 1.00 1.00
404 A87a 85c + 5c like #398 1.00 1.00
405 A87a 85c + 5c like #399 1.00 1.00

500th birth anniv. of Raphael.
Issued: #395-400, 11/25; #401-405, 12/29.

Nos. 317-318, 323-328, 341, 355, 342, 356 and 331 Surcharged in Black or Gold with One or Two Bars

1983, Nov. 30 Photo.

406 A77 52c on 30c #317 .70 .70
407 A77 52c on 30c #318 .70 .70
408 A77 58c on 50c #323 .80 .80
409 A77 58c on 50c #324 .80 .80
410 A77 70c on 60c #325 1.00 1.00
411 A77 70c on 60c #326 1.00 1.00
412 A77 83c on 80c #327 1.25 1.25
413 A77 83c on 80c #328 1.25 1.25
413A A79 $1.10 on 95c #341 1.50 1.50

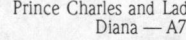

413B A82 $1.10 on $1.25 #355 (G) 1.50 1.50
413C A79 $2.60 on $1.20 #342 3.75 3.75
413D A82 $2.60 on $2.50 #356 (G) 3.75 3.75
413E A77a $3.70 on $3 #331 5.00 5.00
Nos. 406-413E (13) 23.00 23.00

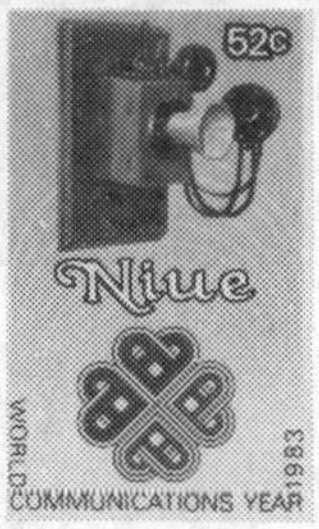

World Communications Year — A88

1984, Jan. 23 Photo. *Perf. 13x13½*
414 A88 40c Telegraph sender .45 .45
415 A88 52c Early telephone .55 .55
416 A88 83c Satellite .90 .90
a. Souvenir sheet of 3, #414-416 2.00 2.00
Nos. 414-416 (3) 1.90 1.90

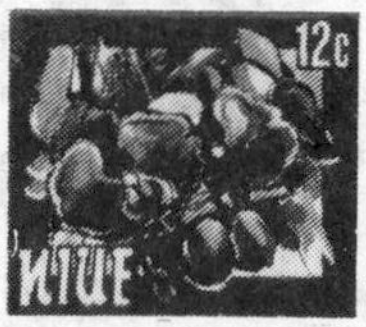

Moth Orchid — A89

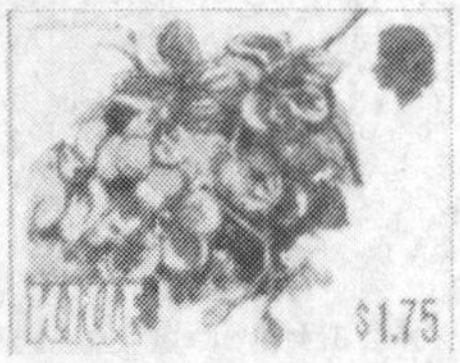

Golden Shower Tree — A90

1984 *Perf. 13x13½*
417 A89 12c shown .18 .18
418 A89 25c Poinsettia .35 .35
419 A89 30c Buttercup tree .42 .42
420 A89 35c Begonia .50 .50
421 A89 40c Frangipani .55 .55
422 A89 52c Bird of paradise .70 .70
423 A89 58c Rose of Sharon .75 .75
424 A89 70c Princess flower .95 .95
425 A89 83c Lotus 1.10 1.10
426 A89 $1.05 Yellow hibiscus 1.50 1.50
427 A90 $1.75 shown 1.65 1.65
428 A90 $2.30 Orchid var. 2.25 2.25
429 A90 $3.90 Orchid sp. 3.50 3.50
430 A90 $5 Poinsettia, diff. 4.50 4.50
431 A90 $6.60 Hybrid hibiscus 5.75 5.75
431A A90 $8.30 Hibiscus rosasinensis 7.75 7.75
Nos. 417-431A (16) 32.40 32.40

Issued: #417-426, 2/20; #427-429, 5/10; others 6/18.

For overprints see #O1-O13, O15, O17-O18.

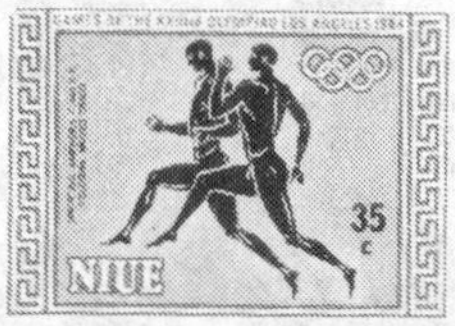

1984 Summer Olympics A91

Designs: Greek pottery designs, 3rd cent. BC. 30c, 70c vert.

1984, Mar. 15 Photo. *Perf. 14*
432 A91 30c Discus .40 .40
433 A91 35c Running .45 .45
434 A91 40c Equestrian .52 .52
435 A91 58c Boxing .75 .75
436 A91 70c Javelin .90 .90
Nos. 432-436 (5) 3.02 3.02

For overprints and surcharges see #446-450, 480-483.

Niue stamps can be mounted in the Scott New Zealand Dependencies album.

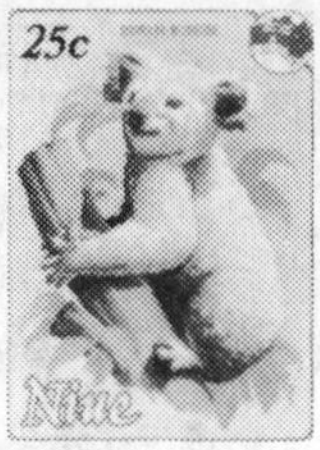

AUSIPEX '84, Australian Animals — A92

1984 Photo. *Perf. 14*
437 A92 25c Koala .28 .28
438 A92 35c Koala, diff. .35 .35
439 A92 40c Koala, diff. .42 .42
440 A92 58c Koala, diff. .60 .60
441 A92 70c Koala, diff. .75 .75
442 A92 83c Kangaroo with joey .90 .90
443 A92 $1.05 Kangaroo with joey, diff. 1.10 1.10
444 A92 $2.50 Kangaroo, diff. 2.50 2.50
Nos. 437-444 (8) 6.90 6.90

Souvenir Sheets
445 Sheet of 2 + label 3.00 3.00
a. A92 $1.75 Wallaby 1.50 1.50
b. A92 $1.75 Koala, diff. 1.50 1.50
c. Sheet of 6, #437-441, 445b, perf. 13½ 3.50 3.50
d. Sheet of 4, #442-444, 445a, perf. 13½ 5.00 5.00

Nos. 442-444 airmail.
Issued: #437-444, Aug. 24; $445, Sept. 20.

Nos. 432-436 Ovptd. with Event, Names of Gold Medalists, Country in Gold or Red

1984, Sept. 7 *Perf. 14*
446 A91 30c Danneberg .30 .30
447 A91 35c Coe (R) .35 .35
448 A91 40c Todd .40 .40
449 A91 58c Biggs .58 .58
450 A91 70c Haerkoenen .70 .70
Nos. 446-450 (5) 2.33 2.33

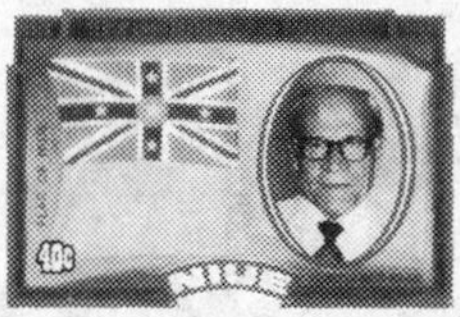

10th Anniv. of Self Government — A93

1984, Oct. 19 Photo. *Perf. 13*
451 A93 40c Niue flag .40 .40
452 A93 58c Niue map .58 .58
453 A93 70c Ceremony .70 .70
a. Souvenir sheet of 3, #451-453 1.75 1.75
Nos. 451-453 (3) 1.68 1.68

Souvenir Sheet
454 A93 $2.50 like 70c 2.50 2.50

For overprints and surcharges see Nos. 655-660.

Nos. 340, 354 Surcharged: "Prince Henry / 15.9.84" and Bars and New Values in Red or Silver

1984, Oct. 22 Photo. *Perf. 14*
455 A79 $2 on 75c multi (R) 2.00 2.00
456 A79 $2 on 50c multi (S) 2.00 2.00

Nos. 455-456 issued in sheets of 5 + label.

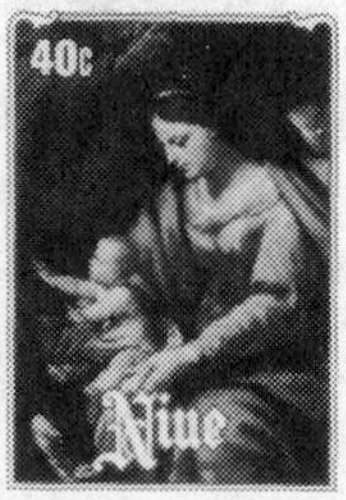

Christmas — A94

Paintings: 40c, The Nativity, by A. Vaccaro. 58c, Virgin with Fly, anonymous. 70c, Adoration of the Shepherds, by B. Murillo. 83c, Flight into Egypt, by B. Murillo.

1984, Oct. 19 Photo. *Perf. 13x13½*
457 A94 40c multicolored .50 .50
458 A94 58c multicolored .70 .70
459 A94 70c multicolored .80 .80
460 A94 83c multicolored 1.00 1.00
Nos. 457-460 (4) 3.00 3.00

Souvenir Sheets
461 Sheet of 4 2.70 2.70
a. A94 40c + 5c Like 40c .45 .45
b. A94 58c + 5c Like 58c .58 .58
c. A94 70c + 5c Like 70c .75 .75
d. A94 83c + 5c Like 83c .82 .82

Perf. 13½
462 A94 95c + 10c Like 40c 1.05 1.05
463 A94 95c + 10c Like 58c 1.05 1.05
464 A94 95c + 10c Like 70c 1.05 1.05
465 A94 95c + 10c Like 83c 1.05 1.05

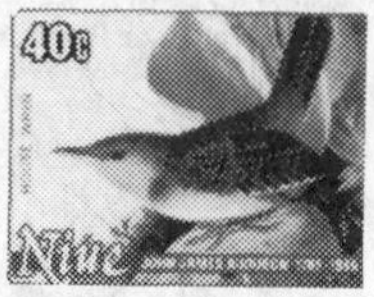

Audubon Birth Bicentenary A95

Illustrations of North American bird species by artist/naturalist John J. Audubon.

1985, Apr. 15 Photo. *Perf. 14½*
466 A95 40c House wren .32 .32
467 A95 70c Veery .55 .55
468 A95 83c Grasshopper sparrow .70 .70
469 A95 $1.05 Henslow's sparrow .85 .85
470 A95 $2.50 Vesper sparrow 2.00 2.00
Nos. 466-470 (5) 4.42 4.42

Souvenir Sheets
Perf. 14
471 A95 $1.75 like #466 1.50 1.50
472 A95 $1.75 like #467 1.50 1.50
473 A95 $1.75 like #468 1.50 1.50
474 A95 $1.75 like #469 1.50 1.50
475 A95 $1.75 like #470 1.50 1.50
Nos. 471-475 (5) 7.50 7.50

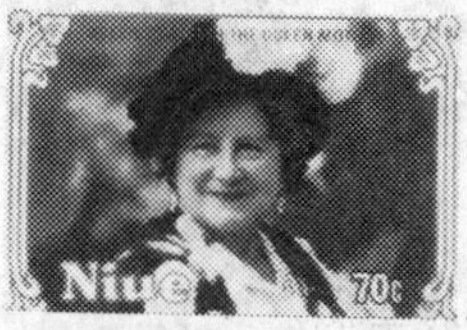

Queen Mother, 85th Birthday A96

Designs: 70c, Wearing mantle of the Order of the Garter. $1.15, With Queen Elizabeth II. $1.50, With Prince Charles. $3, Writing letter.

1985, June 14 *Perf. 13½x13*
476 A96 70c multicolored .70 .70
477 A96 $1.15 multicolored 1.15 1.15
478 A96 $1.50 multicolored 1.50 1.50
a. Souvenir sheet of 3 + label, #476-478 3.35 3.35
Nos. 476-478 (3) 3.35 3.35

Souvenir Sheet
Perf. 13½
479 A96 $3 multicolored 3.00 3.00

Nos. 476-478 issued in sheets of 5 plus label. No. 479 contains one 39x36mm stamp.
No. 478a issued Aug. 4, 1986, for 86th birthday.

Nos. 432-433, 435-436 Overprinted: "Mini South Pacific Games, Rarotonga" and Surcharged with Gold Bar and New Value in Black

1985, July 26 *Perf. 14*
480 A91 52c on 95c multi .52 .52
481 A91 83c on 58c multi .85 .85
482 A91 95c on 35c multi .95 .95
483 A91 $2 on 30c multi 2.00 2.00
Nos. 480-483 (4) 4.32 4.32

Nos. 368-371 Overprinted with Conference Emblem and: "Pacific Islands Conference, Rarotonga"

1985, July 26 *Perf. 13½x13*
484 A84 70c on #368 .70 .70
485 A84 70c on #369 .70 .70
486 A84 70c on #370 .70 .70
487 A84 70c on #371 .70 .70
a. Block of 4, #484-487 2.80 2.80

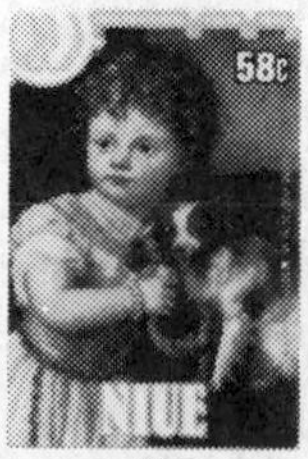

A97

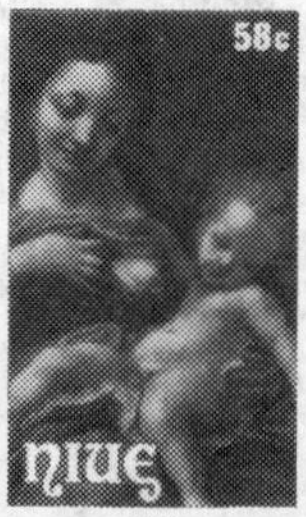

A98

Paintings of children: 38c, Portrait of R. Strozzi's Daughter, by Titian. 70c, The Fifer, by Manet. $1.15, Portrait of a Young Girl, by Renoir. $1.50, Portrait of M. Berard, by Renoir.

1985, Oct. 11 *Perf. 13*
488 A97 58c multicolored .58 .58
489 A97 70c multicolored .70 .70
490 A97 $1.15 multicolored 1.15 1.15
491 A97 $1.50 multicolored 1.50 1.50
Nos. 488-491 (4) 3.93 3.93

Souvenir Sheets
Perf. 13x13½
492 A97 $1.75 + 10c like #488 2.00 2.00
493 A97 $1.75 + 10c like #489 2.00 2.00
494 A97 $1.75 + 10c like #490 2.00 2.00
495 A97 $1.75 + 10c like #491 2.00 2.00

Intl. Youth Year.

1985, Nov. 29 Photo. *Perf. 13x13½*

Christmas, Paintings (details) by Correggio: 58c, No. 500a, Virgin and Child. 85c, No. 500b, Adoration of the Magi. $1.05, No. 500c, Virgin and Child, diff. $1.45, No. 500d, Virgin and Child with St. Catherine.

496 A98 58c multicolored .70 .70
497 A98 85c multicolored 1.05 1.05
498 A98 $1.05 multicolored 1.25 1.25
499 A98 $1.45 multicolored 1.75 1.75
Nos. 496-499 (4) 4.75 4.75

Souvenir Sheets
500 Sheet of 4 3.50 3.50
a.-d. A98 60c + 10c, any single .85 .85

Imperf
501 A98 65c like #496 .78 .78
502 A98 95c like #497 1.15 1.15
503 A98 $1.20 like #498 1.50 1.50
504 A98 $1.75 like #499 2.25 2.25
Nos. 500-504 (5) 9.18 9.18

Nos. 501-504 each contain one 61x71mm stamp.

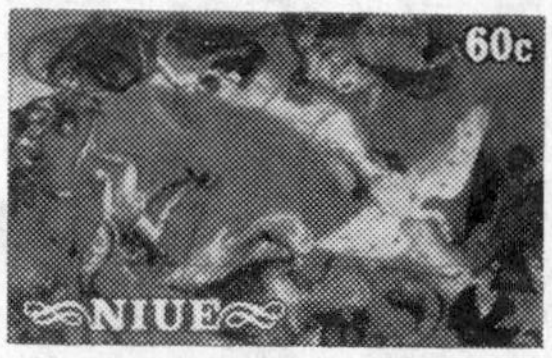

Halley's Comet — A99

The Constellations, fresco by Giovanni De Vecchi, Farnesio Palace, Caprarola, Italy.

1986, Jan. 24 *Perf. 13½*
505 A99 60c multicolored .68 .68
506 A99 75c multicolored .85 .85
507 A99 $1.10 multicolored 1.25 1.25
508 A99 $1.50 multicolored 1.75 1.75
Nos. 505-508 (4) 4.53 4.53

Souvenir Sheet
509 Sheet of 4 4.50 4.50
a. A99 95c like #505 1.10 1.10
b. A99 95c like #506 1.10 1.10
c. A99 95c like #507 1.10 1.10
d. A99 95c like #508 1.10 1.10

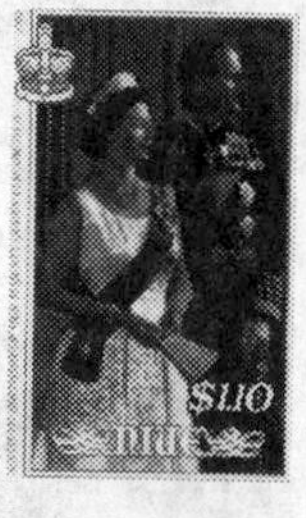

Elizabeth II, 60th Birthday — A100

Designs: $1.10, No. 513a, Elizabeth and Prince Philip at Windsor Castle. $1.50, No. 513b, At Balmoral. $2, No. 513c, Elizabeth at Buckingham Palace. $3, Elizabeth seated and Prince Philip.

1986, Apr. 28 *Perf. 14½x13½*
510 A100 $1.10 multicolored 1.10 1.10
511 A100 $1.50 multicolored 1.65 1.65
512 A100 $2 multicolored 2.25 2.25
Nos. 510-512 (3) 5.00 5.00

Souvenir Sheets
513 Sheet of 3 2.75 2.75
a.-c. A100 75c, any single .90 .90
514 A100 $3 multicolored 3.50 3.50

For surcharges see Nos. 546-547.

Mt. Rushmore — A101   Statue of Liberty, Cent. — A102

1986, May 22   Photo.   Perf. 14
515 A101 $1 Washington, US #1   1.15 1.15
516 A101 $1 Jefferson, Roosevelt, Lincoln   1.15 1.15

AMERIPEX '86. Nos. 515-516 printed se-tenant in a continuous design.

1986, July 4   Perf. 13x13¹/₂
Paintings: $1, Statue under construction, 1883, by Victor Dargaud. $2.50, Unveiling the Statue of Liberty, 1886, by Edmund Morand (1829-1901).
517 A102 $1 multicolored   1.15 1.15
518 A102 $2.50 multicolored   2.75 2.75

Souvenir Sheet
519   Sheet of 2   2.90 2.90
a.   A102 $1.25 like #517   1.45 1.45
b.   A102 $1.25 like #518   1.45 1.45

Wedding of Prince Andrew and Sarah Ferguson — A103

Designs: $2.50, Portraits, Westminster Abbey. $5, Portraits.

1986, July 23   Perf. 13¹/₂x13
520 A103 $2.50 multicolored   2.75 2.75

Souvenir Sheet
521 A103 $5 Portraits   5.50 5.50

No. 520 printed in sheets of 4. No. 521 contains one 45x32mm stamp.

STAMPEX '86, Adelaide, Aug. 4-10 — A104

Birds.

Perf. 13x13¹/₂, 13¹/₂x13
1986, Aug. 4   Photo.
522 A104 40c Egretta alba, vert.   .45 .45
523 A104 60c Emblema picta   .65 .65
524 A104 75c Aprosmictus scapularis, vert.   .80 .80
525 A104 80c Malurus lamberti   .88 .88
526 A104 $1 Falco peregrinus, vert.   1.10 1.10
527 A104 $1.65 Halcyon azurea   1.80 1.80
528 A104 $2.20 Melopsittacus undulatus, vert.   2.40 2.40
529 A104 $4.25 Dromaius novaehollandiae   4.60 4.60
   Nos. 522-529 (8)   12.68 12.68

Christmas — A105

Paintings in the Vatican Museum: 80c, No. 534a, Virgin and Child, by Perugino (1446-1523). $1.15, No. 534b, Virgin of St. N. dei Frari, by Titian. $1.80, No. 534c, Virgin with Milk, by Lorenzo di Credi (1459-1537). $2.60, $7.50, No. 534d, Foligno Madonna, by Raphael.

1986, Nov. 14   Litho.   Perf. 14
530 A105 80c multi   .85 .85
531 A105 $1.15 multi   1.25 1.25
532 A105 $1.80 multi   1.90 1.90
533 A105 $2.60 multi   2.75 2.75
   Nos. 530-533 (4)   6.75 6.75

Souvenir Sheets
Perf. 13¹/₂
534   Sheet of 4   6.40 6.40
a.-d.   A105 $1.50, any single   1.60 1.60
Perf. 14¹/₂x13¹/₂
535 A105 $7.50 multi   8.00 8.00

For surcharges see Nos. B56-B61.

Souvenir Sheets

Statue of Liberty, Cent. A106

Photographs: No. 536a, Tall ship, bridge. No. 536b, Workmen, flame from torch. No. 536c, Workman, flame, diff. No. 536d, Ships, New York City. No. 536e, Tall ship, sailboat, bridge. No. 537a, Statue, front. No. 537b, Statue, left side. No. 537c, Torch dismantled. No. 537d, Statue, right side. No. 537e, Welder.

1987, May 20
536   Sheet of 5+label   4.50 4.50
a.-e.   A106 75c any single   .90 .90
537   Sheet of 5+label   4.50 4.50
a.-e.   A106 75c any single   .90 .90

Tennis Champions — A107

Olympic emblem, coin and: 80c, $1.15, $1.40, $1.80, Boris Becker. 85c, $1.05, $1.30, $1.75, Steffi Graf. Various action scenes.

1987
538 A107 80c multi   1.10 1.10
539 A107 85c multi   1.20 1.20
540 A107 $1.05 multi   1.45 1.45
541 A107 $1.15 multi   1.60 1.60
542 A107 $1.30 multi   1.80 1.80
543 A107 $1.40 multi   1.95 1.95
544 A107 $1.75 multi   2.40 2.40
545 A107 $1.80 multi   2.50 2.50
   Nos. 538-545 (8)   14.00 14.00

Issue dates: 80c, $1.15, $1.40, $1.80, Sept. 25. Others, Oct. 20.
For overprints see Nos. 560-563.

Nos. 511-512 Surcharged "40th /WEDDING / ANNIV." with Denomination in Black on Gold
Perf. 14¹/₂x13¹/₂
1987, Nov. 20   Photo.
546 A100 $4.85 on $1.50 No. 511   6.00 6.00
547 A100 $4.85 on $2 No. 512   6.00 6.00

40th Wedding anniv. of Queen Elizabeth II and Prince Philip, Duke of Edinburgh.

Christmas — A108

Paintings (details) by Albrecht Durer (Angel with Lute on 80c, $1.05, $2.80): 80c, No. 551a, The Nativity. $1.05, No. 551b, Adoration of the Magi. $2.80, No. 551c, $7.50, Celebration of the Rosary.

1987, Dec. 4   Photo.   Perf. 13¹/₂
548 A108 80c multi   .90 .90
549 A108 $1.05 multi   1.25 1.25
550 A108 $2.80 multi   3.00 3.00
   Nos. 548-550 (3)   5.15 5.15

Souvenir Sheets
551   Sheet of 3   4.50 4.50
a.-c.   A108 $1.30 any single   1.50 1.50
552 A108 $7.50 multi   8.50 8.50

Size of Nos. 551a-551c: 49¹/₂x38¹/₂mm. No. 552 contains one 51x33mm stamp.

European Soccer Championships — A109

Highlights from Franz Beckenbauer's career: 20c, Match scene. 40c, German all-star team. 60c, Brussels, 1974. 80c, England, 1966. $1.05, Mexico, 1970. $1.30, Munich, 1974. $1.80, FC Bayern Munchen vs. Athletico Madrid.

1988, June 20   Litho.   Perf. 14
553 A109 20c multi   .25 .25
554 A109 40c multi   .50 .50
555 A109 60c multi   .75 .75
556 A109 80c multi   .95 .95
557 A109 $1.05 multi   1.25 1.25
558 A109 $1.30 multi   1.65 1.65
559 A109 $1.80 multi   2.25 2.25
   Nos. 553-559 (7)   7.60 7.60

Nos. 539-540, 542 and 543 Ovptd.
a. "Australia 24 Jan 88 / French Open 4 June 88"
b. "Wimbledon 2 July 88 / U S Open 10 Sept. 88"
c. "Women's Tennis Grand / Slam: 10 September 88"
d. "Seoul Olympic Games / Gold Medal Winner"

1988, Oct. 14   Litho.   Perf. 13¹/₂x14
560 A107(a) 85c on No. 539   1.00 1.00
561 A107(b) $1.05 on No. 540   1.25 1.25
562 A107(c) $1.30 on No. 542   1.50 1.50
563 A107(d) $1.75 on No. 543   2.00 2.00
   Nos. 560-563 (4)   5.75 5.75

Steffi Graf, 1988 Olympic gold medalist; opportunities for youth in sports.

Christmas A110

Adoration of the Shepherds, by Rubens: 60c, Angels. 80c, Joseph and witness. $1.05, Madonna. $1.30, Christ child. $7.20, Entire painting.

1988, Oct. 28   Photo.   Perf. 13¹/₂
564 A110 60c multi   .75 .75
565 A110 80c multi   1.05 1.05
566 A110 $1.05 multi   1.35 1.35
567 A110 $1.30 multi   1.65 1.65
   Nos. 564-567 (4)   4.80 4.80

Souvenir Sheet
568 A110 $7.20 multi   8.50 8.50

No. 568 contains one 40x50mm stamp.

First Moon Landing, 20th Anniv. A111

Apollo 11: No. 569, Mission emblem and astronaut. No. 570, Earth, Moon and simplified flight plan. No. 571, Olive branch, Apollo 1 mission emblem and astronaut on Moon. Printed se-tenant in a continuous design.

1989, July 20   Photo.   Perf. 14
569 A111 $1.50 multi   1.75 1.75
570 A111 $1.50 multi   1.75 1.75
571 A111 $1.50 multi   1.75 1.75
   Nos. 569-571 (3)   5.25 5.25

Souvenir Sheet
Perf. 13¹/₂x13
572   Sheet of 3   4.05 4.05
a.-c.   A111 $1.15 like #569-571   1.35 1.35

Christmas — A112

Details of Presentation in the Temple, 1631, by Rembrandt, Royal Cabinet of Paintings, The Hague: 70c, Priests. 80c, Madonna. $1.05, Joseph, Christ child. $7.20, Entire painting.

1989, Nov. 22   Photo.   Perf. 13x13¹/₂
573 A112 70c multicolored   .80 .80
574 A112 80c multicolored   .90 .90
575 A112 $1.05 multicolored   1.10 1.10
576 A112 $1.30 multicolored   1.40 1.40
   Nos. 573-576 (4)   4.20 4.20

Souvenir Sheet
Perf. 13¹/₂
577 A112 $7.20 multicolored   8.50 8.50

No. 577 contains one 39x50mm stamp.

Emblem of the German Natl. Soccer Team and Signatures — A113

Former team captains: 80c, Fritz Walter. $1.15, Franz Beckenbauer. $1.40, Uwe Seeler.

1990, Feb. 5   Photo.   Perf. 13¹/₂
578 A113 80c multicolored   .95 .95
579 A113 $1.15 multicolored   1.40 1.40
580 A113 $1.40 multicolored   1.70 1.70
581 A113 $1.80 shown   2.20 2.20
   Nos. 578-581 (4)   6.25 6.25

1990 World Cup Soccer Championships, Italy.

First Postage Stamp, 150th Anniv. — A114

Paintings by Rembrandt showing letters: 80c, No. 586d, Merchant Maarten Looten (1632). $1.05, No. 586c, Rembrandt's son Titus holding pen (1655). $1.30, No. 586b, The Shipbuilder and his Wife (1633). $1.80, No. 586a, Bathsheba with King David's letter (1654).

1990, May 2   Photo.   Perf. 13¹/₂
582 A114 80c multicolored   .95 .95
583 A114 $1.05 multicolored   1.25 1.25
584 A114 $1.30 multicolored   1.50 1.50
585 A114 $1.80 multicolored   2.10 2.10
   Nos. 582-585 (4)   5.80 5.80

Souvenir Sheet
586   Sheet of 4   7.00 7.00
a.-d.   A114 $1.50 any single   1.75 1.75

A115

A116

1990, July 23   Perf. 13x13½
587 A115 $1.25 multicolored   1.50 1.50

Souvenir Sheet
588 A115 $7 multicolored   8.25 8.25

Queen Mother, 90th birthday.

1990, Nov. 27   Litho.   Perf. 14

Christmas (Paintings): 70c, Adoration of the Magi by Bouts. 80c, Holy Family by Fra Bartolomeo. $1.05, The Nativity by Memling. $1.30, Adoration of the King by Pieter Bruegel, the Elder. $7.20, Virgin and Child Enthroned by Cosimo Tura.

589 A116 70c multicolored   .85 .85
590 A116 80c multicolored   1.00 1.00
591 A116 $1.05 multicolored   1.30 1.30
592 A116 $1.30 multicolored   1.60 1.60
    Nos. 589-592 (4)   4.75 4.75

Souvenir Sheet
593 A116 $7.20 multicolored   8.75 8.75

No. 334 Overprinted in Silver

1990, Dec. 5   Perf. 13x13½
594 A77a $10 multicolored   12.00 12.00

Birdpex '90, 20th Intl. Ornithological Congress, New Zealand.

No. 333 Overprinted
"SIXTY FIFTH BIRTHDAY
QUEEN ELIZABETH II"

1991, Apr. 22   Litho.   Perf. 13x13½
595 A77a $6 multicolored   7.25 7.25

Nos. 340-342 Overprinted in Black or Silver

T E N T H   T E N T H
ANNIVERSARY   ANNIVERSARY
Typo.   Litho.

1991, June 26   Photo.   Perf. 14
596 A79 75c on #340 (S)   .90 .90
  a.   Litho. overprint   .90 .90
597 A79 95c on #341   1.15 1.15
  a.   Litho. overprint   1.15 1.15
598 A79 $1.20 on #342   1.45 1.45
  a.   Litho. overprint   1.45 1.45
    Nos. 596-598 (3)   3.50 3.50
    Nos. 596a-598a (3)   3.50 3.50

Nos. 596-598 issued in miniature sheets of 5 with typo. overprint. Nos. 596a-598a issued in uncut panes of 4 miniature sheets of 5. Letters of typo. overprint are taller and thinner than litho. overprint.

Christmas — A117   Birds — A118

Paintings: 20c, The Virgin and Child with Saints Jerome and Dominic, by Filippino Lippi. 50c, The Isenheim Altarpiece, The Virgin and Child, by Grunewald. $1, The Nativity, by Pittoni. $2, Adoration of the Kings, by Jan Brueghel, the Elder. $7, The Adoration of the Shepherds, by Reni.

1991, Nov. 11   Litho.   Perf. 14
599 A117 20c multicolored   .25 .25
600 A117 50c multicolored   .60 .60
601 A117 $1 multicolored   1.20 1.20
602 A117 $2 multicolored   2.40 2.40
    Nos. 599-602 (4)   4.45 4.45

Souvenir Sheet
603 A117 $7 multicolored   8.40 8.40

1992-93   Litho.   Perf. 14x13½
604 A118 20c Banded rail   .25 .25
605 A118 50c Red-tailed tropic-bird   .60 .60
606 A118 70c Purple swamphen   .85 .85
607 A118 $1 Pacific pigeon   1.20 1.20
608 A118 $1.50 White-collared kingfisher   1.80 1.80
609 A118 $2 Blue-crowned lory   2.40 2.40
610 A118 $3 Crimson-crowned fruit dove   3.60 3.60
611 A118 $5 Barn owl   5.60 5.60

Perf. 13
Size: 51x38mm
612 A118 $7 Longtailed cockoo   7.35 7.35

Size: 49x35mm
613 A118 $10 Reef heron   10.50 10.50
614 A118 $15 Polynesian triller   16.50 16.50
    Nos. 604-614 (11)   50.65 50.65

Issued $1.50, $2, 3/20; $3, 4/16; $5, 5/15; $7, 3/26/93; $10, 4/16/93; $15, 8/10/93; others, 2/92.
For overprints see Nos. O20-O25.
This is an expanding set. Numbers may change.

Discovery of America, 500th Anniv. — A119

Designs: $2, Queen Isabella supports Columbus. $3, Columbus' fleet. $5, Columbus landing in America.

1992   Litho.   Perf. 13
621 A119 $2 multicolored   2.25 2.25
622 A119 $3 multicolored   3.40 3.40
623 A119 $5 multicolored   5.60 5.60
    Nos. 621-623 (3)   11.25 11.25

1992 Summer Olympics, Barcelona — A120

Designs: No. 624a, $10 coin, tennis player. b, Flags, torch. c, Gymnast, $10 coin. $5, Water polo player.

1992, July 22   Litho.   Perf. 13½x13
624 A120 $2.50 Strip of 3, #a.-c.   8.50 8.50

Souvenir Sheet
625 A120 $5 multicolored   5.60 5.60

Nos. 265-280 Surcharged

$1   ═

1992, Sept. 30   Photo.   Perf. 13
626 A72 $1 on 20c #265   1.10 1.10
627 A72 $1 on 20c #266   1.10 1.10
628 A72 $1 on 20c #267   1.10 1.10
629 A72 $1 on 20c #268   1.10 1.10
  a.   Strip of 4, #626-629   4.40 4.40
630 A72 $1 on 25c #269   1.10 1.10
631 A72 $1 on 25c #270   1.10 1.10
632 A72 $1 on 25c #271   1.10 1.10
633 A72 $1 on 25c #272   1.10 1.10
  a.   Strip of 4, #630-633   4.40 4.40
634 A72 $1 on 30c #273   1.10 1.10
635 A72 $1 on 30c #274   1.10 1.10
636 A72 $1 on 30c #275   1.10 1.10
637 A72 $1 on 30c #276   1.10 1.10
  a.   Strip of 4, #634-637   4.40 4.40
638 A72 $1 on 35c #277   1.10 1.10
639 A72 $1 on 35c #278   1.10 1.10
640 A72 $1 on 35c #279   1.10 1.10

641 A72 $1 on 35c #280   1.10 1.10
  a.   Strip of 4, #638-641   4.40 4.40
    Nos. 626-641 (16)   17.60 17.60

6th South Pacific Festival of the Arts.

Christmas
A121

Design: Different details from St. Catherine's Mystic Marriage, by Hans Memling.

1992, Nov. 18   Litho.   Perf. 13½
642 A121 20c multicolored   .20 .20
643 A121 50c multicolored   .52 .52
644 A121 $1 multicolored   1.05 1.05
645 A121 $2 multicolored   2.10 2.10
    Nos. 642-645 (4)   3.87 3.87

Souvenir Sheet
646 A121 $7 like #643   7.35 7.35

No. 646 contains one 39x48mm stamp.

Queen Elizabeth II's Accession to the Throne, 40th Anniv. — A122

Various portraits of Queen Elizabeth II.

1992, Dec. 7   Perf. 14
647 A122 70c multicolored   .75 .75
648 A122 $1 multicolored   1.05 1.05
649 A122 $1.50 multicolored   1.60 1.60
650 A122 $2 multicolored   2.10 2.10
    Nos. 647-650 (4)   5.50 5.50

Dolphins
A123

Designs: 20c, Rough-toothed dolphin. 50c, Fraser's dolphin. 75c, Pantropical spotted dolphin. $1, Risso's dolphin.

1993, Jan. 13   Litho.   Perf. 14
651 A123 20c multicolored   .20 .20
652 A123 50c multicolored   .52 .52
653 A123 75c multicolored   .80 .80
654 A123 $1 multicolored   1.05 1.05
    Nos. 651-654 (4)   2.57 2.57

World Wildlife Fund.

Nos. 451-453 Ovptd.   1909 IN MEMORIAM 1992 / SIR ROBERT R. REX K.B.E.

1993, Mar. 15   Photo.   Perf. 13
655 A93 40c on #451 multi   .42 .42
656 A93 58c on #452 multi   .60 .60
657 A93 70c on #453 multi   .75 .75

Nos. 655-657 Surcharged

1993, Mar. 15
658 A93 $1 on 40c #655   1.05 1.05
659 A93 $1 on 58c #656   1.05 1.05
660 A93 $1 on 70c #657   1.05 1.05
    Nos. 655-660 (6)   4.92 4.92

Queen Elizabeth II, 40th Anniv. of Coronation — A124

1993, June 2   Litho.   Perf. 14
661 A124 $5 multicolored   5.25 5.25

Christmas — A125

Details from Virgin of the Rosary, by Guido Reni: 20c, Infant Jesus. 70c, Cherubs. $1, Two men, one pointing upward. $1.50, Two men looking upward. $3, Madonna and child.

1993, Oct. 29   Litho.   Perf. 14
662 A125 20c multicolored   .22 .22
663 A125 70c multicolored   .75 .75
664 A125 $1 multicolored   1.10 1.10
665 A125 $1.50 multicolored   1.65 1.65

Size: 32x47mm
Perf. 13½
666 A125 $3 multicolored   3.25 3.25
    Nos. 662-666 (5)   6.97 6.97

1994 World Cup Soccer Championships, US — A126

Illustration reduced.

1994, June 17   Litho.   Perf. 14
667 A126 $4 multicolored   5.25 5.25

First Manned Moon Landing, 25th Anniv. — A127

Designs: a, Flight to Moon, astronaut opening solar wind experiment lunar surface. b, Astronaut holding flag. c, Astronaut standing by lunar experiment package.

1994, July 20   Litho.   Perf. 14
668 A127 $2.50 Tryptic, #a.-c.   9.00 9.00

Christmas
A128

Entire paintings or details: No. 669a, The Adoration of the Kings, by Jan Gossaert. b, Madonna & Child with Saints John & Catherine, by Titian. c, The Holy Family and Shepherd, by Titian. d, Virgin & Child with Saints, by Gerard David.
No. 670a-670b, Adoration of the Shepherds, by N. Poussin. c, Madonna & Child with Saints Joseph & John, by Sebastiano. d, Adoration of the Kings, by Veronese.

1994, Nov. 28 Litho. *Perf. 14*

669 A128 70c Block of 4, #a.-d. 3.50 3.50
670 A128 $1 Block of 4, #a.-d. 5.00 5.00

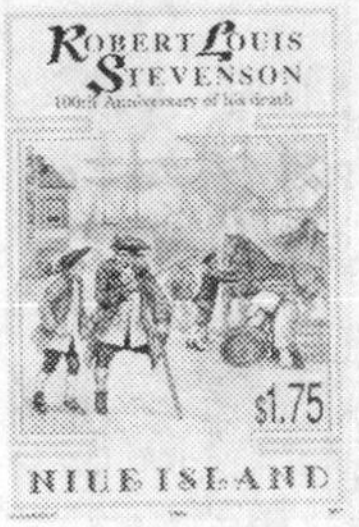

Robert Louis Stevenson (1850-94), Writer — A129

Designs: a, Treasure Island. b, Dr. Jekyll and Mr. Hyde. c, Kidnapped. d, Stevenson, tomb, inscription.

1994, Dec. 14 *Perf. 15x14*

671 A129 $1.75 Block of 4, #a.-d. 8.75 8.75

SEMI-POSTAL STAMPS

Catalogue values for unused stamps in this section are for Never Hinged items.

Easter Type of 1978
Souvenir Sheets

Designs: No. B1, Descent from the Cross, by Caravaggio. No. B2, Burial of Christ, by Bellini. Sheets show paintings from which stamp designs were taken.

1978, Mar. 15 Photo. *Perf. 13½*

B1 A61 70c + 5c multi 1.25 1.25
B2 A61 70c + 5c multi 1.25 1.25

Surtax was for school children in Niue.

Christmas Type of 1978
Souvenir Sheets

1978, Nov. 30 Photo. *Perf. 13*

B3 A63 60c + 5c like #232 1.25 1.25
B4 A63 60c + 5c like #233 1.25 1.25
B5 A63 60c + 5c like #234 1.25 1.25
Nos. B3-B5 (3) 3.75 3.75

Surtax was for school children of Niue. The sheets show paintings from which designs of stamps were taken.

Easter Type of 1979
Souvenir Sheets

1979, Apr. 2

B6 A64 70c + 5c like #235 1.50 1.50
B7 A64 70c + 5c like #236 1.50 1.50

Surtax was for school children of Niue. The sheets show altarpiece from which designs of stamps were taken.

IYC Type of 1979
Souvenir Sheets

1979, May 31 Photo. *Perf. 13*

B8 A65 70c + 5c like #237 1.25 1.25
B9 A65 70c + 5c like #238 1.25 1.25
B10 A65 70c + 5c like #239 1.25 1.25
B11 A65 70c + 5c like #240 1.25 1.25
Nos. B8-B11 (4) 5.00 5.00

Sheets show paintings from which designs of stamps were taken.

Christmas Type of 1979
Souvenir Sheets

1979, Nov. 29 Photo. *Perf. 13*

B12 A70 85c + 5c like #258 1.25 1.25
B13 A70 85c + 5c like #259 1.25 1.25
B14 A70 85c + 5c like #260 1.25 1.25
B15 A70 85c + 5c like #261 1.25 1.25
Nos. B12-B15 (4) 5.00 5.00

Multicolored margins show entire paintings.

Nos. 241-245, 251-254, 255-257, 258-261 Surcharged in Black (2 lines) or Silver (3 lines):
HURRICANE RELIEF Plus 2c

1980, Jan. 25 Photo. *Perf. 14, 13½*

B16 A66 20c + 2c pair .60 .60
B18 A68 20c + 2c multi (S) .30 .30
B19 A70 20c + 2c multi (S) .30 .30
B20 A70 25c + 2c multi (S) .40 .40
B21 A66 30c + 2c pair .90 .90
B23 A68 30c + 2c multi (S) .45 .45
B24 A69 30c + 2c multi (S) .45 .45
B25 A70 30c + 2c multi (S) .45 .45
B26 A66 35c + 2c pair 1.10 1.10
B28 A68 35c + 2c multi (S) .55 .55
B29 A69 35c + 2c multi (S) .55 .55
B30 A66 50c + 2c pair 1.40 1.40
B32 A70 50c + 2c multi (S) .70 .70
B33 A66 60c + 2c pair 1.75 1.75
B35 A69 60c + 2c multi (S) .90 .90
B36 A68 75c + 2c multi (S) 1.10 1.10
Nos. B16-B36 (16) 11.90 11.90

Easter Type of 1980
Souvenir Sheets

1980, Apr. 2 Photo. *Perf. 13*

B37 Sheet of 3 1.00 1.00
a. A71 25c + 2c like #262 .28 .28
b. A71 30c + 2c like #263 .32 .32
c. A71 35c + 2c like #264 .38 .38

1980, Apr. 2

B38 A71 85c + 5c like #262 1.10 1.10
B39 A71 85c + 5c like #263 1.10 1.10
B40 A71 85c + 5c like #264 1.10 1.10
Nos. B38-B40 (3) 3.30 3.30

Surtax was for hurricane relief.

No. 245a Overprinted Like Nos. 281-285 and Surcharged
Souvenir Sheet

1980, Aug. 22 Photo. *Perf. 14*

B41 Sheet of 10 4.50 4.50
a. A66 20c + 2c pair .45 .45
b. A66 30c + 2c pair .60 .60
c. A66 35c + 2c pair .80 .80
d. A66 50c + 2c pair 1.25 1.25
e. A66 60c + 2c pair 1.40 1.40

ZEAPEX '80, New Zealand Intl. Stamp Exhib., Auckland, Aug. 23-31.

Souvenir Sheet

1980, Oct. 30 Photo. *Perf. 14*

B42 Sheet of 8 3.75 3.75
a. A74 20c + 2c like #293 .32 .32
b. A75 20c + 2c like #294 .32 .32
c. A74 25c + 2c like #295 .42 .42
d. A75 25c + 2c like #296 .42 .42
e. A74 30c + 2c like #297 .48 .48
f. A75 30c + 2c like #298 .48 .48
g. A74 35c + 2c like #299 .55 .55
h. A75 35c + 2c like #300 .55 .55

22nd Summer Olympic Games, Moscow, July 19-Aug. 3.

Christmas Type of 1980
Souvenir Sheets

1980, Nov. 28 Photo. *Perf. 13½x13*

B43 A76 80c + 5c like #301 .90 .90
B44 A76 80c + 5c like #302 .90 .90
B45 A76 80c + 5c like #303 .90 .90
B46 A76 80c + 5c like #304 .90 .90
Nos. B43-B46 (4) 3.60 3.60

Nos. B43-B46 each contain one 31x39mm stamp.

Easter Type of 1981
Souvenir Sheets

1981, Apr. 10 Photo. *Perf. 13½*

B47 Sheet of 3 2.25 2.25
a. A78 35c + 2c like #337 .52 .52
b. A78 50c + 2c like #338 .65 .65
c. A78 60c + 2c like #339 .80 .80
B48 A78 80c + 5c like #337 1.00 1.00
B49 A78 80c + 5c like #338 1.00 1.00
B50 A78 80c + 5c like #339 1.00 1.00
Nos. B47-B50 (4) 5.25 5.25

Soccer Type of 1981

1981, Oct. 16 Photo. *Perf. 13*

B51 A80 Sheet of 9 4.50 4.50

#B51 contains #343-345 each with 3c surtax.

Royal Wedding Type of 1981
Nos. 340-342a Surcharged

1981, Nov. 3 Photo. *Perf. 14*

B52 A79 75c + 5c like #340 1.60 1.60
B53 A79 95c + 5c like #341 2.00 2.00
B54 A79 $1.20 + 5c like #342 2.50 2.50
Nos. B52-B54 (3) 6.10 6.10

Souvenir Sheet

B55 Sheet of 3 6.50 6.50
a. A79 75c + 10c like #340 1.70 1.70
b. A79 95c + 10c like #341 2.10 2.10
c. A79 $1.20 + 10c like #342 2.60 2.60

Intl. Year of the Disabled. Surtax was for disabled.

Nos. 530-535 Surcharged "CHRISTMAS VISIT TO SOUTH PACIFIC OF / POPE JOHN PAUL II, NOVEMBER 21-24 1986" in Black on Silver

1986, Nov. 21 Litho. *Perf. 14*

B56 A105 80c + 10c multi .95 .95
B57 A105 $1.15 + 10c multi 1.35 1.35
B58 A105 $1.80 + 10c multi 2.00 2.00
B59 A105 $2.60 + 10c multi 2.90 2.90
Nos. B56-B59 (4) 7.20 7.20

Souvenir Sheets

Perf. 13½

B60 Sheet of 4 6.80 6.80
a.-d. A105 $1.50 + 10c on #534a-534d 1.70 1.70

Perf. 14½x13½

B61 A105 $7.50 + 50c multi 8.50 8.50

No. B60 ovptd. "FIRST VISIT OF A POPE TO SOUTH PACIFIC" and "HIS HOLINESS POPE JOHN PAUL II" on margin. No. B61 ovptd. on margin only "Visit of Pope John Paul II, Nov 21-24 1986 / First Papal Visit to the South Pacific."

AIR POST STAMPS

Catalogue values for unused stamps in this section are for Never Hinged items.

Type of 1977

Designs: 15c, Preparing ground for taro. 20c, Banana harvest. 23c, Bush plantation. 50c, Canoe fishing. 90c, Reef fishing. $1.35, Preparing ground for taro. $2.10, Shellfish gathering. $2.60, Luku harvest.

1979 Litho. *Perf. 14*

C1 A54 15c gold & multi .16 .16
C2 A54 20c gold & multi .22 .22
C3 A54 23c gold & multi .26 .26
C4 A54 50c gold & multi .60 .60
C5 A54 90c gold & multi .90 .90
C6 A54 $1.35 gold & multi 1.40 1.40
C7 A54 $2.10 gold & multi 2.25 2.25
C8 A54 $2.60 gold & multi 2.75 2.75
C9 A54 $5.10 like #187 5.25 5.25
C10 A54 $6.35 like #188 6.75 6.75
Nos. C1-C10 (10) 20.54 20.54

Issue dates: Nos. C1-C5, Feb. 26. Nos. C6-C8, Mar. 30. C9-C10, May 28.

OFFICIAL STAMPS

Catalogue values for unused stamps in this section are for Never Hinged items.

Nos. 417-430, 332-334, 431-431A Overprinted "O.H.M.S." in Metallic Blue or Gold

Perf. 13½, 13½x13, 13x13½, 13

1985-87 Photo.

O1 A89 12c multi .15 .15
O2 A89 25c multi .18 .18
O3 A89 30c multi .22 .22
O4 A89 35c multi .25 .25
O5 A89 40c multi .30 .30
O6 A89 52c multi .40 .40
O7 A89 58c multi .48 .48
O8 A89 70c multi .55 .55
O9 A89 83c multi .65 .65
O10 A89 $1.05 multi .75 .75
O11 A90 $1.75 multi 1.40 1.40
O12 A90 $2.30 multi 2.00 2.00
O13 A90 $3.90 multi 3.75 3.75
O14 A77a $4 multi (G) 3.50 3.50
O15 A90 $5 multi 4.25 4.25
O16 A77a $6 multi ('87) (G) 9.00 9.00
O17 A90 $6.60 multi ('86) 5.50 5.50
O18 A90 $8.30 multi ('86) 7.00 7.00
O19 A77a $10 multi ('87) (G) 15.00 15.00
Nos. O1-O19 (19) 55.33 55.33

Nos. 604-613 Ovptd. "O.H.M.S." in Gold

1993-94 Litho. *Perf. 14x13½*

O20 A118 20c multicolored .22 .22
O21 A118 50c multicolored .55 .55
O22 A118 70c multicolored .80 .80
O23 A118 $1 multicolored 1.10 1.10
O24 A118 $1.50 multicolored 1.65 1.65
O25 A118 $2 multicolored 2.25 2.25
O26 A118 $3 multicolored 3.25 3.25
O27 A118 $5 multicolored 5.50 5.50
O28 A118 $7 multicolored 8.50 8.50
O29 A118 $10 multicolored 12.00 12.00
O30 A118 $15 multicolored 18.00 18.00
Nos. O20-O30 (11) 53.82 53.82

Nos. O20-O30 were not sold unused to local customers.

Issued: 20c-$2, 12/10/93; $3, $5, 4/27/94; $7, $10, 9/1/94; $15, 9/30/94.

NORFOLK ISLAND

'nȯr–fək 'ī–lənd

LOCATION — Island in the south Pacific Ocean, 900 miles east of Australia
GOVT. — Territory of Australia
AREA — 13 ½ sq. mi.
POP. — 1,800 (est. 1982)

12 Pence = 1 Shilling
100 Cents = 1 Dollar (1966)

Catalogue values for all unused stamps in this country are for Never Hinged items.

Watermark

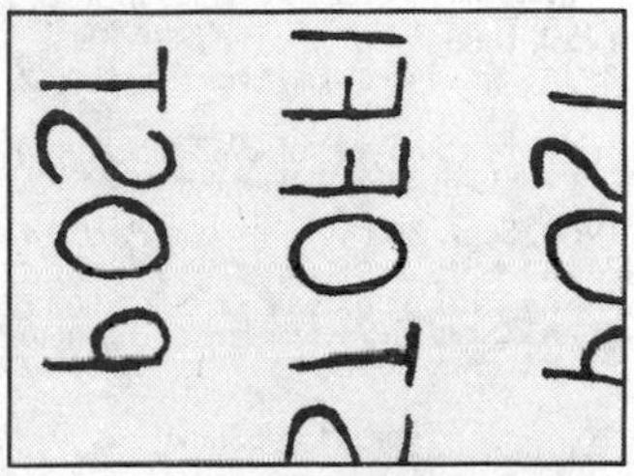

Wmk. 380- "POST OFFICE"

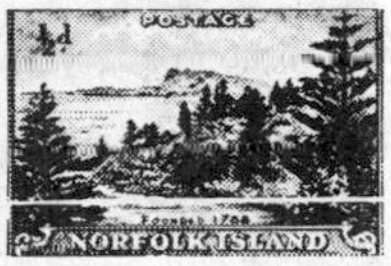

View of Ball Bay — A1

Unwmk.

1947, June 10 Engr. *Perf. 14*

1 A1 ½p deep orange .25 .25
2 A1 1p violet .40 .45
3 A1 1½p bright green .60 .40
4 A1 2p red violet .70 .45
5 A1 2½p red .90 .60
6 A1 3p brown orange .80 .65
7 A1 4p rose lake 1.10 .70
8 A1 5½p slate 1.25 .80
9 A1 6p sepia 1.50 1.00
10 A1 9p lilac rose 2.25 1.50
11 A1 1sh gray green 2.25 1.50
12 A1 2sh olive bister 6.00 3.25
Nos. 1-12 (12) 18.00 11.55

See Nos. 23-24.

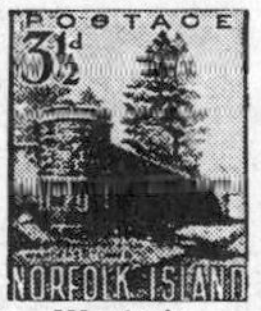

Warder's Tower — A2

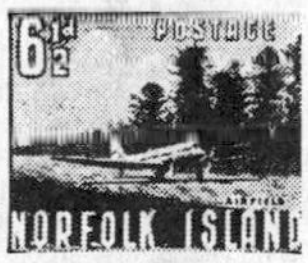

Airfield — A3

Designs: 7½p, First Governor's Residence. 8½p, Barracks entrance. 10p, Salt House. 5sh, Bloody Bridge.

1953, June 10 *Perf. 14½*

13 A2 3½p rose brown 2.50 .80
14 A3 6½p dark green 2.75 1.25
15 A3 7½p deep ultra 4.25 1.75
16 A2 8½p chocolate 6.25 2.75
17 A2 10p rose lilac 5.00 2.25
18 A3 5sh dark brown 47.50 21.00
Nos. 13-18 (6) 68.25 29.80

See Nos. 35, 40. For surcharges see Nos. 21-22, 27. For types surcharged see Nos. 26, 28.

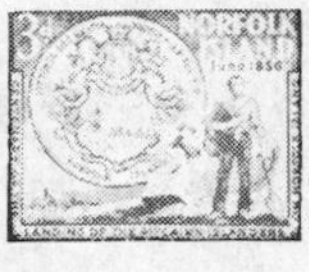

Original Norfolk Seal and First Settlers — A4

1956, June 8

19	A4	3p bluish green	1.10	1.00
20	A4	2sh violet	5.25	*8.00*

Cent. of the landing of the Pitcairn Islanders on Norfolk Island.

Nos. 15 and 16 Surcharged with New Value and Bars

1958, July 1

21	A3	7p on 7½p dp ultra	2.25	*3.25*
22	A2	8p on 8½p choc	3.00	*4.50*

Ball Bay Type of 1947

1959, July 6 **Engr.** ***Perf. 14***

23	A1	3p green	12.50	5.50
24	A1	2sh dark blue	25.00	14.00

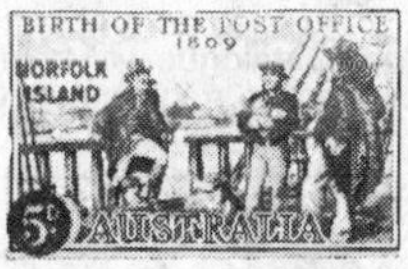

A5

Australia #332 Surcharged in Red

1959, Dec. 7

25	A5	5p on 4p dk gray blue	2.00	2.00

No. 14 and Types of 1953 Surcharged with New Values and Bars

1960, Sept. 26 ***Perf. 14½***

26	A2	1sh1p on 3½p dk bl	6.00	5.00
27	A3	2sh5p on 6½p dk grn	8.00	7.50
28	A3	2sh8p on 7½p dk brn	12.50	10.00
		Nos. 26-28 (3)	26.50	22.50

Types of 1953 and

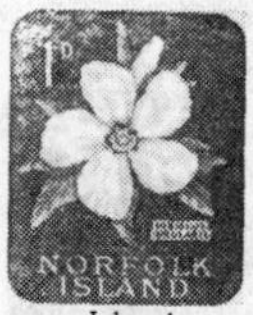

Island Hibiscus — A6

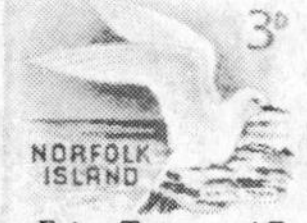

Fairy Tern — A7

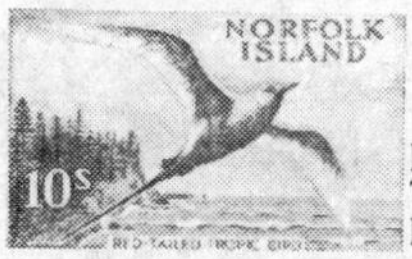

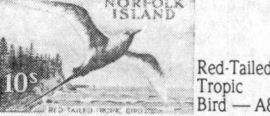

Red-Tailed Tropic Bird — A8

Designs: 2p, Lagunaria patersonii (flowers). 5p, Lantana. 8p, Red hibiscus. 9p, Cereus and Queen Elizabeth II. 10p, Salt House. 1sh1p, Fringed hibiscus. 2sh, Providence petrel, vert. 2sh5p, Passion flower. 2sh8p, Rose apple. 5sh, Bloody Bridge.

1960-62 **Unwmk.** **Engr.** ***Perf. 14½***

29	A6	1p blue green	.15	.15
30	A6	2p gray grn & brt pink	.20	.15
31	A7	3p brt green ('61)	.55	.25
32	A6	5p lilac	1.10	.75
33	A6	8p vermilion	2.00	1.50
34	A6	9p ultramarine	2.00	1.50
35	A2	10p pale pur & brn ('61)	3.50	1.75
36	A6	1sh1p dark red ('61)	2.75	1.50
37	A6	2sh sepia ('61)	2.75	1.75
38	A6	2sh5p dk purple ('62)	2.75	1.75
39	A6	2sh8p green & sal ('62)	4.25	2.00
40	A3	5sh green & gray ('61)	6.50	3.00

Perf. 14½x14

41	A8	10sh green ('61)	42.50	30.00
		Nos. 29-41 (13)	71.00	46.05

See #585-586. For surcharges see #71-82.

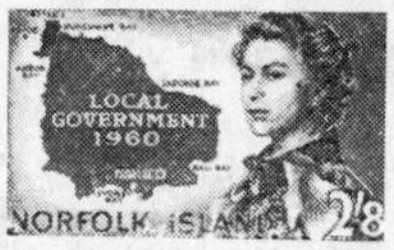

Map of Norfolk Island — A9

1960, Oct. 24 **Engr.** ***Perf. 14***

42	A9	2sh8p rose violet	30.00	30.00

Introduction of local government for Norfolk Island.

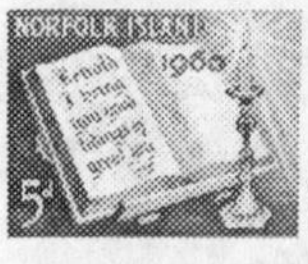

Open Bible and Candle — A9a

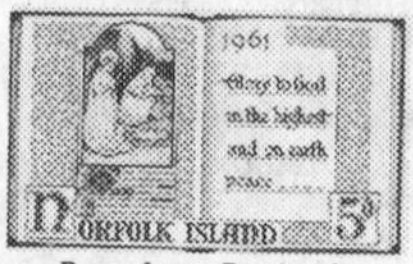

Page from Book of Hours, 15th Century — A9b

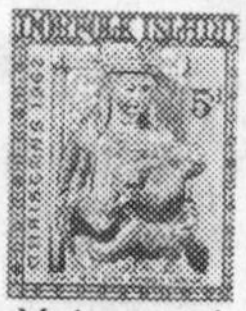

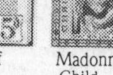

Madonna and Child — A9c

1960, Nov. 21 ***Perf. 14½***

43	A9a	5p bright lilac rose	5.00	5.00

Christmas.

1961, Nov. 20 ***Perf. 14½x14***

44	A9b	5p slate blue	1.75	1.75

Nos. 43-44 were issued to mark the beginning and the end of the 350th anniversary year of the publication of the King James translation of the Bible.

1962, Nov. 19 ***Perf. 14½***

45	A9c	5p blue	1.75	1.75

Christmas.

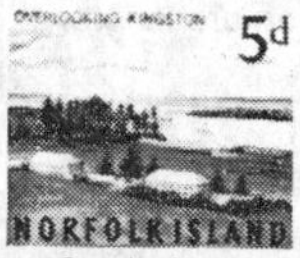

Overlooking Kingston — A10

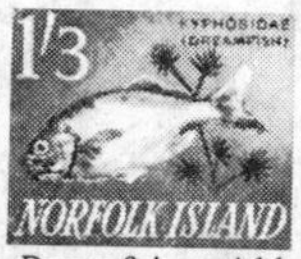

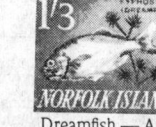

Dreamfish — A11

Designs: 6p, Tweed trousers (fish). 8p, Kingston scene. 9p, "The Arches." 10p, Slaughter Bay. 11p, Trumpeter fish. 1sh, Po'ov (wrasse). 1sh6p, Queensland grouper. 2sh3p, Ophie (carangidae).

Perf. 14½x14

1962-64 **Unwmk.** **Photo.**

49	A10	5p multicolored ('64)	.70	.60
50	A11	6p multicolored	.80	.80
51	A10	8p multicolored ('64)	1.10	.90
52	A10	9p multicolored ('64)	1.65	1.40
53	A10	10p multicolored ('64)	2.00	1.90
54	A11	11p multicolored ('63)	2.75	1.90
55	A11	1sh olive, bl & pink	3.25	2.75
57	A11	1sh3p bl, mar & grn ('63)	3.75	3.25
58	A11	1sh6p bl, brn & lil ('63)	4.25	4.25
60	A11	2sh3p dl bl, yel & red ('63)	4.75	4.50
		Nos. 49-60 (10)	25.00	22.25

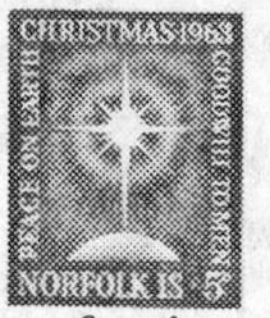

Star of Bethlehem — A11a

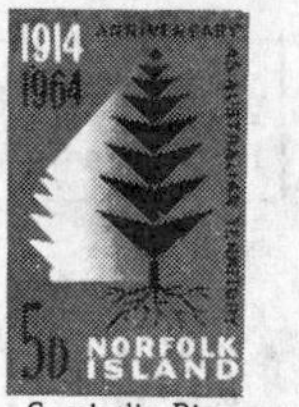

Symbolic Pine Tree — A12

1963, Nov. 11 **Engr.** ***Perf. 14½***

65	A11a	5p vermilion	1.50	1.50

Christmas.

1964, July 1 **Photo.** ***Perf. 13½x13***

66	A12	5p orange, blk & red	1.00	.65
67	A12	8p gray green, blk & red	1.60	1.60

50th anniv. of Norfolk Island as an Australian Territory.

Scott Catalogue Tabs

Scott Catalogue Tabs make referencing listings quick and easy. The peel-and-stick tabs feature country names and specialty areas for each volume of the catalogue including the Specialized and the Classic.

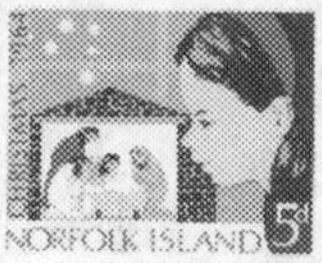

Child Looking at Nativity Scene — A12a

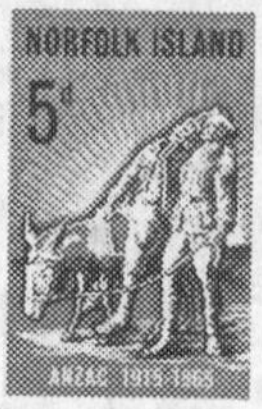

"Simpson and His Donkey" by Wallace Anderson — A12b

1964, Nov. 9 ***Perf. 13½***

68	A12a	5p multicolored	1.10	1.10

Christmas.

1965, Apr. 14 **Photo.** ***Perf. 13½x13***

69	A12b	5p brt green, sepia & blk	.75	.75

ANZAC issue. See note after Australia No. 387.

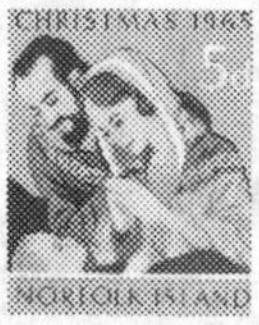

Nativity — A12c

1965, Oct. 25 **Unwmk.** ***Perf. 13½***

70	A12c	5p gold, blk, ultra & redsh brn	.50	.50

Christmas. No. 70 is luminescent. See note after Australia No. 331.

Nos. 29-33 and 35-41 Surcharged in Black on Overprinted Metallic Rectangles

Two types of 1c on 1p:
I. Silver rectangle 4x5½mm.
II. Silver rectangle 5½x5¼mm.
Two types of $1 on 10sh:
I. Silver rectangle 7x6½mm.
II. Silver rectangle 6x4mm.

Perf. 14½, 14½x14

1966, Feb. 14 **Engr.**

71	A6	1c on 1p bl grn (I)	.15	.15
a.		Type II	.35	.35
72	A6	2c on 2p gray grn & brt pink	.15	.15
73	A7	3c on 3p brt green	.20	.20
74	A6	4c on 5p lilac	.25	.25
75	A6	5c on 8p vermilion	.30	.30
76	A2	10c on 10p pale pur & brn	.65	.65
77	A6	15c on 1sh1p dark red	1.00	1.00
78	A6	20c on 2sh sepia	1.25	1.25
79	A6	25c on 2sh5p dk pur	1.90	1.90
80	A6	30c on 2sh8p grn & sal	2.50	2.50
81	A3	50c on 5sh grn & gray	5.00	5.00
82	A8	$1 on 10sh green (I)	6.50	6.50
a.		Type II	7.00	7.00
		Nos. 71-82 (12)	19.85	19.85

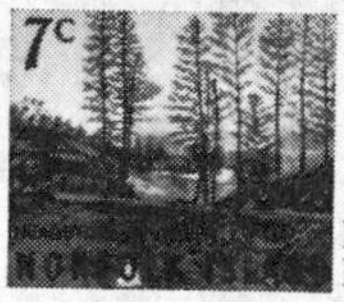

Headstone Bridge — A13

1966, June 27 **Photo.** ***Perf. 14½***

88	A13	7c shown	.32	.32
89	A13	9c Cemetary road	.48	.48

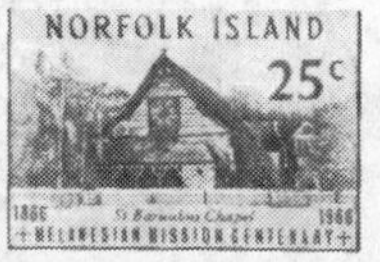

St. Barnabas Chapel — A14

Design: 4c, Interior of St. Barnabas Chapel.

Perf. 14x14½

1966, Aug. 23 **Photo.** **Unwmk.**

97	A14	4c multicolored	.15	.15
98	A14	25c multicolored	.75	.75

Centenary of the Melanesian Mission.

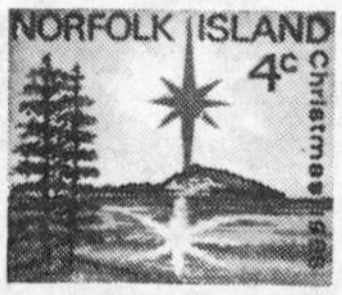

Star over Philip Island — A15

1966, Oct. 24 **Photo.** ***Perf. 14½***

99	A15	4c violet, grn, blue & sil	.40	.40

Christmas.

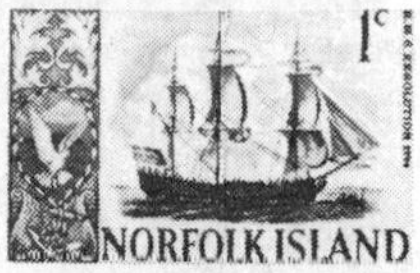

H.M.S. Resolution, 1774 — A16

Ships: 2c, La Boussole and Astrolabe, 1788. 3c, Brig Supply, 1788. 4c, Sirius, 1790. 5c, The Norfolk, 1798. 7c, Survey cutter Mermaid, 1825. 9c, The Lady Franklin, 1853. 10c The Morayshire, 1856. 15c, Southern Cross, 1866. 20c, The Pitcairn, 1891. 25c, Norfolk Island whaleboat, 1895. 30c, Cable ship Iris, 1907. 50c, The Resolution, 1926. $1, S.S. Morinda, 1931.

1967-68 **Photo.** ***Perf. 14x14½***

100	A16	1c multicolored	.15	.15
101	A16	2c multicolored	.15	.15
102	A16	3c multicolored	.15	.15
103	A16	4c multicolored	.18	.16
104	A16	5c multicolored	.28	.22
105	A16	7c multicolored	.32	.30
106	A16	9c multicolored	.42	.40
107	A16	10c multicolored	.55	.52
108	A16	15c multicolored	.85	.80
109	A16	20c multicolored	1.25	1.10
110	A16	25c multicolored	2.00	1.65
111	A16	30c multicolored	2.50	2.25
112	A16	50c multicolored	3.00	2.75
113	A16	$1 multicolored	5.00	4.75
		Nos. 100-113 (14)	16.80	15.35

Issued: #100-103, 4/17; #104-107, 8/19; #108-110, 3/18/68; #111-113, 6/18/68.

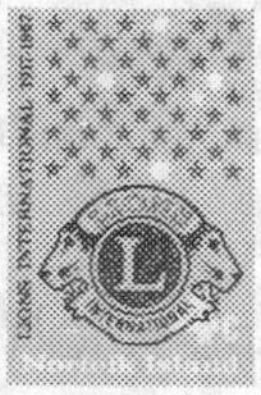

Lions Intl., 50th Anniv. — A16a

1967, June 7 **Photo.** ***Perf. 13½***

114	A16a	4c citron, blk & blue grn	.40	.40

Printed on luminescent paper; see note after Australia No. 331.

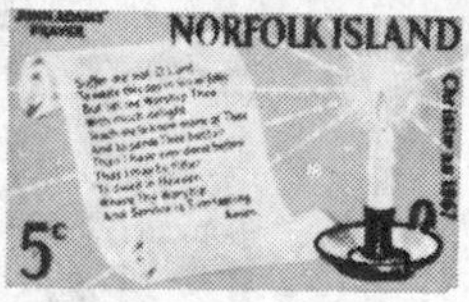

John Adams' Prayer A17

1967, Oct. 16 **Photo.** ***Perf. 14x14½***

115	A17	5c brick red, black & buff	.40	.40

Christmas.

Queen Elizabeth II Type of Australia, 1966-67

Coil Stamps

Perf. 15 Horizontally

1968-71 **Photo.** **Unwmk.**

116	A157	3c brn org, blk & buff	.15	.15
117	A157	4c blue grn, blk & buff	.15	.15
118	A157	5c brt purple, blk & buff	.20	.20
118A	A157	6c dk red, brn, blk & buff	.40	.40
		Nos. 116-118A (4)	.90	.90

Issued: 6c, Aug. 25, 1971; others, Aug. 5, 1968.

DC-4 Skymaster and Lancastrian
Plane — A18

1968, Sept. 25   Perf. 14½x14
119 A18 5c dk car, sky blue & indigo .20 .20
120 A18 7c dk car, blue grn & sepia .30 .30

21st anniv. of the Sydney to Norfolk Island air service by Qantas Airways.

Star and Hibiscus
Wreath — A19

Photo.; Silver Impressed (Star)
1968, Oct. 24   Perf. 14½x14
121 A19 5c sky blue & multi .30 .30

Christmas.

Map of Pacific, Transit of Venus before
Sun, Capt. Cook and Quadrant
A20

1969, June 3 Photo.   Perf. 14x14½
122 A20 10c brn, ol, pale brn & yel .35 .35

Bicent. of the observation at Tahiti by Capt. James Cook of the transit of the planet Venus across the sun.

Map of Van
Diemen's Land
and Norfolk
Island — A21

1969, Sept. 29   Perf. 14x14½
123 A21 5c multicolored .15 .15
124 A21 30c multicolored .90 .90

125th anniv. of the annexation of Norfolk Island by Van Diemen's Land (Tasmania).

Nativity (Mother-of-Pearl
carving) — A22

1969, Oct. 27 Photo.   Perf. 14½x14
125 A22 5c brown & multi .30 .30

Christmas.

Norfolk Island
Flyeater
A23

Birds of Norfolk Island from Book by Gregory Mathews: 1c, Robins, vert. 2c, Norfolk Island whistlers (thickheads), vert. 4c, Long-tailed cuckoos. 5c, Red-fronted parakeet, vert. 7c, Long-tailed trillers, vert. 9c, Island thrush. 10c, Owl, vert. 15c, Norfolk Island pigeon (extinct; vert.). 20c, White-breasted white-eye. 25c, Norfolk Island parrots,

vert. 30c, Gray fantail. 45c, Norfolk Island starlings. 50c, Crimson rosella, vert. $1, Sacred kingfisher.

Perf. 14x14½, 14½x14
1970-71   **Photo.**   **Unwmk.**
126 A23 1c multicolored .15 .15
127 A23 2c multicolored ('71) .20 .15
128 A23 3c multicolored .25 .20
129 A23 4c multicolored .32 .25
130 A23 5c multicolored ('71) .35 .30
131 A23 7c multicolored .50 .38
132 A23 9c multicolored .70 .50
133 A23 10c multicolored .80 .70
134 A23 15c multicolored ('71) 1.00 .70
135 A23 20c multicolored ('71) 2.00 1.00
136 A23 25c multicolored 2.00 1.25
137 A23 30c multicolored 5.00 3.00
138 A23 45c multicolored 5.50 4.25
139 A23 50c multicolored ('71) 6.75 4.75
140 A23 $1 multicolored ('71) 8.25 7.00
Nos. 126-140 (15) 33.77 24.58

Issue dates: 3c, 4c, 9c, 45c, Feb. 25. 1c, 7c, 10c, 25c, July 22. 2c, 2c, 5c, 15c, 50c, Feb. 24, 1971. 20c, 30c, $1, June 16, 1971.

Map of
Australia,
James
Cook and
Southern
Cross
A24

Design: 10c, "Endeavour" entering Botany Bay, Apr. 29, 1770, and aborigine with spear. The 1776 portrait of James Cook on the 5c is by John Webber.

1970, Apr. 29 Photo.   Perf. 14x14½
141 A24 5c multicolored .22 .20
142 A24 10c multicolored .42 .38

200th anniv. of Cook's discovery and exploration of the eastern coast of Australia.

First Christmas, Sydney
Bay, 1788 — A25

1970, Oct. 15 Photo.   Perf. 14x14½
143 A25 5c multicolored .32 .32

Christmas.

Bishop
Patteson, Open
Bible — A26

Designs: No. 145, Bible opened to Acts Chap 7, martyrdom of St. Stephen, and knotted palm fronds. No. 146, Bishop Patteson, rose window of Melanesian Mission Chapel on Norfolk Island. No. 147, Cross erected at Nukapu where Patteson died and his arms.

1971, Sept. 20
144 A26 6c brown & multi .22 .22
145 A26 6c brown & multi .22 .22
  a. Pair, #144-145 .45 .45
146 A26 10c purple & multi .40 .40
147 A26 10c purple & multi .40 .40
  a. Pair, #146-147 .80 .80
Nos. 144-147 (4) 1.24 1.24

Centenary of the death of Bishop John Coleridge Patteson (1827-1871), head of the Melanesian mission.

Rose Window, St.
Barnabas Chapel,
Norfolk Island — A27

1971, Oct. 25   Perf. 14x13½
148 A27 6c dk vio blue & multi .25 .25

Christmas.

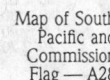 

Map of South
Pacific and
Commission
Flag — A28

1972, Feb. 6   Perf. 14x14½
149 A28 7c multicolored .50 .50

So. Pacific Commission, 25th anniv.

Stained-glass
Window — A29

Cross, Church,
Pines — A30

1972, Oct. 16 Photo.   Perf. 14x14½
150 A29 7c dark olive & multi .30 .30

Christmas. The stained-glass window by Edward Coley Burne-Jones is in All Saints Church, Norfolk Island.

1972, Nov. 20
151 A30 12c multicolored .50 .50

Centenary of All Saints Church, first built by Pitcairners on Norfolk Island.

"Resolution" in Antarctica — A31

1973, Jan. 17 Photo.   Perf. 14½x14
152 A31 35c multicolored 2.75 2.75

200th anniv. of the 1st crossing of the Antarctic Circle by Cook, Jan. 17, 1773.

Sleeping Child, and
Christmas Tree — A32

Christmas: 35c, Star over lagoon.

1973, Oct. 22 Photo.   Perf. 14x14½
153 A32 7c black & multi .28 .28
154 A32 12c black & multi .50 .50
155 A32 35c black & multi 1.75 1.75
Nos. 153-155 (3) 2.53 2.53

Protestant
Clergyman's
House
A33

Designs: 2c, Royal Engineer Office. 3c, Double quarters for free overseers. 4c, Guard House. 5c, Pentagonal Gaol entrance. 7c, Pentagonal Gaol, aerial view. 8c, Convict barracks. 10c, Officers' quarters, New Military Barracks. 12c, New Military Barracks. 14c, Beach stores. 15c, Magazine. 20c, Old Military Barracks, entrance. 25c, Old Military Barracks. 30c, Old stores, Crankmill. 50c, Commissariat stores. $1, Government House.

1973-75   **Photo.**   **Perf. 14x14½**
156 A33 1c multicolored .15 .15
157 A33 2c multicolored .15 .15
158 A33 3c multicolored .15 .15
159 A33 4c multicolored .18 .18
160 A33 5c multicolored .20 .20

161 A33 7c multicolored .30 .30
162 A33 8c multicolored .35 .35
163 A33 10c multicolored .40 .40
164 A33 12c multicolored .45 .45
165 A33 14c multicolored .60 .60
166 A33 15c multicolored .65 .65
167 A33 20c multicolored .75 .75
168 A33 25c multicolored .90 .90
169 A33 30c multicolored 1.25 1.25
170 A33 50c multicolored 2.25 2.25
171 A33 $1 multicolored 3.75 3.75
Nos. 156-171 (16) 12.48 12.48

Issued: 1c, 5c, 10c, 50c, 11/19/73; 2c, 7c, 12c, 30c, 5/1/74; 4c, 14c, 20c, $1, 7/12/74; 3c, 8c, 15c, 25c, 2/19/75.

Map of Norfolk
Island — A34

1974, Feb. 8 Photo.   Perf. 14x14½
172 A34 7c red lilac & multi .40 .40
173 A34 25c dull blue & multi 1.75 1.75

Visit of Queen Elizabeth II and the Duke of Edinburgh, Feb. 11-12.

Gipsy Moth
over Norfolk
Island — A35

1974, Mar. 28 Litho.   Perf. 14x14½
174 A35 14c multicolored 2.00 2.00

1st aircraft to visit Norfolk, Sir Francis Chichester's "Mme. Elijah," Mar. 28, 1931.

Capt. Cook — A36

Nativity — A37

Designs: 10c, "Resolution," by Henry Roberts. 14c, Norfolk Island pine, cone and seedling. 25c, Norfolk Island flax, by George Raper, 1790. Portrait of Cook on 7c by William Hodges, 1770.

1974, Oct. 8   **Litho.**   **Perf. 14**
175 A36 7c multicolored .60 .60
176 A36 10c multicolored .75 .75
177 A36 14c multicolored 1.50 1.50
178 A36 25c multicolored 4.50 4.50
Nos. 175-178 (4) 7.35 7.35

Bicentenary of the discovery of Norfolk Island by Capt. James Cook.

1974, Oct. 18   **Photo.**   **Perf. 14**
179 A37 7c rose & multi .30 .30
180 A37 30c violet & multi 1.50 1.50

Christmas.

Norfolk
Island
Pine
A38

Designs: 15c, Off-shore islands. 35c, Crimson rosella and sacred kingfisher. 40c, Map showing Norfolk's location. Stamps in shape of Norfolk Island.

1974, Dec. 16   **Litho.**   **Imperf.**
Self-adhesive
181 A38 10c brown & multi .42 .42
182 A38 15c dk blue & multi .65 .65
183 A38 35c dk purple & multi 1.50 1.50

184 A38 40c dk blue grn & multi 1.90 3.50
   a. Souvenir sheet of 4 30.00 27.50
     Nos. 181-184 (4) 4.47 6.07

Cent. of UPU. Stamps printed on peelable paper backing. No. 184a contains 4 imperf. stamps similar to Nos. 181-184 in reduced size on a background of map of Norfolk Island. Peelable paper backing shows beach scene on Norfolk Island.

Survey Cutter "Mermaid," 1825 — A39

Design: 35c, Kingston, 1835, after painting by Thomas Seller. Stamps outlined in shape of Norfolk Island map.

1975, Aug. 18   **Litho.**   *Imperf.*
Self-adhesive
185 A39 10c multicolored .25 .25
186 A39 35c multicolored 1.00 1.00

Sesquicentennial of 2nd settlement of Norfolk Island. Printed on peelable paper backing with green and black design and inscription.

Star over Norfolk Island Pine and Map — A40

Brass Memorial Cross — A41

1975, Oct. 6   **Photo.**   *Perf. 14¹/₂x14*
187 A40 10c lt blue & multi .32 .32
188 A40 15c lt brown & multi .45 .45
189 A40 35c lilac & multi 1.25 1.25
     Nos. 187-189 (3) 2.02 2.02

Christmas.

Perf. 14¹/₂x14, 14x14¹/₂
1975, Nov. 24   **Photo.**

Design: 60c, Laying foundation stone, 1875, and chapel, 1975, horiz.

190 A41 30c multicolored .65 .65
191 A41 60c multicolored 1.50 1.50

St. Barnabas Chapel, centenary.

Launching "Resolution" A42

Design: 45c, "Resolution" under sail.

1975, Dec. 1   **Perf. 14x14¹/₂**
192 A42 25c multicolored .75 .75
193 A42 45c multicolored 1.25 1.25

50th anniversary of launching of schooner "Resolution."

Bedford Flag, Charles W. Morgan Whaler — A43

Designs: 25c, Grand Union Flag, church interior. 40c, 15-star flag, 1795, and plane over island, WWII. 45c, 13-star flag and California quail.

1976, July 5   **Photo.**   *Perf. 14*
194 A43 18c multicolored .40 .40
195 A43 25c multicolored .60 .60
196 A43 40c multicolored .80 .80
197 A43 45c multicolored .90 .90
     Nos. 194-197 (4) 2.70 2.70

American Bicentennial.

Bird in Flight, Brilliant Sun — A44

1976, Oct. 4   **Photo.**   *Perf. 14*
198 A44 18c blue grn & multi .48 .48
199 A44 25c dp blue & multi .70 .70
200 A44 45c violet & multi 1.25 1.25
     Nos. 198-200 (3) 2.43 2.43

Christmas.

Bassaris Itea — A45

Butterflies and Moths: 2c, Utetheisa pulchelloides vaga. 3c, Agathia asterias jowettorum. 4c, Cynthia kershawi. 5c, Leucania loreyimima. 10c, Hypolimnas bolina nerina. 15c, Pyrrhorachis pyrrhogona. 16c, Austrocarea iocephala millsi. 17c, Pseudocoremia christiani. 18c, Cleora idiocrossa. 19c, Simplicia caeneusalis buffetti. 20c, Austrocidaria ralstonae. 30c, Hippotion scrofa. 40c, Papilio ilioneus. 50c, Tiracola plagiata. $1, Precis vilida. $2, Cepora perimale.

1976-77   **Photo.**   *Perf. 14*
201 A45 1c multicolored .15 .15
202 A45 2c multicolored .15 .15
203 A45 3c multicolored .15 .15
204 A45 4c multicolored .15 .15
205 A45 5c multicolored .15 .15
206 A45 10c multicolored .16 .16
207 A45 15c multicolored .22 .22
208 A45 16c multicolored .26 .26
209 A45 17c multicolored .32 .32
210 A45 18c multicolored .35 .35
211 A45 19c multicolored .35 .35
212 A45 20c multicolored .38 .38
213 A45 30c multicolored .55 .55
214 A45 40c multicolored .65 .65
215 A45 50c multicolored 1.00 1.00
216 A45 $1 multicolored 1.25 1.25
217 A45 $2 multicolored 2.75 2.75
     Nos. 201-217 (17) 8.99 8.99

Issued: 1c, 5c, 10c, 16c, 18c, $1, 11/17; others, 1977.

View of Kingston A46

1977, June 10
218 A46 25c multicolored .80 .80

25th anniv. of reign of Elizabeth II.

Hibiscus and 19th Century Whaler's Lamp — A47

Capt. Cook, by Nathaniel Dance — A48

1977, Oct. 4   **Photo.**   *Perf. 14¹/₂*
219 A47 18c multicolored .35 .35
220 A47 25c multicolored .55 .55
221 A47 45c multicolored .80 .80
     Nos. 219-221 (3) 1.70 1.70

Christmas.

1978, Jan. 18   **Photo.**   *Perf. 14¹/₂*
Designs: 25c, Discovery of Northern Hawaiian Islands (Cook aboard ship), horiz. 80c, British flag and Island, horiz.

222 A48 18c multicolored .32 .32
223 A48 25c multicolored .60 .60
224 A48 80c multicolored 1.40 1.40
     Nos. 222-224 (3) 2.32 2.32

Bicentenary of Capt. Cook's arrival in Hawaiian Islands.

World Guides Flag and Globe A49

Designs: 25c, Norfolk Guides' scarf badge and trefoil. 35c, Elizabeth II and trefoil. 45c, FAO Ceres medal with portrait of Lady Olive Baden-Powell, and trefoil. Stamps outlined in shape of Norfolk Island map.

1978, Feb. 22   **Litho.**   *Imperf.*
Self-adhesive
225 A49 18c lt ultra & multi .30 .30
226 A49 25c yellow & multi .40 .40
227 A49 35c lt green & multi .65 .65
228 A49 45c yellow grn & multi .90 .90
     Nos. 225-228 (4) 2.25 2.25

50th anniversary of Norfolk Island Girl Guides. Printed on peelable paper backing with green multiple pines and tourist publicity inscription.

St. Edward's Crown — A50

Design: 70c, Coronation regalia.

1978, June 29   **Photo.**   *Perf. 14¹/₂*
229 A50 25c multicolored .45 .45
230 A50 70c multicolored 1.25 1.25

25th anniv. of coronation of Elizabeth II.

Norfolk Island Boy Scouts, 50th Anniv. A51

Designs: 20c, Cliffs, Duncombe Bay, Scout Making Fire. 25c, Emily Bay, Philip and Nepean Islands from Kingston. 35c, Anson Bay, Cub and Boy Scouts. 45c, Sunset and Lord Baden-Powell. Stamps outlined in shape of Norfolk Island map.

1978, Aug. 22   **Litho.**   *Imperf.*
Self-adhesive
231 A51 20c multicolored .35 .35
232 A51 25c multicolored .50 .50
233 A51 35c multicolored .70 .70
234 A51 45c multicolored .90 .90
     Nos. 231-234 (4) 2.45 2.45

Printed on peelable paper backing with green multiple pines and tourist publicity inscription and picture.

Map of Bering Sea and Pacific Ocean, Routes of Discovery and Resolution A52

Design: 90c, Discovery and Resolution trapped in ice, by John Webber.

1978, Aug. 29   **Photo.**   *Perf. 14¹/₂*
235 A52 25c multicolored .45 .45
236 A52 90c multicolored 1.75 1.75

Northernmost point of Cook's voyages.

Poinsettia and Bible — A53

Christmas: 30c, Native oak (flowers) and Bible. 55c, Hibiscus and Bible.

1978, Oct. 3   **Photo.**   *Perf. 14¹/₂*
237 A53 20c multicolored .40 .40
238 A53 30c multicolored .60 .60
239 A53 55c multicolored 1.00 1.00
     Nos. 237-239 (3) 2.00 2.00

Capt. Cook, View of Staithes A54

Design: 80c, Capt. Cook and view of Whitby harbor.

1978, Oct. 27
240 A54 20c multicolored .45 .45
241 A54 80c multicolored 1.75 1.75

Resolution, Map of Asia and Australia A55

Designs: No. 243, Map of Hawaii and Americas, Cook's route and statue. No. 244, Capt. Cook's death. No. 245, Ships off Hawaii.

1979, Feb. 14   **Photo.**   *Perf. 14¹/₂*
242 A55 20c multicolored .50 .50
243 A55 20c multicolored .50 .50
   a. Pair, #242-243 1.00 1.00
244 A55 40c multicolored 1.00 1.00
245 A55 40c multicolored 1.00 1.00
   a. Pair, #244-245 2.00 2.00
     Nos. 242-245 (4) 2.96 2.96

Bicentenary of Capt. Cook's death.

Rowland Hill and Tasmania No. 1 A56

Rowland Hill and: 30c, Great Britain No. 8. 55c, Norfolk Island No. 2.

1979, Aug. 27   **Perf. 14x14¹/₂**
246 A56 20c multicolored .25 .25
247 A56 30c multicolored .35 .35
248 A56 55c multicolored .70 .70
   a. Souvenir sheet of 1 1.40 1.40
     Nos. 246-248 (3) 1.30 1.30

Sir Rowland Hill (1795-1879), originator of penny postage.

Legislative Assembly — A57

1979, Aug.   Photo.   Perf. 14¹/₂x14
249 A57 $1 multicolored   1.50 1.50
First session of Legislative Assembly.

Map of Pacific Ocean, IYC Emblem A58

1979, Sept. 25   Litho.   Perf. 15
250 A58 80c multicolored   1.25 1.25
International Year of the Child.

Emily Bay Beach — A59

1979, Oct. 2   Photo.   Perf. 12¹/₂x13
251 A59 15c shown   .25 .25
252 A59 20c Emily Bay   .32 .32
253 A59 30c Salt House   .52 .52
 a.   Souv. sheet of 3, #251-253, perf.
        14x14¹/₂   2.00 2.00
 b.   Strip of 3, #251-253   1.10 1.10
Christmas. #253b has continuous design.

Lions District Convention 1980 — A60

1980, Jan. 25   Litho.   Perf. 15
254 A60 50c multicolored   .80 .80

Rotary International, 75th Anniversary A61

1980, Feb. 21
255 A61 50c multicolored   .80 .80

DH-60 "Gypsy Moth" A62

1980-81   Litho.   Perf. 14¹/₂
256 A62 1c Hawker Siddeley
            HS-748   .15 .15
257 A62 2c shown   .15 .15
258 A62 3c Curtiss P-40 Kit-
            tyhawk   .15 .15
259 A62 4c Chance Vought
            Corsair   .15 .15
260 A62 5c Grumman Avenger   .15 .15
261 A62 15c Douglas Dauntless   .28 .28
262 A62 20c Cessna 172   .35 .35
262A A62 25c Lockheed Hudson   .45 .45
263 A62 30c Lockheed PV-1 Ven-
            tura   .55 .55
264 A62 40c Avro York   .70 .70
265 A62 50c DC-3   .90 .90

266 A62 60c Avro 691 Lancastri-
            an   1.00 1.00
267 A62 80c DC-4   1.50 1.50
268 A62 $1 Beechcraft Super
            King Air   1.75 1.75
269 A62 $2 Fokker Friendship   2.25 2.25
270 A62 $5 Lockheed C-130
            Hercules   5.75 5.75
     Nos. 256-270 (16)   16.23 16.23
   Issue dates: 2c, 3c, 20c, $5, Mar. 25. 4c, 5c,
15c, $2, Aug. 19. 30c, 50c, 60c, 80c, Jan. 13,
1981. 1c, 25c, 40c, $1, Mar. 3, 1981.

Queen Mother Elizabeth, 80th Birthday A63

1980, Aug. 4   Litho.   Perf. 14¹/₂
271 A63 22c multicolored   .35 .35
272 A63 60c multicolored   .85 .85

Red-tailed Tropic Birds — A64

1980, Oct. 28   Litho.   Perf. 14x14¹/₂
273 A64 15c shown   .25 .25
274 A64 22c Fairy terns   .35 .35
275 A64 35c White-capped noddys   .60 .60
 a.   Strip of 3, #273-275   1.20 1.20
276 A64 60c Fairy terns, diff.   1.00 1.00
     Nos. 273-276 (4)   2.20 2.20
Christmas. No. 275a has continuous design.

Citizens Arriving at Norfolk Island A65

1981, June 5   Litho.   Perf. 14¹/₂
277 A65 5c Departure   .15 .15
278 A65 35c shown   .55 .55
279 A65 60c Settlement   .95 .95
 a.   Souvenir sheet of 3, #277-279   1.65 1.65
     Nos. 277-279 (3)   1.65 1.65
Pitcairn migration to Norfolk Island, 125th anniv.

Royal Wedding Issue
Common Design Type

1981, July 22   Litho.   Perf. 14
280 CD331 35c Bouquet   .50 .50
281 CD331 55c Charles   .80 .80
282 CD331 60c Couple   .90 .90
     Nos. 280-282 (3)   2.20 2.20

#280-282 each se-tenant with decorative label.

Uniting Church of Australia A66

1981, Sept. 15   Litho.   Perf. 14¹/₂
283 A66 18c shown   .30 .30
284 A66 24c Seventh Day Adventist
            Church   .40 .40
285 A66 30c Church of the Sacred
            Heart   .50 .50
286 A66 $1 St. Barnabas Church   1.60 1.60
     Nos. 283-286 (4)   2.80 2.80
Christmas.

White-breasted Silvereye A67

1981, Nov. 10   Litho.   Perf. 14¹/₂
287   Strip of 5   3.00 3.00
 a.-e.   A67 35c any single   .60 .60

Philip Island A68

Views, Flora and Fauna: No. 288, Philip Isld. No. 289, Nepean Island.

1982, Jan. 12   Litho.   Perf. 14
288   Strip of 5   1.75 1.75
 a.-e.   A68 24c any single   .35 .35
289   Strip of 5   2.75 2.75
 a.-e.   A68 35c any single   .55 .55

Sperm Whale A69

1982, Feb. 23   Litho.   Perf. 14¹/₂
290 A69 24c shown   .40 .40
291 A69 55c Southern right whale   .90 .90
292 A69 80c Humpback whale   1.50 1.50
     Nos. 290-292 (3)   2.80 2.80

Shipwrecks A70

1982   Litho.   Perf. 14¹/₂
293 A70 24c Sirius, 1790   .40 .40
294 A70 27c Diocet, 1873   .45 .45
295 A70 35c Friendship, 1835   .55 .55
296 A70 40c Mary Hamilton, 1873   .65 .65
297 A70 55c Fairlie, 1840   .80 .80
298 A70 65c Warrigal, 1918   1.00 1.00
     Nos. 293-298 (6)   3.85 3.85

Christmas and 40th Anniv. of Aircraft Landing A71

1982, Sept. 7   Perf. 14
299 A71 27c Supplies drop   .40 .40
300 A71 40c Landing   .65 .65
301 A71 75c Sharing supplies   1.25 1.25
     Nos. 299-301 (3)   2.30 2.30

Battalion Company Officer, 50th Regiment, 1835-1842 — A72

British Army Uniforms, Second Settlement, 1839-1848: 40c, Light Company Officer, 58th Reg., 1845. 55c, Private, 80th Bat., 1838. 65c, Bat. Company Officer, 11th Reg., 1847.

1982, Nov. 9   Perf. 14¹/₂
302 A72 27c multicolored   .40 .40
303 A72 40c multicolored   .65 .65
304 A72 55c multicolored   .80 .80
305 A72 65c multicolored   1.00 1.00
     Nos. 302-305 (4)   2.85 2.85

Norfolk Island

Local Mushrooms — A73

1983, Mar. 29   Litho.   Perf. 14x13¹/₂
306 A73 27c Panaeolus papilionaceus   .40 .40
307 A73 40c Coprinus domesticus   .65 .65
308 A73 55c Marasmius niveus   .80 .80
309 A73 65c Cymatoderma elegans   1.00 1.00
     Nos. 306-309 (4)   2.85 2.85

Manned Flight Bicentenary A74

1983, July 12   Litho.   Perf. 14¹/₂x14
310 A74 10c Beech 18, aerial map-
            ping   .18 .18
311 A74 27c Fokker F-28   .40 .40
312 A74 45c DC4   .80 .80
313 A74 75c Sikorsky helicopter   1.25 1.25
 a.   Souvenir sheet of 4, #310-313   2.75 2.75
     Nos. 310-313 (4)   2.63 2.63

Christmas — A75

Stained-glass Windows by Edward Burne-Jones (1833-1898), St. Barnabas Chapel.

1983, Oct. 4   Litho.   Perf. 14
314 A75 5c multicolored   .15 .15
315 A75 24c multicolored   .40 .40
316 A75 30c multicolored   .45 .45
317 A75 55c multicolored   .65 .65
318 A75 85c multicolored   1.25 1.25
     Nos. 314-318 (5)   2.90 2.90

World Communications Year — A76

ANZCAN Cable Station: 30c, Chantik, Cable laying Ship. 45c, Shore end. 75c, Cable Ship Mercury. 85c, Map of cable route.

1983, Nov. 15   Litho.   Perf. 14¹/₂x14
319 A76 30c multicolored   .40 .40
320 A76 45c multicolored   .60 .60
321 A76 75c multicolored   1.00 1.00
322 A76 85c multicolored   1.10 1.10
     Nos. 319-322 (4)   3.10 3.10

Local Flowers — A77

1984   Litho.   Perf. 14
323 A77 1c Myoporum obsurum   .15 .15
324 A77 2c Ipomoea pes-caprae   .15 .15
325 A77 3c Phreatia crassiuscula   .15 .15
326 A77 4c Streblorrhiza speciosa   .15 .15
327 A77 5c Rhopalostylis baueri   .15 .15
328 A77 10c Alyxia gynopogon   .15 .15
329 A77 15c Ungeria floribunda   .22 .22
330 A77 20c Capparis nobilis   .28 .28
331 A77 25c Lagunaria patersonia   .35 .35
332 A77 30c Cordyline obtecta   .45 .45
333 A77 35c Hibiscus insularis   .50 .50
334 A77 40c Millettia australis   .55 .55
335 A77 50c Jasminum volubile   .65 .65
336 A77 $1 Passiflora aurantia   1.40 1.40
337 A77 $3 Oberonia titania   4.25 4.25
338 A77 $5 Araucaria heterophyl-
            la   7.00 7.00
     Nos. 323-338 (16)   16.55 16.55
   Issue dates: Jan. 10: 2c, 3c, 10c, 20c, 25c, 40c, 50c, $5; others Mar. 27.

Reef Fish — A78

Perf. 13½x14

1984, Apr. 17   Litho.   Wmk. 373
339 A78 30c Painted morwong .60 .60
340 A78 45c Black-spot goatfish .90 .90
341 A78 75c Ring-tailed surgeon fish 1.50 1.50
342 A78 85c Three-striped butterfly fish 1.65 1.65
 Nos. 339-342 (4) 4.65 4.65

Boobook Owl — A79

Designs: a, Laying eggs. b, Standing at treehole. c, Sitting on branch looking sideways. d, Looking head on. e, Flying.

Wmk. 373
1984, July 17   Litho.   Perf. 14
343 Strip of 5 4.25 4.25
 a.-e. A79 30c any single .85 .85

AUSIPEX '84 — A80

1984, Sept. 18   Litho.   Perf. 14½
344 A80 30c Nos. 15 and 176 .65 .65
345 A80 45c First day cover 1.00 1.00
346 A80 75c Presentation pack 2.00 2.00
 a. Souvenir sheet of 3, #344-346 3.50 3.50
 Nos. 344-346 (3) 3.65 3.65

Christmas — A81   A82

1984, Oct. 9   Litho.   Perf. 13½
347 A81 5c The Font .15 .15
348 A81 24c Church at Kingston, interior .45 .45
349 A81 30c Pastor and Mrs. Phelps .60 .60
350 A81 45c Phelps, Church of Chester .90 .90
351 A81 85c Phelps, Methodist Church, modern interior 1.75 1.75
 Nos. 347-351 (5) 3.85 3.85

1984, Nov. 6   Litho.   Perf. 14x15
352 A82 30c As teacher .55 .55
353 A82 45c As minister .85 .85
354 A82 75c As chaplain 1.40 1.40
355 A82 85c As community leader 1.75 1.75
 Nos. 352-355 (4) 4.55 4.55

Rev. George Hunn Nobbs, death centenary.

Whaling Ships — A83

1985   Litho.   Perf. 13½x14
356 A83 5c Fanny Fisher .15 .15
357 A83 15c Waterwitch .30 .30
358 A83 20c Canton .38 .38
359 A83 33c Costa Rica Packet .62 .62

360 A83 50c Splendid .90 .90
361 A83 60c Aladin 1.50 1.50
362 A83 80c California 1.75 1.75
363 A83 90c Onward 2.25 2.25
 Nos. 356-363 (8) 7.85 7.85

Issued: 5c, 33c, 50c, 90c, 2/19; others 4/30.

Queen Mother 85th Birthday
Common Design Type
Perf. 14½x14

1985, June 6   Litho.   Wmk. 384
364 CD336 5c Portrait, 1926 .15 .15
365 CD336 33c With Princess Anne .52 .52
366 CD336 50c Photograph by N. Parkinson .80 .80
367 CD336 90c Holding Prince Henry 1.65 1.65
 Nos. 364-367 (4) 3.12 3.12

Souvenir Sheet
368 CD336 $1 With Princess Anne, Ascot Races 2.25 2.25

Intl. Youth Year — A84

Children's drawings.

1985, July 9   Litho.   Perf. 13½x14
369 A84 33c Swimming .75 .75
370 A84 50c Nature walk 1.25 1.25

Girl, Prize-winning Cow — A85

Designs: 90c, Embroidery, jam-making, baking, animal husbandry.

1985, Sept. 10   Litho.   Perf. 13½x14
371 A85 80c multicolored 1.15 1.15
372 A85 90c multicolored 1.25 1.25
 a. Souvenir sheet of 2, #371-372 3.25 3.25

Royal Norfolk Island Agricultural & Horticultural Show, 125th anniv.

Christmas — A86

1985, Oct. 3   Perf. 13½
373 A86 27c Three Shepherds .45 .45
374 A86 33c Journey to Bethlehem .60 .60
375 A86 50c Three Wise Men .80 .80
376 A86 90c Nativity 1.65 1.65
 Nos. 373-376 (4) 3.50 3.50

Marine Life — A87

1986, Jan. 14   Perf. 13½x14
377 A87 5c Long-spined sea urchin .15 .15
378 A87 33c Blue starfish .75 .75
379 A87 55c Eagle ray 1.25 1.25
380 A87 75c Moray eel 1.75 1.75
 a. Souvenir sheet of 4, #377-380 4.00 4.00
 Nos. 377-380 (4) 3.90 3.90

Halley's Comet — A88

Designs: a, Giotto space probe. b, Comet.

1986, Mar. 11   Perf. 15
381 Pair 4.00 4.00
 a.-b. A88 $1 any single 2.00 2.00

Se-tenant in continuous design.

AMERIPEX '86 — A89

Designs: 33c, Isaac Robinson, US consul in Norfolk, 1887-1908, vert. 50c, Ford Model-T. 80c, Statue of Liberty.

1986, May 22   Litho.   Perf. 13½
382 A89 33c multicolored .60 .60
383 A89 50c multicolored .90 .90
384 A89 80c multicolored 1.50 1.50
 a. Souvenir sheet of #382-384 3.25 3.25
 Nos. 382-384 (3) 3.00 3.00

Queen Elizabeth II, 60th Birthday — A90

Various portraits.

1986, June 12
385 A90 5c As Princess .15 .15
386 A90 33c Contemporary photograph .65 .65
387 A90 80c Opening N.I. Golf Club 1.40 1.40
388 A90 90c With Prince Philip 1.75 1.75
 Nos. 385-388 (4) 3.95 3.95

Christmas A91

1986, Sept. 23   Litho.   Perf. 13½x14
389 A91 30c multicolored .50 .50
390 A91 40c multicolored .65 .65
391 A91 $1 multicolored 1.60 1.60
 Nos. 389-391 (3) 2.75 2.75

Commission of Gov. Phillip, Bicent. — A92

1986   Litho.   Perf. 14x13½
392 A92 36c British prison, 1787 .55 .55
393 A92 55c Transportation, Court of Assize .85 .85
394 A92 90c Gov. meeting Home Society 1.40 1.40

395 A92 90c Gov. meeting Home Secretary 1.40 1.40
396 A92 $1 Gov. Phillip, 1738-1814 1.50 1.50
 Nos. 392-396 (5) 5.70 5.70

No. 395 was issued because No. 394 is incorrectly inscribed.
 Issued: #395, Dec. 16; others, Oct. 14.
 See #417-420, 426-436.

Commission of Gov. Phillip, Bicent. — A93

1986, Dec. 16   Perf. 13½
397 A93 36c Maori chief .55 .55
398 A93 36c Bananas, taro .55 .55
399 A93 36c Stone tools .55 .55
400 A93 36c Polynesian outrigger .55 .55
 Nos. 397-400 (4) 2.20 2.20

Pre-European occupation of the Island.

Island Scenery — A94   — A96

1987-88   Litho.   Perf. 13½
401 A94 1c Cockpit Creek Bridge .15 .15
402 A94 2c Cemetery Bay Beach .15 .15
403 A94 3c Guesthouse .15 .15
404 A94 5c Philip Island from Point Ross .15 .15
405 A94 15c Cattle grazing .20 .20
406 A94 30c Rock fishing .40 .40
407 A94 37c Old home .50 .50
408 A94 40c Shopping center .50 .50
409 A94 50c Emily Bay .65 .65
410 A94 60c Bloody Bridge .80 .80
411 A94 80c Pitcairner-style shop 1.10 1.10
412 A94 90c Government House 1.25 1.25
413 A94 $1 Melanesian Memorial Chapel 1.40 1.40
414 A94 $2 Kingston convict settlement 2.00 2.00
415 A94 $3 Ball Bay 4.00 4.00
416 A94 $5 Northerly cliffs 10.00 10.00
 Nos. 401-416 (16) 23.40 23.40

Issue dates: 5c, 50c, 90c, $1, Feb. 17. 30c, 40c, 80c, $2, Apr. 17. 15c, 37c, 60c, $3, July 27. 1c, 2c, 3c, $5, May 17, 1988.

Bicentennial Type of 1986

Designs: 5c, Loading supplies at Deptford, England, 1787. No. 418, First Fleet sailing from Spithead (buoy in water). No. 419, Sailing from Spithead (ship flying British merchant flag). $1, Convicts below deck.

1987, May 13   Litho.   Perf. 14x13½
417 A92 5c multicolored .15 .15
418 A92 55c multicolored .65 .65
419 A92 55c multicolored .65 .65
 a. Pair, #418-419 1.30 1.30
420 A92 $1 multicolored 1.25 1.25
 Nos. 417-420 (4) 2.70 2.70

No. 419a has a continuous design.

1987, Sept. 16   Unwmk.

World Wildlife Fund: Green parrot.
421 Strip of 4 3.00 3.00
 a. A96 5c Parrot facing right .15 .15
 b. A96 15c Parrot, chick, egg .40 .40
 c. A96 36c Parrots .95 .95
 d. A96 55c Parrot facing left 1.50 1.50

Christmas A97

Children's party: 30c, Norfolk Island pine tree, restored convicts' settlement. 42c, Santa Claus, children opening packages. 58c, Santa, children, gifts in fire engine. 63c, Meal.

Perf. 13½x14

1987, Oct. 13 Litho. Wmk. 384

422 A97 30c multicolored .45 .45
423 A97 42c multicolored .65 .65
424 A97 58c multicolored .85 .85
425 A97 63c multicolored .95 .95
Nos. 422-425 (4) 2.90 2.90

Bicentennial Type of 1986

Designs: 5c, Lt. Philip Gidley King. No. 427, La Perouse and Louis XVI of France. No. 428, Gov. Phillip sailing in ship's cutter from Botany Bay to Port Jackson. No. 429, Flag raising on Norfolk Is. 55c, Lt. King and search party exploring the island. 70c, Landfall, Sydney Bay. No. 432, L'Astrolabe and La Boussole off coast of Norfolk. No. 433, HMS Supply. No. 434, Wrecking of L'Astrolabe off the Solomon Isls. No. 435, First Fleet landing at Sydney Cove. No. 436, First settlement, Sydney Bay, 1788.

1987-88 Litho. *Perf. 14x13½*

426 A92 5c multicolored .15 .15
427 A92 37c multicolored .52 .52
428 A92 37c multicolored .52 .52
429 A92 37c multicolored .52 .52
430 A92 55c multicolored .80 .80
431 A92 70c multicolored 1.00 1.00
432 A92 90c multicolored 1.25 1.25
433 A92 90c multicolored 1.25 1.25
434 A92 $1 multicolored 1.50 1.50
435 A92 $1 multicolored 1.50 1.50
436 A92 $1 multicolored 1.50 1.50
Nos. 426-436 (11) 10.51 10.51

Visit of Jean La Perouse (1741-88), French navigator, to Norfolk Is. (Nos. 427, 432, 434); arrival of the First Fleet at Sydney Cove (Nos. 428, 435); founding of Norfolk Is. (Nos. 426, 429-431, 433, 436).

Issued: #427, 432, 434, Dec. 8, 1987; #428, 435, Jan. 25, 1988; others, Mar. 4, 1988.

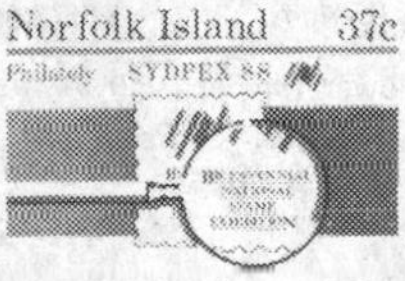

SYDPEX '88, July 30-Aug. 7
A98

Sydney-Norfolk transportation and communication links.

Perf. 14x13½ 13½x14

1988, July 30 Litho.

437 A98 37c Air and sea transports, vert. .62 .62
438 A98 37c shown .62 .62
439 A98 37c Telecommunications, vert. .62 .62
a. Souvenir sheet of 3, #437-439 1.90 1.90
Nos. 437-439 (3) 1.86 1.86

No. 438 exists perf. 13½ within No. 439a.

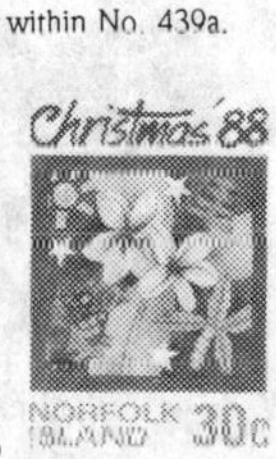

Christmas — A99

1988, Sept. 27 Litho. *Perf. 14x13½*

440 A99 30c shown .48 .48
441 A99 42c Flowers, diff. .68 .68
442 A99 58c Trees, fish .95 .95
443 A99 63c Trees, sailboats 1.00 1.00
Nos. 440-443 (4) 3.11 3.11

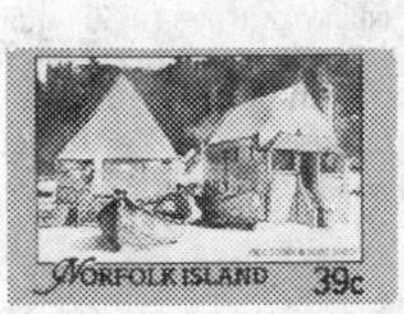

Convict Era Georgian Architecture, c. 1825-1850
A100

Designs: 39c, Waterfront shop and boat shed. 55c, Royal Engineers' Building. 90c, Old military barracks. $1, Commissary and new barracks.

1988, Dec. 6 Litho. *Perf. 13½x14*

444 A100 39c multicolored .62 .62
445 A100 55c multicolored .88 .88
446 A100 90c multicolored 1.40 1.40
447 A100 $1 multicolored 1.60 1.60
Nos. 444-447 (4) 4.50 4.50

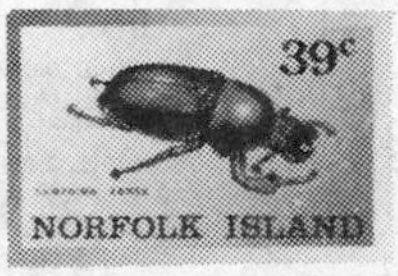

Indigenous Insects
A101

Perf. 13½x14

1989, Feb. 14 Litho. Unwmk.

448 A101 39c *Lamprima aenea* .68 .68
449 A101 55c *Insulascirtus nythos* .95 .95
450 A101 90c *Caedicia araucariae* 1.50 1.50
451 A101 $1 *Thrincophora aridela* 1.70 1.70
Nos. 448-451 (4) 4.83 4.83

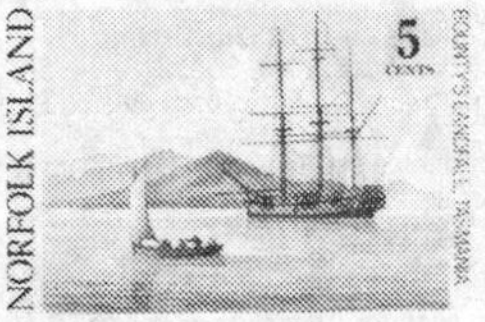

Mutiny on the Bounty
A102

Designs: 5c, *Bounty's* landfall, Adventure Bay, Tasmania. 39c, Mutineers and Polynesian maidens, c. 1790. 55c, Cumbria, Christian's home county. $1.10, Capt. Bligh and crewmen cast adrift.

Perf. 13½

1989, Apr. 28 Litho. Unwmk.

452 A102 5c multicolored .15 .15
453 A102 39c multicolored .70 .70
454 A102 55c multicolored 1.00 1.00
455 A102 $1.10 multicolored 1.75 1.75
Nos. 452-455 (4) 3.60 3.60

Souvenir Sheet

456 Sheet of 3 + label (#453, 456a-456b) 4.00 4.00
a. A102 90c Isle of Man No. 393 1.55 1.55
b. A102 $1 Pitcairn Isls. No. 321d 1.75 1.75

See Isle of Man Nos. 389-394 and Pitcairn Isls. Nos. 320-322.

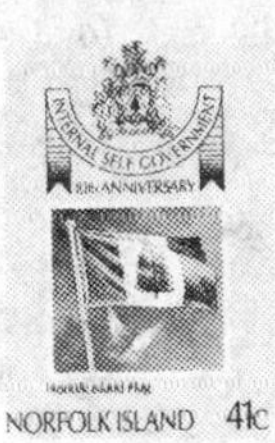

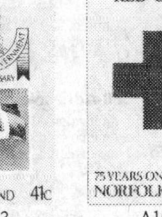

A103

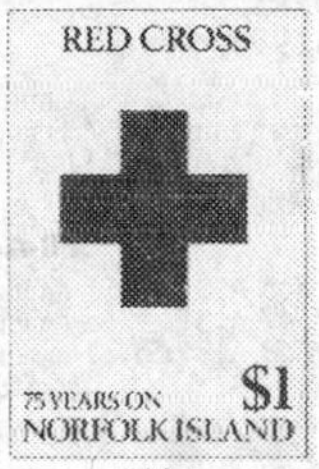

A104

Perf. 14x13½

1989, Aug. 10 Litho. Unwmk.

457 A103 41c Flag .62 .62
458 A103 55c Ballot box .85 .85
459 A103 $1 Norfolk Is. Act of 1979 1.50 1.50
460 A103 $1.10 Norfolk Is. crest 1.65 1.65
Nos. 457-460 (4) 4.62 4.62

Self-Government, 10th anniv.

Perf. 13½x13

1989, Sept. 25 Litho. Unwmk.

461 A104 $1 dark ultra & dark red 1.50 1.50

Natl. Red Cross, 75th anniv.

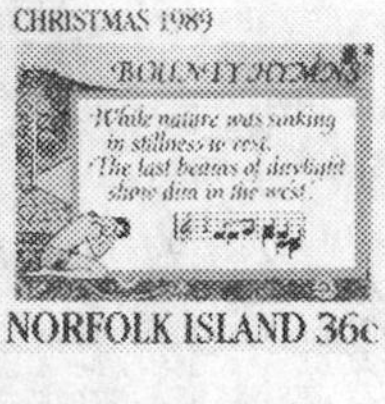

Bounty Hymns — A105

Designs: 36c, "While nature was sinking in stillness to rest, The last beams of daylight show dim in the west." 60c, "There's a land that is fairer than day, And by faith we can see it afar." 75c, "Let the lower lights be burning, Send a gleam across the wave." 80c, "Oh, have you not heard of that beautiful stream That flows through our father's lands."

1989, Oct. 9 *Perf. 13½x14*

462 A105 36c multicolored .55 .55
463 A105 60c multicolored .95 .95
464 A105 75c multicolored 1.20 1.20
465 A105 80c multicolored 1.25 1.25
Nos. 462-465 (4) 3.95 3.95

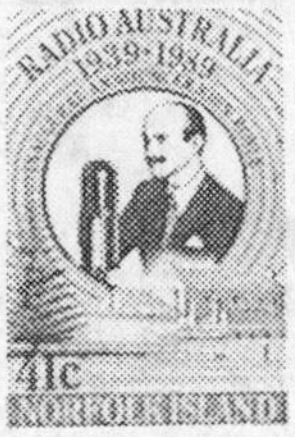

A106

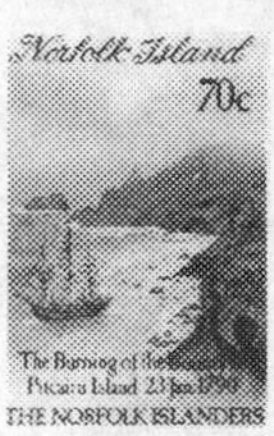

A107

1989, Nov. 21 *Perf. 14x13½*

466 A106 41c Announcer John Royle .65 .65
467 A106 65c Sound waves on map 1.00 1.00
468 A106 $1.10 Jacko, the laughing kookaburra 1.75 1.75
Nos. 466-468 (3) 3.40 3.40

Radio Australia, 50th anniv.

Perf. 15x14½

1990, Jan. 23 Litho. Unwmk.

Settlement of Pitcairn (The Norfolk Islanders): 70c, The *Bounty* on fire. $1.10, Armorial ensign of Norfolk.

469 A107 70c multicolored 1.10 1.10
470 A107 $1.10 multicolored 1.75 1.75

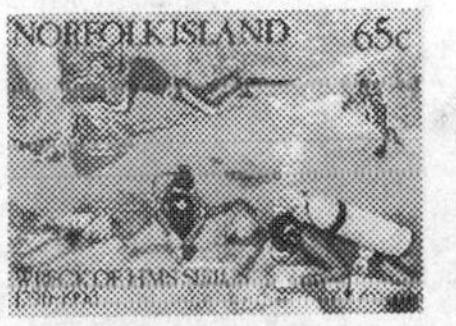

Salvage Team at Work
A108

Designs: No. 471, HMS *Sirius* striking reef. No. 472, HMS *Supply* clearing reef. $1, Map of salvage sites, artifacts.

1990, Mar. 19 *Perf. 14x13½*
Size of Nos. 471-472: 40x27

471 A108 41c multicolored .65 .65
472 A108 41c multicolored .65 .65
a. Pair, #471-472 1.30 1.30
473 A108 65c shown 1.00 1.00
474 A108 $1 multicolored 1.55 1.55
Nos. 471-474 (4) 3.85 3.85

Wreck of HMS *Sirius*, 200th anniv. No. 472a has continuous design.

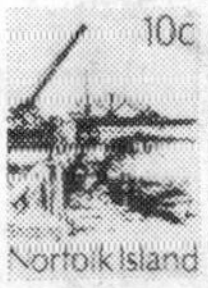

Lightering Cargo Ashore, Kingston
A109

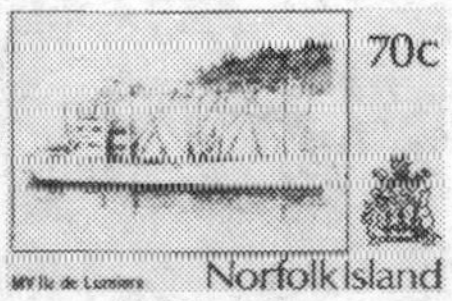

MV Ile de Lumiere
A110

1990-91 Litho. *Perf. 14x14½*

479 A109 5c like #480 .15 .15
480 A109 10c shown .15 .15

Perf. 14½

481 A110 45c La Dunkerquoise .65 .65
482 A110 50c Dmitri Mendeleev .78 .78
483 A110 65c Pacific Rover 1.00 1.00
484 A110 70c shown 1.10 1.10
485 A110 75c Norfolk Trader 1.15 1.15
486 A110 80c Roseville 1.25 1.25
487 A110 90c Kalia 1.40 1.40
488 A110 $1 HMS Bounty 1.55 1.55
489 A110 $2 HMAS Success 3.05 3.05
490 A110 $5 HMAS Whyalia 7.75 7.75
Nos. 479-490 (12) 19.98 19.98

Issued: 5c, 10c, 70c, $2, 7/17/90; 45c, 50c, 65c, $5, 2/19/91; 75c, 80c, 90c, $1, 8/13/91.

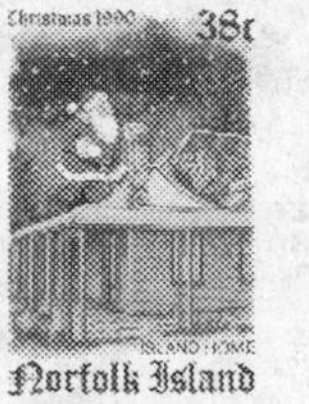

Christmas — A111

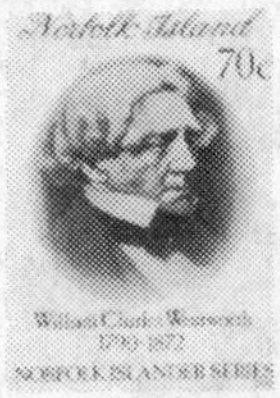

A112

1990, Sept. 25 Litho. *Perf. 14½*

491 A111 38c Island home .60 .60
492 A111 43c New post office .68 .68
493 A111 65c Sydney Bay, Kingston, horiz. 1.00 1.00
494 A111 85c Officers' Quarters, 1836, horiz. 1.35 1.35
Nos. 491-494 (4) 3.63 3.63

1990, Oct. 11 Litho. *Perf. 15x14½*

Designs: 70c, William Charles Wentworth (1790-1872), Australian politician. $1.20, Thursday October Christian (1790-1831).

495 A112 70c brown 1.15 1.15
496 A112 $1.20 brown 2.00 2.00

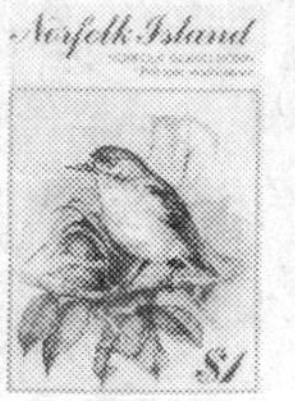

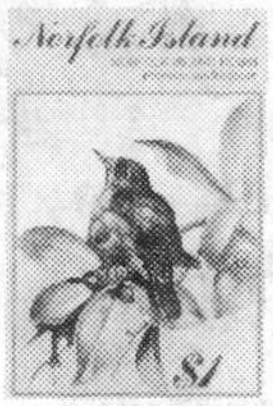

Norfolk Island Robin
A113 A114

1990, Dec. 3 Litho. *Perf. 14½*

497 A113 65c multicolored .90 .90
498 A113 $1 shown 1.40 1.40
499 A113 $1.20 multi, diff. 1.70 1.70
Nos. 497-499 (3) 4.00 4.00

Souvenir Sheet

500 Sheet of 2 2.80 2.80
a. A114 $1 shown 1.40 1.40
b. A114 $1 Two robins 1.40 1.40

Birdpex '90, 20th Intl. Ornithological Congress, New Zealand.

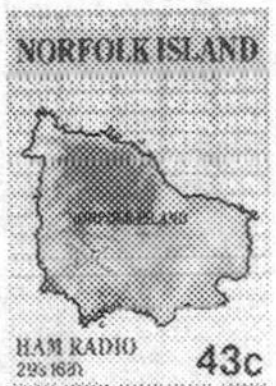

Ham Radio — A115

1991, Apr. 9 Litho. *Perf. 14½*

501 A115 43c Island map .65 .65
502 A115 $1 World map 1.55 1.55
503 A115 $1.20 Regional location 1.85 1.85
Nos. 501-503 (3) 4.05 4.05

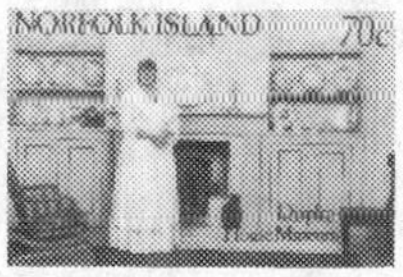

Museum Displays
A116

1991, May 16 Litho. *Perf. 14½*

504 A116 43c Ship's bow, Sirius Museum, vert. .65 .65
505 A116 70c House Museum 1.10 1.10
506 A116 $1 Carronade, Sirius Museum 1.55 1.55
507 A116 $1.20 Pottery, Archaeology Museum, vert. 1.85 1.85
Nos. 504-507 (4) 5.15 5.15

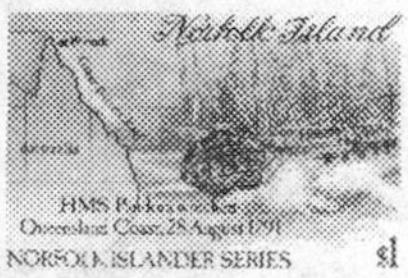

Wreck of HMS Pandora, Aug. 28, 1791 — A117

Design: $1.20, HMS Pandora searching for Bounty mutineers.

1991, July 2 Litho. *Perf. 13½x14*

508 A117 $1 shown 1.55 1.55
509 A117 $1.20 multicolored 1.85 1.85

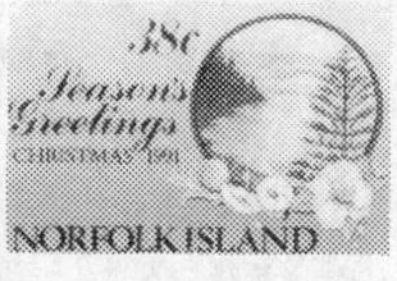

Christmas
A118

1991, Sept. 23 Litho. *Perf. 14½*
510 A118 38c multicolored .58 .58
511 A118 43c multicolored .65 .65
512 A118 65c multicolored 1.00 1.00
513 A118 85c multicolored 1.30 1.30
Nos. 510-513 (4) 3.53 3.53

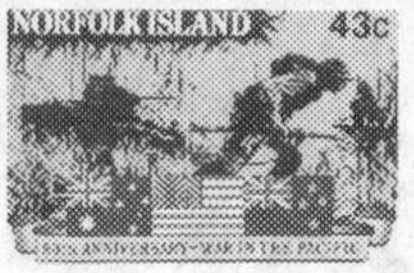

Start of World War II in the Pacific, 50th Anniv. A119

1991, Dec. 9 Litho. *Perf. 14½*
514 A119 43c Tank and soldier .65 .65
515 A119 70c B-17 1.05 1.05
516 A119 $1 War ships 1.50 1.50
Nos. 514-516 (3) 3.20 3.20

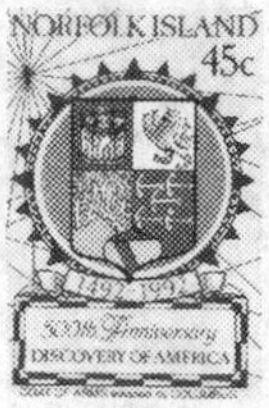

A120

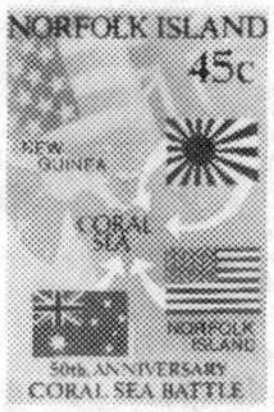

A121

1992, Feb. 11 Litho. *Perf. 14½*
517 A120 45c Columbus' Coat of Arms .65 .65
518 A120 $1.05 Santa Maria 1.60 1.60
519 A120 $1.20 Columbus at globe 1.85 1.85
Nos. 517-519 (3) 4.10 4.10

Discovery of America, 500th anniv.

1992, May 4 Litho. *Perf. 14½*

Designs: No. 520, Map of Coral Sea Battle area. No. 521, Battle area, Midway. No. 522, HMAS Australia. No. 523, Catalina PBY5. No. 524, USS Yorktown. No. 525, Dauntless dive bomber.

520 A121 45c multicolored .65 .65
521 A121 45c multicolored .65 .65
522 A121 70c multicolored 1.05 1.05
523 A121 70c multicolored 1.05 1.05
524 A121 $1.05 multicolored 1.60 1.60
525 A121 $1.05 multicolored 1.60 1.60
Nos. 520-525 (6) 6.60 6.60

Battles of the Coral Sea and Midway, 50th anniv.

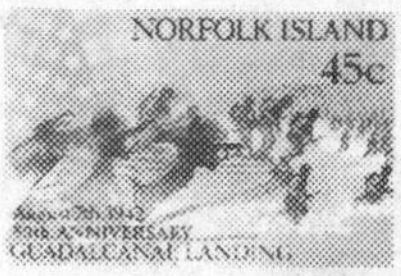

US Invasion of Guadalcanal, 50th Anniv. — A122

Designs: 45c, Troops landing on beach. 70c, Troops in battle. $1.05, Map, flags.

1992, Aug. 6 Litho. *Perf. 14½*
526 A122 45c multicolored .65 .65
527 A122 70c multicolored 1.05 1.05
528 A122 $1.05 multicolored 1.60 1.60
Nos. 526-528 (3) 3.30 3.30

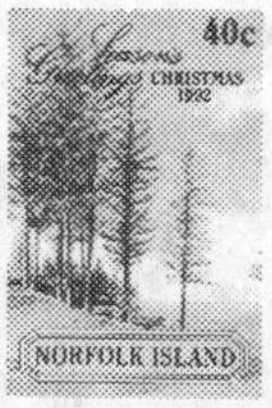

Christmas — A123

Scenes of Norfolk Island: 40c, Ball Bay, looking over Point Blackbourne. 45c, Headstone Creek. 75c, Ball Bay. $1.20, Rocky Point Reserve.

1992, Oct. 29 Litho. *Perf. 15x14½*
529 A123 40c multicolored .60 .60
530 A123 45c multicolored .68 .68
531 A123 75c multicolored 1.10 1.10
532 A123 $1.20 multicolored 1.80 1.80
Nos. 529-532 (4) 4.18 4.18

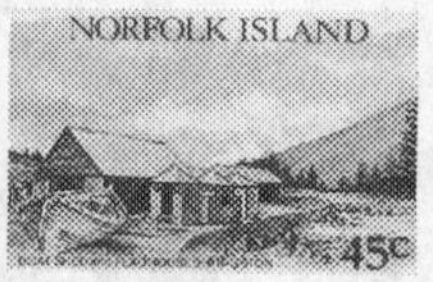

Tourism A124

Tourist sites at Kingston: a, Boat shed, flaghouses. b, Old military barracks. c, All Saints Church. d, Officers quarters. e, Quality row.

1993, Feb. 23 Litho. *Perf. 14½*
533 A124 45c Strip of 5, #a.-e. 3.40 3.40

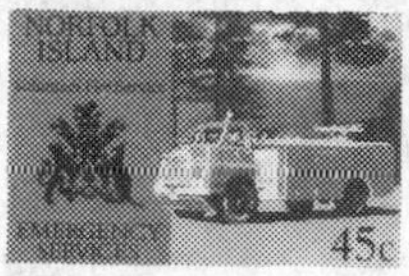

Emergency Services A125

1993, May 18 Litho. *Perf. 14½*
534 A125 45c Volunteer fire service .55 .55
535 A125 70c Rescue squad .90 .90
536 A125 75c St. John ambulance .95 .95
537 A125 $1.20 Police service 1.50 1.50
Nos. 534-537 (4) 3.90 3.90

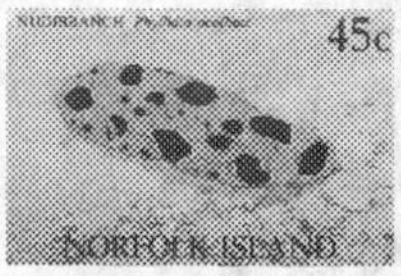

Nudibranchs A126

1993, July 7 Litho. *Perf. 14½*
538 A126 45c Phyllidia ocellata .55 .55
539 A126 45c Glaucus atlanticus .55 .55
540 A126 75c Bornella sp. .95 .95
541 A126 85c Glossodoris rubroannolata 1.10 1.10
542 A126 95c Halgerda willeyi 1.20 1.20
543 A126 $1.05 Chromodoris amoena 1.35 1.35
Nos. 538-543 (6) 5.70 5.70

No. 539 identified as "glauc."

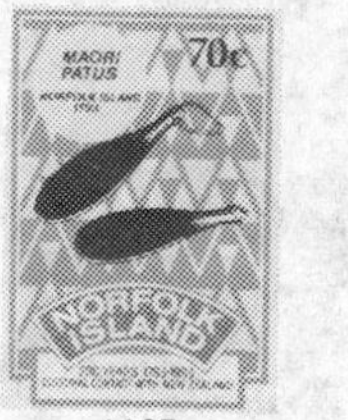

A127

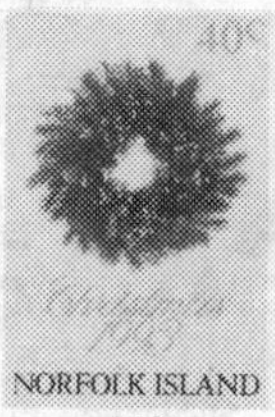

A128

Designs: 70c, Maori patus. $1.20, First Maori map of New Zealand on paper, 1793.

1993, Oct. 28 Litho. *Perf. 14½*
544 A127 70c tan, buff & black .90 .90
545 A127 $1.20 tan, buff & black 1.50 1.50

Cultural contact with New Zealand, bicent.

1993, Oct. 28
546 A128 40c blue & multi .52 .52
547 A128 45c red & multi .58 .58
548 A128 75c green & multi 1.00 1.00
549 A128 $1.20 black & multi 1.50 1.50
Nos. 546-549 (4) 3.60 3.60

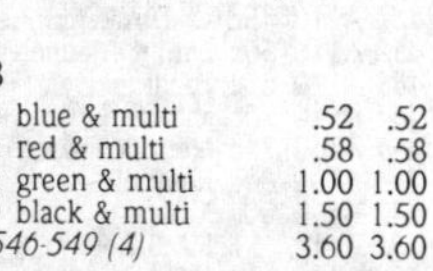

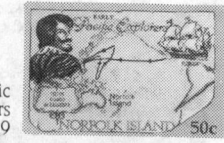

Early Pacific Explorers A129

Explorer, ship: 5c, Vasco Nunez de Balboa, Barbara. 10c, Ferdinand Magellan, Victoria. 20c, Juan Sebastian de Elcano, Victoria. 50c, Alvaro de Saavedra, Florida. 70c, Ruy Lopez de Villalobos, San Juan. 75c, Miguel Lopez de Legaspi, San Lesmes. 80c, Sir Frances Drake, Golden Hinde. 85c, Alvaro de Mendana, Santiago. 90c, Pedro Fernandes de Quiros, San Pedro Paulo. $1, Luis Baez de Torres, San Perico. $2, Abel Tasman, Heemskerk. $5, William Dampier, Cygnet. No. 562, Golden Hinde (Francis Drake).

1994 Litho. *Perf. 14½*
550 A129 5c multicolored .15 .15
551 A129 10c multicolored .15 .15
552 A129 20c multicolored .28 .28
554 A129 50c multicolored .65 .65
556 A129 70c multicolored .90 .90
557 A129 75c multicolored 1.00 1.00
558 A129 80c multicolored 1.10 1.10
559 A129 85c multicolored 1.25 1.25
560 A129 90c multicolored 1.25 1.25
560A A129 $1 multicolored 1.40 1.40
561 A129 $2 multicolored 2.50 2.50
561A A129 $5 multicolored 6.75 6.75
Nos. 550-561A (12) 17.38 17.38

Souvenir Sheet
Perf. 13
562 A129 $1.20 multicolored 1.50 1.50

No. 562 contains one 32x52mm stamp.
Issued: 50c, 70c, 75c, $2, No. 562, 2/8/94; 5c, 10c, 20c, $5, 5/3/94. 80c, 85c, 90c, $1, 7/26/94.
This is an expanding set. Numbers may change.

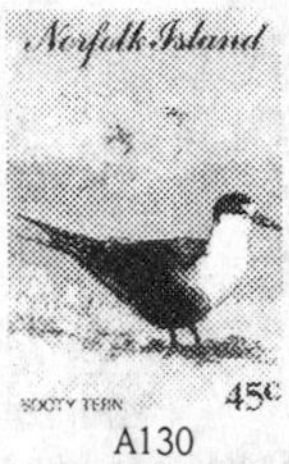

A130

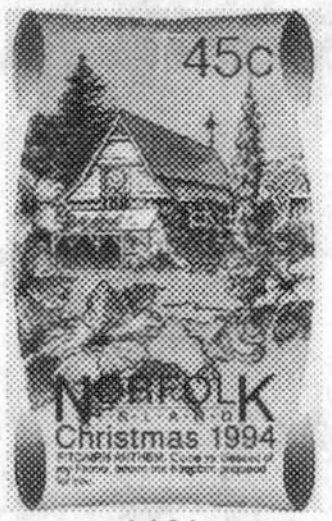

A131

Seabirds: a, Sooty tern. b, Red-tailed tropic bird. c, Australasian gannet. d, Wedge-tail shearwater. e, Masked booby.

1994, Aug. 17 Litho. *Perf. 14½x14*
565 A130 45c Strip of 5, #a.-e. 3.25 3.25
Booklet, 2 #565 6.50

1994, Oct. 27 Litho. *Die Cut*

Christmas: 45c, Church, flowers, words from Pitcairn anthem. 75c, Stained glass windows, "To God be the glory." $1.20, Rainbow, ship, "Ship of Fame."

Self-Adhesive
566 A131 45c multicolored .65 .65
567 A131 75c multicolored 1.10 1.10
568 A131 $1.20 multicolored 1.75 1.75
Nos. 566-568 (3) 3.50 3.50

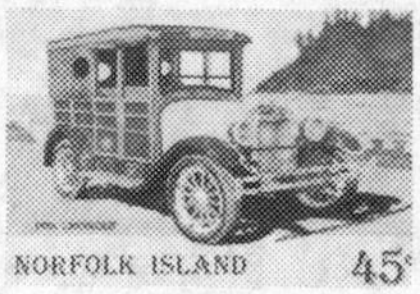

Vintage Cars — A132

1995, Feb. 7 Litho. *Perf. 14x14½*
569 A132 45c 1926 Chevrolet .65 .65
570 A132 75c 1928 Model A Ford 1.10 1.10
571 A132 $1.05 1929 Model A A/C Ford truck 1.50 1.50
572 A132 $1.20 1930 Model A Ford 1.75 1.75
Nos. 569-572 (4) 5.00 5.00

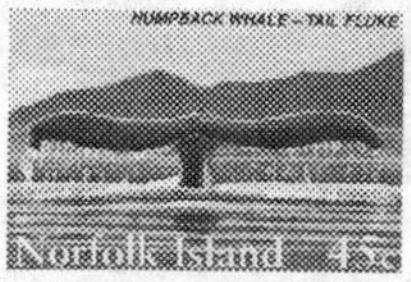

Humpback Whales A133

Perf. 14x14½, 14½x14
1995, May 9 Litho.
573 A133 45c Tail fluke .65 .65
574 A133 75c Mother & calf 1.10 1.10
575 A133 $1.05 Breaching, vert. 1.50 1.50
Nos. 573-575 (3) 3.25 3.25

Souvenir Sheet
Perf. 14x14½
576 A133 $1.20 Bubble netting, vert. 1.75 1.75
a. Overprinted in gold & black 1.75 1.75

No. 576 contains one 30x50mm stamp and is a continuous design.
Overprint in margin of No. 576a has "Selamat Hari Merdeka" and JAKARTA '95 exhibition emblem.

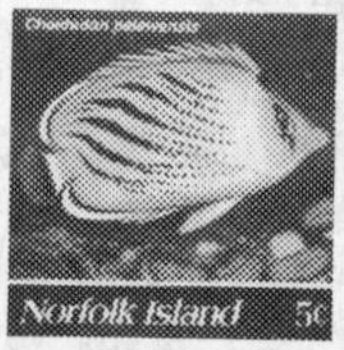

Butterfly Fish — A134

Chaetodon...: 5c, pelewensis. 45c, plebeius. $1.20, tricinctus. $1.50, auriga.

1995, June 15 Litho. *Perf. 14*
577 A134 5c multicolored .15 .15
578 A134 45c multicolored .65 .65
579 A134 $1.20 multicolored 1.75 1.75
580 A134 $1.50 multicolored 2.00 2.00
Nos. 577-580 (4) 4.55 4.55

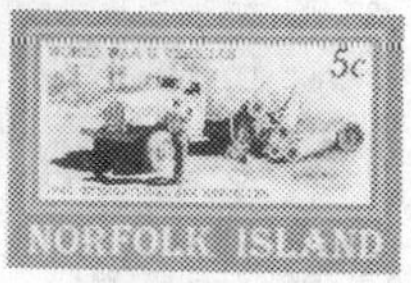

World War II Vehicles A135

Designs: 5c, 1942 Intl. 4x4 refueler. 45c, 1942 Ford 5 passenger sedan. $1.20, 1942 Ford 3-ton tipper. $2, D8 Caterpillar with scraper.

1995, Aug. 8 Litho. *Perf. 14x15*
Black Vignettes
581 A135 5c brown & tan .15 .15
582 A135 45c blue & red lilac .65 .65
583 A135 $1.20 green & orange 1.75 1.75
584 A135 $2 red & gray 3.00 3.00
Nos. 581-584 (4) 5.55 5.55

Island Flower Type of 1960

1995, Sept. 1 Litho. *Rouletted 7*
Booklet Stamps
585 A6 5c like No. 30 .15 .15
a. Booklet pane of 18 + 3 labels 1.35
586 A6 5c like No. 33 .15 .15
a. Booklet pane of 18 + 3 labels 1.35
Complete booklet, 1 each #585a-586a 2.75

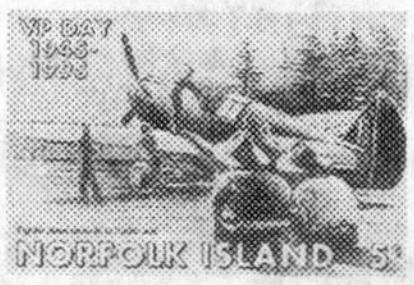

A136

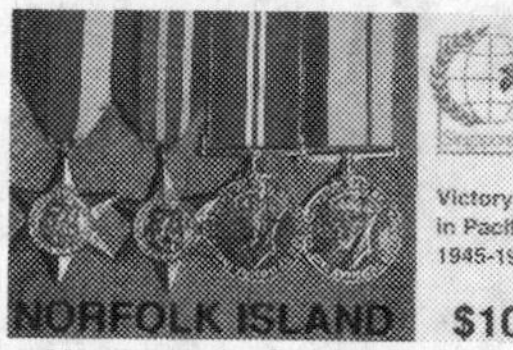

Victory in the Pacific Day, 50th Anniv. — A136a

Designs: 5c, Fighter plane en route. 45c, Sgt. T.C. Derrick, VC, vert. 75c, Gen. MacArthur, vert. $1.05, Girls at victory party.

1995, Sept. 1 Litho. *Perf. 12*
587 A136 5c multicolored .15 .15
588 A136 45c multicolored .65 .65
589 A136 75c multicolored 1.10 1.10
590 A136 $1.05 multicolored 1.50 1.50
Nos. 587-590 (4) 3.40 3.40

Litho. & Embossed
591 A136a $10 Medals 15.00 15.00

Singapore '95.

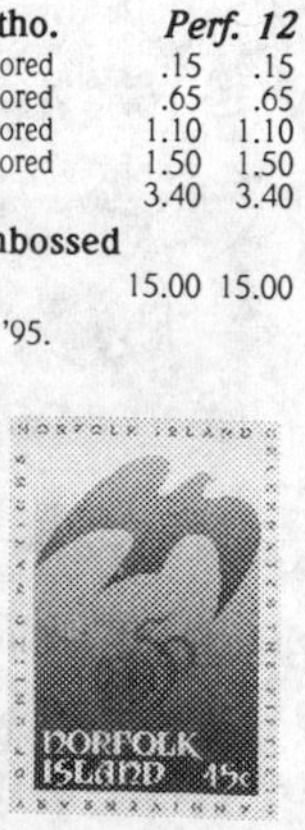

UN, 50th Anniv. — A137

1995, Nov. 7   Litho.   Perf. 14½x14

592	A137	45c Dove	.65	.65
593	A137	75c Christmas star	1.10	1.10
594	A137	$1.05 Christmas candles	1.50	1.50
595	A137	$1.20 Olive branch	1.75	1.75
		Nos. 592-595 (4)	5.00	5.00

Christmas (#593-594).

NORTH BORNEO

'nȯrth 'bȯr–nē–ˌō

LOCATION — Northeast part of island of Borneo, Malay archipelago
GOVT. — Former British colony
AREA — 29,388 sq. mi.
POP. — 470,000 (est. 1962)
CAPITAL — Jesselton

The British North Borneo Company administered North Borneo, under a royal charter granted in 1881, until 1946 when it became a British colony. Labuan (q.v.) became part of the new colony. As "Sabah," North Borneo joined with Singapore, Sarawak and Malaya to form the Federation of Malaysia on Sept. 16, 1963.

100 Cents = 1 Dollar

Quantities of most North Borneo stamps through 1912 have been canceled to order with an oval of bars. Values given for used stamps beginning with No. 6 are for those with this form of cancellation. Stamps from No. 6 through Nos. 159 and J31 that do not exist CTO have used values in italics. Stamps with dated town cancellations sell for much higher prices.

> Catalogue values for unused stamps in this country are for Never Hinged items, beginning with Scott 238.

North Borneo

Coat of Arms — A1

1883-84   Unwmk.   Litho.   Perf. 12

1	A1	2c brown	15.00	45.00
a.		Horiz. pair, imperf. btwn.		
2	A1	4c rose ('84)	24.00	45.00
3	A1	8c green ('84)	47.50	50.00
		Nos. 1-3 (3)	86.50	140.00

For surcharges see Nos. 4, 19-21.

No. 1 Surcharged in Black   EIGHT CENTS

4	A1	8c on 2c brown	350.00	165.00
a.		Double surcharge		4,250.

Coat of Arms with Supporters
A4   A5

Perf. 14

6	A4	50c violet	65.00	12.50
7	A5	$1 red	45.00	9.00

1886   Perf. 14

8	A1	½c magenta	45.00	90.00
9	A1	1c orange	140.00	200.00
a.		Imperf., pair	275.00	
10	A1	2c brown	14.00	14.00
a.		Horiz. pair, imperf. between	425.00	
11	A1	4c rose	15.00	35.00
12	A1	8c green	16.00	35.00
a.		Horiz. pair, imperf. between		

13	A1	10c blue	17.00	35.00
a.		Imperf., pair	275.00	
		Nos. 8-13 (6)	247.00	409.00

Nos. 8, 11, 12 and 13 Surcharged or Overprinted in Black:

and Revenue b

3 CENTS c   **3 CENTS** d

1886

14	A1	(b) ½c magenta	60.00	100.00
15	A1	(c) 3c on 4c rose	55.00	90.00
16	A1	(c) 3c on 4c rose	1,100.	
17	A1	(c) 5c on 8c green	60.00	70.00
a.		Inverted surcharge	2,250.	
18	A1	(b) 10c blue	100.00	175.00

On Nos. 2 and 3   Perf. 12

19	A1	(c) 3c on 4c rose	110.00	200.00
20	A1	(d) 3c on 4c rose	—	
a.		Double surcharge, both types of "3"		
21	A1	(c) 5c on 8c green	110.00	165.00

Common Design Types pictured in section before Great Britain.

British North Borneo

A9

1886   Unwmk.   Litho.   Perf. 12

22	A9	½c lilac rose	100.00	250.00
23	A9	1c orange	82.50	110.00

Perf. 14

25	A9	½c rose	2.00	1.75
a.		½c lilac rose	10.00	
b.		Imperf., pair	12.00	4.00
26	A9	1c orange	.90	1.00
a.		Imperf., pair	10.50	3.00
27	A9	2c brown	1.25	1.25
a.		Imperf., pair	5.50	3.00
b.		Horiz. pair, imperf. between	52.50	
28	A9	4c rose	.90	.90
a.		Cliché of 1c in plate of 4c	165.00	250.00
b.		Imperf., pair	6.00	3.00
c.		As "a," imperf. in pair with #28	2,750.	
29	A9	8c green	2.25	3.50
a.		Imperf., pair	9.50	3.75
30	A9	10c blue	5.25	7.50
a.		Imperf., pair	9.50	5.75
		Nos. 25-30 (6)	12.55	15.90

For surcharges see Nos. 54-55.

A10   A11

A12   A13

31	A10	25c slate blue	85.00	7.75
a.		Imperf., pair	77.50	12.00
32	A11	50c violet	100.00	6.00
a.		Imperf., pair	70.00	8.50
33	A12	$1 red	150.00	7.25
a.		Imperf., pair	85.00	8.50
34	A13	$2 sage green	175.00	16.00
a.		Imperf., pair	100.00	15.00
		Nos. 31-34 (4)	510.00	37.00
		Nos. 22-34 (12)	705.05	412.90

See Nos. 44-47.

A14

1887-92   Perf. 14

35	A14	½c rose	.45	.25
a.		½c magenta	2.50	3.00
36	A14	1c orange	.65	.25
37	A14	2c red brown	1.10	.25
a.		Horiz. pair imperf. between		200.00
38	A14	3c violet	1.90	.25
39	A14	4c rose	2.50	.25
a.		Horiz. pair, imperf. vert.		
40	A14	5c slate	2.00	.25
41	A14	6c lake ('92)	5.25	.25
42	A14	8c green	8.00	.35
a.		Horiz. pair, imperf. between		
43	A14	10c blue	5.25	.35
		Nos. 35-43 (9)	27.10	2.45

Exist imperf. Value $7 each, unused, $4 used.
Forgeries exist, perf. 11½.
For surcharges see Nos. 52-53, 56-57.

Redrawn

25c. The letters of "BRITISH NORTH BORNEO" are 2mm high instead of 1½mm.
50c. The club of the native at left does not touch the frame. The 0's of "50" are flat at top and bottom instead of being oval.
$1.00. The spear of the native at right does not touch the frame. There are 14 pearls at each side of the frame instead of 13.
$2.00. "BRITISH" is 11mm long instead of 12mm. There are only six oars at the side of the dhow.

1888

44	A10	25c slate blue	21.00	.42
b.		Horiz. pair, imperf. between		
c.		Imperf., pair	80.00	2.75
45	A11	50c violet	40.00	.45
a.		Imperf., pair	85.00	3.50
46	A12	$1 red	22.50	.45
a.		Imperf., pair	85.00	3.50
47	A13	$2 sage green	70.00	1.25
a.		Imperf., pair	110.00	4.25
		Nos. 44-47 (4)	153.50	2.57

For surcharges see Nos. 50-51, 58.

A15

A16

1889

48	A15	$5 red violet	92.50	6.00
a.		Imperf., pair	140.00	12.00
49	A16	$10 brown	110.00	8.50
b.		Imperf., pair	250.00	21.00

Two Cents. e   **6 cents.** f

No. 44 Surcharged Type "e" in Red

1890

50	A10	2c on 25c slate blue	35.00	45.00
a.		Inverted surcharge	250.00	275.00
b.		With additional surcharge "2 cents" in black		
51	A10	8c on 25c slate blue	55.00	60.00

Surcharged Type "f" in Black On #42-43

1891-92

52	A14	6c on 8c green	7.00	9.00
a.		"c" of "cents" inverted	300.00	325.00
b.		"cetns"	325.00	400.00
c.		Inverted surcharge	200.00	275.00
53	A14	6c on 10c blue	45.00	9.50

On Nos. 29 and 30

54	A9	6c on 8c green	5,250.	4,500.
55	A9	6c on 10c blue	35.00	9.00
a.		Inverted surcharge	140.00	140.00
b.		Double surcharge	900.00	
c.		Triple surcharge	300.00	

Nos. 39, 40 and 44 Surcharged in Red:

1 cent.   **8 Cents.**

1892

56	A14	1c on 4c rose	8.00	12.00
a.		Double surcharge	325.00	
b.		Surcharged on face & back		400.00
57	A14	1c on 5c slate	3.00	4.75
58	A10	8c on 25c blue	90.00	125.00
		Nos. 56-58 (3)	101.00	141.75

North Borneo

Dyak Chief — A21

Malayan Sambar — A22   Malay Dhow — A26

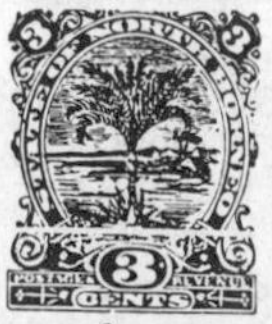
Sago Palm — A23

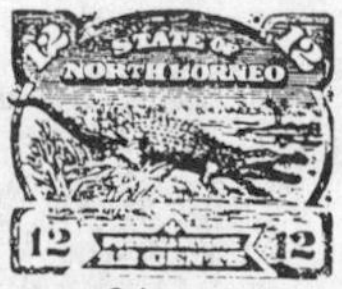
Saltwater Crocodile — A27

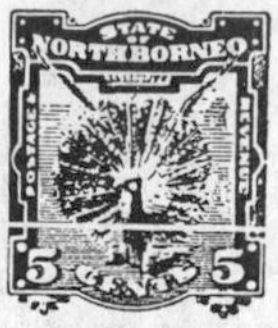
Argus Pheasant — A24

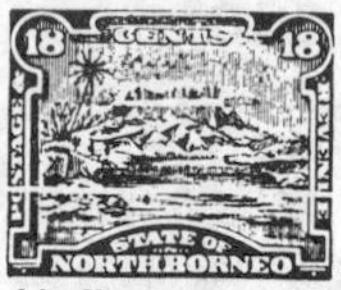
Mt. Kinabalu — A28

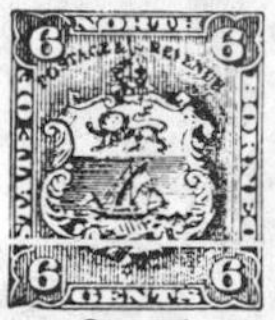
Coat of Arms — A25

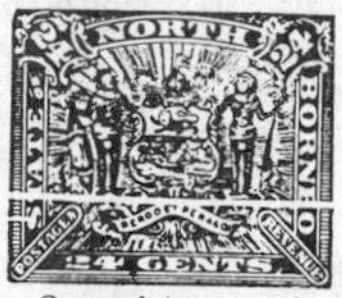
Coat of Arms with Supporters — A29

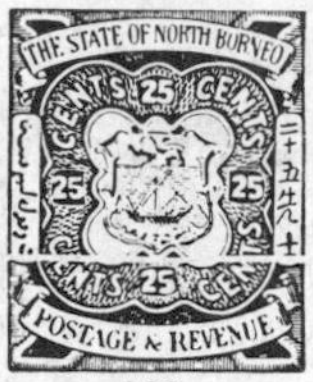
A30

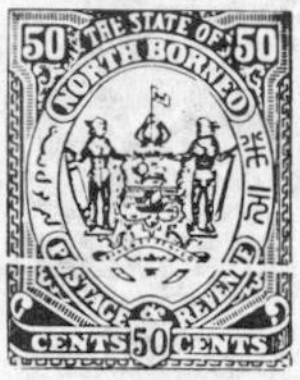
A31

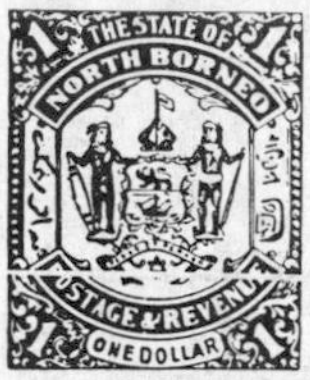
A32

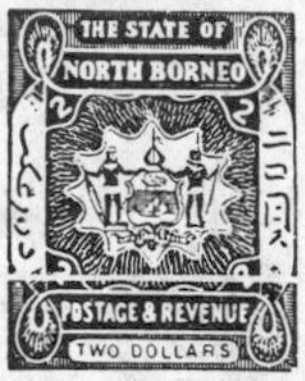
A33

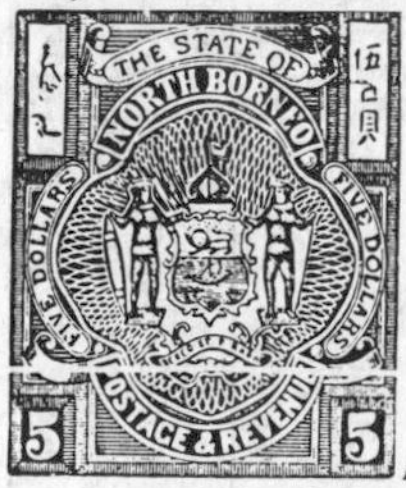
A34

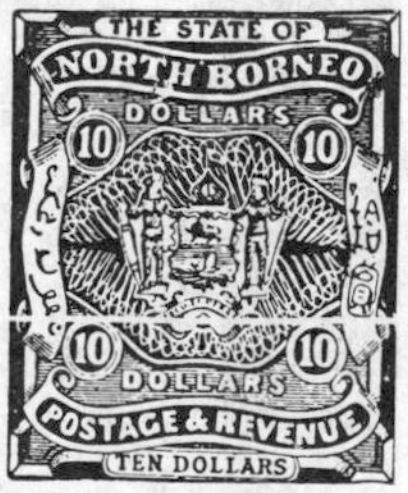
A35

Perf. 12 to 15 and Compound

1894 **Engr.** **Unwmk.**

59 A21 1c bis brown & blk 1.40 .40
a. Vert. pair, imperf. btwn.
60 A22 2c rose & black 4.00 .75
61 A23 3c vio & ol green 4.00 .55
a. Horiz. pair, imperf. btwn. 325.00
62 A24 5c org red & black 3.25 .75
a. Horiz. pair, imperf. btwn. 325.00
63 A25 6c brn ol & blk 3.00 .55
64 A26 8c lilac & black 2.50 .75
a. Vert. pair, imperf. btwn. 325.00 *350.00*
b. Horiz. pair, imperf. btwn. *325.00*
65 A27 12c ultra & black 21.00 1.25
a. 12c blue & black 27.50 1.75
66 A28 18c green & black 15.00 1.75
67 A29 24c claret & blue 17.00 1.75

Litho. *Perf. 14*

68 A30 25c slate blue 15.00 .55
a. Imperf., pair 3.00
69 A31 50c violet 21.00 .60
a. Imperf., pair 3.00
70 A32 $1 red 9.50 .75
a. Perf. 14x11 175.00
b. Imperf., pair 6.00
71 A33 $2 gray green 18.00 .75
a. Imperf., pair 4.50
72 A34 $5 red violet 140.00 4.75
a. Imperf., pair 15.00
73 A35 $10 brown 150.00 6.00
a. Imperf., pair 15.00
Nos. 59-73 (15) 424.65 21.90

For #68-70 in other colors see Labuan #63a-65a.
For surcharges & overprints see #74-78, 91-94, 97-102, 115-119, 130-135, 115-119, 150-151, 158-159.

No. 70 Surcharged in Black

4
CENTS

1895, June

74 A32 4c on $1 red 2.50 1.25
a. Double surcharge 325.00
75 A32 10c on $1 red 5.25 .60
76 A32 20c on $1 red 17.00 .60
77 A32 30c on $1 red 11.00 .75
78 A32 40c on $1 red 12.50 .75
Nos. 74-78 (5) 48.25 3.95

See No. 99.

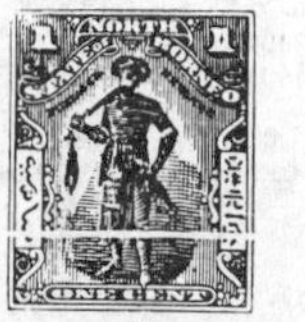
A37

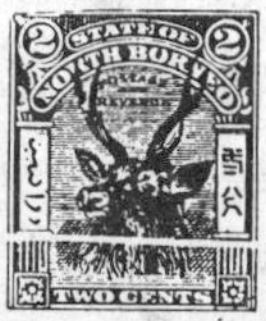
A38

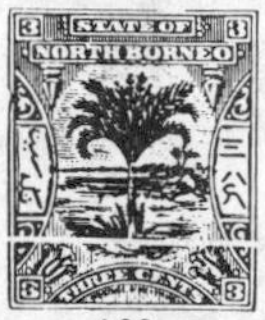
A39

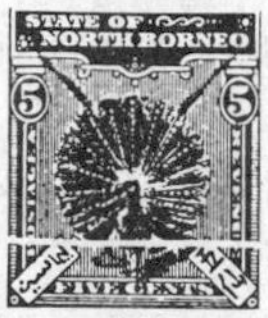
A40

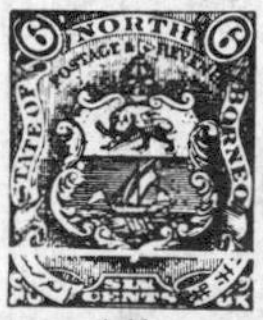
A41

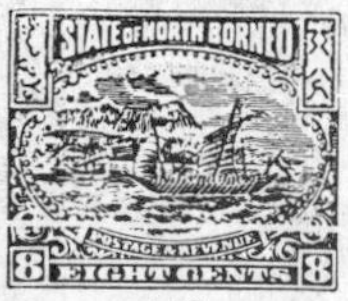
A42

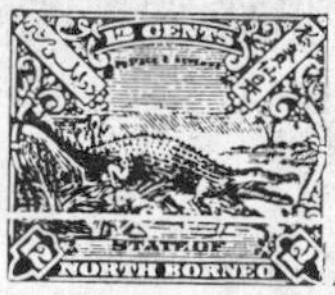
A43

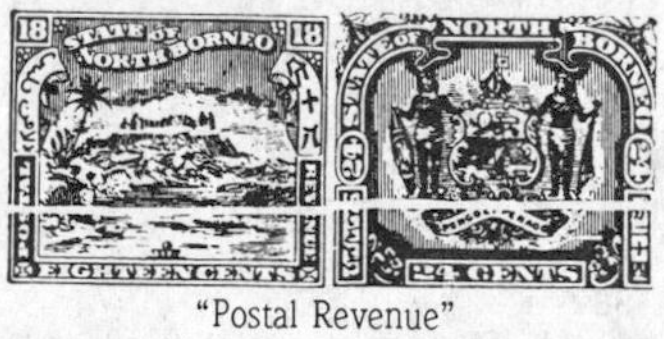
"Postal Revenue"
A44 A45

Perf. 13 to 16 and Compound

1897-1900 **Engr.**

79 A37 1c bis brown & blk 5.00 .55
a. Horiz. pair, imperf. btwn. —
80 A38 2c dp rose & blk 10.00 .55
81 A38 2c green & blk ('00) 15.00 .55
82 A39 3c lilac & ol green 5.00 .55
83 A40 5c orange & black 22.50 .50
84 A41 6c ol brown & blk 15.00 .35
85 A42 8c brn lilac & blk 6.50 .50
86 A43 12c blue & black 80.00 .85
87 A44 18c green & black 12.50 .55
a. Vert. pair, imperf. btwn. *100.00*
88 A45 24c claret & blue 11.00 .85
Nos. 79-88 (10) 182.50 5.80

For overprints see Nos. 105-107, 109-112. For surcharges see Nos. 124-127.

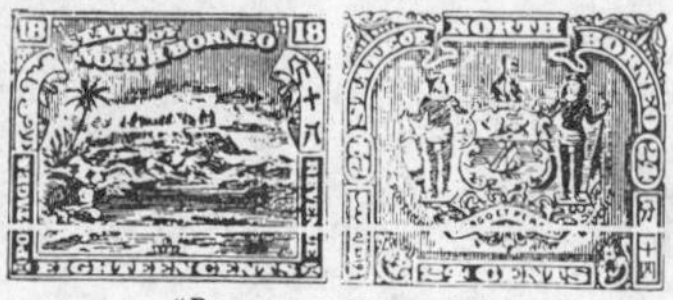
"Postage & Revenue"
A46 A47

1897

89 A46 18c green & black 40.00 .75
90 A47 24c claret & blue 40.00 .75

For surcharges & overprints see #95-96, 128-129, 113-114.

Stamps of 1894-97 Surcharged in Black

4
CENTS

1899

91 A40 4c on 5c orange & blk 10.00 *14.00*
92 A41 4c on 6c ol brn & blk 7.75 *18.00*
93 A42 4c on 8c brn lil & blk 11.00 *13.00*
94 A43 4c on 12c blue & blk 11.00 *18.00*
a. Horiz. or vert. pair, imperf. btwn. 425.00 *500.00*
95 A46 4c on 18c green & blk 11.00 *18.00*
96 A47 4c on 24c cl & blue 11.00 *18.00*
a. Perf. 16 42.50 *50.00*
97 A30 4c on 25c sl blue 7.75 *14.00*
98 A31 4c on 50c violet 11.00 *18.00*
99 A32 4c on $1 red 7.75 *14.00*
100 A33 4c on $2 gray grn 9.00 *19.00*
101 A34 4c on $5 red vio 32.50 *40.00*
a. "CENTS" 8½mm below "4" 11.00 *18.00*
102 A35 4c on $10 brown 32.50 *40.00*
a. "CENTS" 8½mm below "4" 11.00 *18.00*

No. 99 differs from No. 74 in the distance between "4" and "cents" which is 4¾mm on No. 99 and 3¾mm on No. 74.

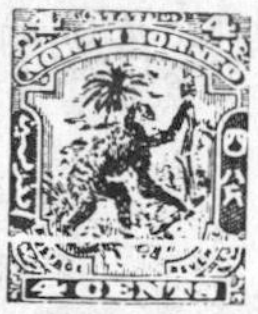
Orangutan — A48

1899-1900 **Engr.**

103 A48 4c green & black 6.25 3.25
104 A48 4c dp rose & blk ('00) 16.00 .55

For overprint see No. 108.

Stamps of 1894-1900 Overprinted in Red, Black, Green or Blue

BRITISH

m

PROTECTORATE.

1901-05

105 A37 1c bis brn & blk (R) 1.90 .25
106 A38 2c green & blk (R) 1.65 .25
107 A39 3c lilac & ol grn (Bk) 1.10 .35
108 A48 4c dp rose & blk (G) 2.25 .35
109 A40 5c org & blk (G) 2.25 .35
110 A41 6c ol brn & blk (R) 2.75 .35
111 A42 8c brown & blk (Bl) 4.00 .35
a. Vert. pair, imperf. btwn.
112 A43 12c blue & blk (R) 27.50 .65
113 A46 18c green & blk (R) 8.50 .65
114 A47 24c red & blue (Bk) 15.00 .65
115 A30 25c slate blue (R) 3.00 .45
a. Inverted overprint 425.00
116 A31 50c violet (R) 7.50 .50
117 A32 $1 red (R) 20.00 3.75
118 A32 $1 red (Bk) 10.00 2.75
a. Double overprint 325.00
119 A33 $2 gray green (R) 32.50 3.25
a. Double overprint 950.00
Nos. 105-119 (15) 139.90 14.90

Nos. 110, 111 and 122 are known without period after "PROTECTORATE."
See Nos. 122-123, 150-151.

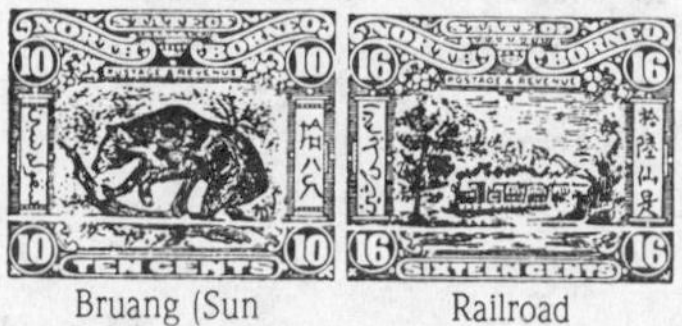
Bruang (Sun Bear) — A49
Railroad Train — A50

1902 **Engr.**

120 A49 10c slate & dk brown 47.50 2.50
a. Vertical pair, imperf. between
121 A50 16c yel brown & grn 80.00 .90

Overprinted type "m" in Red or Black

122 A49 10c sl & dk brn (R) 16.00 .35
a. Double overprint 350.00 275.00
123 A50 16c yel brn & grn (Bk) 55.00 .45
Nos. 120-123 (4) 198.50 4.20

Stamps of 1894-97 Surcharged in Black

4.
cents

1904

124 A40 4c on 5c org & blk 14.00 *22.50*
125 A41 4c on 6c ol brn & blk 4.25 *8.75*
a. Inverted surcharge 250.00 *250.00*
126 A42 4c on 8c brn lil & blk 9.50 *11.00*
a. Inverted surcharge 250.00 *250.00*
127 A43 4c on 12c blue & blk 14.00 *26.00*
128 A46 4c on 18c grn & blk 15.00 *27.50*
129 A47 4c on 24c cl & bl 14.00 *14.00*
130 A30 4c on 25c sl blue 4.50 *4.50*
131 A31 4c on 50c violet 4.50 *5.25*
132 A32 4c on $1 red 5.75 *6.25*
133 A33 4c on $2 gray grn 10.50 *8.75*
134 A34 4c on $5 red vio 11.00 *10.50*
135 A35 4c on $10 brown 11.00 *10.50*
a. Inverted surcharge 1,700.
Nos. 124-135 (12) 118.00 *155.50*

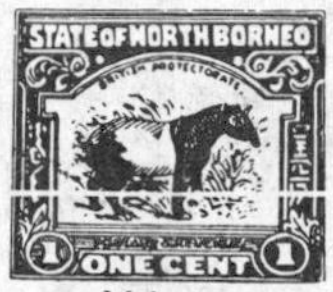
Malayan Tapir — A51

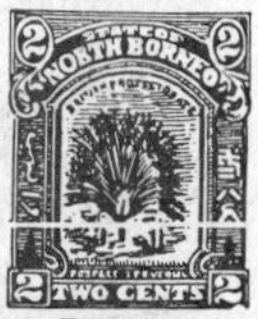
Traveler's Palm — A52

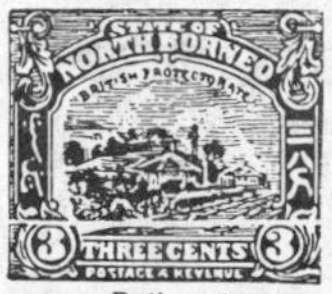
Railroad Station — A53

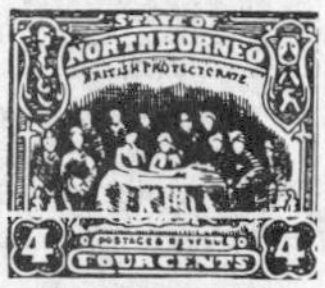
Meeting of the Assembly — A54

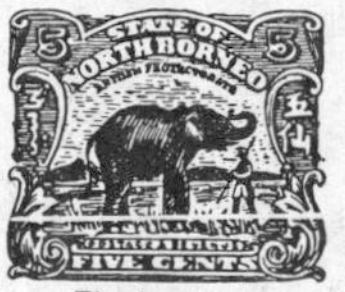
Elephant and Mahout A55

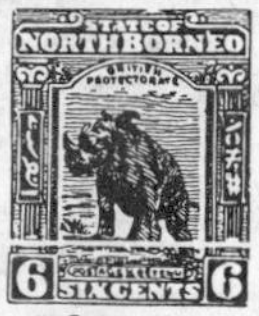
Sumatran Rhinoceros A56

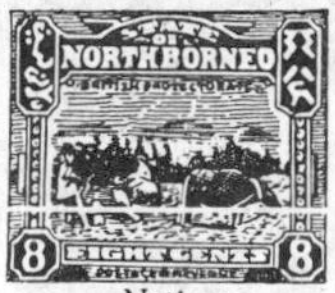
Natives Plowing — A57

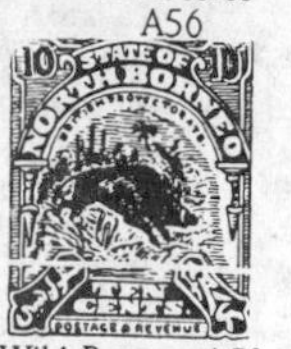
Wild Boar — A58

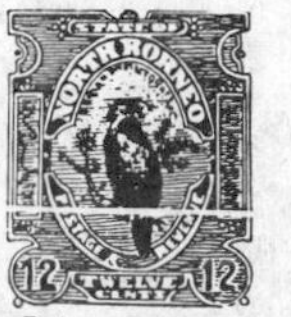
Palm Cockatoo A59

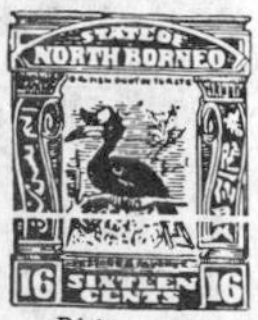
Rhinoceros Hornbill A60

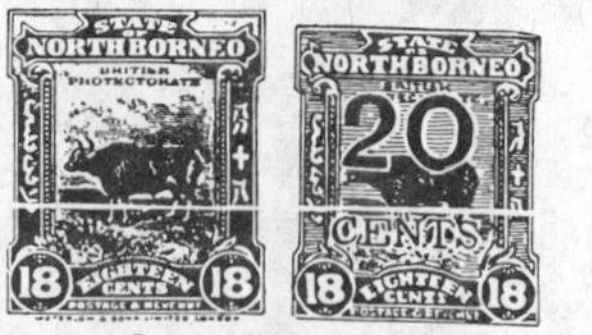
Banteng (Wild Ox)
A61 A62

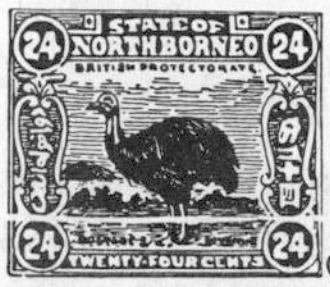
Cassowary — A63

1909-22 Unwmk. Engr. *Perf. 14*
Center in Black

136 A51 1c chocolate	3.00	.15
b. Perf. 13½		
c. Perf. 15	15.00	4.25
137 A52 2c green	.85	.15
b. Perf. 15	3.00	1.50
138 A53 3c deep rose	.95	.30
b. Perf. 15		.75
139 A53 3c green ('22)	8.50	.40
140 A54 4c dull red	1.50	.15
b. Perf. 13½	11.00	10.50
c. Perf. 15	7.50	1.00
141 A55 5c yellow brn	4.00	.30
b. Perf. 15		
142 A56 6c olive green	5.75	.30
b. Perf. 15	19.00	1.00
143 A57 8c rose	3.50	.30
144 A58 10c blue	12.00	.30
b. Perf. 13½		2.50
c. Perf. 15	16.00	6.50
145 A59 12c deep blue	15.00	.75
c. Perf. 15		
146 A60 16c red brown	16.00	1.25
b. Perf. 13½	20.00	6.50
147 A61 18c blue green	45.00	1.25
148 A62 20c on 18c bl grn (R)	3.50	.55
b. Perf. 15	190.00	75.00
149 A63 24c violet	17.50	1.50
Nos. 136-149 (14)	137.05	7.65

Issued: #139, 1922; others, July 1, 1909.
See #167-178. #136a-149a follow #162.
For surcharges and overprints see #160-162, 166, B1-B12, B14-B24, B31-B41.

Nos. 72-73 Overprinted type "m" in Red

1910

150 A34 $5 red violet	100.00	4.50
151 A35 $10 brown	92.50	6.75
a. Double overprint		
b. Inverted overprint		

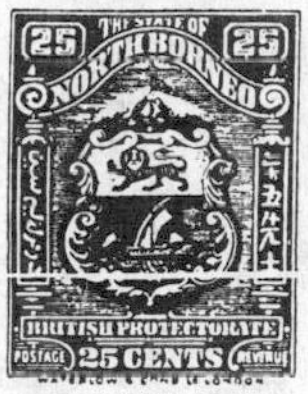
A64

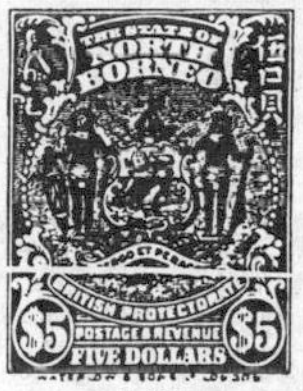
A65

1911 Engr. *Perf. 14*
Center in Black

152 A64 25c yellow green	4.00	1.50
a. Perf. 15	10.00	
b. Imperf., pair	50.00	
153 A64 50c slate blue	7.00	2.25
a. Perf. 15	24.00	8.50
b. Imperf., pair	67.50	
154 A64 $1 brown	14.00	2.25
a. Perf. 15	32.50	6.75
c. Imperf., pair	67.50	
155 A64 $2 dk violet	32.50	12.00
156 A65 $5 claret	57.50	60.00
a. Perf. 13½	82.50	
b. Imperf., pair	100.00	
157 A65 $10 vermilion	135.00	125.00
a. Imperf. pair	100.00	
Nos. 152-157 (6)	250.00	203.00

See #179-184. #152c-153c follow #162.
For overprint and surcharges see Nos. B13, B25-B30, B42-B47.

BRITISH

Nos. 72-73 Overprinted in Red

PROTECTORATE

1912

158 A34 $5 red violet	800.00	9.25
159 A35 $10 brown	1,200.	9.25

Nos. 158 and 159 were prepared for use but not regularly issued.

Nos. 138, 142 and 145 Surcharged in Black or Red

2
cents

1916 Center in Black *Perf. 14*

160 A53 2c on 3c dp rose	10.00	6.50
a. Inverted "S"	87.50	87.50
161 A56 4c on 6c ol grn (R)	10.00	6.50
a. Inverted "S"	100.00	100.00
162 A59 10c on 12c bl (R)	25.00	37.50
a. Inverted "S"	110.00	110.00
Nos. 160-162 (3)	45.00	50.50

Stamps and Types of 1909-11 Overprinted in Red or Blue in Three Lines: "MALAYA-BORNEO EXHIBITION 1922."

1922
Center in Black

136a A51 1c brown	5.50	22.50
137a A52 2c green	1.90	13.00
138a A53 3c deep rose (B)	4.75	18.00
140a A54 4c dull red (B)	2.50	13.00
141a A55 5c yel brown (B)	5.50	22.50
142a A56 6c olive green	4.75	27.50
143a A57 8c rose (B)	4.75	27.50
144a A58 10c gray blue	5.25	35.00
145a A59 12c deep blue	7.50	45.00
146a A60 16c red brown (B)	7.50	50.00
148a A62 20c on 18c bl grn	13.00	57.50
149a A63 24c violet	11.00	55.00
152c A64 25c yel green	11.00	40.00
153c A64 50c slate blue	9.50	45.00
Nos. 136a-153c (14)	94.40	471.50

Industrial fair, Singapore, Mar. 31-Apr. 15, 1922.

THREE

No. 140 Surcharged in Black

CENTS

1923

166 A54 3c on 4c dull red & blk	1.50	1.65
a. Double surcharge		

Types of 1909-22 Issues

1926-28 Engr. *Perf. 12½*
Center in Black

167 A51 1c chocolate	.60	.50
168 A52 2c lake	.40	.40
169 A53 3c green	1.25	.75
170 A54 4c dull red	.40	.25
171 A55 5c yellow brown	3.50	3.50
172 A56 6c yellow green	3.75	.45
173 A57 8c rose	2.25	.30
174 A58 10c bright blue	1.90	.65
175 A59 12c deep blue	5.00	.65
176 A60 16c orange brn	12.50	22.50
177 A62 20c on 18c bl grn (R)	3.50	4.00
178 A63 24c dull violet	35.00	50.00
179 A64 25c yellow grn	5.50	5.50
180 A64 50c slate blue	8.50	12.50
181 A64 $1 brown	30.00	75.00
182 A64 $2 dark violet	50.00	125.00
183 A65 $5 deep rose	85.00	250.00
184 A65 $10 dull vermilion	200.00	350.00
Nos. 167-184 (18)	449.05	901.95

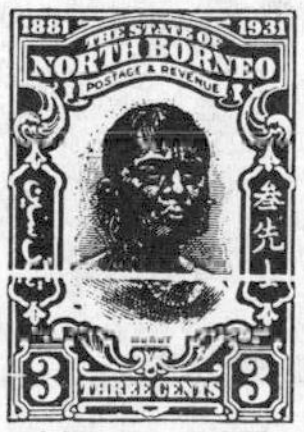
Murut — A66

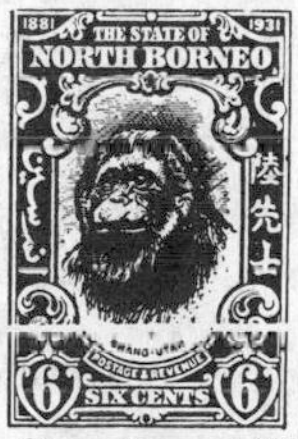
Orangutan — A67

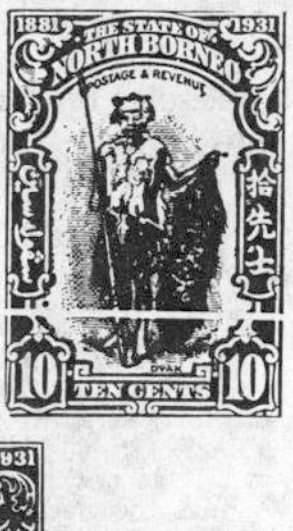
Dyak — A68

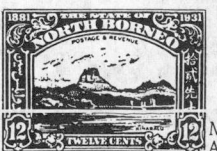

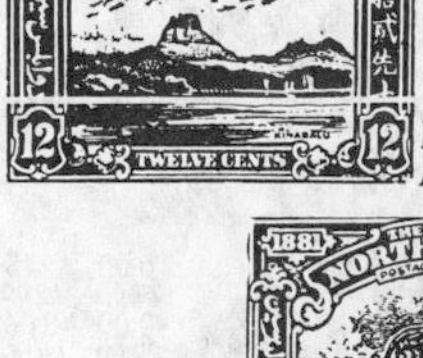
Mt. Kinabalu A69

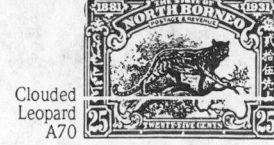

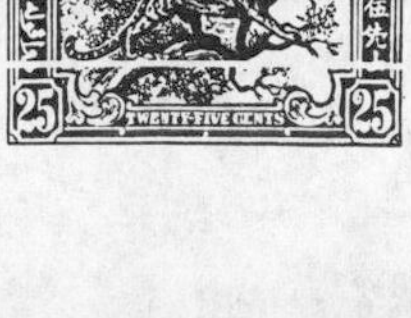
Clouded Leopard A70

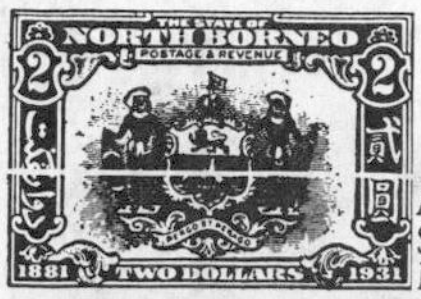
Arms with Supporters and Motto — A72

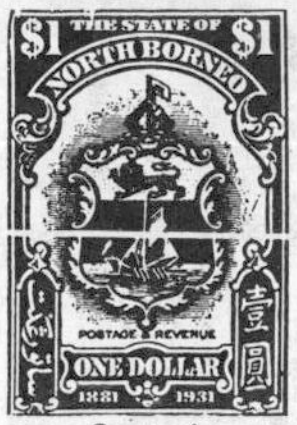
Coat of Arms — A71

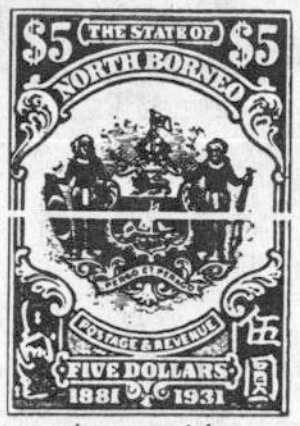
Arms with Supporters — A73

1931, Jan. 1 Engr. *Perf. 12½*
Center in Black

185 A66 3c blue green	1.90	1.50
186 A67 6c orange red	10.50	4.75
187 A68 10c carmine	4.50	6.25
188 A69 12c ultra	3.00	4.00
189 A70 25c deep violet	20.00	22.50
190 A71 $1 yellow green	24.00	30.00
191 A72 $2 red brown	32.50	37.50
192 A73 $5 red violet	77.50	110.00
Nos. 185-192 (8)	173.90	216.50

50th anniv. of the North Borneo Co.

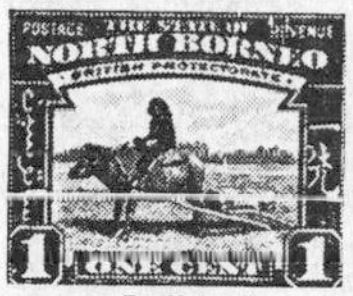
Buffalo Transport — A74

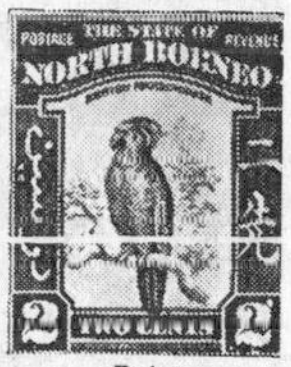
Palm Cockatoo — A75

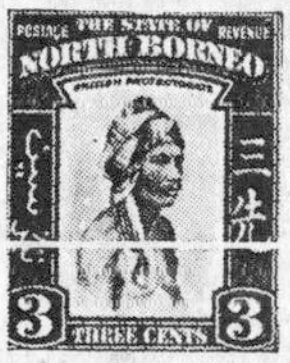
Murut — A76

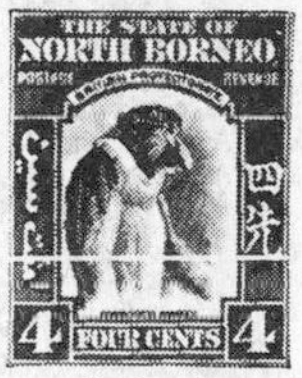
Proboscis Monkey — A77

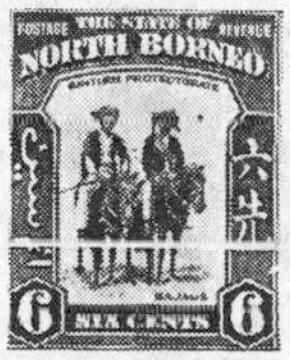
Bajaus — A78

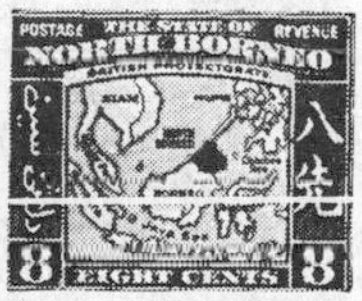
Map of North Borneo and Surrounding Lands — A79

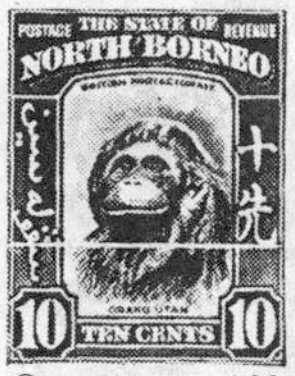
Orangutan — A80

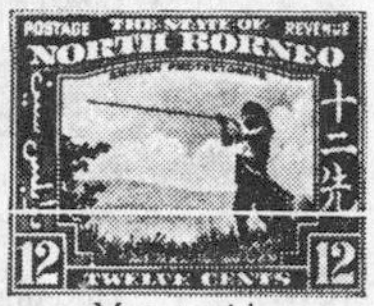
Murut with Blowgun — A81

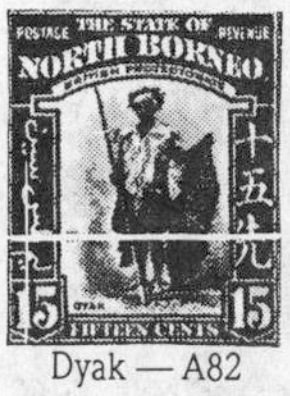
Dyak — A82

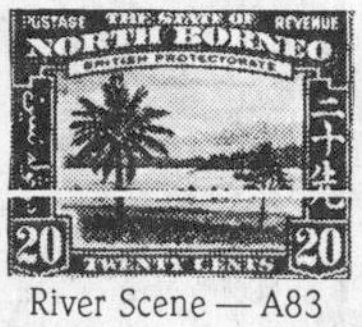
River Scene — A83

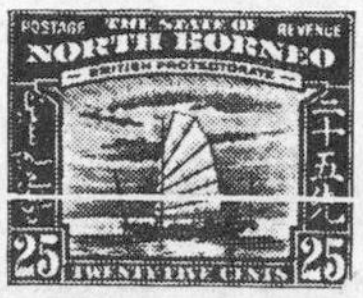
Proa — A84

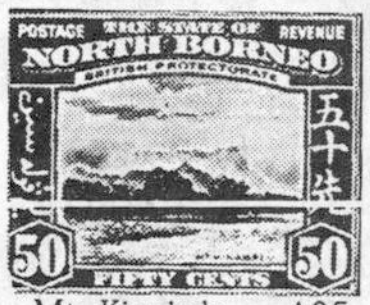
Mt. Kinabalu — A85

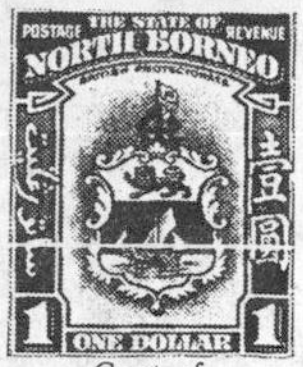
Coat of Arms — A86

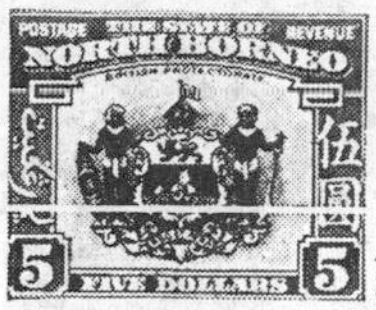
Arms with Supporters — A87

1939, Jan. 1 *Perf. 12½*

193 A74 1c red brn & dk grn	.20	.40
194 A75 2c Prus bl & red vio	.50	.40
195 A76 3c dk grn & sl blue	.25	.75
196 A77 4c rose vio & ol grn	.45	.30
197 A78 6c dp cl & dk blue	.40	1.50
198 A79 8c red	2.50	.50
199 A80 10c olive grn & vio	10.00	5.00
200 A81 12c ultra & grn	2.50	2.50
201 A82 15c bis brn & brt bl grn	5.00	2.50
202 A83 20c ind & rose vio	4.00	2.00
203 A84 25c dk brn & bl grn	5.00	3.50
204 A85 50c purple & brn	5.00	3.50
205 A86 $1 car & brown	25.00	12.50
206 A86 $2 ol grn & pur	47.50	55.00
207 A87 $5 blue & indigo	140.00	125.00
Nos. 193-207 (15)	248.30	215.35

For overprints see #208-237, N1-N15, N16-N31.

Nos. 193 to 207 Overprinted in Black **BMA**

1945, Dec. 17 Unwmk. *Perf. 12½*

208 A74 1c red brn & dk grn	.30	.30
209 A75 2c Prus bl & red vio	.35	.30
210 A76 3c dk grn & sl bl	.30	.30
211 A77 4c rose vio & ol grn	12.00	8.00
212 A78 6c dp cl & dk bl	.35	.35
213 A79 8c red	.55	.55
214 A80 10c ol green & vio	1.40	1.00
215 A81 12c ultra & green	.70	.65
216 A82 15c bis brn & brt bl grn	4.00	4.00
217 A83 20c ind & rose vio	1.10	1.10
218 A84 25c dk brn & bl grn	1.10	1.10
219 A85 50c purple & brn	2.25	2.25
220 A86 $1 carmine & brn	15.00	16.00
221 A86 $2 ol green & pur	15.00	16.00
a. Double overprint		
222 A87 $5 blue & indigo	15.00	15.00
Nos. 208-222 (15)	69.40	66.90

"BMA" stands for British Military Administration.

Nos. 193 to 207 Overprinted in Black or Carmine With Bars

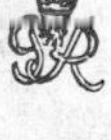

1947

223 A74 1c red brn & dk grn	.15	.15
224 A75 2c Prus bl & red vio	.25	.15
225 A76 3c dk grn & sl bl (C)	.25	.15
226 A77 4c rose vio & ol grn	.25	.15
227 A78 6c dp cl & dk bl (C)	.25	.25
228 A79 8c red	.25	.15
229 A80 10c olive grn & vio	.40	.25
230 A81 12c ultra & grn	.25	.25
231 A82 15c bis brn & brt bl grn	.25	.25
232 A83 20c ind & rose vio	.30	.30
233 A84 25c dk brn & bl grn	.45	.45
234 A85 50c purple & brn	.50	.50
235 A86 $1 carmine & brn	.60	.60
236 A86 $2 ol green & pur	3.25	3.25
237 A87 $5 blue & ind (C)	5.50	5.50
Nos. 223-237 (15)	12.90	12.35

The bars obliterate "The State of" and "British Protectorate."

Catalogue values for unused stamps in this section, from this point to the end of the section, are for Never Hinged items.

Silver Wedding Issue
Common Design Types
Perf. 14x14½

1948, Nov. 1 Wmk. 4 Photo.
238 CD304 8c scarlet .30 .20

Engraved; Name Typographed
Perf. 11½x11
239 CD305 $10 purple 12.50 6.75

UPU Issue
Common Design Types
Engr.; Name Typo. on 10c and 30c

1949, Oct. 10 *Perf. 13½, 11x11½*
240 CD306 8c rose carmine .25 .20
241 CD307 10c chocolate .35 .30
242 CD308 30c deep orange 1.10 .85
243 CD309 55c blue 1.75 1.40
Nos. 240-243 (4) 3.45 2.75

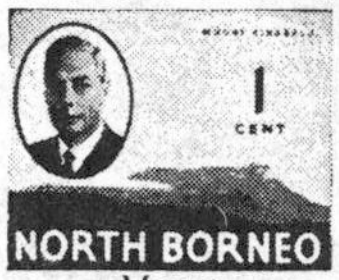
Mount Kinabalu — A88

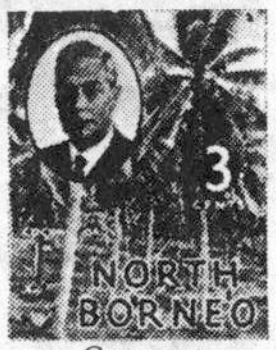
Coconut Grove — A89

Designs: 2c, Musician. 4c, Hemp drying. 5c, Cattle at Kota Belud. 8c, Map. 10c, Logging. 15c, Proa at Sandakan. 20c, Bajau Chief. 30c, Suluk Craft. 50c, Clock tower. $1, Bajau horsemen. $2, Murut with blowgun. $5, Net fishing. $10, Arms.

Perf. 13½x14½, 14½x13½

1950, July 1 Photo.
244 A88 1c red brown .15 .15
245 A88 2c blue .15 .15
246 A89 3c green .30 .15
247 A89 4c red violet .35 .15
248 A89 5c purple 1.75 .15
249 A88 8c red .90 .15
250 A88 10c violet brn .45 .15
251 A88 15c brt ultra .55 .20
252 A88 20c dk brown .70 .25
253 A89 30c brown 1.10 .20
254 A89 50c cer *(Jessleton)* 1.10 .45
255 A89 $1 red orange 1.75 .75
256 A88 $2 dark green 4.50 1.90
257 A88 $5 emerald 12.00 5.00
258 A88 $10 gray blue 22.50 9.25
Nos. 244-258 (15) 48.25 19.05

Redrawn

1952, May 1 *Perf. 14½x13½*
259 A89 50c cerise *(Jesselton)* .50 .50

Coronation Issue
Common Design Type

1953, June 3 Engr. *Perf. 13½x13*
260 CD312 10c carmine & black .35 .35

Types of 1950 with Portrait of Queen Elizabeth II
Perf. 13½x14½, 14½x13½

1954-57 Photo.
261 A88 1c red brown .15 .15
262 A88 2c brt blue ('56) .35 .20
263 A89 3c green ('57) .35 .20
264 A89 4c red violet ('55) .15 .15
265 A89 5c purple .25 .15
266 A88 8c red .15 .15
267 A88 10c violet brown .20 .15
268 A88 15c brt ultra ('55) .35 .15
269 A88 20c dk brown .50 .15
270 A89 30c brown .50 .20
271 A89 50c cerise ('56) .75 .30
272 A89 $1 red orange ('55) 1.90 .65
273 A88 $2 dk green ('55) 3.75 1.65
274 A88 $5 emerald ('57) 11.50 6.25
275 A88 $10 gray blue ('57) 22.50 11.00
Nos. 261-275 (15) 43.35 21.50

Issue dates: 10c, Mar. 1. 5c, July 1. 20c, 30c, Aug. 3. 1c, 8c, Oct. 1. $1, Apr. 1, 1955. 4c, 15c, May 16, 1955. $2, Oct. 1, 1955. 50c, Feb. 10, 1956. 2c, June 1, 1956. 3c, $5, $10, Feb. 1, 1957.

In 1960, the 30c plate was remade, using a finer, smaller-dot (250) screen instead of the 200 screen. The background appears smoother. Value $2.75 unused.

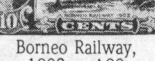

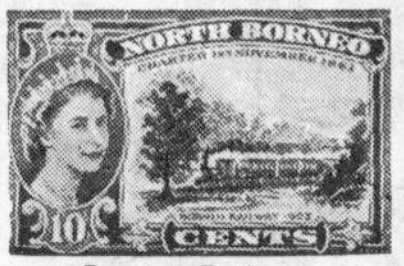
Borneo Railway, 1902 — A90

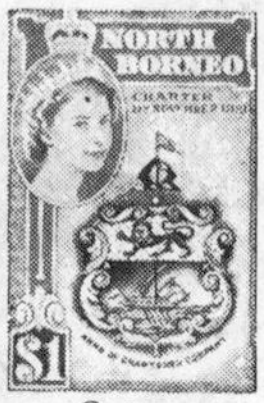
Comp. Arms — A91

Designs: 15c, Proa (sailboat). 35c, Mount Kinabalu.

Perf. 13x13½, 13½x13

1956, Nov. 1 Engr. Wmk. 4
276 A90 10c rose car & blk .20 .20
277 A90 15c red brown & blk .30 .30
278 A90 35c green & blk .50 .50
279 A91 $1 slate & blk 1.25 1.25
Nos. 276-279 (4) 2.25 2.25

75th anniv. of the founding of the Chartered Company of North Borneo.

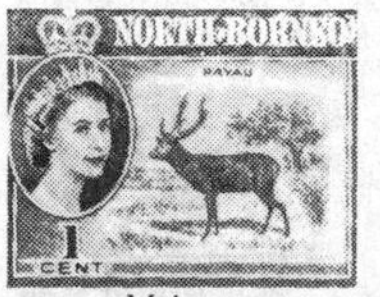
Malayan Sambar — A92

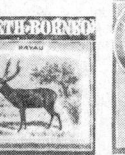

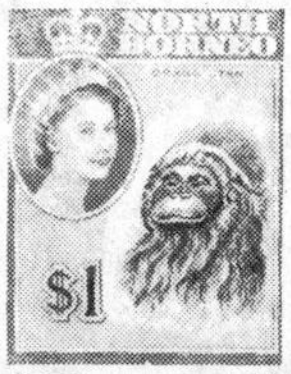
Orangutan — A93

Designs: 4c, Honey bear. 5c, Clouded leopard. 6c, Dusun woman with gong. 10c, Map of Borneo. 12c, Banteng (wild ox). 20c, Butterfly orchid. 25c, Rhinoceros. 30c, Murut with blowgun. 35c, Mount Kinabalu. 50c, Dusun with buffalo transport. 75c, Bajau horsemen. $2, Rhinoceros hornbill. $5, Crested wood partridge. $10, Coat of arms.

Perf. 13x12½, 12½x13

1961, Feb. 1 Wmk. 314 Engr.
280 A92 1c lt red brn & grn .15 .15
281 A92 4c orange & olive .20 .15
282 A92 5c violet & sepia .25 .15
283 A92 6c bluish grn & sl .25 .15
284 A92 10c rose red & lt grn .25 .15
285 A92 12c dull grn & brn .35 .35
286 A92 20c ultra & bl grn .50 .35
287 A92 25c rose red & gray .65 .60
288 A92 30c gray ol & sep .65 .45
289 A92 35c redsh brn & stl bl .80 .55
290 A92 50c brn org & bl grn .95 .60
291 A92 75c red vio & sl bl 1.25 .95
292 A93 $1 yel grn & brn 2.50 1.25
293 A93 $2 slate & brown 5.00 2.50
294 A93 $5 brn vio & grn 16.00 6.75
295 A93 $10 blue & car 32.50 18.00
Nos. 280-295 (16) 62.25 33.10

Freedom from Hunger Issue
Common Design Type

1963, June 4 Photo. *Perf. 14x14½*
296 CD314 12c ultramarine .90 .40

Sabah (Malaysia) stamps replaced those of North Borneo in 1964.

SEMI-POSTAL STAMPS

Nos. 136-138, 140-146, 148-149, 152 Overprinted in Carmine or Vermilion

1916 Unwmk. *Perf. 14*
Center in Black
B1 A51 1c chocolate 4.50 12.00
B2 A52 2c green 17.50 27.50
a. Perf. 15 25.00 32.50
B3 A53 3c deep rose 13.00 20.00
B4 A54 4c dull red 6.50 12.00
a. Perf. 15 72.50
B5 A55 5c yellow brown 26.00 24.00
B6 A56 6c olive green 20.00 30.00
a. Perf. 15
B7 A57 8c rose 13.00 24.00
B8 A58 10c brt blue 26.00 35.00
B9 A59 12c deep blue 26.00 37.50
B10 A60 16c red brown 27.50 37.50
B11 A62 20c on 18c bl grn 27.50 40.00
B12 A63 24c violet 42.50 45.00

Perf. 15
B13 A64 25c yellow green 450.00 475.00
Nos. B1-B13 (13) 700.00 819.50

All values exist with the vermilion overprint and all but the 4c with the carmine.

Of the total overprinting, a third was given to the National Philatelic War Fund Committee in London to be auctioned for the benefit of the wounded and veterans' survivors. The balance was lost en route from London to Sandakan when a submarine sank the ship. Very few were postally used.

Nos. 136-138, 140-146, 149, 152-157 Surcharged

RED CROSS
TWO CENTS

1918 *Perf. 14*
Center in Black
B14 A51 1c + 2c choc 3.25 7.00
B15 A52 2c + 2c green .70 7.00
B16 A53 3c + 2c deep rose 5.00 13.00
a. Perf. 15 25.00 60.00
B17 A54 4c + 2c dull red .50 4.00
a. Inverted surcharge 275.00
B18 A55 5c + 2c yellow brn 5.50 21.00
B19 A56 6c + 2c olive grn 4.50 15.00
a. Perf. 15 125.00
B20 A57 8c + 2c rose 4.50 6.00
B21 A58 10c + 2c brt blue 5.00 20.00
B22 A59 12c + 2c deep blue 12.50 35.00
a. Inverted surcharge 475.00
B23 A60 16c + 2c red brown 14.00 30.00
B24 A63 24c + 2c violet 15.00 30.00
B25 A64 25c + 2c yel grn 12.00 35.00
B26 A64 50c + 2c sl blue 14.00 35.00
B27 A64 $1 + 2c brown 35.00 45.00
B28 A64 $2 + 2c dk vio 50.00 85.00
B29 A65 $5 + 2c claret 240.00 325.00
B30 A65 $10 + 2c ver 240.00 325.00
Nos. B14-B30 (17) 661.45 1,038.

On Nos. B14-B24 the surcharge is 15mm high, on Nos. B25-B30 it is 19mm high.

Nos. 136-138, 140-146, 149, 152-157 Surcharged in Red

+
FOUR CENTS

1918
Center in Black
B31 A51 1c + 4c choc .40 4.00
B32 A52 2c + 4c green .60 6.00
B33 A53 3c + 4c dp rose .60 3.00
B34 A54 4c + 4c dull red .40 4.00
B35 A55 5c + 4c yellow brn 1.40 15.00
B36 A56 6c + 4c olive grn 1.40 10.00
a. Vert. pair, imperf. btwn. 900.00
B37 A57 8c + 4c rose 1.00 8.50
B38 A58 10c + 4c brt blue 3.25 10.00
B39 A59 12c + 4c dp blue 6.00 10.00
B40 A60 16c + 4c red brown 4.25 15.00
B41 A63 24c + 4c violet 4.25 17.50
B42 A64 25c + 4c yellow grn 5.00 40.00
B43 A64 50c + 4c sl blue 13.00 40.00
a. Perf. 15 50.00
B44 A64 $1 + 4c brown 15.00 50.00
a. Perf. 15 60.00
B45 A64 $2 + 4c dk vio 35.00 65.00
B46 A65 $5 + 4c claret 200.00 350.00
B47 A65 $10 + 4c ver 200.00 350.00
Nos. B31-B47 (17) 491.55 998.00

POSTAGE DUE STAMPS

Regular Issues Overprinted **POSTAGE DUE**

Reading Up Vert. (V), or Horiz. (H)

1895, Aug. 1 Unwmk. *Perf. 14, 15*
On Nos. 60 to 67
J1 A22 2c rose & blk (V) 15.00 .95
J2 A23 3c vio & ol grn (V) 5.00 .80
J3 A24 5c org red & blk (V) 25.00 1.25
a. Period after "DUE" (V) 45.00
J4 A25 6c ol brn & blk (V) 12.00 1.50
J5 A26 8c lilac & blk (H) 32.50 2.00
a. Double ovpt. (H)
J6 A27 12c blue & blk (H) 60.00 1.50
a. Double overprint (H) 325.00
J7 A28 18c green & blk (V) 65.00 3.00
a. Ovpt. reading down 400.00 275.00
b. Overprinted horizontally 20.00 2.75
c. Same as "b" inverted 300.00 275.00
J8 A29 24c claret & bl (H) 60.00 1.65
Nos. J1-J8 (8) 274.50 12.65

On Nos. 80 and 85

1897
J9 A38 2c dp rose & blk (V) 6.00 .45
a. Overprinted horizontally 12.00 15.00
J10 A42 8c brn lil & blk (H) 40.00 40.00
a. Period after "DUE" 30.00 60.00

On Nos. 81-88 and 104
Vertically reading up

1901
J11 A38 2c green & blk 21.00 .55
a. Overprinted horizontally 27.50
J12 A39 3c lilac & ol grn 8.00 .35
a. Period after "DUE" 18.00 30.00
J13 A48 4c dp rose & blk 18.00 .45
J14 A40 5c orange & blk 21.00 .55
a. Period after "DUE" 30.00
J15 A41 6c olive brn & blk 3.50 .45
J16 A42 8c brown & blk 7.00 .45
a. Overprinted horizontally 30.00
b. Period after "DUE" (H) 60.00
J17 A43 12c blue & blk 65.00 .90
J18 A46 18c green & blk 35.00 .90
J19 A47 24c red & blue 17.50 .90
Nos. J11-J19 (9) 196.00 5.50

On Nos. 105-114, 122-123 Horizontally

1903-11 *Perf. 14*
J20 A37 1c bis brn & blk, period after "DUE" 13.00 13.00
a. Period omitted
J21 A38 2c green & blk 6.00 .25
a. Ovpt. vert., perf. 16 150.00
b. Perf 15 (ovpt. horiz.) 55.00 55.00
J22 A39 3c lilac & ol grn 6.00 .35
a. Ovpt. vert. 110.00 110.00
b. Perf. 15 (ovpt. horiz.) 95.00 17.00
J23 A48 4c dp rose & blk, perf. 15 4.50 .45
a. "Postage Due" double 110.00
b. Perf. 14 4.75 1.00
J24 A40 5c orange & blk 7.00 .45
a. Ovpt. vert., perf. 15 165.00 110.00
b. Perf. 13½ (ovpt. horiz.)
c. Perf. 15 (ovpt. horiz.) 13.00 10.00
J25 A41 6c olive brn & blk 7.25 .35
a. "Postage Due" double
b. "Postage Due" inverted 110.00
c. Perf. 16 25.00 25.00
J26 A42 8c brown & blk 14.00 .50
a. Overprint vertical 150.00 125.00
J27 A49 10c slate & brn 35.00 .90
J28 A43 12c blue & blk 10.50 .75
J29 A50 16c yel brn & grn 18.00 .90
J30 A46 18c green & blk 7.00 .60
a. "Postage Due" double 80.00
J31 A47 24c claret & blue 15.00 1.25
a. "Postage Due" double 125.00
b. Overprint vertical 85.00
Nos. J20-J31 (12) 143.25 19.75

On Nos. 137 and 139-146

1921-31 *Perf. 14, 15*
J32 A52 2c green & blk 9.00 60.00
a. Perf. 13½ 12.00 12.00
J33 A53 3c green & blk 4.25 20.00
J34 A54 4c dull red & blk 1.00 1.25
J35 A55 5c yel brn & blk 4.25 10.00
J36 A56 6c olive grn & blk 11.00 11.00
J37 A57 8c rose & blk 4.25 4.25
J38 A58 10c blue & blk 5.50 12.00
a. Perf. 15 40.00 60.00
J39 A59 12c dp vio & blk 7.50 25.00
J40 A60 16c red brn & blk 20.00 65.00
Nos. J32-J40 (9) 66.75 208.50

On Nos. 168 to 176

1926-28 *Perf. 12½*
J41 A52 2c lake & blk .40 2.00
J42 A53 3c green & blk 1.75 12.50
J43 A54 4c dull red & blk 3.00 1.00
J44 A55 5c yel brown & blk 5.25 50.00
J45 A56 6c yel green & blk 7.25 3.00
J46 A57 8c rose & black 6.50 8.50
J47 A58 10c brt blue & blk 8.50 50.00
J48 A59 12c dp blue & blk 15.00 85.00
J49 A60 16c org brn & blk 32.50 125.00
Nos. J41-J49 (9) 80.15 337.00

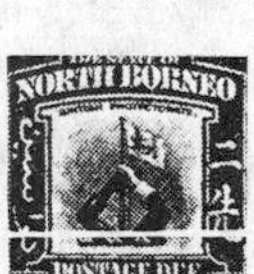
Crest of British North Borneo Company — D1

1939, Jan. 1 Engr. *Perf. 12½*
J50 D1 2c brown 3.25 25.00
J51 D1 4c carmine 4.25 32.50
J52 D1 6c dp rose violet 7.00 42.50
J53 D1 8c dk blue green 10.00 52.50
J54 D1 10c deep ultra 16.00 70.00
Nos. J50-J54 (5) 40.50 222.50

WAR TAX STAMPS

Nos. 193-194 Overprinted

WAR TAX
No. MR1

WAR TAX
No. MR2

1941, Feb. 24 Unwmk. *Perf. 12½*

MR1	A74	1c red brown & dk green	.30	.30
MR2	A75	2c Prus blue & red violet	.50	.55

For overprints see Nos. N15A-N15B.

OCCUPATION STAMPS

Issued under Japanese Occupation

Nos. 193-207 Handstamped in Violet or Black

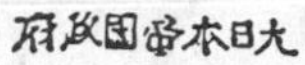

On Nos. N1-N15B, the violet overprint is attributed to Jesselton, the black to Sandakan. Nos. N1-N15 are generally found with violet overprint, Nos. N15A-N15B with black.

1942 Unwmk. *Perf. 12½*

N1	A74	1c	100.00	120.00
N2	A75	2c	95.00	125.00
N3	A76	3c	95.00	125.00
N4	A77	4c	50.00	95.00
N5	A78	6c	110.00	125.00
N6	A79	8c	95.00	125.00
N7	A80	10c	95.00	125.00
N8	A81	12c	120.00	190.00
N9	A82	15c	120.00	190.00
N10	A83	20c	200.00	*250.00*
N11	A84	25c	175.00	*250.00*
N12	A85	50c	275.00	*300.00*
N13	A86	$1	210.00	*400.00*
N14	A86	$2	275.00	*550.00*
N15	A87	$5	400.00	*700.00*
		Nos. N1-N15 (15)	2,415.	*3,670.*

For overprints see Nos. N22a, N31a.

Same Overprint on Nos. MR1-MR2 in Black or Violet

1942

N15A	A74	1c	*350.00*	*190.00*
N15B	A75	2c	*800.00*	*250.00*

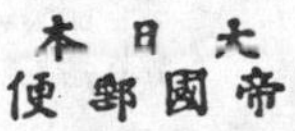

Nos. 193 to 207 Overprinted in Black

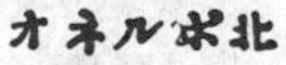

1944, Sept. 30 Unwmk. *Perf. 12½*

N16	A74	1c	3.00	6.25
N17	A75	2c	5.75	6.25
N18	A76	3c	2.25	3.50
N19	A77	4c	3.00	5.00
N20	A78	6c	3.00	3.50
N21	A79	8c	4.00	11.00
N22	A80	10c	4.00	9.00
a.		On No. N7	150.00	
N23	A81	12c	4.00	9.00
N24	A82	15c	3.00	9.00
N25	A83	20c	8.50	21.00
N26	A84	25c	8.50	*21.00*
N27	A85	50c	35.00	*57.50*
N28	A86	$1	55.00	*95.00*
		Nos. N16-N28 (13)	139.00	*257.00*

Nos. 193 and 205 Surcharged in Black

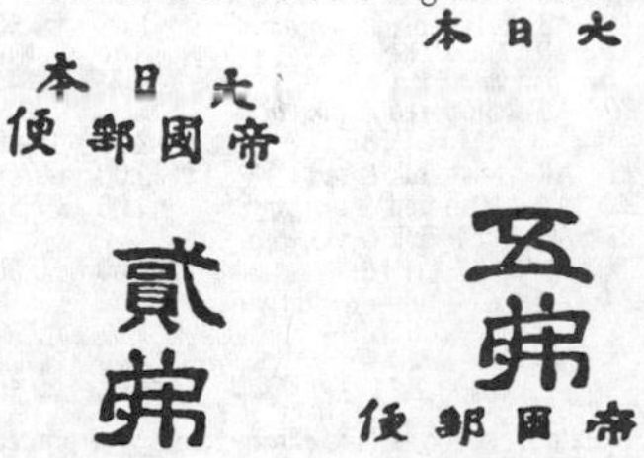

No. N30 No. N31

1944, May

N30	A74	$2 on 1c	*3,750.*	*3,250.*
N31	A86	$5 on $1	3,800.	3,800.
a.		On No. N13	2,750.	2,750.

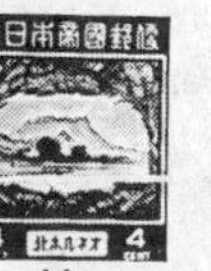

Mt. Kinabalu — OS1

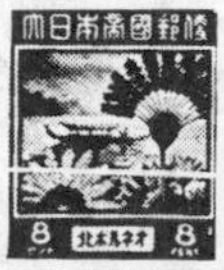

Boat and Traveler's Palm — OS2

1943, Apr. 29 Litho.

N32	OS1	4c dull rose red	15.00	18.00
N33	OS2	8c dark blue	15.00	18.00

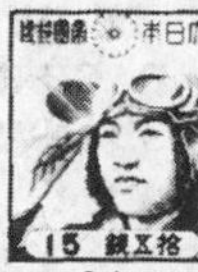

Aviator Saluting and Japanese Flag — A150

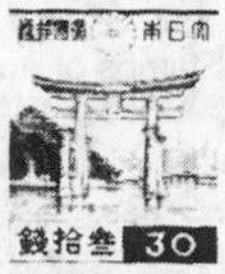

Miyajima Torii, Itsukushima Shrine — A96

Stamps of Japan, 1938-43, Overprinted in Black

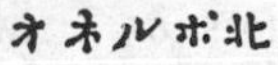

Designs: 1s, War factory girl. 2s, Gen. Maresuke Nogi. 3s, Power plant. 4s, Hyuga Monument and Mt. Fuji. 5s, Adm. Heihachiro Togo. 6s, Garambi Lighthouse, Formosa. 8s, Meiji Shrine, Tokyo. 10s, Palms and map of "Greater East Asia." 20s, Mt. Fuji and cherry blossoms. 25s, Horyu Temple, Nara. 50s, Golden Pavilion, Kyoto. 1y, Great Buddha, Kamakura. (See Burma for illustrations of 2s, 3s, 5s, 8s, 20s and watermark. For others, see Japan, Vol. 4.)

Wmk. Curved Wavy Lines (257)

1944, Sept. 30 *Perf. 13*

N34	A144	1s orange brown	5.25	12.00
N35	A84	2s vermilion	5.25	12.00
N36	A85	3s green	3.50	12.00
N37	A146	4s emerald	5.25	12.00
N38	A86	5s brown lake	6.25	13.00
N39	A88	6s orange	5.75	13.00
N40	A90	8s dk purple & pale vio	3.25	13.00
N41	A148	10s crim & dull rose	4.75	13.00
N42	A150	15s dull blue	4.75	13.00
N43	A94	20s ultra	100.00	200.00
N44	A95	25s brown	65.00	55.00
N45	A96	30s peacock blue	225.00	125.00
N46	A97	50s olive	70.00	55.00
N47	A98	1y lt brown	65.00	100.00
		Nos. N34-N47 (14)	569.00	648.00

The overprint translates "North Borneo."

NORTHERN NIGERIA

'nor–th̲ə(r)n nī–'jir–ē–ə

LOCATION — Western Africa
GOVT. — A former British Protectorate
AREA — 281,703 sq. mi.
POP. — 11,866,250
CAPITAL — Zungeru

In 1914 Northern Nigeria united with Southern Nigeria to form the Colony and Protectorate of Nigeria.

12 Pence = 1 Shilling
20 Shillings = 1 Pound

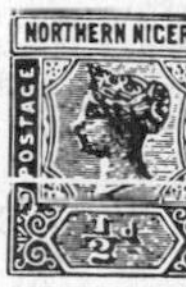

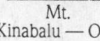

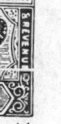

Victoria — A1

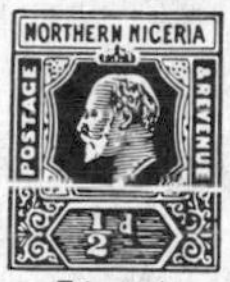

Edward VII — A2

Numerals of 5p and 6p, types A1 and A2, are in color on plain tablet.

Wmk. Crown and C A (2)

1900, Mar. Typo. *Perf. 14*

1	A1	½p lilac & grn	.65	1.00
2	A1	1p lilac & rose	3.50	1.00
3	A1	2p lilac & yel	2.50	*18.00*
4	A1	2½p lilac & blue	2.50	*7.50*
5	A1	5p lilac & brn	6.75	*22.50*
6	A1	6p lilac & vio	9.75	*15.00*
7	A1	1sh green & blk	12.00	*37.50*
8	A1	2sh6p green & blue	55.00	*100.00*
9	A1	10sh green & brn	200.00	*275.00*
		Nos. 1-9 (9)	292.65	*477.50*

1902, July 1

10	A2	½p violet & green	.20	.30
11	A2	1p violet & car rose	.85	.25
12	A2	2p violet & org	2.00	1.50
13	A2	2½p violet & ultra	.40	.45
14	A2	5p violet & org brn	1.65	3.25
15	A2	6p violet & pur	5.00	3.50
16	A2	1sh green & black	2.25	2.50
17	A2	2sh6p green & ultra	8.50	*15.00*
18	A2	10sh green & brown	32.50	*45.00*
		Nos. 10-18 (9)	53.35	*71.75*

1904, Apr. Wmk. 3

18A	A2	£25 green & carmine	*27,500.*	

No. 18A was available for postage but probably was used only for fiscal purposes.

1905

19	A2	½p violet & grn	3.25	2.00
20	A2	1p violet & car rose	2.00	.20
21	A2	2p violet & org	3.50	7.50
22	A2	2½p violet & ultra	2.00	2.00
23	A2	5p violet & org brn	5.75	12.50
24	A2	6p violet & pur	6.50	10.50
25	A2	1sh green & black	16.00	*25.00*
26	A2	2sh6p green & ultra	19.00	*22.00*
		Nos. 19-26 (8)	58.00	*81.70*

All values exist on ordinary paper and all but the ½p on chalky paper.

1910-11 Ordinary Paper

28	A2	½p green	1.00	.50
29	A2	1p carmine	.80	.30
30	A2	2p gray	1.25	2.00
31	A2	2½p ultra	.90	3.50

Chalky Paper

32	A2	3p violet, *yel*	2.75	.25
33	A2	5p vio & ol grn	2.50	4.25
34	A2	6p vio & red vio ('11)	1.25	4.50
a.		6p violet & deep violet	4.50	10.00
35	A2	1sh black, *green*	1.10	.55
36	A2	2sh6p blk & red, *bl*	8.00	16.00
37	A2	5sh grn & red, *yel*	17.50	47.50
38	A2	10sh grn & red, *grn*	37.50	40.00
		Nos. 28-38 (11)	74.55	119.35

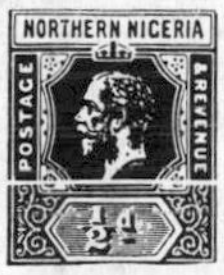

George V — A3

For description of dies I and II see back of this section of the Catalogue.

Die I

1912 Ordinary Paper

40	A3	½p green	.55	.55
41	A3	1p carmine	.45	.15
42	A3	2p gray	1.00	1.25

Chalky Paper

43	A3	3p violet, *yel*	.75	.35
44	A3	4p blk & red, *yel*	.45	.45
45	A3	5p vio & ol grn	1.25	1.40
46	A3	6p vio & red vio	1.25	.70
47	A3	9p violet & scar	1.10	*2.50*
48	A3	1sh blk, *green*	1.75	1.00
49	A3	2sh6p blk & red, *bl*	6.50	*20.00*
50	A3	5sh grn & red, *yel*	17.50	*45.00*
51	A3	10sh grn & red, *grn*	37.50	*45.00*
52	A3	£1 vio & blk, *red*	150.00	100.00
		Nos. 40-52 (13)	220.05	*218.35*

Numerals of 3p, 4p, 5p and 6p, type A3, are in color on plain tablet.

Stamps of Northern Nigeria were replaced in 1914 by those of Nigeria.

NORTHERN RHODESIA

'nor–th̲ə(r)n rō–'dē–zh(ē–)ə

LOCATION — In southern Africa, east of Angola and separated from Southern Rhodesia by the Zambezi River.
GOVT. — Former British Protectorate
AREA — 287,640 sq. mi.
POP. — 2,550,000 (est. 1962)
CAPITAL — Lusaka

Prior to April 1, 1924, Northern Rhodesia was administered by the British South Africa Company. It joined the Federation of Rhodesia and Nyasaland in 1953 and used its stamps in 1954-63. It resumed issuing its own stamps in December, 1963, after the Federation was dissolved. On Oct. 24, 1964, Northern Rhodesia became the independent republic of Zambia. See Rhodesia, Southern Rhodesia, Rhodesia and Nyasaland, Zambia.

12 Pence = 1 Shilling
20 Shillings = 1 Pound

Catalogue values for unused stamps in this country are for Never Hinged items, beginning with Scott 46 in the regular postage section and Scott J5 in the postage due section.

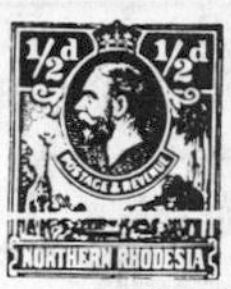

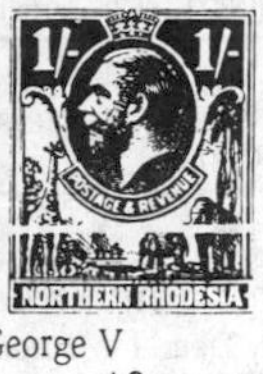

King George V
A1 A2

1925-29 Engr. Wmk. 4 *Perf. 12½*

1	A1	½p dk green	.25	.15
2	A1	1p dk brown	.25	.15
3	A1	1½p carmine	.25	.20
4	A1	2p brown org	.60	.15
5	A1	3p ultra	.60	.50
6	A1	4p dk violet	.80	.50
7	A1	6p gray	.75	.35
8	A1	8p rose lilac	4.75	14.00
9	A1	10p olive grn	4.75	12.50
10	A2	1sh black & org	2.00	1.25
11	A2	2sh ultra & brn	8.50	10.50
12	A2	2sh6p green & blk	3.50	3.75
13	A2	3sh indigo & vio	12.00	9.00
14	A2	5sh dk vio & gray	11.00	9.50
15	A2	7sh6p blk & lil rose	80.00	*140.00*
16	A2	10sh black & green	30.00	32.50
17	A2	20sh rose lil & red	140.00	140.00
		Nos. 1-17 (17)	300.00	375.00

High values with revenue cancellations are inexpensive.

Issue dates: 3sh, 1929; others, Apr. 1.

Silver Jubilee Issue

Common Design Type

1935, May 6 *Perf. 13½x14*

18	CD301	1p olive grn & ultra	.55	.50
19	CD301	2p indigo & grn	.95	.90
20	CD301	3p blue & brown	1.00	1.00
21	CD301	6p brt vio & indigo	3.75	3.75
		Nos. 18-21 (4)	6.25	6.15

Coronation Issue

Common Design Type

1937, May 12 *Perf. 11x11½*

22	CD302	1½p dark carmine	.15	.15
23	CD302	2p yellow brown	.30	.30
24	CD302	3p deep ultra	.50	.50
		Nos. 22-24 (3)	.95	.95

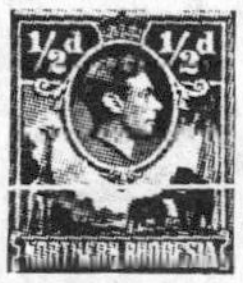

King George VI — A3

1938-52 Wmk. 4 *Perf. 12½*

Size: 19x24mm

25	A3	½p green	.15	.15
26	A3	½p dk brown ('51)	.15	.40
a.		Perf. 12½x14	.15	.25
27	A3	1p dk brown	.25	.25
28	A3	1p green ('51)	.45	1.40
29	A3	1½p carmine	26.00	.25
a.		Horiz. pair, imperf. between	*12,500.*	
30	A3	1½p brown org ('41)	.25	.25
31	A3	2p brown org	40.00	1.40
32	A3	2p carmine ('41)	.25	.25
33	A3	2p rose lilac ('51)	.35	.25
34	A3	3p ultra	.25	.25
35	A3	3p red ('51)	.45	.35
36	A3	4p dk violet	.25	.325
37	A3	4½p dp blue ('52)	.35	2.75
38	A3	6p dark gray	.25	.25
39	A3	9p violet ('52)	.35	3.00

Size: 21½x26¾mm

40	A3	1sh blk & brn org	1.25	.40
41	A3	2sh6p green & blk	4.25	1.40
42	A3	3sh ind & dk vio	8.00	2.00
43	A3	5sh violet & gray	4.50	3.25

44	A3	10sh black & green	5.50	11.00
45	A3	20sh rose lil & red	20.00	40.00
		Nos. 25-45 (21)	113.25	69.60

Catalogue values for unused stamps in this section, from this point to the end of the section, are for Never Hinged items.

Peace Issue
Common Design Type

1946, Nov. 26 Engr. *Perf. 13½x14*

46	CD303	1½p deep orange	.15	.15
a.		Perf. 13½	.30	.30
47	CD303	2p carmine	.25	.25

Common Design Types pictured in section in the front of the Catalogue.

Silver Wedding Issue
Common Design Types

1948, Dec. 1 Photo. *Perf. 14x14½*

48	CD304	1½p orange	.15	.15

Engr. *Perf. 11½x11*

49	CD305	20sh rose brown	50.00	57.50

UPU Issue
Common Design Types

Engr.; Name Typo. on 3p, 6p
Perf. 13½, 11x11½

1949, Oct. 10 Wmk. 4

50	CD306	2p rose carmine	.25	.25
51	CD307	3p indigo	.40	.40
52	CD308	6p gray	.85	.85
53	CD309	1sh red orange	1.65	1.65
		Nos. 50-53 (4)	3.15	3.15

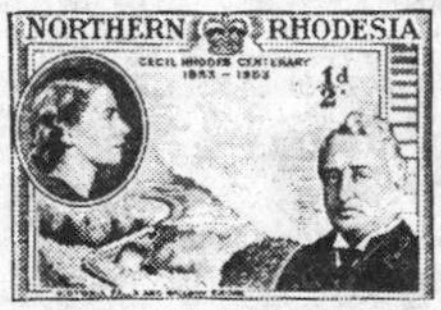

Victoria Falls and Railway Bridge, Cecil Rhodes and Elizabeth II — A4

1953, May 30 Engr. *Perf. 12x11*

54	A4	½p brown	.15	.15
55	A4	1p green	.20	.15
56	A4	2p deep claret	.25	.15
57	A4	4½p deep blue	.75	.75
58	A4	1sh gray & orange	.95	.95
		Nos. 54-58 (5)	2.30	2.15

Cecil Rhodes (1853-1902).

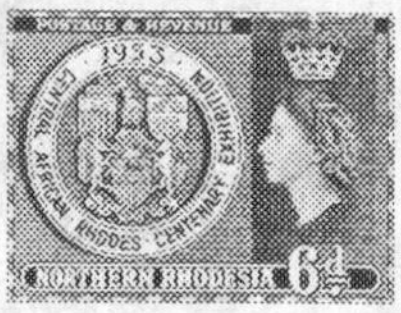

Exhibition Seal — A5

1953, May 30 *Perf. 14x13½*

59	A5	6p purple	.45	.45

Central African Rhodes Centenary Exhib.

Coronation Issue
Common Design Type

1953, June 2 *Perf. 13½x13*

60	CD312	1½p orange & black	.35	.25

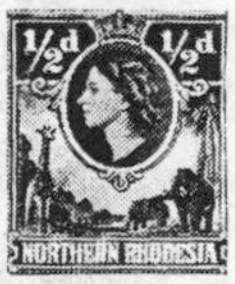

Elizabeth II A6

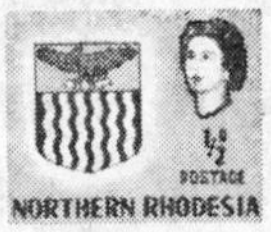

Coat of Arms A7

Perf. 12½x13½

1953, Sept. 15 Engr.

Size: 19x23mm

61	A6	½p dark brown	.25	.15
62	A6	1p green	.25	.15
63	A6	1½p brown orange	.25	.15
64	A6	2p rose lilac	.25	.15
65	A6	3p red	.25	.25
66	A6	4p dark violet	.35	.35
67	A6	4½p deep blue	.45	.45
68	A6	6p dark gray	.55	.55
69	A6	9p violet	.95	.95

Size: 21x27mm

70	A6	1sh black & brn org	1.10	1.10
71	A6	2sh6p green & blk	3.00	3.00
72	A6	5sh violet & gray	5.00	5.00
73	A6	10sh black & green	8.00	8.00
74	A6	20sh rose lilac & red	20.00	20.00
		Nos. 61-74 (14)	40.65	40.25

Perf. 14½

1963, Dec. 1 Unwmk. Photo.

Size: 23x19mm

Arms in Black, Blue and Orange

75	A7	½p violet & blk	.15	.15
a.		Value omitted	375.00	
76	A7	1p blue & blk	.15	.15
a.		Value omitted	11.50	
77	A7	2p brown & blk	.15	.15
78	A7	3p orange & blk	.15	.15
a.		Bklt. pane of 4	.85	
b.		Value omitted	90.00	
79	A7	4p green & blk	.15	.15
a.		Value omitted	80.00	
80	A7	6p yellow grn & blk	.15	.15
a.		Value omitted	175.00	
81	A7	9p ocher & blk	.30	.25
a.		Value omitted	150.00	
82	A7	1sh dk gray & blk	.25	.25
a.		Value omitted		
83	A7	1sh3p brt red lil & blk	.60	.55

Perf. 13

Size: 27x23mm

84	A7	2sh dp orange & blk	.70	.60
85	A7	2sh6p maroon & blk	.90	.90
86	A7	5sh dk car rose & blk	1.75	1.65
87	A7	10sh brt pink & blk	3.50	3.00
88	A7	20sh dk blue & blk	8.75	8.00
a.		Value omitted	750.00	
		Nos. 75-88 (14)	17.65	16.10

Stamps of Northern Rhodesia were replaced by those of Zambia, starting Oct. 24, 1964.

POSTAGE DUE STAMPS

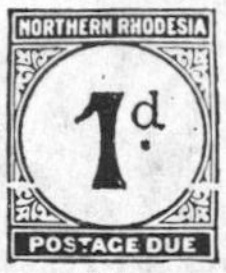

D1

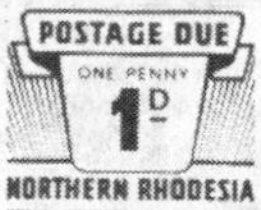

D2

1929 Typo. Wmk. 4 *Perf. 14*

J1	D1	1p black	1.75	3.75
a.		Wmk. 4a (error)	110.00	
J2	D1	2p black	2.75	6.50
J3	D1	3p black	6.75	22.50
a.		Wmk. 4a (error)	150.00	
J4	D1	4p black	7.25	25.00
		Nos. J1-J4 (4)	18.50	57.75

Catalogue values for unused stamps in this section, from this point to the end of the section, are for Never Hinged items.

1964 Unwmk. Litho. *Perf. 12½*

J5	D2	1p orange	.40	1.00
J6	D2	2p dark blue	.80	2.00
J7	D2	3p rose claret	1.25	2.50
J8	D2	4p violet blue	2.00	4.00
J9	D2	6p purple	3.00	6.00
J10	D2	1sh emerald	4.00	8.00
		Nos. J5-J10 (6)	11.45	23.50

NORTH WEST PACIFIC ISLANDS

'north 'west pə–'si–fik 'ī–ləndz

LOCATION — Group of islands in the West Pacific Ocean including a part of New Guinea and adjacent islands of the Bismarck Archipelago
GOVT. — Australian military government
AREA — 96,160 sq. mi.
POP. — 636,563

Stamps of Australia were overprinted for use in the former German possessions of Nauru and German New Guinea which Australian troops had captured. Following the League of Nations' decision which placed these territories under mandate to Australia, these provisional issues were discontinued. See German New Guinea, New Britain, Nauru and New Guinea.

12 Pence = 1 Shilling
20 Shillings = 1 Pound

Stamps of Australia Overprinted **N. W. PACIFIC ISLANDS**

There are two varieties of the letter "S" in the overprint: variety a, normal "S"; variety b, "S" with small head and long bottom stroke. Three combinations of these letters are found in the word "Islands": I, both are variety a; II, varieties b and a; III, both are variety b.

1915-16 Wmk. 8 *Perf. 12*

1	A1	2p gray	16.00	30.00
2	A1	2½p dark blue	2.50	14.00
3	A1	3p olive bister	16.00	32.50
4	A1	6p ultra	22.50	42.50
5	A1	9p violet	30.00	50.00
6	A1	1sh blue green	35.00	50.00
8	A1	5sh yel & gray ('16)	700.00	850.00
9	A1	10sh pink & gray	100.00	140.00
		Revenue cancel		27.50
10	A1	£1 ultra & brown	750.00	625.00
		Nos. 1-6,8-10 (9)	1,672.	1,834.

For surcharge see No. 39.

Wmk. Wide Crown and Narrow A (9)
Perf. 12, 14

11	A4	½p emerald	.90	2.50
a.		Double overprint		
12	A4	1p car (Die I)	2.00	1.50
a.		1p carmine rose (Die I)	5.00	5.00
b.		1p carmine (Die Ia)	125.00	125.00
13	A1	2p gray	10.00	12.00
14	A1	2½p dk bl ('16)	7,000.	7,000.
16	A4	4p orange	3.25	9.00
17	A4	5p org brown	1.50	14.00
18	A1	6p ultra	9.00	11.00
19	A1	9p violet	12.00	14.00
20	A1	1sh blue green	8.50	21.00
21	A1	2sh brown	70.00	90.00
22	A1	5sh yellow & gray	75.00	95.00
		Nos. 11-13,16-22 (10)	192.15	270.00

For description of the dies of No. 12 see Australia.
For surcharge see No. 40.

1915-19 Wmk. 10

27	A1	2p gray	4.50	10.00
28	A1	2½p dk bl ('19)	4.00	14.00
a.		"1" of fraction omitted	5,500.	6,250.
29	A1	3p ol bister	4.00	10.00
32	A1	6p ultra ('19)	4.75	13.00
33	A1	9p violet ('19)	9.50	30.00
34	A1	1sh bl grn ('18)	5.50	26.00
35	A1	2sh brown ('16)	25.00	40.00
36	A1	5sh yel & gray ('19)	55.00	55.00
37	A1	10sh pink & gray ('19)	150.00	175.00
38	A1	£1 ultra & brn ('16)	425.00	550.00
		Nos. 27-29,32-38 (10)	687.25	923.00

Nos. 6 and 17 Surcharged **One Penny**

1918, May 23 Wmk. 8 *Perf. 12*

39	A1	1p on 1sh bl grn	100.00	80.00

Wmk. 9 *Perf. 14*

40	A4	1p on 5p org brn	100.00	85.00

1919 Wmk. 11

41	A4	½p emerald	.65	3.00

1921-22 Wmk. 9

42	A4	1p violet ('22)	1.00	5.00
43	A4	2p orange	3.25	4.00
44	A4	2p red ('22)	5.00	7.50
45	A4	4p violet ('22)	26.00	45.00
46	A4	4p light ultra ('22)	10.00	45.00
		Nos. 42-46 (5)	45.25	106.50

North West Pacific Islands stamps were largely used in New Britain. Some were used in Nauru. They were intended to serve the Bismarck Archipelago and other places.

NYASALAND PROTECTORATE

nī–'a–sə–,land prə–'tek–t(ə–)rət

LOCATION — In southern Africa, bordering on Lake Nyasa
GOVT. — British Protectorate
AREA — 49,000 sq. mi.
POP. — 2,950,000 (est. 1962)
CAPITAL — Zomba

For previous issues, see British Central Africa.

Nyasaland joined the Federation of Rhodesia and Nyasaland in 1953, using its stamps until 1963. As the Federation began to dissolve in 1963, Nyasaland withdrew its postal services and issued provisional stamps. On July 6, 1964, Nyasaland became the independent state of Malawi.

12 Pence = 1 Shilling
20 Shillings = 1 Pound

Catalogue values for unused stamps in this country are for Never Hinged items, beginning with Scott 68 in the regular postage section and Scott J1 in the postage due section.

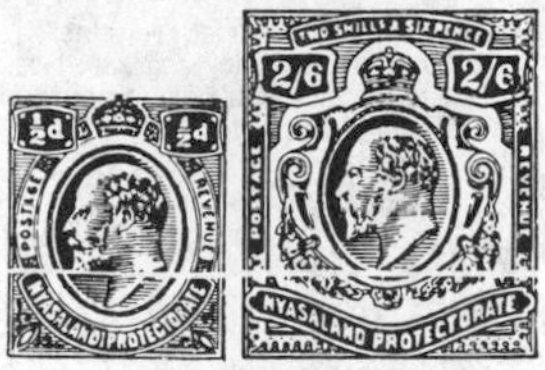

King Edward VII
A1 A2

Wmk. Crown and C A (2)

1908, July 22 Typo. *Perf. 14*

Chalky Paper

1	A1	1sh black, *green*	2.00	4.50

Wmk. Multiple Crown and C A (3)

Ordinary Paper

2	A1	½p green	.60	.40
3	A1	1p carmine	.90	.20

Chalky Paper

4	A1	3p violet, *yel*	1.25	2.00
5	A1	4p scar & blk, *yel*	1.50	2.00
6	A1	6p red vio & vio	3.25	4.75
7	A2	2sh 6p car & blk, *bl*	30.00	30.00
8	A2	4sh black & car	55.00	65.00
9	A2	10sh red & grn, *grn*	65.00	90.00
10	A2	£1 blk & vio, *red*	375.00	375.00
11	A2	£10 ultra & lilac	8,500.	8,500.
		Nos. 1-10 (10)	534.50	573.85

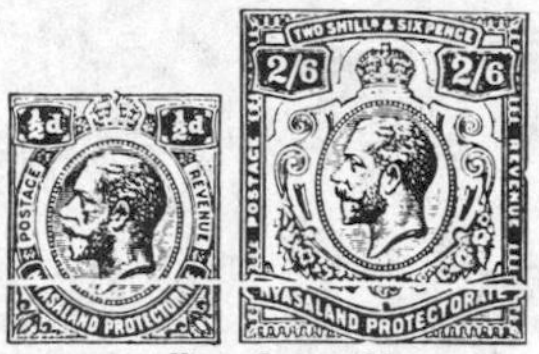

King George V
A3 A4

1913-18

Ordinary Paper

12	A3	½p green	.40	.40
13	A3	1p scarlet	.40	.25
a.		1p carmine	.65	.40
14	A3	2p gray	1.25	.50
15	A3	2½p ultra	.50	.60

Chalky Paper

16	A3	3p violet, *yel*	1.50	1.50
17	A3	4p scar & blk, *yel*	1.25	1.50
18	A3	6p red vio & dull vio	1.50	1.75
19	A3	1sh black, *green*	1.65	1.50
a.		1sh black, *emerald*	1.10	1.10
b.		1sh blk, *bl grn*, olive back	1.25	1.25
20	A4	2sh6p red & blk, *bl* ('18)	12.50	16.00
21	A4	4sh blk & red ('18)	20.00	21.00
22	A4	10sh red & grn, *grn*	60.00	77.50
23	A4	£1 blk & vio, *red* ('18)	150.00	150.00
24	A4	£10 ultra & dull vio ('14)	2,750.	1,750.
		Revenue cancel		250.00
		Nos. 12-23 (12)	250.95	272.50

Stamps of Nyasaland Protectorate overprinted "N. F." are listed under German East Africa.

1921-30 Wmk. 4

Ordinary Paper

25	A3	½p green	.35	.15
26	A3	1p rose red	.35	.15
27	A3	1½p orange	7.00	10.00
28	A3	2p gray	.75	.30

Chalky Paper

29	A3	3p violet, *yel*	2.25	.65
30	A3	4p scar & blk, *yel*	1.90	1.65
31	A3	6p red vio & dl vio	2.75	2.75
32	A3	1sh blk, *grn* ('30)	5.50	4.00
33	A4	2sh ultra & dl vio, *bl*	10.00	10.00
34	A4	2sh6p red & blk, *bl* ('24)	14.00	11.50
35	A4	4sh black & car	10.00	8.25
36	A4	5sh red & grn, *yel* ('29)	30.00	27.50
37	A4	10sh red & grn, *emer*	82.50	100.00
		Nos. 25-37 (13)	167.35	176.90

George V and Leopard — A5

1934-35		Engr.	Perf. 12½	
38	A5	½p green	.60	.40
39	A5	1p dark brown	.60	.35
40	A5	1½p rose	.60	.55
41	A5	2p gray	.75	.55
42	A5	3p dark blue	1.50	1.50
43	A5	4p rose lilac ('35)	2.50	2.50
44	A5	6p dk violet	3.00	3.00
45	A5	9p olive bis ('35)	3.75	5.75
46	A5	1sh orange & blk	3.75	3.75
		Nos. 38-46 (9)	17.05	18.35

Silver Jubilee Issue
Common Design Type

1935, May 6			Perf. 11x12	
47	CD301	1p gray blk & ultra	.65	.65
48	CD301	2p indigo & grn	3.75	2.25
49	CD301	3p ultra & brn	4.50	9.00
50	CD301	1sh brown vio & ind	14.00	17.00
		Nos. 47-50 (4)	22.90	28.90

Coronation Issue
Common Design Type

1937, May 12			Perf. 11x11½	
51	CD302	½p deep green	.15	.20
52	CD302	1p dark brown	.35	.20
53	CD302	2p gray black	.35	.35
		Nos. 51-53 (3)	.85	.75

A6

King George VI — A7

1938-44		Engr.	Perf. 12½	
54	A6	½p green	.15	.30
54A	A6	½p dk brown ('42)	.15	.40
55	A6	1p dark brown	.15	.15
55A	A6	1p green ('42)	.15	.20
56	A6	1½p dark carmine	.65	1.90
56A	A6	1½p gray ('42)	.15	1.25
57	A6	2p gray	1.25	.40
57A	A6	2p dark car ('42)	.15	.30
58	A6	3p blue	.30	.15
59	A6	4p rose lilac	.80	.30
60	A6	6p dark violet	.85	.25
61	A6	9p olive bister	1.40	1.40
62	A6	1sh orange & blk	1.40	.55

Typo.
Perf. 14
Chalky Paper

63	A7	2sh ultra & dl vio, bl	5.50	4.50
64	A7	2sh6p red & blk, bl	6.50	4.50
65	A7	5sh red & grn, yel	22.50	11.00
a.		5sh dk red & dp grn, yel ('44)	50.00	37.50
66	A7	10sh red & grn, grn	32.50	14.00

Wmk. 3

67	A7	£1 blk & vio, red	16.00	15.00
		Nos. 54-67 (18)	90.55	56.55

Catalogue values for unused stamps in this section, from this point to the end of the section, are for Never Hinged items.

Canoe on Lake Nyasa — A8

Soldier of King's African Rifles — A9

Tea Estate, Mlanje Mountain A10

Map and Coat of Arms — A11

Fishing Village, Lake Nyasa — A12

Tobacco Estate — A13

Arms of Nyasaland and George VI A14

1945, Sept. 1		Engr.	Perf. 12	
68	A8	½p brown vio & blk	.15	.15
69	A9	1p dp green & blk	.15	.15
70	A10	1½p gray grn & blk	.30	.15
71	A11	2p scarlet & blk	.15	.15
72	A12	3p blue & blk	.40	.15
73	A13	4p rose vio & blk	.80	.70
74	A10	6p violet & blk	.80	.70
75	A8	9p ol grn & blk	1.25	2.25
76	A11	1sh myr grn & ind	.85	.65
77	A12	2sh dl red brn & grn	3.00	2.25
78	A13	2sh6p ultra & green	3.25	4.00
79	A14	5sh ultra & lt vio	4.50	4.50
80	A11	10sh green & lake	9.00	8.50
81	A14	20sh black & scar	20.00	32.50
		Nos. 68-81 (14)	44.60	56.80

Peace Issue
Common Design Type
Perf. 13½x14

1946, Dec. 16			Wmk. 4	
82	CD303	1p bright green	.20	.20
83	CD303	2p red orange	.25	.25

A15

1947, Oct. 20			Perf. 12	
84	A15	1p emer & org brn	.25	.15

Silver Wedding Issue
Common Design Types

1948, Dec. 15		Photo.	Perf. 14x14½	
85	CD304	1p dark green	.15	.15

Engr.; Name Typo.
Perf. 11½x11

86	CD305	10sh purple	13.00	11.50

UPU Issue
Common Design Types
Engr.; Name Typo. on 3p, 6p
Perf. 13½, 11x11½

1949, Nov. 21			Wmk. 4	
87	CD306	1p blue green	.15	.15
88	CD307	3p Prus blue	.45	.45
89	CD308	6p rose violet	1.40	.90
90	CD309	1sh violet blue	2.25	2.75
		Nos. 87-90 (4)	4.25	4.25

Arms of British Central Africa and Nyasaland Protectorate — A16

1951, May 15		Engr.	Perf. 11x12	
		Arms in Black		
91	A16	2p rose	.20	.20
92	A16	3p blue	.25	.25
93	A16	6p purple	.40	.80
94	A16	5sh deep blue	2.50	3.50
		Nos. 91-94 (4)	3.35	4.75

60th anniv. of the Protectorate, originally British Central Africa.

Exhibition Seal — A17

1953, May 30			Perf. 14x13½	
95	A17	6p purple	.45	.40

Central African Rhodes Cent. Exhib.

Coronation Issue
Common Design Type

1953, June 2			Perf. 13½x13	
96	CD312	2p orange & black	.25	.25

Types of 1945-47 with Portrait of Queen Elizabeth II and

Grading Cotton — A18

1953, Sept. 1			Perf. 12	
97	A8	½p red brown & blk	.15	.15
a.		Booklet pane of 4	3.25	
b.		Perf. 12x12½ ('54)	.15	.15
98	A15	1p emer & org brn	.15	.15
a.		Booklet pane of 4	3.25	
99	A10	1½p gray grn & blk	.20	.20
100	A11	2p orange & blk	.15	.15
a.		Booklet pane of 4	3.25	
b.		Perf. 12x12½ ('54)	.15	.15
101	A18	2½p blk & brt grn	.15	.20
102	A13	3p scarlet & blk	.25	.15
103	A12	4½p blue & blk	.40	.40
104	A10	6p violet & blk	.45	.45
a.		Booklet pane of 4	3.00	
b.		Perf. 12x12½ ('54)	.45	.45
105	A8	9p olive & blk	.70	1.65
106	A11	1sh myr grn & ind	.85	.85
107	A12	2sh rose brn & grn	1.50	1.50
108	A13	2sh6p ultra & grn	2.00	2.00
109	A14	5sh Prus bl & rose lil	3.00	3.00
110	A11	10sh green & lake	6.75	7.75
111	A14	20sh black & scar	10.50	12.50
		Nos. 97-111 (15)	27.20	31.20

Issue date: Nos. 97b, 100b, 104b, Mar. 8.

Revenue Stamps Overprinted "POSTAGE" and Bars in Black

Arms of Nyasaland A19

Perf. 11½x12

1963, Nov. 1		Engr.	Unwmk.	
112	A19	½p on 1p blue	.15	.15
113	A19	1p green	.15	.15
114	A19	2p rose red	.15	.15
115	A19	3p dark blue	.24	.20
116	A19	6p rose lake	.40	.40
117	A19	9p on 1sh car rose	.50	.50
118	A19	1sh purple	.55	.55
119	A19	2sh6p black	1.00	1.00
120	A19	5sh brown	1.40	1.40
121	A19	10sh gray olive	3.50	3.50
122	A19	£1 violet	6.25	6.25
		Nos. 112-122 (11)	14.29	14.25

Nos. 112, 117 have 3 bars over old value.

Mother and Child — A20

Designs: 1p, Chambo fish. 2p, Zebu bull. 3p, Peanuts. 4p, Fishermen in boat. 6p, Harvesting tea. 1sh, Lumber and tropical pine branch. 1sh3p, Tobacco industry. 2sh6p, Cotton industry. 5sh, Monkey Bay, Lake Nyasa. 10sh, Afzelia tree (pod mahogany). £1, Nyala antelope, vert.

Perf. 14½

1964, Jan. 1		Unwmk.	Photo.	
		Size: 23x19mm		
123	A20	½p lilac	.15	.15
124	A20	1p green & blk	.15	.15
125	A20	2p red brown	.20	.15
126	A20	3p pale brn, brn red & grn	.20	.15
127	A20	4p org yel & indigo	.25	.25
		Size: 41½x25mm, 25x41½mm		
128	A20	6p bl pur & brt yel grn	.30	.30
129	A20	1sh yel brn & dk grn	.65	.65
130	A20	1sh3p red brn & ol	.70	.65
131	A20	2sh6p blue & brn	1.25	1.25
132	A20	5sh grn, bl, sep & yel	1.75	1.75
133	A20	10sh org brn & grn & gray	3.00	3.00
134	A20	£1 yel & dk brn	6.00	6.00
		Nos. 123-134 (12)	14.60	14.45

Stamps of Malawi replaced those of Nyasaland Protectorate starting July 6, 1964.

POSTAGE DUE STAMPS

Catalogue values for unused stamps in this section are for Never Hinged items.

D1

1950, July 1		Wmk. 4	Typo.	Perf. 14	
J1	D1	1p rose red		2.50	8.00
J2	D1	2p ultramarine		6.00	16.00
J3	D1	3p green		9.00	10.00
J4	D1	4p claret		16.00	35.00
J5	D1	6p ocher		25.00	65.00
		Nos. J1-J5 (5)		58.50	134.00

Nyasaland Protectorate stamps can be mounted in the Scott British Africa album.

OMAN

ō-'män

(Muscat and Oman)

LOCATION — Southeastern corner of the Arabian Peninsula
GOVT. — Sultanate
AREA — 105,000 sq. mi.
POP. — 1,500,000 (est. 1982)
CAPITAL — Muscat

Nos. 16-93, the stamps with "value only" surcharges, were used not only in Muscat, but also in Dubai (Apr. 1, 1948 - Jan. 6, 1961), Qatar (Aug. 1950 - Mar. 31, 1957), Abu Dhabi (Mar. 30, 1963 - Mar. 29, 1964). Occasionally they also were used in Bahrain and Kuwait.

The Sultanate of Muscat and Oman changed its name to Oman in 1970.

12 Pies = 1 Anna
16 Annas = 1 Rupee
100 Naye Paise = 1 Rupee (1957)
64 Baizas = 1 Rupee (1966)
1000 Baizas = 1 Rial Saidi (1970)

Catalogue values for all unused stamps in this country are for Never Hinged items.

Muscat

Stamps of India 1937-43 Overprinted in Black

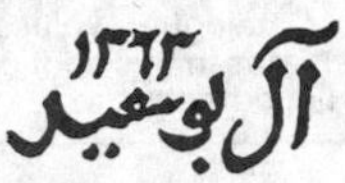

Wmk. Multiple Stars (196)

1944, Nov. 20 *Perf. 13½x14*

1	A83	3p slate	.15	.15
2	A83	½a rose violet	.15	.15
3	A83	9p lt green	.15	.15
4	A83	1a carmine rose	.15	.15
5	A84	1½a dark purple	.15	.25
a.		Double overprint	400.00	
6	A84	2a scarlet	.30	.45
7	A84	3a violet	.40	.55
8	A84	3½a ultra	.40	.55
9	A85	4a chocolate	.45	.65
10	A85	6a pck blue	.60	.90
11	A85	8a blue violet	.90	1.25
12	A85	12a car lake	1.25	1.75
13	A81	14a rose violet	1.25	1.75
14	A82	1r brown & slate	2.50	3.75
15	A82	2r dk brn & dk vio	4.00	6.00
		Nos. 1-15 (15)	12.80	18.45

200th anniv. of Al Busaid Dynasty. On Nos. 1-13 the overprint is smaller—13x6mm.

Great Britain, Nos. 258 to 263, 243, 248, 249A Surcharged

Perf. 14½x14

1948, Apr. 1 **Wmk. 251**

16	A101	½a on ½p green	.15	.15
17	A101	1a on 1p vermilion	.15	.20
18	A101	1½a on 1½p lt red brn	.30	.40
19	A101	2a on 2p lt org	.35	.55
20	A101	2½a on 2½p ultra	.40	.60
21	A101	3a on 3p violet	.15	.20
22	A102	6a on 6p rose lilac	.30	.25
23	A103	1r on 1sh brown	1.40	1.60

Wmk. 259 *Perf. 14*

24	A104	2r on 2sh6p yel grn	11.00	17.50
		Nos. 16-24 (9)	14.20	21.45

Silver Wedding Issue

Great Britain, Nos. 267 and 268, Surcharged with New Value in Black

Perf. 14½x14, 14x14½

1948, Apr. 26 **Wmk. 251**

25	A109	2½a on 2½p brt ultra	.15	.15
26	A110	15r on £1 dp chlky bl	35.00	35.00

Three bars obliterate the original denomination on No. 26.

Olympic Games Issue

Great Britain, Nos. 271 to 274, Surcharged with New Value in Black

1948, July 29 *Perf. 14½x14*

27	A113	2½a on 2½p brt ultra	.25	.20
28	A114	3a on 3p dp violet	.30	.20
29	A115	6a on 6p red violet	.45	.40
30	A116	1r on 1sh dk brown	1.10	.75
a.		Double surcharge	300.00	
		Nos. 27-30 (4)	2.10	1.55

A square of dots obliterates the original denomination on Nos. 28-30.

UPU Issue

Great Britain Nos. 276 to 279 Surcharged with New Value and Square of Dots in Black

1949, Oct. 10 **Photo.**

31	A117	2½a on 2½p brt ultra	.30	.30
32	A118	3a on 3p brt violet	.50	.50
33	A119	6a on 6p red violet	.85	.85
34	A120	1r on 1sh brown	1.50	1.50
		Nos. 31-34 (4)	3.15	3.15

Great Britain Nos. 280-286 Surcharged with New Value in Black

1951

35	A101	½a on ½p lt org	.30	.30
36	A101	1a on 1p ultra	.45	.45
37	A101	1½a on 1½p green	1.75	1.75
38	A101	2a on 2p lt red brn	.90	.90
39	A101	2½a on 2½p vermilion	1.75	1.75
40	A102	4a on 4p ultra	1.50	1.50

Wmk. 259 *Perf. 11x12*

41	A121	2r on 2sh6p green	20.00	17.50
		Nos. 35-41 (7)	26.65	24.15

Two types of surcharge on No. 41.

Stamps of Great Britain, 1952-54, Surcharged with New Value in Black and Dark Blue

1952-54 **Wmk. 298** *Perf. 14½x14*

42	A126	½a on ½p red org ('53)	.15	.15
43	A126	1a on 1p ultra ('53)	.15	.15
44	A126	1½a on 1½p green ('52)	.15	.15
45	A126	2a on 2p red brn ('53)	.20	.20
46	A127	2½a on 2½p scar ('52)	.25	.25
47	A127	3a on 3p dk pur (Dk Bl)	.30	.30
48	A128	4a on 4p ultra ('53)	.45	.45
49	A129	6a on 6p lilac rose	.60	.45
50	A132	12a on 1sh3p dk grn ('53)	1.60	1.40
51	A131	1r on 1sh6p dk bl ('53)	2.00	1.60
		Nos. 42-51 (10)	5.85	5.10

Coronation Issue

Great Britain Nos. 313-316 Surcharged with New Value in Black

1953, June 10

52	A134	2½a on 2½p scarlet	.70	.70
53	A135	4a on 4p brt ultra	1.10	1.10
54	A136	12a on 1sh3p dk green	3.50	3.50
55	A137	1r on 1sh6p dk blue	3.75	3.75
		Nos. 52-55 (4)	9.05	9.05

Squares of dots obliterate the original denominations on Nos. 54-55.

Great Britain Stamps of 1955-56 Surcharged with New Value in Black

Perf. 14½x14

1955-57 **Wmk. 308** **Photo.**

56	A126	1a on 1p ultra	.35	.35
56A	A126	1½a on 1½p grn		400.00
57	A126	2a on 2p red brn	.55	.55
58	A127	2½a on 2½p scar	.85	.85
59	A127	3a on 3p dk pur	1.25	1.25
60	A128	4a on 4p ultra	1.75	1.75
61	A129	6a on 6p lilac rose	1.00	1.00
62	A131	1r on 1sh6p dk bl	1.40	1.40

Engr. *Perf. 11x12*

63	A133	2r on 2sh6p dk brown	8.50	8.50
64	A133	5r on 5sh crimson	15.00	15.00
		Nos. 56,57-64 (9)	30.65	30.65

Surcharge on No. 63 exists in three types, on No. 64 in two types.

Issued: 2r, 9/23/55; 2a, 2½a, 6/8/56; 1r, 8/2/56; 4a, 12/9/56; 1½a, 1956; 3a, 2/3/57; 6a, 2/10/57; 5r, 3/1/57; 1a, 3/4/57.

Great Britain Nos. 317-325, 328, 332 Surcharged with New Value in Black

1957, Apr. 1 *Perf. 14½x14*

65	A129	1np on 5p lt brown	.15	.15
66	A126	3np on ½p red org	.15	.15
67	A126	6np on 1p ultra	.35	.35
68	A126	9np on 1½p green	.90	.70
69	A126	12np on 2p red brown	.50	.50
70	A127	15np on 2½p scar, I	.80	.80
a.		Type II	.60	.60
71	A127	20np on 3p dk pur	.30	.30
72	A128	25np on 4p ultra	.60	.60
73	A129	40np on 6p lilac rose	.80	.80
74	A130	50np on 9p dp ol grn	.80	.80
75	A132	75np on 1sh3p dk grn	1.25	1.25
		Nos. 65-75 (11)	6.60	6.40

The arrangement of the surcharge varies on different values; there are three bars through value on No. 74.

Jubilee Jamboree Issue

Great Britain Nos. 334-336 Surcharged with New Value and Square of Dots in Black

Perf. 14½x14

1957, Aug. 1 **Wmk. 308**

76	A138	15np on 2½p scar	.50	.50
77	A138	25np on 4p ultra	.75	.75
78	A138	75np on 1sh3p dk grn	.90	.90
		Nos. 76-78 (3)	2.15	2.15

50th anniv. of the Boy Scout movement and the World Scout Jubilee Jamboree, Aug. 1-12.

Great Britain Stamps of 1958-60 Surcharged with New Value in Black

Perf. 14½x14

1960-61 **Wmk. 322** **Photo.**

79	A129	1np on 5p lt brown	.15	.15
80	A126	3np on ½p red org	.90	.90
81	A126	5np on 1p ultra	.15	.15
82	A126	6np on 1p ultra	1.60	1.60
83	A126	10np on 1½p green	.40	.25
84	A126	12np on 2p red brn	2.75	2.75
85	A127	15np on 2½p scar	.30	.30
86	A127	20np on 3p dk pur	.30	.30
87	A128	30np on 4½p hn brn	.65	.60
88	A129	40np on 6p lil rose	.55	.55
89	A130	50np on 9p dp ol grn	.80	.65
90	A132	75np on 1sh3p dk grn	1.40	1.10
91	A131	1r on 1sh6p dk blue	1.65	1.40
92	A133	2r on 2sh6p dk brn	9.00	5.00
93	A133	5r on 5sh crimson	14.00	12.00
		Nos. 79-93 (15)	34.60	27.70

Issue dates: 15np, Apr. 26. 3np, 6np, 12np, June 21. 1np, Aug. 8. 20np, 40np, Sept. 28. 5np, 10np, 30np, 50np-5r, Apr. 8, 1961.

Muscat and Oman

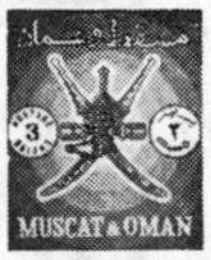

Crest — A1

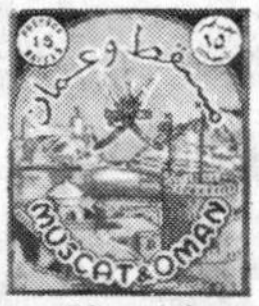

View of Harbor — A2

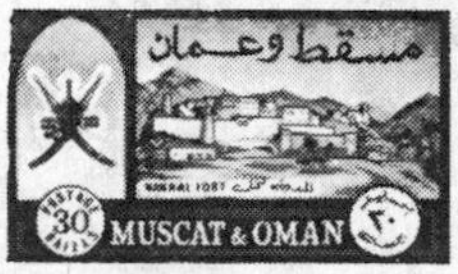

Nakhal Fort — A3

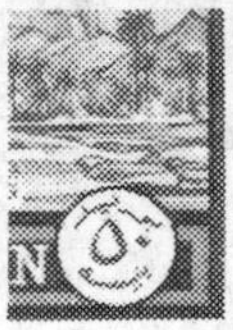

Baizas

Designs (Crest and): 50b, Samail Fort. 1r, Sohar Fort. 2r, Nizwa Fort. 5r, Matrah Fort. 10r, Mirani Fort.

Perf. 14½x14 (A1), 14x14½ (A2), 14x13½ (A3)

1966, Apr. 29 **Photo.** **Unwmk.**

94	A1	3b plum	.15	.15
95	A1	5b brown	.15	.15
96	A1	10b red brown	.15	.15
97	A2	15b black & violet	.30	.20
98	A2	20b black & ultra	.40	.25
99	A2	25b black & orange	.50	.35
100	A3	30b dk blue & lil rose	.65	.45
101	A3	50b red brn & brt grn	1.00	.60
a.		Value in "baizas" in Arabic	18.00	9.50
102	A3	1r org & dk bl	2.00	1.10
103	A3	2r grn & brn org	4.00	2.25
104	A3	5r dp car & vio	10.00	6.50
105	A3	10r dk vio & car rose	16.00	14.00
		Nos. 94-105 (12)	35.30	26.15

No. 101 has value in rupees in Arabic.
For surcharges see Nos. 133A, 133C.

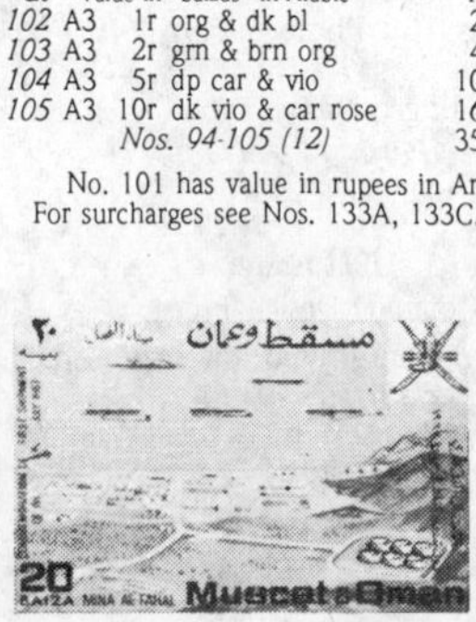

Mina al Fahal Harbor A4

Designs: 25b, Oil tanks. 40b, Oil installation in the desert. 1r, View of Arabian Peninsula from Gemini IV.

Perf. 13½x13

1969, Jan. 1 **Litho.** **Unwmk.**

106	A4	20b multicolored	.80	.60
107	A4	25b multicolored	1.00	.75
108	A4	40b multicolored	1.60	1.25
109	A4	1r multicolored	4.00	3.00
		Nos. 106-109 (4)	7.40	5.60

1st oil shipment from Muscat & Oman, July, 1967.

Types of 1966

Designs: 50b, Nakhal Fort. 75b, Samail Fort. 100b, Sohar Fort. ¼r, Nizwa Fort. ½r, Matrah Fort. 1r, Mirani Fort.

Perf. 14½x14 (A1), 14x14½ (A2), 14x13½ (A3)

1970, June 27 **Photo.** **Unwmk.**

110	A1	5b plum	.15	.15
111	A1	10b brown	.15	.15
112	A1	20b red brown	.30	.15
113	A2	25b black & vio	.35	.20
114	A2	30b black & ultra	.40	.30
115	A2	40b black & org	.55	.40
116	A3	50b dk blue & lil rose	.75	.45
117	A3	75b red brn & brt grn	1.00	.65
118	A3	100b orange & dk bl	1.40	.95
119	A3	¼r grn & brn org	4.00	2.75
120	A3	½r brn car & vio	8.50	5.50
121	A3	1r dk vio & car rose	16.50	11.00
		Nos. 110-121 (12)	34.05	22.65

Sultanate of Oman

Nos. 110-121 Overprinted

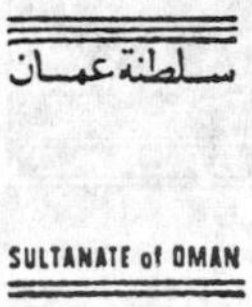

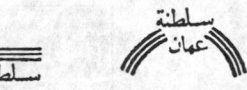

a

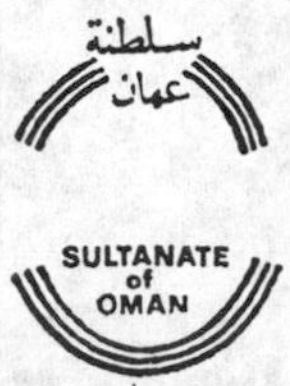

b

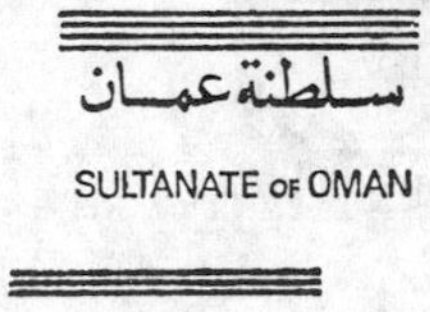

c

5b, 10b 20b:
Type 1- Lower bars 15¼mm long; letter "A" has low, thick crossbar.
Type 2- Lower bars 14¾mm; "A" crossbar high, thin.

Perf. 14½x14, 14x14½, 14x13½

1971, Jan. 16 **Photo.** **Unwmk.**

122	A1 (a)	5b plum	.15	.15
a.		Type 2	2.00	2.00
123	A1 (a)	10b brown	.15	.15
a.		Type 2	2.00	2.00
124	A1 (a)	20b red brown	.35	.20
a.		Type 2	5.00	5.00
125	A2 (b)	25b black & vio	.40	.25
126	A2 (b)	30b black & ultra	.50	.35
127	A2 (b)	40b black & org	.65	.50
128	A3 (c)	50b dk bl & lil rose	.85	.55
129	A3 (c)	75b red brn & brt grn	1.20	.80
130	A3 (c)	100b org & dk bl	1.60	1.10
131	A3 (c)	¼r grn & brn org	5.00	3.25
132	A3 (c)	½r brn car & vio	10.00	6.50
133	A3 (c)	1r dk vio & car rose	20.00	14.00
		Nos. 122-133 (12)	40.85	27.80

For surcharge see No. 133B.

No. 94 Surcharged Type "a," Nos. 127, 102 Surcharged

Perf. 14½x14, 14x14½, 14½x13½

1971-72

133A	A1	5b on 3b	7.00	4.00
133B	A2	25b on 40b	9.00	5.00
133C	A3	25b on 1r	11.00	6.00
		Nos. 133A-133C (3)	27.00	15.00

No. 133C surcharge resembles type "c" with "Sultanate of Oman" omitted and bars of crisscross lines.

No. 133A exists with inverted surchagre and in pair, one with surcharge omitted. No. 133C exist with Arabic "2" or "5" omitted.

Issue dates: 5b, Nov. No. 133C, June 6, 1972. No. 133B, July 1, 1972.

Sultan Qaboos bin Said and New
Buildings — A5

National Day: 40b, Sultan Qaboos and freedom
symbols. 50b, Crest of Oman and health clinic.
100b, Crest of Oman, classrooms and school.

1971, July 23   Litho.   Perf. 13¹/₂x14
134	A5	10b multicolored	1.90	.25
135	A5	40b multicolored	1.90	.65
136	A5	50b multicolored	2.50	1.00
137	A5	100b multicolored	4.25	1.65
		Nos. 134-137 (4)	10.55	3.55

Open
Book
A6

1972, Jan. 3   Perf. 14x14¹/₂
138	A6	25b ap grn, dk bl & dk red	5.00	2.00

International Book Year, 1972.

View of
Muscat,
1809
A7

Designs: 5, 10, 20, 25b, View of Matrah, 1809.
30, 40, 50, 75b, View of Shinas, 1809.

Wmk. 314 Sideways
1972, July 23   Litho.   Perf. 14x14¹/₂
Size: 21x17mm
139	A7	5b tan & multi	.20	.15
140	A7	10b blue & multi	.20	.15
141	A7	20b gray green & multi	.40	.20
142	A7	25b violet & multi	.55	.25

Perf. 14¹/₂x14
Size: 25x21mm
143	A7	30b tan & multi	.70	.30
144	A7	40b gray blue & multi	.90	.35
145	A7	50b rose brown & multi	1.25	.50
146	A7	75b olive & multi	2.00	.75

Perf. 14
Size: 41x25mm
147	A7	100b lilac & multi	2.00	.80
148	A7	¹/₄r green & multi	4.25	1.65
149	A7	¹/₂r bister & multi	8.00	3.25
150	A7	1r dull bl grn & multi	17.00	6.25
		Nos. 139-150 (12)	37.45	14.60

Perf. 14x14¹/₂, 14¹/₂x14
1972-75   Wmk. 314 Upright
139a	A7	5b tan & multi ('75)	.15	.15
140a	A7	10b blue & multi ('75)	.60	.35
141a	A7	20b gray grn & multi ('75)	1.10	.65
142a	A7	25b violet & multi ('75)	1.50	.90
143a	A7	30b tan & multi	2.00	1.20
144a	A7	40b blue & multi	2.50	1.50
145a	A7	50b rose brn & multi	3.00	1.75
146a	A7	75b olive & multi	5.00	3.00
		Nos. 139a-146a (8)	15.85	9.50

Issue dates: Nov. 17, 1972, Sept. 11, 1975.

Perf. 14x14¹/₂, 14¹/₂x14, 14
1976-82   Wmk. 373
139b	A7	5b tan & multi ('78)	.15	.15
140b	A7	10b blue & multi ('78)	.25	.25
141b	A7	20b gray grn & multi ('82)	.35	.25
142b	A7	25b vio & multi ('78)	.40	.25
143b	A7	30b tan & multi	.45	.30
144b	A7	40b blue & multi	.65	.45
145b	A7	50b rose brn & multi	.75	.50
146b	A7	75b olive & multi	1.20	.75
147b	A7	100b lilac & multi	1.65	1.10
148a	A7	¹/₄r grn & multi ('78)	4.00	2.50
149a	A7	¹/₂r bister & multi	7.50	5.00
150a	A7	1r dull bl grn & multi	15.00	10.00
		Nos. 139b-150a (12)	32.35	21.50

Issued: Apr. 12, 1976; Jan. 27, 1978; Mar. 15,
1982.

Ministerial Complex — A8

Litho.; Date Typo.
1973, Sept. 20   Unwmk.   Perf. 13
151	A8	25b emerald & multi	1.00	.50
152	A8	50b brown org & multi	3.50	1.75

Opening of ministerial complex.
Nos. 151-152 exist with date omitted and
hyphen omitted.

Dhows — A9

Perf. 12¹/₂x12
1973, Nov. 18   Litho.   Wmk. 314
153	A9	15b shown	.55	.35
154	A9	50b Seeb Airport	2.00	1.40
155	A9	65b Dhow and tanker	2.75	1.75
156	A9	100b Camel rider	3.75	2.50
		Nos. 153-156 (4)	9.05	6.00

National Day.

Port Qaboos — A10

1974, July 30   Litho.   Perf. 13
157	A10	100b multicolored	4.00	3.00

Opening of Port Qaboos.

Open Book,
Map of Arab
World — A11

Design: 100b, Hands reaching for book, vert.

1974, Sept. 8   Wmk. 314   Perf. 14¹/₂
158	A11	25b multicolored	1.00	.50
159	A11	100b multicolored	3.50	1.75

International Literacy Day, Sept. 8.

Sultan Qaboos, UPU and Arab Postal
Union Emblems — A12

1974, Oct. 29   Litho.   Perf. 13¹/₂
160	A12	100b multicolored	2.50	1.25

Centenary of Universal Postal Union.

Old Man
Learning to
Write
A13

1975, May 8   Photo.   Perf. 13x14
161	A13	25b multicolored	5.00	3.00

Eradication of illiteracy.

New Harbor at Mina Raysoot — A14

Designs: 50b, Stadium and map of Oman. 75b,
Water desalination plant. 100b, Oman color television station. 150b, Satellite earth station and map.
250b, Telephone, radar, cable and map.

Perf. 14x13¹/₂
1975, Nov. 18   Litho.   Wmk. 373
162	A14	30b multicolored	.35	.20
163	A14	50b multicolored	.65	.30
164	A14	75b multicolored	1.00	.45
165	A14	100b multicolored	1.40	.60
166	A14	150b multicolored	2.50	.95
167	A14	250b multicolored	3.75	1.60
		Nos. 162-167 (6)	9.65	4.10

National Day 1975.
For surcharges see Nos. 190A-190C.

Mother with Child, Nurse, Globe, Red
Crescent, IWY Emblem — A15

Design: 150b, Hand shielding mother and children, Omani flag, IWY emblem, vert.

Perf. 13¹/₂x14, 14x13¹/₂
1975, Dec. 27   Litho.
168	A15	75b citron & multi	1.50	1.10
169	A15	150b ultra & multi	3.00	2.00

International Women's Year 1975.

Sultan Presenting Colors and Opening
Seeb-Nizwa Road — A16

National Day: 40b, Paratroopers bailing out from
plane and mechanized harvester. 75b, Helicopter
squadron and Victory Day procession. 150b, Army
building road and Salalah television station.

1976, Nov. 15   Litho.   Perf. 14¹/₂
173	A16	25b multicolored	.50	.25
174	A16	40b multicolored	.70	.45
175	A16	75b multicolored	1.20	.80
176	A16	150b multicolored	2.00	1.75
		Nos. 173-176 (4)	4.40	3.25

Great Bath at Mohenjo-Daro — A17

1977, Jan. 6   Wmk. 373   Perf. 13¹/₂
177	A17	125b multicolored	3.00	2.00

UNESCO campaign to save Mohenjo-Daro excavations in Pakistan.

APU Emblem,
Members' Flags
A18

Coffeepots
A19

1977, Apr. 4   Litho.   Perf. 12
178	A18	30b emerald & multi	1.00	.60
179	A18	75b blue & multi	2.75	1.50

Arab Postal Union, 25th anniversary.

1977, Nov. 18   Litho.   Perf. 13¹/₂
Designs: 75b, Earthenware. 100b, Stone tablet,
Khor Rori, 100 B.C. 150b, Jewelry.
180	A19	40b multicolored	.75	.35
181	A19	75b multicolored	1.40	.65
182	A19	100b multicolored	1.75	.80
183	A19	150b multicolored	3.00	1.25
		Nos. 180-183 (4)	6.90	3.05

National Day 1977.

Forts
A20

Wmk. 373
1978, Nov. 18   Litho.   Perf. 14
184	A20	20b Jalali	.40	.25
185	A20	25b Nizwa	.50	.40
186	A20	40b Rostaq	.90	.60
187	A20	50b Sohar	1.00	.65
188	A20	75b Bahla	1.50	1.00
189	A20	100b Jibrin	2.00	1.25
		Nos. 184-189 (6)	6.30	4.15

National Day 1978.

Pilgrims, Mt.
Arafat, Holy
Kaaba
A21

1978, Nov. 1   Litho.   Perf. 13¹/₂
190	A21	40b multicolored	2.50	2.00

Pilgrimage to Mecca.

Nos. 166, 169 and 167 Surcharged
Perf. 14x13¹/₂
1978, July 30   Litho.   Wmk. 373
190A	A14	40b on 150b #166	17.50	17.50
190B	A15	50b on 150b #169	21.00	21.00
190C	A14	75b on 250b #167	32.50	32.50
		Nos. 190A-190C (3)	71.00	71.00

World Map,
Book,
Symbols of
Learning
A22

1979, Mar. 22   Litho.   Perf. 14x13½
191 A22   40b multicolored   .65   .45
192 A22   100b multicolored   1.60 1.10
Cultural achievements of the Arabs.

Girl on
Swing, IYC
Emblem
A23

1979, Oct. 28   Litho.   Perf. 14
193 A23   40b multicolored   2.75 1.75
International Year of the Child.

Gas
Plant
A24

National Day: 75b, Fisheries.

1979, Nov. 18   Photo.   Perf. 11½
194 A24   25b multicolored   1.50   .55
195 A24   75b multicolored   2.00 1.60

Sultan on Horseback, Military
Symbols — A25

Design: 100b, Soldier, parachutes, tank.

1979, Dec. 11
196 A25   40b multicolored   2.50 1.10
197 A25   100b multicolored   4.25 2.75
Armed Forces Day.

Hegira (Pilgrimage
Year) — A26

1980, Nov. 9   Photo.   Perf. 11½
198 A26   50b shown   1.00   .55
199 A26   150b Hegira emblem   3.00 1.75

Omani Women — A27

1980, Nov. 18
Granite Paper
200 A27   75b Bab Alkabir   .70   .45
201 A27   100b Corniche Highway   .95   .55
202 A27   250b Polo match   2.50 1.40
203 A27   500b shown   4.50 2.75
        Nos. 200-203 (4)   8.65 5.15
10th National Day.
For surcharges see Nos. 212-213.

Sultan and Patrol Boat — A28

1980, Dec. 11
Granite Paper
204 A28   150b shown   3.00 1.50
205 A28   750b Sultan, mounted
                 troops   13.00 6.50
Armed Forces Day.
For surcharges, see Nos. 210-211.

Policewoman and Children Crossing
Street — A29

1981, Feb. 7   Litho.   Perf. 13½x14
206 A29   50b shown   .65   .30
207 A29   100b Marching band   1.10   .55
208 A29   150b Mounted police on
                 beach   1.75   .85
209 A29   ½r Headquarters   6.00 2.80
        Nos. 206-209 (4)   9.50 4.50
First National Police Day.

Nos. 204-205, 200, 203 Surcharged in
Black on Silver

1981, Apr. 8   Photo.   Perf. 11½
210 A28   20b on 150b multi   1.90   .40
211 A28   30b on 750b multi   2.75   .60
212 A27   50b on 75b multi   4.75   .90
213 A27   100b on 500b multi   8.25 1.75
        Nos. 210-213 (4)   17.65 3.65

Welfare of the Blind — A30

1981, Oct. 14   Photo.   Perf. 11½
214 A30   10b multicolored   .60   .15

World
Food
Day
A31

1981, Oct. 16   Photo.   Perf. 12
215 A31   50b multicolored   2.25   .75

Hegira
(Pilgrimage
Year)
A32

1981, Oct. 25   Litho.   Perf. 14½
216 A32   50b multicolored   2.50   .75

11th
Natl.
Day
A32a

1981, Nov. 18   Photo.   Perf. 12
216A A32a   160b Al-Razha match
                  (sword vs. stick)   2.00 1.00
216B A32a   300b Sultan, map, vert.   3.75 1.90

Voyage of
Sinbad — A33

1981, Nov. 23   Litho.   Perf. 14½x14
217 A33   50b Muscat Port, 1981   .65   .35
218 A33   100b Dhow Shohar   1.25   .75
219 A33   130b Map   1.50 1.00
220 A33   200b Muscat Harbor,
                 1650   2.50 1.50
  a. Souvenir sheet of 4, #217-220   10.00 4.50
        Nos. 217-220 (4)   5.90 3.60

Armed
Forces
Day
A34

1981, Dec. 11   Photo.   Perf. 11½
221 A34   100b Sultan, planes   1.75   .80
222 A34   400b Patrol boats   6.50 3.50

Natl. Police
Day
A35

1982, Jan. 5   Litho.   Perf. 14½
223 A35   50b Patrol launch   .80   .55
224 A35   100b Band, vert.   1.60 1.10

Nerium
Mascatense
A36

Red-legged
Partridge
A37

1982, July 7   Photo.   Perf. 12½
Granite Paper
225 A36   5b shown   .25   .25
226 A36   10b Dionysia mira   .25   .25
227 A36   20b Teucrium mascat-
                 ense   .25   .25
228 A36   25b Geranium mascat-
                 ense   .25   .25
229 A36   30b Cymatium boschi,
                 horiz.   .30   .30
230 A36   40b Acteon eloiseae,
                 horiz.   .45   .45
231 A36   50b Cypraea teulerei,
                 horiz.   .50   .50
232 A36   75b Cypraea pulchra,
                 horiz.   .75   .75
233 A37   100b shown   1.00 1.00
234 A37   ¼r Hoopoe   2.50 2.50
Size: 25x38mm
235 A37   ½r Tahr   5.00 5.00
236 A37   1r Arabian oryx   10.00 10.00
        Nos. 225-236 (12)   21.50 21.50

2nd Municipalities Week (1981) — A38

Perf. 13½x14½
1982, Oct. 28   Litho.
237 A38   40b multicolored   2.25   .65

ITU
Plenipotentiaries
Conference,
Nairobi,
Sept. — A39

1982, Nov. 6   Perf. 14½x13½
238 A39   100b multicolored   3.00   .75

12th
Natl.
Day
A40

1982, Nov. 18   Perf. 12
239 A40   40b State Consultative
                 Council inaugural
                 session   1.00   .40
240 A40   100b Oil refinery   2.25   .80

Armed
Forces
Day
A41

1982, Dec. 11   Perf. 13½x14
241 A41   50b Soldiers   1.10   .45
242 A41   100b Mounted band   2.25   .90

Arab
Palm
Tree
Day
A42

Perf. 13½x14½
1982, Sept. 19   Litho.
243 A42   40b Picking coconuts   .90   .40
244 A42   100b Dates   2.25   .90

Natl. Police
Day — A43

1983, Jan. 5   Litho.   Perf. 14x13½
245 A43   50b multicolored   2.25   .75

World Communications Year — A44

1983, May 17   Perf. 13¹/₂x14
246 A44 50b multicolored   2.25 .75

Beehive
A45

1983, Aug. 15   Litho.   Perf. 13¹/₂
247   Strip of 2   2.25 1.00
a.-b. A45 50b any single   1.10 .50

Hegira (Pilgrimage Year) — A46

1983, Sept. 14   Photo.   Perf. 13¹/₂
248 A46 40b multicolored   3.00 .75

Youth
Year
A47

Perf. 12¹/₂x13¹/₂
1983, Nov. 15   Litho.
249 A47 50b multicolored   2.00 .65

National Day 1983 — A48

1983, Nov. 18   Litho.   Perf. 13¹/₂x14
250 A48 50b Sohar Copper Factory 1.25 .40
251 A48 100b Sultan Qaboos University   2.25 .80

Armed
Forces
Day
A49

1983, Dec. 11   Litho.   Perf. 13¹/₂x14
252 A49 100b multicolored   2.25 .65

Police
Day
A50

1984, Jan. 5   Litho.   Perf. 13¹/₂x14
253 A50 100b multicolored   2.75 .65

7th Arabian Gulf Soccer Tournament,
Muscat, Mar. 9-26 — A51

1984, Mar. 9   Litho.   Perf. 13¹/₂
254 A51 40b Players, cup, vert. 1.00 .25
255 A51 50b Emblem   1.25 .40

Pilgrims at Stone-Throwing
Ceremony — A52

1984, Sept. 5   Litho.   Perf. 13¹/₂x14
256 A52 50b multicolored   2.25 .50
Pilgrimage to Mecca.

National Day 1984 — A53

Perf. 13¹/₂x14, 14x13¹/₂
1984, Nov. 18   Litho.
257 A53 130b Mail sorting, new p.o. 1.90 .70
258 A53 160b Map, vert.   2.25 .80
Inauguration of the new Central P.O., development of telecommunications.

16th Arab Scout Conference,
Muscat — A54

1984, Dec. 5   Litho.   Perf. 14¹/₂
259 A54 50b Setting-up camp .65 .65
260 A54 50b Map reading .65 .65
  a.   Pair, #259-260 1.00 1.00
261 A54 130b Saluting natl. flag 1.65 1.65
262 A54 130b Scouts and girl guides 1.65 1.65
  a.   Pair, #261-262 2.50 2.50
   Nos. 259-262 (4) 4.60 4.60

Armed
Forces
Day
A55

1984, Dec. 11   Perf. 13¹/₂x14
263 A55 100b multicolored   3.00 .60

Police Day — A56

1985, Jan. 5   Perf. 14x13¹/₂
264 A56 100b multicolored   2.75 .60

Hegira
(Pilgrimage
Year)
A57

1985, Aug. 20   Litho.   Perf. 13¹/₂x14
265 A57 50b Al-Khaif Mosque, Mina   1.50 .50

Intl. Youth
Year
A58

1985, Sept. 22   Litho.   Perf. 13¹/₂x14
266 A58 50b Emblems .70 .30
267 A58 100b Emblem, youth activities   1.40 .55

Jabrin Palace Restoration — A59

1985, Sept. 22   Litho.   Perf. 13¹/₂x14
268 A59 100b Interior 1.25 .75
269 A59 250b Restored ceiling 3.75 2.00

Intl. Symposium on Traditional
Music — A60

1985, Oct. 6   Litho.   Perf. 13¹/₂x14
270 A60 50b multicolored   1.50 .50

UN Child
Survival
Campaign
A61

1985, Oct. 25   Litho.   Perf. 13¹/₂x14
271 A61 50b multicolored   1.50 .50

Flags, Map and Sultan Qaboos — A62

1985, Nov. 3   Litho.   Perf. 12¹/₂
272 A62 40b shown .90 .30
273 A62 50b Supreme Council, vert. 1.10 .35
6th Session of Arab Gulf States Supreme Council, Muscat.

Natl.
Day
1985
A63

Progress and development. 20b, Sultan Qaboos University. 50b, Date picking, plowing field. 100b, Port Qaboos Cement Factory. 200b, Post, transportation and communications. 250b, Sultan Qaboos, vert.

1985, Nov. 18
274 A63 20b multicolored .20 .15
275 A63 50b multicolored .50 .30
276 A63 100b multicolored 1.00 .60
277 A63 200b multicolored 1.90 1.15
278 A63 250b multicolored 2.50 1.40
   Nos. 274-278 (5) 6.10 3.60

Armed
Forces
Day
A64

1985, Dec. 11   Perf. 13¹/₂x14
279 A64 100b multicolored   1.75 .65

Fish and
Crustaceans — A65

Perf. 11¹/₂x12, 12x11¹/₂
1985, Dec. 15   Photo.
280 A65 20b Chaetodon collaris .20 .15
281 A65 50b Chaetodon melapterus .65 .40
282 A65 100b Chaetodon gardineri 1.25 .75
283 A65 150b Scomberomorus commerson 1.75 1.10
284 A65 200b Panulirus homarus 2.25 1.50
   Nos. 380-284 (5) 6.10 3.90
   Nos. 280-282, vert.

Frankincense Trees in Oman — A66

1985, Dec. 15   Litho.   Perf. 13¹/₂x14
285 A66 100b multicolored .85 .55
286 A66 3r multicolored 30.00 15.00

Police
Day
A67

1986, Jan. 5   Litho.   Perf. 13¹/₂x14
287 A67 50b Camel Corps, Muscat 1.50 .30

Statue of
Liberty,
Cent.
A68

Maps and: 50b, Sultanah, voyage from Muscat to US 1840. 100b, Statue, Shabab Oman voyage from Oman to US, 1986, and fortress.

1986, July 4   *Perf. 14¹/₂*
288 A68 50b multicolored   .80   .30
289 A68 100b multicolored   1.65   .60
a.   Souvenir sheet of 2, #288-289   3.75   1.50

No. 289a sold for 250b.

Pilgrimage to Mecca
A69

1986, Aug. 9
290 A69 50b Holy Kaaba   1.25   .30

17th Arab Scout Camp — A70

1986, Aug. 20
291 A70 50b Erecting tent   .85   .30
292 A70 100b Surveying   1.75   .60

Sultan Qaboos Sports Complex Inauguration — A71

1986, Oct. 18   Litho.   *Perf. 14¹/₂*
293 A71 100b multicolored   1.75   .60

Intl. Peace Year A72

1986, Oct. 24   *Perf. 13¹/₂x13*
294 A72 130b multicolored   1.75   .80

A73

A74   100

Natl. Day 1986 — A75

1986, Nov. 18   *Perf. 14¹/₂*
295 A73 50b mutlicolored   .45   .30
296 A74 100b multicolored   .85   .60

Perf. 13¹/₂x13
297 A75 130b multicolored   3.00   .80
   Nos. 295-297 (3)   4.30   1.70

Police Day A76

1987, Jan. 5   *Perf. 13¹/₂x14*
298 A76 50b multicolored   1.25   .30

Second Arab Gulf Week for Social Work, Bahrain A77

1987, Mar. 21   Litho.   *Perf. 13¹/₂x13*
299 A77 50b multicolored   1.25   .25

Intl. Environment Day — A78

Perf. 13¹/₂x13, 13x13¹/₂
1987, June 5   Litho.
300 A78 50b Flamingos in flight   .75   .30
301 A78 130b Irrigation canal, vert.   1.75   .70

Pilgrimage to Mecca A79

Stages of Pilgrimage (not in consecutive order): a, Pilgrims walking the tawaf, circling the Holy Kaaba 7 times. b, Tent City, Mina. c, Symbolic stoning of Satan. d, Pilgrims in Muzdalifah at dusk, picking up stones. e, Veneration of the prophet (pilgrims praying), Medina. f, Pilgrims wearing ihram, Pilgrim's Village, Jeddah.

1987, July 29   Litho.   *Perf. 13¹/₂*
302   Strip of 6   5.00   1.80
a.-f.   A79 50b any single   .80   .30

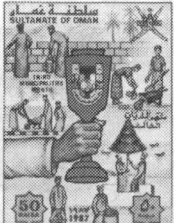

Third Municipalities Month — A80

1987, Oct. 1   *Perf. 13x13¹/₂*
303 A80 50b multicolored   1.10   .30

Natl. Day A81

Designs: 50b, Marine Biology and Fisheries Center. 130b, Royal Hospital.

1987, Nov. 18   Litho.   *Perf. 13¹/₂x13*
304 A81 50b multicolored   .70   .70
305 A81 130b multicolored   1.75   1.75

Royal Omani Amateur Radio Soc., 15th Anniv. — A82

1987, Dec. 23   Litho.   *Perf. 13¹/₂x13*
306 A82 130b multicolored   1.10   1.10

Traditional Handicrafts A83

1988, June 1   Photo.   *Perf. 12x11¹/₂*
Granite Paper
307 A83 50b Weaver   .40   .40
308 A83 100b Potter   .75   .75
309 A83 150b Halwa maker   1.25   1.25
310 A83 200b Silversmith   1.50   1.50
a.   Souvenir sheet of 4, #307-310   5.25   5.25
   Nos. 307-310 (4)   3.90   3.90

No. 310a sold for 600b.

A84   A85

1988, Sept. 17   Litho.   *Perf. 14¹/₂*
311 A84 100b Equestrian   .70   .70
312 A84 100b Field hockey   .70   .70
313 A84 100b Soccer   .70   .70
314 A84 100b Running   .70   .70
315 A84 100b Swimming   .70   .70
316 A84 100b Shooting   .70   .70
a.   Block of 6, #311-316   4.25   4.25
b.   Souvenir sheet of 6, #311-316   5.25   5.25
   Nos. 311-316 (6)   4.20   4.20

1988 Summer Olympics, Seoul.

1988, Nov. 1   Litho.   *Perf. 13¹/₂*
317 A85 100b multicolored   1.10   1.10

WHO, 40th anniv.

Natl. Day, Agriculture Year — A86

1988, Nov. 18   *Perf. 14¹/₂x13¹/₂*
318 A86 100b Tending crops   1.00   1.00
319 A86 100b Animal husbandry   1.00   1.00
a.   Pair, #318-319   2.00   2.00

No. 319a has a continuous design.

Women Wearing Regional Folk Costume — A87

Designs: 200b-1r, Men wearing regional folk costumes.

Perf. 11¹/₂x12
1989   Photo.   **Granite Paper**
320 A87 30b Dhahira   .20   .20
321 A87 40b Eastern   .25   .25
322 A87 50b Batinah   .35   .35
323 A87 100b Interior   .65   .65
324 A87 130b Southern   .90   .90
325 A87 150b Muscat   1.00   1.00
a.   Souvenir sheet of 6, #320-325   6.00   6.00
326 A87 200b Dhahira   1.40   1.40
327 A87 ¼r Eastern   1.65   1.65
328 A87 ½r Southern   5.00   5.00
329 A87 1r Muscat   6.75   6.75
a.   Souvenir sheet of 4, #326-329   15.00   15.00
   Nos. 320-329 (10)   18.15   18.15

No. 325a sold for 700b, No. 329a for 2r.
Issued: 30b-150b, Aug. 26; 200b-1r, Nov. 11.

National Day, Agriculture Year — A88

1989, Nov. 18   *Perf. 12¹/₂x13*
330 A88 100b Fishing   .55   .55
331 A88 100b Farming   .55   .55
a.   Pair, #330-331   1.10   1.10

Printed se-tenant in a continuous design.

10th Session of Supreme Council of the Cooperation Council for Arab Gulf States — A89

1989, Dec. 18   Litho.   *Perf. 13x12*
332 A89 50b Flags, Omani crest   .30   .30
333 A89 50b Sultan Qaboos, council emblem   .30   .30
a.   Pair, #332-333   .55   .55

Printed se-tenant in a continuous design.

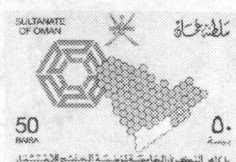

Gulf Investment Corp., 5th Anniv. (in 1989) — A90

1990, Jan. 1   Litho.   *Perf. 13x12*
334 A90 50b multicolored   .30   .30
335 A90 130b multicolored   .70   .70

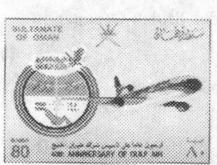

Gulf Air, 40th Anniv. A91

1990, Mar. 24 Perf. 13x13½
336 A91 80b multicolored .40 .40

Symposium on the Oman Ophiolite — A92

1990, Apr. 22 Photo. Perf. 11½
Granite Paper
337 A92 80b shown .45 .45
338 A92 150b multicolored .80 .80

First Omani Envoy to the US, 150th Anniv. — A93

1990, Apr. 30 Litho. Perf. 13
339 A93 200b multicolored 1.05 1.05

Sultan Qaboos Rose — A94

1990, May 5 Photo. Perf. 11½
Granite Paper
340 A94 200b multicolored 1.05 1.05

20th National Day A95

Designs: 100b, National Day emblem. 200b, Sultan Qaboos.

Litho. & Embossed
1990, Nov. 18 Perf. 12x11½
Granite Paper
341 A95 100b gold, red & green .55 .55
342 A95 200b gold, green & red 1.10 1.10
a. Souvenir sheet of 2, #341-342 2.85 2.85
No. 342a sold for 500b.

Blood Donors — A96

1991, Apr. 22 Litho. Perf. 13½x13
343 A96 50b multicolored .25 .25
344 A96 200b multicolored 1.10 1.10
a. Pair, #343-344 1.35 1.35

National Day — A97

1991, Nov. 18 Photo. Perf. 13½
345 A97 100b shown .50 .50
346 A97 200b Sultan Qaboos 1.10 1.10
a. Souvenir sheet of 2, #345-346 2.00 2.00
No. 346a sold for 400b.

Armed Forces Day A98

1991, Dec. 11 Litho. Perf. 14½
347 A98 100b multicolored .50 .50

A99 A100

1992, Jan. 29 Litho. Perf. 13½x14
348 A99 100b multicolored .50 .50
a. Sheet of 1, perf. 13x13½ 1.50 1.50
Inauguration of Omani-French Museum, Muscat. No. 348a sold for 300b.

1992, Mar. 23 Litho. Perf. 14½
349 A100 200b multicolored 1.00 1.00
World Meteorological Day.

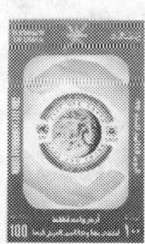 

A101 A102

1992, June 5 Litho. Perf. 13x13½
350 A101 100b multicolored .50 .50
World Environment Day.

1992, Sept. 26 Litho. Perf. 13½x14
351 A102 70b multicolored .35 .35
Welfare of Handicapped Children.

Sultan Qaboos Encyclopedia of Arab Names — A103

1992, Oct. 10 Perf. 14½
352 A103 100b gold & multi .55 .55

National Day — A104

Sultan Qaboos and emblems of: 100b, Year of Industry. 200b, Majlis As'shura.

1992, Nov. 18 Litho. Perf. 14x13½
353 A104 100b multicolored .55 .55
354 A104 200b multicolored 1.05 1.05

Royal Oman Police Day A105

1993, Jan. 5 Litho. Perf. 13½x14
355 A105 80b multicolored .45 .45

1993 Census A106

1993, Sept. 4 Litho. Perf. 14x13½
356 A106 100b multicolored .55 .55

Royal Navy Day — A107

1993, Nov. 3 Litho. Perf. 13
357 A107 100b multicolored .55 .55

23rd National Day A108

1993, Nov. 18 Photo. Perf. 12
Granite Paper
358 A108 100b Year of Youth emblem .55 .55
359 A108 200b Sultan Qaboos 1.00 1.00

Scouting — A109

Designs: No. 360, Emblem of Scouts and Guides, Scout Headquarters. No. 361, Scout camp, Sultan Qaboos.

1993, Nov. 20 Litho. Perf. 13x13½
360 A109 100b multicolored .55 .55
361 A109 100b multicolored .55 .55
a. Pair, #360-361 1.10 1.10
Scouting movement in Oman, 61st anniv. (#360). Installation of Sultan Qaboos as chief scout, 10th anniv. (#361).

Whales and Dolphins — A110

Designs: No. 362, Dolphins, humpback whale. No. 363, Dolphins, sperm whale. Illustration reduced.

1993, Dec. 8 Perf. 14½
362 A110 100b multicolored .55 .55
363 A110 100b multicolored .55 .55
a. Pair, #362-363 1.10 1.10
b. Souvenir sheet of 2, #362-363 2.25 2.25
No. 363a has a continuous design. No. 363b sold for 400b and has a white border surrounding the stamps.

World Day for Water — A111   Muscat Municipality, 70th Anniv. — A112

1994, Mar. 22 Litho. Perf. 13½
364 A111 50b multicolored .25 .25

1994, Apr. 16
365 A112 50b multicolored .25 .25

Intl. Olympic Committee, Cent. — A113

1994, Aug. 29 Litho. Perf. 13½
366 A113 100b multicolored .55 .55

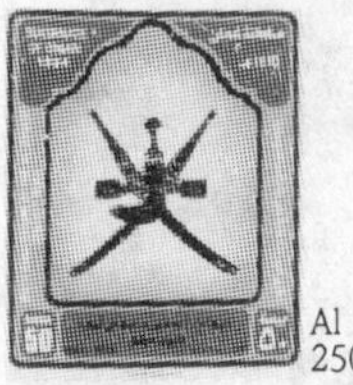

Al Busaid Dynasty, 250th Anniv. — A114

Natl. arms or sultan, dates: a, 1744-75. b, 1775-79. c, 1779-92. d, 1792-1804. e, 1804-7. f, Sa'id ibn Sultan, 1807-56. g, 1856-65. h, 1866-68. i, 1868-71. j, Sultan, 1871-88. k, Sultan, 1888-1913. l, Sultan Taymur ibn Faysal, 1913-32. m, Sultan Qaboos, laurel tree. n, Sultan Sa'id ibn Taymur, 1932-70. o, Sultan Qaboos, 1970-.

Litho. & Embossed

1994, Dec. 28 *Perf. 11½*

367	A114	50b Block of 15, #a.-o.	4.50	4.50

Nos. 367f, 367j-367o contain portraits of sultans.

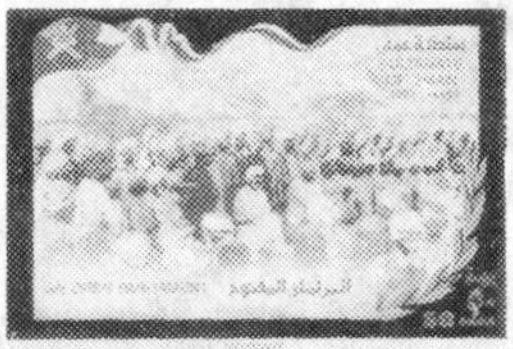

Open Parliament — A115

1995, Jan. 7 Litho. *Perf. 14*

Granite Paper

368	A115	50b silver & multi	*.50*	*.50*

SEMI-POSTAL STAMP

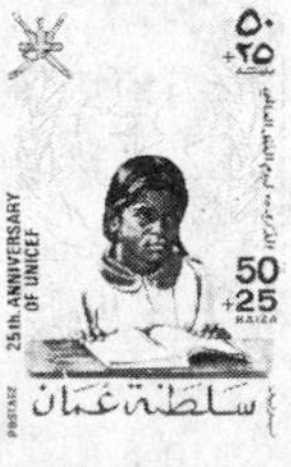

UNICEF Emblem, Girl with Book — SP1

Wmk. 314

1971, Dec. 25 Litho. *Perf. 14*

B1	SP1	50b + 25b multicolored	10.00	6.50

25th anniv. of UNICEF.

OFFICIAL STAMPS

Official Stamps of India 1938-43 Overprinted in Black

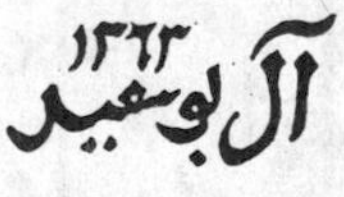

Perf. 13½x14

1944, Nov. 20 **Wmk. 196**

O1	O8	3p slate	.20	.15
O2	O8	½a dk rose violet	.20	.15
O3	O8	9p green	.20	.15
O4	O8	1a carmine rose	.20	.15
O5	O8	1½a dull purple	.40	.20
O6	O8	2a scarlet	.45	.20
O7	O8	2½a purple	.55	.25
O8	O8	4a dark brown	.60	.30
O9	O8	8a blue violet	1.00	.50
O10	A82	1r brown & slate	2.50	1.10
		Nos. O1-O10 (10)	6.30	3.15

Al Busaid Dynasty, 200th anniv. On Nos. O1-O9 the overprint is smaller — 13x6mm.

ORANGE RIVER COLONY

'är-inj 'ri-vər 'kä-lə-nē

(Orange Free State)

LOCATION — South Africa, north of the Cape of Good Hope between the Orange and Vaal Rivers

GOVT. — A former British Crown Colony
AREA — 49,647 sq. mi.
POP. — 528,174 (1911)
CAPITAL — Bloemfontein

Orange Free State was an independent republic, 1854-1900. Orange River Colony existed from May, 1900, to June, 1910, when it united with Cape of Good Hope, Natal and the Transvaal to form the Union of South Africa.

12 Pence = 1 Shilling

Values for unused stamps are for examples with original gum as defined in the catalogue introduction. Very fine examples of Nos. 1-60c will have perforations touching the design on one or more sides due to the narrow spacing of the stamps on the plates. Stamps with perfs clear of the design on all four sides are scarce and will command higher prices.

Een = 1
Twee = 2
Drie = 3
Vier = 4

Issues of the Republic

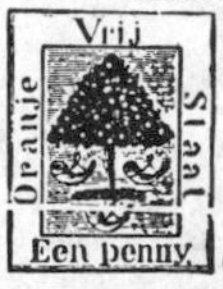

Orange Tree — A1

1868-1900 Unwmk. Typo. *Perf. 14*

1	A1	½p red brown ('83)	1.00	.50
2	A1	½p orange ('97)	1.00	.35
3	A1	1p brown	4.00	.40
4	A1	1p violet ('94)	1.00	.25
5	A1	2p violet ('83)	3.25	.40
6	A1	3p ultra ('83)	1.50	1.25
7	A1	4p ultra ('78)	3.25	1.25
8	A1	6p car rose ('90)	2.75	.85
a.		6p rose ('68)	12.00	4.00
b.		6p ultramarine ('00)	90.00	
10	A1	1sh orange	15.00	1.10
a.		1sh orange buff	*50.00*	*6.00*
11	A1	1sh brown ('97)	7.00	2.00
12	A1	5sh green ('78)	9.00	10.00
		Nos. 1-8,10-12 (11)	48.75	18.35

No. 8b was not placed in use without surcharge.
For surcharges see #13-53, 44j-53c, 57-60.

No. 8a Surcharged:

4 4 4 4
a b c d

1877

13	(a)	4p on 6p rose	110.00	40.00
a.		Inverted surcharge	*1,000.*	500.00
b.		Double surcharge, one inverted ("a" and "c")		1,000.
14	(b)	4p on 6p rose	1,100.	225.00
a.		Inverted surcharge	*1,400.*	1,000.
b.		Double surcharge, one inverted ("b" and "d")	*1,500.*	750.00
15	(c)	4p on 6p rose	75.00	27.50
a.		Inverted surcharge	*500.00*	300.00
16	(d)	4p on 6p rose	125.00	50.00
a.		Inverted surcharge	*900.00*	400.00

No. 12 Surcharged with Bar and:

1d. 1d. 1d. 1d. 1d.
f g h i k

1881

17	(f)	1p on 5sh green	50.00	11.00
18	(g)	1p on 5sh green	75.00	37.50
a.		Inverted surcharge	600.00	500.00
b.		Double surcharge		600.00
19	(h)	1p on 5sh green	30.00	9.00
a.		Inverted surcharge	625.00	600.00
b.		Double surcharge	625.00	600.00
20	(i)	1p on 5sh green	40.00	10.00
a.		Double surcharge	*725.00*	500.00
b.		Inverted surcharge	575.00	450.00
21	(k)	1p on 5sh green	250.00	190.00
a.		Inverted surcharge	1,250.	1,100.
b.		Double surcharge		—
		Nos. 17-21 (5)	445.00	257.50

No. 12 Surcharged: ½d

1882

22	A1	½p on 5sh green	3.50	4.00
a.		Double surcharge	350.00	325.00
b.		Inverted surcharge	*800.00*	*800.00*

No. 7 Surcharged with Thin Line and:

3d 3d 3d 3d 3d
m n o p q

1882

23	(m)	3p on 4p ultra	65.00	24.00
a.		Double surcharge		625.00
24	(n)	3p on 4p ultra	50.00	19.00
a.		Double surcharge		625.00
25	(o)	3p on 4p ultra	27.50	18.00
a.		Double surcharge		625.00
26	(p)	3p on 4p ultra	150.00	60.00
a.		Double surcharge		750.00
27	(q)	3p on 4p ultra	50.00	25.00
a.		Double surcharge		625.00
		Nos. 23-27 (5)	342.50	146.00

No. 6 Surcharged 2d

1888

28	A1	2p on 3p ultra	10.00	1.75
a.		Wide "2"	25.00	10.00
b.		As No. 28, invtd. surch.		350.00
c.		As No. 28a, invtd. surch.		900.00

Nos. 6 and 7 Surcharged:

1d 1d Id
r s t

1890-91

29	(r)	1p on 3p ultra ('91)	1.50	.85
a.		Double surcharge	75.00	75.00
30	(r)	1p on 4p ultra	15.00	5.00
a.		Double surcharge	120.00	100.00
31	(s)	1p on 3p ultra ('91)	8.00	3.00
a.		Double surcharge	165.00	165.00
32	(s)	1p on 4p ultra	75.00	50.00
a.		Double surcharge	250.00	225.00
b.		Triple surcharge		
33	(t)	1p on 4p ultra	*950.00*	*750.00*

No. 6 Surcharged 2½d.

1892

34	A1	2½p on 3p ultra	4.00	1.00
a.		Without period	50.00	50.00

No. 6 Surcharged:

½d ½d ½d ½d ½d
v w x y z

1896

35	(v)	½p on 3p ultra	2.50	2.50
a.		Double surcharge "v" and "y"	14.00	12.00
36	(w)	½p on 3p ultra	5.00	3.00
a.		Double surcharge "w" and "y"	15.00	15.00
37	(x)	½p on 3p ultra	5.00	3.00
38	(y)	½p on 3p ultra	2.25	2.25
a.		Double surcharge	12.50	11.00
39	(z)	½p on 3p ultra	4.50	2.75

Surcharged as "v" but "1" with Straight Serif

40	A1	½p on 3p ultra	5.00	5.00
a.		Double surcharge, one type "y"	13.00	13.00

Surcharged as "z" but "1" with Straight Serif

41	A1	½p on 3p ultra	4.75	5.00
a.		Double surcharge, one type "y"	12.50	11.00
		Nos. 35-41 (7)	29.00	23.50

No. 6 Surcharged

Halve
Penny.

1896

42	A1	½p on 3p ultra	.65	.65
a.		No period after "Penny"	10.00	15.00
b.		"Peuny"	8.50	8.50
c.		Inverted surcharge	60.00	60.00
d.		Double surch., one inverted	165.00	165.00
e.		Without bar	5.00	5.00
f.		With additional surcharge as on Nos. 35-41	75.00	75.00

Nos. 42c, 42d, 42f probably were created as favors. They were not available to the public.

No. 6 Surcharged 2½

1897

43	A1	2½p on 3p ultra	2.00	.75
a.		Roman "I" instead of "1" in "½"	150.00	90.00

Issued under British Occupation

V. R. I.

Nos. 2-8, 8a, 10-12 Surcharged or Overprinted

½d

1900, Mar.-Apr. Unwmk. *Perf. 14*

Periods in "V.R.I." Level with Bottoms of Letters

44	A1	½p on ½p orange	1.50	1.50
a.		No period after "V"	15.00	15.00
b.		No period after "I"	170.00	170.00
c.		"I" and period after "R" omitted		
f.		"½" omitted	*175.00*	*175.00*
g.		Small "½"	45.00	45.00
h.		Double surcharge	125.00	*125.00*
i.		As "g," double surcharge	300.00	
45	A1	1p on 1p violet	1.65	.75
a.		No period after "V"	10.50	10.50
b.		"I" and period after "R" omitted	155.00	170.00
d.		"1" of "1d" omitted	165.00	175.00
e.		"d" omitted	300.00	300.00
f.		"1d" omitted, "V.R.I." at top	375.00	
45O	A1	1p on 1p brown	*600.00*	*500.00*
y.		No period after "V"	*2,250.*	
46	A1	2p on 2p violet	.35	.60
a.		No period after "V"	10.00	12.00
b.		No period after "R"	250.00	
c.		No period after "I"	250.00	
47	A1	'2½' on 3p ultra	4.50	4.00
a.		No period after "V"	70.00	65.00
b.		Roman "I" in "½"	165.00	275.00
48	A1	3p on 3p ultra	1.50	1.00
a.		No period after "V"	13.00	13.00
b.		Dbl. surch. one diagonal	600.00	
49	A1	4p on 4p ultra	4.50	6.00
a.		No period after "V"	50.00	52.50
50	A1	6p on 6p car rose	35.00	35.00
a.		No period after "V"	250.00	300.00
b.		"6" omitted	300.00	300.00
51	A1	6p on 6p ultra	2.75	3.25
a.		No period after "V"	30.00	30.00
c.		"6" omitted	65.00	65.00
52	A1	1sh on 1sh brown	3.50	3.50
a.		No period after "V"	30.00	30.00
c.		"1" of "1s" omitted	110.00	110.00
52G	A1	1sh on 1sh org	*2,250.*	*2,000.*
53	A1	5sh on 5sh green	18.00	30.00
a.		No period after "V"	175.00	175.00
b.		"5" omitted	700.00	700.00

#47, 47c overprinted "V.R.I." on #43.

No. 45f ("1d" omitted) with "V.R.I." at bottom is a shift which sells for a fifth of the value of the listed item. Varieties such as "V.R.I." omitted, denomination omitted and pair, one without surcharge are also the result of shifts.

For surcharges see Nos. 57, 60.

1900-01

Periods in "V.R.I." Raised Above Bottoms of Letters

44j	A1	½p on ½p orange	.25	.15
k.		Mixed periods	1.75	1.75
l.		Pair, one with level periods	8.00	13.00
m.		No period after "V"	3.00	3.00
n.		No period after "I"	25.00	25.00
o.		"V" omitted	400.00	400.00
p.		Small "½"	12.00	13.00
q.		"1" for "I" in "V.R.I."	9.00	9.00
r.		Thick "V"	.28	.45
45i	A1	1p on 1p violet	.30	.15
j.		Mixed periods	1.50	1.65
k.		Pair, one with level periods	17.00	17.00
l.		No period after "V"	6.00	6.00
m.		No period after "R"	12.00	12.00
n.		No period after "I"	12.00	12.00
p.		Double surcharge	90.00	90.00
q.		Inverted surcharge	200.00	
s.		Small "1" in "1d"	165.00	165.00
t.		"1" for "I" in "V.R.I."	13.00	13.00
u.		Thick "V"	.28	.25
v.		As "u," invtd. "1" for "I" in "V.R.I."	7.25	7.25
w.		As "u," double surcharge	300.00	300.00
z.		As "u," no period after "R"	30.00	30.00
46e	A1	2p on 2p violet	.50	.25
f.		Mixed periods	4.50	4.50
g.		Pair, one with level periods	7.25	7.25
h.		Inverted surcharge	300.00	300.00
i.		Thick "V"	.35	.28
j.		As "i," invtd. "1" for "I" in "V.R.I."	15.00	15.00
47c	A1	'2½' on 3p ultramarine	190.00	165.00
d.		Thick "V"	350.00	350.00
f.		As "d," Roman "I" on "½"		
48d	A1	3p on 3p ultramarine	.35	.20
e.		Mixed periods	5.00	5.00
f.		Pair, one with level periods	15.00	15.00
g.		Double surcharge	425.00	
h.		Thick "V"	.90	.90
i.		As "h," invtd. "1" for "I" in "V.R.I."	80.00	80.00
49b	A1	4p on 4p ultramarine	1.10	2.00
c.		Mixed periods	7.00	7.00
d.		Pair, one with level periods	15.00	18.00
50c	A1	6p on 6p carmine rose	35.00	47.50
d.		Mixed periods	175.00	175.00
e.		Pair, one with level periods	175.00	
f.		Thick "V"	*450.00*	*450.00*
51d	A1	6p on 6p ultramarine	.60	.30
e.		Mixed periods	6.00	6.00
f.		Pair, one with level periods	15.00	15.00
g.		Thick "V"	3.00	3.00
52e	A1	1sh on 1sh brown	1.00	.45
f.		Mixed periods	10.00	10.00
h.		Pair, one with level periods	25.00	26.00
i.		Thick "V"	1.75	1.50
52j	A1	1sh on 1sh orange	*1,050.*	*1,050.*
53c	A1	5sh on 5sh green	6.50	9.00
d.		Mixed periods	325.00	325.00
e.		Pair, one with level periods	*1,600.*	*2,500.*
f.		"5" with short flag	60.00	60.00
g.		Thick "V"	18.00	18.00

Stamps with mixed periods have one or two periods level with the bottoms of letters. One stamp in

each pane had all periods level. Later settings had several stamps with thick "V." No. 52j may not have been issued. Excellent forgeries of the scarcer varieties exist.

"V.R.I." stands for Victoria Regina Imperatrix. On No. 59, "E.R.I." stands for Edward Rex Imperator.

Cape of Good Hope Stamps of 1893-98 Overprinted

ORANGE RIVER COLONY.

1900		**Wmk. 16**		
54	A15	½p green	.20	.15
a.		No period after "COLONY"	8.50	12.00
b.		Double overprint	500.00	600.00
55	A13	2½p ultramarine	.30	.30
a.		No period after "COLONY"	45.00	57.50

Overprinted as in 1900

1902, May				
56	A15	1p carmine rose	.30	.30
a.		No period after "COLONY"	10.00	15.00

Nos. 51d, 53c, Surcharged and No. 8b Surcharged like No. 51 but Reading "E.R.I."

4d

One Shilling *

Carmine or Vermilion and Black Surcharges

1902		**Unwmk.**		
57	A1	4p on 6p on 6p ultra	.60	.70
a.		Thick "V"	1.75	1.25
b.		As "a," inverted "1" instead of "I"	4.50	4.50
c.		No period after "R"	30.00	30.00
		Black Surcharge		
59	A1	6p on 6p ultra	2.00	6.00
a.		Double surcharge, one invtd.	*600.00*	*600.00*
		Orange Surcharge		
60	A1	1sh on 5sh on 5sh grn	5.00	6.00
a.		Thick "V"	13.00	18.00
b.		"5" with short flag	60.00	60.00
c.		Double surcharge		
		Nos. 57-60 (3)	7.60	12.70

"E.R.I." stands for Edward Rex Imperator.

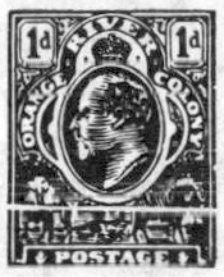

King Edward VII — A8

1903-04		**Wmk. 2**		**Typo.**
61	A8	½p yellow green	5.00	1.10
62	A8	1p carmine	1.50	.20
63	A8	2p chocolate	3.00	.70
64	A8	2½p ultra	.90	.45
65	A8	3p violet	3.50	.80
66	A8	4p olive grn & car	18.00	2.50
67	A8	6p violet & car	5.00	1.00
68	A8	1sh bister & car	20.00	2.00
69	A8	5sh red brn & bl ('04)	62.50	18.00
		Nos. 61-69 (9)	119.40	26.75

Some of the above stamps are found with the overprint "C. S. A. R." for use by the Central South African Railway.

The "IOSTAGE" variety on the 4p is the result of a broken "P."

Issue dates: 1p, Feb. 3. ½p, 2p, 2½p, 3p, 4p, 6p, 1sh, July 6. 5sh, Oct. 31.

1907-08		**Wmk. 3**		
70	A8	½p yellow green	4.00	.45
71	A8	1p carmine	3.00	.20
72	A8	4p olive grn & car	4.00	1.50
73	A8	1sh bister & car	25.00	8.00
		Nos. 70-73 (4)	36.00	10.15

The "IOSTAGE" variety on the 4p is the result of a broken "P."

Stamps of Orange River Colony were replaced by those of Union of South Africa.

PAKISTAN

'pa–ki–,stan

LOCATION — In southern, central Asia
GOVT. — Republic
AREA — 307,293 sq. mi.
POP. — 88,000,000 (est. 1983)
CAPITAL — Islamabad

Pakistan was formed August 15, 1947, when India was divided into the Dominions of the Union of India and Pakistan, with some princely states remaining independent. Pakistan became a republic on March 23, 1956.

Pakistan had two areas made up of all or part of several predominantly Moslem provinces in the northwest and northeast corners of pre-1947 India. Western Pakistan consists of the entire provinces of Baluchistan, Sind (Scinde) and "Northwest Frontier," and 15 districts of the Punjab. Eastern, consisting of the Sylhet district in Assam and 14 districts in Bengal Province, became independent as Bangladesh in December 1971.

The state of Las Bela was incorporated into Pakistan.

12 Pies = 1 Anna
16 Annas = 1 Rupee
100 Paisa = 1 Rupee (1961)

Catalogue values for all unused stamps in this country are for Never Hinged items.

Watermarks

Wmk. 274

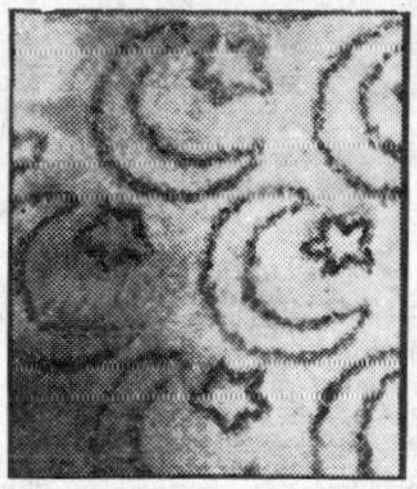

Wmk. 351 Crescent and Star Multiple

Stamps of India, 1937-43, Overprinted in Black:

PAKISTAN Nos. 1-12   **PAKISTAN** Nos. 13-19

Perf. 13½x14

1947, Oct. 1			**Wmk. 196**	
1	A83	3p slate	.15	.15
2	A83	½a rose violet	.15	.15
3	A83	9p lt green	.15	.15
4	A83	1a carmine rose	.15	.15
4A	A84	1a3p bister ('49)	.55	.55
5	A84	1½a dk purple	.15	.15
6	A84	2a scarlet	.15	.15
7	A84	3a violet	.15	.15
8	A84	3½a ultra	.35	.35
9	A85	4a chocolate	.15	.15
10	A85	6a peacock blue	.50	.50
11	A85	8a blue violet	.20	.20
12	A85	12a carmine lake	.60	.60
13	A81	14a rose violet	1.40	1.40
14	A82	1r brown & slate	1.10	1.10
a.		Inverted overprint	110.00	
b.		Pair, one without ovpt.	425.00	
15	A82	2r dk brn & dk vio	1.10	1.10
16	A82	5r dp ultra & dk grn	2.50	2.50
17	A82	10r rose car & dk vio	2.50	2.50
18	A82	15r dk grn & dk brn	30.00	30.00
19	A82	25r dk vio & bl vio	35.00	35.00
		Nos. 1-19 (20)	77.00	77.00

The overprint on Nos. 14-19 is slightly smaller than the illustration.

Provisional use of stamps of India with handstamped or printed "PAKISTAN" was authorized in 1947-49. Nos. 4A, 14a 14b exist only as provisional issues.

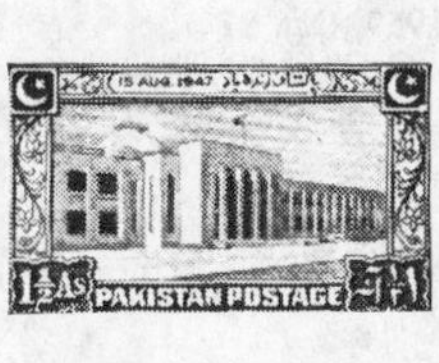

Constituent Assembly Building, Karachi A1

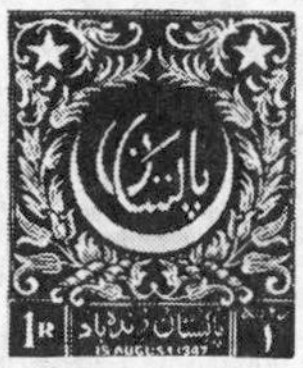

Crescent and Urdu Inscription — A2

Designs: 2½a, Karachi Airport entrance. 3a, Lahore Fort gateway.

1948, July 9	**Unwmk.**	**Engr.**	***Perf. 14***	
20	A1	1½a bright ultra	.15	.15
21	A1	2½a green	.15	.15
22	A1	3a chocolate	.15	.15
		Perf. 12		
23	A2	1r red	.55	.52
a.		Perf. 14	4.00	4.00
		Nos. 20-23 (4)	1.00	.97

Pakistan's independence, Aug. 15, 1947.

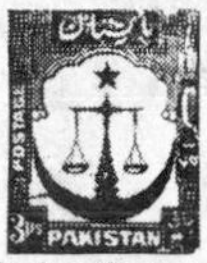

Scales, Star and Crescent — A3

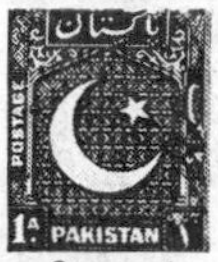

Star and Crescent — A4

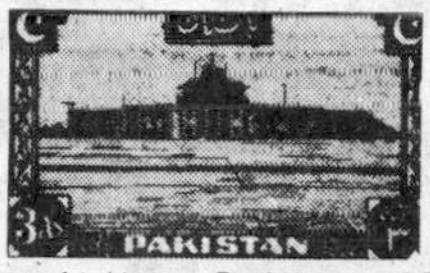

Karachi Airport Building — A5

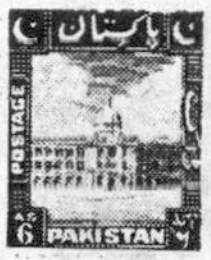

Karachi Port Authority Building — A6

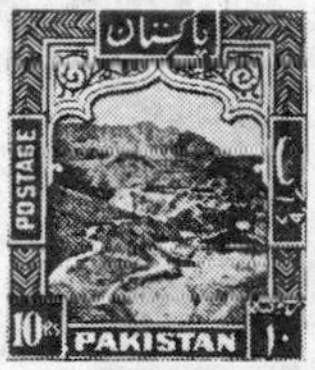

Khyber Pass — A7

Designs: 2½a, 3½a, 4a, Ghulan Muhammed Dam, Indus River, Sind. 1r, 2r, 5r, Salimullah Hostel.

Perf. 12½, 13½x14, 14x13½

1948-57			**Unwmk.**	
24	A3	3p org red, perf. 13 ('54)	.15	.15
a.		Perf. 12½	.15	.15
25	A3	6p pur, perf. 13 ('54)	.25	.15
a.		Perf. 12½	.15	.15
26	A3	9p dk grn, perf. 12½	.15	.15
a.		Perf. 13 ('54)	.15	.15
27	A4	1a dark blue	.15	.15
28	A4	1½a gray green	.15	.15
29	A4	2a orange red	.15	.15
30	A6	2½a green	.15	.15
31	A5	3a olive green	.15	.15
32	A6	3½a violet blue	.18	.15
33	A6	4a chocolate	.15	.15
34	A6	6a deep blue	.18	.15
35	A6	8a black	.30	.15
36	A5	10a red	.32	.15
37	A6	12a red	.42	.15
38	A5	1r ultra, perf. 13 ('54)	.75	.15
a.		Perf. 13½x14	.48	.15
39	A5	2r dark brown, perf. 13 ('54)	1.50	.25
a.		Perf. 13½x14	.90	.25
40	A5	5r car, perf. 13½x14	2.00	.15
a.		Perf. 13 ('54)	5.25	1.00
		Perf. 13½x13		
41	A7	10r rose lilac ('51)	7.50	.30
a.		Perf. 14x13½	5.25	4.00
b.		Perf. 12	7.50	1.25
42	A7	15r blue green ('57)	9.00	3.50
a.		Perf. 14x13½	11.00	9.00
b.		Perf. 12	5.25	1.50
43	A7	25r purple ('54)	16.00	7.50
a.		Perf. 14x13½	16.00	8.00
b.		Perf. 12	16.00	8.00
		Nos. 24-43 (20)	39.60	13.95

See No. 259, types A9-A11. For surcharges and overprints see Nos. 124, O14-O26, O35-O37, O41-O43A, O52, O63, O68.

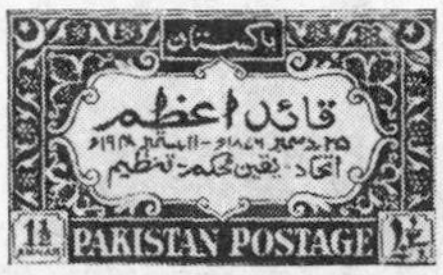

"Quaid-i-Azam" (Great Leader), "Mohammed Ali Jinnah" — A8

1949, Sept. 11		**Engr.**	***Perf. 13½x14***	
44	A8	1½a brown	.55	.20
45	A8	3a dark green	.75	.25
46	A8	10a blk *(English inscriptions)*	3.50	1.50
		Nos. 44-46 (3)	4.80	1.95

1st anniv. of the death of Mohammed Ali Jinnah (1876-1948), Moslem lawyer, pres. of All-India Moslem League.

Re-engraved (Crescents Reversed)

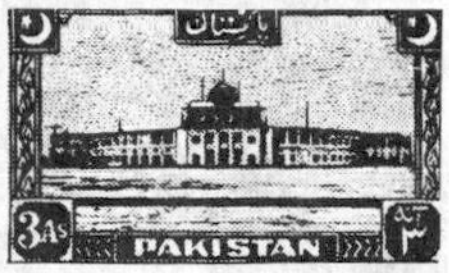

A9

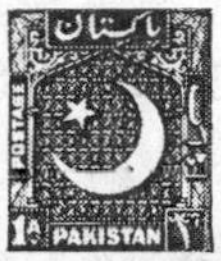

A10

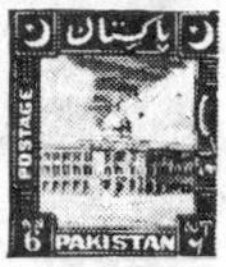

A11

Perf. 12½, 13½x14 (3a, 10a), 14x13½ (6a, 12a)

1949-53				
47	A10	1a dk blue ('50)	.15	.15
a.		Perf. 13 ('52)	.15	.15
48	A10	1½a gray green	.15	.15
a.		Perf. 13 ('53)	.15	.15
49	A10	2a orange red	.15	.15
a.		Perf. 13 ('52)	.15	.15
50	A9	3a olive green	.40	.15
51	A11	6a deep blue ('50)	.45	.15
52	A11	8a black ('50)	.45	.15
53	A9	10a red	1.00	.15
54	A11	12a red ('50)	1.75	.20
		Nos. 47-54 (8)	4.50	
		Set value		.60

For overprints see #O27-O31, O38-O40.

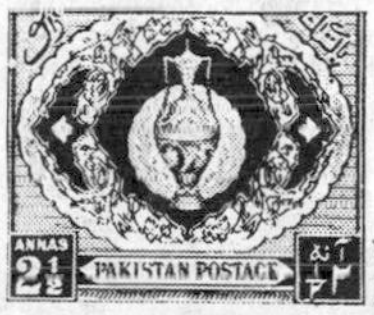

Vase and Plate — A12

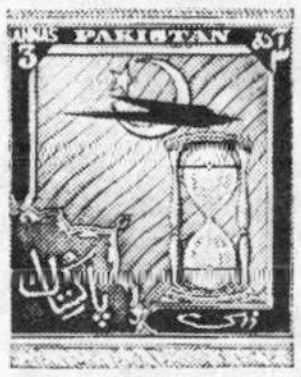

Star and Crescent, Plane and Hour Glass — A13

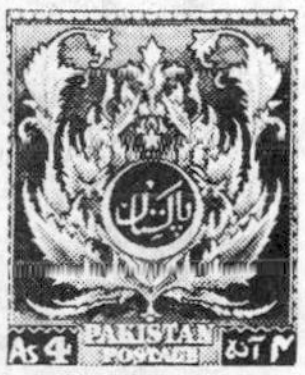

Moslem Leaf Pattern — A14

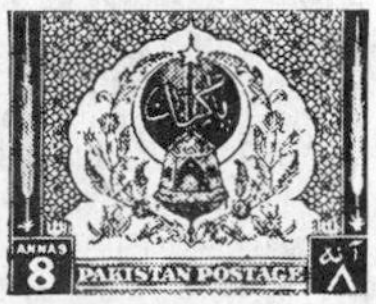

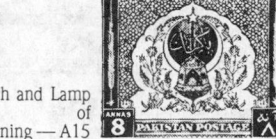

Arch and Lamp of Learning — A15

1951, Aug. 14		**Engr.**	***Perf. 13***	
55	A12	2½a dark red	.15	.15
56	A13	3a dk rose lake	.15	.15
57	A12	3½a dp ultra (Urdu "1/23")	.70	.45
57A	A12	3½a dp ultra (Urdu "3½") ('56)	1.25	1.00
58	A14	4a deep green	.25	.15
59	A14	6a red orange	.35	.15
60	A15	8a brown	.45	.15
61	A15	10a purple	.80	.35
62	A13	12a dk slate blue	1.00	.35
		Nos. 55-62 (9)	5.10	2.90

Fourth anniversary of independence.

On No. 57, the characters of the Urdu denomination at right appears as "1/23." On the reengraved No. 57A, they read "3½."

Issue date: Dec. 1956.

See Nos. 88, O32-O34.
For surcharges see Nos. 255, 257.

Scinde District Stamp and Camel Train — A16

1952, Aug. 14
63 A16 3a olive green, *citron* .80 .45
64 A16 12a dark brown, *salmon* 2.25 1.25

5th anniv. of Pakistan's Independence and the cent. of the 1st postage stamps in the Indo-Pakistan sub-continent.

Peak K-2, Karakoram Mountains — A17

1954, Dec. 25
65 A17 2a violet .30 .15

Conquest of K-2, world's 2nd highest mountain peak, in July 1954.

Kaghan Valley — A18

Gilgit Mountains — A19

Tea Garden, East Pakistan — A20

Designs: 1a, Badshahi Mosque, Lahore. 1½a, Emperor Jahangir's Mausoleum, Lahore. 1r, Cotton field. 2r, River craft and jute field.

1954, Aug. 14   **Engr.**
66 A18 6p rose violet .15 .15
    a.   Booklet pane of 4 .20
67 A19 9p blue .15 .15
68 A19 1a carmine rose .15 .15
69 A19 1½a light ultra .15 .15
    a.   Booklet pane of 4 .22
70 A20 14a dark green .60 .15
71 A20 1r yellow green .85 .15
72 A20 2r orange 1.75 .15
         Nos. 66-72 (7) 3.80
         Set value .40

Seventh anniversary of independence.
For overprints & surcharges see #77, 101, 123, 126, O44-O50, O53-O56, O60-O62, O67, O69-O71.

Karnaphuli Paper Mill, East Pakistan (Urdu "½2") — A21

Designs: 6a, Textile mill. 8a, Jute mill. 12a, Sui gas plant.

1955, Aug. 14   Unwmk.   Perf. 13
73   A21 2½a dk car (Urdu "½2") .30 .15
73A A21 2½a dk car (Urdu "2½2") .32 .15
              ('56)
74   A21 6a dark blue .38 .15
75   A21 8a violet .50 .15
76   A21 12a car lake & org .90 .15
              Nos. 73-76 (5) 2.40
              Set value .44

Eighth anniversary of independence.
On No. 73, the characters of the Urdu denomination at right appear as "½2." On the reengraved No. 73A, they read "2½2."
    Issue date: Dec. 1956.
For No. 87. For overprints and surcharges see Nos. 78, 102-103, 256, O51, O58-O59.

Nos. 69 and 76 Overprinted in Ultramarine

TENTH ANNIVERSARY UNITED NATIONS

24. 10. 55.

1955, Oct. 24
77 A18 1½a red 1.75 1.75
78 A21 12a car lake & org 1.75 1.75
         UN, 10th anniv.

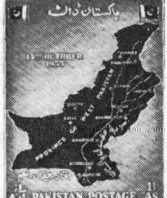

Map of West Pakistan — A22

1955, Dec. 7   Unwmk.   Perf. 13½x13
79 A22 1½a dark green .15 .15
80 A22 2a dark brown .18 .15
81 A22 12a deep carmine .75 .50
         Nos. 79-81 (3) 1.08 .80

West Pakistan unification, Nov. 14, 1955.

National Assembly A23

1956, Mar. 23   Litho.   Perf. 13x12½
82 A23 2a green .15 .15

Proclamation of the Republic of Pakistan, Mar. 23, 1956.

Crescent and Star — A24

Map of East Pakistan — A25

1956, Aug. 14   Engr.   Perf. 13
83 A24 2a red .15 .15

Ninth anniversary of independence.
For surcharges and overprints see Nos. 127, O57, O72-O73.

1956, Oct. 15   Perf. 13½x13
84 A25 1½a dark green .20 .15
85 A25 2a dark brown .20 .15
86 A25 12a deep red .85 .50
         Nos. 84-86 (3) 1.25 .80

1st Session at Dacca (East Pakistan) of the National Assembly of Pakistan.

Redrawn Types of 1951, 1955 and

Orange Tree — A26

Perf. 13x13½, 13½x13
1957, Mar. 23   Engr.
87 A21 2½a dark carmine .15 .15
88 A12 3½a bright blue .15 .15
89 A26 10r dk green & orange 2.75 1.10
         Nos. 87-89 (3) 3.05 1.40

Nos. 87-89 inscribed "Pakistan" in English, Urdu and Bengali. Denomination in English only.
Islamic Republic of Pakistan, 1st anniv.
See Nos. 95, 258, 475A. For surcharge and overprint see Nos. 159, O64.

Flag and Broken Chain — A27

1957, May 10   Litho.   Perf. 13
90 A27 1½a green .18 .15
91 A27 12a blue .40 .35

Cent. of the struggle for Independence (Indian Mutiny).

Industrial Plants and Roses as Symbols of Progress A28

1957, Aug. 14   Unwmk.   Perf. 13½
92 A28 1½a light ultra .15 .15
93 A28 4a orange vermilion .25 .15
94 A28 12a red lilac .50 .50
         Nos. 92-94 (3) .90 .80

Tenth anniversary of independence.

Type of 1957.
Design: 15r, Coconut Tree.

1958, Mar. 23   Engr.   Perf. 13½x13
95 A26 15r rose lilac & red 5.00 4.25

Issued to commemorate the second anniversary of the Islamic Republic of Pakistan.

Verse of Iqbal Poem — A29

1958, Apr. 21   Photo.   Perf. 14½x14
Black Inscriptions
96 A29 1½a citron .15 .15
97 A29 2a orange brown .15 .15
98 A29 14a aqua .40 .30
         Nos. 96-98 (3) .70
         Set value .44

20th anniv. of the death of Mohammad Iqbal (1877-1938), Moslem poet and philosopher.

Globe and Book — A30

1958, Dec. 10   Litho.   Perf. 13
99   A30 1½a Prus blue .15 .15
100 A30 14a dark brown .40 .35
          Set value .47 .41

10th anniv. of the signing of the Universal Declaration of Human Rights.

Nos. 66 and 75 Overprinted: "Pakistan Boy Scout 2nd National Jamboree Chittagong Dec. 58-Jan. 59"

1958, Dec. 28   Engr.   Perf. 13
101 A18 6p rose violet .15 .15
102 A21 8a violet .40 .40

2nd National Boy Scout Jamboree held at Chittagong, Dec. 28-Jan. 4.

No. 74 Overprinted in Red: "Revolution Day, Oct. 27, 1959."

1959, Oct. 27
103 A21 6a dark blue .18 .15

First anniversary of the 1958 Revolution.

Red Cross — A31

Engr.; Cross Typo.
1959, Nov. 19   Unwmk.   Perf. 13
104 A31 2a green & red .18 .15
105 A31 10a dk blue & red .85 .18
          Set value .28

Armed Forces Emblem — A32

1960, Jan. 10   Litho.   Perf. 13
106 A32 2a blue grn, red & ultra .15 .15
107 A32 14a ultra & red .35 .22
          Set value .41 .27

Issued for Armed Forces Day.

Map Showing Disputed Areas A33

1960, Mar. 23   Engr.   Unwmk.
108 A33 6p purple .15 .15
109 A33 2a copper red .15 .15
110 A33 8a green .18 .15
111 A33 1r blue .38 .28
          Set value .67 .48

Publicizing the border dispute with India over Jammu and Kashmir, Junagarh and Manavadar.
For overprints and surcharges see Nos. 122, 125, 128, 178, O65-O66, O74-O75.

Uprooted Oak Emblem — A34

1960, Apr. 7
112 A34 2a carmine rose .15 .15
113 A34 10a green .28 .22
          Set value .34 .27

Issued to publicize World Refugee Year, July 1, 1959-June 30, 1960.

House, Field and Column (Allegory of Democratic Development) A35

1960, Oct. 27   Photo.   Perf. 13
114 A35 2a brown, pink & grn .15 .15
     a.   Green & pink omitted 13.50
115 A35 14a multicolored .35 .28
          Set value .41 .33

Revolution Day, Oct. 27, 1960.
No. 114a is easily counterfeited.

Punjab Agricultural College, Lyallpur A36

Design: 8a, College shield.

1960, Oct.   Engr.   Perf. 12½x14
116 A36 2a rose red & gray blue .15 .15
117 A36 8a lilac & green .35 .28
          Set value .41 .33

50th anniv. of the Punjab Agricultural College, Lyallpur.

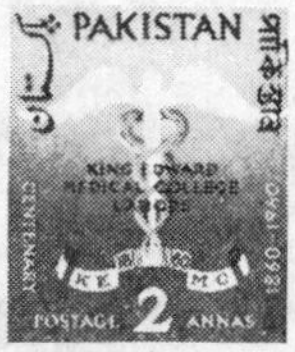

Caduceus, College Emblem — A37

1960, Nov. 16 Photo. *Perf. 13½x13*
118 A37 2a blue, yel & blk .15 .15
119 A37 14a car rose, blk & emerald .35 .30
Set value .42 .37

King Edward Medical College, Lahore, cent.

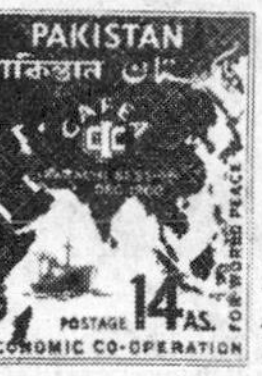

Map of South-East Asia and Commission Emblem — A38

1960, Dec. 5 Engr. *Perf. 13*
120 A38 14a red orange .40 .30

Conf. of the Commission on Asian and Far Eastern Affairs of the Intl. Chamber of Commerce, Karachi, Dec. 5-9.

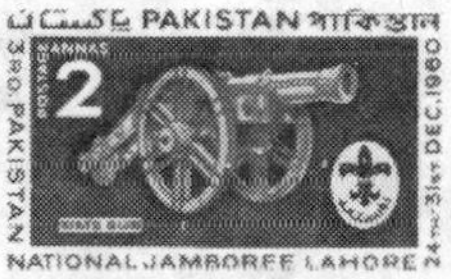

"Kim's Gun" and Scout Badge A39

Perf. 12½x14

1960, Dec. 24 Unwmk.
121 A39 2a dk green, car & yel .18 .15

3rd Natl. Boy Scout Jamboree, Lahore, Dec. 24-31.

No. 110 Overprinted in Red — LAHORE STAMP EXHIBITION 1961

1961, Feb. 12
122 A33 8a green .28 .20

10th Lahore Stamp Exhibition, Feb. 12.

New Currency

Nos. 24, 68-69, 83, 108-109 Surcharged with New Value in Paisa

1961 *Perf. 13*
123 A18 1p on 1½a red .15 .15
124 A3 2p on 3p orange red .15 .15
125 A33 3p on 6p purple .15 .15
126 A19 7p on 1a car rose .15 .15
127 A24 13p on 2a red .16 .15
128 A33 13p on 2a copper red .22 .15
Set value .65 .40

Various violet handstamped surcharges were applied to a variety of regular-issue stamps. Most of these repeat the denomination of the basic stamp and add the new value. Example: "8 Annas (50 Paisa)" on No. 75. Many errors exist.
For overprints see Nos. O74-O75.

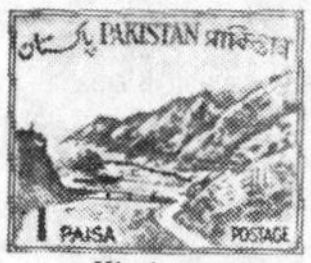

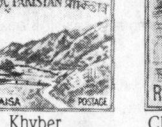

Khyber Pass — A40

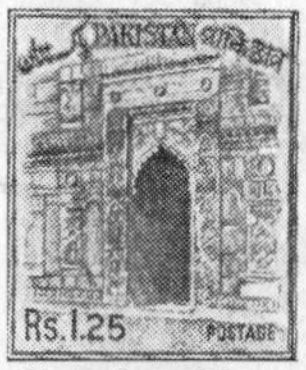

Chota Sona Masjid Gate — A41

Design: 10p, 13p, 25p, 40p, 50p, 75p, 90p, Shalimar Gardens, Lahore.

Type I Type II

Two types of 1p, 2p and 5p:
I - First Bengali character beside "N" lacks appendage at left side of loop.
II - This character has a downward-pointing appendage at left side of loop.

1961-63 Engr. *Perf. 13½x14*
129 A40 1p violet (II) .20 .20
a. Type I .15 .15
130 A40 2p rose red (II) .25 .20
a. Type I .15 .15
131 A40 3p magenta .15 .15
132 A40 5p ultra (II) .20 .20
a. Type I .15 .15
133 A40 7p emerald .15 .15
134 A40 10p brown .15 .15
135 A40 13p blue vio .18 .15
136 A40 25p dark blue ('62) .18 .15
137 A40 40p dull purple ('62) .30 .15
138 A40 50p dull green ('62) .50 .15
139 A40 75p dk carmine ('62) .75 .15
140 A40 90p lt olive grn ('62) .75 .15

Perf. 13½x13
141 A41 1r vermilion ('63) .80 .15
142 A41 1.25r purple 1.00 .50
143 A41 2r orange ('63) 1.65 .15
144 A41 5r green ('63) 5.25 2.00
Nos. 129-144 (16) 12.46
Set value 4.00

See #200-203. For surcharge and overprints see Nos. 184, O76-O82, O85-O93A.

Designs Redrawn

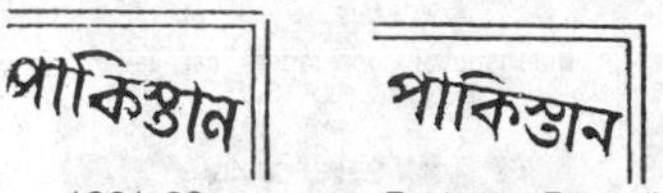

1961-62 Bengali Inscription — Redrawn Bengali Inscription

Bengali inscription redrawn with straight connecting line across top of characters. Shading of scenery differs, especially in Shalimar Gardens design where reflection is strengthened and trees at right are composed of horizontal lines instead of vertical lines and dots.
Designs as before; 15p, 20p, Shalimar Gardens.

1963-70 *Perf. 13½x14*
129b A40 1p violet .15 .15
130b A40 2p rose red ('64) .15 .15
131a A40 3p magenta ('70) .15 .15
132b A40 5p ultra .15 .15
133a A40 7p emerald ('64) .15 .15
134a A40 10p brown .15 .15
135a A40 13p blue violet .15 .15
135B A40 15p rose lilac ('64) .15 .15
135C A40 20p dull green ('70) .15 .15
136a A40 25p dark blue .15 .15
137a A40 40p dull purple ('64) .15 .15
138a A40 50p dull green ('64) .28 .15
139a A40 75p dark carmine ('64) .32 .15
140a A40 90p lt olive green ('64) .75 .15
Set value 2.15 1.00

For overprints see Nos. 174, O76b, O77b, O78a, O79b, O80a, O81a, O82a, O83-O84A, O85a, O86a.

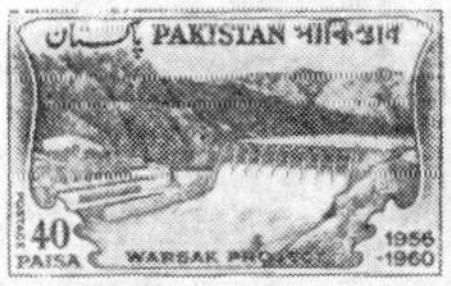

Warsak Dam, Kabul River — A42

1961, July 1 Engr. *Perf. 12½x13½*
150 A42 40p black & lt ultra .20 .15

Dedication of hydroelectric Warsak Project.

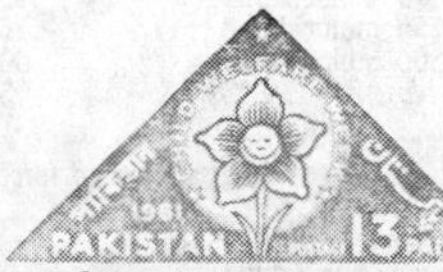

Symbolic Flower — A43

1961, Oct. 2 Unwmk. *Perf. 14*
151 A43 13p greenish blue .15 .15
152 A43 90p red lilac .42 .28
Set value .34

Issued for Children's Day.

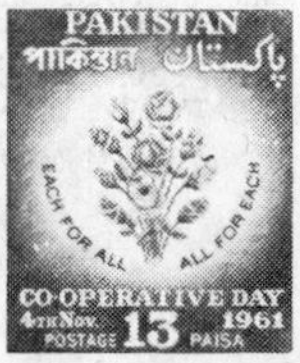

Roses — A44

1961, Nov. 4 *Perf. 13½x13*
153 A44 13p deep green & ver .15 .15
154 A44 90p blue & vermilion .62 .22
Set value .27

Cooperative Day.

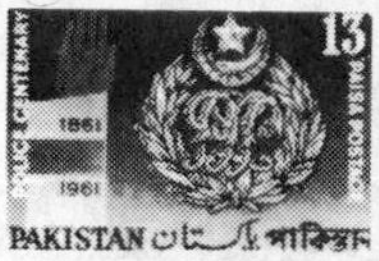

Police Crest and Traffic Policeman's Hand — A45

1961, Nov. 30 Photo. *Perf. 13x12½*
155 A45 13p dk blue, sil & blk .15 .15
156 A45 40p red, silver & blk .55 .40
Set value .45

Centenary of the police force.

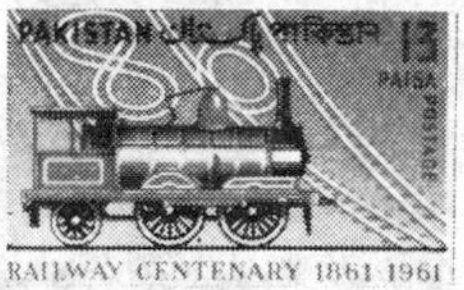

"Eagle Locomotive, 1861" A46

Design: 50pa, Diesel Engine, 1961.

1961, Dec. 31 *Perf. 13½x14*
157 A46 13p yellow, green & blk .25 .15
158 A46 50p green, blk & yellow .75 .35

Centenary of Pakistan railroads.

No. 87 Surcharged in Red with New Value, Boeing 720-B Jetliner and: "FIRST JET FLIGHT KARACHI-DACCA"

1962, Feb. 6 Engr. *Perf. 13*
159 A21 13p on 2½a dk carmine .20 .15

1st jet flight from Karachi to Dacca, Feb. 6, 1962.

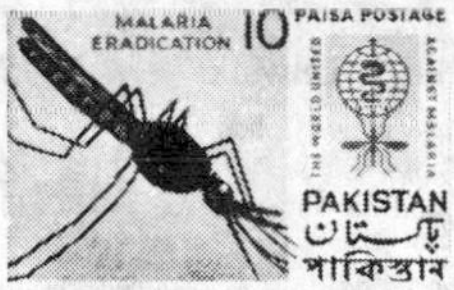

Mosquito and Malaria Eradication Emblem A47

Design: 13p, Dagger pointing at mosquito, and emblem.

1962, Apr. 7 Photo. *Perf. 13½x14*
160 A47 10p multicolored .15 .15
161 A47 13p multicolored .15 .15
Set value .15

WHO drive to eradicate malaria.

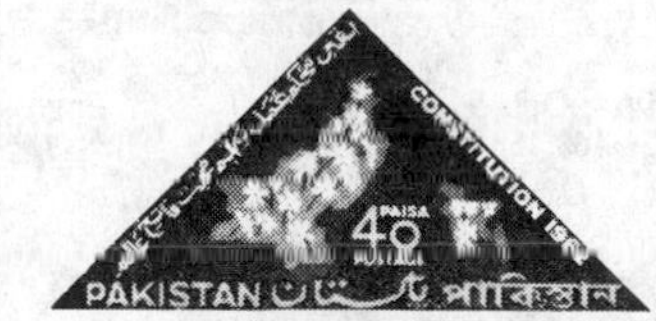

Map of Pakistan and Jasmine — A48

1962, June 8 Unwmk. *Perf. 12*
162 A48 40p grn, yel grn & gray .28 .18

Introduction of new Pakistan Constitution.

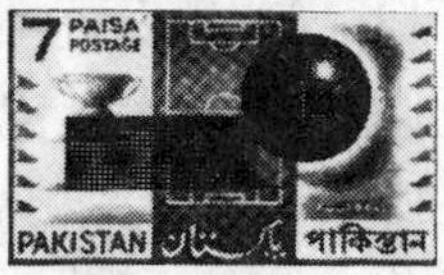

Soccer A49

Designs: 13p, Hockey and Olympic gold medal. 25p, Squash rackets and British squash rackets championship cup. 40p, Cricket and Ayub challenge cup.

Perf. 12½x13½

1962, Aug. 14 Engr.
163 A49 7p blue & black .15 .15
164 A49 13p green & black .18 .15
165 A49 25p lilac & black .30 .15
166 A49 40p brown org & blk 1.10 .18
Nos. 163-166 (4) 1.73
Set value .36

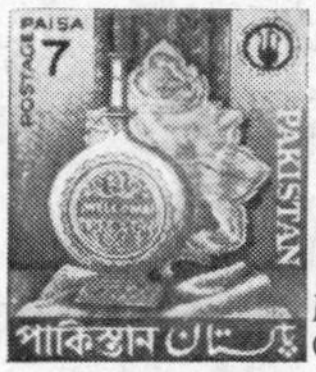

Marble Fruit Dish and Clay Flask — A50

Designs: 13p, Sporting goods. 25p, Camel skin lamp and brass jug. 40p, Wooden powder bowl and cane basket. 50p, Inlaid box and brassware.

1962, Nov. 10 *Perf. 13½x13*
167 A50 7p dark red .15 .15
168 A50 13p dark green .15 .15
169 A50 25p bright purple .15 .15
170 A50 40p yellow green .45 .15
171 A50 50p dull red .48 .25
Nos. 167-171 (5) 1.38
Set value .58

Pakistan Intl. Industries Fair, Oct. 12-Nov. 20, publicizing Pakistan's small industries.

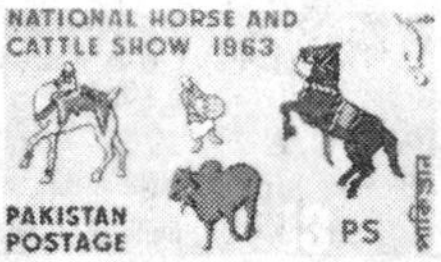

Children's Needs A51

1962, Dec. 11 Photo. *Perf. 13½x14*
172 A51 13p blue, plum & blk .15 .15
173 A51 40p multicolored .20 .18
Set value .26 .23

16th anniv. of UNICEF.

No. 135a Overprinted in Red: "U.N. FORCE W. IRIAN"

1963, Feb. 15 Engr. Unwmk.
174 A40 13p blue violet .15 .15

Issued to commemorate the dispatch of Pakistani troops to West New Guinea.

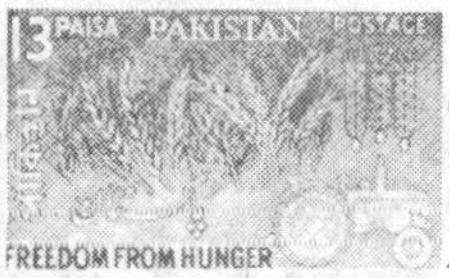

Camel, Bull, Dancing Horse and Drummer A52

1963, Mar. 13 Photo. *Perf. 12*
175 A52 13p multicolored .15 .15

National Horse and Cattle Show, 1963.

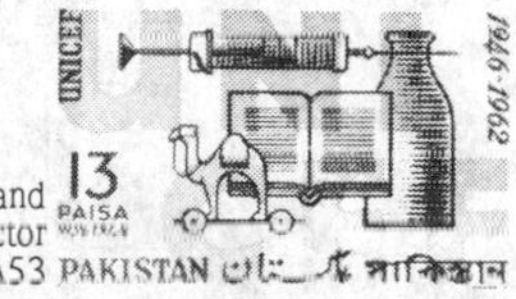

Wheat and Tractor A53

Design: 50p, Hands and heap of rice.

Perf. 12½x13½

1963, Mar. 21 Engr.
176 A53 13p brown orange .22 .15
177 A53 50p brown .85 .18
Set value .24

FAO "Freedom from Hunger" campaign.

No. 109 Surcharged with New Value and: "INTERNATIONAL/DACCA STAMP/EXHIBITION/1963"

1963, Mar. 23 *Perf. 13*
178 A33 13p on 2a copper red .25 .22

International Stamp Exhibition at Dacca.

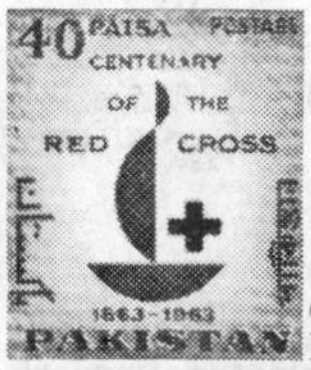

Centenary Emblem — A54

Perf. 13¹/₂x12¹/₂

1963, June 25   **Engr. and Typo.**
179 A54 40p dark gray & red   .30 .15
International Red Cross, cent.

Paharpur Stupa — A55

Designs: 13p, Cistern, Mohenjo-Daro, vert. 40p, Stupas, Taxila. 50pa, Stupas, Mainamati.

Perf. 12¹/₂x13¹/₂, 13¹/₂x12¹/₂

1963, Sept. 16   **Engr.**   **Unwmk.**
180 A55 7p ultra   .15 .15
181 A55 13p brown   .15 .15
182 A55 40p carmine rose   .22 .18
183 A55 50p dark violet   .35 .20
    Set value   .71 .48

No. 131 Surcharged and Overprinted:
"100 YEARS OF P.W.D. OCTOBER, 1963"

1963, Oct. 7   *Perf. 13¹/₂x14*
184 A40 13p on 3pa magenta   .15 .15
Centenary of Public Works Department.

Atatürk Mausoleum, Ankara — A56

1963, Nov. 10   *Perf. 13x13¹/₂*
185 A56 50p red   .22 .18
25th anniv. of the death of Kemal Atatürk, pres. of Turkey.

Globe and UNESCO Emblem A57

1963, Dec. 10   **Photo.**   *Perf. 13¹/₂x14*
186 A57 50p dk brn, vio blue & red   .15 .15
15th anniv. of the Universal Declaration of Human Rights.

Multan Thermal Power Station A58

Perf. 12¹/₂x13¹/₂
1963, Dec. 25   **Engr.**
187 A58 13p ultra   .15 .15
Issued to mark the opening of the Multan Thermal Power Station.

Type of 1961-63
Perf. 13¹/₂x13
1963-65   **Engr.**   **Wmk. 351**
200 A41 1r vermilion   .40 .15
201 A41 1.25r purple ('64)   .50 .22
202 A41 2r orange   .80 .15
203 A41 5r green ('65)   2.25 .62
   Nos. 200-203 (4)   3.95 1.14

For overprints see Nos. O92-O93A.

A59   SAVE THE MONUMENTS OF NUBIA

Designs: 13p, Temple of Thot, Dakka, and Queen Nefertari with Goddesses Hathor and Isis. 50p, Ramses II, Abu Simbel, and View of Nile.

Perf. 13x13¹/₂
1964, Mar. 30   **Unwmk.**
204 A59 13p brick red & turq blue   .15 .15
205 A59 50p black & rose lilac   .30 .22
    Set value   .38 .26
UNESCO world campaign to save historic monuments in Nubia.

Pakistan Pavilion and Unisphere A60

Design: 1.25r, Pakistan pavilion and Unisphere, vert.

Perf. 12¹/₂x14, 14x12¹/₂
1964, Apr. 22   **Engr.**   **Unwmk.**
206 A60 13p ultramarine   .15 .15
207 A60 1.25r dp orange & ultra   .60 .40
New York World's Fair, 1964-65.

Mausoleum of Shah Abdul Latif — A61   Mausoleum of Jinnah — A62

1964, June 25   *Perf. 13¹/₂x13*
208 A61 50p magenta & ultra   .25 .15
Bicentenary (?) of the death of Shah Abdul Latif of Bhit (1689-1752).

1964, Sept. 11   **Unwmk.**   *Perf. 13*
Design: 15p, Mausoleum, horiz.
209 A62 15p green   .15 .15
210 A62 50p greenish gray   .22 .20
    Set value   .30 .26
16th anniv. of the death of Mohammed Ali Jinnah (1876-1948), the Quaid-i-Azam (Great Leader), founder and president of Pakistan.

Bengali Alphabet on Slate and Slab with Urdu Alphabet — A63

1964, Oct. 5   **Engr.**
211 A63 15p brown   .15 .15
Issued for Universal Children's Day.

West Pakistan University of Engineering and Technology A64

1964, Dec. 21   *Perf. 12¹/₂x14*
212 A64 15p henna brown   .15 .15
1st convocation of the West Pakistan University of Engineering & Technology, Lahore, Dec. 1964.

Eyeglasses and Book — A65

Perf. 13x13¹/₂
1965, Feb. 28   **Litho.**   **Unwmk.**
213 A65 15p yellow & ultra   .15 .15
Issued to publicize aid for the blind.

ITU Emblem, Telegraph Pole and Transmission Tower — A66

1965, May 17   **Engr.**   *Perf. 12¹/₂x14*
214 A66 15p deep claret   .85 .15
Cent. of the ITU.

ICY Emblem A67

1965, June 26   **Litho.**   *Perf. 13¹/₂*
215 A67 15p blue & black   .40 .15
216 A67 50p yellow & green   .70 .15
    Set value   .17
International Cooperation Year, 1965.

Hands Holding Book — A68

Design: 50p, Map and flags of Turkey, Iran and Pakistan.

Perf. 13¹/₂x13, 13x12¹/₂
1965, July 21   **Litho.**   **Unwmk.**
    Size: 46x35mm
217 A68 15p org brn, dk brn & buff   .15 .15
    Size: 54x30¹/₂mm
218 A68 50p multicolored   .22 .20
    Set value   .26
1st anniv. of the signing of the Regional Cooperation for Development Pact by Turkey, Iran and Pakistan.

Tanks, Army Emblem and Soldier A69

Designs: 15p, Navy emblem, corvette No. O204 and officer. 50p, Air Force emblem, two F-104 Starfighters and pilot.

1965, Dec. 25   **Litho.**   *Perf. 13¹/₂x13*
219 A69 7p multicolored   .15 .15
220 A69 15p multicolored   .18 .15
221 A69 50p multicolored   .60 .18
   Nos. 219-221 (3)   .93
    Set value   .29
Issued to honor the Pakistani armed forces.

Emblems of Pakistan Armed Forces — A70

1966, Feb. 13   **Litho.**   *Perf. 13¹/₂x13*
222 A70 15p buff, grn & dk bl   .15 .15
Issued for Armed Forces Day.

Atomic Reactor, Islamabad — A71

Unwmk.
1966, Apr. 30   **Engr.**   *Perf. 13*
223 A71 15p black   .15 .15
Pakistan's first atomic reactor.

Habib Bank Emblem A72

Perf. 12¹/₂x13¹/₂
1966, Aug. 25   **Litho.**   **Unwmk.**
224 A72 15p brown, org & dk grn   .15 .15
25th anniversary of the Habib Bank.

Boy and Girl — A73

1966, Oct. 3   **Litho.**   *Perf. 13x13¹/₂*
225 A73 15p multicolored   .15 .15
Issued for Children's Day.

UNESCO Emblem — A74

1966, Nov. 24   **Unwmk.**   *Perf. 14*
226 A74 15p multicolored   .15 .15
20th anniv. of UNESCO.

Secretariat Buildings, Islamabad, Flag and Pres. Mohammed Ayub Khan — A75

1966, Nov. 29   **Litho.**   *Perf. 13*
227 A75 15p multicolored   .15 .15
228 A75 50p multicolored   .18 .15
    Set value   .25 .18
Issued to publicize the new capital, Islamabad.

Avicenna — A76

Mohammed Ali Jinnah — A77

1966, Dec. 3   *Perf. 13½*
229 A76 15p salmon pink & slate grn   .15   .15
Issued to publicize the Health Institute.

Lithographed and Engraved
1966, Dec. 25   Unwmk.   *Perf. 13*
Design: 50p, Different frame.
230 A77 15p orange, blk & bl   .15   .15
231 A77 50p lilac, blk & vio bl   .18   .15
    Set value   .25   .18
90th anniv. of the birth of Mohammed Ali Jinnah (1876-1948), 1st Governor General of Pakistan.

ITY Emblem A78

1967, Jan. 1   Litho.
232 A78 15p bister brn, blue & blk   15   15
International Tourist Year, 1967.

Red Crescent Emblem — A79

1967, Jan. 10   Litho.   *Perf. 13½*
233 A79 15p brn, brn org & red   .15   .15
Tuberculosis eradication campaign.

Scout Sign and Emblem A80

Perf. 12½x13½
1967, Jan. 29   Photo.
234 A80 15p dp plum & brn org   .18   .15
4th National Pakistan Jamboree.

Justice Holding Scales — A81

Unwmk.
1967, Feb. 17   Litho.   *Perf. 13*
235 A81 15p multicolored   .15   .15
Centenary of High Court of West Pakistan.

Mohammad Iqbal — A82

1967, Apr. 21   Litho.   *Perf. 13*
236 A82 15p red & brown   .15   .15
237 A82 1r dk green & brn   .28   .22
    Set value   .35   .27
90th anniv. of the birth of Mohammad Iqbal (1877-1938), poet and philosopher.

Holy War Flag — A83

1967, May 15   Litho.   *Perf. 13*
238 A83 15p multicolored   .15   .15
Holy War Flag awarded for valor to the cities of Lahore, Sialkot and Sargodha.

Star and "20" — A84

1967, Aug. 14   Photo.   Unwmk.
239 A84 15p red & slate green   .15   .15
20th anniversary of independence.

Rice Plant and Globe — A85

Cotton Plant, Bale and Cloth — A86

Design: 50p, Raw jute, bale and cloth.
1967, Sept. 26   Photo.   *Perf. 13x13½*
240 A85 10p dk blue & yellow   .15   .15
     Perf. 13
241 A86 15p orange, bl grn & yel   .15   .15
242 A86 50p blue grn, brn & tan   .18   .15
    Set value   .30   .22
Issued to publicize major export products.

Toys — A87

1967, Oct. 2   Litho.   *Perf. 13*
243 A87 15p multicolored   .15   .15
Issued for International Children's Day.

Shah and Empress Farah of Iran — A88

Lithographed and Engraved
1967, Oct. 26   *Perf. 13*
244 A88 50p yellow, blue & lilac   .22   .20
Coronation of Shah Mohammed Riza Pahlavi and Empress Farah of Iran.

"Each for all, . . ." — A89

1967, Nov. 4   Litho.   *Perf. 13*
245 A89 15p multicolored   .15   .15
Cooperative Day, 1967.

Mangla Dam — A90

1967, Nov. 23   Litho.   *Perf. 13*
246 A90 15p multicolored   .15   .15
Issued to publicize the Indus Basin Project, to harness the Indus River for flood control and irrigation.

"Fight Against Cancer" — A91   Human Rights Flame — A92

1967, Dec. 26
247 A91 15p red & dk brown   .15   .15
Issued to publicize the fight against cancer.

1968, Jan. 31   Photo.   *Perf. 14x12½*
248 A92 15p Prus green & red   .15   .15
249 A92 50p yellow, silver & red   .28   .15
    Set value   .36   .20
International Human Rights Year 1968.

Agricultural University and Produce A93

1968, Mar. 28   Litho.   *Perf. 13½*
250 A93 15p multicolored   .15   .15
Issued to publicize the first convocation of the East Pakistan Agricultural University.

WHO Emblem — A94

Perf. 13½x12½
1968, Apr. 7   Photo.
251 A94 15p emerald & orange   .15   .15
252 A94 50p orange & dk blue   .28   .15
    Set value   .36   .18
20th anniv. of WHO.

Kazi Nazrul Islam A95

Lithographed and Engraved
1968, June 25   Unwmk.   *Perf. 13*
253 A95 15p dull yellow & brown   .15   .15
254 A95 50p rose & brown   .22   .15
    Set value   .30   .20
Issued to honor Kazi Nazrul Islam, poet and composer.

Nos. 56, 61 and 74 Surcharged with New Value and Bars in Black or Red
1968, Sept.   Engr.   *Perf. 13*
255 A13   4p on 3a dk rose lake   .15   .15
256 A21   4p on 6a dk blue (R)   .15   .15
257 A15   60p on 10a purple (R)   .32   .20
  a.   Black surcharge
    Set value   .42   .30

Types of 1948-57
1968   Wmk. 351   Engr.   *Perf. 13*
258 A26 10r dk green & orange   1.00   .90
259 A7   25r purple   3.00   2.75

Children with Hoops A96

Unwmk.
1968, Oct. 7   Litho.   *Perf. 13*
260 A96 15p buff & multi   .15   .15
Issued for International Children's Day.

Symbolic of Political Reforms — A97

Designs: 15p, Agricultural and industrial development. 50p, Defense. 60p, Scientific and cultural advancement.

1968, Oct. 27   Litho.   *Perf. 13*
261 A97 10p multicolored   .15   .15
262 A97 15p multicolored   .15   .15
263 A97 50p multicolored   .20   .15
264 A97 60p multicolored   .28   .18
    Set value   .60   .43
Development Decade, 1958-1968.

Chittagong Steel Mill — A98

1969, Jan. 7   Unwmk.   *Perf. 13*
265 A98 15p lt gray grn, lt blue & blk   .15   .15
Opening of Pakistan's first steel mill.

Family of Four — A99

1969, Jan. 14 Litho. Perf. 13½
266 A99 15p lt blue & plum .15 .15
Issued to publicize family planning.

Hockey Player and Medal — A100

1969, Jan. 30 Photo. Perf. 13½
267 A100 15p green, lt bl, blk & gold .15 .15
268 A100 1r grn, sal pink, blk & gold .60 .25
Set value .32
Pakistan's hockey victory at the 19th Olympic Games in Mexico.

Mirza Ghalib A101

1969, Feb. 15 Litho. Perf. 13
269 A101 15p blue & multi .15 .15
270 A101 50p multicolored .18 .15
Set value .25 .20
Mirza Ghalib (Asad Ullab Beg Khan, 1797-1869), poet who modernized the Urdu language.

Dacca Railroad Station A102

1969, Apr. 27 Litho. Perf. 13
271 A102 15p yel, grn, blk & dull bl .25 .15
Opening of the new railroad station in Kamalpur area of Dacca.

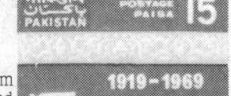

ILO Emblem and Ornamental Border A103

1969, May 15 Litho. Perf. 13½
272 A103 15p bright green & ocher .15 .15
273 A103 50p carmine rose & ocher .28 .18
Set value .35 .24
50th anniv. of the ILO.

Lady on Balcony, Mogul Miniature, Pakistan — A104

Designs: 50p, Lady Serving Wine, Safavi miniature, Iran. 1r, Sultan Suleiman Receiving Sheik Abdul Latif, 16th century miniature, Turkey.

1969, July 21 Litho. Perf. 13
274 A104 20p multicolored .15 .15
275 A104 50p multicolored .18 .15
276 A104 1r multicolored .35 .28
Nos. 274-276 (3) .68
Set value .48
5th anniv. of the signing of the Regional Cooperation for Development Pact by Turkey, Iran and Pakistan.

Eastern Refinery, Chittagong A105

1969, Sept. 14 Photo. Perf. 13½
277 A105 20p yel, blk & vio bl .15 .15
Issued to commemorate the opening of the first oil refinery in East Pakistan.

Children Playing — A106

1969, Oct. 6 Perf. 13
278 A106 20p blue & multi .15 .15
Issued for Universal Children's Day.

Japanese Doll, Map of Dacca-Tokyo Pearl Route A107

1969, Nov. 1 Litho. Perf. 13½x13
279 A107 20p multicolored .15 .15
280 A107 50p ultra & multi .24 .16
Set value .34 .24
Inauguration of the Pakistan International Airways' Dacca-Tokyo "Pearl Route."

Reflection of Light Diagram — A108

1969, Nov. 4 Perf. 13
281 A108 20p multicolored .16 .15
Alhazen (abu-Ali al Hasan ibn-al-Haytham, 965-1039), astronomer and optician.

Vickers Vimy and London-Darwin Route over Karachi — A109

1969, Dec. 2 Photo. Perf. 13½x13
282 A109 50p multicolored .40 .22
50th anniv. of the 1st England to Australia flight.

View of EXPO '70, Sun Tower, Flags of Pakistan, Iran and Turkey — A110

1970, Feb. 15 Litho. Perf. 13
283 A110 50p multicolored .22 .16
Issued to publicize EXPO '70 International Exhibition, Osaka, Japan, Mar. 15-Sept. 13.

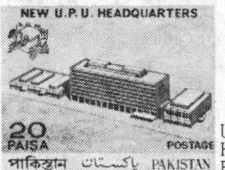

UPU Headquarters, Bern — A111

1970, May 20 Litho. Perf. 13½x13
284 A111 20p multicolored .15 .15
285 A111 50p multicolored .30 .15
Set value .38 .20
Opening of new UPU headquarters in Bern. A souvenir sheet of 2 exists, inscribed "U.P.U. Day 9th Oct. 1971". It contains stamps similar to Nos. 284-285, imperf.

UN Headquarters, New York — A112

Design: 50p, UN emblem.

1970, June 26
286 A112 20p green & multi .15 .15
287 A112 50p violet & multi .28 .15
Set value .36 .20
25th anniversary of the United Nations.

Education Year Emblem and Open Book A113

1970, July 6 Litho. Perf. 13
288 A113 20p blue & multi .15 .15
289 A113 50p orange & multi .22 .16
Set value .30 .15
International Education Year, 1970.

Saiful Malook Lake, Pakistan A114

Designs: 50p, Seeyo-Se-Pol Bridge, Esfahan, Iran. 1r, View, Fethiye, Turkey.

1970, July 21
290 A114 20p yellow & multi .15 .15
291 A114 50p yellow & multi .24 .15
292 A114 1r yellow & multi .45 .24
Nos. 290-292 (3) .84
Set value .39
6th anniv. of the signing of the Regional Cooperation for Development Pact by Pakistan, Iran and Turkey.

Asian Productivity Year Emblem A115

1970, Aug. 18 Photo. Perf. 12½x14
293 A115 50p black, yellow & green .18 .15
Asian Productivity Year, 1970.

Dr. Maria Montessori — A116

1970, Aug. 31 Litho. Perf. 13
294 A116 20p red & multi .15 .15
295 A116 50p multicolored .20 .15
Set value .28 .17
Maria Montessori (1870-1952) Italian educator and physician.

Tractor and Fertilizer Factory — A117

1970, Sept. 12
296 A117 20p yel grn & brn org .15 .15
10th Regional Food and Agricultural Organization Conf. for the Near East in Islamabad.

Boy, Girl, Open Book A118

Flag and Inscription A119

1970, Oct. 5 Photo. Perf. 13
297 A118 20p multicolored .15 .15
Issued for Children's Day.

1970, Dec. 7   Litho.   *Perf. 13½x13*
298 A119 20p violet & green   .15 .15
299 A119 20p brt pink & green   .15 .15
       Set value   .16 .16

No. 298 inscribed "Elections for National Assembly 7th Dec. 1970," No. 299 inscribed "Elections for Provincial Assemblies 17th Dec. 1970."

Emblem and Burning of Al Aqsa Mosque — A120

1970, Dec. 26   *Perf. 13½x12½*
300 A120 20p multicolored   .50 .25

Islamic Conference of Foreign Ministers, Karachi, Dec. 26-28.

Coastal Embankment — A121

1971, Feb. 25   Litho.   *Perf. 13*
301 A121 20p multicolored   .15 .15

Development of coastal embankments in East Pakistan.

Men of Different Races — A122

1971, Mar. 21   Litho.   *Perf. 13*
302 A122 20p multicolored   .15 .15
303 A122 50p lilac & multi   .18 .15
       Set value   .25 .15

Intl. Year against Racial Discrimination.

Cement Factory, Daudkhel A123

1971, July 1   Litho.   *Perf. 13*
304 A123 20p purple, blk & brn   .15 .15

20th anniversary of Colombo Plan.

Badshahi Mosque, Lahore — A124

Designs: 10pa, Mosque of Selim, Edirne, Turkey. 50pa, Religious School, of Chaharbagh, Isfahan, Iran, vert.

1971, July 21   Litho.   *Perf. 13*
305 A124 10p red & multi   .15 .15
306 A124 20p green & multi   .15 .15
307 A124 50p blue & multi   .28 .18
       Set value   .45 .28

7th anniversary of Regional Cooperation among Pakistan, Iran and Turkey.

Electric Train and Boy with Toy Locomotive — A125

1971, Oct. 4   Litho.   *Perf. 13*
308 A125 20p slate & multi   .40 .22

Children's Day.

Messenger and Statue of Cyrus the Great — A126

1971, Oct. 15
309 A126 10p green & multi   .15 .15
310 A126 20p blue & multi   .15 .15
311 A126 50p red & multi   .38 .22
       Set value   .40 .32

2500th anniversary of the founding of the Persian Empire by Cyrus the Great.
A souvenir sheet of 3 contains stamps similar to Nos. 309-311, imperf.

Hockey Player and Cup — A127

1971, Oct. 24
312 A127 20p red & multi   .35 .15

First World Hockey Cup, Barcelona, Spain, Oct. 15-24.

Great Bath at Mohenjo-Daro — A128

1971, Nov. 4
313 A128 20p dp org, dk brn & blk   .15 .15

25th anniv. of UNESCO.

UNICEF Emblem A129

1971, Dec. 11   Litho.   *Perf. 13*
314 A129 50p dull blue, org & grn   .30 .15

25th anniv. of UNICEF.

King Hussein and Jordan Flag A130

1971, Dec. 25
315 A130 20p blue & multi   .15 .15

50th anniversary of the Hashemite Kingdom of Jordan.

Pakistan Hockey Federation Emblem, and Cup A131

1971, Dec. 31
316 A131 20p yellow & multi   .18 .15

Pakistan, world hockey champions, Barcelona, Oct. 1971.

Arab Scholars — A132

1972, Jan. 15   Litho.   *Perf. 13½*
317 A132 20p brown, blk & blue   .15 .15

International Book Year 1972.

Angels and Grand Canal, Venice — A133

1972, Feb. 5   *Perf. 13*
318 A133 20p blue & multi   .15 .15

UNESCO campaign to save Venice.

ECAFE Emblem A134

1972, Mar. 28   Litho.   *Perf. 13*
319 A134 20p blue & multi   .15 .15

Economic Commission for Asia and the Far East (ECAFE), 25th anniversary.

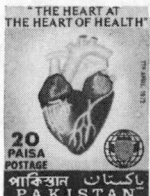

"Your Heart is your Health" — A135

1972, Apr. 7   *Perf. 13x13½*
320 A135 20p vio blue & multi   .15 .15

World Health Day 1972.

"Only One Earth" — A136

1972, June 5   Litho.   *Perf. 12½x14*
321 A136 20p ultra & multi   .18 .15

UN Conference on Human Environment, Stockholm, June 5-16.

Young Man, by Abdur Rehman Chughtai — A137

Paintings: 10p, Fisherman, by Cevat Dereli (Turkey). 20p, Persian Woman, by Behzad.

1972, July 21   Litho.   *Perf. 13*
322 A137 10p multicolored   .15 .15
323 A137 20p multicolored   .15 .15
324 A137 50p multicolored   .18 .15
       Set value   .30 .20

Regional Cooperation for Development Pact among Pakistan, Turkey and Iran, 8th anniversary.

Jinnah and Independence Memorial — A138

"Land Reforms" — A139

Designs: Nos. 326-329, Principal reforms. 60pa, State Bank, Islamabad, meeting-place of National Assembly, horiz.

Perf. 13 (A138), 13½x12½ (A139)
1972, Aug. 14
325 A138 10p shown   .15 .15
326 A139 20p shown   .15 .15
327 A139 20p Labor reforms   .15 .15
328 A139 20p Education   .15 .15
329 A139 20p Health care   .15 .15
  a.   Vert. strip of 4, #326-329   .50
330 A138 60p rose lilac & car   .22 .15
       Set value   .80 .35

25th anniversary of independence. No. 329a has decorative labels adjoining.

Blood Donor, Society Emblem — A140

1972, Sept. 6 Litho. Perf. 14x12½
331 A140 20p multicolored .15 .15
Pakistan National Blood Transfusion Service.

Census Chart — A141

1972, Sept. 16 Litho. Perf. 13½
332 A141 20p multicolored .15 .15
Centenary of population census.

Children Leaving Slum for Modern City — A142

1972, Oct. 2 Litho. Perf. 13
333 A142 20p multicolored .15 .15
Children's Day.

Giant Book and Children A143

1972, Oct. 23
334 A143 20p purple & multi .15 .15
Education Week.

Nuclear Power Plant, Karachi A144

1972, Nov. 28 Litho. Perf. 13
335 A144 20p multicolored .15 .15
Pakistan's first nuclear power plant.

Copernicus in Observatory, by Jan Matejko — A145

1973, Feb. 19 Litho. Perf. 13
336 A145 20p multicolored .15 .15
500th anniversary of the birth of Nicolaus Copernicus (1473-1543), Polish astronomer.

Dancing Girl, Public Baths, Mohenjo-Daro — A146

1973, Feb. 23 Perf. 13½x13
337 A146 20p multicolored .15 .15
50th anniv. of the Mohenjo-Daro excavations.

Radar, Lightning, WMO Emblem — A147

1973, Mar. 23 Litho. Perf. 13
338 A147 20p multicolored .15 .15
Cent. of intl. meteorological cooperation.

Prisoners of War A148

1973, Apr. 18
339 A148 1.25r black & multi .18 .15
A plea for Pakistani prisoners of war in India.

National Assembly, Islamabad A149

1973, Apr. 21 Perf. 12½x13½
340 A149 20p green & multi .15 .15
Constitution Week.

State Bank and Emblem A150

1973, July 1 Litho. Perf. 13
341 A150 20p multicolored .15 .15
342 A150 1r multicolored .25 .15
Set value .15
State Bank of Pakistan, 25th anniversary.

Street, Mohenjo-Daro, Pakistan — A151

Designs: 20p, Statue of man, Shahdad, Kerman, Persia, 4000 B.C. 1.25r, Head from mausoleum of King Antiochus I (69-34 B.C.), Turkey.

1973, July 21 Perf. 13x13½
343 A151 20p blue & multi .15 .15
344 A151 60p emerald & multi .16 .15
345 A151 1.25r red & multi .35 .25
Nos. 343-345 (3) .66
Set value .40
Regional Cooperation for Development Pact among Pakistan, Turkey and Iran, 9th anniversary.

Pakistani Flag and Constitution A152

1973, Aug. 14 Litho. Perf. 13
346 A152 20p blue & multi .15 .15
Independence Day.

Mohammed Ali Jinnah — A153

1973, Sept. 11 Litho. Perf. 13
347 A153 20p emerald, yel & blk .15 .15
Mohammed Ali Jinnah (1876-1948), president of All-India Moslem League.

Wallago Attu — A154

Fish: 20p, Labeo rohita. 60p, Tilapia mossambica. 1r, Catla catla.

1973, Sept. 24 Litho. Perf. 13½
348 A154 10p multicolored .20 .15
349 A154 20p multicolored .25 .15
350 A154 60p multicolored .50 .20
351 A154 1r ultra & multi .85 .35
a. Strip of 4, #348-351 1.80 .75

Book, Torch, Child and School A155

1973, Oct. 1
352 A155 20p multicolored .15 .15
Universal Children's Day.

Sindhi Farmer and FAO Emblem A156

1973, Oct. 15 Litho. Perf. 13
353 A156 20p multicolored .15 .15
World Food Organization, 10th anniv.

Kemal Ataturk and Ankara A157

1973, Oct. 29
354 A157 50p multicolored .15 .15
50th anniversary of Turkish Republic.

Scout Pointing to Planet and Stars — A158

Human Rights Flame, Sheltered Home — A159

Perf. 13½x12½
1973, Nov. 11 Litho.
355 A158 20p dull blue & multi .30 .15
25th anniversary of Pakistani Boy Scouts and Silver Jubilee Jamboree.

1973, Nov. 16
356 A159 20p multicolored .15 .15
25th anniversary of the Universal Declaration of Human Rights.

al-Biruni and Jhelum Observatory — A160

1973, Nov. 26 Litho. Perf. 13
357 A160 20p multicolored .15 .15
358 A160 1.25r multicolored .50 .35
Set value .40
International Congress on Millenary of abu-al-Rayhan al-Biruni, Nov. 26-Dec. 12.

Dr. A. G. Hansen — A161

1973, Dec. 29
359 A161 20p ultra & multi .15 .15
Centenary of the discovery by Dr. Armauer Gerhard Hansen of the Hansen bacillus, the cause of leprosy.

Family and WPY Emblem A162

1974, Jan. 1 Litho. Perf. 13
360 A162 20p yellow & multi .15 .15
361 A162 1.25r salmon & multi .35 .25
Set value .41 .30
World Population Year 1974.

Summit Emblem and Ornament — A163

Emblem, Crescent and Rays A164

1974, Feb. 22   Perf. 14x12½, 13
362 A163 20p multicolored   .15 .15
363 A164 65p multicolored   .18 .15
  a.   Souvenir sheet of 2   1.75 1.75
        Set value   .24 .19

Islamic Summit Meeting. No. 363a contains two stamps similar to Nos. 362-363 with simulated perforations.

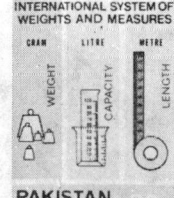

Metric Measures — A165

1974, July 1   Litho.   Perf. 13
364 A165 20p multicolored   .15 .15

Introduction of metric system.

Kashan Rug, Lahore — A166

Designs: 60p, Persian rug, late 16th century. 1.25r, Anatolian rug, 15th century.

1974, July 21
365 A166 20p multicolored   .15 .15
366 A166 60p multicolored   .16 .15
367 A166 1.25r multicolored   .35 .25
  Nos. 365-367 (3)   .66
        Set value   .40

10th anniversary of the Regional Cooperation for Development Pact among Pakistan, Iran and Turkey.

Hands Protecting Sapling — A167

1974, Aug. 9   Litho.   Perf. 13
368 A167 20p multicolored   .15 .15

Arbor Day.

Torch over Map of Africa with Namibia — A168

1974, Aug. 26
369 A168 60p green & multi   .20 .15

Namibia (South-West Africa) Day. See note after United Nations No. 241.

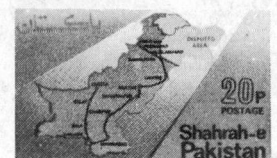

Map of Pakistan with Highways and Disputed Area — A169

1974, Sept. 23
370 A169 20p multicolored   .15 .15

Highway system under construction.

Child and Students — A170

1974, Oct. 7   Litho.   Perf. 13
371 A170 20p multicolored   .15 .15

Universal Children's Day.

UPU Emblem — A171   Liaqat Ali Khan — A172

Design: 2.25r, Jet, UPU emblem, mail coach.

1974, Oct. 9
        Size: 24x36mm
372 A171 20p multicolored   .15 .15
        Size: 29x41mm
373 A171 2.25r multicolored   .60 .50
  a. Souv. sheet of 2, #372-373, imperf. 1.75 1.75

Centenary of Universal Postal Union.

1974, Oct. 16   Litho.   Perf. 13x13½
374 A172 20p black & red   .15 .15

Liaqat Ali Khan, Prime Minister 1947-1951.

Mohammad Allama Iqbal — A173

1974, Nov. 9   Litho.   Perf. 13
375 A173 20p multicolored   .15 .15

Mohammad Allama Iqbal (1877-1938), poet and philosopher.

Dr. Schweitzer on Ogowe River, 1915 A174

1975, Jan. 14   Litho.   Perf. 13
376 A174 2.25r multicolored   .85 .50

Dr. Albert Schweitzer (1875-1965), medical missionary, birth centenary.

Tourism Year 75 Emblem — A175

1975, Jan. 15
377 A175 2.25r multicolored   .50 .40

South Asia Tourism Year, 1975.

Flags of Participants, Memorial and Prime Minister Bhutto — A176

1975, Feb. 22   Litho.   Perf. 13
378 A176 20p lt blue & multi   .15 .15
379 A176 1r brt pink & multi   .28 .28
        Set value   .34 .32

1st anniversary of 2nd Lahore Islamic Summit, Feb. 22.

IWY Emblem and Woman Scientist — A177

Design: 2.25r, Old woman and girl learning to read and write.

1975, June 15   Litho.   Perf. 13
380 A177 20p multicolored   .15 .15
381 A177 2.25r multicolored   .60 .50
        Set value   .55

International Women's Year 1975.

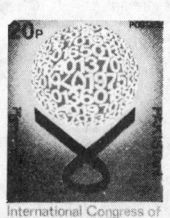

Globe with Dates, Arabic "X" — A178   Camel Leather Vase, Pakistan — A179

1975, July 14   Litho.   Perf. 13
382 A178 20p multicolored   .15 .15

International Congress of Mathematical Sciences, Karachi, July 14-20.

1975, July 21
Designs: 60p, Ceramic plate and RCD emblem, Iran, horiz. 1.25r, Porcelain vase, Turkey.

383 A179 20p lilac & multi   .15 .15
384 A179 60p violet blk & multi   .16 .15
385 A179 1.25r blue & multi   .30 .18
        Set value   .53 .32

Regional Cooperation for Development Pact among Turkey, Iran and Pakistan.

Sapling, Trees and Ant — A180   Black Partridge — A181

1975, Aug. 9   Litho.   Perf. 13x13½
386 A180 20p multicolored   .15 .15

Tree Planting Day.

1975, Sept. 30   Litho.   Perf. 13
387 A181 20p blue & multi   .30 .15
388 A181 2.25r yellow & multi   1.40 .55

Wildlife Protection.

Girls — A182

1975, Oct. 6
389 A182 20p multicolored   .15 .15

Universal Children's Day.

Hazrat Amir Khusrau, Sitar and Tabla — A183

1975, Oct. 24   Litho.   Perf. 14x12½
390 A183 20p lt blue & multi   .15 .15
391 A183 2.25r pink & multi   .50 .40
        Set value   .45

700th anniversary of Hazrat Amir Khusrau (1253-1325), musician who invented the sitar and tabla instruments.

Mohammad Iqbal — A184

1975, Nov. 9   Perf. 13
392 A184 20p multicolored   .15 .15

Mohammad Allama Iqbal (1877-1938), poet and philosopher, birth centenary.

Wild Sheep of the
Punjab — A185

1975, Dec. 31　Litho.　Perf. 13
393 A185 20p multicolored　　　　.35　.18
394 A185 3r multicolored　　　　2.00　.65
　　Wildlife Protection. See Nos. 410-411.

Mohenjo-Daro
and UNESCO
Emblem
A186

Designs: View of Mohenjo-Daro excavations.

1976, Feb. 29　Litho.　Perf. 13
395 A186 10p multicolored　　　　.15　.15
396 A186 20p multicolored　　　　.15　.15
397 A186 65p multicolored　　　　.15　.15
398 A186 3r multicolored　　　　.50　.40
399 A186 4r multicolored　　　　.65　.60
　a.　Strip of 5, #395-399　　　1.40　1.40
　　UNESCO campaign to save Mohenjo-Daro excavations.

Dome and Minaret
of Rauza-e-Mubarak
Mausoleum
A187

1976, Mar. 3　Photo.　Perf. 13¹/₂x14
400 A187 20p blue & multi　　　　.15　.15
401 A187 3r gray & multi　　　　.50　.40
　　Set value　　　　　　　.55　.45
　　International Congress on Seerat, the teachings of Mohammed, Mar. 3-15.

Alexander Graham Bell, 1876 Telephone
and Dial — A188

1976, Mar. 10　　　　Perf. 13
402 A188 3r blue & multi　　　　.85　.85
　　Centenary of first telephone call by Alexander Graham Bell, Mar. 10, 1876.

College Emblem — A189

1976, Mar. 15　Litho.　Perf. 13
403 A189 20p multicolored　　　　.15　.15
　　Cent. of Natl. College of Arts, Lahore.

Peacock
A190

1976, Mar. 31　Litho.　Perf. 13
404 A190 20p lt blue & multi　　　.35　.18
405 A190 3r pink & multi　　　　2.00　.65
　　Wildlife protection.

Eye and WHO Emblem — A191

1976, Apr. 7
406 A191 20p multicolored　　　　.15　.15
　　World Health Day: "Foresight prevents blindness."

Mohenjo-Daro, UNESCO Emblem, Bull
(from Seal) — A192

1976, May 31　Litho.　Perf. 13
407 A192 20p multicolored　　　　.15　.15
　　UNESCO campaign to save Mohenjo-Daro excavations.

Jefferson Memorial, US Bicentennial
Emblem — A193

Declaration of Independence, by John
Trumbull — A194

1976, July 4　　　　Perf. 13
408 A193 90p multicolored　　　　.15　.15
**　　　　Perf. 13¹/₂x13**
409 A194 4r multicolored　　　　1.10　1.10
　　American Bicentennial.

**　　Wildlife Type of 1975**
　Wildlife protection: 20p, 3r, Ibex.

1976, July 12
410 A185 20p multicolored　　　　.35　.18
411 A185 3r multicolored　　　　2.00　.65

Mohammed Ali Jinnah — A195

Designs: 65p, Riza Shah Pahlavi. 90p, Kemal
Ataturk.

1976, July 21　Litho.　Perf. 14
412 A195 20p multicolored　　　　.15　.15
413 A195 65p multicolored　　　　.15　.15
414 A195 90p multicolored　　　　.18　.15
　a.　Strip of 3, #412-414　　　　.35　.35
　　Regional Cooperation for Development Pact among Pakistan, Turkey and Iran, 12th anniversary.

Ornament
A196

Jinnah and Wazir Mansion
A197

Designs (Jinnah and): 40p, Sind Madressah
(building). 50p, Minar Qarardad (minaret). 3r,
Mausoleum.

1976, Aug. 14　Litho.　Perf. 13¹/₂
415 A196 5p multicolored　　　　.15　.15
416 A196 10p multicolored　　　　.15　.15
417 A196 15p multicolored　　　　.15　.15
418 A197 20p multicolored　　　　.18　.15
419 A197 40p multicolored　　　　.20　.15
420 A197 50p multicolored　　　　.28　.15
421 A196 1r multicolored　　　　.35　.15
422 A197 3r multicolored　　　　.65　.50
　a.　Block of 8, #415-422　　　2.25　2.00
　　Set value　　　　　　　1.00
　　Mohammed Ali Jinnah (1876-1948), first Governor General of Pakistan, birth centenary. Horizontal rows of types A196 and A197 alternate in sheet.

Mohenjo-Daro and UNESCO
Emblem — A198

1976, Aug. 31　　　　Perf. 14
423 A198 65p multicolored　　　　.15　.15
　　UNESCO campaign to save Mohenjo-Daro excavations.

Racial Discrimination Emblem — A199

**　　Perf. 12¹/₂x13¹/₂**
1976, Sept. 15　　　　Litho.
424 A199 65p multicolored　　　　.22　.18
　　Fight against racial discrimination.

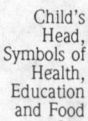

Child's
Head,
Symbols of
Health,
Education
and Food
A200

1976, Oct. 4　　　　Perf. 13
425 A200 20p blue & multi　　　　.15　.15
　　Universal Children's Day.

Verse by
Allama
Iqbal
A201

1976, Nov. 9　Litho.　Perf. 13
426 A201 20p multicolored　　　　.15　.15
　　Mohammed Allama Iqbal (1877-1938), poet and philosopher, birth centenary.

Scout Emblem,　　Children
Jinnah Giving　　Reading — A203
Salute — A202

1976, Nov. 20
427 A202 20p multicolored　　　　.15　.15
　　Quaid-I-Azam Centenary Jamboree, Nov. 1976.

1976, Dec. 15　Litho.　Perf. 13
428 A203 20p multicolored　　　　.15　.15
　　Books for children.

Mohammed Ali
Jinnah — A204

**　　Lithographed and Embossed**
1976, Dec. 25　　　　Perf. 12¹/₂
429 A204 10r gold & green　　　　1.25　1.25
　　Mohammed Ali Jinnah (1876-1948), 1st Governor General of Pakistan.

Farm Family and
Village, Tractor,
Ambulance
A205

1977, Apr. 14　Litho.　Perf. 13
430 A205 20p multicolored　　　　.15　.15
　　Social Welfare and Rural Development Year, 1976-77.

Terracotta Bullock Cart, Pakistan A206

Designs: 20p, Terra-cotta jug, Turkey. 90p, Decorated jug, Iran.

1977, July 21   Litho.   Perf. 13
431 A206 20p ultra & multi .15 .15
432 A206 65p blue green & multi .20 .15
433 A206 90p lilac & multi .35 .18
Nos. 431-433 (3) .70
Set value .32

Regional Cooperation for Development Pact among Pakistan, Turkey and Iran, 13th anniversary.

Trees — A207

1977, Aug. 9   Litho.   Perf. 13
434 A207 20p multicolored .15 .15
Tree planting program.

Desert A208

1977, Sept. 5   Litho.   Perf. 13
435 A208 65p multicolored .15 .15
UN Conference on Desertification, Nairobi, Kenya, Aug. 29-Sept. 9.

"Water for the Children" — A209

1977, Oct. 3   Litho.   Perf. 14x12½
436 A209 50p multicolored .15 .15
Universal Children's Day.

Aga Khan III — A210

1977, Nov. 2   Litho.   Perf. 13
437 A210 2r multicolored .35 .35
Aga Khan III (1877-1957), spiritual ruler of Ismaeli sect, statesman, birth centenary.

Mohammad Iqbal — A211

Designs: 20p, Spirit appearing to Iqbal, painting by Behzad. 65p, Iqbal looking at Jamaluddin Afghani and Saeed Halim offering prayers, by Behzad. 1.25r, Verse in Urdu. 2.25r, Verse in Persian.

1977, Nov. 9
438 A211 20p multicolored .15 .15
439 A211 65p multicolored .15 .15
440 A211 1.25r multicolored .20 .18
441 A211 2.25r multicolored .40 .35
442 A211 3r multicolored .85 .65
a. Strip of 5, #438-442 1.60 1.60

Mohammad Allama Iqbal (1877-1938), poet and philosopher, birth centenary.

Holy Kaaba, Mecca — A212

1977, Nov. 21   Perf. 14
443 A212 65p green & multi .15 .15
1977 pilgrimage to Mecca.

Healthy and Sick Bodies A213

Woman from Rawalpindi-Islamabad A214

1977, Dec. 19   Litho.   Perf. 13
444 A213 65p blue green & multi .15 .15
World Rheumatism Year.

1978, Feb. 5   Litho.   Perf. 12½x13½
445 A214 75p multicolored .20 .15
Indonesia-Pakistan Economic and Cultural Cooperation Organization.

Blood Circulation and Pressure Gauge A215

1978, Apr. 20   Litho.   Perf. 13
446 A215 20p blue & multi .15 .15
447 A215 2r yellow & multi .35 .35
Set value .40 .40
Campaign against hypertension.

Henri Dunant, Red Cross, Red Crescent A216

1978, May 8   Perf. 14
448 A216 1r multicolored .18 .18
Henri Dunant (1828-1910), founder of Red Cross, 150th birth anniversary.

Red Roses, Pakistan — A217

Designs: 90p, Pink roses, Iran. 2r, Yellow rose, Turkey.

1978, July 21   Litho.   Perf. 13½
449 A217 20p multicolored .15 .15
450 A217 90p multicolored .15 .15
451 A217 2r multicolored .35 .35
a. Strip of 3, #449-451 .55 .55

Regional Cooperation for Development Pact among Turkey, Iran and Pakistan.

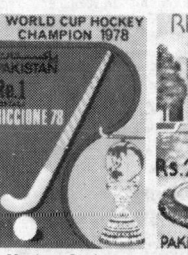

Hockey Stick and Ball, Championship Cup — A218

Fair Building, Fountain, Piazza Tourismo — A219

1978, Aug. 26   Litho.   Perf. 13
452 A218 1r multicolored .18 .18
453 A219 2r multicolored .35 .35

Riccione '78, 30th International Stamp Fair, Riccione, Italy, Aug. 26-28. No. 452 also commemorates Pakistan as World Hockey Cup Champion.

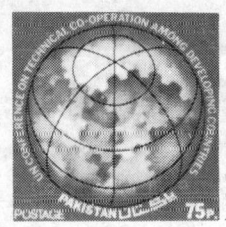

Globe and Cogwheels A220

1978, Sept. 3
454 A220 75p multicolored .15 .15
UN Conference on Technical Cooperation among Developing Countries, Buenos Aires, Argentina, Sept. 1978.

St. Patrick's Cathedral, Karachi — A221

Design: 2r, Stained-glass window.

1978, Sept. 29   Litho.   Perf. 13
455 A221 1r multicolored .22 .18
456 A221 2r multicolored .50 .35

St. Patrick's Cathedral, Karachi, centenary.

"Four Races" — A222

1978, Nov. 20   Litho.   Perf. 13
457 A222 1r multicolored .18 .15
Anti-Apartheid Year.

Maulana Jauhar — A223

1978, Dec. 10   Litho.   Perf. 13
458 A223 50p multicolored .15 .15
Maulana Muhammad Ali Jauhar, writer, journalist and patriot, birth centenary.

Type of 1957 and

Qarardad Monument A224

Tractor A225

Tomb of Ibrahim Khan Makli — A225a

Engr.; Litho. (10p, 25p, 40p, 50p, 90p)
1978-81   Perf. 14
459 A224 2p dark green .15 .15
460 A224 3p black .15 .15
461 A224 5p violet blue .15 .15
462 A225 10p lt blue & blue ('79) .15 .15
463 A225 20p yel green ('79) .15 .15
464 A225 25p rose car & grn ('79) .15 .15
465 A225 40p carmine & blue .15 .15
466 A225 50p bl grn & vio ('79) .15 .15
467 A225 60p black .18 .15
468 A225 75p dull red .20 .15
469 A225 90p blue & carmine .25 .15

Perf. 13½x13
Engr.   Wmk. 351
470 A225a 1r olive ('80) .28 .15
471 A225a 1.50r dp orange ('79) .40 .15
472 A225a 2r car rose ('79) .55 .16
473 A225a 3r indigo ('80) .85 .22
474 A225a 4r black ('81) 1.10 .35
475 A225a 5r dk brown ('81) 1.40 .40
475A A26 15r rose lil & red ('79) 5.00 4.00
Nos. 459-475A (18) 11.41
Set value 5.75

Lithographed stamps, type A225, have bottom panel in solid color with colorless lettering and numerals 2mm high instead of 3mm.
For overprints see Nos. O94-O110.

Tornado Jet Fighter, de Havilland Rapide
and Flyer A — A226

Designs (Wright Flyer A and): 1r, Phantom F4F
jet fighter and Tristar airliner. 2r, Bell X15 fighter
and TU-104 airliner. 2.25r, MiG fighter and
Concorde.

Unwmk.

1978, Dec. 24		Litho.	Perf. 13	
476	A226	65p multicolored	.15	.15
477	A226	1r multicolored	.20	.15
478	A226	2r multicolored	.35	.18
479	A226	2.25r multicolored	.40	.20
a.		Block of 4, #476-479	1.10	
		Set value		.52

75th anniv. of 1st powered flight. Nos. 476-479
printed se-tenant in sheets of 40.

Koran Lighting
the World and
Mohammed's
Tomb — A227

1979, Feb. 10		Litho.	Perf. 13	
480	A227	20p multicolored	.15	.15

Mohammed's birth anniversary.

Mother
and
Children
A228

1979, Feb. 25
481 A228 50p multicolored .15 .15

APWA Services, 30th anniversary.

Lophophorus Impejanus — A229

Pheasants: 25p, Lophura leucomelana. 40p, Puc-
crasia macrolopha. 1r, Catreus walichii.

1979, June 17		Litho.	Perf. 13	
482	A229	20p multicolored	.15	.15
483	A229	25p multicolored	.15	.15
484	A229	40p multicolored	.15	.15
485	A229	1r multicolored	.35	.15
		Set value	.55	.22

For overprint see No. 525.

At the Well, by Allah Baksh — A230

Paintings: 75p, Potters, by Kamalel Molk, Iran.
1.60r, Plowing, by Namik Ismail, Turkey.

1979, July 21		Litho.	Perf. 14x13	
486	A230	40p multicolored	.15	.15
487	A230	75p multicolored	.15	.15
488	A230	1.60r multicolored	.22	.15
a.		Strip of 3, #486-488	.38	.38
		Set value		.22

Regional Cooperation for Development Pact
among Pakistan, Iran and Turkey, 15th anniversary.

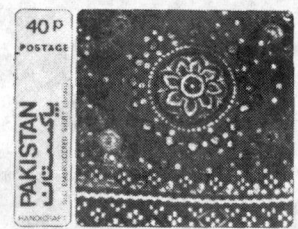

Guj Embroidery — A231

Handicrafts: 1r, Enamel inlay brass plate. 1.50r,
Baskets. 2r, Peacock, embroidered rug.

1979, Aug. 23		Litho.	Perf. 14x13	
489	A231	40p multicolored	.15	.15
490	A231	1r multicolored	.15	.15
491	A231	1.50r multicolored	.20	.15
492	A231	2r multicolored	.28	.16
a.		Block of 4, #489-492	.80	.80
		Set value		.40

Children,
IYC and
SOS
Emblems
A232

1979, Sept. 10		Litho.	Perf. 13	
493	A232	50p multicolored	.15	.15

SOS Children's Village, Lahore, opening.

Playground, IYC Emblem — A233

IYC Emblem and: Children's drawings.

1979, Oct. 22			Perf. 14x12½	
494	A233	40p multicolored	.15	.15
495	A233	75p multicolored	.15	.15
496	A233	1r multicolored	.15	.15
497	A233	1.50r multicolored	.20	.15
a.		Block of 4, #494-497	.50	.50
		Set value		.28

Souvenir Sheet

Imperf

498	A233	2r multi, vert.	1.75	1.40

IYC. For overprints see #520-523.

Fight Against
Cancer — A234

Unwmk.

1979, Nov. 12		Litho.	Perf. 14	
499	A234	40p multicolored	.15	.15

Pakistan Customs
Service
Centenary — A235

1979, Dec. 10			Perf. 13x13½	
500	A235	1r multicolored	.15	.15

Tippu Sultan Shaheed — A236

1979, Mar. 23		Wmk. 351	Perf. 14	
501	A236	10r shown	1.75	1.25
502	A236	15r Syed Ahmad Khan	2.75	2.00
503	A236	25r Altaf Hussain Hali	4.75	3.25
a.		Strip of 3, #501-503	10.00	10.00

See No. 699.

A237　A238

Ornament — A239

Perf. 12x11½, 11½x12

1980			Unwmk.	
506	A237	10p dk grn & yel org	.15	.15
507	A237	15p dk grn & apple grn	.15	.15
508	A237	25p multicolored	.15	.15
509	A237	35p multicolored	.15	.15
510	A238	40p red & lt brown	.15	.15
511	A239	50p olive & vio bl	.15	.15
512	A239	80p black & yel grn	.22	.15
		Set value	.76	.35

Issued: 25, 35, 50, 80p, Mar. 10; others, Jan. 15.
See Nos. O111-O117.

Pakistan International Airline, 25th
Anniversary — A240

1980, Jan. 10		Litho.	Perf. 13	
516	A240	1r multicolored	.15	.15

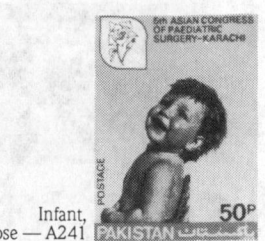

Infant,
Rose — A241

1980, Feb. 16			Perf. 13	
517	A241	50p multicolored	.15	.15

5th Asian Congress of Pediatric Surgery, Karachi,
Feb. 16-19.

Conference
Emblem
A242

1980, May 17		Litho.	Perf. 13	
518	A242	1r multicolored	.20	.15

11th Islamic Conference of Foreign Ministers,
Islamabad, May 17-21.

Lighthouse, Oil Terminal, Map Showing
Karachi Harbor — A243

1980, July 15			Perf. 13½	
519	A243	1r multicolored	.20	.15

Karachi Port, centenary of independent
management.

Nos. 494-497 Overprinted in Red:
RICCIONE 80

1980, Aug. 30			Perf. 14x12½	
520	A233	40p multicolored	.15	.15
521	A233	75p multicolored	.18	.15
522	A233	1r multicolored	.35	.15
523	A233	1.50r multicolored	.65	.15
		Nos. 520-523 (4)	1.33	
		Set value		.28

RICCIONE 80 International Stamp Exhibition,
Riccione, Italy, Aug. 30-Sept. 2.

Quetta Command
and Staff College,
75th Anniversary
A244

1980, Sept. 18		Litho.	Perf. 13	
524	A244	1r multicolored	.15	.15

No. 485 Overprinted: "World Tourism
Conference/Manila 80"

1980, Sept. 27
525 A229 1r multicolored .15 .15

World Tourism Conf., Manila, Sept. 27.

Birth Centenary of Mohammed
Shairani — A245

1980, Oct. 5   **Litho.**   **Perf. 13**
526 A245 40p multicolored   .15 .15

Aga Khan Architecture Award — A246

1980, Oct. 23   **Litho.**   **Perf. 13½**
527 A246 2r multicolored   .28 .15

Rising Sun
A247

1981, Mar. 7   **Litho.**   **Perf. 13**
Size: 30x41mm
528 A247 40p Hegira emblem   .15 .15

1980, Nov. 6   **Litho.**   **Perf. 13**
529 A247 40p shown   .15 .15
Perf. 14
Size: 33x33mm
530 A247 2r Moslem symbols   .28 .15
Perf. 13x13½
Size: 31x54mm
531 A247 3r Globe, hands holding
Koran   .40 .20
Nos. 528-531 (4)   .98 .65

Souvenir Sheet
Imperf
532 A247 4r Candles   1.75 .65
Hegira (Pilgrimage Year).

Airmail Service, 50th Anniversary — A248

Postal History: No. 533, Postal card cent. No.
534, Money order service cent.

1980-81   **Perf. 13**
533 A248 40p multicolored   .15 .15
534 A248 40p multicolored   .15 .15
535 A248 1r multicolored   .15 .15
Set value   .26 .17

Issue dates: No. 533, Dec. 20; No. 534, Dec. 27;
No. 535, Feb. 15, 1981.

Heinrich von Stephan, UPU Emblem
A249

1981, Jan. 7   **Perf. 13½**
536 A249 1r multicolored   .15 .15
Von Stephan (1831-97), founder of UPU.

Conference Emblem, Afghan Refugee
A250

Conference Emblem,
Flags of Participants,
Men — A251

Conference Emblem, Map of
Afghanistan — A252

1981, Mar. 29   **Litho.**   **Perf. 13**
537 A250 40p multicolored   .15 .15
538 A251 40p multicolored   .15 .15
539 A250 1r multicolored   .28 .15
540 A251 1r multicolored   .28 .15
541 A252 2r multicolored   .50 .35
Nos. 537-541 (5)   1.36
Set value   .65

3rd Islamic Summit Conference, Makkah al-
Mukarramah, Jan. 25-28.

Conference Emblem in
Ornament
A253

Conference Emblem,
Flags of
Participants — A254

1981, Mar. 29   **Litho.**   **Perf. 13½**
542 A253 40p multicolored   .15 .15
543 A254 40p multicolored   .15 .15
544 A253 85p multicolored   .22 .15
545 A254 85p multicolored   .22 .15
Set value   .58 .30

3rd Islamic Summit Conference, Makkah al-
Mukarramah, Jan. 25-28.

Kemal Ataturk
(1881-1938), First
President of
Turkey — A255

1981, May 19   **Litho.**   **Perf. 13x13½**
546 A255 1r multicolored   .20 .15

Green
Turtle — A256

1981, June 20   **Litho.**   **Perf. 12x11½**
547 A256 40p multicolored   .30 .15

Palestinian
Cooperation
A257

1981, July 25   **Litho.**   **Perf. 13**
548 A257 2r multicolored   .65 .35

Mt. Haramosh
A258   A259

Designs: Mountain ranges and peaks.

1981, Aug. 20   **Perf. 14x13½**
549 A258 40p Malubiting West,
range   .15 .15
550 A259 40p Peak   .15 .15
   a. Pair, #549-550   .25
551 A258 1r shown   .18 .15
552 A259 1r shown   .18 .15
   a. Pair, #551-552   .36
553 A258 1.50r K6, range   .28 .15
554 A259 1.50r Peak   .28 .15
   a. Pair, #553-554   .56
555 A258 2r K2, range   .35 .15
556 A259 2r Peak   .35 .15
   a. Pair, #555-556   .70
Nos. 540-556 (8)   1.92
Set value   .70

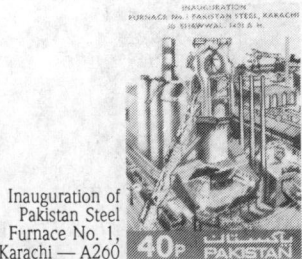

Inauguration of
Pakistan Steel
Furnace No. 1,
Karachi — A260

1981, Aug. 31   **Perf. 13**
557 A260 40p multicolored   .15 .15
558 A260 2r multicolored   .28 .15
Set value   .34 .18

Western
Tragopan in
Summer
A261

1981, Sept. 15   **Litho.**   **Perf. 14**
559 A261 40p shown   .15 .15
560 A261 2r Winter   .55 .28
Set value   .34

Intl. Year
of the
Disabled
A262

1981, Dec. 12   **Litho.**   **Perf. 13**
561 A262 40p multicolored   .15 .15
562 A262 2r multicolored   .28 .15
Set value   .34 .18

World Cup
Championship
A263

1982, Jan. 31   **Litho.**   **Perf. 13½x13**
563 A263 1r Cup, flags in arc   .15 .15
564 A263 1r shown   .15 .15
   a. Pair, #563-564   .30 .30
Set value   .15

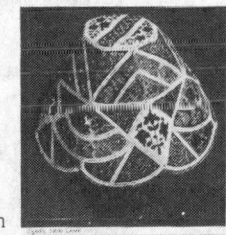

Camel Skin
Lampshade
A264

1982, Feb. 20   **Litho.**   **Perf. 14**
565 A264 1r shown   .15 .15
566 A264 1r Hala pottery   .15 .15
Set value   .15

See Nos. 582-583.

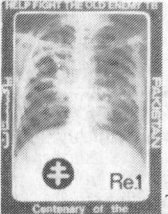

TB Bacillus
Centenary — A265

1982, Mar. 24
567 A265 1r multicolored   .20 .18

Blind Indus
Dolphin
A266

1982, Apr. 24   Litho.   *Perf. 12x11½*
568 A266 40p Dolphin   .15 .15
569 A266 1r Dolphin, diff.   .28 .15
       Set value   .20

Peaceful Uses of Outer Space — A267

1982, June 7   Litho.   *Perf. 13*
570 A267 1r multicolored   .20 .15

50th Anniv. of Sukkur Barrage — A268

1982, July 17   Litho.   *Perf. 13*
571 A268 1r multicolored   .15 .15
    For overprint, see No. 574.

Independence
Day — A269

1982, Aug. 14
572 A269 40p Flag   .15 .15
573 A269 85p Map   .15 .15
       Set value   .18 .15

No. 571 Overprinted:
"RICCIONE-82/1932-1982"

1982, Aug. 28
574 A268 1r multicolored   .35 .18
  RICCIONE '82 Intl. Stamp Exhibition, Riccione,
Italy, Aug. 28-30.

University of the Punjab
Centenary — A270

1982, Oct. 14   Litho.   *Perf. 13½*
575 A270 40p multicolored   .15 .15

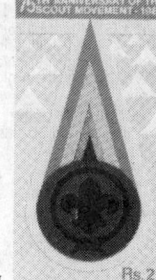

Scouting
Year — A271

1982, Dec. 23   Litho.   *Perf. 13*
576 A271 2r Emblem   .50 .20

Quetta Natural
Gas Pipeline
Project
A272

1983, Jan. 6   Litho.   *Perf. 13*
577 A272 1r multicolored   .20 .15

Common
Peacock
A273

1983, Feb. 15   Litho.   *Perf. 14*
578 A273 40p shown   .15 .15
579 A273 50p Common rose   .15 .15
580 A273 60p Plain tiger   .15 .15
581 A273 1.50r Lemon butterfly .28 .15
       Set value   .49 .28

Handicraft Type of 1982

1983, Mar. 9
582 A264 1r Straw mats   .15 .15
583 A264 1r Five-flower cloth design .15 .15
       Set value   .15

Opening of Aga Khan University — A274

1983, Mar. 16   *Perf. 13½*
584 A274 2r multicolored   .28 .15

Yak Caravan, Zindiharam-Darkot Pass,
Hindu Kush Mountains — A275

1983, Apr. 28   Litho.   *Perf. 13*
585 A275 1r multicolored   .20 .15

Marsh
Crocodile
A276

1983, May 19   *Perf. 13½x14*
586 A276 3r multicolored   .55 .28

1983, June 20   Litho.   *Perf. 14*
       Size: 50x40mm
587 A276 1r Gazelle   .28 .15

36th Anniv. of
Independence
A277

1983, Aug. 14   *Perf. 13*
588 A277 60p Star   .15 .15
589 A277 4r Torch   .55 .28
       Set value   .32

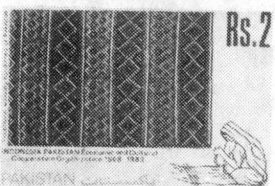

25th Anniv. of Indonesia-Pakistan
Economic and Cultural Cooperation
Org. — A278

Weavings.

1983, Aug. 19   Litho.   *Perf. 13*
590 A278 2r Pakistani (geometric) .28 .15
591 A278 2r Indonesian (figures) .28 .15

Siberian Cranes — A279

1983, Sept. 8   *Perf. 13½*
592 A279 3r multicolored   .50 .20

World Communications Year — A280

1983, Oct. 9   Litho.   *Perf. 13*
593 A280 2r multicolored   .28 .15
       Size: 33x33mm
594 A280 3r Symbol, diff.   .40 .20

World Food
Day — A281

1983, Oct. 24   Litho.   *Perf. 13*
595 A281 3r Livestock   .42 .20
596 A281 3r Fruit   .42 .20
597 A281 3r Grain   .42 .20
598 A281 3r Seafood   .42 .20
  a.   Strip of 4, #595-598 1.75 1.75

A282   A283

1983, Oct. 24   Litho.   *Perf. 13½*
599 A282 60p multicolored   .15 .15
  National Fertilizer Corp.

1983, Nov. 13   Litho.   *Perf. 13*
600   Strip of 6, View of Lahore
      City, 1852   .85 .28
  a.-f. A283 60p any single   .15 .15
  PAKPHILEX '83 Natl. Stamp Exhibition.

Yachting Victory in
9th Asian Games,
1982 — A284

1983, Dec. 31   Litho.   *Perf. 13*
601 A284 60p OK Dinghy   .15 .15
602 A284 60p Enterprise   .15 .15
       Set value   .15

Snow Leopard — A285

1984, Jan. 21   *Perf. 14*
603 A285 40p lt green & multi   .15 .15
604 A285 1.60r blue & multi   .40 .15
       Set value   .15

Jehangir Khan (b.
1963), World
Squash
Champion — A286

1984, Mar. 17   Litho.   *Perf. 13*
605 A286 3r multicolored   .30 .15

Pakistan Intl. Airway China Service, 20th
Anniv. — A287

1984, Apr. 29   Litho.   *Perf. 13*
606 A287 3r Jet   .30 .15

Glass
Work,
Lahore
Fort
A288

Various glass panels.

1984, May 31		Litho.	Perf. 13
607 A288	1r green & multi	.15	.15
608 A288	1r purple & multi	.15	.15
609 A288	1r vermilion & multi	.15	.15
610 A288	1r brt blue & multi	.15	.15
	Set value	.40	.24

Forts — A289

1984-88		Litho.	Perf. 11
613 A289	5p Kot Diji	.15	.15
614 A289	10p Rohtas	.15	.15
615 A289	15p Bala Hissar ('86)	.15	.15
616 A289	20p Attock	.15	.15
617 A289	50p Hyderabad ('86)	.15	.15
618 A289	60p Lahore	.15	.15
619 A289	70p Sibi ('88)	.16	.15
620 A289	80p Ranikot ('86)	.19	.15
	Set value	.75	.32

Issued: 5p, Nov. 1; 10p, Sept. 25; 80p, July 1.
For overprints see Nos. O118-O124.

Shah Rukn-i-Alam Tomb, Multan — A290

1984, June 26		Litho.	Perf. 13
624 A290	60p multicolored	.15	.15

Aga Khan Award for Architecture.

Asia-Pacific
Broadcasting Union,
20th
Anniv. — A290a

1984, July 1		Litho.	Perf. 13
625 A290a	3r multicolored	.28	.15

1984 Summer Olympics, Los
Angeles — A291

1984, July 31
626 A291	3r Athletics	.50	.15
627 A291	3r Boxing	.50	.15
628 A291	3r Hockey	.50	.15
629 A291	3r Yachting	.50	.15
630 A291	3r Wrestling	.50	.15
	Nos. 626-630 (5)	2.50	.75

Issued in sheets of 10.

Independence, 37th Anniv. — A292

1984, Aug. 14
631 A292	60p Jasmine	.15	.15
632 A292	4r Lighted torch	.65	.35
	Set value		.41

Intl. Trade Fair,
Sept. 1-21,
Karachi
A293

1984, Sept. 1
633 A293	60p multicolored	.15	.15

PAKISTAN TOURISM
CONVENTION 1984

1984 Natl. Tourism Convention, Karachi,
Nov. 5-8 — A293a

Shah Jahan Mosque: a, Main dome interior. b,
Tile work. c, Entrance. d, Archways. e, Dome interior, diff.

1984, Nov. 5		Litho.	Perf. 13½
634	Strip of 5	.50	.28
a.-e.	A293a 1r any single	.15	.15

United Bank
Limited, 25th
Anniv.
A294

1984, Nov. 7
635 A294	60p multicolored	.15	.15

UNCTAD, UN Conference on Trade and
Development, 20th Anniv. — A294a

1984, Dec. 24			Perf. 14½x14
636 A294a	60p multicolored	.15	.15

Postal Life Insurance,
Cent. — A295

1984, Dec. 29		Perf. 13½x14
637 A295	60p multicolored	.15 .15
638 A295	1r multicolored	.15 .15
	Set value	.16 .15

UNESCO World
Heritage
Campaign — A296

1984, Dec. 31
639 A296	2r Unicorn, rock painting	.20	.15
640 A296	2r Unicorn seal, round	.20	.15
a.	Pair, #639-640	.40	.30
	Set value		.20

Restoration of Mohenjo-Daro.

IYY, Girl Guides
75th
Anniv. — A297

1985, Jan. 5		Perf. 13½
641 A297	60p Emblems	.15 .15

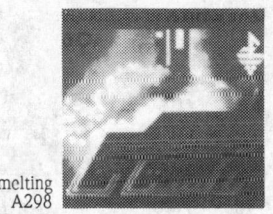

Smelting
A298

Pouring
Steel — A299

1985, Jan. 15		Perf. 13
642 A298	60p multicolored	.15 .15
643 A299	1r multicolored	.15 .15
	Set value	.16 .15

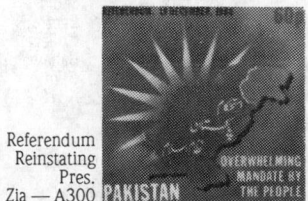

Referendum
Reinstating
Pres.
Zia — A300

1985, Mar. 20		Litho.	Perf. 13
644 A300	60p Map, sunburst	.15	.15

Minar-e-Qarardad-e-Pakistan
Tower — A301

Ballot
Box — A302

1985 Elections.

1985, Mar. 23
645 A301	1r multicolored	.15	.15
646 A302	1r multicolored	.15	.15
	Set value	.20	.15

Mountaineering — A303

1985, May 27		Litho.	Perf. 14
647 A303	40p Mt. Rakaposhi, Kara-koram	.15	.15
648 A303	2r Mt. Nangaparbat, Western Himalayas	.20	.15
	Set value	.25	.15

Championship Pakistani Men's Field
Hockey Team — A304

Design: 1984 Olympic gold medal, 1985 Dhaka
Asia Cup, 1982 Bombay World Cup.

1985, June 5		Litho.	Perf. 13
649 A304	1r multicolored	.15	.15

King Edward Medical College, Lahore,
125th Anniv. — A305

1985, July 28		Litho.	Perf. 13
650 A305	3r multicolored	.40	.20

Natl. Independence Day — A306

Designs: No. 651a, 37th Independence Day written in English. No. 651b, In Arabic.

1985, Aug. 14
651	Pair	.20	.15
a.-b.	A306 60p any single	.15	.15

Sind Madressah-Tul-Islam, Karachi,
Education Cent. — A307

1985, Sept. 1
652 A307 2r multicolored   .35   .18

Mosque, Jinnah Avenue, Karachi — A308

1985, Sept. 14
653 A308 1r Mosque by day   .18   .15
654 A308 1r At night   .18   .15
   Set value   .16

35th anniv. of the Jamia Masjid Pakistan Security
Printing Corporation's miniature replica of the Badshahi Mosque, Lahore.

Lawrence College, Murree, 125th
Anniv. — A309

1985, Sept. 21
655 A309 3r multicolored   .50   .25

UN, 40th Anniv. — A310

1985, Oct. 24   Litho.   Perf. 14x14½
656 A310 1r UN building, sun   .15   .15
657 A310 2r Building emblem   .20   .15
   Set value   .30   .16

10th Natl. Scouting Jamboree, Lahore,
Nov. 8-15 — A311

1985, Nov. 8   Perf. 13
658 A311 60p multicolored   .15   .15

Islamabad and
Capital
Development
Authority
Emblem — A312

1985, Nov. 30   Perf. 14½
659 A312 3r multicolored   .50   .25
Islamabad, capital of Pakistan, 25th anniv.

Flags and Map
of SAARC
Nations
A313

Flags as
Flower Petals
A314

1985, Dec. 8   Perf. 13½, 13
660 A313 1r multicolored   .15   .15
661 A314 2r multicolored   .20   .15
   Set value   .30   .16

SAARC, South Asian Assoc. for Regional
Cooperation.

Dove and
World Map
A315

1985, Dec. 14   Perf. 13
662 A315 60p multicolored   .15   .15

UN Declaration on the Granting of Independence
to Colonial Countries and Peoples, 25th Anniv.

Shaheen
Falcon — A316

1986, Jan. 20   Perf. 13½x14
663 A316 1.50r multicolored   .35   .18

Agricultural Development Bank, 25th
Anniv. — A317

1986, Feb. 18   Litho.   Perf. 13
664 A317 60p multicolored   .15   .15

Sadiq
Egerton
College,
Bahawalpur,
Cent.
A318

1986, Apr. 25
665 A318 1r multicolored   .15   .15

A319

A320

1986, May 11   Perf. 13½
666 A319 1r multicolored   .15   .15
Asian Productivity Organization, 25th anniv.

1986, Aug. 14   Litho.   Perf. 14½x14
667 A320 80p "1947-1986"   .15   .15
668 A320 1r Urdu text, fireworks   .15   .15
   Set value   .20   .15

Independence Day, 39th anniv.

A321

A322

1986, Sept. 8   Perf. 13
669 A321 1r Teacher, students   .15   .15
Intl. Literacy Day.

1986, Oct. 28   Litho.   Perf. 13½x13
670 A322 80p multicolored   .15   .15
UN Child Survival Campaign.

Aitchison College, Lahore, Cent. — A323

1986, Nov. 3   Perf. 13½
671 A323 2.50r multicolored   .28   .15

Intl. Peace
Year — A324

1986, Nov. 20   Perf. 13
672 A324 4r multicolored   .42   .22

4th Asian Cup
Table Tennis
Tournament,
Karachi
A325

1986, Nov. 25   Perf. 14½
673 A325 2r multicolored   .22   .15

Marcopolo Sheep — A326

1986, Dec. 4   Litho.   Perf. 14
674 A326 2r multicolored   .22   .15
See No. 698.

Eco Philex
'86 — A327

Mosques: No. 675a, Selimiye, Turkey. No. 675b,
Gawhar Shad, Iran. No. 675c, Grand Mosque,
Pakistan.

1986, Dec. 20   Perf. 13
675   Strip of 3   1.00   .48
a.-c. A327 3r any single   .32   .16

St. Patrick's School, Karachi, 125th
Anniv. — A328

1987, Jan. 29   Litho.   Perf. 13
676 A328 5r multicolored   .55   .28

Savings Bank
Week — A329

Birds, berries and: a, National defense. b, Education. c, Agriculture. d, Industry.

1987, Feb. 21   Litho.   Perf. 13
677   Block of 4 + 2 labels   2.25   1.10
a.-d. A329 5r any single   .55   .28

Parliament House Opening,
Islamabad — A330

1987, Mar. 23
678 A330 3r multicolored   .32   .16

Fight Against Drug Abuse — A331

1987, June 30   Litho.   Perf. 13
679 A331 1r multicolored   .15   .15

Natl. Independence, 40th Anniv. — A332

Natl. flag and: 80p, Natl. anthem, written in Urdu. 3r, Jinnah's first natl. address, the Minar-e-Qarardad-e-Pakistan and natl. coat of arms.

1987, Aug. 14   Litho.   Perf. 13
680 A332 80p multicolored   .15   .15
681 A332 3r multicolored   .40   .20
        Set value   .26

Miniature Sheet

Air Force, 40th Anniv. — A333

Aircraft: a, Tempest II. b, Hawker Fury. c, Super Marine Attacker. d, F86 Sabre. e, F104 Star Fighter. f, C130 Hercules. g, F-6. h, Mirage III. i, A5. j, F16 Fighting Falcon.

1987, Sept. 7   Litho.   Perf. 13½
682   Sheet of 10   4.00   2.00
a.-j. A333 3r any single   .40   .20

Tourism Convention 1987 — A334

Views along Karakoram Highway: a, Pasu Glacier. b, Apricot trees. c, Highway winding through hills. d, Khunjerab peak.

1987, Oct. 1   Perf. 13
683   Block of 4   .80   .40
a.-d. A334 1.50r any single   .20   .15

Shah Abdul Latif Bhitai Mausoleum — A335

1987, Oct. 8   Perf. 13
684 A335 80p multicolored   .15   .15

D.J. Sind Government Science College, Karachi, Cent. — A336

1987, Nov. 7
685 A336 80p multicolored   .15   .15

College of Physicians and Surgeons, 25th Anniv. — A337

1987, Dec. 9   Litho.   Perf. 13
686 A337 1r multicolored   .15   .15

Intl. Year of Shelter for the Homeless — A338

1987, Dec. 15
687 A338 3r multicolored   .45   .22

Cathedral Church of the Resurrection, Lahore, Cent. — A339

1987, Dec. 20
688 A339 3r multicolored   .45   .22

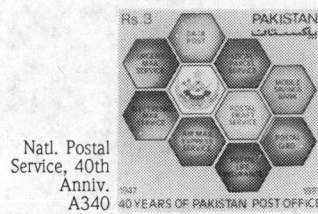

Natl. Postal Service, 40th Anniv. A340

1987, Dec. 28
689 A340 3r multicolored   .45   .22

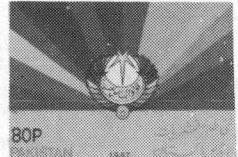

Radio Pakistan A341

1987, Dec. 31
690 A341 80p multicolored   .15   .15

Jamshed Nusserwanjee Mehta (1886-1952), Mayor of Karachi, Member of the Sind Legislative Assembly — A342

1988, Jan. 7
691 A342 3r multicolored   .45   .22

World Leprosy Day — A343

1988, Jan. 31
692 A343 3r multicolored   .45   .22

World Health Organization, 40th Anniv. A344

1988, Apr. 7   Litho.   Perf. 13
693 A344 4r multicolored   .50   .25

Intl. Red Cross and Red Crescent Organizations, 125th Annivs. — A345

1988, May 8
694 A345 3r multicolored   .45   .22

Independence Day, 41st Anniv. — A346

1988, Aug. 14   Litho.   Perf. 13½
695 A346 80p multicolored   .15   .15
696 A346 4r multicolored   .50   .25
        Set value   .31

Miniature Sheet

1988 Summer Olympics, Seoul — A347

Events: a, Discus, shot put, hammer throw, javelin. b, Relay, hurdles, running, walking. c, High jump, long jump, triple jump, pole vault. d, Gymnastic floor exercises, rings, parallel bars. e, Table tennis, field hockey, baseball. f, Volleyball, soccer, basketball, team handball. g, Wrestling, judo, boxing, weight lifting. h, Sport pistol, fencing, rifle shooting, archery. i, Swimming, diving, yachting, quadruple-sculling, kayaking. j, Equestrian jumping, cycling, steeplechase.

1988, Sept. 17   Litho.   Perf. 13½x13
697   Sheet of 10+32 labels   12.50   6.25
a.-j. A347 10r any single   1.25   .62
Labels contained in No. 697 picture the Seoul Games character trademark or emblem. Size of No. 697: 251x214mm.

Fauna Type of 1986

1988, Oct. 29   Litho.   Perf. 14
698 A326 2r Suleman markhor, vert.   .25   .15

Pioneers of Freedom Type of 1979

1989, Jan. 23   Litho.   Wmk. 351
699 A236 3r Maulana Hasrat Mohani   .38   .20

Islamia College, Peshawar, 75th Anniv. — A348

1988, Dec. 22   Unwmk.   Perf. 13½
700 A348 3r multicolored   .38   .20

SAARC Summit Conference, Islamabad — A349

Designs: 25r, Flags, symbols of commerce. 50r, Globe, communication and transportation. 75r, Bangladesh #69, Maldive Islands #1030, Bhutan #98, Pakistan #403, Ceylon #451, India #580, Nepal #437.

1988, Dec. 29   Perf. 13
701 A349 25r shown   2.50   1.25
        Size: 33x33mm
        Perf. 14
702 A349 50r multicolored   5.00   2.50
        Size: 52x28mm
        Perf. 13½x13
703 A349 75r multicolored   7.50   3.75
        Nos. 701-703 (3)   15.00   7.50

Adasia '89, 16th Asian Advertising Congress, Lahore, Feb. 18-22 — A350

1989, Feb. 18   Litho.   Perf. 13
704   Strip of 3   .38   .20
a. A350 1r deep rose lilac & multi   .15   .15
b. A350 1r green & multi   .15   .15
c. A350 1r bright vermilion & multi   .15   .15
Printed in sheets of 9.

Pres. Zulfikar Ali Bhutto (1928-1979), Ousted by Military Coup and Executed — A351

Portraits.

1989, Apr. 4   Litho.   Perf. 13
705   A351 1r shown   .15   .15
706   A351 2r multi, diff.   .25   .15
    Set value   .18

Submarine Operations, 25th Anniv. — A352

Submarines: a, *Agosta.* b, *Daphne.* c, *Fleet Snorkel.* Illustration reduced.

1989, June 1   Litho.   Perf. 13½
707   Strip of 3   .36   .18
a.-c.   A352 1r any single   .15   .15

Oath of the Tennis Court, by David — A353

1989, June 24   Litho.   Perf. 13½
708   A353 7r multicolored   .75   .38
    French revolution, bicent.

Archaeological Heritage A354

Terra cotta vessels excavated in Baluchistan: a, Pirak, c. 2200 B.C. b, Nindo Damb, c. 2300 B.C. c, Mehrgarh, c. 3600 B.C. d, Nausharo, c. 2600 B.C.

1989, June 28   Perf. 14½x14
709   Block of 4   .45   .22
a.-d.   A354 1r any single   .15   .15

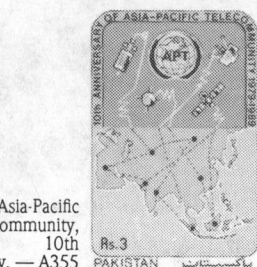

Asia-Pacific Telecommunity, 10th Anniv. — A355

1989, July 1   Perf. 13½x14
710   A355 3r multicolored   .32   .16

Laying the Foundation Stone for the 1st Integrated Container Terminal, Port Qasim — A356

1989, Aug. 5   Litho.   Perf. 14
711   A356 6r Ship in berth   .65   .32

Mohammad Ali Jinnah — A357

Litho & Engr.
1989, Aug. 14   Wmk. 351   Perf. 13
712   A357 1r multicolored   .15   .15
713   A357 1.50r multicolored   .16   .15
714   A357 2r multicolored   .22   .15
715   A357 3r multicolored   .33   .16
716   A357 4r multicolored   .45   .22
717   A357 5r multicolored   .55   .28
    Nos. 712-717 (6)   1.86
    Set value   .90
    Independence Day.

Abdul Latif Bhitai Memorial — A358

1989, Sept. 16   Litho.   Unwmk.
718   A358 2r multicolored   .22   .15
    245th death and 300th birth annivs. of Shah Abdul Latif Bhitai.

World Wildlife Fund — A359

Himalayan black bears and WWF emblem: a, Bear on slope, emblem UR. b, Bear on slope, emblem UL. c, Bear on top of rock, emblem UR. d, Seated bear, emblem UL.

Perf. 14x13½
1989, Oct. 7   Litho.   Unwmk.
719   Block of 4   1.80   .90
a.-d.   A359 4r any single   .45   .22

World Food Day — A360

1989, Oct. 16   Perf. 14x12½
720   A360 1r multicolored   .15   .15

Quilt and Bahishiti Darwaza (Heavenly Gate) — A361

1989, Oct. 20   Perf. 13
721   A361 3r multicolored   .35   .16
    800th Birth anniv. of Baba Farid.

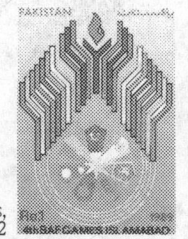

4th SAF Games, Islamabad — A362

1989, Oct. 20
722   A362 1r multicolored   .15   .15

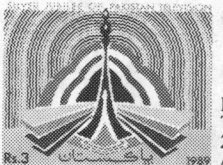

Pakistan Television, 25th Anniv. A363

1989, Nov. 26   Litho.   Perf. 13½
723   A363 3r multicolored   .35   .16

SAARC Year Against Drug Abuse and Drug Trafficking A364

1989, Dec. 8   Perf. 13
724   A364 7r multicolored   .80   .40

Murray College, Sialkot, Cent. A365

1989, Dec. 18   Perf. 14
725   A365 6r multicolored   .70   .35

Government College, Lahore, 125th Anniv. — A366

1989, Dec. 21   Perf. 13
726   A366 6r multicolored   .70   .35

Center on Integrated Rural Development for Asia and the Pacific (CIRDAP), 10th Anniv. — A367

1989, Dec. 31
727   A367 3r multicolored   .35   .16

Organization of the Islamic Conference (OIC), 20th Anniv. — A368

1990, Feb. 9   Litho.   Perf. 13
728   A368 1r multicolored   .15   .15

7th World Field Hockey Cup, Lahore, Feb. 12-23 — A369

Illustration reduced.

1990, Feb. 12   Perf. 14x13½
729   A369 2r multicolored   .24   .15

A370

Pakistan Resolution, 50th Anniv. — A371

Designs: a, Allama Mohammad Iqbal addressing the Allahabad Session of the All-India Muslim League and swearing-in of Liat Ali Khan as league secretary-general. b, Freedom fighter Maulana Mohammad Ali Jauhar at Muslim rally and Mohammed Ali Jinnah at microphone. c, Muslim woman holding flag and swearing-in of Mohammed Ali Jinnah as governor-general of Pakistan, Aug. 14, 1947.

7r, English and Urdu translations of the resolution, natl. flag and Minar-e-Qarardade Pakistan.

1990, Mar. 23 Litho. Perf. 13
730 Strip of 3 .36 .18
a.-c. A370 1r any single .15 .15

Size: 90x45mm
Perf. 13½
731 A371 7r multicolored .85 .42

Safe Motherhood South Asia Conference, Lahore — A372

1990, Mar. 24 Perf. 13½
732 A372 5r multicolored .60 .30

Calligraphic Painting of a Ghalib Verse, by Shakir Ali (1916-1975) — A373

1990, Apr. 19 Litho. Perf. 13½x13
733 A373 1r multicolored .15 .15
See Nos. 757-758.

Badr-1 Satellite — A374

1990, July 26 Litho. Perf. 13
734 A374 3r multicolored .28 .15

Pioneers of Freedom — A375

No. 735: a, Allama Mohammad Iqbal (1877-1938). b, Mohammad Ali Jinnah (1876-1948). c, Sir Syed Ahmad Khan (1817-1898). d, Nawab Salimullah (1884-1915). e, Mohtarma Fatima Jinnah (1893-1967). f, Aga Khan III (1877-1957). g, Nawab Mohammad Ismail Khan (1884-1958). h, Hussain Shaheed Suhrawardy (1893-1963). i, Syed Ameer Ali (1849-1928).
No. 736: a, Nawab Bahadur Yar Jung (1905-1944). b, Khawaja Nazimuddin (1894-1964). c, Maulana Obaidullah Sindhi (1872-1944). d, Sahibzada Abdul Qaiyum Khan (c. 1863-1937). e, Begum Jahanara Shah Nawaz (1896-1979). f, Sir Shulam Hussain Hidayatullah (1879-1948). g, Qazi Mohammad Isa (1913-1976). h, Sir M. Shahnawaz Khan Mamdot (1883-1942). i, Pir Shaib of Manki Sharif (1923-1960).
No. 737: a, Liaquat Ali Khan (1895-1951). b, Maulvi A.K. Fazl-Ul-Haq (1873-1962). c, Allama Shabbir Ahmad Usmani (1885-1949). d, Sardar Abdur Rab Nishtar (1899-1958). e, Bi Amma (c. 1850-1924). f, Sir Abdullah Haroon (1872-1942). g, Chaudhry Rahmat Ali (1897-1951). h, Raja Sahib of Mahmudabad (1914-1973). i, Hassanally Effendi (1830-1895).
No. 737J: k, Maulana Zafar Ali Khan (1873-1956). l, Maulana Mohamed Ali Jauhar (1878-1931). m, Chaudhry Khaliquzzaman (1889-1973). n, Hameed Nizami (1915-1962). o, Begum Ra'ana

Liaquat Ali Khan (1905-1990). p, Mirza Abol Hassan Ispahani (1902-1981). q, Raja Ghazanfar Ali Khan (1895-1963). r, Malik Barkat Ali (1886-1946). s, Mir Jaffer Khan Jamali (c. 1911-1967).

1990-91 Litho. Perf. 13
Miniature Sheets
735 Sheet of 9 .90 .90
a.-i. A375 1r any single .15 .15
736 Sheet of 9 .90 .90
a.-i. A375 1r any single .15 .15
737 Sheet of 9 .90 .90
a.-i. A375 1r any single .15 .15
737J Sheet of 9 ('91) .90 .90
k.-s. A375 1r any single .15 .15
Nos. 735-737J (4) 3.60 3.60
Issued: #735-737, Aug. 19; #737J, 1991.
See Nos. 773, 792, 804.

Indonesia Pakistan Economic and Cultural Cooperation Organization, 1968-1990 — A376

1990, Aug. 19
738 A376 7r multicolored .65 .32

Intl. Literacy Year — A377

1990, Sept. 8
739 A377 3r multicolored .28 .15

A378

1990, Sept. 22
740 A378 2r multicolored .18 .15
Joint meeting of Royal College of Physicians, Edinburgh and College of Physicians and Surgeons, Pakistan.

World Summit for Children — A379

1990, Sept. 19
741 A379 7r multicolored .65 .32

Year of the Girl Child A380

1990, Nov. 21 Litho. Perf. 13½
742 A380 2r multicolored .18 .15

Security Papers Ltd., 25th Anniv. — A381

1990, Dec. 8 Perf. 13
743 A381 3r multicolored .28 .15

Intl. Civil Defense Day — A382

1991, Mar. 1 Litho. Perf. 13
744 A382 7r multicolored .28 .15

South & West Asia Postal Union — A383

1991, Mar. 21
745 A383 5r multicolored .20 .15

World Population Day — A384

1991, July 11
746 A384 10r multicolored .40 .20

Intl. Special Olympics — A385

1991, July 19
747 A385 7r multicolored .28 .15

Habib Bank Limited, 50th Anniv. — A386

1991, Aug. 25 Litho. Perf. 13
748 A386 1r brt red & multi .15 .15
749 A386 5r brt green & multi .20 .15
Set value .30 .15

St. Joseph's Convent School, Karachi — A387

1991, Sept. 8
750 A387 5r multicolored .20 .15

Emperor Sher Shah Suri (c. 1472-1545) A388

1991, Oct. 5
751 A388 5r multicolored .20 .15

Souvenir Sheet
Size: 90x81mm
Imperf
752 A388 7r multicolored .90 .45

Pakistani Scientific Expedition to Antarctica — A389

1991, Oct. 28
753 A389 7r multicolored .28 .15

Houbara Bustard — A390

1991, Nov. 4
754 A390 7r multicolored .28 .15

Asian Development Bank, 25th Anniv. — A391

1991, Dec. 19   Litho.   *Perf. 13*
755 A391 7r multicolored   .90 .45

Hazrat Sultan Bahoo, 300th Death Anniv. A392

1991, Dec. 22
756 A392 7r multicolored   .90 .45

Painting Type of 1990

Paintings and artists: No. 757, Village Life, by Allah Ustad Bux (1892-1978). No. 758, Miniature of Royal Procession, by Muhammad Haji Sharif (1889-1978).

1991, Dec. 24
757 A373 1r multicolored   .15 .15
758 A373 1r multicolored   .15 .15

American Express Travelers Cheques, 100th Anniv. — A393

Illustration reduced.

1991, Dec. 26   *Perf. 13½*
759 A393 7r multicolored   .90 .45

First year of Privatisation

Muslim Commercial Bank, First Year of Private Operation — A394

7r, City skyline, worker, cogwheels, computer operators.

1992, Apr. 8   Litho.   *Perf. 13*
760 A394 1r multicolored   .15 .15
761 A394 7r multicolored   .90 .45
   Set value   .52

Pakistan, 1992 World Cricket Champions — A395

World Cricket Cup and: 2r, Pakistani player, vert. 7r, Pakistan flag, fireworks, vert.

1992, Apr. 27
762 A395 2r multicolored   .25 .15
763 A395 5r multicolored   .65 .65
764 A395 7r multicolored   .90 .45
   Nos. 762-764 (3)   1.80 1.25

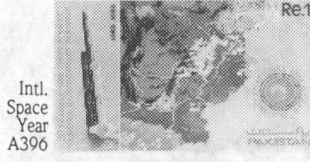

Intl. Space Year A396

Design: 2r, Globe, satellite.

1992, June 7   Litho.   *Perf. 13*
771 A396 1r multicolored   .15 .15
772 A396 2r multicolored   .22 .22

30th anniv. of first Pakistani rocket (#771).

Pioneers of Freedom Type of 1990

Designs: a, Syed Suleman Nadvi (1884-1953). b, Nawab Iftikhar Hussain Khan Mamdot (1906-1969). c, Maulana Muhammad Shibli Naumani (1857-1914).

1992, Aug. 14   Litho.   *Perf. 13*
773 A375 1r Strip of 3, #a.-c.   .30 .30

World Population Day A397

1992, July 25
774 A397 6r multicolored   .65 .65

Medicinal Plants A398

1992, Nov. 22   Litho.   *Perf. 13*
775 A398 6r multicolored   .58 .58
   See No. 791.

Extraordinary Session of Economic Cooperation Organization Council of Ministers, Islamabad — A399

1992, Nov. 28
776 A399 7r multicolored   .70 .70

Intl. Conference on Nutrition, Rome — A400

1992, Dec. 5   *Perf. 14*
777 A400 7r multicolored   .70 .70

A401   A402

1992, Dec. 14   *Perf. 13*
778 A401 7r Alhambra, Spain   .70 .70

Islamic cultural heritage.

1992, Aug. 23   *Perf. 14x12½*
779 A402 6r 6th Jamboree   .58 .58
780 A402 6r 4th Conference   .58 .58

Islamic Scouts, Islamabad.

Government Islamia College, Lahore, Cent. — A403

1992, Nov. 1   *Perf. 13*
781 A403 3r multicolored   .35 .35

Industries A404

Designs: a, 10r, Surgical instruments. b, 15r, Leather goods. c, 25r, Sports equipment.

1992, July 5   Litho.   *Perf. 13½x13*
782 A404 Strip of 3, #a.-c.   5.00 5.00

World Telecommunications Day — A405

1993, May 17   Litho.   *Perf. 13*
783 A405 1r multicolored   .15 .15

21st Islamic Foreign Ministers Conference A406

1993, Apr. 25
784 A406 1r buff & multi   .15 .15
785 A406 6r green & multi   .60 .60

Traditional Costumes of Provinces A407

1993, Mar. 10
786 A407 6r Sindh   .60 .60
787 A407 6r North West Frontier   .60 .60
788 A407 6r Baluchistan   .60 .60
789 A407 6r Punjab   .60 .60
   Nos. 786-789 (4)   2.40 2.40

Birds — A408

Designs: a, Gadwall. b, Common shelduck. c, Mallard. d, Greylag goose. The order of the birds is different on each row. Therefore the arc of the rainbow is different on each of the 4 Gadwalls, etc.

1992, Dec. 31   *Perf. 14x13*
790 A408 5r Sheet of 16   10.00 10.00

Medicinal Plants Type

1993, June 20   Litho.   *Perf. 13*
791 A398 6r Fennel, chemistry equipment   .60 .60

Pioneers of Freedom Type of 1990

Designs: a, Rais Ghulam Mohammad Bhurgri (1878-1924). b, Mir Ahmed Yar Khan, Khan of Kalat (1902-1977). c, Mohammad Abdul Latif Pir Sahib Zakori Sharif (1914-1978).

1993, Aug. 14   Litho.   *Perf. 13*
792 A375 1r Strip of 3, #a.-c.   .30 .30

Gordon College, Rawalpindi, Cent. — A410

1993, Sept. 1
793 A410 2r multicolored   .22 .22

SAVE JUNIPER FORESTS AT ZIARAT Juniper Forests, Ziarat — A411

1993, Sept. 30
794 A411 7r multicolored   .80 .80
   See No. 827.

World Food Day — A412

1993, Oct. 16   *Perf. 14*
795 A412 6r multicolored   .65 .65

A413   A414

**   *Perf. 13½***
1993, Dec. 25   Litho.   Wmk. 351
796 A413 1r multicolored   .15 .15

Wazir Mansion, birthplace of Muhammad Ali Jinnah.

**   *Perf. 13x13½***
1993, Oct. 28   Unwmk.
797 A414 7r multicolored   .55 .55

Burn Hall Institutions, 50th anniv.

South & West Asia
Postal Union — A415

1993, Nov. 18 *Perf. 13*
798 A415 7r multicolored .55 .55

Pakistani College of
Physicians &
Surgeons, Intl.
Medical
Congress — A416

1993, Dec. 10
799 A416 1r multicolored .15 .15

ILO,
75th
Anniv.
A417

1994, Apr. 11 *Litho.* *Perf. 13*
800 A417 7r multicolored .55 .55

Bio-diversity
A418

Designs: a, Ratan jot, medicinal plant. b, Wetlands. c, Mahseer fish. d, Himalayan brown bear.

1994, Apr. 20 *Litho.* *Perf. 13½*
801 A418 6r Strip or block of 4,
#a.-d. 1.90 1.90

Intl. Year of the
Family — A419

1994, May 15 *Perf. 13*
802 A419 7r multicolored .52 .52

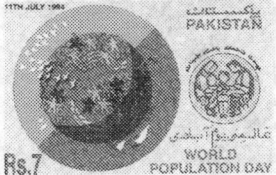

World Population Day — A420

1994, July 11 *Litho.* *Perf. 13*
803 A420 7r multicolored .52 .52

Pioneers of Freedom Type of 1990
Miniature Sheet of 8

Designs: a, Nawab Mohsin-Ul-Mulk (1837-1907). b, Sir Shahnawaz Bhutto (1888-1957). c, Nawab Viqar-Ul-Mulk (1841-1917). d, Pir Ilahi Bux (1890-1975). e, Sheikh Sir Abdul Qadir (1874-1950). f, Dr. Sir Ziauddin Ahmed (1878-1947). g,

Jam Mir Ghulam Qadir Khan (1920-88). h, Sardar Aurangzeb Khan (1899-1953).

1994, Aug. 14 *Litho.* *Perf. 13*
804 A375 1r #a.-h. + label .70 .70

A421 A422

1994, Oct. 2 *Perf. 13x13½*
805 A421 2r multicolored .22 .22

First Intl. Festival of Islamic Artisans.

1994, Sept. 8
806 A422 7r multicolored .55 .55

Intl. Literacy Day.

Hyoscyamus
Niger — A423

1994 *Perf. 13*
807 A423 6r multicolored .50 .50

Mohammed
Ali Jinnah
A424

Litho. & Engr.
1994, Sept. 11 *Wmk. 351* *Perf. 13*
808 A424 1r slate & multi .15 .15
809 A424 2r claret & multi .15 .15
810 A424 3r bright blue & multi .22 .22
811 A424 4r emerald & multi .30 .30
812 A424 5r lake & multi .38 .38
813 A424 7r blue & multi .50 .50
814 A424 10r green & multi .75 .75
815 A424 12r orange & multi .90 .90
816 A424 15r violet & multi 1.10 1.10
817 A424 20r rose & multi 1.50 1.50
818 A424 25r brown & multi 1.90 1.90
819 A424 30r olive brown & multi 2.25 2.25
Nos. 808-819 (12) 10.10 10.10

2nd SAARC & 12th
Natl. Scout
Jamboree,
Quetta — A425

1994, Sept. 22 *Litho.*
820 A425 7r multicolored .60 .60

Publication of
Ferdowsi's Book of
Kings, 1000th
Anniv. — A426

1994, Oct. 27
821 A426 1r multicolored .15 .15

Indonesia-Pakistan
Economic & Cultural
Cooperation
Organization
A427

1994, Aug. 19
822 A427 10r Hala pottery .75 .75
823 A427 10r Lombok pottery .75 .75
a. Pair, #822-823 1.50 1.50

See Indonesia Nos. 1585-1586.

Lahore Museum,
Cent. — A428

Wmk. 351
1994, Dec. 27 *Litho.* *Perf. 13*
824 A428 4r multicolored .25 .25

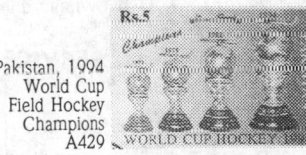

Pakistan, 1994
World Cup
Field Hockey
Champions
A429

1994, Dec. 31
825 A429 5r multicolored .32 .32

World Tourism Organization, 20th
Anniv. — A430

1995, Jan. 2
826 A430 4r multicolored .25 .25

Juniper Forests Type of 1993

1995 *Litho.* *Perf. 13*
827 A411 1r like #794 .15 .15

Third Economic
Cooperation
Organization
Summit,
Islamabad
A431

1995 *Litho.* *Perf. 14*
828 A431 6r multicolored .48 .48

Khushall Khan
Khatak (1613-
89) — A432

1995 *Perf. 13*
829 A432 7r multicolored .55 .55

Earth
Day — A433

1995 *Litho.* *Wmk. 351* *Perf. 13*
830 A433 6r multicolored .60 .60

Snakes
A434

Designs: a, Krait. b, Cobra. c, Python. d, Viper.

1995, Apr. 15 *Unwmk.* *Perf. 13½*
831 A434 6r Block of 4, #a.-d. 2.25 2.25

Traditional Means of
Transportation — A435

1995 *Litho.* *Wmk. 351* *Perf. 13*
832 A435 5r Horse-drawn carriage .40 .40

Louis Pasteur (1822-
95) — A436

1995 *Litho.* *Wmk. 351* *Perf. 13*
833 A436 5r multicolored .40 .40

UN, FAO, 50th Anniv. A437

1995
834 A437 1.25r multicolored   .20 .20

Kinnaird College for Women, Lahore — A438   4th World Conference on Women, Beijing — A439

1995   *Perf. 14x13*
835 A438 1.25r multicolored   .20 .20

1995   *Perf. 13*

Women in various activities: a, Playing golf, in armed forces, repairing technical device. b, Graduates, student, chemist, computer operator, reading gauge. c, At sewing machine, working with textiles. d, Making rugs, police woman, laborers.

836 A439 1.25r Strip of 4, #a.-d.   .45 .45

Presentation Convent School, Rawalpindi, Cent. — A440

1995 Litho. Wmk. 351   *Perf. 13½*
837 A440 1.25r multicolored   .20 .20

Liaquat Ali Khan (1895-1951) — A441

1995   *Perf. 13*
838 A441 1.25r multicolored   .20 .20

1st Conference of Women Parliamentarians from Muslim Countries — A442

Designs: No. 839, Dr. Tansu Ciller, Prime Minister of Turkey. No. 840, Mohtarma Benazir Bhutto, Prime Minister of Pakistan.

1995   **Unwmk.**
839 A442 5r multicolored   .40 .40
840 A442 5r multicolored   .40 .40
  a.   Pair, #839-840   .80 .80

OFFICIAL STAMPS

Official Stamps of India, 1939-43, Overprinted in Black **PAKISTAN**

1947-49   Wmk. 196   Perf. 13½x14
O1   O8   3p slate   .55 .15
O2   O8   ½a dk rose vio   .25 .15
O3   O8   9p green   2.50 .15
O4   O8   1a carmine rose   .25 .15
O4A O8   1a3p bister ('49)   3.00 2.50

O5   O8   1½a dull purple   .25 .15
O6   O8   2a scarlet   .25 .15
O7   O8   2½a purple   3.25 .15
O8   O8   4a dk brown   .60 .15
O9   O8   8a blue violet   .75 .50

India Nos. O100-O103 Overprinted in Black **PAKISTAN**

O10 A82 1r brown & slate   .65 .50
O11 A82 2r dk brn & dk vio   2.75 .25
O12 A82 5r dp ultra & dk grn   11.00 7.50
O13 A82 10r rose car & dk vio   27.50 20.00
   Nos. O1-O13 (14)   53.55 32.45

Regular Issue of 1948 Overprinted in Black or Carmine — a   **SERVICE**

Perf. 12½, 13, 13½x14, 14x13½

1948, Aug. 14   Unwmk.
O14 A3   3p orange red   .15 .15
O15 A3   6p purple (C)   .15 .15
O16 A3   9p dk green (C)   .15 .15
O17 A4   1a dk blue (C)   .15 .15
O18 A4   1½a gray grn (C)   .15 .15
O19 A4   2a orange red   .15 .15
O20 A5   3a olive green   .15 .15
O21 A6   4a chocolate   .15 .15
O22 A6   8a black (C)   .25 .20
O23 A5   1r ultra   .55 .15
O24 A5   2r dark brown   1.10 .35
O25 A5   5r carmine   2.25 1.25
O26 A7   10r rose lil, perf. 14x13½   6.00 2.75
  a.   Perf. 12   10.00 2.75
  b.   Perf. 13   8.00 1.75
   Nos. O14-O26 (13)   11.35
    Set value   5.00

Issued: #O26a, Oct. 10, 1951; #O26b, 1954(?).

Nos. 47-50 and 52 Overprinted Type "a" in Black or Carmine

1949-50   Perf. 12½, 13½x14
O27 A10 1a dark blue (C)   .15 .15
O28 A10 1½a gray brn (C)   .15 .15
  a.   Inverted ovpt.   35.00
O29 A10 2a orange red   .15 .15
O30 A9   3a olive green ('49)   .18 .60
O31 A11 8a black (C)   .45 1.50
   Nos. O27-O31 (5)   1.08 2.55

Types of Regular Issue of 1951, "Pakistan" or "Pakistan Postage" Replaced by "SERVICE"

    Unwmk.

1951, Aug. 14   Engr.   Perf. 13
O32 A13 3a dark rose lake   .20 1.25
O33 A14 4a deep green   .22 .15
O34 A15 8a brown   .54 .20
   Nos. O32-O34 (3)   .96 1.60

Nos. 24-26, 47-49, 38-41 Overprinted in Black or Carmine   b   **SERVICE**

1954
O35 A3   3p orange red   .15 .15
O36 A3   6p purple (C)   .15 .15
O37 A3   9p dk green (C)   .15 .15
O38 A10 1a dk blue (C)   .15 .15
O39 A10 1½a gray grn (C)   .15 .15
O40 A10 2a orange red   .15 .15
O41 A5   1r ultra   1.75 .32
O42 A5   2r dark brown   1.50 .15
O43 A5   5r carmine   5.25 1.10
O43A A7 10r rose lilac   8.00 16.00
   Nos. O35-O43A (10)   17.40 18.47

Nos. 66-72 Overprinted Type "b" in Carmine or Black

1954, Aug. 14
O44 A18 6p rose violet (C)   .15 .30
O45 A19 9p blue (C)   .15 2.00
O46 A19 1a carmine rose   .15 .25
O47 A18 1½a red   .15 .25
O48 A20 14a dk green (C)   .60 1.25
O49 A20 1r yellow grn (C)   .75 .15
O50 A20 2r orange   1.25 .20
   Nos. O44-O50 (7)   3.20 4.40

No. 75 Overprinted in Carmine Type "b"
Overprint: 13x2½mm

1955, Aug. 14   Unwmk.   Perf. 13
O51 A21 8a violet   .18 .15

Nos. 24, 40, 66-72, 74-75, 83, 89 Overprinted in Black or Carmine   c   **SERVICE**

1957-61
O52 A3   3p orange red ('58)   .15 .15
O53 A18 6p rose vio (C)   .15 .15
O54 A19 9p blue (C) ('58)   .15 .25
O55 A19 1a carmine rose   .15 .15
O56 A18 1½a red   .15 .15

O57 A24 2a red ('58)   .15 .15
O58 A21 6a dk bl (C) ('60)   .15 .15
O59 A21 8a vio (C) ('58)   .15 .15
O60 A20 14a dk grn (C) ('58)   .40 1.00
O61 A20 1r yel grn (C) ('58)   .40 .15
O62 A20 2r orange ('58)   2.25 .15
O63 A5   5r carmine ('58)   3.00 .25
O64 A26 10r dk grn & org (C) ('61)   6.00 4.00
   Nos. O52-O64 (13)   13.25
    Set value   5.90

For surcharges see Nos. O67-O73.

Nos. 110-111 Overprinted Type "c"

1961, Apr.
O65 A33 8a green   .18 .15
O66 A33 1r blue   .25 .15
  a.   Inverted overprint   8.25
    Set value   .15

New Currency

Nos. O52, O55-O57 Surcharged with New Value in Paisa

1961
O67 A18 1p on 1½a red   .15 .15
  a.   Overprinted type "b"   .85 .85
O68 A3   2p on 3p orange red   .15 .15
  a.   Overprinted type "b"   1.75 1.75
O69 A19 6p on 1a car rose   .15 .15
O70 A19 7p on 1a car rose   .15 .15
  a.   Overprinted type "b"   2.25 2.25
O71 A18 9p on 1½a red   .15 .15
O72 A24 13p on 2a red ("PAISA")   .15 .15
O73 A24 13p on 2a red ("Paisa")

Nos. O68, O71, O73 were locally overprinted at Mastung.

Nos. 125, 128 Overprinted Type "c"

1961
O74 A33 3p on 6p purple   .15 .15
O75 A33 13p on 2a copper red   .15 .15
    Set value   .15

Various violet handstamped surcharges were applied to several official stamps. Most of these repeat the denomination of the basic stamp and add the new value. Example: "4 ANNAS (25 Paisa)" on No. O33.

Nos. 129-135, 135B, 135C, 136a, 137-140a Overprinted in Carmine   d   **SERVICE**

1961-78   Perf. 13½x14
O76 A40 1p violet (II)   .15 .15
   Type I
O77 A40 2p rose red (II)   .15 .15
   Type I
O78 A40 3p magenta   .15 .15
O79 A40 5p purple (II)   .15 .15
   Type I
O80 A40 7p emerald   .15 .15
O81 A40 10p brown   .15 .15
O82 A40 13p blue violet   .15 .15
O83 A40 15p rose lil (#135B) ('64)   .15 .15
O84 A40 20p dl grn (#135C) ('70)   .15 .15
O84A A40 25p dark blue (#136a) ('77)   .15 .15
O85 A40 40p dull pur ('62)   .15 .15
O86 A40 50p dull grn ('62)   .18 .15
O87 A40 75p dk car ('62)   .22 .15
O88 A40 90p lt ol grn ('78)   .30 .15
    Set value   1.35 .75

Designs Redrawn

1961-66
O76b A40 1p violet (#129b) ('63)   .15 .15
O77b A40 2p rose red (#130b) ('64)   .15 .15
O78a A40 3p magenta (#131a) ('66)   .15 .15
O79b A40 5p ultra (#132b) ('63)   .15 .15
O80a A40 7p emerald (#133a)   2.00 .15
O81a A40 10p brown (#134a) ('64)   .15 .15
O82a A40 13p blue vio (#135a) ('63)   .15 .15
O85a A40 40p dull purple (#137a)   .35 .15
O86a A40 50p dull grn (#138a) ('64)   .18 .15
    Set value   2.75 .45

Nos. 141, 143-144 Overprinted Type "c" in Black or Carmine

1963, Jan. 7   Unwmk.   Perf. 13½x13
O89 A41 1r vermilion   .50 .15
O90 A41 2r orange   2.00 .30
O91 A41 5r green (C)   5.00 4.00
   Nos. O89-O91 (3)   7.50 4.45

Nos. 200, 202-203 Overprinted Type "c"

1968-?   Wmk. 351   Perf. 13½x13
O92 A41 1r vermilion   .40 .15
O93 A41 2r orange   1.25 .25
O93A A41 5r green (C)   6.00 5.00
   Nos. O92-O93A (3)   7.65 5.35

Nos. 459-468, 470-475 Overprinted Type "d" in Carmine or Black

1980-84
O94 A224 2p dark green   .15 .15
O95 A224 3p black   .15 .15
O96 A224 5p violet blue   .15 .15
O97 A225 10p grnsh blue   .15 .15
O98 A225 20p yel grn ('81)   .15 .15

O99 A225 25p rose car & grn ('81)   .15 .15
O100 A225 40p car & bl ('81)   .15 .15
O101 A225 50p bl grn & vio   .15 .15
O102 A225 60p black   .15 .15
O103 A225 75p dp orange   .15 .15
O105 A225a 1r olive ('81)   .15 .15
O106 A225a 1.50r dp orange   .20 .18
O107 A225a 2r car rose (B)   .28 .15
O108 A225a 3r indigo ('81)   .40 .35
O109 A225a 4r black ('84)   .65 .50
O110 A225a 5r dk brown ('84)   .85 .65
    Set value   3.00 2.40

Types A237-A239 Inscribed "SERVICE POSTAGE"

1980 Litho.   Perf. 12x11½, 11½x12
O111 A237 10p dk grn & yel org   .15 .15
O112 A237 15p dk grn & ap grn   .15 .15
O113 A237 25p dp vio & rose car   .15 .15
O114 A237 35p rose pink & brt yel grn   .15 .15
O115 A238 40p red & lt brn   .15 .15
O116 A239 50p olive & vio bl   .15 .15
O117 A239 80p blk & yel grn   .15 .15
    Set value   .50 .35

Issued: 10p, 15p, 40p, Jan. 15, others, Mar. 10.

Nos. 613-614, 616-620 Ovptd. "SERVICE" in Red

1984-87   Litho.   Perf. 11
O118 A289 5p Kot Diji   .15 .15
O119 A289 10p Rohtas   .15 .15
O120 A289 20p Attock Fort   .15 .15
O121 A289 50p Hyderabad   .15 .15
O122 A289 60p Lahore ('86)   .15 .15
O123 A289 70p Sibi   .16 .15
O124 A289 80p Ranikot   .19 .15
    Set value   .60 .40

Issued: 10p, Sept. 25, 1984; 80p, Aug. 3, 1987.

No. 712 Ovptd. "SERVICE"

1989, Dec. 24   Litho. & Engr.   Perf. 13
O124A A357 1r multicolored   .15 .15

National Assembly, Islamabad   O1

1991, Apr. 12   Litho.   Wmk. 351
O125 O1 1r green & red   .20 .15
O126 O1 2r rose car & red   .40 .15
O127 O1 3r ultra & red   .60 .15
O128 O1 4r red brown & red   .80 .15
O129 O1 5r rose lilac & red   1.00 .15
   Nos. O125-O129 (5)   3.00
    Set value   .25

BAHAWALPUR

LOCATION — A State of Pakistan.
AREA — 17,494 sq. mi.
POP. — 1,341,209 (1941)
CAPITAL — Bahawalpur

Bahawalpur was a State of India until 1947. These stamps had franking power solely within Bahawalpur.

Seventeen King George VI stamps of India exist overprinted with star, cresent and a line of Arabic. These are not considered to be legitimate stamps.

Amir Muhammad Bahawal Khan I Abbasi — A1

Perf. 12½x12

1947, Dec. 1   Wmk. 274   Engr.
1 A1 ½a brt car rose & blk   .15 .15
   Bicentenary of the ruling family.

Nawab Sadiq Muhammad Khan V Abbasi Bahadur — A2

Tombs of the Amirs — A3

Mosque, Sadiq Garh — A4

Fort Dirawar — A5

Nur-Mahal Palace — A6

Palace, Sadiq Garh — A7

Nawab Sadiq Muhammad Khan V Abbasi Bahadur — A8

A9

Perf. 12½ (A2), 12x12½ (A3, A5, A6, A7), 12½x12 (A4, A8), 13x13½ (A9)

1948, Apr. 1   Engr.   Wmk. 274

2	A2	3p dp blue & blk	.15	.15
3	A2	½a lake & blk	.15	.15
4	A2	9p dk green & blk	.15	.15
5	A2	1a dp car & blk	.15	.15
6	A2	1½a violet & blk	.15	.18
7	A3	2a car & dp grn	.15	.20
8	A4	4a brn & org red	.18	.35
9	A5	6a dp bl & vio brn	.20	.42
10	A6	8a brt pur & car	.30	.45
11	A7	12a dp car & dk bl grn	.45	.80
12	A8	1r chocolate & vio	.55	1.00
13	A8	2r dp mag & dk grn	.60	1.25
14	A8	5r purple & black	2.00	4.25
15	A9	10r black & carmine	8.50	
		Nos. 2-15 (14)	11.18	18.10

See #18-21. For overprints see #O17-O24.

Soldiers of 1848 and 1948 — A10

1948, Oct. 15   Engr.   Perf. 11½

16   A10   1½a dp car & blk   .15   2.00

Centenary of the Multan Campaign.

Amir Khan V and Mohammed Ali Jinnah — A11

1948, Oct. 3   Perf. 13x12½

17   A11   1½a grn & car rose   .15   .75

1st anniv. of the union of Bahawalpur with Pakistan.

Types of 1948

1948   Perf. 12x11½

18	A8	1r orange & dp grn	.15	.35
19	A8	2r carmine & blk	.15	.50
20	A8	5r ultra & red brn	.28	1.40

Perf. 13½

21	A9	10r green & red brn	.55	2.50
		Nos. 18-21 (4)	1.13	4.75

Panjnad Weir — A12

1949, Mar. 3   Perf. 14

22	A12	3p shown	.15	2.00
23	A12	½a Wheat	.15	2.00
24	A12	9p Cotton	.15	2.00
25	A12	1a Sahiwal Bull	.15	2.00
		Nos. 22-25 (4)		8.00
		Set value		.20

25th anniv. of the acquisition of full ruling powers by Amir Khan V.

UPU Monument, Bern — A13

1949, Oct. 10   Perf. 13
Center in Black

26	A13	9p green	.15	1.00
27	A13	1a red violet	.15	1.00
28	A13	1½a brown orange	.15	1.00
29	A13	2½a blue	.45	2.00
		Nos. 26-29 (4)	.90	5.00

UPU, 75th anniv. Exist perf 17½x17. Exist imperf.
For overprints see Nos. O25-O28.

OFFICIAL STAMPS

Panjnad Weir — O1

Camel and Colt — O2

Antelopes — O3

Pelicans — O4

Juma Masjid Palace, Fort Derawar — O5

Temple at Pattan Munara — O6

Red Overprint
Wmk. 274

1945, Jan. 1   Engr.   Perf. 14

O1	O1	½a brt grn & blk	.65	2.25
O2	O2	1a carmine & blk	1.40	1.25
O3	O3	2a violet & blk	2.00	2.50
O4	O4	4a olive & blk	3.50	5.75
O5	O5	8a brown & blk	2.50	4.50
O6	O6	1r orange & blk	2.50	4.50
		Nos. O1-O6 (6)	12.55	20.75

For types overprinted see Nos. O7-O9, O11-O13.

Types of 1945, Without Red Overprint, Surcharged in Black

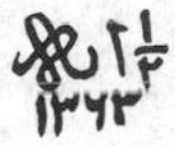

1945   Unwmk.

O7	O5	½a on 8a lake & blk	4.00	2.00
O8	O6	1½a on 1r org & blk	12.00	2.50
O9	O1	1½a on 2r ultra & blk	22.50	3.00
		Nos. O7-O9 (3)	38.50	7.50

Camels — O7

1945, Mar. 10   Red Overprint

O10   O7   1a brown & black   27.50   35.00

Types of 1945, Without Red Overprint Overprinted in Black

SERVICE

1945

O11	O1	½a carmine & black	.65	3.50
O12	O2	1a carmine & black	.65	3.50
O13	O3	2a orange & black	1.40	6.50
		Nos. O11-O13 (3)	2.70	13.50

Nawab Sadiq Muhammad Khan V Abbasi Bahadur — O8

1945

O14	O8	3p dp blue & blk	.20	1.40
O15	O8	1½a dp violet & blk	1.50	3.25

Flags of Allied Nations — O9

1946, May 1

O16   O9   1½a emerald & gray   1.25   1.25

Victory of Allied Nations in World War II.

Stamps of 1948 Overprinted in Carmine or Black

Perf. 12½, 12½x12, 12x11½, 13½

1948   Wmk. 274

O17	A2	3p dp bl & blk (C)	.15	2.00
O18	A2	1a dp carmine & blk	.15	1.50
O19	A3	2a car & dp grn	.15	2.00
O20	A4	4a brown & org red	.15	3.00
O21	A8	1r org & dp grn (C)	.15	3.00
O22	A8	2r car & blk (C)	.15	4.00
O23	A8	5r ultra & red brn (C)	.18	7.00
O24	A9	10r grn & red brn (C)	.28	8.50
		Set value	.80	

Same Ovpt. in Carmine on #26-29

1949   Perf. 13, 18
Center in Black

O25	A13	9p green	.25	2.00
O26	A13	1a red violet	.25	2.00
O27	A13	1½a brown orange	.25	2.00
O28	A13	2½a blue	.25	2.00
		Nos. O25-O28 (4)	.00	

75th anniv. of the UPU. Exist perf 17½x17. Exist imperf.

PALESTINE

'pa–lə–‚stin

LOCATION — Western Asia bordering on the Mediterranean Sea
GOVT. — Former British Mandate
AREA — 10,429 sq. mi.
POP. — 1,605,816 (estimated)
CAPITAL — Jerusalem

Formerly a part of Turkey, Palestine was occupied by the Egyptian Expeditionary Forces of the British Army in World War I and was mandated to Great Britain in 1923. Mandate ended May 14, 1948.

10 Milliemes = 1 Piaster
1000 Milliemes = 1 Egyptian Pound
1000 Mils = 1 Palestine Pound (1928)

Watermark

Wmk. 33

Issued under British Military Occupation

For use in Palestine, Transjordan, Lebanon, Syria and in parts of Cilicia and northeastern Egypt

A1

Wmk. Crown and "GvR" (33)

1918, Feb. 10 Litho. *Rouletted 20*

1	A1	1pi deep blue	200.00	125.00
2	A1	1pi ultra	2.00	1.50

No. 2 Surcharged in Black

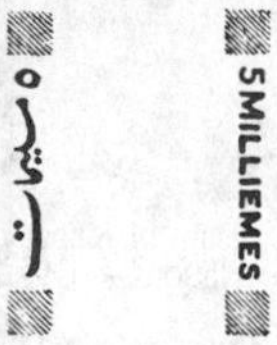

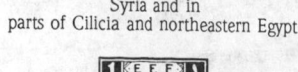

1918, Feb. 16

3	A1	5m on 1pi ultra	5.00	4.00
a.		5m on 1pi gray blue	125.00	650.00

Nos. 1 and 3a were issued without gum. No. 3a is on paper with a surface sheen.

1918 Typo. *Perf. 15x14*

4	A1	1m dark brown	.15	.15
5	A1	2m blue green	.20	.20
6	A1	3m light brown	.25	.30
7	A1	4m scarlet	.30	.35
8	A1	5m orange	.30	.30
9	A1	1pi indigo	.30	.20
10	A1	2pi olive green	.45	.50
11	A1	5pi plum	1.50	1.65
12	A1	9pi bister	2.50	3.25
13	A1	10pi ultramarine	2.50	3.25
14	A1	20pi gray	8.00	11.00
		Nos. 4-14 (11)	16.45	21.15

Many shades exist.

Nos. 4-11 exist with rough perforation.

Issued: 1m, 2m, 4m, 2pi, 5pi, July 16; 5m, Sept. 25; 1pi, Nov. 9; 3m, 9pi, 10pi, Dec. 17; 20pi, Dec. 27.

Nos. 4-11 with overprint "O. P. D. A." (Ottoman Public Debt Administration) or "H.J.Z." (Hejaz-Jemen Railway) are revenue stamps; they exist postally used.

For overprints on stamps and types see #15-62 & Jordan #1-63, 73-90, 92-102, 130-144, J12-J23.

Issued under British Administration

Overprinted at Jerusalem

فلسطين

Stamps and Type of 1918 Overprinted in Black or Silver — PALESTINE

פלשתינה א״י

1920, Sept. 1 Wmk. 33 *Perf. 15x14*

Arabic Overprint 8mm long

15	A1	1m dark brown	1.25	1.25
16	A1	2m blue green, perf. 14	1.00	1.10
d.		Perf. 15x14	6.00	3.00
17	A1	3m lt brown	3.00	3.25
d.		Perf. 14	40.00	45.00
e.		Inverted overprint	350.00	600.00
18	A1	4m scarlet	1.25	1.50
19	A1	5m orange, perf. 14	1.25	.95
e.		Perf. 15x14	7.00	3.75
20	A1	1pi indigo (S)	1.00	.50
21	A1	2pi olive green	1.25	1.25
22	A1	5pi plum	9.00	10.00
23	A1	9pi bister	10.00	15.00
24	A1	10pi ultra	10.00	15.00
25	A1	20pi gray	20.00	32.50
		Nos. 15-25 (11)	59.00	82.30

Forgeries exist of No. 17e.

Similar Overprint, with Arabic Line 10mm Long, Arabic "S" and "T" Joined, "‘" Extends Above Other Letters

فلسطين

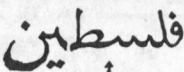

1920-21 *Perf. 15x14*

15a	A1	1m dark brown	.50	.75
e.		Perf. 14	600.00	750.00
g.		As "a," invtd. ovpt.		
16a	A1	2m blue green	2.25	2.75
e.		"PALESTINE" omitted	2,500.	1,500.
f.		Perf. 14	2.25	2.75
17a	A1	3m light brown	.50	.75
18a	A1	4m scarlet	1.00	1.40
b.		Perf. 14	60.00	80.00
19a	A1	5m orange	1.75	.60
f.		Perf. 14	1.50	1.00
20a	A1	1pi indigo, perf. 14 (S) ('21)	25.00	1.75
d.		Perf. 15x14	500.00	37.50
21a	A1	2pi olive green ('21)	65.00	30.00
22a	A1	5pi plum ('21)	20.00	8.00
d.		Perf. 14	190.00	650.00
		Nos. 15a-22a (8)	116.00	46.00

This overprint often looks grayish to grayish black. In the English line the letters are frequently uneven and damaged.

Similar Overprint, with Arabic Line 10mm Long, Arabic "S" and "T" Separated and 6mm Between English and Hebrew Lines

فلسطين

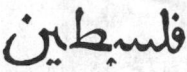

1920, Dec. 6

15b	A1	1m dk brown, perf. 14	24.00	30.00
17b	A1	3m lt brown, perf. 15x14	30.00	35.00
19b	A1	5m orange, perf. 14	350.00	30.00
d.		Perf. 15x14	17,500.	15,000.
		Nos. 15b-19b (3)	404.00	95.00

Overprinted as Before, 7 1/2mm Between English and Hebrew Lines, "‘" Even With Other Letters

1921 *Perf. 15x14*

15c	A1	1m dark brown	4.50	2.00
f.		1m dull brown, perf. 14		2,500.
16c	A1	2m blue green	5.50	3.25
17c	A1	3m light brown	15.00	1.50
18c	A1	4m scarlet	11.00	1.50
19c	A1	5m orange	12.00	.75
20c	A1	1pi indigo (S)	15.00	.70
21c	A1	2pi olive green	20.00	5.00
22c	A1	5pi plum	18.00	8.00
23c	A1	9pi bister	30.00	100.00
24c	A1	10pi ultra	30.00	15.00
25c	A1	20pi pale gray	90.00	60.00
d.		Perf. 14	14,000.	2,000.
		Nos. 15c-25c (11)	251.00	197.70

Overprinted at London

فلسطين

Stamps of 1918 Overprinted — PALESTINE

פלשתינה א״י

1921 *Perf. 15x14*

37	A1	1m dark brown	.30	.22
38	A1	2m blue green	.30	.22
39	A1	3m light brown	.30	.22
40	A1	4m scarlet	1.00	.50
41	A1	5m orange	.30	.20
42	A1	1pi bright blue	.50	.20
43	A1	2pi olive green	1.00	.50
44	A1	5pi plum	4.00	5.50
45	A1	9pi bister	13.00	16.00
46	A1	10pi ultra	15.00	—
47	A1	20pi gray	42.50	—
		Nos. 37-47 (11)	78.20	
		Nos. 37-45 (9)		23.56

The "‘ (2nd from left on bottom line) consists of long thin lines.

Deformed or damaged letters exist in all three lines of the overprint.

Similar Overprint on Type of 1921 Issue

1922 Wmk. 4 *Perf. 14*

48	A1	1m dark brown	.20	.15
a.		Inverted overprint		15,000.
b.		Double overprint	225.00	400.00
49	A1	2m yellow	.40	.15
50	A1	3m Prus blue	.20	.15
51	A1	4m rose	.20	.15
52	A1	5m orange	.35	.15
53	A1	6m blue green	.50	.15
54	A1	7m yellow brown	.60	.20
55	A1	8m red	.55	.15
56	A1	1pi gray	.55	.15
57	A1	13m ultra	.60	.15
58	A1	2pi olive green	1.00	.25
a.		Inverted overprint	350.00	400.00
b.		2pi yellow bister	125.00	6.00
59	A1	5pi plum	5.00	1.00
a.		Perf. 15x14	25.00	3.00

Perf. 15x14

60	A1	9pi bister	10.00	9.00
a.		Perf. 14	1,200.	225.00
61	A1	10pi light blue	20.00	6.50
a.		Perf. 14	20.00	7.00
62	A1	20pi violet	7.50	4.00
a.		Perf. 14	175.00	100.00
		Nos. 48-62 (15)	47.65	22.30

The "" (2nd from left on bottom line) consists of short thick lines.

The "E. F. F." for "E. E. F." on No. 61 is caused by damaged type.

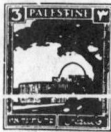

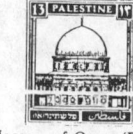

Rachel's Tomb — A3

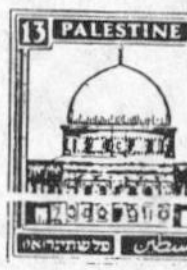

Mosque of Omar (Dome of the Rock) — A4

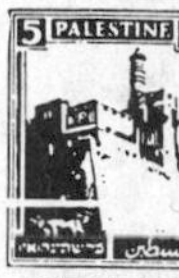

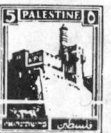

Citadel at Jerusalem
A5

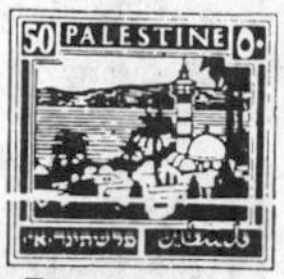

Tiberias and Sea of Galilee
A6

1927-42 Typo. *Perf. 13 1/2x14 1/2*

63	A3	2m Prus blue	.15	.15
64	A3	3m yellow green	.15	.15
65	A4	4m rose red	.90	.35
66	A4	4m violet brn ('32)	.15	.15
67	A5	5m brown org	.15	.15
c.		Perf. 14 1/2x14 (coil stamp) ('36)	2.25	2.75
68	A4	6m deep green	.15	.15
69	A5	7m deep red	1.40	.25
70	A5	7m dk violet ('32)	.15	.15
71	A4	8m yellow brown	6.00	3.00
72	A4	8m scarlet ('32)	.25	.15
73	A3	10m deep gray	.15	.15
a.		Perf. 14 1/2x14 (coil stamp) ('38)	2.50	3.00
74	A4	13m ultra	2.00	.20
75	A4	13m olive bister ('32)	.15	.15
76	A4	15m ultra ('32)	.15	.15
77	A5	20m olive green	.15	.15

Perf. 14

78	A6	50m violet brown	.50	.15
79	A6	90m bister	30.00	27.50
80	A6	100m bright blue	.50	.15
81	A6	200m dk violet	1.00	.55
82	A6	250m dp brown ('42)	.60	.80
83	A6	500m red ('42)	1.50	1.70
84	A6	£1 gray black ('42)	2.00	2.50
		Nos. 63-84 (22)	48.15	38.80

Issue dates: 3m, No. 74, June 1. 2m, 5m, 6m, 10m, Nos. 65, 69, 71, 77-81, Aug. 14. Nos. 70, 72, June 1, 1932. No. 75, 15m, Aug. 1, 1932. No. 66, Nov. 1, 1932. Nos. 82-84, Jan. 15, 1942.

Jordan stamps overprinted with "Palestine" in English and Arabic are listed under Jordan.

POSTAGE DUE STAMPS

D1

1923 Unwmk. Typo. *Perf. 11*

J1	D1	1m bister brown	11.00	15.00
b.		Horiz. pair, imperf. btwn.	1,300.	
J2	D1	2m green	8.00	9.00
J3	D1	4m red	7.00	8.00
J4	D1	8m violet	4.50	4.50
b.		Horiz. pair, imperf. btwn.		2,750.
J5	D1	13m dark blue	4.50	4.50
a.		Horiz. pair, imperf. btwn.	1,150.	
		Nos. J1-J5 (5)	35.00	41.00

Imperfs. of 1m, 2m, 8m, are from proof sheets.
Values for Nos. J1-J5 are for fine centered copies.

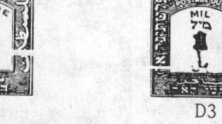

D2

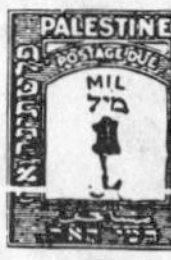

D3

1924, Dec. 1 Wmk. 4

J6	D2	1m brown	.90	.90
J7	D2	2m yellow	1.00	1.00
J8	D2	4m green	1.10	.90
J9	D2	8m red	1.50	.50
J10	D2	13m ultramarine	3.00	1.90
J11	D2	5pi violet	7.00	1.50
		Nos. J6-J11 (6)	14.50	6.70

1928-45 *Perf. 14*

J12	D3	1m lt brown	.35	.70
a.		Perf. 15x14 ('45)	21.00	37.50
J13	D3	2m yellow	.45	.50
J14	D3	4m green	.60	1.25
a.		4m bluish grn, perf. 15x14 ('45)	35.00	50.00
J15	D3	6m brown org ('33)	6.00	5.50
J16	D3	8m red	1.25	.60
J17	D3	10m light gray	1.00	.45
J18	D3	13m ultra	1.25	1.40
J19	D3	20m olive green	1.40	1.00
J20	D3	50m violet	2.00	1.00
		Nos. J12-J20 (9)	14.30	12.40

The Hebrew word for "mil" appears below the numeral on all values but the 1m.

Issue dates: 6m, Oct. 1933, others, Feb. 1, 1928.

PAPUA NEW GUINEA

ˈpa–pyə–wə ˈnü ˈgi–nē

LOCATION — Eastern half of island of New Guinea, north of Australia
GOVT. — Independent state in British Commonwealth.
AREA — 185,136 sq. mi.
POP. — 3,260,000 (est. 1984)
CAPITAL — Port Moresby

In 1884 a British Protectorate was proclaimed over this part of the island, called "British New Guinea." In 1905 the administration was transferred to Australia and in 1906 the name was changed to Territory of Papua.

In 1949 the administration of Papua and New Guinea was unified, as the 1952 issue indicates. In 1972 the name was changed to Papua New Guinea. In 1974 came self-government, followed by independence on September 16, 1975.

Issues of 1925-39 for the mandated Territory of New Guinea are listed under New Guinea.

12 Pence = 1 Shilling
20 Shillings = 1 Pound
100 Cents = 1 Dollar (1966)
100 Toea = 1 Kina (1975)

Catalogue values for unused stamps in this country are for Never Hinged items, beginning with Scott 122 in the regular postage section and Scott J1 in the postage due section.

Watermarks

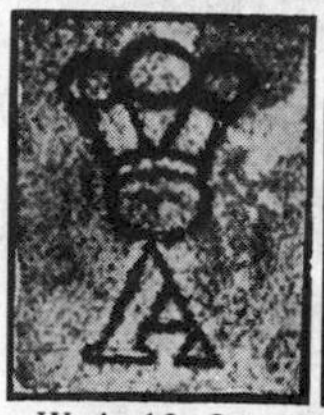

Wmk. 13- Crown and Double-Lined A

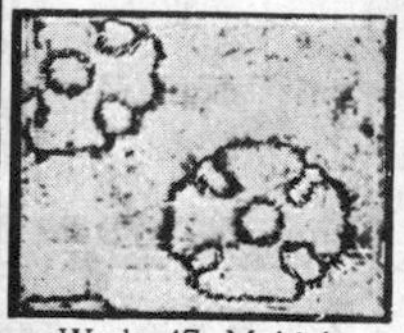

Wmk. 47- Multiple Rosette

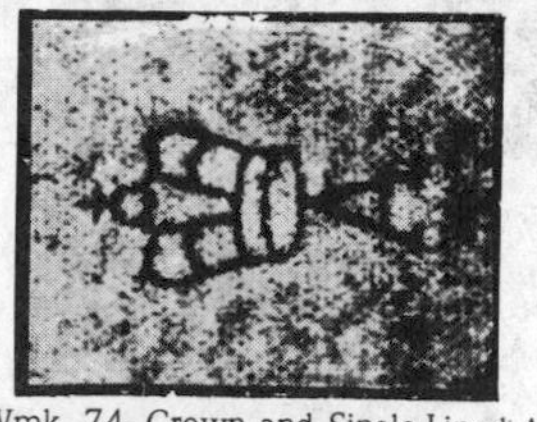

Wmk. 74- Crown and Single-Lined A Sideways

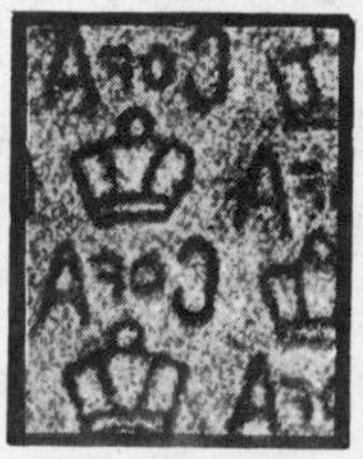

Wmk. 228- Small Crown and C of A Multiple

Wmk. 387

British New Guinea

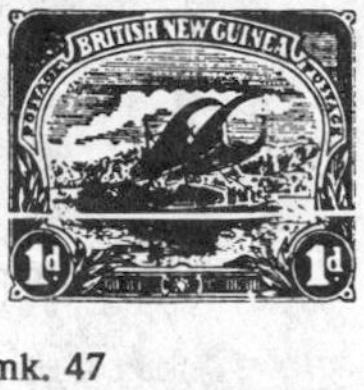

Lakatoi — A1

Wmk. 47

1901, July 1 Engr. *Perf. 14*

Center in Black

1	A1	½p yellow green	3.00	3.75
2	A1	1p carmine	3.00	2.00
3	A1	2p violet	6.50	4.00
4	A1	2½p ultra	8.00	11.00
5	A1	4p black brown	30.00	35.00
6	A1	6p dark green	40.00	40.00
7	A1	1sh orange	55.00	70.00
8	A1	2sh6p brown ('05)	575.00	575.00
		Nos. 1-8 (8)	720.50	740.75

The paper varies in thickness and the watermark is found in two positions, with the greater width of the rosette either horizontal or vertical.

For overprints see Nos. 11-36.

Papua

Stamps of British New Guinea, Overprinted **Papua.**

1906, Nov. 8 Wmk. 47 *Perf. 14*

Center in Black

11	A1	½p yellow green	5.00	10.00
12	A1	1p carmine	8.50	11.00
13	A1	2p violet	4.50	4.50
14	A1	2½p ultra	5.00	10.00
15	A1	4p black brown	175.00	150.00
16	A1	6p dark green	22.50	27.50
17	A1	1sh orange	22.50	27.50
18	A1	2sh6p brown	140.00	150.00
		Nos. 11-18 (8)	383.00	390.50

Overprinted **Papua.**

1907 **Center in Black**

19	A1	½p yellow green	4.00	4.25
a.		Double overprint	1,750.	
20	A1	1p carmine	3.50	3.75
a.		Vertical overprint, up	750.00	750.00
21	A1	2p violet	3.50	3.00
22	A1	2½p ultra	6.00	5.50
a.		Double overprint		
23	A1	4p black brown	27.50	33.50
24	A1	6p dark green	26.00	30.00
a.		Double overprint	1,750.	1,750.
25	A1	1sh orange	32.50	40.00
a.		Double overprint		
26	A1	2sh6p brown	32.50	42.50
b.		Vert. ovpt., down	1,500.	
d.		Double horiz. ovpt.		1,500.
		Nos. 19-26 (8)	135.50	161.50

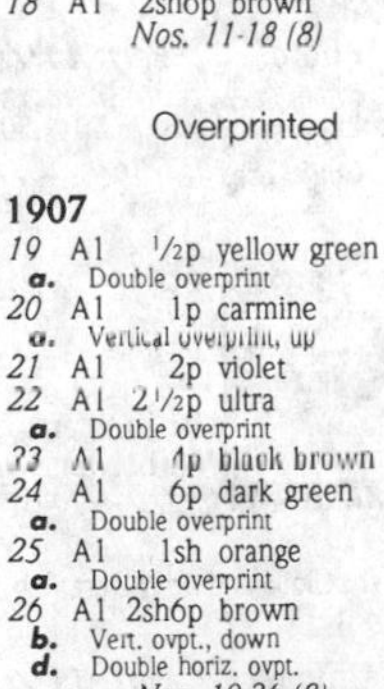

A2

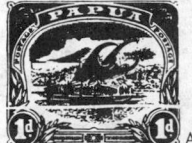

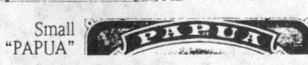

Small "PAPUA"

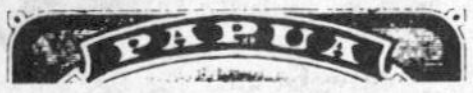

Perf. 11, 12½

1907-08 Litho. Wmk. 13

Center in Black

28	A2	1p carmine ('08)	5.00	4.00
29	A2	2p violet ('08)	5.00	4.00
30	A2	2½p ultra ('08)	6.50	5.25
31	A2	4p black brown	4.00	6.00
32	A2	6p dk green ('08)	14.00	14.00
33	A2	1sh orange ('08)	17.00	12.00
		Nos. 28-33 (6)	51.50	45.25

Perf. 12½

30a	A2	2½p	45.00	65.00
31a	A2	4p	8.50	8.75
33a	A2	1sh	65.00	75.00
		Nos. 30a-33a (3)	118.50	148.75

1909-10 **Wmk. Sideways**

Center in Black

34	A2	½p yellow green	1.40	1.75
a.		Perf. 11x12½	2,000.	2,000.
b.		Perf. 11	1.40	1.75
35	A2	1p carmine	6.25	6.00
a.		Perf. 11	10.00	10.00
36	A2	2p violet ('10)	3.00	1.75
a.		Perf. 11x12½	750.00	
b.		Perf. 11	4.00	3.00
37	A2	2½p ultra ('10)	4.00	5.00
a.		Perf. 12½	6.50	7.00
38	A2	4p black brn ('10)	4.75	5.00
a.		Perf. 11x12½	3,750.	
39	A2	6p dark green	16.00	15.00
a.		Perf. 12½	1,500.	1,750.
40	A2	1sh orange ('10)	12.00	20.00
a.		Perf. 11	50.00	65.00
		Nos. 34-40 (7)	47.40	54.50

One stamp in each sheet has a white line across the upper part of the picture which is termed the "rift in the clouds."

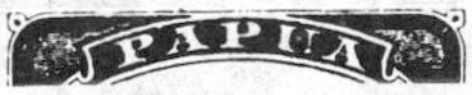

Large "PAPUA"

2sh6p:

Type I - The numerals are thin and irregular. The body of the "6" encloses a large spot of color. The dividing stroke is thick and uneven.

Type II - The numerals are thick and well formed. The "6" encloses a narrow oval of color. The dividing stroke is thin and sharp.

1910 **Wmk. 13**

Center in Black

41	A2	½p yellow green	1.50	1.75
42	A2	1p carmine	5.00	3.50
43	A2	2p violet	4.25	4.00
44	A2	2½p blue violet	3.75	4.00
45	A2	4p black brown	5.00	8.25
46	A2	6p dark green	6.50	10.00
47	A2	1sh orange	8.25	12.50
48	A2	2sh6p brown, type II	55.00	70.00
a.		Type I	55.00	70.00
		Nos. 41-48 (8)	89.25	114.00

Wmk. Sideways

49	A2	2sh6p choc, type I	80.00	100.00

1911 **Typo.** **Wmk. 74** *Perf. 12½*

50	A2	½p yellow green	.70	.70
51	A2	1p lt red	1.25	1.25
52	A2	2p lt violet	1.10	1.10
53	A2	2½p ultra	4.00	4.00
54	A2	4p olive green	4.50	5.50
55	A2	6p orange brown	4.25	4.25
56	A2	1sh yellow	8.00	11.00
57	A2	2sh6p rose	25.00	37.50
		Nos. 50-57 (8)	48.80	65.30

For surcharges see Nos. 74-79.

1915, June *Perf. 14*

59	A2	1p light red	10.00	5.50

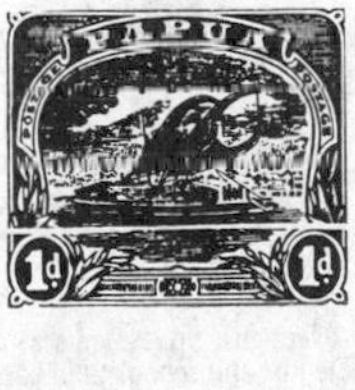

A3

1916-31

60	A3	½p pale yel grn & myr grn ('19)	.22	.22
61	A3	1p rose red & blk	.90	.90
62	A3	1½p yel brn & gray bl ('25)	.60	.60
63	A3	2p red vio & vio brn ('19)	2.50	1.00
64	A3	2p red brn & vio brn ('31)	3.25	2.25
a.		2p cop red & vio brn ('31)	35.00	7.50
65	A3	2½p ultra & dk grn ('19)	2.25	2.50
66	A3	3p emerald & blk	1.00	1.00
a.		3p dp bl grn & blk	2.00	2.00
67	A3	4p org & lt brn ('19)	3.75	3.75
68	A3	5p ol brn & sl ('31)	5.25	6.00
69	A3	6p vio & dl vio ('23)	2.25	2.50
70	A3	1sh ol grn & dk brn ('19)	3.00	3.25
71	A3	2sh6p rose & red brn ('19)	11.25	13.50
72	A3	5sh dp grn & blk	17.50	17.50
73	A3	10sh gray bl & grn ('25)	175.00	190.00
		Nos. 60-73 (14)	228.72	244.97

Type A3 is a redrawing of type A2.

The lines of the picture have been strengthened, making it much darker, especially the sky and water.

For surcharges & overprints see #88-91, O1-O10.

Stamps of 1911 Surcharged **ONE PENNY**

1917 *Perf. 12½*

74	A2	1p on ½p yellow grn	.70	1.00
75	A2	1p on 2p lt violet	7.00	10.00
76	A2	1p on 2½p ultra	2.00	4.50
77	A2	1p on 4p olive green	2.00	4.50
78	A2	1p on 6p orange brown	7.00	12.50
79	A2	1p on 2sh6p rose	1.75	4.50
		Nos. 74-79 (6)	20.45	37.00

No. 62 Surcharged **TWO PENCE**

1931, Jan. 1 *Perf. 14*

88	A3	2p on 1½p yellow brn & gray blue	1.25	1.25

Nos. 70, 71 and 72 Surcharged in Black **5d.** **FIVE PENCE**

1931

89	A3	5p on 1sh #70	2.00	1.75
90	A3	9p on 2sh6p #71	3.50	8.00
91	A3	1sh3p on 5sh #72	5.00	12.50
		Nos. 89-91 (3)	10.50	22.25

Type of 1916 Issue

1932 **Wmk. 228** *Perf. 11*

92	A3	9p dp violet & gray	15.00	27.50
93	A3	1sh3p pale blue & gray blk	17.50	30.00

For overprints see Nos. O11-O12.

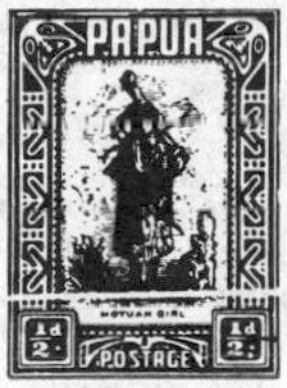

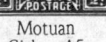

Motuan Girl — A5

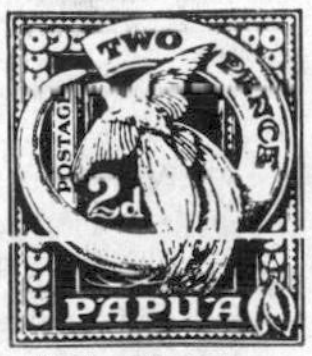

Bird of Paradise and Boar's Tusk — A6

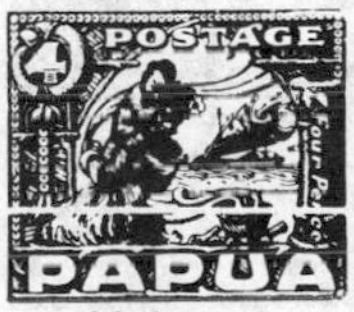

Mother and Child — A7

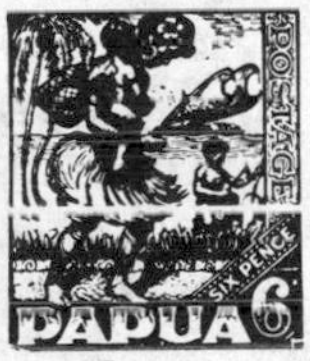

Papuan Motherhood — A8

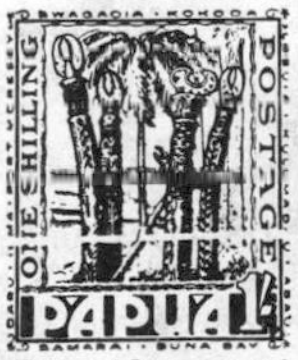

Dubu (Ceremonial Platform) — A9

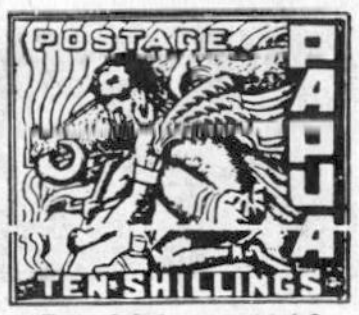

Fire Maker — A10

Designs: 1p, Steve, son of Oala. 1½p, Tree houses. 3p, Papuan dandy. 5p, Masked dancer. 9p, Shooting fish. 1sh3p, Lakatoi. 2sh, Delta art. 2sh6p, Pottery making. 5sh, Sgt.-Major Simoi. £1, Delta house.

Unwmk.

1932, Nov. 14 **Engr.** *Perf. 11*

94	A5	½p orange & blk	.22	.22
95	A5	1p yel green & blk	.15	.15
96	A5	1½p red brn & blk	.90	.90
97	A6	2p light red	2.00	.45
98	A5	3p blue & blk	2.50	2.25
99	A7	4p olive green	2.00	2.00
100	A5	5p grnsh sl & blk	2.25	2.25
101	A8	6p bister brown	4.00	3.75
102	A5	9p lilac & blk	7.50	9.00
103	A9	1sh bluish gray	3.00	3.00
104	A5	1sh3p brown & blk	12.50	14.50
105	A5	2sh bluish slate & blk	14.50	21.00
106	A5	2sh6p rose lilac & blk	21.00	32.50
107	A5	5sh olive & blk	45.00	45.00
108	A10	10sh gray lilac	82.50	82.50
109	A5	£1 lt gray & black	200.00	140.00
		Nos. 94-109 (16)	400.02	359.47

For overprints see Nos. 114-117.

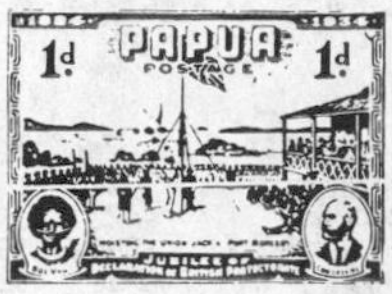

Hoisting Union Jack at Port Moresby — A21

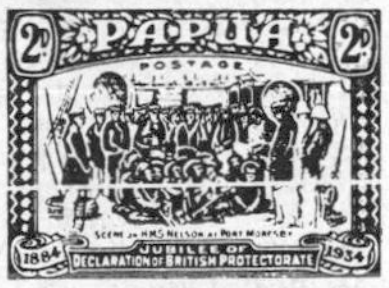

H. M. S. "Nelson" at Port Moresby — A22

1934, Nov. 6

110	A21	1p dull green	.90	.90
111	A22	2p red brown	1.10	1.10
112	A21	3p blue	2.75	2.75
113	A22	5p violet brown	6.25	6.25
		Nos. 110-113 (4)	11.00	11.00
		Set, never hinged	17.00	

50th anniv. of the Declaration of British Protection.

Silver Jubilee Issue

Stamps of 1932 Issue Overprinted in Black:

HIS MAJESTY'S JUBILEE.
1910 1935
a

HIS MAJESTY'S
JUBILEE.
1910 — 1935
b

1935, July 9

Glazed Paper

114	A5(a)	1p yellow grn & blk	.25	.35
115	A6(b)	2p light red	.65	.85
116	A5(a)	3p lt blue & blk	2.50	3.25
117	A5(a)	5p grnsh slate & blk	5.00	6.50
		Nos. 114-117 (4)	8.40	10.95
		Set, never hinged	14.00	

25th anniv. of the reign of George V.

Coronation Issue

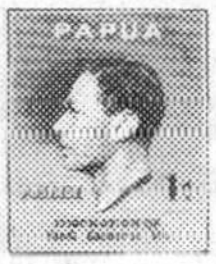

King George VI — A22a

Unwmk.

1937, May 14 **Engr.** *Perf. 11*

118	A22a	1p green	.25	.20
119	A22a	2p salmon rose	.25	.20
120	A22a	3p blue	.25	.25
121	A22a	5p brown violet	.35	.35
		Nos. 118-121 (4)	1.10	1.00
		Set, never hinged	2.00	

Catalogue values for unused stamps in this section, from this point to the end of the section, are for Never Hinged items.

Papua and New Guinea

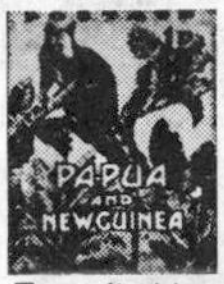

Tree-climbing Kangaroo — A23

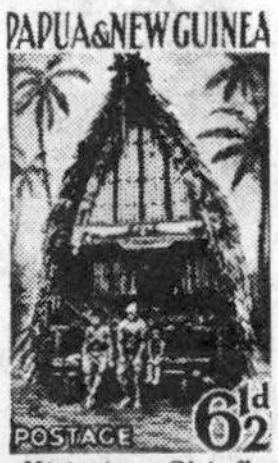

Kiriwina Chief's House — A24

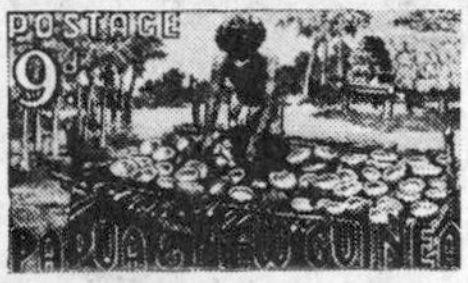

Copra Making A25

Designs: 1p, Buka head-dress. 2p, Youth. 2½p, Bird of paradise. 3p, Policeman. 3½p, Chimbu headdress. 7½p, Kiriwina yam house. 1sh, Trading canoe. 1sh6p, Rubber tapping. 2sh, Shields and

spears. 2sh6p, Plumed shepherd. 10sh, Map. £1, Spearing fish.

Unwmk.

1952, Oct. 30 Engr. *Perf. 14*

122 A23	½p	blue green	.22	.15
123 A23	1p	chocolate	.22	.15
124 A23	2p	deep ultra	.60	.15
125 A23	2½p	orange	2.50	.52
126 A23	3p	dark green	.90	.16
127 A23	3½p	dk carmine	1.10	.20
128 A24	6½p	vio brown	1.75	.32
129 A24	7½p	dp ultra	13.00	5.75
130 A25	9p	chocolate	4.00	.80
131 A25	1sh	yellow green	2.50	.42
132 A24	1sh6p	dark green	7.25	1.10
133 A24	2sh	deep blue	7.75	.90
134 A25	2sh6p	dk red brown	8.75	1.50
135 A25	10sh	gray black	72.50	15.00
136 A24	£1	chocolate	77.50	22.50
		Nos. 122-136 (15)	200.54	49.62
		Set, hinged	155.00	

See Nos. 139-141. For surcharges and overprints see Nos. 137-138, 147, J1-J3, J5-J6.

Nos. 125 and 131 Surcharged with New Values and Bars

1957, Jan. 29 *Perf. 14*

137 A23	4p on 2½p orange	.50	.30
138 A25	7p on 1sh yellow green	1.00	.80

Type of 1952 and

Klinki Plymill A26

Designs: 3½p, Chimbu headdress. 4p, 5p, Cacao. 8p, Klinki Plymill. 1sh7p, Cattle. 2sh5p, Cattle. 5sh, Coffee, vert.

1958-60 Engr. *Perf. 14*

139 A23	3½p	black	8.50	4.50
140 A23	4p	vermilion	.70	.15
141 A23	5p	green ('60)	.70	.15
142 A26	7p	gray green	4.50	.90
143 A26	8p	dk ultra	3.25	2.00
144 A26	1sh7p	red brown	47.50	32.50
145 A26	2sh5p	vermilion	7.50	6.75
146 A26	5sh	gray olive & brn red	9.50	3.25
		Nos. 139-146 (8)	82.15	50.20

Issue dates: June 2, 1958, Nov. 10, 1960.
For surcharge see No. J4.

No. 122 Surcharged with New Value

1959, Dec. 1

147 A23	5p on ½p blue green	.70	.30

Council Chamber and Frangipani Flowers A27

1961, Apr. 10 Photo. *Perf. 14½x14*

148 A27	5p	green & yellow	2.25	1.40
149 A27	2sh3p	green & salmon	18.00	16.00

Reconstitution of the Legislative Council.

Woman's Head — A28

Red-plumed Bird of Paradise — A29

Port Moresby Harbor A30

Constable Ragas Amis Matia, Port Moresby A32

View of Rabaul, by Samuel Terarup Cham — A33

Woman Dancer A31

Elizabeth II A34

Designs: 3p, Man's head. 6p, Golden opossum. 2sh, Male dancer with drum. 2sh3p, Piaggio transport plane landing at Tapini.

Perf. 14 (A28, A31, A32), 11½ (A29, A33), 14x13½ (A30), 14½ (A34)

1961-63 Engr. Unwmk.

153 A28	1p	dk carmine	.18	.15
154 A28	3p	bluish black	.22	.15
		Photo.		
155 A29	5p	lt brn, red brn, blk & yel	.25	.15
156 A29	6p	gray, ocher & slate	.90	.90
		Engr.		
157 A30	8p	green	.45	.35
158 A31	1sh	gray green	6.00	.75
159 A31	2sh	rose lake	1.40	.70
160 A30	2sh3p	dark blue	1.20	.75
161 A32	3sh	green	1.50	1.20
		Photo.		
162 A33	10sh	multicolored	30.00	22.50
163 A34	£1	brt grn, blk & gold	20.00	12.50
		Nos. 153-163 (11)	62.10	40.10

The 5p and 6p are on granite paper.
Issue dates: 3sh, Sept. 5, 1962; 10sh, Feb. 13; 5p, 6p, Mar. 27, 1963; 8p, 2sh3p, May 8, 1963; £1, July 3, 1963; others, July 26, 1961.

Malaria Eradication Emblem — A35

1962, Apr. 7 Litho. *Perf. 14*

164 A35	5p	lt blue & maroon	.45	.15
165 A35	1sh	lt brown & red	2.25	.95
166 A35	2sh	yellow green & blk	4.75	3.00
		Nos. 164-166 (3)	7.45	4.10

WHO drive to eradicate malaria.

Map of Australia and South Pacific A36

1962, July 9 Engr. Unwmk.

167 A36	5p	dk red & lt green	.50	.25
168 A36	1sh6p	dk violet & yel	2.75	2.25
169 A36	2sh6p	green & lt blue	8.75	6.00
		Nos. 167-169 (3)	12.00	8.50

5th So. Pacific Conf., Pago Pago, July 1962.

High Jump — A37

Games Emblem — A38

1962, Oct. 24 Photo. *Perf. 11½*

Size: 26x21mm

Granite Paper

171 A37	5p	shown	.55	.25
172 A37	5p	Javelin	.55	.25

Size: 32½x22½mm

173 A37	2sh3p	runners	5.00	3.75
		Nos. 171-173 (3)	6.10	4.25

British Empire and Commonwealth Games, Perth, Australia, Nov. 22-Dec. 1.

Nos. 171 and 172 printed in alternating horizontal rows in sheet.

Red Cross Centenary Emblem — A38a

1963, May 1 *Perf. 13½*

174 A38a	5p blue grn, gray & red	.75	.40

Centenary of the International Red Cross.

1963, Aug. 14 Engr. *Perf. 13½x14*

176 A38	5p	olive bister	.30	.15
177 A38	1sh	green	1.25	1.10

So. Pacific Games, Suva, Aug. 29-Sept. 7.

Top of Wooden Shield — A39

Casting Ballot — A40

Various Carved Heads.

Perf. 11½

1964, Feb. 5 Unwmk. Photo.

Granite Paper

178 A39	11p	multicolored	.40	.28
179 A39	2sh5p	multicolored	1.25	.85
180 A39	2sh6p	multicolored	1.00	.65
181 A39	5sh	multicolored	2.75	1.75
		Nos. 178-181 (4)	5.40	3.53

1964, Mar. 4 Unwmk. *Perf. 11½*

Granite Paper

182 A40	5p	dk brown & pale brn	.16	.16
183 A40	2sh3p	dk brown & lt blue	1.10	1.10

First Common Roll elections.

A41

A42

Designs: 5p, Patients at health center clinic. 8p, Dentist and school child patient. 1sh, Nurse holding infant. 1sh2p, Medical student using microscope.

1964, Aug. 5 Engr. *Perf. 14*

184 A41	5p	violet	.15	.15
185 A41	8p	green	.32	.32
186 A41	1sh	deep ultra	.45	.45
187 A41	1sh2p	rose brown	.60	.60
		Nos. 184-187 (4)	1.52	1.52

Territorial health services.

1964-65 Unwmk. Photo. *Perf. 11½*

Designs: 1p, Striped gardener bower birds. 3p, New Guinea regent bower birds. 5p, Blue birds of paradise. 6p, Lawes six-wired birds of paradise. 8p, Sickle-billed birds of paradise. 1sh, Emperor birds of paradise. 2sh, Brown sickle-billed bird of paradise. 2sh3p, Lesser bird of paradise. 3sh, Magnificent bird of paradise. 5sh, Twelve-wired bird of paradise. 10sh, Magnificent rifle birds.

Birds in Natural Colors

Size: 21x26mm

188 A42	1p	brt citron & dk brn	.15	.15
189 A42	3p	gray & dk brown	.20	.15
190 A42	5p	salmon pink & blk	.20	.15
191 A42	6p	pale grn & sepia	.30	.20
192 A42	8p	pale lilac & dk brn	.45	.25

Size: 25x36mm

193 A42	1sh	salmon & blk	.60	.45
194 A42	2sh	blue & dk brn	2.00	1.25
195 A42	2sh3p	lt green & dk brn	3.00	1.75
196 A42	3sh	yellow & dk brn	3.25	2.25
197 A42	5sh	lt ultra & dk brn	9.00	5.00
198 A42	10sh	gray & dk blue	8.00	6.00
		Nos. 188-198 (11)	27.15	17.60

Issued: 6p, 8p, 1sh, 10sh, 10/28/64; others, 1/20/65.

Carved Crocodile's Head — A43

Designs: Wood carvings from Sepik River Region used as ship's prows and as objects of religious veneration.

1965, Mar. 24 Photo. *Perf. 11½*

199 A43	4p	multicolored	.50	.20
200 A43	1sh2p	gray brown, bister & dk brown	2.00	1.50
201 A43	1sh6p	lilac, dk brn & buff	.85	.65
202 A43	4sh	blue, dk vio & mar	2.50	2.00
		Nos. 199-202 (4)	5.85	4.35

"Simpson and His Donkey" by Wallace Anderson — A43a

1965, Apr. 14 *Perf. 13½x13*

203 A43a	2sh3p brt grn, sep & blk	1.00	1.00

ANZAC issue. See note after Australia No. 387.

Urbanized Community and Stilt House — A44

Design: 1sh, Stilt house at left.

1965, July 7 Photo. *Perf. 11½*

204 A44	6p	multicolored	.25	.16
205 A44	1sh	multicolored	.50	.50

6th South Pacific Conf., Lae, July, 1965.

UN Emblem, Mother and Child — A45

UN Emblem and: 1sh, Globe and orbit, vert. 2sh, Four globes in orbit, vert.

1965, Oct. 13 Unwmk. *Perf. 11½*

206 A45	6p	brown, grnsh bl & dp bl	.22	.18
207 A45	1sh	dull pur, blue & org	.42	.42
208 A45	2sh	dp blue, pale grn & grn	.55	.55
		Nos. 206-208 (3)	1.19	1.15

20th anniversary of the United Nations.

New Guinea Birdwing — A46

Molala Harai and Paiva Streamer — A47

Discus — A48

Butterflies: 1c, Blue emperor, vert. 3c, White-banded map butterfly, vert. 4c, Mountain swallow-tail, vert. 5c, Port Moresby terinos, vert. 12c, Blue crow. 15c, Euchenor butterfly. 20c, White-spotted parthenos. 25c, Orange Jezebel. 50c, New Guinea emperor. $1, Blue-spotted leaf-wing. $2, Paradise birdwing.

Myths of Elema People: 7c, Marai, the fisherman. 30c, Meavea Kivovia and the Black Cockatoo. 60c, Toivita Tapaivita (symbolic face decorations).

1966 Photo. *Perf. 11½*
Granite Paper

209 A46	1c	salmon, blk & aqua	.15	.15
210 A47	2c	black & carmine	.16	.16
211 A46	3c	gray grn, brn & org	.15	.15
212 A46	4c	multicolored	.16	.15
213 A46	5c	multicolored	.18	.15
214 A47	7c	blue, blk & yel	.45	.40
215 A46	10c	multicolored	.40	.35
216 A46	12c	salmon & multi	1.00	1.00
217 A46	15c	pale vio, dk brn & buff	1.00	.80
218 A46	20c	yel bister, dk brn & yel orange	1.50	1.00
219 A46	25c	gray, blk & yel	3.00	2.00
220 A47	30c	blk, yel grn & car	1.50	.90
221 A46	50c	multicolored	4.50	3.25
222 A47	60c	blk, org & car	3.00	2.50
223 A46	$1	pale blue, dk brn & dp org	5.75	5.00
224 A46	$2	multicolored	10.00	9.00
		Nos. 209-224 (16)	32.90	26.96

In 1967 Courvoisier made new plates for the $1 and $2. Stamps from these plates show many minor differences and slight variations in shade.

Issued: 12c, 10/10: A47, 6/8; others, 2/14.

1966, Aug. 31 *Perf. 11½*
Granite Paper

225 A48	5c	shown	.15	.15
226 A48	10c	Soccer	.55	.55
227 A48	20c	Tennis	.70	.70
		Nos. 225-227 (3)	1.40	1.40

Second South Pacific Games, Noumea, New Caledonia, Dec. 8-18.

d'Albertis' Creeper — A49

Book and Pen ("Fine Arts") — A50

Flowers: 10c, Tecomanthe dendrophila. 20c, Rhododendron macgregoriae. 60c, Rhododendron konori.

1966, Dec. 7 Photo. *Perf. 11½*

228 A49	5c	multicolored	.16	.15
229 A49	10c	multicolored	.40	.40
230 A49	20c	multicolored	.70	.70
231 A49	60c	multicolored	2.00	2.00
		Nos. 228-231 (4)	3.26	3.25

1967, Feb. 8 Photo. *Perf. 12½x12*

Designs: 3c, "Surveying," transit, view finder and pencil. 4c, "Civil Engineering," buildings and compass. 5c, "Science," test tubes and chemical formula. 20c, "Justice," Justitia and scales.

232 A50	1c	orange & multi	.15	.15
233 A50	3c	blue & multi	.15	.15
234 A50	4c	brown & multi	.15	.15
235 A50	5c	green & multi	.16	.16
236 A50	20c	pink & multi	.70	.70
		Nos. 232-236 (5)	1.31	1.31

Issued to publicize the development of the University of Papua and New Guinea and the Institute of Higher Technical Education.

Leaf Beetle — A51

Hydroelectric Power — A52

Beetles: 10c, Eupholus schoenherri. 20c, Sphingnotus albertisi. 25c, Cyphogastra albertisi.

1967, Apr. 12 Unwmk. *Perf. 11½*

237 A51	5c	blue & multi	.16	.16
238 A51	10c	lt green & multi	.40	.40
239 A51	20c	rose & multi	.65	.65
240 A51	25c	yellow & multi	.85	.85
		Nos. 237-240 (4)	2.06	2.06

1967, June 28 Photo. *Perf. 12x12½*

Designs: 10c, Pyrethrum (Chrysanthemum cinerariaefolium). 20c, Tea. 25c, like 5c.

241 A52	5c	multicolored	.15	.15
242 A52	10c	multicolored	.32	.32
243 A52	20c	multicolored	.50	.50
244 A52	25c	multicolored	.65	.65
		Nos. 241-244 (4)	1.62	1.62

Completion of part of the Laloki River Hydroelectric Works near Port Moresby, and the Hydrological Decade (UNESCO), 1965-74.

Battle of Milne Bay — A53

Designs: 5c, Soldiers on Kokoda Trail, vert. 20c, The coast watchers. 50c, Battle of the Coral Sea.

1967, Aug. 30 Unwmk. *Perf. 11½*

245 A53	2c	multicolored	.15	.15
246 A53	5c	multicolored	.15	.15
247 A53	20c	multicolored	.50	.50
248 A53	50c	multicolored	1.25	1.25
		Nos. 245-248 (4)	2.05	2.05

25th anniv. of the battles in the Pacific, which stopped the Japanese from occupying Papua and New Guinea.

Pesquet's Parrot — A54

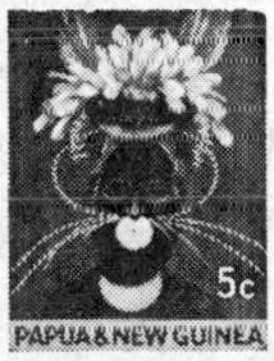

Chimbu District Headdress — A55

Parrots: 5c, Fairy lory. 20c, Dusk-orange lory. 25c, Edward's fig parrot.

1967, Nov. 29 Photo. *Perf. 12*

249 A54	5c	multicolored	.15	.15
250 A54	7c	multicolored	.25	.25
251 A54	20c	multicolored	.70	.70
252 A54	25c	multicolored	.90	.90
		Nos. 249-252 (4)	2.00	2.00

Perf. 12x12½, 12½x12
1968, Feb. 21 Photo. Unwmk.

Headdress from: 10c, Southern Highlands District, horiz. 20c, Western Highlands District, horiz. 60c, Chimbu District (different from 5c).

253 A55	5c	multicolored	.15	.15
254 A55	10c	multicolored	.20	.15
255 A55	20c	multicolored	.42	.32
256 A55	60c	multicolored	1.40	1.00
		Nos. 253-256 (4)	2.17	1.62

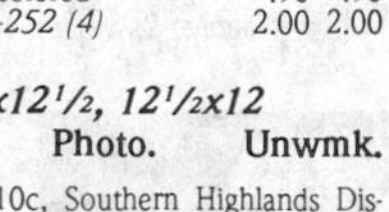

Frogs — A56

1968, Apr. 24 Photo. *Perf. 11½*

257 A56	5c	Tree	.20	.20
258 A56	10c	Tree, diff.	.45	.45
259 A56	15c	Swamp	.65	.65
260 A56	20c	Tree, diff.	.90	.85
		Nos. 257-260 (4)	2.20	2.15

Human Rights Flame and Headdress A57

Symbolic Designs: 10c, Human Rights Flame surrounded by the world. 20c, 25c, "Universal Suffrage" in 2 abstract designs.

1968, June 26 Litho. *Perf. 14x13*

261 A57	5c	black & multi	.15	.15
262 A57	10c	black & multi	.30	.30
263 A57	20c	black & multi	.75	.55
264 A57	25c	black & multi	.85	.75
		Nos. 261-264 (4)	2.05	1.75

Issued for Human Rights Year, 1968, and to publicize free elections.

Frilled Clam — A58

Sea Shells: 1c, Egg cowry. 3c, Crested stromb. 4c, Lithograph bone. 5c, Marble cone. 7c, Orange-spotted miter. 10c, Red volute. 12c, Checkerboard helmet shell. 15c, Scorpion shell. 25c, Chocolate-flamed Venus shell. 30c, Giant murex. 40c, Chambered nautilus. 60c, Triton's trumpet. $1, Emerald snails. $2, Glory of the sea, vert.

Perf. 12½x12, 12x12½
1968-69 Photo.
Granite Paper

265 A58	1c	multicolored	.15	.15
266 A58	3c	multicolored	.15	.15
267 A58	4c	multicolored	.18	.15
268 A58	5c	multicolored	.25	.15
269 A58	7c	multicolored	.35	.18
270 A58	10c	multicolored	.45	.30
271 A58	12c	multicolored	.65	.45
272 A58	15c	multicolored	.75	.50
273 A58	20c	multicolored	.85	.55
274 A58	25c	multicolored	1.25	.85
275 A58	30c	multicolored	1.50	1.10
276 A58	40c	multicolored	2.50	1.50
277 A58	60c	multicolored	3.00	2.00
278 A58	$1	multicolored	5.00	4.25
279 A58	$2	multicolored	13.00	8.50
		Nos. 265-279 (15)	30.03	20.78

Issued: 5c, 20c, 25c, 30c, 60c, 8/28/68; 3c, 10c, 15c, 40c, $1, 10/30/68; others, 1/29/69.

Legend of Tito-Iko — A59

Fireball Class Sailboat, Port Moresby Harbor — A60

Myths of Elema People: No. 281, 5c inscribed "Iko." No. 282, 10c inscribed "Luvuapo." No. 283, 10c inscribed "Miro."

#280 & 282:
Perf. 12½x13½xRoul. 9xPerf. 13½
#281 & 283:
Roul. 9 x Perf. 13½x12½x13½

1969, Apr. 9 Litho. Unwmk.

280 A59	5c	black, yellow & red	.16	.15
281 A59	5c	black, yellow & red	.16	.15
a.		Vert. pair, #280-281	.32	.32
282 A59	10c	black, gray & red	.40	.35
283 A59	10c	black, gray & red	.40	.35
a.		Vert. pair, #282-283	.80	.80
		Nos. 280-283 (4)	1.12	1.00

Nos. 281a, 283a have continuous designs, rouletted between.

Perf. 14x14½, 14½x14
1969, June 25 Engr.

Designs: 10c, Games' swimming pool, Boroko, horiz. 20c, Main Games area, Konedobu, horiz.

284 A60	5c	black	.16	.16
285 A60	10c	bright violet	.35	.35
286 A60	20c	green	.65	.65
		Nos. 284-286 (3)	1.16	1.16

3rd S. Pacific Games, Port Moresby, Aug. 13-23.

Dendrobium Ostrinoglossum A61

Potter A62

Orchids: 10c, Dendrobium lawesii. 20c, Dendrobium pseudofrigidum. 30c, Dendrobium conanthum.

1969, Aug. 27 Photo. *Perf. 11½*
Granite Paper

287 A61	5c	multicolored	.20	.20
288 A61	10c	multicolored	.50	.40
289 A61	20c	multicolored	.85	.85
290 A61	30c	multicolored	1.50	1.40
		Nos. 287-290 (4)	3.05	2.85

Issued to publicize the 6th World Orchid Conference, Sydney, Australia, Sept. 1969.

1969, Sept. 24 Photo. *Perf. 11½*
Granite Paper

291 A62	5c	multicolored	.28	.20

50th anniv. of the ILO.

Bird of Paradise A63

Seed Pod Rattle (Tareko) A64

Coil Stamps

1969-71 *Perf. 14½ Horiz.*

291A	A63 2c	red, dp blue & blk	.15	.15
292	A63 5c	orange & emerald	.20	.15
		Set value	.30	.20

Issue dates: 5c, Sept. 24; 2c, Apr. 1, 1971.

1969, Oct. 29 Photo. *Perf. 12½*

Musical Instruments: 10c, Hand drum (garamut). 25c, Pan pipes (iviliko). 30c, Hourglass drum (kundu).

293 A64	5c	multicolored	.13	.13
294 A64	10c	multicolored	.38	.28
295 A64	25c	multicolored	.90	.70
296 A64	30c	multicolored	1.10	.80
		Nos. 293-296 (4)	2.53	1.93

Prehistoric Ambum Stone and Skull — A65

Designs: 10c, Masawa canoe of the Kula Circuit. 25c, Map of Papua and New Guinea made by Luis Valez de Torres, 1606. 30c, H.M.S. Basilisk, 1873.

1970, Feb. 11 Photo. *Perf. 12½*

297 A65	5c	violet brown & multi	.16	.15
298 A65	10c	ocher & multi	.38	.30
299 A65	25c	orange brown & multi	.95	.75
300 A65	20c	olive green & multi	1.25	.95
		Nos. 297-300 (4)	2.74	2.15

Papua New Guinea stamps can be mounted in the Scott Australian Dependencies album.

King of Saxony Bird of Paradise — A66

Birds of Paradise: 10c, King. 15c, Augusta Victoria. 25c, Multi-crested.

1970, May 13 Photo. *Perf. 11½*

301 A66	5c tan & multi	.50	.20
302 A66	10c multicolored	1.00	.45
303 A66	15c lt blue & multi	2.00	1.40
304 A66	25c multicolored	3.50	2.00
	Nos. 301-304 (4)	7.00	4.05

Canceled to Order

Starting in 1970 or earlier, the Philatelic Bureau at Port Moresby began to sell new issues canceled to order at face value.

Douglas DC-3 and Matupi Volcano — A67

Aircraft: No. 305, DC-6B and Mt. Wilhelm. No. 306, Lockheed Mark II Electra and Mt. Yule. No. 307, Boeing 727 and Mt. Giluwe. No. 308, Fokker F27 Friendship and Manam Island Volcano. 30c, Boeing 707 and Hombom's Bluff.

1970, July 8 Photo. *Perf. 14½x14*

305 A67	5c "TAA" on tail	.16	.16
306 A67	5c Striped tail	.16	.16
307 A67	5c "T" on tail	.16	.16
308 A67	5c Red tail	.16	.16
a.	Block of 4, #305-308	.65	.65
309 A67	25c multicolored	1.10	1.00
310 A67	30c multicolored	1.40	1.10
	Nos. 305-310 (6)	3.14	2.74

Development of air service during the last 25 years between Australia and New Guinea.

Nicolaus N. de Miklouho-Maclay, Explorer, and Mask — A68

Designs: 10c, Bronislaw Kaspar Malinowski, anthropologist, and hut. 15c, Count Tommaso Salvadori, ornithologist, and cassowary. 20c, Friedrich R. Schlechter, botanist, and orchid.

1970, Aug. 19 Photo. *Perf. 11½*

311 A68	5c brown, blk & lilac	.16	.16
312 A68	10c multicolored	.42	.32
313 A68	15c dull lilac & multi	.70	.55
314 A68	20c slate & multi	1.20	.85
	Nos. 311-314 (4)	2.48	1.88

42nd Cong. of the Australian and New Zealand Assoc. for the Advancement of Science, Port Moresby, Aug. 17-21.

Wogeo Island Food Bowl — A69

Eastern Highlands Round House — A70

National Handicraft: 10c, Lime pot. 15c, Aibom sago storage pot. 30c, Manus Island bowl, horiz.

1970, Oct. 28 Photo. *Perf. 12½*

315 A69	5c multicolored	.18	.18
316 A69	10c multicolored	.42	.42
317 A69	15c multicolored	.60	.60
318 A69	30c multicolored	1.25	1.10
	Nos. 315-318 (4)	2.45	2.30

1971, Jan. 27 Photo. *Perf. 11½*

Local Architecture: 7c, Milne Bay house. 10c, Purari Delta house. 40c, Sepik or Men's Spirit House.

319 A70	5c dark olive & multi	.20	.16
320 A70	7c Prus blue & multi	.32	.30
321 A70	10c deep orange & multi	.50	.42
322 A70	40c brown & multi	1.50	1.25
	Nos. 319-322 (4)	2.52	2.13

Spotted Cuscus — A71

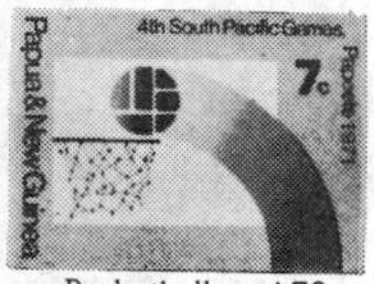

Basketball — A72

Animals: 10c, Brown and white striped possum. 15c, Feather-tailed possum. 25c, Spiny anteater, horiz. 30c, Good-fellow's tree-climbing kangaroo, horiz.

1971, Mar. 31 Photo. *Perf. 11½*

323 A71	5c blue green & multi	.30	.20
324 A71	10c multicolored	.75	.50
325 A71	15c multicolored	1.25	.85
326 A71	25c dull yellow & multi	1.90	1.10
327 A71	30c olive & multi	2.50	1.50
	Nos. 323-327 (5)	6.70	4.15

1971, June 9 Litho. *Perf. 14*

328 A72	7c shown	.24	.24
329 A72	14c Yachting	.45	.42
330 A72	21c Boxing	.85	.65
331 A72	28c Field events	1.00	.85
	Nos. 328-331 (4)	2.54	2.16

Fourth South Pacific Games, Papeete, French Polynesia, Sept. 8-19.

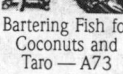

Bartering Fish for Coconuts and Taro — A73

Siaa Dancer — A74

Primary industries: 9c, Man stacking yams and taro. 14c, Market scene. 30c, Farm couple tending yams.

1971, Aug. 18 Photo. *Perf. 11½*

332 A73	7c multicolored	.28	.25
333 A73	9c multicolored	.50	.40
334 A73	14c multicolored	.75	.60
335 A73	30c multicolored	1.50	1.40
	Nos. 332-335 (4)	3.03	2.65

1971, Oct. 27 Photo. *Perf. 11½*

Designs: 9c, Urasena masked dancer. 20c, Two Siassi masked dancers, horiz. 28c, Three Siaa dancers, horiz.

336 A74	7c orange & multi	.20	.20
337 A74	9c yel green & multi	.40	.38
338 A74	20c bister & multi	1.10	1.00
339 A74	28c multicolored	1.75	1.50
	Nos. 336-339 (4)	3.45	3.08

Papua New Guinea and Australia Arms — A75

Design: No. 341, Papua New Guinea and Australia flags.

1972, Jan. 26 *Perf. 12½x12*

340 A75	7c gray blue, org & blk	.45	.32
341 A75	7c gray blue, blk, red & yel	.45	.32
a.	Pair, #340-341	.90	.65

Constitutional development for the 1972 House of Assembly elections.

Papua New Guinea Map, South Pacific Commission Emblem — A76

Design: No. 343, Man's head and South Pacific Commission flag.

1972, Jan. 26

342 A76	15c brt green & multi	1.00	.60
343 A76	15c brt green & multi	1.00	.60
a.	Pair, #342-343	2.00	1.25

South Pacific Commission, 25th anniv.

Pitted-shelled Turtle — A77

Designs: 14c, Angle-headed agamid. 21c, Green python. 30c, Water monitor.

1972, Mar. 15 Photo. *Perf. 11½*

344 A77	7c multicolored	.38	.18
345 A77	14c car rose & multi	1.25	.55
346 A77	21c yellow & multi	1.65	.80
347 A77	30c yel green & multi	2.00	1.25
	Nos. 344-347 (4)	5.28	2.78

Curtiss Seagull MF 6 and Ship A78

Designs: 14c, De Havilland 37 and porters from gold fields. 20c, Junkers G 31 and heavy machinery. 25c, Junkers F 13 and Lutheran mission church.

1972, June 7

Granite Paper

348 A78	7c dp yellow & multi	.30	.24
349 A78	14c dp orange & multi	.85	.55
350 A78	20c olive & multi	1.40	.85
351 A78	25c multicolored	1.65	.90
	Nos. 348-351 (4)	4.20	2.54

50th anniv. of aviation in Papua New Guinea.

National Day Unity Emblem — A79

Designs: 10c, Unity emblem and kundu (drum). 30c, United emblem and conch.

1972, Aug. 16 *Perf. 12x12½*

352 A79	7c violet blue & multi	.16	.16
353 A79	10c orange & multi	.65	.40
354 A79	30c vermilion & multi	1.40	.90
	Nos. 352-354 (3)	2.21	1.46

National Day, Sept. 15, 1972.

Rev. Copland King — A80

Pioneering Missionaries: No. 356, Pastor Ruatoka. No. 357, Bishop Stanislaus Henry Verjus. No. 358, Rev. Dr. Johannes Flierl.

1972, Oct. 25 Photo. *Perf. 11½*

355 A80	7c dark blue & multi	.60	.45
356 A80	7c dark red & multi	.60	.45
357 A80	7c dark green & multi	.60	.45
358 A80	7c dark olive bister & multi	.60	.45
	Nos. 355-358 (4)	2.40	1.80

Christmas 1972.

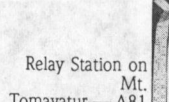

Relay Station on Mt. Tomavatur — A81

1973, Jan. 24 Photo. *Perf. 12½*

359 A81	7c shown	.48	.24
360 A81	7c Mt. Kerigomna	.48	.24
361 A81	7c Sattelburg	.48	.24
362 A81	7c Wideru	.48	.24
a.	Block of 4, #359-362	2.00	1.25
363 A81	9c Teleprinter	.75	.30
364 A81	30c Map of network	2.25	1.25
	Nos. 359-364 (6)	4.92	2.51

Telecommunications development 1968-1972. No. 362a has a unifying frame.

Queen Carol's Bird of Paradise — A82

Birds of Paradise: 14c, Goldie's. 21c, Ribbon-tailed astrapia. 28c, Princess Stephanie's.

1973, Mar. 30 Photo. *Perf. 11½*

Size: 22½x38mm

365 A82	7c citron & multi	.70	.45
366 A82	14c dull green & multi	1.50	.85

Size: 17x48mm

367 A82	21c lemon & multi	2.00	1.25
368 A82	28c lt blue & multi	3.00	1.75
	Nos. 365-368 (4)	7.20	4.30

Wood Carver, Milne Bay — A83

Designs: 3c, Wig makers, Southern Highlands. 5c, Bagana Volcano, Bougainville. 6c, Pig Exchange, Western Highlands. 7c, Coastal village, Central District. 8c, Arawe mother, West New Britain. 9c, Fire dancers, East New Britain. 10c, Tifalmin hunter, West Sepik District. 14c, Crocodile hunters, Western District. 15c, Mt. Elimbari, Chimbu. 20c, Canoe racing, Manus District. 21c, Making sago, Gulf District. 25c, Council House, East Sepik. 28c, Menyamya bowmen, Morobe. 30c, Shark snaring, New Ireland. 40c, Fishing canoes, Madang. 60c, Women making tapa cloth, Northern District. $1, Asaro mudmen, Eastern Highlands. $2, Sing festival, Enga District.

1973-74 Photo. *Perf. 11½*

Granite Paper

369 A83	1c multicolored	.15	.15
370 A83	3c multi ('74)	.15	.15
371 A83	5c multicolored	.15	.15
372 A83	6c multi ('74)	.16	.15
373 A83	7c multicolored	.20	.15
374 A83	8c multi ('74)	.20	.15
375 A83	9c multicolored	.26	.16
376 A83	10c multi ('74)	.26	.18
377 A83	14c multicolored	.38	.18
378 A83	15c multicolored	.42	.28
379 A83	20c multi ('74)	.55	.38
380 A83	21c multicolored	.55	.38
381 A83	25c multicolored	.70	.45
382 A83	28c multicolored	.80	.52
383 A83	30c multicolored	.80	.55
385 A83	40c multicolored	1.00	.80
386 A83	60c multi ('74)	1.65	1.00
387 A83	$1 multi ('74)	6.00	3.50
388 A83	$2 multi ('74)	10.00	6.00
	Nos. 369-383,385-388 (19)	24.38	15.28

Issue dates: 1c, 7c, 9c, 15c, 25c, 40c, June 13. 5c, 14c, 21c, 28c, 30c, Aug.

Papua New Guinea No. 7 A84

Designs: 1c, German New Guinea Nos. 1-2. 6c, German New Guinea No. 17. 7c, New Britain No. 43. 25c, New Guinea No. 1. 30c, Papua New Guinea No. 108.

Litho. (1c, 7c); Litho. & Engr. (others)
1973, Oct. 24   Perf. 13½x14

Size: 54x31mm

389	A84	1c gold, brn, grn & blk	.15	.15
390	A84	6c silver, blue & indigo	.32	.32
391	A84	7c gold, red, blk & buff	.40	.40

Perf. 14x14½
Size: 45x38mm

392	A84	9c gold, org, blk & brn	.50	.50
393	A84	25c gold & orange	1.50	1.50
394	A84	30c silver & dp lilac	1.65	1.65
		Nos. 389-394 (6)	4.52	4.52

75th anniv. of stamps in Papua New Guinea.

Masks — A85

1973, Dec. 5   Photo.   Perf. 12½
Granite Paper

395	A85	7c multicolored	.35	.30
396	A85	10c violet blue & multi	.65	.55

Self-government.

Queen Elizabeth II — A86

1974, Feb. 22   Photo.   Perf. 14x14½

397	A86	7c dp carmine & multi	.30	.30
398	A86	30c vio blue & multi	1.65	1.50

Visit of Queen Elizabeth II and the Royal Family, Feb. 22-27.

Wreathed Hornbill A87

Size of No. 400, 32½x48mm.

Perf. 12, 11½ (10c)
1974, June 12   Photo.
Granite Paper

399	A87	7c shown	1.50	1.25
400	A87	10c Great cassowary	2.50	2.25
401	A87	10c Kapul eagle	6.00	5.50
		Nos. 399-401 (3)	10.00	9.00

Dendrobium Bracteosum — A88

Orchids: 10c, Dendrobium anosmum. 20c, Dendrobium smillieae. 30c, Dendrobium insigne.

1974, Nov. 20   Photo.   Perf. 11½
Granite Paper

402	A88	7c dark green & multi	.35	.20
403	A88	10c dark blue & multi	.50	.28
404	A88	20c bister & multi	1.00	.55
405	A88	30c green & multi	1.75	.80
		Nos. 402-405 (4)	3.60	1.83

Motu Lakatoi A89

Traditional Canoes: 10c, Tami two-master morobe. 25c, Aramia racing canoe. 30c, Buka Island canoe.

1975, Feb. 26   Photo.   Perf. 11½
Granite Paper

406	A89	7c multicolored	.22	.22
407	A89	10c orange & multi	.40	.32
408	A89	25c apple green & multi	1.10	.95
409	A89	30c citron & multi	1.40	1.10
		Nos. 406-409 (4)	3.12	2.59

Paradise Birdwing Butterfly, 1t Coin — A90

Ornate Butterfly Cod on 2t and Plateless Turtle on 5t — A91

New coinage: 10t, Cuscus on 10t. 20t, Cassowary on 20t. 1k, River crocodiles on 1k coin with center hole; obverse and reverse of 1k.

Perf. 11, 11½ (A91)
1975, Apr. 21   Photo.
Granite Paper

410	A90	1t green & multi	.15	.15
411	A91	7t brown & multi	.32	.18
412	A90	10t violet blue & multi	.45	.25
413	A91	20t carmine & multi	.60	.50
414	A91	1k dull blue & multi	4.50	2.75
		Nos. 410-414 (5)	6.02	3.83

Ornithoptera Alexandrae — A92

Boxing and Games' Emblem — A93

Birdwing Butterflies: 10t, O. victoriae regis. 30t, O. allottei. 40t, O. chimaera.

1975, June 11   Photo.   Perf. 11½
Granite Paper

415	A92	7t multicolored	.28	.20
416	A92	10t multicolored	.40	.30
417	A92	30t multicolored	1.40	.90
418	A92	40t multicolored	2.00	1.20
		Nos. 415-418 (4)	4.08	2.60

1975, Aug. 2   Photo.   Perf. 11½
Granite Paper

419	A93	7t shown	.25	.22
420	A93	20t Track and field	.70	.60
421	A93	25t Basketball	.90	.75
422	A93	30t Swimming	1.25	.90
		Nos. 419-422 (4)	3.10	2.47

5th South Pacific Games, Guam, Aug. 1-10.

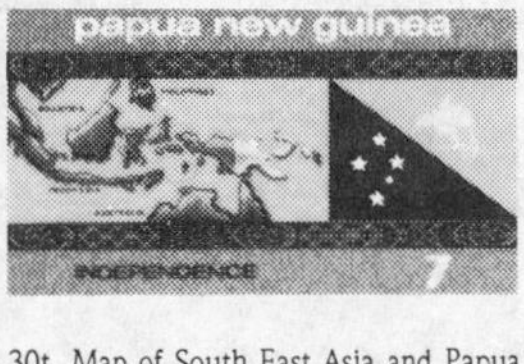

Map of South East Asia and Flag of PNG A94

Design: 30t, Map of South East Asia and Papua New Guinea coat of arms.

1975, Sept. 10   Photo.   Perf. 11½
Granite Paper

423	A94	7t red & multi	.28	.28
424	A94	30t blue & multi	1.10	1.10
a.		Souvenir sheet of 2, #423-424	2.00	2.00

Papua New Guinea independence, Sept. 16, 1975.

M. V. Bulolo A95

Ships of the 1930's: 15t, M.V. Macdhui. 25t, M.V. Malaita. 60t, S.S. Montoro.

1976, Jan. 21   Photo.   Perf. 11½
Granite Paper

425	A95	7t multicolored	.24	.15
426	A95	15t multicolored	.42	.28
427	A95	25t multicolored	.70	.45
428	A95	60t multicolored	1.65	1.25
		Nos. 425-428 (4)	3.01	2.13

Rorovana Carvings — A96

Bougainville Art: 20t, Upe hats. 25t, Kapkaps (tortoise shell ornaments). 30t, Carved canoe paddles.

1976, Mar. 17   Photo.   Perf. 11½
Granite Paper

429	A96	7t multicolored	.25	.22
430	A96	20t blue & multi	.75	.60
431	A96	25t dp orange & multi	.90	.75
432	A96	30t multicolored	1.10	.90
		Nos. 429-432 (4)	3.00	2.47

Houses — A97

1976, June 9   Photo.   Perf. 11½
Granite Paper

433	A97	7t Rabaul	.25	.15
434	A97	15t Aramia	.50	.35
435	A97	30t Telefomin	.90	.75
436	A97	40t Tapini	1.40	.90
		Nos. 433-436 (4)	3.05	2.15

Boy Scouts and Scout Emblem A98

De Havilland Sea Plane, Map of Pacific — A99

Designs: 15t, Sea Scouts on outrigger canoe, Scout emblem. 60t, Plane on water.

1976, Aug. 18   Photo.   Perf. 11½
Granite Paper

437	A98	7t multicolored	.22	.18
438	A99	10t lilac & multi	.32	.25
439	A99	15t multicolored	.60	.38
440	A99	60t multicolored	1.90	1.50
		Nos. 437-440 (4)	3.04	2.31

50th anniversaries: Papua New Guinea Boy Scouts; 1st flight from Australia.

Father Ross and Mt. Hagen — A100

1976, Oct. 28   Photo.   Perf. 11½
Granite Paper

441	A100	7t multicolored	.45	.30

Rev. Father William Ross (1896-1973), American missionary in New Guinea.

Clouded Rainbow Fish A101

Tropical Fish: 15t, Imperial angelfish. 30t, Freckled rock cod. 40t, Threadfin butterflyfish.

1976, Oct. 28
Granite Paper

442	A101	5t multicolored	.24	.16
443	A101	10t multicolored	.70	.48
444	A101	30t multicolored	1.40	.85
445	A101	40t multicolored	1.65	1.10
		Nos. 442-445 (4)	3.99	2.59

Kundiawa Man — A102

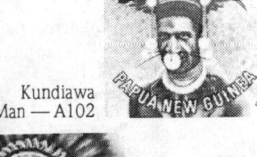

Mekeo Headdress A103

Headdresses: 5t, Masked dancer, East Sepik Province. 10t, Dancer, Koiari area. 15t, Hanuabada woman. 20t, Young woman, Orokaiva. 25t, Haus Tambaran dancer, East Sepik Province. 30t, Asaro Valley man. 35t, Garaina man, Morobe. 40t, Waghi Valley man. 50t, Trobriand dancer, Milne Bay. 1k, Wasara.

Perf. 11½ (1, 5, 10, 20, 35, 40, 50t),
12 (15, 25, 30t), Perf 14½x14 (1k),
14½x15 (2k)
1977-78   Photo.
Size: 25x30mm (1, 5, 20t), 26x26mm
(10, 15, 25, 30, 50t), 23x38mm
(35, 40t), 28x35½mm (1k),
33x23mm (2k)

446	A102	1t multicolored	.15	.15
447	A102	5t multicolored	.15	.15
448	A102	10t multicolored	.24	.24
449	A102	15t multicolored	.35	.35
450	A102	20t multicolored	.48	.48
451	A102	25t multicolored	.60	.60
452	A102	30t multicolored	.70	.70
453	A102	35t multicolored	.80	.80
454	A102	40t multicolored	.90	.90
455	A102	50t multicolored	1.25	1.25

Litho.

456	A102	1k multicolored	2.50	2.50
457	A103	2k multicolored	4.75	4.75
		Nos. 446-457 (12)	12.87	12.87

Issued: #456-457, Jan. 12, 1977; #448, 450, 453, 455, June 7, 1978; others, Mar. 29, 1978.

Elizabeth II and P.N.G. Arms A104

Designs: 7t, Queen and P.N.G. flag. 35t, Queen and map of P.N.G.

1977, Mar. 16   Photo.   Perf. 15x14

462	A104	7t multicolored	.25	.16
463	A104	15t multicolored	.50	.40
464	A104	35t multicolored	1.10	1.00
		Nos. 462-464 (3)	1.85	1.56

25th anniv. of the reign of Elizabeth II.

Whitebreasted Ground Dove — A105

Protected Birds: 7t, Victoria crowned pigeon. 15t, Pheasant pigeon. 30t, Orange-fronted fruit dove. 50t, Banded imperial pigeon.

1977, June 8　Photo.　Perf. 11½
Granite Paper

465	A105	5t multicolored	.15　.15
466	A105	7t multicolored	.25　.16
467	A105	15t multicolored	.50　.35
468	A105	30t multicolored	1.00　.65
469	A105	50t multicolored	1.75　1.10
		Nos. 465-469 (5)	3.65　2.41

Girl Guides and Gold Badge — A106

Designs (Girl Guides): 15t, Mapping and blue badge. 30t, Doing laundry in brook and red badge. 35t, Wearing grass skirts, cooking and green badge.

1977, Aug. 10　Litho.　Perf. 14½

470	A106	7t multicolored	.20　.16
471	A106	15t multicolored	.40　.35
472	A106	30t multicolored	.80　.65
473	A106	35t multicolored	1.00　.85
		Nos. 470-473 (4)	2.40　2.01

Papua New Guinea Girl Guides, 50th anniv.

Legend of Kari Marupi — A107

Myths of Elema People: 20t, Savoripi Clan. 30t, Oa-Laea. 35t, Oa-Iriarapo.

1977, Oct. 19　Litho.　Perf. 13½

474	A107	7t black & multi	.20　.16
475	A107	20t black & multi	.55　.45
476	A107	30t black & multi	.80　.65
477	A107	35t black & multi	1.00　.85
		Nos. 474-477 (4)	2.55　2.11

Blue-tailed Skink A108

Lizards: 15t, Green tree skink. 35t, Crocodile skink. 40t, New Guinea blue-tongued skink.

1978, Jan. 25　Photo.　Perf. 11½
Granite Paper

478	A108	10t blue & multi	.28　.25
479	A108	15t lilac & multi	.40　.38
480	A108	35t olive & multi	.80　.75
481	A108	40t orange & multi	1.00　.85
		Nos. 478-481 (4)	2.48　2.23

Roboastra Arika — A109

Sea Slugs: 15t, Chromodoris fidelis. 35t, Flabellina macassarana. 40t, Chromodoris trimarginata.

1978, Aug. 29　Photo.　Perf. 11½

482	A109	10t multicolored	.25　.20
483	A109	15t multicolored	.35　.28
484	A109	35t multicolored	.85　.65
485	A109	40t multicolored	1.00　.85
		Nos. 482-485 (4)	2.45　1.98

Mandated New Guinea Constabulary A110

Constabulary and Badge: 10t, Royal Papua New Guinea. 20t, Armed British New Guinea. 25t, German New Guinea police. 30t, Royal Papua and New Guinea.

1978, Oct. 26　Photo.　Perf. 14½x14

486	A110	10t multicolored	.20　.18
487	A110	15t multicolored	.30　.28
488	A110	20t multicolored	.40　.38
489	A110	25t multicolored	.50　.45
490	A110	30t multicolored	.60　.55
		Nos. 486-490 (5)	2.00　1.84

Ocarina, Chimbu Province — A111

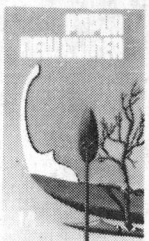

Prow and Paddle, East New Britain — A112

Musical Instruments: 20t, Musical bow, New Britain, horiz. 28t, Launut, New Ireland. 35t, Nose flute, New Hanover, horiz.

Perf. 14½x14, 14x14½
1979, Jan. 24　　　　　Litho.

491	A111	7t multicolored	.15　.15
492	A111	20t multicolored	.40　.38
493	A111	28t multicolored	.55　.50
494	A111	35t multicolored	.75　.65
		Nos. 491-494 (4)	1.85　1.68

1979, Mar. 28　Litho.　Perf. 14½

Canoe Prows and Paddles: 21t, Sepik war canoe. 25t, Trobriand Islands. 40t, Milne Bay.

495	A112	14t multicolored	.35　.30
496	A112	21t multicolored	.50　.45
497	A112	25t multicolored	.60　.55
498	A112	40t multicolored	1.00　.90
		Nos. 495-498 (4)	2.45　2.20

Belt of Shell Disks — A113

Traditional Currency: 15t, Tusk chest ornament. 25t, Shell armband. 35t, Shell necklace.

1979, June 6　Litho.　Perf. 12½x12

499	A113	7t multicolored	.15　.15
500	A113	15t multicolored	.40　.40
501	A113	25t multicolored	.65　.60
502	A113	35t multicolored	1.00　.90
		Nos. 499-502 (4)	2.20　2.05

Oenetus A114

Moths: 15t, Celerina vulgaris. 20t, Alcidis aurora, vert. 25t, Phyllodes conspicillator. 30t, Nyctalemon patroclus, vert.

1979, Aug. 29　Photo.　Perf. 11½

503	A114	7t multicolored	.16　.16
504	A114	15t multicolored	.35　.35
505	A114	20t multicolored	.40　.40
506	A114	25t multicolored	.50　.50
507	A114	40t multicolored	.65　.65
		Nos. 503-507 (5)	2.06　2.06

Baby in String Bag Scale — A115

IYC (Emblem and): 7t, Mother nursing baby. 30t, Boy playing with dog and ball. 60t, Girl in classroom.

1979, Oct. 24　Litho.　Perf. 14x13½

508	A115	7t multicolored	.16　.16
509	A115	15t multicolored	.35　.35
510	A115	30t multicolored	.65　.65
511	A115	60t multicolored	1.25　1.25
		Nos. 508-511 (4)	2.41　2.41

Mail Sorting, Mail Truck A116

UPU Membership: 25t, Wartime mail delivery. 35t, UPU monument, airport and city. 40t, Hand canceling, letter carrier.

1980, Jan. 23　Litho.　Perf. 13½x14

512	A116	7t multicolored	.15　.15
513	A116	25t multicolored	.50　.50
514	A116	35t multicolored	.75　.75
515	A116	40t multicolored	.90　.90
		Nos. 512-515 (4)	2.30　2.30

Male Dancer, Betrothal Ceremony — A117

Third South Pacific Arts Festival, Port Moresby (Minj Betrothal Ceremony Mural): No. 516 has continuous design.

1980, Mar. 26　Photo.　Perf. 11½
Granite Paper

516		Strip of 5	2.00　2.00
a.	A117	20t single stamp	.40　.40

National Census A118

1980, June 4　Litho.　Perf. 14

517	A118	7t shown	.15　.15
518	A118	15t Population symbol	.30　.30
519	A118	40t P. N. G. map	.75　.75
520	A118	50t Faces	1.00　1.00
		Nos. 517-520 (4)	2.20　2.20

Blood Transfusion, Donor's Badge — A119

1980, Aug. 27　Litho.　Perf. 14½

521	A119	7t shown	.15　.15
522	A119	15t Donating blood	.30　.30
523	A119	30t Map of donation centers	.60　.60
524	A119	60t Blood components and types	1.10　1.10
		Nos. 521-524 (4)	2.15　2.15

Dugong — A120

1980, Oct. 29　Photo.　Perf. 11½

525	A120	7t shown	.15　.15
526	A120	30t Native spotted cat, vert.	.65　.65
527	A120	35t Tube-nosed bat, vert.	.75　.75
528	A120	45t Raffray's bandicoot	1.00　1.00
		Nos. 525-528 (4)	2.55　2.55

Beach Kingfisher A121

Mask A122

1981, Jan. 21　Photo.　Perf. 12
Granite Paper

529	A121	3t shown	.15　.15
530	A121	7t Forest kingfisher	.15　.15
531	A121	20t Sacred kingfisher	.45　.45
		Size: 26x45½mm	
532	A121	25t White-tailed paradise kingfisher	.50　.50
		Size: 26x36mm	
533	A121	60t Blue-winged kookaburra	1.40　1.40
		Nos. 529-533 (5)	2.65　2.65

Coil Stamps
Perf. 14½ Horiz.
1981, Jan. 21　　　　　Photo.

534	A122	2t shown	.15　.15
535	A122	5t Hibiscus	.15　.15
		Set value	.15　.15

Defense Force Soldiers Firing Mortar A123

1981, Mar. 25　Photo.　Perf. 13½x14

536	A123	7t shown	.15　.15
537	A123	15t DC-3 military plane	.32　.32
538	A123	40t Patrol boat Eitape	.85　.85
539	A123	50t Medics treating civilians	1.00　1.00
		Nos. 536-539 (4)	2.32　2.32

For surcharge see No. 615.

Missionary Aviation Fellowship Plane — A124

Planes of Missionary Organizations: 15t, Holy Ghost Society. 20t, Summer Institute of Linguistics. 30t, Lutheran Mission. 35t, Seventh Day Adventist.

1981, June 17　Litho.　Perf. 14

540	A124	10t multicolored	.25　.25
541	A124	15t multicolored	.35　.35
542	A124	20t multicolored	.45　.45
543	A124	30t multicolored	.70　.70
544	A124	35t multicolored	.80　.80
		Nos. 540-544 (5)	2.55　2.55

Scoop Net Fishing A125

1981, Aug. 26

545	A125	10t shown	.20	.20
546	A125	15t Kite fishing	.30	.30
547	A125	30t Rod fishing	.60	.60
548	A125	60t Scissor net fishing	1.20	1.20
		Nos. 545-548 (4)	2.30	2.30

Forcartia Buhleri A126

1981, Oct. 28 Photo. *Perf. 12*
Granite Paper

549	A126	5t shown	.15	.15
550	A126	15t Naninia citrina	.35	.35
551	A126	20t Papuina adonis, papuina hermione	.45	.45
552	A126	30t Papustyla hindei, papustyla novaepommeraniae	.70	.70
553	A126	40t Rhynchotrochus strabo	.90	.90
		Nos. 549-553 (5)	2.55	2.55

75th Anniv. of Boy Scouts — A127

1982, Jan. 20 Photo. *Perf. 11½*
Granite Paper

554	A127	15t Lord Baden-Powell, flag raising	.30	.30
555	A127	25t Leader, campfire	.50	.50
556	A127	35t Scout, hut building	.65	.65
557	A127	50t Percy Chatterton, first aid	1.00	1.00
		Nos. 554-557 (4)	2.45	2.45

Wanigela Pottery A128

1982, Mar. 24 Litho. *Perf. 14*
Size: 29x29mm

558	A128	10t Boiken, East Sepik	.25	.25
559	A128	20t Gumalu, Madang	.48	.48

Perf. 14½
Size: 36x23mm

560	A128	40t shown	1.00	1.00
561	A128	50t Ramu Valley, Madang	1.25	1.25
		Nos. 558-561 (4)	2.98	2.98

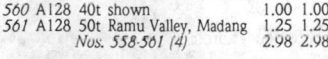

Nutrition A129

1982, May 5 Litho. *Perf. 14½x14*

562	A129	10t Mother, child	.30	.30
563	A129	15t Protein	.45	.45
564	A129	30t Fruits, vegetables	.90	.90
565	A129	40t Carbohydrates	1.20	1.20
		Nos. 562-565 (4)	2.85	2.85

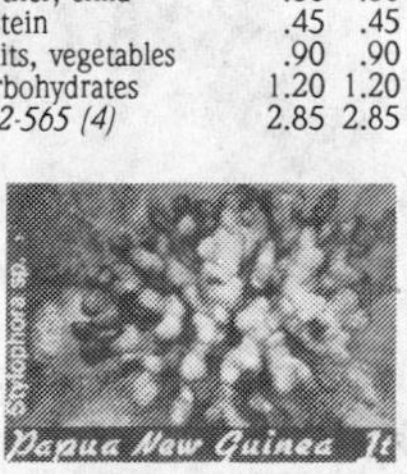

Coral — A130

1982, July 21 Photo. *Perf. 11½*
Granite Paper

566	A130	1t Stylophora sp.	.15	.15
567	A130	5t Acropora humilis	.15	.15
568	A130	15t Distichopora sp.	.30	.30
569	A130	1k Xenia sp.	2.00	2.00
		Nos. 566-569 (4)	2.60	2.60

See Nos. 575-579, 588-591, 614.

Centenary of Catholic Church in Papua New Guinea — A131

1982, Sept. 15 Photo. *Perf. 11½*

570	Strip of 3	1.00	1.00
a.	A131 10t any single	.30	.30

12th Commonwealth Games, Brisbane, Australia, Sept. 30-Oct. 9 — A132

1982, Oct. 6 Litho. *Perf. 14½*

571	A132	10t Running	.20	.20
572	A132	15t Boxing	.30	.30
573	A132	45t Shooting	.90	.90
574	A132	50t Lawn bowling	1.00	1.00
		Nos. 571-574 (4)	2.40	2.40

Coral Type of 1982

1983, Jan. 12 Photo. *Perf. 11½*
Granite Paper

575	A130	3t Dendrophyllia	.15	.15
576	A130	10t Dendronephthya	.20	.20
577	A130	30t Dendrone-phthya, diff.	.65	.65
578	A130	40t Antipathes	.90	.70
579	A130	3k Distichopora	7.00	7.00
		Nos. 575-579 (5)	8.90	8.70

Nos. 575-579 vert.

Commonwealth Day — A133

1983, Mar. 9 Litho. *Perf. 14*

580	A133	10t Flag, arms	.20	.20
581	A133	15t Youth, recreation	.30	.30
582	A133	20t Technical assistance	.40	.40
583	A133	50t Export assistance	1.00	1.00
		Nos. 580-583 (4)	1.90	1.90

World Communications Year — A134

1983, Sept. 7 Litho. *Perf. 14*

584	A134	10t Mail transport	.20	.20
585	A134	25t Writing & receiving letter	.50	.50
586	A134	30t Telephone calls	.60	.60
587	A134	60t Family reunion	1.20	1.20
		Nos. 584-587 (4)	2.50	2.50

Coral Type of 1982

1983, Nov. 9 Photo. *Perf. 11½*

588	A130	20t Isis sp.	.60	.60
589	A130	25t Acropora sp.	1.00	1.00
590	A130	35t Stylaster elegans	1.50	1.50
591	A130	45t Turbinarea sp.	1.90	1.90
		Nos. 588-591 (4)	5.00	5.00

Nos. 588-591 vert.

Turtles — A135

1984, Feb. 8 Photo.
Granite Paper

592	A135	5t Chelonia depressa	.20	.20
593	A135	10t Chelonia mydas	.40	.40
594	A135	15t Eretkmochelys imbricata	.60	.60
595	A135	20t Lepidochelys olivacea	.75	.75
596	A135	25t Caretta caretta	.95	.95
597	A135	40t Dermochelys coriacea	1.65	1.65
		Nos. 592-597 (6)	4.55	4.55

Papua-Australia Airmail Service, 50th Anniv. A136

Mail planes.

1984, May 9 Litho. *Perf. 14½x14*

598	A136	20t Avro X VH-UXX	.65	.65
599	A136	25t DH86B VH-UYU Carmania	.80	.80
600	A136	40t Westland Widgeon	1.40	1.40
601	A136	60t Consolidated Catalina NC777	2.00	2.00
		Nos. 598-601 (4)	4.85	4.85

Parliament House Opening — A137

1984, Aug. 7 Litho. *Perf. 13½x14*

602	A137	10t multicolored	.40	.40

Bird of Paradise — A138

1984, Aug. 7 Photo. *Perf. 11½*
Granite Paper

603	A138	5k multicolored	9.50	9.50

Ceremonial Shield — A139

1984, Sept. 21

604	A139	10t Central Province	.32	.32
605	A139	20t West New Britain	.75	.75
606	A139	30t Madang	1.10	1.10
607	A139	50t East Sepik	1.90	1.90
		Nos. 604-607 (4)	4.07	4.07

A140

British New Guinea Proclamation Centenary A141

1984, Nov. 6 Litho. *Perf. 14½x14*

608	Pair	.75	.75
a.	A140 10t Nelson, Port Moresby, 1884	.38	.38
b.	A141 10t Port Moresby, 1984	.38	.38
609	Pair	3.25	3.25
a.	A140 45t Rabaul, 1984	1.65	1.65
b.	A141 45t Elizabeth, Rabaul, 1884	1.65	1.65

Chimbu Gorge — A142

1985, Feb. 6 Photo. *Perf. 11½*

610	A142	10t Fergusson Island, vert.	.30	.30
611	A142	25t Sepik River, vert.	.80	.80
612	A142	40t shown	1.25	1.25
613	A142	60t Dali Beach, Vanimo	2.00	2.00
		Nos. 610-613 (4)	4.35	4.35

Coral Type of 1982

1985, May 29 Photo. *Perf. 11½*

614	A130	12t Dendronephthya sp.	.50	.50

For surcharge see No. 686.

No. 536 Surcharged

1985, Apr. 1 Litho. *Perf. 13½x14*

615	A123	12t on 7t multi	.50	.50

Ritual Structures — A143

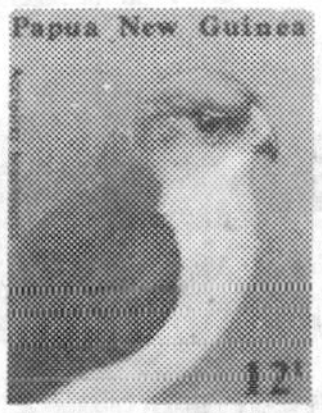

Indigenous Birds of Prey — A144

Designs: 15t, Dubu platform, Central Province. 20t, Tamuniai house, West New Britain. 30t, Yam tower, Trobriand Island. 60t, Huli grave, Tari.

1985, May 1 *Perf. 13x13½*

616	A143	15t multicolored	.55	.55
617	A143	20t multicolored	.75	.75
618	A143	30t multicolored	1.10	1.10
619	A143	60t multicolored	2.00	2.00
		Nos. 616-619 (4)	4.40	4.40

1985, Aug. 26 *Perf. 14x14½*

620	A144	12t Accipiter brachyurus	.50	.50
621	A144	12t In flight	.50	.50
a.		Pair, #620-621	1.00	1.00
622	A144	30t Megatriorchis doriae	1.25	1.25
623	A144	30t In Flight	1.25	1.25
a.		Pair, #622-623	2.50	2.50
624	A144	60t Henicopernis longicauda	2.50	2.50
625	A144	60t In flight	2.50	2.50
a.		Pair, #624-625	5.00	5.00
		Nos. 620-625 (6)	8.50	8.50

Flag and Gable of Parliament House, Port Moresby — A145

1985, Sept. 11 *Perf. 14½x15*

626	A145	12t multicolored	.50	.50

Post Office Centenary A146

Designs: 12t, No. 631a, 1901 Postal card, aerogramme, spectacles and inkwell. 30t, No. 631b, Queensland Type A15, No. 628. 40t, No. 631c, Plane and news clipping, 1885. 60t, No. 631d, 1892 German canceler, 1985 first day cancel.

1985, Oct. 9 *Perf. 14½x14*

627	A146	12t multicolored	.35	.35
628	A146	30t multicolored	.90	.90
629	A146	40t multicolored	1.25	1.25
630	A146	60t multicolored	1.90	1.90
		Nos. 627-630 (4)	4.40	4.40

Souvenir Sheet

631		Sheet of 4	5.00	5.00
a.	A146	12t multicolored	.40	.40
b.	A146	30t multicolored	1.00	1.00
c.	A146	40t multicolored	1.40	1.40
d.	A146	60t multicolored	2.00	2.00

Nombowai Cave Carved Funerary Totems — A147

1985, Nov. 13   Perf. 11½

632	A147	12t	Bird Rulowlaw, headman	.30	.30
633	A147	30t	Barn owl Raus, headman	.75	.75
634	A147	60t	Melerawuk	1.50	1.50
635	A147	80t	Cockerel, woman	2.00	2.00
			Nos. 632-635 (4)	4.55	4.55

Conch Shells — A148

1986, Feb. 12   Perf. 11½

636	A148	15t	Cypraea valentia	.32	.32
637	A148	35t	Oliva buelowi	.75	.75
638	A148	45t	Oliva parkinsoni	.95	.95
639	A148	70t	Cypraea aurantium	1.50	1.50
			Nos. 636-639 (4)	3.52	3.52

Queen Elizabeth II 60th Birthday
Common Design Type

Designs: 15t, In ATS officer's uniform, 1945. 35t, Silver wedding anniv. portrait by Patrick Lichfield, Balmoral, 1972. 50t, Inspecting troops, Port Moresby, 1982. 60t, Banquet aboard Britannia, state tour, 1982. 70t, Visiting Crown Agents' offices, 1983.

    Perf. 14½

1986, Apr. 21   Litho.   Unwmk.

640	CD337	15t	scar, blk & sil	.30	.30
641	CD337	35t	ultra & multi	.70	.70
642	CD337	50t	green & multi	1.00	1.00
643	CD337	60t	violet & multi	1.20	1.20
644	CD337	70t	rose vio & multi	1.40	1.40
			Nos. 640-644 (5)	4.60	4.60

AMERIPEX '86 A149

Small birds.

1986, May 22   Photo.   Perf. 12½
Granite Paper

645	A149	15t	Pitta erythrogaster	.65	.65
646	A149	35t	Melanocharis striativentris	1.50	1.50
647	A149	45t	Rhipidura rufifrons	1.90	1.90
648	A149	70t	Poecilodryas placens, vert.	3.00	3.00
			Nos. 645-648 (4)	7.05	7.05

Lutheran Church, Cent. — A150

1986, July 7   Litho.   Perf. 14x15

649	A150	15t	Monk, minister	.55	.55
650	A150	70t	Churches from 1886, 1986	2.50	2.50

Indigenous Orchids — A151   Folk Dancers — A152

1986, Aug. 4   Litho.   Perf. 14

651	A151	15t	Dendrobium vexillarius	.65	.65
652	A151	35t	Dendrobium lineale	1.50	1.50
653	A151	45t	Dendrobium johnsoniae	1.90	1.90
654	A151	70t	Dendrobium cuthbertsonii	3.00	3.00
			Nos. 651-654 (4)	7.05	7.05

1986, Nov. 12   Litho.   Perf. 14

655	A152	15t	Maprik	.65	.65
656	A152	35t	Kiriwina	1.50	1.50
657	A152	45t	Kundiawa	1.90	1.90
658	A152	70t	Fasu	3.00	3.00
			Nos. 655-658 (4)	7.05	7.05

Fish A153

Unwmk.

1987, Apr. 15   Litho.   Perf. 15

659	A153	17t	White-cap anemonefish	.50	.50
660	A153	30t	Black anemonefish	.85	.85
661	A153	35t	Tomato clownfish	1.00	1.00
662	A153	70t	Spine-cheek anemonefish	2.00	2.00
			Nos. 659-662 (4)	4.35	4.35

For surcharges see Nos. 720, 823, 868.

Ships — A154

1987-88   Photo.   Unwmk.   Perf. 11½
Granite Paper

663	A154	1t	La Boudeuse, 1768	.15	.15
664	A154	5t	Roebuck, 1700	.15	.15
665	A154	10t	Swallow, 1767	.22	.22
666	A154	15t	Fly, 1845	.28	.28
667	A154	17t	like 15t	.35	.35
668	A154	20t	Rattlesnake, 1849	.40	.40
669	A154	30t	Vitiaz, 1871	.65	.65
670	A154	35t	San Pedrico, Zabre, 1606	.65	.65
671	A154	40t	L'Astrolabe, 1827	.80	.80
672	A154	45t	Neva, 1876	.80	.80
673	A154	60t	Caravel of Jorge De Meneses, 1526	1.25	1.25
674	A154	70t	Eendracht, 1616	1.25	1.25
675	A154	1k	Blanche, 1872	2.25	2.25
676	A154	2k	Merrie England, 1889	3.75	3.75
676A	A154	3k	Samoa, 1884	6.50	6.50
			Nos. 663-676A (15)	19.45	19.45

Issued: 5, 35, 45, 70t, 2k, 6/15/87; 15, 20, 40, 60t, 2/17/88; 17t, 1k, 3/1/88; 1, 10, 30t, 3k, 11/16/88.
For surcharge see No. 824.

War Shields — A155

    Perf. 11½x12

1987, Aug. 19   Photo.   Unwmk.

677	A155	15t	Elema shield, Gulf Province, c. 1880	.32	.32
678	A155	35t	East Sepik Province	.75	.75
679	A155	45t	Simbai region, Madang Province	.95	.95
680	A155	70t	Telefomin region, West Sepik	1.45	1.45
			Nos. 677-680 (4)	3.47	3.47

Starfish A156

1987, Sept. 30   Litho.   Perf. 14

682	A156	17t	Protoreaster nodosus	.45	.45
683	A156	35t	Gomophia egeriae	1.00	1.00
684	A156	45t	Choriaster granulatus	1.25	1.25
685	A156	70t	Neoferdina ocellata	2.00	2.00
			Nos. 682-685 (4)	4.70	4.70

No. 614 Surcharged **15t** ═

1987, Sept. 23   Photo.   Perf. 11½
Granite Paper

686	A130	15t on 12t multi	.50	.50

Aircraft A157

Designs: 15t, Cessna Stationair 6, Rabaraba Airstrip. 35t, Britten-Norman Islander over Hombrum Bluff. 45t, DHC Twin Otter over the Highlands. 70t, Fokker F28 over Madang.

Unwmk.

1987, Nov. 11   Litho.   Perf. 14

687	A157	15t	multicolored	.45	.45
688	A157	35t	multicolored	1.00	1.00
689	A157	45t	multicolored	1.25	1.25
690	A157	70t	multicolored	2.00	2.00
			Nos. 687-690 (4)	4.70	4.70

Royal Papua New Guinea Police Force, Cent. — A158

Historic and modern aspects of the force: 17t, Motorcycle constable and pre-independence officer wearing a lap-lap. 35t, Sir William McGregor, Armed Native Constabulary founder, 1890, and recruit. 45t, Badges. 70t, Albert Hahl, German official credited with founding the island's police movement in 1888, and badge, early officer.

    Perf. 14x15

1988, June 15   Litho.   Unwmk.

691	A158	17t	multicolored	.45	.45
692	A158	35t	multicolored	.85	.85
693	A158	45t	multicolored	1.25	1.25
694	A158	70t	multicolored	1.75	1.75
			Nos. 691-694 (4)	4.30	4.30

Sydney Opera House and a Lakatoi (ship) — A159

Fireworks and Globes — A160

1988, July 30   Litho.   Perf. 13½

695	A159	35t	multicolored	.80	.80
696	A160		Pair	1.60	1.60
a.-b.			35t any single	.80	.80
c.			Souvenir sheet of 2, #696a-696b	1.60	1.60

SYDPEX '88, Australia (No. 695); Australia bicentennial (No. 696).

World Wildlife Fund A161

Metamorphosis of a Queen Alexandra's birdwing butterfly.

1988, Sept. 19   Perf. 14½

697	A161	5t	Courtship	.15	.15
698	A161	17t	Ovipositioning and larvae, vert.	.40	.40
699	A161	25t	Emergence from pupa, vert.	.60	.60
700	A161	35t	Adult male on leaf	.80	.80
			Nos. 697-700 (4)	1.95	1.95

1988 Summer Olympics, Seoul — A162

1988, Sept. 19   Litho.   Perf. 13½

701	A162	17t	Running	.40	.40
702	A162	45t	Weight lifting	1.05	1.05

Rhododendrons A163

Wmk. 387

1989, Jan. 25   Litho.   Perf. 14

703	A163	3t	R. zoelleri	.15	.15
704	A163	20t	R. cruttwellii	.50	.50
705	A163	60t	R. superbum	1.50	1.50
706	A163	70t	R. christianae	1.75	1.75
			Nos. 703-706 (4)	3.90	3.90

Intl. Letter Writing Week — A164

1989, Mar. 22   Perf. 14½

707	A164	20t	Writing letter	.50	.50
708	A164	35t	Mailing letter	.88	.88
709	A164	60t	Stamping letter	1.50	1.50
710	A164	70t	Reading letter	1.75	1.75
			Nos. 707-710 (4)	4.63	4.63

Thatched Dwellings — A165

1989, May 17   Wmk. 387   Perf. 15
711 A165 20t Buka Is., 1880s   .50   .50
712 A165 35t Koiari tree houses   .90   .90
713 A165 60t Lauan, New Ireland,
              1890s   1.50 1.50
714 A165 70t Basilaki, Milne Bay
              Province, 1930s   1.75 1.75
        Nos. 711-714 (4)   4.65 4.65

Small
Birds — A166

1989, July 12   Unwmk.   Perf. 14½
715 A166 20t Oreocharis arfaki fe-
              male, shown   .55   .55
716 A166 20t Male   .55   .55
  a.   Pair, #715-716   1.10 1.10
717 A166 35t Ifrita kowaldi   .95   .95
718 A166 45t Poecilodryas albo
              notata   1.20 1.20
719 A166 70t Sericornis nouhuysi   1.90 1.90
        Nos. 715-719 (5)   5.15 5.15

No. 659 Surcharged

1989, July 12   Unwmk.   Perf. 15
720 A153 20t on 17t multi   .50   .50

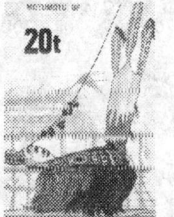

Traditional
Dance — A167

Designs: 20t, Motumotu, Gulf Province. 35t, Baining, East New Britain Province. 60t, Vailala River, Gulf Province. 70t, Timbunke, East Sepik Province.

Perf. 14x14½
1989, Sept. 6   Litho.   Wmk. 387
721 A167 20t multicolored   .60   .60
722 A167 35t multicolored   1.00 1.00
723 A167 60t multicolored   1.75 1.75
724 A167 70t multicolored   2.00 2.00
        Nos. 721-724 (4)   5.35 5.35

For surcharge see No. 860.

Christmas
A168

Designs: 20t, Hibiscus, church and symbol from a gulf gope board, Kavaumai. 35t, Rhododendron, madonna and child, and mask, Murik Lakes region. 60t, D'Albertis creeper, candle, and shield from Oksapmin, West Sepik highlands. 70t, Pacific frangipani, peace dove and flute mask from Chungrebu, a Rao village in Ramu.

Perf. 14x14½
1989, Nov. 8   Litho.   Unwmk.
725 A168 20t multicolored   .55   .55
726 A168 35t multicolored   .90   .90
727 A168 60t multicolored   1.75 1.75
728 A168 70t multicolored   2.00 2.00
        Nos. 725-728 (4)   5.20 5.20

Waterfalls — A169

Unwmk.
1990, Feb. 1   Litho.   Perf. 14
729 A169 20t Guni Falls   .48   .48
730 A169 35t Rouna Falls   .82   .82
731 A169 60t Ambua Falls   1.45 1.45
732 A169 70t Wawoi Falls   1.65 1.65
        Nos. 729-732 (4)   4.40 4.40

For surcharges see Nos. 866, 870.

Natl.
Census — A170

1990, May 2   Perf. 14½x15
733 A170 20t Three youths, form   .48   .48
734 A170 70t Man, woman, child,
              form   1.65 1.65

For surcharge see No. 869.

Gogodala Dance
Masks — A171

1990, July 11   Litho.   Perf. 13½
735 A171 20t shown   .48   .48
736 A171 35t multi, diff.   .82   .82
737 A171 60t multi, diff.   1.45 1.45
738 A171 70t multi, diff.   1.65 1.65
        Nos. 735-738 (4)   4.40 4.40

For surcharges see Nos. 867, 871.

Waitangi Treaty,
150th
Anniv. — A172

Designs: 20t, Dwarf Cassowary, Great Spotted Kiwi. No. 740, Double Wattled Cassowary, Brown Kiwi. No. 741, Sepik mask and Maori carving.

1990, Aug. 24   Litho.   Perf. 14½
739 A172 20t multicolored   .48   .48
740 A172 35t multicolored   .82   .82
741 A172 35t multicolored   .82   .82
        Nos. 739-741 (3)   2.12 2.12

No. 741 for World Stamp Exhibition, New Zealand 1990.
For surcharges see Nos. 862-863.

Birds — A173

1990, Sept. 26   Litho.   Perf. 14
742 A173 20t Whimbrel   .48   .48
743 A173 35t Sharp-tailed sandpiper   .82   .82
744 A173 60t Ruddy turnstone   1.45 1.45
745 A173 70t Terek sandpiper   1.65 1.65
        Nos. 742-745 (4)   4.40 4.40

Musical
Instruments
A174

1990, Oct. 31   Litho.   Perf. 13
746 A174 20t Jew's harp   .48   .48
747 A174 35t Musical bow   .82   .82
748 A174 60t Wantoat drum   1.45 1.45
749 A174 70t Gogodala rattle   1.65 1.65
        Nos. 746-749 (4)   4.40 4.40

For surcharge see No. 861.

Snail Shells
A174a

Designs: 21t, Rhynchotrochus weigmani. 40t, Forcartia globula, Canefriula azonata. 50t, Planispira deaniana. 80t, Papuina chancel, Papuina xanthocheila.

1991, Mar. 6   Litho.   Perf. 14x14½
750 A174a 21t multicolored   .50   .50
751 A174a 40t multicolored   .95   .95
752 A174a 50t multicolored   1.20 1.20
753 A174a 80t multicolored   1.90 1.90
        Nos. 750-753 (4)   4.55 4.55

For surcharge see No. 864.

A175

A176

1991-93   Litho.   Perf. 14½
755 A175   1t Ptiloris magnificus   .15   .15
756 A175   5t Loria loriae   .15   .15
757 A175 10t Cnemophilus mac-
              gregorii   .20   .20
758 A175 20t Parotia wahnesi   .40   .40
759 A175 21t Manucodia
              chalybata   .45   .45
760 A175 30t Paradisaea decora   .60   .60
761 A175 40t Loboparadisea ser-
              icea   .80   .80
762 A175 45t Cicinnurus regius   .95   .95
763 A175 50t Paradigalla brevi-
              cauda   1.00 1.00
764 A175 60t Parotia carolae   1.30 1.30
765 A175 90t Paradisaea guilielmi   1.95 1.95
766 A175   1k Diphyllodes
              magnificus   2.00 2.00
767 A175   2k Lophorina superba   4.00 4.00
  a.   Strip of 4, #761, 763, 766-767 +
        label   8.00 8.00
768 A175   5k Phonygammus ker-
              audrenii   10.00 10.00
                                       Perf. 13
769 A176 10k Paradisaea minor   21.00 21.00
        Nos. 755-769 (15)   44.95 44.95

No. 767a for Hong Kong '94 and sold for 4k.
Issued: 21t, 45t, 60t, 90t, 3/25/92; 5t, 40t, 50t, 1k, 2k, 9/2/92; 1t, 10t, 20t, 30t, 5k, 1993; 10k, 5/1/91; No. 767a, 2/18/94.
For surcharges see Nos. 862, 865.

Large T — A176a

1993   Litho.   Perf. 14½
770A A176a 21t like #758   .45   .45
770B A176a 45t like #762   .95   .95
770C A176a 60t like #764   1.30 1.30
770D A176a 90t like #765   1.95 1.95
        Nos. 770A-770D (4)   4.65 4.65

Originally scheduled for release on Feb. 19, 1992, #770A-770D were withdrawn when the denomination was found to have an upper case "T." Corrected versions with a lower case "T" are #759, 762, 764-765. A quantity of the original stamps appeared in the market and to prevent speculation in these items, the Postal Administration of Papua New Guinea released the stamps with the upper case "T."
For surcharges see Nos. 863B, 865A.

1991
South
Pacific
Games
A177

1991, June 26   Litho.   Perf. 13
771 A177 21t Cricket   .50   .50
772 A177 40t Running   .95   .95
773 A177 50t Baseball   1.20 1.20
774 A177 80t Rugby   1.90 1.90
        Nos. 771-774 (4)   4.55 4.55

Anglican
Church in
Papua New
Guinea,
Cent.
A178

Churches: 21t, Cathedral of St. Peter & St. Paul, Dogura. 40t, Kaieta Shrine, Anglican landing site. 80t, First thatched chapel, modawa tree.

1991, Aug. 7   Litho.   Perf. 14½
775 A178 21t multicolored   .50   .50
776 A178 40t multicolored   .95   .95
777 A178 80t multicolored   1.90 1.90
        Nos. 775-777 (3)   3.35 3.35

Traditional
Headdresses — A179

Designs: 21t, Rambutso, Manus Province. 40t, Marawaka, Eastern Highlands. 50t, Tufi, Oro Province. 80t, Sina Sina, Simbu Province.

1991, Oct. 16   Litho.   Perf. 13
778 A179 21t multicolored   .50   .50
779 A179 40t multicolored   .95   .95
780 A179 50t multicolored   1.20 1.20
781 A179 80t multicolored   1.90 1.90
        Nos. 778-781 (4)   4.55 4.55

Discovery of
America,
500th
Anniv.
A180

1992, Apr. 15   Litho.   Perf. 14
782 A180 21t Nina   .45   .45
783 A180 45t Pinta   .90   .90
784 A180 60t Santa Maria   1.30 1.30

*785 A180 90t Columbus, ships 1.95 1.95
   a. Souvenir sheet of 2, #784-785 2.75 2.75
   Nos. 782-785 (4) 4.60 4.60

World Columbian Stamp Expo '92, Chicago.
Issue date: No. 785a, June 3.

A181   A182

Papuan Gulf Artifacts: 21t, Canoe prow shield, Bamu. 45t, Skull rack, Kerewa. 60t, Ancestral figure, Era River. 90t, Gope (spirit) board, Urama.

1992, June 3   Litho.   Perf. 14
*786 A181 21t multicolored .45 .45
787 A181 45t multicolored .90 .90
788 A181 60t multicolored 1.30 1.30
789 A181 90t multicolored 1.95 1.95
   Nos. 786-789 (4) 4.60 4.60*

1992, July 22   Litho.   Perf. 14
Soldiers from: 21t, Papuan Infantry Battalion. 45t, Australian Militia. 60t, Japanese Nankai Force. 90t, US Army.

*790 A182 21t multicolored .45 .45
791 A182 45t multicolored .90 .90
792 A182 60t multicolored 1.30 1.30
793 A182 90t multicolored 1.90 1.90
   Nos. 790-793 (4) 4.55 4.55*

World War II, 50th anniv.

Flowering Trees — A183

1992, Oct. 28   Litho.   Perf. 14
*794 A183 21t Hibiscus tiliaceus .45 .45
795 A183 45t Castanospermum australe .95 .95
796 A183 60t Cordia subcordata 1.25 1.25
797 A183 90t Acacia auriculiformis 1.85 1.85
   Nos. 794-797 (4) 4.50 4.50*

Mammals A184

1993, Apr. 7   Litho.   Perf. 14
*798 A184 21t Myoictis melas .42 .42
799 A184 45t Microperoryctes longicauda .90 .90
800 A184 60t Mallomys rothschildi 1.20 1.20
801 A184 90t Pseudocheirus forbesi 1.80 1.80
   Nos. 798-801 (4) 4.32 4.32*

Small Birds — A185

1993, June 9   Litho.   Perf. 14
*802 A185 21t Clytomyias insignis .40 .40
803 A185 45t Pitta superba .88 .88
804 A185 60t Rhagologus leucostigma 1.15 1.15
805 A185 90t Toxorhamphus poliopterus 1.75 1.75
   Nos. 802-805 (4) 4.18 4.18*

Nos. 802-805 Redrawn with Taipei '93 emblem
in Blue and Yellow

1993, Aug. 13   Litho.   Perf. 14
*806 A185 21t multicolored .40 .40
807 A185 45t multicolored .88 .88
808 A185 60t multicolored 1.15 1.15
809 A185 90t multicolored 1.75 1.75
   Nos. 806-809 (4) 4.18 4.18*

Freshwater Fish A186

Designs: 21t, Iriatherina werneri. 45t, Tateurndina ocellicauda. 60t, Melanotaenia affinis. 90t, Pseudomugil connieae.

1993, Sept. 29   Litho.   Perf. 14x14½
*810 A186 21t multicolored .45 .45
811 A186 45t multicolored .95 .95
812 A186 60t multicolored 1.25 1.25
813 A186 90t multicolored 1.90 1.90
   Nos. 810-813 (4) 4.55 4.55*

For surcharges see Nos. 876-878.

Air Niugini, 20th Anniv. A187

1993, Oct. 27   Perf. 14
*814 A187 21t DC3 .45 .45
815 A187 45t F27 .95 .95
816 A187 60t Dash 7 1.25 1.25
817 A187 90t Airbus A310-300 1.90 1.90
   Nos. 814-817 (4) 4.55 4.55*

Souvenir Sheet

Paradisaea Rudolphi — A188

1993, Sept. 29   Litho.   Perf. 14
818 A188 2k multicolored 4.25 4.25

Bangkok '93.

Huon Tree Kangaroo — A189

1994, Jan. 19   Litho.   Perf. 14½
*819 A189 21t Domesticated joey .40 .40
820 A189 45t Adult male .90 .90
821 A189 60t Female, joey in pouch 1.25 1.25
822 A189 90t Adolescent 1.75 1.75
   Nos. 819-822 (4) 4.30 4.30*

No. 661 Surcharged

21t

No. 671 Surcharged

 K1.20

1994, Mar. 23
Perfs. and Printing Methods as Before
*823 A153 21t on 35t multi .40 .40
824 A154 1.20k on 40t multi 2.50 2.50*

Artifacts — A190

Designs: 1t, Hagen ceremonial axe, Western Highlands. 2t, Telefomin war shield, West Sepik. 20t, Head mask, Gulf of Papua. 21t, Kanganaman stool, East Sepik. 45t, Trobriand lime gourd, Milne Bay. 60t, Yuat River flute stopper, East Sepik. 90t, Tami island dish, Morobe. 1k, Kundu drum, Ramu River estuary. 5k, Gogodala dance mask, Western Province. 10k, Malanggan mask, New Ireland.

1994-95   Litho.   Perf. 14½
*825 A190 1t multicolored .15 .15
826 A190 2t multicolored .15 .15
828 A190 20t multicolored .40 .40
829 A190 21t multicolored .40 .40
833 A190 45t multicolored .90 .90
835 A190 60t multicolored 1.25 1.25
836 A190 90t multicolored 1.75 1.75
837 A190 1k multicolored 1.75 1.75
839 A190 5k multicolored 10.00 10.00
840 A190 10k multicolored 17.50 17.50
   Nos. 825-840 (10) 34.25 34.25*

Issued: 21, 45, 60, 90t, 3/23; 1, 2, 20t, 5k, 6/29/94; 1k, 10k, 4/12/95.
This is an expanding set. Numbers may change.

Classic Cars — A191

1994, May 11   Litho.   Perf. 14
*841 A191 21t Model T Ford .42 .42
842 A191 45t Chevrolet 490 .90 .90
843 A191 60t Baby Austin 1.25 1.25
844 A191 90t Willys Jeep 1.90 1.90
   Nos. 841-844 (4) 4.47 4.47*

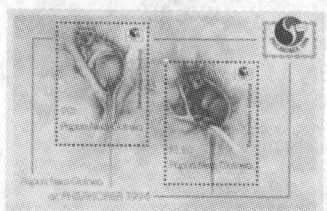

PHILAKOREA '94 — A192

Tree kangaroos: 90t, Dendrolagus inustus. 1.20k, Dendrolagus dorianus.

1994, Aug. 10   Litho.   Perf. 14
845 A192 Sheet of 2, #a.-b. 4.50 4.50

Moths A193

Designs: 21t, Daphnis hypothous pallescens. 45t, Tanaorhinus unipuncta. 60t, Neodiphthera sciron. 90t, Parotis maginata.

1994, Oct. 26   Litho.   Perf. 14
*846 A193 21t multicolored .45 .45
847 A193 45t multicolored 1.00 1.00
848 A193 60t multicolored 1.25 1.25
849 A193 90t multicolored 2.00 2.00
   Nos. 846-849 (4) 4.70 4.70*

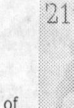

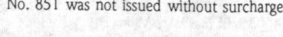

Beatification of Peter To Rot — A194

1995, Jan. 11   Litho.   Perf. 14
*850 A194 21t Peter To Rot .45 .45
851 A194 1k on 90t Pope John Paul II 2.25 2.25
   a. Pair, #850-851 + label 2.75 2.75*
No. 851 was not issued without surcharge.

Tourism A195

Designs: No. 852, Cruising. No. 853, Handicrafts. No. 854, Jet. No. 855, Resorts. No. 856, Trekking adventure. No. 857, White-water rafting. No. 858, Boat, diver. No. 859, Divers, sunken plane.

1995, Jan. 11
*852 A195 21t multicolored .45 .45
853 A195 21t multicolored .45 .45
   a. Pair, #852-853 .90 .90
854 A195 50t on 45t multi 1.10 1.10
855 A195 50t on 45t multi 1.10 1.10
   a. Pair, #854-855 2.25 2.25
856 A195 65t on 60t multi 1.40 1.40
857 A195 65t on 60t multi 1.40 1.40
   a. Pair, #856-857 2.75 2.75
858 A195 1k on 90t multi 2.25 2.25
859 A195 1k on 90t multi 2.25 2.25
   a. Pair, #858-859 4.50 4.50
   Nos. 852-859 (8) 10.40 10.40*

Nos. 854-859 were not issued without surcharge.

Nos. 662, 722, 730, 732, 734, 736, 738, 740-741, 747, 753, 762, 765, 770B, 770D Surcharged

 5t

1994-95   Perfs., Etc. as Before
*860 A167 5t on 35t #722 .15 .15
861 A174 5t on 35t #747
862 A172 10t on 35t #740
863 A172 10t on 35t #741
863A A175 21t on 45t #762 .38 .38
863B A176a 21t on 45t #770B .38 .38
864 A174a 21t on 80t #753
865 A175 21t on 90t #765 .45 .45
865A A176a 21t on 90T #770D
866 A169 50t on 35t #730
867 A171 50t on 35t #736
868 A153 65t on 70t #662 1.40 1.40
869 A170 65t on 70t #734 1.40 1.40
870 A169 1k on 70t #732
871 A171 1k on 70t #738 2.00 2.00
   Nos. 860-871 (7) 6.16 6.16*

Size, style and location of surcharge varies.
Issued: #862, 864, 8/23/94; #861, 863, 10/3/94; #860, 871, 10/6/94; #866-868, 869-870, 11/28/94; #863A-863B, 1995; #860, 3/27/95; #865A, 4/25/95.
Numbers have been reserved for additional surcharges.

Mushrooms — A196

Designs: 25t, Lentinus umbrinus. 50t, Amanita hemibapha. 65t, Boletellus emodensis. 1k, Ramaria zippellii.

1995, June 21   Litho.   Perf. 14
*872 A196 25t multicolored .40 .40
   Complete booklet, 10 #872 4.00
873 A196 50t multicolored .85 .85
   Complete booklet, 10 #873 8.50*

874	A196	65t multicolored	1.10 1.10
875	A196	1k multicolored	1.75 1.75
		Nos. 872-875 (4)	4.10 4.10

Nos. 811-813 Surcharged

21t

1995　　Litho.　　Perf. 14x14½

876	A186	21t on 45t #811	.40 .40
877	A186	21t on 60t #812	.40 .40
878	A186	21t on 90t #813	.40 .40
		Nos. 876-878 (3)	1.20 1.20

Independence, 20th
Anniv. — A197

Designs: 50t, 1k, "20" emblem.

1995, Aug. 30　　　Perf. 14

879	A197	21t shown	.40 .40
880	A197	50t blue & multi	.90 .90
881	A197	1k green & multi	1.75 1.75
		Nos. 879-881 (3)	3.05 3.05

Souvenir Sheet

Singapore
'95 — A198

Orchids: a, 21t, Dendrobium rigidifolium. b, 45t, Dendrobium convolutum. c, 60t, Dendrobium spectabile. d, 90t, Dendrobium tapiniense.

1995, Aug. 30　　Litho.　　Perf. 14

882	A198	Sheet of 4, #a.-d.	4.50 4.50

No. 882 sold for 3k.

Souvenir Sheet

New Year 1995 (Year of the Boar) — A199

Illustration reduced.

1995, Sept. 14

883	A199	3k multicolored	4.50 4.50

Beijing '95.

Eruption of
Rabaul Volcano, 1st
Anniv.
A200

1995, Sept. 19

884	A200	2k multicolored	3.00 3.00

Crabs — A201

1995, Oct. 25　　Litho.　　Perf. 14

885	A201	21t Zosimus aeneus	.40 .40
886	A201	50t Cardisoma carnifex	1.00 1.00
887	A201	65t Uca tetragonon	1.30 1.30
888	A201	1k Eriphia sebana	2.00 2.00
		Nos. 885-888 (4)	4.70 4.70

AIR POST STAMPS

Regular Issue of
1916 Overprinted **AIR MAIL**

1929　　Wmk. 74　　Perf. 14

C1	A3	3p blue grn & dk gray	1.25 1.40
b.		Vert. pair, one without ovpt.	3,000.
c.		Horiz. pair, one without ovpt.	3,000.
d.		3p blue green & sepia black	50.00 62.50
e.		Overprint on back, vert.	2,500.

No. C1 exists on white and on yellowish paper, No. C1d on yellowish paper only.

Regular Issues of
1916-23
Overprinted in Red

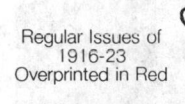

1930, Sept. 15　　　Wmk. 74

C2	A3	3p blue grn & blk	1.00 2.50
a.		Yellowish paper	1,000.
b.		Double overprint	1,400.
C3	A3	6p violet & dull violet	3.50 7.50
a.		Yellowish paper	6.50 7.00
C4	A3	1sh ol green & ol brn	7.50 17.00
a.		Inverted overprint	3,500.
b.		Yellowish paper	15.00 35.00
		Nos. C2-C4 (3)	12.00 20.00

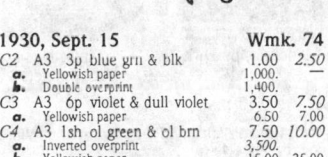

Port
Moresby — AP1

Unwmk.

1938, Sept. 6　　Engr.　　Perf. 11

C5	AP1	2p carmine	1.25 1.40
C6	AP1	3p ultra	1.50 1.65
C7	AP1	5p dark green	2.00 2.25
C8	AP1	8p red brown	3.00 3.25
C9	AP1	1sh violet	12.50 7.50
		Nos. C5-C9 (5)	20.25 16.05
		Set, never hinged	35.00

50th anniv. of Papua as a British possession.

Papuans Poling
Rafts — AP2

1939-41

C10	AP2	2p carmine	2.50 2.00
C11	AP2	3p ultra	2.50 2.75
C12	AP2	5p dark green	4.00 3.25
C13	AP2	8p red brown	3.00 3.00
C14	AP2	1sh violet	6.00 3.50
C15	AP2	1sh6p lt olive ('41)	27.50 32.50
		Nos. C10-C15 (6)	46.50 47.00
		Set, never hinged	70.00

POSTAGE DUE STAMPS

Catalogue values for unused
stamps in this section are for Never
Hinged items.

Nos. 128, 122, 129, 139　　**POSTAL**
and 125 Surcharged in　　**CHARGES**
Black, Blue, Red or
Orange　　　　　　　　　**6d.**

1960　　Unwmk.　　Engr.　　Perf. 14

J1	A24	1p on 6½p	8.00 6.00
J2	A23	3p on 1½p (Bl)	12.00 8.00
a.		Double surcharge	525.00
J3	A24	6p on 7½p (R)	20.00 12.00
a.		Double surcharge	525.00
J4	A23	1sh3p on 3½p (O)	27.50 20.00
J5	A23	3sh on 2½p (G)	35.00 32.50
		Nos. J1-J5 (5)	102.50 78.50

**POSTAL
CHARGES
6d.**

No. 129 Surcharged
with New Value in
Red

 IXIXIXIXIX

J6	A24	6p on 7½p	650.00 425.00
a.		Double surcharge	2,750. 1,750.

D1

Perf. 13½x14

1960, June 2　　Litho.　　Wmk. 228

J7	D1	1p orange	.20 .15
J8	D1	3p ocher	.50 .30
J9	D1	6p light ultra	.85 .40
J10	D1	9p vermilion	1.40 .65
J11	D1	1sh emerald	2.00 1.00
J12	D1	1sh3p bright violet	3.50 1.75
J13	D1	1sh6p light blue	4.00 3.75
J14	D1	3sh yellow	5.00 3.50
		Nos. J7-J14 (8)	17.45 11.50

OFFICIAL STAMPS

Nos. 60-63, 66-71,　　**O** 　　**S**
92-93 Overprinted

1931　　Wmk. 74　　Perf. 14½

O1	A3	½p #60	.65 2.25
O2	A3	1p #61	.65 2.75
O3	A3	1½p #62	2.25 6.50
O4	A3	2p #63	2.75 8.25
O5	A3	3p #66	3.00 10.00
O6	A3	4p #67	3.00 10.00
O7	A3	5p #68	4.50 14.00
O8	A3	6p #69	5.00 10.00
O9	A3	1sh #70	6.50 14.00
O10	A3	2sh6p #71	27.50 52.50
		Nos. O1-O10 (10)	55.80 130.25

1932　　Wmk. 228　　Perf. 11½

O11	A3	9p #92	20.00 50.00
O12	A3	1sh3p #93	27.50 52.50

PENRHYN ISLAND

pen-'rin 'ī-lənd

(Tongareva)

AREA — 3 sq. mi.
POP. — 395 (1926)

Stamps of Cook Islands were used in
Penrhyn from 1932 until 1973.

12 Pence = 1 Shilling

Catalogue values for unused
stamps in this country are for Never
Hinged items, beginning with Scott
35 in the regular postage section,
Scott B1 in the semi-postal section
and Scott O1 in the officials
section.

Stamps of New Zealand Surcharged in
Carmine, Vermilion, Brown or Blue:

PENRHYN ISLAND.

½ PENI.　　　　　**PENRHYN ISLAND.**
½ pence　　　　　　　　**TAI PENI.**
　　　　　　　　　　　　　1 pence

1902　　Wmk. 63　　Perf. 14

1	A18	½p green (C)	1.25 2.50
a.		No period after "ISLAND"	90.00 100.00
2	A35	1p carmine (Br)	3.25 5.00
a.		Perf. 11	1,000. 1,000.
b.		Perf. 11x14	1,000. 1,000.

Wmk. 61　　Perf. 14

5	A18	½p green (V)	1.00 2.50
a.		No period after "ISLAND"	60.00 65.00
6	A35	1p carmine (Bl)	1.00 2.75
a.		No period after "ISLAND"	37.50 40.00
b.		Perf. 11x14	9,000. 8,500.
		Nos. 1-6 (4)	6.50 12.75

Stamps with compound perfs. also exist perf. 11
or 14 on one or more sides.

PENRHYN ISLAND.

2½ PENI.

1902　　Unwmk.　　Perf. 11

8	A22	2½p blue (C)	2.00 2.75
a.		"½" and "PENI" 2mm apart	10.50 16.00
9	A22	2½p blue (V)	2.00 2.75
a.		"½" and "PENI" 2mm apart	10.50 16.00

**PENRHYN
ISLAND.**　　　　**PENRHYN
ISLAND.**

Toru Pene.　　　　**Ono Pene.**
d　　　　　　　　　e

**PENRHYN
ISLAND.**

Tahi Silingi.
f

1903　　　　　Wmk. 61

10	A23(d)	3p yellow brn (Bl)	8.00 16.00
11	A26(e)	6p rose (Bl)	13.00 24.00
12	A29(f)	1sh orange red (Bl)	37.50 52.50
a.		1sh bright red (Bl)	37.50 52.50
b.		1sh brown red (Bl)	37.50 52.50
		Nos. 10-12 (3)	58.50 92.50

1914-15　　　Perf. 14, 14x14½

13	A41(a)	½p yellow grn (C)	1.25 3.00
a.		No period after "ISLAND"	32.50 50.00
b.		No period after "PENI"	75.00 90.00
14	A41(a)	½p yel grn (V) ('15)	.90 2.50
a.		No period after "ISLAND"	16.00 22.50
b.		No period after "PENI"	37.50 50.00
15	A41(e)	6p carmine rose (Bl)	25.00 37.50
16	A41(f)	1sh vermilion (Bl)	35.00 62.50
		Nos. 13-16 (4)	62.15 105.50

New Zealand Stamps of　　**PENRHYN**
1915-19 Overprinted in　　**ISLAND.**
Red or Dark Blue

Perf. 14x13½, 14x14½

1917-20　　　　　　　　Typo.

17	A13	½p yel grn (R) ('20)	.75 1.05
18	A47	1½p gray black (R)	3.00 4.00
19	A47	1½p brn org (R) ('19)	1.50 4.00
20	A43	3p choc (Bl) ('19)	2.50 4.50

Engr.

21	A44	2½p dull bl (R) ('20)	1.75 2.75
22	A45	3p vio brn (Bl) ('18)	7.00 16.00
23	A45	6p car rose (Bl) ('18)	5.25 11.00
24	A45	1sh vermilion (Bl)	11.00 22.50
		Nos. 17-24 (8)	32.75 66.40

Landing of Capt.　　　Avarua
Cook　　　　　　　Waterfront
A10　　　　　　　　A11

Capt. James　　　　Coconut
Cook — A12　　　　Palm — A13

Arorangi Village, Rarotonga — A14 | Avarua Harbor — A15

1920   Unwmk.   Perf. 14

25	A10	½p emerald & blk	1.00	5.00
a.		Center inverted		625.00
26	A11	1p red & black	1.25	5.00
a.		Center inverted		850.00
27	A12	1½p violet & blk	5.00	10.00
28	A13	3p red org & blk	3.75	7.50
29	A14	6p dk brn & red brn	4.50	17.50
30	A15	1sh dull bl & blk	10.00	20.00
		Nos. 25-30 (6)	25.50	65.00

Rarotongan Chief (Te Po) — A16

1927   Engr.   Wmk. 61

31	A16	2½p blue & red brn	1.75	4.00

Types of 1920 Issue

1928-29

33	A10	½p yellow grn & blk	3.50	4.00
34	A11	1p carmine rose & blk	3.50	5.25

PENRHYN

Northern Cook Islands

POP. — 2,030 (1976).

The Northern Cook Islands include six besides Penrhyn that are inhabited: Nassau, Palmerston (Avarua), Manihiki (Humphrey), Rakahanga (Reirson), Pukapuka (Danger) and Suwarrow (Anchorage).

100 Cents = 1 Dollar

Catalogue values for unused stamps in this section are for Never Hinged items.

PENRHYN

Cook Islands Nos. 200-201, 203, 205-208, 211-212, 215-217 Overprinted

NORTHERN

1973 Photo. Unwmk. Perf. 14x13½

35	A34	1c gold & multi	.15	.15
36	A34	2c gold & multi	.15	.15
37	A34	3c gold & multi	.15	.15
38	A34	4c gold & multi	.16	.16
a.		Overprinted on #204		
39	A34	5c gold & multi	.20	.20
40	A34	6c gold & multi	.25	.25
41	A34	8c gold & multi	.35	.35
42	A34	15c gold & multi	.65	.65
43	A34	20c gold & multi	.80	.80
44	A34	50c gold & multi	2.50	2.50
45	A35	$1 gold & multi	2.75	2.75
46	A35	$2 gold & multi	6.00	6.00
		Nos. 35-46 (12)	14.11	14.11

Nos. 45-46 are overprinted "Penrhyn" only. Overprint exists with broken "E" or "O." Issue dates: #35-45, Oct. 24; #46, Nov. 14.

Penrhyn Island stamps can be mounted in the Scott New Zealand Dependencies album.

Cook Islands Nos. 369-371 Overprinted in Silver: "PENRHYN / NORTHERN"

1973, Nov. 14   Photo.   Perf. 14

47	A60	25c Princess Anne	1.25	1.25
48	A60	30c Mark Phillips	1.65	1.65
49	A60	50c Princess and Mark Phillips	2.00	2.00
		Nos. 47-49 (3)	4.90	4.90

Wedding of Princess Anne and Capt. Mark Phillips.

Fluorescence

Starting with No. 50, stamps carry a "fluorescent security underprinting" in a multiple pattern combining a sailing ship, "Penrhyn Northern Cook Islands" and stars.

Ostracion A17

Aerial View of Penrhyn Atoll — A18

Designs: ½c-$1, Various fish of Penrhyn. $5, Map showing Penrhyn's location.

1974-75   Photo.   Perf. 13½x14

50	A17	½c multicolored	.15	.15
51	A17	1c multicolored	.15	.15
52	A17	2c multicolored	.15	.15
53	A17	3c multicolored	.15	.15
54	A17	4c multicolored	.15	.15
55	A17	5c multicolored	.15	.15
56	A17	8c multicolored	.15	.15
57	A17	10c multicolored	.20	.20
58	A17	20c multicolored	.45	.45
59	A17	25c multicolored	.48	.48
60	A17	60c multicolored	1.20	1.20
61	A17	$1 multicolored	2.00	2.00
62	A18	$2 multicolored	4.00	4.00
63	A18	$5 multicolored	9.50	9.50
		Nos. 50-63 (14)	18.88	18.88

Issue dates: $2, Feb. 12, 1975; $5, Mar. 12, 1975; others Aug. 15, 1974.
For surcharges and overprints see Nos. 72, 352-353, O1-O12.

Map of Penrhyn and Nos. 1-2 — A19

UPU, cent.: 50c, UPU emblem, map of Penrhyn and Nos. 27-28.

1974, Sept. 27   Perf. 13

64	A19	25c violet & multi	.60	.60
65	A19	50c slate grn & multi	1.25	1.25

Adoration of the Kings, by Memling — A20

Christmas: 10c, Adoration of the Shepherds, by Hugo van der Goes. 25c, Adoration of the Kings, by Rubens. 30c, Holy Family, by Orazio Borgianni.

1974, Oct. 30

66	A20	5c multicolored	.15	.15
67	A20	10c multicolored	.28	.28
68	A20	25c multicolored	.65	.65
69	A20	30c multicolored	.75	.75
		Nos. 66-69 (4)	1.83	1.83

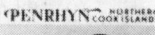 

Churchill Giving "V" Sign — A21

1974, Nov. 30   Photo.

70	A21	30c shown	.80	.80
71	A21	50c Portrait	1.25	1.25

Winston Churchill (1874-1965).

No. 63 Overprinted   KIA ORANA ASTRONAUTS

1975, July 24   Perf. 13½x13

72	A18	$5 multicolored	8.50	8.50

Safe splashdown of Apollo space capsule.

Madonna, by Dirk Bouts A22 | Pietà, by Michelangelo A23

Madonna Paintings: 15c, by Leonardo da Vinci. 35c, by Raphael.

1975, Nov. 21   Photo.   Perf. 14½x13

73	A22	7c gold & multi	.18	.18
74	A22	15c gold & multi	.42	.42
75	A22	35c gold & multi	.90	.90
		Nos. 73-75 (3)	1.50	1.50

Christmas 1975.

1976, Mar. 19   Photo.   Perf. 14x13

76	A23	15c gold & dark brown	.32	.32
77	A23	20c gold & deep purple	.42	.42
78	A23	35c gold & dark green	.65	.65
a.		Souvenir sheet of 3, #76-78	1.90	1.90
		Nos. 76-78 (3)	1.39	1.39

Easter and for the 500th birth anniv. of Michelangelo Buonarroti (1475-1564), Italian sculptor, painter and architect.

The Spirit of '76, by Archibald M. Willard — A24

Design: No. 79, Washington Crossing the Delaware, by Emmanuel Leutze.

1976, May 20   Photo.   Perf. 13½

79	A24	Strip of 3	2.00	2.00
a.		30c Boatsman	.60	.60
b.		30c Washington	.60	.60
c.		30c Men in boat	.60	.60
80	A24	Strip of 3	3.50	3.50
a.		50c Drummer boy	1.00	1.00
b.		50c Old drummer	1.00	1.00
c.		50c Fifer	1.00	1.00
d.		Souvenir sheet, #79-80		

American Bicentennial. Nos. 79-80 printed in sheets of 15, 5 strips of 3 and 3-part corner labels. For overprint see No. O13.

Running A25

Montreal Olympic Games Emblem and: 30c, Long jump. 75c, Javelin.

1976, July 9   Photo.   Perf. 13½

81	A25	25c multicolored	.35	.35
82	A25	30c multicolored	.40	.40
83	A25	75c multicolored	1.25	1.25
a.		Souvenir sheet of 3, #81-83, perf. 14½x13½	3.00	3.00
		Nos. 81-83 (3)	2.00	2.00

21st Olympic Games, Montreal, Canada, July 17-Aug. 1. Nos. 81-83 printed in sheets of 6 (2x3).

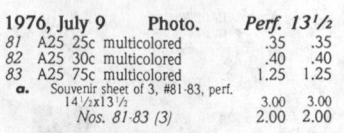

Flight into Egypt, by Dürer — A26

Etchings by Albrecht Dürer: 15c, Adoration of the Shepherds. 35c, Adoration of the Kings.

1976, Oct. 20   Photo.   Perf. 13x13½

84	A26	7c silver & dk brown	.16	.16
85	A26	15c silver & slate grn	.28	.28
86	A26	35c silver & purple	.60	.60
		Nos. 84-86 (3)	1.04	1.04

Christmas. Nos. 84-86 printed in sheets of 8 (2x4) with decorative border.

Elizabeth II and Westminster Abbey — A27

Designs: $1, Elizabeth II and Prince Philip. $2, Elizabeth II.

1977, Mar. 24   Photo.   Perf. 13½x13

87	A27	50c silver & multi	1.00	.90
88	A27	$1 silver & multi	2.50	2.25
89	A27	$2 silver & multi	5.00	4.25
a.		Souvenir sheet of 3, #87-89	8.50	8.50
		Nos. 87-89 (3)	8.50	7.40

25th anniversary of reign of Queen Elizabeth II. Nos. 87-89 issued in sheets of 4. For overprints see Nos. O14-O15.

Annunciation — A28

Designs: 15c, Announcement to Shepherds. 35c, Nativity. Designs from "The Bible in Images," by Julius Schnorr von Carolsfeld (1794-1872).

1977, Sept. 23   Photo.   Perf. 13½

90	A28	7c multicolored	.15	.15
91	A28	15c multicolored	.30	.30
92	A28	35c multicolored	.75	.75
		Nos. 90-92 (3)	1.20	1.20

Christmas. Issued in sheets of 6.

Red Sickle-bill (I'wii) — A29  | Chief's Feather Cloak — A30

Designs: No. 95, Crimson creeper (apapane). No. 96, Feathered head of Hawaiian god. No. 97, Hawaiian gallinule (alae). No. 98, Chief's regalia: feather cape, staff (kahili) and helmet. No. 99, Yellow-tufted bee-eater (o'o). No. 100, Scarlet

feathered image (head). Birds are extinct; their feathers were used for artifacts shown.

1978, Jan. 19 Photo. *Perf. 12½x13*

93	A29 20c silver & multi	.38	.38
94	A30 20c silver & multi	.38	.38
95	A29 30c silver & multi	.60	.60
96	A30 30c silver & multi	.60	.60
97	A29 35c silver & multi	.65	.65
98	A30 35c silver & multi	.65	.65
99	A29 75c silver & multi	1.40	1.40
a.	Souv. sheet of 4, #93, 95, 97, 99	3.75	3.75
100	A30 75c silver & multi	1.40	1.40
a.	Souv. sheet of 4, #94, 96, 98, 100	3.75	3.75
	Nos. 93-100 (8)	6.06	6.06

Bicentenary of Capt. Cook's arrival in Hawaii. Stamps of same denomination printed se-tenant in sheets of 8 (4x2).

A31

A32

Rubens' Paintings: 10c, St. Veronica by Rubens. 15c, Crucifixion. 35c, Descent from the Cross.

1978, Mar. 10 Photo. *Perf. 13½x13*

Size: 25x36mm

101	A31 10c multicolored	.20	.20
102	A31 15c multicolored	.30	.30
103	A31 35c multicolored	.70	.70
a.	Souvenir sheet of 3	1.25	1.25
	Nos. 101-103 (3)	1.20	1.20

Easter and 400th birth anniv. of Peter Paul Rubens (1577-1640). Nos. 101-103 issued in sheets of 6. No. 103a contains one each of Nos. 101-103 (27x36mm).

Miniature Sheet

1978, May 24 Photo. *Perf. 13*

104	Sheet of 6	7.00	7.00
a.	A32 90c Arms of United Kingdom	1.10	.90
b.	A32 90c shown	1.10	.90
c.	A32 90c Arms of New Zealand	1.10	.90
d.	Souvenir sheet of 3, #104a-104c	5.00	4.00

25th anniv. of coronation of Elizabeth II.

No. 104 contains 2 horizontal se-tenant strips of Nos. 104a-104c, separated by horizontal gutter showing coronation.

A33

A34

Paintings by Dürer: 30c, Virgin and Child. 35c, Virgin and Child with St. Anne.

1978, Nov. 29 Photo. *Perf. 14x13½*

105	A33 30c multicolored	.50	.50
106	A33 35c multicolored	.60	.60
a.	Souvenir sheet of 2, #105-106	1.25	1.25

Christmas and 450th death anniv. of Albrecht Dürer (1471-1528), German painter. Nos. 105-106 issued in sheets of 6.

1979, Sept. 26 Photo. *Perf. 14*

Designs: No. 107, Penrhyn #64-65. No. 108, Rowland Hill, Penny Black. No. 109, Penrhyn #104b. No. 110, Hill portrait.

107	A34 75c multicolored	1.00	1.00
108	A34 75c multicolored	1.00	1.00
109	A34 90c multicolored	1.25	1.25
110	A34 90c multicolored	1.25	1.25
a.	Souvenir sheet of 4, #107-110	5.00	5.00
	Nos. 107-110 (4)	4.50	4.50

Sir Rowland Hill (1795-1879), originator of penny postage. Nos. 107-108 and 109-110 issued se-tenant in sheets of 8.

Max and Moritz, IYC Emblem — A35

IYC: Scenes from Max and Moritz, by Wilhelm Busch (1832-1908).

1979, Nov. 20 Photo. *Perf. 13x12½*

111	Sheet of 4	.75
a.	A35 12c shown	.18
b.	A35 12c Looking down chimney	.18
c.	A35 12c With stolen chickens	.18
d.	A35 12c Woman and dog, empty pan	.18
112	Sheet of 4	.90
a.	A35 15c Sawing bridge	.20
b.	A35 15c Man falling into water	.20
c.	A35 15c Broken bridge	.20
d.	A35 15c Running away	.20
113	Sheet of 4	1.25
a.	A35 20c Baker	.30
b.	A35 20c Sneaking into bakery	.30
c.	A35 20c Falling into dough	.30
d.	A35 20c Baked into breads	.30
	Nos. 111-113 (3)	2.90

A36

A37

Easter (15th Century Prayerbook Illustrations): 12c, Jesus Carrying the Cross. 20c, Crucifixion, by William Vreland. 35c, Descent from the Cross.

1980, Mar. 28 Photo. *Perf. 13x13½*

114	A36 12c multicolored	.20	.20
115	A36 20c multicolored	.35	.35
116	A36 35c multicolored	.60	.60
a.	Souvenir sheet of 3, #114-116	1.10	1.10
	Nos. 114-116 (3)	1.15	1.15

See Nos. B4-B6.

1980, Sept. 17 Photo. *Perf. 13*

117	A37 $1 multicolored	2.00	2.00

Souvenir Sheet

118	A37 $2.50 multicolored	4.25	4.25

Queen Mother Elizabeth, 80th birthday.

A38

A39

Designs: Nos. 119-120, Platform diving. Nos. 121-122, Archery. Nos. 123-124, Soccer. Nos. 125-126, Running. Stamps of same denomination se-tenant in continuous design.

1980, Nov. 14 Photo. *Perf. 13½*

119	A38 10c Falk Hoffman, DDR	.15	.15
120	A38 10c Martina Jaschke	.15	.15
121	A38 20c Tomi Polkolainen	.30	.30
122	A38 20c Kete Losaberidse	.30	.30
123	A38 30c Czechoslovakia, gold	.40	.40
124	A38 30c DDR, silver	.40	.40
125	A38 50c Barbel Wockel	.75	.75
126	A38 50c Pietro Mennea	.75	.75
a.	Souvenir sheet of 8, #119-126	3.75	3.75
	Nos. 119-126 (8)	3.20	3.20

22nd Summer Olympic Games, Moscow, July 19-Aug. 3.

1980, Dec. 5 Photo. *Perf. 13*

Christmas (15th Century Virgin and Child Paintings by): 20c, Virgin and Child, by Luis Dalmau. 35c, Serra brothers. 50c, Master of the Porciuncula.

127	A39 20c multicolored	.35	.35
128	A39 35c multicolored	.50	.50
129	A39 50c multicolored	.65	.65
a.	Souvenir sheet of 3, #127-129	1.75	1.75
	Nos. 127-129 (3)	1.50	1.50

See Nos. B7-B9.

Amatasi — A40

A41

Cutty Sark, 1869 A42

1981 Photo. *Perf. 14*

130	A40 1c shown	.15	.15
131	A40 1c Ndrua	.15	.15
132	A40 1c Waka	.15	.15
133	A40 1c Tongiaki	.15	.15
134	A40 3c Va'a teu'ua	.15	.15
135	A40 3c Victoria, 1500	.15	.15
136	A40 3c Golden Hinde, 1560	.15	.15
137	A40 3c Boudeuse, 1760	.15	.15
138	A40 4c Bounty, 1787	.15	.15
139	A40 4c Astrolabe, 1811	.15	.15
140	A40 4c Star of India, 1861	.15	.15
141	A40 4c Great Rep., 1853	.15	.15
142	A40 6c Balcutha, 1886	.15	.15
143	A40 6c Coonatto, 1863	.15	.15
144	A40 6c Antiope, 1866	.15	.15
145	A40 6c Teaping, 1863	.15	.15
146	A40 10c Preussen, 1902	.20	.20
147	A40 10c Pamir, 1921	.20	.20
148	A40 10c Cap Hornier, 1910	.20	.20
149	A40 10c Patriarch, 1869	.20	.20

Perf. 13½x14½

150	A41 15c shown	.28	.28
151	A41 15c Ndrua	.28	.28
152	A41 15c Waka	.28	.28
153	A41 15c Tongiaki	.28	.28
154	A41 20c Va'a Teu'ua	.40	.40
155	A41 20c Victoria, 1500	.40	.40
156	A41 20c Golden Hind, 1560	.40	.40
157	A41 20c Boudeuse, 1760	.40	.40
158	A41 30c Bounty, 1787	.60	.60
159	A41 30c Astrolabe, 1811	.60	.60
160	A41 30c Star of India, 1861	.60	.60
161	A41 30c Great Rep., 1853	.60	.60
162	A41 50c Balcutha, 1886	1.00	1.00
163	A41 50c Coonatto, 1863	1.00	1.00
164	A41 50c Antiope, 1866	1.00	1.00
165	A41 50c Teaping, 1863	1.00	1.00
166	A41 $1 Preussen, 1902	2.00	2.00
167	A41 $1 Pamir, 1921	2.00	2.00
168	A41 $1 Cap Hornier, 1910	2.00	2.00
169	A41 $1 Patriarch, 1869	2.00	2.00

Perf. 13½

170	A42 $2 shown	4.00	4.00
171	A42 $4 Mermerus, 1872	8.00	8.00
172	A42 $6 Resolution, Discovery, 1776	12.00	12.00
	Nos. 130-172 (43)	44.32	44.32

Stamps of same denomination se-tenant.

Issue dates: 1c-10c, Feb. 16. 15c-50c, Mar. 16. $1, May 15. $2, $4, June 26. $6, Sept. 21.

For surcharges and overprints see Nos. 232-243, 251, 254, 395, O35, O37, O39.

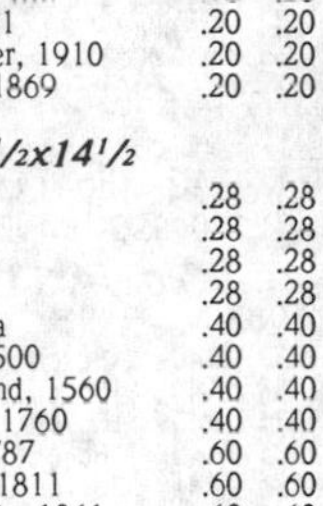

Christ with Crown of Thorns, by Titan — A44

Easter: 30c, Jesus at the Grove, by Paolo Veronese. 50c, Pieta, by Van Dyck.

1981, Apr. 5 *Perf. 14*

173	A44 30c multicolored	.50	.50
174	A44 40c multicolored	.65	.65
175	A44 50c multicolored	.80	.80
a.	Souv. sheet of 3, #173-175, perf. 13½	2.25	2.25
	Nos. 173-175 (3)	1.95	1.95

See Nos. B10-B12.

A45

A46

Designs: Portraits of Prince Charles.

1981, July 10 Photo. *Perf. 14*

176	A45 40c multicolored	.65	.65
177	A45 50c multicolored	.80	.80
178	A45 60c multicolored	1.00	1.00
179	A45 70c multicolored	1.25	1.25
180	A45 80c multicolored	1.40	1.40
a.	Souv. sheet of 5, #176-180+label	5.00	5.00
	Nos. 176-180 (5)	5.10	5.10

Royal wedding. Nos. 176-180 each issued in sheets of 5 plus label showing couple.

For overprints and surcharges see Nos. 195-199, 244-245, 248, 299-300, B13-B18.

1981, Dec. 7 Photo. *Perf. 13*

181	Strip of 3	.60	.60
a.	A46 15c, any single	.20	.20
182	Strip of 3	1.50	1.50
a.	A46 35c, any single	.50	.50
183	Strip of 3	2.00	2.00
a.	A46 50c, any single	.65	.65
	Nos. 181-183 (3)	4.10	4.10

1982 World Cup Soccer. See No. B19.

Christmas — A47

21st Birthday of Princess Diana — A48

Dürer Engravings: 30c, Virgin on a Crescent, 1508. 40c, Virgin at the Fence, 1503. 50c, Holy Virgin and Child, 1505.

1981, Dec. 15 Photo. *Perf. 13x13½*

184	A47 30c multicolored	.45	.45
185	A47 40c multicolored	.60	.60
186	A47 50c multicolored	.75	.75
a.	Souvenir sheet of 3	2.00	2.00
	Nos. 184-186 (3)	1.80	1.80

Souvenir Sheets

Perf. 14x13½

187	A47 70c + 5c like #184	1.50	1.50
188	A47 70c + 5c like #185	1.50	1.50
189	A47 70c + 5c like #186	1.50	1.50

No. 186a contains Nos. 184-186 each with 2c surcharge. Nos. 187-189 each contain one 25x40mm stamp. Surtaxes were for childrens' charities.

1982, July 1 Photo. *Perf. 14*

Designs: Portraits of Diana.

190	A48 30c multicolored	.38	.38
191	A48 50c multicolored	.65	.65
192	A48 70c multicolored	.95	.95
193	A48 80c multicolored	1.10	1.10
194	A48 $1.40 multicolored	1.90	1.90
a.	Souv. sheet of 5, #190-194 + label	5.25	5.25
	Nos. 190-194 (5)	4.98	4.98

For new inscriptions, overprints and surcharges, see Nos. 200-204, 246-247, 249-250, 301-302.

Nos. 176-180a Overprinted: "BIRTH OF PRINCE WILLIAM OF WALES 21 JUNE 1982"

1982, July 30

195	A45 40c multicolored	.95	.95
196	A45 50c multicolored	1.15	1.15
197	A45 60c multicolored	1.50	1.50
198	A45 70c multicolored	1.60	1.60
199	A45 80c multicolored	1.85	1.85
a.	Souvenir sheet of 5	10.00	10.00
	Nos. 195-199 (5)	7.05	7.05

Nos. 190-194a Inscribed in Silver: 21 JUNE 1982 BIRTH OF/PRINCE WILLIAM OF WALES or COMMEMORATING THE BIRTH OF/PRINCE WILLIAM OF WALES

1982 Photo. *Perf. 14*

200	A48	30c	21 June 1982	.50	.50
200A	A48	30c	Commem...	.50	.50
201	A48	50c	21 June 1982	.80	.80
201A	A48	50c	Commem...	.80	.80
202	A48	70c	21 June 1982	1.25	1.25
202A	A48	70c	Commem...	1.25	1.25
203	A48	80c	21 June 1982	1.40	1.40
203A	A48	80c	Commem...	1.40	1.40
204	A48	$1.40	21 June 1982	2.50	2.50
204A	A48	$1.40	Commem...	2.50	2.50
b.			Souvenir sheet of 5	6.50	6.50
			Nos. 200-204A (10)	12.90	12.90

Miniature sheets of each denomination were issued containing 2 "21 JUNE 1982...," 3 "COMMEMORATING...," and a label.

For surcharges see Nos. 247, 250, 253.

A49

A50

Christmas: Virgin and Child Paintings.

1982, Dec. 10 Photo. *Perf. 14*

205	A49	35c	Joos Van Cleve (1485-1540)	.60	.60
206	A49	48c	Filippino Lippi (1457-1504)	.80	.80
207	A49	60c	Cima Da Conegliano (1459-1517)	1.00	1.00
a.			Souvenir sheet of 3	2.75	2.75
			Nos. 205-207 (3)	2.40	2.40

Souvenir Sheets

208	A49	70c	+ 5c like 35c	1.40	1.40
209	A49	70c	+ 5c like 48c	1.40	1.40
210	A49	70c	+ 5c like 60c	1.40	1.40

No. 207a contains Nos. 205-207 each with 2c surcharge. Nos. 208-210 each contain one stamp, perf. 13½. Surtaxes were for childrens' charities.

1983, Mar. 14 *Perf. 13½x13*

211	A50	60c	Red coral	.80	.80
212	A50	60c	Aerial view	.80	.80
213	A50	60c	Eleanor Roosevelt, grass skirt	.80	.80
214	A50	60c	Map	.80	.80
			Nos. 211-214 (4)	3.20	3.20

Commonwealth day. Nos. 211-214 se-tenant.

For surcharges see Nos. O27-O30.

Scouting Year A51

Emblem and various tropical flowers.

1983, Apr. 5 *Perf. 13½x14½*

215	A51	36c	multicolored	.60	.60
216	A51	48c	multicolored	.80	.80
217	A51	60c	multicolored	1.00	1.00
			Nos. 215-217 (3)	2.40	2.40

Souvenir Sheet

218	A51	$2	multicolored	3.25	3.25

Nos. 215-218 Overprinted: "XV / WORLD JAMBOREE / CANADA / 1983"

1983, July 8 Photo. *Perf. 13½x14½*

219	A51	36c	multicolored	.60	.60
220	A51	48c	multicolored	1.00	1.00
221	A51	60c	multicolored	1.00	1.00
			Nos. 219-221 (3)	2.60	2.60

Souvenir Sheet

222	A51	$2	multicolored	3.25	3.25

15th World Boy Scout Jamboree.

Save the Whales Campaign A52

Various whale hunting scenes.

1983, July 29 Photo. *Perf. 13*

223	A52	8c	multicolored	.15	.15
224	A52	15c	multicolored	.25	.25
225	A52	35c	multicolored	.60	.60
226	A52	60c	multicolored	1.00	1.00
227	A52	$1	multicolored	1.75	1.75
			Nos. 223-227 (5)	3.75	3.75

World Communications Year — A53

Designs: Cable laying Vessels.

1983, Sept. Photo. *Perf. 13*

228	A53	36c	multicolored	.60	.60
229	A53	48c	multicolored	.80	.80
230	A53	60c	multicolored	1.00	1.00
			Nos. 228-230 (3)	2.40	2.40

Souvenir Sheet

231	Sheet of 3	2.50	2.50
a.	A53 36c + 3c like No. 228	.65	.65
b.	A53 48c + 3c like No. 229	.85	.85
c.	A53 60c + 3c like No. 230	.95	.95

Surtax was for local charities.

Nos. 146-149, 154-161, 170, 172, 178-180, 192-194, 202-204 Surcharged

Perf. 14, 13½x14½, 13½

1983 Photo.

232	A40	18c	on 10c #146	.35	.35
233	A40	18c	on 10c #147	.35	.35
234	A40	18c	on 10c #148	.35	.35
235	A40	18c	on 10c #149	.35	.35
236	A41	36c	on 20c #154	.70	.70
237	A41	36c	on 20c #155	.70	.70
238	A41	36c	on 20c #156	.70	.70
239	A41	36c	on 20c #157	.70	.70
240	A41	36c	on 30c #158	.70	.70
241	A41	36c	on 30c #159	.70	.70
242	A41	36c	on 30c #160	.70	.70
243	A41	36c	on 30c #161	.70	.70
244	A45	48c	on 60c multi	.90	.90
245	A45	72c	on 70c multi	1.50	1.50
246	A48	72c	on 70c #192	1.50	1.50
247	A48	72c	on 70c #202	1.50	1.50
247A	A48	72c	on 70c #202A	1.50	1.50
248	A45	96c	on 80c multi	1.75	1.75
249	A48	96c	on 80c #193	1.75	1.75
250	A48	96c	on 80c #203	1.75	1.75
250A	A48	96c	on 80c #203A	1.75	1.75
251	A42	$1.20	on $2 multi	2.25	2.25
252	A48	$1.20	on $1.40 #194	2.25	2.25
253	A48	$1.20	on $1.40 #204	2.25	2.25
253A	A48	$1.20	on $1.40 #204A	2.25	2.25
254	A42	$5.60	on $6 multi	10.50	10.50
			Nos. 232-254 (26)	40.40	40.40

Issued: #232-243, 245, 251, Sept. 26; #244, 246, 249, 252, 254, Oct. 28; others Dec. 1.

First Manned Balloon Flight, 200th Anniv. — A54

Designs: 36c, Airship, Sir George Cayley (1773-1857). 48c, Man-powered airship, Dupuy de Lome (1818-1885). 60c, Brazilian Aviation Pioneer, Alberto Santos Dumont (1873-1932). 96c, Practical Airship, Paul Lebaudy (1858-1937). $1.32, L-Z 127 Graf Zeppelin.

1983, Oct. 31 Litho. *Perf. 13*

255	A54	36c	multicolored	.60	.60
256	A54	48c	multicolored	.80	.80
257	A54	60c	multicolored	.95	.95
258	A54	96c	multicolored	1.50	1.50
259	A54	$1.32	multicolored	2.25	2.25
a.			Souvenir sheet of 5, #255-259	6.00	6.00
			Nos. 255-259 (5)	6.10	6.10

Nos. 255-259 se-tenant with labels. Sheets of 5 for each value exist.

Nos. 255-259 are misspelled "ISLANS." For correcting overprints see Nos. 287-291.

Christmas — A55

Raphael Paintings: 36c, Madonna in the Meadow. 42c, Tempi Madonna. 48c, Small Cowper Madonna. 60c, Madonna Della Tenda.

1983, Nov. 30 Photo. *Perf. 13x13½*

260	A55	36c	multicolored	.55	.55
261	A55	42c	multicolored	.65	.65
262	A55	48c	multicolored	.75	.75
263	A55	60c	multicolored	.95	.95
a.			Souvenir sheet of 4	3.00	3.00
			Nos. 260-263 (4)	2.90	2.90

Souvenir Sheets

Perf. 13½

264	A55	75c	+ 5c like #260	1.25	1.25
265	A55	75c	+ 5c like #261	1.25	1.25
266	A55	75c	+ 5c like #262	1.25	1.25
267	A55	75c	+ 5c like #263	1.25	1.25

No. 263a contains Nos. 260-263 each with 3c surcharge. Nos. 264-267 each contain one 29x41mm stamp. Issued Dec. 28. Surtaxes were for children's charities.

Waka Canoe — A56

1984 Photo. *Perf. 14½*

268	A56	2c	shown	.15	.15
269	A56	4c	Amatasi fishing boat	.15	.15
270	A56	5c	Ndrua canoe	.15	.15
271	A56	8c	Tongiaki canoe	.15	.15
272	A56	10c	Victoria, 1500	.15	.15
273	A56	18c	Golden Hind, 1560	.25	.25
274	A56	20c	Boudeuse, 1760	.28	.28
275	A56	30c	Bounty, 1787	.40	.40
276	A56	36c	Astrolabe, 1811	.50	.50
277	A56	48c	Great Republic, 1853	.65	.65
278	A56	50c	Star of India, 1861	.68	.68
279	A56	60c	Coonatto, 1863	.80	.80
280	A56	72c	Antiope, 1866	1.00	1.00
281	A56	80c	Balcutha, 1886	1.10	1.10
282	A56	96c	Cap Hornier, 1910	1.40	1.40
283	A56	$1.20	Pamir, 1921	1.60	1.60

Perf. 13

Size: 42x34mm

284	A56	$3	Mermerus, 1872	3.00	3.00
285	A56	$5	Cutty Sark, 1869	4.75	4.75
286	A56	$9.60	Resolution, Discovery	9.00	9.00
			Nos. 268-286 (19)	26.16	26.16

Issue dates: Nos. 268-277, Feb. 8. Nos. 278-283, Mar. 23. Nos. 284-286 June 15.

For overprints and surcharges see Nos. O16-O26, O31-O34, O36, O38, O40.

Nos. 255-259a Ovptd. with Silver Bar and "NORTHERN COOK ISLANDS" in Black

1984 Litho. *Perf. 13*

287	A54	36c	multicolored	.90	.90
288	A54	48c	multicolored	1.20	1.20
289	A54	60c	multicolored	1.50	1.50
290	A54	96c	multicolored	2.40	2.40
291	A54	$1.32	multicolored	3.25	3.25
a.			Souvenir sheet of 5, #287-291	9.25	9.25
			Nos. 287-291 (5)	9.25	9.25

1984 Los Angeles Summer Olympic Games A57

1984, July 20 Photo. *Perf. 13½x13*

292	A57	35c	Olympic flag	.38	.38
293	A57	60c	Torch, flags	.60	.60
294	A57	$1.80	Classic runners, Memorial Coliseum	1.90	1.90
			Nos. 292-294 (3)	2.88	2.88

Souvenir Sheet

295	Sheet of 3 + label	2.75	2.75
a.	A57 35c + 5c like #292	.30	.30
b.	A57 50c + 5c like #293	.55	.55
c.	A57 $1.80 + 5c like #294	1.90	1.90

Surtax for amateur sports.

AUSIPEX '84 — A57a

1984, Sept. 20

296	A57a	60c	Nos. 136, 108, 180, 104b	.60	.60
297	A57a	$1.20	Map of South Pacific	1.25	1.25

Souvenir Sheet

298	Sheet of 2	2.00	2.00
a.	A57a 96c like #296	1.00	1.00
b.	A57a 96c like #297	1.00	1.00

For surcharge see No. 345.

Nos. 176-177, 190-191 Ovptd. "Birth of/Prince Henry/15 Sept. 1984" and Surcharged in Black or Gold

1984, Oct. 18 *Perf. 14*

299	A45	$2	on 40c	2.25	2.25
300	A45	$2	on 50c	2.25	2.25
301	A48	$2	on 30c	2.25	2.25
302	A48	$2	on 50c	2.25	2.25
			Nos. 299-302 (4)	9.00	9.00

Nos. 209-302 printed in sheets of 5 plus one label each picturing a portrait of the royal couple or an heraldic griffin.

Christmas 1984 — A58

Paintings: 36c, Virgin and Child, by Giovanni Bellini. 48c, Virgin and Child, by Lorenzo di Credi. 60c, Virgin and Child, by Palma, the Older. 96c, Virgin and Child, by Raphael.

1984, Nov. 15 Photo. *Perf. 13x13½*

303	A58	36c	multicolored	.32	.32
304	A58	48c	multicolored	.45	.45
305	A58	60c	multicolored	.55	.55
306	A58	96c	multicolored	.90	.90
a.			Souvenir sheet of 4	3.00	3.00
			Nos. 303-306 (4)	2.22	2.22

Souvenir Sheets

307	A58	96c	+ 10c like #303	1.20	1.20
308	A58	96c	+ 10c like #304	1.20	1.20
309	A58	96c	+ 10c like #305	1.20	1.20
310	A58	96c	+ 10c like #306	1.20	1.20

No. 306a contains Nos. 303-306, each with 5c surcharge. Nos. 307-310 issued Dec. 10. Surtax for children's charities.

Audubon Bicentenary A59

1985, Apr. 9 — Photo. — Perf. 13

311	A59	20c Harlequin duck	.18	.18
312	A59	55c Sage grouse	.50	.50
313	A59	65c Solitary sandpiper	.60	.60
314	A59	75c Red-backed sandpiper	.70	.70
		Nos. 311-314 (4)	1.98	1.98

Souvenir Sheets
Perf. 13½x13

315	A59	95c Like #311	.85	.85
316	A59	95c Like #312	.85	.85
317	A59	95c Like #313	.85	.85
318	A59	95c Like #314	.85	.85

For surcharges see Nos. 391-394.

Queen Mother, 85th Birthday — A60

1985, June 24 — Photo. — Perf. 13x13½

319	A60	75c Photograph, 1921	.75	.75
320	A60	95c New mother, 1926	.90	.90
321	A60	$1.20 Coronation day, 1937	1.10	1.10
322	A60	$2.80 70th birthday	2.75	2.75
a.		Souvenir sheet of 4, #319-322	3.50	3.50
		Nos. 319-322 (4)	5.50	5.50

Souvenir Sheet

323	A60	$5 Portrait, c. 1980	4.75	4.75

No. 322a issued on 8/4/86, for 86th birthday.

Intl. Youth Year — A61

Grimm Brothers' fairy tales.

1985, Sept. 10 — Perf. 13x13½

324	A61	75c House in the Wood	.90	.90
325	A61	95c Snow White and Rose Red	1.15	1.15
326	A61	$1.15 Goose Girl	1.40	1.40
		Nos. 324-326 (3)	3.45	3.45

Christmas 1985 — A62

Paintings (details) by Murillo: 75c, No. 330a, The Annunciation. $1.15, No. 330b, Adoration of the Shepherds. $1.80, No. 330c, The Holy Family.

1985, Nov. 25 — Photo. — Perf. 14

327	A62	75c multicolored	.90	.90
328	A62	$1.15 multicolored	1.40	1.40
329	A62	$1.80 multicolored	2.25	2.25
		Nos. 327-329 (3)	4.55	4.55

Souvenir Sheets
Perf. 13½

330		Sheet of 3	3.50	3.50
a.-c.		A62 95c any single	1.15	1.15
331	A62	$1.20 like #327	1.25	1.25
332	A62	$1.45 like #328	1.50	1.50
333	A62	$2.75 like #329	2.75	2.75

Halley's Comet — A63

Fire and Ice, by Camille Rendal. Nos. 334-335 se-tenant in continuous design.

1986, Feb. 4 — Perf. 13½x13

334	A63	$1.50 Comet head	1.75	1.75
335	A63	$1.50 Comet tail	1.75	1.75

Size: 109x43mm
Imperf

336	A63	$3 multicolored	3.50	3.50
		Nos. 334-336 (3)	7.00	7.00

Elizabeth II, 60th Birthday A64

1986, Apr. 21 — Perf. 14

337	A64	95c Age 3	1.15	1.15
338	A64	$1.45 Wearing crown	1.75	1.75

Size: 60x34mm
Perf. 13½x13

339	A64	$2.50 Both portraits	3.00	3.00
		Nos. 337-339 (3)	5.90	5.90

A65   A66

Statue of Liberty, Cent.: 95c, Statue, scaffolding. $1.75 Removing copper facade. $3, Restored statue on Liberty Island.

1986, June 27 — Photo. — Perf. 13½

340	A65	95c gold, pale grn & sep	1.00	1.00
341	A65	$1.75 gold, pale grn & sep	1.90	1.90
342	A65	$3 gold, pale grn & sep	3.25	3.25
		Nos. 340-342 (3)	6.15	6.15

1986, July 23 — Perf. 13x13½

343	A66	$2.50 Portraits	2.75	2.75
344	A66	$3.50 Profiles	4.00	4.00

Wedding of Prince Andrew and Sarah Ferguson. Nos. 343-344 each printed in sheets of 4 plus 2 center decorative labels.

No. 298 Surcharged with Gold Circle, Bar, New Value in Black and Exhibition Emblem in Gold and Black

1986, Aug. 4

345		Sheet of 2	4.50	4.50
a.		A57a S2 on 96c #208a	2.25	2.25
b.		A57a S2 on 96c #208b	2.25	2.25

STAMPEX '86, Adelaide, Aug. 4-10.

Christmas — A67

Engravings by Rembrandt: 65c, No. 349a, Adoration of the Shepherds. $1.75, No. 349b, Virgin and Child. $2.50, No. 349c, The Holy Family.

1986, Nov. 20 — Litho. — Perf. 13x13½

346	A67	65c gold, hn brn & buff	.70	.70
347	A67	$1.75 gold, hn brn & buff	1.85	1.85
348	A67	$2.50 gold, hn brn & buff	2.65	2.65
		Nos. 346-348 (3)	5.20	5.20

Souvenir Sheet
Perf. 13½x13

349		Sheet of 3	4.80	4.80
a.-c.		A67 $1.50 any single	1.60	1.60

Corrected inscription is black on silver. For surcharges see Nos. B20-B23.

Souvenir Sheets

Statue of Liberty, Cent. A68

Photographs: No. 350a, Workmen, crown. No. 350b, Ellis Is., aerial view. No. 350c, Immigration building, Ellis Is. No. 350d, Buildings, opposite side of Ellis Is. No. 350e, Workmen inside torch structure. No. 351a, Liberty's head and torch. No. 351b, Torch. No. 351c, Workmen on scaffold. No. 351d, Statue, full figure. No. 351e, Workmen beside statue. Nos. 351a-351e vert.

1987, Apr. 15 — Litho. — Perf. 14

350		Sheet of 5 + label	3.50	3.50
a.-e.		A68 65c any single	.70	.70
351		Sheet of 5 + label	3.50	3.50
a.-e.		A68 65c any single	.70	.70

Nos. 62-63 Ovptd. "Fortieth Royal Wedding / Anniversary 1947-87" in Lilac Rose

1987, Nov. 20 — Photo. — Perf. 13½x14

352	A18	$2 multicolored	2.00	2.00
353	A18	$5 multicolored	5.25	5.25

Christmas — A69

Paintings (details) by Raphael: 95c, No. 357a, The Garvagh Madonna, the National Gallery, London. $1.60, No. 357b, The Alba Madonna, the National Gallery of Art, Washington. $2.25, No. 357c, The Madonna of the Fish, Prado Museum, Madrid.

1987, Dec. 11 — Photo. — Perf. 13½

354	A69	95c multicolored	1.25	1.25
355	A69	$1.60 multicolored	2.05	2.05
356	A69	$2.25 multicolored	2.90	2.90
		Nos. 354-356 (3)	6.20	6.20

Souvenir Sheets

357		Sheet of 3 + label	4.35	4.35
a.-c.		A69 $1.15 any single	1.45	1.45
358	A69	$4.80 multicolored	6.25	6.25

No. 358 contains one 31x39mm stamp.

1988 Summer Olympics, Seoul — A70

Events and: 55c, $1.25, Seoul Games emblem. 95c, Obverse of a $50 silver coin issued in 1987 to commemorate the participation of Cook Islands athletes in the Olympics for the 1st time. $1.50, Coin reverse.

Perf. 13½x13, 13x13½

1988, July 29 — Photo.

359	A70	55c Running	.70	.70
360	A70	95c High jump, vert.	1.25	1.25
361	A70	$1.25 Shot put	1.50	1.50
362	A70	$1.50 Tennis, vert.	1.75	1.75
		Nos. 359-362 (4)	5.20	5.20

Souvenir Sheet

363		Sheet of 2	5.00	5.00
a.		A70 $2.50 like 95c	2.25	2.25
b.		A70 $2.50 like $1.50	2.25	2.25

Nos. 359-363 Ovptd. for Olympic Gold Medalists

a. "CARL LEWIS / UNITED STATES / 100 METERS"
b. "LOUISE RITTER / UNITED STATES / HIGH JUMP"
c. "ULF TIMMERMANN / EAST GERMANY / SHOT-PUT"
d. "STEFFI GRAF / WEST GERMANY / WOMEN'S TENNIS"
e. "JACKIE / JOYNER-KERSEE / United States / Heptathlon"
f. "STEFFI GRAF / West Germany / Women's Tennis / MILOSLAV MECIR / Czechoslovakia / Men's Tennis"

Perf. 13½x13, 13x13½

1988, Oct. 14 — Photo.

364	A70(a)	55c on No. 359	.75	.75
365	A70(b)	95c on No. 360	1.30	1.30
366	A70(c)	$1.25 on No. 361	1.70	1.70
367	A70(d)	$1.50 on No. 362	2.00	2.00
		Nos. 364-367 (4)	5.75	5.75

Souvenir Sheet

368		Sheet of 2	6.75	6.75
a.		A70(e) $2.50 on No. 363a	3.35	3.35
b.		A70(f) $2.50 on No. 363b	3.35	3.35

Christmas — A71

Virgin and Child paintings by Titian.

1988, Nov. 9 — Perf. 13x13½

369	A71	70c multicolored	.80	.80
370	A71	85c multi, diff.	.95	.95
371	A71	95c multi, diff.	1.00	1.00
372	A71	$1.25 multi, diff.	1.40	1.40
		Nos. 369-372 (4)	4.15	4.15

Souvenir Sheet
Perf. 13

373	A71	$6.40 multi, diff.	7.00	7.00

No. 373 contains one diamond-shaped stamp, size: 55x55mm.

1st Moon Landing, 20th Anniv. A72

Apollo 11 mission emblem, US flag and: 55c, First step on the Moon. 75c, Astronaut carrying equipment. 95c, Conducting experiment. $1.25, Crew members Armstrong, Collins and Aldrin. $1.75, Armstrong and Aldrin aboard lunar module.

1989, July 24 — Photo. — Perf. 14

374	A72	55c multicolored	.65	.65
375	A72	75c multicolored	.90	.90
376	A72	95c multicolored	1.15	1.15
377	A72	$1.25 multicolored	1.50	1.50
378	A72	$1.75 multicolored	2.10	2.10
		Nos. 374-378 (5)	6.30	6.30

Christmas — A73

Details from The Nativity, by Albrecht Durer, 1498, center panel of the Paumgartner altarpiece: 55c, Madonna. 70c, Christ child, cherubs. 85c, Joseph. $1.25, Attendants. $6.40, Entire painting.

1989, Nov. 17 — Photo. — Perf. 13x13½

379	A73	55c multicolored	.65	.65
380	A73	70c multicolored	.82	.82
381	A73	85c multicolored	1.00	1.00
382	A73	$1.25 multicolored	1.45	1.45
		Nos. 379-382 (4)	3.92	3.92

Souvenir Sheet

383	A73	$6.40 multicolored	6.75	6.75

No. 383 contains one 31x50mm stamp.

Queen Mother, 90th Birthday — A74

1990, July 24   Photo.   Perf. 13½
384 A74 $2.25 multicolored   2.75 2.75

Souvenir Sheet
385 A74 $7.50 multicolored   8.75 8.75

Christmas — A75

Paintings: 55c, Adoration of the Magi by Veronese. 70c, Virgin and Child by Quentin Metsys. 85c, Virgin and Child Jesus by Van Der Goes. $1.50, Adoration of the Kings by Jan Gossaert. $6.40, Virgin and Child with Saints Francis, John the Baptist, Zenobius and Lucy by Domenico Veneziano.

1990, Nov. 26   Litho.   Perf. 14
386 A75   55c multicolored   .68   .68
387 A75   70c multicolored   .85   .85
388 A75   85c multicolored   1.00 1.00
389 A75 $1.50 multicolored   1.85 1.85
    Nos. 386-389 (4)   4.38 4.38

Souvenir Sheet
390 A75 $6.40 multicolored   7.00 7.00

Nos. 311-314
Surcharged in **$1.50**
Red or Black

1990, Dec. 5   Photo.   Perf. 13
391 A59 $1.50 on 20c (R)   1.85 1.85
392 A59 $1.50 on 55c   1.85 1.85
393 A59 $1.50 on 65c   1.85 1.85
394 A59 $1.50 on 75c (R)   1.85 1.85
    Nos. 391-394 (4)   7.40 7.40

Birdpex '90, 20th Intl. Ornithological Cong., New Zealand. Surcharge appears in various locations.

No. 172 Overprinted
"COMMEMORATING 65th BIRTHDAY OF H.M. QUEEN ELIZABETH II"

1991, Apr. 22   Photo.   Perf. 13½
395 A42 $6 multicolored   7.00 7.00

Christmas A76

Paintings: 55c, Virgin and Child with Saints, by Gerard David. 85c, The Nativity, by Tintoretto. $1.15, Mystic Nativity, by Botticelli. $1.85, Adoration of the Shepherds, by Murillo. $6.40, Madonna of the Chair, by Raphael.

1991, Nov. 11   Litho.   Perf. 14
396 A76   55c multicolored   .65   .65
397 A76   85c multicolored   1.00 1.00
398 A76 $1.15 multicolored   1.35 1.35
399 A76 $1.85 multicolored   2.15 2.15
    Nos. 396-399 (4)   5.15 5.15

Souvenir Sheet
400 A76 $6.40 multicolored   7.40 7.40

1992 Summer Olympics, Barcelona — A77

1992, July 27   Litho.   Perf. 14
401 A77   75c Runners   .90   .90
402 A77   95c Boxing   1.20 1.20
403 A77 $1.15 Swimming   1.45 1.45
404 A77 $1.50 Wrestling   1.90 1.90
    Nos. 401-404 (4)   5.45 5.45

6th Festival of Pacific Arts, Rarotonga — A78

Festival poster and: $1.15, Marquesan canoe. $1.75, Statue of Tangaroa. $1.95, Manihiki canoe.

1992, Oct. 16   Litho.   Perf. 14x15
405 A78 $1.15 multicolored   1.20 1.20
406 A78 $1.75 multicolored   1.80 1.80
407 A78 $1.95 multicolored   2.00 2.00
    Nos. 405-407 (3)   5.00 5.00

Overprinted "ROYAL VISIT"

1992, Oct. 16
408 A78 $1.15 on #405   1.20 1.20
409 A78 $1.75 on #406   1.80 1.80
410 A78 $1.95 on #407   2.00 2.00
    Nos. 408-410 (3)   5.00 5.00

Christmas A79

Paintings by Ambrogio Borgognone: 55c, $6.40, Virgin with Child and Saints. 85c, Virgin on Throne. $1.05, Virgin on Carpet. $1.85, Virgin of the Milk.

1992, Nov. 18   Litho.   Perf. 13½
411 A79   55c multicolored   .58   .58
412 A79   85c multicolored   .90   .90
413 A79 $1.05 multicolored   1.10 1.10
414 A79 $1.85 multicolored   1.90 1.90
    Nos. 411-414 (4)   4.48 4.48

Souvenir Sheet
415 A79 $6.40 multicolored   6.50 6.50

No. 415 contains one 38x48mm stamp.

Discovery of America, 500th Anniv. — A80

Designs: $1.15, Vicente Yanez Pinzon, Nina. $1.35, Martin Alonso Pinzon, Pinta. $1.75, Columbus, Santa Maria.

1992, Dec. 4   Perf. 15x14
416 A80 $1.15 multicolored   1.20 1.20
417 A80 $1.35 multicolored   1.40 1.40
418 A80 $1.75 multicolored   1.85 1.85
    Nos. 416-418 (3)   4.45 4.45

Coronation of Queen Elizabeth II, 40th Anniv. — A81

1993, June 4   Litho.   Perf. 14x14½
419 A81 $6 multicolored   6.75 6.75

Marine Life — A82

Marine Life — A82a

1993-94   Litho.   Perf. 14
420 A82   5c Helmet shell   .15   .15
421 A82   10c Daisy coral   .15   .15
422 A82   15c Hydroid coral   .18   .18
423 A82   20c Feather star   .22   .22
424 A82   25c Sea star   .28   .28
425 A82   30c Nudibranch   .35   .35
426 A82   50c Smooth sea star   .58   .58
427 A82   70c Black pearl oyster .80   .80
428 A82   80c Pyjama nudibranch   .90   .90
429 A82   85c Prickly sea cucumber .95 .95
430 A82   90c Organ pipe coral   1.00 1.00
431 A82 $1 Aeolid nudibranch   1.10 1.10
432 A82 $2 Textile cone shell 2.25 2.25
433 A82a $3 pink & multi   3.25 3.25
434 A82a $5 lilac & multi   5.50 5.50
    Nos. 420-434 (15)   17.66 17.66

Issued: 80c, 85c, 90c, $1, $2, 12/3/93; $3, $5, 11/21/94; others, 10/18/93.
This is an expanding set. Numbers will change if necessary.

Christmas — A83

Details from Virgin on Throne with Child, by Cosimo Tura: 55c, Madonna and Child. 85c, Musicians. $1.05, Musicians, diff. $1.95, Woman. $4.50, Entire painting.

1993, Nov. 2   Litho.   Perf. 14
436 A83   55c multicolored   .60   .60
437 A83   85c multicolored   .95   .95
438 A83 $1.05 multicolored   1.10 1.10
439 A83 $1.95 multicolored   2.25 2.25

Size: 32x47mm
Perf. 13½
440 A83 $4.50 multicolored   5.00 5.00
    Nos. 436-440 (5)   9.90 9.90

First Manned Moon Landing, 25th Anniv. A84

1994, July 20   Litho.   Perf. 14
441 A84 $3.25 multicolored   3.50 3.50

Christmas — A85

Details or entire paintings: No. 442a, Virgin and Child with Saints Paul & Jerome, by Vivarini. b, The Virgin and Child with St. John, by B. Luini. c, The Virgin and Child with Saints Jerome & Dominic, by F. Lippi. d, Adoration of Shepherds, by Murillo.
No. 443a, Adoration of the Kings, by Raphael. c, Madonna & Child with the Infant Baptist, by Raphael. c, Adoration of the Kings, by Reni, diff. d, Virgin and Child, by Bergognone.

1994, Nov. 30   Litho.   Perf. 14
442 A85 90c Block of 4, #a.-d.   4.50 4.50
443 A85 $1 Block of 4, #a.-d.   5.00 5.00

End of World War II, 50th Anniv. — A86

Designs: a, Battleships on fire, Pearl Harbor, Dec. 7, 1941. b, B-29 bomber Enola Gay, A-bomb cloud, Aug. 1945.

1995, Sept. 4   Litho.   Perf. 13
444 A86 $3.75 Pair, #a.-b.   10.00 10.00

Queen Mother, 95th Birthday A87

1995, Sept. 14   Litho.   Perf. 13½
445 A87 $4.50 multicolored   6.00 6.00

No. 445 was issued in sheets of 4.

UN, 50th Anniv. — A88

1995, Oct. 20   Litho.   Perf. 13½
446 A88 $4 multicolored   5.25 5.25

No. 446 was issued in sheets of 4.

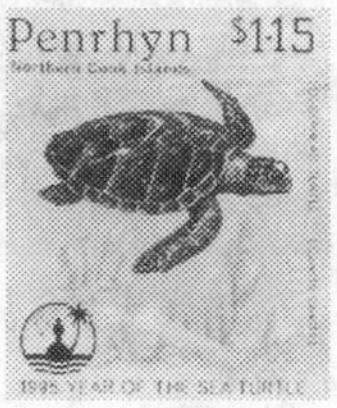

1995, Year of the Sea Turtle — A89

Turtles: No. 447a, Loggerhead. b, Hawksbill. No. 448a, Olive ridley. b, Green.

1995, Dec. 7 Litho. *Perf. 13½*

447	A89	$1.15 Pair, #a.-b.	3.00	3.00
448	A89	$1.65 Pair, #a.-b.	4.50	4.50

SEMI-POSTAL STAMPS

Catalogue values for unused stamps in this section are for Never Hinged items.

Easter Type of 1978

Souvenir Sheets

Rubens Paintings: No. B1, like #101. No. B2, like #102. No. B3, like #103.

1978, Apr. 17 Photo. *Perf. 13½x13*

B1	A31	60c + 5c multi	1.25	1.25
B2	A31	60c + 5c multi	1.25	1.25
B3	A31	60c + 5c multi	1.25	1.25

Surtax was for school children.

Easter Type of 1980

Souvenir Sheets

1980, Mar. 28 Photo. *Perf. 13x13½*

B4	A36	70c + 5c like #114	1.25	1.25
B5	A36	70c + 5c like #115	1.25	1.25
B6	A36	70c + 5c like #116	1.25	1.25

Surtax was for local charities.

Christmas Type of 1980

Souvenir Sheets

1980, Dec. 5 Photo. *Perf. 13*

B7	A39	70c + 5c like #127	1.25	1.25
B8	A39	70c + 5c like #128	1.25	1.25
B9	A39	70c + 5c like #129	1.25	1.25

Surtax was for local charities.

Easter Type of 1981

Souvenir Sheets

1981, Apr. 5 Photo. *Perf. 13½*

B10	A44	70c + 5c like #173	1.25	1.25
B11	A44	70c + 5c like #174	1.25	1.25
B12	A44	70c + 5c like #175	1.25	1.25

Surtax was for local charities.

Nos. 176-180a Surcharged

1981, Nov. 30 Photo. *Perf. 14*

B13	A45	40c + 5c like #176	1.15	1.15
B14	A45	50c + 5c like #177	1.40	1.40
B15	A45	60c + 5c like #178	1.65	1.65
B16	A45	70c + 5c like #179	1.90	1.90
B17	A45	80c + 5c like #180	2.15	2.15
		Nos. B13-B17 (5)	8.25	8.25

Souvenir Sheet

B18		Sheet of 5	5.75	5.75
a.	A45	40c + 10c like #176	.80	.80
b.	A45	50c + 10c like #177	.90	.90
c.	A45	60c + 10c like #178	1.10	1.10
d.	A45	70c + 10c like #179	1.40	1.40
e.	A45	80c + 10c like #180	1.50	1.50

Intl. Year of the Disabled. Surtax was for the disabled.

Soccer Type of 1981

1981, Dec. 7 *Perf. 13*

B19	A46	Sheet of 9	5.50	5.50

No. B19 contains Nos. 181-183. Surtax was for local sports.

Nos. 346-349 Surcharged ".SOUTH PACIFIC PAPAL VISIT . 21 TO 24 NOVEMBER 1986" in Metallic Blue

1986, Nov. 24 Litho. *Perf. 13x13½*

B20	A67	65c + 10c multi	.80	.80
B21	A67	$1.75 + 10c multi	2.00	2.00
B22	A67	$2.50 + 10c multi	2.75	2.75
		Nos. B20-B22 (3)	5.55	5.55

Souvenir Sheet

Perf. 13½x13

B23		Sheet of 3	5.25	5.25
a.-c.		A67 $1.50 + 10c on #349a-349c	1.75	1.75

No. B23 inscribed "COMMEMORATING FIRST PAPAL VISIT TO SOUTH PACIFIC / VISIT OF POPE JOHN PAUL II . NOVEMBER 1986."

OFFICIAL STAMPS

Catalogue values for unused stamps in this section are for Never Hinged items.

Nos. 51-60, 80, 88-89 Overprinted or Surcharged in Black, Silver or Gold **O.H.M.S**

Perf. 13½x14, 13½, 13½x13

1978, Nov. 14 Photo.

O1	A17	1c multi	.15	.15
O2	A17	2c multi	.15	.15
O3	A17	3c multi	.15	.15
O4	A17	4c multi	.15	.15
O5	A17	5c multi	.15	.15
O6	A17	8c multi	.15	.15
O7	A17	10c multi	.18	.18
O8	A17	15c on 60c multi	.25	.25
O9	A17	18c on 60c multi	.35	.35
O10	A17	20c multi	.38	.38
O11	A17	25c multi (S)	.40	.40
O12	A17	30c on 60c multi	.60	.60
O13	A24	Strip of 3, multi	2.75	2.75
a.		50c, No. 80a (G)	.80	.80
b.		50c, No. 80b (G)	.80	.80
c.		50c, No. 80c (G)	.80	.80
O14	A27	$1 multi (S)	2.00	2.00
O15	A27	$2 multi (G)	4.00	4.00
		Nos. O1-O15 (15)	11.81	11.81

Overprint on No. O14 diagonal.

Nos. 260-276, 278, 277, 211-214, 280, 282, 281, 283, 170, 284, 171, 285, 172, 286 Surcharged with Bar and New Value or Ovptd. "O.H.M.S." in Silver or Metallic Red

1985-87 Photo. *Perfs. as before*

O16	A56	2c multi	.15	.15
O17	A56	4c multi	.15	.15
O18	A56	5c multi	.15	.15
O19	A56	8c multi	.15	.15
O20	A56	10c multi	.15	.15
O21	A56	18c multi	.20	.20
O22	A56	20c multi	.22	.22
O23	A56	30c multi	.35	.35
O24	A56	40c on 36c	.45	.45
O25	A56	50c multi	.55	.55
O26	A56	55c on 48c	.62	.62
O27	A50	65c on 60c #211	.72	.72
O28	A50	65c on 60c #212	.72	.72
O29	A50	65c on 60c #213	.72	.72
O30	A50	65c on 60c #214	.72	.72
O31	A56	75c on 72c	.85	.85
O32	A56	75c on 96c	.85	.85
O33	A56	80c multi	.90	.90
O34	A56	$1.20 multi	1.35	1.35
O35	A42	$2 multi (R)	2.25	2.25
O36	A56	$3 multi	3.35	3.35
O37	A42	$4 multi (R)	4.50	4.50
O38	A56	$5 multi	6.00	6.00
O39	A42	$6 multi (R)	7.25	7.25
O40	A56	$9.60 multi	11.75	11.75
		Nos. O16-O40 (25)	45.07	45.07

Issue dates: Nos. O16-O30, Aug. 15. Nos. O31-O37, Apr. 29, 1986. Nos. O38-O40, Nov. 2, 1987.

PITCAIRN ISLANDS

'pit-ˌkarn 'ī-ləndz

LOCATION — South Pacific Ocean, nearly equidistant from Australia and South America

GOVT. — British colony under the British High Commissioner in New Zealand

AREA — 1.75 sq. mi.

POP. — 57 (1984)

The district of Pitcairn also includes the uninhabited islands of Ducie, Henderson and Oeno.

Postal affairs are administered by Fiji.

12 Pence = 1 Shilling

100 Cents = 1 Dollar (1967)

Catalogue values for all unused stamps in this country are for Never Hinged items.

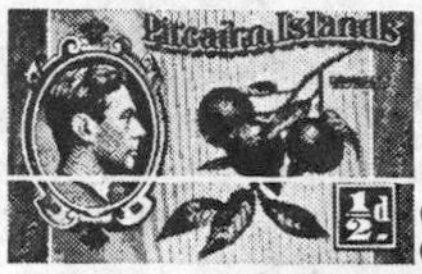

Cluster of Oranges — A1

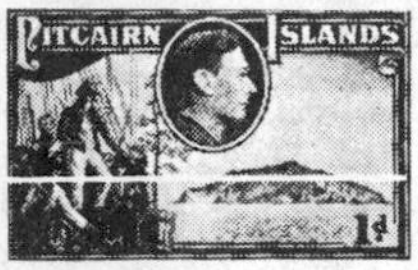

Fletcher Christian with Crew and View of Pitcairn Island — A2

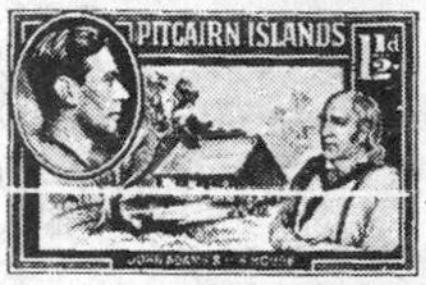

John Adams and His House — A3

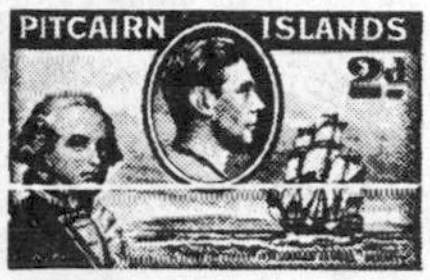

William Bligh and H. M. Armed Vessel "Bounty" A4

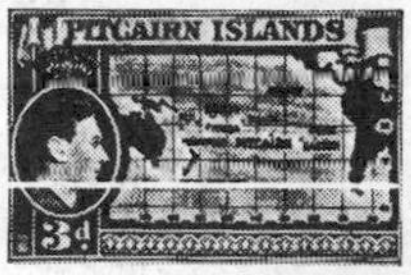

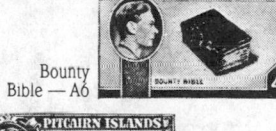

Map of Pitcairn and Pacific Ocean — A5

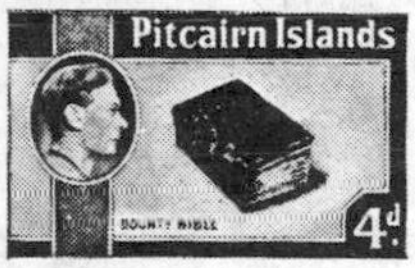

Bounty Bible — A6

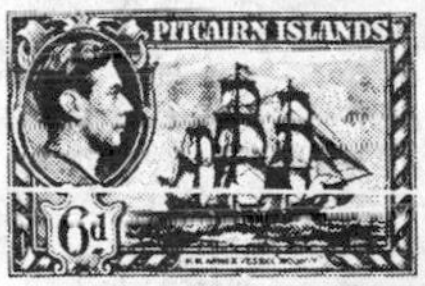

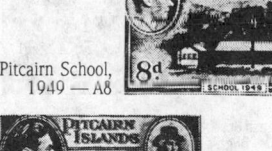

H.M. Armed Vessel "Bounty" A7

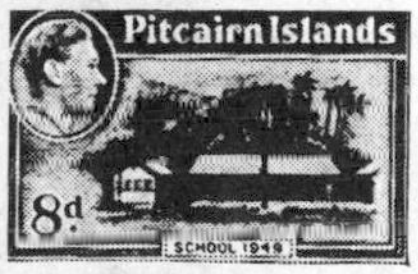

Pitcairn School, 1949 — A8

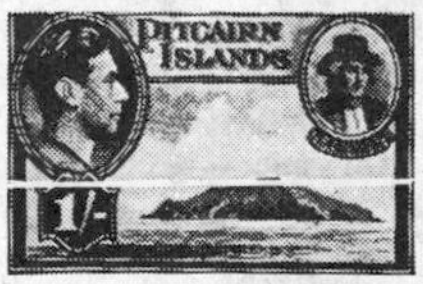

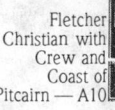

Fletcher Christian and View of Pitcairn Island — A9

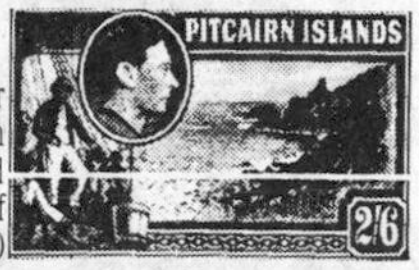

Fletcher Christian with Crew and Coast of Pitcairn — A10

Perf. 12½, 11½x11

1940-51 Engr. Wmk. 4

1	A1	½p blue grn & org	.35	.25
2	A2	1p red lil & rose vio	.50	.40
3	A3	1½p rose car & blk	.50	.65
4	A4	2p dk brn & brt grn	1.50	1.00
5	A5	3p dk blue & yel grn	1.25	1.25
5A	A6	4p dk blue grn & blk	13.00	6.50
6	A7	6p sl grn & dp brn	4.50	2.00
6A	A8	8p lil rose & grn	13.00	6.50
7	A9	1sh slate & vio	3.50	2.25
8	A10	2sh6p dk brn & brt grn	7.50	5.00
		Nos. 1-8 (10)	45.60	25.80

Nos. 1-5, 6 and 7-8 exist in a booklet of eight panes of one.

Issued: 4p, 8p, 9/1/51; others, 10/15/40.

Peace Issue

Common Design Type

1946, Dec. 2 *Perf. 13½x14*

9	CD303	2p brown	.50	.50
10	CD303	3p deep blue	.95	.95

Common Design Types pictured in section before Great Britain.

Silver Wedding Issue

Common Design Types

1949, Aug. 1 Photo. *Perf. 14x14½*

11	CD304	1½p scarlet	1.50	.75

Engraved; Name Typographed

Perf. 11½x11

12	CD305	10sh purple	80.00	*60.00*

UPU Issue

Common Design Types

Engr.; Name Typo. on 3p & 6p

1949, Oct. 10 *Perf. 13½, 11x11½*

13	CD306	2½p red brown	6.00	2.75
14	CD307	3p indigo	6.00	2.75
15	CD308	6p green	11.00	5.00
16	CD309	1sh rose violet	22.50	10.00
		Nos. 13-16 (4)	45.50	20.50

Coronation Issue

Common Design Type

1953, June 2 *Perf. 13½x13*

19	CD312	4p dk green & blk	3.00	1.10

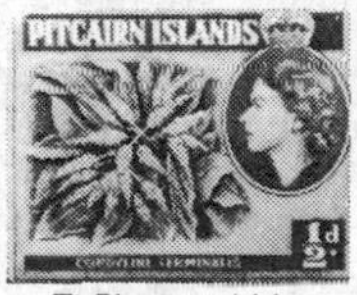

Ti Plant — A11

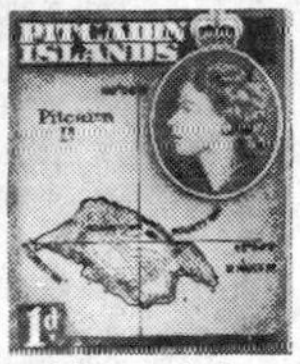

Map — A12

Designs: 2p, John Adams and Bounty Bible. 2½p, Handicraft (Carving). 3p, Bounty Bay. 4p, School (actually Schoolteacher's House). 6p, Fiji-Pitcairn connection (Map). 8p, Inland scene. 1sh, Handicraft (Ship model). 2sh, Wheelbarrow. 2sh6p, Whaleboat.

Perf. 13x12½, 12½x13

1957, July 2 Engr. Wmk. 4

20	A11	½p lilac & green	.35	.15
21	A12	1p olive grn & blk	.50	.20
22	A12	2p blue & brown	.60	.26
23	A11	2½p orange & brn	.85	.30
24	A11	3p ultra & emer	.95	.40
25	A11	4p ultra & rose red *(Pitcairn School)*	3.50	1.35
26	A11	6p indigo & buff	2.00	.70
27	A11	8p magenta & grn	2.50	.80
28	A11	1sh brown & blk	2.75	1.00
29	A12	2sh dp orange & grn	21.00	7.25
30	A11	2sh6p magenta & ultra	14.00	6.00
		Nos. 20-30 (11)	49.00	18.31

See Nos. 31, 38.

Type of 1957 Corrected

1958, Nov. 5 *Perf. 13x12½*

31	A11	4p ultra & rose red *(Schoolteacher's House)*	.75	.50

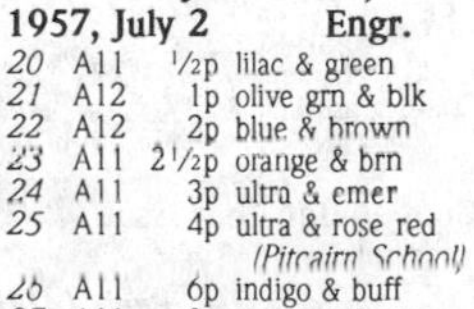

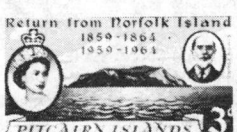

Simon Young and Pitcairn A13

Designs: 6p, Maps of Norfolk and Pitcairn Islands. 1sh, Schooner Mary Ann.

Perf. 14½x13½

1961, Nov. 15 Photo. Wmk. 314

32	A13	3p yellow & black	.70	.50
33	A13	6p blue & red brown	1.25	.90
34	A13	1sh brt green & dp org	3.00	2.25
		Nos. 32-34 (3)	4.95	3.65

Pitcairn Islanders return from Norfolk Island.

Freedom from Hunger Issue
Common Design Type

1963, June 4 *Perf. 14x14½*

35	CD314	2sh6p ultra	25.00	6.50

Red Cross Centenary Issue
Common Design Type

1963, Dec. 9 Litho. *Perf. 13*

36	CD315	2p black & red	.50	.30
37	CD315	2sh6p ultra & red	14.00	10.00

Type of 1957
Perf. 13x12½

1963, Dec. 4 Engr. Wmk. 314

38	A11	½p lilac & green	1.25	1.25

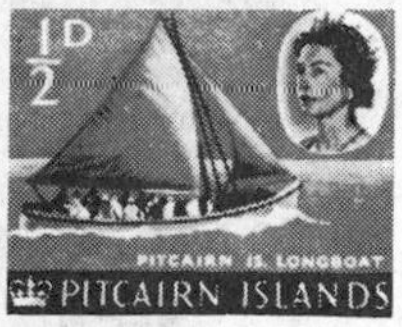

Pitcairn Longboat A14

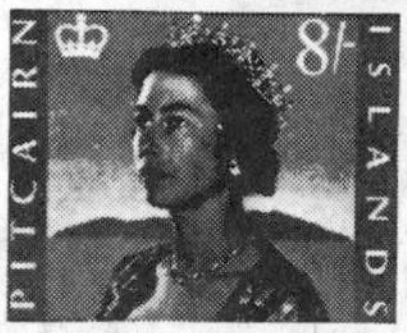

Queen Elizabeth II — A15

Designs: 1p, H.M. Armed Vessel Bounty. 2p, Oarsmen rowing longboat. 3p, Great frigate bird. 4p, Fairy tern 6p, Pitcairn reed warbler. 8p, Red-footed booby. 10p, Red-tailed tropic birds. 1sh, Henderson Island flightless rail. 1sh6p, Henderson Island lory. 2sh6p, Murphy's petrel. 4sh, Henderson Island fruit pigeon.

1964-65 Photo. *Perf. 14x14½*

39	A14	½p multicolored	.15	.15
40	A14	1p vio bl, blk & tan	.15	.15
41	A14	2p multicolored	.15	.15
42	A14	3p ocher & multi	.18	.15
43	A14	4p multicolored	.28	.18
44	A14	6p multicolored	.48	.28
45	A14	8p multicolored	.60	.36
a.		Gray (beak) omitted	100.00	
46	A14	10p blue, blk & org	.80	.40
47	A14	1sh multicolored	.90	.55
48	A14	1sh6p multicolored	1.25	.90
49	A14	2sh6p multicolored	3.25	2.00
50	A14	4sh brown & multi	5.00	3.50
51	A15	8sh multicolored	13.00	9.00
		Nos. 39-51 (13)	26.19	17.77

Issued: ½p-4sh, 8/5/64; 8sh, 4/5/65.
For surcharges see Nos. 72-84.

ITU Issue
Common Design Type

1965, May 17 Litho. *Perf. 11x11½*

52	CD317	1p red lilac & org brn	.42	.22
53	CD317	2sh6p grnsh blue & ultra	17.50	11.00

Intl. Cooperation Year Issue
Common Design Type

1965, Oct. 25 *Perf. 14½*

54	CD318	1p bl grn & claret	.35	.22
55	CD318	1sh6p lt vio & grn	15.00	11.00

Churchill Memorial Issue
Common Design Type

1966, Jan. 24 Photo. *Perf. 14*

Design in Black, Gold and Carmine Rose

56	CD319	2p brt blue	1.00	.50
57	CD319	3p green	2.00	1.00
58	CD319	6p brown	5.00	4.00
59	CD319	1sh violet	15.00	10.00
		Nos. 56-59 (4)	23.00	15.50

World Cup Soccer Issue
Common Design Type

1966, Aug. 1 Litho. *Perf. 14*

60	CD321	4p multi	1.50	1.00
61	CD321	2sh6p multi	8.25	6.50

WHO Headquarters Issue
Common Design Type

1966, Sept. 20 Litho. *Perf. 14*

62	CD322	8p multi	2.00	1.50
63	CD322	1sh6p multi	11.00	6.50

UNESCO Anniversary Issue
Common Design Type

1966, Dec. 1 Litho. *Perf. 14*

64	CD323	½p "Education"	.18	.15
65	CD323	10p "Science"	2.00	1.50
66	CD323	2sh "Culture"	12.00	8.00
		Nos. 64-66 (3)	14.18	9.65

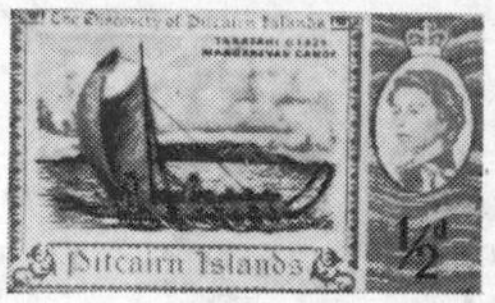

Mangarevan Canoe, c. 1325, and Pitcairn Island — A16

Designs: 1p, Pedro Fernandez de Quiros and galleon, 1606. 8p, "San Pedro," 17th century Spanish brigantine, 1606. 1sh, Capt. Philip Carteret and H.M.S. Swallow. 1sh6p, "Hercules," 1819.

Perf. 14½

1967, Mar. 1 Photo. Wmk. 314

67	A16	½p multicolored	.15	.15
68	A16	1p multicolored	.15	.15
69	A16	8p multicolored	.35	.35
70	A16	1sh multicolored	.65	.50
71	A16	1sh6p multicolored	.90	.85
		Nos. 67-71 (5)	2.20	2.00

Bicentenary of the discovery of Pitcairn Islands by Capt. Philip Carteret.

Nos. 39-51 Surcharged in Gold

20c

1967, July 10 *Perf. 14x14½*

72	A14	½c on ½p	.15	.15
a.		Brown omitted	400.00	
73	A14	1c on 1p	.15	.15
74	A14	2c on 2p	.18	.15
75	A14	2½c on 3p	.22	.18
76	A14	3c on 4p	.32	.28
77	A14	5c on 6p	.52	.52
78	A14	10c on 8p	.95	.85
a.		"10c" omitted	240.00	
79	A14	15c on 10p	1.50	1.25
80	A14	20c on 1sh	2.25	1.90
81	A14	25c on 1sh6p	2.75	2.75
82	A14	30c on 2sh6p	4.00	3.50
83	A14	40c on 4sh	5.25	5.25
84	A15	45c on 8sh	8.50	8.50
		Nos. 72-84 (13)	26.74	25.43

Size of gold rectangle and anchor varies. The anchor symbol is designed after the anchor of H.M.S. Bounty.

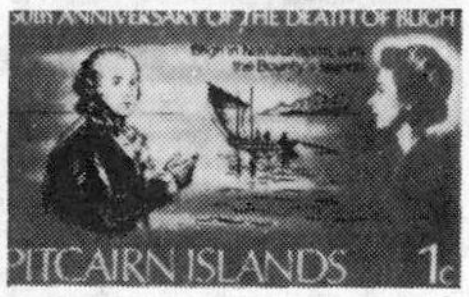

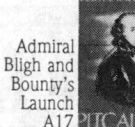

Admiral Bligh and Bounty's Launch A17

Designs: 8c, Bligh and his followers adrift in a boat. 20c, Bligh's tomb, St. Mary's Cemetery, Lambeth, London.

Unwmk.

1967, Dec. 7 Litho. *Perf. 13*

85	A17	1c ultra, lt blue & blk	.15	.15
86	A17	8c brt rose, yel & blk	.50	.50
87	A17	20c brown, yel & blk	1.65	1.50
		Nos. 85-87 (3)	2.30	2.15

150th anniv. of the death of Admiral William Bligh (1754-1817), capt. of the Bounty.

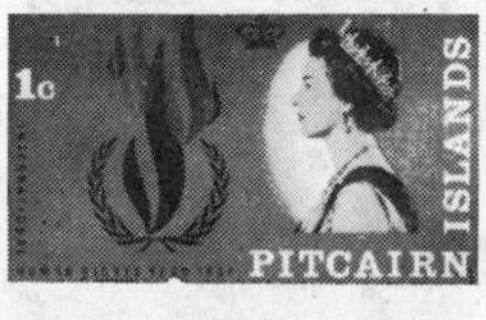

Human Rights Flame A18

Perf. 13½x13

1968, Mar. 4 Litho. Wmk. 314

88	A18	1c rose & multi	.15	.15
89	A18	2c ocher & multi	.15	.15
90	A18	25c multicolored	1.65	1.25
		Nos. 88-90 (3)	1.95	1.55

International Human Rights Year.

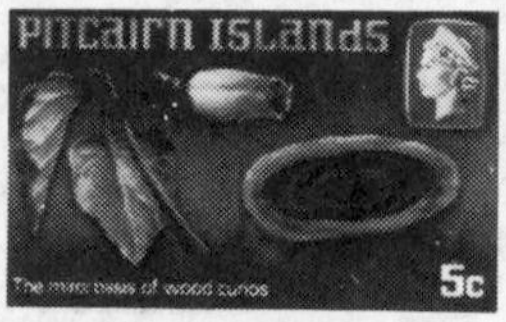

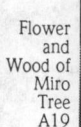

Flower and Wood of Miro Tree A19

Pitcairn Handicraft: 10c, Carved flying fish. 15c, Two "hand" vases, vert. 20c, Old and new woven baskets, vert.

Perf. 14½x14, 14x14½

1968, Aug. 19 Photo. Wmk. 314

91	A19	5c chocolate & multi	.42	.28
92	A19	10c dp green & multi	.85	.55
93	A19	15c brt violet & multi	1.25	.95
94	A19	20c black & multi	1.75	1.40
		Nos. 91-94 (4)	4.27	3.18

See Nos. 194-197.

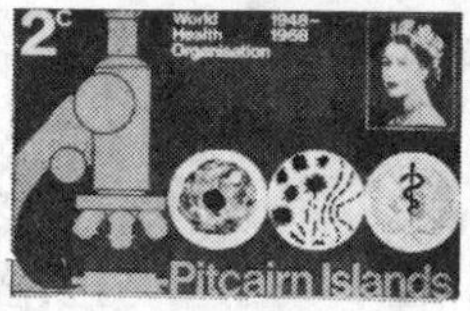

Microscope, Cell, Germs and WHO Emblem A20

Design: 20c, Hypodermic and jars containing pills.

1968, Nov. 25 Litho. *Perf. 14*

95	A20	2c vio blue, grnsh bl & blk	.15	.15
96	A20	20c black, magenta & org	1.50	1.25

20th anniv. of WHO.

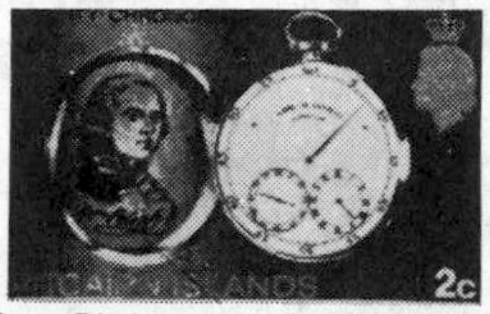

Capt. Bligh and his Larcum-Kendall Chronometer — A21

Designs: 1c, Pitcairn Island. 3c, Bounty's anchor, vert. 4c, Plan of the Bounty, drawn 1787. 5c, Breadfruit and method of transporting young plants. 6c, Bounty Bay. 8c, Pitcairn longboat. 10c, Ship Landing Point and palms. 15c, Fletcher Christian's Cave. 20c, Thursday October Christian's house. 25c, "Flying Fox" cable system (for hauling cargo), vert. 30c, Radio Station at Taro Ground. 40c, Bounty Bible.

Perf. 13x12½, 12½x13

1969, Sept. 17 Litho. Wmk. 314

97	A21	1c brn, yel & gold	.15	.15
98	A21	2c brn, blk & gold	.16	.15
99	A21	3c red, blk & gold	.22	.15
100	A21	4c buff, brn & gold	.28	.16
101	A21	5c gold & multi	.32	.22
102	A21	6c gold & multi	.40	.28
103	A21	8c gold & multi	.60	.40
104	A21	10c gold & multi	1.10	.75
105	A21	15c gold & multi	1.40	1.00
a.		Gold (Queen's head) omitted	500.00	
106	A21	20c gold & multi	1.75	1.40
107	A21	25c gold & multi	3.25	2.25
108	A21	30c gold & multi	4.00	3.25
109	A21	40c red lil, blk & gold	5.50	3.50
		Nos. 97-109 (13)	19.13	13.66

For overprint see No. 118.

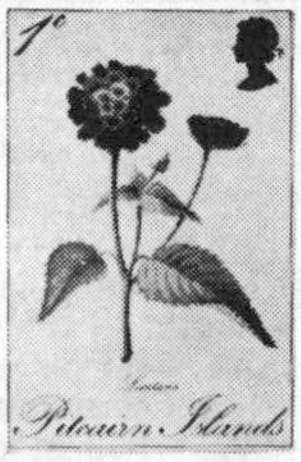

Lantana — A22

Pitcairn Islands Flowers: 2c, Indian shot (canna indica). 5c, Pulau (hibiscus tiliaceus). 25c, Wild gladioli.

1970, Mar. 23 Litho. *Perf. 14*

110	A22	1c black & multi	.15	.15
111	A22	2c black & multi	.50	.25
112	A22	5c black & multi	1.25	.65
113	A22	25c black & multi	10.00	5.00
		Nos. 110-113 (4)	11.90	6.05

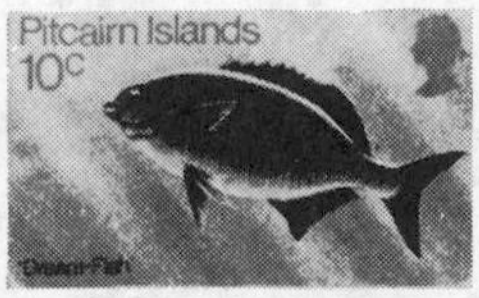

Rudderfish (Dream Fish) A23

Fish: 5c, Groupers (Auntie and Ann). 15c, Wrasse (Elwyn's trousers). 20c, Wrasse (Whistling daughter).

Perf. 14½x14

1970, Oct. 12 Photo. Wmk. 314

114	A23	5c black & multi	1.10	1.00
115	A23	10c grnsh bl & blk	2.25	2.00
116	A23	15c multicolored	3.25	3.00
117	A23	20c multicolored	4.50	3.50
		Nos. 114-117 (4)	11.10	9.50

No. 104 Overprinted in Silver: "ROYAL VISIT 1971"

1971, Feb. 22 Litho. *Perf. 13x12½*

118	A21	10c gold & multi	9.50	5.75

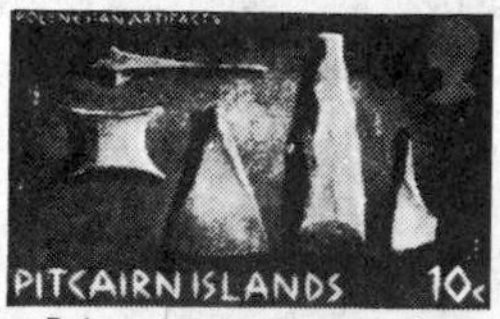

Polynesian Artifacts — A24

Polynesian Art on Pitcairn: 5c, Rock carvings, vert. 15c, Making of stone fishhook. 20c, Seated deity, vert.

1971, May 3 Litho. *Perf. 13½*

Queen's Head in Gold

119	A24	5c dk brown & bis	1.00	1.00
120	A24	10c ol green & blk	2.00	2.00
121	A24	15c black & lt vio	3.25	2.50
122	A24	20c black & rose red	4.00	3.25
		Nos. 119-122 (4)	10.25	8.75

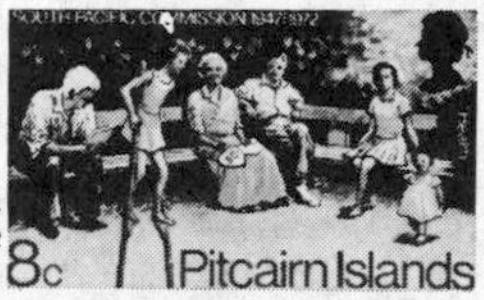

Health Care A25

Designs: 4c, South Pacific Commission flag and Southern Cross, vert. 18c, Education (elementary school). 20c, Economy (country store).

1972, Apr. 4 Litho. *Perf. 14x14½*

123	A25	4c vio blue, yel & ultra	1.10	.60
124	A25	8c brown & multi	2.00	1.50
125	A25	18c yellow grn & multi	2.75	2.00
126	A25	20c orange & multi	3.50	2.75
		Nos. 123-126 (4)	9.35	6.85

So. Pacific Commission, 25th anniv.

Silver Wedding Issue, 1972
Common Design Type

Design: Queen Elizabeth II, Prince Philip, skuas and longboat.

1972, Nov. 20 Photo. Wmk. 314

127	CD324	4c slate grn & multi	.38	.25
128	CD324	20c ultra & multi	1.65	1.00

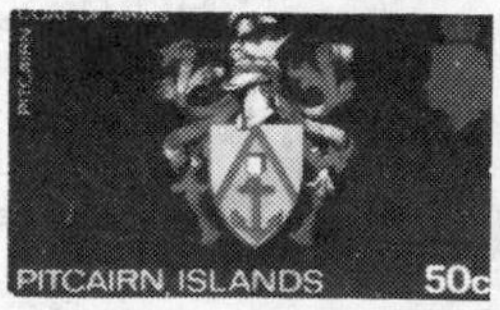

Pitcairn Coat of Arms A26

1973, Jan. 2 Litho. *Perf. 14½x14*

129	A26	50c multicolored	3.50	3.50

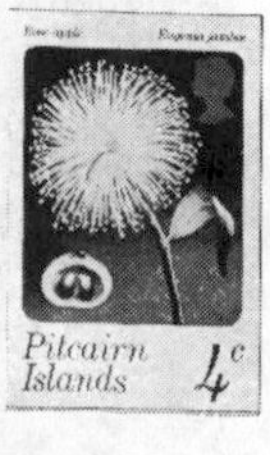

Rose Apple — A27

1973, June 25 *Perf. 14*

130 A27	4c shown	.90	.40
131 A27	8c Mountain apple	1.50	.75
132 A27	15c Lata (myrtle)	2.25	1.40
133 A27	20c Cassia	2.50	1.75
134 A27	35c Guava	5.00	3.50
	Nos. 130-134 (5)	12.15	7.80

Princess Anne's Wedding Issue
Common Design Type

1973, Nov. 14 **Litho.** *Perf. 14*

135 CD325	10c lilac & multi	.48	.40
136 CD325	25c gray green & multi	1.10	1.00

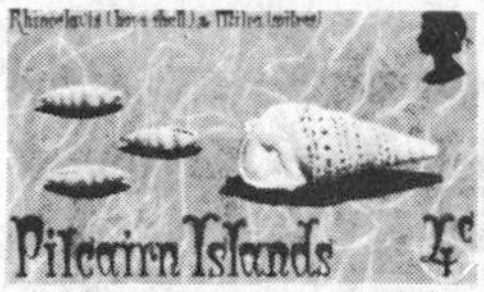

Miter and Horn Shells A28

1974, Apr. 15

137 A28	4c shown	.60	.48
138 A28	10c Dove shells	1.50	1.40
139 A28	18c Limpets and false limpet	2.50	2.25
140 A28	50c Lucine shells	6.50	6.25
a.	Souvenir sheet of 4, #137-140	14.00	8.75
	Nos. 137-140 (4)	11.10	10.38

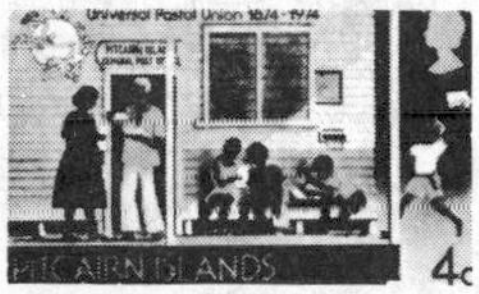

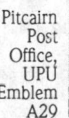

Pitcairn Post Office, UPU Emblem A29

UPU, cent.: 20c, Stampless cover, "Posted at Pitcairn Island No Stamps Available." 35c, Longboat leaving Bounty Bay for ship offshore.

1974, July 22 **Wmk. 314** *Perf. 14½*

141 A29	4c multicolored	.20	.18
142 A29	20c multicolored	.85	.80
143 A29	35c multicolored	1.90	1.75
	Nos. 141-143 (3)	2.95	2.73

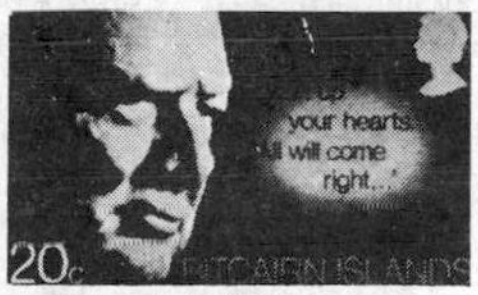

Churchill: "Lift up your hearts . . ." — A30

Design: 35c, Churchill and "Give us the tools and we will finish the job."

1974, Nov. 30 **Litho.** **Wmk. 373**

144 A30	20c black & citron	1.00	.90
145 A30	35c black & yellow	1.50	1.25

Sir Winston Churchill (1874-1965).

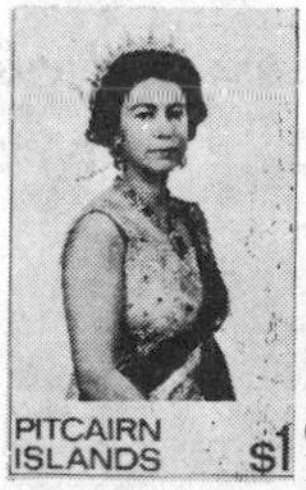

Queen Elizabeth II — A31

1975, Apr. 21 **Wmk. 314** *Perf. 14½*

146 A31	$1 multicolored	9.50	9.50

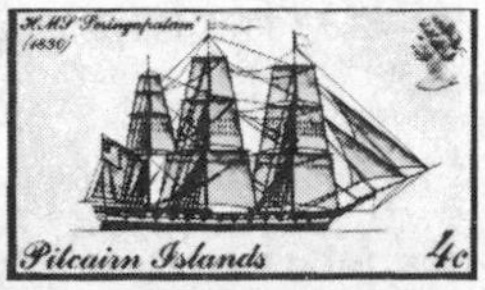

Mailboats A32

1975, July 22 **Litho.** *Perf. 14½*

147 A32	4c Seringapatam, 1830	.35	.30
148 A32	10c Pitcairn, 1890	.95	.85
149 A32	18c Athenic, 1901	1.65	1.50
150 A32	50c Gothic, 1948	4.75	4.25
a.	Souvenir sheet of 4, #147-150, perf. 14	14.00	12.00
	Nos. 147-150 (4)	7.70	6.90

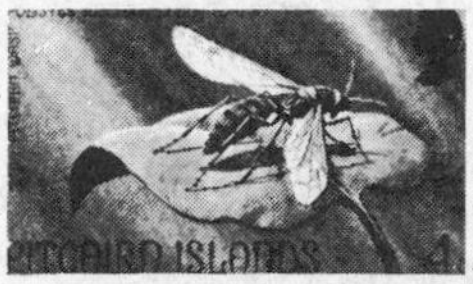

Pitcairn Wasp A33

Insects: 6c, Grasshopper. 10c, Pitcairn moths. 15c, Dragonfly. 20c, Banana moth.

Perf. 14½

1975, Nov. 9 **Litho.** **Wmk. 314**

151 A33	4c blue grn & multi	.60	.30
152 A33	6c carmine & multi	.85	.45
153 A33	10c purple & multi	1.50	1.10
154 A33	15c black & multi	2.25	1.25
155 A33	20c multicolored	2.50	1.75
	Nos. 151-155 (5)	7.70	4.85

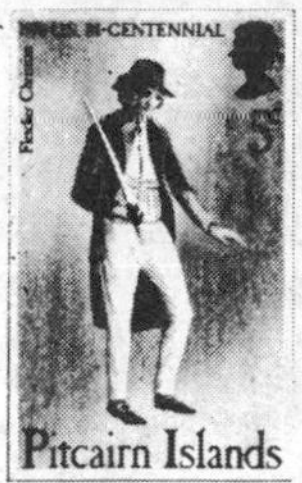

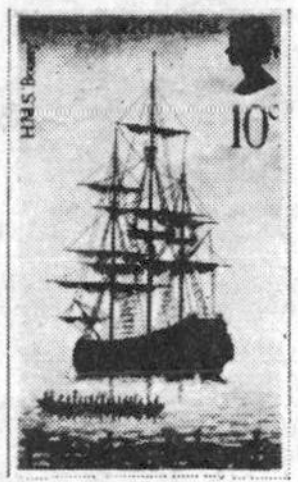

Fletcher Christian — A34 H.M.S. Bounty — A35

American Bicentennial: 30c, George Washington. 50c, Mayflower.

1976, July 4 **Wmk. 373** *Perf. 13½*

156 A34	5c multicolored	.30	.28
157 A35	10c multicolored	.60	.55
158 A34	30c multicolored	1.50	1.40
a.	Pair, #156, 158	1.80	1.80
159 A35	50c multicolored	2.00	1.75
a.	Pair, #157, 159	2.60	2.60
	Nos. 156-159 (4)	4.40	3.98

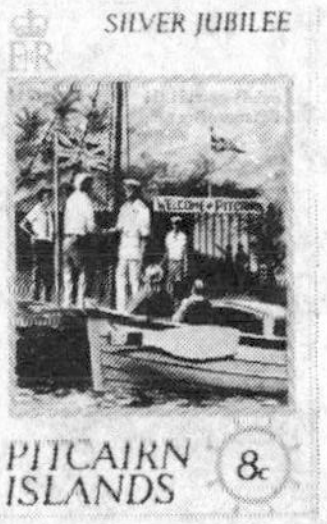

Prince Philip's Arrival, 1971 Visit — A36

Designs: 20c, Chair of homage. 50c, The enthronement.

1977, Feb. 6 *Perf. 13*

160 A36	8c silver & multi	.30	.28
161 A36	20c silver & multi	.75	.65
162 A36	50c silver & multi	1.75	1.65
	Nos. 160-162 (3)	2.80	2.58

25th anniv. of the reign of Elizabeth II.

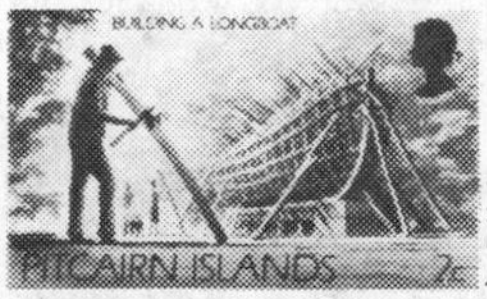

Building Longboat A37

Designs: 1c, Man ringing Island Bell, vert. 5c, Landing cargo. 6c, Sorting supplies. 9c, Cleaning wahoo (fish), vert. 10c, Farming. 15c, Sugar mill. 20c, Women grating coconuts and bananas. 35c, Island church. 50c, Gathering miro logs, Henderson Island. 70c, Burning obsolete stamps, vert. $1, Prince Philip and "Britannia." $2, Elizabeth II, vert.

1977-81 **Litho.** *Perf. 14½*

163	A37	1c multicolored	.15	.15
164	A37	2c multicolored	.15	.15
165	A37	5c multicolored	.15	.15
166	A37	6c multicolored	.15	.15
167	A37	9c multicolored	.15	.15
168	A37	10c multicolored	.15	.15
168A	A37	15c multicolored	.20	.20
169	A37	20c multicolored	.25	.25
170	A37	35c multicolored	.42	.42
171	A37	50c multicolored	.60	.60
171A	A37	70c multicolored	.80	.80
172	A37	$1 multicolored	1.25	1.25
173	A37	$2 multicolored	2.50	2.50
		Nos. 163-173 (13)	6.92	6.92

Issued: #168A, 171A, 10/1/81; others, 9/12/77.

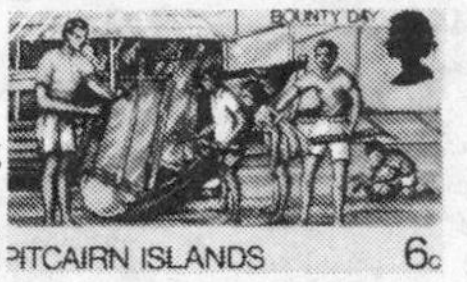

Building "Bounty" Model A38

Bounty Day: 20c, Bounty model afloat. 35c, Burning Bounty.

1978, Jan. 9 *Perf. 14½*

174 A38	6c yellow & multi	.28	.24
175 A38	20c yellow & multi	1.25	1.00
176 A38	35c yellow & multi	2.00	1.90
a.	Souvenir sheet of 3, #174-176	9.25	8.25
	Nos. 174-176 (3)	3.53	3.14

Souvenir Sheet

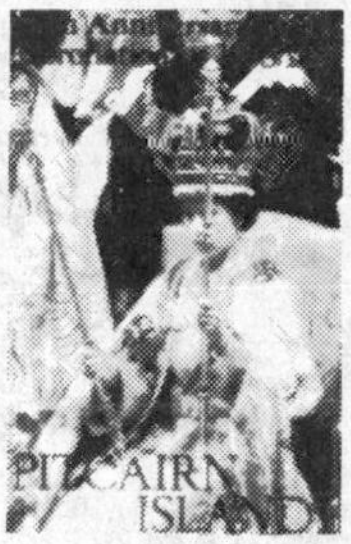

Elizabeth II in Coronation Regalia — A39

Wmk. 373

1978, Sept. **Litho.** *Perf. 12*

177 A39	$1.20 silver & multi	5.00	4.00

25th anniv. of coronation of Elizabeth II.

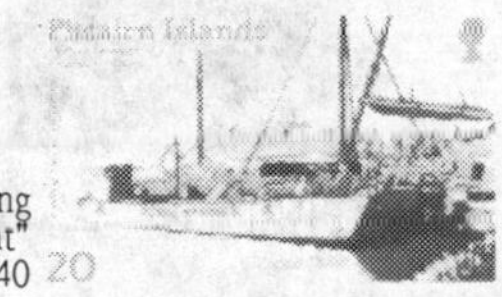

Unloading "Sir Geraint" A40

Designs: 15c, Harbor before development. 30c, Work on the jetty. 35c, Harbor after development.

Perf. 13½

1978, Dec. 18 **Litho.** **Wmk. 373**

178 A40	15c multicolored	.32	.32
179 A40	20c multicolored	.50	.50
180 A40	30c multicolored	.85	.85
181 A40	35c multicolored	1.00	1.00
	Nos. 178-181 (4)	2.67	2.67

Development of new harbor on Pitcairn.

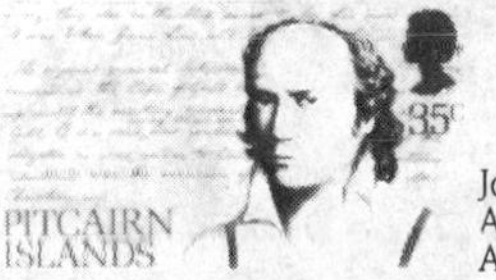

John Adams A41

Design: 70c, John Adams' grave.

1979, Mar. 5 **Litho.** *Perf. 14½*

182 A41	35c multicolored	.90	.90
183 A41	70c multicolored	1.75	1.75

John Adams (1760-1829), founder of Pitcairn Colony, 150th death anniversary.

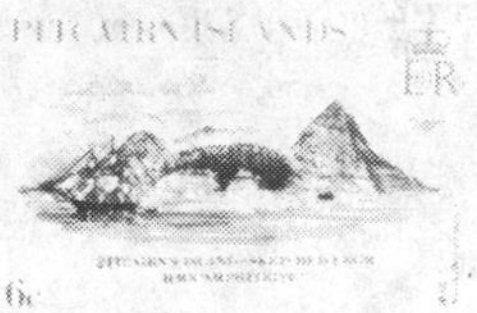

Pitcairn Island Seen from "Amphitrite" — A42

Engravings (c. 1850): 9c, Bounty Bay and Pitcairn Village, 20c, Lookout Ridge. 70c, Church and schoolhouse.

1979, Sept. 12 **Litho.** *Perf. 14*

184 A42	6c multicolored	.16	.16
185 A42	9c multicolored	.24	.24
186 A42 20c multicolored		.48	.48
187 A42	70c multicolored	1.65	1.65
	Nos. 184-187 (4)	2.53	2.53

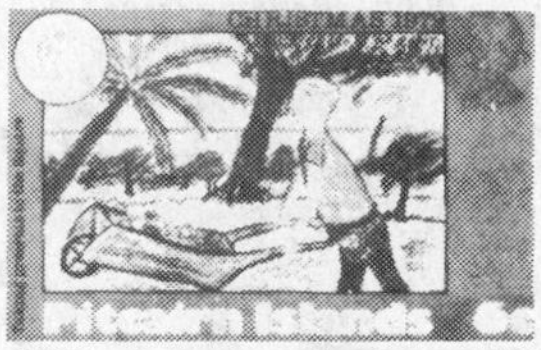

Taking Presents to the Square, IYC Emblem — A43

IYC Emblem and Children's Drawings: 9c, Decorating trees with presents. 20c, Distributing presents. 35c, Carrying the presents home.

Perf. 13½

1979, Nov. 28 **Litho.** **Wmk. 373**

188 A43	6c multicolored	.16	.16
189 A43	9c multicolored	.24	.24
190 A43	20c multicolored	.55	.55
191 A43	35c multicolored	1.00	1.00
a.	Souvenir sheet of 4, #188-191	3.75	3.50
	Nos. 188-191 (4)	1.95	1.95

Christmas and IYC.

Souvenir Sheet

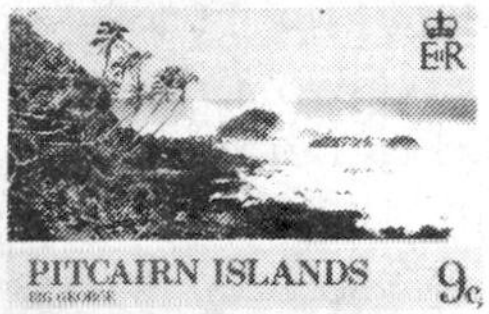

Mail Transport by Longboat A44

Perf. 14½

1980, May 6 **Litho.** **Wmk. 373**

192	Sheet of 4	2.25	2.25
a.	A44 35c shown	.55	.55
b.	A44 35c Mail crane lift	.55	.55
c.	A44 35c Tractor transport	.55	.55
d.	A44 35c Arrival at post office	.55	.55

London 80 Intl. Phil. Exhib., May 6-14.

Queen Mother Elizabeth Birthday Issue
Common Design Type

Wmk. 373

1980, Aug. 4 **Litho.** *Perf. 14*

193 CD330	50c multicolored	1.00	1.00

Handicraft Type of 1968

Perf. 14½x14, 14x14½

1980, Sept. 29 **Litho.** **Wmk. 373**

194 A19	9c Turtles	.16	.16
195 A19	20c Wheelbarrow	.38	.38
196 A19	35c Gannet, vert.	.65	.65
197 A19	40c Bonnet and fan, vert.	.75	.75
	Nos. 194-197 (4)	1.94	1.94

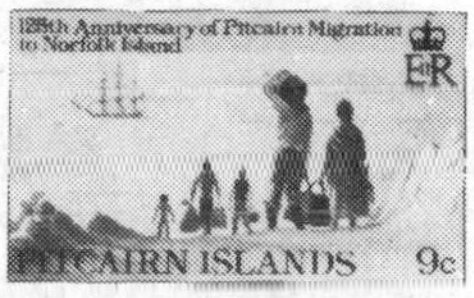

Big George A45

Wmk. 373

1981, Jan. 22 **Litho.** *Perf. 14*

198 A45	6c View of Adamstown	.15	.15
199 A45	9c shown	.15	.15
200 A45	20c Christian's Cave, Gannet's Ridge	.35	.35
201 A45	35c Pawala Valley Ridge	.60	.60
202 A45	70c Tatrimoa	1.25	1.25
	Nos. 198-202 (5)	2.50	2.50

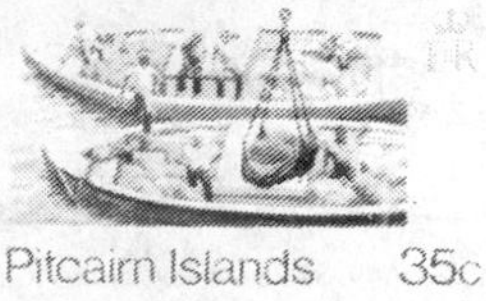

Citizens Departing for Norfolk Island A46

1981, May 3 **Photo.** *Perf. 13x14½*

203 A46	9c shown	.18	.18
204 A46	35c Norfolk Isld. from Morayshire	.75	.75
205 A46	70c Morayshire	1.50	1.50
	Nos. 203-205 (3)	2.43	2.43

Migration to Norfolk Is., 125th anniv.

Royal Wedding Issue
Common Design Type
Wmk. 373

1981, July 22 Litho. *Perf. 14*

206 CD331 20c Bouquet .28 .28
207 CD331 35c Charles .50 .50
208 CD331 $1.20 Couple 1.65 1.65
Nos. 206-208 (3) 2.43 2.43

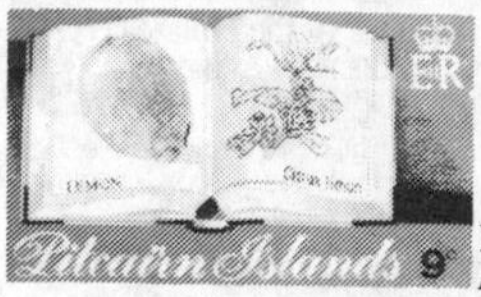

Lemon A47

1982, Feb. 23 Litho. *Perf. 14½*

209 A47 9c shown .22 .22
210 A47 20c Pomegranate .50 .50
211 A47 35c Avocado .90 .90
212 A47 70c Pawpaw 1.80 1.80
Nos. 209-212 (4) 3.42 3.42

Princess Diana Issue
Common Design Type

1982, July 1 Litho. *Perf. 14½x14*

213 CD333 6c Arms .15 .15
214 CD333 9c Diana .15 .15
215 CD333 70c Wedding 1.10 1.10
216 CD333 $1.20 Portrait 1.75 1.75
Nos. 213-216 (4) 3.15 3.15

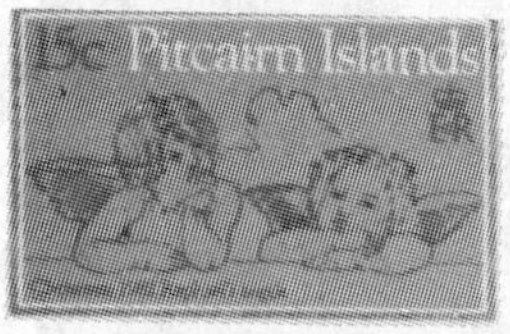

Christmas — A48

Designs: Various paintings of angels by Raphael. 50c, $1 vert.

1982, Oct. 19 Litho. *Perf. 14*

217 A48 15c multicolored .22 .22
218 A48 20c multicolored .28 .28
219 A48 50c multicolored .70 .70
220 A48 $1 multicolored 1.40 1.40
Nos. 217-220 (4) 2.60 2.60

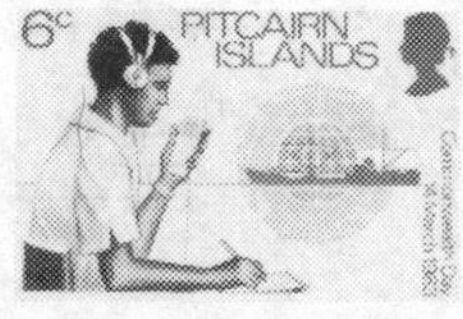

A48a

1983, Mar. 14

221 A48a 6c Radio operator .15 .15
222 A48a 9c Postal clerk .15 .15
223 A48a 70c Fisherman .85 .85
224 A48a $1.20 Artist 1.50 1.50
Nos. 221-224 (4) 2.65 2.65

Commonwealth Day.

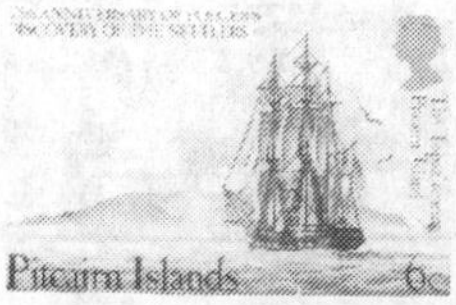

175th Anniv. of Capt. Folger's Discovery of the Settlers A49

Wmk. 373

1983, June 14 Litho. *Perf. 14*

225 A49 6c Topaz off Pitcairn Isld. .15 .15
226 A49 20c Topaz, islanders .30 .30
227 A49 70c John Adams welcoming Folger 1.10 1.10
228 A49 $1.20 Presentation of Chronometer 1.75 1.75
Nos. 225-228 (4) 3.30 3.30

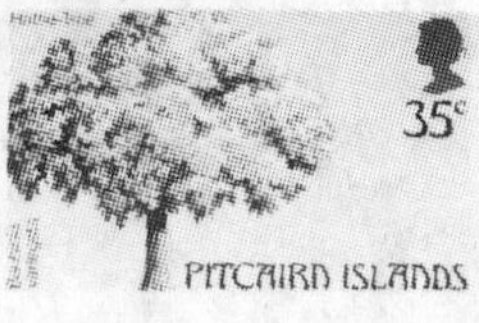

Local Trees A50

1983, Oct. 6 Litho. *Perf. 13½*

229 Pair 1.25 1.25
a. A50 35c Hattie .60 .60
b. A50 35c Branch, wood painting .60 .60
230 Pair 2.25 2.25
a. A50 70c Pandanus 1.10 1.10
b. A50 70c Branch, basket weaving 1.10 1.10

See Nos. 289-290.

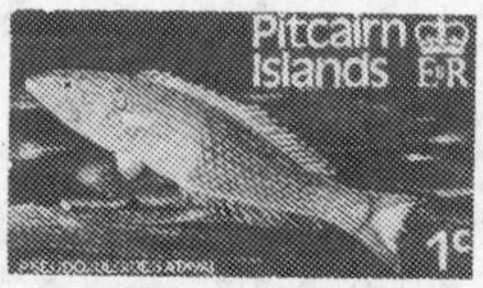

Pseudojuloides Atavai — A51

Perf. 14½

1984, Jan. 11 Litho. Wmk. 373

231 A51 1c shown .15 .15
232 A51 4c Halichoeres melasmapomus .15 .15
233 A51 6c Scarus longippinis .15 .15
234 A51 9c Variola louti .15 .15
235 A51 10c Centropyge hotumatua .15 .15
236 A51 15c Stegastes emeryi .22 .22
237 A51 20c Chaetodon smithi .28 .28
238 A51 35c Xanthichthys mento .50 .50
239 A51 50c Chrysiptera galba .70 .70
240 A51 70c Genicanthus spinus .95 .95
241 A51 $1 Myripristis tiki 1.10 1.10
242 A51 $1.20 Anthias ventralis 1.10 1.10
243 A51 $2 Pseudocaranx dentex 2.25 2.25
Nos. 231-243 (13) 7.85 7.85

See Nos. 295-296.

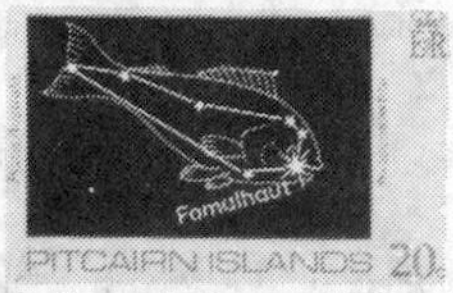

Constellations — A52

1984, May 14 Wmk. 373

244 A52 15c Crux Australis .25 .25
245 A52 20c Piscis Australis .35 .35
246 A52 70c Canis Minor 1.25 1.25
247 A52 $1 Virgo 1.75 1.75
Nos. 244-247 (4) 3.60 3.60

Souvenir Sheet

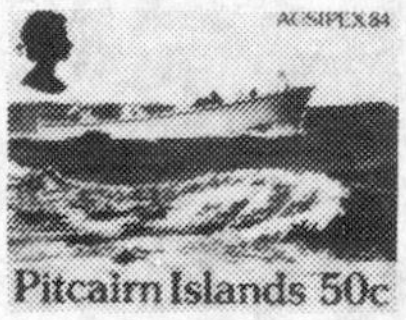

AUSIPEX '84 — A53

Longboats.

1984, Sept. 21 Litho. Wmk. 373

248 Sheet of 2 4.00 4.00
a. A53 50c multicolored .75 .75
b. A53 $2 multicolored 3.25 3.25

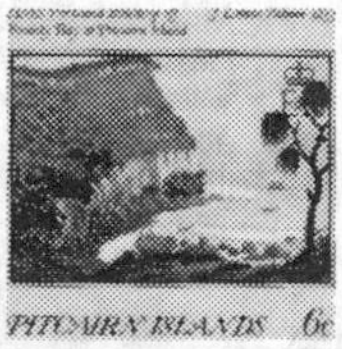

HMS Portland off Bounty Bay, by J. Linton Palmer, 1853 — A54

Paintings by J. Linton Palmer, 1853, and William Smyth, 1825: 9c, Christian's Look Out at Pitcairn Island. 35c, The Golden Age. $2, View of Village, by Smyth.

Wmk. 373

1985, Jan. 16 Litho. *Perf. 14*

249 A54 6c multicolored .15 .15
250 A54 9c multicolored .15 .15
251 A54 35c multicolored .48 .48

Size: 48x32mm

252 A54 $2 multicolored 2.75 2.75
Nos. 249-252 (4) 3.53 3.53

Copies of No. 252 with "1835" date were not issued. Value, $45.
See Nos. 291-294.

Queen Mother 85th Birthday
Common Design Type
Perf. 14½x14

1985, June 7 Litho. Wmk. 384

253 CD336 6c In Dundee, 1964 .15 .15
254 CD336 35c At 80th birthday celebration .30 .30
255 CD336 70c Queen Mother .55 .55
256 CD336 $1.20 Holding Prince Henry 1.00 1.00
Nos. 253-256 (4) 2.00 2.00

Souvenir Sheet

257 CD336 $2 In coach at the Races, Ascot 2.00 2.00

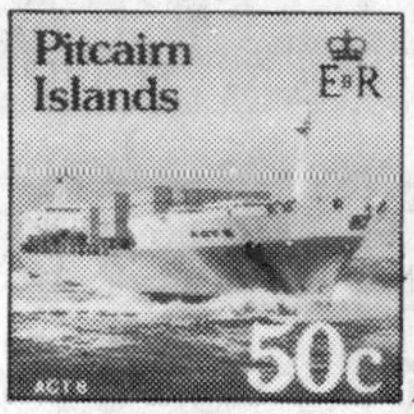

Act 6 — A55

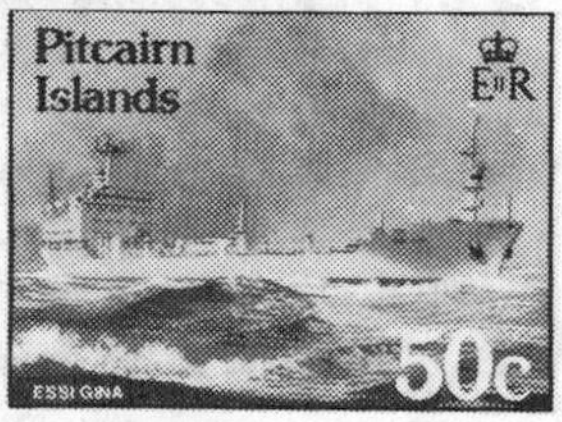

Essi Gina A56

1985, Aug. 28 *Perf. 14½x14*

258 A55 50c shown .90 .90
259 A55 50c Columbus Louisiana .90 .90

Perf. 14

260 A56 50c shown .90 .90
261 A56 50c Stolt Spirit .90 .90
Nos. 258-261 (4) 3.60 3.60

See Nos. 281-284.

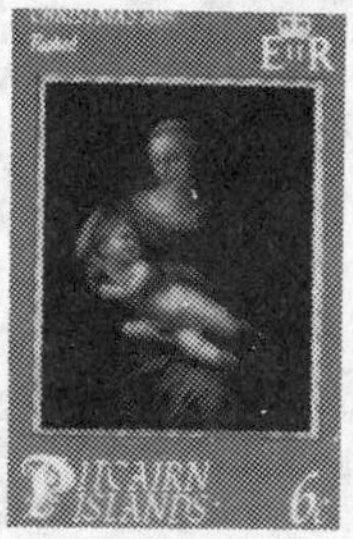

Christmas — A57

Madonna & child paintings: 6c, by Raphael. 9c, by Krause. 35c, by Andreas Mayer. $2, by an unknown Austrian master.

1985, Nov. 26 *Perf. 14*

262 A57 6c multicolored .15 .15
263 A57 9c multicolored .15 .15
264 A57 35c multicolored .45 .45
265 A57 $2 multicolored 2.50 2.50
Nos. 262-265 (4) 3.25 3.25

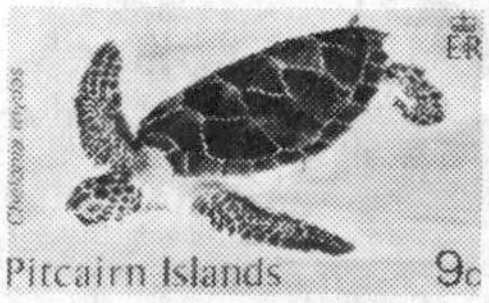

Turtles A58

Designs: 9c, 20c, Chelonia mydas. 70c, $1.20, Eretmochelys imbricata.

Perf. 14½

1986, Feb. 12 Litho. Wmk. 384

266 A58 9c multicolored .15 .15
267 A58 20c multi, diff. .28 .28
268 A58 70c multicolored 1.00 1.00
269 A58 $1.20 multi, diff. 1.90 1.90
Nos. 266-269 (4) 3.33 3.33

Queen Elizabeth II 60th Birthday
Common Design Type

Designs: 6c, In Royal Lodge garden, Windsor, 1946. 9c, Wedding of Princess Anne and Capt. Mark Philips, 1973. 20c, Wearing mantle and robes of Order of St. Paul's Cathedral, 1961. $1.20, Concert, Royal Festival Hall, London, 1971. $2, Visting Crown Agents' offices, 1983.

1986, Apr. 21 Litho. *Perf. 14½*

270 CD337 6c multi .15 .15
271 CD337 9c multi .15 .15
272 CD337 20c multi .24 .24
273 CD337 $1.20 multi 1.45 1.45
274 CD337 $2 multi 2.40 2.40
Nos. 270-274 (5) 4.39 4.39

Royal Wedding Issue, 1986
Common Design Type

Designs: 20c, Informal portrait. $1.20, Andrew aboard royal navy vessel.

Wmk. 384

1986, July 23 Litho. *Perf. 14*

275 CD338 20c multi .32 .32
276 CD338 $1.20 multi 2.00 2.00

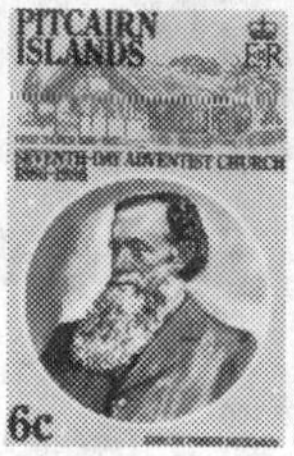

7th Day Adventist Church, Cent. — A59

Designs: 6c, First church, 1886, and John I. Tay, missionary. 20c, Second church, 1907, and mission ship Pitcairn, 1890. 35c, Third church, 1945, baptism and Down Isaac. $2, Church, 1954, and sailing ship.

1986, Oct. 18

277 A59 6c multicolored .15 .15
278 A59 20c multicolored .22 .22
279 A59 35c multicolored .38 .38
280 A59 $2 multicolored 2.15 2.15
Nos. 277-280 (4) 2.90 2.90

Ship Type of 1985

1987, Jan. 20 *Perf. 14x14½*

281 A55 50c Brussel .70 .70
282 A55 50c Samoan Reefer .70 .70

Perf. 14

283 A56 50c Australian Exporter .70 .70
284 A56 50c Taupo .70 .70
Nos. 281-284 (4) 2.80 2.80

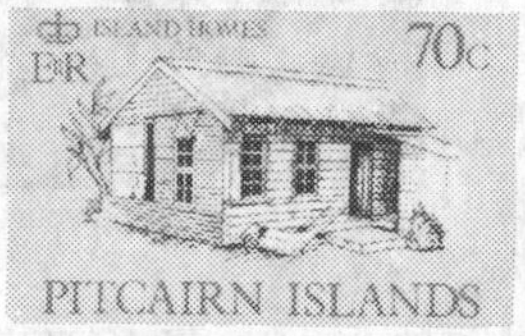

Island Houses A60

1987, May 21 Wmk. 373 *Perf. 14*

285 A60 70c lt greenish blue, bluish grn & blk .70 .70
286 A60 70c cream, yel bister & blk .70 .70
287 A60 70c lt blue, brt blue & blk .70 .70
288 A60 70c lt lil, brt vio & blk .70 .70
Nos. 285-288 (4) 2.80 2.80

Tree Type of 1983

1987, Aug. 10 Wmk. 384 *Perf. 14½*

289 Pair .80 .80
a. A50 40c Leaves, blossoms .40 .40
b. A50 40c Monkey puzzle tree .40 .40
290 Pair 3.50 3.50
a. A50 $1.80 Leaves, blossoms, nuts 1.75 1.75
b. A50 $1.80 Duduinut tree 1.75 1.75

Art Type of 1985

Paintings by Lt. Conway Shipley, 1848: 20c, House and Tomb of John Adams. 40c, Bounty Bay, with H.M.S. Calypso. 90c, School House and Chapel. $1.80, Pitcairn Island with H.M.S. Calypso.

1987, Dec. 7 Litho. *Perf. 14*

291 A54 20c multi .25 .25
292 A54 40c multi .48 .48
293 A54 90c multi 1.10 1.10

Size: 48x32mm

294 A54 $1.80 multi 2.25 2.25
Nos. 291-294 (4) 4.08 4.08

Fish Type of 1984
Perf. 14½

1988, Jan. 14 Litho. Wmk. 384

295 A51 90c Variola louti 1.15 1.15
296 A51 $3 Gymnothorax eurostus 3.75 3.75

Souvenir Sheet

Australia Bicentennial — A61

1988, May 9 **Wmk. 384** **Perf. 14**
297 A61 $3 HMS *Bounty* replica under sail 4.00 4.00

Visiting Ships A62

Perf. 13½
1988, Aug. 14 **Litho.** **Wmk. 373**
298 A62 5c HMS *Swallow*, 1767 .15 .15
299 A62 10c HMS *Pandora*, 1791 .15 .15
300 A62 15c HMS *Briton* and HMS *Tagus*, 1814 .18 .18
301 A62 20c HMS *Blossom*, 1825 .25 .25
 a. Wmk. 384 .22 .22
 b. Booklet pane of 4, #301a .88
302 A62 30c S.V. *Lucy Anne*, 1831 .35 .35
303 A62 35c S.V. *Charles Doggett*, 1831 .45 .45
304 A62 40c HMS *Fly*, 1838 .50 .50
305 A62 60c LMS *Camden*, 1840 .75 .75
306 A62 90c HMS *Virago*, 1853 1.10 1.10
 a. Wmk. 384 1.05 1.05
 b. Booklet pane of 4, #306a 4.25
307 A62 $1.20 S.S. *Rakaia*, 1867 1.50 1.50
308 A62 $1.80 HMS *Sappho*, 1882 2.25 2.25
309 A62 $5 HMS *Champion*, 1893 6.00 6.00
  Nos. 298-309 (12) 13.63 13.63

20c, 90c exist dated "1990." Issue date: Nos. 301a-301b, 306a-306b, May 3, 1990.

Constitution, 150th Anniv. — A63

Text and: 20c, Raising the Union Jack. 40c, Signing of the constitution aboard the H.M.S. "Fly," 1838. $1.05, Suffrage. $1.80, Equal education.

1988, Nov. 30 **Wmk. 373** **Perf. 14**
315 A63 20c multicolored .22 .22
316 A63 40c multicolored .45 .45
317 A63 $1.05 multicolored 1.25 1.25
318 A63 $1.80 multicolored 2.00 2.00
  Nos. 315-318 (4) 3.92 3.92

Christmas A64

Designs: a, Angel, animals in stable. b, Holy Family. c, Two Magi. d, Magus and shepherd boy.

1988, Nov. 30 **Wmk. 384** **Perf. 14**
319 Strip of 4 4.00 4.00
 a.-d. A64 90c any single 1.00 1.00

Miniature Sheets

Pitcairn Isls., Bicent. A65

No. 320 (*Bounty* sets sail for the South Seas, Dec. 23, 1787): a, Fitting out the *Bounty* at Deptford. b, *Bounty* leaving Spithead. c, *Bounty* trying to round Cape Horn. d, Anchored in Adventure Bay, Tasmania. e, Ship's mates collecting breadfruit. f, Breadfruit in great cabin.
No. 321 (the mutiny, Apr. 28, 1789): a, *Bounty* leaving Matavai Bay. b, Mutineers waking Capt. Bligh. c, Confrontation between Fletcher Christian and Bligh. d, Bligh and crew members set adrift in an open boat. e, Castaways. f, Throwing breadfruit overboard.
No. 322: a, like No. 321e. b, Isle of Man #393. c, Norfolk Is. #453.

1989 **Litho.** **Wmk. 373**
320 Sheet of 6 1.50 1.50
 a.-f. A65 20c any single .25 .25
321 Sheet of 6 6.30 6.30
 a.-f. A65 90c any single 1.05 1.05

Souvenir Sheet
Wmk. 384
322 Sheet of 3 + label 3.15 3.15
 a.-c. A65 90c any single 1.05 1.05

See #331, Isle of Man #389-394 and Norfolk Is. #452-456.
Issued: #320, Feb. 22; #321-322, Apr. 28.
Difference between #. 321e and 322a is inscription at bottom of #322a: "C. Abbott 1989 BOT."

Aircraft — A66

Perf. 14½
1989, July 25 **Litho.** **Wmk. 384**
323 A66 20c RNZAF Orion .25 .25
324 A66 80c Beechcraft Queen Air 1.05 1.05
325 A66 $1.05 Navy helicopter, USS *Breton* 1.35 1.35
326 A66 $1.30 RNZAF Hercules 1.70 1.70
  Nos. 323-326 (4) 4.35 4.35

Second mail drop on Pitcairn, Mar. 21, 1985 (20c); photo mission from Tahiti, Jan. 14, 1983 (80c); diesel fuel delivery by the navy, Feb. 12, 1969 ($1.05); and parachute delivery of a bulldozer, May 31, 1983 ($1.30).

The Islands A67

Wmk. 373
1989, Oct. 23 **Litho.** **Perf. 14**
327 A67 15c Ducie Is. .18 .18
328 A67 90c Henderson Is. 1.00 1.00
329 A67 $1.05 Oeno Is. 1.20 1.20
330 A67 $1.30 Pitcairn Is. 1.50 1.50
  Nos. 327-330 (4) 3.88 3.88

Bicentennial Type of 1989
Miniature Sheet

Designs: a, Mutineers aboard *Bounty* anticipating landing on Pitcairn. b, Landing. c, Exploration of the island. d, Carrying goods ashore. e, Burning the *Bounty*. f, Settlement.

1990, Jan. 15 **Wmk. 384** **Perf. 14**
331 Sheet of 6 + 3 labels 2.90 2.90
 a.-f. A65 40c any single .48 .48

Stamp World London '90 — A68

Links with the UK: 80c, Peter Heywood and Ennerdale, Cumbria. 90c, John Adams and The Tower of St. Augustine, Hackney. $1.05, William Bligh and The Citadel Gateway, Plymouth. $1.30, Fletcher Christian and birthplace, Cockermouth.

1990, May 3 **Wmk. 373** **Perf. 14**
332 A68 80c multicolored .95 .95
333 A68 90c multicolored 1.05 1.05
334 A68 $1.05 multicolored 1.25 1.25
335 A68 $1.30 multicolored 1.55 1.55
  Nos. 332-335 (4) 4.80 4.80

Queen Mother 90th Birthday
Common Design Types
1990, Aug. 4 **Wmk. 384** **Perf. 14x15**
336 CD343 40c Portrait, 1937 .45 .45
Perf. 14½
337 CD344 $3 King, Queen in carriage 3.50 3.50

First Pitcairn Island Postage Stamps, 50th Anniv — A69

Designs: Historical items and Pitcairn Islands stamps.

Perf. 13½x14
1990, Oct. 15 **Wmk. 373**
338 A69 20c Chronometer, #2 .24 .24
339 A69 80c Bounty's Bible, #31 .95 .95
340 A69 90c Bounty's Bell, #108 1.05 1.05
341 A69 $1.05 Bounty, #172 1.20 1.20
342 A69 $1.30 Penny Black, #300 1.50 1.50
  Nos. 338-342 (5) 4.94 4.94

Birds — A70

1990, Dec. 5 **Wmk. 373** **Perf. 14**
343 A70 20c Redbreast .25 .25
344 A70 90c Wood pigeon 1.10 1.10
345 A70 $1.30 Sparrow 1.60 1.60
346 A70 $1.80 Flightless chicken 2.25 2.25
  Nos. 343-346 (4) 5.20 5.20

Birdpex '90, 20th Intl. Ornithological Congress, New Zealand.

Miniature Sheet

Pitcairn Islands, Bicent. A71

Bicentennial celebrations: a, Re-enacting the landing. b, Commemorative plaque. c, Memorial church service. d, Cricket match. e, Bounty model burning. f, Fireworks.

Perf. 14½
1991, Mar. 24 **Litho.** **Wmk. 384**
347 A71 80c Sheet of 6, #a.-f. 5.75 5.75

Elizabeth & Philip, Birthdays
Common Design Types
Perf. 14½
1991, July 12 **Litho.** **Wmk. 384**
348 CD346 20c multicolored .20 .20
349 CD345 $1.30 multicolored 1.40 1.40
 a. Pair, #348-349 + label 1.60 1.60

Cruise Ships A72

1991, June 17
350 A72 15c Europa .16 .16
351 A72 80c Royal Viking Star .85 .85
352 A72 $1.30 World Discoverer 1.40 1.40
353 A72 $1.80 Sagafjord 1.95 1.95
  Nos. 350-353 (4) 4.36 4.36

Island Vehicles A73

1991, Sept. 25 **Wmk. 373** **Perf. 14**
354 A73 20c Bulldozer .22 .22
355 A73 80c Motorcycle .92 .92
356 A73 $1.30 Tractor 1.50 1.50
357 A73 $1.80 All-terrain vehicle 2.10 2.10
  Nos. 354-357 (4) 4.74 4.74

Christmas — A74

1991, Nov. 18 **Perf. 14x14½**
358 A74 20c The Annunciation .22 .22
359 A74 80c Shepherds .92 .92
360 A74 $1.30 Nativity scene 1.50 1.50
361 A74 $1.80 Three wise men 2.10 2.10
  Nos. 358-361 (4) 4.74 4.74

Queen Elizabeth II's Accession to the Throne, 40th Anniv.
Common Design Type
Wmk. 384
1992, Feb. 6 **Litho.** **Perf. 14**
362 CD349 20c multicolored .24 .24
363 CD349 60c multicolored .70 .70
364 CD349 90c multicolored 1.00 1.00
365 CD349 $1 multicolored 1.15 1.15
Wmk. 373
366 CD349 $1.80 multicolored 2.10 2.10
  Nos. 362-366 (5) 5.19 5.19

Sharks A75

Designs: 20c, Carcharhinus galapagensis. $1, Eugomphodus taurus. $1.50, Carcharhinus melanopterus. $1.80, Carcharhinus amblyrhynchos.

Perf. 15x14½
1992, June 30 **Litho.** **Wmk. 373**
367 A75 20c multicolored .24 .24
368 A75 $1 multicolored 1.15 1.15
369 A75 $1.50 multicolored 1.75 1.75
370 A75 $1.80 multicolored 2.10 2.10
  Nos. 367-370 (4) 5.24 5.24

Sir Peter Scott Commemorative Expedition to Pitcairn Islands, 1991-92 — A76

Designs: 20c, Montastrea, acropora coral sticks. $1, Henderson sandalwood. $1.50, Murphy's petrel. $1.80, Henderson hawkmoth.

Perf. 14x15

1992, Sept. 11　Litho.　Wmk. 373

371	A76	20c multicolored	.24	.24
372	A76	$1 multicolored	1.15	1.15
373	A76	$1.50 multicolored	1.75	1.75
374	A76	$1.80 multicolored	2.10	2.10
		Nos. 371-374 (4)	5.24	5.24

Captain William Bligh, 175th Anniv. of Death A77

Designs: 20c, Bligh's birthplace, St. Tudy, Cornwall. HMS Resolution. $1, On deck of HMAV Bounty, breadfruit plant. $1.50, Voyage in open boat, Bligh's answers at court martial. $1.80, Portrait by Rachel H. Combe, Battle of Camperdown, 1797.

Perf. 14½

1992, Dec. 7　Litho.　Wmk. 373

375	A77	20c multicolored	.22	.22
376	A77	$1 multicolored	1.10	1.10
377	A77	$1.50 multicolored	1.65	1.65
378	A77	$1.80 multicolored	1.95	1.95
		Nos. 375-378 (4)	4.92	4.92

Royal Naval Vessels A78

Wmk. 384

1993, Mar. 10　Litho.　Perf. 14

379	A78	15c HMS Chichester	.15	.15
380	A78	20c HMS Jaguar	.20	.20
381	A78	$1.80 HMS Andrew	1.80	1.80
382	A78	$3 HMS Warrior	3.00	3.00
		Nos. 379-382 (4)	5.15	5.15

Coronation of Queen Elizabeth II, 40th Anniv. A79

Wmk. 373

1993, June 17　Litho.　Perf. 13

| 383 | A79 | $5 multicolored | 5.00 | 5.00 |

Scenic Views A80

Designs: 10c, Pawala Valley Ridge. 90c, St. Pauls. $1.20, Matt's Rocks from Water Valley. $1.50, Ridge Rope to St. Paul's Pool. $1.80, Ship Landing Point.

Wmk. 373

1993, Sept. 8　Litho.　Perf. 14

384	A80	10c multicolored	.15	.15
385	A80	90c multicolored	.95	.95
386	A80	$1.20 multicolored	1.25	1.25
387	A80	$1.50 multicolored	1.65	1.65
388	A80	$1.80 multicolored	1.90	1.90
		Nos. 384-388 (5)	5.90	5.90

Lizards A81

Designs: 20c, Indopacific tree gecko. No. 390, Stump-toed gecko. No. 391, Mourning gecko. $1, Moth skink No. 393, Snake-eyed skink. No. 394, White-bellied skink.

Perf. 13x13½

1993, Dec. 14　Litho.　Wmk. 373

389	A81	20c multicolored	.22	.22
390	A81	45c multicolored	.50	.50
391	A81	45c multicolored	.50	.50
a.		Pair, #390-391	1.00	1.00
392	A81	$1 multicolored	1.10	1.10
393	A81	$1.50 multicolored	1.75	1.75
394	A81	$1.50 multicolored	1.75	1.75
a.		Pair, #393-394	3.50	3.50
		Nos. 389-394 (6)	5.82	5.82

Nos. 390-391, 393-394 Ovptd. with Hong Kong '94 Emblem

Perf. 13x13½

1994, Feb. 18　Litho.　Wmk. 373

395	A81	45c on #390	.50	.50
396	A81	45c on #391	.50	.50
a.		Pair, #395-396	1.00	1.00
397	A81	$1.50 on #393	1.75	1.75
398	A81	$1.50 on #394	1.75	1.75
a.		Pair, #397-398	3.50	3.50
		Nos. 395-398 (4)	4.50	4.50

Early Pitcairners — A82

Designs: 5c, Friday October Christian. 20c, Moses Young. $1.80, James Russell McCoy. $3, Rosalind Amelia Young.

1994, Mar. 7　　　　Perf. 14

399	A82	5c multicolored	.15	.15
400	A82	20c multicolored	.22	.22
401	A82	$1.80 multicolored	2.00	2.00
402	A82	$3 multicolored	3.25	3.25
		Nos. 399-402 (4)	5.62	5.62

Shipwrecks A83

Designs: 20c, Wildwave, Oeno Island, 1858. 90c, Cornwallis, Pitcairn Island, 1875. $1.80, Acadia, Ducie Island, 1881. $3, Oregon, Oeno Island, 1883.

Wmk. 373

1994, June 22　Litho.　Perf. 14

403	A83	20c multicolored	.22	.22
404	A83	90c multicolored	1.00	1.00
405	A83	$1.80 multicolored	2.00	2.00
406	A83	$3 multicolored	3.50	3.50
		Nos. 403-406 (4)	6.72	6.72

Corals A84

Designs: 20c, Fire coral, vert. 90c, Cauliflower coral, arc-eye hawkfish. $1, Snubnose chub, lobe coral, vert. $3, Coral garden, butterflyfish, vert.

Wmk. 373

1994, Sept. 15　Litho.　Perf. 14

407	A84	20c multicolored	.25	.25
408	A84	90c multicolored	1.10	1.10
409	A84	$1 multicolored	1.25	1.25
		Nos. 407-409 (3)	2.60	2.60

Souvenir Sheet

| 410 | A84 | $3 multicolored | 3.75 | 3.75 |

Christmas A85

Flowers: 20c, Morning glory. 90c, Hibiscus, vert. $1, Frangipani. $3, Ginsey, vert.

Wmk. 373

1994, Nov. 24　Litho.　Perf. 14

411	A85	20c multicolored	.25	.25
412	A85	90c multicolored	1.10	1.10
413	A85	$1 multicolored	1.25	1.25
414	A85	$3 multicolored	3.75	3.75
		Nos. 411-414 (4)	6.35	6.35

Birds A86

Designs: 5c, Fairy tern. 10c, Red-tailed tropicbird chick, vert. 15c, Henderson rail. 20c, Red-footed booby, vert. 45c, Blue-gray noddy. 50c, Henderson reed warbler. 90c, Common noddy. $1, Masked booby, chick, vert. $1.80, Henderson fruit dove. $2, Murphy's petrel. $3, Christmas shearwater. $5, Red-tailed tropicbird juvenile.

1995, Mar. 8　　　　Perf. 13½

415	A86	5c multicolored	.15	.15
416	A86	10c multicolored	.15	.15
417	A86	15c multicolored	.18	.18
418	A86	20c multicolored	.25	.25
419	A86	45c multicolored	.55	.55
420	A86	50c multicolored	.62	.62
421	A86	90c multicolored	1.10	1.10
422	A86	$1 multicolored	1.25	1.25
423	A86	$1.80 multicolored	2.25	2.25
424	A86	$2 multicolored	2.50	2.50
425	A86	$3 multicolored	3.75	3.75
426	A86	$5 multicolored	6.25	6.25
		Nos. 415-426 (12)	19.00	19.00

Oeno Island Vacation — A87

Designs: 20c, Boating. 90c, Volleyball on the beach. $1.80, Picnic. $3, Sing-a-long.

1995, June 26　　　　Perf. 14x15

427	A87	20c multicolored	.25	.25
428	A87	90c multicolored	1.25	1.25
429	A87	$1.80 multicolored	2.50	2.50
430	A87	$3 multicolored	4.00	4.00
		Nos. 427-430 (4)	8.00	8.00

Souvenir Sheet

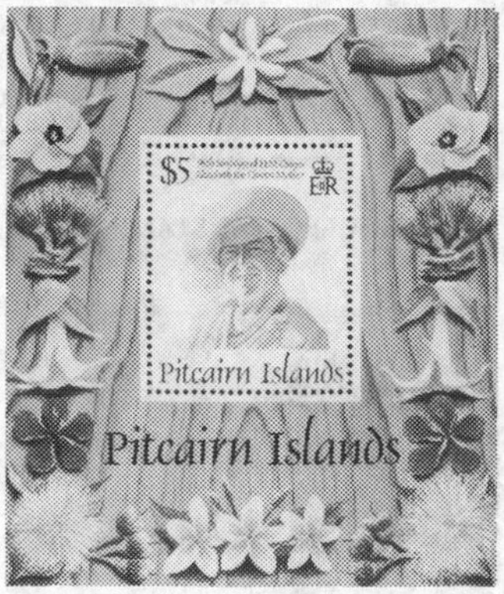

Queen Mother, 95th Birthday — A88

1995, Aug. 4 *Perf. 14½*
431 A88 $5 multicolored 6.75 6.75

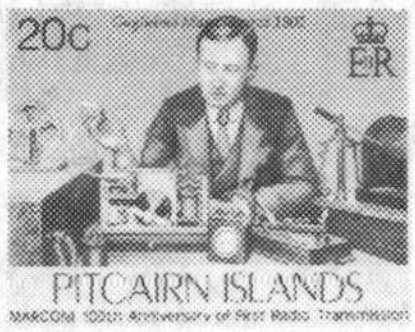

Radio, Cent. — A89

Designs: 20c, Guglielmo Marconi, radio equipment, 1901. $1, Man, Pitcairn radio, 1938. $1.50, Woman, satellite earth station equipment, 1994. $3, Satellite in orbit, 1992.

1995, Sept. 5 *Perf. 13*
432 A89 20c multicolored .25 .25
433 A89 $1 multicolored 1.25 1.25
434 A89 $1.50 multicolored 2.00 2.00
435 A89 $3 multicolored 4.00 4.00
Nos. 432-435 (4) 7.50 7.50

UN, 50th Anniv.
Common Design Type

Designs: 20c, Lord Mayor's Show. $1, RFA Brambleleaf. $1.50, UN ambulance. $3, Royal Air Force Tristar.

Wmk. 373
1995, Oct. 24 Litho. *Perf. 14*
436 CD353 20c multicolored .25 .25
437 CD353 $1 multicolored 1.25 1.25
438 CD353 $1.50 multicolored 2.00 2.00
439 CD353 $3 multicolored 4.00 4.00
Nos. 436-439 (4) 7.50 7.50

QUEENSLAND

ˈkwēnz-ˌland

LOCATION — Northeastern part of Australia
GOVT. — A former British Crown Colony
AREA — 670,500 sq. mi.
POP. — 498,129 (1901)
CAPITAL — Brisbane

Originally a part of New South Wales, Queensland was constituted a separate colony in 1859. It was one of the six British Colonies that united in 1901 to form the Commonwealth of Australia.

12 Pence = 1 Shilling
20 Shillings = 1 Pound

Values for unused stamps are for examples with original gum as defined in the catalogue introduction. Very fine examples of Nos. 4-73, 84-125, 128-140, and F1-F3b will have perforations touching the design on at least one or more sides due to the narrow spacing of the stamps on the plates. Stamps with perfs clear of the design on all four sides are scarce and will command higher prices.

Watermarks

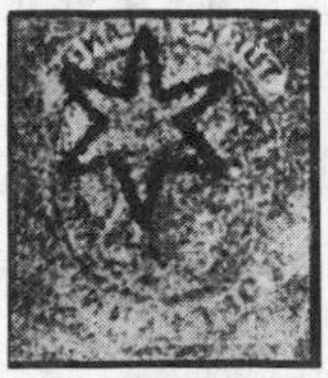

Wmk. 5- Small Star

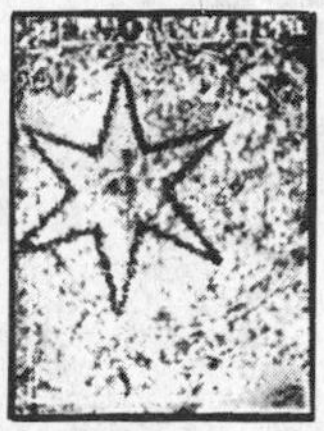

Wmk. 6- Large Star

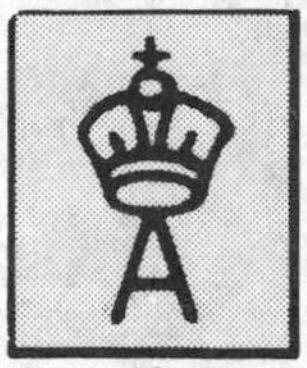

Wmk. 12- Crown and Single-lined A

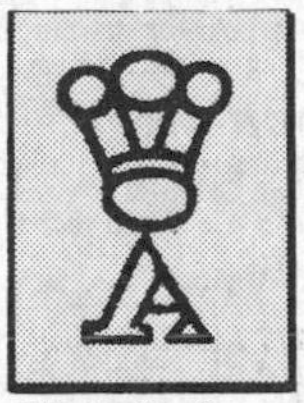

Wmk. 13- Crown and Double-lined A

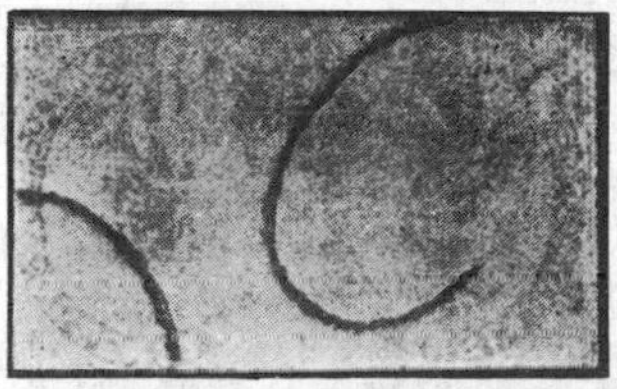

Wmk. 65- "Queensland Postage Stamps" in Sheet in Script Capitals

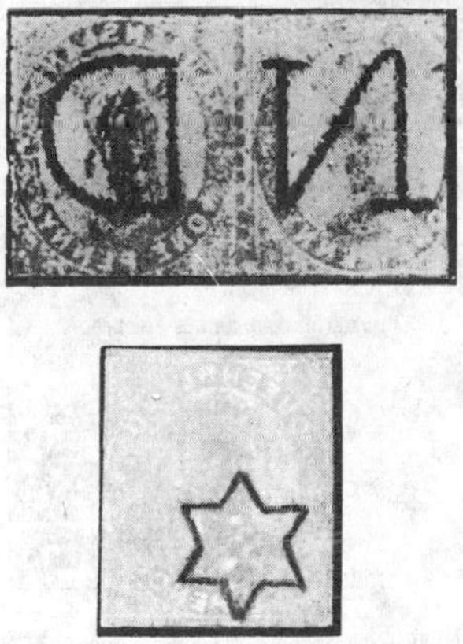

Wmks. 66 & 67- "Queensland" in Large Single-lined Roman Capitals in the Sheet and Short-pointed Star to Each Stamp (Stars Vary Slightly in Size and Shape)

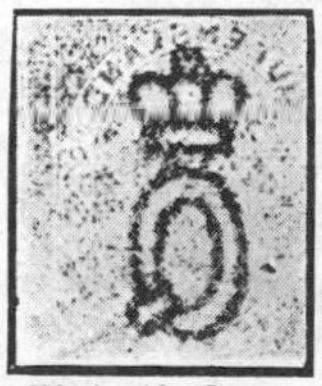

Wmk. 68- Crown and Q

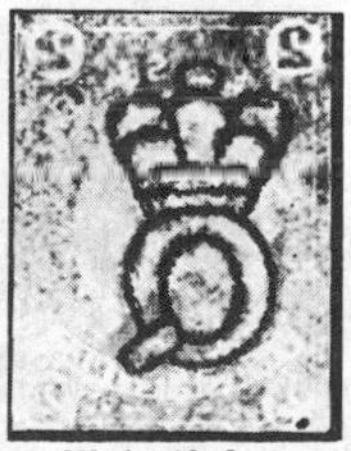

Wmk. 69- Large Crown and Q

There are two varieties of the watermark 68, differing slightly in the position and shape of the crown and the tongue of the "Q."

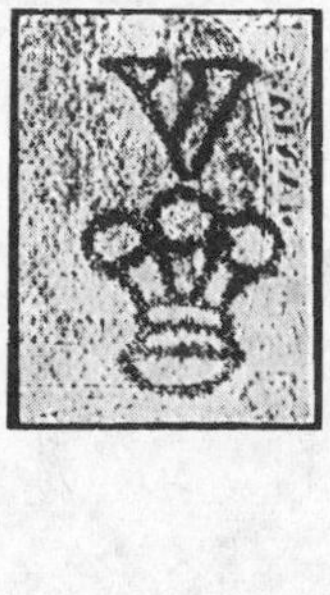

Wmk. 70- V and Crown

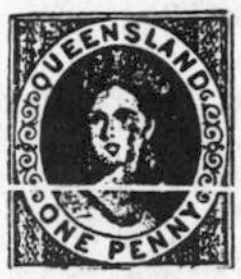

Queen Victoria — A1

1860, Nov. 1 Engr. Wmk. 6 *Imperf.*
1 A1 1p deep rose 3,000. 675.
2 A1 2p deep blue 6,250. 2,250.
3 A1 6p deep green 4,250. 675.

Clean-Cut Perf. 14 to 16
4 A1 1p deep rose 1,750. 150.
5 A1 2p deep blue 475. 100.
6 A1 6p deep green 475. 60.

Clean-Cut Perf. 14 to 16
1860-61 Wmk. 5
6A A1 2p blue 525.00 80.00
b. Horiz. pair, imperf. vert 675.00
6D A1 3p brown ('61) 225.00 45.00
6E A1 6p deep green 550.00 45.00
6F A1 1sh gray violet 475.00 47.50

Regular Perf. 14
6H A1 1p rose 125.00 25.00
6I A1 2p deep blue 325.00 37.50

Rough Perf. 14 to 16
7 A1 1p deep rose 80.00 35.00
8 A1 2p blue 90.00 35.00
9 A1 3p brown ('61) 55.00 17.50
a. Horiz. pair, imperf. vert. 2,000.
10 A1 6p deep green 175.00 20.00
11 A1 1sh dull violet 400.00 85.00

Thick Yellowish Paper

Square Perf. 12½ to 13
1862-67 Unwmk.
12 A1 1p indian red 325.00 70.00
13 A1 1p orange ('63) 60.00 15.00
a. Perf. 13, round holes ('67) 45.00 15.00
b. Horiz. pair, imperf. between
c. Imperf., pair 200.00
14 A1 2p deep blue 40.00 17.00
a. 2p pale blue 90.00 30.00
b. Perf. 13, round holes ('67) 60.00 14.00
c. Imperf., pair 175.00
e. Horiz. pair, imperf. between *900.00*
15 A1 3p brown ('63) 55.00 19.00
a. Imperf.
b. Perf. 13, round holes ('67) 300.00
16 A1 6p yellow grn ('63) 80.00 15.00
a. 6p grn 85.00 17.00
b. Perf. 13, round holes ('67) 95.00 9.25
c. Imperf., pair 275.00
17 A1 1sh gray ('63) 125.00 20.00
b. Imperf. horizontally
c. Horiz. pair, imperf. between 900.00
d. Perf. 13, round holes ('67)

White Wove Paper

1865 Wmk. 5 ***Rough Perf. 13***
18 A1 1p orange 50.00 8.75
a. Horiz. pair, imperf. vert. 425.00
19 A1 2p light blue 50.00 16.00
a. Vert. pair, imperf. horiz. 900.00
b. Half used as 1p on cover 2,000.
20 A1 6p yellow green 135.00 24.00
Nos. 18-20 (3) 235.00 48.75

Perf. 13, Round Holes
1866 Wmk. 65
21 A1 1p orange vermilion 160.00 15.00
22 A1 2p blue 45.00 18.00
b. Diagonal half used as 1p on cover

1866 Unwmk. Litho. *Perf. 13*
23 A1 4p lilac 90.00 18.00
a. 4p slate 135.00 16.00
24 A1 5sh pink 225.00 30.00
b. Vert. pair, imperf between 725.00

Wmk. 66, 67
1868-74 Engr. *Perf. 13*
25 A1 1p orange ('71) 45.00 5.00
26 A1 2p blue 45.00 1.90
27 A1 3p grnsh brn ('71) 85.00 2.50
a. 3p brown 87.50 3.50
b. 3p olive brown 87.50 3.50
28 A1 6p yel green ('71) 125.00 8.50
a. 6p deep green 175.00 11.00
30 A1 1sh grnsh gray ('72) 375.00 40.00
31 A1 1sh violet ('74) 200.00 20.00

Perf. 12
32 A1 1p orange 275.00 30.00
33 A1 2p blue 37.50
34 A1 3p brown 275.00 110.00
35 A1 6p deep green 900.00 42.50
36 A1 1sh violet — 37.50

Perf. 13x12
36A A1 1p orange 250.00
37 A1 2p blue *1,500.* 100.00
37A A1 3p brown *1,250.*

The reprints are perforated 13 and the colors differ slightly from those of the originals.

1868-75 Wmk. 68 *Perf. 13*
38 A1 1p orange 45.00 5.00
39 A1 1p rose ('74) 50.00 9.00
40 A1 2p blue 35.00 2.50
b. Imperf., pair 315.00
41 A1 3p brown ('75) 65.00 14.00
42 A1 6p yel green ('69) 100.00 7.50
a. 6p apple green 135.00 10.00
b. 6p deep green 125.00 10.00
43 A1 1sh violet ('75) *150.00* 26.00
Nos. 38-43 (6) *445.00* 64.00

No. 40 exists in vert. pair, imperf. btwn.

1876-78 *Perf. 12*
44 A1 1p orange 35.00 3.00
a. Imperf. 300.00
45 A1 1p rose 45.00 11.00
46 A1 2p blue 22.50 1.50
a. Imperf.
47 A1 3p brown 60.00 10.00
48 A1 6p yellow green 125.00 5.00
a. 6p apple green 135.00 4.75
b. 6p deep green 135.00 4.75
49 A1 1sh violet 42.50 5.00
Nos. 44-49 (6) 330.00 35.50

#44, 49 exist in vertical pairs, imperf. between.

Perf. 13x12
49B A1 1p orange 165.00
49C A1 2p blue *1,800.* 200.00
49D A1 4p yellow
49E A1 6p deep green 200.00

The reprints are perforated 12 and are in paler colors than the originals.

1879 Unwmk. *Perf. 12*
50 A1 6p pale emerald 200.00 25.00
a. Horiz. pair, imperf. vert. 650.00

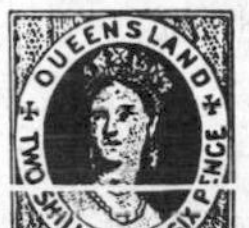

A2

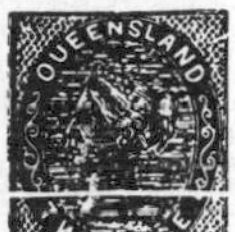

A3

1875-81 Litho. Wmk. 68 *Perf. 13*
50B A1 4p yellow ('75) 800.00 42.50

Perf. 12
51 A1 4p buff ('76) 600.00 22.50
a. 4p yellow 600.00 22.50
52 A1 2sh pale blue ('81) 55.00 12.00
a. 2sh deep blue 67.50 12.00
b. Imperf.
53 A2 2sh6p lt red ('81) 110.00 30.00
54 A1 5sh orange brn ('81) 120.00 27.50
a. 5sh fawn 125.00 27.50
55 A1 10sh brown ('81) 325.00 110.00
a. Imperf., pair 550.00
56 A1 20sh rose ('81) 650.00 90.00
Nos. 50B-56 (7) 2,660. 334.50

Nos. 53-56, 62-64, 74-83 with pen (revenue) cancellations removed are often offered as unused.

1879-81 Typo. Wmk. 68 *Perf. 12*
57 A3 1p rose red 9.50 1.50
a. 1p red orange 9.50 1.75
b. 1p brown orange 30.00 5.50
c. "QOEENSLAND" 110.00 32.50
d. Imperf.
e. Vert. pair, imperf. horiz. 90.00
58 A3 2p gray blue 22.50 .70
a. 2p deep ultra 27.50 .80
b. Imperf.
c. "PENGE" 70.00
d. "TW" joined 25.00 1.10
e. Vert. pair, imperf. horiz. 450.00
59 A3 4p orange yellow 60.00 8.00
a. Imperf.
60 A3 6p yellow green 55.00 5.00
a. Imperf.
61 A3 1sh pale violet ('81) 50.00 5.00
a. 1sh deep violet 45.00 3.75
Nos. 57-61 (5) 197.00 20.20

The stamps of type A3 were electrotyped from plates made up of groups of four types, differing in minor details. Two dies were used for the 1p and 2p, giving eight varieties for each of those values.

Nos. 59-60 exist imperf. vertically.

For surcharge see No. 65.

Moire on Back

1878-79 Unwmk.
62 A3 1p brown org ('79) 450.00 60.00
a. "QOEENSLAND" 2,000.
63 A3 2p deep ultra ('79) 600.00 30.00
a. "PENGE" 4,750. 725.00
64 A1 1sh red violet 100.00 47.50
Nos. 62-64 (3) 1,150. 137.50

No. 57b Surcharged Vertically in Black **Half-penny**

1881 Wmk. 68
65 A3 ½p on 1p brn org 175.00 95.00
a. "QOEENSLAND" 1,000. 825.00

A4

A5

1882-83   Typo.   Perf. 12

66	A4	1p pale red	5.75	.20
a.		1p rose	5.75	.20
b.		Imperf., pair	30.00	30.00
67	A4	2p gray blue	9.00	.20
a.		2p deep ultra	9.00	.20
b.		Imperf.		
68	A4	4p yellow ('83)	20.00	1.00
a.		"PENCE"	125.00	45.00
b.		Imperf., pair		150.00
69	A4	6p yellow green	10.00	.70
70	A4	1sh violet ('83)	12.00	1.00
		Nos. 66-70 (5)	56.75	3.10

There are eight minor varieties of the 1p, twelve of the 2p and four each of the other values. On the 1p there is a period after "PENNY." On all values the lines of shading on the neck extend from side to side.
Compare design A4 with A6, A10, A11, A15, A16.

1883   Perf. 9¹/₂x12

71	A4	1p rose	160.00	25.00
72	A4	2p gray blue	350.00	55.00
73	A4	1p pale violet	225.00	30.00
		Nos. 71-73 (3)	735.00	110.00

Beware of faked perfs.
See Nos. 94, 95, 100.

Wmk. 68 Twice Sideways
1882-85   Engr.   Perf. 12
Thin Paper

74	A5	2sh ultra	60.00	18.00
75	A5	2sh6p vermilion	50.00	22.50
76	A5	5sh car rose ('85)	50.00	22.50
77	A5	10sh brown	95.00	42.50
78	A5	£1 dark green ('83)	165.00	55.00
		Nos. 74-78 (5)	420.00	163.00

The 2sh, 5sh and £1 exist imperf.
There are two varieties of the watermark on Nos. 74-78, as in the 1879-81 issue.
Copies with revenue cancels sell for $3.25-6.50.

1886 Thick Paper Wmk. 69 Perf. 12

79	A5	2sh ultra	100.00	35.00
80	A5	2sh6p vermilion	40.00	22.50
81	A5	5sh car rose	37.50	30.00
82	A5	10sh dark brown	100.00	40.00
83	A5	£1 dark green	175.00	60.00
		Nos. 79-83 (5)	452.50	187.50

High value stamps with cancellations removed are offered as unused.
Copies with revenue cancels sell for $3.25-6.50.
See Nos. 126-127, 141-144.

A6

Redrawn
1887-89   Typo.   Wmk. 68   Perf. 12

84	A6	1p orange	4.50	.20
a.		Imperf., pair	40.00	60.00
85	A6	2p gray blue	9.00	.20
a.		2p deep ultra	11.50	.24
86	A6	2sh red brown ('89)	65.00	20.00

Perf. 9¹/₂x12

88	A6	2p deep ultra	250.00	110.00
		Nos. 84-88 (4)	328.50	130.40

The 1p has no period after the value.
In the redrawn stamps the shading lines on the neck are not completed at the left, leaving an irregular white line along that side.
Variety "LA" joined exists on Nos. 84-86, 88, 90, 91, 93, 97, 98, 102.
On No. 88 beware of faked perfs.

A7

A8

1890-92   Perf. 12¹/₂, 13

89	A7	¹/₂p green	4.50	.32
90	A6	1p orange red	3.00	.15
91	A6	2p gray blue	5.00	.15
92	A8	2¹/₂p rose carmine	11.00	.35
93	A6	3p brown ('92)	9.00	2.00
94	A4	4p orange	15.00	1.25
a.		4p yellow	16.00	1.25
b.		"PENCE"	65.00	27.50
95	A6	6p green	11.00	2.00
96	A6	2sh red brown	40.00	8.25
		Nos. 89-96 (8)	98.50	14.47

The ¹/₂p and 3p exist imperf.

1895   Wmk. 69   Perf. 12¹/₂, 13
Thick Paper

98	A6	1p orange	3.50	.50
99	A6	2p gray blue	3.50	.50

Perf. 12

100	A4	1sh pale violet	17.00	3.75
		Nos. 98-100 (3)	24.00	4.75

A9

A10

Moiré on Back
1895   Unwmk.   Perf. 12¹/₂, 13

101	A9	¹/₂p green	1.90	1.90
a.		Without moire	55.00	
102	A6	1p orange	2.25	2.25
a.		"PE" missing		

Wmk. 68

103	A9	¹/₂p green	2.25	.35
a.		¹/₂p deep green	1.65	.35
b.		Printed on both sides	60.00	
104	A10	1p orange	2.50	.15
105	A10	2p gray blue	3.25	.25

Wmk. 69
Thick Paper

106	A9	¹/₂p green	1.90	1.90

1895-96   Unwmk.   Thin Paper
Crown and Q Faintly Impressed

107	A9	¹/₂p green	2.75	.80
108	A10	1p orange	4.00	1.10
108A	A6	2p gray blue	11.00	

A11

A12

A13

1895-96   Wmk. 68

109	A11	1p red	8.50	.16
110	A12	2¹/₂p violet	9.00	1.75
111	A13	5p violet brown	11.00	1.75
111A	A11	6p yellow green		

A14

A15

A16

A17

A18

A19

1897-1900

TWO PENCE:
Type I - Point of bust does not touch frame.
Type II - First redrawing. The top of the crown, the chignon and the point of the bust touch the frame. The forehead is completely shaded.
Type III - Second redrawing. The top of crown does not touch the frame, though the chignon and the point of the bust do. The forehead and the bridge of the nose are not shaded.

1897-1900   Perf. 12¹/₂, 13

112	A14	¹/₂p deep green	3.50	1.40
a.		Perf. 12	150.00	
113	A15	1p red	1.50	.15
a.		Perf. 12	1.75	.20
114	A16	2p gray blue (I)	2.00	.15
a.		Perf. 12		6.00
115	A17	2¹/₂p rose	17.00	6.25
116	A17	2¹/₂p violet, blue	8.50	.70
117	A15	3p brown	8.00	.70
118	A15	4p bright yellow	8.00	.70
119	A18	5p violet brown	7.50	1.25
120	A15	6p yellow green	9.00	.70
121	A19	1sh lilac	13.00	1.65
a.		1sh light violet	16.00	1.65
122	A19	2sh turq blue	32.50	4.75
		Nos. 112-122 (11)	110.50	18.40

1898   Serrated Roulette 13

123	A15	1p scarlet	5.00	2.00
a.		Serrated and perf. 13	6.00	3.00
b.		Serrated in black	10.00	10.00
c.		Serrated without color and in black	9.00	9.00
d.		Same as "b," and perf. 13	85.00	
e.		Same as "c," and perf. 13	110.00	

Queen Victoria — A20

1899   Typo.   Perf. 12, 12¹/₂, 13

124	A20	¹/₂p blue green	1.00	.25

Unwatermarked stamps are proofs.

A13

"Australia" — A21

NINE PENCE:
Type I- "QUEENSLAND" 18x1¹/₂mm.
Type II- "QUEENSLAND" 17¹/₂x1¹/₄mm.

1903   Wmk. 70   Perf. 12¹/₂

125	A21	9p org brn & ultra, type I	13.00	3.50
a.		9p org brn & ultra, type II	12.00	3.00

See No. 128.

Type of 1882
Perf. 12, 12¹/₂, 13

1906   Litho.   Wmk. 68

126	A5	5sh rose	150.00	82.50
127	A5	£1 dark green	500.00	150.00

1907   Typo.   Wmk. 13   Perf. 12¹/₂

128	A21	9p yel brn & ultra, type	15.00	3.00
a.		9p yel brn & ultra, type II	27.50	4.25
b.		Perf. 11, type II		240.00

1907   Wmk. 68   Perf. 12¹/₂, 13

129	A16	2p ultra, type II	9.00	1.25
129A	A18	5p dark brown	9.00	1.90
b.		5p olive brown	9.00	1.90

1907-09   Wmk. 12

130	A20	¹/₂p deep green	1.25	.30
131	A15	1p red	1.25	.15
a.		Imperf., pair	200.00	
132	A16	2p ultra, type II	7.50	.15
133	A16	2p ultra, type III	2.25	.15
134	A15	3p pale brown	10.00	1.00
135	A15	4p bright yellow	12.00	2.75
136	A15	4p gray black ('09)	12.00	4.00
137	A18	5p brown	8.50	1.65
138	A15	6p yellow green	12.00	2.50
139	A19	1sh violet	15.00	3.75
140	A19	2sh turquoise bl	35.00	9.00

Wmk. 12 Sideways
Litho.

141	A5	2sh6p deep orange	50.00	37.50
142	A5	5sh rose	55.00	37.50
143	A5	10sh dark brown	100.00	35.00
144	A5	£1 blue green	225.00	135.00
		Nos. 130-144 (15)	546.75	268.05

SEMI-POSTAL STAMPS

Queen Victoria, Colors and Bearers — SP1

SP2

Perf. 12, 12¹/₂
1900, June 19   Wmk. 68

B1	SP1	1p red lilac	80.00	90.00
B2	SP2	2p deep violet	200.00	210.00

These stamps were sold at 1sh and 2sh respectively. The difference was applied to a patriotic fund in connection with the Boer War.

REGISTRATION STAMPS

R1

Clean-Cut Perf. 14 to 16
1861   Wmk. 5   Engr.

F1	R1	(6p) olive yellow	400.00	75.00
a.		Horiz. pair, imperf. vert.	4,500.	

Rough Perf. 14 to 16

F2	R1	(6p) dull yellow	50.00	35.00

1864   Perf. 12¹/₂ to 13

F3	R1	(6p) golden yellow	80.00	40.00
a.		Imperf.		
b.		Double impression	900.00	

The reprints are watermarked with a small truncated star and perforated 12.

> Queensland stamps can be mounted in the Scott Australia album.

RHODESIA

rō-'dē–zh(ē–)ə

(British South Africa)

LOCATION — Southeastern Africa
GOVT. — Formerly administered by the
British South Africa Company
AREA — 440,653 sq. mi.
POP. — 1,738,000 (estimated 1921)
CAPITAL — Salisbury

In 1923 the area was divided and the
portion south of the Zambezi River became
the British Crown Colony of Southern Rhodesia. In the following year the remaining
territory was formed into the Protectorate of
Northern Rhodesia. The Federation of Rhodesia and Nyasaland (comprising Southern
Rhodesia, Northern Rhodesia and Nyasaland) was established Sept. 3, 1953.

12 Pence = 1 Shilling
20 Shillings = 1 Pound

A1

A2

Coat of Arms — A3

Thin Paper
Engr. (A1, A3); Engr., Typo. (A2)

		1890-94 Unwmk.	Perf. 14, 14½	
1	A2	½p blue & ver ('91)	2.25	1.00
2	A1	1p black	8.50	1.00
3	A2	2p gray grn & ver ('91)	8.00	1.25
4	A2	3p gray & grn ('91)	7.50	1.25
5	A2	4p red brn & blk ('91)	8.00	1.50
6	A1	6p ultra	47.50	18.00
7	A1	6p deep blue	21.00	3.75
8	A2	8p rose & bl ('91)	8.50	2.75
9	A1	1sh gray brown	25.00	10.00
10	A1	2sh vermilion	35.00	22.50
11	A1	2sh6p dull lilac	22.50	25.00
		Revenue cancellation		.60
12	A2	3sh brn & grn ('94)	90.00	65.00
		Revenue cancellation		2.00
13	A2	4sh gray & ver ('93)	42.50	25.00
		Revenue cancellation		.80
14	A1	5sh yellow	35.00	42.50
		Revenue cancellation		1.00
15	A1	10sh deep green	65.00	65.00
		Revenue cancellation		1.00
16	A3	£1 dark blue	165.00	125.00
		Revenue cancellation		.30
17	A3	£2 rose	350.00	140.00
		Revenue cancellation		4.00
18	A3	£5 yellow grn	1,750.	500.00
		Revenue cancellation		6.00
19	A3	£10 orange brn	2,250.	900.00
		Revenue cancellation		10.00
		Nos. 1-16 (16)	591.25	410.50

The paper of the 1891 issue has the trademark
and initials of the makers in a monogram
watermarked in each sheet. Some of the lower values were also printed on a slightly thicker paper
without watermark.
Copies of #16-19 with cancellations removed are
frequently offered as unused specimens.
See #24-25, 58.
For surcharges see #20-23, 40-42. For overprints
see British Central Africa #1-20.

Nos. 6 and 9 Surcharged
in Black

½d.

1891, Mar.

20	A1	½p on 6p ultra	65.00	100.00
21	A1	2p on 6p ultra	70.00	125.00
22	A1	4p on 6p ultra	75.00	175.00
23	A1	8p on 1sh brown	110.00	250.00
		Nos. 20-23 (4)	320.00	650.00

Beware of forged surcharges.

Thick Soft Paper

		1895	Perf. 12½	
24	A2	2p green & red	20.00	4.00
25	A2	4p ocher & black	22.50	8.00
a.		Imperf., pair	1,750.	

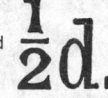
A4

		1896 Engraved, Typo.	Perf. 14	
26	A4	½p slate & violet	.65	.38
27	A4	1p scarlet & emer	2.00	2.00
28	A4	2p brown & rose lil	1.75	.75
29	A4	3p red brown & ultra	.90	.38
30	A4	4p blue & red lil	.90	.28
a.		4p ultra & red lilac	3.00	2.25
b.		Horiz. pair, imperf. btwn.		
31	A4	6p vio & pale rose	1.75	.45
a.		6p violet & pink	65.00	10.00
32	A4	8p dp grn & vio, buff	3.50	.85
a.		Imperf. pair	3,000.	
b.		Horiz. pair, imperf. btwn.		
33	A4	1sh brt grn & ultra	15.00	2.50
34	A4	2sh dk bl & grn, buff	17.50	5.00
35	A4	2sh6p brn & vio, yel	45.00	37.50
36	A4	3sh grn & red vio, bl	45.00	25.00
a.		Imperf. pair	3,500.	
37	A4	4sh red & bl, grn	35.00	3.00
38	A4	5sh org red & grn	30.00	12.00
39	A4	10sh sl & car, rose	100.00	60.00
		Nos. 26-39 (14)	298.95	150.09

The plates for this issue were made from two
dies. Stamps of die I have a small dot at the right of
the tail of the supporter at the right of the shield,
and the body of the lion is not fully shaded. Stamps
of die II have not the dot and the lion is heavily
shaded.
See type A7.

Nos. 4, 13-14 Surcharged in Black

One Penny **THREE**
 PENCE.

1896, Apr.

			Perf. 14	
40	A2	1p on 3p	350.00	350.00
a.		"P" of "Penny" inverted	10,000.	
41	A2	1p on 4sh	375.00	275.00
a.		"P" of "Penny" inverted	10,000.	
b.		Single bar in surch.	2,000.	2,500.
c.		"y" of "Penny" inverted	10,000.	
42	A1	3p on 5s yellow	210.00	250.00
a.		"T" of "THREE" inverted	10,000.	
b.		"R" of "THREE" inverted	10,000.	
		Nos. 40-42 (3)	935.00	875.00

Cape of Good Hope
Stamps Overprinted
in Black

BRITISH
SOUTH AFRICA
COMPANY.

1896, May 22

			Wmk. 16	
43	A6	½p slate	6.00	10.00
44	A15	1p carmine	7.50	10.50
45	A6	2p bister brown	8.75	6.00
46	A6	4p deep blue	10.50	10.50
a.		"COMPANY" omitted	10,000.	
47	A3	6p violet	37.50	47.50
48	A6	1sh yellow buff	70.00	85.00

Wmk. 2

49	A6	3p claret	40.00	45.00
		Nos. 43-49 (7)	180.25	214.00

Forgeries are plentiful.

Remainders

Rhodesian authorities made available
remainders in large quantities of all
stamps in 1897, 1898-1908, 1905, 1909
and 1910 issues, CTO. Some varieties
exist only as remainders. See notes following Nos. 100 and 118.

A7

Type A7 differs from type A4 in having the ends
of the scroll which is below the shield curved

between the hind legs of the supporters instead of
passing behind one leg of each. There are other
minor differences.

			Perf. 13½ to 16	
		1897 Unwmk.	Engr.	
50	A7	½p slate & violet	2.50	1.25
51	A7	1p ver & gray grn	2.75	1.25
52	A7	2p brown & lil rose	2.00	.50
53	A7	3p red brn & gray bl	2.00	.50
a.		Vert. pair, imperf. btwn.	1,500.	
54	A7	4p ultra & red lilac	2.75	.32
a.		Horiz. pair, imperf. btwn.	5,000.	5,000.
55	A7	6p violet & salmon	2.75	1.00
56	A7	8p dk grn & vio, buff	11.50	1.25
57	A7	£1 black & red, grn	425.00	200.00
		Revenue cancellation		10.00
		Nos. 50-56 (7)	26.25	6.07

Thick Paper
Perf. 15

58	A3	£2 bright red	1,300.	425.00
		Revenue cancellation		10.00

See note on remainders following No. 49.

A8

A9

A10

		1898-1908	Perf. 13½ to 16	
59	A8	½p yellow green	1.00	.15
a.		Imperf. pair	900.00	
b.		Horiz. pair, imperf. vert.	900.00	
60	A8	1p rose	1.10	.15
a.		1p red	.75	.15
b.		Horiz. or vert. pair, imperf. btwn.	500.00	
d.		Imperf. pair	500.00	500.00
61	A8	2p brown	1.00	.15
62	A8	2½p cobalt bl ('03)	3.00	.40
a.		Horiz. pair, imperf. between	750.00	750.00
63	A8	3p claret ('08)	3.00	.40
a.		Vert. pair, imperf. between	900.00	
64	A8	4p olive green	3.00	.15
a.		Vert. pair, imperf. between	700.00	
65	A8	6p lilac	5.50	1.50
a.		Vert. pair, imperf. between		
66	A9	1sh olive bister	6.50	1.00
a.		Imperf., pair	3,500.	
b.		Horiz. or vert. pair, imperf. btwn.	3,500.	
67	A9	2sh6p bluish gray ('06)	27.50	.65
a.		Vert. pair, imperf. between	1,300.	750.00
68	A9	3sh purple ('08)	7.00	1.00
69	A9	5sh orange ('01)	18.00	8.00
70	A9	7sh6p black ('01)	35.00	14.00
71	A9	10sh bluish grn ('08)	12.00	2.00
72	A10	£1 gray vio ('01)	140.00	50.00
		Revenue cancellation		1.00
73	A10	£2 red brown ('08)	55.00	50.00
74	A10	£5 dk blue ('01)	2,100.	
		Revenue cancellation		6.00
75	A10	£10 blue lil ('01)	2,750.	
		Revenue cancellation		5.50
		Nos. 59-73 (15)	318.60	89.55

For overprints and surcharges, see #82-100.
See note on remainders following #49.

Victoria
Falls — A11

		1905, July 13	Perf. 13½ to 15	
76	A11	1p rose red	2.25	3.25
77	A11	2½p ultra	6.50	3.25
78	A11	5p magenta	15.00	35.00
79	A11	1sh blue green	16.00	20.00
a.		Pair, imperf. between	10,750.	
b.		Imperf., pair	12,500.	
80	A11	2sh6p black	85.00	125.00
81	A11	5sh violet	72.50	60.00
		Nos. 76-81 (6)	197.25	226.50

Opening of the Victoria Falls bridge across the
Zambezi River.
See note on remainders following No. 49.

Stamps of 1898-1908 Overprinted or Surcharged:

RHODESIA. RHODESIA. 5d

1909			Perf. 14, 15	
82	A8	½p yellow green	.15	.15
83	A8	1p red	.15	.15
a.		Horiz. pair, imperf., vert.	450.00	
84	A8	2p brown	.90	.90
85	A8	2½p cobalt blue	.30	.15
86	A8	3p claret	.60	.18
b.		Double overprint		
87	A8	4p olive green	1.75	.45
88	A8	5p on 6p lilac	1.10	1.65
89	A8	6p lilac	4.25	.60
90	A9	7½p on 2sh6p	.75	.60
91	A9	10p on 3sh pur	1.25	1.25
92	A9	1sh olive bis	3.00	.35
93	A9	2sh on 5sh org	2.50	1.65
94	A9	2sh6p bluish gray	9.00	3.50
95	A9	3sh purple	9.00	4.00
96	A9	5sh orange	18.00	5.50
97	A9	7sh6p black	60.00	22.50
98	A9	10sh bluish grn	22.50	6.00
99	A10	£1 gray violet	95.00	60.00
a.		Pair, one without overprint	15,000.	
b.		Violet overprint	250.00	180.00
100	A10	£2 red brown	2,400.	325.00
		Nos. 82-99 (18)	230.20	111.58

See note on remainders following No. 49. The remainders included inverted overprints of the 3p ($35), 4p ($15) and 2s6p ($27.50).

Nos. 82-87, 89, 92, 94, 96 and 98 exist without period after "Rhodesia."

Queen Mary and King George V
A12   A13

1910	Engr.		Perf. 14, 15x14, 14x15	
101	A12	½p green	6.00	1.00
a.		½p olive green	14.00	1.25
b.		Perf. 15	225.00	13.00
c.		Imperf., pair	6,000.	6,750.
d.		Perf. 13½	250.00	37.50
102	A12	1p rose carmine	9.00	.50
a.		Vertical pair, imperf. btwn.	18,500.	
b.		Perf. 15	200.00	7.00
c.		Perf. 13½	1,500.	55.00
103	A12	2p gray & blk	27.50	6.00
a.		Horiz. pair, imperf. btwn.		
b.		Perf. 15	650.00	27.50
104	A12	2½p light blue	12.50	6.00
a.		2½p ultramarine	10.50	6.00
b.		Perf. 15	75.00	37.50
c.		Perf. 13½	30.00	37.50
105	A12	3p ol yel & vio	20.00	8.50
a.		Perf. 15	1,600.	55.00
106	A12	4p orange & blk	22.50	15.00
a.		4p orange & violet blk	52.50	35.00
b.		Perf. 15x14	400.00	
107	A12	5p ol grn & brn	20.00	27.50
a.		5p olive yel & brn (error)	400.00	115.00
b.		Perf. 15	450.00	115.00
108	A12	6p claret & brn	20.00	7.25
a.		Perf. 15	1,000.	55.00
109	A12	8p brn vio & gray blk	90.00	55.00
a.		Perf. 13½	50.00	150.00
110	A12	10p plum & rose red	25.00	42.50
111	A12	1sh turq grn & black	27.50	8.00
a.		Horiz. pair, imperf. btwn.		
b.		Perf. 15	550.00	35.00
112	A12	2sh gray bl & black	50.00	40.00
a.		Perf. 15	900.00	325.00
113	A12	2sh6p car rose & blk	325.00	275.00
114	A12	3sh vio & bl grn	120.00	120.00
115	A12	5sh yel grn & brn red	250.00	225.00
116	A12	7sh6p brt bl & car	500.00	450.00
117	A12	10sh red org & myr grn	400.00	200.00
a.		10sh red org & bl grn	300.00	200.00
118	A12	£1 bluish sl & car	900.00	350.00
a.		£1 black & red	900.00	250.00
c.		Perf. 15	8,000.	4,750.
		Nos. 101-118 (18)	2,825.	1,832.

See note on remainders following No. 49. The £1 in plum and red is from the remainders.

1913-19			Perf. 14	
119	A13	½p green	2.50	.55
a.		Horiz. pair, imperf. vert.	525.00	525.00
b.		Perf. 15	4.00	2.50
c.		Perf. 14x15	2,000.	200.00
d.		Perf. 15x14	2,000.	225.00
120	A13	1p bright rose	4.00	.50
a.		1p brown rose	1.50	.15
b.		Horiz. pair, imperf. btwn.	525.00	525.00
c.		Perf. 15	2.00	2.50

121	A13	1½p bister	2.50	.50
a.		Perf. 15	20.00	3.25
b.		Perf. 15x14		
c.		Vert. pair, imperf. btwn.	525.00	525.00
d.		Horiz. pair, imperf. btwn.	525.00	525.00
122	A13	2p gray & blk	4.00	3.00
a.		2p vio blk & blk	3.00	1.10
b.		Perf. 15	3.00	3.00
c.		Horiz. pair, imperf. btwn.	3,250.	3,500.
123	A13	2½p ultra	3.50	12.00
a.		Perf. 15	14.00	20.00
124	A13	3p yellow & blk	5.00	3.00
a.		3p orange yel & blk	3.50	1.25
b.		Perf. 15	6.00	5.25
125	A13	4p orange red & blk	7.00	3.25
a.		Perf. 15	30.00	13.00
126	A13	5p yel grn & blk	3.75	6.00
127	A13	6p lilac & blk	4.00	1.50
a.		Perf. 15	4.00	4.00
128	A13	8p gray grn & violet	10.00	25.00
a.		Perf. 15	30.00	30.00
129	A13	10p car rose & bl, perf. 15	6.50	16.00
a.		Perf. 14	8.50	18.00
130	A13	1sh turq bl & blk	5.00	2.50
131	A13	1sh lt grn & blk ('19)	6.50	1.75
			45.00	15.00
132	A13	2sh brn & blk, perf. 15	11.00	20.00
a.		Perf. 14	11.00	13.00
133	A13	2sh6p gray & blue	20.00	22.50
a.		2sh6p ol gray & vio bl	20.00	8.50
b.		Perf. 15	20.00	20.00
134	A13	3sh brt blue & red brown	25.00	13.00
a.		Perf. 15	140.00	100.00
135	A13	5sh green & blue	55.00	45.00
a.		Perf. 15	75.00	75.00
136	A13	7sh6p black & vio, perf. 15	82.50	110.00
a.		Perf. 14	165.00	165.00
137	A13	10sh yel grn & car	140.00	140.00
a.		Perf. 15	140.00	225.00
138	A13	£1 violet & blk	400.00	475.00
a.		£1 magenta & black	400.00	475.00
b.		Perf. 15	650.00	650.00
		Nos. 119-138 (20)	836.25	914.30

Three dies were used for the stamps of this issue: 1) Outline at top of cap absent or very faint and broken. Left ear not shaded or outlined and appears white; 2) Outline at top of cap faint and broken. Ear shaded all over, with no outline; 3) Outline at top of cap continuous. Ear shaded all over, with continuous outline.

No. 120 Surcharged in Dark Violet:

= = = =

Half **Half.**
Penny **Penny.**
No. 139 No. 140

1917				
139	A13	½p on 1p	1.00	1.00
a.		Inverted surcharge	1,500.	1,600.
140	A13	½p on 1p	.65	.65

Nos. 141-190 are accorded to Rhodesia and Nyasaland.

RHODESIA

rō-'dē–zh(ē-)ə

Self-Governing State (formerly Southern Rhodesia)

LOCATION — Southeastern Africa, bordered by Zambia, Mozambique, South Africa and Botswana
GOVT. — Self-governing member of British Commonwealth
AREA — 150,333 sq. mi.
POP. — 4,670,000 (est. 1968)
CAPITAL — Salisbury

In 1965, Southern Rhodesia assumed the name Rhodesia. On Nov. 11, 1965, the white minority government declared Rhodesia independent. Rhodesia became Zimbabwe on Dec. 31, 1978. For earlier issues, see Southern Rhodesia and Rhodesia and Nyasaland.

12 Pence = 1 Shilling
20 Shillings = 1 Pound
100 Cents = 1 Dollar (1967)

ITU Emblem, Old and New Communication Equipment — A27

1965, May 17	Unwmk. Photo.		Perf. 14	
200	A27	6p apple grn & brt vio	1.00	.38
201	A27	1sh3p brt vio & dk vio	1.50	1.00
202	A27	2sh6p org brn & dk vio	5.00	4.25
		Nos. 200-202 (3)	7.50	5.63

Cent. of the ITU.

Bangala Dam — A28

Designs: 4p, Irrigation canal through sugar plantation. 2sh6p, Worker cutting sugar cane.

1965, July 19	Photo.		Perf. 14	
203	A28	3p dull bl, grn & ocher	.28	.15
204	A28	4p blue, grn & brn	.85	.70
205	A28	2sh6p multicolored	4.50	3.75
		Nos. 203-205 (3)	5.63	4.60

Issued to publicize Conservation Week of the Natural Resources Board.

Churchill, Parliament, Quill and Sword A29

1965, Aug. 16				
206	A29	1sh3p ultra & black	.90	.65

Sir Winston Spencer Churchill (1874-1965), statesman and WWII leader. For surcharge see No. 222.

Issues of Smith Government

Arms of Rhodesia A30

1965, Dec. 8	Photo.		Perf. 11	
207	A30	2sh6p violet & multi	.60	.50
a.		Imperf., pair	825.00	

Declaration of independence by the government of Prime Minister Ian Smith.

Southern Rhodesia Nos. 95-108 Overprinted

INDEPENDENCE
11th November 1965

Southern Rhodesia Nos. 95-108 Overprinted

INDEPENDENCE
11th November 1965

1966, Jan. 17	Unwmk.	Perf. 14½	Photo.	
		Size: 23x19mm		
208	A30	½p lt bl, yel & grn	.15	.15
209	A30	1p ocher & purple	.15	.15
210	A30	2p violet & org yel	.15	.15
211	A30	3p lt blue & choc	.15	.15
212	A30	4p sl green & choc	.15	.15
		Perf. 13½x13		
		Size: 27x23mm		
213	A30	6p dull grn, red & yel	.16	.15
a.		Pair, one without overprint		
214	A30	9p ol grn, yel & brn	.28	.24
a.		Double overprint	125.00	
b.		Inverted overprint		
215	A30	1sh ocher & brt grn	.30	.28
a.		Double overprint	150.00	
216	A30	1sh3p grn, vio & dk red	.35	.30
217	A30	2sh dull bl & yel	1.00	.90
218	A30	2sh6p ultra & red	.65	.55
a.		Red omitted		

Advertisement (Column 1 lower)

Perf. 14½x14
Size: 32x27mm
Overprint 26mm Wide

219 A30 5sh bl, grn, ocher & lt brn 13.00 9.25
220 A30 10sh ocher, blk, red & bl 3.25 3.00
221 A30 £1 rose, sep, ocher & grn 6.00 5.50
Nos. 208-221 (14) 25.74 20.92

No. 206 Surcharged in Red

INDEPENDENCE
11th November
1965
= 5/-

Perf. 14

222 A29 5sh on 1sh3p 45.00 *62.50*

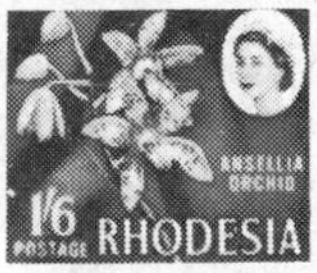
Ansellia Orchid — A31

Designs: 1p, Cape Buffalo. 2p, Oranges. 3p, Kudu. 4p, Emeralds. 6p, Flame lily. 9p, Tobacco. 1sh, Corn. 1sh3p, Lake Kyle. 2sh, Aloe. 2sh6p, Tigerfish. 5sh, Cattle. 10sh, Gray-breasted helmet guinea fowl. £1, Arms of Rhodesia.

Printed by Harrison & Sons, London.

1966, Feb. 9 Photo. *Perf. 14½*
Size: 23x19mm

223 A31 1p ocher & pur .15 .15
224 A31 2p slate grn & org .15 .15
225 A31 3p lt blue & choc .15 .15
b. Queen's head omitted
c. Booklet pane of 4 .85
226 A31 4p gray & brt grn .15 .15

Perf. 13½x13
Size: 27x23mm

227 A31 6p dull grn, red & yel .15 .15
228 A31 9p purple & ocher .25 .25
229 A31 1sh lt blue, yel & grn .28 .15
230 A31 1sh3p dull blue & yel .45 .28
231 A31 1sh6p ol grn, yel & brn .60 .38
232 A31 2sh lt ol grn, vio & dk red .70 .45
233 A31 2sh6p brt grnsh bl, ultra & ver .80 .55

Perf. 14½x14
Size: 32x27mm

234 A31 5sh bl, grn, ocher & lt brn 2.75 1.90
235 A31 10sh dl yel, blk, red & bl 7.00 6.25
236 A31 £1 sal pink, sep, ocher & grn 16.00 14.00
Nos. 223-236 (14) 29.58 24.96

Printed by Mardon Printers, Salisbury

1966-68 Litho. *Perf. 14½*

223a A31 1p ocher & purple .15 .15
224a A31 2p sl grn & org ('68) .20 .15
225a A31 3p lt bl & choc ('68) .30 .20
226a A31 4p sepia & brt grn .40 .32
227a A31 6p gray grn, red & yel .60 .48
228a A31 9p pur & ocher ('68) .80 .60
230a A31 1sh3p dl bl & yel 1.00 .80
232a A31 2sh lt ol grn, vio & dk red 4.00 3.25

Perf. 14

234a A31 5sh brt bl, grn, ocher & brn 11.00 8.25
235a A31 10sh ocher, blk, red & bl 35.00 27.50
236a A31 £1 sal pink, sep, ocher & grn 50.00 40.00
Nos. 223a-236a (11) 103.45 81.70

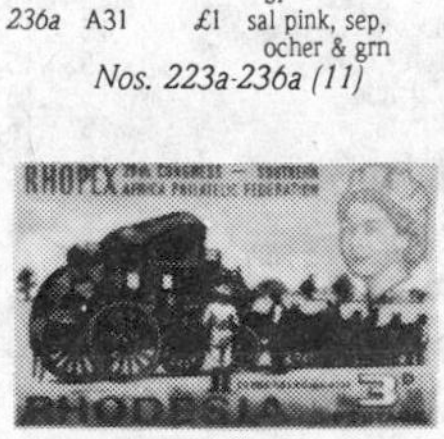
Zeederberg Coach A32

Designs: 9p, Sir Rowland Hill. 1sh6p, Penny Black. 2sh6p, Rhodesia No. 18, £5.

Perf. 14½

1966, May 2 Litho. Unwmk.

237 A32 3p blue, org & blk .40 .32
238 A32 9p beige & brown .55 .48
239 A32 1sh6p blue & black 1.40 1.10
240 A32 2sh6p rose, yel grn & blk 2.50 2.50
a. Souvenir sheet of 4, #237-240 15.00 *25.00*
Nos. 237-240 (4) 4.85 4.40

28th Cong. of the Southern Africa Phil. Fed. and the RHOPEX Exhib., Bulawayo, May 2-7.

No. 240a was printed in sheets of 12 and comes with perforations extending through the margins in four different versions. Many have holes in the top margin made when the sheet was cut into individual panes. Sizes of panes vary.

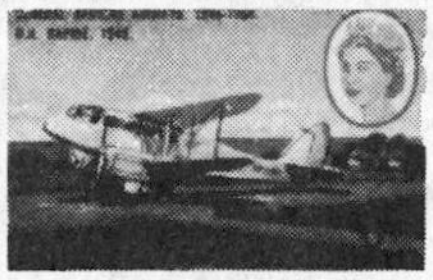
De Havilland Dragon Rapide — A33

Planes: 1sh3p, Douglas DC-3. 2sh6p, Vickers Viscount. 5sh, Jet.

1966, June 1

241 A33 6p multicolored 1.00 .85
242 A33 1sh3p multicolored 1.65 1.00
243 A33 2sh6p multicolored 4.50 4.00
244 A33 5sh blue & black 7.50 6.25
Nos. 241-244 (4) 14.65 12.10

20th anniv. of Central African Airways.

Dual Currency Issue
Type of 1966 with Denominations in Cents and Pence-Shillings

1967-68 Litho. *Perf. 14½*

245 A31 3p/2½c lt blue & choc .42 .35
246 A31 1sh/10c multi 1.75 1.25
247 A31 1sh6p/15c multi 13.00 6.50
248 A31 2sh/20c multi 19.00 13.00
248A A31 2sh6p/25c multi 52.50 60.00
Nos. 245-248A (5) 86.67 81.10

These locally printed stamps were issued to acquaint Rhodesians with the decimal currency to be introduced in 1969-1970.

Issued: 3p, Mar. 15, 1967. 1sh, Nov. 1, 1967. 1sh6p, 2sh, Mar. 11, 1968. 2sh6p, Dec. 9, 1968.

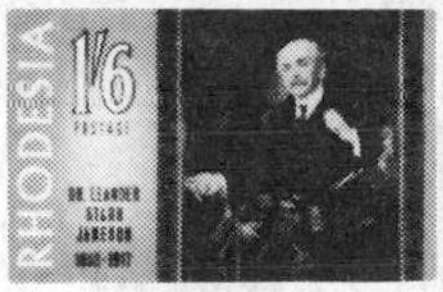
Leander Starr Jameson, by Frank Moss Bennett A34

1967, May 17

249 A34 1sh6p emerald & multi 1.25 1.10

Dr. Leander Starr Jameson (1853-1917), pioneer with Cecil Rhodes and Prime Minister of Cape Colony. See No. 262.

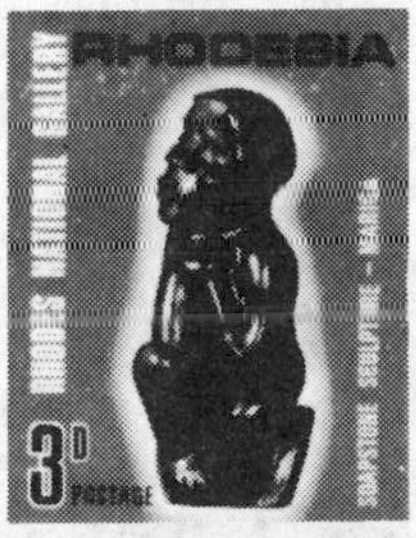
Soapstone Sculpture, by Joram Mariga A35

Designs: 9p, Head of Burgher of Calais, by Auguste Rodin. 1sh3p, "Totem," by Roberto Crippa. 2sh6p, St. John the Baptist, by Michele Tosini.

1967, July 12 Litho. *Perf. 14*

250 A35 3p brn, blk & ol grn .24 .22
251 A35 9p brt bl, blk & ol grn .75 .70
252 A35 1sh3p multicolored 1.10 1.10
253 A35 2sh6p multicolored 2.25 2.00
Nos. 250-253 (4) 4.34 4.02

10th anniv. of the Rhodes Natl. Gallery, Salisbury.

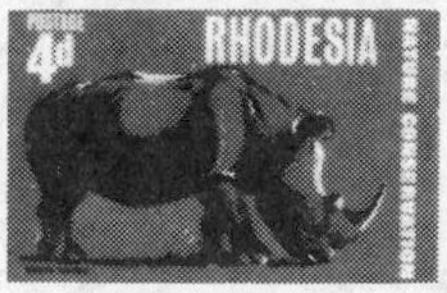
White Rhinoceros A36

Designs: No. 255, Parrot's beak gladioli, vert. No. 256, Baobab tree. No. 257, Elephants.

1967, Sept. 6 Unwmk. *Perf. 14½*

254 A36 4p olive & black .55 .55
255 A36 4p dp orange & blk .55 .55
256 A36 4p brown & blk .55 .55
257 A36 4p gray & blk .55 .55
Nos. 254-257 (4) 2.20 2.20

Issued to publicize nature conservation.

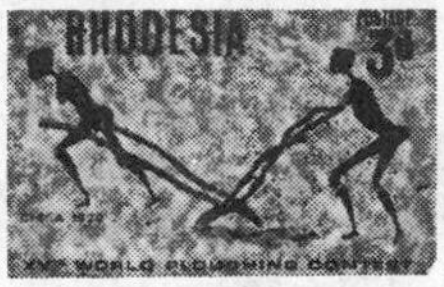
Wooden Hand Plow, c. 1820 A37

Designs: 9p, Ox-drawn plow, c. 1860. 1sh6p, Steam tractor and plows, c. 1905. 2sh6p, Tractor and moldboard plow, 1968.

1968, Apr. 26 Litho. *Perf. 14½*

258 A37 3p multicolored .15 .15
259 A37 9p multicolored .30 .30
260 A37 1sh6p multicolored .70 .70
261 A37 2sh6p multicolored 1.90 1.90
Nos. 258-261 (4) 3.05 3.05

15th world plowing contest, Kent Estate, Norton.

Portrait Type of 1967

Design: 1sh6p, Alfred Beit (portrait at left).

1968, July 15 Unwmk. *Perf. 14½*

262 A34 1sh6p orange, blk & red 1.25 1.25

Alfred Beit (1853-1906), philanthropist and friend of Cecil Rhodes.

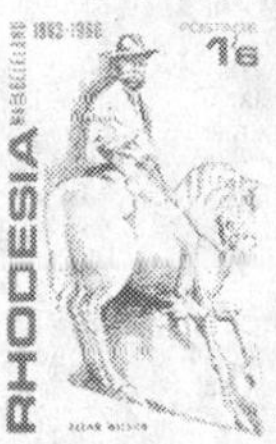
Allan Wilson, Matopos Hills — A38

Matabeleland, 75th Anniversary: 3p, Flag raising, Bulawayo, 1893. 9p, Bulawayo arms, view of Bulawayo.

1968, Nov. 4 Litho. *Perf. 14½*

263 A38 3p multicolored .25 .25
264 A38 9p multicolored .90 .90
265 A38 1sh6p multicolored 1.75 1.75
Nos. 263-265 (3) 2.90 2.90

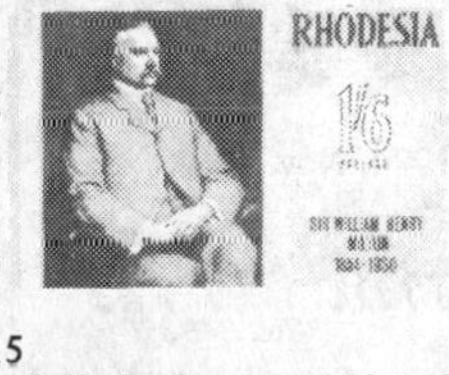
William Henry Milton (1854-1930), Adminstrator A39

1969, Jan. 15

266 A39 1sh6p multicolored 1.00 1.00

See Nos. 298-303.

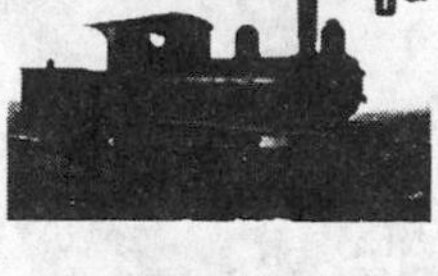
Locomotive, 1890's A40

Beira-Salisbury Railroad, 70th Anniversary: 9p, Steam locomotive, 1901. 1sh6p, Garratt articulated locomotive, 1950, 2sh6p, Diesel, 1955.

1969, May 22

267 A40 3p multicolored .50 .22
268 A40 9p multicolored 1.50 .85
269 A40 1sh6p multicolored 6.00 4.50
270 A40 2sh6p multicolored 9.50 7.75
Nos. 267-270 (4) 17.50 13.32

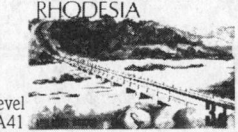

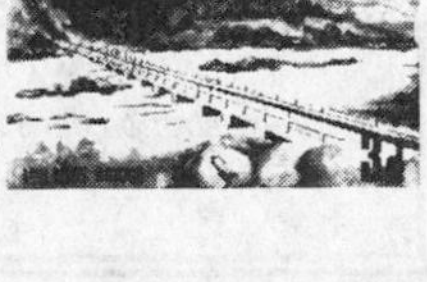
Low Level Bridge — A41

Bridges: 9p, Mpudzi River. 1sh6p, Umniati River. 2sh6p, Birchenough over Sabi River.

1969, Sept. 18

271 A41 3p multicolored .35 .25
272 A41 9p multicolored 1.25 .70
273 A41 1sh6p multicolored 4.50 3.25
274 A41 2sh6p multicolored 5.75 4.00
Nos. 272-274 (4) 11.85 8.20

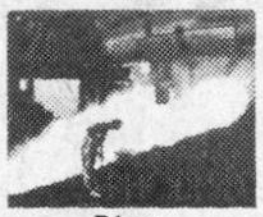
Blast Furnace — A42

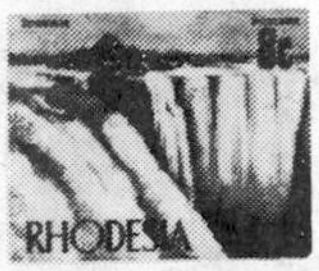
Devil's Cataract, Victoria Falls — A43

Designs: 1c, Wheat harvest. 2½c, Ruins, Zimbabwe. 3c, Trailer truck. 3½c, 4c, Cecil Rhodes statue. 5c, Mining. 6c, Hydrofoil, "Seaflight." 7½c, like 8c. 10c, Yachting, Lake McIlwaine. 12½c, Hippopotamus. 14c, 15c, Kariba Dam. 20c, Irrigation canal. 25c, Bateleur eagles. 50c, Radar antenna and Viscount plane. $1, "Air Rescue." $2, Rhodesian flag.

1970-73 Litho. *Perf. 14½*
Size: 22x18mm

275 A42 1c multicolored .15 .15
a. Booklet pane of 4 .28
b. Min. sheet of 4, Rhophil 2.50
276 A42 2c multicolored .15 .15
277 A42 2½c multicolored .15 .15
a. Booklet pane of 4 .18
b. Min. sheet of 4, Rhophil 2.50
278 A42 3c multi ('73) 1.75 .22
a. Booklet pane of 4 7.25
279 A42 3½c multicolored .15 .15
a. Booklet pane of 4 .70
b. Min. sheet of 4, Rhophil 2.50
280 A42 4c multi ('73) 1.75 .22
a. Booklet pane of 4 8.00
281 A42 5c multicolored .20 .15

Size: 27x23mm

282 A43 6c multi ('73) 2.75 1.00
283 A43 7½c multi ('73) 5.25 3.25
284 A43 8c multicolored 2.25 .80
285 A43 10c multicolored .45 .28
286 A43 12½c multicolored .55 .28
287 A43 14c multi ('73) 7.75 2.75
288 A43 15c multi ('71) 2.25 .40
289 A43 20c multicolored 2.75 .45

Size: 30x25mm

290 A43 25c multicolored 3.00 1.00
291 A43 50c multicolored 5.25 4.00
292 A43 $1 multicolored 10.00 8.50
293 A43 $2 multicolored 27.50 25.00
Nos. 275-293 (19) 74.05 48.90

Booklet panes and miniature sheets were made by altering the plates used to print the stamps, eliminating every third horizontal and vertical row of stamps. The perforations extend through the margins in four different versions. In 1972 sheets of 4 overprinted in the margins were issued for Rhophil '72 Philatelic Exhibition.

Issue dates: Feb. 17, 1970, Jan. 1, 1973.

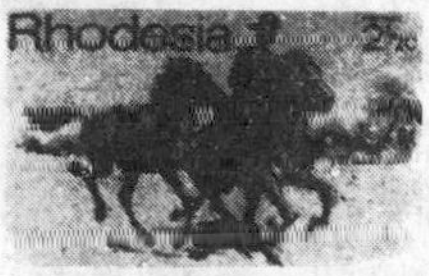
Despatch Rider, c. 1890 — A44

Posts and Telecommunications Corporation, Inauguration: 3½c, Loading mail, Salisbury Airport. 15c, Telegraph line construction, c.1890. 25c, Telephone and telecommunications equipment.

1970, July 1

294 A44 2½c multicolored .25 .25
295 A44 3½c multicolored .60 .60
296 A44 15c multicolored 1.90 1.90
297 A44 25c multicolored 3.25 3.25
Nos. 294-297 (4) 6.00 6.00

Famous Rhodesians Type of 1969

Portraits: 13c Dr. Robert Moffat (1795-1883), missionary. No. 299, Dr. David Livingstone (1813-73), explorer. No. 300, George Pauling (1854-1919), engineer No. 301, Thomas Baines (1820-75), self-portrait. No. 302, Mother Patrick (1863-1900), Dominican nurse and teacher. No. 303, Frederick Courteney Selous (1851-1917), explorer, big game hunter.

1970-75 Litho. *Perf. 14½*

298 A39 13c multi ('72) 1.50 1.50
299 A39 14c multi ('73) 1.50 1.50
300 A39 14c multi ('74) 1.50 1.50
301 A39 14c multi ('75) 1.50 1.50

302	A39	15c multi	1.50	1.50
303	A39	15c multi ('71)	1.50	1.50
		Nos. 298-303 (6)	9.00	9.00

Issued: Feb. 14, 1972, Apr. 2, 1973, May 15, 1974, Feb. 12, 1975, Nov. 16, 1970, Mar. 1, 1971.

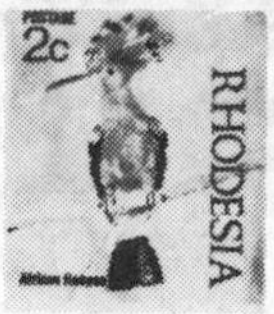

African Hoopoe — A45

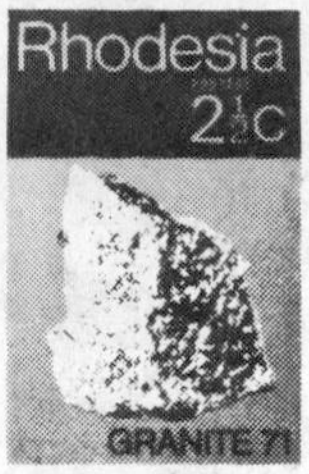

Porphyritic Granite — A46

Birds: 2½c, Half-collared kingfisher, horiz. 5c, Golden-breasted bunting. 7½c, Carmine bee-eater. 8c, Red-eyed bulbul. 25c, Wattled plover, horiz.

1971, June 1

304	A45	2c multicolored	1.00	.45
305	A45	2½c multicolored	1.25	.50
306	A45	5c multicolored	2.75	1.10
307	A45	7½c multicolored	3.50	1.75
308	A45	8c multicolored	3.50	1.75
309	A45	25c multicolored	10.00	4.25
		Nos. 304-309 (6)	22.00	9.80

1971, Aug. 30

Granite '71, Geological Symposium, Aug. 30-Sept. 19: 7½c, Muscovite mica, seen through microscope. 15c, Granite, seen through microscope. 25c, Geological map of Rhodesia.

310	A46	2½c multicolored	.38	.32
311	A46	7½c multicolored	1.65	1.25
312	A46	15c multicolored	2.50	2.00
313	A46	25c multicolored	3.75	3.25
		Nos. 310-313 (4)	8.28	6.82

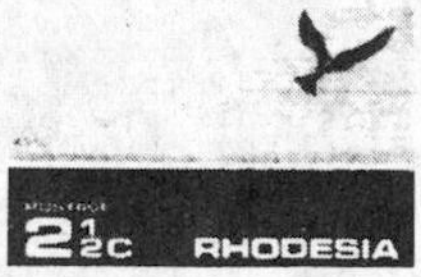

"Be Airwise" A47

Prevent Pollution: 3½c, Antelope (Be Countrywise). 7c, Fish (Be Waterwise). 13c, City (Be Citywise).

1972, July 17

314	A47	2½c multicolored	.15	.15
315	A47	3½c multicolored	.32	.32
316	A47	7c multicolored	.70	.70
317	A47	13c multicolored	1.10	1.10
		Nos. 314-317 (4)	2.27	2.27

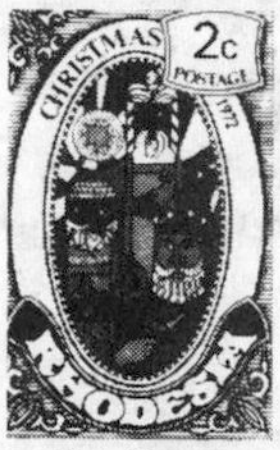

The Three Kings — A48

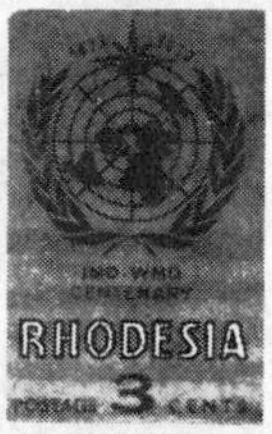

W.M.O. Emblem — A49

1972, Oct. 18

318	A48	2c multicolored	.15	.15
319	A48	5c multicolored	.35	.35
320	A48	13c multicolored	1.00	1.00
		Nos. 318-320 (3)	1.50	1.50

Christmas.

1973, July 2

321	A49	3c multicolored	.15	.15
322	A49	14c multicolored	.80	.80
323	A49	25c multicolored	1.50	1.50
		Nos. 321-323 (3)	2.45	2.45

Intl. Meteorological Cooperation, cent.

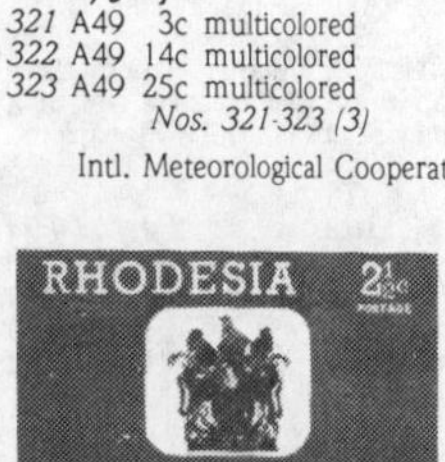

Arms of Rhodesia A50

1973, Oct. 10

324	A50	2½c multicolored	.32	.32
325	A50	4c multicolored	.60	.60
326	A50	7½c multicolored	1.40	1.40
327	A50	14c multicolored	2.50	2.50
		Nos. 324-327 (4)	4.82	4.82

Responsible Government, 50th Anniversary.

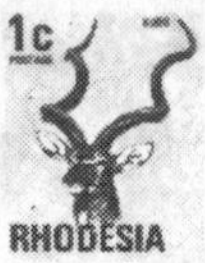

Kudu A51

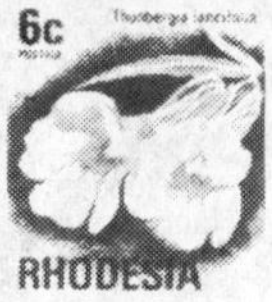

Thunbergia A52

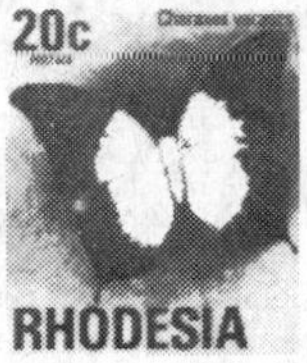

Pearl Charaxes — A53

1974-76 Litho. *Perf. 14½*

328	A51	1c shown	.16	.15
329	A51	2½c Eland	.48	.15
330	A51	3c Roan antelope	.16	.15
331	A51	4c Reedbuck	.16	.15
332	A51	5c Bushbuck	.20	.15
333	A52	6c shown	.28	.15
334	A52	7½c Flame lily	3.25	1.75
335	A52	8c like 7½c ('76)	.25	.15
336	A52	10c Devil thorn	.25	.15
337	A52	12c Hibiscus ('76)	.40	.18
338	A52	12½c Pink sabi star	3.25	1.75
339	A52	14c Wild pimpernel	4.75	2.50
340	A52	15c like 12½c ('76)	.48	.25
341	A52	16c like 14c ('76)	.48	.25
342	A53	20c shown	.48	.25
343	A53	24c Yellow pansy ('76)	.95	.52
344	A53	25c like 24c	4.75	2.50
345	A53	50c Queen purple tip	1.25	.65
346	A53	$1 Striped swordtail	2.50	1.25
347	A53	$2 Guinea fowl butterfly	4.75	2.50
		Nos. 328-347 (20)	29.23	15.55

Issue dates: Aug. 14, 1974, July 1, 1976.
For surcharges see Nos. 364-366.

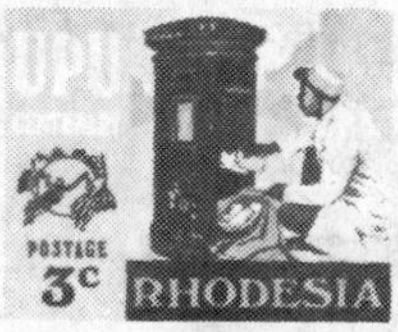

Mail Collection and UPU Emblem A54

1974, Nov. 20 *Perf. 14½*

348	A54	3c shown	.30	.30
349	A54	4c Mail sorting	.42	.42
350	A54	7½c Mail delivery	.80	.80
351	A54	14c Parcel post	1.40	1.40
		Nos. 348-351 (4)	2.92	2.92

Universal Postal Union Centenary.

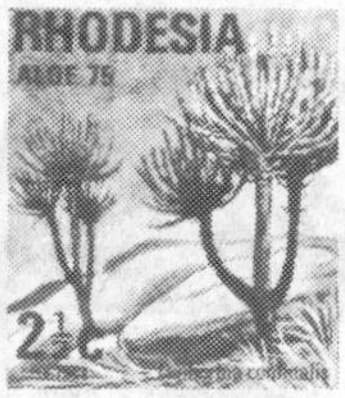

Euphorbia Confinalis — A55

1975, July 16

352	A55	2½c shown	.16	.16
353	A55	3c Aloe excelsa	.18	.18
354	A55	4c Hoodia lugardii	.35	.25
355	A55	7½c Aloe ortholopha	.65	.48
356	A55	14c Aloe musapana	1.50	1.25
357	A55	25c Aloe saponaria	2.00	1.90
		Nos. 352-357 (6)	4.84	4.22

Intl. Succulent Cong., Salisbury, July 1975.

Rhodesia stamps can be mounted in the Scott British Africa album.

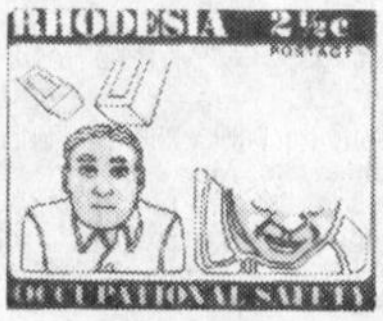

Head Injury and Safety Helmet — A56

Occupational Safety: 4c, Bandaged hand and safety glove. 7½c, Injured eye and safety eyeglass. 14c, Blind man and protective shield.

1975, Oct. 15

358	A56	2½c multicolored	.15	.15
359	A56	4c multicolored	.45	.45
360	A56	7½c multicolored	.70	.70
361	A56	14c multicolored	1.25	1.25
		Nos. 358-361 (4)	2.55	2.55

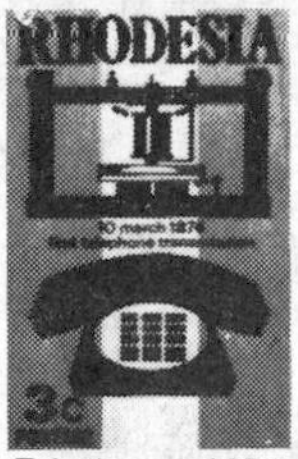

Telephones, 1876 and 1976 — A57

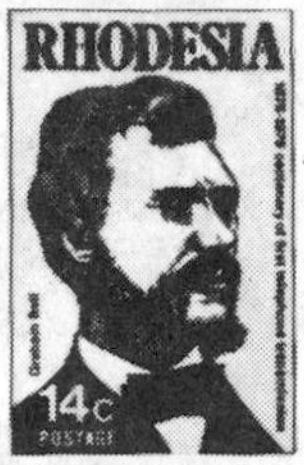

Alexander Graham Bell — A58

1976, Mar. 10

362	A57	3c light blue & blk	.15	.15
363	A58	14c buff & black	.48	.48

Centenary of first telephone call, by Alexander Graham Bell, Mar. 10, 1876.

Nos. 334, 339 and 344 Surcharged with New Value and Two Bars

1976, July 1

364	A52	8c on 7½c multi	.18	.18
365	A52	16c on 14c multi	.38	.38
366	A53	24c on 25c multi	1.25	1.25
		Nos. 364-366 (3)	1.81	1.81

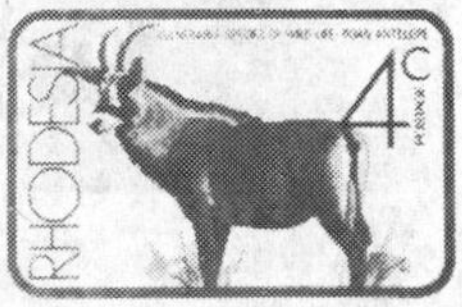

Wildlife Protection A59

1976, July 21

367	A59	4c Roan Antelope	.22	.22
368	A59	6c Brown hyena	.32	.32
369	A59	8c Wild dog	.45	.45
370	A59	16c Cheetah	1.00	1.00
		Nos. 367-370 (4)	1.99	1.99

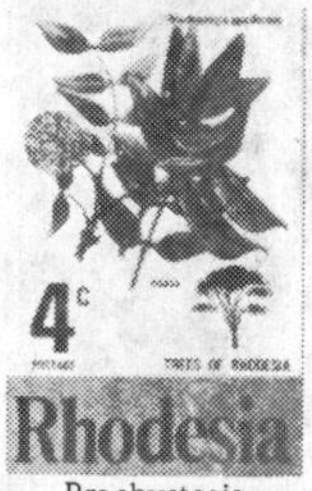

Brachystegia Spiciformis — A60

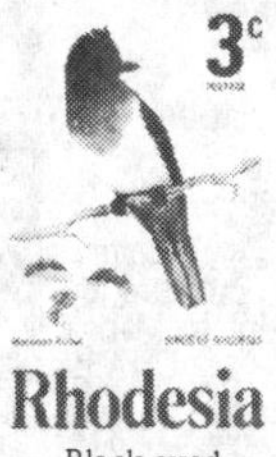

Black-eyed Bulbul — A61

1976, Nov. 17

371	A60	4c shown	.15	.15
372	A60	6c Red mahogany	.15	.15
373	A60	8c Pterocarpus angolensis	.38	.38
374	A60	16c Rhodesian teak	.75	.75
		Nos. 371-374 (4)	1.43	1.43

Flowering trees.

1977, Mar. 16

Birds: 4c, Yellow-mantled whydah. 6c, Orange-throated longclaw. 8c, Long-tailed shrike. 16c, Lesser blue-eared starling. 24c, Red-billed wood hoopoe.

375	A61	3c multicolored	.15	.15
376	A61	4c multicolored	.20	.20
377	A61	6c multicolored	.30	.30
378	A61	8c multicolored	.45	.45
379	A61	16c multicolored	.90	.90
380	A61	24c multicolored	1.10	1.10
		Nos. 375-380 (6)	3.10	3.10

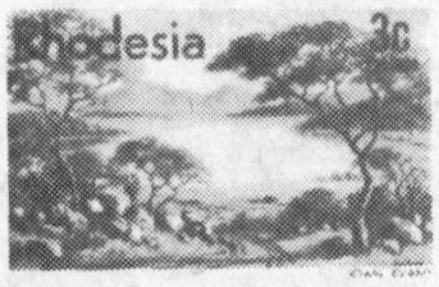

Lake Kyle, by Joan Evans — A62

Landscape Paintings: 4c, Chimanimani Mountains, by Evans. 6c, Rocks near Bonsor Reef, by Alice Balfour. 8c, Dwala (rock) near Devil's Pass, by Balfour. 16c, Zimbabwe, by Balfour. 24c, Victoria Falls, by Thomas Baines.

1977, July 20 Litho. *Perf. 14½*

381	A62	3c multicolored	.15	.15
382	A62	4c multicolored	.15	.15
383	A62	6c multicolored	.20	.20
384	A62	8c multicolored	.28	.28
385	A62	16c multicolored	.50	.50
386	A62	24c multicolored	.80	.80
		Nos. 381-386 (6)	2.08	2.08

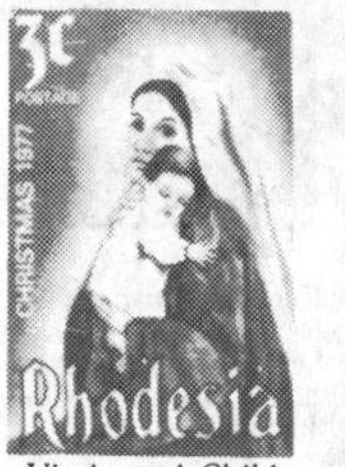

Virgin and Child A63

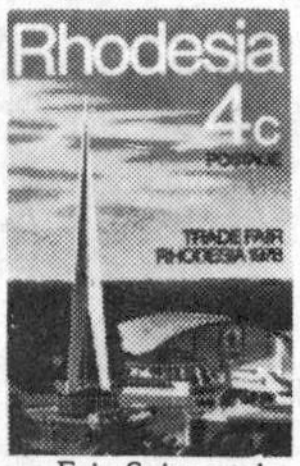

Fair Spire and Fairgrounds A64

1977, Nov. 16

387	A63	3c multicolored	.15	.15
388	A63	6c multicolored	.16	.16
389	A63	8c multicolored	.25	.25
390	A63	16c multicolored	.50	.50
		Nos. 387-390 (4)	1.06	1.06

Christmas.

1978, Mar. 15

19th Rhodesian Trade Fair, Bulawayo: 8c, Fair spire.

391	A64	4c multicolored	.15	.15
392	A64	8c multicolored	.32	.32

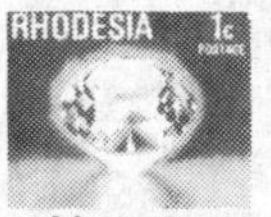

Morganite A65

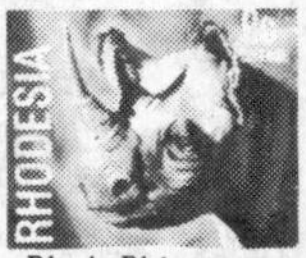

Black Rhinoceros A66

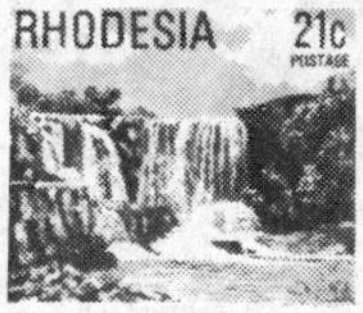

Odzani Falls — A67

1978, Aug. 16 Litho. *Perf. 14½*

393	A65	1c shown	.15	.15
394	A65	3c Amethyst	.15	.15
395	A65	4c Garnet	.15	.15
396	A65	5c Citrine	.15	.15
397	A65	7c Blue topaz	.15	.15
398	A66	9c shown	.15	.15
399	A66	11c Lion	.15	.15
400	A66	13c Warthog	.15	.15
401	A66	15c Giraffe	.15	.15
402	A66	17c Zebra	.16	.15
403	A67	21c shown	.20	.20
404	A67	25c Goba Falls	.22	.22
405	A67	30c Inyangombe Falls	.32	.32
406	A67	$1 Bridal Veil Falls	1.40	1.40
407	A67	$2 Victoria Falls	2.25	1.40
		Nos. 393-407 (15)	5.90	5.04
		Set value	5.25	4.25

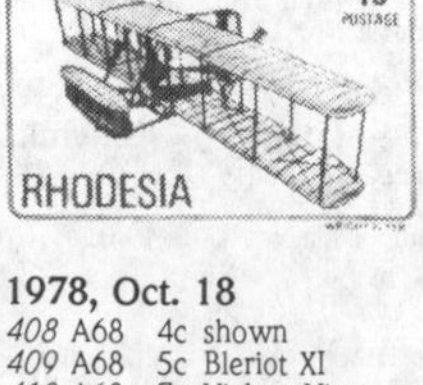

Wright's Flyer A68

1978, Oct. 18

408	A68	4c shown	.15	.15
409	A68	5c Bleriot XI	.15	.15
410	A68	7c Vickers Vimy	.15	.15

411 A68 9c A.W. 15 Atalanta .25 .25
412 A68 17c Vickers Viking 1B .50 .50
413 A68 25c Boeing 720 .70 .70
Nos. 408-413 (6) 1.90 1.90

75th anniversary of powered flight.

Rhodesia stamps were replaced in 1978 by stamps of Zimbabwe.

POSTAGE DUE STAMPS

Type of Rhodesia and Nyasaland, 1961, Inscribed "RHODESIA"

Hyphen Hole Perf. 5

1965, June 17 Typo. Unwmk.

J5 D1 1p vermilion .90 .90
a. Rouletted 9½ .45 .45

Rouletted 9½

J6 D1 2p dark blue .45 .45
J7 D1 4p emerald .70 .70
J8 D1 6p purple 1.50 1.50
Nos. J5-J8 (4) 3.55 3.55

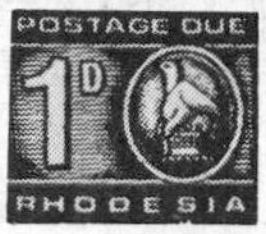

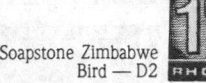

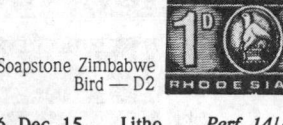

Soapstone Zimbabwe Bird — D2

1966, Dec. 15 Litho. *Perf. 14½*

J9 D2 1p crimson .80 .80
J10 D2 2p violet blue 1.00 1.00
J11 D2 4p emerald 1.75 1.75
J12 D2 6p lilac 2.00 2.00
J13 D2 1sh dull red brown 2.75 2.75
J14 D2 2sh black 4.00 4.00
Nos. J9-J14 (6) 12.30 12.30

1970-73 Litho. *Perf. 14½*

Size: 26x22½mm

J15 D2 1c bright green .40 .40
J16 D2 2c ultramarine .00 .00
J17 D2 5c red violet 1.25 1.25
J18 D2 6c lemon 4.00 4.00
J19 D2 10c rose red 3.00 3.00
Nos. J15-J19 (5) 9.45 9.45

Issued: 6c, 5/7/73; others, 2/1/70.

RHODESIA AND NYASALAND

rō-'dē-zh(ē-)ə ən(d) nī-'a-sə-,land

LOCATION — Southern Africa
GOVT. — Former Federal State in British Commonwealth
AREA — 486,973 sq. mi.
POP. — 8,510,000 (est. 1961)
CAPITAL — Salisbury, Southern Rhodesia

The Federation of Southern Rhodesia, Northern Rhodesia and Nyasaland was created in 1953, dissolved at end of 1963.

12 Pence = 1 Shilling
20 Shillings = 1 Pound

Catalogue values for all unused stamps in this country are for Never Hinged items.

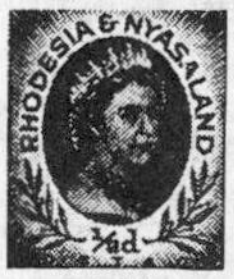

A14

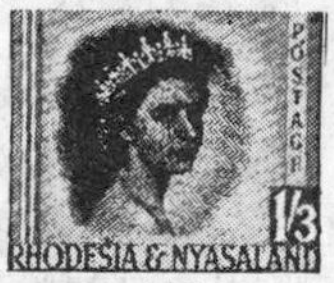

A15

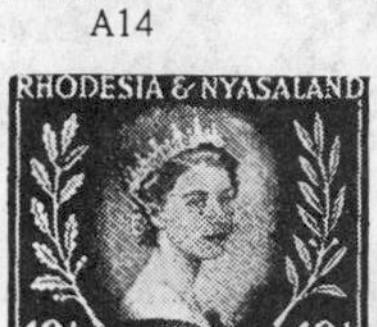

Queen Elizabeth II A16

Perf. 13½ (A14), 13½x13 (A15), 14x13 (A16)

1954-56 Engr. Unwmk.

141 A14 ½p vermilion .15 .15
a. Booklet pane of 6 1.25
b. Perf. 12½x13½ .60 .40
142 A14 1p ultra .15 .15
a. Booklet pane of 6 1.25
b. Perf. 12½x13½ .80 .50
143 A14 2p emerald .15 .15
a. Booklet pane of 6 1.65
143B A14 2½p ocher ('56) .60 .15
144 A14 3p carmine .18 .15
145 A14 4p red brown .45 .15
146 A14 4½p blue green .50 .16
147 A14 6p red lilac .70 .15
148 A14 9p purple .90 .35
149 A14 1sh gray .75 .15
150 A15 1sh3p ultra & ver .90 .15
151 A15 2sh brn & dp bl 3.50 .70
152 A15 2sh6p carmine & blk 3.75 .55
153 A15 5sh olive & pur 7.50 1.40
154 A16 10sh red org & aqua 18.00 7.00
155 A16 £1 brn car & ol 32.50 12.50
Nos. 141-155 (16) 70.68 24.01

Issue dates: 2½p, Feb. 15, others, July 1.

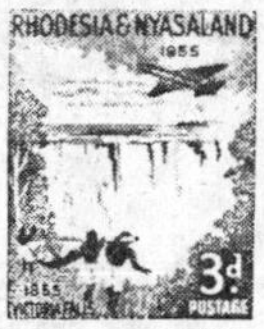

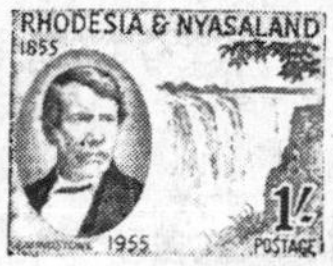

Victoria Falls
A17 A18

1955, June 15 *Perf. 13½*

156 A17 3p Plane .30 .15
157 A18 1sh David Livingstone .85 .55

Centenary of discovery of Victoria Falls.

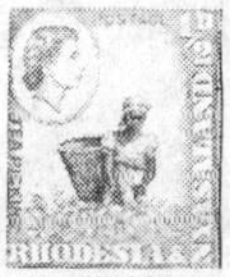

Tea Picking A19

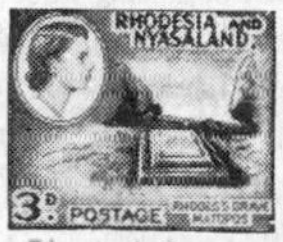

Rhodes' Grave, Matopos A20

Designs: 1p, V. H. F. Mast. 2p, Copper mining. 2½p, Kingsley Fairbridge Memorial. 4p, Boat on Lake Bangweulu. 6p, Victoria Falls. 9p, Railroad trains. 1sh, Tobacco. 1sh3p, Ship on Lake Nyasa. 2sh, Chirundu Bridge, Zambezi River. 2sh6p, Salisbury Airport. 5sh, Cecil Rhodes statue, Salisbury. 10sh, Mlanje mountain. £1, Coat of arms.

Perf. 13½x14, 14x13½

1959-63 Engr. Unwmk.

Size: 18½x22½mm, 22½x18½mm

158 A19 ½p emerald & blk .15 .15
a. Perf. 12½x13½ .65 .65
159 A19 1p blk & rose red .15 .15
a. Perf. 12½x13½ .65 .65
160 A19 2p ocher & violet .15 .15
161 A19 2½p slate & lil, perf. 14½ .35 .30
162 A20 3p blue & black .25 .15
a. Booklet pane of 4 ('63) 1.50
b. Black omitted

Perf. 14½

Size: 24x27mm, 27x24mm

163 A19 4p olive & mag .25 .15
164 A19 6p green & ultra .30 .15
164A A20 9p pur & ocher ('62) 2.75 2.75
165 A20 1sh ultra & yel grn .65 .20
166 A20 1sh3p sep & brt grn, perf. 14 1.40 .20
167 A20 2sh lake & grn 3.75 1.00
168 A20 2sh6p ocher & blue 4.75 1.00

Perf. 11½

Size: 32x27mm

169 A20 5sh yel grn & choc 8.00 1.65
170 A20 10sh brt rose & ol 22.50 9.50
171 A20 £1 violet & blk 30.00 19.00
Nos. 158-171 (15) 75.40 36.50

Nos. 158a and 159a are coils.
Issue dates: 9p, May 15, others, Aug. 12.

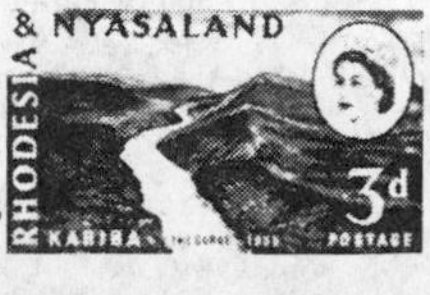

Kariba Gorge, 1955 — A21

Designs: 6p, Power lines. 1sh, View of dam. 1sh3p, View of dam and lake. 2sh6p, Power station. 5sh, Dam and Queen Mother Elizabeth.

1960, May 17 Photo. *Perf. 14½x14*

172 A21 3p orange & sl grn .40 .15
173 A21 6p yel brn & brn .55 .35
174 A21 1sh dull bl & emer 1.10 .55
175 A21 1sh3p grnsh bl & ocher 1.75 .70
176 A21 2sh6p org ver & blk 4.00 2.25
177 A21 5sh grnsh bl & lilac 7.75 4.00
Nos. 172-177 (6) 15.55 8.00

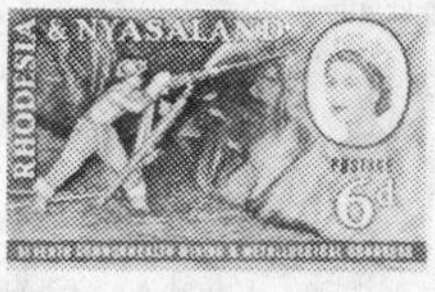

Miner with Drill — A22

Design: 1sh3p, Mining surface installations.

1961, May 8 Unwmk.

178 A22 6p chnt brn & ol grn .60 .35
179 A22 1sh3p lt blue & blk .95 .80

7th Commonwealth Mining and Metallurgical Cong., Apr. 10-May 20.

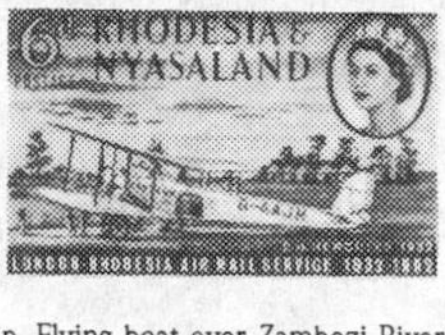

DH Hercules Biplane A23

Designs: 1sh3p, Flying boat over Zambezi River. 2sh6p, DH Comet, Salisbury Airport.

1962, Feb. 6

180 A23 6p ver & ol grn .45 .45
181 A23 1sh3p bl, blk, grn & yel 1.00 1.00
182 A23 2sh6p dk pur & car rose 6.50 6.50
Nos. 180-182 (3) 7.95 7.95

30th anniv. of the inauguration of the Rhodesia-London airmail service.

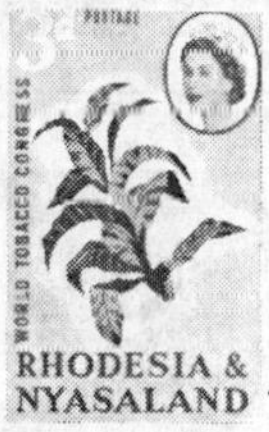

Tobacco Plant — A24

Designs: 6p, Tobacco field. 1sh3p, Auction floor. 2sh6p, Cured tobacco.

1963, Feb. 18 Photo. *Perf. 14x14½*

184 A24 3p gray brown & grn .20 .15
185 A24 6p blue, grn & brn .35 .30
186 A24 1sh3p slate & red brn 1.00 .75
187 A24 2sh6p brown & org yel 4.00 3.25
Nos. 184-187 (4) 5.55 4.45

3rd World Tobacco Scientific Cong., Salisbury, Feb. 18-26 and the 1st Intl. Tobacco Trade Cong., Salisbury, March 6-16.

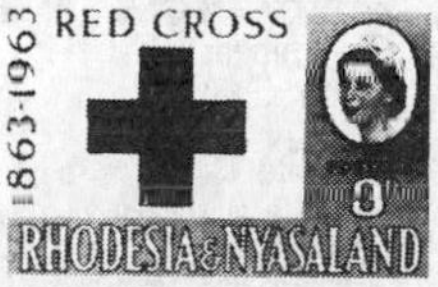

Red Cross — A25

1963, Aug. 6 *Perf. 14½x14*

188 A25 3p red .35 .20

Centenary of the International Red Cross.

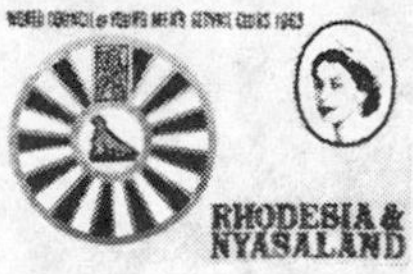

"Round Table" Emblem A26

1963, Sept. 11 Unwmk.

189 A26 6p multicolored .45 .45
190 A26 1sh3p multicolored .70 .70

World Council of Young Men's Service Clubs at University College of Rhodesia and Nyasaland, Sept. 8-15.

POSTAGE DUE STAMPS

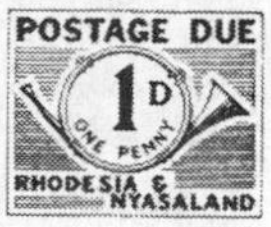

D1

Perf. 12½

1961, Apr. 19 Unwmk. Typo.

J1 D1 1p vermilion .80 *3.00*
a. Horiz. pair, imperf. btwn. *450.00*
J2 D1 2p dark blue 1.65 *2.50*
J3 D1 4p emerald 2.50 *7.00*
J4 D1 6p dark purple 3.25 *7.00*
a. Horiz. pair, imperf. btwn. —
Nos. J1-J4 (4) 8.20 *19.50*

ST. HELENA

sānt 'he-lə-nə

LOCATION — Island in the Atlantic Ocean, 1,200 miles west of Angola
GOVT. — British Crown Colony
AREA — 47 sq. mi.
POP. — 5,499 (1982)
CAPITAL — Jamestown

12 Pence = 1 Shilling
20 Shillings = 1 Pound
100 Pence = 1 Pound (1971)

Catalogue values for unused stamps in this country are for Never Hinged items, beginning with Scott 128 in the regular postage section, Scott B1 in the semi-postal section and Scott J1 in the postage due section.

Values for unused stamps are for examples with original gum as defined in the catalogue introduction. Very fine examples of Nos. 2-39a and 47-47b will have perforations touching the design on one or more sides due to the narrow spacing of the stamps on the plates. Stamps with perfs clear of the design on all four sides are scarce and will command higher prices.

Watermark

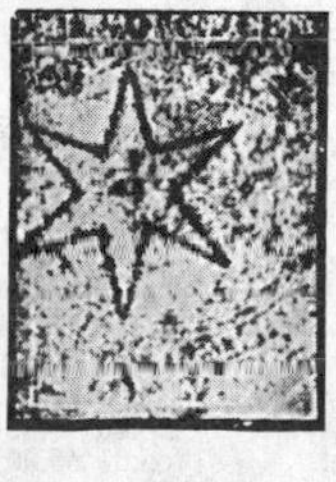

Wmk. 6- Star

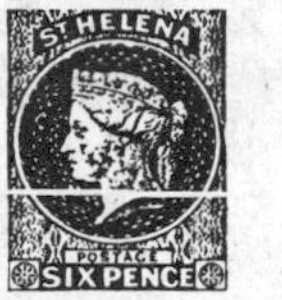

Queen Victoria — A1

1856, Jan. Wmk. 6 Engr. *Imperf.*

1 A1 6p blue 550.00 175.00

For types surcharged see Nos. 8-39, 47.

1861 *Clean-Cut Perf. 14 to 15½*

2 A1 6p blue 1,200. 225.00

1863 *Rough Perf. 14 to 15½*

2B A1 6p blue 375.00 125.00

1873-74 Wmk. 1 *Perf. 12½*

3 A1 6p dull blue 550.00 90.00
4 A1 6p ultra ('74) 275.00 75.00

1879 *Perf. 14x12½*

5 A1 6p gray blue 275.00 32.50

1889 *Perf. 14*

6 A1 6p gray blue 250.00 37.50

1889 Wmk. Crown and C A (2)

7 A1 6p gray 8.00 5.50

Type of 1856 Surcharged

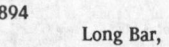

ONE PENNY a **ONE PENNY** b

1863 Wmk. 1 *Imperf.*

Long Bar, 16, 17, 18 or 19mm

8 A1(a) 1p on 6p brown red (surch. 17mm) 110.00 150.00
a. Double surcharge 5,500. 2,750.
9 A1(a) 1p on 6p brown red (surch. 19mm) 110.00 150.00
10 A1(b) 4p on 6p carmine 400.00 165.00
a. Surcharge omitted
b. Double surcharge *9,000. 9,000.*

1864-73 *Perf. 12½*

11 A1(a) 1p on 6p brn red 25.00 24.00
12 A1(b) 1p on 6p brn red ('71) 50.00 17.00
a. Blue black surcharge *1,300. 875.00*
13 A1(b) 2p on 6p yel ('73) 65.00 35.00
a. Blue black surcharge *6,750. 4,000.*
14 A1(b) 3p on 6p dk vio ('73) 65.00 40.00
15 A1(b) 4p on 6p carmine 85.00 37.50
a. Double surcharge *9,000. 6,250.*
16 A1(b) 1sh on 6p grn (bar 16 to 17mm) 125.00 24.00
17 A1(b) 1sh on 6p dp grn (bar 18mm) ('73) 225.00 14.00
a. Blue black surcharge

1868

Short Bar, 14 or 15mm

18 A1(a) 1p on 6p brn red ('68) 85.00 45.00
a. Imperf., pair 7,500.
b. Double surcharge
19 A1(b) 2p on 6p yel ('68) 100.00 50.00
a. Imperf., pair 17,000.
20 A1(b) 3p on 6p dk vio ('68) 57.50 40.00
a. Double surcharge 6,750.
b. Imperf., pair 2,250.
21 A1(b) 4p on 6p car (words 18mm) ('68) 62.50 40.00
a. Double surcharge *5,500.* 5,500.
b. Imperf., pair 19,000.
22 A1(b) 4p on 6p car (words 19mm) ('68) 165.00 100.00
a. Words double, 18mm and 19mm *12,500. 12,500.*
b. Imperf.
23 A1(a) 1sh on 6p yel grn ('68) 325.00 140.00
a. Double surcharge 10,000.
b. Pair, one without surcharge 7,750.
24 A1(a) 5sh on 6p org ('68) 32.50 42.50

No. 21 exists with surcharge omitted.

1882 *Perf. 14x12½*

25 A1(a) 1p on 6p brown red 42.50 12.00
26 A1(b) 2p on 6p yellow 55.00 45.00
27 A1(b) 3p on 6p violet 165.00 65.00
28 A1(b) 4p on 6p carmine (words 16mm) 75.00 45.00

1883 *Perf. 14*

29 A1(a) 1p on 6p brown red 40.00 15.00
30 A1(b) 2p on 6p yellow 30.00 22.50
31 A1(a) 1sh on 6p yel grn 20.00 11.00

1882 *Perf. 14x12½*

Long Bar, 18mm

32 A1(b) 1sh on 6p dp green 300.00 20.00

1884-94 Wmk. 2 *Perf. 14*

Short Bar, 14 or 14½mm

33 A1(b) ½p on 6p grn (words 17mm) 2.75 2.50
a. ½p on 6p emer, blurred print (words 17mm) ('84) 5.00 5.00
b. Double surcharge 1,200.
34 A1(b) ½p on 6p grn (words 15mm) ('94) .80 1.10
35 A1(a) 1p on 6p red ('87) 2.25 1.40
36 A1(b) 2p on 6p yel ('94) 1.10 1.90
37 A1(b) 3p on 6p dp vio ('87) 1.75 2.00
a. 3p on 6p red violet 3.50 2.00
b. Double surcharge *6,750. 6,750.*
38 A1(b) 4p on 6p dk brn ('90) 8.75 5.50
a. With thin bar below thick one

1894

Long Bar, 18mm

39 A1(b) 1sh on 6p yel grn 22.50 11.00
a. Double surcharge *4,000.*

See note after No. 47.

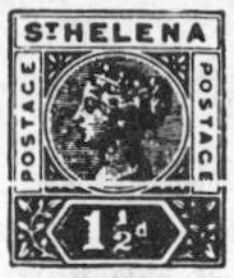
Queen Victoria — A3

1890-97 Typo. *Perf. 14*

40 A3 ½p green ('97) 3.00 4.00
41 A3 1p rose ('96) 7.00 1.00
42 A3 1½p red brn & grn 4.00 6.00
43 A3 2p yellow ('96) 4.00 8.00
44 A3 2½p ultra ('96) 6.00 9.00
45 A3 5p violet ('96) 10.00 22.50
46 A3 10p brown ('96) 15.00 *45.00*
Nos. 40-46 (7) 49.00 *95.50*

Type of 1856 Surcharged **2½d**

1893 Engr. Wmk. 2

47 A1 2½p on 6p blue 2.00 4.00
a. Double surcharge *16,500.*
b. Double impression 7,500.

In 1905 remainders of Nos. 34-47 were sold by the postal officials. They are canceled with bars, arranged in the shape of diamonds, in purple ink. No such cancellation was ever used on the island and the stamps so canceled are of slight value. With this cancellation removed, these remainders are sometimes offered as unused. Some have been recanceled with a false dated postmark.

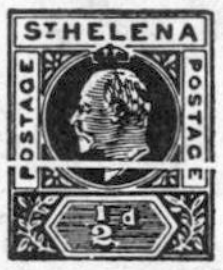
King Edward VII — A5

1902 Typo. Wmk. 2

48 A5 ½p green 1.40 *1.10*
49 A5 1p carmine rose 3.50 .85

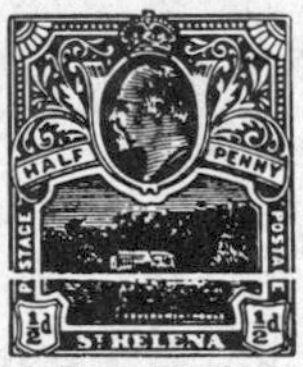
Government House — A6

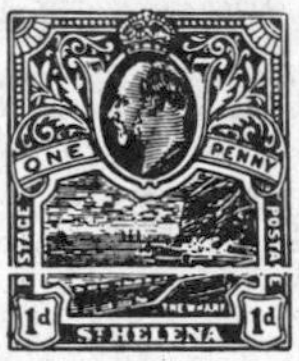
"The Wharf" — A7

1903, June Wmk. 1

50 A6 ½p gray green & brn 1.50 2.00
51 A7 1p carmine & blk 1.10 .50
52 A6 2p ol grn & blk 4.50 1.50
53 A7 8p brown & blk 11.00 *30.00*
54 A6 1sh org buff & brn 12.00 *27.50*
55 A7 2sh violet & blk 37.50 *70.00*
Nos. 50-55 (6) 67.60 *131.50*

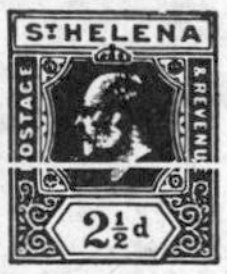
A8

1908, May Wmk. 3

56 A8 2½p ultra 1.40 *1.50*
57 A8 4p black & red, *yel* 2.75 *8.00*
58 A8 6p dull violet 6.00 *15.00*
Nos. 56-58 (3) 10.15 *24.50*

Wmk. 2

60 A8 10sh grn & red, *grn* 175.00 *200.00*

Nos. 57 and 58 exist on both ordinary and chalky paper; No. 56 on ordinary and No. 60 on chalky paper.

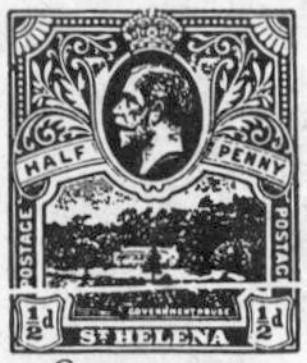
Government House — A9

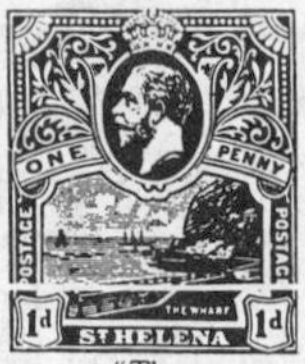
"The Wharf" — A10

1912-16 Ordinary Paper Wmk. 3

61 A9 ½p green & blk 1.25 5.00
62 A10 1p carmine & blk 1.40 1.90
a. 1p scarlet & black ('16) 22.50 *27.00*
63 A10 1½p orange & blk 2.25 4.00
64 A9 2p gray & black 2.25 1.75
65 A10 2½p ultra & blk 1.90 5.00
66 A9 3p vio & blk, *yel* 1.90 5.00
67 A10 8p dull vio & blk 5.25 40.00
68 A9 1sh black, *green* 7.50 20.00
69 A10 2sh ultra & blk, *bl* 25.00 *55.00*
70 A10 3sh violet & blk 45.00 *90.00*
Nos. 61-70 (10) 93.70 *227.65*

See Nos. 75-77.

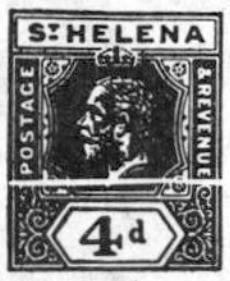
A11

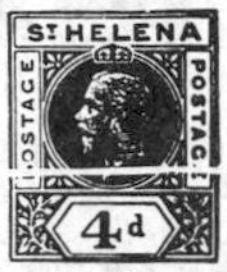
A12

Die I

For description of dies I and II see back of this section of the Catalogue.

1912

Chalky Paper

71 A11 4p black & red, *yel* 4.25 *14.00*
72 A11 6p dull vio & red vio 2.50 *8.00*

1913

Ordinary Paper

73 A12 4p black & red, *yel* 1.75 1.75
74 A12 6p dull vio & red vio 7.50 *22.50*

1922 Wmk. 4

75 A10 1p green 1.00 *17.00*
76 A10 1½p rose red 6.00 *22.50*
77 A9 3p ultra 11.00 *35.00*
Nos. 75-77 (3) 18.00 *74.50*

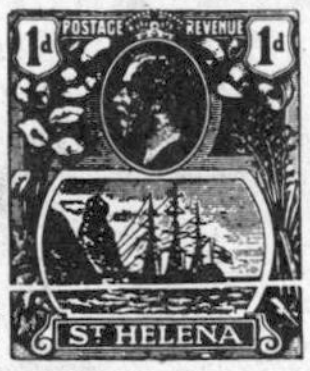
Badge of the Colony — A13

1922-27 Wmk. 4

Chalky Paper

79 A13 ½p black & gray 1.00 1.50
80 A13 1p green & black 1.00 1.25
81 A13 1½p rose red 2.25 *7.00*
82 A13 2p pale gray & gray 1.90 1.90
83 A13 3p ultra 1.90 *3.75*
84 A13 5p red & grn, *emer* 2.50 *5.00*
85 A13 6p red vio & black 3.00 *8.00*
86 A13 8p violet & blk 3.00 *6.00*
87 A13 1sh dk brown & blk 5.00 *8.00*
88 A13 1sh6p grn & blk, *emer* 10.00 *40.00*
89 A13 2sh ultra & vio, *bl* 12.50 *32.50*
90 A13 2sh6p car & blk, *yel* 12.50 *45.00*
91 A13 5sh grn & blk, *yel* 32.50 *65.00*
92 A13 7sh6p orange & blk 75.00 *110.00*
93 A13 10sh ol grn & blk 100.00 *150.00*
94 A13 15sh vio & blk, *bl* 875.00 *1,250.*
Nos. 79-93 (15) 264.05 *484.90*

Nos. 88, 90, and 91 are on ordinary paper.

Wmk. 3

Chalky Paper

95 A13 4p black, *yel* 6.00 *7.00*
96 A13 1sh6p bl grn & blk, *grn* 20.00 *45.00*
97 A13 2sh6p car & blk, *yel* 24.00 *47.50*
98 A13 5sh grn & blk, *yel* 37.50 *70.00*
99 A13 £1 red vio & blk, *red* 375.00 *400.00*
Nos. 95-99 (5) 462.50 *569.50*

Issue dates: ½p, 1½p, 2p, 3p, 4p, 8p, February, 1923; 5p, Nos. 88-91, 1927; others, June 1922.

Centenary Issue

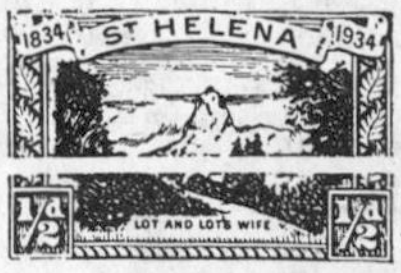
Lot and Lot's Wife — A14

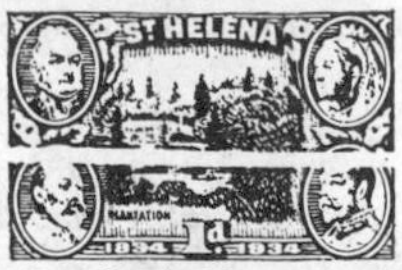
Plantation; Queen Victoria and Kings William IV, Edward VII, George V A15

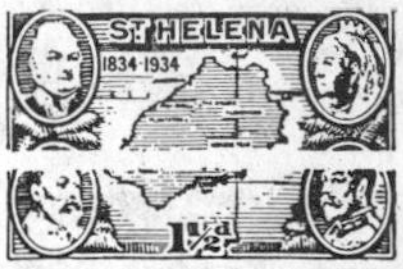
Map of the Colony — A16

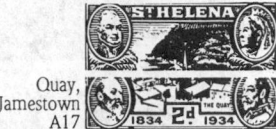

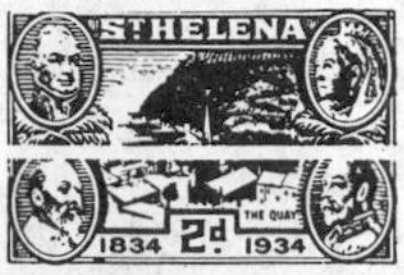
Quay, Jamestown A17

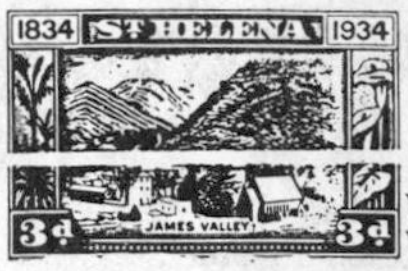
View of James Valley — A18

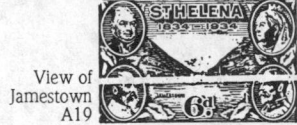

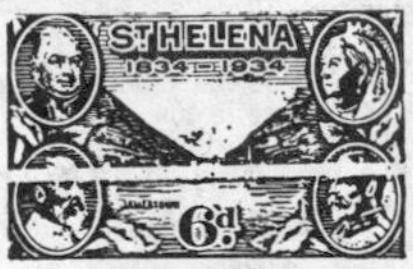
View of Jamestown A19

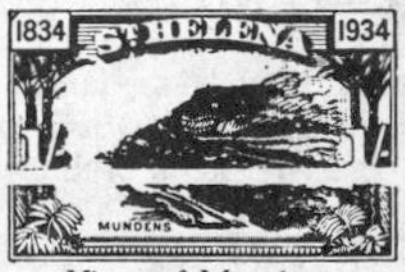
View of Mundens A20

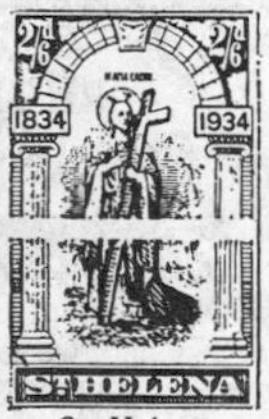
St. Helena A21

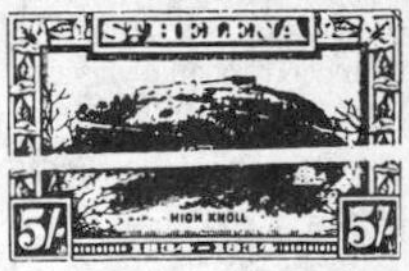
View of High Knoll — A22

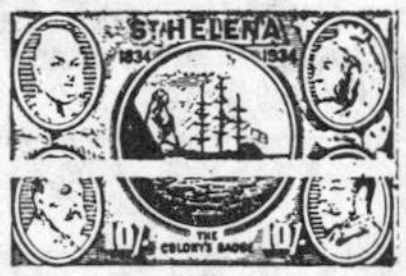
Badge of the Colony — A23

Wmk. 4

1934, Apr. 23 Engr. *Perf. 12*

101 A14 ½p dk vio & black .52 .60
102 A15 1p green & blk .70 .85
103 A16 1½p red & blk 2.25 2.75
104 A17 2p orange & blk 1.75 1.90
105 A18 3p blue & blk 1.50 *5.00*
106 A19 6p lt blue & blk 3.00 *3.50*
107 A20 1sh dk brown & blk 6.50 *18.00*
108 A21 2sh6p carmine & blk 32.50 *45.00*
109 A22 5sh choc & blk 70.00 80.00
110 A23 10sh red vio & black 190.00 225.00
Nos. 101-110 (10) 308.72 382.60

Silver Jubilee Issue

Common Design Type

1935, May 6 *Perf. 13½x14*

111 CD301 1½p car & dk blue .50 *2.00*
112 CD301 2p gray blk & ultra 1.10 1.10
113 CD301 6p indigo & grn 3.75 3.75
114 CD301 1sh brt vio & indigo 5.00 *9.00*
Nos. 111-114 (4) 10.35 *15.85*
Set, never hinged 22.50

Coronation Issue
Common Design Type

1937, May 19

115	CD302	1p deep green	.15	.15
116	CD302	2p deep orange	.20	.20
117	CD302	3p bright ultra	.30	.30
		Nos. 115-117 (3)	.65	.65
		Set, never hinged	1.65	

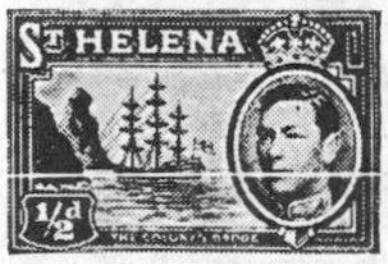

Badge of the Colony — A24

1938-40 *Perf. 12½*

118	A24	½p purple	.15	.15
119	A24	1p dp green	9.50	3.00
119A	A24	1p org yel ('40)	.15	.20
120	A24	1½p carmine	.15	.20
121	A24	2p orange	.15	.20
122	A24	3p ultra	42.50	27.50
122A	A24	3p gray ('40)	.15	.25
122B	A24	4p ultra ('40)	.80	.25
123	A24	6p gray blue	.80	.40
123A	A24	8p olive ('40)	1.50	1.10
124	A24	1sh sepia	.35	.55
125	A24	2sh6p deep claret	7.00	3.00
126	A24	5sh brown	7.50	*7.00*
127	A24	10sh violet	7.50	*14.00*
		Nos. 118-127 (14)	78.20	*57.80*
		Set, never hinged	160.00	

Issue dates: May 12, 1938, July 8, 1940.
See Nos. 136-138.

Catalogue values for unused stamps in this section, from this point to the end of the section, are for Never Hinged items.

Peace Issue
Common Design Type

Perf. 13½x14

1946, Oct. 21 Wmk. 4 Engr.

128	CD303	2p deep orange	.20	.20
129	CD303	4p deep blue	.25	.25

Silver Wedding Issue
Common Design Types

1948, Oct. 20 Photo. *Perf. 14x14½*

130	CD304	3p black	.25	.25

Engr.; Name Typo.
Perf. 11½x11

131	CD305	10sh blue violet	19.00	*27.50*

UPU Issue
Common Design Types

Engr.; Name Typo. on 4p, 6p

1949, Oct. 10 *Perf. 13½, 11x11½*

132	CD306	3p rose carmine	.30	.30
133	CD307	4p indigo	.80	.80
134	CD308	6p olive	1.75	1.75
135	CD309	1sh slate	2.75	2.75
		Nos. 132-135 (4)	5.60	5.60

George VI Type of 1938

1949, Nov. 1 Engr. *Perf. 12½*

Center in Black

136	A24	1p blue green	.60	.60
137	A24	1½p carmine rose	.80	.80
138	A24	2p carmine	.80	.80
		Nos. 136-138 (3)	2.20	2.20

Coronation Issue
Common Design Type

1953, June 2 *Perf. 13½x13*

139	CD312	3p purple & black	1.00	1.00

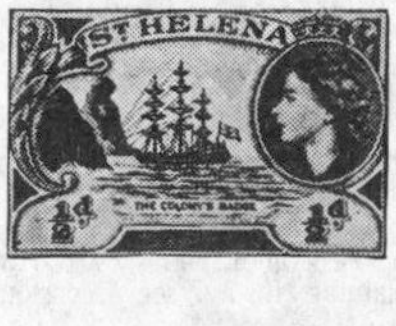

Badge of the Colony — A25

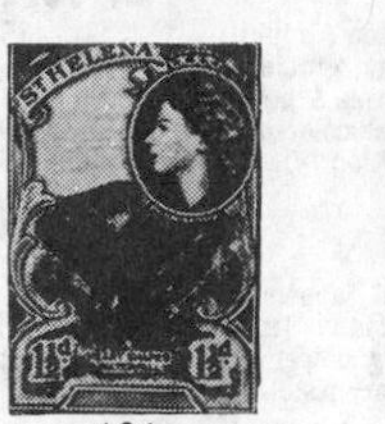
A26

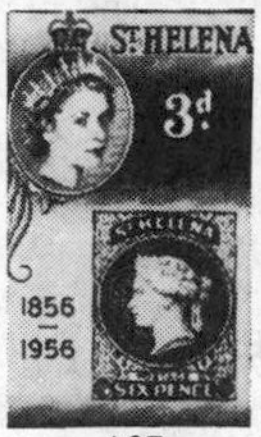

A27

Designs: 1p, Flax plantation. 1½p, Heart-shaped waterfall. 2p, Lace making. 2½p, Drying flax. 3p, Wire bird. 4p, Flagstaff and barn. 6p, Donkeys carrying flax. 7p, Map. 1sh, Entrance, government offices. 2sh 6p, Cutting flax. 5sh, Jamestown. 10sh, Longwood house.

1953, Aug. 4 *Perf. 13½x14, 14x13½*

Center and Denomination in Black

140	A25	½p emerald	.15	.15
141	A25	1p dark green	.15	.15
142	A26	1½p red violet	.20	.15
143	A25	2p rose lake	.25	.20
144	A25	2½p red	.25	.20
145	A25	3p brown	.35	.25
146	A25	4p deep blue	.50	.30
147	A25	6p purple	.70	.45
148	A25	7p gray	.90	.55
149	A25	1sh dk car rose	1.25	.80
150	A25	2sh 6p violet	7.00	3.75
151	A25	5sh chocolate	15.00	8.00
152	A25	10sh orange	40.00	20.00
		Nos. 140-152 (13)	66.70	34.95

Perf. 11½

1956, Jan. 3 Wmk. 4 Engr.

153	A27	3p dk car rose & blue	.20	.20
154	A27	4p redsh brown & blue	.35	.35
155	A27	6p purple & blue	.55	.55
		Nos. 153-155 (3)	1.10	1.10

Cent. of the 1st St. Helena postage stamp.

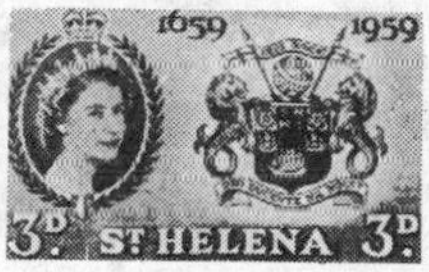

Arms of East India Company A28

Designs: 6p, Dutton's ship "London" off James Bay. 1sh, Memorial stone from fort built by Governor Dutton.

Perf. 12½x13

1959, May 5 Wmk. 314

156	A28	3p rose & black	.18	.18
157	A28	6p gray & yellow green	.45	.45
158	A28	1sh orange & black	.65	.65
		Nos. 156-158 (3)	1.28	1.28

300th anniv. of the landing of Capt. John Dutton on St. Helena and of the 1st settlement.

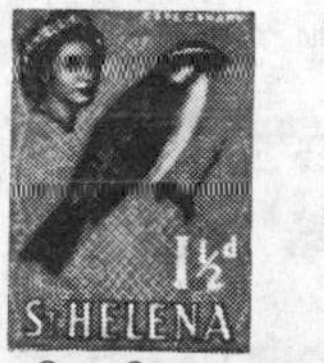

Cape Canary A29

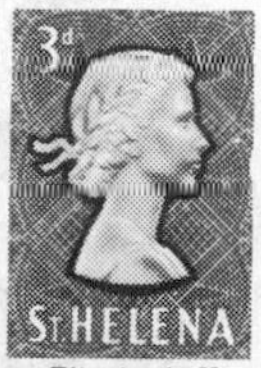

Elizabeth II A30

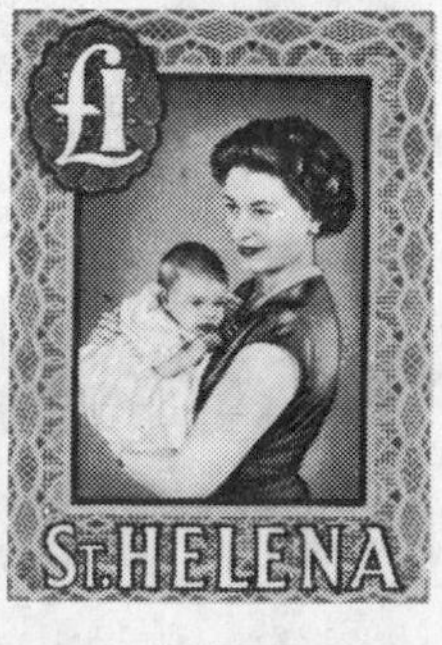

Queen and Prince Andrew A31

Designs: 1p, Cunning fish, horiz. 2p, Brittle starfish, horiz. 4½p, Redwood flower. 6p, Red fody (Madagascar weaver). 7p, Trumpetfish, horiz. 10p, Keeled feather starfish, horiz. 1sh, Gumwood flowers. 1sh6p, Fairy tern. 2sh6p, Orange starfish, horiz. 5sh, Night-blooming cereus. 10sh, Deepwater bull's-eye, horiz.

Perf. 11½x12, 12x11½

1961, Dec. 12 Photo. Wmk. 314

159	A29	1p multicolored	.15	.15
160	A29	1½p multicolored	.25	.15
161	A29	2p gray & red	.15	.18
162	A30	3p dk blue, rose & grnsh blue	.40	.35
163	A29	4½p slate, brn & grn	.50	.35
164	A29	6p cit, brn & dp car	2.00	.42
165	A29	7p vio, blk & red brn	.40	.42
166	A29	10p blue & dp claret	.65	.65
167	A29	1sh red brn, grn & yel	.65	.65
168	A29	1sh6p gray bl & blk	5.00	1.75
169	A29	2sh6p grnsh bl, yel & red	3.75	2.75
170	A29	5sh green, brown & yel	7.50	4.25
171	A29	10sh gray bl, blk & sal	10.50	9.50

Perf. 14x14½

172	A31	£1 turq blue & choc	20.00	22.50
		Nos. 159-172 (14)	51.90	44.07

For overprints see Nos. 176-179.

Freedom from Hunger Issue
Common Design Type

1963, June 4 *Perf. 14x14½*

173	CD314	1sh6p ultra	4.00	3.00

Red Cross Centenary Issue
Common Design Type

Wmk. 314

1963, Sept. 2 Litho. *Perf. 13*

174	CD315	3p black & red	.32	.32
175	CD315	1sh6p ultra & red	4.50	3.50

Nos. 159, 162, 164 and 168 Overprinted: "FIRST LOCAL POST / 4th JANUARY 1965"

Perf. 11½x12, 12x11½

1965, Jan. 4 Photo. Wmk. 314

176	A29	1p multicolored	.15	.15
177	A30	3p dk bl, rose & grnsh bl	.16	.16
178	A29	6p cit, brn & dp car	.30	.30
179	A29	1sh6p gray blue & blk	.60	.60
		Nos. 176-179 (4)	1.21	1.21

Establishment of the 1st internal postal service on the island.

ITU Issue
Common Design Type

Perf. 11x11½

1965, May 17 Litho. Wmk. 314

180	CD317	3p ultra & gray	.32	.32
181	CD317	6p red lil & blue grn	.75	.75

Intl. Cooperation Year Issue
Common Design Type

1965, Oct. 25 Litho. *Perf. 14½*

182	CD318	1p blue grn & claret	.15	.15
183	CD318	6p lt violet & green	1.50	1.50

Churchill Memorial Issue
Common Design Type

1966, Jan. 24 Photo. *Perf. 14*

Design in Black, Gold and Carmine Rose

184	CD319	1p bright blue	.15	.15
185	CD319	3p green	.22	.22
186	CD319	6p brown	.65	.65
187	CD319	1sh6p violet	2.25	2.25
		Nos. 184-187 (4)	3.27	3.27

World Cup Soccer Issue
Common Design Type

1966, July 1 Litho. *Perf. 14*

188	CD321	3p multicolored	.45	.45
189	CD321	6p multicolored	1.25	1.00

WHO Headquarters Issue
Common Design Type

1966, Sept. 20 Litho. *Perf. 14*

190	CD322	3p multicolored	.45	.45
191	CD322	1sh6p multicolored	2.75	2.25

UNESCO Anniversary Issue
Common Design Type

1966, Dec. 1 Litho. *Perf. 14*

192	CD323	3p "Education"	.90	.65
193	CD323	6p "Science"	1.40	1.10
194	CD323	1sh6p "Culture"	4.50	4.00
		Nos. 192-194 (3)	6.80	5.75

St. Helena stamps can be mounted in the Scott British Africa album.

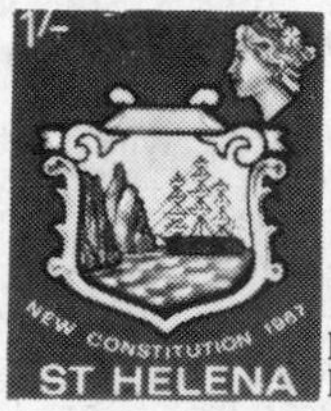

Badge of St. Helena — A32

Perf. 14½x14

1967, May 5 Photo. Wmk. 314

195	A32	1sh dk green & multi	.30	.30
196	A32	2sh6p blue & multi	.70	.70
a.		Carmine omitted	450.00	

St. Helena's New Constitution.

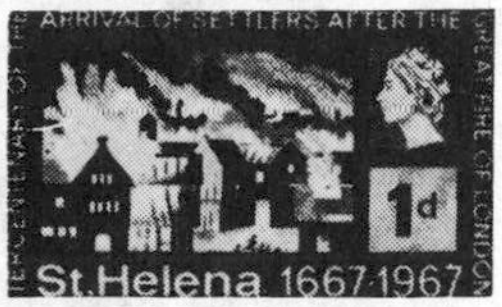

The Great Fire of London A33

Designs: 3p, Three-master Charles. 6p, Boats bringing new settlers to shore. 1sh6p, Settlers at work.

Perf. 13½x13

1967, Sept. 4 Engr. Wmk. 314

197	A33	1p black & carmine	.15	.15
198	A33	3p black & vio blue	.16	.16
199	A33	6p black & dull violet	.28	.28
200	A33	1sh6p black & ol green	.75	.75
		Nos. 197-200 (4)	1.34	1.34

Tercentenary of the arrival of settlers from London after the Great Fire of Sept. 2-4, 1666.

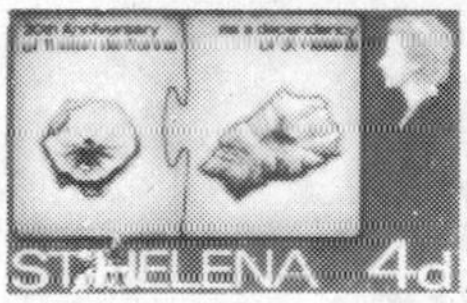

Maps of Tristan da Cunha and St. Helena A34

Designs: 8p, 2sh3p, Maps of St. Helena and Tristan da Cunha.

Perf. 14x14½

1968, June 4 Photo. Wmk. 314

Maps in Sepia

201	A34	4p dp red lilac	.15	.15
202	A34	8p olive	.20	.20
203	A34	1sh9p deep ultra	.48	.48
204	A34	2sh3p Prus blue	.75	.75
		Nos. 201-204 (4)	1.58	1.58

30th anniv. of Tristan da Cunha as a Dependency of St. Helena.

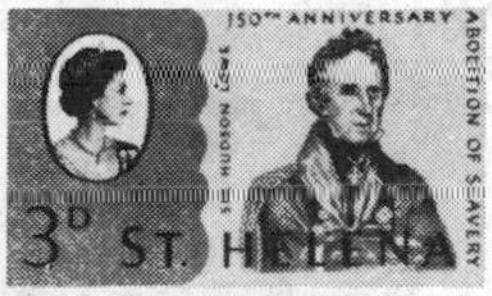

Sir Hudson Lowe A35

Designs: 1sh6p, 2sh6p, Sir George Bingham.

Perf. 13½x13

1968, Sept. 4 Litho. Wmk. 314

205	A35	3p multicolored	.15	.15
206	A35	9p multicolored	.25	.25
207	A35	1sh6p multicolored	.55	.55
208	A35	2sh6p multicolored	.85	.85
		Nos. 205-208 (4)	1.80	1.80

Abolition of slavery in St. Helena, 150th anniv.

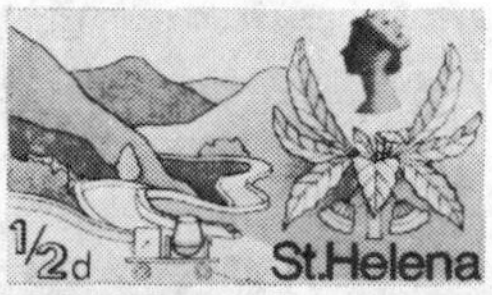

Road Construction — A36

Designs: 1p, Electricity development. 1½p, Dentist. 2p, Pest control. 3p, Apartment houses in Jamestown. 4p, Pasture and livestock improvement. 6p, School children listening to broadcast. 8p, Country cottages. 10p, New school buildings. 1sh, Reforestation. 1sh6p, Heavy lift crane. 2sh6p, Playing children in Lady Field Children's Home. 5sh,

Agricultural training. 10sh, Ward in New General Hospital. £1, Lifeboat "John Dutton."

Perf. 13½

1968, Nov. 4 Litho. Wmk. 314

209	A36	½p multicolored	.15	.15
210	A36	1p multicolored	.15	.15
211	A36	1½p multicolored	.15	.15
212	A36	2p multicolored	.15	.15
213	A36	3p multicolored	.16	.16
214	A36	4p multicolored	.24	.24
215	A36	6p multicolored	.26	.26
216	A36	8p multicolored	.35	.35
217	A36	10p multicolored	.40	.40
218	A36	1sh multicolored	.50	.50
219	A36	1sh6p multicolored	.65	.65
220	A36	2sh6p multicolored	1.25	1.25
221	A36	5sh multicolored	2.25	2.25
222	A36	10sh multicolored	4.50	4.50
223	A36	£1 multicolored	12.00	12.00
		Nos. 209-223 (15)	23.16	23.16

See Nos. 244-256.

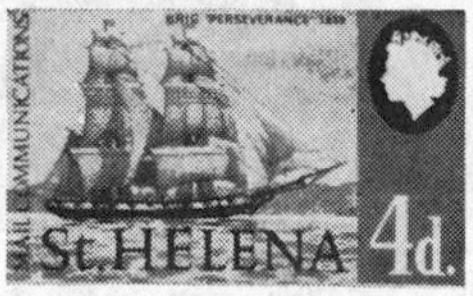

Brig Perseverance, 1819 — A37

Ships: 8p, M.S. Dane, 1857. 1sh9p, S.S. Llandovery Castle, 1925. 2sh3p, M.S. Good Hope Castle, 1969.

1969, Apr. 19 Litho. *Perf. 13½*

224	A37	4p violet & multi	.15	.15
225	A37	8p ocher & multi	.45	.45
226	A37	1sh9p ver & multi	1.25	1.25
227	A37	2sh3p dk blue & multi	1.40	1.40
		Nos. 224-227 (4)	3.25	3.25

Issued in recognition of St. Helena's dependence on sea mail.

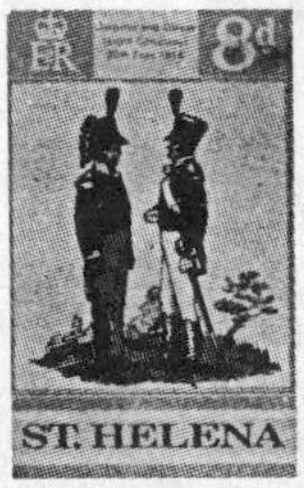

Surgeon and Officer (Light Company) 20th Foot, 1816 — A38

British Uniforms: 6p, Warrant Officer and Drummer, 53rd Foot, 1815. 1sh8p, Drum Major, 66th Foot, 1816, and Royal Artillery Officer, 1820. 2sh6p, Private 91st Foot and 2nd Corporal, Royal Sappers and Miners, 1832.

Perf. 14x14½

1969, Sept. 3 Litho. Wmk. 314

228	A38	6p red & multi	.28	.22
229	A38	8p blue & multi	.45	.32
230	A38	1sh8p green & multi	1.25	1.10
231	A38	2sh6p gray & multi	2.25	2.00
		Nos. 228-231 (4)	4.23	3.64

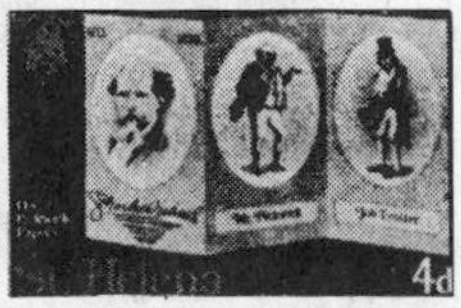

Charles Dickens, "The Pickwick Papers" A39

Dickens and: 8p, "Oliver Twist." 1sh6p, "Martin Chuzzlewit." 2sh6p, "Bleak House."

Perf. 13½x13

1970, June 9 Litho. Wmk. 314

232	A39	4p dk brown & multi	.25	.24
233	A39	8p slate & multi	.60	.50
234	A39	1sh6p multicolored	1.00	.90
235	A39	2sh6p multicolored	1.90	1.50
		Nos. 232-235 (4)	3.75	3.14

Charles Dickens (1812-70), English novelist.

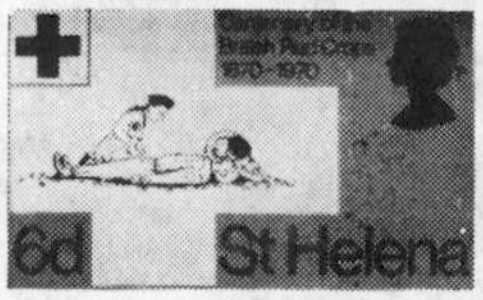

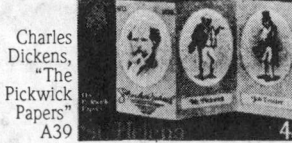

Mouth to Mouth Resuscitation — A40

Centenary of British Red Cross Society: 9p, Girl in wheelchair and nurse. 1sh9p, First aid. 2sh3p, British Red Cross Society emblem.

1970, Sept. 15 *Perf. 14½*

236	A40	6p bister, red & blk	.15	.15
237	A40	9p lt blue grn, red & blk	.24	.24
238	A40	1sh9p gray, red & blk	.60	.60
239	A40	2sh3p pale vio, red & blk	.70	.70
		Nos. 236-239 (4)	1.69	1.69

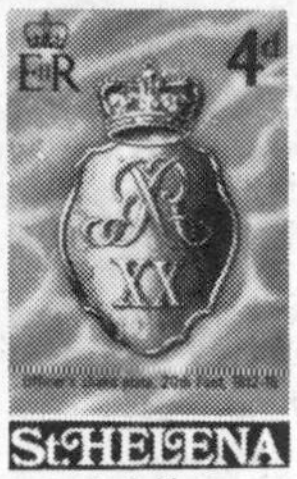

A41

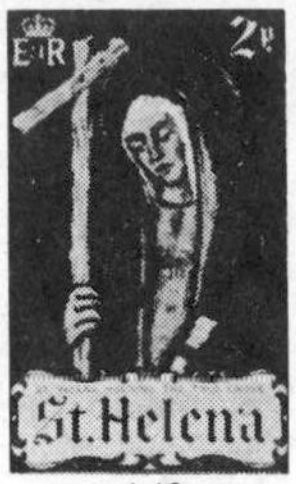

A42

Regimental Emblems: 4p, Officer's Shako Plate, 20th Foot, 1812-16. 9p, Officer's breast plate, 66th Foot, before 1818. 1sh3p, Officer's full dress shako, 91st Foot, 1816. 2sh11p, Ensign's shako, 53rd Foot, 1815.

Perf. 14½

1970, Nov. 2 Litho. Wmk. 314

240	A41	4p multicolored	.30	.22
241	A41	9p red & multi	.90	.65
242	A41	1sh3p dk gray & multi	1.50	1.10
243	A41	2sh11p dk gray grn & multi	3.25	2.50
		Nos. 240-243 (4)	5.95	4.47

See Nos. 263-270, 273-276.

Type of 1968
"P" instead of "d"

1971, Feb. 15 Litho. *Perf. 13½*

244	A36	½p like #210	.15	.15
245	A36	1p like #211	.15	.15
246	A36	1½p like #212	.20	.20
247	A36	2p like #213	.30	.30
a.		Perf. 14½ ('75)	.55	.55
248	A36	2½p like #214	.35	.35
249	A36	3½p like #215	.45	.45
250	A36	4½p like #216	.55	.55
251	A36	5p like #217	.70	.70
252	A36	7½p like #218	.95	.95
253	A36	10p like #219	1.10	1.10
254	A36	12½p like #220	1.50	1.50
255	A36	25p like #221	3.00	3.00
256	A36	50p like #222	13.00	13.00
		Nos. 244-256 (13)	22.40	22.40

The paper of Nos. 244-256 is thinner than the paper of Nos. 209-223 and No. 223 (£1) has been reprinted in slightly different colors.

Perf. 14x14½

1971, Apr. 5 Litho. Wmk. 314

St. Helena, from Italian Miniature, 1460

257	A42	2p violet blue & multi	.15	.15
258	A42	5p multicolored	.28	.28
259	A42	7½p multicolored	.50	.50
260	A42	12½p olive & multi	.75	.75
		Nos. 257-260 (4)	1.68	1.68

Easter 1971.

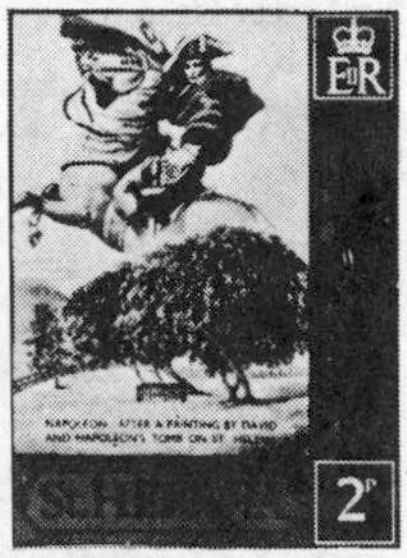

Napoleon, after J. L. David, and Tomb in St. Helena — A43

Design: 34p, Napoleon, by Hippolyte Paul Delaroche.

1971, May 5 *Perf. 13½*

261	A43	2p multicolored	.25	.18
262	A43	34p multicolored	4.00	3.00

Sesquicentennial of the death of Napoleon Bonaparte (1769-1821).

Military Type of 1970

Designs: 1½p, Sword Hilt, Artillery Private, 1815. 4p, Baker rifle and socket bayonet, c. 1816. 6p, Infantry officer's sword hilt, 1822. 22½p, Baker rifle and light sword bayonet, c. 1823.

1971, Nov. 10 *Perf. 14½*

263	A41	1½p green & multi	.30	.25
264	A41	4p gray & multi	.95	.75
265	A41	6p purple & multi	1.50	1.25
266	A41	22½p multicolored	4.75	4.00
		Nos. 263-266 (4)	7.50	6.25

1972, June 19

Designs: 2p, Royal Sappers and Miners breastplate, 1823. 5p, Infantry sergeant's pike, 1830. 7½p, Royal Artillery officer's breastplate, 1830. 12½p, English military pistol, 1800.

267	A41	2p multicolored	.28	.22
268	A41	5p plum & black	.85	.70
269	A41	7½p dp blue & multi	1.40	1.10
270	A41	12½p olive & multi	2.75	2.25
		Nos. 267-270 (4)	5.28	4.27

Silver Wedding Issue, 1972
Common Design Type

Design: Queen Elizabeth II, Prince Philip, St. Helena plover and white fairy tern.

1972, Nov. 20 Photo. *Perf. 14x14½*

271	CD324	2p slate green & multi	.15	.15
272	CD324	16p rose brown & multi	1.00	1.00

Military Type of 1970

Designs: 2p, Shako, 53rd Foot, 1815. 5p, Band and Drums sword hilt, 1830. 7½p, Royal Sappers and Miners officers' hat, 1830. 12½p, General's sword hilt, 1831.

1973, Sept. 20 Litho. *Perf. 14½*

273	A41	2p dull brown & multi	.60	.30
274	A41	5p multicolored	.85	.85
275	A41	7½p olive grn & multi	3.50	2.00
276	A41	12½p lilac & multi	4.75	3.75
		Nos. 273-276 (4)	9.70	6.90

Princess Anne's Wedding Issue
Common Design Type

1973, Nov. 14 Wmk. 314 *Perf. 14*

277	CD325	2p multicolored	.15	.15
278	CD325	18p multicolored	.60	.60

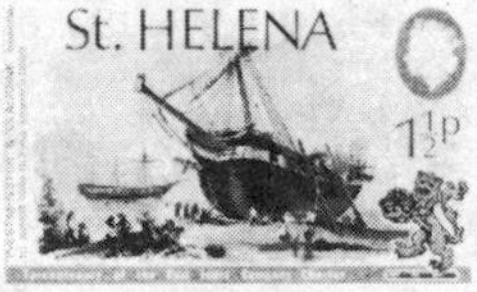

Westminster and Claudine Beached During Storm, 1849 — A45

Designs: 4p, East Indiaman True Briton, 1790. 6p, General Goddard in action off St. Helena, 1795. 22½p, East Indiaman Kent burning in Bay of Biscay, 1825.

Perf. 14½x14

1973, Dec. 17 Litho. Wmk. 314

279	A45	1½p multicolored	.38	.18
280	A45	4p multicolored	.75	.60
281	A45	6p multicolored	1.10	.80
282	A45	22½p multicolored	3.50	3.00
		Nos. 279-282 (4)	5.73	4.58

Tercentenary of the East India Company Charter.

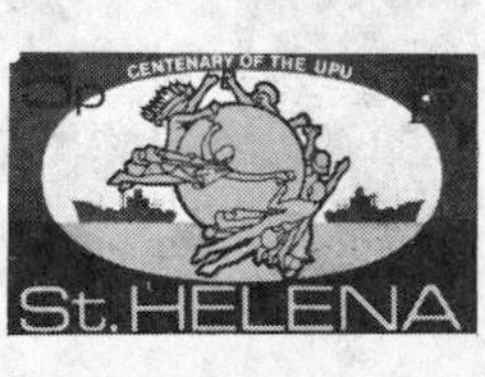

UPU Emblem, Ships A46

Design: 25p, UPU emblem and letters.

1974, Oct. 15 *Perf. 14½x14*

283	A46	5p blue & multi	.22	.22
284	A46	25p red & multi	.90	.90
a.		Souvenir sheet of 2, #283-284	1.25	1.25

Centenary of Universal Postal Union.

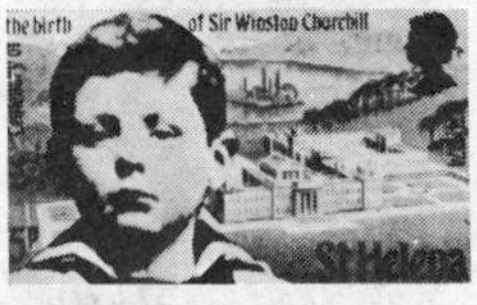

Churchill and Blenheim Palace A47

Design: 25p, Churchill, Tower Bridge and Thames.

1974, Nov. 30 Wmk. 373 *Perf. 14½*

285	A47	5p black & multi	.22	.22
286	A47	25p black & multi	.90	.90
a.		Souvenir sheet of 2, #285-286	1.75	1.25

Sir Winston Churchill (1874-1965).

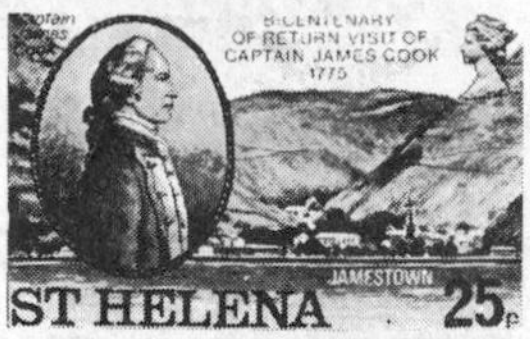

Capt. Cook and Jamestown — A48

Design: 5p, Capt. Cook and "Resolution," vert.

Perf. 14x13½, 13½x14

1975, July 14 Litho.

287	A48	5p multicolored	.60	.60
288	A48	25p multicolored	3.25	3.25

Return of Capt. James Cook to St. Helena, bicent.

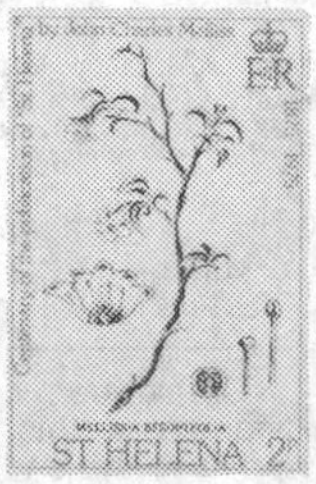

Mellissia Begonifolia — A49

Designs: 5p, Mellissius adumbratus (insect). 12p, Aegialitis St. Helena (bird), horiz. 25p, Scorpaenia mellissii (fish), horiz.

1975, Oct. 20 Wmk. 373 *Perf. 13*

289	A49	2p gray & multi	.16	.16
290	A49	5p gray & multi	.38	.38
291	A49	12p gray & multi	.80	.80
292	A49	25p gray & multi	1.65	1.65
		Nos. 289-292 (4)	2.99	2.99

Centenary of the publication of "St. Helena," by John Charles Melliss.

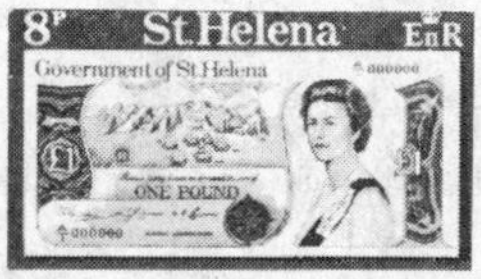

Pound Note A50

Design: 33p, 5-pound note.

1976, Apr. 15 Wmk. 314 *Perf. 13½*

293	A50	8p claret & multi	.45	.35
294	A50	33p multicolored	1.40	1.10

First issue of St. Helena bank notes.

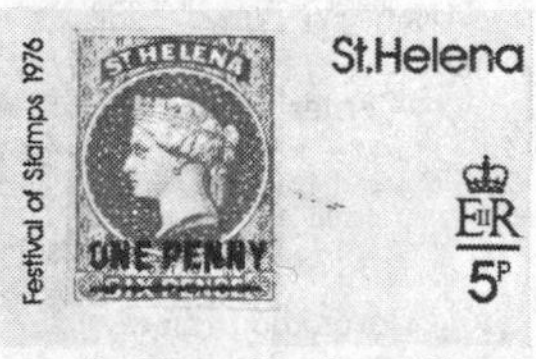

St. Helena No. 8 — A51

Designs: 8p, St. Helena No. 80, vert. 25p, Freighter Good Hope Castle.

Perf. 13½x14, 14x13½

1976, May 4 Litho. Wmk. 373

295	A51	5p buff, brown & blk	.20	.20
296	A51	8p lt grn, grn & blk	.32	.32
297	A51	25p multicolored	1.10	1.10
		Nos. 295-297 (3)	1.62	1.62

Festival of stamps 1976. For souvenir sheet containing No. 297 see Ascension No. 214a.

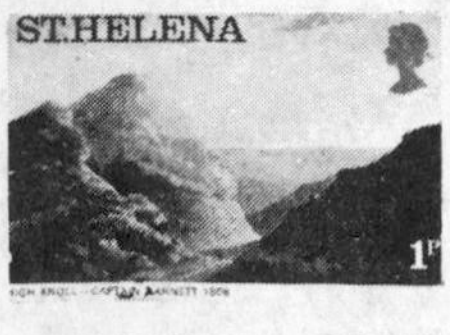

High Knoll, by Capt. Barnett A52

Views on St. Helena, lithographs: 3p, Friar Rock, by G. H. Bellasis, 1815. 5p, Column Lot, by Bellasis. 6p, Sandy Bay Valley, by H. Salt, 1809. 8p, View from Castle terrace, by Bellasis. 9p, The Briars, 1815. 10p, Plantation House, by J. Wathen, 1821. 15p, Longwood House, by Wathen, 1821. 18p, St. Paul's Church, by Vincent Brooks. 26p, St. James's Valley, by Capt. Hastings, 1815. 40p, St. Matthew's Church, Longwood, by Brooks. £1, St. Helena and sailing ship, by Bellasis. £2, Sugar Loaf Hill, by Wathen, 1821.

Wmk. 373

1976, Nov. 28 Litho. *Perf. 14*

Size: 38½x25mm

298	A52	1p multicolored	.15	.15
299	A52	3p multicolored	.15	.15
300	A52	5p multicolored	.15	.15
301	A52	6p multicolored	.16	.16
302	A52	8p multicolored	.20	.20
303	A52	9p multicolored	.22	.22
304	A52	10p multicolored	.25	.25
305	A52	15p multicolored	.38	.38
306	A52	18p multicolored	.48	.48
307	A52	26p multicolored	.70	.70
308	A52	40p multicolored	.95	.95

Size: 47½x35mm

Perf. 13½

309	A52	£1 multicolored	2.50	2.50
310	A52	£2 multicolored	5.00	5.00
		Nos. 298-310 (13)	11.29	11.29

Issue dates: 1p, 3p, 5p, 8p, 10p, 18p, 26p, 40p, £1, Sept. 28; others Nov. 23.
1p, 10p and £2 reissued inscribed 1982.
For overprints see Nos. 376-377.

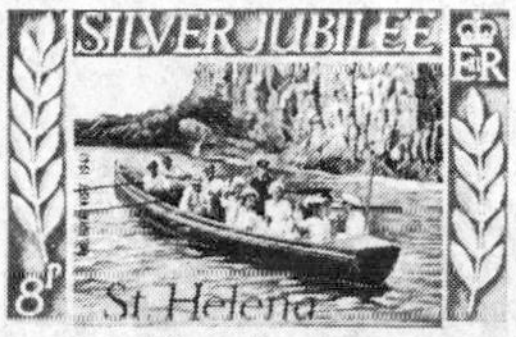

Royal Party Leaving St. Helena, 1947 — A53

Designs: 15p, Queen's scepter and dove. 26p, Prince Philip paying homage to the Queen.

1977, Feb. 7 Wmk. 373 *Perf. 13*

311	A53	8p multicolored	.24	.24
312	A53	15p multicolored	.40	.40
313	A53	26p multicolored	.80	.80
		Nos. 311-313 (3)	1.44	1.44

25th anniv. of the reign of Elizabeth II.

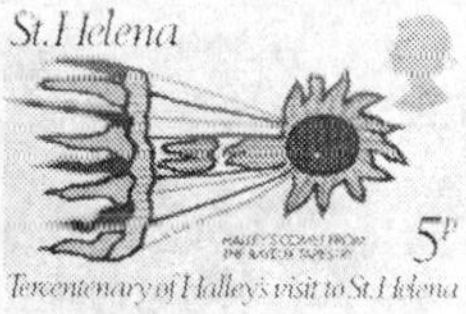

Halley's Comet, from Bayeux Tapestry A54

Designs: 8p, 17th century sextant. 27p, Edmund Halley and Halley's Mount, St. Helena.

1977, Aug. 23 Litho. *Perf. 14*

314	A54	5p multicolored	.60	.60
315	A54	8p multicolored	.90	.90
316	A54	27p multicolored	2.50	2.50
		Nos. 314-316 (3)	4.00	4.00

Edmund Halley's visit to St. Helena, 300th anniv.

Elizabeth II Coronation Anniversary Issue

Common Design Types

Souvenir Sheet

Unwmk.

1978, June 2 Litho. *Perf. 15*

317	Sheet of 6	3.00	3.00
a.	CD326 25p Black dragon of Ulster	.45	.45
b.	CD327 25p Elizabeth II	.45	.45
c.	CD328 25p Sea Lion	.45	.45

No. 317 contains 2 se-tenant strips of Nos. 317a-317c, separated by horizontal gutter.

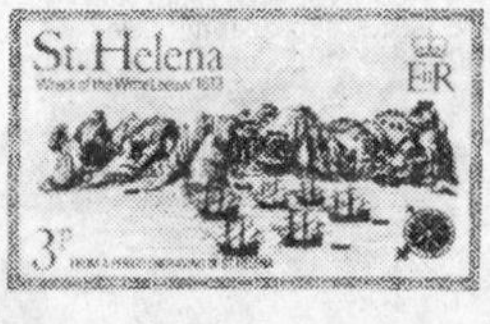

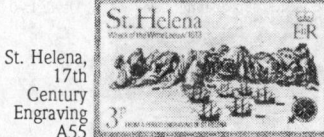

St. Helena, 17th Century Engraving A55

Designs: 5p, 9p, 15p, Various Chinese porcelain and other utensils salvaged from wreck. 8p, Bronze cannon. 20p, Dutch East Indiaman.

Perf. 14½

1978, Aug. 14 Litho. Wmk. 373

318	A55	3p multicolored	.15	.15
319	A55	5p multicolored	.18	.18
320	A55	8p multicolored	.32	.32
321	A55	9p multicolored	.38	.38
322	A55	15p multicolored	.55	.55
323	A55	20p multicolored	.75	.75
		Nos. 318-323 (6)	2.33	2.33

Wreck of the Witte Leeuw, 1613.

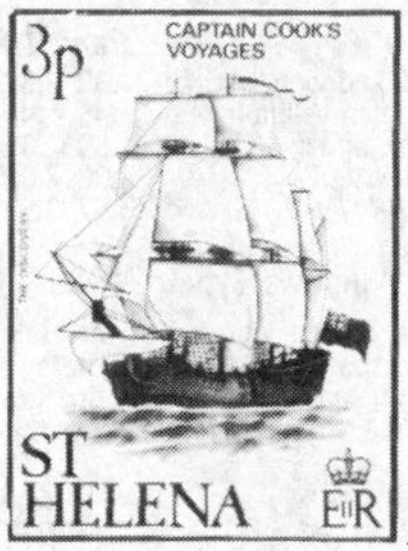

"Discovery" A56

Capt. Cook's voyages: 8p, Cook's portable observatory. 12p, Pharnaceum acidum (plant), after sketch by Joseph Banks. 25p, Capt. Cook, after Flaxman/Wedgwood medallion.

1979, Feb. 19 Litho. *Perf. 11*

324	A56	3p multicolored	.15	.15
325	A56	8p multicolored	.40	.30
326	A56	12p multicolored	.55	.50

Litho.; Embossed

327	A56	25p multicolored	1.10	.95
		Nos. 324-327 (4)	2.20	1.90

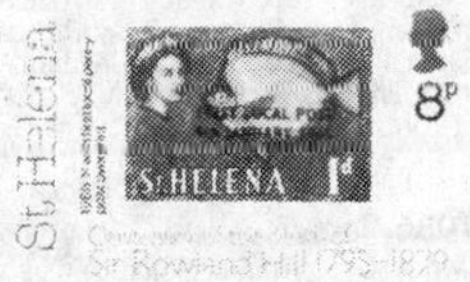

St. Helena No. 176 A57

Designs: 5p, Rowland Hill and his signature, vert. 20p, St. Helena No. 8. 32p, St. Helena No. 49.

1979, Aug. 20 Litho. *Perf. 14*

328	A57	5p multicolored	.15	.15
329	A57	8p multicolored	.22	.22
330	A57	20p multicolored	.60	.60
331	A57	32p multicolored	.90	.90
		Nos. 328-331 (4)	1.87	1.87

Sir Rowland Hill (1795-1879), originator of penny postage.

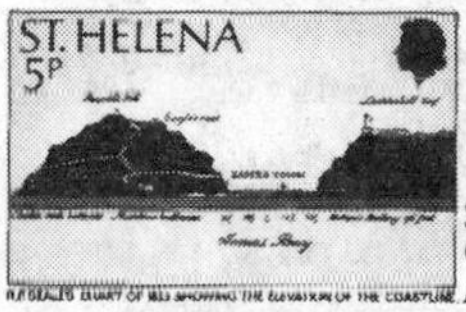

Seale's Chart, 1823 A58

Designs: 8p, Jamestown and Inclined Plane, 1829. 50p, Inclined Plane (stairs), 1979, vert.

1979, Dec. 10 Litho. *Perf. 14*

332	A58	5p multicolored	.15	.15
333	A58	8p multicolored	.22	.22
334	A58	50p multicolored	1.40	1.40
		Nos. 332-334 (3)	1.77	1.77

Inclined Plane, 150th anniversary.

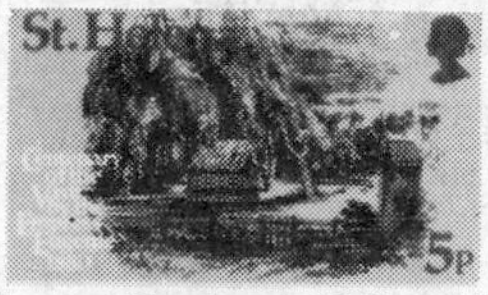

Tomb of Napoleon I, 1848 — A59

Empress Eugenie: 8p, Landing at St. Helena. 62p, Visiting Napoleon's tomb.

1980, Feb. 23 Litho. *Perf. 14½*

335	A59	5p multicolored	.15	.15
336	A59	8p multicolored	.22	.22
337	A59	62p multicolored	1.75	1.75
a.		Souvenir sheet of 3, #335-337	2.25	2.25
		Nos. 335-337 (3)	2.12	2.12

Visit of Empress Eugenie (widow of Napoleon III) to St. Helena, centenary.

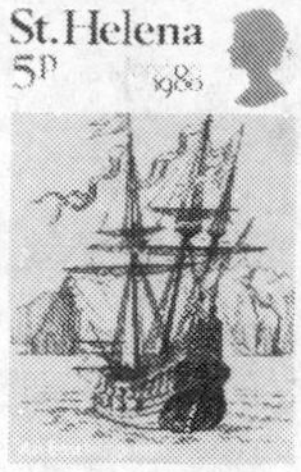

East Indiaman, London 1980 Emblem — A60

1980, May 6 Litho. *Perf. 14½*

338	A60	5p shown	.15	.15
339	A60	8p "Dolphin" postal stone	.22	.22
340	A60	47p Jamestown castle postal stone	1.25	1.25
a.		Souvenir sheet of 3, #338-340	1.90	1.90
		Nos. 338-340 (3)	1.62	1.62

London 1980 Intl. Stamp Exhib., May 6-14.

Queen Mother Elizabeth Birthday Issue

Common Design Type

1980, Aug. 18 Litho. *Perf. 14*

341	CD330	24p multicolored	.60	.60

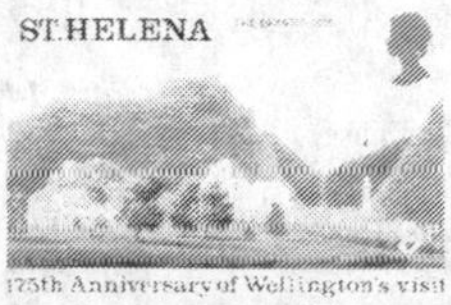

The Briars, 1815 — A61

1980, Nov. 17 Litho. *Perf. 14*

342	A61	9p shown	.25	.25
343	A61	30p Wellington, by Goya, vert	.80	.80

Duke of Wellington's visit to St. Helena, 175th anniv. Nos. 342-343 issued in sheets of 10 with gutter giving historical background.

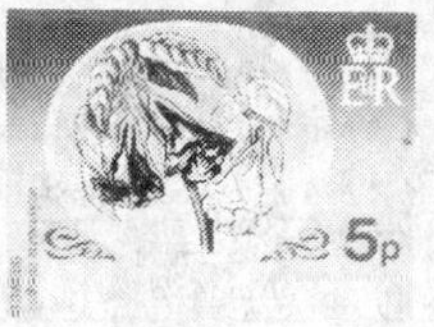

Redwood Flower — A62

1981, Jan. 5 *Perf. 13½*

344	A62	5p shown	.15	.15
345	A62	8p Old father-live-forever	.24	.24
346	A62	15p Gumwood	.45	.45
347	A62	27p Black cabbage	.80	.80
		Nos. 344-347 (4)	1.64	1.64

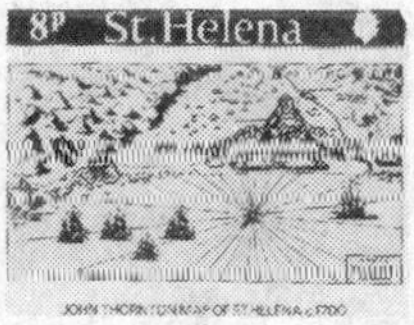

John Thornton's Map of St. Helena, 1700 — A63

1981, May 22 Litho. *Perf. 14½*

348	A63	5p Reinel Portolan Chart, 1530	.15	.15
349	A63	8p shown	.22	.22
350	A63	20p St. Helena, 1815	.52	.52
351	A63	30p St. Helena, 1817	.80	.80
		Nos. 348-351 (4)	1.69	1.69

Souvenir Sheet

352	A63	24p Gastaldi's map of Africa, 16th cent.	.85	.85

Royal Wedding Issue

Common Design Type

Wmk. 373

1981, July 22 Litho. *Perf. 14*

353	CD331	14p Bouquet	.38	.38
354	CD331	29p Charles	.80	.80
355	CD331	32p Couple	.90	.90
		Nos. 353-355 (3)	2.08	2.08

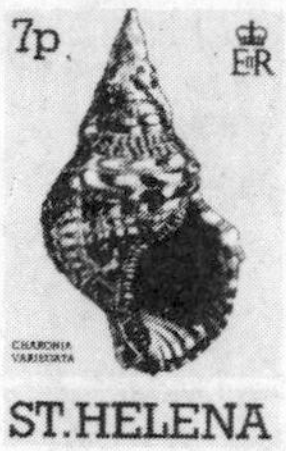

Charonia Variegata — A64

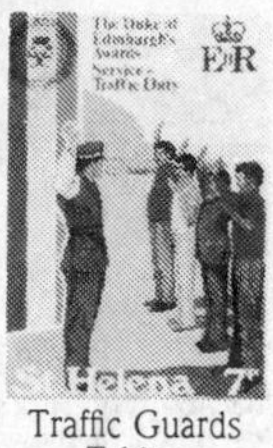

Traffic Guards Taking Oath — A65

1981, Sept. 10 Litho. *Perf. 14*

356	A64	7p shown	.20	.20
357	A64	10p Cypraea spurca sanctahelenae	.30	.30
358	A64	25p Janthina janthina	.75	.75
359	A64	53p Pinna rudis	1.65	1.65
		Nos. 356-359 (4)	2.90	2.90

1981, Nov. 5

360	A65	7p shown	.22	.22
361	A65	11p Posting signs	.35	.35
362	A65	25p Animal care	.75	.75
363	A65	50p Duke of Edinburgh	1.50	1.50
		Nos. 360-363 (4)	2.82	2.82

Duke of Edinburgh's Awards, 25th anniv.

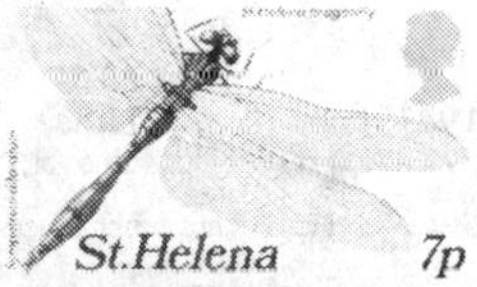

St. Helena Dragonfly A66

1982, Jan. 4 Litho. *Perf. 14½*

364	A66	7p shown	.16	.16
365	A66	10p Burchell's beetle	.32	.32
366	A66	25p Cockroach wasp	.85	.85
367	A66	32p Earwig	1.10	1.10
		Nos. 364-367 (4)	2.43	2.43

See Nos. 386-389.

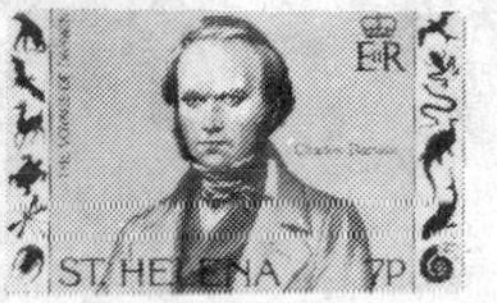

Sesquicentennial of Charles Darwin's Visit — A67

1982, Apr. 19 Litho. *Perf. 14*

368	A67	7p Portrait	.20	.20
369	A67	14p Flagstaff Hill, hammer	.45	.45
370	A67	25p Ring-necked pheasants	.75	.75
371	A67	29p Beagle	.90	.90
		Nos. 368-371 (4)	2.30	2.30

Princess Diana Issue

Common Design Type

1982, July 1 Litho. *Perf. 14*

372	CD333	7p Arms	.20	.20
373	CD333	11p Honeymoon	.32	.32
374	CD333	29p Diana	.85	.85
375	CD333	55p Portrait	1.65	1.65

Nos. 305, 307 Overprinted: "1st PARTICIPATION / COMMONWEALTH GAMES 1982"

1982, Oct. 25 Litho. *Perf. 14*

376	A52	15p multicolored	.48	.48
377	A52	26p multicolored	.80	.80

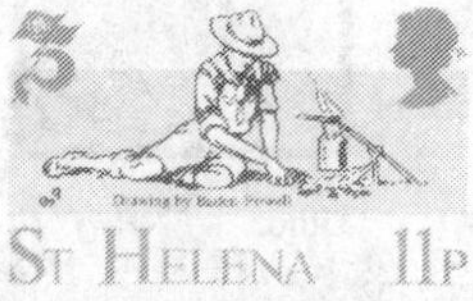

Scouting Year A68

1982, Nov. 29

378	A68	3p Baden-Powell, vert.	.15	.15
379	A68	11p Campfire	.32	.32
380	A68	29p Canon Walcott, vert.	.90	.90
381	A68	59p Thompsons Wood camp	1.75	1.75
		Nos. 378-381 (4)	3.12	3.12

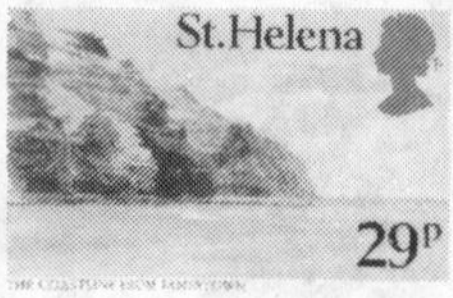

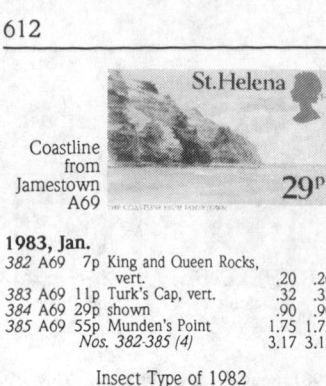

Coastline from Jamestown A69

1983, Jan.

382	A69	7p King and Queen Rocks, vert.	.20	.20
383	A69	11p Turk's Cap, vert.	.32	.32
384	A69	29p shown	.90	.90
385	A69	55p Munden's Point	1.75	1.75
		Nos. 382-385 (4)	3.17	3.17

Insect Type of 1982

1983, Apr. 22 Litho. *Perf. 14½*

386	A66	11p Death's-head hawk-moth	.32	.32
387	A66	15p Saldid-shore bug	.42	.42
388	A66	29p Click beetle	.85	.85
389	A66	59p Weevil	1.65	1.65
		Nos. 386-389 (4)	3.24	3.24

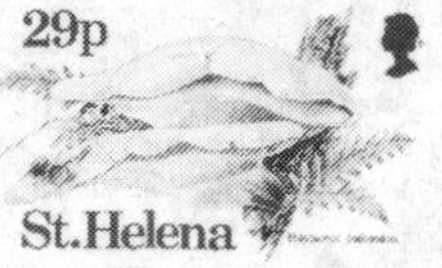

Local Fungi A70

Wmk. 373

1983, June 16 Litho. *Perf. 14*

390	A70	11p Coriolus versicolor, vert.	.32	.32
391	A70	15p Pluteus brunneisucus, vert.	.42	.42
392	A70	29p Polyporus induratus	.85	.85
393	A70	59p Coprinus angulatus, vert.	1.65	1.65
		Nos. 390-393 (4)	3.24	3.24

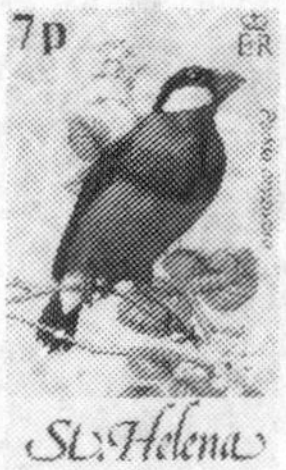

Local Birds — A71

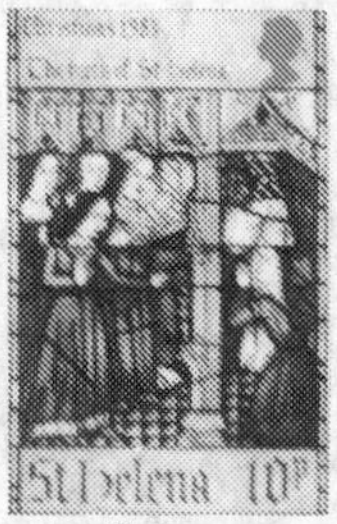

Christmas 1983 — A72

1983, Sept. 12 Litho. *Perf. 14x14½*

394	A71	7p Padda oryzivora	.20	.20
395	A71	15p Foudia madagascariensis	.40	.40
396	A71	33p Estrilda astrild	.90	.90
397	A71	59p Serinus flaviventris	1.65	1.65
		Nos. 394-397 (4)	3.15	3.15

Souvenir Sheet

1983, Oct. 17 Litho. *Perf. 14x13½*

Stained Glass, Parish Church of St. Michael.

398	Sheet of 10	3.25	3.25
a.	A72 10p multicolored	.25	.25
b.	A72 15p multicolored	.38	.38

Sheet contains strips of 10p and 15p with center margin telling St. Helena story.

See Nos. 424-427, 442-445.

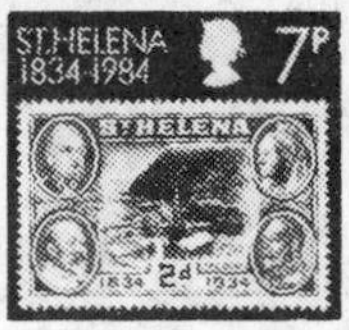

150th Anniv. of the Colony — A73

1984, Jan. 3 Litho. *Perf. 14*

399	A73	1p No. 101	.15	.15
400	A73	3p No. 102	.15	.15
401	A73	6p No. 103	.16	.16
402	A73	7p No. 104	.18	.18
403	A73	11p No. 105	.30	.30
404	A73	15p No. 106	.42	.42
405	A73	29p No. 107	.85	.85
406	A73	33p No. 109	.95	.95
407	A73	59p No. 110	1.65	1.65
408	A73	£1 No. 108	2.75	2.75
409	A73	£2 New coat of arms	5.75	5.75
		Nos. 399-409 (11)	13.31	13.31

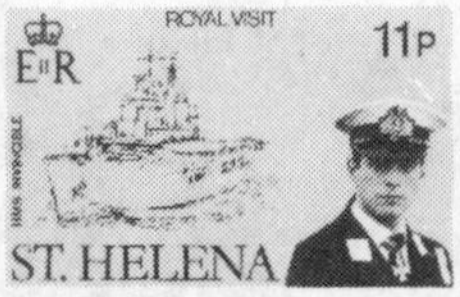

Visit of Prince Andrew A74

1984, Apr. 4 Litho. *Perf. 14*

410	A74	11p Andrew, Invincible	.30	.30
411	A74	60p Andrew, Herald	1.65	1.65

Lloyd's List Issue

Common Design Type

1984, May *Perf. 14½x14*

412	CD335	10p St. Helena, 1814	.28	.28
413	CD335	18p Solomon's facade	.50	.50
414	CD335	25p Lloyd's Coffee House	.70	.70
415	CD335	50p Papanui, 1898	1.40	1.40
		Nos. 412-415 (4)	2.88	2.88

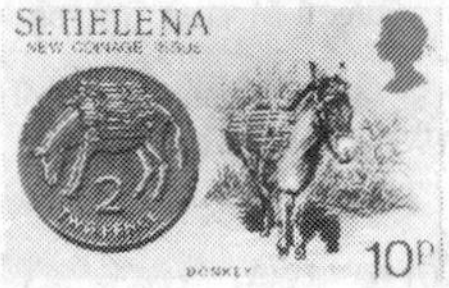

New Coin Issue — A75

1984, July *Perf. 14*

416	A75	10p 2p, Donkey	.30	.30
417	A75	15p 5p, Wire bird	.45	.45
418	A75	29p 1p, Yellowfin tuna	.90	.90
419	A75	50p 10p, Arum lily	1.50	1.50
		Nos. 416-419 (4)	3.15	3.15

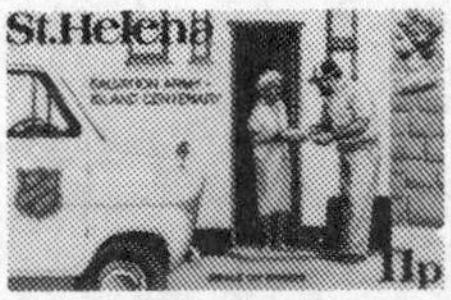

Centenary of Salvation Army in St. Helena A76

1984, Sept. Litho. Wmk. 373

420	A76	7p Secretary Rebecca Fuller, vert.	.20	.20
421	A76	11p Meals on Wheels service	.30	.30
422	A76	25p Jamestown SA Hall	.65	.65
423	A76	60p Hymn playing, clock tower	1.65	1.65
		Nos. 420-423 (4)	2.80	2.80

Stained Glass Windows Type of 1983

1984, Nov. 9

424	A72	6p St. Helena visits prisoners	.16	.16
425	A72	10p Betrothal of St. Helena	.28	.28
426	A72	15p Marriage of St. Helena & Constantius	.40	.40
427	A72	33p Birth of Constantine	.90	.90
		Nos. 424-427 (4)	1.74	1.74

Queen Mother 85th Birthday Issue

Common Design Type

Perf. 14½x14

1985, June 7 Litho. Wmk. 384

428	CD336	11p Portrait, age 2	.32	.32
429	CD336	15p Queen Mother, Elizabeth II	.45	.45
430	CD336	29p Attending ballet, Covent Garden	.85	.85
431	CD336	55p Holding Prince Henry	1.75	1.75
		Nos. 428-431 (4)	3.37	3.37

Souvenir Sheet

432	CD336	70p Queen Mother and Ford V8 Pilot	3.00	3.00

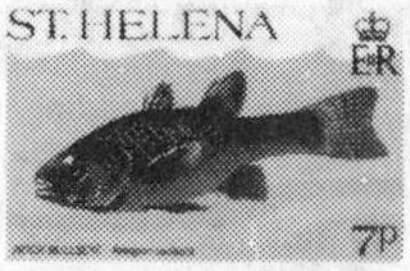

Marine Life — A78

Perf. 13x13½

1985, July 12 Litho. Wmk. 373

433	A78	7p Rock bullseye	.18	.18
434	A78	11p Mackerel	.30	.30
435	A78	15p Skipjack tuna	.42	.42
436	A78	33p Yellowfin tuna	1.00	1.00
437	A78	50p Stump	1.40	1.40
		Nos. 433-437 (5)	3.30	3.30

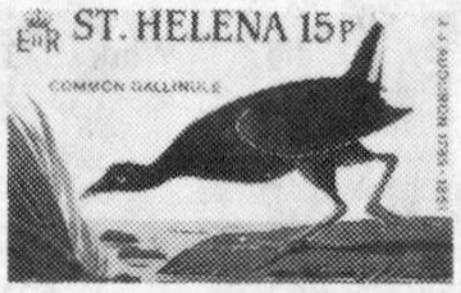

Audubon Birth Bicent. A79

Portrait of naturalist and his illustrations of American bird species.

1985, Sept. 2 *Perf. 14*

438	A79	11p John Audubon, vert.	.32	.32
439	A79	15p Common gallinule	.45	.45
440	A79	25p Tropic bird	.80	.80
441	A79	60p Noddy tern	2.00	2.00
		Nos. 438-441 (4)	3.57	3.57

Stained Glass Windows Type of 1983

Christmas: 7p, St. Helena journeys to the Holy Land. 10p, Zambres slays the bull. 15p, The bull restored to life, conversion of St. Helena. 60p, Resurrection of the corpse, the true cross identified.

1985, Oct. 14

442	A72	7p multicolored	.22	.22
443	A72	10p multicolored	.30	.30
444	A72	15p multicolored	.50	.50
445	A72	60p multicolored	1.90	1.90
		Nos. 442-445 (4)	2.92	2.92

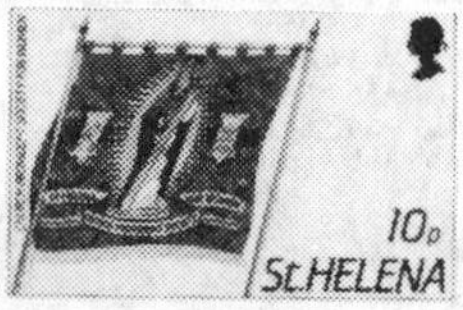

Society Banners A80

Designs: 10p, Church Provident Society for Women. 11p, Working Men's Christian Assoc. 25p, Church Benefit Society for Children. 29p, Mechanics & Friendly Benefit Society. 33p, Ancient Order of Foresters.

Perf. 13x13½

1986, Jan. 7 Wmk. 384

446	A80	10p multicolored	.30	.30
447	A80	11p multicolored	.32	.32
448	A80	25p multicolored	.75	.75
449	A80	29p multicolored	.85	.85
450	A80	33p multicolored	1.00	1.00
		Nos. 446-450 (5)	3.22	3.22

Queen Elizabeth II 60th Birthday

Common Design Type

Designs: 10p, Making 21st birthday broadcast, royal tour of South Africa, 1947. 15p, In robes of state, Throne Room, Buckingham Palace, Silver Jubilee, 1977. 20p, Onboard HMS Implacable, en route to South Africa, 1947. 50p, State visit to U.S., 1976. 65p, Visiting Crown Agents' offices, 1983.

1986, Apr. 21 *Perf. 14½*

451	CD337	10p scarlet, blk & sil	.28	.28
452	CD337	15p ultra & multi	.42	.42
453	CD337	20p green, blk & sil	.55	.55
454	CD337	50p violet & multi	1.40	1.40
455	CD337	65p rose vio & multi	1.75	1.75
		Nos. 451-455 (5)	4.40	4.40

For overprints see Nos. 488-492.

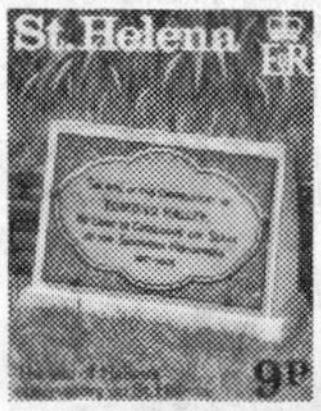

Halley's Comet — A81

Designs: 9p, Site of Halley's observatory on St. Helena. 12p, Edmond Halley, astronomer. 20p, Halley's planisphere of the southern stars. 65p, Voyage to St. Helena on the Unity.

1986, May 15 Wmk. 373 *Perf. 14½*

456	A81	9p multicolored	.28	.28
457	A81	12p multicolored	.38	.38
458	A81	20p multicolored	.48	.48
459	A81	65p multicolored	1.40	1.40
		Nos. 456-459 (4)	2.54	2.54

Royal Wedding Issue, 1986

Common Design Type

Designs: 10p, Informal portrait. 40p, Andrew in dress uniform at parade.

Wmk. 384

1986, July 23 Litho. *Perf. 14*

460	CD338	10p multicolored	.32	.32
461	CD338	40p multicolored	1.25	1.25

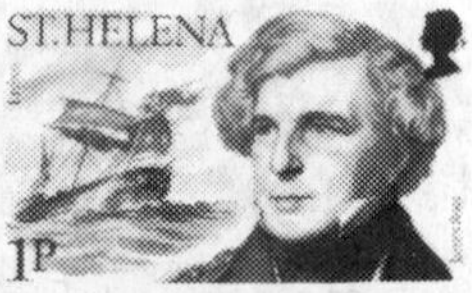

Explorers and Ships A82

Designs: 1p, James Ross (1800-62), Erebus. 3p, Robert FitzRoy (1805-65), Beagle. 5p, Adam Johann von Krusenstern (1770-1846), Nadezhda, Russia. 9p, William Bligh (1754-1817), Resolution. 10p, Otto von Kotzebue (1786-1846), Rurik, Germany. 12p, Philip Carteret (1639-82), Swallow, 15p, Thomas Cavendish (c.1560-92), Desire. 20p, Louis-Antoine de Bougainville (1729-1811), La Boudeuse, France. 25p, Fyodor Petrovitch Litke (1797-1882), Seniavin, Russia. 40p, Louis Isidore Duperrey (1786-1865), La Coquille, France. 60p, John Byron (1723-86), Dolphin. £1, James Cook, Endeavour. £2, Jules Dumont d'Urville (1790-1842), L'Astrolabe, France.

Perf. 14½

1986, Sept. 22 Litho. Wmk. 384

462	A82	1p red brown	.15	.15
463	A82	3p bright ultra	.15	.15
464	A82	5p olive green	.15	.15
465	A82	9p deep claret	.28	.28
466	A82	10p sepia	.30	.30
467	A82	12p brt blue green	.36	.36
468	A82	15p brown lake	.45	.45
469	A82	20p sapphire	.60	.60
470	A82	25p red brown	.75	.75
471	A82	40p myrtle green	1.20	1.20
472	A82	60p brown	1.80	1.80
473	A82	£1 Prussian blue	3.00	3.00
474	A82	£2 bright violet	6.00	6.00
		Nos. 462-474 (13)	15.19	15.19

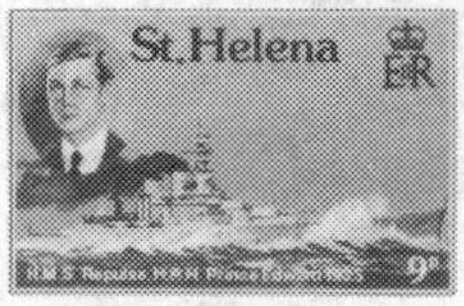

Ships of Royal Visitors A83

Portraits and vessels: 9p, Prince Edward, HMS Repulse, 1925. 13p, King George VI, HMS Vanguard, 1947. 38p, Prince Philip, HMY Britannia, 1957. 45p, Prince Andrew, HMS Herald, 1984.

1987, Feb. 16 Wmk. 373 *Perf. 14*

475	A83	9p multicolored	.35	.35
476	A83	13p multicolored	.50	.50
477	A83	38p multicolored	1.50	1.50
478	A83	45p multicolored	1.75	1.75
		Nos. 475-478 (4)	4.10	4.10

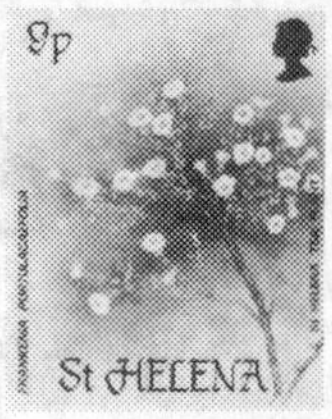

Rare Plants — A84

1987, Aug. 3 *Perf. 14½x14*

479	A84	9p St. Helena tea plant	.35	.35
480	A84	13p Baby's toes	.50	.50
481	A84	38p Salad plant	1.50	1.50
482	A84	45p Scrubwood	1.75	1.75
		Nos. 479-482 (4)	4.10	4.10

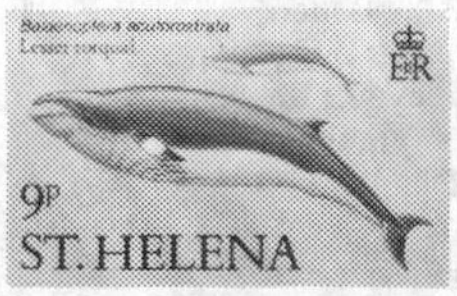

Marine Mammals A85

Wmk. 384

1987, Oct. 24 Litho. *Perf. 14*

483	A85	9p Lesser rorqual	.35	.35
484	A85	13p Risso's dolphin	.52	.52
485	A85	45p Sperm whale	1.90	1.90
486	A85	60p Euphrosyne dolphin	2.50	2.50
		Nos. 483-486 (4)	5.27	5.27

Souvenir Sheet

487	A85	75p Humpback whale	3.75	3.75

Nos. 451-455 Ovptd. "40TH WEDDING ANNIVERSARY" in Silver.

Perf. 14½
1987, Dec. 9 Litho. Wmk. 384
488 CD337 10p scarlet, blk & sil .35 .35
489 CD337 15p ultra & multi .50 .50
490 CD337 20p green, blk & sil .68 .68
491 CD337 38p violet & multi 1.70 1.70
492 CD337 65p rose vio & multi 2.20 2.20
Nos. 488-492 (5) 5.43 5.43

Australia Bicentennial A86

Ships and signatures: 9p, HMS Defence, 1691, and William Dampier. 13p, HMS Resolution, 1775, and James Cook. 45p, HMS Providence, 1792, and William Bligh. 60p, HMS Beagle, 1836, and Charles Darwin.

Perf. 14½
1988, Mar. 1 Litho. Wmk. 384
493 A86 9p multicolored .35 .35
494 A86 13p multicolored .48 .48
495 A86 45p multicolored 1.65 1.65
496 A86 60p multicolored 2.20 2.20
Nos. 493-496 (4) 4.68 4.68

Christmas — A87   Rare Plants — A88

Religious paintings by unknown artists: 5p, The Holy Family with Child. 20p, Madonna. 38p, The Holy Family with St. John. 60p, The Holy Virgin with the Child.

Wmk. 373
1988, Oct. 11 Litho. Perf. 14
497 A87 5p multicolored .18 .18
498 A87 20p multicolored .68 .68
499 A87 38p multicolored 1.30 1.30
500 A87 60p multicolored 2.05 2.05
Nos. 497-500 (4) 4.21 4.21

Lloyds of London, 300th Anniv.
Common Design Type
Designs: 9p, Underwriting room, 1886. 20p, Edinburgh Castle, horiz. 45p, Bosun Bird, horiz. 60p, Spangereid on fire off St. Helena, 1920.

Wmk. 384
1988, Nov. 1 Litho. Perf. 14
501 CD341 9p multicolored .30 .30
502 CD341 20p multicolored .68 .68
503 CD341 45p multicolored 1.50 1.50
504 CD341 60p multicolored 2.00 2.00
Nos. 501-504 (4) 4.48 4.48

1989, Jan. 6 Perf. 14
505 A88 9p Ebony .30 .30
506 A88 20p St. Helena lobelia .68 .68
507 A88 45p Large bellflower 1.55 1.55
508 A88 60p She cabbage tree 2.05 2.05
Nos. 505-508 (4) 4.58 4.58

Flags and Military Uniforms, 1815 — A89

Designs: 9p, Soldier, 53rd Foot. 13p, Officer, 53rd Foot. 20p, Royal marine. 45p, Officer, 66th Foot. 60p, Soldier, 66th Foot.

1989, June 5 Litho. Perf. 14
509 Strip of 5 5.25 5.25
a. A89 9p multicolored .32 .32
b. A89 13p multicolored .45 .45

c. A89 20p multicolored .70 .70
d. A89 45p multicolored 1.60 1.60
e. A89 60p multicolored 2.10 2.10

Nos. 509a-509e Overprinted

1989, July 7 Litho. Perf. 14
510 Strip of 5 5.25 5.25
a. A89 9p multicolored .32 .32
b. A89 13p multicolored .45 .45
c. A89 20p multicolored .70 .70
d. A89 45p multicolored 1.60 1.60
e. A89 60p multicolored 2.10 2.10
PHILEXFRANCE '89.

New Central (Prince Andrew) School — A90

1989, Aug. 24 Perf. 14½
511 A90 13p Agriculture .48 .48
512 A90 20p Literacy .75 .75
513 A90 25p Building exterior .92 .92
514 A90 60p Campus 2.20 2.20
Nos. 511-514 (4) 4.35 4.35

Christmas — A91

Paintings: 10p, The Madonna with the Pear, by Durer. 20p, The Holy Family Under the Apple Tree, by Rubens. 45p, The Virgin in the Meadow, by Raphael. 60p, The Holy Family with Saint John, by Raphael.

1989, Oct. 10 Wmk. 373 Perf. 14
515 A91 10p multicolored .32 .32
516 A91 20p multicolored .65 .65
517 A91 45p multicolored 1.40 1.40
518 A91 60p multicolored 1.90 1.90
Nos. 515-518 (4) 4.27 4.27

Early Vehicles A92

1989, Dec. 1 Wmk. 384 Perf. 14½
519 A92 9p 1930 Chevrolet .30 .30
520 A92 20p 1929 Austin Seven .65 .65
521 A92 45p 1929 Morris Cowley 1.40 1.40
522 A92 60p 1932 Sunbeam 1.90 1.90
Nos. 519-522 (4) 4.25 4.25

Souvenir Sheet
523 A92 £1 Ford Model A 3.15 3.15

Farm Animals — A93

1990, Feb. 1 Litho. Perf. 14
524 A93 9p Sheep .28 .28
525 A93 13p Pigs .42 .42
526 A93 45p Cow, calf 1.40 1.40
527 A93 60p Geese 1.90 1.90
Nos. 524-527 (4) 4.00 4.00

Great Britain No. 2 A94

Exhibition emblem and: 20p, Great Britain No. 1. 38p, Mail delivery to branch p.o. 45p, Main p.o., mail van.

1990, May 3 Wmk. 373
528 A94 13p shown .40 .40
529 A94 20p multicolored .65 .65
530 A94 38p multicolored 1.20 1.20
531 A94 45p multicolored 1.40 1.40
Nos. 528-531 (4) 3.65 3.65
Stamp World London '90, 150th anniv. of the Penny Black.

Queen Mother, 90th Birthday
Common Design Types
1990, Aug. 4 Wmk. 384 Perf. 14x15
532 CD343 25p As Duchess of York, 1923 .85 .85
Perf. 14½
533 CD344 £1 Visiting communal feeding center, 1940 3.40 3.40

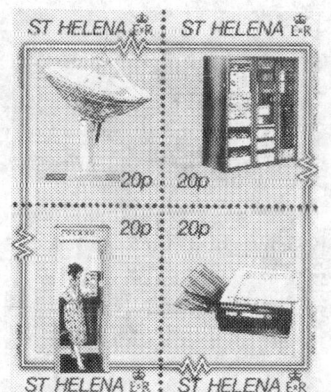

Telecommunications — A95

1990, July 28 Wmk. 373 Perf. 14
534 A95 Block of 4 3.25 3.25
a.-d. 20p any single .80 .80

Dane, 1857 — A96

Designs: 20p, RMS St. Helena offloading cargo. 38p, Launching new RMS St. Helena, 1989. 45p, Duke of York launching new RMS St. Helena. £1, New RMS St. Helena.

1990, Sept. 13 Perf. 14½
535 A96 13p multicolored .45 .45
536 A96 20p multicolored .70 .70
537 A96 38p multicolored 1.35 1.35
538 A96 45p multicolored 1.60 1.60
Nos. 535-538 (4) 4.10 4.10

Souvenir Sheet
539 A96 £1 multicolored 3.50 3.50
See Ascension Nos. 493-497, Tristan da Cunha Nos. 482-486.

Christmas A97

Parish Churches.
1990, Oct. 18 Perf. 13
540 A97 10p Baptist Chapel, Sandy Bay .35 .35
541 A97 13p St. Martin in the Hills .45 .45

542 A97 20p St. Helena and the Cross .70 .70
543 A97 38p St. James Church 1.35 1.35
544 A97 45p St. Paul's Church 1.60 1.60
Nos. 540-544 (5) 4.45 4.45

Removal of Napoleon's Body from St. Helena, 150th Anniv. — A98

Designs: 13p, Funeral cortege, Jamestown wharf. 20p, Moving coffin to Belle Poule, James Bay. 38p, Transfer of coffin from Belle Poule to Normandie, Cherbourg. 45p, Napoleon's Tomb, St. Helena.

1990, Dec. 15 Wmk. 373 Perf. 14
545 A98 13p green & black .45 .45
546 A98 20p blue & black .70 .70
547 A98 38p violet & black 1.35 1.35
548 A98 45p multicolored 1.60 1.60
Nos. 545-548 (4) 4.10 4.10

A99   A100

Military Uniforms 1897: 13p, Officer, Leicestershire Regiment. 15p, Officer, York and Lancaster Regiment. 20p, Color Sergeant, Leicestershire Regiment. 38p, Drummer/Flautist, York and Lancaster Regiment. 45p, Lance Corporal, York and Lancaster Regiment.

1991, May 2
549 A99 13p multicolored .45 .45
550 A99 15p multicolored .52 .52
551 A99 20p multicolored .70 .70
552 A99 38p multicolored 1.35 1.35
553 A99 45p multicolored 1.60 1.60
Nos. 549-553 (5) 4.62 4.62

Elizabeth & Philip, Birthdays
Common Design Types
1991, July 1 Wmk. 384 Perf. 14½
554 CD345 25p multicolored .88 .88
555 CD346 25p multicolored .88 .88
a. Pair, #554-555 + label 1.76 1.76

1991, Nov. 2 Wmk. 373 Perf. 14
Christmas (Paintings): 10p, Madonna and Child, Titian. 13p, Holy Family, Mengs. 20p, Madonna and Child, Dyce. 38p, Two Trinities, Murillo. 45p, Virgin and Child, Bellini.

556 A100 10p multicolored .35 .35
557 A100 13p multicolored .45 .45
558 A100 20p multicolored .70 .70
559 A100 38p multicolored 1.35 1.35
560 A100 45p multicolored 1.60 1.60
Nos. 556-560 (5) 4.45 4.45

Phila Nippon '91 — A101

Motorcycles: 13p, Matchless 346cc (ohv), 1947. 20p, Triumph Tiger 100, 500cc, 1950. 38p, Honda CD 175cc, 1967. 45p, Yamaha DTE 400, 1976. 65p, Suzuki RM 250cc, 1984.

Perf. 14x14½
1991, Nov. 16 Litho. Wmk. 384
561 A101 13p multicolored .45 .45
562 A101 20p multicolored .70 .70
563 A101 38p multicolored 1.35 1.35
564 A101 45p multicolored 1.60 1.60
Nos. 561-564 (4) 4.10 4.10

Souvenir Sheet
565 A101 65p multicolored 3.50 3.50

Discovery of America, 500th
Anniv. — A102

Wmk. 373

1992, Jan. 24	Litho.		*Perf. 14*
566 A102	15p STV Eye of the Wind	.52	.52
567 A102	25p STV Soren Larsen	.88	.88
568 A102	35p Santa Maria, Nina & Pinta	1.25	1.25
569 A102	50p Columbus, Santa Maria	1.75	1.75
	Nos. 566-569 (4)	4.40	4.40

World Columbian Stamp Expo '92, Chicago and Genoa '92 Intl. Philatelic Exhibitions.

Queen Elizabeth II's Accession to the Throne, 40th Anniv.
Common Design Type

1992, Feb. 6

570 CD349	11p multicolored	.38	.38
571 CD349	15p multicolored	.50	.50
572 CD349	25p multicolored	.85	.85
573 CD349	35p multicolored	1.25	1.25
574 CD349	50p multicolored	1.75	1.75
	Nos. 570-574 (5)	4.73	4.73

Liberation of
Falkland Islands,
10th
Anniv. — A103

Designs: No. 579a, 13p + 3p, like No. 575. b, 20p + 4p, like No. 576. c, 38p + 8p, like No. 577. d, 45p + 8p, like No. 578.

1992, June 12

575 A103	13p HMS Ledbury	.45	.45
576 A103	20p HMS Brecon	.70	.70
577 A103	38p RMS St. Helena	1.35	1.35
578 A103	45p First mail drop, 1982	1.60	1.60
	Nos. 575-578 (4)	4.10	4.10

Souvenir Sheet

579 A103	Sheet of 4, #a.-d.	5.00	5.00

Surtax for Soldiers', Sailors' and Airmens' Families Association.

Christmas — A104

Children in scenes from Nativity plays: 13p, Angel, shepherds. 15p, Magi, shepherds. 20p, Joseph, Mary. 45p, Nativity scene.

1992, Oct. 12		**Wmk. 384**	
580 A104	13p multicolored	.45	.45
581 A104	15p multicolored	.52	.52
582 A104	20p multicolored	.70	.70
583 A104	45p multicolored	1.60	1.60
	Nos. 580-583 (4)	3.27	3.27

Anniversaries
A105

Designs: 13p, Man broadcasting at radio station. 20p, Scouts marching in parade. 38p, Breadfruit, HMS Providence, 1792. 45p, Governor Colonel Brooke, Plantation House.

1992, Dec. 4		**Wmk. 373**	*Perf. 14½*
584 A105	15p multicolored	.45	.45
585 A105	20p multicolored	.70	.70
586 A105	35p multicolored	1.35	1.35
587 A105	45p multicolored	1.60	1.60
	Nos. 584-587 (4)	4.10	4.10

Radio St. Helena, 25th anniv. (#584). Scouting on St. Helena, 75th anniv. (#585). Captain Bligh's visit, 200th anniv. (#586). Plantation House, 200th anniv. (#587).

Flowers — A106

Perf. 14½x14

1993, Mar. 19	Litho.	**Wmk. 384**	
588 A106	9p Moses in the bulrush	.28	.28
589 A106	13p Periwinkle	.45	.45
590 A106	20p Everlasting flower	.65	.65
591 A106	38p Cigar plant	1.25	1.25
592 A106	45p Lobelia erinus	1.45	1.45
	Nos. 588-592 (5)	4.08	4.08

See Nos. 635-640.

Wirebird
A107

Perf. 13½

1993, Aug. 16	Litho.	**Wmk. 373**	
593 A107	3p Adult with eggs	.15	.15
594 A107	5p Male, brooding female	.15	.15
595 A107	12p Downy young, adult	.38	.38
596 A107	25p Two immature birds	.75	.75
597 A107	40p Adult in flight	1.15	1.15
598 A107	60p Immature bird	1.75	1.75
	Nos. 593-598 (6)	4.33	4.33

Birds — A108

1993, Aug. 26			*Perf. 14½*
599 A108	1p Swainson's canary	.15	.15
600 A108	3p Chuckar partridge	.15	.15
601 A108	11p Pigeon	.32	.32
602 A108	12p Waxbill	.35	.35
603 A108	15p Common myna	.42	.42
604 A108	18p Java sparrow	.52	.52
605 A108	25p Red-billed tropicbird	.70	.70
606 A108	35p Maderian storm petrel	1.00	1.00
607 A108	75p Madagascar fody	2.25	2.25
608 A108	£1 Common fairy tern	3.00	3.00
609 A108	£2 Southern giant petrel	5.75	5.75
610 A108	£5 Wirebird	15.00	15.00
	Nos. 599-610 (12)	29.61	29.61

Nos. 599-604, 607, 610 are vert.

Christmas — A109

Toys: 12p, Teddy bear, soccer ball. 15p, Sailboat, doll. 18p, Paint palette, rocking horse. 25p, Kite, airplane. 60p, Guitar, roller skates.

1993, Oct. 1		*Perf. 13½x14*	
611 A109	12p multicolored	.35	.35
612 A109	15p multicolored	.42	.42
613 A109	18p multicolored	.52	.52
614 A109	25p multicolored	.70	.70
615 A109	60p multicolored	1.75	1.75
	Nos. 611-615 (5)	3.74	3.74

Flowers — A110

Photographs: No. 616a, Arum lily. No. 617a, Ebony. No. 618a, Shell ginger.
Nos. 616b-618b: Child's painting of same flower as in "a."

1994, Jan. 6		**Wmk. 384**	*Perf. 14*
616 A110	12p Pair, #a.-b.	.65	.65
617 A110	25p Pair, #a.-b.	1.40	1.40
618 A110	35p Pair, #a.-b.	1.90	1.90

Pets — A111

Designs: 12p, Abyssinian guinea pig. 25p, Common tabby cat. 53p, Plain white, black rabbits. 60p, Golden labrador.

1994, Feb. 18		**Wmk. 373**	*Perf. 14½*
619 A111	12p multicolored	.35	.35
620 A111	25p multicolored	.70	.70
621 A111	53p multicolored	1.50	1.50
622 A111	60p multicolored	1.65	1.65
	Nos. 619-622 (4)	4.20	4.20

Hong Kong '94.

Fish — A112

Designs: 12p, Springer's blenny. 25p, Bastard five finger. 53p, Deepwater gurnard. 60p, Green fish.

1994, June 6		**Wmk. 384**	*Perf. 14*
623 A112	12p multicolored	.35	.35
624 A112	25p multicolored	.75	.75
625 A112	53p multicolored	1.65	1.65
626 A112	60p multicolored	1.75	1.75
	Nos. 623-626 (4)	4.50	4.50

Butterflies
A113

1994, Aug. 9		**Wmk. 373**	
627 A113	12p Lampides boeticus	.35	.35
628 A113	25p Cynthia cardui	.75	.75
629 A113	53p Hypolimnas bolina	1.65	1.65
630 A113	60p Danaus chrysippus	1.75	1.75
	Nos. 627-630 (4)	4.50	4.50

Christmas
Carols
A114

Designs: 12p, "Silent night, holy night..." 15p, "While shepherds watched..." 25p, "Away in a manger..." 38p, "We three kings..." 60p, Angels from the realms of glory.

1994, Oct. 6			
631 A114	12p multicolored	.50	.50
632 A114	15p multicolored	.65	.65
633 A114	18p multicolored	1.00	1.00
634 A114	38p multicolored	1.65	1.65
635 A114	60p multicolored	2.50	2.50
	Nos. 631-635 (5)	6.30	6.30

Flower Type of 1993

1994, Dec. 15		*Perf. 14½*	
	Litho.	**Wmk. 384**	
636 A106	12p Honeysuckle	.38	.38
637 A106	15p Gobblegheer	.45	.45
638 A106	25p African lily	.80	.80
639 A106	38p Prince of Wales feathers	1.25	1.25
640 A106	60p St. Johns lily	1.90	1.90
	Nos. 636-640 (5)	4.78	4.78

Emergency
Services
A115

Wmk. 384

1995, Feb. 2	Litho.	*Perf. 14*	
641 A115	12p Fire engine	.38	.38
642 A115	25p Inshore rescue craft	.80	.80
643 A115	53p Police, rural patrol	1.65	1.65
644 A115	60p Ambulance	1.90	1.90
	Nos. 641-644 (4)	4.73	4.73

Harpers Earth
Dam Project
A116

Designs: a, Site clearance. b, Earthworks in progress. c, Laying the outlet pipe. d, Revetment block protection. e, Completed dam, June 1994.

Perf. 14½

1995, Apr. 6	Litho.	**Wmk. 373**	
645 A116	25p Strip of 5, #a.-e.	4.00	4.00

No. 645 is a continuous design.

End of World War II, 50th Anniv.
Common Design Types

Designs: No. 646, CS Lady Denison Pender. No. 647, HMS Dragon. No. 648, RFA Darkdale. No. 649, HMS Hermes. No. 650, St. Helena Rifles on parade. No. 651, Gov. Maj. W.J. Bain Gray during Victory Parade. No. 652, 6-inch gun, Ladder Hill. No. 653, Signal Station, flag hoist signalling VICTORY.
No. 654, Reverse of War Medal 1939-45.

1995, May 8	**Wmk. 373**	*Perf. 14*	
646 CD351	5p multicolored	.16	.16
647 CD351	5p multicolored	.16	.16
a.	Pair, #646-647	.32	.32
648 CD351	12p multicolored	.38	.38
649 CD351	12p multicolored	.38	.38
a.	Pair, #648-649	.75	.75
650 CD351	25p multicolored	.75	.75
651 CD351	25p multicolored	.75	.75
a.	Pair, #650-651	1.50	1.50
652 CD351	53p multicolored	1.65	1.65
653 CD351	53p multicolored	1.65	1.65
a.	Pair, #652-653	3.25	3.25
	Nos. 646-653 (8)	5.88	5.88

Souvenir Sheet

654 CD352	£1 multicolored	3.25	3.25

Invertebrates — A117

Designs: 12p, Blushing snail. 25p, Golden sail spider. 53p, Spiky yellow woodlouse. 60p, St. Helena shore crab. £1, Giant earwig.

1995, Aug. 29		**Wmk. 373**	*Perf. 14*
655 A117	12p multicolored	.40	.40
656 A117	25p multicolored	.80	.80
657 A117	53p multicolored	1.75	1.75
658 A117	60p multicolored	2.00	2.00
	Nos. 655-658 (4)	4.95	4.95

Souvenir Sheet

659 A117	£1 multicolored	3.25	3.25

Souvenir Sheet

Orchids — A118

Designs: a, Epidendrum ibaguense. b, Vanda Miss Joquim.

Perf. 14¹/₂x14

1995, Sept. 1   **Wmk. 384**
660 A118 50p Sheet of 2, #a.-b.   2.00 2.00
    Singapore '95.

Christmas
A119

Children's drawings: 12p, Christmas Eve in Jamestown. 15p, Santa, musicians. 25p, Party at Blue Hill Community Center. 38p, Santa walking in Jamestown. 60p, RMS St. Helena.

Perf. 14x14¹/₂

1995, Oct. 17 **Litho.** **Wmk. 373**
661 A119 12p multicolored   .40 .40
662 A119 15p multicolored   .45 .45
663 A119 25p multicolored   .80 .80
664 A119 38p multicolored   1.20 1.20
665 A119 60p multicolored   1.90 1.90
    Nos. 661-665 (5)   4.75 4.75

SEMI-POSTAL STAMPS

Catalogue values for unused stamps in this section are for Never Hinged items.

Tristan da Cunha Nos. 46, 49-51 Overprinted "ST. HELENA / Tristan Relief" and Surcharged with New Value and "+"

Perf. 12¹/₂x13

1961, Oct. 12 **Wmk. 314** **Engr.**
B1 A3 2¹/₂c + 3p   425.
B2 A3 5c + 6p   425.
B3 A3 7¹/₂c + 9p   500.
B4 A3 10c + 1sh   600.
    Nos. B1-B4 (4)   5,000. 1,950.

Withdrawn from sale Oct. 19.

POSTAGE DUE STAMPS

Catalogue values for unused stamps in this section are for Never Hinged items.

Map — D1

Perf. 15x14

1986, June 9 **Litho.** **Wmk. 384**
    Background Color
J1 D1 1p tan   .15 .15
J2 D1 2p orange   .15 .15
J3 D1 5p vermilion   .15 .15
J4 D1 7p violet   .22 .22
J5 D1 10p chalky blue   .30 .30
J6 D1 25p dull yel grn   .78 .78
    Nos. J1-J6 (6)   1.75 1.75

WAR TAX STAMPS

No. 62a
Surcharged

ONE PENNY

1916 **Wmk. 3** **Perf. 14**
MR1 A10 1p + 1p scarlet & blk   .60 .60
  a. Double surcharge   9,500.

WAR TAX

No. 62
Surcharged

1919
MR2 A10 1p + 1p carmine & blk   .40 .40

SAMOA

sə-ˈmō-ə

(Western Samoa)

LOCATION — Archipelago in the south Pacific Ocean, east of Fiji
GOVT. — Independent state; former territory mandated by New Zealand
AREA — 1,093 sq. mi.
POP. — 156,349 (1981)
CAPITAL — Apia

In 1861-99, Samoa was an independent kingdom under the influence of the US, to which the harbor of Pago Pago had been ceded, and that of Great Britain and Germany. In 1898 a disturbance arose, resulting in the withdrawal of Great Britain, and the partitioning of the islands between Germany and the US. Early in World War I the islands under German domination were occupied by New Zealand troops and in 1920 the League of Nations declared them a mandate to New Zealand. Western Samoa became independent Jan. 1, 1962. See Vol. 5 for German issues.

12 Pence = 1 Shilling
20 Shillings = 1 Pound
100 Sene (Cents) = 1 Tala (Dollar) (1967)

Catalogue values for unused stamps in this country are for Never Hinged items, beginning with Scott 191 in the regular postage section, Scott B1 in the semi-postal section and Scott C1 in the air post section.

Watermarks

Wmk. 62- NZ and
Star Wide Apart

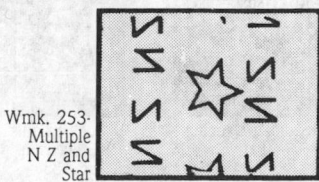

Wmk. 253-
Multiple
N Z and
Star

Wmk. 355- Kava Bowl and WS, Multiple

Issues of the Kingdom

A1

Type I - Line above "X" is usually unbroken. Dots over "SAMOA" are uniform and evenly spaced. Upper right serif of "M" is horizontal.
Type II - Line above "X" is usually broken. Small dot near upper right serif of "M."
Type III - Line above "X" roughly retouched. Upper right serif of "M" bends down.
Type IV - Speck of color on curved line below center of "M."

Perf. 12, 12¹/₂

1877-82 **Litho.** **Unwmk.**
1 A1 1p blue (III) ('79)   25.00 40.00
  a. 1p ultra (III) ('79)   30.00 40.00
  b. 1p ultra (I) ('78)   90.00 90.00
  c. 1p ultra (I) ('77)   250.00 100.00
2 A1 2p lil rose (IV) ('82)   25.00
3 A1 3p ver (III) ('79)   50.00 70.00
  a. 3p brt scarlet (III)   50.00 70.00
  b. 3p scarlet (II) ('77)   250.00 125.00
  c. 3p deep scarlet (I) ('77)   250.00 125.00
4 A1 6p violet (III) ('79)   42.50 47.50
  a. 6p violet (II) ('78)   165.00 85.00
  b. 6p violet (I) ('77)   275.00 90.00
5 A1 9p yel brn (IV) ('80)   62.50 125.00
  a. 9p orange brown (IV) ('80)   62.50 125.00
6 A1 1sh org yel (II) ('78)   70.00 85.00
  a. 1sh dull yellow (I) ('77)   150.00 100.00
7 A1 2sh dp brn (III) ('79)   125.00 200.00
  a. 2sh red brown (II) ('78)   275.00 175.00
  b. 2sh brown (II) ('78)   250.00 300.00
8 A1 5sh yel grn (III) ('79)   425.00 550.00
  a. 5sh deep green (III) ('79)   425.00 550.00
  b. 5sh gray green (II) ('78)   1,750. 1,250.

The 1p often has a period after "PENNY." The 2p was never placed in use since the Samoa Express service was discontinued late in 1881.
Imperforates of this issue are proofs. pSheets of the first issue were not perforated around the outer sides. All values except the 2p were printed in sheets of 10 (2x5). The 1p, 3p and 6p type I and the 1p type III were also printed in sheets of 20 (4x5), and six stamps on each of these sheets were perforated all around. The 2p was printed in sheets of 21 (3x7) and five stamps in the second row were perforated all around. These are the only varieties of the original stamps which have not one or two imperforate edges.
Reprints are of type IV and nearly always perforated on all sides. They have a spot of color at the edge of the panel below the "M." This spot is not on any originals except the 2p, which may be distinguished by its color, and the 9p which may be distinguished by having a rough blind perf. 12.
Forgeries exist.

Palms — A2   King Malietoa Laupera — A3

1895-99 **Typo.** **Wmk. 62** **Perf. 11**
9 A2 ¹/₂p brown vio   .65 1.75
10 A2 ¹/₂p green ('99)   .65 1.40
11 A2 1p green   1.25 1.75
12 A2 1p red brown ('99)   .55 1.25
13 A2 2p brt yellow   5.00 1.00
14 A2 2¹/₂p rose   .80 4.50
15 A3 2¹/₂p blk, perf. 10x11 ('96)   .90 3.00
  a. Perf. 11   75.00 65.00
16 A2 4p blue   1.00 2.00
17 A2 6p maroon   1.75 3.00
18 A2 1sh rose   1.50 3.75
19 A2 2sh6p red violet   4.75 7.50
  c. Vert. pair, imperf. btwn.   400.00
    Nos. 9-19 (11)   18.80 30.90

1886-92   **Perf. 12¹/₂**
9a A2 ¹/₂p brown violet   17.00 35.00
11a A2 1p green   6.50 12.00
13a A2 2p orange   14.00 8.50
14a A3 2¹/₂p rose ('92)   22.50 4.75
16a A2 4p blue   25.00 8.50
17a A2 6p maroon   750.00

18a A2 1sh rose   65.00 8.00
  c. Diagonal half used as 6p on cover   350.00
19a A2 2sh6p purple   60.00 60.00
    Nos. 9a-16a,18a-19a (7)   210.00 136.75

1887-92   **Perf. 12x11¹/₂**
9b A2 ¹/₂p brown violet   2.50 2.50
11b A2 1p green   15.00 1.40
13b A2 2p brown orange   18.00 1.75
14b A3 2¹/₂p rose ('92)   75.00 3.50
16b A2 4p blue   125.00 5.00
17b A2 6p maroon   22.50 8.00
18b A2 1sh rose   250.00 4.00
19b A2 2sh6p red violet   325.00 8.00
    Nos. 9b-19b (8)   833.00 34.65

Three forms of watermark 62 are found on stamps of type A2:
1 - Wide "N Z" and wide star, 6mm apart (used 1886-87).
2 - Wide "N Z" and narrow star, 4mm apart (1890).
3 - Narrow "NZ" and narrow star, 7mm apart (1890-1900). The 2¹/₂p has only the 3rd form.
For surcharges or overprints on stamps or types of design A2 see Nos. 20-22, 24-38.

No. 16b Handstamp Surcharged in Black or Red:

FIVE PENCE   **FIVE PENCE**   **5d**

    a   b   c

1893   **Perf. 12x11¹/₂**
20 A2(a) 5p on 4p blue   45.00 45.00
21 A2(b) 5p on 4p blue   60.00 100.00
22 A2(c) 5p on 4p blue (R)   15.00 22.50
    Nos. 20-22 (3)   140.00 167.50

As the surcharges on Nos. 20-21 were hand-stamped in two steps and on No. 22 in three steps, various varieties exist.

Flag Design — A7

1894-95 **Typo.** **Perf. 11¹/₂x12**
23 A7 5p vermilion   18.00 2.50
  a. Perf. 11 ('95)   10.00 7.00

Types of 1887-1895 Surcharged in Blue, Black, Red or Green:

Surcharged   **R**

1¹/₂d.   **3d.**

1¹/₂p, 2¹/₂p   3p

1895   **Perf. 11**
24 A2 1¹/₂p on 2p orange (Bl)   1.50 3.75
  a. 1¹/₂p on 2p brn org, perf. 12x11¹/₂ (Bl)   7.50 5.50
  b. 1¹/₂p on 2p yellow, "2" ends with vertical stroke   2.50 22.50
25 A2 3p on 2p orange (Bk)   6.00 8.00
  a. 3p on 2p brn org, perf. 12x11¹/₂ (Bk)   25.00 8.50
  b. 3p on 2p yel, perf. 11 (Bk)   75.00 60.00
  c. Vert. pair, imperf. btwn.   425.00

1898-1900   **Perf. 11**
26 A2 2¹/₂p on 1sh rose (Bk)   3.50 9.00
  a. Double surcharge   425.00
27 A2 2¹/₂p on 2sh6p vio (Bk)   4.75 12.00
28 A2 2¹/₂p on 1p bl grn (R)   .55 2.25
  a. Inverted surcharge   425.00
29 A2 2¹/₂p on 1sh rose (R)   3.50 9.00
30 A2 3p on 2p orange (G)   5.00 6.25
    Nos. 26-30 (5)   13.80

No. 30 was a reissue, available for postage.

Stamps of 1886-99 Overprinted in Red or Blue

PROVISIONAL

GOVT.

1899
31 A2 ¹/₂p green (R)   .30 1.40
32 A2 1p red brown (Bl)   1.00 3.00
33 A2 2p orange (R)   .90 3.50
    2p yellow   .80 3.50
34 A2 4p blue (R)   .45 3.25
35 A7 5p scarlet (Bl)   .90 4.75
36 A2 6p maroon (Bl)   1.00 4.00

37	A2 1sh rose (Bl)	1.40	12.00
38	A2 2sh6p violet (R)	4.50	*18.00*
	Nos. 31-38 (8)	10.45	*49.90*

In 1900 the Samoan islands were partitioned between the US and Germany. The part which became American has since used US stamps.

Issued under British Dominion

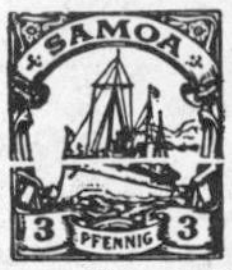

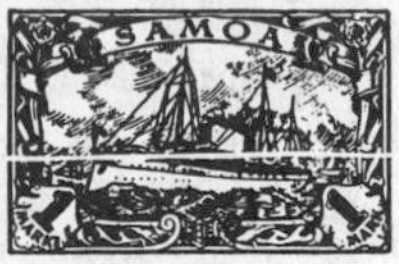

Kaiser's Yacht "Hohenzollern"
A12 A13

Stamps of German Samoa Surcharged:

G.R.I. 2½ d. — On A12
G.R.I. 1 Shillings. — On A13

1914 **Unwmk.** ***Perf. 14***

101	A12 ½p on 3pf brown	20.00	9.00
a.	Double surcharge	500.00	400.00
b.	Fraction bar omitted	50.00	30.00
c.	Comma after "I"	435.00	360.00
102	A12 ½p on 5pf green	42.50	10.00
a.	Double surcharge	450.00	325.00
b.	Fraction bar omitted	125.00	55.00
d.	Comma after "I"	360.00	300.00
103	A12 1p on 10pf car	100.00	40.00
a.	Double surcharge	375.00	375.00
104	A12 2½p on 20pf ultra	30.00	10.00
a.	Fraction bar omitted	65.00	37.50
b.	Inverted surcharge	725.00	650.00
c.	Double surcharge	650.00	600.00
d.	Commas after "I"	375.00	310.00
105	A12 3p on 25pf org & blk, *yel*	50.00	40.00
a.	Double surcharge	425.00	360.00
b.	Comma after "I"	4,000.	800.00
106	A12 4p on 30pf org & blk, *sal*	110.00	57.50
107	A12 5p on 40pf lake & blk	110.00	70.00
108	A12 6p on 50pf pur & blk, *sal*	55.00	35.00
a.	Inverted "9" for "6"	165.00	110.00
b.	Double surcharge	500.00	500.00
109	A12 9p on 80pf lake & blk, *rose*	200.00	82.50

Perf. 14½x14

110	A13 1sh on 1m car ("1 Shillings.")	3,000.	2,000.
a.	"1 Shilling."	*9,500.*	*7,000.*
111	A13 2sh on 2m blue	3,500.	3,500.
112	A13 3sh on 3m blk vio	1,200.	750.00
a.	Double surcharge	*7,500.*	*7,500.*
113	A13 5sh on 5m slate & car	850.00	800.00

G.R.I. stands for Georgius Rex Imperator.
The 3d on 30pf and 4d on 40pf were produced at a later time.

Stamps of New Zealand Overprinted in Red or Blue:

SAMOA. k — **SAMOA.** m

Perf. 14, 14x13½, 14x14½

1914, Sept. 29 **Wmk. 61**

114	A41(k) ½p yellow grn (R)	.30	.30
115	A42(k) 1p carmine	.30	.15
116	A41(k) 2p mauve (R)	.60	.95
117	A22(m) 2½p blue (R)	1.50	1.75
118	A41(k) 6p car rose, perf. 14x14½	1.50	1.75
a.	Perf. 14x13½	17.00	20.00
119	A41(k) 1sh vermilion	3.50	*10.00*
	Nos. 114-119 (6)	7.70	*14.90*

Overprinted Type "m"

1914-25 ***Perf. 14, 14½x14***

120	PF1 2sh blue (R)	4.00	*5.50*
121	PF1 2sh6p brown (Bl)	4.50	*8.50*
122	PF1 3sh vio (R) ('22)	12.00	*32.50*
123	PF1 5sh green (R)	9.00	*11.00*
124	PF1 10sh red brown (Bl)	20.00	*27.50*
125	PF2 £1 rose (Bl)	52.50	*45.00*
126	PF2 £2 vio (R) ('25)	350.00	
	Nos. 120-126 (7)	452.00	

Postal use of the £2 is questioned.

Overprinted Type "k"
Perf. 14x13½, 14x14½

1916-19 **Typo.**

127	A43 ½p yellow grn (R)	.15	.18
128	A47 1½p gray blk (R) ('17)	.22	.25
129	A47 1½p brn org (R) ('19)	.18	.25
130	A43 2p yellow (R) ('18)	.38	.30
131	A43 3p chocolate (Bl)	1.25	3.00

Engr.

132	A44 2½p dull blue (R)	.50	.55
133	A45 3p violet brn (Bl)	.50	.65
134	A45 6p carmine rose (Bl)	1.40	1.50
135	A45 1sh vermilion (Bl)	1.75	1.75
	Nos. 127-135 (9)	6.33	8.43

Overprinted Type "k" On New Zealand Victory Issue of 1919

1920, June ***Perf. 14***

136	A48 ½p yellow grn (R)	1.75	.40
137	A49 1p carmine (Bl)	1.50	.50
138	A50 1½p brown org (R)	1.25	1.10
139	A51 3p black brn (Bl)	4.75	4.25
140	A52 6p purple (R)	3.50	5.00
141	A53 1sh vermilion (Bl)	11.00	10.00
	Nos. 136-141 (6)	23.75	21.25

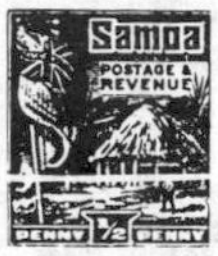

British Flag and Samoan House — A22

1921, Dec. 23 **Engr.** ***Perf. 14x13½***

142	A22 ½p green	.32	.32
a.	Perf. 14x14½	.50	.60
143	A22 1p lake	.32	.20
a.	Perf. 14x14½	.32	.42
144	A22 1½p orange brn, perf. 14x14½	.48	.55
a.	Perf. 14x13½	3.00	3.25
145	A22 2p yel, perf. 14x14½	.48	.48
a.	Perf. 14x13½	1.90	1.50
146	A22 2½p dull blue	.75	.75
147	A22 3p dark brown	1.65	1.75
148	A22 4p violet	1.50	1.75
149	A22 5p brt blue	1.50	1.75
150	A22 6p carmine rose	2.25	2.50
151	A22 8p red brown	3.00	3.50
152	A22 9p olive green	3.00	3.50
153	A22 1sh vermilion	4.00	4.25
	Nos. 142-153 (12)	19.25	21.30

For overprints see Nos. 163-165.

New Zealand Nos. 182-183 Overprinted Type "m" in Red

1926-27 ***Perf. 14½x14***

154	A56 2sh dark blue	4.50	*8.75*
a.	2sh blue ('27)	10.00	*20.00*
155	A56 3sh deep violet	10.00	*20.00*
a.	3sh violet ('27)	42.50	*55.00*

Issue dates: 2sh, Nov., 3sh, Oct., Nos. 154a, 155a, Nov. 10.

New Zealand Postal-Fiscal Stamps, Overprinted Type "m" in Blue or Red

1932, Aug. ***Perf. 14***

156	PF5 2sh6p brown	15.00	*25.00*
157	PF5 5sh green (R)	18.00	*32.50*
158	PF5 10sh lake	40.00	70.00
159	PF5 £1 pink	55.00	*80.00*
160	PF5 £2 violet (R)	*700.00*	
161	PF5 £5 dark blue (R)	*1,800.*	

See Nos. 175-180, 195-202, 216-219.

Silver Jubilee Issue

Stamps of 1921 Overprinted in Black

SILVER JUBILEE OF KING GEORGE V 1910 - 1935.

1935, May 7 ***Perf. 14x13½***

163	A22 1p lake	.28	.30
a.	Perf. 14x14½	*75.00*	*110.00*
164	A22 2½p dull blue	.80	.95
165	A22 6p carmine rose	3.00	3.00
	Nos. 163-165 (3)	4.08	4.25

25th anniv. of the reign of George V.

Western Samoa

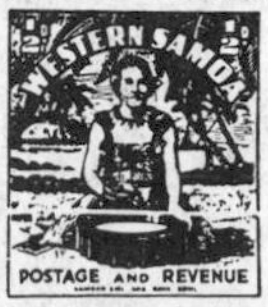

Samoan Girl and Kava Bowl — A23

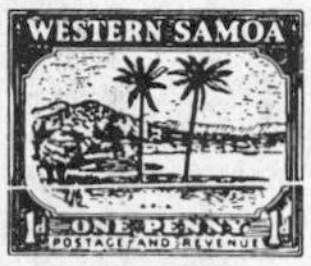

View of Apia — A24

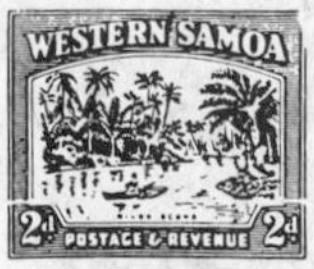

River Scene — A25

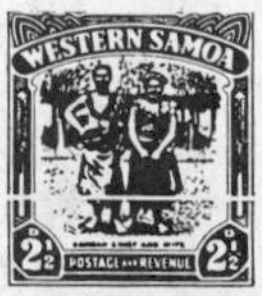

Samoan Chief and Wife — A26

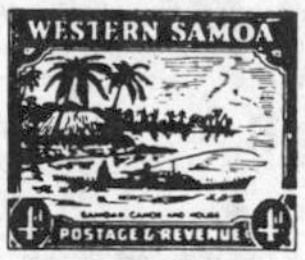

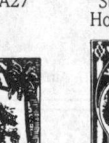

Samoan Canoe and House — A27

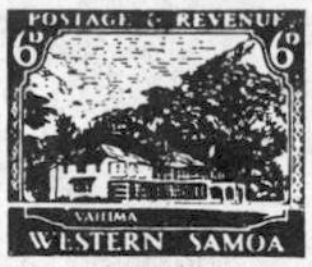

"Vailima," Stevenson's Home — A28

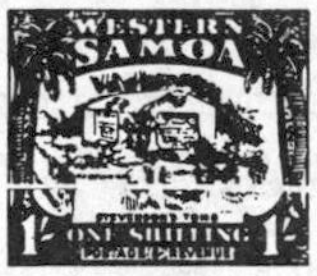

Stevenson's Tomb — A29

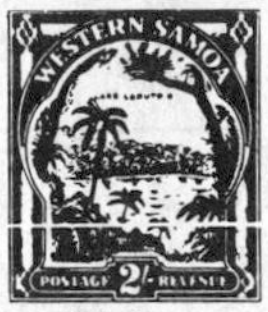

Lake Lanuto'o — A30

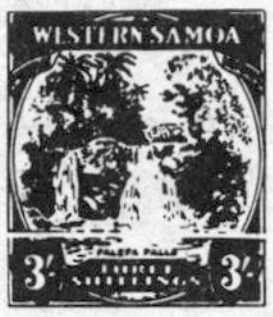

Falefa Falls — A31

Perf. 14x13½, 13½x14

1935, Aug. 7 **Engr.** **Wmk. 61**

166	A23 ½p yellow grn	.15	.15
167	A24 1p car lake & blk	.15	.15
168	A25 2p red org & blk, perf. 14	.40	.40
a.	Perf. 13½x14	1.40	2.75
169	A26 2½p dp blue & blk	.22	.22
170	A27 4p blk brn & dk gray	.50	.50
171	A28 6p plum	.50	.50
172	A29 1sh brown & violet	.80	.80
173	A30 2sh red brn & yel grn	1.25	1.25
174	A31 3sh org brn & brt bl	2.00	2.00
	Nos. 166-174 (9)	5.97	5.97

See Nos. 186-188.

Postal-Fiscal Stamps of New Zealand Overprinted in Blue or Carmine

WESTERN SAMOA.

1935 ***Perf. 14***

175	PF5 2sh6p brown	5.00	*12.50*
176	PF5 5sh green	10.00	*15.00*
177	PF5 10sh dp carmine	40.00	*55.00*
178	PF5 £1 pink	55.00	*80.00*
179	PF5 £2 violet (C)	125.00	*250.00*
180	PF5 £5 dark blue (C)	300.00	*500.00*
	Nos. 175-180 (6)	535.00	*912.50*

See Nos. 195-202, 216-219.

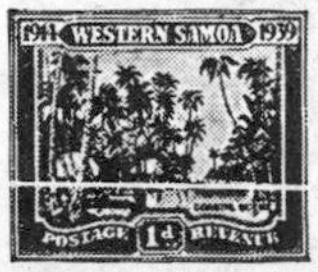

Samoan Coastal Village — A32

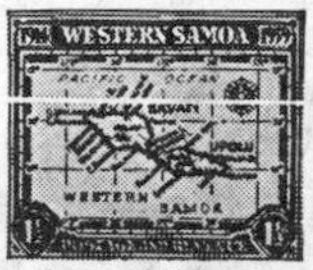

Map of Western Samoa — A33

Samoan Dancing Party A34

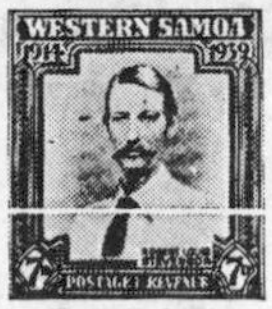

Robert Louis Stevenson A35

Perf. 13½x14

1939, Aug. 29 **Engr.** **Wmk. 253**

181	A32 1p scar & olive	.25	.25
182	A33 1½p copper brn & bl	.50	.50
183	A34 2½p dk blue & brn	1.00	1.00

Perf. 14x13½

184	A35 7p dp sl grn & vio	6.00	2.00
	Nos. 181-184 (4)	7.75	3.75

25th anniv. of New Zealand's control of the mandated territory of Western Samoa.

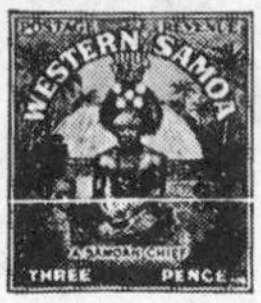

Samoan Chief — A36

1940, Sept. 2 ***Perf. 14x13½***

185	A36 3p on 1½p brown	.15	.15

Types of 1935 and A37

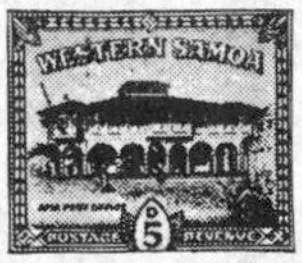

Apia Post Office — A37

1944-49 **Wmk. 253** ***Perf. 14***

186	A23 ½p yellow green	.38	.38
187	A25 2p red orange & blk	.50	.50
188	A26 2½p dp blue & blk ('48)	1.25	1.25

Perf. 13½x14

189	A37 5p dp ultra & ol brn ('49)	.25	.25
	Nos. 186-189 (4)	2.38	2.38

Issue date: 5p, June 8.

Catalogue values for unused stamps in this section, from this point to the end of the section, are for Never Hinged items.

Peace Issue

New Zealand Nos. 248, 250, 254, and 255 Overprinted in Black or Blue

WESTERN SAMOA p — **WESTERN SAMOA** q

1946, June 1 ***Perf. 13x13½, 13½x13***

191	A94(p) 1p emerald	.15	.15
192	A96(q) 2p rose violet (Bl)	.15	.15
193	A100(p) 6p org red & red brn	.25	.25
194	A101(p) 8p brn lake & blk (Bl)	.30	.30
	Nos. 191-194 (4)	.85	.85

Stamps and Type of New Zealand, 1931-50 Overprinted Like Nos. 175-180 in Blue or Carmine

1945-50 **Wmk. 253** ***Perf. 14***

195	PF5 2sh6p brown	1.10	2.25
196	PF5 5sh green	4.25	5.25
197	PF5 10sh carmine ('48)	13.00	13.00
198	PF5 £1 pink ('48)	47.50	50.00
199	PF5 30sh choc ('48)	125.00	150.00
200	PF5 £2 violet (C)	140.00	150.00
201	PF5 £3 lt green ('50)	175.00	225.00
202	PF5 £5 dk bl (C) ('50)	300.00	350.00

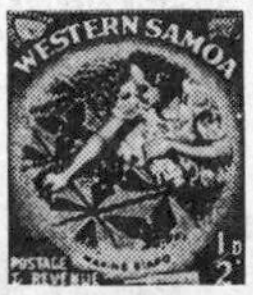

Making Siapo Cloth — A38

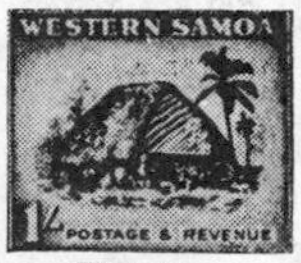

Thatching Hut — A40

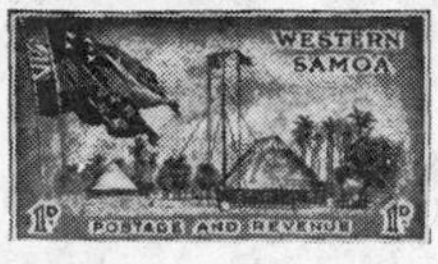

Western Samoa and New Zealand Flags, Village A39

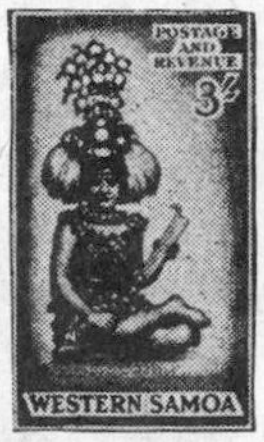

Samoan Chieftainess — A41

Designs: 2p, Western Samoa seal. 3p, Aleisa Falls (actually Malifa Falls). 5p, Manumea (tooth-billed pigeon). 6p, Fishing canoe. 8p, Harvesting cacao. 2sh, Preparing copra.

Perf. 13, 13½x13

1952, Mar. 10 Engr. Wmk. 253

203	A38	½p org brn & claret	.15	.15
204	A39	1p green & olive	.18	.15
205	A38	2p deep carmine	.24	.20
206	A39	3p indigo & blue	.38	.32
207	A38	5p dk grn & org brn	.55	.45
208	A39	6p dp rose pink & bl	.60	.50
209	A39	8p rose carmine	.90	.70
210	A40	1sh blue & brown	1.10	.90
211	A39	2sh yellow brown	2.75	2.25
212	A41	3sh ol gray & vio brn	4.75	3.75
		Nos. 203-212 (10)	11.60	9.37

Coronation Issue

Types of New Zealand 1953

1953, May 25 Photo. *Perf. 14x14½*

214	A113	2p brown	.38	.38
215	A114	6p slate black	1.10	1.10

Type of New Zealand 1944-52 Overprinted in Blue or Carmine

WESTERN

SAMOA

Wmk. 253

1955, Nov. 14 Typo. *Perf. 14*

216	PF5	5sh yellow green	9.50	15.00
217	PF5	10sh carmine rose	12.00	19.00
218	PF5	£1 dull rose	26.00	35.00
219	PF5	£2 violet (C)	62.50	115.00
		Nos. 216-219 (4)	110.00	184.00

Redrawn Types of 1952 and

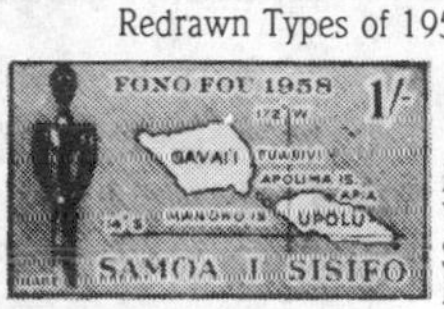

Map of Western Samoa and Mace — A42

Designs: 4p, as 1p. 6p, as 2p.

Inscribed: "Fono Fou 1958" and "Samoa I Sisifo"

Perf. 13½x13, 13

1958, Mar. 21 Engr. Wmk. 253

220	A39	4p rose carmine	.18	.18
221	A38	6p dull purple	.18	.18
222	A42	1sh light violet blue	.32	.32
		Nos. 220-222 (3)	.68	.68

INDEPENDENT STATE

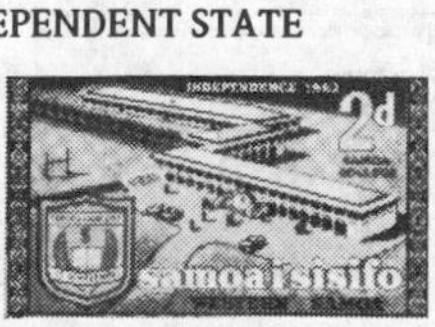

Samoa College A43

Designs: 1p, Woman holding ceremonial mat, vert. 3p, Public Library. 4p, Fono House (Parliament). 6p, Map of Western Samoa, ship and plane. 8p, Faleolo airport. 1sh, Talking chief with fly whisk, vert. 1sh3p, Government House, Vailima. 2sh6p, Flag of Western Samoa. 5sh, State Seal.

Perf. 13½

1962, July 2 Wmk. 253 Litho.

223	A43	1p carmine & brown	.15	.15
224	A43	2p org, lt grn, red & brown	.15	.15
225	A43	3p blue, grn & brn	.22	.22
226	A43	4p dk grn, bl & car	.35	.35
227	A43	6p yel, grn & ultra	.42	.42
228	A43	8p blue & emerald	.55	.55
229	A43	1sh brt grn & brn	.85	.85
230	A43	1sh3p blue & emerald	1.10	1.10
231	A43	2sh6p vio blue & red	1.65	1.65
232	A43	5sh olive gray, red & dk blue	4.00	4.00
		Nos. 223-232 (10)	9.44	9.44

Western Samoa's independence. See #242-247.

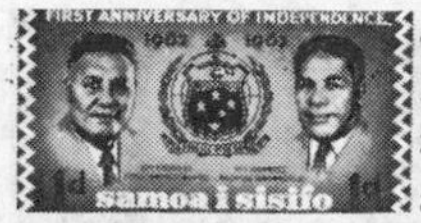

Tupua Tamasese Mea'ole, Malietoa Tanumafili II and Seal — A44

1963, Oct. 1 Photo. *Perf. 14*

233	A44	1p green & blk	.15	.15
234	A44	4p dull blue & blk	.15	.15
235	A44	8p carmine rose & blk	.16	.16
236	A44	2sh orange & blk	.42	.42
		Set value	.70	.70

First anniversary of independence.

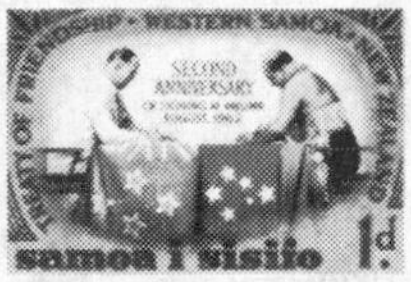

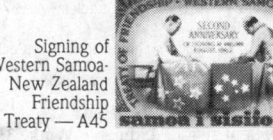

Signing of Western Samoa-New Zealand Friendship Treaty — A45

1964, Sept. 1 Unwmk. *Perf. 13½*

237	A45	1p multicolored	.15	.15
238	A45	8p multicolored	.15	.15
239	A45	2sh multicolored	.32	.32
240	A45	3sh multicolored	.45	.45
		Nos. 237-240 (4)	1.07	1.07

2nd anniv. of the signing of the Treaty of Friendship between Western Samoa and New Zealand. Signers: J. B. Wright, N. Z. High Commissioner for Western Pacific, and Fiame Mata'afa, Prime Minister of Western Samoa.

Type of 1962

Perf. 13½

1965, Oct. 4 Litho. Wmk. 355

242	A43	1p carmine & brn	.35	.35
243	A43	3p blue, grn & brn	30.00	12.00
244	A43	4p dk green, bl & car	.35	.35
245	A43	6p yellow, grn & ultra	.38	.38
246	A43	8p blue & emerald	.45	.45
247	A43	1sh brt green & brn	.60	.60
		Nos. 242-247 (6)	32.13	14.13

For surcharge see No. B1.

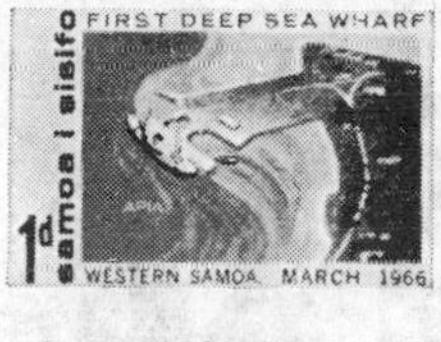

Aerial View of Deep-Sea Wharf A46

Design: 8p, 2sh, View of Apia harbor and deep-sea wharf.

1966, Mar. 2 Photo. *Perf. 13½*

251	A46	1p multicolored	.15	.15
252	A46	8p multicolored	.15	.15
253	A46	2sh multicolored	.32	.32
254	A46	3sh multicolored	.50	.50
		Nos. 251-254 (4)	1.12	1.12

Opening of Western Samoa's first deep-sea wharf at Apia.

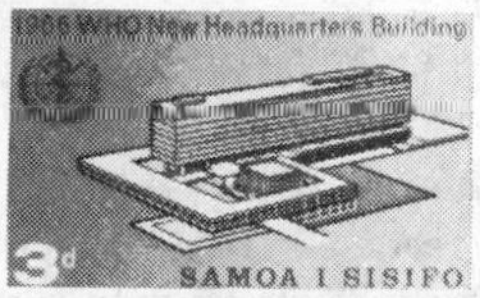

Inauguration of WHO Headquarters, Geneva — A47

Design: 4p, 1sh, WHO building and flag.

1966, July 4 Photo. Wmk. 355

255	A47	3p gray, ultra & bister	.15	.15
256	A47	4p multicolored	.15	.15
257	A47	6p lt olive grn, pur & grn	.25	.25
258	A47	1sh multicolored	.50	.50
		Nos. 255-258 (4)	1.05	1.05

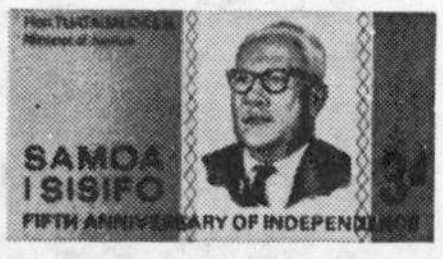

Tuatagaloa L.S., Minister of Justice A48

Designs: 8p, F.C.F. Nelson, Minister of Works, Marine and Civil Aviation. 2sh, To'omata T. L., Minister of Lands. 3sh, Fa'alava'au Galu, Minister of Post Office, Radio and Broadcasting.

Perf. 14½x14

1967, Jan. 16 Photo. Wmk. 355

259	A48	3p violet & sepia	.15	.15
260	A48	8p blue & sepia	.16	.16
261	A48	2sh lt olive grn & sepia	.30	.30
262	A48	3sh lilac rose & sepia	.48	.48
		Nos. 259-262 (4)	1.09	1.09

Fifth anniversary of Independence.

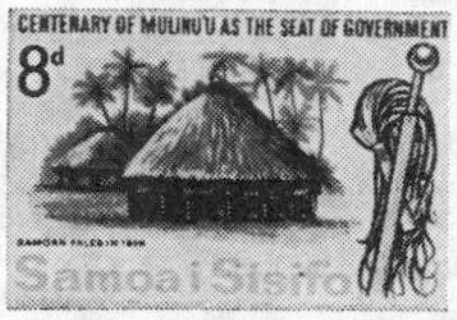

Samoan Fales, 1900, and Fly Whisk A49

Design: 1sh, Fono House (Parliament) and mace.

1967, May 16 *Perf. 14½*

263	A49	8p multicolored	.20	.20
264	A49	1sh multicolored	.30	.30

Centenary of Mulinu'u as Government Seat.

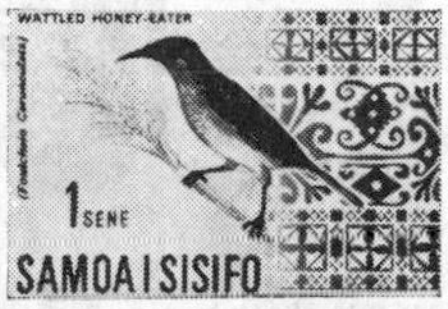

Wattled Honey-Eater A50

Birds of Western Samoa: 2s, Pacific pigeon. 3s, Samoan starling. 5s, Samoan broadbill. 7s, Red-headed parrot finch. 10s, Purple swamp hen. 20s, Barn owl. 25s, Tooth-billed pigeon. 50s, Island thrush. $1, Samoan fantail. $2, Mao (gymnomyza samoensis). $4, Samoan white-eye (zosterops samoensis).

Perf. 14x14½

1967, July 10 Photo. Wmk. 355

Birds in Natural Colors

Size: 37x24mm

265	A50	1s black & lt brown	.15	.15
266	A50	2s lt ultra, blk & brn org	.15	.15
267	A50	3s black, lt brn & emer	.15	.15
268	A50	5s lilac, blk & vio bl	.22	.18
269	A50	7s blk, vio bl & gray	.30	.25
270	A50	10s Prus blue & blk	.45	.38
271	A50	20s dk gray & blue	.95	.75
272	A50	25s pink, blk & dk grn	1.10	.95
273	A50	50s brn, blk & lt ol grn	2.25	1.90
274	A50	$1 yellow & black	4.50	3.75

1969 Size: 43x28mm *Perf. 13½*

274A	A50	$2 blk & lt grnsh bl	11.00	9.25
274B	A50	$4 dp orange & blk	37.50	40.00
		Nos. 265-274B (12)	58.72	57.86

For surcharge see No. 294.

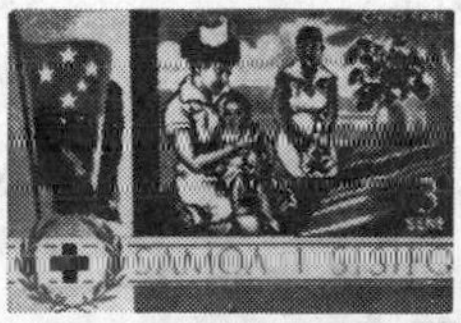

Child Care A51

Designs: 7s, Leprosarium. 20s, Mobile X-ray unit. 25s, Apia Hospital.

1967, Dec. 1 Litho. *Perf. 14*

275	A51	3s multicolored	.15	.15
276	A51	7s multicolored	.15	.15
277	A51	20s multicolored	.38	.38
278	A51	25s multicolored	.50	.50
		Nos. 275-278 (4)	1.18	1.18

South Pacific Health Service.

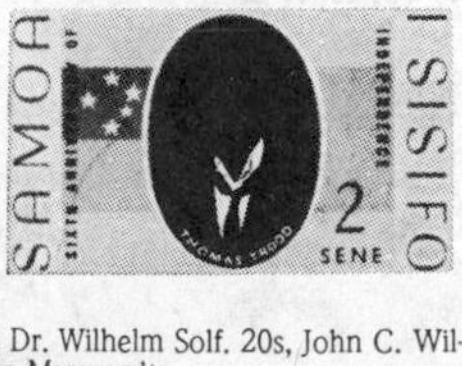

Thomas Trood A52

Portraits: 7s, Dr. Wilhelm Solf. 20s, John C. Williams. 25s, Fritz Marquardt.

1968, Jan. 1 Unwmk. *Perf. 13½*

279	A52	2s multicolored	.15	.15
280	A52	7s multicolored	.15	.15
281	A52	20s multicolored	.32	.32
282	A52	25s multicolored	.38	.38
		Nos. 279-282 (4)	1.00	1.00

Sixth anniversary of independence.

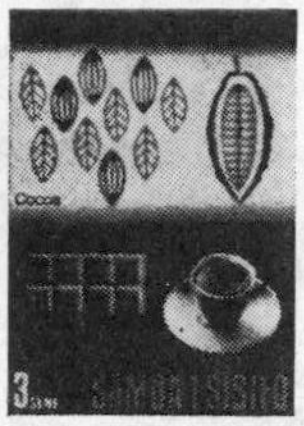

Samoan Agricultural Development — A53

Perf. 13x12½

1968, Feb. 15 Photo. Wmk. 355

283	A53	3s Cocoa	.15	.15
284	A53	5s Breadfruit	.15	.15
285	A53	10s Copra	.22	.22
286	A53	20s Bananas	.45	.45
		Nos. 283-286 (4)	.97	.97

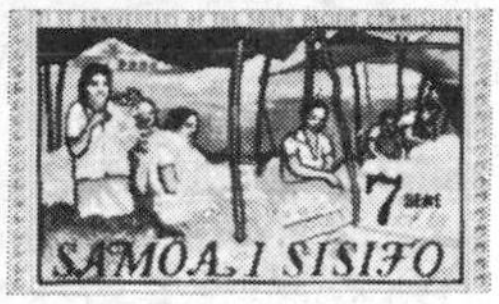

Curio Vendors, Pago Pago A54

Designs: 20s, Palm trees at the shore. 25s, A'Umi Beach.

Perf. 14½x14

1968, Apr. 22 Photo. Wmk. 355

287	A54	7s multicolored	.15	.15
288	A54	20s multicolored	.32	.32
289	A54	25s multicolored	.42	.42
		Nos. 287-289 (3)	.89	.89

South Pacific Commission, 21st anniv.

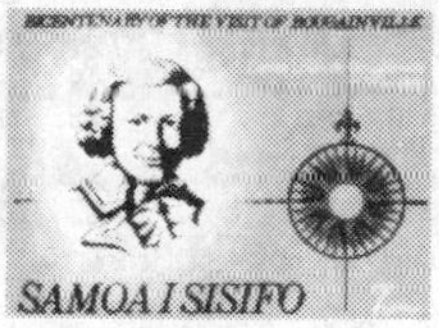

Bougainville and Compass Rose — A55

Designs: 3s, Map showing Western Samoa Archipelago and Bougainville's route. 20s, Bougainvillea. 25s, Bougainville's ships La Boudeuse and L'Etoile.

1968, June 10 Litho. *Perf. 14*

290	A55	3s brt blue & blk	.15	.15
291	A55	7s ocher & blk	.15	.15
292	A55	20s grnsh blk, brt rose & grn	.50	.50
293	A55	25s brt lil, vio, blk & org	.65	.65
		Nos. 290-293 (4)	1.45	1.45

200th anniv. of the visit of Louis Antoine de Bougainville (1729-1811) to Samoa.

No. 270 Surcharged with New Value, Three Bars and: "1928-1968 / KINGSFORD-SMITH / TRANSPACIFIC FLIGHT"

1968, June 13 Photo. *Perf. 14x14½*

294	A50	20s on 10s multicolored	.35	.35

40th anniv. of the 1st Transpacific flight under Capt. Charles Kingsford-Smith (Oakland, CA to Brisbane, Australia, via Honolulu and Fiji).

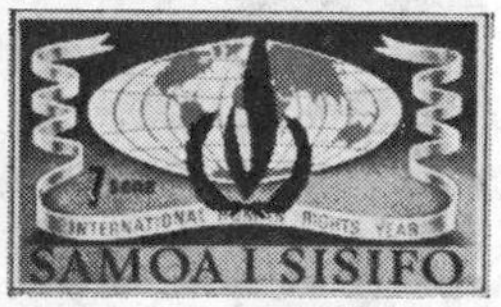

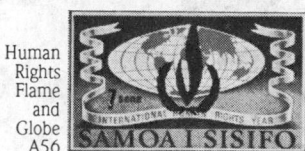

Human Rights Flame and Globe A56

Perf. 14½x14

1968, Aug. 26 Photo. Wmk. 355

295	A56	7s multicolored	.15	.15
296	A56	20s multicolored	.32	.32
297	A56	25s multicolored	.42	.42
		Nos. 295-297 (3)	.89	.89

International Human Rights Year, 1968.

Martin Luther
King, Jr. — A57

Polynesian
Madonna — A58

1968, Sept. 23   Litho.   Perf. 14
298 A57 7s green & black   .15 .15
299 A57 20s brt rose lilac & black .40 .40

Rev. Dr. Martin Luther King, Jr. (1929-68),
American civil rights leader.

1968, Oct. 12   Wmk. 355
300 A58 1s olive & multi   .15 .15
301 A58 3s multicolored   .15 .15
302 A58 20s crimson & multi   .40 .40
303 A58 30s dp orange & multi   .50 .50
      Nos. 300-303 (4)   1.20 1.20

Christmas 1968.

Frangipani
A59

Flowers: 7s, Chinese hibiscus, vert. 20s, Red ginger, vert. 30s, Cananngium odoratum.

1969, Jan. 20   Unwmk.   Perf. 14
304 A59 2s brt blue & multi   .15 .15
305 A59 7s multicolored   .22 .22
306 A59 20s yellow & multi   .70 .70
307 A59 30s multicolored   1.00 1.00
      Nos. 304-307 (4)   2.07 2.07

Seventh anniversary of independence.

R. L.
Stevenson
and Silver
from
"Treasure
Island"
A60

Robert Louis Stevenson and: 7s, Stewart and Balfour on the moor from "Kidnapped," 20s, "Doctor Jekyll and Mr. Hyde." 22s, Archie Weir and Christiana Elliot from "Weir of Hermiston."

Perf. 14x13½
1969, Apr. 21   Litho.   Wmk. 355
308 A60 3s gray & multi   .15 .15
309 A60 7s gray & multi   .16 .16
310 A60 20s gray & multi   .50 .50
311 A60 22s gray & multi   .60 .60
      Nos. 308-311 (4)   1.41 1.41

75th anniv. of the death of Robert Louis Stevenson, who is buried in Samoa.

Weight Lifting — A61

Perf. 13½x13
1969, July 21   Photo.   Unwmk.
312 A61 3s shown   .15 .15
313 A61 20s Sailing   .40 .40
314 A61 22s Boxing   .45 .45
      Nos. 312-314 (3)   1.00 1.00

3rd Pacific Games, Port Moresby, Papua and New Guinea, Aug. 13-23.

American Astronaut on Moon, Splashdown
and Map of Samoan Islands — A62

1969, July 24   Photo.
315 A62 7s red, blk, silver & grn .15 .15
316 A62 20s car, blk, silver & ultra .40 .40

US astronauts. See note after US No. C76.

Holy Family by
El Greco — A63

Christmas (Paintings): 1s, Virgin and Child, by Murillo. 20s, Nativity, by El Greco. 30s, Virgin and Child (from Adoration of the Kings), by Velazquez.

1969, Oct. 13   Unwmk.   Perf. 14
317 A63 1s gold, red & multi   .15 .15
318 A63 3s gold, red & multi   .15 .15
319 A63 20s gold, red & multi   .38 .38
320 A63 30s gold, red & multi   .55 .55
  a. Souvenir sheet of 4, #317-320 1.25 1.25
      Nos. 317-320 (4)   1.23 1.23

Seventh Day Adventists' Sanatorium,
Apia — A64

Designs: 7s, Father Louis Violette and R. C. Cathedral, Apia. 20s, Church of Latter Day Saints (Mormon), Tuasivi, Safotulafai, vert. 22s, John Williams and London Missionary Society Church, Sapapali'i.

1970, Jan. 19   Litho.   Wmk. 355
321 A64 2s brown, blk & gray   .15 .15
322 A64 7s violet, blk & bister   .15 .15
323 A64 20s rose, blk & lt violet .38 .38
324 A64 22s olive, blk & bister   .42 .42
      Nos. 321-324 (4)   1.10 1.10

Eighth anniversary of independence.

U.S.S.
Nipsic
A65

Designs: 5s, Wreck of German ship Adler. 10s, British ship Calliope in storm. 20s, Apia after hurricane.

1970, Apr. 27   Perf. 13½x14
325 A65 5s multicolored   .40 .40
326 A65 7s multicolored   .55 .55
327 A65 10s multicolored   .90 .90
328 A65 20s multicolored   1.75 1.75
      Nos. 325-328 (4)   3.60 3.60

The great Apia hurricane of 1889.

Cook Statue,
Whitby,
England — A66

"Peace for the
World" by Frances
B. Eccles — A67

Designs: 1s, Kendal's chronometer and Cook's sextant. 20s, Capt. Cook bust, in profile. 30s, Capt. Cook, island scene and "Endeavour," horiz.

Perf. 14x14½
1970, Sept. 14   Litho.   Wmk. 355
Size: 25x41mm
329 A66 1s silver, dp car & blk   .15 .15
330 A66 2s multicolored   .24 .15
331 A66 20s gold, black & ultra   2.25 1.50

Perf. 14½x14
Size: 83x25mm
332 A66 30s multicolored   3.25 2.25
      Nos. 329-332 (4)   5.89 4.05

Bicentenary of Capt. James Cook's exploration of South Pacific.

Perf. 13½
1970, Oct. 26   Photo.   Unwmk.
Christmas: 3s, Samoan coat of arms and Holy Family, by Werner Erich Jahnke. 20s, Samoan Mother and Child, by F. B. Eccles. 30s, Prince of Peace, by Sister Melane Fe'ao.
333 A67 2s gold & multi   .15 .15
334 A67 3s gold & multi   .15 .15
335 A67 20s gold & multi   .48 .48
336 A67 30s gold & multi   .70 .70
  a. Souvenir sheet of 4, #333-336 1.75 1.75
      Nos. 333-336 (4)   1.48 1.48

Pope Paul
VI — A68

Lumberjack — A69

Wmk. 355
1970, Nov. 29   Litho.   Perf. 14
337 A68 8s Prus blue & black   .18 .18
338 A68 20s deep plum & black   .48 .48

Visit of Pope Paul VI, Nov. 29, 1970.

Perf. 14x13½, 13½x14
1971, Feb. 1   Litho.   Unwmk.
Designs: 8s, Woman and tractor in clearing, horiz. 10s, Log and saw carrier, horiz. 22s, Logging and ship.
339 A69 3s multicolored   .15 .15
340 A69 8s multicolored   .15 .15
341 A69 20s multicolored   .35 .35
342 A69 20s multicolored   .42 .42
      Nos. 339-342 (4)   1.07 1.07

Development of the timber industry on Savaii Island by the American Timber Company of Potlatch.

Souvenir Sheet

Longboat in Apia Harbor; Samoa #3 and
US #3 — A70

1971, Mar. 12   Photo.   Perf. 11½
Granite Paper
343 A70 70s blue & multi   2.00 2.00

INTERPEX, 13th Intl. Stamp Exhib., NYC, Mar. 12-14.

Siva Dance
A71

Tourist Publicity: 7s, Samoan cricket game. 8s, Hideaway Resort Hotel. 10s, Aggie Grey and Aggie's Hotel.

Wmk. 355
1971, Aug. 9   Litho.   Perf. 14
344 A71 5s orange brn & multi   .45 .45
345 A71 7s orange brn & multi   .60 .60
346 A71 8s orange brn & multi   .75 .75
347 A71 10s orange brn & multi   .90 .90
      Nos. 344-347 (4)   2.70 2.70

A72

A73

Samoan Legends, carved by Sven Ortquist: 3s, Queen Salamasina. 8s, Lu and his sacred hens (Samoa). 10s, God Tagaloa fishing Samoan islands of Upolu and Savaii from the sea. 22s, Mt. Vaea and Pool of Tears.

1971, Sept. 20
348 A72 3s dark violet & multi   .15 .15
349 A72 8s multicolored   .24 .24
350 A72 10s dark blue & multi   .26 .26
351 A72 22s dark blue & multi   .65 .65
      Nos. 348-351 (4)   1.30 1.30

See Nos. 399-402.

1971, Oct. 4   Perf. 14x13½
Christmas: 2s, 3s, Virgin and Child, by Giovanni Bellini. 20c, 30c, Virgin and Child with St. Anne and St. John the Baptist, by Leonardo da Vinci.
352 A73 2s blue & multi   .15 .15
353 A73 3s black & multi   .15 .15
354 A73 20s yellow & multi   .55 .55
355 A73 30s dark red & multi   .80 .80
      Nos. 352-355 (4)   1.65 1.65

Samoan
Islands, Scales
of
Justice — A74

1972, Jan. 10   Photo.   Perf. 11½x12
356 A74 10s light blue & multi   .35 .35

1st So. Pacific Judicial Conf., Samoa, Jan. 1972.

Asau Wharf,
Savaii
A75

Designs: 8s, Parliament Building. 10s, Mothers' Center. 22s, Portraits of Tupua Tamasese Mea'ole and Malietoa Tanumafili II, and view of Vailima.

Perf. 13x13½

1972, Jan. 10 Litho. Wmk. 355

357	A75	1s bright pink & multi	.15	.15
358	A75	8s lilac & multi	.20	.20
359	A75	10s green & multi	.26	.26
360	A75	22s multicolored	.60	.60
		Nos. 357-360 (4)	1.21	1.21

10th anniversary of independence.

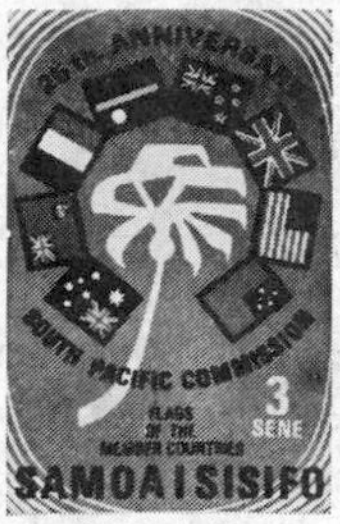

Commission Members' Flags — A76

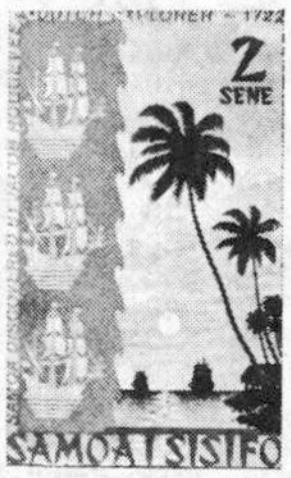

Sunset and Ships — A77

Designs: 7s, Afoafouvale Misimoa, Secretary-General, 1970-71 and Commission flag. 8s, Headquarters Building, Noumea, New Caledonia, horiz. 10s, Flag of Samoa, flag and map of South Pacific Commission area, horiz.

Perf. 14x13½, 13½x14

1972, Mar. 17

361	A76	3s ultra & multi	.15	.15
362	A76	7s yellow, black & ultra	.25	.25
363	A76	8s multicolored	.28	.28
364	A76	10s lt green & multi	.35	.35
		Nos. 361-364 (4)	1.03	1.03

South Pacific Commission, 25th anniv.

1972, June 14 *Perf. 14½*

Designs: 8s, Sailing ships Arend, Thienhoven and Africaansche Galey in storm. 10s, Outrigger canoe and Roggeveen's ships. 30s, Hemispheres with exploration route and map of Samoan Islands. All horiz.

365	A77	2s carmine rose & multi	.15	.15
366	A77	8s violet blue & multi	.38	.32
367	A77	10s ultra & multi	.45	.38

Size: 85x25mm

368	A77	30s ocher & multi	2.00	1.10
		Nos. 365-368 (4)	2.98	1.95

250th anniv. of Jacob Roggeveen's Pacific voyage and discovery of Samoa in June 1722.

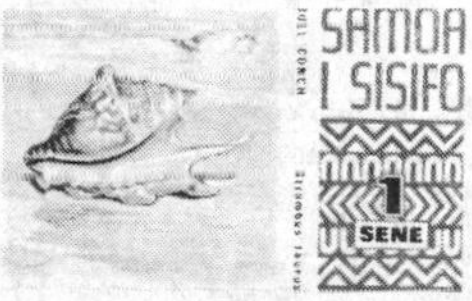

Bull Conch A78

1972-75 Litho. *Perf. 14½*

Size: 41x24mm

369	A78	1s shown	.15	.15
370	A78	2s Rhinoceros beetle	.15	.15
371	A78	3s Skipjack (fish)	.15	.15
372	A78	4s Painted crab	.15	.15
373	A78	5s Butterflyfish	.15	.15
374	A78	7s Samoan monarch	.20	.20
375	A78	10s Triton shell	.26	.26
376	A78	20s Jewel beetle	.55	.55
377	A78	50s Spiny lobster	1.40	1.40

Perf. 14x13½

Size: 29x45mm

378	A78	$1 Hawk moth	2.75	2.75
378A	A78	$2 Green turtle	5.50	5.50
378B	A78	$4 Black marlin	11.00	11.00
378C	A78	$5 Green tree lizard	14.00	14.00
		Nos. 369-378C (13)	36.41	36.41

Issued: 1s-$1, Oct. 18, 1972; $2, June 18, 1973; $4, Mar. 27, 1974; $5, June 30, 1975.

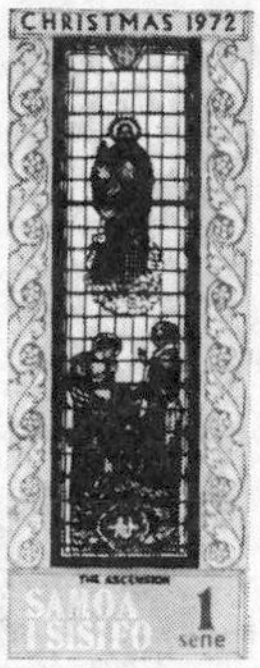

Ascension, Stained Glass Window — A79

Stained Glass Windows in Apia Churches: 4s, Virgin and Child. 10s, St. Andrew blessing Samoan canoe. 30s, The Good Shepherd.

Perf. 14x14½

1972, Nov. 1 Wmk. 355

379	A79	1s ocher & multi	.15	.15
380	A79	4s gray & multi	.15	.15
381	A79	10s dull green & multi	.32	.32
382	A79	30s blue & multi	.90	.90
	a.	Souvenir sheet of 4, #379-382	1.65	1.65
		Nos. 379-382 (4)	1.52	1.52

Christmas.

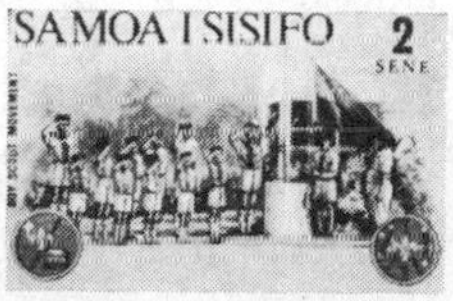

Scouts Saluting Flag, Emblems A80

1973, Jan. 29 *Perf. 14*

383	A80	2s shown	.15	.15
384	A80	3s First aid	.16	.16
385	A80	8s Pitching tent	.38	.38
386	A80	20s Action song	1.00	1.00
		Nos. 383-386 (4)	1.69	1.69

Boy Scouts of Samoa.

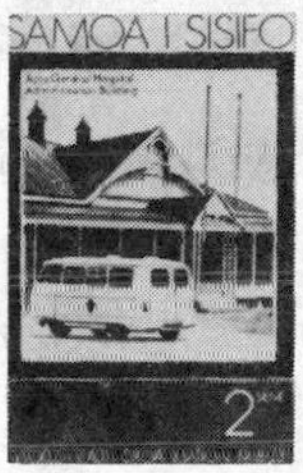

Apia General Hospital — A81

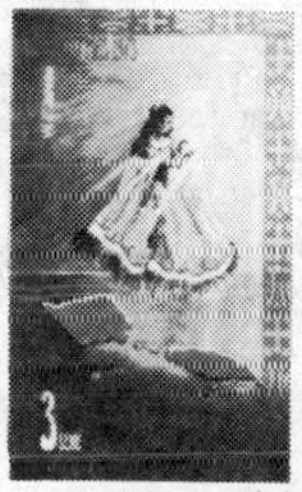
"A Prince is Born," by Jahnke — A82

WHO, 25th anniv.: 8s, Baby clinic. 20s, Filariasis research. 22s, Family welfare.

1973, Aug. 20 Wmk. 355

387	A81	2s green & multi	.15	.15
388	A81	8s multicolored	.24	.24
389	A81	20s brown & multi	.55	.55
390	A81	22s vermilion & multi	.65	.65
		Nos. 387-390 (4)	1.59	1.59

1973, Oct. 15 Litho. *Perf. 14*

Christmas: 4s, "Star of Hope," by Fiasili Keil. 10s, "Mother and Child," by Ernesto Coter. 30s, "The Light of the World," by Coter.

391	A82	3s blue & multi	.15	.15
392	A82	4s purple & multi	.15	.15
393	A82	10s red & multi	.32	.32
394	A82	30s blue & multi	.95	.95
	a.	Souvenir sheet of 4, #391-394	2.00	2.00
		Nos. 391-394 (4)	1.57	1.57

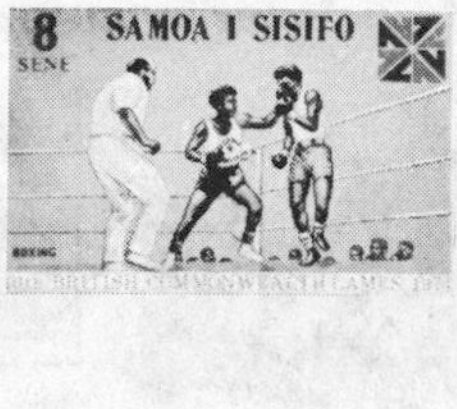

Boxing and Games' Emblem A83

1974, Jan. 24

395	A83	8s shown	.45	.45
396	A83	10s Weight lifting	.60	.60
397	A83	20s Lawn bowling	1.25	1.25
398	A83	30s Stadium	1.75	1.75
		Nos. 395-398 (4)	4.05	4.05

10th British Commonwealth Games, Christchurch, New Zealand, Jan. 24-Feb. 2.

Legends Type of 1971

Samoan Legends, Wood Carvings by Sven Ortquist: 2s, Tigilau and dove. 8s, Pili with his sons and famous fish net. 20s, The girl Sina and the eel which became the coconut tree. 30s, Nafanua who returned from the spirit world to free her village.

1974, Aug. 13 Wmk. 355 *Perf. 14*

399	A72	2s lemon & multi	.15	.15
400	A72	8s rose red & multi	.24	.24
401	A72	20s yellow grn & multi	.70	.70
402	A72	30s lt violet & multi	1.00	1.00
		Nos. 399-402 (4)	2.09	2.09

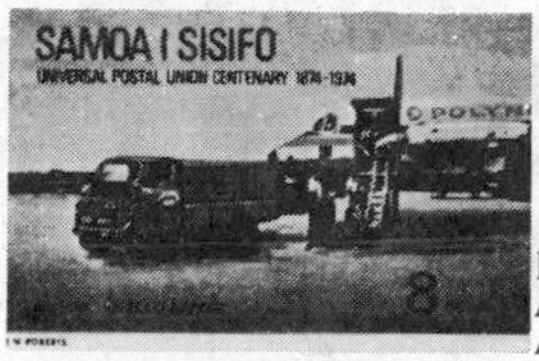

Faleolo Airport A84

Designs: 20s, Apia Wharf. 22s, Early post office, Apia. 50s, William Willis, raft "Age Unlimited" and route from Callao, Peru, to Tully, Western Samoa.

1974, Sept. 4 Unwmk. *Perf. 13½*

Size: 47x29mm

403	A84	8s multicolored	.18	.18
404	A84	20s multicolored	.45	.45
405	A84	22s multicolored	.60	.60

Size: 86x29mm

406	A84	50s multicolored	1.25	1.25
	a.	Souvenir sheet of 1, perf. 13	1.75	1.75
		Nos. 403-406 (4)	2.48	2.48

Cent. of UPU. The 8s is inscribed "Air Mail"; 20s, "Sea Mail"; 22s, "Raft Mail."

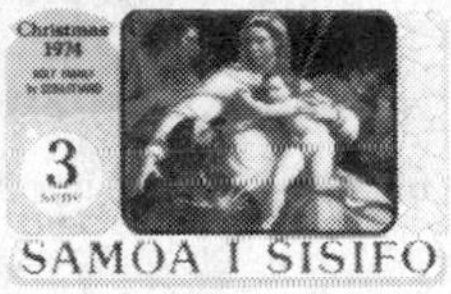

Holy Family, by Sebastiano A85

Christmas: 4s, Virgin and Child with Saints, by Lotto. 10s, Virgin and Child with St. John, by Titian. 30s, Adoration of the Shepherds, by Rubens.

1974, Nov. 18 Litho. *Perf. 13x13½*

407	A85	3s ocher & multi	.15	.15
408	A85	4s fawn & multi	.15	.15
409	A85	10s dull green & multi	.26	.26
410	A85	30s blue & multi	.80	.80
	a.	Souvenir sheet of 4, #407-410	1.40	1.40
		Nos. 407-410 (4)	1.36	1.36

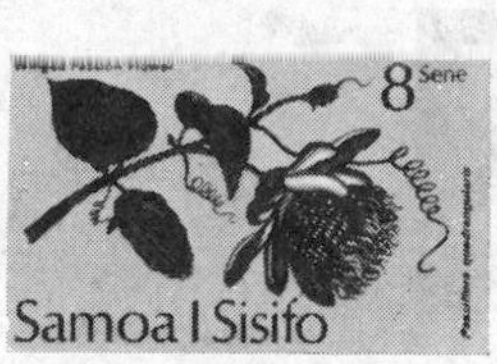

Winged Passion Flower A86

Flowers: 20s, Gardenias, vert. 22s, Lecythidaceae, vert. 30s, Malay apple.

Perf. 14½

1975, Jan. 17 Litho. Wmk. 355

411	A86	8s dull yellow & multi	.22	.22
412	A86	20s pale pink & multi	.55	.55
413	A86	22s pink & multi	.60	.60
414	A86	30s lt green & multi	.85	.85
		Nos. 411-414 (4)	2.22	2.22

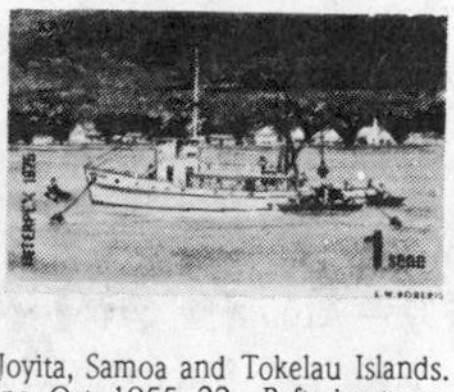
Joyita Loading at Apia — A87

Designs: 8s, Joyita, Samoa and Tokelau Islands. 20s, Joyita sinking, Oct. 1955. 22s, Rafts in storm. 50s, Plane discovering wreck.

1975, Mar. 14 Photo. *Perf. 13*

415	A87	1s multicolored	.15	.15
416	A87	8s multicolored	.16	.16
417	A87	20s multicolored	.40	.40
418	A87	22s multicolored	.45	.45
419	A87	50s multicolored	1.00	1.00
	a.	Souvenir sheet of 5, #415-419	2.50	2.50
		Nos. 415-419 (5)	2.16	2.16

17th INTERPEX Phil. Exhib., NYC, Mar. 14-16.

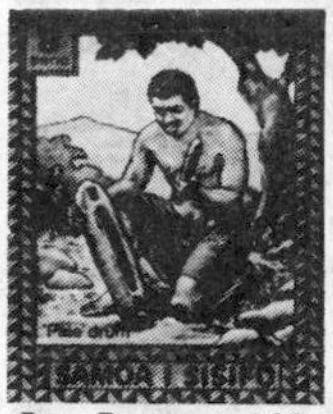

Pate Drum — A88

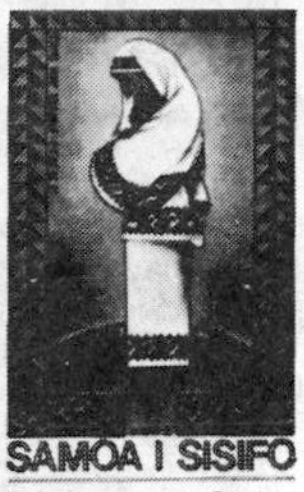

Mother and Child, by Meleane Fe'ao — A89

1975, Sept. 30 Litho. *Perf. 14½x14*

420	A88	8s shown	.20	.20
421	A88	20s Lali drum	.50	.50
422	A88	22s Logo drum	.55	.55
423	A88	30s Pu shell horn	.75	.75
		Nos. 420-423 (4)	2.00	2.00

1975, Nov. 25 Litho. Wmk. 355

Christmas (Paintings): 4s, Christ Child and Samoan flag, by Polataia Tuigamala. 10s, "A Star is Born," by Iosua Toafa. 30s, Mother and Child, by Ernesto Coter.

424	A89	3s multicolored	.15	.15
425	A89	4s multicolored	.15	.15
426	A89	10s multicolored	.25	.25
427	A89	30s multicolored	.75	.75
	a.	Souvenir sheet of 4, #424-427	1.40	1.40
		Nos. 424-427 (4)	1.30	1.30

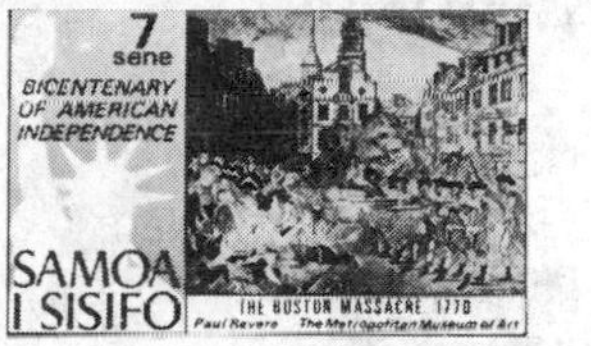

Boston Massacre, by Paul Revere — A90

Designs (Statue of Liberty and): 8s, Declaration of Independence, by John Trumbull. 20s, The Sinking of the Bonhomme Richard, by J. L. G. Ferris. 22s, Wm. Pitt Addressing House of Commons, by R. A. Hickel. 50s, Battle of Princeton, by William Mercer.

Perf. 13½x14

1976, Jan. 20 Litho. Wmk. 355

428	A90	7s salmon & multi	.22	.22
429	A90	8s green & multi	.26	.26
430	A90	20s lilac & multi	.65	.65
431	A90	22s blue & multi	.70	.70
432	A90	50s yellow & multi	1.65	1.65
	a.	Souvenir sheet of 5, #428-432 + label	4.75	4.75
		Nos. 428-432 (5)	3.48	3.48

Bicentenary of American Independence.

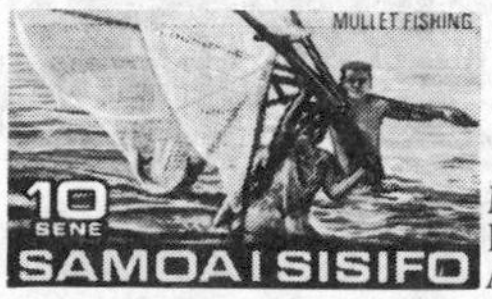

Mullet Fishing A91

1976, Apr. 27 Litho. *Perf. 14½*

433	A91	10s shown	.28	.28
434	A91	12s Fish traps	.32	.32
435	A91	22s Fishermen	.60	.60
436	A91	50s Net fishing	1.40	1.40
		Nos. 433-436 (4)	2.60	2.60

Souvenir Sheet

Samoan $100 Gold Coin with Paul Revere
and US Map — A92

1976, May 29   Unwmk.   Photo.   Perf. 13
437 A92 $1 green & gold   3.00 3.00

American Bicentennial and Interphil 76 Intl.
Phil. Exhib., Philadelphia, PA, May 29-June 6.

Boxing
A93

Designs (Olympic Rings and): 12s, Wrestling.
22s, Javelin. 50s, Weight lifting.

Perf. 14¹/₂x14
1976, June 21   Litho.   Wmk. 355
438 A93 10s black & multi   .22 .22
439 A93 12s dark brown & multi   .25 .25
440 A93 22s dark purple & multi   .45 .45
441 A93 50s dark blue & multi   1.10 1.10
     Nos. 438-441 (4)   2.02 2.02

21st Olympic Games, Montreal, Canada, July 17-
Aug. 1.

Mary and Joseph on
Road to
Bethlehem — A94

Christmas: 5s, Adoration of the Shepherds. 22s,
Nativity. 50s, Adoration of the Kings.

1976, Oct. 18   Litho.   Perf. 14x13¹/₂
442 A94 3s multicolored   .15 .15
443 A94 5s multicolored   .15 .15
444 A94 22s multicolored   .60 .60
445 A94 50s multicolored   1.50 1.50
     a. Souvenir sheet of 4, #442-445   2.50 2.50
     Nos. 442-445 (4)   2.40 2.40

Presentation of the Spurs of
Chivalry — A95

Designs: 12s, Queen and view of Apia. 32s,
Royal Yacht Britannia and Queen. 50s, Queen leaving Westminster Abbey.

Perf. 13¹/₂x14
1977, Feb. 11   Wmk. 355
446 A95 12s multicolored   .18 .18
447 A95 22s multicolored   .35 .35
448 A95 32s multicolored   .55 .55
449 A95 50s multicolored   .90 .90
     Nos. 446-449 (4)   1.98 1.98

25th anniv. of the reign of Elizabeth II.

Lindbergh
and Spirit of
St. Louis
A96

Designs: 22s, Map of transatlantic route and
plane. 24s, Spirit of St. Louis in flight. 26s, Spirit of
St. Louis taking off.

1977, May 20   Litho.   Perf. 14
450 A96 22s multicolored   .42 .42
451 A96 24s multicolored   .48 .48
452 A96 26s multicolored   .50 .50
453 A96 50s multicolored   1.00 1.00
     a. Souvenir sheet of 4, #450-453   2.50 2.50
     Nos. 450-453 (4)   2.40 2.40

Charles A. Lindbergh's solo transatlantic flight
from New York to Paris, 50th anniv.

Apia
Automatic
Telephone
Exchange
A97

Designs: 13s, Mulinuu radio terminal. 26s, Old
wall and new dial telephones. 50s, Global communications (2 telephones and globe).

1977, July 11   Litho.   Perf. 14
454 A97 12s multicolored   .18 .18
455 A97 13s multicolored   .20 .20
456 A97 26s multicolored   .45 .45
457 A97 50s multicolored   .80 .80
     Nos. 454-457 (4)   1.63 1.63

Telecommunications.

Samoa
No. 3
and
First
Mail
Notice
A98

Designs: 13s, Samoa No. 4 and 1881 cover. 26s,
Samoa No. 1 and Chief Post Office, Apia. 50s,
Samoa No. 4 and schooner "Energy," which carried
first mail.

1977, Aug. 29   Wmk. 355   Perf. 13¹/₂
458 A98 12s multicolored   .22 .22
459 A98 13s multicolored   .25 .25
460 A98 26s multicolored   .50 .50
461 A98 50s multicolored   1.00 1.00
     Nos. 458-461 (4)   1.97 1.97

Samoan postage stamp centenary.

Nativity — A99

Christmas: 6s, People bringing gifts to Holy Family in Samoan hut. 26s, Virgin and Child. 50s, Stars
over Christ Child.

1977, Oct. 11   Litho.   Perf. 14
462 A99 4s multicolored   .15 .15
463 A99 6s multicolored   .15 .15
464 A99 26s multicolored   .50 .50
465 A99 50s multicolored   1.65 1.65
     a. Souvenir sheet of 4, #462-465   2.50 2.50
     Nos. 462-465 (4)   2.45 2.45

Polynesian
Airlines'
Boeing
737 — A100

Aviation Progress: 24s, Kitty Hawk. 26s, Kingsford-Smith Fokker. 50s, Concorde.

Unwmk.
1978, Mar. 21   Litho.   Perf. 14
466 A100 12s multicolored   .22 .22
467 A100 24s multicolored   .45 .45
468 A100 26s multicolored   .48 .48
469 A100 50s multicolored   .95 .95
     a. Souvenir sheet of 4, #466-469, perf.
      13¹/₂   2.50 2.50
     Nos. 466-469 (4)   2.10 2.10

Turtle
Hatchery,
Aleipata
A101

Design: $1, Hawksbill turtle and Wildlife Fund
emblem.

1978, Apr. 14   Wmk. 355   Perf. 14¹/₂
470 A101 24s multicolored   .45 .45
471 A101 $1 multicolored   1.90 1.90

Project to replenish endangered hawksbill turtles.

**Elizabeth II Coronation Anniversary
Issue**
Souvenir Sheet
Common Design Types

1978, Apr. 21   Unwmk.   Perf. 15
472   Sheet of 6   3.00 3.00
     a. CD326 26s King's lion   .45 .45
     b. CD327 26s Elizabeth II   .45 .45
     c. CD328 26s Pacific pigeon   .45 .45

No. 472 contains 2 se-tenant strips of Nos. 472a-
472c, separated by horizontal gutter with commemorative and descriptive inscriptions and showing central part of coronation procession with
coach.

Souvenir Sheet

Canadian
and Samoan
Flags
A102

Perf. 14¹/₂
1978, June 9   Wmk. 355   Litho.
473 A102 $1 multicolored   2.75 2.75

CAPEX Canadian Intl. Phil. Exhib., Toronto,
June 9-18.

Capt. James
Cook — A103

Designs: 24s, Cook's cottage, now in Melbourne,
Australia. 26s, Old drawbridge over River Esk,
Whitby, 1766-1833. 50s, Resolution and map of
Hawaiian Islands.

1978, Aug. 28   Litho.   Perf. 14¹/₂x14
474 A103 12s multicolored   .32 .32
475 A103 24s multicolored   .65 .65
476 A103 26s multicolored   .85 .85
477 A103 50s multicolored   1.65 1.65
     Nos. 474-477 (4)   3.47 3.47

A104   A105

Cowrie Shells: 1s, Thick-edged Cowrie. 2s, Isabella cowrie. 3s, Money cowrie. 4s, Eroded cowrie.

6s, Honey cowrie. 7s, Banded cowrie. 10s, Globe
cowrie. 11s, Mole cowrie. 12s, Children's cowrie.
13s, Flag cone. 14s, Soldier cone. 24s, Cloth-of-gold
cone. 26s, Lettered cone. 50s, Tiled cone. $1, Black
marble cone. $2, Marlin-spike auger. $3, Scorpion
spider conch. $5, Common harp.

1978-80   Photo.   Unwmk.   Perf. 12¹/₂
Size: 31x24mm
Granite Paper
478 A104 1s multicolored   .15 .15
479 A104 2s multicolored   .15 .15
480 A104 3s multicolored   .15 .15
481 A104 4s multicolored   .15 .15
482 A104 6s multicolored   .15 .15
483 A104 7s multicolored   .15 .15
484 A104 10s multicolored   .15 .15
485 A104 11s multicolored   .15 .15
486 A104 12s multicolored   .15 .15
487 A104 13s multicolored   .15 .15
488 A104 14s multicolored   .20 .20
489 A104 24s multicolored   .32 .32
490 A104 26s multicolored   .32 .32
491 A104 50s multicolored   .65 .65
492 A104 $1 multicolored   1.25 1.25

Perf. 11¹/₂
Size: 36x26mm
493 A104 $2 multi ('79)   2.50 2.50
494 A104 $3 multi ('79)   4.00 4.00
494A A104 $5 multi ('80)   10.50 10.50
     Nos. 478-494A (18)   21.24 21.24

Issue dates: 1s-12s, Sept. 15. 13s-$1, Nov. 20.
$2, $3, July 18. $5, Aug. 26.

Wmk. 355
1978, Nov. 6   Litho.   Perf. 14

Works by Dürer: 4s, The Virgin in Glory. 6s,
Nativity. 26s, Adoration of the Kings. 50s,
Annunciation.

495 A105 4s lt brown & blk   .15 .15
496 A105 6s grnsh blue & blk   .15 .15
497 A105 26s violet blue & blk   .50 .50
498 A105 50s purple & blk   1.00 1.00
     a. Souvenir sheet of 4, #495-498   1.75 1.75
     Nos. 495-498 (4)   1.80 1.80

Christmas and for 450th death anniv. of Albrecht
Dürer.

Boy
Carrying
Coconuts
A106

Designs: 24s, Children leaving church on White
Sunday. 26s, Children pumping water. 50s, Girl
playing ukulele.

1979, Apr. 10   Litho.   Perf. 14
499 A106 12s multicolored   .20 .20
500 A106 24s multicolored   .42 .42
501 A106 26s multicolored   .45 .45
502 A106 50s multicolored   .95 .95
     Nos. 499-502 (4)   2.02 2.02

International Year of the Child.

Charles W.
Morgan
A107

1979, May 29   Litho.   Perf. 13¹/₂
503 A107 12s multicolored   .25 .25
504 A107 14s Lagoda   .32 .32
505 A107 24s James T. Arnold   .52 .52
506 A107 50s Splendid   1.10 1.10
     Nos. 503-506 (4)   2.19 2.19

See Nos. 521-524, 543-546.

Saturn V   Penny Black, Hill
Launch — A108   Statue — A109

Designs: 14s, Landing module and astronaut on moon, horiz. 24s, Earth seen from moon. 26s, Astronaut on moon, horiz. 50s, Lunar and command modules. $1, Command module after splashdown, horiz.

Perf. 14½x14, 14x14½

1979, June 20 Litho. Wmk. 355

507 A108 12s multicolored .16 .16
508 A108 14s multicolored .18 .18
509 A108 24s multicolored .32 .32
510 A108 26s multicolored .35 .35
511 A108 50s multicolored .65 .65
512 A108 $1 multicolored 1.40 1.40
a. Souvenir sheet 1.75 1.75
Nos. 507-512 (6) 3.06 3.06

1st moon landing, 10th anniv.

1979, Aug. 27 *Perf. 14*

Designs: 24s, Great Britain No. 2 with Maltese Cross postmark. 26s, Penny Black and Rowland Hill. $1, Great Britain No. 2 and Hill statue.

513 A109 12s multicolored .15 .15
514 A109 24s multicolored .30 .30
515 A109 26s multicolored .32 .32
516 A109 $1 multicolored 1.25 1.25
a. Souvenir sheet of 4, #513-516 1.90 1.90
Nos. 513-516 (4) 2.02 2.02

Sir Rowland Hill (1795-1879), originator of penny postage.

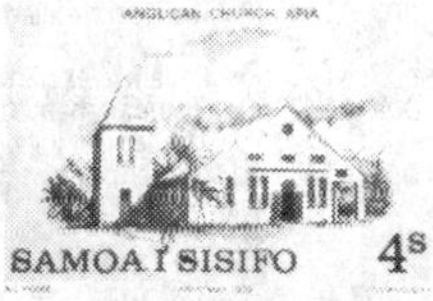

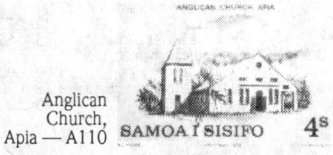

Anglican Church, Apia — A110

Samoan Churches: 6s, Congregational Christian Church, Leulumoega. 26s, Methodist Church, Piula. 50s, Protestant Church, Apia.

1979, Oct. 22 Photo. *Perf. 12x11½*

517 A110 4s lt blue & blk .15 .15
518 A110 6s lt yellow grn & blk .15 .15
519 A110 26s dull yellow & blk .40 .40
520 A110 50s lt lilac & blk .75 .75
a. Souvenir sheet of 4, #517-520 1.40 1.40
Nos. 517-520 (4) 1.45 1.45

Christmas.

Ship Type of 1979

Wmk. 355

1980, Jan. 22 Litho. *Perf. 14*

521 A107 12s William Hamilton .20 .20
522 A107 14s California .25 .25
523 A107 24s Liverpool II .42 .42
524 A107 50s Two Brothers .90 .90
Nos. 521-524 (4) 1.77 1.77

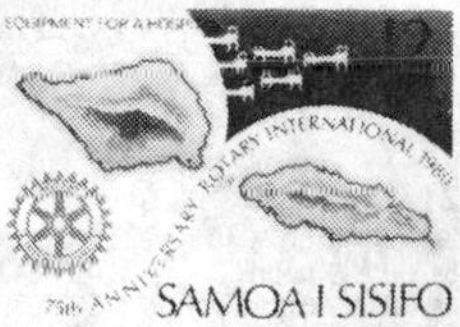

Map of Samoan Islands, Rotary Emblem A111

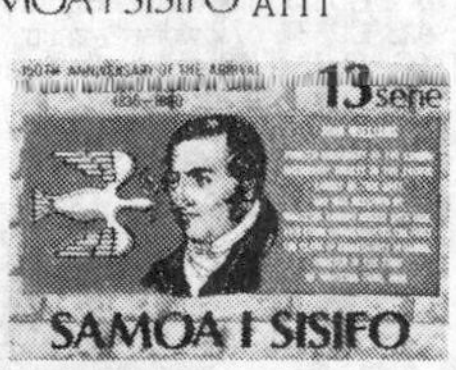

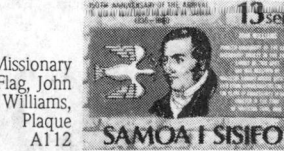

Missionary Flag, John Williams, Plaque A112

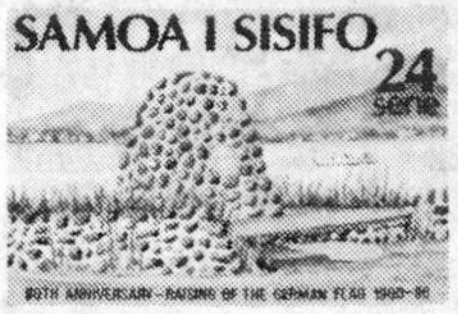

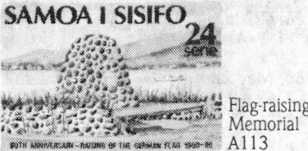

Flag-raising Memorial A113

1980, Mar. 26 Photo. *Perf. 14*

525 A111 12s shown .16 .16
526 A112 13s shown .20 .20
527 A112 14s German flag, Dr. Wilhelm Solf, plaque .20 .20
528 A113 24s shown .35 .35
529 A113 26s Williams Memorial, Savai'i .38 .38
530 A111 50s Emblem, Paul P. Harris, founder .70 .70
Nos. 525-530 (6) 1.99 1.99

Rotary Intl., 75th anniv. (A111); arrival of Williams, missionary in Samoa, 150th anniv. (13s, 26s); raising of the German flag, 80th anniv. (14s, 24s).

Souvenir Sheet

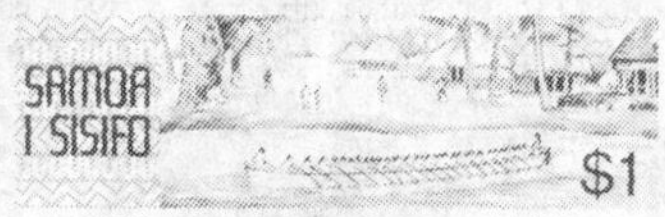

Village and Long Boat — A114

Wmk. 355

1980, May 6 Litho. *Perf. 14*

531 A114 $1 multicolored 2.00 2.00

London 80 Intl. Phil. Exhib., May 6-14.

Queen Mother Elizabeth Birthday Issue

Common Design Type

1980, Aug. 4 Litho.

532 CD330 50s multicolored .70 .70

Souvenir Sheet

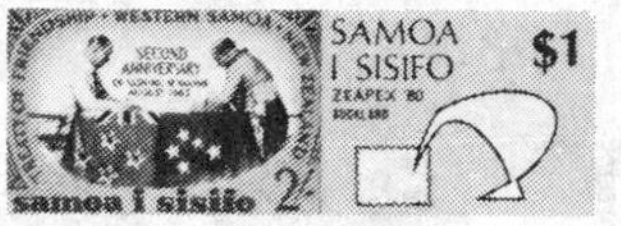

Samoa No. 239, ZEAPEX Emblem — A115

Unwmk.

1980, Aug. 23 Litho. *Perf. 14*

533 A115 $1 multicolored 2.00 2.00

ZEAPEX '80, New Zealand International Stamp Exhibition, Auckland, Aug. 23-31.

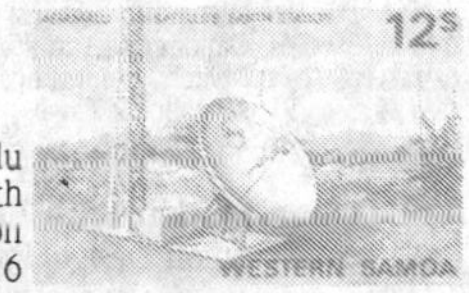

Afiamalu Satellite Earth Station A116

Designs: 14s, Station, diff. 24s, Station, map of Samoa. 50s, Satellite sending waves to earth. $2, Samoa No. 536, Sydpex '80 emblem.

1980, Sept. 17 Litho. *Perf. 11½*

Granite Paper

534 A116 12s multicolored .18 .18
535 A116 14s multicolored .22 .22
536 A116 24s multicolored .35 .35
537 A116 50s multicolored .80 .80
Nos. 534-537 (4) 1.55 1.55

Souvenir Sheet

1980, Sept. 29 *Imperf.*

538 A116 $2 multicolored 3.00 3.00

Sydpex '80 Natl. Phil. Exhib., Sydney.

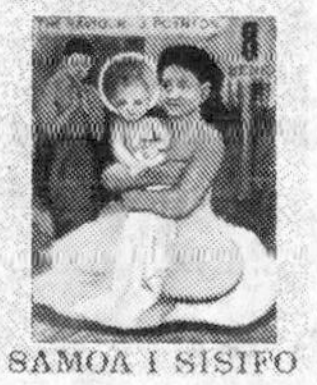

The Savior, by John Poynton — A117

Christmas (Paintings by Local Artists): 14s, Madonna and Child, by Lealofi F. Siaopo. 27s, Nativity, by Pasila Feata. 50s, Yuletide, by R.P. Aiono.

Wmk. 355

1980, Oct. 28 Litho. *Perf. 14*

539 A117 8s multicolored .15 .15
540 A117 14s multicolored .15 .15
541 A117 27s multicolored .28 .28
542 A117 50s multicolored .50 .50
a. Souvenir sheet of 4, #539-542 1.40 1.40
Nos. 539-542 (4) 1.08 1.08

Ship Type of 1979

1981, Jan. 26 Litho. *Perf. 13½*

543 A107 12s Ocean .24 .24
544 A107 18s Horatio .38 .38
545 A107 27s Calliope .55 .55
546 A107 32s Calypso .65 .65
Nos. 543-546 (4) 1.82 1.82

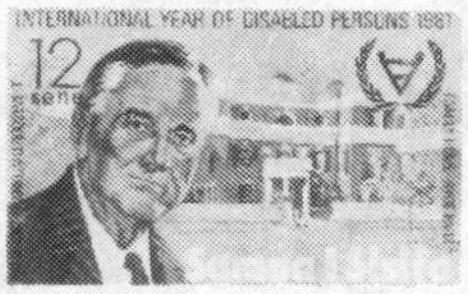

Pres. Franklin Roosevelt and Hyde Park Home A118

International Year of the Disabled: Scenes of Franklin D. Roosevelt.

Wmk. 355

1981, Apr. 29 Litho. *Perf. 14*

547 A118 12s shown .15 .15
548 A118 18c Inauguration .18 .18
549 A118 27s Pres. & Mrs. Roosevelt .25 .25
550 A118 32s Atlantic convoy (Lend Lease Bill) .28 .28
551 A118 38s With stamp collection .35 .35
552 A118 $1 Campobello House .85 .85
Nos. 547-552 (6) 2.06 2.06

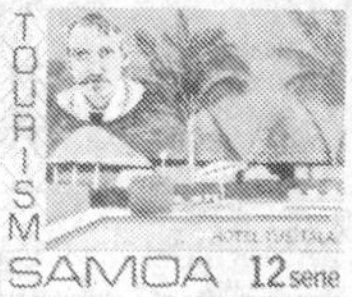

Hotel Tusitala — A119

Perf. 14½x14

1981, June 29 Litho. Wmk. 355

553 A119 12s shown .15 .15
554 A119 18s Apia Harbor .20 .20
555 A119 27s Aggie Grey's Hotel .30 .30
556 A119 32s Ceremonial kava preparation .35 .35
557 A119 54s Piula Pool .60 .60
Nos. 553-557 (5) 1.60 1.60

Royal Wedding Issue

Common Design Type

Wmk. 355

1981, July 22 Litho. *Perf. 14*

558 CD331 18s Bouquet .15 .15
559 CD331 32s Charles .20 .20
560 CD331 $1 Couple .65 .65
Nos. 558-560 (3) 1.00 1.00

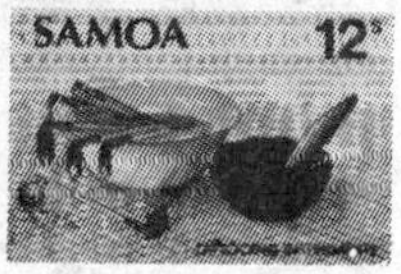

Tattooing Instruments A120

1981, Sept. 29 Litho. *Perf. 13½x14*

561 Strip of 4 1.75 1.75
a. A120 12s shown .15 .15
b. A120 18s 1st stage .20 .20
c. A120 27s Later stage .30 .30
d. A120 $1 Tattooed man 1.10 1.10

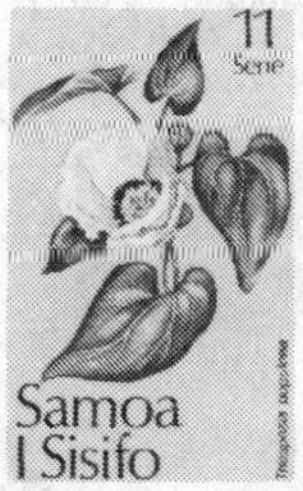

Christmas — A121

1981, Nov. 30 Litho. *Perf. 13½*

562 A121 11s Milo tree blossom .15 .15
563 A121 15s Copper leaf .16 .16
564 A121 23s Yellow allamanda .25 .25
565 A121 $1 Mango blossom 1.00 1.00
a. Souvenir sheet of 4, #562-565 2.00 2.00
Nos. 562-565 (4) 1.56 1.56

Souvenir Sheet

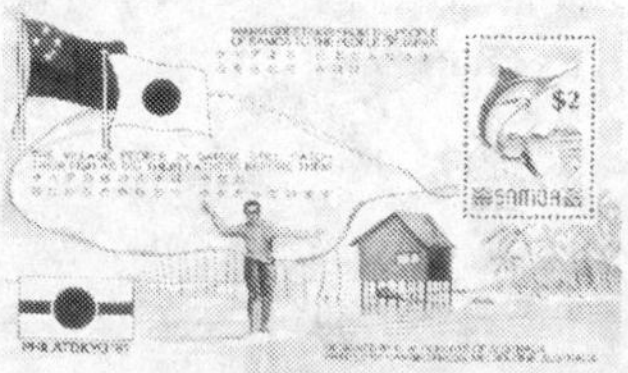

Philatokyo '81 Intl. Stamp Exhibition — A122

1981, Oct. 9 Litho. *Perf. 14x13½*

566 A122 $2 multicolored 2.25 2.25

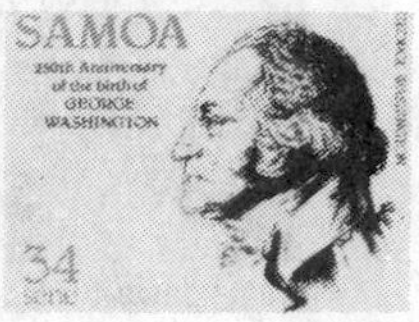

250th Birth Anniv. of George Washington A123

1982, Feb. 26 Litho. *Perf. 14*

567 A123 23s Pistol .45 .45
568 A123 25s Mt. Vernon .50 .59
569 A123 34s Portrait .70 .70
Nos. 567-569 (3) 1.65 1.74

Souvenir Sheet

570 A123 $1 Taking oath 2.00 2.00

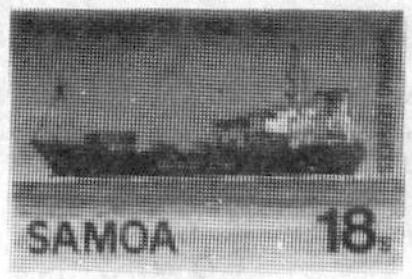

20th Anniv. of Independence A124

1982, May 24 Litho. *Perf. 13½x14*

571 A124 18s Freighter Forum Samoa .24 .24
572 A124 23s Jet, routes .32 .32
573 A124 25s Natl. Provident Fund building .35 .35
574 A124 $1 Intl. subscriber dialing system 1.25 1.25
Nos. 571-574 (4) 2.16 2.16

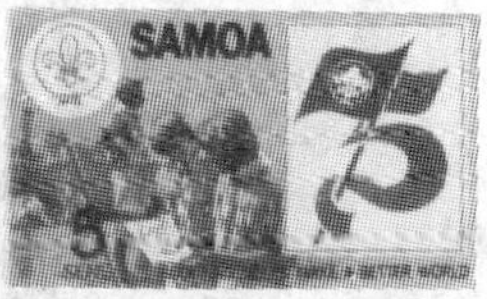

Scouting Year A125

1982, July 20 Wmk. 355 *Perf. 14½*

575 A125 5s Map reading .15 .15
576 A125 38s Salute .50 .50
577 A125 44s Rope bridge .60 .60
578 A125 $1 Troop 1.10 1.10
a. Souvenir sheet 1.50 1.50
Nos. 575-578 (4) 2.35 2.35

No. 578a contains one stamp similar to No. 578, 48x36mm.

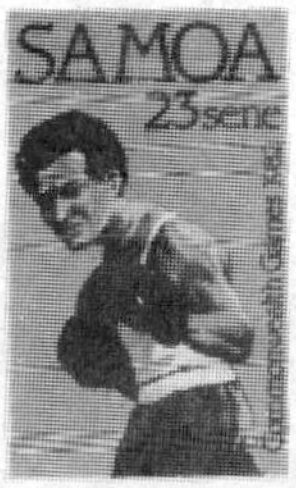

12th Commonwealth Games, Brisbane, Australia, Sept. 30-Oct. 9 — A126

Perf. 14x14½

1982, Sept. 20 Wmk. 373

579 A126 23s Boxing .28 .28
580 A126 25s Hurdles .30 .30
581 A126 34s Weightlifting .42 .42
582 A126 $1 Lawn bowling 1.10 1.10
Nos. 579-582 (4) 2.10 2.10

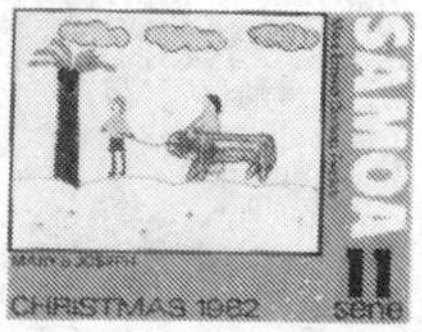

Christmas A127

Children's Drawings: 11s, 15s, Flight into Egypt (diff.). 38s, $1, Virgin and Child (diff.).

1982, Nov. 15 Litho. Wmk. 355

583 A127 11s multicolored .15 .15
584 A127 15s multicolored .20 .20
585 A127 38s multicolored .50 .50
586 A127 $1 multicolored 1.10 1.10
a. Souvenir sheet of 4, #583-586 2.00 2.00
Nos. 583-586 (4) 1.95 1.95

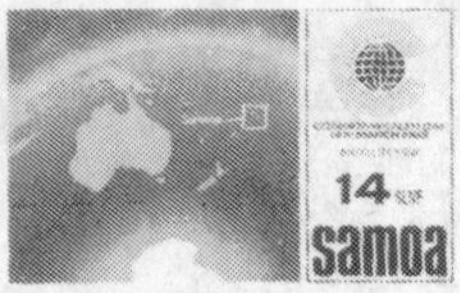

Commonwealth Day — A128

Perf. 13½x14

1983, Feb. 23 Litho. Wmk. 373

587 A128 14s Map .16 .16
588 A128 29s Flag .35 .35
589 A128 43s Harvesting copra .50 .50
590 A128 $1 Malietoa Tanumafili II 1.10 1.10
Nos. 587-590 (4) 2.11 2.11

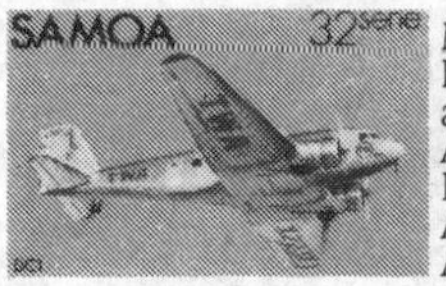

Manned Flight Bicentenary and 50th Anniv. of Douglas Aircraft A129

Designs: a, DC-1. b, DC-2. c, DC-3. d, DC-4. e, DC-5. f, DC-6. g, DC-7. h, DC-8. i, DC-9. j, DC-10.

Wmk. 373

1983, June 7 Litho. *Perf. 14*

591 Sheet of 10 3.50 3.50
a.-j. A129 32s any single .35 .35

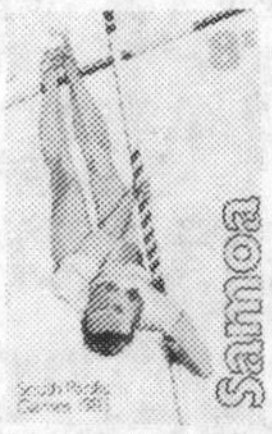

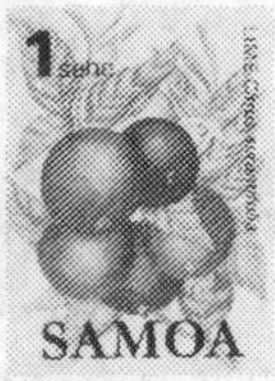

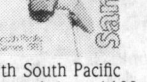

7th South Pacific Games, Apia — A130 Local Fruit — A131

1983, Aug. 29 Litho. *Perf. 14x14½*

592 A130 8s Pole vault .15 .15
593 A130 15s Basketball .15 .15
594 A130 25c Tennis .22 .22
595 A130 32s Weightlifting .28 .28
596 A130 35s Boxing .30 .30
597 A130 46s Soccer .40 .40
598 A130 48s Golf .45 .45
599 A130 56s Rugby .50 .50
Nos. 592-599 (8) 2.45 2.45

Perf. 14x13½

1983-84 Litho. Wmk. 373

600 A131 1s Limes .15 .15
601 A131 2s Star fruit .15 .15
602 A131 3s Mangosteen .15 .15
603 A131 4s Lychee .15 .15
604 A131 7s Passion fruit .15 .15
605 A131 8s Mangoes .15 .15
606 A131 11s Papaya .15 .15
607 A131 13s Pineapple .15 .15
608 A131 14s Breadfruit .16 .16
609 A131 15s Bananas .18 .18
610 A131 21s Cashew nut .25 .25
611 A131 25s Guava .28 .28
612 A131 32s Water Melon .35 .35
613 A131 48s Sasalapa .55 .55
614 A131 56s Avocado .65 .65
615 A131 $1 Coconut 1.10 1.10

Perf. 13½

616 A131 $2 Apples ('84) 2.25 2.25
617 A131 $4 Grapefruit ('84) 4.50 4.50
618 A131 $5 Oranges ('84) 5.50 5.50
Nos. 600-618 (19) 16.97 16.97

Issue dates: 1s-15s, Sept. 28. 21s-$1, Nov. 30. $2-$5, Apr. 11.

For overprint see No. 628.

Miniature Sheet

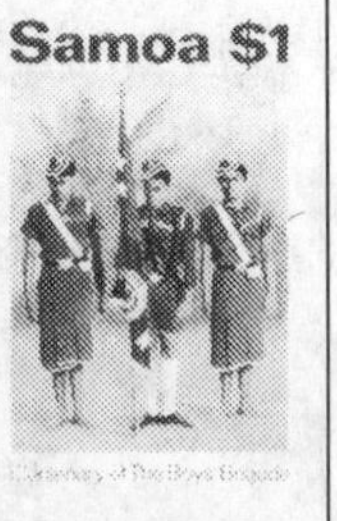

Boys' Brigade Centenary — A132

1983, Oct. 10 *Perf. 14½*

619 A132 $1 multicolored 1.00 1.00

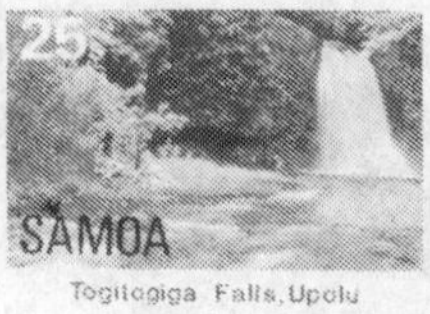

Togitogiga Falls, Upolu A133

Wmk. 373

1984, Feb. 15 Litho. *Perf. 14*

620 A133 25s shown .24 .24
621 A133 32s Lano Beach, Savai'i .30 .30
622 A133 48s Mulinu'u Point, Upolu .45 .45
623 A133 56s Nu'utele Isld. .52 .52
Nos. 620-623 (4) 1.51 1.51

Lloyd's List Issue

Common Design Type

Perf. 14½x14

1984, May 24 Litho. Wmk. 373

624 CD335 32s Apia Harbor .28 .28
625 CD335 48s Apia hurricane, 1889 .45 .45
626 CD335 60s Forum Samoa .55 .55
627 CD335 $1 Matua .90 .90
Nos. 624-627 (4) 2.18 2.18

No. 615 Overprinted: "19th U.P.U. CONGRESS / HAMBURG 1984"

1984, June 7 *Perf. 14x13½*

628 A131 $1 multicolored 1.00 1.00

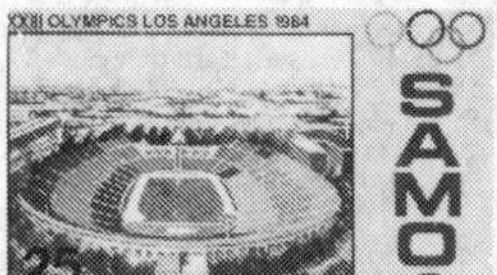

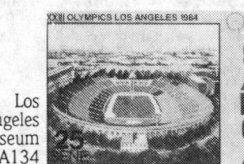

Los Angeles Coliseum A134

1984, June 26 Litho. *Perf. 14½*

629 A134 25s shown .25 .25
630 A134 32s Weightlifting .35 .35
631 A134 48s Boxing .52 .52
632 A134 $1 Running 1.10 1.10
a. Souvenir sheet of 4, #629-632 2.25 2.25
Nos. 629-632 (4) 2.22 2.22

1984 Summer Olympics and Samoa's first Olympic participation.

Souvenir Sheet

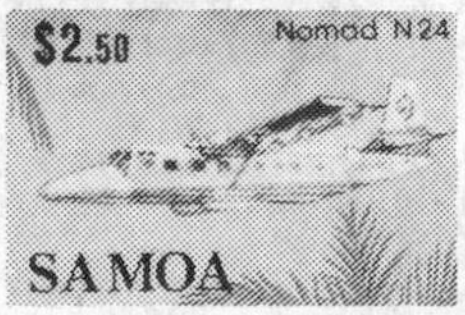

Ausipex '84 A135

1984, Sept. 21 Litho. *Perf. 14*

633 A135 $2.50 Nomad N24 2.50 2.50

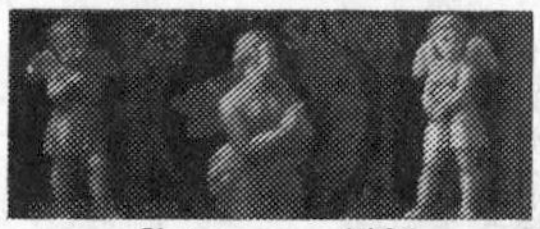

Christmas — A136

The Three Virtues, by Raphael.

1984, Nov. 7 *Perf. 14½x14*

634 A136 25s Faith .24 .24
635 A136 35s Hope .30 .30
636 A136 $1 Charity .95 .95
a. Souvenir sheet of 3, #634-636 1.50 1.50
Nos. 634-636 (3) 1.49 1.49

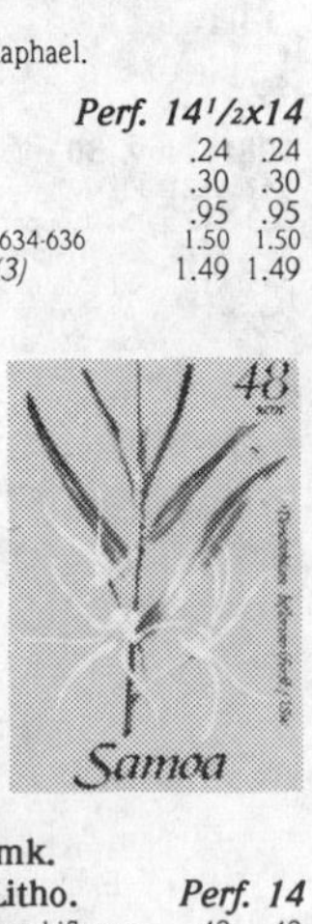

Orchids — A137

Unwmk.

1985, Jan. 23 Litho. *Perf. 14*

637 A137 48s Dendrobium biflorum .42 .42
638 A137 56s Dendrobium vaupelianum kraenzl .50 .50
639 A137 67s Glomera montana .60 .60
640 A137 $1 Spathoglottis plicata .90 .90
Nos. 637-640 (4) 2.42 2.42

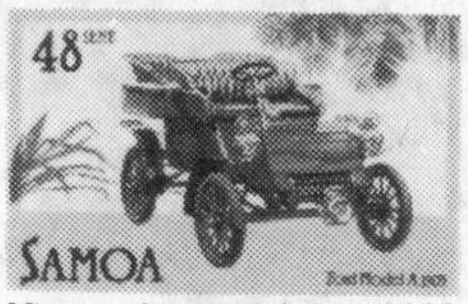

Vintage Automobiles — A138

Wmk. 373

1985, Mar. 26 Litho. *Perf. 14*

641 A138 48s Ford Model A, 1903 .45 .45
642 A138 56s Chevrolet Tourer, 1912 .52 .52
643 A138 67s Morris Oxford, 1913 .60 .60
644 A138 $1 Austin Seven, 1923 .95 .95
Nos. 641-644 (4) 2.52 2.52

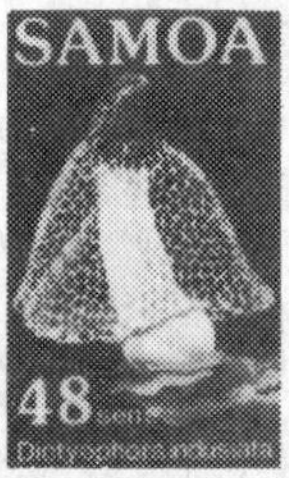

Fungi — A139

1985, Apr. 17 Litho. *Perf. 14½*

645 A139 48s Dictyophora indusiata .45 .45
646 A139 56s Ganoderma tornatum .52 .52
647 A139 67s Mycena chlorophos .60 .60
648 A139 $1 Mycobonia flava .95 .95
Nos. 645-648 (4) 2.52 2.52

Queen Mother 85th Birthday

Common Design Type

Perf. 14½x14

1985, June 7 Litho. Wmk. 384

649 CD336 32s Photo., age 9 .32 .32
650 CD336 48s With Prince William at christening of Prince Henry .50 .50
651 CD336 56s At Liverpool street station .60 .60
652 CD336 $1 Holding Prince Henry 1.00 1.00
Nos. 649-652 (4) 2.42 2.42

Souvenir Sheet

653 CD336 $2 Arriving at Tattenham corner station 2.00 2.00

Souvenir Sheet

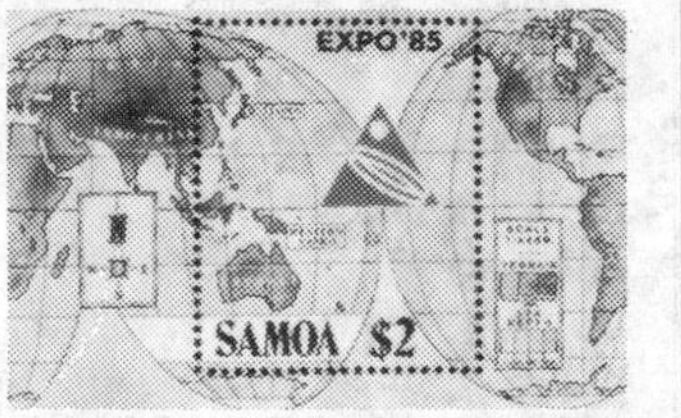

EXPO '85, Tsukuba, Japan — A140

Unwmk.

1985, Aug. 26 Litho. *Perf. 14*

654 A140 $2 Emblem, elevation map 1.75 1.75

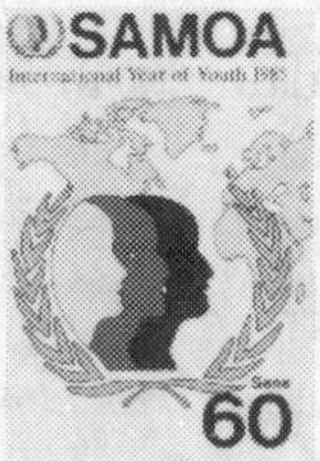

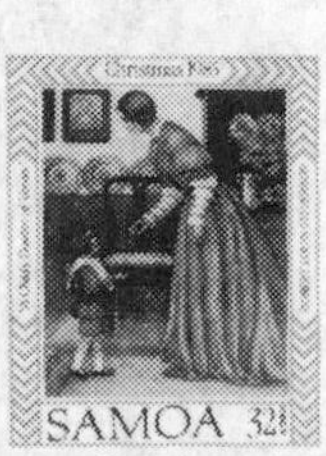

Intl. Youth Year — A141 Christmas 1985 — A142

Portions of world map and: a, Emblem, map of No. America, Europe and Africa. b, Hands reaching high. c, Arms reaching, hands limp. d, Hands clenched. e, Emblem and map of Africa, Asia and Europe.

1985, Sept. 18 Wmk. 373

655 Strip of 5 2.60 2.60
a.-e. A141 60s any single .52 .52

1985, Nov. 5 Unwmk. *Perf. 14x14½*

Illustrations by Millicent Sowerby from A Child's Garden of Verses, by Robert Louis Stevenson.

656 A142 32s System .28 .28
657 A142 48s Time to Rise .42 .42
658 A142 56s Auntie's skirts .50 .50
659 A142 $1 Good Children .90 .90
a. Souvenir sheet of 4, #656-659 2.10 2.10
Nos. 656-659 (4) 2.10 2.10

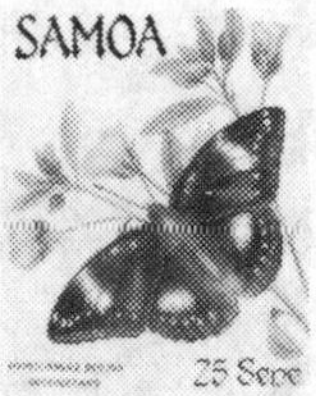

Butterflies — A143

1986, Feb. 13 Wmk. 384 *Perf. 14½*

660 A143 25s Hypolimnas bolina inconstans .40 .40
661 A143 32s Anapheis java sparrman .50 .50
662 A143 48s Deudorix epijarbas doris .70 .70
663 A143 56s Badamia exclamationis .85 .85
664 A143 60s Tirumala hamata melitula 1.00 1.00
665 A143 $1 Catochrysops taitensis 1.75 1.75
Nos. 660-665 (6) 5.20 5.20

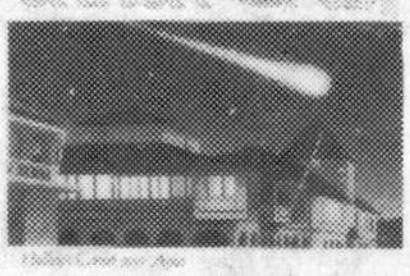

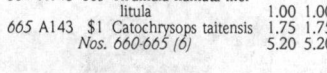

Halley's Comet A144

Designs: 32s, Comet over Apia. 48s, Edmond Halley, astronomer. 60s, Comet orbiting the Earth. $2, Giotto space probe under construction at British Aerospace.

1986, Mar. 24

666 A144 32s multicolored .28 .28
667 A144 48s multicolored .42 .42
668 A144 60s multicolored .52 .52
669 A144 $2 multicolored 1.75 1.75
Nos. 666-669 (4) 2.97 2.97

Queen Elizabeth II 60th Birthday

Common Design Type

Designs: 32s, Engagement to the Duke of Edinburgh, 1947. 48s, State visit to US, 1976. 56s, Attending outdoor ceremony, Apia, 1977. 67s, At Badminton Horse Trials, 1978. $2, Visiting Crown Agents' offices, 1983.

1986, Apr. 21

670 CD337 32s scarlet, blk & sil .28 .28
671 CD337 48s ultra & multi .42 .42
672 CD337 56s green & multi .50 .50
673 CD337 67s violet & multi .60 .60
674 CD337 $2 rose violet & multi 1.75 1.75
Nos. 670-674 (5) 3.55 3.55

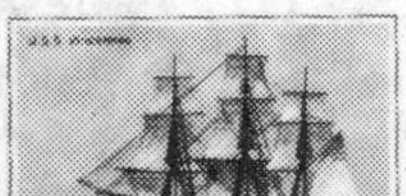

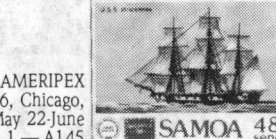

AMERIPEX '86, Chicago, May 22-June 1 — A145

1986, May 22 Unwmk.

675 A145 48s USS Vincennes .42 .42
676 A145 56s Sikorsky S-42 .50 .50
677 A145 60s USS Swan .52 .52
678 A145 $2 Apollo 10 splashdown 1.75 1.75
Nos. 675-678 (4) 3.19 3.19

Souvenir Sheet

Vailima, Estate of Novelist Robert Louis Stevenson, Upolu Is. — A146

1986, Aug. 4   Litho.   Perf. 13½
679 A146 $3 multicolored   3.25 3.25

STAMPEX '86, Adelaide, Aug. 4-10.

Fish — A147

1986, Aug. 13   Unwmk.   Perf. 14
680 A147 32s Spotted grouper   .30   .30
681 A147 48s Sabel squirrelfish   .45   .45
682 A147 60s Lunartail grouper   .55   .55
683 A147 67s Longtail snapper   .70   .70
684 A147 $1 Berndt's soldierfish   1.10 1.10
  Nos. 680-684 (5)   3.10 3.10

US Peace Corps in Samoa, 25th Anniv. A148

Statesmen: Vaai Kolone of Samoa, Ronald Reagan of US and: 45s, Fiame Mata'afa, John F. Kennedy (1961) and Parliament House. 60s, Jules Grevy, Grover Cleveland (1886) and the Statue of Liberty.

1986, Dec. 1   Perf. 14½
685 A148 45s multicolored   .40   .40
686 A148 60s multicolored   .55   .55
  a. Souvenir sheet of 2, #685-686 2.00 2.00

Christmas, Statue of Liberty, cent.

Natl. Independence, 25th Anniv. — A149

Perf. 14x14½
1987, Feb. 16   Litho.   Unwmk.
687 A149 15s Map, hibiscus   .15   .15
688 A149 45s Parliament   .40   .40
689 A149 60s Rowing race, 1987   .55   .55
690 A149 70s Dove   .62   .62
691 A149 $2 Prime minister, flag   1.75 1.75
  Nos. 687-691 (5)   3.47 3.47

Nos. 687-690 vert.

Marine Life A150

1987, Mar. 31
692 A150 45s Gulper   .45   .45
693 A150 60s Hatchet-fish   .60   .60
694 A150 70s Angler   .70   .70
695 A150 $2 Gulper, diff.   1.90 1.90
  Nos. 692-695 (4)   3.65 3.65

Souvenir Sheet

CAPEX '87 — A151

1987, June 13   Perf. 14½
696 A151 $3 Logger, construction
              workers   2.75 2.75

Landscapes A152

1987, July 29   Perf. 14
697 A152 45s Lefaga Beach, Upolu   .42   .42
698 A152 60s Vaisala Beach, Savaii .55   .55
699 A152 70s Solosolo Beach, Upolu .65   .65
700 A152 $2 Neiafu Beach, Savaii   1.90 1.90
  Nos. 697-700 (4)   3.52 3.52

Australia Bicentennial A153

Explorers of the Pacific: 40s, Abel Tasman (c. 1603-1659), Dutch navigator, discovered Tasmania, 1642. 45s, James Cook. 80s, Count Louis-Antoine de Bougainville (1729-1811), French navigator, discovered Bougainville Is., largest of the Solomon Isls., 1768. $2, Comte de La Perouse (1741-1788), French navigator, discovered La Perouse Strait.

1987, Sept. 30   Litho.   Perf. 14½
701 A153 40s multicolored   .38   .38
702 A153 45s multicolored   .42   .42
703 A153 80s multicolored   .78   .78
704 A153 $2 multicolored   1.90 1.90
  a. Souvenir sheet of 1   1.95 1.95
  Nos. 701-704 (13)   66.70 34.95

No. 704a Ovptd. with HAFNIA '87 Emblem in Scarlet

1987, Oct. 16
705 A153 $2 multicolored   1.95 1.95

Christmas 1987 — A154

1987, Nov. 30   Perf. 14
706 A154 40s Christmas tree   .38   .38
707 A154 45s Going to church   .42   .42
708 A154 50s Bamboo fire-gun   .48   .48
709 A154 80s Going home   .78   .78
  Nos. 706-709 (4)   2.06 2.06

Australia Bicentennial A155

Designs: a, Samoan natl. crest, Australia Post emblem. b, Two jets, postal van. c, Loading airmail. d, Jet, van, postman. e, Congratulatory aerogramme.

1988, Jan. 27   Perf. 14½
710   Strip of 5   3.00 3.00
  a.-e. A155 45s any single   .60   .60

Faleolo Intl. Airport A156

Perf. 13x13½
1988, Mar. 24   Litho.   Unwmk.
711 A156 40s Terminal, Boeing 727   .40   .40
712 A156 45s Boeing 727, Fuatino   .45   .45
713 A156 60s So. Pacific Is. N43SP,
              terminal   .60   .60
714 A156 70s Air New Zealand Boe-
              ing 737   .68   .68
715 A156 80s Tower, jet   .78   .78
716 A156 $1 Hawaian Air DC-9,
              VIP house   .98   .98
  Nos. 711-716 (6)   3.89 3.89

EXPO '88, Brisbane, Australia A157

1988, Apr. 27   Perf. 14½
717 A157 45s Island village display .45   .45
718 A157 70s EXPO complex, mono-
              rail and flags   .70   .70
719 A157 $2 Map   2.00 2.00
  Nos. 717-719 (3)   3.15 3.15

Souvenir Sheet

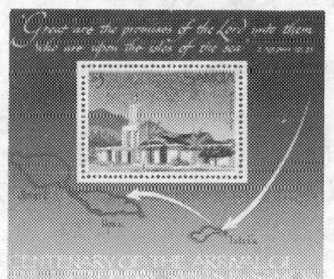

Arrival of the Latter Day Saints in Samoa, Cent. — A158

1988, June 9   Litho.   Perf. 13½
720 A158 $3 The Temple, Apia   3.00 3.00

1988 Summer Olympics, Seoul — A159   Birds — A160

1988, Aug. 10   Litho.   Perf. 14
721 A159 15s Running   .15   .15
722 A159 60s Weight lifting   .60   .60
723 A159 80s Boxing   .80   .80
724 A159 $2 Olympic Stadium   2.00 2.00
  a. Souvenir sheet of 4, #721-724 3.55 3.55
  Nos. 721-724 (4)   3.55 3.55

1988-89   Unwmk.   Perf. 13½
725 A160 10s Polynesian triller   .15   .15
726 A160 15s Samoan wood rail   .15   .15
727 A160 20s Flat-billed kingfisher .20   .20
728 A160 25s Samoan fantail   .25   .25
729 A160 35s Scarlet robin   .35   .35
730 A160 40s Mao   .38   .38
731 A160 50s Cardinal honeyeater   .48   .48
732 A160 65s Samoan whistler   .62   .62
733 A160 75s Many-colored fruit
              dove   .72   .72
734 A160 85s White-throated pigeon .80   .80
Perf. 14
Size:45x39mm
735 A160 75s Silver gull   .72   .72
736 A160 85s Great frigatebird   .80   .80
737 A160 90s Eastern reef heron   .86   .86
738 A160 $3 Short-tailed alba-
              tross   2.90 2.90

739 A160 $10 Common fairy tern   9.25 9.25
740 A160 $20 Shy albatross   18.50 18.50
  Nos. 725-740 (16)   37.13 37.13
  Issue dates: #725-734, 8/17/88; #735-738,
2/28/89; #739-740, 7/31/89.

Conservation — A161

1988, Oct. 25   Perf. 14
741 A161 15s Forests, vert.   .15   .15
742 A161 40s Culture, vert.   .38   .38
743 A161 45s Wildlife, vert.   .45   .45
744 A161 50s Water   .48   .48
745 A161 60s Marine resources   .58   .58
746 A161 $1 Land and soil   .95   .95
  Nos. 741-746 (6)   2.99 2.99

Christmas — A162   Orchids — A163

Designs: 15s, 40s, Congregational Church of Jesus, Apia. 40s, Roman Catholic Church, Leauvaa. 45s, Congregational Christian Church, Moataa. $2, Baha'i Temple, Vailima.

Perf. 14x14½
1988, Nov. 14   Litho.   Unwmk.
747 A162 15s multicolored   .15   .15
748 A162 40s multicolored   .38   .38
749 A162 45s multicolored   .45   .45
750 A162 $2 multicolored   1.95 1.95
  a. Souvenir sheet of 4, #747-750 3.00 3.00
  Nos. 747-750 (4)   2.93 2.93

1989, Jan. 31   Litho.   Perf. 14
751 A163 15s Phaius flavus   .16   .16
752 A163 45s Calanthe triplicata   .50   .50
753 A163 60s Luisia teretifolia   .65   .65
754 A163 $3 Dendrobium moh-
              lianum   3.25 3.25
  Nos. 751-754 (4)   4.56 4.56

Apia Hurricane, 1889 — A164

1989, Mar. 16   Litho.   Unwmk.
755   Strip of 4   4.00 4.00
  a. A164 50s SMS Eber   .50   .50
  b. A164 65s SMS Olga   .65   .65
  c. A164 85s SMS Calliope   .85   .85
  d. A164 $2 SMS Vandalia   2.00 2.00
  e. Souv. sheet of 2, #c-d, imperf. 2.85 2.85

World Stamp Expo '89.
#755e, issued Nov. 17, is wmk. 355.

Intl. Red Cross and Red Crescent Organizations, 125th Annivs. — A165

1989, May 15   Perf. 14½x14
756 A165 50s Youths in parade   .45   .45
757 A165 65s Blood donation   .60   .60
758 A165 75s First Aid   .68   .68
759 A165 $3 Volunteers   2.75 2.75
  Nos. 756-759 (4)   4.48 4.48

Moon Landing, 20th Anniv.
Common Design Type

Apollo 14: 18s, Saturn-Apollo vehicle and mobile launcher. 50s, Alan Shepard, Stuart Roosa and Edgar Mitchell. 65s, Mission emblem. $2, Tracks of the modularised equipment transporter. $3, Buzz Aldrin and American flag raised on the Moon, Apollo 11 mission.

1989, July 20   Wmk. 384   *Perf. 14*
Size of Nos. 761-762: 29x29mm
760	CD342	18s multicolored	.16	.16
761	CD342	50s multicolored	.45	.45
762	CD342	65s multicolored	.60	.60
763	CD342	$2 multicolored	1.80	1.80
		Nos. 760-763 (4)	3.01	3.01

Souvenir Sheet
764	CD342	$3 multicolored	2.75	2.75

"Roosa" is misspelled on No. 761.

Christmas
A166

Perf. 13½x13
1989, Nov. 1   Litho.   Unwmk.
765	A166	18s Joseph and Mary	.16	.16
766	A166	50s Shepherds	.45	.45
767	A166	55s Animals	.50	.50
768	A166	$2 Three kings	1.75	1.75
		Nos. 765-768 (4)	2.86	2.86

Local Transport — A167

Designs: 18s, Pao pao (outrigger canoe). 55s, Fautasi (longboat). 60s, Polynesian Airlines propeller plane. $3, Lady Samoa ferry.

1990, Jan. 31   Unwmk.   *Perf. 14x15*
769	A167	18s multicolored	.16	.16
770	A167	55s multicolored	.48	.48
771	A167	60s multicolored	.52	.52
772	A167	$3 multicolored	2.60	2.60
		Nos. 769-772 (4)	3.76	3.76

Otto von Bismarck, Brandenburg Gate — A168

1990, May 3   *Perf. 14x13½*
773	A168	75s shown	.65	.65
774	A168	$3 SMS Adler	2.60	2.60
a.		Pair, #773-774	3.25	3.25

Opening of the Berlin Wall, 1989, and cent. of the Treaty of Berlin (in 1989). No. 774a has a continuous design.

Great Britain No. 1 and Alexandra Palace — A169

Illustration reduced.

1990, May 3
775	A169	$3 multicolored	2.60	2.60

Stamp World London '90 and 150th anniv. of the Penny Black.

Tourism
A170

1990, July 30   Litho.   *Perf. 14*
776	A170	18s Visitors Bureau	.16	.16
777	A170	50s Samoa Village Resorts	.45	.45
778	A170	65s Aggies Hotel	.60	.60
779	A170	$3 Tusitala Hotel	2.75	2.75
		Nos. 776-779 (4)	3.96	3.96

Souvenir Sheet

No. 240, Exhibition Emblem — A171

1990, Aug. 24   Litho.   *Perf. 13*
780	A171	$3 multicolored	2.30	2.30

World Stamp Exhib., New Zealand 1990.

Christmas — A172

Paintings of Madonna and Child.

1990, Oct. 31   *Perf. 12½*
781	A172	18s Bellini	.16	.16
782	A172	50s Bouts	.45	.45
783	A172	55s Correggio	.50	.50
784	A172	$3 Cima	2.75	2.75
		Nos. 781-784 (4)	3.86	3.86

The 55s is "The School of Love," not "Madonna of the Basket."

UN Development Program, 40th Anniv. — A173

1990, Nov. 26   *Perf. 13½*
785	A173	$3 multicolored	2.75	2.75

Parrots — A174

1991, Apr. 8   Litho.   *Perf. 13½*
786	A174	18s Black-capped lory	.15	.15
787	A174	50s Eclectus parrot	.42	.42
788	A174	65s Scarlet macaw	.55	.55
789	A174	$3 Palm cockatoo	2.50	2.50
		Nos. 786-789 (4)	3.62	3.62

Elizabeth & Philip, Birthdays
Common Design Types
Perf. 14½
1991, June 17   Litho.   Wmk. 384
790	CD346	75s multicolored	.60	.60
791	CD345	$2 multicolored	1.60	1.60
a.		Pair, #790-791 + label	2.20	2.20

Souvenir Sheet

1991 Rugby World Cup — A175

1991, Oct. 12   Litho.   *Perf. 14½*
792	A175	$5 multicolored	4.25	4.25

Christmas
A176

Orchids and Christmas carols: 20s, O Come All Ye Faithful. 60s, Joy to the World. 75s, Hark! the Herald Angels Sing. $4, We Wish You a Merry Christmas.

1991, Oct. 31   Litho.   *Perf. 14½*
793	A176	20s multicolored	.16	.16
794	A176	60s multicolored	.48	.48
795	A176	75s multicolored	.60	.60
796	A176	$4 multicolored	3.20	3.20
		Nos. 793-796 (4)	4.44	4.44

See Nos. 815-818, 836-840.

Phila Nippon '91
A177

Samoan hawkmoths: 60s, Herse convolvuli. 75s, Gnathothlibus erotus. 75s, Hippotion celerio. $3, Cephonodes armatus.

1991, Nov. 16   *Perf. 13½x14*
797	A177	60s multicolored	.48	.48
798	A177	75s multicolored	.60	.60
799	A177	85s multicolored	.70	.70
800	A177	$3 multicolored	2.40	2.40
		Nos. 797-800 (4)	4.18	4.18

Independence, 30th Anniv. — A178

1992, Jan. 8   Litho.   *Perf. 14*
801	A178	50s Honor guard	.40	.40
802	A178	65s Siva scene	.52	.52
803	A178	$1 Parade float	.80	.80
804	A178	$3 Raising flag	2.40	2.40
		Nos. 801-804 (4)	4.12	4.12

Queen Elizabeth II's Accession to the Throne, 40th Anniv.
Common Design Type
1992, Feb. 6   Wmk. 384
805	CD349	20s multicolored	.15	.15
806	CD349	60s multicolored	.48	.48
807	CD349	75s multicolored	.60	.60
808	CD349	85s multicolored	.70	.70

Wmk. 373
809	CD349	$3 multicolored	2.40	2.40
		Nos. 805-809 (5)	4.33	4.33

Souvenir Sheet

Discovery of America, 500th Anniv. — A179

1992, Apr. 17   Unwmk.   *Perf. 14½*
810	A179	$4 No. 1	3.20	3.20

World Columbian Stamp Expo '92, Granada '92 and Genoa '92 Philatelic Exhibitions.

1992 Summer Olympics, Barcelona — A180

1992, July 28   Wmk. 373   *Perf. 14*
811	A180	60s Weight lifting	.50	.50
812	A180	75s Boxing	.65	.65
813	A180	85s Running	.75	.75
814	A180	$3 Stadium, statue	2.60	2.60
		Nos. 811-814 (4)	4.50	4.50

Christmas Type of 1991

Christmas carol, orchid: 50s, "God rest you, merry gentlemen...," liparis layardii. 60s, "While shepherds watched...," corymborkis veratrifolia. 75s, "Away in a manger...," phaius flavus. $4, "O little town...," bulbophyllum longifolium.

1992, Oct. 28   Litho.   *Perf. 14½*
815	A176	50s multicolored	.45	.45
816	A176	60s multicolored	.52	.52
817	A176	75s multicolored	.65	.65
818	A176	$4 multicolored	3.50	3.50
		Nos. 815-818 (4)	5.12	5.12

Fish
A182

1993, Mar. 17   Litho.   *Perf. 14*
819	A182	60s Batfish	.48	.48
820	A182	75s Lined surgeonfish	.58	.58
821	A182	$1 Red-tail snapper	.78	.78
822	A182	$3 Long-nosed emperor	2.35	2.35
		Nos. 819-822 (4)	4.19	4.19

World Cup Seven-a-Side Rugby Championships, Scotland — A183

Designs: 60s, Team performing traditional dance. 75c, Two players, vert. 85c, Player, vert. $3, Edinburgh Castle.

1993, May 12   *Perf. 13½x14*
823	A183	60s multicolored	.48	.48
824	A183	75s multicolored	.58	.58
825	A183	85s multicolored	.68	.68
826	A183	$3 multicolored	2.35	2.35
		Nos. 823-826 (4)	4.09	4.09

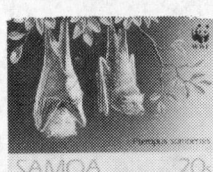

Bats
A184

1993, June 10   *Perf. 14x14¹/₂*
827 A184 20s Two hanging .16 .16
828 A184 50s Two flying .38 .38
829 A184 60s Three flying .48 .48
830 A184 75s One on flower .58 .58
    Nos. 827-830 (4) 1.60 1.60

World Wildlife Fund.

Souvenir Sheet

Taipei '93, Asian Intl. Invitation Stamp
Exhibition — A185

Illustration reduced.

1993, Aug. 16   Litho.   *Perf. 14*
831 A185 $5 multicolored 4.00 4.00

World Post
Day
A186

Designs: 60s, Globe, letter, flowers. 75s, Customers at Post Office. 85s, Black, white hands exchanging letter. $4, Globe, national flags, letter.

1993, Oct. 8   Litho.   *Perf. 14*
832 A186 60s multicolored .45 .45
833 A186 75s multicolored .55 .55
834 A186 85s multicolored .65 .65
835 A186 $4 multicolored 3.00 3.00
    Nos. 832-835 (4) 4.65 4.65

Christmas Type of 1991

Flowers, Christmas carol: 20s, "Silent Night! Holy Night!..." 60s, "As with gladness men of old..." 75s, "Mary had a Baby, Yes Lord..." $1.50, "Once in Royal David's City..." $3, "Angels, from the realms of Glory..."

       Perf. 14¹/₂
1993, Nov. 1   Litho.   Unwmk.
836 A176 20s multicolored .15 .15
837 A176 60s multicolored .45 .45
838 A176 75s multicolored .55 .55
839 A176 $1.50 multicolored 1.10 1.10
840 A176 $3 multicolored 2.25 2.25
    Nos. 836-840 (5) 4.50 4.50

Corals
A187

1994, Feb. 18   Litho.   *Perf. 14*
841 A187 20s Alveropora allingi .15 .15
842 A187 60s Acropora polystoma .45 .45
843 A187 90s Acropora listeri .70 .70
844 A187 $4 Acropora grandis 3.00 3.00
    Nos. 841-844 (4) 4.30 4.30

Ovptd. with Hong Kong '94 Emblem

1994, Feb. 18
845 A187 20s on #841 .15 .15
846 A187 60s on #842 .45 .45
847 A187 90s on #843 .70 .70
848 A187 $4 on #844 3.00 3.00
    Nos. 845-848 (4) 4.30 4.30

Manu
Samoa
Rugby
Team
A188

Designs: 70s, Management. 90s, Test match with Wales. 95s, Test match with New Zealand. $4, Apia Park Stadium.

1994, Apr. 11   Litho.   *Perf. 14*
849 A188 70s multicolored .50 .50
850 A188 90s multicolored .68 .68
851 A188 95s multicolored .70 .70
852 A188 $4 multicolored 3.00 3.00
    Nos. 849-852 (4) 4.88 4.88

Souvenir Sheet

PHILAKOREA '94 — A189

Butterflies: $5, White caper, glasswing. Illustration reduced.

1994, Aug. 16   Litho.   *Perf. 13*
853 A189 $5 multicolored 4.00 4.00

Teuila
Tourism
Festival
A190

1994, Sept. 22   Litho.   *Perf. 13¹/₂*
854 A190 70s Singers .55 .55
855 A190 90s Fire dancer .70 .70
856 A190 95s Parade float .75 .75
857 A190 $4 Police band 3.25 3.25
    Nos. 854-857 (4) 5.25 5.25

A191   A192

1994, Nov. 21   *Perf. 14*
858 A191 70s Schooner Equator .55 .55
859 A191 90s Portrait .70 .70
860 A191 $1.20 Tomb, Mount Vaea .95 .95
861 A191 $4 Vailima House,
      horiz. 3.25 3.25
    Nos. 858-861 (4) 5.45 5.45

Robert Louis Stevenson (1850-94), writer.

1994, Nov. 30

Children's Christmas paintings: 70s, Father Christmas. 95s, Nativity. $1.20, Picnic. $4, Greetings.

862 A192 70s multicolored .55 .55
863 A192 95s multicolored .75 .75
864 A192 $1.20 multicolored .95 .95
865 A192 $4 multicolored 3.25 3.25
    Nos. 862-865 (4) 5.50 5.50

Scenic
Views
A193

Designs: 5s, Lotofaga Beach, Aleipata. 10s, Nuutele Island. 30s, Satuatua, Savaii. 50s, Sinalele, Aleipata. 60s, Paradise Beach, Lefaga. 70s, Houses, Piula Cave. 80s, Taga blowholes. 90s, View from east coast road. 95s, Canoes, Leulumoega. $1, Parliament Building.

1995   Litho.   *Perf. 14¹/₂x13*
866 A193 5s multicolored .15 .15
867 A193 10s multicolored .15 .15
871 A193 30s multicolored .25 .25
874 A193 50s multicolored .40 .40
875 A193 60s multicolored .50 .50
876 A193 70s multicolored .55 .55
877 A193 80s multicolored .65 .65
878 A193 90s multicolored .70 .70
879 A193 95s multicolored .75 .75
880 A193 $1 multicolored .80 .80
    Nos. 866-880 (10) 4.90 4.90

Issued: Nos. 866-867, 871, 874-880, 3/29/95. This is an expanding set. Numbers may change.

1995 World Rugby Cup Championships,
South Africa — A194

Designs: 70s, Players under age 12. 90s, Secondary Schools' rugby teams. $1, Manu Samoa test match with New Zealand. $4, Ellis Park Stadium, Johannesburg.

1995, May 25   Litho.   *Perf. 14x13¹/₂*
886 A194 70s multicolored .55 .55
887 A194 90s multicolored .70 .70
888 A194 $1 multicolored .80 .80
889 A194 $4 multicolored 3.25 3.25
    Nos. 886-889 (4) 5.30 5.30

End of World War II, 50th Anniv.
Common Design Types

Designs: 70s, OS2U Kingfisher over Faleolo Air Base. 90s, F4U Corsair, Faleolo Air Base. 95s, US troops in landing craft. $3, US Marines landing on Samoan beach. $4, Reverse of War Medal 1939-45.

1995, May 31   Litho.   *Perf. 13¹/₂*
890 CD351 70s multicolored .55 .55
891 CD351 90s multicolored .70 .70
892 CD351 95s multicolored .75 .75
893 CD351 $3 multicolored 2.50 2.50
    Nos. 890-893 (4) 4.50 4.50

Souvenir Sheet
Perf. 14
894 CD352 $4 multicolored 3.25 3.25

Year of the Sea
Turtle — A195

1995, Aug. 24   Litho.   *Perf. 13x13¹/₂*
895 A195 70s Leatherback .55 .55
896 A195 90s Loggerhead .70 .70
897 A195 $1 Green turtle .80 .80
898 A195 $4 Pacific Ridley 3.25 3.25
    Nos. 895-898 (4) 5.30 5.30

Souvenir Sheet

Singapore '95 — A196

1995, Sept. 1   *Perf. 14*
899 A196 $5 Phaius tankervilleae 4.00 4.00

UN, 50th Anniv.
Common Design Type

Designs: 70s, Mobile hospital. 90s, Bell Sioux helicopter. $1, Bell 212 helicopter. $4, RNZAF Andover.

Unwmk.
1995, Oct. 24   Litho.   *Perf. 14*
900 CD353 70s multicolored .55 .55
901 CD353 90s multicolored .70 .70
902 CD353 $1 multicolored .80 .80
903 CD353 $4 multicolored 3.25 3.25
    Nos. 900-903 (4) 5.30 5.30

Christmas — A197

1995, Nov. 15   *Perf. 14¹/₂*
904 A197 25s Madonna & Child .20 .20
905 A197 70s Wise Man .55 .55
906 A197 90s Wise Man, diff. .70 .70
907 A197 $5 Wise Man, diff. 4.00 4.00
    Nos. 904-907 (4) 5.45 5.45

SEMI-POSTAL STAMP

Catalogue values for unused stamps in this section are for Never Hinged items.

No. 246 Surcharged: "HURRICANE
RELIEF / 6d"

Perf. 13¹/₂
1966, Sept. 1   Wmk. 355   Litho.
B1 A43 8p + 6p blue & emerald .20 .20

Surtax for aid to plantations destroyed by the hurricane of Jan. 29, 1966.

AIR POST STAMPS

Catalogue values for unused stamps in this section are for Never Hinged items.

Red-tailed
Tropic
Bird — AP1

The index in each volume of the Scott Catalogue contains many listings that help identify stamps.

Perf. 14½

1965, Dec. 29 Wmk. 355 Photo.

C1	AP1 8p shown	.26	.26
C2	AP1 2sh Flying fish	.65	.65

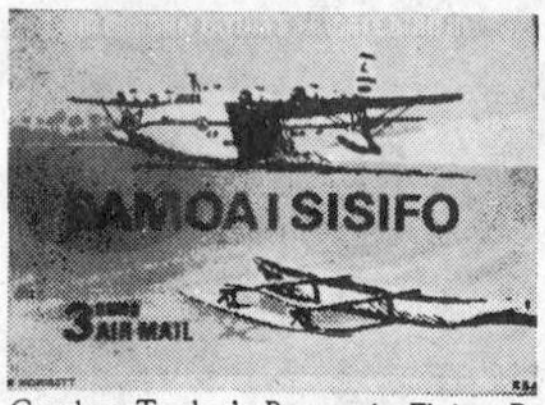

Sir Gordon Taylor's Bermuda Flying Boat "Frigate Bird III" — AP2

Designs: 7s, Polynesian Airlines DC-3. 20s, Pan American Airways "Samoan Clipper." 30s, Air Samoa Britten-Norman "Islander."

Perf. 13½x13

1970, July 27 Photo. Unwmk.

C3	AP2 3s multicolored	.15	.15
C4	AP2 7s multicolored	.30	.30
C5	AP2 20s multicolored	.90	.90
C6	AP2 30s multicolored	1.40	1.40
	Nos. C3-C6 (4)	2.75	2.75

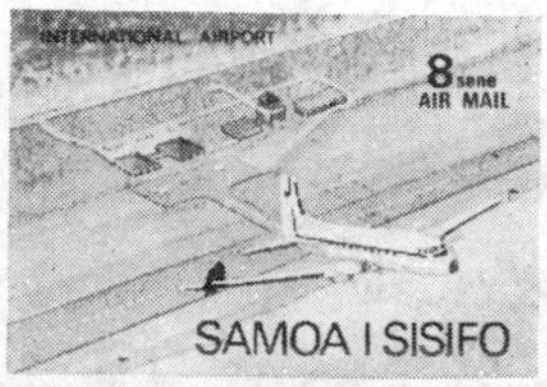

Hawker Siddeley 748 — AP3

Planes at Faleolo Airport: 10s, Hawker Siddeley 748 in the air. 12s, Hawker Siddeley 748 on ground. 22s, BAC 1-11 planes on ground.

1973, Mar. 9 *Perf. 11½*

Granite Paper

C7	AP3 8s multicolored	.30	.30
C8	AP3 10s multicolored	.38	.38
C9	AP3 12s multicolored	.45	.45
C10	AP3 22s multicolored	.85	.85
	Nos. C7-C10 (4)	1.98	1.98

SARAWAK

sə-'rä-(,)wä(k)

LOCATION — Northwestern part of the island of Borneo, bordering on the South China Sea
GOVT. — Former British Crown Colony
AREA — 48,250 sq. mi. (approx.)
POP. — 975,918 (1970)
CAPITAL — Kuching

The last ruling Raja, who retired in 1946 when he ceded Sarawak to the British Crown, was Sir Charles Vyner Brooke, an Englishman. He inherited the title from his father, Sir Charles Johnson Brooke, who in turn received it from his uncle, Sir James Brooke. The title of Raja was conferred on Sir James by Raja Muda Hassim after Sir James had aided him in subduing a rebellion. The title and right of succession were duly recognized by the Sultan of Brunei and by Great Britain.

Sarawak joined the Federation of Malaysia in 1963.

100 Cents = 1 Dollar

Catalogue values for unused stamps in this country are for Never Hinged items, beginning with Scott 155.

Watermarks

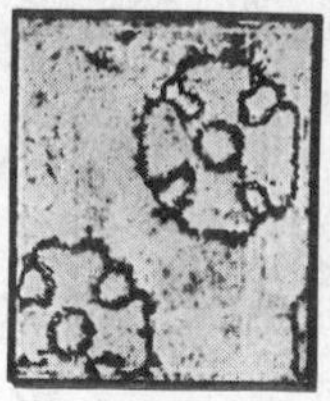

Wmk. 47- Multiple Rosettes

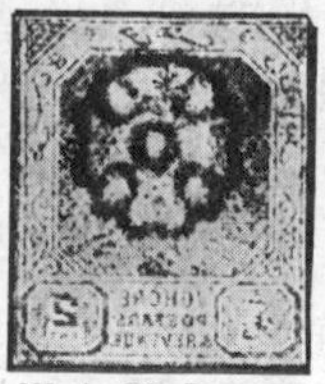

Wmk. 71- Rosette

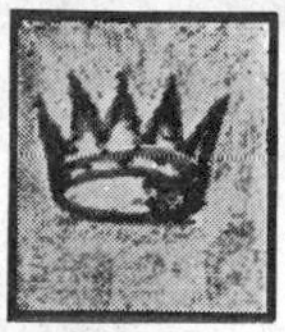

Wmk. 231- Oriental Crown

Unused examples of Nos. 1-7, 25 and 32-35 are valued without gum. Stamps with original gum are worth more.

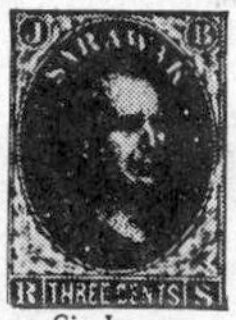

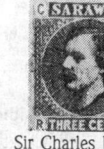

Sir James Brooke — A1

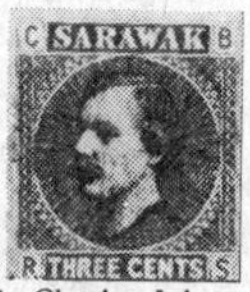

Sir Charles Johnson Brooke — A2

Unwmk.

1869, Mar. 1 Litho. *Perf. 11*

1	A1 3c brown, *yellow*	45.00	*225.00*

1871, Jan.

2	A2 3c brown, *yellow*	1.50	*3.25*

No. 2 surcharged "TWO CENTS" is believed to be bogus.

There are a number of varieties including narrow A, "period" after THREE, etc.

Imperfs. of Nos. 1, 2 are proofs.

For surcharges, see Nos. 25, 32.

1875, Jan. 1 *Perf. 12*

3	A2 2c gray lilac, *lilac*	3.25	*6.00*
4	A2 4c brown, *yellow*	3.00	*4.00*
b.	Vertical pair, imperf between	*525.00*	
5	A2 6c green, *green*	3.00	*5.00*
6	A2 8c blue, *blue*	3.00	*4.00*
c.	Laid paper		
7	A2 12c red, *rose*	6.00	*9.00*
	Nos. 3-7 (5)	18.25	*28.00*

Nos. 3-7 have each five varieties of the words of value.

For surcharges see Nos. 33-35.

Imperfs are proofs.

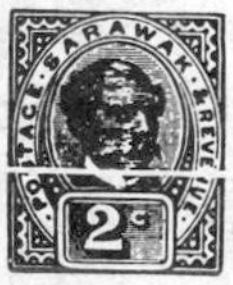

Sir Charles Johnson Brooke — A4

1888-97 Typo. *Perf. 14*

8	A4 1c lilac & black ('92)	1.00	.45
9	A4 2c lilac & rose	1.25	.60
10	A4 3c lilac & blue	1.10	.75
11	A4 4c lilac & yellow	9.00	*12.00*
12	A4 5c lilac & green ('91)	6.00	4.00
13	A4 6c lilac & brown	10.00	*30.00*
14	A4 8c green & rose	4.00	2.00
a.	8c green & carmine	10.00	4.25
15	A4 10c green & vio ('93)	21.00	12.50
16	A4 12c green & blue	3.00	*6.00*
17	A4 16c gray grn & org ('97)	27.50	*40.00*
18	A4 25c green & brown	22.50	*27.50*
19	A4 32c gray grn & blk ('97)	20.00	*30.00*
20	A4 50c gray green ('97)	22.50	*60.00*
21	A4 $1 gray grn & blk ('97)	42.50	*60.00*
	Nos. 8-21 (14)	191.35	*285.80*

No. 21 shows the numeral on white tablet.

Three higher values —$2, $5, $10— were prepared but not issued. Value $300 each.

For surcharges see Nos. 22-24, 26-27.

Nos. 14 and 16 Surcharged in Black:

2c. a **5c.** No. 23 **5c.** No. 24

1889-91

22	A4 2c on 8c	2.25	4.50
a.	Double surcharge	300.00	
b.	Pair, one without surcharge	2,000.	
c.	Inverted surcharge	2,000.	
23	A4 5c on 12c ('91)	15.00	15.00
a.	Double surcharge	1,100.	*1,100.*
b.	Pair, one without surcharge	—	
c.	No period after "C"	18.00	21.00
d.	Without "C"	250.00	—
e.	Dbl. surch., one vert.	1,750.	
24	A4 5c on 12c ('91)	55.00	*105.00*
a.	No period after "C"	45.00	*105.00*
b.	Double surcharge	750.00	
c.	"C" omitted	375.00	300.00

No. 2 Surcharged in Black **ONE CENT**

1892, May 23 *Perf. 11*

25	A2 1c on 3c brown, *yel*	.70	2.00
b.	Without bar	2.75	
c.	Period after "THREE"	13.00	18.00
d.	Double surcharge	375.00	

No. 10 Surcharged in Black:

one cent. e **One Cent.** f

1892 *Perf. 14*

26	A4(e) 1c on 3c lilac & blue	2.75	5.50
a.	No period after "cent"	100.00	100.00
27	A4(f) 1c on 3c lilac & blue	30.00	30.00
b.	Double surcharge	375.00	275.00

Issued: #26, Feb.; #27, Jan. 12.

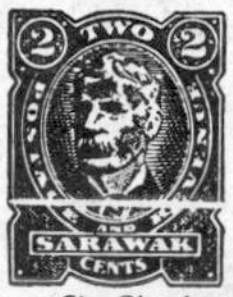

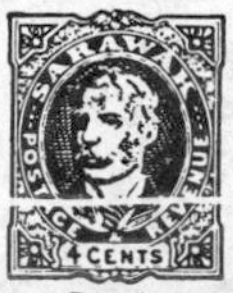

Sir Charles Johnson Brooke
A11 A12

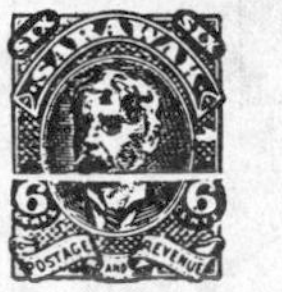

A13

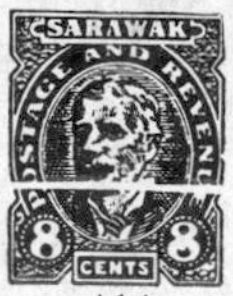

A14

1895, Jan. 1 Engr. *Perf. 11½, 12*

28	A11 2c red brn, perf. 12½	5.00	5.00
a.	Perf. 11½	4.00	4.25
29	A12 4c black	3.00	3.00
30	A13 6c violet	3.00	6.00
31	A14 8c deep green	12.50	10.50
	Nos. 28-31 (4)	23.50	24.50

The 2c and 8c imperf are proofs.

Stamps of 1871-75 Surcharged in Black or Red **2 CENTS.**

1899 *Perf. 11*

32	A2 2c on 3c brown, *yel*	1.25	2.00
a.	Period after "THREE"	50.00	

Perf. 12

33	A2 2c on 12c red, *rose*	2.50	*2.00*
a.	Inverted surcharge	900.00	*1,050.*
34	A2 4c on 6c green, *grn* (R)	17.50	*40.00*
a.	Inverted surcharge		
35	A2 4c on 8c blue, *bl* (R)	3.50	7.25
	Nos. 32-35 (4)	24.75	*51.25*

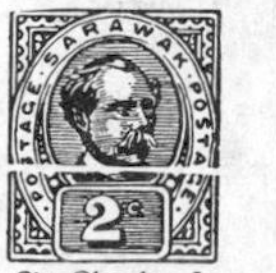

Sir Charles J. Brooke
A16

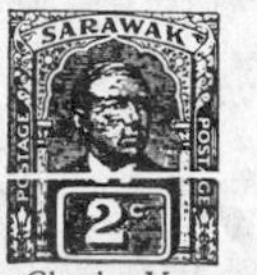

Sir Charles Vyner Brooke
A17

1899-1908 Typo. *Perf. 14*

36	A16 1c blue & car ('01)	.40	.65
37	A16 2c gray green	.75	.40
38	A16 3c dull violet ('08)	2.25	.35
39	A16 4c rose	1.25	2.00
40	A16 8c yellow & black	1.25	1.00
41	A16 10c ultra	1.25	.50
42	A16 12c light violet	1.90	1.75
43	A16 16c org brn & grn	1.25	1.75
44	A16 20c brn ol & vio ('00)	3.00	2.25
45	A16 25c brown & ultra	2.00	4.00
46	A16 50c ol grn & rose	10.00	*15.00*
47	A16 $1 rose & green	22.50	*50.00*
	Nos. 36-47 (12)	47.80	*79.65*

A 5c was prepared but not issued. Value $15.

1901 Wmk. 71

48	A16 2c gray green	15.00	10.00

1918-23 Unwmk.

50	A17 1c slate blue & rose	.60	.15
51	A17 2c deep green	1.10	.20
52	A17 2c violet ('23)	1.10	.30
53	A17 3c violet brown	2.25	1.00
54	A17 3c deep green ('22)	.75	.30
55	A17 4c carmine rose	2.00	.40
56	A17 4c purple brn ('23)	.75	.15
57	A17 5c orange ('23)	.90	.20
58	A17 6c lake brown ('22)	.75	1.00
59	A17 8c yellow & blk	4.75	*30.00*
60	A17 8c carmine rose ('22)	1.75	.65
61	A17 10c ultra	1.75	1.50
a.	10c blue	1.75	1.50
62	A17 10c black ('23)	1.50	2.00
63	A17 12c violet	5.50	8.00
64	A17 12c ultra ('22)	5.75	*10.00*
65	A17 16c brn & blue grn	3.75	4.00
66	A17 20c olive bis & vio	3.00	4.00
a.	20c olive green & violet	3.00	4.00
67	A17 25c brown & blue	3.00	*5.00*
68	A17 30c bis & gray ('22)	2.75	*2.50*
69	A17 50c olive grn & rose	4.75	6.00
70	A17 $1 car rose & grn	9.50	*12.00*
	Nos. 50-70 (21)	57.95	*89.35*

In 1918 a supply of the 1c (No. 50) had the value tablet printed, by error, in slate blue instead of rose. It is officially stated that this stamp was never issued and had no franking power. Value $20.

The $1 denomination shows numeral of value in color on white tablet.

Nos. 61 and 63 Surcharged **ONE cent**

1st Printing - bars 1¼mm apart.
2nd Printing - Bars ¾mm apart.

1923, Jan.

77	A17 1c on 10c ultra	15.00	*50.00*
a.	"cnet"	300.00	*600.00*
b.	Bars ¾mm apart	75.00	
78	A17 2c on 12c violet	5.00	*10.00*
a.	Bars ¾mm apart	50.00	

Type of 1918 Issue

1928-29 Typo. Wmk. 47

79	A17 1c slate blue & rose	.50	.30
80	A17 2c dull violet	.75	.25
81	A17 3c deep green	.50	*1.00*
82	A17 4c purple brown	1.25	.20
83	A17 5c orange ('29)	4.00	*4.00*
84	A17 6c brown lake	.90	.40
85	A17 8c carmine	1.90	*6.00*
86	A17 10c black	1.50	1.00
87	A17 12c ultra	2.25	*7.50*
88	A17 16c dp brn & bl grn	1.90	*2.00*
89	A17 20c dp olive & vio	1.50	1.40
90	A17 25c dk brown & ultra	3.00	*3.00*
91	A17 30c olive bis & gray	3.00	2.50
92	A17 50c olive grn & rose	3.50	*3.00*
93	A17 $1 car rose & grn	12.50	*20.00*
	Nos. 79-93 (15)	38.95	*52.55*

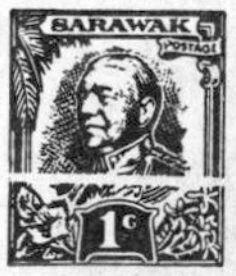

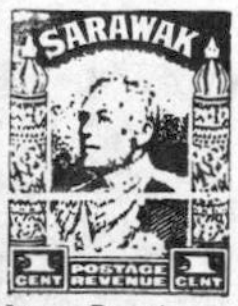

Sir Charles Vyner Brooke
A18 A19

Perf. 12½

1932, Jan. 1 Engr. Wmk. 231

94	A18 1c indigo	.60	.40
95	A18 2c dark green	.60	.40
96	A18 3c deep violet	2.50	.65
97	A18 4c deep orange	.90	.25
98	A18 5c brown lake	2.50	.65
99	A18 6c deep red	3.50	*4.00*
100	A18 8c orange yel	2.50	*5.00*
101	A18 10c black	2.50	*5.00*
102	A18 12c violet blue	2.50	*4.00*
103	A18 15c orange brown	3.75	*4.00*
104	A18 20c violet & org	2.50	*4.00*
105	A18 25c org brn & yel	5.00	*6.00*
106	A18 30c org red & ol brn	5.00	*10.00*
107	A18 50c olive grn & red	5.75	*8.75*
108	A18 $1 car & green	10.00	*17.50*
	Nos. 94-108 (15)	50.10	*70.60*

1934-41 Unwmk. *Perf. 12*

109	A19 1c brown violet	.15	.15
110	A19 2c blue green	.15	.15
111	A19 2c black ('41)	.70	*1.40*
112	A19 3c black	.20	.15
113	A19 3c blue grn ('41)	1.00	1.00

114 A19 4c magenta .45 .15
115 A19 5c violet .20 .15
116 A19 6c deep rose .20 .40
117 A19 6c red brn ('41) 2.50 *4.00*
118 A19 8c red brown .20 .20
119 A19 8c deep rose ('41) 2.00 .25
120 A19 10c red .90 .45
121 A19 12c deep ultra .45 .50
122 A19 12c orange ('41) .70 *5.25*
123 A19 15c orange .80 *5.00*
124 A19 15c deep blue ('41) 2.50 *5.25*
125 A19 20c dp rose & olive 1.00 .60
126 A19 25c orange & vio 1.00 *.70*
127 A19 30c violet & red brn 1.00 1.00
128 A19 50c red & violet 1.00 .50
129 A19 $1 dk brown & red 1.00 1.00
130 A19 $2 violet & mag 2.75 *5.50*
131 A19 $3 blue grn & rose 15.00 *10.00*
132 A19 $4 red & ultra 16.00 *12.00*
133 A19 $5 red brn & red 18.00 *27.50*
134 A19 $10 orange & blk 20.00 *42.50*
Nos. 109-134 (26) 89.85 *125.75*

Issue dates: May 1, 1934, Mar. 1, 1941.
For overprints see #135-154, 159-173, N1-N22.

Stamps of 1934-41 Overprinted in Black or Red **B M A**

1945, Dec. 17
135 A19 1c brown violet .15 .20
136 A19 2c black (R) .15 .20
137 A19 3c blue green .15 .20
138 A19 4c magenta .15 .20
139 A19 5c violet (R) .20 .45
140 A19 6c red brown .20 .45
141 A19 8c deep rose 6.00 7.00
142 A19 10c red .25 .45
143 A19 12c orange .40 *2.75*
144 A19 15c deep blue .60 .25
145 A19 20c dp rose & ol 1.00 1.00
146 A19 25c org & vio (R) 1.00 *1.50*
147 A19 30c vio & red brn 1.00 *2.00*
148 A19 50c red & violet .85 .25
149 A19 $1 dk brown & red 2.00 .95
150 A19 $2 violet & mag 5.00 3.50
151 A19 $3 blue grn & rose 10.50 19.00
152 A19 $4 red & ultra 15.00 19.00
153 A19 $5 red brn & red 60.00 70.00
154 A19 $10 org & blk (R) 60.00 85.00
Nos. 135-154 (20) 164.60 214.35

Catalogue values for unused stamps in this section, from this point to the end of the section, are for Never Hinged items.

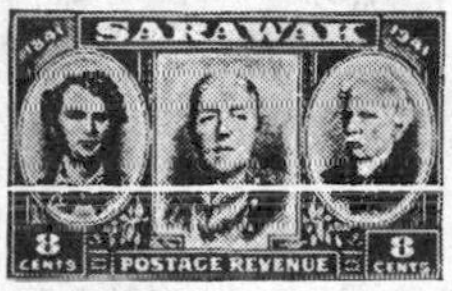
Sir James Brooke, Sir Charles V. Brooke and Sir Charles J. Brooke A20

1946, May 18
155 A20 8c dark carmine .15 .15
156 A20 15c dark blue .35 .35
157 A20 50c red & black .60 .60
158 A20 $1 sepia & black 2.25 *3.75*
Nos. 155-158 (4) 3.35 *4.85*

Type of 1934-41 Overprinted in Blue or Red
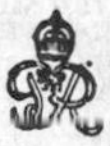

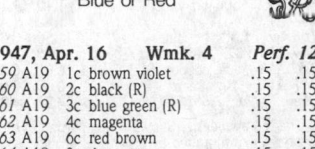

1947, Apr. 16 Wmk. 4 *Perf. 12*
159 A19 1c brown violet .15 .15
160 A19 2c black (R) .15 .15
161 A19 3c blue green (R) .15 .15
162 A19 4c magenta .15 .15
163 A19 6c red brown .15 .15
164 A19 8c deep rose .15 .15
165 A19 10c red .15 .15
166 A19 12c orange .15 .15
167 A19 15c deep blue (R) .20 .20
168 A19 20c dp rose & ol (R) .24 .24
169 A19 25c orange & vio (R) .24 .24
170 A19 50c red & vio (R) .40 .40
171 A19 $1 dk brown & red 1.10 1.10
172 A19 $2 violet & mag 1.90 1.90
173 A19 $5 red brown & red 4.25 4.25
Nos. 159-173 (15) 9.53 9.53

Silver Wedding Issue
Common Design Types
1948, Oct. 25 Photo. *Perf. 14x14½*
174 CD304 8c scarlet .15 .15

Engraved; Name Typographed
Perf. 11½x11
175 CD305 $5 light brown 24.00 25.00

UPU Issue
Common Design Types
Engr.; Name Typo. on 15c, 25c
Perf. 13½, 11x11½
1949, Oct. 10 Wmk. 4
176 CD306 8c rose carmine .55 .55
177 CD307 15c indigo .75 .75
178 CD308 25c green 1.40 1.40
179 CD309 50c violet 3.50 3.50
Nos. 176-179 (4) 6.20 6.20

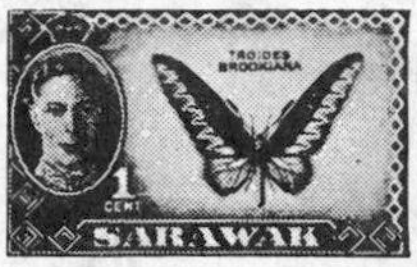
Troides Brookiana A21

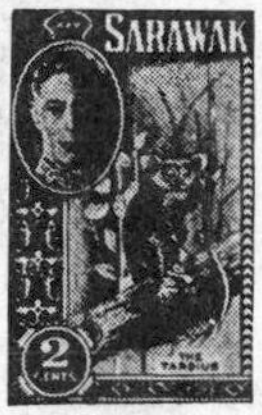
Western Tarsier — A22

Designs: 3c, Kayan tomb. 4c, Kayan girl and boy. 6c, Bead work. 8c, Dyak dancer. 10c, Scaly anteater. 12c, Kenyah boys. 15c, Fire making. 20c, Kelemantan rice barn. 25c, Pepper vines. 50c, Iban woman. $1, Kelabit smithy. $2, Map of Sarawak. $5, Arms of Sarawak.

Perf. 11½x11, 11x11½
1950, Jan. 3 Engr.
180 A21 1c black .20 .15
181 A22 2c orange red .20 .15
182 A22 3c green .24 .20
183 A22 4c brown .24 .20
184 A22 6c aquamarine .30 .20
185 A21 8c red .45 .30
186 A21 10c orange 2.25 2.25
187 A21 12c purple .45 .30
188 A21 15c deep blue .50 .24
189 A21 20c red org & brn .75 .50
190 A21 25c carmine & grn .85 .60
191 A22 50c purple & brn 1.25 1.00
192 A21 $1 dk brn & bl grn 2.25 2.25
193 A21 $2 rose car & blue 16.00 10.50

Engr. and Typo.
194 A21 $5 dp vio, blk, red & yel 16.00 8.75
Nos. 180-194 (15) 41.93 27.59

1952, Feb. 1
195 A21 10c orange *(Map)* .70 .35

Coronation Issue
Common Design Type
1953, June 3 Engr. *Perf. 13½x13*
196 CD312 10c ultra & black .60 .60

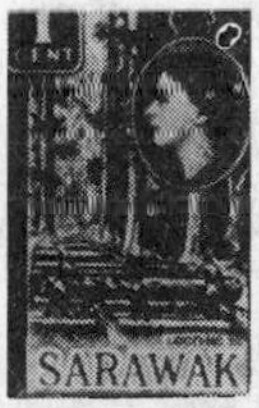
Logging — A23

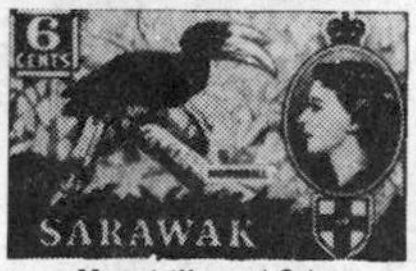
Hornbill — A24

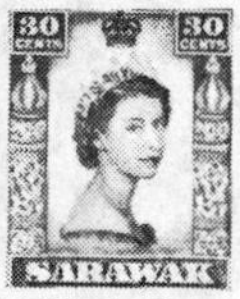
Elizabeth II — A25

Designs: 2c, Young Orangutan. 4c, Kayan Dancing. 8c, Shield with spears. 10c, Kenyah ceremonial carving. 12c, Barong Panau (sailboat). 15c, Turtles. 20c, Melanau basket making. 25c, Astana, Kuching (Governor's Residence). $1, $2, Queen Elizabeth II (Portrait like Fiji A39). $5, Arms.

Perf. 11x11½, 11½x11, 12x12½ (A25)
1955-57 Wmk. 4 Engr.
197 A23 1c green .15 .15
198 A23 2c red orange .15 .15
199 A23 4c brown carmine .15 .15
200 A24 6c greenish blue .25 .22
201 A24 8c rose red .15 .15
202 A24 10c dark green .25 .15
203 A24 12c purple .30 .15
204 A24 15c ultra .40 .15
205 A24 20c brown & olive .45 .25
206 A24 25c brt green & brn .65 .25
207 A25 30c violet & red brn 1.00 .15
208 A25 50c car rose & blk .95 .45
209 A25 $1 orange brn & grn 3.00 .75
210 A25 $2 green & violet 6.75 2.25

Engr. and Typo.
211 A24 $5 dp vio, blk, red & yel 21.00 6.00
Nos. 197-211 (15) 35.60 11.37

Issued: 30c, June 1, 1955; others, Oct. 1, 1957.
See Nos. 215-222.

Freedom from Hunger Issue
Common Design Type
Perf. 14x14½
1963, June 4 Photo. Wmk. 314
212 CD314 12c sepia 1.25 .20

STATE OF MALAYSIA
Types of 1955-57
Perf. 11x11½, 11½x11
1964-65 Engr. Wmk. 314
215 A23 1c green .15 .15
216 A23 2c red orange .50 *2.00*
217 A24 6c green blue 3.25 *2.00*
218 A24 10c dark green .80 .60
219 A24 12c purple 1.25 *3.00*
220 A24 15c ultra 1.00 *5.00*
221 A24 20c brown & olive .40 1.25
222 A24 25c brt green & brown 1.65 2.25
Nos. 215-222 (8) 9.00 *16.25*

Issued: 20c, 6/9/64; 2c, 15c, 8/17/65; others, 9/9/64.

Orchid Type of Johore (Malaysia), 1965, with State Crest
Perf. 14½
1965, Nov. 15 Wmk. 338 Photo.
Flowers in Natural Colors
228 A14 1c black & lt grnsh bl .15 .15
229 A14 2c black, red & gray .15 .15
230 A14 5c black & Prus blue .24 .15
231 A14 6c black & lt lilac .35 .20
232 A14 10c black & lt ultra .80 .30
233 A14 15c black, lil rose & grn 1.00 .30
234 A14 20c black & brown 1.25 .50
Nos. 228-234 (7) 3.94
Set value 1.45

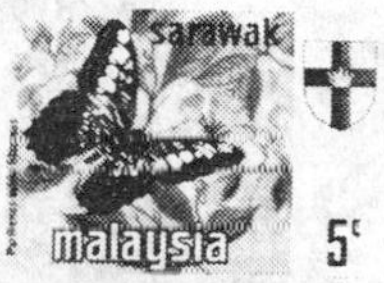
Clipper and State Crest — A26

Perf. 13½x13
1971, Feb. 1 Litho. Unwmk.
235 A26 1c Delias ninus .15 .15
236 A26 2c Danaus melanippus .15 .15
237 A26 5c Parthenos sylvia .15 .15
a. Booklet pane of 4 ('73) .75
238 A26 6c Papilio demoleus .18 .15
239 A26 10c Hebomnia glaucippe .38 .15
a. Booklet pane of 4 ('73) 1.90
240 A26 15c Precis orithya .45 .22
a. Booklet pane of 4 ('73) 2.25
241 A26 20c Valeria valeria .90 .38
Nos. 235-241 (7) 2.36
Set value .95

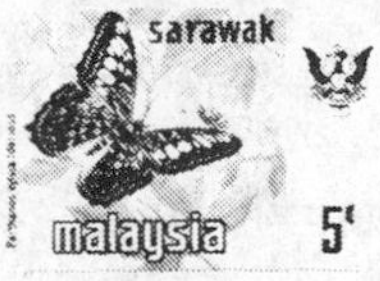
Clipper and New State Crest — A27

Changed Colors, Designs as Before
1977-78 Photo. Unwmk.
242 A27 1c multi ('78) 4.00 4.00
243 A27 2c multi ('78) 1.00 *2.00*
244 A27 5c multicolored .20 .15
245 A27 10c multicolored .35 .20
246 A27 15c multicolored 1.00 .30
247 A27 20c multi ('78) 1.00 .40
Nos. 242-247 (6) 7.55 7.05

Flower Type of Johore, 1979, with State Crest
1979, Apr. 30 Wmk. 47 *Perf. 14½*
248 A16 1c multicolored .15 .15
249 A16 2c multicolored .15 .15
250 A16 5c multicolored .15 .15
251 A16 10c multicolored .15 .15
252 A16 15c multicolored .15 .15
253 A16 20c multicolored .16 .15
254 A16 25c multicolored .20 .15
Set value .70 .44

1984-86 Unwmk.
250a A16 5c ('86) 1.05
251a A16 10c ('85) 2.15
253a A16 20c 4.25

Agriculture and State Arms Type of Johore
Wmk. 388
1986, Oct. 25 Litho. *Perf. 12*
255 A19 1c multicolored .15 .15
256 A19 2c multicolored .15 .15
257 A19 5c multicolored .15 .15
258 A19 10c multicolored .15 .15
259 A19 15c multicolored .15 .15
260 A19 20c multicolored .16 .15
261 A19 30c multicolored .24 .15
Set value .75 .45

OCCUPATION STAMPS

Issued under Japanese Occupation

Stamps of 1934-41 Handstamped in Violet 府政国帝本日大

1942 Unwmk. *Perf. 12*
N1 A19 1c brown violet 17.50 20.00
N2 A19 2c blue green 32.50 35.00
N3 A19 2c black 37.50 45.00
N3A A19 3c black *110.00 125.00*
N4 A19 3c blue green 37.50 45.00
N5 A19 4c magenta 24.00 24.00
N6 A19 5c violet 20.00 22.50
N7 A19 6c deep rose 35.00 35.00
N8 A19 6c red brown 35.00 42.50
N8A A19 8c red brown *110.00 125.00*
N9 A19 8c deep rose 77.50 140.00
N10 A19 10c red 24.00 26.00
N11 A19 12c deep ultra 32.50 35.00
N12 A19 12c orange 77.50 82.50
N12A A19 15c orange *110.00 125.00*
N13 A19 15c deep blue 26.00 35.00
N14 A19 20c dp rose & ol 22.50 35.00
N15 A19 25c orange & vio 22.50 35.00
N16 A19 30c violet & red brn 27.50 42.50
N17 A19 50c red & violet 32.50 35.00
N18 A19 $1 dk brown & red 37.50 47.50
N19 A19 $2 violet & mag 77.50 82.50
N19A A19 $3 blue grn & rose *450.00 500.00*
N20 A19 $4 red & ultra 77.50 100.00
N21 A19 $5 red brown & red 77.50 100.00
N22 A19 $10 orange & blk 110.00 140.00
Nos. N1-N22 (26) 1,741. 2,080.

Stamps overprinted with Japanese characters in oval frame or between 2 vertical black lines were not for paying postage.

SEYCHELLES

sā-'shel(z)

LOCATION — A group of islands in the Indian Ocean, off the coast of Africa north of Madagascar.
GOVT. — Republic
AREA — 156 sq. mi.
POP. — 64,718 (est. 1984)
CAPITAL — Victoria

The islands were attached to the British colony of Mauritius from 1810 to 1903, when they became a separate colony. Seychelles achieved internal self-government in October 1975 and independence on June 29, 1976.

100 Cents = 1 Rupee

Catalogue values for unused stamps in this country are for Never Hinged items, beginning with Scott 149 in the regular postage section and Scott J1 in the postage due section.

Watermark

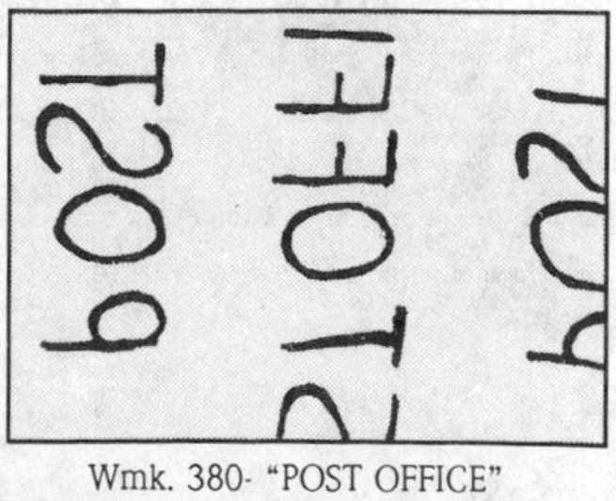
Wmk. 380- "POST OFFICE"

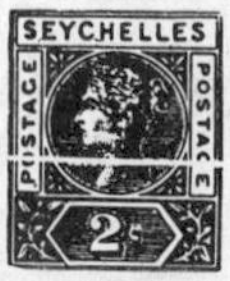

Queen Victoria — A1

Two dies of 2c, 4c, 8c, 10c, 13c, 16c:

Die I - Shading lines at right of diamond in tiara band.

Die II - No shading lines in this rectangle.

1890-1900 Typo. Wmk. 2 *Perf. 14*

1 A1 2c green & rose (II) .65 *.85*
a. Die I 1.10 *7.00*
2 A1 2c org brn & grn ('00) .55 .40
3 A1 3c dk vio & org ('93) .70 .35
4 A1 4c car rose & grn (II) .75 .75
a. Die I 11.00 *9.00*
5 A1 6c car rose ('00) 2.00 *.50*
6 A1 8c brn vio & ultra (II) 3.00 1.50
a. 8c brn vio & bl (I) 3.50 *3.00*
7 A1 10c ultra & brn (II) 3.25 3.00
a. 10c bl & brn (I) 4.50 *10.00*
8 A1 12c ol gray & grn ('93) .85 .60
9 A1 13c slate & blk (II) .85 1.75
a. Die I 4.50 *8.50*
10 A1 15c ol grn & vio ('93) 3.00 2.25
11 A1 15c ultra ('00) 2.25 2.75
12 A1 16c org brn & bl (I) 1.65 3.00
a. 16c org brn & ultra (II) 32.50 6.50
13 A1 18c ultra ('97) 1.50 1.00
14 A1 36c brn & rose ('97) 12.50 4.00
15 A1 45c brn & rose ('93) 18.00 27.50
16 A1 48c ocher & green 14.00 15.00
17 A1 75c yel & pur ('00) 32.50 60.00
18 A1 96c violet & car 32.50 *45.00*
19 A1 1r vio & red ('97) 7.00 4.00
20 A1 1.50r blk & rose ('00) 40.00 70.00
21 A1 2.25r vio & grn ('00) 55.00 *70.00*
Nos. 1-21 (21) 232.50 314.20

Numerals of 75c, 1r, 1.50r and 2.25r of type A1 are in color on plain tablet.

For surcharges see Nos. 22-37.

Surcharged in Black **3 cents**

1893

22 A1 3c on 4c car rose & green (II) 1.00 1.10
a. Inverted surcharge 300.00 *325.00*
b. Double surcharge 600.00
d. Pair, one without surcharge *4,750.*
23 A1 12c on 16c org brown & ultra (II) 2.50 1.10
a. 12c on 16c org brn & bl (I) 1.50 1.35
b. Inverted surcharge (I) 325.00 325.00
d. Double surcharge (I) *4,250.* *5,000.*
e. Double surcharge (II)
24 A1 15c on 16c org brn & ultra (II) 6.00 2.25
a. 15c on 16c org brn & bl (I) 8.00 10.00
b. Inverted surcharge (I) 300.00 300.00
c. Inverted surcharge (II) 650.00 650.00
d. Double surcharge (I) 650.00 650.00
e. Double surcharge (II) 1,000. 1,000.
f. Triple surcharge (II) *3,250.*
25 A1 45c on 48c ocher & grn 8.50 5.00
26 A1 90c on 96c vio & car 22.50 24.00
Nos. 22-26 (5) 40.50 33.45

No. 15 Surcharged in Black **18 CENTS**

1896

27 A1 18c on 45c brn & rose 7.50 3.00
a. Double surcharge 1,100. 1,100.
b. Triple surcharge *1,500.*
28 A1 36c on 45c brn & rose 10.00 *40.00*
a. Double surcharge 1,100.

Surcharged in Black:

3 cents

6 cents

1901

29 A1 3c on 10c bl & brn (II) .60 .70
a. Double surcharge 825.00
30 A1 3c on 16c org brn & ultra (II) .60 *1.75*
a. "3 cents" omitted (II) 500.00 500.00
b. Inverted surcharge (II) 600.00 600.00
c. Double surcharge (II) 550.00
31 A1 3c on 36c brn & rose .60 .95
a. Without bars
b. Double surcharge 600.00 *825.00*
c. "3 cents" omitted 550.00 600.00
32 A1 6c on 8c brn vio & ultra (II) .60 *1.40*
a. Inverted surcharge 775.00 700.00
Nos. 29-32 (4) 2.40 *4.80*

Stamps of 1890-1900 Surcharged **2 cents**

1902, June

33 A1 2c on 4c car rose & grn (II) 2.50 2.50
34 A1 30c on 75c yel & pur 2.50 *7.75*
a. Narrow "0" in "30" 25.00 *50.00*
35 A1 30c on 1r vio & red 5.25 *15.00*
a. Narrow "0" in "30" 40.00 *87.50*
b. Double surcharge *850.00*
36 A1 45c on 1r vio & red 5.25 *13.00*
37 A1 45c on 2.25r vio & grn 17.50 *32.50*
a. Narrow "5" in "45" 150.00 165.00
Nos. 33-37 (5) 33.00 *70.75*

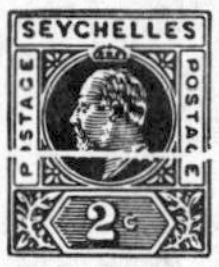

King Edward VII — A6

Numerals of 75c, 1.50r and 2.25r of type A6 are in color on plain tablet.

1903, May 26 Typo. Wmk. 2

38 A6 2c red brn & grn .90 .40
39 A6 3c green .90 1.10
40 A6 6c carmine rose 1.50 .30
41 A6 12c ol gray & grn 1.75 1.25
42 A6 15c ultra 3.25 1.75
43 A6 18c pale yel grn & rose 2.75 *5.75*
44 A6 30c purple & grn 4.75 *8.00*
45 A6 45c brown & rose 6.25 *10.00*
46 A6 75c yel & pur 8.00 *18.00*
47 A6 1.50r black & rose 30.00 *50.00*
48 A6 2.25r red vio & grn 21.00 *60.00*
Nos. 38-48 (11) 81.05 *156.55*

Nos. 42-43, 45 Surcharged **3 cents**

1903

49 A6 3c on 15c 1.00 *1.50*
50 A6 3c on 18c 2.00 *22.00*
51 A6 3c on 45c 1.25 *1.75*
Nos. 49-51 (3) 4.25 *25.25*

Type of 1903

1906 Wmk. 3

52 A6 2c red brn & grn .75 *2.00*
53 A6 3c green .75 .40
54 A6 6c car rose 1.40 .24
55 A6 12c ol gray & grn 2.75 1.25
56 A6 15c ultra 1.75 *2.75*
57 A6 18c pale yel grn & rose 3.00 *5.00*
58 A6 30c purple & grn 5.50 *7.50*
59 A6 45c brown & rose 2.75 *5.25*
60 A6 75c yellow & pur 8.00 *35.00*
61 A6 1.50r black & rose 40.00 *35.00*
62 A6 2.25r red vio & grn 27.50 *42.50*
Nos. 52-62 (11) 94.15 *136.89*

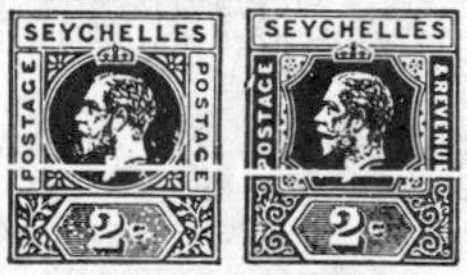

King George V
A7 A8

Numerals of 75c, 1.50r and 2.25r of type A7 are in color on plain tablet.

1912 *Perf. 14*

63 A7 2c org brn & grn .35 .75
64 A7 3c green .40 .35
65 A7 6c car rose 5.00 3.00
66 A7 12c ol gray & grn .90 2.75
67 A7 15c ultra 1.40 1.40
68 A7 18c pale yel grn & rose 1.25 2.75
69 A7 30c purple & grn 4.50 1.75
70 A7 45c brown & rose 2.25 *12.50*
71 A7 75c yellow & pur 3.50 5.00
72 A7 1.50r black & rose 15.00 1.75
73 A7 2.25r violet & grn 27.50 3.50
Nos. 63-73 (11) 62.05 35.50

Die I

For description of dies I and II see back of this section of the Catalogue.

The 5c of type A8 has a colorless numeral on solid-color tablet. Numerals of 9c, 20c, 25c, 50c, 75c, and 1r to 5r of type A8 are in color on plain tablet.

1917-20

74 A8 2c org brn & grn .20 .75
75 A8 3c green .75 .50
76 A8 5c brown ('20) .90 *2.50*
77 A8 6c carmine rose .50 .40
78 A8 12c gray .40 *1.50*
79 A8 15c ultra .50 *1.10*
80 A8 18c violet, *yel* 2.00 *12.50*
a. Die II ('20) 1.00 *10.00*
81 A8 25c blk & red, *yel* ('20) 1.90 *12.50*
a. Die II ('20) 1.90 *5.00*
82 A8 30c dull vio & ol grn 1.90 *5.50*
83 A8 45c dull vio & org 2.50 *15.00*
84 A8 50c dull vio & blk ('20) 2.50 *10.00*
85 A8 75c blk, *bl grn,* ol back 2.75 *6.75*
a. 75c blk, *emer* (Die II) ('20) 3.50 *10.00*
86 A8 1r dl vio & red ('20) 13.00 *20.00*
87 A8 1.50r vio & bl, *bl* 12.50 *32.50*
a. Die II ('20) 9.25 *18.00*
88 A8 2.25r gray grn & dp vio 27.50 *75.00*
89 A8 5r gray grn & ultra ('20) 65.00 *140.00*
Nos. 74-89 (16) 134.80 *336.50*

Die II

1921-32 Wmk. 4

Ordinary Paper

91 A8 2c org brn & grn .15 .20
92 A8 3c green .15 .20
93 A8 3c black ('22) .30 .30
94 A8 4c green ('22) .50 .80
95 A8 4c ol grn & rose red ('28) 2.50 *9.00*
96 A8 5c dk brown 1.25 *2.50*
97 A8 6c car rose 1.25 *4.50*
98 A8 6c violet ('22) .30 .20
99 A8 9c rose red ('27) 1.00 2.00
100 A8 12c gray .50 .20
a. Die I ('32) 2.25 .65
101 A8 12c carmine ('22) .35 .30
102 A8 15c ultra 5.00 *32.50*
103 A8 15c yellow ('22) .80 1.75
104 A8 18c violet, *yel* 1.50 5.00
105 A8 20c ultra ('22) .90 .65

Chalky Paper

106 A8 25c blk & red, *yel* ('22) 1.50 *5.00*
107 A8 30c dull vio & ol grn 1.25 *7.50*
108 A8 45c dull vio & org .95 *6.25*
109 A8 50c dull vio & blk .95 *3.75*
110 A8 75c blk, *emerald* 7.75 *14.00*
111 A8 1r dull vio & red 10.00 *21.00*
a. Die I ('32) 14.00 *27.50*
112 A8 1.50r vio & bl, *bl* 10.00 *16.00*
113 A8 2.25r green & vio 12.50 *25.00*
114 A8 5r green & ultra 65.00 *90.00*
Nos. 91-114 (24) 126.35 *248.60*

Silver Jubilee Issue
Common Design Type

1935, May 6 Engr. *Perf. 11x12*

118 CD301 6c black & ultra .20 .40
119 CD301 12c indigo & green .45 .45
120 CD301 20c ultra & brown .75 .50
121 CD301 1r brn vio & indigo 2.75 *7.50*
Nos. 118-121 (4) 4.15 *8.85*

Coronation Issue
Common Design Type

1937, May 12 *Perf. 11x11½*

122 CD302 6c olive green .15 .15
123 CD302 12c deep orange .15 .15
124 CD302 20c deep ultra .30 .30
Nos. 122-124 (3) .60 .60

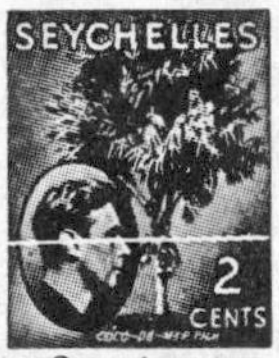

Coco-de-mer Palm — A9

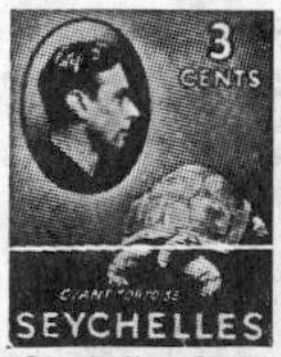

Seychelles Giant Tortoise — A10

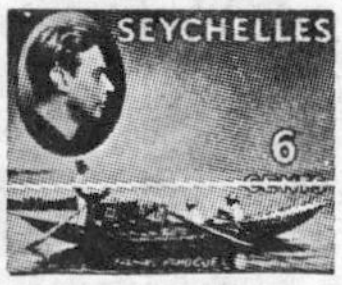

Fishing Canoe — A11

Perf. 13½x14½, 14½x13½

1938-41 Photo. Wmk. 4

125 A9 2c violet brown .15 .15
126 A10 3c green .50 .30
127 A10 3c orange ('41) .15 .15
128 A11 6c orange .50 .30
129 A11 6c green ('41) .15 .15
130 A9 9c rose red 2.50 *1.65*
131 A9 9c pck blue ('41) .15 .15
132 A10 12c violet 7.50 2.50
133 A10 15c copper red ('41) .15 .15
134 A9 18c rose lake ('41) .15 .15
135 A11 20c brt blue 4.00 2.00
136 A11 20c ocher ('41) .15 .15
137 A9 25c ocher 17.50 7.00
138 A10 30c rose lake 17.50 7.00
139 A9 30c brt blue ('41) .20 .15
140 A11 45c brown .30 .25
141 A9 50c dull violet .35 .30
142 A10 75c gray blue 30.00 27.50
143 A10 75c dull vio ('41) .40 .30
144 A11 1r yellow grn 42.50 26.00
145 A11 1r gray ('41) .40 .30
146 A9 1.50r ultra 1.25 .55
147 A10 2.25r olive bister 2.00 .85
148 A11 5r copper red 2.50 2.75
Nos. 125-148 (24) 130.95 80.75

Issue dates: Nos. 126, 128, 132, 135, 137, Jan. 1, 1938. Nos. 125, 130, 138, 140-142, 144, 146-148, Feb. 10, 1938. Others, Aug. 8, 1941.

See Nos. 158-169, 174-188.

Catalogue values for unused stamps in this section, from this point to the end of the section, are for Never Hinged items.

Peace Issue
Common Design Type
Perf. 13½x14

1946, Sept. 23 Engr. Wmk. 4

149 CD303 9c light blue .15 .15
150 CD303 30c dark blue .15 .15
Set value .25 .25

Silver Wedding Issue
Common Design Types

1948, Nov. 11 Photo. *Perf. 14x14½*

151 CD304 9c bright ultra .20 .20

Engraved; Name Typographed
Perf. 11½x11

152 CD305 5r rose carmine 7.00 10.00

UPU Issue
Common Design Types
Perf. 13½, 11x11½

1949, Oct. 10 Engr.

153 CD306 18c red violet .15 .15
154 CD307 50c dp rose violet .35 .35
155 CD308 1r gray .55 .55
156 CD309 2.25r olive 1.00 1.00
Nos. 153-156 (4) 2.05 2.05

Types of 1938-41 Redrawn and

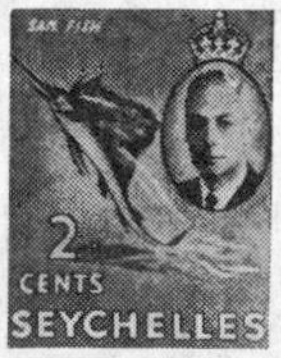

Sailfish — A12

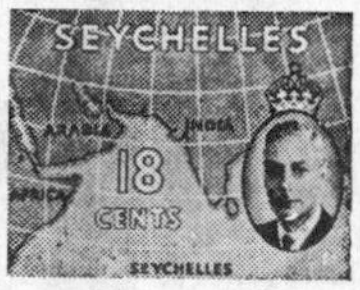

Map — A13

Perf. 14½x13½, 13½x14½

1952, Mar. 3 Photo. Wmk. 4

157 A12 2c violet .15 .15
158 A10 3c orange .30 .30
159 A9 9c peacock blue .52 .52
160 A11 15c yellow green .52 .52
161 A13 18c rose lake .52 .52
162 A11 20c ocher .52 .52
163 A10 25c bright red .60 .60
164 A12 40c ultra 1.40 1.40
165 A11 45c violet brown 1.10 1.10
166 A9 50c brt violet 1.10 1.10
167 A13 1r gray 1.40 1.40
168 A9 1.50r brt blue 2.50 2.50
169 A10 2.25r olive bister 3.75 3.75
170 A13 5r copper red 8.00 8.00
171 A12 10r green 12.00 12.00
Nos. 157-171 (15) 34.38 34.38

The redrawn design shows a new portrait of King George VI surmounted by crown, as on type A12.

Nos. 157-170 exist with watermark 4a.

Coronation Issue
Common Design Type

1953, June 2 Engr. *Perf. 13½x13*

172 CD312 9c dark blue & blk .30 .30

Types of 1938-52 with Portrait of Queen Elizabeth II

Perf. 14½x13½, 13½x14½

1954-56 Photo.

173 A12 2c violet .22 .22
174 A10 3c orange .26 .26
175 A9 9c peacock blue .26 .26
176 A9 10c blue ('56) .35 .35
177 A11 15c yellow grn .15 .15
178 A13 18c rose lake .45 .45
179 A11 20c ocher .18 .18
180 A10 25c bright red .22 .22
181 A13 35c mag ('56) .55 .55
182 A12 40c ultra .42 .42
183 A11 45c violet brn .75 .75
184 A9 50c brt violet .35 .35
185 A11 70c vio brn ('56) 1.00 1.00
186 A13 1r gray .70 .70

187 A9	1.50r brt blue		1.50	1.50
188 A10	2.25r olive bister		3.50	3.00
189 A13	5r copper red		10.00	5.25
190 A12	10r green		19.00	11.00
	Nos. 173-190 (18)		39.86	26.61

Issue dates: 10c, 35c, 70c, Sept. 15, 1956. Others, Feb. 1, 1954.

For surcharge see No. 193.

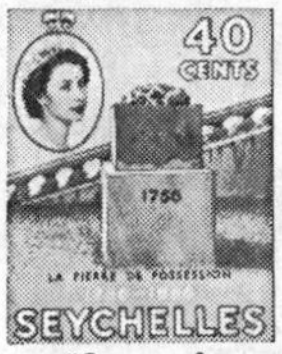

"Stone of Possession" A14

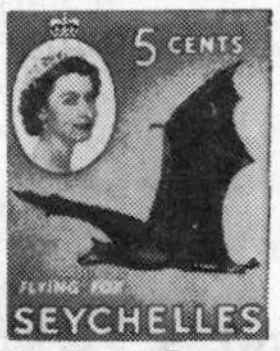

Flying Fox A15

Perf. 14½x14

1956, Nov. 15 Wmk. 4

191 A14	40c ultra	.38	.38
192 A14	1r gray black	.65	.65

Bicentenary of French colonization.

No. 183 Surcharged "5 cents" and Bars

1957, Sept. 16 ***Perf. 13½x14½***

193 A11	5c on 45c violet brn	.30	.30
a.	Double surcharge	200.00	
b.	Thick bars omitted	450.00	

The "c," "e" or "s" of surcharge may be found in italic.

1957, Oct. 25 ***Perf. 14½x13½***

194 A15	5c light violet	.15	.15

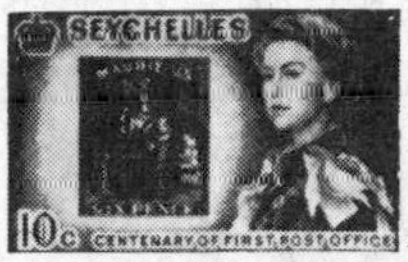

Mauritius Stamp of 1859 with Seychelles "B64" Cancellation A16

Perf. 11½x11

Engr. & Typo.

1961, Dec. 11 Wmk. 314

Stamp in Dull Blue & Black

195 A16	10c lilac	.15	.15
196 A16	35c dull green	.30	.30
197 A16	2.25r orange brown	1.10	1.10
	Nos. 195-197 (3)	1.55	1.55

1st post office in Victoria, Seychelles, cent.

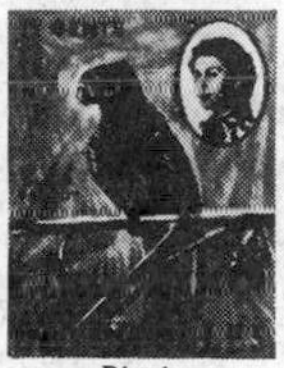

Black Parrot — A17

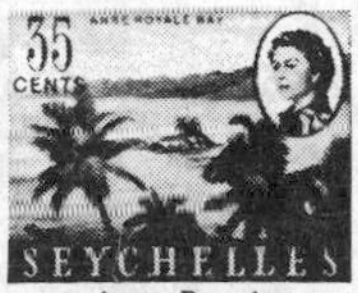

Anse Royal Bay — A18

Designs: 10c, Vanilla. 15c, Fisherman. 20c, Denis Island Lighthouse. 25c, Clock Tower, Victoria. 30c, 35c, Anse Royal Bay. 40c, Government House. 45c, Fishing boat. 50c, Cascade Church. 60c, Flying fox. 70c, 85c, Sailfish. 75c, Coco-de-mer palm. 1r, Cinnamon. 1.50r, Copra. 2.25r, Map of Indian Ocean. 3.50r, Settlers' homes. 5r, Regina Mundi Convent. 10r, Badge of Seychelles.

Perf. 14½x13½, 13½x14½

1962-69 Photo. Wmk. 314

Size: 24x31mm, 31x24mm

198	A17	5c yel grn, brn & crimson	.15	.15
a.		Wmkd. sideways ('67)	.16	.15
199	A17	10c ocher, grn & dk bl	.15	.15
a.		Wmkd. sideways ('68)	.20	.16
200	A17	15c multicolored	.15	.15
201	A17	20c brt bl, blk & grn	.15	.15
202	A17	25c Prus bl, org brn & grn	.15	.15
202A	A18	30c multi ('68)	.80	.80
203	A18	35c bl, grn & dk brn	1.00	1.00
204	A18	40c bl, dk grn & yel grn	.24	.24
204A	A18	45c brt bl & yel ('66)	1.00	.65
205	A17	50c multicolored	.35	.35
b.		Wmkd. sideways ('69)	.80	.80
205A	A17	60c bl, rose & blk ('68)	.80	.80
206	A17	70c grnsh bl & vio bl	2.25	2.25
206A	A17	75c multi ('66)	1.00	1.00
206B	A17	85c grnsh bl & vio bl ('68)	1.00	1.00
207	A18	1r yel brn, emer & yel	.65	.65
208	A18	1.50r dk grn, choc & yel	1.40	1.40
209	A18	2.25r ocher, bl grn & crimson	2.25	2.25
210	A18	3.50r multicolored	3.50	3.50
211	A18	5r multicolored	4.75	4.75

Perf. 13x14

Size: 22½x39mm

212	A17	10r multicolored	14.00	14.00
		Nos. 198-212 (20)	35.74	35.39

Issue dates: 45c and 75c, Aug. 1, 1966. No. 198a, Feb. 7, 1967. The 30c, 60c, 85c, July 15, 1968. Others, Feb. 21, 1962.

The 60c and 85c have watermark sideways.

For surcharges see Nos. 216-217, 241-243. For overprints see Nos. 233-236.

Freedom from Hunger Issue

Common Design Type

1963, June 4 ***Perf. 14x14½***

213 CD314	70c lilac	.75	.60

Red Cross Centenary Issue

Common Design Type

1963, Sept. 2 Litho. ***Perf. 13***

214 CD315	10c black & red	.16	.15
215 CD315	75c ultra & red	.85	.60

Nos. 203 and 206 Surcharged with New Value and Bars

Perf. 14x14½, 14½x14

1965, Apr. Photo. Wmk. 314

216 A18	45c on 35c	.20	.20
217 A17	75c on 70c	.30	.30

ITU Issue

Common Design Type

Perf. 11x11½

1965, June 1 Litho. Wmk. 314

218 CD317	5c orange & vio bl	.15	.15
219 CD317	1.50r red lil & apple grn	.90	.80

Intl. Cooperation Year Issue

Common Design Type

1965, Oct. 25 ***Perf. 14½***

220 CD318	5c blue green & claret	.15	.15
221 CD318	40c lt violet & green	.48	.48

Churchill Memorial Issue

Common Design Type

1966, Jan. 24 Photo. ***Perf. 14***

Design in Black, Gold and Carmine Rose

222 CD319	5c bright blue	.15	.15
223 CD319	15c green	.16	.15
224 CD319	75c brown	.80	.55
225 CD319	1.50r violet	1.50	1.10
	Nos. 222-225 (4)	2.61	1.95

World Cup Soccer Issue

Common Design Type

1966, July 1 Litho. ***Perf. 14***

226 CD321	15c multicolored	.15	.15
227 CD321	1r multicolored	.45	.45

WHO Headquarters Issue

Common Design Type

1966, Sept. 20 Litho. ***Perf. 14***

228 CD322	20c multicolored	.15	.15
229 CD322	50c multicolored	.55	.55

UNESCO Anniversary Issue

Common Design Type

1966, Dec. 1 Litho. ***Perf. 14***

230 CD323	15c "Education"	.15	.15
231 CD323	1r "Science"	.40	.40
232 CD323	5r "Culture"	2.25	2.25
	Nos. 230-232 (3)	2.80	2.80

Nos. 200, 204A, 206A and 210 Overprinted: "UNIVERSAL / ADULT / SUFFRAGE / 1967"

Perf. 14½x14, 14x14½

1967, Sept. 18 Photo. Wmk. 314

233 A17	15c multicolored	.15	.15
234 A18	45c brt blue & yel	.16	.16
235 A17	75c multicolored	.24	.24
236 A18	3.50r multicolored	.90	.90
	Nos. 233-236 (4)	1.45	1.45

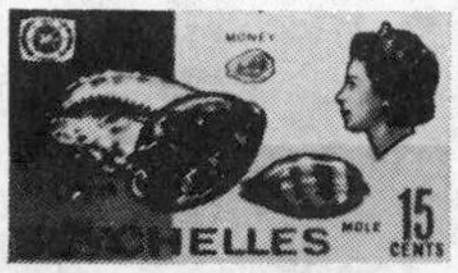

Cowries: Tiger, Mole, Money A19

Sea Shells (ITY Emblem and): 40c, Textile, betulinus and virgin cones. 1r, Arthritic spider conch. 2.25r, Triton and subulate auger.

Perf. 14x13½

1967, Dec. 4 Photo. Wmk. 314

237 A19	15c multicolored	.15	.15
238 A19	40c multicolored	.26	.26
239 A19	1r multicolored	.60	.60
240 A19	2.25r multicolored	1.25	1.25
	Nos. 237-240 (4)	2.26	2.26

Issued for International Tourist Year, 1967.

Nos. 204, 204A and 206A Surcharged

Perf. 14x14½, 14½x14

1968, Apr. 16 Photo. Wmk. 314

241 A18	30c on 40c multicolored	.15	.15
242 A18	60c on 45c blue & yel	.16	.16
243 A17	85c on 75c multicolored	.26	.26
	Nos. 241-243 (3)	.57	.57

The surcharge on No. 241 includes 2 bars; on Nos. 242-243 it includes 3 bars and "CENTS."

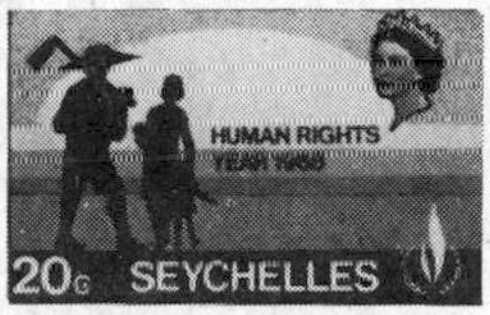

Family, Rising Sun and Human Rights Flame A20

Perf. 14½x14

1968, Sept. 2 Litho. Wmk. 314

244 A20	20c chocolate & multi	.15	.15
245 A20	50c vio blue & multi	.15	.15
246 A20	85c black & multi	.22	.22
247 A20	2.25r brown & multi	.65	.65
	Nos. 244-247 (4)	1.17	1.17

International Human Rights Year.

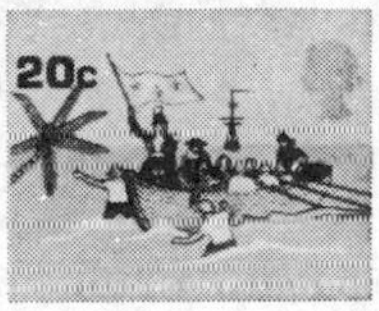

First Landing on Praslin Island — A21

Designs: 50c, La Digue and La Curieuse at anchor, vert. 85c, Coco-de-mer and black parrot, vert. 2.25r, La Digue and La Curieuse under sail.

Litho.; Head Embossed in Gold

Perf. 14x14½

1968, Dec. 30 Wmk. 314

248 A21	20c multicolored	.15	.15
249 A21	50c dk blue, blk & red	.24	.24
250 A21	85c rose red & multi	.40	.40
251 A21	2.25r ultra & multi	1.90	1.90
	Nos. 248-251 (4)	2.60	2.60

Landing on Praslin Island of the Chevalier Marion Dufresne expedition, 200th anniv.

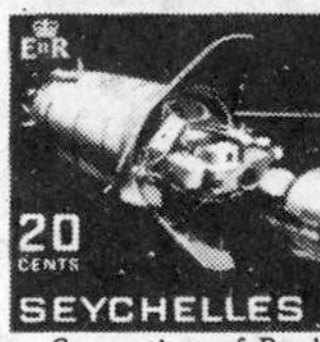

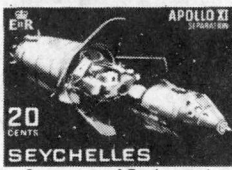

Separation of Rocket and Spacecraft — A22

Designs: 5c, Launching of Apollo XI, vert. 50c, Landing module and men on the moon. 85c, Seychelles tracking station. 2.25r, Moonscape and earth.

1969, Sept. 9 Litho. ***Perf. 13½***

252 A22	5c multicolored	.15	.15
253 A22	20c multicolored	.15	.15
254 A22	50c multicolored	.22	.22
255 A22	85c multicolored	.35	.35
256 A22	2.25r multicolored	1.10	1.10
	Nos. 252-256 (5)	1.97	1.97

See note after US No. C76.

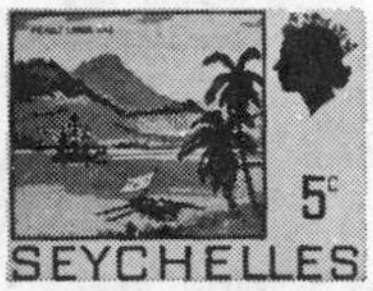

Lazare Picault Landing in 1741 — A23

History of Seychelles: 10c, US satellite tracking station. 15c, German cruiser Königsberg at Aldabra, 1915. 20c, British fleet refueling, St. Anne, 1939-45. 25c, Ashanti King Prempeh in exile, 1896. 30c, 40c, Stone of Possession placed, 1756. 50c, 65c, Pirates. 60c, Corsairs. 85c, 95c, Jet and airport. 1r, First capitulation of the French to the British, 1794. 1.50r, Battle between the sailing vessels Sybille and Chiffone, 1801. 3.50r, Visit of Duke of Edinburgh, 1956. 5r, Chevalier Queau de Quincy. 10r, Map of Indian Ocean, 1574. 15r, Seychelles coat of arms.

Perf. 13x12½

1969-72 Litho. Wmk. 314

257	A23	5c multicolored	.15	.15
258	A23	10c multicolored	.15	.15
259	A23	15c multicolored	.15	.15
260	A23	20c multicolored	.15	.15
261	A23	25c multicolored	.15	.15
262	A23	30c multicolored	.65	.65
262A	A23	40c multicolored	.32	.32
263	A23	50c multicolored	.22	.22
264	A23	60c multicolored	.95	.95
264A	A23	65c multicolored	.48	.48
265	A23	85c multicolored	1.00	1.00
265A	A23	95c multicolored	.48	.48
266	A23	1r multicolored	.42	.42
267	A23	1.50r multicolored	.65	.65
268	A23	3.50r multicolored	1.65	1.65
269	A23	5r multicolored	2.25	2.25
270	A23	10r multicolored	4.50	4.50
271	A23	15r multicolored	7.25	7.25
		Nos. 257-271 (18)	21.57	21.57

Issued: 40, 65, 95c, Dec. 11, 1972; others, Nov. 3.

For overprints & surcharges see Nos. 294-298, 323-330, 361-369.

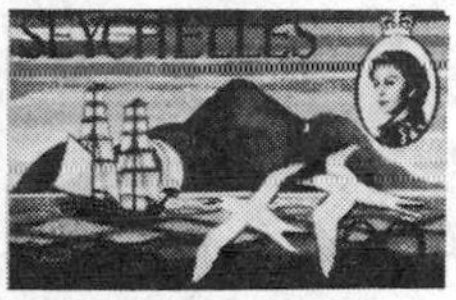

St. Anne Island, Ship and Gulls — A24

Designs: 50c, Flying fish, island and ship. 85c, Map of Seychelles and compass rose. 3.50r, Anchor, chain on sea bottom.

1970, Apr. 27 ***Perf. 14***

272 A24	20c multicolored	.15	.15
273 A24	50c multicolored	.32	.32
274 A24	85c multicolored	.50	.50
275 A24	3.50r multicolored	1.50	1.50
	Nos. 272-275 (4)	2.47	2.47

Bicentenary of first settlement on St. Anne.

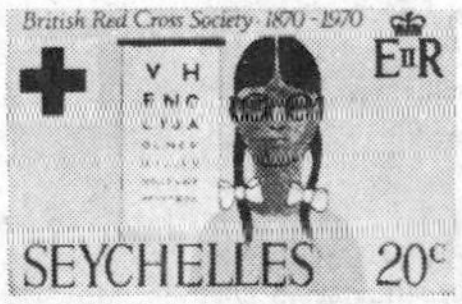

Girl and Eye Chart A25

Designs: 50c, Infant on scales and milk bottles. 85c, Mother and child, vert. 3.50r, Red Cross branch headquarters.

1970, Aug. 4 Litho. Wmk. 314

276 A25	20c lt blue & multi	.15	.15
277 A25	50c multicolored	.32	.32
278 A25	85c multicolored	.52	.52
279 A25	3.50r multicolored	1.50	1.50
	Nos. 276-279 (4)	2.49	2.49

Centenary of British Red Cross Society.

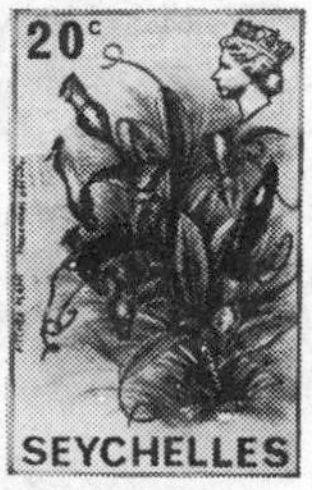

Pitcher Plant — A26

Flowers: 50c, Wild vanilla. 85c, Tropic-bird flower. 3.50r, Vare hibiscus.

1970, Dec. 29 *Perf. 14½*

280 A26	20c	multicolored	.20	.20
281 A26	50c	multicolored	.52	.52
282 A26	85c	multicolored	1.00	1.00
283 A26	3.50r	multicolored	5.25	5.25
a.		Souvenir sheet of 4, #280-283	16.00	13.00
		Nos. 280-283 (4)	6.97	6.97

Souvenir Sheet

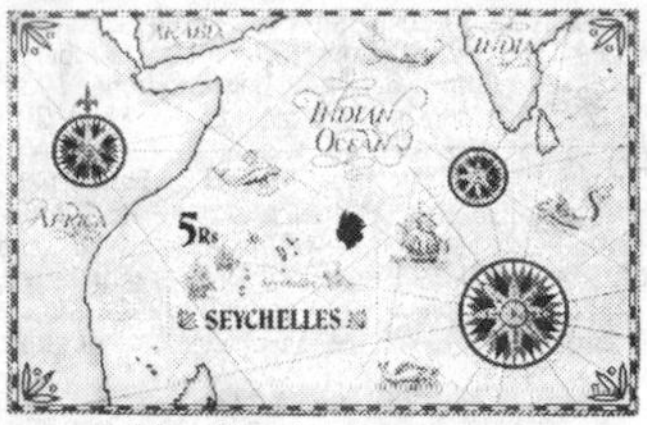

Map Showing Location of Seychelles — A27

Perf. 13½x14

1971, Apr. 20 **Litho.** **Wmk. 314**

284 A27	5r	yellow grn & multi	10.00	10.00

Issued to publicize Seychelles' location.

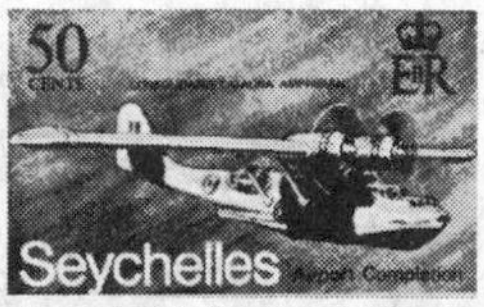

Consolidated Catalina Amphibian — A28

Designs: 5c, Piper Navajo, vert. 20c, Westland Wessex, vert. 60c, Grumman Albatross amphibian, vert. 85c, "G" class Short Brothers flying boat. 3.50r, Vickers supermarine "Walrus" amphibian.

Perf. 14x14½, 14½x14

1971, June 28 **Litho.** **Wmk. 314**

285 A28	5c	orange & multi	.15	.15
286 A28	20c	purple & multi	.18	.15
287 A28	50c	olive & multi	.35	.18
288 A28	60c	sepia & multi	.45	.22
289 A28	85c	brown & multi	.60	.35
290 A28	3.50r	blue & multi	5.00	1.90
		Nos. 285-290 (6)	6.73	2.95

Completion of Seychelles Airport.

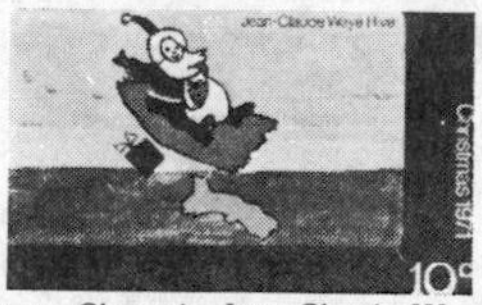

Santa Claus, by Jean-Claude Waye Hive — A29

Christmas (Children's Drawings): 15c, Santa Claus riding a tortoise, by Edison Thérésine. 3.50r, Santa Claus on the seashore, by Isabelle Tirant.

1971, Oct. 12 *Perf. 13½*

291 A29	10c	dark blue & multi	.15	.15
292 A29	15c	dark green & multi	.15	.15
293 A29	3.50r	violet & multi	1.50	1.50
		Nos. 291-293 (3)	1.80	1.80

Nos. 262, 264-265 Surcharged with New Value and 5 Bars

1971, Dec. 21 *Perf. 13x12½*

294 A23	40c	on 30c multicolored	.28	.28
295 A23	65c	on 60c multicolored	.42	.42
296 A23	95c	on 85c multicolored	.60	.60
		Nos. 294-296 (3)	1.30	1.30

Nos. 260, 269 Overprinted in Black or Gold: "ROYAL VISIT 1972"

1972, Mar. 21 **Litho.** **Wmk. 314**

297 A23	20c	multicolored	.15	.15
298 A23	5r	multicolored (G)	2.50	2.50

Visit of Elizabeth II and Prince Philip.

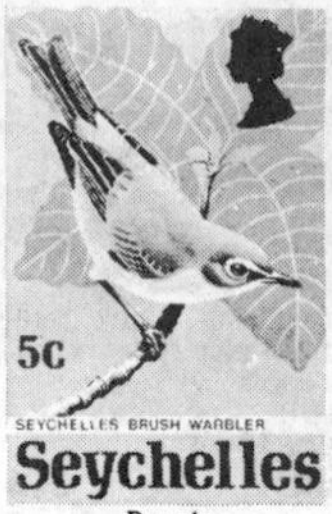

Brush Warbler — A30

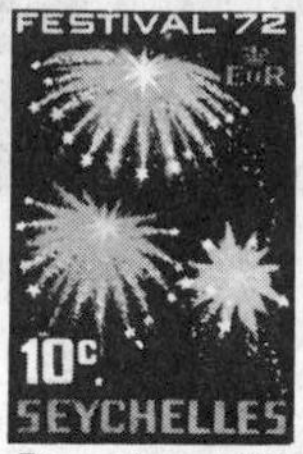

Fireworks — A31

1972, July 15 *Perf. 14x13½*

299 A30	5c	shown	.15	.15
300 A30	20c	Scops owl	.32	.22
301 A30	50c	Blue pigeons	.90	.45
302 A30	65c	Magpie robin	1.25	.70
303 A30	95c	Paradise flycatchers	2.25	1.25
304 A30	3.50r	Kestrel	9.00	4.50
a.		Souvenir sheet of 6, #299-304	24.00	19.00
		Nos. 299-304 (6)	13.87	7.27

1972, Sept. 18 **Litho.** *Perf. 14*

305 A31	10c	shown	.15	.15
306 A31	15c	Canoe race, horiz.	.15	.15
307 A31	25c	Women in local costumes	.15	.15
308 A31	5r	Water-skiing, horiz.	1.65	1.65
		Nos. 305-308 (4)	2.10	2.10

Seychelles Festival 1972.

Silver Wedding Issue, 1972

Common Design Type

Design: Queen Elizabeth II, Prince Philip, giant tortoise and leaping sailfish.

1972, Nov. 20 **Photo.** *Perf. 14x14½*

309 CD324	95c	multicolored	.35	.35
310 CD324	1.50r	multicolored	.55	.55

Princess Anne's Wedding Issue

Common Design Type

1973, Nov. 14 **Litho.** *Perf. 14*

311 CD325	95c	ocher & multi	.25	.25
312 CD325	1.50r	slate & multi	.40	.40

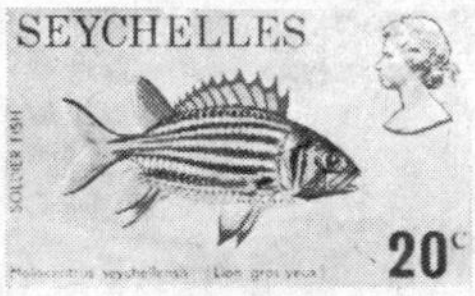

Soldierfish A32

Wmk. 314

1974, Mar. 5 **Litho.** *Perf. 14*

313 A32	20c	shown	.20	.20
314 A32	50c	Filefish	.42	.42
315 A32	95c	Butterflyfish	.80	.80
316 A32	1.50r	Gaterin	1.75	1.75
		Nos. 313-316 (4)	3.17	3.17

Envelope and Globe A33

UPU, cent.: 50c, Globe with location of Seychelles and radio tower. 95c, Cancellation and globe. 1.50r, "UPU" with emblems.

Perf. 12½x12

1974, Oct. 9 **Wmk. 314**

317 A33	20c	multicolored	.15	.15
318 A33	50c	multicolored	.22	.22
319 A33	95c	multicolored	.42	.42
320 A33	1.50r	multicolored	.65	.65
		Nos. 317-320 (4)	1.44	1.44

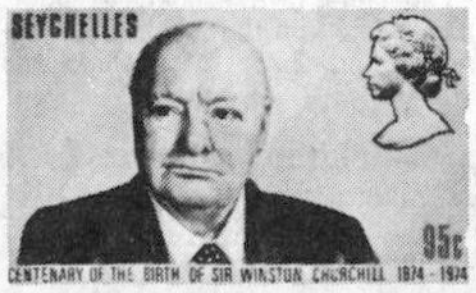

Winston Churchill A34

Design: 1.50r, Churchill, different portrait.

1974, Nov. 30 **Litho.** *Perf. 14½*

321 A34	95c	lt blue & multi	.40	.40
322 A34	1.50r	lt green & multi	.60	.60
a.		Souvenir sheet of 2, #321-322	1.10	1.10

Sir Winston Churchill (1874-1965).

Nos. 260, 263, 265A and 267 Overprinted in Black or Silver

VISIT OF
Q.E. II

Perf. 13x12½

1975, Feb. 8 **Wmk. 314**

323 A23	20c	multi (B)	.15	.15
324 A23	50c	multi (B)	.22	.22
325 A23	95c	multi (S)	.35	.35
326 A23	1.50r	multi (B)	.55	.55
		Nos. 323-326 (4)	1.27	1.27

Visit of cruise ship Queen Elizabeth II, Mahe, Seychelles.

Nos. 260, 264A, 266, 268 Overprinted in Gold

INTERNAL
SELF-GOVERNMENT
OCTOBER
1975

1975, Oct. 1 **Litho.** **Wmk. 314**

327 A23	20c	multicolored	.15	.15
328 A23	65c	multicolored	.24	.24
329 A23	1r	multicolored	.32	.32
330 A23	3.50r	multicolored	1.10	1.10
		Nos. 327-330 (4)	1.81	1.81

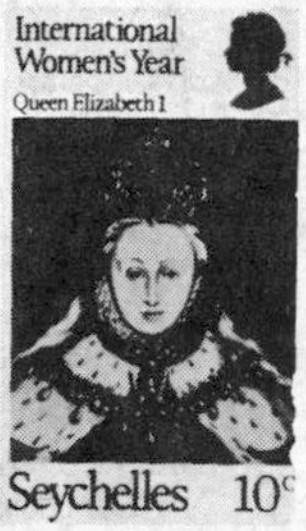

Queen Elizabeth I — A35

Portraits: 15c, Gladys Aylward. 20c, Elizabeth Fry. 25c, Emmeline Pankhurst. 65c, Florence Nightingale. 1r, Amy Johnson. 1.50r, Joan of Arc. 3.50r, Eleanor Roosevelt.

Perf. 13½

1975, Dec. 15 **Litho.** **Wmk. 314**

331 A35	10c	dp brown & multi	.15	.15
332 A35	15c	dk brown & multi	.15	.15
333 A35	20c	dk green & multi	.15	.15
334 A35	25c	purple & multi	.15	.15
335 A35	65c	dk blue & multi	.30	.30
336 A35	1r	Prus blue & multi	.42	.42
337 A35	1.50r	dp violet & multi	.65	.65
338 A35	3.50r	dk olive & multi	1.75	1.75
		Nos. 331-338 (8)	3.72	3.72

International Women's Year.

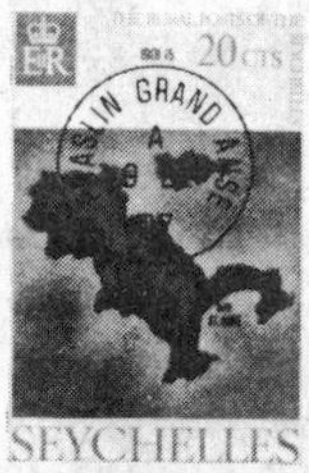

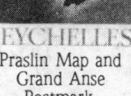

Praslin Map and Grand Anse Postmark, 1907 — A36

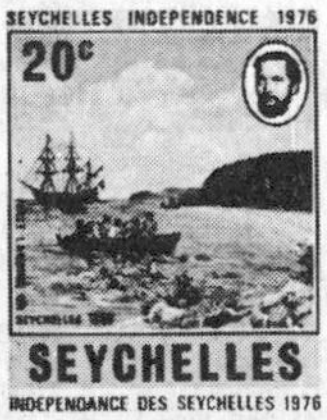

First Landing, 1609, and James Mancham — A37

Designs: 65c, La Digue map and postmark, 1916. 1r, Partial map of Mahé and Victoria postmark, 1917. 1.50r, Southern part of Mahé and Anse Royale postmark, 1938.

1976, Mar. 30 **Wmk. 373** *Perf. 14*

339 A36	20c	lt blue & multi	.15	.15
340 A36	65c	lt blue & multi	.32	.32
341 A36	1r	lt blue & multi	.50	.50
342 A36	1.50r	lt blue & multi	.75	.75
a.		Souvenir sheet of 4, #339-342	2.50	2.50
		Nos. 339-342 (4)	1.72	1.72

Rural posts of Seychelles.

1976, June 29 *Perf. 14*

Designs: 25c, Stone of Possession. 40c, Arrival of 1st settlers, 1770 (ship). 75c, Le Chevalier Quéau de Quincy. 1r, Sir Bickham Sweet-Escott. 1.25r, Government House. 1.50r, Coat of arms of Internal Self-government. 3.50r, Seychelles flag.

343 A37	20c	rose & multi	.15	.15
344 A37	25c	yellow & multi	.15	.15
345 A37	40c	lilac & multi	.16	.16
346 A37	75c	green & multi	.24	.24
347 A37	1r	salmon & multi	.35	.35
348 A37	1.25r	multicolored	.40	.40
349 A37	1.50r	ocher & multi	.48	.48
350 A37	3.50r	blue & multi	1.10	1.10
		Nos. 343-350 (8)	3.03	3.03

Seychelles' independence, June 29, 1976.

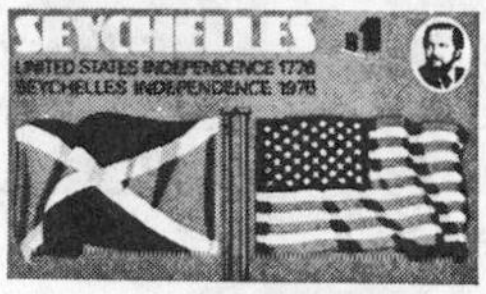

Flags of Seychelles and US — A38

US bicent.: 10r, State House, Seychelles, and Independence Hall, Philadelphia.

1976, July 12 **Litho.**

351 A38	1r	blue & multi	.25	.25
352 A38	10r	red & multi	2.50	2.50

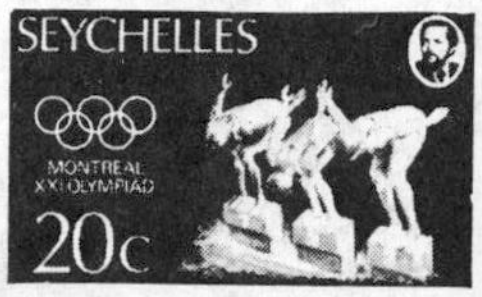

Swimming A39

Designs (Olympic Rings and): 65c, Hockey. 1r, Basketball. 3.50r, Soccer.

1976, July 26 *Perf. 14½*

353 A39	20c	vio blue & blk	.15	.15
354 A39	65c	dk grn, yel grn & blk	.25	.25
355 A39	1r	brown, grn & blk	.35	.35
356 A39	3.50r	car rose & blk	1.25	1.25
		Nos. 353-356 (4)	2.00	2.00

21st Olympic Games, Montreal, Canada, July 17-Aug. 1.

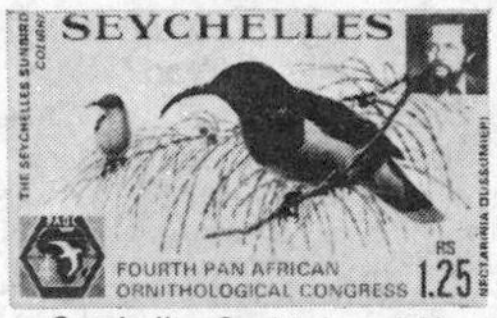

Seychelles Sunbird — A40

Seychelles Birds (James R. Mancham, Congress Emblem and): 20c, Paradise flycatcher, vert. 1.50r, Gray white-eye. 5r, Black parrot, vert.

Perf. 14½

1976, Nov. 8 **Litho.** **Wmk. 373**

357 A40	20c	multicolored	.15	.15
358 A40	1.25r	multicolored	.80	.65
359 A40	1.50r	multicolored	.95	.85
360 A40	5r	multicolored	2.75	2.50
a.		Souvenir sheet of 4, #357-360	5.50	5.50
		Nos. 357-360 (4)	4.65	4.15

4th Pan-African Ornithological Cong., Mahe Beach Hotel, Nov. 6-13.

Nos. 260, 263, 265A-266, 268-271, 264A Overprinted or Surcharged: "Independence / 1976"

Perf. 13x12½

1976, Nov. 22 **Litho.** **Wmk. 314**

361 A23	20c	multicolored	.15	.15
362 A23	50c	multicolored	.28	.24
363 A23	95c	multicolored	.48	.40
364 A23	1r	multicolored	.48	.40
365 A23	3.50r	multicolored	2.00	1.75
366 A23	5r	multicolored	2.50	2.00
367 A23	10r	multicolored	4.75	4.00
368 A23	15r	multicolored	6.75	6.00
369 A23	25r	on 65c multi	12.00	10.00
		Nos. 361-369 (9)	29.39	24.94

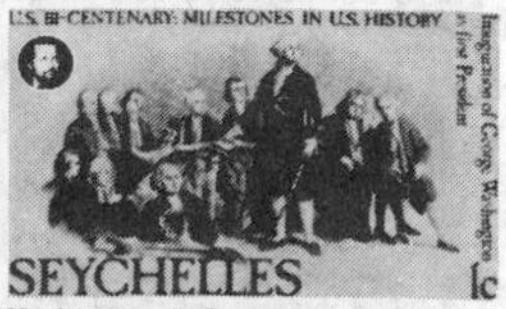

Washington's Inauguration — A41

American Bicentennial: 2c, Jefferson and map of Louisiana Purchase. 3c, Seward and map of Alaska Purchase. 4c, Pony Express, 1860. 5c, Lincoln's

Emancipation Proclamation, 1863. 1.50r, Completion of Transcontinental Railroad, 1869. 3.50r, Wright Brothers' 1st flight, 1903. 5r, Ford assembly line, 1913. 10r, Kennedy and Apollo 11 moon landing, 1969. 25r, Declaration of Independence, 1776.

Perf. 14x13½

1976, Dec. 21 — Wmk. 373

370 A41	1c rose & plum	.15	.15
371 A41	2c lilac & vio	.15	.15
372 A41	3c blue & vio bl	.15	.15
373 A41	4c yellow & brn	.15	.15
374 A41	5c brt yel & grn	.15	.15
375 A41	1.50r yel brn & brn	.35	.35
376 A41	3.50r brt grn & bl grn	.80	.80
377 A41	5r yellow & brn	1.25	1.25
378 A41	10r dull bl & dk bl	2.50	2.50
	Nos. 370-378 (9)	5.65	5.65

Souvenir Sheet

379 A41	25r lilac rose & pur	6.00	6.00

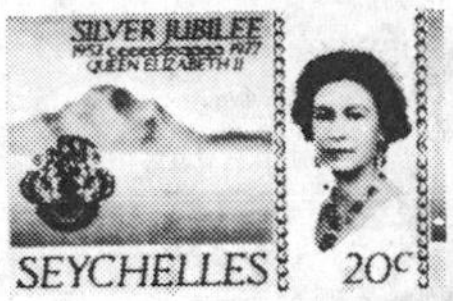

Seychelles Islands and Arms — A42

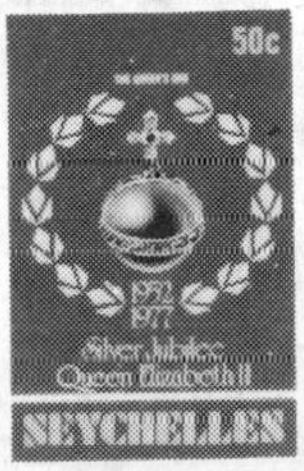

The Orb — A43

Designs: 40c, 5r, 10r, similar to 20c. 1r, St. Edward's Crown. 1.25r, Ampulla and Spoon. 1.50r, Scepter with Cross.

1977, Sept. 5 — Litho. — *Perf. 14*

380 A42	20c multicolored	.15	.15
381 A42	40c multicolored	.15	.15
382 A43	50c multicolored	.15	.15
383 A43	1r multicolored	.20	.20
384 A43	1.25r multicolored	.25	.25
385 A43	1.50r multicolored	.30	.30
386 A42	5r multicolored	1.00	1.00
387 A42	10r multicolored	2.00	2.00
a.	Souv. sheet of 4, #380, 382, 383, 387	3.00	3.00
	Nos. 380-387 (8)	4.20	4.20

25th anniv. of reign of Elizabeth II.

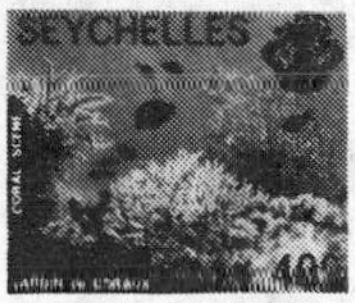

Coral Reef — A44

Perf. 14, 14x14½ (40c, 1, 1.25, 1.50r)

1977-78 — Litho. — Wmk. 373

Sizes: 40c, 1, 1.25, 1.50r, 30x25mm, Others 28x23mm

388 A44	5c Reef fish	.15	.15
389 A44	10c Hawksbill turtle	.15	.15
390 A44	15c Coco de mer	.15	.15
391 A44	20c Wild vanilla	.15	.15
392 A44	25c Butterfly	.15	.15
393 A44	40c Coral reef	.15	.15
394 A44	50c Giant tortoise	.16	.16
a.	Wmk. 384, perf. 14x14½	.22	.22
395 A44	75c Crayfish	.18	.18
396 A44	1r Madagascar cardinal	.25	.25
397 A44	1.25r Fairy tern	.32	.32
398 A44	1.50r Flying fox	.38	.38
398A A44	3r like #399, wmk. 384	1.40	1.40
399 A44	3.50r Green gecko	.85	.85

Perf. 13

Size: 27x35mm

400 A44	5r Octopus, vert.	1.25	1.25
401 A44	10r Tiger cowrie, vert.	2.50	2.50
402 A44	15r Pitcher plant, vert.	3.75	3.75
403 A44	20r Arms, vert.	5.25	5.25
	Nos. 388-403 (17)	17.19	17.19

Issue dates: 40c, 1r, 1.25r, 1.50r, Oct. 31, 1977. No. 394a and 398A, Nov., 1991. Others, 1978.

Reissued dated "1979" below design: 10, 15, 25, 40, 50, 75c, 1r, 1.50r. Dated "1981": 40c. Dated "1982": 40c.

See No. 446. For surcharge and overprint see Nos. 446, 605.

Denomination "R" Instead of "Re." or "Rs."

Perf. 14x14½, 14 (1.10r)

1981, Jan. 6 — Litho.

Sizes: 1.10r, 28x23mm, Others, 30x25mm

403A A44	1r like No. 396	.30	.30
403B A44	1.10r like No. 399	.35	.35
403C A44	1.25r like No. 397	.38	.38
i.	Wmk. 384 ('89)	.45	.45
403D A44	1.50r like No. 398	.45	.45

Perf. 13

403E A44	5r like No. 400	1.50	1.50
j.	Perf. 14x14½, Wmk 384 ('90)	1.85	1.85
403F A44	10r like No. 401	3.00	3.00
403G A44	15r like No. 402	4.50	4.50
403H A44	20r like No. 403	6.00	6.00
	Nos. 403A-403H (8)	16.48	16.48

Reissued dated "1981" below design: 1.50r. Dated "1982": 1r, 1.50r. Dated "1985": 5r, Dated "1986": 1r, Dated "1990": 1r, Dated "1991": 1r, 1.50r.

See No. 576 for No. 403C with commemorative inscription.

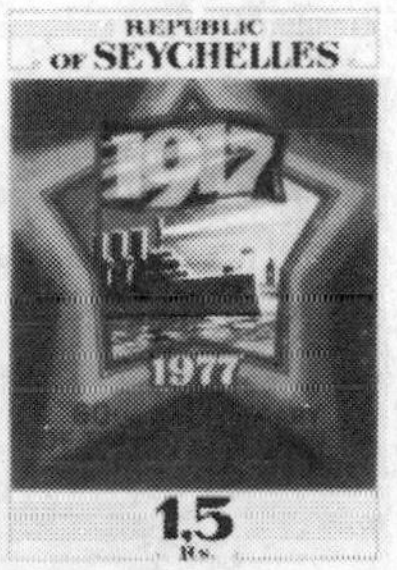

Cruiser Aurora, Star and Flag — A45

1977, Nov. 7 — Unwmk. — *Perf. 12*

404 A45	1.50r red, black & gold	.45	.45
a.	Souvenir sheet	.55	.55

60th anniv. of Russian Oct. Revolution.

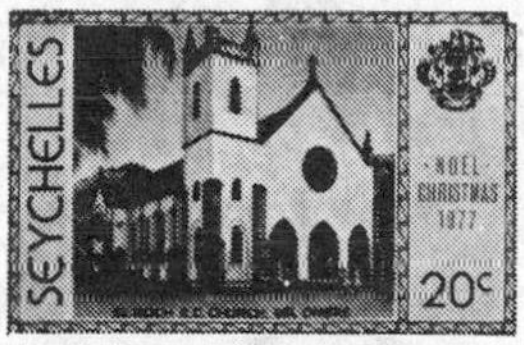

St. Roch Roman Catholic Church, Bel Ombre — A46

Christmas: 1r, Anglican Cathedral, Victoria. 1.50r, R. C. Cathedral, Victoria. 5r, St. Mark's Anglican Church, Praslin.

Perf. 13½x14

1977, Dec. 5 — Wmk. 373

405 A46	20c multicolored	.15	.15
406 A46	1r multicolored	.18	.18
407 A46	1.50r multicolored	.28	.28
408 A46	5r multicolored	.90	.90
	Nos. 405-408 (4)	1.51	1.51

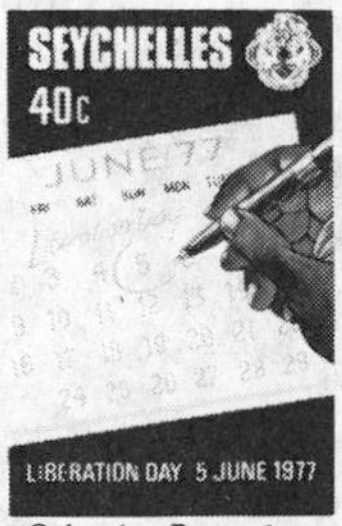

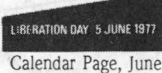

Calendar Page, June 5, 1977 — A47

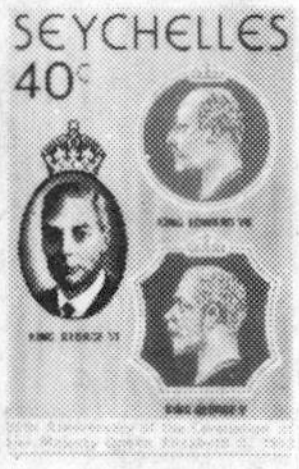

Edward VII, George V, George VI — A48

Designs: 1.25r, Hands holding rifle, torch and Seychelles flag. 1.50r, Fisherman and farmer holding hands. 5r, Soldiers and waving children.

Perf. 14x13½

1978, June 5 — Litho. — Wmk. 373

409 A47	40c multicolored	.15	.15
410 A47	1.25r multicolored	.16	.16
411 A47	1.50r multicolored	.24	.24
412 A47	5r multicolored	.85	.85
	Nos. 409-412 (4)	1.40	1.40

First anniversary of Liberation Day.

1978, Aug. 21 — Litho. — *Perf. 14*

Designs: 1.50r, Queens Victoria and Elizabeth II. 3r, Queen Victoria Monument, Seychelles. 5r, Queen's Building, Victoria, Seychelles.

413 A48	40c multicolored	.15	.15
414 A48	1.50r multicolored	.26	.26
415 A48	3r multicolored	.55	.55
416 A48	5r multicolored	.90	.90
a.	Souvenir sheet of 4, #413-416	2.50	2.50
	Nos. 413-416 (4)	1.86	1.86

25th anniv. of coronation of Elizabeth II.

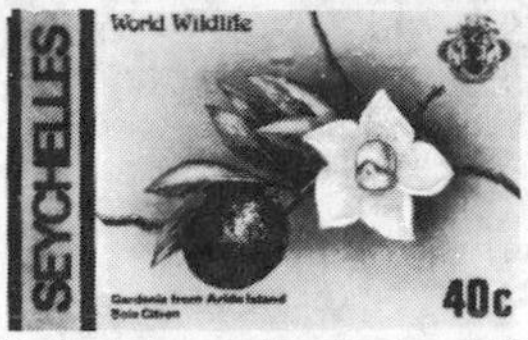

Gardenia from Aride Island — A49

Designs (Coat of Arms and): 1.25r, Magpie robin of Fregate Island. 1.50r, Seychelles paradise flycatchers. 5r, Green turtle.

Perf. 13½x14

1978, Oct. 16 — Litho. — Wmk. 373

417 A49	40c multicolored	.16	.16
418 A49	1.25r multicolored	.42	.42
419 A49	1.50r multicolored	.50	.50
420 A49	5r multicolored	1.90	1.90
	Nos. 417-420 (4)	2.98	2.98

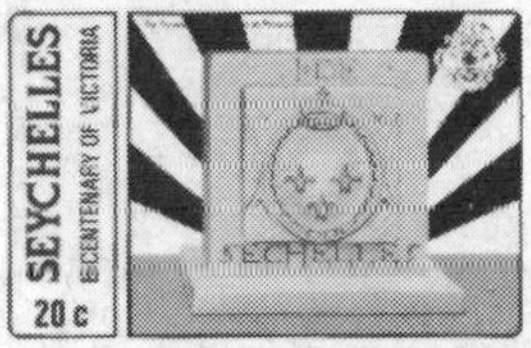

"Stone of Possession" — A50

1978, Dec. 15 — Litho. — *Perf. 13½*

421 A50	20c shown	.15	.15
422 A50	1.25r Map, 1782	.24	.24
423 A50	1.50r Clock tower	.30	.30
424 A50	5r Pierre Poivre	.90	.90
	Nos. 421-424 (4)	1.59	1.59

Bicentennary of the founding of Victoria.

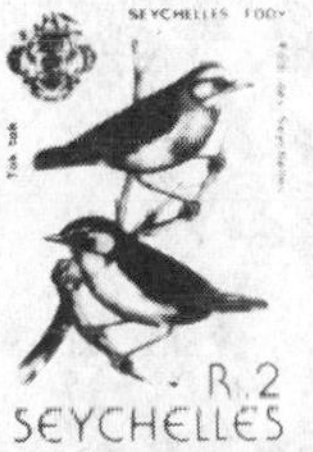

Seychelles Fody — A51

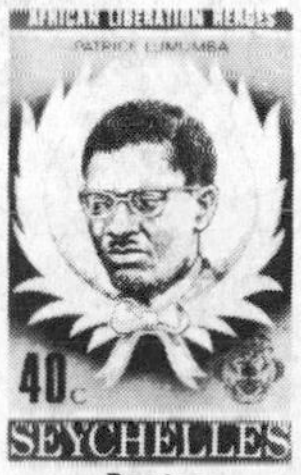

Patrice Lumumba — A52

Birds: No. 426, Green-backed heron. No. 427, Seychelles bulbul. No. 428, Seychelles cave swiftlets. No. 429, Grayheaded lovebirds.

1979, Feb. 27 — Litho. — *Perf. 14*

425 A51	2r multicolored	.70	.70
426 A51	2r multicolored	.70	.70
427 A51	2r multicolored	.70	.70
428 A51	2r multicolored	.70	.70
429 A51	2r multicolored	.70	.70
a.	Strip of 5, #425-429	3.50	3.50
	Nos. 425-429 (5)	3.50	3.50

1979, June 5 — Litho. — *Perf. 14½*

African Liberation Heroes: 2r, Kwame Nkrumah. 2.25r, Dr. Eduardo Mondlane. 5r, Amilcar Cabral.

430 A52	40c violet & blk	.15	.15
431 A52	2r dark blue & blk	.32	.32
432 A52	2.25r orange brn & blk	.35	.35
433 A52	5r olive grn & blk	.75	.75
	Nos. 430-433 (4)	1.57	1.57

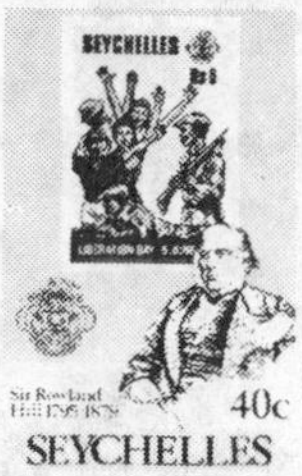

Coat of Arms, Rowland Hill, Seychelles No. 412 — A53

Coat of Arms, Hill, Seychelles stamps: 2.25r, No. 301. 3r, No. 205. 5r, No. 4.

1979, Aug. — Litho. — *Perf. 14x14½*

434 A53	40c multicolored	.15	.15
435 A53	2.25r multicolored	.45	.45
436 A53	3r multicolored	.60	.60
	Nos. 434-436 (3)	1.20	1.20

Souvenir Sheet

437 A53	5r multicolored	1.25	1.25

Sir Rowland Hill (1795-1879), originator of penny postage.

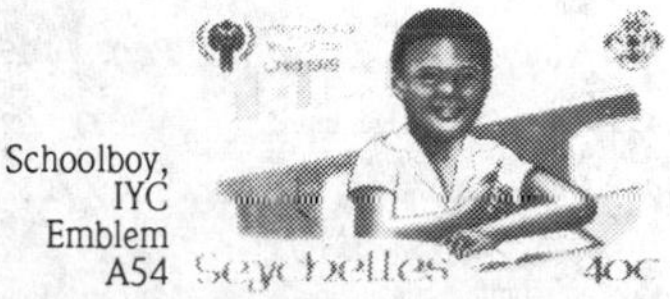

Schoolboy, IYC Emblem A54

IYC Emblem and: 2.25r, Children. 3r, Boy with ball, vert. 5r, Girl with puppet, vert.

Perf. 14½x14, 14x14½

1979, Oct. 25 — Litho.

438 A54	40c multicolored	.15	.15
439 A54	2.25r multicolored	.35	.35
440 A54	3r multicolored	.45	.45
441 A54	5r multicolored	.75	.75
	Nos. 438-441 (4)	1.70	1.70

International Year of the Child.

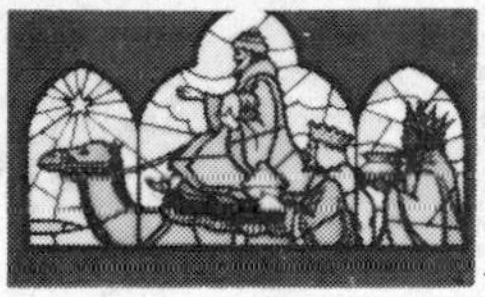
Three Kings Bearing Gifts A55

Christmas (Stained Glass Windows): 20c, Angel, vert. 2.25r, Virgin and Child, vert. 5r, Flight into Egypt.

1979, Dec. 3 — Litho. — *Perf. 14½*

442 A55	20c multicolored	.15	.15
443 A55	2.25r multicolored	.55	.55
444 A55	3r multicolored	.75	.75
	Nos. 442-444 (3)	1.45	1.45

Souvenir Sheet

445 A55	5r multicolored	1.40	1.40

No. 399 Surcharged

Wmk. 373

1979, Dec. 7 — Litho. — *Perf. 14*

446 A44	1.10r on 3.50r multicolored	.35	.35

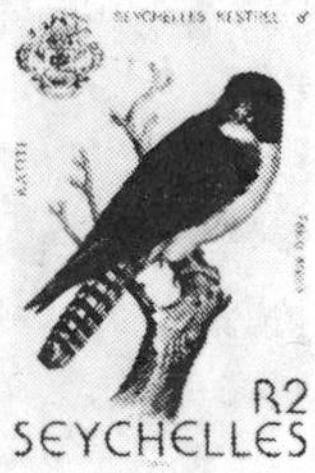

Seychelles Kestrel — A56

Seychelles Kestrel: a, shown. b, Pair. c, Female, eggs. d, Mother and chick. e, Chicks nesting.

1980, Feb. 29 — Litho. — *Perf. 14*

447	Strip of 5	3.50	3.50
a.-e.	A56 2r any single	.70	.70

See Nos. 468, 483.

50-Rupee Bank Note, London 1980 Emblem — A57

Sprinting, Moscow '80 Emblem — A58

New Currency: 40c, 1.50r, horiz.

1980, Apr. 18 Litho. *Perf. 14*

448	A57	40c	multicolored	.15	.15
449	A57	1.50r	multicolored	.28	.28
450	A57	2.25r	multicolored	.42	.42
451	A57	5r	multicolored	.90	.90
a.			Souvenir sheet of 4, #448-451	1.90	1.90
			Nos. 448-451 (4)	1.75	1.75

London 1980 Intl. Stamp Exhib., May 6-14.

1980, June 13 *Perf. 14½*

452	A58	40c	shown	.15	.15
453	A58	2.25r	Weight lifting	.32	.32
454	A58	3r	Boxing	.42	.42
455	A58	5r	Yachting	1.50	1.50
a.			Souvenir sheet of 4, #452-455	2.75	2.75
			Nos. 452-455 (4)	2.39	2.39

22nd Summer Olympic Games, Moscow, July 19-Aug. 3.

Boeing 747 — A59

1980, Aug. 22 Litho. *Perf. 14*

456	A59	40c	shown	.15	.15
457	A59	2.25r	Tour bus	.45	.45
458	A59	3r	Ocean liner, pirogue	.65	.65
459	A59	5r	Tour motor boat	1.10	1.10
			Nos. 456-459 (4)	2.35	2.35

World Tourism Conf., Manila, Sept. 27.

Female Coco-de-Mer Palm Tree — A60

1980, Oct. 31 Litho. *Perf. 14*

460	A60	40c	shown	.15	.15
461	A60	2.25r	Male tree	.42	.42
462	A60	3r	Bowls	.55	.55
463	A60	5r	Gourds, canoes	.95	.95
a.			Souvenir sheet of 4, #460-463	2.25	2.25
			Nos. 460-463 (4)	2.07	2.07

Vasco da Gama's San Gabriel, 1497 A61

Perf. 14½

1981, Feb. Litho. Wmk. 373

464	A61	40c	shown	.15	.15
465	A61	2.25r	Mascarenhas' Caravel, 1505	.48	.48
466	A61	3.50r	Darwin's Beagle, 1831	.75	.75
467	A61	5r	Queen Elizabeth 2, 1968	1.00	1.00
a.			Souvenir sheet of 4, #464-467	2.50	2.50
			Nos. 464-467 (4)	2.38	2.38

Bird Type of 1980

1981, Apr. 10 Litho. *Perf. 14*

468		Strip of 5, multi	5.00	5.00
a.	A56	2r Male fairy tern	1.00	1.00
b.	A56	2r Pair	1.00	1.00
c.	A56	2r Female	1.00	1.00
d.	A56	2r Female, diff.	1.00	1.00
e.	A56	2r Adult bird, chick	1.00	1.00

Prince Charles, Lady Diana, Royal Yacht Charlotte A61a

Prince Charles and Lady Diana — A61b

Illustration A61b is reduced.

Wmk. 380

1981, June 23 Litho. *Perf. 14*

469	A61a	1.50r	Couple, Victoria & Albert I	.48	.48
a.			Bklt. pane of 4, perf. 12	1.50	
470	A61b	1.50r	Couple	.48	.48
471	A61a	5r	Cleveland	1.50	1.50
472	A61b	5r	like #470	1.50	1.50
a.			Bklt. pane of 2, perf. 12	2.50	
473	A61a	10r	Britannia	3.25	3.25
474	A61b	10r	like #470	3.25	3.25
			Nos. 469-474 (6)	10.46	10.46

Each denomination issued in sheets of 7 (6 type A61a, 1 type A61b).

For surcharges see Nos. 528-533.

Souvenir Sheet

1981 Litho. *Perf. 12*

474A	A61b	7.50r	Couple	2.25	2.25

Seychelles Intl. Airport, 10th Anniv. A62

Perf. 14½

1981, July 27 Litho. Wmk. 373

475	A62	40c	Britten-Norman Islander	.15	.15
476	A62	2.25r	Britten-Norman Trislander	.55	.55
477	A62	3.50r	Vickers VC-10	.80	.80
478	A62	5r	Boeing 747	1.10	1.10
			Nos. 475-478 (4)	2.60	2.60

A63

A65

Designs: Various flying foxes.

1981, Oct. 9 Litho. *Perf. 14*

479	A63	40c	multicolored	.15	.15
480	A63	2.25r	multicolored	.75	.75
481	A63	3r	multicolored	.95	.95
482	A63	5r	multicolored	1.65	1.65
a.			Souvenir sheet, #479-482	4.75	4.75
			Nos. 479-482 (4)	3.50	3.50

Bird Type of 1980

Designs: a, Male Chinese bittern. b, Female. c, Hen on nest. d, Nest, eggs. e, Hen, chicks.

Wmk. 373

1982, Feb. 4 Litho. *Perf. 14*

483		Strip of 5	6.50	6.50
a.-e.	A56	3r any single	1.25	1.25

1982, Apr. 22 Litho. *Perf. 14½*

487	A65	40c	Map of Silhouette Island and La Digue	.15	.15
488	A65	1.50r	Denis & Bird Islds.	.30	.30
489	A65	2.75r	Curieuse Isld., Praslin	.60	.60
490	A65	7r	Mahe	1.40	1.40
a.			Souvenir sheet of 4, #487-490	3.25	3.25
			Nos. 487-490 (4)	2.45	2.45

5th Anniv. of Liberation A66

1982, June 5 *Perf. 14*

491	A66	40c	Bookmobile	.15	.15
492	A66	1.75r	Mobile dental clinic	.35	.35
493	A66	2.75r	Farming	.52	.52
494	A66	7r	Construction site	1.40	1.40
a.			Souvenir sheet of 4, #491-494	3.00	3.00
			Nos. 491-494 (4)	2.42	2.42

Tourist Board Emblem A67

Tourism: Hotels.

1982, Sept. 1

495	A67	1.75r	Northolme	.40	.40
496	A67	1.75r	Reef	.40	.40
497	A67	1.75r	Barbarons Beach	.40	.40
498	A67	1.75r	Coral Strand	.40	.40
499	A67	1.75r	Beau Vallon Bay	.40	.40
500	A67	1.75r	Fisherman's Cove	.40	.40
501	A67	1.75r	Mahe Beach, shown	.40	.40
502	A67	1.75r	Island scene	.40	.40
			Nos. 495-502 (8)	3.20	3.20

Tata Bus — A68

Wmk. 373

1982, Nov. 18 Litho. *Perf. 14*

503	A68	20c	shown	.15	.15
504	A68	1.75r	Mini moke	.35	.35
505	A68	2.75r	Ox cart	.55	.55
506	A68	7r	Truck	1.40	1.40
			Nos. 503-506 (4)	2.45	2.45

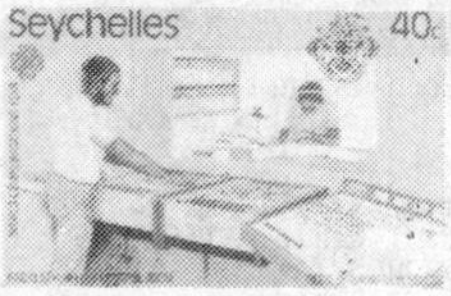

World Communications Year — A69

1983, Feb. 25

507	A69	40c	Radio control room	.15	.15
508	A69	2.75r	Satellite earth station	.60	.60
509	A69	3.50r	TV control room	.75	.75
510	A69	5r	Postal services	1.10	1.10
			Nos. 507-510 (4)	2.60	2.60

Commonwealth Day — A70

1983, Mar. 14

511	A70	40c	Agricultural research	.15	.15
512	A70	2.75r	Food processing plant	.60	.60
513	A70	3.50r	Fishing industry	.80	.80
514	A70	7r	Flag	1.65	1.65
			Nos. 511-514 (4)	3.20	3.20

Denis Isld. Lighthouse, 1910 — A71

1983, July 14 *Perf. 14x13½*

515	A71	40c	shown	.15	.15
516	A71	2.75r	Seychelles Hospital, 1924	.75	.75
517	A71	3.50r	Supreme Court, 1894	1.00	1.00
518	A71	7r	State House, 1911	2.00	2.00
a.			Souvenir sheet of 4, #515-518	4.50	4.50
			Nos. 515-518 (4)	3.90	3.90

Manned Flight Bicentenary A72

1983, Sept. 15 *Perf. 14*

519	A72	40c	Royal Vauxhall balloon, 1836	.15	.15
520	A72	1.75r	DeHavilland D.H.-50j	.50	.50
521	A72	2.75r	Grumman Albatross	.80	.80
522	A72	7r	Sweavingen Merlin	2.00	2.00
			Nos. 519-522 (4)	3.45	3.45

First Intl. Air Seychelles Flight A73

1983, Oct. 26 Litho.

523	A73	2r	DC10 aircraft	.65	.65

Paintings, Marianne North — A74

1983, Nov. 17 Litho. *Perf. 14*

524	A74	40c	Swamp Plant and Moorhen	.15	.15
525	A74	1.75r	Wormia flagellaria	.50	.50
526	A74	2.75r	Asiatic Pancratium	.80	.80
527	A74	7r	Pitcher Plant	2.00	2.00
a.			Souvenir sheet of 4, #524-527	3.75	3.75
			Nos. 524-527 (4)	3.45	3.45

Nos. 469-474 Surcharged

Wmk. 380

1983, Dec. 28 Litho. *Perf. 14*

528	A61a	50c	on 1.50r multi	.16	.16
529	A61b	50c	on 1.50r multi	.16	.16
530	A61a	2.25r	on 5r multi	.75	.75
531	A61b	2.25r	on 5r multi	.75	.75
532	A61a	3.75r	on 10r multi	1.25	1.25
533	A61b	3.75r	on 10r multi	1.25	1.25
			Nos. 528-533 (6)	4.32	4.32

Handicrafts A75

Wmk. 373

1984, Feb. 29 Litho. *Perf. 14*

534	A75	50c	Coconut kettle	.15	.15
535	A75	2r	Scarf, doll	.60	.60
536	A75	3r	Coconut-fiber roses	.90	.90
537	A75	10r	Carved fishing boat, doll	2.75	2.75
			Nos. 534-537 (4)	4.40	4.40

Lloyd's List Issue

Common Design Type

1984, May 21 Litho. *Perf. 14½x14*

538	CD335	50c	Port Victoria	.15	.15
539	CD335	2r	Steamship, 1930s	.60	.60
540	CD335	3r	Cruise liner	.90	.90
541	CD335	10r	Ennerdale	2.75	2.75
			Nos. 538-541 (4)	4.40	4.40

People's United Party, 20th Anniv. A76

1984, June 2 Litho. *Perf. 14*

542 A76 50c Original headquarters .15 .15
543 A76 2r Liberation statue, vert. .60 .60
544 A76 3r New headquarters .90 .90
545 A76 10r Pres. Rene, vert. 2.75 2.75
Nos. 542-545 (4) 4.40 4.40

Souvenir Sheet

UPU Congress A77

1984, June 18 *Perf. 14½*

546 A77 5r No. 156 1.50 1.50

1984 Summer Olympics A78

1984, July 28 *Perf. 14*

547 A78 50c Long jump .15 .15
548 A78 2r Boxing .55 .55
549 A78 3r Diving .80 .80
550 A78 10r Weight lifting 2.75 2.75
a. Souvenir sheet of 4, #547-550 4.25 4.25
Nos. 547-550 (4) 4.25 4.25

Scuba Diving A79

1984, Sept. 24

551 A79 50c shown .18 .18
552 A79 2r Paragliding .70 .70
553 A79 3r Sailing 1.00 1.00
554 A79 10r Water skiing 3.25 3.25
Nos. 551-554 (4) 5.13 5.13

Whale Conservation A80

1984, Nov. **Litho.**

555 A80 50c Humpback whale .18 .18
556 A80 2r Sperm whale .70 .70
557 A80 3r Right whale 1.00 1.00
558 A80 10r Blue whale 3.50 3.50
Nos. 555-558 (4) 5.38 5.38

Audubon Birth Bicent. — A81

EXPO '85, Tsukuba — A82

Bare-legged scops owls.

1985, Mar. 11 Litho. *Perf. 14*

559 A81 50c multicolored .18 .18
560 A81 2r multicolored .70 .70
561 A81 3r multicolored 1.00 1.00
562 A81 10r multicolored 3.50 3.50
Nos. 559-562 (4) 5.38 5.38

Wmk. 373

1985, Mar. 15 Litho. *Perf. 14*

563 A82 50c Giant tortoise .15 .15
564 A82 2r Fairy tern .55 .55
565 A82 3r Wind surfing .80 .80
566 A82 5r Coco de mer 1.40 1.40
a. Souvenir sheet of 4, #563-566 3.00 3.00
Nos. 563-566 (4) 2.90 2.90

See No. 604.

Queen Mother 85th Birthday

Common Design Type

Perf. 14½x14

1985, June 7 Litho. Wmk. 384

567 CD336 50c Queen Elizabeth, 1930 .15 .15
568 CD336 2r With grandchildren, 1970 .60 .60
569 CD336 3r 75th birthday celebration .90 .90
570 CD336 5r Holding Prince Henry 1.50 1.50
Nos. 567-570 (4) 3.15 3.15

Souvenir Sheet

571 CD336 10r Exiting from helicopter 3.00 3.00

2nd Indian Ocean Islands Games A83

1985, Aug. 24

572 A83 50c Boxing .15 .15
573 A83 2r Soccer .55 .55
574 A83 3r Swimming .80 .80
575 A83 10r Wind surfing 2.75 2.75
Nos. 572-575 (4) 4.25 4.25

A83a A84

1985, Nov. 1 **Wmk. 384**

576 A83a 1.25r Fairy tern .35 .35

Air Seychelles 1st Airbus.

1985, Nov. 28

577 A84 50c Agriculture .15 .15
578 A84 2r Construction .55 .55
579 A84 3r Carpentry .80 .80
580 A84 10r Science education 2.75 2.75
Nos. 577-580 (4) 4.25 4.25

Intl. Youth Year.

Vintage Cars — A85

1985, Dec. 18

581 A85 50c 1919 Ford Model T .15 .15
582 A85 2r 1922 Austin Seven .60 .60
583 A85 3r 1924 Morris Bullnose Oxford .85 .85
584 A85 10r 1929 Humber Coupe 3.00 3.00
Nos. 581-584 (4) 4.60 4.60

Halley's Comet — A86

1986, Feb. Wmk. 384 *Perf. 14x14½*

585 A86 50c Transit instrument .15 .15
586 A86 2r Quadrant .60 .60
587 A86 3r Trajectory diagram .85 .85
588 A86 10r Edmond Halley 3.00 3.00
Nos. 585-588 (4) 4.60 4.60

Giselle, Performed by the Ballet Louvre, Apr. 4-8 — A87

Wmk. 384

1986, Apr. 4 Litho. *Perf. 14*

589 A87 2r Heroine .60 .60
590 A87 3r Hero .90 .90

Souvenir Sheet

591 A87 10r United 3.00 3.00

First ballet performed in the Seychelles.

Queen Elizabeth II 60th Birthday

Common Design Type

Designs: 50c, Marrying the Duke of Edinburgh, 1947. 1.25r, Silver Jubilee celebration. 2r, Greeting child aboard the Britannia, Qatar Harbor. 3r, State opening of Parliament, 1982. 5r, Visiting Crown Agents' offices, 1983.

1986, Apr. 21 *Perf. 14½*

592 CD337 50c scarlet, blk & sil .15 .15
593 CD337 1.25r ultra & multi .38 .38
594 CD337 2r green & multi .60 .60
595 CD337 3r violet & multi .90 .90
596 CD337 5r rose vio & multi 1.50 1.50
Nos. 592-596 (5) 3.53 3.53

For overprints see Nos. 625-629.

AMERIPEX '86, Inter-island Communications — A88

Wmk. 384

1986, May 22 Litho. *Perf. 14*

597 A88 50c La Digue Ferry .16 .16
598 A88 2r Phone booth, vert. .62 .62
599 A88 3r Victoria P.O., vert. .90 .90
600 A88 7r Air Seychelles trislander 2.25 2.25
Nos. 597-600 (4) 3.93 3.93

Coptic Catholic Knights of Malta Celebration Day — A89

Perf. 14½x14

1986, June 7 Litho. Wmk. 384

601 A89 5r Natl. arms, assoc. emblem 1.50 1.50
a. Souvenir sheet of 1 1.65 1.65

Royal Wedding Issue, 1986

Common Design Type

Designs: 2r, Informal portrait. 10r, Andrew, helicopter.

1986, July 23 Litho. *Perf. 14*

602 CD338 2r multicolored .60 .60
603 CD338 10r multicolored 3.00 3.00

Tsukuba Expo Type of 1985

Souvenir Sheet

Wmk. 384

1986, July 12 Litho. *Perf. 14*

604 Sheet of 4 3.00 3.00
a. A82 50c multicolored .15 .15
b. A82 2r multicolored .55 .55
c. A82 3r multicolored .80 .80
d. A82 5r multicolored 1.40 1.40

No. 604 inscribed "Seychelles Philatelic Exhibition-Tokyo-1986" and printed without EXPO '85 emblem on margin or on individual stamps. Nos. 604a-604d inscribed "1986."

No. 396 Overprinted

LAZOURNEN ENTERNASYONAL KREOL

Perf. 14½x14

1986, Oct. 28 **Wmk. 373**

605 A44 1r multicolored .30 .30

Intl. Creole Day.

State Visit of Pope John Paul II — A90

Pope and: 50c, Seychelles Airport. 2r, Cathedral. 3r, Baie Lazare parish church. 10r, People's Stadium.

1986, Dec. 1 Wmk. 384 *Perf. 14½*

606 A90 50c multicolored .18 .18
607 A90 2r multicolored .70 .70
608 A90 3r multicolored 1.00 1.00
609 A90 10r multicolored 3.25 3.25
a. Souvenir sheet of 4, #606-609 5.00 5.00
Nos. 606-609 (4) 5.13 5.13

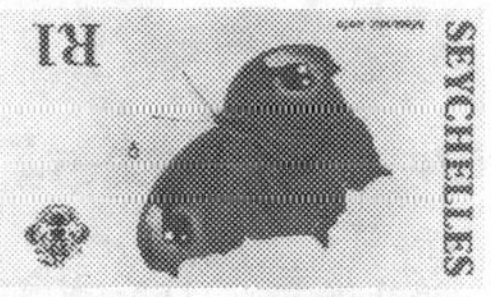

Butterflies A91

Perf. 14½

1987, Feb. 18 Litho. Wmk. 384

610 A91 1r Melanitis leda .38 .38
611 A91 2r Phalanta philiberti .75 .75
612 A91 3r Danaus chrysippus 1.10 1.10
613 A91 10r Euploea mitra 3.50 3.50
Nos. 610-613 (4) 5.73 5.73

Seashells — A92

Liberation, 10th Anniv. — A93

1987, May 7 **Wmk. 373**

614 A92 1r Gloripallium pallium .38 .38
615 A92 2r Spondylus aurantius .70 .70
616 A92 3r Harpa ventricosa, Lioconcha ornata 1.10 1.10
617 A92 10r Strombus lentiginosus 3.50 3.50
Nos. 614-617 (4) 5.68 5.68

Perf. 14x14½, 14½x14

1987, June 5 **Wmk. 384**

618 A93 1r Liberation monument .32 .32
619 A93 2r Hospital, horiz. .62 .62
620 A93 3r Orphanage, horiz. .92 .92
621 A93 10r Fish monument 3.00 3.00
Nos. 618-621 (4) 4.86 4.86

Natl. Banking Cent. — A94

1987, June 25 *Perf. 14½x14*

622 A94 1r Savings Bank, Praslin .32 .32
623 A94 2r Development Bank .60 .60
624 A94 10r Central Bank 3.00 3.00
Nos. 622-624 (3) 3.92 3.92

Nos. 592-596 Ovptd. in Silver

40TH WEDDING ANNIVERSARY

Perf. 14½

1987, Dec. 9 Litho. Wmk. 384

625 CD337 50c scarlet, blk & sil .16 .16
626 CD337 1.25r ultra & multi .42 .42
627 CD337 2r green & multi .70 .70

628	CD337	3r violet & multi	1.00	1.00
629	CD337	5r rose vio & multi	1.75	1.75
		Nos. 625-629 (5)	4.03	4.03

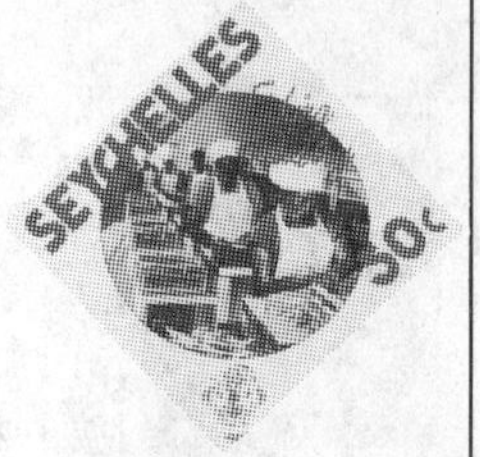

Fishing Industry A95

Wmk. 384

1987, Dec. 11 Litho. *Perf. 14*

630	A95	50c Tuna cannery	.16	.16
631	A95	2r Fishing trawler	.65	.65
632	A95	3r Weighing fish	1.00	1.00
633	A95	10r Hauling catch from net	3.50	3.50
		Nos. 630-633 (4)	5.31	5.31

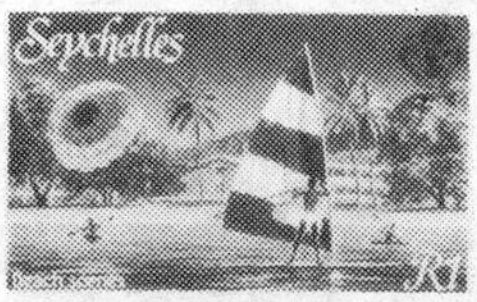

Beach Scenes A96

Perf. 14¹/₂

1988, Feb. 9 Litho. Wmk. 384

634	A96	1r Para-sailing, windsurfing, kayaks	.32	.32
635	A96	2r Boating	.65	.65
636	A96	3r Yacht at anchor	.95	.95
637	A96	10r Hotel, cabanas	3.00	3.00
		Nos. 634-637 (4)	4.92	4.92

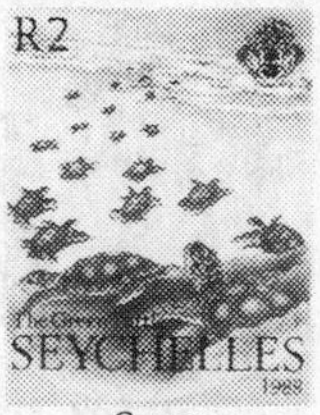

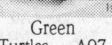

Green Turtles — A97

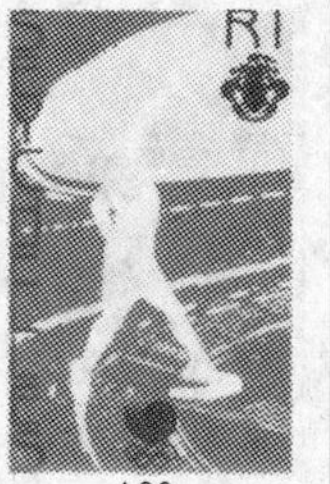

A98

No. 638, Newly hatched turtles headed toward ocean. No. 639, Offspring hatching. No. 640, Female emerging from ocean. No. 641, Female laying eggs in sand. Stamps of same denomination printed se-tenant in a continuous design.

1988, Apr. 22 Wmk. 373

638	A97	2r multicolored	.75	.75
639	A97	2r multicolored	.75	.75
640	A97	3r multicolored	1.15	1.15
641	A97	3r multicolored	1.15	1.15
		Nos. 638-641 (4)	3.80	3.80

1988, July 29 Wmk. 384 *Perf. 14¹/₂*

Designs: 1r, No. 647a, Shot put. Nos. 643, 647b, High jump. 3r, No. 647c, Medal winner, grandstand and flags. 4r, No. 647d, Running. 5r, No. 647e, Javelin. 10r, Tennis.

642	A98	1r multicolored	.30	.30
643	A98	2r multicolored	.60	.60
644	A98	3r multicolored	.90	.90
645	A98	4r multicolored	1.25	1.25
646	A98	5r multicolored	1.40	1.40
647		Strip of 5	3.00	3.00
a.-e.		A98 2r any single	.60	.60
		Nos. 642-647 (6)	7.45	7.45

Souvenir Sheet

Wmk. 373

648	A98	10r multicolored	3.75	3.75

No. 647 has a continuous design.

1988 Summer Olympics, Seoul, (1r-5r). Intl. Tennis Fed., 75th anniv. (10r). No. 648 contains one stamp, size: 28x39mm.

Lloyds of London, 300th Anniv.

Common Design Type

Designs: 1r, Leadenhall Street, London, 1928. 2r, Cinq Juin, horiz. 3r, Queen Elizabeth II, horiz. 10r, Explosion of the Hindenburg, Lakehurst, New Jersey, 1937.

Wmk. 384

1988, Sept. 30 Litho. *Perf. 14*

649	CD341	1r multicolored	.38	.38
650	CD341	2r multicolored	.72	.72
651	CD341	3r multicolored	1.05	1.05
652	CD341	10r multicolored	3.50	3.50
		Nos. 649-652 (4)	5.65	5.65

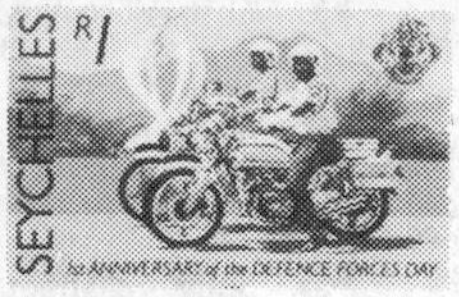

Defense Forces Day, 1st Anniv. A99

1988, Nov. 25 Litho. Wmk. 373

653	A99	1r Motorcycle police	.38	.38
654	A99	2r Air force helicopter	.72	.72
655	A99	3r Navy patrol boat	1.05	1.05
656	A99	10r Tank	3.50	3.50
		Nos. 653-656 (4)	5.65	5.65

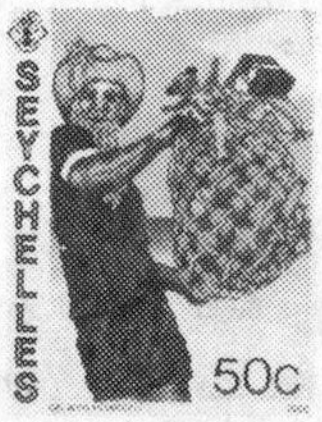

Christmas — A100

Illustrations by local artists.

1988, Dec. 1 Litho. Wmk. 373

657	A100	50c Selwyn Hoareau	.15	.15
658	A100	2r Robin Leste	.72	.72
659	A100	3r France Anacoura	1.10	1.10
660	A100	10r Andre McGaw	3.65	3.65
		Nos. 657-660 (4)	5.62	5.62

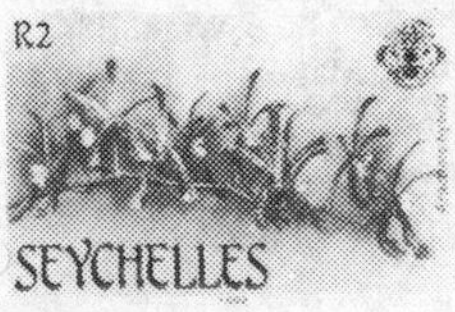

Orchids A101

Wmk. 384

1988, Dec. 21 Litho. *Perf. 14*

661	A101	1r Dendrobium, vert.	.38	.38
662	A101	2r Arachnis hybrid	.75	.75
663	A101	3r Vanda caerulea, vert.	1.15	1.15
664	A101	10r Dendrobium phalaenopsis	3.75	3.75
		Nos. 661-664 (4)	6.03	6.03

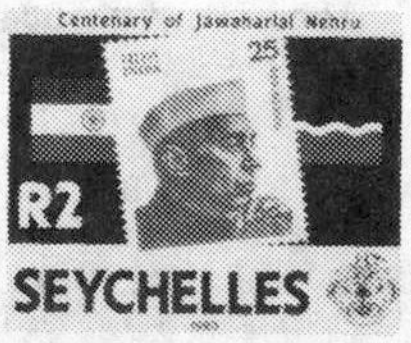

Jawaharlal Nehru (1889-1964), 1st Prime Minister of Independent India — A102

1989, Mar. 30 *Perf. 13¹/₂*

665	A102	2r India Type A409	.75	.75
666	A102	10r Portrait	3.75	3.75

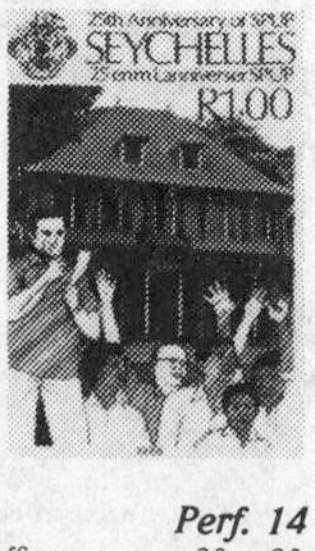

People's United Party (SPUP), 25th Anniv. — A103

1989, June 5 *Perf. 14*

667	A103	1r Rally, old office	.38	.38
668	A103	2r Maison Du Peuple	.75	.75
669	A103	3r Pres. Rene, banner, torch	1.10	1.10
670	A103	10r Torch, flag, Rene	3.65	3.65
		Nos. 667-670 (4)	5.88	5.88

Moon Landing, 20th Anniv.

Common Design Type

Apollo 15: 1r, Saturn 5 lift-off. 2r, David R. Scott, Alfred M. Worden and James B. Irwin. 3r, Mission emblem. 5r, Irwin salutes flag in front of the Hadley Delta. 10r, Buzz Aldrin about to step onto the Moon, Apollo 11 mission.

1989, July 20

Size of Nos. 677-678: 29x29mm

676	CD342	1r multicolored	.35	.35
677	CD342	2r multicolored	.72	.72
678	CD342	3r multicolored	1.10	1.10
679	CD342	5r multicolored	1.80	1.80
		Nos. 676-679 (4)	3.97	3.97

Souvenir Sheet

680	CD342	10r multicolored	3.65	3.65

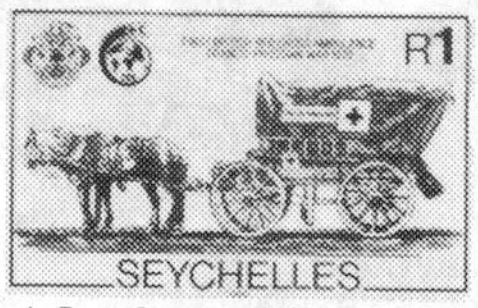

Intl. Red Cross and Red Crescent Organizations, 125th Annivs. — A104

1989, Sept. 12 *Perf. 14¹/₂*

681	A104	1r Ambulance, 1870	.40	.40
682	A104	2r H.M. Hospital Ship Liberty, 1914-18	.78	.78
683	A104	3r Sunbeam Standard Army Ambulance, 1914-18	1.20	1.20
684	A104	10r The White Train, 1899-1902	4.00	4.00
		Nos. 681-684 (4)	6.38	6.38

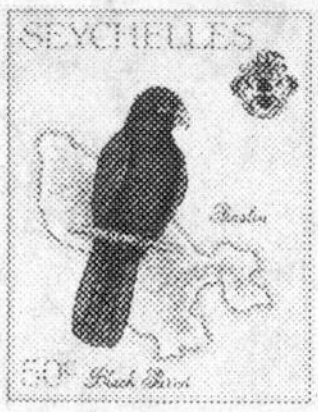

Island Birds — A105

1989, Oct. 16 *Perf. 14¹/₂x14*

685	A105	50c Black parrot	.22	.22
686	A105	2r Sooty tern	.85	.85
687	A105	3r Magpie robin	1.40	1.40
688	A105	5r Roseate tern	2.25	2.25
a.		Souvenir sheet of 4, #685-688	4.75	4.75
		Nos. 685-688 (4)	4.72	4.72

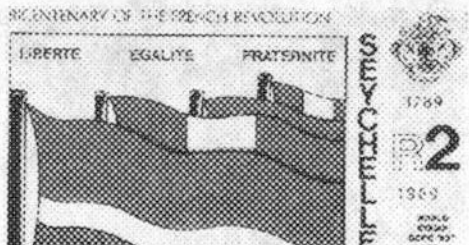

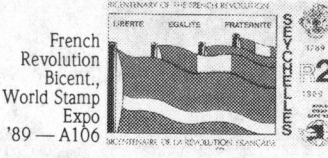

French Revolution Bicent., World Stamp Expo '89 — A106

1989, Nov. 17 *Perf. 14*

689	A106	2r Flags	.70	.70
690	A106	5r Storming of the Bastille	1.75	1.75

Souvenir Sheet

691	A106	10r Raising French flag, Seychelles, 1791	3.50	3.50

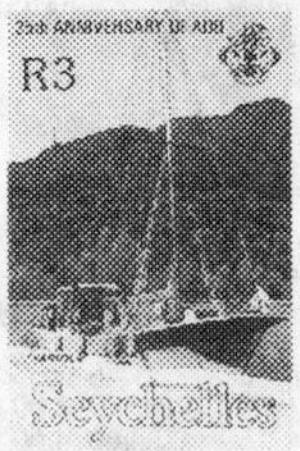

African Development Bank, 25th Anniv. — A107

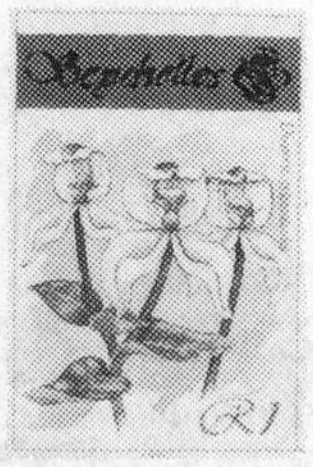

Orchids — A108

Designs: 1r, Beau Vallon School, horiz. 2r, Fishing Authority headquarters, horiz. 3r, Variola. 10r, Deneb.

1989, Dec. 29 Wmk. 384

692	A107	1r multicolored	.35	.35
693	A107	2r multicolored	.70	.70
694	A107	3r multicolored	1.05	1.05
695	A107	10r multicolored	3.50	3.50
		Nos. 692-695 (4)	5.60	5.60

1990, Jan. 26

696	A108	1r Disperis tripetaloides	.35	.35
697	A108	2r Vanilla phalaenopsis	.70	.70
698	A108	3r Angraecum eburneum superbum	1.05	1.05
699	A108	10r Polystachya concreta	3.50	3.50
		Nos. 696-699 (4)	5.60	5.60

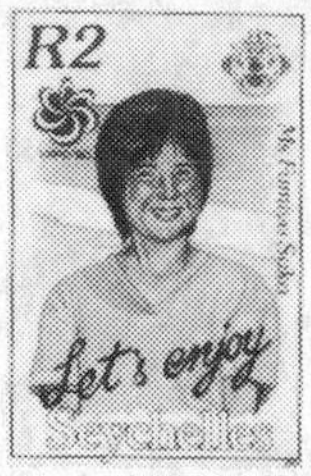

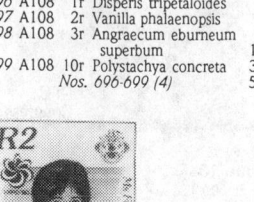

Expo '90 (International Garden & Greenery Exposition), Japan — A109

Designs: 2r, Fumiyo Sako. 3r, Coco-de-mer, male and female plants. 5r, Pitcher plant, Aldabra lily. 7r, Gardenia, Arms of Seychelles.

1990, June 8 Litho. Wmk. 373

700	A109	2r multicolored	.70	.70
701	A109	3r multicolored	1.05	1.05
702	A109	5r multicolored	1.75	1.75
703	A109	7r multicolored	2.50	2.50
a.		Souvenir sheet of 4, #700-703	6.05	6.05
		Nos. 700-703 (4)	6.00	6.00

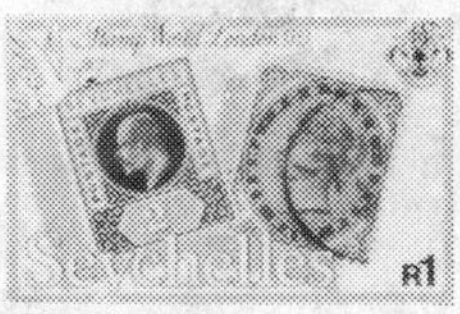

Penny Black 150th Anniv., Stamp World London '90 A110

Exhibition emblem and stamps on stamps: 1r, Seychelles #38, Great Britain #80 canceled. 2r, Seychelles #81, Great Britain #64 canceled. 3r, Seychelles #74, Great Britain #62 canceled. 5r, Seychelles #2, Great Britain #3 canceled. 10r, Seychelles #197, Great Britain #1 canceled.

1990, May 3 *Perf. 12¹/₂*

704	A110	1r multicolored	.35	.35
705	A110	2r multicolored	.70	.70
706	A110	3r multicolored	1.05	1.05
707	A110	5r multicolored	1.75	1.75
		Nos. 704-707 (4)	3.85	3.85

Souvenir Sheet

708	A110	10r multicolored	3.50	3.50

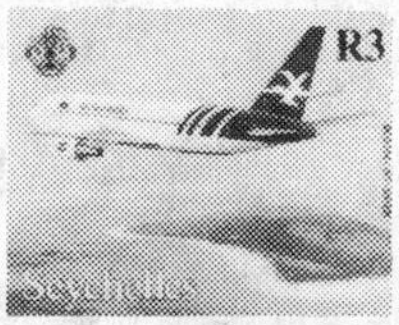

Boeing 767-200ER A111

Perf. 14¹/₂x14¹/₂

1990, July 27 Litho. Wmk. 384

709	A111	3r multicolored	1.05	1.05

Printed in panes of 10 (2 strips of 5 separated by pictorial gutter).

Queen Mother, 90th Birthday

Common Design Types

1990, Aug. 4 Wmk. 384 *Perf. 14x15*

710	CD343	2r Queen Elizabeth in coronation robes, 1937	.70	.70

Perf. 14¹/₂

711	CD344	10r Visiting workshops, 1947	3.50	3.50

A112   A113

1990, Sept. 8   Wmk. 373   *Perf. 14*

712	A112	1r Blackboard	.36 .36
713	A112	2r Reading mail	.72 .72
714	A112	3r Reading directions	1.10 1.10
715	A112	10r Crossword puzzle	3.60 3.60
		Nos. 712-715 (4)	5.78 5.78

Intl. Literacy Year.

1990, Oct. 27   *Perf. 13¹/₂x14*

Various Sega Dancers: a, Pink and white skirt, white blouse. b, Yellow dress. c, Blue, sky blue and pink dress. d, Yellow, green and pink dress. e, White and pink skirt, green blouse.

716		Strip of 5	3.60 3.60
a.-e.	A113	2r any single	.72 .72

Festival Kreol 1990.

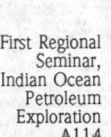

First Regional Seminar, Indian Ocean Petroleum Exploration A114

1990, Dec. 10   Wmk. 384   *Perf. 14¹/₂*

717	A114	3r Beach	1.10 1.10
718	A114	10r Geological map	3.65 3.65

Orchids — A115

1991, Feb. 1   *Perf. 14*

719	A115	1r Bulbophyllum intertextum	.36 .36
720	A115	2r Agrostophyllum occidentale	.72 .72
721	A115	3r Vanilla planifolia	1.10 1.10
722	A115	10r Malaxis seychellarum	3.60 3.60
		Nos. 719-722 (4)	5.78 5.78

Elizabeth & Philip, Birthdays
Common Design Types

1991, June 17   *Perf. 14¹/₂*

723	CD345	4r multicolored	1.40 1.40
724	CD346	4r multicolored	1.40 1.40
a.		Pair, #723-724 + label	2.80 2.80

Butterflies A116

1991, Nov. 15   Litho.   Wmk. 373
Perf. 14¹/₂x14

725	A116	1.50r Precis rhadama	.58 .58
726	A116	3r Lampides boeticus	1.15 1.15
727	A116	3.50r Zizeeria knysna	1.35 1.35
728	A116	10r Phalanta phalanta aethiopica	4.00 4.00
		Nos. 725-728 (4)	7.08 7.08

Souvenir Sheet

729	A116	10r Eagris sabadius	4.00 4.00

Phila Nippon '91.

Christmas — A117

Woodcuts: 50c, The Holy Virgin, Joseph, the Holy Child and St. John by Raphael, engraved by S. Vouillemont. 1r, The Holy Virgin, the Child and an Angel by Van Dyck, engraved by A. Blooting. 2r, The Holy Family, St. John and St. Anna by Rubens, engraved by Lucas Vorsterman. 7r, The Holy Family, an Angel and St. Catherine, painting and engraving by Cornelius Bloemaert.

1991, Dec. 2   Wmk. 384   *Perf. 14*

730	A117	50c multicolored	.18 .18
731	A117	1r multicolored	.40 .40
732	A117	3r multicolored	.80 .80
733	A117	7r multicolored	2.75 2.75
		Nos. 730-733 (4)	4.13 4.13

Queen Elizabeth II's Accession to the Throne, 40th Anniv.
Common Design Type

1992, Feb. 6   Wmk. 373

734	CD349	1r multicolored	.38 .38
735	CD349	1.50r multicolored	.55 .55
736	CD349	1.15r multicolored	1.15 1.15
737	CD349	3.50r multicolored	1.30 1.30
738	CD349	5r multicolored	1.85 1.85
		Nos. 734-738 (5)	5.23 5.23

Flora and Fauna — A118

Designs: 10c, Brush warbler. 25c, Bronze gecko, vert. 50c, Seychelles tree frog. 1r, Seychelles splendid palm, vert. 1.50r, Seychelles skink, vert. 2r, Giant tenebrionid beetle. 3r, Seychelles sunbird. 3.50r, Seychelles killifish. 4r, Magpie robin. 5r, Seychelles vanilla, vert. 10r, Tiger chameleon. 15r, Coco-de-mer, vert. 25r, Paradise flycatcher, vert. 50r, Giant tortoise.

Perf. 13¹/₂

1993, Mar. 1   Litho.   Wmk. 373

739	A118	10c multicolored	.15 .15
740	A118	25c multicolored	.15 .15
741	A118	50c multicolored	.20 .20
742	A118	1r multicolored	.38 .38
743	A118	1.50r multicolored	.58 .58
744	A118	2r multicolored	.80 .80
745	A118	3r multicolored	1.15 1.15
746	A118	3.50r multicolored	1.35 1.35
747	A118	4r multicolored	1.55 1.55
748	A118	5r multicolored	1.95 1.95
749	A118	10r multicolored	3.85 3.85
750	A118	15r multicolored	5.75 5.75
751	A118	25r multicolored	9.50 9.50
752	A118	50r multicolored	19.00 19.00
		Nos. 739-752 (14)	46.36 46.36

#742, 748-749, 751-752 exist inscribed "1994."

First Visit to Seychelles by Archbishop of Canterbury — A119

Archbishop and: 3r, Anglican Cathedral, Victoria. 10r, Air France, Air Seychelles airplanes.

1993, June 8   *Perf. 13¹/₂*

753	A119	3r multicolored	1.15 1.15
754	A119	10r multicolored	3.85 3.85

4th Indian Ocean Island Games — A120

1993, Aug. 21   *Perf. 14¹/₂*

755	A120	1.50r Running	.58 .58
756	A120	3r Soccer	1.10 1.10
757	A120	3.50r Cycling	1.40 1.40
758	A120	10r Sailing	3.75 3.75
		Nos. 755-758 (4)	6.83 6.83

Telecommunications, Cent. — A121

Designs: 1r, Cable ship Scotia, Victoria, 1893. 3r, Eastern Telegraph Company's Office, Victoria, 1904. 4r, HF Transmitting Station, operational 1971. 10r, New Telecoms House, Victoria, 1993.

1993, Nov. 12   *Perf. 13*

759	A121	1r multicolored	.40 .40
760	A121	3r multicolored	1.25 1.25
761	A121	4r multicolored	1.65 1.65
762	A121	10r multicolored	4.00 4.00
		Nos. 759-762 (4)	7.30 7.30

Zil Elwannyen Sesel Nos. 59, 61, 63, 64
Surcharged

R1

R1

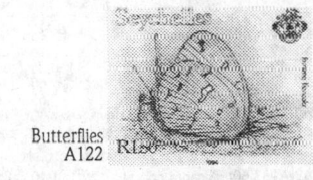

Butterflies A122

1994, Feb. 18   *Perf. 14x14¹/₂*

763	A9	1r on 2.10r #59	.38 .38
764	A9	1.50r on 2.75r #61	.55 .55
765	A9	3.50r on 7r #63	1.40 1.40
766	A9	10r on 15r #64	3.75 3.75
		Nos. 763-766 (4)	6.08 6.08

Hong Kong '94. Size and location of surcharge varies.

1994, Aug. 16   Wmk. 384   *Perf. 14*

767	A122	1.50r Eurema floricola	.60 .60
768	A122	3r Coeliades forestan	1.25 1.25
769	A122	3.50r Borbo borbonica	1.40 1.40
770	A122	10r Zizula hylax	4.00 4.00
		Nos. 767-770 (4)	7.25 7.25

Queen Mother, 95th Birthday — A123

1995, Sept. 26   Wmk. 373

771	A123	1.50r Age 9	.65 .65
772	A123	3r Wedding day	1.25 1.25
773	A123	3.50r 1936 Portrait	1.50 1.50
774	A123	10r 1975 Photograph	4.25 4.25
		Nos. 771-774 (4)	7.65 7.65

POSTAGE DUE STAMPS

Catalogue values for unused stamps in this section are for Never Hinged items.

D1

Engr.; Denomination Typo. in Carmine
1951, Mar. 1   Wmk. 4   *Perf. 11¹/₂*

J1	D1	2c carmine	1.50 3.25
J2	D1	3c blue green	1.50 3.25
J3	D1	6c ocher	1.00 1.65
J4	D1	9c brown orange	1.25 5.00
J5	D1	15c purple	1.50 6.25
J6	D1	18c deep blue	1.90 7.00
J7	D1	20c black brown	2.00 8.25
J8	D1	30c red brown	2.50 10.50
		Nos. J1-J8 (8)	13.15 45.15

Engr.; Denomination Typo.
1964-65   Wmk. 314

J9	D1	2c carmine	.80 .80
J10	D1	3c green & red ('65)	2.50 2.50

Issue dates: July 7, 1964, Sept. 14, 1965.

Dated "1980"
1980   Litho.   *Perf. 14*

J11	D1	5c lilac rose & red	.15 .15
J12	D1	10c dk green & red	.15 .15
J13	D1	15c bister & red	.15 .15
J14	D1	20c brown org & red	.15 .15
J15	D1	25c violet & red	.15 .15
J16	D1	75c dk red brown & red	.25 .25
J17	D1	80c dk blue & red	.28 .28
J18	D1	1r claret & red	.30 .30
		Set value	1.10 1.10

ZIL ELWANNYEN SESEL

LOCATION — South of Seychelles

The islands of Aldabra, Farquhar and Des Roches. Formerly part of the British Indian Ocean Territory.

Catalogue values for unused stamps in this country are for Never Hinged items.

Type of Seychelles, 1977-78
Perf. 14, 14¹/₂x14 (40c, 1r, 1.25r, 1.50r)

1980-81   Litho.   Wmk. 373
Size: 30x26mm (40c, 1r, 1.25r, 1.50r)

1	A44	5c Reef fish	.15 .15
2	A44	10c Hawksbill turtle	.15 .15
3	A44	15c Coco-de-mer	.15 .15
4	A44	20c Wild vanilla	.15 .15
5	A44	25c Butterfly	.15 .15
6	A44	40c Coral reef	.15 .15
7	A44	50c Giant tortoise	.15 .15
8	A44	75c Crayfish	.20 .20
9	A44	1r Madagascar fody	.25 .25
10	A44	1.10r Green gecko	.28 .28
11	A44	1.25r Fairy tern	.32 .32
12	A44	1.50r Flying fox	.40 .40

Size: 27x35mm

13	A44	5r Octopus, vert.	1.25 1.25
a.		Perf. 13 ('81)	1.25 1.25
14	A44	10r Giant tiger cowrie, vert.	2.50 2.50
a.		Perf. 13 ('81)	2.50 2.50
15	A44	15r Pitcher plant, vert.	4.00 4.00
a.		Perf. 13 ('81)	4.00 4.00
16	A44	20r Natl. arms, vert.	5.00 5.00
a.		Perf. 13 ('81)	5.00 5.00
		Nos. 1-16 (16)	15.25 15.25

Nos. 1-12 exist with 1981 imprint.

Traveling Post Office A1

1980, Oct. 24   *Perf. 14*

17	A1	1.50r Cinq Juin	.38 .38
18	A1	2.10r Canceling letters	.55 .55
19	A1	5r Map	1.25 1.25
		Nos. 17-19 (3)	2.18 2.18

The 5r showing Agalega as part of the Seychelles was not issued.

Yellowfin
Tuna — A2   R1.50

1980, Nov. 28
20 A2   1.50r shown   .38   .38
21 A2   2.10r Blue marlin   .55   .55
22 A2   5r Sperm whale   1.25   1.25
    Nos. 20-22 (3)   2.18   2.18

Royal Wedding Types of Seychelles
1981, June 23   Wmk. 380   Perf. 14
23 A61a   40c Royal Escape   .15   .15
  a.   Bklt. pane of 4, perf. 12½x12,
         unwmkd.   .45   .45
24 A61a   40c Couple   .15   .15
25 A61a   5r Victoria & Albert II 1.25   1.25
26 A61b   5r like #24   1.25   1.25
  a.   Bklt pane of 2, perf. 12½x12,
         unwmkd.   2.50   2.50
27 A61a   10r Britannia   2.50   2.50
28 A61b   10r like #24   2.50   2.50
    Nos. 23-28 (6)   7.80   7.80

Souvenir Sheet
Perf. 12½x12
29 A61b   7.50r like #24   2.00   2.00
  Each denomination issued in sheets of 7 (6 type
A61a, 1 type A61b).
  For surcharges see Nos. 70-75.

Wildlife — A3   R1.40

1981, Dec. 11   Wmk. 373   Perf. 14
30 A3   1.40r Wright's skink   .35   .35
31 A3   2.25r Tree frog   .60   .60
32 A3   5r Robber crab   1.25   1.25
    Nos. 30-32 (3)   2.20   2.20

Workboats
A4   R1.75

1982, Mar. 11   Perf. 14x14½
33 A4   1.75r Cinq Juin   .45   .45
34 A4   2.10r Junon   .55   .55
35 A4   5r Diamond M. Dragon   1.25   1.25
    Nos. 33-35 (3)   2.25   2.25

Mailboats
A5

1982, July 22   Wmk. 373   Perf. 14
36 A5   40c Paulette   .15   .15
37 A5   1.75r Janette   .45   .45
38 A5   2.75r Lady Esme   .70   .70
39 A5   3.50r Cinq Juin   .90   .90
    Nos. 36-39 (4)   2.20   2.20

Aldabra,
World
Heritage
Site — A6

1982, Nov. 19
40 A6   40c Birds flying over island .15 .15
41 A6   2.75r Map   .70   .70
42 A6   7r Giant tortoises   1.90   1.90
    Nos. 40-42 (3)   2.75   2.75

Wildlife — A7   R1.75

1983, Feb. 25   Perf. 14x14½
43 A7   1.75r Red land crab   .55   .55
44 A7   2.75r Black terrapin   .90   .90
45 A7   7r Madagascar green gecko 2.25 2.25
    Nos. 43-45 (3)   3.70   3.70

Maps — A8

1983, Apr. 27   Perf. 14½
46 A8   40c Poivre Island, Ile du Sud .15 .15
47 A8   1.50r Ile des Roches   .50   .50
48 A8   2.75r Astove Island   .90   .90
49 A8   7r Coetivy Island   2.25   2.25
  a.   Souvenir sheet of 4, #46-49 4.00 4.00
    Nos. 46-49 (4)   3.80   3.80

5c   Birds — A9

Perf. 14x14½
1983, July 13   Wmk. 373
50 A9   5c Aldabra brush warbler .15   .15
51 A9   10c Barred ground dove   .15   .15
52 A9   15c Aldabra nightjar   .15   .15
53 A9   20c Malagasy grass war-
             bler   .15   .15
54 A9   25c Aldabra white-eye   .15   .15
55 A9   40c Aldabra fody   .15   .15
56 A9   50c Aldabra rail   .16   .16
57 A9   75c Aldabra bulbul   .25   .25
58 A9   2r Dimorphic little egret .60   .60
59 A9   2.10r Aldabra sunbird   .65   .65
60 A9   2.50r Aldabra turtle dove .80   .80
61 A9   2.75r Aldabra sacred ibis .90   .90

Perf. 14½x14
62 A9   3.50r Aldabra coucal   1.10   1.10
63 A9   7r Aldabra kestrel   2.25   2.25
64 A9   15r Aldabra blue pigeon 5.00   5.00
65 A9   20r Greater flamingo   6.25   6.25
    Nos. 50-65 (16)   18.86 18.86
  Nos. 62-65 vert. See Nos. 96-100. For surcharges
see Seychelles Nos. 763-766.

World
Tourism
Day — A10

1983, Sept. 27   Perf. 14
66 A10   50c Windsurfing   .16   .16
67 A10   2r Hotel   .60   .60
68 A10   3r Beach   .95   .95
69 A10   10r Sunset   3.25   3.25
    Nos. 66-69 (4)   4.96   4.96

Nos. 23-28 Surcharged
1983   Wmk. 380   Perf. 14
70 A61a   30c on 40c multi   .15   .15
71 A61a   30c on 40c multi   .15   .15
72 A61a   2r on 5r multi   .65   .65
73 A61a   2r on 5r multi   .65   .65
74 A61b   3r on 10r multi   .95   .95
75 A61b   3r on 10r multi   .95   .95
    Nos. 70-75 (6)   3.50   3.50
  Each denomination issued in sheets of 7 (6 type
A61a, 1 type A61b).

Aldabra Post
Office,
Reopening
A11   50c

1984, Mar. 30   Wmk. 373   Perf. 14
76 A11   50c Map, postmark   .16   .16
77 A11   2.75r Aldabra rail   .85   .85
78 A11   3r Giant tortoise   .95   .95
79 A11   10r Red-footed booby   3.25   3.25
    Nos. 76-79 (4)   5.21   5.21

Game
Fishing
A12   50c

1984, May 31
80 A12   50c Fishing boat   .16   .16
81 A12   2r Hooked fish, vert.   .65   .65
82 A12   3r Weighing catch, vert. .95   .95
83 A12   10r Fishing boat, stern view 3.25 3.25
    Nos. 80-83 (4)   5.01   5.01

Crabs
A13   50c

1984, Aug. 24   Perf. 14½
84 A13   50c Giant hermit crab   .16   .16
85 A13   2r Fiddler crabs   .65   .65
86 A13   3r Ghost crab   .95   .95
87 A13   10r Spotted pebble crab 3.25   3.25
    Nos. 84-87 (4)   5.01   5.01

Constellations   Mushrooms
A14   A15

1984, Oct. 16   Perf. 14
88 A14   50c Orion   .16   .16
89 A14   2r Cygnus   .65   .65
90 A14   3r Virgo   .95   .95
91 A14   10r Scorpio   3.25   3.25
    Nos. 88-91 (4)   5.01   5.01

Wmk. 373
1985, Jan. 31   Litho.   Perf. 14
92 A15   50c Lenzites elegans   .15   .15
93 A15   2r Xylaria telfairei   .55   .55
94 A15   3r Lentinus sajor-caju   .80   .80
95 A15   10r Hexagonia tenuis   2.75   2.75
    Nos. 92-95 (4)   4.25   4.25

Bird Type of 1983
Inscribed "Zil Elwannyen Sesel"
Wmk. 373, 384 (5c)
1985-88   Perf. 14x14½
96 A9   5c Like #50 ('88)   .15   .15
97 A9   10c Like #51   .15   .15
  a.   Wmk. 384 ('88)   .15   .15
98 A9   25c Like #54   .15   .15
99 A9   50c Like #56 ('87)   .15   .15
  a.   Wmk. 384 ('88)   .15   .15
100 A9   2r Like #58   .55   .55
  a.   Wmk. 384 ('88)   .55   .55
    Set value   .78   .78
  No. 97 exists with 1987 imprint, No. 100a with
1990 imprint.

Queen Mother 85th Birthday
Common Design Type
Perf. 14½x14
1985, June 1   Wmk. 384
101 CD336   1r Coronation portrait   .28   .28
102 CD336   2r With Princess Anne   .55   .55
103 CD336   3r Wearing tiara   .80   .80

104 CD336   5r Holding Prince Hen-
               ry   1.40   1.40
    Nos. 101-104 (4)   3.03   3.03
Souvenir Sheet
105 CD336   10r In river taxi, Venice 2.75   2.75

Giant
Tortoise
A16   50c

1985, Sept. 27   Perf. 14
106 A16   50c shown   .15   .15
107 A16   75c Tortoises crossing
               stream   .20   .20
108 A16   1r Three tortoises   .28   .28
109 A16   2r Tortoise facing right .55 .55
    Nos. 106-109 (4)   1.18   1.18
Souvenir Sheet
Perf. 13x13½
110 A16   10r Two tortoises   2.75   2.75
  World Wildlife Fund. See Nos. 131-134.

Famous
Visitors
A17   50c

  Visitors and their ships: 50c, Phoenician trader,
600 B.C. 2r, Sir Hugh Scott, HMS Sealark, 1908.
10r, Vasco de Gama, Sao Gabriel, 1502.

1985, Oct. 25   Wmk. 373   Perf. 14
111 A17   50c multicolored   .15   .15
112 A17   2r multicolored   .55   .55
113 A17   10r multicolored   2.75   2.75
    Nos. 111-113 (3)   3.45   3.45

Queen Elizabeth II, 60th Birthday
Common Design Type

Designs: 75c, As princess. 1r, With Prince Philip.
1.50r, Wearing blue cape. 3.75r, Portrait. 5r, Wearing red hat.

Perf. 14½x14
1986, Apr. 21   Wmk. 384
114 CD337   75c scar, blk & sil   .20   .20
115 CD337   1r blue & multi   .28   .28
116 CD337   1.50r grn & multi   .40   .40
117 CD337   3.75r vio & multi   1.00   1.00
118 CD337   5r rose vio & multi   1.40   1.40
    Nos. 114-118 (5)   3.28   3.28

  For overprints see Nos. 135-139.

Royal Wedding
Common Design Type

Designs: 3r, Sarah Ferguson, Prince Andrew. 7r,
Andrew.

1986, July 23   Perf. 14
119 CD338   3r multicolored   .80   .80
120 CD338   7r multicolored   1.90   1.90

Coral — A18   Flowers — A19

  Continuous design: a, Acropora palifera, Tubastraea coccinea. b, Echinopora lamellosa, Favia pal-
lida. c, Sarcophyton sp, Porites lutea. d, Goniopora
sp, Goniastrea retiformis. e, Tubipora musica,
Fungia fungites.

1986, Sept. 17
121 A18   2r Strip of 5, #a.-e.   2.75   2.75

1986, Nov. 12
122 A19   50c Hibiscus tiliaceus   .15   .15
123 A19   2r Crinum angustum   .55   .55
124 A19   3r Phaius tetragonus   .80   .80
125 A19   10r Rothmannia annae   2.75   2.75
    Nos. 122-125 (4)   4.25   4.25

Fish — A20   Trees — A21

Continuous design: a, Chaetodon unimaculatus. b, Ostorhincus fleurieu. c, Platax orbicularis. d, abudefduf annularus. e, Chaetodon lineolatus.

1987, Mar. 26
126 A20 2r Strip of #126a-126e   2.75 2.75

1987, Aug. 26   *Perf. 14¹/₂*
127 A21 1r Coconut .28 .28
128 A21 2r Mangrove .55 .55
129 A21 3r Pandanus palm .80 .80
130 A21 5r Indian almond 1.40 1.40
   Nos. 127-130 (4) 3.03 3.03

Nos. 106-110 Redrawn
World Wildlife Fund Emblem without Circle

1987, Sept. 9   **Wmk. 384**   *Perf. 14*
131 A16 50c multicolored .15 .15
132 A16 75c multicolored .20 .20
133 A16 1r multicolored .28 .28
134 A16 2r multicolored .55 .55
   Nos. 131-134 (4) 1.18 1.18

Nos. 114-118 Ovptd. in Silver
"40TH WEDDING ANNIVERSARY"

1987, Dec. 9   *Perf. 14¹/₂x14*
135 CD337 75c scar, blk & sil .22 .22
136 CD337 1r blue & multi .30 .30
137 CD337 1.50r grn & multi .45 .45
138 CD337 3.75r vio & multi 1.10 1.10
139 CD337 5r rose vio & multi 1.50 1.50
   Nos. 135-139 (5) 3.57 3.57

Mai Valley Tropical Forest — A22

Continuous design: b, Trunk of palm tree at right. c, Bamboo.

1987, Dec. 16   *Perf. 14*
140 A22 3r Strip of 3, #a. c. 2.75 2.75

Insects A23

1988, July 28   **Wmk. 373**
141 A23 1r Yanga seychellensis .30 .30
142 A23 2r Belenois aldabraensis .60 .60
143 A23 3r Polyspilota seychelliana .90 .90
144 A23 5r Polposipus herculeanus 1.50 1.50
   Nos. 141-144 (4) 3.30 3.30

Souvenir Sheet

1988 Summer Olympics, Seoul — A24

1988, Aug. 31   **Wmk. 384**
145 A24 10r multicolored 3.00 3.00

Lloyds' of London, 300th Anniv.
Common Design Type

Designs: 1r, Lloyd's building, 1988. 2r, Cable ship Retriever, horiz. 3r, Chantel, horiz. 5r, Torrey Canyon aground off Cornwall, 1967.

1988, Oct. 28   **Wmk. 373**
146 CD341 1r multicolored .30 .30
147 CD341 2r multicolored .60 .60
148 CD341 3r multicolored .90 .90
149 CD341 5r multicolored 1.50 1.50
   Nos. 146-149 (4) 3.30 3.30

Christmas — A25

Perf. 13¹/₂x14, 14x13¹/₂

1988, Nov. 18   **Wmk. 384**
150 A25 1r Santa, toys in canoe .30 .30
151 A25 2r Church, vert. .60 .60
152 A25 3r Santa riding bird, vert. .90 .90
153 A25 5r Sleigh over island 1.50 1.50
   Nos. 150-153 (4) 3.30 3.30

Moon Landing, 20th Anniv.
Common Design Type

Apollo 18: 1r, Firing room, Launch Control Center. 2r, Astronauts Slayton, Stafford, Brand and cosmonauts Leonov and Kubasov. 3r, Mission emblem. 5r, Apollo and Soyuz docking in space. 10r, Apollo 11 lifted aboard USS Hornet.

Perf. 14x13¹/₂, 14 (#155-156)

1989, July 20
Size of Nos. 155-156: 29x29mm
154 CD342 1r multicolored .38 .38
155 CD342 2r multicolored .75 .75
156 CD342 3r multicolored 1.10 1.10
157 CD342 5r multicolored 1.75 1.75
   Nos. 154-157 (4) 3.98 3.98

Souvenir Sheet
158 CD342 10r multicolored 3.75 3.75

Poisonous Plants A26

1989, Oct. 9   *Perf. 14*
159 A26 1r Dumb cane .38 .38
160 A26 2r Star of Bethlehem .75 .75
161 A26 3r Indian licorice 1.10 1.10
162 A26 5r Black nightshade 1.75 1.75
   Nos. 159-162 (4) 3.98 3.98

See Nos. 173-176.

Creole Cooking — A27

1989, Dec. 18
163 A27 1r Tec-tec broth .38 .38
164 A27 2r Pilaf a la Seychelloise .75 .75
165 A27 3r Mullet grilled in banana leaves 1.10 1.10
166 A27 5r Daube 1.75 1.75
   a. Souvenir sheet of 4, #163-166 4.00 4.00
   Nos. 163-166 (4) 3.98 3.98

Stamps in No. 166a have continuous design.

Stamp World London '90 — A28

Designs: 1r, #22. 2r, #13. 3r, #61. 5r, #32.

Perf. 12¹/₂

1990, May 3   **Litho.**   **Wmk. 373**
167 A28 1r multicolored .35 .35
168 A28 2r multicolored .70 .70
169 A28 3r multicolored 1.05 1.05
170 A28 5r multicolored 1.75 1.75
   a. Souvenir sheet of 4, #167-170 4.00 4.00
   Nos. 167-170 (4) 3.85 3.85

Queen Mother 90th Birthday
Common Design Types

Designs: 2r, As Duchess of York with infant Elizabeth. 10r, With King George VI viewing bomb-damaged London, 1940.

1990, Aug. 4   **Wmk. 384**   *Perf. 14x15*
171 CD343 2r multi .70 .70

Perf. 14¹/₂
172 CD344 10r yel brn & blk 3.50 3.50

Poisonous Plants Type of 1989

Perf. 12¹/₂

1990, Nov. 5   **Litho.**   **Wmk. 373**
173 A26 1r Ordeal plant .35 .35
174 A26 2r Thorn apple .70 .70
175 A26 3r Strychnine tree 1.05 1.05
176 A26 5r Bwa zasmen 1.75 1.75
   Nos. 173-176 (4) 3.85 3.85

Elizabeth & Philip, Birthdays
Common Design Types

Perf. 14¹/₂

1991, June 17   **Litho.**   **Wmk. 384**
177 CD345 4r multicolored 1.40 1.40
178 CD346 4r multicolored 1.40 1.40
   a. Pair, #177-178 + label 2.80 2.80

Shipwrecks A29

Wmk. 373

1991, Oct. 28   **Litho.**   *Perf. 14*
179 A29 1.50r St. Abbs, 1860 .55 .55
180 A29 3r Norden, 1862 1.05 1.05
181 A29 3.50r Clan Mackay, 1894 1.25 1.25
182 A29 10r Glenlyon, 1905 3.50 3.50
   Nos. 179-182 (4) 6.35 6.35

Queen Elizabeth II's Accession to the Throne, 40th Anniv.
Common Design Type

1992, Feb. 6
183 CD349 1r multicolored .38 .38
184 CD349 1.50r multicolored .55 .55
185 CD349 3r multicolored 1.15 1.15
186 CD349 3.50r multicolored 1.30 1.30
187 CD349 5r multicolored 1.85 1.85
   Nos. 183-187 (5) 5.23 5.23

Aldabra World Heritage Site, 10th Anniv. — A30

Designs: 1.50r, Lomatopyllum aldabrense. 3r, Dryolimnas cuvieri aldabranus. 3.50r, Birgus latro. 10r, Dicrurus aldabranus.

1992, Nov. 19   *Perf. 14¹/₂*
188 A30 1.50r multicolored .60 .60
189 A30 3r multicolored 1.25 1.25
190 A30 3.50r multicolored 1.45 1.45
191 A30 10r multicolored 4.10 4.10
   Nos. 188-191 (4) 7.40 7.40

SIERRA LEONE

sē-,er-ə lē-'ōn

LOCATION — West coast of Africa, between Guinea and Liberia
GOVT. — Republic in British Commonwealth
AREA — 27,925 sq. mi.

POP. — 3,354,000 (est. 1982)
CAPITAL — Freetown

Sierra Leone was a British colony and protectorate. In 1961 it became fully independent, remaining within the Commonwealth. It became a republic April 19, 1971.

   12 Pence = 1 Shilling
   20 Shillings = 1 Pound
   100 Cents = 1 Leone (1964)

Catalogue values for unused stamps in this country are for Never Hinged items, beginning with Scott 186 in the regular postage section and Scott C1 in the air post section.

Watermark

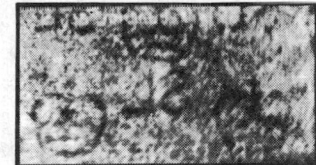

Wmk. 336- St. Edwards Crown & SL, Multiple

Queen Victoria
A1   A2

1859   **Unwmk.**   **Typo.**   *Perf. 14*
3 A1 6p bright violet 37.50 25.00
   a. 6p dull violet 200.00 40.00

1872   *Perf. 12¹/₂*
5 A1 6p violet 300.00 50.00

1872   **Wmk. 1 Sideways**   *Perf. 12¹/₂*
6 A2 1p rose 55.00 25.00
8 A2 3p yellow buff 100.00 30.00
9 A2 4p blue 140.00 35.00
10 A2 1sh yellow green 225.00 45.00

1873   **Wmk. 1 Upright**
6a A2 1p 50.00 27.50
7 A2 2p magenta 100.00 45.00
8a A2 3p 500.00 75.00
9a A2 4p 200.00 45.00
10a A2 1sh 350.00 85.00

1876-96   **Wmk. 1 Upright**   *Perf. 14*
11 A2 ¹/₂p bister 1.90 4.50
12 A2 1p rose 40.00 9.50
13 A2 1¹/₂p violet ('77) 40.00 6.00
14 A2 2p magenta 45.00 3.50
15 A2 3p yellow buff 45.00 3.50
16 A2 4p blue 100.00 6.00
17 A1 6p brt violet ('85) 50.00 20.00
   a. Half used as 3p on cover
18 A1 6p violet brn ('90) 12.50 13.00
19 A1 6p brown vio ('96) 2.00 5.50
20 A2 1sh green 47.50 5.00
   Nos. 11-20 (10) 383.90 76.50

For surcharge see No. 32.

1883-93   **Wmk. Crown and C A (2)**
21 A2 ¹/₂p bister 19.00 35.00
22 A2 ¹/₂p dull green ('84) .35 .45
23 A2 1p carmine ('84) 1.75 .45
   a. 1p rose carmine 27.50 8.00
   b. 1p rose 190.00 30.00
24 A2 1¹/₂p violet ('93) 1.50 4.00
25 A2 2p magenta 35.00 6.00
26 A2 2p slate ('84) 18.00 1.50
27 A2 2¹/₂p ultra ('91) 6.00 .65
28 A2 3p org yel ('92) 1.50 4.25
29 A2 4p blue 825.00 25.00
30 A2 4p bister ('88) 1.25 .90
31 A2 1sh org brn ('88) 11.00 10.00
   Nos. 21-28,30-31 (10) 95.35 63.20

For surcharge see No. 33.

HALF PENNY

Nos. 13 and 24 Surcharged in Black

1893 **Wmk. 1**

32	A2	½p on 1½p violet	400.00	425.00
a.		"PFNNY"	2,000.	2,500.

Wmk. 2

33	A2	½p on 1½p violet	2.50	2.75
a.		"PFNNY"	65.00	65.00
b.		Inverted surcharge	110.00	110.00
c.		Same as "a," inverted	1,500.	
d.		Double surcharge	900.00	

A4

1896-97

34	A4	½p	lilac & grn ('97)	.75	1.00
35	A4	1p	lilac & car	.75	1.00
36	A4	1½p	lilac & blk ('97)	2.50	7.00
37	A4	2p	lilac & org	2.00	4.50
38	A4	2½p	lilac & ultra	1.25	.75
39	A4	3p	lilac & sl ('97)	6.50	6.50
40	A4	4p	lilac & car ('97)	6.00	11.00
41	A4	5p	lilac & blk	7.00	11.00
42	A4	6p	lilac ('97)	6.50	13.00
43	A4	1sh	green & blk	5.50	14.00
44	A4	2sh	green & ultra	22.50	27.50
45	A4	5sh	green & car	35.00	75.00
46	A4	£1	violet, *red*	140.00	275.00
			Nos. 34-46 (13)	236.25	447.25

Numerals of Nos. 39-46 of type A4 are in color on plain tablet.

A5

A6

2½d. 2½d. 2½d.
a b c

2½d. 2½d. 2½d.
d e f

1897 **Wmk. C A over Crown (46)**

47	A5	1p lilac & grn	1.65	1.75
48	A6(a)	2½p on 3p lil & grn	12.00	14.00
49	A6(b)	2½p on 3p	60.00	67.50
50	A6(c)	2½p on 3p	140.00	150.00
51	A6(d)	2½p on 3p	275.00	325.00
52	A6(a)	2½p on 6p lil & grn	10.00	12.50
53	A6(b)	2½p on 6p	42.50	47.50
54	A6(c)	2½p on 6p	110.00	125.00
55	A6(d)	2½p on 6p	210.00	240.00
56	A6(a)	2½p on 1sh lilac	85.00	65.00
57	A6(b)	2½p on 1sh lilac	1,100.	1,100.
58	A6(c)	2½p on 1sh lilac	400.00	400.00
59	A6(e)	2½p on 1sh lilac	1,750.	2,000.
59A	A6(f)	2½p on 1sh lilac	1,300.	1,300.
60	A6(a)	2½p on 2sh lilac	1,200.	1,450.
61	A6(b)	2½p on 2sh lilac	*10,000.*	
62	A6(c)	2½p on 2sh lilac	7,500.	
63	A6(e)	2½p on 2sh lilac	*30,000.*	
63A	A6(f)	2½p on 2sh lilac	*30,000.*	

The words "POSTAGE AND REVENUE" on Nos. 56-63A are set in two lines and overprinted below instead of above "2½d."

The "d" in type "f" is 3½mm wide; that in type "a" is 3mm.

Very fine examples of Nos. 47-63A will have perforations touching the frameline on one or more sides.

Nos. 56-59A are often found discolored. Such copies sell for about half the values quoted.

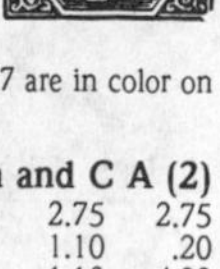
King Edward VII — A7

Numerals of 3p to £1 of type A7 are in color on plain tablet.

1903 **Wmk. Crown and C A (2)**

64	A7	½p	violet & grn	2.75	2.75
65	A7	1p	violet & car	1.10	.20
66	A7	1½p	violet & blk	1.10	4.00
67	A7	2p	violet & brn org	3.50	9.00
68	A7	2½p	violet & ultra	4.00	4.50
69	A7	3p	violet & gray	6.00	8.00
70	A7	4p	violet & car	6.50	8.00
71	A7	5p	violet & blk	6.50	15.00
72	A7	6p	violet & dull vio	10.00	10.00
73	A7	1sh	green & blk	11.00	27.50
74	A7	2sh	green & ultra	32.50	45.00
75	A7	5sh	green & car	45.00	70.00
76	A7	£1	violet, *red*	200.00	215.00
			Nos. 64-76 (13)	329.95	418.95

1904-05 **Wmk. 3**

Chalky Paper

77	A7	½p	violet & grn	4.50	2.25
78	A7	1p	violet & car	.75	.25
79	A7	1½p	violet & blk	2.50	7.50
80	A7	2p	violet & brn org	4.00	3.00
81	A7	2½p	violet & ultra	4.00	1.75
82	A7	3p	violet & gray	19.00	3.00
83	A7	4p	violet & car	5.00	5.50
84	A7	5p	violet & blk	10.00	16.00
85	A7	6p	violet & dl vio	4.50	3.00
86	A7	1sh	green & blk	7.00	8.00
87	A7	2sh	green & ultra	12.00	18.00
88	A7	5sh	green & car	30.00	45.00
89	A7	£1	violet, *red*	200.00	200.00
			Nos. 77-89 (13)	303.25	313.25

The 1p also exists on ordinary paper.

1907-10

Ordinary Paper

90	A7	½p	green	.40	.25
91	A7	1p	carmine	6.00	.25
92	A7	1½p	orange ('10)	.48	1.25
93	A7	2p	gray	.70	1.25
94	A7	2½p	ultra	1.75	1.10

Chalky Paper

95	A7	3p	violet, *yel*	5.00	2.50
96	A7	4p	blk & red, *yel*	2.00	1.00
97	A7	5p	vio & ol grn	5.00	3.50
98	A7	6p	vio & red vio	3.00	4.50
99	A7	1sh	black, *green*	5.00	4.00
100	A7	2sh	vio & bl, *bl*	14.00	12.00
101	A7	5sh	grn & red, *yel*	25.00	35.00
102	A7	£1	vio & blk, *red*	150.00	160.00
			Nos. 90-102 (13)	218.33	226.60

The 3p also exists on ordinary paper.

King George V and Seal of the Colony
A8 A9

Die I

For description of dies I and II see back of this volume.

Numerals of 3p, 4p, 5p, 6p and 10p of type A8 are in color on plain tablet. Numerals of 7p and 9p are on solid-color tablet.

1912-24 **Ordinary Paper** **Wmk. 3**

103	A8	½p	green	1.00	.65
104	A8	1p	scarlet	1.00	.50
a.			1p carmine	1.00	.15
105	A8	1½p	orange	1.00	.75
106	A8	2p	gray	.90	.18
107	A8	2½p	ultra	7.00	2.00

Chalky Paper

108	A9	3p	violet, *yel*	2.50	2.00
109	A8	4p	blk & red, *yel*	1.25	5.00
a.			Die II ('24)	3.00	3.00
110	A8	5p	violet & ol grn	.85	2.75
111	A8	6p	vio & red vio	3.00	3.50
112	A8	7p	violet & org	1.40	4.00
113	A8	9p	violet & blk	4.50	6.00
114	A8	10p	violet & red	3.00	12.00
115	A9	1sh	black, *green*	3.50	3.00
a.			1sh black, *emerald*		165.00
116	A9	2sh	vio & ultra, *bl*	8.00	3.75
117	A9	5sh	grn & red, *yel*	10.00	17.00
118	A9	10sh	grn & red, *grn*	45.00	70.00
119	A9	£1	vio & blk, *red*	110.00	140.00
120	A9	£2	violet & ultra	500.00	600.00
121	A9	£5	gray grn & org	*1,250.*	----
			Nos. 103-119 (17)	203.90	273.08

The status of No. 115a has been questioned.

Die II

1921-27 **Wmk. 4**

Ordinary Paper

122	A8	½p	green	.75	.15
123	A8	1p	violet ('26)	1.00	.65
a.			Die I ('24)	1.00	.15
124	A8	1½p	scarlet	.70	.25
125	A8	2p	gray ('22)	.50	.15
126	A8	2½p	ultra	.50	2.00
127	A8	3p	ultra ('22)	.55	.28
128	A8	4p	blk & red, *yel*	2.00	2.00
129	A8	5p	vio & ol grn	.48	.75

Chalky Paper

130	A8	6p	dp vio & red vio	1.40	1.75
131	A8	7p	vio & org ('27)	2.00	11.00
132	A8	9p	dl vio & blk ('22)	2.25	8.00
133	A8	10p	violet & red	1.75	14.00
134	A9	1sh	blk, *emerald*	4.00	4.00
135	A9	2sh	vio & ultra, *bl*	8.00	8.00
136	A9	5sh	grn & red, *yel*	8.00	30.00
137	A9	10sh	grn & red, *grn*	55.00	100.00
138	A9	£2	violet & ultra	450.00	525.00
139	A9	£5	gray grn & org	*1,000.*	*1,500.*
			Nos. 122-137 (16)	88.88	182.98

Rice Field — A10

Palms and Kola Tree — A11

1932, Mar. 1 **Engr.** ***Perf. 12½***

140	A10	½p	green	.15	.15
141	A10	1p	dk violet	.15	.15
142	A10	1½p	rose car	.30	1.00
143	A10	2p	yellow brn	.30	.15
144	A10	3p	ultra	.70	1.00
145	A10	4p	orange	.70	2.25
146	A10	5p	olive green	.70	1.25
147	A10	6p	light blue	.70	1.25
148	A10	1sh	red brown	2.50	3.00

Perf. 12

149	A11	2sh	dk brown	6.00	8.25
150	A11	5sh	indigo	10.00	14.00
151	A11	10sh	deep green	40.00	85.00
152	A11	£1	deep violet	75.00	125.00
			Nos. 140-152 (13)	137.20	242.45

Wilberforce Issue

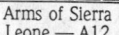

Arms of Sierra Leone — A12

Slave Throwing Off Shackles — A13

Map of Sierra Leone — A14

Old Slave Market, Freetown — A15

Fruit Seller A16

Government Sanatorium A17

Bullom Canoe — A18

Punting near Banana Islands — A19

Government Buildings, Freetown — A20

Old Slavers' Resort, Bunce Island — A21

African Elephant — A22

George V — A23

Freetown Harbor — A24

1933, Oct. 2

153	A12	½p	deep green	.45	.75
154	A13	1p	brown & blk	.45	.40
155	A14	1½p	orange brn	4.00	4.50
156	A15	2p	violet	2.50	.40
157	A16	3p	ultra	2.00	1.25
158	A17	4p	dk brown	6.50	10.00
159	A18	5p	red brn & sl grn	6.50	15.00
160	A19	6p	dp org & blk	6.50	7.00
161	A20	1sh	dk violet	5.25	14.00
162	A21	2sh	bl & dk brn	21.00	30.00
163	A22	5sh	red vio & blk	125.00	175.00
164	A23	10sh	green & blk	140.00	225.00
165	A24	£1	yel & dk vio	350.00	375.00
			Nos. 153-165 (13)	670.15	858.30

Abolition of slavery in the British colonies and cent. of the death of William Wilberforce, English philanthropist and agitator against the slave trade.

Silver Jubilee Issue
Common Design Type

1935, May 6 ***Perf. 11x12***

166	CD301	1p	black & ultra	.20	.20
167	CD301	3p	ultra & brown	1.00	1.00
168	CD301	5p	indigo & green	1.50	2.50
169	CD301	1sh	brown vio & ind	3.25	3.25
			Nos. 166-169 (4)	5.95	6.95

Coronation Issue
Common Design Type

1937, May 12 ***Perf. 11x11½***

170	CD302	1p	deep orange	.25	.25
171	CD302	2p	dark violet	.30	.30
172	CD302	3p	deep ultra	.40	.40
			Nos. 170-172 (3)	.95	.95

Freetown Harbor A25

Rice Harvesting A26

1938-44 ***Perf. 12½***

173	A25	½p	green & blk	.15	.15
174	A25	1p	dp claret & blk	.25	.15
175	A26	1½p	rose red	5.00	.25
175A	A26	1½p	red vio ('41)	.20	.15
176	A26	2p	red violet	9.00	1.25
176A	A26	2p	dark red ('41)	.20	.30
177	A25	3p	ultra & blk	.25	.15
178	A25	4p	red brn & blk	.35	.50
179	A26	5p	olive green	2.00	1.65
180	A26	6p	gray	.50	.20
181	A25	1sh	ol grn & blk	.60	.20
181A	A26	1sh3p	org yel ('44)	.30	.25
182	A25	2sh	sepia & blk	1.75	.60
183	A26	5sh	red brown	3.00	2.00

184	A26	10sh emerald	4.00	2.75
185	A25	£1 dk blue	5.00	7.25
		Nos. 173-185 (16)	32.55	17.80

Catalogue values for unused stamps in this section, from this point to the end of the section, are for Never Hinged items.

Peace Issue
Common Design Type

Perf. 13½x14

1946, Oct. 1 Engr. Wmk. 4

186	CD303	1½p lilac	.15	.15
187	CD303	3p bright ultra	.15	.15

Silver Wedding Issue
Common Design Types

1948, Dec. 1 Photo. *Perf. 14x14½*

188	CD304	1½p brt red violet	.15	.15

Engraved; Name Typographed

Perf. 11½x11

189	CD305	£1 dark blue	16.00	17.00

UPU Issue
Common Design Types

Engr.; Name Typo. on 3p, 6p

1949, Oct. 10 *Perf. 13½, 11x11½*

190	CD306	1½p rose violet	.20	.25
191	CD307	3p indigo	.35	.35
192	CD308	6p gray	.60	.60
193	CD309	1sh olive	1.25	1.25
		Nos. 190-193 (4)	2.40	2.45

Coronation Issue
Common Design Type

1953, June 2 Engr. *Perf. 13½x13*

194	CD312	1½p purple & black	.15	.15

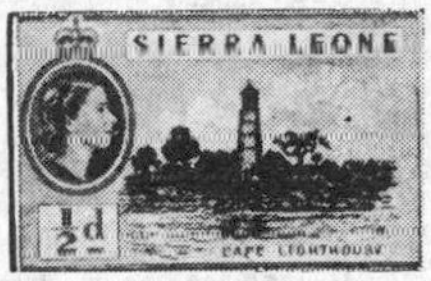

Cape Lighthouse A27

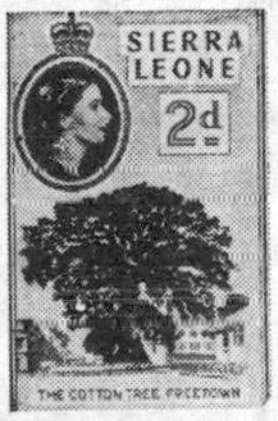

Cotton Tree, Freetown — A28

Designs: 1p, Queen Elizabeth II Quay. 1½d, Piassava workers. 3p, Rice harvesting. 4p, Iron ore production, Marampa. 6p, Whale Bay, York Village. 1sh, Bullom boat. 1sh3p, Map of Sierra Leone and plane. 2sh6p, Orugu Bridge. 5sh, Kuranko chief. 10sh, Law Courts, Freetown. £1, Government House.

Perf. 13 (A27), 13½ (A28)

1956, Jan. 2 Engr. Wmk. 4

Center in Black

195	A27	½p lt violet	.50	.75
196	A27	1p reseda	.50	.15
197	A27	1½p ultra	1.00	2.00
198	A28	2p lt brown	.30	.15
199	A28	3p ultra	.75	.15
a.		Perf 13x13½	1.25	5.00
200	A27	4p gray blue	1.90	.65
201	A27	6p violet	.60	.15
202	A28	1sh carmine	.60	.20
203	A27	1sh3p gray brown	5.00	.20
204	A28	2sh6p brown org	6.00	2.50
205	A28	5sh green	.95	.75
206	A27	10sh red violet	2.50	1.90
207	A27	£1 orange	7.00	12.00
		Nos. 195-207 (13)	27.60	21.55

For surcharges and overprints see Nos. 242-247, 251-253, 255-256, 319, 322, C1-C7, C13.

Independent State

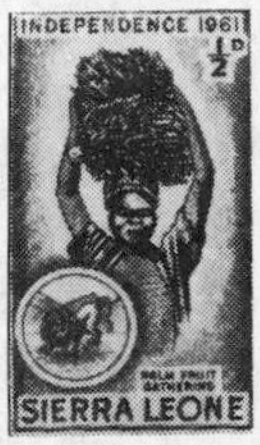

Carrying Oil Palm Fruit — A29

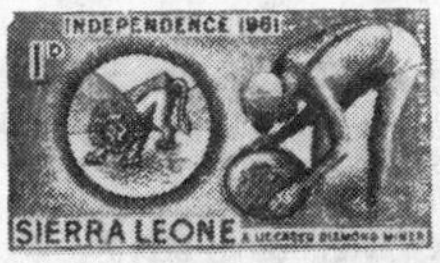

Diamond Miner and Badge — A30

Badge and: 1½p, 5sh, Bundu mask. 2p, 10sh, Bishop Crowther and Old Fourah Bay College. 3p, 6p, Sir Milton Margai. 4p, 1sh3p, Lumley Beach, Freetown. £1, Bugler.

Perf. 13x13½, 13½x13

1961, Apr. 27 Engr. Wmk. 336

208	A29	½p blue grn & dk brn	.15	.15
209	A30	1p gray grn & brn org	.15	.15
210	A29	1½p green & blk	.15	.15
211	A29	2p vio blue & blk	.15	.15
212	A30	3p brn org & ultra	.15	.15
213	A30	4p rose red & grnsh bl	.15	.15
214	A30	6p lilac & gray	.16	.15
215	A29	1sh org & dk brn	.30	.30
216	A30	1sh3p vio & grnsh bl	.30	.22
217	A30	2sh6p black & grn	.65	.60
218	A29	5sh rose red & blk	1.25	1.10
219	A29	10sh emerald & blk	2.50	2.50
220	A29	£1 carmine & yel	4.50	4.50
		Nos. 208-220 (13)	10.56	10.27

Sierra Leone's Independence.

For surcharges see Nos. 254, 274, 279-280, 285-286, 290-291, 294, 296, 299, C10, C29-C31, C132-C133.

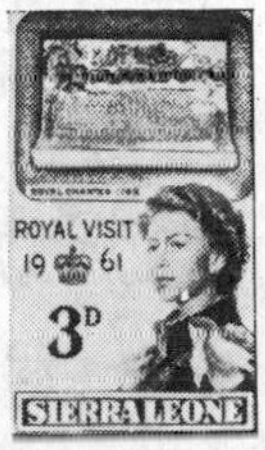

Royal Charter, 1799 — A31

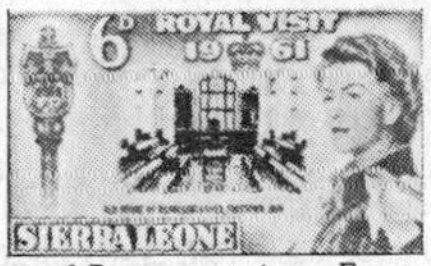

House of Representatives, Freetown, 1924 — A32

Designs: 4p, King's Yard Gate, Freetown, 1817. 1sh3p, Yacht "Britannia."

1961, Nov. 25 Engr. Wmk. 336

221	A31	3p vermilion & blk	.15	.15
222	A31	4p violet & blk	.22	.22
223	A32	6p orange & blk	.30	.30
224	A32	1sh3p blue & blk	.60	.60
		Nos. 221-224 (4)	1.27	1.27

Visit of Elizabeth II to Sierra Leone, Nov., 1961.

For overprints and surcharges see Nos. 272, 278, C8-C9, C11-C12.

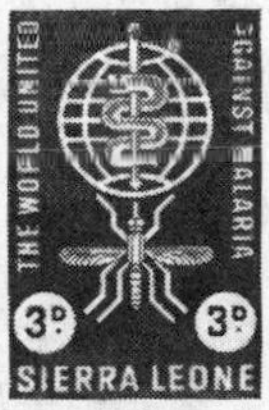

Malaria Eradication Emblem — A33

1962, Apr. 7 *Perf. 11x11½*

225	A33	3p crimson	.15	.15
226	A33	1sh3p green	.38	.38
		Set value	.45	.45

WHO drive to eradicate malaria.

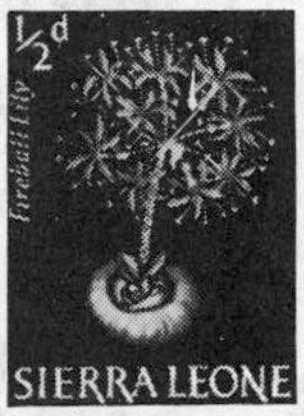

Fireball Lily — A34

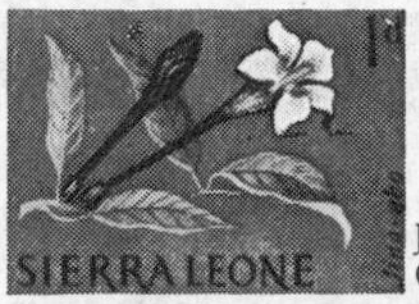

Jina Gbo — A35

Plants: 1½p, Stereospermum. 2p, Black-eyed Susan. 3p, Beniseed. 4p, Blushing hibiscus. 6p, Climbing lily. 1sh, Beautiful crinum. 1sh3p, Bluebells. 2sh6p, Broken hearts. 5sh, Ra-ponthi. 12sh, Blue plumbago. £1, African tulip tree.

1963, Jan. 1 Photo. *Perf. 14*

Flowers in Natural Colors

227	A34	½p olive brown	.15	.15
228	A35	1p org ver & dk red	.15	.15
229	A34	1½p green	.15	.15
230	A35	2p lemon	.15	.15
231	A34	3p dark green	.15	.15
232	A34	4p lt violet blue	.15	.15
233	A35	6p indigo	.16	.15
234	A34	1sh brt yel grn & red	.40	.24
235	A35	1sh3p dk yellow grn	.48	.24
236	A34	2sh6p dk gray	1.00	.70
237	A34	5sh deep violet	1.50	1.25
238	A34	10sh red lilac	3.25	2.75
239	A35	£1 bright blue	8.50	6.75
		Nos. 227-239 (13)	16.19	12.98

For surcharges see Nos. 271, 273, 276-277, 283-284, 289, 295, 300-305, 317-318, 320-321, 329-332, C37-C41, C57-C60, C134.

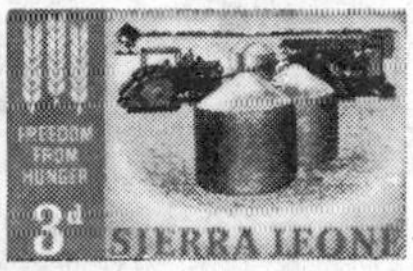

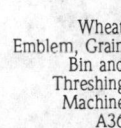

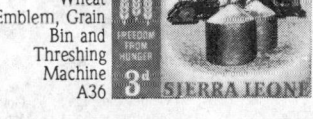

Wheat Emblem, Grain Bin and Threshing Machine A36

Design: 1sh3p, Bullom woman examining onion crop.

Perf. 11½x11

1963, Mar. 21 Engr. Wmk. 336

240	A36	3p orange yel & blk	.15	.15
241	A36	1sh3p green & brown	.40	.40

FAO "Freedom from Hunger" campaign.

For surcharges see Nos. 275, C28.

Nos. 195, 197 and 199 Surcharged in Red, Brown, Orange, Violet or Blue:

2ND YEAR OF INDEPENDENCE 19 PROGRESS 63 DEVELOPMENT **3d.**	2nd Year Independence Progress Development 1963 **10d.**
on A27	on A28

Perf. 13, 13½

1963, Apr. 27 Wmk. 4

Center in Black

242	A27	3p on ½p lt vio (R)	.15	.15
243	A27	4p on 1½p ultra (Br)	.15	.15
244	A27	6p on ½p lt vio (O)	.15	.15
245	A28	10p on 3p ultra (R)	.28	.28
246	A28	1sh6p on 3p ultra (V)	.38	.38
247	A28	3sh6p on 3p ultra (Bl)	.85	.85
		Nos. 242-247 (6)	1.96	1.96

Type "a" exists in two settings, varying in the width of the line "19 Progress 63". In each sheet of 60, this line measures 19½-21mm on 55 stamps, and 17½-18mm on 5 stamps. See Nos. C1-C7.

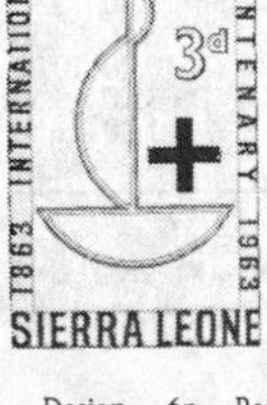

Centenary Emblem — A37

Design: 6p, Red Cross. 1sh3p, Centenary Emblem with curved-lines background.

Perf. 11x11½

1963, Nov. 1 Engr. Wmk. 336

248	A37	3p purple & red	.15	.15
249	A37	6p black & red	.15	.15
250	A37	1sh3p dark green & red	.32	.32
		Nos. 248-250 (3)	.62	.62

Centenary of International Red Cross.

For surcharge see No. C56.

Nos. 199, 197, 216 and 195 Overprinted or Surcharged in Pink, Red, Violet or Brown

1853–1859–1963 Oldest Postal Service Newest G.P.O. in West Africa

4d.

Perf. 13, 13½, 13½x13

1963, Nov. 4 Engr. Wmk. 4

Center in Black except No. 254

251	A28	3p (P)	.15	.15
252	A27	4p on 1½p (R)	.15	.15
253	A27	9p on 1½p (V)	.18	.18
254	A30	1sh on 1sh3p (R)	.20	.20
255	A27	1sh6p on ½p (P)	.28	.28
256	A28	2sh on 3p (Br)	.35	.35
		Nos. 251-256,C8-C13 (12)	12.58	12.58

Oldest postal service (1st stamps in 1859) and the newest GPO in West Africa. Overprint in 5 lines on Nos. 251 and 256. A number of surcharge varieties and errors exist.

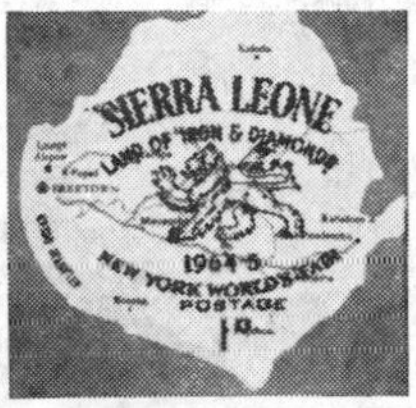

Map and Lion of Sierra Leone — A38

Engraved and Lithographed

1964, Feb. 10 Unwmk. *Imperf.*

Self-adhesive

257	A38	1p multicolored	.15	.15
258	A38	3p multicolored	.15	.15
259	A38	4p multicolored	.15	.15
260	A38	6p multicolored	.15	.15
261	A38	1sh multicolored	.16	.16
262	A38	2sh multicolored	.30	.30
263	A38	5sh multicolored	.80	.80
		Nos. 257-263,C14-C20 (14)	5.49	5.49

New York World's Fair, 1964-65.

For surcharges see Nos. 288, 297, 335 and note under No. 299.

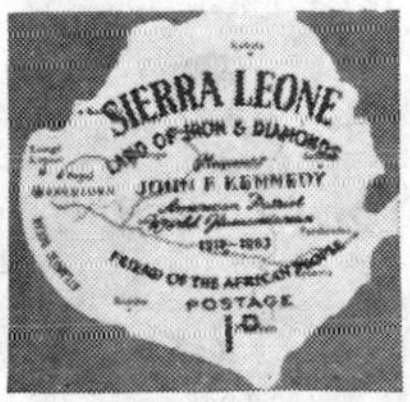

"John F. Kennedy, American Patriot, World Humanitarian" A39

1964, May 11

Self-adhesive

264	A39	1p multicolored	.15	.15
265	A39	3p multicolored	.15	.15
266	A39	4p multicolored	.15	.15
267	A39	6p multicolored	.15	.15
268	A39	1sh multicolored	.18	.18
269	A39	2sh multicolored	.35	.35
270	A39	5sh multicolored	.95	.95
		Nos. 264-270,C21-C27 (14)	6.47	6.47

For surcharges see Nos. 281-282, 287, 292-293, 298, 333, 336, and note under No. 299.

Issues of 1961-63 Surcharged in Red, Black, Dark Blue, Violet or Orange

1964, Aug. 4

271	A35	1c on 6p (#233) (R)	.15	.15
272	A31	2c on 3p (#221)	.15	.15
273	A34	3c on 3p (#231)	.15	.15
274	A29	5c on ½p (#208) (DB)	.15	.15
275	A36	8c on 3p (#240) (R)	.20	.20
276	A35	10c on 1sh3p (#235) (R)	.28	.25
277	A34	15c on 1sh (#234)	.40	.40
278	A32	25c on 6p (#223) (V)	.60	.60
279	A30	50c on 2sh6p (#217) (O)	1.20	1.20
		Nos. 271-279,C28-C31 (13)	5.47	5.44

Issues of 1961-64 Surcharged in Black or Gold

1965, Jan. 20

280	A30	1c on 3p (#212)	.15	.15
281	A39	2c on 1p (#264)	.15	.15
282	A39	4c on 3p (#265)	.15	.15
283	A35	5c on 2p (#230)	.15	.15

284	A34	1 le on 5sh (#237) (G)	2.50 2.50
285	A29	2 le on £1 (#220)	5.25 5.25
		Nos. 280-285 (6)	8.35 8.35

The surcharges on Nos. 284-285 are given in numerals and spelled out in two lines; numeral on Nos. 280-283.

Issues of 1961-64 Surcharged in Red, Black, Orange, Blue or Pink

1965, Apr.

286	A29	1c on 1½p (#210) (R)	.15 .15
287	A39	2c on 3p (#265)	.15 .15
288	A38	2c on 4p (#259)	.15 .15
289	A35	3c on 1p (#228)	.15 .15
290	A29	3c on 2p (#211) (O)	.15 .15
291	A30	5c on 1sh3p (#216) (O)	.15 .15
292	A39	15c on 6p (#267)	.95 .95
293	A39	15c on 1sh (#268) (O)	1.65 1.65
294	A30	20c on 6p (#214) (O)	.40 .40
295	A35	25c on 6p (#233) (R)	.55 .55
296	A30	50c on 3p (#212) (R)	1.10 1.10
297	A38	60c on 5sh (#263) (Bl)	2.50 2.50
298	A39	1 le on 6p (#266) (P)	3.25 3.25
299	A29	2 le on £1 (#220) (Bl)	6.00 6.00
		Nos. 286-299 (14)	17.30 17.30

Additional surcharges exist: "1c" on Nos. 260, 262, 269-270. See note after No. C41 for airmails. Value $4 each.

For surcharges see Nos. 333, 335-336.

Nos. 228, 231, 234, 235, 232, 237 Surcharged

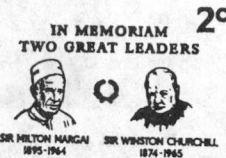

IN MEMORIAM 2c TWO GREAT LEADERS

SIR MILTON MARGAI 1895-1964 — SIR WINSTON CHURCHILL 1874-1965

Designs of Surcharge: Nos. 301, 304, Sir Milton Margai. Nos. 302, 305, Sir Winston Churchill.

Wmk. 336

1965, May 19 Photo. Perf. 14

300	A35	2c on 1p multi	.15 .15
301	A34	3c on 3p multi	.15 .15
302	A34	10c on 1sh multi	.30 .30
303	A34	20c on 1sh3p multi	.55 .55
304	A34	50c on 4p multi	1.25 1.25
305	A34	75c on 5sh multi	2.25 2.25
		Nos. 300-305,C37-C41 (11)	14.20 14.20

For surcharges see Nos. 329-332.

Cola Nut and Plant — A40

Coat of Arms — A41

Typographed; Embossed on Silver Foil

1965 Unwmk. Imperf.

Self-adhesive

310	A40	1c multicolored	.15 .15
311	A40	2c multicolored	.20 .20
312	A40	3c multicolored	.20 .20
313	A40	4c multicolored	.30 .30
314	A40	5c multicolored	.30 .30

Engr.; Embossed on Paper

315	A41	20c multi, cream	.75 .60
316	A41	50c multi, cream	2.00 1.75
		Nos. 310-316,C53-C55 (10)	6.75 6.35

Various advertisements printed on peelable paper backing. Nos. 310-316 have side tabs for handling and come packed in boxes of 100. Nos. 310-312

---

and 314 were released during November due to a stamp shortage; official release date for set, Dec. 17, 1965. See #338-356, C67, C97. For surcharges see #334, 337, 364-368.

Nos. 197-198, and 232-234, 236 Surcharged with New Value in Black or Ultramarine and Overprinted: "FIVE YEARS / INDEPENDENCE / 1961-1966"

1966, Apr. 27 Wmk. 4, 336

317	A35	1c on 6p multi	.15 .15
318	A34	2c on 4p multi	.15 .15
319	A27	3c on 1½p ultra & blk (U)	.15 .15
320	A34	8c on 1sh multi (U)	.16 .16
321	A34	10c on 2sh6p multi (U)	.20 .20
322	A28	20c on 2p lt brown (U)	.42 .42
		Nos. 317-322,C56-C60 (11)	5.88 5.88

5th anniv. of independence. The surcharge on No. 317 includes an "X" over old denomination.

Lion's Head Coin — A42

Designs: 2c, 3c, ¼ Golde coin. 5c, 8c, ½ Golde coin. 25c, 1 le, 1 Golde coin. (3c, 8c, 1 le, Map of Sierra Leone.)

Litho.; Embossed on Gilt Foil

1966, Nov. 12 Unwmk. Imperf.

Self-adhesive

Diameter: 2c, 3c, 38mm; 5c, 8c, 54mm; 25c, 1 le, 82mm

323	A42	2c orange & dp plum	.15 .15
324	A42	3c red lilac & emerald	.15 .15
325	A42	5c vio blue & red org	.15 .15
326	A42	8c black & Prus blue	.15 .15
327	A42	25c emerald & violet	.38 .38
328	A42	1 le red & orange	1.75 1.75
		Nos. 323-328,C61-C66 (12)	8.13 8.13

1st gold coinage of Sierra Leone. Advertising printed on paper backing.

Nos. 297-298, 303-305 and 316 Surcharged in Red, Silver, Violet, Green, Blue or Black:

12½ on A34, A35

17½ on A38, A39

=17½ on A41

1967, Dec. 2

329	A34	6½c on 75c on 5sh (R)	.30 .30
330	A34	7½c on 75c on 5sh (S)	.30 .30
331	A34	9½c on 50c on 4p (G)	.40 .40
332	A35	12½c on 20c on 1sh3p (V)	.50 .50
333	A39	17½c on 1 le on 4p (Bl)	3.50 3.50
334	A41	17½c on 50c	3.50 3.50
335	A38	18½c on 60c on 5sh	10.00 10.00
336	A39	18½c on 1 le on 4p	3.50 3.50
337	A41	25c on 50c	1.00 1.00
		Nos. 329-337,C67-C69 (12)	24.90 24.90

Self-adhesive & Imperf.

Nos. 338-421 are self-adhesive and imperforate.

Cola Nut Type of 1965

Typographed; Embossed on White Paper

1967-68 Unwmk.

White Numeral Tablet

338	A40	½c brt car, grn & yel	.15 .15
339	A40	1c brt car, grn & yel	.15 .15
340	A40	1½c orange, grn & yel	.15 .15
341	A40	2c brt car, grn & yel	.25 .25
342	A40	2½c emer, bl grn & yel	.40 .40
343	A40	3c brt car, grn & yel	.25 .25
344	A40	3½c olive, rose & ultra	.25 .25

345	A40	4½c gray ol, grn & yel	.40 .40
346	A40	5c brt car, grn & yel	.40 .40
347	A40	5½c red brn, grn & yel	.40 .40
		Nos. 338-347 (10)	2.80 2.80

Advertisements printed on peelable backing except on the 2c, 3c, 3½c and 5c.

Colored Numeral Tablet

348	A40	½c brt car, grn & yel	.15 .15
349	A40	1c brt car, grn & yel	.15 .15
350	A40	2c pink, brn & car	.20 .20
351	A40	3c brt car, grn & yel	.75 .60
352	A40	2½c bl grn, vio & org	1.00 .75
353	A40	2½c emer, bl grn & yel	.30 .20
354	A40	3c brt car, grn & yel	.20 .20
355	A40	3½c lilac rose, grn & yel	.30 .30
356	A40	4c brt car, grn & yel	.30 .25
		Nos. 348-356 (9)	3.30 2.80

Nos. 344, 348-354 issued in 1968. Advertisements printed on peelable backing on the 3½c and 4c.

Map of Africa Showing Rhodesia A43

Designs: Each denomination shows map of Africa with map of one of the following countries—Portuguese Guinea, South Africa, Mozambique, Rhodesia, South West Africa or Angola.

1968, Sept. 25 Unwmk. Litho.

357	A43	½c multicolored	.15 .15
358	A43	2c multicolored	.15 .15
359	A43	2½c multicolored	.15 .15
360	A43	3½c multicolored	.20 .20
361	A43	10c multicolored	.40 .40
362	A43	11½c multicolored	.45 .45
363	A43	15c multicolored	.60 .60
		Nos. 357-363 (7)	2.10 2.10
		7 Strips of 6 (1 of each design) (42)	11.40

Intl. Human Rights Year. Sheets of 30 have 5 horizontal rows containing one stamp of each design. Advertisements printed on peelable backing. See #C72-C78. For surcharges see #C106-C111.

No. 316 Surcharged

MEXICO 1968 OLYMPIC PARTICIPATION

✱6½c

Engraved; Embossed on Paper

1968, Nov. 30

364	A41	6½c on 50c multi	.15 .15
365	A41	17½c on 50c multi	.28 .28
366	A41	22½c on 50c multi	.38 .38
367	A41	28½c on 50c multi	.52 .52
368	A41	50c on 50c multi	.85 .85
		Nos. 364-368,C79-C83 (10)	4.49 4.49

19th Olympic Games, Mexico City, Oct. 12-27.

Sierra Leone Type A1, 1859 A44

Designs: 2c, Type A40, 2c, 1965. 3½c, #220. 5c, #315. 12½c, #189. 1 le, Type A9, #2, 1912.

1969, Mar. 1 Litho.

369	A44	1c multicolored	.15 .15
370	A44	2c multicolored	.15 .15
371	A44	3½c multicolored	.15 .15
372	A44	5c multicolored	.15 .15
373	A44	12½c multicolored	.38 .38
374	A44	1 le multicolored	4.75 4.75
		Nos. 369-374,C84-C89 (12)	25.00 25.00

5th anniv. of free-form self-adhesive postage stamps. Various advertisements printed on peelable paper backing. No. 369 has side tab for handling and comes packed in boxes of 50. Nos. 370-374 are without side tabs and come 20 stamps attached to one sheet.

Globe, Freighter, Flags of Sierra Leone and Japan — A45

Map of Europe and Africa, Freighter, Flags of Sierra Leone and Netherlands — A46

Anvil Shape with Flags of Sierra Leone and: 3½c, Union Jack. 10c, 50c, West Germany. 18½c, Netherlands.

1969, July 10

375	A45	1c multicolored	.15 .15
376	A46	2c multicolored	.15 .15
377	A46	3½c multicolored	.15 .15
378	A46	10c multicolored	.16 .16
379	A46	18½c multicolored	.30 .30
380	A46	50c multicolored	.80 .80
		Nos. 375-380,C90-C95 (12)	7.58 7.58

Completion of the Pepel Port iron ore carrier terminal. Various advertisements printed on peelable paper backing. No. 375 has side tab for handling and comes packed in boxes of 50. Nos. 376-380 are without side tabs and come 20 stamps attached to one sheet.

African Development Bank Emblem — A47

Lithographed; Gold Impressed

1969, Sept. 10

381	A47	3½c lt blue, grn & gold	.30 .30

5th anniv. of the African Development Bank. Advertising printed on peelable paper backing, 20 imperf. stamps to a sheet of backing, roulette 10. See No. C96.

Diamond and Boy Scout Emblem A48

1969, Dec. 6 Litho.

382	A48	1c multicolored	.15 .15
383	A48	2c multicolored	.15 .15
384	A48	3½c multicolored	.20 .16
385	A48	4½c multicolored	.24 .20

386	A48	5c multicolored	.32	.28
387	A48	75c multicolored	10.00	8.00

Nos. 382-387,C100-C105 (12) 123.39 91.02

60th anniv. of the Sierra Leone Boy Scouts. Various advertising printed on peelable paper backing. No. 382 has side tab for handling and comes packed in boxes of 100. Nos. 383-387 are without side tabs and come 20 stamps attached to one sheet.

EXPO '70 Emblems, Torii, Maps of Sierra Leone and Japan — A49

1970, June 22

388	A49	2c multicolored	.15	.15
389	A49	3½c multicolored	.15	.15
390	A49	10c multicolored	.20	.20
391	A49	12½c multicolored	.28	.28
392	A49	20c multicolored	.45	.45
393	A49	45c multicolored	1.00	1.00

Nos. 388-393,C112-C117 (12) 12.89 12.89

EXPO '70 Intl. Exhib., Osaka, Japan, Mar. 15-Sept. 13. Various advertising printed on peelable paper backing.

Diamond A50

Palm Kernel — A51

Lithographed and Embossed
1970, Oct. 3   **Unwmk.**
Light Blue Background

394	A50	1c carmine & blk	.15	.15
395	A50	1½c brt green & car	.15	.15
396	A50	2c lilac & yel grn	.15	.15
397	A50	2½c ocher & dk blue	.15	.15
398	A50	3c vio bl & org red	.22	.22
399	A50	3½c dk blue & grn	.28	.28
400	A50	4c olive & ultra	.28	.28
401	A50	5c black & lilac	.32	.32

Orange Brown Background

402	A51	6c bright green	.32	.32
403	A51	7c rose lilac	.45	.45
404	A51	8½c orange	.50	.50
405	A51	9c lilac	.50	.50
406	A51	10c dark blue	.55	.55
407	A51	11½c blue	.75	.75
408	A51	18½c yellow green	1.10	1.10

Nos. 394-408,C118-C124 (22) 28.37 24.57

Advertisements printed on peelable paper backing. Packed in boxes of 500.

Sewa Diadem in Jewelry Box — A52

1970, Dec. 30

409	A52	2c multicolored	.15	.15
410	A52	3½c multicolored	.15	.15
411	A52	10c multicolored	.35	.35
412	A52	12½c multicolored	.45	.45
413	A52	40c multicolored	1.50	1.35
414	A52	1 le multicolored	7.50	5.00

Nos. 409-414,C125-C130 (12) 39.15 30.50

Diamond industry. Advertisement printed on peelable paper backing. Sheets of 20.

Traffic Pattern — A53

1971, Mar. 1   **Litho.**

415	A53	3½c orange & vio blue	.25	.25

Right hand traffic change-over. See No. C131. Advertisements printed on peelable paper backing.

Flag and Lion's Head — A54

Litho.; Embossed in Silver
1971, Apr. 27

416	A54	2c multicolored	.15	.15
417	A54	3½c multicolored	.15	.15
418	A54	10c multicolored	.18	.18
419	A54	12½c multicolored	.20	.20
420	A54	40c multicolored	.80	.80
421	A54	1 le multicolored	1.75	1.75

Nos. 416-421,C137-C142 (12) 12.03 12.03

10th anniversary of independence. Advertisements printed on peelable paper backing. Stamps are in shape of Sierra Leone map.

Pres. Siaka Stevens — A55

1972   **Litho.**   **Perf. 13**

422	A55	1c pink & multi	.15	.15
423	A55	2c violet & multi	.15	.15
424	A55	4c lt ultra & multi	.15	.15
425	A55	5c buff & multi	.15	.15
426	A55	7c rose & multi	.15	.15
427	A55	10c olive & multi	.18	.18
428	A55	15c emerald & multi	.24	.24
429	A55	18c yellow & multi	.30	.30
430	A55	20c lt blue & multi	.35	.35
431	A55	25c orange & multi	.42	.42
432	A55	50c brt green & multi	.90	.90
433	A55	1 le multicolored	1.65	1.65

434	A55	2 le red org & multi	3.25	3.25
435	A55	5 le multicolored	8.50	8.50

Nos. 422-435 (14) 16.54 16.54

Shades from later printings are found on several denominations including 1c, 2c, 7c, 10c, 1 le, 2 le.

Guma Valley Dam and Bank Emblem — A56

1975, Jan. 14   **Litho.**   **Perf. 13½**

436	A56	4c multicolored	125.00	82.50

African Development Bank, 10th anniversary. See No. C143.

Pres. Siaka Stevens and Opening of Congo Bridge — A57

1975, Aug. 24   **Litho.**   **Perf. 13x13½**

437	A57	5c multicolored	11.00	11.00

Congo Bridge opening and Pres. Siaka Stevens' 70th birthday. See No. C144.

Pres. Tolbert and Stevens, Hands across Mano River — A58

1975, Oct. 3   **Litho.**   **Perf. 13x13½**

438	A58	4c multicolored	1.40	1.40

Mano River Union Agreement between Liberia and Sierra Leone, signed Oct. 3, 1973. See No. C145.

Mohammed Ali Jinnah, Flags of Sierra Leone and Pakistan A59

Elizabeth II A60

1977, Jan. 28   **Litho.**   **Perf. 13 rough**

439	A59	30c multicolored	.80	.80

Mohammed Ali Jinnah (1876-1948), First Governor General of Pakistan.

1977, Nov. 28   **Litho.**   **Perf. 12½x12**

440	A60	5c multicolored	.15	.15
441	A60	1 le multicolored	1.40	1.40

25th anniv. of the reign of Elizabeth II.

REPUBLIC OF SIERRA LEONE
Fourah Bay College — A61

Design: 20c, Old College, vert.

Perf. 12x12½, 12½x12
1977, Dec. 19   **Litho.**

442	A61	5c multicolored	.15	.15
443	A61	20c multicolored	.35	.35

Fourah Bay College, Mt. Aureol, Freetown, founded 1827.

St. Edward's Crown and Scepters — A62

Designs: 50c, Elizabeth II in coronation coach. 1 le, Elizabeth II and Prince Philip on coronation day.

1978, Sept. 14   **Litho.**   **Perf. 14½x14**

444	A62	5c multicolored	.15	.15
445	A62	50c multicolored	.60	.60
446	A62	1 le multicolored	1.10	1.10

Nos. 444-446 (3) 1.85 1.85

25th anniv. of coronation of Elizabeth II.

Fig Tree Blue A63

Butterflies: 15c, Narrow blue-banded swallowtail. 25c, Pirate. 1 le, African giant swallowtail.

1979, Apr. 9   **Litho.**   **Perf 14½**

447	A63	5c multicolored	.15	.15
448	A63	15c multicolored	.35	.35
449	A63	25c multicolored	.60	.60
450	A63	1 le multicolored	2.50	2.50

Nos. 447-450 (4) 3.60 3.60

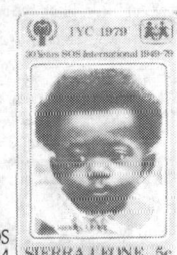

Child, IYC and SOS Emblems — A64

Designs (Emblems and): 27c, Girl and infant. 1 le, Mother and infant.

Perf. 14x13½
1979, Aug. 13   **Litho.**   **Wmk. 373**

451	A64	5c multicolored	.15	.15
452	A64	27c multicolored	.55	.55
453	A64	1 le multicolored	2.25	2.25
a.		Souvenir sheet of 1	2.50	2.50

Nos. 451-453 (3) 2.95 2.95

Intl. Year of the Child and 30th anniv. of SOS villages (villages for homeless children).

Presidents Stevens and Tolbert, Pigeon Post, Mano River A65

1979, Oct. 3   **Perf. 13½**

454	A65	5c multicolored	.15	.15
455	A65	22c multicolored	.30	.30
456	A65	27c multicolored	.38	.38
457	A65	35c multicolored	.45	.45
458	A65	1 le multicolored	1.40	1.40
a.		Souvenir sheet of 1	1.40	1.40

Nos. 454-458 (5) 2.68 2.68

Mano River Union, 5th anniv.; Postal Union, 1st anniv.

Sierra Leone No. 9,
Hill — A66

1979, Dec. 19   Litho.   Perf. 14½x14
459 A66 10c Grt. Britain #6   .18   .18
460 A66 15c shown   .25   .25
461 A66 50c Sierra Leone #220   .90   .90
      Nos. 459-461 (3)   1.33 1.33
          Souvenir Sheet
462 A66 1 le Sierra Leone #119   1.25 1.25
Sir Rowland Hill (1795-1879), originator.

Touraco
A67

1980, Jan. 29   Perf. 14
463 A67 1c shown   .15   .15
464 A67 2c Olive-bellied sunbird   .15   .15
465 A67 3c Black-headed oriole   .15   .15
466 A67 5c Spur-winged goose   .15   .15
467 A67 7c White-bellied didric
              cuckoo   .15   .15
468 A67 10c Gray parrot, vert.   .16   .16
469 A67 15c African blue quail,
              vert.   .25   .25
470 A67 20c West African wood
              owl, vert.   .32   .32
471 A67 30c Blue plantain eater,
              vert.   .50   .50
472 A67 40c Nigerian blue-breast-
              ed kingfisher, vert.   .65   .65
473 A67 50c Black crake, vert.   .90   .90
474 A67 1 le Hartlaub's duck   1.65 1.65
475 A67 2 le Black bee-eater   3.25 3.25
476 A67 5 le Denham's bustard   8.50 8.50
      Nos. 463-476 (14)   16.93 16.93
Reissues: Nos. 464-476 inscribed 1982. Nos. 463-464, 466, 468-473, 475-476 inscribed 1983. For surcharges see Nos. 632-636. For overprints see Nos. 637-638.

Rotary
Intl.,
75th
Anniv.
A68

1980, Feb. 23   Perf. 14
477 A68 5c orange & multi   .15   .15
478 A68 27c red & multi   .35   .35
479 A68 50c green & multi   .70   .70
480 A68 1 le blue & multi   1.40 1.40
      Nos. 477-480 (4)   2.60 2.60

Mail Ship
"Maria,"
1884,
London '80
Emblem
A69

1980, May 6   Litho.   Perf. 14
481 A69 6c shown   .15   .15
482 A69 31c "Tarquah," 1902   .45   .45
483 A69 50c "Aureol," 1951   .75   .75
484 A69 1 le "Africa Palm," 1974   1.50 1.50
      Nos. 481-484 (4)   2.85 2.85
London 80 Intl. Stamp Exhib., May 6-14.

Conf.
Emblem — A70

Small Striped
Swordtail — A71

1980, July 1   Litho.   Perf. 14½
485 A70 20c multicolored   .25   .25
486 A70 1 le multicolored   1.25 1.25
17th African Summit Conf., Freetown, July 1-4.

1980, Oct. 6   Litho.   Perf. 14
487 A71 5c shown   .15   .15
488 A71 27c Pearl charaxes   .45   .45
489 A71 35c White barred charaxes   .55   .55
490 A71 1 le Zaddach's forester   1.65 1.65
      Nos. 487-490 (4)   2.80 2.80

Freetown
Airport — A72

1980, Dec. 5   Litho.   Perf. 13½
491 A72 6c shown   .15   .15
492 A72 26c Mammy Yoko Hotel   .30   .30
493 A72 31c Freetown Cotton Tree   .35   .35
494 A72 40c Beindomgo Falls   .50   .50
495 A72 50c Water skiing   .60   .60
496 A72 1 le Elephant   1.25 1.25
      Nos. 491-496 (6)   3.15 3.15

Servals
A73

Cats and Kittens: No. 498, Serval kittens. No. 500a, African golden cats. No. 502a, Leopards. No. 504a, Lions. Pairs have continuous design.

1981, Feb. 23   Litho.   Perf. 14
497 A73 6c multicolored   .15   .15
498 A73 6c multicolored   .15   .15
   a.   Pair, #497-498   .18   .18
499 A73 31c multicolored   .45   .45
500 A73 31c multicolored   .45   .45
   a.   Pair, #499-500   .90   .90
501 A73 50c multicolored   .75   .75
502 A73 50c multicolored   .75   .75
   a.   Pair, #501-502   1.50 1.50
503 A73 1 le multicolored   1.50 1.50
504 A73 1 le multicolored   1.50 1.50
   a.   Pair, #503-504   3.00 3.00
      Nos. 497-504 (8)   5.70 5.70

Ambulance Clinic — A74

Perf. 14½
1981, Apr. 18   Litho.   Wmk. 373
505 A74 6c Soldiers, vert.   .15   .15
506 A74 31c shown   .50   .50
507 A74 40c Traffic policeman, vert. .65 .65
508 A74 1 le Coast Guard ship   1.65 1.65
      Nos. 505-508 (4)   2.95 2.95
Anniv.: independence, 20th; republic, 10th.

Royal Wedding Issue
Common Design Type
1981   Litho.   Perf. 12, 14
509 CD331 31c Bouquet   .60   .60
510 CD331 35c Sandringham   .70   .70
511 CD331 45c Charles   .95   .95

512 CD331 60c Charles   1.25 1.25
513 CD331 70c like 35c   1.50 1.50
514 CD331 1 le Couple   2.00 2.00
515 CD331 1.30 le Charles   2.50 2.50
516 CD331 1.50 le Couple   3.00 3.00
517 CD331 2 le Couple   4.00 4.00
      Nos. 509-517 (9)   16.50 16.50
          Souvenir Sheet
518 CD331 3 le Royal landau   5.00 5.00
31c, 45c, 1 le, 3 le issued July 22, perf. 14. 35c, 60c, 1.50 le issued in sheets of 5 plus label; perf. 12, Sept. 9. 70c, 1.30 le, 2 le issued in booklets only, perf. 14.
For surcharges see #540-546, 714, 716, 721.

Soccer Player — A75

Wmk. 373
1981, Sept. 30   Litho.   Perf. 14
519 A75 6c shown   .15   .15
520 A75 31c Boys planting trees   .45   .45
521 A75 1 le Duke of Edinburgh   1.50 1.50
522 A75 1 le Pres. Stevens   1.50 1.50
      Nos. 519-522 (4)   3.60 3.60
Duke of Edinburgh's Awards and Pres. Steven's Awards, 25th anniv.

SIERRA LEONE Pineapples — A76

Woman
Tending
Rice
Plants
A77

Perf. 14, 14½ (A77)
1981   Litho.   Wmk. 373
523 A76 6c shown   .15   .15
524 A77 6c Peanuts for export   .15   .15
525 A76 31c Peanuts   .50   .50
526 A77 31c Crushing, eating cassa-
              va   .50   .50
527 A76 50c Cassava fruits   .85   .85
528 A77 50c shown   .85   .85
529 A76 1 le Rice plants   1.65 1.65
530 A77 1 le Men tending pineapple
              plants   1.65 1.65
      Nos. 523-530 (8)   6.30 6.30
World Food Day. Issue dates: Nos. 523, 525, 527, 529, Oct. 16; others, Nov. 2.

Princess Diana Issue
Common Design Type
1982, July   Litho.   Perf. 14½
531 CD332 31c Caernarvon Castle   .50   .50
532 CD332 50c Honeymoon   .85   .85
533 CD332 2 le Wedding   3.00 3.00
      Nos. 531-533 (3)   4.35 4.35
          Souvenir Sheet
534 CD332 3 le Diana   4.75 4.75
Also issued in sheetlets of 5 + label.
For overprints and surcharges see Nos. 552-555, 713, 715, 717-720, 722-723.

Scouting
Year — A78

1982, Aug. 23   Perf. 14
535 A78 20c Studying animal hus-
              bandry   .32   .32
536 A78 50c Botanical study   .85   .85

537 A78 1 le Baden-Powell   1.65 1.65
538 A78 2 le Fishing at campsite   3.00 3.00
      Nos. 535-538 (4)   5.82 5.82
          Souvenir Sheet
539 A78 3 le Raising flag   4.75 4.75
For surcharges see Nos. 694-698.

Nos. 509-512, 514, 516, 518 Surcharged
1982, Aug. 30   Wmk. 373
540 CD331 50c on 31c   .90   .90
541 CD331 50c on 35c   .90   .90
542 CD331 50c on 45c   .90   .90
543 CD331 50c on 60c   .90   .90
544 CD331 90c on 1 le   1.40 1.40
545 CD331 2 le on 1.50 le   3.25 3.25
      Nos. 540-545 (6)   8.25 8.25
          Souvenir Sheet
546 CD331 3.50 le on 3 le   6.00 6.00

1982 World
Cup — A79

Designs: Various soccer players.

1982, Sept. 7
547 A79 20c multicolored   .32   .32
548 A79 30c multicolored   .45   .45
549 A79 1 le multicolored   1.65 1.65
550 A79 3 le multicolored   3.00 3.00
      Nos. 547-550 (4)   5.42 5.42
          Souvenir Sheet
551 A79 3 le multicolored   4.75 4.75
For overprints see Nos. 561-565.

Nos. 531-534 Overprinted: "ROYAL
BABY/ 21.6.82"
1982, Oct. 15   Litho.   Perf. 14½
552 CD332 31c multicolored   .50   .50
553 CD332 50c multicolored   .85   .85
554 CD332 2 le multicolored   3.00 3.00
      Nos. 552-554 (3)   4.35 4.35
          Souvenir Sheet
555 CD332 3 le multicolored   4.75 4.75
Birth of Prince William of Wales, June 21. Also issued in sheetlets of 5 + label.
For surcharges see Nos. 715, 719-720, 723.

George
Washington
A80

Designs: Various paintings of Washington. 31c, 1 le, vert.

1982, Oct. 30   Litho.   Perf. 14
556 A80 6c multicolored   .15   .15
557 A80 31c multicolored   .45   .45
558 A80 50c multicolored   .75   .75
559 A80 1 le multicolored   1.50 1.50
      Nos. 556-559 (4)   2.85 2.85
          Souvenir Sheet
560 A80 2 le multicolored   3.00 3.00

Nos. 547-551 Overprinted with Finalists
and Score
1982, Nov. 9   Perf. 14
561 A79 20c multicolored   .30   .30
562 A79 30c multicolored   .42   .42
563 A79 1 le multicolored   1.50 1.50
564 A79 2 le multicolored   2.75 2.75
      Nos. 561-564 (4)   4.97 4.97
          Souvenir Sheet
565 A79 3 le multicolored   4.25 4.25
Italy's victory in 1982 World Cup.

Christmas — A81

Stained-glass Windows, St. George's Cathedral, Freetown.

1982, Nov. 18   *Perf. 14*
566	A81	6c Temptation of Christ	.15	.15
567	A81	31c Baptism of Christ	.45	.45
568	A81	50c Annunciation	.75	.75
569	A81	1 le Nativity	1.50	1.50
		Nos. 566-569 (4)	2.85	2.85

Souvenir Sheet
570	A81	2 le Mary and Joseph	3.00	3.00

Charles Darwin (1809-82)   6c   A82

1982, Dec. 10
571	A82	6c Long-snouted crocodile	.18	.18
572	A82	31c Rainbow lizard	.50	.50
573	A82	50c River turtle	.90	.90
574	A82	1 le Chameleon	1.75	1.75
		Nos. 571-574 (4)	3.33	3.33

Souvenir Sheet
575	A02	2 le Royal python, vert.	3.25	3.25

500th Birth Anniv. of Raphael — A83

School of Athens, Fresco, Vatican. Nos. 576-579 show details.

1983, Jan. 28   Litho.   *Perf. 14*
576	A83	6c Diogenes	.15	.15
577	A83	31c Euclid, Ptolemy	.45	.45
578	A83	50c Euclid and his Students	.75	.75
579	A83	2 le Pythagoras, Heraclitus	3.00	3.00
		Nos. 576-579 (4)	4.35	4.35

Souvenir Sheet
580	A83	3 le Entire painting	4.50	4.50

A83a

1983, Mar. 14   Litho.   *Perf. 14*
581	A83a	6c Agricultural training	.15	.15
582	A83a	10c Tourism development	.15	.15
583	A83a	50c Broadcast training	.75	.75
584	A83a	1 le Airport services	1.50	1.50
		Nos. 581-584 (4)	2.55	2.55

Commonwealth Day.

25th Anniv. of Economic Commission for Africa — A84

1983, Apr. 29   Litho.   *Perf. 13½x13*
585	A84	1 le multicolored	1.40	1.40

Endangered Chimpanzees, World Wildlife Fund Emblem — A85

Various chimpanzees from Outamba-Kilimi Natl. Park. 10c, 31c, vert.

1983, May   Litho.   *Perf. 14*
586	A85	6c multicolored	.15	.15
587	A85	10c multicolored	.24	.24
588	A85	31c multicolored	.70	.70
589	A85	60c multicolored	1.50	1.50
		Nos. 586-589 (4)	2.59	2.59

Souvenir Sheet
590	A85	3 le Elephants	4.00	4.00

World Communications Year — A86

1983, July 14   *Perf. 14*
591	A86	6c Traditional communications	.15	.15
592	A86	10c Mano River mail	.15	.15
593	A86	20c Satellite ground station	.30	.30
594	A86	1 le English packet, 1805	1.50	1.50
		Nos. 591-594 (4)	2.10	2.10

Souvenir Sheet
595	A86	2 le Map, phone, envelope	3.00	3.00

Manned Flight Bicentenary A87

1983, Aug 31   Litho.   *Perf. 14*
596	A87	6c Montgolfiere, 1783, vert.	.15	.15
597	A87	20c Deutschland blimp, 1897	.32	.32
598	A87	50c Norge I blimp, North Pole, 1926	.80	.80
599	A87	1 le Cape Sierra sport balloon, Freetown, 1983, vert.	1.65	1.65
		Nos. 596-599 (4)	2.92	2.92

Souvenir Sheet
600	A87	2 le Futuristic airship	2.75	2.75

Walt Disney, Space Ark Fantasy — A88

1983, Nov.
601	A88	1c Hippopotamus, Huey, Dewey and Louie	.15	.15
602	A88	1c Mickey Mouse and Snake	.15	.15
603	A88	3c Elephant and Donald Duck	.15	.15
604	A88	3c Zebra and Goofy	.15	.15
605	A88	10c Lion and Ludwig von Drake	.15	.15
606	A88	10c Rhinoceros and Goofy	.15	.15
607	A88	2 le Giraffe and Mickey Mouse	1.75	1.75
608	A88	3 le Monkey and Donald Duck	2.50	2.50
		Nos. 601-608 (8)	5.15	5.15

Souvenir Sheet
609	A88	5 le Mickey Mouse and animals	4.50	4.50

10th Anniv. of Mano River Union A89

1984, Feb. 8   Litho.   *Perf. 15*
610	A89	6c Teaching Program graduates	.15	.15
611	A89	25c Emblem	.20	.20
612	A89	31c Map, presidents	.25	.25
613	A89	41c Guinea Accession signing	.35	.35
a.		Souvenir sheet of 1	.50	.50
		Nos. 610-613 (4)	.95	.95

23rd Olympic Games, Los Angeles, July 28-Aug. 12 — A90

1984, Mar. 15   *Perf. 14*
614	A90	90c Gymnastics	.65	.65
615	A90	1 le Hurdles	.70	.70
616	A90	3 le Javelin	2.25	2.25
		Nos. 614-616 (3)	3.60	3.60

Souvenir Sheet
617	A90	7 le Boxing	5.25	5.25

For surcharges see Nos. 699-702.

Apollo 11, 15th Anniv.— A91

1984, May 14   Litho.   *Perf. 14*
618	A91	50c Lift off	.40	.40
619	A91	75c Lunar landing	.60	.60
620	A91	1.25 le 1st step on moon	1.00	1.00
621	A91	2.50 le Walking on moon	2.00	2.00
		Nos. 618-621 (4)	4.00	4.00

Souvenir Sheet
622	A91	5 le TV transmission, horiz.	4.00	4.00

UPU Congress A92

1984, June 19
623	A92	4 le Concorde	2.75	2.75

Souvenir Sheet
624	A92	4 le UPU emblem, von Stephan	2.75	2.75

UN Decade for African Transportation — A93

Various cars.

1984, July 16   *Perf. 14½x15*
625	A93	12c Citroen	.15	.15
626	A93	60c Locomobile	.42	.42
627	A93	90c AC Ace	.60	.60
628	A93	1 le Vauxhall Prince Henry	.70	.70
629	A93	1.50 le Delahaye-185	1.10	1.10
630	A93	2 le Mazda	1.40	1.40
		Nos. 625-630 (6)	4.37	4.37

Souvenir Sheet
Perf. 15
631	A93	6 le Volkswagon Beetle	4.00	4.00

Nos. 466, 468, 475 Surcharged

1984, Aug. 3   Litho.   *Perf. 14*
632	A67	25c on 10c multi	.20	.20
633	A67	40c on 10c multi	.32	.32
634	A67	50c on 2 le multi	.50	.50
635	A67	70c on 5c multi	.56	.56
636	A67	10 le on 5c multi	8.00	8.00
		Nos. 632-636 (5)	9.58	9.58

#473, 476 Ovptd.: "AUSIPEX 84"
Wmk. 373

1984, Aug. 22   Litho.   *Perf. 14*
637	A67	50c multicolored	.40	.40
638	A67	5 le multicolored	4.00	4.00

Portuguese Caravel Da Sintra A94

1984
639	A94	2c shown	.15	.15
640	A94	5c Merlin of Bristol	.15	.15
641	A94	10c Golden Hind	.15	.15
642	A94	15c Interloper Morquant	.15	.15
643	A94	20c Navy Board Transport Atlantic	.15	.15
644	A94	25c Navy Vessel Lapwing	.16	.16
645	A94	30c Brig Traveller	.20	.20
646	A94	40c Schooner Amistad	.25	.25
647	A94	50c Teazer	.32	.32
648	A94	70c Cable Ship Scotia	.45	.45
649	A94	1 le Alecto	.65	.65
650	A94	2 le Blonde	1.25	1.25
651	A94	5 le Fox	3.25	3.25
652	A94	10 le Mail ship Accra	6.50	6.50
		Nos. 639-652 (14)	13.78	13.78

Issue dates: Nos. 639-649, Sept. 5; Nos. 650-651, Oct. 9; 10 le, Nov. 7.
See #739-740. For surcharges see #809-812.

1985   *Perf. 12½x12*
639a	A94	2c	.15	.15
640a	A94	5c	.15	.15
641a	A94	10c	.15	.15
643a	A94	20c	.15	.15
644a	A94	25c	.15	.15
645a	A94	30c	.15	.15
646a	A94	40c	.15	.15
647a	A94	50c	.15	.15
648a	A94	70c	.18	.18
649a	A94	1 le	.25	.25
650a	A94	2 le	.50	.50
651a	A94	5 le	1.25	1.25
652a	A94	10 le	2.50	2.50
		Nos. 639a-652a (13)	5.88	5.88

125th Anniv. of Sierra Leone Postage Stamps A95

1984, Oct. 9
653	A95	50c Mail messenger, No. 2	.32	.32
654	A95	2 le Post Master receiving letters, No. 2	1.25	1.25
655	A95	3 le Cover	2.00	2.00
		Nos. 653-655 (3)	3.57	3.57

Souvenir Sheet
656	A95	5 le Penny Black, No. 2	3.25	3.25

50th Anniv. of Donald Duck — A95a

1984, Nov. Litho. *Perf. 14x13½*

657	A95a	1c	Wise Little Hen	.15	.15
658	A95a	2c	Boat Builders	.15	.15
659	A95a	3c	Three Caballeros	.15	.15
660	A95a	4c	Mathematic Land	.15	.15
661	A95a	5c	Mickey Mouse Club	.15	.15
662	A95a	10c	On Parade	.15	.15
663	A95a	1 le	Don Donald	.80	.80
663A	A95a	2 le	Donald gets drafted, p. 12½x12	1.60	1.60
664	A95a	4 le	Tokyo Disneyland	3.25	3.25
			Nos. 657-664 (9)	6.55	6.55

Souvenir Sheet

665 A95a 5 le Sketches 4.00 4.00

Christmas — A96

Mother and Child paintings.

1984, Nov. 28 *Perf. 14*

666	A96	20c	Pisanello	.15	.15
667	A96	1 le	Memling	.70	.70
668	A96	2 le	Raphael	1.40	1.40
669	A96	3 le	van der Werff	2.00	2.00
			Nos. 666-669 (4)	4.25	4.25

Souvenir Sheet

670 A96 6 le Picasso 4.25 4.25

Songbirds A97

1985, Jan. 31 Litho.

671	A97	40c	Straw-tailed whydah	.40	.40
672	A97	90c	Spotted flycatcher	.95	.95
673	A97	1.30 le	Garden warbler	1.40	1.40
674	A97	3 le	Speke's weaver	3.00	3.00
			Nos. 671-674 (4)	5.75	5.75

Souvenir Sheet

675 A97 5 le Great gray shrike 5.00 5.00

International Youth Year — A98

1985, Feb. 14 Litho.

676	A98	1.15 le	Fishing	1.10	1.10
677	A98	1.50 le	Timber	1.40	1.40
678	A98	2.15 le	Rice farming	2.00	2.00
			Nos. 676-678 (3)	4.50	4.50

Souvenir Sheet

679 A98 5 le Diamond polishing 4.50 4.50

Intl. Civil Aviation Org., 40th Anniv. A100

Early aviators and their aircraft: 70c, Eddie Rickenbacker, Spad XIII (1918). 1.25 le, Samuel P. Langley, Aerodrome No. 5. 1.30 le, Orville and Wilbur Wright, Flyer 1. 2 le, Charles Lindbergh, Spirit of St. Louis.

1985, Feb. 28 Litho. *Perf. 14*

680	A100	70c	multicolored	.60	.60
681	A100	1.25 le	multicolored	1.10	1.10
682	A100	1.30 le	multicolored	1.10	1.10
683	A100	2 le	multicolored	1.90	1.90
			Nos. 680-683 (4)	4.70	4.70

Souvenir Sheet

684 A100 5 le Jet over Freetown 4.50 4.50

Easter A101

Religious paintings: Nos. 685, 687, 689 by Botticelli (1445-1510). Nos. 686, 688 by Velazquez (1599-1660).

1985, Apr. 29

685	A101	45c	The Temptation of Christ	.15	.15
686	A101	70c	Christ at the Column	.25	.25
687	A101	1.55 le	Pieta	.55	.55
688	A101	10 le	Christ on the Cross	4.00	4.00
			Nos. 685-688 (4)	4.95	4.95

Souvenir Sheet

689 A101 12 le Man of Sorrows 4.75 4.75

Queen Mother, 85th Birthday — A102

Designs: 1 le, Queen Mother at St. Peter's Cathedral, London, vert. 1.70 le, With Double Star at Sandown Racetrack. 10 le, Attending the gala ballet at Covent Garden, 1971, vert. 12 le, With Princess Anne at Ascot, vert.

1985, July 8 Litho. *Perf. 14*

690	A102	1 le	multicolored	.32	.32
691	A102	1.70 le	multicolored	.60	.60
692	A102	10 le	multicolored	3.25	3.25
			Nos. 690-692 (3)	4.17	4.17

Souvenir Sheet

693 A102 12 le multicolored 4.00 4.00

Nos. 535-539 Surcharged "75th Anniversary / of Girl Guides," Black Bar and New Value

1985, July 25

694	A78	70c on 20c multi	.60	.60
695	A78	1.30 le on 50c multi	1.25	1.25
696	A78	5 le on 1 le multi	.90	.90
697	A78	7 le on 2 le multi	1.75	1.75
		Nos. 694-697 (4)	4.50	4.50

Souvenir Sheet

698 A78 15 le on 3 le multi 5.00 5.00

Nos. 614-617 Surcharged with Winners Names, Country, "Gold Medal," Black Bar and New Value

1985, July 25

699	A90	2 le on 90c Ma Yanhonjg, China	.65	.65
700	A90	4 le on 1 le E. Moses, USA	1.25	1.25
701	A90	8 le on 3 le A. Haerkoenen, Finland	2.50	2.50
		Nos. 699-701 (3)	4.40	4.40

Souvenir Sheet

702 A90 15 le on 7 le M. Taylor, USA 4.75 4.75

1905 Chater-Lea, Hill Station House A103

Designs: 2 le, Honda XR 350 R, QE II Quay. 4 le, Kawasaki Vulcan, Bo Clock Tower. 5 le, Harley-Davidson Electra-Glide, Makeni. 12 le, 1893 Millet.

1985, Aug. 15

703	A103	1.40 le	multicolored	.45	.45
704	A103	2 le	multicolored	.65	.65
705	A103	4 le	multicolored	1.25	1.25
706	A103	5 le	multicolored	1.65	1.65
			Nos. 703-706 (4)	4.00	4.00

Souvenir Sheet

707 A103 12 le multicolored 4.00 4.00

Motorcycle cent., Decade for African Transport.

A104

Christmas — A105

1985, Sept. 3

708	A104	70c	Viola pomposa	.24	.24
709	A104	3 le	Spinet	1.00	1.00
710	A104	4 le	Lute	1.25	1.25
711	A104	5 le	Oboe	1.65	1.65
			Nos. 708-711 (4)	4.14	4.14

Souvenir Sheet

712 A104 12 le Portrait 4.00 4.00

Johann Sebastian Bach (1685-1750), composer. Nos. 708-712 show music from "Clavier Ubang."

Nos. 510, 512, 516, 531-534, 552-555 Surcharged

1985, Sept. 30 *Perfs. as Before*

Designs CD331-CD332

713	70c on 31c #531	.48	.48
714	1.30 le on 60c #512	.90	.90
715	1.30 le on 31c #552	.90	.90
716	2 le on 35c #510	1.25	1.25
717	4 le on 50c #532	2.75	2.75
718	5 le on 2 le #533	3.25	3.25
719	5 le on 50c #553	3.25	3.25
720	7 le on 2 le #554	4.50	4.50
721	8 le on 1.50 le #516	5.50	5.50
	Nos. 713-721 (9)	22.78	22.78

Souvenir Sheets

722	15 le on 3 le #534	7.00	7.00
723	15 le on 3 le #555	7.00	7.00

1985, Oct. 18 Litho. *Perf. 14*

Madonna and child paintings by: 70c, Carlo Crivelli (c. 1430-1494). 3 le, Dirk Bouts (c. 1400-1475). 4 le, Antonello de Messina (c. 1430-1479). 5 le, Stefan Lochner (c. 1400-1451). 12 le, Miniature from the Book of Kells, 9th cent., Ireland.

724	A105	70c	multicolored	.24	.24
725	A105	3 le	multicolored	1.00	1.00
726	A105	4 le	multicolored	1.35	1.35
727	A105	5 le	multicolored	1.65	1.65
			Nos. 724-727 (4)	4.24	4.24

Miniature Sheet

728 A105 12 le multicolored 4.00 4.00

Jacob and Wilhelm Grimm, Fabulists — A106

Mark Twain, American Humorist A107

Walt Disney characters acting out Twain quotes or in Rumpelstiltskin.

1985, Oct. 30 Litho. *Perf. 14*

729	A106	70c	multicolored	.22	.22
730	A106	1.30 le	multicolored	.38	.38
731	A107	1.50 le	multicolored	.42	.42
732	A106	2 le	multicolored	.55	.55
733	A107	3 le	multicolored	.85	.85
734	A107	4 le	multicolored	1.25	1.25
735	A107	5 le	multicolored	1.40	1.40
736	A106	10 le	multicolored	2.75	2.75
			Nos. 729-736 (8)	7.82	7.82

Souvenir Sheets

737	A106	15 le	multicolored	4.25	4.25
738	A107	15 le	multicolored	4.25	4.25

Nos. 731, 733-735 bear the Intl. Youth Year emblem.

Ship Type of 1984

1985, Nov. 15

739	A94	15 le	Favourite	4.50	4.50
740	A94	25 le	Euryalus	7.50	7.50

UN, 40th Anniv. A108

Stamps of UN and famous men: 2 le, No. 30, Kennedy. 4 le, No. 59, Einstein. 7 le, No. 44, Maimonides (1135-1204), medieval Judaic scholar. 12 le, Martin Luther King, Jr. (1929-1968), civil rights leader, vert.

1985, Nov. 28 Litho. *Perf. 14½*

741	A108	2 le	multicolored	.65	.65
742	A108	4 le	multicolored	1.35	1.35
743	A108	7 le	multicolored	2.30	2.30
			Nos. 741-743 (3)	4.30	4.30

Souvenir Sheet

744 A108 12 le multicolored 4.00 4.00

1986 World Cup Soccer Championships A109

Statue of Liberty, Cent. A110

Various soccer plays.

1986, Mar. 3 *Perf. 14*

745	A109	70c	multicolored	.28	.28
746	A109	3 le	multicolored	1.10	1.10
747	A109	4 le	multicolored	1.50	1.50
748	A109	5 le	multicolored	1.90	1.90
			Nos. 745-748 (4)	4.78	4.78

Souvenir Sheet

749 A109 12 le multicolored 4.50 4.50

For overprints and surcharges see Nos. 788-792.

1986, Mar. 11

New York City: 40c, Times Square, 1905. 70c, Times Square, 1986. 1 le, Tally Ho Coach, c. 1880, horiz. 10 le, Liberty Lines express bus, 1986. 12 le, Statue of Liberty.

750	A110	40c	multicolored	.16	.16
751	A110	70c	multicolored	.28	.28
752	A110	1 le	multicolored	.42	.42
753	A110	10 le	multicolored	4.00	4.00
			Nos. 750-753 (4)	4.86	4.86

Souvenir Sheet

754 A110 12 le multicolored 4.00 4.00

A111

Halley's Comet A112

Designs: 15c, Johannes Kepler (1571-1630), German astronomer, and Paris Observatory. 50c, US space shuttle landing, 1985. 70c, Bayeux Tapestry (detail), 1066 sighting. 10 le, Arthurian magician, Merlin, sights comet, 530. 12 le, Comet over Sierra Leone.

1986, Apr. 1

755 A111 15c multicolored .15 .15
756 A111 50c multicolored .16 .16
757 A111 70c multicolored .24 .24
758 A111 10 le multicolored 3.35 3.35
Nos. 755-758 (4) 3.90 3.90

Souvenir Sheet

759 A112 12 le multicolored 4.00 4.00

For overprints and surcharges see Nos. 813-817.

Queen Elizabeth II, 60th Birthday
Common Design Type

1986, Apr. 21

760 CD339 10c Cranwell, 1951 .15 .15
761 CD339 1.70 le Garter Ceremony .55 .55
762 CD339 10 le Braemar Games, 1970 3.35 3.35
Nos. 760-762 (3) 4.05 4.05

Souvenir Sheet

763 CD339 12 le Windsor Castle, 1943 4.00 4.00

For surcharges see Nos. 793-795.

AMERIPEX '86 — A113

Locomotives.

1986, May 22

764 A113 50c Hiawatha, Milwaukee .16 .16
765 A113 2 le The Rocket, Rock Is. .65 .65
766 A113 4 le Prospector, Rio Grande 1.35 1.35
767 A113 7 le Daylight, So. Pacific 2.35 2.35
Nos. 764-767 (4) 4.51 4.51

Souvenir Sheet

768 A113 12 le Broadway, Pennsylvania 4.00 4.00

Royal Wedding Issue, 1986
Common Design Type

Designs: 10c, Prince Andrew and Sarah Ferguson. 1.70 le, Andrew with shotgun. 10 le, Andrew saluting. 12 le, Couple, diff.

1986, July 23

769 CD340 10c multi .15 .15
770 CD340 1.70 le multi .55 .55
771 CD340 10 le multi 3.35 3.35
Nos. 769-771 (3) 4.05 4.05

Souvenir Sheet

772 CD340 12 le multi 4.00 4.00

For surcharges see Nos. 796-798.

Indigenous Flowers — A114

1986, Aug. 25 Litho. *Perf. 15*

773 A114 70c Monodora myristica .15 .15
774 A114 1.50 le Gloriosa simplex .15 .15
775 A114 4 le Mussaenda erythrophylla .35 .35
776 A114 6 le Crinum ornatum .52 .52
777 A114 8 le Bauhinia purpurea .75 .75
778 A114 10 le Bombax costatum .90 .90
779 A114 20 le Hibiscus rosa-sinensis 1.75 1.75
780 A114 30 le Cassia fistula 2.75 2.75
Nos. 773-780 (8) 7.32 7.32

Souvenir Sheets

781 A114 40 le Clitoria ternatea 3.50 3.50
782 A114 40 le Plumbago auriculata 3.50 3.50

US Peace Corps in Sierra Leone, 25th Anniv. A115

1986, Aug. 26 Litho. *Perf. 14*

783 A115 10 le multi 1.25 1.25

Intl. Peace Year — A116

1986, Sept. 1

784 A116 1 le Transportation .15 .15
785 A116 2 le Education .24 .24
786 A116 5 le Communications .60 .60
787 A116 10 le Fishing 1.25 1.25
Nos. 784-787 (4) 2.24 2.24

Nos. 745-749 Ovptd. or Surcharged "WINNERS / Argentina 3 / West Germany 2" in Gold

1986, Sept. 15 *Perf. 14*

788 A109 70c multi .15 .15
789 A109 3 le multi .24 .24
790 A109 4 le multi .32 .32
791 A109 40 le on 5 le multi 3.20 3.20
Nos. 788-791 (4) 3.91 3.91

Souvenir Sheet

792 A109 40 le on 12 le multi 3.20 3.20

Nos. 760, 762-763 Surcharged in Silver or Black

1986, Sept. 15

793 CD339 70c on 10c multi .15 .15
794 CD339 45 le on 10 le multi 3.60 3.60

Souvenir Sheet

795 CD339 50 le on 12 le (B) 4.00 4.00

Nos. 769, 771-772 Surcharged in Silver

1986, Sept. 15

796 CD340 70c on 10c multi .15 .15
797 CD340 45 le on 10 le multi 3.60 3.60

Souvenir Sheet

798 CD340 50 le on 12 le multi 4.00 4.00

STOCKHOLMIA '86 — A117

Disney characters in Mother Goose fairy tales.

1986, Sept. 22 *Perf. 11*

799 A117 70c Jack and Jill .15 .15
800 A117 1 le Wee Willie Winkie .15 .15
801 A117 2 le Little Miss Muffet .16 .16
802 A117 4 le Old King Cole .32 .32
803 A117 5 le Mary Quite Contrary .40 .40
804 A117 10 le Little Bo Peep .80 .80
805 A117 25 le Polly Put the Kettle On 2.00 2.00
806 A117 35 le Rub-a-Dub-Dub 2.80 2.80
Nos. 799-806 (8) 6.78 6.78

Souvenir Sheets

807 A117 40 le Old Woman in the Shoe 3.20 3.20
808 A117 40 le Simple Simon 3.20 3.20

Nos. 639, 645-646 and 648 Surcharged

1986, Oct. 15

809 A94 30 le on 2c multi 2.75 2.75
810 A94 40 le on 30c multi 3.75 3.75
811 A94 45 le on 40c multi 4.25 4.25
812 A94 50 le on 70c multi 4.75 4.75
Nos. 809-812 (4) 15.50 15.50

Nos. 755-759 Ovptd. or Surcharged with Halley's Comet Emblem in Black or Silver

HALLEY'S COMET 1985 OFFICIAL 1986

1986, Oct. 15

813 A111 50c multi .15 .15
814 A111 70c multi .15 .15
815 A111 1.50 le on 15c multi .15 .15
816 A111 45 le on 10 le multi 4.25 4.25
Nos. 813-816 (4) 4.70 4.70

Souvenir Sheet

817 A112 50 le on 12 le multi (S) 4.75 4.75

Christmas A118

Paintings by Titian: 70c, Virgin and Child with St. Dorothy. $1.50 le, The Gypsy Madonna, vert. 20 le, The Holy Family. 30 le, Virgin and Child in an Evening Landscape, vert. 40 le, Madonna with the Pesaro Family.

1986, Nov. 17 Litho. *Perf. 14*

818 A118 70c multi .15 .15
819 A118 1.50 le multi .15 .15
820 A118 20 le multi 1.60 1.60
821 A118 30 le multi 2.40 2.40
Nos. 818-821 (4) 4.30 4.30

Souvenir Sheet

822 A118 40 le multi 3.25 3.25

Statue of Liberty, Cent. A119

Pictures of the statue by Peter B. Kaplan before and after renovation. Nos. 823, 825-826, 828-829, 831, vert.

1987, Jan. 2 *Perf. 14*

823 A119 70c Torch assembly .15 .15
824 A119 1.50 le Liberty holding torch .15 .15
825 A119 2 le Torch assembly, diff. .16 .16
826 A119 3 le Man, torch .24 .24
827 A119 4 le Crown .32 .32
828 A119 5 le Lighting of the statue .40 .40
829 A119 10 le Lighting, diff. .80 .80
830 A119 25 le Liberty Is. 2.00 2.00
831 A119 30 le Face 2.40 2.40
Nos. 823-831 (9) 6.62 6.62

UNICEF, 40th Anniv. A120

1987, Mar. 18 Litho. *Perf. 14*

832 A120 10 le multi .80 .80

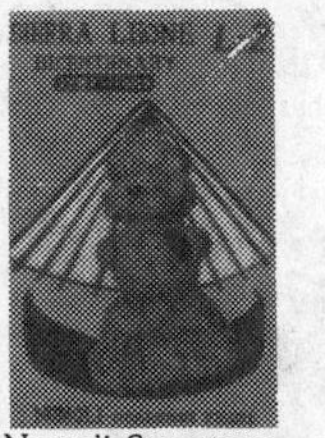

Nomoli Soapstone Sculpture — A121

Tall Ship in Harbor, Freetown — A122

1987, Jan. 2 *Perf. 15*

833 A121 2 le shown .15 .15
834 A121 5 le King's Yard Gate, 1817 .35 .35

Souvenir Sheet

835 A122 60 le shown 4.00 4.00

First settlement of liberated slaves returned to the African continent by the British, Freetown, bicent.

America's Cup — A123

Constellation, 1964 — A124

1987, June 15 Litho. *Perf. 14*

836 A123 1 le USA, 1987 .15 .15
837 A123 1.50 le New Zealand, 1987 .15 .15
838 A123 2.50 le French Kiss, 1987 .15 .15
839 A123 10 le Stars & Stripes, 1987 .60 .60
840 A123 15 le Australia II, 1983 .90 .90
841 A123 25 le Freedom, 1980 1.50 1.50
842 A123 30 le Kookaburra III, 1987 1.75 1.75
Nos. 836-842 (7) 5.20 5.20

Souvenir Sheet

843 A124 50 le shown 3.00 3.00

Nos. 837, 839 and 842 horiz.
For overprint see No. 964.

CAPEX '87 — A125

Disney characters, Canadian sights.

1987, June 15 *Perf. 11*

849 A125 2 le Parliament .15 .15
850 A125 5 le Totem poles .25 .25
851 A125 10 le Perce Rock .52 .52
852 A125 20 le Canadian Rockies 1.00 1.00
853 A125 25 le Old Quebec City 1.40 1.40
854 A125 45 le Aurora Borealis 2.25 2.25
855 A125 50 le Yukon P.O. 2.75 2.75
856 A125 75 le Niagara Falls 4.00 4.00
Nos. 849-856 (8) 12.32 12.32

Souvenir Sheets

857 A125 100 le Exploring Newfoundland 5.25 5.25
858 A125 100 le Calgary Exhibition and Stampede 5.25 5.25

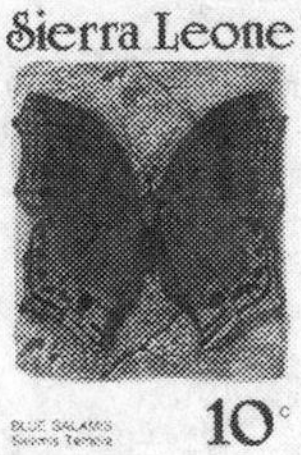

Butterflies — A126

1988 Summer Olympics, Seoul — A127

1987, Aug. 4 *Perf. 14*

859 A126 10c Blue salamis .15 .15
860 A126 20c Pale-tailed blue .15 .15
861 A126 40c Acraea swallowtail .15 .15
862 A126 1 le Broad blue-banded swallowtail .15 .15
863 A126 2 le Giant blue swallowtail .15 .15

864 A126 3 le Blood-red cymothoe .15 .15
865 A126 5 le Green-spotted swallowtail .20 .20
866 A126 10 le Small-striped swordtail .40 .40
867 A126 20 le Congo long-tailed blue .80 .80
868 A126 25 le Blue monarch 1.00 1.00
869 A126 30 le Black and yellow swallowtail 1.20 1.20
870 A126 45 le Western blue charaxes 1.75 1.75
871 A126 60 le Violet-washed charaxes 2.40 2.40
872 A126 75 le Orange admiral 3.00 3.00
873 A126 100 le Blue-patched judy 4.00 4.00
Nos. 859-873 (15) 15.65 15.65

Nos. 859-864 exist with 1989 date, No. 871 with 1990.
See Nos. 1332A-1332I.

1988-89 ***Perf. 12x12½***

859a A126 10c .15 .15
860a A126 20c .15 .15
861a A126 40c .15 .15
862a A126 1 le .15 .15
863a A126 2 le .15 .15
864a A126 3 le .15 .15
865a A126 5 le .20 .20
866a A126 10 le .40 .40
867a A126 20 le .80 .80
868a A126 25 le 1.00 1.00
869a A126 30 le 1.20 1.20
870a A126 45 le 1.75 1.75
873a A126 100 le 5.00 5.00
Nos. 859a-873a (13) 11.25 11.25

1987, Aug. 10

874 A127 5 le Cycling .25 .25
875 A127 10 le Equestrian .50 .50
876 A127 45 le Running 2.25 2.25
877 A127 50 le Tennis 2.50 2.50
Nos. 874-877 (4) 5.50 5.50

Souvenir Sheet

878 A127 100 le Gold medal, map 5.50 5.50

Works of Art by Marc Chagall, (1887-1985) A128

1987, Aug. 17 ***Perf. 14***

879 A128 3 le The Quarrel, 1911-1912 .15 .15
880 A128 5 le Rebecca Giving Abraham's Servant a Drink .22 .22
881 A128 10 le The Village .45 .45
882 A128 20 le Ida at the Window, 1924 .45 .45
883 A128 25 le Promenade, 1913 1.10 1.10
884 A128 45 le Peasants 2.00 2.00
885 A128 50 le Turquoise Plate 2.25 2.25
886 A128 75 le Cemetery Gate, 1917 3.25 3.25
Nos. 879-886 (8) 9.87 9.87

Size: 111x95mm

Imperf

887 A128 100 le Wedding Feast, Stravinsky's Ballet, 1945 4.50 4.50
888 A128 100 le The Falling Angel 4.50 4.50

Nos. 879-886 printed in sheets of 10 (5x2). Stamp selvage inscribed with name of painting.

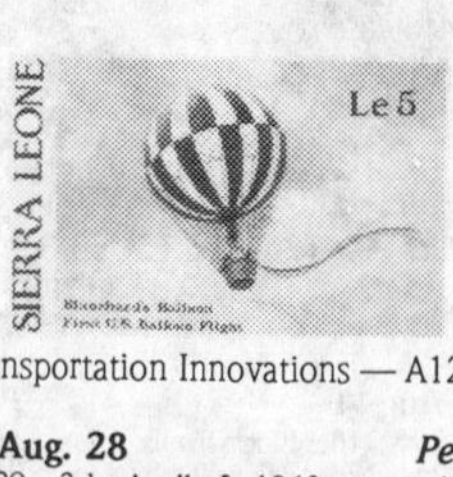

Transportation Innovations — A129

1987, Aug. 28 ***Perf. 15***

889 A129 3 le Apollo 8, 1968, vert. .15 .15
890 A129 5 le Blanchard's Balloon, 1793 .20 .20
891 A129 10 le Lockheed Vega, 1932 .40 .40
892 A129 15 le Vicker's Vimy, 1919 .60 .60
893 A129 20 le Tank Mk1, c. 1918 .80 .80
894 A129 25 le Sikorsky VS-300, 1939 1.00 1.00
895 A129 30 le Flyer 1, 1903 1.20 1.20
896 A129 35 le Bleriot XI, 1909 1.40 1.40
897 A129 40 le Paraplane, 1983, vert. 1.60 1.60
898 A129 50 le Daimler's motorcycle, 1885 2.00 2.00
Nos. 889-898 (10) 9.35 9.35

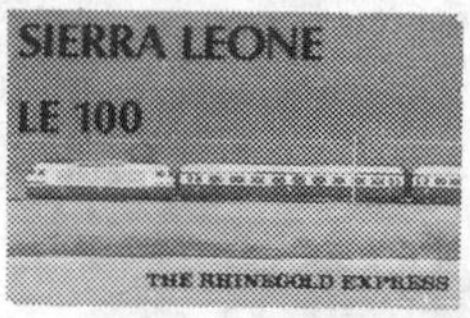

Rhinegold Express, Ireland (1st Electric Railroad, 1884) A129a

1987, Aug. 28 Litho. ***Perf. 15***

898A A129a 100 le multi 4.00 4.00

Wimbledon Tennis Champions A130

1987, Sept. 4 ***Perf. 14***

899 A130 2 le Evonne Goolagong, Australia .15 .15
900 A130 5 le Martina Navratilova, US-Czechoslovakia .30 .30
901 A130 10 le Jimmy Connors, US .60 .60
902 A130 15 le Bjorn Borg, Sweden .90 .90
903 A130 30 le Boris Becker, West Germany 1.90 1.90
904 A130 40 le John McEnroe, US 2.50 2.50
905 A130 50 le Chris Evert Lloyd, US 3.00 3.00
906 A130 75 le Virgina Wade, Great Britain 4.75 4.75
Nos. 899-906 (8) 14.10 14.10

Souvenir Sheets

907 A130 100 le Steffi Graf, German Open 1986 6.25 6.25
908 A130 100 le Boris Becker 6.25 6.25

For overprints see Nos. 965, 1023-1024.

Discovery of America, 500th Anniv. (in 1992) A131

Designs: 5 le, Ducats, Santa Maria, Issac Abravanel (1437-1508), fundraiser. 10 le, Astrolabe, Pinta, Abraham Zacuto (1452-1515), astronomer. 45 le, Maravedis (coins), Nina, Luis de Santangel (1448-1498), fund raiser. 50 le, Tobacco leaves, plant, Luis de Torres (1453-1522), translator.

1987, Sept. 11

909 A131 5 le multicolored .22 .22
910 A131 10 le multicolored .45 .45
911 A131 45 le multicolored 2.00 2.00
912 A131 50 le multicolored 2.25 2.25
Nos. 909-912 (4) 4.92 4.92

Souvenir Sheet

913 A131 100 le Columbus, map 4.50 4.50

For overprint see No. 966.

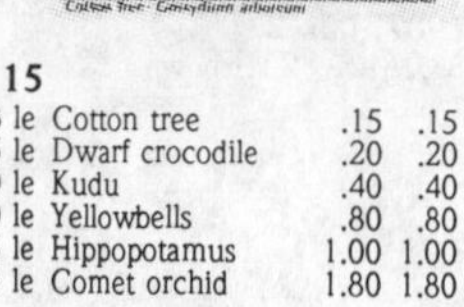

Fauna and Flora A132

1987, Sept. 15

914 A132 3 le Cotton tree .15 .15
915 A132 5 le Dwarf crocodile .20 .20
916 A132 10 le Kudu .40 .40
917 A132 20 le Yellowbells .80 .80
918 A132 25 le Hippopotamus 1.00 1.00
919 A132 45 le Comet orchid 1.80 1.80
920 A132 50 le Baobab tree 2.00 2.00
921 A132 75 le Elephant 3.00 3.00
Nos. 914-921 (8) 9.35 9.35

Souvenir Sheets

922 A132 100 le Banana, papaya, coconut, pineapple 4.00 4.00
923 A132 100 le Leopard 4.00 4.00

16th World Scout Jamboree, Australia, 1987-88 A133

Scouts, jamboree emblem, map of Australia and: 5 le, Ayers Rock. 15 le, Sailing. 40 le, Sydney skyline. 50 le, Sydney harbor bridge, opera house. 100 le, Flags of Sierra Leone, Australia and Scouts.

1987, Oct. 5 Litho. ***Perf. 15***

924 A133 5 le multicolored .45 .45
925 A133 15 le multicolored 1.35 1.35
926 A133 40 le multicolored 3.60 3.60
927 A133 50 le multicolored 4.50 4.50
Nos. 924-927 (4) 9.90 9.90

Souvenir Sheet

928 A133 100 le multicolored 9.00 9.00

1.50 le stamps like the 50 le were printed but not issued.

US Constitution Bicentennial A134

Designs: 5 le, White House. 10 le, George Washington. 30 le, Patrick Henry. 65 le, New Hampshire state flag. 100 le, John Jay.

1987, Nov. 9 ***Perf. 14***

929 A134 5 le multi .45 .45
930 A134 10 le multi, vert. .90 .90
931 A134 30 le multi, vert. 2.70 2.70
932 A134 65 le multi 5.85 5.85
Nos. 929-932 (4) 9.90 9.90

Souvenir Sheet

933 A134 100 le multi, vert. 9.00 9.00

Tokyo Disneyland, 5th Anniv. — A135

Disney animated characters and attractions at Tokyo Disneyland.

1987, Dec. 9 Litho. ***Perf. 14***

934 A135 20c Space Mountain .15 .15
935 A135 40c Country Bear Jamboree .15 .15
936 A135 80c Mickey Mouse Review .15 .15
937 A135 1 le Mark Twain's River Boat .15 .15
938 A135 2 le Western River Railroad .18 .18
939 A135 3 le Pirates of the Caribbean .28 .28
940 A135 10 le Big Thunder Mountain train .90 .90
941 A135 20 le It's a Small World 1.80 1.80
942 A135 30 le Park entrance 2.70 2.70
Nos. 934-942 (9) 6.46 6.46

Souvenir Sheet

943 A135 65 le Cinderella's Castle 5.85 5.85

Mickey Mouse, 60th anniv.

Christmas A136

Paintings by Titian: 2 le, The Annunciation. 10 le, Madonna and Child with Saints. 20 le, Madonna and Child with Saints Ulfus and Brigid. 35 le, Madonna of the Cherries. 65 le, Pesaro Altarpiece, vert.

1987, Dec. 21

944 A136 2 le multicolored .18 .18
945 A136 10 le multicolored .90 .90
946 A136 20 le multicolored 1.80 1.80
947 A136 35 le multicolored 3.20 3.20
Nos. 944-947 (4) 6.08 6.08

Souvenir Sheet

948 A136 65 le multicolored 5.85 5.85

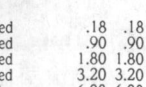

40th Wedding Anniv. of Queen Elizabeth II and Prince Philip A137

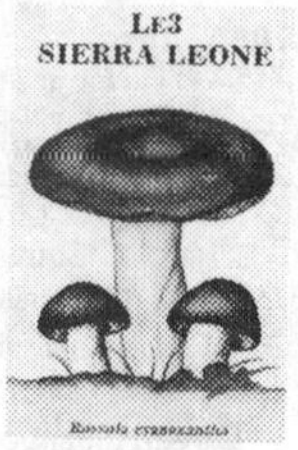

Mushrooms A138

1988, Feb. 15 Litho. ***Perf. 14***

949 A137 2 le Ceremony, 1947 .18 .18
950 A137 3 le Elizabeth, Charles, 1948 .28 .28
951 A137 10 le Elizabeth, Anne, Charles, c. 1950 .90 .90
952 A137 50 le Elizabeth, c. 1970 4.50 4.50
Nos. 949-952 (4) 5.86 5.86

Souvenir Sheet

953 A137 65 le Wedding portrait 5.85 5.85

1988, Feb. 29

954 A138 3 le Russula cyanoxantha .18 .18
955 A138 10 le Lycoperdon perlatum .90 .90
956 A138 20 le Lactarius deliciosus 1.80 1.80
957 A138 30 le Boletus edulis 2.70 2.70
Nos. 954-957 (4) 5.58 5.58

Miniature Sheet

958 A138 65 le Amanita muscaria 5.80 5.80

Fish A139

1988, Apr. 13 ***Perf. 15***

959 A139 3 le Golden pheasant .28 .28
960 A139 10 le Banded toothcarp .90 .90
961 A139 20 le Jewel fish 1.80 1.80
962 A139 35 le Butterfly fish 3.20 3.20
Nos. 959-962 (4) 6.18 6.18

Miniature Sheet

963 A139 65 le African longfin 5.90 5.90

Nos. 841, 903 and 911 Ovptd. for Philatelic Exhibitions in Black

a INDEPENDENCE 40

b OLYMPHILEX '88

c Praga '88

1988, Apr. 19 Litho. ***Perf. 14***

964 A123(a) 25 le multicolored 2.00 2.00
965 A130(b) 30 le multicolored 2.40 2.40
966 A131(c) 45 le multicolored 3.60 3.60
Nos. 964-966 (3) 8.00 8.00

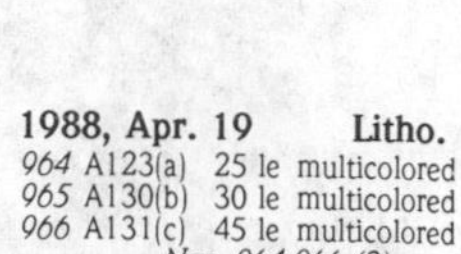

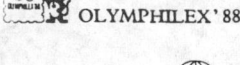

Intl. Fund for Agricultural Development (IFAD), 10th Anniv. A140

1988, May 3 Litho. *Perf. 14*

967	A140	3 le Cocoa, coffee	.28	.28
968	A140	15 le Tropical fruit	1.35	1.35
969	A140	25 le Rice harvest	2.25	2.25
		Nos. 967-969 (3)	3.88	3.88

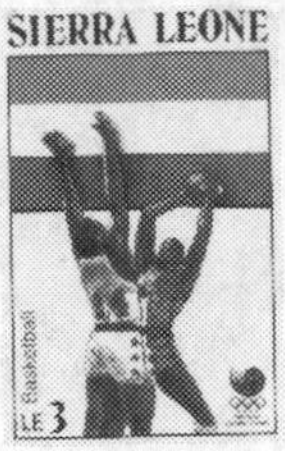

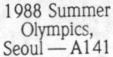

1988 Summer Olympics, Seoul — A141

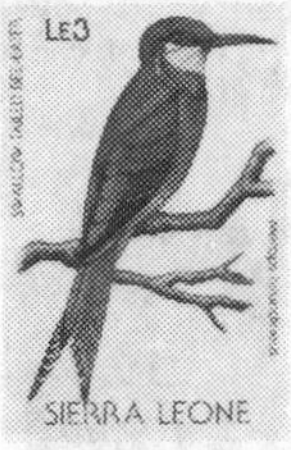

Birds — A142

1988, June 15

970	A141	3 le Basketball	.24	.24
971	A141	10 le Judo	.80	.80
972	A141	15 le Gymnastics	1.20	1.20
973	A141	40 le Synchronized swimming	3.20	3.20
		Nos. 970-973 (4)	5.44	5.44

Souvenir Sheet

974	A141	65 le Torch-bearer	5.25	5.25

1988, June 25

975	A142	3 le Swallow-tailed bee-eater	.24	.24
976	A142	5 le Tooth-billed barbet	.40	.40
977	A142	8 le African golden oriole	.65	.65
978	A142	10 le Red bishop	.80	.80
979	A142	12 le Red-billed shrike	.95	.95
980	A142	20 le European bee-eater	1.60	1.60
981	A142	35 le Barbary shrike	2.80	2.80
982	A142	40 le Black-headed oriole	3.20	3.20
		Nos. 975-982 (8)	10.64	10.64

Souvenir Sheets

983	A142	65 le Saddlebill stork	5.25	5.25
984	A142	65 le Purple heron	5.25	5.25

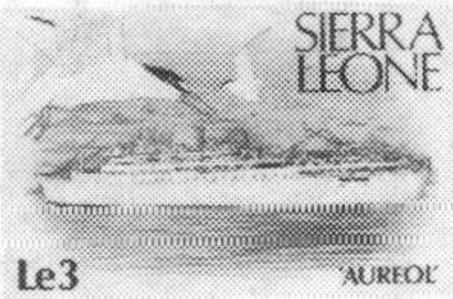

Merchant Marine A143

1988, July 1

985	A143	3 le Aureol	.24	.24
986	A143	10 le Dunkwa	.80	.80
987	A143	15 le Melampus	1.20	1.20
988	A143	30 le Dumbaia	2.40	2.40
		Nos. 985-988 (4)	4.64	4.64

Souvenir Sheet

989	A143	65 le Loading containers	5.25	5.25

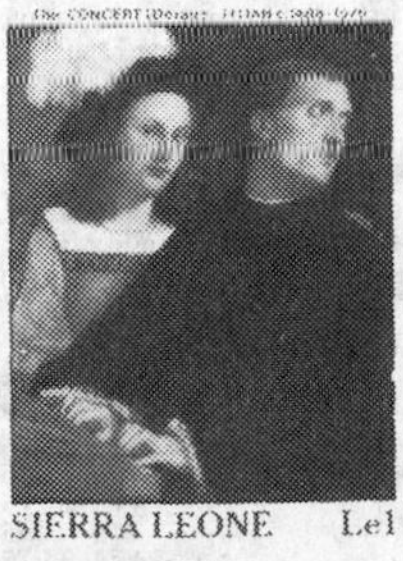

Paintings by Titian — A144

Designs: 1 le, The Concert, 1512. 2 le, Philip II of Spain, c. 1550-51. 3 le, St. Sebastian, c. 1520-22. 5 le, Martyrdom of St. Peter Martyr, c. 1528-30. 15 le, St. Jerome, 1560. 20 le, St. Mark Enthroned with Saints Cosmas and Damian, Roch and Sebastian, c. 1508-09. 25 le, Portrait of a Young Man, 1506. 30 le, St. Jerome in Penitence, 1555. No. 998, Self-portrait, 1567. No. 999, Orpheus and Eurydice, 1508.

1988, Aug. 22 Litho. *Perf. 13½x14*

990	A144	1 le multicolored	.15	.15
991	A144	2 le multicolored	.16	.16
992	A144	3 le multicolored	.24	.24
993	A144	5 le multicolored	.40	.40
994	A144	15 le multicolored	1.20	1.20
995	A144	20 le multicolored	1.60	1.60
996	A144	25 le multicolored	2.00	2.00
997	A144	30 le multicolored	2.40	2.40
		Nos. 990-997 (8)	8.15	8.15

Souvenir Sheets

998	A144	50 le multicolored	4.00	4.00
999	A144	50 le multicolored	4.00	4.00

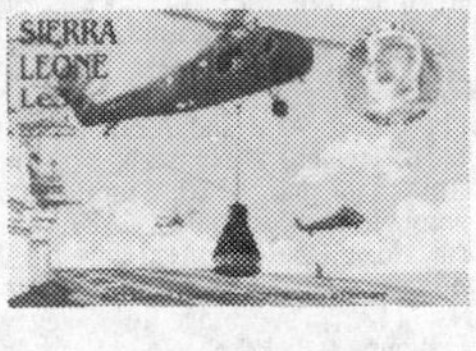

John F. Kennedy A145

Kennedy half-dollar and space achievements: 3 le, Recovery of a Mercury capsule by the US Navy. 5 le, Splashdown and recovery of Liberty Bell 7, July 21, 1961, piloted by Virgil "Gus" Grissom, vert. 15 le, Launch of Freedom 7, piloted by Alan B. Shepherd, May 5, 1961, vert. 40 le, Friendship 7 in orbit, piloted by John Glenn, Feb. 20, 1962. 65 le, Kennedy, speech excerpt.

1988, Sept. 26 Litho. *Perf. 14*

1000	A145	3 le multicolored	.25	.25
1001	A145	5 le multicolored	.40	.40
1002	A145	15 le multicolored	1.20	1.20
1003	A145	40 le multicolored	1.60	1.60
		Nos. 1000-1003 (4)	3.45	3.45

Souvenir Sheet

1004	A145	65 le multicolored	5.25	5.25

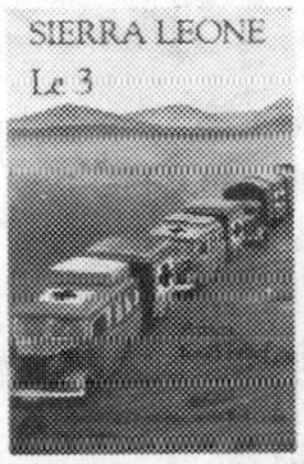

Intl. Red Cross and Red Crescent Organizations, 125th Annivs. — A146

1988, Nov. 1

1005	A146	3 le Africa food relief	.25	.25
1006	A146	10 le Battle of Solferino	.80	.80
1007	A146	20 le WWII Pacific	1.60	1.60
1008	A146	40 le WWI Europe	3.20	3.20
		Nos. 1005-1008 (4)	5.85	5.85

Souvenir Sheet

Size: 41x28mm

1009	A146	65 le Alfred Nobel, Dunant, horiz.	5.25	5.25

Miniature Sheet

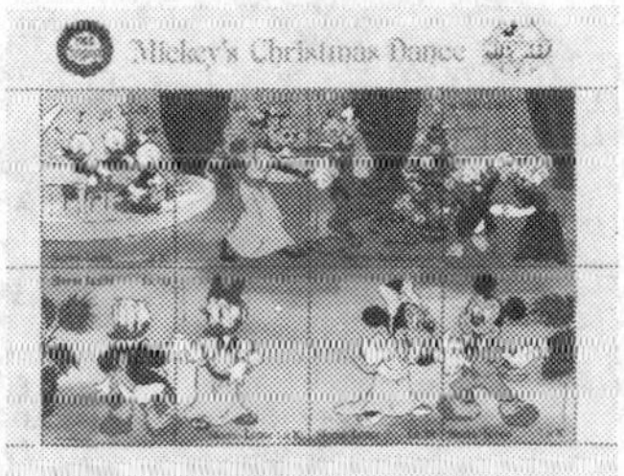

Christmas, Mickey Mouse 60th Anniv. — A147

Walt Disney characters dancing: No. 1010a, Huey, Dewey and Louie. No. 1010b, Clarabelle Cow. No. 1010c, Goofy. No. 1010d, Scrooge McDuck and Grandma Duck. No. 1010e, Donald Duck. No. 1010f, Daisy Duck. No. 1010g, Minnie Mouse. No. 1010h, Mickey Mouse. No. 1011, Dance, c. 1920. No. 1012, Dance, c. 1950.

1988, Dec. 1 *Perf. 13½x14*

1010	A147	Sheet of 8	5.50	5.50
a.-h.		10 le any single	.70	.70

Souvenir Sheets

1011	A147	70 le multicolored	4.50	4.50
1012	A147	70 le multicolored	4.50	4.50

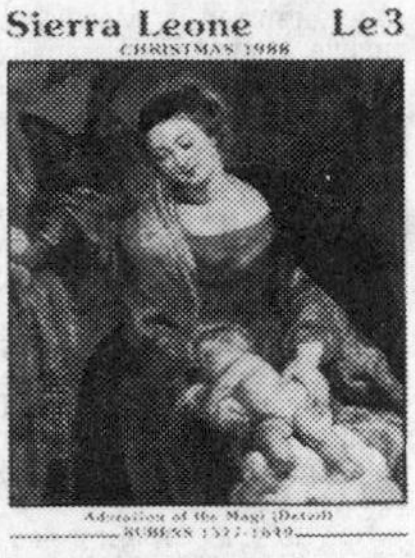

Christmas A148

Paintings by Rubens (details): 3 le, Adoration of the Magi (Virgin and Child). 3.60 le, Adoration of the Shepherds (shepherds and child). 5 le, Adoration of the Magi (Magi). 10 le, Adoration of the Shepherds (Virgin and Child). 20 le, Virgin and Child Surrounded by Flowers. 40 le, St. Gregory the Great and Other Saints (Virgin and Child). 60 le, Adoration of the Magi, (Virgin, Child and Magi), diff. 80 le, Madonna and Child with Saints. No. 1021, St. Gregory the Great and Other Saints. No. 1022, Virgin and Child Enthroned with Saints.

1988, Dec. 15 Litho. *Perf. 13½x14*

1013	A148	3 le multicolored	.18	.18
1014	A148	3.60 le multicolored	.22	.22
1015	A148	5 le multicolored	.30	.30
1016	A148	10 le multicolored	.60	.60
1017	A148	20 le multicolored	1.20	1.20
1018	A148	40 le multicolored	2.40	2.40
1019	A148	60 le multicolored	3.60	3.60
1020	A148	80 le multicolored	4.80	4.80
		Nos. 1013-1020 (8)	13.30	13.30

Souvenir Sheets

1021	A148	100 le multicolored	6.00	6.00
1022	A148	100 le multicolored	6.00	6.00

No. 907 Ovptd. "GRAND SLAM WINNER" in Gold

1989, Jan. 16 *Perf. 14*

Souvenir Sheets

1023	A130	100 le multicolored	5.20	5.20

No. 1023 exists with four diff. gold marginal overprints: "AUSTRALIAN OPEN / JANUARY 11-24, 1988 / GRAF v EVERET / 6-1 / 7-6," "FRENCH OPEN / MAY 23-JUNE 5, 1988 / GRAF v ZVEREVA / 6-0 / 6-0," "WIMBLEDON / JUNE 20-JULY 4, 1988 / GRAF v NAVRATILOVA / 5-7 / 6-2 / 6-1," or "U.S. OPEN / AUGUST 29-SEPTEMBER 11, 1988 / GRAF v SABATINI / 6-3 / 3-6 / 6-1."

No. 907 Ovptd. "GOLD MEDALIST" in Gold

1989, Jan. 16 Litho. *Perf. 14*

1024	A130	100 le multi	5.20	5.20

Marginal overprint: "SEOUL OLYMPICS 1988 / GRAF v SABATINI / 6-3 / 6-3."

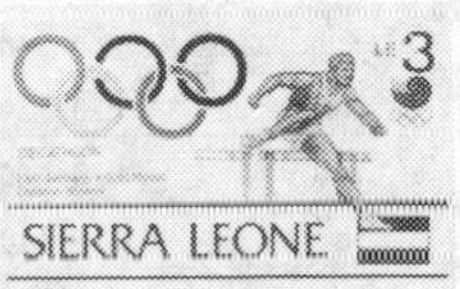

Medalists of the 1988 Summer Olympics, Seoul A149

Designs: 3 le, Christian Schenk, German Democratic Republic, decathlon. 6 le, Hitoshi Saito, Japan, heavyweight judo. 10 le, Jutta Niehaus, Federal Republic of Germany, women's road race. 15 le, Tomas Lange, German Democratic Republic, single sculls. 20 le, Matthew Biondi, US, 50m and 100m freestyle. 30 le, Carl Lewis, US, 100m sprint. 40 le, Nicole Uphoff, Federal Republic of Germany, individual dressage. 50 le, Andras Sike, Hungary, 126-pound Greco-Roman wrestling. No. 1033, Gold medal, five-ring emblem. No. 1034, Torch, five-ring emblem.

1989, Apr. 28 Litho. *Perf. 14*

1025	A149	3 le multicolored	.15	.15
1026	A149	6 le multicolored	.30	.30
1027	A149	10 le multicolored	.50	.50
1028	A149	15 le multicolored	.75	.75
1029	A149	20 le multicolored	1.00	1.00
1030	A149	30 le multicolored	1.50	1.50
1031	A149	40 le multicolored	2.00	2.00
1032	A149	50 le multicolored	2.50	2.50
		Nos. 1025-1032 (8)	8.70	8.70

Souvenir Sheets

1033	A149	100 le multicolored	5.00	5.00
1034	A149	100 le multicolored	5.00	5.00

Name of athlete not inscribed on No. 1031.

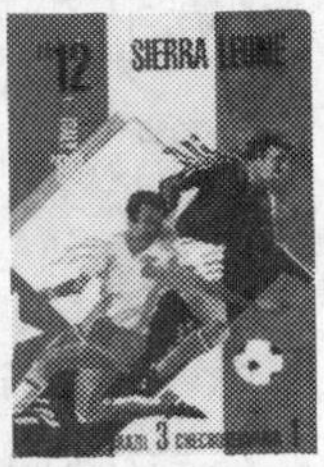

1990 World Cup Soccer Championships, Italy — A150

1989, May 8

1035	A150	3 le Brazil vs. Sweden	.15	.15
1036	A150	6 le Germany vs. Hungary	.30	.30
1037	A150	8 le England vs. Germany	.40	.40
1038	A150	10 le Argentina vs. The Netherlands	.50	.50
1039	A150	12 le Brazil vs. Czechoslovakia	.60	.60
1040	A150	20 le Germany vs. The Netherlands	1.00	1.00
1041	A150	30 le Italy vs. Germany	1.50	1.50
1042	A150	40 le Brazil vs. Italy	2.00	2.00
		Nos. 1035-1042 (8)	6.45	6.45

Souvenir Sheets

1043	A150	100 le Uruguay vs. Brazil	5.00	5.00
1044	A150	100 le Argentina vs. Germany	5.00	5.00

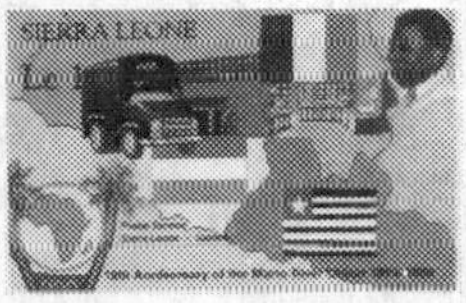

Mano River Union, 15th Anniv. A151

Designs: 1 le, Sierra Leone-Guinea postal service. 3 le, Presidents Momoh, Conte of Guinea and Doe of Liberia. 10 le, Freetown-Monrovia Highway under construction. 15 le, Presidents signing the Communique at a 1988 summit.

1989, May 19 *Perf. 14*

1045	A151	1 le multicolored	.15	.15
1046	A151	3 le multicolored	.24	.24
1047	A151	10 le multicolored	.80	.80
		Nos. 1045-1047 (3)	1.19	1.19

Souvenir Sheet

1048	A151	15 le multicolored	1.20	1.20

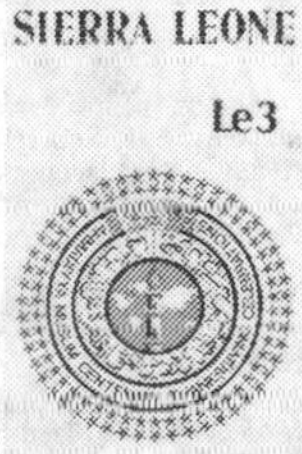

Ahmadiyya Muslim Centenary Thanksgiving Celebrations — A152

1989, June 8

1049	A152	3 le black & brt blue	.24	.24

Miniature Sheets

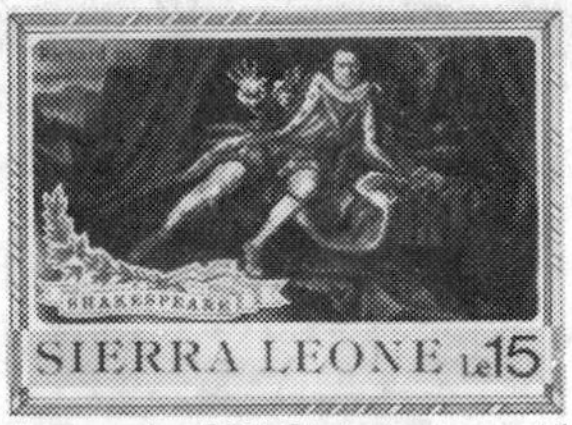

Shakespeare's 425th Birth Anniv. — A153

Scenes from the playwright's works.

No. 1050: a, Richard III. b, Othello (Desdemona and two men). c, The Two Gentlemen of Verona. d, Macbeth (chamber). e, Hamlet. f, Taming of the Shrew (scene with dog). g, The Merry Wives of Windsor. h, Henry IV (assembly room).

No. 1051: a, Macbeth (horsemen). b, Romeo and Juliet. c, Merchant of Venice. d, As You Like It. e, Taming of the Shrew (ruined meal). f, King Lear. g, Othello (death scene). h, Henry IV (street scene).

1989, May 30 *Perf. 13*

1050		Sheet of 8 + label	6.00	6.00
a.-h.		A153 15 le any single	.75	.75
1051		Sheet of 8 + label	6.00	6.00
a.-h.		A153 15 le any single	.75	.75

648 SIERRA LEONE

Souvenir Sheets

1052 A153 100 le Portrait 5.00 5.00
1053 A153 100 le Portrait, coat of arms 5.00 5.00

Nos. 1050-1051 contain center label picturing Shakespeare's portrait (No. 1050) or his birthplace in Stratford (No. 1051).

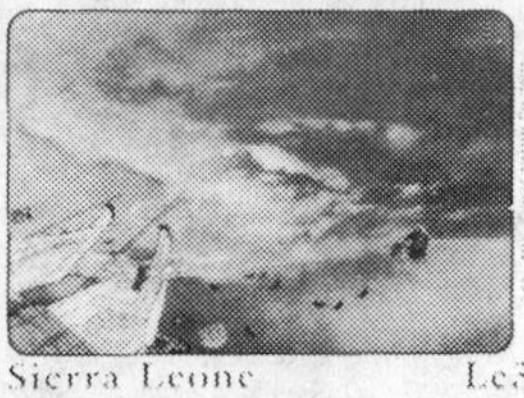
Sierra Leone Le3

Paintings by Takeuchi Seiho (1864-1942) — A154

Designs: 3 le, Lapping Waves. 6 le, Hazy Moon, vert. 8 le, Passing Spring, vert. 10 le, Mackerels. 12 le, Calico Cat. 30 le, The First Time To Be a Model, vert. 40 le, Kingly Lion. 75 le, After a Shower, vert. No. 1062, Domesticated Monkeys and Rabbits. No. 1063, Dozing in the Midst of All the Chirping, vert.

Perf. 14x13½, 13½x14

1989, July 3 Litho.

1054 A154 3 le multicolored .15 .15
1055 A154 6 le multicolored .22 .22
1056 A154 8 le multicolored .28 .28
1057 A154 10 le multicolored .35 .35
1058 A154 12 le multicolored .42 .42
1059 A154 30 le multicolored 1.05 1.05
1060 A154 40 le multicolored 1.45 1.45
1061 A154 75 le multicolored 2.65 2.65
Nos. 1054-1061 (8) 6.57 6.57

Souvenir Sheets

1062 A154 150 le multicolored 4.50 4.50
1063 A154 150 le multicolored 4.50 4.50

Hirohito (1901-89) and enthronement of Akihito as emperor of Japan.
See Nos. 1098-1129.

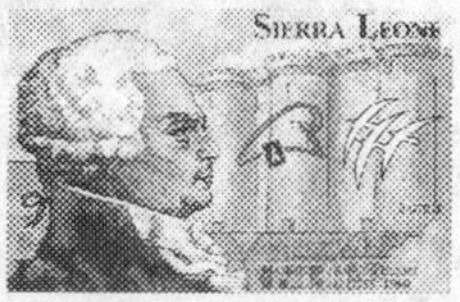
SIERRA LEONE

PHILEXFRANCE '89, French Revolution Bicent. — A155

Famous people, sites, exhibition and anniv. emblems: 6 le, Robespierre (1758-94), the Bastille. 20 le, Georges Jacques Danton (1759-94), the Louvre. 45 le, Marie Antoinette (1755-93), Notre Dame Cathedral interior. 80 le, Louis XVI (1754-93), Palace of Versailles. 150 le, Revolutionaries in Paris, vert.

1989, July 14 Litho. *Perf. 14*

1064 A155 6 le multicolored .30 .30
1065 A155 20 le multicolored 1.00 1.00
1066 A155 45 le multicolored 2.25 2.25
1067 A155 80 le multicolored 4.00 4.00
Nos. 1064-1067 (4) 7.55 7.55

Souvenir Sheet

1068 A155 150 le multicolored 7.50 7.50

Miniature Sheets

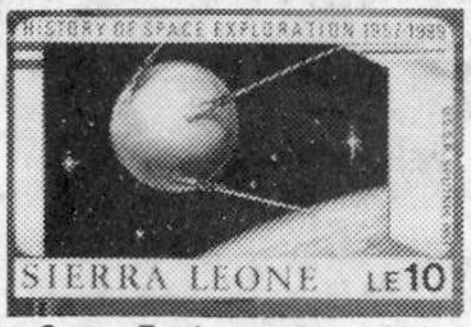
SIERRA LEONE LE10

Space Exploration — A156

Satellites, probes and spacecraft.

No. 1069: a, Sputnik, 1957. b, Telstar, 1962. c, Rendezvous of Gemini 6 and 7, 1965. d, Yuri Gagarin, 1st man in space, 1961. e, Mariner, 1964. f, Surveyor on Mars, 1966. g, US-Canadian Alouette satellite, 1962. h, Edward White, 1st American to walk in space, 1965. i, OGO-4 satellite, 1967.

No. 1070: a, Buzz Aldrin on the Moon, Apollo 11 mission, 1969. b, Apollo 15 mission lunar rover. c, Apollo 15 crew member. d, Conducting experiments on the lunar surface. e, Splitrock, Valley of Taurus-Littrow. f, Saluting the flag, Apollo 15 lunar module. g, Solar wind experiment. h, Lunar rover, diff. i, Apollo command module.

No. 1071: a, Module separation. b, Docking maneuvers. c, Lunar module in space. d, Second stage separation. e, Module transposition. f, Lunar module controlled descent, Moon's surface. g, Apollo 11 liftoff, 1969. h, Lunar module separates from command module. i, Neil Armstrong's first step on the Moon.

No. 1072: a, Mariner-Mars, 1971. b, Mariner 10, 1973. c, Viking, 1975. d, Skylab, 1974. e, Soyuz-Salyut, 1974. f, Viking robot craft, 1974. g, Pioneer 2, 1973. h, Apollo-Soyuz, 1975. i, Pioneer-Venus, 1978.

No. 1073: a, Apollo 17 lunar module, 1972. b, Command module jettison of service module before reentry. c, Soyuz 11, 1971. d, Lunar module liftoff. e, U.S. Navy recovery operation. f, Mars 2, 1971. g, Command module in docking position. h, Luna 17, 1970. i, Mars 3, 1971.

No. 1074: a, Voyager 1 and 2, 1977. b, Columbia space shuttle, 1981. c, Mir space station, 1986. d, IUE-Ultraviolet Explorer, US, U.K. and the European Space Agency, 1978. e, Astronaut operating out of shuttle cargo bay, 1983. f, Magellan, 1989. g, Soyuz-Salyut, 1978. h, STS-10, 1984. i, Shuttle, space telescope, 1989.

No. 1075, Spacelab. No. 1076, Future space station. No. 1077, Voyager.

1989, July 20 Litho. *Perf. 14*

1069 Sheet of 9 2.75 2.75
a.-i. A156 10 le any single .30 .30
1070 Sheet of 9 2.75 2.75
a.-i. A156 10 le any single .30 .30
1071 Sheet of 9 2.75 2.75
a.-i. A156 10 le any single .30 .30
1072 Sheet of 9 4.05 4.05
a.-i. A156 15 le any single .45 .45
1073 Sheet of 9 4.05 4.05
a.-i. A156 15 le any single .45 .45
1074 Sheet of 9 4.05 4.05
a.-i. A156 15 le any single .45 .45

Souvenir Sheets

1075 A156 100 le multicolored 3.00 3.00
1076 A156 100 le multicolored 3.00 3.00
1077 A156 100 le multicolored 3.00 3.00

Nos. 1069f is incorrectly inscribed "Mars" instead of "Moon."

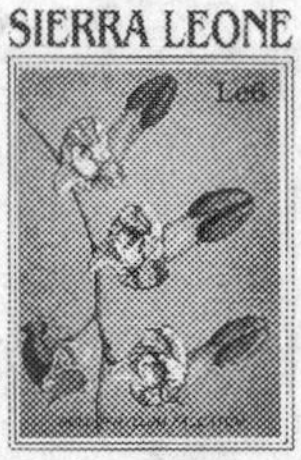
SIERRA LEONE

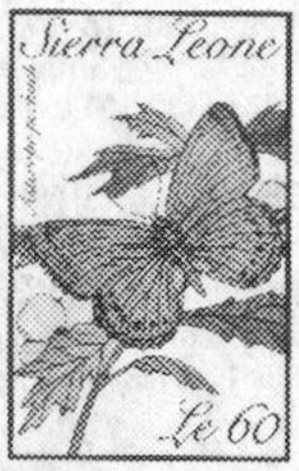
Sierra Leone
Le 60

Orchids — A157 Butterflies — A158

1989, Sept. 8 Litho. *Perf. 14*

1078 A157 3 le Bulbophyllum barbigerum .15 .15
1079 A157 6 le Bulbophyllum falcatum .20 .20
1080 A157 12 le Habenaria macrara .38 .38
1081 A157 20 le Eurychone rothchildiana .60 .60
1082 A157 50 le Calyptrochilum christyanum 1.50 1.50
1083 A157 60 le Bulbophyllum distans 1.80 1.80
1084 A157 70 le Eulophia guineensis 2.10 2.10
1085 A157 80 le Diaphananthe pellucida 2.40 2.40
Nos. 1078-1085 (8) 9.13 9.13

Souvenir Sheets

1086 A157 100 le Cyrtorchis arcuata 3.00 3.00
1087 A157 100 le Butterflies, Eulophia cucullata 3.00 3.00

1989, Sept. 11

1088 A158 6 le Salamis temora .20 .20
1089 A158 12 le Pseudacraea lucretia .38 .38
1090 A158 18 le Charaxes boueti .55 .55
1091 A158 30 le Graphium antheus .90 .90
1092 A158 40 le Colotis protomedia 1.20 1.20
1093 A158 60 le Asterope pechueli 1.80 1.80
1094 A158 72 le Coenura aurantiaca 2.15 2.15
1095 A158 80 le Precis octavia 2.40 2.40
Nos. 1088-1095 (8) 9.58 9.58

Souvenir Sheets

1096 A158 100 le Charaxes cithaeron 3.00 3.00
1097 A158 100 le Euphaedra themis 3.00 3.00

Nos. 1088-1090, 1095 and 1097 horiz.

Art Type of 1989

Paintings by Hiroshige in the series Fifty-three Stations on the Tokaido: No. 1098, Coolies Warming Themselves at Hamamatsu. No. 1099, Imakiri Ford at Maisaka. No. 1100, Pacific Ocean Seen from Shirasuka. No. 1101, Futakawa Street Singers. No. 1102, Repairing Yoshida Castle. No. 1103, The Inn at Akasaka. No. 1104, The Bridge to Okazaki. No. 1105, Samurai's Wife Entering Narumi. No. 1106, Harbour at Kuwana. No. 1107, Autumn in Ishiyakushi. No. 1108, Snowfall at Kameyama. No. 1109, The Frontier Station of Seki. No. 1110, Teahouse at Sakanoshita. No. 1111, Kansai Houses at Minakushi. No. 1112, Kusatsu Station. No. 1113, Ferry to Kawasaki. No. 1114, The Hilly Town of Hodogaya. No. 1115, Lute Players at Fujisawa. No. 1116, Mild Rainstorm at Oiso. No. 1117, Lake Ashi and Mountains of Hakone. No. 1118, Twilight at Numazu. No. 1119, Mount Fuji From Hara. No. 1120, Samurai's Children Riding Through Yoshiwara. No. 1121, Mountain Pass at Yui. No. 1122, Harbour at Ejiri. No. 1123, Stopping at Fujieda. No. 1124, Misty Kanaya on the Oi River. No. 1125, The Bridge to Kakegawa. No. 1126, Teahouse at Fukuroi. No. 1127, The Ford at Mistuke. No. 1128, Sanjo Bridge in Kyoto. No. 1129, Nibonbashi Bridge in Edo.

1989, Nov. 13 Litho. *Perf. 14x13½*

1098-1127 A154 25 le Set of 30 22.50 22.50

Souvenir sheets

1128-1129 A154 120 le each 4.00 4.00

Hirohito (1901-1989) and enthronement of Akihito as emperor of Japan.

Souvenir Sheet

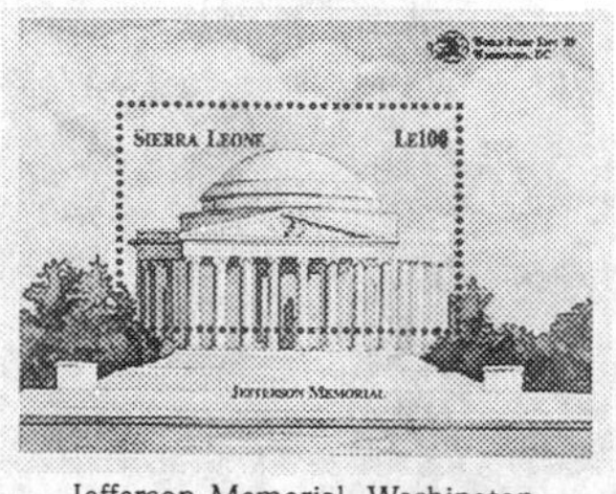
SIERRA LEONE
LE100
JEFFERSON MEMORIAL

Jefferson Memorial, Washington, DC — A159

1989, Nov. 17 Litho. *Perf. 14*

1136 A159 100 le multicolored 3.00 3.00

World Stamp Expo '89.

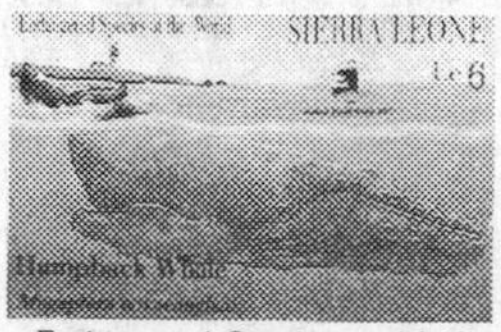
SIERRA LEONE
Le6
Humpback Whale

Endangered Species — A160

1989, Nov. 29 *Perf. 14*

1137 A160 6 le Humpback whale .18 .18
1138 A160 9 le Formosan sika deer .28 .28
1139 A160 16 le Spanish lynx .48 .48
1140 A160 20 le Goitered gazelle .60 .60
1141 A160 30 le Japanese sea lion .90 .90
1142 A160 50 le Long-eared owl 1.50 1.50
1143 A160 70 le Chinese copper pheasant 2.10 2.10
1144 A160 100 le Siberian tiger 3.00 3.00
Nos. 1137-1144 (8) 9.04 9.04

Souvenir Sheets

1145 A160 150 le Mauritius kestrel falcon 4.50 4.50
1146 A160 150 le Crested ibis 4.50 4.50

World Stamp Expo '89.

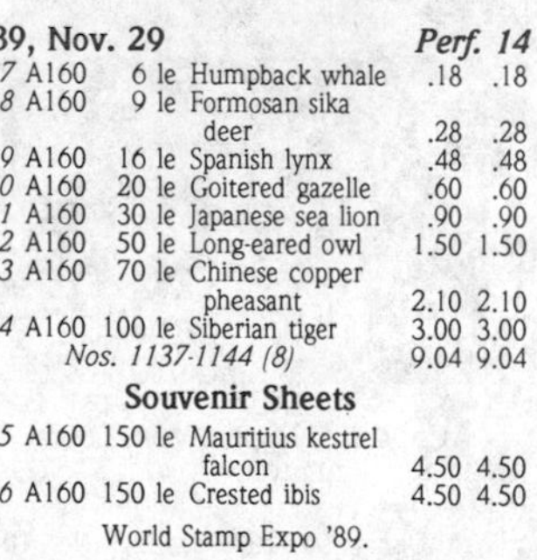
SIERRA-LEONE
Le3
1934 PHANTOM II ROLLS-ROYCE ROADSTAR

Christmas — A161

Disney characters and classic automobiles: 3 le, 1934 Phantom II Rolls-Royce Roadstar. 6 le, 1935 Mercedes-Benz 500K. 10 le, 1938 Jaguar SS-100. 12 le, 1941 Jeep. 20 le, 1937 Buick Roadmaster Sedan Model 91. 30 le, 1948 Tucker. 40 le, 1933 Alfa Romeo. 50 le, 1937 Cord. No. 1155, 1938 Fiat Topolino. No. 1156, 1931 Pontiac Model 401, 1929 Pontiac Landau.

1989, Dec. 18 *Perf. 14x13½*

1147 A161 3 le multicolored .15 .15
1148 A161 6 le multicolored .20 .20
1149 A161 10 le multicolored .32 .32
1150 A161 12 le multicolored .38 .38
1151 A161 20 le multicolored .65 .65
1152 A161 30 le multicolored .98 .98
1153 A161 40 le multicolored 1.30 1.30
1154 A161 50 le multicolored 1.60 1.60
Nos. 1147-1154 (8) 5.58 5.58

Souvenir Sheets

1155 A161 100 le multicolored 3.25 3.25
1156 A161 100 le multicolored 3.25 3.25

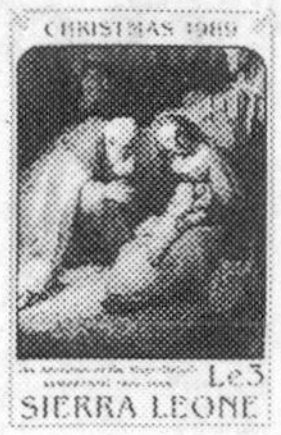
CHRISTMAS 1989
Le3
SIERRA LEONE

Christmas — A162

Religious paintings by Rembrandt: 3 le, Adoration of the Magi. 6 le, The Holy Family with a Cat. 10 le, The Holy Family with Angels. 15 le, Simeon in the Temple. 30 le, The Circumcision. 90 le, The Holy Family. 100 le, The Visitation. 120 le, The Flight into Egypt. No. 1165, The Adoration of the Shepherds. No. 1166, The Presentation of Jesus in the Temple.

1989, Dec. 22 *Perf. 14*

1157 A162 3 le multicolored .15 .15
1158 A162 6 le multicolored .20 .20
1159 A162 10 le multicolored .32 .32
1160 A162 15 le multicolored .48 .48
1161 A162 30 le multicolored .98 .98
1162 A162 90 le multicolored 2.90 2.90
1163 A162 100 le multicolored 3.25 3.25
1164 A162 120 le multicolored 4.00 4.00
Nos. 1157-1164 (8) 12.28 12.28

Souvenir Sheets

1165 A162 150 le multicolored 4.75 4.75
1166 A162 150 le multicolored 4.75 4.75

Miniature Sheets

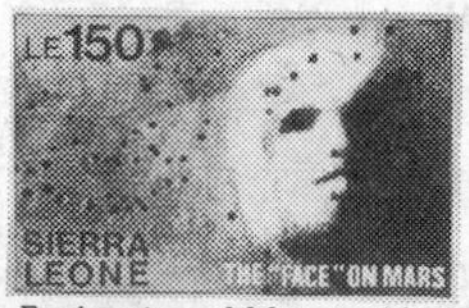
LE150
SIERRA LEONE
THE "FACE" ON MARS

Exploration of Mars — A163

No. 1167: a, Kepler. b, Galileo. c, Drawings by Huygens in 1672 and Schiaparelli in 1886. d, Sir W. Herschel. e, Percival Lowell in Arizona, 1896-1907. f, Mars. g, Mariner 4, 1965. h, Mars 2, 1971. i, Mars 3, 1971.

No. 1168: a, Mariner 9, 1971. b, Mariner 9, Phobos. c, Cydonia Region. d, South polar cap. e, Profile of Mars. f, Polar cap, diff. g, Nix Olympica. h, Grand Canyon of Mars. i, North Pole.

No. 1169: a, Olympus Mons. b, Viking 1, July 1976. c, Viking 2 releases Lander, Sept. 1976. d, Lander entering Mars's atmosphere. e, Parachute deployed. f, Terminal descent. g, Viking Lander on Mars. h, Soil sampler (robotic arm). i, Soil Sampler (US flag, machine).

No. 1170: a, Martian dusk. b, Project Deimos. c, Exploration of Mars (astronauts surveying land). d, Return to Rombus. e, US rocket bound for Mars. f, Spacecraft bound for Mars. g, Spacecraft in Martian orbit. h, Mission to Mars (astronauts weightless in spacecraft cabin). i, Space station.

No. 1171, "The Face," Mars.

1990 Litho. *Perf. 14*

1167 Sheet of 9 24.75 24.75
a.-i. A163 175 le any single 2.75 2.75
1168 Sheet of 9 24.75 24.75
a.-i. A163 175 le any single 2.75 2.75
1169 Sheet of 9 24.75 24.75
a.-i. A163 175 le any single 2.75 2.75
1170 Sheet of 9 24.75 24.75
a.-i. A163 175 le any single 2.75 2.75

Souvenir Sheet

1171 A163 150 le multicolored 2.35 2.35
1171A A163 150 le Space station 2.35 2.35

Issue dates: No. 1171A, Dec. 24. Others, Jan. 15.

Extreme speculation has occured with this issue, centered around No. 1171, the face on Mars stamp.

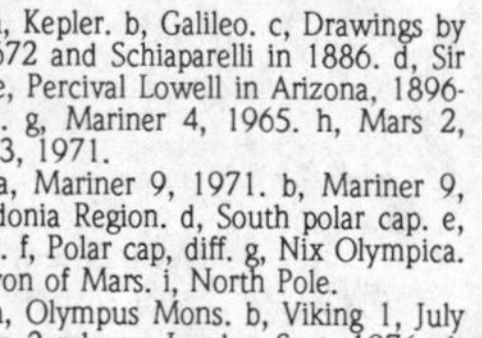
LE1
SIERRA LEONE

World War II — A164

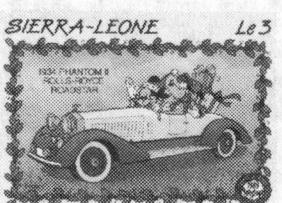

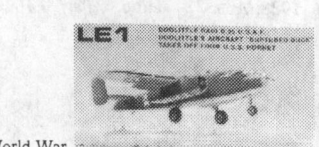

USAF aircraft.

1990, Feb. 5 Litho. *Perf. 14*

1172	A164	1 le	Doolittle Raid B-25	.15	.15
1173	A164	2 le	B-24 Liberator	.15	.15
1174	A164	3 le	A-20 Boston	.15	.15
1175	A164	9 le	P-38 Lightning	.28	.28
1176	A164	12 le	B-26	.35	.35
1177	A164	16 le	B-17 F	.48	.48
1178	A164	50 le	B-25 D Mitchell	1.50	1.50
1179	A164	80 le	Boeing B-29	2.40	2.40
1180	A164	90 le	B-17 G	2.70	2.70
1181	A164	100 le	The Enola Gay	3.00	3.00
			Nos. 1172-1181 (10)	11.16	11.16

Souvenir Sheets

1182	A164	150 le	B-25, USS Hornet	4.50	4.50
1183	A164	150 le	B-17 G	4.50	4.50

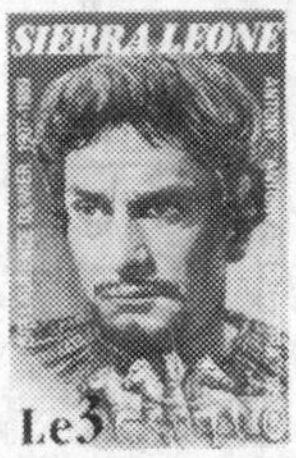

Stage and Screen Roles Played by Sir Laurence Olivier (1907-1989) — A165

1990, Apr. 27 *Perf.*

1184	A165	3 le	Antony & Cleopatra, 1951	.15	.15
1185	A165	9 le	Henry V, 1943	.18	.18
1186	A165	16 le	Oedipus, 1945	.32	.32
1187	A165	20 le	Wuthering Heights, 1939	.40	.40
1188	A165	30 le	Marathon Man, 1976	.60	.60
1189	A165	70 le	Othello, 1964	1.40	1.40
1190	A165	175 le	Beau Geste, 1929	3.50	3.50
1191	A165	200 le	Richard III, 1956	4.00	4.00
			Nos. 1184-1191 (8)	10.55	10.55

Souvenir Sheets

1192	A165	250 le	The Battle of Britain, 1969	5.00	5.00
1193	A165	250 le	Hamlet, 1947	5.00	5.00

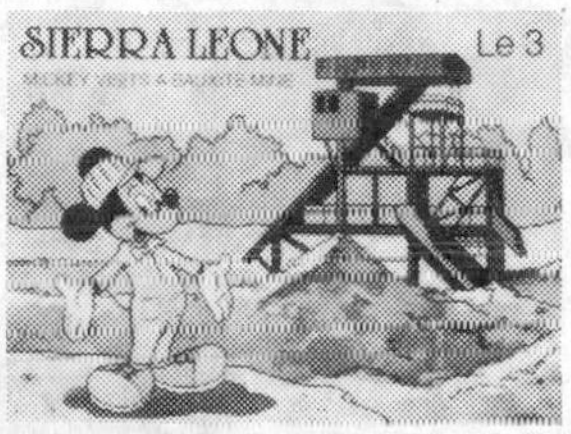

Walt Disney Characters, Settings in Sierra Leone — A166

1990, Apr. 23 Litho. *Perf.*

1194	A166	3 le	Bauxite mine	.15	.15
1195	A166	6 le	Panning for gold	.15	.15
1196	A166	10 le	Lungi Intl. Airport	.24	.24
1197	A166	12 le	Old Fourah Bay College	.30	.30
1198	A166	16 le	Mining bauxite	.42	.42
1199	A166	20 le	Rice harvest	.48	.48
1200	A166	30 le	The Cotton Tree	.75	.75
1201	A166	100 le	Rutile Mine	2.50	2.50
1202	A166	200 le	Fishing at Goderich	5.00	5.00
1203	A166	225 le	Bintumani Hotel	5.50	5.50
			Nos. 1194-1203 (10)	15.49	15.49

Souvenir Sheets

1204	A166	250 le	Market Place, King Jimmy	5.00	5.00
1205	A166	250 le	Diamond mining	5.00	5.00

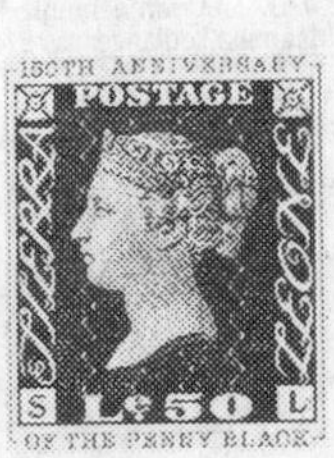

Penny Black, 150th Anniv. — A167

1990, May 3 *Perf. 14*

1206	A167	50 le	deep ultra	1.00	1.00
1207	A167	100 le	violet brown	2.50	2.50

Souvenir Sheet

1208	A167	250 le	black	5.00	5.00

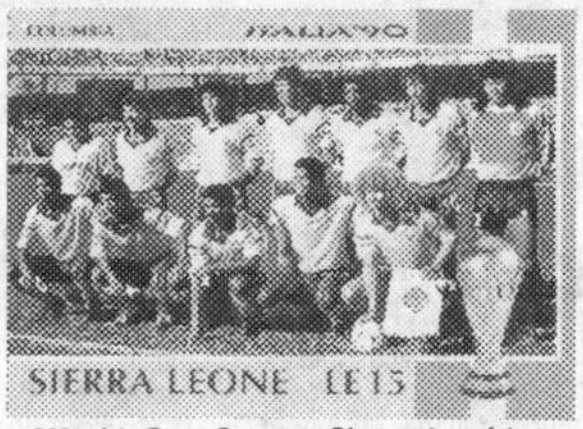

World Cup Soccer Championships, Italy — A168

Team photographs.

1990, May 11 Litho. *Perf. 14*

1209	A168	15 le	Colombia	.25	.25
1210	A168	15 le	United Arab Emirates	.25	.25
1211	A168	15 le	South Korea	.25	.25
1212	A168	15 le	Cameroun	.25	.25
1213	A168	15 le	Costa Rica	.25	.25
1214	A168	15 le	Romania	.25	.25
1215	A168	15 le	Yugoslavia	.25	.25
1216	A168	15 le	Egypt	.25	.25
1217	A168	30 le	Netherlands	.50	.50
1218	A168	30 le	Uruguay	.50	.50
1219	A168	30 le	USSR	.50	.50
1220	A168	30 le	Czechoslovakia	.50	.50
1221	A168	30 le	Scotland	.50	.50
1222	A168	30 le	Belgium	.50	.50
1223	A168	30 le	Austria	.50	.50
1224	A168	30 le	Sweden	.50	.50
1225	A168	45 le	West Germany	.75	.75
1226	A168	45 le	England	.75	.75
1227	A168	45 le	United States	.75	.75
1228	A168	45 le	Ireland	.75	.75
1229	A168	45 le	Spain	.75	.75
1230	A168	45 le	Brazil	.75	.75
1231	A168	45 le	Italy	.75	.75
1232	A168	45 le	Argentina	.75	.75
			Nos. 1209-1232 (24)	12.00	12.00

No. 1209 spelled "Columbia," No. 1218 "Uraguay," No. 1220 "Czecheslovakia" on stamps.

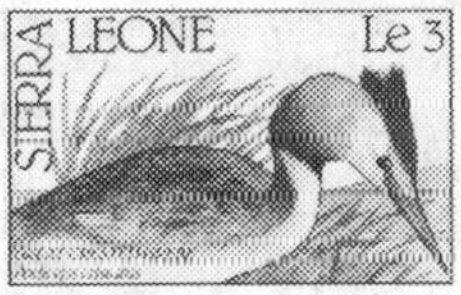

Great Crested Grebe A169

1990, June 4

1233	A169	3 le	shown	.15	.15
1234	A169	6 le	Green woodhoopoe	.15	.15
1235	A169	10 le	African jacana	.18	.18
1236	A169	12 le	Avocet	.20	.20
1237	A169	20 le	African finfoot	.35	.35
1238	A169	80 le	Glossy ibis	1.40	1.40
1239	A169	150 le	Hamerkop	2.50	2.50
1240	A169	200 le	Greater honey guide	3.40	3.40
			Nos. 1233-1240 (8)	8.33	8.33

Souvenir Sheets

1241	A169	250 le	Painted snipe	4.25	4.25
1242	A169	250 le	Palm swift	4.25	4.25

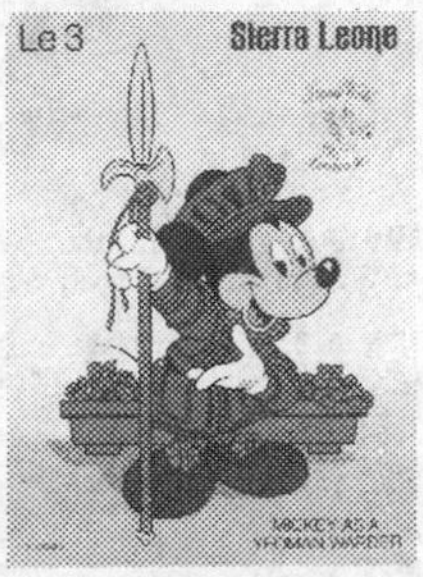

Mickey as Yeoman Warder A170

Disney characters: 6 le, Scrooge as lamplighter. 12 le, Knight Goofy. 15 le, Clarabell as Anne Boleyn. 75 le, Minnie Mouse as Queen Elizabeth I. 100 le, Donald Duck as chimney sweep. 125 le, Pete as King Henry VIII. 150 le, May dancers in Salisbury. No. 1251, Boadicea, Queen of the Iceni. No. 1252, Lawyers at Parliament House.

1990, June 6 *Perf. $13^1/_2$x14*

1243	A170	3 le	multicolored	.15	.15
1244	A170	6 le	multicolored	.15	.15
1245	A170	12 le	multicolored	.20	.20
1246	A170	15 le	multicolored	.25	.25
1247	A170	75 le	multicolored	1.25	1.25
1248	A170	100 le	multicolored	1.75	1.75
1249	A170	125 le	multicolored	2.25	2.25
1250	A170	150 le	multicolored	2.50	2.50
			Nos. 1243-1250 (8)	8.50	8.50

Souvenir Sheets

1251	A170	250 le	multicolored	4.50	4.50
1252	A170	250 le	multicolored	4.50	4.50

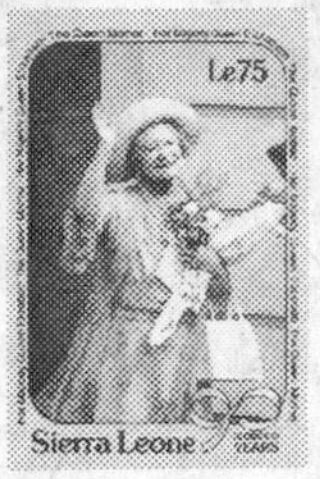

Queen Mother, 90th Birthday — A171

1990, July 5 *Perf. 14*

1253	A171	75 le	shown	1.25	1.25
1254	A171	75 le	Wearing black hat	1.25	1.25
1255	A171	75 le	Wearing yellow hat	1.25	1.25
			Nos. 1253-1255 (3)	3.75	3.75

Souvenir Sheet

1256	A171	250 le	Like No. 1252	4.50	4.50

Butterfly Type of 1987

1990 *Perf. $12^1/_2$x$11^1/_2$*

1257	A126	3 le	like No. 861	.15	.15
1258	A126	9 le	like No. 864	.15	.15
1259	A126	12 le	like No. 859	.20	.20
1260	A126	16 le	like No. 860	.28	.28
			Nos. 1257-1260 (4)	.78	.78

Inscribed 1989.

Miniature Sheet

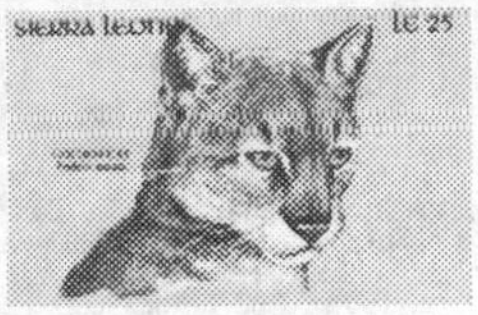

Wildlife A172

Designs: No. 1261a, Golden cat. b, White-backed night heron. c, Bateleur eagle. d, Marabou stork. e, White-faced whistling duck. f, Aardvark. g, Royal antelope. h, Pygmy hippopotamus. i, Leopard. j, Sacred ibis. k, Mona monkey. l, Darter. m, Chimpanzee. n, African elephant. o, Potto. p, African manatee. q, African fish eagle. r, African spoonbill.

1990, Sept. 24 Litho. *Perf. 14*

1261			Sheet of 18	7.60	7.60
a.-r.	A172	25 le	any single	.42	.42

Souvenir Sheet

1262	A172	150 le	Crowned eagle, vert.	2.50	2.50

No. 1261 printed in continuous design showing map of Sierra Leone in background.

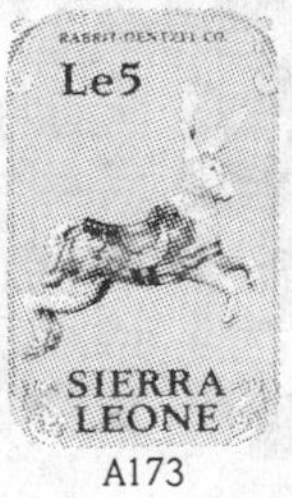

A173

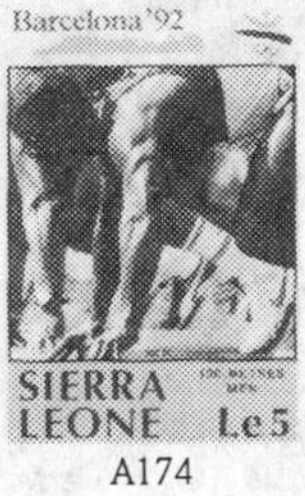

A174

Carousel animals.

1990, Oct. 22 Litho. *Perf. 14*

1263	A173	5 le	Rabbit	.15	.15
1264	A173	10 le	Horse with panther saddle	.16	.16
1265	A173	20 le	Ostrich	.32	.32
1266	A173	30 le	Zebra	.48	.48
1267	A173	50 le	White horse	.80	.80
1268	A173	80 le	Sea monster	1.30	1.30
1269	A173	100 le	Giraffe	1.60	1.60
1270	A173	150 le	Armored horse	2.40	2.40
1271	A173	200 le	Camel	3.20	3.20
			Nos. 1263-1271 (9)	10.41	10.41

Souvenir Sheets

1272	A173	300 le	Centaur, Lord Baden-Powell	4.75	4.75
1273	A173	300 le	Horse head	4.75	4.75

1990, Nov. 12 Litho. *Perf. 14*

1274	A174	5 le	Men's 100-meter race	.15	.15
1275	A174	10 le	Men's 4x400-meter relay	.16	.16
1276	A174	20 le	Men's 100-meter race, diff.	.32	.32
1277	A174	30 le	Weight lifting	.48	.48
1278	A174	40 le	Freestyle wrestling	.65	.65
1279	A174	80 le	Water polo	1.30	1.30
1280	A174	150 le	Women's gymnastics	2.40	2.40
1281	A174	200 le	Cycling	3.20	3.20
			Nos. 1274-1281 (8)	8.66	8.66

Souvenir Sheets

1282	A174	400 le	Boxing	6.40	6.40
1283	A174	400 le	Olympic flag	6.40	6.40

1992 Summer Olympics, Barcelona.

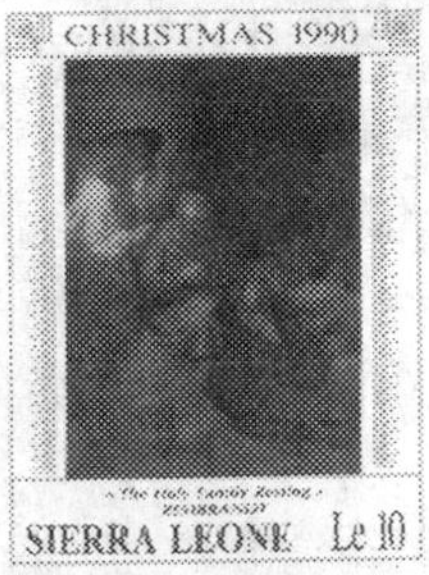

Christmas A175

Paintings: 10 le, The Holy Family Resting by Rembrandt. 20 le, The Holy Family with St. Elizabeth by Andrea Mantegna. 30 le, Virgin and Child with an Angel by Correggio. 50 le, The Annunciation by Bernardo Strozzi. 100 le, Madonna and Child Appearing to St. Anthony by Filippino Lippi. 175 le, Virgin and Child by Giovanni Boltraffio. 200 le, The Esterhazy Madonna by Raphael. 300 le, Coronation of Mary by Orcagna. No. 1292, Adoration of the Shepherds by Bronzino. No. 1293, Adoration of the Shepherds by Gerard David.

1990, Dec. 17 *Perf. 13*

1284	A175	10 le	multicolored	.16	.16
1285	A175	20 le	multicolored	.32	.32
1286	A175	30 le	multicolored	.48	.48
1287	A175	50 le	multicolored	.80	.80
1288	A175	100 le	multicolored	1.60	1.60
1289	A175	175 le	multicolored	2.80	2.80
1290	A175	200 le	multicolored	3.20	3.20
1291	A175	300 le	multicolored	4.80	4.80
			Nos. 1284-1291 (8)	14.16	14.16

Souvenir Sheets

1292	A175	400 le	multicolored	6.40	6.40
1293	A175	400 le	multicolored	6.40	6.40

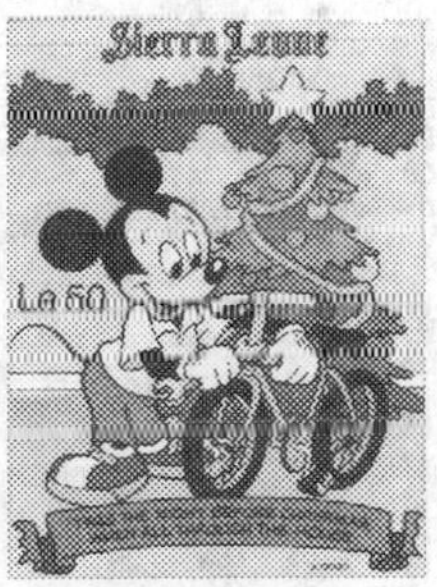

Christmas A176

Walt Disney characters in "The Night Before Christmas."

No. 1294a, 'Twas the night. . . b, Not a creature. . . c, The stockings were hung. . . d, And Mama in her kerchief. . . e, When out on the lawn. . . f, I sprang from my bed. . . g, Away to the window. . . h, Tore open the shutter. . .

No. 1295a, The moon on the breast. . . b, When what to my wondering. . . c, With a little old driver. . . d, More rapid than eagles. . . e, To the top of the porch. . . f, And then in a twinkling. . . g, As I drew in my head. . . h, He was dressed. . .

No. 1296a, A bundle of toys. . . b, The stump of a pipe. . . c, He had a broad face. . . d, He was chubby and plump. . . e, A wink of his eye. . . f, Then turned with a jerk. . . g, And giving a nod. . . h, He sprang to his sleigh. . .

No. 1297, The children were nestled. . . No. 1298, His eyes, how they twinkled. . . No. 1299, He spoke not a word. . . No. 1300, And he whistled. . . No. 1301, As dry leaves. . . No. 1302, But I heard him exclaim. . .

1990, Dec. 17 Litho. *Perf. 13*

Miniature Sheets of 8

1294	A176	50 le	#a.-h.	4.50	4.50
1295	A176	75 le	#a.-h.	6.75	6.75
1296	A176	100 le	#a.-h.	9.00	9.00

Souvenir Sheets

1297	A176	400 le	multi	4.50	4.50
1298	A176	400 le	multi, horiz.	4.50	4.50
1299	A176	400 le	multi	4.50	4.50
1300	A176	400 le	multi, horiz.	4.50	4.50
1301	A176	400 le	multi, horiz.	4.50	4.50
1302	A176	400 le	multi	4.50	4.50

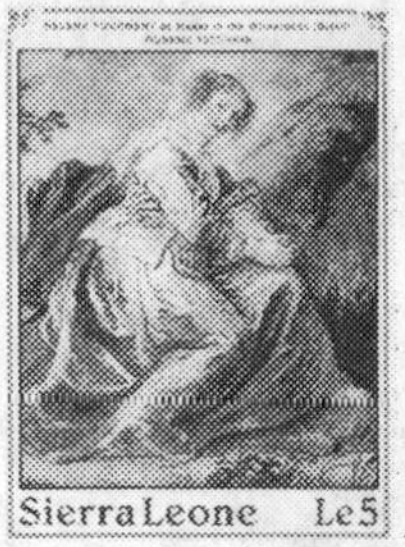

Peter Paul Rubens (1577-1640), Painter A177

Entire paintings or different details from: 5 le, Helena Fourment as Hagar in the Wilderness. 10 le, Isabella Brant. 20 le, 60 le, Countess of Arundel and Her Party. 80 le, Nicolaas Rockox. 100 le, Adriana Perez. 150 le, George Villiers, Duke of Buckingham. 300 le, Countess of Buckingham. No. 1311, Veronica Spinola Dorio. No. 1312, Giovanni Carlo Dorio.

1990, Dec. 24 ***Perf. 14***

1303	A177	5 le	multicolored	.15	.15
1304	A177	10 le	multicolored	.16	.16
1305	A177	20 le	multicolored	.32	.32
1306	A177	60 le	multicolored	.95	.95
1307	A177	80 le	multicolored	1.30	1.30
1308	A177	100 le	multicolored	1.60	1.60
1309	A177	150 le	multicolored	2.40	2.40
1310	A177	300 le	multicolored	4.80	4.80
			Nos. 1303-1310 (8)	11.68	11.68

Souvenir Sheets

1311	A177	350 le	multicolored	5.60	5.60
1312	A177	350 le	multicolored	5.60	5.60

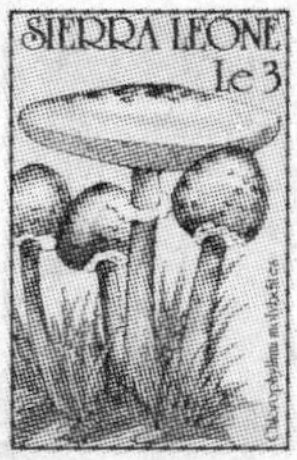

Mushrooms — A178

Designs: 3 le, Chlorophyllum molybdites. 5 le, Lepista nuda. 10 le, Clitocybe nebularis. 15 le, Cyathus striatus. 20 le, Bolbitius vitellinus. 25 le, Leucoagaricus naucinus. 30 le, Suillus luteus. 40 le, Podaxis pistillaris. 50 le, Oudemansiella radicata. 60 le, Phallus indusiatus. 80 le, Macrolepiota rhacodes. 100 le, Mycena pura. 150 le, Volvariella volvacea. 175 le, Omphalotus olearius. 200 le, Sphaerobolus stellatus. 250 le, Schizophyllum commune. No. 1329, Agaricus campestris. No. 1330, Hypholama fasciculare. No. 1331, Suillus granulatus. No. 1332, Psilocybe coprophila.

1990, Dec. 31 ***Perf. 14***

1313	A178	3 le	multicolored	.15	.15
1314	A178	5 le	multicolored	.15	.15
1315	A178	10 le	multicolored	.16	.16
1316	A178	15 le	multicolored	.24	.24
1317	A178	20 le	multicolored	.32	.32
1318	A178	25 le	multicolored	.40	.40
1319	A178	30 le	multicolored	.48	.48
1320	A178	40 le	multicolored	.65	.65
1321	A178	50 le	multicolored	.80	.80
1322	A178	60 le	multicolored	.95	.95
1323	A178	80 le	multicolored	1.30	1.30
1324	A178	100 le	multicolored	1.60	1.60
1325	A178	150 le	multicolored	2.40	2.40
1326	A178	175 le	multicolored	2.80	2.80
1327	A178	200 le	multicolored	3.20	3.20
1328	A178	250 le	multicolored	4.00	4.00
			Nos. 1313-1328 (16)	19.60	19.60

Souvenir Sheets

1329-1332	A178	350 le each	5.60	5.60

Butterfly Type of 1987
"Sierra Leone" in Blue

1990(?) **Litho.**

1332A	A126	50c	like #861	.15	.15
1332B	A126	2 le	like #863		
1332C	A126	5 le	like #865		
1332D	A126	10 le	like #866		
1332E	A126	30 le	like #864		
1332F	A126	50 le	like No. 859		
1332G	A126	60 le	like #871		
1332H	A126	80 le	like No. 860		
1332I	A126	300 le	like No. 869		

Issued: 2, 5, 10, 30, 60 le, 1990(?), perf. 14; 50c, 50, 80, 300 le, Aug, 1991, perf. 12½x11½; Nos. 1332A, 1332F, 1332H-1332I inscribed 1990.

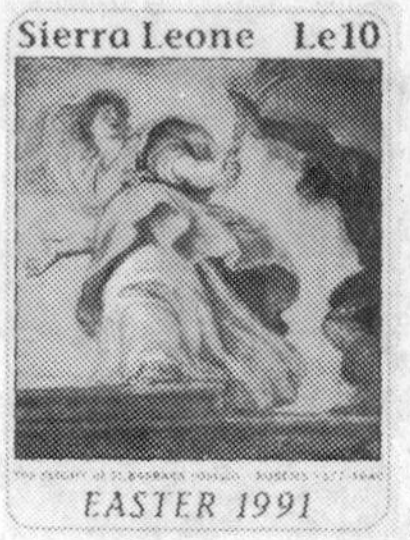

Easter — A179

Entire works or details from paintings by Rubens: 10 le, Flight of St. Barbara. 20 le, No. 1341, The Last Judgement. 30 le, St. Gregory of Nazianzus. 50 le, Doubting Thomas. 80 le, No. 1342, The Way to Calvary. 100 le, St. Gregory with Sts. Domitilla, Maurus and Papianus. 175 le, Sts. Gregory, Maurus and Papianus. 300 le, Christ and the Penitent Sinners.

1991, Apr. 8 **Litho.** ***Perf. 13½x14***

1333	A179	10 le	multicolored	.16	.16
1334	A179	20 le	multicolored	.32	.32
1335	A179	30 le	multicolored	.48	.48
1336	A179	50 le	multicolored	.80	.80
1337	A179	80 le	multicolored	1.30	1.30
1338	A179	100 le	multicolored	1.60	1.60
1339	A179	175 le	multicolored	2.80	2.80
1340	A179	300 le	multicolored	4.80	4.80
			Nos. 1333-1340 (8)	12.26	12.26

Souvenir Sheets

1341-1342	A179	400 le each	6.40	6.40

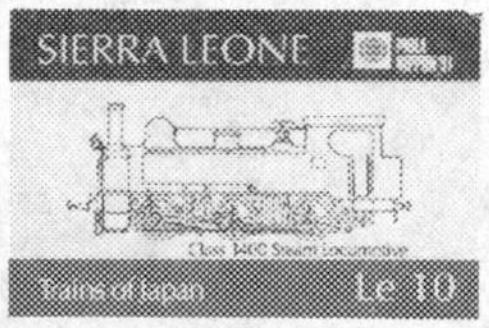

Phila Nippon '91 A180

Japanese locomotives: 10 le, Class 1400 steam. 20 le, Streamlined C55 steam. 30 le, ED17 electric. 60 le, EF13 electric. 100 le, Baldwin Mikado steam. 150 le, C62 steam. 200 le, KiHa 81 class diesel. 300 le, Class 8550 steam. No. 1351, Hikari bullet train. No. 1352, Class 7000 electric. No. 1353, D51 steam. No. 1354, Class 9600 steam.

1991, May 13 **Litho.** ***Perf. 14***

1343	A180	10 le	multicolored	.16	.16
1344	A180	20 le	multicolored	.32	.32
1345	A180	30 le	multicolored	.48	.48
1346	A180	60 le	multicolored	.95	.95
1347	A180	100 le	multicolored	1.60	1.60
1348	A180	150 le	multicolored	2.40	2.40
1349	A180	200 le	multicolored	3.20	3.20
1350	A180	300 le	multicolored	4.80	4.80
			Nos. 1343-1350 (8)	13.91	13.91

Souvenir Sheets

1351-1354	A180	400 le each	6.40	6.40

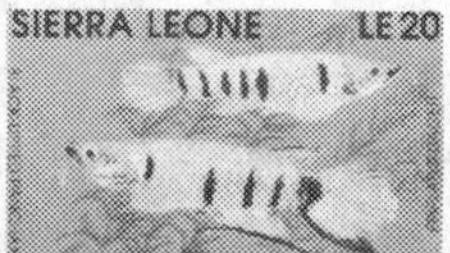

Fish A181

1991, June 3 **Litho.** ***Perf. 14***

1355	A181	10 le	Aphyosemion ghana	.15	.15
1356	A181	20 le	Black-lipped panchax	.24	.24
1357	A181	30 le	Peter's killie	.36	.36
1358	A181	60 le	Micro-walkeri killie	.72	.72
1359	A181	100 le	Butterfly fish	1.20	1.20
1360	A181	150 le	Green panchax	1.80	1.80
1361	A181	200 le	Six-barred panchax	2.40	2.40
1362	A181	300 le	Banded puffer	3.60	3.60
			Nos. 1355-1362 (8)	10.47	10.47

Souvenir Sheets

1363	A181	400 le	Spotfin synodontis	4.80	4.80
1364	A181	400 le	Two-striped panchax	4.80	4.80

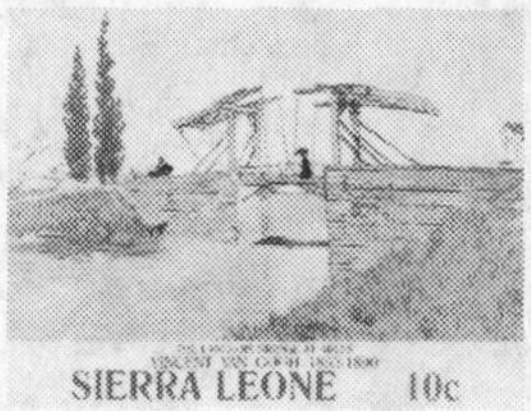

Paintings by Vincent Van Gogh — A182

Designs: 10c, The Langlois Bridge at Arles. 50c, Trees in the Garden of Saint-Paul Hospital, vert. 1 le, Wild Flowers and Thistles in a Vase, vert. 2 le, Still Life: Vase with Oleanders and Books. 5 le, Farmhouses in a Wheat Field Near Arles. 10 le, Self-Portrait, Sept. 1889, vert. 20 le, Portrait of Patience Escalier, vert. 30 le, Portrait of Doctor Felix Rey, vert. 50 le, The Iris, vert. 60 le, The Shepherdess, vert. 80 le, Vincent's House in Arles (The Yellow House). 100 le, The Road Menders. 150 le, The Garden of Saint-Paul Hospital, vert. 200 le, View of the Church of Saint-Paul-De-Mausole. 250 le, Seascape at Saintes- Maries. 300 le, Pieta, vert. No. 1381, Church at Auvers Sur Dise, vert. No. 1382, Vineyards with a View of Auvers. No. 1383, The Trinquetaille Bridge. No. 1384, Two Poplars on a Road Through the Hills, vert. No. 1385, Haystacks in Provence. No. 1386, The Garden of Saint-Paul Hospital, diff.

1991, June 28 **Litho.** ***Perf. 13½***

1365	A182	10c	multicolored	.15	.15
1366	A182	50c	multicolored	.15	.15
1367	A182	1 le	multicolored	.15	.15
1368	A182	2 le	multicolored	.15	.15
1369	A182	5 le	multicolored	.15	.15
1370	A182	10 le	multicolored	.15	.15
1371	A182	20 le	multicolored	.24	.24
1372	A182	30 le	multicolored	.35	.35
1373	A182	50 le	multicolored	.60	.60
1374	A182	60 le	multicolored	.72	.72
1375	A182	80 le	multicolored	.95	.95
1376	A182	100 le	multicolored	1.20	1.20
1377	A182	150 le	multicolored	1.80	1.80
1378	A182	200 le	multicolored	2.40	2.40
1379	A182	250 le	multicolored	3.00	3.00
1380	A182	300 le	multicolored	3.60	3.60
			Nos. 1365-1380 (16)	15.76	15.76

Size: 102x76mm

Imperf

1381-1386	A182	400 le each	4.80	4.80

Royal Family Birthday, Anniversary
Common Design Type

1991, July 5 **Litho.** ***Perf. 14***

1387	CD347	10 le	multi	.16	.16
1388	CD347	20 le	multi	.32	.32
1389	CD347	30 le	multi	.48	.48
1390	CD347	80 le	multi	1.30	1.30
1391	CD347	100 le	multi	1.60	1.60
1392	CD347	200 le	multi	3.20	3.20
1393	CD347	250 le	multi	4.00	4.00
1394	CD347	300 le	multi	4.80	4.80
			Nos. 1387-1394 (8)	15.86	15.86

Souvenir Sheets

1395	CD347	400 le	Elizabeth, Philip	6.40	6.40
1396	CD347	400 le	Charles, Diana, sons	6.40	6.40

10 le, 30 le, 200 le, 250 le, No. 1395, Queen Elizabeth II, 65th birthday. Others, Charles and Diana, 10th wedding anniversary.

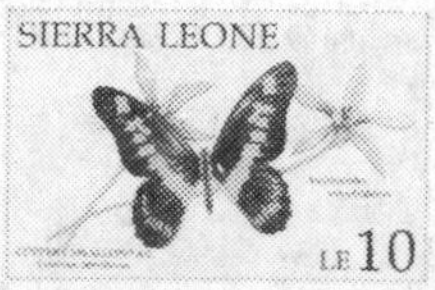

Butterflies A183

1991, Aug. 5 **Litho.** ***Perf. 14x13½***

1397	A183	10 le	Coppery swallowtail	.15	.15
1398	A183	30 le	Orange forester	.36	.36
1399	A183	50 le	Large striped swordtail	.60	.60
1400	A183	60 le	Lilac beauty	.72	.72
1401	A183	80 le	African leaf	.95	.95
1402	A183	100 le	Blue diadem	1.20	1.20
1403	A183	200 le	Beautiful monarch	2.40	2.40
1404	A183	300 le	Veined swallowtail	3.60	3.60
			Nos. 1397-1404 (8)	9.98	9.98

Souvenir Sheets

Perf. 13x12

1405	A183	400 le	Blue banded nymph	4.80	4.80
1406	A183	400 le	Western red charaxes	2.75	2.75
1407	A183	400 le	Broad-bordered grass yellow	2.75	2.75
1408	A183	400 le	African clouded yellow	3.25	3.25

A number has been reserved for additional value in this set. While numbers 1406-1407 have the same issue date as Nos. 1397-1405, the dollar value of Nos. 1406-1407 was lower when they were released. While No. 1408 has the same issue date as Nos. 1397-1407, the value of No. 1408 was different when released.

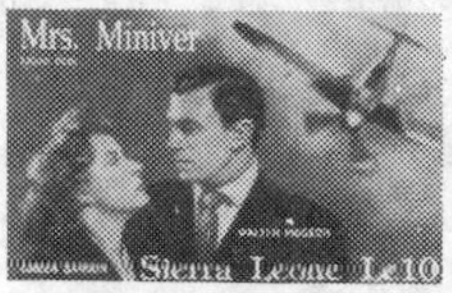

World War II Motion Pictures A184

Designs: 2 le, To Hell and Back, Audie Murphy. 5 le, Attack, Jack Palance. 10 le, Mrs. Miniver, Greer Garson and Walter Pidgeon. 20 le, The Guns of Navarone. 30 le, The Great Dictator, Paulette Goddard and Charlie Chaplin. 50 le, The Train. 60 le, The Diary of Anne Frank. 80 le, The Bridge on the River Kwai, William Holden. 100 le, Lifeboat, Alfred Hitchcock, Tallulah Bankhead. 200 le, Sands of Iwo Jima, John Wayne. 300 le, Thirty Seconds Over Tokyo, Van Johnson and Spencer Tracy. 350 le, Casablanca, Humphrey Bogart and Ingrid Bergman. No. 1421, Twelve O'Clock High, Gregory Peck. No. 1422, Tora! Tora! Tora!. No. 1423, Patton, George C. Scott.

1991, Oct. 14 **Litho.** ***Perf. 14***

1409	A184	2 le	multicolored	.15	.15
1410	A184	5 le	multicolored	.15	.15
1411	A184	10 le	multicolored	.15	.15
1412	A184	20 le	multicolored	.24	.24
1413	A184	30 le	multicolored	.35	.35
1414	A184	50 le	multicolored	.60	.60
1415	A184	60 le	multicolored	.72	.72
1416	A184	80 le	multicolored	.95	.95
1417	A184	100 le	multicolored	1.20	1.20
1418	A184	200 le	multicolored	2.40	2.40
1419	A184	300 le	multicolored	3.60	3.60
1420	A184	350 le	multicolored	4.25	4.25
			Nos. 1409-1420 (12)	14.76	14.76

Souvenir Sheets

1421	A184	450 le	multicolored	5.40	5.40
1422	A184	450 le	multicolored	5.40	5.40
1423	A184	450 le	multicolored	5.40	5.40

Miniature Sheets

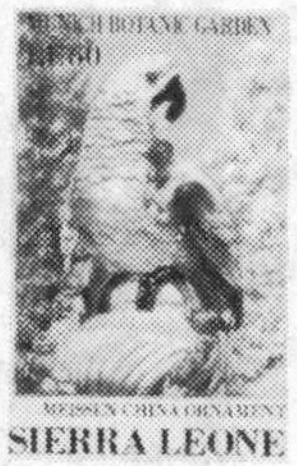

Botanic Gardens — A185

Munich Botanic Garden: No. 1424a, Meissen China ornament. b, Masdevallia. c, White Egyptian lotus. d, French marigold. e, Pitcher plant. f, The Palm House. g, Dog's tooth violet. h, Passion flower. i, Hedge rose. j, Sensitive plant. k, Pitcher plant, diff. l, Trillium. m, Wild plantain. n, German primrose. o, Tulip. p, Spring walk.

Kyoto Botanic Garden: No. 1425a, Flowering cherry. b, Gardenia. c, The Domed Conservatory. d, Chrysanthemums. e, Bleeding heart. f, Hibiscus. g, Hiryu azalea. h, Sweet honeysuckle. i, Goldband lily. j, Non-traditional garden art. k, Viburnum. l, Japanese iris. m, Orchid. n, Hydrangea. o, View of Kyoto Botanic Garden. p, Camelia.

Brooklyn Botanic Garden: No. 1426a, The Palm House. b, Kurume azalea. c, Southern magnolia. d, Oleander. e, Chinese wisteria. f, Sourwood tree. g, Cattleya orchid. h, Gingko tree. i, Japanese Hill and Pond Garden. j, Rose. k, German iris. l, East Indian lotus. m, Speciosum lily. n, Lilac. o, Rose bay. p, Cranford Rose Garden.

No. 1427, Rhododendron, Munich, horiz. No. 1428, Chrysanthemum, Kyoto, horiz. No. 1429, Magnolia soulangeana, Brooklyn, horiz.

1991, Oct. 28

Sheets of 16

1424	A185	60 le	#a.-p.	11.50	11.50
1425	A185	60 le	#a.-p.	11.50	11.50
1426	A185	60 le	#a.-p.	11.50	11.50

Souvenir Sheets

1427-1429	A185	600 le each	7.25	7.25

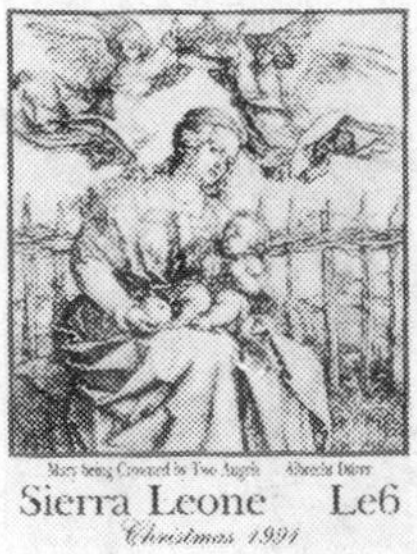

Christmas
A186

Details from paintings or engravings by Albrecht Durer: 6 le, Mary being Crowned by Two Angels. 60 le, St. Christopher. 80 le, Virgin and Child. 100 le, Madonna and Child (Virgin with the Pear). 200 le, Madonna and Child. 300 le, The Virgin in Half-Length. 700 le, The Madonna with the Siskin. No. 1437, The Feast of the Rose Garlands. No. 1438, Virgin and Child with St. Anne.

1991, Dec. 9 Litho. *Perf. 12*

1430 A186	6 le pink & black	.15	.15
1431 A186	60 le blue & black	.48	.48
1432 A186	80 le multicolored	.65	.65
1433 A186	100 le multicolored	.80	.80
1434 A186	200 le multicolored	1.60	1.60
1435 A186	300 le multicolored	2.40	2.40
1436 A186	700 le multicolored	5.60	5.60
	Nos. 1430-1436 (7)	11.68	11.68

Souvenir Sheets

Perf. 14½

1437-1438 A186 600 le each 4.75 4.75

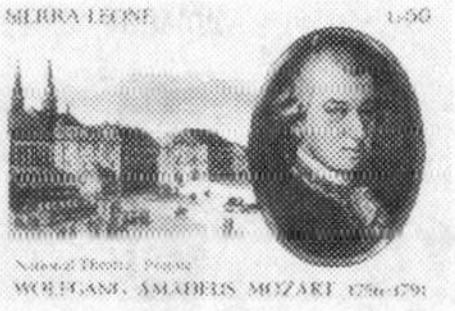

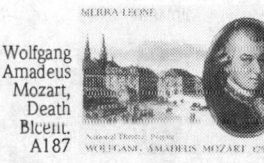

Wolfgang Amadeus Mozart, Death Bicent. A187

Mozart and: 50 le, National Theatre, Prague. 100 le, St. Peter's Abbey, Salzburg. 500 le, Scene from opera, "Idomeneo."

1991, Dec. 20 *Perf. 14*

1439 A187	50 le multicolored	.40	.40
1440 A187	100 le multicolored	.80	.80
1441 A187	500 le multicolored	4.00	4.00
	Nos. 1439-1441 (3)	5.20	5.20

Souvenir Sheet

1442 A187 600 le Bust, vert. 4.75 4.75

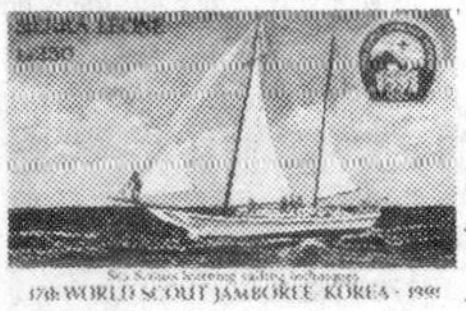

17th World Scout Jamboree, Korea A188

Designs: 250 le, Scouts learning to sail. 300 le, Lord Robert Baden-Powell, founder. 400 le, Scouts playing baseball. 750 le, Jamboree emblem, vert.

1991, Dec. 20

1443 A188	250 le multicolored	2.00	2.00
1444 A188	300 le multicolored	2.40	2.40
1445 A188	400 le multicolored	3.20	3.20
	Nos. 1443-1445 (3)	7.60	7.60

Souvenir Sheet

1446 A188 750 le multicolored 6.00 6.00

Miniature Sheet

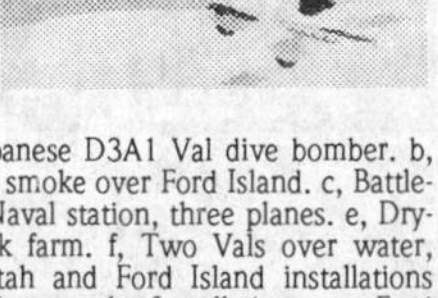

Attack on Pearl Harbor, 50th Anniv. A189

Designs: a, Japanese D3A1 Val dive bomber. b, Plane amid rising smoke over Ford Island. c, Battleships ablaze. d, Naval station, three planes. e, Drydock ablaze, tank farm. f, Two Vals over water, ships. g, USS Utah and Ford Island installations ablaze, ship underway. h, Installations on Ford Island ablaze. i, US P-40 Warhawk fighter plane. j, Two Japanese torpedo bombers, plane on fire falling from sky. k, Three Japanese bombers over Pearl City. l, Two Japanese bombers diving on four ships, one burning ship. m, Japanese plane on fire. n, Two Japanese planes. o, One Japanese plane over Waipio Peninsula.

1991, Dec. 20 *Perf. 14½x15*

1447 A189 75 le Sheet of 15, #a.-o. 9.00 9.00

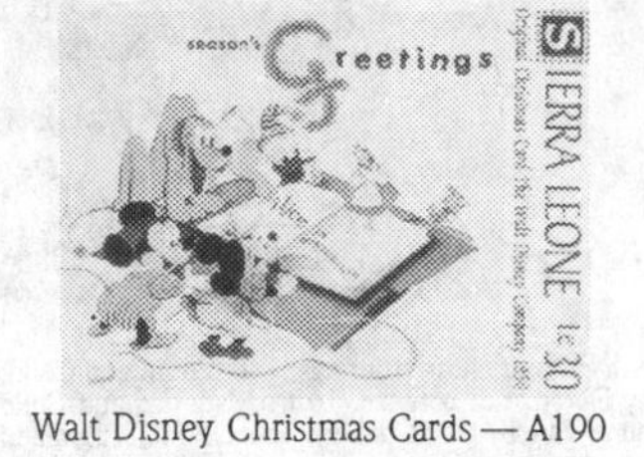

Walt Disney Christmas Cards — A190

Designs and year of issue: 12 le, Mickey and Donald decorating tree, 1952. 30 le, Characters surrounding book with "Alice in Wonderland", 1950. 60 le, Dwarf asleep with hare and tortoise, 1938. 75 le, Minnie, Donald, Mickey and Pluto mailing Christmas card, 1936. 100 le, Costumed characters in front of Magic Kingdom, 1984. 125 le, Mickey singing, Donald's nephews and Pluto reading 20,000 Leagues Under the Sea, 1954. 150 le, 101 Dalmations with season's greetings, 1960. 200 le, Donald and Mickey among gifts, 1948. 300 le, Mickey, Minnie at home for Christmas, 1983. 400 le, Donald and ducks preparing for Christmas watching Mickey Mouse Club, 1956. Characters on parade with Christmas cheer. 500 le, Disney characters, 50th birthday of Walt Disney Productions, 1972. No. 1460, Map of Magic Kingdom, 1955, vert. No. 1461, Seven dwarfs in bobsled, 1959, vert. No. 1462, Alice in Wonderland at tea party, 1950, vert.

1991, Dec. 24 Litho. *Perf. 14x13½*

1448 A190	12 le multicolored	.15	.15
1449 A190	30 le multicolored	.20	.20
1450 A190	60 le multicolored	.35	.35
1451 A190	75 le multicolored	.40	.40
1452 A190	100 le multicolored	.55	.55
1453 A190	125 le multicolored	.75	.75
1454 A190	150 le multicolored	.85	.85
1455 A190	200 le multicolored	1.25	1.25
1456 A190	300 le multicolored	1.75	1.75
1457 A190	400 le multicolored	2.25	2.25
1458 A190	500 le multicolored	2.75	2.75
1459 A190	600 le multicolored	3.25	3.25
	Nos. 1448-1459 (12)	14.50	14.50

Souvenir Sheets

Perf. 13½x14

1460-1462 A190 900 le each 5.25 5.25

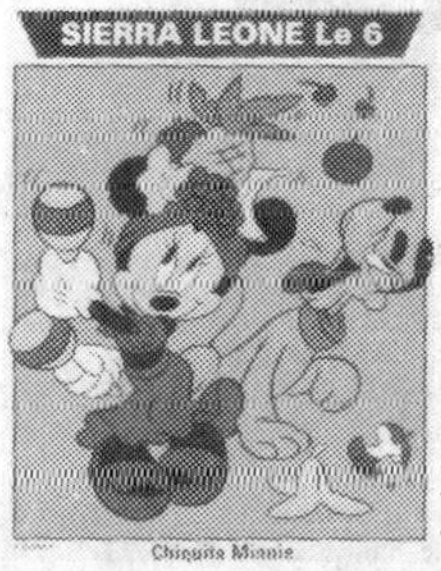

Disney Characters on World Tour — A192

Designs: 6 le, Chiquita Minnie in Central America. 10 le, Gold Medal Goofy in Ancient Greece. 20 le, Donald, Daisy having Flamenco Fun in Spain. 30 le, Goofy guarding Donald at London's Buckingham Palace. 50 le, Mickey and Minnie dressed in Paris originals. 100 le, Goofy with mountain goat in Switzerland. 200 le, Daisy, Minnie as luau ladies in Hawaii. 350 le, Mickey, Donald and Goofy as ancient Egyptian comic strips, horiz. 500 le, Daisy and Minnie as can-can dancers in Paris, horiz. No. 1479, Mickey playing bagpipes in Scotland. No. 1480, Goofy fishes from Donald's gondola in Venice, Italy. No. 1481, Mickey and Goofy taking crash course in Greek.

Perf. 13x13½, 13½x13

1992, Feb. Litho.

1470 A192	6 le multicolored	.15	.15
1471 A192	10 le multicolored	.15	.15
1472 A192	20 le multicolored	.16	.16
1473 A192	30 le multicolored	.24	.24
1474 A192	50 le multicolored	.40	.40
1475 A192	100 le multicolored	.80	.80
1476 A192	200 le multicolored	1.60	1.60
1477 A192	350 le multicolored	2.80	2.80
1478 A192	500 le multicolored	4.00	4.00
	Nos. 1470-1478 (9)	10.30	10.30

Souvenir Sheets

1479-1481 A192 700 le each 5.60 5.60

Queen Elizabeth II's Accession to the Throne, 40th Anniv.

Common Design Type

1992, Feb. 6 Litho. *Perf. 14*

1482 CD348	60 le multicolored	.48	.48
1483 CD348	100 le multicolored	.80	.80
1484 CD348	300 le multicolored	2.40	2.40
1485 CD348	400 le multicolored	3.20	3.20
	Nos. 1482-1485 (4)	6.88	6.88

Souvenir Sheets

1486 CD348	700 le Queen, hillside	5.60	5.60
1487 CD348	700 le Queen, houses	5.60	5.60

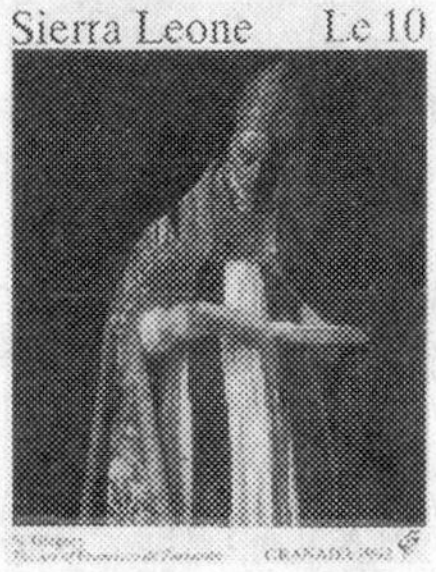

Spanish Art — A193

Paintings by Francisco de Zurbaran: 1 le, The Visit of St. Thomas Aquinas to St. Bonaventure. 10 le, St. Gregory. 30 le, St. Andrew. 50 le, St. Gabriel the Archangel. 60 le, The Blessed Henry Suso. 100 le, St. Lucy. 300 le, St. Casilda. 400 le, St. Margaret of Antioch. 500 le, St. Apollonia. 600 le, St. Bonaventure at the Council of Lyons. 700 le, St. Bonaventure on His Bier. 800 le, The Martyrdom of St. James (detail). No. 1496, St. Hugh in the Refectory, horiz. No. 1497, The Martyrdom of St. James. No. 1497A, The Young Virgin.

1992, May 25 Litho. *Perf. 13*

1487A A193	1 le multi	.15	.15
1488 A193	10 le multi	.15	.15
1489 A193	30 le multi	.22	.22
1490 A193	50 le multi	.38	.38
1491 A193	60 le multi	.48	.48
1491A A193	100 le multi	.50	.50
1491B A193	300 le multi	1.50	1.50
1492 A193	400 le multi	3.00	3.00
1493 A193	500 le multi	4.00	4.00
1494 A193	600 le multi	4.80	4.80
1495 A193	700 le multi	3.50	3.50
1495A A193	800 le multi	4.00	4.00

Size: 120x95mm

Imperf

1496 A193	900 le multi	7.20	7.20
1497 A193	900 le multi	6.85	6.85
1497A A193	900 le multi	4.65	4.65
	Nos. 1487A-1497A (15)	41.38	41.38

Granada '92.

While Nos. 1487A-1497A all have the same issue date, the dollar value of Nos. 1487A, 1489-1490, 1491A-1491B, 1492, 1495, 1497-1497A was lower when they were released.

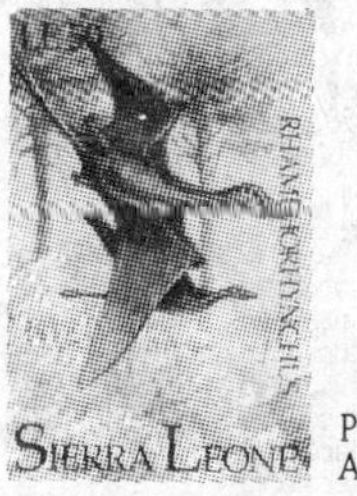

Prehistoric Animals — A194

Designs: No. 1498a, Rhamphorhynchus. b, Pteranodon. c, Dimorphodon. d, Pterodactyl. e, Archaeopteryx. f, Iguanodon. g, Hypsilophodon. h, Nothosaurus. i, Brachiosaurus. j, Kentrosaurus. k, Plesiosaurus. l, Trachodon. m, Hesperornis. n, Henodus. o, Steneosaurus. p, Stenopterygius. q, Eurhinosaurus r, Placodus. s, Mosasaurus. t, Mixosaurus. No. 1499, Herperornis, diff.

1992, June 8 *Perf. 14*

1498 A194 50 le Sheet of 20, #a.-t. 8.00 8.00

Souvenir Sheet

1499 A194 50 le multicolored .40 .40

"Sierra Leone" is 22mm wide on No. 1499.

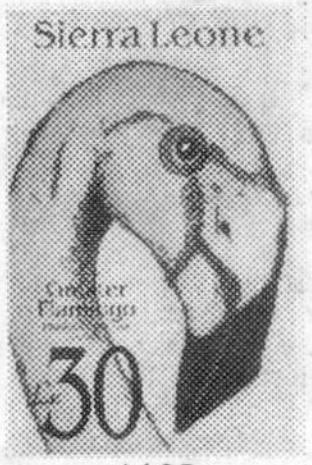

A195

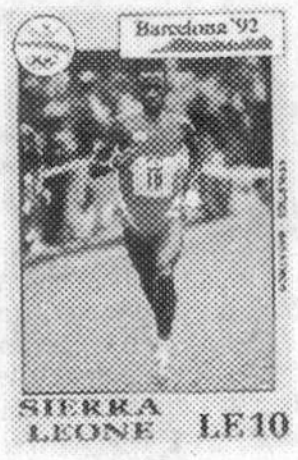

A196

Tropical Birds: 30 le, Greater flamingo. 50 le, White-crested hornbill. 100 le, Verreaux's touraco. 170 le, Yellow-spotted barbet. 200 le, African spoonbill. 250 le, Saddlebill stork. 300 le, Red-headed lovebird. 600 le, Yellow-billed barbet. No. 1508, Fire-bellied woodpecker. No. 1509, Swallow-tailed bee-eater.

1992, July 20 Litho. *Perf. 14*

1500 A195	30 le multicolored	.25	.25
1501 A195	50 le multicolored	.38	.38
1502 A195	100 le multicolored	.52	.52
1503 A195	170 le multicolored	.90	.90
1504 A195	200 le multicolored	1.55	1.55
1505 A195	250 le multicolored	1.30	1.30
1506 A195	300 le multicolored	1.60	1.60
1507 A195	600 le multicolored	4.65	4.65
	Nos. 1500-1507 (8)	11.15	11.15

Souvenir Sheets

1508 A195	1000 le multicolored	7.60	7.60
1509 A195	1000 le multicolored	5.25	5.25

While Nos. 1500-1509 all have the same release date, the value of Nos. 1502-1503, 1505-1506, 1509 was lower when they were released.

1992 Litho. *Perf. 14*

1992 Summer Olympics, Barcelona: 10 le, Marathon. 20 le, Gymnastics, parallel bars. 30 le, Discus. 50 le, 110-meter hurdles, horiz. 60 le, Women's long jump. 100 le, Gymnastics, floor exercise, horiz. 200 le, Windsurfing. 300 le, Road race cycling. 400 le, Weight lifting. 900 le, Soccer, horiz.

1510 A196	10 le multicolored	.15	.15
1511 A196	20 le multicolored	.15	.15
1512 A196	30 le multicolored	.22	.22
1513 A196	50 le multicolored	.38	.38
1514 A196	60 le multicolored	.45	.45
1515 A196	100 le multicolored	.75	.75
1516 A196	200 le multicolored	1.55	1.55
1517 A196	300 le multicolored	2.30	2.30
1518 A196	400 le multicolored	3.00	3.00
	Nos. 1510-1518 (9)	8.95	8.95

Souvenir Sheet

1519 A196 900 le multicolored 6.75 6.75

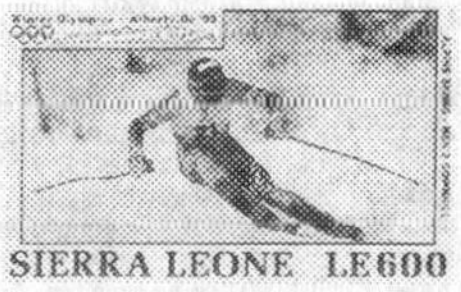

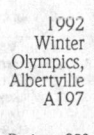

1992 Winter Olympics, Albertville A197

Designs: 250 le, Women's biathlon, vert. 500 le, Speed skating, vert. 600 le, Men's downhill skiing. No. 1523, Men's single luge. No. 1524, Ice dancing, vert.

1992, Sept. 8 Litho. *Perf. 14*

1520 A197	250 le multicolored	1.30	1.30
1521 A197	500 le multicolored	2.60	2.60
1522 A197	600 le multicolored	3.10	3.10
	Nos. 1520-1522 (3)	7.00	7.00

Souvenir Sheets

1523-1524 A197 900 le each 4.65 4.65

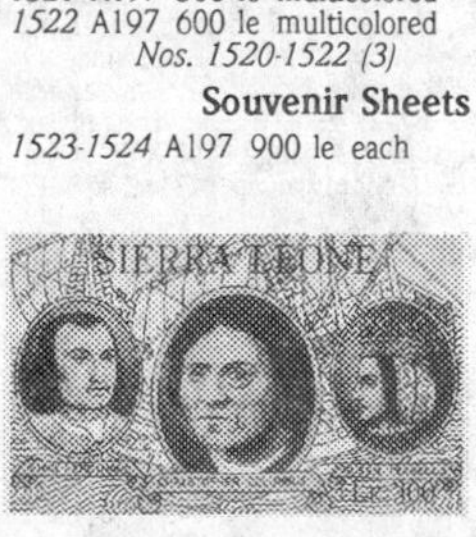

Discovery of America, 500th Anniv. A198

Designs: 300 le, Ferdinand, Isabella, Columbus. 500 le, Landing in New World. 900 le, Columbus, vert.

1992, Oct. Litho. *Perf. 14*

1525 A198	300 le multicolored	1.60	1.60
1526 A198	500 le multicolored	2.60	2.60

Souvenir Sheet

1527 A198 900 le multicolored 4.65 4.65

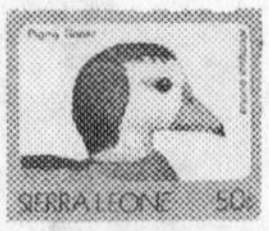

Birds — A199

Designs: 50c, Pygmy goose. 1 le, Spotted eagle owl. 2 le, Verreaux's touraco. 5 le, Saddlebill stork. 10 le, African golden oriole. 20 le, Malachite kingfisher. 30 le, Fire-crowned bishop. 40 le, Fire-bellied woodpecker. 50 le, Red-billed fire-finch. 80 le, Blue fairy flycatcher. 100 le, Crested malimbe. 150 le, Vitelline masked weaver. 170 le, Blue plantain-eater. 200 le, Superb sunbird. 250 le, Swallow-tailed bee-eater. 300 le, Cabani's yellow bunting. 500 le, Crocodile bird. 750 le, White-faced owl. 1000 le, Blue cuckoo-shrike. 2000 le, Bare-headed rock-fowl. 3000 le, Red-tailed buzzard.

1992-93 Litho. *Perf. 14x15*

1528	A199	50c multi	.15	.15
1529	A199	1 le multi	.15	.15
1530	A199	2 le multi	.15	.15
1531	A199	5 le multi	.15	.15
1532	A199	10 le multi	.15	.15
1533	A199	20 le multi	.15	.15
1534	A199	30 le multi	.16	.16
1535	A199	40 le multi	.20	.20
1536	A199	50 le multi	.26	.26
1537	A199	80 le multi	.42	.42
1538	A199	100 le multi	.52	.52
1539	A199	150 le multi	.80	.80
1540	A199	170 le multi	.90	.90
1541	A199	200 le multi	1.05	1.05
1542	A199	250 le multi	1.30	1.30
1543	A199	300 le multi	1.60	1.60
1544	A199	500 le multi	2.65	2.65
1545	A199	750 le multi	4.00	4.00
1546	A199	1000 le multi	5.25	5.25
1546A	A199	2000 le multi	10.50	10.50
1546B	A199	3000 le multi	15.75	15.75
		Nos. 1528-1546B (21)	46.26	46.26

Nos. 1536, 1538-1539, 1541, 1543 exist inscribed 1994.

Issue dates: Nos. 1528-1546, Sept. 1992. Nos. 1546A-1546B, 1993.

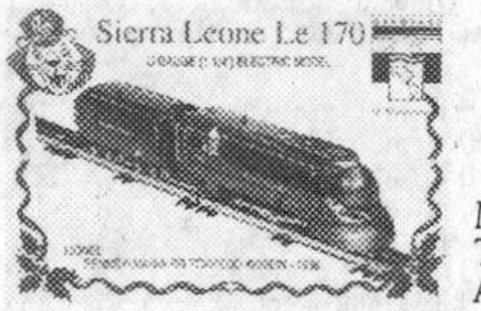

Model Trains A200

Lionel models: No. 1547a, Pennsylvannia RR GG-1 electric #6-18306, O gauge, 1992. b, Wabash RR Hudson #8610, O gauge, 1985. c, Locomotive #1911, standard gauge, 1911. d, Chesapeake & Ohio 4-4-2 #6-18627, O gauge, 1992. e, Gang car #50, O gauge, 1954. f, #8004, 1980 model of Rock Island & Peoria RR engine built for Columbian Exposition of 1893, O gauge. g, Western Maryland RR Shay #6-18023, O gauge, 1992. h, (Kenner-Parker) Boston & Albany Hudson #784, O gauge, 1986. i, Locomotive #6, standard gauge, 1906.

No. 1548a, Pennsylvania RR Torpedo #238EW, O gauge, 1936. b, Denver & Rio Grande Western Alco Pa No. 6-18107, O gauge, 1992. c, #408E Locomotive, standard gauge, 1930. d, Mickey Mouse 60th birthday boxcar No. 19241, O gauge, 1991. e, Polished brass locomotive, No. 54, standard gauge, 1913. f, Broadway limited #392E, standard gauge, 1936. g, Great Northern RR EP-5 #18302, O gauge, 1988. h, 4-4-0 Locomotive #6, standard gauge, 1918. i, 4-4-4 Locomotive No. 400E, standard gauge, 1933.

No. 1549a, Special F-3 diesel engine, O gauge, 1947. b, Pennsylvania RR GE 44-ton switcher #6-18905, O gauge, 1992. c, #1 trolley, standard gauge, 1913. d, Seaboard RR freight diesel, O gauge, 1958. e, Pennsylvannia S-2 turbine, O gauge, 1991. f, Western Pacific RR GP-9 diesel #6-18822, O gauge, 1992. g, #10 with Ives plates transition model, standard gauge, 1929. h, 4-4-4 locomotive #400E, standard gauge, 1931. i, #384E, standard gauge, 1928.

No. 1550, Hudson No. 8210 Special, O gauge. No. 1551, #381E, standard gauge, 1928. No. 1552, 2-Rail electric model #300 trolley with converse body, 2 7/8-inch gauge.

1992, Nov. 23 Litho. *Perf. 14*

1547	A200	150 le Sheet of 9, #a.-i.	7.00	7.00
1548	A200	170 le Sheet of 9, #a.-i.	8.00	8.00
1549	A200	170 le Sheet of 9, #a.-i.	8.00	8.00

Souvenir Sheets

Perf. 13

1550-1552	A200	1000 le each	5.25	5.25

Genoa '92 (#1547-1549). Nos. 1550-1552 contains one 51x39mm stamp.

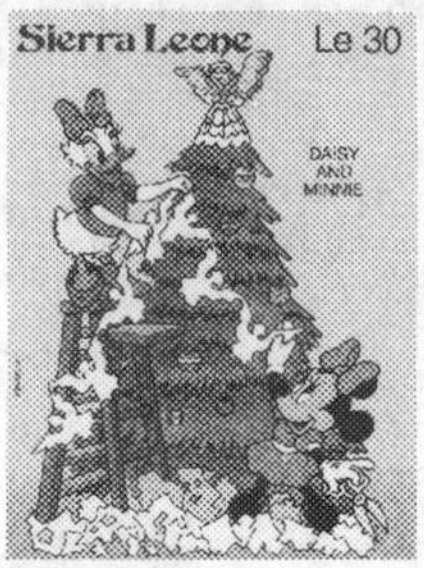

Walt Disney Characters in Christmas Scenes A201

1992, Nov. 16 *Perf. 13 1/2x14*

1553 A201	10 le	Minnie & Chip	.15	.15
1554 A201	20 le	Goofy as Santa	.15	.15
1555 A201	30 le	Daisy, Minnie	.15	.15
1556 A201	50 le	Mickey, Goofy	.26	.26
1557 A201	80 le	Pete	.42	.42
1558 A201	100 le	Donald Duck	.52	.52
1559 A201	150 le	Morty & Ferdie	.78	.78
1560 A201	200 le	Mickey	1.05	1.05
1561 A201	300 le	Goofy with ornament	1.60	1.60
1562 A201	500 le	Chip & Dale	2.60	2.60
1563 A201	600 le	Donald & Dale	3.20	3.20
1564 A201	800 le	Huey, Dewey & Louie	4.15	4.15
		Nos. 1553-1564 (12)	15.03	15.03

Souvenir Sheets

1565 A201	900 le	Mickey Mouse	4.75	4.75

Perf. 14x13 1/2

1566 A201	900 le	Angel with Chip, horiz.	4.75	4.75
1567 A201	900 le	Mickey & Minnie, horiz.	4.75	4.75

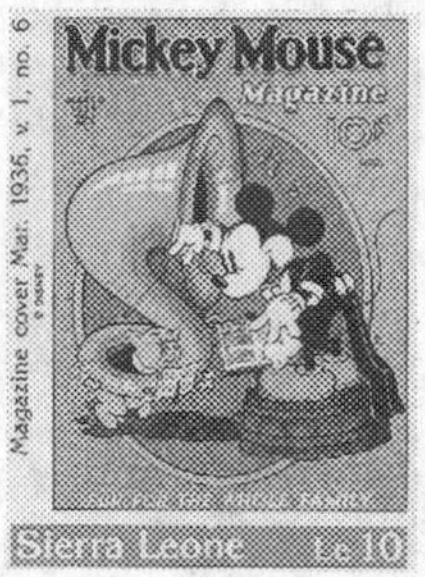

Mickey Mouse Magazines and Books — A202

Designs: 10 le, Magazine cover, Mar. 1936, v. 1, No. 6. 20 le, Magazine cover, June 1936, v. 1, No. 9. 30 le, Magazine cover, Nov. 1936, v. 2, No. 2. 40 le, Magazine cover, Aug. 1937, v. 2, No. 11. 50 le, Magazine cover, Oct. 1937, v. 2, No. 13. 60 le, Magazine cover, Dec. 1937, v. 3, No. 3. 70 le, Magazine cover, Jan. 1938, v. 3, No. 4. 150 le, Cover, Big Book No. 4062, 1935. 170 le, Story book cover, 1936. 200 le, Comic book cover, unnumbered. 300 le, Comic book cover, No. 181. 400 le, Comic book cover #194. 500 le, Story book cover, Book 1, 1931. No. 1581, Boys' and Girls' March of Comics cover, 1948. No. 1582, First Mickey Mouse Magazine cover for June-Aug. 1935, v. 1, No. 1, horiz. No. 1583, Cover of early Mickey Mouse story book published in England, 1933, horiz.

1992 *Perf. 13 1/2x14*

1568 A202	10 le	multicolored	.15	.15
1569 A202	20 le	multicolored	.15	.15
1570 A202	30 le	multicolored	.15	.15
1571 A202	40 le	multicolored	.20	.20
1572 A202	50 le	multicolored	.28	.28
1573 A202	60 le	multicolored	.32	.32
1574 A202	70 le	multicolored	.38	.38
1575 A202	150 le	multicolored	.78	.78
1576 A202	170 le	multicolored	.90	.90
1577 A202	200 le	multicolored	1.05	1.05
1578 A202	300 le	multicolored	1.60	1.60
1579 A202	400 le	multicolored	2.05	2.05
1580 A202	500 le	multicolored	2.60	2.60
		Nos. 1568-1580 (13)	10.61	10.61

Souvenir Sheets

1581 A202	900 le	multicolored	4.65	4.65

Perf. 14x13 1/2

1582 A202	900 le	multicolored	4.65	4.65
1583 A202	900 le	multicolored	4.65	4.65

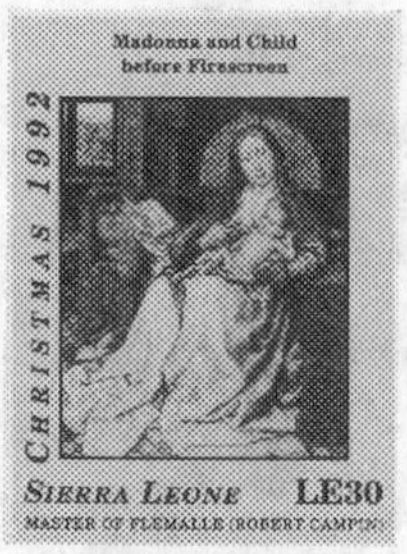

Christmas A203

Details or entire paintings: 1 le, Virgin and Child, by Fiorenzo di Lorenzo. 10 le, Madonna and Child on a Wall, by Circle of Dirk Bouts. 20 le, Virgin and Child with the Flight into Egypt, by Master of Hoogstraeten. 30 le, Madonna and Child before Firescreen, by Master of Flemalle. 50 le, Mary in a Rose Garden, by Hans Memling. 100 le, Virgin Mary and Child, by Lucas Cranach the Elder. 170 le, Virgin and Child, by Rogier van der Weyden. 200 le, Madonna and Saints, by Perugino. 250 le, Madonna Enthroned with Saints Catherine and Barbara, by Master of Hoogstraeten. 300 le, The Virgin in a Rose Arbor, by Stefan Lochner. 500 le, Madonna and Child with Angels, by Sandro Botticelli. 1000 le, Madonna and Child with Young St. John the Baptist, by Fra Bartolemmeo. No. 1596, The Virgin with the Green Cushion, by Andrea Solario. No. 1597, The Virgin and Child, by Jan Gossaert. No. 1598, The Virgin and Child, by Lucas Cranach the Younger.

1992, Dec. 7 Litho. *Perf. 13 1/2x14*

1584 A203	1 le	multicolored	.15	.15
1585 A203	10 le	multicolored	.15	.15
1586 A203	20 le	multicolored	.15	.15
1587 A203	30 le	multicolored	.15	.15
1588 A203	50 le	multicolored	.28	.28
1589 A203	100 le	multicolored	.52	.52
1590 A203	170 le	multicolored	.90	.90
1591 A203	200 le	multicolored	1.05	1.05
1592 A203	250 le	multicolored	1.30	1.30
1593 A203	300 le	multicolored	1.60	1.60
1594 A203	500 le	multicolored	2.60	2.60
1595 A203	1000 le	multicolored	5.20	5.20
		Nos. 1584-1595 (12)	14.05	14.05

Souvenir Sheets

1596-1598 A203	900 le	each	4.75	4.75

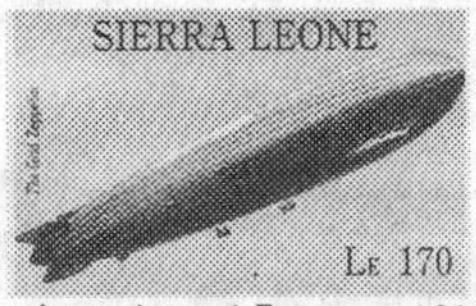

Anniversaries and Events — A204

Designs: 150 le, Emblems of FAO, ICN, WHO. No. 1600, Graf Zeppelin. No. 1601, Cow, emblems, grain stalk. 200 le, Starving child. No. 1603, Lions Intl. emblem, map. No. 1604, Cottonwood tree. 300 le, African elephant. 600 le, Space Shuttle. 700 le, Graf Zeppelin LZ 127, specifications. No. 1608, Astronaut. No. 1609, Count Zeppelin.

1992, Dec. Litho. *Perf. 14*

1599 A204	150 le	multicolored	.78	.78
1600 A204	170 le	multicolored	.90	.90
1601 A204	170 le	multicolored	.90	.90
1602 A204	200 le	multicolored	1.05	1.05
1603 A204	250 le	multicolored	1.30	1.30
1604 A204	250 le	multicolored	1.30	1.30
1605 A204	300 le	multicolored	1.60	1.60
1606 A204	600 le	multicolored	3.25	3.25
1607 A204	700 le	multicolored	3.65	3.65
		Nos. 1599-1607 (9)	14.73	14.73

Souvenir Sheets

1608-1609 A204	900 le	each	4.75	4.75

Intl. Conference on Nutrition, Rome (#1599, 1601). Count Zeppelin, 75th anniv. of death (#1600, 1607, 1609). World Health Organization (#1602). Lions Intl., 75th anniv. (#1603). Earth Summit, Rio de Janeiro (#1604-1605). Intl. Space Year (#1606, 1608).

Miniature Sheet

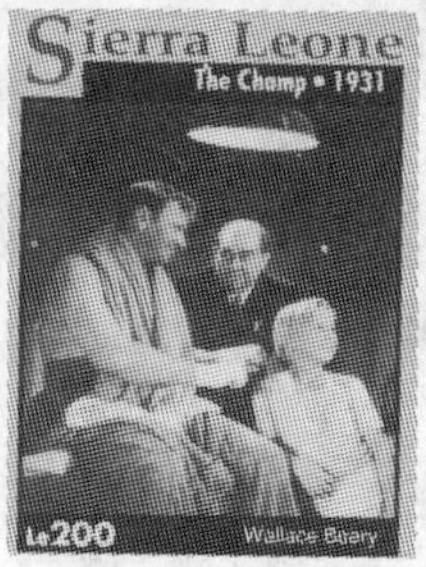

Boxing A205

Boxing movies, stars: No. 1610a, The Champ, Wallace Beery. b, Golden Boy, William Holden. c, Body and Soul, John Garfield. d, Champion, Kirk Douglas. e, The Set-Up, Robert Ryan. f, Requiem for a Heavyweight, Anthony Quinn. g, Kid Galahad, Elvis Presley. h, Fat City, Jeff Bridges.

No. 1612, Gentlemen Jim, Errol Flynn. No. 1614, Rocky III, Sylvester Stallone.

Boxing champions: No. 1611a, Joe Louis. b, Archie Moore. c, Muhammad Ali. d, George Foreman. e, Joe Frazier. f, Marvin Hagler. g, Sugar Ray Leonard. h, Evander Holyfield.

No. 1613, Muhammad Ali, diff.

1993, Feb. 8 Litho. *Perf. 13 1/2x14*

1610 A205	200 le	Sheet of 8, #a.-h.	8.50	8.50
1611 A205	200 le	Sheet of 8, #a.-h.	8.50	8.50

Souvenir Sheets

1612-1614 A205	1000 le	each	5.20	5.20

Miniature Sheets

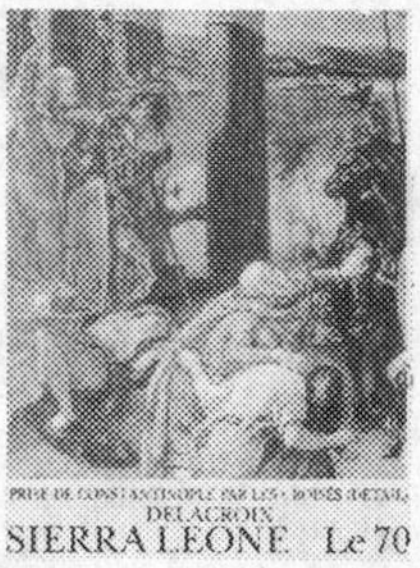

Louvre Museum, Bicent. A206

Details or entire paintings by Eugene Delacroix (1798-1863): Nos. 1615a-1615b, Entry of the Crusaders into Constantinople (left, right). c-d, Jews Purchasing Brides in Morocco (left, right). e-f, The Death of Sardanapalus (left, right). g-h, Liberty Guiding the People (left, right).

No. 1616a, An Orphan at the Cemetery. b-c, Women of Algiers in their Apartment (left, right). d, Dante and Virgil in the Infernal Regions. e, Self-Portrait. f-g, Massacre at Chios (left, right). h, Frederic Chopin.

No. 1617, Rape of the Sabine Women, by Jacques-Louis David (1748-1825).

1993, Mar. 8 Litho. *Perf. 12x12 1/2*

1615 A206	70 le	Sheet of 8, #a.-h. + label	3.00	3.00
1616 A206	70 le	Sheet of 8, #a.-h. + label	3.00	3.00

Souvenir Sheet

Perf. 14 1/2

1617 A206	900 le	multicolored	4.75	4.75

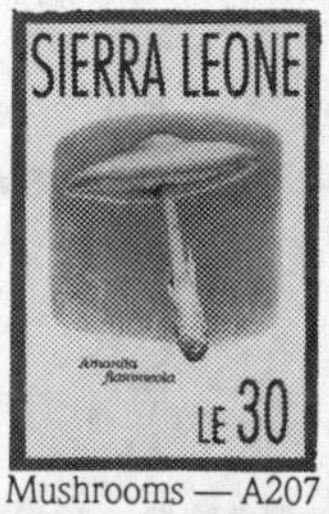

Mushrooms — A207

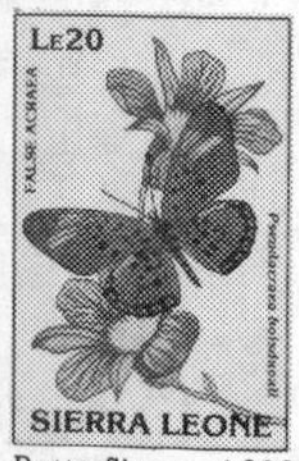

Butterflies — A208

Designs: 30 le, Amanita flammeola. 50 le, Cantharellus pseudocbarius. 100 le, Volvariella volvacea. 200 le, Termitomyces microcarpus. 300 le, Auricularia auricula. 400 le, Pleurotus tuberregium. 500 le, Schizophyllum commune. 600 le, Termitomyces robustus. No. 1626, Phallus rubicundus. No. 1627, Daldina concentrica.

1993, May 5 *Perf. 14*

1618 A207	30 le	multicolored	.15	.15
1619 A207	50 le	multicolored	.28	.28
1620 A207	100 le	multicolored	.52	.52

SIERRA LEONE 653

1621 A207 200 le multicolored 1.05 1.05
1622 A207 300 le multicolored 1.55 1.55
1623 A207 400 le multicolored 2.10 2.10
1624 A207 500 le multicolored 2.60 2.60
1625 A207 600 le multicolored 3.20 3.20
Nos. 1618-1625 (8) 11.45 11.45

Souvenir Sheets

1626-1627 A207 1000 le each 5.25 5.25

1993, May 5

1628 A208 20 le False acraea .15 .15
1629 A208 30 le Blue temora .15 .15
1630 A208 50 le Foxy charaxes .28 .28
1631 A208 100 le Leaf blue .52 .52
1632 A208 150 le Blue-banded swallowtail .78 .78
1633 A208 170 le African monarch .90 .90
1634 A208 200 le Mountain beauty 1.05 1.05
1635 A208 250 le Gaudy commodore 1.30 1.30
1636 A208 300 le Palla butterfly 1.60 1.60
1637 A208 500 le Pirate butterfly 2.60 2.60
1638 A208 600 le Painted lady 3.25 3.25
1639 A208 700 le Gold-banded forester 3.75 3.75
Nos. 1628-1639 (12) 16.33 16.33

Souvenir Sheets

1640 A208 1000 le Blue diadem 5.25 5.25
1641 A208 1000 le Blue swallowtail 5.25 5.25
1642 A208 1000 le African leaf butterfly 5.25 5.25

Miniature Sheets

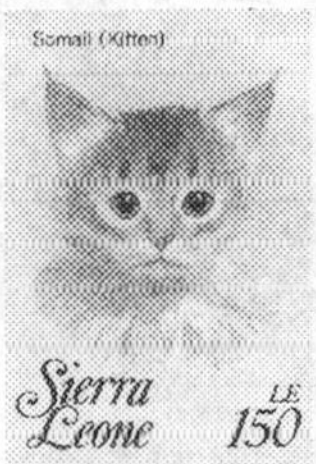
Somali (Kitten)
Sierra Leone
LE 150

Cats — A209

Designs: No. 1643a, Somali. b, Egyptian Mau smoke. c, Chocolate-point Siamese. d, Mi-Ke Japanese bobtail. e, Chinchilla. f, Red Burmese. g, British shorthair brown tabby. h, Blue Persian. i, British silver classic tabby. j, Oriental ebony. k, Red Persian. l, British calico shorthair.

No. 1644a, Black Persian. b, Blue-point Siamese. c, American wirehair. d, Birman. e, Scottish fold (silver tabby). f, American shorthair red tabby. g, Blue & white Persian bicolor. h, Havana brown. i, Norwegian forest cat. j, Brown tortie Burmese. k, Angora. l, Exotic shorthair.

No. 1645, American shorthair blue tabby, horiz. No. 1646, Seal-point colorpoint, horiz.

1993, May 17 Litho. *Perf. 14*

1643 A209 150 le Sheet of 12, #a.-l. 9.50 9.50
1644 A209 150 le Sheet of 12, #a.-l. 9.50 9.50

Souvenir Sheets

1645-1646 A209 1000 le each 5.25 5.25

Nos. 1643-1646 Ovptd. with Hong Kong '94 Emblem

1994 Litho. *Perf. 14*

1643m On #1643b & in sheet margin 9.50 9.50
1644m On #1644b & in sheet margin 9.50 9.50
1645a Ovptd. in sheet margin 5.25 5.25
1646a Ovptd. in sheet margin 5.25 5.25

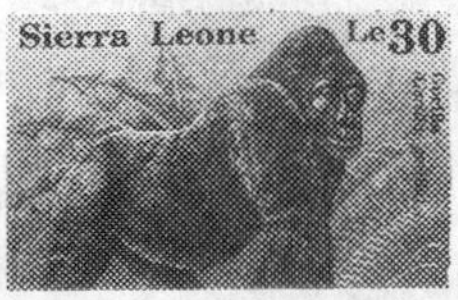
Sierra Leone Le30

Wild Animals A210

1993, June 17

1647 A210 30 le Gorilla .16 .16
1648 A210 100 le Bongo .52 .52
1649 A210 150 le Potto .78 .78
1650 A210 170 le Chimpanzee .90 .90
1651 A210 200 le Dwarf galago 1.05 1.05
1652 A210 300 le African linsang 1.60 1.60
1653 A210 500 le Banded duiker 2.65 2.65
1654 A210 750 le Diana monkey 4.00 4.00
Nos. 1647-1654 (8) 11.66 11.66

Souvenir Sheets

1655 A210 1200 le Leopard 6.25 6.25
1656 A210 1200 le Elephant 6.25 6.25

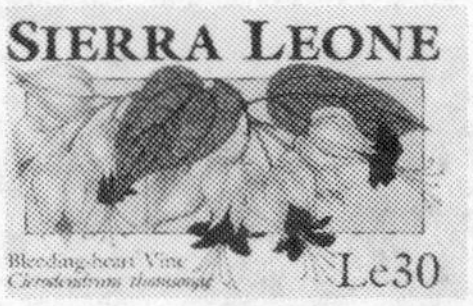
SIERRA LEONE
Le30

Flowers A211

Designs: 30 le, Bleeding-heart vine. 40 le, Passion vine. 50 le, Hydrangea. 60 le, Wax begonia. 100 le, Hibiscus. 150 le, Crape-myrtle. 170 le, Bougainvillea. 200 le, Leadwort. 250 le, Gerbera daisy. 300 le, Black-eyed susan. 500 le, Gloriosa lily. 900 le, Sweet violet. No. 1669, Gloriosa lily, diff. No. 1670, Passion vine, diff. No. 1671, Hibiscus, diff.

1993, July 15 Litho. *Perf. 14*

1657 A211 30 le multicolored .15 .15
1658 A211 40 le multicolored .20 .20
1659 A211 50 le multicolored .25 .25
1660 A211 60 le multicolored .30 .30
1661 A211 100 le multicolored .52 .52
1662 A211 150 le multicolored .80 .80
1663 A211 170 le multicolored .90 .90
1664 A211 200 le multicolored 1.00 1.00
1665 A211 250 le multicolored 1.25 1.25
1666 A211 300 le multicolored 1.50 1.50
1667 A211 500 le multicolored 2.50 2.50
1668 A211 900 le multicolored 3.00 3.00
Nos. 1657-1668 (12) 12.37 12.37

Souvenir Sheets

1669-1671 A211 1200 le each 6.25 6.25

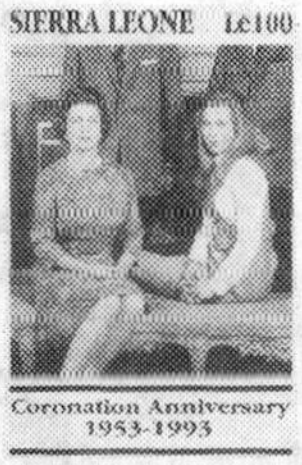
SIERRA LEONE Le100
Coronation Anniversary
1953-1993

Coronation of Queen Elizabeth II, 40th Anniv. — A212

Designs: 100 le, Queen, Princess Anne. 200 le, Coronation procession. 600 le, Official coronation photograph. 1500 le, Portrait, by Pietro Annigoni, 1954-55.

1993, Oct. Litho. *Perf. 14*

1672 A212 100 le multicolored .52 .52
1673 A212 200 le black 1.00 1.00
1674 A212 600 le multicolored 3.25 3.25
Nos. 1672-1674 (3) 4.77 4.77

Souvenir Sheet

1675 A212 1500 le multicolored 7.75 7.75

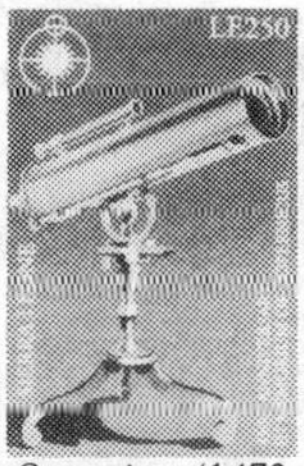
LE250

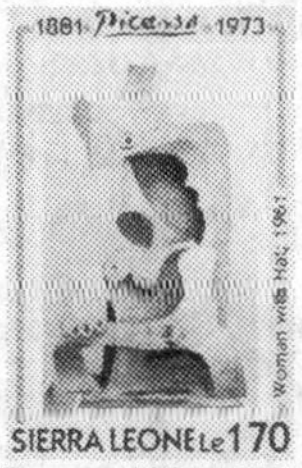
1881 Picasso 1973
SIERRA LEONE Le170

Copernicus (1473-1543) A213

Picasso (1881-1973) A214

Designs: 250 le, Early telescope. 800 le, Moon's surface.

1993, Oct.

1676 A213 250 le multicolored 1.25 1.25
1677 A213 800 le multicolored 4.25 4.25

1993, Oct.

Sculpture: 170 le, Woman with Hat, 1961.
Paintings: 200 le, Buste de Femme, 1958. 800 le, Maya with a Doll, 1938. 1000 le, Women of Algiers (after Delacroix), 1955.

1678 A214 170 le multicolored .90 .90
1679 A214 200 le multicolored 1.00 1.00
1680 A214 800 le multicolored 4.25 4.25
Nos. 1678-1680 (3) 6.15 6.15

Souvenir Sheet

1681 A214 1000 le multicolored 5.25 5.25

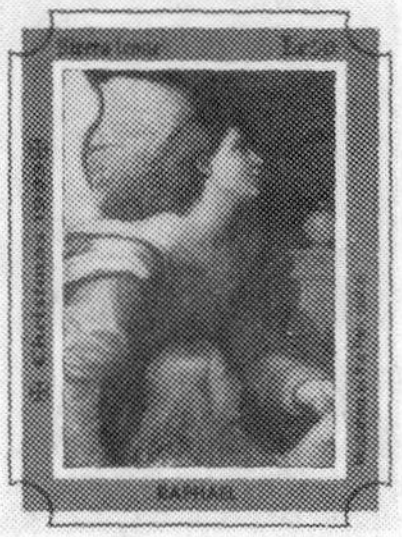

Christmas A215

Details or entire paintings, by Raphael: 50 le, 100 le, No. 1690, Madonna of the Fish. 150 le, Madonna & Child Enthroned with Five Saints. 800 le, The Holy Family with the Lamb.

Details or entire woodcuts, by Durer: 200 le, 250 le, 300 le, The Circumcision. 500 le, No. 1691, Holy Clan with Saints and Two Angels Playing Music.

1993, Dec. *Perf. 13½x14*

1682 A215 50 le multicolored .25 .25
1683 A215 100 le multicolored .52 .52
1684 A215 150 le multicolored .80 .80
1685 A215 200 le multicolored 1.00 1.00
1686 A215 250 le multicolored 1.25 1.25
1687 A215 300 le multicolored 1.50 1.50
1688 A215 500 le multicolored 2.50 2.50
1689 A215 800 le multicolored 4.25 4.25
Nos. 1682-1689 (8) 12.07 12.07

Souvenir Sheets

1690-1691 A215 1200 le each 6.25 6.25

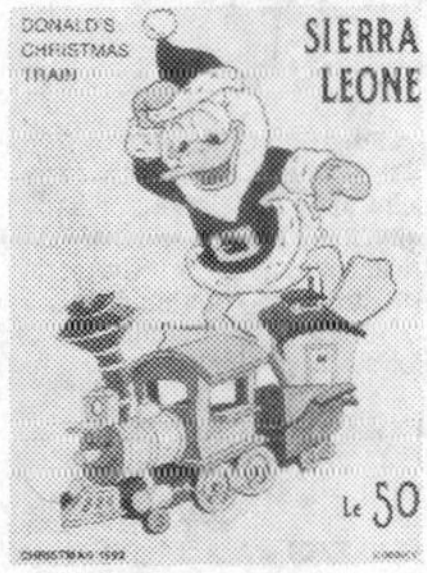
DONALD'S CHRISTMAS TRAIN
SIERRA LEONE
Le 50

Christmas A216

Disney characters celebrate Christmas: different. No. 1700, Santa. No. 1701, Elves, horiz. No. 1702, Santa, horiz. No. 1703, Mickey, Minnie, horiz.

1993, Dec. 17 *Perf. 13½x14*

1692 A216 50 le multicolored .25 .25
1693 A216 100 le multicolored .52 .52
1694 A216 170 le multicolored .90 .90
1695 A216 200 le multicolored 1.00 1.00
1696 A216 250 le multicolored 1.25 1.25
1697 A216 500 le multicolored 2.50 2.50
1698 A216 600 le multicolored 3.00 3.00
1699 A216 800 le multicolored 4.25 4.25
Nos. 1692-1699 (8) 13.67 13.67

Souvenir Sheets

Perf. 13½x14, 14x13½

1700-1703 A216 1200 le each 6.25 6.25

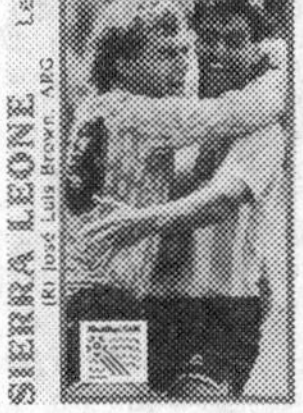
Le30
SIERRA LEONE

1994 World Cup Soccer Championships, US — A217

Players, country: 30 le, Jose Luis Brown (R), Argentina. 50 le, Gary Lineker, England. 100 le, Carlos Valderrama, Colombia. 250 le, Skuhravy, Czechoslovakia; Marchena, Costa Rica. 300 le, Butragueno, Spain. 400 le, Roger Milla, Cameroun. 500 le, Roberto Donadoni, Italy. 700 le, Enzo Scifo, Belgium.

No. 1712, 1200 le, Socrates, Brazil. No. 1713, 1200 le, Wright, England; Demol, Belgium.

1993 *Perf. 13½x14*

1704-1711 A217 Set of 8 10.00 10.00

Souvenir Sheets

1712-1713 A217 1200 le Set of 2 12.50 12.50

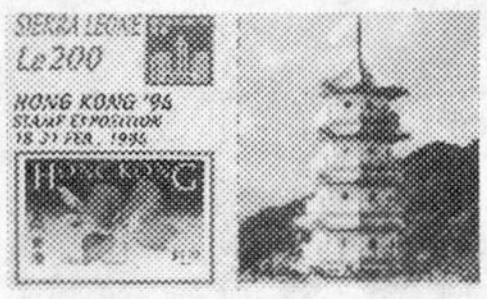
SIERRA LEONE
Le200
HONG KONG '94

A218

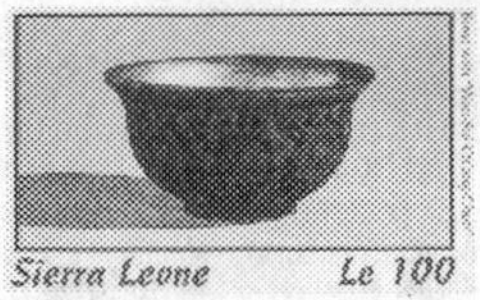
Sierra Leone Le 100

Hong Kong '94 A219

Stamps and: No. 1714, Hong Kong #455, pagoda, Tiger Baum Garden. No. 1715, Ai Par Garden, #1084.

Carved lacquer, Qing Dynasty: No. 1716a, Bowl with "Wan-Sui-Ch'ang-Chun." b, Four-wheeled box. c, Flower container. d, Box with human figure design. e, Shishi dog (not lacquer). f, Persimmon.

1994, Feb. 18 Litho. *Perf. 14*

1714 A218 200 le multicolored 1.00 1.00
1715 A218 200 le multicolored 1.00 1.00
a. Pair, #1714-1715 2.00 2.00

Miniature Sheet

1716 A219 100 le Sheet of 6, #a.-f. 3.25 3.25

Nos. 1714-1715 issued in sheets of 5 pairs. No. 1715a is a continuous design.

New Year 1994 (Year of the Dog) (#1716e).

Miniature Sheet

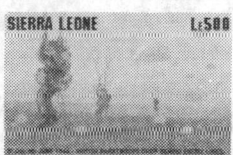

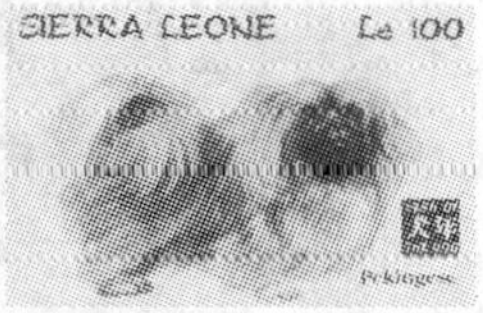
SIERRA LEONE Le 100
Pekingese

New Year 1994 (Year of the Dog) A220

Designs: a, 100 le, Pekingese. b, 150 le, Doberman pinscher. c, 200 le, Tibetan terrier. d, 250 le, Weimaraner. e, 400 le, Rottweiler. f, 500 le, Akita. g, 600 le, Schnauzer. h, 1000 le, Tibetan spaniel.

No. 1718, Wire-haired pointing Griffon. No. 1719, Shih Tzu.

1994, June 20 Litho. *Perf. 14*

1717 A220 Sheet of 8, #a.-h. 13.00 13.00

Souvenir Sheets

1718-1719 A220 1200 le each 4.75 4.75

SIERRA LEONE Le500

D-Day, 50th Anniv. A221

Designs: 500 le, British paratroops drop behind enemy lines. 750 le, US paratrooper jumps from C47 transport.

1000 le, C47 Douglas Dakota, paratroops.

1994, July 11 Litho. *Perf. 14*

1720 A221 500 le multicolored 2.00 2.00
1721 A221 750 le multicolored 3.00 3.00

Souvenir Sheet

1722 A221 1000 le multicolored 4.00 4.00

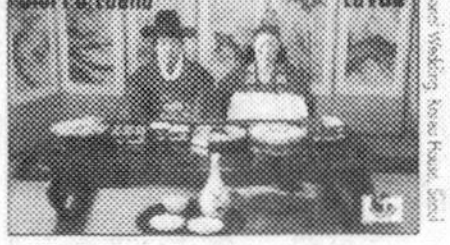
Sierra Leone Le100

A222

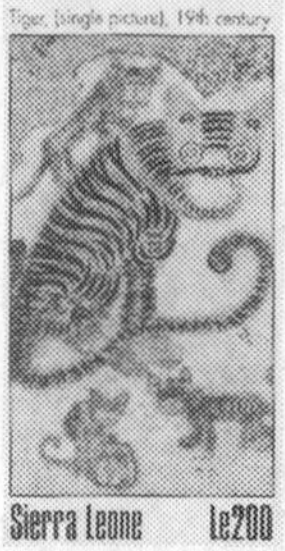

PHILAKOREA '94 — A223

Designs: 100 le, Traditional wedding, Korea House, Seoul. 400 le, Royal tombs, Koryo Dynasty, Kaesong. 600 le, Terraced farm land, near Chungmu.

Tiger paintings, Choson Dynasty: No. 1726a, Tiger, cubs, 19th cent. b, Munsa-pasal seated on lion. c, Extinct Korean tiger. d, Tiger, bamboo. e, Tiger guarding 3 cubs, 4 magpies. f, Tiger, 19th cent. g, Mountain Spirit. h, Tiger, bird in tree.

No. 1727, Wall painting of mounted hunters from Tomb of the Dancers of Kungnaesong, Koguryo period.

Perf. 14, 13½ (#1726)

1994, July 11 **Litho.**

1723-1725 A222 Set of 3 4.50 4.50

Miniature Sheet of 8

1726 A223 200 le #a.-h. 6.50 6.50

Souvenir Sheet

1727 A222 1200 le multicolored 4.75 4.75

Miniature Sheets of 6

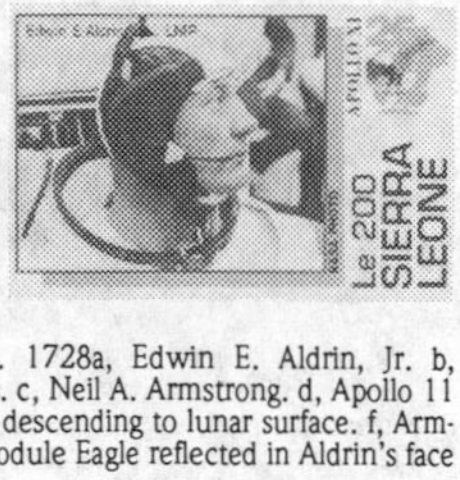

First Manned Moon Landing, 25th Anniv. A224

Designs: No. 1728a, Edwin E. Aldrin, Jr. b, Michael Collins. c, Neil A. Armstrong. d, Apollo 11 liftoff. e, Aldrin descending to lunar surface. f, Armstrong, lunar module Eagle reflected in Aldrin's face shield.

No. 1729a, Aldrin gathering soil samples. b, Eagle with Aldrin deploying solar wind experiment. c, Aldrin, ALSEP & Eagle at Tranquility Base. d, US flag, Aldrin, Tranquility Base. e, Plaque on moon. f, Apollo 11 crew, stamp ceremony.

1000 le, First footprint on moon.

1994, July 11 ***Perf. 14***

1728-1729 A224 200 le #a.-f, each 4.75 4.75

Souvenir Sheet

1730 A224 1000 le multicolored 4.00 4.00

Miniature Sheet of 6

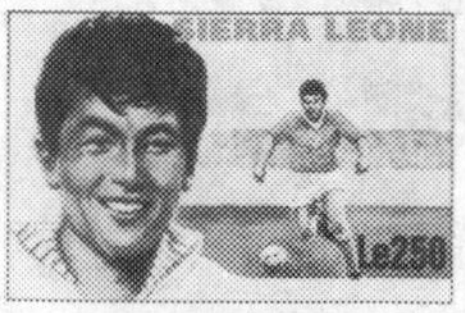

A225

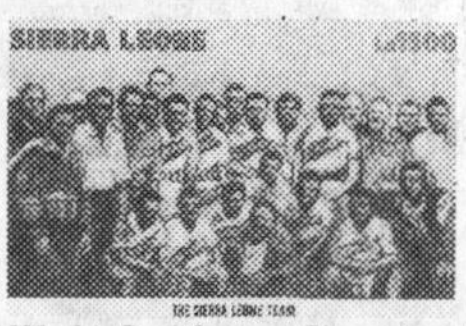

1994 World Cup Soccer Championships, US — A226

Players: No. 1731a, Kim Ho, South Korea. b, Cobi Jones, US. c, Claudio Suarez, Mexico. d, Tomas Brolin, Sweden. e, Ruud Gullit, Netherlands. f, Andreas Herzog, Austria.

No. 1732, Sierra Leone team. No. 1733, Giants Stadium, New Jersey.

1994, July 15

1731 A225 250 le #a.-f. 6.00 6.00

Souvenir Sheets

1732-1733 A226 1500 le each 6.00 6.00

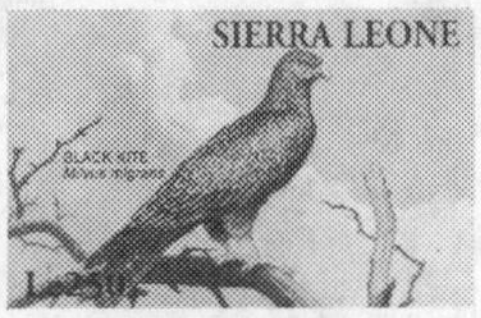

Birds A227

Designs: 250 le, Black kite. 300 le, Superb sunbird. 500 le, Martial eagle. 800 le, Red bishop.

White-necked picathartes: No. 1738a, 50 le, Feeding young. b, 100 le, On brown tree limb. c, 150 le, Two at nest. d, On gray limb, green leaves.

No. 1739, Greater flamingo, vert. No. 1740, White-necked picathartes up close, vert.

1994, Aug. 10

1734-1737 A227 Set of 4 8.50 8.50

Miniature Sheet of 9

1738 A227 3 each, #a.-d. 6.00 6.00

Souvenir Sheets

1739-1740 A227 1200 le each 4.75 4.75

World Wildlife Fund (#1738).

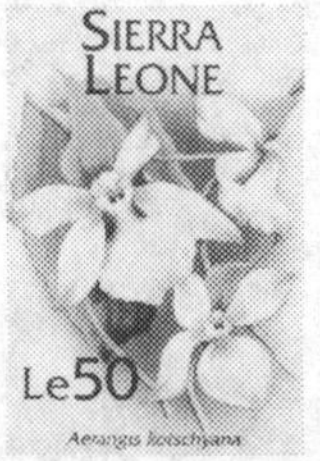

Orchids — A228

Designs: 50 le, Aerangis kotschyana. 100 le, Brachycorythis kalbreyeri. 150 le, Diaphananthe pellucida. 200 le, Eulophia guineensis. 300 le, Eurychone rothschildana. 500 le, Tridactyle tridactylites. 750 le, Cyrtorchis arcuata. 900 le, Ancistrochilus rothschildianus.

No. 1749, Plectrelminthus caudatus. No. 1750, Polystachaya affinis.

1994, Sept. 1

1741-1748 A228 Set of 8 12.00 12.00

Souvenir Sheets

1749-1750 A228 1500 le each 6.00 6.00

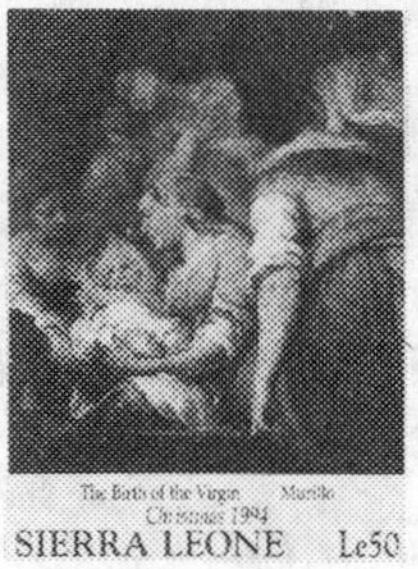

Christmas A229

Details or entire paintings: 50 le, The Birth of the Virgin, by Murillo. 100 le, Education of the Virgin, by Murillo. 150 le, Annunciation, by Filippino Lippi. 200 le, Marriage of the Virgin, by Bernard van Orley. 250 le, The Visitation, by Nicolas Vleughels. 300 le, Holy Infant from Castelfranco altarpiece, by Giorgione. 400 le, Adoration of the Magi, Workshop of Bartholome Zeitblom. 600 le, Presentation of Infant Jesus in the Temple, by Master of the Prado.

No. 1759, Nativity Altarpiece, by Lorenzo Monado. No. 1760, Allendale Nativity, by Giorgione.

1994, Dec. 1 **Litho.** ***Perf. 13½x14***

1751-1758 A229 Set of 8 6.75 6.75

Souvenir Sheets

1759-1760 A229 1500 le each 5.00 5.00

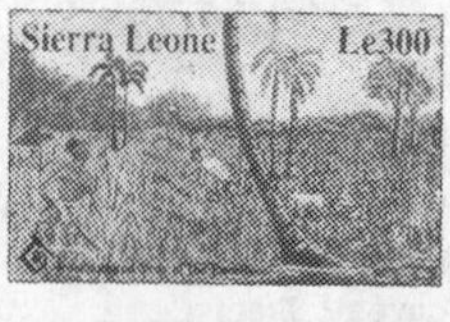

Intl. Year of the Family A230

1994, Dec. 20 **Litho.** ***Perf. 14***

1761 A230 300 le Working in field 1.00 1.00

1762 A230 350 le At beach 1.10 1.10

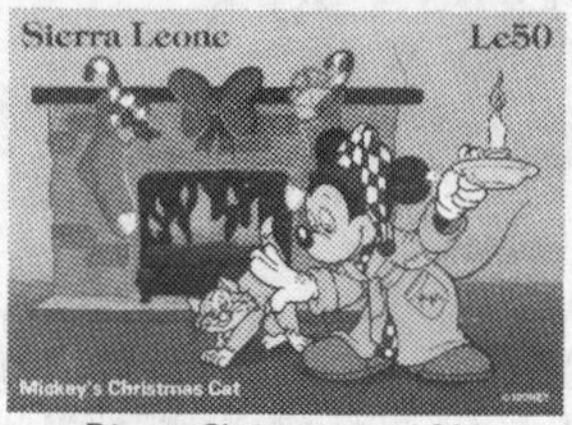

Disney Christmas — A231

Designs: 50 le, Mickey's Christmas cat. 100 le, Goofy's Christmas tree, vert. 150 le, Daisy's Christmas gift. 200 le, Donald's Christmas surprise, vert. 250 le, Minnie's Christmas flight. 300 le, Goofy's Christmas snowball, vert. 400 le, Goofy's Christmas letters. 500 le, Christmas sled ride, vert. 600 le, Mickey's Christmas snowman. 800 le, Pluto's Christmas treat, vert.

No. 1773, Goofy hanging outdoor lights. No. 1774, Mickey asleep in chair, vert.

Perf. 14x13½, 13½x14

1995, Jan. 23 **Litho.**

1763-1772 A231 Set of 10 11.00 11.00

Souvenir Sheets

1773-1774 A231 1500 le each 5.00 5.00

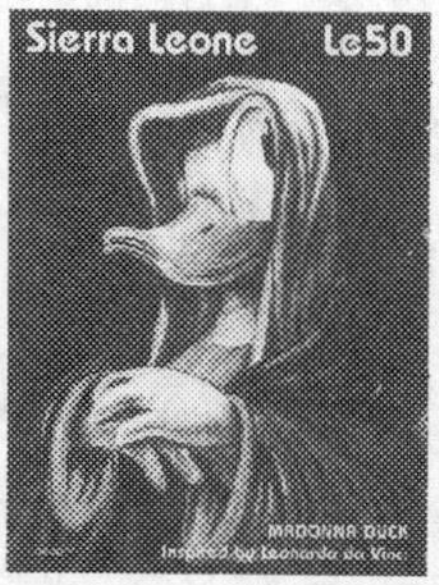

Donald Duck's Gallery of Old Masters A232

Name of painting, inspiration: 50 le, Madonna Duck, Leonardo da Vinci. 100 le, Portrait of a Venetian Duck, Tintoretto. 150 le, Duck with a Glove, Frans Hals. 200 le, Donald with a Pink, Quentin Massys. 250 le, Pinkie Daisy, Sir Thomas Lawrence. 300 le, Donald's Whistling Mother, Whistler. 400 le, El Quacko, El Greco. 500 le, The Noble Snob, Rembrandt. 600 le, The Blue Duck, by Gainsborough. 800 le, Modern Quack, Picasso.

No. 1785, Soup's On, Brueghel. No. 1786, Duck Dancers, Degas, horiz.

Perf. 13½x14, 14x13½

1995, Jan. 23

1775-1784 A232 Set of 10 11.00 11.00

Souvenir Sheets

1785-1786 A232 1500 le each 5.00 5.00

Miniature Sheets of 12

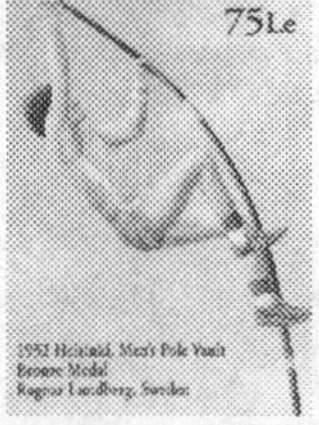

Olympic Medal Winners — A233

Summer Olympics: No. 1787a, Ragnar Lundberg, 1952 men's pole vault. b, Karin Janz, 1972 all-round gymnastics. c, Matthias Volz, 1936 gymnastics. d, Carl Lewis, 1988 long jump. e, Sara Simeoni, 1976 high jump. f, Daley Thompson, 1980 decathlon. g, Japan vs. Britain, 1964 soccer. h, Gabriella Dorio, 1984 1500-meters run. i, Daniela Hunger, 1988 200-meters individual medley swimming. j, Kyoko Iwasaki, 1992 200-meters breast stroke. k, Italian team member, 1960 water polo. l, David Wilkie, 1976 200-meters breast stroke.

1994 Winter Olympics, Lillehammer: No. 1788a, Katja Seizinger, downhill skiing. b, Hot air balloon (no medalist). c, Elvis Stojko, figure skating. d, Jens Weissflog, individual large hill ski jump. e, Bjorn Daehlie, 10k cross-country skiing. f, Germany, four-man bobsled. g, Markus Wasmeier, men's super giant slalom. h, Georg Hackl, luge. i, Trovill & Dean, ice dancing. j, Bonnie Blair, speed skating. k, Nancy Kerrigan, figure skating. l, Team Sweden, hockey.

No. 1789, torchbearer, horiz. No. 1790, Oksana Baiul, Nancy Kerrigan, Chen Lu, 1994 figure skating, horiz.

1995, Feb. 6 **Litho.** ***Perf. 14***

1787 A233 75 le #a.-l. 3.00 3.00

1788 A233 200 le #a.-l. 8.00 8.00

Souvenir Sheets

1789-1790 A233 1000 le each 3.50 3.50

Miniature Sheets

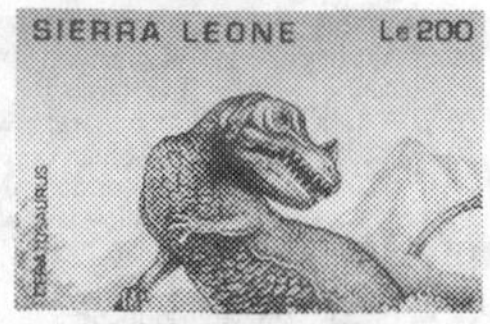

Dinosaurs A234

No. 1791: a, Ceratosaurus (d). b, Brachiosaurus. c, Pteranodon (b). d, Stegoceras. e, Saurolophus (h). f, Ornithomumus. g, Compsognathus (j). h, Deinonychus (i). i, Ornitholestes. j, Archaeopteryx. k, Heterodontosaurus (l). l, Lesothosaurus.

No. 1792: a, 100 le, Triceratops. b, 250 le, Protoceratops (c). c, 400 le, Monoclonius (b). d, 800 le, Styracosaurus (c).

No. 1793, Deinonychus. No. 1794, Rhamphorynchus.

1995, May 4 **Litho.** ***Perf. 14***

1791 A234 200 le Sheet of 12, #a.-l. 8.00 8.00

1792 A234 Sheet of 4, #a.-d. 5.25 5.25

Souvenir Sheets

1793-1794 A234 2500 le each 8.25 8.25

Miniature Sheets of 9

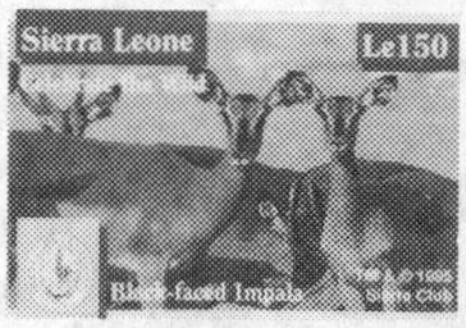

Sierra Club, Cent. A235

No. 1795, vert: a, L'Hoest's guenon. b, Black-footed cat. c, Colobus monkey up close. d, Colobus monkey in tree. e, Mandrill facing forward. f, Bonobo with young. g, Bonobo lying down. h, Mandrill facing right. i, Colobus monkey standing.

No. 1796: a, Black-faced impala facing forward. b, Herd of black-faced impala. c, Black-faced impala drinking. d, Bonobo. e, Black-footed cat. f, Black-footed cat up close. g, L'Hoest's guenon. h, L'Hoest's guenon, seated. i, Mandrills.

1995, May 10

1795-1796 A235 150 le #a.-i., each 4.50 4.50

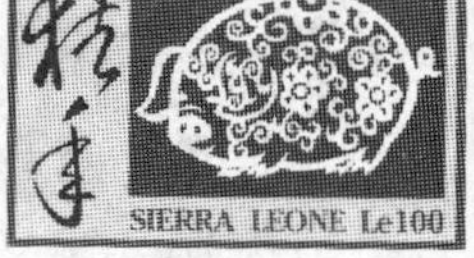

New Year 1995 (Year of the Boar) A236

Stylized boars: No. 1797a, red & multi, facing left. b, green & multi, facing right. c, green & multi, facing left. d, red & multi, facing right.

500 le, Two boars, vert.

1995, May 8 **Litho.** ***Perf. 14***

1797 A236 100 le Block of 4, #a.-d. 1.25 1.25

Souvenir Sheet

1798 A236 500 le multicolored 1.65 1.65

Miniature Sheets of 9

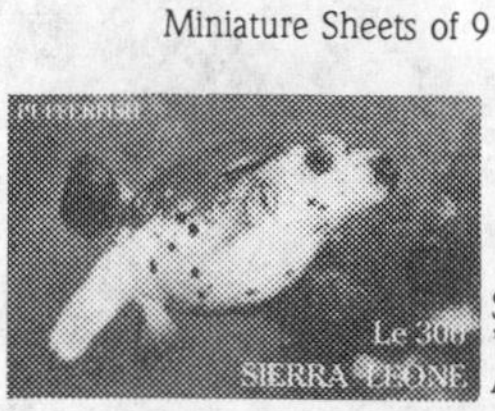

Singapore '95 A237

Marine life: No. 1799a, Pufferfish. b, Coral grouper. c, Hawksbill turtle. d, Hogfish. e, Emperor angelfish. f, Butterflyfish. g, Lemon butterflyfish. h, Parrotfish. i, Moray eel.

Water birds, marine life: No. 1800a, Cape pigeons. b, Pelican. c, Puffin. d, Humpback whale. e, Greater shearwater. f, Bottlenose dolphin. g, Gurnard. h, Salmon. i, John dory.

No. 1801, Surgeonfish. No. 1802, Angelfish, vert.

1995
1799-1800 A237 300 le #a.-i., each 9.00 9.00

Souvenir Sheets
1801-1802 A237 1500 le each 5.00 5.00

Miniature Sheets of 6 or 8

A238

End of
World War
II, 50th
Anniv.
A239

No. 1803: a, USS Idaho. b, HMS Ark Royal. c, Admiral Graf Spee. d, Destroyer. e, HMS Nelson. f, PT 109. g, USS Iowa. h, Bismark.
No. 1804: a, B-17. b, B-25. c, B-24 Liberator. d, USS Missouri. e, A-20 Boston. f, Pennsylvania, Colorado, Louisville, Portland, Columbia enter Lingayen Gulf. No. 1805, HMS Indomitable launching aircraft. No. 1806, B-29 bomber.

1995, July 10
1803 A238 250 le #a.-h. + label 6.75 6.75
1804 A239 300 le #a.-f. + label 6.00 6.00

Souvenir Sheet
1805 A238 1500 le multicolored 5.00 5.00
1806 A239 1500 le multicolored 5.00 5.00

No. 1805 contains one 57x42mm stamp.

UN, 50th
Anniv. — A240

No. 1807: a, 300 le, Dais, UN General Assembly. 400 le, Sec. Gen. U. Thant. 500 le, UN building, dove.
1500 le, Sec. Gen. Dag Hammarskjold.

1995, July 10   Litho.   Perf. 14
1807 A240 Strip of 3, #a.-c. 4.00 4.00

Souvenir Sheet
1808 A240 1500 le multicolored 5.00 5.00

No. 1807 is a continuous design.

1995 Boy
Scout
Jamboree,
Holland
A241

No. 1809: a, 400 le, Natl. flag. b, 500 le, Lord Baden-Powell. c, 600 le, Scout sign.
1500 le, Scout salute.

1995, July 10
1809 A241 Strip of 3, #a.-c. 5.00 5.00

Souvenir Sheet
1810 A241 1500 le multicolored 5.00 5.00

Queen Mother,
95th Birthday
A242

No. 1811: a, Drawing. b, Holding bouquet of flowers. c, Formal portrait. d, Without hat. 1500 le, Blue hat, dress.

1995, July 10   Perf. 13½x14
1811 A242 400 le Block or strip of 4, #a.-d. 5.25 5.25

Souvenir Sheet
1812 A242 1500 le multicolored 5.00 5.00

No. 1811 was issued in sheets of 8 stamps.

FAO,
50th
Anniv.
A243

No. 1813: a, 300 le, Man working with sack of food. b, 400 le, Boy carrying bundle of sticks on head. c, 500 le, Woman holding bowl of fruit. 1500 le, Woman holding baby, vert.

1995, July 10   Perf. 14
1813 A243 Strip of 3, #a.-c. 4.00 4.00

Souvenir Sheet
1814 A243 1500 le multicolored 5.00 5.00

Rotary Intl.,
90th Anniv.
A244

Designs: 500 le, Natl. flag, Rotary emblem. 1000 le, Paul Harris, Rotary emblem.

1995, July 10
1815 A244 500 le multicolored 1.75 1.75

Souvenir Sheet
1816 A244 1000 le multicolored 3.50 3.50

Miniature Sheets of 8

Singapore
'95 — A245

Flora & fauna: No. 1817a, African tulip tree. b, Senegal bush locust. c, Killifish. d, Bird of paradise. e, Mandrill. f, Painted reed frog. g, Large spotted acraea. h, Carmine bee-eater.
No. 1818: a, Flame lily. b, Grants gazelle. c, Dogbane. d, Gold-banded forester. e, Horned chameleon. f, Malachite kingfisher. g, Leaf beetle. h, Acanthus.
No. 1819, Lion. No. 1820, African elephant.

1995, Sept. 5   Litho.   Perf. 14
1817-1818 A245 300 le #a.-h., each 8.00 8.00

Souvenir Sheets
1819-1820 A245 1500 le each 5.00 5.00

Third UN Decade
for Advancement of
Women — A246

Designs: 300 le, Development. 500 le, Peace. 700 le, Equality.

1995   Litho.   Perf. 14
1821-1823 A246 Set of 3 5.00 5.00

Sierra
Leone
Grammar
School,
150th
Anniv.
A247

1995, Sept. 27   Litho.   Perf. 14
1824 A247 300 le multicolored 1.00 1.00

Christmas
A248

Details or entire paintings: 50 le, Holy Family, by Beccafumi. 100 le, Rest on Flight into Egypt, by Barocci. 150 le, La Vierge, by Bellini. 200 le, The Flight, by d'Arpino. 600 le, Adoration of the Magi, by Francken. 800 le, The Annunciation, by da Conegliano.
No. 1831, Virgin and child, by Cranach. No. 1832, Madonna and Child, by Berlinghiero.

1995, Dec. 1   Litho.   Perf. 13½x14
1825-1830 A248 Set of 6 6.50 6.50

Souvenir Sheets
1831-1832 A248 1500 le each 5.00 5.00

Disney
Christmas
A249

Antique Disney toys: 5 le, Mickey Mouse doll. 10 le, Donald rag drum major. 15 le, Donald wind up. 20 le, Toothbrush holder. 25 le, Mickey telephone, 30 le, Walking wind-up. 800 le, Movie projector. 1000 le, Goofy tricycle.
No. 1841, Black Mickey Mouse. No. 1842, First Mickey book.

1995, Dec. 4   Perf. 13½x14
1833-1840 A249 Set of 8 6.50 6.50

Souvenir Sheets
1841-1842 A249 1500 le each 5.00 5.00

Miniature Sheets of 9

Nobel Prize Fund
Established,
Cent. — A250

Recipients: No. 1843a, Andrew Huxley, medicine, 1963. b, Nelson Mandela, peace, 1993. c, Gabriela Mistral, literature, 1945. d, Otto Diels, chemistry, 1950. e, Hannes Alfven, physics, 1970. f, Wole Soyinka, literature, 1986. g, Hans G. Dehmelt, physics, 1989. h, Desmond Tutu, peace, 1984. i, Leo Esaki, physics, 1973.
No. 1844: a, Maria Goeppert Mayer, physics, 1963. b, Irène Joliot-Curie, chemistry, 1935. c, Mother Teresa, peace, 1979. d, Selma Lagerlöf, literature, 1909. e, Rosalyn Yalow, medicine, 1977. f, Dorothy Hodgkin, chemistry, 1964. g, Rita Levi-Montalcini, medicine, 1986. h, Mairead Corrigan, peace, 1976. i, Betty Williams, peace, 1976.
No. 1845: a, Tobias Asser, peace, 1911. b, Andrei Sakharov, peace, 1975. c, Frederic Passy, peace, 1901. d, Dag Hammarskjöld, peace, 1961. e, Aung San Suu Kyi, peace, 1991. f, Ludwig Quidde,

peace, 1927. g, Elie Wiesel, peace, 1986. h, Bertha von Suttner, peace, 1905. i, Dalai Lama, peace, 1989.
No. 1846: a, Richard Zsigmondy, chemistry, 1925. b, Robert Huber, chemistry, 1988. c, Wilhelm Ostwald, chemistry, 1909. d, Johann Deisenhofer, chemistry, 1988. e, Heinrich Wieland, chemistry, 1927. f, Gerhard Herzberg, chemistry, 1971. g, Hans von Euler-Chelpin, chemistry, 1929. h, Richard Willstätter, chemistry, 1915. i, Fritz Haber, chemistry, 1918.
No. 1847, Albert Einstein, physics, 1921. No. 1848, Wilhelm Röentgen, physics, 1901. No. 1849, Sin-Itiro Tomonaga, physics, 1965.

1995, Dec. 29   Litho.   Perf. 14
1843-1846 A250 250 le #a.-i., each 7.50 7.50

Souvenir Sheets
1847-1849 A250 1500 le each 5.00 5.00

New Year
1996 (Year
of the Rat)
A252

Different stylized rats: No. 1854a, Facing left, purple & multi. b, Facing right, blue green & multi. c, Facing left, blue green & multi. d, Facing right, blue & multi.
No. 1856, Rat, vert.

1996, Jan. 6
1854 A252 200 le Block of 4, #a.-d. 2.00 2.00

Miniature Sheet of 4
1855 A252 200 le #1854a-1854d 2.00 2.00

Souvenir Sheet
1856 A252 500 le multicolored 1.25 1.25

No. 1854 was issued in sheets of 16 stamps.

AIR POST STAMPS

Catalogue values for unused stamps in this section are for Never Hinged items.

Independence — Progress Issue
Nos. 197, 199, 204 and 206 Surcharged Like Nos. 242-247 plus "AIRMAIL" in Carmine, Red, Violet, Blue or Orange

Perf. 13, 13½

1963, Apr. 27   Wmk. 4   Engr.
Center in Black

C1	A27	7p on 1½p (C)	.15	.15
C2	A27	1sh3p on 1½p (R)	.18	.18
C3	A27	2sh6p brown org (V)	.38	.38
C4	A28	3sh on 3p (Bl)	.42	.42
C5	A28	6sh on 3p (O)	.52	.52
C6	A27	11sh on 10sh (C)	1.65	1.65
C7	A27	11sh on £1 (C)	500.00	175.00
		Nos. C1-C6 (6)	3.30	3.30

Nos. 221, 224, 213, 223 and 207 Surcharged or Overprinted in Brown, Red, Black, Violet, Ultramarine or Orange

1853–1859–1963
Oldest Postage Stamp
Newest G.P.O.
in West Africa

AIRMAIL   2/6

Perf. 13x13½, 13½x13, 13

1963, Nov. 4   Wmk. 4, 336

C8	A31	7p on 3p (Br)	.20	.20
C9	A32	1sh3p blue & blk (R)	.24	.24
C10	A30	2sh6p on 4p (Bk)	.48	.48
C11	A31	3sh on 3p (V)	.60	.60
C12	A32	6sh on 6p (U)	1.25	1.25
C13	A27	£1 orange & blk (O)	8.50	8.50
		Nos. C8-C13 (6)	11.27	11.27

Overprint is in 6 lines on Nos. C8, C11 and C12. A number of surcharge varieties and errors exist.

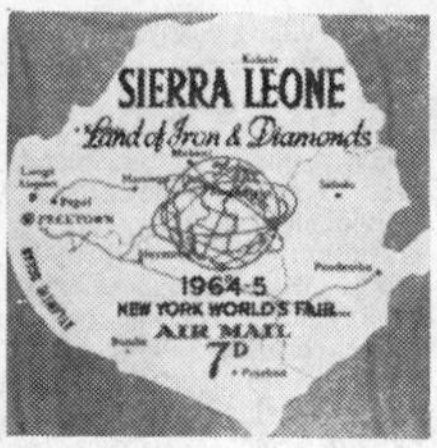

Unisphere and Map of Sierra Leone — AP1

Engraved and Lithographed

1964, Feb. 10 Unwmk. *Imperf.*

Self-adhesive

C14	AP1	7p multicolored	.15	.15
C15	AP1	9p multicolored	.15	.15
C16	AP1	1sh3p multicolored	.18	.18
C17	AP1	2sh6p multicolored	.35	.35
C18	AP1	3sh6p multicolored	.50	.50
C19	AP1	6sh multicolored	.90	.90
C20	AP1	11sh multicolored	1.40	1.40
		Nos. C14-C20 (7)	3.63	3.63

New York World's Fair, 1964-65.
For surcharge see No. C33.

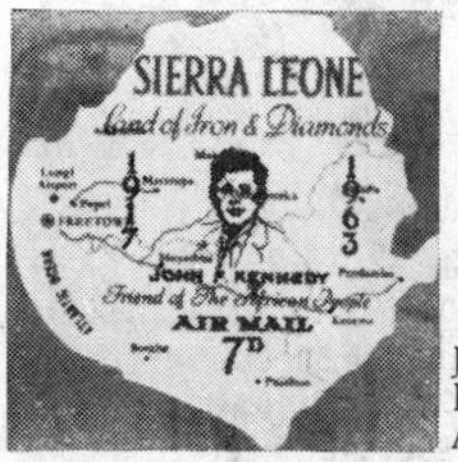

John F. Kennedy AP2

Self-adhesive

1964, May 11

C21	AP2	7p multicolored	.15	.15
C22	AP2	9p multicolored	.15	.15
C23	AP2	1sh3p multicolored	.22	.22
C24	AP2	2sh6p multicolored	.42	.42
C25	AP2	3sh6p multicolored	.60	.60
C26	AP2	6sh multicolored	1.10	1.10
C27	AP2	11sh multicolored	1.75	1.75
		Nos. C21-C27 (7)	4.39	4.39

For surcharges see Nos. C32, C34-C36.

Nos. 241, 213, 219 and 218 Surcharged in Dark Blue, Black, Red or Violet Blue

Perf. 11½x11, 13½x13, 13x13½

1964, Aug. 4 Engr. Wmk. 336

C28	A36	7c on 1sh3p (#241) (DB)	.22	.22
C29	A30	20c on 4p (#213)	.42	.42
C30	A29	30c on 10sh (#219) (R)	.70	.70
C31	A29	40c on 5sh (#218) (VB)	.85	.85
		Nos. C28-C31 (4)	2.19	2.19

Map-shaped Issues of 1964 Surcharged in Red or Black

Engraved and Lithographed

1964-65 Unwmk. *Imperf.*

C32	AP2	7c on 7p (#C21) (R)	.15	.15
C33	AP1	7c on 9p (#C15)	.85	.85
C34	AP2	60c on 9p (#C22)	1.25	1.25
C35	AP2	1 le on 1sh3p (#C23) (R)	2.00	2.00
C36	AP2	2 le on 11sh (#C27)	4.25	4.25
		Nos. C32-C36 (5)	8.50	8.50

Issue dates: Aug. 4, 1964, Nos. C35-C36. Jan. 20, 1965, Nos. C32, C34. April, 1965, No. C33.

Regular Issue of 1963 Surcharged like Nos. 300-305 with "AIRMAIL" added

Wmk. 336

1965, May 19 Photo. *Perf. 14*

Designs of Surcharge: No. C37, C39-C40, Sir Milton Margai and Sir Winston Churchill. No. C38, Margai. No. C41, Churchill.

C37	A35	7c on 2p (#230)	.15	.15
C38	A34	15c on ½p (#227)	.40	.40
C39	A35	30c on 6p (#233)	.75	.75
C40	A35	1 le on £1 (#239)	2.75	2.75
C41	A34	2 le on 10sh (#238)	5.50	5.50
		Nos. C37-C41 (5)	9.55	9.55

The portraits and inscription on No. C39 are white, the denomination and "AIRMAIL" are orange.

Ten more surcharges were issued Nov. 9, 1965: "2c" on Nos. C16, C23 and C25. "3c" on Nos. C14 and C22. "5c" on Nos. C17-C19, C24, and C26. Value $4 each.

One further surcharge was issued Jan. 28, 1966: "TWO/Leones" on No. C39. Value $10.

Type of Regular Issue and

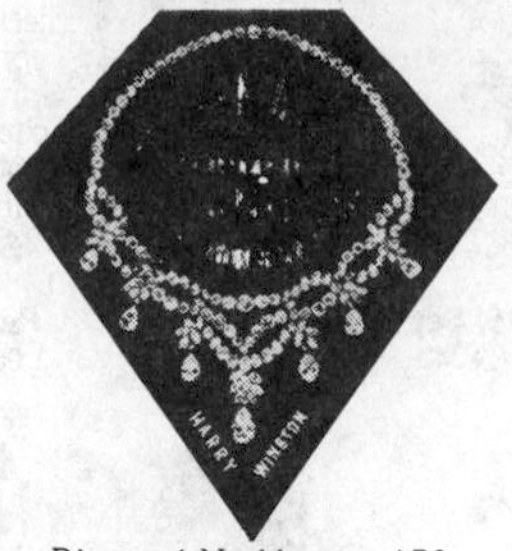

Diamond Necklace — AP3

Litho.; Reversed Embossing

1965, Dec. 17 Unwmk. *Imperf.*

Self-adhesive

C53	AP3	7c black, grn, gold & bl	.35	.35
C54	AP3	15c black, brnz, car & bl	.75	.75

Engr. and Embossed on Paper

C55	A41	40c multi, *cream*	1.75	1.75
		Nos. C53-C55 (3)	2.85	2.85

Various advertisements printed on peelable paper backing. Nos. C54-C55 have side tabs for handling and come packed in boxes of 100. No. C53 is without side tab and comes 25 stamps attached to one sheet.

For overprints and surcharges see Nos. C68-C69, C79-C83.

Nos. 248, 229, 232, 234 and 236 Surcharged and Overprinted: "AIRMAIL/FIVE YEARS/INDEPENDENCE/1961-1966"

1966, Apr. 27 Wmk. 336

C56	A37	7c on 3p pur & red	.15	.15
C57	A34	15c on 1sh multi	.35	.35
C58	A34	25c on 2sh6p multi	.55	.55
C59	A34	50c on 1½p multi	1.10	1.10
C60	A34	1 le on 4p multi	2.50	2.50
		Nos. C56-C60 (5)	4.65	4.65

The denomination on No. C60 is spelled out "One Leone."

Self-adhesive & Imperf.

Nos. C61-C131, C135-C142 are self-adhesive and imperforate.

Gold Coin Type of Regular Issue

Designs: 7c, 10c, ¼ Golde coin. 15c, 30c, ½ Golde coin. 50c, 2 le, 1 Golde coin. (7c, 15c, 50c, Map of Sierra Leone. 10c, 30c, 2 le, Lion's head.)

Diameter: 7c, 10c, 38mm; 15c, 30c, 54mm; 50c, 2 le, 82mm.

Lithographed; Embossed on Gilt Foil

1966, Nov. 12 Unwmk.

C61	A42	7c red & orange	.15	.15
C62	A42	10c dull blue & red	.15	.15
C63	A42	15c red & orange	.20	.20
C64	A42	30c black & rose lilac	.40	.40
C65	A42	50c rose lilac & emer	.75	.75
C66	A42	2 le green & black	3.75	3.75
		Nos. C61-C66 (6)	5.40	5.40

Advertising printed on paper backing.

Type of Regular Issue, 1965 and No. C55 Surcharged **=11½**

1967, Dec. 2 Engr. & Embossed

C67	A41	10c multi (red frame), *cream*	.50	.50
a.		Black frame	.50	.50
C68	A41	11½c on 40c multi, *cr*	.40	.40
C69	A41	25c on 40c multi, *cr*	1.00	1.00
		Nos. C67-C69 (3)	1.90	1.90

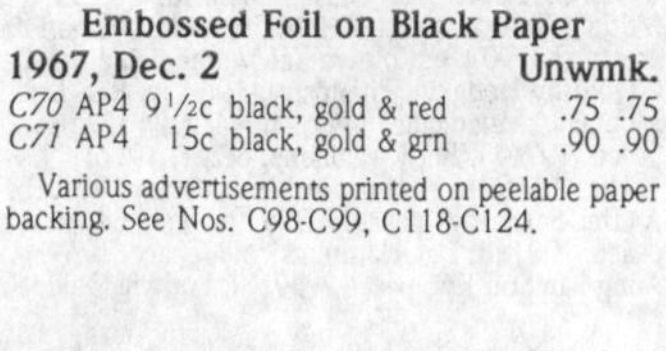

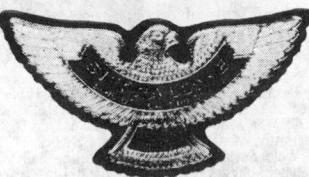

Eagle — AP4

Embossed Foil on Black Paper

1967, Dec. 2 Unwmk.

C70	AP4	9½c black, gold & red	.75	.75
C71	AP4	15c black, gold & grn	.90	.90

Various advertisements printed on peelable paper backing. See Nos. C98-C99, C118-C124.

Map Type of Regular Issue

Designs: Each denomination shows map of Africa with map of one of the following countries — Portuguese Guinea, South Africa, Mozambique, Rhodesia, South West Africa or Angola. Sheets of 30 (6x5) have 5 horizontal rows containing one stamp of each design.

1968, Sept. 25 Litho.

C72	A43	7½c multicolored	.30	.30
C73	A43	9½c multicolored	.45	.45
C74	A43	14½c multicolored	.65	.65
C75	A43	18½c multicolored	.75	.75
C76	A43	25c multicolored	1.25	1.25
C77	A43	1 le multicolored	7.50	7.50
C78	A43	2 le multicolored	17.50	17.50
		Nos. C72-C78 (7)	28.40	28.40
		7 Strips of 6, 1 of each design (42)	170.40	

No. C55 Overprinted and Surcharged in Red Similar to Nos. 364-368

Engraved and Embossed on Paper

1968, Nov. 30

C79	A41	6½c on 40c multi	.15	.15
C80	A41	17½c on 40c multi	.38	.38
C81	A41	22½c on 40c multi	.38	.38
C82	A41	28½c on 40c multi	.55	.55
C83	A41	40c multicolored	.85	.85
		Nos. C79-C83 (5)	2.31	2.31

Scroll Type of Regular Issue

Designs: 7½c, #C54. 9½c, #C70. 20c, #C16. 30c, #C26. 50c, #165. 2 le, #207 with "2nd Year of Independence" overprint. All are horiz.

1969, Mar. 1 Litho.

C84	A44	7½c multicolored	.24	.24
C85	A44	9½c multicolored	.28	.28
C86	A44	20c multicolored	.60	.60
C87	A44	30c multicolored	.90	.90
C88	A44	50c multicolored	2.25	2.25
C89	A44	2 le multicolored	15.00	15.00
		Nos. C84-C89 (6)	19.27	19.27

Various advertisements printed on peelable paper backing. No. C84 has side tab for handling and comes packed in boxes of 50. Nos. C85-C89 are without side tabs and come 20 stamps attached to one sheet.

For surcharges see Nos. C135-C136.

Pepel Port Types of Regular Issue

Designs: 7½c, 15c, Globe, tanker, flags of Sierra Leone and Japan. Anvil Shape with Flags of Sierra Leone and: 9½c, 2 le, Union Jack. 25c, Netherlands. 1 le, West Germany.

1969, July 10

C90	A45	7½c multicolored	.15	.15
C91	A46	9½c multicolored	.16	.16
C92	A45	15c multicolored	.26	.26
C93	A46	25c multicolored	.40	.40
C94	A46	1 le multicolored	1.65	1.65
C95	A46	2 le multicolored	3.25	3.25
		Nos. C90-C95 (6)	5.87	5.87

Various advertisements printed on peelable paper backing. No. C90 has side tab for handling and comes packed in boxes of 50. Nos. C91-C95 are without side tabs and come 20 stamps attached to one sheet.

Bank Type of Regular Issue

Lithographed; Gold Impressed

1969, Sept. 10

C96	A47	9½c yel grn, vio & gold	.90	.90

Advertising printed on peelable paper backing; 20 imperf. stamps to a sheet of backing, roulette 10.

Cola Nut Type of Regular Issue and Type of 1967

Typo.; Embossed on White Paper

1969, Sept. 10

C97	A40	7c yellow, maroon & car	.40	.40

Embossed Foil on Black Paper

C98	AP4	9½c black, gold & blue	.50	.50
C99	AP4	15c black, gold & red	.75	.75
		Nos. C97-C99 (3)	1.65	1.65

No. C97 has side tab for handling and comes packed in boxes of 100. Nos. C98-C99 have advertisements printed on peelable paper backing, side tabs and come packed in boxes of 50.

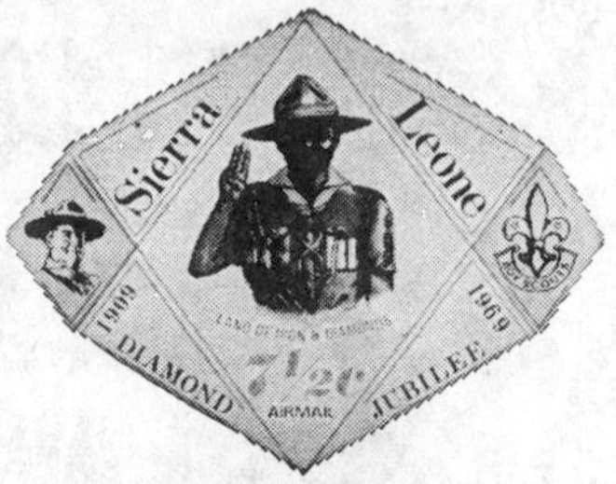

Boy Scout, Lord Baden-Powell and Scout Emblem — AP5

1969, Dec. 6 Litho.

C100	AP5	7½c multicolored	.48	.40
C101	AP5	9½c multicolored	.60	.48
C102	AP5	15c multicolored	1.25	.80
C103	AP5	22c multicolored	2.00	1.40
C104	AP5	55c multicolored	8.00	6.50
C105	AP5	3 le multicolored	100.00	72.50
		Nos. C100-C105 (6)	112.33	82.08

60th anniv. of the Sierra Leone Boy Scouts. Various advertising printed on peelable paper backing. No. C100 has side tab for handling and comes packed in boxes of 100. Nos. C101-C105 are without side tabs and come 20 stamps attached to one sheet.

No. 357 Surcharged "AIRMAIL" and New Denomination in Metallic Emerald, Lilac, Blue, Green, Bronze or Silver

1970, Mar 28

C106	A43	7½c on ½c (E)	.30	.30
C107	A43	9½c on ½c (L)	.40	.40
C108	A43	15c on ½c (Bl)	.50	.50
C109	A43	28c on ½c (G)	1.00	1.00
C110	A43	40c on ½c (Br)	1.75	1.75
C111	A43	2 le on ½c (S)	9.00	9.00
		Nos. C106-C111 (6)	12.95	12.95

See design paragraph over No. 357.

EXPO Type of Regular Issue

Design: EXPO '70 emblem, maps of Sierra Leone and Japan.

1970, June 22 Litho.

C112	A49	7½c multicolored	.16	.16
C113	A49	9½c multicolored	.20	.20
C114	A49	15c multicolored	.35	.35
C115	A49	25c multicolored	.70	.70
C116	A49	50c multicolored	1.50	1.50
C117	A49	3 le multicolored	7.75	7.75
		Nos. C112-C117 (6)	10.66	10.66

Various advertising printed on peelable paper backing.

Eagle Type of 1967

1970, Oct. 3 Embossed Foil

C118	AP4	7½c crimson & gold	.45	.45
C119	AP4	9½c emerald & cop	.55	.50
C120	AP4	15½c grnsh bl & sil	.85	.65
C121	AP4	25c brt red lil & gold	1.40	1.10
C122	AP4	50c gold & emer	2.75	2.25
C123	AP4	1 le silver & dk bl	5.50	4.50
C124	AP4	2 le gold & brt bl	11.00	9.25
		Nos. C118-C124 (7)	22.50	18.70

Advertisements printed on peelable paper backing. Issued in sheets of 10.

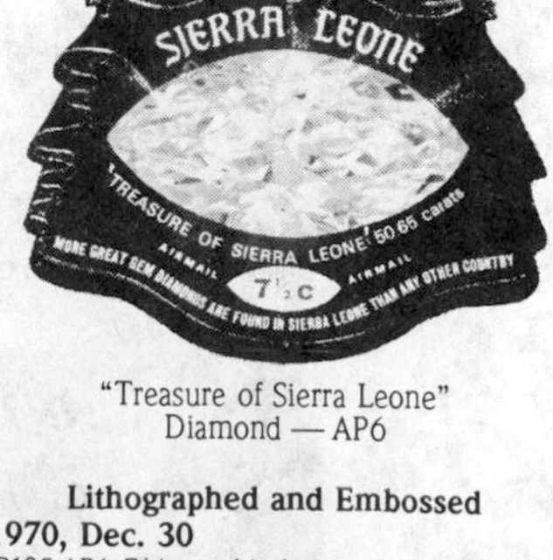

"Treasure of Sierra Leone" Diamond — AP6

Lithographed and Embossed

1970, Dec. 30

C125	AP6	7½c multicolored	.25	.25
C126	AP6	9½c multicolored	.30	.30
C127	AP6	15c multicolored	.50	.50
C128	AP6	25c multicolored	.50	.50
C129	AP6	75c multicolored	5.00	4.00
C130	AP6	2 le multicolored	22.50	17.50
		Nos. C125-C130 (6)	29.05	23.05

Diamond industry. Advertisement printed on peelable paper backing. Sheets of 20.

Traffic Type of Regular Issue

1971, Mar. 1			**Litho.**
C131	A53	9½c vio blue & org	.75 .75

Advertisements printed on peelable paper backing.

Nos. 211, 215, 228 and C87 Surcharged in Dark Red, Dark Blue or Black

10c 70c
AIRMAIL
a   b

1971, Mar. 1		**Engr.**	**Wmk. 336**
C132	A29(a)	10c on 2p (DR)	.35 .32
C133	A29(a)	20c on 1sh (DB)	.70 .65
		Photo.	**Perf. 14**
C134	A35(a)	50c on 1p (Bk)	1.75 1.50
		Unwmk.	
		Litho.	*Imperf.*
C135	A44(b)	70c on 30c (DB)	2.75 2.50
C136	A44(b)	1 le on 30c (Bk)	4.00 3.25
	Nos. C132-C136 (5)		9.55 8.22

Lion's Head and Bugles — AP7

Lithographed and Embossed (Gold)

1971, Apr. 27			
C137	AP7	7½c multicolored	.16 .16
C138	AP7	9½c multicolored	.18 .18
C139	AP7	15c multicolored	.26 .26
C140	AP7	25c multicolored	.45 .45
C141	AP7	75c multicolored	1.75 1.75
C142	AP7	2 le multicolored	6.00 6.00
	Nos. C137-C142 (6)		8.80 8.80

10th anniversary of independence. Advertisements printed on peelable paper backing. Stamps are in shape of Sierra Leone map and in flag colors.

Guma Valley Dam and Bank Emblem — AP8

1975, Jan. 14		**Litho.**	**Perf. 13½**
C143	AP8	15c multicolored	1.00 1.00

African Development Bank, 10th anniv.

Congo River Type of 1975

1975, Aug. 24		**Litho.**	**Perf. 13x13½**
C144	A57	20c multicolored	.75 .75

Mano River Type of 1975

1975, Oct. 3			**Perf. 13x13½**
C145	A58	15c multicolored	.60 .60

SINGAPORE

'siŋ-ə-ˌpȯr

LOCATION — An island just off the southern tip of the Malay Peninsula, south of Johore
GOVT. — Republic in British Commonwealth
AREA — 239 sq. mi.
POP. — 2,529,100 (est. 1984)
CAPITAL — Singapore

Singapore, Malacca and Penang were the British settlements which, together with the Federated Malay States, composed the former colony of Straits Settlements. On April 1, 1946, Singapore became a separate colony when the Straits Settlements colony was dissolved. Malacca and Penang joined the Malayan Union, which was renamed the Federation of Malaya in 1948. In 1959 Singapore became a state with internal self-government.

Singapore joined the Federation of Malaysia in 1963 and withdrew in 1965.

100 Cents = 1 Dollar

> Catalogue values for all unused stamps in this country are for Never Hinged items.

Watermark

Wmk. 366- S multiple

King George VI — A1

1948		**Wmk. 4**	**Typo.**	**Perf. 14**
1	A1	1c black		.15 .15
2	A1	2c orange		.15 .15
3	A1	3c green		.25 .15
4	A1	4c chocolate		.25 .15
6	A1	6c gray		.25 .15
7	A1	8c rose red		.35 .30
9	A1	10c plum		.30 .15
11	A1	15c ultra		2.25 .15
12	A1	20c dk green & blk		1.50 .40
14	A1	25c org & rose lilac		1.40 .15
16	A1	40c dk vio & rose red		6.25 17.50
17	A1	50c ultra & black		7.50 .25
18	A1	$1 vio brn & ultra		11.00 .40
19	A1	$2 rose red & emer		62.50 3.00
20	A1	$5 chocolate & emer		135.00 3.75
	Nos. 1-20 (15)			229.10 26.80
	Set, hinged			120.00

1949-52				**Perf. 18**
1a	A1	1c black ('52)		.55 .15
2a	A1	2c orange		.55 .15
4a	A1	4c chocolate		.55 .15
5	A1	5c rose violet ('52)		2.75 .15
6a	A1	6c gray ('52)		1.40 .15
8	A1	8c green ('52)		5.50 2.50
9a	A1	10c plum ('50)		.90 .15
10	A1	12c rose red ('52)		5.50 2.50
11a	A1	15c ultra ('50)		6.50 .30
12a	A1	20c dark green & black		5.50 1.25
13	A1	20c ultra ('52)		4.50 .75
14a	A1	25c org & rose lil ('50)		2.75 .15
15	A1	35c dk vio & rose red ('52)		8.25 3.00
16a	A1	40c dk vio & rose red ('51)		22.50 15.00
17a	A1	50c ultra & black ('50)		8.25 .15
18a	A1	$1 violet brn & ultra		16.00 .75
b.		Wmk. 4a (error)		1,000.
19a	A1	$2 rose red & emer ('51)		125.00 3.00
b.		Wmk. 4a (error)		1,000.
20a	A1	$5 choc & emerald ('51)		225.00 3.75
	Nos. 1a-20a (18)			441.95 34.00
	Set, hinged			225.00

Silver Wedding Issue
Common Design Types
Inscribed: "Singapore"

1948, Oct. 25	**Photo.**	**Perf. 14x14½**	
21	CD304	10c purple	.85 .15

Engraved; Name Typographed
Perf. 11½x11

22	CD305	$5 light brown	95.00 22.50

UPU Issue
Common Design Types
Inscribed: "Malaya-Singapore"
Engr.; Name Typo. on 15c, 25c
Perf. 13½, 11x11½

1949, Oct. 10				**Wmk. 4**
23	CD306	10c rose violet		1.25 .25
24	CD307	15c indigo		2.50 .55
25	CD308	25c orange		4.00 .95
26	CD309	50c slate		8.75 3.25
	Nos. 23-26 (4)			16.50 5.00

Coronation Issue
Common Design Type

1953, June 2	**Engr.**	**Perf. 13½x13**	
27	CD312	10c magenta & black	1.75 .15

Chinese Sampans — A2

Sir Stamford Raffles Statue — A3

Singapore River — A4

Designs: 2c, Malay kolek. 4c, Twa-kow. 5c, Lombok sloop. 6c, Trengganu pinas. 8c, Palari. 10c, Timber tongkong. 12c, Hylam trader. 20c, Cocos-Keeling schooner. 25c, Argonaut plane. 30c, Oil tanker. 50c, Liner (M.S. Chusan). $5, Arms of Singapore.

Perf. 13½x14½

1955, Sept. 4		**Photo.**	**Wmk. 4**	
28	A2	1c sepia		.15 .15
29	A2	2c orange yellow		.15 .15
30	A2	2c orange brown		.22 .15
31	A2	5c magenta		.22 .15
32	A2	6c gray blue		.22 .15
33	A2	8c aqua		.65 .32
34	A2	10c dark purple		.32 .15
35	A2	12c rose red		1.40 .65
36	A2	20c violet blue		1.40 .15
37	A2	25c orange & purple		.75 .15
38	A2	30c purple & plum		1.10 .15
39	A2	50c bright blue		2.25 .15

Perf. 13½x14, 14x13½
Engr.

40	A3	$1 blue & purple	6.50 .18
41	A4	$2 blue green & red	22.50 .50

Engr.; Arms Typo.

42	A3	$5 multicolored	45.00 2.25
	Nos. 28-42 (15)		82.83
	Set value		4.50

For a later printing of the 10c and 50c, plates with finer screen (250) than normal (200) were used.

Singapore Lion and Administrative Center — A5

1959, June 1	**Photo.**	**Wmk. 314**	
Lion in Gold			
43	A5	4c deep rose red	.20 .15
44	A5	10c magenta	.38 .15
45	A5	20c ultra	1.00 .45
46	A5	25c yellow green	1.20 .50

47	A5	30c bright violet	1.40 .95
48	A5	50c bluish gray	3.25 1.90
	Nos. 43-48 (6)		7.43 4.10

New Constitution of Singapore.

State Flag of Singapore — A6

1960, June 3	**Litho.**	**Perf. 13½**	
49	A6	4c blue, red & yellow	.35 .15
50	A6	10c gray, red & yellow	.70 .30

Issued for National Day, June 3, 1960.

Hands and Map of Singapore — A7

1961, June 3		**Photo.**	
51	A7	4c brown, yellow & gray	.40 .20
52	A7	10c green, yellow & gray	.60 .25

Issued for National Day, June 3, 1961.

Sea Horse — A8

Malayan Fish: 4c, Tiger barb, horiz. 5c, Anemone fish, horiz. 6c, Archerfish. 10c, Harlequin fish, horiz. 20c, Butterflyfish. 25c, Two-spot gournami, horiz.

Perf. 14½x13½, 13½x14½

1962, Mar. 31				**Wmk. 314**
53	A8	2c lt green & red brown		.15 .15
54	A8	4c red orange & blk		.15 .15
a.		Black omitted		110.00
55	A8	5c gray & red org		.15 .15
a.		Red orange omitted		110.00
b.		Wmkd. sideways ('67)		.22 .15
56	A8	6c yellow & blk		.18 .15
57	A8	10c dk gray & red org		.28 .15
a.		Red orange omitted		85.00
b.		Wmkd. sideways ('67)		.42 .15
58	A8	20c blue & orange		.80 .15
a.		Orange omitted		125.00
59	A8	25c orange & black		.80 .15
a.		Black omitted		100.00
b.		Wmkd. sideways ('67)		.85 .25
	Nos. 53-59 (7)			2.51
	Set value			.40

For surcharge see No. 370.

Symbolic of Labor's Role in Building the Nation — A9

1962, June 3   Unwmk.   Perf. 11½
60	A9	4c brt rose, blk & yel	.35 .15
61	A9	10c brt blue, blk & yel	.55 .22

Issued for National Day, June 3, 1962.

Vanda Tan Chay Yan — A10

Yellow-Breasted Sunbird — A11

Designs: 1c, Arachnis Maggie Oei, horiz. 12c, Grammatophyllum speciosum. 30c, Vanda Miss Joaquim. 50c, Shama, horiz. $1, White-breasted kingfisher, horiz. $5, White-tailed sea eagle.

Perf. 12½, 13½x13 (50c, $1), 13x13½ ($2, $5)

1963, Mar. 10   Photo.   Wmk. 314
Flowers and Birds in Natural Colors
Size: 37x26mm, 26x37mm
62	A10	1c brt pink & ultra	.15 .15
a.		Wmkd. sideways ('67)	.15 .15
63	A10	8c lt blue & mag	.55 .55
64	A10	12c salmon & brown	1.10 .15
65	A10	30c tan & ol green	1.65 .15
a.		tan omitted	50.00

Size: 35½x25½mm, 25½x35½mm
66	A11	50c yel green & blk	1.90 .15
a.		Wmkd. sideways ('66)	3.00 .85
67	A11	$1 yellow & blk	5.75 .20
a.		Wmkd. sideways ('67)	6.25 3.25
68	A11	$2 dull blue & blk	11.00 1.10
69	A11	$5 pale blue & blk	32.50 2.75
		Nos. 62-69 (8)	54.60 5.35

See No. 76.

Government Housing Project A12

1963, June 3   Perf. 12½
70	A12	4c multicolored	.35 .15
71	A12	10c multicolored	.50 .22

Issued for National Day, June 3, 1963.

Folk Dancers — A13

1963, Aug. 8   Photo.   Perf. 14x14½
72	A13	5c multicolored	.20 .15

Southeast Asia Cultural Festival.

Workers, Factory and Apartment House — A14

Wmk. 314 (30c), Unwmd. (15, 20c)
1966, Aug. 9   Photo.   Perf. 12½x13
73	A14	15c ultra & multi	.40 .20
74	A14	20c red & multi	.60 .40
75	A14	30c yellow & multi	1.00 .65
		Nos. 73-75 (3)	2.00 1.25

First anniversary of the Republic.

Bird Type of 1963

Design: 15c, Black-naped tern (sterna).

1966, Nov. 9   Wmk. 314   Perf. 12½
Bird in Natural Colors
Size: 26x37mm
76	A11	15c blue & black	.35 .15
a.		Orange (eye) omitted	12.50

Marching Women, Chinese Inscription A15

Designs: 15c, Malay inscription. 50c, Tamil inscription.

Perf. 14x14½
1967, Aug. 9   Photo.   Unwmk.
77	A15	6c lt brown, gray & red	.15 .15
78	A15	15c multicolored	.30 .20
79	A15	50c multicolored	1.25 1.00
		Nos. 77-79 (3)	1.70 1.35

"Build a Vigorous Singapore" campaign.

Buildings and Map of Africa and Southeast Asia — A16

1967, Oct. 7   Perf. 14x13½
Black Overprint
80	A16	10c multicolored	.16 .15
81	A16	25c multicolored	.52 .45
82	A16	50c multicolored	1.10 .90
		Nos. 80-82 (3)	1.78 1.50

2nd Afro-Asian Housing Cong., Oct. 7-15. No. 80 exists without overprint.

Map of Singapore and Symbolic Worker — A17

Sword Dance — A18

Stamps are inscribed "Work for Prosperity" in English and: 6c, Chinese. 15c, Malay. 50c, Tamil.

Perf. 13½x14½
1968, Aug. 9   Photo.   Unwmk.
83	A17	6c red, black & gold	.18 .16
84	A17	15c brt yel grn, blk & gold	.40 .30
85	A17	50c brt blue, blk & gold	1.25 1.10
		Nos. 83-85 (3)	1.83 1.56

Issued for National Day, 1968.

Wmk. Rectangles (334)
1968   Photo.   Perf. 14
Designs: 6c, Lion dance. 10c, Bharatha Natyam, Indian dance. 15c, Tari Payong, Sumatran dance. 20c, Kathak Kali, Indian dance mask. 25c, Lu Chih Shen and Lin Chung, Chinese opera masks. 30c, Dragon dance, horiz. 50c, Tari Lilin, Malayan candle dance. 75c, Tarian Kuda Kepang, Javanese dance. $1, Yao Chi, Chinese opera mask.
86	A18	5c yellow & multi	.18 .15
87	A18	6c orange & multi	.22 .15
88	A18	10c blue green & multi	.35 .15
89	A18	15c lt brown & multi	.48 .22
a.		Booklet pane of 4 ('69)	1.90
90	A18	20c brown & multi	.60 .22
91	A18	25c dp car & multi	.90 .38
92	A18	30c pink & multi	1.25 .38
93	A18	50c brown org & multi	1.40 .75

94	A18	75c brt rose & multi	2.50 1.20
95	A18	$1 olive grn & multi	3.25 1.50
		Nos. 86-95 (10)	11.13 5.10

Issue dates: 6c, 20c, 30c, 50c, 75c, Dec. 1; 5c, 10c, 15c, 25c, $1, Dec. 29.

1973   Perf. 13
86a	A18	5c yellow & multi	.60 .42
88a	A18	10c blue green & multi	.85 .50
90a	A18	20c brown & multi	1.50 .85
91a	A18	25c deep carmine & multi	2.50 1.40
92a	A18	30c pink & multi	3.50 1.75
93a	A18	50c brown orange & multi	5.00 3.00
95a	A18	$1 olive green & multi	12.00 6.00
		Nos. 86a-95a (7)	25.95 13.92

Cogwheel and Emblem — A19

1969, Apr. 15   Unwmk.   Perf. 13
96	A19	15c blue, black & silver	.40 .24
97	A19	30c red, black & silver	.80 .65
98	A19	75c violet, black & silver	2.00 1.50
		Nos. 96-98 (3)	3.20 2.39

25th Plenary Session of the Economic Commission for Asia and the Far East (ECAFE), Singapore, Apr. 15-28.

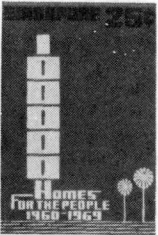
"Homes for the People" A20

Plane over Docks of Singapore A21

Perf. 13x13½
1969, July 20   Litho.   Unwmk.
99	A20	25c emerald & black	1.00 .70
100	A20	50c dark blue & black	1.50 1.25

1960-69 building program of the Housing and Development Board.

1969, Aug. 9   Perf. 14x14½
Designs: 30c, UN emblem and map of Singapore. 75c, Flags and map of Malaya and Borneo. $1, Uplifted hands and Singapore flag. $5, Tail of Japanese plane and searchlights. $10, Statue of Sir Thomas Stamford Raffles.
101	A21	15c yellow, blk & org	.28 .24
102	A21	30c brt blue & blk	.60 .52
103	A21	75c orange & multi	1.90 1.25
104	A21	$1 red & black	4.25 2.25
105	A21	$5 gray, blk & red	27.50 17.50
106	A21	$10 emerald & blk	52.50 35.00
a.		Souvenir sheet of 6, #101-106	375.00 325.00
		Nos. 101-106 (6)	87.03 56.76

Sesquicent. of the founding of Singapore.

Mirudhangam, South Indian Drum — A22

Musical Instruments: 4c, Pi Pa, Chinese, 4 strings, vert. $2, Rebab, Malay violin, 3 strings, vert. $5, Vina, Indian, 7 strings. $10, Ta Ku, Chinese drum.

1969   Photo.   Wmk. 366   Perf. 13
107	A22	1c multicolored	.15 .15
108	A22	4c multicolored	.15 .15
109	A22	$2 multicolored	5.00 2.75
110	A22	$5 multicolored	11.00 6.75
111	A22	$10 multicolored	27.50 15.00
		Nos. 107-111 (5)	43.80 24.80

Issue dates: 1c, 4c, $2, $5, Nov. 10; $10, Dec. 6.

Sea Shells — A23

Designs: 30c, Tropical fish. 75c, Greater flamingo and helmeted hornbill. $1, Orchids.

Perf. 13½
1970, Mar. 15   Unwmk.   Litho.
112	A23	15c pale violet & multi	.45 .18
113	A23	30c lt blue & multi	1.40 .60
114	A23	75c yellow & multi	4.00 2.75
115	A23	$1 lt green & multi	4.75 3.00
a.		Souvenir sheet of 4, #112-115	13.00 6.75
		Nos. 112-115 (4)	10.60 6.53

EXPO '70 International Exposition, Osaka, Japan, Mar. 15-Sept. 13.

Common Design Types pictured in section before Great Britain.

Child Playing (Kindergarten) — A24

Designs: 50c, Sports activities. 75c, Cultural activities.

1970, July   Unwmk.   Perf. 13½
116	A24	15c deep orange & blk	.55 .22
117	A24	50c orange, blk & vio bl	1.90 1.10
118	A24	75c black & dp lilac rose	2.75 1.90
		Nos. 116-118 (3)	5.20 3.22

People's Association, 10th anniversary.

Soldier and Map of Singapore — A25

Designs: Map and soldiers in various positions.

1970, Aug. 9   Litho.   Unwmk.
119	A25	15c emerald, blk & org	.48 .20
120	A25	50c orange, blk & brt mag	2.50 1.50
121	A25	$1 brt mag, blk & emer	3.50 3.25
		Nos. 119-121 (3)	6.48 4.95

National military service.

Runners A26

Designs: 15c, Swimmers. 25c, Badminton. 50c, Automobile race.

1970, Aug. 23   Photo.   Perf. 13
122	A26	10c black, dp car & ultra	.45 .20
123	A26	15c black, ultra & brn org	.80 .14
124	A26	25c black, brn org & emer	1.40 1.40
125	A26	50c black, dp car & emer	2.50 2.50
a.		Strip of 4, #122-125	5.25 5.25

1970 Festival of Sports.

Ship and Emblem of National Line (Neptune Oriental Lines) — A27

Designs: 30c, Ship in first container berth. 75c, Ship repairing and ship building.

1970, Nov. 1   Litho.   Perf. 12
126 A27 15c vio blue, lemon & red   1.10   .30
127 A27 30c dp ultra & lemon   2.50   1.10
128 A27 75c red & lemon   6.50   3.25
    Nos. 126-128 (3)   10.10   4.65

Singapore shipping industry.

Flags of Commonwealth Nations — A28

Designs: 15c, Circular arrangement of names of Commonwealth members. 30c, Flags arranged in circle. $1, Flags (different arrangement).

1971, Jan. 14   Perf. 15x14¹/₂
Size: 46¹/₂x31mm
129 A28 15c gold & multi   .45   .20
130 A28 30c gold & multi   1.00   .65
131 A28 75c gold & multi   1.65   1.65
Size: 67x31mm
Perf. 14
132 A28 $1 gold & multi   4.00   2.50
    Nos. 129-132 (4)   7.10   5.00

Commonwealth Heads of Government Meeting, Singapore, Jan. 12-14.

Cycle Rickshaws — A29

Houses of Worship in Singapore — A30

Perf. 11¹/₂
1971, Apr. 4   Unwmk.   Litho.
133 A29 15c shown   .32   .18
134 A29 20c Sampans   .48   .35
135 A29 30c Market place   1.50   .60
Perf. 13x13¹/₂
136 A30 50c Waterfront   1.75   1.00
137 A30 75c shown   3.00   1.25
    Nos. 133-137 (5)   7.05   3.38

Tourist publicity.

Chinese New Year — A31

Singapore Festivals: 30c, Hari Raya Puasa (Moslem). 50c, Deepavali (Hindu). 75c, Christmas.

1971, Aug. 9   Litho.   Perf. 14
138 A31 15c multicolored   .62   .25
139 A31 30c multicolored   1.35   .80
140 A31 50c multicolored   2.50   1.50

141 A31 75c multicolored   3.75   2.25
    a.   Souvenir sheet of 4, #138-141   67.50   67.50
    Nos. 138-141 (4)   8.22   4.80

Satellite Earth Station, Sentosa Island — A32

Design: No. 143 as 15c, enlarged to cover 4 stamps. Sheets of 100.

1971, Oct. 23   Unwmk.   Perf. 13¹/₂
142 A32 15c red & multi   4.00   1.25
143 A32   Block of 4   42.50   37.50
    a.   30c (yellow numeral)   10.50   9.25
    b.   30c (green numeral)   10.50   9.25
    c.   30c (rose numeral)   10.50   9.25
    d.   30c (orange numeral)   10.50   9.25

Establishment of Singapore's satellite earth station, Sentosa Island.

Singapore River and Fort Canning, 1843-1847 — A33

Views of Singapore, from 19th century art works: 15c, The Padang, 1851. 20c, Waterfront, 1848-1849. 35c, View from Fort Canning, 1846. 50c, View from Mount Wallich, 1857. $1, Waterfront with ships, from the sea, 1861.

1971, Dec. 5   Unwmk.   Perf. 13x12¹/₂
Size: 52x45mm
144 A33 10c gold & multi   .60   .32
145 A33 15c gold & multi   .90   .45
146 A33 20c gold & multi   1.50   .75
147 A33 35c gold & multi   3.50   2.00
Perf. 12¹/₂x13
Size: 68x47mm
148 A33 50c gold & multi   6.25   3.50
149 A33 $1 gold & multi   15.00   8.00
    Nos. 144-149 (6)   27.75   15.02

George V 1c Copper Coin, 1920 — A34

Singapore Coins: 35c, Silver dollar, 1969. $1, Gold $150, 1969 commemorative coin for sesquicentennial of founding of Singapore.

1972, June 4   Litho.   Perf. 13¹/₂
150 A34 15c dk grn, dp org & blk   .85   .22
151 A34 35c red & black   2.00   .75
152 A34 $1 ultra, yellow & blk   3.00   3.00
    Nos. 150-152 (3)   5.85   3.97

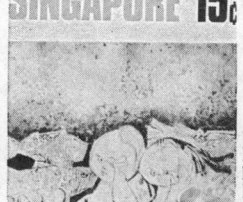

"Moon Festival," by Seah Kim Joo — A35

Paintings by Singapore Artists: 35c, "Complimentary Force," by Thomas Yeo. 50c, "Rhythm in Blue," by Yusman Aman. $1, "Gibbons," by Chen Wen Hsi.

1972, July 9   Litho.   Perf. 12¹/₂
Size: 40x43¹/₂mm
153 A35 15c brown org & multi   .50   .20
Size: 35¹/₂x53¹/₂mm
154 A35 35c blue green & multi   1.40   .70
155 A35 50c dull violet & multi   2.00   1.00
Size: 40x43¹/₂mm
156 A35 $1 bister & multi   4.75   2.25
    Nos. 153-156 (4)   8.65   4.15

Chinese New Year — A36

Festivals: 35c, Hari Raya Puasa (candles and ornament). 50c, Deepavali (incense and teapot). 75c, Christmas (candle and stained glass window).

1972, Aug. 9   Litho.   Perf. 13x12¹/₂
157 A36 15c deep rose & multi   .45   .25
158 A36 35c violet & multi   1.25   .85
159 A36 50c green & multi   1.65   1.10
160 A36 75c blue & multi   2.50   1.65
    Nos. 157-160 (4)   5.85   3.85

Technical and Scientific Training — A37

Designs: 35c, Sport. $1, Art and culture.

1972, Oct. 1   Photo.   Perf. 12
161 A37 15c orange & multi   .50   .30
162 A37 35c blue & multi   1.25   1.00
163 A37 $1 orange & multi   3.50   3.00
    Nos. 161-163 (3)   5.25   4.30

Youth of Singapore.

Neptune Ruby A38

1972, Dec. 17   Litho.   Perf. 14x14¹/₂
Size: 42x28¹/₂mm
164 A38 15c shown   .25   .20
Size: 29¹/₂x28¹/₂mm
165 A38 75c Maria Rickmers   2.00   2.00
166 A38 $1 Chinese junk   6.00   6.00
    a.   Souvenir sheet of 3, #164-166   17.00   10.00
    Nos. 164-166 (3)   8.25   8.20

Singapore shipping industry.

Quality and Reliability Emblem — A39

Birds, Jurong Bird Park — A40

Designs: 15c, Emblem and initials of participating organizations: Singapore Institute of Standards and Industrial Research, Singapore Manufacturers' Association, National Trades Union Congress. 75c, Emblem and "Prosperity through Quality and Reliability" in multiple rows. $1, Quality and Reliability emblem.

1973, Feb. 25   Litho.   Perf. 14¹/₂x14
167 A39 15c gold & multi   .30   .25
168 A39 35c gold & multi   .75   .65
169 A39 75c gold & multi   1.75   1.65
170 A39 $1 gold & multi   2.50   2.25
    Nos. 167-170 (4)   5.30   4.80

Prosperity through Quality and Reliability campaign.

1973, Apr. 29   Perf. 12¹/₂
Landmarks: 35c, Dancers, National Theater. 50c, City Hall and ballplayers. $1, Singapore River with boats and buildings.

171 A40 15c vermilion & blk   .40   .25
172 A40 35c dull green & blk   1.25   .90
173 A40 50c brown & blk   2.00   1.10
174 A40 $1 dark violet & blk   4.00   2.25
    Nos. 171-174 (4)   7.65   4.35

Airline Emblems A41

Designs: 35c, Emblem of Singapore Airlines and international destinations. 75c, SIA emblem on stylized tail of Boeing jet. $1, SIA emblems circling globe.

1973, June 24   Litho.   Perf. 13¹/₂
175 A41 10c multicolored   .35   .20
176 A41 35c multicolored   .90   .90
177 A41 75c multicolored   2.25   1.75
178 A41 $1 multicolored   3.25   3.00
    Nos. 175-178 (4)   6.75   5.85

Singapore Intl. Airport at Paya Lebar.

Entertainers — A42

Running, Judo, Boxing — A43

Design: Composite of various forms of entertainment.

1973, Aug. 9   Litho.   Perf. 13¹/₂x14
179 A42 10c black & orange red   .50   .25
180 A42 35c black & orange red   1.40   1.10
181 A42 50c black & orange red   2.00   1.75
182 A42 75c black & orange red   3.50   2.75
    a.   Block of 4, #179-182   7.50   7.50

National Day 1973.

1973, Sept. 1   Photo.   Perf. 14
Designs: 15c, Bicycling, weight lifting, pistol shoot, yachting. 25c, Various balls. 35c, Tennis racket, ball, hockey stick. 50c, Swimming. $1, Singapore National Stadium.

Size: 25x25mm
183 A43 10c gold, silver & ind   .45   .22
184 A43 15c gold & dk brown   .50   .24
185 A43 25c silver, gold & blk   .85   .60
186 A43 35c gold, silver & dk pur   1.25   .95
Perf. 13x14
Size: 40¹/₂x25mm
187 A43 50c gold & multi   1.50   1.25
188 A43 $1 silver, vio bl & emer   4.00   3.50
    a.   Souvenir sheet of 6, #183-188   15.00   5.00
    Nos. 183-188 (6)   8.55   6.76

7th South East Asia (SEAP) Games, Singapore.

Agave A44

Mangosteen A45

Designs: Stylized flowers and fruit.

1973 Photo. *Perf. 13*

189 A44 1c shown .15 .15
190 A44 5c Coleus blumei .15 .15
a. Booklet pane of 10 (4 #190, 4 #191 + 2 #193) 2.25
191 A44 10c Madagascar periwinkle .20 .15
192 A44 15c Sunflower .22 .15
193 A44 20c Dwarf palm .35 .15
194 A44 25c Yellow daisy .38 .15
195 A44 35c Chrysanthemum .65 .35
196 A44 50c Costus .90 .45
197 A44 75c Transvaal daisy 1.25 .65
198 A45 $1 shown 1.65 1.00
199 A45 $2 Jackfruit 3.50 2.25
200 A45 $5 Coconuts 8.75 5.50
201 A45 $10 Pineapple 17.00 11.00
Nos. 189-201 (13) 35.15 22.10

Nos. 189-201 have fluorescent underprint "Singapore" in multiple rows.

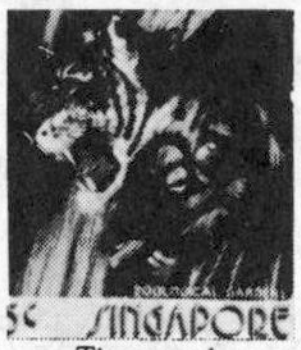

Tiger and Orangutans — A46

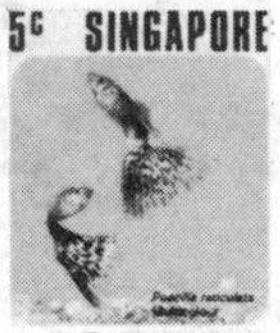

Tropical Fish — A47

1973, Dec. 16 Litho. *Perf. 13*

202 A46 5c shown .40 .15
203 A46 10c Leopard and deer .80 .25
204 A46 35c Panther and stag 2.50 1.00
205 A46 75c White horse & lion 4.50 2.50
Nos. 202-205 (4) 8.20 3.90

Opening of Singapore Zoo.

1974, Apr. 21 *Perf. 13½x14*

Designs: Various poecilia reticulata fish.

206 A47 5c apple green & multi .35 .15
207 A47 10c pink & multi .55 .28
208 A47 35c brt blue & multi 1.40 1.25
209 A47 $1 brt green & multi 4.75 3.50
Nos. 206-209 (4) 7.05 5.18

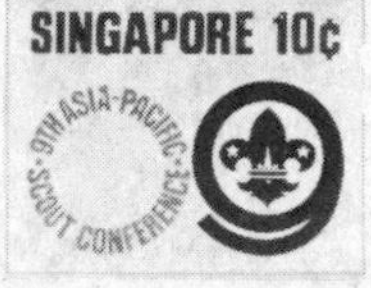

Scout Conference Emblem — A48

1974, June 9 *Perf. 13½x14½*

210 A48 10c multicolored .45 .28
211 A48 75c multicolored 2.75 2.75

9th Asia-Pacific Boy Scout Conf., Singapore.

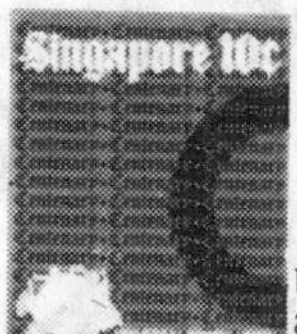

UPU Emblem, Circle and "Centenary" Multiple — A49

UPU, cent.: 35c, Circle and UN emblems, multiple. 75c, Circle and pigeons, multiple.

1974, July 7 Litho. *Perf. 14½x13½*

212 A49 10c orange brn & multi .24 .15
213 A49 35c blue & multi .80 .55
214 A49 75c emerald & multi 2.00 1.40
Nos. 212-214 (3) 3.04 2.10

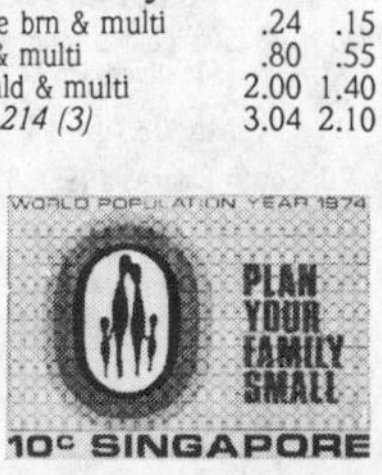

Family — A50

1974, Aug. 9 Litho. *Perf. 13x13½*

215 A50 10c shown .22 .15
216 A50 35c Symbols for male & female .80 .65
217 A50 75c World map and WPY emblem 2.00 1.90
Nos. 215-217 (3) 3.02 2.70

Natl. Day and World Population Year 1974.

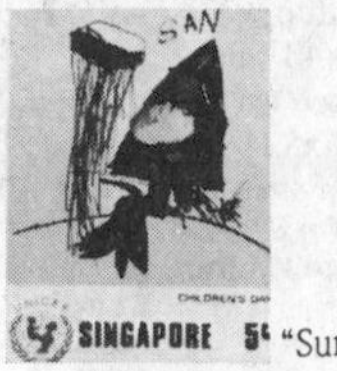

"Sun and Tree" — A51

Children's Drawings: 10c, "My Daddy and Mommy." 35c, "A Dump Truck." 50c, "My Aunt."

1974, Oct. 1 Photo. *Perf. 14x13½*

218 A51 5c multicolored .35 .15
219 A51 10c multicolored .75 .50
220 A51 35c multicolored 2.00 1.65
221 A51 50c multicolored 3.25 2.50
a. Souv. sheet of 4, #218-221, perf. 13 11.00 3.50
Nos. 218-221 (4) 6.35 4.80

Children's drawings for Children's Day (UNICEF).

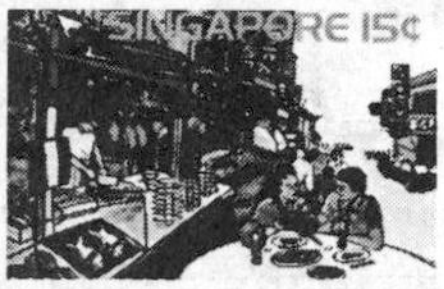

Alfresco Dining A52

Tourist publicity: 20c, Singapore River. $1, "Kelong" fish traps.

1975, Jan. 26 Litho. *Perf. 14*

222 A52 15c multicolored .40 .25
223 A52 20c multicolored .48 .40
224 A52 $1 multicolored 4.00 3.00
Nos. 222-224 (3) 4.88 3.65

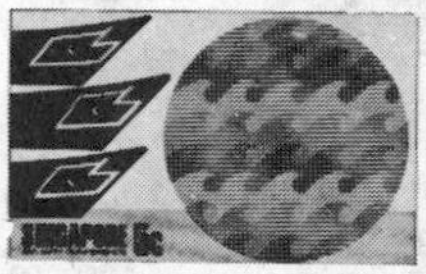

Prows of Barges and Wave Design — A53

Designs: 25c, Cargo ships and ship's wheel. 50c, Tanker and signal flags. $1, Container ship and propellers.

1975, Mar. 10 Litho. *Perf. 13½*

225 A53 5c multicolored .20 .15
226 A53 25c multicolored .80 .70
227 A53 50c multicolored 1.50 1.40
228 A53 $1 multicolored 3.50 2.75
Nos. 225-228 (4) 6.00 5.00

9th Biennial Conf. of the Intl. Assoc. of Ports and Harbors, Singapore, Mar. 8-15.

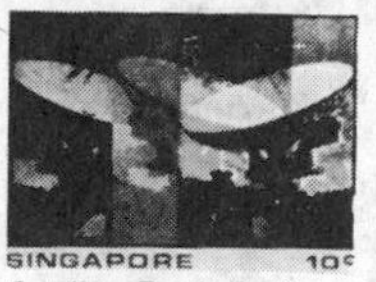

Satellite Earth Stations, Sentosa Island — A54

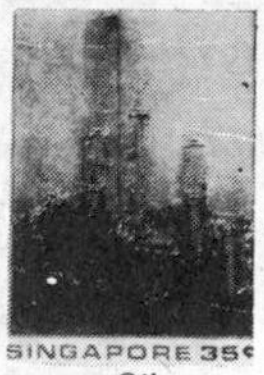

Oil Refinery — A55

Science and Industry: 75c, Brain surgery, Medical Center, Jurong.

1975, June 29 Photo. *Perf. 13½*

229 A54 10c multicolored .25 .15
230 A55 35c multicolored .75 .55
231 A54 75c multicolored 2.50 1.50
Nos. 229-231 (3) 3.50 2.20

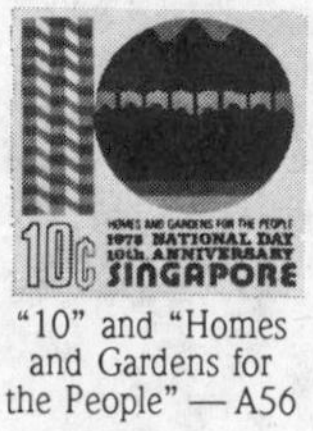

"10" and "Homes and Gardens for the People" — A56

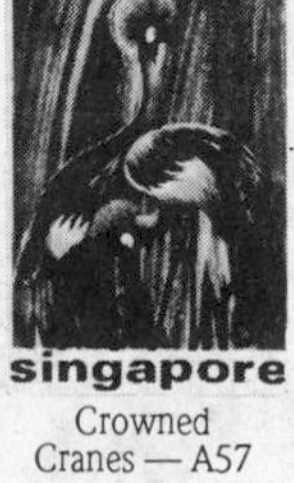

Crowned Cranes — A57

Tenth Natl. Day ("10" and): 35c, "Shipping and ship building." 75c, "Communications and technology." $1, "Trade, commerce and industry."

1975, Aug. 9 Litho. *Perf. 13½*

232 A56 10c multicolored .25 .15
233 A56 35c multicolored .80 .55
234 A56 75c multicolored 2.00 1.25
235 A56 $1 multicolored 2.50 1.50
Nos. 232-235 (4) 5.55 3.45

1975, Oct. 5 Litho. *Perf. 14½x13½*

Birds: 10c, Great hornbill. 35c, White-breasted and white-collared kingfishers. $1, Sulphur-crested cockatoo and blue and yellow macaw.

236 A57 5c emerald & multi .35 .15
237 A57 10c emerald & multi .55 .20
238 A57 35c emerald & multi 3.00 1.25
239 A57 $1 emerald & multi 7.25 3.75
Nos. 236-239 (4) 11.15 5.35

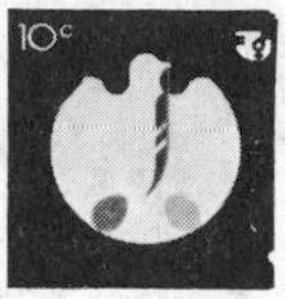

IWY Emblem, Peace Dove as "Equality" — A58

Designs (IWY Emblem): 35c, Peace dove with eggs in basket, symbolizing "Development." 75c, Peace dove and young, symbolizing "Peace."

1975, Dec. 7 Litho. *Perf. 13½*

240 A58 10c blk, blue & pink .45 .25
241 A58 35c orange & multi 1.50 1.10
242 A58 75c dp violet & multi 3.00 2.25
a. Souvenir sheet of 3, #240-242 12.00 12.00
Nos. 240-242 (3) 4.95 3.60

International Women's Year 1975.

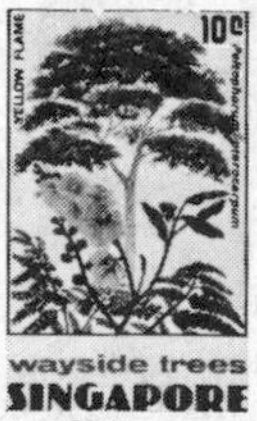

Yellow Flame — A59

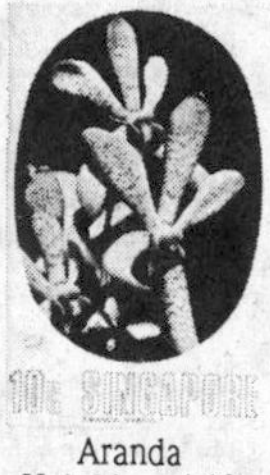

Aranda Hybrid — A60

Wayside Trees: 35c, Cabbage tree. 50c, Rose of India. 75c, Variegated coral tree.

1976, Apr. 18 Litho. *Perf. 14*

243 A59 10c multicolored .30 .20
244 A59 35c multicolored 1.00 .85
245 A59 50c multicolored 1.50 1.25
246 A59 75c multicolored 3.00 1.90
Nos. 243-246 (4) 5.80 4.20

1976, June 20 Litho. *Perf. 14*

Designs: Varieties of aranda orchids.

247 A60 10c black & multi .40 .15
248 A60 35c black & multi 1.50 .75
249 A60 50c black & multi 3.00 1.10
250 A60 75c black & multi 4.50 1.60
Nos. 247-250 (4) 9.40 3.60

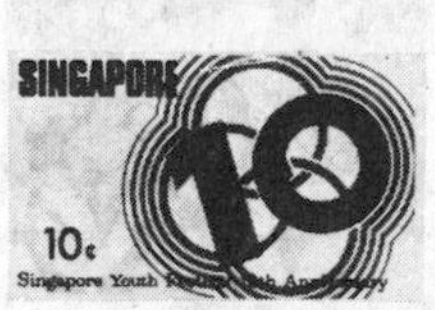

"10" and Children's Band — A61

Designs ("10" and): 35c, Running boys. 75c, Dancing children.

1976, Aug. 9 Litho. *Perf. 12½*

251 A61 10c multicolored .30 .20
252 A61 35c multicolored 1.00 .70
253 A61 75c multicolored 3.00 1.65
Nos. 251-253 (3) 4.30 2.55

Singapore Youth Festival, 10th anniversary.

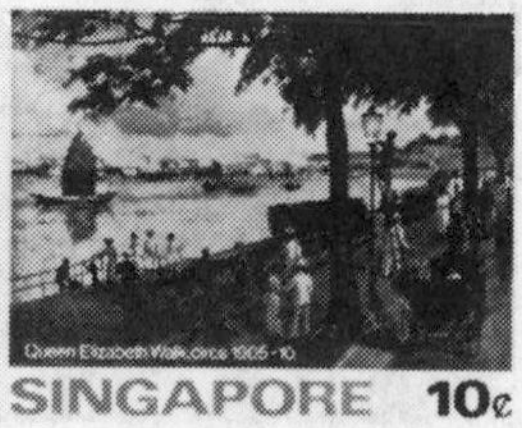

Queen Elizabeth Walk — A62

Paintings of Old Singapore, c. 1905-10: 50c, The Padang. $1, Raffles Place.

1976, Nov. 14 Litho. *Perf. 14*

254 A62 10c multicolored .35 .15
255 A62 50c multicolored 1.50 1.00
256 A62 $1 multicolored 3.50 2.00
a. Souvenir sheet of 3, #254-256, perf. 13½ 10.00 10.00
Nos. 254-256 (3) 5.35 3.15

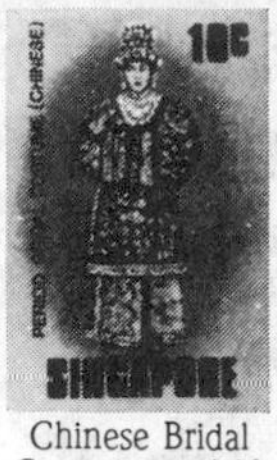

Chinese Bridal Costume — A63

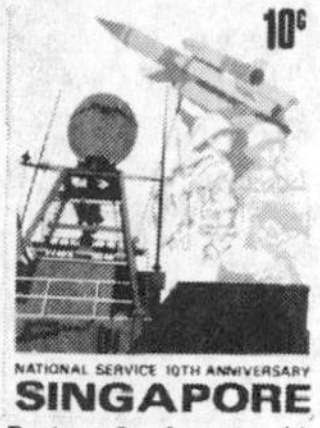

Radar, Surface to Air Missile, Soldiers — A64

Designs: 35c, Indian bridal costume. 75c, Malay bridal costume.

1976, Dec. 19 Litho. *Perf. 14½*

257 A63 10c lt green & multi .40 .15
258 A63 35c lilac & multi 1.40 .70
259 A63 75c yellow & multi 3.00 1.75
Nos. 257-259 (3) 4.80 2.60

1977, Mar. 12 Litho. *Perf. 14½*

Designs: 50c, Infantry soldiers and tank. 75c, Jet fighter, pilot, telecommunications center.

260 A64 10c multicolored .30 .15
261 A64 50c multicolored 1.40 .85
262 A64 75c multicolored 2.50 1.40
Nos. 260-262 (3) 4.20 2.40

National Service, 10th anniversary.

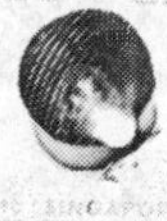
Lyrate Cockle A65

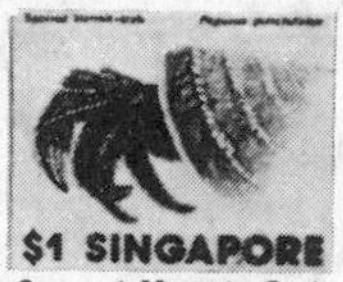

Spotted Hermit Crab A66

Sea Shells: 5c, Folded scallop. 10c, Marble cone. 15c, Scorpion conch. 20c, Amplustre bubble. 25c, Spiral Babylon. 35c, Regal thorny oyster. 50c, Winged frog shell. 75c, Troschel's murex.

Marine Life: $2, Stingray. $5, Cuttlefish. $10, Lionfish.

1977 *Perf. 13½*

263 A65 1c orange & multi .15 .15
264 A65 5c orange & multi .15 .15
a. Bklt. pane of 12 (4 #264, 8 #265) 1.25
265 A65 10c orange & multi .15 .15
266 A65 15c orange & multi .15 .15
267 A65 20c orange & multi .25 .15
268 A65 25c orange & multi .25 .20
269 A65 35c orange & multi .35 .25
270 A65 50c orange & multi .55 .45
271 A65 75c orange & multi .80 .65

Perf. 14

272 A66 $1 multicolored 1.10 .90
273 A66 $2 multicolored 2.25 1.75
274 A66 $5 multicolored 5.50 4.50
275 A66 $10 multicolored 10.50 9.00
Nos. 263-275 (13) 22.15 18.45

No. 264a has a large inscribed selvage, the size of 6 stamps.

Issue dates: #263-271, Apr. 9; others, June 4.

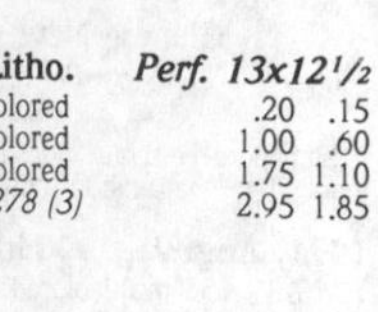

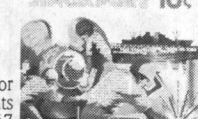

Singapore Harbor Improvements A67

Labor Day: 50c, Construction workers. 75c, Road workers.

1977, May 1 Litho. *Perf. 13x12½*

276 A67 10c multicolored .20 .15
277 A67 50c multicolored 1.00 .60
278 A67 75c multicolored 1.75 1.10
Nos. 276-278 (3) 2.95 1.85

"Key to Savings" — A68

Grain and Cattle — A69

Designs: 35c, "On-line Banking Service." 75c, "GIRO Service."

1977, July 16   Litho.   Perf. 13
279 A68 10c multicolored .20 .15
280 A68 35c multicolored .75 .45
281 A68 75c multicolored 2.25 1.40
Nos. 279-281 (3) 3.20 2.00

Centenary of Post Office Savings Bank.

1977, Aug. 8   Litho.   Perf. 14
Designs: 10c, Flags of founding members: Thailand, Indonesia, Singapore, Malaysia and Philippines. 75c, Steel, oil and chemical industries.
282 A69 10c multicolored .20 .15
283 A69 35c multicolored .60 .40
284 A69 75c multicolored 1.90 .85
Nos. 282-284 (3) 2.70 1.40

Association of South East Asian Nations (ASEAN), 10th anniversary.

Bus Stop — A70

Children's Drawings: 10c, Chingay procession, vert. 75c, Playground.

1977, Oct. 1   Perf. 12½
285 A70 10c multicolored .35 .15
286 A70 35c multicolored 1.00 .65
287 A70 75c multicolored 3.25 1.50
a.   Souvenir sheet of 3, #285-287 4.75 4.75
Nos. 285-287 (3) 4.60 2.30

Symbols of Life Sciences — A71

Botanical Gardens — A72

Singapore Science Center; 35c, "Physical sciences." 75c, "Science and technology." $1, Science Center.

1977, Dec. 10   Litho.   Perf. 14½x14
288 A71 10c multicolored .15 .15
289 A71 35c multicolored .50 .30
290 A71 75c multicolored 1.10 .70
291 A71 $1 multicolored 1.65 1.10
Nos. 288-291 (4) 3.40 2.25

1978, Apr. 22   Litho.   Perf. 14½
Singapore Parks and Gardens: 10c, Jurong Bird Park, horiz. 35c, East Coast Lagoon and Park.
292 A72 10c multicolored .20 .15
293 A72 35c multicolored .60 .45
294 A72 75c multicolored 1.50 1.10
Nos. 292-294 (3) 2.30 1.70

Red-whiskered Bulbul — A73

Songbirds: 35c, White eyes. 50c, White-rumped shama. 75c, White-crested laughing thrush.

Thian Hock Keng Temple — A74

1978, July 1   Litho.   Perf. 13½
295 A73 10c multicolored .25 .15
296 A73 35c multicolored .70 .42
297 A73 50c multicolored 1.25 .70
298 A73 75c multicolored 1.65 1.10
Nos. 295-298 (4) 3.85 2.37

National Monuments: No. 303a, like No. 299. Nos. 300, 303b, Hajjah Fatimah Mosque. Nos. 301, 303c, Armenian Church. Nos. 302, 303d, Sri Mariamman Temple.

1978, Aug. 9
299 A74 10c tan & multi .30 .15
300 A74 10c green & multi .30 .15
301 A74 10c blue & multi .30 .15
302 A74 10c lilac & multi .30 .15
Nos. 299-302 (4) 1.20
Set value .40

Souvenir Sheet
303   Sheet of 4 4.00 4.00
a.   A74 35c tan & multi .55
b.   A74 35c green & multi .55
c.   A74 35c blue & multi .55
d.   A74 35c lilac & multi .55

Map of Proposed Cable Network — A75

1978, Oct. 30   Litho.   Perf. 14
304 A75 10c multicolored .15 .15
305 A75 35c multicolored .55 .45
306 A75 50c multicolored .80 .65
307 A75 75c multicolored 1.10 1.00
Nos. 304-307 (4) 2.60 2.25

ASEAN Submarine Cable Network. Nos. 304-307 printed in sheets of 100. Stamps have perforations around design and around edges. See No. 429a.

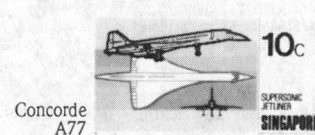

Neptune Spinel — A76

Ships: 35c, Neptune Aries. 50c, Arno Temasek. 75c, Neptune Pearl.

1978, Nov. 18   Litho.   Perf. 13½x14
308 A76 10c multicolored .16 .15
309 A76 35c multicolored .52 .52
310 A76 50c multicolored .80 .80
311 A76 75c multicolored 1.25 1.25
Nos. 308-311 (4) 2.73 2.72

Neptune Oriental Shipping Lines, 10th anniversary.

Concorde A77

Aviation Development: 35c, Vickers-Vimy, 1st aircraft to land in Singapore. 50c, Boeing 747B. 75c, Wright Brothers' Flyer I.

1978, Dec. 16   Perf. 13½
312 A77 10c yellow green & blk .20 .15
313 A77 35c blue & black .55 .55
314 A77 50c carmine & black .80 .80
315 A77 75c brown & black 1.25 1.25
Nos. 312-315 (4) 2.80 2.75

75th anniversary of 1st powered flight.

Distance Marker in Kilometers A78

Vanda Orchids A79

Designs: 35c, Tape measure in centimeters. 75c, Scales in grams and kilograms.

1979, Jan. 24   Litho.   Perf. 13x13½
316 A78 10c multicolored .15 .15
317 A78 35c multicolored .50 .35
318 A78 75c multicolored 1.00 .75
Nos. 316-318 (3) 1.65 1.25

Introduction of metric system.

Perf. 14½x14, 14x14½
1979, Apr. 14   Litho.
Designs: Varieties of vanda hybrids. 10c, 35c, horiz.
319 A79 10c multicolored .55 .55
320 A79 35c multicolored .52 .52
321 A79 50c multicolored .75 .75
322 A79 75c multicolored 1.10 1.10
Nos. 319-322 (4) 2.92 2.92

Envelope Addressed to Postmaster A80

Design: 50c, Envelope addressed to Philatelic Bureau.

1979, July 1   Litho.   Perf. 12½x13
323 A80 10c orange & multi .20 .15
324 A80 50c dark blue & multi .80 .50

Singapore's postal code system.

Old Phone, Telephone Lines — A81

Designs: 35c, Dial, world map. 50c, Push-button phone, skyline. 75c, Line network.

1979, Oct. 5   Litho.   Perf. 13½
325 A81 10c multicolored .20 .15
326 A81 35c multicolored .40 .35
327 A81 50c multicolored .65 .45
328 A81 75c multicolored .90 .65
Nos. 325-328 (4) 2.15 1.60

Telephone service centenary

IYC Emblem, Lanterns Festival A82

IYC Emblem, Children's Drawings: 35c, Singapore Harbor. 50c, "Use Your Hands." 75c, Soccer.

1979, Nov. 10   Litho.   Perf. 13
329 A82 10c multicolored .15 .15
330 A82 35c multicolored .45 .45
331 A82 50c multicolored .60 .60
332 A82 75c multicolored .90 .90
a.   Souvenir sheet of 4, #329-332 3.00 3.00
Nos. 329-332 (4) 2.10 2.10

International Year of the Child.

Botanic Gardens, 120th Anniversary A83

1979, Dec. 15   Perf. 13½
333 A83 10c shown .16 .15
334 A83 50c Gazebo .60 .50
335 A83 $1 Greenhouse 1.25 1.00
Nos. 333-335 (3) 2.01 1.65

Hainan Junk — A84

1980   Litho.   Perf. 14
336 A84 1c shown .15 .15
337 A84 5c Clipper .15 .15
338 A84 10c Fujian junk .15 .15
a.   Booklet pane of 10 1.00
339 A84 15c Golekkan .15 .15
340 A84 20c Palari .16 .16
341 A84 25c East Indiaman .22 .22
342 A84 35c Galleon .30 .30
343 A84 50c Caravel .42 .42
344 A84 75c Jiangsu trader .60 .60

Size: 41½x24½mm
Perf. 13½
345 A84 $1 Coaster .85 .85
346 A84 $2 Oil tanker 1.65 1.65
347 A84 $5 Screw steamer 4.25 4.25
348 A84 $10 Paddle wheel steamer 8.50 8.50
Nos. 336-348 (13) 17.55 17.55

Issue dates: #336-344, Apr. 26; others, Apr. 5.

Straits Settlements No. 1, Old Singapore Map, London 1980 Emblem A85

London 1980 Emblem and: 35c, Straits Settlements No. 146, letter. $1, Singapore No. 19, map of Straits. $2, Singapore No. 106, letter, 1819.

1980, May 6   Litho.   Perf. 13
349 A85 10c multicolored .16 .15
350 A85 35c multicolored .30 .30
351 A85 $1 multicolored .85 .85
352 A85 $2 multicolored 1.65 1.65
a.   Souvenir sheet of 4, #349-352 4.00 4.00
Nos. 349-352 (4) 2.96 2.95

London 1980 Intl. Stamp Exhib., May 6-14.

Fund Board Emblem, Keys to Retirement — A86

1980, July 1   Litho.   Perf. 13
353 A86 10c shown .15 .15
354 A86 50c Home ownership savings .55 .55
355 A86 $1 Old age savings 1.10 1.10
Nos. 353-355 (3) 1.80 1.80

Central Provident Fund Board, 25th anniv.

Map Showing Singapore-Indonesia Cable Route — A87

1980, Aug. 8   Litho.   Perf. 14
356 A87 10c multicolored .15 .15
357 A87 35c multicolored .35 .35
358 A87 50c multicolored .45 .45
359 A87 75c multicolored .70 .70
  Nos. 356-359 (4) 1.65 1.65

ASEAN Submarine Cable Network extension. Stamps perforated around design and around edges. See No. 429a.

Fair Emblem
A88   **SINGAPORE**   10c

1980, Oct. 3   Litho.   Perf. 13
360 A88 10c multicolored .15 .15
361 A88 35c multicolored .42 .42
362 A88 75c multicolored .95 .95
  Nos. 360-362 (3) 1.52 1.52

Asean Trade Fair, Oct. 3-12.

singapore
A89   A90

1980, Nov. 2   Litho.   Perf. 13½
363 A89 10c Flame of the wood .15 .15
364 A89 35c Golden trumpet .38 .38
365 A89 50c Sky vine .50 .50
366 A89 75c Bougainvillea .80 .80
  Nos. 363-366 (4) 1.83 1.83

1981, Jan. 24   Litho.   Perf. 14x14½
367 A90 10c multicolored .15 .15
368 A90 35c multicolored .35 .35
369 A90 75c multicolored .75 .75
  Nos. 367-369 (3) 1.25 1.25

Monetary Authority of Singapore, 10th anniv.

10
CENTS

No. 54
Surcharged

Perf. 13½x14½
1981, Mar. 5   Photo.   Wmk. 314
370 A8 10c on 4c red org & blk .15 .15

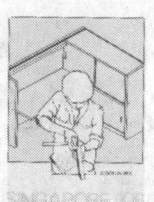

A91   A92

Unwmk.
1981, Apr. 11   Litho.   Perf. 13
371 A91 10c Technical Training
        (Woodworking) .15 .15
372 A91 35c Building construction .30 .30
373 A91 50c Electronics .42 .42
374 A91 75c Precision machinery .60 .60
  Nos. 371-374 (4) 1.47 1.47

1981, Aug. 25   Litho.   Perf. 14
Sports For All: Various sports.
375 A92 10c multicolored .15 .15
376 A92 75c multicolored .75 .75
377 A92 $1 multicolored 1.10 1.10
  Nos. 375-377 (3) 2.00 2.00

A93   A94

1981, Nov. 24   Litho.   Perf. 14½
378 A93 10c Man in wheelchair .15 .15
379 A93 35c Group .35 .35
380 A93 50c Teacher, student .50 .50
381 A93 75c Blind communications
        worker .75 .75
  Nos. 378-381 (4) 1.75 1.75

Intl. Year of the Disabled.

1981, Dec. 29   Litho.   Perf. 14x13½
382 A94 10c multicolored .15 .15
383 A94 35c multicolored .30 .30
384 A94 40c multicolored .40 .40
385 A94 75c multicolored .60 .60
386 A94 $1 multicolored .80 .80
  a. Souvenir sheet of 5, #382-386 4.00 4.00
  Nos. 382-386 (5) 2.25 2.25

Changi airport opening.

A95

1982, Mar. 3   Litho.   Perf. 14x14½
387 A95 10c Clipper .15 .15
388 A95 50c Blue grassy tiger .65 .65
389 A95 $1 Raja Brooke's birdwing 1.25 1.25
  Nos. 387-389 (3) 2.05 2.05

A96   A97

1982, June 14   Litho.   Perf. 14
390 A96 10c multicolored .15 .15
391 A96 35c multicolored .32 .32
392 A96 50c multicolored .45 .45
393 A96 75c multicolored .70 .70
  Nos. 390-393 (4) 1.62 1.62

15th ASEAN Ministerial meeting.

1982, July 9   Litho.   Perf. 12
394 A97 10c multicolored .15 .15
395 A97 75c multicolored .70 .70
396 A97 $1 multicolored 1.00 1.00
  Nos. 394-396 (3) 1.85 1.85

1982 World Cup.

Sultan Shoal
Lighthouse,
1896 — A98

1982, Aug. 7
397 A98 10c shown .15 .15
398 A98 75c Horsburgh, 1851 .70 .70
399 A98 $1 Raffles, 1855 1.00 1.00
  a. Souvenir sheet of 3, #397-399 2.25 2.25
  Nos. 397-399 (3) 1.85 1.85

10th Anniv. of
PSA Container
Terminal
A99

1982, Sept. 15   Litho.   Perf. 13½
400 A99 10c Yard gantry cranes .15 .15
401 A99 35c Computer .38 .38
402 A99 50c Freightlifter .55 .55
403 A99 75c Straddle carrier .85 .85
  Nos. 400-403 (4) 1.93 1.93

A100

A101

1982, Oct. 15   Litho.   Perf. 14x13½
404 A100 10c Color guard .15 .15
405 A100 35c Hiking .40 .40
406 A100 50c Building tower .55 .55
407 A100 75c Kayaking .85 .85
  Nos. 404-407 (4) 1.95 1.95

Scouting Year.

1982, Nov. 17   Perf. 13½
408 A101 10c Text .15 .15
409 A101 35c Housing .38 .38
410 A101 50c Quality control meet-
        ing .55 .55
411 A101 75c Participation .85 .85
  Nos. 408-411 (4) 1.93 1.93

Productivity movement.

A102   A103

1983, May 14   Litho.   Perf. 13½x13
412 A102 10c multicolored .15 .15
413 A102 35c multicolored .30 .30
414 A102 75c multicolored .60 .60
415 A102 $1 multicolored .85 .85
  Nos. 412-415 (4) 1.90 1.90

Commonwealth Day.

1983, May 28   Litho.   Perf. 14x13½
416 A103 10c Soccer .15 .15
417 A103 35c Racket games .35 .35
418 A103 75c Athletics .75 .75
419 A103 $1 Swimming 1.00 1.00
  Nos. 416-419 (4) 2.25 2.25

12th Southeast Asia Games.

Neighborhood
Watch Safety
Campaign — A104

1983, June 24   Litho.   Perf. 14
420 A104 10c Family .15 .15
421 A104 35c Children .35 .35
422 A104 75c Community .75 .75
  Nos. 420-422 (3) 1.25 1.25

BANGKOK '83
Intl. Stamp Show,
Aug. 4-13 — A105

Designs: 10c, Nos. 282-284, statue of King Chulalongkorn (1868-1910). 35c, Nos. 304-307, map of southeast Asia. $1, Nos. 390-393, Declaration of ASEAN (Assoc. of South East Asian Nations) signatures, 1976.

1983, Aug. 4   Litho.   Perf. 14x14½
423 A105 10c multicolored .15 .15
424 A105 35c multicolored .42 .42
425 A105 $1 multicolored 1.25 1.25
  a. Souvenir sheet of 3, #423-425 2.00 2.00
  Nos. 423-425 (3) 1.82 1.82

ASEAN Submarine
Cable
Network — A106

1983, Sept. 27   Litho.   Perf. 14
426 A106 10c multicolored .15 .15
427 A106 35c multicolored .42 .42
428 A106 50c multicolored .60 .60
429 A106 75c multicolored .90 .90
  a. Souv. sheet of 6, #304, 359, 426-
      429 3.00 3.00
  Nos. 426-429 (4) 2.07 2.07

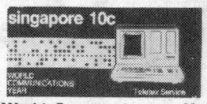

World Communications Year — A107

1983, Nov. 10   Litho.   Perf. 13
430 A107 10c Telex service .15 .15
431 A107 35c Telephone numbering
        plan .35 .35
432 A107 75c Satellite transmission .70 .70
433 A107 $1 Sea communications .95 .95
  Nos. 430-433 (4) 2.15 2.15

Coastal
Birds — A108

Perf. 14½x13½
1984, Mar. 15   Litho.
434 A108 10c Slaty-breasted rail .15 .15
435 A108 35c Black bittern .42 .42
436 A108 50c Brahminy kite .60 .60
437 A108 75c Common moorhens .90 .90
  Nos. 434-437 (4) 2.07 2.07

Natl. Monuments
A109

Designs: 10c, House of Tan Yeok Nee (merchant), 1885. 35c, Thong Chai Building (former hospital), 1892. 50c, Telok Ayer Market, 1894. $1, Nagore Durgha Muslim Shrine, 1828.

1984, June 7   Litho.   Perf. 12
438 A109 10c multicolored .15 .15
439 A109 35c multicolored .40 .40
440 A109 50c multicolored .55 .55
441 A109 $1 multicolored 1.10 1.10
  Nos. 438-441 (4) 2.20 2.20

A110　　　A111

1984, Aug. 9　　Litho.　Perf. 14
442	A110	10c No. 121	.15	.15
443	A110	35c No. 377	.35	.35
444	A110	50c No. 99	.50	.50
445	A110	75c No. 243	.75	.75
446	A110	$1 No. 386	1.00	1.00
447	A110	$2 No. 367	2.00	2.00
a.		Souvenir sheet of 6, #442-447	4.75	4.75
		Nos. 442-447 (6)	4.75	4.75

25th anniv. of self-government.

1984, Oct. 26　　Litho.　Perf. 12

Total Defense: a, This is our country. b, We are one. c, We work together. d, We are prepared. e, We are ready.

448		Strip of 5	.50	.50
a.-e.	A111	10c any single	.15	.15

Bridges
A112

1985, Mar. 15　Engr.　Perf. 14½x14
449	A112	10c Coleman	.15	.15
450	A112	35c Cavenagh	.28	.28
451	A112	75c Elgin	.60	.60
452	A112	$1 Benjamin Sheares	.85	.85
		Nos. 449-452 (4)	1.00	1.88

Insects — A113 SINGAPORE 5c

1985　　Litho.　Perf. 13x13½
453	A113	5c Ceriagrion cerinorubellum	.15	.15
454	A113	10c Apis javana	.15	.15
455	A113	15c Delta arcuata	.15	.15
456	A113	20c Xylocopa caerulea	.15	.15
457	A113	25c Donacia javana	.20	.20
458	A113	35c Heteroneda reticulata	.28	.28
459	A113	50c Catacanthus nigripes	.40	.40
460	A113	75c Chremistica pontianaka	.60	.60

Litho. & Engr.
Size: 35x30mm
461	A113	$1 Homoeoxipha lycoides	.80	.80
462	A113	$2 Traulia azureipennis	1.65	1.65
463	A113	$5 Trillemus aurora	3.75	3.75
464	A113	$10 Scambophyllum sanguinolentum	7.50	7.50
		Nos. 453-464 (12)	15.78	15.78

Issued: #453-460, Apr. 24; #461-464, June 5.

People's Assoc., 25th Anniv. — A114

Montage of public services.

1985, July 1　　Perf. 13½x14
465	A114	10c multicolored	.15	.15
466	A114	35c multicolored	.30	.30
467	A114	50c multicolored	.45	.45
468	A114	75c multicolored	.65	.65
		Nos. 465-468 (4)	1.55	1.55

Public Housing, 25th Anniv. — A115

Modern housing developments.

1985, Aug. 9
469	A115	10c multicolored	.15	.15
470	A115	35c multicolored	.35	.35
471	A115	50c multicolored	.50	.50
472	A115	75c multicolored	.80	.80
a.		Souvenir sheet of 4, #469-472	1.90	1.90
		Nos. 469-472 (4)	1.80	1.80

Girl Guides, 75th Anniv. — A116

Activities.

1985, Nov 6　　Perf. 14½x14
473	A116	10c Brownies	.15	.15
474	A116	35c Guides	.38	.38
475	A116	55c Seniors	.55	.55
476	A116	75c Guide leaders	.85	.85
		Nos. 473-476 (4)	1.93	1.93

Intl. Youth Year — A117

1985, Dec. 18　　Perf. 13
477	A117	10c Youth assoc. emblems	.15	.15
478	A117	75c Hand, sapling	.75	.75
479	A117	$1 Dove, stick figures	1.00	1.00
		Nos. 477-479 (3)	1.90	1.90

Indigenous Fruit — A118　　Natl. Trade Unions Cong., 25th Anniv. — A119

1986, Feb. 26　Litho.　Perf. 14½x14
480	A118	10c Psidium guajava	.15	.15
481	A118	35c Eugenia aquea	.35	.35
482	A118	50c Nephelium lappaceum	.50	.50
483	A118	75c Manilkara zapota	.75	.75
		Nos. 480-483 (4)	1.75	1.75

1986, May 1　　Perf. 13½

Progress: a, Science and technology. b, Communications. c, Industry. d, Education.

484		Strip of 4	.40	.40
a.-d.	A119	10c any single	.20	.20

Souvenir Sheet
485		Sheet of 4	1.40	1.40
a.-d.	A119	35c any single	.35	.35

EXPO '86, Vancouver A120

1986, May 2　　Perf. 14½x14
486		Strip of 3	2.00	2.00
a.	A120	50c Calligraphy	.45	.45
b.	A120	75c Garland making	.65	.65
c.	A120	$1 Batik printing	.90	.90

Economic Development Board, 25th Anniv. — A121

1986, Aug. 1　　Perf. 15
487	A121	10c Automation	.15	.15
488	A121	35c Precision engineering	.32	.32
489	A121	50c Electronics	.45	.45
490	A121	70c Biotechnology	.70	.70
		Nos. 487-490 (4)	1.62	1.62

Submarine Cable — A122

1986, Sept. 8　　Perf. 13½
491	A122	10c multicolored	.15	.15
492	A122	35c multicolored	.32	.32
493	A122	45c multicolored	.45	.45
494	A122	75c multicolored	.65	.65
		Nos. 491-494 (4)	1.57	1.57

Citizens' Consultative Committees, 21st Anniv. — A123

1986, Oct 15　　Perf. 12
495	A123	Block of 4	1.50	1.50
a.		10c multicolored	.15	.15
b.		35c multicolored	.30	.30
c.		50c multicolored	.45	.45
d.		75c multicolored	.65	.65

Intl. Peace Year — A124

1986, Dec. 17　Litho.　Perf. 14x13½
496	A124	10c People	.15	.15
497	A124	35c Southeast Asia map	.35	.35
498	A124	$1 Globe	1.00	1.00
		Nos. 496-498 (3)	1.50	1.50

Views of Singapore A125

1986, Feb. 25　　Perf. 12x12½
499	A125	10c Orchard Road	.15	.15
500	A125	50c Central business district	.42	.42
501	A125	75c Marina Center, Raffles City	.60	.60
		Nos. 499-501 (3)	1.17	1.17

Assoc. of Southeast Asian Nations (ASEAN), 20th Anniv. — A126　　National Service, 20th Anniv. — A127

1987, June 15　　Perf. 12
502	A126	10c multicolored	.15	.15
503	A126	35c multicolored	.28	.28
504	A126	50c multicolored	.40	.40
505	A126	60c multicolored	.60	.60
		Nos. 502-505 (4)	1.43	1.43

1987, July 1　　Perf. 15x14

Designs: a, Army. b, Navy. c, Air Force. d, Pledge of Allegiance. e, Singapore Lion.

506		Strip of 4	.40	.40
a.-d.	A127	10c any single	.15	.15
507		Sheet of 5	1.50	1.50
a.-e.	A127	35c any single	.30	.30

River Life — A128

1987, Sept. 2　　Perf. 14
508	A128	10c Singapore River	.15	.15
509	A128	50c Kallang Basin	.45	.45
510	A128	$1 Kranji Reservoir	.95	.95
		Nos. 508-510 (3)	1.55	1.55

Natl. Museum Cent. A129

Views of the museum and artifacts: 10c, Majapahis gold bracelet, 14th-15th cent. 75c, Ming fluted kendi (water jar). $1, Seventeen-wave kris (sword with silver hilt, sheath), property of Sultan Abdul Jalil Sabat, 1699.

1987, Oct. 12　Litho.　Perf. 13½x14
511	A129	10c multicolored	.15	.15
512	A129	75c multicolored	.72	.72
513	A129	$1 multicolored	.95	.95
		Nos. 511-513 (3)	1.82	1.82

Singapore Science Center, 10th Anniv. A130

Attractions.

1987, Dec. 10　　Perf. 14½
514	A130	10c Omni Theater	.15	.15
515	A130	35c Omni Planetarium	.35	.35
516	A130	75c Cellular model	.72	.72
517	A130	$1 Science exhibits	.95	.95
		Nos. 514-517 (4)	2.17	2.17

Artillery, Cent. A131

Designs: 10c, 155-Gun Howitzer and Khatib Camp, headquarters of the Singapore Gunners. 35c, 25-Pound gun salute and Singapore City Hall. 50c, 4.5-inch Howitzer and Singapore Cricket Club, c. 1928. $1, Ft. Fullerton Drill Hall, c. 1893, and .405 Maxim gun.

1988, Feb. 22 Litho. Perf. 13¹/₂x14

518	A131	10c multicolored	.15	.15
519	A131	35c multicolored	.35	.35
520	A131	50c multicolored	.50	.50
521	A131	$1 multicolored	1.00	1.00
		Nos. 518-521 (4)	2.00	2.00

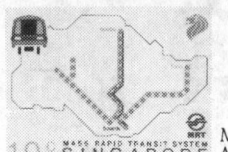

Mass Transit A132

1988, Mar. 12 Perf. 14

522	A132	10c Rail car, map	.15	.15
523	A132	50c Elevated train	.48	.48
524	A132	$1 Urban subway	.95	.95
		Nos. 522-524 (3)	1.58	1.58

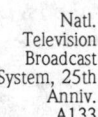 

Natl. Television Broadcast System, 25th Anniv. A133

1988, Apr. 4 Perf. 13¹/₂x14

525	A133	10c shown	.15	.15
526	A133	35c Studio	.35	.35
527	A133	75c Television, transmission tower	.75	.75
528	A133	$1 Screen, satellite dish	1.00	1.00
		Nos. 525-528 (4)	2.25	2.25

Public Utilities Board, 25th Anniv. — A134

1988, May 4 Litho. Perf. 13¹/₂

529	A134	10c Water works	.15	.15
530	A134	50c Electric company	.50	.50
531	A134	$1 Fossil fuels	1.00	1.00
a.		Souvenir sheet of 3, #529-531	1.60	1.60
		Nos. 529-531 (3)	1.65	1.65

Courtesy Campaign, 10th Anniv. A135

Singa the lion (character trademark) and: 10c, Neighbors. 30c, Store service counter. $1, Helping the elderly.

1988, July 6 Litho. Perf. 14¹/₂

532	A135	10c multicolored	.15	.15
533	A135	30c multicolored	.30	.30
534	A135	$1 multicolored	1.00	1.00
		Nos. 532-534 (3)	1.45	1.45

Fire Service, Cent. — A136

1988, Nov. 1 Litho. Perf. 13¹/₂

535	A136	10c Turntable ladder truck	.15	.15
536	A136	$1 1890s Steam pump	1.00	1.00

Port Authority, 25th Anniv. — A137

Various facilities.

1989, Apr. 3 Litho. Perf. 14x13¹/₂

537	A137	10c multicolored	.15	.15
538	A137	30c multi, diff.	.30	.30
539	A137	75c multi, diff.	.75	.75
540	A137	$1 multi, diff.	1.00	1.00
		Nos. 537-540 (4)	2.20	2.20

Old Chinatown A138

1989, May 17 Litho. Perf. 14¹/₂

541	A138	10c Sago St.	.15	.15
542	A138	35c Pagoda St.	.35	.35
543	A138	75c Trengganu St.	.78	.78
544	A138	$1 Temple St.	1.00	1.00
		Nos. 541-544 (4)	2.28	2.28

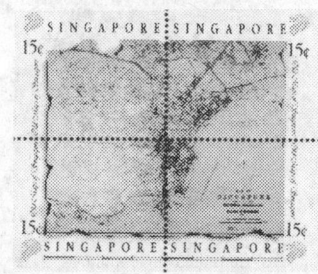

Maps of Singapore — A139

Early 19th cent. map Singapore Showing Principal Residences and Places of Interest: No. 545a, Upper left. No. 545b, Upper right. No. 545c, Lower left. No. 545d, Lower right. (Illustration reduced).

1989, July 26 Litho. Perf. 14¹/₂

545	A139	Block of 4	.65	.65
a.-d.		15c any single	.16	.16

Size: 33x31mm
Perf. 12¹/₂x13

546	A139	50c Singapore and Dependencies	.52	.52
547	A139	$1 Plan of the British Settlement	1.05	1.05
		Nos. 545-547 (3)	2.22	2.22

Fish — A140

1989, Sept. 6 Perf. 14

548	A140	15c Clown triggerfish	.16	.16
549	A140	30c Majestic angelfish	.30	.30
550	A140	75c Emperor angelfish	.78	.78
551	A140	$1 Royal empress angelfish	1.05	1.05
		Nos. 548-551 (4)	2.29	2.29

Festivals — A141

Children's drawings: 15c, Hari Raya Puasa, by Loke Yoke Yen. 35c, Chinese New Year, by Simon Koh. 75c, Thaipusam, by Henry Setiono. $1, Christmas, by Wendy Ang Lin.

1989, Oct. 25 Litho. Perf. 14¹/₂

552	A141	15c multicolored	.16	.16
553	A141	35c multicolored	.38	.38
554	A141	75c multicolored	.80	.80
555	A141	$1 multicolored	1.10	1.10
a.		Souv. sheet of 4, #552-555, perf. 14	2.45	2.45
		Nos. 552-555 (4)	2.44	2.44

Singapore Indoor Stadium A142

1989, Dec. 27 Litho. Perf. 14¹/₂

556	A142	30c North entrance	.32	.32
557	A142	75c Interior	.80	.80
558	A142	$1 East entrance	1.10	1.10
a.		Souvenir sheet of 3, #556-558	2.25	2.25
		Nos. 556-558 (3)	2.22	2.22

Sports issue.

Lithographs of 19th Cent. Singapore A143

1990, Feb. 21 Litho. Perf. 13

559	A143	15c Singapore River, 1839	.16	.16
560	A143	30c Chinatown, 1837	.32	.32
561	A143	75c Waterfront, 1837	.78	.78
562	A143	$1 View from Ft. Canning, 1824	1.05	1.05
		Nos. 559-562 (4)	2.31	2.31

First Postage Stamps, 150th Anniv. — A144

Maps and: 50c, Nos. 101-106. 75c, Cover to Scotland. $1, Cover to Ireland $2, Great Britain Nos. 1, 2.

1990, May 3 Litho. Perf. 13¹/₂

563	A144	50c multicolored	.50	.50
564	A144	75c multicolored	.75	.75
565	A144	$1 multicolored	1.00	1.00
566	A144	$2 multicolored	2.00	2.00
a.		Souvenir sheet of 4, #563-566	4.60	4.60
		Nos. 563-566 (4)	4.25	4.25

Tourism — A145

1990, July 4 Perf. 14¹/₂

567	A145	5c Zoo	.15	.15
568	A145	15c Resort	.16	.16
a.		Booklet pane of 10	1.60	
569	A145	20c City	.22	.22
570	A145	25c Dragon boat race	.28	.28
571	A145	30c Hotel	.32	.32
572	A145	35c Caged birds	.38	.38
573	A145	40c Park	.44	.44

574	A145	50c Festival	.55	.55
575	A145	75c Building, diff.	.82	.82
		Nos. 567-575 (9)	3.32	3.32

Independence, 25th Anniv. — A146

1990, Aug. 16 Litho. Perf. 14x14¹/₂

576	A146	15c shown	.16	.16
a.		Booklet pane of 10	1.60	
577	A146	35c One Singapore	.38	.38
578	A146	75c One hope	.82	.82
579	A146	$1 One people	1.10	1.10
		Nos. 576-579 (4)	2.46	2.46

Tourism A147

Designs: $1, Chinese opera singer, Siong Lim Temple. $2, Malay dancer, Sultan Mosque. $5, Indian dancer, Sri Mariamman Temple. $10, Ballet dancer, Victoria Memorial Hall.

Photo. & Engr.

1990, Oct. 10 Perf. 15x14

580	A147	$1 multicolored	1.35	1.35
581	A147	$2 multicolored	2.70	2.70
582	A147	$5 multicolored	6.75	6.75
583	A147	$10 multicolored	11.35	11.35
		Nos. 580-583 (4)	22.15	22.15

15c Ferns — A148

1990, Nov. 14 Litho. Perf. 14

584	A148	15c Stag's horn	.16	.16
585	A148	35c Maiden hair	.38	.38
586	A148	75c Bird's nest	.82	.82
587	A148	$1 Rabbit's foot	1.10	1.10
		Nos. 584-587 (4)	2.46	2.46

A149

Houses of Worship A150

Designs: 20c, Hong San See Temple, 1912. 50c, Abdul Gattoor Mosque, 1910. 75c, Sri Perumal Temple, 1961. $1, St. Andrew's Cathedral, 1863.

1991, Jan. 23 Litho. Perf. 14¹/₂

588	A149	20c multicolored	.22	.22
589	A150	20c multicolored	.22	.22
a.		Pair, #588-589	.44	.44
590	A149	50c multicolored	.55	.55
591	A150	50c multicolored	.55	.55
a.		Pair, #590-591	1.10	1.10
592	A149	75c multicolored	.82	.82
593	A150	75c multicolored	.82	.82
a.		Pair, #592-593	1.65	1.65
594	A149	$1 multicolored	1.10	1.10
595	A150	$1 multicolored	1.10	1.10
a.		Pair, #594-595	2.20	2.20
		Nos. 588-595 (8)	5.38	5.38

Vanda Miss
Joaquim — A151

Design: No. 597, Dendrobium Anocha.

1991, Apr. 24   Litho.   Perf. 14
596 A151 $2 multicolored   2.20 2.20
597 A151 $2 multicolored   2.20 2.20
  a.   Pair, #596-597 + label   4.40 4.40

Singapore '95 Intl. Philatelic Exhibition.
See Nos. 615-616, 664-665, 685-686, 716-717.

Civilian
Airports — A152

Designs: 20c, Boeing 747, Changi Terminal II,
1991. 75c, Boeing 747, Changi Terminal I, 1981.
$1, Concorde, Paya Lebar, 1955-1981. $2, DC-3,
Kallang, 1937-1955.

Perf. 13¹/₂x14¹/₂
1991, July 1   Litho. & Engr.
598 A152 20c multicolored   .22 .22
599 A152 75c multicolored   .82 .82
600 A152 $1 multicolored   1.10 1.10
601 A152 $2 multicolored   2.20 2.20
    Nos. 598-601 (4)   4.34 4.34

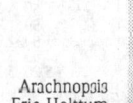

Arachnopsis
Eric Holttum
A153

Orchids: 30c, Cattleya Meadii. $1, Calanthe
vestita.

1991, Aug. 8 Litho. Perf. 14¹/₂x13¹/₂
602 A153 20c multicolored   .22 .22
603 A153 30c multicolored   .34 .34
604 A153 $1 multicolored   1.10 1.10
    Nos. 602-604 (3)   1.66 1.66

SINGAPORE 20c Birds — A154

Designs: 20c, Common tailorbird. 35c, Scarlet-
backed flowerpecker. 75c, Black-naped oriole. $1,
Common tora.

1991, Sept. 19   Perf. 14
605 A154 20c multicolored   .22 .22
  a.   Booklet pane of 10   2.05 2.05
606 A154 35c multicolored   .38 .38
607 A154 75c multicolored   .82 .82
608 A154 $1 multicolored   1.10 1.10
    Nos. 605-608 (4)   2.52 2.52

10 Years of   Phila Nippon
Productivity — A155   '91 — A156

1991, Nov. 1 Litho. Perf. 14x14¹/₂
609 A155 20c shown   .24 .24
610 A155 $1 Construction engineers 1.15 1.15

1991, Nov. 16   Perf. 14¹/₂x14
Flowers: 30c, Railway creeper. 75c, Asystasia.
$1, Singapore rhododendron. $2, Coat buttons.
611 A156 30c multicolored   .35 .35
612 A156 75c multicolored   .85 .85
613 A156 $1 multicolored   1.15 1.15
614 A156 $2 multicolored   2.30 2.30
  a.   Souvenir sheet of 4, #611-614 4.65 4.65
    Nos. 611-614 (4)   4.65 4.65

Flower Type of 1991

Designs: No. 615, Dendrobium Sharifah
Fatimah. No. 616, Phalaenopsis Shim Beauty.

1992, Jan. 22   Litho.   Perf. 14
615 A151 $2 multicolored   2.35 2.35
616 A151 $2 multicolored   2.35 2.35
  a.   Pair, #615-616 + label   4.70 4.70
  b.   Souvenir sheet of 2, #615-616 4.70 4.70

Singapore '95 Intl. Philatelic Exhibition.

Paintings — A157

1992, Mar. 11   Litho.   Perf. 14
617 A157 20c Singapore Waterfront,
           1958   .24 .24
618 A157 75c Kampung Hut, 1973   .85 .85
619 A157 $1 Bridge, 1983   1.15 1.15
620 A157 $2 Singapore River, 1984 2.30 2.30
    Nos. 617-620 (4)   4.54 4.54

1992
Summer
Olympics,
Barcelona
A158

1992, Apr. 24   Perf. 14
621 A158 20c Soccer   .24 .24
622 A158 35c Relay races   .40 .40
623 A158 50c Swimming   .58 .58
624 A158 75c Basketball   .85 .85
625 A158 $1 Tennis   1.15 1.15
626 A158 $2 Sailing   2.30 2.30
  a.   Souvenir sheet of 6, #621-626 5.55 5.55
    Nos. 621-626 (6)   5.52 5.52

Costumes,
1910 — A159

1992, Apr. 24   Litho.   Perf. 14¹/₂
627 A159 20c Chinese family   .24 .24
628 A159 35c Malay family   .42 .42
629 A159 75c Indian family   .90 .90
630 A159 $2 Straits Chinese family 2.40 2.40
    Nos. 627-630 (4)   3.96 3.96

Natl. Military
Forces, 25th
SINGAPORE 20¢ Anniv. — A160

Designs: 35c, Frogman with gun, fighter plane,
artillery. $1, Fighter, tank, ship.

1992, July 1
631 A160 20c multicolored   .24 .24
632 A160 35c multicolored   .42 .42
633 A160 $1 multicolored   1.20 1.20
    Nos. 631-633 (3)   1.86 1.86

Visit ASEAN
Year, 25th
Anniv.
A161

Designs: 20c, Mask, bird, sea life. 35c, Costumed
women. $1, Outdoor scenery.

1992, Aug. 8
634 A161 20c multicolored   .24 .24
635 A161 35c multicolored   .42 .42
636 A161 $1 multicolored   1.20 1.20
    Nos. 634-636 (3)   1.86 1.86

Crabs
A162

Designs: 20c, Mosaic crab. 50c, Johnson's freshwater crab. 75c, Singapore freshwater crab. $1,
Swamp forest crab.

1992, Aug. 21   Perf. 14¹/₂x15
637 A162 20c multicolored   .24 .24
  a.   Booklet pane of 10   2.40
638 A162 50c multicolored   .60 .60
639 A162 75c multicolored   .90 .90
640 A162 $1 multicolored   1.20 1.20
    Nos. 637-640 (4)   2.94 2.94

Currency,
Notes and
Coins
A163

1992, Oct. 2   Litho.   Perf. 14¹/₂
641 A163 20c Coins   .25 .25
642 A163 75c Coin, flowers on note .90 .90
643 A163 $1 Boat on note, coins 1.20 1.20
644 A163 $2 Bird on note   2.40 2.40
  a.   Block of 4, #641-644   4.75 4.75

Wild Animals
A164

1993, Jan. 13   Litho.   Perf. 14¹/₂x15
645 A164 20c Sun bear   .25 .25
646 A164 30c Orangutan   .35 .35
647 A164 75c Slow loris   .90 .90
648 A164 $2 Large mouse deer   2.40 2.40
    Nos. 645-648 (4)   3.90 3.90

Greetings
Stamps — A165

Designs: a, Thank you. b, Congratulations. c,
Best wishes. d, Happy birthday. e, Get well soon.

Perf. 14¹/₂x14 on 3 Sides
1993, Feb. 10
Booklet Stamps
649 A165 20c Strip of 5, #a.-e. 1.20 1.20
  f.   Booklet pane of 2 #649   2.40 2.40

Preservation of Tanjong Pagar — A166

1993, Mar. 10   Litho.   Perf. 14
650 A166 20c shown   .24 .24
651 A166 30c Building facade, tower .35 .35
652 A166 $2 Aerial view   2.40 2.40
    Nos. 650-652 (3)   2.99 2.99

A167   A168

1993, May 29   Perf. 12x11¹/₂
653 A167 $2 Cranes, by Chen Wen
           Hsi   2.40 2.40

Indopex '93.

1993, June 12   Litho.   Perf. 14
654 A168 20c Soccer   .24 .24
655 A168 35c Basketball   .42 .42
656 A168 50c Badminton   .60 .60
657 A168 75c Running   .90 .90
658 A168 $1 Water polo   1.25 1.25
659 A168 $2 Yachting   2.50 2.50
    Nos. 654-659 (6)   5.91 5.91

17th Sea Games, Singapore.

Butterflies — A169   Fruits — A170

1993, Aug. 21   Litho.   Perf. 14¹/₂
660 A169 20c Plain tiger   .25 .25
  a.   Booklet pane of 10   2.50
661 A169 50c Malay lacewing   .60 .60
662 A169 75c Palm king   .90 .90
663 A169 $1 Banded swallowtail 1.25 1.25
    Nos. 660-663 (4)   3.00 3.00

Flower Type of 1991

1993, Aug. 13
Size: 26x34mm
664 A151 $2 Phalaenopsis amabilis 2.50 2.50
665 A151 $2 Vanda sumatrana   2.50 2.50
  a.   Pair, #664-665 + label   5.00 5.00
  b.   Souvenir sheet of 2, #664-665, perf.
        15x14¹/₂   5.00 5.00

Singapore '95 World Stamp Exhibition and Taipei
'93, Asian Intl. Invitation Stamp Exhibition
(#665b).

1993, Oct. 1   Litho.   Perf. 14¹/₂x14
666 A170 20c Papaya   .25 .25
667 A170 35c Pomegranate   .42 .42
668 A170 75c Starfruit   .95 .95
669 A170 $2 Durian   2.50 2.50
  a.   Souvenir sheet of 4, #666-669 4.25 4.25
    Nos. 666-669 (4)   4.12 4.12

Bangkok '93 (#669a).

Chinese
Egrets — A171

Designs: 20c, Two, one with bill in water. 25c, Two, one with fish in mouth. 30c, Two facing opposite directions. 35c, In flight.

1993, Nov. 10   Litho.   Perf. 13¹/₂x14
670 A171 20c multicolored .25 .25
671 A171 25c multicolored .32 .32
672 A171 30c multicolored .38 .38
673 A171 35c multicolored .45 .45
a.   Strip of 4, #670-673 1.40 1.40

World Wildlife Fund.

Palm
Tree — A171a

1993, Nov. 24   Photo.   Die Cut
Self-Adhesive
Booklet Stamp
673B A171a (20c) multicolored .25 .25
c.   Booklet pane of 15 3.75

By its nature, No. 673c is a complete booklet. The peelable backing serves as a booklet cover.

Marine
Life — A172

Type A Perforations

A. On two longer sides, groups of three and eighteen holes separated by an oval hole equal in width to three holes.

Perf. 13x13¹/₂, 13¹/₂x14 (675B)
1994   Litho.
674 A172 5c Tiger cowrie .15 .15
675 A172 25c Sea fan .25 .25
a.   Booklet pane of 10 2.50
675B A172 (20c) Blue-spotted
              stingray .30 .30
676 A172 25c Tunicate .32 .32
677 A172 30c Clownfish .38 .38
678 A172 35c Nudibranch .42 .42
679 A172 40c Sea urchin .50 .50
680 A172 50c Soft coral .65 .65
681 A172 75c Pin cushion star .95 .95

Litho. & Embossed
Perf. 14 Syncopated Type A (2 Sides)
682 A172 $1 Knob coral 1.40 1.40
683 A172 $2 Mushroom coral 2.75 2.75
684 A172 $5 Bubble coral 7.00 7.00
684A A172 $10 Octopus coral 14.00 14.00
      Nos. 674-684A (13) 29.07 29.07

Self-Adhesive
Die Cut Perf. 8¹/₂
684B A172 (20c) Blue-spotted
              stingray .30 .30
c.   Booklet pane of 10 3.00

Nos. 675B, 684B inscribed "FOR LOCAL ADDRESSES ONLY". By its nature, No. 684c is a complete booklet. The peelable paper backing serves as a booklet cover.
Issued: 5c-75c, 1/12/94; $1-$10, 3/23/94; #675B, 684B, 11/16/94.

Flower Type of 1991
Designs: No. 685, Paphiopedilum vicotriaregina. No. 686, Dendrobium smillieae.

1994, Feb. 18   Litho.   Perf. 14¹/₂
Size: 26x35mm
685 A151 $2 multicolored 2.75 2.75
686 A151 $2 multicolored 2.75 2.75
a.   Pair, #685-686 + label 5.50 5.50
b.   Souvenir sheet of 2, #685-686 5.50 5.50

Singapore '95 and Hong Kong '94 (#686b).

Spring Festival — A173

1994, May 18   Litho.   Perf. 13¹/₂
687 A173 20c Ballet .28 .28
688 A173 30c Mime, puppets .40 .40
689 A173 50c Musicians .70 .70
690 A173 $1 Crafts 1.40 1.40
      Nos. 687-690 (4) 2.78 2.78

Operationally Ready Natl. Servicemen,
25th Anniv. — A174

Civilian-soldiers: 20c, Saluting flag, aiming anti-tank missile. 30c, With family, on jungle patrol with automatic rifle. 35c, Reading newspaper, aiming machine gun. 75c, Working with computer, and as commander, looking through binoculars.

1994, July 1   Litho.   Perf. 13¹/₂
691 A174 20c multicolored .28 .28
692 A174 30c multicolored .42 .42
693 A174 35c multicolored .48 .48
694 A174 75c multicolored 1.10 1.10
      Nos. 691-694 (4) 2.28 2.28

Herons — A175

1994, Aug. 16   Litho.   Perf. 14
695 A175 20c Black-crowned night
              heron .28 .28
a.   Booklet pane of 10 2.80
696 A175 50c Little heron .70 .70
697 A175 75c Purple heron 1.00 1.00
698 A175 $1 Gray heron 1.40 1.40
a.   Block of 4, #695-698 3.40 3.40
      Nos. 695-698 (4) 3.38 3.38

Greetings
Stamps — A175a

Designs: No. 698B, Birthday cake. No. 698C, Bouquet of flowers. No. 698D, Gift-wrapped present. No. 698E, Fireworks. No. 698F, Balloons.

Die Cut Perf. 11¹/₂
1994, Sept. 14   Litho.
Self-Adhesive
Booklet Stamps
698B A175a (20c) multicolored .30 .30
698C A175a (20c) multicolored .30 .30
698D A175a (20c) multicolored .30 .30
698E A175a (20c) multicolored .30 .30
698F A175a (20c) multicolored .30 .30
g.   Bklt. pane, 2 each #698B-698F 1.50 1.50
      Nos. 698B-698F (5)

Nos. 698B-693F inscribed "For Local Addresses Only." By its nature, No. 698g is a complete booklet. The peelable paper backing serves as a booklet cover. The outside of the cover contains 10 peelable labels.

Modern Singapore, 175th Anniv. — A176

Early, modern scenes: 20c, Schoolchildren reading, graduating seniors. 50c, Horse-drawn carriages, high-speed train. 75c, Small boats, container ship dock. $1, Skyline.

1994, Sept. 30   Perf. 13¹/₂x14
699 A176 20c multicolored .28 .28
700 A176 50c multicolored .70 .70
701 A176 75c multicolored 1.00 1.00
702 A176 $1 multicolored 1.40 1.40
a.   Souvenir sheet of 4, #699-702 3.40 3.40
      Nos. 699-702 (4) 3.38 3.38

ICAO, 50th
Anniv. — A177

Designs: 35c, Control tower, passenger jet. 75c, Terminal, Concord jet. $2, Control tower, communication satellite, passenger jet.

1994, Oct. 5   Litho.   Perf. 14
703 A177 20c multicolored .28 .28
704 A177 35c multicolored .50 .50
705 A177 75c multicolored 1.10 1.10
706 A177 $2 multicolored 3.00 3.00
      Nos. 703-706 (4) 4.88 4.88

Love Stamps — A178

Designs: No. 707, "Love" in three different inscriptions. No. 708, Spiral of "Love." No. 709, "Love" on two lines. No. 710, "Love" in different languages. No. 711, Geometrical "Love."

Die Cut Perf. 11¹/₂
1995, Feb. 8   Litho.
Self-Adhesive
Booklet Stamps
707 A178 (20c) multicolored .30 .30
708 A178 (20c) multicolored .30 .30
709 A178 (20c) multicolored .30 .30
710 A178 (20c) multicolored .30 .30
711 A178 (20c) multicolored .30 .30
a.   Booklet pane, 2 each #707-711 3.00
      Nos. 707-711 (5) 1.50 1.50

Nos. 707-711 inscribed "FOR LOCAL ADDRESSES ONLY." By its nature, No. 711a is a complete booklet. The peelable paper backing serves as a booklet cover. The outside of the cover contains 10 peelable labels.

Meet in
Singapore
A179

Scenes in Suntec City: (20c), Intl. Convention & Exhibition Center. 75c, High rise buildings. $1, Temasek Boulevard. $2, Fountain Terrace.

1995, Jan. 11   Perf. 13¹/₂x14
712 A179 (20c) multicolored .30 .30
713 A179 75c multicolored 1.10 1.10
714 A179 $1 multicolored 1.50 1.50
715 A179 $2 multicolored 3.00 3.00
      Nos. 712-715 (4) 5.90 5.90

Singapore '95. No. 712 inscribed "FOR LOCAL ADDRESSES ONLY."

Souvenir Sheets of 2, #712, 715
Inscribed:
715a FIP DAY 4.00 4.00
715b OLYMPIC DAY-YOUTH 4.00 4.00
715c FIAP DAY 4.00 4.00
715d LETTER WRITING DAY 4.00 4.00
715e STAMP COLLECTING DAY 4.00 4.00
715f SINGAPORE '95 DAY .50 .50
715g PHILATELIC MUSEUM DAY 4.00 4.00
715h SINGAPORE POST DAY 4.00 4.00
715i AWARDS DAY 4.00 4.00
715j THEMATIC PHILATELY DAY 4.00 4.00

Flower Type of 1991
Designs: No. 716, Vanda Marlie Dolera, No. 717, Vanda limbata.

1995, Mar. 15   Litho.   Perf. 14
716 A151 $2 multicolored 3.00 3.00
717 A151 $2 multicolored 3.00 3.00
a.   Pair, #716-717 + label 6.00 6.00
b.   Souvenir sheet, #716-717 6.00 6.00

Singapore '95 (#717a-717b).

Independence,
30th Anniv.
A180

"My Singapore, My Country, Happy Birthday" in various languages and: 20c, "30" formed in ribbon, vert. 50c, #471, flower. 75c, #598, Music sheet. $1, Natl. flag, #489, music sheets, vert.

Perf. 14x13¹/₂, 13¹/₂x14
1995, Apr. 19   Litho.
718 A180 (20c) multicolored .28 .28
719 A180 50c multicolored .70 .70
720 A180 75c multicolored 1.10 1.10
721 A180 $1 multicolored 1.40 1.40
a.   Souvenir sheet of 4, #718-721 3.75 3.75
      Nos. 718-721 (4) 3.48 3.48

No. 718 inscribed "For Local Addresses Only." No. 721a is a continuous design.

End of
World
War II,
50th
Anniv.
A181

Designs: (20c), Crowd celebrating, Straits Settlements #271, vert. 60c, Lord Mountbatten receiving Japanese surrender of Singapore, Straits Settlements #265, vert. 70c, Food kitchen. $2, Police road block.

Perf. 14x13¹/₂, 13¹/₂x14
1995, June 21   Litho.
723 A181 (20c) multicolored .30 .30
724 A181 60c multicolored .90 .90
725 A181 70c multicolored 1.00 1.00
726 A181 $2 multicolored 3.00 3.00
      Nos. 723-726 (4) 5.20 5.20

No. 723 inscribed "For Local Addresses Only" and sold for 20c on day of issue.

New Six
Digit
Postal
Code
A182

1995   Litho.   Perf. 14x14¹/₂
727 A182 (20c) shown .30 .30
728 A182 $2 Six boxes, numbers 3.00 3.00

No. 728 inscribed "For Local Addresses Only."

Philatelic
Museum,
Singapore
A183

Museum building, various stamps, featuring: 20c, #12. 50c, #157. 60c, #661. $2, Displays of stamps.

1995   Perf. 13x13¹/₂
729 A183 (20c) multicolored .30 .30
730 A183 50c multicolored .75 .75
731 A183 60c multicolored .90 .90
732 A183 $2 multicolored 3.00 3.00
      Nos. 729-732 (4) 4.95 4.95

No. 729 inscribed "For Local Addresses Only."

Fish — A184

1995   Litho.   Perf. 13¹/₂x14
733 A184 (20c) Yellow-faced angel-
              fish .30 .30
734 A184 60c Harlequin sweetlips .90 .90

735 A184 70c Lionfish 1.00 1.00
736 A184 $1 Longfin bannerfish 1.50 1.50
Nos. 733-736 (4) 3.70 3.70

No. 733 inscribed "For Local Addresses Only."

Paintings in Singapore Art Museum
A185

Designs: (20c), Tropical Fruits, by Georgette Chen. 30c, Bali Beach, by Cheong Soo Pieng. 70c, Gibbons, by Chen Wen Hsi. $2, Shi (Lion), by Pan Shou (calligraphy).

1995 Litho. Perf. 12½
737 A185 (20c) multicolored .30 .30
738 A185 30c multicolored .45 .45
739 A185 70c multicolored 1.00 1.00

Perf. 13½x13
740 A185 $2 multicolored 3.00 3.00
Nos. 737-740 (4) 4.75 4.75

No. 737 inscribed "For Local Addresses Only."
No. 740 is 22½x39mm.

POSTAGE DUE STAMPS

 D1
 D2

Wmk. 314
1968, Feb. 1 Litho. Perf. 9
J1 D1 1c emerald .20 .20
J2 D1 2c red org .30 .30
J3 D1 4c yel org .65 .65
J4 D1 8c brown .75 .75
J5 D1 10c rose mag 1.90 1.90
J6 D1 12c dl vio 1.00 1.00
J7 D1 20c brt bl 2.25 2.25
J8 D1 50c gray grn 5.50 5.50
Nos. J1-J8 (8) 12.55 12.55

1973-77 Perf. 13x13½
J1a D1 1c Unwmkd. ('77)
J3a D1 4c Unwmkd. ('77)
J5a D1 10c
b. Unwmkd. ('77) .75 .75
J7a D1 20c Unwmkd. ('77)
J8a D1 50c 4.25 4.25
b. Unwmkd. ('77)

1981 Unwmk. Perf. 12x11½
J9 D2 1c emerald .15 .15
J10 D2 4c orange .15 .15
J11 D2 10c carmine .55 .55
J12 D2 20c light blue .60 .60
J13 D2 50c light yellow green .85 .85
Nos. J9-J13 (5) 2.30 2.30

1978, Sept. 25 Perf. 13x13½
J9a D2 1c .70 .70
J10a D2 4c .80 .80
J11a D2 10c .80 .80
J12a D2 20c 1.00 1.00
J13a D2 50c 1.75 1.75
Nos. J9a-J13a (5) 5.05 5.05

 D3

1989, July 12 Litho. Perf. 13x13½
J14 D3 5c lind lilac .15 .15
J15 D3 10c red .15 .15
J16 D3 20c light blue .25 .25
J17 D3 50c yellow green .70 .70
Set value 1.10 1.10

SOLOMON ISLANDS

'sä-lə-mən 'ī-ləndz

British Solomon Islands

LOCATION — West Pacific Ocean, east of Papua
GOVT. — Independent state in British Commonwealth
AREA — 11,500 sq. mi.
POP. — 258,193 (1984)
CAPITAL — Honiara

The Solomons include 10 large islands and four groups of small islands extending over an area of 375,000 square miles.
The British protectorate of British Solomon Islands changed its name to Solomon Islands in 1975 and achieved independence July 7, 1978.

12 Pence = 1 Shilling
20 Shillings = 1 Pound
100 Cents = 1 Dollar (1966)

Catalogue values for unused stamps in this country are for Never Hinged items, beginning with Scott 80 in the regular postage section and Scott B1 in the semi-postal section.

War Canoe — A1

Unwmk.
1907, Feb. 14 Litho. Perf. 11
1 A1 ½p ultra 10.00 15.00
2 A1 1p red 25.00 32.50
3 A1 2p dull blue 37.50 32.50
a. Horiz. pair, imperf. btwn. 10,000.
4 A1 2½p orange 35.00 37.50
a. Vert. pair, imperf. btwn. 4,500.
b. Horiz. pair, imperf. btwn. 5,000. 4,250.
5 A1 5p yellow green 55.00 65.00
6 A1 6p chocolate 55.00 65.00
a. Vertical pair, imperf. btwn. 3,750.
b. Horiz. pair, imperf. btwn.
7 A1 1sh violet 85.00 95.00
Nos. 1-7 (7) 292.50 342.50

Excellent counterfeits are plentiful.

War Canoe A2

George V A3

Wmk. Multiple Crown and CA (3)
1908-11 Engr. Perf. 14
8 A2 ½p green .80 .90
9 A2 1p carmine .95 .55
10 A2 2p gray 1.00 .90
11 A2 2½p ultra 2.25 2.50
12 A2 4p red, yel ('11) 2.50 10.00
13 A2 5p olive green 8.00 8.50
14 A2 6p claret 8.00 7.00
15 A2 1sh black, green 9.00 12.00
16 A2 2sh vio, bl ('10) 27.50 45.00
17 A2 2sh6p red, bl ('10) 40.00 65.00
18 A2 5sh bl, yel ('10) 70.00 90.00
Nos. 8-18 (11) 170.00 242.35

Inscribed "POSTAGE - POSTAGE"
1913-24 Typo.
19 A3 ½p green .85 2.50
20 A3 1p carmine 2.00 8.75
21 A3 3p violet, yel 2.00 5.75
22 A3 11p dull violet & red 6.00 12.50
Wmk. 4
23 A3 1½p scarlet ('24) 1.50 3.75
Nos. 19-23 (5) 12.35 33.25

Inscribed "POSTAGE - REVENUE"
1914-23 Wmk. 3
28 A3 ½p green .70 6.00
29 A3 1p carmine 1.10 1.00
a. 1p scarlet ('17) 3.50 6.00
30 A3 2p gray 1.50 8.00
31 A3 2½p ultra 2.00 5.00
Chalky Paper
32 A3 3p violet, yel ('23) 20.00 65.00
33 A3 4p blk & red, yel 2.00 3.00
34 A3 5p dull vio & ol grn 15.00 25.00

35 A3 6p dull vio & red vio 5.00 13.00
36 A3 1sh blk, green 4.00 6.75
a. 1sh blk, bl grn, ol back 6.00 13.00
37 A3 2sh dull vio & ultra, bl 6.50 10.50
38 A3 2sh6p blk & red, bl 8.00 18.00
39 A3 5sh grn & red, yel 25.00 40.00
40 A3 10sh grn & red, grn 75.00 80.00
41 A3 £1 vio & blk, red 210.00 125.00
Nos. 28-41 (14) 375.80 406.25

Inscribed "POSTAGE - REVENUE"
1922-31 Wmk. 4
43 A3 ½p green .45 1.75
44 A3 1p carmine ('23) 10.00 8.00
45 A3 1p violet ('27) .90 5.00
46 A3 2p gray ('23) 2.25 8.00
47 A3 3p ultra ('23) .90 3.00
Chalky Paper
48 A3 4p blk & red, yel ('27) 3.50 15.00
49 A3 4½p red brn ('31) 3.00 15.00
50 A3 5p dull vio & ol grn 3.00 20.00
51 A3 6p dull vio & red vio 3.50 15.00
52 A3 1sh black, emer 2.75 11.00
53 A3 2sh dull vio & ultra, bl ('27) 7.75 30.00
54 A3 2sh6p blk & red, bl 7.00 30.00
55 A3 5sh grn & red, yel 22.50 47.50
56 A3 10sh grn & red, emer ('25) 90.00 100.00
Nos. 43-56 (14) 157.50 309.25

No. 49 is on ordinary paper.

Silver Jubilee Issue
Common Design Type
1935, May 6 Engr. Perf. 13½x14
60 CD301 1½p car & dk bl 1.20 1.25
61 CD301 3p blue & brown 4.50 5.25
62 CD301 6p ol grn & lt bl 4.75 5.75
63 CD301 1sh brt vio & ind 7.00 8.50
Nos. 60-63 (4) 17.45 20.75

Coronation Issue
Common Design Type
1937, May 13 Perf. 11x11½
64 CD302 1p dark purple .20 .30
65 CD302 3p dark carmine .25 .35
66 CD302 3p deep ultra .35 .35
Nos. 64-66 (3) .80 .90

Spears and Shield — A4

Policeman and Chief — A5

Artificial Island, Malaita — A6

Canoe House, New Georgia — A7

Roviana War Canoe — A8

View of Munda Point — A9

Meeting House, Reef Islands A10

Coconut Plantation A11

Breadfruit — A12

Tinakula Volcano, Santa Cruz Islands — A13

Scrub Fowl — A14

Malaita Canoe — A15

Perf. 12½, 13½ (A7, A13, A14)
1939-51 Wmk. 4
67 A4 ½p deep grn & ultra .15 .45
68 A5 1p dk pur & choc .15 .40
69 A6 1½p car & sl grn .25 .60
70 A7 2p blk & org brn .30 .60
a. 2p black & red brown ('43) .30 .60
b. Perf. 12 ('51) .50 1.00
71 A8 2½p ol grn & rose vio .50 .75
a. Vert. pair, imperf. horiz. 8,000.
72 A9 3p ultra & blk, perf. 12 ('51) .55 1.00
a. Perf. 13½ .85 .85
73 A10 4½p dk brn & yel grn 6.00 11.00
74 A11 6p rose lil & dk pur .40 .60
75 A12 1sh black & green .60 .60
76 A13 2sh dp org & blk 3.25 2.00
a. 2sh6p dull vio & blk ('43) 3.25 2.00
77 A14 2sh6p dull vio & blk green 9.00 6.00
78 A15 5sh red & brt bl green 11.00 7.50
79 A10 10sh red lil & ol ('42) 7.00 8.50
Nos. 67-79 (13) 39.15 40.00

Catalogue values for unused stamps in this section, from this point to the end of the section, are for Never Hinged items.

Peace Issue
Common Design Type
Perf. 13½x14
1946, Oct. 15 Wmk. 4 Engr.
80 CD303 1½p carmine .20 .30
81 CD303 3p deep blue .20 .30

Silver Wedding Issue
Common Design Types
1949, Mar. 14 Photo. Perf. 14x14½
82 CD304 2p black .20 .20
Perf. 11½x11
Engr.; Name Typo.
83 CD305 10sh red violet 22.50 22.50

UPU Issue
Common Design Types
Engr.; Name Typo. on 3p and 5p
Perf. 13½, 11x11½
1949, Oct. 10 Wmk. 4
84 CD306 2p red brown .90 .90
85 CD307 3p indigo 1.25 1.25
86 CD308 5p green 2.25 2.25
87 CD309 1sh slate 3.50 3.50
Nos. 84-87 (4) 7.90 7.90

Coronation Issue
Common Design Type

1953, June 2 Engr. *Perf. 13½x13*

88	CD312	2p gray & black	.50	.50

Ysabel Canoe — A16

Prow of Roviana Canoe — A17

Designs: 1p, Roviana canoe. 1½p, Artificial Island, Malaita. 2p, Canoe house. 3p, Malaita canoe. 5p, 1sh3p, Map. 6p, Trading schooner. 8p, 9p, Henderson Field, Guadalcanal. 1sh, Chart of Solomons and H.M.S. Swallow, recalling Capt. Philip Carteret's voyage of 1767. 2sh, Tinakula Volcano. 2sh6p, Meeting house, Reef Islands. 5sh, Alvaro de Mendana de Neyra and Caravel. 10sh, Constable and Chief. £1, Coat of Arms.

Perf. 11½x11, 11x11½, 12, 13

1956-60 Engr. Wmk. 4

89	A16	½p	lilac & orange	.15	.15
90	A16	1p	red brn & ol grn	.15	.15
91	A16	1½p	dk car & sl bl	.15	.15
92	A16	2p	gray grn & choc	.25	.25
93	A17	2½p	gray bl & blk	.40	.40
94	A16	3p	dull red & grn	.40	.20
95	A16	5p	blue & black	.85	.85
96	A16	6p	bluish grn & blk	.35	.30
97	A16	8p	black & ultra	.85	.55
98	A16	9p	black & brt grn	4.75	1.40
99	A16	1sh	brn org & sl bl	.85	.55
100	A16	1sh3p	blue & black	3.50	1.50
101	A16	2sh	car rose & blk	3.50	1.00
102	A17	2sh6p	rose lil & emer	4.00	.50
103	A16	5sh	red brown	8.50	3.00
104	A17	10sh	black brown	16.00	4.00
105	A16	£1	lt blue & blk	42.50	35.00
			Nos. 89-105 (17)	87.15	49.95

Issue dates: £1, Nov. 5, 1958. 9p, 1sh3p, Jan. 28, 1960. Others, Mar. 1, 1956.

See Nos. 113-125.

Great Frigate Bird — A18

Perf. 13x12½

1961, Jan. 19 Litho. Wmk. 314

106	A18	2p blue green & black	.15	.25
107	A18	3p rose red & black	.15	.15
108	A18	9p lilac & black	.25	.40
		Nos. 106-108 (3)	.55	.80

New constitution, brought into operation Oct. 18, 1960. The watermark is sideways and may be found facing both left and right.

Freedom from Hunger Issue
Common Design Type

1963, June 4 Photo. *Perf. 14x14½*

109	CD314	1sh3p ultra	3.50	2.00

Red Cross Centenary Issue
Common Design Type

1963, Sept. 2 Litho. *Perf. 13*

110	CD315	2p black & red	.40	.25
111	CD315	9p ultra & red	2.00	1.75

Types of 1956-60

Perf. 12, 13, 11½x11

1963-64 Engr. Wmk. 314

113	A16	1p	red brn & ol grn	.25	.25
114	A16	1½p	dk car & sl bl	.25	.40
115	A16	2p	gray grn & choc	.25	.20
117	A16	3p	dull red & grn	.40	.20
119	A16	6p	bluish grn & blk	.90	.40
121	A16	9p	black & brt grn	.90	.40
123	A16	1sh3p	blue & blk	1.10	.70
124	A16	2sh	car rose & blk	2.50	4.25
125	A17	2sh6p	rose lil & emer	9.00	9.00
			Nos. 113-125 (9)	15.55	15.80

Issue dates: 3p, Nov. 16. 6p, 9p, 1sh3p, July 7, 1964. 1p, 1½p, 2p, 2sh, 2sh6p, July 9, 1964.

ITU Issue
Common Design Type

Perf. 11x11½

1965, June 28 Litho. Wmk. 314

126	CD317	2p ver & grnsh blue	.35	.35
127	CD317	3p grnsh blue & olive bis	.55	.55

Makira Food Bowl — A19

Designs: 1p, 1sh, 1sh3p, Various orchids. 1½p, Scorpion shell. 2p, Papuan hornbill. 2½p, Ysabel shield. 3p, Rennellese club. 6p, Moorish idol (fish). 9p, Great frigate bird. 2sh, Sanford's sea eagle. 2sh6p, Malaita belt. 5sh, Ornithoptera Victoreae (butterfly). 10sh, White cockatoo. £1, Figurehead, western canoe.

Perf. 13x12½

1965, May 24 Litho. Wmk. 314

Design Subject in Black

128	A19	½p	sl blue & lt bl	.15	.15
129	A19	1p	orange & yel	.15	.15
130	A19	1½p	blue & yel grn	.15	.15
131	A19	2p	vio blue & lt blue	.15	.15
132	A19	2½p	red brn & buff	.15	.15
133	A19	3p	green & lt green	.15	.15
134	A19	6p	brt car rose & org	.22	.22
135	A19	9p	slate grn & buff	.32	.32
136	A19	1sh	dp cl & rose	.48	.48
137	A19	1sh3p	ver & buff	2.25	.75
138	A19	2sh	dp mag & lil	3.75	1.50
139	A19	2sh6p	ol brn & buff	2.50	2.25
140	A19	5sh	dk vio bl & lil	5.50	4.50
141	A19	10sh	ol grn & yel	9.50	8.75
142	A19	£1	purple & red	15.00	15.00
			Nos. 128-142 (15)	40.42	34.67

For surcharges see Nos. 149-166.

Intl. Cooperation Year Issue
Common Design Type

1965, Oct. 25 Litho. *Perf. 14½*

143	CD318	1p blue green & cl	.15	.15
144	CD318	2sh6p lt violet & grn	1.25	1.25

Churchill Memorial Issue
Common Design Type

1966, Jan. 24 Photo. *Perf. 14*

145	CD319	2p multicolored	.15	.15
146	CD319	9p multicolored	.40	.35
147	CD319	1sh6p multicolored	.85	.70
148	CD319	2sh6p multicolored	1.40	1.25
		Nos. 145-148 (4)	2.80	2.45

Nos. 128-142 Surcharged with New Value and Three Bars in Black or Red

Perf. 13x12½

1966-67 Litho. Wmk. 314

149	A19	1c on ½p multi	.15	.15
150	A19	2c on 1p multi	.15	.15
151	A19	3c on 1½p multi	.15	.15
152	A19	4c on 2p multi	.15	.15
153	A19	5c on 6p multi	.18	.18
154	A19	6c on 2½p multi	.20	.20
155	A19	7c on 3p multi	.30	.30
156	A19	8c on 9p multi	.32	.32
b.		"8" inverted	13.00	13.00
157	A19	10c on 1sh	.45	.45
158	A19	12c on 1sh3p multi	.45	.45
159	A19	13c on 1sh3p multi	.50	.50
160	A19	14c on 3p multi	.50	.50
161	A19	20c on 2sh multi	.85	.85
162	A19	25c on 2sh6p multi	1.10	1.10
163	A19	35c on 2p multi	2.00	1.65
164	A19	50c on 5sh multi (R)	2.50	2.25
165	A19	$1 on 10sh multi	4.25	4.25
166	A19	$2 on £1 multi	8.75	8.75
		Nos. 149-166 (18)	22.95	22.35

The 12c, 14c, 35c have watermark sideways.
Issued: 12c, 14c, 35c, 3/1/67; others, 2/14/66.

1966 Wmk. 314 Sideways

149a	A19	1c on ½p	.15	.15
150a	A19	2c on 1p	.15	.15
151a	A19	3c on 1½p	.18	.18
152a	A19	4c on 2p	.24	.24
153a	A19	5c on 6p	.30	.30
154a	A19	6c on 2½p	.35	.35
155a	A19	7c on 3p	.42	.42
156a	A19	8c on 9p	.48	.48
157a	A19	10c on 1sh	.60	.60
159a	A19	13c on 1sh3p	.75	.75
161a	A19	20c on 2sh	1.25	1.25
162a	A19	25c on 2sh6p	1.50	1.50
164a	A19	50c on 5sh (R)	3.00	3.00
165a	A19	$1 on 10sh	6.00	6.00
166a	A19	$2 on £1	9.00	9.00
		Nos. 149a-166a (15)	24.37	24.37

World Cup Soccer Issue
Common Design Type

1966, July 1 Litho. *Perf. 14*

167	CD321	8c multicolored	.30	.30
168	CD321	35c multicolored	1.10	1.10

WHO Headquarters Issue
Common Design Type

1966, Sept. 20 Litho. *Perf. 14*

169	CD322	3c multicolored	.15	.15
170	CD322	50c multicolored	1.65	1.65

UNESCO Anniversary Issue
Common Design Type

1966, Dec. 1 Litho. *Perf. 14*

171	CD323	3c "Education"	.15	.15
172	CD323	25c "Science"	.65	.65
173	CD323	$1 "Culture"	3.50	2.75
		Nos. 171-173 (3)	4.30	3.55

Henderson Field, Guadalcanal — A20

Design: 35c, US Marines landing, Red Beach, Guadalcanal, 1942.

Perf. 14x14½

1967, Aug. 28 Photo. Wmk. 314

174	A20	8c multi & silver	.20	.20
175	A20	35c multi & gold	.75	.75

Guadalcanal campaign in WW II, 25th anniv.

Mendana's Ship Off Puerta de la Cruz (Honiara), Guadalcanal, 1568 — A21

Designs: 8c, Arrival of Missionaries. 35c, Naval battle during World War II. $1, Honor guard raising Union Jack during proclamation of Protectorate.

1968, Feb. 2 Photo. *Perf. 14½*

176	A21	3c pink & multi	.15	.15
177	A21	8c emerald & multi	.22	.22
178	A21	35c multicolored	.75	.75
179	A21	$1 blue & multi	2.25	2.25
		Nos. 176-179 (4)	3.37	3.37

400th anniv. of the discovery of the British Solomon Islands by the Spanish navigator Alvaro de Mendana de Neyra.

Vine Fishing — A22

Designs: 2c, Kite fishing. 3c, Platform fishing. 4c, Net fishing. 6c, Gold lip shell diving. 8c, Night fishing. 12c, Boat building. 14c, Cocoa harvest. 15c, Road building. 20c, Geological survey by plane. 24c, Hauling timber. 35c, Copra. 45c, Harvesting rice. $1, Honiara Port. $2, Map of the Islands, plane and route of Internal Air Service.

Perf. 14½

1968, May 20 Wmk. 314 Photo.

180	A22	1c aqua, brn & blk	.15	.15
181	A22	2c lt yel grn, brn & blk	.15	.15
182	A22	3c brt grn, dk grn & blk	.15	.15
183	A22	4c brt rose lil, brn & blk	.15	.15
184	A22	6c multicolored	.20	.20
185	A22	8c dp ultra, org & blk	.28	.28
186	A22	12c bister, red & blk	.42	.42
187	A22	14c red org, brn & blk	.52	.52
188	A22	15c multicolored	.55	.55
189	A22	20c ultra, red & blk	.80	.80
190	A22	24c scarlet, yel & blk	.90	.90
191	A22	35c multicolored	1.75	1.75
192	A22	45c yellow, red & blk	2.50	2.50
193	A22	$1 vio bl, emer & blk	4.50	4.50
194	A22	$2 multicolored	9.00	9.00
		Nos. 180-194 (15)	22.02	22.02

Map of South Pacific and University Degrees A23

Perf. 12½x12

1969, Feb. 10 Litho. Unwmk.

195	A23	3c multicolored	.15	.15
196	A23	12c multicolored	.25	.25
197	A23	35c multicolored	.60	.60
		Nos. 195-197 (3)	1.00	1.00

Inauguration of the University of the South Pacific in 1969, at the Royal New Zealand Air Force Seaplane Station, Laucala Bay, Fiji.

Field Ball and Games' Emblem — A24

Stained Glass Window with Melanesian Peace Symbol — A25

Perf. 14½x14

1969, Aug. 13 Photo. Wmk. 314

198	A24	3c shown	.15	.15
199	A24	8c Soccer	.16	.16
200	A24	14c Running	.30	.30
201	A24	45c Rugby	.95	.95
a.		Souvenir sheet of 4, #198-201	5.00	5.00
		Nos. 198-201 (4)	1.56	1.56

3rd S. Pacific Games, Port Moresby, Aug. 13-23.

In No. 201a, shading was added below athlete's foot on 14c, and strengthened on 8c and 45c.

1969, Nov. 21 Photo. Wmk. 314

Christmas: 8c, South Sea Islands scene with palms and Star of Bethlehem.

202	A25	8c violet, grnsh bl & blk	.22	.22
203	A25	35c black & multi	.85	.85

C. M. Woodford and Stamp of 1907 — A26

Designs: 7c, British Solomon Islands 1906 handstamp and cancellation, and New South Wales No. 99. 18c, British Solomon Islands No. 18 and 1913 Tulagi cancellation. 23c, New General Post Office, Honiara.

1970, Apr. 15 Litho. *Perf. 13*

204	A26	7c lilac rose & black	.15	.15
205	A26	14c lt olive & black	.35	.35
206	A26	18c orange, yel & blk	.48	.48
207	A26	23c multicolored	.65	.65
		Nos. 204-207 (4)	1.63	1.63

Issued to publicize the opening of the new General Post Office in Honiara.

Map of Solomon Islands — A27

Design: 18c, British Solomon Islands coat of arms, vert.

Perf. 14½x14, 14x14½

1970, June 15 Litho. Wmk. 314

208	A27	18c multicolored	.55	.55
209	A27	35c multicolored	1.00	1.00

Adoption of the new 1970 Constitution.

Red Cross Headquarters, Honiara — A28

Design: 35c, Map of British Solomon Islands showing Red Cross stations, and wheelchair.

1970, Aug. 17 *Perf. 14½x14*

210	A28	3c multicolored	.15	.15
211	A28	35c multicolored	.95	.95

Centenary of British Red Cross Society.

Carved Angel and Southern Cross — A29

Reredos: Symbols of Trinity and Light at St. Luke's Church, Kia
A30

Perf. 14x13½, 13½x14

1970, Oct. 19 **Litho.** **Wmk. 314**

212	A29	8c violet & bister brn	.28	.28
213	A30	45c multicolored	1.00	1.00

Christmas 1970.

Count de La Pérouse and "La Boussole"
A31

Designs: 4c, Astrolabe and Polynesian reed map. 12c, Abel Tasman and sailing ship Heemskerk, 1643. 35c, Te Puki canoe, Santa Cruz.

1971, Jan. 28 *Perf. 14½x14*

214	A31	3c multicolored	.38	.20
215	A31	4c multicolored	.45	.30
216	A31	12c multicolored	1.40	.75
217	A31	35c multicolored	3.50	2.75
		Nos. 214-217 (4)	5.73	4.00

In honor of famous explorers and ships. See Nos. 228-231, 250-253.

Bishop Patteson, J. Atkin and S. Taroniara
A32

Designs: 4c, Last landing of the "Southern Cross" at Nukapu. 14c, Memorial for Bishop Patteson and map of Nukapu, vert. 45c, Ceremonial leaf tag (had been attached to Bishop's body; vert.).

Perf. 14½x14, 14x14½

1971, Apr. 5 **Litho.** **Wmk. 314**

218	A32	2c lt green & multi	.15	.15
219	A32	4c blue green & multi	.16	.16
220	A32	14c brt pink & multi	.45	.45
221	A32	45c brown & multi	1.50	1.50
		Nos. 218-221 (4)	2.26	2.26

Bishop John Coleridge Patteson (1827-71), head of the Melanesian mission.

Boxing, Games Emblem
A33

Designs (Games Emblem and): 8c, Soccer. 12c, Running. 35c, Spear fishing.

1971, Aug. 9 *Perf. 14½x14*

222	A33	3c orange & multi	.15	.15
223	A33	8c emerald & multi	.22	.22
224	A33	12c yellow & multi	.32	.32
225	A33	35c blue & multi	1.10	1.10
		Nos. 222-225 (4)	1.79	1.79

4th South Pacific Games, Papeete, French Polynesia, Sept. 8-19.

Melanesian Lectern (wood carving) — A34

Christmas: 45c, Stylized birds, painted by school girl Margarita Bara.

1971, Nov. 15 **Litho.** **Wmk. 314**

226	A34	9c orange & multi	.20	.20
227	A34	45c blue & multi	1.10	1.10

Explorer Type of 1971

Designs: 4c, Louis Antoine de Bougainville and La Boudeuse, 1776. 9c, Horizontal planisphere, 1574, and ivory backstaff, 1695. 15c, Philip Carteret and H.M.S. Swallow, 1707. 45c, Small canoe of Malaita.

1972, Feb. 1 *Perf. 14½*

228	A31	4c brown & multi	.25	.25
229	A31	9c green & multi	.60	.60
230	A31	15c lt blue & multi	1.10	1.10
231	A31	45c blue & multi	3.75	3.75
		Nos. 228-231 (4)	5.70	5.70

Cupha Woodfordi
A35

Designs: 1c, 2c, 3c, 4c, $2, Butterflies. 5c, 8c, 9c, 15c, $1, Fishes. 12c, 20c, 25c, 35c, 45c, Orchids. $5, Birds.

1972-73 *Perf. 14*

232	A35	1c *shown*	.15	.15
233	A35	2c *Ornithoptera priamus*	.15	.15
234	A35	3c *Vindula sapor*	.15	.15
235	A35	4c *Papilio orssippus*	.15	.15
236	A35	5c *Great trevally*	.16	.16
237	A35	8c *Little bonito*	.28	.20
238	A35	9c *Sapphire demoiselle*	.30	.30
239	A35	12c *Costus speciosus*	.50	.45
240	A35	15c *Orange anemone*	.70	.60
241	A35	20c *Spathoglottis plicata*	.90	.75
242	A35	25c *Ephemerantha comata*	1.10	1.00
243	A35	35c *Dendrobium cuthbertsonii*	1.75	1.25
244	A35	45c *Heliconia salomonica*	2.00	1.75
245	A35	$1 *Blue-finned triggerfish*	5.00	3.50
246	A35	$2 *Ornithoptera allotti*	10.50	7.00
247	A35	$5 *Great frigate bird*	17.00	17.00
		Nos. 232-247 (16)	40.79	34.56

Issued: $5, July 2, 1973; others, July 2, 1972. For overprints see Nos. 300-311.

Silver Wedding Issue, 1972
Common Design Type

Design: Queen Elizabeth II, Prince Philip, scroll and message drum on woven mat.

1972, Nov. 20 **Photo.** *Perf. 14x14½*

248	CD324	8c car rose & multi	.15	.15
249	CD324	45c olive & multi	.65	.65

Explorer Type of 1971

Designs: 4c, Antoine R. J. d'Entrecasteaux and "The Recherche," 1791. 9c, Ship's hourglass, 17th century, and chronometer, 1761. 15c, Lieutenant Shortland and "The Alexander," 1788. 35c, Tomoko (war canoe).

Perf. 14½

1973, Mar. 9 **Litho.** **Wmk. 314**

250	A31	4c blue & multi	.20	.20
251	A31	9c blue & multi	.60	.60
252	A31	15c blue & multi	1.00	1.00
253	A31	35c blue & multi	3.25	3.25
		Nos. 250-253 (4)	5.05	5.05

Pan Pipes
A36

Musical Instruments: 9c, Castanets. 15c, Bamboo flute. 35c, Bauro gongs. 45c, Bamboo band.

1973, Oct. 1 *Perf. 13½x14*

254	A36	4c brick red & multi	.15	.15
255	A36	9c yellow bis & multi	.25	.25
256	A36	15c pink & multi	.42	.42
257	A36	35c blue green & multi	1.00	1.00
258	A36	45c multicolored	1.25	1.25
		Nos. 254-258 (5)	3.07	3.07

Princess Anne's Wedding Issue
Common Design Type

1973, Nov. 14 *Perf. 14*

259	CD325	4c slate & multi	.15	.15
260	CD325	35c multicolored	.60	.60

Adoration of the Kings, by Jan Brueghel
A37

Adoration of the Kings by: 22c, Peter Brueghel, vert. 45c, Botticelli.

1973, Nov. 26 **Litho.** *Perf. 14*

Size: 39x25mm, 25x39mm

261	A37	8c pink & multi	.35	.35
262	A37	22c lilac & multi	.85	.85

Perf. 13½

Size: 47x35mm

263	A37	45c gray & multi	1.90	1.90
		Nos. 261-263 (3)	3.10	3.10

Christmas 1973.

Map of Solomon Islands — A38

1974, Feb. 18 **Litho.** *Perf. 13½*

264	A38	4c blue & multi	.15	.15
265	A38	9c citron & multi	.28	.28
266	A38	15c violet gray & multi	.48	.48
267	A38	35c emerald & multi	1.50	1.25
		Nos. 264-267 (4)	2.41	2.16

Visit of British Royal Family.

First Resident Commissioner Landing at Tulagi — A39

Designs: 9c, Marine radar and scanner unit, map of Islands. 15c, Islanders taken to "Blackbirder" ship. 45c, John F. Kennedy's P.T. 109 off Lumbari Island, 1943.

1974, May 15 **Litho.** *Perf. 14½*

268	A39	4c multicolored	.20	.20
269	A39	9c multicolored	.45	.45
270	A39	15c multicolored	.65	.65
271	A39	45c multicolored	2.75	2.75
		Nos. 268-271 (4)	4.05	4.05

Ships and navigators.

Mailman, Map of Islands — A40

Designs (UPU Emblem, map of Solomon Islands and): 9c, Carrier pigeon, horiz. 15c, Angel Gabriel. 45c, Pegasus, horiz. Designs based on origami (folded paper) figures.

1974, Aug. 29 **Wmk. 314** *Perf. 14*

272	A40	4c brt green & multi	.15	.15
273	A40	9c lemon & multi	.30	.22
274	A40	15c multicolored	.45	.35
275	A40	45c blue & multi	1.25	1.10
		Nos. 272-275 (4)	2.15	1.82

Centenary of Universal Postal Union.

Solomon Islands No. 208
A41

1974, Dec. 16 **Litho.** *Perf. 14½*

276	A41	4c shown	.15	.15
277	A41	9c No. 107	.30	.30
278	A41	15c same	.50	.50
279	A41	35c like 4c	1.10	1.10
a.		Souvenir sheet of 4, #276-279	4.00	3.50
		Nos. 276-279 (4)	2.05	2.05

New Constitution, inaugurated Oct. 18, 1960.

Golden Whistler
A42

Birds: 2c, River kingfisher. 3c, Red-throated fruit dove. 4c, Button quail. $2, Duchess lorikeet.

1975, Apr. 7 **Wmk. 314** *Perf. 14*

280	A42	1c yellow grn & multi	.15	.15
281	A42	2c lt blue & multi	.16	.15
282	A42	3c brt pink & multi	.25	.15
283	A42	4c orange & multi	.35	.18
284	A42	$2 dp orange & multi	15.00	6.25
		Nos. 280-284 (5)	15.91	6.88

See Nos. 316-320, 323, 330-331. For overprints see Nos. 296-299.

Motor Vessel Walande
A43

1975, May 29 *Perf. 13½*

285	A43	4c shown	.15	.15
286	A43	9c M. V. Melanesian	.38	.28
287	A43	15c Ship Marsina, house flag	.60	.50
288	A43	45c S. S. Himalaya	1.90	1.50
		Nos. 285-288 (4)	3.03	2.43

Runner, 800-meters — A44

1975, Aug. 4 **Litho.** *Perf. 13½*

289	A44	4c shown	.15	.15
290	A44	9c Long jump	.24	.24
291	A44	15c Javelin	.35	.35
292	A44	45c Soccer	1.00	1.00
a.		Souvenir sheet of 4, #289-292	4.25	2.50
		Nos. 289-292 (4)	1.74	1.74

5th South Pacific Games, Guam, Aug. 1-10.

Nativity and Candles A45

Christmas: 35c, Angels, shepherds and candles. 45c, Three Kings approaching Bethlehem, and candles.

1975, Oct. 13 Wmk. 373 *Perf. 14*

293 A45 15c multicolored .35 .35
294 A45 35c multicolored .80 .80
295 A45 45c multicolored 1.10 1.10
a. Souvenir sheet of 3, #293-295 4.25 3.75
Nos. 293-295 (3) 2.25 2.25

Nos. 236-245, 247, 280-284 Overprinted with Bar Obliterating "British" in Black or Silver

1975, Nov. 12 Litho. Wmk. 314

296 A42 1c multicolored .15 .15
297 A42 2c multicolored .15 .15
298 A42 3c multicolored .15 .15
299 A42 4c multicolored .15 .15
300 A35 5c multicolored .22 .22
301 A35 8c multicolored .40 .40
302 A35 9c multicolored .40 .40
303 A35 12c multicolored .50 .50
304 A35 15c multicolored .70 .70
305 A35 20c multicolored .90 .90
306 A35 25c multicolored 1.00 1.00
307 A35 35c multicolored 1.50 1.50
308 A35 45c multicolored 1.75 1.75
309 A35 $1 multicolored 3.50 3.50
310 A42 $2 multicolored 7.00 7.00
311 A35 $5 multicolored (S) 18.00 18.00
Nos. 296-311 (16) 36.47 36.47

Ceremonial Food Bowl A46

Artifacts: 15c, Barava, chief's money. 35c, Nguzu-nguzu, canoe protector spirit, vert. 45c, Nguzu-nguzu on canoe prow.

Wmk. 314

1976, Jan. 12 Litho. *Perf. 14*

312 A46 4c scarlet & black .15 .15
313 A46 15c lt violet & multi .32 .32
314 A46 35c multicolored .85 .85
315 A46 45c multicolored .95 .95
Nos. 312-315 (4) 2.27 2.27

Type of 1975 Inscribed "Solomon Islands" and

Golden Cowries A47

Designs: 1c, Golden whistler. 2c, River kingfisher. 3c, Red-throated fruit dove. 4c, Button quail. 5c, Willie wagtail. 10c, Glory-of-the-sea cones. 12c, Rainbow lory. 15c, Pearly nautilus. 20c, Venus comb murex. 25c, Commercial trochus. 35c, Melon or baler shell. 45c, Orange spider conch. $1, Pacific triton. $2, Duchess lorikeet. $5, Great frigate bird.

1976 Wmk. 373 *Perf. 14*

316 A42 1c yellow grn & multi .15 .15
317 A42 2c lt blue & multi .15 .15
318 A42 3c pink & multi .15 .15
319 A42 4c orange & multi .15 .15
320 A42 5c red brown & multi .15 .15
321 A47 6c rose & multi .15 .15
322 A47 10c multicolored .25 .25
323 A42 12c yellow grn & multi .30 .30
324 A47 15c lilac & multi .35 .35
325 A47 20c ultra & multi .50 .50
326 A47 25c dull grn & multi .60 .60
327 A47 35c bister & multi .90 .90
328 A47 45c fawn & multi 1.10 1.10
329 A47 $1 olive & multi 2.50 2.50
330 A42 $2 multicolored 5.00 5.00
331 A42 $5 multicolored 12.00 12.00
Nos. 316-331 (16) 24.40 24.40

Issue dates: $5, Dec. 6; others Mar. 8.

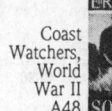

Coast Watchers, World War II A48

American Bicentennial: 20c, "Amagiri" ramming "P.T.109" and Lt. John F. Kennedy. 35c, Plane on Henderson Airfield. 45c, Map showing landing of US forces on Guadalcanal.

1976, May 24 *Perf. 14*

333 A48 6c black & multi .18 .15
334 A48 20c black & multi .70 .55
335 A48 35c black & multi 1.10 .90
336 A48 45c black & multi 1.40 1.10
a. Souvenir sheet of 4, #333-336 5.50 4.75
Nos. 333-336 (4) 3.38 2.70

Alexander Graham Bell — A49

Designs: 20c, Radio-telephone and satellite. 35c, Ericsson's magneto telephone. 45c, Telephone, 1876, and stick telephone.

1976, July 26 Litho. *Perf. 14½x14*

337 A49 6c lt ultra & multi .15 .15
338 A49 20c multicolored .48 .48
339 A49 35c orange & multi .70 .70
340 A49 45c bister & multi 1.00 1.00
Nos. 337-340 (4) 2.33 2.33

Centenary of first telephone call by Alexander Graham Bell, Mar. 10, 1876.

One-Eleven BAC — A50

Planes: 20c, Solair Britten Norman Islander. 35c, DC-3 Dakota. 45c, De Havilland DH50A.

1976, Sept. 13 Wmk. 373 *Perf. 14*

341 A50 6c black & multi .18 .18
342 A50 20c black & multi .65 .65
343 A50 35c black & multi 1.10 1.10
344 A50 45c black & multi 1.40 1.40
Nos. 341-344 (4) 3.33 3.33

1st flight to Solomon Islands, 50th anniv.

Queen Receiving Lei, 1974 Visit — A51

Carved Wooden Figure — A52

Designs: 35c, Communion plate and cup. 45c, Communion.

1977, Feb. 7 Litho. *Perf. 14x13½*

345 A51 6c multicolored .15 .15
346 A51 35c multicolored .52 .52
347 A51 45c multicolored .65 .65
Nos. 345-347 (3) 1.32 1.32

25th anniv. of the reign of Elizabeth II.

1977, May 9 *Perf. 14*

Artifacts: 20c, Sea adaro or spirit. 35c, Shark-headed man. 45c, Seated man.

348 A52 6c yellow & multi .16 .16
349 A52 20c blue & multi .50 .50
350 A52 35c rose & multi .85 .85
351 A52 45c multicolored 1.10 1.10
Nos. 348-351 (4) 2.61 2.61

Man Spraying House, Anopheles Mosquito A53

Designs: 20c, Taking blood samples. 35c, Microscope, map of Solomon Islands, Malaria Eradication Program emblem. 45c, Messenger delivering medicine to malaria patient.

1977, July 27 Litho. Wmk. 373

352 A53 6c multicolored .15 .15
353 A53 20c multicolored .42 .42
354 A53 35c multicolored .75 .75
355 A53 45c multicolored 1.10 1.10
Nos. 352-355 (4) 2.42 2.42

Malaria eradication.

Adoration of the Shepherds — A54

Christmas: 20c, Nativity. 35c, Adoration of the Kings. 45c, Flight into Egypt.

Wmk. 373

1977, Sept. 12 Litho. *Perf. 14*

356 A54 6c multicolored .15 .15
357 A54 20c multicolored .45 .45
358 A54 35c multicolored .80 .80
359 A54 45c multicolored 1.00 1.00
Nos. 356-359 (4) 2.40 2.40

Traditional Feather Money A55

Designs: No. 361, New coins. No. 362, Banknotes. No. 363, Traditional shell money.

1977, Oct. 24 Litho. *Perf. 14x14½*

360 A55 6c brt green & multi .16 .16
361 A55 6c brt green & multi .16 .16
a. Pair, #360-361 .35 .35
362 A55 45c buff & multi 1.00 1.00
363 A55 45c buff & multi 1.00 1.00
a. Pair, #362-363 2.00 2.00
Nos. 360-363 (4) 2.32 2.32

New coinage.

Shortland Islands Figure — A56

Artifacts: 20c, Ceremonial shield. 35c, Santa Cruz ritual figure. 45c, Decorative combs.

1978, Jan. 11 *Perf. 14*

364 A56 6c multicolored .15 .15
365 A56 20c multicolored .45 .45
366 A56 35c multicolored .80 .80
367 A56 45c multicolored 1.00 1.00
Nos. 364-367 (4) 2.40 2.40

Elizabeth II Coronation Anniversary Issue

Common Design Types

Souvenir Sheet

Unwmk.

1978, Apr. 21 Litho. *Perf. 15*

368 Sheet of 6 3.00 3.00
a. CD326 45c King's dragon .45 .45
b. CD327 45c Elizabeth II .45 .45
c. CD328 45c Sandford eagle .45 .45

No. 368 contains 2 se-tenant strips of Nos. 368a-368c, separated by horizontal gutter with commemorative and descriptive inscriptions and showing central part of coronation procession with coach.

National Flag — A57

Apostles by Dürer — A58

Independence: 15c, Governor General's flag. 35c, Cenotaph, Honiara, flags of U.S., Great Britain, New Zealand and Australia. 45c, Coat of Arms.

Wmk. 373

1978, July 7 Litho. *Perf. 14*

369 A57 6c multicolored .15 .15
370 A57 15c multicolored .30 .30
371 A57 35c multicolored .70 .70
372 A57 45c multicolored .95 .95
Nos. 369-372 (4) 2.10 2.10

1978, Oct. 4 Litho. *Perf. 14*

373 A58 6c John .15 .15
374 A58 20c Peter .42 .42
375 A58 35c Paul .70 .70
376 A58 45c Mark .90 .90
Nos. 373-376 (4) 2.17 2.17

Albrecht Dürer (1471-1528), German painter, 450th death anniversary.

Scouts Making Fire — A59

Designs: 20c, Camping. 35c, Solomon Islands Scouts. 45c, Canoeing.

1978, Nov. 15 Litho. *Perf. 14*

377 A59 6c multicolored .15 .15
378 A59 20c multicolored .42 .42
379 A59 35c multicolored .75 .75
380 A59 45c multicolored 1.00 1.00
Nos. 377-380 (4) 2.32 2.32

50 years of Scouting in Solomon Islands.

Discovery A60

Designs: 18c, Capt. Cook, 1776, painting by Nathaniel Dance. 35c, Sextant. 45c, Capt. Cook after Flaxman / Wedgwood medallion.

Wmk. 373

1979, Jan. 16 Litho. *Perf. 11*

381 A60 8c multicolored .20 .20
382 A60 18c multicolored .42 .42
383 A60 35c multicolored .80 .80

Litho.; Embossed

384 A60 45c multicolored 1.00 1.00
Nos. 381-384 (4) 2.42 2.42

Capt. Cook's voyages.

Fish Net Float A61

Artifacts: 20c, Armband made of shell money, vert. 35c, Ceremonial food bowl. 45c, Forehead ornament, vert.

1979, Mar. 21   Litho.   Perf. 14
385 A61 8c multicolored .18 .18
386 A61 20c multicolored .40 .40
387 A61 35c multicolored .70 .70
388 A61 45c multicolored .85 .85
     Nos. 385-388 (4) 2.13 2.13

6th South Pacific Games — A62

1979, June 4   Litho.   Wmk. 373
389 A62 8c Running .15 .15
390 A62 20c Hurdles .30 .30
391 A62 35c Soccer .52 .52
392 A62 45c Swimming .65 .65
     Nos. 389-392 (4) 1.62 1.62

Solomon Islands No. 14 — A63   Sea Snake — A64

Designs (Rowland Hill and): 20c, Great Britain No. 27. 35c, Solomon Islands No. 372. 45c, Solomon Islands No. 40.

1979, Aug. 16   Litho.   Perf. 14
393 A63 8c multicolored .15 .15
394 A63 20c multicolored .35 .35
395 A63 35c multicolored .60 .60
     Nos. 393-395 (3) 1.10 1.10

Souvenir Sheet
396 A63 45c multicolored .90 .90
Sir Rowland Hill (1795-1879), originator of penny postage.

Perf. 13½x13
1979-83   Litho.   Wmk. 373
397 A64 1c Sea snake .15 .15
398 A64 3c Red-banded tree
          snake .15 .15
399 A64 4c Whip snake .15 .15
400 A64 6c Pacific boa .15 .15
401 A64 8c Skink .15 .15
402 A64 10c Gecko .16 .16
403 A64 12c Monitor .20 .20
404 A64 15c Angelhead .24 .24
405 A64 20c Giant toad .32 .32
406 A64 25c Marsh frog .40 .40
407 A64 30c Horned frog .48 .48
408 A64 35c Tree frog .55 .55
408A A64 40c Burrowing snake .52 .52
409 A64 45c Guppy's snake .65 .65
409A A64 50c Tree gecko .60 .60
410 A64 $1 Large skink 1.40 1.40
411 A64 $2 Guppy's frog 2.75 2.75
412 A64 $5 Estuarine crocodile 7.00 7.00
412A A64 $10 Hawksbill turtle 14.00 14.00
     Nos. 397-412A (19) 30.02 30.02

Issue dates: $10, Sept. 20, 1982. 40c, 50c, Jan. 24, 1983. Others, Sept. 18, 1979 (undated).
Nos. 403, 406, 410, 412 reissued inscribed "1982." No. 407, "1983."

Madonna and Child, by Morando — A65

IYC Emblem and Madonna and Child: 20c, Bernardino Luini. 35c, Bellini. 50c, Raphael.

1979, Nov. 15   Perf. 14½
413 A65 4c multicolored .15 .15
414 A65 20c multicolored .26 .26
415 A65 35c multicolored .45 .45
416 A65 50c multicolored .65 .65
  a. Souvenir sheet of 4, #413-416 1.75 1.75
     Nos. 413-416 (4) 1.51 1.51

Christmas 1979, Intl. Year of the Child.

Curacoa and Crest — A66

Ships and Crests: 20c, Herald, 1854. 35c, Royalist, 1889. 45c, Beagle, 1878.

Wmk. 373
1980, Jan. 23   Litho.   Perf. 14
417 A66 8c multicolored .15 .15
418 A66 20c multicolored .38 .38
419 A66 35c multicolored .65 .65
420 A66 45c multicolored .85 .85
     Nos. 417-420 (4) 2.03 2.03

See Nos. 435-438.

Steel Fishery Training Ship A67

1980, Mar. 27   Litho.   Perf. 13½
421 A67 8c shown .15 .15
422 A67 20c Fishery training ship .28 .28
423 A67 45c Refrigerated carrier .65 .65
424 A67 80c Research ship 1.10 1.10
     Nos. 421-424 (4) 2.18 2.18

"Comliebank," Tulag Cancel — A68

1980, May 6   Litho.   Perf. 14½
425   Sheet of 4 2.50 2.50
  a. A68 45c shown .60 .60
  b. A68 45c Douglas C-47 .60 .60
  c. A68 45c BAC 1-11, Honiara cancel .60 .60
  d. A68 45c "Corabank," Auki cancel .60 .60
London 1980 Intl. Stamp Exhib., May 6-14.

Queen Mother Elizabeth Birthday Issue
Common Design Type
Wmk. 373
1980, Aug. 4   Litho.   Perf. 14
426 CD330 45c multicolored .60 .60

Angel with Trumpet — A69

Christmas: 20c, Angel with violin. 45c, Angel with trumpet. 80c, Angel with lute.

Perf. 14½
1980, Sept. 2   Litho.   Wmk. 373
427 A69 8c multicolored .15 .15
428 A69 20c multicolored .28 .28
429 A69 45c multicolored .60 .60
430 A69 80c multicolored 1.00 1.00
     Nos. 427-430 (4) 2.03 2.03

Parthenos Sylvia — A70

Perf. 13½
1980, Nov. 12   Litho.   Wmk. 373
431 A70 8c shown .15 .15
432 A70 20c Delias schoenbergi .30 .30
433 A70 45c Jamides cephion .70 .70
434 A70 80c Ornithoptera victoriae 1.25 1.25
     Nos. 431-434 (4) 2.40 2.40

See Nos. 461-464.

Ship Crest Type of 1980
Ships and Crests: 8c, Mounts Bay, 1959. 20c, Charybdis, 1970. 45c, Hydra, 1972-1973. $1, Britannia, 1974.

1981, Jan. 14
435 A66 8c multicolored .15 .15
436 A66 20c multicolored .30 .30
437 A66 45c multicolored .65 .65
438 A66 $1 multicolored 1.50 1.50
     Nos. 435-438 (4) 2.60 2.60

Maurelle's Map, 1742 — A71

Wmk. 373
1981, Mar. 23   Litho.   Perf. 14
439 A71 8c Francisco Maurelle,
          vert. .15 .15
440 A71 10c shown .16 .16
441 A71 45c La Princesa .70 .70
442 A71 $1 Compass cards, vert. 1.65 1.65
     Nos. 439-442 (4) 2.66 2.66

Souvenir Sheet
443   Sheet of 4 1.65 1.65
  a. A71 25c any single .38 .38
Bicent. of arrival of Francisco Antonio Maurelle and of charts of mapmaker Jean Nicholas Buache (1741-1825). No. 443 contains 4 44x28mm stamps, perf. 14½.

Women's Basketball — A72

Wmk. 373
1981, July 7   Litho.   Perf. 12
444 A72 8c shown .15 .15
445 A72 10c Tennis .18 .18
446 A72 25c Women's running .42 .42
447 A72 30c Soccer .52 .52
448 A72 45c Boxing .80 .80
     Nos. 444-448 (5) 2.07 2.07

Souvenir Sheet
449 A72 $1 Emblem 1.75 1.75
Mini South Pacific Games, July.

Royal Wedding Issue
Common Design Type
1981, July 22   Perf. 13½x13
450 CD331 8c Bouquet .15 .15
451 CD331 45c Charles .70 .70
452 CD331 $1 Couple 1.50 1.50
     Nos. 450-452 (3) 2.35 2.35
For surcharge see No. B1.

Duke of Edinburgh's Awards, 25th Anniv. — A73

Wmk. 373
1981, Sept. 28   Litho.   Perf. 14
453 A73 8c Music .15 .15
454 A73 25c Handicrafts .28 .28
455 A73 45c Canoeing .52 .52
456 A73 $1 Duke of Edinburgh 1.10 1.10
     Nos. 453-456 (4) 2.05 2.05

Holy Cross Cathedral, Honiara A74 $2

Christmas 1981 (Churches): 8c, 25c, Old churches, diff. 10c, St. Barnabas Anglican Cathedral, Honiara.

1981, Oct. 12
457 A74 8c multicolored .15 .15
458 A74 10c multicolored .15 .15
459 A74 25c multicolored .30 .30
460 A74 $2 multicolored 2.75 2.75
     Nos. 457-460 (4) 3.35 3.35

Butterfly Type of 1980
Perf. 13½
1982, Jan. 5   Litho.   Wmk. 373
461 A70 10c Doleschallia bisaltide .16 .16
462 A70 25c Papilio bridgei hecat-
          aeus .45 .45
463 A70 35c Taenaris phorcas .65 .65
464 A70 $1 Graphium sarpedon 1.75 1.75
     Nos. 461-464 (4) 3.01 3.01

Sanford's Eagle — A75

1982, May 15   Litho.   Perf. 14
465 A75 12c Pair facing left .42 .42
466 A75 12c Chick .42 .42
467 A75 12c Mother feeding chicks .42 .42
468 A75 12c Pair facing right .42 .42
469 A75 12c Male flying .42 .42
470 A75 12c Pair flying .42 .42
     Nos. 465-470 (6) 2.52 2.52

Se-tenant in sheets of 24. The center horiz. row consists of 4 No. 470 + label. No block of 6 contains all 6 designs.

Princess Diana Issue
Common Design Type
Perf. 14½x14
1982, July 1   Litho.   Wmk. 373
471 CD333 12c Arms .15 .15
472 CD333 40c Diana .52 .52
473 CD333 50c Wedding .65 .65
474 CD333 $1 Portrait 1.25 1.25
     Nos. 471-474 (4) 2.57 2.57

A76

1982, Oct. 11   Litho.   Perf. 14
475 A76 25c Running .50 .50
476 A76 25c Boxing .50 .50

Souvenir Sheet
477 Sheet of 3, #475-476, 477a 2.50 2.50
a. A76 $1 Britannia facing left 1.50 1.50

12th Commonwealth Games, Brisbane, Australia, Sept. 30-Oct. 9.

1982, Oct. 11
478 A76 12c Royal couple .25 .25
479 A76 12c Flags .25 .25

Souvenir Sheet
480 Sheet of 3, #478-479, 480a 2.25 2.25
a. A76 $1 Britannia facing right 1.75 1.75

Visit of Queen Elizabeth II and Prince Philip.

Scouting Year — A78

Designs: Nos. 481, 485, Scout patroller. Nos. 482, 486, Brigade bugler. Nos. 483, 487, Baden-Powell. Nos. 484-488, William Smith.

1982, Nov. 30
481 A78 12c dark blue & multi .18 .18
482 A78 12c brown & multi .18 .18
483 A78 25c dark blue & multi .35 .35
484 A78 25c brown & multi .35 .35
485 A78 35c green & multi .50 .50
486 A78 35c red & multi .50 .50
487 A78 50c green & multi .70 .70
488 A78 50c red & multi .70 .70
Nos. 481-488 (8) 3.46 3.46

Turtles A79

1983, Jan. 5   Perf. 14
489 A79 18c Leatherback .28 .28
490 A79 35c Loggerhead .55 .55
491 A79 45c Pacific Ridley .70 .70
492 A79 50c Green .80 .80
Nos. 489-492 (4) 2.33 2.33

Commonwealth Day — A80

1983, Mar. 14
493 A80 12c Oliva vidum, conus
generalis, murex tribulus .18 .18
494 A80 35c Romu, kurila, kakadu,
money belt .55 .55
495 A80 45c Shells, bride necklaces .70 .70
496 A80 50c Trochus niloticus, natural, polished .75 .75
Nos. 493-496 (4) 2.18 2.18

Manned Flight Bicentenary — A81

Wmk. 373
1983, June 30   Litho.   Perf. 14
497 A81 30c Montgolfliere, 1783 .38 .38
498 A81 35c Lockheed Hercules .45 .45
499 A81 40c Wright Brothers' Flyer III, 1905 .50 .50
500 A81 45c Columbia space shuttle .55 .55
501 A81 50c Beechcraft Baron-Solair .65 .65
Nos. 497-501 (5) 2.53 2.53

Christmas 1983 A82

1983, Aug. 25
502 A82 12c Weto dance .18 .18
503 A82 15c Custom wrestling .22 .22
504 A82 18c Girl dancers .26 .26
505 A82 20c Devil dancers .30 .30
506 A82 25c Bamboo band .38 .38
507 A82 35c Gilbertese dancers .52 .52
508 A82 40c Pan pipers .60 .60
509 A82 45c Afufu girl dancers .65 .65
510 A82 50c Cross, flowers .75 .75
a. Souvenir sheet of 9, #502-510 3.75 3.75
Nos. 502-510 (9) 3.86 3.86

Stamps in #510a do not have "Christmas 1983."
For overprints see Nos. 519-520.

World Communications Year — A83

Wmk. 373
1983, Dec. 19   Litho.   Perf. 14
511 A83 12c Telephone Exchange building .15 .15
512 A83 18c Ham radio operator .22 .22
513 A83 25c No. 11 .32 .32
514 A83 $1 No. 14 1.25 1.25
a. Souvenir sheet of 1 1.50 1.50
Nos. 511-514 (4) 1.94 1.94

No. 514a is inscribed "1908-1983." See No. 525 for sheet inscribed "1907-1984."

Local Fungi — A84

1984, Jan. 30   Perf. 13½
515 A84 6c Calvatia gardneri .15 .15
516 A84 18c Marasmiellus inoderma .25 .25
517 A84 35c Pycnoporus sanguineus .50 .50
518 A84 $2 Filoboletus manipularis 2.75 2.75
Nos. 515-518 (4) 3.65 3.65

Type of No. 510 overprinted "VISIT OF POPE JOHN PAUL II May 9th, 1984"

1984, Apr. 16   Wmk. 373
519 A82 12c multicolored .18 .18
520 A82 50c multicolored .70 .70

Lloyd's List Issue
Common Design Type

1984, Apr. 21   Litho.   Perf. 14½x14
521 CD335 12c Olivebank, 1892 .18 .18
522 CD335 15c Tinhow, 1906 .22 .22
523 CD335 18c Oriana, Point Cruz .25 .25
524 CD335 $1 Point Cruz view 1.40 1.40
Nos. 521-524 (4) 2.05 2.05

WCY Type of 1983
Souvenir Sheet
Wmk. 373
1984, June 18   Litho.   Perf. 14
525 A83 $1 multicolored 1.40 1.40

UPU Congress. No. 514a is inscribed "1908-1983," No. 525 inscribed "1907-1984."

Asia-Pacific Broadcasting Union, 20th Anniv. — A86

1984, July 2   Perf. 13½
526 A86 12c Village drums .18 .18
527 A86 45c Radio City Guadalcanal .60 .60
528 A86 60c Broadcasting studio .80 .80
529 A86 $1 Broadcasting station 1.40 1.40
Nos. 526-529 (4) 2.98 2.98

1984 Summer Olympics — A87

Perf. 13½x14
1984, Aug. 4   Litho.   Wmk. 373
530 A87 12c Flag, vert. .22 .22
531 A87 25c Lawson Tama Stadium, Honiara .45 .45
532 A87 50c Honiara Community Center .85 .85
533 A87 $1 Olympic Stadium 1.75 1.75
Nos. 530-533 (4) 3.27 3.27

Souvenir Sheet
534 A87 95c Bronte Baths 4.50 4.50

Solomon Islds. first olympic participation. No. 534 available in booklet only. Margin shows swimmer A. Wickham (1886-1976).

Little Pied Cormorant (Ausipex '84) — A88

Perf. 14½
1984, Sept. 21   Litho.   Wmk. 373
535 A88 12c shown .25 .25
536 A88 18c Australian grey duck .35 .35
537 A88 35c Nankeen night-heron .70 .70
538 A88 $1 Dollarbird 1.90 1.90
a. Souvenir sheet of 4, #535-538 3.50 3.50
Nos. 535-538 (4) 3.20 3.20

EXPO '85, Tsukuba, Japan A89

Designs: 12c, Japanese Memorial Shrine, Mt. Austen, Guadalcanal. 25c, Digital telephone exchange equipment. 45c, Soltai No. 7 fishing vessel. 85c, Coastal village.

Wmk. 373
1985, June 28   Litho.   Perf. 14
539 A89 12c multicolored .18 .18
540 A89 25c multicolored .35 .35
541 A89 45c multicolored .60 .60
542 A89 85c multicolored 1.10 1.10
Nos. 539-542 (4) 2.23 2.23

Queen Mother 85th Birthday
Common Design Type
Perf. 14½x14
1985, June 7   Litho.   Wmk. 384
543 CD336 12c VE Day, 1945 .15 .15
544 CD336 25c With Margaret .30 .30
545 CD336 35c St. Patrick's Day celebration .40 .40
546 CD336 $1 Holding Prince Henry 1.25 1.25
Nos. 543-546 (4) 2.10 2.10

Souvenir Sheet
547 CD336 $1.50 In a gondola, Venice 2.00 2.00

For surcharge see No. B2.

Christmas A90

1985, Aug. 30 Wmk. 373   Perf. 14½
548 A90 12c Titiana Village .18 .18
549 A90 25c Sigana, Santa Isabel .38 .38
550 A90 35c Artificial Island, Langa Lagoon .52 .52
Nos. 548-550 (3) 1.08 1.08

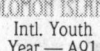

Intl. Youth Year — A91   Audubon Birth Bicent. — A92

Designs: 12c, Girl Guide activities. 15c, Stop Polio Campaign. 25c, Relay runners, views of the islands. 35c, Relay runners, views of Australia. 45c, Saluting natl. flag, badges.

1985, Sept. 30   Perf. 14
551 A91 12c multicolored .18 .18
552 A91 15c multicolored .22 .22
553 A91 25c multicolored .38 .38
554 A91 35c multicolored .52 .52
a. Souvenir sheet of 2, #553-554 .90 .90
555 A91 45c multicolored .70 .70
Nos. 551-555 (5) 2.00 2.00

Girl Guides 75th anniv., 12c, 45c; IYY, others.

Souvenir Sheet
Bird illustration by Audubon.

1985, Nov. 25   Wmk. 384
556 Sheet of 3, 45c, 2 50c 3.75 3.75
a. A92 45c Portrait 1.10 1.10
b. A92 50c Osprey 1.25 1.25

Souvenir Sheet

Mini Hydro-Electric Project, Iriri Village — A93

Designs: 30c, Water-driven generator. 60c, Illuminated village house.

1986, Jan. 24   Perf. 14
557 A93 Sheet of 2 1.10 1.10
a. 30c multicolored .35 .35
b. 60c multicolored .65 .65

Halley's Comet A94

Operation Raleigh, 1986: 18c, Construction of Red Cross Center, Gizo. 30c, Exploring rain forest. 60c, Observing Halley's Comet. $1, Ships Sir Walter Raleigh and Zebu.

Perf. 14½x14

1986, Mar. 27 **Wmk. 373**

558 A94 18c multicolored .22 .22
559 A94 30c multicolored .38 .38
560 A94 60c multicolored .75 .75
561 A94 $1 multicolored 1.25 1.25
Nos. 558-561 (4) 2.60 2.60

Queen Elizabeth II 60th Birthday

Common Design Type

Designs: 5c, Visiting Clydebank Town Hall with Prince Philip, 1947. 18c, At Queen Mother's 80th birthday, St. Paul's Cathedral, 1980. 22c, Walking among children of the islands, Pacific tour, 1982. 55c, 50th birthday, Windsor Castle, 1976. $2, Visiting Crown Agents' offices, 1983.

1986, Apr. 21 **Wmk. 384** *Perf. 14½*

562 CD337 5c scarlet, blk & sil .15 .15
563 CD337 18c ultra & multi .20 .20
564 CD337 22c green & multi .25 .25
565 CD337 55c violet & multi .65 .65
566 CD337 $2 rose vio & multi 2.25 2.25
Nos. 562-566 (5) 3.50 3.50

Royal Wedding Issue, 1986

Common Design Type

Designs: 55c, Informal portrait. 60c, Andrew aboard royal navy vessel.

Wmk. 384

1986, July 23 **Litho.** *Perf. 14*

567 CD338 55c multicolored .60 .60
568 CD338 60c multicolored .70 .70

Souvenir Sheet

AMERIPEX '86 — A95

Designs: 55c, US Memorial, Henderson Field, Guadalcanal. $1.65, Peace Corps emblem, Statue of Liberty, Pres. John F. Kennedy.

1986, May 22 **Litho.** *Perf. 13½*

569 A95 Sheet of 2 2.50 2.50
a. 55c multicolored .60 .60
b. $1.65 multicolored 1.75 1.75

Intl. Peace Year, Peace Corps 25th anniv.
For surcharge see No. B3.

1987 America's Cup — A96

Previous winners, challengers, maps and club emblems: No. 570a, America, US, 1851. b, Magic, US, 1870. c, Madeleine, US, 1876. d, Mischief, US, 1881. e, Columbia, US, 1871. f, British Cup course, 1851. g, America II, US, 1987. h, America's Cup. i, Heart of America, US, 1987. j, French Kiss, France, 1987.

No. 571a, Puritan, US, 1885. b, Mayflower, US, 1886. c, Defender, US, 1895. d, Vigilant, US, 1893. e, Volunteer, US, 1887. f, America Cup course, Newport, 1930-1962. g, South Australia, Australia, 1987. h, KA14, Australia, 1987. i, New Zealand II, New Zealand, 1987. j, St. Francis IX, US, 1987.

No. 572a, Columbia, US, 1899. b, Columbia, US, 1901. c, Enterprise, US, 1930. d, Resolute, US, 1920. e, Reliance, US, 1903. f, America Cup course, 1964-1983. g, Kookaburra, Australia, 1987. h, Eagle, US, 1987. i, True North, Canada, 1987. j, Italia, Italy, 1987.

No. 573a, Rainbow, US, 1934. b, Ranger, US, 1937. c, Constellation, US, 1964. d, Weatherly, US, 1962. e, Columbia, US, 1958. f, Western Australia Cup course, 1987. g, Secret Cove, syndicate, 1987. h, Courageous III, US, 1987. i, France, France, 1987. j, Azzurra, Italy, 1987.

No. 574a, Intrepid, US, 1967. b, Intrepid, US, 1970. c, Freedom, US, 1980. d, Courageous, US, 1977. e, Courageous, US, 1974. f, Australia II, Australia, 1983. g, Crusader, Great Britain, 1987. h, Sail America, US, 1987. i, Australia III, Australia, 1987. j, Royal Perth Yacht Club/America's Cup '87 emblem, 1987.

1986, Aug. 22 **Litho.** *Perf. 14½*

570 Strip of 10 + label 4.75 4.75
a.-d. A96 18c any single .15 .15
e.-f. A96 30c any single .26 .26
g.-j. A96 $1 any single .85 .85
571 Strip of 10 + label 4.75 4.75
a.-d. A96 18c any single .15 .15
e.-f. A96 30c any single .26 .26
g.-j. A96 $1 any single .85 .85
572 Strip of 10 + label 4.75 4.75
a.-d. A96 18c any single .15 .15
e.-f. A96 30c any single .26 .26
g.-j. A96 $1 any single .85 .85
573 Strip of 10 + label 4.75 4.75
a.-d. A96 18c any single .15 .15
e.-f. A96 30c any single .26 .26
g.-j. A96 $1 any single .85 .85
574 Strip of 10 + label 4.75 4.75
a.-d. A96 18c any single .15 .15
e.-f. A96 30c any single .26 .26
g.-j. A96 $1 any single .85 .85
Nos. 570-574 (5) 23.75 23.75

Nos. 570-574 printed se-tenant with center labels picturing natl. arms, 1987 America's Cup emblem and trophy in sheets of 50.

Souvenir Sheet

1987, Feb. 4 **Litho.** *Perf. 14½*

575 A96 $5 Stars and Stripes, US, victor 5.25 5.25

Coral — A97

Perf. 14½x14

1987, Feb. 11 **Litho.** **Wmk. 384**

576 A97 18c Dendrophyllia gracilis .18 .18
577 A97 45c Dendronephthya .42 .42
578 A97 60c Clavularia .55 .55
579 A97 $1.50 Melithaea squamata 1.40 1.40
Nos. 576-579 (4) 2.55 2.55

Flowering Plants — A98

1987-88

580 A98 1c Cassia fistula .15 .15
581 A98 5c Allamanda cathartica .15 .15
582 A98 10c Catharanthus roseus .15 .15
583 A98 18c Mimosa pudica .20 .20
584 A98 20c Hibiscus rosa-sinensis .22 .22
585 A98 22c Clerodendrum thomsonae .24 .24
586 A98 25c Bauhinia variegata .28 .28
587 A98 28c Gloriosa rothschildiana .30 .30
588 A98 30c Heliconia solomonensis .32 .32
589 A98 40c Episcia hybrid .44 .44
590 A98 45c Bougainvillea hybrid .48 .48
591 A98 50c Alpinia purpurata .55 .55
592 A98 55c Plumeria rubra .60 .60
593 A98 60c Acacia farnesiana .65 .65
594 A98 $1 Ipomea purpurea 1.10 1.10
595 A98 $2 Dianella ensifolia 2.25 2.25
596 A98 $5 Passiflora foetida 5.25 5.25
596A A98 $10 Hemigraphis specie ('88) 10.00 10.00
Nos. 580-596A (18) 23.33 23.33

Issue dates: $10, Mar. 1; others, May 12.

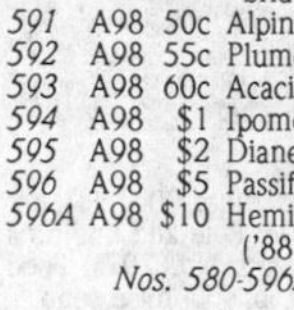

Mangrove Kingfisher — A99

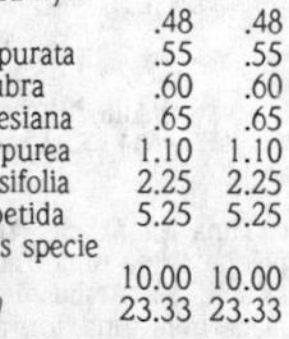

Orchids — A100

Designs: a, Perched on root. b, Diving. c, Landing in water. d, Emerging with fish.

Perf. 14x14½

1987, July 15 **Wmk. 373**

597 Strip of 4 3.25 3.25
a.-d. A99 60c any single .80 .80

No. 597 has a continuous design.

Perf. 13½x13

1987, Sept. 23 **Wmk. 384**

598 A100 18c Dendrobium conanthum .18 .18
599 A100 30c Spathoglottis plicata .30 .30
600 A100 55c Dendrobium gouldii .55 .55
601 A100 $1.50 Dendrobium goldfinchii 1.50 1.50
Nos. 598-601 (4) 2.53 2.53

Christmas 1987.

Transportation and Communications Decade — A101

Designs: 18c, Telecommunications link. 30c, Express mail service. 60c, Guadalcanal Road Improvement Project. $2, Beechcraft Queen Air, Henderson Airfield control tower.

Perf. 14x13½

1987, Oct. 31 **Litho.** **Unwmk.**

602 A101 18c multicolored .18 .18
603 A101 30c multicolored .28 .28
604 A101 60c multicolored .60 .60
605 A101 $2 multicolored 2.00 2.00
Nos. 602-605 (4) 3.06 3.06

Queen Victoria's Birdwing Butterfly — A102

Designs: No. 606a, Male. No. 606b, Larva. No. 606c, Pupa. No. 606d, Female.

1987, Nov. 25 **Wmk. 384** *Perf. 14½*

606 Strip of 4 3.00 3.00
a.-d. A102 45c any single .70 .70

Intl. Fund for Agricultural Development (IFAD), 10th Anniv. — A103

Natl. colors and: No. 607, Student, Natl. Agricultural Training Institute (NATI) farm and emblem (left stamp). No. 608, Students in working in NATI field and emblem (right stamp). No. 609, Flatbed truck transporting produce and emblem (left stamp). No. 610, Canoes, seagulls and emblem (right stamp).

Perf. 14½

1988, Feb. 12 **Litho.** **Wmk. 384**

607 A103 50c multicolored .45 .45
608 A103 50c multicolored .45 .45
a. Pair, #607-608 .90 .90
609 A103 $1 multicolored .90 .90
610 A103 $1 multicolored .90 .90
a. Pair, #609-610 1.80 1.80
Nos. 607-610 (4) 2.70 2.70

EXPO '88, Brisbane, Apr. 30-Oct. 30 — A104

Designs: 22c, Yacht in dry dock. 80c, Canoe. $1.50, Huts.

Perf. 13½x14

1988, Apr. 30 **Unwmk.**

611 A104 22c multicolored .20 .20
612 A104 80c multicolored .80 .80
613 A104 $1.50 multicolored 1.50 1.50
a. Souvenir sheet of 3, #611-613 2.50 2.50
b. As "a," surcharged $3.50 in margin ('90) 12.00 12.00
Nos. 611-613 (3) 2.50 2.50

National Independence, 10th Anniv. A105

Perf. 13x13½

1988, July 7 **Litho.** **Wmk. 373**

614 A105 22c *Capitana* in Estrella Bay .20 .20
615 A105 55c Flag raising, 1893 .55 .55
616 A105 80c Supreme Court .80 .80
617 A105 $1 Traditional celebration 1.00 1.00
Nos. 614-617 (4) 2.55 2.55

Australia Bicentennial — A106

Ships: 35c, M.V. *Papuan Chief.* 60c, M.V. *Nimos.* 70c, S.S. *Malaita.* $1.30, S.S. *Makambo.*

1988, July 30 **Wmk. 384** *Perf. 14*

618 A106 35c multicolored .32 .32
619 A106 60c multicolored .55 .55
620 A106 70c multicolored .65 .65
621 A106 $1.30 multicolored 1.25 1.25
a. Souvenir sheet of 4, #618-621 2.75 2.75
Nos. 618-621 (4) 2.77 2.77

A107

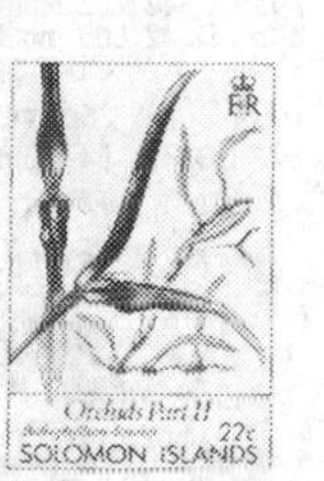

Orchids — A108

Perf. 14½

1988, Aug. 5 **Litho.** **Wmk. 384**

622 A107 22c Archery .22 .22
623 A107 55c Weight lifting .55 .55
624 A107 70c Running .70 .70
625 A107 80c Boxing .80 .80
Nos. 622-625 (4) 2.27 2.27

Souvenir Sheet

Wmk. 373

626 A107 $2 Olympic Stadium, horiz. 2.00 2.00

1988 Summer Olympics, Seoul.

Lloyds of London, 300th Anniv.

Common Design Type

Designs: 22c, King George V and Queen Mary at Lloyd's ground-breaking ceremony, 1925. 50c, *Forthbank,* horiz. 65c, Soltel Satellite Ground Station, horiz. $2, *Empress of China.*

1988, Oct. 31 *Perf. 14*

627 CD341 22c multicolored .20 .20
628 CD341 50c multicolored .48 .48
629 CD341 65c multicolored .60 .60
630 CD341 $2 multicolored 1.85 1.85
Nos. 627-630 (4) 3.13 3.13

Perf. 13½x13

1989, Jan. 20 **Litho.** **Wmk. 373**

631 A108 22c *Bulbophyllum dennisii* .22 .22
632 A108 35c *Calanthe langei* .35 .35
633 A108 55c *Bulbophyllum blumei* .55 .55
634 A108 $2 *Grammatophyllum speciosum* 2.00 2.00
Nos. 631-634 (4) 3.12 3.12

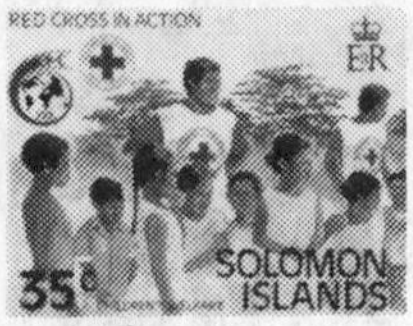

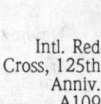

Intl. Red Cross, 125th Anniv. A109

Perf. 14x14½

1989, May 16 Wmk. 384

635 A109 35c Disabled children .32 .32
636 A109 35c Children's Center minibus .32 .32
a. Pair, #635-636 .65 .65
637 A109 $1.50 Patient abed 1.40 1.40
638 A109 $1.50 Physical therapy 1.40 1.40
a. Pair, #637-638 2.80 2.80
Nos. 635-638 (4) 3.44 3.44

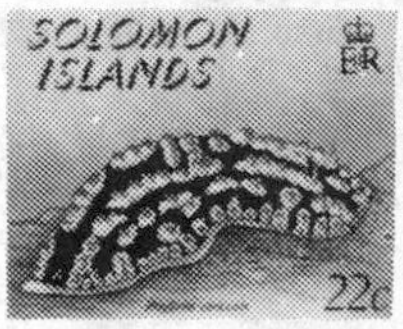

Sea Slugs A110

1989, June 30 Wmk. 373 *Perf. 14½*

639 A110 22c *Phyllidia varicosa* .20 .20
640 A110 70c *Chromodoris bullocki* .65 .65
641 A110 80c *Chromodoris leopardus* .72 .72
642 A110 $1.50 *Phidiana indica* 1.35 1.35
Nos. 639-642 (4) 2.92 2.92

Moon Landing, 20th Anniv.

Common Design Type

Apollo 16: 22c, Splashdown. 35c, Launch. 70c, Mission emblem. 80c, Ultraviolet color enhancement of Earth. $4, The Moon, as photographed during the *Apollo 11* mission.

1989, July 20 Wmk. 384 *Perf. 14*

Size of Nos. 644-645: 29x29mm

643 CD342 22c multicolored .20 .20
644 CD342 35c multicolored .32 .32
645 CD342 70c multicolored .62 .62
646 CD342 80c multicolored .70 .70
Nos. 643-646 (4) 1.84 1.84

Souvenir Sheet

647 CD342 $4 multicolored 3.55 3.55

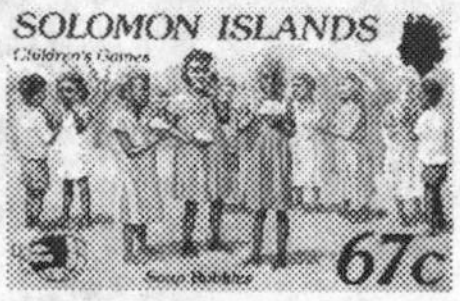

Blowing Soap Bubbles A111

Children's games.

1989, Nov. 17 Wmk. 384

648 A111 5c Five stones catch, vert. .15 .15
649 A111 67c shown .65 .65
650 A111 73c Coconut shell empire .68 .68
651 A111 $1 Seed wind sound, vert. .95 .95
Nos. 648-651 (4) 2.43 2.43

Souvenir Sheet

Wmk. 373

652 A111 $3 Baseball, softball, vert. 2.85 2.85

World Stamp Expo '89.

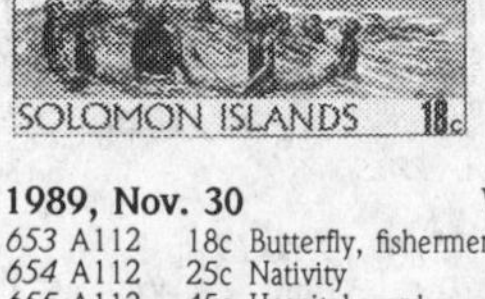

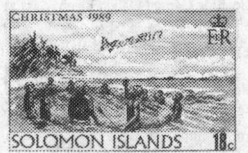

Christmas A112

1989, Nov. 30 Wmk. 384

653 A112 18c Butterfly, fishermen .28 .28
654 A112 25c Nativity .40 .40
655 A112 45c Hospital ward .70 .70
656 A112 $1.50 Tug of war 2.35 2.35
Nos. 653-656 (4) 3.73 3.73

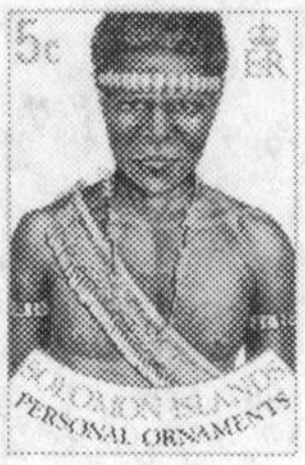

Personal Ornaments — A113

1990, Feb. 14 Litho. Wmk. 373

657 A113 5c shown .15 .15
658 A113 12c Necklace .15 .15
659 A113 18c Islander, diff. .17 .17
660 A113 $2 Head ornament 1.90 1.90
Nos. 657-660 (4) 2.37 2.37

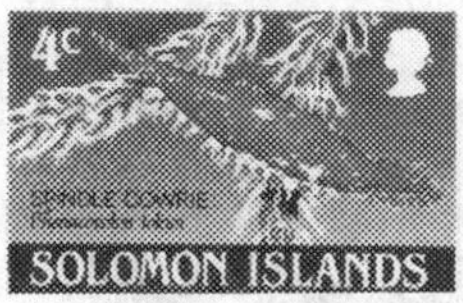

Cowrie Shells A114

1990, July 23

666 A114 4c Spindle cowrie .15 .15
667 A114 20c Map cowrie .18 .18
668 A114 35c Sieve cowrie .32 .32
669 A114 50c Egg cowrie .48 .48
670 A114 $1 Prince cowrie .95 .95
Nos. 666-670 (5) 2.08 2.08

Queen Mother, 90th Birthday

Common Design Types

Designs: 25c, Queen Mother, 1987. $5, Inspecting damage to Buckingham Palace, 1940.

1990, Aug. 4 Wmk. 384 *Perf. 14x15*

671 CD343 25c multicolored .23 .23

Perf. 14½

672 CD344 $5 brown & blk 4.75 4.75

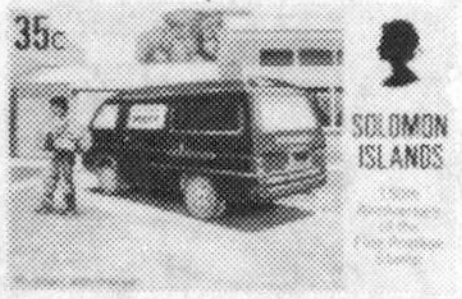

First Postage Stamp, 150th Anniv. A115

Designs: 35c, Postman, mail van. 45c, Solomon Islands Post Office. 50c, Solomon Islands No. 1. 55c, Young philatelist. 60c, Solomon Islands No. 20, Penny Black.

1990, Oct. 15 Wmk. 373 *Perf. 14*

673 A115 35c multicolored .58 .58
674 A115 45c multicolored .75 .75
675 A115 50c multicolored .85 .85
676 A115 55c multicolored .92 .92
677 A115 60c multicolored 1.00 1.00
Nos. 673-677 (5) 4.10 4.10

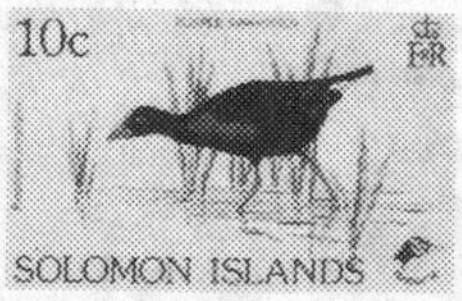

Birds A116

1990, Dec. 5

678 A116 10c Purple swamphen .15 .15
679 A116 25c Rufous brown pheasant dove .38 .38
680 A116 30c Superb fruit dove .45 .45
681 A116 45c Cardinal honeyeater .70 .70
682 A116 $2 Pigmy parrot 3.00 3.00
Nos. 678-682 (5) 4.68 4.68

Birdpex '90, 20th Intl. Ornithological Congress, New Zealand.

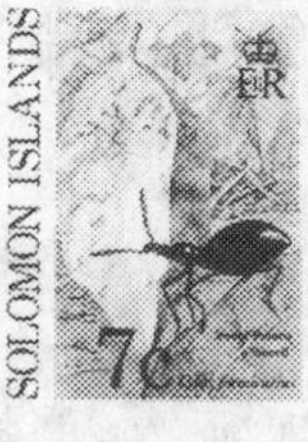

Crop Pests — A117

Perf. 14x13½

1991, Jan. 16 Litho. Wmk. 373

683 A117 7c Sweet potato weevil .15 .15
684 A117 25c Melon fly .38 .38
685 A117 40c Taro beetle .62 .62
686 A117 90c Cocoa weevil borer 1.40 1.40
687 A117 $1.50 Rhinoceros beetle 2.30 2.30
Nos. 683-687 (5) 4.85 4.85

Elizabeth & Philip, Birthdays

Common Design Types

Perf. 14½

1991, June 17 Litho. Wmk. 384

688 CD346 90c multicolored 1.40 1.40
689 CD345 $2 multicolored 3.10 3.10
a. Pair, #688-689 + label 4.50 4.50

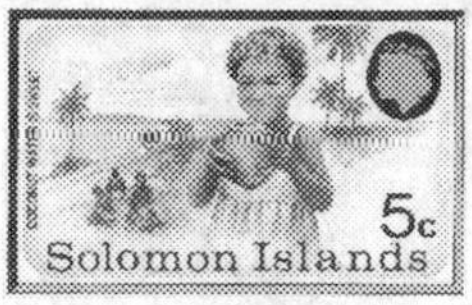

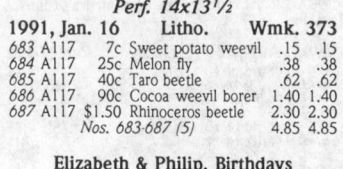

Nutritional Foods A118

1991, June 24 Wmk. 373 *Perf. 14*

690 A118 5c Coconut water .15 .15
691 A118 75c Feed your child 1.15 1.15
692 A118 80c Mother's milk 1.25 1.25
693 A118 90c Local food 1.40 1.40
Nos. 690-693 (4) 3.95 3.95

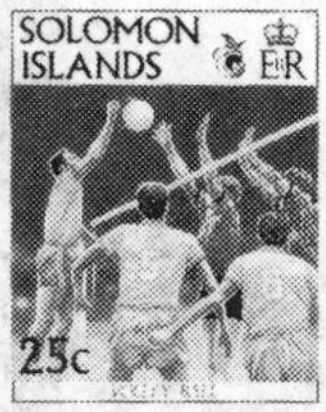

9th South Pacific Games — A119

Wmk. 384

1991, Aug. 8 Litho. *Perf. 14*

694 A119 25c Volleyball .38 .38
695 A119 40c Judo .62 .62
696 A119 65c Squash 1.00 1.00
697 A119 90c Lawn bowling 1.40 1.40
Nos. 694-697 (4) 3.40 3.40

Souvenir Sheet

698 A119 $2 Games emblem 3.10 3.10

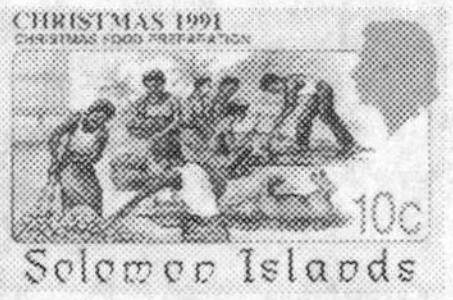

Christmas A120

Wmk. 373

1991, Oct. 28 Litho. *Perf. 14*

699 A120 10c Food preparation .15 .15
700 A120 25c Church service .38 .38
701 A120 65c Feast 1.00 1.00
702 A120 $2 Cricket match 3.10 3.10
a. Souvenir sheet of 4, #699-702 4.65 4.65
Nos. 699-702 (4) 4.63 4.63

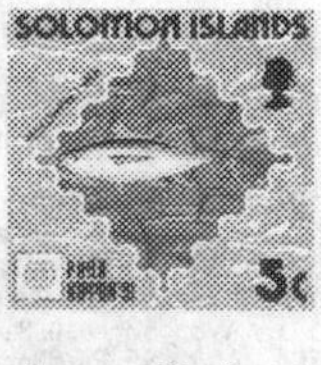

Phila Nippon '91 — A121

Tuna fishing: 5c, Yellowfin tuna. 30c, Boat for pole and line tuna fishing. 80c, Pole and line tuna fishing. $2, Arabushi processing. No. 707a, Food made from tuna, tori nanban. b, Aka miso soup.

Wmk. 384

1991, Nov. 16 Litho. *Perf. 14*

703 A121 5c multicolored .15 .15
704 A121 30c multicolored .45 .45
705 A121 80c multicolored 1.20 1.20
706 A121 $2 multicolored 3.10 3.10
Nos. 703-706 (4) 4.90 4.90

Souvenir Sheet

707 A121 80c Sheet of 2, #a.-b. 2.40 2.40

No. 707 contains two 28x45mm stamps.

Queen Elizabeth II's Accession to the Throne, 40th Anniv.

Common Design Type

Wmk. 384 (5c, 60c), 373

1992, Feb. 6 Litho. *Perf. 14*

708 CD349 5c multicolored .15 .15
709 CD349 20c multicolored .15 .15
710 CD349 40c multicolored .28 .28
711 CD349 60c multicolored .45 .45
712 CD349 $5 multicolored 3.60 3.60
Nos. 708-712 (5) 4.63 4.63

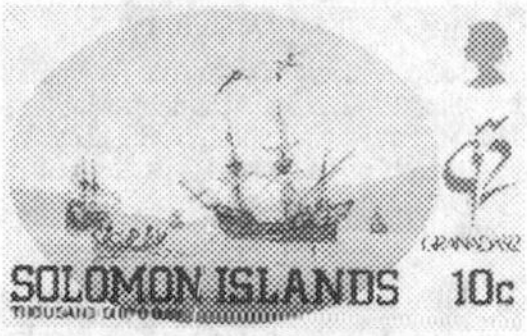

Alvaro Mendana de Niera (1541-1595), Discoveries in the Solomon Islands — A122

Granada '92: 10c, Thousand Ships Bay. 65c, Route to the Solomon Islands. 80c, Alvaro Mendana de Niera. $1, Graciosa Bay settlement. $5, Sailing ships.

Perf. 15x14½

1992, Apr. 24 Litho. Wmk. 373

713 A122 10c multicolored .15 .15
714 A122 65c multicolored .48 .48
715 A122 80c multicolored .58 .58
716 A122 $1 multicolored .75 .75
717 A122 $5 multicolored 3.60 3.60
Nos. 713-717 (5) 5.56 5.56

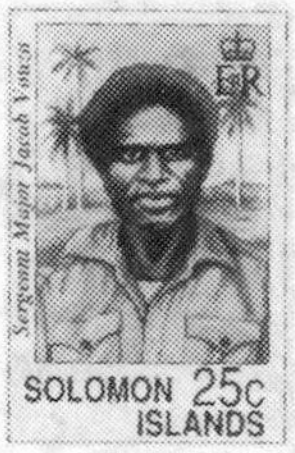

A123

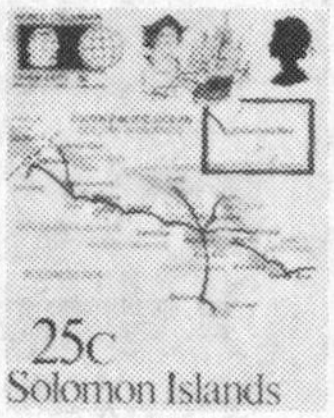

A124

Perf. 14x13½

1992, May 3 Litho. Wmk. 373

718 A123 25c Early portrait .15 .15
719 A123 70c Wearing USMC fatigues .45 .45
720 A123 90c Wearing uniform, cap .65 .65
a. Booklet pane, 2 each #718, #720 1.50
721 A123 $2 Statue 1.40 1.40
a. Booklet pane, 2 each #719, #721 3.75
Nos. 718-721 (4) 2.65 2.65

Souvenir Sheet

722 A123 $4 In dress uniform 2.75 2.75
a. Booklet pane of 1 2.75

Sergeant Major Jacob Vouza (1891-1984). One margin of Nos. 720a, 721a, and 722a is rouletted 8.

1992, May 22

World Columbian Stamp Expo '92, Chicago: 25c, Solomon Airlines domestic routes. 80c, Boeing 737-400 airplanes. $1.50, Solomon Airlines international routes. $5, Columbus and Santa Maria.

723 A124 25c multicolored .18 .18
724 A124 80c multicolored .60 .60
725 A124 $1.50 multicolored 1.15 1.15
726 A124 $5 multicolored 3.75 3.75
a. Souvenir sheet of 4, #723-726 5.75 5.75
b. As "a," ovptd. with Taipei '93 emblem in sheet margin 7.25 7.25
Nos. 723-726 (4) 5.68 5.68

No. 726b issued Aug. 14, 1993.

Miniature Sheets

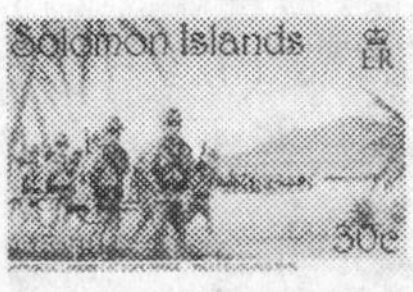

Battle of Guadalcanal, 50th Anniv. A125

Scenes from battle of Guadalcanal: No. 727a, Japanese landing at Esperance. b, US landings. c, Australian Navy cruiser. d, US Navy post office. e, Royal New Zealand Air Force PBY Catalina.

No. 728a, US Marine Wildcat fighters. b, Henderson Field under construction and attack. c, Heavy cruiser USS Quincy. d, Australian Navy heavy cruiser Canberra. e, US Marines land on Guadalcanal. f, Japanese aircraft carrier Ryujo. g,

Japanese Zeke fighters attack US positions. h, Japanese bombers attack American beachhead. i, Japanese destroyers of Tokyo Express. j, Japanese heavy cruiser Chokai.

Wmk. 384

1992, Aug. 7	Litho.		Perf. 14	
727 A125 30c Sheet of 5, #a.-e.			1.15	1.15
728 A125 80c Sheet of 10, #a.-j.			5.50	5.50

Orchids A126

Perf. 14¹/₂x14

1992, Dec. 14	Litho.		Wmk. 373	
729 A126	15c Dendrobium hybrid		.15	.15
730 A126	70c Vanda "Amy Laycock"		.52	.52
731 A126	95c Dendrobium mirbelianum		.75	.75
732 A126	$2.50 Dendrobium macrophyllum		1.90	1.90
Nos. 729-732 (4)			3.32	3.32

See Nos. 752-755.

Crabs — A127

Wmk. 373

1993, Jan. 15	Litho.		Perf. 13	
733 A127	5c Stalk-eyed ghost		.15	.15
734 A127	10c Red-spotted		.15	.15
735 A127	25c Flat		.16	.16
736 A127	30c Land hermit		.20	.20
737 A127	40c Grapsid		.28	.28
738 A127	45c Red & white painted		.30	.30
739 A127	55c Swift footed		.38	.38
740 A127	60c Spanner		.40	.40
741 A127	70c Red hermit		.48	.48
742 A127	80c Red-eyed		.55	.55
743 A127	90c Rathbun red		.60	.60
744 A127	$1 Coconut		.70	.70
745 A127	$1.10 Red-spotted white		.75	.75
746 A127	$4 Ghost		2.70	2.70
747 A127	$10 Mangrove fiddler		7.00	7.00
Nos. 733-747 (15)			14.80	14.80

World War II, 50th Anniv. A128

Designs: 30c, US War Memorial, Skyline Ridge. 80c, Country flags, Guadalcanal. 95c, Major General Alexander A. Vandegrift, map. $4, WWII Scouts, Gino Islands.

Wmk. 373

1993, Apr. 19	Litho.		Perf. 14	
748 A128 30c multicolored			.20	.20
749 A128 80c multicolored			.55	.55
750 A128 95c multicolored			.65	.65
751 A128 $4 multicolored			2.75	2.75
Nos. 748-751 (4)			4.15	4.15

Orchid Type of 1992
Perf. 14¹/₂x14

1993	Litho.		Wmk. 373	
752 A126 20c like #729			.15	.15
753 A126 85c like #730			.60	.60
754 A126 $1.15 like #731			.80	.80
755 A126 $3 like #732			2.10	2.10
Nos. 752-755 (4)			3.65	3.65

Issued: #752, 755, Apr. 24; #753-754, May 29.
Nos. 752, 755 are inscribed "World Orchid Conference." Nos. 753-754 are inscribed "Indopex '93 Exhibition."

Sinking of PT 109, 50th Anniv. A129

Wmk. 373

Designs: 30c, PT 109 about to be rammed. 50c, Native, Lt. John F. Kennedy. 95c, Message for help written on coconut, natives in canoe. $1.10, Kennedy, Navy and Marine Corps Medal. $5, PT 109.

1993, July 30	Litho.		Perf. 13	
756 A129 30c multicolored			.20	.20
757 A129 50c multicolored			.35	.35
758 A129 95c multicolored			.65	.65
759 A129 $1.10 multicolored			.75	.75
Nos. 756-759 (4)			1.95	1.95

Souvenir Sheet
Perf. 13x13¹/₂

| 760 A129 $5 multicolored | | | 3.50 | 3.50 |

Nicobar Pigeon — A130

Wmk. 373

1993, Sept. 21	Litho.		Perf. 14	
761 A130	30c shown		.18	.18
762 A130	50c One on ground		.32	.32
763 A130	65c Two on branches		.40	.40
764 A130	70c One on branch		.45	.45
765 A130	$1.10 One on berry branch		.75	.75
766 A130	$3 Two in flight		1.90	1.90
Nos. 761-766 (6)			4.00	4.00

World Wildlife Fund.

Dogs A131

Perf. 14¹/₂

1994, Feb. 18	Litho.		Wmk. 373	
767 A131	30c Dachshund		.28	.28
768 A131	80c German shepherd		.75	.75
769 A131	95c Dobermann pinscher		.90	.90
770 A131	$1.10 Australian cattle dog		1.00	1.00
Nos. 767-770 (4)			2.93	2.93

Souvenir Sheet

| 771 A131 $4 Boxer | | | 3.75 | 3.75 |

Hong Kong '94.

Dolphins A132

Wmk. 373

1994, May 9	Litho.		Perf 14	
772 A132	75c Striped		.45	.45
773 A132	85c Risso's		.52	.52
774 A132	$1.15 Common		.70	.70
775 A132	$2.50 Spinner		1.50	1.50
776 A132	$3 Bottlenose		1.90	1.90
Nos. 772-776 (5)			5.07	5.07

Miniature Sheet

Butterflies A133

Designs: a, Vindula sapor. b, Papilio aegeus. c, Graphium hicetaon. d, Graphium mendana. e, PHILAKOREA '94 emblem. f, Graphium meeki. g, Danaus schenkii. h, Papilio ptolychus. i, Phaedyma fissizonata.

Perf. 13¹/₂

1994, Aug. 16			Wmk. 373	
777 A133 70c Sheet of 9, #a.-i.			3.50	3.50

Intl. Year of the Family — A134

Designs: a, Girl writing letter in Brisbane, Australia, family reading letter on Santa Isabel, Solomon Islands. b, Boeing 737-400, Brisbane Intl. Airport, Australia. c, Boeing 737-400, Henderson Airfield, Guadalcanal, DHC 6-Twin Otter. d, Fera Airfield, Buala, Santa Isabel. e, Family.

1994, Aug. 18			Perf. 13	
778 A134 $1.10 Strip of 5, #a.-e.			3.50	3.50

Volcanoes of the Solomon Islands A135

Designs: 30c, Cook Island Volcano erupting under sea, 1967. 70c, Kavachi Volcano erupting from sea, 1977. 80c, Kavachi Volcano forming temporary island, 1978. 90c, Tinakulu Volcano, permanent island.
No. 783a, Map of Solomon Island volcanoes. b, Diagram illustrating formation of volcanic island archipelago.

Wmk. 373

1994, Oct. 24	Litho.		Perf. 14	
779 A135 30c multicolored			.18	.18
780 A135 70c multicolored			.45	.45
781 A135 80c multicolored			.50	.50
782 A135 90c multicolored			.55	.55
Nos. 779-782 (4)			1.68	1.68

Souvenir Sheet

| 783 A135 $2 Sheet of 2, #a.-b. | | | 2.50 | 2.50 |

La Perouse Expedition, 210th Anniv. A136

Designs: 30c, La Perouse, King Louis XVI. 80c, Map of Ile de La Perouse. 95c, L'Astrolabe. $1.10, La Boussole. $3, L'Astrolabe foundering on reef.

Wmk. 384

1994, Dec. 16	Litho.		Perf. 14	
784 A136	30c multicolored		.18	.18
785 A136	80c multicolored		.50	.50
786 A136	95c multicolored		.60	.60
787 A136	$1.10 multicolored		.70	.70
788 A136	$3 multicolored		1.90	1.90
Nos. 784-788 (5)			3.88	3.88

Visit South Pacific Year A137

Designs: 30c, Tourists watching traditional dance, land hermit crab. 50c, Dendrobium rennellii, milkweed butterfly. 95c, Diver, moorish idol, fish. $1.15, Boats at shore, grapsid crab. $4, Flower, yellow-bibbed lorry.

Perf. 15x14¹/₂

1995, Feb. 17	Litho.		Wmk. 373	
789 A137 30c multicolored			.20	.20
790 A137 50c multicolored			.32	.32
791 A137 95c multicolored			.60	.60
792 A137 $1.15 multicolored			.75	.75
Nos. 789-792 (4)			1.87	1.87

Souvenir Sheet

| 793 A137 $4 multicolored | | | 2.50 | 2.50 |

FAO, 50th Anniv. A138

1995, Apr. 5			Perf. 12	
794 A138 70c Banana			.42	.42
795 A138 75c Paw paw			.45	.45
796 A138 95c Pomelo			.60	.60
797 A138 $2 Star fruit			1.25	1.25
Nos. 794-797 (4)			2.72	2.72

Souvenir Sheet

| 798 A138 $3 Mango | | | 1.75 | 1.75 |

End of World War II, 50th Anniv.
Common Design Types

Admirals, aircraft carriers: 95c, Vice Adm. Chuichi Nagumo, Akagi. $1, Rear Adm. Frank J. Fletcher, USS Yorktown. $2, Vice Adm. Robert L. Ghormley, USS Wasp. $3, Vice Adm. William F. Halsey, USS Enterprise.
$5, Reverse of War Medal 1939-45.

1995, May 8			Perf. 13¹/₂	
799 CD351 95c multicolored			.60	.60
800 CD351 $1 multicolored			.65	.65
801 CD351 $2 multicolored			1.25	1.25
802 CD351 $3 multicolored			1.90	1.90
Nos. 799-802 (4)			4.40	4.40

Souvenir Sheet
Perf. 14

| 803 CD352 $5 multicolored | | | 3.25 | 3.25 |

Orchids — A139

Designs: 45c, Calanthe triplicata. 75c, Dendrobium mohlianum. 85c, Flickingeria comata. $1.15, Dendrobium spectabile. $4, Coelogyne asperata.

Wmk. 373

1995, Sept. 1	Litho.		Perf. 14	
804 A139 45c multicolored			.30	.30
805 A139 75c multicolored			.50	.50
806 A139 85c multicolored			.55	.55
807 A139 $1.15 multicolored			.75	.75
Nos. 804-807 (4)			2.10	2.10

Souvenir Sheet

| 808 A139 $4 multicolored | | | 2.50 | 2.50 |

Singapore '95 (#808).

Christmas — A140

Designs: 90c, Start of canoe race. $1.05, Pan pipers, Christmas tree. $1.25, Picnic on beach. $1.45, Local church, nativity.

1995, Nov. 6			Perf. 13x13¹/₂	
810 A140 90c multicolored			.60	.60
811 A140 $1.05 multicolored			.70	.70
812 A140 $1.25 multicolored			.85	.85
813 A140 $1.45 multicolored			1.00	1.00
Nos. 810-813 (4)			3.15	3.15

SEMI-POSTAL STAMPS

Catalogue values for unused stamps in this section are for Never Hinged items.

No. 452 Overprinted in Red: "+ 50c SURCHARGE / CYCLONE RELIEF FUND / 1982"

Perf. 13½x13

1982, May 3 Litho. Wmk. 373
B1 CD331 $1 + 50c multi 3.50 3.50

Nos. 546 and 569 Surcharged "Cyclone Relief Fund 1986" and New Value in Scarlet

Perf. 14½x14

1986, Sept. 23 Litho. Wmk. 384
B2 CD336 $1 + 50c multi 1.50 1.50

Souvenir Sheet
Perf. 13½

B3 Sheet of 2 3.25 3.25
a. A95 55c + 25c multi .75 .75
b. A95 $1.65 + 75c multi 2.50 2.50

POSTAGE DUE STAMPS

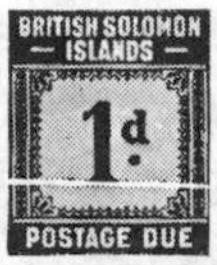

D1

Wmk. 4

1940, Sept. 1 Typo. *Perf. 12*
J1 D1 1p emerald 3.00 *5.00*
J2 D1 2p dark red 3.50 *5.00*
J3 D1 3p chocolate 4.00 *8.00*
J4 D1 4p dark blue 4.25 *9.00*
J5 D1 5p deep green 5.50 *12.00*
J6 D1 6p brt red vio 6.25 *14.00*
J7 D1 1sh dull violet 11.00 *24.00*
J8 D1 1sh6p turq green 22.50 *45.00*
Nos. J1-J8 (8) 60.00 *122.00*

SOMALILAND PROTECTORATE

sō-ˈmä-lē-ˌland

prə-ˈtek-t(ə-)rət

LOCATION — Eastern Africa, bordering on the Gulf of Aden
GOVT. — Former British Protectorate
AREA — 68,000 sq. mi.
POP. — 640,000 (estimated)
CAPITAL — Hargeisa

Formerly administered by the Indian Government, the territory was taken over by the British Foreign Office in 1898 and transferred to the Colonial Office in 1905.

Somaliland Protectorate became part of independent Somalia in 1960.

16 Annas = 1 Rupee
100 Cents = 1 Shilling (1951)

Catalogue values for unused stamps in this country are for Never Hinged items, beginning with Scott 108.

Stamps of India, 1882-1900, Overprinted at Top of Stamp — BRITISH SOMALILAND

1903 Wmk. 39 *Perf. 14*
1 A17 ½a light green 1.25 *2.00*
2 A19 1a carmine rose 1.25 *2.00*
3 A21 2a violet 1.25 .75
a. Double overprint *750.00*
4 A28 2½a ultra 1.75 *3.75*
5 A22 3a brown orange 1.50 *2.50*
6 A23 4a olive green 3.00 *3.75*
7 A25 8a red violet 1.50 *4.75*
8 A26 12a brown, *red* 1.75 *6.25*
a. Inverted overprint *1,200.*
9 A29 1r car rose & grn 3.50 *10.00*
10 A30 2r yel brn & car rose 18.00 *35.00*
11 A30 3r green & brown 14.00 *37.50*
12 A30 5r violet & blue 20.00 *42.50*

Wmk. Elephant's Head (38)

13 A14 6a bister 1.75 *4.00*
Nos. 1-13 (13) 70.50 *154.75*

Nos. 1-5 exist without the 2nd "I" of "BRITISH."

Same, but Overprinted at Bottom of Stamp

1903 Wmk. 39
14 A28 2½a ultra 1.75 *4.00*
15 A26 12a violet, *red* 4.00 *10.00*
16 A29 1r car rose & grn 2.50 *10.00*
17 A30 2r yel brn & car rose 50.00 70.00
18 A30 3r green & brn 45.00 70.00
a. Inverted overprint 500.00
19 A30 5r violet & blue 45.00 67.50

Wmk. 38

20 A14 6a bister 1.50 *3.75*
Nos. 14-20 (7) 149.75 235.25

Stamps of India, 1902-03, Ovptd.

1903 Wmk. 39
21 A33 ½a light green .40 .40
22 A34 1a car rose .50 .45
23 A35 2a violet 1.40 2.25
24 A37 3a brown orange 1.75 *2.75*
25 A38 4a olive green 2.00 *3.25*
26 A40 8a red violet 2.50 *4.50*
Nos. 21-26 (6) 8.55 *13.60*

The above overprints vary in length, also in the relative positions of the letters. Nos. 21 to 23 exist without the second "I" of "British."

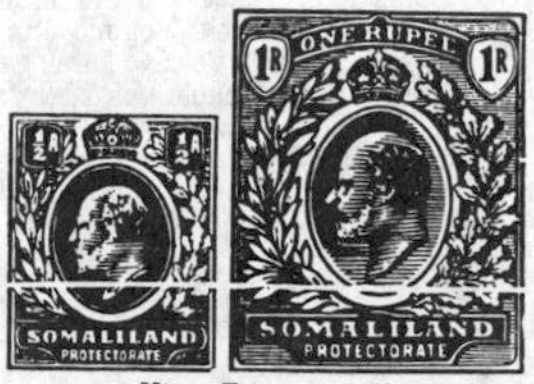

King Edward VII
A1 A2

1904 Wmk. 2 Typo.
27 A1 ½a gray green .55 .50
28 A1 1a carmine & blk 1.25 1.40
29 A1 2a red vio & dull vio .80 .95
30 A1 2½a ultramarine 1.10 1.25
31 A1 3a gray grn & vio brn 1.60 *3.00*
32 A1 4a black & gray grn 1.75 *3.50*
33 A1 6a vio & gray grn 3.50 *4.50*
34 A1 8a pale blue & blk 4.50 *7.25*
35 A1 12a ocher & blk 6.75 *8.00*

Wmk. Crown and C C (1)

36 A2 1r gray grn 9.00 *12.50*
37 A2 2r red vio & dull vio 20.00 *27.50*
38 A2 3r blk & gray grn 30.00 *37.50*
39 A2 5r carmine & blk 32.50 *45.00*
Nos. 27-39 (13) 113.30 *152.85*

1905 Wmk. 3
40 A1 ½a gray green .40 1.00
41 A1 1a carmine & blk 2.75 1.00
42 A1 2a red vio & dull vio 3.50 *5.00*
43 A1 2½a ultramarine 2.75 3.75
44 A1 3a gray grn & vio brn 2.75 *6.50*
45 A1 4a black & gray grn 2.75 *5.75*
46 A1 6a violet & gray grn 3.25 *9.00*
47 A1 8a pale blue & blk 3.75 *6.75*
48 A1 12a ocher & black 3.00 *7.75*
Nos. 40-48 (9) 24.90 *46.50*

Nos. 41, 42, 44-48 are on both ordinary and chalky paper.

1909
50 A1 1a carmine 1.50 1.10

For overprints see Nos. O11-O16.

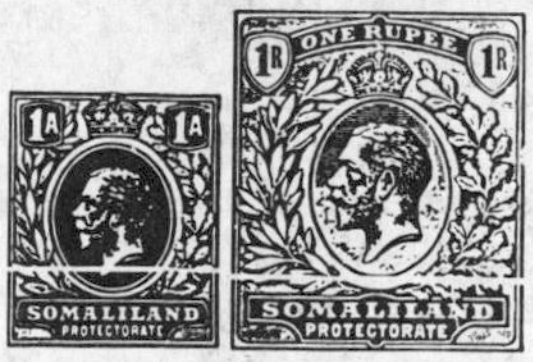

King George V
A3 A4

The ½, 1 and 2½a of type A3 are on ordinary paper, the other values of types A3 and A4 are on chalky paper.

1912-19
51 A3 ½a green .30 4.00
52 A3 1a carmine 2.50 1.00
53 A3 2a red vio & dull vio 4.00 *7.50*
54 A3 2½a ultramarine .75 *5.00*
55 A3 3a gray grn & vio brn .75 *3.00*
56 A3 4a blk & grn ('13) 1.00 *5.50*
57 A3 6a violet & green 1.00 *3.00*
58 A3 8a lt blue & blk 1.75 *8.00*
59 A3 12a ocher & blk 1.50 *13.00*
60 A4 1r dull grn & grn 6.00 *9.00*
61 A4 2r red vio & dull vio ('19) 16.00 *40.00*
62 A4 3r blk & gray grn ('19) 45.00 *75.00*
63 A4 5r car & blk ('19) 45.00 *100.00*
Nos. 51-63 (13) 125.55 *274.00*

1921 Wmk. 4
64 A3 ½a blue green .40 *3.00*
65 A3 1a scarlet .50 .25
66 A3 2a vio & dull vio .90 *.80*
67 A3 2½a ultramarine .75 *2.50*
68 A3 3a gray grn & vio brown 1.50 *5.00*
69 A3 4a black & grn 1.50 *4.00*
70 A3 6a violet & grn 1.00 *10.00*
71 A3 8a lt blue & blk 1.25 *4.00*
72 A3 12a ocher & blk 5.00 *12.50*
73 A4 1r dull grn & grn 5.00 *20.00*
74 A4 2r vio & dull vio 12.50 *27.50*
75 A4 3r blk & gray grn 25.00 *75.00*
76 A4 5r scarlet & blk 45.00 *100.00*
Nos. 64-76 (13) 100.30 *264.55*

Silver Jubilee Issue
Common Design Type

1935, May 6 Engr. *Perf. 11x12*
77 CD301 1a car & dk blue .70 1.00
78 CD301 2a black & ultra 1.25 1.75
79 CD301 3a ultra & brown 1.75 2.50
80 CD301 1r brown vio & ind 5.50 7.50
Nos. 77-80 (4) 9.20 12.75
Set, never hinged 15.00

Coronation Issue
Common Design Type

1937, May 13 *Perf. 13½x14*
81 CD302 1a carmine .15 .15
82 CD302 2a black .30 .40
83 CD302 3a bright ultra .40 .30
Nos. 81-83 (3) .85 .85
Set, never hinged 1.50

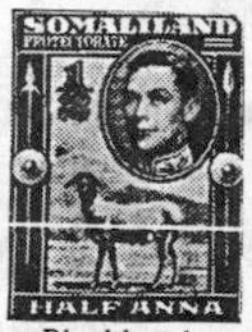

Blackhead Sheep — A5

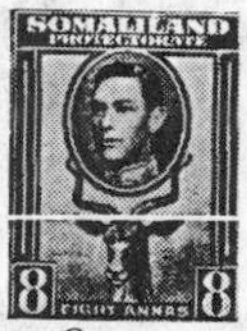

Greater Kudu — A6

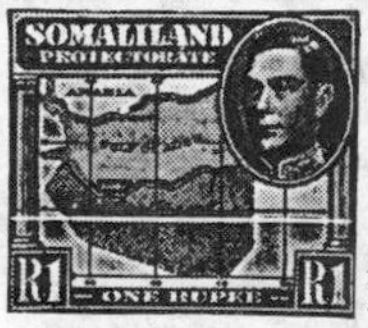

Map of Somaliland Protectorate — A7

1938, May 10 Wmk. 4 *Perf. 12½*
84 A5 ½a green .25 1.00
85 A5 1a carmine .25 .25
86 A5 2a deep claret .50 .45
87 A5 3a ultra 2.00 *2.50*
88 A6 4a dark brown 1.00 *2.25*
89 A6 6a purple 1.50 *5.00*
90 A6 8a gray black 1.00 *5.00*
91 A6 12a orange 1.50 *6.50*
92 A7 1r green 7.50 *17.50*
93 A7 2r rose violet 7.50 *17.50*
94 A7 3r ultramarine 10.00 *15.00*
95 A7 5r black 10.00 *15.00*
a. Horiz. pair, imperf. btwn. *4,500.*
Nos. 84-95 (12) 43.00 *87.95*
Set, never hinged 57.50

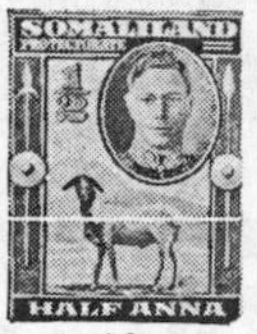

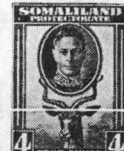

A8

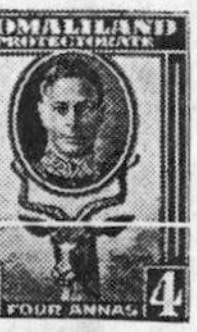

A9

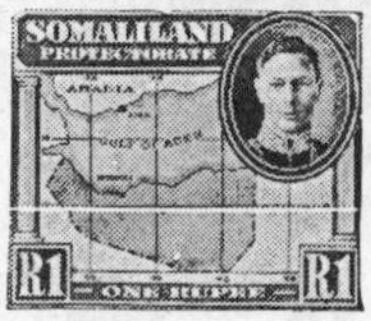

A10

1942, Apr. 22
96 A8 ½a green .15 .15
97 A8 1a carmine .15 .15
98 A8 2a deep claret .15 .15
99 A8 3a ultramarine .30 .15
100 A9 4a dark brown .50 .15
101 A9 6a purple .30 .30
102 A9 8a gray .45 *.85*
103 A9 12a orange .75 *.85*
104 A10 1r green .70 *1.25*
105 A10 2r rose violet 1.10 *2.00*
106 A10 3r ultra 1.65 *3.00*
107 A10 5r black 2.75 *4.25*
Nos. 96-107 (12) 8.95 *13.25*
Set, never hinged 13.00

For surcharges see Nos. 116-126.

Catalogue values for unused stamps in this section, from this point to the end of the section, are for Never Hinged items.

Peace Issue
Common Design Type
Perf. 13½x14

1946, Oct. 15 Engr. Wmk. 4
108 CD303 1a carmine .15 .15
a. Perf. 13½ 5.00 *20.00*
109 CD303 3a deep blue .15 .15
Set value .25 .25

Silver Wedding Issue
Common Design Types

1949, Jan. 28 Photo. *Perf. 14x14½*
110 CD304 1a scarlet .15 .15

Engraved; Name Typographed
Perf. 11½x11

111 CD305 5r gray black 5.00 *7.00*

UPU Issue
Common Design Types
Surcharged in Black or Carmine with New Values in Annas

Engr.; Name Typo. on 3a, 6a

1949, Oct. 10 *Perf. 13½, 11x11½*
112 CD306 1a on 10c rose car .15 .15
113 CD307 3a on 30c ind (C) .30 .15
114 CD308 6a on 50c rose vio .60 .30
115 CD309 12a on 1sh red org 1.25 .60
Nos. 112-115 (4) 2.30 1.20

Nos. 96 and 98 to 107 Surcharged with New Value in Black or Carmine

1951, Apr. 2 Wmk. 4 *Perf. 12½*
116 A8 5c on ½a green .15 .15
117 A8 10c on 2a deep claret .30 .15
118 A8 15c on 3a ultramarine .35 .18
119 A9 20c on 4a dark brown .40 .20
120 A9 30c on 6a purple .45 .22
121 A9 50c on 8a gray .50 .25
122 A9 70c on 12a red .65 .32
123 A10 1sh on 1r green .85 .42
124 A10 2sh on 2r rose violet 1.25 .65
125 A10 2sh on 3r ultra 2.00 1.00
126 A10 5sh on 5r black (C) 5.00 2.50
Nos. 116-126 (11) 11.90 6.04

Coronation Issue
Common Design Type

1953, June 2 Engr. *Perf. 13½x13*
127 CD312 15c dark green & blk .20 .20

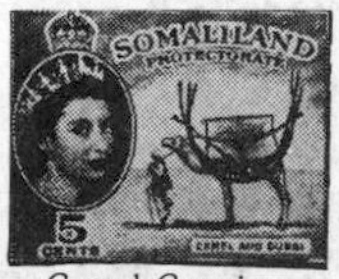

Camel Carrying Somali House
A11

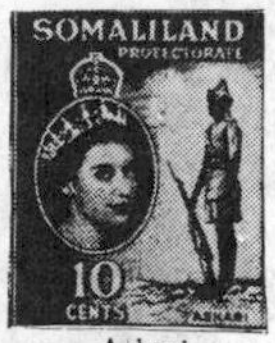

Askari Militiaman
A12

Designs: 35c, 2sh, Rock Pigeon. 50c, 5sh, Martial eagle. 1sh, Blackhead sheep. 1sh30c, Tomb of Sheik Isaaq, Mait. 10sh, Taleh Fort.

1953-58 Engr. *Perf. 12½*
128 A11 5c gray .15 .15
129 A12 10c red orange 1.25 .15
130 A11 15c blue green .40 .20
131 A11 20c rose red .40 .20
132 A12 30c lt chocolate .40 .18
133 A11 35c blue 1.25 1.00
134 A11 50c lilac rose & brn 1.25 .30
135 A11 1sh grnsh blue .80 .35
136 A11 1sh30c dark gray & ultra ('58) 4.50 2.00
137 A11 2sh violet & brn 12.00 2.25
138 A11 5sh emerald & brn 12.00 2.25
139 A11 10sh rose lilac & brn 9.00 12.00
Nos. 128-139 (12) 43.40 21.03

Nos. 131 and 135 Overprinted:
"Opening of the Legislative
Council 1957"

1957, May 21
140 A11 20c rose red .15 .15
141 A11 1sh greenish blue .30 .30

Nos. 131 and 136 Overprinted:
"Legislative Council Unofficial
Majority, 1960"

1960, Apr. 5
142 A11 20c rose red .15 .15
143 A11 1sh30c dk gray & ultra .28 .28
Changes in the Legislative Council.

Three stamps of Somalia were overprinted "Somaliland Independence 26 June 1960" and issued in Hargeisa on that day. Somaliland Protectorate became part of Somalia on July 1, 1960. These three stamps are listed in Vol. 5 as Somalia Nos. 242, C68-C69.

Stamps of Somaliland Protectorate were replaced by those of Somalia in 1960.

OFFICIAL STAMPS

Official Stamps of
India, 1883-1900,
Overprinted

BRITISH SOMALILAND

1903, June 1   Wmk. 39   Perf. 14
O1 A17 ½a light green 4.00 42.50
O2 A19 1a carmine rose 9.00 9.00
O3 A21 2a violet 8.00 42.50
O4 A25 8a red violet 22.50 450.00
O5 A29 1r car rose & green 22.50 450.00
Nos. O1-O5 (5) 66.00

SERVICE

India Nos. 61-63, 68,
10 Overprinted

BRITISH SOMALILAND

1903
O6 A33 ½a green .75
O7 A34 1a carmine rose .75
O8 A35 2a violet .75
O9 A40 8a red violet 15.00
O10 A29 1r car rose & green 25.00
Nos. O6-O10 (5) 42.25
Nos. O6-O10 were not regularly issued.

Regular Issue of 1904
Overprinted **O.H.M.S.**

1904   Wmk. Crown and C A (2)
O11 A1 ½a gray green 5.50 18.00
O12 A1 1a carmine & blk 8.50 9.00
O13 A1 2a red vio & dull vio 175.00 50.00
O14 A1 8a pale blue & blk 55.00 110.00
Nos. O11-O14 (4) 244.00 187.00

Wmk. Crown and C C (1)
O15 A2 1r gray green 175.00 500.00

Same Overprint on No. 42

1905   Wmk. 3
O16 A1 2a red vio & dull vio 70.00 400.00
The period after "M" may be found missing on Nos. O11-O14 and O16.

SOUTH AFRICA

saúth 'a–fri–kə

LOCATION — Southern Africa
GOVT. — Republic
AREA — 433,678 sq. mi.
POP. — 26,749,000 (est. 1984)
CAPITAL — Pretoria (administrative); Cape Town (legislative)

The union was formed on May 31, 1910, comprising the former British colonies of Cape of Good Hope, Natal, Transvaal and the Orange Free State, which became provinces. The union became a republic in 1961.

For previous listings, see individual headings.

12 Pence = 1 Shilling
20 Shillings = 1 Pound
100 Cents = 1 Rand (1961)

Catalogue values for unused stamps in this country are for Never Hinged items, beginning with Scott 74 in the regular postage section, Scott B1 in the semi-postal section, Scott J22 in the postage due section, and Scott O21 in the officials section.

Watermarks

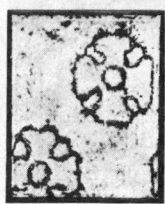
Wmk. 47- Multiple Rosette

Wmk. 177- Springbok's Head

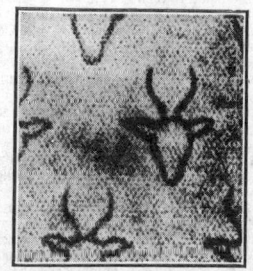
Wmk. 201- Multiple Springbok's Head

Wmk. 330- Coat of Arms, Multiple

Wmk. 348- RSA in Triangle, Multiple

Wmk. 359- RSA in Triangle, Tete Beche

A1   A2
George V

1910   Engr.   Wmk. 47   Perf. 14
1 A1 2½p deep blue 5.00 1.90
Union Parliament opening, Nov. 4, 1910.

Type A2 stamps have very small margins at top and bottom. Values are for copies with perfs close to, or touching the frame.

1913-24   Typo.   Wmk. 177
2 A2 ½p green .15 .15
a. Double impression 16,500.
3 A2 1p scarlet .30 .15
4 A2 1½p orange brn ('20) .45 .15
a. Tête bêche pair 5.00 10.00
5 A2 2p dull violet .90 .15
6 A2 2½p ultra 1.40 .75
7 A2 3p brn org & blk 1.75 .15
8 A2 3p ultra ('22) 2.00 .70
9 A2 4p ol grn & org 4.25 .20
10 A2 6p violet & blk 3.25 .15
11 A2 1sh orange 14.00 .20
12 A2 1sh3p violet ('20) 17.50 10.00
13 A2 2sh6p green & cl 55.00 2.00
14 A2 5sh blue & claret 125.00 11.00
15 A2 10sh ol grn & blue 250.00 16.00
16 A2 £1 red & dp grn ('16) 1,000. 450.00
a. £1 red & gray green ('24) 1,100. 1,750.
Nos. 2-16 (15) 1,475. 491.75

The ½p, 1p and 1½p have the words "Revenue" and "Inkomst" on the stamps. On other stamps of this type these words are replaced by short vertical lines.

All values exist in many shades. No. 4a exists with and without gutter between.

Unwatermarked copies of the 1p are the result of misplaced watermarks.

For overprint see No. O1.

Coil Stamps
Perf. 14 Horizontally
17 A2 ½p green 4.25 .85
18 A2 1p scarlet ('14) 6.25 1.65
19 A2 1½p orange brown ('20) 7.75 3.00
20 A2 2p dull violet ('21) 7.75 2.75
Nos. 17-20 (4) 26.00 8.25

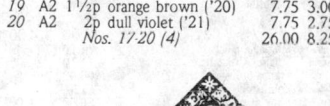
"Hope"
A3

Design: No. 22, inscribed SUIDAFRIKA.

1926   Engr.   Wmk. 201   Imperf.
21 A3 4p blue gray .75 .65
22 A3 4p blue gray .75 .65
Nos. 21 and 22 were privately rouletted and perforated, but such varieties were not officially made.

No. 21 (English inscription) was printed in a separate sheet from No. 22 (Afrikaans inscription).

English-Afrikaans Se-Tenant
Stamps with English inscriptions and with Afrikaans inscriptions were printed alternately in the same sheets, starting with No. 23. Major-number listings and values are for horizontal pairs (vertical pairs sell for about one-third less) of such stamps consisting of one English and one Afrikaans-inscribed stamp, unless otherwise described.

Springbok — A5

Jan van Riebeek's Ship, Drommedaris — A6   Orange Tree — A7

1926   Typo.   Perf. 14½x14

23	A5 ½p dk grn & blk, pair	1.50	1.25
a.	Single, English	.25	.15
b.	Single, Afrikaans	.25	.15
c.	Tete beche pair	1,000.	
d.	Center omitted	275.00	
e.	Booklet pane of 6	50.00	
f.	As "e," perf. 14	725.00	
24	A6 1p car & blk, pair	1.50	1.10
a.	Single, English	.25	.15
b.	Single, Afrikaans	.25	.15
c.	Imperf., pair	650.00	
d.	Tete beche pair	1,000.	
e.	Center omitted	275.00	
f.	Booklet pane of 6	40.00	
g.	As "f," perf. 14	550.00	
25	A7 6p org & grn, pair	25.00	8.25
a.	Single, English	1.65	.15
b.	Single, Afrikaans	1.65	.15

Nos. 23c and 24d are from uncut sheets printed for the perf. 14 booklet panes of 1928, Nos. 23f and 24g.

See Nos. 33-35, 42, 45-50, 59-61, 98-99. For overprints see Nos. O2-O4, O6-O9, O12-O15, O18, O21-O25, O30-O32, O42-O45, O48.

Government Buildings, Pretoria — A8   "Groote Schuur," Rhodes's Home — A9

Native Kraal — A10   Gnu — A11

Trekking — A12    Ox Wagon — A13

Cape Town and Table Mountain — A14

Perf. 14, 14x13½

1927-28	Engr.		Wmk. 201
26	A8 2p vio brn & gray, pair	13.00	15.00
a.	Single, English	2.00	.15
b.	Single, Afrikaans	2.00	.15
27	A9 3p red & blk, pair	18.00	18.00
a.	Single, English	3.50	.25
b.	Single, Afrikaans	3.50	.25
c.	Perf. 14x13, pair	80.00	100.00
d.	As "c," single, English	11.00	3.50
e.	As "c," single, Afrikaans	11.00	3.50
28	A10 4p brown, pair ('28)	21.00	25.00
a.	Single, English	3.00	.40
b.	Single, Afrikaans	3.00	.40
29	A11 1sh dp bl & bis brn, pair	27.50	30.00
a.	Single, English	4.50	1.00
b.	Single, Afrikaans	4.50	1.00
30	A12 2sh6p brn & bl grn, pair	82.50	140.00
a.	Single, English	14.00	7.50
b.	Single, Afrikaans	14.00	7.50
c.	Perf. 14x13½, pair	300.00	200.00
d.	As "c," single, English	60.00	25.00
e.	As "c," single, Afrikaans	60.00	25.00
31	A13 5sh dp grn & blk, pair	200.00	475.00
a.	Single, English	32.50	35.00
b.	Single, Afrikaans	32.50	35.00
c.	Perf. 14x13½, pair	425.00	500.00
d.	As "c," single, English	90.00	100.00
e.	As "c," single, Afrikaans	90.00	100.00
32	A14 10sh ol brn & bl, pair	150.00	90.00
a.	Single, English	32.50	15.00
b.	Single, Afrikaans	32.50	15.00
c.	Perf. 14x13½, pair	275.00	250.00

d.	As "c," single, English	75.00	35.00
e.	As "c," single, Afrikaans	75.00	35.00
	Nos. 26-32 (7)	512.00	793.00

See Nos. 36-41, 43-44, 53-54, 58, 62-66. For overprints see Nos. O5, O10-O111, O16-O17, O19-O20, O28, O33-O35, O39, O41, O49-O53.

Types of 1926-28 Redrawn "SUIDAFRIKA" (No Hyphen) on Afrikaans Stamps

The photogravure, unhyphenated stamps of 1930-45 are distinguished from the 1926-28 typographed or engraved stamps (also unhyphenated) by the following characteristics:

½p, 1p, 6p. Leg of "R" in AFRICA or AFRIKA ends in a straight line in the photogravure set; in a curved line in the typographed. No. 35 differs from No. 34, having 2mm space between POSSEEL—INKOMSTE instead of 1mm.

2p. A memorial statue has been added just above and leftward of the "2" in value tablet on Nos. 36-37 (photogravure).

3p. Top frame on No. 38 consists of 3 heavy lines. On No. 27 it has 3 heavy and 2 very thin lines.

4p. On Nos. 40-41 the background in upper corners is solid. On No. 28 it consists of horizontal and vertical lines. No. 41 has pretzel-shaped scroll endings at bottom. On No. 40 these scroll endings enclose a solid mass of color.

1sh. No. 43 has no fine shading lines projecting from the curved top of the left inner frame, as No. 29 has. On No. 43 the shading of the last "A" of the country name partly covers the flower below it.

2sh6p. On No. 44 the shading below the country name is solid or shows signs of wear. On No. 30 it is composed of fine lines.

The engraved pictorials are much more finely executed and show details more clearly than the photogravure.

Perf. 15x14 (½p, 1p, 6p), 14

1930-45	Photo.		Wmk. 201
33	A5 ½p bl grn & blk, pair	2.00	1.40
a.	Single, English	.25	.15
b.	Single, Afrikaans	.25	.15
c.	Tete-beche pair	1,100.	
d.	As "c," gutter between	950.00	
e.	Booklet pane of 6	30.00	30.00
f.	Vert. pair, monolingual	60.00	65.00
34	A6 1p car & blk, pair	2.50	1.10
a.	Single, English	.45	.15
b.	Single, Afrikaans	.45	.15
c.	Center omitted	850.00	
d.	Frame omitted	650.00	
e.	Tete-beche pair	1,000.	
f.	As "e," gutter between	750.00	
g.	Booklet pane of 6	30.00	30.00
35	A6 1p rose & blk, pair ('32)	25.00	3.25
a.	Single, English	1.50	.15
b.	Single, Afrikaans	1.50	.15
c.	Center omitted	750.00	
36	A8 2p vio & gray, pair ('31)	14.00	4.00
a.	Single, English	1.10	.40
b.	Single, Afrikaans	1.10	.40
c.	Frame omitted	800.00	
d.	Tete-beche pair	2,750.	
e.	Booklet pane of 4	50.00	50.00
37	A8 2p vio & ind, pair ('38)	150.00	50.00
a.	Single, English	8.25	2.50
b.	Single, Afrikaans	8.25	2.50
38	A9 3p red & blk, pair ('31)	45.00	45.00
a.	Single, English	4.25	2.50
b.	Single, Afrikaans	4.25	2.50
39	A9 3p ultra & bl, pair ('33)	7.00	4.00
a.	Single, English	.85	.30
b.	Single, Afrikaans	.85	.30
c.	Center omitted	1,000.	
40	A10 4p redsh brn, pair ('32)	37.50	22.50
a.	Single, English	2.50	.60
b.	Single, Afrikaans	2.50	.60
41	A10 4p brn, pair ('36)	4.00	2.50
a.	Single, English	.60	.15
b.	Single, Afrikaans	.60	.15
42	A7 6p org & grn, pair ('31)	16.00	3.00
a.	Single, English	2.00	.30
b.	Single, Afrikaans	2.00	.30
43	A11 1sh dp bl & brn, pair ('32)	45.00	20.00
a.	Single, English	5.25	.40
b.	Single, Afrikaans	5.25	.40
c.	1sh dp bl & yel brn, pair	40.00	17.50
d.	As "c," single, English	4.50	.35
e.	As "c," single, Afrikaans	4.50	.35
44	A12 2sh 6p red brn & grn, pair ('32)	100.00	67.50
a.	Single, English	8.75	3.00
b.	Single, Afrikaans	8.75	3.00
c.	2sh6p brn & sl grn ('36), pair	65.00	37.50
d.	As "c," single, English	7.25	3.00
e.	As "c," single, Afrikaans	7.25	3.00
f.	2sh6p choc & dp grn ('37), pair	57.50	30.00
g.	As "f," single, English	6.50	3.00
h.	As "f," single, Afrikaans	6.50	3.00
i.	2sh6p brn & bl ('45), pair	16.00	8.25
j.	As "i," single, English	1.65	.30
k.	As "i," single, Afrikaans	1.65	.30
	Nos. 33-44 (12)	448.00	224.25

No. 34 unwatermarked, or watermarked multiple clover leaf, is a proof.

Types of 1926-28 with "SUID-AFRIKA" Hyphenated on Afrikaans Stamps, and

Gold Mine — A15   Government Buildings, Pretoria — A16

Groote Schuur — A17    Groot Constantia — A18

½p. No. 45 shading in leaves and ornaments strengthened; 40 lines in center background. Size: 18½x22½mm.

No. 46 has 28 heavy horizontal shading lines in center background and similar thicker lines in frame. Top and bottom green bars are scored by a white horizontal line. Size: 18½x22½mm.

No. 47 is smaller, 18x22mm.

1p. No. 48, size 18½x22½mm.

No. 49, size 18x22mm.

No. 50. Size: 17½x21½mm.

2p. On Nos. 53-54, S's in SOUTH and POSTAGE are narrower than on Nos. 36-37.

6p. Die I, "SUID-AFRIKA" 16½mm. Shading in leaves framing oval very faint and broken. Size: 18½x22½mm.

Die II, "SUID-AFRIKA" 17mm. Leaves strongly shaded. Heavy lines of shading in background of tree. Size: 18½x22½mm.

Die III, "question mark" scrolls below top panel are cleanly defined without intrusion of background shading. Size: 18x22mm.

Nos. 45-67 were printed in many shades. Some denominations in some printings were partly or wholly screened. Except for No. 47, the screened stamps were issued after 1947.

5sh. No. 65. Type I, letters "U" and "A" in SOUTH AFRICA have projections. Size: 27x21½mm.

No. 66. Type II, letters "U" and "A" redrawn to eliminate projections. Size: 26½x21½mm.

Perf. 15x14 (½p, 1p, 6p), 14

1933-54	Photo.		Wmk. 201
45	A5 ½p grn & gray, pair ('36)	4.00	.80
a.	Single, English	.22	.15
b.	Single, Afrikaans	.22	.15
c.	Bklt. pane of 6, marginal ads	30.00	30.00
d.	Perf. 13½x14 (coil), pair	22.50	22.50
e.	As "d," single, English	1.80	.80
f.	As "d," single, Afrikaans	1.80	.80
46	A5 ½p grn & gray, redrawn, pair ('37)	4.00	.18
a.	Single, English	.15	.15
b.	Single, Afrikaans	.15	.15
c.	Booklet pane of 6	37.50	30.00
d.	Booklet pane of 2	8.00	1.00
e.	As "c," 4 blank margins	35.00	35.00
f.	Perf. 14½x14 (coil), pair	12.50	7.25
g.	As "f," single, English	2.25	.80
h.	As "f," single, Afrikaans	2.25	.80
47	A5 ½p grn & gray, pair ('47)	1.25	.18
a.	Single, English	.15	.15
b.	Single, Afrikaans	.15	.15
c.	Bklt. pane of 6, marginal ads	5.00	3.50
d.	As "c," no horiz. margins	5.00	3.00
48	A6 1p car & gray, pair ('34)	1.25	.22
a.	Single, English	.15	.15
b.	Single, Afrikaans	.15	.15
c.	Booklet pane of 6	37.50	37.50
d.	Booklet pane of 2	3.00	1.25
e.	Perf. 13½x14 (coil), pair	27.50	27.50
f.	As "e," single, English	1.40	1.00
g.	As "e," single, Afrikaans	1.40	1.00
h.	Center omitted pair	310.00	
j.	Bklt. pane of 6, marginal ads	27.50	27.50
k.	As "j," 4 blank margins	30.00	30.00
m.	Perf. 14½x14 (coil), pair	11.00	11.00
n.	As "m," single, English	1.40	1.40
p.	As "m," single, Afrikaans	1.40	1.40
49	A6 1p rose car & gray blk, pair ('40)	1.25	.28
a.	Single, English	.15	.15
b.	Single, Afrikaans	.15	.15
c.	Unwmkd., pair	325.00	325.00
d.	Booklet pane of 6	3.75	2.75
e.	Perf. 14½x14 (coil), pair	14.00	11.50
f.	As "e," single, English	1.40	.90
g.	As "e," single, Afrikaans	1.40	.90
h.	As "d," marginal ads	5.00	4.25
50	A6 1p car & blk, pair ('51)	1.25	.15
a.	Single, English	.15	.15
b.	Single, Afrikaans	.15	.15
51	A15 1½p dk grn & gold, 27x21½mm, pair ('36)	2.00	.60
a.	Single, English	.35	.15
b.	Single, Afrikaans	.35	.15
c.	Booklet pane of 4	9.00	8.00
d.	Center omitted, pair	1,000.	

52	A15 1½p sl grn & ocher, 22x18mm, pair ('41)	1.25	.22
a.	Single, English	.15	.15
b.	Single, Afrikaans	.15	.15
c.	Center omitted, pair	900.00	
d.	Booklet pane of 6	5.75	4.50
53	A8 2p bl vio & dl bl, pair ('38)	40.00	25.00
a.	Single, English	3.00	1.00
b.	Single, Afrikaans	3.00	1.00
54	A8 2p dl vio & gray, pair ('41)	24.00	.80
a.	Single, English	.90	.15
b.	Single, Afrikaans	.90	.15
55	A16 2p pur & sl bl, 27x21½mm, pair ('45)	.75	.15
a.	Single, English	.15	.15
b.	Single, Afrikaans	.15	.15
56	A16 2p same, 21½ x 17¼mm, pair ('50)	.25	.15
a.	Single, English	.15	.15
b.	Single, Afrikaans	.15	.15
c.	Booklet pane of 6 ('51)	3.75	2.75
57	A17 3p ultra, pair ('40)	2.00	.55
a.	Single, English	.20	.15
b.	Single, Afrikaans	.20	.15
c.	3p bl, pair ('49)	.55	.28
d.	As "c," single, English	.15	.15
e.	As "c," single, Afrikaans	.15	.15
58	A10 4p choc brn, pair ('52)	.70	.55
a.	Single, English	.18	.15
b.	Single, Afrikaans	.18	.15
59	A7 6p org & bl grn, I, pair ('37)	50.00	15.00
a.	Single, English	3.75	1.10
b.	Single, Afrikaans	3.75	1.10
60	A7 6p org & grn, II, pair ('38)	18.00	2.75
a.	Single, English	.90	.22
b.	Single, Afrikaans	.90	.22
61	A7 6p org & grn, III, pair ('46)	7.00	1.90
a.	Single, English	.80	.15
b.	Single, Afrikaans	.80	.15
c.	6p red org & bl grn, III ('50), pair	.95	.40
d.	As "c," single, English	.15	.15
e.	As "c," single, Afrikaans	.15	.15
62	A11 1sh lt bl & ol brn, pair ('39)	15.00	4.00
a.	Single, English	.75	.15
b.	Single, Afrikaans	.75	.15
c.	1sh chlky bl & lt brn ('50), pair	3.50	.55
d.	As "c," single, English	.55	.15
e.	As "c," single, Afrikaans	.55	.15
f.	1sh vio bl & brnsh blk, pair	5.50	1.10
g.	As "f," single, English	.35	.15
h.	As "f," single, Afrikaans	.35	.15
63	A12 2sh6p brn & brt grn, pair ('49)	6.50	4.50
a.	Single, English	.90	.25
b.	Single, Afrikaans	.90	.25
64	A13 5sh grn & blk, I, pair	35.00	14.00
a.	Single, English	2.50	.45
b.	Single, Afrikaans	2.50	.45
65	A13 5sh bl grn & blk, I, pair ('49)	32.50	13.00
a.	Single, English	2.50	.60
b.	Single, Afrikaans	2.50	.60
66	A13 5sh grn & blk, II, pair ('54)	45.00	25.00
a.	Single, English	1.65	.32
b.	Single, Afrikaans	1.65	.32
67	A18 10sh ol blk & bl, pair ('39)	27.50	5.50
a.	Single, English	3.00	.38
b.	Single, Afrikaans	3.00	.38
	Nos. 45-67 (23)	320.45	115.48

See Nos. 98-99. For overprints see Nos. O26-O27, O29, O36-O38, O40, O46-O47, O54.

George V and Springboks A19

1935, May 1   Wmk. 201   Perf. 15x14

68	A19 ½p Prus grn & blk, pair	1.65	2.75
a.	Single, English top	.20	.15
b.	Single, Afrikaans top	.20	.15
69	A19 1p car rose & blk, pair	1.75	1.75
a.	Single, English top	.28	.15
b.	Single, Afrikaans top	.28	.15
70	A19 3p bl & dk bl, pair	27.50	55.00
a.	Single, English top	3.00	2.50
b.	Single, Afrikaans top	3.00	2.50
71	A19 6p org & grn, pair	40.00	75.00
a.	Single, English top	3.00	2.00
b.	Single, Afrikaans top	3.00	2.00
	Nos. 68-71 (4)	70.90	134.50

25th anniv. of the reign of George V.

English and Afrikaans inscriptions are transposed on alternate stamps. On the ½p, 3p and 6p with "SOUTH AFRICA" at top, "SILWER JUBILEUM" is at left of medallion, but on 1p with English at top, it is at the right.

Johannesburg International Philatelic Exhibition Issue
Souvenir Sheets

A20

A21

Black Overprint, "JIPEX 1936"

1936, Nov. 2 *Perf. 15x14*
72 A20 Sheet of 6 (½p) 5.00 7.50
73 A21 Sheet of 6 (1p) 4.25 6.00

Sheets made by overprinting booklet panes Nos. 45c and 48j. Sheets exist with and without horizontal perforations through right margin. Sheet size: 81x72½mm.

Catalogue values for unused stamps in this section, from this point to the end of the section, are for Never Hinged items.

George VI — A22

"KRONING SUID-AFRIKA" on alternate stamps.

1937, May 12 *Perf. 14*
74 A22 ½p grn & ol blk, pair .55 .35
a. Single, English .15 .15
b. Single, Afrikaans .15 .15
75 A22 1p car & ol blk, pair .80 .50
a. Single, English .15 .15
b. Single, Afrikaans .15 .15
76 A22 1½p Prus grn & org, pair .80 .50
a. Single, English .15 .15
b. Single, Afrikaans .15 .15
77 A22 3p bl & ultra, pair 1.75 1.10
a. Single, English .18 .18
b. Single, Afrikaans .18 .18
78 A22 1sh Prus bl & org brn, pair 5.00 3.00
a. Single, English .50 .50
b. Single, Afrikaans .50 .50
Nos. 74-78 (5) 8.90 5.45

Coronation of George VI and Queen Elizabeth.

Wagon Wheel A23

Voortrekker Family A24

Alternate stamps inscribed "SOUTH AFRICA," "SUID-AFRIKA."

1938, Dec. 14 *Perf. 15x14*
79 A23 1p rose & slate, pair 5.00 5.00
a. Single, English .30 .25
b. Single, Afrikaans .30 .25
80 A24 1½p red brn & Prus bl, pair 6.00 6.00
a. Single, English .40 .30
b. Single, Afrikaans .40 .30

Issued to commemorate the Voortrekkers.

Infantry A25

Nurse and Ambulance A26

Airman and Spitfires (Flight Lt. Robert Kershaw) — A27

Sailor — A28

Women's Services A29

Artillery A30

Welder A31

Tank Corps A32

Signal Corps A33

Bilingual inscriptions on 2p and 1sh.

Perf. 14 (2p, 4p, 6p), 15x14

1941-43 **Photo.** **Wmk. 201**
81 A25 ½p dp blue grn, pair .65 .65
a. Single, English .15 .15
b. Single, Afrikaans .15 .15
82 A26 1p brt rose, pair 1.40 1.40
a. Single, English .15 .15
b. Single, Afrikaans .15 .15
83 A27 1½p Prus grn, pair ('42) 1.10 1.10
a. Single, English .15 .15
b. Single, Afrikaans .15 .15
84 A28 2p dk violet .50 .15
85 A29 3p dp blue, pair 14.00 14.00
a. Single, English .20 .15
b. Single, Afrikaans .20 .15
86 A30 4p org brn, pair 13.00 13.00
a. Single, English .45 .20
b. Single, Afrikaans .45 .20
c. 4p red brown, pair 27.50 10.00
d. As "c," single, English .60 .15
e. As "c," single, Afrikaans .60 .15
87 A31 6p brt red org, pair 7.75 7.75
a. Single, English .50 .30
b. Single, Afrikaans .50 .30
88 A32 1sh dark brown 2.25 1.00
89 A33 1sh3p dk ol brn, pair ('43) 8.00 5.00
a. Single, English .40 .18
b. Single, Afrikaans .40 .18
c. 1sh3p dark brown, pair 3.50 5.00
d. As "c," single, English .40 .18
e. As "c," single, Afrikaans .40 .18
Nos. 81-89 (9) 48.65 44.05

Infantry-Nurse-Airman-Sailor
A34 A35 A36 A37

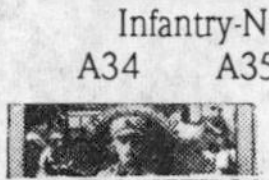

Women's Services — A38

Artillery — A39

Welder A40

Tank Corps A41

Bilingual inscriptions on 4p and 1sh.

Pairs: Perf. 14, Roul. 6½ btwn. Strips of 3: Perf. 15x14, Roul. 6½ btwn.

1942-43 **Photo.** **Wmk. 201**
90 A34 ½p Horiz. strip of 3 .65 .65
a. Single, English .15 .15
b. Single, Afrikaans .15 .15
c. As #90, imperf. between 350.00
91 A35 1p Horiz. strip of 3 ('43) .90 .45
a. Single, English .15 .15
b. Single, Afrikaans .15 .15
c. As #91, imperf. between 350.00
92 A36 1½p Horiz. pair .60 .60
a. Single, English .15 .15
b. Single, Afrikaans .15 .15
c. As #92, roul. 13 4.50 4.50
d. As #92, imperf. btwn. 350.00
93 A37 2p Horiz. pair ('43) .85 .75
a. Single, English .15 .15
b. Single, Afrikaans .15 .15
c. As #93, imperf. btwn. 350.00
94 A38 3p Vert strip of 3 6.50 8.00
a. Single, English .15 .15
b. Single, Afrikaans .15 .15
95 A39 4p Vert. strip of 3 13.00 3.75
a. Single .16 .15
96 A40 6p Horiz. pair 1.90 1.25
a. Single, English .16 .15
b. Single, Afrikaans .16 .15
97 A41 1sh Vert. pair 11.00 1.10
a. Single .25 .15
Nos. 90-97 (8) 35.40 16.55

Because of the rouletting these are collected as pairs or strips of three, even on the bilingual stamps.

Types of 1926, Redrawn
"SUID-AFRIKA" Hyphenated
Coil Stamps

1943 **Photo.** *Perf. 15x14*
98 A5 ½p myrtle grn, pair 1.40 1.40
a. Single, English .20 .15
b. Single, Afrikaans .20 .15
99 A6 1p rose pink, pair 1.65 1.65
a. Single, English .20 .15
b. Single, Afrikaans .20 .15

"Victory" — A42

"Peace" — A43

Design: 3p, Profiles of couple ("Hope").

1945, Dec. 3 **Photo.** *Perf. 14*
100 A42 1p rose pink & choc, pair .18 .15
a. Single, English .15 .15
b. Single, Afrikaans .15 .15
101 A43 2p vio & sl bl, pair .22 .15
a. Single, English .15 .15
b. Single, Afrikaans .15 .15
102 A43 3p ultra & dp ultra, pair .32 .28
a. Single, English .15 .15
b. Single, Afrikaans .15 .15
Nos. 100-102 (3) .72 .58

World War II victory of the Allies.

George VI A44

King George VI and Queen Elizabeth A45

Princesses Margaret Rose and Elizabeth A46

1947, Feb. 17 **Wmk. 201** *Perf. 15x14*
103 A44 1p cer & gray, pair .15 .15
a. Single, English .15 .15
b. Single, Afrikaans .15 .15
104 A45 2p purple, pair .16 .15
a. Single, English .15 .15
b. Single, Afrikaans .15 .15
105 A46 3p dk blue, pair .30 .24
a. Single, English .15 .15
b. Single, Afrikaans .15 .15
Nos. 103-105 (3) .61 .54

Visit of the British Royal Family, Mar.-Apr., 1947.

George VI, Elizabeth — A47

Gold Mine — A48

1948, Apr. 26 **Photo.** *Perf. 14*
106 A47 3p dp chlky bl & sil, pair .50 .30
a. Single, English .15 .15
b. Single, Afrikaans .15 .15

25th anniv. of the marriage of George VI and Queen Elizabeth.

Vertical Pairs Perf. 14 all around, Rouletted 6½ between

1948, Apr.
107 A48 1½p sl & ocher, vert. pair .16 .15
a. Single, English .15 .15
b. Single, Afrikaans .15 .15

"Wanderer" in Port Natal — A49

1949, May 2 **Photo.** *Perf. 15x14*
108 A49 1½p red brown, pair .25 .15
a. Single, English .15 .15
b. Single, Afrikaans .15 .15

Mercury and Globe — A50

1949, Oct. 1 *Perf. 14x15*
109 A50 ½p dk green, pair .60 .24
a. Single, English .15 .15
b. Single, Afrikaans .15 .15
110 A50 1½p dk red, pair 1.00 .24
a. Single, English .15 .15
b. Single, Afrikaans .15 .15
111 A50 3p ultra, pair 1.50 .60
a. Single, English .15 .15
b. Single, Afrikaans .15 .15
Nos. 109-111 (3) 3.10 1.08

75th anniv. of the UPU.

Except for Nos. 216, 310-313, 518a, 669a this is the end of bi-lingual multiples in the postage section

Voortrekkers en Route to Natal — A51

Voortrekker Monument, Pretoria A52

Voortrekkers Looking Toward Natal, and Open Bible — A53

1949, Dec. 1 *Perf. 15x14*
112 A51 1p magenta .15 .15
113 A52 1½p dull green .15 .15
114 A53 3p dark blue .18 .15
Set value .34 .22

Inauguration of the Voortrekker Monument at Pretoria.

Riebeeck's Seal and Dutch East India Company Monogram
A54

Maria de la Quellerie — A55

Designs: 2p, van Riebeeck's Ships. 4½p, Jan van Riebeeck. 1sh, Landing of van Riebeeck.

Perf. 15x14, 14x15

1952, Mar. 14 Wmk. 201

115	A54	½p dk brn & red vio	.15	.15
116	A55	1p dark green	.15	.15
117	A54	2p dark purple	.15	.15
118	A55	4½p dark blue	.18	.18
119	A54	1sh brown	.55	.50
		Set value	1.00	.85

300th anniv. of the landing of Jan van Riebeeck at the Cape of Good Hope.

Nos. 116-117 Overprinted "SATISE" (1p) and "SADIPU" (2p)

1952, Mar. 26

120	A55	1p dark green	.18	.15
121	A54	2p dark purple	.22	.18

South African Tercentenary Intl. Stamp Exhib., Cape Town, Mar. 26-Apr. 5, 1952.

Coronation Issue

Queen Elizabeth II — A97

1953, June 3 *Perf. 14x15*

192	A97	2p violet blue	.20	.15

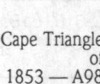

Cape Triangle of 1853 — A98

1953, Sept. 1 *Perf. 15x14*

193	A98	1p red & dk brown	.15	.15
194	A98	4p blue & indigo	.25	.20
		Set value	.33	.26

Cent. of the introduction of postage stamps in South Africa.

Merino Ram and Sheep — A99

1953, Oct. 1 *Perf. 14*

195	A99	4½p shown	.70	.30
196	A99	1sh3p Springbok	2.50	.18
197	A99	1sh6p Aloes	2.00	.40
		Nos. 195-197 (3)	5.20	.88

Arms of Orange Free State, Pen and Scroll
A100

1954, Feb. 23 *Perf. 15x14*

198	A100	2p red org & dk brown	.15	.15
199	A100	4½p gray & rose violet	.25	.25
		Set value	.35	.33

Orange Free State centenary.

Wart Hog
A101

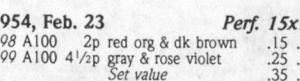

White Rhinoceros
A102

Lion — A103

1954, Oct. 14 *Perf. 15x14*

200	A101	½p shown	.15	.15
201	A101	1p Gnu	.15	.15
202	A101	1½p Leopard	.15	.15
203	A101	2p Zebra	.15	.15

Perf. 14

204	A102	3p shown	.15	.15
205	A102	4p Elephant	.22	.15
206	A102	4½p Hippopotamus	1.40	.70
207	A103	6p shown	.42	.15
208	A102	1sh Kudu	.95	.15
209	A103	1sh3p Springbok	1.40	.15
210	A102	1sh6p Gemsbok	1.75	.32
211	A102	2sh6p Nyala	2.00	.18
212	A102	5sh Giraffe	13.00	.75
213	A102	10sh Sable antelope	19.00	2.00
		Nos. 200-213 (14)	40.89	
		Set value		4.50

See Nos. 221-228, 241-244, 247, 250-253.

Paul Kruger — A104

Portrait: 6p, Martinus Wessels Pretorius.

Perf. 14x15

1955, Oct. 21 Photo. Wmk. 201

214	A104	3p slate green	.25	.15
215	A104	6p brown violet	.50	.25

Centenary of Pretoria.

Andries Pretorius, Church of the Vow and Flag of Natalia — A105

German Wagon and House — A106

1955, Dec. 1 *Perf. 14*

Inscribed alternately in English and Afrikaans.

216	A105	2p ultra & cer, pair	.75	.45
a.		Single, English	.15	.15
b.		Single, Afrikaans	.15	.15

Union Covenant Celebrations, Pietermaritzburg, Dec. 13-18, 1955.

1958, July 1 *Perf. 14*

218	A106	2p pale lilac & brown	.15	.15

Cent. of the arrival of German settlers.

Seal of Academy
A107

Perf. 15x14

1959, May 1 Photo. Wmk. 201

219	A107	3p brt blue & dk blue	.18	.15
a.		Dark blue omitted	2,000.	

50th anniv. of the South African Academy of Science and Art, Pretoria.

Globe Showing Antarctica and South Africa — A108

Perf. 14x15

1959, Nov. 16 Wmk. 330

220	A108	3p blue grn, brn & org	.20	.15

South African Natl. Antarctic Expedition.

Animal Types of 1954

1959-60 Wmk. 330 *Perf. 15x14*

221	A101	½p Wart hog ('60)	.35	.65
222	A101	1p Gnu	.15	.15
a.		Redrawn	.42	.22

Perf. 14

223	A102	3p White rhinoceros	.42	.15
224	A102	4p Elephant	1.10	.35
225	A103	6p Lion	2.25	.15
226	A102	1sh Kudu	3.25	.15
227	A102	2sh6p Nyala	10.00	6.50
228	A102	5sh Giraffe ('60)	21.00	20.00
		Nos. 221-228 (8)	38.52	28.10

On No. 222a, the numeral "1" is centered above "S." On No. 222, "1" is slightly to right of "S."

Prime Ministers Botha, Smuts, Hertzog, Malan, Strydom and Verwoerd
A109

Flag and Notes from National Anthem — A110

Pushing Wheel Uphill
A111

Designs: 6p, Arms of the Union and of four provinces. 1sh6p, Official Union festival emblem.

Perf. 14x15, 15x14

1960 Photo. Wmk. 330

235	A109	3p chocolate	.20	.15
236	A110	4p lt blue & red org	.30	.15
237	A110	6p yel grn, red & brn	.45	.20
238	A111	1sh yel, dk bl & blk	.75	.20
239	A111	1sh6p lt blue & blk	2.75	1.75
		Nos. 235-239 (5)	4.45	2.45

50th anniv. of the founding of the Union.

See Nos. 245-246, 248-249.

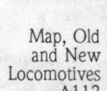

Map, Old and New Locomotives
A112

1960, May 2 *Perf. 15x14*

240	A112	1sh3p dark blue	3.50	.90

Centenary of railways in South Africa.

Types of 1954 and 1960.

Designs: ½c, Wart hog. 1c, Gnu. 1½c, Leopard. 2c, Zebra. 2½c, Prime Ministers. 3½c, Flag and music notes. 5c, Lion. 7½c, Arms of Union and four provinces. 10c, Pushing wheel uphill. 12½c, Springbok. 20c, Gemsbok. 50c, Giraffe. 1r, Sable antelope.

Perf. 15x14, 14x15, 14 (A102, A103)

1961, Feb. 14 Photo. Wmk. 330

241	A101	½c dk bluish green	.15	.15
242	A101	1c rose brown	.15	.15
243	A101	1½c sepia	.15	.15
244	A101	2c purple	.16	.15
245	A109	2½c chocolate	.30	.15
246	A110	3½c lt bl & red org	.50	.15
247	A103	5c orange & dk brn	.60	.15
248	A110	7½c yel grn, red & brn	.75	.15
249	A111	10c yel, dk bl & blk	.85	.15
250	A103	12½c dull grn & dk brn	1.25	.15
251	A102	20c pink & dk brown	2.25	.42
252	A102	50c org yel & blk brn	9.25	2.00
253	A102	1r blue & black	21.00	8.50
		Nos. 241-253 (13)	37.36	12.42

Republic

Natal Pigmy Kingfisher
A112a

Coral Tree Flower
A112b

Pouring Gold
A113

Groot Constantia
A114

Designs: 1½c, Afrikander bull. 3c, Crimson-breasted shrike. 5c, Baobab tree. 7½c, Corn. 10c, Castle entrance, Cape Town. 12½c, Protea flower. 20c, Secretary bird. 50c, Cape Town, harbor. 1r, Bird of Paradise flower.

Two types of 2½c.

Type I - Lines of building faint.

Type II - Lines of building very strong; strong line between bottom of building and top of name panel.

Perf. 14x15, 15x14

1961, May 31 Photo. Wmk. 330

254	A112a	½c blue, mag & brn	.15	.15
a.		Perf. 14x13½ ('63)	.15	.15
255	A112b	1c gray & red	.15	.15
256	A112a	1½c brown carmine	.15	.15
		Nos. 254-256 (3)	.45	.45

Perf. 14

257	A113	2c ultra & orange	.15	.15
258	A114	2½c violet & grn (I)	.32	.15
a.		Type II	.40	.15
259	A113	3c pink, dk bl & red	.28	.15
260	A114	5c grnsh bl & yel	.35	.15
261	A114	7½c emerald & brn	.55	.15
a.		Brown omitted		
262	A114	10c emer & dk brn	.70	.15
263	A114	12½c dk grn, red & yel	1.65	.15
a.		Yellow omitted		
264	A114	20c sal, sl bl & pink	4.00	.30
265	A113	50c ultra & blk	32.50	1.65
266	A113	1r blue, org & grn	22.50	1.90
		Nos. 254-266 (13)	63.45	
		Set value		4.35

1961-63 Unwmk. *Perf. 15x14*

269	A112b	1c gray & red	.25	.15

Perf. 14

270	A113	2c ultra & org ('63)	.40	.15
271	A114	2½c violet & grn (II)	.45	.15
272	A113	3c pink, dk bl & red	.45	.15
273	A114	5c grnsh blue & yel	.75	.15
274	A114	7½c emer & brn ('62)	1.10	.15
275	A114	10c green & dk brn	1.50	.15
276	A114	20c sal, sl bl & pink ('63)	17.00	.40
277	A113	50c ultra & blk ('62)	24.00	3.25
		Nos. 269-277 (9)	45.90	
		Set value		4.25

See Nos. 289-298, 317-322, 324, 326-338, 340-342, 376-377, 379-382, 383-385 and designs A135-A136.

Boeing 707
and Bleriot
Monoplane
A115

Folk Dancers
A116

Perf. 14x15

1961, Dec. 1   Photo.   Wmk. 330
280 A115   3c blue & red   .50 .15
  50th anniv. of South Africa's 1st air mail.

1962, Mar. 1
281 A116   2½c lt brn, choc & red org   .25 .15
  50th anniv. of folk dancing in South Africa.

"Chapman"
Arriving in
1820
A117

Perf. 15x14

1962, Aug. 20   Photo.   Wmk. 330
282 A117   2½c dp plum & bl grn   .35 .15
283 A117   12½c choc & blue   3.00 1.50
  Unveiling of the precinct stone of the British
Settlers Monument at Grahamstown.

Red Disa Orchid, Castle Rock,
Kirstenbosch Botanic Gardens
A118

1963, Mar. 14   Perf. 14
284 A118   2½c multicolored   .35 .15
  50th anniv. of the Kirstenbosch Botanic Gardens,
Cape Town.

Centenary Emblem and
Nurse — A119

  Design: 12½c, Centenary emblem and globe,
horiz.

1963, Aug. 30   Wmk. 348   Perf. 14
285 A119   2½c rose claret, blk &
              red   .35 .15

Perf. 15x14
286 A119   12½c dk bl gray & red   3.50 1.60
  a.   Red Cross omitted   1,000.
  Centenary of the International Red Cross.

Assembly
Seat, Bunga
Building,
Umtata
A120

Perf. 14½x14

1963, Dec. 11   Wmk. 348
287 A120   2½c dk brown & lt grn   .30 .15
  a.   Light green omitted   850.00
  Transkei Legislative Assembly, 1st meeting.

Types of 1961
Perf. 15x14, 14x15

1963-67   Photo.   Wmk. 348
Colors as Before
289 A112b   1c   .15 .15
290 A112a   1½c ('67)   1.40 .35

Perf. 14
291 A113   2c ('64)   .15 .15
292 A114   2½c (II) ('64)   .15 .15
293 A114   5c ('66)   1.10 .15
294 A114   7½c ('66)   7.00 .15
295 A114   10c ('64)   .55 .15
296 A114   20c ('64)   1.25 .28
297 A113   50c ('66)   35.00 3.50
298 A113   1r ('64)   60.00 21.00
  Nos. 289-298 (10)   106.75 26.03

Rugby Board Emblem,
Springbok and
Ball — A121

John
Calvin — A122

  Design: 12½c, Rugby player diving over goal
line, horiz.

Perf. 14x15, 15x14

1964, May 8   Photo.   Wmk. 348
301 A121   2½c dk green & brn   .25 .15
302 A121   12½c yellow grn & blk 3.75 2.50
  South African Rugby Board, 75th anniv.

1964, July 10   Perf. 14
303 A122   2½c choc, brt car & violet   .35 .15
  John Calvin (1509-64), French theologian and
leader of the Reformation.

Nurse's Lamp — A123

  Design: 12½c, Nurse holding lamp, horiz.

Perf. 14x15, 15x14

1964, Oct. 12   Photo.   Wmk. 348
304 A123   2½c dp & ultra   .24 .15
305 A123   12½c ultra & gold   2.75 2.75
  a.   Gold omitted   800.00
  South African Nursing Assoc., 50th anniv.

ITU Emblem
and Satellites
A124

  Design: 12½c, ITU emblem, old and new communication equipment.

1965, May 17   Perf. 15x14
306 A124   2½c brt blue & org   .28 .15
307 A124   12½c green & claret   3.00 2.50
  Cent. of the ITU.

Pulpit, Groote Kerk,
Cape Town
A125

Diamond
A126

  Design: 12½c, Emblem of Dutch Reformed
Church of South Africa, horiz.

1965, Oct. 21   Photo.   Wmk. 348
308 A125   2½c dp brown & yel   .28 .15
309 A125   12½c lt ultra, ocher & blk 3.25 2.75
  Tercentenary of the Dutch Reformed Church in
South Africa.

1966, May 31   Perf. 14
  Designs: 2½c, Flying bird, symbol of freedom
and the future, horiz. 3c, Corn. 7½c, Table Mountain, horiz. Inscribed alternately in English and
Afrikaans.

310 A126   1c blk, yel, dk &
              lt grn, pair   .50 .50
  a.   Single, English   .15 .15
  b.   Single, Afrikaans   .15 .15
311 A126   2½c dk bl, ultra & yel
              grn, pair   1.25 1.25
  a.   Single, English   .15 .15
  b.   Single, Afrikaans   .15 .15

Perf. 14x15, 15x14
312 A126   3c red brn, red & yel,
              pair   2.50 2.50
  a.   Single, English   .15 .15
  b.   Single, Afrikaans   .15 .15
313 A126   7½c ultra, vio bl, ocher
              & blk, pair   7.00 7.00
  a.   Single, English   .50 .40
  b.   Single, Afrikaans   .50 .40
  Nos. 310-313 (4)   11.25 11.25
  5th anniversary of the Republic.

Hendrik F.
Verwoerd and
Union
Buildings,
Pretoria
A127

  Designs: 3c, Verwoerd's portrait, vert. 12½c,
Verwoerd and map of South Africa.

Perf. 15x14, 14x15

1966, Dec. 6   Photo.   Wmk. 348
314 A127   2½c grnsh blue & blk   .18 .15
315 A127   3c yellow grn & blk   .25 .15
316 A127   12½c dull blue & blk 1.65 1.40
  Nos. 314-316 (3)   2.08 1.70
  Issued in memory of Dr. Hendrik F. Verwoerd
(1901-1966), Prime Minister.

Types of 1961 Redrawn and

Industry — A128

(Inscriptions in larger, bolder type)

½c, 1½c
and 1r

On the 1r, the "N" of "VAN" is over the final "A"
of "AFRIKA." On Nos. 286 and 298, the "N" is
over "KA."

1c, 7½c and 12½c

2½c, 5c, 10c and 20c

2c, 3c and
50c (similar)

Perf. 14x15, 15x14

1964-68   Photo.   Wmk. 348
Colors as Before
317 A112a   ½c   .16 .15
  a.   Imperf., pair   400.00
318 A112b   1c   .25 .15

Perf. 14
319 A113   2c ('68)   .28 .15
320 A113   2½c   .32 .15
321 A113   3c   .55 .15
322 A113   12½c   2.25 .15

---

323 A128   15c ('67)   5.00 .15
324 A113   1r   16.00 2.50
  Nos. 317-324 (8)   24.81
    Set value   3.00
    See No. 339.

  Redrawn Types of 1964-68

  Designs: 4c, Groot Constantia (like 2½c). 6c,
Corn (like 7½c). 9c, Protea flower (like 12½c).

1967-71   Photo.   Wmk. 359
326 A112a   ½c   .18 .15
327 A112b   1c   .24 .15
328 A112a   1½c   .30 .15
329 A114   2c ('68)   .30 .15
330 A114   2½c   .35 .15
331 A113   3c   .35 .15
332 A114   4c ('71)   .48 .15
333 A114   5c ('68)   .75 .15
334 A114   6c ('71)   .90 .15
335 A114   7½c   1.50 .15
336 A114   9c ('71)   1.50 .15
337 A114   10c ('68)   1.90 .15
338 A114   12½c ('70)   3.00 .15
339 A128   15c ('69)   3.00 .15
340 A114   20c ('68)   3.00 .25
341 A113   50c ('68)   7.25 .60
342 A113   1r ('68)   15.00 1.50
  Nos. 326-342 (17)   40.00
    Set value   3.00

  Luminescence
  Starting in 1969, South Africa began
to add phosphorescent "frames" to its
definitive stamps.
  In 1971, stamps began to appear with
the phosphorescent element throughout
the paper.
  Phosphorescent commemoratives
include Nos. 357, 359 et cetera.

Martin Luther
A129

Door of
Wittenberg
Church
A130

Perf. 14x15

1967, Oct. 31   Litho.   Wmk. 348
343 A129   2½c pink & black   .22 .15

Wmk. 359
344 A130   12½c black & orange 2.25 2.00
  450th anniversary of the Reformation.

Pres. J. J.
Fouché — A133

James B. M.
Hertzog
Statue — A134

  Design: 12½c, Full-face portrait.

Perf. 14x15

1968, Apr. 10   Photo.   Wmk. 348
345 A133   2½c lt rose brn & dk
              brn   .35 .15
346 A133   12½c grysh bl & vio bl 2.75 2.25

Wmk. 359
347 A133   12½c grysh bl & vio bl 2.75 2.25
  Nos. 345-347 (3)   5.85 4.65
  Pres. Jacobus Johannes Fouché, inauguration.

Perf. 13½x14, 14x13½

1968, Sept. 21 Photo.   Wmk. 359
  Designs: 2½c, Hertzog in 1902, with hat, horiz.
3c, Hertzog in 1924, horiz.

348 A134   2½c dk brn, lem & blk .20 .15

Wmk. 348

349 A134   3c multicolored   .32   .15
350 A134   12½c org brn, org & blk   2.00 1.75
        Nos. 348-350 (3)   2.52 2.05

Unveiling of a monument in Bloemfontein honoring James Barry Munnik Hertzog (1866-1942), Boer general, prime minister of South Africa (1924-39).

Natal Pigmy Kingfisher A135   Kaffir Boom Flower A136

1969   Wmk. 359   Photo.   Perf. 14

351 A135   ½c blue & multi   .18   .15
 a.   Perf. 14x14½ (coil)   .50   .20
352 A136   1c grysh brown & multi   .18   .15
        Set value   .16
           See Nos. 374-375.

Springbok, Torch and Rings — A137

1969, Mar. 15   Perf. 14x13½

353 A137   2½c olive, ind & red   .18   .15
354 A137   12½c bister, ind & red   1.90 1.75

South African Natl. Games, Bloemfontein, Mar. 15-Apr. 19.

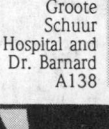

Groote Schuur Hospital and Dr. Barnard A138

Hands Holding Heart A139

Perf. 13½x14

1969, July 7   Photo.   Wmk. 348

355 A138   2½c dp rose, pink & plum   .32   .15

Wmk. 359   Perf. 15x14

356 A139   12½c dp bl & dp car   3.25 2.50

1st heart transplant operation (by Dr. Christiaan Barnard) and opening of the 47th South African Medical Cong., Pretoria.

Stagecoach of 1869 A140

Transvaal No. 1 — A141    Water Drop and Flower — A142

Perf. 13½x14, 14x13½

1969, Oct. 6   Photo.   Wmk. 359

357 A140   2½c ocher, Prus bl & yel   .35   .15
358 A141   12½c salmon, grn & gold   3.00 2.25
        Centenary of South African postage stamps.

1970, Feb. 14   Perf. 14

Design: 3c, Waves, horiz.

359 A142   2½c brn, brt bl & grn   .16   .15
360 A142   3c pale gray, bl & indigo   .35   .22
        Set value   .27

Issued to publicize the Water 70 campaign of the Department of Water Affairs.

Sower — A143

"BIBLIA" A144

1970, Aug. 24   Photo.   Perf. 14

361 A143   2½c multicolored   .28   .15

Photo; Gold Impressed

362 A144   12½c ultra, blk & gold   3.00 2.50
        150th anniv. of the South African Bible Soc.

Strijdom Tower, Johannes G. Strijdom — A145

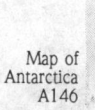 

Map of Antarctica A146

Perf. 14x13½, 13½x14

1971, May 22   Photo.   Wmk. 359

363 A145   5c blue, yel & blk   .60   .20
364 A146   12½c grnsh bl, vio bl &
               red   8.00 7.00
        Nos. 363-365 (3)   9.85 8.10

Wmk. 330

365 A145   5c blue, yel & blk   1.25   .90

Intl. Stamp Exhib. (INTERSTEX), Cape Town, May 22-31. No. 364 also for the 10th anniv. of the Antarctic Treaty pledging peaceful uses of and scientific cooperation in Antarctica.

Landing of British Settlers, 1820, by Thomas Baines A147

Martinus Steyn, Paul Kruger, Unification Monument — A148

1971, May 31   Wmk. 359

366 A147   2c magenta & rose red   .15   .15
367 A148   4c blue green & blk   .30   .15
        Set value   .18

10th anniv. of the Republic of South Africa.

Hendrik Verwoerd Dam A149

1972, Mar. 4   Photo.   Perf. 14

Size: 37x22mm

368 A149   4c shown   .26   .15
369 A149   5c Aerial view of dam   .45   .15

Size: 57x22mm

370 A149   10c Dam, reservoir and
                 Verwoerd   1.50   .90
        Nos. 368-370 (3)   2.21 1.20

Inauguration of the Hendrik F. Verwoerd Dam of the Orange River Project.

Ram's Head and Wool Mark — A150    Lamb and Wool Mark — A151

1972, May 15   Wmk. 359   Perf. 14

371 A150   4c blue & multi   .18   .15
372 A151   15c dull bl & dk bl   .85   .40

South African wool industry. Issued in sheets of 100 with advertisements in margin. See Nos. 378-378A, 382A.

Cats — A152   Pylon — A153

1972, Sept. 19   Wmk. 359

373 A152   5c multicolored   1.25   .25
           Centenary of the SPCA.

Redrawn Types of 1964-69 and Types of 1972

Perf. 14x15 (½c), 14 (1c, #382A), 12½

1972-74		Photo.	Unwmk.	
374	A135	½c blue & multi	1.00	.15
375	A136	1c grysh brn & red	.15	.15
376	A113	2c brt blue & org	.50	.15
377	A113	3c rose red & bluish		
		black	.55	.15
378	A150	4c blue & multi	.85	.15
378A	A150	4c brown & multi	.32	.15
379	A114	5c grnsh bl & yel	1.00	.15
380	A114	6c emerald & brn	1.40	.15
381	A114	9c dk grn, red & yel	2.25	.35
382	A114	10c emer & dk brn	2.50	.15
382A	A151	15c dull bl & dk bl	2.75	.85
383	A114	20c sal, sl bl & pink	2.75	.55
384	A113	50c ultra & black	7.25	2.25
385	A113	1r blue, org & grn	41.95	5.00
		Nos. 374-385 (13)	41.95	10.20

Issue years: 2c, 1972. 6c, 15c, 1974. Others, 1973.

1973, Feb. 1   Photo.   Perf. 12x12½

Designs: 4c, Electrical usage, pylon, power plant, horiz. 15c, Smokestacks.

Size: 37½x20mm

386 A153   4c blue & multi   .25   .15

Size: 20x27mm

Perf. 12½

387 A153   5c blue & black   .35   .15
388 A153   15c ocher & multi   3.75 1.50
        Nos. 386-388 (3)   4.35 1.80

Electricity Supply Commission, 50th anniv.

Arms of University — A154    Old University, Cape Town — A156

New University, Pretoria A155

1973, Apr. 2   Unwmk.   Perf. 12½

389 A154   4c blue & multi   .28   .15

Perf. 12x12½
Wmk. 359

390 A155   5c gold & multi   .38   .18

Unwmk.   Perf. 12½

391 A156   15c gold & blk   3.25 1.65

Cent. of the Univ. of South Africa (UNISA).

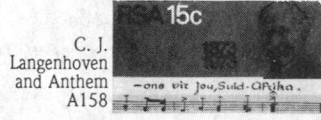

Woltemade, Sailor and Horse A157

Designs: 5c, Sinking ship in storm. 15c, "De Jonge Thomas" sinking.

1973, June 2   Photo.   Perf. 12x12½

392 A157   4c brown red, ol & blk   .26   .18
393 A157   5c olive, blk & citron   .45   .20
394 A157   15c brown, blk & ocher   5.50 4.50
        Nos. 392-394 (3)   6.21 4.88

Bicentenary of Wolraad Woltemade's heroism in saving 14 people from the ship "De Jonge Thomas" in Table Bay.

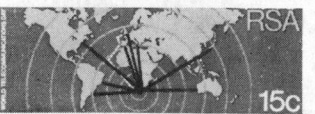

C. J. Langenhoven and Anthem A158

Designs: 4c, 5c, vert., Portrait and signature.

1973, Aug. 1   Perf. 12½

Size: 27x20mm

395 A158   4c orange, blk & ultra   .48   .15

Perf. 12½x12, 12x12½

Size: 21x38mm, 37x21mm

396 A158   5c orange, blk & ultra   .60   .15
397 A158   15c orange, blk & ultra   3.00 1.00
        Nos. 395-397 (3)   4.08 1.30

Cornelis Jacob Langenhoven (1873-1932), lawyer, writer, who worked for recognition of Afrikaans language.

World Map and Communications Network — A159

Perf. 12½

1973, Oct. 1   Photo.   Unwmk.

398 A159   15c ultra & multi   2.00 1.65
 a.   Wmk. 359   3.00 2.25
        International Telecommunications Day.

Restored Houses, Tulbagh — A160

Design: 5c, Church Street, Tulbagh.

1974, Mar. 14   Unwmk.   Perf. 12½

Size: 27x21mm

400 A160   4c Prus green & multi   .24   .15

Size: 57x20mm

401 A160 5c ocher & multi .45 .15
  Set value .22
Restoration of historic Church Street in Tulbagh after 1969 earthquake.

Burgerspond A161 — Prime Minister D. F. Malan A162

1974, Apr. 7 Photo. Perf. 12¹/₂x12
402 A161 9c multicolored .70 .52
Centenary of the first official coin struck in South Africa, 1874. The £1 gold coin shows portrait of Pres. Thomas Francois Burger.

1974, May 22 Photo. Unwmk.
403 A162 4c lt ultra & dk blue .30 .15
Centenary of the birth of Daniel F. Malan (1874-1959), prime minister of South Africa.

Congress Emblem A163

1974, June 13 Perf. 12x12¹/₂
404 A163 15c silver & dk blue 1.75 .50
15th World Sugar Cong., Durban, June 13-30.

"50" A164

1974, July 13 Photo. Unwmk.
405 A164 4c red & black .32 .15
50th anniversary of radio in South Africa.

Cultural Center, Grahamstown — A165

1974, July 13 Perf. 12x12¹/₂
406 A165 5c red & black .32 .15
Natl. Monument to British settlers of 1820.

Natal No. 78, Transvaal No. 145, Cape of Good Hope No. 28 and Orange River Colony No. 4 — A166

1974, Oct. 9 Photo. Perf. 12¹/₂
407 A166 15c multicolored 1.50 .90
Centenary of Universal Postal Union.

Wild Iris — A167 — Cape Gannet — A168

Galjoen — A169

Bokmakierie (Shrike) A170

Designs: 2c, Heather. 3c, Geranium. 4c, Calla lily. 7c, Zebrafish. 9c, Angelfish. 10c, Moorish idol. 14c, Roman fish. 15c, Greater double-collared sunbird. 20c, Yellow-billed hornbill. 25c, Barberton daisy. 50c, Blue cranes. 1r, Bateleur eagles.

Photo. and Engr.
1974, Nov. 11 Unwmk. Perf. 12¹/₂
408 A167 1c pink & multi .15 .15
409 A167 2c yellow & multi .15 .15
410 A167 3c multicolored .15 .15
411 A167 4c multicolored .15 .15
412 A168 5c dull blue & multi .20 .15
413 A169 6c multicolored .25 .15
414 A169 7c lilac & multi .30 .15
415 A169 9c buff & multi .35 .15
416 A169 10c lt blue & multi .40 .20
417 A169 14c salmon & multi .60 .20
418 A168 15c gray & multi .60 .20
419 A168 20c yellow & multi .80 .30
420 A167 25c dk brown & multi 1.10 .35

Perf. 12x12¹/₂
421 A170 30c gray & multi 4.50 .75
422 A170 50c citron & multi 4.00 1.00
423 A170 1r multicolored 7.50 2.00
  Nos. 408-423 (16) 21.20 6.20
The coils that follow are two colors while the above sheet stamps are multicolored.

1974 Photo. Coil Stamps Perf. 12¹/₂
430 A167 1c pink & violet .25 .15
431 A167 2c yellow & grn .25 .15
432 A168 5c dull blue & blk .35 .18
433 A169 10c lt blue & indigo .85 .70
  Nos. 430-433 (4) 1.70 1.18

See note on color that follows No. 423.

1975-76 Perf. 14
Same Designs
430a A167 1c .15 .15
431a A167 2c ('76) .15 .15
433a A169 10c ('76) .75 .70
  Nos. 430a-433a (3) 1.05 1.00
No. 430a has black control number on back of every fifth stamp.

Voortrekker Monument and Encampment — A171

1974, Dec. 6 Unwmk. Perf. 12¹/₂
438 A171 4c multicolored .35 .15
Voortrekker Monument, 25th anniversary.

Sasolburg Refinery A172

Perf. 12x12¹/₂, 12¹/₂
1975, Feb. 26 Litho.
439 A172 15c red & multi 1.50 .90
25th anniversary of South Africa Coal, Oil and Gas Corp., Ltd. (SASOL).

Pres. Nicolaes Diederichs — A173 — Jan C. Smuts — A174

Litho. and Engr.
1975, Apr. 19 Perf. 12¹/₂x12
440 A173 4c brown & gold .15 .15

Litho.
441 A173 15c ultra & gold .85 .85
Installation of Dr. Nicolaes Diederichs as third State President.

1975, May 24 Litho. and Engraved
442 A174 4c black .30 .15
Smuts (1870-1950), lawyer, gen., statesman.

Dutch East Indiaman, by Baines A175

Designs: Paintings by John Thomas Baines.

1975, June 18 Photo. Perf. 12x12¹/₂
443 A175 5c gold & multi .22 .15
444 A175 9c gold & multi .45 .40
445 A175 15c gold & multi .80 .65
446 A175 30c gold & multi 1.50 1.50
  a. Souvenir sheet of 4 4.50 4.50
  Nos. 443-446 (4) 2.97 2.70
John Thomas Baines (1820-1875), painter. No. 446a contains 4 litho. stamps similar to Nos. 443-446.

Gideon Malherbe House, Paarl — A176

Photo. and Engr.
1975, Aug. 14 Perf. 12¹/₂
447 A176 4c multicolored .30 .15
Society of Real Afrikanders (Genootskap of Regte Afrikaaners), cent.

Automatic Letter Sorting — A177

1975, Sept. 11 Photo. Perf. 12¹/₂x12
448 A177 4c brt blue & multi .30 .15
Postal automation.

Title Page, First Afrikaans Paper — A178 — Afrikaans Monument, Paarl — A179

1975, Oct. 10 Litho. Perf. 12¹/₂x12
449 A178 4c black & orange .20 .15
450 A179 5c multicolored .28 .15
  Set value .18
Inauguration of Afrikaans Language Monument.

Table Mountain — A180

1975, Nov. 13 Litho. Perf. 12¹/₂
451 A180 15c shown 1.75 1.50
452 A180 15c Johannesburg 1.75 1.50
453 A180 15c Cape vineyards 1.75 1.50
454 A180 15c Lions, Kruger Natl. Park 1.75 1.50
  a. Block of 4, #451-454 7.00 7.00
Tourist publicity.

Satellites, Radar and Africa on Globe — A181

1975, Dec. 3 Litho. Perf. 12¹/₂
455 A181 15c dk vio blue & multi .75 .50
Satellite communications.

Lawn Bowler — A182

Designs: No. 457, Cricket batsman. No. 458, Polo player. No. 459, Golfer (Gary Player).

1976 Photo. Perf. 12¹/₂x12
456 A182 15c green & blk .60 .35
457 A182 15c yellow grn & blk .60 .35
458 A182 15c olive & blk .60 .35
459 A182 15c brt green & blk .60 .35
  a. Miniature sheet of 4, #456-459 3.75 2.75
  Nos. 456-459 (4) 2.40 1.40
3rd World Bowling Championships, Zoo Lake Club, Johannesburg, Feb. 1976 (No. 456); cent. of cricket in South Africa (No. 457); Intl. polo (No. 458); Gary Player, South African golf champion (No. 459).
Issue dates: #456, Feb. 18. #457, Mar. 12. #458, Aug. 16. #459, 459a, Dec. 2.

No. 456 Overprinted in Gold

WÊRELDKAMPIOENE WORLD CHAMPIONS

1976, Apr. 6 Photo. Perf. 12¹/₂x12
460 A182 15c green & black .45 .52
Victory of South Africa in 3rd World Bowling championships.

Picnic under Baobab Tree — A183

Paintings by Erich Mayer: 10c, Wagons at Foot of Blauberg, Transvaal. 15c, Hartbeesspoort Dam, near Pretorial. 20c, Street in Doornfontein.

1976, Apr. 20 Photo. Perf. 12x12¹/₂
461 A183 4c ocher & multi .28 .15
462 A183 10c dk green & multi .55 .45
463 A183 15c multicolored .80 .60

464 A183 20c multicolored	1.40	1.00
a. Souvenir sheet of 4, #461-464	4.00	4.00
Nos. 461-464 (4)	3.03	2.20

Erich Mayer (1876-1960), painter. Artist's signature in horizontal gutter between 2 se-tenant pairs.

Wildlife
Protection
A184

1976, June 5 Litho.   Perf. 12x12½

465 A184 3c Cheetah	.25	.15
466 A184 10c Black rhinoceros	.48	.35
467 A184 15c Biesbok	.95	.70
468 A184 20c Zebra	1.25	.95
Nos. 465-468 (4)	2.93	2.15

Emily Hobhouse, by Johan
Hoekstra — A185

1976, June 8 Photo.   Perf. 12½x12

469 A185 4c multicolored   .25 .15

Emily Hobhouse (1860-1926), the "Angel of Mercy" during Anglo-Boer War.

S.S.
Dunrobin
Castle, 1876
A186

1976, Oct. 5 Litho.   Perf. 12x12½

470 A186 10c multicolored   .75 .30

Ocean Mail Service contract, centenary.

Family with
Globe — A187

1976, Nov. 6 Photo.   Perf. 12½x12

471 A187 4c salmon & dull red   .28 .15

Family planning.

Wine
Glasses — A188

Jacob Daniel
du
Toit — A189

1977, Feb. 14 Litho.   Perf. 12½x12

472 A188 15c multicolored   .50 .25

Quality of the Vintage Symposium, Cape Town, Feb. 14-21.

1977, Feb. 21   Photo.

473 A189 4c multicolored   .28 .15

Dr. Jacob Daniel du Toit (Totius; 1877-1953), theologian, educator, poet.

Transvaal
Supreme
Court
A190

1977, May 18 Photo.   Perf. 12x12½

474 A190 4c red brown   .28 .15

Transvaal Supreme Court, centenary.

Sugarbush (Protea
Repens) — A191

**Photo. (1-5, 8, 10, 15, 20c); Litho.
(others)**

1977, May 27   Perf. 12½

475 A191 1c shown	.15	.15
476 A191 2c P. punctata	.15	.15
477 A191 3c P. neriifolia	.15	.15
478 A191 4c P. longifolia	.15	.15
479 A191 5c P. cynaroides	.15	.15
480 A191 6c P. canaliculata	.15	.15
481 A191 7c P. lorea	.15	.15
482 A191 8c P. mundii	.15	.15
483 A191 9c P. roupelliae	.16	.15
484 A191 10c P. aristata	.18	.15
485 A191 15c P. eximia	.28	.15
486 A191 20c P. magnifica	.38	.15
487 A191 25c P. grandiceps	.48	.18
488 A191 30c P. amplexicaulis	.55	.18
489 A191 50c Leucospermum cordifolium	1.00	.32
490 A191 1r Paranomus reflexus	2.00	.65
491 A191 2r Orothamnus zeyheri	3.75	1.25
Nos. 475-491 (17)	9.98	
Set value		3.00

Perf. 14

477a A191 3c Litho.	.15	.15
479a A191 5c	.15	.15
480a A191 6c	.15	.15
481a A191 7c	.18	.15
482a A191 8c	.18	.15
483a A191 9c	.20	.15
484a A191 10c	.24	.15
486a A191 20c Litho.	.75	.30
487a A191 25c	.60	.22
488a A191 30c	.70	.24
489a A191 50c	1.25	.40
490a A191 1r	2.50	.80
491a A191 2r	4.75	1.50
Nos. 477a-491a (13)	11.80	
Set value		3.60

Perf. 14 Vertically

	Photo.	Coil Stamps	
492 A191 1c Silver tree	.15	.15
493 A191 2c Bottle brush	.15	.15
494 A191 5c Blushing bride	.16	.15
495 A191 10c Leucadendrom sessile	.30	.15
Set value	.60	.20

Some printings have control number on back of every fifth stamp.

Gymnastics — A192

1977, Aug. 15 Litho.   Perf. 12½x12

496 A192 15c multicolored   .42 .32

8th Intl. Cong. of Physical Education and Sports for Girls and Women, Cape Town, Aug. 14-20.

World Map
and
"M" — A193

1977, Sept. 15 Litho.   Perf. 12x12½

497 A193 15c multicolored   .42 .32

Introduction of international metric system.

Nuclear
Power Plant
and
Uranium
Atom
A194

1977, Oct. 8

498 A194 15c multicolored   .42 .32

Uranium development.

Flag of South
Africa
A195

1977, Nov. 11

499 A195 5c multicolored   .20 .15

50th anniversary of national flag.

Walvis Bay, 1878 — A196

1978, Mar. 10 Litho.   Perf. 12½

500 A196 15c multicolored   .55 .38

Centenary of Walvis Bay annexation.

Dr. Andrew
Murray — A197

1978, May 9   Perf. 12½x12

501 A197 4c multicolored   .15 .15

Dr. Andrew Murray, pioneer theologian, 150th birth anniversary.

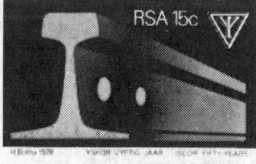

Railroad
Rail and
ISCOR
Emblem
A198

1978, June 5 Litho.   Perf. 12

502 A198 15c multicolored   .45 .38

50th anniversary of ISCOR (Iron and Steel Industrial Corporation).

Saldanha Bay — A199

Design: No. 504, Richard's Bay.

1978, July 21 Litho.   Perf. 12½

503 A199 15c multicolored	.52	.52
504 A199 15c multicolored	.52	.52
a. Pair, #503-504	1.05	1.05

Opening of new harbors on east and west coasts of South Africa.

Landscape by Volschenk — A200

Designs: Landscapes by J. E. A. Volschenk.

1978, Aug. 21

505 A200 10c multicolored	.35	.35
506 A200 15c multicolored	.50	.50
507 A200 20c multicolored	.70	.70
508 A200 25c multicolored	.90	.90
a. Souvenir sheet of 4, #505-508	3.00	3.00
Nos. 505-508 (4)	2.45	2.45

Jan Ernst Abraham Volschenk (1853-1936), first South African professional artist.

B. J. Vorster — A201

1978, Oct. 10 Litho.   Perf. 12½x12

509 A201 4c maroon & gold	.15	.15
a. Perf. 14½x14	.75	.30

Perf. 14½x14

510 A201 15c violet & gold	.40	.32
Set value	.48	.37

Inauguration of Balthazar John Vorster as president of South Africa.

Golden Gate Highlands National
Park — A202

Designs: 15c, Blyde River Canyon, Transvaal. 20c, Amphitheater, Natal National Park. 25c, Cango Caves, Cape Province.

1978, Nov. 13   Perf. 12½

511 A202 10c multicolored	.35	.35
512 A202 15c multicolored	.50	.50
513 A202 20c multicolored	.70	.70
514 A202 25c multicolored	1.10	1.00
Nos. 511-514 (4)	2.65	2.55

Tourist publicity.

Tellurometer and Dr. I. R. Wadley — A203

1979, Feb. 12 Litho.   Perf. 12½

515 A203 15c multicolored   .30 .25

15th anniversary of the invention of the tellurometer (to measure radio distances).

South
Africa
No. C5
A204

1979, Mar. 30 Litho.   Perf. 14½x14

516 A204 15c multicolored   .35 .30

First stamp printed by South African Government Printer, 50th anniversary.

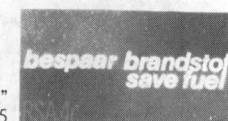

"Save Fuel"
A205

Fuel Economy: No. 518, Language inscriptions reversed.

1979, Apr. 2   Photo.   Perf. 12x12½

517	A205	4c red & black	.15 .15
518	A205	4c red & black	.15 .15
a.		Pair, #517-518	.24 .24
		Set value	.15

Battle of Isandlwana, by Melton
Prior — A206

Designs: 15c, Battle of Ulundi, by Louis
Creswicke. 20c, Battle of Rorke's Drift, by Lt. Col.
Crealock.

1979, May 25   Litho.   Perf. 14x13½

519	A206	4c red & black	.15 .15
520	A206	15c red & black	.38 .35
521	A206	20c red & black	.52 .42
a.		Souv. sheet of 3, #519-521 + label	3.00 3.00
		Nos. 519-521 (3)	1.05 .92

Centenary of Zulu War.

"Health Care and
Service" — A207

1979, June 19   Litho.   Perf. 12½x12

522	A207	4c multicolored	.15 .15
a.		Perf. 14	

Health Year.

Boy and Girl Watching Candle — A208

1979, Sept. 13   Litho.   Perf. 14½x14

523	A208	4c multicolored	.15 .15

South African Christmas Stamp Fund, 50th
anniversary.

Cape Town
University,
150th
Anniversary
A209

1979, Oct. 1   Litho.   Perf. 14x14½

524	A209	4c multicolored	.15 .15
a.		Perf. 12x12½	

Southern Sun
Rose — A210

Designs: Roses.

1979, Oct. 4   Litho.   Perf. 14½x14

525	A210	4c multicolored	.15 .15
526	A210	15c multicolored	.38 .30
527	A210	20c multicolored	.48 .40
528	A210	25c multicolored	.65 .55
a.		Souvenir sheet of 4, #525-528	2.25 2.25
		Nos. 525-528 (4)	1.66 1.40

Rosafari 1979, 4th World Rose Convention, Pretoria, October.

Stellenbosch University — A211

1979, Nov. 8

529	A211	4c shown	.15 .15
530	A211	15c Rhenish Church	.32 .26
		Set value	.40 .35

Stellenbosch (oldest town in South Africa), 300th
anniversary.

A212   A213

1979, Dec. 18   Photo.   Perf. 12½x12

531	A212	4c multicolored	.15 .15

Federation of Afrikaans Cultural Societies, 50th
anniv.

1980, May 6   Litho.   Perf. 14½x14

Paintings by Pieter Wenning (1873-1921): 5c,
Still Life with Sweet Peas. 25c, House in the Suburbs, Cape Town.

532	A213	5c multicolored	.15 .15

Size: 45x37mm

533	A213	25c multicolored	.50 .35
a.		Souvenir sheet of 2, #532-533	2.00 1.00

Great Star of Africa
Diamond — A214

1980, May 12   Litho.   Perf. 14x14½

534	A214	15c shown	.50 .35
535	A214	20c Cullinan II diamond	.65 .50

World Diamond Congress.

A215   A216

1980, Sept. 3   Litho.   Perf. 14½x14

536	A215	5c multicolored	.15 .15

Christian Louis Leipoldt (1880-1947), writer and
physician.

1980, Oct. 9   Litho.

537	A216	5c multicolored	.15 .15

University of Pretoria, 50th anniv.

Marine
With
Ships,
by Willem
van de
Velde
A217

Paintings: 10c, Firetail and Trainer, by George
Stubbs. 15c, Lavinia, by Thomas Gainsborough,
vert. 20c, Landscape, by Pieter Post.

1980, Nov. 3   Perf. 14½x14

538	A217	5c multicolored	.15 .15
539	A217	10c multicolored	.22 .16
540	A217	15c multicolored	.32 .24
541	A217	20c multicolored	.40 .32
a.		Souvenir sheet of 4, #538-541	1.90 1.25
		Nos. 538-541 (4)	1.09 .87

Natl. Gallery, 50th anniv.

P.J. Joubert, Paul Kruger, M.W. Pretorius
(First Leaders of Triumvirate Government)
A218

Design: 10c, Monument, flag of South African
Republic, 1880, vert.

Perf. 14x14½ 14½x14

1980, Dec. 15

542	A218	5c multicolored	.15 .15
543	A218	10c multicolored	.20 .16
		Set value	.30 .25

Paardekraal Monument (built on site of founding
of triumverate government) centennial.

British Troops in Battle of
Amajuba — A219

1981, Feb. 27   Litho.   Perf. 14x14½

544	A219	5c Boer snipers, vert.	.15 .15
545	A219	15c shown	.36 .30

Battle of Amajuba centenary (led to independence of Orange Free State).

Scene
from
Verdi's
Aida
A220

1981, May 23   Litho.   Perf. 14½x14

546	A220	20c Raka ballet scene	.35 .30
547	A220	25c shown	.45 .35
a.		Souvenir sheet of 2, #546-547	1.00 .80

Opening of State Theater, Pretoria.

Pres. Marais
Viljoen — A221

Deaf Girl
Learning to
Speak — A222

1981, May 30   Perf. 14x14½

Size: 57x21mm

548	A221	5c Former presidents	.15 .15
549	A221	15c shown	.30 .26
		Set value	.33

1981, June 12   Perf. 14½x14

550	A222	5c shown	.15 .15
551	A222	15c Man reading braille	.30 .25
		Set value	.33

Institute for the Deaf and Blind, Worcester,
centenary.

Natl. Cancer Assn. 50th
Anniv. — A223

1981, July 10

552	A223	5c multicolored	.15 .15

Calanthe
Natalensis
A224

Voortrekker
Movement, 50th
Anniv.
A225

1981, Sept. 11   Litho.

553	A224	5c shown	.15 .15
554	A224	15c Eulophia speciosa	.30 .25
555	A224	20c Disperis fanniniae	.40 .32
556	A224	25c Disa uniflora	.50 .40
a.		Souvenir sheet of 4, #553-556	2.50 2.25
		Nos. 553-556 (4)	1.35 1.12

10th World Orchid Conf., Durban, Sept. 11-17.

1981, Sept. 30   Perf. 14x14½

557	A225	5c multicolored	.20 .15

Scouting Year
A226

TB Bacillus
Centenary
A227

1982, Feb. 22   Litho.   Perf. 14½x14

558	A226	15c Baden Powell	.30 .25

1982, Mar. 24   Litho.

559	A227	20c multicolored	.30 .25

Return of Simonstown Naval Base, 25th
Anniv. — A228

1982, Apr. 2   Perf. 14½x14

560	A228	8c Submarine	.16 .15
561	A228	15c Strike craft	.28 .24
562	A228	20c Mine sweeper	.40 .32
563	A228	25c Harbor patrol boats	.50 .40
a.		Souvenir sheet of 4, #560-563	2.00 1.90
		Nos. 560-563 (4)	1.34 1.11

Old Provost,
Grahamstown
A229

Design: 2c, Tuynhuys, Kaapstad (Cape Town).
3c, Appelhof, Bloemfontein. 4c, Raadsaal, Pretoria.
5c, Die Kasteel, Kaapstad. 6c, Goewermentsgebou,
Bloemfontein. 7c, Drostdy, Graaf-Reinet. 8c,

Leeuwenhof, Cape Town. 9c, Libertas, Pretoria. 10c, City Hall, Pietermaritzburg. 11c, City Hall, Kimberley. 12c, City Hall, Port Elizabeth. 14c, Johannesburg City Hall. 15c, Hotel Milner, Matjesfontein. 16c, Durban City Hall. 20c, Post Office, Durban. 25c, Melrose House, Pretoria. 30c, Old Legislative Assembly Building, Pietermaritzburg. 50c, Raadsaal, Bloemfontein. 1r, Houses of Parliament, Cape Town. 2r, Uniegebou, Pretoria.

Coils have different designs.

1982-87 Litho. *Perf. 14x14½*

564 A229 1c brown ('84) .15 .15
565 A229 2c apple green .15 .15
566 A229 2c green ('83) .15 .15
567 A229 2c slate grn ('85) .15 .15
568 A229 3c purple ('85) .15 .15
569 A229 4c olive grn ('85) .15 .15
570 A229 5c carmine .15 .15
571 A229 6c brt green .15 .15
572 A229 7c gray green .15 .15
573 A229 8c blue .15 .15
574 A229 8c intense blue ('83) .15 .15
575 A229 9c brt rose lilac .15 .15
576 A229 10c lt red brown .15 .15
577 A229 10c violet brn ('83) .15 .15
578 A229 11c cerise ('84) .20 .15
579 A229 12c dp ultra ('85) .15 .15
580 A229 14c rose brn ('86) .15 .15
581 A229 16c red ('87) .24 .24
582 A229 20c vermilion .30 .24
583 A229 20c black ('85) .15 .15
584 A229 25c bister .38 .30

Size: 45x27mm

Perf. 14½x14

586 A229 30c brown ('86) .80 .50
587 A229 50c Prus blue ('86) 1.25 1.00
588 A229 1r violet blue ('86) 1.50 1.25
589 A229 2r cerise ('85) 2.75 2.50
Set value 7.50 6.25

For surcharge see No. B12.

Engr.

590 A229 1c dark brown .15 .15
591 A229 2c slate grn ('83) .15 .15
592 A229 3c violet .15 .15
593 A229 4c olive green .15 .15
594 A229 5c dark lake ('83) .15 .15
595 A229 6c green blk ('84) .15 .15
596 A229 15c blue .22 .20
597 A229 20c black ('83) .50 .40
598 A229 30c violet brown .45 .35
599 A229 50c Prus blue .70 .60
600 A229 1r violet blue 1.50 1.25
601 A229 2r rose carmine 3.00 2.50
Nos. 590-601 (12) 7.27 6.20

In some cases there are slight design differences from litho. stamp.

Perf. 14 Horiz.

Photo. Coil Stamps

602 A229 1c Residence, Swellendam .15 .15
603 A229 2c City Hall, East London .15 .15
604 A229 5c Rissik St. PO, Johannesburg .15 .15
605 A229 10c Morgenster, Somerset West .25 .20
Set value .49 .40

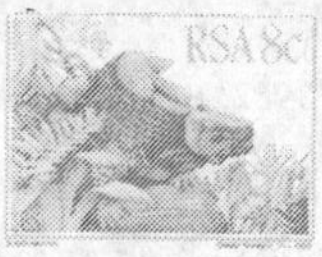

Bradysaurus
A230

Prehistoric Animals (Karoo Fossils).

1982, Dec. 1 Litho. *Perf. 14x14½*

606 A230 8c shown .15 .15
607 A230 15c Lystrosaurus .24 .20
608 A230 20c Euparkeria .32 .25
609 A230 25c Thrinaxodon .40 .32
a. Souvenir sheet of 4, #606-609 3.00
Nos. 606-609 (4) 1.11 .92

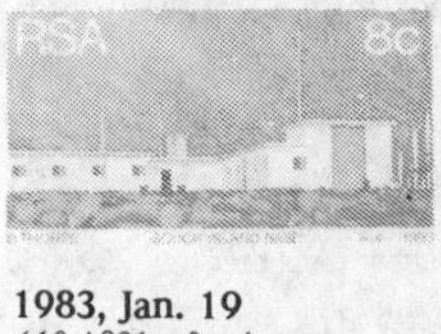

Weather Station, Gough Island
A231

1983, Jan. 19 Litho.

610 A231 8c shown .15 .15
611 A231 20c Marion Isld. station .32 .25
612 A231 25c Reading instruments .40 .32
613 A231 40c Weather balloon, Antarctica .65 .52
Nos. 610-613 (4) 1.52 1.24

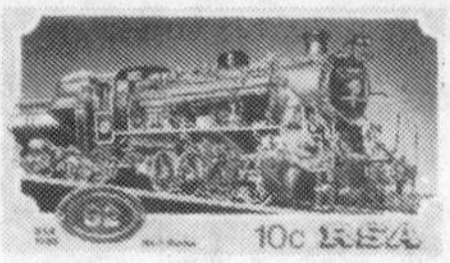

Steam Locomotives
A232

1983, Apr. 27 Litho.

614 A232 10c Class 82, 1952 .20 .16
615 A232 20c Class 16E, 1935 .42 .35
616 A232 25c Class 6H, 1901 .52 .42
617 A232 40c Class 15F, 1939 .85 .70
Nos. 614-617 (4) 1.99 1.63

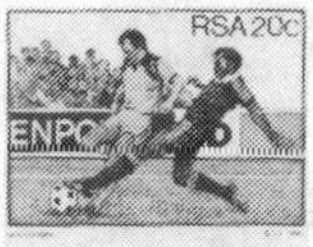

Soccer — A233

Perf. 14½x14 (10c, 25c), 14x14½ (20c, 40c)

1983, July 20 Litho.

618 A233 10c Rugby, vert. .15 .15
619 A233 20c shown .30 .25
620 A233 25c Sailing, vert. .40 .30
621 A233 40c Equestrian .62 .48
Nos. 618-621 (4) 1.47 1.18

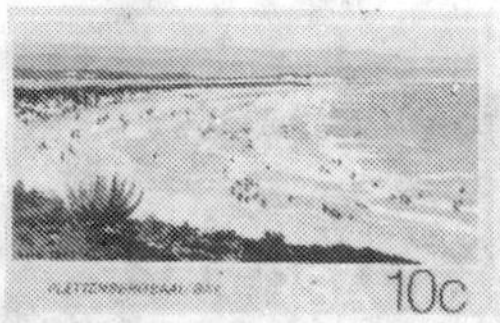

Plettenberg Bay — A234

1983, Oct. 12 Litho. *Perf. 14½x14*

622 A234 10c shown .15 .15
623 A234 20c Durban Beach .32 .22
624 A234 25c West Coast beach .40 .25
625 A234 40c Clifton beach scene .65 .45
a. Souvenir sheet of 4, #622-625 1.75 1.25
Nos. 622-625 (4) 1.52 1.07

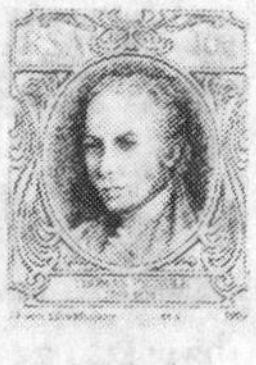

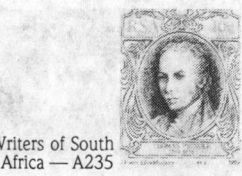

English Writers of South Africa — A235

Designs: 10c, Thomas Pringle (1789-1834). 20c, Pauline Smith (1882-1959). 25c, Olive Schreiner (1855-1920). 40c, Percy FitzPatrick (1862-1931).

1984, Feb. 24 Litho. *Perf. 14½x14*

626 A235 10c multicolored .15 .15
627 A235 20c multicolored .28 .18
628 A235 25c multicolored .35 .25
629 A235 40c multicolored .60 .35
Nos. 626-629 (4) 1.38 .93

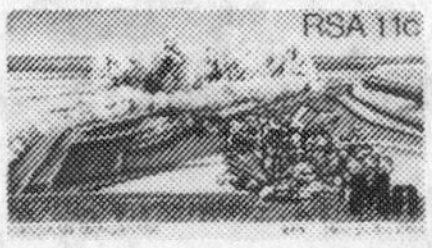

Manganese
A236

1984, June 8 Litho. *Perf. 14x14½*

630 A236 11c shown .20 .15
631 A236 20c Chromium .38 .24
632 A236 25c Vanadium .48 .32
633 A236 30c Titanium .55 .35
Nos. 630-633 (4) 1.61 1.06

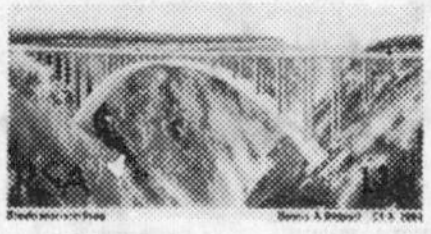

Bloukrans River Bridge
A237

1984, Aug. 24

634 A237 11c shown .18 .15
635 A237 25c Durban 4-level Bridge Interchange .40 .25
636 A237 30c Mfolozi Railroad Bridge .48 .30
637 A237 45c Gouritz River Bridge .72 .45
Nos. 634-637 (4) 1.78 1.15

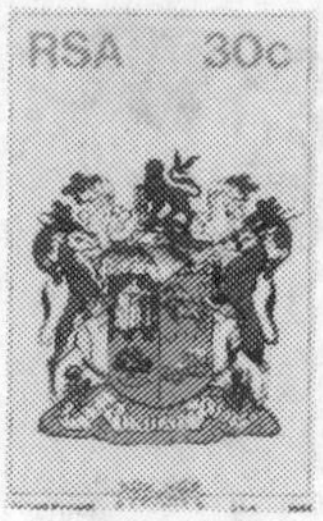

New Constitution
A238

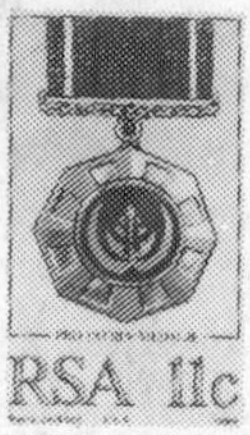

Military Medals
A239

1984, Sept. 3 Litho. *Perf. 14x14½*

638 A238 11c Preamble (English) .24 .16
639 A238 11c Preamble (Africaans) .24 .16
a. Pair, #638-639 .48 .35
640 A238 25c Symbolic pillars, anthem .55 .35
641 A238 30c Arms .65 .42
Nos. 638-641 (4) 1.68 1.09

1984, Nov. 9 *Perf. 14½x14*

642 A239 11c Pro Patria .18 .15
643 A239 25c De Wet .40 .25
644 A239 30c John Chard Decoration .48 .30
645 A239 45c Honoris Crux .72 .45
a. Miniature sheet of 4, #642-645 2.00 1.25
Nos. 642-645 (4) 1.78 1.15

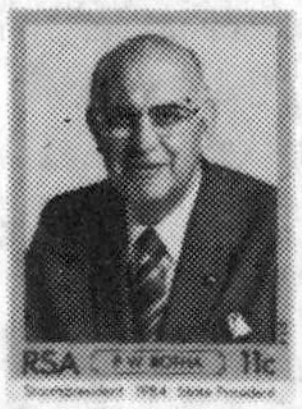

Pres. Pieter Willem Botha (b. 1916) — A240

1984, Nov. 2 Litho. *Perf. 14x14½*

646 A240 11c multicolored .18 .15
647 A240 25c multicolored .40 .25

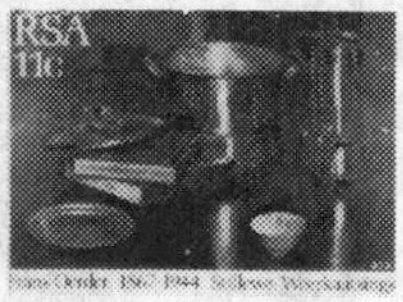

Frans David Oerder, Painter (1867-1944)
A241

1985, Feb. 22 Litho. *Perf. 14½x14*

648 A241 11c Reflections .15 .15
649 A241 25c Ladies in a Garden .32 .22
650 A241 30c Still-Life with Lobster .42 .28
651 A241 50c Still-Life with Marigolds .65 .45
a. Souvenir sheet of 4, #648-651 2.00 2.00
Nos. 648-651 (4) 1.54 1.10

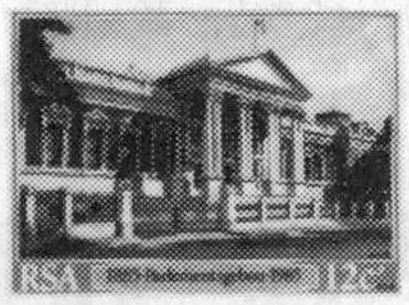

Cape Parliament Cent. — A242

1985, May 15 Litho.

652 A242 12c Parliament .18 .15
653 A242 25c Speaker's chair .35 .25
654 A242 30c The National Convention, by Edward Roworth .40 .28
655 A242 50c South African arms .70 .48
Nos. 652-655 (4) 1.63 1.16

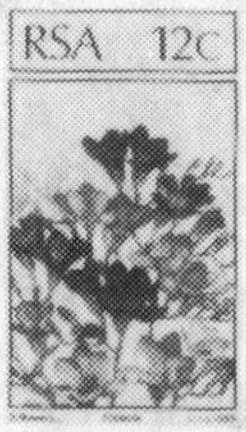

Indigenous Flowers
A243

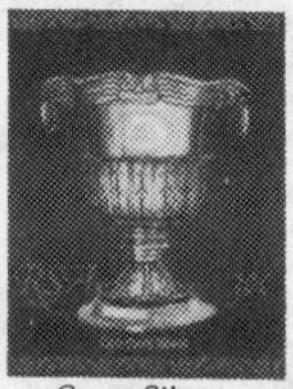

Cape Silver
A244

1985, Aug. 23 Litho. *Perf. 14½x14*

656 A243 12c Freesia .20 .16
657 A243 25c Nerine .65 .45
658 A243 30c Ixia .75 .50
659 A243 50c Gladiolus 1.40 .90
Nos. 656-659 (4) 3.00 2.01

1985, Nov. 5 *Perf. 14½x14, 14x14½*

660 A244 12c Sugar bowl, horiz. .15 .15
661 A244 25c Tea pot, horiz. .28 .18
662 A244 30c Goblet .35 .25
663 A244 50c Coffee pot .60 .38
Nos. 660-663 (4) 1.38 .96

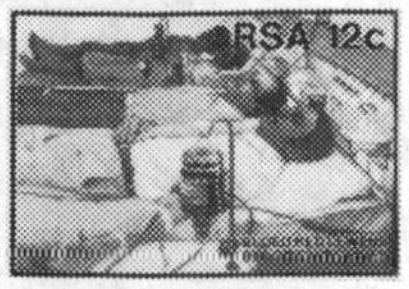

Blood Transfusion Services
A245

1986, Feb. 20 *Perf. 14½x14*

664 A245 12c Blood donation .15 .15
665 A245 20c Transfusion .24 .15
666 A245 25c Surgery .30 .22
667 A245 30c Emergency aid .35 .24
Nos. 664-667 (4) 1.04 .76

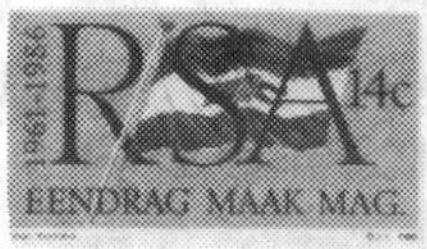

Republic of South Africa, 25th Anniv.
A246

1986, May 30 Litho. *Perf. 14x14½*

668 A246 14c Text in Afrikaans .25 .20
669 A246 14c Text in English .25 .20
a. Pair, #668-669 .50 .50

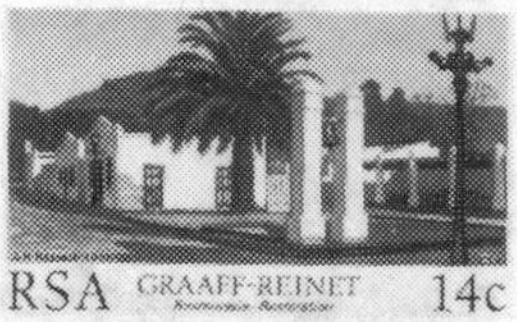

Cultural Heritage — A247

Restoration projects: 14c, Drostdyhof, Free Street, Graaff-Reinet, 19th cent. 20c, Pilgrim's Rest, Eastern Transvaal, 1873. 25c, J.T. Strapp and Son importers, c. 1893, Bethlehem. 30c, Palmdene, c. 1897, Pietermaritzburg.

1986, Aug. 14 *Perf. 14½x14*

670 A247 14c multicolored .25 .20
671 A247 20c multicolored .35 .25
672 A247 25c multicolored .40 .30
673 A247 30c multicolored .50 .35
Nos. 670-673 (4) 1.50 1.10

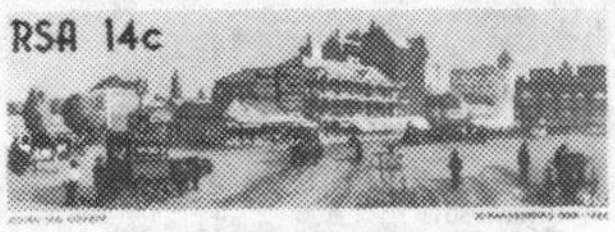

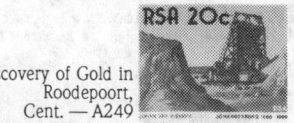

Johannesburg, Cent. — A248

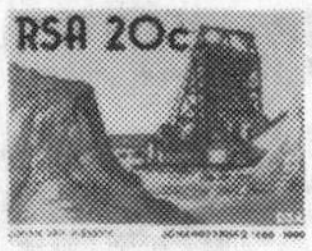

Discovery of Gold in Roodepoort, Cent. — A249

1986, Sept. 25 *Perf. 14x14½*

674 A248 14c Johannesburg, 1886 .24 .18
675 A249 20c Gold mine .35 .28
676 A248 25c Johannesburg, 1986 .42 .32
677 A249 30c Gold .50 .35
a. Souvenir sheet of 1 3.00 3.00
Nos. 674-677 (4) 1.51 1.13

No. 677a for Johannesburg stamp exhibition. Sold for 50c.

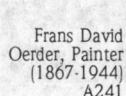

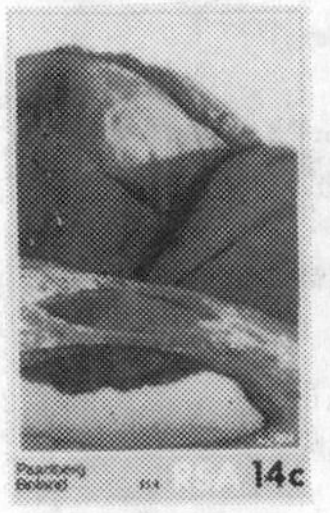

Pearl Mountain — A250

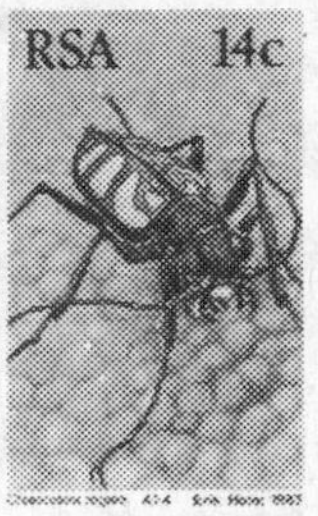

Beetles — A251

1986, Nov. 20 Litho. *Perf. 14x14½*

678 A250 14c shown .22 .22
679 A250 20c The Column, Drakensburg .32 .32
680 A250 25c Maltese Cross, Cedarberg .42 .42
681 A250 30c Bourke's Luck Potholes .52 .52
Nos. 678-681 (4) 1.48 1.48

1987, Mar. 6 Litho. *Perf. 14x14½*

690 A251 14c *Chaetodera regalis* .28 .28
691 A251 20c *Trichostetha fascicularis* .40 .40
692 A251 25c *Julodis viridipes* .50 .50
693 A251 30c *Ceroplesis militaris* .60 .60
Nos. 690-693 (4) 1.78 1.78

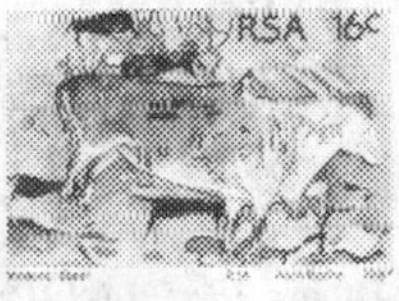

Petroglyphs A252

1987, June 4 *Perf. 14½x14*

694 A252 16c Eland, Sebaaleni Cave .32 .32
695 A252 20c Leaping lion, Clocolan .40 .40
696 A252 25c Black wildebeest, uMhlwazini Valley .50 .50
697 A252 30c San dance, Floukraal .60 .60
Nos. 694-697 (4) 1.82 1.82

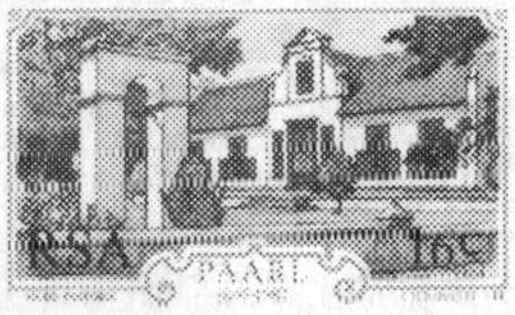

Paarl, 300th Anniv. A253

1987, Sept. 3

698 A253 16c Oude Pastorie .32 .32
699 A253 20c Winegrowing .40 .40
700 A253 25c Wagon-building .50 .50
701 A253 30c KWV Cathedral Cellar .60 .60
Nos. 698-701 (4) 1.82 1.82

A souvenir sheet of one, No. 701, has decorative margin picturing emblem of the natl. philatelic exhibition at Paarl, Sept. 16-19. Sold for 50c.

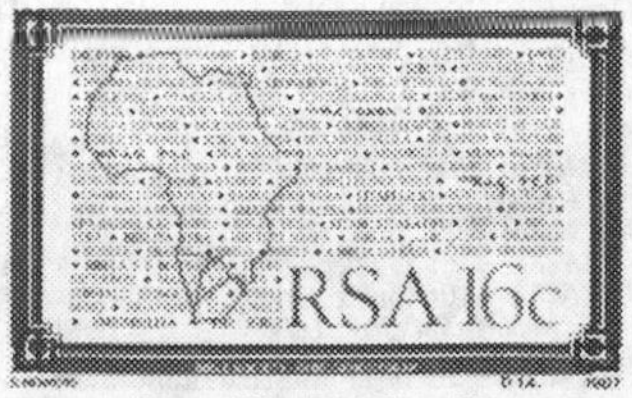

Map, "The Bible" in 76 Languages — A254

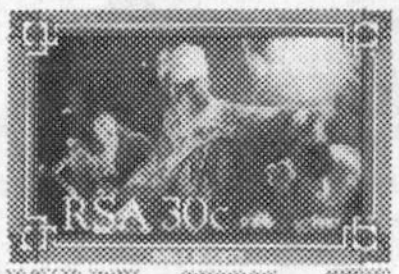

Religious Paintings by Rembrandt A255

Designs: 30c, *Belshazzar's Feast.* 50c, *St. Matthew and the Angel,* vert.

Perf. 14x14½, 14½x14 (30c)

1987, Nov. 19

702 A254 16c shown .32 .32
703 A255 30c shown .60 .60
704 A255 50c multicolored 1.00 1.00
Nos. 702-704 (3) 1.92 1.92

Bible Society of South Africa.
For surcharge see No. B13.

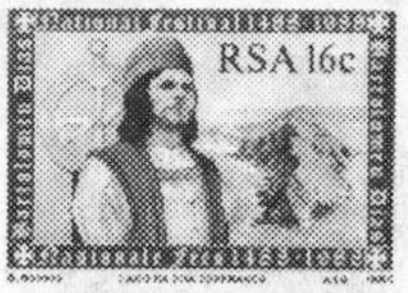

Discovery of the Cape of Good Hope by Bartolomeu Dias — A256

Designs: 16c, Dias, astrolabe, Cape of Good Hope. 30c, Kwaaihoek Memorial. 40c, Caravels, 1488. 50c, Martellus Map, c. 1489.

1988, Feb. 3 *Perf. 14½x14*

706 A256 16c multicolored .30 .30
707 A256 30c multicolored .55 .55
708 A256 40c multicolored .75 .75
709 A256 50c multicolored .95 .95
Nos. 706-709 (4) 2.55 2.55

A souvenir sheet of one, No. 709, has decorative margin picturing emblem of the natl. philatelic exhibition held at Pietermaritzburg, Nov. 22-27. Sold for 70c.
For surcharge see No. B14 .

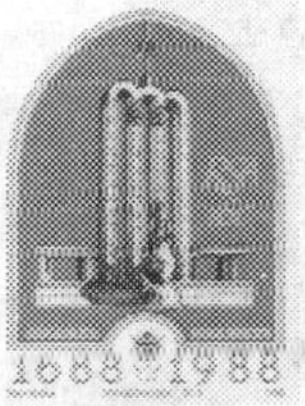

French Huguenot Settlement of the Cape, 300th Anniv. — A257

1988, Apr. 13 *Perf. 14x14½*

710 A257 16c Memorial, Franschhoek .30 .30
711 A257 30c Map of France .55 .55
712 A257 40c French-Dutch Bible, 1672 .75 .75
713 A257 50c St. Bartholomew's Day Massacre, 1572 .95 .95
Nos. 710-713 (4) 2.55 2.55

For surcharges see Nos. B15-B18 .

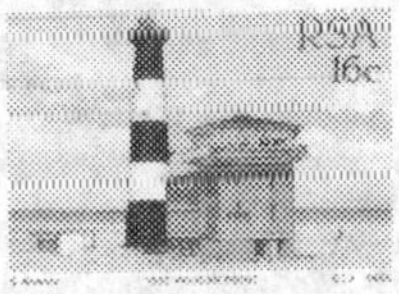

Lighthouses A258

1988, June 9 *Perf. 14½x14*

714 A258 16c Pelican Point, 1932 .30 .30
715 A258 30c Groenpunt, 1824 .55 .55
716 A258 40c Agulhas, 1849 .75 .75
717 A258 50c Umhlanga Rocks, 1954 .95 .95
a. Souvenir sheet of 4, #714-717 3.00 3.00
Nos. 714-717 (4) 2.55 2.55

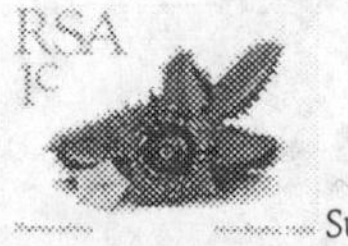

Succulents — A259

1988-93 Litho. *Perf. 14x14½*

735 A259 1c *Huernia zebrina* .15 .15
736 A259 2c *Euphorbia symmetrica* .15 .15
737 A259 5c *Lithops dorotheae* .15 .15
738 A259 7c *Gibbaeum newbrownii* .15 .15
739 A259 10c *Didymaotus lapidiformis* .15 .15
740 A259 16c *Vanheerdea divergens* .15 .15
741 A259 18c *Faucaria tigrina* .15 .15
742 A259 20c *Conophytum mundum* .15 .15
743 A259 21c *Gasteria armstrongii* .15 .15
744 A259 25c *Cheiridopsis peculiaris* .16 .16
745 A259 30c *Tavaresia barklyi* .20 .20
a. Strip, 2 each 1c, 2c, 5c, 7c, 30c *2.00*
746 A259 35c *Dinteranthus wilmotianus* .24 .24
747 A259 40c *Frithia pulchra* .28 .28
748 A259 (45c) *Stapelia grandiflora* .28
749 A259 50c *Lapidaria margaretae* .32 .32
750 A259 90c *Dioscorea elephantipes* .65 .65
751 A259 1r *Trichocaulon cactiforme* .70 .70
752 A259 2r *Crassula columnaris* 1.40 1.40
753 A259 5r *Anacampseros albissima* 3.50 3.50
Nos. 735-753 (19) 9.08 8.80

Coil Stamps

Photo.

Perf. 14 Horiz.

754 A259 1c *Adromischus marianiae* .15 .15
755 A259 2c *Titanopsis calcarea* .25 .25
756 A259 5c *Dactylopsis digitata* .70 .70
757 A259 10c *Pleiospilos bolusii* 1.40 1.40
Nos. 754-757 (4) 2.50 2.50

Issued: 18c, 4/1/89; 5r, 3/1/90; 21c, 4/2/90; #748, 4/1/93; others, 9/1/88.
No. 748 is inscribed "Gestandaardiseerde pos / Standardised mail," and initially sold for 45c.

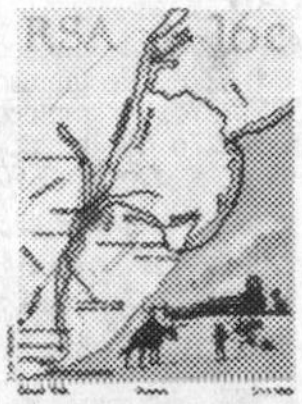

Map and Settlers — A260

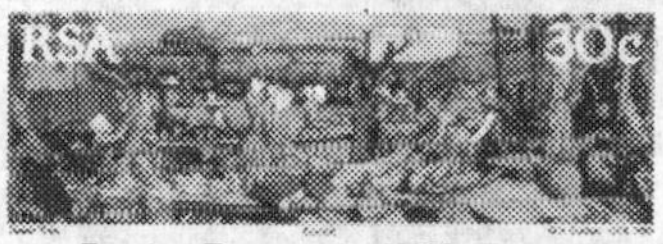

Exodus, Tapestry by W.H. Coetzer Studio — A261

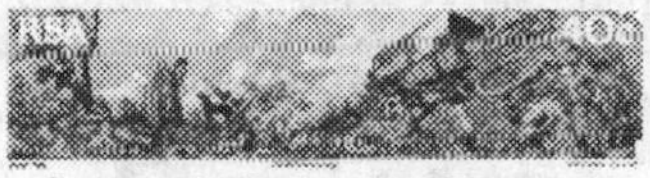

Crossing the Drakensburg, Tapestry by Coetzer Studio (illustration reduced) — A262

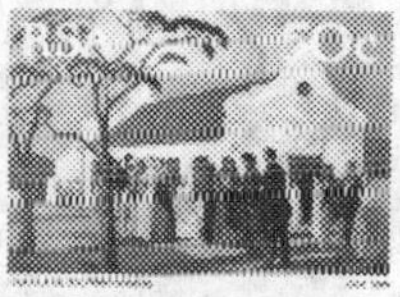

Church of the Vow, Pietermaritzburg — A263

Perf. 14x14½, 14½x14 (50c)

1988, Nov. 21 Litho.

758 A260 16c multicolored .22 .22
759 A261 30c multicolored .45 .45
760 A262 40c multicolored .60 .60
761 A263 50c multicolored .75 .75
Nos. 758-761 (4) 2.02 2.02

The Great Trek, 150th anniv.

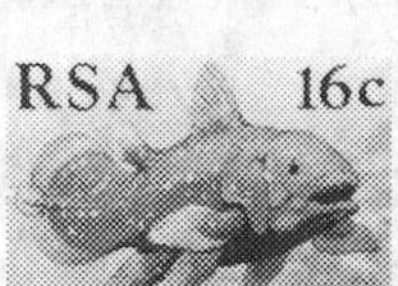

Discovery of a Living Specimen of the Coelacanth, 50th Anniv. A264

Designs: 16c, *Latimeria chalumnae.* 30c, J. L. B. Smith, Margaret Courtenay-Latimer. 40c, Smith Institute of Ichthyology, Grahamstown. 50c, Fish, GEO two-man research submarine.

1989, Feb. 9 *Perf. 14½x14*

762 A264 16c multicolored .30 .30
763 A264 30c multicolored .55 .55
764 A264 40c multicolored .75 .75
765 A264 50c multicolored .95 .95
a. Souvenir sheet of 1 3.25 3.25
Nos. 762-765 (4) 2.55 2.55

No. 765a has decorative margin picturing emblem of the natl. philatelic exhibition WANDERERS 101, held Sept. 6-9. Sold for 1.50r.

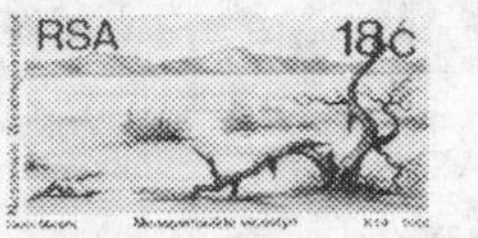

Soil Conservation Campaign of the Natl. Grazing Strategy A265

1989, May 3 *Perf. 14x14½*

766 A265 18c Desertification .35 .35
767 A265 30c Eroded gullies .55 .55
768 A265 40c Barrage .75 .75
769 A265 50c Verdant plain .95 .95
Nos. 766-769 (4) 2.60 2.60

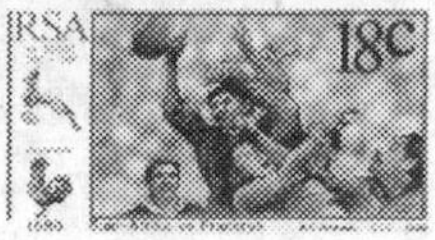

Natl. Rugby Board, Cent. A266

Springboks, foreign team emblems, match scenes.

1989, June 22

770 A266 18c France, 1980 .25 .25
771 A266 30c Australia, 1963 .45 .45
772 A266 40c New Zealand, 1937 .60 .60
773 A266 50c British Isles, 1896 .75 .75
Nos. 770-773 (4) 2.05 2.05

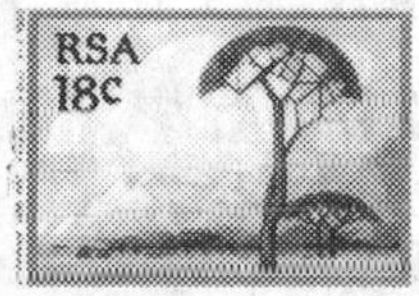

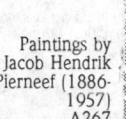

Paintings by Jacob Hendrik Pierneef (1886-1957) A267

1989, Aug. 3 *Perf. 14½x14*

774 A267 18c *Composition in Blue,* 1928 .15 .15
775 A267 30c *Zanzibar,* 1926 .22 .22
776 A267 40c *The Bushveld,* 1949 .30 .30
777 A267 50c *Cape Homestead,* 1942 .38 .38
a. Souvenir sheet of 4, #774-777 2.50 2.50
Nos. 774-777 (4) 1.05 1.05

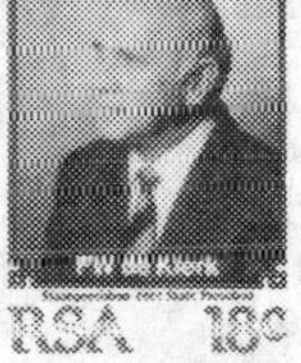

Election of Pres. Frederik Willem de Klerk, Aug. 15 — A268

1989, Sept. 20 *Perf. 14x14½*

778 A268 18c shown .20 .20
779 A268 45c Portrait, diff. .50 .50

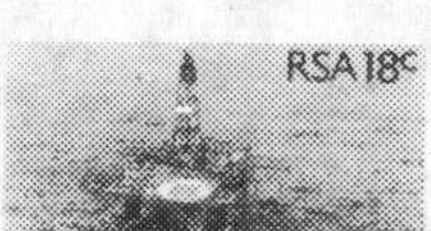

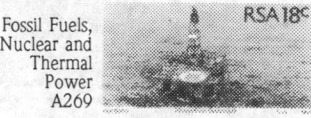

Fossil Fuels, Nuclear and Thermal Power A269

Designs: 18c, SOEKOR gas project, Mossel Bay. 30c, SASOL coal conversion plant. 40c, Koeberg nuclear power plant. 50c, ESKOM thermal power station.

1989, Oct. 19

780 A269 18c multicolored .16 .16
781 A269 30c multicolored .28 .28
782 A269 40c multicolored .35 .35
783 A269 50c multicolored .45 .45
Nos. 780-783 (4) 1.24 1.24

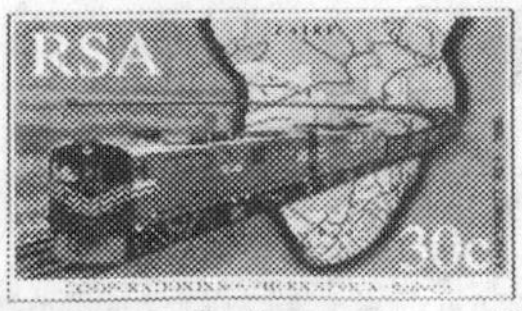

Cooperation in Southern Africa — A270

Maps and: 18c, Cahora Bassa hydroelectric power project. 30c, Railway network. 40c, Lesotho Highlands water project. 50c, Veterinary care.

1990, Feb. 15 ***Perf. 14½x14***

Size of 18c, 40c: 68x26mm

784	A270	18c multicolored	.22	.22
785	A270	30c multicolored	.38	.38
786	A270	40c multicolored	.50	.50
787	A270	50c multicolored	.65	.65
a.		Miniature sheet of 4, #784-787	1.75	1.75
		Nos. 784-787 (4)	1.75	1.75

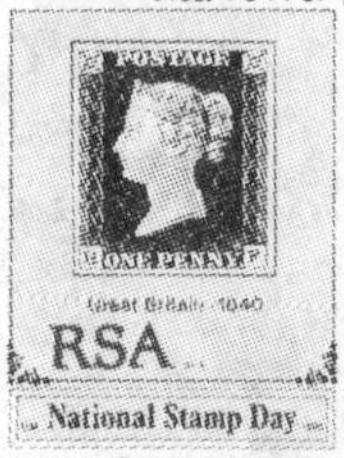

Stamp Day — A271

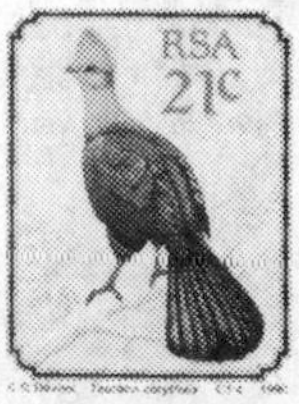

Birds — A272

Stamps on stamps: a, Great Britain #1. b, Cape of Good Hope #2. c, Natal #4. d, Orange River Colony #10. e, Transvaal #3.

1990, May 12 **Litho.**

788		Strip of 5	1.50	1.50
a.-e.		A271 21c any single	.30	.30

Penny Black, 150th anniv.

1990, Aug. 2 **Litho.** ***Perf. 14x14½***

Designs: 21c, *Tauraco corythaix*. 35c, *Cossypha natalensis*. 40c, *Mirafra africana*. 50c, *Telophorus zeylonus*.

789	A272	21c multicolored	.25	.25
790	A272	35c multicolored	.42	.42
791	A272	40c multicolored	.48	.48
792	A272	50c multicolored	.60	.60
		Nos. 789-792 (4)	1.75	1.75

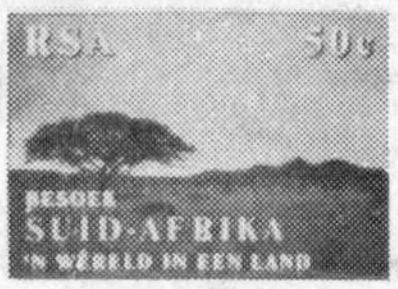

Karoo Landscape, Near Britstown A273

Tourism: No. 794, Camps Bay, Cape Peninsula. No. 795, Giraffes, Kruger National Park. No. 796, Boschendal homestead, Drakenstein.

1990, Nov. 1 **Litho.** ***Perf. 14½x14***

793	A273	50c multicolored	.42	.42
794	A273	50c multicolored	.42	.42
795	A273	50c multicolored	.42	.42
796	A273	50c multicolored	.42	.42
a.		Block of 4, #793-796	1.75	1.75

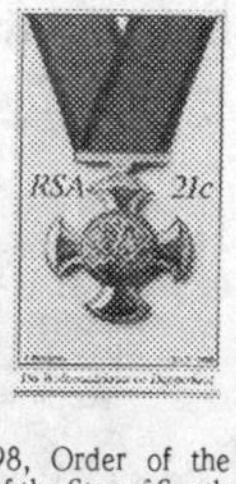

Woltemade Cross for Bravery — A274

National Decorations: No 798, Order of the Southern Cross. No. 799, Order of the Star of South Africa. No. 800, Order for Meritorious Service. No. 801, Order of Good Hope.

1990, Dec. 6

797	A274	21c multicolored	.25	.25
798	A274	21c multicolored	.25	.25
799	A274	21c multicolored	.25	.25
800	A274	21c multicolored	.25	.25
801	A274	21c multicolored	.25	.25
a.		Souv. sheet of 5, #797-801	1.25	1.25
b.		Strip of 5, #797-801	1.25	1.25

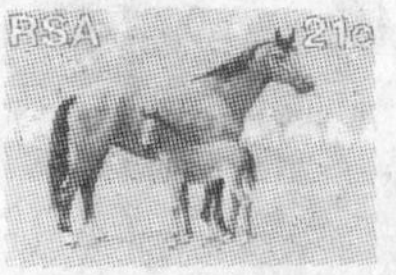

Animal Breeding A275

Designs: a, Boer horse. b, Bonsmara cattle. c, Dorper sheep. d, Ridgeback dog. e, Putterie racing pigeon.

1991, Feb. 21 **Litho.**

802	A275	21c Strip of 5, #a.-e.	1.25	1.25

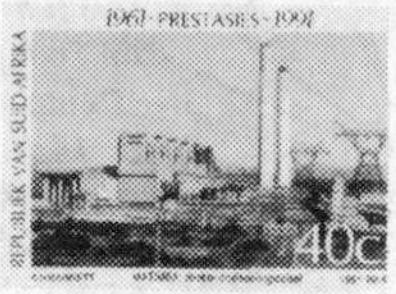

Achievements A276

Designs: 25c, First heart transplant, vert. 40c, Matimba power plant. 50c, Dolos breakwater blocks. 60c, Western Deep Levels Gold Mine, world's deepest mine, vert.

Perf. 14½x14 (25c, 60c), 14x14½ (40c, 50c)

1991, May 30 **Litho.**

803	A276	25c multicolored	.15	.15
804	A276	40c multicolored	.22	.22
805	A276	50c multicolored	.28	.28
806	A276	60c multicolored	.35	.35
		Nos. 803-806 (4)	1.00	1.00

30th anniv. of Republic of South Africa.

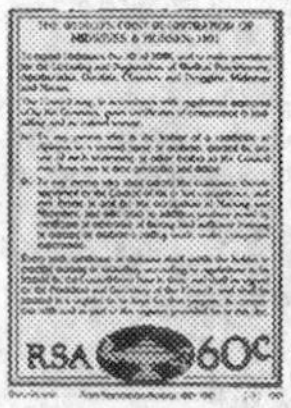

1st Registration of Nurses & Midwives, Cent. — A277

1991, Aug. 15 **Litho.** ***Perf. 14x14½***

807	A277	60c multicolored	.48	.48

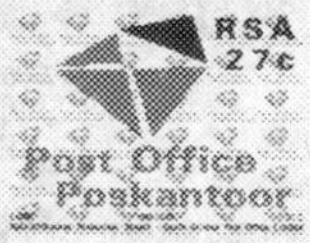

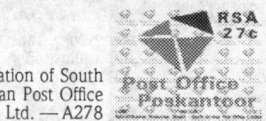

Creation of South African Post Office Ltd. — A278

1991, Oct. 1 **Litho.**

808	A278	27c shown	.16	.16
809	A278	27c Telkom SA Ltd.	.16	.16
a.		Pair, #808-809	.32	.32

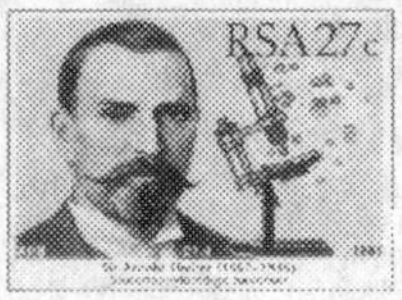

South African Scientists A279

Designs: 27c, Sir Arnold Theiler (1867-1936), veterinarian. 45c, Sir Basil Schonland (1896-1972), physicist. 65c, Dr. Robert Broom (1866-1951), paleontologist. 85c, Dr. Alexander L. du Toit (1878-1948), geologist.

1991, Oct. 9 ***Perf. 14½x14***

810	A279	27c multicolored	.16	.16
811	A279	45c multicolored	.28	.28
812	A279	65c multicolored	.40	.40
813	A279	85c multicolored	.50	.50
		Nos. 810-813 (4)	1.34	1.34

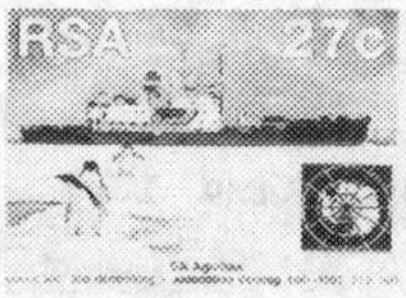

Antarctic Treaty, 30th Anniv. — A280

1991, Dec. 5 **Litho.**

814	A280	27c SA Agulhas, penguins	.16	.16
815	A280	65c Meteorological chart	.40	.40

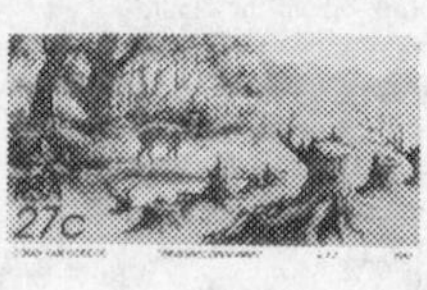

Conservation A281

1992, Feb. 6 **Litho.** ***Perf. 14x14½***

816	A281	27c Prevent erosion	.16	.16
817	A281	65c Water pollution	.40	.40
818	A281	85c Air pollution	.50	.50
		Nos. 816-818 (3)	1.06	1.06

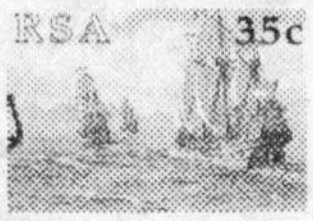

Stamp Day — A282

Designs depicting history of postal stones: No. 819, Sailing ships at Table Bay. No. 820, Sailors going ashore at Aguada de Saldanha. No. 821, Sailors discovering postal stone near Versse River. No. 822, Finding letters under postal stones. No. 823, Reading news from other mariners.

1992, May 9 **Litho.** ***Perf. 14x14½***

819	A282	35c multicolored	.28	.28
820	A282	35c multicolored	.28	.28
821	A282	35c multicolored	.28	.28
822	A282	35c multicolored	.28	.28
823	A282	35c multicolored	.28	.28
a.		Strip of 5, #819-823	1.40	1.40

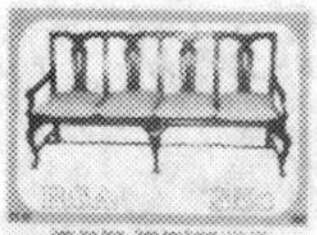

Antique Cape Furniture — A283

Designs: No. 824, Queen Anne settee, c. 1750-1770. No. 825, Stinkwood settee, c. 1800. No. 826, Canopy bed, c. 1800, vert. No. 827, Rocking cradle, 19th cent. No. 828, Waterbutt, c. 1800, vert. No. 829, Flemish style cabinet, c. 1700, vert. No. 830, Armoire, c. 1780-1790, vert. No. 831, Church chair, late 17th cent, vert. No. 832, Tub chair, c. 1770-1790, vert. No. 833, Bible desk, c. 1770, vert.

Perf. 14½x14, 14x14½

1992, July 9 **Litho.**

824	A283	35c multicolored	.28	.28
825	A283	35c multicolored	.28	.28
826	A283	35c multicolored	.28	.28
827	A283	35c multicolored	.28	.28
828	A283	35c multicolored	.28	.28
829	A283	35c multicolored	.28	.28
830	A283	35c multicolored	.28	.28
831	A283	35c multicolored	.28	.28
832	A283	35c multicolored	.28	.28
833	A283	35c multicolored	.28	.28
a.		Miniature sheet of 10, #824-833	2.80	

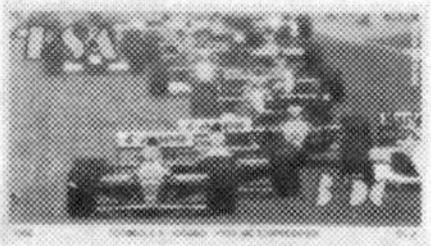

Sports A284

1992, July 24 ***Perf. 14x14½***

834	A284	35c Formula 1 Grand Prix	.28	.28
835	A284	35c Soccer	.28	.28
836	A284	55c Paris-le Cap Rally	.45	.45
837	A284	70c Track	.55	.55
838	A284	90c Rugby	.72	.72
839	A284	1.05r Cricket	.85	.85
a.		Souvenir sheet of 6, #834-839	3.25	3.25
		Nos. 834-839 (6)	3.13	3.13

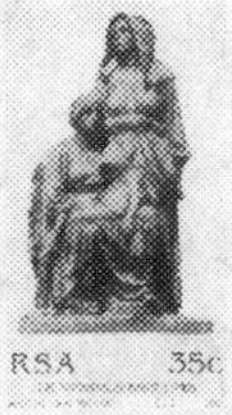

Sculptures by Anton van Wouw (1862-1945) — A285

1992, Oct. 8 **Litho.** ***Perf. 14½x14***

840	A285	35c Women's Monument	.28	.28
841	A285	70c Sekupu Player	.55	.55
842	A285	90c The Hunter	.72	.72
843	A285	1.05r Postman Lehman	.85	.85
a.		Souvenir sheet of 4, #840-843	2.75	2.75
		Nos. 840-843 (4)	2.40	2.40

No. 843a sold for 3.30r.

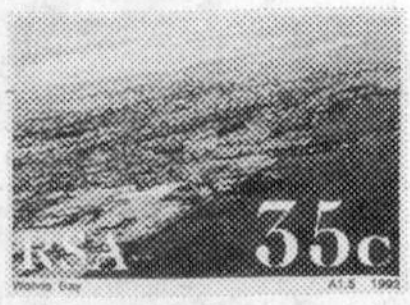

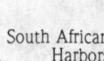

South African Harbors A286

1993, Jan. 28 **Litho.**

844	A286	35c Walvis Bay	.22	.22
845	A286	55c East London	.35	.35
846	A286	70c Port Elizabeth	.45	.45
847	A286	90c Cape Town	.58	.58
848	A286	1.05r Durban	.70	.70
a.		Souv. sheet of 5, #844-848 + label	2.60	2.60
		Nos. 844-848 (5)	2.30	2.30

No. 848a sold for 3.90r.

Miniature Sheet

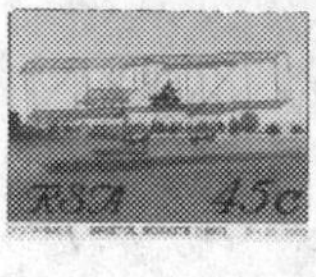

Aircraft — A287

Designs: a, Bristol Boxkite, 1907. b, Voisin, 1909. c, Bleriot XI, 1911. d, Paterson No. 2 biplane, 1913. e, Henri Farman F.27, 1915. f, BE2e, 1918. g, Vickers Vimy Silver Queen, 1920. h, SE-5a, 1921. i, Avro 504K, 1921. j, Armstrong-Whitworth Atalanta, 1930. k, DH66 Hercules, 1931. l, Westland Wapiti, 1931. m, Junkers F.13, 1932. n, Handley Page HP-42, 1933. o, Junkers Ju52/3m, 1934. p, Junkers Ju86, 1936. q, Hawker Hartbees, 1936. r, Short Empire flying boat Canopus, 1937. s, Miles Master II and Airspeed AS-10 Oxford, 1940. t, Harvard Mk IIa, 1942. u, Short Sunderland, 1945. v, Avro York, 1946. w, Douglas DC-7B, 1955. x, Sikorsky S-55C, 1956. y, Boeing 707-344, 1959.

1993, May 7 **Litho.** ***Perf. 14x14½***

849	A287	45c Sheet of 25, #a.-y.	7.25	

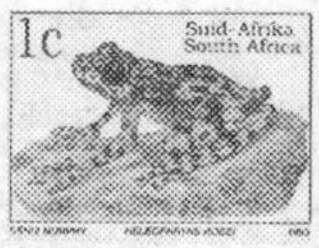

Endangered Fauna — A288

Designs: 1c, Heleophryne rosei. 2c, Bradypodion taeniabronchum. 5c, Cordylus giganteus. 10c, Psammobates geometricus. 20c, Atelerix frontalis. 40c, Bonolagus monticularis. No. 856, Diceros bicornis. 50c, Cercopithecus mitis. 55c, Proteles cristatus. 60c, Lycaon pictus. 70c, Hippotragus equinus. 75c, Poecilogale albinucha. 80c, Otis kori. 90c, Spheniscus demersus. 1r, Grus carunculatus. 2r, Hirundo atrocaerulea. 5r, Polemaetus bellicosus. 10r, Terathopius ecaudatus.

1993, Sept. 3 **Litho.** ***Perf. 14x14½***

850	A288	1c multicolored	.15	.15
851	A288	2c multicolored	.15	.15
852	A288	5c multicolored	.15	.15
853	A288	10c multicolored	.15	.15
854	A288	20c multicolored	.15	.15
a.		Strip of 5, 1c, 2 each 2c, 20c	*1.00*	
855	A288	40c multicolored	.25	.25
856	A288	(45c) multicolored	.28	.28
857	A288	50c multicolored	.30	.30
858	A288	55c multicolored	.32	.32
859	A288	60c multicolored	.35	.35
860	A288	70c multicolored	.42	.42
861	A288	75c multicolored	.45	.45
862	A288	80c multicolored	.48	.48
863	A288	90c multicolored	.55	.55
864	A288	1r multicolored	.60	.60
865	A288	2r multicolored	1.25	1.25
866	A288	5r multicolored	3.00	3.00
867	A288	10r multicolored	6.00	6.00
		Nos. 850-867 (18)	15.00	15.00

No. 856 is inscribed "Gestandaardiseerde pos / Standardised mail," and initially sold for 45c.

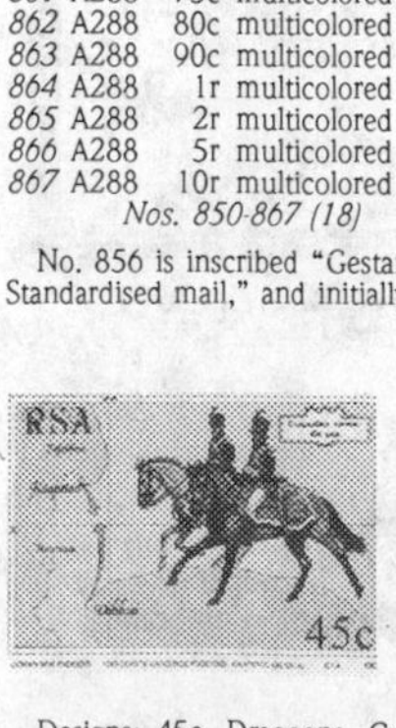

First Postal Services in South Africa, 190th Anniv. — A289

Designs: 45c, Dragoons, Cape Town-False Bay Route. 65c, Ox train, Cape Town-Stellenbosch. 85c, Khoi-Khoin runners. 1.05r, Post riders, Cape Town-eastern districts.

1993, Oct. 8   *Perf. 14x14½*
868	A289	45c multicolored	.28	.28
869	A289	65c multicolored	.40	.40
870	A289	85c multicolored	.50	.50
871	A289	1.05r multicolored	.62	.62
		Nos. 868-871 (4)	1.80	1.80

Tourism
A290

Designs: a, Namaqualand. b, North Beach, Durban. c, Lion. d, Apple Express. e, Oryx gazella.

1993, Nov. 12   *Litho.*   *Perf. 14½x14*
872	A290	85c Strip of 5, #a.-e.	2.50	2.50

Export
Fruits
A291

1994, Jan. 28   *Litho.*   *Perf. 14½x14*
873	A291	85c Grapes	.50	.50
a.		Souvenir sheet of 1	.50	.50
874	A291	90c Apples	.52	.52
875	A291	1.05r Plums	.60	.60
876	A291	1.25r Oranges	.75	.75
877	A291	1.40r Avocados	.85	.85
		Nos. 873-877 (5)	3.22	3.22

Peace and Goodwill — A292

Childrens' drawings: 45c, Smiling faces, by Nicole Davies. 70c, Dove flying toward olive tree, by Robynne Lawrie. 95c, Three girls, dove, scattered cartridge cases, by Batami Nothmann. 1.15r, Faces surrounding "peace," by Karen Uys.

1994, Apr. 8   *Litho.*   *Perf. 14½x14*
878	A292	45c multicolored	.25	.25
879	A292	70c multicolored	.40	.40
880	A292	95c multicolored	.55	.55
881	A292	1.15r multicolored	.65	.65
		Nos. 878-881 (4)	1.85	1.85

Inauguration of Pres.
Nelson
Mandela — A293

Perf. 14x14½, 14½x14
1994, May 10   *Litho.*
882	A293	45c shown	.25	.25
883	A293	70c Anthems, horiz.	.40	.40
884	A293	95c Flag, horiz.	.55	.55
885	A293	1.15r Union Bldgs., horiz.	.65	.65
		Nos. 882-885 (4)	1.85	1.85

Tugboats
A294

1994, May 13   *Perf. 14½x14*
886	A294	45c TS McEwen	.25	.25
887	A294	70c Sir William Hoy	.40	.40
888	A294	95c Sir Charles Elliott	.55	.55
889	A294	1.15r Eland	.65	.65
890	A294	1.35r Pioneer	.75	.75
a.		Souvenir sheet of 5, #886-890	2.60	2.60
		Nos. 886-890 (5)	2.60	2.60

Our Family — A295

Children's paintings: a, Mother Hands Out Work (C1.5). b, My Friends and I at Play (C2.5). c, Family Life (C3.5). d, Sunday in Church (C4.5). e, I Visit My Brother in the Hospital (C5.5).

1994, July 10   *Litho.*   *Perf. 14x14½*
891	A295	45c Strip of 5, #a.-e.	1.25	1.25

Stamp Day — A296

1994, Sept. 30   *Litho.*   *Perf. 14*
892	A296	50c Bulk mail	.28	.28
893	A296	70c Proof of delivery	.40	.40
894	A296	95c Registered mail	.55	.55
895	A296	1.15r Express delivery	.65	.65
		Nos. 892-895 (4)	1.88	1.88

Heath — A297

Designs: a, Erica tenuifolia. b, Erica urna-viridis. c, Erica decora. d, Erica aristata. e, Erica dichrus.

1994, Nov. 18   *Litho.*   *Perf. 14*
896	A297	95c Strip of 5, #a.-e.	2.75	2.75

Tourism — A298

Designs: No. 897, Phacochoerus aethiopicus, Eastern Transvaal Province. No. 898, Lost City, Sun City, North West Province. No. 899, Ceratotherium simum, KwaZulu/Natal Province. No. 900, Waterfront, Cape Town, Western Cape Province. No. 901, Adansonia digitata, Northern Transvaal Province. No. 902, Highland Route, Free State. No. 903, Augrabies Falls, Northern Cape Province. No. 904, Addo Elephant Natl. Park, Eastern Cape Province. No. 905, Union Buildings, Pretoria, Gauteng.
Illustration reduced.

1995   *Litho.*   *Perf. 14*
897	A298	50c multicolored	.28	.28
898	A298	50c multicolored	.28	.28
899	A298	60c multicolored	.35	.35
900	A298	60c multicolored	.35	.35
901	A298	60c multicolored	.35	.35
902	A298	60c multicolored	.35	.35
903	A298	60c multicolored	.35	.35
904	A298	60c multicolored	.35	.35
905	A298	60c multicolored	.35	.35
a.		Strip of 5, #901-905	1.75	1.75
		Nos. 897-905 (9)	3.01	3.01

Nos. 899-905 were inscribed "Standardized Mail" and sold for 60c on date of issue.
Issued: #897, 1/18; #898, 2/15; #899, 4/28; #900, 5/12; #901-905, 6/30.

South African Airforce, 75th
Anniv. — A299

Design: 50c, DeHavilland DH-9 biplane, Cheetah D fighter.

1995, Feb. 1   *Litho.*   *Perf. 14*
906	A299	50c multicolored	.28	.28

First Trans-Africa Flight, 75th
Anniv. — A300

Design: 95c, Vickers Vimy bomber Silver Queen, map of route.

1995, Feb. 1
907	A300	95c multicolored	.55	.55

South Africa,
1995 Rugby
World Cup
Champions
A301

Designs: No. 908, Shown. No. 909, Player running with ball, vert. No. 910, Player holding trophy, vert. No. 911, Like #908, World Champions. No. 912, Scrum, two players.

1995, May 25   *Litho.*   *Perf. 14*
908	A301	(60c) multicolored	.35	.35
909	A301	(60c) multicolored	.35	.35
a.		Souvenir sheet of 1	.35	.35
910	A301	(60c) multicolored	.35	.35
911	A301	(60c) multicolored	.35	.35

Size: 68x26mm
912	A301	1.15r multicolored	.65	.65
		Nos. 908-912 (5)	2.05	2.05

See note following Nos. 899-905.

CSIR (Council
for Scientific
and Industrial
Research), 50th
Anniv — A302

1995, June 15
913	A302	(60c) Purifying water	.35	.35

See note following Nos. 899-905.

Marine Science
in South Africa,
Cent. — A303

1995, Aug. 25   *Litho.*   *Perf. 14*
914	A303	(60c) Dr. JDF Gilchrist	.35	.35

No. 914 inscribed "Standard Postage."

Singapore '95 — A304

Illustration reduced.

1995, Sept. 1
915	A304	(60c) multicolored	.35	.35

See note following No. 914.

Masakhane
Campaign
A305

1995, Sept. 16
916	A305	(60c) multicolored	.35	.35

See note following No. 914.

Visit of Pope John
Paul II
A306

Mahatma
Gandhi
A307

1995, Sept. 16
917	A306	(60c) multicolored	.35	.35

See note following No. 914.

1995, Oct. 2

Designs: (60c), 1906 Photograph. 1.40r, Ghandhi in later years.
918	A307	(60c) blue	.35	.35
919	A307	1.40r brown	.80	.80
a.		Souvenir sheet of 1	.80	.80

No. 918 is inscribed "STANDARD POSTAGE." Design on stamp in No. 919a extends to perforations.
See India Nos. 1534-1535.

World Post Day — A308

1995
920	A308	(60c) multicolored	.35	.35

Size: 65x60mm
Imperf
921	A308	5r multicolored	3.00	3.00

Stampex '95.
Issued: (60c), 10/9; 5r, 10/19.
See note following No. 914.

Market value for a particular scarce stamp may remain relatively low if few collectors want it.

UN, 50th
Anniv. — A309

1995, Oct. 24   Litho.   Perf. 14
922 A309 (60c) multicolored   .35   .35
No. 922 inscribed "Standard Postage."

Souvenir Sheet

UNESCO, 50th Anniv. — A310

Illustration reduced.

1995, Oct. 24
923 A310 (60c) multicolored   .35   .35
See note following No. 922.

Shells — A311

1995, Nov. 24
924 A311 (60c) Afrivoluta priglei   .35   .35
925 A311 (60c) Lyria africana   .35   .35
926 A311 (60c) Marginella mosaica   .35   .35
927 A311 (60c) Conus pictus   .35   .35
928 A311 (60c) Gypreaea fultoni   .35   .35
   a.   Strip of 5, #924-928   1.75   1.75
See note following No. 922.

SEMI-POSTAL STAMPS

> Catalogue values for unused stamps in this section are for Never Hinged items.

English-Afrikaans Se-Tenant
Stamps with English inscriptions and with Afrikaans inscriptions of Nos. B1-B11 were printed alternately in the same sheets. Major-number listings and values are for pairs consisting of one English and one Afrikaans-inscribed stamp.

Church of the
Vow — SP1

Cradock's
Pass — SP2

Voortrekker
SP3

Voortrekker
Woman
SP4

1933-36   Photo.   Wmk. 201   Perf. 14
B1   SP1   ½p + ½p grn & blk,
        pair ('36)   3.25   3.75
   a.   Single, English   .30   .35
   b.   Single, Afrikaans   .30   .35
B2   SP2   1p + ½p rose & blk,
        pair   3.75   4.00
   a.   Single, English   .40   .45
   b.   Single, Afrikaans   .40   .45
B3   SP3   2p + 1p dull vio & gray,
        pair   7.50   7.50
   a.   Single, English   1.50   1.50
   b.   Single, Afrikaans   1.50   1.50
B4   SP4   3p + 1½p dp blue &
        gray, pair   15.00   15.00
   a.   Single, English   2.25   2.25
   b.   Single, Afrikaans   2.25   2.25
     Nos. B1-B4 (4)   29.50   30.25

Issued to commemorate the Voortrekkers. Surtax went to the National Memorial Fund for a national Voortrekker monument.

Voortrekker
Plowing — SP5

Crossing the
Drakensberg — SP6

Signing Dingaan-Relief Treaty — SP7

Proposed
Monument
SP8

1938, Dec. 14   Perf. 14
B5   SP5   ½p + ½p dl grn & ind,
        pair   5.75   4.75
   a.   Single, English   .35   .40
   b.   Single, Afrikaans   .35   .40
B6   SP6   1p + 1p rose & sl, pair   7.75   6.75
   a.   Single, English   .45   .50
   b.   Single, Afrikaans   .45   .50
             Perf. 15x14
B7   SP7   1½p + ½p Prus grn &
        choc, pair   14.00   13.50
   a.   Single, English   1.10   1.10
   b.   Single, Afrikaans   1.10   1.10
B8   SP8   3p + 3p chlky bl, pair   20.00   16.00
   a.   Single, English   2.25   2.50
   b.   Single, Afrikaans   2.25   2.50
     Nos. B5-B8 (4)   47.50   41.00

Voortrekker centenary. Surtax went to the Natl. Memorial Fund for a Voortrekker monument.

"The Old Vicarage,"
Huguenot
Museum — SP9

Rising Sun and
Cross — SP10

Huguenot
Dwelling,
Drakenstein
Mountain
Valley
SP11

1939, July 17   Photo.   Perf. 14
B9   SP9   ½p + ½p Prus grn &
        gray brn, pair   6.00   6.75
   a.   Single, English   .60   .60
   b.   Single, Afrikaans   .60   .60
B10   SP10   1p + 1p rose car & Prus
        grn, pair   6.75   7.00
   a.   Single, English   .90   .90
   b.   Single, Afrikaans   .90   .90

              Perf. 15x14
B11   SP11   1½p + 1½p, pair   9.00   11.00
   a.   Single, English   1.50   1.50
   b.   Single, Afrikaans   1.50   1.50
     Nos. B9-B11 (3)   21.75   24.75

250th anniv. of the landing of the Huguenots in South Africa. Surtax went to a fund to build a Huguenot memorial at Paarl.

No. 581 Surcharged in English or Afrikaans

a   +10c
          NATAL
     FLOOD DISASTER

b   +10c
     VLOEDRAMP
       NATAL

c   Nasionale   National
     Vloedramp   Flood Disaster
              +10c

d   +10c

1987, Nov. 16   Litho.   Perf. 14x14½
B12   Pair   1.25   1.25
   a.   A229(a) 16c +10c red   .60   .60
   b.   A229(b) 16c +10c red   .60   .60

Surcharge for flood relief.

No. 702 Surcharged in English or Afrikaans

1987, Dec. 1
B13   Pair   1.25   1.25
   a.   A254(a) 16c +10c multicolored   .60   .60
   b.   A254(b) 16c +10c multicolored   .60   .60

"+10c" is overprinted below text on Nos. B13a-B13b. Surcharge for flood relief.

No. 706 Surcharged in English or Afrikaans

1988, Mar. 1   Perf. 14½x14
B14   Pair   1.25   1.25
   a.   A256(a) 16c +10c multicolored   .60   .60
   b.   A256(b) 16c +10c multicolored   .60   .60

Surcharge for flood relief.

Nos. 710-713 Surcharged in English or Afrikaans

1988, Apr. 13   Perf. 14x14½
B15   Pair   .85   .85
   a.   A257(c) 16c +10c multicolored   .42   .42
   b.   A257(d) 16c +10c multicolored   .42   .42
B16   Pair   1.65   1.65
   a.   A257(c) 30c +10c multicolored   .80   .80
   b.   A257(d) 30c +10c multicolored   .80   .80
B17   Pair   2.25   2.25
   a.   A257(c) 40c +10c multicolored   1.10   1.10
   b.   A257(d) 40c +10c multicolored   1.10   1.10
B18   Pair   2.75   2.75
   a.   A257(c) 50c +10c multicolored   1.25   1.25
   b.   A257(d) 50c +10c multicolored   1.25   1.25
     Nos. B12-B18 (7)   11.25   11.25

Surcharge for flood relief.
On Nos. B16a, B16b, the "+ 10" is in upper left corner.

AIR POST STAMPS

Mail
Plane — AP1

Biplane in
Flight — AP2

Unwmk.

1925, Feb. 26   Litho.   Perf. 12
C1   AP1   1p red   6.00   9.00
C2   AP1   3p ultramarine   9.00   10.50
C3   AP1   6p violet   10.50   15.00
C4   AP1   9p gray green   24.00   40.00
     Nos. C1-C4 (4)   49.50   74.50

1929, Aug. 16   Typo.   Perf. 14x13½
C5   AP2   4p blue green   3.25   2.00
C6   AP2   1sh orange   13.00   12.00

POSTAGE DUE STAMPS

D1   D2

Wmk. Springbok's Head (177)
1914-15   Typo.   Perf. 14
J1   D1   ½p green & blk   1.10   1.25
J2   D1   1p red & blk   .90   .35
J3   D1   2p vio & blk ('14)   2.00   .15
J4   D1   3p ultra & blk   1.10   .20
J5   D1   5p brown & blk   4.50   12.00
J6   D1   6p gray & blk   7.50   15.00
J7   D1   1sh black & red   65.00   110.00
     Nos. J1-J7 (7)   82.10   138.95

1922   Unwmk.   Litho.   Rouletted 7-8
J8   D1   ½p blue grn & blk   .40   .50
J9   D1   1p dull red & blk   .60   .70
J10   D1   1½p yellow brn & blk   .90   1.00
     Nos. J8-J10 (3)   1.90   2.20

1922-26   Perf. 14
J11   D1   ½p blue grn & blk   .20   .20
J12   D1   1p rose & blk ('23)   .35   .15
J13   D1   1½p yel brn & blk ('24)   1.00   .80
J14   D1   2p vio & blk ('23)   .85   .38
   a.   Imperf. pair   250.00
J15   D1   3p blue & blk ('26)   5.00   2.25
J16   D1   6p gray & blue ('23)   5.50   3.25
     Nos. J11-J16 (6)   12.90   7.03

1927-28   Typo.
J17   D2   ½p blue green & blk   .40   .50
J18   D2   1p rose & black   .40   .40
J19   D2   2p violet & black   .70   .60
J20   D2   3p ultra & black   6.50   6.50
J21   D2   6p gray & black   10.00   10.00
     Nos. J17-J21 (5)   18.00   18.00

> Catalogue values for unused stamps in this section, from this point to the end of the section, are for Never Hinged items.

Type of 1927-28 Redrawn
Perf. 15x14
1932-40   Photo.   Wmk. 201
J22   D2   ½p blue grn & blk ('34)   1.00   1.25
J23   D2   1p rose car & blk ('34)   .95   .95
J24   D2   2p blk violet & blk   4.00   .30
   a.   2p dark purple & black ('40)   11.00   .20
J25   D2   3p dp blue & blk   18.00   12.00
J26   D2   3p ultra & dk bl ('35)   3.50   .40
J27   D2   3p blk & dk bl ('40)   21.00   2.00
J28   D2   6p brn org & grn ('33)   18.00   6.00
J29   D2   6p red org & grn ('38)   8.50   2.00
     Nos. J22-J29 (8)   81.95   24.80

The ½p No. J22 photogravure has larger but thinner numeral and the "d" is taller and thinner than on No. J17.
The 1p No. J23 photogravure has numeral with parallel sides. The "d" is taller and thicker than on No. J18.
On Nos. J25 and J27 the numeral is followed by a large "d" with thick lines and a large round period below it.
Nos. J22, J24 and J25 have frame in photogravure, value typographed.

See "English-Afrikaans Se-tenant" note preceding No. 23.

D3

Horiz. strips of Three, Perf. 15x14 All Around, Rouletted 6½ Between

1943-44 Photo. Wmk. 201

J30 D3 ½p Prus green ('44)	8.50	9.00
a. Single	.16	.18
J31 D3 1p brt carmine	9.50	5.25
a. Single	.16	.18
J32 D3 2p dark purple	9.00	7.75
a. Single	.16	.18
J33 D3 3p dark blue	55.00	55.00
a. Single	.16	.18
Nos. J30-J33 (4)	82.00	77.00

Catalogued as strips of 3 because of the perforations.

Type of 1932-38, Redrawn
Thick Numerals, Capital "D"

1948-49 ***Perf. 15x14***

J34 D2 ½p blue green & blk	8.00	6.00
J35 D2 1p deep rose & blk	8.50	2.50
J36 D2 2p dk pur & blk ('49)	11.00	2.50
J37 D2 3p ultra & dk blue	12.00	9.00
J38 D2 6p dp org & grn ('49)	35.00	7.00
Nos. J34-J38 (5)	74.50	27.00

Redrawn Type of 1948-49
Hyphen between Suid-Afrika

1950-58 ***Perf. 15x14***

J40 D2 1p car rose & blk	.95	.40
J41 D2 2p dk pur & blk ('51)	.65	.25
J42 D2 3p ultra & dk blue	5.25	2.25
J43 D2 4p emer & dk grn ('58)	10.00	10.00
J44 D2 6p dp org & grn ('52)	9.50	10.50
J45 D2 1sh brn red & dk brn ('58)	13.00	13.00
Nos. J40-J45 (6)	39.35	36.40

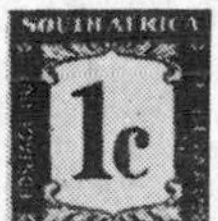

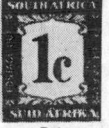

D4

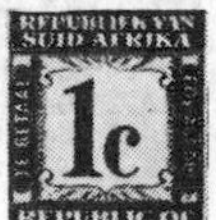

D5

Perf. 15x14

1961, Feb. 14 Photo. Wmk. 330

J46 D4 1c cerise & blk	.15	2.50
J47 D4 2c purple & blk	.15	2.50
J48 D4 4c brt & dk green	1.00	*6.00*
J49 D4 5c chalky blue & slate	2.00	*6.50*
J50 D4 6c vermilion & dk grn	8.00	*7.00*
J51 D4 10c maroon & dk brn	8.50	*10.00*
Nos. J46-J51 (6)	19.80	*34.50*

Republic

1961-69 ***Perf. 15x14***

Afrikaans Inscription on Top and Left Side

J52 D5 1c cerise & blk	.40	.40
J53 D5 4c brt & dk green	.45	.45
J54 D5 6c vermilion & dk grn	1.50	1.75

English Inscription on Top and Left Side

J55 D5 1c cerise & blk ('62)	.25	3.00
J56 D5 2c purple & blk	.35	.35
J57 D5 4c brt & dk grn ('69)	8.00	11.00
J58 D5 5c chlky bl & dk bl	2.00	2.50
J59 D5 5c chlky bl & blk ('62)	1.50	7.00
J60 D5 10c maroon & dk brn	4.00	2.50
Nos. J52-J60 (9)	18.45	28.95

1967-70 Photo. Wmk. 359

Afrikaans Inscription on Top and Left Side

J61 D5 1c carmine rose & blk	.15	.15
J62 D5 2c brt purple & blk	.20	.20
a. Perf. 14 ('71)	18.00	18.00
J63 D5 4c lt grn & blk ('71)	15.00	18.00
a. 4c bright & dark green ('70)	*75.00*	*75.00*
J64 D5 5c chky blue & blk	.60	.60
J65 D5 6c orange & dk grn	3.00	7.00
J66 D5 10c dk rose brown & blk	1.50	1.50

English Inscription on Top and Left Side

J67 D5 1c car rose & blk	.15	.15
J68 D5 2c brt purple & blk	.30	.30
a. Perf. 14 ('71)	18.00	18.00
J69 D5 4c lt green & blk ('71)	15.00	18.00
a. 4c bright & dark green ('70)	*25.00*	*25.00*
b. As "a," perf. 14 ('71)	*42.50*	42.50
J70 D5 5c dk blue & blk	.60	.60
J71 D5 6c orange & dk grn	3.00	7.00
J72 D5 10c dk rose brown & blk	1.50	1.50
Nos. J61-J72 (12)	41.00	55.00

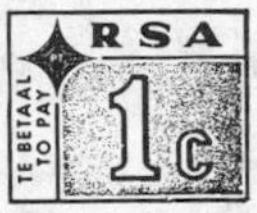

D6

1972, Mar. 22 ***Perf. 14x13½***

J73 D6 1c brt yellow green	.40	1.50
J74 D6 2c orange	.50	1.50
J75 D6 4c dull purple	1.50	2.50
J76 D6 6c yellow	1.50	3.50
J77 D6 8c bright blue	1.50	4.00
J78 D6 10c rose red	4.00	5.00
Nos. J73-J78 (6)	9.40	18.00

On the 2c, 6c and 10c "TO PAY" in first row at left.

OFFICIAL STAMPS

Type A2 stamps have very small margins at top and bottom. Values are for copies with perfs close to, or touching the frame.

Regular Issues Overprinted in Black

OFFICIAL. OFFISIEEL.

Periods in Overprint
On No. 5

1926 Wmk. 177 ***Perf. 14***

O1 A2 2p dull violet	10.00	2.00

See "English-Afrikaans Se-tenant" note preceding No. 23.

On Nos. 23-25
Perf. 14½x14
Wmk. 201

O2 A5 ½p dk grn & blk, pair	4.25	4.25
a. Single, English	.75	.30
b. Single, Afrikaans	.75	.30
O3 A6 1p car & blk, pair	1.75	1.75
a. Single, English	.25	.20
b. Single, Afrikaans	.25	.20
O4 A7 6p org & grn, pair	600.00	100.00
a. Single, English	25.00	7.50
b. Single, Afrikaans	25.00	7.50

Nos. 26 and 25 Overprinted (Reading Up)

b OFFICIAL OFFISIEEL

No Periods in Overprint

1928-29 ***Perf. 14, 14½x14***

Space between words 19mm

O5 A8 2p vio brn & gray, pair ('29)	2.50	2.50
a. Single, English	.40	.30
b. Single, Afrikaans	.40	.30
c. Space 17½mm, pair	2.50	2.50
d. As "c," single, English	.25	.20
e. As "c," single, Afrikaans	.25	.20

Space between words 11½mm

O6 A7 6p org & grn, pair	10.00	*15.00*
a. Single, English	1.00	.70
b. Single, Afrikaans	1.00	.70

#23-25 Ovptd. type "b" Reading Down
Space between words 13½-14mm

1929 ***Perf. 14½x14***

O7 A5 ½p grn & blk, pair	.50	.50
a. Single, English	.15	.15
b. Single, Afrikaans	.15	.15
c. Period after "OFFISIEEL" on English stamp	2.75	2.75
d. Pair, "c" + normal ½p	7.00	7.00
e. Period after "OFFISIEEL." on Afrikaans stamp	3.25	3.25
f. Pair, "e" + normal ½p	8.50	7.25
O8 A6 1p car & blk, pair	.65	.45
a. Single, English	.15	.15
b. Single, Afrikaans	.15	.15
O9 A7 6p org & grn, pair	2.75	1.80
a. Single, English	.50	.40
b. Single, Afrikaans	.50	.40
c. Period after "OFFISIEEL." on English stamp	8.00	8.00
d. Pair, "c" + normal 6p	18.00	18.00
e. Period after "OFFISIEEL." on Afrikaans stamp	8.00	8.00
f. Pair, "e" + normal 6p	18.00	18.00
Nos. O7-O9 (3)	3.90	2.75

#29-30 Ovptd. type "b" Reading Down
Space between words 17½-19mm

1931 Engr. ***Perf. 14, 14x13½***

O10 A11 1sh dp bl & bis brn, pair	12.00	12.00
a. Single, English	2.25	2.25
b. Single, Afrikaans	2.25	2.25
c. Period after "OFFICIAL." on Afrikaans stamp	50.00	50.00
d. Pair, "c" + normal 1sh	75.00	75.00
O11 A12 2sh6p brn & bl grn, pair	15.00	15.00
a. Single, English	2.50	2.50
b. Single, Afrikaans	2.50	2.50
c. Period after "OFFICIAL." on Afrikaans stamp	72.50	72.50
d. Pair, "c" + normal 2sh6p	300.00	300.00

Regular Issues of 1930-45 Overprinted type "b" Reading Down
("SUIDAFRIKA" on Afrikaans stamps)

Perf. 15x14 (½p, 1p, 6p), 14

1930-47 Photo. Wmk. 201

Space between words 9½-12mm
(Various spacings occur in same setting)

O12 A5 ½p bl grn & blk (#33), pair ('31)	.30	.25
a. Single, English	.15	.15
b. Single, Afrikaans	.15	.15
c. Period after "OFFISIEEL." on English stamp	4.50	4.50
d. Pair, "c" + normal ½p	7.50	7.50
e. Period after "OFFISIEEL." on Afrikaans stamp	5.00	5.00
f. Pair, "e" + normal ½p	9.00	9.00

Space between words 12½-13½mm

O13 A5 ½p bl grn & blk, pair (#33)	.75	.75
a. Single, English	.15	.15
b. Single, Afrikaans	.15	.15
O14 A6 1p car & blk, pair (#34)	.45	.35
a. Single, English	.15	.15
b. Single, Afrikaans	.15	.15
c. Period after "OFFISIEEL." on English stamp	4.75	4.75
d. Pair, "c" + normal 1p	6.00	6.00
e. Period after "OFFISIEEL." on Afrikaans stamp	5.75	5.75
f. Pair, "e" + normal 1p	10.00	10.00
O15 A6 1p rose & blk, pair (#35) ('33)	.90	.75
a. Single, English	.25	.20
b. Single, Afrikaans	.25	.20
c. Double ovpt., pair	400.00	
d. As "c," English	57.50	
e. As "c," Afrikaans	57.50	

Space between words 20½-22mm

O16 A8 2p vio & gray, pair (#36) ('31)	1.25	.85
a. Single, English	.25	.15
b. Single, Afrikaans	.25	.15
O17 A8 2p vio & ind, pair (#37)	16.00	10.00
a. Single, English	1.25	.50
b. Single, Afrikaans	1.25	.50

Space between words 12½-13½mm

O18 A7 6p org & grn, pair (#42)	9.50	3.00
a. Single, English	.55	.35
b. Single, Afrikaans	.55	.35
c. Period after "OFFISIEEL." on English stamp	11.00	11.00
d. Pair, "c" + normal 6p	18.00	18.00
e. Period after "OFFISIEEL." on Afrikaans stamp	13.50	13.50
f. Pair, "e" + normal 6p	22.50	22.50

Space between words 21mm

O19 A11 1sh dp bl & brn, pair (#43) ('32)	8.00	6.25
a. Single, English	1.00	.30
b. Single, Afrikaans	1.00	.30
c. 1sh dk bl & yel brn (#43c), 19mm, pair	25.00	35.00
d. As "c," single, English	.70	.25
e. As "c," single, Afrikaans	.70	.25
f. As "c," spaced 21mm, pair	30.00	35.00
g. As "f," single, English	9.00	4.50
h. As "f," single, Afrikaans	9.00	4.50

Space between words 17½-18½mm

O20 A12 2sh6p red brn & grn, pair (#44) ('33)	32.50	37.50
a. Single, English	3.25	1.75
b. Single, Afrikaans	3.25	1.75
c. Spaced 21mm, pair	50.00	50.00
d. As "c," single, English	2.75	1.75
e. As "c," single, Afrikaans	2.75	1.75
f. 2sh6p brn & sl grn (#44c) ('37), pair	22.50	22.50
g. As "f," single, English	3.50	2.75
h. As "f," single, Afrikaans	3.50	2.75
j. 2sh6p brn & bl, 19-20mm (#44i) ('47), pair	32.50	40.00
k. As "j," single, English	2.25	1.40
m. As "j," single, Afrikaans	2.25	1.40
Nos. O12-O20 (9)	69.65	59.70

Catalogue values for unused stamps in this section, from this point to the end of the section, are for Never Hinged items.

Regular Issue of 1933-54 Overprinted type "b" Reading Down
("SUID-AFRIKA" Hyphenated)

1935-50 Photo. ***Perf. 15x14, 14***

Space between words given with each listing

O21 A5 ½p grn & gray (#45), 12½-13mm, pair ('36)	3.00	1.00
a. Single, English	.15	.15
b. Single, Afrikaans	.15	.15
O22 A5 ½p grn & gray, (#46), 11½-13mm, pair ('38)	.70	.30
a. Single, English	.15	.15
b. Single, Afrikaans	.15	.15
O23 A5 ½p grn & gray (#47), 11½mm, pair ('48)	.55	.35
a. Single, English	.15	.15
b. Single, Afrikaans	.15	.15
O24 A6 1p car & gray (#48), 11-13mm, pair	.40	.40
a. Single, English	.15	.15
b. Single, Afrikaans	.15	.15
O25 A6 1p rose car & gray blk (#49), 11½-12mm, pair ('41)	.75	.50
a. Single, English	.15	.15
b. Single, Afrikaans	.15	.15
O26 A15 1½p dk grn & gold (#51), 19-21mm, pair ('37)	14.00	1.00
a. Single, English	.25	.15
b. Single, Afrikaans	.25	.15
O27 A15 1½p sl grn & ocher (#52), 14-14½mm, pair ('44)	.50	.30
a. Single, English	.15	.15
b. Single, Afrikaans	.15	.15
c. Ovpt. spaced 16mm, pair	1.50	1.50
d. As "c," single, English	.30	.25
e. As "c," single, Afrikaans	.30	.25
O28 A8 2p bl vio & dl bl (#53), 20-21mm, pair ('39)	55.00	3.00
a. Single, English	.60	.30
b. Single, Afrikaans	.60	.30
O29 A16 2p pur & sl (#55), 19-21mm, pair ('48)	3.00	.35
a. Single, English	.15	.15
b. Single, Afrikaans	.15	.15
O30 A7 6p org & bl grn, I (#59), 12-13mm, pair ('38)	77.50	21.00
a. Single, English	5.25	3.50
b. Single, Afrikaans	5.25	3.50
O31 A7 6p org & grn, II (#60), 12-13mm, pair ('39)	10.00	3.00
a. Single, English	.30	.25
b. Single, Afrikaans	.30	.25
O32 A7 6p org & grn III (#61), 11½-12mm, pair ('47)	2.25	1.80
a. Single, English	.25	.20
b. Single, Afrikaans	.25	.20
O33 A11 1sh lt bl & ol brn (#62), 19-21mm, pair ('40)	40.00	1.50
a. Single, English	.30	.15
b. Single, Afrikaans	.30	.15
c. "OFFICIAL" on both sides	90.00	
d. "OFFISIEEL" on both sides	90.00	
e. 1sh chlky bl & lt brn (#62c) ('50), pair	3.00	1.80
f. As "e," single, English	.60	.15
g. As "e," single, Afrikaans	.60	.15
h. 1sh vio bl & brnsh blk (#62f), 18-19mm, pair	40.00	1.80
j. As "h," single, English	.60	.15
k. As "h," single, Afrikaans	.60	.15
O34 A13 5sh grn & blk (#64) 19-20mm, pair	40.00	12.00
a. Single, English	3.00	1.80
b. Single, Afrikaans	3.00	1.80
O35 A13 5sh bl grn & blk (#65), 20mm, pair	40.00	12.00
a. Single, English	2.00	1.10
b. Single, Afrikaans	2.00	1.10
O36 A18 10sh ol blk & bl (#67), 19½-20mm, pair ('48)	70.00	25.00
a. Single, English	4.50	2.00
b. Single, Afrikaans	4.50	2.00
Nos. O21-O36 (16)	357.65	83.50

Nos. 52 and 56 Overprinted type "b" Reading Up
Space between words 16mm

1949-50 Size: 22x18mm ***Perf. 14***

O37 A15 1½p sl grn & ocher, pair	2.00	.75
a. Single, English	.15	.15

b. Single, Afrikaans .15 .15

Size: 21½x17½mm

O38 A16 2p pur & sl bl, pair ('50) 900. 1,100.
a. Single, English 100. 50.
b. Single, Afrikaans 100. 50.

Nos. 64, 67 Overprinted

OFFICIAL OFFISIEEL

c

Space between words 18-19mm

1940 ***Perf. 14***

O39 A13 5sh grn & blk, pair 15.00 9.00
a. Single, English 2.50 1.10
b. Single, Afrikaans 2.50 1.10
O40 A18 10sh ol brn & bl, pair 30.00 25.00
a. Single, English 4.50 2.50
b. Single, Afrikaans 4.50 2.50

No. 54 Overprinted type "c" Reading Up
Space between words 19mm

1945 ***Perf. 14***

O41 A8 2p dl vio & gray, pair .75 .55
a. Single, English .15 .15
b. Single, Afrikaans .15 .15

No. 47 Overprinted

OFFICIAL OFFISIEEL

1947 ***Perf. 15x14***

O42 A5 ½p grn & gray, pair .75 .50
a. Single, English .15 .15
b. Single, Afrikaans .15 .15

Stamps of 1937-54 Overprinted

OFFISIEEL OFFICIAL

1950-54 ***Perf. 15x14, 14***

Space between words 10mm

O43 A5 ½p grn & gray, pair (#47) .30 .20
a. Single, English .15 .15
b. Single, Afrikaans .15 .15
O44 A6 1p rose car & gray blk, pair (#49) .70 .70
a. Single, English .15 .15
b. Single, Afrikaans .15 .15
O45 A6 1p car & blk, pair (#50) .25 .15
a. Single, English .15 .15
b. Single, Afrikaans .15 .15

Space between words 14½mm

O46 A15 1½p sl grn & ocher, pair (#52) .50 .45
a. Single, English .15 .15
b. Single, Afrikaans .15 .15
O47 A16 2p pur & sl bl, pair (#56) .50 .45
a. Single, English .15 .15
b. Single, Afrikaans .15 .15
c. Ovpt. reading up, pair

Space between words 10mm

O48 A7 6p red org & bl grn, III, pair (#61c) .85 .45
a. Single, English .15 .15
b. Single, Afrikaans .15 .15

Space between words 19mm

O49 A11 1sh chky bl & lt brn, pair (#62c) 6.75 2.10
a. Single, English .30 .15
b. Single, Afrikaans .30 .15
c. 1sh vio bl & brnsh blk (#62f), pair 125.00 32.50
d. As "c," single, English 6.00 2.50
e. As "c," single, Afrikaans 6.00 2.50
O50 A12 2sh6p brn & brt grn, pair (#63) 10.00 6.50
a. Single, English .80 .60
b. Single, Afrikaans .80 .60
O51 A13 5sh grn & blk, pair (#64) 125.00 8.50
a. Single, English 1.75 .90
b. Single, Afrikaans 1.75 .90
O52 A13 5sh bl grn & blk, I, pair (#65) 35.00 6.50
a. Single, English 2.00 .70
b. Single, Afrikaans 2.00 .70
O53 A13 5sh grn & blk, II, pair (#66) 60.00 10.00
a. Single, English 1.75 1.50
b. Single, Afrikaans 1.75 1.50
O54 A18 10sh ol blk & bl, pair (#67) 60.00 16.00
a. Single, English 4.50 2.50
b. Single, Afrikaans 4.50 2.50
Nos. O43-O54 (12) 299.85 52.00

BOPHUTHATSWANA

ˌbō–(ˌ)pü–tät–ˈswä–nə

LOCATION — Noncontiguous enclaves, Republic of South Africa
GOVT. — Self-governing tribal homeland
AREA — 27,340 sq. mi.
POP. — 1,660,000 (1985)
CAPITAL — Mmabatho

Catalogue values for all unused stamps in this country are for Never Hinged items.

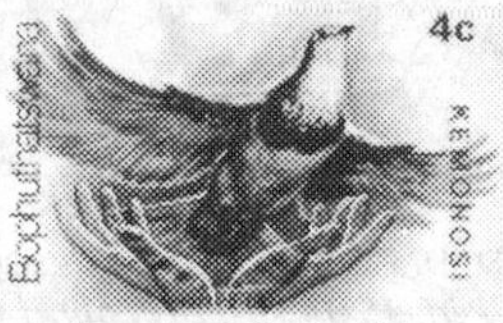

Independence from South Africa — A1

Perf. 12½

1977, Dec. 6 **Litho.** **Unwmk.**

1 A1 4c Hands, dove released 1.00 1.00
2 A1 10c Leopard (state emblem) 2.50 2.50
3 A1 15c Coat of arms 3.75 3.75
4 A1 20c Flag 5.25 5.25
Nos. 1-4 (4) 12.50 12.50

An imperf. souvenir sheet exists containing Nos. 1-4 printed in one color (blue). Not valid for postage.

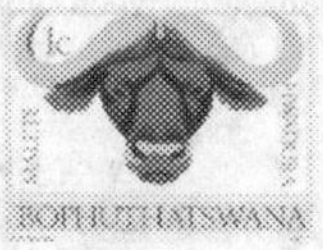

Tribal Totems — A2

Designs: 1c, African buffalo (Malete, Hwaduba). 2c, Bush pig (Kolobeng). 3c, Chacma baboon (Hurutshe, Thlaro). 4c, Leopard (state emblem). 5c, Crocodile (Kwena-Fokeng). 6c, Savanna monkey (Kgatla). 7c, Lion (Taung). 8c, Spotted hyena (Phiring). 9c, Cape porcupine (Rokologadi). 10c, Aardvark (Tlokwa). 15c, Fish (Tlhaping). 20c, Hunting dog (Tlhalerwa). 25c, Common duiker (Mfatlha). 30c, African elephant (Tlhako, Tloung). 50c, Python (Nogeng). 1r, Hippopotamus (Kubung). 2r, Greater kudu (Rolong).

1977, Dec. 6

5 A2 1c multicolored .15 .15
6 A2 2c multicolored .15 .15
7 A2 3c multicolored .15 .15
8 A2 4c multicolored .15 .15
9 A2 5c on 4c multi .50 .50
10 A2 6c multicolored .18 .18
11 A2 7c multicolored .21 .21
12 A2 8c multicolored .24 .24
13 A2 9c multicolored .27 .27
14 A2 10c multicolored .30 .30
15 A2 15c multicolored .45 .45
16 A2 20c multicolored .60 .60
17 A2 25c multicolored .75 .75
18 A2 30c multicolored .90 .90
19 A2 50c multicolored 1.50 1.50
20 A2 1r multicolored 3.00 3.00
21 A2 2r multicolored 6.00 6.00
Nos. 5-21 (17) 15.50 15.50

No. 9 was printed as a 4c stamp. Grass was printed over the 4c at upper right and 5c printed at upper left. Copies exist without the surcharge. No. 9A does not have the 4c.

Perf. 14

5a A2 1c .15 .15
6a A2 2c .15 .15
7a A2 3c .15 .15
8a A2 4c .15 .15
9A A2 5c multicolored .15 .15
11a A2 7c .15 .15
12a A2 8c .20 .20
14a A2 10c .20 .20
Nos. 5a-14a (8) 1.30 1.30

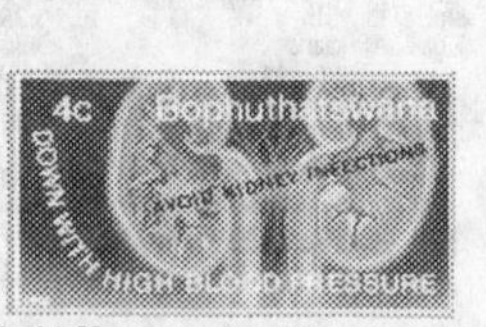

World Hypertension Month — A3

1978, Apr. 7 ***Perf. 12x12½***

22 A3 4c Avoid kidney infections .90 .90
23 A3 10c Lower salt intake 2.25 2.25
24 A3 15c Overeating is dangerous 3.25 3.25
Nos. 22-24 (3) 6.40 6.40

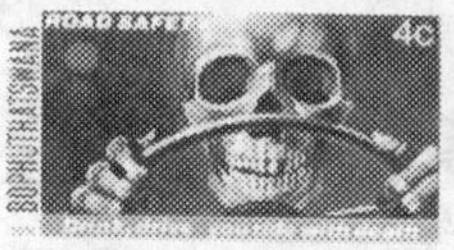

Road Safety — A4

1978, July 12

25 A4 4c Don't drink and drive .52 .52
26 A4 10c Keep children off roads 1.25 1.25
27 A4 15c Pedestrians observe crossing signals 2.00 2.00
28 A4 20c Observe stop signs 2.50 2.50
Nos. 25-28 (4) 6.27 6.27

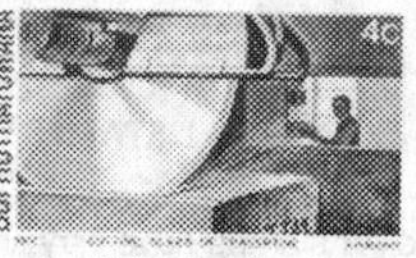

Cutting and Polishing Semi-precious Stones — A5

1978, Oct. 3

29 A5 4c Cutting slabs of travertine .45 .45
30 A5 10c Polishing travertine 1.10 1.10
31 A5 15c Sorting stones 1.65 1.65
32 A5 20c Factory at Taung 2.25 2.25
Nos. 29-32 (4) 5.45 5.45

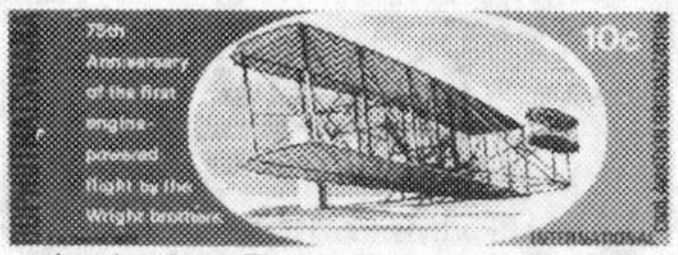

1st Airplane Flight, 75th Anniv. — A6

Illustration reduced.

1978, Dec. 1 ***Perf. 12½***

33 A6 10c Wright Flyer 1.40 1.40
34 A6 15c Orville and Wilbur Wright 2.25 2.25

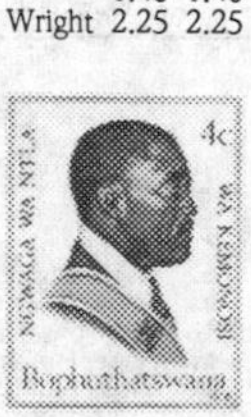

Pres. Lucas M. Mangope — A7

1978, Dec. 6

35 A7 4c Profile .32 .32
36 A7 15c Portrait 1.25 1.25

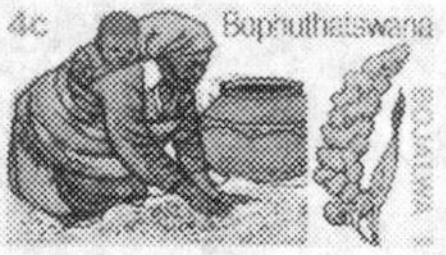

Sorghum Beer Production A8

1979, Feb. 28 ***Perf. 14x14½***

37 A8 4c Drying germinated wheat .28 .28
38 A8 15c Cooking ground grain 1.00 1.00
39 A8 20c Straining the liquid 1.40 1.40
40 A8 25c Drinking beer 1.75 1.75
Nos. 37-40 (4) 4.43 4.43

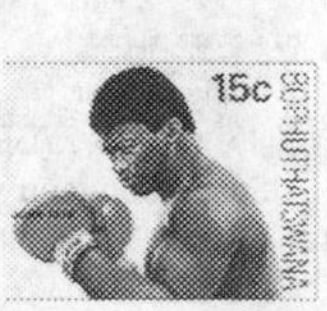

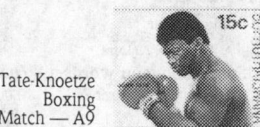

Tate-Knoetze Boxing Match — A9

1979, June 2

41 A9 15c John Tate 1.65 1.65
42 A9 15c Kallie Knoetze 1.65 1.65
a. Pair, #41-42 3.30 3.30

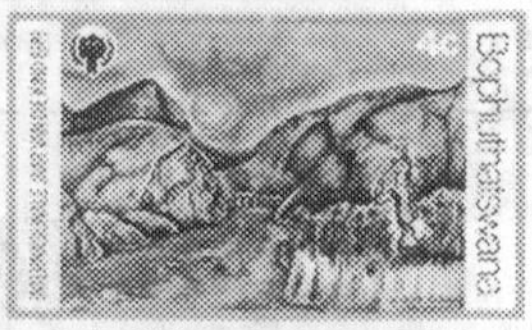

Intl. Children's Year — A10

Illustrations by local youths: 4c, Boy dazzled by sun, from a folk tale, by Hendrick Sebapo. 15c, Africans and animal silhouettes, by Daisy Morapedi. 20c, Man in profile and landscape, by Peter Tladi. 25c, Old man, boy and mule, by Sebapo.

1979, June 7 ***Perf. 14½x14***

43 A10 4c multicolored .24 .24
44 A10 15c multicolored .90 .90
45 A10 20c multicolored 1.25 1.25
46 A10 25c multicolored 1.50 1.50
Nos. 43-46 (4) 3.89 3.89

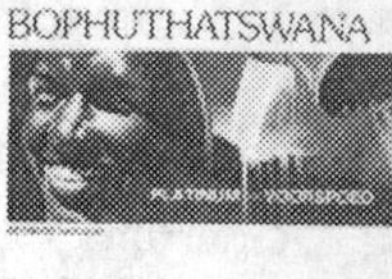

Platinum Industry A11

Designs: 4c, Pouring molten metal. 15c, Platinum in industrial use. 20c, Telecommunications satellite in orbit. 25c, Jewelry.

1979, Aug. 15 ***Perf. 14x14½***

47 A11 4c multicolored .16 .16
48 A11 15c multicolored .60 .60
49 A11 20c multicolored .80 .80
50 A11 25c multicolored 1.00 1.00
Nos. 47-50 (4) 2.56 2.56

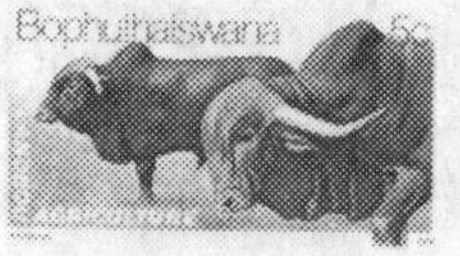

Agriculture A12

1979, Oct. 25

51 A12 5c Cattle .20 .20
52 A12 15c Picking cotton .60 .60
53 A12 20c Researchist in corn field .80 .80
54 A12 25c Fish in net 1.00 1.00
Nos. 51-54 (4) 2.60 2.60

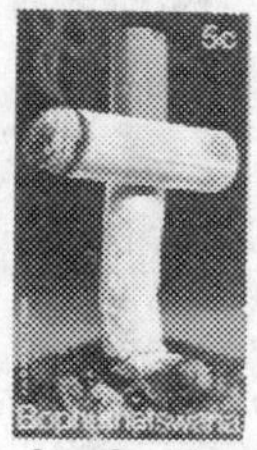

Stop Smoking Campaign A13

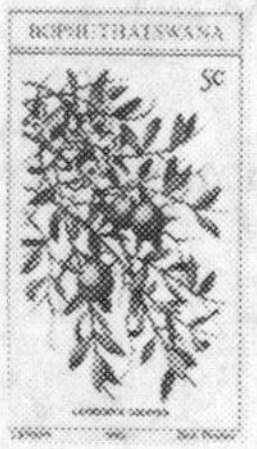

Edible Wild Fruit A14

1980, Mar. 5 ***Perf. 14½x14***

55 A13 5c multicolored .70 .70

1980, June 4

56 A14 5c *Landolphia capensis* .15 .15
57 A14 10c *Vangueria infausta* .30 .30
58 A14 15c *Bequaertiodendron magalismontanum* .45 .45
59 A14 20c *Sclerocarya caffra* .60 .60
Nos. 56-59 (4) 1.50 1.50

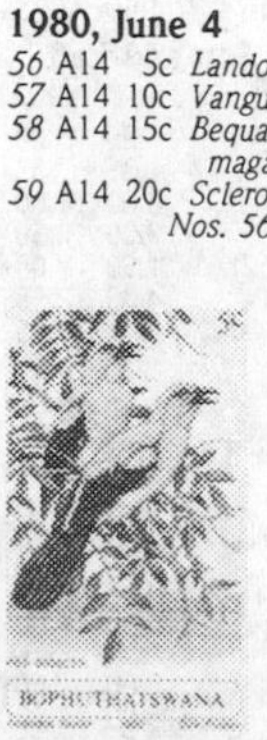

Birds — A15

1980, Sept. 10

60 A15 5c Pied babbler .15 .15
61 A15 10c Carmine bee-eater .30 .30
62 A15 15c Shaft-tailed whydah .45 .45
63 A15 20c Meyer's parrot .60 .60
Nos. 60-63 (4) 1.50 1.50

Sun City
Tourist
Attractions
A16

1980, Dec. 5 — Perf. 14x14½
64 A16 5c Hotel, casino, country
        club .20 .20
65 A16 10c Golfer at Gary Player
        Country Club .40 .40
66 A16 15c Casino interior .60 .60
67 A16 20c Night club dancers .80 .80
    Nos. 64-67 (4) 2.00 2.00

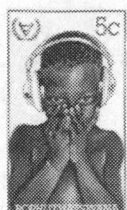

Intl. Year for the
Disabled — A17

1981, Jan. 30 — Perf. 14½x14
68 A17 5c shown .15 .15
69 A17 15c Blind boy .30 .30
70 A17 20c Archer in wheelchair .40 .40
71 A17 25c X-ray (tuberculosis) .50 .50
    Nos. 68-71 (4) 1.35 1.35

Easter
A18

Bible quotes and: 5c, Lamb, sunset. 15c, Bread.
20c, Man holding lamb. 25c, Wheat field.

1981, Apr. 1 — Perf. 14x14½
72 A18 5c multicolored .15 .15
73 A18 15c multicolored .30 .30
74 A18 20c multicolored .40 .40
75 A18 25c multicolored .50 .50
    Nos. 72-75 (4) 1.35 1.35

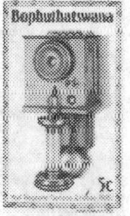

Telephones   Grasses
A19   A20

Designs: 5c, Siemens & Halske wall telephone,
1885. 15c, Ericsson table model, 1895. 20c, Hasler
table model, 1900. 25c, Mix & Genest wall model,
1904.

1981, July 31 — Perf. 14½x14
76 A19 5c multicolored .15 .15
77 A19 15c multicolored .30 .30
78 A19 20c multicolored .40 .40
79 A19 25c multicolored .50 .50
    Nos. 76-79 (4) 1.35 1.35

1981, Nov. 25
80 A20 5c Themeda triandra .15 .15
81 A20 15c Rhynchelytrum repens .30 .30
82 A20 20c Eragrostis capensis .40 .40
83 A20 25c Monocymbium ceresi-
        iforme .50 .50
    Nos. 80-83 (4) 1.35 1.35

Boy Scouts,   Easter — A22
75th
Anniv. — A21

1982, Jan. 29
84 A21 5c Scout, 1982 .15 .15
85 A21 15c Mafeking Siege stamps .45 .45
86 A21 20c Scout cadet, 1907 .60 .60
87 A21 25c Lord Baden-Powell .75 .75
    Nos. 84-87 (4) 1.95 1.95

1982, Apr. 1
88 A22 15c John 12:1 .15 .15
89 A22 20c Matthew 21:1-2 .20 .20
90 A22 25c Mark 11:5-6 .50 .50
91 A22 30c Matthew 21:7 .60 .60
    Nos. 88-91 (4) 1.45 1.45

Table Telephones — A23

1982, Sept. 3
92 A23 8c Ericsson, 1878 .16 .16
93 A23 15c Ericsson, 1885 .30 .30
94 A23 20c Ericsson, 1893 .40 .40
95 A23 25c Siemens & Halske, 1898 .50 .50
    Nos. 92-95 (4) 1.36 1.36

Independence, 5th Anniv. — A24

8c, Old parliament building. 15c, New government offices. 20c, University, Mmabatho. 25c,
Civic Center, Mmabatho.

1982, Dec. 6 — Perf. 14x14½
96 A24 8c multicolored .16 .16
97 A24 15c multicolored .30 .30
98 A24 20c multicolored .40 .40
99 A24 25c multicolored .50 .50
    Nos. 96-99 (4) 1.36 1.36

Pilanesberg
Nature
Reserve
A25

1983, Jan. 5
100 A25 8c Ceratotherium simum .24 .24
101 A25 20c Equus burchelli .60 .60
102 A25 25c Hippotragus niger .75 .75
103 A25 40c Alcelaphus caama 1.25 1.25
    Nos. 100-103 (4) 2.84 2.84

Easter
A26

1983, Mar. 30 — Perf. 14½x14
104 A26 8c Matthew 21:7 .16 .16
105 A26 20c Mark 11:7 .40 .40
106 A26 25c Matthew 21:8 .50 .50
107 A26 40c Mark 11:9 .80 .80
    Nos. 104-107 (4) 1.86 1.86

Telephones   Birds of the
A27   Veld
                   A28

Designs: 10c, ATM table model, c. 1920. 20c,
A/S Elektrisk wall model, c. 1900. 25c, Ericsson
wall model, c. 1900. 40c, Ericsson wall model, c.
1900, diff.

1983, June 22
108 A27 10c multicolored .20 .20
109 A27 20c multicolored .40 .40
110 A27 25c multicolored .50 .50
111 A27 40c multicolored .80 .80
    Nos. 108-111 (4) 1.90 1.90

1983, Sept. 14
112 A28 10c Kori bustard .30 .30
113 A28 20c Black korhaan .60 .60
114 A28 25c Red-crested korhaan .75 .75
115 A28 40c Stanley bustard 1.25 1.25
    Nos. 112-115 (4) 2.90 2.90

Grasses — A29

1984, Jan. 20
116 A29 10c Panicum maximum .20 .20
117 A29 20c Hyparrhenia dregeana .40 .40
118 A29 25c Cenchrus ciliaris .50 .50
119 A29 40c Urochloa brachyura .80 .80
    Nos. 116-119 (4) 1.90 1.90

Easter
A30

1984, Mar. 23 — Perf. 14½x14
120 A30 10c Mark 11:11 .20 .20
121 A30 20c Mark 11:15 .40 .40
122 A30 25c Matthew 21:19 .50 .50
123 A30 40c Matthew 21:19, diff. .80 .80
    Nos. 120-123 (4) 1.90 1.90

See Nos. 165-168, 173-176.

Mining
Industry
A31

1984, Apr. 2 — Perf. 14½x14
124 A31 11c multicolored .20 .20

Telephones — A32

Designs: 11c, Shuchhardt table model, c. 1905.
20c, Siemens wall model, c. 1925. 25c, Ericsson
table model, c. 1900. 30c, Oki table model, c.
1930.

1984, July 20
125 A32 11c multicolored .22 .22
126 A32 20c multicolored .40 .40
127 A32 25c multicolored .50 .50
128 A32 30c multicolored .60 .60
    Nos. 125-128 (4) 1.72 1.72

Lizards
A33

Designs: 11c, Yellow-throated plated lizard. 25c,
Transvaal girdled lizard. 30c, Ocellated sand lizard.
45c, Bibron's thick-toed gecko.

1984, Sept. 25 — Perf. 14x14½
129 A33 11c multicolored .22 .22
130 A33 25c multicolored .50 .50
131 A33 30c multicolored .60 .60
132 A33 45c multicolored .90 .90
    Nos. 129-132 (4) 2.22 2.22

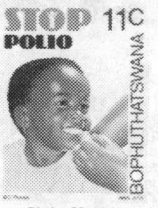 

Child Health   Mafeking,
Care — A34   Cent. — A35

1985, Jan. 25
133 A34 11c Stop Polio .22 .22
134 A34 25c Stop Measles .50 .50
135 A34 30c Stop Diphtheria .60 .60
136 A34 50c Stop Whooping Cough 1.00 1.00
    Nos. 133-136 (4) 2.32 2.32

1985, Mar. 11
Portraits: 11c, Montshiwa (1814-1896), chief of
the Barolong booRatshidi. 25c, Sir Charles Warren
(1840-1927), army commander who established
the Crown Colony and layed-out the town of
Mafeking.
137 A35 11c multicolored .22 .22
138 A35 25c multicolored .50 .50

Industries
A36

Designs: 1c, Textile mill, Bophuthatswana. 2c,
Sewing cloth sacks, Selosesha. 3c, Ceramic tile production line. 4c, Processing sheepskin. 5c, Manufacture of crossbows. 6c, Automobile parts. 7c,
Hosiery factory, Babelegi. 8c, Specialized bicycle
factory. 9c, Lawn mower assembly line. 10c, Dress
factory, Thaba Nchu. 12c, Automobile upholstery
factory. 14c, Milling industry, Mafeking. 15c, Manufacturing of plastic bags. 16c, Brickworks,
Mmabatho. 18c, Manufacturing of cutlery. 20c,
Men's clothing factory. 25c, Chromium plating
baby carriage parts. 30c, Spray-painting metal beds.
50c, Milk processing plant. 1r, Printing works. 2r,
Industrial complex, Babelegi.

1985-89 — Perf. 14½x14
139 A36 1c multicolored .15 .15
140 A36 2c multicolored .15 .15
141 A36 3c multicolored .15 .15
142 A36 4c multicolored .15 .15
143 A36 5c multicolored .15 .15
144 A36 6c multicolored .15 .15
145 A36 7c multicolored .15 .15
146 A36 8c multicolored .15 .15
147 A36 9c multicolored .15 .15
148 A36 10c multicolored .15 .15
149 A36 12c multicolored .15 .15
150 A36 14c multicolored .15 .15
151 A36 15c multicolored .15 .15
152 A36 16c multicolored .16 .16
153 A36 18c multicolored .18 .18
154 A36 20c multicolored .20 .20
155 A36 25c multicolored .25 .25
156 A36 30c multicolored .30 .30
157 A36 50c multicolored .50 .50
158 A36 1r multicolored 1.00 1.00
159 A36 2r multicolored 2.00 2.00
    Set value 5.34 5.34

Issued: 1c-10c, 15c, 20c, 25c, 30c-2r,
10/25/85; 12c, 4/1/85; 14c, 4/1/86; 16c,
4/1/87; 18c, 7/3/89.

Easter Type of 1984

1985, Apr. 2
165 A30 12c Matthew 21:14 .15 .15
166 A30 25c Matthew 21:14, diff. .25 .25
167 A30 30c Matthew 21:15 .30 .30
168 A30 50c Matthew 21:15-16 .50 .50
    Nos. 165-168 (4) 1.20 1.20

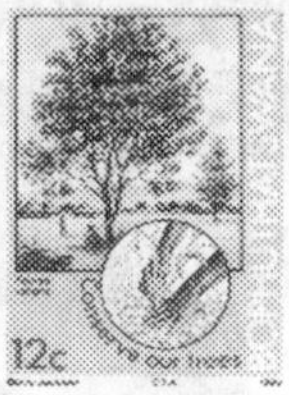
Tree Conservation — A37

1985, July 4 *Perf. 14x14½*

169 A37 12c *Fourea saligna*	.24	.24
170 A37 25c *Boscia albitrunca*	.50	.50
171 A37 30c *Erythrina lysistemon*	.60	.60
172 A37 50c *Bequaertiodendron magalismontanum*	1.00	1.00
Nos. 169-172 (4)	2.34	2.34

Easter Type of 1984

1986, Mar. 6 *Perf. 14½x14*

173 A30 12c John 12:2	.18	.18
174 A30 20c John 12:3	.30	.30
175 A30 25c John 12:3, diff.	.38	.38
176 A30 30c Matthew 26:7	.45	.45
Nos. 173-176 (4)	1.31	1.31

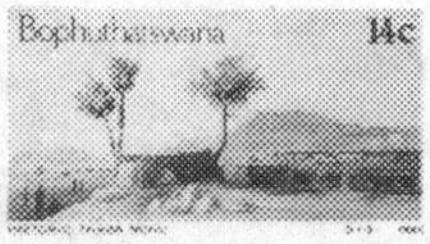
Paintings of Thaba Nchu in the Africana Museum, Johannesburg A38

Designs: 14c, *Wesleyan Mission Station and Residence of Moroka, Chief of the Barolong, 1834,* by Charles Davidson Bell. 20c, *James Archbell's Congregation, 1834,* by Bell. 25c, *Mission Station at Thaba Nchu, 1850,* by Thomas Baines (1822-1875).

1986, May 15 *Perf. 14x14½*

177 A38 14c multicolored	.20	.20
178 A38 20c multicolored	.30	.30
179 A38 25c multicolored	.38	.38
Nos. 177-179 (3)	.88	.88

Incorporation of Thaba Nchu and Bophuthatswana, Oct. 1, 1983.

A souvenir sheet of one No. 179 has decorative margin continuing the painting and picturing the emblem of the philatelic exhibition held at Johannesburg, Oct. 6-11. Sold for 50c.

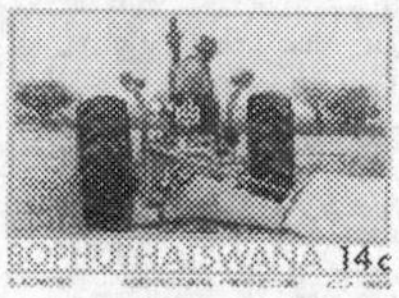
Temisano Development Projects — A39

1986, Aug. 6 *Perf. 14½x14*

180 A39 14c Agricultural production	.20	.20
181 A39 20c Community development	.30	.30
182 A39 25c Vocational training	.38	.38
183 A39 30c Secondary industries	.45	.45
Nos. 180-183 (4)	1.33	1.33

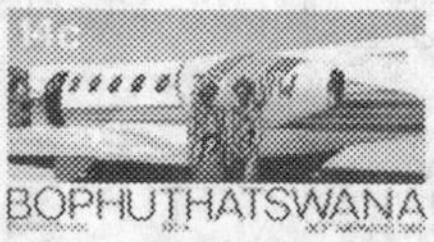
BOP Airways, 5th Anniv. A40

1986, Oct. 16 *Perf. 14x14½*

184 A40 14c Airline personnel, aircraft	.20	.20
185 A40 20c Passengers	.30	.30
186 A40 25c Mmabatho Intl. Airport	.38	.38
187 A40 30c Cessna Citation	.45	.45
Nos. 184-187 (4)	1.33	1.33

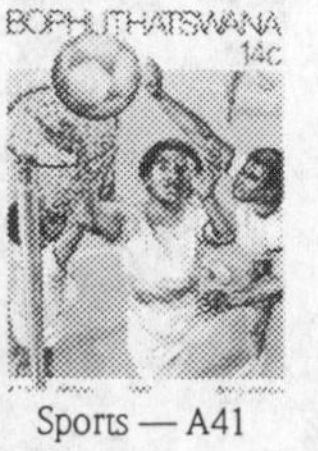
Sports — A41

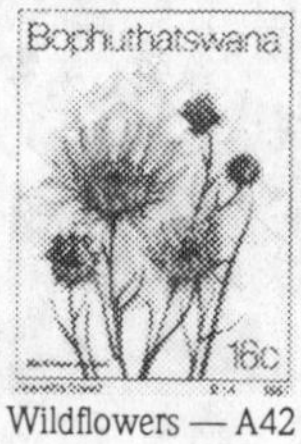
Wildflowers — A42

1987, Jan. 22

188 A41 14c Netball	.22	.22
189 A41 20c Tennis	.32	.32
190 A41 25c Soccer	.40	.40
191 A41 30c Running	.50	.50
Nos. 188-191 (4)	1.44	1.44

1987, Apr. 23

192 A42 16c *Berkheya zeyheri*	.25	.25
193 A42 20c *Plumbago auriculata*	.32	.32
194 A42 25c *Pterodiscus speciosus*	.42	.42
195 A42 30c *Gazania krebsiana*	.50	.50
Nos. 192-195 (4)	1.49	1.49

A souvenir sheet of one No. 194 has decorative black and white inscribed margin picturing the emblem of the natl. philatelic exhibition held at Paarl, Sept. 16-19. Sold for 70c.

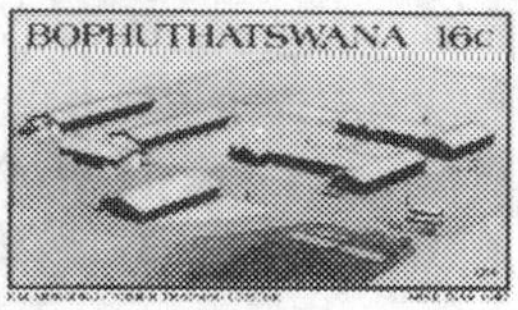
Education — A43

Designs: 16c, E.M. Mokgoko Farmer Training Center, Ramatlabama. 20c, Main lecture block, University of Bophuthatswana, Mmabatho. 25c, Manpower Center. 30c, Hotel training school, Odi.

1987, Aug. 6 *Perf. 14½x14*

196 A43 16c multicolored	.25	.25
197 A43 20c multicolored	.32	.32
198 A43 25c multicolored	.42	.42
199 A43 30c multicolored	.50	.50
Nos. 196-199 (4)	1.49	1.49

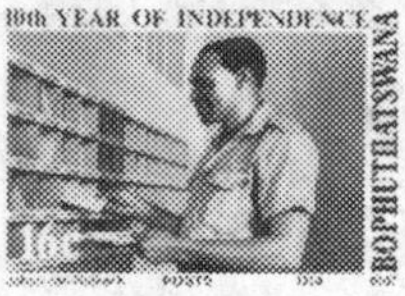
Independence, 10th Anniv. — A44

Communications.

1987, Dec. 4

200 A44 16c Postal service	.20	.20
201 A44 30c Telephone	.38	.38
202 A44 40c Radio	.52	.52
203 A44 50c Television	.65	.65
Nos. 200-203 (4)	1.75	1.75

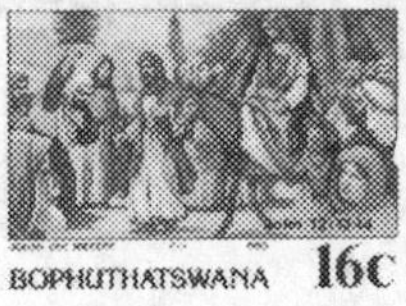
Easter — A45

1988, Mar. 31

204 A45 16c John 12:12-14	.16	.16
205 A45 30c Mark 14:10-11	.32	.32
206 A45 40c John 13:5	.45	.45
207 A45 50c John 13:26	.55	.55
Nos. 204-207 (4)	1.48	1.48

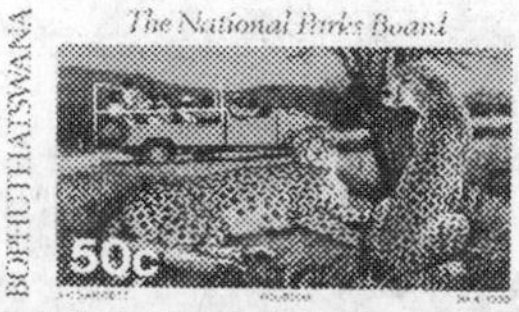
Natl. Parks Board Activities — A46

1988, June 23 *Perf. 14½x14*

208 A46 16c Environmental education	.20	.20
209 A46 30c Conservation	.38	.38
210 A46 40c Catering	.52	.52
211 A46 50c Tourism	.65	.65
Nos. 208-211 (4)	1.75	1.75

A souvenir sheet of one No. 211 has black and white decorative margin picturing the emblem of the natl. philatelic exhibition held at Pietermaritzburg, Nov. 22-27. Sold for 70c.

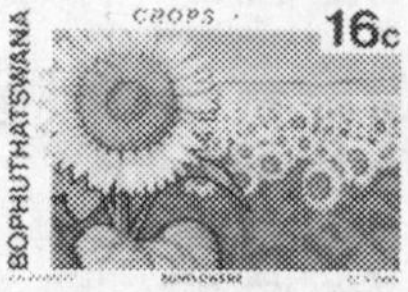
Crops — A47

1988, Sept. 15 *Perf. 14½x14*

212 A47 16c Sunflowers	.16	.16
213 A47 30c Peanuts	.32	.32
214 A47 40c Cotton	.45	.45
215 A47 50c Cabbages	.55	.55
Nos. 212-215 (4)	1.48	1.48

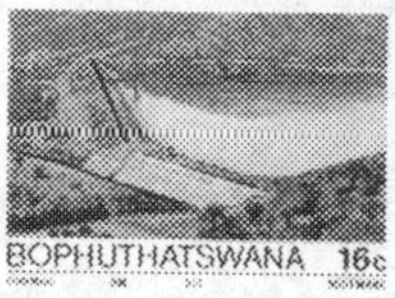
Dams — A48

1988, Nov. 17

216 A48 16c Ngotwane	.16	.16
217 A48 30c Groothoek	.32	.32
218 A48 40c Sehujwane	.45	.45
219 A48 50c Molatedi	.55	.55
Nos. 216-219 (4)	1.48	1.48

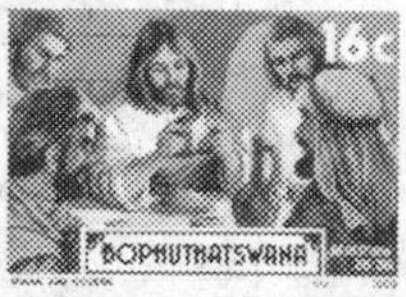
Easter — A49

1989, Mar. 9

220 A49 16c Mark 26:26	.15	.15
221 A49 30c Matthew 26:39	.28	.28
222 A49 40c Mark 14:45	.38	.38
223 A49 50c John 18:10	.48	.48
Nos. 220-223 (4)	1.29	1.29

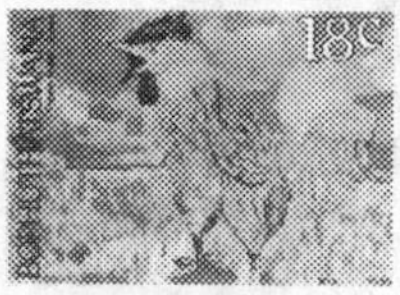
Children's Art — A50

Designs: 18c, "Rooster," by Thembi Atong. 30c, "Thatched Hut in Rural Setting," by Muhammad Mahri. 40c, "Modern World," by Tshepo Mashokwe. 50c, "Cityscape," by Miles Brown.

1989, May 11

224 A50 18c multicolored	.25	.25
225 A50 30c multicolored	.42	.42
226 A50 40c multicolored	.55	.55
227 A50 50c multicolored	.70	.70
Nos. 224-227 (4)	1.92	1.92

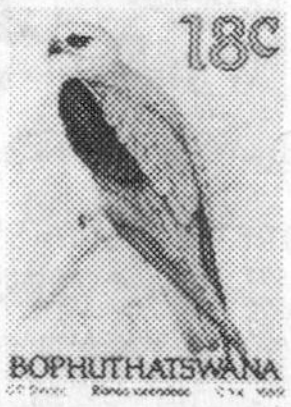
Birds of Prey — A51

1989, Sept. 1 *Perf. 14x14½*

228 A51 18c *Elanus caeruleus*	.22	.22
229 A51 30c *Melierax canorus*	.38	.38
230 A51 40c *Falco naumanni*	.50	.50
231 A51 50c *Circaetus gallicus*	.60	.60
a. Souvenir sheet of 1	1.75	1.75
Nos. 228-231 (4)	1.70	1.70

No. 231a has multicolored decorative margin picturing emblem of the WANDERERS 101 natl. philatelic exhibition held Sept. 6-9. Sold for 1.50r.

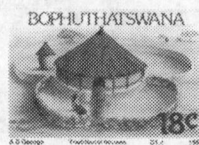

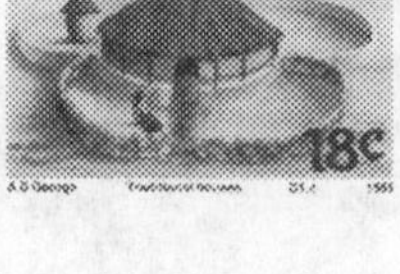
Traditional Thatched Dwellings A52

1989, Nov. 28 *Perf. 14½x14*

232 A52 18c shown	.16	.16
233 A52 30c multi, diff.	.28	.28
234 A52 40c multi, diff.	.35	.35
235 A52 50c multi, diff.	.45	.45
Nos. 232-235 (4)	1.24	1.24

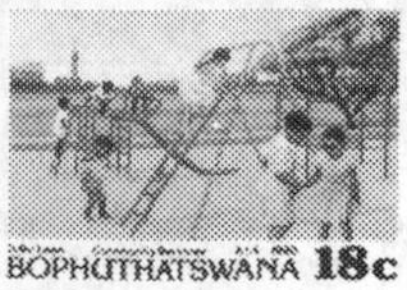
Community Services A53

1990, Jan. 11

236 A53 18c Playground	.18	.18
237 A53 30c Immunization clinic	.32	.32
238 A53 40c Library	.45	.45
239 A53 50c Hospital	.55	.55
Nos. 236-239 (4)	1.50	1.50

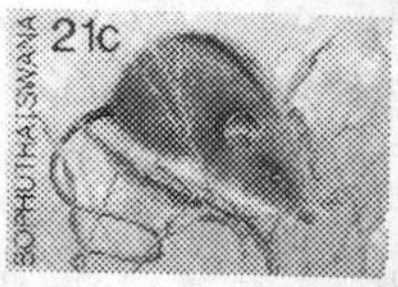
Wildlife (Small Mammals) A54

1990, Apr. 11 Litho. *Perf. 14½x14*

240 A54 21c *Dendromus mystacalis*	.20	.20
241 A54 30c *Ictonyx striatus*	.28	.28
242 A54 40c *Elephantulus myurus*	.35	.35
243 A54 50c *Procavia capensis*	.45	.45
a. Souvenir sheet of 1	2.25	2.25
Nos. 240-243 (4)	1.28	1.28

No. 243a has multicolored inscribed margin; text publicizes the natl. philatelic exhibition. Sold for 1.50r.

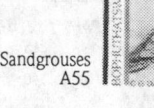

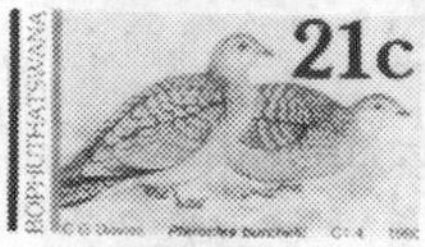
Sandgrouses A55

1990, July 12 Litho. *Perf. 14x14½*

244 A55 21c *Pterocles burchelli*	.20	.20
245 A55 35c *Pterocles bicinctus*	.35	.35
246 A55 40c *Pterocles namaqua*	.40	.40
247 A55 50c *Pterocles gutturalis*	.50	.50
Nos. 244-247 (4)	1.45	1.45

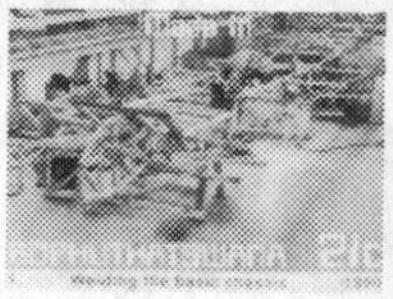
Bus Manufacturing A56

Designs: a, Chassis welding. b, Mounting the engine. c, Body construction. d, Spray painting. e, Completed models and bare chassis.

1990, Aug. 3 *Perf. 14½x14*

248 Strip of 5	1.25	1.25
a.-e. A56 21c any single	.25	.25

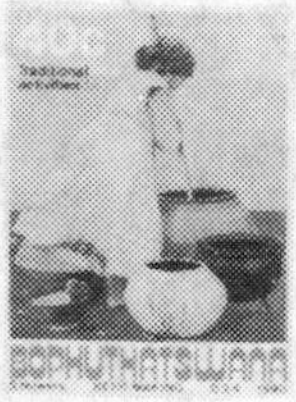
Traditional Activities — A57

1990, Oct. 4 *Perf. 14x14½*

249 A57 21c Basketry	.18	.18
250 A57 35c Tanning	.30	.30
251 A57 40c Beer making	.35	.35
252 A57 50c Pottery making	.45	.45
Nos. 249-252 (4)	1.28	1.28

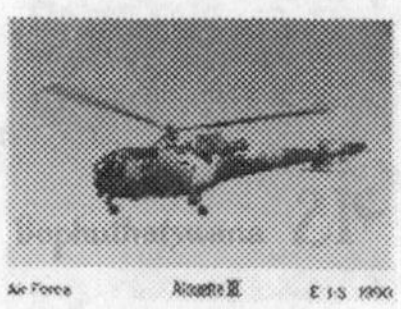
Bophuthatswana Air Force, 10th Anniv. — A58

Helicopters: a, Alouette III. b, BK117. Airplanes: c, Pilatus Trainer PC-7. d, Pilatus Porter PC-6. e, Casa 212.

1990, Dec. 12   *Perf. 14¹/₂x14*
253   Strip of 5   1.25   1.25
a.-e.   A58 21c any single   .25   .25

Edible Wild Fruit — A59

1991, Jan. 24   Litho.   *Perf. 14x14¹/₂*
254 A59 21c Annona senegalensis   .18   .18
255 A59 35c Strychnos pungens   .30   .30
256 A59 40c Ficus sycomorus   .35   .35
257 A59 50c Dovyalis caffra   .42   .42
    Nos. 254-257 (4)   1.25   1.25

Easter — A60

1991, Mar. 21   Litho.   *Perf. 14¹/₂x14*
258 A60 21c Mark 14:46   .15   .15
259 A60 35c Mark 14:53   .22   .22
260 A60 40c Mark 14:65   .28   .28
261 A60 50c Mark 14:67   .32   .32
    Nos. 258-261 (4)   .97   .97

Locomotives A61

1991, July 4   Litho.
   Size: 72x25mm (25c, 50c)
262 A61 25c Class 6A   .15   .15
263 A61 40c Class 7A   .24   .24
264 A61 50c Class 6Z   .30   .30
265 A61 60c Class 8   .38   .38
    Nos. 262-265 (4)   1.07   1.07

    See Nos. 291-294.

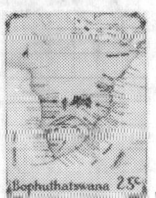

Maps of Africa — A62

1991, Sept. 12   Litho.   *Perf. 14x14¹/₂*
266 A62 25c Caneiro chart, 1502   .15   .15
267 A62 40c Cantino chart, 1502   .24   .24
268 A62 50c Contarini map, 1506   .30   .30
269 A62 60c Waldseemuller map, 1507   .38   .38
    Nos. 266-269 (4)   1.07   1.07

Maps of Africa — A63

1992, Jan. 9   Litho.   *Perf. 14¹/₂x14*
270 A63 27c Fracanzano, 1508   .16   .16
271 A63 45c Waldseemuller, 1513   .28   .28
272 A63 65c Waldseemuller, 1516   .40   .40
273 A63 85c Laurent Fries, 1522   .50   .50
    Nos. 270-273 (4)   1.34   1.34

Easter — A64

1992, Apr. 1   Litho.
274 A64 27c Mark 15:1   .16   .16
275 A64 45c Mark 15:15   .28   .28
276 A64 65c Mark 15:17-18   .40   .40
277 A64 85c Mark 15:19   .50   .50
    Nos. 274-277 (4)   1.34   1.34

Acacia Trees — A65

1992, Sept. 17   Litho.
278 A65 35c Karroo   .28   .28
279 A65 70c Erioloba   .58   .58
280 A65 90c Tortilis   .75   .75
281 A65 1.05r Mellifera   .85   .85
    Nos. 278-281 (4)   2.46   2.46

Lost City Hotel Complex, Sun City — A66

Designs: a, View from lake. b, Palace. c, Porte cochere. d, Lobby of Palace. e, Tusk bar.

1992, Nov. 19   Litho.   *Perf. 14x14¹/₂*
282   Strip of 5   1.25   1.25
a.-e. A66 35c any single   .25   .25

Chickens A67

1993, Feb. 12   Litho.   *Perf. 14¹/₂x14*
283 A67 35c Light Sussex   .22   .22
284 A67 70c Rhode Island red   .45   .45
285 A67 90c Brown leghorn   .58   .58
286 A67 1.05r White leghorn   .68   .68
    Nos. 283-286 (4)   1.93   1.93

Easter — A68

1993, Mar. 5
287 A68 35c Luke 23:25   .22   .22
288 A68 70c John 19:17   .45   .45
289 A68 90c Mark 15:21   .58   .58
290 A68 1.05r Mark 15:23   .68   .68
    Nos. 287-290 (4)   1.93   1.93

Trains Type of 1991

Designs: 45c, Mafeking locomotive shed, c. 1933, RR classes 10, 8, & 12. 65c, Locomotive No. 5. 85c, 1934 Royal visit, White Train, SAR Class 16B. 1.05r, SAR class 19D.

1993, June 18   Litho.
   Size: 72x25mm (45c, 85c)
291 A61 45c multicolored   .28   .28
292 A61 65c multicolored   .40   .40
293 A61 85c multicolored   .52   .52
294 A61 1.05r multicolored   .65   .65
    Nos. 291-294 (4)   1.85   1.85

Maps of Africa — A69

Name of cartographer, year published: 45c, Sebastian Munster, 1540. 65c, Jacopo Gastaldi, 1564. 85c, Gerardus Mercator the Younger, 1595. 1.05r, Abraham Ortelius, 1570.

1993, Aug. 20   Litho.
295 A69 45c multicolored   .28   .28
296 A69 65c multicolored   .40   .40
297 A69 85c multicolored   .52   .52
298 A69 1.05r multicolored   .65   .65
    Nos. 295-298 (4)   1.85   1.85

Easter — A70

1994, Mar. 25   Litho.   *Perf. 14¹/₂x14*
299 A70 35c Luke 22:33   .20   .20
300 A70 65c Luke 23:35-36   .38   .38
301 A70 85c Luke 23:36   .50   .50
302 A70 1.05r Luke 23:38   .60   .60
    Nos. 299-302 (4)   1.68   1.68

Bophuthatswana ceased to exist April 27, 1994.

CISKEI

'sis-ˌkī

LOCATION — Enclave, Republic of South Africa
GOVT. — Self-governing tribal homeland
AREA — 5,592 sq. mi.
POP. — 1,000,000
CAPITAL — Bisho

> Catalogue values for all unused stamps in this country are for Never Hinged Items.

Independence from South Africa — A1

    Perf. 14x14¹/₂
1981, Dec. 4   Litho.   Unwmk.
1 A1 5c Pres. Sebe   .15   .15
2 A1 15c Coat of arms   .40   .40
3 A1 20c Flag   .55   .55
4 A1 25c Mace   .70   .70
    Nos. 1-4 (4)   1.80   1.80

An imperf. souvenir sheet exists containing Nos. 1-4 printed in one color (black). Not valid for postage.

Birds
A2   A3

1981-89   *Perf. 14¹/₂x14*
5 A2 1c Tauraco corythaix   .15   .15
6 A2 2c Motacilla capensis   .15   .15
7 A2 3c Centropus superciliosus   .15   .15
8 A2 4c Nectarinia famosa   .15   .15
9 A2 5c Anthropoides paradisea   .15   .15
10 A2 6c Onychognathus morio   .15   .15
11 A2 7c Ceryle maxima   .15   .15
12 A2 8c Bostrychia hagedash   .15   .15
13 A2 9c Cuculus clamosus   .15   .15
14 A2 10c Lybius torquatus   .15   .15
15 A2 11c Oriolus larvatus   .15   .15
16 A2 12c Alcedo cristata   .18   .18
17 A2 14c Upupa epops   .20   .20
18 A2 15c Haliaeetus vocifer   .22   .22
19 A2 16c Batis capensis   .24   .24
20 A3 18c Euplectes progne   .26   .26
21 A2 20c Macronyx capensis   .30   .30
22 A2 21c Aplopelia larvata   .75   .75
23 A2 25c Burhinus capensis   .38   .38
24 A2 30c Treron calva   .45   .45
25 A2 50c Poicephalus robustus   .75   .75
26 A2 1r Apaloderma narina   1.75   1.75
27 A2 2r Bubo capensis   3.50   3.50
    Nos. 5-27 (22)   9.88   9.88

   Issued: 11c, 4/4/82; 12c, 4/1/85; 14c, 4/1/86; 16c, 4/1/87; 18c, 7/3/89; others, 12/4/81.

Nursing A4

    Perf. 14¹/₂x14, 14x14¹/₂
1982, Apr. 30
34 A4 8c Cecilia Makiwane, vert.   .15   .15
35 A4 15c Surgery, vert.   .22   .22
36 A4 20c Nurses pledge to serve   .30   .30
37 A4 25c Hospital care   .38   .38
    Nos. 34-37 (4)   1.05   1.05

Pineapple Industry A5

1982, Aug. 20   *Perf. 14x14¹/₂*
38 A5 8c Spraying   .15   .15
39 A5 15c Harvesting   .22   .22
40 A5 20c Transporting fruit to cannery   .30   .30
41 A5 30c Packing   .45   .45
    Nos. 38-41 (4)   1.12   1.12

Small Mammals A6

1982, Oct. 29
42 A6 8c Lepus capensis   .15   .15
43 A6 15c Vulpes chama   .22   .22
44 A6 20c Xerus inauris   .30   .30
45 A6 25c Felis caracal   .38   .38
    Nos. 42-45 (4)   1.05   1.05

Trees — A7

1983, Feb. 2   *Perf. 14¹/₂x14*
46 A7 8c Cussonia spicata   .15   .15
47 A7 20c Curtisia dentata   .30   .30
48 A7 25c Calodendrum capense   .38   .38
49 A7 40c Podocarpus falcatus   .60   .60
    Nos. 46-49 (4)   1.43   1.43

1984, Jan. 6
50 A7 10c Rhus chirindensis   .15   .15
51 A7 20c Phoenix reclinata   .30   .30
52 A7 25c Ptaeroxylon obliquum   .38   .38
53 A7 40c Apodytes dimidiata   .60   .60
    Nos. 50-53 (4)   1.43   1.43

Sharks — A8

1983, Apr. 13   *Perf. 14¹/₂x14*
54 A8 8c Dusky   .24   .24
55 A8 20c Ragged-tooth   .60   .60

    Size: 57x21mm
56 A8 25c Tiger   .75   .75
57 A8 30c Scalloped hammerhead   .90   .90
58 A8 40c Great white   1.25   1.25
    Nos. 54-58 (5)   3.74   3.74

Educational
Institutions
A9

1983, July 6
59	A9	10c	Lovedale	.15	.15
60	A9	20c	Fort Hare	.30	.30
61	A9	25c	Headtown	.38	.38
62	A9	40c	Lennox Sebe	.60	.60
			Nos. 59-62 (4)	1.43	1.43

Military
Ciskei 0.. 20c Uniforms — A10

6th Foot, 1st Warwickshire Regiment, 1821-27
(No. 63): a, White drill uniform (D1.5). b, Light
Company privates (D2.5). c, Grenadier Company
sergeants (D3.5). d, Light Co. Officers (D4.5). e,
Officer and field officer (D5.5).
Cape Mounted Rifles, 1827-35 (No. 64): a,
Trooper and sergeant, 1830 (D1.5). b, Trooper and
sergeant in full dress, 1835 (D2.5). c, Officers,
1830 (D3.5). d, Officers in full dress, 1827-34
(D4.5). e, Officers in full dress, 1834 (D5.5).

1983, Sept. 28   *Perf. 14¹/₂x14*
| 63 | | Strip of 5 | 2.00 | 2.00 |
| a.-e. | A10 20c any single | | .40 | .40 |

1984, Oct. 26
| 64 | | Strip of 5 | 2.50 | 2.50 |
| a.-e. | A10 25c any single | | .50 | .50 |

Sheets of 10 containing two strips of five.

Coastal
Angling
A11

Bait.

1984, Apr. 12   *Perf. 14x14¹/₂*
65	A11	11c	Sand prawn	.15	.15
66	A11	20c	Coral worm	.30	.30
67	A11	25c	Bloodworm	.38	.38
68	A11	30c	Red-bait	.45	.45
			Nos. 65-68 (4)	1.28	1.28

1985, May 7
Game fish.
69	A11	11c	Lithognathus		
			lithognathus	.15	.15
70	A11	25c	Pachymetopon grande	.38	.38
71	A11	30c	Argyrosomus		
			hololepidotus	.45	.45
72	A11	50c	Pomadasys commersonni	.75	.75
			Nos. 69-72 (4)	1.73	1.73

Migratory Birds and Maps — A12

1984, Aug. 17   *Perf. 14¹/₂x14*
73	A12	11c	Banded sand martin	.15	.15
74	A12	25c	House martin	.38	.38
75	A12	30c	Greater striped swallow	.45	.45
76	A12	50c	European swallow	.65	.65
			Nos. 73-76 (4)	1.63	1.63

Brownies
A13

1985, May 3
77	A13	12c	shown	.18	.18
78	A13	25c	Rangers planting saplings	.38	.38
79	A13	30c	Guide color guard	.45	.45
80	A13	50c	Camping	.75	.75
			Nos. 77-80 (4)	1.76	1.76

Intl. Year of the Child, 75th anniv. of the Girl
Guide movement.

Small
Businesses
A14

1985, Aug. 8   *Perf. 14x14¹/₂*
81	A14	12c	Furniture	.18	.18
82	A14	25c	Dress making	.38	.38
83	A14	30c	Welding	.45	.45
84	A14	50c	Basketry	.75	.75
			Nos. 81-84 (4)	1.76	1.76

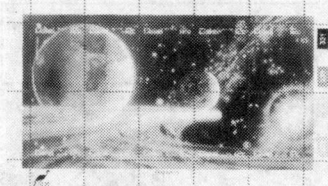

Troop
Ships — A15

1985, Nov. 15   *Perf. 14¹/₂x14*
85	A15	12c	Antelope	.18	.18
86	A15	25c	Pilot	.38	.38
87	A15	30c	Salisbury	.45	.45
88	A15	50c	Olive Branch	.75	.75
			Nos. 85-88 (4)	1.76	1.76

Miniature Sheet

Halley's Comet — A16

Comet streaking through the solar system: a,
A1.10. b, A2.10. c, A3.10. d, A4.10. e, A5.10. f,
A6.10. g, A7.10. h, A8.10. i, A9.10. j, A10.10.
Illustration reduced.

1986, Mar. 20
| 89 | A16 | Sheet of 10 | 11.00 | 11.00 |
| a.-j. | 12c any single | 1.10 | 1.10 |

Military Uniforms — A17

98th Foot Regiment: 14c, Fifer in winter. 20c,
Private in summer. 25c, Grenadier Company sergeant in summer. 30c, Sergeant-major in winter.

1986, June 12
90	A17	14c	multicolored	.20	.20
91	A17	20c	multicolored	.30	.30
92	A17	25c	multicolored	.38	.38
93	A17	30c	multicolored	.45	.45
a.	Souvenir sheet of 1		2.75	2.75
			Nos. 90-93 (4)	1.33	1.33

No. 93a for the natl. philatelic exhibition held at
Johannesberg, Oct. 6-11. Sold for 50c.

Bicycle Factory,
Dimbaza
A18

1986, Sept. 18
94	A18	14c	Welding frames	.20	.20
95	A18	20c	Painting	.30	.30
96	A18	25c	Spoke installation	.38	.38
97	A18	30c	Assembly	.45	.45
			Nos. 94-97 (4)	1.33	1.33

Independence, 5th Anniv. — A19

Designs: 14c, Pres. Sebe. 20c, Natl. shrine,
Ntaba kaNdoda. 25c, Legislative Assembly, Bisho.
30c, Automatic telephone exchange, Bisho.

1986, Dec. 4   *Perf. 14x14¹/₂*
98	A19	14c	multicolored	.20	.20
99	A19	20c	multicolored	.28	.28
100	A19	25c	multicolored	.35	.35
101	A19	30c	multicolored	.42	.42
			Nos. 98-101 (4)	1.25	1.25

Edible
Mushrooms — A20

1987, Mar. 19
102	A20	14c	Boletus edulis	.24	.24
103	A20	20c	Macrolepiota zeyheri	.35	.35
a.	Souvenir sheet of 1		3.00	3.00
104	A20	25c	Termitomyces	.42	.42
105	A20	30c	Russula capensis	.50	.50
			Nos. 102-105 (4)	1.51	1.51

No. 103a has fawn and black decorative margin
picturing emblem of the natl. philatelic exhibition
held at Paarl, Sept. 16-19. Sold for 50c.

Nkone
Cattle — A21

1987, June 18   *Perf. 14¹/₂x14*
106	A21	16c	Cow and calf	.22	.22
107	A21	20c	Cow	.28	.28
108	A21	25c	Bull	.35	.35
109	A21	30c	Herd	.42	.42
			Nos. 106-109 (4)	1.27	1.27

Toys — A22

Perf. 14x14¹/₂, 14¹/₂x14
1987, Sept. 17
110	A22	16c	Windmill, vert.	.18	.18
111	A22	20c	Rag doll, vert.	.22	.22
112	A22	25c	Clay horse	.28	.28
113	A22	30c	Wire vehicle	.32	.32
			Nos. 110-113 (4)	1.00	1.00

Folklore — A23

Legend of Sikulume: 16c, Seven birds. 20c,
Sikulume escapes cannibals. 25c, Fights sea monster. 30c, Elopes and is pursued by bride's father.

1987, Nov. 6   *Perf. 14¹/₂x14*
114	A23	16c	multicolored	.18	.18
115	A23	20c	multicolored	.22	.22
116	A23	25c	multicolored	.28	.28
117	A23	30c	multicolored	.32	.32
			Nos. 114-117 (4)	1.00	1.00

See Nos. 122, 139-142, 147-150.

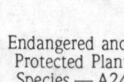

Endangered and
Protected Plant
Species — A24

1988, Mar. 17   *Perf. 14x14¹/₂*
118	A24	16c	Clivia nobilis	.22	.22
119	A24	30c	Dierama pulcherrimum	.42	.42
120	A24	40c	Moraea reticulata	.55	.55
121	A24	50c	Crinum campanulatum	.70	.70
a.	Souvenir sheet of 1		3.00	3.00
			Nos. 118-121 (4)	1.89	1.89

No. 121a margin pictures the emblem of the
natl. philatelic exhibition held at Pietermaritzburg,
Nov. 22-27. Sold for 1r.

Folklore Type of 1987
Miniature Sheet

Legend of Mbulukazi: a, Two wives (B1.10). b,
Two doves appear to Numbakatali (B2.10). c, Birth
of Mbulukazi and brother (B3.10). d, Mbulukazi
and brother at river (B4.10). e, Chief's son
announces marriage (B5.10). f, Chief's son presents
wives Mbulukazi and Mahlunguluza with huts
(B6.10). g, Mahlunguluza drowns Mbulukazi
(B7.10). h, Ox tears down Mahlunguluza's hut
(B8.10). i, Mbulukazi revived (B9.10). j, Chief's son
embraces Mbulukazi, banishes Mahlunguluza
(B10.10).

1988, Aug. 26
Size of Nos. 122a-122j: 36x20mm
| 122 | Sheet of 10 | 3.50 | 3.50 |
| a.-j. | A23 16c any single | .35 | .35 |

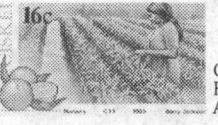

Citrus
Farming
A25

1988, Sept. 29
123	A25	16c	Nursery	.20	.20
124	A25	30c	Grafting	.38	.38
125	A25	40c	Picking fruit	.52	.52
126	A25	50c	Grading	.65	.65
			Nos. 123-126 (4)	1.75	1.75

Poisonous
Mushrooms — A26

1988, Dec. 1
127	A26	16c	Amanita phalloides	.20	.20
128	A26	30c	Chlorophyllum		
			molybdites	.38	.38
129	A26	40c	Amanita muscaria	.52	.52
130	A26	50c	Amanita pantherina	.65	.65
			Nos. 127-130 (4)	1.75	1.75

Dams — A27

1989, Mar. 2   *Perf. 14¹/₂x14*
131	A27	16c	Kat River	.18	.18
132	A27	30c	Cata	.35	.35
133	A27	40c	Binfield Park	.45	.45
134	A27	50c	Sandile	.55	.55
			Nos. 131-134 (4)	1.53	1.53

Trout
Hatcheries
A28

Artificial fertilization: 18c, Obtaining eggs from trout. 30c, Fertilized ova, alevins. 40c, Rainbow trout at 5 weeks. 40c, Adult male rainbow trout.

1989, June 8

135	A28	18c multicolored	.20	.20
136	A28	30c multicolored	.32	.32
137	A28	40c multicolored	.45	.45
138	A28	50c multicolored	.55	.55
a.		Souvenir sheet of 1	1.50	1.50
		Nos. 135-138 (4)	1.52	1.52

No. 138a margin pictures emblem of the natl. philatelic exhibition WANDERERS 101, held Sept. 6-9. Sold for 1.50r.

Folklore Type of 1987

Legend of the Little Jackal and the Lion: 18c, Lion and Jackal hunt large eland. 30c, Jackal and offspring climbing to lair. 40c, Lion roaring, jackal under rock. 50c, Lion falling.

1989, Sept. 21

139	A23	18c multicolored	.20	.20
140	A23	30c multicolored	.32	.32
141	A23	40c multicolored	.45	.45
142	A23	50c multicolored	.55	.55
		Nos. 139-142 (4)	1.52	1.52

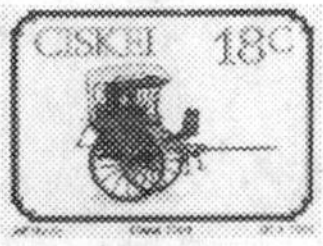

Early Transportation A29

1989, Dec. 7 *Perf. 14x14½*

143	A29	18c Cape cart	.20	.20
144	A29	30c Jubilee Spider	.32	.32
145	A29	40c Transport wagon	.45	.45
146	A29	50c Voortrekker wagon	.55	.55
		Nos. 143-146 (4)	1.52	1.52

Folklore Type of 1987

The Legend of Five Heads: 18c, Mpunzikazi presenting offering to Makanda Mahlanu, the 5-headed snake chief. 30c, Snake chief kills Mpunzikazi. 40c, Mpunzanyan presents offering to snake chief. 50c, Snake chief transformed into a man and marries Mpunzanyan.

1990, Mar. 15 *Perf. 14½x14*

147	A23	18c multicolored	.20	.20
148	A23	30c multicolored	.32	.32
149	A23	40c multicolored	.45	.45
150	A23	50c multicolored	.55	.55
		Nos. 147-150 (4)	1.52	1.52

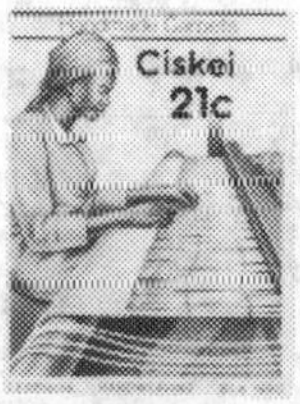

Handmade Carpets — A30

1990, June 14 Litho. *Perf. 14x14½*

151	A30	21c Hand weaving	.18	.18
152	A30	35c Spinning	.30	.30
153	A30	40c Dyeing yarn	.35	.35
154	A30	50c Hand weaving, diff.	.42	.42
a.		Souvenir sheet of 1	2.25	2.25
		Nos. 151-154 (4)	1.25	1.25

No. 154a for the 150th anniv. of the Penny Black. Sold for 1.50r.

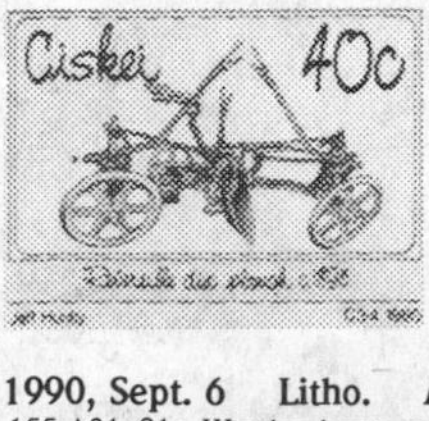

Plows A31

1990, Sept. 6 Litho. *Perf. 14½x14*

155	A31	21c Wooden beam, c. 1855	.18	.18
156	A31	35c Triple disc, c. 1895	.30	.30
157	A31	40c Reversible disc, c. 1895	.35	.35
158	A31	50c "Het Volk", c. 1910	.42	.42
		Nos. 155-158 (4)	1.25	1.25

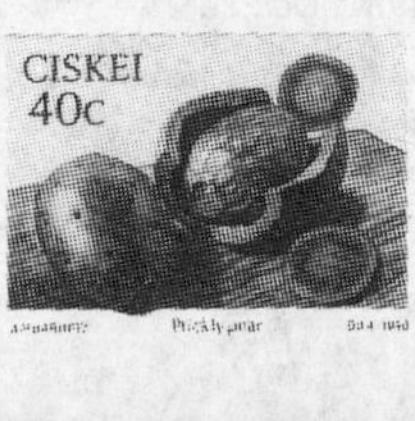

Prickly Pear — A32

1990, Nov. 29 Litho.

159	A32	21c Vendor	.18	.18
160	A32	35c Prickly pear bush	.30	.30
161	A32	40c shown	.35	.35
162	A32	50c Flowering prickly pear	.42	.42
		Nos. 159-162 (4)	1.25	1.25

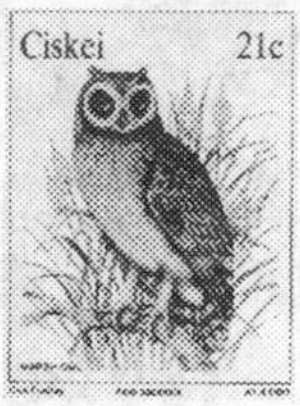

Owls — A33

1991, Feb. 2 Litho. *Perf. 14x14½*

163	A33	21c Marsh owl	.18	.18
164	A33	35c Scops owl	.30	.30
165	A33	40c Barn owl	.35	.35
166	A33	50c Wood owl	.42	.42
a.		Miniature sheet of 1	1.50	1.50
		Nos. 163-166 (4)	1.25	1.25

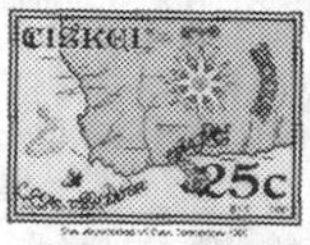

First Letter From South Africa — A34

Designs: a, Map showing location of Sao Bras (Mossel Bay), 1500. b, Storm-damaged ship off Cabo Tormentoso, 1500. c, Pedro d'Ataide lands at Sao Bras, 1501. d, D'Ataide leaves letter in boot, 1501. e, Joao da Nova finds letter, 1501.

1991, May 11 Litho.

167	A34	25c Strip of 5, #a.-e.	1.00	1.00

Inscriptions on #167a & 167b are reversed.

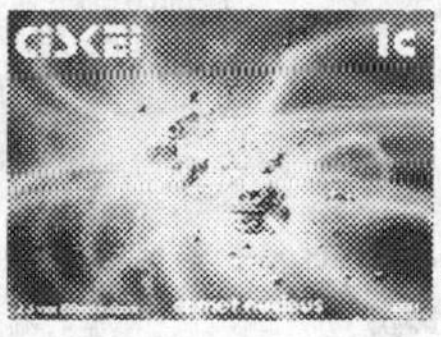

Solar System A35

1991, Aug. 1 Litho. *Perf. 14½x14*

168	A35	1c Comet nucleus	.15	.15
169	A35	2c Trojan asteroids	.15	.15
170	A35	5c Meteoroid	.15	.15
171	A35	7c Pluto	.15	.15
172	A35	10c Neptune	.15	.15
173	A35	20c Uranus	.16	.16
174	A35	25c Saturn	.20	.20
175	A35	30c Jupiter	.24	.24
176	A35	35c Asteroid belt	.28	.28
177	A35	40c Mars	.32	.32
178	A35	50c Earth's moon	.40	.40
179	A35	60c Earth	.48	.48
180	A35	1r Venus	.80	.80
181	A35	2r Mercury	1.60	1.60
182	A35	5r Sun	4.00	4.00
a.		Miniature sheet of 15, #168-182	8.70	8.70
		Nos. 168-182 (15)	9.23	9.23

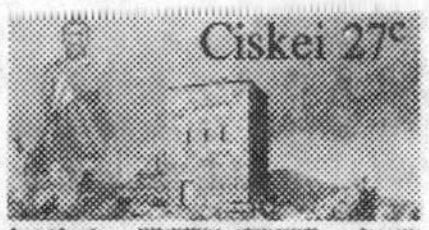

Frontier Forts — A36

Designs: 27c, Xhosa warrior, Fort Armstrong. 45c, Sir George Grey, Keiskamma Hoek Post. 65c, Chief Sandile, Fort Hare. 85c, Cavalryman, Cavalry Barracks, Peddie.

1991, Nov. 7 Litho. *Perf. 14x14½*

183	A36	27c multicolored	.22	.22
184	A36	45c multicolored	.38	.38
185	A36	65c multicolored	.52	.52
186	A36	85c multicolored	.70	.70
		Nos. 183-186 (4)	1.82	1.82

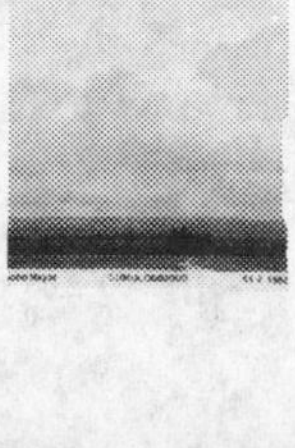

Cloud Formations — A37

1992, Mar. 19 Litho.

187	A37	27c Cumulonimbus	.22	.22
188	A37	45c Altocumulus	.38	.38
189	A37	65c Cirrus	.52	.52
190	A37	85c Cumulus	.70	.70
		Nos. 187-190 (4)	1.82	1.82

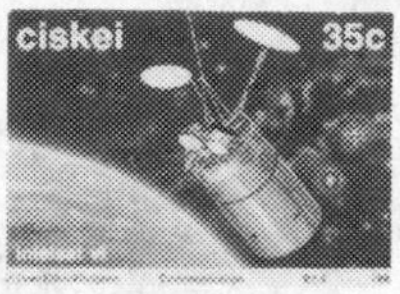

Satellites A38

1992, June 4 Litho. *Perf. 14½x14*

191	A38	35c Intelsat VI	.28	.28
192	A38	70c GPS Navstar	.58	.58
193	A38	90c Meteosat	.75	.75
194	A38	1.05r Landsat VI	.85	.85
		Nos. 191-194 (4)	2.46	2.46

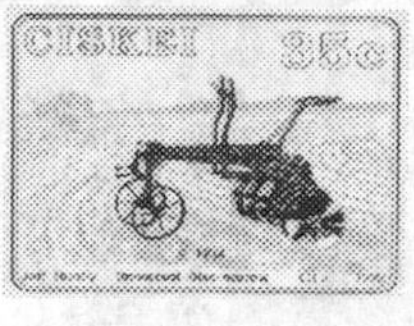

Farm Implements A39

Designs: 35c, John Deere universal disc-harrow, c. 1914. 70c, John Deere clod crusher and pulverizer, c. 1914. 90c, Self-dump hay rake, c. 1910. 1.05r, McCormick hay tedder, c. 1900.

1992, Aug. 20 Litho.

195	A39	35c multicolored	.28	.28
196	A39	70c multicolored	.58	.58
197	A39	90c multicolored	.75	.75
198	A39	1.05r multicolored	.85	.85
		Nos. 195-198 (4)	2.46	2.46

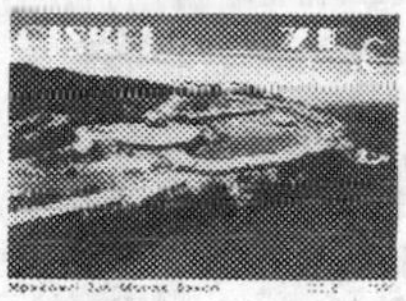
Hotels — A40

Designs: 35c, Mpekweni Sun Marine Resort. 70c, Katberg Protea Hotel. 90c, Fish River Sun Hotel. 1.05r, Amatola Sun Hotel.

1992, Nov. 5 Litho.

199	A40	35c multicolored	.25	.25
200	A40	70c multicolored	.48	.48
201	A40	90c multicolored	.60	.60
202	A40	1.05r multicolored	.70	.70
		Nos. 199-202 (4)	2.03	2.03

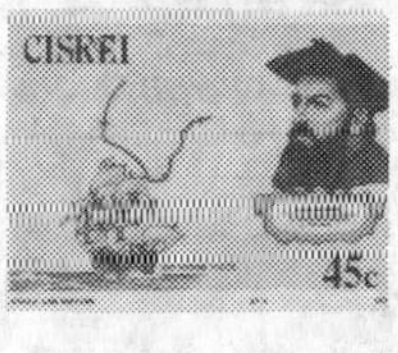

Famous Explorers A41

Map of voyage, sailing ship, and explorer: 45c, San Gabriel, 1497-98, Vasco da Gama. 65c, Endeavour, 1768-71, James Cook. 85c, Victoria, 1519, Ferdinand Magellan. 90c, Golden Hinde, 1577-80, Sir Francis Drake. 1.05r, Heemskerck, 1642, Abel Tasman.

1993, May 19 Litho.

203	A41	45c multicolored	.30	.30
204	A41	65c multicolored	.45	.45
205	A41	85c multicolored	.58	.58
206	A41	90c multicolored	.60	.60
207	A41	1.05r multicolored	.70	.70
		Nos. 203-207 (5)	2.63	2.63

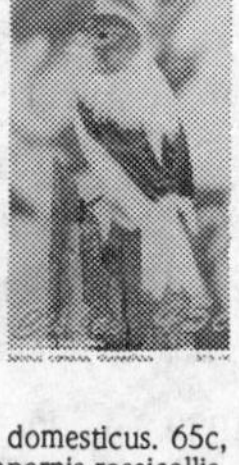
Small Cage Birds — A42

Designs: 45c, Serinus canarius domesticus. 65c, Melopsittacus undulatus. 85c, Agapornis roseicollis. 90c, Nymphicus hollandicus. 1.05r, Chloebia gouldiae.

1993, July 16 Litho.

208	A42	45c multicolored	.28	.28
209	A42	65c multicolored	.40	.40
210	A42	85c multicolored	.52	.52
211	A42	90c multicolored	.55	.55
212	A42	1.05r multicolored	.65	.65
		Nos. 208-212 (5)	2.40	2.40

A souvenir sheet of one No. 209 has inscription for National Philatelic Exhibition. Sold for 3r.

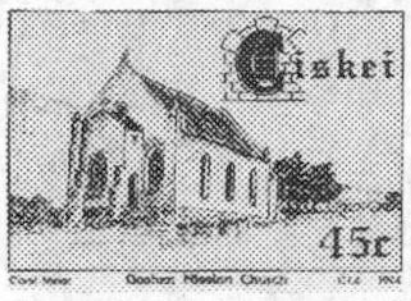

Churches A43

Designs: 45c, Goshen Mission Church. 65c, Kamastone Mission Church. 85c, Richie Thompson Memorial Church. 1.05r, Bryce Ross Memorial Church.

1993, Sept. 17 Litho.

213	A43	45c black, buff & red	.28	.28
214	A43	65c black, blue & red	.40	.40
215	A43	85c black, tan & red	.52	.52
216	A43	1.05r black, lt yellow & red	.65	.65
		Nos. 213-216 (4)	1.85	1.85

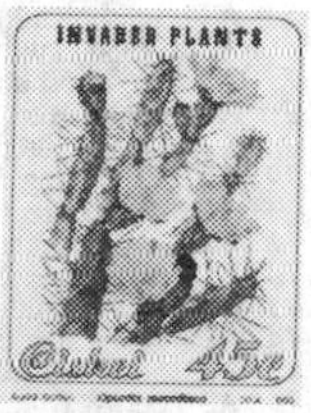

Invader Plants — A44

1993, Nov. 5 Litho. *Perf. 14x14½*

217	A44	45c Opuntia aurantiaca	.28	.28
218	A44	65c Datura stramonium	.40	.40
219	A44	85c Sesbania punicea	.52	.52
220	A44	1.05r Nicotiana glauca	.65	.65
a.		Souvenir sheet, #217-220		
		Nos. 217-220 (4)	1.85	1.85

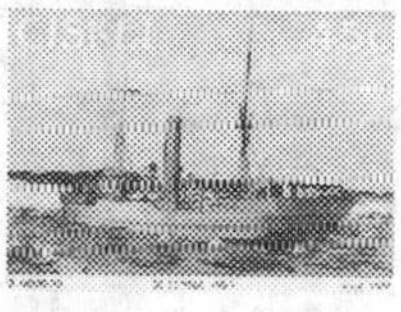
Shipwrecks A45

1994, Feb. 18 Litho. *Perf. 14½x14*

221	A45	45c SS Lostia, 1921	.28	.28
222	A45	65c Catherine, 1846	.40	.40
223	A45	85c Bennebroek, 1713	.50	.50
224	A45	1.05r Sao Joao Bapista, 1622	.65	.65
		Nos. 221-224 (4)	1.83	1.83

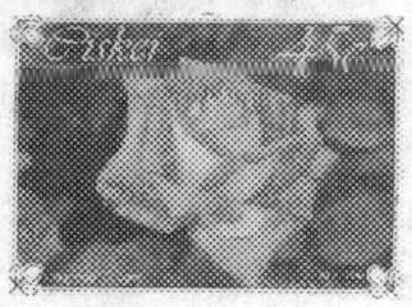

Roses — A46

1994, Apr. 15 Litho. *Perf. 14½x14*

225	A46	45c Herman Steyn	.25	.25
226	A46	70c Esther Geldenhuys	.40	.40
227	A46	95c Margaret Wasserfall	.55	.55
228	A46	1.15r Prof. Fred Ziady	.65	.65
a.		Souvenir sheet of 4, #225-228	1.90	1.90
		Nos. 225-228 (4)	1.85	1.85

Ciskei ceased to exist April 27, 1994.

TRANSKEI

(,)tran(t)s-'kī

LOCATION — Enclave, East Cape Province, Republic of South Africa
GOVT. — Self-governing tribal homeland
AREA — 16,910 sq. mi.
POP. — 2,876,122 (1985)
CAPITAL — Umtata

Catalogue values for all unused stamps in this country are for Never Hinged items.

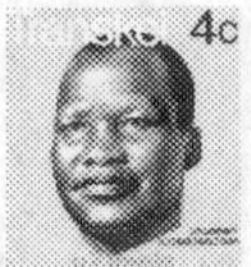

Independence from South Africa — A1

Perf. 12½

1976, Oct. 26 Litho. Unwmk.

1 A1 4c Paramount Chief K.D. Matanzima .80 .80
2 A1 10c Mace, flag 1.90 1.90
3 A1 15c Matanzima, diff. 3.00 3.00
4 A1 20c Coat of arms 4.00 4.00
Nos. 1-4 (4) 9.70 9.70

An imperf. souvenir sheet exists containing Nos. 1-4 printed in one color (black). Not valid for postage.

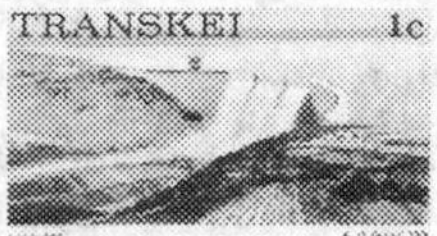

Lubisi Dam — A2

1976, Oct. 26 *Perf. 12x12½*

5 A2 1c shown .15 .15
6 A2 2c Soil cultivation .15 .15
7 A2 3c Threshing sorghum .15 .15
8 A2 4c Transkei matron .15 .15
9 A2 5c Grinding corn .15 .15
10 A2 6c Cutting *Phormium tenax* .18 .18
11 A2 7c Shepherd boy .20 .20
12 A2 8c Felling timber .24 .24
13 A2 9c Agricultural school .27 .27
14 A2 10c Picking tea .40 .40
15 A2 15c Wood gathering .60 .60
16 A2 20c Weaving industry .80 .80
17 A2 25c Improving cattle breeds 1.00 1.00
18 A2 30c Sledge transportation 1.25 1.25
19 A2 50c Map, coat of arms 2.00 2.00
20 A2 1r Administrative Building, Umtata 4.00 4.00
21 A2 2r The Bunga, flag 8.00 8.00
Nos. 5-21 (17) 19.69 19.69

Perf. 14

5a A2 1c .15 .15
6a A2 2c .15 .15
7a A2 3c .15 .15
8a A2 4c .15 .15
9a A2 5c .15 .15
10a A2 6c .18 .18
12a A2 8c .24 .24
13a A2 9c .27 .27
14a A2 10c .40 .40
15a A2 15c .60 .60
16a A2 20c .80 .80
17a A2 25c 1.00 1.00
18a A2 30c 1.25 1.25
19a A2 50c 2.00 2.00
Nos. 5a-19a (14) 7.49 7.49

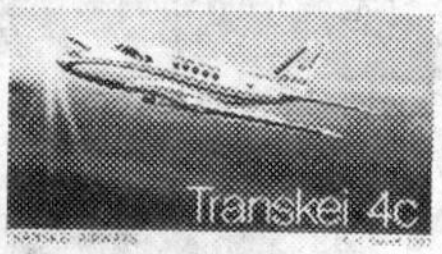

Transkei Airways Inaugural Flight, Umtata-Johannesburg — A3

1977, Feb. 11

22 A3 4c Aircraft 1.00 1.00
23 A3 15c Aircraft, terminal 3.75 3.75

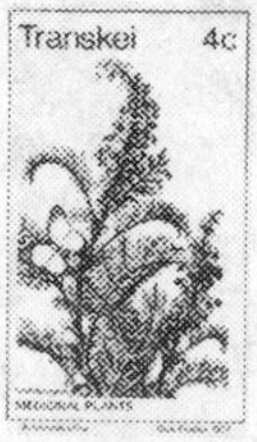

Artemesia affra — A4

Medicinal plants.

1977, May 16 *Perf. 12½x12*

24 A4 4c shown .50 .50
25 A4 10c *Bulbine natalensis* 2.00 2.00
26 A4 15c *Melianthus major* 3.00 3.00
27 A4 20c *Cotyledon orbiculata* 4.00 4.00
Nos. 24-27 (4) 9.50 9.50

1978, Sept. 25

Edible fruit.

28 A4 4c *Carissa bispinosa* .25 .25
29 A4 10c *Dovyalis caffra* .60 .60
30 A4 15c *Harpephyllum caffrum* .90 .90
31 A4 20c *Syzygium cordatum* 1.25 1.25
Nos. 28-31 (4) 3.00 3.00

1981, Apr. 15

Medicinal plants.

32 A4 5c *Leonotis leonurus* .15 .15
33 A4 15c *Euphorbia bupleurifolia* .30 .30
34 A4 20c *Pelargonium reniforme* .40 .40
35 A4 25c *Hibiscus trionum* .50 .50
Nos. 32-35 (4) 1.35 1.35

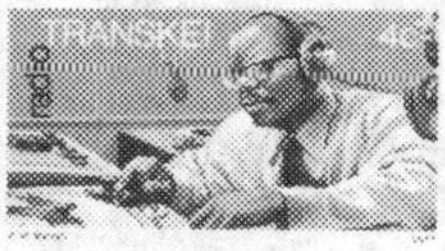

Transkei Radio, 1st Anniv. — A5

1977, Oct. 26 *Perf. 12x12½*

36 A5 4c Disc jockey .60 .60
37 A5 15c Announcer 2.50 2.50

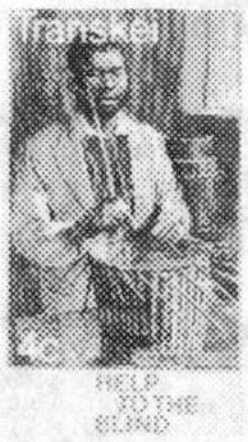

"Help the Blind" — A6

1977, Nov. 18 *Perf. 12½x12*

38 A6 4c Basket weaver .40 .40
39 A6 15c Reading Braille 1.50 1.50
40 A6 20c Spinning wool 2.00 2.00
Nos. 38-40 (3) 3.90 3.90

1978, Nov. 30

"Care for Cripples."

41 A6 4c Leg brace on boy .35 .35
42 A6 10c Man in wheelchair .90 .90
43 A6 15c Nurse examining boy 1.40 1.40
Nos. 41-43 (3) 2.65 2.65

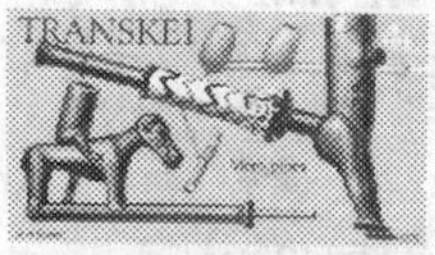

Men's Pipes — A7

1978, Mar. 1 *Perf. 12x12½*

44 A7 4c shown .48 .48
45 A7 10c multi, diff. 1.25 1.25
46 A7 15c multi, diff. 1.75 1.75
47 A7 20c Woman's and witch doctor's pipes 2.50 2.50
Nos. 44-47 (4) 5.98 5.98

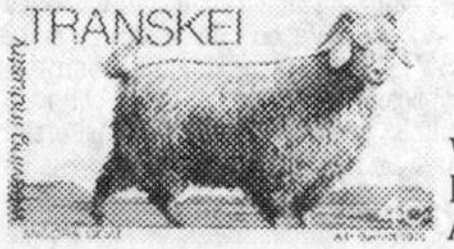

Weaving Industry A8

1978, June 9

48 A8 4c Angora goat .32 .32
49 A8 10c Spinning mohair .80 .80
50 A8 15c Dyeing mohair 1.25 1.25
51 A8 20c Weaving mohair rug 1.65 1.65
Nos. 48-51 (4) 4.02 4.02

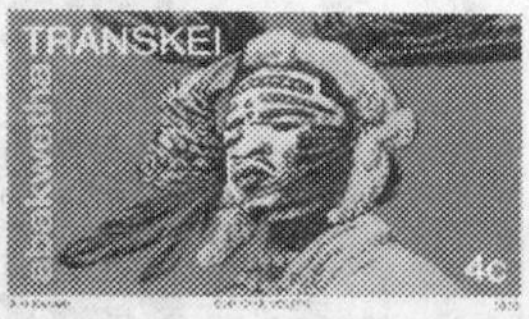

Initiation Ceremony of Xhosa Men — A9

1979, Jan. 30 *Perf. 12½*

52 A9 4c Chi Cha youth .32 .32
53 A9 10c Youths in seclusion .90 .90
54 A9 15c Umtshilo dance 1.40 1.40
55 A9 20c Leaving the Sutu 1.75 1.75
Nos. 52-55 (4) 4.37 4.37

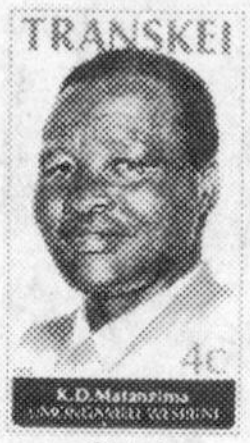

Chief Matanzima A10

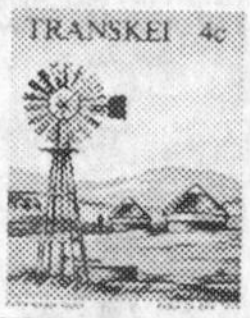

Water Resources A11

1979, Feb. 20 *Perf. 14½x14*

56 A10 4c brn car & gold .28 .28
57 A10 15c olive grn & gold 1.00 1.00

Inauguration of Matanzima, second state president.

Perf. 14½x14, 14x14½

1979, Mar. 13

58 A11 4c Windmill .20 .20
59 A11 10c Woman filling water jar .50 .50
60 A11 15c Irrigation, Indwe River, horiz. .75 .75
61 A11 20c Ncora dam, horiz. 1.00 1.00
Nos. 58-61 (4) 2.45 2.45

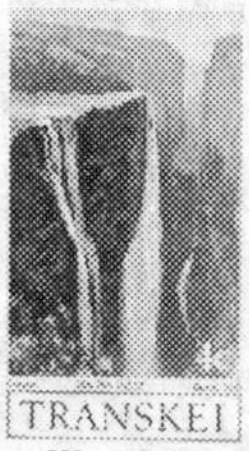

Waterfalls A12

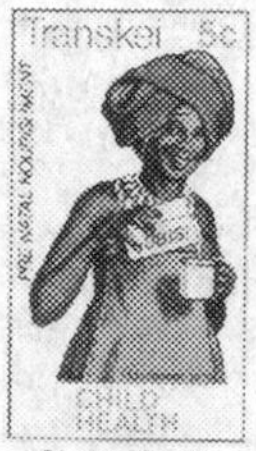

Child Health Care A13

1979, Sept. 4

62 A12 4c Magwa Falls .16 .16
63 A12 10c Bawa Falls .40 .40
64 A12 15c Waterfall Bluff, horiz. .60 .60
65 A12 20c Tsitsa Falls, horiz. .80 .80
Nos. 62-65 (4) 1.96 1.96

1979, Dec. 3 *Perf. 14½x14*

66 A13 5c Pre-natal nourishment .15 .15
67 A13 15c Primary feeding .45 .45
68 A13 20c Immunization .60 .60
Nos. 66-68 (3) 1.20 1.20

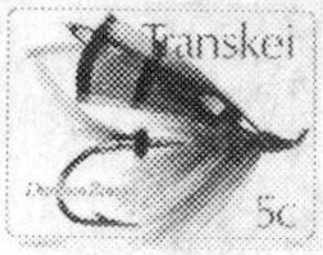

Fishing Flies — A14

Designs: a, Durham ranger. b, Colonel Bates. c, Black gnat. d, Zug bug. e, March brown.

1980, Jan. 15 *Perf. 14x14½*

69 Strip of 5 2.50 2.50
a.-e. A14 5c any single .50 .50

1981, Jan. 15

Designs: a, Kent's lightning. b, Wickham's fancy. c, Jock Scott. d, Green highlander. e, Tan nymph.

70 Strip of 5 1.50 1.50
a.-e. A14 10c any single .30 .30

1982, Jan. 6

Designs: a, Royal coachman. b, Light spruce. c, Montana nymph. d, Butcher. e, Blue charm.

71 Strip of 5 1.50 1.50
a.-e. A14 10c any single .30 .30

1983, Mar. 2

Designs: a, Alexandra. b, Kent's marbled sedge. c, White marabou. d, Mayfly nymph. e, Silver Wilkinson.

72 Strip of 5 2.00 2.00
a.-e. A14 20c any single .40 .40

1984, Feb. 10

Designs: a, Silver gray. b, Ginger quill. c, Hardy's favorite. d, March brown nymph. e, Kent's spectrum Mohawk.

73 Strip of 5 2.00 2.00
a.-e. A14 20c any single .40 .40

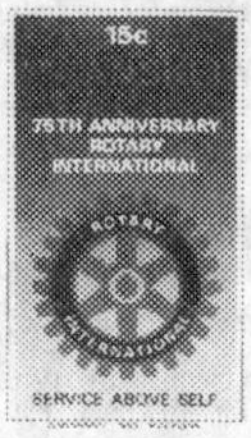

Rotary Intl., 75th Anniv. — A15

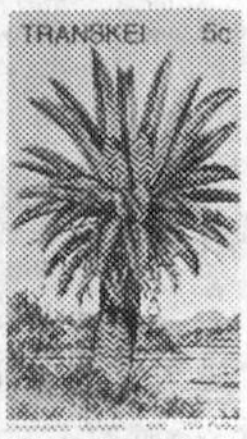

Cycads — A16

1980, Feb. 22 *Perf. 14½x14*

74 A15 15c blk, ultra & gold .45 .45

1980, Apr. 30

75 A16 5c *Encephalartos altensteinii* .15 .15
76 A16 10c *Encephalartos princeps* .30 .30
77 A16 15c *Encephalartos vilosus* .45 .45
78 A16 20c *Encephalartos friderici-guilielmi* .60 .60
Nos. 75-78 (4) 1.50 1.50

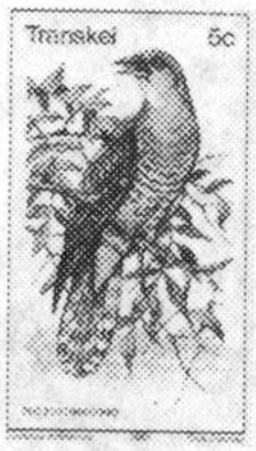

Birds — A17

1980, July 30

79 A17 5c *Cuculus solitarius* .20 .20
80 A17 10c *Batis capensis* .40 .40
81 A17 15c *Balearica pavonina* .60 .60
82 A17 20c *Ploceus ocularius* .80 .80
Nos. 79-82 (4) 2.00 2.00

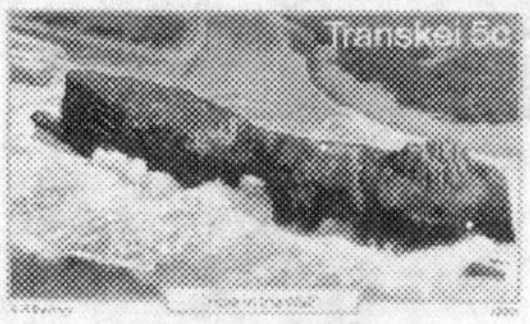

Tourism — A18

1980, Oct. 26

83 A18 5c Hole in the Wall .15 .15
84 A18 10c Port St. Johns .30 .30
85 A18 15c The Citadel .45 .45
86 A18 20c The Archway .60 .60
Nos. 83-86 (4) 1.50 1.50

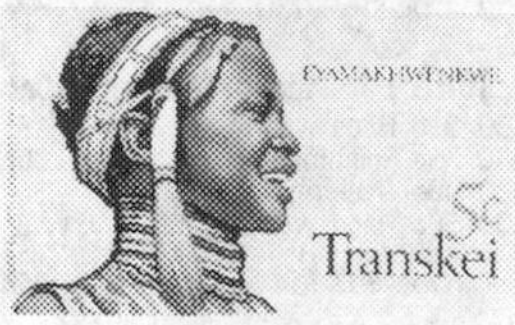

Xhosa Women's Headdresses — A19

1981, Aug. 28

87 A19 5c Eyamakhwenkwe .15 .15
88 A19 15c Eyabafana .30 .30
89 A19 20c Umfazana .40 .40
90 A19 25c Ixhegokazi .50 .50
a. Souvenir sheet of 4, #87-90 1.30 1.30
Nos. 87-90 (4) 1.35 1.35

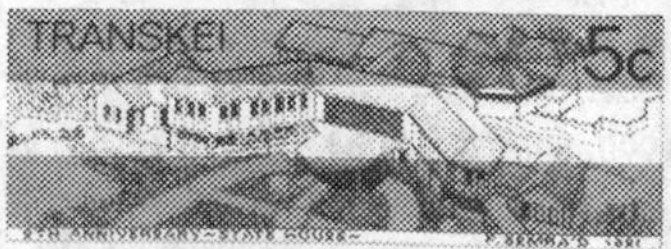

Independence, 5th Anniv. — A20

1981, Oct. 26 *Perf. 14x14½*

91 A20 5c State House .20 .20
92 A20 15c University .60 .60

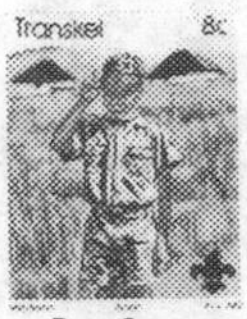

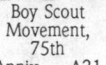

Boy Scout Movement, 75th Anniv. — A21

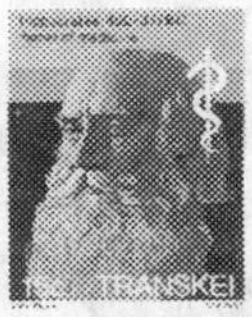

Great Medical Pioneers — A22

1982, May 14 *Perf. 14½x14*

93 A21 8c Salute .16 .16
94 A21 10c Planting tree .20 .20
95 A21 20c Rafting .40 .40
96 A21 25c Nature hike with dog .50 .50
Nos. 93-96 (4) 1.26 1.26

1982, Oct. 5

97 A22 15c Hippocrates .15 .15
98 A22 20c Anton van Leeuwenhoek .60 .60
99 A22 25c William Harvey .75 .75
100 A22 30c Joseph Lister .90 .90
Nos. 97-100 (4) 2.40 2.40

1983, Aug. 17

101 A22 10c Edward Jenner .30 .30
102 A22 20c Gregor Mendel .60 .60
103 A22 25c Louis Pasteur .75 .75
104 A22 40c Florence Nightingale 1.25 1.25
Nos. 101-104 (4) 2.90 2.90

1984, Oct. 12

105 A22 11c Nicholas of Cusa .45 .45
106 A22 25c William Morton 1.00 1.00
107 A22 30c Wilhelm Roentgen 1.25 1.25
108 A22 45c Karl Landsteiner 1.75 1.75
Nos. 105-108 (4) 4.45 4.45

1985, Sept. 20

109 A22 12c Andreas Vesalius .48 .48
110 A22 25c Marcello Malpighi 1.00 1.00
111 A22 30c Francois Magendie 1.25 1.25
112 A22 50c William Stewart Halsted 2.00 2.00
Nos. 109-112 (4) 4.73 4.73
Nos. 97-112 (16) 14.48 14.48

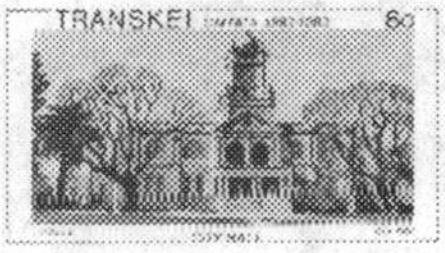

Umtata, Cent. A23

Architecture: 8c, City Hall. 15c, The Bunga. 20c, Botha Sigcau Building. 25c, Palace of Justice, Matanzima Building.

1982, Nov. 10 *Perf. 14x14½*

113 A23 8c multicolored .15 .15
114 A23 15c multicolored .30 .30
115 A23 20c multicolored .40 .40
116 A23 25c multicolored .50 .50
Nos. 113-116 (4) 1.35 1.35

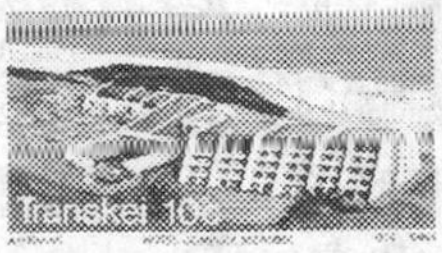

Wildcoast Holiday Resort, Mzamba A24

1983, May 25

117 A24 10c Hotel complex .20 .20
118 A24 20c Beach scene .40 .40
119 A24 25c Casino .50 .50
120 A24 40c Carousel .80 .80
Nos. 117-120 (4) 1.90 1.90

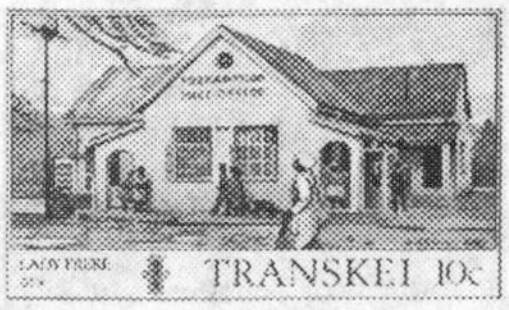

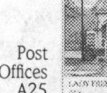

Post Offices A25

1983, Nov. 9 *Perf. 14½x14*

121 A25 10c Lady Frere .20 .20
122 A25 20c Idutywa .40 .40
123 A25 25c Lusikisiki .50 .50
124 A25 40c Cala .80 .80
Nos. 121-124 (4) 1.90 1.90

1984, May 11

125 A25 11c Umzimkulu .22 .22
126 A25 20c Mount Fletcher .40 .40
127 A25 25c Qumbu .50 .50
128 A25 30c Umtata .80 .80
Nos. 125-128 (4) 1.92 1.92

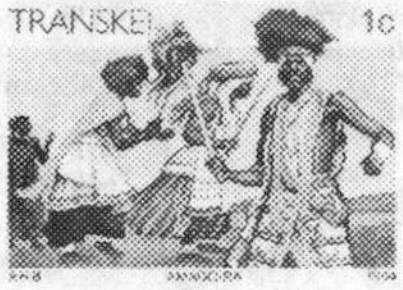

Xhosa Lifestyle A26

1984-90

129 A26 1c Amaggira .15 .15
130 A26 2c Horsemen .15 .15
131 A26 3c Mat maker .15 .15
132 A26 4c Xhosa dancers .15 .15
133 A26 5c Man, donkeys .15 .15
134 A26 6c Musicians .15 .15
135 A26 7c Fingo brides .15 .15
136 A26 8c Tasting beer .15 .15
137 A26 9c Thinning corn .15 .15
138 A26 10c Dance demonstration .15 .15
139 A26 11c Carrying water from the river .18 .18
140 A26 12c Meal preparation .18 .18
141 A26 14c Weeding .20 .20
142 A26 15c Stick fighting .22 .22
143 A26 16c Morning pasture .24 .24
144 A26 20c Abakhwetha dancers .30 .30
145 A26 21c Building initiation hut .32 .32
146 A26 25c Tribesmen singing .38 .38
147 A26 30c Matrons .40 .40
148 A26 50c Pipe maker .75 .75
149 A26 1r Intonjane women 1.50 1.50
150 A26 2r Abakhwetha 3.00 3.00
Nos. 129-150 (22) 9.17 9.17

Issued: 11c, 4/2/84; 12c, 4/1/85; 14c, 4/1/86; 16c, 4/1/87; 21c, 7/3/90; others, 7/6/84.

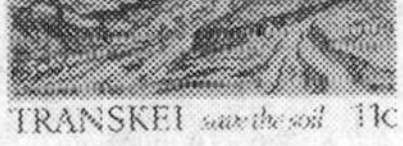

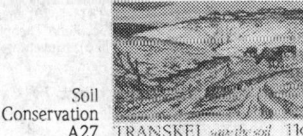

Soil Conservation A27

Designs: 11c, Erosion from over-grazing. 25c, Wall construction to collect sediment. 30c, Regeneration of vegetation. 50c, Cattle grazing on verdant plain.

1985, Feb. 7

155 A27 11c shown .22 .22
156 A27 25c multicolored .50 .50
157 A27 30c multicolored .60 .60
158 A27 50c multicolored 1.00 1.00
Nos. 155-158 (4) 2.32 2.32

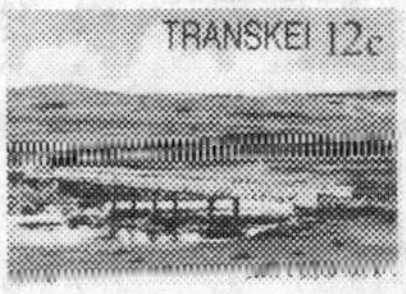

Bridges — A28

1985, Apr. 18

159 A28 12c Tsitsa .24 .24
160 A28 25c White Kei .50 .50
161 A28 30c Mitchell .60 .60
162 A28 50c Umzimvubu 1.00 1.00
Nos. 159-162 (4) 2.34 2.34

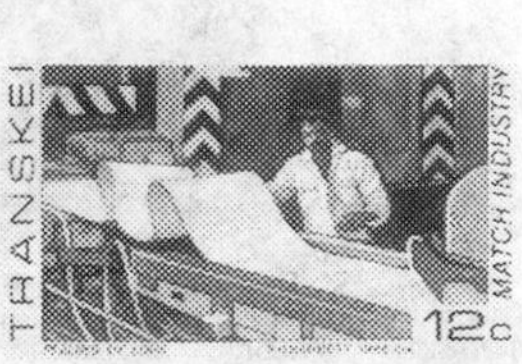

Match Industry A29

1985, July 25 *Perf. 14½x14*

163 A29 12c Peeling logs .24 .24
164 A29 25c Splint chopping .50 .50
165 A29 30c VPO machine .60 .60
166 A29 50c Filling boxes 1.00 1.00
Nos. 163-166 (4) 2.34 2.34

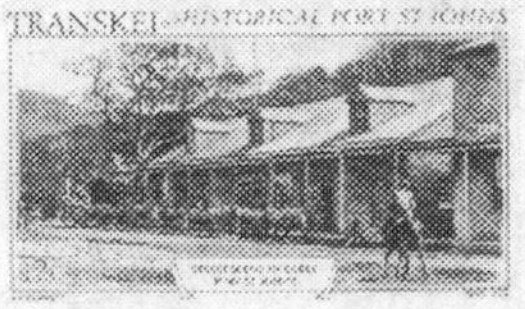

Port St. Johns A30

Designs: 12c, Early street scene. 20c, Coaster *Umzimvubu* at the Old Jetty. 25c, Unloading corn from wagons at the Jetty. 30c, View of the town, 1890's.

1986, Feb. 6

167 A30 12c multicolored .18 .18
168 A30 20c multicolored .30 .30
169 A30 25c multicolored .38 .38
170 A30 30c multicolored .45 .45
a. Souvenir sheet of 4, #167-170 2.00 2.00
Nos. 167-170 (4) 1.31 1.31

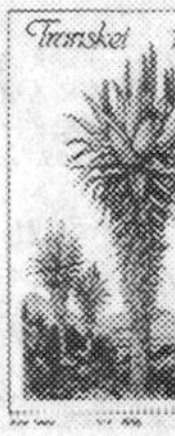

Aloes — A31

1986, May 1

171 A31 14c *Aloe ferox* .20 .20
172 A31 20c *Aloe arborescens* .30 .30
173 A31 25c *Aloe maculata* .38 .38
174 A31 30c *Aloe ecklonis* .45 .45
a. Souvenir sheet of 1 3.00 3.00
Nos. 171-174 (4) 1.33 1.33

No. 174a margin pictures emblem of the natl. philatelic exhibition held at Johannesburg, Oct. 6-11. Sold for 50c.

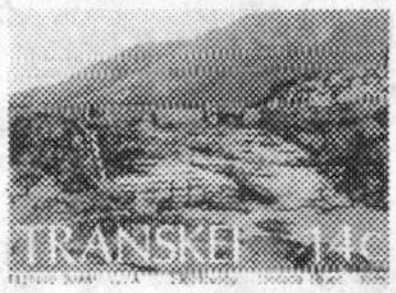

Hydroelectric Power Stations — A32

Designs: 14c, First Falls, Umtata River. 20c, Second Falls, Umtata River. 25c, Ncora, Qumanco River. 30c, Collywobbles, Mbashe River.

1986, July 24

175 A32 14c shown .20 .20
176 A32 20c multicolored .30 .30
177 A32 25c multicolored .38 .38
178 A32 30c multicolored .45 .45
Nos. 175-178 (4) 1.33 1.33

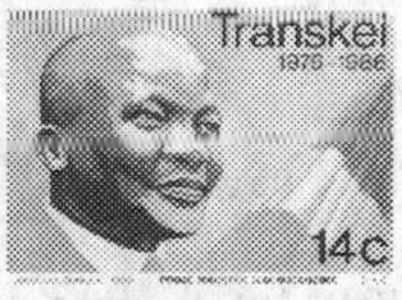

Independence, 10th Anniv. — A33

Designs: 14c, Prime Minister G. M. Matanzima. 20c, Technical College, Umtata. 25c, University of Transkei, Umtata. 30c, Palace of Justice, Umtata.

1986, Oct. 26

179 A33 14c multicolored .20 .20
180 A33 20c multicolored .30 .30
181 A33 25c multicolored .38 .38
182 A33 30c multicolored .45 .45
Nos. 179-182 (4) 1.33 1.33

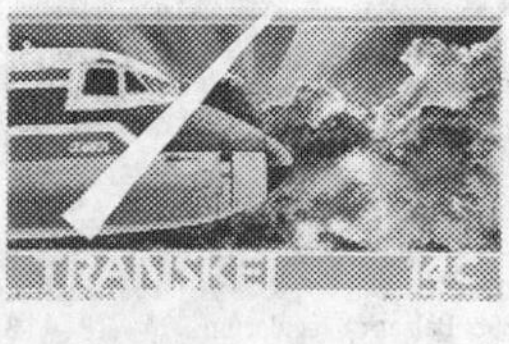

Transkei Airways, 10th Anniv. A34

1987, Feb. 5

183 A34 14c shown .26 .26
184 A34 20c Aircraft tail .40 .40
185 A34 25c Nose, propellers .50 .50
186 A34 30c Plane, control tower .60 .60
Nos. 183-186 (4) 1.76 1.76

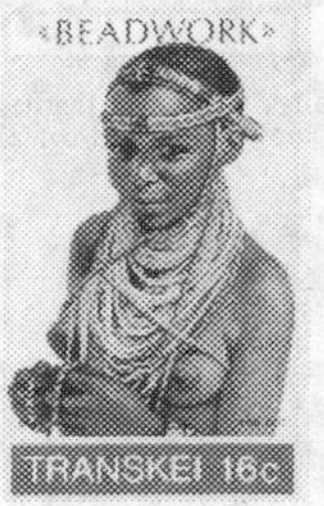

Beadwork — A35

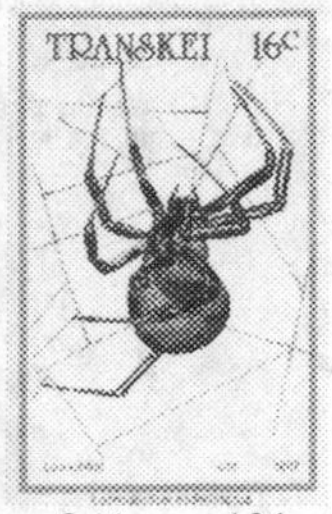

Spiders — A36

1987, May 22 *Perf. 14x14½*

187 A35 16c Pondo girl .30 .30
188 A35 20c Bomvana woman .38 .38
189 A35 25c Xessibe woman .48 .48
a. Souvenir sheet of 1 3.50 3.50
190 A35 30c Xhosa man .60 .60
Nos. 187-190 (4) 1.76 1.76

No. 189a has blue and black decorative margin picturing the emblem of the natl. philatelic exhibition held at Paarl, Sept. 16-19. Sold for 50c.

1987, Aug. 24

191 A36 16c *Latrodectus indistinctus* .30 .30
192 A36 20c *Nephila pilipes fenestrata* .38 .38
193 A36 25c *Lycosidae* .48 .48
194 A36 30c *Argiope nigrovittata* .60 .60
Nos. 191-194 (4) 1.76 1.76

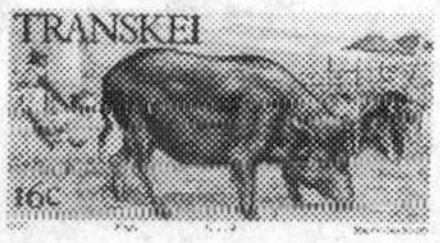

Domestic Animals A37

1987, Oct. 22

195 A37 16c Black pigs .25 .25
196 A37 30c Goats .50 .50
197 A37 40c Merino sheep .65 .65
198 A37 50c Cattle .85 .85
Nos. 195-198 (4) 2.25 2.25

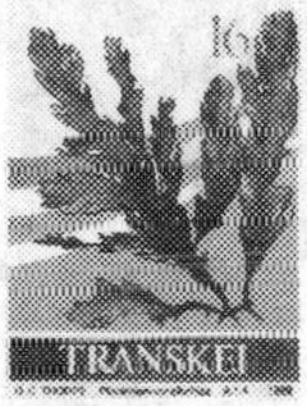

Seaweed — A38

1988, Feb. 18

199 A38 16c *Plocamium corallorhiza* .22 .22
200 A38 30c *Gelidium amanzil* .42 .42
201 A38 40c *Ecklonia biruncinata* .60 .60
202 A38 50c *Halimeda cuneata* .70 .70
Nos. 199-202 (4) 1.94 1.94

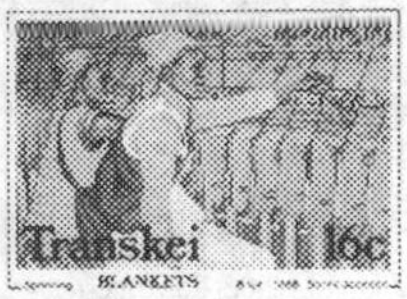

Blanket Factory, Butterworth A39

1988, May 5 *Perf. 14½x14*

203 A39 16c Spinning machines .22 .22
204 A39 30c Warping machine .42 .42
205 A39 40c Weaving machine .60 .60
206 A39 50c Raising the nap .70 .70
Nos. 203-206 (4) 1.94 1.94

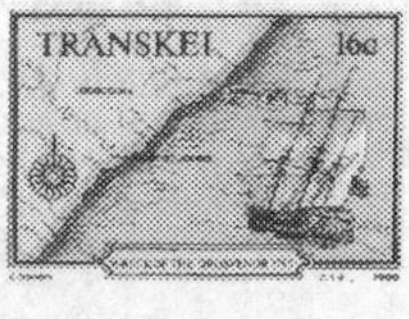

Wreck of the *Grosvenor,* 1782 — A40

Designs: 16c, Ship, map. 30c, *The Wreck of the Grosvenor,* by R. Smirke. 40c, Dirk hilt, compass and coins salvaged. 50c, *African Hospitality,* by G. Morland.

1988, Aug. 4

207 A40 16c multicolored .28 .28
208 A40 30c multicolored .55 .55
209 A40 40c multicolored .75 .75

210 A40 50c multicolored .90 .90
a. Souvenir sheet of 1 3.50 3.50
Nos. 207-210 (4) 2.48 2.48

No. 210a margin pictures emblem of the natl. philatelic exhibition at Pietermaritzburg, Nov. 22-27. Sold for 1r.

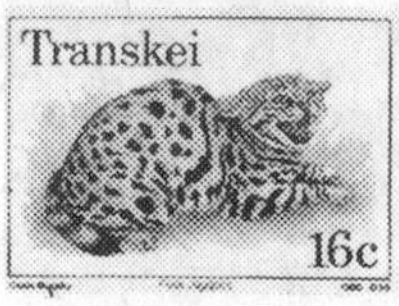

Endangered Species — A41

1988, Oct. 20
211 A41 16c *Felis nigripes* .22 .22
212 A41 30c *Philantomba monticola* .42 .42
213 A41 40c *Ourebia ourebi* .60 .60
214 A41 50c *Lycaon pictus* .70 .70
Nos. 211-214 (4) 1.94 1.94

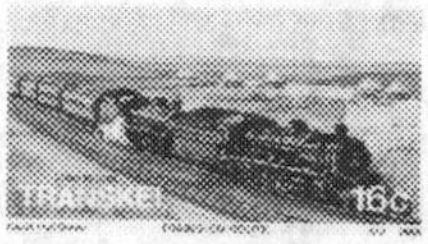

Locomotive, Trains and Bridges A42

Designs: 16c, Class 14 CRB locomotive. 30c, CRB pulling train over Toleni-Halt Bridge. 40c, Train on the Great Kei River Bridge, vert. 50c, Train in the Kei Valley.

Perf. 14x14¹/₂, 14¹/₂x14
1989, Jan. 19
215 A42 16c multi .18 .18
216 A42 30c multi .32 .32
217 A42 40c multi .45 .45
218 A42 50c multi, vert. .55 .55
Nos. 215-218 (4) 1.50 1.50

A souvenir sheet of one No. 218 has margin picturing the emblem of the natl. philatelic exhibition WANDERERS 101, held Sept. 6-9. Sold for 1.50r.

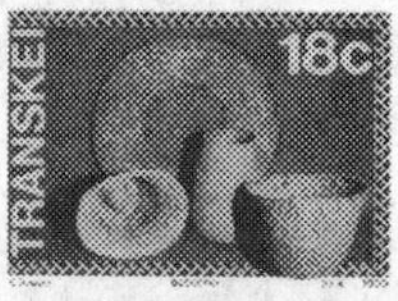

Basketry A43

1989, Apr. 20 ***Perf. 14¹/₂x14***
219 A43 18c shown .20 .20
220 A43 30c multi, diff. .32 .32
221 A43 40c multi, diff. .42 .42
222 A43 50c multi, diff. .55 .55
Nos. 219-222 (4) 1.49 1.49

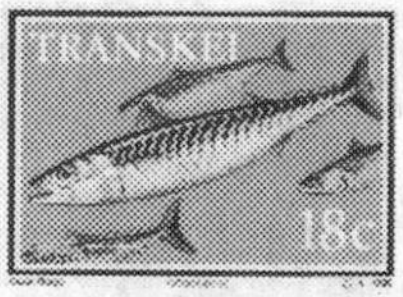

Mackerel A44

1989, July 20
223 A44 18c shown .20 .20
224 A44 30c Squid .32 .32
225 A44 40c Brown mussel .42 .42
226 A44 50c Rock lobster .55 .55
Nos. 223-226 (4) 1.49 1.49

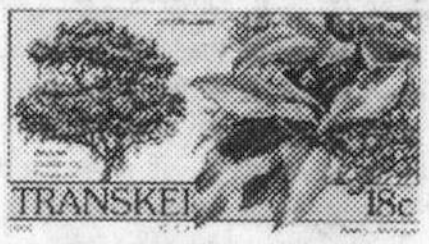

Trees — A45

1989, Oct. 5 ***Perf. 14x14¹/₂***
227 A45 18c Broom cluster fig .20 .20
228 A45 30c Natal fig .32 .32
229 A45 40c Broad-leaved coral .42 .42
230 A45 50c Cabbage tree .55 .55
Nos. 227-230 (4) 1.49 1.49

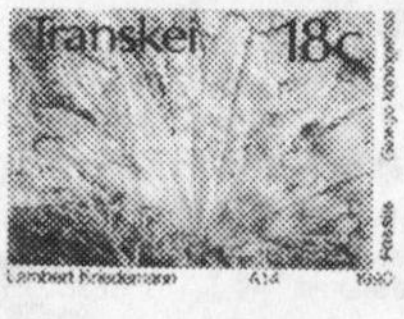

Fossils — A46

1990, Jan. 18
231 A46 18c *Ginkgo koningensis* .18 .18
232 A46 30c *Pseudoctenis spatulata* .32 .32
233 A46 40c *Rissikia media* .42 .42
234 A46 50c *Taeniopteris anavolans* .55 .55
Nos. 231-234 (4) 1.47 1.47

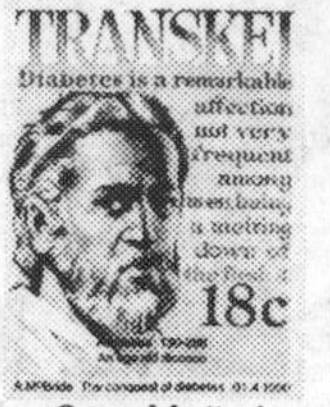

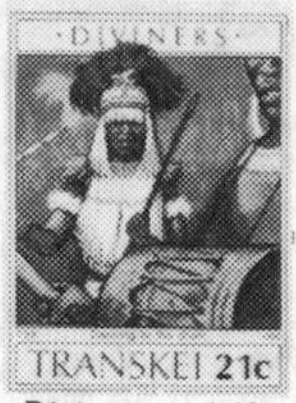

Great Medical Pioneers — A47

Diviners — A48

1990, Mar. 29 ***Perf. 14x14¹/₂***
235 A47 18c Aretaeus .18 .18
236 A47 30c Claude Bernard .32 .32
237 A47 40c Oscar Minkowski .42 .42
238 A47 50c Frederick Banting .55 .55
Nos. 235-238 (4) 1.47 1.47

1990, June 28 Litho. ***Perf. 14x14¹/₂***
239 A48 21c Dancing to the Drum .18 .18
240 A48 35c Lecturing Imichetywa .30 .30
241 A48 40c Initiation ceremony .35 .35
242 A48 50c Induction ceremony .42 .42
a. Souvenir sheet of 1 2.25 2.25
Nos. 239-242 (4) 1.25 1.25

No. 242a for the 150th anniv. of the Penny Black. Sold for 1.50r.

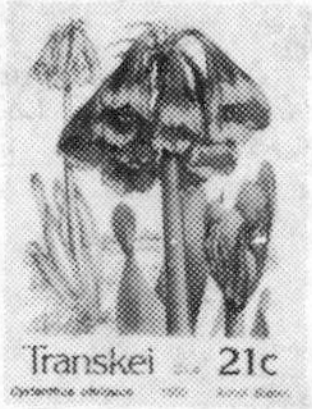

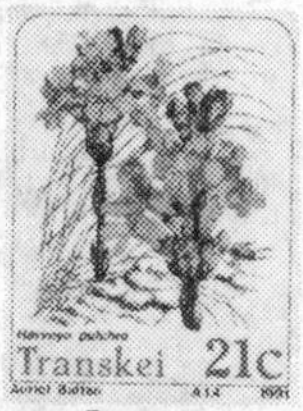

Flowers — A49

Parasitic Plants — A50

1990, Sept. 20 Litho. ***Perf. 14x14¹/₂***
243 A49 21c Cyrtanthus obliquus .18 .18
244 A49 35c Disa crassicornis .30 .30
245 A49 40c Sandersonia aurantiaca .35 .35
246 A49 50c Podranea ricasoliana .42 .42
Nos. 243-246 (4) 1.25 1.25

1991, Jan. 10 **Litho.**
247 A50 21c Harveya pulchra .15 .15
248 A50 35c Harveya speciosa .24 .24
249 A50 40c Alectra sessiliflora .28 .28
250 A50 50c Hydnora africana .35 .35
Nos. 247-250 (4) 1.02 1.02

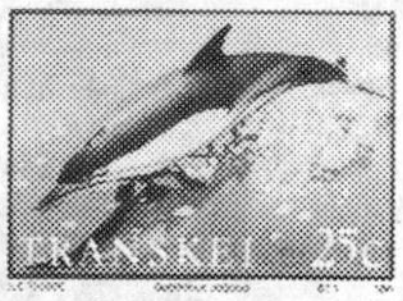

Dolphins A51

1991, Apr. 4 Litho. ***Perf. 14¹/₂x14***
251 A51 25c Delphinus delphis .15 .15
252 A51 40c Tursiops truncatus .22 .22
253 A51 50c Sousa plumbea .28 .28
254 A51 60c Grampus griseus .35 .35
Nos. 251-254 (4) 1.00 1.00

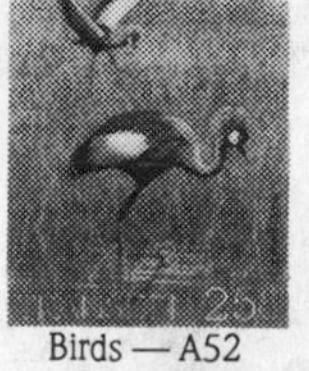
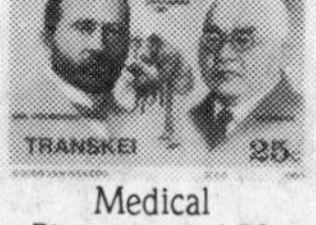

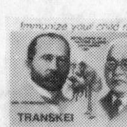

Birds — A52

Medical Pioneers — A53

1991, June 20 **Litho.**
255 A52 25c Balearica regulorum .18 .18
256 A52 40c Gyps coprotheres .28 .28
257 A52 50c Grus carunculata .35 .35
258 A52 60c Neophron percnopterus .42 .42
Nos. 255-258 (4) 1.23 1.23

1991, Sept. 26 Litho. ***Perf. 14x14¹/₂***

Developers of vaccines: 25c, Emil von Behring (1854-1917) and Shibasaburo Kitasato (1852-1931), diphtheria. 40c, Leon Albert Calmette (1863-1933) and Camille Guerin (1872-1961), tuberculosis. 50c, Jonas Salk (b. 1914), polio. 60c, John Franklin Enders (1897-1985), measles.

259 A53 25c multicolored .15 .15
260 A53 40c multicolored .24 .24
261 A53 50c multicolored .30 .30
262 A53 60c multicolored .38 .38
Nos. 259-262 (4) 1.07 1.07

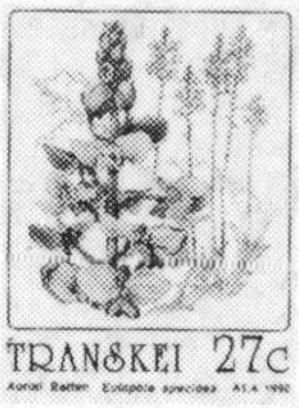

Orchids — A54

1992, Feb. 20 **Litho.**
263 A54 27c Eulophia speciosa .16 .16
264 A54 45c Satyrium sphaerocarpum .26 .26
265 A54 65c Disa scullyi .40 .40
266 A54 85c Disa tysonii .52 .52
Nos. 263-266 (4) 1.34 1.34

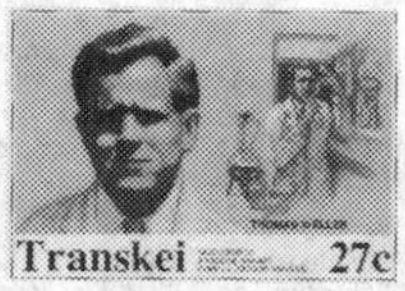

Medical Pioneers A55

Designs: 27c, Thomas Huckle Weller (b. 1915), developer of rubella vaccine. 45c, Ignaz Philipp Semmelweis (1818-1865), diagnosed septicaemia. 65c, Sir James Young Simpson (1811-1870), first to use chloroform in obstetrics. 85c, Rene Theophile Hyacinthe Laennec (1781-1826), inventor of stethoscope.

1992, Apr. 1 Litho. ***Perf. 14¹/₂x14***
267 A55 27c multicolored .16 .16
268 A55 45c multicolored .28 .28
269 A55 65c multicolored .40 .40
270 A55 85c multicolored .50 .50
Nos. 267-270 (4) 1.34 1.34

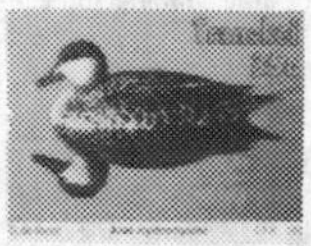
Waterfowl — A56

1992, July 16 Litho. ***Perf. 14x14¹/₂***
271 A56 35c Anas erythrorhyncha .28 .28
272 A56 35c Anas hottentota .28 .28
a. Pair, #271-272 .56 .56
273 A56 70c Oxyura punctata .56 .56
274 A56 70c Thalassornis leuconotus .56 .56
a. Pair, #273-274 1.12 1.12
275 A56 90c Anas sparsa .72 .72
276 A56 90c Alopochen aegyptiacus .72 .72
a. Pair, #275-276 1.45 1.45
277 A56 1.05r Anas smithi .85 .85
278 A56 1.05r Anas capensis .85 .85
a. Pair, #277-278 1.70 1.70
Nos. 271-278 (8) 4.82 4.82

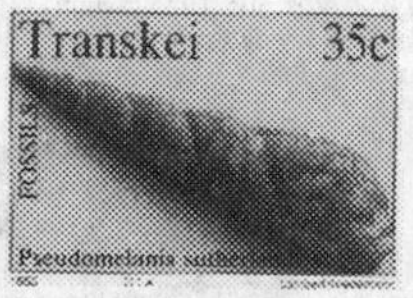

Fossils — A57

Designs: 35c, Pseudomelania sutherlandi. 70c, Gaudryceras denseplicatum. 90c, Neithea quinquecostata. 1.05r, Pugilina (Mayeria) acuticarinatus.

1992, Sept. 17 Litho. ***Perf. 14¹/₂x14***
279 A57 35c multicolored .28 .28
280 A57 70c multicolored .56 .56
281 A57 90c multicolored .72 .72
282 A57 1.05r multicolored .85 .85
Nos. 279-282 (4) 2.41 2.41

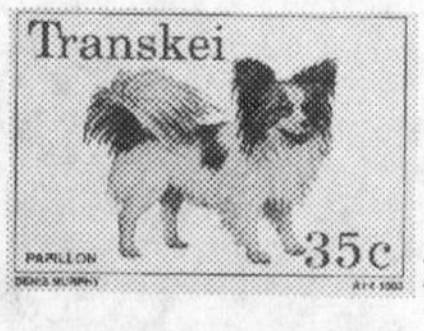

Dogs — A58

1993, Feb. 12 **Litho.**
283 A58 35c Papillon .22 .22
284 A58 70c Pekingese .45 .45
285 A58 90c Chihuahua .58 .58
286 A58 1.05r Dachshund .68 .68
Nos. 283-286 (4) 1.93 1.93

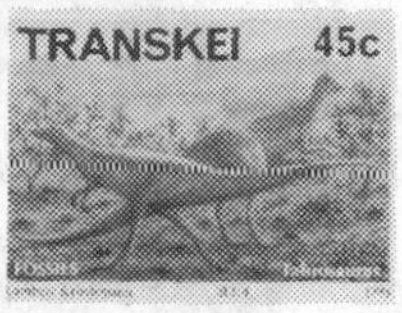

Prehistoric Animals — A59

1993, June 18 **Litho.**
287 A59 45c Fabrosaurus .28 .28
288 A59 65c Diictodon .40 .40
289 A59 85c Chasmatosaurus .52 .52
290 A59 1.05r Rubidgea .65 .65
Nos. 287-290 (4) 1.85 1.85

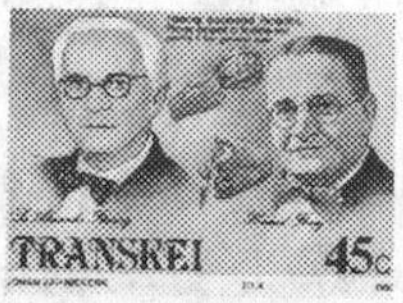

Medical Pioneers A60

Designs: 45c, Sir Alexander Fleming (1881-1955), discovered penicillin and Lord Howard Walter Florey (1898-1968), purified penicillin for general use. 65c, Alexis Carrel (1873-1944), developed Carrel-Dakin fluid and method to suture blood vessels. 85c, James Lind (1716-1794), recommended citrus fruit to combat scurvy. 1.05r, Santiago Ramon y Cajal (1852-1934), established neuron as basic unit of nervous structure.

1993, Aug. 20 **Litho.**
291 A60 45c multicolored .28 .28
292 A60 65c multicolored .40 .40
293 A60 85c multicolored .52 .52
294 A60 1.05r multicolored .65 .65
Nos. 291-294 (4) 1.85 1.85

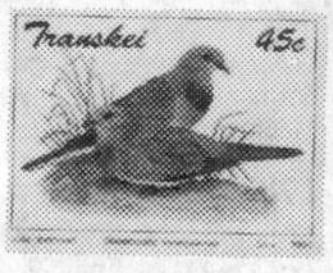

Doves — A61

Designs: 45c, Streptopelia senegalensis. 65c, Turtur tympanistria. 85c, Turtur chalcospilos. 1.05r, Oena capensis.

1993, Oct. 15 Litho. ***Perf. 14x14¹/₂***
295 A61 45c multicolored .28 .28
296 A61 65c multicolored .40 .40
297 A61 85c multicolored .52 .52
298 A61 1.05r multicolored .65 .65
a. Souvenir sheet of 4, #295-298 2.25 2.25
Nos. 295-298 (4) 1.85 1.85

No. 298a sold for 3.50r.

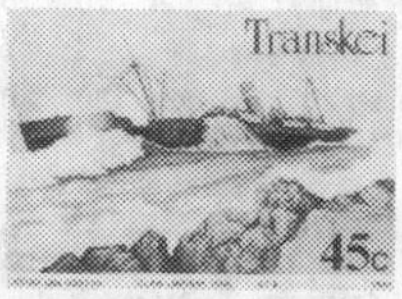

Modern Shipwrecks A62

1994, Mar. 18 Litho. ***Perf. 14¹/₂x14***
299 A62 45c Clan Lindsay, 1898 .25 .25
300 A62 65c Horizon, 1967 .38 .38
301 A62 85c Oceanos, 1991 .50 .50
a. Souvenir sheet of 1 .50 .50
302 A62 1.05r Forresbank, 1958 .60 .60
Nos. 299-302 (4) 1.73 1.73

Transkei ceased to exist April 27, 1994.

VENDA

'ven–də

LOCATION — Enclave, Republic of South Africa

GOVT. — Self-governing tribal homeland
AREA — 4,040 sq. mi.
POP. — 343,480 (1980)
CAPITAL — Thohoyandou

Catalogue values for all unused stamps in this country are for Never Hinged items.

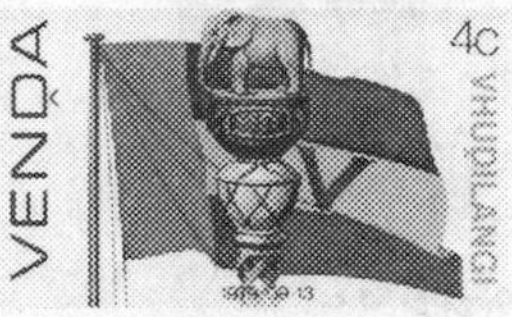

Independence from South Africa — A1

Designs: 4c, Mace, flag. 15c, Administrative buildings. 20c, P.R. Mphephu, paramount chief and president. 25c, Coat of arms.

Perf. 14½x14

1979, Sept. 13 **Litho.** **Unwmk.**

1 A1 4c multicolored .60 .60
2 A1 15c multicolored 2.25 2.25
3 A1 20c multicolored 3.00 3.00
4 A1 25c multicolored 3.75 3.75
Nos. 1-4 (4) 9.60 9.60

An imperf. souvenir sheet exists containing Nos. 1-4 printed in one color (black). Not valid for postage.

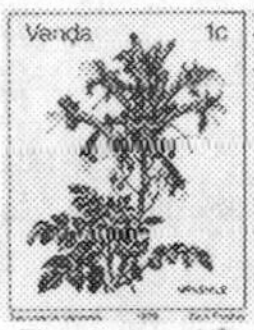

Flowers — A2

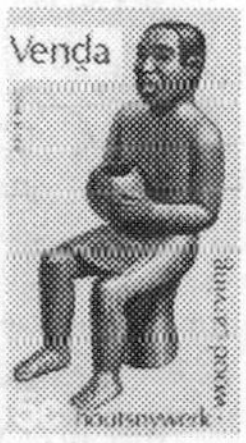

Wood Carvings — A3

1979-85 *Perf. 12½, 14 (11c, 12c)*

5 A2 1c *Tecomaria capensis* .15 .15
6 A2 2c *Catophractes alexandri* .15 .15
7 A2 3c *Tricliceras longipedunculatum* .15 .15
8 A2 4c *Dissotis princeps* .15 .15
9 A2 5c *Gerbera jamesonii* .15 .15
10 A2 6c *Hibiscus mastersianus* .15 .15
11 A2 7c *Nymphaea caerulaea* .15 .15
12 A2 8c *Crinum lugardiae* .15 .15
13 A2 9c *Xerophyta retinervis* .15 .15
14 A2 10c *Hypoxis angustifolia* .30 .30
15 A2 11c *Combretum microphyllum* .32 .32
16 A2 12c *Clivia caulescens* .35 .35
17 A2 15c *Pycnostachys urticifolia* .45 .45
18 A2 20c *Zantedeschia jucunda* .60 .60
19 A2 25c *Leonotis mollis* .75 .75
20 A2 30c *Littonia modesta* .90 .90
21 A2 50c *Protea caffra* 1.50 1.50
22 A2 1r *Adenium multiflorum* 3.00 3.00
23 A2 2r *Strelitzia caudata* 6.00 6.00
Nos. 5-23 (19) 15.52 15.52

Issue dates: 11c, Apr. 2, 1984; 12c, Apr. 1, 1985; others, Sept. 13, 1979.

Perf. 14

5a A2 1c .15 .15
6a A2 2c .15 .15
9a A2 5c .15 .15
12a A2 8c .15 .15
19a A2 25c .75 .75
21a A2 50c 1.50 1.50
Nos. 5a-21a (6) 2.85 2.85

Perf. 14½x14, 14x14½

1980, Feb. 13

Designs: 5c, Man with cup. 10c, Woman with corn, bowl and spoon. 15c, King Nebuchadnezzar, horiz. 20c, Python killing woman, horiz.

24 A3 5c multicolored .40 .40
25 A3 10c multicolored .80 .80
26 A3 15c multicolored 1.25 1.25
27 A3 20c multicolored 1.65 1.65
Nos. 24-27 (4) 4.10 4.10

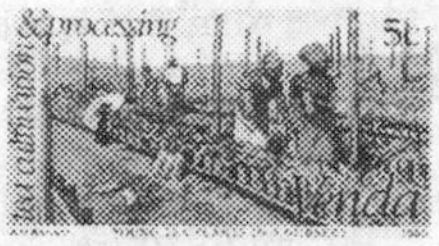

Tea Cultivation A4

1980, May 14 *Perf. 14x14½*

28 A4 5c Plants in nursery .20 .20
29 A4 10c Harvest .40 .40
30 A4 15c Withering .60 .60
31 A4 20c Cut, twist, curl unit .80 .80
Nos. 28-31 (4) 2.00 2.00

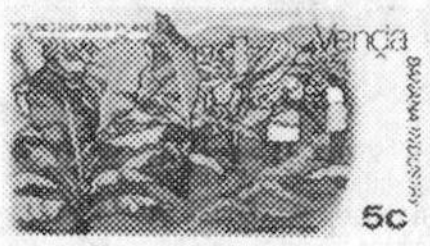

Banana Industry A5

1980, Aug. 13

32 A5 5c Plants .20 .20
33 A5 10c Cutting "hands" .40 .40
34 A5 15c Sorting .60 .60
35 A5 20c Packing .80 .80
Nos. 32-35 (4) 2.00 2.00

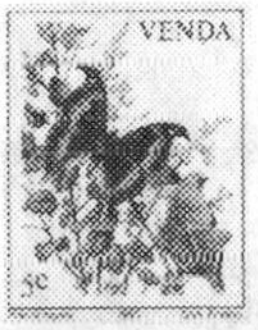

Butterflies — A6

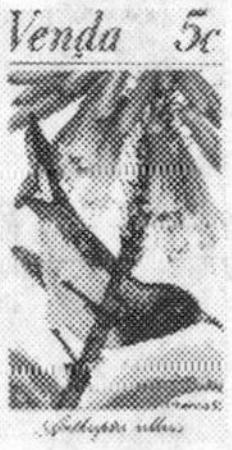

Sunbirds — A7

1980, Nov. 13 *Perf. 14½x14*

36 A6 5c *Precis tugela* .20 .20
37 A6 10c *Charaxes bohemani* .40 .40
38 A6 15c *Catacroptera cloanthe* .60 .60
39 A6 20c *Papilio dardanus* .80 .80
Nos. 36-39 (4) 2.00 2.00

1981, Feb. 16

40 A7 5c *Anthreptes collaris* .15 .15
41 A7 15c *Nectarinia mariquensis* .45 .45
42 A7 20c *Nectarinia talatala* .60 .60
43 A7 25c *Nectarinia senegalensis* .75 .75
Nos. 40-43 (4) 1.95 1.95

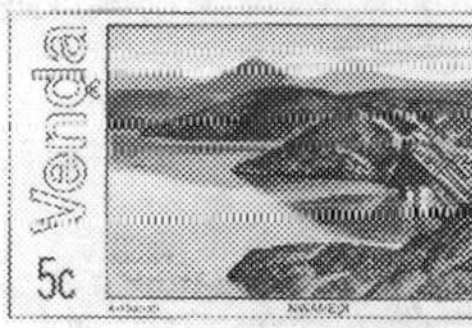

Nwanedi Dam — A8

1981, May 6

44 A8 5c shown .15 .15
45 A8 15c Mahovhohovho Falls .45 .45
46 A8 20c Phiphidi Falls .60 .60
47 A8 25c Lake Fundudzi .75 .75
Nos. 44-47 (4) 1.95 1.95

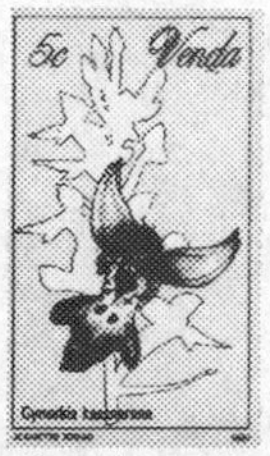

Orchids — A9

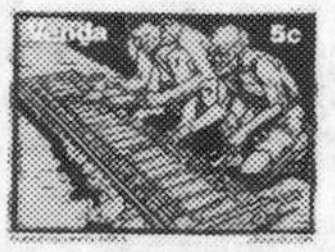

Musical Instruments — A10

1981, Sept. 11

48 A9 5c *Cynorkis kassnerana* .15 .15
49 A9 15c *Eulophia fridericii* .45 .45
50 A9 20c *Bonatea densiflora* .60 .60
51 A9 25c *Mystacidium brayboniae* .75 .75
a. Souvenir sheet of 4, #48-51 2.00 2.00
Nos. 48-51 (4) 1.95 1.95

1981, Nov. 13 *Perf. 14x14½*

52 A10 5c Mbila .15 .15
53 A10 15c Phalaphala .45 .45
54 A10 20c Tshizambi .60 .60
55 A10 25c Ngoma .75 .75
Nos. 52-55 (4) 1.95 1.95

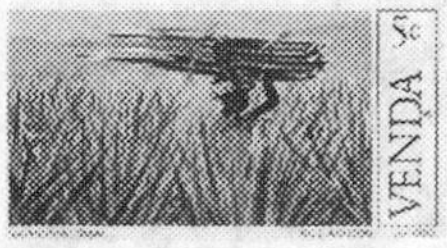

Sisal Cultivation A11

1982, Feb. 26

56 A11 5c Harvesting .15 .15
57 A11 10c Drying .25 .25
58 A11 20c Grading .50 .50
59 A11 25c Baling .60 .60
Nos. 56-59 (4) 1.50 1.50

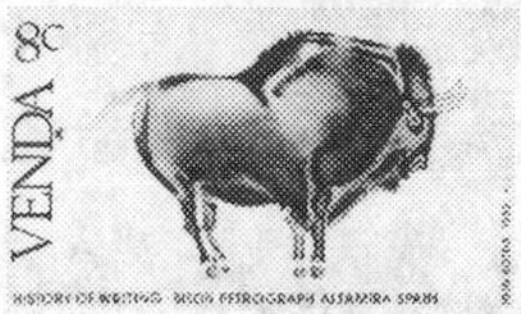

History of Writing A12

Designs: 8c, Bison, petroglyph, Atlamira, Spain. 15c, Animal, petroglyph, eastern California. 20c, Pictographic script on a Sumerian tablet. 25c, Bushman burial stone, Humansdorp, South Africa.

1982, June 15 *Perf. 14½x14*

60 A12 8c multicolored .16 .16
61 A12 15c multicolored .30 .30
62 A12 20c multicolored .40 .40
63 A12 25c multicolored .50 .50
Nos. 60-63 (4) 1.36 1.36

1983, May 11 **Size: 21x37mm**

Designs: 10c, Indus Valley script, 3000 B.C. 20c, Sumerian cuneiform, 2000 B.C. 25c, Egyptian hieroglyphics, 1300 B.C. 40c, Chinese handscroll, A.D. 1100.

64 A12 10c multicolored .20 .20
65 A12 20c multicolored .40 .40
66 A12 25c multicolored .50 .50
67 A12 40c multicolored .80 .80
Nos. 64-67 (4) 1.90 1.90

1984, Feb. 17 *Perf. 14x14½*
Size: 37½x20½mm

Designs: 10c, Evolution of the cuneiform sign. 20c, Evolution of the Chinese character. 25c, Development of Cretan hieroglyphics. 40c, Development of Egyptian hieroglyphics.

68 A12 10c multicolored .20 .20
69 A12 20c multicolored .40 .40
70 A12 25c multicolored .50 .50
71 A12 40c multicolored .80 .80
Nos. 68-71 (4) 1.90 1.90

1985, Mar. 21 *Perf. 14½x14*
Size: 34x24½mm

Designs: 11c, Southern Arabic characters. 25c, Phoenician characters. 30c, Aramaic characters. 50c, Canaanite characters.

72 A12 11c multicolored .22 .22
73 A12 25c multicolored .50 .50
74 A12 30c multicolored .60 .60
75 A12 50c multicolored 1.00 1.00
Nos. 72-75 (4) 2.32 2.32

1986, Apr. 10 *Perf. 14x14½*
Size: 24½x34mm

76 A12 14c Etruscan .20 .20
77 A12 20c Greek .30 .30
78 A12 25c Roman .38 .38
79 A12 30c Cyrillic .45 .45
Nos. 76-79 (4) 1.33 1.33

1988, Apr. 28 *Perf. 14½x14*
Size: 34x26mm

80 A12 16c Chinese .18 .18
81 A12 30c Hindi .32 .32
82 A12 40c Russian .45 .45
83 A12 50c Arabic .55 .55
Nos. 80-83 (4) 1.50 1.50
Nos. 60-83 (24) 10.31 10.31

See Nos. 209-212.

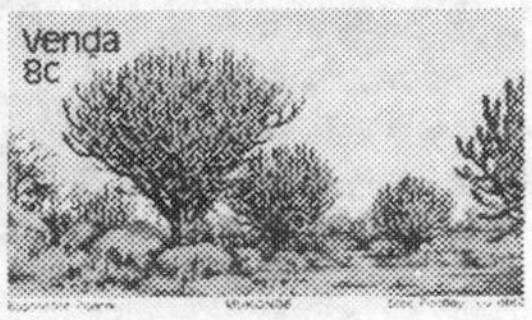

Trees A13

1982, Sept. 17

84 A13 8c *Euphorbia ingens* .16 .16
85 A13 15c *Pterocarpus angolensis* .30 .30
86 A13 20c *Ficus ingens* .40 .40
87 A13 25c *Adansonia digitata* .50 .50
Nos. 84-87 (4) 1.36 1.36

1983, Aug. 3

88 A13 10c *Gardenia spatulifolia* .20 .20
89 A13 20c *Hyphaene natalensis* .40 .40
90 A13 25c *Albizia adianthifolia* .50 .50
91 A13 40c *Sesamothamnus lugardii* .80 .80
Nos. 88-91 (4) 1.90 1.90

1984, June 21

92 A13 11c *Afzelia quanzensis* .22 .22
93 A13 20c *Peltophorum africanum* .40 .40
94 A13 25c *Gyrocarpus americanus* .50 .50
95 A13 30c *Acacia sieberana* .60 .60
Nos. 92-95 (4) 1.72 1.72
Nos. 84-95 (12) 4.98 4.98

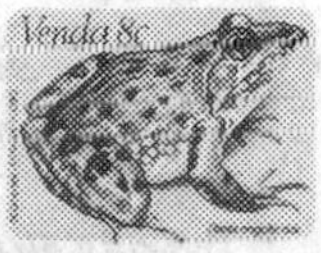

Frogs — A14

1982, Nov. 26 *Perf. 14x14½*

96 A14 8c *Rana angolensis* .16 .16
97 A14 15c *Chiromantis xerampelina* .30 .30
98 A14 20c *Leptopelis* .40 .40
99 A14 25c *Ptychadena anchietae* .50 .50
Nos. 96-99 (4) 1.36 1.36

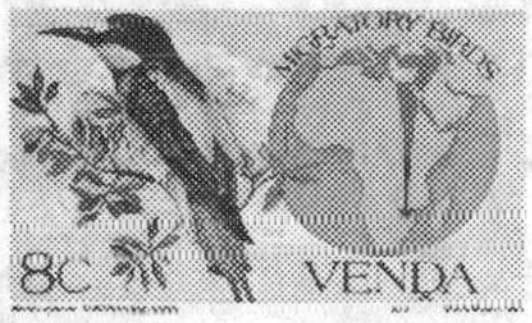

Migratory Birds and Maps — A15

1983, Feb. 16 *Perf. 14½x14*

100 A15 8c European bee-eater .20 .20
101 A15 20c Steppe eagle .50 .50
102 A15 25c Plum-colored starling .60 .60
103 A15 40c White-bellied stork 1.00 1.00
Nos. 100-103 (4) 2.30 2.30

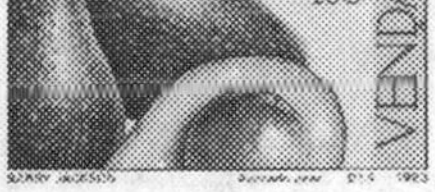

Subtropical Fruit — A16

1983, Oct. 26 *Perf. 14x14½*

104 A16 10c Avocado .20 .20
105 A16 20c Mango .40 .40
106 A16 25c Papaya .50 .50
107 A16 40c Litchi .80 .80
Nos. 104-107 (4) 1.90 1.90

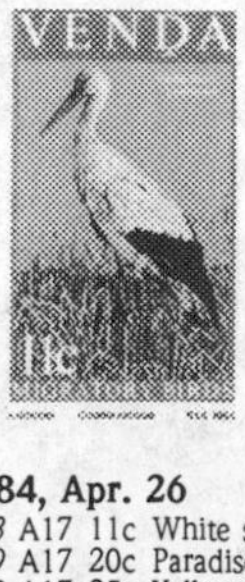

Migratory Birds — A17

1984, Apr. 26 *Perf. 14½x14*

108 A17 11c White stork .22 .22
109 A17 20c Paradise flycatcher .40 .40
110 A17 25c Yellow-billed kite .50 .50
111 A17 30c Wood sandpiper .60 .60
Nos. 108-111 (4) 1.72 1.72

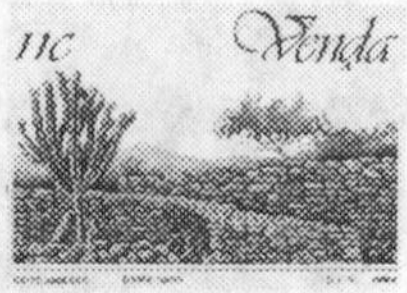

Independence, 5th Anniv. — A18

1984, Sept. 13 *Perf. 14½x14*
112 A18 11c Dzata Ruins .15 .15
113 A18 25c Traditional hut .38 .38
114 A18 30c Low-income housing .45 .45
115 A18 45c Modern home .65 .65
Nos. 112-115 (4) 1.63 1.63

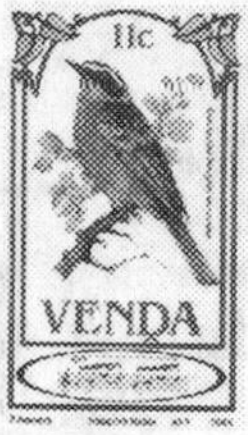

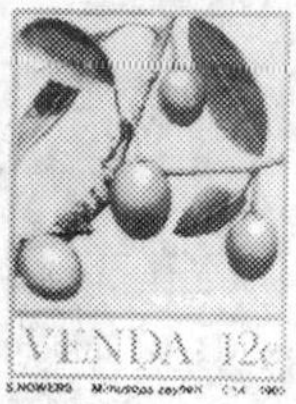

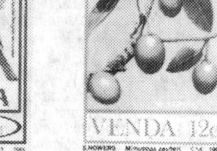

Songbirds A19 Food of the Veld A20

1985, Jan. 10
116 A19 11c Heuglin's robin .22 .22
117 A19 25c Black-collared barbet .50 .50
118 A19 30c Black-headed oriole .60 .60
119 A19 50c Kurrichane thrush 1.00 1.00
Nos. 116-119 (4) 2.32 2.32

1985, June 21 *Perf. 14x14½*
120 A20 12c *Mimusops zeyheri* .24 .24
121 A20 25c *Ziziphus mucronata* .50 .50
122 A20 30c *Citrullus lanatus* .60 .60
123 A20 50c *Berchemia discolor* 1.00 1.00
Nos. 120-123 (4) 2.34 2.34

See Nos. 173-176.

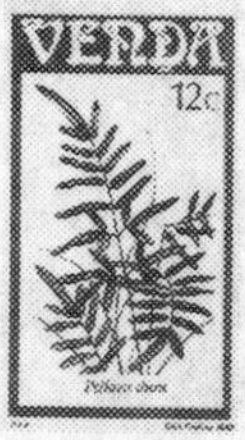

Ferns — A21

1985, Sept. 5 *Perf. 14½x14*
124 A21 12c *Pellaea dura* .24 .24
125 A21 25c *Actiniopteris radiata* .50 .50
126 A21 30c *Adiantum hispidulum* .60 .60
127 A21 50c *Polypodium polypodioides* 1.00 1.00
Nos. 124-127 (4) 2.34 2.34

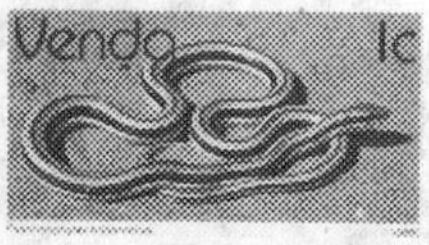

Reptiles A22

1986-90 *Perf. 14x14½*
128 A22 1c *Psammophylax tritaeniatus* .15 .15
129 A22 2c *Pseudaspis cana* .15 .15
130 A22 3c *Nucras taeniolata ornata* .15 .15
131 A22 4c *Bitis arietans* .15 .15
132 A22 5c *Mabuya capensis* .15 .15
133 A22 6c *Naja haje annulifera* .15 .15
134 A22 7c *Mabuya quinquetaeniata margaritifer* .15 .15
135 A22 8c *Philothamnus semivariegatus* .15 .15
136 A22 9c *Gerrhosaurus flavigularis* .15 .15
137 A22 10c *Prosymna sundevallii lineata* .15 .15
138 A22 14c *Platysaurus intermedius* .15 .15
139 A22 15c *Lacerta rupicola* .18 .18
140 A22 16c *Varanus niloticus* .18 .18
141 A22 18c *Dendroaspis polylepis* .18 .18
142 A22 20c *Afroedura transvaalica* .20 .20
143 A22 21c *Chamaeleo dilepsis* .20 .20
144 A22 25c *Elapsoidea sundevallii longicauda* .25 .25
145 A22 30c *Pachydactylus tigrinus* .30 .30
146 A22 50c *Mehelya capensis* .50 .50
147 A22 1r *Cordylus warreni depressus* 1.00 1.00
148 A22 2r *Python sebae natalensis* 2.00 2.00
Nos. 128-148 (21) 6.64 6.64

Issued: 14c, 4/1/86; 16c, 4/1/87; 18c, 7/3/89; 21c, 8/3/90; others, 1/16/86.

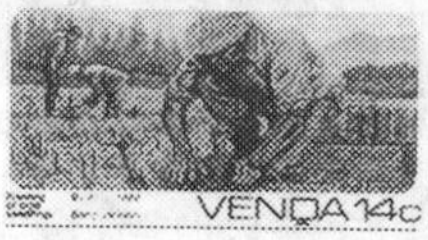

Forestry A23

Designs: 14c, Planting pine seedlings. 20c, Felling and extracting saw timber. 25c, Unloading timber at sawmill. 30c, Construction workers using pre-cut lumber.

1986, June 26 *Perf. 14x14½*
153 A23 14c multicolored .20 .20
154 A23 20c multicolored .30 .30
155 A23 25c multicolored .38 .38
156 A23 30c multicolored .45 .45
Nos. 153-156 (4) 1.33 1.33

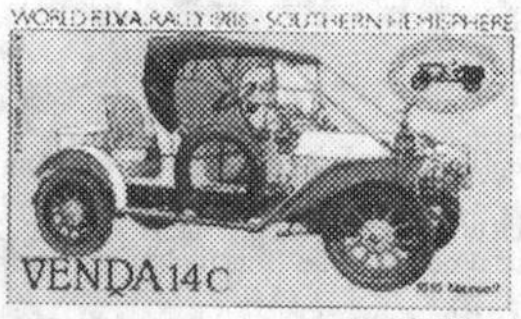

FIVA World Classic Car Rally A24

1986, Sept. 4 *Perf. 14½x14*
157 A24 14c 1910 Maxwell .20 .20
158 A24 20c 1929 Bentley 4½ l .30 .30
159 A24 25c 1933 Plymouth Coupe .38 .38
160 A24 30c 1958 Mercedes Cabriolet .45 .45
a. Souvenir sheet of 1 1.50 1.50
Nos. 157-160 (4) 1.33 1.33

No. 160a for the natl. philatelic exhibition held at Johannesburg, Oct. 6-11. Sold for 50c.

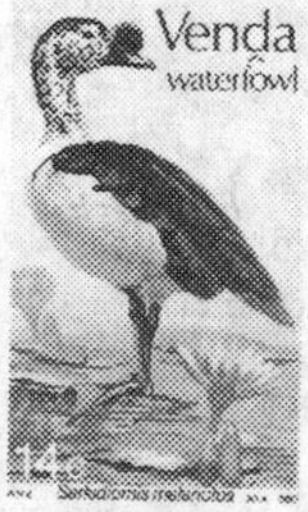

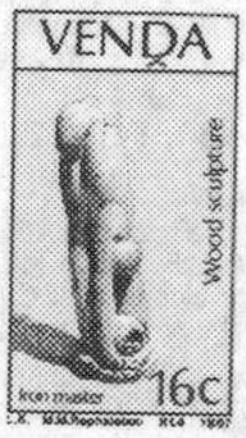

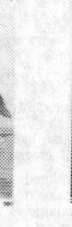

Waterfowl A25 Wood Carvings A26

1987, Jan. 8 *Perf. 14x14½, 14½x14*
161 A25 14c *Sarkidiornis melanotos* .40 .40
162 A25 20c *Dendrocygna viduata* .55 .55
163 A25 25c *Plectropterus gambensis* .70 .70
a. Souvenir sheet of 1 3.50 3.50
164 A25 30c *Alopochen aegyptiacus* .85 .85
Nos. 161-164 (4) 2.50 2.50

Nos. 163-164 are horiz. No. 163a margin pictures emblem of the natl. philatelic exhibition held at Paarl, Sept. 16-19. Sold for 50c.

1987, Apr. 9 *Perf. 14½x14*
165 A26 16c *Iron Master* .25 .25
166 A26 20c *Distant Drums* .32 .32
167 A26 25c *Sunrise* .40 .40
168 A26 30c *Obedience* .50 .50
Nos. 165-168 (4) 1.47 1.47

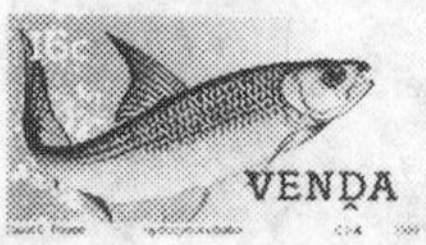

Freshwater Fish — A27

1987, July 2 *Perf. 14x14½*
169 A27 16c *Hydrocynus vittatus* .40 .40
170 A27 20c *Opsardium zambezense* .50 .50
171 A27 25c *Oreochromis mossambicus* .60 .60
172 A27 30c *Clarias gariepinus* .75 .75
Nos. 169-172 (4) 2.25 2.25

Food of the Veld Type of 1985

1987, Oct. 2
173 A20 16c *Grewia occidentalis* .20 .20
174 A20 30c *Phoenix reclinata* .38 .38
175 A20 40c *Halleria lucida* .52 .52
176 A20 50c *Cucumis africanus* .65 .65
Nos. 173-176 (4) 1.75 1.75

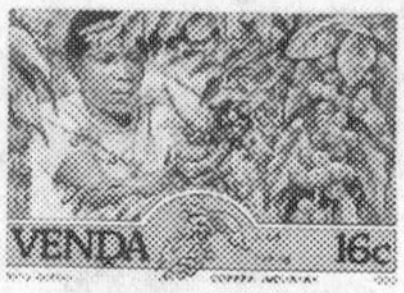

Coffee Industry A28

1988, Jan. 21 *Perf. 14½x14*
177 A28 16c Harvesting .18 .18
178 A28 30c Weighing .32 .32
179 A28 40c Sun drying .45 .45
180 A28 50c Roasting .55 .55
Nos. 177-180 (4) 1.50 1.50

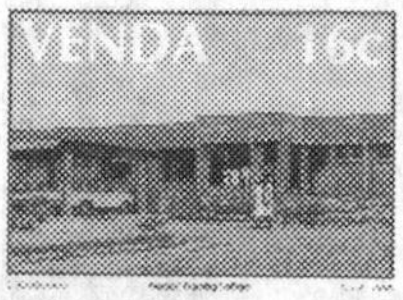

Nurse's Training College, Shayandima A29

1988, Aug. 18
181 A29 16c shown .18 .18
182 A29 30c Microscopy .32 .32
183 A29 40c Anatomy lecture .45 .45
184 A29 50c Clinical training .55 .55
Nos. 181-184 (4) 1.50 1.50

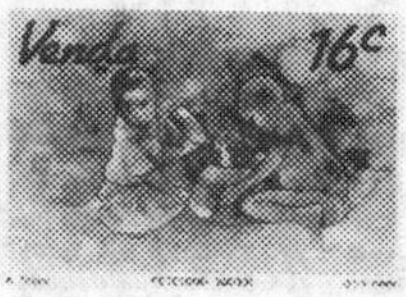

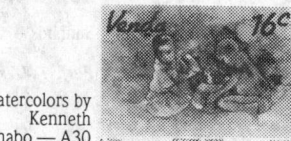

Watercolors by Kenneth Thabo — A30

1988, Oct. 6
185 A30 16c Fetching Water .18 .18
186 A30 30c Grinding Maize .32 .32
187 A30 40c Offering Food .45 .45
188 A30 50c Kindling the Fire .55 .55
a. Souvenir sheet of 1 2.00 2.00
Nos. 185-188 (4) 1.50 1.50

No. 188a for the natl. philatelic exhibition held at Pietermaritzburg, Nov. 22-27. Sold for 1.50r.

See Nos. 193-196.

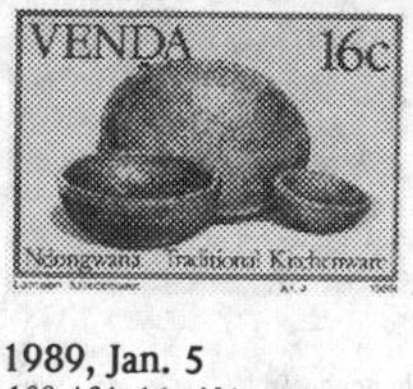

Traditional Kitchenware A31

1989, Jan. 5
189 A31 16c Ndongwana .15 .15
190 A31 30c Ndilo .28 .28
191 A31 40c Mufaro .38 .38
192 A31 50c Muthatha .48 .48
Nos. 189-192 (4) 1.29 1.29

Art Type of 1988

Traditional dances: watercolors by Kenneth Thabo.

1989, Apr. 5
193 A30 18c Domba .16 .16
194 A30 30c Tshinzerere .28 .28
195 A30 40c Malende .38 .38
196 A30 50c Malombo .45 .45
Nos. 193-196 (4) 1.27 1.27

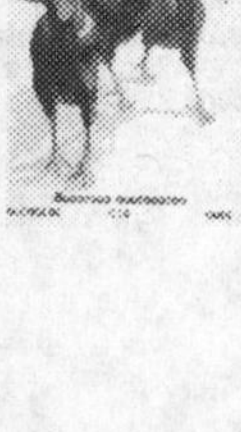

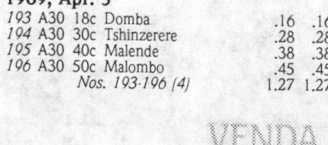

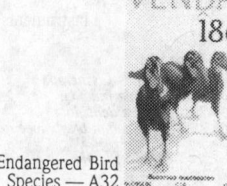

Endangered Bird Species — A32

1989, June 27
197 A32 18c *Bucorvus leadbeateri* .16 .16
198 A32 30c *Torgos tracheliotus* .28 .28
199 A32 40c *Terathopius ecaudatus* .35 .35
200 A32 50c *Polemaetus bellicosus* .45 .45
a. Souvenir sheet of 1 1.50 1.50
Nos. 197-200 (4) 1.24 1.24

No. 200a for the natl. philatelic exhibition WANDERERS 101, held Sept. 6-9. Sold for 1.50r.

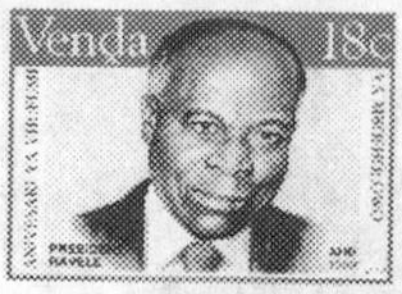

Independence, 10th Anniv. — A33

1989, Sept. 13
201 A33 18c Pres. Ravele .16 .16
202 A33 30c Presidential office .28 .28
203 A33 40c Presidential residence .35 .35
204 A33 50c Thohoyandou Stadium .45 .45
Nos. 201-204 (4) 1.24 1.24

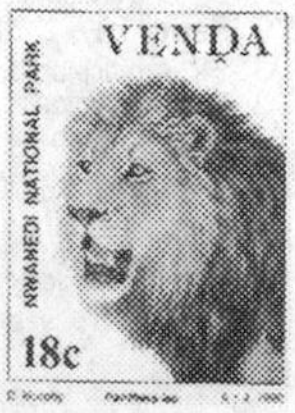

Wildlife Conservation, Nwanedi Natl. Park — A34

1990, Mar. 1
205 A34 18c *Panthera leo* .16 .16
206 A34 30c *Equus burchelli* .28 .28
207 A34 40c *Acinonyx jubatus* .35 .35
208 A34 50c *Ceratotherium simum* .45 .45
a. Souvenir sheet of 1 2.25 2.25
Nos. 205-208 (4) 1.24 1.24

No. 208a for the natl. philatelic exhibition. Sold for 1.50r.

History of Writing Type of 1982

Designs: 21c, Calligraphy. 30c, Musical notation, Beethoven's *Moonlight Sonata.* 40c, Computer characters. 50c, Black-and-white television picture transmitted across interstellar distances by the Arecibo radio telescope.

1990, May 23 Litho. *Perf. 14½x14*
209 A12 21c multicolored .18 .18
210 A12 30c multicolored .26 .26
211 A12 40c multicolored .35 .35
212 A12 50c multicolored .45 .45
Nos. 209-212 (4) 1.24 1.24

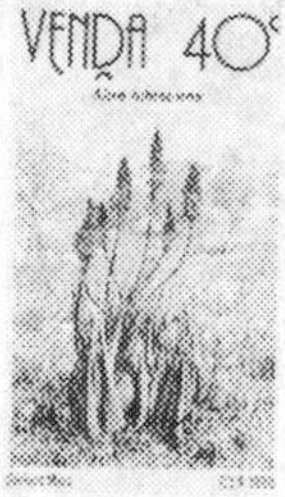

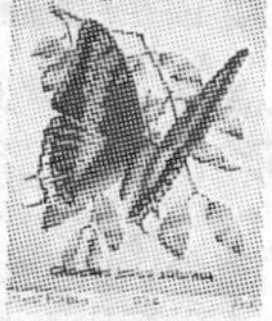

Aloe Plants — A35 Butterflies — A36

1990, Aug. 23 Litho. *Perf. 14½x14*
213 A35 21c Aloe globuligemma .18 .18
214 A35 35c Aloe aculeata .30 .30
215 A35 40c Aloe lutescens .35 .35
216 A35 50c Aloe angelica .42 .42
Nos. 213-216 (4) 1.25 1.25

1990, Nov. 15 *Perf. 14x14½*
217 A36 21c Pseudacraea boisduvalii .18 .18
218 A36 35c Papilio nireus .30 .30
219 A36 40c Charaxes jasius .35 .35
220 A36 50c Aeropetes tulbaghia .42 .42
Nos. 217-220 (4) 1.25 1.25

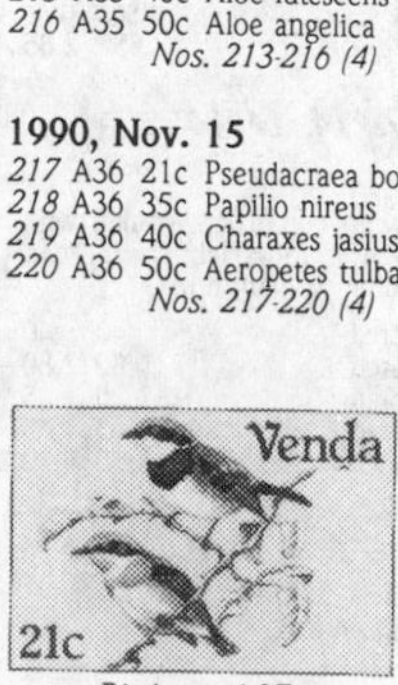

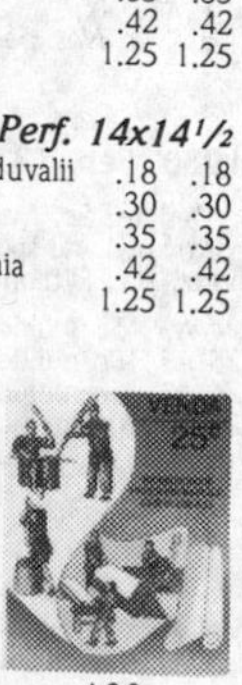

Birds — A37 A38

1991, Mar. 7 Litho. *Perf. 14½x14*

221	A37	21c Batis capensis	.15	.15
222	A37	35c Cossypha natalensis	.22	.22
223	A37	40c Anthreptes collaris	.25	.25
224	A37	50c Phyllastrephus flavostriatus	.32	.32
		Nos. 221-224 (4)	.94	.94

1991, June 6 Litho. *Perf. 14½x14*

Chinese inventions.

225	A38	25c Paper made from pulp	.15	.15
226	A38	40c Magnetic compass	.22	.22
227	A38	50c Abacus	.28	.28
228	A38	60c Gunpowder	.35	.35
		Nos. 225-228 (4)	1.00	1.00

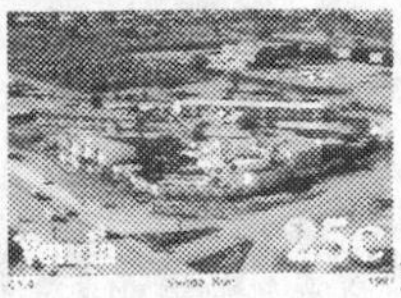

Hotels — A39

1991, Aug. 29 Litho.

229	A39	25c Venda Sun	.15	.15
230	A39	40c Mphephu Resort	.24	.24
231	A39	50c Sagole Spa	.30	.30
232	A39	60c Luphephe-Nwanedi Resort	.38	.38
		Nos. 229-232 (4)	1.07	1.07

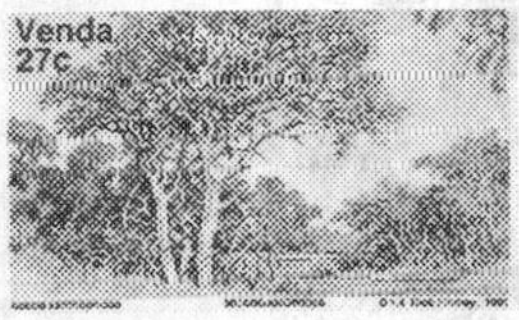

Trees A40

1991, Nov. 21 Litho.

233	A40	27c Acacia xanthophloea	.16	.16
234	A40	45c Faurea saligna	.28	.28
235	A40	65c Strelitzia caudata	.40	.40
236	A40	85c Kigelia africana	.50	.50
		Nos. 233-236 (4)	1.34	1.34

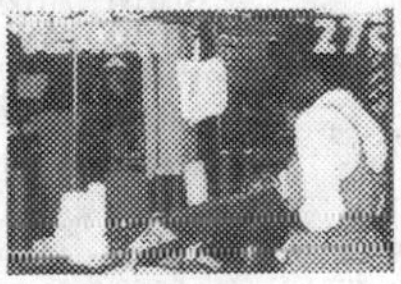

Clothing Factory — A41

1992, Mar. 5 Litho.

237	A41	27c Setting the web	.16	.16
238	A41	45c Knitting a pattern	.26	.26
239	A41	65c Using sewing machine	.40	.40
240	A41	85c Testing for flaws	.52	.52
		Nos. 237-240 (4)	1.34	1.34

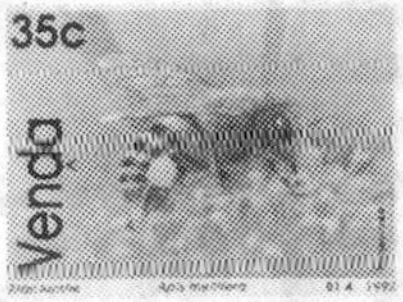

Bees — A42

1992, May 21 Litho.

241	A42	35c Honey bee	.25	.25
242	A42	70c Carder bee	.48	.48
243	A42	90c Leafcutter bee	.60	.60
244	A42	1.05r Carpenter bee	.70	.70
		Nos. 241-244 (4)	2.03	2.03

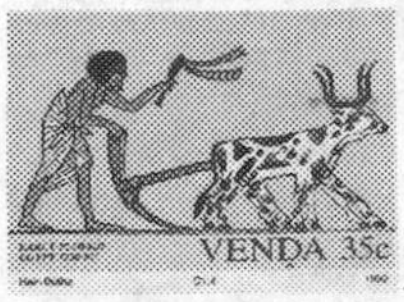

Inventions A43

Designs: 35c, Plow, Egypt 1259 B.C. 70c, Wheel, Mesopotamia, 3200 B.C. 90c, Brickmaking, Egypt, 3000 B.C. 1.05r, Sailing ship, Egypt, 1600 B.C.

1992, Aug. 13

245	A43	35c multicolored	.25	.25
246	A43	70c multicolored	.48	.48
247	A43	90c multicolored	.60	.60
248	A43	1.05r multicolored	.70	.70
		Nos. 245-248 (4)	2.03	2.03

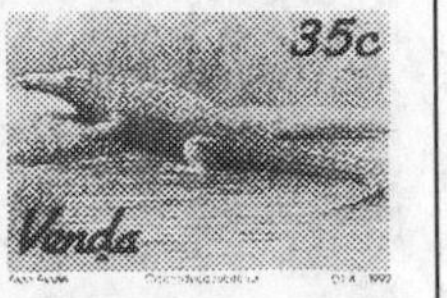

Crocodile Farming — A44

1992, Oct. 15 Litho.

249	A44	35c Emerging from water	.25	.25
250	A44	70c Egg laying	.48	.48
251	A44	90c Hatchlings	.60	.60
252	A44	1.05r Maternal care	.70	.70
		Nos. 249-252 (4)	2.03	2.03

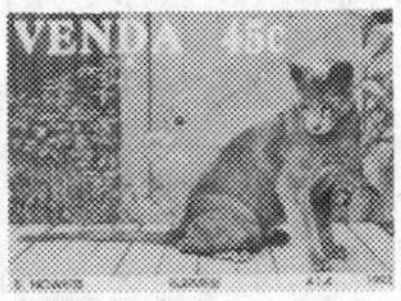

Domestic Cats — A45

1993, Mar. 19 Litho.

253	A45	45c Burmese	.30	.30
254	A45	65c Tabby	.45	.45
255	A45	85c Siamese	.60	.60
256	A45	1.05r Persian	.70	.70
		Nos. 253-256 (4)	2.05	2.05

A souvenir sheet of one No. 254 has inscription for National Philatelic Exhibition. Sold for 3r.

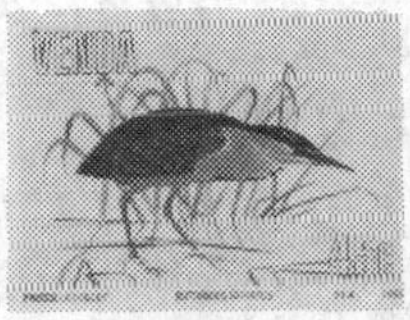

Herons — A46

Designs: 45c, Butorides striatus. 65c, Nycticorax nycticorax. 85c, Ardea purpurea. 1.05r, Ardea melanocephala.

1993, July 16 Litho. *Perf. 14½x14*

257	A46	45c multicolored	.28	.28
258	A46	65c multicolored	.40	.40
259	A46	85c multicolored	.52	.52
260	A46	1.05r multicolored	.65	.65
a.		Souvenir sheet of 4, #257-260	1.85	1.85
		Nos. 257-260 (4)	1.85	1.85

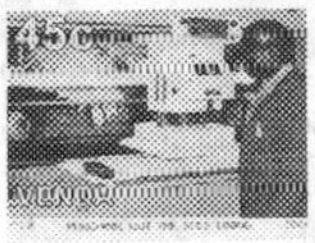

Shoe Factory — A47

1993, Sept. 17 Litho. *Perf. 14x14½*

261	A47	45c Punching out sole lining	.28	.28
262	A47	65c Shaping heel	.40	.40
263	A47	85c Joining upper to inner sole	.52	.52
264	A47	1.05r Forming sole	.65	.65
		Nos. 261-264 (4)	1.85	1.85

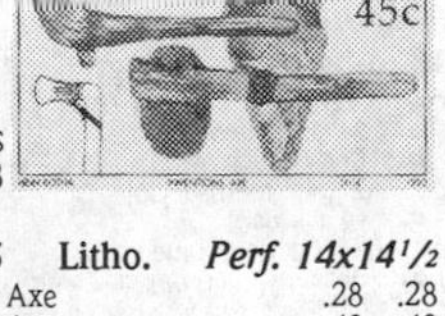

Inventions A48

1993, Nov. 5 Litho. *Perf. 14x14½*

265	A48	45c Axe	.28	.28
266	A48	65c Armor	.40	.40
267	A48	85c Arch	.52	.52
268	A48	1.05r Aqueduct	.65	.65
		Nos. 265-268 (4)	1.85	1.85

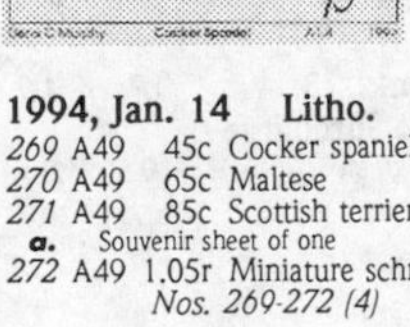

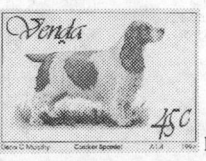

Dogs — A49

1994, Jan. 14 Litho. *Perf. 14½x14*

269	A49	45c Cocker spaniel	.28	.28
270	A49	65c Maltese	.40	.40
271	A49	85c Scottish terrier	.52	.52
a.		Souvenir sheet of one	.52	.52
272	A49	1.05r Miniature schnauzer	.65	.65
		Nos. 269-272 (4)	1.85	1.85

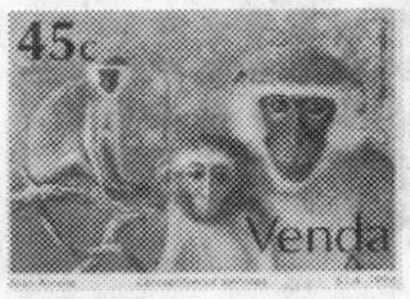

Monkeys A50

Designs: 45c, Cercopithecus aethiops. 65c, Galago moholi. 85c, Cercopithecus mitis. 1.05r, Otolemur crassicaudatus.

1994, Mar. 4 Litho. *Perf. 14½x14*

273	A50	45c multicolored	.25	.25
274	A50	65c multicolored	.38	.38
275	A50	85c multicolored	.50	.50
276	A50	1.05r multicolored	.60	.60
a.		Souvenir sheet of 4, #273-276	1.75	1.75
		Nos. 273-276 (4)	1.73	1.73

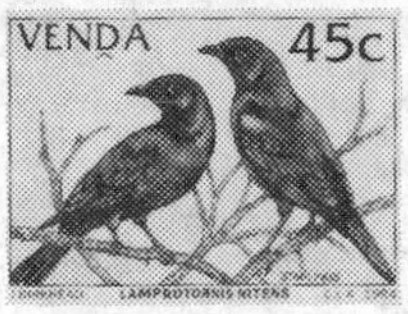

Starlings A51

Designs: 45c, Lamprotornis nitens. 70c, Cinnyricinclus leucogaster. 95c, Onychognathus morio. 1.15r, Creatophora cinerea.

1994, Apr. 29 Litho. *Perf. 14½x14*

277	A51	45c multicolored	.25	.25
278	A51	70c multicolored	.40	.40
279	A51	95c multicolored	.55	.55
280	A51	1.15r multicolored	.65	.65
		Nos. 277-280 (4)	1.85	1.85

Venda ceased to exist April 27, 1994.

SOUTH ARABIA

saủth ə-'rā-bē-ə

LOCATION — Southern Arabia
GOVT. — Federation; British dependency
AREA — 61,890 sq. mi.
POP. — 771,000 (est. 1966)
CAPITAL — Al Ittihad

The Federation of South Arabia was established in 1959 and consists of 14 states including Aden colony and part of Aden protectorate. When the Federation became independent, Nov. 30, 1967, it became the People's Republic of Southern Yemen. See People's Democratic Republic of Yemen, Vol. 5.

100 Cents = 1 Shilling
1000 Fils = 1 Dinar (1965)

Catalogue values for all unused stamps in this country are for Never Hinged items.

Red Cross Centenary Issue
Common Design Type
Wmk. 314

1963, Nov. 25 Litho. *Perf. 13*

1	CD315	15c black & red	.20	.15
2	CD315	1sh25c ultra & red	.60	.45

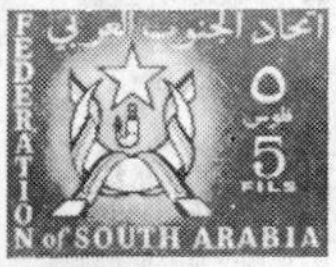

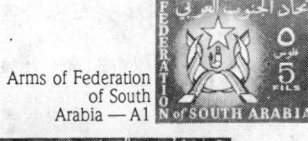

Arms of Federation of South Arabia — A1

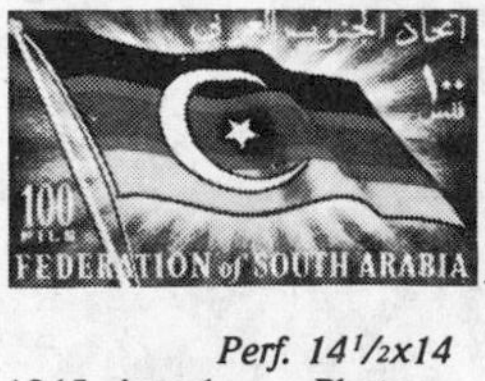

Flag of Federation A2

Perf. 14½x14

1965, Apr. 1 Photo. Unwmk.

3	A1	5f blue	.15	.15
4	A1	10f light violet blue	.15	.15
5	A1	15f blue green	.15	.15
6	A1	20f green	.15	.15
7	A1	25f orange brown	.15	.15
8	A1	30f lemon	.15	.15
9	A1	35f red brown	.15	.15
10	A1	50f rose red	.20	.15
11	A1	65f light yellow green	.25	.15
12	A1	75f rose carmine	.30	.20

Perf. 14½

Flag in Black, Yellow, Green and Blue

13	A2	100f reddish brown	.45	.30
14	A2	250f dark blue	1.00	.60
15	A2	500f dark red	3.00	1.00
16	A2	1d violet	5.00	2.50
		Nos. 3-16 (14)	11.25	5.95

Intl. Cooperation Year Issue
Common Design Type with Coat of Arms Replacing Queen's Portrait
Perf. 14½

1965, Oct. 24 Wmk. 314 Litho.

17	CD318	5f blue grn & claret	.15	.15
18	CD318	65f lt violet & green	.40	.35
		Set value	.45	.40

Churchill Memorial Issue
Common Design Type with Coat of Arms Replacing Queen's Portrait
Unwmk.

1966, Jan. 24 Photo. *Perf. 14*
Design in Black, Gold and Carmine Rose

19	CD319	5f bright blue	.15	.15
20	CD319	10f green	.15	.15
21	CD319	65f brown	.50	.40
22	CD319	125f violet	1.00	.75
		Nos. 19-22 (4)	1.80	1.45

World Cup Soccer Issue
Common Design Type with Coat of Arms Replacing Queen's Portrait

1966, July 1 Litho. *Perf. 14*

23	CD321	10f multicolored	.15	.15
24	CD321	50f multicolored	.35	.30
		Set value		.35

WHO Headquarters Issue
Common Design Type with Coat of Arms Replacing Queen's Portrait

1966, Sept. 20 Litho. Unwmk.

25	CD322	10f multicolored	.15	.15
26	CD322	75f multicolored	.50	.40
		Set value		.45

UNESCO Anniversary Issue
Common Design Type with Coat of Arms Replacing Queen's Portrait

1966, Dec. 15 Litho. *Perf. 14*

27	CD323	10f "Education"	.15	.15
28	CD323	65f "Science"	.35	.30
29	CD323	125f "Culture"	.65	.50
		Nos. 27-29 (3)	1.15	.95

SOUTH AUSTRALIA

'saủth ȯ-'strāl-yə

LOCATION — Central part of southern Australia
GOVT. — A former British Colony
AREA — 380,070 sq. mi.
POP. — 358,346 (1901)
CAPITAL — Adelaide

South Australia was one of the six British colonies that united in 1901 to form the Commonwealth of Australia.

12 Pence = 1 Shilling
20 Shillings = 1 Pound

Values for unused stamps are for examples with original gum as defined in the catalogue introduction. Very fine examples of Nos. 10-60 and O1-O60 will have perforations slightly cutting into the framelines or design on one or more sides due to the narrow spacing of the stamps on the plates. Stamps with perfs clear on all sides are scarce to rare and will command higher to substantially higher prices.

Watermarks

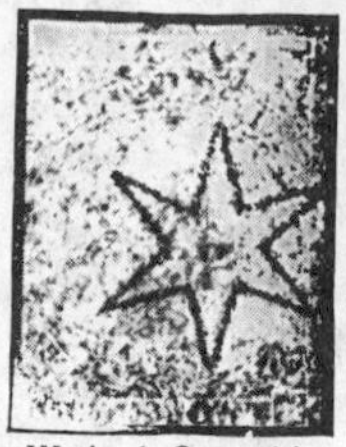

Wmk. 6- Star with Long Narrow Points

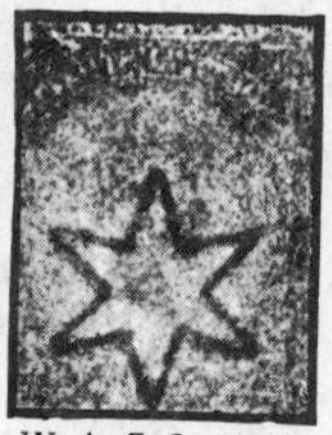

Wmk. 7- Star with Short Broad Points

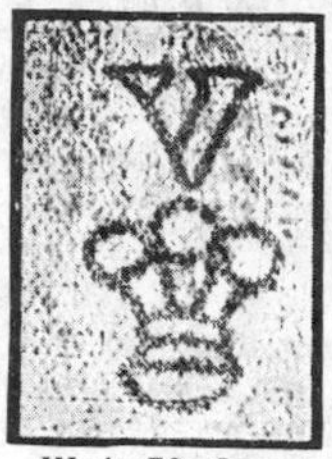

Wmk. 70- Crown and V

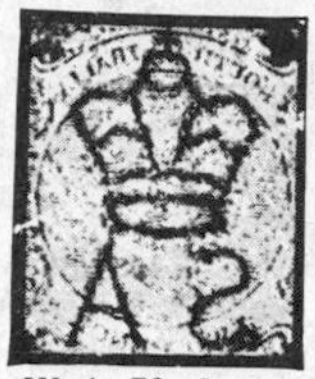

Wmk. 72- Crown and SA

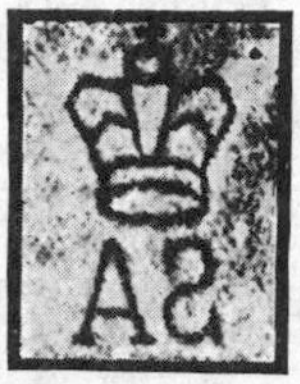

Wmk. 73- Crown and SA, Letters Close

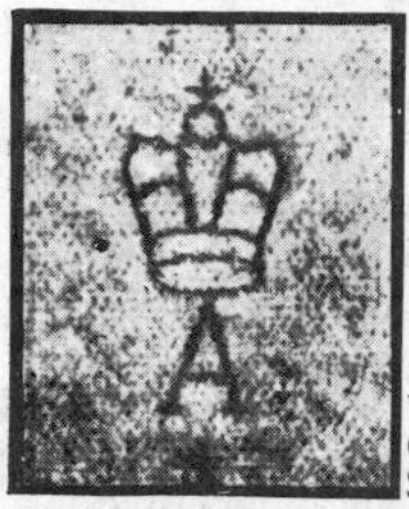

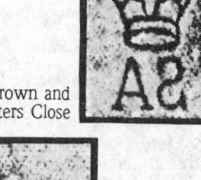

Wmk. 74- Crown and Single-lined A

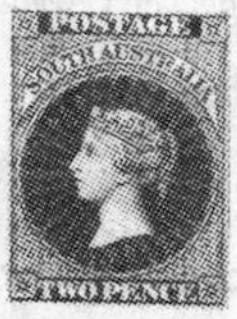

Queen Victoria — A1

1855-56 Engr. Wmk. 6 *Imperf.*
London Print

1 A1 1p dark green 2,750. 400.
2 A1 2p dull carmine 600. 80.
3 A1 6p deep blue 2,500. 140.
4 A1 1sh violet ('56) *4,500.*

No. 4 was never put in use. Nos. 1 and 3 without watermark are proofs.

1856-59 Local Print

5 A1 1p yellow grn ('58) *6,000.* 550.00
6 A1 2p blood red 1,500. 90.00
a. Printed on both sides
7 A1 2p pale red ('57) 700.00 60.00
a. Printed on both sides *650.00*
8 A1 6p slate blue ('57) 2,500. 175.00
9 A1 1sh orange ('57) 4,750. 375.00
a. Printed on both sides

1858-59 *Rouletted*

10 A1 1p yellow grn ('59) 400.00 45.00
a. Horiz. pair, imperf. between
11 A1 2p pale red ('59) 125.00 22.50
a. Printed on both sides
12 A1 6p slate blue 375.00 27.50
13 A1 1sh orange ('59) 1,250. 35.00
c. Printed on both sides *1,400.*

See Nos. 14-16, 19-20, 25-26, 28-29, 32, 35-36, 41-43, 47, 51-52, 69-70, 73, 113, 118. For overprints see Nos. O1-O2, O5, O7, O9, O11-O13, O17, O20, O27, O30, O32, O39-O40, O42, O52, O76, O85.

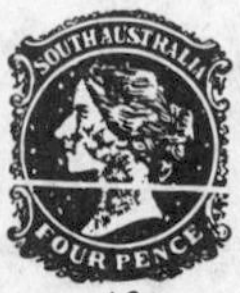

A2

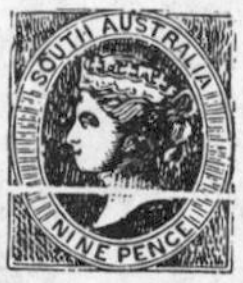

A3

Surcharge on #22-24, 34, 49-50

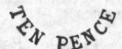

TEN PENCE

1860-69 *Rouletted*

14 A1 1p bright green 50.00 25.00
a. 1p deep green 250.00 65.00
15 A1 1p sage green 72.50 25.00
16 A1 2p vermilion ('62) 40.00 4.00
a. Horiz. pair, imperf. btwn. 650.00 350.00
b. Rouletted and perf. all around *700.00*
c. Printed on both sides 500.00
18 A2 4p dull violet ('67) 75.00 17.00
19 A1 6p grnsh blue ('63) 55.00 3.75
20 A1 6p dull blue 85.00 3.75
a. 6p sky blue 125.00 6.50
b. 6p Prussian blue 750.00 50.00
c. Horiz. pair, imperf. between 850.00
21 A3 9p gray lilac ('69) 50.00 9.00
a. Double impression
22 A3 10p on 9p red orange (Bl) ('66) 110.00 25.00
23 A3 10p on 9p yel (Bl) ('67) 165.00 21.00
24 A3 10p on 9p yel (Blk) ('69) 1,300. 32.50
a. Inverted surcharge *2,750.*
c. Printed on both sides 1,100.
25 A1 1sh red brown 135.00 13.00
26 A1 1sh brown ('62) 140.00 11.00
a. 1sh chestnut ('64) 125.00 11.00
27 A2 2sh carmine ('67) 165.00 27.50
a. Horiz. pair, imperf. btwn. 1,000.

There are six varieties of the surcharge "TEN PENCE" in this and subsequent issues.

Nos. 16b, 28a, 32c, 33a are rouletted remainders that were later perforated.

See Nos. 31, 33, 46, 48, 53, 63, 68, 72, 74, 112, 113B, 119-120. For overprints see Nos. O4, O6, O8, O10, O16, O18, O21, O26, O29, O31, O33, O37-O38, O41B, O43, O53. For surcharges see Nos. 34, 44-45, 49-50, 59, 67, 71, O19, O28, O36, O41.

1867-72 *Perf. 11½ to 12½xRoulette*

28 A1 1p blue green 225.00 32.50
a. Rouletted and perf. all around 650.00
29 A1 1p yellow green 135.00 20.00
31 A2 4p dull violet 1,500. 140.00
32 A1 6p Prus blue 450.00 21.00
a. 6p sky blue 500.00 17.50
b. Printed on both sides
c. Rouletted and perf. all around 300.00
33 A3 9p gray lilac ('72) 275.00
a. Rouletted and perf. all around 1,800. 275.00
34 A3 10p on 9p yel (Bl) ('68) 800.00 35.00
a. Printed on both sides 500.00
35 A1 1sh brown ('68) 275.00 30.00
36 A1 1sh red brown ('69) 275.00 25.00

#44-45 **3-PENCE**

Perf. 10, 11½, 12½ and Compound
1867-74

41 A1 1p yellow green 45.00 17.50
42 A1 1p blue green 60.00 12.50
a. Printed on both sides
43 A1 2p vermilion 1,250.
44 A2 3p on 4p dp bl (Blk) ('70) 60.00 5.50
a. 3p on 4p ultra, black surcharge 125.00 5.50
b. Surcharge omitted *20,000.* *5,000.*
c. Double surcharge 4,500.
d. Surcharged on both sides 3,250.
45 A2 3p on 4p sl bl (Red) ('70) 425.00 32.50
46 A2 4p dull violet 60.00 9.00
47 A1 6p dark blue 90.00 8.00
a. 6p sky blue 350.00 9.25
b. Imperf. vert., pair
48 A3 9p red lilac ('72) 47.50 5.00
a. 9p violet 115.00 5.50
b. 9p red violet 115.00 5.50
c. Printed on both sides 350.00
49 A3 10p on 9p yel (Bl) ('68) 1,500. 26.00
50 A3 10p on 9p yel (Blk) ('69) 150.00 21.00
51 A1 1sh deep brown 150.00 12.00
52 A1 1sh red brown 100.00 12.00
a. 1sh chestnut 125.00 12.50
53 A2 2sh carmine 60.00 7.50
a. Printed on both sides 400.00
b. Horiz. pair, imperf. vert.

See Nos. 67, O14, O28, O36.

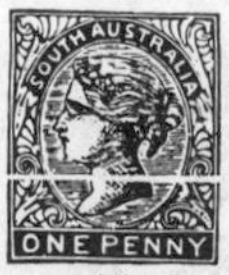

A6

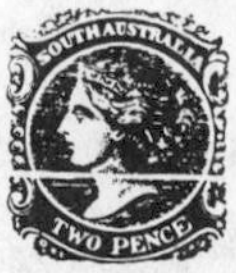

A6a

1868 Typo. Wmk. 72 *Rouletted*

54 A6a 2p orange red 65.00 4.00
a. Imperf.
b. Printed on both sides 275.00
c. Horiz. pair, imperf. btwn. 275.00

1869 *Perf. 11½ to 12½xRoulette*

55 A6a 2p orange red 150.00

1870 *Perf. 10xRoulette*

56 A6a 2p orange red 350.00 30.00

Perf. 10, 11½, 12½ and Compound
1868-75

57 A6 1p blue green ('75) 24.00 4.50
58 A6a 2p orange red 13.00 1.00
a. Printed on both sides 200.00
b. Horiz. pair, imperf. vert.

Engr.

59 A3 10p on 9p yellow (Bl) *1,500.*

1869 Typo. Wmk. 6 *Rouletted*

60 A6a 2p orange red 65.00 11.50
a. Imperf.
b. Printed on both sides

Perf. 11½ to 12½xRoulette

61 A6a 2p orange red 125.00

Perf. 11½ to 12½

61B A6a 2p orange red

See Nos. 62, 64-66, 97-98, 105-106, 115-116, 133-134, 145-146. For overprints see Nos. O3, O22-O25, O34-O35, O44-O47, O55-O56, O62-O63, O68-O69, O74, O78-O79. For surcharges see Nos. 75, O49.

1871 Wmk. 70 *Perf. 10*

62 A6a 2p orange red 75.00 16.00

Engr.

63 A2 4p dull violet 2,250. 350.00
a. Printed on both sides

Copies of the 4p from edge of sheet sometimes lack watermark.

Perf. 10, 11½, 12½ and Compound
1876-80 Typo. Wmk. 73

64 A6 1p green 6.00 .50
65 A6a 2p orange 4.25 .50
66 A6a 2p blood red ('80) 225.00 7.50
Nos. 64-66 (3) 235.25 8.50

See #97-98, 105-106, 115-116, 133-134, 145-146.

8 PENCE
No. 71

HALF- PENNY
No. 75

1876-84 Engr. Wmk. 7

67 A2 3p on 4p ultra (Blk) 65.00 17.50
a. 3p on 4p deep blue 15.00
b. Double surcharge *1,500.*
68 A2 4p reddish violet 50.00 5.50
a. 4p dull violet 60.00 9.00
69 A1 6p deep blue 65.00 4.50
a. Horiz. pair, imperf. vert.
b. Imperf.
70 A1 6p pale ultra ('84) 40.00 2.25
71 A3 8p on 9p bister brn 65.00 5.50
a. 8p on 9p yellow brown 57.50 2.50
b. 8p on 9p gray brown ('80) 52.50 4.00
d. Double surcharge 380.00
72 A3 9p rose lilac 10.00 5.50
a. Printed on both sides 300.00
73 A1 1sh red brown 37.50 3.25
a. 1sh brown 40.00 2.50
b. Horiz. pair, imperf. btwn. 300.00
74 A2 2sh carmine 35.00 4.50
a. Horiz. pair, imperf. vert. *400.00*
b. Imperf., pair

For overprint see No. O41.

1882 Wmk. 73 *Perf. 10*
Black Surcharge

75 A6 ½p on 1p green 10.50 4.00

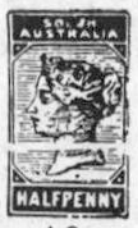

A9

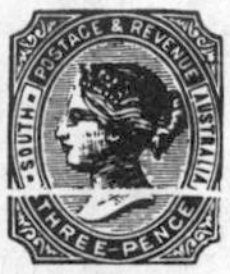

A10

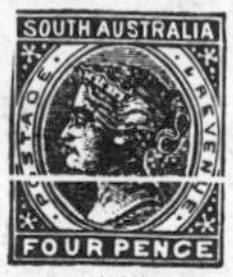

A11

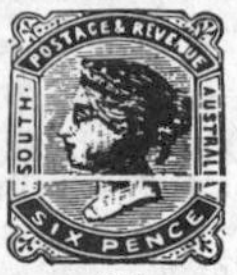

A12

Perf. 10, 11½, 12½ and Compound
1883-90 Typo.

76 A9 ½p chocolate brown 2.25 .25
a. ½p red brown ('89) 2.25 .25
b. ½p bister brown 3.50 .25
78 A10 3p deep green ('86) 6.50 .75
a. 3p olive green ('90) 11.00 1.50
79 A11 4p violet ('90) 7.75 1.75
80 A12 6p blue ('87) 7.75 1.00
Nos. 76-80 (4) 24.25 3.75

See Nos. 96, 100-101, 104, 108-109, 111. For overprints see Nos. O50-O51, O54, O58, O60-O61, O64, O66-O67, O71, O73, O75, O81-O82. For surcharges see Nos. 94-95, 99, O48, O57, O59.

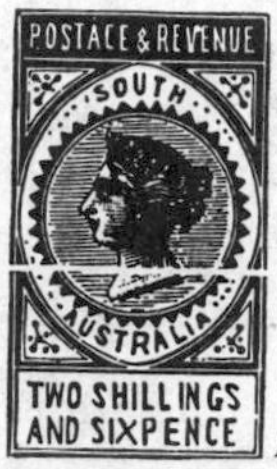

A13

1886-96 *Perf. 10, 11½ to 12½*

81 A13 2sh6p violet 27.50 6.50
82 A13 5sh rose 40.00 16.00
83 A13 10sh green 100.00 25.00
84 A13 15sh buff 200.00 140.00
85 A13 £1 blue 165.00 60.00
86 A13 £2 red brown 475.00 150.00
87 A13 50sh rose red 600.00 200.00
88 A13 £3 olive green 825.00
89 A13 £4 lemon 1,000.
90 A13 £5 gray *2,700.*
90A A13 £5 brown ('96) *2,600.*
91 A13 £10 bronze *3,000.* *700.00*
92 A13 £15 silver *6,500.*
93 A13 £20 lilac *8,250.*

For overprints see Nos. O83-O84.

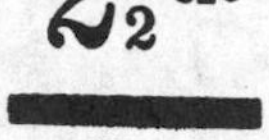

2½d.
#94, 99

5D.
#95

Perf. 10, 11½x12½ and Compound
1891

Brown Surcharge

94 A11 2½p on 4p green 8.00 1.40
a. "½" nearer the "2" 30.00 20.00
b. Pair, imperf. between 375.00
c. Fraction bar omitted 90.00 80.00

Carmine Surcharge

95 A12 5p on 6p red brown 17.00 6.00
a. No period after "D" 165.00

See #99. For overprints see #O48, O57, O59.

Many stamps of the issues of 1855-91 have been reprinted; they are all on paper watermarked Crown and SA, letters wide apart, and are overprinted "REPRINT."

1893 Typo. *Perf. 15*

96 A9 ½p brown 3.00 .18
a. Horiz. pair, imperf. between 125.00
b. Pair, perf. 12 between and perf. 15 around 195.00 50.00
97 A6 1p green 3.50 .20
98 A6a 2p orange 6.50 .15
a. Vert. pair, imperf. between 225.00
99 A11 2½p on 4p green 12.00 1.65
a. "½" nearer the "2" 40.00 35.00
b. Fraction bar omitted
100 A11 4p gray violet 13.00 2.00
101 A12 6p blue 32.50 4.25
Nos. 96-101 (6) 70.50 8.43

Kangaroo, Palm — A16

Coat of Arms — A17

1894, Mar. 1

102 A16 2½p blue violet 13.00 1.50
103 A17 5p dull violet 15.00 2.50

See Nos. 107, 110, 117, 135-136, 147, 151. For overprints see Nos. O65, O70, O72, O80.

1895-97 ***Perf. 13***

104 A9 ½p pale brown 3.00 .25
105 A6 1p green 5.25 .50
a. Vert. pair, imperf. between
106 A6a 2p orange 4.25 .15
107 A16 2½p blue violet 7.50 .32
108 A10 3p olive green ('97) 5.00 .30
109 A11 4p bright violet 6.50 .32
110 A17 5p dull violet 7.00 .32
111 A12 6p blue 8.00 .38
Nos. 104-111 (8) 46.50 2.54

Some authorities regard the so-called redrawn 1p stamps with thicker lettering (said to have been issued in 1897) as impressions from a new or cleaned plate.

Perf. 11½, 12½, Clean-Cut, Compound

1896 **Engr.** **Wmk. 7**

112 A3 9p lilac rose 12.50 6.50
113 A1 1sh dark brown 26.00 5.50
a. Horiz. pair, imperf. vert.
c. Vert. pair, imperf. btwn. 180.00
113B A2 2sh carmine 32.50 8.00
Nos. 112-113B (3) 71.00 20.00

Adelaide Post Office — A18

1899 **Typo.** **Wmk. 73** ***Perf. 13***

114 A18 ½p yellow green 1.75 .25
115 A6 1p carmine 3.00 .20
a. 1p scarlet 2.75 .50
116 A6a 2p purple 2.25 .25
117 A16 2½p dark blue 7.00 .75
Nos. 114-117 (4) 14.00 1.45

See #132, 144. For overprint see #O77.

Perf. 11½, 12½

1901 **Engr.** **Wmk. 72**

118 A1 1sh dark brown 24.00 16.00
a. 1sh red brown 24.00 10.00
b. Horiz. pair, imperf. vert.
119 A2 2sh carmine 27.50 15.00

1902

120 A3 9p magenta 20.00 20.00

A19

A20

Perf. 11½, 12½ and Compound

1902-03 **Typo.** **Wmk. 73**

121 A19 3p olive green 4.75 .75
122 A19 4p red orange 7.50 1.50
123 A19 6p blue green 6.50 1.50
124 A19 8p ultra (value 19mm long) 8.50 2.25
124A A19 8p ultra (value 16½mm long) ('03) 13.00 3.00
b. "EIGNT" 900.00 *3,000.*
125 A19 9p claret 8.50 2.25
a. Pair, imperf. between 300.00
126 A19 10p org buff 11.00 3.50
127 A19 1sh brown ('03) 12.00 3.00
a. Horiz. or vert. pair, imperf. btwn. 700.00
128 A19 2sh6p purple 32.50 9.00
129 A19 5sh rose 75.00 52.50
130 A19 10sh green ('03) 110.00 65.00
131 A19 £1 blue 275.00 150.00
Nos. 121-131 (12) 564.25 294.25

1904 ***Perf. 12x11½***

132 A18 ½p yellow green 3.00 .60
133 A6 1p rose 6.50 .60
134 A6a 2p purple 6.50 .60
135 A16 2½p dark blue 14.00 1.50
136 A17 5p dull violet 11.00 1.75
Nos. 132-136 (5) 41.00 5.05

1904-08 ***Perf. 12 and 12x11½***

137 A20 6p blue green 8.25 1.75
138 A20 8p ultra ('06) 11.50 2.25
139 A20 9p claret 8.00 1.65
139A A20 10p org buff ('07) 20.00 5.25
b. Pair, imperf. between 325.00 225.00
140 A20 1sh brown 12.00 2.00
a. Pair, imperf. between 250.00
141 A20 2sh6p purple ('05) 55.00 8.25
142 A20 5sh scarlet 55.00 32.50
142B A20 10sh green ('08) 165.00 125.00
143 A20 £1 deep blue 200.00 140.00
Nos. 137-143 (9) 534.75 318.65

See Nos. 148-150, 152-157.

1906-12 **Wmk. 74**

144 A18 ½p green 1.50 .15
145 A6 1p carmine 1.50 .15
146 A6a 2p purple 2.50 .15
a. Horiz. pair, imperf. between
147 A16 2½p dk blue ('11) 10.50 1.50
148 A20 3p ol grn (value 19mm long) 6.50 1.25
a. Horiz. pair, imperf. between
149 A20 3p ol grn (value 17mm long) ('09) 8.50 1.50
150 A20 4p red orange 9.75 1.75
151 A17 5p dull vio ('08) 8.50 2.00
152 A20 6p blue grn ('07) 7.50 1.10
a. Vert. pair, imperf. between 240.00
153 A20 8p ultra ('09) 15.00 5.50
154 A20 9p claret 15.00 3.00
a. Vert. pair, imperf. between 195.00
b. Horiz. pair, imperf. between 225.00
155 A20 1sh brown 11.00 3.00
a. Pair, imperf. between 175.00
156 A20 2sh6p purple ('09) 32.50 10.50
157 A20 5sh lt red ('12) 82.50
Nos. 144-157 (14) 212.75 31.55

OFFICIAL STAMPS

For Departments
Regular Issues Overprinted in Red, Black or Blue:

A. (Architect), A. G. (Attorney General), A. O. (Audit Office), B. D. (Barracks Department), B. G. (Botanical Gardens), B. M. (Bench of Magistrates), C. (Customs), C. D. (Convict Department), C. L. (Crown Lands), C. O. (Commissariat Officer), C. S. (Chief Secretary), C. Sgn. (Colonial Surgeon), C. P. (Commissioner of Police), C. T. (Commissioner of Titles), D. B. (Destitute Board), D. R. (Deed Registry), E. (Engineer), E. B. (Education Board),

G. P. (Government Printer), G. S. (Government Storekeeper), G. T. (Goolwa Tramway), G. F. (Gold Fields), H. (Hospital), H. A. (House of Assembly), I. A. (Immigration Agent), I. E. (Intestate Estates), I. S. (Inspector of Sheep), L. A. (Lunatic Asylum), L. C. (Legislative Council), L. L. (Legislative Library), L. T. (Land Titles), M. (Military), M. B. (Marine Board), M. R. (Manager of Railways), M. R. G. (Main Roads Gambierton), N. T. (Northern Territory),

O. A. (Official Assignee), P. (Police), P. A. (Protector of Aborigines), P. O. (Post Office), P. S. (Private Secretary), P. W. (Public Works), R. B. (Road Board), R. G. (Registrar General of Births, &c.), S. (Sheriff), S. C. (Supreme Court), S.G. (Surveyor General), S. M. (Stipendiary Magistrate), S. T. (Superintendent of Telegraph), T. (Treasurer), T. R. (Titles Registry), V. (Volunteers), V. A. (Valuator), V. N. (Vaccination), W. (Waterworks).

1868-74 **Wmk. 6** ***Rouletted***

O1 A1 1p green
O2 A1 2p pale red
O3 A6a 2p vermilion
O4 A2 4p dull violet
O5 A1 6p slate blue
O6 A3 9p gray lilac
O7 A1 1sh brown
O8 A2 2sh carmine

Perf. 11½ to 12½ x Roulette

O9 A1 1p green
O10 A2 4p dull violet
O11 A1 6p blue
O12 A1 1sh brown

Perf. 10, 11½, 12½ and Compound

O13 A1 1p green
O14 A2 3p on 4p slate blue (Red)
O16 A2 4p dull violet
O17 A1 6p deep blue
O18 A3 9p violet
O19 A3 10p on 9p yellow (Blk)
O20 A1 1sh brown
O21 A2 2sh carmine

Rouletted
Wmk. 72

O22 A6a 2p orange

Perf. 10 x Roulette

O23 A6a 2p orange

Perf. 10, 11½, 12½ and Compound

O24 A6a 2p orange

Wmk. 70
Perf. 10

O25 A6a 2p orange
O26 A2 4p dull violet

For General Use

Overprinted in Black **O.S.**

Perf. 10, 11½, 12½ and Compound

1874 **Wmk. 6**

O27 A1 1p green — *450.00*
a. Printed on both sides
O28 A2 3p on 4p ultra 150.00
a. No period after "S" 375.00
O29 A2 4p dull violet 27.50 9.50
a. Inverted overprint
b. No period after "S" 25.00
c. Perf. 10 1,650. 400.00
O30 A1 6p deep blue 55.00 9.50
a. No period after "S" 22.50
O31 A3 9p violet 250.00 60.00
a. No period after "S" 300.00
O32 A1 1sh red brown 55.00 16.00
a. Double overprint 27.50
b. No period after "S" 110.00 40.00
O33 A2 2sh carmine 67.50 14.00
a. Double overprint
b. No period after "S" 32.50

1874-75 **Wmk. 72**

O34 A6 1p blue green 100.00 27.50
a. Inverted overprint
O35 A6a 2p orange 14.00 1.40

1876-86 **Wmk. 7**

O36 A2 3p on 4p ultra
O37 A2 4p dull violet 100.00 17.00
O38 A2 4p reddish vio 37.50 3.00
a. Double overprint
b. Inverted overprint
c. Dbl. ovpt., one inverted
O39 A1 6p dark blue 62.50 5.00
a. Double overprint 37.50
b. Inverted overprint
O40 A1 6p ultramarine 57.50 4.50
a. Double overprint
b. Inverted overprint
O41 A3 8p on 9p yel brn 425.00 125.00
a. Double overprint 750.00
O41B A3 9p violet *3,000.*
O42 A1 1sh red brown 45.00 5.00
a. Inverted overprint 150.00 75.00
b. Double overprint
O43 A2 2sh carmine 110.00 8.00
a. Double overprint 70.00
b. Inverted overprint 75.00

1880-91 **Wmk. 73**

O44 A6 1p blue green 11.00 .50
a. Inverted overprint 22.50
b. Double overprint 35.00 20.00
c. Dbl. ovpt., one inverted
O45 A6 1p yellow green 12.00 .50
O46 A6a 2p orange 11.00 .25
a. Inverted overprint 10.00
b. Double overprint 70.00 25.00
c. Overprinted sideways
d. Dbl. ovpt., one inverted
e. Dbl. ovpt., both inverted 57.50
O47 A6a 2p blood red 52.50 5.00
O48 A11 2½p on 4p green 35.00 9.50
a. "½" nearer the "2" 75.00
b. Double overprint
c. Pair, one without ovpt.
Nos. O44-O48 (5) 131.50 15.75

1882-90 ***Perf. 10***

O49 A6 ½p on 1p green 25.00 8.00
a. Inverted overprint
O50 A11 4p violet 21.00 1.90
O51 A12 6p blue 12.00 1.25
a. Double overprint
Nos. O49-O51 (3) 58.00 11.15

Overprinted in Black **O.S.**

Perf. 10, 11½, 12½ and Compound

1891 **Wmk. 7**

O52 A1 1sh red brown 42.50 3.50
O53 A2 2sh carmine 100.00 10.00
a. Double overprint

1891-95 **Wmk. 73**

O54 A9 ½p brown 12.00 2.50
O55 A6 1p blue green 12.00 .30
a. Double overprint 80.00
O56 A6a 2p orange 12.00 .30
O57 A11 2½p on 4p green 45.00 2.75
a. "½" nearer the "2" 52.50 18.00
b. Inverted overprint 100.00
O58 A11 4p violet 17.50 1.25
a. Double overprint
O59 A12 5p on 6p red brn 55.00 2.50
O60 A12 6p blue 9.75 .75
a. Double overprint
Nos. O54-O60 (7) 163.25 10.35

1893 ***Perf. 15***

O61 A9 ½p brown 15.00 1.75
O62 A6 1p green 11.00 .30
O63 A6a 2p orange 12.00 .15
a. Inverted overprint 18.00
b. Double overprint 32.50
O64 A11 4p gray violet 65.00 1.75
a. Double overprint 21.00
O65 A17 5p dull violet 80.00 4.50
O66 A12 6p blue 20.00 .70
Nos. O61-O66 (6) 203.00 9.15

1896 ***Perf. 13***

O67 A9 ½p brown 12.50 1.75
a. Triple overprint
O68 A6 1p green 16.00 .15
O69 A6a 2p orange 11.00 .15
O70 A16 2½p blue violet 60.00 1.40
O71 A11 4p brt violet 65.00 1.75
a. Double overprint 30.00 40.00
O72 A17 5p dull violet 60.00 4.25
O73 A12 6p blue 25.00 .90
Nos. O67-O73 (7) 249.50 10.35

On No. O67a, one overprint is upright, two sideways.

Same Overprint in Dark Blue

1891-95 ***Perf. 10***

O74 A6 1p green 150.00 15.00
O75 A12 6p blue

Black Overprint

Perf. 11½, 12½, Clean-Cut

1897 **Wmk. 7**

O76 A1 1sh brown 40.00 4.50
a. Double overprint

Overprinted in Black **O. S.**

1900 **Wmk. 73** ***Perf. 13***

O77 A18 ½p yellow green 10.00 1.75
O78 A6 1p carmine rose 11.50 .15
a. Inverted overprint
b. Double overprint
O79 A6a 2p purple 11.50 .15
a. Inverted ovpt. 40.00
O80 A16 2½p dark blue 82.50 1.40
a. Inverted overprint 30.00
O81 A11 4p violet 65.00 .70
a. Inverted overprint 125.00
O82 A12 6p blue 20.00 .70
Nos. O77-O82 (6) 200.50 4.85

1901 ***Perf. 10***

O83 A13 2sh6p violet *2,000. 2,000.*
O84 A13 5sh rose *2,250. 2,250.*

On Nos. O77-O82 the letters "O.S." are 11½mm apart; on Nos. O83-O84, 14½mm apart.

Overprinted in Black **O.S.**

1903 **Wmk. 72** ***Perf. 11½, 12½***

O85 A1 1sh red brown 40.00 25.00

Many of the official stamps are found with one or both the periods after "O.S." missing. This occurs more often in the later than in the earlier issues.

South Australia stamps can be mounted in the Scott Australia album.

SOUTHERN NIGERIA

'sə–th͟ərn nī–'jir–ē–ə

LOCATION — In western Africa bordering on the Gulf of Guinea
GOVT. — A former British Crown Colony and Protectorate
AREA — 90,896 sq. mi.
POP. — 8,590,545
CAPITAL — Lagos

The Protectorate of Southern Nigeria, formed in 1900, absorbed in that year the Niger Coast Protectorate. In 1906 it united with Lagos and became the Colony and Protectorate of Southern Nigeria. An amalgamation was effected in 1914 between Northern and Southern Nigeria to form the Colony and Protectorate of Nigeria. See Nigeria, Northern Nigeria, Niger Coast Protectorate and Lagos.

12 Pence = 1 Shilling
20 Shillings = 1 Pound

Victoria — A1

Edward VII — A2

Wmk. Crown and C A (2)

1901 Typo. *Perf. 14*

1	A1	½p yel grn & blk	.75	.75
2	A1	1p car rose & blk	.80	.50
3	A1	2p org brn & blk	.80	*2.50*
4	A1	4p ol grn & blk	1.50	*5.00*
5	A1	6p red vio & blk	1.65	*4.00*
6	A1	1sh blk & gray grn	4.00	*10.00*
7	A1	2sh6p brn & blk	25.00	*35.00*
8	A1	5sh yellow & blk	30.00	*55.00*
9	A1	10sh vio & blk, *yel*	72.50	*110.00*
		Nos. 1-9 (9)	137.00	*222.75*

1903-04

10	A2	½p yel grn & blk	.40	.20
11	A2	1p car rose & blk	.50	.25
12	A2	2p org brn & blk	1.75	.95
13	A2	2½p ultra & blk ('04)	3.50	.70
14	A2	4p ol grn & blk	1.10	2.75
15	A2	6p red vio & blk	3.75	5.00
16	A2	1sh blk & gray grn	10.00	7.50
17	A2	2sh6p brown & blk	7.50	20.00
18	A2	5sh yellow & blk	27.50	65.00
19	A2	10sh vio & blk, *yel*	25.00	50.00
20	A2	£1 pur & gray grn	225.00	325.00
		Nos. 10-20 (11)	306.00	477.35

1904-07 Wmk. 3

Chalky Paper

21	A2	½p yel grn & blk	.35	.15
22	A2	1p carmine & blk	4.25	.20
23	A2	2p org brn & blk	1.25	.35
24	A2	2½p ultra & blk	.65	.55
24A	A2	3p vio & org brn ('07)	5.00	1.25
25	A2	4p ol grn & blk ('05)	7.50	1.40
26	A2	6p red vio & blk	3.50	1.10
27	A2	1sh blk & gray grn	2.50	.55
28	A2	2sh6p brn & blk ('05)	10.00	3.25
29	A2	5sh yellow & blk	25.00	20.00
30	A2	10sh vio & blk, *yel* ('08)	75.00	*90.00*
31	A2	£1 pur & gray grn ('05)	125.00	*150.00*
		Nos. 21-31 (12)	260.00	*268.80*

#23 and 24 are on ordinary paper, #24A and 25 on chalky, and the other values on both papers.

1907-10

Ordinary Paper

32	A2	½p green ('08)	.55	.15
33	A2	1p carmine	1.25	.15
34	A2	2p gray	.85	.65
35	A2	2½p ultra	.90	1.50

Chalky Paper

36	A2	3p violet, *yel*	.80	.30
37	A2	4p scar & blk, *yel*	.65	.60
38	A2	6p red vio & dl vio	11.00	.90
39	A2	1sh black, *green*	5.50	.60
40	A2	2sh6p car & blk, *bl*	3.50	1.10
41	A2	5sh scar & grn, *yel*	22.50	*35.00*
42	A2	10sh red & grn, *grn*	42.50	*60.00*
43	A2	£1 blk & vio, *red*	125.00	125.00
		Nos. 32-43 (12)	215.00	*225.95*

1910 Ordinary Paper Redrawn

44	A2	1p carmine	.50	.40

In the redrawn stamp the "1" of "1d" is not as thick as in No. 33 but the "d" is taller and broader.

King George V — A3

1912

45	A3	½p green	.75	.15
46	A3	1p carmine	.50	.15
47	A3	2p gray	.45	.50
48	A3	2½p ultra	2.00	2.25
49	A3	3p violet, *yel*	.65	.25
50	A3	4p scar & blk, *yel*	.60	.80
51	A3	6p red vio & dl vio	.55	.60
52	A3	1sh black, *green*	2.00	.60
53	A3	2sh6p red & blk, *bl*	5.00	12.50
54	A3	5sh red & grn, *yel*	12.50	42.50
55	A3	10sh red & grn, *grn*	35.00	65.00
56	A3	£1 blk & vio, *red*	110.00	125.00
		Nos. 45-56 (12)	170.00	250.30

Stamps of Southern Nigeria were replaced in 1914 by those of Nigeria.

SOUTHERN RHODESIA

'sə–th͟ərn rō–'dē–zh(ē–)ə

LOCATION — Southeastern Africa between Northern Rhodesia and Mozambique
GOVT. — British Colony
AREA — 150,333 sq. mi.
POP. — 4,010,000 (est. 1963)
CAPITAL — Salisbury

Prior to 1923 this territory was administered by the British South Africa Company. The colony was created in that year by the British Government at the request of the inhabitants. In 1953, Southern Rhodesia joined Northern Rhodesia and Nyasaland to form the Federation of Rhodesia and Nyasaland. When the Federation dissolved at the end of 1963, Southern Rhodesia again became an internally self-governing colony. See Rhodesia and Northern Rhodesia.

12 Pence = 1 Shilling
20 Shillings = 1 Pound

Catalogue values for unused stamps in this country are for Never Hinged items, beginning with Scott 56 in the regular postage section and Scott J1 in the postage due section.

King George V — A1

1924-30 Unwmk. Engr. *Perf. 14*

1	A1	½p dark green	1.00	.15
a.		Vert. pair, imperf. btwn.	750.00	
b.		Horiz. pair, imperf. btwn.	750.00	
c.		Horiz. pair, imperf. vert.	800.00	
2	A1	1p scarlet	1.40	.15
a.		Horiz. pair, imperf. btwn.	650.00	
b.		Perf. 12½ (coil) ('30)	3.00	*95.00*
c.		Vert. pair, imperf. btwn.	650.00	
d.		Vert. pair, imperf. horiz.	800.00	
3	A1	1½p bister brown	1.00	.15
a.		Horiz. pair, imperf. btwn.	*7,000.*	
b.		Vert. pair, imperf. btwn.	*3,000.*	
4	A1	2p vio blk & blk	1.25	.25
a.		Horiz. pair, imperf. btwn.	*6,000.*	
5	A1	3p deep blue	2.25	1.50
6	A1	4p org red & blk	1.90	1.50
7	A1	6p lilac & blk	2.25	1.50
a.		Horiz. pair, imperf. btwn.	*7,500.*	
8	A1	8p gray grn & vio	11.00	16.00
9	A1	10p rose red & bl	11.00	16.00
10	A1	1sh turq bl & blk	5.25	1.50
11	A1	1sh6p yellow & blk	17.50	16.00
12	A1	2sh brown & blk	18.00	16.00
13	A1	2sh6p blk brn & bl	35.00	42.50
14	A1	5sh bl grn & bl	57.50	75.00
		Nos. 1-14 (14)	166.30	188.20

Values for imperf between pairs are for stamps from the same sheet.

George V
A2

Victoria Falls
A3

1931-37 *Perf. 11½, 12 (1p)*

16	A2	½p dp green ('33)	.55	.15
a.		Bklt. pane of 6 ('32)	*150.00*	
b.		Perf. 12	.85	.35
c.		Perf. 14 ('35)	.85	.15
17	A2	1p scarlet	.75	.15
a.		Bklt. pane of 6 ('32)	*150.00*	
b.		Perf. 11½ ('33)	1.00	.15
c.		Perf. 14 ('35)	.65	.15
18	A2	1½p dp brown ('32)	1.10	.50
a.		Bklt. pane of 6 ('32)	*600.00*	
b.		Perf. 12 ('33)	52.50	*35.00*
		Nos. 16-18 (3)	2.40	.80

Typo. *Perf. 14½x14*

19	A3	2p blk brn & blk	2.25	.65
20	A3	3p dark blue	5.50	10.00

Perf. 12, 11½ (10p)

Engr.

21	A2	4p org red & blk	.70	.65
a.		Perf. 14 ('37)	32.50	37.50
b.		Perf. 11½ ('35)	16.00	4.50
22	A2	6p rose lilac & blk	1.40	.75
a.		Perf. 14 ('36)	14.00	.55
b.		Perf. 11½ ('33)	13.00	.60
23	A2	8p green & violet	1.40	*3.00*
a.		Perf. 11½ ('34)	19.00	*27.50*
24	A2	9p gray grn & ver ('34)	3.75	7.75
25	A2	10p car & ultra ('33)	5.50	*12.00*
a.		Perf. 12	6.00	2.75
26	A2	1sh turq bl & blk	1.40	2.00
a.		Perf. 11½ ('36)	75.00	50.00
b.		Perf. 14 ('37)	165.00	110.00
27	A2	1sh6p ocher & blk	7.50	*14.00*
a.		Perf. 11½ ('36)	50.00	*85.00*
28	A2	2sh dk brn & blk	15.00	4.00
a.		Perf. 11½ ('33)	40.00	27.50
29	A2	2sh6p ol brn & ultra	27.50	32.50
a.		Perf. 11½ ('33)	30.00	27.50
30	A2	5sh bl grn & ultra	32.50	42.50
		Nos. 16-30 (15)	106.80	130.60

Victoria Falls — A4

1932, May *Perf. 12½*

31	A4	2p dark brown & grn	.85	.15
32	A4	3p dark blue	3.75	.55
a.		Vert. pair, imperf. horiz.	*9,000.*	*10,000.*
b.		Vert. pair, imperf. btwn.	—	

See Nos. 37-37A.

Silver Jubilee Issue

Victoria Falls and George V
A5

1935, May 6 *Perf. 11x12*

33	A5	1p car rose & olive	.40	.35
34	A5	2p blk brn & lt grn	1.10	.90
35	A5	3p blue & violet	6.25	*7.00*
36	A5	6p dp violet & blk	8.25	*8.00*
		Nos. 33-36 (4)	16.00	*16.25*
		Set, never hinged	27.50	

25th anniv. of the reign of George V.

"Postage and Revenue"
A6

1935-41 *Perf. 14*

37	A6	2p dk brn & grn ('41)	.25	.15
b.		Perf. 12½	1.50	1.50
37A	A6	3p deep blue ('38)	.75	.20
		Set value		.26
		Set, never hinged	3.25	

Queen Elizabeth, George VI
A7

1937, May 12 *Perf. 12½*

38	A7	1p carmine & gray grn	.18	.18
39	A7	2p brown & green	.25	.25
40	A7	3p lt blue & violet	1.40	1.40
41	A7	6p red violet & blk	.95	.95
		Nos. 38-41 (4)	2.78	2.78
		Set, never hinged	7.00	

Coronation of George VI & Elizabeth.

King George VI — A8

1937, Nov. 25 *Perf. 14*

42	A8	½p yellow green	.30	.15
43	A8	1p red	.20	.15
44	A8	1½p red brown	.60	.15
45	A8	4p orange red	.90	.15
46	A8	6p dark gray	.90	.15
47	A8	8p blue green	1.25	.35
48	A8	9p blue	.75	.32
49	A8	10p violet	1.25	1.10
50	A8	1sh green & blk	.90	.15
51	A8	1sh6p ocher & blk	4.00	.35
52	A8	2sh brown & blk	6.50	.85
53	A8	2sh6p violet & blue	2.75	1.90
54	A8	5sh green & blue	7.25	1.25
		Nos. 42-54 (13)	27.55	7.02
		Set, never hinged	57.50	

Catalogue values for unused stamps in this section, from this point to the end of the section, are for Never Hinged items.

Seal of British South Africa Co. — A9

Fort Salisbury, 1890 — A10

Cecil John Rhodes — A11

Pioneer Fort and Mail Coach — A12

Rhodes Makes Peace, 1896 — A13

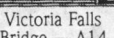

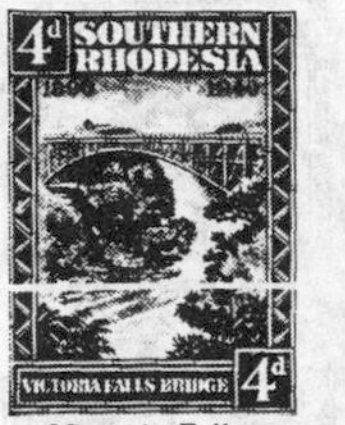
Victoria Falls Bridge — A14

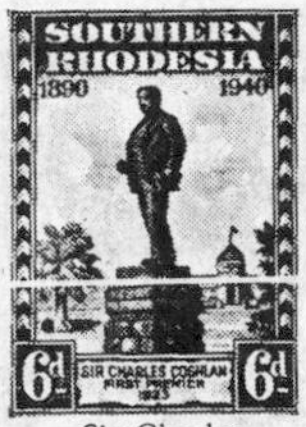
Sir Charles Coghlan — A15

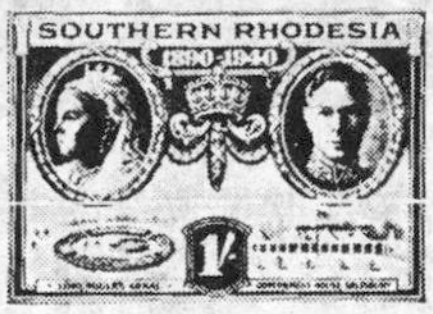
Queen Victoria, George VI, Lobengula's Kraal and Government House — A16

Unwmk.

1940, June 3 Engr. *Perf. 14*

56	A9	½p dp grn & dull vio	.18	.16
57	A10	1p red & vio blue	.18	.16
58	A11	1½p cop brn & blk	.20	.20
59	A12	2p pur & brt grn	.20	.20
60	A13	3p dk blue & blk	.35	.25
61	A14	4p brn & bl grn	.85	.60
62	A15	6p sepia & dull grn	1.25	.60
63	A16	1sh dk bl & brt grn	2.00	.85
		Nos. 56-63 (8)	5.21	3.02

50th anniv. of the founding of Southern Rhodesia by Cecil John Rhodes.

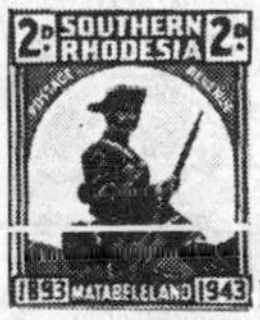
Pioneer — A17

1943, Nov. 1 Photo. Wmk. 201

64	A17	2p Prus grn & choc	.20	.15

50th anniv. of Matabeleland under British control.

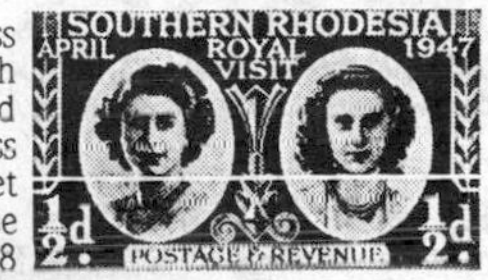
Princess Elizabeth and Princess Margaret Rose A18

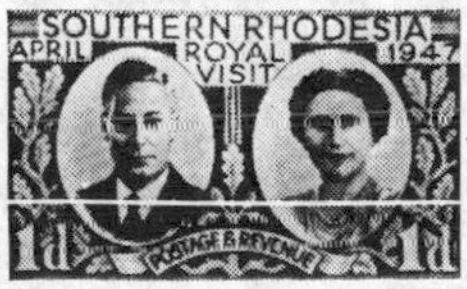
King George VI and Queen Elizabeth A19

Unwmk.

1947, Apr. 1 Engr. *Perf. 14*

65	A18	½p dk green & blk	.15	.15
66	A19	1p carmine & blk	.15	.15

Visit of the British Royal Family, Apr., 1947.

Victory Issue

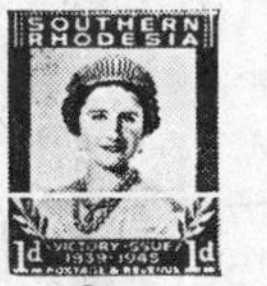
Queen Elizabeth — A20

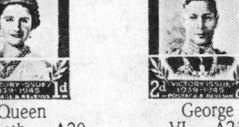

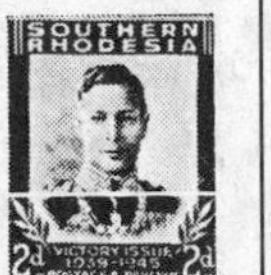
George VI — A21

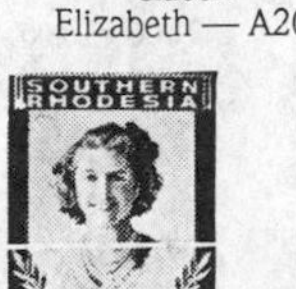
Princess Elizabeth A22

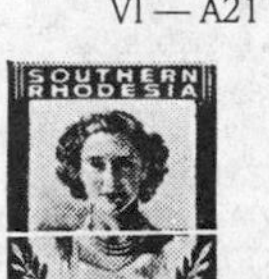
Princess Margaret Rose A23

1947, May 8

67	A20	1p deep carmine	.15	.15
68	A21	2p slate black	.16	.16
69	A22	3p deep blue	.20	.20
70	A23	6p red orange	.35	.35
		Nos. 67-70 (4)	.86	.86

Victory of the Allied Nations in WW II.

UPU Issue

Common Design Types

Engr.; Name Typo.

Perf. 11x11½

1949, Oct. 10 Wmk. 4

71	CD307	2p slate black	.55	.45
72	CD308	3p slate blue	1.40	1.40

75th anniv. of the UPU.

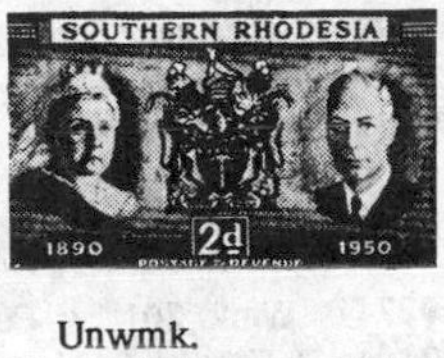
Queen Victoria and King George VI A24

Unwmk.

1950, Sept. 12 Engr. *Perf. 14*

73	A24	2p choc & blue grn	.20	.15

60th anniversary of Rhodesia.

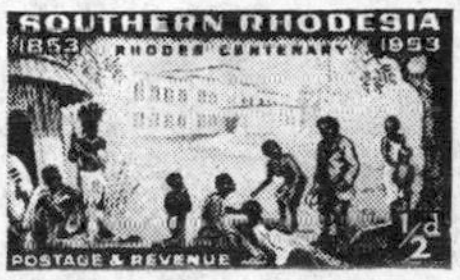
Hospital, Doctor and Natives A25

Designs: 1p, African Scene. 2p, Native Houses, Modern City and Cecil Rhodes. 4½p, Dam and Natives. 1sh, Transportation.

1953, Apr. 15

74	A25	½p dk brown & blue	.22	.15
75	A25	1p blue grn & fawn	.22	.15
76	A25	2p vio & dk bl grn	.35	.22
77	A25	4½p dk bl & bl grn	1.65	.85
78	A25	1sh chestnut & blk	2.50	.95
		Nos. 74-78 (5)	4.94	2.32

#77 is inscribed Matabeleland Diamond Jubilee.

Type of Nyasaland Prot., 1953

1953, May 30 *Perf. 14x13½*

79	A17	6p purple	.45	.45

Nos. 74-79 were issued to commemorate the Central African Cecil Rhodes Centenary Exhibition.

Coronation Issue

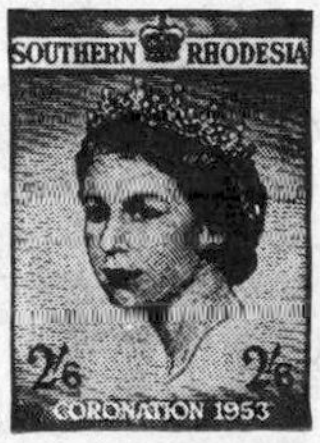
Elizabeth II — A26

1953, June 1 *Perf. 12x12½*

80	A26	2sh6p cerise	5.00	5.00

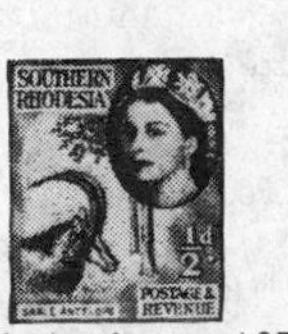
Sable Antelope — A27

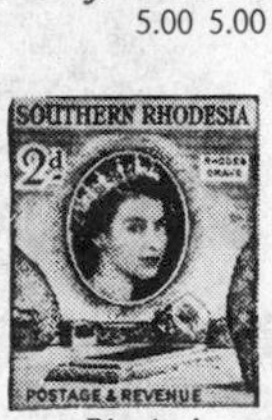
Rhodes' Grave — A28

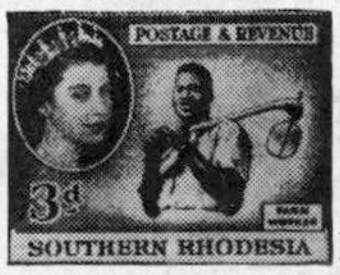
Farm Worker — A29

Designs: 1p, Tobacco planter. 4p, Flame lily. 4½p, Victoria Falls. 6p, Baobab tree. 9p, Lion. 1sh, Zimbabwe ruins. 2sh, Birchenough Bridge. 2sh6p, Kariba Gorge. 5sh, Basket maker. 10sh, Balancing rocks. £1, Arms.

Perf. 14x13½, 13½x14

1953, Aug. 31

Portrait in Various Positions

81	A27	½p rose lake & dk ol grn	.20	.25
82	A27	1p choc & green	.20	.15
83	A28	2p rose vio & org brn	.20	.15

Size: 28x22½mm

84	A29	3p carmine & sep	.45	.50
85	A29	4p gray, brn, car & grn	2.25	.15
86	A29	4½p ultra & blk	1.50	1.75
87	A28	6p aqua & olive	2.00	.20
88	A29	9p org brn & dp bl	3.00	1.50
89	A29	1sh grnsh bl & rose vio	.85	.15
90	A29	2sh red & rose vio	8.00	2.50
91	A29	2sh6p org brn & ol grn	6.00	3.00
92	A28	5s dk grn & org brn	13.00	7.00

Size: 37x27mm

93	A29	10sh ol grn & red brn	17.00	32.50
94	A29	£1 dk gray & car	27.50	32.50
		Nos. 81-94 (14)	82.15	82.30

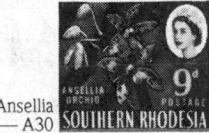

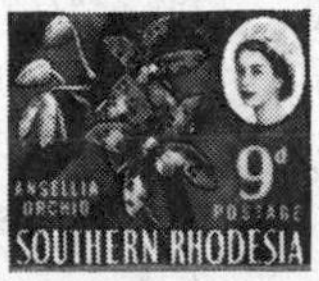
Ansellia Orchid — A30

1964, Feb. 19 Photo. *Perf. 14½*

Size: 23x19mm

95	A30	½p Corn	.20	.15
96	A30	1p Cape buffalo	.15	.15
a.		Purple omitted	*650.00*	
97	A30	2p Tobacco	.15	.15
98	A30	3p Kudu	.15	.15
99	A30	4p Oranges	.15	.15

Perf. 13½x13

Size: 27x23mm

100	A30	6p Flame lily	.15	.15
101	A30	9p shown	.75	.20
102	A30	1sh Emeralds	.75	.15
a.		Green omitted	*1,250.*	
103	A30	1sh3p Aloe	.90	.15
104	A30	2sh Lake Kyle	1.50	.50
105	A30	2sh6p Tiger fish	1.65	.60
a.		Red omitted	375.00	

Perf. 14½x14

Size: 32x27mm

106	A30	5sh Cattle	3.50	2.00
107	A30	10sh Guinea fowl	10.50	5.50
108	A30	£1 Arms	17.50	12.00
		Nos. 95-108 (14)	38.00	22.00

#95-108 with overprint "Independence 11th November 1965" are listed as Rhodesia #208-221.

Stamps of Southern Rhodesia were replaced in 1965 by those of Rhodesia (formerly Southern Rhodesia).

POSTAGE DUE STAMPS

Catalogue values for unused stamps in this section are for Never Hinged items.

Great Britain Postage Due Stamps of 1938-51 Overprinted in Black

SOUTHERN

RHODESIA

1951 Wmk. 251 *Perf. 14x14½*

J1	D1	½p emerald	2.50	*3.75*
J2	D1	1p violet blue	1.50	*.65*
J3	D1	2p black brown	3.25	*1.50*
J4	D1	3p violet	3.25	*1.50*
J5	D1	4p brt blue	1.50	*3.00*
a.		4p slate green	150.00	*200.00*
J6	D1	1sh blue	3.25	*1.50*
		Nos. J1-J6 (6)	15.25	*11.90*

SOUTH WEST AFRICA

saùth 'west 'a–fri–kə

(Namibia)

LOCATION — Southwestern Africa between Angola, Botswana and South Africa, bordering on the Atlantic Ocean

GOVT. — Administered by the Republic of South Africa under a mandate of the League of Nations

AREA — 318,261 sq. mi.

POP. — 1,039,800 (1982)

CAPITAL — Windhoek

Formerly a German possession, South West Africa was occupied by South African forces in 1915 and by the Treaty of Versailles was mandated to the Union of South Africa. On March 20, 1990 it became Namibia.

12 Pence = 1 Shilling
20 Shillings = 1 Pound
100 Cents = 1 Rand (1961)

Catalogue values for unused stamps in this country are for Never Hinged items, beginning with Scott 125 in the regular postage section, Scott B1 in the semi-postal section, Scott J86 in the postage due section, and Scott O13 in the officials section.

Stamps of South Africa, Nos. 2-3, 5 and 9-16, Overprinted in English or Dutch alternately throughout the sheets.

Major-number listings and values of Nos. 1-40 and 85-93 are for multiples with both overprints.

Setting I

South West / **Africa.** — a

Zuid-West / **Afrika.** — b

"South West" 14½mm wide
"Zuid-West" 13mm wide
Overprint Spaced 14mm

1923, Jan. 2 Wmk. 177 *Perf. 14*

1	A2	½p green, pair	1.50	*6.00*
a.		Single, Dutch	.15	*.50*
2	A2	1p red, pair	2.00	*6.00*
a.		Single, Dutch	.15	*.50*
b.		Inverted overprint, pair	900.00	
c.		As "b," single, English	140.00	
d.		As "b," single, Dutch	140.00	
e.		"Af,rica"	175.00	
f.		Double overprint, pair	—	
g.		As "f," single, English	1,000.	
h.		As "f," single, Dutch	1,000.	
3	A2	2p dull vio, pair	2.25	*8.00*
a.		Single, Dutch	.15	*.90*
b.		Inverted overprint, pair	775.00	—
c.		As "b," single, English	110.00	
d.		As "b," single, Dutch	110.00	
4	A2	3p ultra, pair	7.00	*15.00*
a.		Single, Dutch	.25	*1.75*
5	A2	4p ol grn & org, pair	10.00	*35.00*
a.		Single, Dutch	.40	*4.00*
6	A2	6p vio & blk, pair	7.50	*30.00*
a.		Single, Dutch	.40	*4.00*
7	A2	1sh orange, pair	21.00	*45.00*
a.		Single, Dutch	1.00	*4.50*
8	A2	1sh3p violet, pair	27.50	*50.00*
a.		Single, Dutch	1.25	*5.00*
b.		Inverted overprint, pair	225.00	
c.		As "b," single, English	45.00	
d.		As "b," single, Dutch	45.00	
9	A2	2sh6p grn & cl, pair	65.00	*120.00*
a.		Single, Dutch	3.75	*15.00*
10	A2	5sh blue & cl, pair	200.00	*250.00*
a.		Single, Dutch	15.00	*30.00*
11	A2	10sh ol grn & bl, pair	1,600.	*2,250.*
a.		Single, Dutch	150.00	*300.00*
12	A2	£1 red & dp grn, pair	1,100.	*1,400.*
a.		Single, Dutch	100.00	*200.00*
		Nos. 1-12 (12)	3,043.	*4,215.*

Most values exist with "t" of "West" partly or totally missing. Vertical displacement in overprinting accounts for the copies with only one line of overprint.

For English from setting I "a," see note after No. 27.

Setting II

South West / **Africa.** — c

Zuid-West / **Afrika.** — d

Words Same Width as Setting I
Overprint Spaced 9½-10mm

1923, Apr.

13 A2 5sh blue & cl, pair 250.00 275.00
a. Single, English 25.00 50.00
b. Single, Dutch 25.00 50.00
c. As #13, without period after "Afrika" 1,800. —
14 A2 10sh ol grn & bl, pair 850.00 1,250.
a. Single, English 85.00 175.00
b. Single, Dutch 85.00 175.00
c. As #14, without period after "Afrika" 2,500. 3,000.
15 A2 £1 red & green, pair 1,250. 1,900.
a. Single, English 125.00 200.00
b. Single, Dutch 125.00 200.00
c. As #15, without period after "Afrika" 7,000. —

Setting III

South West **Zuidwest**

Africa. **Afrika.**
a f

English as in Setting I
"Zuidwest" 11mm wide, No Hyphen
Overprint Spaced 14mm

1923-24

16 A2 ½p green, pair ('24) 4.00 22.50
a. Single, English .30 3.00
b. Single, Dutch .30 3.00
17 A2 1p red, pair 4.00 6.50
a. Single, English .30 1.25
b. Single, Dutch .30 1.25
18 A2 2p dull vio, pair 4.00 6.00
a. Single, English .30 1.10
b. Single, Dutch .30 1.10
c. Dbl. ovpt., pair 1,000.
d. As "c," single, English 90.00
e. As "c," single, Dutch 90.00
19 A2 3p ultra, pair 4.00 5.00
a. Single, English .30 1.00
b. Single, Dutch .30 1.00
20 A2 4p ol grn & org, pair 5.00 15.00
a. Single, English .40 2.50
b. Single, Dutch .40 2.50
21 A2 6p vio & blk, pair 11.00 30.00
a. Single, English 1.00 4.00
b. Single, Dutch 1.00 4.00
22 A2 1sh orange, pair 13.00 37.50
a. Single, English 1.25 4.75
b. Single, Dutch 1.25 4.75
23 A2 1sh3p violet, pair 26.00 40.00
a. Single, English 2.50 5.00
b. Single, Dutch 2.50 5.00
24 A2 2sh6p green & cl, pair 40.00 75.00
a. Single, English 4.00 9.00
b. Single, Dutch 4.00 9.00
25 A2 5sh blue & cl, pair 72.50 120.00
a. Single, English 7.50 17.50
b. Single, Dutch 7.50 17.50
26 A2 10sh ol grn & bl, pair 250.00 275.00
a. Single, English 25.00 45.00
b. Single, Dutch 25.00 45.00
27 A2 £1 red & green, pair 400.00 475.00
a. Single, English 40.00 75.00
b. Single, Dutch 40.00 75.00
Nos. 16-27 (12) 833.50 1,107.

The English overprint of Setting III is the same as that of Setting I.

Setting IV

South West **Zuidwest**

Africa. **Afrika.**
g h

"South West" 16mm wide
"Zuidwest" 12mm wide
Overprint Spaced 14mm

1924, July

28 A2 2sh6p green & cl, pair 125.00 150.00
a. Single, English 13.00 25.00
b. Single, Dutch 13.00 25.00

Setting VI

South West **Zuidwest**

Africa. **Afrika.**
k l

"South West" 16, 16½mm wide
"Zuidwest" 12½mm wide
Overprint Spaced 9½mm

1924, Dec.

29 A2 ½p green, pair 6.00 30.00
a. Single, English .50 4.00
b. Single, Dutch .50 4.00
30 A2 1p red, pair 2.50 7.50
a. Single, English .25 1.00
b. Single, Dutch .25 1.00
31 A2 2p dull vio, pair 4.00 15.00
a. Single, English .45 1.75
b. Single, Dutch .45 1.75
32 A2 3p ultra, pair 4.00 22.50
a. Single, English .45 2.50
b. Single, Dutch .45 2.50
33 A2 4p ol grn & org, pair 6.00 30.00
a. Single, English .75 4.25
b. Single, Dutch .75 4.25
34 A2 6p vio & blk, pair 7.00 40.00
a. Single, English .75 5.00
b. Single, Dutch .75 5.00
35 A2 1sh orange, pair 10.00 40.00
a. Single, English 1.00 5.00
b. Single, Dutch 1.00 5.00
36 A2 1sh3p violet, pair 14.00 42.50
a. Single, English 1.50 5.25
b. Single, Dutch 1.50 5.25
37 A2 2sh6p green & cl, pair 35.00 75.00
a. Single, English 3.50 11.00
b. Single, Dutch 3.50 11.00
38 A2 5sh blue & cl, pair 60.00 100.00
a. Single, English 6.00 15.00
b. Single, Dutch 6.00 15.00
39 A2 10sh ol grn & bl, pair 90.00 125.00
a. Single, English 10.00 20.00
b. Single, Dutch 10.00 20.00
40 A2 £1 red & grn, pair 325.00 425.00
a. Single, English 32.50 80.00
b. Single, Dutch 32.50 80.00
Nos. 29-40 (12) 563.50 952.50

Setting VII
South Africa Nos. 21-22 Overprinted:

SOUTH WEST AFRICA **SUIDWES-AFRIKA**
m n

SOUTH WEST AFRICA
o

1926-27 **Wmk. 201** ***Imperf.***

81 A3 (m) 4p blue gray .75 1.75
82 A3 (n) 4p blue gray .75 1.75
83 A3 (o) 4p blue gray ('27) 7.00 18.00
Nos. 81-83 (3) 8.50 21.50

Nos. 81-83 were not officially perforated, but firms and individuals applied various forms of perforation and rouletting for their own convenience. Perf. 11 examples of Nos. 81-82 were made by John Meinert, Ltd., Windhoek, same values.

Setting VIII
South Africa Nos. 23-25 Overprinted Alternately with type "p" on English-inscribed Stamps and type "q" on Afrikaans-inscribed Stamps

South West Africa. **Suidwes Afrika.**
p q

"South West" 16½mm wide
"Suidwes" 11mm wide
Overprint Spaced 11½mm

1926 **Typo.** ***Perf. 14½x14***

85 A5 ½p dk green & blk, pair 4.50 7.50
a. Single, English .35 1.00
b. Single, Afrikaans .35 1.00
c. Ovpt. "q" on English stamp .35 1.00
d. Ovpt. "p" on Afrikaans stamp .35 1.00
e. Pair, "c" + "d" 4.50 7.50
f. As "e," without period after "Africa" 200.00
86 A6 1p car & blk, pair 2.00 7.50
a. Single, English .20 1.00
b. Single, Afrikaans .20 1.00
c. Ovpt. "q" on English stamp .20 1.00
d. Ovpt. "p" on Afrikaans stamp .20 1.00
e. Pair, "c" + "d" 2.50 8.00
f. As "e," without period after "Africa" 275.00
87 A7 6p org & grn, pair 24.00 45.00
a. Single, English 2.50 6.00
b. Single, Afrikaans 2.50 6.00
c. Ovpt. "q" on English stamp 2.00 5.00
d. Ovpt. "p" on Afrikaans stamp 2.00 5.00
e. Pair, "c" + "d" 20.00 40.00
f. As "e," without period after "Africa" 200.00
Nos. 85-87 (3) 30.50 60.00

For overprints see Nos. O1-O3.

Setting IX
South Africa Nos. 26-27, 29-32 Overprinted in Blue with types "p" and "q" Spaced 16mm

1927 **Engr.** ***Perf. 14***

88 A8 2p vio brn & gray, pair 3.00 12.50
a. Single, English .25 1.50
b. Single, Afrikaans .25 1.50
89 A9 3p red & blk, pair 3.00 22.50
a. Single, English .25 2.50
b. Single, Afrikaans .25 2.50
90 A11 1sh dp bl & bis brn, pair 13.00 30.00
a. Single, English 1.25 3.50
b. Single, Afrikaans 1.25 3.50
91 A12 2sh6p brn & bl grn, pair 42.50 55.00
a. Single, English 4.50 10.00
b. Single, Afrikaans 4.50 10.00
92 A13 5sh dp grn & blk, pair 75.00 110.00
a. Single, English 8.00 17.50
b. Single, Afrikaans 8.00 17.50
93 A14 10sh ol brn & bl, pair 85.00 110.00
a. Single, English 9.00 17.50
b. Single, Afrikaans 9.00 17.50
Nos. 88-93 (6) 221.50 340.00

South Africa Nos. 12 and 16a Overprinted at Foot

S.W.A.
r

1927 **Typo.** **Wmk. 177**

94 A2 1sh3p violet 2.75 5.00
a. Without period after "A" 110.00
95 A2 £1 lt red & gray grn 190.00 165.00
a. Without period after "A" 1,750. 2,250.

South Africa Nos. 23-25 Overprinted type "r" at Foot

1927 **Wmk. 201** ***Perf. 14½x14***

96 A5 ½p green & blk, pair 1.25 5.00
a. Single, English .15 .75
b. Single, Afrikaans .15 .75
c. As #96, without period after "A" on one stamp 75.00
97 A6 1p car & blk, pair 1.25 3.00
a. Single, English .15 .50
b. Single, Afrikaans .15 .50
c. As #97, without period after "A" on one stamp 75.00 75.00
d. Ovpt. at top, pair ('30) 3.25 12.50
e. As "d," single, English .35 1.75
f. As "d," single, Afrikaans .35 1.75
98 A7 6p org & grn, pair 12.50 21.00
a. Single, English 1.25 2.75
b. Single, Afrikaans 1.25 2.75
c. As #98, without period after "A" on one stamp 125.00
Nos. 96-98 (3) 15.00 29.00

For overprints see Nos. O5-O7.

South Africa Nos. 26-32 Overprinted type "r" at Top

1927-28 **Engr.** ***Perf. 14***

99 A8 2p vio brn & gray, pair 4.00 9.00
a. Single, English .35 1.25
b. Single, Afrikaans .35 1.25
c. As #99, without period after "A" on one stamp 100.00 100.00
d. Double ovpt., one inverted 675.00 800.00
100 A9 3p red & blk, pair 5.50 21.00
a. Single, English .60 3.00
b. Single, Afrikaans .60 3.00
c. As #100, without period after "A" on one stamp 125.00 125.00
101 A10 4p brn, pair ('28) 17.00 45.00
a. Single, English 1.75 6.50
b. Single, Afrikaans 1.75 6.50
c. As #101, without period after "A" on one stamp 85.00 125.00
102 A11 1sh dp bl & bis brn, pair 22.50 40.00
a. Single, English 2.50 5.00
b. Single, Afrikaans 2.50 5.00
c. As #102, without period after "A" on one stamp 1,600.
103 A12 2sh6p brn & bl grn, pair 45.00 70.00
a. Single, English 5.00 10.00
b. Single, Afrikaans 5.00 10.00
c. As #103, without period after "A" on one stamp 175.00 225.00
104 A13 5sh dp grn & blk, pair 60.00 95.00
a. Single, English 7.00 17.50
b. Single, Afrikaans 7.00 17.50
c. As #104, without period after "A" on one stamp 250.00 —
105 A14 10sh ol brn & bl, pair 165.00 190.00
a. Single, English 17.50 25.00
b. Single, Afrikaans 17.50 25.00
c. As #105, without period after "A" on one stamp 325.00 —
Nos. 99-105 (7) 319.00 470.00

For overprint see No. O8.

South Africa Nos. 33-34 Overprinted type "r" at Foot

1930 **Photo.** ***Perf. 15x14***

106 A5 ½p bl grn & blk, pair 6.00 20.00
a. Single, English .50 2.50
b. Single, Afrikaans .50 2.50
107 A6 1p car rose & blk, pair 5.00 20.00
a. Single, English .50 2.50
b. Single, Afrikaans .50 2.50

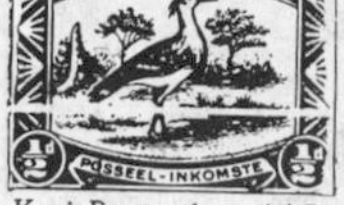

Kori Bustard — A15

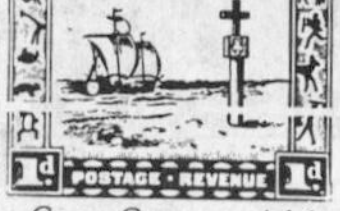

Cape Cross — A16

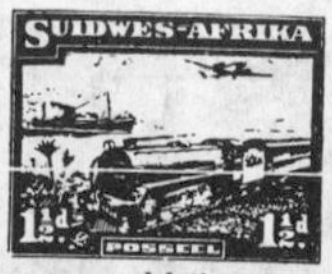

Mail Transport — A17

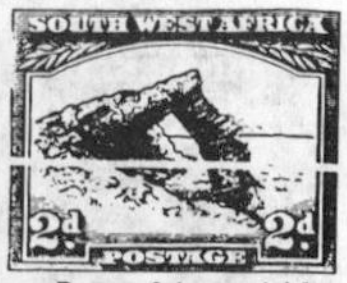

Bogenfels — A18

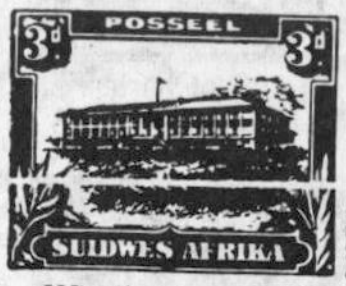

Windhoek — A19

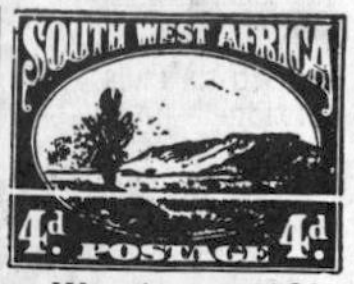

Waterberg — A20

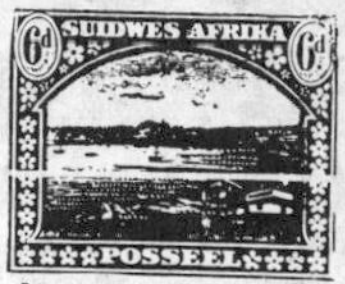

Lüderitz Bay — A21

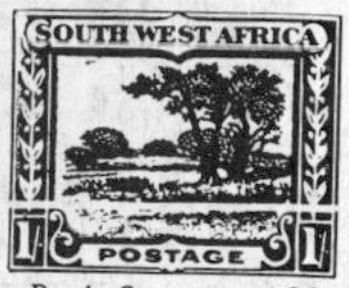

Bush Scene — A22

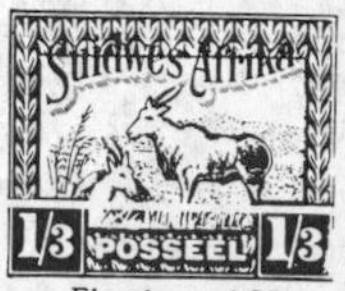

Elands — A23

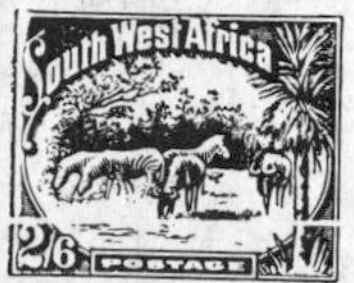

Zebras and Brindled Gnus — A24

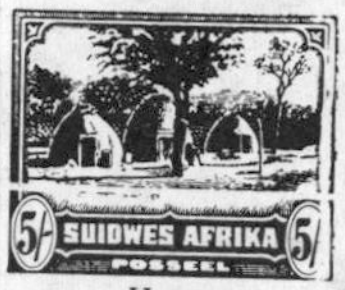

Herero Houses — A25

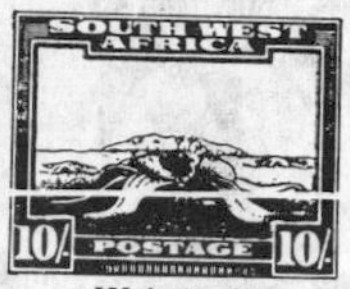

Welwitschia Plant — A26

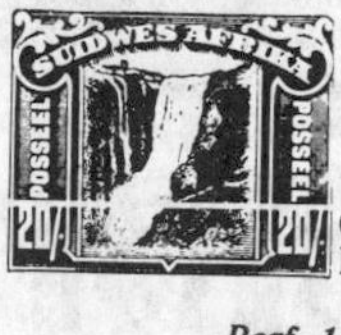

Okuwahakan Falls — A27

Perf. 14x13½

1931-37 **Wmk. 201** **Engr.**

108 A15 ½p grn & blk, pair 1.40 1.00
a. Single, English .15 .15
b. Single, Afrikaans .15 .15
109 A16 1p red & ind, pair 1.40 1.75
a. Single, English .15 .15
b. Single, Afrikaans .15 .15
110 A17 1½p vio brn, pair ('37) 12.00 2.25
a. Single, English .15 .25
b. Single, Afrikaans .15 .25
111 A18 2p dk brn & dk bl, pair .45 2.25
a. Single, English .15 .15
b. Single, Afrikaans .15 .15
112 A19 3p dp bl & gray blk, pair .55 2.50
a. Single, English .15 .15
b. Single, Afrikaans .15 .15
113 A20 4p brn vio & grn, pair .75 4.50
a. Single, English .15 .20
b. Single, Afrikaans .15 .20
114 A21 6p ol brn & bl, pair .75 6.00
a. Single, English .15 .20
b. Single, Afrikaans .15 .20
115 A22 1sh bl & vio brn, pair 1.25 6.00
a. Single, English .18 .20
b. Single, Afrikaans .18 .20
116 A23 1sh3p ocher & pur, pair 9.00 10.00
a. Single, English .45 .50
b. Single, Afrikaans .45 .50
117 A24 2sh6p dk gray & rose, pair 21.00 16.00
a. Single, English 1.25 1.75
b. Single, Afrikaans 1.25 1.75
118 A25 5sh vio brn & ol grn, pair 19.00 35.00
a. Single, English 1.25 2.50
b. Single, Afrikaans 1.25 2.50
119 A26 10sh grn & brn, pair 50.00 55.00
a. Single, English 4.50 6.50
b. Single, Afrikaans 4.50 6.50
120 A27 20sh bl grn & mar, pair 110.00 110.00
a. Single, English 12.50 12.50
b. Single, Afrikaans 12.50 12.50
Nos. 108-120 (13) 227.55 252.25

For overprints see Nos. O13-O27.

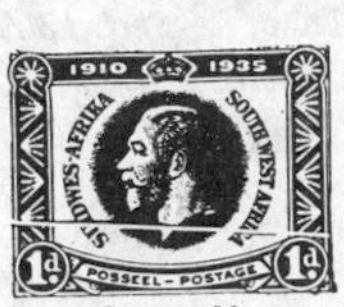

George V
A28

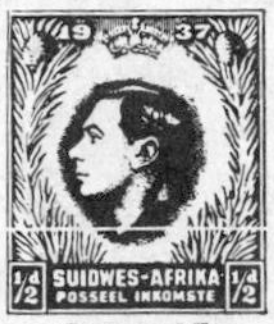

George VI
A29

1935, May 6 *Perf. 14x13½*
121 A28 1p carmine & blk .90 .25
122 A28 2p dk brown & blk .90 .25
123 A28 3p blue & blk 12.50 *13.00*
124 A28 6p violet & blk 5.00 4.00
Nos. 121-124 (4) 19.30 17.50

25th anniv. of the reign of George V.

Catalogue values for unused stamps in this section, from this point to the end of the section, are for Never Hinged items.

Coronation Issue

Inscribed alternately in English and Afrikaans

1937, May 12 Engr. *Perf. 13½x14*
125 A29 ½p emer & blk, pair .50 .40
a. Single, English .15 .15
b. Single, Afrikaans .15 .15
126 A29 1p car & blk, pair .60 .40
a. Single, English .15 .15
b. Single, Afrikaans .15 .15
127 A29 1½p org & blk, pair .60 .50
a. Single, English .15 .15
b. Single, Afrikaans .15 .15
128 A29 2p dk brn & blk, pair .60 .50
a. Single, English .15 .15
b. Single, Afrikaans .15 .15
129 A29 3p brt bl & blk, pair .60 .50
a. Single, English .15 .15
b. Single, Afrikaans .15 .15
130 A29 4p dk vio & blk, pair .75 .50
a. Single, English .15 .15
b. Single, Afrikaans .15 .15
131 A29 6p yel & blk, pair .75 *1.50*
a. Single, English .15 .20
b. Single, Afrikaans .15 .20
132 A29 1sh gray & blk, pair 1.10 1.50
a. Single, English .20 .20
b. Single, Afrikaans .20 .20
Nos. 125-132 (8) 5.50 5.80

George VI & Queen Elizabeth coronation.

Voortrekker Issue

South Africa Nos. 79-80 Overprinted type "r"

1938, Dec. 14 Photo. *Perf. 15x14*
133 A23 1p rose & sl, pair 8.25 8.25
a. Single, English 1.00 1.00
b. Single, Afrikaans 1.00 1.00
134 A24 1½p red brn & Prus bl, pair 15.00 15.00
a. Single, English 1.50 1.50
b. Single, Afrikaans 1.50 1.50

Issued to commemorate the Voortrekkers.

South Africa Nos. 81-89 Overprinted

SWA
s

Perf. 14 (2p, 4p, 6p); 15x14

1941-43 Wmk. 201
135 A25 ½p dp blue grn, pair 1.25 1.90
a. Single, English .15 .15
b. Single, Afrikaans .15 .15
136 A26 1p brt rose, pair 1.50 1.75
a. Single, English .15 .15
b. Single, Afrikaans .15 .15
137 A27 1½p Prus grn, pair ('42) 2.50 2.75
a. Single, English .20 .15
b. Single, Afrikaans .20 .15
138 A28 2p dk violet .60 .50
139 A29 3p dp blue, pair 12.50 7.50
a. Single, English 1.00 .85
b. Single, Afrikaans 1.00 .85
140 A30 4p brown, pair 5.00 7.50
a. Single, English .50 .85
b. Single, Afrikaans .50 .85
141 A31 6p brt red org, pair 2.75 3.50
a. Single, English .30 .40
b. Single, Afrikaans .30 .40
142 A32 1sh dk brown 1.00 .75
143 A33 1sh3p dk ol brn, pair ('43) 12.50 10.00
a. Single, English 1.00 1.25
b. Single, Afrikaans 1.00 1.25
Nos. 135-143 (9) 39.60 36.15

South Africa Nos. 90-97 Overprinted

SWA **SWA**
t u

Pairs or Strips of 3 Perf. 14 or 15x14 all around, Rouletted 6½ or 13 btwn.

1942-45 Wmk. 201
144 A34 (t) ½p dp grn, horiz. strip of 3 .80 1.75
a. Single, English .15 .15
b. Single, Afrikaans .15 .15
c. ½p dp bl grn, horiz. strip of 3 1.50 2.25
d. As "c," single, English .15 .15
e. As "c," single, Afrikaans .15 .15
145 A35 (t) 1p brt car, horiz. strip of 3 1.75 2.00
a. Single, English .15 .15
b. Single, Afrikaans .15 .15
c. 1p rose car, horiz. strip of 3 .95 1.50
d. As "c," single, English .15 .15
e. As "c," single, Afrikaans .15 .15
146 A36 (u) 1½p cop brn, horiz. pair .75 .65
a. Single, English .15 .15
b. Single, Afrikaans .15 .15
147 A37 (t) 2p dk vio, horiz. pair 3.00 2.00
a. Single, English .15 .15
b. Single, Afrikaans .15 .15
148 A38 (t) 3p dp bl, vert. strip of 3 3.50 *7.50*
a. Single, English .20 .40
b. Single, Afrikaans .20 .40
149 A39 (t) 4p sl grn, vert. strip of 3 3.25 7.50
a. Single .25 .40
b. As "c," single 50.00
c. Inverted overprint, strip of 3 500.00 300.00
150 A40 (t) 6p brt red org, horiz. pair 3.50 2.00
a. Single, English .30 .30
b. Single, Afrikaans .30 .30
c. Inverted overprint, pair 425.00
d. As "c," single, English 50.00 50.00
e. As "c," single, Afrikaans 50.00 50.00
151 A41 (u) 1sh dk brn, vert. pair 9.00 15.00
a. Single 1.00 1.50
b. As "c," single 75.00
c. Inverted overprint, pair 500.00 375.00
152 A41 (t) 1sh dk brn, vert. pair 4.75 3.50
a. Single .60 .30
b. As "c," single 50.00 45.00
c. Inverted overprint, vert. pair 400.00 300.00
Nos. 144-152 (9) 30.30 41.90

Issue years: #144-145, 147-151, 1943, #152, 1944; #144c, 145c, 149c, 1945.

Peace Issue

South Africa Nos. 100-102 Overprinted Type "w"

1945 Wmk. 201 *Perf. 14*
153 A42 1p rose pink & choc, pair .30 .40
a. Single, English .15 .15
b. Single, Afrikaans .15 .15
c. Inverted overprint, pair 275.00 275.00
d. As "c," single, English 42.50
e. As "c," single, Afrikaans 42.50
154 A43 2p vio & sl bl, pair .35 .45
a. Single, English .15 .15
b. Single, Afrikaans .15 .15
155 A43 3p ultra & dp ultra, pair .60 .75
a. Single, English .15 .15
b. Single, Afrikaans .15 .15
Nos. 153-155 (3) 1.25 1.60

WW II victory of the Allies.

Royal Visit Issue

South Africa Nos. 103-105 Overprinted **S W A**

1947, Feb. 17 *Perf. 15x14*
156 A44 1p cerise & gray, pair .20 .20
a. Single, English .15 .15
b. Single, Afrikaans .15 .15
157 A45 2p purple, pair .20 .25
a. Single, English .15 .15
b. Single, Afrikaans .15 .15
158 A46 3p dk blue, pair .25 .30
a. Single, English .15 .15
b. Single, Afrikaans .15 .15
Nos. 156-158 (3) .65 .75

Visit of the British Royal Family, Mar.-Apr., 1947.

South Africa No. 106 Overprinted **SWA**

1948, Apr. 26 *Perf. 14*
159 A47 3p dp chalky bl & sil, pair 1.25 .30
a. Single, English .15 .15
b. Single, Afrikaans .15 .15

25th anniv. of the marriage of George VI and Queen Elizabeth.

UPU Issue

South Africa Nos. 109-111 Overprinted type "w" 13mm wide

1949, Oct. 1 *Perf. 14x15*
160 A50 ½p dk green, pair 1.00 1.50
a. Single, English .15 .25
b. Single, Afrikaans .15 .25
161 A50 1½p dk red, pair 1.00 1.25
a. Single, English .15 .15
b. Single, Afrikaans .15 .15
162 A50 3p ultra, pair 1.25 1.25
a. Single, English .15 .25
b. Single, Afrikaans .15 .25
Nos. 160-162 (3) 3.25 4.00

75th anniv. of the UPU.

Except for Nos. 312-313, 423-428, this ends the bi-lingual multiples in the postage section.

Voortrekker Monument Issue

South Africa Nos. 112-114 Overprinted **S W A**

1949, Dec. 1 *Perf. 15x14*
163 A51 1p magenta .15 .15
164 A52 1½p dull green .15 .15
165 A53 3p dark blue .25 .25
Nos. 163-165 (3) .55 .55

Inauguration of the Voortrekker Monument at Pretoria.

South Africa Nos. 115-119 Overprinted

SWA **SWA**
w x

1952, Mar. 14 *Perf. 15x14, 14x15*
166 A54(w) ½p dk brown & red vio .15 .15
167 A55(x) 1p dark green .15 .15
168 A54(w) 2p dark purple .15 .15
169 A55(x) 4½p dark blue .65 .65
170 A54(w) 1sh brown 1.25 1.25
Nos. 166-170 (5) 2.35 2.35

300th anniv. of the landing of Jan van Riebeeck at the Cape of Good Hope.

Coronation Issue

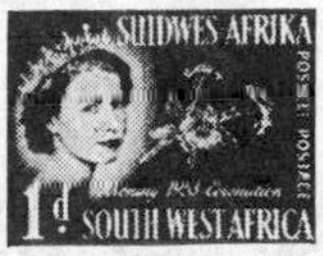

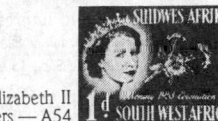

Queen Elizabeth II and Flowers — A54

Various flowers.

1953, June 2 Photo. *Perf. 14*
244 A54 1p carmine rose .45 .30
245 A54 2p dark green .60 .45
246 A54 4p deep magenta 1.50 1.25
247 A54 6p deep blue 1.75 1.50
248 A54 1sh chestnut brown 2.50 1.90
Nos. 244-248 (5) 6.80 5.40

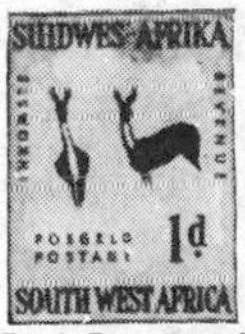

Rock Painting of Two Bucks — A55

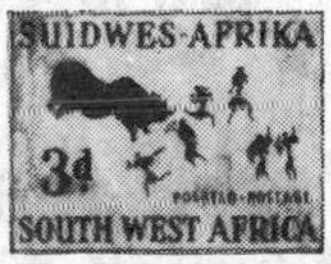

Rhinoceros Hunt — A56

Designs: 2p, "White Lady" (rock painting). 4p, Elephant and giraffe (rock painting). 4½p, Karakul lamb. 6p, Orambo blowing Kudu horn. 1sh, Ukuanjama woman. 1sh3p, Herero woman. 1sh6p, Ukuanjama girl. 2sh6p, Lioness. 5sh, Cape Oryx. 10sh, Elephant.

1954, Nov. 15 Wmk. 201 *Perf. 14*
249 A55 1p rose brown .15 .15
250 A55 2p dk brown .25 .15
251 A56 3p brown vio .50 .15
252 A56 4p olive gray .70 .22
253 A55 4½p blue vio .95 .42
254 A55 6p gray green .95 .30
255 A55 1sh magenta 2.00 .50
256 A55 1sh3p rose pink 3.50 1.10
257 A55 1sh6p dull purple 4.00 1.40
258 A55 2sh6p yel brown 8.00 2.00
259 A55 5sh blue 15.00 4.00
260 A55 10sh dk green 52.50 20.00
Nos. 249-260 (12) 88.50 30.39

1960 Wmk. 330 *Perf. 14*
261 A55 1p rose brown .42 .15
262 A55 2p dark brown .60 .28
263 A56 3p brown vio 1.25 .75
264 A56 4p olive gray 5.00 5.00
265 A55 1sh6p dull purple 25.00 22.50
Nos. 261-265 (5) 32.27 28.68

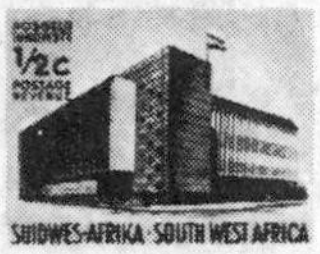

General Post Office, Windhoek
A57

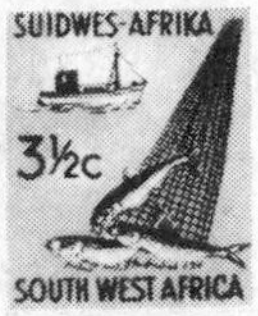

Fishing Industry
A58

Designs: 1c, Finger Rock, Asab. 1½c, Monument, Mounted Soldier. 2c, Quivertree (aloe dichotoma masson). 2½c, Administrator's residence. 3p, Swakopmund Lighthouse and flamingoes. 5c, Flamingo. 7½c, Christchurch. 10c, Diamonds. 12½c, Fort Namutoni. 15c, Hardap Dam. 20c, Topaz. 50c, Tourmaline. 1r, Heliodor.

1961-63 Wmk. 330 Photo. *Perf. 14*
266 A57 ½c blue & brown .20 .15
267 A58 1c pale lil & brn .25 .15
268 A58 1½c salmon & dk pur .35 .16
269 A58 2c yel & green .40 .15
270 A57 2½c lt blue & red brn .55 .16
271 A58 3c dp rose & vio bl .65 .18
272 A58 3½c blue grn & ind 1.10 .42
273 A58 5c bluish gray & red 1.10 .22
274 A58 7½c yellow & brn 1.40 .95
275 A58 10c brt blue & yel 2.75 .75
276 A57 12½c yellow & ind 4.00 .95
277 A57 15c dp brn & blue 4.25 1.25
278 A58 20c salmon, brn & blk 5.75 1.50
279 A58 50c org yel & Prus grn 10.50 5.00
280 A58 1r brt blue, mar & yel 27.50 12.50
Nos. 266-280 (15) 60.75 24.49

Issue dates: 3c, Oct. 1, 1962. 15c, Mar. 16, 1963. Others, Feb. 14.

1962-73 Unwmk.
281 A57 ½c blue & brn 1.25 .42
282 A58 1½c sal & dk pur ('63) 1.65 .42
283 A58 2c yellow & grn 1.65 .35
284 A57 2½c lt bl & red brn ('64) 2.75 .42
285 A58 3c dp rose & vio bl ('73) 3.25 2.50
286 A58 3½c bl grn & ind ('66) 14.00 7.25
287 A58 5c bluish gray & red 5.50 1.00
Nos. 281-287 (7) 30.05 12.36

See Nos. 304-308, 314-328.

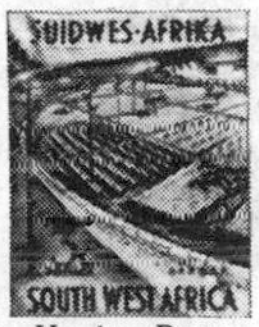

Hardap Dam and Development
A59

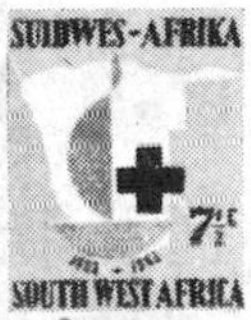

Centenary Emblem and S.W.A. Map
A60

1963, Mar. 16 Wmk. 330
294 A59 3c sepia green .90 .90

Opening of Hardap Dam near Mariental.

1963, Aug. 30 Unwmk. *Perf. 14*

Design: 15c, Emblem and globe.

295 A60 7½c blue, blk & red 6.50 3.50
296 A60 15c brn org, blk & red 13.00 7.00

Centenary of the International Red Cross.

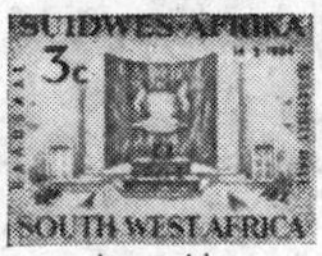

Assembly Hall — A61

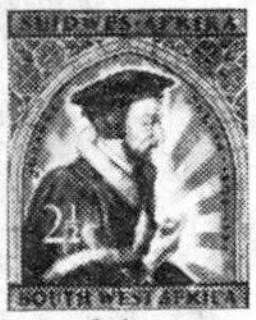

John Calvin — A62

1964, May 14 Photo. Wmk. 330
297 A61 3c salmon pink & vio bl .90 .75

Issued to commemorate the opening of the new hall of the Legislative Assembly.

1964, Oct. 1 Unwmk. *Perf. 14*
298 A62 2½c magenta & gold .85 .55
299 A62 15c green & gold 4.50 3.50

John Calvin (1509-64), French theologian and leader of the Reformation.

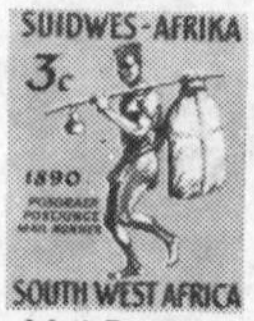

Mail Runner, 1890
A63

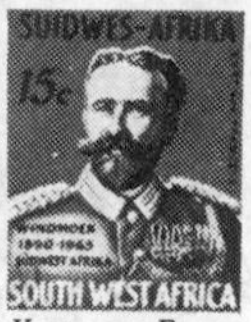

Kurt von François
A64

Wmk. 348

1965, Oct. 18 Photo. *Perf. 14*
300 A63 3c red & dp brown .45 .30
301 A64 15c green & dp brown 2.75 1.75

75th anniversary of Windhoek.

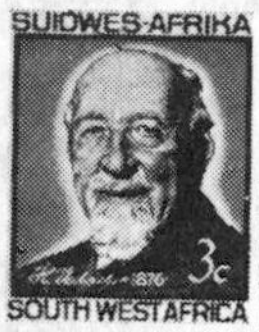

Dr. H. H. Vedder, Missionary, Educator and Senator, 90th Birthday — A65

1966, July 4 *Perf. 14*
302 A65 3c black & salmon .45 .30
303 A65 15c black & lt blue 2.75 2.25

Types of 1961-62

1966-67 Wmk. 348 Photo. *Perf. 14*
Chalky Paper
304 A57 ½c lt blue & brn ('67) .30 .15
304A A58 1c pale lil & brn ('67) .35 .16
305 A58 2c brt yel & dp grn .35 .16
306 A57 2½c gray blue & red brn .45 .20
307 A58 3½c pale grn & vio bl ('67) 3.50 2.00
308 A58 7½c brt yel & brn ('67) 1.90 .80
Nos. 304-308 (6) 6.85 3.47

The watermark on Nos. 304, 305-308 is very faint, and these stamps can be distinguished by the shades and by the thick chalky paper. The watermark on No. 304A is clear.

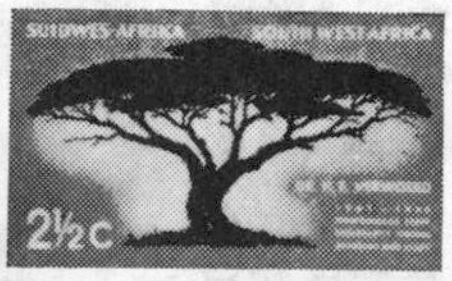

Camelthorn Tree — A66

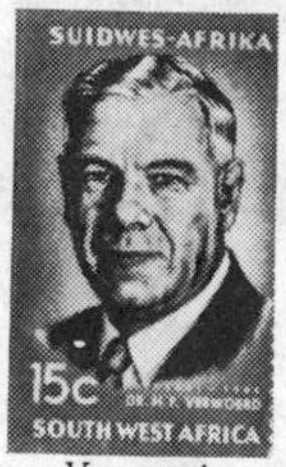

Verwoerd
A67

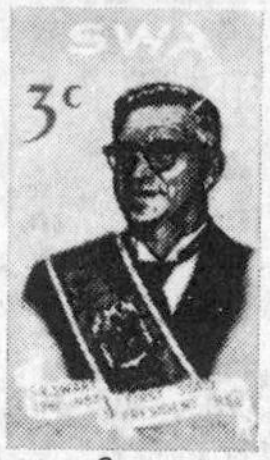

Swart
A68

Design: 3c, Waves breaking against rock.

Perf. 14, 14x15 (15c)
1967, Jan. 6 Litho. Wmk. 348
309 A66 2½c green & black .38 .22
310 A67 3c brt blue & brown .55 .25
311 A67 15c rose lilac & black 3.75 3.50
Nos. 309-311 (3) 4.68 3.97

Dr. Hendrik F. Verwoerd (1901-1966), Prime Minister of South Africa.

Perf. 14x15
1968, Jan. 2 Photo. Wmk. 359

Design: 15c, President and Mrs. C. R. Swart.

312 Strip of 3 3.75 3.75
a. A68 3c Single, English .52 .30
b. A68 3c Single, Afrikaans .52 .30
c. A68 3c Single, German .52 .30
313 Strip of 3 10.50 10.50
a. A68 15c Single, English 3.00 2.50
b. A68 15c Single, Afrikaans 3.00 2.50
c. A68 15c Single, German 3.00 2.50

Charles Robberts Swart, 1st president of South Africa, (1961-67).

Types of 1961-62

Designs: 4c, like 2½c. 6c, Christchurch. 9c, Fort Namutoni.

1968-72 Wmk. 359 Photo. *Perf. 14*
314 A57 ½c blue & brown 1.00 .24
315 A57 ½c blue & brn, redrawn ('70) 2.50 1.00
316 A58 1c pale lilac & brn ('70) 1.00 .24
317 A58 1½c salmon & dk pur 1.25 .35
318 A58 1½c sal & dk pur, redrawn ('71) 14.00 6.50
319 A58 2c yel & grn, redrawn ('70) 1.40 .35
320 A57 2½c lt bl & red brn ('70) 1.25 .24
321 A58 3c dp rose & vio bl ('70) 2.25 .30
322 A57 4c lt bl & red brn ('71) 5.50 .85
323 A58 5c bluish gray & red 2.25 .42
324 A58 6c yel & brn ('71) 10.50 3.50
325 A57 9c yel & ind ('71) 13.00 4.50
326 A58 10c brt bl & yel ('70) 5.75 1.65
327 A57 15c dp brn & bl ('72) 10.50 3.50
328 A58 20c org, brn & blk 9.50 2.00
Nos. 314-328 (15) 81.65 25.64

Nos. 315, 318-319 are without inscription "Posgeld Incomste Postage Revenue" and the numerals have been enlarged. The ½c (#315), 2c and 10c were also issued as coils.

Water Type of South Africa, 1970

Designs: 2½c, Water drop and flower, vert. 3c, Waves, horiz.

1970, Feb. 14 *Perf. 14*
329 A142 2½c brown, brt bl & grn .90 .65
330 A142 3c pale gray, bl & ind 1.10 .80

Water '70 campaign of the South African Department of Water Affairs.

Bible Society Types of South Africa

Designs: 2½c, Sower, stained glass window. 12½c, "BIBLIA" and open book.

1970, Aug. 24 Photo. *Perf. 14*
331 A143 2½c multicolored 1.00 .55

Photo.; Gold Impressed
332 A144 12½c ultra, blk & gold 9.50 8.00

South African Bible Soc., 150th anniv.

Stamp Exhibition Types of South Africa
Perf. 14x13½, 13½x14
1971, May 31 Photo. Wmk. 359
333 A145 5c blue, yel & blk 4.75 3.25
334 A146 12½c grnsh bl, vio bl & red 55.00 27.50

Intl. Stamp Exhib. (INTERSTEX), Cape Town, May 22-31. No. 334 also for the 10th anniv. of the Antarctic Treaty pledging peaceful uses of and scientific cooperation in Antarctica.

Republic Anniversary Types of South Africa
1971, May 31 *Perf. 14*
335 A147 2c mag, rose red & buff 2.75 1.10
336 A148 4c blue green & black 4.75 1.40

10th anniv. of the Republic of South Africa.

Cat Type of South Africa
1972, Sept. 19 *Perf. 14*
337 A152 5c multicolored 2.00 1.40

Cent. of the SPCA.

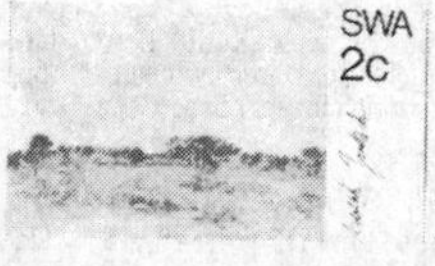

Landscape, by Adolph Jentsch
A69

Designs: Various landscapes by Adolph Jentsch (1888-). 10c, 15c, vert.

Perf. 11½x12½
1973, Apr. 28 Litho.
338 A69 2c multicolored .85 .85
339 A69 4c multicolored 2.00 2.00
340 A69 5c multicolored 2.50 2.50
341 A69 10c multicolored 5.50 5.50
342 A69 15c multicolored 8.25 8.25
Nos. 338-342 (5) 19.10 19.10

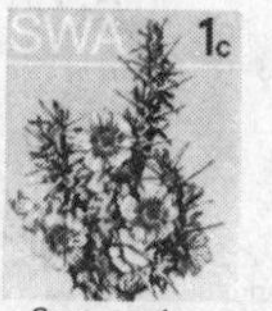

Sarcocaulon Rigidum
A70

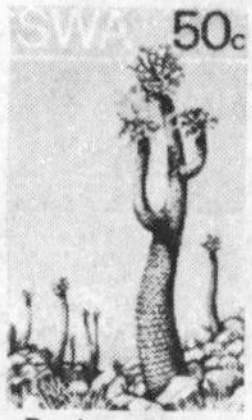

Pachypodium Namaqua-num
A71

Designs: 1c-50c, Various succulent plants. 1r, Welwitschia. 30c, 1r, horiz.

1973, Sept. 1 Litho. *Perf. 12½*
Plants in Natural Colors
343 A70 1c light blue .20 .16
344 A70 2c yellow .20 .16
345 A70 3c salmon pink .20 .16
346 A70 4c gray .25 .16
347 A70 5c blue .30 .18
348 A70 6c greenish gray .40 .18
349 A70 7c bright yellow .45 .20
350 A70 9c dull yellow .50 .20
351 A70 10c blue green .55 .22
352 A70 14c yellow green .80 .38
353 A70 15c light brown 1.10 .38
354 A70 20c light olive 1.25 .45
355 A70 25c orange 1.65 .55

Perf. 12x12½, 12½x12
356 A71 30c dull yellow 2.00 .60
357 A71 50c light green 3.50 1.10
358 A71 1r blue green 7.00 2.25
Nos. 343-358 (16) 20.35 7.33

1979 Same Designs *Perf. 14*
344a A70 2c .15 .15
345a A70 3c .18 .16
347a A70 5c .42 .42
351a A70 10c .60 .60
356a A70 30c 3.00 3.00
357a A70 50c 2.75 2.75
Nos. 344a-357a (6) 7.10 7.08

Coil Stamps
1973, Sept. 1 Photo. *Perf. 14*
359 A70 1c brt pink & black .15 .15
360 A70 2c yellow & black .15 .15
361 A70 5c red & black .30 .30
Set value .50 .50

1978 *Perf. 14 Vertically*
361A A70 1c brt pink & black 1.75 1.75
362 A70 2c yellow & black .15 .15
362A A70 5c red & black .15 .15
Nos. 361A-362A (3) 2.05 2.05

See Nos. 423-428.

NOTE: coil stamps, Nos. 359-362A, are printed in two colors, sheet stamps are multicolored.

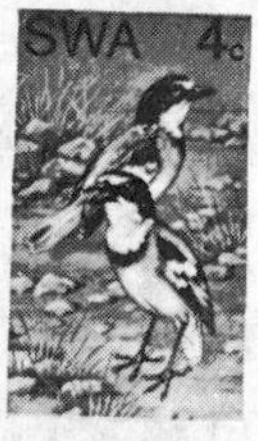

Chat-shrike — A72

Designs: Rare birds.

Perf. 12½x11½
1974, Feb. 13 Litho.
363 A72 4c shown 2.75 2.25
364 A72 5c Rosy-faced lovebirds 4.00 2.75
365 A72 10c Damara rockjumper 9.00 8.00
366 A72 15c Ruppell's parrot 16.00 12.50
Nos. 363-366 (4) 31.75 25.50

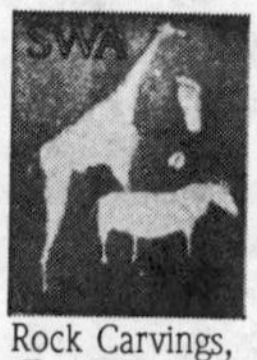

Rock Carvings, Twyfelfontein
A73

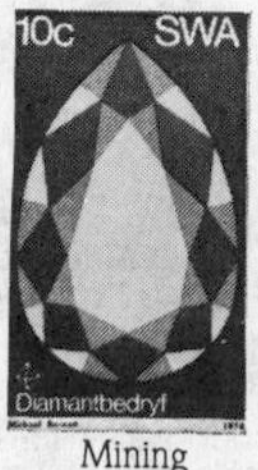

Mining
A74

1974, Apr. 10 Litho. *Perf. 12½*
367 A73 4c Giraffe & horse 1.90 .90
368 A73 5c Elephant 2.50 1.25

Perf. 12x12½
Size: 37x21½mm
369 A73 15c Deer, horiz. 11.50 5.50
Nos. 367-369 (3) 15.90 7.65

1974, Sept. 30 *Perf. 12½x11½*
370 A74 10c Diamonds 3.00 2.00
371 A74 15c Diamond washing diagram 4.25 3.00

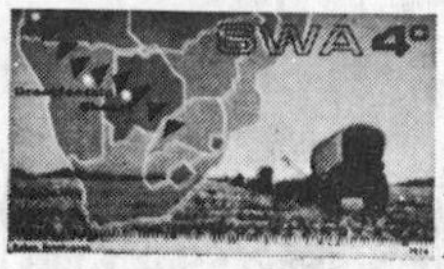

Map Showing Route, Covered Wagons
A75

Perf. 11½x12
1974, Nov. 13 Unwmk.
372 A75 4c yellow & multi 1.25 .85

Centenary of "Thirstland Trek" from Transvaal through Kalahari Desert to Angola.

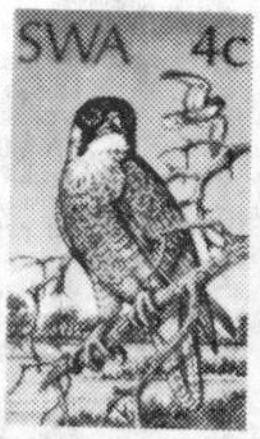

Peregrine Falcon — A76

Designs: Protected Birds of Prey.

1975, Mar. 19 *Perf. 12½x11½*
373 A76 4c shown 1.90 1.00
374 A76 5c Black eagle 2.50 1.25
375 A76 10c Martial eagle 5.50 2.75
376 A76 15c Egyptian vulture 7.50 4.25
Nos. 373-376 (4) 17.40 9.25

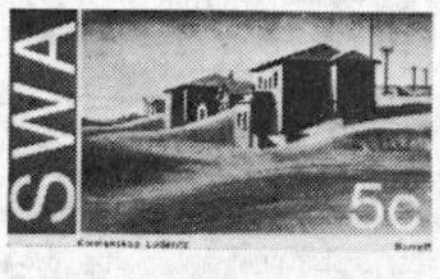

Kolmanskop, Ghost Diamond Mining Town — A77

Designs: 9c, German steam traction engine, 1896. 15c, Old Fort, Windhoek and statue of Colonial German trooper on horseback.

1975, July 23 Litho. *Perf. 12x12½*
377 A77 5c violet & multi .35 .30
378 A77 9c ocher & multi .75 .75
379 A77 15c yellow & multi 1.25 1.25
Nos. 377-379 (3) 2.35 2.30

Historic monuments.

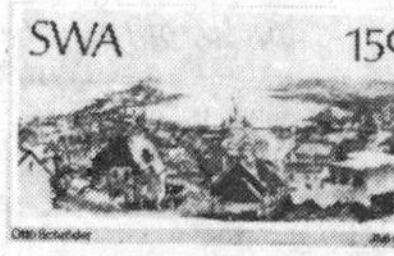

Swakopmund, by Otto Schröder — A78

Paintings by Otto Schröder (1913-75).

1975, Oct. 15 Litho. *Perf. 12x12½*
380 A78 15c shown 1.50 1.40
381 A78 15c Luderitz 1.50 1.40
382 A78 15c Unloading freighters 1.50 1.40
383 A78 15c Ships at anchor, Walvis Bay 1.50 1.40
a. Souvenir sheet of 4, #380-383 7.00 7.00
b. Block of 4, #380-383 6.00 6.00
Nos. 380-383 (4) 6.00 5.60

No. 383a has a horizontal gutter with black inscription on silver panel.

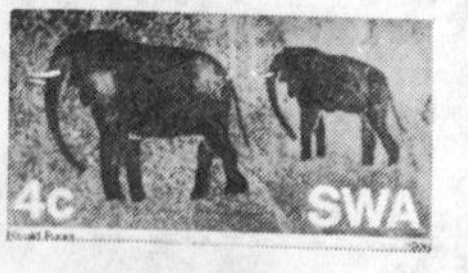

Elephants
A79

Pre-historic Rock Paintings: 10c, Rhinoceros. 15c, Deer and hunter. 20c, Hunter with bow and arrow.

1976, Mar. 12 Litho. *Perf. 12x12½*

384	A79	4c red brown & multi	.27	.22
385	A79	10c red brown & multi	.65	.65
386	A79	15c red brown & multi	1.00	1.00
387	A79	20c red brown & multi	1.65	1.65
a.		Souvenir sheet of 4, #384-387	6.25	6.25
		Nos. 384-387 (4)	3.57	3.52

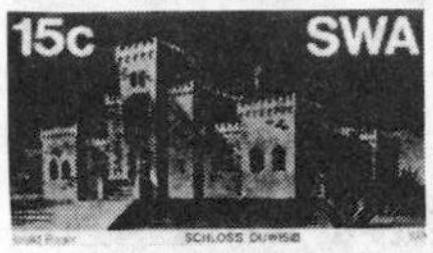

Schloss Duwisib A80

Castles Built by German Settlers: 10c, Schwerinsburg. 20c, Heynitzburg.

1976, May 14 Litho. *Perf. 12x12½*

388	A80	10c multicolored	.60	.60
389	A80	15c multicolored	.90	.90
390	A80	20c multicolored	1.25	1.25
		Nos. 388-390 (3)	2.75	2.75

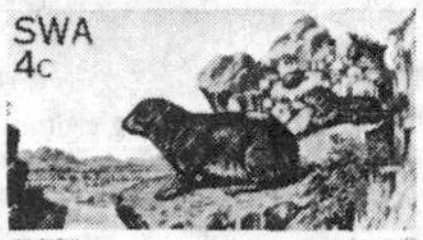

Nature Protection A81

Perf. 11½x12½

1976, July 16 Litho.

391	A81	4c Daman	.35	.22
392	A81	10c Dik-diks	.90	.70
393	A81	15c Tree squirrel	1.40	1.10
		Nos. 391-393 (3)	2.65	2.02

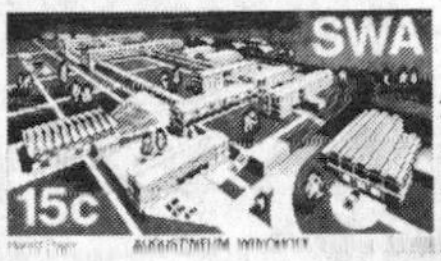

Augustineum Training Institute, Windhoek A82

Design: 20c, Katutura State Hospital, Windhoek.

1976, Sept. 17 Litho. *Perf. 12x12½*

394	A82	15c ocher & black	.60	.60
395	A82	20c citron & black	.80	.80

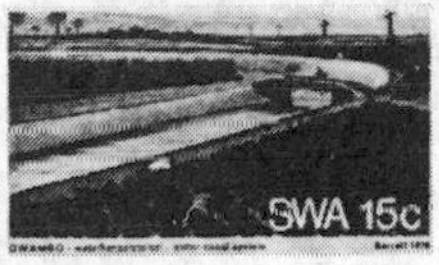

Owambo Canal System A83

Design: 20c, Ruacana Dam and hydroelectric station.

1976, Nov. 19 Litho. *Perf. 12x12½*

396	A83	15c multicolored	.60	.60
397	A83	20c multicolored	.80	.80

Water and electricity supply.

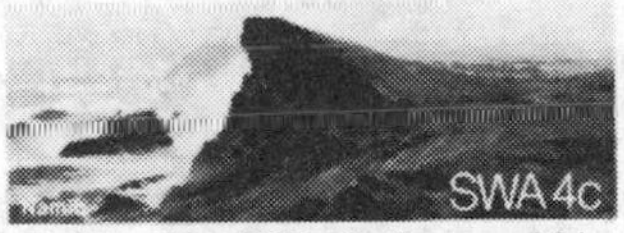

Sinking Ship off Namib Shore — A84

Designs: Namib Desert, various views.

1977, Mar. 29 Litho. *Perf. 12½*

398	A84	4c multicolored	.25	.16
399	A84	10c multicolored	.60	.50
400	A84	15c multicolored	.85	.75
401	A84	20c multicolored	1.25	1.10
		Nos. 398-401 (4)	2.95	2.51

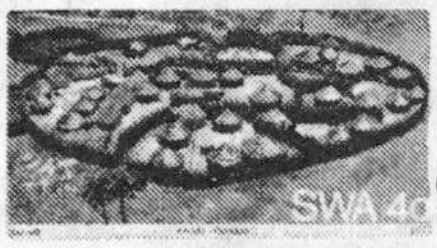
Owambo Kraal — A85

Designs: 10c, Giant grain baskets. 15c, Women pounding corn. 20c, Body painting.

1977, July 15 Litho. *Perf. 12x12½*

402	A85	4c multicolored	.16	.15
403	A85	10c multicolored	.42	.42
404	A85	15c multicolored	.60	.60
405	A85	20c multicolored	.85	.85
		Nos. 402-405 (4)	2.03	2.02

Traditions of the Wambo people.

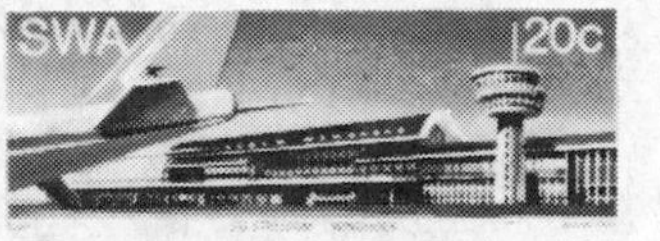

J. G. Strijdom Airport, Windhoek — A86

1977, Aug. 22 *Perf. 12½*

406	A86	20c multicolored	.65	.65

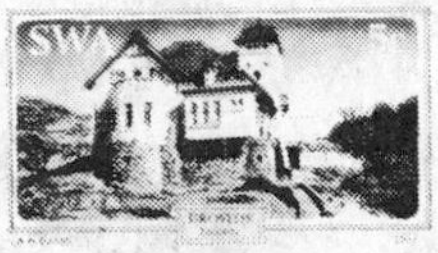

Drostdy, Lüderitz, 1910 — A87

Historic Houses: 10c, Woermannhaus, Swakopmund, 1895. 15c, Neu-Heusis, Windhoek. 20c, Schmelenhaus, Bethanie, 1814.

1977, Nov. 4 Litho. *Perf. 12x12½*

407	A87	5c multicolored	.20	.16
408	A87	10c multicolored	.40	.40
409	A87	15c multicolored	.60	.60
410	A87	20c multicolored	.80	.80
a.		Souvenir sheet of 4, #407-410	2.75	2.75
		Nos. 407-410 (4)	2.00	1.96

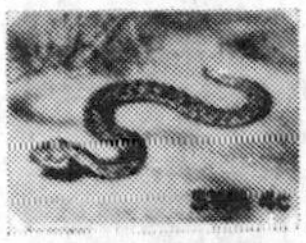

Side-winding Adder — A88

Small Animals of the Namib Desert: 10c, Golden sand mole. 15c, Palmato gecko. 20c, Namaqua chameleon.

1978, Feb. 6 Litho. *Perf. 12½*

411	A88	4c multicolored	.18	.15
412	A88	10c multicolored	.45	.45
413	A88	15c multicolored	.65	.65
414	A88	20c multicolored	.90	.90
		Nos. 411-414 (4)	2.18	2.15

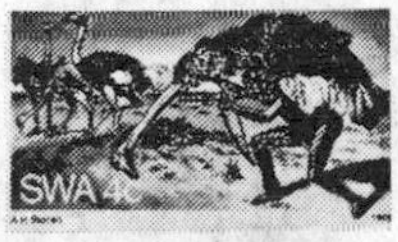

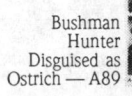

Bushman Hunter Disguised as Ostrich — A89

Bushmen: 10c, Woman carrying melons on back. 15c, Making fire. 20c, Family sitting in front of hut.

1978, Apr. 14 Litho. *Perf. 12x12½*

415	A89	4c brown, buff & blk	.15	.15
416	A89	10c brown, buff & blk	.35	.35
417	A89	15c brown, buff & blk	.55	.55
418	A89	20c brown, buff & blk	.70	.70
		Nos. 415-418 (4)	1.75	1.75

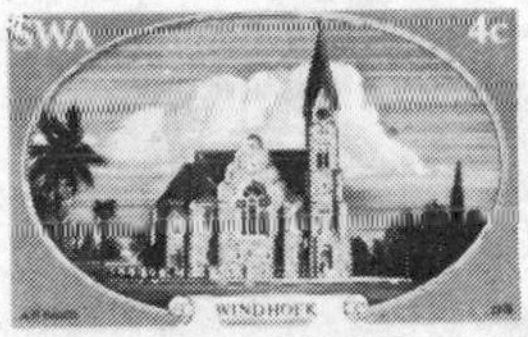

Lutheran Church, Windhoek — A90

Designs: 10c, Lutheran Church, Swakopmund. 15c, Rhenish Mission Church, Otjimbingwe. 20c, Rhenish Mission Church, Keetmanshoop.

1978, June 16 Litho. *Perf. 12½*

419	A90	4c ol bister & blk	.15	.15
420	A90	10c bister & blk	.40	.40
421	A90	15c pale red brn & blk	.60	.60
422	A90	20c blue gray & blk	.80	.80
a.		Souvenir sheet of 4, #419-422	2.50	2.50
		Nos. 419-422 (4)	1.95	1.95

Type of 1973 Inscribed in English, German or Afrikaans:

a, UNIVERSAL / SUFFRAGE
b, ALLGEMEINES / WAHLRECHT
c, ALGEMENE / STEMREG

1978, Nov. 1 Litho. *Perf. 12½*

423		Strip of 3	.25	.25
a.-c.		A70 4c any single	.15	.15
424		Strip of 3	.32	.32
a.-c.		A70 5c any single	.15	.15
425		Strip of 3	.60	.60
a.-c.		A70 10c any single	.20	.20
426		Strip of 3	.95	.95
a.-c.		A70 15c any single	.30	.30
427		Strip of 3	1.25	1.25
a.-c.		A70 20c any single	.40	.40
428		Strip of 3	1.65	1.65
a.-c.		A70 25c any single	.55	.55
		Nos. 423-428 (6)	5.02	5.02

General suffrage. Printed se-tenant with inscriptions alternating horizontally and vertically in sheets of 30 (3x10).

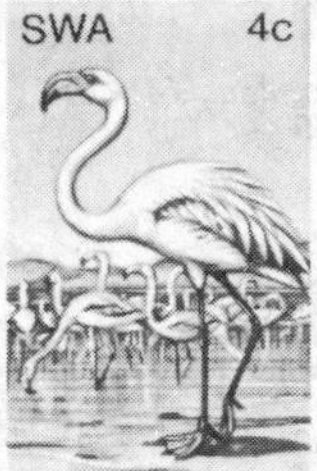

Greater Flamingoes — A91

Water Birds: 15c, White-breasted cormorants. 20c, Chestnut-banded plovers. 25c, White pelicans.

1979, Apr. 5 Litho. *Perf. 14x14½*

429	A91	4c multicolored	.15	.15
430	A91	15c multicolored	.45	.45
431	A91	20c multicolored	.60	.60
432	A91	25c multicolored	.75	.75
		Nos. 429-432 (4)	1.95	1.95

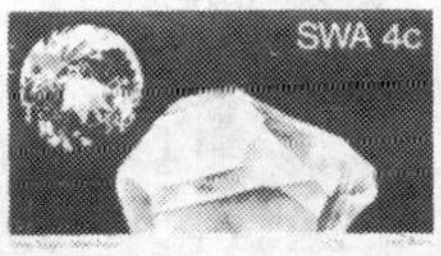

Silver Topaz — A92

1979, Nov. 26 Litho. *Perf. 14x14½*

433	A92	4c shown	.15	.15
434	A92	15c Aquamarine	.40	.40
435	A92	20c Malachite	.60	.60
436	A92	25c Amethyst	.70	.70
		Nos. 433-436 (4)	1.85	1.85

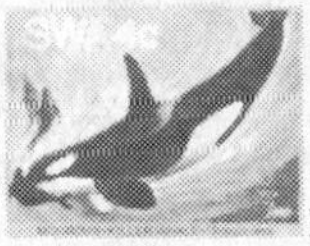
Killer Whale — A93

1980, Mar. 25 Litho. *Perf. 14x14½*

437	A93	4c shown	.25	.16

Size: 37½x21mm

438	A93	5c Humpback whale	.25	.20
439	A93	10c Southern right whale	.50	.42

Size: 57½x21mm

440	A93	15c Sperm whale, octopus	.85	.60
441	A93	20c Fin whale	1.10	.85

Size: 87½x21mm

442	A93	25c Blue whale, diver	1.25	1.00
a.		Souvenir sheet of 6, #437-442	3.75	3.75
		Nos. 437-442 (6)	4.20	3.23

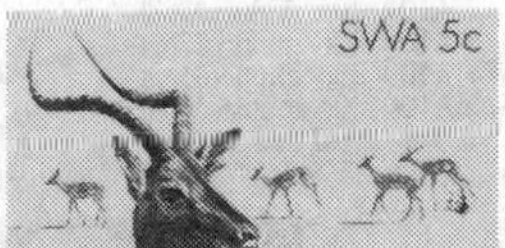

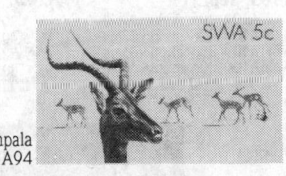

Impala A94

1980, June 25 Litho. *Perf. 14½x14*

443	A94	5c shown	.16	.16
444	A94	10c Roan antelope	.30	.30
445	A94	15c Tsessebe	.45	.45
446	A94	20c Black-nosed impala	.60	.60
		Nos. 443-446 (4)	1.51	1.51

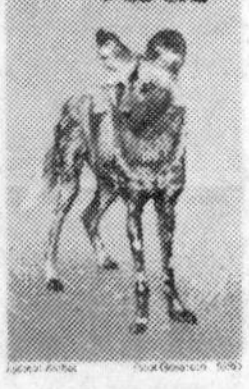

Cape Hunting Dog — A95

1980-85 Litho. *Perf. 14½x14*

447	A95	1c Black backed jackal	.15	.15
448	A95	2c shown	.15	.15
449	A95	3c Hyena	.15	.15
450	A95	4c Dorcas antelope	.15	.15
451	A95	5c Oryx	.15	.15
452	A95	6c Greater kudu	.15	.15

Perf. 14x14½

453	A95	7c Zebra, horiz.	.15	.15
454	A95	8c Porcupine, horiz.	.15	.15
455	A95	9c Honey badger, horiz.	.16	.16
456	A95	10c Cheetah, horiz.	.18	.18
456A	A95	11c Blue wildebeest ('84)	.15	.15
456B	A95	12c Syncerus caffer, horiz.	.15	.15
c.		Booklet pane of 10	.80	
457	A95	15c Hippopotamus, horiz.	.25	.25
458	A95	20c Taurotagus oryx, horiz.	.38	.38
459	A95	25c Rhinoceros, horiz.	.45	.45
460	A95	30c Lion, horiz.	.55	.55

Perf. 14½x14

461	A95	50c Giraffe	.95	.95
462	A95	1r Leopard	1.75	1.75
463	A95	2r Elephant	3.50	3.50
		Nos. 447-463 (19)	9.67	9.67

Coil Stamps

1980, Oct. 1 Litho. *Perf. 14 Vert.*

464	A95	1c Suricate suricate	.15	.15
465	A95	2c Guenon	.15	.15
466	A95	5c South African chacma	.18	.18
		Set value	.28	.28

See Nos. 556-557.

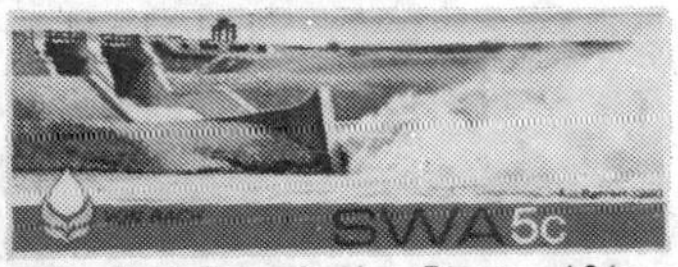

Von Bach Dam, Swakop River — A96

1980, Nov. 25 Litho. *Perf. 14x14½*

467	A96	5c shown	.15	.15
468	A96	10c Swakoppoort Dam	.25	.25
469	A96	15c Naute Dam	.35	.35
470	A96	20c Hardap Dam	.50	.50
		Nos. 467-470 (4)	1.25	1.25

Water conservation in the desert.

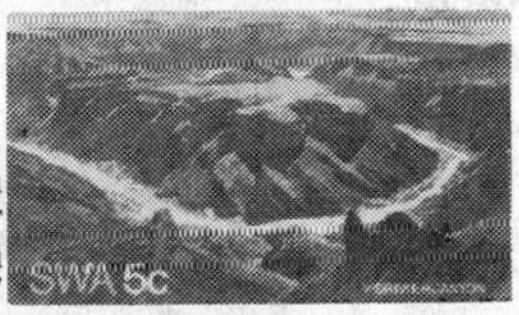

Fish River Canyon A97

Designs: Views of Fish River Canyon.

1981, Mar. 20 Litho. *Perf. 14½x14*

471	A97	5c multicolored	.15	.15
472	A97	15c multicolored	.28	.28
473	A97	20c multicolored	.40	.40
474	A97	25c multicolored	.50	.50
		Nos. 471-474 (4)	1.33	1.33

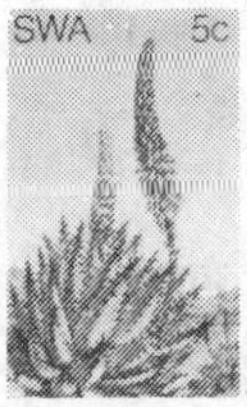

Aloe Erinacea — A98

1981, Aug. 14

475	A98	5c shown	.15	.15
476	A98	15c Aloe viridiflora	.28	.28
477	A98	20c Aloe pearsonii	.40	.40
478	A98	25c Aloe littoralis	.50	.50
		Nos. 475-478 (4)	1.33	1.33

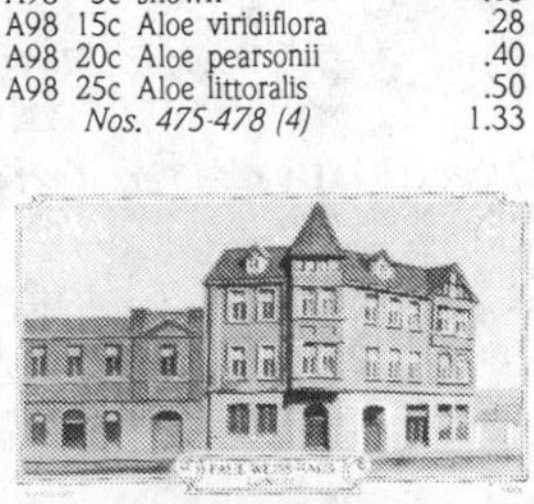
Paul Weiss-Haus Building, 1909, Luderitz — A99

Designs: Historic buildings in Luderitz.

1981, Oct. 16

479	A99	5c shown	.15	.15
480	A99	15c Deutsche Afrika Bank, 1906	.28	.28
481	A99	20c Schroederhaus, 1911	.40	.40

482 A99 25c Imperial P.O., 1908 .50 .50
   a. Souvenir sheet of 4, #479-482 1.40 1.40
     Nos. 479-482 (4) 1.33 1.33

Salt Making
A100

1981, Dec. 4 Litho. Perf. 14x14½
483 A100 5c Salt pan .15 .15
484 A100 15c Dumping and washing .28 .28
485 A100 20c Stockpiling .40 .40
486 A100 25c Loading .50 .50
     Nos. 483-486 (4) 1.33 1.33

Kalahari
Starred
Tortoise
A101

1982, Mar. 12
487 A101 5c shown .15 .15
488 A101 15c Leopard tortoise .28 .28
489 A101 20c Angulated tortoise .40 .40
490 A101 25c Speckled padloper .50 .50
     Nos. 487-490 (4) 1.33 1.33

Discoverers of South-West Africa — A102

1982, May 28 Litho. Perf. 14½x14
491 A102 15c Archbishop Olaus
     Magnus, sea monster .25 .25
492 A102 20c Bartolomeu Dias,
     ships, map .38 .38
493 A102 25c Caravel .45 .45
494 A102 30c Dias erecting cross,
     Angra das Voltas .55 .55
     Nos. 491-494 (4) 1.63 1.63

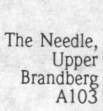

The Needle,
Upper
Brandberg
A103

Designs: Mountain peaks.

1982, Aug. 3 Litho. Perf. 14x14½
495 A103 6c Brandberg .15 .15
496 A103 15c Omatako twin peaks .28 .28
497 A103 20c shown .38 .38
498 A103 25c Spitzkuppe, Karakul
     sheep .45 .45
     Nos. 495-498 (4) 1.26 1.26

Traditional
Headdress, Herero
Tribe — A104

1982, Oct. 15 Litho. Perf. 14x14½
499 A104 6c shown .15 .15
500 A104 15c Himba .28 .28
501 A104 20c Ngandjera .38 .38
502 A104 25c Kwanyama .45 .45
     Nos. 499-502 (4) 1.26 1.26

See Nos. 524-527.

Fort
Vogelsang
A105

Bethany Chief Joseph
Fredericks — A106

**Perf. 14x14½ (6c, 25c), 14½x14
(20c, 30-40c)**

1983, Mar. 16
503 A105 6c shown .15 .15
504 A106 20c shown .38 .38
505 A105 25c Angra Pequena Bay .45 .45
506 A106 30c Explorer Heinrich
     Vogelsang .55 .55
507 A106 40c Adolf Luderitz (1834-
     1886) .75 .75
     Nos. 503-507 (5) 2.28 2.28

City of Luderitz centenary (1982).

Diamond
Field, 1908
A107

Ernest Oppenheimer
(1880-1957), Diamond
Industry Leader — A108

**Perf. 14x14½ (10-20c), 14½x14 (25-
40c)**

1983, June 8   Litho.
508 A107 10c shown .20 .20
509 A107 20c Field, diff. .40 .40
510 A108 25c shown .50 .50
511 A108 40c August Stauch, pros-
     pector .80 .80
     Nos. 508-511 (4) 1.90 1.90

75th anniv. of discovery of diamonds at Luderitz.

Zebras Drinking, by J.J. van Ellinckhuijzen
(b. 1940) — A109

Paintings: 20c, Rossing Mountain, by Herman
H.J. Henckert (b. 1906). 25c, Stampeding Buffalo,
by Fritz Krampe (1913-1966). 40c, Erongo Mountains, by Johann Blatt (1905-1973).

1983, Sept. 1   Perf. 14x14½
512 A109 10c multicolored .20 .20
513 A109 20c multicolored .40 .40
514 A109 25c multicolored .52 .52
515 A109 40c multicolored .80 .80
     Nos. 512-515 (4) 1.92 1.92

Lobster
Industry
A110

1983, Nov. 23   Perf. 13½x14
516 A110 10c Lobsters .20 .20
517 A110 20c Dinghies .40 .40
518 A110 25c Raising trap .50 .50
519 A110 40c Packaging .80 .80
     Nos. 516-519 (4) 1.90 1.90

Historic Buildings, Swakopmund — A111

1984, Mar. 8 Litho. Perf. 14x13½
520 A111 10c Hohenzollern House .20 .20
521 A111 20c Railway Station .40 .40
522 A111 25c Imperial District Bu-
     reau .50 .50
523 A111 30c Ritterburg .60 .60
     Nos. 520-523 (4) 1.70 1.70

Headdress Type of 1982

1984, May 25   Litho.
524 A104 11c Kwambi .22 .22
525 A104 20c Bushman .40 .40
526 A104 25c Kwaluudhi .50 .50
527 A104 30c Mbukushu .60 .60
     Nos. 524-527 (4) 1.72 1.72

German
Colonization
Centenary
A112

1984, Aug. 7 Litho. Perf. 13½x14
528 A112 11c Map, flag .25 .25
529 A112 25c Flag raising .60 .60
530 A112 30c Land marker .70 .70
531 A112 45c Corvettes Elisabeth &
     Leipzig 1.10 1.10
     Nos. 528-531 (4) 2.65 2.65

Spring Flowers — A113

1984, Nov. 22 Litho. Perf. 14½x14
532 A113 11c Sweet thorn .24 .24
533 A113 25c Camel thorn .55 .55
534 A113 30c Hook thorn .65 .65
535 A113 45c Candle-pod acacia 1.00 1.00
     Nos. 532-535 (4) 2.44 2.44

Ostrich — A114

1985, Mar. 15
536 A114 11c Head of bird .30 .30
537 A114 25c Female nesting .75 .75
538 A114 30c Chick, eggs .90 .90
539 A114 50c Male mating dance 1.50 1.50
     Nos. 536-539 (4) 3.45 3.45

Historic Buildings, 1900-1912,
Windhoek — A115

1985, June 6
540 A115 12c Erkrath, Gathemann
     Buildings, Kaiser
     Street .20 .20
541 A115 25c Gymnasium .42 .42
542 A115 30c Supreme Court .50 .50
543 A115 50c Railway Station .85 .85
     Nos. 540-543 (4) 1.97 1.97

600mm
Narrow-gauge
Locomotives
A116

1985, Aug. 2
544 A116 12c Zwilling Schmalspur,
     1898 .24 .24
545 A116 25c Feldspur Side-Tank .52 .52
546 A116 30c 0-6-2 Side-Tank, 1904 .60 .60
547 A116 50c Henschel hd Smal-
     spoor, 1912 1.10 1.10
     Nos. 544-547 (4) 2.46 2.46

Swakopmund-Tsumeb Railway line, 79th anniv.

Endemic
Musical
Instruments
A117

1985, Oct. 17
548 A117 12c Lidumu-dumu .18 .18
549 A117 25c Ngoma .35 .35
550 A117 30c Okambulum bumbwa .42 .42
551 A117 50c Gwashi .70 .70
     Nos. 548-551 (4) 1.65 1.65

Diogo Cao,
Portuguese
Explorer, 1486
Visit to
SWA — A118

1986, Jan. 24   Perf. 14½x14
552 A118 12c Erecting padroes on
     shore .30 .30
553 A118 20c Cao coat of arms .55 .55
554 A118 25c Caravel .70 .70
555 A118 30c Portrait .90 .90
     Nos. 552-555 (4) 2.45 2.45

Wildlife Type of 1980

1986-87 Litho. Perf. 14x14½
556 A95 14c Caracal, horiz. .20 .20
557 A95 16c Warthog, horiz. .20 .20

Issue dates: 14c, Apr. 1; 16c, Apr. 1, 1987.

Rock
Formations
A119

Designs: 14c, Granite bornhardt, Erongo. 20c,
Vingerklip, Outjo. 25c, Aeolian sandstone, Kuiseb
River. 30c, Columnar dolerite, Twifelfontein.

1986, Apr. 24   Perf. 14½x14
566 A119 14c multicolored .28 .28
567 A119 20c multicolored .45 .45
568 A119 25c multicolored .52 .52
569 A119 30c multicolored .75 .75
     Nos. 566-569 (4) 2.00 2.00

Karakul Wool
(Swakara)
Industry — A120

1986, July 10   Perf. 14x14½
570 A120 14c Model .24 .24
571 A120 20c Hand loom .35 .35
572 A120 25c Sheep .45 .45
573 A120 30c Rams .55 .55
   a. Souvenir sheet of 1 2.75 2.75
     Nos. 570-573 (4) 1.59 1.59

No. 573a margin pictures design of No. 570 and
Johannesburg stamp exhib. emblem. Sold for 50c to
benefit stamp exhib.

Caprivi
Strip — A121

1986, Nov. 6 Litho. Perf. 14½x14
574 A121 14c Lake Liambezi .22 .22
575 A121 20c Stock and crop farm-
     ing .35 .35
576 A121 25c Settlement .42 .42
577 A121 30c Map .55 .55
     Nos. 574-577 (4) 1.54 1.54

Paintings by Thomas Baines (1820-1875)
A122

Designs: 14c, *Rhenish Mission Church at Gababis*, 1863. 20c, *Outspan in October*, 1861. 25c, *Outspan Under Oomahaama Tree*, 1862. 30c, *Swa-Kop River S.W. Africa*, 1861.

1987, Feb. 19 Litho. *Perf. 14½x14*

578 A122 14c multicolored	.30	.30
579 A122 20c multicolored	.45	.45
580 A122 25c multicolored	.55	.55
a. Souvenir sheet of 1	2.75	2.75
581 A122 30c multicolored	.70	.70
Nos. 578-581 (4)	2.00	2.00

No. 580a for the natl. philatelic exhibition at Paarl, Sept. 16-19. Sold for 50c.

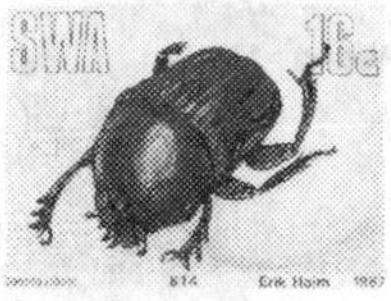

Insects
A123

1987, May 7

582 A123 16c *Garreta nitens*	.45	.45
583 A123 20c *Alcimus stenurus*	.55	.55
584 A123 25c *Anthophora caerulea*	.70	.70
585 A123 30c *Hemiempusa capensis*	.85	.85
Nos. 582-585 (4)	2.55	2.55

Resorts
A124

1987, July 23

586 A124 16c Okaukuejo, Etosha Natl. Park	.40	.40
587 A124 20c Daan Viljoen Game Park	.50	.50
588 A124 25c Ai-Ais Hot Springs	.60	.60
589 A124 30c Hardap, Mariental	.70	.70
Nos. 586-589 (4)	2.20	2.20

Shipwrecks
A125

1987, Oct. 15

590 A125 16c *Hope*, 1804	.35	.35
591 A125 30c *Tilly*, 1885	.70	.70
592 A125 40c *Eduard Bohlen*, 1909	.90	.90
593 A125 50c *Dunedin Star*, 1942	1.25	1.25
Nos. 590-593 (4)	3.20	3.20

Discovery of the Cape of Good Hope by Bartolomeu Dias, 500th Anniv. — A126

1988, Jan. 7 *Perf. 14x14½*

594 A126 16c shown	.38	.38
595 A126 30c Caravel	.70	.70
596 A126 40c The Cantino Map, 1502	1.00	1.00
597 A126 50c King John II	1.25	1.25
Nos. 594-597 (4)	3.33	3.33

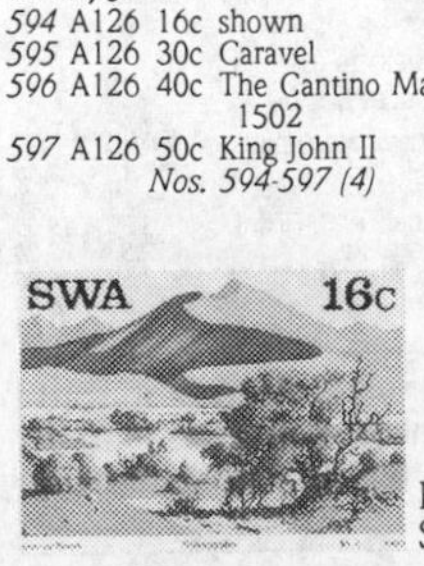

Historic Sites — A127

1988, Mar. 3 *Perf. 14½x14*

598 A127 16c Sossusvlei Clay Pans	.35	.35
599 A127 30c Sesriem Canyon	.60	.60
600 A127 40c Hoaruseb clay castles	.80	.80
601 A127 50c Hoba meteorite	1.25	1.25
Nos. 598-601 (4)	3.00	3.00

Postal Service, Cent.
A128

1988, July 7 *Perf. 14x14½*

602 A128 16c Otyimbingue P.O., 1888	.32	.32
603 A128 30c Windhoek P.O., 1904	.60	.60
604 A128 40c Mail runner, 1888	.80	.80
605 A128 50c Camel post, 1904	1.00	1.00
a. Souvenir sheet of 1	2.75	2.75
Nos. 602-605 (4)	2.72	2.72

No. 605a for the natl. philatelic exhibition held at Windhoek, July 7-9. Sold for 1r.

Birds — A129

1988, Nov. 3

606 A129 16c *Namibornis hereo*	.45	.45
607 A129 30c *Ammomanes grayi*	1.00	1.00
608 A129 40c *Eupodotis rueppellii*	1.25	1.25
609 A129 50c *Tockus monteiri*	1.65	1.65
Nos. 606-609 (4)	4.35	4.35

Missionaries and Mission Stations
A130

Designs: 16c, Carl Hahn (1818-1895) and Gross-Barmen Mission. 30c, Johann Kronlein (1826-1892) and Berseba Mission. 40c, Franz Kleinschmidt (1812-1864) and Rehoboth Mission. 50c, Johann Schmelen (1777-1848) and Bethanien Mission.

1989, Feb. 16

610 A130 16c multicolored	.32	.32
611 A130 30c multicolored	.55	.55
612 A130 40c multicolored	.75	.75
613 A130 50c multicolored	1.00	1.00
Nos. 610-613 (4)	2.62	2.62

Aviation Industry, 75th Anniv.
A131

Maps and aircraft.

1989, May 18 *Perf. 14½x14*

614 A131 18c Beechcraft 1900, 1988	.30	.30
615 A131 30c Ryan Navion, 1948	.45	.45
616 A131 40c Junkers F13, 1930	.60	.60
617 A131 50c Pfalz Otto biplane, 1914	.80	.80
a. Souvenir sheet of 1	3.00	3.00
Nos. 614-617 (4)	2.15	2.15

No. 617a has decorative bright blue and black inscribed margin picturing emblem of natl. philatelic exhibition WANDERERS 101, held Sept. 6-9. Sold for 1.50r.

Namib Desert Sand Dunes — A132

1989, Aug. 14 *Perf. 14x14½*
Size of 30c, 50c: 31x21½mm

618 A132 18c Barchan dunes	.32	.32
619 A132 30c Star dunes	.52	.52
620 A132 40c Transverse dunes	.75	.75
621 A132 50c Crescent dunes	.90	.90
Nos. 618-621 (4)	2.49	2.49

Suffrage, UN Resolution
435 — A133

1989, Aug. 24

622 A133 18c dull orange & gray vio	.30	.30
623 A133 35c green & blue	.60	.60
624 A133 45c yellow & purple	.85	.85
625 A133 60c golden brn & gray grn	1.25	1.25
Nos. 622-625 (4)	3.00	3.00

Minerals A134 — Mines A135

1989, Nov. 16-90 *Perf. 14½x14*

626 A134 1c Gypsum	.15	.15
627 A134 2c Fluorite	.15	.15
628 A134 5c Mimetite	.15	.15
629 A134 7c Cuprite	.15	.15
630 A134 10c Azurite	.15	.15
631 A134 18c Boltwoodite	.18	.18
631A A134 18c see footnote		
632 A134 20c Dioptase	.20	.20
633 A135 25c Alluvial diamond field, Oranjemund	.25	.25
634 A135 30c Lead, copper & zinc mine, Tsumeb	.30	.30
635 A135 35c Zinc mine, Rosh Pinah	.35	.35
636 A134 40c Diamonds	.40	.40
637 A134 45c Wulfenite	.45	.45
638 A135 50c Tin mine, Uis	.50	.50
639 A135 1r Uranium mine, Rossing	1.00	1.00
640 A134 2r Gold	2.00	2.00
Nos. 626-640 (15)	6.38	6.38

No. 631 has formula, K(H3O)(UO2)(SiO4), No. 631A has K2(UO2)2(SiO3)2(OH)2.5H2O.

No. 631A was issued Oct. 25, 1990. This set remained in use until Namibia issued a definitive set Jan. 2, 1991.

Flora — A136

1990, Feb. 1 *Perf. 14½x14*

641 A136 18c *Adenium boehmianum*	.24	.24
642 A136 35c *Adansonia digitata*	.48	.48
643 A136 45c *Kigelia africana*	.62	.62
644 A136 60c *Harpagophytum procumbens*	.85	.85
a. Souvenir sheet of 1	2.50	2.50
Nos. 641-644 (4)	2.19	2.19

No. 644a margin publicizes the natl. phil. exhib. Sold for 1.50r.

SEMI-POSTAL STAMPS

Catalogue values for unused stamps in this section are for Never Hinged items.

Voortrekker Monument Issue
South Africa Nos. B1-B4 Overprinted **S.W.A.**

1935-36 Wmk. 201 *Perf. 14*

B1 SP1 ½p + ½p grn & blk, pair	2.00	*4.50*
a. Single, English	.25	*.60*
b. Single, Afrikaans	.25	*.60*
B2 SP2 1p + ½p rose & blk, pair	2.75	4.25
a. Single, English	.30	.40
b. Single, Afrikaans	.30	.40
B3 SP3 2p + 1p dl vio & gray, pair	9.00	10.00
a. Single, English	.75	.85
b. Single, Afrikaans	.75	.85
B4 SP4 3p + 1½p dp bl & gray, pair	16.00	*22.50*
a. Single, English	1.50	*3.00*
b. Single, Afrikaans	1.50	*3.00*
Nos. B1-B4 (4)	29.75	*41.25*

Voortrekker Centenary Issue
South Africa Nos. B5-B8 Overprinted **S.W.A.**

1938, Dec. 14 *Perf. 14*

B5 SP5 ½p + ½p dl grn & indigo, pair	7.25	7.25
a. Single, English	.75	1.25
b. Single, Afrikaans	.75	1.25
Perf. 15x14		
B6 SP6 1p + 1p rose & sl, pair	15.00	6.00
a. Single, English	1.00	.75
b. Single, Afrikaans	1.00	.75
B7 SP7 1½p + 1½p Prus grn & choc, pair	20.00	17.00
a. Single, English	1.25	2.00
b. Single, Afrikaans	1.25	2.00
B8 SP8 3p + 3p chlky bl, pair	40.00	42.50
a. Single, English	2.75	5.00
b. Single, Afrikaans	2.75	5.00
Nos. B5-B8 (4)	82.25	72.75

Same Overprint on South Africa Nos. B9-B11

1939, July 17 *Perf. 14*

B9 SP9 ½p + ½p Prus grn & gray brn, pair	6.00	6.00
a. Single, English	.65	.85
b. Single, Afrikaans	.65	.85
B10 SP10 1p + 1p rose car & Prus grn, pair	10.00	8.50
a. Single, English	.75	1.25
b. Single, Afrikaans	.75	1.25
Perf. 15x14		
B11 SP11 1½p + 1½p rose vio, dk vio & Prus grn, pair	15.00	11.50
a. Single, English	1.25	1.25
b. Single, Afrikaans	1.25	1.25
Nos. B9-B11 (3)	31.00	26.00

250th anniv. of the landing of the Huguenots in South Africa. Surtax went to a fund to build a Huguenot memorial at Paarl.

AIR POST STAMPS

South Africa Nos. C5-C6 Overprinted **S.W.A.**

1930 Unwmk. *Perf. 14x13½*

C1 AP2 4p blue green	9.00	*17.50*
a. Without period after "A"	80.00	110.00
C2 AP2 1sh orange	17.00	*35.00*
a. Without period after "A"	425.00	*500.00*

Overprinted **S.W.A.**

C3 AP2 4p blue green	2.25	*5.00*
a. Double overprint	150.00	
b. Inverted overprint	150.00	
c. Small "I" in "AIR"	6.00	
C4 AP2 1sh orange	4.00	*12.50*
a. Double overprint	550.00	

Monoplane over Windhoek — AP3   Biplane over Windhoek — AP4

Wmk. 201

1931, Mar. 5 Engr. *Perf. 14*

C5 AP3 3p blue & dk brn, pair	25.00	*35.00*
a. Single, English	2.00	*3.00*
b. Single, Afrikaans	2.00	*3.00*
C6 AP4 10p brn vio & blk, pair	40.00	*75.00*
a. Single, English	3.00	*7.50*
b. Single, Afrikaans	3.00	*7.50*

POSTAGE DUE STAMPS

Postage Due Stamps of South Africa and Transvaal Overprinted like Regular Issues.

Setting I

On South Africa Nos. J11, J14

1923 Unwmk. *Perf. 14*

J1 D1 ½p blue grn & blk, pair 3.00 *15.00*
a. Single, English .35 *4.00*
b. Single, Dutch .35 *4.00*
c. As #J1, without period after "Afrika" 100.00
d. Inverted ovpt., pair 325.00
J2 D1 2p violet & blk, pair 2.00 2.00
a. Single, English .20 .20
b. Single, Dutch .20 .20
c. As #J2, without period after "Afrika" 70.00 70.00

On South Africa Nos. J9-J10

Rouletted 7-8

J3 D1 1p dull red & blk, pair 6.00 6.00
a. Single, English .15 .15
b. Single, Dutch .15 .15
c. As #J3, without period after "Afrika" 70.00 70.00
d. Pair, imperf. between 825.00
J4 D1 1½p yel brn & blk, pair 1.00 1.00
a. Single, English .15 .15
b. Single, Dutch .15 .15
c. As #J4, without period after "Afrika" 42.50 42.50

On South Africa Nos. J3-J4, J6

Perf. 14

Wmk. 177

J5 D1 2p violet & blk, pair 17.00 *27.50*
a. Single, English 1.75 *7.50*
b. Single, Dutch 1.75 *7.50*
c. As #J5, without period after "Afrika" 150.00
J6 D1 3p ultra & blk, pair 7.50 *27.50*
a. Single, English .85 *7.50*
b. Single, Dutch .85 *7.50*
J7 D1 6p gray & blk, pair 23.00 *40.00*
a. Single, English 2.50 *12.50*
b. Single, Dutch 2.50 *12.50*
Nos. J1-J7 (7) 59.50 *118.70*

On Transvaal Nos. J5-J6

Wmk. Multiple Crown and C A (3)

J8 D1 5p violet & blk, pair 4.00 *27.50*
a. Single, English .50 *7.50*
b. Single, Dutch .50 *7.50*
c. As #J8, without period after "Afrika" 85.00 85.00
J9 D1 6p red brn & blk, pair 17.00 *27.50*
a. Single, Dutch 1.75 *7.50*
b. As #J9, without period after "Afrika" 77.50

For No. J9 single in English see No. J17a and note after No. 27.

The "t" of "West" may be found partly or entirely missing on Nos. J1, J3-J6, J8-J9.

Setting II

On South Africa No. J9

Rouletted

Unwmk.

J10 D1 1p dull red & blk, pair *8,000.*
a. Single, English 800.00 —
b. Single, Dutch 800.00 —

On South Africa Nos. J3-J4

Perf. 14

Wmk. 177

J11 D1 2p violet & blk, pair 12.00 *25.00*
a. Single, English 1.25 *7.00*
b. Single, Dutch 1.25 *7.00*
c. As #J11, without period after "Afrika" 110.00 125.00
J12 D1 3p ultra & blk, pair 7.00 20.00
a. Single, English .75 5.00
b. Single, Dutch .75 5.00
c. As #J12, without period after "Afrika" 70.00 80.00

On Transvaal No. J5

Wmk. Multiple Crown and C A (3)

J13 D1 5p violet & blk, pair 75.00 110.00
a. Single, English 15.00
b. Single, Dutch 15.00

Setting III

On South Africa Nos. J11, J12, J9

Unwmk.

J14 D1 ½p blue grn & blk, pair 7.00 *17.50*
a. Single, Dutch .75 *4.50*
J15 D1 1p rose & black, pair 7.00 *17.50*
a. Single, English .75 *4.50*
b. Single, Dutch .75 *4.50*

Rouletted 7

J16 D1 1p dull red & blk, pair 2.00 *15.00*
a. Single, Dutch .15 *4.00*

For Nos. J14 and J16 singles in English see Nos. J1a and J3a and note after No. 27.

On Transvaal No. J6

Perf. 14

Wmk. 3

J17 D1 6p red brown & blk, pair 17.00 *60.00*
a. Single, English 1.75 *17.50*
b. Single, Dutch 1.75 *17.50*

See note below No. 27.

Setting IV

On South Africa Nos. J11-J12, J16

1924 Unwmk.

J18 D1 ½p blue grn & blk, pair 3.50 *20.00*
a. Single, English .45 *5.00*
b. Single, Dutch .45 *5.00*
J19 D1 1p rose & blk, pair 5.00 *20.00*
a. Single, English .60 *5.00*
b. Single, Dutch .60 *5.00*
J20 D1 6p gray & blk, pair 2.00 *27.50*
a. Single, English .30 *8.00*
b. Single, Dutch .30 *8.00*

On Transvaal No. J5

Wmk. Multiple Crown and C A (3)

J21 D1 5p violet & blk, pair 400.00 —
a. Single, English 100.00
b. Single, Dutch 100.00

Setting V

South West **Zuidwest**

Africa. **Afrika.**
i j

"South West" 16mm wide
"Zuidwest" 12mm wide
Overprint Spaced 12mm
On South Africa Nos. J4, J11, J13

1924 Unwmk.

J22 D1 ½p green & blk, pair 2.00 *22.50*
a. Single, English .25 *6.50*
b. Single, Dutch .25 *6.50*
J23 D1 1½p yel brown & blk 4.00 *22.50*
a. Single, English .50 *6.50*
b. Single, Dutch .50 *6.50*

Wmk. Springbok's Head (177)

J24 D1 3p ultra & black, pair 12.50 *37.50*
a. Single, English 1.40 *10.00*
b. Single, Dutch 1.40 *10.00*

On Transvaal No. J5

Wmk. Multiple Crown and C A (3)

J25 D1 5p violet & blk, pair 3.00 *25.00*
a. Single, English .40 *7.50*
b. Single, Dutch .40 *7.50*

Setting VI

On South Africa Nos. J4, J11-J16

1924, Dec. Unwmk.

J26 D1 ½p blue grn & blk, pair 5.00 *25.00*
a. Single, English .60 *6.00*
b. Single, Dutch .60 *6.00*
J27 D1 1p rose & black, pair 1.50 *7.50*
a. Single, English .15 *1.75*
b. Single, Dutch .15 *1.75*
c. As #J27, without period after "Africa" 87.50
J28 D1 1½p yel brown & blk, pair 2.50 *22.50*
a. Single, English .30 *5.50*
b. Single, Dutch .30 *5.50*
c. As #J28, without period after "Africa" 75.00
J29 D1 2p violet & blk, pair 2.50 *12.50*
a. Single, English .30 *3.00*
b. Single, Dutch .30 *3.00*
c. As #J29, without period after "Africa" 55.00
J30 D1 3p blue & black, pair 3.00 *15.00*
a. Single, English .75 *3.50*
b. Single, Dutch .75 *3.50*
c. As #J30, without period after "Africa" 70.00
J31 D1 6p gray & black, pair 8.00 *45.00*
a. Single, English 1.00 *12.50*
b. Single, Dutch 1.00 *12.50*
c. As #J31, without period after "Africa" 100.00
Nos. J26-J31 (6) 22.50 *127.50*

Wmk. Springbok's Head (177)

J32 D1 3p ultra & black, pair 6.00 *35.00*
a. Single, English .75 *9.00*
b. Single, Dutch .75 *9.00*

On Transvaal No. J5

Wmk. 3

J33 D1 5p violet & blk, pair 2.00 *12.50*
a. Single, English .25 *3.00*
b. Single, Dutch .25 *3.00*
c. As #J33, without period after "Africa" 55.00 *75.00*

Setting VIII

On South Africa Nos. J18, J13-J16

1927 Unwmk.

J34 D2 1p rose & black, pair .90 *9.00*
a. Single, English .15 *2.00*
b. Single, Afrikaans .15 *2.00*
c. As #J34, without period after "Africa" 10.50 *17.50*
J35 D1 1½p yel brown & blk, pair .90 *10.00*
a. Single, English .15 *2.50*
b. Single, Afrikaans .15 *2.50*
c. As #J35, without period after "Africa" 50.00 *60.00*
J36 D1 2p violet & blk, pair 2.50 *12.50*
a. Single, English .30 *3.25*
b. Single, Afrikaans .30 *3.25*
c. As #J36, without period after "Africa" 50.00 *60.00*
J37 D1 3p blue & black, pair 10.00 *40.00*
a. Single, English 1.25 *10.00*
b. Single, Afrikaans 1.25 *10.00*
c. As #J37, without period after "Africa" 70.00 70.00
J38 D1 6p gray & black, pair 7.50 *27.50*
a. Single, English 1.00 *8.00*
b. Single, Afrikaans 1.00 *8.00*
c. As #J38, without period after "Africa" 100.00 115.00
Nos. J34-J38 (5) 21.80 *99.00*

On Transvaal No. J5

Wmk. Multiple Crown and C A (3)

J39 D1 5p violet & blk, pair 16.00 *75.00*
a. Single, English 1.75 *20.00*
b. Single, Afrikaans 1.75 *20.00*

South Africa Nos. J15-J16 Overprinted **S.W.A.**

1928 Unwmk.

J79 D1 3p blue & black 1.65 *12.00*
a. Without period after "A" 30.00 35.00
J80 D1 6p gray & black 7.50 *22.50*
a. Without period after "A" 125.00

Same Overprint on South Africa Nos. J17-J21

J81 D2 ½p blue grn & blk .40 *6.00*
J82 D2 1p rose & black .50 *3.00*
a. Without period after "A" 40.00 *45.00*
J83 D2 2p violet & black .65 *3.75*
a. Without period after "A" 60.00
J84 D2 3p ultra & black 1.50 *17.50*
J85 D2 6p gray & black 1.75 *15.00*
a. Without period after "A" 40.00 *55.00*
Nos. J81-J85 (5) 4.80 *45.25*

Catalogue values for unused stamps in this section, from this point to the end of the section, are for Never Hinged items.

D3

D4

Wmk. 201

1931, Feb. 23 Litho. *Perf. 12*

Size: 19x22mm

J86 D3 ½p yel green & blk .85 *8.50*
J87 D3 1p rose & black .85 *1.65*
J88 D3 2p violet & black .85 *3.25*
J89 D3 3p blue & black 3.25 *18.00*
J90 D3 6p gray & black 13.00 *27.50*
Nos. J86-J90 (5) 18.80 *63.45*

Photo. (Frame) & Typo. (Center)

1959 *Perf. 14½x14*

Size: 17x21mm

J91 D3 1p rose & black 1.50 *10.00*
J92 D3 2p violet & black 1.50 *10.00*
J93 D3 3p blue & black 1.50 *11.00*
Nos. J91-J93 (3) 4.50 *31.00*

1960 Wmk. 330

Size: 17x21mm

J94 D3 1p rose & black 3.50 4.00
J95 D3 3p blue & black 3.50 5.50

1961, Feb. Photo. *Perf. 14½x14*

J96 D4 1c green & black .80 *4.00*
J97 D4 2c red & black .80 *4.00*
J98 D4 4c lilac & black .80 *4.00*
J99 D4 5c blue & black 1.25 *4.75*
J100 D4 6c emerald & black 1.50 *6.75*
J101 D4 10c yellow & black 3.00 *8.50*
Nos. J96-J101 (6) 8.15 *32.00*

Type of South Africa, 1972

1972 Wmk. 359 *Perf. 14x13½*

J102 D6 1c bright green .65 *3.25*
J106 D6 8c violet blue 2.50 *6.00*

OFFICIAL STAMPS

Nos. 85-87 (Setting VIII) Overprinted at top with type "c" on English-inscribed Stamps and type "d" on Afrikaans-inscribed Stamps

OFFICIAL **OFFISIEEL**
c d

Without Periods after Words

1927 Wmk. 201 *Perf. 14½x14*

O1 A5 ½p dk green & blk, pair 75.00 *125.00*
a. Single, English 9.00 *25.00*
b. Single, Afrikaans 9.00 *25.00*
O2 A6 1p car & blk, pair 75.00 *125.00*
a. Single, English 9.00 *25.00*
b. Single, Afrikaans 9.00 *25.00*
O3 A7 6p org & grn, pair 80.00 *125.00*
a. Single, English 9.50 *25.00*
b. Single, Afrikaans 9.50 *25.00*

South Africa No. 5 Overprinted As Nos. 85-87 plus "c" and "d"

Perf. 14

Wmk. 177

O4 A2 2p dull violet 125.00 *200.00*
a. Single, English 22.50 *40.00*
b. Single, Afrikaans 22.50 *40.00*

Nos. 96-98 Overprinted like Nos. J79-J85 at foot, Overprinted Types "c" and "d" at Top

1929 *Perf. 14½x14*

O5 A5 ½p green & blk, pair .85 *10.00*
a. Single, English .15 *2.50*
b. Single, Afrikaans .15 *2.50*
O6 A6 1p car & blk, pair 1.00 *11.00*
a. Single, English .20 *2.50*
b. Single, Afrikaans .20 *2.50*
O7 A7 6p org & grn, pair 3.75 *15.00*
a. Single, English .75 *3.50*
b. Single, Afrikaans .75 *3.50*
Nos. O5-O7 (3) 5.60 *36.00*

No. 99 Overprinted like Nos. J79-J85 at foot,
Overprinted at top

OFFICIAL. **OFFISIEEL.**

With Periods after Words

Perf. 14

O8 A8 2p vio brn & gray, pair 2.50 *17.00*
a. Single, English .30 *3.75*
b. Single, Afrikaans .30 *3.75*
c. Without period after "OFFICIAL" 5.00 *30.00*
d. Pair, "c" + normal 2p 15.00 *80.00*
e. Without period after "OFFISIEEL" 5.00 *30.00*
f. Pair, "e" + normal 2p 15.00 *80.00*
g. Pair, "c" + "e" 15.00 *80.00*

In each sheet of 120 stamps there were 12 No. O8c and 10 No. O8e.

South Africa Nos. 23-25 Overprinted

OFFICIAL **S.W.A.** **OFFISIEEL** **S.W.A.**

Without Periods after Words

1929 Wmk. 201 *Perf. 14½x14*

O9 A5 ½p green & blk, pair .60 *11.00*
a. Single, English .15 *2.50*
b. Single, Afrikaans .15 *2.50*
O10 A6 1p car & blk, pair .70 *11.00*
a. Single, English .15 *2.50*
b. Single, Afrikaans .15 *2.50*
O11 A7 6p org & grn, pair 2.50 *25.00*
a. Single, English .30 *6.00*
b. Single, Afrikaans .30 *6.00*
Nos. O9-O11 (3) 3.80 *47.00*

South Africa No. 26 Overprinted

OFFICIAL. **OFFISIEEL.**
S.W.A. **S.W.A.**

With Periods after Words

Perf. 14

O12 A8 2p vio brn & gray, pair 1.00 *15.00*
a. Single, English .15 *3.50*
b. Single, Afrikaans .15 *3.50*
c. Without period after "OFFICIAL" 3.50 *35.00*
d. Pair, "c" + normal 2p 12.50 *70.00*
e. Without period after "OFFISIEEL" 3.50 *35.00*
f. Pair, "e" + normal 2p 12.50 *70.00*
g. Pair, "c" + "e" 17.50 *80.00*

Catalogue values for unused stamps in this section, from this point to the end of the section, are for Never Hinged items.

Nos. 108-109, 111 and 114 Overprinted
in Red

OFFICIAL   OFFISIEEL

1931
O13 A15	½p green & blk, pair	8.50	15.00
a.	Single, English	1.00	3.50
b.	Single, Afrikaans	1.00	3.50
O14 A16	1p red & indigo, pair	.65	15.00
a.	Single, English	.15	3.50
b.	Single, Afrikaans	.15	3.50
O15 A18	2p dk brn & dk bl, pair	1.00	9.00
a.	Single, English	.15	2.00
b.	Single, Afrikaans	.15	2.00
O16 A21	6p ol brn & bl, pair	2.00	13.00
a.	Single, English	.25	3.00
b.	Single, Afrikaans	.25	3.00
	Nos. O13-O16 (4)	12.15	52.00

No. 110 Overprinted in Red

OFFICIAL   OFFISIEEL

1938, July 1   Wmk. 201
O17 A17	1½p violet brn, pair	25.00	35.00
a.	Single, English	2.75	6.00
b.	Single, Afrikaans	2.75	6.00

Nos. 108-111, 114 Ovptd. in Red

OFFICIAL   OFFISIEEL

1945-50   Wmk. 201   Perf. 14x13½
O18 A15	½p green & blk, pair	8.00	21.00
a.	Single, English	1.00	4.25
b.	Single, Afrikaans	1.00	4.25
O19 A16	1p red & ind, pair ('50)	2.00	12.50
a.	Single, English	.25	3.00
b.	Single, Afrikaans	.25	3.00
O20 A17	1½p vio brown, pair	30.00	27.50
a.	Single, English	5.00	5.00
b.	Single, Afrikaans	5.00	5.00
O21 A18	2p dk brn & dk bl, pair ('47)	425.00	600.00
a.	Single, English	75.00	100.00
b.	Single, Afrikaans	75.00	100.00
O22 A21	6p ol brn & bl, pair	7.00	37.50
a.	Single, English	.80	5.00
b.	Single, Afrikaans	.80	5.00

Nos. 108-111, 114 Ovptd. in Red

OFFICIAL   OFFISIEEL

1951-52
O23 A15	½p grn & blk, pair ('52)	11.00	15.00
a.	Single, English	1.25	4.00
b.	Single, Afrikaans	1.25	4.00
O24 A16	1p red & ind, pair	2.25	9.00
a.	Single, English	.30	1.75
b.	Single, Afrikaans	.30	1.75
c.	Ovpt. transposed, pair	50.00	82.50
d.	As "c," single, English ovpt.	10.00	
e.	As "c," single, Afrikaans ovpt.	10.00	
O25 A17	1½p violet brn, pair	22.50	22.50
a.	Single, English	3.00	5.00
b.	Single, Afrikaans	3.00	5.00
c.	Ovpt. transposed, pair	60.00	75.00
d.	As "c," single, English ovpt.	7.50	
e.	As "c," single, Afrikaans ovpt.	7.50	
O26 A18	2p dk brn & dk bl, pair	1.50	13.00
a.	Single, English	.20	3.50
b.	Single, Afrikaans	.20	3.50
c.	Ovpt. transposed, pair	32.50	90.00
d.	As "c," single, English ovpt.	4.50	
e.	As "c," single, Afrikaans ovpt.	4.50	
O27 A21	6p ol brn & blue, pair	2.75	30.00
a.	Single, English	.35	7.00
b.	Single, Afrikaans	.35	7.00
c.	Ovpt. transposed, pair	20.00	110.00
d.	As "c," single, English ovpt.	4.00	
e.	As "c," single, Afrikaans ovpt.	4.00	
	Nos. O23-O27 (5)	89.50	

"Overprint transposed" means English inscription
on Afrikaans stamp, or vice versa.
Use of official stamps ceased in Jan. 1955.

SRI LANKA

(ˌ)srē ˈlän-kə

LOCATION — Indian Ocean south of India
GOVT. — Democratic Socialist Republic
AREA — 26,244 sq. mi.
POP. — 14,850,001 (1981)
CAPITAL — Colombo

Sri Lanka was named Ceylon until May
22, 1972. Issues inscribed "Ceylon" are
listed under that name in this volume.

100 Cents = 1 Rupee

Catalogue values for all unused
stamps in this country are for Never
Hinged items.

Watermark

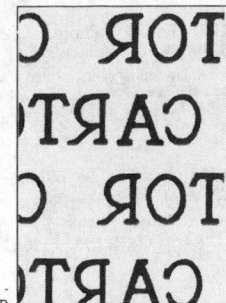

Wmk. 385 -
CARTOR

Lotus and Sunrise
over Adam's
Peak — A162

1972, May 22   Litho.   Perf. 13½x13
470 A162	15c blue & multi	.15	.15

Inauguration of Ceylon as Republic of Sri Lanka.

A162a

Overprinted "1972" in Red

1972, May 26   Perf. 14x13½
471 A162a	5c orange brn & multi	.15	.15

World Fellowship of Buddhists, Sri Lanka, May
22-28.

Supposedly not issued without overprint, copies
sell for 25-cents.

Book Year Emblem,
Oil Lamp — A163

1972, Sept. 8   Photo.   Perf. 13
472 A163	20c yellow & dk brn	.15	.15

International Book Year 1972.

Imperial
Angelfish — A164

Tropical Fish: 3c, Green chromide. 30c, Skipjack
bonito. 2r, Black ruby barbs.

**   Perf. 14x13½**

1972, Oct. 12   Litho.   Unwmk.
473 A164	2c ultra & multi	.15	.15
474 A164	3c dp orange & multi	.15	.15
475 A164	30c brt green & multi	.15	.15
476 A164	2r dp green & multi	.80	.40
	Set value	1.00	.58

3rd Session of Indian Ocean Fisheries Commission, Colombo, Oct. 9-14.

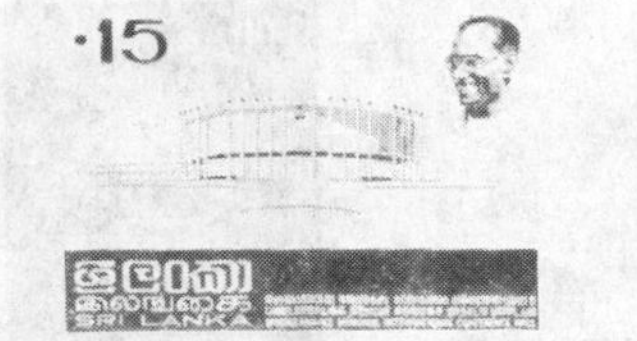

Bandaranaike Memorial Hall — A165

1973, May 17   Litho.   Perf. 14
477 A165	15c ultra & vio blue	.15	.15

Opening of Bandaranaike Memorial International
Conference Hall.

Women
Holding
Lotus — A166

Rock and Temple Paintings: 35c, King giving
away his children, Degaldoruwa Temple, near
Kandy, 18th cent. 50c, Prince and gravedigger,
Polonaruwa, 12th cent. 90c, Holy man holding
lotus, Polonaruwa, 12th cent. Design of 1.55r is
from Sigiriya, 5th cent.

1973, Sept. 3   Perf. 13½x14
478 A166	35c lt gray & multi	.15	.15
479 A166	50c gray & multi	.20	.15
480 A166	90c slate & multi	.36	.18
481 A166	1.55r brown & multi	.55	.27
a.	Souvenir sheet of 4, #470-401	1.50	1.50
	Nos. 478-481 (4)	1.26	
	Set value		.63

For surcharges see Nos. 538-540.

Bandaranaike
Conference
Hall — A167

1974, Sept. 6   Litho.   Perf. 14
482 A167	85c multicolored	.25	.25

20th Commonwealth Parliamentary Conference,
Sri Lanka, Sept. 1-15.

S.W.R.D.
Bandaranaike
A168

"UPU," "100" and
UPU Emblem
A170

1974, Sept. 25   Photo.   Perf. 14½
486 A168	15c ultra & multi	.15	.15

For surcharge see No. 541.

1974, Oct. 9   Litho.   Perf. 13
490 A170	50c multicolored	.50	.50

Parliament,
Colombo
A171

1975, Apr. 1   Litho.   Perf. 13½
491 A171	1r multicolored	.30	.30

Interparliamentary Union, Spring Meeting at
Bandaranaike Memorial International Conference
Hall, Sri Lanka, Mar. 31-Apr. 5.

Ponnambalam
Ramanathan
A172

D. J.
Wimalasurendra
A173

1975, Sept. 4   Litho.   Perf. 13½
492 A172	75c multicolored	.25	.25

Sir Ponnambalam Ramanathan (1851-1930),
lawyer and educator.

1975, Sept. 17
493 A173	75c ultra & blue blk	.40	.40

Devapura Jayasena Wimalasurendra (1874-
1953), engineer and irrigation specialist.

Map, Mrs.
Bandaranaike,
Dove — A174

1975, Dec. 22   Litho.   Perf. 13½
494 A174	1.15r blue & multi	.35	.35

International Women's Year 1975.

Rhododendron
Zeylanicum — A175

Flowers: 50c, Exacum trinerve. 75c, Daffodil
orchid. 10r, Wormia triquetra.

1976, Jan. 1   Litho.   Perf. 13
495 A175	25c blue & multi	.15	.15
496 A175	50c ocher & multi	.20	.20
497 A175	75c black & multi	.40	.40
498 A175	10r black & multi	2.00	2.00
a.	Souvenir sheet of 4, #495-498	3.50	3.50
	Nos. 495-498 (4)	2.75	2.75

Mahaveli-ganga Sluice — A176

1976, Jan. 8   Litho.   Perf. 13x12½
499 A176	85c lt blue, lt grn & lilac	.45	.45

Mahaveli-ganga River diversion.

Radar
Station — A177

1976, May 6   Litho.   Perf. 14
500 A177	1r blue & multi	.30	.30

Opening of Satellite Earth Station, Padukka.

Prince Siddhartha as White Elephant and
Sleeping Queen — A178

Birth of Buddha: 10c, King consulting astrologers. 1.50r, King entertaining astrologers at banquet. 2r, Queen taken in procession to her parents. 2.25r, Flag bearers, musicians in procession. 5r, Queen giving birth to Prince Siddhartha, the Buddha. Designs taken from 18th cent. wall paintings in Dambawa Vihara Temple.

1976, May 7   **Litho.**   **Perf. 13¹/₂**

501	A178	5c blue & multi	.15	.15
502	A178	10c blue & multi	.15	.15
503	A178	1.50r blue & multi	.25	.25
504	A178	2r blue & multi	.30	.30
505	A178	2.25r blue & multi	.35	.35
506	A178	5r blue & multi	.75	.75
a.		Souvenir sheet of 6, #501-506	3.50	3.50
		Nos. 501-506 (6)	1.95	1.95

Blue Sapphire — A179

Gems of Sri Lanka: 1.15r, Cat's-eye. 2r, Star sapphire. 5r, Ruby.

1976, June 16   **Perf. 12x12¹/₂**

507	A179	60c multicolored	.30	.30
508	A179	1.15r multicolored	.40	.40
509	A179	2r multicolored	.60	.60
510	A179	5r multicolored	1.50	1.50
a.		Souvenir sheet of 4, #507-510	3.75	3.75
		Nos. 507-510 (4)	2.80	2.80

Prime Minister Sirimavo Bandaranaike — A180

Statue of Liberty — A181

1976, Aug. 3   **Photo.**   **Perf. 14x14¹/₂**

511	A180	1.15r pink & multi	.35	.35
512	A180	2r pink & multi	.40	.40

5th Summit Conference of Non-aligned Countries, Colombo, Aug. 9-19.

1976, Nov. 29   **Litho.**   **Perf. 14**

513	A181	2.25r lt blue & indigo	.80	.80

American Bicentennial.

A. G. Bell, Telephone and Telephone Line — A182

Maitreya Bodhisattva — A183

1976, Dec. 21   **Litho.**   **Perf. 13x13¹/₂**

514	A182	1r orange & multi	.30	.30

Centenary of first telephone call by Alexander Graham Bell, Mar. 10, 1876.

1977, Jan. 1   **Litho.**   **Perf. 12¹/₂x13**

Bronze Statues: 1r, Sundara Murti Swami, 11th century. 5r, Goddess Tara.

515	A183	50c multicolored	.15	.15
516	A183	1r multicolored	.20	.20
517	A183	5r multicolored	.75	.75
		Nos. 515-517 (3)	1.10	1.10

Colombo Museum, centenary.

Kandyan Crown, 1737-1815 — A184

Design: 2r, Kandyan throne and footstool, 1693-1815.

1977, Jan. 18

518	A184	1r multicolored	.60	.60
519	A184	2r multicolored	.80	.80

Rahula Thero — A185   Brass Lamps — A186

Portrait: No. 521, Ponnambalam Arunachalam.

1977   **Litho.**   **Perf. 13¹/₂**

520	A185	1r multicolored	.30	.30
521	A185	1r multicolored	.30	.30

Sri Rahula Thero, 15th cent. poet and scholar, and Sir Ponnambalam Arunachalam (1851-1930), 1st president of Ceylon University Assoc., member of Congress.

Issue dates: #520, Feb. 23; #521, Mar. 10.

1977, Apr. 7   **Perf. 13**

Handicrafts: 25c, Jewelry box and jewelry. 50c, Caparisoned ivory elephant. 5r, Sinhala wooden mask.

522	A186	20c multicolored	.15	.15
523	A186	25c multicolored	.15	.15
524	A186	50c multicolored	.22	.22
525	A186	5r multicolored	1.10	1.10
a.		Souvenir sheet of 4, #522-525	3.00	3.00
		Nos. 522-525 (4)	1.62	1.62

Mohammed Cassim Siddi Lebbe — A187

1977, June 11   **Litho.**   **Perf. 13**

526	A187	1r multicolored	.60	.60

Lebbe (1838-98), lawyer, educator and Moslem journalist.

Girl Guide — A188

1977, Dec. 13   **Litho.**   **Perf. 15**

527	A188	75c multicolored	.40	.40

60th anniversary of Sri Lanka Girl Guides.

Parliament and Wheel of Life — A189   Runners — A190

1978, Feb. 4   **Photo.**   **Perf. 12x12¹/₂**

528	A189	15c green & gold	.15	.15

J.R. Jayewardene, first elected president, assumption of office.

See Nos. 559, 611-611A, 847. For surcharges see Nos. 542, 572, 698A-698B.

1978, Apr. 27   **Litho.**   **Perf. 15**

529	A190	15c multicolored	.15	.15

National Youth Service Council.
For surcharge see No. 543.

Bodhisattva in Royal Attire in Lotus Position — A191

Vesak Festival: 50c, Bodhisattva without royal attire cutting off his hair with sword. Both designs from rock carvings in Borobudur Temple, Java.

1978, May 16   **Perf. 13**

530	A191	15c multicolored	.15	.15
531	A191	50c multicolored	.30	.30

Veera Puran Appu and his Flag — A192   Birdwing Butterfly — A193

1978, Aug. 8   **Litho.**   **Perf. 13**

532	A192	15c multicolored	.15	.15

Veera Puran Appu (1848-1908), revolutionist, 130th birth anniversary.

1978, Nov. 28   **Litho.**   **Perf. 14x13¹/₂**

Butterflies: 50c, Tamil lacewing. 5r, Blue oakleaf. 10r, Blue mormon.

534	A193	25c multicolored	.15	.15
535	A193	50c multicolored	.15	.15
536	A193	5r multicolored	.80	.60
537	A193	10r multicolored	1.75	1.25
a.		Souvenir sheet of 4, #534-537	3.50	3.50
		Nos. 534-537 (4)	2.85	2.15

Nos. 478, 480-481 Surcharged with New Value and Bar

1978   **Litho.**   **Perf. 13¹/₂x14**

538	A166	5c on 90c multi	.15	.15
539	A166	10c on 35c multi	.15	.15
540	A166	1r on 1.55r multi	.35	.35
		Set value	.50	.50

Nos. 486, 528 Surcharged with New Value and 2 Bars; No. 529 with New Value on Pink Panel

Perf. 14¹/₂, 12x12¹/₂, 15

1979, Jan.   **Litho.; Engr.**

541	A168	25c on 15c multi	.75	.75
542	A189	25c on 15c multi	.75	.75
543	A190	25c on 15c multi	.75	.75
		Nos. 541-543 (3)	2.25	2.25

Ceylon No. 390 Overprinted Vertically "SRI LANKA" in Green and Surcharged in Black

1979, Mar. 22   **Photo.**   **Perf. 11¹/₂**
Granite Paper

544	A118	15c on 10c brt green	.15	.15

Arrival of Sacred Tooth — A194   Wrestlers — A195

Wall Paintings from Kelaniya Temple: 25c, Prince Danta and Princess Hema Mala bringing Sacred Tooth from Kalinga, 4th century A.D. 1r, Princess Theri Sanghamitta bringing, by ship, the bodhi tree branch, 3rd century B.C. 10r, King Kirti offering fan of authority to supreme patriarch, 18th century.

1979, May 3   **Perf. 13¹/₂**

546	A194	25c multicolored	.15	.15
547	A194	1r multicolored	.15	.15
548	A194	10r multicolored	1.50	1.50
a.		Souvenir sheet of 3, #546-548	1.75	1.75
		Nos. 546-548 (3)	1.80	1.80

2523rd Vesak Festival, May 11.

1979, May 18   **Litho.**   **Perf. 14**

Design: 50r, Dancer. Woodcarvings from Embekke Temple.

549	A195	20r multicolored	2.00	2.00
550	A195	50r multicolored	6.00	6.00

Piyadasa Sirisena — A196   Dudley S. Senanayake — A197

1979, May 22   **Perf. 13x13¹/₂**

551	A196	1.25r deep green	.20	.20

Piyadasa Sirisena (1875-1946), patriot, journalist, novelist and poet.

1979, June 19   **Photo.**

552	A197	1.25r deep green	.20	.20

27th death anniversary of Prime Minister Dudley S. Senanayake.

Mother Feeding Child, IYC Emblem — A198

Designs: 3r, Faces and IYC emblem. 5r, Children with rope and ball, IYC emblem.

1979, July 31   **Litho.**   **Perf. 12¹/₂**

553	A198	5c multicolored	.15	.15
554	A198	3r multicolored	.30	.30
555	A198	5r multicolored	.50	.50
		Nos. 553-555 (3)	.95	.95

International Year of the Child.

Ceylon No. 2, Rowland
Hill
A199

Airlanka
Emblem
A200

1979, Aug. 27   Litho.   Perf. 13½
556 A199 3r multicolored   .35   .35
Sir Rowland Hill (1795-1879), originator of
penny postage.

1979, Sept. 1   Litho.   Perf. 12½
557 A200 3r red, dk grn & blk   .35   .35
Airlanka National Airline, inaugural flight,
Colombo-Bangkok.

Coconut Palm — A201

1979, Oct. 9   Litho.   Perf. 13½
558 A201 2r multicolored   .25   .25
Asian and Pacific Coconut Community, 10th
anniversary.

No. 528 Redrawn Without Date
1979, Oct. 9   Photo.   Perf. 13
Size: 20x24mm
559 A189 25c green & gold   .15   .15

Family in
Cogwheel,
Parliament
A202

1979, Oct.   Litho.   Perf. 13½
560 A202 2r multicolored   .30   .30
Intl. Conf. of Parliamentarians on Population &
Development, Colombo, Aug. 28-Sept. 1.

Swami Vipulananda
(1892-1947), Philosopher
& Theologian — A203

1979, Nov. 18   Perf. 12½
561 A203 1.25r multicolored   .20   .20

Text and
Crescent — A204

1979, Nov. 22
562 A204 3.75r multicolored   .60   .60
Hegira (pilgrimage year).

Institute
Emblem
A205

Blue Magpie
A206

1979, Nov. 29   Perf. 13
563 A205 15c multicolored   .15   .15
Ayurveda Medical Institute, 50th anniversary.

1979, Dec. 13   Litho.   Perf. 14
564 A206 10c shown   .15   .15
565 A206 15c Lorikeet   .15   .15
566 A206 75c Arrenga   .15   .15
567 A206 1r Spurfowl   .18   .15
568 A206 5r Yellow-fronted barbet   .75   .60
569 A206 10r Yellow-eared bulbul   1.50   .60
a.   Souvenir sheet of 6, #564-569   3.00   3.00
Nos. 564-569 (6)   2.88
Set value   1.50
For surcharge see No. 1062B.

Rotary Emblem,
Map of Sri
Lanka — A207

1979, Dec. 27   Litho.   Perf. 14½
570 A207 1.50r multicolored   .35   .35
Rotary International, 75th anniversary.

A. Ratnayake, Educator
and Pres. of
Senate — A208

1980, Jan. 7   Photo.   Perf. 14x13½
571 A208 1.25r slate green   .20   .20

No. 559 Surcharged
1980, Mar. 17   Photo.   Perf. 13
572 A189 35c on 25c multi   .15   .15
One position has ".33" instead of ".35."

Leaf, Wheel, Fan
(Buddhist
Symbols) — A209

1980, Mar. 25   Photo.   Perf. 13½x14
573 A209 10c Steeple   .15   .15
574 A209 35c shown   .15   .15
Set value   .15   .15
All Ceylon Buddhist Cong., 60th anniv.

Col. Henry Olcott,
Buddhist
Emblem — A210

Journey of
Patachara, Temple
Painting — A211

1980, May 17   Litho.   Perf. 14
575 A210 2r multicolored   .28   .28
Col. Henry S. Olcott (1832-1907), American theosophist and Buddhist lecturer, centenary of arrival
in Sri Lanka.

1980, May 23   Perf. 13½x14
Vesak Festival (Paintings, life of Buddha): 1.60r,
Patachara crossing river.
576 A211 35c multicolored   .15   .15
577 A211 1.60r multicolored   .25   .25
Set value   .30   .30

George E. De
Silva — A212

1980, June 8   Perf. 13x13½
578 A212 1.60r multicolored   .25   .25
George E. de Silva (1879-1950), politician.

Siva Temples,
Polonnaruwa
A213

1980, Aug. 25   Litho.   Perf. 13½
579 A213 35c shown   .15   .15
580 A213 35c Cave Temples,
Dambulla   .15   .15
581 A213 35c Sacred Tooth Temple, Kandy   .15   .15
582 A213 1.60r Abhayagiri Hill   .20   .20
583 A213 1.60r Jetavanarama Hill   .20   .20
584 A213 1.60r Sigiri   .20   .20
a.   Souvenir sheet of 6, #579-584   .90   .90
Set value   .75   .75
UNESCO "Cultural Triangle" Project.

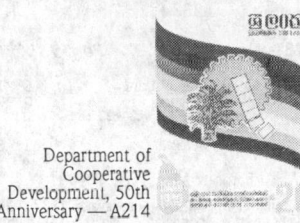

Department of
Cooperative
Development, 50th
Anniversary — A214

1980, Oct. 1   Litho.   Perf. 13½
585 A214 20c multicolored   .15   .15

Women's
Movement
Emblem
A215

1980, Oct. 10   Photo.   Perf. 14x13½
586 A215 35c multicolored   .15   .15
Mahila Samiti (Rural Women's Movement), 50th
anniversary.

Nativity — A216

1980, Nov. 20   Litho.   Perf. 13½
587 A216 35c shown   .15   .15
588 A216 3.75r Three kings   .50   .50
a.   Souvenir sheet of 2, #587-588   .65   .65
Set value   .55   .55
Christmas 1980/Year of the family.

Colombo
Public
Library
Opening
A217

1980, Dec. 17   Perf. 12x12½
589 A217 35c multicolored   .15   .15

Peacock
Banner — A218

Designs: Ancient flags.

1980, Dec. 18   Perf. 13
590 A218 10c shown   .15   .15
591 A218 25c Elephant banner   .15   .15
592 A218 1.60r Sinhalese royal flag   .20   .20
593 A218 20r Kings Civil Standard   2.25   2.25
a.   Souvenir sheet of 4, #590-593   2.75   2.75
Nos. 590-593 (4)   2.75   2.75

Fishing Cat — A219

1981, Feb. 10   Litho.   Perf. 14
594 A219 2.50r on 1.60r, shown   .40   .30
595 A219 3r on 1.30r, Golden
palm cat   .45   .30
596 A219 4r on 2r, Mouse deer   .60   .45
597 A219 5r on 3.75r, Rusty-spotted cat   .75   .60
a.   Souvenir sheet of 4, #594-597   2.25   2.25
Nos. 594-597 (4)   2.20   1.65
See #728-730A, 928. For surcharge see #731.

Population and
Housing
Census — A220

1981, Mar. 2   Litho.   Perf. 12½x12
598 A220 50c multicolored   .15   .15

Ceylon Light
Infantry
Centenary — A221

The Death of
Buddha, Carved
Panel, 1st
Cent. — A222

1981, Apr. 1   Litho.   Perf. 12
599 A221 2r multicolored   .30   .30

1981, May 5   Perf. 13x13½
600 A222 35c shown   .15   .15
601 A222 50c Silk banner   .15   .15
602 A222 7r Statuette   .90   .90
a.   Souvenir sheet of 3, #600-602   1.00   1.00
Set value   1.00   1.00
Vesak Festival.

St. John Baptist de la Salle
A223

1981, May 15   Litho.   Perf. 12½x12
603 A223 2r multicolored   .30   .30

De la Salle Brothers Order, 300th anniv.

Polwatte Sri Buddadatta
A224

Intl. Year of the Disabled
A225

Famous Men: No. 605, Mohottiwatte Guna-nanda, Buddhist leader. No. 606, Gnanapra Kasar, Catholic missionary. No. 607, Al-Haj T.B. Jayah, Muslim teacher. No. 608, James Peiris. No. 609, N.M. Perera, founded first Marxist Party in Sri Lanka, 1935.

1981   Photo.   Perf. 12
604 A224 50c olive bister   .15   .15
605 A224 50c dull red brown   .15   .15
606 A224 50c lilac   .15   .15
607 A224 50c gray green   .15   .15
608 A224 50c brown   .15   .15
609 A224 50c crimson rose   .15   .15
        Set value   .48   .48

Issue dates: Nos. 604-606 May 22; No. 607, May 31; No. 609, June 6.
See #623-624, 640-642, 646, 672-676, 713-717.

1981, June 19   Litho.   Perf. 12x12½
610 A225 2r multicolored   .25   .25

No. 528 Redrawn with Denomination in Upper Right Corner

1981-83   Photo.   Perf. 13
                 Size: 20x24mm
611 A189 50c green & gold   .15   .15
611A A189 60c green & gold   .15   .15

Issue dates: 50c, June 6; 60c, Dec. 30, 1983.
For surcharges see Nos. 698A-698B.

Hand Putting Ballot in Box — A226

**   Perf. 12½x12, 12x12½**
1981, July 7   Litho.
612 A226 50c shown   .15   .15
613 A226 7r Ballot box on map, vert.   .90   .90

Universal Franchise, 50th anniv.

Rhys Davids (Society Founder)
A227

1981, July 14   Perf. 12½x12
614 A227 35c multicolored   .15   .15

All Ceylon Buddhist Students' Federation, 25th Anniv.
A228

1981, July 21   Litho.   Perf. 13½
615 A228 2r multicolored   .25   .25

Family Planning — A229

7th World Acupuncture Cong. — A230

1981, Sept. 25
616 A229 50c multicolored   .15   .15

1981, Oct. 20   Litho.   Perf. 12x12½
617 A230 2r multicolored   .30   .30

Visit of Queen Elizabeth II, Oct. — A231

Designs: Flags of Gt. Britain and Sri Lanka.

1981, Oct. 21   Perf. 14
618 A231 50c multicolored   .15   .15
619 A231 5r multicolored   .75   .75
a.   Souvenir sheet of 2, #618-619   .85   .85

Forest Conservation
A232

1981, Nov. 27   Perf. 13½x13
620 A232 35c Forest   .15   .15
621 A232 50c Tree planting   .15   .15
622 A232 5r Jack tree   .70   .70
a.   Souvenir sheet of 3, #620-622, perf.
          14x13   .80   .80
          Set value   .83   .83

Famous Men Type of 1981

Designs: No. 623, F.R. Senanayaka (1882-1926), lawyer and politician. No. 624, Philip Gunawardhane, politician, 10th death anniv.

1982   Litho.   Perf. 14
623 A224 50c brown   .15   .15
624 A224 50c bright rose   .15   .15
          Set value   .20   .20

Issue dates: #623, Jan. 1; #624, Jan. 11.

Dept. of Inland Revenue, 50th Anniv.
A233

Natl. Television Inauguration
A234

1982, Feb. 9   Litho.   Perf. 14
625 A233 50c multicolored   .15   .15

1982, Feb. 15
626 A234 2.50r multicolored   .38   .38

Sesquicentennial of Cricket Introduction and Centenary of Sri Lanka vs. England Match — A235

1982, Feb. 17
627 A235 2.50r multicolored   .38   .38

Osbeckia Wightiana
A236

1982, Apr. 1   Perf. 12
628 A236 35c shown   .15   .15
629 A236 2r Mesua nagassarium   .25   .25
630 A236 7r Rhodomyrtus to-
            mentosa   .80   .80
631 A236 20r Phaius tancarvilleae   2.25   2.25
a.   Souvenir sheet of 4, #628-631   3.75   3.75
           Nos. 628-631 (4)   3.45   3.45

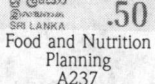

Food and Nutrition Planning
A237

World Hindu Conference
A238

1982, Apr. 6   Litho.   Perf. 13
632 A237 50c multicolored   .15   .15

1982, Apr. 21   Perf. 14x14½
633 A238 50c multicolored   .15   .15

Vesak Festival 1982
A239

Scenes from Jataka Story (Pre-incarnation of Buddha), Cloth Painting, 3rd cent. B.C., Hanguranketa Temple (King Vessantara and): 35c, Giving away white elephant. 50c, Royal Family in Vankagiri Forest. 2.50r, Giving away his children to a Brahmin. 5r, Royal family in chariot.

1982, Apr. 23   Perf. 14
634 A239 35c multicolored   .15   .15
635 A239 50c multicolored   .15   .15
636 A239 2.50r multicolored   .38   .38
637 A239 5r multicolored   .75   .75
a.   Souvenir sheet of 4, #634-637   1.25   1.25
           Nos. 634-637 (4)   1.43   1.43

New Parliament Building Opening
A240

1982, Apr. 29
638 A240 50c multicolored   .15   .15

Scouting Year
A241

1982, May 24   Litho.   Perf. 12½x12
639 A241 50c multicolored   .15   .15

Famous Men Type of 1981

1982   Perf. 12x12½
640 A224 50c C.W.W. Kannangara   .15   .15
641 A224 50c G.P. Malalasekara   .15   .15
642 A224 50c John Kotelawala   .15   .15
          Set value   .30   .30

Issue dates: No. 640, May 22; No. 641, May 26; No. 642, June 8.

World Buddhist Leaders Conference
A242

1982, June 10   Perf. 12½x12
643 A242 50c multicolored   .15   .15

World Environment Day — A243

1982, June 5
644 A243 50c multicolored   .15   .15

YMCA Centenary — A244

1982, June 24   Photo.   Perf. 11½
645 A244 2.50r multicolored   .50   .50

Famous Men Type of 1981

1982, June 14   Litho.   Perf. 12x12½
646 A224 50c Waitialingam Durais-
            wamy   .15   .15

Weliwita Saranankara Sangharaja — A245

1982, July 5
647 A245 50c orange & black   .15   .15

25th Anniv. of Sasana Sevaka Samithiya
A246

1982, Aug. 8
648 A246 50c multicolored   .15   .15

TB Bacillus Centenary A247

1982, Sept. 21
649 A247 50c Koch, microscope, bacillus .15 .15

Eye Donation Society — A248

1982, Nov. 16 Litho. Perf. 12x12½
650 A248 2.50r Emblems, map .40 .40

125th Anniv. of Ceylon Postage Stamps A249

1982, Dec. 1 Litho. Perf. 13½
651 A249 50c Ceylon #5, 302 .15 .15
652 A249 2.50r Ceylon #12, #611 .40 .40
  a. Souv. sheet of 2, #651-652, perf. 12 .50 .50

Natl. Stamp Exhibition.

Sir Oliver Goonetilleke — A250

1982, Dec. 17 Litho. Perf. 12x12½
653 A250 50c black & brown .15 .15

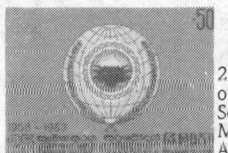

25th Anniv. of Sarvodaya Social Movement A251

1983, Jan. 1 Perf. 13½
654 A251 50c multicolored .15 .15

55th Anniv. of Amateur Radio Society A252

1983, Jan. 17
655 A252 2.50r multicolored .30 .30

Customs Cooperation Council and First Intl. Customs Day — A253

1983, Jan. 26 Litho. Perf. 12
656 A253 50c orange & multi .15 .15
657 A253 5r green & multi .30 .30
  Set value .36 .36

Bottlenose Dolphin A254

1983, Feb. 22 Perf. 14½x14
658 A254 50c shown .15 .15
659 A254 2r Dugongs .25 .25
660 A254 2.50r Humpback whale .30 .30
661 A254 10r Great sperm whale 1.25 1.25
  Nos. 658-661 (4) 1.95 1.95

Ceylon Shipping Corp. A255

1983, Mar. 1 Perf. 12x12½
662 A255 50c Container ship .15 .15
663 A255 2.50r Liner services map .28 .28
664 A255 5r Conventional ship .60 .60
665 A255 20r Oil tanker 2.50 2.50
  Nos. 662-665 (4) 3.53 3.53

Intl. Women's Day — A256

1983, Mar. 8 Perf. 13½
666 A256 50c Woman, flag .15 .15
667 A256 5r Woman, map .60 .60

Commonwealth Day — A257

1983, Mar. 14
668 A257 50c Waterfall .15 .15
669 A257 2.50r Tea picking .20 .20
670 A257 5r Harvesting .50 .50
671 A257 20r Cultural pageant 1.75 1.75
  Nos. 668-671 (4) 2.60 2.60

Famous Men Type of 1981
1983 Litho. Perf. 12
672 A224 50c Henry W. Amarasuriya .15 .15

Size: 29x40mm
673 A224 50c Charles A. Lorenz .15 .15
674 A224 50c Simon G. Perera .15 .15
675 A224 50c Nordeen H.M. Abdul Cader .15 .15
676 A224 50c C.W. Tamotherampillai .15 .15
  Set value .35 .35

Issued: No. 676, Oct. 1; others, May 22.
No. 676 shows Tamotherampillai looking towards the right of the stamp. A version that was to be issued May 22, showed someone labeled C. W. Tamotherampillai looking straight ahead.

25th Anniv. of Lions Club A258

1983, May 7 Litho. Perf. 14
677 A258 2.50r multicolored .35 .35

Vesak Festival 1983 — A259

Various Colombo murals.

1983, May 13 Perf. 12½x12
678 A259 35c multicolored .15 .15
679 A259 50c multicolored .15 .15
680 A259 5r multicolored .40 .40
681 A259 10r multicolored .80 .80
  a. Souvenir sheet of 4, #678-681 1.75 1.75
  Nos. 678-681 (4) 1.50 1.50

125th Anniv. of Telecommunication Service — A260

1983, May 17 Perf. 12x12½
682 A260 2r shown .20 .20
683 A260 10r World Communications Year 1.00 1.00

Gam Udawa Village Re-awakening Movement — A261

1983, June 23 Litho. Perf. 12x12½
684 A261 50c Family .15 .15
685 A261 5r Village .50 .50

Cattle Transport A262

1983, Aug. 1 Litho. Perf. 12
686 A262 35c shown .15 .15
687 A262 2r Train .20 .20
688 A262 2.50r Cattle cart .25 .25
689 A262 5r Model T Ford .50 .50
  Nos. 686-689 (4) 1.10 1.10

Sir Tikiri Banda Panabokke, 20th Death Anniv. — A263

1983, Sept. 2 Litho. Perf. 13½x14
690 A263 50c dark red .15 .15

Ceylon Wood Pigeon — A264

1983, Dec. 1 Litho. Perf. 14½
691 A264 25c shown .15 .15
692 A264 35c Ceylon white-eye .15 .15
693 A264 2r Dusky-blue flycatcher .20 .20

694 A264 20r Ceylon coucal 2.00 2.00
  a. Souvenir sheet of 4, #691-694 2.25 2.25
  Nos. 691-694 (4) 2.50 2.50

See No. 877. For surcharge see No. 780A.

Christmas, Stone Carvings — A265

1983, Dec. 5 Litho. Perf. 12½x13
695 A265 50c multicolored .15 .15
696 A265 5r ultra & bister .50 .50
  a. Souv. sheet of 2, #695-696+label .60 .60
  Set value .55 .55

A266   A267

1983, Nov. 25 Litho. Perf. 14x15
697 A266 50c brown .15 .15

Rev. Pelene Thero (1878-1955), Buddhist leader.

1983 Litho. Perf. 13½
698 A267 50c Ahamed Orabi Al-Misri .15 .15

No. 611 Surcharged with Four Bars, No. 611A with Three Bars and New Denomination in Black or Green
1983-85 Photo. Perf. 13
698A A189 60c on 50c .15 .15
Size: 20x24mm
698B A189 75c on 60c (G) .15 .15

Ovpt. on No. 698A also exists with two bars. Issue dates: both Dec. 1.

World Food Day (Oct. 16) — A268

1984, Jan. 2 Perf. 12½x12
699 A268 3r Rice paddy .24 .24

Colombo Tea Auctions Centenary A269

1984, Jan. 31
700 A269 1r Auction House .15 .15
701 A269 2r Emblem .16 .16
702 A269 5r Tea picker .40 .40
703 A269 10r Auction .80 .80
  Nos. 700-703 (4) 1.51 1.51

Mahapola Anniversary (Educational System) — A270

1984, Feb. 10 — *Perf. 12*
704 A270 60c Students .15 .15
705 A270 1r Classroom .15 .15
706 A270 5.50r Student in library, lab .50 .50
707 A270 6r Emblem .60 .60
Nos. 704-707 (4) 1.40 1.40

Vesak Festival 1984 — A271 .35

Wooden Casket Paintings, Temple Godapitiya Rajamaha Vihara, Akuressa: Scenes from Daham Sonda Jathaka legend.

1984, Apr. 27 Litho. — *Perf. 14*
708 A271 35c multicolored .15 .15
709 A271 60c multicolored .15 .15
710 A271 5r multicolored .55 .55
711 A271 10r multicolored 1.25 1.25
a. Souv. sheet of 4, #708-711, perf. 13x13½ 2.00 2.00
Nos. 708-711 (4) 2.10 2.10

Lions Club Intl., District 306A — A272

1984, May 5 Litho. — *Perf. 14x14½*
712 A272 60c multicolored .15 .15

Famous Men Type of 1981

Designs: No. 713, K. Balasingham, lawyer. No. 714, Mohamed Macan Markar (1879-1952), Muslim politician. No. 715, W. Arthur de Silva (d. 1942), industrialist. No. 716, Tissa Mahanayake Thero (1826-1907), Buddhist educator. No. 717, G.P. Wickremarachchi, medical pioneer.

1984, May 22 Litho. — *Perf. 12x12½*
713 A224 60c brown .15 .15
714 A224 60c green .15 .15
715 A224 60c orange red .15 .15
716 A224 60c bister .15 .15
717 A224 60c yellow green .15 .15
Set value .40 .40

Public Service Mutual Provident Assoc. Centenary A273

1984, June 16 — *Perf. 13x13½*
718 A273 4.60r Emblem .35 .35

Village Re-awakening Movement — A274

1984, June 23 — *Perf. 12x12½*
719 A274 60c "One Million Houses" .15 .15

Asia-Pacific Broadcasting Union, 20th Anniv. — A275

1984, June 30 — *Perf. 12½x12*
720 A275 7r Map .65 .65
For surcharge see No. 776.

Cultural Pageant A276

Procession: a, Drummers, elephant. b, Torch bearers, 3 elephants (green or red masks). c, Torch bearers, 3 elephants (orange or yellow masks). d, Dancers. Continuous design.

1984, Aug. 11 Litho. — *Perf. 12½x12*
721 Strip of 4 1.65 1.65
a.-d. A276 4.60r any single .40 .40
e. Souvenir sheet of 4 1.65 1.65

Orchid Circle of Sri Lanka, 50th Anniversary — A277

1984, Aug. 31 — *Perf. 14*
722 A277 60c Vanda memoria .15 .15
723 A277 4.60r Acanthephippium bicolor .45 .45
724 A277 5r Vanda Tessellata .50 .50
725 A277 10r Anoectochillus setaceus 1.10 1.10
a. Souvenir sheet of 4, #722-725 2.25 2.25
Nos. 722-725 (4) 2.20 2.20

Natl. Coat of Arms — A278

Perf. 14½x14
1984, Aug. 15 Engr. — *Wmk.*
726 A278 50r vermilion 5.00 5.00
727 A278 100r deep claret 10.00 10.00

Wildlife Type of 1981

1984(?)-89 Litho. — *Perf. 14*
728 A219 2.50r Felis viverrina .18 .18
729 A219 3r Paradoxurus zeylonensis .22 .22
730 A219 4r Tragulus meminna .30 .30
730A A219 5r Felis rubiginosa ('89) .40 .40
Nos. 728-730A (4) 1.10 1.10

No. 729 has brown inscriptions. See No. 928 for black inscriptions.

No. 728 Surcharged in Brown

1985, Dec. 1 Litho. — *Perf. 14*
731 A219 5.75r on 2.50r multi .40 .40

The Observer Newspaper, 150th Anniv. — A280

1984, Aug. 31 Litho. — *Perf. 13x13½*
732 A280 4.60r Publisher, Colombo .32 .32

Natl. School Games — A281

1984, Oct. 5 — *Perf. 13½x13*
733 A281 60c blue, gray & blk .15 .15

D. S. Senanayake (1884-1952), Prime Minister A282

1984, Oct. 20 — *Perf. 14½x14*
734 A282 35c Irrigated field .15 .15
735 A282 60c Statue .15 .15
736 A282 4.60r Reservoir .32 .32
737 A282 6r Parliament House, Colombo .42 .42
Set value .84 .84

World Food Program — A284

Baari Arabic College, Weligama, Cent. — A285

1984, Dec. 10 Litho. — *Perf. 13x13½*
738 A284 7r Globe, Sri Lankans working field .60 .60

1984, Dec. 24 — *Perf. 13x12½*
739 A285 4.60r dull bl grn & blk .35 .35

Intl. Youth Year — A286

World Religion Day — A287

1985, Jan. 1 — *Perf. 12½x13*
740 A286 4.60r multicolored .35 .35
741 A286 20r multicolored 1.50 1.50
For surcharge see No. 790.

1985, Jan. 20 — *Perf. 12*
Design: Emblems of World religions.
742 A287 4.60r multicolored .35 .35

Royal College, Colombo, 150th Anniv. — A288

Mahapola Scholarship Program for Development & Education, 5th Anniv. — A289

1985, Jan. 29 — *Perf. 13x12½*
743 A288 60c College crest .15 .15
744 A288 7r Campus .60 .60

1985, Feb. 7 — *Perf. 14*
745 A289 60c Diplomas, freighter, office buildings .15 .15

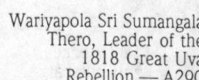 

Wariyapola Sri Sumangala Thero, Leader of the 1818 Great Uva Rebellion — A290

1985, Mar. 2 — *Perf. 13x13½*
746 A290 60c brown & yellow .15 .15

Victoria Project A291

Perf. 12½x12, 12x12½
1985, Apr. 12 — *Litho.*
747 A291 60c Victoria Dam .15 .15
748 A291 7r Dam, map, vert. .50 .50
Set value .55 .55

Vesak Festival 1985 A292

Natl. Heroes A293

Designs: 35c, Frontispiece of the Buddhist Annual golden jubilee issue. 60c, Women worshiping at temple, Vesak Poya Holiday cent. 6r, Bauddha Mandiraya, Colombo. 9r, Buddhist flag cent.

1985, Apr. 26 — *Perf. 13x12½*
749 A292 35c multicolored .15 .15
750 A292 60c multicolored .15 .15
751 A292 6r multicolored .45 .45
752 A292 9r multicolored .70 .70
a. Souvenir sheet of 4, #749-752 1.40 1.40
Nos. 749-752 (4) 1.45 1.45

1985, May 22 — *Perf. 13x12½*
Portraits: No. 753, Waskaduwe Sri Subhuthi Thero (1835-1917), Pali scholar, philologist responsible for the Sinhala dictionary. No. 754, Rev. Fr. Peter A. Pillai (1904-1964), educational and social reformer. No. 755, Dr. Senarath Paranavitane (c. 1900-1972), epigraphist. No. 756, A.M. Wapche Marikar (1829-1925), educational reformer, architect.

Pale Yellow Orange and
753 A293 60c tan .15 .15
754 A293 60c brt rose lilac .15 .15
755 A293 60c brown .15 .15
756 A293 60c emerald .15 .15
Set value .20 .20

Gam Udawa — Yovur Udanaya Village Reformation Movement A294

1985, June 23 — *Perf. 13½x13*
757 A294 60c multicolored .15 .15

Colombo Young Poets Assoc., 50th Anniv. — A295

1985, June 25 — *Perf. 14*
758 A295 60c Emblem .15 .15

Kothmale Project Commission A296

1985, Aug. 24
759 A296 60c Dam, lake .15 .15
760 A296 6r Hydro-electric power
station .45 .45
Set value .50 .50

A297 A298

Child Survival: 35c, Mother breastfeeding. 60c, Infant, oral inoculant. 6r, Weighing toddler. 9r, Infant, intravenous inoculant.

1985, Sept. 1 Wmk. 385 Perf. 13½
761 A297 35c multicolored .15 .15
762 A297 6r multicolored .15 .15
763 A297 6r multicolored .45 .45
764 A297 9r multicolored .70 .70
a. Souvenir sheet of 4, #761-764 1.25 1.25
Nos. 761-764 (4) 1.45 1.45

1985, Sept. 2 Unwmk. Perf. 14
765 A298 7r Womb, infant .52 .52

10th Asian & Oceanic Congress of Obstetrics & Gynecology.

World
Tourism
Org., 10th
Anniv. —
A299

1985, Sept. 27 Litho. Perf. 14
766 A299 1r Conch shell horn .15 .15
767 A299 6r Parliament complex .42 .42
768 A299 7r Tea plantation .50 .50
769 A299 10r Buddhist monastery,
Ruwanveliseya .72 .72
a. Souv. sheet of 4, #766-769, perf.
13½ 1.75 1.75
Nos. 766-769 (4) 1.79 1.79

Land Development
Ordinance, 50th
Anniv. — A300

Sinhal Translation,
Koran — A301

1985, Oct. 15 Perf. 14x15
770 A300 4.60r Deeds presentation .40 .40

1985, Oct. 17 Wmk. 385 Perf. 13½
771 A301 60c violet & gold .15 .15

Christmas — A302

1985, Nov. 5 Perf. 12
772 A302 60c Our Lady of Matara .15 .15
773 A302 9r Our Lady of Madhu .65 .65
a. Souvenir sheet of 2, #772-773 .70 .70

SAARC 1st
Summit, Dec.
7-8 — A303

1985, Dec. 8 Perf. 14½x14
774 A303 60c shown .15 .15
775 A303 5.50r Flags on UN emblem .50 .50

No. 720 Surcharged in Intense Blue

1986, Jan. 20 Perf. 12½x12
776 A275 1r on 7r Map .15 .15

Viceroy
Special
Train — A304

1986, Feb. 2 Perf. 12½x13
777 A304 1r multicolored .15 .15

Colombo-Kandy line inauguration.

Students
A305

1986, Feb. 14 Perf. 14
778 A305 75c multicolored .15 .15

Mahapola Scholarship Program for development and education, 6th anniv.

Don Richard
Wijewardene
(1886-1950),
Newspaper
Publisher A306

Welttara
Gnanatillake
Mahanayake Thero
(1858-1941),
Scientist — A307

1986, Feb. 23 Perf. 14x15
779 A306 75c sage green & brown .15 .15

1986, Feb. 26 Wmk. 385 Perf. 13½
780 A307 75c multicolored .15 .15

No. 692 Surcharged

1986, Mar. 10 Litho. Perf. 14½
780A A264 7r on 35c 1.00 1.00

Natl. Red
Cross Society,
50th Anniv.
A308

1986, Mar. 31 Perf. 12½x13
781 A308 75c multicolored .15 .15

Halley's Comet
A309

1986, Apr. 5 Perf. 12½
782 A309 50c Comet is not an
omen .15 .15
783 A309 75c Constellations .15 .15
784 A309 6.50r Trajectory diagrams .48 .48

785 A309 8.50r Edmond Halley .62 .62
a. Souvenir sheet of 4, #782-785, perf.
12½x13 1.25 1.25
Set value 1.20 1.20

Sinhalese and Tamil
New Year — A310

Designs: 50c, Woman lighting lamp. 75c, Woman, holiday foods. 6.50r, Women celebrating around table. 8.50r, Food preparation, feast, anointment ritual.

1986, Apr. 10
786 A310 50c multicolored .15 .15
787 A310 75c multicolored .15 .15
788 A310 6.50r multicolored .48 .48
789 A310 8.50r multicolored .62 .62
a. Souvenir sheet of 4, #786-789, perf.
13x12½ 1.25 1.25
Set value 1.20 1.20

No. 740 Surcharged

1986, Apr. 29 Perf. 12½x13
790 A286 1r on 4.60r multi .20 .20

Vesak Festival
A311

Jathaka Story frescoes from the house Samudragiri Vihara, Mirissa, recounting the life of Siddhartha (583-463 B.C.): 50c, King Kurudhamma Jathakaya gives elephant to the brahman. 75c, Vasavarthi heaven. 5r, Sujatha's milk rice offering. 10d, Thapassu and Bhalluka's parched corn and honey offering.

1986, May 16
791 A311 50c multicolored .15 .15
792 A311 75c multicolored .15 .15
793 A311 5d multicolored .35 .35
794 A311 10d multicolored .72 .72
Nos. 791-794 (4) 1.37 1.37

Natl.
Heroes — A312

Natl. Cooperative
Movement, 75th
Anniv. — A313

Designs: No. 795, Kalukondayave Sri Prajnasekhara Mahanayake Thero (1895-1977), theologian. No. 796, Brahmachari Walisinghe Harischandra (1876-1913), historian, social reformer. No. 797, Martin Wickramasinghe (1890-1970), author. No. 798, Ganapathipillai Gangaser Ponnambalam (1901-1972), diplomat. No. 799, Aboobucker Mohammed Abdul Azeez (1911-1973), scholar.

1986, May 22 Perf. 13x12½
795 A312 75c multicolored .15 .15
796 A312 75c multicolored .15 .15
797 A312 75c multicolored .15 .15
798 A312 75c multicolored .15 .15
799 A312 75c multicolored .15 .15
Set value .30 .30

1986, June 23
800 A313 1r multicolored .15 .15

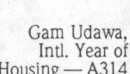

Gam Udawa,
Intl. Year of
Housing — A314

1986, June 23 Perf. 13½x13
801 A314 75c multicolored .15 .15

Arthur V.
Dias — A315

1986, July 31 Perf. 14x15
802 A315 1r multicolored .15 .15

World
Wildlife
Fund
A316

Elephants: a, Adult with tusks. b, Adult, calf. c, Adult. d, Family in river.

1986, Aug. 5 Perf. 15x14
803 Strip of 4 1.40 1.40
a.-d. A316 5r any single .35 .33

2nd Indo-Pacific
Congress on Legal
Medicine and
Forensic
Sciences — A317

1986, Aug. 14 Perf. 13½x13
804 A317 8.50r multicolored .62 .62

Submarine
Cable
A318

1986, Sept. 8 Perf. 13½x14
805 A318 5.75r Handset, map .40 .40

South-East Asia, Middle East, Western Europe Submarine Cable System.

Dag Hammarskjold
Award — A320

Second Natl.
School Games,
Sept. 22-
27 — A321

1986, Sept. 20 Litho. Perf. 13x12½
808 A320 2r multicolored .16 .16

1986, Sept. 22 Perf. 12
809 A321 1r multicolored .15 .15

Natl. Surveyor's Institute, 60th Anniv. — A322

1986, Sept. 27   *Perf. 13¹/₂x13*
810 A322 75c multicolored   .15   .15

Ananda College, Cent. — A323

College crest and: 75c, College. 5r, Athletic field. 5.75r, Founders Migettuwatte Gunananda, Hikkaduwe Sumangala and Col. H.S. Olcott, Buddhist flag and College, 1886, 1986. 6r, Crest on flag.

1986, Nov. 1   *Perf. 12*
811 A323 75c multicolored   .15   .15
812 A323 5r multicolored   .40   .40
813 A323 5.75r multicolored   .45   .45
814 A323 6r multicolored   .48   .48
       Nos. 811-814 (4)   1.48   1.48

Wildlife Conservation A324

1986, Nov. 11
815 A324 35c Mangrove habitat   .15   .15
816 A324 50c Rhizophora apiculata   .15   .15
817 A324 75c Germinating flower   .15   .15
818 A324 6r Fiddler crab   .48   .48
       Set value   .64   .64

Preservation of mangrove habitats.

Intl. Year of Shelter for the Homeless A325

1987, Jan. 1   Litho.   *Perf. 13x13¹/₂*
819 A325 75c multicolored   .15   .15

A.I. Thero, 19th Cent. Theologian A326   Proctor John De Silva (b. 1854), Lawyer and Playwright A327

1987, Jan. 29   *Perf. 12*
820 A326 5.75r multicolored   .45   .45

1987, Jan. 31
821 A327 5.75r multicolored   .45   .45

Mahapola Educational Plan, 7th Anniv. — A328

1987, Feb. 6
822 A328 75c multicolored   .15   .15

Dr. R.L. Brohier, Historian — A329

1987, Feb. 14
823 A329 5.75r multicolored   .45   .45

Sri Lanka Tire Corp., 25th Anniv. A330

1987, Mar. 23   *Perf. 14*
824 A330 5.75r multicolored   .45   .45

Sri Lanka Medical Assoc., Cent. A331

1987, Mar. 24   *Perf. 13x13¹/₂*
825 A331 5.75r multicolored   .45   .45

Farmers' Pension and Social Security Plan A332   AGRO MAHAWELI '87 Agricultural Exposition A333

1987, Mar. 29   *Perf. 14*
826 A332 75c multicolored   .15   .15

1987, Apr. 2   *Perf. 12*
827 A333 75c multicolored   .15   .15

Child Immunization Program A334

1987, Apr. 7   *Perf. 13¹/₂*
828 A334 1r multicolored   .15   .15

World Health Day.

Sinhalese and Tamil New Year — A335

1987, Apr. 9   *Perf. 12*
829 A335 75c Three girls, swing   .15   .15
830 A335 5r Lamp, women   .40   .40

Vesak Festival Lanterns A336

1987, May 4   *Perf. 12*
831 A336 50c Lotus   .15   .15
832 A336 75c Octagonal   .15   .15
833 A336 5r Star   .40   .40
834 A336 10r Gok   .80   .80
   a.   Souvenir sheet of 4, #831-834   1.40   1.40
       Nos. 831-834 (4)   1.50   1.50

Natl. Olympic Committee, 50th Anniv. A337

1987, May 8   *Perf. 13¹/₂*
835 A337 10r multicolored   .80   .80

Birds A338

1987, May 18   *Perf. 14*
836 A338 50c Layard's parakeet   .15   .15
837 A338 1r Legge's flowerpecker   .15   .15
838 A338 5r Sri Lanka white-headed starling   .40   .40
839 A338 10r Sri Lanka rufous babbler   .80   .80
   a.   Souvenir sheet of 4, #836-839   1.40   1.40
       Nos. 836-839 (4)   1.50   1.50

Natl. Heroes — A339

Designs: No. 840, Heenatiyana Sri Dhammaloka Thero, 20th cent. theologian. No. 841, P. de S. Kularatne, educator. No. 842, M.C. Abdul Rahuman, politician.

1987, May 22   *Perf. 12*
840 A339 75c multicolored   .15   .15
841 A339 75c multicolored   .15   .15
842 A339 75c multicolored   .15   .15
       Set value   .18   .18

Gam Udawa A340

1987, June 23
843 A340 75c multicolored   .15   .15

Village reformation movement.

Natl. Forestry Agency, Cent. A341

1987, June 25
844 A341 75c Mesua nagassarium   .15   .15
845 A341 5r Elephants in forest   .40   .40

Founder H.S. Olcott and College A342

1987, June 30
846 A342 75c multicolored   .15   .15

Dharmaraja College, cent.

No. 528 Redrawn with Denomination in Upper Right Corner

1987, July 1   Photo.   *Perf. 13x13¹/₂*
       Size: 20x24mm

847 A189 75c green & gold   .15   .15

Youth Services Emblem A343

1987, July 15   Litho.   *Perf. 12*
848 A343 75c multicolored   .15   .15

Natl. Youth Services Act, 20th anniv.

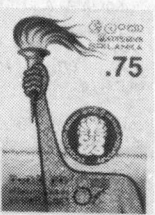 

Mahaweli Games — A344   Ceylon Bible Society, 175th Anniv. — A345

1987, Sept. 5   Litho.   *Perf. 12*
849 A344 75c multicolored   .15   .15

1987, Oct. 2
850 A345 5.75r multicolored   .48   .48

Kandy Friend-in-Need Society, 150th Anniv. — A346

1987, Nov. 4   *Perf. 13¹/₂x13*
851 A346 75c multicolored   .15   .15

Christmas
1987 — A347

Sir Ernest de Silva
(1887-1957),
Banker,
Philatelist — A348

1987, Nov. 25 Litho. **Perf. 12**
852 A347 75c Mother and Child .15 .15
853 A347 10r Infant, star, dove .80 .80
  a. Souvenir sheet of 2, #852-853 .90 .90

1987, Nov. 25 **Perf. 13x13½**
854 A348 75c multicolored .15 .15

1st Convocation
Ceremony at
Buddhist and Pali
University — A349

Missionary Work of
Fr. Joseph Vaz
(1651-1711),
300th
Anniv. — A350

1987, Dec. 14 **Perf. 12**
855 A349 75c yel, lake & org yel .15 .15

1987, Dec. 15
856 A350 75c multicolored .15 .15

Buddhist Publication
Soc., Kandy, 30th
Anniv. — A351

Design: Wheel of Life, dagaba (temple cupola)
and Bo (Tree of Life) leaf.

1988, Jan. 1 Litho. **Perf. 12**
857 A351 75c multicolored .15 .15

Mahapola
Dharmayatra, 5th
Anniv. — A352

1988, Jan. 4 **Perf. 13½x13**
858 A352 75c multicolored .15 .15

Ceylon Arts Soc.,
Cent. — A353

1988, Jan. 8 **Perf. 12**
859 A353 75c multicolored .15 .15

Opening of the
Natl. Youth
Center,
Maharagama
A354

1988, Jan. 31 **Perf. 13½x13**
860 A354 1r multicolored .15 .15

Natl. Independence,
40th
Anniv. — A355

Mahapola
Movement, 8th
Anniv. — A356

1988, Feb. 4 **Perf. 12**
861 A355 75c shown .15 .15
862 A355 8.50r Heraldic lion, "40" .68 .68

1988, Feb. 11
863 A356 75c Youth Education Services .15 .15

Transportation Board, 30th Anniv. — A357

1988, Feb. 19
864 A357 5.75r multicolored .48 .48

Weligama Sri
Sumangala Maha
Nayake Thero (1825-
1905), Buddhist
Monk, Sanskrit
Scholar — A358

1988, Mar. 13
865 A358 75c multicolored .15 .15

Artillery
Regiment,
Cent. — A359

1988, Apr. 20
866 A359 5.75r multicolored .48 .48

Chevalier I.X.
Pereira (1888-1951),
Politician — A360

1988, Apr. 26 Litho. **Perf. 12**
867 A360 5.75r multicolored .48 .48

Vesak
Festival
A361

Paintings in Suriyagoda Sri Narendraramaya
Viharaya temple, Kandy District: 50c, Buddha inviting deities and brahmas to be born into the world as
Buddhists. 75c, Buddha walking seven steps on
seven lotus flowers, followers paying homage.

1988, May 13 **Perf. 12½x12**
868 A361 50c multicolored .15 .15
869 A361 75c multicolored .15 .15
  a. Souvenir sheet of 2, #868-869 .15 .15
    Set value .15 .15

Natl. Heroes — A362

Designs: No. 870, Rev. Father Ferdinand Bonnel
(1873-1945), Jesuit priest who founded St.
Michael's College, Batticaloa. No. 871, Sir Razik
Fareed (1893-1984), political and social reformer.
No. 872, W.F. Gunawardhana (b. 1861), founder
of the Oriental Studies Soc. No. 873, Edward Alexander Nugawela (1898-1972), politician. No. 874,
Sir Edwin Arthur Lewis Wijeyewardene (b. 1887),
first Ceylonese chief justice, attorney general.

1988, May 22 **Perf. 12x12½**
870 A362 75c multicolored .15 .15
871 A362 75c multicolored .15 .15
872 A362 75c multicolored .15 .15
873 A362 75c multicolored .15 .15
874 A362 75c multicolored .15 .15
    Set value .30 .30

Gam Udawa,
10th Anniv.
A363

1988, June 23 Litho. **Perf. 12**
875 A363 75c multicolored .15 .15

Village reformation movement.

Maliyadeva
College,
Cent. — A364

1988, June 30 **Perf. 13½x13**
876 A364 75c multicolored .15 .15

Bird Type of 1983

1988, Sept. 28 Litho. **Perf. 14½**
877 A264 7r like No. 692 .42 .42

Mohamed
J.M. Lafir
(1929-1980),
World
Amateur
Billiards
Champion
A365

1988, July 5 Litho. **Perf. 12½x12**
878 A365 5.75r multicolored .45 .45

Australia
Bicentennial
A366

1988, July 19 Litho. **Perf. 12**
879 A366 8.50r multicolored .52 .52

Gunaratna Maha
Nayake Thero
(1752-1832),
Buddhist and
Sinhalese Language
Scholar — A367

Mahaweli
Games — A368

1988, Aug. 11 **Perf. 12x12½**
880 A367 75c multicolored .15 .15

1988, Sept. 3 **Perf. 12**
881 A368 75c multicolored .15 .15

1988 Summer
Olympics,
Seoul — A369

WHO, 40th
Anniv. — A370

1988, Sept. 6 **Perf. 12x12½**
882 A369 75c Running .15 .15
883 A369 1r Swimming .15 .15
884 A369 5.75r Boxing .45 .45
885 A369 8.50r Handshake, map,
    emblems .68 .68
  a. Souvenir sheet of 4, #882-885 1.30 1.30
    Nos. 882-885 (4) 1.43 1.43

1988, Sept. 12 **Perf. 12**
886 A370 75c multicolored .15 .15

3rd Natl.
School
Games, Sept.
20-25
A371

1988, Sept. 20
887 A371 1r multicolored .15 .15

Mahatma
Gandhi — A372

1988, Oct. 2 **Perf. 12**
888 A372 75c multicolored .15 .15

Transportation and Communication
Decade, 1978-88 — A373

Modes of transportation and: 75c, Globe. 5.75r,
Communication tower.

1988, Oct. 24   Litho.   *Perf. 12¹/₂x12*
889 A373 75c multicolored .15 .15
890 A373 5.75r multicolored .45 .45

Randenigala
Project
A374

1988, Oct. 31   *Perf. 12*
891 A374 75c Woman, dam, power
station .15 .15
892 A374 5.75r Hydrelectric dam .45 .45

Some copies were distributed at the time the set
was originally planned to be issued in 1986.

A375   Christmas — A376

1988, Nov. 17   Litho.   *Perf. 13¹/₂*
893 A375 75c multicolored .15 .15

Opening of Gramodaya Folk Art Center.

1988, Nov. 25   *Perf. 12x12¹/₂*
894 A376 75c shown .15 .15
895 A376 8.50r Shepherds see star .68 .68
a. Souvenir sheet of 2, #894-895 .75 .75

A377   Waterfalls — A378

1988, Dec. 28   *Perf. 12*
896 A377 75c multicolored .15 .15

E.W. Adikaram (1905-85), educator.

1989, Aug. 11   Litho.   *Perf. 12*
897 A378 75c Dunhinda .15 .15
898 A378 1r Rawana .15 .15
899 A378 5.75r Laxapana .40 .40
900 A378 8.50r Diyaluma .60 .60
Nos. 897-900 (4) 1.30 1.30

Free
Distribution
of School
Text Books,
10th Anniv.
A379

1989, Jan. 23   Litho.   *Perf. 13¹/₂x13*
901 A379 75c multicolored .15 .15

Poets — A380

1989, Jan. 27   *Perf. 13*
902 A380 75c Wimalaratne
Kumaragama .15 .15
903 A380 75c G.H. Perera .15 .15
904 A380 75c Sagara Palansuriya .15 .15
905 A380 75c P.B. Alwis Perera .15 .15
Set value .24 .24

Mahapola
Educational
Plan, 8th
Anniv.
A381

1989, Feb.   *Perf. 13¹/₂*
906 A381 75c multicolored .15 .15

Chamber of
Commerce, 150th
Anniv. — A382

1989, Mar. 25   Litho.   *Perf. 12*
907 A382 75c multicolored .15 .15

AGRO
Mahaweli
A383

1989, Sept. 2   Litho.   *Perf. 12*
908 A383 75c multicolored .15 .15

Famous Men
A384

1989, May 22
909 A384 75c Simon Casie Chitty .15 .15
910 A384 75c Parawahera Sri
Vajiragnana Thero .15 .15
911 A384 75c Fr. Maurice Le Goc .15 .15
912 A384 75c Hemapala Munidasa .15 .15
913 A384 75c Ananda Samarakoon .15 .15
Set value .35 .35

Nos. 910-913 vert.

Hartley College,
150th Anniv. (in
1988) — A385

1989, June 5
914 A385 75c multicolored .15 .15

Vesak
Festival
A386

Various paintings in Medawala Viharaya,
Harispattuwa.

1989, May 15   Litho.   *Perf. 12¹/₂x12*
915 A386 50c multicolored .15 .15
916 A386 75c multicolored .15 .15
917 A386 5r multicolored .40 .40
918 A386 5.75r multicolored .48 .48
a. Souvenir sheet of 4, #915-918 1.00 1.00
Set value .98 .98

For surcharge see No. 953A.

Pres.
Premadasa's
Declaration
Establishing
the Ministry
of Buddha
Sasana
A387

1989, June 18   Litho.   *Perf. 12¹/₂x12*
919 A387 75c multicolored .15 .15

Gam Udawa,
11th Anniv.
A388

1989, June 23
920 A388 75c multicolored .15 .15

Village reformation movement.

French
Revolution,
Bicent. — A389

1989, Aug. 26   Litho.   *Perf. 13¹/₂x13*
921 A389 8.50r rose & deep blue .68 .68

Bank of Ceylon,
50th
Anniv. — A390

1989, Aug. 31
922 A390 75c Old, new headquarters .15 .15
923 A390 5r Emblem, flowers .40 .40
Set value .46 .46

Jana Saviya
Grants — A391

1989, June 23   Litho.   *Perf. 12x11¹/₂*
924 A391 75c multicolored .15 .15

Development program to eliminate poverty and
improve the standard of living through education
and by providing food, health care, shelter and
clothing.
See No. 953. For surcharge see No. 955.

Baptist
Mission,
177th
Anniv.
A392

1989, Aug. 19   *Perf. 12¹/₂x12*
925 A392 5.75r James Chater,
church, 1812 .45 .45

State Literary   Wilhelm
Festival — A393   Geiger — A394

1989, Sept. 22   *Perf. 12x11¹/₂*
926 A393 75c multicolored .15 .15

1989, Sept. 30   *Perf. 13x13¹/₂*
927 A394 75c multicolored .15 .15

Wilhelm Geiger (1856-1943), German philologist
who studied Sinhalese.

Wildlife Type of 1981

1989, Oct. 11   *Perf. 14*
928 A219 3r like No. 595 .24 .24

No. 928 has black inscriptions and is dated
"1989." See No. 729 for brown inscriptions.

Famous   Sir Cyril de
Lawyers — A395   Zoysa — A396

1989, Oct. 16   *Perf. 12x11¹/₂*
929 A395 75c H.V. Perera (1890-
1969) .15 .15
930 A395 75c Sir Ivor Jennings
(1903-1965) .15 .15
Set value .15 .15

1989, Oct. 26   *Perf. 13x13¹/₂*
931 A396 75c multicolored .15 .15

Sir Cyril de Zoysa (1896-1978), key figure in the
Buddhist cultural reformation.

Asia-Pacific
Telecommunity, 10th
Anniv. — A397

1989, Nov. 1   *Perf. 12x12¹/₂*
932 A397 5.75r multicolored .45 .45

Sri Sucharitha
Viyaparaya
Oratory
Children's
Soc., 50th
Anniv.
A398

1989, Nov. 9   *Perf. 13*
933 A398 75c multicolored .15 .15

1st Moon Landing, 20th Anniv. — A399

Christmas — A400

1989, Nov. 10   *Perf. 12x12¹/₂*
934	A399	75c Apollo 11 liftoff, crew	.15	.15
935	A399	1r Astronaut descending ladder	.15	.15
936	A399	2r Astronaut on lunar surface	.16	.16
937	A399	5.75r Lunar surface, view of Earth	.45	.45
a.		Souvenir sheet of 4, #934-937	.75	.75
		Set value	.75	.75

1989, Nov. 21   *Perf. 13¹/₂*
938	A400	75c Adoration of the Shepherds	.15	.15
939	A400	8.50r Adoration of the Magi	.62	.62
a.		Souvenir sheet of 2, #938-939	.70	.70

Devananda Nayake Thero — A401

1989, Nov. 25   *Perf. 12x11¹/₂*
940	A401	75c multicolored	.15	.15

Devananda Nayake Thero (1921-1983), religious scholar, educator, reformer.

Rev. William Ault, College and Crest — A402

1989, Nov. 29   *Perf. 11¹/₂x12*
941	A402	75c multicolored	.15	.15

Batticaloa Methodist Central College, 175th anniv.

Nuwara Eliya Golf Club, Cent. A403

1989, Dec. 8   *Perf. 14x13¹/₂*
942	A403	75c shown	.15	.15
943	A403	8.50r Course, golf house	.68	.68

Raja — A404

1989, Dec. 12   *Perf. 13x13¹/₂*
944	A404	75c multicolored	.15	.15

Raja (1913-1988), the royal tusker of the Sri Dalada Maligawa that carried the relic casket in the Kandy Esala Procession.

Gampaha Wickamarachchi Ayurveda Medical College, 60th Anniv. — A405

1989, Dec. 14   *Perf. 13¹/₂x13*
945	A405	75c Founder, institute	.15	.15

Udunuwara Sri Sarananda Mahanayake Thero (1867-1947), Educator — A406

1989, Dec. 20   *Perf. 12x12¹/₂*
946	A406	75c multicolored	.15	.15

Railway Dept., 125th Anniv. A407

1989, Dec. 27   *Perf. 11¹/₂x12, 13 (3r)*
947	A407	75c Train, viaduct	.15	.15
948	A407	2r Train, light signal, Maradana Station	.15	.15
949	A407	3r Steam locomotive, semaphore signal	.18	.18
950	A407	7r 1st train in Sri Lanka	.42	.42
		Nos. 947-950 (4)	.90	.90

Thomas Cooray (1901-1988), 1st Native Sri Lankan Cardinal — A408

Justin Wijayawardena (1904-1982), Educator, Politician — A409

1989, Dec. 28   *Perf. 13x13¹/₂*
951	A408	75c multicolored	.15	.15

1990, Jan. 14   *Perf. 12x12¹/₂*
952	A409	1r multicolored	.15	.15

Jana Suviya Grants Type of 1989

1990, Jan. 31   *Litho.*   *Perf. 12x11¹/₂*
953	A391	1r multicolored	.15	.15

No. 918 Surcharged

.25

1990, Feb. 16   *Litho.*   *Perf. 12¹/₂x12*
953A	A386	25c on 5.75r multi	.15	.15

Induruwe Uttarananda Mahanayake Thero — A411

1990, Mar. 15   *Litho.*   *Perf. 12*
954	A411	1r multicolored	.15	.15

No. 924 Surcharged   **1.00** ≡

1990, Mar. 22   *Litho.*   *Perf. 12x11¹/₂*
955	A391	1r on 75c multi	.15	.15

Silver Jubilee of Laksala A413

Traditional handicrafts.

1990, Apr. 2   *Litho.*   *Perf. 12*
956	A413	1r Drums	.15	.15
957	A413	2r Silverware	.16	.16
958	A413	3r Lacquerware	.24	.24
959	A413	8r Dumbara mats	.65	.65
		Nos. 956-959 (4)	1.20	1.20

Vesak Festival A414

Various paintings in Wewurukannala Buduraja Maha Viharaya.

1990, May 2   *Perf. 12¹/₂x12*
960	A414	75c multicolored	.15	.15
961	A414	1r multicolored	.15	.15
962	A414	2r multicolored	.16	.16
963	A414	8r multicolored	.65	.65
a.		Souvenir sheet of 4, #960-963	.95	.95
		Set value	.94	.94

A415

Famous Men — A416

1990, May 22   *Perf. 12*
964	A415	1r Rev. T.M.F. Long	.15	.15

Size: 25x39mm
Perf. 12x12¹/₂
965	A416	1r D.P.A. Wijewardene	.15	.15
966	A416	1r L.T.P. Manjusri	.15	.15
967	A416	1r M.D. Ratnasuriya	.15	.15
		Set value	.32	.32

Gam Udawa Program, 12th Anniv. A417

1990, June 23   *Perf. 12¹/₂x12*
968	A417	1r multicolored	.15	.15

Dept. of Archaeology, Cent. — A418

Designs: 1r, Gold reliquary from Delivala Temple, c. 200 B.C. 2r, Statuette of Ganesha (the Elephant God) from Polonnaruwa. 3r, Terrace of the Bodhi-tree at Isurumuni Vihara. 8r, Stone seat with inscription of King Nissankamalle, 12th century A.D.

1990, July 7   *Perf. 12*
969	A418	1r black & orange	.15	.15
970	A418	2r black & gray	.16	.16
971	A418	3r black, yel grn & gold	.24	.24
972	A418	8r black & gold	.65	.65
		Nos. 969-972 (4)	1.20	1.20

Sri Lanka Tennis Assoc., 75th Anniv. A419

1990, Aug. 14   *Perf. 13¹/₂*
973	A419	1r Player ready to volley	.15	.15
974	A419	1r Player receiving volley	.15	.15
a.		Pair, #973-974	.16	.16
975	A419	8r Men players	.65	.65
976	A419	8r Women players	.65	.65
a.		Pair, #975-976	1.30	1.30
		Nos. 973-976 (4)	1.60	1.60

Fish — A420

1990, Sept. 14   *Perf. 11¹/₂*
977	A420	25c Spotted loach	.15	.15
978	A420	2r Ornate paradise fish	.16	.16
979	A420	8r Mountain labeo	.65	.65
980	A420	20r Cherry barb	1.60	1.60
a.		Souvenir sheet of 4, #977-980	2.46	2.46
		Nos. 977-980 (4)	2.56	2.56

A421

A422

1990, Dec. 26   *Perf. 12*
981	A421	1r Letter box, 1904	.15	.15
982	A421	2r Mail runner, 1815	.16	.16
983	A421	5r Mail coach, 1832	.40	.40
984	A421	10r Nuwara-Eliya Post Office, 1894	.80	.80
		Nos. 981-984 (4)	1.51	1.51

Sri Lanka Postal Service, 175th anniv.

1990, Oct. 28   *Litho.*   *Perf. 12*
985	A422	1r multicolored	.15	.15

Rukmani Devi (1923-78), actress.

Christmas — A423

1990, Nov. 28   *Perf. 13*
986 A423   1r Mary, Joseph at inn   .15   .15
987 A423 10r Adoration of the Magi   .80   .80
  a.   Souv. sheet of 2, #986-987, perf. 12   .88   .88

World AIDS
Day — A424

1990, Nov. 30
988 A424   1r multicolored   .15   .15
989 A424   8r AIDS Virus   .65   .65

A425   A426

1990, Dec. 8   *Perf. 12*
990 A425   1r multicolored   .15   .15
Dharmapala College, 50th anniv.

1990, Dec. 14   *Litho.*   *Perf. 12*
991 A426   1r olive green & brown   .15   .15
Peri Sunderam (b. 1890), political & social
reformer.

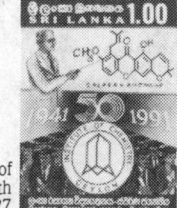

Ceylon Institute of
Chemistry, 50th
anniv. — A427

1991, Jan. 25   *Litho.*   *Perf. 12*
992 A427   1r multicolored   .15   .15

Vesak Festival
A428

Various scenes from Buddha's life.

1991, May 17   *Litho.*   *Perf. 12*
993 A428 75c multicolored   .15   .15
994 A428   1r multicolored   .15   .15
995 A428   2r multicolored   .15   .15
996 A428 11r multicolored   .55   .55
  a.   Souvenir sheet of 4, #993-996   .70   .70
        Set value   .70   .70

A429   A430

1991, May 31   *Perf. 12*
997 A429   1r multicolored   .15   .15
Mahabodhi Society, cent.

1991, May 22   *Litho.*   *Perf. 12x12½*
Famous men.
 998 A430   1r Narada Thero   .15   .15
 999 A430   1r Sir Muttu Coomaras-
                 wamy   .15   .15
1000 A430   1r Dr. Andreas Nell   .15   .15
1001 A430   1r W.A. Silva   .15   .15
        Set value   .20   .20

Gam
Udawa,
13th
Anniv.
A431

1991, June 23   *Litho.*   *Perf. 12½*
1002 A431   1r multicolored   .15   .15

Henpitagedera
Gnanaseeha Nayake
Thero (1909-1981),
Religious
Leader — A432

1991, Aug. 1
1003 A432   1r multicolored   .15   .15

Colombo Plan,
40th Anniv.
A433

1991, July 1   *Litho.*   *Perf. 12*
1004 A433   1r multicolored   .15   .15

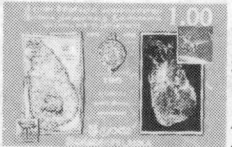

Survey
Dept.,
190th
Anniv.
A434

1991, Aug. 2   *Perf. 12½*
1005 A434   1r multicolored   .15   .15

Police
Service,
125th
Anniv.
A435

1991, Sept. 3   *Litho.*   *Perf. 12½*
1006 A435   1r multicolored   .15   .15

6th SAARC
Summit
A436

1991, Dec. 21   *Litho.*   *Perf. 12½*
1007 A436   1r shown   .15   .15
1008 A436   8r Flags encircling bldg.   .40   .40
        Set value   .45   .45

Kingswood
College,
Cent.
A437

1991, Oct. 26   *Perf. 12½x12*
1009 A437   1r multicolored   .15   .15

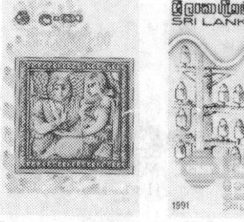

Christmas — A439   A440

1991, Nov. 19   *Litho.*   *Perf. 12½*
1014 A439   1r The Annunciation   .15   .15
1015 A439 10r Nativity scene   .50   .50
  a.   Sheet of 2, #1014-1015   .65   .65

1991, Nov. 23
Telecommunications: 1r, Early telephone network. 2r, Switchboard operations. 8r, Satellite
transmitters, cable network. 10r, Telephone, fiber
optic cable, computer, cordless telephone, FAX
machine.
1016 A440   1r multicolored   .15   .15
1017 A440   2r multicolored   .15   .15
1018 A440   8r multicolored   .40   .40
1019 A440 10r multicolored   .50   .50
        Nos. 1016-1019 (4)   1.20 1.20

5th South
Asian
Federation
Games
A441

1991, Dec. 22   *Perf. 14*
1020 A441   1r Mascot   .15   .15
1021 A441   2r Emblem   .15   .15
1022 A441   4r Stadium, Colombo   .20   .20
1023 A441 11r Globe and flags   .55   .55
        Set value   .90   .90

Year of
Exports
A442

1992, Jan. 13   *Litho.*   *Perf. 11½x12*
1024 A442   1r multicolored   .15   .15

Mahinda
College,
Cent.
A443

1992, Mar. 2   *Litho.*   *Perf. 11½x12*
1025 A443   1r multicolored   .15   .15

General Ranjan
Wijeratne (1931-
1991) — A444

1992, Mar. 2   *Litho.*   *Perf. 12x12½*
1026 A444   1r multicolored   .15   .15

Tea Production,
125th Anniv.
A445

Field of tea and: 1r, Tea picker. 2r, Family, cup
and glass of tea. 5r, Package of tea. 10r, James
Taylor.

1992, Feb. 12   *Perf. 13½*
1027 A445   1r multicolored   .15   .15
1028 A445   2r multicolored   .15   .15
1029 A445   5r multicolored   .25   .25
1030 A445 10r multicolored   .50   .50
        Nos. 1027-1030 (4)   1.05 1.05

Newstead
College,
175th
Anniv. (in
1991)
A446

1992, Mar. 13   *Litho.*   *Perf. 11½x12*
1031 A446   1r multicolored   .15   .15
        Dated 1991.

Mahapola Scholarship
Fund, 11th
Anniv. — A447

1992, Mar. 30   *Perf. 12*
1032 A447   1r multicolored   .15   .15

Vesak Festival
A448

Mural paintings from Kottimbulwala Rajamaha
Vihara: 75c, Dukula and Parika retiring to forest.
1r, Sama and parents living in forest. 8r, Sama
directing blind parents to hermitage. 11r, Sama's
parents approach wounded son.

1992, May 5   *Litho.*   *Perf. 11½x12*
1033 A448 75c multicolored   .15   .15
1034 A448   1r multicolored   .15   .15
1035 A448   8r multicolored   .48   .48
1036 A448 11r multicolored   .68   .68
  a.   Souvenir sheet of 4, #1033-1036 1.30 1.30
        Set value   1.27 1.27

A449   A450

National Heroes: No. 1037, Wadeebhasinha
Dewamottawe Amarawansa Thero. No. 1038, R. A.
Mirando. No. 1039, Gate Mudaliyar N. Cana-
ganayagam. No. 1040, I.L.M. Abdul Azeez.

1992, May 22   **Perf. 14**
1037 A449 1r multicolored   .15 .15
1038 A449 1r multicolored   .15 .15
1039 A449 1r multicolored   .15 .15
1040 A449 1r multicolored   .15 .15
    Set value   .24 .24

1992, June 14 **Litho.** **Perf. 12x12½**
1041 A450 1r multicolored   .15 .15

Introduction of Buddhism on Sri Lanka by Anubudu Mihindu Jayanthi, 2300th anniv.

Gam Udawa, 14th Anniv. A451

1992, June 23   **Perf. 12**
1042 A451 1r multicolored   .15 .15

Postal Excellence Service Awards A452

Designs: 1r, Award presentation, postal work. 10r, Award of excellence medals, No. 1043 canceled on envelope.

1992, July 11 **Litho.** **Perf. 14**
1043 A452 1r multicolored   .15 .15
1044 A452 10r multicolored   .50 .50
    Set value   .55 .55

A453   A454

Masks of Sri Lanka.

1992, Aug. 19 **Litho.** **Perf. 13**
1045 A453 1r Narilata   .15 .15
1046 A453 2r Mudali   .15 .15
1047 A453 5r Queen   .25 .25
1048 A453 10r King   .50 .50
  a. Souvenir sheet of 4, #1045-1048 .90 .90
    Set value   .90 .90

1992, Sept. 15 **Litho.** **Perf. 14**
1049 A454 1r Running   .15 .15
1050 A454 11r Rifle shooting .65 .65
1051 A454 13r Swimming   .78 .78
1052 A454 15r Weight lifting .90 .90
  a. Souvenir sheet of 4, #1049-1052 2.50 2.50
    Nos. 1049-1052 (4)   2.48 2.48

1992 Summer Olympics, Barcelona.

Cricket in Sri Lanka, 160th Anniv. A455

1992, Sept. 8 **Litho.** **Perf. 13**
1053 A455 5r multicolored   .25 .25

Vijaya Kumaratunga, Entertainer and Political Leader, Birth Anniv. — A456

1992, Oct. 9
1054 A456 1r multicolored   .15 .15

Al-Bahjathul Ibraheemiyyah Arabic College, Cent. — A457

1992, Oct. 24   **Perf. 12**
1055 A457 1r multicolored   .15 .15

A458   Christmas — A459

1992, Oct. 25 **Litho.** **Perf. 12x11½**
1056 A458 1r multicolored   .15 .15

Dutch Reformed Church in Sri Lanka, 350th anniv.

1992, Nov. 17 **Litho.** **Perf. 12x11½**
1057 A459 1r Holy Family   .15 .15
1058 A459 9r Church, family .45 .45
  a. Souvenir sheet of 2, #1057-1058 .50 .50
    Set value   .50 .50

Discovery of America, 500th Anniv. A460

Designs: 1r, Ships at sea, Aug. 1492. 11r, First landing in the Americas, Oct. 1492. 13r, Santa Maria aground, Dec. 1492. 15r, Return to Spain, Apr. 1493.

1992, Dec. 1   **Perf. 14**
1059 A460 1r multicolored   .15 .15
1060 A460 11r multicolored .55 .55
1061 A460 13r multicolored .65 .65
1062 A460 15r multicolored .75 .75
  a. Souvenir sheet of 4, #1059-1062 2.00 2.00
    Nos. 1059-1062 (4)   2.10 2.10

No. 564 Surcharged   **2.00 ≡**

1992, Dec. 1 **Litho.** **Perf. 14**
1062B A206 2r on 10c multi .15 .15

Dambagasare Sri Sumedhankara Maha Nayake Thero (1892-1984), Buddhist Monk — A461

1992, Dec. 10 **Litho.** **Perf. 12**
1063 A461 1r multicolored   .15 .15

University Education in Sri Lanka A462

1992, Dec. 12 **Litho.** **Perf. 12**
1064 A462 1r multicolored   .15 .15

No. 1064 was not available until Dec. 1993.

University of Colombo, 50th Anniv. (in 1992) — A463

1993, Mar. 23 **Litho.** **Perf. 13**
1065 A463 1r multicolored   .15 .15

Zahira College, Cent. — A464

1993, Apr. 7
1066 A464 1r multicolored   .15 .15

Vesak Festival — A465

Designs based on verses from the Dhammapada (sermons of Buddha): 75c, Magandiya being presented to Buddha. 1r, Kisa Gotami carrying dead child. 3r, Patachara, dead family members. 10r, Conversion of Angulimala, the murderer.

1993, Apr. 30   **Perf. 12x12½**
1067 A465 75c multicolored .15 .15
1068 A465 1r multicolored   .15 .15
1069 A465 3r multicolored   .16 .16
1070 A465 10r multicolored .50 .50
  a. Souvenir sheet of 4, #1067-1070 .75 .75
    Set value   .75 .75

A466   A467

1993, May 10   **Perf. 12**
1071 A466 1r Guide, tent, emblem .15 .15
1072 A466 5r Activities, map   .25 .25

Girl Guides in Sri Lanka, 75th Anniv. (in 1992).

1993, May 22   **Perf. 14**

National Heroes: No. 1073, Yagirala Sri Pagnananda Maha Nayaka Thero. No. 1074, C.P. De Silva. No. 1075, Wilmot A. Perera. No. 1076, N.D.H. Abdul Caffoor.

1073 A467 1r multicolored   .15 .15
1074 A467 1r multicolored   .15 .15
1075 A467 1r multicolored   .15 .15
1076 A467 1r multicolored   .15 .15
    Set value   .20 .20

Gam Udawa, 15th Anniv. A468

1993, June 23 **Litho.** **Perf. 12½**
1077 A468 1r multicolored   .15 .15

Co-operative Consumer Service, 50th Anniv. A469

1993, July 3   **Perf. 13**
1078 A469 1r multicolored   .15 .15

Birds A470

Designs: 3r, Ashy-headed laughing thrush. 4r, Ceylon brown-capped babbler. 5r, Red-faced malkoha. 10r, Ceylon hill-mynah.

1993, July 14   **Perf. 12½x12**
1079 A470 3r multicolored   .15 .15
1080 A470 4r multicolored   .15 .15
1081 A470 5r multicolored   .18 .18
1082 A470 10r multicolored .38 .38
  a. Souvenir sheet of 4, #1079-1082 .85 .85
    Nos. 1079-1082 (4)   .86 .86

Talawila Church, 150th Anniv. A471

1993, July 26   **Perf. 13**
1083 A471 1r multicolored   .15 .15

Postal Excellence Service Awards — A472

1993, Aug. 22
1084 A472 1r multicolored   .15 .15

Technical Education in Sri Lanka, Cent. — A473

1993, Dec. 17
1085 A473 1r multicolored   .15 .15

Musaeus College, Cent. — A474

1993, Nov. 15
1086 A474 1r multicolored .15 .15

Christmas A475

Designs: 1r, Presentation of infant Jesus in Temple of Jerusalem. 17r, Boy Jesus in Temple.

1993, Nov. 30   Perf. 14x13½
1087 A475 1r multicolored .15 .15
1088 A475 17r multicolored .85 .85
a.   Souvenir sheet of 2, #1087-1088 .90 .90

Youth and Health — A476

1993, Dec. 16   Perf. 14
1089 A476 1r multicolored .15 .15

Old Boy's Assoc., Trinity College, Kandy, Cent. — A478

1994, Feb. 11   Litho.   Perf. 12½
1091 A478 1r multicolored .15 .15

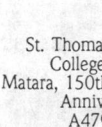 

St. Thomas College, Matara, 150th Anniv. A479

1994, Mar. 10   Litho.   Perf. 13
1092 A479 1r multicolored .15 .15

St. Joseph's College, 125th Anniv. A480

1994, Apr. 4   Litho.   Perf. 12½
1093 A480 1r multicolored .15 .15

Siyambalangamuwe Sri Gunaratana Thero — A481

1994, Apr. 2   Litho.   Perf. 13
1094 A481 1r multicolored .15 .15

ILO, 75th Anniv. — A482

1994, May. 12
1095 A482 1r multicolored .15 .15

Vesak Festival A483

Designs show actions by Bodhisatva in four of ten perfections: 1r, Dana, displaying generosity. 2r, Sila, morality. 5r, Nekkhamma, ascetic surrounded by worshippers. 17r, Panna, wisdom dispensed by Bodhisatva to others.

1994, May 7   Litho.   Perf. 12½
1096 A483 1r multicolored .15 .15
1097 A483 2r multicolored .15 .15
1098 A483 5r multicolored .20 .20
1099 A483 17r multicolored .70 .70
a.   Souvenir sheet of 4, #1096-1099 1.00 1.00
     Set value 1.00 1.00

Famous People A484

Designs: No. 1100, Pres. Ranasinghe Premadasa. No. 1101, Ven. Mihiripanne Dhammaratana Thero. No. 1102, E. Periyathambipillai, poet. No. 1103, Dr. Colvin R. De Silva, politician.

1994, May 22   Litho.   Perf. 14
1100 A484 1r multicolored .15 .15
1101 A484 1r multicolored .15 .15
1102 A484 1r multicolored .15 .15
1103 A484 1r multicolored .15 .15
     Set value .20 .20

World Conference of Intl. Federation of Social Workers, Colombo A485

1994, July 9   Litho.   Perf. 12½
1104 A485 8r blue, lt blue & black .40 .40

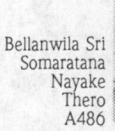 

Bellanwila Sri Somaratana Nayake Thero A486

1994, Aug. 2   Litho.   Perf. 12½
1105 A486 1r multicolored .15 .15

Infotel Lanka '94 — A487

1994, Sept. 8
1106 A487 10r multicolored .40 .40

Intl. Year of Indigenous People — A488

Designs: 1r, Veddah man making bow. 17r, Veddah man seated by rock art paintings.

1994, Sept. 12   Litho.   Perf. 12
1107 A488 1r multicolored .15 .15
1108 A488 17r multicolored .70 .70
     Set value .72 .72

Natl. Wildlife & Nature Protection Society, Cent. A489

1994, Nov. 24   Litho.   Perf. 12½
1109 A489 1r Emblem .15 .15
1110 A489 2r Rhino-horned lizard .15 .15
1111 A489 10r Giant squirrel .40 .40
1112 A489 17r Sloth bear .70 .70
a.   Souvenir sheet of 4, #1109-1111 1.40 1.40
     Nos. 1109-1112 (4) 1.40 1.40

Gam Udawa, 16th Anniv. A490

1994, Sept.   Litho.   Perf. 13
1113 A490 1r multicolored .15 .15

A491   A492

1994, Oct. 11   Litho.   Perf. 12½
1114 A491 1r multicolored .15 .15
Double entry bookkeeping, 500th anniv.

1995, Feb. 22   Perf. 14
1115 A492 1r Water lily .15 .15

Richmond College Old Boys Assoc., Cent. A493

1994   Perf. 12½
1116 A493 1r multicolored .15 .15

ICAO, 50th Anniv. A494

1994, Dec. 7   Litho.   Perf. 13
1117 A494 10r multicolored .40 .40

Christmas A495

Designs: 1r, Nativity. 17r, Jesus growing up, at home with Joseph and Mary.

1994, Dec. 8   Litho.   Perf. 13
1118 A495 1r multicolored .15 .15
1119 A495 17r multicolored .70 .70
a.   Souvenir sheet, #1118-1119 .75 .75

Assoc. for Advancement of Science, 50th Anniv. A496

1994, Dec. 19   Litho.   Perf. 13
1120 A496 1r multicolored .15 .15

Orchid Circle of Ceylon, 60th Anniv. — A498

Orchids: 50c, Dendrobium maccarthiae. 1r, Cottonia peduncularis. 5r, Bulbophyllum wightii. 17r, Habenaria crinifera.

1994, Dec. 27   Litho.   Perf. 13
1122 A498 50c multicolored .15 .15
1123 A498 1r multicolored .15 .15
1124 A498 5r multicolored .20 .20
1125 A498 17r multicolored .70 .70
a.   Souvenir sheet, #1122-1125 .95 .95
     Set value .95 .95

Visit of Pope John Paul II, Beatification of Fr. Joseph Vaz — A499

1995, Jan. 20
1126 A499 1r multicolored .15 .15

St. Joseph's College, Colombo, Cent. A500

1995, Mar. 2   Litho.   Perf. 13
1127 A500 1r multicolored .15 .15

Royal Asiatic Society of Sri Lanka, 150th Anniv. — A501

1995, Apr. 4
1128 A501 1r multicolored .15 .15

Sirimavo Bandaranaike, World's First Woman Prime Minister — A502

1995, Apr. 17   Litho.   Perf. 12
1129 A502 2r multicolored .15 .15

Vesak Festival — A503

Designs show actions by a Bodhisatva in four of ten perfections: 1r, Endeavor, standing on shore. 2r, Forebearance, one holding another. 10r, Veracity, two people listening to truths. 17r, Resolution, man holding hoe.

1995, May 5   Perf. 12x12½
1130 A503 1r multicolored .15 .15
1131 A503 2r multicolored .15 .15
1132 A503 10r multicolored .42 .42
1133 A503 17r multicolored .70 .70
  a. Souvenir sheet, #1130-1133 1.25 1.25
    Nos. 1130-1133 (4) 1.42 1.42

M. C. Abdul Cader — A504

1995, June 3   Perf. 11
1134 A504 2r multicolored .15 .15

St. Aloysius College, Galle, Cent. A506

1995, June 21   Litho.   Perf. 12½x12
1136 A506 2r multicolored .15 .15

T.B. Ilangaratna (1913-92), Politician A507

1995, July 7   Litho.   Perf. 13
1137 A507 2r multicolored .15 .15

Dhamma School, Cent. A508

1995, Aug. 3
1138 A508 2r multicolored .15 .15

General Post Office, Colombo, Cent. A509

1995, Aug. 22   Litho.   Perf. 13½
1139 A509 1r multicolored .15 .15

Help the Elderly — A510

1995, Oct. 1   Litho.   Perf. 14x13½
1140 A510 2r multicolored .15 .15

41st Commonwealth Parliamentary Conference — A511

1995, Oct. 9   Litho.   Perf. 14x13½
1141 A511 2r multicolored .15 .15

UN, 50th Anniv. — A512   World Thrift Day — A513

1995   Perf. 13½x14
1142 A512 2r multicolored .15 .15

1995
1143 A513 2r multicolored .15 .15

Christmas A514

Designs: 2r, Arms of Colombo and Kurunegla, Persian cross from Anuradhapura, Christian church. 20r, Clasping arms, nativity scene.

1995, Nov. 10   Litho.   Perf. 13
1144 A514 2r multicolored .15 .15
1145 A514 20r multicolored .75 .75
  a. Souvenir sheet, #1144-1145 .80 .80

SAARC, 10th Anniv. — A515

1995
1146 A515 2r multicolored .15 .15

STELLALAND

'ste-lə-ˌland

LOCATION — South Africa
GOVT. — Former Republic
AREA — 5,000 sq. mi. (approx.)
CAPITAL — Vryburg

This short-lived republic was set up by the Boers in an effort to annex territory ruled by the Bechuana chiefs. Great Britain refused to recognize it and in 1885 sent an expeditionary force which ended the political career of the country.

Stellaland was annexed by Great Britain in 1885 and became a part of British Bechuanaland.

12 Pence = 1 Shilling

Coat of Arms
A1   A2

1884, Feb.   Unwmk.   Typo.   Perf. 12
1 A1 1p red 190.00
  a. Horiz. pair, imperf. vert. 2,000.
  b. Vert. pair, imperf. horiz. 2,000.
2 A1 3p orange 18.00
  a. Horiz. pair, imperf. vert. 500.00
  b. Vert. pair, imperf. horiz. 500.00
3 A1 4p gray 18.00
  a. Horiz. pair, imperf. vert. 500.00
4 A1 6p lilac 18.00
  a. Horiz. pair, imperf. vert. 1,000.
  b. Vert. pair, imperf. horiz. 1,000.
5 A1 1sh green 32.50
    Nos. 1-5 (5) 276.50

Imperf. varieties are believed to be proofs.

No. 3 Handstamped "Twee" in Blackish Violet

1885
6 A2 2p on 4p gray 3,750.
The status of No. 6 has long been questioned.

STRAITS SETTLEMENTS

'strāts 'se-t³l-mənt

LOCATION — Malay Peninsula in south-eastern Asia
GOVT. — Former British Colony
AREA — 1,356 sq. mi.
POP. — 1,435,895 (estimated)
CAPITAL — Singapore

The colony comprised the settlements of Malacca, Singapore and Penang, which were incorporated under one government in 1826 and the administration transferred from India to the Secretary of State for the Colonies in 1867.

The colony was dissolved in 1946 when Singapore became a separate crown colony. Malacca and Penang were incorporated into the Malayan Union, which became the Federation of Malaya in 1948.

Stamps of India were used in Malacca, Penang and Singapore, 1854-67.

See Malaya for stamps of the Federated Malay States, the Federation of Malaya,

Johore, Kedah, Kelantan, Malacca, Negri Sembilan, Pahang, Penang, Perak, Perlis, Selangor, Sungei Ujong and Trengganu.

100 Cents = 1 Dollar

Stamps of India Surcharged in Red, Blue, Black Violet or Green:

THREE HALF CENTS Nos. 1-7	**24 CENTS** Nos. 8-9

1867, Sept. 1   Wmk. 38   Perf. 14
1 A7 1½c on ½a bl (R) 60.00 190.00
2 A7 2c on 1a brn (R) 65.00 55.00
3 A7 3c on 1a brn (Bl) 65.00 55.00
4 A7 4c on 1a brn (Bk) 125.00 175.00
5 A7 6c on 2a yel (V) 250.00 175.00
6 A7 8c on 2a yel (G) 90.00 35.00
7 A9 12c on 4a grn (R) 375.00 190.00
  a. Double surcharge 825.00
8 A7 24c on 8a rose (Bl) 190.00 65.00
9 A7 32c on 2a yel (Bk) 190.00 60.00

Manuscript Surcharge, Pen Bar Across "THREE HALF" of No. 1
9A A7 2(c) on 1½c on ½a 6,250. 3,500.

A2   A3

A4   A5

1867-72   Typo.   Wmk. 1   Perf. 14
10 A2 2c bister brown 11.00 2.00
11 A2 4c rose 20.00 3.50
12 A2 6c violet 20.00 7.50
13 A3 8c yellow 50.00 5.50
14 A3 12c ultra 60.00 5.00
  a. 12c blue 22.50 4.50
15 A3 24c green 65.00 4.50
16 A4 30c claret ('72) 65.00 5.25
17 A5 32c pale red 100.00 50.00
18 A5 96c olive gray 150.00 25.00
    Nos. 10-18 (9) 541.00 108.25

Corner ornaments of types A2, A3 and A5 differ for each value.
See Nos. 19. 40-44, 48-50, 52-57. For surcharges see Nos. 20-35, 58-59, 61-66, 73-82, 91. For overprints see Malaya, Johore No. 1, Perak Nos. 1, O1-O2, Selangor Nos. 1-2, Sungei Ujong Nos. 2-3.

Stamps of Straits Settlements, 1867-82, overprinted "B" are listed under Bangkok.

1871   Perf. 12½
19 A5 96c olive gray 1,500. 200.00

Five Cents.	Seven Cents.

1879, May   Perf. 14
20 A3 5c on 8c yellow 60.00 90.00
  a. No period after "CENTS" 400.00 425.00
21 A5 7c on 32c pale red 65.00 75.00
  a. No period after "CENTS" 500.00 550.00

No. 16 Surcharged:

10 e   10 f   10 g   10 h

10 j   10 k   10 m

1880

22 A4(e) 10c on 30c 85.00 50.00
23 A4(f) 10c on 30c 275.00 150.00
24 A4(g) 10c on 30c — —
25 A4(h) 10c on 30c —
25A A4(j) 10c on 30c 1,350. 525.00
25B A4(k) 10c on 30c 1,300. 575.00
25C A4(m) 10c on 30c 1,300. 525.00

Surcharges e & f and g, h, j & m are virtually identical. These must have an expert certificate identifying them. Values can be suspect because of misidentifications.

Unused examples are valued without gum.

With Additional Surcharge *cents*

26 A4(e) 10c on 30c 125.00 50.00
27 A4(f) 10c on 30c
27A A4(g) 10c on 30c 400.00 125.00
28 A4(h) 10c on 30c 1,100. 600.00
28A A4(j) 10c on 30c — 550.00
28B A4(k) 10c on 30c —
28C A4(m) 10c on 30c 1,750. 600.00

Unused examples are valued without gum.

No. 13 Surcharged:

5 *cents.* n — 5 *cents.* o — 5 *cents.* p

1880

29 A3(n) 5c on 8c yellow 50.00 25.00
30 A3(o) 5c on 8c yellow 200.00 250.00
31 A3(p) 5c on 8c yellow 60.00 85.00

No. 11 Surcharged **5 cents.**

1882, Jan.

32 A2 5c on 4c rose 250.00 300.00

Nos. 12, 14a, 16 Surcharged **10 cents.**

1880-81

33 A2 10c on 6c violet 50.00 7.50
34 A3 10c on 12c blue ('81) 30.00 12.50
35 A4 10c on 30c claret 150.00 65.00
Nos. 33-35 (3) 230.00 85.00

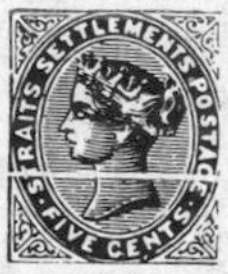
A6

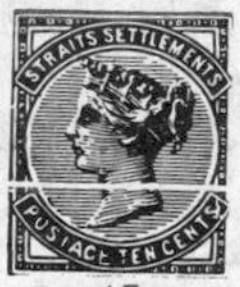
A7

1882, Jan. **Typo.** *Perf. 14*

38 A6 5c violet brown 65.00 60.00
39 A7 10c slate 165.00 50.00

See Nos. 45-47, 51. For surcharges see Nos. 60, 67-72, 89-92.

1882-99 **Wmk. Crown and C A (2)**

40 A2 2c bister brown 175.00 25.00
41 A2 2c car rose ('83) .25 .15
a. 2c rose 5.00 1.00
42 A2 4c rose 60.00 10.50
43 A2 4c car rose ('99) .65 .30
44 A2 4c bister brn ('83) 15.00 .60
45 A6 5c ultra ('83) 7.00 .50
46 A6 5c brown ('94) 2.50 .85
47 A6 5c magenta ('99) 2.00 .85
48 A2 6c violet 2.00 .60
49 A3 8c orange 1.65 .42
50 A3 8c ultra ('94) 4.00 .50
51 A7 10c slate 2.50 .50
52 A3 12c vio brn ('83) 40.00 6.00
53 A3 12c claret ('94) 7.50 7.00
54 A3 24c blue grn ('83) 3.00 1.25
a. 24c yellow green ('84) 15.00 1.25
55 A4 30c claret ('91) 7.00 2.00
56 A5 32c red org ('87) 5.00 2.00
57 A5 96c olive gray ('88) 75.00 25.00
Nos. 40-57 (18) 410.05 84.02

For overprints see Malaya, Perak Nos. O3-O9, Selangor Nos. 3-4, Sungei Ujong Nos. 6-7, 11.

Preceding Issues Surcharged

Surcharged Vertically **TWO CENTS**

1883-84 **Wmk. 2, 1**

58 A3 2c on 8c orange 50.00 40.00
a. Double surcharge 2,400. 950.00
59 A5 2c on 32c pale red 325.00 110.00
a. Double surcharge
60 A6 2c on 5c ultra ('84) 65.00 85.00
a. Pair, one without surcharge
b. Double surcharge
Nos. 58-60 (3) 440.00 235.00

Five types of surcharge on No. 58, two types on No. 59 and three types on No. 60.

Surcharged in Black **2 Cents.**

1883 **Wmk. 2**

61 A2 2c on 4c rose 45.00 50.00
b. "s" of "Cents." inverted 1,000. 1,200.

Wmk. 1

62 A3 2c on 12c blue 125.00 65.00
a. "s" of "Cents." inverted 1,900. 1,600.

Surcharged in Black or Blue **8 Cents**

1884

63 A3 8c on 12c blue 150.00 80.00

Wmk. 2

64 A3 8c on 12c vio brn 125.00 100.00

With Additional Surcharge Handstamped in Red **8**

65 A3 8c on 8c on 12c vio brn (R + Bk) 175.00 200.00
66 A3 8c on 8c on 12c vio brn (R + Bl) 5,000.

Surcharged in Black or Red **4 Cents**

1884

67 A6 4c on 5c ultra (Bk) 2,000. 2,250.
68 A6 4c on 5c ultra (R) 65.00 60.00

No. 68 Surcharged in Red **4**

69 A6 4c on 4c on 5c ultra —

No. 69 may be a trial printing.

Surcharged in Black **3 CENTS**

1885-87

70 A6 3c on 5c ultra 60.00 *150.00*
a. Double surcharge 1,500.

Surcharged in Black **3 cents**

71 A6 3c on 5c vio brn ('86) 110.00 *125.00*

Surcharged **2 Cents.**

72 A6 2c on 5c ultra ('87) 12.50 *30.00*
a. Double surcharge 475.00 375.00
b. "C" omitted *1,750.*

In the surcharged issues of 1883 to 1887, Nos. 59, 62, 63 and 71 are on stamps watermarked Crown and C C, the others are watermarked Crown and C A.

Surcharged **THREE CENTS**

1885-94 **Wmk. Crown and C A (2)**

73 A5 3c on 32c magenta 1.25 .85
74 A5 3c on 32c rose ('94) 2.00 .75
a. Without surcharge *2,750.*

No. 74a value is for copy with perfs touching frame line.

Surcharged **10 CENTS**

1891

75 A3 10c on 24c green 1.50 1.00
a. Narrow "0" in "10" 25.00 30.00

Surcharged **THIRTY CENTS**

76 A5 30c on 32c red orange 5.00 3.25

Surcharged **ONE CENT**

1892

77 A2 1c on 2c rose 1.10 1.25
78 A2 1c on 4c bister brn 3.00 *4.00*
a. Double surcharge 700.00
79 A2 1c on 6c violet 1.00 *2.00*
a. Dbl. surch., one invtd. 650.00 550.00
80 A3 1c on 8c orange 1.00 .70
81 A3 1c on 12c vio brown 4.00 *8.00*
Nos. 77-81 (5) 10.10 15.95

Surcharged **ONE CENT**

82 A3 1c on 8c gray green .50 *1.25*

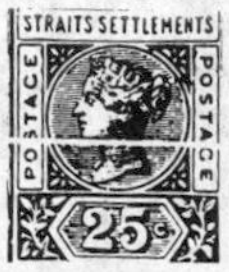
Queen Victoria — A13

1892-99 **Typo.**

83 A13 1c gray green .50 .30
84 A13 3c car rose ('95) 8.00 .55
85 A13 3c brown ('99) 2.50 .50
86 A13 25c dk vio & grn 12.00 3.00
87 A13 50c ol grn & car 15.00 2.50
88 A13 $5 org & car ('98) 250.00 250.00
Nos. 83-88 (6) 288.00 256.85

Denomination of $5, type A13, is in color on plain tablet.

Stamps of 1883-94 Surcharged **4 cents.**

1899

89 A6 4c on 5c ultra 1.10 4.50
90 A6 4c on 5c brown 1.10 6.00
91 A3 4c on 8c ultra .75 2.00
a. Double surcharge *575.00 575.00*
Nos. 89-91 (3) 2.95 12.50

Type of 1882 Issue Surcharged **FOUR CENTS**

92 A6 4c on 5c rose .40 .25
a. Without surcharge *22,500.*

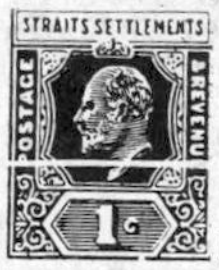
King Edward VII — A14

Numerals of 5c, 8c, 10c, 30c, $1 and $5, type A14, are in color on plain tablet.

1902 **Wmk. 2** **Typo.**

93 A14 1c green .65 1.25
94 A14 3c vio & org 1.25 .15
95 A14 4c violet, *red* 2.25 .25
96 A14 5c violet 1.75 .35
97 A14 8c violet, *blue* 2.50 .40
98 A14 10c vio & blk, *yel* 11.00 .70
99 A14 25c violet & grn 6.50 3.25
100 A14 30c gray & car rose 10.00 6.50
101 A14 50c grn & car rose 13.00 13.00
102 A14 $1 green & blk 22.50 37.50
103 A14 $2 violet & blk 37.50 37.50
104 A14 $5 grn & brn org 110.00 85.00
104A A14 $100 dl vio & grn, *yel* *4,500.*
Nos. 93-104 (12) 218.90 185.85

High values of the 1902 and 1904 issues with revenue cancellations are of minimal value. No. 104A is inscribed "Postage & Revenue" but the limit of weight probably precluded its use postally.

See Nos. 113, 115-128B, 133.

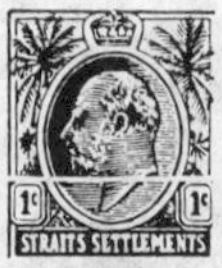
A15

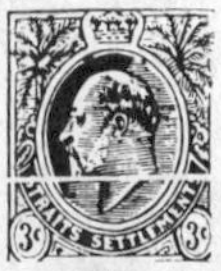
A16

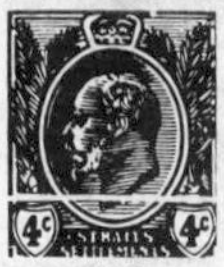
A17

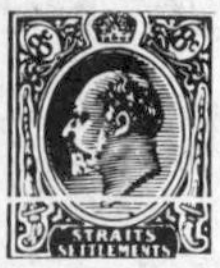
A18

1903-04

105 A15 1c gray green .30 4.25
106 A16 3c dull violet 5.25 2.75
107 A17 4c violet, *red* 1.65 .25
108 A18 8c violet, *blue* 24.00 1.10
Nos. 105-108 (4) 31.20 8.35

See Nos. 109-112, 114, 129-132, 134.

1904-11 **Wmk. 3**

Chalky Paper

109 A15 1c gray green 1.50 .15
110 A16 3c dull violet 1.10 .25
111 A17 4c violet, *red* 2.50 .40
112 A17 4c dull vio ('08) 2.25 .15
113 A14 5c violet ('06) 4.00 1.75
114 A18 8c violet, *bl* 6.00 .40
115 A14 10c vio & blk, *yel* 3.00 .40
116 A14 10c vio, *yel* ('08) 2.50 .40
117 A14 25c vio & grn 14.00 13.00
118 A14 25c violet ('09) 7.00 3.25
119 A14 30c gray & car rose 25.00 2.75
120 A14 30c vio & org ('09) 25.00 1.50
121 A14 50c grn & car rose 17.00 10.00
122 A14 50c blk, *grn* ('10) 4.00 2.00
123 A14 $1 green & blk 27.50 13.00
124 A14 $1 blk & red, *bl* ('11) 9.50 3.00
125 A14 $2 violet & blk 72.50 70.00
Revenue cancel 12.00
126 A14 $2 grn & red, *yel* ('09) 16.00 17.00
127 A14 $5 grn & brn org 70.00 50.00
128 A14 $5 grn & red, *grn* ('10) 90.00 90.00
Revenue cancel 5.00
128A A14 $25 green & blk 850.00
128B A14 $100 dl vio & grn, *yel* *5,000.*
Revenue cancel 225.00
Nos. 109-128 (20) 400.35 279.40

Nos. 125, 128A and 128B are on chalky paper, the other values are on both ordinary and chalky. The note about No. 104A will apply to No. 128B.

1906-11

Ordinary Paper

129 A15 1c blue grn ('10) 1.25 .50
130 A16 3c carmine ('08) .22 .22
131 A17 4c carmine ('07) 1.25 .28
132 A17 4c lake ('11) .65 .65
133 A14 5c orange ('09) 1.75 .35
134 A18 8c ultra ('06) .35 .28
Nos. 129-134 (6) 5.47 2.28

Stamps of Labuan 1902-03, Overprinted or Surcharged in Red or Black

STRAITS SETTLEMENTS. a — **Straits Settlements.** b

STRAITS SETTLEMENTS. **FOUR CENTS.** c

Perf. 12½ to 16 and Compound

1907 **Unwmk.**

134A A38(a) 1c violet & blk 27.50 57.50
135 A38(a) 2c green & blk 95.00 115.00
136 A38(a) 3c brown & blk 9.00 52.50
137 A38(c) 4c on 12c yel & blk 1.40 *3.50*
a. No period after "CENTS" 110.00 110.00
138 A38(c) 4c on 16c org brn & grn (Bk) 1.10 *3.50*
a. With additional name in red 500.00 475.00
139 A38(c) 4c on 18c bis & blk 1.00 *3.00*
a. No period after "CENTS" 100.00 100.00
b. "FOUR CENTS." & bar double 4,000.
140 A38(a) 8c orange & blk 1.00 *4.00*
141 A38(b) 10c sl bl & brn 2.50 *3.25*
a. No period after "Settlements" 125.00

142	A38(a)	25c grnsh bl & grn	3.25	15.00
143	A38(a)	50c gray lil & vio	6.25	4.25
144	A38(a)	$1 org & red brn	26.00	55.00
		Nos. 134A-144 (11)	174.00	316.50

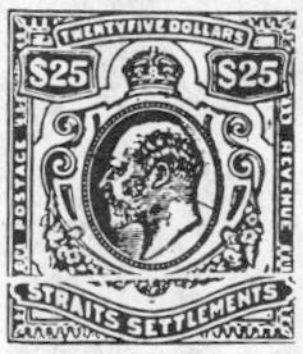

A19

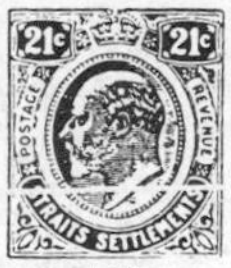

A20

1908-11 Typo. Wmk. 3 Perf. 14

Chalky Paper

145	A19	$25 bl & vio, *bl* ('11)	700.	500.
146	A19	$500 violet & org	50,000.	
		Revenue cancel		275.

No. 146 is inscribed "Postage-Revenue" but was probably used only for revenue.

Excellent forgeries of No. 146 exist.

1910

Chalky Paper

147	A20	21c maroon & vio	4.25	10.00
148	A20	45c black, *green*	4.25	3.50

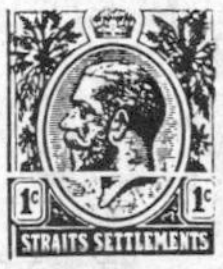

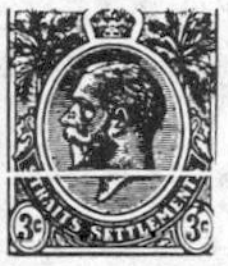

King George V

A21 A22

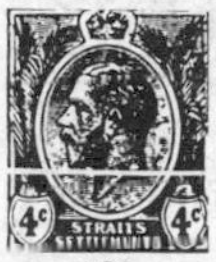

A23

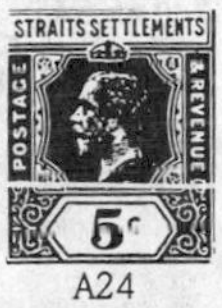

A24

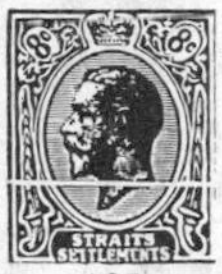

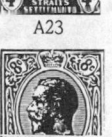

A25

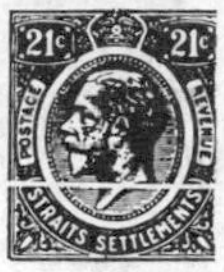

A26

Die I (Type A24).

For description of dies I and II see back of this section of the Catalogue.

The 25c, 50c and $2 denominations of type A24 show the numeral on horizontally-lined tablet.

1912-18 Chalky Paper Wmk. 3

149	A21	1c green	2.50	.50
150	A21	1c black ('18)	.30	.20
151	A25	2c dp green ('18)	.25	.20
152	A22	3c scarlet	.50	.15
a.		3c carmine	1.50	.40
153	A23	4c gray violet	.60	.20
154	A23	4c scarlet ('18)	.90	.15
a.		Booklet pane of 1		
b.		Booklet pane of 12		
c.		4c carmine ('18)	1.00	.15
155	A24	5c orange	1.10	.25
156	A25	6c claret ('10)	1.25	.45
157	A25	8c ultra	.50	.20
158	A24	10c violet, *yel*	.75	.35
159	A24	10c ultra ('18)	3.50	.20
160	A26	21c maroon & vio	2.50	4.50
161	A24	25c vio & red vio	3.50	3.00
162	A24	30c vio & org ('14)	3.50	1.10
163	A26	45c blk, *bl grn*, ol back ('14)	4.25	9.50
a.		45c black, *emerald* ('17)	1.65	8.50
164	A24	50c black, *grn* ('14)	3.50	1.65
a.		50c black, *bl grn*, olive back	8.00	3.50
b.		50c black, *emerald*	8.00	3.50
c.		Die II	2.25	2.50
165	A24	$1 blk & red, *bl* ('14)	5.50	4.25
166	A24	$2 grn & red, *yel* ('15)	6.25	17.00
167	A24	$5 grn & red, *grn* ('15)	40.00	25.00
a.		$5 grn & red, *bl grn*, ol back	50.00	35.00
b.		$5 grn & red, *emer* ('15)	45.00	16.00
c.		Die II	45.00	30.00
		Nos. 149-167 (19)	81.15	68.85

The 1c, 3c, 5c and 8c are on ordinary paper.

Surface-colored Paper

168	A24	10c violet, *yel*	.75	.30
169	A26	45c black, *grn* ('14)	5.00	12.50
170	A24	$2 grn & red, *yel* ('14)	9.00	20.00
171	A24	$5 grn & red, *grn*	57.50	30.00
		Nos. 168-171 (4)	72.25	62.80

See Nos. 179-201. For surcharges see Nos. B1-B2.

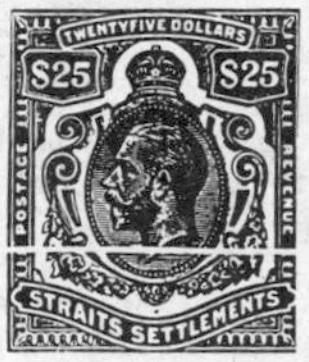

A27

1915

172	A27	$25 bl & vio, *bl*	675.00	300.00
		Revenue cancel		5.75
173	A27	$100 red & blk, *bl*	3,250.	
		Revenue cancel		37.50
174	A27	$500 org & dl vio	30,000.	
		Revenue cancel		150.00

Although Nos. 173 and 174 were available for postage, it is probable that they were used only for fiscal purposes.

See Nos. 202-204.

Die II (Type A24)

1921-32 Wmk. 4

Ordinary Paper

179	A21	1c black	.25	.15
180	A25	2c green	.25	.15
181	A25	2c brown	6.50	2.00
182	A22	3c green	1.25	.55
183	A23	4c scarlet	1.75	2.75
184	A23	4c dp violet ('25)	.35	.15
185	A23	4c orange ('29)	.90	.15
186	A24	5c orange ('23)	2.00	.75
a.		Die I	.90	.15
187	A24	5c dk brown ('32)	1.10	.15
a.		Die I ('32)	3.50	.15
188	A25	6c claret	1.75	.20
189	A25	6c rose red ('25)	12.50	6.00
a.		6c scarlet ('27)	2.00	.15
190	A24	10c ultra (I)	1.50	.16

Chalky Paper

191	A24	10c vio, *yel* ('27)	1.50	.15
a.		Die I ('25)	2.50	4.00
192	A25	12c ultra	.65	.15
193	A26	21c maroon & vio	5.25	30.00
194	A24	25c vio & red vio	2.75	1.25
a.		Die I	16.00	13.00
195	A24	30c violet & org	2.00	.16
a.		Die I	16.00	16.00
196	A26	35c orange & vio	5.25	4.00
197	A26	35c vio & car ('31)	8.50	6.50
198	A24	50c blk, *emerald*	1.65	.32
199	A24	$1 blk & red, *bl*	5.00	.32
200	A24	$2 grn & red, *yel*	9.00	4.25
201	A24	$5 grn & red, *grn*	45.00	16.00
202	A27	$25 bl & vio, *bl*	375.00	82.50
203	A27	$100 red & blk, *bl*	1,600.	
204	A27	$500 org & dl vio	15,000.	
		Nos. 179-201 (23)	116.65	76.26

No. 192 is on ordinary paper.

Nos. 203 and 204 were probably used only for fiscal purposes.

Stamps of 1912-21 Overprinted in Black: "MALAYA-BORNEO EXHIBITION," in Three Lines

1922 Wmk. 3

151d	A25	2c deep green	17.50	50.00
154d	A23	4c scarlet	4.00	8.50
155d	A24	5c orange	4.00	7.25
157d	A25	8c ultra	1.75	3.50
161d	A24	25c vio & red vio	4.75	8.50
163d	A26	45c blk, *bl grn*, ol back	4.75	8.50
165d	A24	$1 blk & red, *bl*	125.00	300.00
166d	A24	$2 grn & red, *yel*	37.50	75.00
167d	A24	$5 grn & red, *grn*	250.00	425.00

Wmk. 4

179d	A21	1c black	.35	1.50
180d	A25	2c green	2.25	5.50
183d	A23	4c scarlet	1.75	7.00
186d	A24	5c orange (II)	3.00	8.50
190d	A24	10c ultra	3.00	10.00
199d	A24	$1 blk & red, *bl*	25.00	70.00
		Nos. 151d-199d (15)	484.60	988.75

Industrial fair at Singapore, Mar. 31-Apr. 15, 1922.

Silver Jubilee Issue

Common Design Type

1935, May 6 Engr. Perf. 11x12

213	CD301	5c black & ultra	.60	.15
214	CD301	8c indigo & green	1.25	1.25
215	CD301	12c ultra & brown	1.25	1.50
216	CD301	25c brown vio & ind	2.75	3.50
		Nos. 213-216 (4)	5.85	6.40

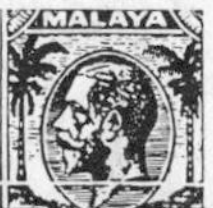

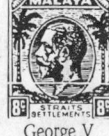

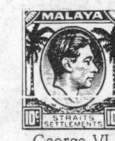

George V

A28

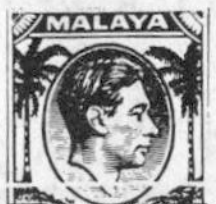

George VI

A29

1936-37 Typo. Perf. 14

Chalky Paper

217	A28	1c black ('37)	.25	.15
218	A28	2c green	.30	.20
220	A28	4c orange brn	.70	.20
221	A28	5c brown	.25	.15
222	A28	6c rose red	.60	.50
223	A28	8c gray	.50	.20
224	A28	10c dull vio	1.00	.25
225	A28	12c ultra	1.65	1.50
226	A28	25c rose red & vio	.80	.20
227	A28	30c org & dk vio	1.00	2.00
229	A28	40c dk vio & car	1.00	2.00
230	A28	50c blk, *emerald*	1.65	.75
232	A28	$1 red & blk, *blue*	8.50	1.00
233	A28	$2 rose red & gray grn	15.00	10.00
234	A28	$5 grn & red, *grn* ('37)	32.50	10.00
		Nos. 217-234 (15)	65.70	29.10

Coronation Issue

Common Design Type

1937, May 12 Engr. Perf. 13½x14

235	CD302	4c deep orange	.15	.15
236	CD302	8c gray black	.24	.15
237	CD302	12c bright ultra	.26	.26
		Nos. 235-237 (3)	.65	.56

Two Dies

Die I. Printed in two operations. Lines of background touch outside of central oval. Foliage of palms touches outer frame line. Palm frond in front of King's eye has two points.

Die II. Printed from a single plate. Lines of background separated from central oval by a white line. Foliage of palms does not touch outer frame line. Palm frond in front of King's eye has one point.

1937-41 Typo. Perf. 14

238	A29	1c black (I)	1.75	.25
239	A29	2c green (I)	9.00	.25
c.		Die II ('38)	1.90	.15
239A	A29	2c brown org ('41) (II)	1.00	.55
239B	A29	3c green ('41) (II)	1.75	.55
240	A29	4c brown org (I)	6.50	.25
a.		Die II ('38)	4.75	.15
241	A29	5c brown (I)	11.00	.25
a.		Die II ('39)	1.50	.15
242	A29	6c rose red ('38) (I)	5.00	.25
243	A29	8c gray ('38) (I)	20.00	.25
244	A29	10c dull vio (I)	3.50	.25
245	A29	12c ultra ('38) (I)	3.50	.25
245A	A29	15c ultra ('41) (II)	2.00	3.50
246	A29	25c rose red & vio (I)	22.00	.50
247	A29	30c org & vio (I)	22.00	1.10
248	A29	40c dk vio & rose red (I)	5.50	1.25
249	A29	50c blk, *emer* ('38) (I)	.75	.55
250	A29	$1 red & blk, *bl* ('38) (I)	1.40	.55
251	A29	$2 rose red & gray grn ('38) (I)	13.00	3.00
252	A29	$5 grn & red, *grn* ('38) (I)	13.00	6.00
		Nos. 238-252 (18)	142.65	19.55

For overprints see #256-271, N1-N29 and Malaya, Malacca #N1-N14, Penang #N1-N26.

Stamps and Type of 1937-41 Overprinted in Red or Black **B M A MALAYA**

1945-48

256	A29	1c black (R)	.15	.15
257	A29	2c brown org (II)	.15	.15
a.		Die I ('46)	.60	.60
258	A29	3c green	.15	.15
259	A29	5c brown	.15	.15
260	A29	6c gray	.15	.15
261	A29	8c rose red	.15	.15
262	A29	10c dull vio (I)	.15	.15
a.		10c claret (II) ('48)	.15	.15
263	A29	12c ultra	.18	.18
264	A29	15c ultra (Bk)	1.25	1.50
265	A29	15c ultra (R)	.15	.15
266	A29	25c rose red & vio	.15	.15
a.		Double overprint		
267	A29	50c blk, *emer* (R)	.24	.15
268	A29	$1 rose red & blk	.60	.15
269	A29	$2 rose red & gray grn	.90	.18
270	A29	$5 grn & red, *grn*	27.50	24.00
271	A29	$5 brn org & vio	2.75	.40
		Nos. 256-271 (16)	34.77	27.91

The letters "B M A" are initials of "British Military Administration".

An 8c gray with BMA overprint was prepared but not issued. Value $5.

The 6c gray, 8c rose red and $5 brown orange & violet exist without BMA overprint, but were issued only with it.

No. 262a does not exist without overprint. No. 262 exists in at least three shades.

SEMI-POSTAL STAMPS

RED CROSS

Nos. 152-153 Surcharged

2c.

1917 Wmk. 3 Perf. 14

B1	A22	3c + 2c scarlet	.75	2.00
a.		No period after "C"	55.00	
B2	A23	4c + 2c gray violet	.75	2.00
a.		No period after "C"	77.50	

POSTAGE DUE STAMPS

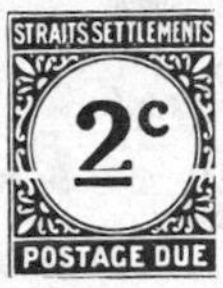

D1

1924-26 Typo. Wmk. 4 Perf. 14

J1	D1	1c violet	3.50	2.25
J2	D1	2c black	3.50	.30
J3	D1	4c green ('26)	2.00	7.50
J4	D1	8c red	3.75	.38
J5	D1	10c orange	3.75	1.10
J6	D1	12c ultramarine	6.25	.75
		Nos. J1-J6 (6)	22.75	12.28

OCCUPATION STAMPS

Issued Under Japanese Occupation

Straits Settlements Nos. 238, 239A, 239B, 243 and 245A Handstamped in Red

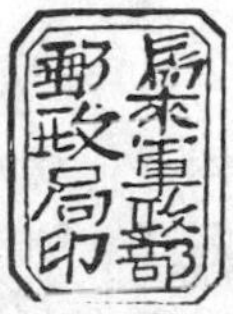

1942, Mar. 16 Wmk. 4 Perf. 14

N1	A29	1c black	12.00	12.00
N2	A29	2c brown orange	12.00	12.00
N3	A29	3c green	60.00	85.00
N4	A29	8c gray	30.00	27.50
N5	A29	15c ultra	20.00	22.50
		Nos. N1-N5 (5)	134.00	159.00

Other denominations with this handstamp are believed to be proofs.

The handstamp reads: "Seal of Post Office of Malayan Military Department."

Stamps of Straits Settlements, 1937-41, Handstamped in Red, Black, Violet or Brown

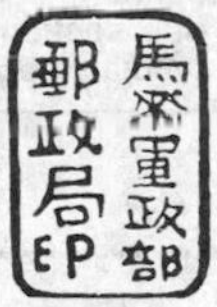

1942, Apr. 3

N6	A29	1c black	4.00	4.00
N6A	A29	2c green (V)	500.00	500.00
N7	A29	2c brown orange	4.00	3.50
N8	A29	3c green	4.00	3.50
N9	A29	5c brown	30.00	30.00
N10	A29	8c gray	4.00	3.50
N11	A29	10c dull violet	45.00	45.00
N12	A29	12c ultra	80.00	80.00
N13	A29	15c ultra	4.50	4.00
N14	A29	30c orange & vio	350.00	350.00
N15	A29	40c dk vio & rose red	100.00	125.00
N16	A29	50c blk, *emerald*	60.00	60.00
N17	A29	$1 red & blk, *bl*	80.00	80.00
N18	A29	$2 rose red & gray grn	140.00	150.00
N19	A29	$5 grn & red, *grn*	200.00	165.00

Nos. N6-N7, N9, N11-N12, N15-N19 with red handstamp were used in Sumatra. The 2c green with red handstamp was not regularly issued.

Straits Settlements Nos. 239A, 239B, 243 and 245A Overprinted in Black

DAI NIPPON
2602
MALAYA

1942

N20	A29	2c brown orange	.50	.50
a.		Inverted overprint	7.00	5.00
b.		Dbl. ovpt., one invtd.	25.00	
N21	A29	3c green	50.00	50.00
N22	A29	8c gray	1.75	1.65
a.		Inverted overprint	19.00	
N23	A29	15c ultra	4.00	3.25
		Nos. N20-N23 (4)	56.25	55.40

Straits Settlements Nos. 239A and 243 Overprinted in Black

SELANGOR EXHIBITION DAI NIPPON 2602 MALAYA

1942, Nov. 3

N24	A29	2c brown orange	17.50	25.00
a.		Inverted overprint	225.00	225.00
N25	A29	8c gray	12.50	20.00
a.		Inverted overprint	225.00	225.00

Agricultural-Horticultural Exhibition held at Kuala Lumpur, Selangor, Nov. 1-2, 1942. Sold only at a temporary post office at the exhibition.

大日本郵便

Straits Settlements Nos. 243, 245 and 248 Overprinted in Black or Red

1943

N26	A29	8c gray (Bk)	.85	.85
a.		Inverted overprint	30.00	
N27	A29	8c gray (R)	.85	.85
N28	A29	12c ultramarine	1.50	.85
N29	A29	40c dk vio & rose red	1.75	2.25
		Nos. N26-N29 (4)	4.95	4.80

The Japanese characters read: "Japanese Postal Service."

SUDAN

sü–'dan

LOCATION — Northeastern Africa, south of Egypt
GOVT. — Republic
AREA — 967,500 sq. mi.
POP. — 20,564,364 (1983)
CAPITAL — Khartoum

10 Milliemes = 1 Piaster
100 Piasters = 1 Egyptian Pound

Catalogue values for unused stamps in this country are for Never Hinged items, beginning with Scott 79 in the regular postage section, Scott C35 in the air post section, Scott CO1 in the air post official section, Scott J12 in the postage due section, and Scott O28 in the officials section.

Watermarks

Wmk. 71- Rosette   Wmk. 179- Multiple Crescent and Star

Wmk. 214- Multiple S G

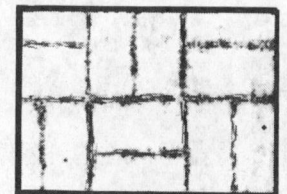

Wmk. 334- Rectangles

Wmk. 345- Rhinoceros

Egyptian Stamps of 1884-93 Overprinted in Black

السودان SOUDAN

1897, Mar. 1   Wmk. 119   Perf. 14

1	A18	1m brown	1.25	1.40
a.		Inverted overprint	300.00	
2	A19	2m green	1.10	1.40
3	A21	3m orange	1.25	1.10
4	A20	5m carmine rose	1.75	.60
a.		Inverted overprint	400.00	
5	A14	1p ultra	6.00	1.75
6	A15	2p orange brown	42.50	11.00
7	A16	5p gray	37.50	11.00
a.		Double overprint		
8	A22	10p violet	27.50	35.00
		Nos. 1-8 (8)	118.85	63.25

Counterfeits of Nos. 1-8 are plentiful.

Camel Post — A1

1898, Mar. 1   Typo.   Wmk. 71

9	A1	1m rose & brn	.25	.25
10	A1	2m brown & grn	.85	1.50
11	A1	3m green & vio	1.75	2.00
12	A1	5m black & rose	1.25	.70
13	A1	1p yel brn & ultra	4.25	3.25
14	A1	2p ultra & blk	15.00	6.25
15	A1	5p grn & org brn	20.00	7.50
16	A1	10p dp vio & blk	20.00	1.75
		Nos. 9-16 (8)	63.35	23.20

See Nos. 17-27, 43-50. For overprints see Nos. C3, MO1-MO15, O1-O9, O17-O24. For surcharges see Nos. 28, 62, C16.

1902-21   Wmk. 179

17	A1	1m car rose & brn ('05)	.40	.15
18	A1	2m brown & grn	1.25	.15
19	A1	3m grn & vio ('03)	1.50	.20
20	A1	4m ol brn & bl ('07)	1.25	2.00
21	A1	4m brn & red ('07)	1.25	.65
22	A1	5m blk & rose red ('03)	1.50	.15
23	A1	1p brn & ultra ('03)	1.50	.20
24	A1	2p ultra & blk ('08)	19.00	1.25
25	A1	2p org & vio brn ('21)	3.25	5.50
26	A1	5p grn & org brn ('08)	19.00	.25
27	A1	10p dp vio & blk ('11)	19.00	2.00
		Nos. 17-27 (11)	68.90	12.50

No. 15 Surcharged in Black   **5 Milliemes**

1903, Sept.   Wmk. 71

28	A1	5m on 5p	6.00	8.50
a.		Inverted surcharge	350.00	350.00

A2

1921-22   Typo.   Wmk. 179

29	A2	1m orange & blk ('22)	.65	1.75
30	A2	2m dk brn & org ('22)	6.50	7.00
31	A2	3m green & vio ('22)	2.00	4.50
32	A2	4m brown & grn ('22)	3.25	1.40
33	A2	5m blk & ol brn ('22)	1.40	.15
34	A2	10m black & car ('22)	1.40	.15
35	A2	15m grn brn & ultra	2.25	.85
		Nos. 29-35 (7)	17.45	15.80

See Nos. 36-42. For overprints see Nos. C1-C2, O10-O16. For surcharges see Nos. 60-61.

1927-40   Wmk. 214

36	A2	1m org yel & blk	.15	.15
37	A2	2m dk brn & org	.15	.15
38	A2	3m green & violet	.15	.15
39	A2	4m brown & green	.20	.15
40	A2	5m blk & ol brn	.20	.15
a.		Booklet pane of 4		
41	A2	10m black & car	.40	.15
42	A2	15m org brn & ultra	.30	.15
43	A1	2p orange & vio brn	.30	.15
44	A1	3p dk bl & red brn ('40)	2.25	.15
45	A1	4p black & ultra ('36)	2.75	.15
46	A1	5p dk grn & org brn	.60	.15
47	A1	6p blk & pale bl ('36)	2.50	.15
48	A1	8p blk & pck grn ('36)	4.50	1.00
49	A1	10p dp vio & blk	.90	.15
50	A1	20p bl & lt bl ('35)	2.25	.15
		Nos. 36-50 (15)	17.60	
		Set value		2.15

Charles George Gordon — A3

Gordon Memorial College A4

Memorial Service at Khartoum — A5

1935, Jan. 1   Engr.   Perf. 13½x14

51	A3	5m deep green	.40	.40
52	A3	10m brown	.40	.40
53	A3	13m ultra	1.75	2.75
54	A3	15m carmine	1.00	1.00
55	A4	2p deep blue	1.00	1.00
56	A4	5p orange	1.40	1.40
57	A4	10p dull violet	5.00	5.00
58	A5	20p black	25.00	27.50
59	A5	50p red brown	65.00	67.50
		Nos. 51-59 (9)	100.95	106.95

50th anniv. of the death of Gen. Charles George ("Chinese") Gordon (1833-85).

5 Mills.

No. 41 Surcharged in Black   ٥ مليم

Wmk. Multiple S G (214)

1940, Feb. 25   Typo.   Perf. 14

60	A2	5m on 10m black & car	.15	.20

Nos. 40 and 48 Surcharged in Black

4½ Piastres

4½ PIASTRES	٤١/٢ قرش
a	b

1940-41

61	A2(a)	4½p on 5m ('41)	40.00	5.00
62	A1(b)	4½p on 8p	27.50	5.00

Sudan Landscape — A6

Perf. 13½, 14x13½

1941   Litho.   Unwmk.

Size: 21½x17½mm

63	A6	1m orange & slate bl	.30	1.10
64	A6	2m chocolate & org	.40	1.00
65	A6	3m grn & rose vio	.45	.15
66	A6	4m choc & bl grn	.20	.20
67	A6	5m indigo & ol bis	.20	.15
68	A6	10m indigo & rose pink	4.50	2.00
69	A6	15m chestnut & ultra	.35	.15

Size: 29x25mm

71	A6	2p orange & claret	2.75	.40
72	A6	3p dk blue & fawn	.50	.15
73	A6	4p blk & brt ultra	.50	.15
74	A6	5p dk grn & brn org	2.75	4.50
75	A6	6p ind & turq bl	11.00	.30
76	A6	8p black & green	9.00	.35
77	A6	10p rose vio & gray	32.50	.45
78	A6	20p dk & lt blue	32.50	15.00
		Nos. 63-78 (15)	97.90	26.05

Catalogue values for unused stamps in this section, from this point to the end of the section, are for Never Hinged items.

Types of 1898-1940 with Changed Arabic Wording Below Camel

A7

A8

Wmk. 214

1948, Jan. 1   Typo.   Perf. 14

79	A7	1m dk orange & blk	.25	1.25
80	A7	2m chocolate & org	.65	1.50
81	A7	3m green & rose lilac	.20	1.25
82	A7	4m choc & sl grn	.20	.15
83	A7	5m black & ol brn	1.75	.60
84	A7	10m black & car	2.00	.15
a.		Center inverted		
85	A7	15m org brn & ultra	2.00	.15
86	A8	2p org yel & vio brn	3.50	.40
87	A8	3p dk bl & red brn	3.00	.15
88	A8	4p black & ultra	2.50	.75
89	A8	5p dk grn & org	3.00	.40
90	A8	6p blk & pale bl	3.25	2.00
91	A8	8p blk & peacock grn	3.25	2.00
92	A8	10p dp rose lil & blk	6.50	1.50
93	A8	20p dk blue & blue	4.50	.20
a.		Perf. 13	19.00	37.50
94	A8	50p ultra & carmine	5.25	.65
		Nos. 79-94 (16)	41.80	13.10

Arabic inscription, types A7 and A8: "Berid es-Sudan"; types A1 and A2; "Postai-Sudaniye." For overprints see Nos. O28-O43.

Stamp of 1898 — A9

1948, Oct. 1   Perf. 12½x13

95	A9	2p dull blue & gray blk	.35	.30

50th anniv. of Sudan's 1st postage stamp.

A10

1948, Dec. 19 *Perf. 13*

96 A10 10m black & carmine .20 .15
97 A10 5p dk green & orange .50 .30

Legislative Assembly opening, Dec., 1948.

Nubian Ibex — A11

Cotton Picking — A12

Camel Post — A13

Designs: 2m, Shoebill. 3m, Giraffe. 4m, Baggara girl. 5m, Shilluk warrior. 10m, Hadendowa. 15m, Sudan policeman. 3p, Ambatch canoe. 3½p, Nuba wrestlers. 4p, Weaving. 5p, Saluka farming. 6p, Gum tapping. 8p, Darfur chief. 10p, Stack laboratory. 20p, Nile lechwe.

1951, Sept. 1 Typo. *Perf. 14*

Center in Black (#98-104)

98 A11 1m orange .15 .65
99 A11 2m ultra .75 .15
100 A11 3m dark green 2.00 1.00
101 A11 4m emerald .45 1.10
102 A11 5m plum .60 .15
103 A11 10m light blue .15 .15
104 A11 15m dp orange brn .70 .15

Perf. 13

105 A12 2p lt blue & dk blue .15 .15
106 A12 3p vio blue & brn 1.40 .15
107 A12 3½p brown & bl grn .25 .15
108 A12 4p black & dp blue .25 .15
109 A12 5p emer & org brn .25 .15
110 A12 6p black & blue 2.50 1.10
111 A12 8p brown & dp bl 3.25 .75
112 A12 10p green & black .75 .32
113 A12 20p black & blue grn 2.50 .65
114 A13 50p black & carmine 6.50 .50
Nos. 98-114 (17) 22.60
Set value 4.15

See #159. For overprints see #O44-O61, O75.

Camel Post — A14

1954, Jan. 9 *Perf. 12½x13*

115 A14 15m emerald & brn org .15 .15
116 A14 3p black & blue .22 .20
117 A14 5p red violet & blk .40 .35
Nos. 115-117 (3) .77 .70

Self-government in the Sudan.
A quantity of these sets inscribed "1953" was sold in London. They were not valid for postage. Value, set $15.

Independent Republic

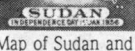

Map of Sudan and Sun — A15

Rhinoceros Carrying Globe — A16

Wmk. 214

1956, Sept. 15 Engr. *Perf. 14*

118 A15 15m rose lilac & org .15 .15
119 A15 3p dk blue & org .20 .16
120 A15 5p green & org .30 .28
Nos. 118-120 (3) .65 .59

Independence Day, Jan. 1, 1956.

1958, Aug. 2

Center in Orange

121 A16 15m plum .15 .15
122 A16 3p blue .22 .20
123 A16 5p green .35 .30
Nos. 121-123 (3) .72 .65

APU Cong., Khartoum, Aug. 2, 1958.

Soldier, Farmer and Map of Nile — A17

Lithographed and Engraved

1959, Nov. 17 Unwmk. *Perf. 14*

124 A17 15m brown, yel & ultra .15 .15
125 A17 3p multicolored .20 .16
126 A17 55m multicolored .35 .30
Nos. 124-126 (3) .70 .61

Sudanese army revolution, 1st anniv.

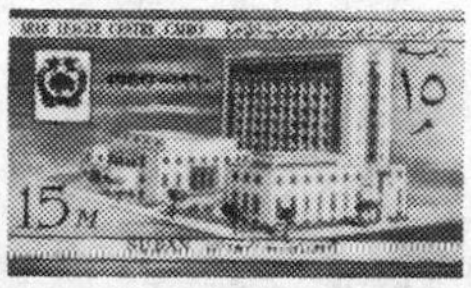

Arab League Center A17a

Perf. 13x13½

1960, Mar. 22 Photo. Wmk. 328

127 A17a 15m dull green & blk .15 .15

Opening of the Arab League Center and the Arab Postal Museum in Cairo.

Uprooted Oak Emblem, Refugee Man and Child — A18

Wmk. 214

1960, Apr. 7 Litho. *Perf. 14*

128 A18 15m black, buff & ultra .15 .15
129 A18 55m black, beige & org .35 .35

World Refugee Year, July 1, 1959-June 30, 1960.

Soccer Player — A19

Forest — A20

1960, Aug. 25 Wmk. 214 *Perf. 14*

130 A19 15m ultra, blk & yel .15 .15
131 A19 3p yellow, blk & grn .22 .20
132 A19 55m emerald, blk & yel .38 .35
Nos. 130-132 (3) .75 .70

17th Olympic Games, Rome, Aug. 25-Sept. 11.

1960, Sept. 6

133 A20 15m multicolored .15 .15
134 A20 3p multicolored .16 .16
135 A20 55m multicolored .30 .28
Nos. 133-135 (3) .61 .59

5th World Forestry Cong., Seattle, WA, Aug. 29-Sept. 10.

King Tirhaqah, 689-663 B.C. — A21

Girl with Book — A22

Unwmk.

1961, Mar. 1 Engr. *Perf. 14*

136 A21 15m yellow grn & brown .15 .15
137 A21 3p salmon & violet .16 .16
138 A21 55m lt blue & red brown .30 .28
Nos. 136-138 (3) .61 .59

Save historic monuments in Nubia.
An imperf. souvenir sheet exists, not sold at post offices, containing one each of Nos. 136-138. Size: 154x97mm. The sheet was not issued for postal purposes and cancellation requests are declined.

1961, Nov. 17 Litho. Wmk. 214

139 A22 15m violet, claret & pink .15 .15
140 A22 3p orange, blk & blue .16 .15
141 A22 55m gray grn, blk & ocher .30 .28
Nos. 139-141 (3) .61 .58

50 years of girls' education in the Sudan.

Malaria Eradication Emblem A23

Arab League Building, Cairo — A24

1962, Apr. 7 Unwmk. *Perf. 14*

142 A23 15m black, pur & blue .15 .15
143 A23 55m dk brown & green .30 .30

WHO drive to eradicate malaria.

1962, Apr. 22 Photo. *Perf. 13½x13*

144 A24 15m deep orange .15 .15
145 A24 55m blue green .28 .22
Set value .35 .28

Arab League Week, Mar. 22-28.

Type of 1951 and

Palace of the Republic, Khartoum A25

Cotton Picker A26

Designs: 15m, Straw cover. 35m, 4p, Wild animals. 55m, 6p, Cattle. 8p, Date palms. 10p, Sailboat. 20p, Bohein Temple, 1500 B.C. 50p, Sennar Dam. £1, Camel Post (A13 redrawn).

Perf. 14½x14, 14x14½

1962, Oct. 1 Litho. Wmk. 345

Size: 23x19mm, 19x23mm

146 A25 5m blue .15 .15
147 A26 10m blue & lilac .15 .15
148 A25 15m multicolored .15 .15
149 A25 2p lt purple .15 .15
150 A26 3p bl grn, red brn & blk .15 .15
151 A26 35m yel grn, brn & org brn .15 .15
152 A26 4p red, lt bl & lil .15 .15
153 A25 55m gray & yel ol .25 .15
154 A25 6p brown & lt blue .25 .15
155 A25 8p green .35 .15

Perf. 14x14½, 13x13½, 14x13½, 13½x14

Size: 24½x30mm, 30x24½mm

156 A26 10p lt bl, red brn & blk .42 .15
157 A25 20p gray ol & yel grn 1.00 .38
158 A25 50p dk gray, ol & bl 2.50 .60

Engr.

159 A13 £1 green & brn org 5.00 3.75
Nos. 146-159 (14) 10.82
Set value 5.50

The frame of No. 159 has been altered with Arabic inscription on top and English at bottom.
See Nos. 420, 427-428. For surcharge and overprints see Nos. 430, O62-O74, O92, O99-O100.

1975-79 Unwmk.

Perfs, Sizes and Printing Methods as Before

146a A25 5m ('76) .15 .15
147a A26 10m ('76) .15 .15
148a A25 15m .15 .15
149a A25 2p .15 .15
150a A26 3p ('76) .15 .15
151a A26 35m .15 .15
152a A26 4p .15 .15
153a A25 55m ('79) .25 .15
154a A25 6p .25 .15
155a A25 8p ('77) .35 .15
156a A26 10p .42 .15
157a A25 20p 1.00 .38
158a A25 50p 2.50 .60
159a A13 £1
Nos. 146a-158a (13) 5.82
Set value 1.75

Corn and Millet — A27

Centenary Emblem and Medals — A28

1963, Mar. 21 Litho. Wmk. 345

160 A27 15m. emerald, gray & brn .15 .15
161 A27 55m violet, lt & dk blue .30 .25
Set value .39 .33

FAO "Freedom from Hunger" campaign.

1963, Oct. 1 *Perf. 14*

162 A28 15m blk, red, gray & gold .15 .15
163 A28 55m grn, gray, red & gold .30 .25
Set value .39 .33

Centenary of the International Red Cross.

Melchior — A29

Khashm El Girba Dam — A30

Designs: 30m, St. Joseph seated, with cross and manuscript, horiz. 55m, Archangel with cross. Designs from frescoes in excavated Faras Church.

1964, Mar. 8 Litho. *Perf. 14*

164 A29 15m multicolored .15 .15
165 A29 30m red brn, blk & brn .35 .30
166 A29 55m red brn, blk & brn .60 .55
Nos. 164-166 (3) 1.10 1.00

UNESCO world campaign to save historic monuments in Nubia.

Perf. 14x14½, 14½x14

1964, Apr. 22 Wmk. 345

New York World's Fair, 1964-65: 3p, Pavilion 55m, Illustrated map of Sudan, vert.

167 A30 15m lt vio blue & vio brn .15 .15
168 A30 3p multicolored .18 .15
169 A30 55m multicolored .35 .25
Nos. 167-169 (3) .68
Set value .43

Eleanor Roosevelt and People Breaking Chains — A31

Arab Postal Union Emblem — A32

1964, Dec. 10 *Perf. 14*

170 A31 15m grnsh blue & blk .15 .15
171 A31 3p violet & black .16 .15
172 A31 55m orange brn & blk .35 .25
Nos. 170-172 (3) .66 .55

Eleanor Roosevelt (1884-1962), on the 16th anniv. of the Universal Declaration of Human Rights.

1964, Dec. 30   *Litho.*
173 A32 15m brick red, blk & gold   .15   .15
174 A32 3p gray green, blk & gold   .18   .15
175 A32 55m violet, blk & gold   .35   .25
   Nos. 173-175 (3)   .68   .55

10th anniv. of the Permanent Office of the Arab Postal Union.

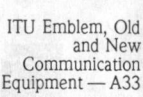

ITU Emblem, Old and New Communication Equipment — A33

1965, May 17   *Wmk. 345*   *Perf. 13½*
176 A33 15m brown & gold   .15   .15
177 A33 3p black & gold   .18   .15
178 A33 55m green & gold   .35   .25
   Nos. 176-178 (3)   .68   .55

Cent. of the ITU.

"Gurashi" and Revolutionists A34

1965, Nov. 10   *Litho.*   *Perf. 12*
179 A34 15m deep ocher & black   .15   .15
180 A34 3p bright red & black   .18   .15
181 A34 55m dark gray & black   .30   .25
   Nos. 179-181 (3)   .63   .55

1st anniv. of the October 21st Revolution and to honor "Gurashi," one of its heroes.

ICY Emblem — A35   El Siddig el Mahdi — A36

Perf. 14½x14
1965, Dec. 10   *Litho.*   *Wmk. 345*
182 A35 15m violet & blk   .15   .15
183 A35 3p yellow green & blk   .15   .15
184 A35 55m vermilion & blk   .30   .25
   Nos. 182-184 (3)   .60   .55

International Cooperation Year, 1965.

1966, Jan. 1   *Perf. 13*
185 A36 15m lt blue & vio blue   .15   .15
186 A36 3p orange & brown   .15   .15
187 A36 55m gray & red brown   .30   .22
   Nos. 185-187 (3)   .60
   Set value   .40

El Siddig el Mahdi (1911-61), imam of Ansar region and political leader.

Mubarak Zaroug A37

1966, Jan. 1   *Litho.*
188 A37 15m pink & lt olive grn   .15   .15
189 A37 3p brt yel grn & dk grn   .18   .15
190 A37 55m orange brn & dk brn   .30   .22
   Nos. 188-190 (3)   .63
   Set value   .40

Issued in memory of Mubarak Zaroug (1917-65), lawyer and political leader.

WHO Headquarters, Geneva — A38

1966, June 11   *Photo.*
191 A38 15m blue   .15   .15
192 A38 3p magenta   .15   .15
193 A38 55m brown   .30   .22
   Nos. 191-193 (3)   .60
   Set value   .40

Inauguration of WHO Headquarters, Geneva.

Map of Sudan and Crests of Upper Nile, Blue Nile and Kassala Provinces — A39

Designs: 3p, Map of Sudan and crests of Equatoria, Kordofan and Khartoum Provinces. 55m, Map of Sudan and crests of Bahr El Gazal, Darfur and Northern Provinces.

1967, Apr. 1   *Litho.*   *Perf. 14*
194 A39 15m org, pur & lt blue grn   .15   .15
195 A39 3p dp org, vio & lt blue   .15   .15
196 A39 55m yel, dp claret & yel grn   .25   .22
   Nos. 194-196 (3)   .55
   Set value   .40

Month of the South.

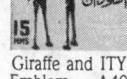

Giraffe and ITY Emblem — A40   Clasped Hands and Arab League Emblem — A41

Perf. 12½x13
1967, Aug. 15   *Litho.*   *Wmk. 345*
197 A40 15m multicolored   .25   .15
198 A40 3p multicolored   .15   .15
199 A40 55m multicolored   .75   .35
   Nos. 197-199 (3)   1.15   .65

International Tourist Year 1967.

Perf. 11x11½
1967, Aug. 29   *Photo.*   *Unwmk.*
200 A41 15m orange & ultra   .15   .15
201 A41 3p brown org & emerald   .15   .15
202 A41 55m lemon & violet   .25   .22
   Nos. 200-202 (3)   .55
   Set value   .40

Arab League Summit Conference.

Emblem of Palestine Liberation Organization — A42

1967, Aug. 29   *Perf. 11½x11*
203 A42 15m olive, car & yel   .15   .15
204 A42 3p green, car & yel   .22   .22
205 A42 55m brt green, car & yel   .38   .30
   Nos. 203-205 (3)   .75   .67

Palestine Liberation Organization.

Abdullahi el Fadil el Mahdi A43

Perf. 11½x11
1968, Feb. 15   *Photo.*   *Unwmk.*
206 A43 15m ultra & brt purple   .15   .15
207 A43 3p dp ultra & brt green   .15   .15
208 A43 55m orange & green   .25   .18
   Nos. 206-208 (3)   .55
   Set value   .33

Issued in memory of Abdullahi el Fadil el Mahdi (1892-1966), political leader.

Mohammed Nur el Din — A44

1968, Feb. 15
209 A44 15m sl blue & apple grn   .15   .15
210 A44 3p blue & olive   .15   .15
211 A44 55m blue & violet blue   .25   .18
   Nos. 209-211 (3)   .55
   Set value   .33

Issued in memory of Mohammed Nur el Din (1898-1964), political leader.

Ahmed Yousif Hashim A45

Perf. 11½x11
1968, Mar. 5   *Photo.*   *Unwmk.*
212 A45 15m green & brown   .15   .15
213 A45 3p brt blue & sepia   .15   .15
214 A45 55m indigo & violet   .25   .18
   Nos. 212-214 (3)   .55
   Set value   .33

Issued in memory of Ahmed Yousif Hashim (1906-1958), journalist.

Mohammed Ahmed el Mardi (1905-1966), Political Lader — A46

Perf. 11x11½
1968, Mar. 5   *Unwmk.*
215 A46 15m Prus blue & vio blue   .30   .15
216 A46 3p ultra, ocher & dl rose   .50   .15
217 A46 55m dk blue & brown   .65   .22
   Nos. 215-217 (3)   1.45   .52

DC-3 A47

20th anniv. of Sudan Airways: 2p, De Havilland Dove. 3p, Fokker Friendship. 55m, De Havilland Comet 4C.

1968, Dec. 15   *Litho.*   *Perf. 13½x13*
218 A47 15m multicolored   .15   .15
219 A47 2p multicolored   .15   .15
220 A47 3p multicolored   .22   .18
221 A47 55m multicolored   .35   .30
   Nos. 218-221 (4)   .87   .78

African Development Bank Emblem (right) — A48

Wmk. Rectangles (334)
1969, Dec. 20   *Photo.*   *Perf. 13*
222 A48 2p black, gray & gold   .15   .15
223 A48 4p dark red & gold   .20   .15
224 A48 65m green & gold   .35   .22
   Nos. 222-224 (3)   .70   .52

5th anniv. of the African Development Bank.

ILO Emblem — A49

Unwmk.
1969, Dec. 27   *Litho.*   *Perf. 14*
225 A49 2p blue, blk & pink   .15   .15
226 A49 4p yellow, blk & silver   .20   .15
227 A49 65m green, blk & lilac   .35   .22
   Nos. 225-227 (3)   .70   .52

50th anniv. of the ILO.

Citizens A50

1970, May 25   *Perf. 11½x11*
228 A50 2p brown org, olive & blue

First anniv. of May 25th Revolution.
This set was withdrawn on day of issue; 1721 sets of the 2p, 4p and 65m stamps in same design were sold through the Philatelic service. A few copies of No. 228 were sold at Post offices. Nos. 229-231 were issued instead.

Citizens A51

1970, Oct. 21   *Photo.*   *Perf. 11½x11*
229 A51 2p brown, olive & red   .15   .15
230 A51 4p lt blue, olive & red   .20   .15
231 A51 65m olive, dk blue & red   .35   .22
   Nos. 229-231 (3)   .70   .52

1st anniv. of the May 25th Revolution.

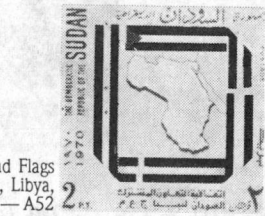

Map and Flags of UAR, Libya, Sudan — A52

1971, Jan. 2   *Unwmk.*   *Perf. 11½*
232 A52 2p lt green, carmine & blk   .15   .15

Signing of the Charter of Tripoli affirming the unity of UAR, Libya and the Sudan, Dec. 27, 1970.

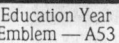

Education Year Emblem — A53   Emblem — A54

1971, May 2   *Photo.*   *Perf. 11x11½*
233 A53 2p blue, blk & brn   .15   .15
234 A53 4p carmine, blk & brn   .20   .15
235 A53 65m violet brn, blk & brn   .35   .22
   Nos. 233-235 (3)   .70   .52

International Education Year.

1971, Nov. 10 *Perf. 11x11½*
236 A54   2p yellow, grn & blk   .15   .15
237 A54   4p blue, grn & blk   .35   .30
238 A54   10½p gray, grn & blk   .90   .75
Nos. 236-238 (3)   1.40   1.20

2nd anniversary of May 25th Revolution.

Arab League and Sudanese Emblems — A55

UN Emblem — A56

1972, Feb. 10 Photo. *Perf. 11x11½*
239 A55   2p yellow, grn & blk   .15   .15
240 A55   4p orange, bl & blk   .25   .22
241 A55   10½p orange, brn & blk   .70   .60
Nos. 239-241 (3)   1.10   .97

25th anniv. (in 1971) of the Arab League.

1972, Mar. 12 Photo. *Perf. 11x11½*
242 A56   2p emer, rose red & org   .15   .15
243 A56   4p ultra, rose red & org   .25   .22
244 A56   10½p black, rose red & org   .70   .60
Nos. 242-244 (3)   1.10   .97

25th anniv. (in 1970) of the UN.

Emblems and Measure A57

1972, Apr. 22 Photo. *Perf. 11½x11*
245 A57   2p multicolored   .15   .15
246 A57   4p lt blue & multi   .25   .22
247 A57   10½p pink & multi   .70   .60
Nos. 245-247 (3)   1.10   .97

World Standards Day, Oct. 14, 1970.

Pres. Nimeiry and Arms of Sudan — A58

1972, May 2 Litho. *Perf. 13x13½*
248 A58   2p vio blue, blk & gold   .15   .15
249 A58   4p dp org, blk & gold   .25   .22
250 A58   10½p ol grn, blk & gold   .70   .60
Nos. 248-250 (3)   1.10   .97

Election of Gaafar al Nimeiry as President, Oct. 1971.

Arms of Sudan and Congress Emblem A59

1972, Oct. 15 Photo. *Perf. 11½x11*
251 A59   2p blue & multi   .15   .15
252 A59   4p multicolored   .25   .22
253 A59   10½p lt olive & multi   .70   .60
Nos. 251-253 (3)   1.10   .97

Founding Congress of the Sudanese Socialist Union.

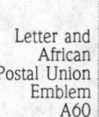 

Letter and African Postal Union Emblem A60

1972, Dec. 16
254 A60   2p yellow & multi   .15   .15
255 A60   4p multicolored   .25   .22
256 A60   10½p blue & multi   .70   .60
Nos. 254-256 (3)   1.10   .97

10th anniv. (in 1971) of the APU.

Emblems of Sudanese Provinces A61

Designs: 4p, Governing Council of Sudan. 10½p, Heraldic eagle and Unity emblem, vert.

1973, Jan. 1 Litho. *Perf. 13*
257 A61   2p gold & multi   .15   .15
258 A61   4p dk red brn & blk   .25   .22
259 A61   10½p silver, org & grn   .70   .55
Nos. 257-259 (3)   1.10   .92

National Unity Day, March 3, 1972.

Emperor Haile Selassie — A62

1973, June 25 Unwmk. *Perf. 13*
260 A62   2p tan & multi   .15   .15
261 A62   4p silver & multi   .25   .22
262 A62   10½p gold & multi   .70   .55
Nos. 260-262 (3)   1.10   .92

80th birthday of Haile Selassie, Emperor of Ethiopia.

Nasser and Crowd A63

1973, July 15 Photo. *Perf. 11½x11*
263 A63   2p black   .15   .15
264 A63   4p pale green & blk   .25   .22
265 A63   10½p lilac & blk   .70   .55
Nos. 263-265 (3)   1.10   .92

Gamal Abdel Nasser (1918-70), President of Egypt.

UN and FAO Emblems, Portal and Map of Resettlement Project A64

1973, Dec. 30 Litho. *Perf. 13*
266 A64   2p multicolored   .15   .15
267 A64   4p multicolored   .25   .22
268 A64   10½p multicolored   .70   .60
Nos. 266-268 (3)   1.10   .97

World Food Program, 10th anniversary.

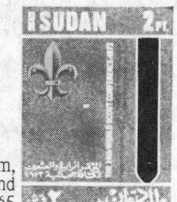

Scout Emblem, Knotted Rope and Stave — A65

1974, Jan. 15
269 A65   2p multicolored   .16   .15
270 A65   4p multicolored   .38   .15
271 A65   10½p multicolored   .75   .38
Nos. 269-271 (3)   1.29   .68

24th World Boy Scout Conference.

INTERPOL Emblem A66

1974, Feb. 16 Litho. *Perf. 13x13½*
272 A66   2p orange & multi   .15   .15
273 A66   4p gray & multi   .20   .15
274 A66   10½p lt blue & multi   .50   .38
Nos. 272-274 (3)   .85   .68

50th anniv. of Intl. Criminal Police Organ.

K.S.M. Building A67

1974, July 1 Litho. *Perf. 13x13½*
275 A67   2p lilac rose & multi   .18   .15
276 A67   4p green & multi   .38   .15
277 A67   10½p vermilion & multi   .90   .38
Nos. 275-277 (3)   1.46   .68

50th anniversary of the Faculty of Medicine, University of Khartoum.

African Postal Union and UPU Emblems — A68

Designs: 4p, Letters, UPU and APU emblems. 10½p, Letters, UPU and APU emblems.

1974, Sept. 9 Litho. *Perf. 13½*
278 A68   2p multicolored   .15   .15
279 A68   4p lt blue & multi   .20   .15
280 A68   10½p lilac & multi   .50   .38
Nos. 278-280 (3)   .85   .68

Centenary of Universal Postal Union.

Ali Abdel Latif, Abdel Fadil Elmaz, Revolutionary Flag and Nile — A69

1975, July 26 Litho. *Perf. 14x13½*
281 A69   2½p green & vio blue   .22   .15
282 A69   4p rose & vio blue   .50   .15
283 A69   10½p sepia & vio blue   .90   .38
Nos. 281-283 (3)   1.62   .68

50th anniversary of 1924 revolution. Portraits show political and military leaders of the revolution.

ADB Emblem with Map of Africa — A70

1975, July 26
284 A70   2½p multicolored   .22   .15
285 A70   4p multicolored   .45   .15
286 A70   10½p multicolored   .90   .38
Nos. 284-286 (3)   1.57   .68

African Development Bank, 10th anniv.

Radar Station and Camel Rider — A71

1976, Feb. 2 Litho. *Perf. 13½x14*
287 A71   2½p lt green & multi   .15   .15
288 A71   4p lilac & multi   .20   .15
289 A71   10½p vio blue & multi   .50   .38
Nos. 287-289 (3)   .85   .68

Umm Haraz Satellite Station.

IWY Emblem, Flag and Woman A72

1976, May 10 Litho. *Perf. 14x13½*
290 A72   2½p multicolored   .15   .15
291 A72   4p multicolored   .22   .15
292 A72   10½p dk blue & multi   .50   .38
Nos. 290-292 (3)   .87   .68

International Women's Year 1975.

Arms of Sudan, Olympic Rings, Track — A73

1976, July 17 Litho. *Perf. 13½x14*
293 A73   2½p green & multi   .22   .15
294 A73   4p green & multi   .50   .30
295 A73   10½p green & multi   .90   .55
Nos. 293-295 (3)   1.62   1.00

21st Olympic Games, Montreal, Canada, July 17-Aug. 1.

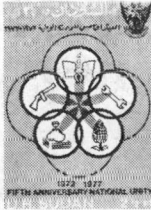

Education, Engineering, Forestry, Agriculture and Defense — A74

1977, July 20 Litho. *Perf. 13½x14*
296 A74   2½p multicolored   .15   .15
297 A74   4p multicolored   .20   .15
298 A74   10½p multicolored   .50   .38
Nos. 296-298 (3)   .85   .68

5th anniversary of national unity.

Archbishop Capucci — A75

1977, Oct. 22 Photo. *Perf. 11x11½*
299 A75   2½p black   .42   .16
300 A75   4p black & green   .70   .42
301 A75   10½p black & red   1.10   .60
Nos. 299-301 (3)   2.22   1.18

Palestinian Archbishop Hilarion Capucci, jailed by Israel in 1974.

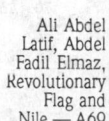

Fair Emblem, Sudanese Flag — A76

Perf. 11½x11

1978, Jan. 19   Photo.   Wmk. 342
302 A76 3p multicolored .15 .15
303 A76 4p multicolored .20 .15
304 A76 10½p multicolored .50 .38
Nos. 302-304 (3) .85 .68

International Khartoum Fair, Jan. 19-27.

APU Emblem A77

1978, Mar. 8   Litho.   Perf. 14x13½
305 A77 3p black, car & sil .22 .15
306 A77 4p dk green, blk & sil .30 .15
307 A77 10½p ultra, blk & sil .75 .38
Nos. 305-307 (3) 1.27 .68

APU, 25th anniv. (in 1977).

Jinnah and Sudanese Flag — A78

1978, May 6   Litho.   Perf. 13
308 A78 3p multicolored .15 .15
309 A78 4p multicolored .30 .15
310 A78 10½p multicolored .50 .38
Nos. 308-310 (3) .95 .68

Mohammed Ali Jinnah (1876-1948), first Governor General of Pakistan.

Desert A79

1978, May 6   Perf. 14x13½
311 A79 3p multicolored .15 .15
312 A79 4p multicolored .20 .15
313 A79 10½p multicolored .50 .38
Nos. 311-313 (3) .85 .68

UN Desertification Conference.

Lion God Apedemek, African Unity Emblems — A80

1978, July 18   Litho.   Perf. 13½x14
314 A80 3p multicolored .15 .15
315 A80 4p multicolored .20 .15
316 A80 10½p multicolored .40 .38
Nos. 314-316 (3) .75 .68

15th African Summit Conference, Khartoum, July 18-21.

A81 / A82

1979, Oct. 1   Litho.   Perf. 13½x14
317 A81 3½p multicolored .15 .15
318 A81 6p multicolored .20 .15
319 A81 13p multicolored .40 .38
Nos. 317-319 (3) .75 .68

May Revolution, 10th Anniversary.

1980, Jan. 19   Litho.   Perf. 13½x14
320 A82 4½p orange & black .15 .15
321 A82 8p olive green & blk .25 .22
322 A82 15½p blue & black .50 .38
Nos. 320-322 (3) .90 .82

UNESCO emblem, children holding globe.

IYC Emblem, Hands Protecting Child — A83

1980, Mar. 15   Perf. 14x13½
323 A83 4½p multicolored .15 .15
324 A83 8p multicolored .25 .22
325 A83 15½p multicolored .50 .45
Nos. 323-325 (3) .90 .82

International Year of the Child (1979).

25th Anniv. of Independence A84

1982, Mar. 4   Photo.   Perf. 11½
326 A84 60m multicolored .20 .15
327 A84 120m multicolored .45 .30
328 A84 250m multicolored .90 .75
Nos. 326-328 (3) 1.55 1.20

World Food Day, Oct. 16, 1981 — A85

1983, Jan. 15   Photo.   Perf. 11½
329 A85 60m Emblem on map, reaching hands .20 .15
330 A85 120m Produce .45 .30
331 A85 250m Map, grain .90 .75
Nos. 329-331 (3) 1.55 1.20

A86 / A87

1984, Feb. 20   Litho.   Perf. 13½
332 A86 10p pink & silver .15 .15
333 A86 25p lt blue & silver .30 .22
334 A86 40p green & silver .40 .38
Nos. 332-334 (3) .85 .75

25th Anniv. of Economic Commission for Africa (1983).

1984, June 16   Litho.   Perf. 14
335 A87 10p multicolored .15 .15
336 A87 25p multicolored .30 .22
337 A87 40p multicolored .45 .38
Nos. 335-337 (3) .90 .75

Cent. of Shaykan Battle, Kordofan (1983).

Olympic Week — A88

1984, Dec. 1   Litho.   Perf. 14
338 A88 10p multicolored .15 .15
339 A88 25p multicolored .30 .22
340 A88 40p multicolored .45 .38
Nos. 338-340 (3) .90 .75

Sudan-Egypt Integration Charter, 2nd Anniv. — A89 / Bakht Erruda, Teacher Training Institute — A90

1985, Mar. 16   Photo.   Perf. 13½x13
341 A89 10p multicolored .15 .15
342 A89 25p multicolored .30 .22
343 A89 40p multicolored .45 .38
Nos. 341-343 (3) .90 .75

1985, Apr. 1
344 A90 10p multicolored .15 .15
345 A90 25p multicolored .30 .22
346 A90 40p multicolored .45 .38
Nos. 344-346 (3) .90 .75

April 6 Uprising, 1st Anniv. — A91

1986, Apr. 1   Litho.   Perf. 14
347 A91 5p multicolored .15 .15
348 A91 25p multicolored .30 .22
349 A91 40p multicolored .45 .38
Nos. 347-349 (3) .90 .75

World Food Day 1986 — A92

Perf. 13x13½, 13½x13 (30p), 14 (50p)

1988, Jan. 1   Litho.
350 A92 25p Net fishermen .15 .15
351 A92 30p Two fish, vert. .15 .15
352 A92 50p Globe .22 .15
353 A92 75p Stylized fish on wave .35 .24
354 A92 300p Fish in sea 1.40 .95
Nos. 350-354 (5) 2.27 1.64

Souvenir Sheet
Imperf
354A A92 75p like 25p .70 .70

Child Survival A93

Perf. 14, Imperf. (No. 357)

1988, Mar. 15   Litho.
355 A93 50p Breast-feeding, vert. .24 .16
356 A93 75p Oral rehydration .35 .24
357 A93 75p like 50p, vert. .35 .24
358 A93 100p Oral vaccine .45 .30
359 A93 150p Growth monitoring .68 .45
Nos. 355-359 (5) 2.07 1.39

No. 357 issued without gum. Size: 63x84mm.

Red Crescent in Sudan, 30th Anniv. (in 1987) — A94 / World Food Day, Oct. 16, 1987, and the Small Farmer — A95

Designs: 100p, Crescent, candle. 150p, Crescent, stylized figure of a man.

1988, Oct. 31   Litho.   Perf. 14
360 A94 40p org yel, blk & dk red .18 .15
361 A94 100p blk, blue grn & dk red .45 .30
362 A94 150p blk, brt blue & dk red .68 .45
Nos. 360-362 (3) 1.31 .90

Nos. 361-362 horiz.

Perf. 13x13½, 13½x13
1988, Oct. 31

FAO emblem and: 40p, Early farming tools, horiz. 100p, Ox-drawn plow. 150p, Crude public water supply.

363 A95 40p multicolored .18 .15
364 A95 100p shown .45 .30
365 A95 150p multicolored .68 .45
Nos. 363-365 (3) 1.31 .90

Khartoum Bank, 75th Anniv. A96

Designs: 40p, Anniv. emblem. 100p, Spheres, emblem, medallion on ribbon. 150p, Text, emblem.

1988, Oct. 31   Perf. 14
366 A96 40p multicolored .18 .15
367 A96 100p multicolored .45 .30
368 A96 150p multicolored .68 .45
Nos. 366-368 (3) 1.31 .90

Declaration of Palestinian State, 1st Anniv. — A97

Design: Nos. 370, 372, 374, Crowd of demonstrators.

1989, Dec. 10   Litho.   Perf. 14
369 A97 100p yellow grn & multi .95 .62
370 A97 100p buff & multi .95 .62
371 A97 150p lt vio & multi 1.40 .92
372 A97 150p lt blue & multi 1.40 .92
373 A97 200p pink & multi 1.90 1.25
374 A97 200p lt green & multi 1.90 1.25
Nos. 369-374 (6) 8.50 5.58

Palestinian Uprising (Nos. 370, 372, 374).

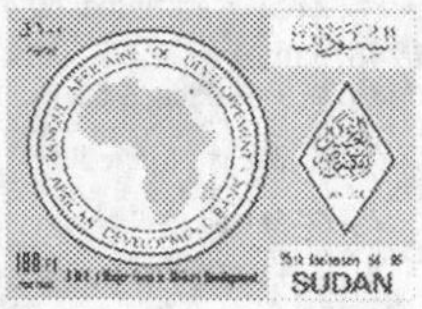

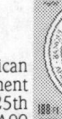

African Development Bank, 25th Anniv. — A99

1989, Dec. 28 *Perf. 13x13½*

375	A99	100p	yel grn, blk & sil	.95	.62
376	A99	150p	blue, blk & sil	1.40	.92
377	A99	200p	plum, blk & sil	1.90	1.25
			Nos. 375-377 (3)	4.25	2.79

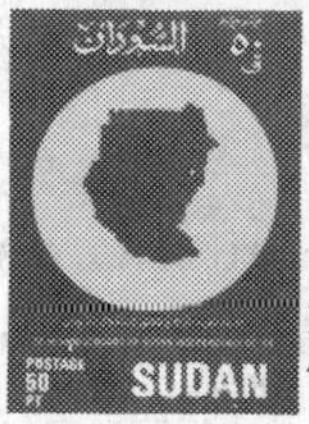

Independence, 33rd Anniv. (in 1989) — A100

1990, Jan. 22 Litho. *Perf. 13½x13*

378	A100	50p	blue & yellow	.35	.22
379	A100	100p	deep claret & yel	.70	.45
380	A100	150p	brt rose & yel	1.05	.70
381	A100	200p	dp rose lilac & yel	1.40	.90
			Nos. 378-381 (4)	3.50	2.27

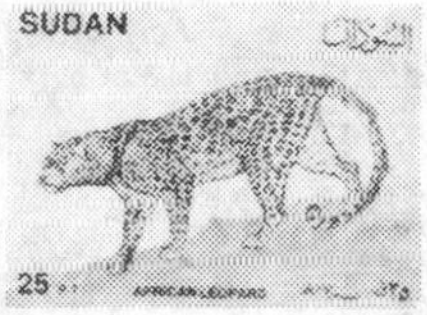

Mammals A101

1990, Feb. 20 *Perf. 13x13½*

382	A101	25p	Leopard	.18	.15
383	A101	50p	Elephant	.35	.22
			Perf. 14		
384	A101	75p	Giraffe, vert.	.52	.35
385	A101	100p	White rhinoceros	.70	.45
386	A101	125p	Addax, vert.	.88	.60
			Nos. 382-386 (5)	2.63	1.77

No. 385 inscribed "Rino."

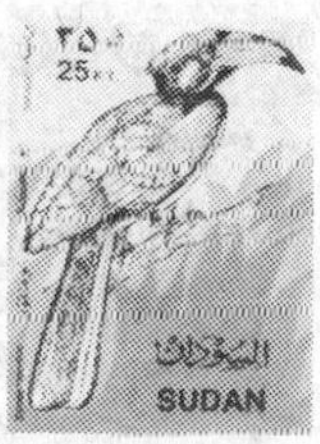

Birds — A102

1990, Mar. 25 *Perf. 13½x13*

387	A102	25p	Zande hornbill	.18	.15
388	A102	50p	Marabou stork	.35	.22
389	A102	75p	Buff-crested bustard	.52	.35
390	A102	100p	Saddle-bill	.70	.45
			Perf. 14		
391	A102	150p	Bald-headed ibis	1.05	.70
			Nos. 387-391 (5)	2.80	1.87

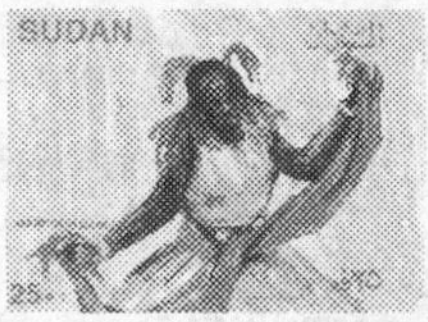

Traditional Dances A103

Perf. 13x13½, 13½x13

1990, May 10 **Litho.**

392	A103	25p	Mardoum	.40	.25
393	A103	50p	Zandi, vert.	.82	.55
394	A103	75p	Kambala, vert.	1.25	.82
395	A103	100p	Nubian, vert.	1.65	1.10
396	A103	125p	Sword	2.10	1.40
			Nos. 392-396 (5)	6.22	4.12

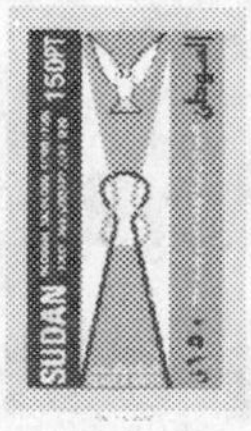

Natl. Salvation Revolution, 1st Anniv. — A104

1991, Apr. 14 Litho. *Perf. 13*

399	A104	150p	multicolored	1.05	.70
400	A104	200p	multicolored	1.40	.90
401	A104	250p	multicolored	1.75	1.15
402	A104	£5	multicolored	3.50	2.30
403	A104	£10	multicolored	7.00	4.60
			Nos. 399-403 (5)	14.70	9.65

For surcharge see No. 438.

Type of 1962 and:

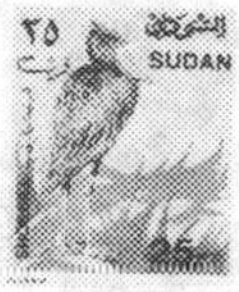

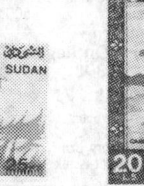

Shoebill A105

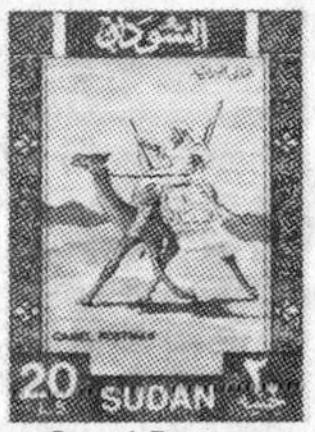

Camel Postman A109

1991, July 1 *Perf. 13½x13*

404	A105	25p	shown	.18	.15
405	A105	50p	Sunflower	.35	.22
406	A105	75p	Gum Arabic	.52	.35
407	A105	100p	Cotton	.70	.45
408	A105	125p	Crowned crane	.90	.58
			Size: 30x24mm		
			Perf. 14x14½, 13½x14		
409	A105	150p	Kenana Sugar Co., horiz.	1.05	.70
410	A105	175p	Secretary bird	1.25	.80
411	A105	£2	Atbara cement factory, horiz.	1.40	.90
			Size: 26x37mm		
			Perf. 14		
412	A105	250p	King Taharqa statue	1.75	1.15
413	A105	£3	Republican palace	2.10	1.40
			Size: 24x30mm		
			Perf. 13½x14		
414	A105	£4	Hug jar	2.75	1.85
415	A105	£5	Gabana coffee pot	3.50	2.25
			Size: 36x27mm		
			Litho. & Engr.		
			Perf. 14		
			Wmk. 334		
416	A105	£8	Pterois volitans, horiz.	5.50	3.75
417	A105	£10	Animal wealth, horiz.	7.00	4.50
418	A105	£15	Nubian ibex	10.50	6.75
419	A109	£20	shown	14.00	9.00
			Nos. 404-419 (16)	53.45	34.80

1992 Litho. Unwmk. *Perf. 14½x14*

420	A25	25p	Cattle	.15	.15

1990 Unwmk. *Perf. 14x13½*

427	A25	£5	Bohein Temple	3.50	2.25
			Perf. 13½x14		
428	A26	£10	Sailboat	7.00	4.50

This is an expanding set. Numbers will change if necessary.

See Nos. O76-O100. For surcharges see Nos. 430, 436-437, 438A-443, O104-O111.

No. 156a Handstamp Surcharged in Blue Violet

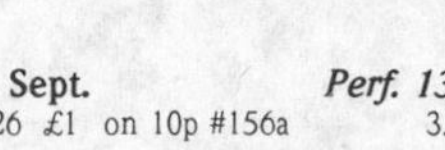

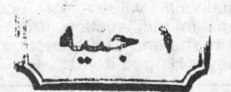

1990, Sept. *Perf. 13½x14*

430	A26	£1	on 10p #156a	3.00	1.95

Surcharge on No. 430 is often incomplete.

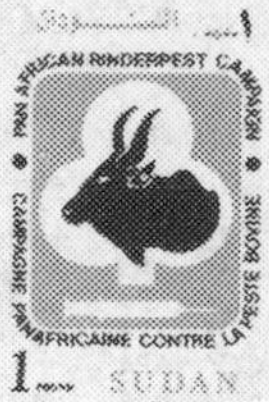

Pan-African Rinderpest Campaign — A114

Perf. 13½x13

1991, July 27 Litho. Unwmk.

431	A114	£1	black & brt grn	.70	.45
432	A114	£2	dp violet & emer	1.40	.90
433	A114	£5	orange & blue grn	3.50	2.30
			Nos. 431-433 (3)	5.60	3.65

Dinar (1992)

Nos. 404, 407, 411, 413-414 Surcharged in Black or Blue Violet

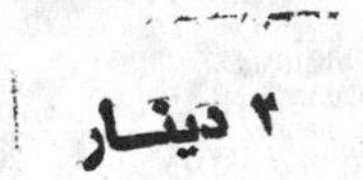

Nos. 406, 409, 420 Surcharged

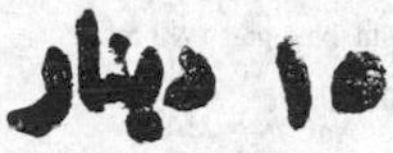

1992?

Perfs. & Printing Methods as Before

436	A105	1d	on 100p #407 (Blk)	3.75	2.50
436A	A105	1.50d	on 150p #409	1.50	1.00
437	A105	2d	on £2 #411	7.25	4.75
438	A104	2.50d	on 25p #404	9.00	5.75
438A	A105	2.50d	on 25p #420	2.50	1.75
439	A105	3d	on £3 #413	11.00	7.00
440	A105	4d	on £4 #414	14.50	9.50
443	A105	7.50d	on 75p #406	7.50	5.00
			Nos. 436-443 (8)	57.00	37.25

This is an expanding set. Numbers will change if necessary.

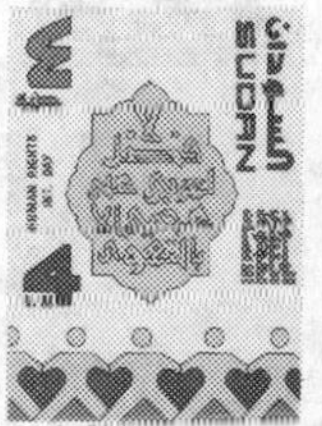

Intl. Human Rights Day — A115

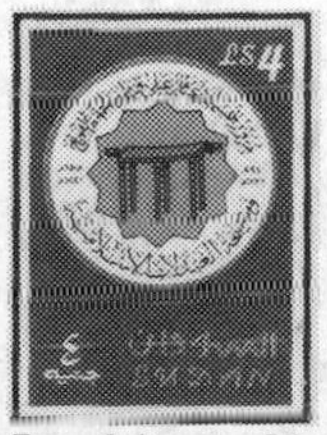

Fung Sultanate, 5th Cent. — A116

Designs: £5, Chain links, rainbow of colors, horiz. 750p, Trellis, rose, inscription.

1993, Dec. 20 Litho. *Perf. 14*

454	A115	£4	multicolored	.80	.52
455	A115	£5	multicolored	1.00	.65
456	A115	750p	multicolored	1.45	1.00
			Nos. 454-456 (3)	3.25	2.17

1993, Dec. 20

Designs: £5, Inscription on tablet. 750p, Inscription in circle, helmet, horiz.

457	A116	£4	multicolored	.80	.52
458	A116	£5	multicolored	1.00	.65
459	A116	750p	multicolored	1.45	1.00
			Nos. 457-459 (3)	3.25	2.17

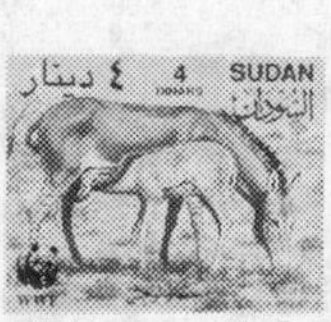

Wild Ass — A117

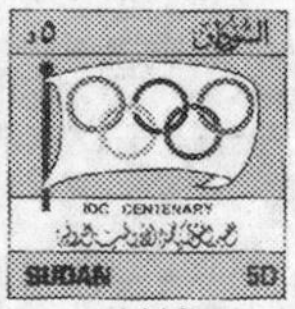

A118

1994, July 15 Litho. *Perf. 14½*

460	A117	4d	With young	.22	.15
461	A117	8d	Standing	.45	.30
462	A117	10d	Running	.55	.38
463	A117	15d	Up close	.85	.55
			Nos. 460-463 (4)	2.07	1.38

1994, Aug. 1 Litho. *Perf. 14*

464	A118	5d	vermilion & multi	.28	.18
465	A118	7d	green & multi	.38	.25
466	A118	15d	gray & multi	.85	.55
			Nos. 464-466 (3)	1.51	.98

Intl. Olympic Committee, cent.

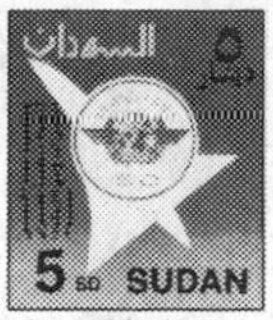

A119

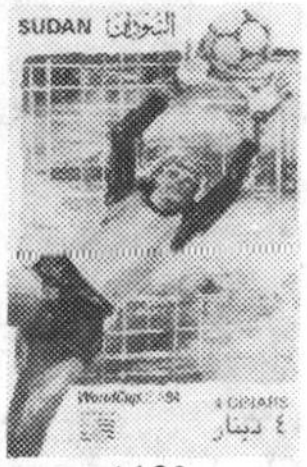

A120

1994, Dec. 7 Litho. *Perf. 13½*

467	A119	5d	lilac & multi	.25	.15
468	A119	7d	brown & multi	.35	.20
469	A119	15d	blue & multi	.80	.50
			Nos. 467-469 (3)	1.40	.85

ICAO, 50th anniv.

1995, July 15 Litho. *Perf. 14*

1994 World Cup Soccer Championships, US: 4d, Goalie, green vest. 5d, Like 4d, blue vest. 7d, Player about to kick ball, green shirt. 8d, Like 7d, brown shirt. 10d, Player, long-sleeved shirt. 15d, Player, yellow shirt. 20d, Player, magenta & blue background. 25d, Player, white shirt & pants. 35d, Like 20d, blue & green background.

75d, Goalie, orange shirt, horiz. 100d, Player kicking ball, horiz.

470	A120	4d	multicolored	.15	.15
471	A120	5d	multicolored	.20	.15
472	A120	7d	multicolored	.25	.15
473	A120	8d	multicolored	.30	.20
474	A120	10d	multicolored	.40	.25
475	A120	15d	multicolored	.60	.40
476	A120	20d	multicolored	.75	.50
477	A120	25d	multicolored	.95	.60
478	A120	35d	multicolored	1.25	.80
			Nos. 470-478 (9)	4.85	3.20

Souvenir Sheets

479	A120	75d	multicolored	5.50	3.75
480	A120	100d	multicolored	7.50	5.00

AIR POST STAMPS

Nos. 40-41, 43 Overprinted in Black

AIR MAIL
Nos. C1-C2

AIR MAIL
No. C3

Perf. 11½x12½, 14

1931 **Wmk. 214**

C1	A2	5m	blk & olive brown	.60	*1.00*
C2	A2	10m	blk & carmine	.60	*2.00*
C3	A1	2p	org & vio brown	.80	*2.75*
			Nos. C1-C3 (3)	2.00	*5.75*

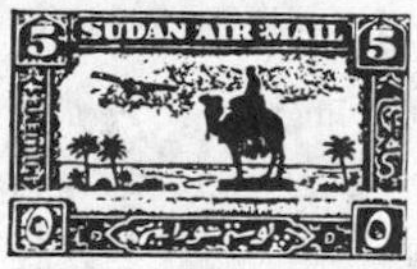

Statue of Gen. C. G. Gordon AP3

1931-35 Engr. *Perf. 14*

C4	AP3	3m	dk brn & grn ('33)	2.00	*5.00*
C5	AP3	5m	grn & blk	.90	.15
C6	AP3	10m	car rose & blk	.90	.25
C7	AP3	15m	dk brn & brn	.35	.15
C8	AP3	2p	org & blk	.25	.15
C9	AP3	2½p	bl & red vio ('33)	3.00	.15
C10	AP3	3p	gray & blk	.50	.15
C11	AP3	3½p	dl vio & blk	1.10	.70
C12	AP3	4½p	gray & brn	9.00	13.00
C13	AP3	5p	ultra & blk	.90	.35
C14	AP3	7½p	pck grn & dk grn ('35)	6.50	3.75
C15	AP3	10p	peacock bl & sep ('35)	7.00	.25
			Nos. C4-C15 (12)	32.40	24.05

See Nos. C23-C30. For surcharges see Nos. C17-C22, C31-C34.

2½ 2½

No. 43 Surcharged in Black

AIR MAIL

٢½ ٢½

1932, July 18 **Typo.**
C16 A1 2½p on 2p 5.00 5.00

Nos. C6, C4-C5, C12 Surcharged

7½ PIASTRES
٧½ فروش

1935 **Engr.** ***Perf. 14***
C17 AP3 15m on 10m .85 .85
a. Double surcharge 575.00 *700.00*
b. Arabic characters omitted 650.00
C18 AP3 2½p on 3m 2.00 2.00
a. "½" 2¼mm high instead of 3mm 8.25 8.25
b. Second Arabic character of surcharge omitted 140.00 140.00
C19 AP3 2½p on 5m 1.00 1.00
a. "½" 2¼mm high instead of 3mm 8.00 8.00
b. Second Arabic character of surcharge omitted 80.00 80.00
c. Inverted surcharge 825.00 825.00
d. As "b," inverted *2,100.*
C20 AP3 3p on 4½p 3.75 *5.00*
C21 AP3 7½p on 4½p 7.50 *10.00*
a. "7¼" instead of "7½"
C22 AP3 10p on 4½p 7.00 *8.00*
Nos. C17-C22 (6) 22.10 *26.85*

Type of 1931-35

1936-37 ***Perf. 11½x12½***
C23 AP3 15m dk brn & brn ('37) .90 .35
C24 AP3 2p org & blk ('37) 4.25 3.00
C25 AP3 2½p bl & red vio .50 .35
C26 AP3 3p gray & blk ('37) 1.50 .75
C27 AP3 3½p dl vio & blk ('37) 3.50 2.25
C28 AP3 5p ultra & blk ('37) 1.25 .60
C29 AP3 7½p pck grn & dk grn ('37) 2.00 1.40
C30 AP3 10p pck bl & sep ('37) 3.25 2.00
Nos. C23-C30 (8) 17.15 10.70

Nos. C25, C11, C14 and C15 Surcharged as in 1935

Perf. 11½x12½, 14

1938 **Wmk. 214**
C31 AP3 5m on 2½p .25 .25
C32 AP3 3p on 3½p 4.00 4.00
a. On No. C27 300.00 *350.00*
C33 AP3 3p on 7½p .90 .90
a. On No. C29 350.00 *400.00*
C34 AP3 5p on 10p 1.10 1.10
a. On No. C30 425.00 *475.00*
Nos. C31-C34 (4) 6.25 6.25

Catalogue values for unused stamps in this section, from this point to the end of the section, are for Never Hinged items.

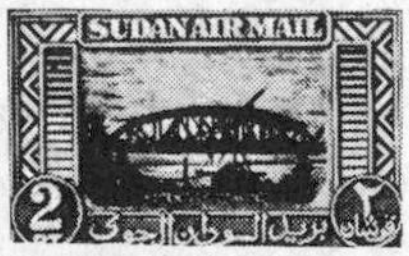

Bridge Over Blue Nile, Khartoum AP4

Designs: 2½p, Kassala Jebel. 3p, Water wheel. 3½p, Port Sudan. 4p, Gordon Memorial College. 4½p, Nile post boat. 6p, Suakin. 20p, General Post Office, Khartoum.

1950, July 1 **Engr.** ***Perf. 12***
C35 AP4 2p dk bl grn & blk .50 .35
C36 AP4 2½p red org & bl .60 .60
C37 AP4 3p dp bl & plum .75 .75
C38 AP4 3½p chnt & choc .75 .75
C39 AP4 4p bl & brn 1.20 1.20
C40 AP4 4½p ultra & blk 1.25 1.25
C41 AP4 6p car & blk 1.25 1.25
C42 AP4 20p plum & blk 5.50 4.00
Nos. C35-C42 (8) 11.80 10.15

For overprints see Nos. CO1-CO8.

AIR POST OFFICIAL

Catalogue values for unused stamps in this section are for Never Hinged items.

Nos. C35 to C42 Overprinted in Carmine or Black

S.G.

1950, July 1 **Wmk. 214** ***Perf. 12***
CO1 AP4 2p dk bl grn & blk (C) 11.00 1.75
CO2 AP4 2½p red org & bl 1.00 1.00
CO3 AP4 3p dp bl & plum .70 .60
CO4 AP4 3½p chnt & choc .70 4.00
CO5 AP4 4p bl & brn .70 2.50
CO6 AP4 4½p ultra & blk (C) 2.00 10.00
CO7 AP4 6p car & blk (C) .90 3.25
CO8 AP4 20p plum & blk (C) 4.50 10.00
Nos. CO1-CO8 (8) 21.50 33.10

POSTAGE DUE STAMPS

Postage Due Stamps of Egypt, 1889, Overprinted in Black

السودان
SOUDAN

1897 **Wmk. 119** ***Perf. 14***
J1 D3 2m green 1.50 7.00
J2 D3 4m maroon 1.50 7.00
J3 D3 1p ultra 8.50 4.00
J4 D3 2p orange 8.50 10.00
Nos. J1-J4 (4) 20.00 28.00

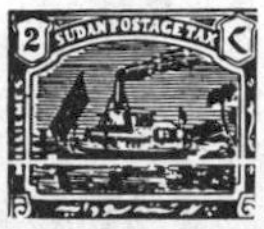

Steamboat on Nile River — D1

1901 **Typo.** **Wmk. 179**
J5 D1 2m orange brn & blk .70 .50
J6 D1 4m blue green & brn 1.00 .60
J7 D1 10m blue vio & blue grn 1.50 .75
J8 D1 20m car rose & ultra 4.50 3.25
Nos. J5-J8 (4) 7.70 5.10

1927-30 **Wmk. Multiple S G (214)**
J9 D1 2m org brn & blk ('30) .60 .60
J10 D1 4m blue grn & brn 1.25 1.25
J11 D1 10m violet & blue grn 1.50 1.50
Nos. J9-J11 (3) 3.35 3.35

Catalogue values for unused stamps in this section, from this point to the end of the section, are for Never Hinged items.

Redrawn

Bottom inscription altered — D2

1948, Jan. 1
J12 D2 2m dp orange & blk 1.75 3.50
J13 D2 4m blue grn & choc 1.75 3.50
J14 D2 10m rose lil & bl grn 6.00 12.50
a. Wmk. 345 ('73)
J15 D2 20m brt car rose & ultra 7.50 15.00
a. Wmk. 345 ('73)
Nos. J12-J15 (4) 17.00 34.50

ARMY OFFICIALS

Regular Issues of 1898 and 1902-08 Overprinted in Black:

ARMY OFFICIAL — Nos. MO1, MO3

ARMY OFFICIAL — Nos. MO2, MO4

1905 **Wmk. 71** ***Perf. 14***
MO1 A1 1m rose & brown 125.00 85.00
a. "OFFICIAL" 1,750.
MO2 A1 1m rose & brown 1,800. *1,800.*

Wmk. 179

MO3 A1 1m car rose & brn 3.00 2.00
a. "OFFICIAL" 32.50 15.00
b. Inverted overprint 70.00 60.00
c. Horizontal overprint 450.00
MO4 A1 1m car rose & brn 35.00 17.50
a. Inverted overprint 350.00 375.00

Regular Issues of 1902-11 Overprinted in Black

Army
Service

1906-11
MO5 A1 1m car rose & brn 1.40 .30
a. "Army" and "Service" 14mm apart 275.00 200.00
b. Inverted overprint 400.00 400.00
c. Pair, one without ovpt. *3,750.*
d. Double overprint 600.00
e. "Service" omitted 3,500.
MO6 A1 2m brown & green 6.25 .50
a. Pair, one without ovpt. 1,800.
b. "Army" omitted 2,250.
MO7 A1 3m green & violet 11.00 .40
a. Inverted overprint 2,000.
MO8 A1 5m blk & rose red 1.75 .15
a. Inverted overprint 200.00
b. Double overprint 275.00 275.00
c. Double ovpt., one invtd. 650.00 350.00
MO9 A1 1p yel brn & ultra 7.50 .25
a. "Army" omitted 2,000. 2,000.
MO10 A1 2p ultra & blk ('09) 12.50 10.00
MO11 A1 5p grn & org brn ('08) 70.00 30.00
MO12 A1 10p dp vio & blk ('11) 500.00 525.00
Nos. MO5-MO12 (8) 610.40 566.60

Same Overprint On Regular Issue of 1898

Wmk. 71

MO13 A1 2p ultra & black 25.00 9.00
a. Inverted overprint
MO14 A1 5p grn & org brn 80.00 *80.00*
MO15 A1 10p dp violet & blk 130.00 150.00

There are two types of this overprint which may be distinguished by the size and shape of the "y."

OFFICIAL STAMPS

Regular Issue of 1898 Overprinted in Black

O.S.G.S.

1902-06 **Wmk. 71** ***Perf. 14***
O1 A1 1m rose & brown 2.00 3.50
a. Inverted overprint 400.00
b. Round periods 7.50 10.00
c. Double overprint 550.00
d. Oval "O" in overprint 90.00
e. As "d," inverted overprint 5,000.
O2 A1 10p dp vio & blk ('06) 8.50 7.00

Same Ovpt. on Stamps of 1902-11

1903-12 **Wmk. 179**
O3 A1 1m car rose & brn ('04) .60 1.00
a. Double overprint
O4 A1 3m grn & vio ('04) .90 1.25
a. Double overprint
O5 A1 5m blk & rose red 2.00 .60
O6 A1 1p yel brn & ultra 4.50 .75
O7 A1 2p ultra & blk 8.50 1.40
O8 A1 5p grn & org brn 3.00 2.50
O9 A1 10p dp vio & blk 4.50 27.50
Nos. O3-O9 (7) 24.00 35.00

Regular Issue of 1927-40 Overprinted in Black

S.G.

Perf. 14, 13½x 14

1936-46 **Wmk. 214**
O10 A2 1m dk org & int blk ('46) .35 *3.50*
O11 A2 2m dk brn & dk org ('45) .15 .15
O12 A2 3m green & vio ('37) .50 .15
O13 A2 4m brown & green .85 .15
O14 A2 5m blk & ol brn ('40) .20 .15
O15 A2 10m blk & car ('46) .30 .15
O16 A2 15m org brn & ultra ('37) 1.75 .15

S.G.

O17 A1 2p org & vio brn ('37) 3.25 .15
O18 A1 3p dk bl & red brn ('46) 1.75 .50
O19 A1 4p blk & ultra ('46) 5.00 1.00
O20 A1 5p dk grn & org brn 2.75 .15
O21 A1 6p blk & pale bl ('46) 3.00 2.00
O22 A1 8p blk & pck grn ('46) 2.25 9.00
O23 A1 10p dp vio & blk ('37) 9.50 2.50
O24 A1 20p bl & lt bl ('46) 9.00 9.00
Nos. O10-O24 (15) 40.60 28.70

Catalogue values for unused stamps in this section, from this point to the end of the section, are for Never Hinged items.

#79-85 Overprinted Like #O10-O16

1948, Jan. 1
O28 A7 1m dk org & blk .15 1.50
O29 A7 2m choc & org .30 .15
O30 A7 3m grn & rose lil .70 3.00
O31 A7 4m choc & sl grn .70 1.00
O32 A7 5m blk & ol brn .70 .15
O33 A7 10m blk & car .65 .35
O34 A7 15m org brn & ultra .65 .15

Nos. 86-94 Overprinted Like Nos. O17-O24

O35 A8 2p org yel & vio brn .85 .15
O36 A8 3p dk bl & red brn .90 .15
O37 A8 4p blk & ultra .90 .15
a. Perf. 13 14.00 16.00
O38 A8 5p dk grn & org 1.00 .15
O39 A8 6p blk & pale bl 1.00 .15
O40 A8 8p blk & pck grn 1.00 1.25
O41 A8 10p dp rose lil & blk 1.00 .20
O42 A8 20p dk bl & bl 3.25 1.00
a. Perf. 13
O43 A8 50p ultra & car 47.50 25.00
Nos. O28-O43 (16) 61.25 34.50

Nos. 98-104 Overprinted Liked Nos. O10-O16 in Red

1951, Sept. 1 **Wmk. 214** ***Perf. 14***

Center in Black

O44 A11 1m orange .15 .15
O45 A11 2m ultra .15 .15
O46 A11 3m dk grn .60 .60
O47 A11 4m emerald .15 .15
O48 A11 5m plum .15 .15
O49 A11 10m light blue .15 .15
O50 A11 15m dp org brn .15 .15

Nos. 105-114 Overprinted Like Nos. O17-O24 in Black or Red

Perf. 13

O51 A12 2p lt bl & dk bl .15 .15
a. Inverted overprint 350.00
O52 A12 3p vio bl & brn .60 .15
O53 A12 3½p brn & bl grn .80 .40
O54 A12 4p blk & dp bl .80 .15
O55 A12 5p emer & org brn .85 .15
O56 A12 6p blk & bl 1.00 .35
O57 A12 8p brn & dp bl 1.40 .35
O58 A12 10p grn & blk (R) 1.75 .35
O59 A12 20p blk & bl grn 2.75 1.25
a. Inverted overprint 700.00
O60 A13 50p blk & car 8.50 4.00
Nos. O44-O60 (17) 20.10
Set value 4.40

No. 112 Overprinted Like Nos.O17-O24 in Black

1958
O61 A12 10p green & black .65 .18

Nos. 146-159 Overprinted ح.س.

Perf. 14½x14, 14x14½

1962, Oct. 1 **Litho.** **Wmk. 345**

Size: 23x19mm, 19x23mm

O62 A25 5m blue .15 .15
O63 A26 10m blue & lilac .15 .15
O64 A25 15m yel, vio, org & brn .18 .15
O65 A25 2p lt pur .22 .15
O66 A26 3p bl grn, red brn & brn .35 .15
O67 A26 35m yel grn, brn & org brn .40 .22
O68 A26 4p red, lt bl & lil .45 .25
O69 A25 55m gray & yel ol .75 .45
O70 A25 6p brn & lt bl .85 .45
O71 A25 8p green 1.10 .55

Size: 24½x30mm, 30x24½mm

O72 A26 10p lt bl, red brn & blk 1.50 .65
O73 A25 20p gray ol & yel grn 3.00 1.40
a. Perf. 13½x12½ 2.75 1.10
O74 A25 50p dk gray, ol & bl 7.50 3.50
a. Perf. 13½x14 6.50 3.25

Engr.

O75 A13 £1 grn & brn org 19.00 12.50
Nos. O62-O75 (14) 35.60 20.72

The overprint measures 12x4½mm on Nos. O62-O71; 16x6mm on Nos. O72-O75.

1975-79 **Unwmk.**

Same Perfs., Sizes and Printing Methods as Before

O62a A25 5m .15 .15
O63a A26 10m ('76) .15 .15
O64a A25 15m .18 .15
O65a A25 2p .22 .15
O66a A26 3p .35 .22
O67a A26 35m .40 .22
O68a A26 4p .45 .25
O69a A25 55m .75 .45
O70a A25 6p ('76) .85 .45
O71a A25 8p 1.10 .55
O72a A26 10p 1.50 .65
O75a A13 £1 ('79) 19.00 12.50
Nos. O62a-O75a (12) 25.10 15.89

Nos. 404-419 Overprinted ح.س.

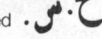

Perf. 13½x13

1991, July 1 Litho. Unwmk.

O76	A105	25p on #404	.15	.15
O77	A105	50p on #405	.22	.15
O78	A105	75p on #406	.32	.20
O79	A105	100p on #407	.45	.30
O80	A105	125p on #408	.55	.35

Size: 30x24mm

Perf. 14x14½, 13½x14

O81	A105	150p on #409	.65	.42
O82	A105	175p on #410	.78	.50
O83	A105	£2 on #411	.90	.58

Size: 26x37mm

Perf. 14

O84	A105	250p on #412	1.10	.70
O85	A105	£3 on #413	1.35	.90

Size: 24x30mm

Perf. 13½x14

O86	A105	£4 on #414	1.75	1.15
O87	A105	£5 on #415	2.20	1.45

Size: 36x27mm

Perf. 14

Wmk. 334

O88	A105	£8 on #416	3.50	2.30
O89	A105	£10 on #417	4.40	2.90
O90	A105	£15 on #418	6.60	4.30
O91	A105	£20 on #419	8.80	5.75
		Nos. O76-O91 (16)	33.72	22.10

For surcharges see Nos. O104-O111.

Nos. 420, 427-428 Overprinted

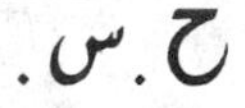

1992 Litho. Unwmk. *Perf. 14½*

O92	A25	25p on #420	.15	.15

Perf. 14x13½, 13½x14

O99	A25	£5 on #427	2.60	1.70
O100	A25	£10 on #428	5.15	3.40
		Nos. O92-O100 (3)	7.90	5.25

Nos. O79, O81, O83, O85-O87 Surcharged in Blue Violet or Black

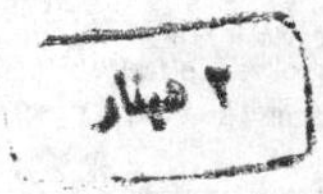

Perf. 13½x13

1993? Litho. Unwmk.

O104	A105	1d on 100p #O79	1.00	.65

Perf. 13½x14

O105	A105	1.50d on 150p #O81	1.50	1.00
O107	A105	2d on £2 #O83	2.00	1.30

Perf. 14

O109	A105	3d on £3 #O85	3.00	2.00

Perf. 14½x14

O110	A105	4d on £4 #O86	4.00	2.75

Perf. 13½x14

O111	A105	5d On £5 #O87 (Blk)	5.00	3.25
		Nos. O104-O110 (5)	11.50	7.70

SWAZILAND

'swä-ze-,land

LOCATION — Southeast Africa bordered by the Transvaal and Zululand in South Africa and by Mozambique
GOVT. — Constitutional monarchy
AREA — 6,705 sq. mi.
POP. — 626,000 (est. 1984)
CAPITAL — Mbabane

An independent state in the 19th century, Swaziland was administered by Transvaal from 1894 to 1906, when the administration was transferred to the British High Commissioner for South Africa. In 1934 Swaziland and Bechuanaland Protectorate came under the administration of the British High Commissioner for Basutoland. The issuing of individual postage stamps had been resumed in 1933. Internal self-government was introduced in 1967. Independence was proclaimed September 6, 1968.

12 Pence = 1 Shilling
20 Shillings = 1 Pound
100 Cents = 1 Rand (1961)
100 Cents = 1 Emalangeni (1975)

Catalogue values for unused stamps in this country are for Never Hinged items, beginning with Scott 38 in the regular postage section and Scott J1 in the postage due section.

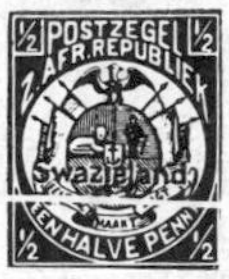
Coat of Arms — A1

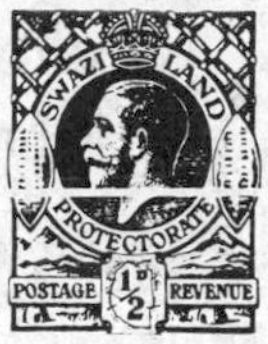
George V — A2

Black Overprint

1889 Unwmk. ***Perf. 12½, 12½x12***

1	A1	½p gray	7.50	*12.50*
a.		Inverted overprint	450.00	500.00
b.		"Swazielan"	900.00	800.00
c.		As "b," inverted overprint		2,750.
2	A1	1p rose	15.00	15.00
a.		Inverted overprint	400.00	*475.00*
3	A1	2p olive bister	13.00	13.00
a.		Inverted overprint	475.00	475.00
b.		"Swazielan"	475.00	475.00
c.		Perf. 12½x12	75.00	21.00
4	A1	6p gray blue	16.00	*27.50*
5	A1	1sh green	9.00	12.00
a.		Inverted overprint	475.00	475.00
6	A1	2sh6p yellow	110.00	*150.00*
7	A1	5sh slate	110.00	150.00
a.		Inverted overprint	*2,400.*	*2,400.*
b.		"Swazielan"	*6,000.*	
c.		As "b," inverted overprint		
8	A1	10sh lt brown	*4,250.*	*3,000.*

1892 Red Overprint

9	A1	½p gray	6.50	11.00
a.		Inverted overprint	475.00	
b.		Double overprint	350.00	*350.00*

Beware of counterfeits.
Reprints have a period after "Swazieland."

Stamps of Swaziland were replaced by those of Transvaal in 1895. Swaziland issues were resumed in 1933.

1933, Jan. 2 Engr. Wmk. 4 ***Perf. 14***

10	A2	½p green	.20	.30
11	A2	1p carmine	.30	.20
12	A2	2p lt brown	.35	.35
13	A2	3p ultra	.35	.40
14	A2	4p orange	.75	.80
15	A2	6p rose violet	1.00	*1.10*
16	A2	1sh olive green	1.75	*3.00*
17	A2	2sh6p violet	9.50	*12.50*
18	A2	5sh gray	37.50	*45.00*
19	A2	10sh black brown	95.00	*125.00*
		Nos. 10-19 (10)	146.70	*188.65*

Silver Jubilee Issue
Common Design Type

1935, May 4 ***Perf. 11x12***

20	CD301	1p carmine & blue	.30	.20
21	CD301	2p black & ultra	.35	.40
22	CD301	3p ultra & brown	.90	1.25
23	CD301	6p brown, vio & ind	1.25	1.25
		Nos. 20-23 (4)	2.80	3.10

Coronation Issue
Common Design Type

1937, May 12 ***Perf. 11x11½***

24	CD302	1p dark carmine	.25	.40
25	CD302	2p brown	.25	.25
26	CD302	3p deep ultra	.50	.40
		Nos. 24-26 (3)	1.00	1.05

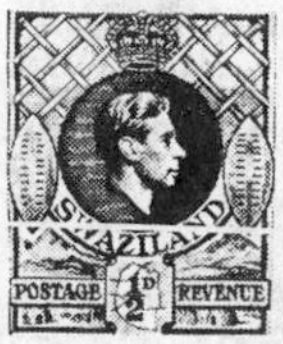
George VI — A3

1938, Apr. 1 ***Perf. 13, 13x13½***

27	A3	½p green	.40	.25
28	A3	1p rose carmine	.40	.25
29	A3	1½p light blue	1.75	.25
a.		Perf. 14 ('42)	.35	.35
30	A3	2p brown	1.25	.15
31	A3	3p ultra	.40	.40
32	A3	4p red orange	.20	.20
33	A3	6p rose violet	.95	.95
34	A3	1sh olive green	.20	.20
35	A3	2sh6p dark violet	1.40	1.40
36	A3	5sh gray	7.00	7.00
37	A3	10sh black brown	2.50	2.50
		Nos. 27-37 (11)	16.45	13.55

Catalogue values for unused stamps in this section, from this point to the end of the section, are for Never Hinged items.

Peace Issue

South Africa, Nos. 100-102 Overprinted **Swaziland**

Basic stamps inscribed alternately in English and Afrikaans.

1945, Dec. 3 Wmk. 201 ***Perf. 14***

38	A42	1p rose pink & choc, pair	.50	.40
a.		Single, English	.15	.15
b.		Single, Afrikaans	.15	.15
39	A43	2p vio & sl blue, pair	.50	.40
a.		Single, English	.15	.15
b.		Single, Afrikaans	.15	.15
40	A43	3p ultra & dp ultra, pair	.50	*1.25*
a.		Single, English	.15	.25
b.		Single, Afrikaans	.15	.25
		Nos. 38-40 (3)	1.50	2.05

World War II victory of the Allies.

Royal Visit Issue
Type of Basutoland, 1947

Perf. 12½

1947, Feb. 17 Wmk. 4 Engr.

44	A3	1p red	.15	.15
45	A4	2p green	.15	.15
46	A5	3p ultramarine	.15	.15
47	A6	1sh dark violet	.20	.20
		Nos. 44-47 (4)	.65	.65

Visit of the British Royal Family, March 25, 1947.

Silver Wedding Issue
Common Design Types

1948, Dec. 1 Photo. ***Perf. 14x14½***

48	CD304	1½p bright ultra	.15	.15

Perf. 11½x11

Engraved; Name Typographed

49	CD305	10sh violet brown	20.00	*25.00*

UPU Issue
Common Design Types

Engr.; Name Typo. on 3p, 6p

Perf. 13½, 11x11½

1949, Oct. 10 Wmk. 4

50	CD306	1½p blue	.15	.15
51	CD307	3p indigo	.30	.30
52	CD308	6p red lilac	.35	.35
53	CD309	1sh olive	.75	.75
		Nos. 50-53 (4)	1.55	1.55

Coronation Issue
Common Design Type

1953, June 3 Engr. ***Perf. 13½x13***

54	CD312	2p yellow brown & blk	.20	.20

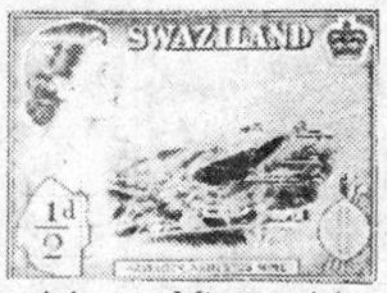
Asbestos Mine — A4

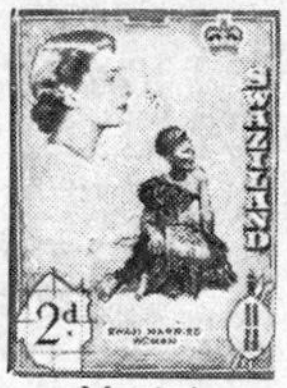
Married Woman — A5

Designs: 1p, 2sh 6p, Highveld view. 3p, 1sh 3p, Courting couple. 4½p, 5sh, Warrior. 6p, £1, Kudu. 1sh, Asbestos mine. 10sh, Married woman.

Perf. 13x13½, 13½x13

1956, July 2 Engr. Wmk. 4

Center in Black, except Nos. 63-64

55	A4	½p orange	.20	.15
56	A4	1p emerald	.20	.15
57	A5	2p redsh brown	.20	.15
58	A5	3p rose red	.25	.15
59	A5	4½p ultra	.55	.25
60	A5	6p magenta	.55	.25
61	A4	1sh gray olive	1.25	.50
62	A5	1sh3p brown	1.40	.60
63	A4	2sh6p car & brt grn	2.00	1.10
64	A5	5sh blue gray & vio	4.75	2.25
65	A5	10sh dull violet	11.00	4.75
66	A5	£1 turquoise	20.00	10.50
		Nos. 55-66 (12)	42.35	20.80

Nos. 55-61 and 63-66 Surcharged with New Value

2½c I **2½c** II **4c** I **4c** II

5c I **5c** II **25c** I **25c** II

50c I **50c** II **50c** III

R1 I **R1** II **R1** III **R2** I **R2** II

1961

67	A4	½c on ½p	2.00	2.00
a.		Inverted surcharge	300.00	
68	A4	1c on 1p	.15	.15
a.		"1c" at center	27.50	
b.		Double surcharge	275.00	
69	A5	2c on 2p	.20	.20
70	A5	2½p on 2p	.20	.20
71	A5	2½c on 3p (I)	.25	.25
a.		Type II	.35	.35
72	A5	3½c on 2p	.15	.15
73	A5	4c on 4½p (II)	.20	.20
a.		Type I	.15	.15
74	A5	5c on 6p (II)	.20	.20
a.		Type I	.20	.20
75	A4	10c on 1sh	17.50	5.50
a.		Double surcharge	350.00	
76	A4	25c on 2sh6p (I)	.80	.90
a.		Type II, "25c" centered	1.25	1.00
b.		Type II, "25c" at lower left	125.00	*150.00*
77	A5	50c on 5sh (I)	.90	1.00
a.		Type II	6.25	5.00
b.		Type III	275.00	*300.00*
78	A5	1r on 10sh (I)	2.50	1.50
a.		Type II	6.25	6.25
b.		Type III	37.50	*40.00*
79	A5	2r on £1 (II, "R2" at middle left)	4.75	4.75
a.		Type I	12.00	12.00
b.		Type II, "R2" at center bottom	27.50	*45.00*
		Nos. 67-79 (13)	29.80	17.00

The type II "25c" surcharge is nearly centered in the sky on No. 76a, and is at lower left touching the value tablet on No. 76b.

Surcharge types are numbered chronologically.

For surcharges see Nos. J3-J6.

Types of 1956

Designs: ½c, 10c, Asbestos mine. 1c, 25c, Highveld view. 2c, 1r, Married woman. 2½c, 12½c, Courting couple. 4c, 50c, Warrior. 5c, 2r, Kudu.

Perf. 13x13½, 13½x13

1961 Engr. Wmk. 4

Center in Black, except Nos. 88-89

80	A4	½c orange	.15	.15
81	A4	1c emerald	.15	.15
82	A5	2c redsh brown	.15	.15
83	A5	2½c rose red	.20	.20
84	A5	4c ultra	.35	.35
85	A5	5c magenta	.35	.35
86	A4	10c gray olive	.50	.50
87	A5	12½c brown	.70	.70
88	A4	25c car & brt green	1.00	1.00
89	A5	50c blue gray & vio	2.25	2.25
90	A5	1r dull violet	4.00	4.00
91	A5	2r turquoise	9.00	9.00
		Nos. 80-91 (12)	18.80	18.80

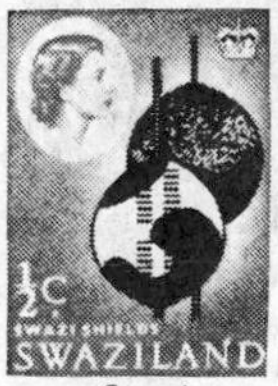
Swazi Shields — A6

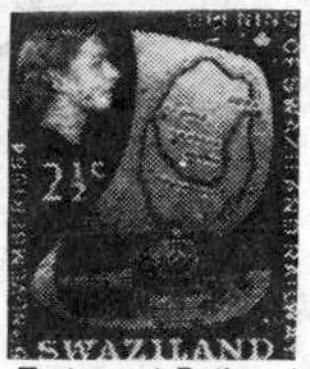
Train and Railroad Map — A7

Designs: 1c, Battle axe. 2c, Forestry. 2½c, Ceremonial headdress. 3½c, Musical instrument. 4c, Irrigation. 5c, Widow bird. 7½c, Rock paintings. 10c, Secretary bird. 12½c, Pink arum lily. 15c, Married woman. 20c, Malaria control. 25c, Swazi warrior. 50c, Ground hornbill, horiz. 1r, Aloes. 2r, Msinsi (flame tree), horiz.

Perf. 12½x14, 14x12½

1962, Apr. 24 Photo. Wmk. 314

92	A6	½c ocher, blk & brn	.20	.20
93	A6	1c gray & orange	.20	.20
94	A6	2c lt yel grn, dk grn & blk	.20	.20
95	A6	2½c vermilion & blk	.20	.20
96	A6	3½c gray & emerald	.25	.25
97	A6	4c aqua & black	.25	.25
98	A6	5c orange red & blk	.30	.30
99	A6	7½c dull ocher & brn	.40	.40
100	A6	10c lt blue & black	.45	.45
101	A6	12½c lt olive & dp car	.65	.65
102	A6	15c red lilac & blk	.75	.75
103	A6	20c emerald & blk	.80	.80
104	A6	25c ultra & blk	1.10	1.10
105	A6	50c rose red & dk brn	2.00	2.00
106	A6	1r bister & emer	4.00	4.00
107	A6	2r ultra & scar	8.00	8.00
		Nos. 92-107 (16)	19.75	19.75

For surcharge & overprints see Nos. 138, 143-159.

Freedom from Hunger Issue
Common Design Type

1963, June 4 *Perf. 14x14½*

108	CD314	15c lilac	.45	.45

Red Cross Centenary Issue
Common Design Type

1963, Sept. 2 Litho. *Perf. 13*

109	CD315	2½c black & red	.16	.16
110	CD315	15c ultra & red	.65	.65

Perf. 11½x12

1964, Nov. 5 Engr. Wmk. 314

111	A7	2½c purple & brt grn	.15	.15
112	A7	3½c dk olive & blue	.20	.20
113	A7	15c dk brown & orange	.48	.48
114	A7	25c dk blue & yellow	.80	.80
		Nos. 111-114 (4)	1.63	1.63

Opening of the Swaziland Railroad linking Ka Dake with Lourenco Marques.

ITU Issue
Common Design Type

Perf. 11x11½

1965, May 17 Litho. Wmk. 314

115	CD317	2½c blue & bister	.15	.15
116	CD317	15c red lil & rose red	.50	.50

Intl. Cooperation Year Issue
Common Design Type

1965, Oct. 25 *Perf. 14½*

117	CD318	½c bl grn & claret	.15	.15
118	CD318	15c lt violet & grn	.40	.40

Churchill Memorial Issue
Common Design Type

1966, Jan. 24 Photo. *Perf. 14*

Design in Black, Gold and Carmine Rose

119	CD319	½c brt blue	.15	.15
120	CD319	2½c green	.16	.15
121	CD319	15c brown	.65	.42
122	CD319	25c violet	1.10	.80
		Nos. 119-122 (4)	2.06	1.52

UNESCO Anniversary Issue
Common Design Type

1966, Dec. 1 Litho. *Perf. 14*

123	CD323	2½c "Education"	.15	.15
124	CD323	7½c "Science"	.30	.30
125	CD323	15c "Culture"	.65	.65
		Nos. 123-125 (3)	1.10	1.10

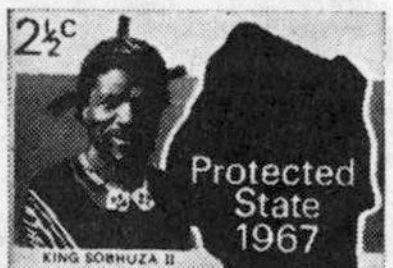

King Sobhuza II and Map of Swaziland — A8

Design: 7½c, 25c, King Sobhuza II, vert.

Perf. 14½x14, 14x14½

1967, Apr. 25 Photo. Wmk. 314

126	A8	2½c multicolored	.15	.15
127	A8	7½c multicolored	.15	.15
128	A8	15c multicolored	.18	.18
129	A8	25c multicolored	.30	.30
		Nos. 126-129 (4)	.78	.78

Attainment of internal self-government.

Common Design Types
pictured in section before Great Britain.

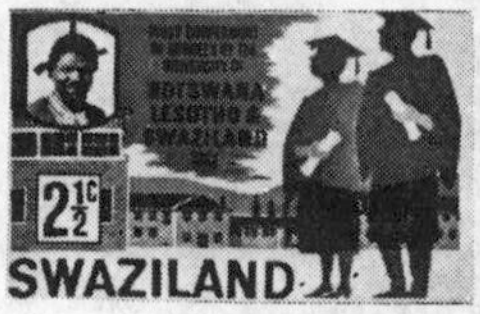

King Sobhuza II, University Buildings and Graduates A9

Perf. 14x14½

1967, Sept. 1 Photo. Unwmk.

130	A9	2½c yel, sepia & dp bl	.15	.15
131	A9	7½c blue, sepia & dp bl	.15	.15
132	A9	15c dl rose, sepia & dp bl	.18	.18
133	A9	25c lt vio, sepia & dp bl	.30	.30
		Nos. 130-133 (4)	.78	.78

1st conferment of degrees by the University of Botswana, Lesotho and Swaziland at Roma, Lesotho.

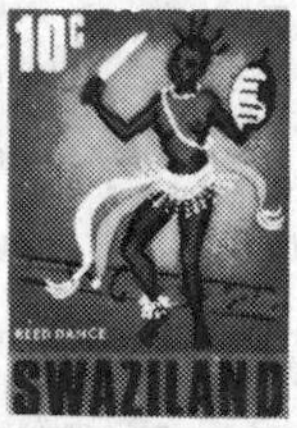

Swazi Reed Dance (Umhlanga) — A10

Designs: 3c, 15c, Feast of the First Fruits, Incwala (bull, sun and king), horiz.

Perf. 14½x14, 14x14½

1968, Jan. 5 Photo. Wmk. 314

134	A10	3c red, blk & silver	.15	.15
135	A10	10c brown, blk, org & sil	.16	.16
136	A10	15c red, blk & gold	.20	.20
137	A10	25c brown, blk, org & gold	.35	.35
		Nos. 134-137 (4)	.86	.86

No. 98 Surcharged with New Value

1968, May 1 *Perf. 12½x14*

138	A6	3c on 5c orange red & blk	.15	.15

Independent Kingdom

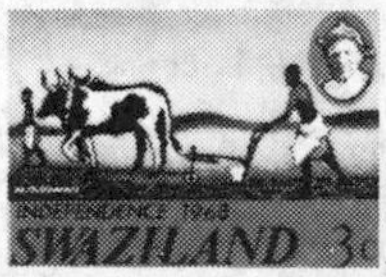

Plowing and King Sobhuza II A11

Designs: 4½c, Cable lift carrying asbestos. 17½c, Worker cutting sugar cane. 25c, Iron ore mining and map showing Swaziland railroad.

Perf. 14x12½

1968, Sept. 6 Photo. Wmk. 314

139	A11	3c gold & multi	.15	.15
140	A11	4½c gold & multi	.15	.15
141	A11	17½c gold & multi	.22	.22
142	A11	25c slate & gold	1.50	1.50
a.		Strip of 4, #139-142	3.25	3.25
		Nos. 139-142 (4)	2.02	2.02

Swaziland's independence.

Nos. 139-142 printed in sheets of 50. No. 142a printed in sheets of 20 (4x5).

Nos. 92-107 Overprinted; No. 96 Surcharged **INDEPENDENCE 1968**

Perf. 12½x14, 14x12½

1968, Sept. 6

143	A6	½c ocher, blk & brn	.15	.15
144	A6	1c gray & orange	.15	.15
145	A6	2c multicolored	.15	.15
146	A6	2½c vermilion & blk	.15	.15
147	A6	3c on 2½c ver & blk	.15	.15
148	A6	3½c gray & emerald	.15	.15
149	A6	4c aqua & black	.20	.20
150	A6	5c org red & blk	.25	.25
151	A6	7½c dull ocher & brn	.35	.35
152	A6	10c lt blue & blk	.50	.50
153	A6	12½c lt olive & dp car	.60	.60
154	A6	15c red lilac & blk	.75	.75
155	A6	20c emerald & blk	.80	.80
156	A6	25c ultra & blk	1.00	1.00
157	A6	50c rose red & dk brn	1.75	1.75
a.		Wmk. sideways	1.65	1.65
158	A6	1r bister & emerald	3.50	3.50
159	A6	2r ultra & scarlet	8.00	8.00
a.		Wmk. sideways	6.75	6.75
		Nos. 143-159 (17)	18.60	18.60

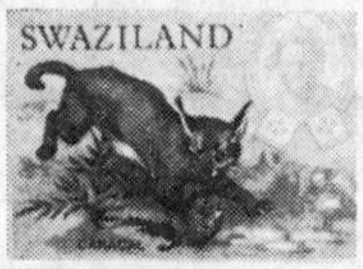

Caracal (African Lynx) A12

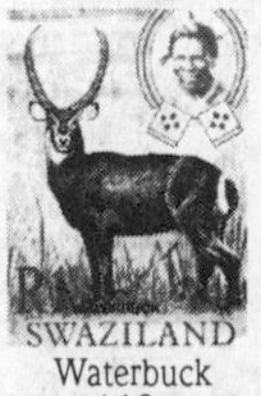

Waterbuck A12a

Designs (Sobhuza II and): 1c, Cape porcupine. 2c, Crocodile. 3c, Lion. 3½c, African elephants. 5c, Bush pig. 7½c, Impalas. 10c, Chacma baboon. 12½c, Ratel (honey badger). 15c, Leopard. 20c, Blue wildebeest (brindled gnu). 25c, White (square-lipped) rhinoceros. 50c, Burchell's zebra. 2r, Giraffe.

Perf. 13x12½, 12½x13

1969, Aug. 1 Litho. Wmk. 314

Size: 30½x21½mm

160	A12	½c multicolored	.15	.15
161	A12	1c multicolored	.15	.15
162	A12	2c multicolored	.16	.15

Size: 35x25mm

163	A12	3c multicolored	.22	.15
a.		Wmk. upright ('75)	.65	.45
164	A12	3½c multicolored	.22	.15

Size: 30½x21½mm, 21½x30½mm

165	A12	5c multicolored	.30	.24
166	A12	7½c multicolored	.38	.32
167	A12	10c multicolored	.60	.50
168	A12	12½c multicolored	.65	.60
169	A12	15c multicolored	.70	.65
170	A12	20c multicolored	.80	.65
171	A12	25c multicolored	1.10	.80
172	A12	50c multicolored	1.90	1.65
173	A12a	1r multicolored	4.50	3.25
174	A12a	2r multicolored	9.50	6.25
		Nos. 160-174 (15)	21.33	15.66

See #228-229. For surcharges see #259-260.

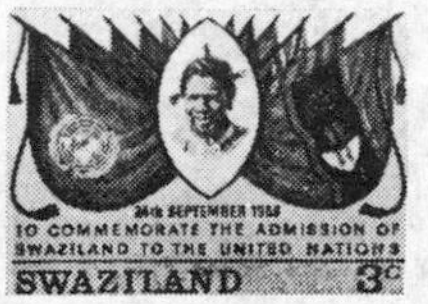

King Sobhuza II and Flags — A13

Designs: 7½c, 25c, UN emblem, UN Headquarters, NY, and King Sobhuza II.

1969, Sept. 24 Litho. *Perf. 13½*

175	A13	3c dp blue & multi	.15	.15
176	A13	7½c pink & multi	.16	.16
177	A13	12½c yellow & multi	.24	.24
178	A13	25c lt blue & multi	.50	.50
		Nos. 175-178 (4)	1.05	1.05

1st anniv. of admission to the UN.

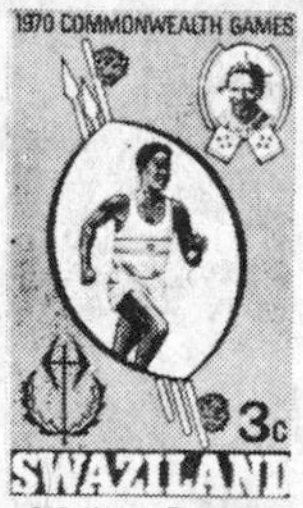

Walking Racer, Shield and King — A14

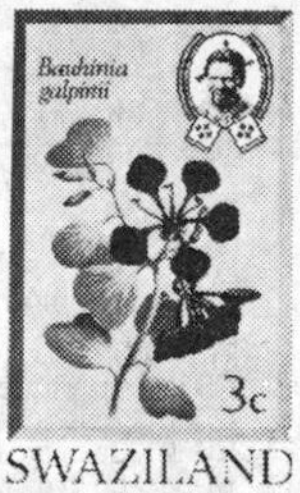

Bauhinia Galpinii and King — A15

Designs: 7½c, Runner. 12½c, Hurdler. 25c, Parade of Swaziland team with flag bearer.

Perf. 14x14½

1970, July 16 Litho. Wmk. 314

179	A14	3c red orange & multi	.15	.15
180	A14	7½c yellow & multi	.16	.16
181	A14	12½c lt blue & multi	.28	.28
182	A14	25c multicolored	.60	.60
		Nos. 179-182 (4)	1.19	1.19

Issued to publicize the 9th Commonwealth Games, Edinburgh, July 16-25.

Perf. 14x14½

1971, Feb. 1 Litho. Wmk. 314

Flowers of Swaziland: 10c, Crocosmia aurea. 15c, Gloriosa superba. 25c, Watsonia densiflora.

183	A15	3c bister & multi	.15	.15
184	A15	10c pale salmon & multi	.50	.40
185	A15	15c pale green & multi	.85	.60
186	A15	25c multicolored	1.25	1.00
		Nos. 183-186 (4)	2.75	2.15

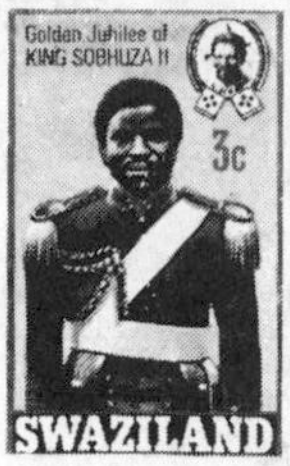

King Sobhuza II — A16

Designs (King Sobhuza II): 3½c, In 1971. 7½c, In tribal costume at gathering of chiefs (Incwala). 25c, Opening Swazi parliament.

1971, Dec. 22

187	A16	3c blue & multi	.15	.15
188	A16	3½c gold, blk, bl & brn	.15	.15
189	A16	7½c gold & multi	.18	.18
190	A16	25c lilac & multi	.65	.65
		Nos. 187-190 (4)	1.13	1.13

50th anniv. of the reign of Sobhuza II.

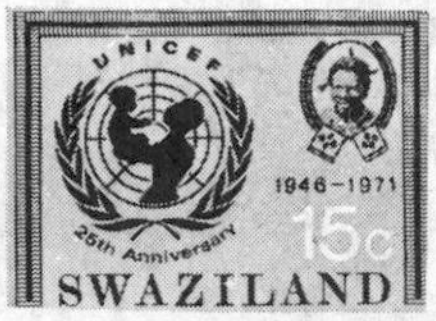

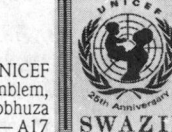

UNICEF Emblem, King Sobhuza II — A17

1972, Apr. 17 *Perf. 14½x14*

191	A17	15c violet & black	.30	.30
192	A17	25c olive & black	.70	.70

25th anniv. (in 1971) of UNICEF.

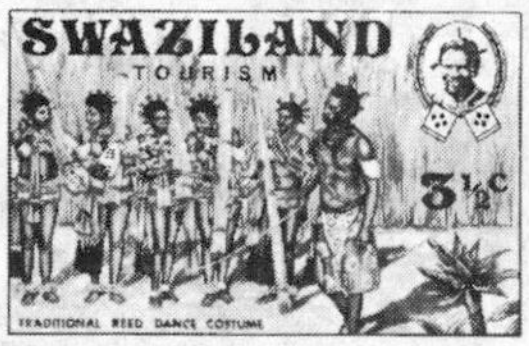

Traditional Reed Dancers — A18

Perf. 13½x14

1972, Sept. 11 Wmk. 314

193	A18	3½c shown	.15	.15
194	A18	7½c Swazi beehive hut	.24	.24
195	A18	15c Ezulwini Valley	.48	.48
196	A18	25c Usutu River fishing	.80	.80
		Nos. 193-196 (4)	1.67	1.67

Tourist publicity.

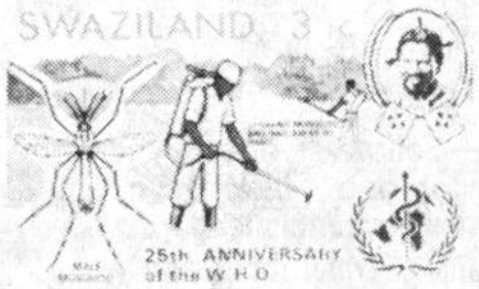

Mosquito Control A19

1973, May 21 Litho. *Perf. 14½*

197	A19	3½c shown	.15	.15
198	A19	7½c Anti-malaria vaccination	.28	.28

25th anniv. of WHO.

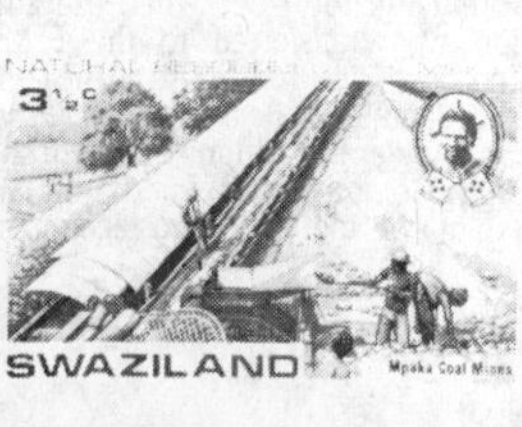

Mpaka Coal Mines A20

Designs: 7½c, Oxen pulling plow. 15c, Weir over Komati River. 25c, Experimental rice plantation.

Perf. 13½x14

1973, June 21 **Wmk. 314**

199 A20 3½c multicolored .15 .15
200 A20 7½c multicolored .16 .16
201 A20 15c multicolored .35 .35
202 A20 25c multicolored .60 .60
Nos. 199-202 (4) 1.26 1.26

Development of natural resources.

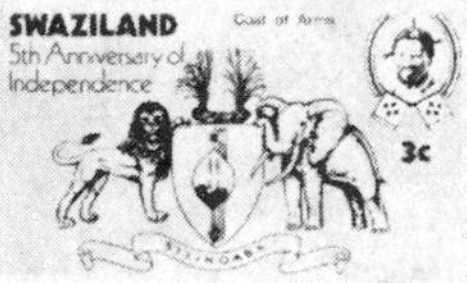

Swaziland Coat of Arms A21

Designs: 10c, King Sobhuza II in dress uniform. 15c, Parliament. 25c, National Somhlolo Stadium.

1973, Sept. 7 **Litho.** *Perf. 14*

203 A21 3c brick red & black .15 .15
204 A21 10c dull orange & multi .25 .25
205 A21 15c blue & multi .35 .35
206 A21 25c yellow & multi .60 .60
Nos. 203-206 (4) 1.35 1.35

5th anniversary of independence.

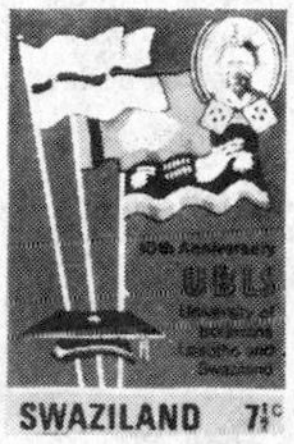

Botswana, Lesotho, Swaziland Flags and Cap — A22

Designs: 12½c, Kwaluseni Campus. 15c, Map of Africa and location of Botswana, Lesotho and Swaziland. 25c, Shield of University.

1974, Mar. 29 **Litho.** *Perf. 14*

207 A22 7½c orange & multi .16 .16
208 A22 12½c emerald & multi .20 .20
209 A22 15c yellow & multi .25 .25
210 A22 25c ultra & multi .38 .38
Nos. 207-210 (4) .99 .99

10th anniversary of the University of Botswana, Lesotho and Swaziland.

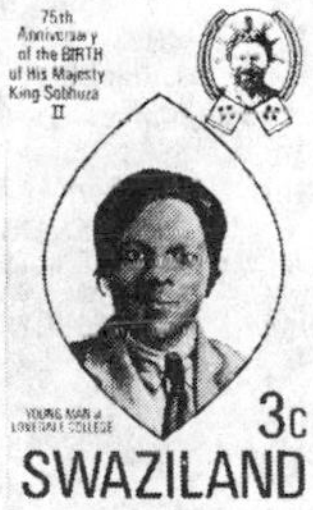

Sobhuza as Student at Lovedale College, South Africa — A23

1974, July 22 **Litho.** *Perf. 13x11*

211 A23 3c shown .15 .15
212 A23 9c Sobhuza as middle-aged man .16 .16
213 A23 50c As old man .80 .80
Nos. 211-213 (3) 1.11 1.11

75th birthday of King Sobhuza II.

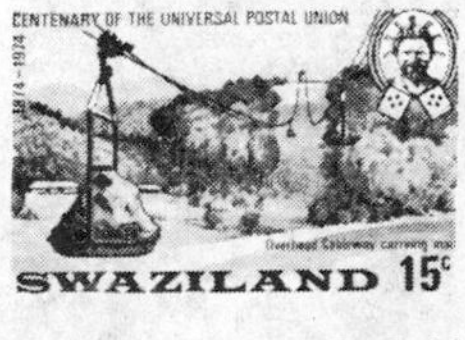

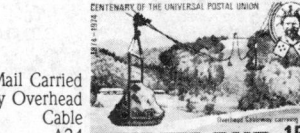

Mail Carried by Overhead Cable A24

1974, Oct. 9 *Perf. 14*

214 A24 4c Post Office, Lobamba .15 .15
215 A24 10c Mbabane temporary P.O., 1902 .24 .24
216 A24 15c shown .35 .35
217 A24 25c Mule-drawn mail coach .75 .75
Nos. 214-217 (4) 1.49 1.49

Centenary of Universal Postal Union.

Animal Type of 1969
"E" instead of "R"

Designs as before.

1975, Jan. 2 **Litho.** *Perf. 12½x13*

228 A12a 1e multicolored 3.25 3.25
229 A12a 2e multicolored 7.00 7.00

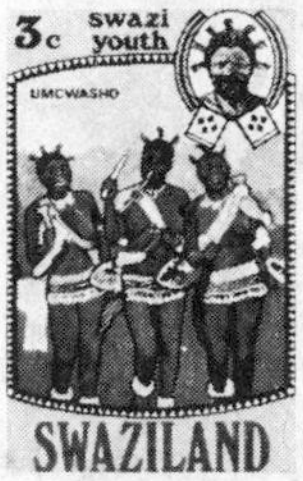

Girl's Umcwasho Ceremony — A26

Swazi youth: 10c, Butimba, hunting ceremony. 15c, Lusekwane, ceremony of preparation, horiz. 25c, Gcina Regiment marching with flags.

1975, Mar. 20 **Wmk. 314** *Perf. 14*

232 A26 3c lt green & multi .15 .15
233 A26 10c lt violet & multi .18 .18
234 A26 15c brown org & multi .28 .28
235 A26 25c yellow & multi .48 .48
Nos. 232-235 (4) 1.09 1.09

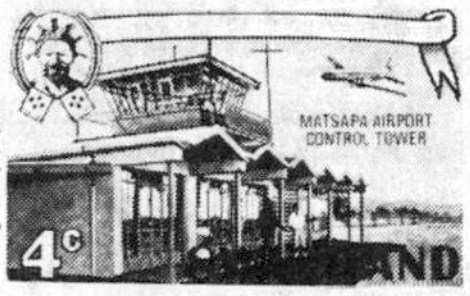

Matsapa Airport Control Tower A27

Designs: 5c, Fire brigade car and staff. 15c, Douglas C-47 Dakota. 25c, Hawker Siddeley 748.

1975, Aug. 18 **Litho.** *Perf. 14½*

236 A27 4c multicolored .25 .25
237 A27 5c multicolored .30 .30
238 A27 15c multicolored 1.00 1.00
239 A27 25c multicolored 1.75 1.75
Nos. 236-239 (4) 3.30 3.30

10th anniversary of internal air service.

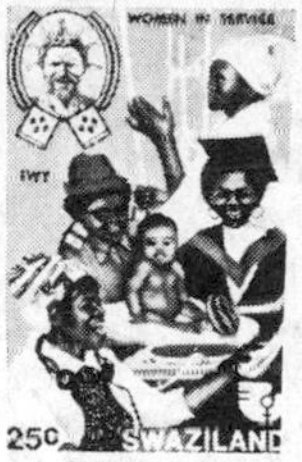

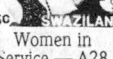

Women in Service — A28

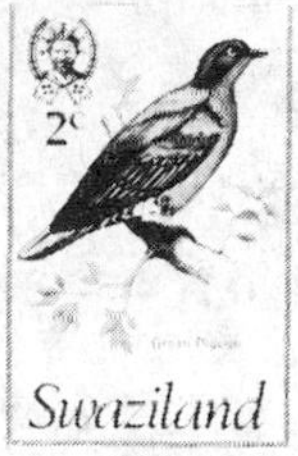

Green Pigeon — A29

Designs: 4c, Elephant with IWY emblem, horiz. 5c, Queen Labotsibeni, grandmother of King Sobhuza II, horiz. 15c, Handicrafts women.

Wmk. 373

1975, Dec. 22 **Litho.** *Perf. 14*

240 A28 4c ultra, blk & gray .15 .15
241 A28 5c bister & multi .15 .15
242 A28 15c multicolored .32 .32
243 A28 25c multicolored .55 .55
Nos. 240-243 (4) 1.17 1.17

International Women's Year 1975.

1976, Jan. 2 **Wmk. 373** *Perf. 14*

Birds: 1c, Black-headed oriole, horiz. 3c, Melba finch, horiz. 4c, Plum-colored starling. 5c, Black-headed heron. 6c, Stonechat. 7c, Chorister robin. 10c, Gorgeous bush shrike. 15c, Black-collared barbet. 20c, Gray heron. 25c, Giant kingfisher. 30c, Black eagle. 50c, Red bishop. 1e, Pin-tailed whydah. 2e, Lilacbreasted roller, horiz.

244 A29 1c orange & multi .15 .15
245 A29 2c lilac & multi .15 .15
246 A29 3c yellow grn & multi .15 .15
247 A29 4c gray blue & multi .15 .15
248 A29 5c orange & multi .18 .18
249 A29 6c orange & multi .22 .22
250 A29 7c orange & multi .30 .30
251 A29 10c slate & multi .42 .42
252 A29 15c lt green & multi .65 .65
253 A29 20c ocher & multi .85 .85
254 A29 25c orange & multi 1.10 1.10
255 A29 30c orange & multi 1.40 1.40
256 A29 50c sepia & multi 2.00 2.00
257 A29 1e vermilion & multi 4.75 4.75
258 A29 2e lt blue & multi 9.00 9.00
Nos. 244-258 (15) 21.47 21.47

Nos. 166 and 168 Surcharged in Ultramarine or Brown

3c

1976 **Wmk. 314** *Perf. 13x12½*

259 A12 3c on 7½c multi (U) .50 .50
260 A12 6c on 12½c multi (B) 1.25 1.25

Denomination at lower left on No. 260.

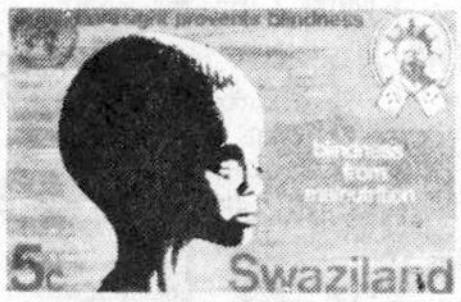

Blindness from Malnutrition — A30

Designs (WHO Emblem and): 10c, Retina, "Operation prevents blindness." 20c, Blind eye, "Blindness from trachoma." 25c, Medicine and syringe, "Medicine and rehabilitation."

Wmk. 373

1976, June 15 **Litho.** *Perf. 14*

261 A30 5c multicolored .15 .15
262 A30 10c multicolored .18 .18
263 A30 20c multicolored .35 .35
264 A30 25c multicolored .45 .45
Nos. 261-264 (4) 1.13 1.13

World Health Day: Foresight prevents blindness.

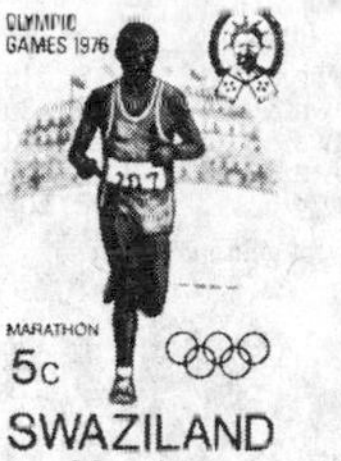

Marathon Runner — A31

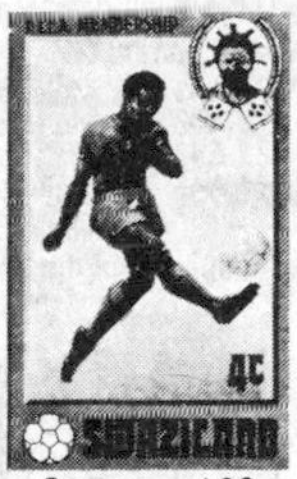

Soccer — A32

Designs (Olympic Rings and): 6c, Boxing. 20c, Soccer. 25c, Olympic torch and flame.

1976, July 17 **Litho.** **Wmk. 373**

265 A31 5c lt blue & multi .15 .15
266 A31 6c olive & multi .15 .15
267 A31 20c lt violet & multi .35 .35
268 A31 25c dull orange & multi .45 .45
Nos. 265-268 (4) 1.10 1.10

21st Olympic Games, Montreal, Canada, July 17-Aug. 1.

1976, Sept. 13 **Litho.** *Perf. 14½*

Designs: 5c, Player heading ball. 20c, Goalkeeper catching ball. 25c, Player kicking ball.

269 A32 4c blue & multi .15 .15
270 A32 5c olive & multi .15 .15
271 A32 20c red & multi .35 .35
272 A32 25c multicolored .48 .48
Nos. 269-272 (4) 1.13 1.13

FIFA membership for Swaziland in 1976 (Federation Internationale de Football Associations).

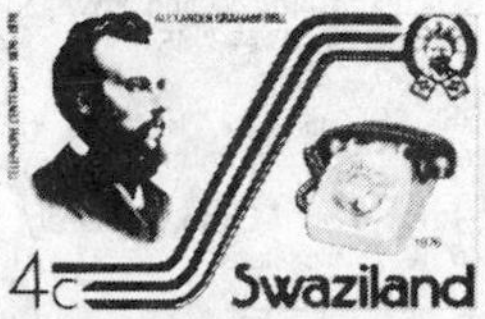

A. G. Bell and 1976 Telephone — A33

Designs (A. G. Bell and Telephone): 5c, 1895. 10c, 1876. 15c, 1877. 20c, 1905.

1976, Nov. 22 *Perf. 14*

273 A33 4c multicolored .15 .15
274 A33 5c multicolored .15 .15
275 A33 10c multicolored .18 .18
276 A33 15c multicolored .28 .28
277 A33 20c multicolored .38 .38
Nos. 273-277 (5) 1.14 1.14

Centenary of first telephone call by Alexander Graham Bell, Mar. 10, 1876.

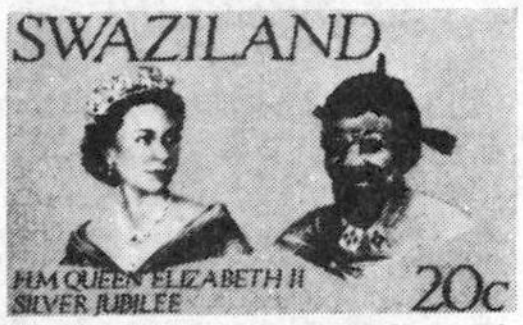

Elizabeth II and Sobhuza II — A34

Designs: 25c, Queen's coach at Admiralty Arch. 50c, Queen seated in coach.

1977, Feb. 7 *Perf. 13½*

278 A34 20c silver & multi .25 .25
279 A34 25c silver & multi .32 .32
280 A34 50c silver & multi .65 .65
Nos. 278-280 (3) 1.22 1.22

25th anniv. of the reign of Elizabeth II.

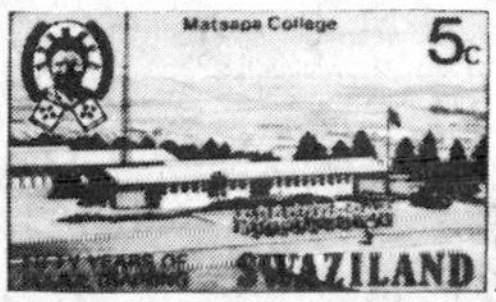

Matsapa College A35

Designs: 10c, Men's and Women's uniforms and jeep. 20c, Police badge, vert. 25c, Dog handler and dog.

1977, May 2 **Litho.** *Perf. 14*

281 A35 5c multicolored .15 .15
282 A35 10c multicolored .22 .22
283 A35 20c multicolored .45 .45
284 A35 25c multicolored .55 .55
Nos. 281-284 (4) 1.37 1.37

50 years of police training in Swaziland.

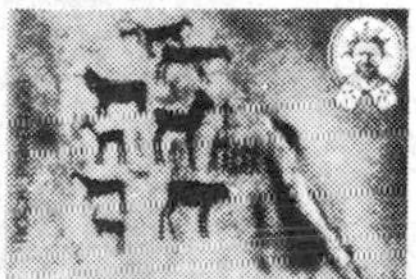

Various Animals — A36

Rock Paintings: 10c, 20c, Groups of men. 15c, Cattle and herdsman.

Perf. 14x14½

1977, Aug. 8 **Wmk. 373**

285 A36 5c multicolored .18 .18
286 A36 10c multicolored .35 .35
287 A36 15c multicolored .55 .55
288 A36 20c multicolored .75 .75
a. Souvenir sheet of 4, #285-288 3.00 3.00
Nos. 285-288 (4) 1.83 1.83

Rock paintings from Highveld area, c. 1700-1850.

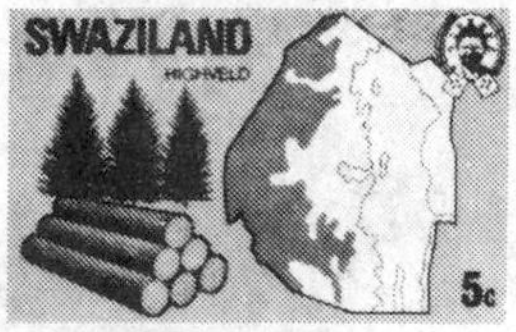

Evergreens, Timber, Map of Highveld — A37

Designs: 10c, Pineapple and map of Middleveld. 15c, Map of Lowveld, orange and lemon. 20c, Map of Lubombo and grazing cattle. No. 293, Map of Swaziland and produce, vert.: UL, Evergreens; UR, Orange and lemon; LL, Pineapple; LR, Cattle.

1977, Oct. 17 **Litho.** *Perf. 13½*

289 A37 5c multicolored .20 .20
290 A37 10c multicolored .38 .38
291 A37 15c multicolored .60 .60
292 A37 20c multicolored .85 .85
Nos. 289-292 (4) 2.03 2.03

Souvenir Sheet

293 Sheet of 4 2.00 2.00
a.-d. A37 25c single stamp .45 .45

No. 293 contains 4 vertical stamps.

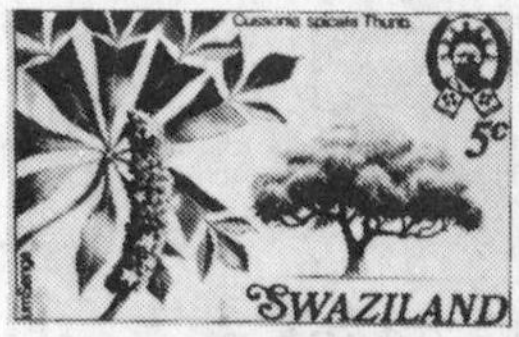

Cussonia Spicata Thunb. A38

Trees: 10c, Sclerocarya birrea. 20c, Pterocarpus angolensis. 25c, Erythrina lysistemon.

1978, Jan. 12 Litho. Wmk. 373

294	A38	5c multicolored	.15	.15
295	A38	10c multicolored	.24	.24
296	A38	20c multicolored	.48	.48
297	A38	25c multicolored	.60	.60
		Nos. 294-297 (4)	1.47	1.47

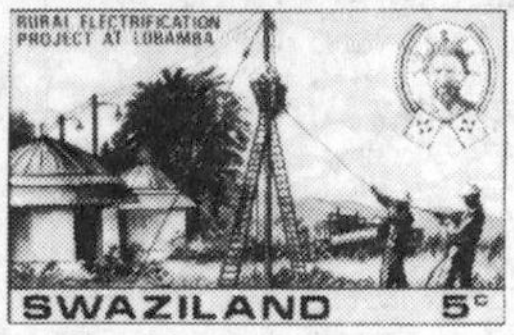

Rural Electrification, Lobamba — A39

Hydroelectric Power: 10c, Edwaleni Power Station. 20c, Switchgear, Maguduza Power Station. 25c, Hydroturbine hall, Edwaleni.

1978, Mar. 6 Litho. *Perf. 13½*

298	A39	5c black & ocher	.15	.15
299	A39	10c black & yellow green	.16	.16
300	A39	20c black & blue	.32	.32
301	A39	25c black & rose magenta	.42	.42
		Nos. 298-301 (4)	1.05	1.05

Elizabeth II Coronation Anniversary Issue

Souvenir Sheet

Common Design Types

1978, Apr. 21 Unwmk. *Perf. 15*

302	Sheet of 6	2.00	2.00
a.	CD326 25c Queen's lion	.35	.35
b.	CD327 25c Elizabeth II	.35	.35
c.	CD328 25c African Elephant	.35	.35

No. 302 contains 2 se-tenant strips of Nos. 302a-302c, separated by horizontal gutter with commemorative and descriptive inscriptions and showing central part of coronation procession with coach.

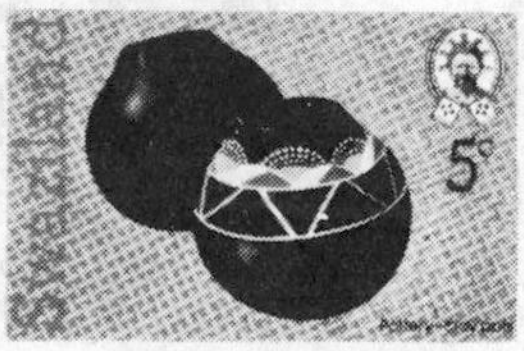

Clay Pots A40

Handicrafts: 10c, Basketwork. 20c, Wooden utensils. 30c, Wooden pot with lid.

Perf. 13½

1978, June 26 Litho. Wmk. 373

303	A40	5c multicolored	.15	.15
304	A40	10c multicolored	.16	.16
305	A40	20c multicolored	.30	.30
306	A40	30c multicolored	.48	.48
		Nos. 303-306 (4)	1.09	1.09

See Nos. 317-320.

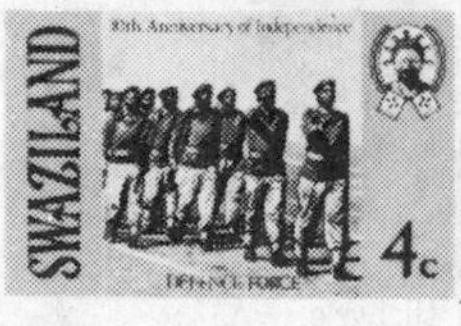

Defense Force A41

Designs: 6c, King's Regiment. 10c, Tinkabi tractor and ox-drawn plow. 15c, Laying water pipe. 25c, Adult literacy class. 50c, Fire engine and ambulance.

1978, Sept. 6 Litho. *Perf. 14*

307	A41	4c multicolored	.15	.15
308	A41	6c multicolored	.15	.15
309	A41	10c multicolored	.15	.15
310	A41	15c multicolored	.22	.22
311	A41	25c multicolored	.35	.35
312	A41	50c multicolored	.70	.70
		Nos. 307-312 (6)	1.72	1.72

10th anniversary of independence.

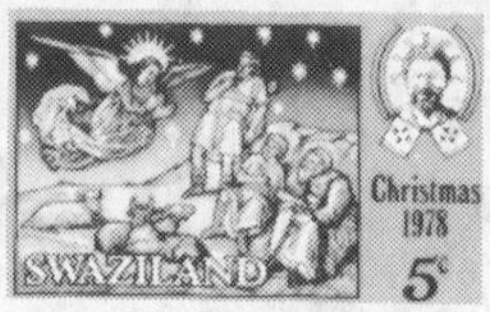

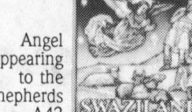

Angel Appearing to the Shepherds A42

Christmas: 10c, Adoration of the Kings. 15c, Angel warning Joseph in a dream. 25c, Flight into Egypt.

1978, Dec. 12 Litho. *Perf. 14*

313	A42	5c multicolored	.15	.15
314	A42	10c multicolored	.18	.18
315	A42	15c multicolored	.26	.26
316	A42	25c multicolored	.45	.45
		Nos. 313-316 (4)	1.04	1.04

Handicrafts Type of 1978

1979, Jan. 10 *Perf. 13½*

317	A40	5c Sisal bowls	.15	.15
318	A40	15c Clay pots	.28	.28
319	A40	20c Basketwork	.35	.35
320	A40	30c Hide shield	.55	.55
		Nos. 317-320 (4)	1.33	1.33

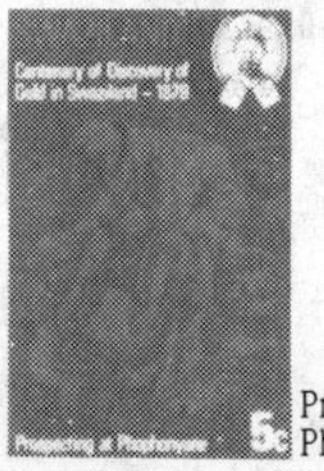

Prospecting at Phophonyane — A43

Designs: 15c, Early 3-stamp battery mill. 25c, Cyanide tanks at Piggs Peak. 50c, Pouring off molten gold.

Wmk. 373

1979, Mar. 27 Litho. *Perf. 14*

321	A43	5c violet brown & gold	.15	.15
322	A43	15c violet brown & gold	.30	.30
323	A43	25c violet brown & gold	.52	.52
324	A43	50c violet brown & gold	1.10	1.10
		Nos. 321-324 (4)	2.07	2.07

Centenary of discovery of gold in Swaziland.

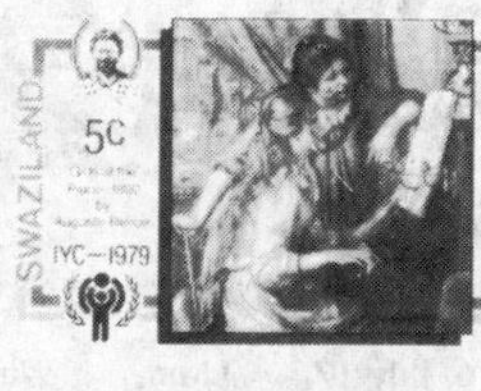

Girls at Piano, 1892, by Renoir A44

Paintings by Renoir: 15c, Madame Charpentier and her Children, 1878. 25c, Girls Picking Flowers, 1889. 50c, Girl with Watering Can, 1876.

1979, May 8 *Perf. 13½*

325	A44	5c multicolored	.15	.15
326	A44	15c multicolored	.24	.24
327	A44	25c multicolored	.40	.40
328	A44	50c multicolored	.80	.80
a.		Souvenir sheet of 4, #325-328	1.90	1.90
		Nos. 325-328 (4)	1.59	1.59

International Year of the Child.

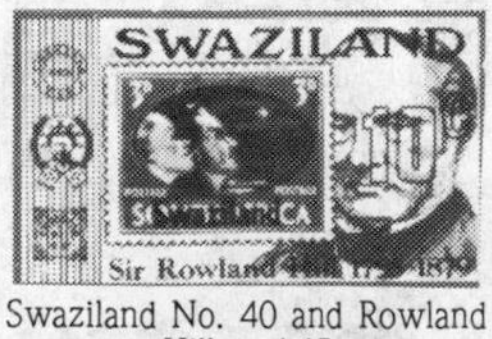

Swaziland No. 40 and Rowland Hill — A45

Rowland Hill and: 10c, Swaziland #18. 25c, Swaziland #142. 50c, Swaziland #105.

1979, July 17 Litho. *Perf. 14½*

329	A45	10c multicolored	.15	.15
330	A45	20c multicolored	.28	.28
331	A45	25c multicolored	.35	.35
		Nos. 329-331 (3)	.78	.78

Souvenir Sheet

332	A45	50c multicolored	.80	.80

Sir Rowland Hill (1795-1879), originator of penny postage.

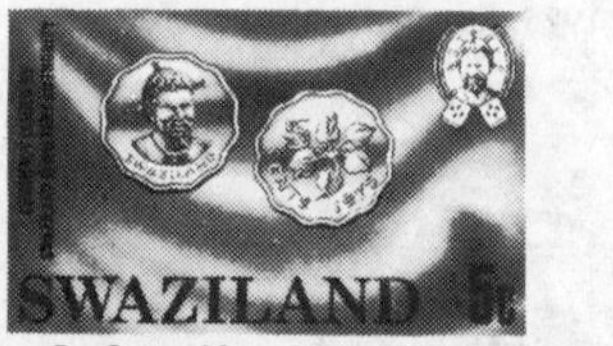

5c Cupro-Nickel Coin — A46

Coins: 10c, King Sobhuza II and sorghum. 20c, King and elephant head. 50c, Coat of arms. 1e, Mother and son.

Perf. 13½x14

1979, Sept. 6 Litho. Wmk. 373

333	A46	5c multicolored	.15	.15
334	A46	10c multicolored	.15	.15
335	A46	20c multicolored	.22	.22
336	A46	50c multicolored	.55	.55
337	A46	1e multicolored	1.10	1.10
		Nos. 333-337 (5)	2.17	2.17

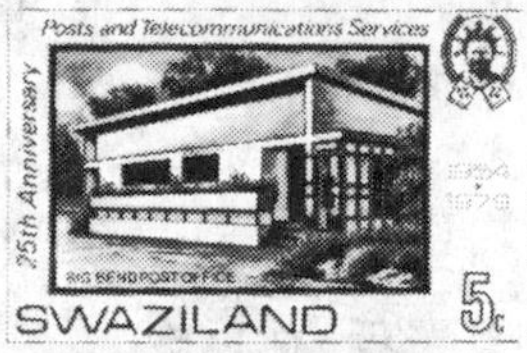

Big Bend Post Office A47

Designs: 15c, Mount Ntondozi microwave station, vert. 20c, Swaziland #53. 50c, Swaziland #217.

1979, Nov. 22

338	A47	5c multicolored	.15	.15
339	A47	15c multicolored	.18	.18
340	A47	20c multicolored	.22	.22
341	A47	50c multicolored	.55	.55
		Nos. 338-341 (4)	1.10	1.10

25th anniv. of Post and Telecommunications service (5c, 15c); 10th anniv. of UPU membership (20c, 50c).

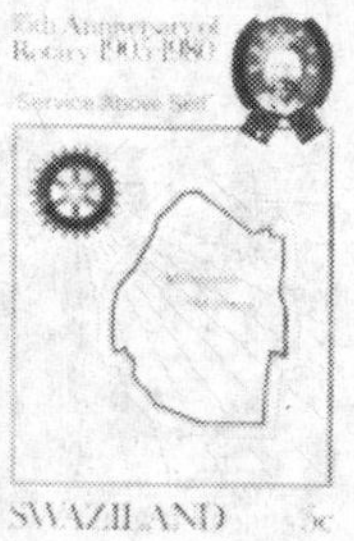

Rotary International, 75th Anniversary — A48

Wmk. 373

1980, Feb. 23 Litho. *Perf. 14*

342	A48	5c shown	.15	.15
343	A48	15c Hospital equipment	.26	.26
344	A48	50c Rotary principles	.90	.90
345	A48	1e Headquarters, Evanston, IL	1.75	1.75
		Nos. 342-345 (4)	3.06	3.06

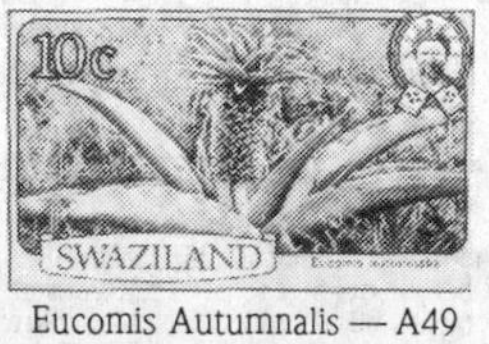

Eucomis Autumnalis — A49

Flowers: 1c, Brunsvigia radulosa. 2c, Aloe suprafoliata. 3c, Haemanthus magificus. 4c, Aloe marlothii. 5c, Dicoma zeyheri. 6c, Aloe kniphofioides. 7c, Cyrtanthus bicolor. 15c, Leucospermum gerrardii. 20c, Haemanthus multiflorus. 30c, Acridocarpus natalitius. 50c, Adenium swazicum. 1e, Protea simplex. 2e, Calodendrum capense. 5e, Gladiolus ecklonii. All vert. except. 15c, 20c, 30c, 50c.

1980, Apr. 28 Litho. *Perf. 13½*

346	A49	1c multicolored	.15	.15
347	A49	2c multicolored	.15	.15
348	A49	3c multicolored	.15	.15
349	A49	4c multicolored	.15	.15
350	A49	5c multicolored	.15	.15
351	A49	6c multicolored	.15	.15
352	A49	7c multicolored	.15	.15
353	A49	10c multicolored	.20	.20
354	A49	15c multicolored	.30	.30
355	A49	20c multicolored	.40	.40
356	A49	30c multicolored	.55	.55
357	A49	50c multicolored	.70	.70

Size: 22x37½mm

358	A49	1e multicolored	1.40	1.40
359	A49	2e multicolored	3.00	3.00
360	A49	5e multicolored	7.00	7.00
		Nos. 346-360 (15)	14.60	14.60

For surcharges see Nos. 465-470.

1983 *Perf. 12*

346a	A49	1c	.15	.15
347a	A49	2c	.15	.15
349a	A49	4c	.15	.15
351a	A49	6c	.15	.15
353a	A49	10c	.22	.22
355a	A49	20c	.45	.45
		Nos. 346a-355a (6)	1.27	1.27

Inscribed 1983.

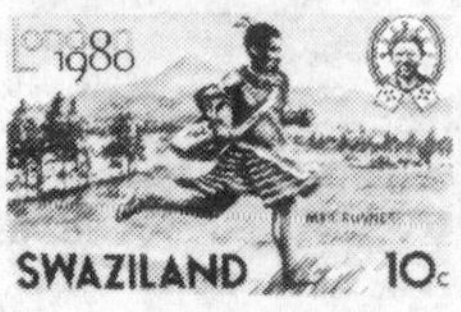

Mail Runner, London 1980 Emblem A50

1980, May 6 Wmk. 373 *Perf. 14*

361	A50	10c shown	.15	.15
362	A50	20c Mail truck	.26	.26
363	A50	25c Mail sorting	.30	.30
364	A50	50c Mail ropeway	.60	.60
		Nos. 361-364 (4)	1.31	1.31

London 80 Intl. Stamp Exhib., May 6-14.

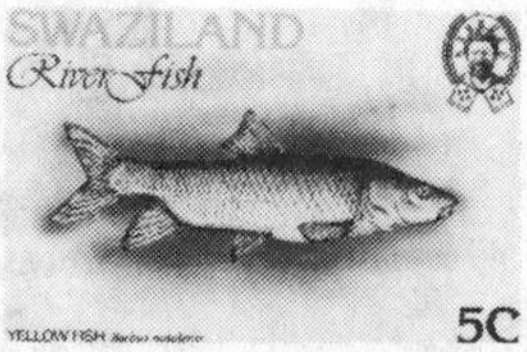

Yellow Fish A51

1980, Aug. 25 Litho. *Perf. 14*

365	A51	5c shown	.15	.15
366	A51	10c Silver barbel	.20	.20
367	A51	15c Tigerfish	.30	.30
368	A51	30c Squeaker fish	.55	.55
369	A51	1e Bream	1.90	1.90
		Nos. 365-369 (5)	3.10	3.10

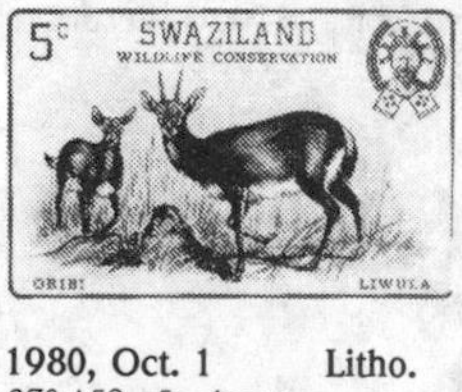

Oribi Antelope A52

1980, Oct. 1 Litho. *Perf. 14*

370	A52	5c shown	.15	.15
371	A52	10c Nile crocodile, vert.	.18	.18
372	A52	50c Pangolin	.90	.90
373	A52	1e Leopard, vert.	1.75	1.75
		Nos. 370-373 (4)	2.98	2.98

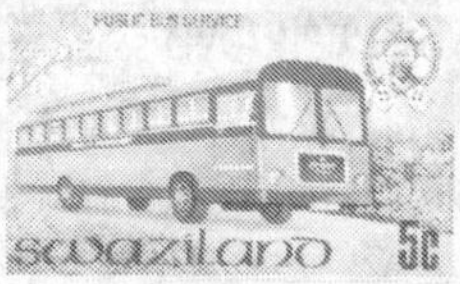

Bus A53

1981, Jan. 5 Litho. *Perf. 14½*

374	A53	5c shown	.15	.15
375	A53	25c Jet	.48	.48
376	A53	30c Truck	.55	.55
377	A53	1e Train	1.90	1.90
		Nos. 374-377 (4)	3.08	3.08

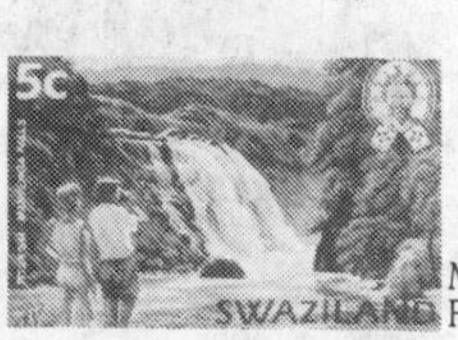

Mantenga Falls — A54

1981, Apr. 16 Litho. *Perf. 14*

378	A54	5c shown	.15	.15
379	A54	15c Mananga Yacht Club	.25	.25
380	A54	30c White rhinoceri, Mlilwane Game Sanctuary	.50	.50
381	A54	1e Gambling	1.65	1.65
		Nos. 378-381 (4)	2.55	2.55

Royal Wedding Issue
Common Design Type
Wmk. 373

1981, July 21   Litho.   *Perf. 14*

382	CD331	10c Bouquet	.16 .16
383	CD331	25c Charles	.38 .38
384	CD331	1e Couple	1.50 1.50
		Nos. 382-384 (3)	2.04 2.04

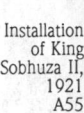

Installation of King Sobhuza II, 1921
A55

60th Anniv. of King Sobhuza II's Reign (King and): 10c, Visit of Royal Family, 1947. 15c, Coronation of Queen Elizabeth II, 1953. 25c, Independence ceremony, 1968. 30c, Early portrait. 1e, Parliament buildings.

Perf. 14½

1981, Aug. 24   Litho.   Wmk. 373

385	A55	5c multicolored	.15 .15
386	A55	10c multicolored	.15 .15
387	A55	15c multicolored	.24 .24
388	A55	25c multicolored	.40 .40
389	A55	30c multicolored	.48 .48
390	A55	1e multicolored	1.65 1.65
		Nos. 385-390 (6)	3.07 3.07

Duke of Edinburgh's Awards, 25th Anniv. — A56   Intl. Year of the Disabled — A57

1981, Nov. 5   Litho.   *Perf. 14*

391	A56	5c Basketball	.15 .15
392	A56	30c Compass reading	.35 .35
393	A56	50c Square	.90 .90
394	A56	1e Duke of Edinburgh	1.75 1.75
		Nos. 391-394 (4)	3.15 3.15

1981, Dec. 7   *Perf. 14x14½, 14½x14*

395	A57	5c Men learning carpentry, horiz.	.15 .15
396	A57	15c Boy learning Braille	.30 .30
397	A57	25c Carpentry, diff.	.52 .52
398	A57	1e Driving, horiz.	2.00 2.00
		Nos. 395-398 (4)	2.97 2.97

Papilio Demodocus
A58

1982, Jan. 6   Litho.   *Perf. 14*

399	A58	5c shown	.20 .20
400	A58	10c Charaxes candiope	.35 .35
401	A58	50c Papilio nireus	1.75 1.75
402	A58	1e Eurema desjardinsii	3.50 3.50
		Nos. 399-402 (4)	5.80 5.80

A59   A60

1982, Apr. 27   Litho.   *Perf. 14*

403	A59	5c Non-smoker, flowers	.15 .15
404	A59	10c Smoker, non-smoker	.25 .25

First Intl. Conference on Smoking and Health, Apr. 25-29

Perf. 13½x13

1982, June 16   Litho.   Wmk. 373

Designs: a, Female fishing owl. b, Pair. c, Owl in nest, egg. d, Adult and young owls. e, Male.

405		Strip of 5, multi	6.00 6.00
a.-e.	A60	35c, any single	1.10 1.10

Princess Diana Issue
Common Design Type

1982, July 1   *Perf. 14½*

406	CD333	5c Arms	.15 .15
407	CD333	20c Diana	.35 .35
408	CD333	50c Wedding	.90 .90
409	CD333	1e Portrait	1.75 1.75
		Nos. 406-409 (4)	3.15 3.15

Sugar Industry
A61

1982, Sept. 1   Litho.

410	A61	5c Planting sugar cane	.15 .15
411	A61	20c Harvesting cane	.45 .45
412	A61	30c Mhlume Mills	.65 .65
413	A61	1e Rail transport	2.25 2.25
		Nos. 410-413 (4)	3.50 3.50

Baphalali Red Cross Society
A62

1982, Nov. 9   *Perf. 14*

414	A62	5c Immunization	.15 .15
415	A62	20c Red Cross Juniors	.35 .35
416	A62	50c Disaster relief	.90 .90
417	A62	1e Red Cross founder Henry Dunant	1.75 1.75
		Nos. 414-417 (4)	3.15 3.15

Scouting Year — A63

Perf. 14½x14

1982, Dec. 6   Litho.   Wmk. 373

418	A63	5c Reciting promise	.15 .15
419	A63	10c Hiking	.25 .25
420	A63	25c Community development	.60 .60
421	A63	75c Baden-Powell	1.90 1.90
		Nos. 418-421 (4)	2.90 2.90

Souvenir Sheet

422	A63	1e Emblem	3.00 3.00

A64   Beaded Vulture — A65

1983, Mar. 14   Litho.   *Perf. 14*

423	A64	6c Satellite view	.15 .15
424	A64	10c King Sobhuza II, flag	.20 .20
425	A64	50c Beehive huts, horiz.	1.00 1.00
426	A64	1e Spraying sugar crop, horiz.	2.00 2.00
		Nos. 423-426 (4)	3.35 3.35

Commonwealth Day.

Perf. 13½x13

1983, May 16   Litho.   Wmk. 373

Designs: a, Male. b, Pair. c, Nest, egg. d, Female at nest. e, Adult, fledgeling.

427		Strip of 5	6.00 6.00
a.-e.	A65	35c, any single	1.10 1.10

Souvenir Sheets

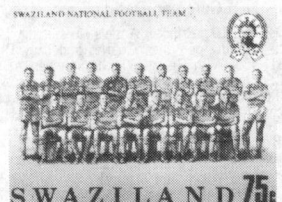

Soccer Tour of Swaziland 1983 — A66

1983, Aug. 20   Litho.   *Perf. 14x13½*

428	A66	75c Natl. team	1.40 1.40
429	A66	75c Tottenham Hotspur	1.40 1.40
430	A66	75c Manchester United	1.40 1.40
		Nos. 428-430 (3)	4.20 4.20

Manned Flight Bicentenary
A67

1983, Sept. 22   Litho.   *Perf. 14*

431	A67	5c Montgolfiere, 1783, vert.	.15 .15
432	A67	10c Wright brothers' plane	.18 .18
433	A67	25c Royal Swazi Fokker Fellowship	.42 .42
434	A67	50c Bell X-1 jet	.85 .85
		Nos. 431-434 (4)	1.60 1.60

Souvenir Sheet

435	A67	1e Columbia space shuttle take-off, vert.	2.00 2.00

Alfred Nobel, 100th Birth Anniv.
A68

1983, Oct. 21

436	A68	6c Albert Schweitzer	.15 .15
437	A68	10c Dag Hammarskjold	.32 .20
438	A68	50c Albert Einstein	1.00 1.00
439	A68	1e shown	2.00 2.00
		Nos. 436-439 (4)	3.47 3.35

World Food Program
A69

1983, Nov. 29

440	A69	6c Maize	.15 .15
441	A69	10c Rice	.28 .28
442	A69	50c Cattle	.85 .85
443	A69	1e Tractor	1.75 1.75
		Nos. 440-443 (4)	3.03 3.03

Women's College
A70

1984, Mar. 12   Litho.   *Perf. 14*

444	A70	6c shown	.15 .15
445	A70	15c Technical training school	.28 .28
446	A70	50c University	.90 .90
447	A70	1e Primary school	1.75 1.75
		Nos. 444-447 (4)	3.08 3.08

SWAZILAND Bald Ibis — A71

Designs: a, Male. b, Male, female. c, Nest, egg. d, Female at nest. e, Adult, fledgeling.

1984, May 18   Litho.   *Perf. 13½x13*

448		Strip of 5	5.50 5.50
a.-e.	A71	35c, any single	1.00 1.00

1984 UPU Congress
A72

Mail Coaches.

1984, June 15   Litho.   *Perf. 14½*

449	A72	7c Mule-drawn coach	.15 .15
450	A72	15c Oxen-drawn post wagon	.28 .28
451	A72	50c Mule-drawn, diff.	.90 .90
452	A72	1e Bristol-London	1.75 1.75
		Nos. 449-452 (4)	3.08 3.08

1984 Summer Olympics
A73

1984, July 28   *Perf. 14*

453	A73	7c Running	.15 .15
454	A73	10c Swimming	.18 .18
455	A73	50c Shooting	.90 .90
456	A73	1e Boxing	1.75 1.75
a.		Souvenir sheet of 4, #453-456	3.50 3.50
		Nos. 453-456 (4)	2.98 2.98

Local Fungi — A74

1984, Sept. 19   Litho.   *Perf. 14*

457	A74	10c Suillus bovinus	.18 .18
458	A74	15c Langermannia gigantea, vert.	.28 .28
459	A74	50c Coriolus versicolor, vert.	.90 .90
460	A74	1e Boletus edulis	1.75 1.75
		Nos. 457-460 (4)	3.11 3.11

20th Anniv. of Swazi Railways
A75

1984, Nov. 5   Litho.   Wmk. 373

461	A75	10c Opening ceremony	.20 .20
462	A75	25c Type 15A locomotive, Siweni Exchange Yard	.50 .50
463	A75	30c Container loading, Matsapha Station	.60 .60
464	A75	1e No. 268, Alto Tunnel	2.00 2.00
a.		Souvenir sheet of 4, #461-464	3.50 3.50
		Nos. 461-464 (4)	3.30 3.30

Nos. 346-349, 351-352 Surcharged

1984, Dec. 15   Litho.   *Perf. 13½*

465	A49	10c on 4c #349	.15 .15
466	A49	15c on 7c #352	.15 .15
467	A49	20c on 3c #348	.16 .16
468	A49	20c on 6c #351	.20 .20
469	A49	30c on 1c #346	.24 .24
470	A49	30c on 2c #347	.24 .24
		Nos. 465-470 (6)	1.14 1.14

Rotary Intl., 80th Anniv.
A76

1985, Feb. 23   Wmk. 373   Perf. 14
471 A76 10c Rotary emblem, world map .15 .15
472 A76 15c Training scholarships .18 .18
473 A76 50c Two children .60 .60
474 A76 1e Nurse, children 1.25 1.25
Nos. 471-474 (4) 2.18 2.18

Life Cycle of the Ground Hornbill — A77

Audubon birth bicentenary.

1985, May 15   Wmk. 373
475 Strip of 5 3.00 3.00
a.-e. A77 25c, any single .52 .52

Queen Mother 85th Birthday
Common Design Type
Perf. 14¹/₂x14
1985, June 7   Litho.   Wmk. 384
476 CD336 10c Visit to South Africa, 1947 .15 .15
477 CD336 15c With Elizabeth II and Margaret .16 .16
478 CD336 50c 75th birthday celebration .52 .52
479 CD336 1e Holding Prince Henry 1.10 1.10
Nos. 476-479 (4) 1.93 1.93

Souvenir Sheet
480 CD336 2e Greeting Prince Andrew 2.00 2.00

Classic Automobiles — A78

Wmk. 373
1985, Sept. 16   Litho.   Perf. 14
481 A78 10c Buick Tourer .15 .15
482 A78 15c Four-cylinder Rover .15 .15
483 A78 50c De Dion Bouton .45 .45
484 A78 1e Ford Model-T .88 .88
Nos. 481-484 (4) 1.63 1.63

Intl. Youth Year — A79

1985, Dec. 2
485 A79 10c Bridge-building .15 .15
486 A79 20c Girl Guides camping .18 .18
487 A79 50c Recreation .45 .45
488 A79 1e Guides collecting branches .88 .88
Nos. 485-488 (4) 1.66 1.66

Girl Guide Movement, 20c, 1e IYY, 10c, 50c.

Halley's Comet
A80

1986, Feb. 27   Wmk. 384   Perf. 14¹/₂
489 A80 1.50e multicolored 1.50 1.50

Queen Elizabeth II 60th Birthday
Common Design Type
Designs: 10c, Princess Anne's christening, 1950. 30c, Wedding of Prince Charles and Lady Diana, 1981. 45c, With George VI, the Dutchess of York and Sobhuza II at Nhlangano, 1947. 1e, At Windsor Polo Ground, 1984. 2e, Visiting Crown Agents' offices, 1983.

1986, Apr. 21   Perf. 14x14¹/₂
490 CD337 10c scar, blk & sil .15 .15
491 CD337 30c ultra & multi .30 .30
492 CD337 45c green, blk & sil .45 .45
493 CD337 1e violet & multi .95 .95
494 CD337 2e rose vio & multi 2.00 2.00
Nos. 490-494 (5) 3.85 3.85

For overprints see Nos. 527-530.

Coronation of Crown Prince Makhosetive
A81

Designs: 10c, Portrait, vert. 20c, Prince and King Sobhuza II at an Incwala ceremony. 25c, Prince at primary school. 30c, At school in England. 40c, Escorted from Matsapha Airport by Guard of Honor. 2e, Dancing the Simemo.

1986, Apr. 25   Perf. 14¹/₂
495 A81 10c multicolored .15 .15
496 A81 20c multicolored .22 .22
497 A81 25c multicolored .28 .28
498 A81 30c multicolored .35 .35
499 A81 40c multicolored .45 .45
500 A81 2e multicolored 2.25 2.25
Nos. 495-500 (6) 3.70 3.70

Assoc. of Round Tables in Central Africa, 50th Anniv. — A82

Club emblems.

Wmk. 384
1986, Oct. 4   Litho.   Perf. 14
501 A82 15c Orbis .15 .15
502 A82 25c Ehlanzeni 51 .22 .22
503 A82 55c Mbabane 30 .48 .48
504 A82 70c Bulembu 54 .62 .62
505 A82 2e Manzini 44 1.75 1.75
Nos. 501-505 (5) 3.22 3.22

Butterflies
A83

Unwmk.
1987, Mar. 17   Litho.   Perf. 14
506 A83 10c Yellow pansy .15 .15
507 A83 15c Guineafowl .15 .15
508 A83 20c Red forest charaxes .18 .18
509 A83 25c Paradise skipper .22 .22
510 A83 30c Broad-bordered acraea .28 .28
511 A83 35c Veined swallowtail .32 .32
512 A83 45c Large striped swordtail .40 .40
513 A83 50c Eyed pansy .45 .45
514 A83 55c Zebra white .48 .48
515 A83 70c Gaudy commodore .62 .62
516 A83 1e Common dotted border .88 .88
517 A83 5e Queen purple tip 4.25 4.25
518 A83 10e Natal barred blue 8.50 8.50
Nos. 506-518 (13) 16.88 16.88

See Nos. 600-611. For surcharges see Nos. 574-577. Compare with design A101.

White Rhinoceros
A84

1987, July 1   Wmk. 384   Perf. 14¹/₂
519 A84 15c Two adults .32 .32
520 A84 25c Adult, calf .50 .50
521 A84 45c Adult walking .90 .90
522 A84 70c Adult in mud 1.40 1.40
Nos. 519-522 (4) 3.12 3.12

World Wildlife Fund.

Flowers — A85

1987, Oct. 19   Litho.   Perf. 14¹/₂
523 A85 15c Blue moon .15 .15
524 A85 35c Danse de feu .35 .35
525 A85 55c Odin .55 .55
526 A85 2e Lilium davidii 2.00 2.00
Nos. 523-526 (4) 3.05 3.05

Nos. 491-494 Ovptd. "40TH WEDDING ANNIVERSARY" in Silver
Perf. 14x14¹/₂
1987, Dec. 9   Litho.   Wmk. 384
527 CD337 30c ultra & multi .30 .30
528 CD337 45c green, blk & sil .45 .45
529 CD337 1e violet & multi 1.00 1.00
530 CD337 2e rose violet & multi 2.00 2.00
Nos. 527-530 (4) 3.75 3.75

Insects
A86

Wmk. 384
1988, Mar. 14   Litho.   Perf. 14
531 A86 15c Zabalius aridus .16 .16
532 A86 55c Callidea bohemani .58 .58
533 A86 1e Phymateus viridipes 1.05 1.05
534 A86 2e Nomadacris septemfasciata 2.05 2.05
Nos. 531-534 (4) 3.84 3.84

1988 Summer Olympics, Seoul
A87

1988, Aug. 22   Litho.   Wmk. 384
535 A87 15c Flag-bearer, stadium .16 .16
536 A87 35c Tae kwon do .38 .38
537 A87 1e Boxing 1.05 1.05
538 A87 2e Tennis 2.00 2.00
Nos. 535-538 (4) 3.59 3.59

Intl. Tennis Federation, 75th anniv. (2e).

Small Mammals
A88

Wmk. 384
1989, Jan. 16   Litho.   Perf. 14
539 A88 35c Green monkey .38 .38
540 A88 55c Rock dassie .58 .58
541 A88 1e Zorilla 1.05 1.05
542 A88 2e African wildcat 2.00 2.00
Nos. 539-542 (4) 4.01 4.01

Intl. Red Cross and Red Crescent Organizations, 125th Anniv.
A89

Wmk. 373
1989, Sept. 21   Litho.   Perf. 12
543 A89 15c David Hynd .15 .15
544 A89 60c First aid .62 .62
545 A89 1e Sigombeni Clinic 1.05 1.05
546 A89 2e Relief work 2.00 2.00
Nos. 543-546 (4) 3.82 3.82

21st Birthday of King Mswati III
A90

King Mswati III: 15c, With Prince of Wales, 1987. 60c, With Pope John Paul II, 1988. 1e, Introduction to the nation while crown prince. 2e, With queen mother.

Perf. 14¹/₂x14
1989, Nov. 15   Unwmk.
547 A90 15c multicolored .15 .15
548 A90 60c multicolored .55 .55
549 A90 1e multicolored .95 .95
550 A90 2e multicolored 1.90 1.90
Nos. 547-550 (4) 3.55 3.55

African Development Bank, 25th Anniv. — A91

Designs: 15c, Manzini-Mahamba Road. 60c, Mbabane microwave radio link. 1e, Mbabane Government Hospital. 2e, Ezulwini Power Switching Station.

Perf. 14x14¹/₂
1989, Dec. 18   Wmk. 384
551 A91 15c multicolored .15 .15
552 A91 60c multicolored .42 .42
553 A91 1e multicolored .70 .70
554 A91 2e multicolored 1.40 1.40
Nos. 551-554 (4) 2.67 2.67

Stamp World London '90 — A92

Perf. 12¹/₂
1990, May 3   Litho.   Wmk. 384
555 A92 15c Intl. priority mail .15 .15
556 A92 60c Facsimile service .45 .45
557 A92 1e Post office .75 .75
558 A92 2e Ezulwini Earth Satellite Station 1.50 1.50
Nos. 555-558 (4) 2.85 2.85

Souvenir Sheet
559 A92 2e Mail runner 1.50 1.50

150th anniv. of the Penny Black.

Queen Mother, 90th Birthday
Common Design Types
1990, Aug. 4   Wmk. 384   Perf. 14x15
565 CD343 75c Queen Mother .42 .42
Perf. 14¹/₂
566 CD344 4e King, Queen visiting Hatfield House 2.25 2.25

Intl. Literacy Year — A94

Wmk. 373
1990, Sept. 21   Litho.   Perf. 14

567 A94	15c shown	.15	.15
568 A94	75c Outdoor class	.60	.60
569 A94	1e Modern instruction	.75	.75
570 A94	2e Receiving diploma	1.50	1.50
	Nos. 567-570 (4)	3.00	3.00

UN Development Program, 40th Anniv. — A95

Perf. 13½x14
1990, Dec. 10   Litho.   Wmk. 373

571 A95	60c Rural water supply	.45	.45
572 A95	1e Seed production	.75	.75
573 A95	2e Low cost housing	1.50	1.50
	Nos. 571-573 (3)	2.70	2.70

Nos. 509-510, 512, 514
Surcharged   **10c**

Unwmk.
1990, Dec. 17   Litho.   Perf. 14

574 A83	10c on 25c multi	.18	.18
575 A83	15c on 30c multi	.26	.26
576 A83	30c on 45c multi	.35	.35
577 A83	40c on 55c multi	.70	.70
	Nos. 574-577 (4)	1.49	1.49

National Heritage A96

Perf. 14x14½
1991, Feb. 11   Wmk. 233

578 A96	15c Lobamba Hot Spring	.15	.15
579 A96	60c Sibebe Rock	.45	.45
580 A96	1e Jolobela Falls	.75	.75
581 A96	2e Mantjolo Sacred Pool	1.50	1.50
	Nos. 578-581 (4)	2.85	2.85

Souvenir Sheet
Perf. 14

581A A96	2e Usushwana River	1.50	1.50

Coronation of King Mswati III, 5th Anniv. A97

Perf. 14x13½
1991, Apr. 24   Litho.   Wmk. 373

582 A97	15c King making radio address	.15	.15
583 A97	75c Butimba royal hunt	.55	.55
584 A97	1e King, schoolmates, 1986	.75	.75
585 A97	2e King opening parliament	1.50	1.50
	Nos. 582-585 (4)	2.95	2.95

Elizabeth & Philip, Birthdays
Common Design Types
Perf. 14½
1991, June 17   Litho.   Wmk. 384

586 CD346	1e multicolored	.75	.75
587 CD345	2e multicolored	1.50	1.50
a.	Pair, #586-587 + label	2.25	2.25

Flowers — A98   Christmas — A99

1991, Sept. 30   Wmk. 373   Perf. 14

588 A98	15c Xerophyta retinervis	.15	.15
589 A98	75c Bauhinia galpinii	.55	.55
590 A98	1e Dombeya rotundifolia	.75	.75
591 A98	2e Kigelia africana	1.50	1.50
	Nos. 588-591 (4)	2.95	2.95

Perf. 13½
1991, Dec. 18   Litho.   Wmk. 373

592 A99	20c Santa Claus, children	.15	.15
593 A99	70c Carolers	.52	.52
594 A99	1e Priest reading Bible	.75	.75
595 A99	2e Nativity Scene	1.50	1.50
	Nos. 592-595 (4)	2.92	2.92

Reptiles A100

1992, Feb. 25

596 A100	20c Lubombo flat lizard	.15	.15
597 A100	70c Natal hinged tortoise	.52	.52
598 A100	1e Swazi thick-toed gecko	.75	.75
599 A100	2e Nile monitor	1.50	1.50
	Nos. 596-599 (4)	2.92	2.92

Butterflies A101

1992, Aug. 26   Litho.   Perf. 14

600 A101	5c Red tip	.15	.15
601 A101	10c like #506	.15	.15
602 A101	15c like #507	.15	.15
603 A101	20c like #508	.16	.16
604 A101	25c like #509	.20	.20
605 A101	30c like #510	.22	.22
606 A101	35c like #511	.28	.28
607 A101	45c like #512	.35	.35
608 A101	50c like #513	.38	.38
609 A101	55c like #514	.42	.42
610 A101	70c like #515	.52	.52
611 A101	1e like #516	.75	.75
	Nos. 600-611 (12)	3.73	3.73

Dated 1991.
Nos. 600-611 have different portrait of King Mswati III from Nos. 506-516.

A102    A103

Designs: 20c, Missionaries with royal family. 1e, Pioneer missionaries.

1992, Dec. 16   Litho.   Perf. 13½x14

614 A102	20c multicolored	.15	.15
615 A102	1e multicolored	.75	.75

Evangelical Alliance Mission in Swaziland, cent.

1993, Mar. 18   Litho.   Perf. 13½x14

Cooking Utensils: 20c, Calabashes. 70c, Contemporary pottery for cooking. 1e, Wooden bowls. 2e, Quern for grinding seeds.

616 A103	20c multicolored	.15	.15
617 A103	70c multicolored	.48	.48
618 A103	1e multicolored	.70	.70
619 A103	2e multicolored	1.40	1.40
	Nos. 616-619 (4)	2.73	2.73

A104   A105

King Mswati, 25th Birthday: 25c, King Mswati as baby with mother. 40c, King Mswati III addressing PTA meeting. 1e, King Sobhuza II receiving Instrument of Independence, 1968. 2e, King Mswati III delivering first speech on Coronation Day, 1986.

1993, Sept. 6   Litho.   Perf. 13½x14

620 A104	25c multicolored	.15	.15
621 A104	40c multicolored	.25	.25
622 A104	1e multicolored	.55	.55
623 A104	2e multicolored	1.25	1.25
	Nos. 620-623 (4)	2.20	2.20

Independence, 25th anniv.

1993, Nov. 25   Perf. 13½

Common Waxbill

624 A105	25c Male & female	.15	.15
625 A105	40c Nest & eggs	.25	.25
626 A105	1e Incubating	.60	.60
627 A105	2e Feeding nestlings	1.25	1.25
	Nos. 624-627 (4)	2.25	2.25

A106    A107

1994, Feb. 22   Litho.   Perf. 13½

628 A106	25c Education	.15	.15
629 A106	40c Rural services	.18	.18
630 A106	1e Swazi culture	.60	.60
631 A106	2e People to people	1.25	1.25
	Nos. 628-631 (4)	2.18	2.18

US Peace Corps, 25th anniv

1994, Sept. 15   Perf. 13½x14

Mushrooms.

632 A107	30c Horse mushroom	.16	.16
633 A107	40c Penny bun bolete	.22	.22
634 A107	1e Russula verdigris	.55	.55
635 A107	2e Honey fungus	1.10	1.10
	Nos. 632-635 (4)	2.03	2.03

ICAO, 50th Anniv. A108

1994, Nov. 30   Litho.   Perf. 14

636 A108	30c Natl. airline	.16	.16
637 A108	40c Control tower	.22	.22
638 A108	1e Air rescue service	.55	.55
639 A108	2e Air traffic control	1.10	1.10
	Nos. 636-639 (4)	2.03	2.03

A109    A110

Traditional handicrafts.

1995, Apr. 7   Litho.   Perf. 13½

640 A109	35c Wooden bowls	.20	.20
641 A109	50c Chicken nests	.28	.28
642 A109	1e Leather crafts	.55	.55
643 A109	2e Wood carvings	1.10	1.10
	Nos. 640-643 (4)	2.13	2.13

1995, June 5   Litho.   Perf. 13½

FAO, 50th anniv.: 35c, Corn harvest. 50c, Planting vegetables. 1e, Herd of cattle. 2e, Sorghum harvest.

644 A110	35c multicolored	.20	.20
645 A110	50c multicolored	.28	.28
646 A110	1e multicolored	.55	.55
647 A110	2e multicolored	1.10	1.10
	Nos. 644-647 (4)	2.13	2.13

Lourie A111

1995, Sept. 27   Litho.   Perf. 13½x13

648 A111	35c Knysna lourie	.20	.20
649 A111	50c Lourie in flight	.30	.30
650 A111	1e Purple crested lourie	.55	.55
651 A111	2e Gray lourie	1.10	1.10
	Nos. 648-651 (4)	2.15	2.15

POSTAGE DUE STAMPS

Catalogue values for unused stamps in this section are for Never Hinged items.

D1    D2

1933   Typo.   Wmk. 4   Perf. 14

J1 D1	1p carmine rose	.30	2.00
a.	Wmk. 4a (error)	100.00	
J2 D1	2p violet	2.25	8.50

No. 57 Surcharged

Postage Due
1c
I

Postage Due
1c
II

1961   Engr.   Perf. 13½x13

J3 A5	(2d) on 2p, type I	10.00	12.00
a.	Type II	.40	
J4 A5	1c on 2p, type I	2.00	3.25
a.	Type II	1.50	1.50
J5 A5	2c on 2p, type I	2.00	3.25
a.	Type II	1.10	1.10
J6 A5	5c on 2p, type I	2.00	3.25
a.	Type II	1.75	1.75
	Nos. J3-J6 (4)	16.00	21.75

No. J3a was surcharged after decimal currency was introduced.

Type of 1933

1961   Typo.   Perf. 14

J7 D1	1c carmine rose	.15	.15
J8 D1	2c violet	.30	.30
J9 D1	5c green	.75	1.00
	Nos. J7-J9 (3)	1.20	1.45

Perf. 11½
1971, Feb. 1   Wmk. 314   Litho.

J10 D2	1c carmine rose	.28	.32
J11 D2	2c dull purple	.40	.48
J12 D2	5c green	.70	.80
	Nos. J10-J12 (3)	1.38	1.60

1977, Jan. 17   Wmk. 373

J10a D2	1c carmine rose	.28	.28
J11a D2	2c dull purple	.40	.40
J12a D2	5c green	.70	.70
	Nos. J10a-J12a (3)	1.38	1.38

1978-91   Perf. 15x14
Size: 17½x21mm

J13 D2	1c carmine lake	.15	.15
J14 D2	2c purple	.15	.15
J15 D2	5c green	.15	.15
J16 D2	10c sky blue	.15	.15
J17 D2	25c brown	.28	.15
	Set value	.70	.34

Nos. J14-J15 reissued dated 1991.
Issue dates: 1c-5c, Apr. 20. 10c-25c, July 17, 1991.

TANGANYIKA

ˌtan–gə–ˈnyē–kə

LOCATION — Southeastern Africa bordering on the Indian Ocean
GOVT. — Republic within British Commonwealth
AREA — 362,688 sq. mi.
POP. — 9,404,000 (est. 1961)
CAPITAL — Dar es Salaam

Before World War I, this area formed part of German East Africa. It was mandated to Britain after World War I and (in 1946) became a trust territory under the United Nations. In 1935, stamps of the mandate were replaced by those used jointly by Kenya, Uganda and Tanganyika (see Kenya, Uganda and Tanzania). On Dec. 9, 1961, Tanganyika became independent. On Dec. 9, 1962, it became a republic. April 26, 1964, it joined Zanzibar to form the United Republic of Tanganyika and Zanzibar (later renamed Tanzania). See Tanzania.

100 Cents = 1 Rupee
100 Cents = 1 Shilling (1922)
20 Shillings = 1 Pound

Catalogue values for unused stamps in this country are for Never Hinged items, beginning with Scott 45 in the regular postage section and Scott O1 in the officials section.

Stamps of Kenya, Uganda & Tanganyika Overprinted **G.E.A.**

1921 Wmk. 4 *Perf. 14*

1	A1	12c gray	3.50	*27.50*
2	A1	15c ultra	.75	*2.50*
3	A1	50c dull violet & blk	10.00	*35.00*

Overprinted **G. E. A.**

4	A2	2r black & red, *blue*	40.00	*85.00*
5	A2	3r gray green & violet	50.00	*100.00*
7	A2	5r dull violet & ultra	60.00	*110.00*
		Nos. 1-7 (6)	164.25	*360.00*

Overprinted in Red or Black **G.E.A.**

1922

8	A1	1c black (R)	.15	*7.50*
9	A1	10c orange (Bk)	.40	*10.00*

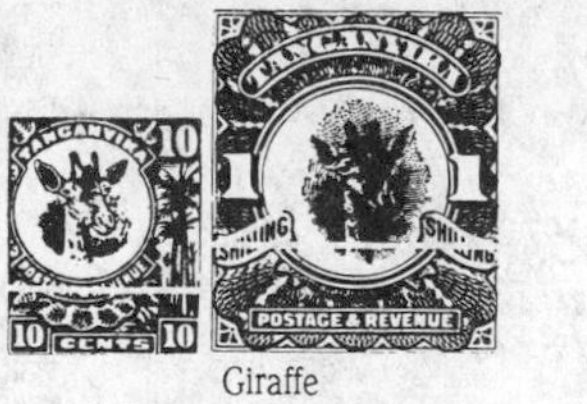

Giraffe
A3 A4

Perf. 14¹/₂x14

1922-25 Engr. Wmk. 4

10	A3	5c dk violet & blk	1.00	.15
11	A3	5c green & blk ('25)	.40	.70
12	A3	10c green & blk	.40	.30
13	A3	10c yellow & blk ('25)	1.50	1.25
14	A3	15c carmine & blk	1.10	.15
15	A3	20c orange & blk	.65	.15
16	A3	25c black	3.00	5.00
17	A3	25c blue & blk ('25)	2.00	*13.00*
18	A3	30c blue & blk	3.50	2.50
19	A3	30c dull vio & blk ('25)	1.50	*7.00*
20	A3	40c brown & black	1.65	3.00
21	A3	50c gray black	1.50	1.50
22	A3	75c bister & black	3.00	*12.00*

Perf. 14

23	A4	1sh green & black	1.10	*7.00*
a.		Wmk. sideways	1.90	*8.00*
24	A4	2sh brown vio & blk	2.00	*16.00*
a.		Wmk. sideways	4.00	*10.00*
25	A4	3sh blk, wmk. sideways	8.00	*20.00*
26	A4	5sh red & black	8.00	*50.00*
a.		Wmk. sideways	15.00	*60.00*
27	A4	10sh dp blue & blk	35.00	70.00
a.		Wmk. sideways	55.00	110.00
28	A4	£1 orange & black	100.00	175.00
a.		Wmk. sideways	100.00	200.00
		Nos. 10-28 (19)	175.30	*384.70*

On No. 28 the words of value are in a curve between the circle and "POSTAGE & REVENUE."

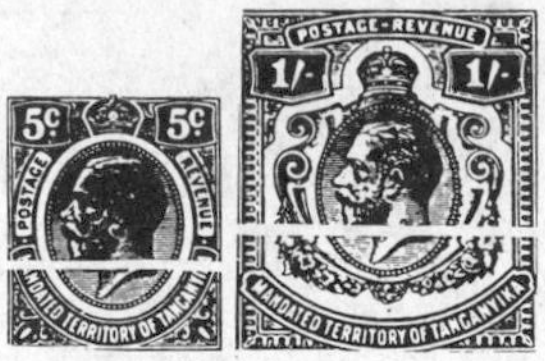

King George V
A5 A6

1927-31 Typo.

29	A5	5c green & black	.25	.15
30	A5	10c yellow & black	.30	.15
31	A5	15c red & black	.30	.15
32	A5	20c orange & black	.30	.15
33	A5	25c ultra & black	.40	.90
34	A5	30c dull violet & blk	.70	1.00
35	A5	30c ultra & blk ('31)	25.00	.40
36	A5	40c brown & black	.80	.95
37	A5	50c gray & black	.45	.18
38	A5	75c olive grn & blk	1.65	7.00
39	A6	1sh green & black	1.40	.60
40	A6	2sh violet brn & blk	4.50	2.50
41	A6	3sh black	5.75	*27.50*
42	A6	5sh scarlet & blk	5.75	12.00
43	A6	10sh ultra & black	25.00	*65.00*
44	A6	£1 brown org & blk	80.00	*125.00*
		Nos. 29-44 (16)	152.55	*243.63*

For issues of 1935-61, see Kenya and Uganda.

Catalogue values for unused stamps in this section, from this point to the end of the section, are for Never Hinged items.

Independent State

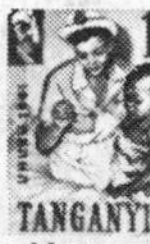

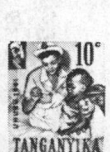

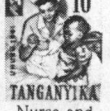

Nurse and Infant — A7

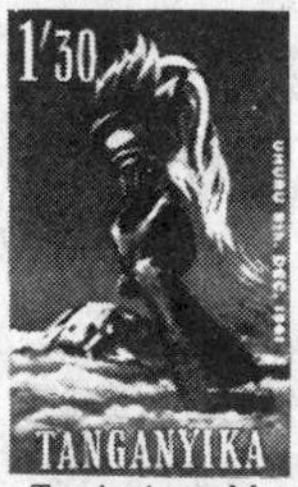

Torch above Mt. Kilimanjaro — A8

Designs: 5c, Teacher instructing villagers, horiz. 15c, Coffee picker. 20c, Harvesting corn. 30c, Flag, horiz. 50c, Serengeti lions. 1sh, Nurse showing infant to mother and hospital. 2sh, Dar es Salaam harbor. 5sh, Tractor and field workers. 10sh, Diamond mine and rose diamond. 1sh, 2sh, 5sh, 10sh, horiz.

Perf. 14x14¹/₂, 14¹/₂x14

1961, Dec. 9 Photo. Unwmk.

45	A7	5c sepia & yel grn	.15	.15
46	A7	10c Prussian green	.15	.15
47	A7	15c sepia & blue	.15	.15
b.		Blue omitted	200.00	
48	A7	20c orange brown	.15	.15
49	A7	30c dp green, blk & yel	.15	.15
50	A7	50c sepia & yellow	.15	.15

Perf. 14¹/₂

51	A8	1sh cit brn & gray bl	.15	.15
52	A8	1sh30c multicolored	.30	.15
53	A8	2sh multicolored	.42	.17
54	A8	5sh Prus grn & dp org	1.00	.35
55	A8	10sh blk, blue & rose	1.75	.75
a.		Rose (diamond) omitted	75.00	
56	A8	20sh multicolored	4.50	1.50
		Nos. 45-56 (12)	9.02	
		Set value		3.20

Tanganyika's independence, Dec. 9, 1961.
For overprints see Nos. O21-O28.

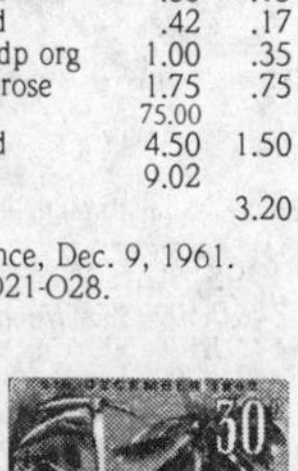

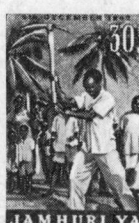

Pres. Julius Nyerere with Pickax — A9

Designs: 50c, Flag hoisting on Mt. Kilimanjaro. 1sh30c, Presidential emblem. 2sh50c, Independence monument, Mnazi Moja.

1962, Dec. 9 *Perf. 14¹/₂x14*

57	A9	30c bright green	.15	.15
58	A9	50c multicolored	.15	.15
59	A9	1sh30c multicolored	.25	.25
60	A9	2sh50c dk blue, blk & red	.50	.50
		Nos. 57-60 (4)	1.05	1.05

Issued to commemorate the establishment of the Republic of Tanganyika, Dec. 9, 1962.

OFFICIAL STAMPS

Catalogue values for unused stamps in this section are for Never Hinged items.

Issued for use by the Tanganyika Government

Stamps of Kenya, Uganda & Tanganyika, 1954-59, Overprinted

OFFICIAL

Perf. 12¹/₂x13, 13x12¹/₂

1959 Engr. Wmk. 4

O1	A18	5c choc & blk	.15	.15
O2	A19	10c carmine	.15	.15
O3	A20	15c lt bl & blk (on #106)	.15	.15
O4	A19	20c orange & blk	.15	.15
a.		Double overprint		*350.00*
O5	A18	30c ultra & black	.16	.15
O6	A19	50c dp red lilac	.22	.16
O7	A19	1sh dp mag & blk	.25	.22
O8	A20	1sh30c pur & red org	.35	.30
O9	A20	2sh dp grn & gray	.52	.52
O10	A20	5sh black & org	1.25	1.25
O11	A20	10sh ultra & blk	3.00	3.00
O12	A21	£1 black & ver	5.75	5.75
		Nos. O1-O12 (12)	12.10	11.95

Stamps of Kenya, Uganda & Tanganyika, 1960, Overprinted **OFFICIAL**

Perf. 14¹/₂x14

1960, Oct. 1 Photo. Wmk. 314

O13	A23	5c dull blue	.15	.15
O14	A23	10c lt olive green	.15	.15
O15	A23	15c dull purple	.15	.15
O16	A23	20c brt lilac rose	.15	.15
O17	A23	30c brt vermilion	.15	.15
O18	A23	50c dull violet	.16	.15

Overprinted **OFFICIAL**

Engr. *Perf. 14*

O19	A24	1sh violet & lilac red	.40	.25
O20	A24	5sh rose red & lilac	1.75	1.50
		Set value	2.60	2.15

Nos. 45-51 and 54 Overprinted "OFFICIAL" in Sans-serif Type of Various Sizes

Perf. 14x14¹/₂, 14¹/₂x14

1961, Dec. 9 Unwmk.

O21	A7	5c sepia & yellow grn	.15	.15
O22	A7	10c Prussian green	.15	.15
O23	A7	15c sepia & blue	.15	.15
O24	A7	20c orange brown	.15	.15
O25	A7	30c dp grn blk & yel	.15	.15
O26	A7	50c sepia & yellow	.20	.15
O27	A8	1sh citron brn & gray bl	.40	.25
O28	A8	5sh Prus grn & dp org	1.50	1.10
		Set value	2.45	1.80

TANZANIA

ˌtan–zə–ˈnē–ə

(Tanganyika and Zanzibar)

LOCATION — Southeastern Africa bordering on the Indian Ocean, and a group of islands about 20 miles off the coast
GOVT. — United republic in British Commonwealth
AREA — 364,886 sq. mi.
POP. — 19,730,000 (est. 1983)
CAPITAL — Dodoma

Tanganyika joined Zanzibar on April 26, 1964, to form the United Republic of Tanganyika and Zanzibar. In October 1965 the name was changed to United Republic of Tanzania.

Zanzibar stamps include two (Nos. 331, 334) inscribed "Tanzania."

100 Cents = 1 Shilling

Catalogue values for all unused stamps in this country are for Never Hinged items.

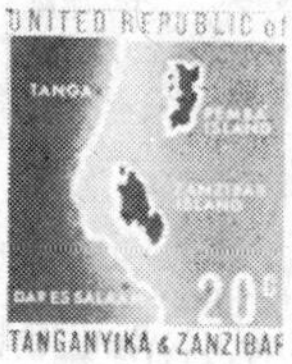

Map — A1

Design: 30c, 1sh30c, Emblem (hands holding torch and spear).

Perf. 14x14¹/₂

1964, July 7 Photo. Unwmk.

1	A1	20c blue & emerald	.15	.15
2	A1	30c brown, dk & lt blue	.15	.15
3	A1	1.30sh ultra, blk & orange	.30	.30
4	A1	2.50sh ultra & purple	.60	.60
		Nos. 1-4 (4)	1.20	1.20

Union of Tanganyika and Zanzibar. Not sold in Zanzibar, nor valid there.

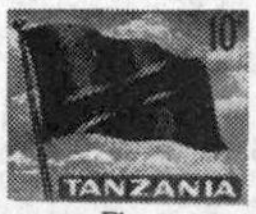

Flag
A2

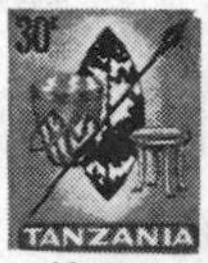

Native Handicraft
A3

Designs: 5c, Hale hydroelectric plant. 15c, Army squad. 20c, Road building. 40c, Giraffes. 50c, Zebras. 65c, Mt. Kilimanjaro. 1sh, Dar es Salaam harbor. 1.30sh, Zinjanthropus skull and Olduvai Gorge excavation. 2.50sh, Sailfish, dhow and map of Mafia Island. 5sh, Sisal industry. 10sh, State House, Dar es Salaam. 20sh, Tanzania coat of arms.

Perf. 14x14¹/₂, 14¹/₂x14

1965, Dec. 9 Photo. Unwmk.

Size: 21x17¹/₂mm, 17¹/₂x21mm

5	A2	5c orange & ultra	.15	.15
6	A2	10c ultra, grn, yel & blk	.15	.15
7	A3	15c grn, bl, brn & buff	.15	.15
8	A2	20c blue & brown	.15	.15
9	A3	30c black & red brn	.15	.15
10	A3	40c blue, yel grn & brn	.15	.15
11	A2	50c yellow grn & blue	.15	.15
12	A2	65c ultra, grn & red brn	.25	.25

Perf. 14¹/₂

Size: 41¹/₂x25, 25x41¹/₂mm

13	A2	1sh bl, grn, yel & brn	.30	.15
14	A2	1.30sh multicolored	.45	.15
15	A2	2.50sh blue & red brown	.65	.30
16	A2	5sh bl, brt grn & red brn	1.40	.45
17	A2	10sh blue & yellow	2.75	1.25
18	A3	20sh gray & multi	5.50	2.75
		Nos. 5-18 (14)	12.35	6.35

For overprints see Nos. O1-O8.

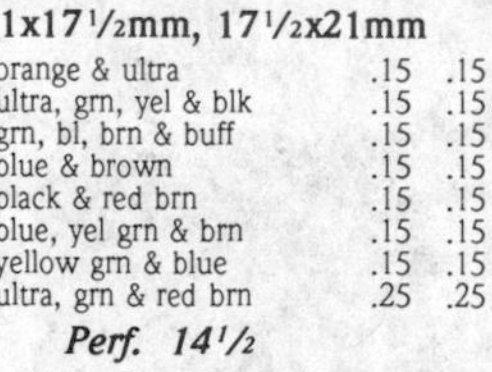

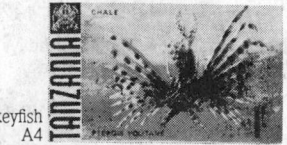

Turkeyfish
A4

Fish: 5c, Cardinalfish. 10c, Mudskipper. 15c, Toby puffer. 20c, Two sea horses. 30c, Batfish. 40c, Sweetlips. 50c, Birdfish. 65c, Butterflyfish. 70c, Grouper. 1.30sh, Surgeonfish. 1.50sh, Caesio xanthonotus. 2.50sh, Emperor snapper. 5sh, Moorish idol. 10sh, Striped triggerfish. 20sh, Squirrelfish.

1967-71 Photo. *Perf. 14x14¹/₂*

Size: 21x17¹/₂mm

Fish in Natural Colors

19	A4	5c black & citron	.15	.15
20	A4	10c brown & olive	.15	.15
21	A4	15c brown & blue	.15	.15
22	A4	20c brown & dk bl grn	.15	.15
23	A4	30c black & yel grn	.15	.15
24	A4	40c brown & emerald	.15	.15
25	A4	50c blk & dull bl grn	.15	.15

26	A4	65c blk & gray grn	.60	.60
27	A4	70c black & olive ('69)	.50	.50

Perf. 14½

Size: 41x25mm

28	A4	1sh brown & multi	.40	.15
29	A4	1.30sh black & olive	.60	.15
30	A4	1.50sh black & ol ('69)	.70	.20
31	A4	2.50sh brn yel & grn	1.25	.15
32	A4	5sh black & bl grn	2.00	.20
33	A4	10sh brown & gray grn	4.50	.60
34	A4	20sh blk & gray olive	10.00	1.40
		Nos. 19-34 (16)	21.60	
		Set value		4.10

Issued: #27, 30, 9/15/69; others, 12/9/67.

Values of Nos. 28-34 are for canceled-to-order stamps with printed cancellations. Postally used copies sell for higher prices.

For overprints see Nos. O9-O16.

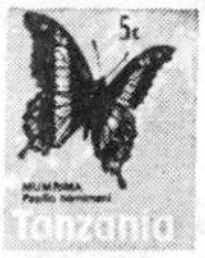

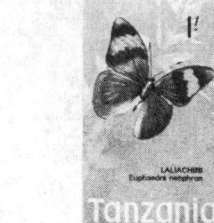

Papilio Hornimani A5

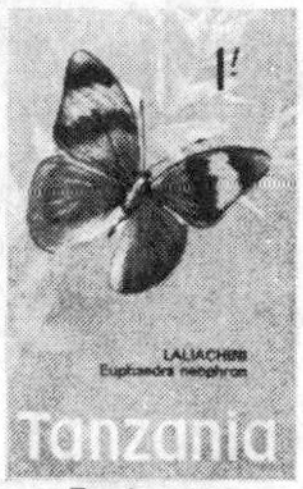

Euphaedra Neophron A6

Butterflies: 10c, Colotis ione. 15c, Amauris makuyuensis. 20c, Libythea laius. 30c, Danaus chrysippus. 40c, Sallya rosa. 50c, Axiocerses styx. 60c, Eurema hecabe. 70c, Acraea insignis. 1.50sh, Precis octavia. 2.50sh, Charaxes eupale. 5sh, Charaxes pollux. 10sh, Salamis parhassus. 20sh, Papilio ophidicephalus.

1973, Dec. 3 Photo. *Perf. 14½x14*

35	A5	5c yellow grn & multi	.15	.15
a.		Booklet pane of 4	.15	
36	A5	10c lt brown & multi	.15	.15
a.		Booklet pane of 4	.15	
37	A5	15c ultra & multi	.15	.15
38	A5	20c fawn & multi	.15	.15
a.		Booklet pane of 4	.20	
39	A5	30c yellow & multi	.15	.15
a.		Booklet pane of 4	.32	
40	A5	40c multicolored	.15	.15
a.		Booklet pane of 4	.40	
41	A5	50c citron & multi	.15	.15
a.		Booklet pane of 4	.52	
42	A5	60c multicolored	.15	.15
43	A5	70c brt green & multi	.18	.15
a.		Booklet pane of 4	.72	

Perf. 14½

44	A6	1sh green & multi	.30	.24
45	A6	1.50sh orange & multi	.45	.35
46	A6	2.50sh multicolored	.75	.60
47	A6	5sh multicolored	1.50	1.20
48	A6	10sh lt green & multi	3.00	2.40
49	A6	20sh blue & multi	6.00	4.80
		Nos. 35-49 (15)	13.38	10.94

For surcharges and overprints see Nos. 50-53, 135-136, O17-O26.

Nos. 42, 45-46, 49 Surcharged with New Value and 2 Bars

Perf. 14½x14, 14½

1975, Nov. 17 Photo.

50	A5	80c on 60c multi	.45	.45
51	A6	2sh on 1.50sh multi	1.10	1.10
52	A6	3sh on 2.50sh multi	9.00	9.00
53	A6	40sh on 20sh multi	11.00	11.00
		Nos. 50-53 (4)	21.55	21.55

Communication Type of Kenya 1976

Designs: 50c, Microwave tower. 1sh, Cordless switchboard and operators, horiz. 2sh, Telephones of 1880, 1930 and 1976. 3sh, Message switching center, horiz.

1976, Apr. 15 Litho. *Perf. 14½*

54	A5	50c blue & multi	.15	.15
55	A5	1sh red & multi	.25	.20
56	A5	2sh yellow & multi	.48	.40
57	A5	3sh multicolored	.72	.60
a.		Souvenir sheet of 4	2.00	2.00
		Nos. 54-57 (4)	1.60	1.35

Telecommunications development in East Africa. No. 57a contains 4 stamps similar to Nos. 54-57 with simulated perforations.

Olympics Type of Kenya 1976

Designs: 50c, Akii Bua, Ugandan hurdler. 1sh, Filbert Bayi, Tanzanian runner. 2sh, Steve Muchoki, Kenyan boxer. 3sh, Olympic torch, flags of Kenya, Tanzania and Uganda.

1976, July 5 Litho. *Perf. 14½*

58	A6	50c blue & multi	.15	.15
59	A6	1sh red & multi	.25	.20
60	A6	2sh yellow & multi	.48	.40
61	A6	3sh blue & multi	.72	.60
a.		Souv. sheet of 4, #58-61, perf. 13	9.25	9.25
		Nos. 58-61 (4)	1.60	1.35

21st Olympic Games, Montreal, Canada, July 17-Aug. 1.

Railway Type of Kenya 1976

Rail Transport in East Africa: 50c, Tanzania-Zambia Railway. 1sh, Nile Bridge, Uganda. 2sh, Nakuru Station, Kenya. 3sh, Class A locomotive, 1896.

1976, Oct. 4 Litho. *Perf. 14½*

62	A7	50c lilac & multi	.20	.15
63	A7	1sh emerald & multi	.35	.24
64	A7	2sh brt rose & multi	.85	.48
65	A7	3sh yellow & multi	1.25	.72
a.		Souv. sheet of 4, #62-65, perf. 13	4.00	3.00
		Nos. 62-65 (4)	2.65	1.59

Fish Type of Kenya 1977

1977, Jan. 10 Litho. *Perf. 14½*

66	A8	50c Nile perch	.16	.15
67	A8	1sh Tilapia	.30	.28
68	A8	3sh Sailfish	.90	.75
69	A8	5sh Black marlin	1.60	1.50
a.		Souvenir sheet of 4, #66-69	3.25	3.25
		Nos. 66-69 (4)	2.96	2.68

African Festival Type of Kenya 1977

Designs (Festival Emblem and): 50c, Masai tribesmen bleeding cow. 1sh, Dancers from Uganda. 2sh, Makonde sculpture. 3sh, Tribesmen skinning hippopotamus.

1977, Jan. 15 *Perf. 13½x14*

70	A9	50c multicolored	.15	.15
71	A9	1sh multicolored	.28	.16
72	A9	2sh multicolored	.50	.32
73	A9	3sh multicolored	.85	.48
a.		Souvenir sheet of 4, #70-73	3.00	3.00
		Nos. 70-73 (4)	1.78	1.11

2nd World Black and African Festival, Lagos, Nigeria, Jan. 15-Feb. 12.

Rally Type of Kenya 1977

Designs (Safari Rally Emblem and): 50c, Automobile passing through village. 1sh, Winner at finish line. 2sh, Car going through washout. 5sh, Car, elephants and Mt. Kenya.

1977, Apr. 5 Litho. *Perf. 14*

74	A10	50c multicolored	.15	.15
75	A10	1sh multicolored	.30	.24
76	A10	2sh multicolored	.80	.48
77	A10	5sh multicolored	2.00	1.25
a.		Souvenir sheet of 4, #74-77	3.50	3.50
		Nos. 74-77 (4)	3.25	2.12

25th Safari rally, Apr. 7-11.

Church Type of Kenya 1977

Designs: 50c, Rev. Canon Apolo Kivebulaya. 1sh, Uganda Cathedral. 2sh, Early grass-topped Cathedral. 5sh, Early tent congregation, Kigezi.

1977, June 20 Litho. *Perf. 14*

78	A11	50c multicolored	.15	.15
79	A11	1sh multicolored	.25	.20
80	A11	2sh multicolored	.50	.32
81	A11	5sh multicolored	1.50	1.00
a.		Souvenir sheet of 4, #78-81	3.00	3.00
		Nos. 78-81 (4)	2.40	1.67

Church of Uganda, centenary.

Wildlife Type of Kenya 1977

Endangered species (Wildlife Fund Emblem and): 50c, Pancake tortoise. 1sh, Nile crocodile. 2sh, Hunter's hartebeest. 3sh, Red Colobus monkey. 5sh, Dugong.

1977, Sept. 26 Litho. *Perf. 14x13½*

82	A13	50c multicolored	.20	.18
83	A13	1sh multicolored	.25	.22
84	A13	2sh multicolored	.85	.45
85	A13	3sh multicolored	1.25	.70
86	A13	5sh multicolored	2.00	1.10
a.		Souvenir sheet of 4, #83-86	4.75	4.75
		Nos. 82-86 (5)	4.55	2.65

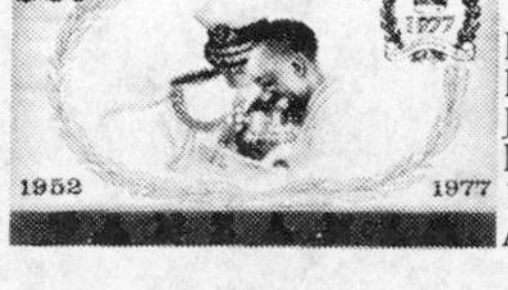

Prince Philip and Julius Nyerere, 1961 A7

Designs: 5sh, Queen Elizabeth II, Prince Philip, Prime Minister Nyerere in London, 1975. 10sh, Royal crown, flags of Tanzania and Commonwealth nations. 20sh, Coronation.

1977, Nov. 23 Litho. *Perf. 14x13½*

87	A7	50c multicolored	.15	.15
88	A7	5sh multicolored	1.10	1.00
89	A7	10sh multicolored	2.25	2.25
90	A7	20sh multicolored	4.50	4.50
a.		Souvenir sheet of 4, #87-90	8.50	8.50
		Nos. 87-90 (4)	8.00	7.90

25th anniv. of reign of Elizabeth II.

For overprints see Nos. 99-102, 179-180.

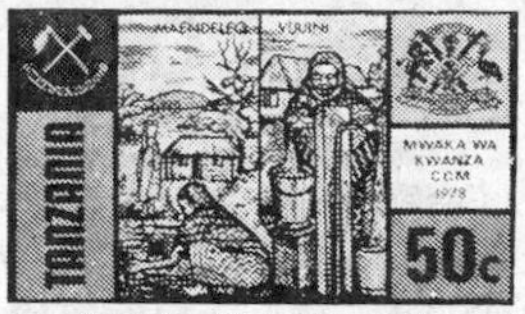

Women Fetching Water from Stream and Tap — A8

Designs: 1sh, Flag raising. 3sh, Health care, laboratory and hospital. 5sh, Pres. Julius Nyerere.

1978, Feb. 5 Litho. *Perf. 13½x14*

91	A8	50c multicolored	.15	.15
92	A8	1sh multicolored	.25	.20
93	A8	3sh multicolored	.72	.60
94	A8	5sh multicolored	1.25	1.10
a.		Souvenir sheet of 4, #91-94	2.50	2.50
		Nos. 91-94 (4)	2.37	2.05

First anniversary of the New Revolutionary Party (Chama cha Mapinduzi).

Soccer Type of Kenya

Designs (Soccer Cup and): 50c, Soccer scene and Joe Kadenge. 1sh, Mohammed Chuma receiving trophy, and his portrait. 2sh, Shot on goal and Omari S. Kidevu. 3sh, Backfield defense and Polly Ouma.

1978, Apr. 17 Litho. *Perf. 14x13½*

95	A17	50c green & multi	.15	.15
96	A17	1sh lt brown & multi	.25	.22
97	A17	2sh lilac & multi	.50	.40
98	A17	3sh dk blue & multi	.75	.60
a.		Souvenir sheet of 4, #95-98	1.75	1.75
		Nos. 95-98 (4)	1.65	1.37

World Soccer Cup Championships, Argentina '78, June 1-25.

Nos. 87-90a Overprinted in Large Serifed Letters: "25th ANNIVERSARY / CORONATION / 2nd JUNE 1953"

1978, June 2

99	A7	50c multicolored	.15	.15
100	A7	5sh multicolored	1.10	1.10
101	A7	10sh multicolored	2.25	2.25
102	A7	20sh multicolored	4.50	4.50
a.		Souvenir sheet of 4, #99-102	8.00	8.00
		Nos. 99-102 (4)	8.00	8.00

25th anniv. of coronation of Elizabeth II.

Nos. 99-102a also exist overprinted with smaller, sans serif letters, perf. 12. Same values or less. The perf. 12 set does not exist without overprint.

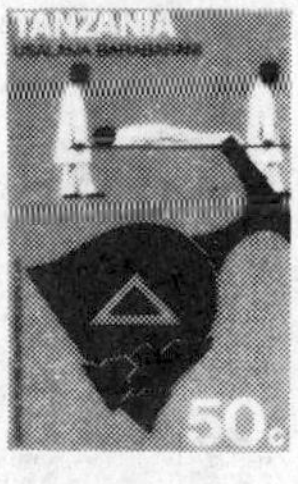

"Do not Drink when Driving" — A9

Designs: 1sh, "Courtesy to the young, old and handicapped." 3sh, "Observe highway code." 5sh, "Do not drive faulty vehicle."

1978, July 1 Litho. *Perf. 13½x13*

103	A9	50c multicolored	.15	.15
104	A9	1sh multicolored	.25	.25
105	A9	3sh multicolored	.65	.60
106	A9	5sh multicolored	1.40	1.10
a.		Souv. sheet of 4, #103-106, perf. 14	3.00	3.00
		Nos. 103-106 (4)	2.45	2.10

Road Safety Campaign.

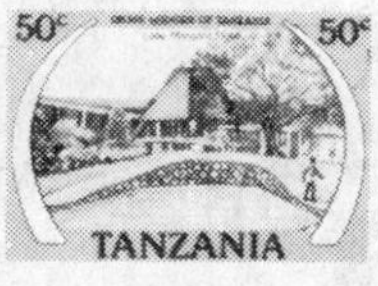

Lake Manyara Hotel — A10

Designs: 1sh, Lobo Wildlife Lodge. 3sh, Ngorongoro Crater Lodge. 5sh, Ngorongoro Wildlife Lodge. 10sh, Mafia Island Lodge. 20sh, Mikumi Wildlife Lodge.

1978, Sept. 11 Litho. *Perf. 13½*

107	A10	50c multicolored	.15	.15
108	A10	1sh multicolored	.25	.25
109	A10	3sh multicolored	.60	.60
110	A10	5sh multicolored	1.10	1.10
111	A10	10sh multicolored	2.25	2.25
112	A10	20sh multicolored	4.50	4.50
a.		Souvenir sheet of 6, #107-112	9.25	9.25
		Nos. 107-112 (6)	8.85	8.85

Game Lodges of Tanzania.

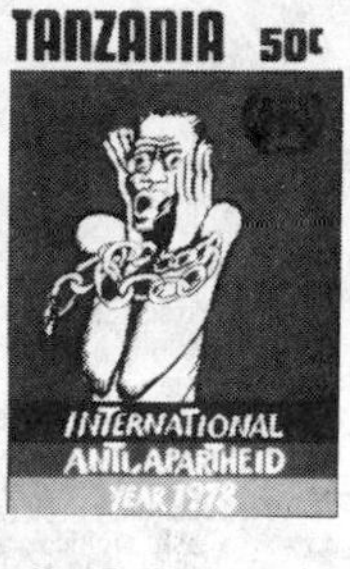

Chained African — A11

Designs (Anti-Apartheid Year Emblem and): 1sh, Division of races (black and white heads). 2.50sh, Racial harmony (black and white handshake and heads). 5sh, End of suppression and rise of freedom (hands breaking loose from chains).

1978, Oct. 24 Litho. *Perf. 14½x14*

113	A11	50c multicolored	.15	.15
114	A11	1sh multicolored	.25	.25
115	A11	2.50sh multicolored	.60	.60
116	A11	5sh multicolored	1.25	1.25
a.		Souvenir sheet of 4, #113-116	2.25	2.25
		Nos. 113-116 (4)	2.25	2.25

Anti-Apartheid Year.

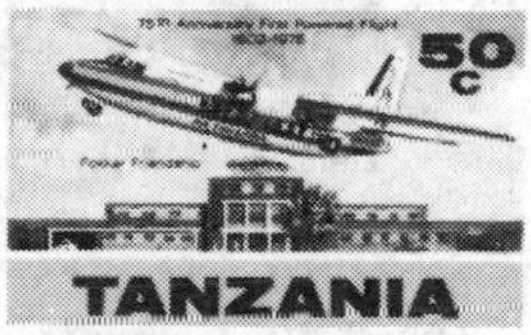

Fokker Friendship at Dar Es Salaam Airport — A12

Designs: 1sh, Single-engine Dragon, 1930, Zanzibar. 2sh, British Airways Concorde. 5sh, Wright Brothers' Flyer 1, 1903.

1978, Dec. 28 Litho. *Perf. 13½*

117	A12	50c multicolored	.15	.15
118	A12	1sh multicolored	.25	.25
119	A12	2sh multicolored	.50	.50
120	A12	5sh multicolored	1.25	1.25
a.		Souvenir sheet of 4, #117-120	2.25	2.25
		Nos. 117-120 (4)	2.15	2.15

75th anniversary of 1st powered flight.

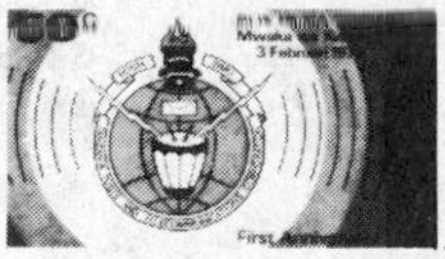

Emblem A13

Design: 5sh, Headquarters buildings.

1979, Feb. 3 Litho. *Perf. 14½x14*

121	A13	50c multicolored	.15	.15
122	A13	5sh multicolored	1.10	1.10
a.		Souvenir sheet of 2, #121-122	1.25	1.25

Tanzania Post and Telecommunications Corporation, 1st anniversary.

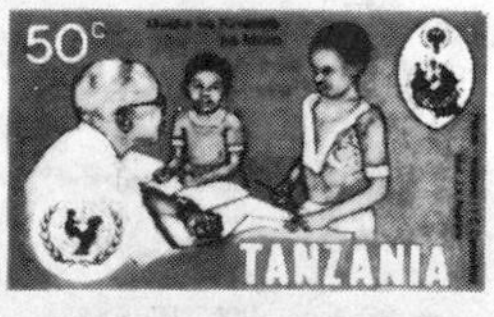

Pres. Nyerere and Children A14

Designs (UNICEF and Tanzanian IYC Emblems and): 1sh, Kindergarten. 2sh, Vaccination of infant. 5sh, Emblems.

1979, June 25 Litho. Perf. 14½
123 A14 50c multicolored .15 .15
124 A14 1sh multicolored .25 .25
125 A14 2sh multicolored .50 .50
126 A14 5sh multicolored 1.25 1.25
a. Souvenir sheet of 4, #123-126 2.25 2.25
Nos. 123-126 (4) 2.15 2.15

International Year of the Child.

Tree Planting — A15

Forest Preservation and Expansion: 1sh, Seedling. 2sh, Rainfall. 5sh, Forest fire.

1979, Sept. 29 Litho. Perf. 14½
127 A15 50c multicolored .15 .15
128 A15 1sh multicolored .25 .25
129 A15 2sh multicolored .50 .50
130 A15 5sh multicolored 1.25 1.25
Nos. 127-130 (4) 2.15 2.15

Mwenge
Satellite
Earth
Station
Opening
A16

1979, Dec. 3 Litho. Perf. 13½
131 A16 10c multicolored .15 .15
132 A16 40c multicolored .15 .15
133 A16 50c multicolored .15 .15
134 A16 1sh multicolored .25 .20
Set value .54 .45

Nos. 36, 43 Surcharged

1979 Litho. Perf. 14½x14
135 A5 40c (10 + 30) multi .15 .15
136 A5 50c on 70c multi .20 .20

Tabata Dispensary, Dar-es-Salaam, Rotary Emblem — A17

1980, Mar. 1 Litho. Perf. 13x13½
137 A17 50c shown .15 .15
138 A17 1sh Ngomvu water project .20 .20
139 A17 5sh Flying doctor service 1.10 1.10
140 A17 20sh Torch, anniversary emblem 4.50 4.50
a. Souvenir sheet of 4, #137-140 6.00 6.00
Nos. 137-140 (4) 5.95 5.95

Rotary International, 75th anniversary.
For overprints see Nos. 149-152.

Zanzibar
Nos. 49
and 309,
"Stamp
History"
Cancel
A18

Cancel and: 50c, Tanganyika #58, postal worker, vert. 10sh, Tanganyika #16, 52. 20sh, Penny Black, Rowland Hill, vert.

1980, Apr. Perf. 14
141 A18 40c multicolored .15 .15
142 A18 50c multicolored .15 .15
143 A18 10sh multicolored 2.00 2.00
144 A18 20sh multicolored 4.00 4.00
a. Souvenir sheet of 4, #141-144 6.25 6.25
Nos. 141-144 (4) 6.30 6.30

Sir Rowland Hill (1795-1879), originator of penny postage; Tanzanian stamp history.

Overprinted: "LONDON 1980" / PHILATELIC EXHIBITION
1980, May 6 Litho. Perf. 14
145 A18 40c multicolored .15 .15
146 A18 50c multicolored .15 .15
147 A18 10sh multicolored 2.25 2.25
148 A18 20sh multicolored 4.50 4.50
a. Souvenir sheet of 4, #145-148 7.00 7.00
Nos. 145-148 (4) 7.05 7.05

London 80 Intl. Stamp Exhib., May 6-14.

Nos. 137-140a with Additional Inscription on 1 or 2 Lines: "District 920-55th Annual / Conference, Arusha, Tanzania"
1980, June 23 Litho. Perf. 13x13½
149 A17 50c multicolored .15 .15
150 A17 1sh multicolored .25 .25
151 A17 5sh multicolored 1.25 1.25
152 A17 20sh multicolored 5.00 5.00
a. Souvenir sheet of 4, #149-152 6.50 6.50
Nos. 149-152 (4) 6.65 6.65

District 920 Rotary Club, 55th Annual Conference, Arusha.

Pan African
Postal Union
and U.P.U.
Emblems
A19

1980, July 1 Perf. 13x13½
153 A19 50c purple & blk .15 .15
154 A19 1sh ultra & blk .25 .25
155 A19 5sh red orange & blk 1.25 1.25
156 A19 10sh green & blk 2.50 2.50
Nos. 153-156 (4) 4.15 4.15

Pan African Postal Union Plenipotentiary Conference, Arusha, Jan. 8-18.

Gidamis
Shahanga,
Marathon
A20

Tanzanian Olympic Team: 1sh, Nzael Kyomo and sprinters. 10sh, Zakayo Malekwa and javelin. 20sh, William Lyimo and boxers.

1980, Aug. 18 Litho. Perf. 13x13½
157 A20 50c multicolored .15 .15
158 A20 1sh multicolored .25 .25
159 A20 10sh multicolored 2.50 2.50
160 A20 20sh multicolored 5.00 5.00
a. Souvenir sheet of 4, #157-160 7.75 7.75
Nos. 157-160 (4) 7.90 7.90

22nd Summer Olympic Games, Moscow, July 19-Aug. 3.
Issued also in sheets of 20 (5 of each value).

Spring Hare — A21

1980, Oct. 1 Litho. Perf. 14
161 A21 10c shown .15 .15
162 A21 20c Genet .15 .15
163 A21 40c Mongoose .15 .15
164 A21 50c Ratel .15 .15
165 A21 75c Rock hyrax .15 .15
166 A21 80c Leopard .16 .16
Perf. 14½
Size: 40x24mm
167 A21 1sh Impalas .20 .20
168 A21 1.50sh Giraffes .30 .30
169 A21 2sh Zebras .40 .40
170 A21 3sh Buffalo .60 .60
171 A21 5sh Lions 1.00 1.00
172 A21 10sh Rhinoceros 2.00 2.00
173 A21 20sh Elephants 4.00 4.00
174 A21 40sh Cheetahs 8.00 8.00
Nos. 161-174 (14) 17.41 17.41

For overprints see Nos. O27-O36.

National
Parks
Emblem
A22

1981, Jan. 26 Litho. Perf. 13x13½
175 A22 50c Ngorongoro Park .15 .15
176 A22 1sh shown .25 .25
177 A22 5sh Friends of Serengeti 1.25 1.25
178 A22 20sh Friends of Ngorongoro 5.00 5.00
Nos. 175-178 (4) 6.65 6.65

Ngorongoro & Serengeti Parks, 60th anniv.
For overprints see Nos. 299-302.

Nos. 89-90 Overprinted: "ROYAL WEDDING/ H.R.H. PRINCE CHARLES/ 29th JULY 1981"
1981, July 29 Litho. Perf. 14x13½
179 A7 10sh multicolored 2.25 2.25
180 A7 20sh multicolored 4.50 4.50
a. Souvenir sheet of 2, #179-180 14.00 14.00

Mail Runner
A23

1981, Oct. 23 Litho. Perf. 12½x12
181 A23 50c shown .15 .15
182 A23 1sh Letter sorting .25 .25
183 A23 5sh Post horn, carrier pigeon 1.10 1.10
184 A23 10sh Commonwealth members' flags 2.25 2.25
a. Souvenir sheet of 4, #181-184 3.75 3.75
Nos. 181-184 (4) 3.75 3.75

Commonwealth Postal Administrations Conference, Arusha, June 29-July 10.

Intl. Year of
the Disabled
A24

1981, Nov. 30 Litho. Perf. 14
185 A24 50c Morris Nyunyusa, blind drummer .15 .15
186 A24 1sh Sewing .25 .25
187 A24 5sh Prostheses 1.10 1.10
188 A24 10sh Children 2.25 2.25
Nos. 185-188 (4) 3.75 3.75

20th Anniv. of Independence — A25

1982, Jan. 13 Litho. Perf. 13x13½
189 A25 50c Pres. Nyerere, flag .15 .15
190 A25 1sh Zanzibar Electricity Plant .25 .25
191 A25 3sh Sisal plant, weaver .75 .75
192 A25 10sh Pupils 2.50 2.50
a. Souvenir sheet of 4, #189-192 3.75 3.75
Nos. 189-192 (4) 3.65 3.65

Ostrich — A26

1982, Jan. 25 Litho. Perf. 13½
193 A26 50c shown .15 .15
194 A26 1sh Secretary bird .25 .25
195 A26 5sh Kori bustard 1.25 1.25
196 A26 10sh Saddle-bill stork 2.50 2.50
Nos. 193-196 (4) 4.15 4.15

1982 World
Cup — A27

1982, June 2 Litho. Perf. 14
197 A27 50c Jella Mtagwa .15 .15
198 A27 1sh Stadium .22 .22
199 A27 10sh Diego Armando Maradona 2.00 2.00
200 A27 20sh Globe 4.25 4.25
a. Souvenir sheet of 4, #197-200 6.75 6.75
Nos. 197-200 (4) 6.62 6.62

Jade of
Seronera
and her
Cubs
A28

Animals Appearing in Movies or TV Shows: 1sh, Wild dog and puppies, Havoc. 5sh, Fifi and sons, Gombe. 10sh, Bahati and twins Rashidi and Ramadhani, Lake Manyara.

1982, July 15 Litho. Perf. 14
201 A28 50c multicolored .15 .15
202 A28 1sh multicolored .25 .25
203 A28 5sh multicolored 1.25 1.25
204 A28 10sh multicolored 2.50 2.50
a. Souv. sheet of 4, #201-204, perf. 14½ 5.00 5.00
Nos. 201-204 (4) 4.15 4.15

Scouting
Year — A29

1982, Aug. 25
205 A29 50c Brick laying .15 .15
206 A29 1sh Camping .15 .15
207 A29 10sh Tracing marks 1.75 1.75
208 A29 20sh Baden-Powell 3.50 3.50
a. Souvenir sheet of 4, #205-208 5.50 5.50
Nos. 205-208 (4) 5.55 5.55

For overprint see No. 303.

World Food
Day — A30

1982, Oct. 16 Litho. Perf. 14
209 A30 50c Plowing .15 .15
210 A30 1sh Dairy cows .20 .20
211 A30 5sh Corn harvest 1.00 1.00
212 A30 10sh Grain storage 2.00 2.00
a. Souvenir sheet of 4, #209-212 3.50 3.50
Nos. 209-212 (4) 3.35 3.35

TB Bacillus
Centenary
A31

1982, Dec. 5 Perf. 12½x12
213 A31 50c Child immunization .15 .15
214 A31 1sh Koch .20 .20
215 A31 5sh TB emblem 1.00 1.00
216 A31 10sh WHO emblem 2.00 2.00
Nos. 213-216 (4) 3.35 3.35

A31a

1983, Mar. 14 Litho. Perf. 14
217 A31a 50c Pres. Nyerere .15 .15
218 A31a 1sh Running, boxing .20 .20
219 A31a 5sh Flags 1.00 1.00
220 A31a 10sh Pres. Nyerere, Royal Family 2.00 2.00
a. Souvenir sheet of 4, #217-220 3.50 3.50
Nos. 217-220 (4) 3.35 3.35

Commonwealth Day. For overprint see #407.

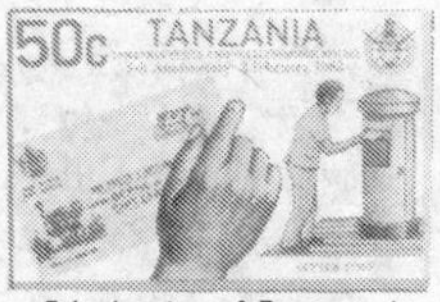

5th Anniv. of Posts and Telecommunications Dept. — A32

1983, Feb. 3 Litho. *Perf. 12½x12*

221 A32 50c Letter post .15 .15
222 A32 1sh Training Institute .20 .20
223 A32 5sh Satellite communications 1.00 1.00
224 A32 10sh Emblems 2.00 2.00
a. Souvenir sheet of 4, #221-224 3.50 3.50
Nos. 221-224 (4) 3.35 3.35

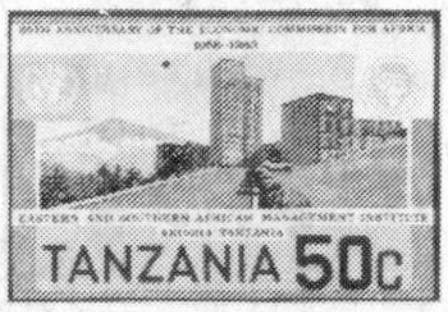

25th Anniv. of Economic Commission for Africa — A33

1983, Sept. 12 Litho. *Perf. 12½x12*

225 A33 50c Eastern & Southern African Management Institute, Arusha .15 .15
226 A33 1sh Emblems .20 .20
227 A33 5sh Mineral collections 1.00 1.00
228 A33 10sh Emblems, diff. 2.00 2.00
a. Souvenir sheet of 4, #225-228 3.25 3.25
Nos. 225-228 (4) 3.35 3.35

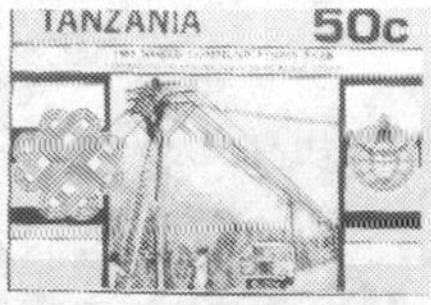

World Communications Year — A34

1983, Oct. 17 Litho. *Perf. 14*

229 A34 50c Rural telephone service .15 .15
230 A34 1sh Emblems .20 .20
231 A34 5sh Post Office 1.00 1.00
232 A34 10sh Microwave tower 2.00 2.00
a. Souvenir sheet of 4, #229-232 3.50 3.50
Nos. 229-232 (4) 3.35 3.35

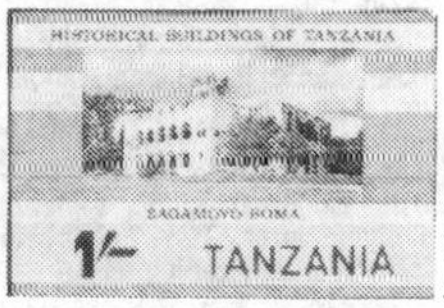

Historical Buildings A35

1983, Dec. 12 Litho. *Perf. 12½x12*

233 A35 1sh Bagamoyo Boma .20 .20
234 A35 1.50sh Beit-El-Ajaib .30 .30
235 A35 5sh Anglican Church .90 .90
236 A35 10sh State House, old and new 1.75 1.75
a. Souvenir sheet of 4, #233-236 3.50 3.50
Nos. 233-236 (4) 3.15 3.15

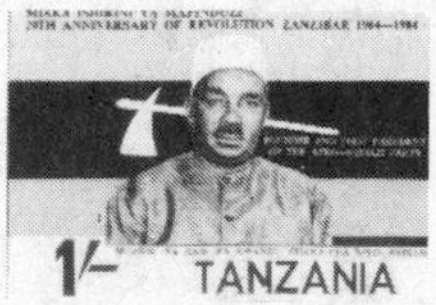

20th Anniv. of Revolution A36

1984, June 18 Litho. *Perf. 14*

237 A36 1sh Muasisi Kwanza .20 .20
238 A36 1.50sh Clove farming .32 .32
239 A36 5sh Industrial development 1.00 1.00
240 A36 10sh Housing developments 2.00 2.00
Nos. 237-240 (4) 3.52 3.52

Souvenir Sheet

241 A36 15sh Map, ship 3.25 3.25

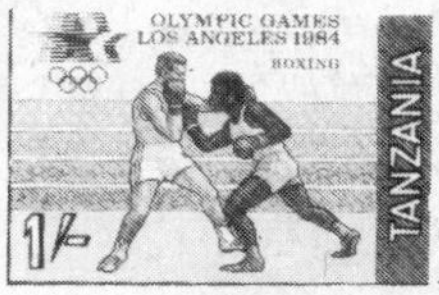

1984 Summer Olympics A37

1984, Aug. 6 *Perf. 12½x12*

242 A37 1sh Boxing .15 .15
243 A37 1.50sh Running .20 .20
244 A37 5sh Basketball .75 .75
245 A37 20sh Soccer 2.50 2.50
a. Souvenir sheet of 4, #242-245 3.50 3.50
Nos. 242-245 (4) 3.60 3.60

For overprints see Nos. 275-278.

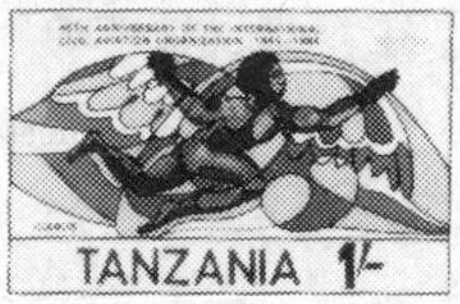

Intl. Civil Aviation Org. 40th Anniv. A38

1984, Nov. 15 Litho. *Perf. 13*

246 A38 1sh Icarus .15 .15
247 A38 1.50sh Air Tanzania jets, traffic controller .20 .20
248 A38 5sh Aircraft maintenance .75 .75
249 A38 10sh ICAO emblem 1.25 1.25
a. Souvenir sheet of 4, #246-249 2.25 2.25
Nos. 246-249 (4) 2.35 2.35

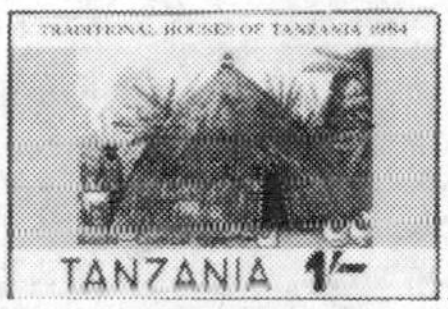

Traditional Houses A39

1984, Dec. 20 *Perf. 12½x12*

250 A39 1sh Sochi .15 .15
251 A39 1.50sh Isyenga .20 .20
252 A39 5sh Tembe .65 .65
253 A39 10sh Banda 1.25 1.25
a. Souvenir sheet of 4, #250-253 2.25 2.25
Nos. 250-253 (4) 2.25 2.25

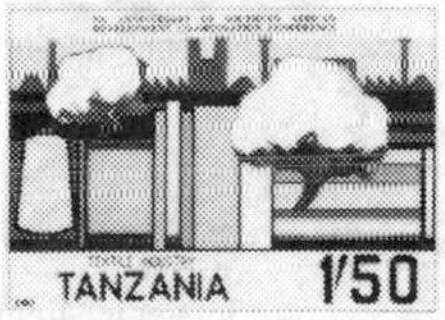

Textile Industry A40

5th anniversary of the Southern Africa Development Coordination Conference.

1985, Apr. 1 *Perf. 14*

254 A40 1.50sh shown .15 .15
255 A40 4sh Mining .45 .45
256 A40 5sh Transportation and communications .55 .55
257 A40 20sh Flags of member nations 2.25 2.25
a. Souvenir sheet of 4, #254-257 3.25 3.25
Nos. 254-257 (4) 3.40 3.40

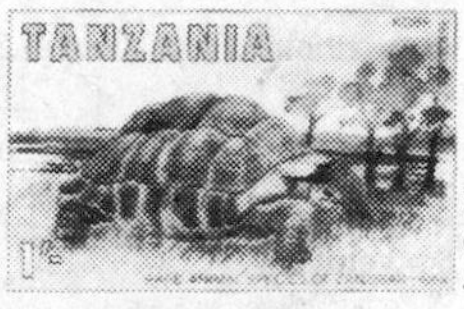

Rare Species of Zanzibar A41

Perf. 13½x13, 13x13½

1985, May 8 **Litho.**

258 A41 1sh Tortoise .15 .15
259 A41 4sh Leopard .45 .45
260 A41 10sh Civet cat 1.10 1.10
261 A41 17.50sh Red colobus, vert. 2.00 2.00
Nos. 258-261 (4) 3.70 3.70

Souvenir Sheet

262 Sheet of 2 3.75 3.75
a. A41 15sh Black rhinoceros 1.60 1.60
b. A41 20sh Giant ground pangolin 2.15 2.15

For overprints see Nos. 408-409, 411.

In 1992 Nos. 263-274, 304-309, 315-322, including souvenir sheets, were being sold as a unit, wholesale, in London for £7.50.

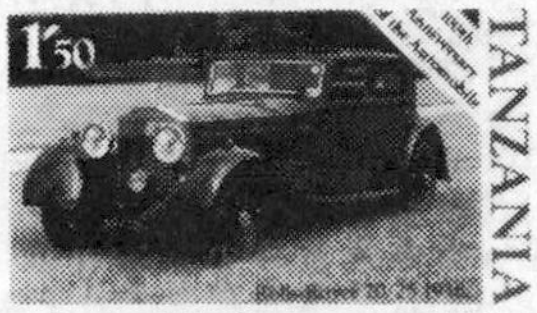

Automobile Centenary — A42

Classic autos manufactured by Rolls-Royce.

1985, May 14 *Perf. 14½x14*

263 A42 1.50sh 1936 20/25 .15 .15
264 A42 5sh 1933 Phantom II .20 .20
265 A42 10sh 1926 Phantom I .40 .40
266 A42 30sh 1907 Silver Ghost 1.25 1.25
a. Souvenir sheet of 4, #263-266 1.90 1.90
Nos. 263-266 (4) 2.00 2.00

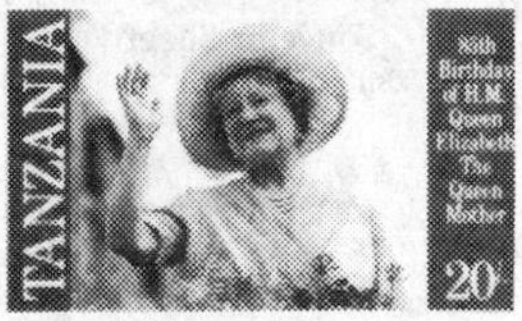

Queen Mother, 85th Birthday — A43

1985, Sept. 30

267 A43 20sh Waving .75 .75
268 A43 20sh Facing left .75 .75
269 A43 100sh Wearing green hat 4.00 4.00
a. Souvenir sheet of 2, #267, 269 4.75 4.75
270 A43 100sh Facing right 4.00 4.00
a. Souvenir sheet of 2, #268, 270 4.75 4.75
Nos. 267-270 (4) 9.50 9.50

For overprints see Nos. 295-298.

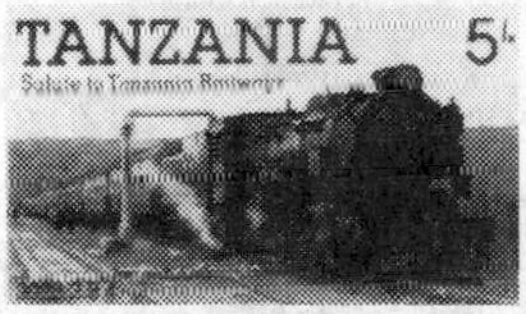

Tanzania Railways Locomotives — A44

1985, Oct. 7 Litho. *Perf. 14½x14*

271 A44 5sh No. 3022 .20 .20
272 A44 10sh No. 3107 .40 .40
273 A44 20sh No. 6004 .75 .75
274 A44 30sh No. 3129 1.25 1.25
a. Souvenir sheet of 4, #271-274 2.60 2.60
Nos. 271-274 (4) 2.60 2.60

Nos. 242-245 Ovptd. with Winners and "GOLD MEDAL" in 2 or 3 Lines

1985, Oct. 22 *Perf. 12½x12*

275 A37 1sh Henry Tillman, USA .15 .15
276 A37 1.50sh USA .18 .18
277 A37 5sh USA .55 .55
278 A37 20sh France 2.15 2.15
a. Souvenir sheet of 4, #275-278 3.00 3.00
Nos. 275-278 (4) 3.03 3.03

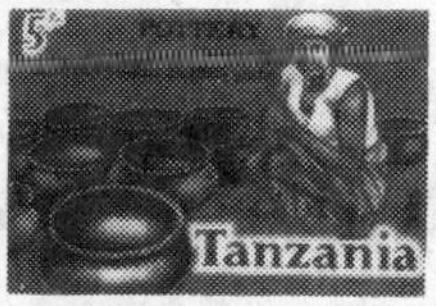

Pottery A45

1985, Nov. 4

279 A45 1.50sh Water and cooking pots .18 .18
280 A45 2sh Frying pot and caldron .22 .22
281 A45 5sh Woman selling pots .55 .55
282 A45 40sh Beer pot 4.25 4.25
Nos. 279-282 (4) 5.20 5.20

Souvenir Sheet

283 A45 30sh Water pot 3.25 3.25

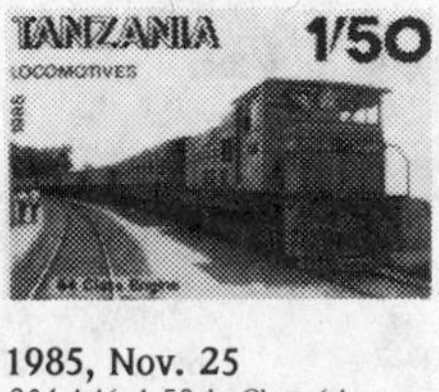

Locomotives A46

1985, Nov. 25

284 A46 1.50sh Class 64 .18 .18
285 A46 2sh Class 36 .22 .22
286 A46 5sh Shunting DFH1013 .55 .55
287 A46 10sh Diesel Electric DE1001 1.10 1.10
288 A46 30sh Zanzibar, 1906 3.25 3.25
Nos. 284-288 (5) 5.30 5.30

Souvenir Sheet

289 Sheet of 2 3.80 3.80
a. A46 15sh Class 30 steam 1.65 1.65
b. A46 20sh Class 11 steam 2.15 2.15

For overprints see Nos. 381A-381E.

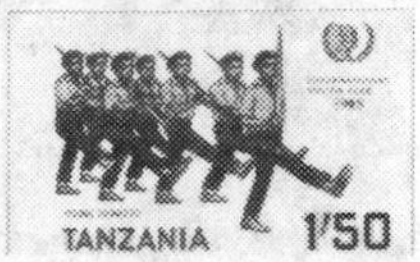

Intl. Youth Year — A47

1986, Jan. 20 *Perf. 14*

290 A47 1.50sh Young Pioneers .18 .18
291 A47 4sh Health care .45 .45
292 A47 10sh Uhuru torch race 1.10 1.10
293 A47 20sh World map 2.15 2.15
Nos. 290-293 (4) 3.88 3.88

Souvenir Sheet

294 A47 30sh Agriculture 3.25 3.25

Nos. 267-270 Ovptd. "CARIBBEAN/ ROYAL VISIT/ 1985" in Silver

1986, Feb. 10 *Perf. 14½x14*

295 A43 20sh on #267 2.15 2.15
296 A43 20sh on #268 2.15 2.15
297 A43 100sh on #269 11.00 11.00
a. Souvenir sheet of 2, #295, 297
298 A43 100sh on #270 11.00 11.00
a. Souvenir sheet of 2, #296, 298
Nos. 295-298 (4) 26.30 26.30

Nos. 175-178, 208a Ovptd. "75th ANNIVERSARY GIRL GUIDES/ 1910-1985" in Silver or Black

1986, Feb. Litho. *Perf. 13x13½, 14*

299 A22 50c multicolored (S)
300 A22 1sh multicolored
301 A22 5sh multicolored
302 A22 20sh multicolored

Souvenir Sheet

303 Sheet of 4
a. A29 50c multicolored
b. A29 1sh multicolored
c. A29 10sh multicolored
d. A29 20sh multicolored

The status of this set and at least 12 stamps overprinted congratulating the Duke and Duchess of York on their marriage are in question.

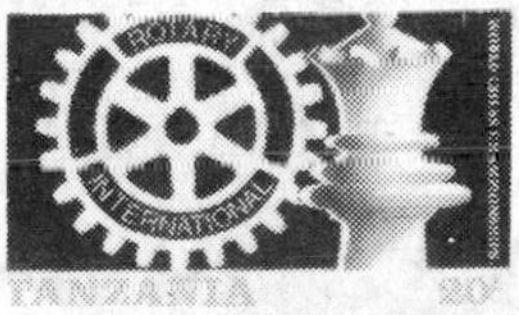

Rotary Intl., World Chess Championships — A48

1986, Mar. 17 *Perf. 14*

304 A48 20sh shown .75 .75
305 A48 100sh Chess board 4.00 4.00
a. Souvenir sheet of 2, #304-305 4.75 4.75

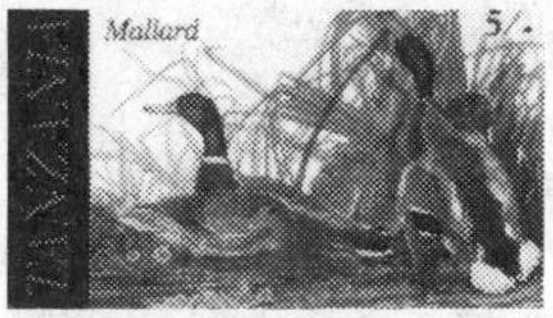

Audubon Birth Bicent. — A49

Illustrations of American bird species by Audubon.

1986, May 22

306 A49 5sh Mallard .20 .20
307 A49 10sh American eider .40 .40
308 A49 20sh Scarlet ibis .75 .75
309 A49 30sh Roseate spoonbill 1.25 1.25
a. Souvenir sheet of 4, #306-309 2.60 2.60
Nos. 306-309 (4) 2.60 2.60

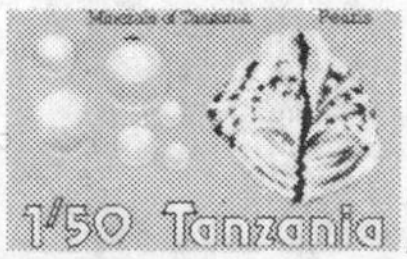

Gemstones A50

1986, May 22
310 A50 1.50sh Pearls .18 .18
311 A50 2sh Sapphires .24 .24
312 A50 5sh Tanzanite .60 .60
313 A50 40sh Diamonds 4.80 4.80
Nos. 310-313 (4) 5.82 5.82

Souvenir Sheet

314 A50 30sh Rubies 3.60 3.60

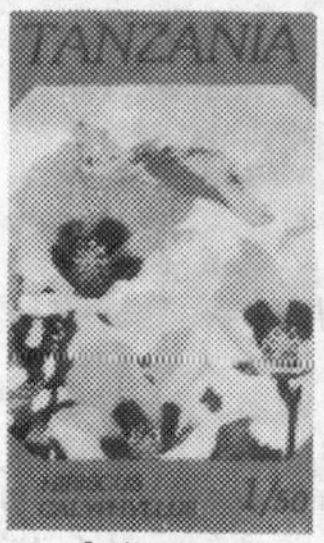

Indigenous Flowers — A51

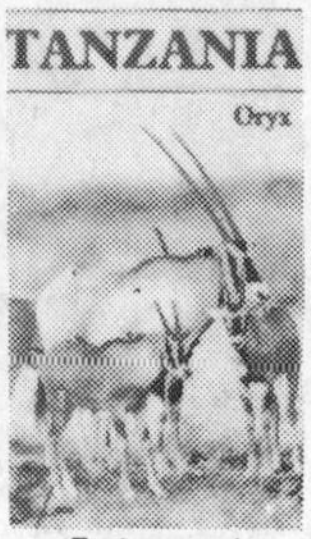

Endangered Wildlife — A52

1986, June 2
315 A51 1.50sh Hibiscus calyphyllus .15 .15
316 A51 5sh Aloe graminicola .20 .20
317 A51 10sh Nersium oleander .40 .40
318 A51 30sh Nymphaea caerulea 1.25 1.25
a. Souvenir Sheet of 4, #315-318 1.90 1.90
Nos. 315-318 (4) 2.00 2.00

1986, June 30 Litho. *Perf. 14x14½*
319 A52 5sh Oryx .20 .20
320 A52 10sh Giraffe .40 .40
321 A52 20sh Rhinoceros .75 .75
322 A52 30sh Cheetah 1.25 1.25
a. Miniature sheet of 4, #319-322 2.60 2.60
Nos. 319-322 (4) 2.60 2.60

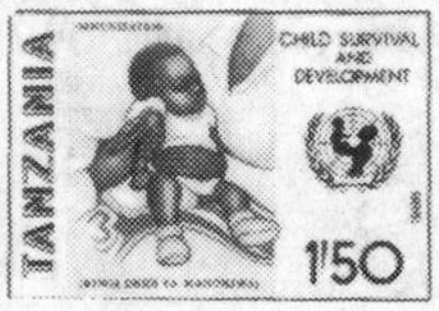

UN Child Survival Campaign A53

1986, July 29 *Perf. 12½x12*
323 A53 1.50sh Immunization .15 .15
324 A53 2sh Growth monitoring .15 .15
325 A53 5sh Oral rehydration therapy .20 .20
326 A53 40sh Breast feeding 1.65 1.65
Nos. 323-326 (4) 2.15 2.15

Souvenir Sheet

327 A53 30sh Healthy child 1.25 1.25

For overprints see Nos. 406, 410, 412.

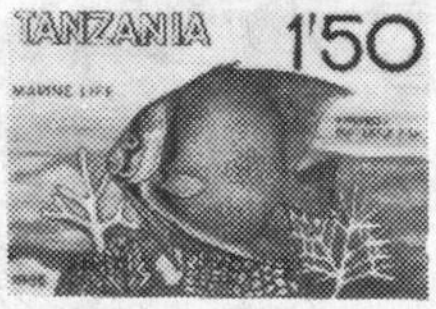

Marine Life — A54

1986, Aug. 20
328 A54 1.50sh Butterflyfish .15 .15
329 A54 4sh Parrotfish .16 .16
330 A54 10sh Sea turtle .40 .40
331 A54 20sh Octopus .85 .85
Nos. 328-331 (4) 1.56 1.56

Souvenir Sheet

332 A54 30sh Coral 1.25 1.25

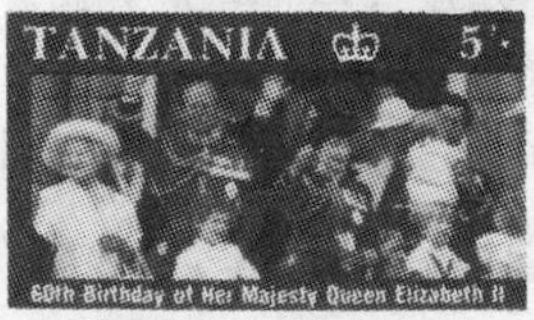

Queen Elizabeth II, 60th Birthday — A55

Photographs: 5sh, Royal family, Buckingham Palace balcony. 10sh, With princes in open carriage. 40sh, Elizabeth II. 60sh, Greeting crowd.

1987, Mar. 24 Litho. *Perf. 14*
333 A55 5sh multicolored *.20*
334 A55 10sh multicolored *.40*
335 A55 40sh multicolored *1.60*
336 A55 60sh multicolored *2.40*
a. Souvenir sheet of 4, #333-336 *4.60*
Nos. 333-336 (4) *4.60*

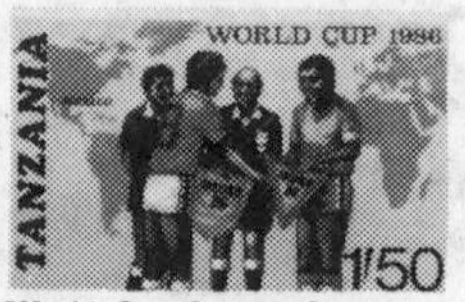

1986 World Cup Soccer Championships, Mexico — A57

Designs: 1.50sh, Map, team captains, officials. 2sh, Foul. 10sh, Goal. 20sh, Goalie save. 30sh, Argentine natl. team.

1986, Oct. 30 Litho. *Perf. 14*
341 A57 1.50sh multicolored .15 .15
342 A57 2sh multicolored .15 .15
343 A57 10sh multicolored .50 .50
344 A57 20sh multicolored 1.00 1.00
Nos. 341-344 (4) 1.80 1.80

Souvenir Sheet

345 A57 30sh multicolored 1.50 1.50

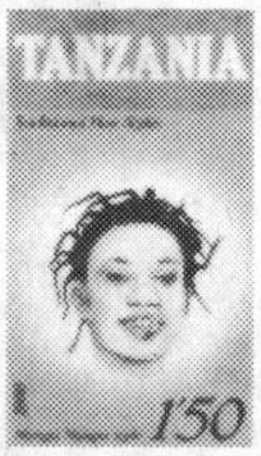

Hair Styles — A58

1987, Mar. 16 *Perf. 14½*
346 A58 1.50sh Nungu Nungu .15 .15
347 A58 2sh Upanga wa Jogoo .15 .15
348 A58 10sh Morani .50 .50
349 A58 20sh Twende Kilioni 1.00 1.00
Nos. 346-349 (4) 1.80 1.80

Souvenir Sheet

350 A58 30sh Kusuka Nywele 1.50 1.50

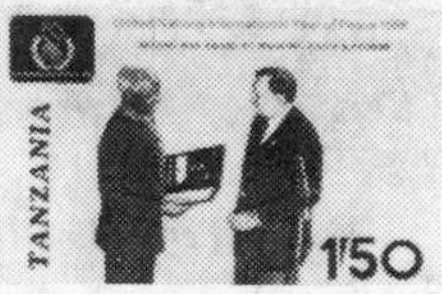

Intl. Peace Year — A59

Designs: 1.50sh, Julius K. Nyerere, Beyond War Award winner. 2sh, Peace among nations. 10sh, Peaceful use of outer space. 20sh, Emblem, UN building. 30sh, Emblem, handshake.

1986, Dec. 22 Litho. *Perf. 14½*
351 A59 1.50sh multicolored .15 .15
352 A59 2sh multicolored .15 .15
353 A59 10sh multicolored .50 .50
354 A59 20sh multicolored 1.00 1.00
Nos. 351-354 (4) 1.80 1.80

Souvenir Sheet

355 A59 30sh multicolored 1.50 1.50

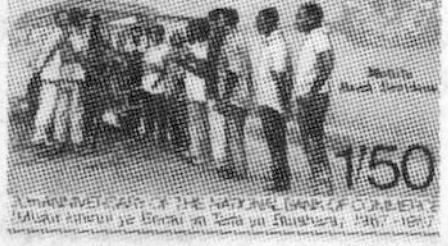

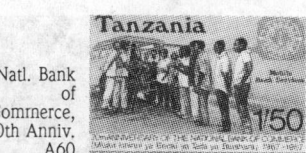

Natl. Bank of Commerce, 20th Anniv. A60

1987, Feb. 6 Litho. *Perf. 14*
356 A60 1.50sh Mobile bank .15 .15
357 A60 2sh Headquarters .15 .15
358 A60 5sh Pres. Mwinyi laying foundation stone .25 .25
359 A60 20sh Cotton harvest 1.00 1.00
Nos. 356-359 (4) 1.55 1.55

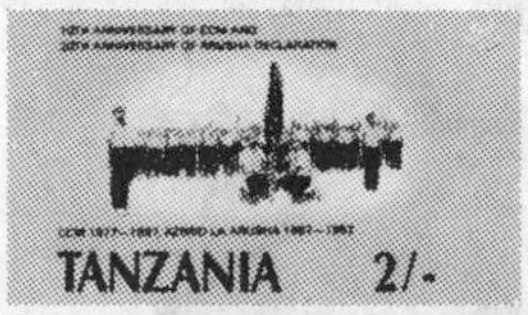

New Revolutionary Party (CCM), 10th Anniv. — A61

1987, Apr. 10 *Perf. 14½x14*
360 A61 2sh Soldiers in formation .15 .15
361 A61 3sh Woman picking coffee beans .15 .15
362 A61 10sh Speaker at podium .40 .40
363 A61 30sh Nyerere, Mwinyi 1.25 1.25
Nos. 360-363 (4) 1.95 1.95

Arush Declaration, 20th anniv.

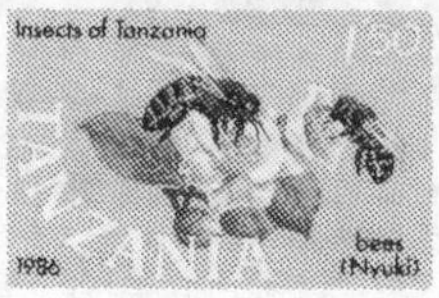

Insects A62

1987, Apr. 22 *Perf. 12½x12*
364 A62 1.50sh Bees .15 .15
365 A62 2sh Greater grain borer .15 .15
366 A62 10sh Tse-tse fly .40 .40
367 A62 20sh Wasp .80 .80
Nos. 364-367 (4) 1.50 1.50

Souvenir Sheet

368 A62 30sh Mosquito 1.25 1.25

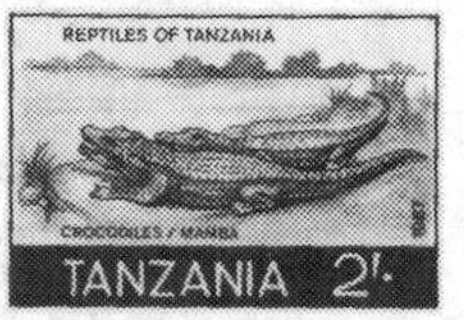

Reptiles A63

1987, July 2
369 A63 2sh Crocodiles .15 .15
370 A63 3sh Black-striped grass snake .15 .15
371 A63 10sh Adder .40 .40
372 A63 20sh Green mamba .80 .80
Nos. 369-372 (4) 1.50 1.50

Souvenir Sheet

373 A63 30sh Tortoise 1.25 1.25

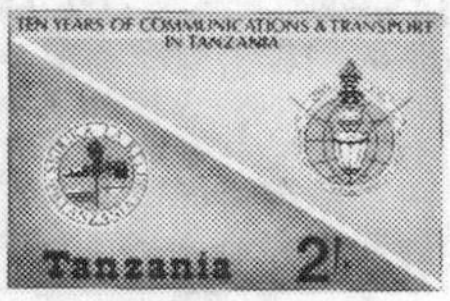

Posts and Telecommunications, Railways Emblems — A64

1987, July 27 *Perf. 14*
374 A64 2sh shown .15 .15
375 A64 8sh Air Tanzania, Port Authority .40 .40

Souvenir Sheet

376 A64 20sh Modes of communication and transportation 1.00 1.00

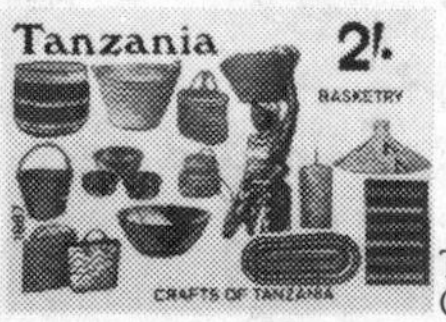

Traditional Crafts — A65

1987, Dec. 15 Litho. *Perf. 12½x12*
377 A65 2sh Baskets .15 .15
378 A65 3sh Gourds .15 .15
379 A65 10sh Stools .30 .30
380 A65 20sh Makonde carvings .60 .60
Nos. 377-380 (4) 1.20 1.20

Souvenir Sheet

381 A65 40sh Makonde carver at work 1.20 1.20

Nos. 284-288 Ovptd.

10th Anniversary of TANZANIA ZAMBIA RAILWAY AUTHORITY 1976-1986

1987, Dec. 30 Litho. *Perf. 12½x12*
381A A46 1.50sh multicolored .15 .15
381B A46 2sh multicolored .15 .15
381C A46 5sh multicolored .24 .24
381D A46 10sh multicolored .50 .50
381E A46 30sh multicolored 1.50 1.50
Nos. 381A-381E (5) 2.54 2.54

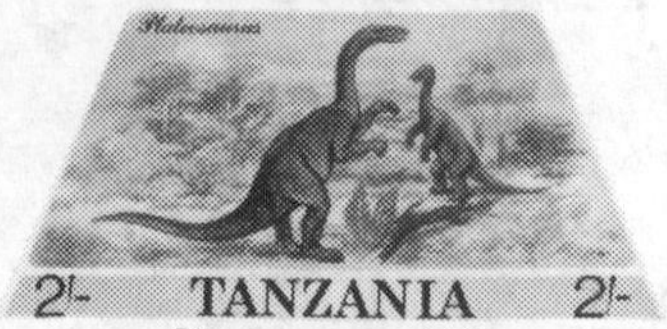

Plateosaurus — A66

1988, Apr. 22 *Perf. 12½*
382 A66 2sh shown .15 .15
383 A66 3sh Pteranodon .15 .15
384 A66 5sh Brontosaurus .15 .15
385 A66 7sh Lions .22 .22
386 A66 8sh Tiger .25 .25
387 A66 12sh Orangutans .35 .35
388 A66 20sh Elephants .60 .60
389 A66 100sh Stegosaurus 3.00 3.00
Nos. 382-389 (8) 4.87 4.87

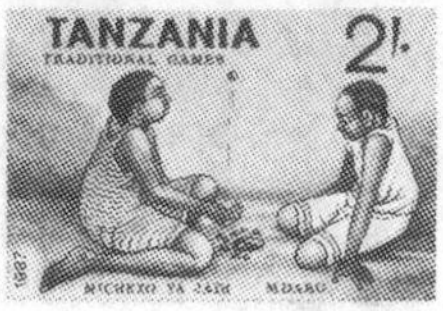

Traditional Games A67

1988, Feb. 15 Litho. *Perf. 12½x12*
390 A67 2sh Mdako (marbles) .15 .15
391 A67 3sh Mieleka (wrestling) .15 .15
392 A67 8sh Bull fight .25 .25
393 A67 20sh Bao (African chess) .60 .60
Nos. 390-393 (4) 1.15 1.15

Souvenir Sheet

394 A67 30sh Kulenga shabaha (archery) .90 .90

Dated 1987.

Miniature Sheets

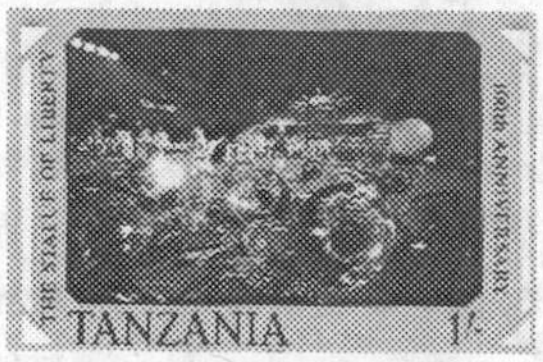

Statue of Liberty, Cent. (in 1986) — A68

No. 395: 1sh, Re-opening gala (evening), 1986. 2sh, Musicians performing. 3sh, Cheerleaders. 15sh, Statue holding tablet. 30sh, Tablet inscription. 40sh, Liberty Island. 50sh, Re-opening gala (afternoon), 1986. 60sh, Blimps over Liberty Island.

No. 396: 4sh, Statue, blimp. 5sh, Torch. 6sh, Torch and crown observatories lit at night, scaffolding. 7sh, Worker gilding torch. 8sh, Statue shrouded in scaffolding. 10sh, Two workers, torch. 12sh, Head, scaffolding. 18sh, Celebrant at re-opening (evening). 20sh, Goodyear blimp, skirt of Statue. 25sh, Boys' choir, statue. 35sh, Torch held aloft, full moon. 45sh, Worker cleaning tablet.

1988, June 15 Litho. *Perf. 14*
395 Sheet of 8 + label 6.00 6.00
a. A68 1sh multicolored .15 .15
b. A68 2sh multicolored .15 .15
c. A68 3sh multicolored .15 .15
d. A68 15sh multicolored .45 .45
e. A68 30sh multicolored .90 .90
f. A68 40sh multicolored 1.20 1.20
g. A68 50sh multicolored 1.50 1.50
h. A68 60sh multicolored 1.75 1.75
396 Sheet of 12 5.85 5.85
a. A68 4sh multicolored .15 .15
b. A68 5sh multicolored .15 .15
c. A68 6sh multicolored .18 .18
d. A68 7sh multicolored .20 .20
e. A68 8sh multicolored .24 .24
f. A68 10sh multicolored .30 .30
g. A68 12sh multicolored .35 .35
h. A68 18sh multicolored .55 .55
i. A68 20sh multicolored .60 .60
j. A68 25sh multicolored .75 .75
k. A68 35sh multicolored 1.05 1.05
l. A68 45sh multicolored 1.35 1.35

No. 395 contains a center label inscribed "THE STATUE / OF LIBERTY / 100th ANNIVERSARY."

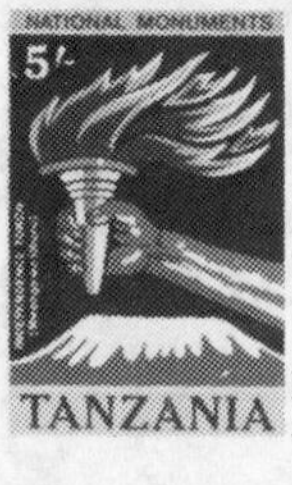

Natl. Monuments — A69

1988, June 15 **Litho.**
397 A69 5sh Independence Torch .15 .15
398 A69 12sh Arusha Declaration .35 .35
399 A69 30sh Askari .85 .85
400 A69 60sh Independence 1.75 1.75
Nos. 397-400 (4) 3.10 3.10

Souvenir Sheet

401 A69 100sh Soldier (Askari detail) 3.00 3.00

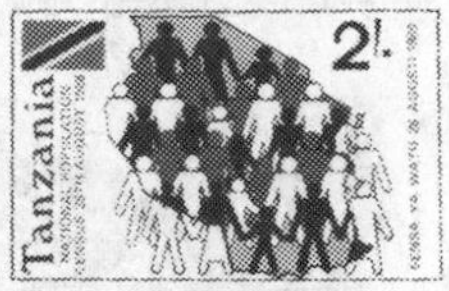

3rd Natl. Census, Aug. 28 — A70

1988, Aug. 8
402 A70 2sh shown .15 .15
403 A70 3sh Enumeration .15 .15
404 A70 10sh Health care .28 .28
405 A70 20sh Population figures .58 .58
Nos. 402-405 (4) 1.16 1.16

Souvenir Sheet

405A A70 40sh Segments of economy and society 1.20 1.20

Stamps of 1983-86 Ovptd:

A53 "125TH ANNIVERSARY / INTERNATIONAL RED CROSS / AND RED CRESCENT"
CD334 "40TH WEDDING ANNIVERSARY / H.M. QUEEN ELIZABETH II / H.R.H. THE DUKE OF EDINBURGH"
A41 "63RD ANNIVERSARY / ROTARY INTERNATIONAL / IN AFRICA"

1988, Aug. 15 ***Perfs. as Before***
406 A53 5sh on #325 .15 .15
407 A31a 10sh on #220 .30 .30
a. Souv. sheet of 4, #218-220, 407 .50 .50
408 A41 10sh on #260 .30 .30
409 A41 17.50sh on #261 .55 .55
410 A53 40sh on #326 1.20 1.20
Nos. 406-410 (5) 2.50 2.50

Souvenir Sheets

411 Sheet of 2 1.05 1.05
a. A41 15sh on #262a .45 .45
b. A41 20sh on #262b .60 .60
412 A53 30sh on #327 .90 .90

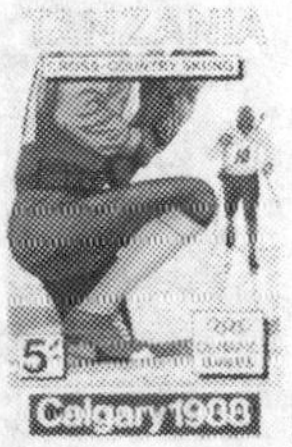

1988 Olympics, Seoul and Calgary — A71

1988, Aug. 29 ***Perf. 14***
414 A71 5sh Biathlon .15 .15
415 A71 10sh Soccer .30 .30
416 A71 20sh Cycling .58 .58
417 A71 25sh Pairs figuring skating .72 .72
418 A71 50sh Fencing 1.45 1.45
419 A71 50sh Downhill skiing 1.45 1.45
420 A71 70sh Volleyball 2.00 2.00
421 A71 75sh Bobsled 2.15 2.15
Nos. 414-421 (8) 8.80 8.80

Souvenir Sheets

422 A71 100sh Flags, hockey sticks 3.00 3.00
423 A71 100sh Gymnastics 3.00 3.00

For overprint see No. 534A-534J.

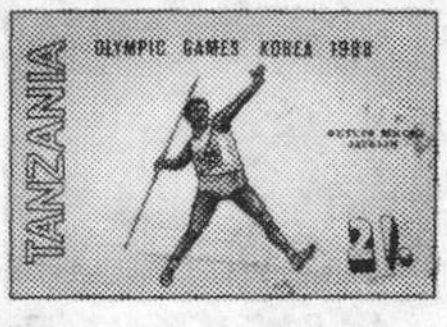

1988 Summer Olympics, Seoul A71a

1988, Sept. 5 **Litho.** ***Perf. 12½x12***
423A A71a 2sh Javelin
423B A71a 3sh Hurdles
423C A71a 7sh Long distance running
423D A71a 12sh Relay race

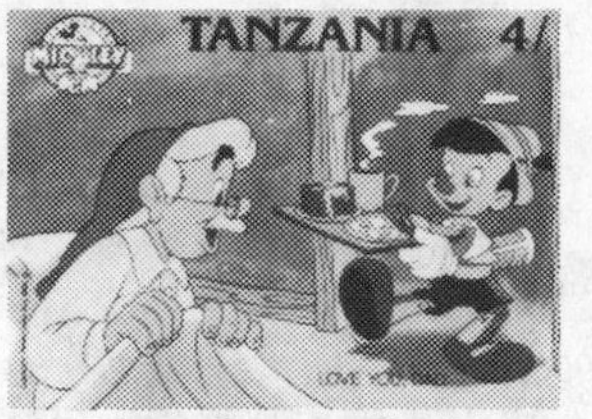

Disney Characters, Special Occasions — A72

1988, Sept. 9 ***Perf. 14***
424 A72 4sh Love You, Dad .15 .15
425 A72 5sh Happy Birthday .15 .15
426 A72 10sh Trick or Treat .30 .30
427 A72 12sh Be Kind to Animals .38 .38
428 A72 15sh Love .45 .45
429 A72 20sh Let's Celebrate .60 .60
430 A72 30sh Keep In Touch .90 .90
431 A72 50sh Love You, Mom 1.50 1.50
Nos. 424-431 (8) 4.43 4.43

Souvenir Sheet

432 A72 150sh Let's Work Together 4.50 4.50
433 A72 150sh Have a Super Sunday 4.50 4.50

Mickey Mouse, 60th anniv.

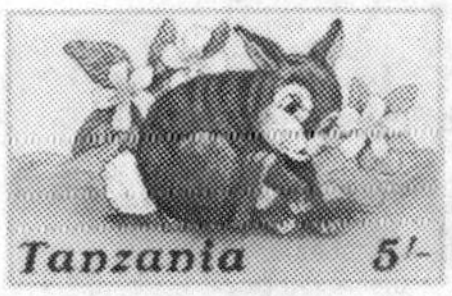

Domestic Animals A73

1988, Sept. 9
434 A73 4sh Goat, vert. .15 .15
435 A73 5sh Rabbit .15 .15
436 A73 8sh Cows .24 .24
437 A73 10sh Cat .30 .30
438 A73 12sh Horse, vert. .38 .38
439 A73 20sh Dog, vert. .60 .60
Nos. 434-439 (6) 1.82 1.82

Souvenir Sheet

440 A73 100sh Chicken 3.00 3.00

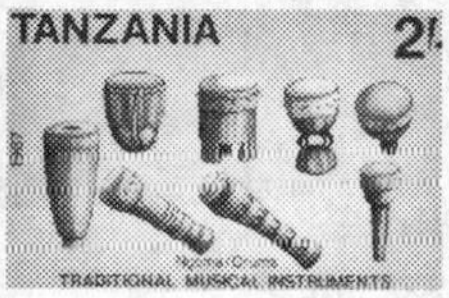

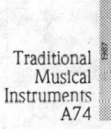

Traditional Musical Instruments A74

1988, Sept. 30 **Litho.** ***Perf. 14***
441 A74 2sh Drums .15 .15
442 A74 3sh Xylophones .15 .15
443 A74 10sh Thumb pianos .30 .30
444 A74 20sh Fiddles .60 .60
Nos. 441-444 (4) 1.20 1.20

Souvenir Sheet

445 A74 40sh Violins with calabash resonators 1.20 1.20

Dated 1987.

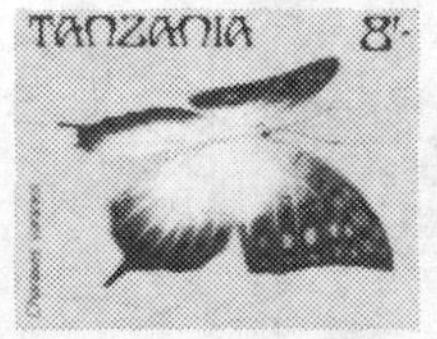

Butterflies A75

1988, Oct. 17 ***Perf. 14½***
446 A75 8sh Charaxes varanes .24 .24
447 A75 30sh Neptis melicerta .90 .90
448 A75 40sh Mylothris chloris 1.20 1.20
449 A75 50sh Charaxes bohemani 1.50 1.50
450 A75 60sh Myrina ficedula 1.80 1.80
451 A75 75sh Papilio phorcas 2.25 2.25
452 A75 90sh Cyrestis camillus 2.70 2.70
453 A75 100sh Salamis temora 3.00 3.00
Nos. 446-453 (8) 13.59 13.59

Souvenir Sheets

454 A75 200sh Asterope rosa 6.00 6.00
455 A75 250sh Kallima rumia 7.50 7.50

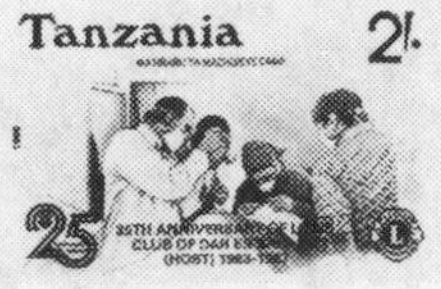

Intl. Lions Club at Dar es Salaam, 25th Anniv. A76

1988, Nov, 30 **Litho.** ***Perf. 14½***
456 A76 2sh Eye operation .15 .15
457 A76 3sh Shallow water well .15 .15
458 A76 7sh Map, rhinoceros .22 .22
459 A76 12sh Donating school desks .35 .35
Set value .73 .73

Souvenir Sheet

460 A76 40sh Emblem 1.20 1.20

Community services: Matibabu Ya Macho Eye Camp (2sh); sanitary water supply in Dar es Salaam (3sh); wildlife conservation (7sh); aid to local schools (12sh).

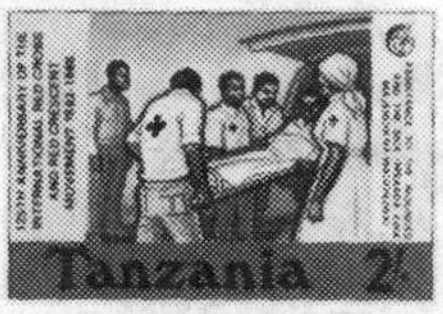

Intl. Red Cross and Red Crescent Organizations, 125th Annivs. — A77

Design: 2sh, Assisting the wounded and sick. 3sh, Postnatal care clinic. 7sh, Red Cross flag. 12sh, Jean-Henry Dunant, founder. 40sh, Dunant, Thomas Maunier, Louis Appia, Gustave Moynier and Gen. Guillaume Henri Dufour, members of intl. committee that sponsored the conference in 1863 where the Red Cross was founded.

1988, Dec. 30 **Litho.** ***Perf. 12½x12***
461 A77 2sh multicolored .15 .15
462 A77 3sh multicolored .15 .15
463 A77 7sh multicolored .15 .15
464 A77 12sh multicolored .25 .25
Set value .50 .50

Souvenir Sheet

465 A77 40sh multicolored .80 .80

Miniature Sheet

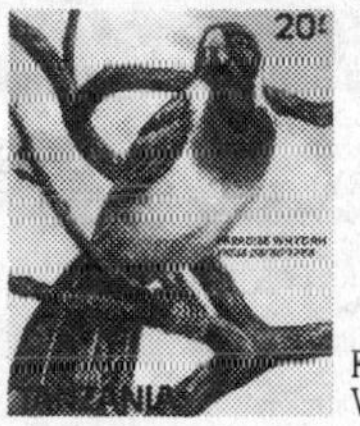

Paradise Whydah — A78

Birds: a, Paradise whydah. b, Black-collared barbet. c, Bataleur eagle. d, Openbill storks, lilac-breasted roller. e, Scarlet tufted malachite sunbird. f, Dark chanting goshawk. g, White-fronted bee-eater, little bee-eater, carmine bee-eater. h, Marabou stork, Narina's trocon. i, African gray parrot. j, Hoopoe. k, Yellow collared lovebird. l, Yellow-billed hornbill. m, Hammerkop. n, Flamingos, violet-crested turaco. o, Malachite kingfisher. p, Greater flamingo. q, Yellow-billed stork. r, Shoebill stork. s, Saddle-billed stork, blacksmith plover. t, Crowned crane.

1989, Jan. 10 ***Perf. 14***
466 Sheet of 20 8.00 8.00
a.-t. A78 20sh any single .40 .40

Souvenir Sheets

467 A78 350sh Helmeted guineafowl 7.00 7.00
467A A78 350sh Ostrich 7.00 7.00

No. 466 has a continuous design.

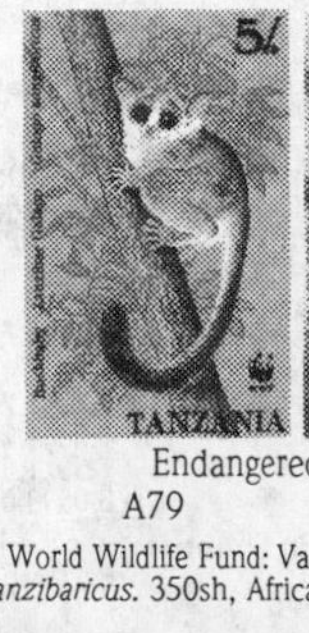
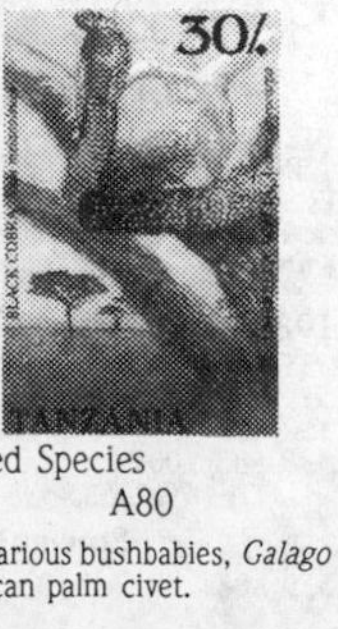

Endangered Species
A79 A80

World Wildlife Fund: Various bushbabies, *Galago zanzibaricus.* 350sh, African palm civet.

1989, Jan. 24 ***Perf. 14***
468 A79 5sh shown .15 .15
469 A79 10sh multi, horiz. .20 .20
470 A79 20sh multi, diff. .40 .40
471 A79 45sh multi, diff., horiz. .90 .90
Nos. 468-471 (4) 1.65 1.65

Souvenir Sheet

472 A79 350sh multi, horiz. 7.00 7.00

1989, Jan. 24

Designs: 30sh, Black cobra, umbrella acacia. 70sh, Red-tailed tropic bird, tree fern. 100sh, African tree frog, cocoa tree. 150sh, African black-necked heron, Egyptian papyrus. 350sh, Pink-backed pelicans, baobab tree.

473 A80 30sh shown .60 .60
474 A80 70sh multicolored 1.40 1.40
475 A80 100sh multicolored 2.00 2.00
476 A80 150sh multicolored 3.00 3.00
Nos. 473-476 (4) 7.00 7.00

Souvenir Sheet

477 A80 350sh multicolored 7.00 7.00

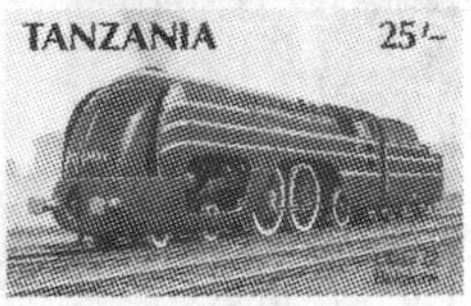

Steam Locomotives A81

1989, Jan. 31
478 A81 10sh Class P36, USSR .15 .15
479 A81 25sh Class 12, Belgium .35 .35
480 A81 60sh Class C62, Japan .85 .85
481 A81 75sh Class T1, Pennsylvania R.R. 1.05 1.05
482 A81 80sh Class WP, India 1.15 1.15
483 A81 90sh Class 59, East African Railways 1.25 1.25
484 A81 150sh People Class 4-6-2, China 2.15 2.15
485 A81 200sh Southern Pacific *Daylight Express,* US 2.85 2.85
Nos. 478-485 (8) 9.80 9.80

Souvenir Sheets

486 A81 350sh Stephenson's *Planet,* Britain 5.00 5.00
487 A81 350sh *Coronation Scot,* Britain 5.00 5.00

Nos. 486-487 vert.

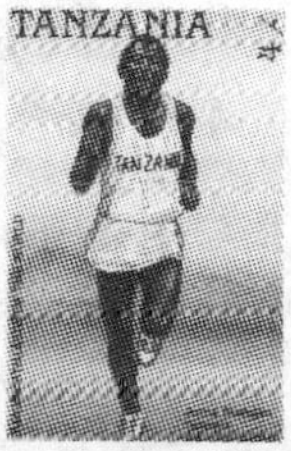

World Class Athletes — A82

Designs: 4sh, Juma Ikangaa, Tanzania, marathon. 8.50sh, Steffi Graf, West Germany, tennis. 12sh, Yannick Noah, France, tennis. 40sh, Pele, Brazil, soccer. 100sh, Erhard Keller, West Germany, speed skater. 125sh, Sadanoyama, Japan, Sumo wrestler. 200sh, Taino, Japan, Sumo wrestler. 250sh, I. Aoki, Japan, golfer. No. 496, Joe Louis, US, world heavyweight boxing champion, 1937-1949. No. 497, T. Nakajima, Japan, golfer.

1989, Feb. 7
488 A82 4sh multicolored .15 .15
489 A82 8.50sh multicolored .15 .15
490 A82 12sh multicolored .18 .18
491 A82 40sh multicolored .58 .58
492 A82 100sh multicolored 1.45 1.45
493 A82 125sh multicolored 1.75 1.75
494 A82 200sh multicolored 2.85 2.85
495 A82 250sh multicolored 3.60 3.60
Nos. 488-495 (8) 10.71 10.71

Souvenir Sheets

496 A82 350sh multicolored 5.00 5.00
497 A82 350sh multicolored 5.00 5.00

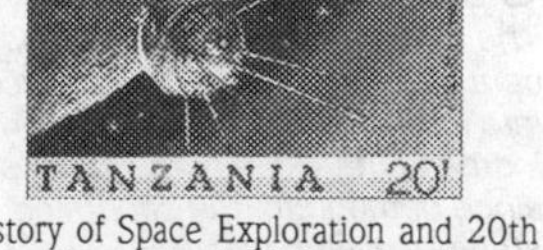

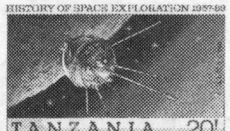

History of Space Exploration and 20th Anniv. of the 1st Moon Landing A83

1989, July 20

498	A83	20sh	Luna 3	.30	.30
499	A83	30sh	Rendezvous of Gemini 6&7	.45	.45
500	A83	40sh	1st US space walk	.60	.60
501	A83	60sh	First man on Moon	.90	.90
502	A83	70sh	Experiments on Moon	1.05	1.05
503	A83	100sh	Apollo 15 lunar rover	1.50	1.50
504	A83	150sh	Apollo-Soyuz	2.25	2.25
505	A83	200sh	Spacelab	3.00	3.00
			Nos. 498-505 (8)	10.05	10.05

Souvenir Sheets

506	A83	250sh	Futuristic space station	3.75	3.75
507	A83	250sh	*Eagle* lunar module	3.75	3.75

History of space exploration (Nos. 498-500, 503-506); others 20th anniv. of 1st Moon Landing.

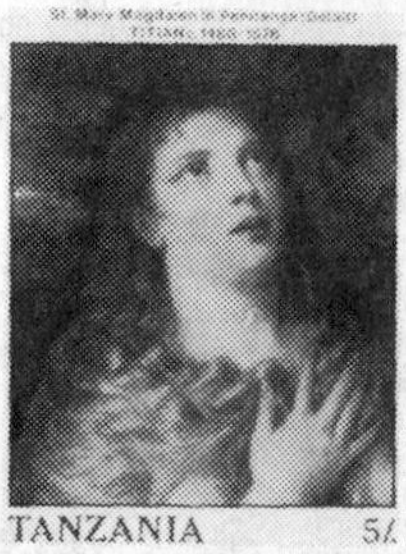

St. Mary Magdalene in Penitence A84

Details from paintings by Titian: 10sh, Averoldi Polyptych. 15sh, St. Margaret. 50sh, Venus and Adonis. 75sh, Venus and the Lutenist. 100sh, Tarquin and Lucretia. 125sh, St. Jerome. 150sh, Madonna and Child with Saints. No. 516, St. Catherine of Alexandria at Prayer. No. 517, Adoration of the Holy Trinity. No. 517A, The Supper at Emmaus.

1989, Nov. 15 Litho. *Perf. 13½x14*

508	A84	5sh	multicolored	.15	.15
509	A84	10sh	multicolored	.15	.15
510	A84	15sh	multicolored	.22	.22
511	A84	50sh	multicolored	.75	.75
512	A84	75sh	multicolored	1.10	1.10
513	A84	100sh	multicolored	1.50	1.50
514	A84	125sh	multicolored	1.90	1.90
515	A84	150sh	multicolored	2.25	2.25
			Nos. 508-515 (8)	8.02	8.02

Souvenir Sheets

516	A84	300sh	multicolored	3.80	3.80
517	A84	300sh	multicolored	3.80	3.80
517A	A84	300sh	multicolored	3.80	3.80

500th birth anniv. of Titian.
#517A was not available until Jan. 8, 1991.

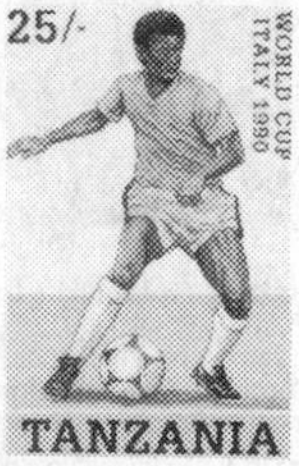

World Cup Soccer Championships, Italy — A85

1989, Nov. 15 *Perf. 14*

Uniform colors

518	A85	25sh	green, red & yel	.38	.38
519	A85	60sh	green, yel & blue	.90	.90
520	A85	75sh	orange & blue	1.10	1.10
521	A85	200sh	blue & white	3.00	3.00
			Nos. 518-521 (4)	5.38	5.38

Souvenir Sheets

522	A85	350sh	orange & bl, diff.	5.25	5.25
523	A85	350sh	grn, yel & bl, diff.	5.25	5.25

15-Cent Minimum Value
The minimum catalogue value is 15 cents. Separating se-tenant pieces into individual stamps does not increase the value of the stamps since demand for the separated stamps may be small.

Souvenir Sheet

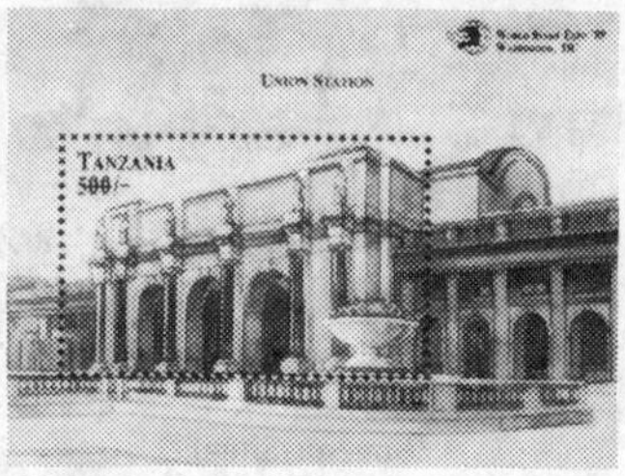

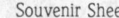

Union Station, Washington, DC — A86

1989, Nov. 17

524	A86	500sh	multicolored	7.50	7.50

World Stamp Expo '89.

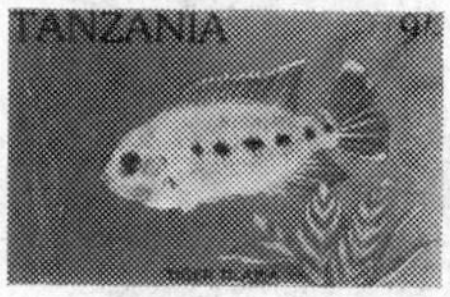

Fish — A87

1989, Dec. 14

525	A87	9sh	Tiger tilapia	.15	.15
526	A87	13sh	Picasso fish	.20	.20
527	A87	20sh	Powder-blue surgeonfish	.30	.30
528	A87	40sh	Butterflyfish	.60	.60
529	A87	70sh	Guenther's notho	1.05	1.05
530	A87	100sh	Ansorge's noelebias	1.50	1.50
531	A87	150sh	Lyretail panchax	2.25	2.25
532	A87	200sh	Regal angelfish	3.00	3.00
			Nos. 525-532 (8)	9.05	9.05

Souvenir Sheets

533	A87	350sh	Batfish	5.25	5.25
534	A87	350sh	Jewel cichlid	5.25	5.25

Nos. 533-534 each contain one 38x51mm stamp.

Nos. 414-423 Ovptd. and Similarly — **Brathlon, Peter-Roetsch, DDR**

1989, Dec. 19 Litho. *Perfs. as Before*

534A	A71	5sh	"Biathlon / Peter-Roetsch, DDR"	.15	.15
534B	A71	10sh	shown	.15	.15
534C	A71	20sh	"Men's Match Sprint / Lutz Hesslich, DDR"	.30	.30
534D	A71	25sh	"Pairs, Gordeeva & Grinkov, USSR"	.40	.40
534E	A71	50sh	"Epee, Schmitt, W. Germany"	.80	.80
534F	A71	50sh	"Zurbriggen, Switzerland"	.80	.80
534G	A71	70sh	"Men's Team, USA"	1.10	1.10
534H	A71	75sh	"Gold-USSR / Silver-DDR / Bronze-DDR"	1.20	1.20
			Nos. 534A-534H (8)	4.90	4.90

Souvenir Sheets

534I	A71	100sh	"Ice Hockey: / Gold-USSR"	1.60	1.60
534J	A71	100sh	"Women's Team, / Gold-USSR"	1.60	1.60

Silver and Bronze medalists overprinted on margins of souvenir sheets.

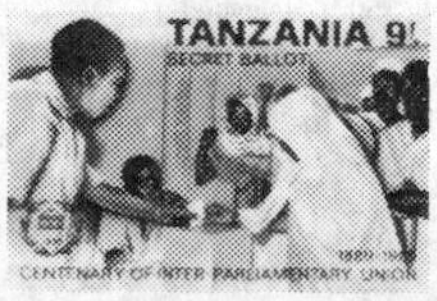

Inter-Parliamentary Union, Cent. — A88

Designs: 9sh, Secret ballot. 13sh, Parliament, Dar Es Salaam. 40sh, Sir William Randal Cremer, Frederic Passy. 80sh, Parliament in session. 100sh, IPU emblem.

1989, Dec. 22 *Perf. 12½x12*

535	A88	9sh	multicolored	.15	.15
536	A88	13sh	multicolored	.20	.20
537	A88	80sh	multicolored	1.20	1.20
538	A88	100sh	lt bl, dp bl & blk	1.50	1.50
			Nos. 535-538 (4)	3.05	3.05

Souvenir Sheet

539	A88	40sh	multicolored	.60	.60

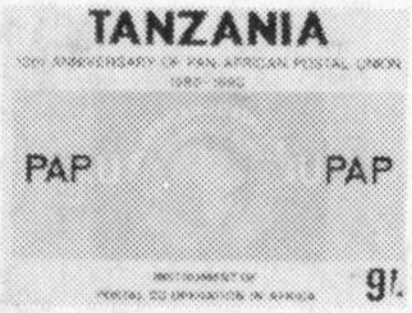

Pan-African Postal Union, 10th Anniv. — A89

1990, Jan. 17 *Perf. 13½*

540	A89	9sh	PAPU emblem	.15	.15
541	A89	13sh	Post offices boxes	.20	.20
542	A89	70sh	Mail early, prompt delivery	1.05	1.05
543	A89	100sh	Modes of mail delivery	1.50	1.50
			Nos. 540-543 (4)	2.90	2.90

Souvenir Sheet

544	A89	40sh	Tanzania Post, PAPU, UPU emblems	.60	.60

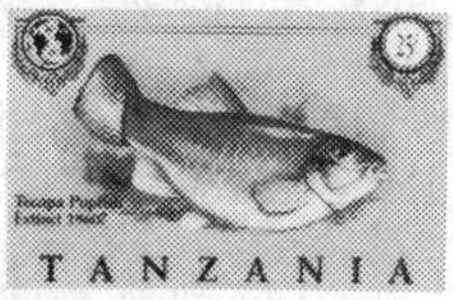

Extinct Animals A90

1990, Feb. 4 *Perf. 14*

545	A90	25sh	Tecopa pupfish	.38	.38
546	A90	40sh	Thylacine	.60	.60
547	A90	50sh	Quagga	.75	.75
548	A90	60sh	Passenger pigeon	.90	.90
549	A90	75sh	Rodriguez saddleback tortoise	1.10	1.10
550	A90	100sh	Toolache wallaby	1.50	1.50
551	A90	150sh	Texas red wolf	2.25	2.25
552	A90	200sh	Utah lake sculpin	3.00	3.00
			Nos. 545-552 (8)	10.48	10.48

Souvenir Sheets

553	A90	350sh	Hawaiian O-O, vert.	5.25	5.25
554	A90	350sh	South island whekau	5.25	5.25

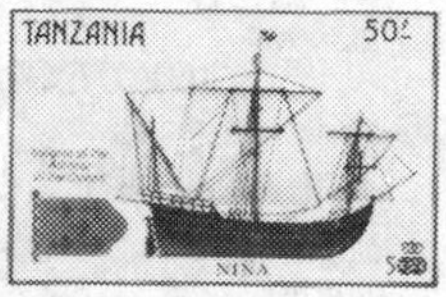

Nina, Admiral's Flag — A91

1990, Feb. 20

555	A91	50sh	shown	.75	.75
556	A91	60sh	Pinta, flag	.90	.90
557	A91	75sh	Santa Maria, flag	1.10	1.10
558	A91	200sh	Map of Columbus' first voyage	3.00	3.00
			Nos. 555-558 (4)	5.75	5.75

Souvenir Sheet

559	A91	350sh	Ships, bird's head	5.25	5.25

Discovery of America, 500th anniv. (in 1992).

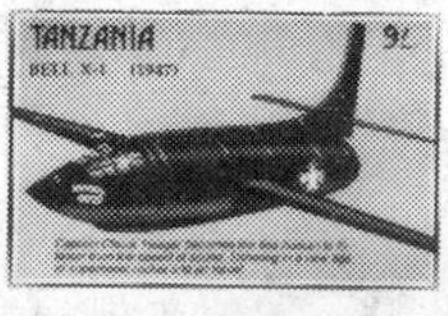

Modern Discoveries A92

Designs: 9sh, Bell X-1 breaking the sound barrier. 13sh, Bathyscaph Trieste reaches the deepest ocean bottom. 150sh, Transistor and computer chips. 250sh, Discovery of DNA structure. 350sh, Voyager 2 visits Neptune.

1990, Feb. 20

560	A92	9sh	multicolored	.15	.15
561	A92	13sh	multicolored	.20	.20
562	A92	150sh	multicolored	2.25	2.25
563	A92	250sh	multicolored	3.75	3.75
			Nos. 560-563 (4)	6.35	6.35

Souvenir Sheet

564	A92	350sh	multicolored	5.25	5.25

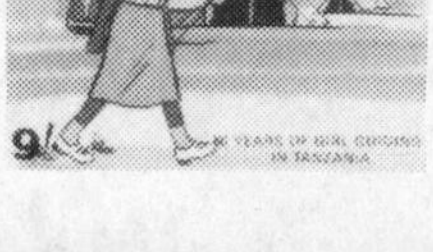

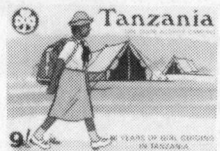

Girl Guides, 60th Anniv. A93

1990, Feb. 22 *Perf. 12½x12*

565	A93	9sh	Hiking	.15	.15
566	A93	13sh	Planting trees	.20	.20
567	A93	50sh	Teaching writing	.75	.75
568	A93	100sh	Teaching health care	1.50	1.50
			Nos. 565-568 (4)	2.60	2.60

Souvenir Sheet

Perf. 12x12½

569	A93	40sh	Nursing school, vert.	.60	.60

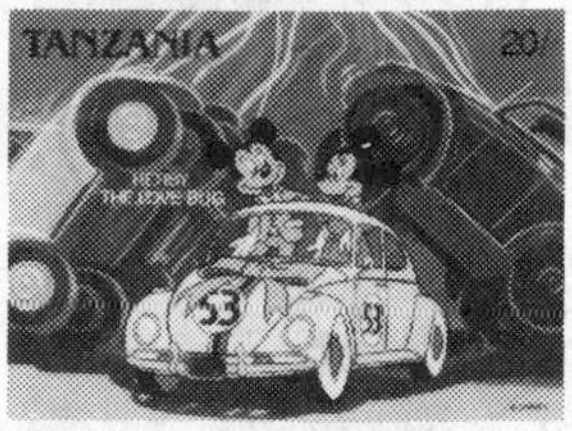

Disney Characters, Automobiles — A94

1990, Mar. 20 *Perf. 14x13½*

570	A94	20sh	Herbie, The Love Bug	.30	.30
571	A94	30sh	The Absent-Minded Professor's car	.45	.45
572	A94	45sh	Chitty-Chitty Bang-Bang	.60	.60
573	A94	60sh	Mr. Toad's wild ride	.75	.75
574	A94	75sh	Scrooge's limousine	.95	.95
575	A94	100sh	Shaggy dog's car	1.25	1.25
576	A94	150sh	Donald Duck's car	2.00	2.00
577	A94	200sh	Firetruck in "Dumbo"	2.50	2.50
			Nos. 570-577 (8)	8.80	8.80

Souvenir Sheets

578	A94	350sh	Cruella de Vil	4.50	4.50
579	A94	350sh	Mickeymobile	4.50	4.50

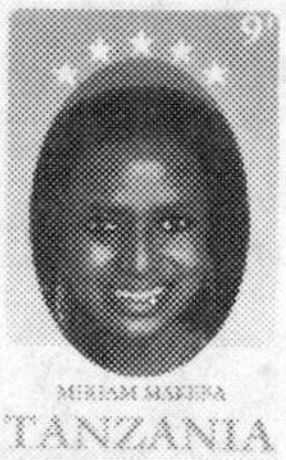

Black Entertainers — A95

1990, Mar. 30 Litho. *Perf. 14*

580	A95	9sh	Miriam Makeba	.15	.15
581	A95	13sh	Manu Dibango	.16	.16
582	A95	25sh	Fela	.30	.30
583	A95	70sh	Smokey Robinson	.85	.85
584	A95	100sh	Gladys Knight	1.20	1.20
585	A95	150sh	Eddie Murphy	1.80	1.80
586	A95	200sh	Sammy Davis, Jr.	2.50	2.50
587	A95	250sh	Stevie Wonder	3.00	3.00
			Nos. 580-587 (8)	9.96	9.96

Souvenir Sheets

Perf. 14½

588	A95	350sh	Bill Cosby	4.25	4.25
589	A95	350sh	Michael Jackson	4.25	4.25

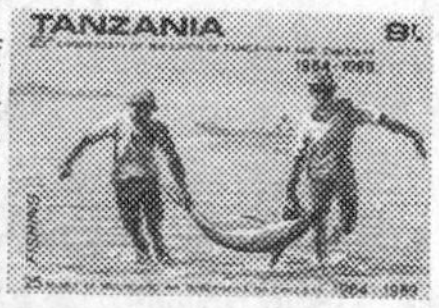

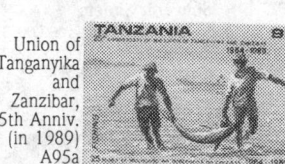

Union of Tanganyika and Zanzibar, 25th Anniv. (in 1989) A95a

Designs: 9sh, Fishing. 13sh, Grapes. 50sh, Cloves. 100sh, Presidents Nyerere and Karume exchanging Union instruments, vert. 40sh, Natl. arms, vert.

Perf. 12½x12, 12x12½

1990, Apr. 25 Litho.

589A	A95a	9sh	multicolored	.15	.15
589B	A95a	13sh	multicolored	.15	.15
589C	A95a	50sh	multicolored	.60	.60
589D	A95a	100sh	multicolored	1.20	1.20
			Nos. 589A-589D (4)	2.10	2.10

Souvenir Sheet

589E	A95a	40sh	multicolored	.48	.48

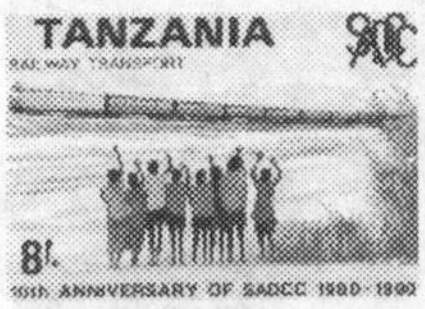

Southern Africa Development Coordinating Conf. (SADCC), 10th Anniv. A96

1990, Aug. 8 *Perf. 13½*
590 A96 8sh Railway transport .15 .15
591 A96 11.50sh Paper industry .15 .15
592 A96 25sh Tractor production .36 .36
593 A96 100sh Flags, map 1.20 1.20
Nos. 590-593 (4) 1.86 1.86

Souvenir Sheet
Perf. 12½
594 A96 50sh Map .60 .60

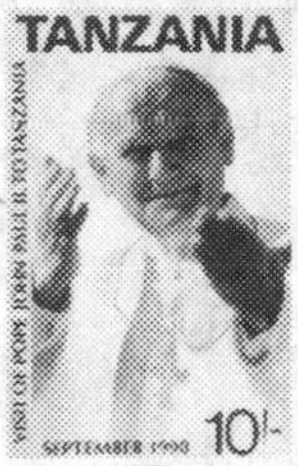

A97

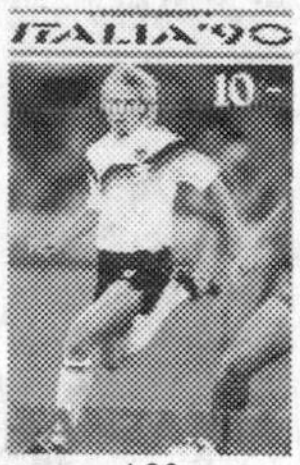

A98

Pope John Paul II's Visit to Tanzania: 15sh, Wearing red vestments. 20sh, Wearing miter. 100sh, Papal arms. No. 599: a, Pope with arms outstretched. b, St. Joseph's Cathedral, Dar Es Salaam. c, Christ the King Cathedral, Moshi. d, Saint Theresa's Cathedral, Tabora. e, Cathedral of the Epiphany, Bugando Mwanza. f, St. Mathias Mulumba Kalemba Cathedral, Songea.

1990, Sept. 1 **Litho.** *Perf. 14*
595 A97 10sh shown .15 .15
596 A97 15sh multicolored .15 .15
597 A97 20sh multicolored .16 .16
598 A97 100sh multicolored .80 .80
Nos. 595-598 (4) 1.26 1.26

Souvenir Sheet
599 Sheet of 6 2.40 2.40
a.-f. A97 50sh any single .40 .40

1990, Sept. 28
Players from participating countries.
600 A98 10sh West Germany .15 .15
601 A98 60sh Italy .48 .48
602 A98 100sh Scotland .80 .80
603 A98 300sh Yugoslavia 2.40 2.40
Nos. 600-603 (4) 3.83 3.83

Souvenir Sheets
604 A98 400sh Costa Rica 3.20 3.20
605 A98 400sh Belgium 3.20 3.20

World Cup Soccer Championships, Italy.

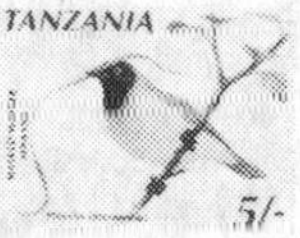

Birds — A99

1990-91 **Litho.** *Perf. 14*
606 A99 5sh Masked weaver .15 .15
607 A99 9sh Emerald cuckoo .15 .15
608 A99 13sh Little bee-eater .15 .15
609 A99 15sh Red bishop .15 .15
610 A99 20sh Bateleur .16 .16
611 A99 25sh Scarlet-chested sunbird .20 .20
a. Booklet pane, 2 each #606-611 2.65
611B A99 30sh Pigeons .24 .24

Size: 42x28mm
612 A99 40sh Lesser flamingo .32 .32
613 A99 70sh Helmeted guineafowl .55 .55
614 A99 100sh White pelican .80 .80
615 A99 170sh Saddle-billed stork 1.35 1.35
616 A99 200sh Crowned crane 1.60 1.60
616A A99 300sh Pied crow 2.40 2.40
616B A99 400sh White-headed vulture 3.20 3.20
617 A99 500sh Ostrich 4.00 4.00
Nos. 606-617 (15) 15.42 15.42

Souvenir Sheet
Stamp size: 42x28mm
617A Sheet of 2 1.25 1.25
b. A99 40sh Superb starling .50 .50
c. A99 60sh Lilac-breasted roller .75 .75

Issued: 30sh, 300sh, 400sh, 1991; others, 10/1/90.

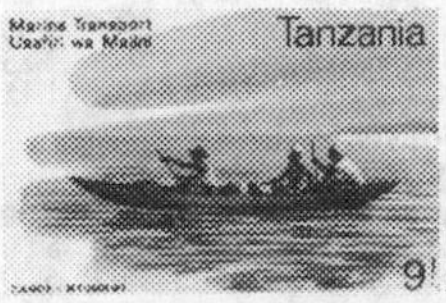

Boats A100

1990, Oct. 10 **Litho.** *Perf. 12½x12*
618 A100 9sh Canoe .15 .15
619 A100 13sh Outrigger canoe .15 .15
620 A100 25sh Dhow .20 .20
621 A100 100sh Freighter .80 .80
Nos. 618-621 (4) 1.30 1.30

Souvenir Sheet
622 A100 40sh Boat .32 .32

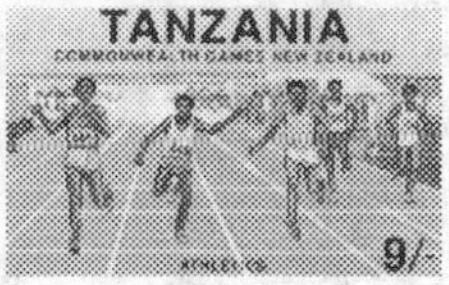

Commonwealth Games, New Zealand — A101

1990, Oct. 22 *Perf. 14*
623 A101 9sh Sprinting .15 .15
624 A101 13sh Netball, vert. .15 .15
625 A101 25sh Pole vault .20 .20
626 A101 100sh Long jump, vert. .80 .80
Nos. 623-626 (4) 1.30 1.30

Souvenir Sheet
627 A101 40sh Boxing .32 .32

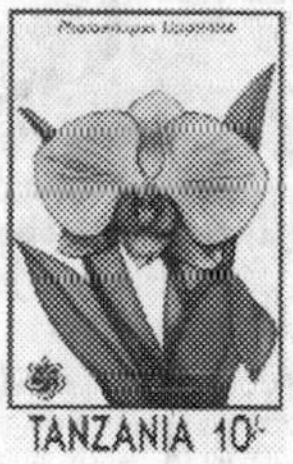

Orchids — A102

1990, Nov. 12
628 A102 10sh Phalaenopsis .15 .15
629 A102 25sh Lycaste .20 .20
630 A102 30sh Vuylstekeara, Cambria "Plush" .24 .24
631 A102 50sh Vuylstekeara, Monica "Burnham" .40 .40
632 A102 90sh Odontocidium .72 .72
633 A102 100sh Oncidioda .80 .80
634 A102 250sh Sophrolaeliocattleya 2.00 2.00
635 A102 300sh Laeliocattleya 2.40 2.40
Nos. 628-635 (8) 6.91 6.91

Souvenir Sheets
636 A102 400sh Cymbidium, Baldoyle "Melbury" 3.20 3.20
637 A102 400sh Cymbidium, Tapestry "Long Beach" 3.20 3.20

Expo '90, the Intl. Garden and Greenery Exposition, Osaka, Japan.

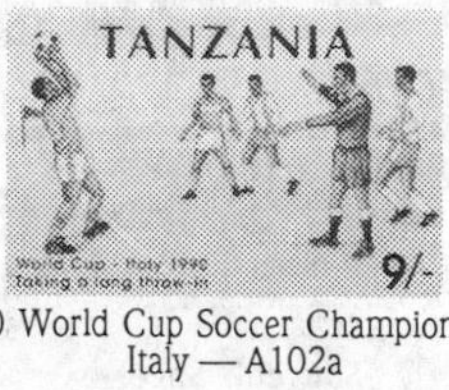

1990 World Cup Soccer Championships, Italy — A102a

1990, Nov. 17 **Litho.** *Perf. 14*
637A A102a 9sh Long throw-in .15 .15
637B A102a 13sh Penalty kick .15 .15
637C A102a 25sh Dribbling .25 .25
637D A102a 100sh Corner kick 1.00 1.00
Nos. 637A-637D (4) 1.55 1.55

Souvenir Sheet
637E A102a 50sh Trophy, map .50 .50

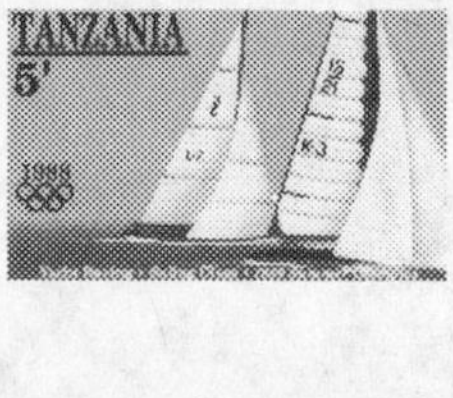

Racing A103

Designs: 5sh, Olympic Soling Class Yacht racing. 20sh, Olympic downhill ski racing. 30sh, Tour de France bicycle race. 40sh, Le Mans 24 hour endurance auto race. 75sh, Olympic 2-man bobsled. 100sh, Belgian Grand Prix motorcycle race. 250sh, Indianapolis 500 auto race. 300sh, Power boat gold cup racing. No. 646, Colorado 500 enduro motorcycle race. No. 647, Schneider Trophy air races.

1990, Nov. 19
638 A103 5sh multicolored .15 .15
639 A103 20sh multicolored .16 .16
640 A103 30sh multicolored .24 .24
641 A103 40sh multicolored .32 .32
642 A103 75sh multicolored .60 .60
643 A103 100sh multicolored .80 .80
644 A103 250sh multicolored 2.00 2.00
645 A103 300sh multicolored 2.40 2.40
Nos. 638-645 (8) 6.67 6.67

Souvenir Sheets
646 A103 400sh multicolored 3.20 3.20
647 A103 400sh multicolored 3.20 3.20

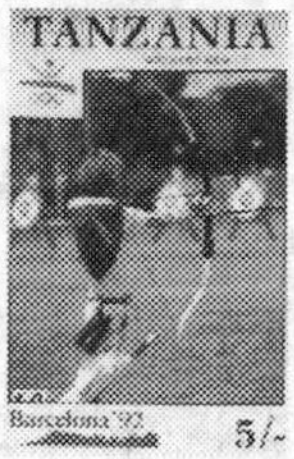

1992 Summer Olympics, Barcelona — A104

1990, Nov. 30
648 A104 5sh Archery .15 .15
649 A104 10sh Women's gymnastics .15 .15
650 A104 25sh Boxing .20 .20
651 A104 50sh Two-man kayak race .40 .40
652 A104 100sh Men's volleyball .80 .80
653 A104 150sh Mens' gymnastics 1.20 1.20
654 A104 200sh 4x100 meter relay 1.60 1.60
655 A104 300sh Judo 2.40 2.40
Nos. 648-655 (8) 6.90 6.90

Souvenir Sheets
656 A104 400sh Men's 400 meter hurdles 3.20 3.20
657 A104 400sh Men's cycling 3.20 3.20

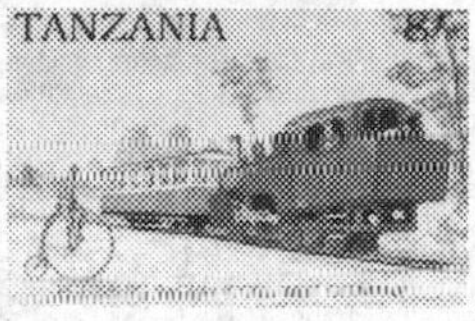

Cog Railroads A105

Cog locomotives: 8sh, Petersberg Cog Railway, West Germany. 25sh, Engine *Waumbek* on Mt. Washington Cog Railway, US. 50sh, Doubleheaded cog engines on Dubrovnik-Sarajevo line, Yugoslavia. 100sh, Cog Railway, Budapest, Hungary 1874. 150sh, Vordenberg-Eisenerz line, Austria. 200sh, Rimutaka Incline, New Zealand, 1955. 250sh, John Stevens' cog engine, Hoboken, NJ, 1825. 300sh, Pilatusbahn Cog Railway, Switzerland, 1889. No. 666, Schneebergbahn of the OBB, Austria. No. 667, Sylvester Marsh, Mt. Washington Cog Railway, 1869.

1990, Dec. 8
658 A105 8sh multicolored .15 .15
659 A105 25sh multicolored .20 .20
660 A105 50sh multicolored .40 .40
661 A105 100sh multicolored .80 .80
662 A105 150sh multicolored 1.20 1.20
663 A105 200sh multicolored 1.60 1.60
664 A105 250sh multicolored 2.00 2.00
665 A105 300sh multicolored 2.40 2.40
Nos. 658-665 (8) 8.75 8.75

Souvenir Sheets
666 A105 400sh multicolored 3.20 3.20
667 A105 400sh multicolored 3.20 3.20

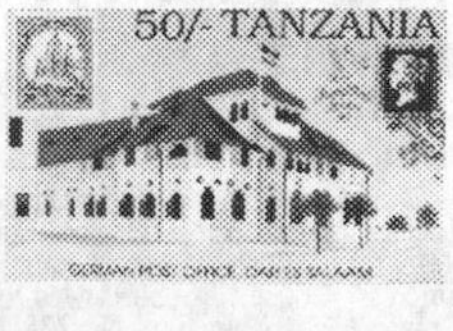

First Postage Stamps, 150th Anniv. A106

Designs: No. 668, German Post Office at Dar Es Salaam, German East Africa No. 16. No. 669, Mailboat S.S. Reichstag, 1890, Germany No. 40 cancelled in Zanzibar. No. 670, Dhows used as mailboats, Zanzibar No. 1. No. 671, Mailplane Singapore I on Lake Victoria, 1928, Tanganyika No. 22. No. 672, Mailplane, Livingston's House, Zanzibar No. 316. No. 673, Passenger-mail train at Moshi Station, Tanganyika No. 52. No. 674, Royal mail coach, 1840. 150sh, Stephenson's *Rocket*, mail car, 1838. 200sh, Handley Page HP-42 mailplane. No. 677, Hand delivery of mail, Thurn & Taxis No. 44 on cover. No. 678, Sir Rowland Hill.

1990, Dec. 12
668 A106 50sh multicolored .40 .40
669 A106 50sh multicolored .40 .40
a. Pair, #668-669 .80 .80
670 A106 75sh multicolored .60 .60
671 A106 75sh multicolored .60 .60
a. Pair, #670-671 1.20 1.20
672 A106 100sh multicolored .80 .80
673 A106 100sh multicolored .80 .80
a. Pair, #672-673 1.60 1.60
674 A106 100sh multicolored .80 .80
675 A106 150sh multicolored 1.20 1.20
676 A106 200sh multicolored 1.60 1.60
Nos. 668-676 (9) 7.20 7.20

Souvenir Sheets
677 A106 350sh multicolored 2.80 2.80
678 A106 350sh multicolored 2.80 2.80

500th anniv. of Thurn and Taxis Post (No. 677).
For overprints see Nos. 928-934.

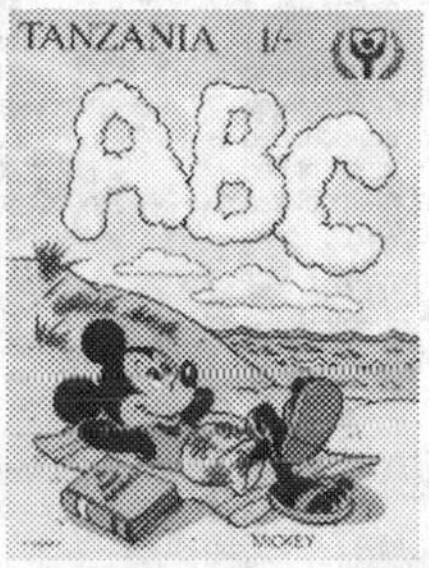

Intl. Literacy Year A107

Nos. 679a-681i depict various Walt Disney characters and a letter of the alphabet.
No. 682, Mickey's train hauls Russian alphabet. No. 683, Children learning Hebrew.

1990, Dec. 27 *Perf. 13½x14*
Miniature Sheets
679 Sheet of 9 5.00 5.00
a. A107 1sh "ABC" .15 .15
b. A107 2sh "A" .15 .15
c. A107 3sh "B" .15 .15
d. A107 15sh "C" .15 .15
e. A107 55sh "D" .45 .45
f. A107 80sh "E" .65 .65
g. A107 120sh "F" .95 .95
h. A107 145sh "G" 1.15 1.15
i. A107 200sh "H" 1.60 1.60
680 Sheet of 9 4.75 4.75
a. A107 10sh "I" .15 .15
b. A107 20sh "J" .16 .16
c. A107 30sh "K" .24 .24
d. A107 40sh "L" .32 .32
e. A107 50sh "M" .40 .40
f. A107 60sh "N" .48 .48
g. A107 100sh "O" .80 .80
h. A107 125sh "P" 1.00 1.00
i. A107 150sh "Q" 1.20 1.20
681 Sheet of 9 5.00 5.00
a. A107 5sh "R" .15 .15
b. A107 18sh "S" .15 .15
c. A107 25sh "T" .20 .20
d. A107 35sh "U" .28 .28
e. A107 45sh "V" .35 .35
f. A107 75sh "W" .60 .60
g. A107 90sh "X" .72 .72
h. A107 160sh "Y" 1.25 1.25
i. A107 175sh "Z" 1.40 1.40

Souvenir Sheets
682 A107 600sh multicolored 4.75 4.75
683 A107 600sh multicolored 4.75 4.75

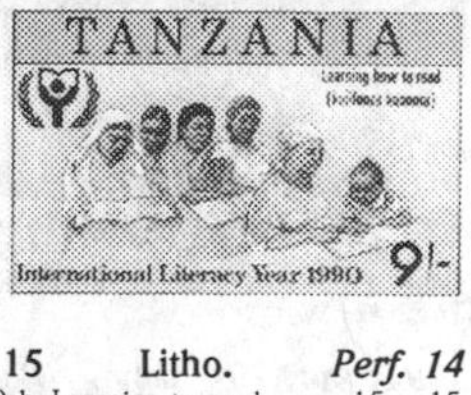

Intl. Literacy Year A108

1991, Mar. 15 **Litho.** *Perf. 14*
684 A108 9sh Learning to read .15 .15
685 A108 13sh Learning to write .15 .15
686 A108 25sh Blackboard, books .20 .20
687 A108 100sh Reading newspapers .80 .80
Nos. 684-687 (4) 1.30 1.30

Souvenir Sheet
688 A108 50sh Adult education .40 .40

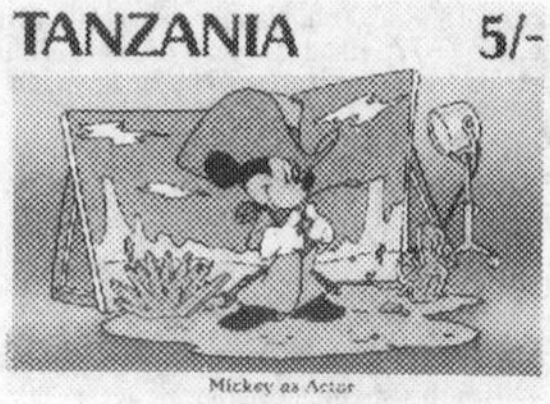
TANZANIA 5/-
Mickey as Actor

Mickey Mouse — A109

Character roles: 5sh, Western cowboy. 10sh, Boxer. 15sh, Astronaut. 20sh, Romantic lead with Minnie. 100sh, Swashbuckling hero. 200sh, Detective with Donald Duck and Pistol Pete. 350sh, King with Donald as court jester. 450sh, Sailor with Donald and Goofy. No. 697, Minnie, Mickey as archaeologists in Egypt, Donald as a mummy. No. 698, Mickey as Canadian Mountie.

1991, Feb. 11 Litho. *Perf. 14x13¹/₂*

689	A109	5sh multicolored	.15	.15
690	A109	10sh multicolored	.15	.15
691	A109	15sh multicolored	.15	.15
692	A109	20sh multicolored	.16	.16
693	A109	100sh multicolored	.80	.80
694	A109	200sh multicolored	1.60	1.60
695	A109	350sh multicolored	2.80	2.80
696	A109	450sh multicolored	3.60	3.60
		Nos. 689-696 (8)	9.41	9.41

Souvenir Sheets

697	A109	600sh multicolored	7.50	7.50
698	A109	600sh multicolored	7.50	7.50

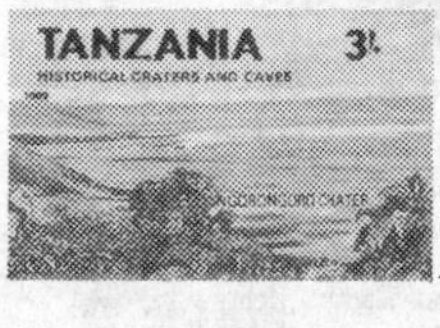
TANZANIA 3/-
HISTORICAL CRATERS AND CAVES

Craters and Caves A109a

Designs: 3sh, Ngorongoro Crater. 5sh, Kondoa Caves, prehistoric rock paintings. 9sh, Mount Kilimanjaro's inner crater. 12sh, Olduvai Gorge.

Amboni Caves: No. 698f, Open area of cave. g, People viewing cave, large stalactite. h, Woman seated beside welcome sign. i, Man climbing up to view cave.

1991, Mar. 28 Litho. *Perf. 14¹/₂*

698A	A109a	3sh multicolored	.15	.15
698B	A109a	5sh multicolored	.15	.15
698C	A109a	9sh multicolored	.15	.15
698D	A109a	12sh multicolored	.15	.15
		Set value	.16	.16

Souvenir Sheet

698E	A109a	10sh Sheet of 4, #f.-i.	.20	.20

Nos. 698A-698E were not available to the philatelic community until Mar. 1994.

Miniature Sheet

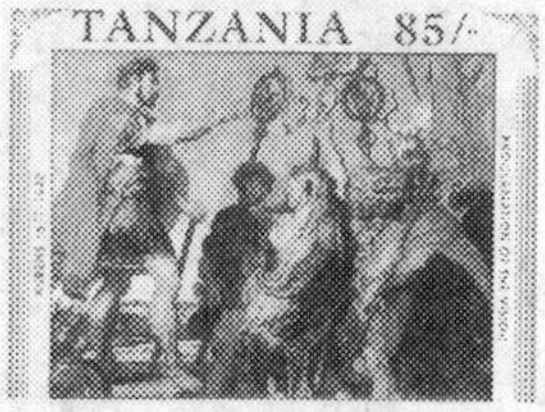
TANZANIA 85/-

Peter Paul Rubens, 350th Death Anniv. — A110

Cycle of Decius Mus: No. 699a, Proclamation of the Vision. b, Divining of the Entrails. c, Dispatch of the Lictors. d, Dedication to Death. e, Victory and Death of Decius Mus. f, Funeral Rites. No. 700, Trophy of War, vert.

1991, Apr. 10 Litho. *Perf. 14x13¹/₂*

699	A110	85sh Sheet of 6, #a.-f.	4.10	4.10

Souvenir Sheet

Perf. 13¹/₂x14

700	A110	500sh multicolored	4.00	4.00

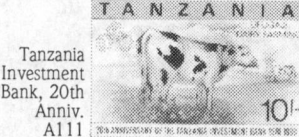

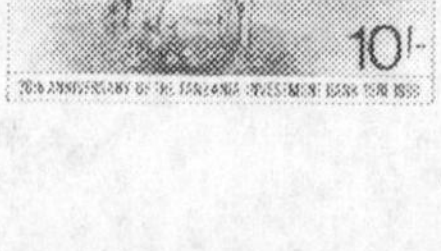
TANZANIA
10/-

Tanzania Investment Bank, 20th Anniv. A111

Designs: 10sh, Dairy farming. 13sh, Industrial development. 25sh, Engineering. 100sh, Tea harvesting.

1991, June 7 *Perf. 14*

701	A111	10sh multicolored	.15	.15
702	A111	13sh multicolored	.15	.15
703	A111	25sh multicolored	.20	.20
704	A111	100sh multicolored	.80	.80
a.		Souvenir sheet of 4, #701-704	1.10	1.10
		Set value	1.10	1.10

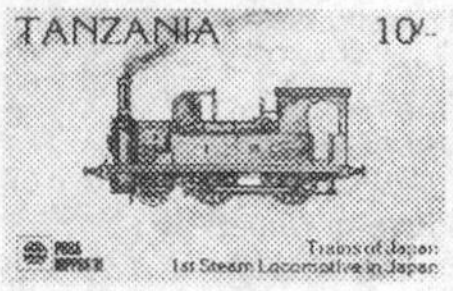
TANZANIA 10/-
Trains of Japan:
1st Steam Locomotive in Japan

Phila Nippon '91 — A112

Japanese locomotives: 10sh, First Japanese steam. 25sh, Series 4500 steam. 35sh, C 62 steam. 50sh, Mikado steam. 75sh, Series 6250 steam. 100sh, C 11 steam. 200sh, E 10 steam. 300sh, Series 8550 steam. No. 713, EF 58 electric. No. 714, DD 51 diesel. No. 715, Series 400 electric. No. 716, EH 10 electric.

1991, Aug. 15 Litho. *Perf. 14*

705	A112	10sh multicolored	.15	.15
706	A112	25sh multicolored	.20	.20
707	A112	35sh multicolored	.30	.30
708	A112	50sh multicolored	.42	.42
709	A112	75sh multicolored	.65	.65
710	A112	100sh multicolored	.85	.85
711	A112	200sh multicolored	1.75	1.75
712	A112	300sh multicolored	2.50	2.50
		Nos. 705-712 (8)	6.82	6.82

Souvenir Sheets

713	A112	400sh multicolored	3.50	3.50
714	A112	400sh multicolored	3.50	3.50
715	A112	400sh multicolored	3.50	3.50
716	A112	400sh multicolored	3.50	3.50

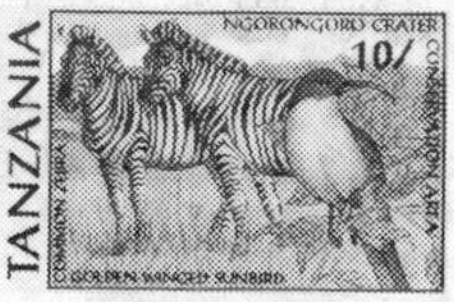
NGORONGORO CRATER
10/-
TANZANIA
GOLDEN WINGED SUNBIRD

Fauna in Natl. Game Parks A113

Species and park: 10sh, Common zebra, golden-winged sunbird, Ngorongoro Crater Conservation Area. 25sh, Greater kudu, African elephant, Ruaha. 30sh, Sable antelope, red and yellow barbet, Mikumi. 50sh, Wildebeest, leopard, Serengeti. 90sh, Giraffe, white-starred bush robin, Ngurdoto Crater. 100sh, Eland, Abbot's duiker, Kilimanjaro. 250sh, Lion, impala, Lake Manyara. 300sh, Black rhinoceros, ostrich, Tarangire. No. 725, Paradise whydah, oryx, Mkomazi Game Reserve. No. 726, Blue-breasted kingfisher, defassa waterbuck, Selous Game Reserve.

1991, Aug. 22 Litho. *Perf. 14*

717	A113	10sh multicolored	.15	.15
718	A113	25sh multicolored	.30	.30
719	A113	30sh multicolored	.38	.38
720	A113	50sh multicolored	.65	.65
721	A113	90sh multicolored	1.10	1.10
722	A113	100sh multicolored	1.25	1.25
723	A113	250sh multicolored	3.10	3.10
724	A113	300sh multicolored	3.75	3.75
		Nos. 717-724 (8)	10.68	10.68

Souvenir Sheets

725	A113	400sh multicolored	5.00	5.00
726	A113	400sh multicolored	5.00	5.00

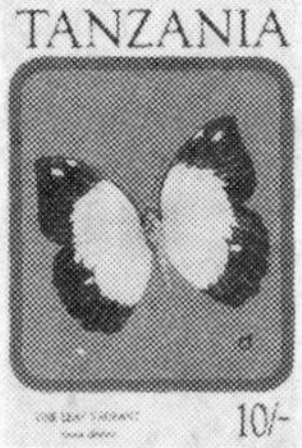
TANZANIA
10/-

Butterflies — A114

Designs: 10sh, Vine leaf vagrant. 15sh, Blue spot commodore. 35sh, Orange admiral. 75sh, Wanderer. 100sh, Jackson's leaf. 150sh, Painted empress. 200sh, Double-banded orange. 300sh, Crawshay's sapphire blue. No. 735, Noble swallowtail. No. 736, Club-tailed charaxes. No. 737, Satyr charaxes. No. 738, Green patch swallowtail.

1991, Aug. 28 Litho. *Perf. 14*

727	A114	10sh multicolored	.15	.15
728	A114	15sh multicolored	.20	.20
729	A114	35sh multicolored	.45	.45
730	A114	75sh multicolored	.95	.95
731	A114	100sh multicolored	1.25	1.25
732	A114	150sh multicolored	1.90	1.90
733	A114	200sh multicolored	2.50	2.50
734	A114	300sh multicolored	3.75	3.75
		Nos. 727-734 (8)	11.15	11.15

Souvenir Sheets

735	A114	400sh multicolored	5.00	5.00
736	A114	400sh multicolored	5.00	5.00
737	A114	400sh multicolored	5.00	5.00
738	A114	400sh multicolored	5.00	5.00

While Nos. 727-736 have the same issue date as Nos. 737-738, the dollar value of Nos. 737-738 was lower when they were released.

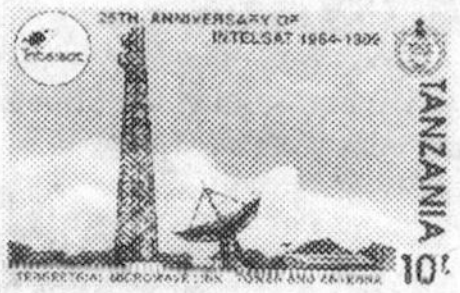
25TH ANNIVERSARY OF INTELSAT 1964-1989
TANZANIA
10/-

Intelsat, 25th Anniv. A115

Designs: 10sh, Microwave link. 25sh, Earth. 100sh, Mwenge standard "B" Earth station. 500sh, Mwenge standard "A" Earth station. 50sh, World map.

1991, Sept. 5 Litho. *Perf. 14*

739	A115	10sh multicolored	.15	.15
740	A115	25sh multicolored	.25	.25
741	A115	100sh multicolored	1.30	1.30
742	A115	500sh multicolored	4.75	4.75
		Nos. 739-742 (4)	6.45	6.45

Souvenir Sheet

743	A115	50sh multicolored	.50	.50

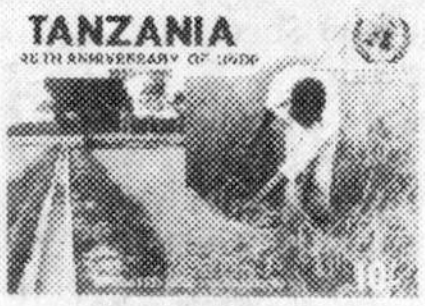
TANZANIA

UN Development Program, 40th Anniv. A116

Designs: 10sh, Irrigated rice farming. 15sh, Vocational training. 100sh, Terrace farming. 500sh, Architectural renovations, vert. 40sh, Helping people to help themselves, vert.

1991, Sept. 16 *Perf. 13¹/₂*

744	A116	10sh multicolored	.15	.15
745	A116	15sh multicolored	.20	.20
746	A116	100sh multicolored	1.30	1.30
747	A116	500sh multicolored	6.50	6.50
		Nos. 744-747 (4)	8.15	8.15

Souvenir Sheet

Perf. 13x12¹/₂

748	A116	40sh black & blue	.52	.52

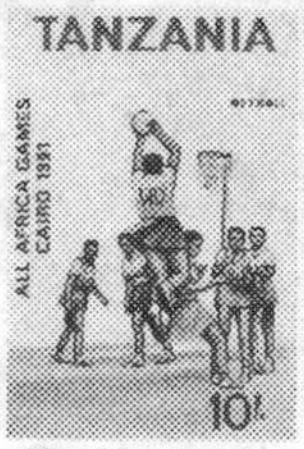
TANZANIA
ALL AFRICA GAMES CAIRO 1991
10/-

All Africa Games, Cairo — A117

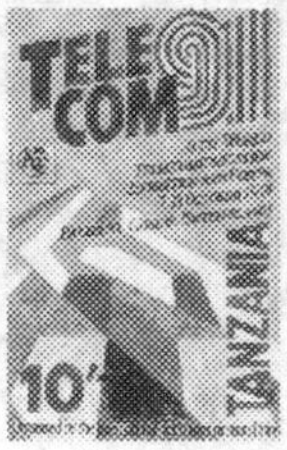
TELECOM 91
10/-
TANZANIA

Telecom '91 — A118

Perf. 12x12¹/₂, 12¹/₂x12

1991, Sept. 20

749	A117	10sh Netball	.15	.15
750	A117	15sh Soccer, horiz.	.20	.20
751	A117	100sh Tennis	1.30	1.30
752	A117	200sh Running	2.60	2.60
753	A117	500sh Baseball, horiz.	6.50	6.50
		Nos. 749-753 (5)	10.75	10.75

Souvenir Sheet

754	A117	500sh Basketball	6.50	6.50

1991, Oct. 1 *Perf. 13¹/₂x14, 14x13¹/₂*

755	A118	10sh shown	.15	.15
756	A118	15sh Telecom '91, horiz.	.20	.20
757	A118	35sh arrows	.45	.45
758	A118	100sh like #757, horiz.	1.30	1.30
		Nos. 755-758 (4)	2.10	2.10

World Telecommunications Day (Nos. 757-758).

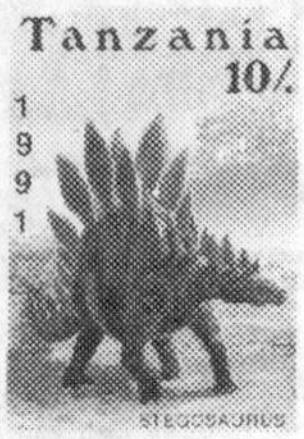
Tanzania
10/-
1991
STEGOSAURUS

Dinosaurs — A119

1991, Oct. 28 *Perf. 12x12¹/₂*

759	A119	10sh Stegosaurus	.15	.15
760	A119	15sh Triceratops	.20	.20
761	A119	25sh Edmontosaurus	.32	.32
762	A119	30sh Plateosaurus	.40	.40
763	A119	35sh Diplodocus	.45	.45
764	A119	100sh Iguanodon	1.30	1.30
765	A119	200sh Silviasaurus	2.60	2.60
		Nos. 759-765 (7)	5.42	5.42

Souvenir Sheet

766	A119	150sh Rhamphorhynchus	2.00	2.00

Miniature Sheets

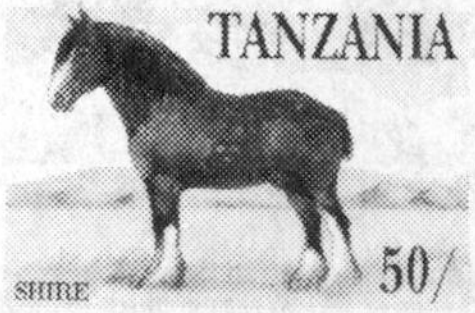
TANZANIA
SHIRE
50/-

Animals and Fish A120

Horses: No. 767a, Shire. b, Thoroughbred. c, Kladruber. d, Appaloosa. e, Hanoverian. f, Arab. g, Breton. h, Exmoor. i, Connemara. j, Lipizzaner. k, Shetland. l, Percheron. m, Pinto. n, Orlov. o, Palomino. p, Welsh cob.

Cats: No. 768a, Japanese bobtail. b, Cornish rex. c, Malayan. d, Tonkinese. e, Abyssinian. f, Russian blue. g, Cymric. h, Somali. i, Siamese. j, Himalayan. k, Singapura. l, Manx. m, Oriental shorthair. n, Maine coon. o, Persian. p, Birman.

African elephants (all designs vert.): No. 769a, One walking left. b, Two with tusks entangled. c, One facing forward. d, One under tree. e, Adult and calf in water, zebra. f, Adult and calf walking into water. g, Two adults and calf in water. h, Adult and calf standing in water. i, One walking right. j, Two, one raising trunk in air. k, One raising trunk in air. l, One facing forward, trunk down, zebra. m, Adult, calf at edge of water, antelope. n, Adult and calf, two more in background. o, One walking toward water. p, Adult with trunk on calf.

Aquarium fish: No. 770a, Jewel tetra. b, Five-banded barb. c, Simpson platy. d, Guppy, e, Zebra danio. f, Neon tetra. g, Siamese fighting fish. h, Tiger barb. i, Red lyretail. j, Goldfish. k, Pearl gourami. l, Angelfish. m, Clown loach. n, Red swordtail. o, Brown discus. p, Rosy barb.

Birds: No. 771a, Budgerigar. b, Rainbow bunting. c, Golden-fronted leafbird. d, Black-headed caique. e, Java sparrow. f, Diamond sparrow. g, Peach-faced lovebird. h, Golden conure. i, Military macaw. j, Celestial parrotlet. k, Sulphur-crested cockatoo. l, Spectacled Amazon parrot. m, Paradise tanager. n, Gouldian finch. o, Masked lovebird. p, Hill mynah.

1991, Oct. 28 Litho. *Perf. 14*

767	A120	50sh Sheet of 16, #a.-p.	10.30	10.30
768	A120	50sh Sheet of 16, #a.-p.	10.30	10.30
769	A120	75sh Sheet of 16, #a.-p.	15.40	15.40
770	A120	75sh Sheet of 16, #a.-p.	15.40	15.40
771	A120	75sh Sheet of 16, #a.-p.	15.40	15.40
		Nos. 767-771 (5)	66.80	66.80

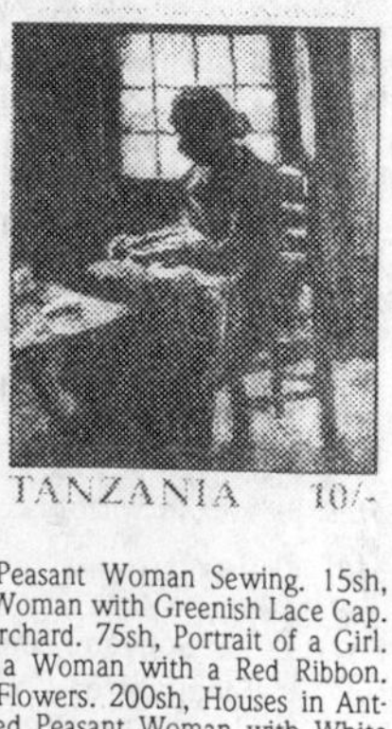
TANZANIA 10/-

Paintings by Vincent Van Gogh — A121

Designs: 10sh, Peasant Woman Sewing. 15sh, Head of a Peasant Woman with Greenish Lace Cap. 35sh, Flowering Orchard. 75sh, Portrait of a Girl. 100sh, Portrait of a Woman with a Red Ribbon. 150sh, Vase with Flowers. 200sh, Houses in Antwerp. 400sh, Seated Peasant Woman with White Cap. No. 780, The Parsonage Garden at Nuenen in the Snow, horiz. No. 781, Bulb Fields, horiz.

1991, Nov. 20 Litho. *Perf. 13½x14*

772 A121 10sh multicolored .15 .15
773 A121 15sh multicolored .20 .20
774 A121 35sh multicolored .45 .45
775 A121 75sh multicolored .95 .95
776 A121 100sh multicolored 1.25 1.25
777 A121 150sh multicolored 1.90 1.90
778 A121 200sh multicolored 2.50 2.50
779 A121 400sh multicolored 5.00 5.00
Nos. 772-779 (8) 12.40 12.40

Size: 127x102mm

Imperf

780 A121 400sh multicolored 5.00 5.00
781 A121 400sh multicolored 5.00 5.00

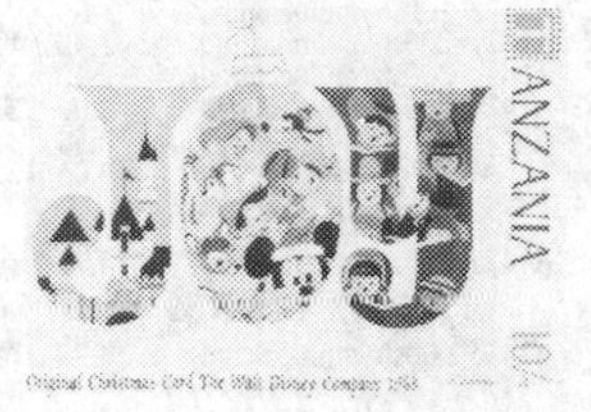

Walt Disney Christmas Cards — A122

Design and date of card: 10sh, "Joy", 1968. 25sh, Mickey, Pluto and Goofy at fireplace, 1981. 35sh, Robin Hood and merry men celebrating, 1973. 75sh, Tree of greetings, Mickey, 1967. 100sh, Goofy, Mickey and Donald trying to catch Santa coming down chimney, 1969, vert. 150sh, Mickey on top of Christmas ornament, 1976, vert. 200sh, Clarabelle Cow with bells, 1935, vert. 300sh, Orphan mice reading book of tricks, 1935, vert. No. 790, Mickey wearing Santa hat and surrounded by Disney characters, 1968, vert. No. 791, Mickey with present for Donald, 1935, vert.

Perf. 13½x14, 14x13½

1991, Dec. Litho.

782 A122 10sh multicolored .15 .15
783 A122 25sh multicolored .30 .30
784 A122 35sh multicolored .45 .45
785 A122 75sh multicolored .95 .95
786 A122 100sh multicolored 1.25 1.25
787 A122 150sh multicolored 1.90 1.90
788 A122 200sh multicolored 2.50 2.50
789 A122 300sh multicolored 3.75 3.75
Nos. 782-789 (8) 11.25 11.25

Souvenir Sheets

790 A122 500sh multicolored 6.25 6.25
791 A122 500sh multicolored 6.25 6.25

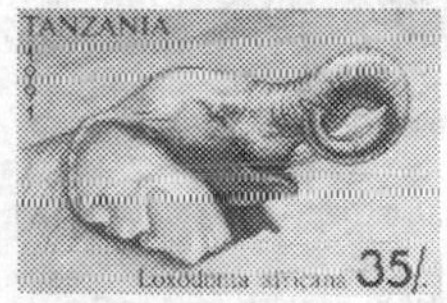

Elephants A123

Designs: 10sh, 15sh, 25sh, 100sh, Various pictures of elephas maximus. 30sh, 35sh, 200sh, Various pictures of loxodonta africana. 400sh, Mammut mammuthus.

Perf. 12x12½, 12½x12

1991, Nov. 28 Litho.

792 A123 10sh multi, vert. .15 .15
793 A123 15sh multi, vert. .20 .20
794 A123 25sh multi, vert. .30 .30
795 A123 30sh multi, vert. .40 .40
796 A123 35sh multicolored .45 .45
797 A123 100sh multicolored 1.25 1.25
798 A123 200sh multicolored 2.50 2.50
Nos. 792-798 (7) 5.25 5.25

Souvenir Sheet

799 A123 400sh multicolored 5.00 5.00

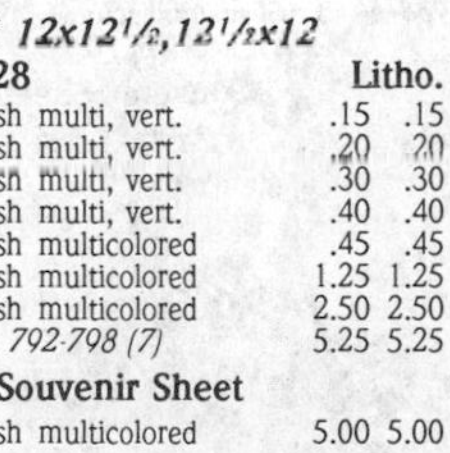

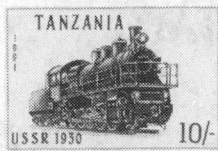

Locomotives A124

Perf. 12½x12, 12x12½

1991, Dec. 10

800 A124 10sh USSR 1930 .15 .15
801 A124 15sh Japan 1964 .20 .20
802 A124 25sh Russia 1834, vert. .30 .30
803 A124 35sh France 1979 .45 .45
804 A124 60sh France 1972 .80 .80
805 A124 100sh United Kingdom 1972 1.25 1.25
806 A124 300sh Russia 1837, vert. 3.75 3.75
Nos. 800-806 (7) 6.90 6.90

Souvenir Sheet

807 A124 100sh France, 1952, vert. 1.25 1.25

Miniature Sheets

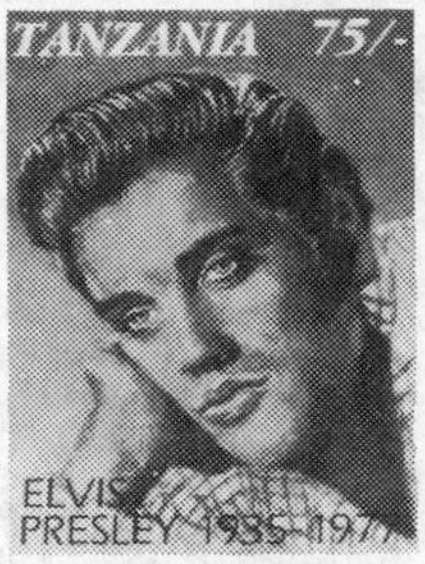

Entertainers A125

Nos. 808a-808i, 812, Various portraits of Elvis Presley.

Nos. 809a-809i, 813, Various portraits of Marilyn Monroe.

Nos. 810a-810i, 814, Various portraits of Bruce Lee.

Black entertainers: No. 813, Scott Joplin. b, Sammy Davis, Jr. c, Joan Armatrading. d, Louis Armstrong. e, Miriam Makeba. f, Lionel Ritchie. g, Whitney Houston, h, Bob Marley. i, Tina Turner. No. 815, Kouyate family.

1992, Feb. 15 *Perf. 14*

808 A125 75sh Sheet of 9, #a.-i. 8.50 8.50
809 A125 75sh Sheet of 9, #a.-i. 8.50 8.50
810 A125 75sh Sheet of 9, #a.-i. 8.50 8.50
811 A125 75sh Sheet of 9, #a.-i. 8.50 8.50
Nos. 808-811 (4) 34.00 34.00

Souvenir Sheets

812 A125 500sh multicolored 6.25 6.25
813 A125 500sh multicolored 6.25 6.25
814 A125 500sh multicolored 6.25 5.25
815 A125 500sh multicolored 6.25 6.25
Nos. 812-815 (4) 25.00 24.00

Nos. 812-815 each contain one 29x43mm stamp.

See #950 for #808 inscribed "15th Anniversary."

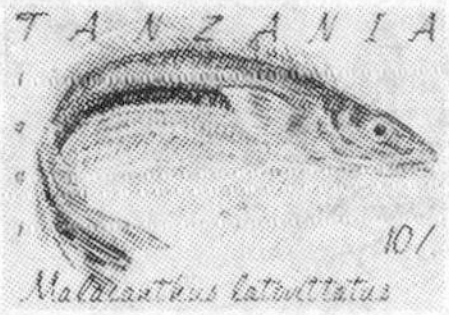

Fish of Tanzania A126

Designs: 10sh, Malacanthus latovittatus. 15sh, Lamprologus tretocephalus. 25sh, Lamprologus calvus. 35sh, Hemichromis bimaculatusl. 60sh, Aphyosemion bivittatum. No. 821, Synanceia verrucosa. 300sh, Aphyosemion ahli. No. 823, Regalecus glesne.

1992, Mar. 8 *Perf. 12½x12*

816 A126 10sh multicolored .15 .15
817 A126 15sh multicolored .20 .20
818 A126 25sh multicolored .32 .32
819 A126 35sh multicolored .45 .45
820 A126 60sh multicolored .75 .75
821 A126 100sh multicolored 1.25 1.25
822 A126 300sh multicolored 3.75 3.75
Nos. 816-822 (7) 6.87 6.87

Souvenir Sheet

823 A126 100sh multicolored 1.25 1.25

Miniature Sheet

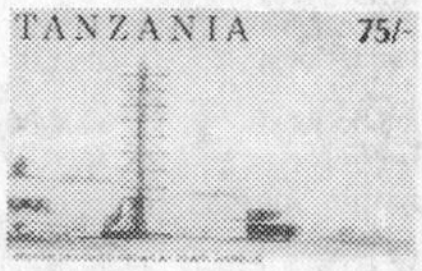

World War II in the Pacific A127

Designs: No. 824a, British-designed radar at Pearl Harbor. b, Churchill declares war on Japan. c, Repulse destroyed. d, Prince of Wales sunk. e, Singapore falls to Japanese. f, Hermes is sunk off Ceylon. g, Airfields in Malaya attacked. h, Hong Kong falls to Japanese. i, Japanese Daihatsu landing craft. j, Japanese cruiser Haguro in Java Sea.

1992, Apr. 27 *Perf. 14½x15*

824 A127 75sh Sheet of 10, #a.-j. 9.50 9.50

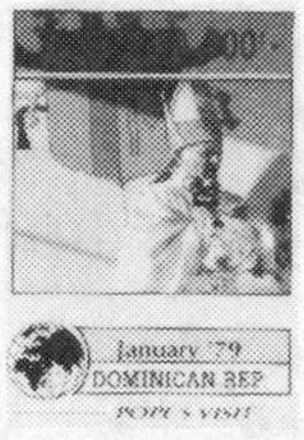

Papal Visits — A128

Pope John Paul II's visits to: No. 825a, Dominican Republic, 1979. b, Mexico, 1979. c, Poland, 1979. d, Ireland, 1979. e, UN, New York, 1979. f, US, 1979. g, Turkey, 1979. h, Zaire, 1980. i, Congo, 1980. j, Kenya, 1980. k, Ghana, 1980. l, Upper Volta, 1980.

No. 826a, Ivory Coast, 1980. b, France, 1980. c, Brazil, 1980. d, West Germany, 1980. e, Pakistan, 1981. f, Philippines, 1981. g, Guam, 1981. h, Japan, 1981. h, Alaska, 1981. i, Nigeria, 1982. j, Benin, 1982. l. Gabon, 1982.

No. 827a, Equatorial Guinea, 1982. b, Portugal, 1982. c, Great Britain, 1982. d, Argentina, 1982. e, UN, Geneva, 1982. f, San Marino, 1982. g, Spain, 1982. h, Costa Rica, 1983. i, Panama, 1983. j, El Salvador, 1983. k, Nicaragua, 1983. l, Guatemala, 1983.

No. 828a, Honduras, 1983. b, Belize, 1983. c, Haiti, 1983. d, Poland, 1983. e, France, 1983. f, Austria, 1983. g, Alaska, 1984. h, South Korea, 1984. i, Papua New Guinea, 1984. j, Solomon Islands, 1984. k, Thailand, 1984. l, Switzerland, 1984.

No. 829a, Canada, 1984. b, Dominican Republic, 1984. c, Puerto Rico, 1984. d, Venezuela, 1985. e, Ecuador, 1985. f, Peru, 1985. g, Trinidad & Tobago, 1985. h, Netherlands, 1985. i, Luxembourg, 1985. j, Belgium, 1985. k, Togo, 1985. l, Ivory Coast, 1985.

No. 830a, Cameroun, 1985. b, Central African Republic, 1985. c, Zaire, 1985. d, Kenya, 1985. e, Morocco, 1985. f, Liechtenstein, 1985. g, India, 1986. h, Colombia, 1986. i, St. Lucia, 1986. j, France, 1986. k, Bangladesh, 1986. l, Singapore, 1986.

No. 831a, Fiji, 1986. b, New Zealand, 1986. c, Australia, 1986. d, Seychelles, 1986. e, Uruguay, 1987. f, Chile, 1987. g, Argentina, 1987. h, West Germany, 1987. i, Poland, 1987. j, US, 1987. k, Canada, 1987. l, Uruguay, 1988.

No. 832a, Bolivia, 1988. b, Peru, 1988. c, Paraguay, 1988. d, Austria, 1988. e, Zimbabwe, 1988. f, Botswana, 1988. g, Lesotho, 1988. h, Swaziland, 1988. i, Mozambique, 1988. j, France, 1988. k, Madagascar, 1989. l, Reunion, 1989.

No. 833a, Zambia, 1989. b, Malawi, 1989. c, Norway, 1989. d, Iceland, 1989. e, Finland, 1989. f, Denmark, 1989. g, Sweden, 1989. h, Spain, 1989. i, South Korea, 1989. j, Indonesia, 1989. k, Mauritius, 1989. l, Cape Verde, 1990.

No. 834a, Mali, 1990. b, Guinea-Bissau, 1990. c, Burkina Faso, 1990. d, Chad, 1990. e, Czechoslovakia, 1990. f, Mexico, 1990. g, Curacao, 1990. h, Malta, 1990. i, Tanzania, 1990. j, Burundi, 1990. k, Rwanda, 1990. l, Ivory Coast, 1990.

1992, Apr. 13 *Perf. 14*

Sheets of 12 + 4 Labels

825 A128 100sh #a.-l. 15.00 15.00
826 A128 100sh #a.-l. 15.00 15.00
827 A128 100sh #a.-l. 15.00 15.00
828 A128 100sh #a.-l. 15.00 15.00
829 A128 100sh #a.-l. 15.00 15.00
830 A128 100sh #a.-l. 15.00 15.00
831 A128 100sh #a.-l. 15.00 15.00
832 A128 100sh #a.-l. 15.00 15.00
833 A128 100sh #a.-l. 15.00 15.00
834 A128 100sh #a.-l. 15.00 15.00
Nos. 825-834 (10) 150.00 150.00

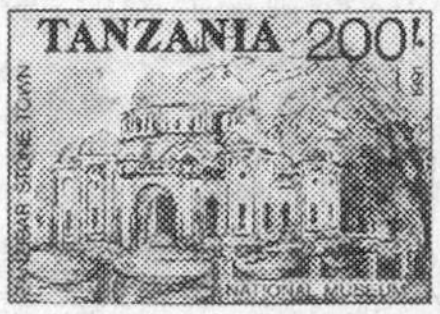

Zanzibar Stone Town A129

Designs: No. 839a, 150sh, Old fort. b, 300sh, Maruhubi ruins.

Perf. 12x12½, 12½x12

1992, Apr. 15

835 A129 10sh Balcony .15 .15
836 A129 20sh Bahlnara mosque .25 .25
837 A129 30sh High Court bldg. .38 .38
838 A129 200sh Natl. museum 2.50 2.50
Nos. 835-838 (4) 3.28 3.28

Souvenir Sheet

839 A129 Sheet of 2, #a.-b. 5.65 5.65

Nos. 835-837 are vert.

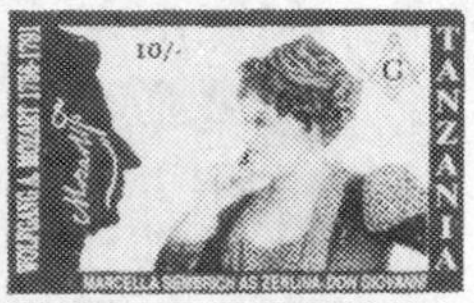

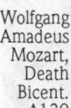

Wolfgang Amadeus Mozart, Death Bicent. A130

Designs: 10sh, Marcella Sembrich as Zerlina in Don Giovanni. 50sh, Symphony Number 41, Jupiter. 300sh, Luciano Pavarotti as Idamente in Idomeneo. 500sh, Wolfgang Amadeus Mozart, vert.

1992, Aug. 1 *Perf. 14*

840 A130 10sh violet & blk .15 .15
841 A130 50sh multicolored .60 .60
842 A130 300sh violet & blk 3.75 3.75
Nos. 840-842 (3) 4.50 4.50

Souvenir Sheet

843 A130 500sh olive brn & blk 5.00 5.00

While No. 843 has the same issue date as Nos. 840-842, the dollar value was lower when it were released.

No. 843 contains one 38x50mm stamp.

1992, Aug. 1

Designs: 10sh, Insignia, giraffe and elephant. 15sh, Scouts in canoe. 400sh, John Glenn's Gemini space capsule orbiting Earth. 500sh, Boy scout, vert.

844 A130 10sh multicolored .15 .15
845 A130 15sh multicolored .20 .20
846 A130 400sh multicolored 5.00 5.00
Nos. 844-846 (3) 5.35 5.35

Souvenir Sheet

847 A130 500sh multicolored 5.00 5.00

Lord Robert Baden-Powell, Founder of Boy Scouts, 50th Death Anniv. (in 1991).

While No. 847 has the same issue date as Nos. 844-846, the dollar value was lower when it were released.

No. 847 contains one 38x50mm stamp.

1992, Aug. 1

Charles de Gaulle (1890-1970): 25sh, French Resistance Monument and medal. 30sh, First Free French tank at Omaha beach, Normandy. 150sh, Concorde at de Gaulle Airport. 500sh, France #439 with Cross of Lorraine overprint and Free French stamp, vert.

848 A130 25sh multicolored .30 .30
849 A130 30sh multicolored .40 .40
850 A130 150sh multicolored 1.90 1.90
Nos. 848-850 (3) 2.60 2.60

Souvenir Sheet

851 A130 500sh multicolored 5.00 5.00

While No. 851 has the same issue date as Nos. 848-850, the dollar value was lower when it was released.

No. 851 contains one 38x50mm stamp.

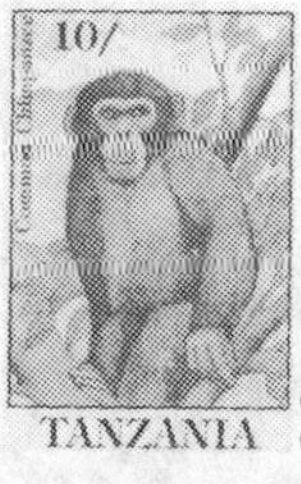

Common Chimpanzee — A131

Various chimpanzees in natural habitat.

1992, Mar. 30

852 A131 10sh multicolored .15 .15
853 A131 15sh multicolored .20 .20
854 A131 35sh multicolored .45 .45
855 A131 75sh multicolored .95 .95
856 A131 100sh multicolored 1.25 1.25
857 A131 150sh multicolored 1.90 1.90
858 A131 200sh multicolored 2.50 2.50
859 A131 300sh multicolored 3.75 3.75
Nos. 852-859 (8) 11.15 11.15

Souvenir Sheets

1992, Mar. 3

860 A131 400sh Swinging from tree 5.00 5.00
861 A131 400sh Eating termites 5.00 5.00

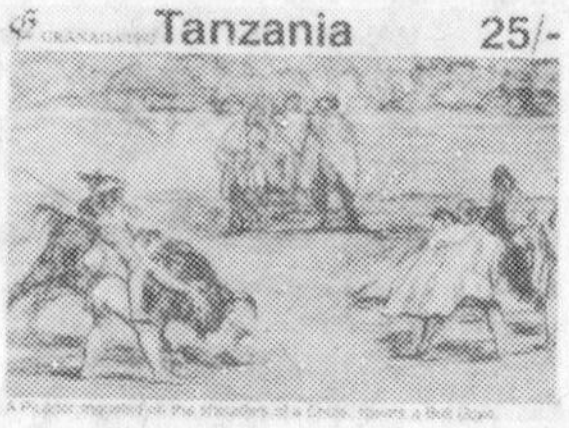

Spanish Art — A132

Drawings by Goya: 25sh, A Picador mounted on the shoulders of a Chulo, spears a Bull. 100sh, The Dream of Reason brings forth Monsters, vert. 150sh, Another Madness (of Martincho) in the Plaza de Zaragoza. 200sh, Recklessness of Martincho in the Plaza de Zaragoza.

No. 866, Seascape, by Mariana Salvador Maella.

1992 *Perf. 13*

862 A132	25sh black & red brn	.30	.30
863 A132	100sh black & brown	1.25	1.25
864 A132	150sh black & red brn	1.90	1.90
865 A132	200sh black & red brn	2.50	2.50

Size: 120x95mm

Imperf

866 A132	400sh multicolored	5.00	5.00
	Nos. 862-866 (5)	10.95	10.95

Granada '92.

1992 *Perf. 13*

Drawings by Diego da Silva Velazquez: 35sh, Philip IV at Fraga. 50sh, The Head of the Stag. 75sh, The Cardinal Infante Don Fernando as a Hunter. 300sh, Pablo de Valladolid. No. 871, Two Men at Table.

867 A132	35sh multicolored	.45	.45
868 A132	50sh multicolored	.65	.65
869 A132	75sh multicolored	.95	.95
870 A132	300sh multicolored	3.75	3.75

Size: 120x95mm

Imperf

871 A132	400sh multicolored	5.00	5.00
	Nos. 867-871 (5)	10.80	10.80

Granada '92.

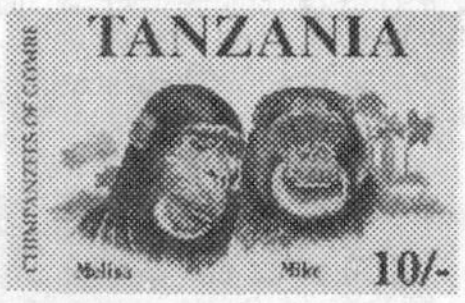

A133

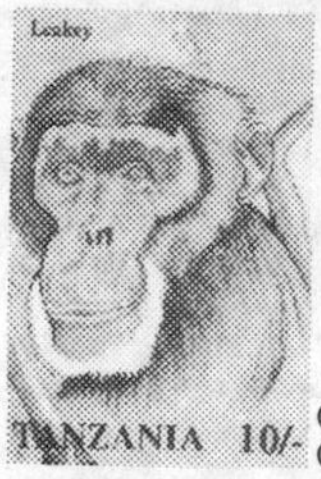

Chimpanzees of Gombe — A134

Designs: No. 872, Melisa and Mike. No. 873, Leakey and David Greybeard. No. 874, Fifi eating termites. No. 875 Galahad.

No. 876a, 10sh, Leakey. b, 15sh, Fifi. c, 20sh, Faben. d, 30sh, David Greybeard. e, 35sh, Mike. f, 50sh, Galahad. g, 100sh, Melisa. h, 200sh, Flo.

No. 877, Fifi, Flo, and Faben.

1992, May 29 **Litho.** *Perf. 14*

872 A133	10sh multicolored	.15	.15
873 A133	15sh multicolored	.15	.15
874 A133	30sh multicolored	.30	.30
875 A133	35sh multicolored	.35	.35
	Nos. 872-875 (4)	.95	.95

Miniature Sheet

876 A134	Sheet of 8, #a.-h.	4.75	4.75

Souvenir Sheet

877 A133	100sh multicolored	1.00	1.00

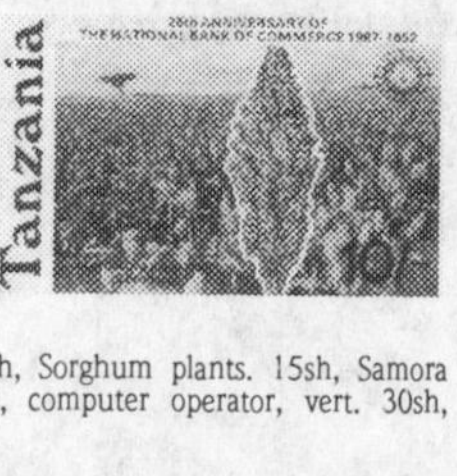

Natl. Bank of Commerce, 25th Anniv. A135

Designs: 10sh, Sorghum plants. 15sh, Samora Avenue branch, computer operator, vert. 30sh, Head office. 35sh, Bankers Training Center. 40sh, Batik tie dyeing.

1992, June 22

878 A135	10sh multicolored	.15	.15
879 A135	15sh multicolored	.15	.15
880 A135	35sh multicolored	.35	.35
881 A135	40sh multicolored	.40	.40
	Nos. 878-881 (4)	1.05	1.05

Souvenir Sheet

882 A135	30sh multicolored	.30	.30

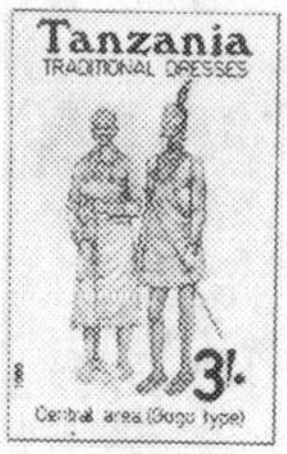

A136

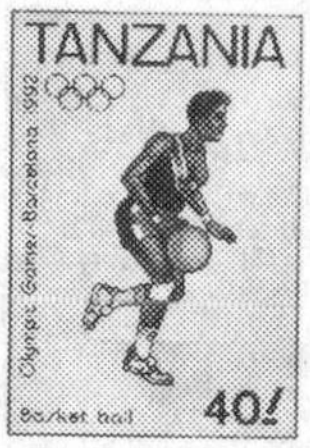

A137

Traditional Dress: 3sh, Gogo, central area. 5sh, Swahili, coastal area. 9sh, Hehe, southern highlands and Makonde, southern area. 12sh, Maasai, northern area. 40sh, Mwarusha.

1992, Apr. 30 **Litho.** *Perf. 14½*

883 A136	3sh multicolored	.15	.15
884 A136	5sh multicolored	.15	.15
885 A136	9sh multicolored	.15	.15
886 A136	12sh multicolored	.15	.15
	Set value	.18	.18

Souvenir Sheet

887 A136	40sh multicolored	.25	.25

Dated 1989.

1992, July 23 *Perf. 12x12½*

888 A137	40sh Basketball	.25	.25
889 A137	100sh Billiards	.68	.68
890 A137	200sh Table tennis	1.35	1.35
891 A137	400sh Darts	2.70	2.70
	Nos. 888-891 (4)	4.98	4.98

Souvenir Sheet

892 A137	500sh Weight lifting	3.40	3.40

1992 Summer Olympics, Barcelona.

Miniature Sheet

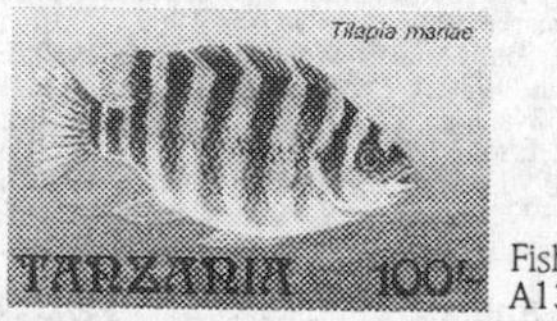

Fish A138

Designs: No. 893a, Tilapia mariae. b, Capoeta hulstaerti. c, Tropheus moorii. d, Synodontis angelicus. e, Julidochromis dickfeldi. f, Tilapia nilotica. g, Nothobranchius rachovii. h, Pseudotropheus crabro. i, Lamprologus leleupi. j, Pseudotropheus zebra. k, Julidochromis marlieri. l, Chalinochromis brichardi.

Designs: No. 894, Haplochromis "electric blue." No. 895, Lamprologus brevis. No. 896, Nothobranchius palmqvisti.

1992, Oct. **Litho.** *Perf. 13½*

893 A138	100sh Sheet of 12, #a.-l.	8.20	8.20

Souvenir Sheets

894 A138	500sh multicolored	3.50	3.50
895 A138	500sh multicolored	3.50	3.50
896 A138	500sh multicolored	3.50	3.50

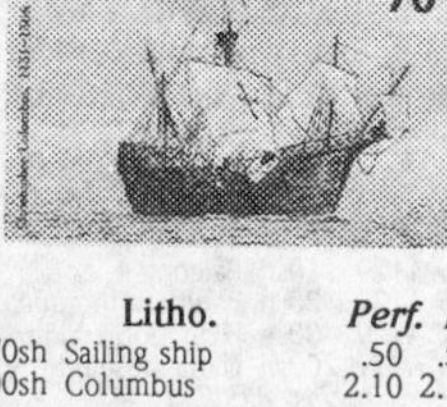

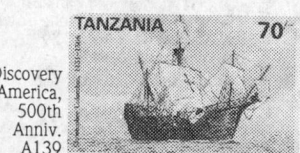

Discovery of America, 500th Anniv. A139

1992, Oct. **Litho.** *Perf. 14*

897 A139	70sh Sailing ship	.50	.50
898 A139	300sh Columbus	2.10	2.10

Souvenir Sheet

899 A139	500sh Columbus, diff.	3.50	3.50

Miniature Sheet

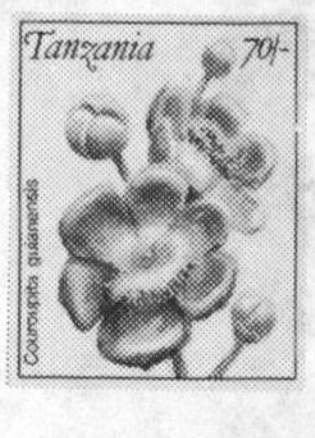

Flowers in Rio de Janeiro Botanical Garden — A140

Designs: No. 900a, Couroupita guianensis. b, Jacaranda acutifolia. c, Psychopsis papilio. d, Nelumbo nucifera. e, Brownea grandiceps. f, Coffea arabica. g, Monodora myristica. h, Calaranthus rosea. i, Hibiscus schizopetalus. j, Carpobrotus edulis. k, Adenium obesum. l, Delonix regia. m, Agapanthus praecox. n, Zantedeschia aethiopica. o, Protea cynaroides. p, Cassia fistula. q, Aganisia cyanea. r, Heliconia rostrata. s, Cattelya luteola. t, Lagerstroemia speciosa.

500sh, Avenue of Royal Palms, Rio.

1992, Nov. 5 **Litho.** *Perf. 14½*

900 A140	70sh Sheet of 20, #a.-t.	7.50	7.50

Souvenir Sheet

901 A140	500sh multicolored	3.50	3.50

Miniature Sheet

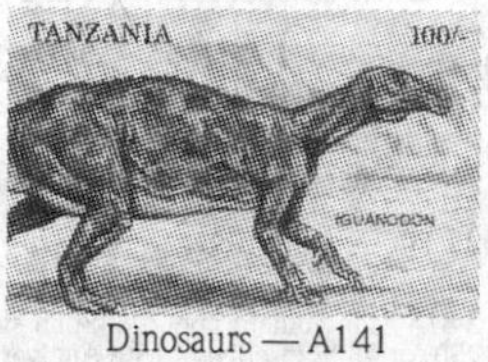

Dinosaurs — A141

Designs: a, Iguanodon. b, Saltasaurus. c, Cetiosaurus. d, Camarasaurus. e, Spinosaurus. f, Stegosaurus. g, Allosaurus. h, Ceratosaurus. i, Lesothosaurus. j, Anchisaurus. k, Ornithomimus. l, Baronyx. m, Pachycephalosaurus. n, Heterodontosaurus. o, Dryosaurus. p, Coelophysis.

1992, Nov. 5 **Litho.** *Perf. 14*

902 A141	100sh Sheet of 16, #a.-p.	11.50	11.50

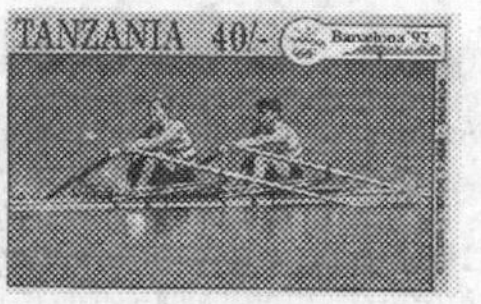

1992 Olympics, Albertville and Barcelona A142

Designs: 20sh, 4000-meter pursuit cycling, vert. 40sh, Double sculls. 50sh, Water polo. 70sh, Women's single luge. 100sh, Marathon. 150sh, Uneven parallel bars. 200sh, Ice hockey, vert, 400sh, Rings, vert.

No. 911, Tennis, vert. No. 912, Soccer, vert.

1992, Nov. 16 **Litho.** *Perf. 14*

903 A142	20sh multicolored	.15	.15
904 A142	40sh multicolored	.28	.28
905 A142	50sh multicolored	.35	.35
906 A142	70sh multicolored	.50	.50
907 A142	100sh multicolored	.70	.70
908 A142	150sh multicolored	1.05	1.05
909 A142	200sh multicolored	1.40	1.40
910 A142	400sh multicolored	2.80	2.80
	Nos. 903-910 (8)	7.23	7.23

Souvenir Sheets

911 A142	500sh multicolored	3.50	3.50
912 A142	500sh multicolored	3.50	3.50

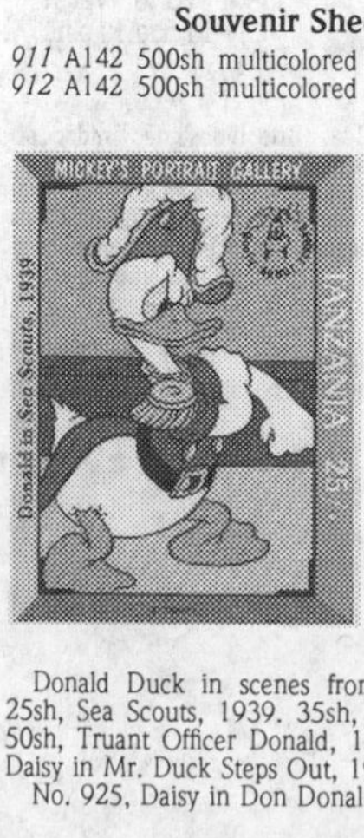

Mickey's Portrait Gallery A142a

Donald Duck in scenes from Disney movies: 25sh, Sea Scouts, 1939. 35sh, Fire Chief, 1940. 50sh, Truant Officer Donald, 1941. 500sh, With Daisy in Mr. Duck Steps Out, 1940.

No. 925, Daisy in Don Donald, 1937.

Disney Characters in scenes from Disney movies: No. 913, Hawaiian Holiday, 1937. No. 914, Society Dog Show, 1939. 75sh, Clock Cleaners, 1937. No. 919, Magician Mickey, 1937. No. 920, Goofy and Wilbur, 1939. 200sh, The Nifty Nineties, 1941. 300sh, Society Dog Show, 1939. 400sh, Pluto's Quin-Puplets, 1937. No. 926, Brave Little Tailor, 1938, horiz. No. 927, Forever Goofy.

1992, Nov. 30 **Litho.** *Perf. 13½x14*

913 A142a	25sh multicolored	.18	.18
914 A142a	25sh multicolored	.18	.18
915 A142a	25sh multicolored	.18	.18
916 A142a	35sh multicolored	.25	.25
917 A142a	50sh multicolored	.35	.35
918 A142a	75sh multicolored	.52	.52
919 A142a	100sh multicolored	.70	.70
920 A142a	100sh multicolored	.70	.70
921 A142a	200sh multicolored	1.40	1.40
922 A142a	300sh multicolored	2.10	2.10
923 A142a	400sh multicolored	3.00	3.00
924 A142a	500sh multicolored	3.50	3.50
	Nos. 913-924 (12)	13.06	13.06

Souvenir Sheets

925 A142a	600sh multicolored	4.25	4.25

Perf. 14x13½

926 A142a	600sh multicolored	4.25	4.25

Perf. 13½x14

927 A142a	600sh multicolored	4.25	4.25

Nos. 668-673 & 678 Ovptd. in Black or Red

40th Anniversary of the Accession HM Queen Elizabeth II 1952-1992

1992 **Litho.** *Perf. 14*

928 A106	50sh on #668	.35	.35
929 A106	50sh on #669	.35	.35
a.	Pair, #928-929	.70	.70
930 A106	75sh on #670	.55	.55
931 A106	75sh on #671	.55	.55
a.	Pair, #930-931	1.10	1.10
932 A106	100sh on #672	.75	.75
933 A106	100sh on #673	.75	.75
a.	Pair, #932-933	1.50	1.50
	Nos. 928-933 (6)	3.30	3.30

Souvenir Sheet

934 A106	350sh on #678 (R)	2.50	2.50

Overprint appears on one line in sheet margin of No. 934.

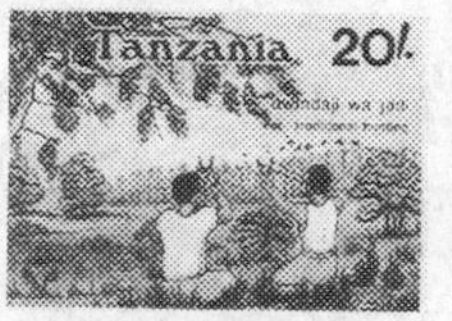

Traditional Hunting A143

Designs: 20sh, Slingshots used on birds. 40sh, Various weapons. 70sh, Bow and arrow used on gazelles. 100sh, Long knife, wooden club used on gazelles. 150sh, Spear and shield used on lion.

1992 **Litho.** *Perf. 13½*

935 A143	20sh multicolored	.15	.15
936 A143	70sh multicolored	.48	.48
937 A143	100sh multicolored	.70	.70
938 A143	150sh multicolored	1.00	1.00
	Nos. 935-938 (4)	2.33	2.33

Souvenir Sheet

Perf. 12½

939 A143	40sh multicolored	.40	.40

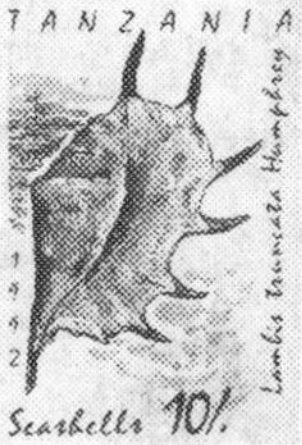

Shells — A144

Designs: 10sh, Lambis truncata Humphrey. 15sh, Cypraecassis rufa. 25sh, Vexillum rugosum. 30sh, Conus litteratus. 35sh, Corculum cardissa. 50sh, Murex ramosus. 250sh, Melo melo. 300sh, Tridacha gigas.

1992, June 30 *Perf. 12x12½*

940 A144	10sh multicolored	.15	.15
941 A144	15sh multicolored	.15	.15
942 A144	25sh multicolored	.18	.18
943 A144	30sh multicolored	.22	.22
944 A144	35sh multicolored	.25	.25

945 A144	50sh multicolored		.35	.35
946 A144	250sh multicolored		1.75	1.75
	Nos. 940-946 (7)		3.05	3.05

Souvenir Sheet

947 A144	300sh multicolored	2.00	2.00

No. 808 Inscribed Vertically "15th Anniversary"

1992 Litho. *Perf. 14*

949 A125	75sh Sheet of 9, #a.-i.	6.50	6.50

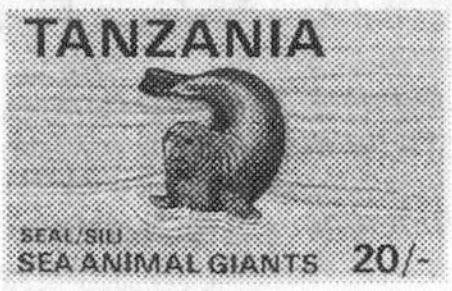

Marine Life — A145

1992 Litho. *Perf. 14*

950 A145	20sh Seal	.15	.15
951 A145	30sh Whale	.22	.22
952 A145	70sh Shark	.50	.50
953 A145	100sh Walrus	.70	.70
	Nos. 950-953 (4)	1.57	1.57

Souvenir Sheet

954 A145	500sh Sea turtle	3.50	3.50

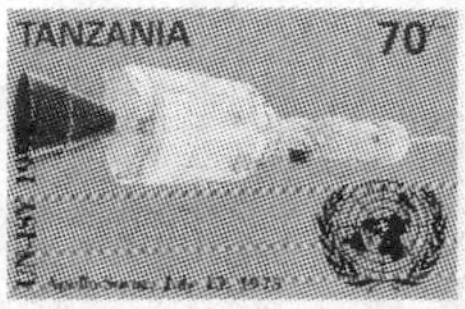

A146

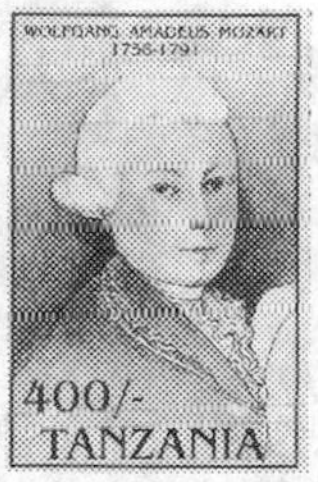

Anniversaries and Events — A147

Designs: 30sh, Count Ferdinand von Zeppelin. 70sh, Apollo-Soyuz. No. 957, Child being offered apple. No. 958, African elephant. No. 959, Lions Intl. emblem, man being given glasses. No. 960, Zebra. 300sh, Graf Zeppelin. No. 962, Space shuttle in Earth orbit. No. 963, Wolfgang Amadeus Mozart. No. 964, Voyager 2. No. 965, Unidentified zeppelin. No. 966, African elephant, diff. No. 967, Scene from "The Magic Flute."

1992 Litho. *Perf. 14*

955 A146	30sh multicolored	.22	.22
956 A146	70sh multicolored	.50	.50
957 A146	150sh multicolored	1.05	1.05
958 A146	150sh multicolored	1.05	1.05
959 A146	200sh multicolored	1.40	1.40
960 A146	200sh multicolored	1.40	1.40
961 A146	300sh multicolored	2.10	2.10
962 A146	400sh multicolored	2.80	2.80
963 A147	400sh multicolored	2.80	2.80
	Nos. 955-963 (9)	13.32	13.32

Souvenir Sheets

964 A146	500sh multicolored	3.50	3.50
965 A146	500sh multicolored	3.50	3.50
966 A146	500sh multicolored	3.50	3.50
967 A147	800sh multicolored	5.50	5.50

Count Zeppelin, 75th death anniv. (#955, 961, 965). Intl. Space Year (#956, 962, 964). Intl. Conference on Nutrition (#957). Earth Summit, Rio de Janeiro (#958, 960, 966).Lions Intl., 75th anniv. (#959). Wolfgang Amadeus Mozart, bicent. of death (in 1991) (#963, 967).

Issued: Nos. 955-956, 961-962, 964-965, Nov.; Nos. 957-960, 966, Dec.

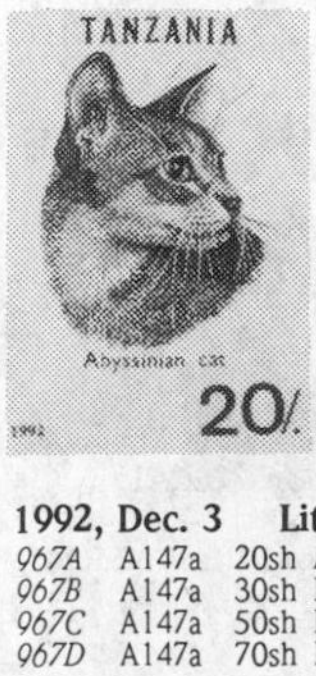

Cats — A147a

1992, Dec. 3 Litho. *Perf. 12x12½*

967A	A147a	20sh Abyssinian	.15	.15
967B	A147a	30sh Havana	.20	.20
967C	A147a	50sh Persian black	.35	.35
967D	A147a	70sh Persian blue	.50	.50
967E	A147a	100sh European silver tabby	.70	.70
967F	A147a	150sh Persian silver tabby	1.00	1.00
967G	A147a	200sh Maine	1.40	1.40
		Nos. 967A-967G (7)	4.30	4.30

Souvenir Sheet

967H	A147a	300sh European	2.00	2.00

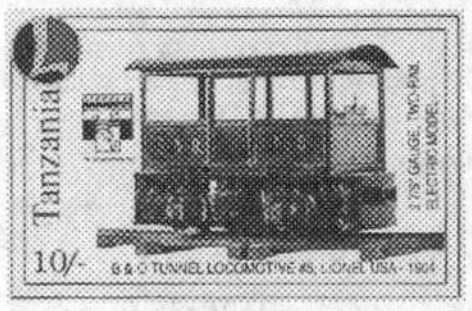

Model Trains A148

Lionel models: 10sh, B & O Tunnel locomotive #5, 2⅞-inch gauge, 1904. 20sh, Liberty Bell #385E, standard gauge, 1930. 30sh, Armored motor car #203, standard gauge, 1917. 50sh, Open trolley #202, standard gauge, 1910-14. 70sh, Macy special #450, standrad gauge. 100sh, Milwaukee Road bi-polar electric #381E, standard gauge, 1929. 200sh, New York Central "S" type, standard gauge, 1912. 300sh, 4-4-0 American #7 (thick rim), standard gauge, 1914. No. 976, Wind-up hand car with Mickey and Minnie Mouse, O-27 gauge, 1936. No. 977, Clear plastic F-3 display model, O gauge, 1947.

1992, Dec. 10 Litho. *Perf. 14*

968 A148	10sh multicolored	.15	.15
969 A148	20sh multicolored	.15	.15
970 A148	30sh multicolored	.22	.22
971 A148	50sh multicolored	.35	.35
972 A148	70sh multicolored	.50	.50
973 A148	100sh multicolored	.70	.70
974 A148	200sh multicolored	1.40	1.40
975 A148	300sh multicolored	2.10	2.10
	Nos. 968-975 (8)	5.57	5.57

Souvenir Sheets

976 A148	500sh multicolored	3.50	3.50
977 A148	500sh multicolored	3.50	3.50

Genoa '92.

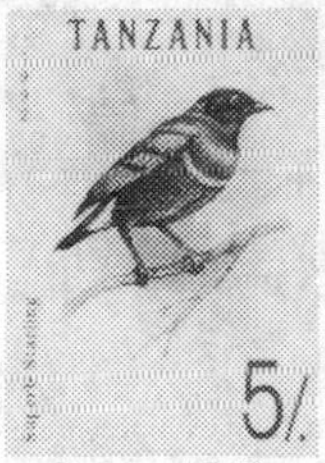

Birds — A149

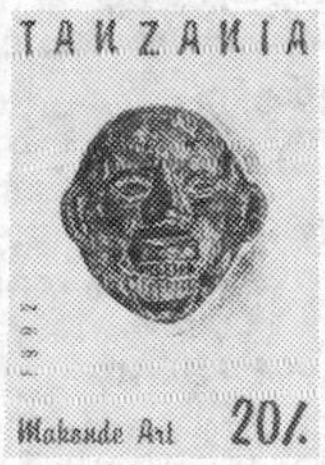

Makonde Art — A149a

1992, Dec. 10 Litho. *Perf. 12x12½*

978 A149	5sh Superb starling	.15	.15
979 A149	10sh Canary	.15	.15
980 A149	15sh Four-colored bush shrike	.15	.15
981 A149	25sh Grey-headed kingfisher	.15	.15
982 A149	30sh Common kingfisher	.15	.15
983 A149	35sh Yellow-billed ox pecker	.16	.16
984 A149	150sh Black throated honeyquide	.75	.75
	Set value	1.30	1.30

Souvenir Sheet

Perf. 12½x12

985 A149	300sh European cuckoo, horiz.	2.00	2.00

1992, Dec. 24 Litho. *Perf. 12x12½*

Various carved faces.

985A	A149a	20sh multicolored	.15	.15
985B	A149a	30sh multicolored	.20	.20
985C	A149a	50sh multicolored	.35	.35
985D	A149a	70sh multicolored	.50	.50
985E	A149a	100sh multicolored	.70	.70
985F	A149a	150sh multicolored	1.00	1.00
985G	A149a	200sh multicolored	1.40	1.40
		Nos. 985A-985G (7)	4.30	4.30

Souvenir Sheet

985H	A149a	350sh multicolored	2.50	2.50

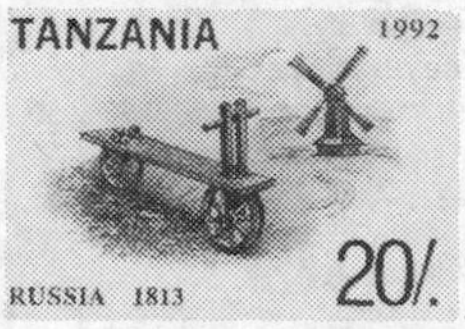

Bicycles A149b

1992, Dec. 30 Litho. *Perf. 12½x12*

985I	A149b	20sh Russia, 1813	.15	.15
985J	A149b	30sh Germany, 1840	.20	.20
985K	A149b	50sh Germany, 1818	.35	.35
985L	A149b	70sh Germany, 1850	.50	.50
985M	A149b	100sh Italy, 1988	.70	.70
985N	A149b	150sh Sweden, 1982	1.00	1.00
985O	A149b	300sh Italy, 1989	2.25	2.25
		Nos. 985I-985O (7)	5.15	5.15

Souvenir Sheet

985P	A149b	350sh Great Britain, 1887	2.50	2.50

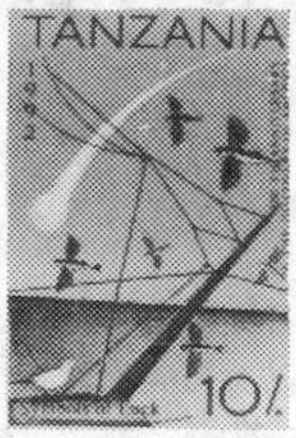

Discovery of America, 500th Anniv. — A150

Perf. 12x12½, 12½x12

1992, Sept. 30 Litho.

Designs: 10sh, Symbols of luck. 15sh, "Is this course right?," compass, chart. 25sh, "Earth!," first sight of land. 30sh, First meetings, horiz. 35sh, Nina, horiz. 75sh, Santa Maria, horiz. 250sh, Ship running aground, vert. 200sh, Columbus.

986 A150	10sh multicolored	.15	.15
987 A150	15sh multicolored	.15	.15
988 A150	25sh multicolored	.18	.18
989 A150	30sh multicolored	.20	.20
990 A150	35sh multicolored	.24	.24
991 A150	75sh multicolored	.52	.52
992 A150	250sh multicolored	1.70	1.70
	Nos. 986-992 (7)	3.14	3.14

Souvenir Sheet

993 A150	200sh multicolored	1.40	1.40

Miniature Sheet

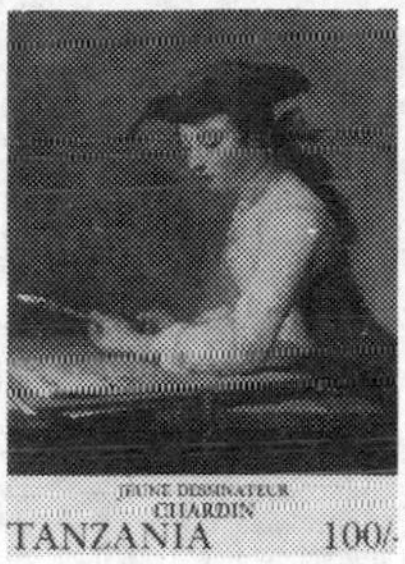

Louvre Museum, Bicent. A151

Paintings by Jean-Baptiste-Simeon Chardin (1699-1779): No. 994a, Young Artist. b, The Buffet. c, The Provider. d, A Mother Working. e, Grace. f, The Copper Fountain. g, House of Cards. h, Child with Teetotum. 500sh, The Ray, horiz.

1993, Mar. 8 Litho. *Perf. 12*

994 A151	100sh Sheet of 8, #a.-h. + label	5.50	5.50

Souvenir Sheet

Perf. 14½

995 A151	500sh multicolored	3.50	3.50

No. 995 contains one 88x55mm stamp.

Miniature Sheet

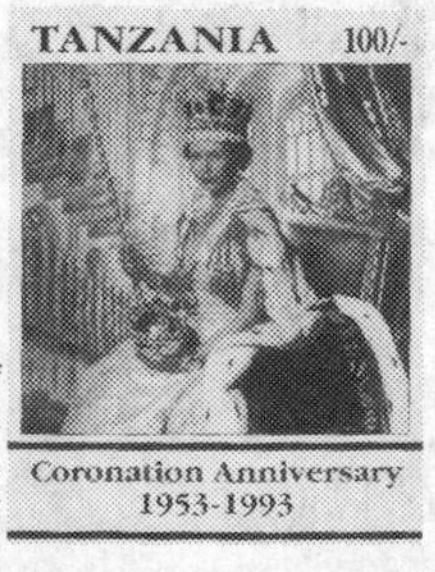

Coronation of Queen Elizabeth II, 40th Anniv. — A152

Designs: a, 100sh, Official coronation photograph. b, 150sh, Exeter salt. c, 200sh, Photograph of ceremony, 1953. d, 300sh, Queen, Prince Andrew.

500sh, Princess Elizabeth Opening the New Broadgate Coventry, by Dame Laura Knight, 1948.

1993, June 2 Litho. *Perf. 13½x14*

996 A152	Sheet, 2 each #a.-d.	10.00	10.00

Souvenir Sheet

Perf. 14

997 A152	500sh multicolored	3.50	3.50

No. 997 contains one 28x43mm stamp.

Miniature Sheet

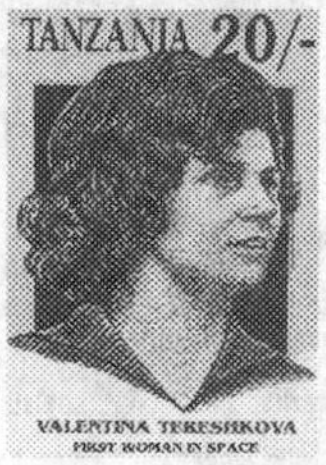

Famous Women — A153

Designs: a, 20sh, Valentina Tereshkova. b, 40sh, Marie Curie. c, 50sh, Indira Gandhi. d, 70sh, Wilma Rudolph. e, 100sh, Margaret Mead. f, 150sh, Golda Meir. g, 200sh, Dr. Elizabeth Blackwell. h, 400sh, Margaret Thatcher.

No. 999, Mother Teresa.

1993, July 15 *Perf. 14*

998 A153	Sheet of 8, #a.-h.	7.00	7.00

Souvenir Sheet

999 A153	500sh multicolored	3.40	3.40

Miniature Sheets

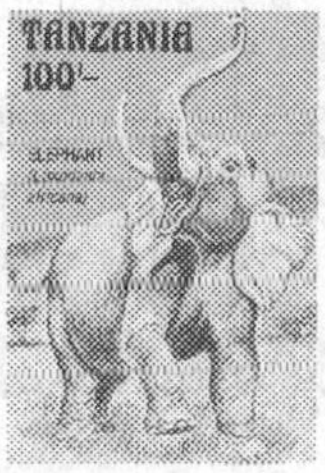

Wildlife — A154

Wildlife at watering hole: No. 1000a, Elephant. b, Gazelles. c, Hartebeest. d, Duiker. e, Genet. f, Civet. g, Pelicans. h, Waterbuck. i, Blacksmith plovers. j, Pied kingfisher. k, Black-winged stilts. l, Bush pig.

No. 1000n, Brown-hooded kingfisher. o, Sable antelope (n). p, Impala (q). q, Buffalo. r, Leopard. s, Aardvark (t). t, Hippopotamus. u, Spotted hyena. v, Crowned crane (w). w, Crocodile. x, Flamingo. y, Baboon.

Wildlife on the plains: No. 1001a, Potto. b, Flamingos. c, Grey-headed kingfisher. d, Red colobus monkey. e, Dik-dik. f, Aardwolf. g, Black-backed jackal. h, Tree pangolin. i, Serval. j, Yellow-billed hornbill. k, Pygmy mongoose. l, Bat-eared fox.

No. 1001n, Bushbaby. o, Egyptian vulture. p, Ostrich. q, Greater kudu. r, Diana monkey. s, Giraffe (w). t, Cheetah (s). u, Wildebeeest (t). v, Chimpanzee. w, Warthog. x, Zebra. y, Rhinoceros.

No. 1002, Lions, horiz. No. 1003, African elephants, horiz.

1993, June 30

Sheets of 12

1000	A154	100sh #a.-l.	8.00	8.00
1000M	A154	100sh #n.-y.	8.00	8.00
1001	A154	100sh #a.-l.	8.00	8.00
1001M	A154	100sh #n.-y.	8.00	8.00
		Nos. 1000-1001M (4)	32.00	32.00

Souvenir Sheets

1002	A154	500sh multicolored	3.50	3.50
1003	A154	500sh multicolored	3.50	3.50

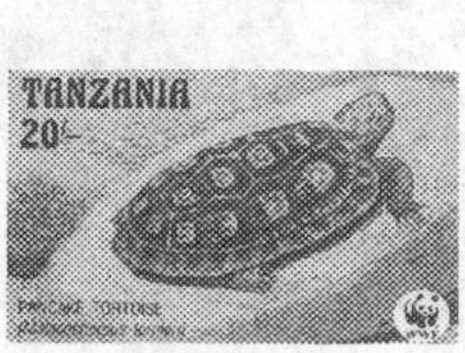

Pancake Tortoise A155

1993, June 30

1004 A155	20sh On rock	.18	.18
1005 A155	30sh Drinking	.26	.26
1006 A155	50sh Crawling from under rocks	.45	.45
1007 A155	70sh Hatchling	.60	.60
	Nos. 1004-1007 (4)	1.49	1.49

World Wildlife Federation.

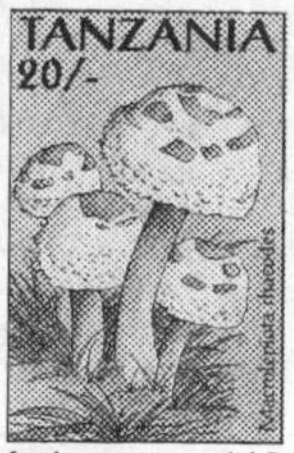

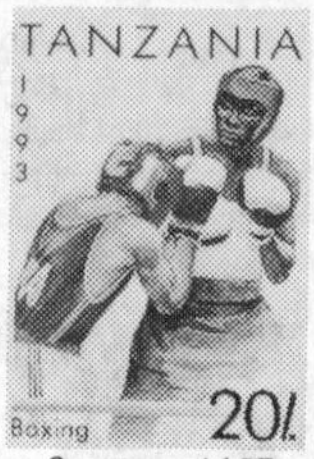

Mushrooms — A156 Sports — A157

Designs: 20sh, Macrolepiota rhacodes. 40sh, Mycena pura. 50sh, Chlorophyllum molybdites. 70sh, Agaricus campestris. 100sh, Volvariella volvacea. 150sh, Leucoagaricus naucinus. 200sh, Oudemansiella radicata. 300sh, Clitocybe nebularis. No. 1016, Omphalotus olearius. No. 1017, Lepista nuda.

1993, June 18 Litho. *Perf. 14*

1008 A156 20sh multicolored .15 .15
1009 A156 40sh multicolored .28 .28
1010 A156 50sh multicolored .35 .35
1011 A156 70sh multicolored .50 .50
1012 A156 100sh multicolored .70 .70
1013 A156 150sh multicolored 1.00 1.00
1014 A156 200sh multicolored 1.40 1.40
1015 A156 300sh multicolored 2.25 2.25
Nos. 1008-1015 (8) 6.63 6.63

Souvenir Sheets

1016 A156 500sh multicolored 3.50 3.50
1017 A156 500sh multicolored 3.50 3.50

1992, May 28 Litho. *Perf. 12x12½*

1018 A157 20sh Boxing .15 .15
1019 A157 50sh Field hockey .35 .35
1020 A157 70sh Horse racing .50 .50
1021 A157 100sh Marathon .70 .70
1022 A157 150sh Soccer 1.00 1.00
1023 A157 200sh Diving 1.40 1.40
1024 A157 400sh Basketball 2.75 2.75
Nos. 1018-1024 (7) 6.85 6.85

Souvenir Sheet

Perf. 12½x12

1025 A157 300sh High jump, horiz. 2.00 2.00

Miniature Sheets

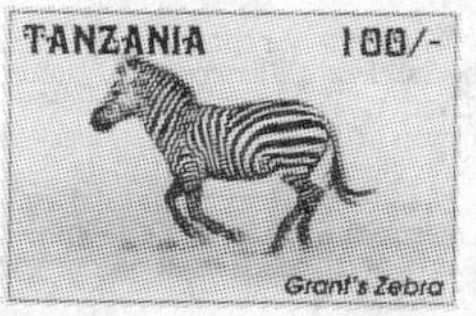

Animals A158

Designs: No. 1026a, Female Grant's zebra, running. b, Male Grant's zebra, standing. c, Female Grant's gazelle. d, Male Grant's gazelle. e, Thompson's gazelle. f, White-bearded gnu, calf.

No. 1027a, Female cheetah, cubs. b, Young cheetah. c, Lioness carrying her cub. d, Two hunting dogs. e, Three hunting dogs. f, Hunting dogs before an attack.

No. 1028, African rhinoceros. No. 1029, African elephant.

1993, June 30 Litho. *Perf. 14*

1026 A158 100sh Sheet of 6, #a.-f. 4.25 4.25
1027 A158 100sh Sheet of 6, #a.-f. 4.25 4.25

Souvenir Sheets

1028 A158 500sh multicolored 3.50 3.50
1029 A158 500sh multicolored 3.50 3.50

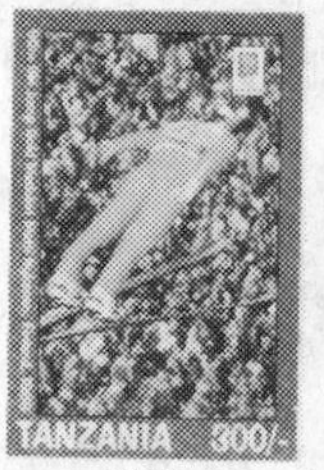

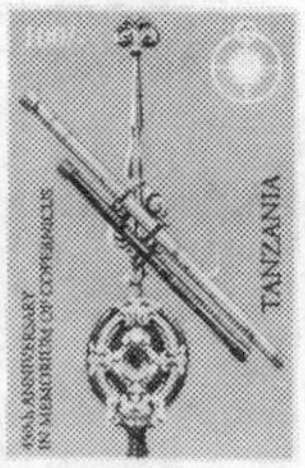

A159 A160

1994 Winter Olympics, Lillehammer, Norway: 300sh, Matti Nykanen, ski jumping, 1988. 400sh, Stefan Krause, Jan Behrendt, double luge, 1992. 500sh, Downhill skiing, 1972.

1993, June 10 Litho. *Perf. 14*

1030 A159 300sh multicolored 2.25 2.25
1031 A159 400sh multicolored 2.75 2.75

Souvenir Sheet

1032 A159 500sh multicolored 3.50 3.50

1993, June 10

1033 A160 100sh Telescope .70 .70
1034 A160 300sh Radio telescope 2.25 2.25

Souvenir Sheet

1035 A160 500sh Copernicus 3.50 3.50

Copernicus, 450th anniv. of death.

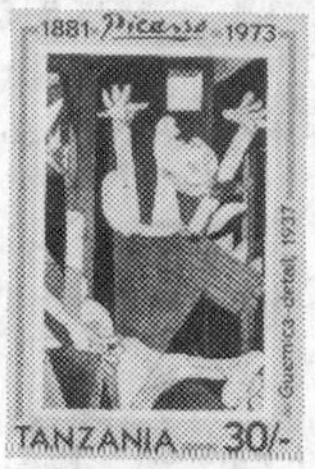

Picasso (1881-1973) A160a

Various details of painting, Guernica, 1937.

1993, June 10 Litho. *Perf. 14*

1035A A160a 30sh multicolored .22 .22
1035B A160a 200sh multicolored 1.40 1.40
1035C A160a 300sh multicolored 2.00 2.00
Nos. 1035A-1035C (3) 3.62 3.62

Souvenir Sheet

1035D A160a 500sh multicolored 3.50 3.50

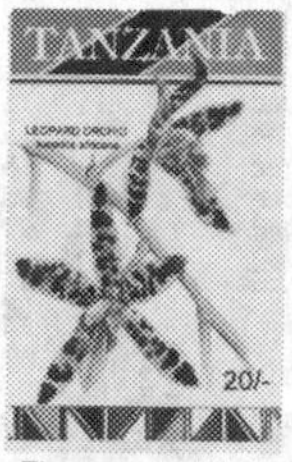

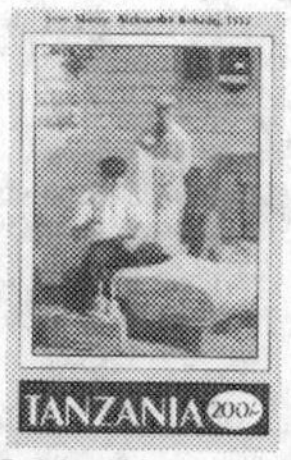

Flowers — A161 Polska '93 — A162

Designs: 20sh, Leopard orchid. 30sh, African violet. 40sh, Stapelia semota lutea. 50sh, Busy Lizzie. 60sh, Senecio petraeus. 70sh, Kalanchoe velutina. 100sh, Dwarf ginger lily. 150sh, Nymphaea colorata. 200sh, Thunbergia battiscombei. 250sh, Crossandra nilotica. 300sh, African tulip tree. 350sh, Ruttya fruticosa. No. 1048, False African violet. No. 1049, Glory lily.

1993, Nov. 8 Litho. *Perf. 13½*

1036 A161 20sh multicolored .15 .15
1037 A161 30sh multicolored .22 .22
1038 A161 40sh multicolored .28 .28
1039 A161 50sh multicolored .35 .35
1040 A161 60sh multicolored .42 .42
1041 A161 70sh multicolored .50 .50
1042 A161 100sh multicolored .70 .70
1043 A161 150sh multicolored 1.10 1.10
1044 A161 200sh multicolored 1.40 1.40
1045 A161 250sh multicolored 1.75 1.75
1046 A161 300sh multicolored 2.00 2.00
1047 A161 350sh multicolored 2.50 2.50
Nos. 1036-1047 (12) 11.37 11.37

Souvenir Sheets

Perf. 13

1048 A161 500sh multicolored 3.50 3.50
1049 A161 500sh multicolored 3.50 3.50

1993 Litho. *Perf. 14*

Paintings: 200sh, Stone Masons, by Aleksander Kobzdej, 1952. 300sh, Child Wearing Plumed Helmut, by Z. Waliszewski, 1932. 500sh, Na Rynku, by Stanislaw Osostowicz, 1939.

1050 A162 200sh multicolored 1.40 1.40
1051 A162 300sh multicolored 2.00 2.00

Souvenir Sheet

1052 A162 500sh multicolored 3.50 3.50

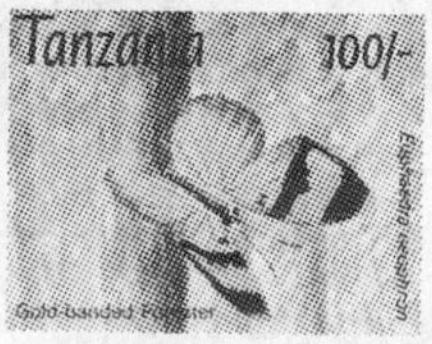

Butterflies A163

Designs: No. 1053a, Gold-banded forester. b, Twin dotted border. c, Aphnaeus flavescens. d, Orange-and-lemon. e, Club-tailed charaxes. f, Broad blue-banded swallowtail. g, African map. h, Buxton's hairstreak. i, Bush charaxes. j, Lilac nymph. k, Large striped swordtail. l, Charaxes acuminatus. m, African leaf. n, African wood white. o, Trimen's false acraea. p, Red line sapphire. q, Mother-of-pearl. r, Flame-bordered charaxes. s, Large blue charaxes. t, Emperor swallowtail.

No. 1054a, Angled grass yellow. b, Figtree blue. c, Iolaus ismenias. d, Green-veined charaxes. e, Commodore. f, African monarch. g, Bush scarlet. h, Eyed pansy. i, Zebra white. j, Azure hairstreak. k, Yellow pansy. l, Regal purple tip.

No. 1054n, Iolaus aphnaeoides. o, Green charaxes. p, Beautiful monarch. q, Short-tailed admiral. r, Dusky dotted border. s, Charaxes anticlea. t, Blue salamis. u, Nepheronia argia. v, Acraea pseudolycia. w, Blue-banded diadem. x, Golden tip. y, Acraea bonasia.

No. 1055, Blood-red cymothoe. No. 1056, Precis octavia. No. 1056A, Noble swallowtail. No. 1056B, Violet-spotted charaxes.

1993, Nov. 8 Litho. *Perf. 13*

Sheet of 25

1053 A163 100sh #a.-t. 16.00 16.00

Sheets of 12

1054 A163 100sh #a.-l. 8.00 8.00
1054M A163 100sh #n.-y. 8.00 8.00

Souvenir Sheets

1055 A163 500sh multicolored 3.50 3.50
1056 A163 500sh multicolored 3.50 3.50
1056A A163 500sh multicolored 3.50 3.50
1056B A163 500sh multicolored 3.50 3.50

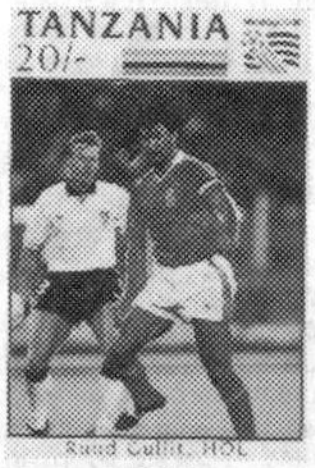

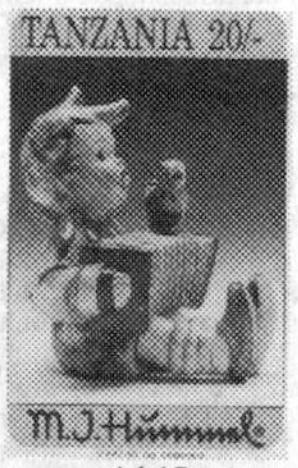

A164 A165

Players, country: 20sh, Gullit, Holland. 30sh, Sheedy, Ireland. 50sh, Giannini, Italy. 70sh, Cesar, Brazil. 250sh, Barnes, England; Grun, Belgium. 300sh, Chendo, Spain. 350sh, Rijkaard, Holland. 400sh, Matthaeus, Germany.

No. 1065, Berti, Italy; Caligiuri, US. No. 1066, Walker, England; Gilhaus, Holland.

1993, Dec. *Perf. 14*

1057-1064 A164 Set of 8 9.00 9.00

Souvenir Sheets

1065-1066 A164 500sh each 3.00 3.00

1994 World Cup Soccer Championships, US.

1994, Feb. 10

Hummel Figurines: 20sh, Boy with accordian. 40sh, Girl with guitar, boy with banjo. 50sh, Boy with tuba. 70sh, Boy with harmonica, bird. 100sh, Bird in tree, boy seated on fence. 150sh, Boy playing horn. 200sh, Boy with horn, bird. 300sh, Girl playing banjo. 350sh, Boy with cello on back. 400sh, Girls with banjo and sheet music.

No. 1077, Four carolers. No. 1078, Two figures in tower blowing horns at angel below.

1067-1076 A165 Set of 10 9.00 9.00

Souvenir Sheets

1077-1078 A165 500sh each 3.00 3.00

Miniature Sheet

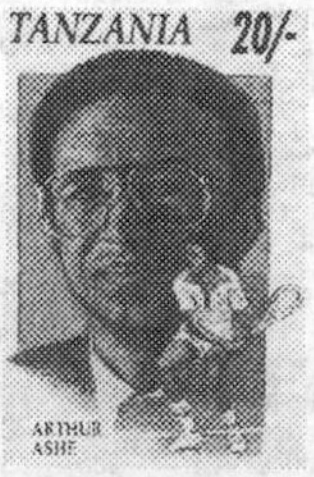

Black Athletes — A166

Designs: a, 20sh, Arthur Ashe. b, 40sh, Michael Jordan. c, 50sh, Daley Thompson. d, 70sh, Jackie Robinson. e, 100sh, Kareem Abdul-Jabbar. f, 150sh, Florence Joyner. g, 200sh, Jesse Owens. h, 400sh, Jack Johnson. 500sh, Muhammad Ali, horiz.

1994, Jan.

1079 A166 Sheet of 8, #a.-h. 5.25 5.25

Souvenir Sheet

1080 A166 500sh multicolored 2.50 2.50

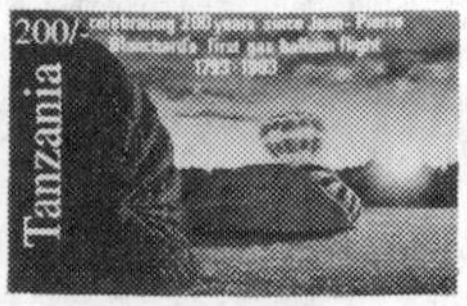

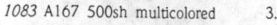

First US Gas Balloon Flight, Bicent. A167

Designs: 200sh, Balloons filling with hot air. 400sh, Jean-Pierre Blanchard (1753-1809), balloon. 500sh, Hot air balloons in flight, vert.

1994, Apr. 25 Litho. *Perf. 14*

1081 A167 200sh multicolored 1.40 1.40
1082 A167 400sh multicolored 2.75 2.75

Souvenir Sheet

1083 A167 500sh multicolored 3.50 3.50

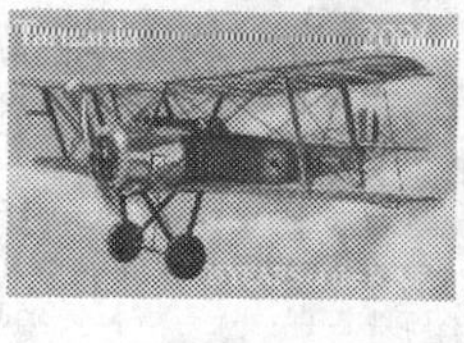

Royal Air Force, 75th Anniv. A168

Designs: 200sh, Sopwith Camel. 400sh, BAE Harrier. 500sh, Supermarine Spitfire.

1993, Dec.

1084 A168 200sh multicolored 1.40 1.40
1085 A168 400sh multicolored 2.75 2.75

Souvenir Sheet

1086 A168 500sh multicolored 3.50 3.50

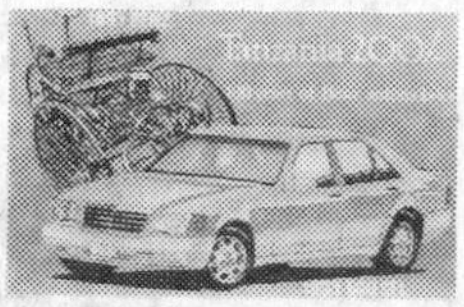

Automotive Anniversaries — A171

Designs: No. 1099, 200sh, 1893 Benz, 1993 500 SEL. No. 1100, 200sh, Henry Ford, 1922 Model T. No. 1101, 400sh, Karl Benz, emblem. No. 1102, 400sh, 1893 Ford, Mustang Cobra.

No. 1103, Emblem, 1937 540 K. No. 1104, Henry Ford, first Ford factory.

1994, Apr. 25 Litho. *Perf. 14*

1099-1102 A171 Set of 4 8.50 8.50

Souvenir Sheets

1103-1104 A171 500sh each 3.50 3.50

First Benz 4-wheel motor car, cent. (#1099, 1101, 1103). First Ford motor, cent. (#1100, 1102, 1104).

Miniature Sheets

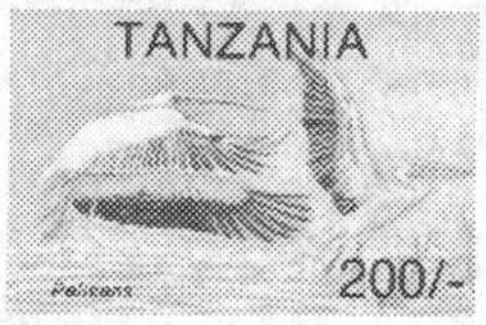

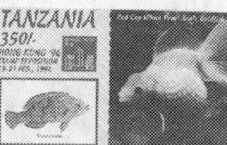

Birds A172

Designs: No. 1105a, 20sh, African hawk eagle. b, 30sh, Shoe-bill stork. c, 50sh, Harrier eagle. d, 70sh, Casqued hornbill. e, 100sh, Crowned crane. f, 150sh, Greater flamingo.

No. 1106a, 200sh, Pelican. b, 250sh, Jacana, black crake. c, 300sh, Ostrich. d, 350sh, Helmeted guinea fowl. e, 400sh, Malachite kingfisher. f, 500sh, Saddle-billed stork.

1994, May 11

1105 A172 Sheet of 6, #a.-f. 3.00 3.00
1106 A172 Sheet of 6, #a.-f. 14.00 14.00

No. 1105 is vert.

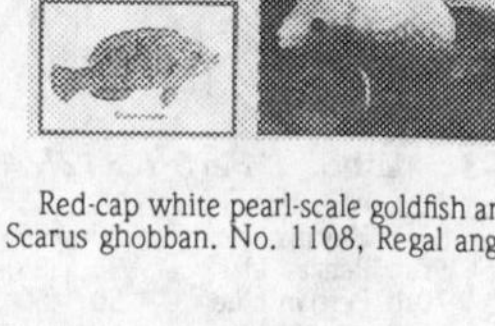

Hong Kong '94 A173

Red-cap white pearl-scale goldfish and: No. 1107, Scarus ghobban. No. 1108, Regal angelfish.

1994, Feb. 18

1107 A173	350sh multicolored		2.50	2.50
1108 A173	350sh multicolored		2.50	2.50
a.	Pair, #1107-1108		5.00	5.00

Nos. 1107-1108 issued in sheets of 5 pairs. No. 1108a is a continuous design.

Numbers have been reserved for additional values in this set.

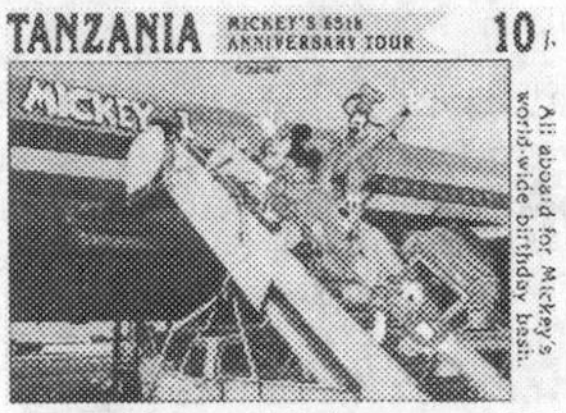

Mickey Mouse, 65th Anniv. — A176

Disney characters on tour: 10sh, Boarding plane. 20sh, Dancing, Tonga. 30sh, Lawn bowling, Australia. 40sh, Building igloo, Arctic region. 50sh, Royal Palace Guard, London. 60sh, Esna bazaar, Egypt. 70sh, Zsambox cowboys, Hungary, vert. 100sh, Grand Canal, Venice, vert. 150sh, Dancing, Bali, Indonesia, vert. 200sh, Monks studying text, Bangkok, Thailand, vert. 300sh, Water skiing, Taj Mahal, India, vert. 400sh, Himalayas, Nepal.

No. 1125, Kilimanjaro Uhuru Peak, Kibo, Tanzania, vert. No. 1126, Kigoma railway station, Dar es Salaam, Tanzania, vert. No. 1127, Memorial to Dr. Livingstone, shores of Lake Tanganyika, Tanzania.

1994, Apr. 6 ***Perf. 14x13¹/₂, 13¹/₂x14***

1113 A176	10sh multicolored	.15	.15
1114 A176	20sh multicolored	.15	.15
1115 A176	30sh multicolored	.22	.22
1116 A176	40sh multicolored	.28	.28
1117 A177	50sh multicolored	.35	.35
1118 A176	60sh multicolored	.42	.42
1119 A176	70sh multicolored	.50	.50
1120 A176	100sh multicolored	.70	.70
1121 A176	150sh multicolored	1.10	1.10
1122 A176	200sh multicolored	1.50	1.50
1123 A176	300sh multicolored	2.00	2.00
1124 A176	400sh multicolored	2.75	2.75
	Nos. 1113-1124 (12)	10.12	10.12

Souvenir Sheets

1125 A176	500sh multicolored	3.50	3.50
1126 A176	500sh multicolored	3.50	3.50
1127 A176	500sh multicolored	3.50	3.50

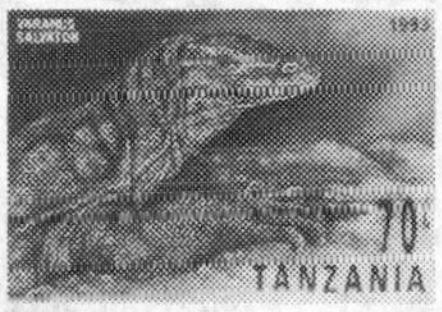

Reptiles A177

Designs: 20sh, Geochelone elephantopus, vert. 50sh, Iguana iguana, vert. 70sh, Varanus salvator. 100sh, Naja oxiana, vert. 150sh, Chamaeleo jacksonii. 200sh, Eunectes murinus. 250sh, Alligator mississippensis.

500sh, Vipera berus, vert.

Perf. 12x12¹/₂, 12¹/₂x12

1993, June 28 **Litho.**

1128-1134 A177	Set of 7	4.35	4.25

Souvenir Sheet

1135 A177	500sh multicolored	2.50	2.50

Nos. 1128-1135 were were not available until July 1994.

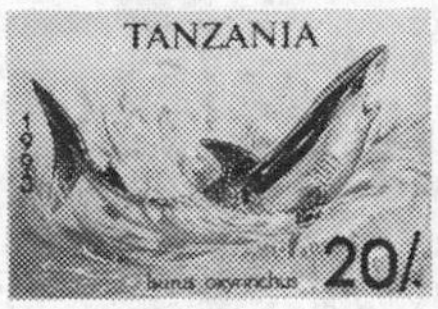

Sharks A178

Designs: 20sh, Isurus oxyrinchus. 30sh, Etmopterus hillianus. 50sh, Galeocerdo cuvier. 70sh, Sguatina afrikana. 100sh, Pristiophorus cirratus. 150sh, Triaenodon obesus. 200sh, Sphyrna lewini.

350sh, Hexanchus grisens, vert.

1993, July 27 ***Perf. 12¹/₂x12***

1136-1142 A178	Set of 7	3.25	3.25

Souvenir Sheet

Perf. 12x12¹/₂

1143 A178	350sh multicolored	1.75	1.75

Nos. 1136-1143 were not available until July 1994.

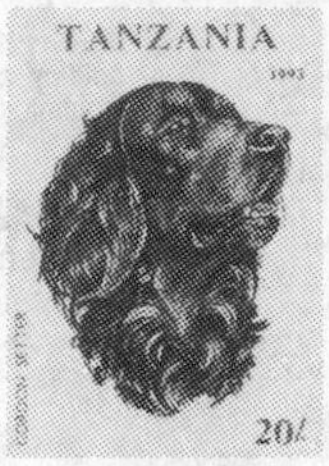

Dogs — A179

Designs: 20sh, Gordon setter. 30sh, Zwergschnauzer. 50sh, Labrador retriever. 70sh, Wire fox terrier. 100sh, English springer spaniel. 150sh, Newfoundlander. 200sh, Moscow toy terrier.

350sh, Doberman pinscher.

1993, Sept. 27 ***Perf. 12x12¹/₂***

1144-1150 A179	Set of 7	3.25	3.25

Souvenir Sheet

1151 A179	350sh multicolored	1.75	1.75

Nos. 1144-1151 were were not available until July 1994.

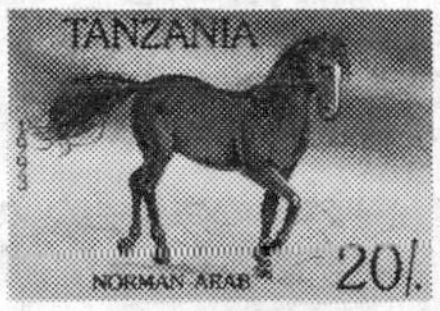

Horses A180

Designs: 20sh, Norman-Arab. 40sh, Nonius. 50sh, Boulonnais. 70sh, Arab. 100sh, Anglo-Arab. 150sh, Tarpon. 200sh, Thorougbred.

No. 1159, Anglo-Norman.

1993, Nov. 30 ***Perf. 12¹/₂x12***

1152-1158 A180	Set of 7	2.00	2.00

Souvenir Sheet

Perf. 12x12¹/₂

1159 A180	400sh multicolored	2.00	2.00

Nos. 1152-1159 were were not available until July 1994.

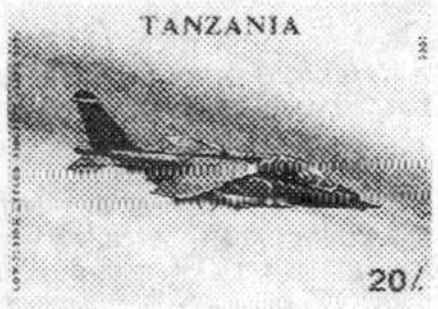

Military Aircraft A181

Designs: 20sh, ALFA jet. 30sh, Northrup F-5E. 50sh, Mirage 3NG. 70sh, MB-339C. 100sh, MIG-31. 150sh, C-101 AVIOJET. 200sh, F-16B.

500sh, EAP fighter, vert.

1994, Apr. 25 **Litho.** ***Perf. 12¹/₂x12***

1160-1166 A181	Set of 7	2.75	2.75

Souvenir Sheet

Perf. 13x12¹/₂

1167 A181	500sh multicolored	2.25	2.25

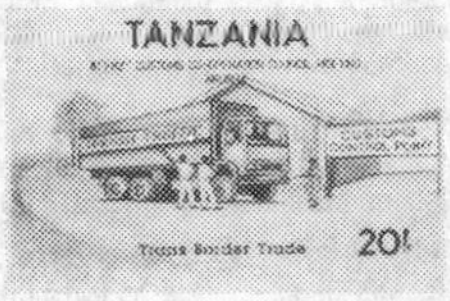

A182

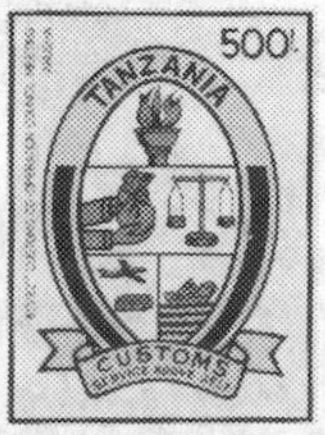

Customs Co-operation Council Meeting, Arusha — A183

Designs: 20sh, Trans-border trade. 50sh, Customs-international trade by ship. 100sh, Customs-air transportation. 150sh, Postal service-customs co-operation, Customs and UPU emblems.

500sh, Emblem.

1994, Aug. 23 **Litho.** ***Perf. 13¹/₂***

1168-1171 A182	Set of 4	1.25	1.25

Souvenir Sheet

Perf. 12¹/₂

1172 A183	500sh multicolored	2.00	2.00

Miniature Sheet of 8

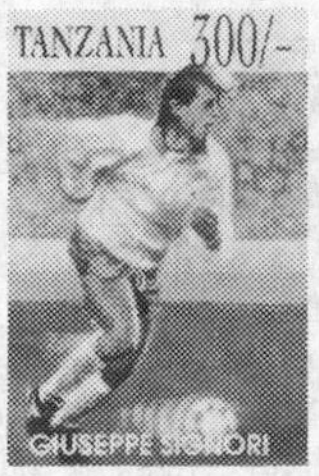

1994 World Cup Soccer Championships, US — A184

Designs: No. 1173a, Giuseppe Signori. b, Ruud Gullit. c, Roberto Mancini. d, Marco Van Bastien. e, Dennis Bergkamp. f, Oscar Ruggeri. g, Frank Rijkaard. h, Peter Schmeichel.

1000sh, World Cup trophy.

1994, Sept. 26 ***Perf. 14***

1173 A184	300sh #a.-h.	9.75	9.75

Souvenir Sheet

1174 A184	1000sh multicolored	4.00	4.00

Miniature Sheets of 9

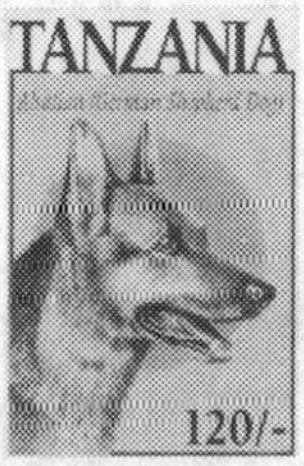

Dogs — A185

Designs: No. 1175a, Alsatian (German Shepherd). b, Japanese chin. c, Shetland sheepdog. d, Italian spinone. e, Great dane. f, English setter. g, Pembroke (welsh corgi). h, St. Bernard. i, Irish wolfhound.

No. 1176a, Afghan hound. b, Basenji (Congo dog). c, Siberian husky. d, Irish setter. e, Norwegian elkhound. f, Bracco Italiano (Italian hound). g, Australian cattle dog. h, German short haired pointer. i, Rhodesian ridgeback.

No. 1177a, Alaskan malamute. b, Scottish cairn terrier. c, American foxhound. d, British bulldog. e, Boston terrier. f, Borzoi (Russian wolfhound). g, Shar pei (Chinese fighting dog). h, Saluki (Persian greyhound). i, Bernese mountain dog.

No. 1178a, Doberman pinscher. b, Chihuahua. c, Bloodhound. d, Keeshond (Dutch barge dog). e, Tibetan spaniel. f, Japanese akita. g, Tervueren (Belgian shepherd dog). h, Chow chow (Chinese Spitz). i, Pharaoh hound.

No. 1179, like #1175e. No. 1180, like #1176b.

1994, Sept. 30

1175-1178 A185	120sh #a.-i, each	4.50	4.50

Souvenir Sheets

1179-1180 A185	1000sh each	4.00	4.00

Miniature Sheets of 8

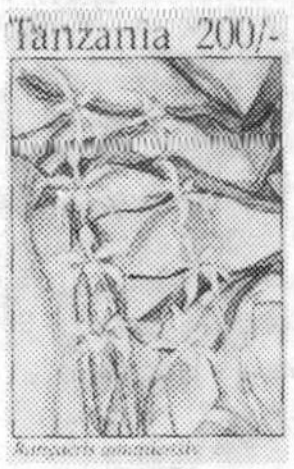

Orchids — A186

Designs: No. 1181a, Rangaeris amaniensis. b, Eulophia macowanii. c, Cyrtorchis arcuata. d, Centrostigma occultans. e, Cirrhopetalum umbellatum. f, Ansellia gigantea. g, Angraecum ramosum. h, Disa englerana.

No. 1182a, Nervilia stolziana. b, Satyrium orbiculare. c, Schzochilus sulphureus. d, Disa stolzii. e, Platycoryne mediocris. f, Satyrium breve. g, Eulophia nuttii. h, Disa ornithantha.

No. 1183, Eulophia thomsonii, horiz. No. 1184, Phaius P. tankervilliae, horiz.

1994, Oct. 7

1181-1182 A186	200sh #a.-h, each	6.50	6.50

Souvenir Sheets

1183-1184 A186	1000sh each	4.00	4.00

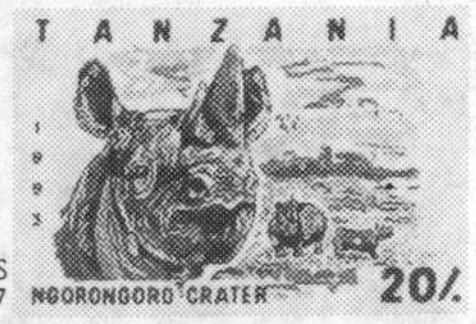

Natl. Parks A187

Designs: 20sh, Ngorongoro Crater. 50sh, Ngurdoto Crater. 70sh, Kilimanjaro Natl. Park. 100sh, Gombe Natl. Park. 150sh, Selous Natl. Park. 200sh, Mikumi Natl. Park. 250sh, Serengeti Natl. Park.

500sh, Lake Manyara Natl. Park, vert.

1994 **Litho.** ***Perf. 12***

1185-1191 A187	Set of 7	3.50	3.50

Souvenir Sheet

1192 A187	500sh multicolored	2.00	2.00

Nos. 1185-1192 are dated 1993 but were not available until Oct. 1994.

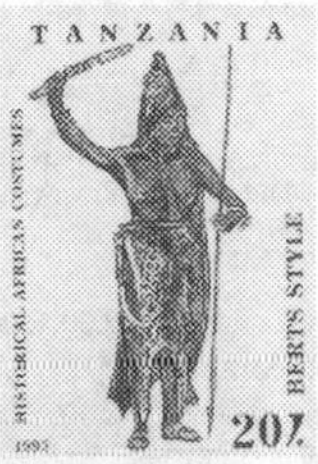

Historical African Costumes A188

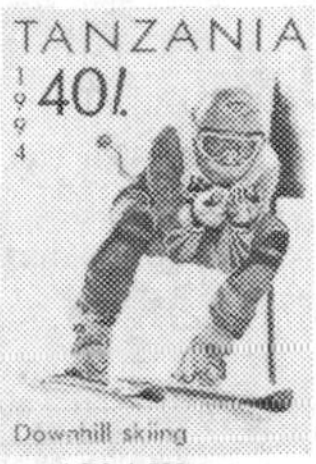

1994 Winter Olympics, Lillehammer A189

Designs: 20sh, Berts style. 40sh, Galla style. 50sh, Guinean warrior. 70sh, Goloff style. 100sh, Peul style. 150sh, Abyssinian warrior. 200sh, Pahuin style.

350sh, Zulu style.

1994

1193-1199 A188	Set of 7	2.50	2.50

Souvenir Sheet

1200 A189	350sh multicolored	1.40	1.40

Nos. 1193-1200 are dated 1993 but were not available until Oct. 1994.

1994

Designs: 40sh, Downhill skiing. 50sh, Ice hockey. 70sh, Speed skating. 100sh, Bobsled. 120sh, Figure skating. 170sh, Free style skiing. 250sh, Biathlon.

500sh, Slalom skiing.

1201-1207 A189	Set of 7	8.00	8.00

Souvenir Sheet

1208 A189	500sh multicolored	2.00	2.00

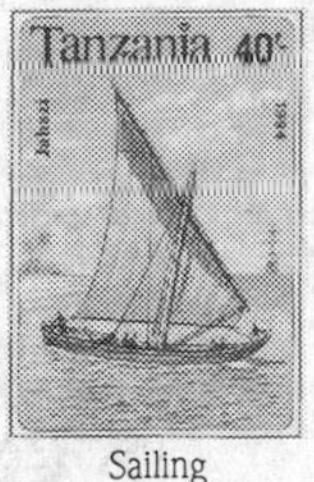

Sailing Ships — A190

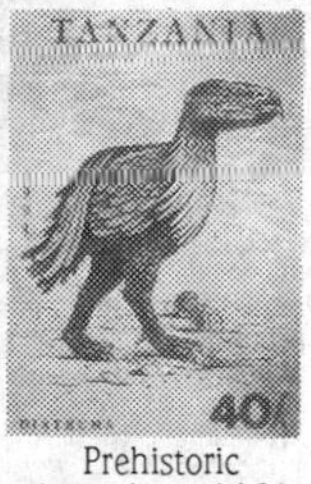

Prehistoric Animals — A191

Designs: 40sh, Jahazi. 50sh, Caravel. 70sh, Carrack. 100sh, Galeas. 170sh, Line of battle ship. 200sh, Frigate. 250sh, Brig.

No. 1210, Bark.

1994

1209-1215 A190	Set of 7	3.50	3.50

Souvenir Sheet

1216 A190	500sh multicolored	2.00	2.00

1994

Designs: 40sh, Diatruma. 50sh, Tyranosaurus. 100sh, Uintaterius. 120sh, Stiracosaurus. 170sh, Diplodocus. 250sh, Archaeopteryx. 300sh, Sordes.

500sh, Dimetrodon, vert.

1217-1223 A191	Set of 7	4.25	4.25

Souvenir Sheet

1224 A191	500sh multicolored	2.00	2.00

A192

A193

Designs: 40sh, Family. 120sh, Father playing ball with children. 170sh, People at clinic, horiz. 250sh, Woman harvesting in field. 300sh, Emblem.

1994 Litho. Perf. 12x12¹/₂, 12¹/₂x12
1225-1228 A192 Set of 4   2.50 2.50

Souvenir Sheet
1229 A192 300sh multicolored   1.25 1.25

Intl. Year of the Family.

1994, Aug. 1
Designs: 40sh, Pres. Salmin Amour. 70sh, Abeid Amani Karume, first president. 120sh, Processing cloves, horiz. 250sh, Zanzibar door. 500sh, Hands clasped over map.

1230-1233 A193 Set of 4   2.00 2.00

Souvenir Sheet
1234 A193 500sh multicolored   2.00 2.00

Zanzibar Revolution, 30th anniv.

Arachnids — A194

Designs: 40sh, Trombidium. 50sh, Eurypelma. 100sh, Salticus. 120sh, Micrommata rosea, vert. 170sh, Araneus, vert. 250sh, Micrathena, vert. 300sh, Araneus diadematus, vert. 500sh, Hadogenes, vert.

Perf. 12¹/₂x12, 12x12¹/₂
1994, Aug. 31
1235-1241 A194 Set of 7   4.25 4.25

Souvenir Sheet
1242 A194 500sh multicolored   2.00 2.00

Miniature Sheets of 9

Butterflies & Flowers A195

Designs: No. 1243a, Lunaria biennis, papilio glaucus. b, Phlox paniculata, danaus plexippus. c, Rudbeckia gloriosa, papilio troilus. d, Tithonia rotundifolia, hypolimnas antevorta. e, Osteospermum, cirrochroa imperatrix. f, Ursinia anethoides, vanessa atalanta. g, Wahlenbergia gloriosa, limenitis archippus. h, Mentzelia lindleyi, hypolimnas pandarus. i, Paeonia suffruticosa, anthocharis belia.
No. 1244a, Coreopsis laneolata, limenitis sydyi. b, Lantana camara, agraulis vanillae. c, Asclepias tuberosa, danaus chrysippus. d, Verbena canadensis, eurytides marcellus. e, Lonicera japonica, artopoetes pryeri. f, Pentas bussei, heliconius charitonius. g, Echinacea purpurea, limenitis weidemeyerii. h, Myosotis alpestris, phoebis sennae. i, Aster amellus, timelaea albescens.
No. 1245, Buddleia davidii, papilio polyxenes. No. 1246, Helianthus annuus, vanessa cardui.

1994, Nov. 19 Perf. 14
1243-1244 A195 150sh #a.-i., each   4.50 4.50

Souvenir Sheets
1245-1246 A195 1000sh each   4.25 4.25

Miniature Sheets of 9

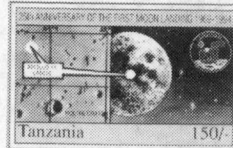
First Manned Moon Landing, 25th Anniv. A196

Apollo 11 mission: No. 1247a, Map of landing site. b, Location of Sea of Tranquility shown on Moon. c, Craters. d, Launch. e, Second stage separation. f, Separation of lunar modules. g, Command module, "Columbia," landing module, "Eagle." h, "Eagle" descending. i, Inside module.
No. 1248a, Michael Collins, Neil Armstrong, Edwin "Buzz" Aldrin. b, "Eagle" on lunar surface. c, Stepping foot on moon. d, Erecting solar wind devices. e, Gathering soil samples. f, Reflection in helmet. g, Astronaut, US flag. h, Carrying equipment. i, "Eagle" ascending from lunar surface.
No. 1249a, "Columbia" above lunar surface, Earth on horizon. b, "Eagle" above lunar surface. c, Release of S-4B rocket. d, Heading toward Earth. e, Re-entering atmosphere. f, Splashdown. g, Pickup at sea. h, Helicopter lifting men on board. i, Astronauts in quarantine.

1994, Nov. 30
1247-1249 A196 150sh #a.-i., each   5.50 5.50

Miniature Sheets of 16

A197

TANZANIA Dinosaurs — A198

Designs: No. 1250a, Brontosaurus (e). b, Albertosaurus. c, Parasaurolophus. d, Pteranodon. e, Stegosaurus. f, Tyrannosaurus. g, Triceratops. h, Ornitholestes. i, Camarasaurus. j, Ankylosaurus. k, Trachodon. l, Allosaurus. m, Corythosaurus. n, Struthiomimus. o, Camptosaurus. p, Heterodontosaurus.
No. 1251a, Deinonychus. b, Styracosaurus. c, Anatosaurus. d, Plateosaurus. e, Iguanodon. f, Oviraptor. g, Dimorphodon. h, Ornithomimus. i, Lambeosaurus. j, Megalosaurus. k, Cetiosaurus. l, Hypsilophodon. m, Rhamphorhynchus. n, Scelidosaurus. o, Antrodemus. p, Dimetrodon.
1000sh, Brachiosaurus, vert.

1994, Dec. 26
1250 A197 120sh #a.-p.   7.75 7.75
1251 A198 120sh #a.-p.   7.75 7.75

Souvenir Sheet
1252 A197 1000sh multicolored   4.00 4.00

No. 1250 is a continuous design.

Mickey Mouse, Safari Club — A199

Designs: No. 1253, 70sh, Donald, Mickey, lion cubs. No. 1254, 70sh, Goofy leaning on Donald. No. 1255, 100sh, Donald wearing tree disguise. No. 1256, 100sh, Donald under elephant. No. 1257, 120sh, Donald, hippopotamus. No. 1258, 120sh, Mickey writing in diary. No. 1259, 150sh, Goofy carrying gear, Donald, Mickey. No. 1260, 150sh, Mickey, elephant, Donald, Goofy in rain. No. 1261, 200sh, Goofy, Mickey reading book, lion. No. 1262, 200sh, Goofy, zebras. No. 1263, 250sh, Mickey, giraffe. No. 1264, 250sh, Donald filming picture.

No. 1265, Goofy hanging from tree, vert. No. 1266, Goofy holding camera, Donald, vert. No. 1267, Mickey holding camera, vert.

1994, Dec. 26 Perf. 14x13¹/₂
1253-1264 A199 Set of 12   7.25 7.25

Souvenir Sheets
Perf. 13¹/₂x14
1265-1267 A199 1000sh each   4.00 4.00

Olympic Gold Medalists
A200   A201

Designs: 350sh, Kristin Otto, Germany, 50m free-style swimming, 1988. 500sh, Carl Lewis, US, track & field, 1984, 1988.
1000sh, Oksana Baiul, Ukraine, women's figure skating, 1994.

1994 Litho. Perf. 14
1268 A200 350sh multicolored   1.50 1.50
1269 A200 500sh multicolored   2.00 2.00

Souvenir Sheet
1270 A201 1000sh multicolored   4.25 4.25

Intl. Olympic Committee, cent. (#1270).

D-Day, 50th Anniv. A202

Designs: 350sh, Combined forces attack Atlantic wall. 600sh, Waterproofed tanks support Marines at Omaha Beach.
No. 1273a, Gen. Eisenhower, US forces, Omaha Beach. b, P-51 Mustang, D-Day armada. c, US Coast Guard cutter, landing craft. d, US troops approaching Omaha Beach. e, US troops landing on Omaha Beach. f, US forces on Omaha Beach.
No. 1274a, Gen. Montgomery, White Ensign flies over Normandy beach. b, British forces with Churchill Avre tank, Gold Beach. c, USS Thompson refueled en route to Omaha Beach. d, HMS Warspite fires on German positions, Sword Beach. e, Royal Marine commandos landing, Juno Beach. f, Sherman Crab flail tank landing on Normandy beach.
No. 1275a, Supermarine Spitfire over Normandy beaches. b, Bren gun carriers, Gold Beach. c, Le Regiment de la Chaudiere, Juno Beach. d, Canadian forces land on Juno Beach. e, Sherman tank on Normandy beach. f, German artillery fires on D-Day Armada.
No. 1276, US forces prepare to embark from England to Normandy beaches. No. 1277, US forces on Utah Beach. No. 1278, Beach obstacles.

1994, Dec. 12 Litho. Perf. 14
1271 A202 350sh multicolored   1.50 1.50
1272 A202 600sh multicolored   2.50 2.50

Miniature Sheets of 6
1273-1275 A202 200sh #a.-f., each   5.00 5.00

Souvenir Sheets
1276-1278 A202 1000sh each   4.25 4.25

Raptors — A203

Designs: 40sh, Terathopius ecaudatus, vert. 50sh, Spizaetus ornatus, vert. 100sh, Pandion haliaetus, vert. 120sh, Vultur gryphus, vert. 170sh, Haliaetus vocifer. 250sh, Sarcoramphus papa, vert. 400sh, Falco peregrinus.
500sh, Pseudogyps africanus, vert.

1994 Perf. 12x12¹/₂, 12¹/₂x12
1279-1285 A203 Set of 7   4.50 4.50

Souvenir Sheet
1286 A203 500sh multicolored   2.00 2.00

Endangered Species A204

Designs: 40sh, Phascolasctos cinereus. 70sh, Ailurus fulgens. 100sh, Aguila. 120sh, Loxodonta africana. 250sh, Monachus tropicalis. 400sh, Eschrichtius gibbosus. 500sh, Cetacea. 500sh, Panthera tigris, vert.

1994 Perf. 12¹/₂x12
1287-1293 A204 Set of 7   6.00 6.00

Souvenir Sheet
Perf. 12x12¹/₂
1294 A204 500sh multicolored   2.00 2.00

No. 1288 shows a Giant Panda, and is incorrectly inscribed with the scientific name of the Lesser Panda.

Crabs — A205

Flowers — A206

Designs: 40sh, Astacus leptodactytus, horiz. 100sh, Eriocheir sinensis. 120sh, Caneer opillo. 170sh, Cardisoma quanhumi, horiz. 250sh, Birgus latro. 300sh, Menippe mercenaria, horiz. 400sh, Dromia vulgaris.
No. 1302, Callinectes sapidus, horiz.

1995 Litho. Perf. 12¹/₂x12, 12x12¹/₂
1295-1301 A205 Set of 7   5.50 5.50

Souvenir Sheet
1302 A205 500sh multicolored   2.00 2.00

Dated 1994.

1995 Perf. 12x12¹/₂
Designs: 40sh, Dicentra spectabilis. 100sh, Thunbergia alata. 120sh, Cyrtanthus minimiflorus. 170sh, Nepenthes hybrida. 250sh, Allamanda cathartica. 300sh, Encyclia pentotis. 400sh, Protea lacticolor.
500sh, Tradescantia.

1303-1309 A206 Set of 7   5.50 5.50

Souvenir Sheet
1310 A206 500sh multicolored   2.00 2.00

Dated 1994.

Woodstock Music Festival, 25th Anniv. — A207

Illustration reduced.

1995, Feb. 27 Litho. Imperf.
Size: 124x84mm
1311 A207 2000sh Jimi Hendrix   7.50 7.50

Souvenir Sheet
Self-Adhesive
1312 A207 2000sh Carlos Santana   7.50 7.50

Numbers have been reserved for additional values in this set.
Issued: #1311, 2/27/95; #1312, 5/15/95.

Space Probes
& Satellites
A208

Designs: 40sh, Hubble telescope. 100sh, Mariner. 120sh, Voyager 2. 170sh, Work Package 03. 250sh, Orbiting solar observatory (OSO). 300sh, Magellan. 400sh, Galileo. 500sh, FOBOS.

1995	Litho.	Perf. 12½x12		
1319-1325	A208	Set of 7	5.50	5.50
Souvenir Sheet				
1326	A208	500sh multicolored	2.00	2.00

Miniature Sheets of 9

Sierra
Club,
Cent.
A209

No. 1327 vert: a, Black rhinoceros. b, Aye-aye. c, Aye-aye, holding claw at mouth. d, Giraffes, Masai Mara Reserve. e, Red lechwe, group. f, Red lechwe running. g, White-handed gibbon, white coat. h, White-handed gibbon, dark coat. i, White-handed gibbon, ready to climb tree.
No. 1328: a, Aye-aye. b, Black rhinoceros facing each other. c, Black rhinoceros. d, Red lechwe. e, Lions fighting, Masai Mara Reserve. f, Hyena, Masai Mara Reserve. g, Nile crocodile in water. h, Nile crocodile, mouth open. i, Nile crocodile in grass.

1995, July 6	Litho.	Perf. 14		
1327-1328	A209	150sh #a.-i., each	5.50	5.50

Fruit
A210

Designs: 70sh, 500sh, Coconuts. 100sh, Pineapple. 150sh, Pawpaw. 200sh, Tomato.

1995, June 30				
1329-1332	A210	Set of 4	2.00	2.00
Souvenir Sheet				
1333	A210	500sh multicolored	2.00	2.00

Miniature Sheets of 9

The Beatles — A211

No. 1334: a, George Harrison. b, d, e, f, h, Various group portraits. c, Ringo Starr. g, Paul McCartney. i, John Lennon.
No. 1335a-1335i, vert: Various portraits of John Lennon.
No. 1336, John Lennon, vert. No. 1337, Paul McCartney.

1995		Perf. 12½		
1334-1335	A211	100sh #a.-i., each	6.25	6.26
Souvenir Sheets				
1336-1337	A211	500sh each	5.25	5.25

No. 1336 contains one 51x76mm stamp. No. 1337 contains one 57x51mm stamp.

Miniature Sheets of 9

Singapore
'95
A212

Trains of the world: No. 1338a, 0-6-0 Italy. b, 0-4-4-OT Mallet, Germany. c, 4-8-0 Tender Engine, Ghana. d, Mallet Tanks, Germany. e, 0-6-2T on the Zillertalbahn, Switzerland. f, Rack Lines, Austria. g, Sweden Jodemans Railway, Norway. h, 4-6-0 Portugal. i, 60CM gauge, Mine Railway, Spain.
No. 1339a, 640 Class 2-6-0s, Italy. b, Norway electric. c, Gordon Highlander 4-40s. d, High Line 9600 class 2-8-0 Japan. e, 4-6-0 Henschel, Portugal. f, Federal German State Railway 220 hydraulic. g, Caledonian 4-2-2, Scotland. h, M2 Locomotive, Denmark. i, Denver & Rio Grande, Western US.
No. 1340, Karl Gosdorf 2-6-0 tank engine, Germany. No. 1341, High speed ET 403, Germany. No. 1342, AKO 1920, US. No. 1343 Porter 2-4-OS, Hawaii.

1995, July 5	Litho.	Perf. 14		
1338-1339	A212	200sh #a.-i., each	7.25	7.25
Souvenir Sheets				
1340-1343	A212	1000sh each	4.00	4.00

A213   A214

FAO, 50th anniv.: No. 1344a, Boy eating. b, Baby, mother eating. c, Two young people eating. 1000sh, Woman picking fruit, horiz.

1995, Aug. 14				
1344	A213	250sh Strip of 3, #a.-c.	4.75	4.75
Souvenir Sheet				
1345	A213	1000sh multicolored	4.00	4.00

No. 1344 is a continuous design.

1995, Aug. 14				

Rotary, Intl., 90th Anniv.: 600sh, Paul Harris, Rotary emblem. 1000sh, Natl. flag, Rotary emblem.

1346	A214	600sh multicolored	3.25	3.25
Souvenir Sheet				
1347	A214	1000sh multicolored	4.00	4.00

Queen Mother,
95th Birthday
A215

No. 1348: a, Drawing. b, With Queen Elizabeth II. c, Formal portrait. d, In black outfit. 1000sh, Blue dress with pearls.

1995, Aug. 14		Perf. 13½x14		
1348	A215	250sh Block or strip of 4, #a.-d.	4.75	4.75
Souvenir Sheet				
1349	A215	1000sh multicolored	4.00	4.00

No. 1348 was issued in sheets of 8 stamps.

Miniature Sheets of 6 or 8

End of
World War
II, 50th
Anniv.
A216

Flags of countries shaped as "VJ:" No. 1350a: Singapore. b, Fiji. c, Malaysia. d, Marshall Islands. e, Philippines. f, Solomon Islands.
No. 1351: a, Pearl Harbor. b, North Africa. c, Battle of Atlantic. d, War in Soviet Union. e, "D" Day, June 6, 1944. f, Holocaust. g, War in Pacific. h, Hiroshima, Enola Gay, mushroom cloud.
No. 1352, Battle of Britain. No. 1353, British soldier, donkey with backpack.

1995, Aug. 14	Litho.	Perf. 14		
1350	A216	250sh #a.-f. + label	6.00	6.00
1351	A216	250sh #a.-h. + label	8.00	8.00
Souvenir Sheets				
1352-1353	A216	1000sh each	4.00	4.00

Miniature Sheet of 12

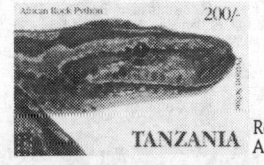

Reptiles
A217

No. 1354: a, African rock python. b, Bell's hinged tortoise. c, Gaboon viper. d, Royal python. e, Savannah monitor. f, Nile monitor. g, Three-horned chameleon. h, Nile crocodile. i, Rough-scaled bush viper. j, Puff adder. k, Rhinoceros viper. l, Leopard tortoise.
No. 1355, Bush viper. No. 1356, Spitting cobra.

1995, Sept. 5				
1354	A217	200sh #a.-l.	9.50	9.50
Souvenir Sheets				
1355-1356	A217	1000sh each	4.00	4.00

UN, 50th
Anniv. — A218

Various races of people, within group: No. 1357a, Woman holding baby on shoulders. b, Man holding child in arms. c, One child standing. 1000sh, UN soldier using binoculars.

1995	Litho.	Perf. 14		
1357	A218	250sh Strip of 3, #a.-c.	3.25	3.25
Souvenir Sheet				
1358	A218	1000sh multicolored	4.25	4.25

No. 1357 is a continuous design.

Miniature Sheets of 9

Summer Olympics
Gold Medal
Winners — A219

No. 1359: a, Tommie Smith, US, 1968. b, Jack Lovelock, New Zealand, 1936. c, Al Oerter, US, 1956-68. d, Daley Thompson, Great Britain, 1980. e, Greg Louganis, US, 1984-88. f, Sammy Lee, US, 1948. g, Dan Gable, US, 1972. h, Helen Meany, US, 1928. i, Sugar Ray Leonard, US, 1976.
No. 1360: a, Robert Mathias, US, 1948-52. b, Larissa Latynina, USSR, 1956. c, Martin Sheridan, US, 1904-08. d, Vera Caslavska, Czechoslovakia, 1968. e, Edwin Moses, US, 1984. f, Jesse Owens, US, 1936. g, Mary Lou Retton, US, 1984. h, Bobby Morrow, US, 1956. i, Joan Benoit, US, 1984.

No. 1361, Florence Griffith Joyner, Jackie Joyner-Kersee, US, 1988. No. 1362, Vasily Alexeyev USSR, 1972-76.

1995, Sept. 18				
1359-1360	A219	200sh #a.-i., each	7.25	7.25
Souvenir Sheets				
1361-1362	A219	1000sh each	4.25	4.25

Miniature Sheets

Wild
Animals
A220

No. 1363: a, Snake, vulture. b, Vulture. c, Giraffe (d, g, h, k, l). d, African bateleur. e, Elephants (f). f, Kob, rhino (b, e, i, j, n). g, Rhinos. h, Baboon. i, Kob (m, n). j, Saddle billed stork, warthog (n). k, Cheetahs (g, j, n). l, African lion (h, k, o, p). m, Vulture. n, Dik-diks. o, Lion cubs. p, Lions (o).
No. 1364: a, Elands. b, Zebras. c, Lions. d, Baboons.
No. 1365, Rhinoceros. No. 1366, Leopard.

1995				
1363	A220	100sh Sheet of 16, #a.-p.	6.50	6.50
1364	A220	250sh Sheet of 4, #a.-d.	4.00	4.00
Souvenir Sheets				
1365-1366	A220	1000sh each	4.25	4.25

UN, 50th
Anniv.
A221

Designs: 70sh, Corn farming, vert. 100sh, Cultivating land. 150sh, Women spinning cotton in factory. 200sh, Boy drawing at desk, vert. 500sh, UN emblem, "50."

	Wmk. 387			
1995, Oct. 24	Litho.	Perf. 14		
1367-1371	A221	Set of 4	2.00	2.00
Souvenir Sheet				
1372	A221	500sh multicolored	2.00	2.00

East
African
Treaty,
2nd
Anniv.
A222

Designs: 100sh, 500sh, Heads of State. 150sh, Map, flags, vert. 180sh, Map, cotton, vert. 200sh, Fishing on Lake Victoria.

1995, Oct. 24				
1373-1376	A222	Set of 4	2.50	2.50
Souvenir Sheet				
1377	A222	500sh multicolored	2.00	2.00

Hoofed   Cactus
Animals — A224   Flowers — A225

Designs: 70sh, Hippopotamus amphibius, horiz. 100sh, Litocranius walleri. 150sh, Sincerus caffer, horiz. 180sh, Antilocapridae, horiz. 200sh, Alcelphus buselaphus. 260sh, Taurotragus oryx. 380sh, Strepsiceros. 500sh, Giraffa camelopardalis.

1995	Litho.	Perf. 12½x12, 12x12½		
1380-1386	A224	Set of 7	5.25	5.25
Souvenir Sheet				
1387	A224	500sh multicolored	2.00	2.00

1995   *Perf. 12x12¹/₂*

Designs: 70sh, Weingartia fidaiana. 100sh, Rebutia spegazziniana. 150sh, Caralluma lugarii. 180sh, Cerochlamys pachyphylla. 200sh, Schlumbergera orssighiana. 260sh, Epiphyllum darrahii. 380sh, Ceropegia nilotica.

500sh, Neoporteria nigrihorrida.

1388-1394 A225   Set of 7   5.25   5.25

Souvenir Sheet

1395 A225   500sh multicolored   2.00   2.00

Bats
A226

Designs: 70sh, Cheiromeles torquatus, vert. 100sh, Hypsignatus monstrosus, vert. 150sh, Rhinolophus, ferrum-equinum, vert. 180sh, Plecotus auritus. 200sh, Syconycteris australis, vert. 260sh, Plecotus auritus, vert. 380sh, Otomops martiensseni.

500sh, Pteropus.

1995   *Perf. 12x12¹/₂, 12¹/₂x12*

1396-1402 A226   Set of 7   5.25   5.25

Souvenir Sheet

1403 A226   500sh multicolored   2.00   2.00

Marine Life
of Coral
Reefs
A227

Designs: 70sh, Medusa. 100sh, Surgeonfish. 150sh, Angelfish. 180sh, Octopus. 200sh, Zebra fish. 250sh, Shark. 380sh, Ray.

500sh, Turtle.

1995   *Perf. 12¹/₂x12*

1404-1410 A227   Set of 7   5.25   5.25

Souvenir Sheet

1411 A227   500sh multicolored   2.00   2.00

Jerry Garcia (d. 1995), Musician
A228

1995, Nov.   Litho.   *Perf. 12¹/₂*

1412 A228   200sh multicolored   .80   .80

Souvenir Sheet

1413 A228   1000sh multicolored   4.00   4.00

No. 1412 was issued in sheets of 9. No. 1413 contains one 51x57mm stamp.

Miniature Sheet

Rock and
Roll Stars
A229

No. 1414: a, Chuck Berry. b, Bob Dylan. c, Aretha Franklin. d, The Supremes. e, Buddy Holly. f, Bruce Springsteen. g, Elton John. h, The Rolling Stones. i, Michael Jackson.

No. 1415, The Beach Boys (Al Jardin, Mike Love, Brian Wilson, Carl Wilson, Dennis Wilson), horiz.

1995, Dec. 1   *Perf. 13¹/₂x14*

1414 A229   250sh Sheet of 9, #a.-i.   9.00   9.00

Souvenir Sheet

Perf. 14x13¹/₂

1415 A229   1000sh multicolored   4.00   4.00

Miniature Sheet

Motion
Pictures,
Cent.
A230

Bible epics: No. 1416a, Noah's Ark, Dolores Costello. b, Ben-Hur, 1926, Ramon Novarro. c, Ben-Hur, 1926, Francis X. Bushman. d, Ben-Hur, 1959, Charlton Heston. e, Ben-Hur, 1959, Haya Harareet. f, Ben-Hur, 1959, Sam Jaffe. g, The Ten Commandments, 1923, Theodore Roberts. h, Samson and Delilah, Victor Mature. i, Samson and Delilah, Hedy Lamarr.

No. 1417, The Ten Commandments, Theodore Roberts.

1995, Dec. 1   *Perf. 13¹/₂x14*

1416 A230   250sh Sheet of 9, #a.-i.   9.00   9.00

Souvenir Sheet

1417 A230   1000sh multicolored   4.00   4.00

World Tourism Organization, 20th
Anniv. — A231

Designs: 100sh, Olduvai Gorge, "Cradle of Mankind." 300sh, First State House, Bagamoyo. 400sh, Mount Kilimanjaro.

500sh, Rhinoceroses, Ngorongoro Crater.

1995, Dec. 18   Litho.   *Perf. 14*

1418-1420 A231   Set of 3   3.25   3.25

Souvenir Sheet

1421 A231   500sh multicolored   2.00   2.00

SEMI-POSTAL STAMPS

Natl. Solidarity
Walk — SP1

1988, July 1   Litho.   *Perf. 14¹/₂*

B1 SP1   2sh +1sh Flag, crowd   .15   .15
B2 SP1   3sh +1sh Map, Pres.   Mwinyi   .15   .15
     Set value   .22   .22

Souvenir Sheet

B3 SP1   50sh +1sh Flag, Pres. Mwinyi   1.50   1.50

Surtax for Chama Cha Mapinduzi party activities.

Natl. Solidarity
Walk — SP2

1989, July 1   Litho.   *Perf. 14¹/₂*

B4 SP2   5sh +1sh Party flag   .15   .15
B5 SP2   10sh +1sh Pres. Mwinyi, walk   .17   .17
     Set value   .27   .27

Souvenir Sheet

B6 SP2   50sh +1sh Pres. Mwinyi   .78   .78

Natl. Solidarity
Walk — SP3

Designs: 4sh +1sh, Pres. Mwinyi marching with crowd. 9sh +1sh, Crowd around party flag. 13sh +1sh, Pres. Mwinyi. 30sh +1sh, Pres. Mwinyi planting tree. No. B11, Pres. Mwinyi sorting cloves. No. B12, Handshake across map, vert.

1991, July 5   Litho.   *Perf. 13¹/₂*

B7 SP3   4sh +1sh multicolored   .15   .15
B8 SP3   9sh +1sh multicolored   .15   .15
B9 SP3   13sh +1sh multicolored   .15   .15
B10 SP3   30sh +1sh multicolored   .25   .25
     Set value   .50   .50

Souvenir Sheets

Perf. 12¹/₂

B11 SP3   50sh +1sh multicolored   .40   .40
B12 SP3   50sh +1sh multicolored   .40   .40

POSTAGE DUE STAMPS

D1   D2

Perf. 14x14¹/₂

1978, July 31   Litho.   Unwmk.

J1 D1   5c red   .15   .15
J2 D1   10c green   .15   .15
J3 D1   20c dark blue   .15   .15
J4 D1   30c reddish brown   .15   .15
J5 D1   40c bright rose lilac   .15   .15
J6 D1   1sh orange   .30   .30
     Set value   .70   .70

1967, Jan. 3   *Perf. 14x13¹/₂*

J1a D1   5c red   .15   .15
J2a D1   10c green   .20   .20
J3a D1   20c dark blue   .40   .40
J4a D1   30c reddish brown   .60   .60
J5a D1   40c bright rose lilac   .80   .80
J6a D1   1sh orange   2.00   2.00
     Nos. J1a-J6a (6)   4.15   4.15

1969-71   *Perf. 14x15*

J1b D1   5c red   .15   .15
J2b D1   10c green   .20   .20
J3b D1   20c dark blue   .40   .40
J4b D1   30c reddish brown   .60   .60
J5b D1   40c bright rose lilac   .80   .80
J6b D1   1sh orange ('71)   2.00   2.00
     Nos. J1b-J6b (6)   4.15   4.15

1973, Dec. 12   *Perf. 15*

J1c D1   5c red   .15   .15
J2c D1   10c green   .15   .15
J3c D1   20c dark blue   .30   .30
J4c D1   30c reddish brown   .45   .45
J5c D1   40c bright rose lilac   .60   .60
J6c D1   1sh orange   1.50   1.50
     Nos. J1c-J6c (6)   3.15   3.15

1990   Litho.   *Perf. 15x14*

J7 D2   50c dark green   .15   .15
J8 D2   80c bright blue   .15   .15
J9 D2   1sh orange brown   .15   .15
J10 D2   2sh light olive green   .15   .15
J11 D2   3sh purple   .15   .15
J12 D2   5sh gray   .15   .15
J13 D2   10sh brown   .15   .15
J14 D2   20sh bister   .15   .15
     Set value   .55   .55

OFFICIAL STAMPS

Nos. 5-9, 11, 13 and 16 Overprinted:
"OFFICIAL"

Perf. 14x14¹/₂, 14¹/₂x14

1965, Dec. 9   Photo.   Unwmk.
Size: 21x17¹/₂mm, 17¹/₂x21mm

O1 A2   5c orange & ultra   .15   .15
O2 A2   10c multicolored   .15   .15
O3 A3   15c grn bl, brn & buff   .15   .15
O4 A2   20c blue & brown   .15   .15
O5 A3   30c black & red brn   .15   .15
O6 A2   50c yellow grn & blk   .15   .15

Perf. 14¹/₂x25
Size: 41¹/₂x25

O7 A2   1sh multicolored   .30   .15
O8 A2   5sh bl, brt grn & red brn   1.50   1.00
     Set value   2.25   1.50

Overprint size: 17mm on 5c, 10c, 20c, 50c. 14mm on 15c, 30c. 29x3¹/₂mm on 1sh, 5sh.

The overprint was also applied in 1967 in Dar es Salaam to 50c, 1sh and 5sh. Size: 29x3mm.

Nos. 19-23, 25, 27 and 30 Overprinted:
"OFFICIAL"

1967, Dec. 9   Photo.   *Perf. 14x14¹/₂*
Fish in Natural Colors
Size: 21x17¹/₂mm

Overprint Litho., 17mm Wide

O9 A4   5c black & citron   .15   .15
O10 A4   10c brown & olive   .15   .15
O11 A4   15c brown & blue   .15   .15
O12 A4   20c brown & dk blue grn   .15   .15
O13 A4   30c black & yel brn   .15   .15
O14 A4   50c black & dull bl grn   .20   .15

Perf. 14¹/₂
Size: 41x25mm

Overprint 29mm Wide

O15 A4   1sh brown & multi   .40   .15
O16 A4   5sh black & blue grn   1.75   1.25
     Nos. O9-O16 (8)   3.10
     Set value   1.70

1970-73
Overprint Typo., 17¹/₂mm Wide

O9a A4   5c black & citron   .15   .15
O10a A4   10c brown & olive   .15   .15
O12a A4   20c brn & dk bl grn   .15   .15
O13a A4   30c blk & yel brn   .30   .22
O13B A4   40c multicolored ('73)   .15   .15
     Set value, #O9a-O13a   .60   .44

The overprint was also applied in 1973 to 15c, 50c, 1sh (28mm wide), and 5sh.

Nos. 35-36, 38, 40-41, 43-47 Overprinted
OFFICIAL   **OFFICIAL**
a   b

1973, Dec. 10   Photo.   *Perf. 14¹/₂x14*

O17 A5(a)   5c multicolored   .15   .15
O18 A5(a)   10c multicolored   .15   .15
O19 A5(a)   20c multicolored   .15   .15
O20 A5(a)   40c multicolored   .15   .15
O21 A5(a)   50c multicolored   .15   .15
O22 A5(a)   70c multicolored   .15   .15

Perf. 14¹/₂

O23 A6(b)   1sh multicolored   .18   .18
O24 A6(b)   1.50sh multicolored   .30   .30
O25 A6(b)   2.50sh multicolored   .50   .50
O26 A6(b)   5sh multicolored   1.00   1.00
     Set value   2.45   2.45

A larger overprint (17¹/₂mm wide instead of 14¹/₂mm) was applied locally to 10c, 20c, 40c, and 50c.
Provisional use of some values for regular postage is known.

Nos. 161-171 Overprinted:
OFFICIAL

1980, Oct. 1   *Perf. 14*

O27 A21   10c multicolored   .15   .15
O28 A21   20c multicolored   .15   .15
O29 A21   40c multicolored   .15   .15
O30 A21   50c multicolored   .15   .15
O31 A21   75c multicolored   .15   .15
O32 A21   80c multicolored   .18   .18

Perf. 14¹/₂

O33 A21   1sh multicolored   .20   .20
O33A A21   1.50sh multicolored
O34 A21   2sh multicolored   .40   .40
O35 A21   3sh multicolored   .60   .60
O36 A21   5sh multicolored   1.00   1.00
     Nos. O27-O33,O34-O36 (10)   3.13   3.13

Overprint measures 13mm on Nos. O33-O36; reads up or down.

Nos. 606-614 Inscribed "OFFICIAL"

1990-91   Litho.   *Perf. 14*

O37 A99   5sh multi   .15   .15
O38 A99   9sh multi   .15   .15
O39 A99   13sh multi   .20   .20
O40 A99   15sh multi   .22   .22
O41 A99   20sh multi   .30   .30
O42 A99   25sh multi   .35   .35
O42A A99   30sh multi ('91)   .45   .45
O43 A99   40sh multi   .60   .60
O44 A99   70sh multi   1.00   1.00
O45 A99   100sh multi   1.50   1.50
     Nos. O37-O45 (10)   4.92   4.92

Inscription on Nos. O37-O42A is 15¹/₂mm long. Insription on Nos. O43-O45 is 19mm long.

TASMANIA

taz–'mā–nē–ə

LOCATION — An island off the southeastern coast of Australia
GOVT. — A former British Colony
AREA — 26,215 sq. mi.
POP. — 172,475 (1901)
CAPITAL — Hobart

Tasmania was one of the six British colonies that united in 1901 to form the Commonwealth of Australia. The island was originally named Van Diemen's Land by its discoverer, Abel Tasman, the present name having been adopted in 1853. Stamps of Australia are now used.

12 Pence = 1 Shilling
20 Shillings = 1 Pound

Watermarks

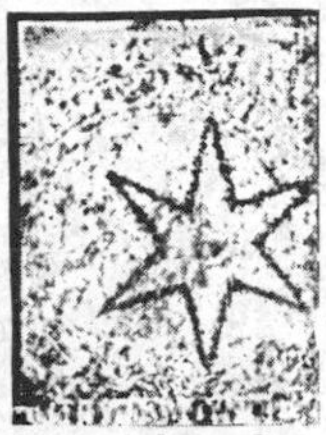
Wmk. 6- Large Star

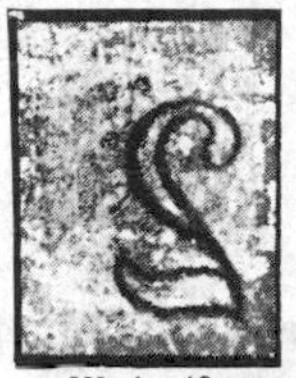
Wmk. 49- Double-lined Numeral

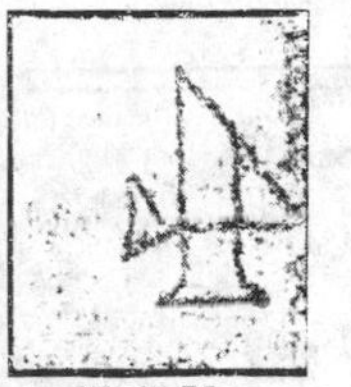
Wmk. 75- Double-lined Numeral

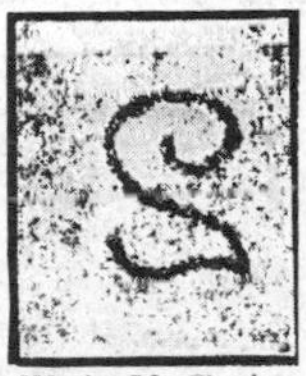
Wmk. 50- Single-lined "2"

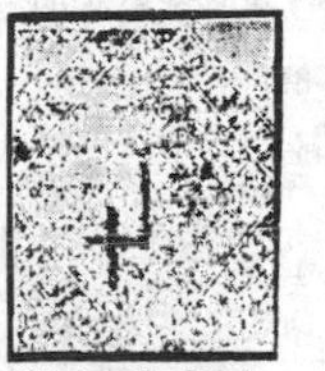
Wmk. 51- Single-lined "4"

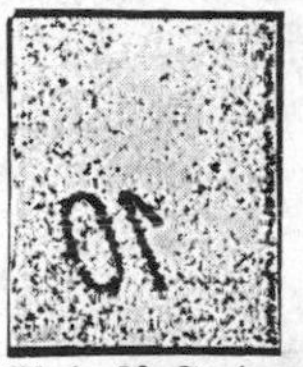
Wmk. 52- Single-lined "10"

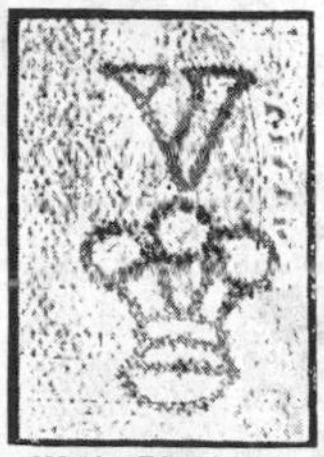
Wmk. 70- V and Crown

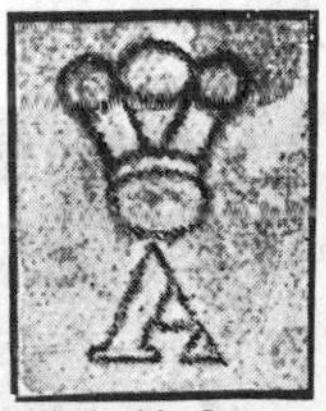
Wmk. 13- Crown & Double-lined A

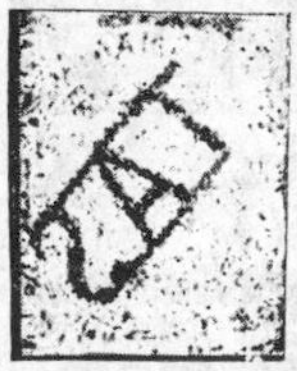
Wmk. 76- TAS

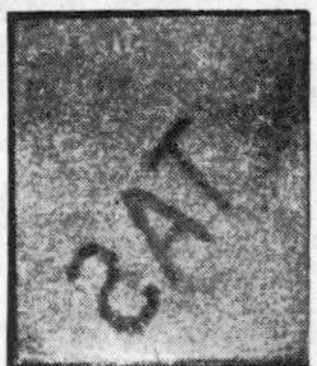
Wmk. 77- TAS

Tasmania stamps can be mounted in the Scott Australia album.

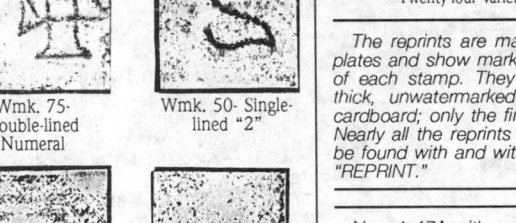

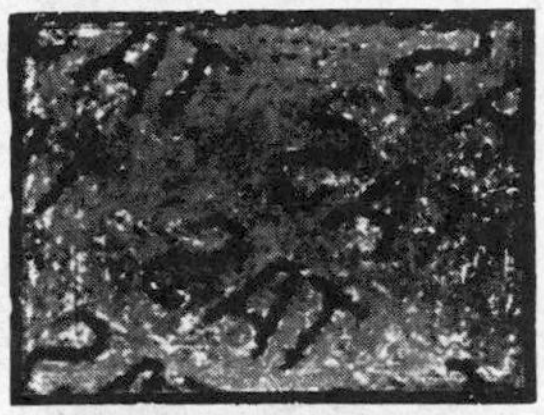
Wmk. 78- Multiple TAS

Values for unused stamps are for examples with original gum as defined in the catalogue introduction except for Nos. 1-2a and 10 which are valued without gum as few examples exist with any remaining original gum. Very fine examples of Nos. 17-75a will have perforations touching the design on one or more sides due to the narrow spacing of the stamps on the plates. Stamps with perfs clear of the design on all four sides are scarce and command higher prices.

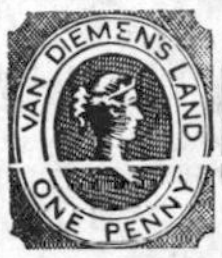
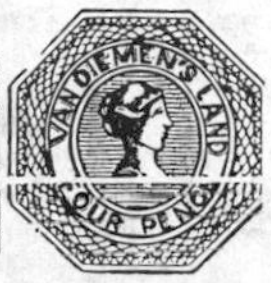
Queen Victoria
A1 A2

1853, Nov. 1 Unwmk. Engr. ***Imperf.***

1	A1 1p blue	3,500.	850.00
2	A2 4p red orange	2,150.	275.00
a.	4p yellow orange	2,250.	200.00
	Cut to shape		1.75

Twenty four varieties of each.

The reprints are made from defaced plates and show marks across the face of each stamp. They are on thin and thick, unwatermarked paper and thin cardboard; only the first are perforated. Nearly all the reprints of Tasmania may be found with and without the overprint "REPRINT."

Nos. 1-47A with pen or revenue cancellations sell for a small fraction of the price of postally used specimens. Copies are found with pen cancellation removed.

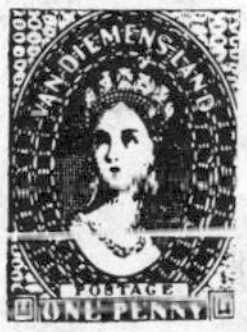
Queen Victoria — A3

1855 Wmk. 6 Wove Paper

4	A3 1p dark carmine	6,000.	825.00
5	A3 2p deep green	1,800.	600.00
6	A3 4p deep blue	1,250.	75.00

1856-57 Unwmk.

7	A3 1p pale red	6,000.	500.00
8	A3 2p emerald ('57)	7,250.	700.00
9	A3 4p blue ('57)	750.00	75.00

1856 Pelure Paper

10	A3 1p brown red	2,750.	600.00

1857 Wmk. 49, 75

11	A3 1p carmine	80.00	15.00
a.	1p orange red	85.00	15.00
b.	1p brown red	400.00	22.50
c.	Double impression		165.00
12	A3 2p green	175.00	35.00
a.	2p yellow green	250.00	50.00
b.	2p sage green	130.00	40.00
13	A3 4p blue	130.00	12.00
b.	Printed on both sides		—
	Nos. 11-13 (3)	385.00	62.00

See #17-19, 23-25, 29-31, 35-37, 39-41, 45-47A.

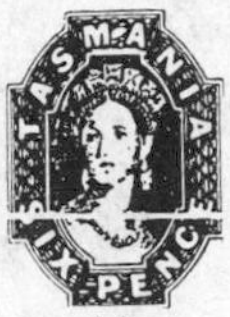
A4

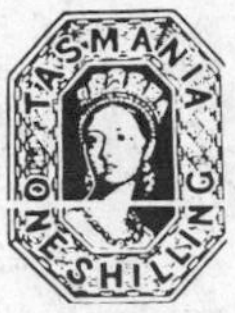
A4a

1858

14	A4 6p gray lilac	125.00	50.00
a.	6p red violet	600.00	150.00
b.	Double impression		200.00
15	A4 6p blue gray	200.00	45.00
16	A4a 1sh vermilion	550.00	50.00
	Nos. 14-16 (3)	875.00	145.00

No. 15 watermarked large star was not regularly issued.

1864 ***Rouletted***

17	A3 1p carmine	375.00	125.00
a.	1p brick red		180.00
18	A3 2p yellow grn		375.00
19	A3 4p blue		180.00
21	A4 6p gray lilac		225.00
22	A4a 1sh vermilion		625.00

1864-69 ***Perf. 10***

23	A3 1p brick red	50.00	19.00
a.	1p carmine	50.00	19.00
b.	1p orange red	50.00	19.00
24	A3 2p yellow green	275.00	55.00
a.	2p sage green	375.00	150.00
25	A3 4p blue	125.00	9.00
a.	Double impression		125.00
26	A4 6p lilac	125.00	10.50
a.	6p red lilac	375.00	55.00
27	A4 6p slate blue	175.00	12.50
28	A4a 1sh vermilion	100.00	11.00
a.	Horiz. pair, imperf. vert.		
	Nos. 23-28 (6)	850.00	117.00

1864-69 ***Perf. 11½, 12, 12½, 13***

29	A3 1p carmine	20.00	6.00
a.	1p orange red	30.00	14.00
b.	1p brick red	42.50	40.00
c.	Double impression		82.50
d.	Wmkd. "2"		650.00
	As "d", pen cancel		165.00
30	A3 2p yellow green	130.00	35.00
a.	2p dark green	100.00	35.00
b.	2p sage green	250.00	115.00
31	A3 4p blue	65.00	32.50
32	A4 6p red lilac	80.00	16.00
a.	6p purple	70.00	21.00
b.	6p violet	65.00	16.00
d.	Horiz. pair, imperf. vert.		
e.	Double impression		100.00
33	A4 6p slate blue	180.00	27.50
34	A4a 1sh vermilion	80.00	12.50
a.	Double impression		120.00
b.	Horiz. pair, imperf. vert.		
	Nos. 29-34 (6)	555.00	129.50

The reprints are on unwatermarked paper, perforated 11½, and on thin cardboard, imperforate and perforated.

Pin-perf. 5½ to 9½, 13½ to 14½

1867

35	A3 1p carmine	350.00	77.50
36	A3 2p yellow green		275.00
37	A3 4p blue		165.00
38	A4 6p gray		150.00
38A	A4 6p red lilac		450.00
38B	A4a 1sh vermilion		650.00

Oblique Roulette

39	A3 1p carmine		165.00
40	A3 2p yellow green		410.00
41	A3 4p blue		325.00
42	A4 6p gray		550.00
43	A4 6p red lilac		350.00
44	A4a 1sh vermilion		750.00

1868 ***Serrate Perf. 19***

45	A3 1p carmine	225.00	90.00
46	A3 2p yellow green		175.00
47	A3 4p blue	650.00	110.00
47A	A3 6p purple		500.00

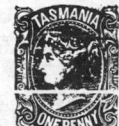

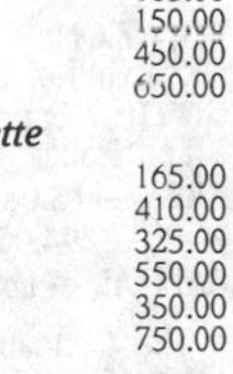
Queen Victoria — A5

1870-71 Typo. Wmk. 50 ***Perf. 12***

48	A5 2p green	65.00	6.50
a.	Imperf.		
b.	Perf. 11½	50.00	3.75
c.	Double impression		

See Nos. 49-75, 98, 108-109.

Wmk. 51

49	A5 1p rose ('71)	60.00	20.00
a.	Imperf., pair	600.00	215.00
50	A5 4p blue	725.00	300.00

Wmk. 52

51	A5 1p rose	40.00	9.00
a.	Imperf. pair	265.00	250.00
c.	Perf. 11½	1,000.	
52	A5 10p black	20.00	6.00
a.	Imperf. pair	120.00	
b.	Perf. 11½	25.00	20.00

The reprints are on unwatermarked paper. The 4p has also been reprinted on thin cardboard, imperf and perf.

1871-76 Wmk. 76 ***Perf. 11½***

53	A5 1p rose	4.50	.60
a.	Imperf.		
c.	Perf. 12	65.00	9.00
53B	A5 1p vermilion ('73)	250.00	95.00
54	A5 2p deep green ('72)	12.00	.60
a.	2p yellow green	120.00	1.25
b.	2p blue green	45.00	.60
c.	Imperf. pair		120.00
d.	2p green, perf. 12	450.00	135.00
e.	Double impression		
55	A5 3p brown	37.50	4.50
a.	3p purple brown	37.50	4.50
b.	As "a," imperf. pair		325.00
56	A5 3p red brown ('71)	37.50	4.50
a.	3p indian red	35.00	4.50
b.	Imperf. pair	120.00	
c.	Vert. pair, imperf. horiz.		
d.	Perf. 12	85.00	21.00
57	A5 4p dull yellow ('76)	40.00	7.50
a.	Perf. 12	225.00	15.00
58	A5 9p blue	20.00	7.50
a.	Imperf. pair	120.00	
b.	Perf. 12	40.00	40.00
59	A5 5sh bright violet	125.00	25.00
a.	Imperf.		
b.	Horiz. pair, imperf. vert.		
c.	Perf. 12	175.00	150.00
	Pen cancel		.30
	Nos. 53-59 (8)	526.50	145.20

The reprints are on unwatermarked paper, the 5sh has also been reprinted on thin cardboard; all are perforated.

1878 Wmk. 77 ***Perf. 14***

60	A5 1p rose	4.50	.60
61	A5 2p deep green	4.50	.60
62	A5 8p violet brown	15.00	4.50
	Nos. 60-62 (3)	24.00	5.70

The 8p has been reprinted on thin unwatermarked paper, perforated 11½.

1880-83 ***Perf. 12, 11½***

63	A5 3p indian red, perf. 12	9.00	2.00
a.	Imperf. pair	85.00	
b.	Horiz. pair, imperf. between	600.00	
c.	Perf. 11½	10.50	3.00
64	A5 4p lem, perf. 11½ ('83)	40.00	7.50
a.	4p olive yellow, perf. 11½	10.00	21.00
b.	Printed on both sides	210.00	
c.	Imperf.		
d.	4p deep yellow, perf. 12	75.00	22.50

Type of 1871 Surcharged in Black **Halfpenny**

1889 ***Perf. 14***

65	A5 ½p on 1p carmine	9.00	1.75
a.	"al" sideways in surcharge	825.00	*500.00*

No. 65 has been reprinted on thin cardboard, perforated 12, with the surcharge "Halfpenny" 19mm long.

1889-96 ***Perf. 11½***

66	A5 ½p red orange	2.25	.70
a.	½p yellow orange	2.25	.70
b.	Perf. 12	2.00	.85
67	A5 1p dull red	8.25	2.00
a.	1p vermilion	5.00	2.00
68	A5 1p car, perf. 12	8.25	3.25
a.	1p pink, perf. 12	27.50	5.00
b.	1p salmon rose, perf. 12	8.25	3.25
c.	Imperf. pair	92.50	92.50

Perf. 12

69	A5 4p bister ('96)	18.00	8.25
70	A5 9p chalky bl ('96)	10.00	3.25
	Nos. 66-70 (5)	46.75	17.45

1891 Wmk. 76 ***Perf. 11½***

71	A5 ½p orange	16.00	8.25
a.	½p brown orange	16.00	8.25
b.	Imperf. pair	82.50	
c.	Perf. 12	35.00	9.25
72	A5 1p salmon rose	21.00	11.50
a.	1p carmine, perf. 12	40.00	20.00
73	A5 4p ol bis, perf. 12	15.00	6.50
	Nos. 71-73 (3)	52.00	26.25

See Nos. 98, 108-109.

Surcharged in Black **d. 2½**

1891 Wmk. 77 ***Perf. 11½***
Surcharge 14mm High

74	A5 2½p on 9p lt blue	6.00	6.50
a.	Dbl. surcharge, one invtd.	210.00	200.00
b.	Imperf. pair	135.00	

Perf. 12

Surcharge 15mm High

75 A5 2½p on 9p lt blue 5.50 5.00
a. Surcharged in blue

No. 74 has been reprinted on thin unwatermarked paper, imperforate. There is also a reprint on thin cardboard, in deep ultramarine, with surcharge 16½mm high, and perforated 12.

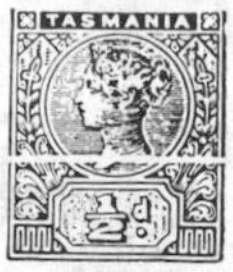
A8

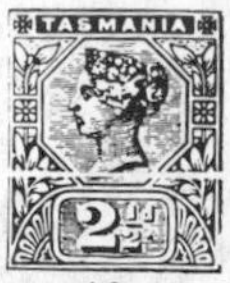
A9

1892-99 Typo. *Perf. 14*

76 A8 ½p orange & vio	.85	.35
77 A9 2½p magenta	2.50	.65
78 A8 5p pale bl & brn	3.50	1.40
79 A8 6p blue vio & blk	3.50	1.50
80 A8 10p red brn & grn ('99)	6.75	5.50
81 A8 1sh rose & green	4.50	1.50
82 A8 2sh6p brown & blue	25.00	8.00
83 A8 5sh brn vio & red	37.50	17.00
84 A8 10sh brt vio & brn	75.00	45.00
85 A8 £1 green & yel	525.00	225.00
Nos. 76-85 (10)	684.10	305.90

No. 80 shows the numeral on white tablet. See Nos. 99, 110-111.

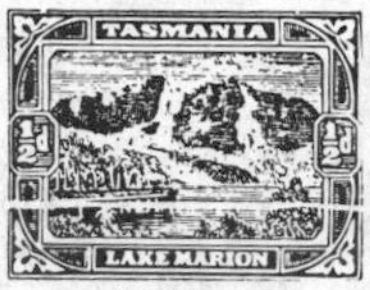
Lake Marion A10

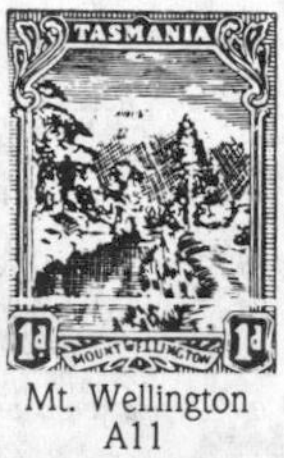
Mt. Wellington A11

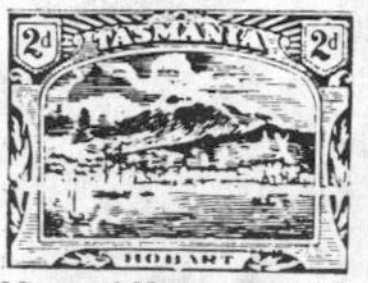
View of Hobart — A12

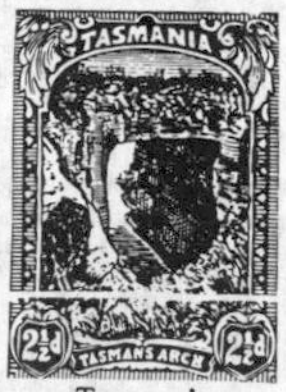
Tasman's Arch — A13

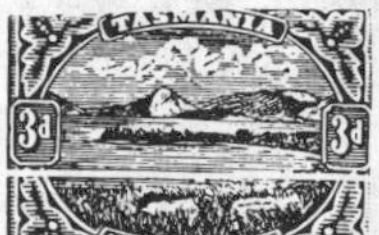
Spring River, Port Davey — A14

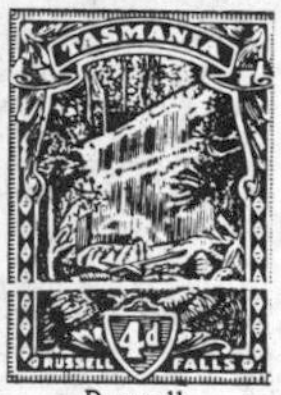
Russell Falls — A15

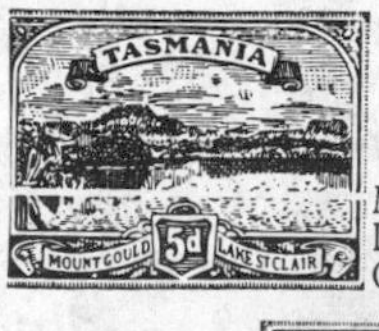
Mt. Gould and Lake St. Clair — A16

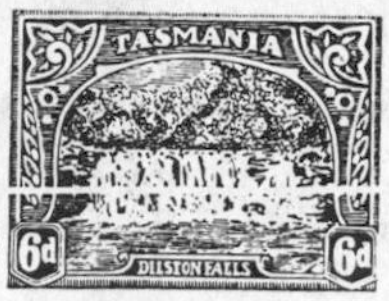
Dilston Falls — A17

1899-1900 Engr. Wmk. 78 *Perf. 14*

86 A10 ½p dark green	5.00	1.75
87 A11 1p carmine	5.00	.60
88 A12 2p violet	5.50	.45
89 A13 2½p dark blue	11.00	5.00
90 A14 3p dark brown	8.50	1.75
91 A15 4p ocher	16.00	2.25
92 A16 5p ultramarine	16.00	7.50
93 A17 6p lake	20.00	6.50
Nos. 86-93 (8)	87.00	25.80

See Nos. 94-97, 102-107, 114-117.

Perf. 11, 12½, 11x12½

1902-03 Litho., Typo. Wmk. 70

94 A10 ½p green	2.25	.30
95 A11 1p carmine	5.50	.15
96 A11 1p dull red	5.00	.20
97 A12 2p violet	3.25	.15
98 A5 9p blue	9.00	3.00
a. 9p ultramarine	225.00	
b. 9p indigo	90.00	
c. Perf. 11	7.25	3.50
99 A8 1sh rose & green	12.00	3.75
a. Perf. 11	27.50	27.50
Nos. 94-99 (6)	37.50	7.55

Nos. 94, 97 are litho., Nos. 96, 98-99 typo. No. 95 was printed both ways.

No. 78 Surcharged in Black **1½d.**

1904 Wmk. 77 *Perf. 14*

100 A8 1½p on 5p blue & brn 1.75 1.25

Perf. 11, 12, 12½ and Compound

1905-08 Typo. Wmk. 13

102 A10 ½p dull green	2.00	.15
a. Booklet pane of 12		
103 A11 1p carmine	2.00	.15
a. Booklet pane of 18		
104 A12 2p violet	3.50	.15
105 A14 3p dark brown	7.00	2.00
106 A15 4p ocher	13.00	2.25
107 A17 6p lake	40.00	5.00
108 A5 8p violet brown	19.00	5.00
109 A5 9p blue	8.00	3.00
110 A8 1sh rose & green	13.00	2.50
111 A8 10sh brt vio & brn	100.00	62.50
a. Perf. 11	175.00	
Nos. 102-111 (10)	207.50	82.70

Nos. 104-107 also printed litho.

1911 Redrawn

114 A12 2p bright violet	3.50	.30
115 A15 4p dull yellow	16.00	8.00
116 A17 6p lake	17.00	8.00
Nos. 114-116 (3)	36.50	16.30

The redrawn 2p measures 33½x25mm instead of 32½x24½mm. There are many slight changes in the clouds and other parts of the design.

The 4p is much lighter, especially the waterfall and trees above it. This appears to be a new or cleaned plate rather than a redrawn one.

In the redrawn 6p there are more colored lines in the waterfall and the river and more white dots in the trees.

No. 114 Surcharged in Red **ONE PENNY**

1912

117 A12 1p on 2p bright violet .85 .50

TOGO

'tō-(,)gō

LOCATION — Western Africa bordering on the Gulf of Guinea
GOVT. — Former mandate of Great Britain and France
AREA — 13,041 sq. mi.
POP. — 294,000. (estimated 1915)
CAPITAL — Lome

The German protectorate of Togo was occupied by Great Britain and France in World War I, and later mandated to them. The British area became part of Ghana. The French area was granted internal authonomy in 1956 and achieved independence in 1958. See "Togo" in Vol. 5 for German, French and Republic issues.

100 Pfennig = 1 Mark
12 Pence = 1 Shilling

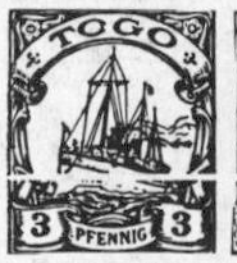
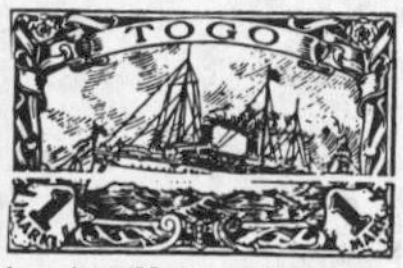
Kaiser's Yacht, the "Hohenzollern"
A3 A4

Stamps of German Togo Overprinted or Surcharged

TOGO
Anglo-French
Occupation

First (Wide) Setting
3mm between Lines
2mm between "Anglo" & "French"

Wmk. 125 (5pf, 10pf); Unwmkd.

1914, Oct. 1 *Perf. 14, 14½*

33 A3 ½p on 3pf brown	250.00	200.00
a. Thin "y" in "penny"	700.00	450.00
34 A3 1p on 5pf green	250.00	200.00
a. Thin "y" in "penny"	700.00	450.00
35 A3 3pf brown	125.00	75.00
36 A3 5pf green	110.00	75.00
37 A3 10pf carmine	125.00	75.00
a. Inverted overprint	10,000.	5,500.
b. Unwmk.		5,500.
38 A3 20pf ultra	27.50	25.00
39 A3 25pf org & blk, *yel*	27.50	22.50
40 A3 30pf org & blk, *sal*	30.00	27.50
41 A3 40pf lake & blk	250.00	175.00
42 A3 50pf pur & blk, *sal*	9,500.	7,000.
43 A3 80pf lake & blk, *rose*	250.00	200.00
44 A4 1m carmine	4,750.	2,250.
45 A4 2m blue	—	—
a. Inverted overprint	—	
b. "Occupation" double	—	—

On Nos. 33-34, the surcharge line ("Half penny" or "One penny") was printed separately and its position varies in relation to the 3-line overprint. On Nos. 46-47, the surcharge and overprint lines were printed simultaneously.

TOGO
Anglo-French
Occupation
Half penny

Second (Narrow) Setting
2mm between Lines
2mm between "Anglo" & "French"

1914, Oct.

46 A3 ½p on 3pf brown	25.00	19.00
a. Thin "y" in "penny"	55.00	45.00
b. "TOG"	425.00	250.00
47 A3 1p on 5pf green	5.00	5.00
a. Thin "y" in "penny"	15.00	15.00
b. "TOG"	125.00	100.00
48 A3 3pf brown	2,750.	1,100.
a. "Occupation" omitted		
49 A3 5pf green	1,500.	1,000.
50 A3 10pf carmine	—	2,750.
51 A3 20pf ultra	13.00	7.50
a. "TOG"	5,500.	3,500.
b. Vert. pair, #51 & #38	—	
52 A3 25pf org & blk, *yel*	20.00	20.00
a. "TOG"	10,000.	
53 A3 30pf org & blk, *sal*	20.00	27.50
54 A3 40pf lake & blk	2,750.	1,250.
55 A3 50pf pur & blk, *sal*		5,750.
56 A3 80pf lake & blk, *rose*	1,250.	1,250.
57 A4 1m carmine	12,000.	4,500.
58 A4 2m blue		9,250.
59 A4 3m black violet		—
60 A4 5m slate & car		—

Third Setting
1¼mm btwn. "Anglo" & "French"
2mm between Lines
"Anglo-French" 15mm Wide

1915, Jan. 7

61 A3 3pf brown	6,000.	3,250.
62 A3 5pf green	200.	125.
63 A3 10pf carmine	200.	125.
64 A3 20pf ultra	1,500.	825.
64A A3 40pf lake & blk		7,500.
65 A3 50pf pur & blk, *sal*	10,000.	7,500.

Stamps of Gold Coast Overprinted Locally

TOGO
ANGLO-FRENCH
OCCUPATION

1915, May Wmk. 3 *Perf. 14*

66 A7 ½p green	.25	.35
a. Double overprint	500.00	500.00
67 A8 1p scarlet	.20	.20
a. Double ovpt.	300.00	300.00
b. Inverted ovpt.	125.00	150.00
c. As "b," "Togo" omitted		
68 A7 2p gray	.20	.30
69 A7 2½p ultra	.30	.45

Chalky Paper

70 A7 3p violet, *yel*	.45	.60
71 A7 6p dl vio & red vio	.60	.90
72 A7 1sh black, *grn*	1.25	1.75
a. Double overprint	675.00	
73 A7 2sh vio & ultra, *bl*	4.25	6.00
74 A7 2sh6p blk & red, *bl*	4.00	7.50
75 A7 10sh grn & red, *grn*	24.00	35.00
76 A7 20sh vio & blk, *red*	80.00	80.00

Surfaced-Colored Paper

77 A7 3p violet, *yel*	3.50	8.00
78 A7 5sh grn & red, *yel*	9.00	18.00
Nos. 66-78 (13)	128.00	159.05

Nos. 66 to 78 exist with small "F" in "French" and thin "G" in "Togo." Several values are known without the hyphen between "Anglo-French" and all but No. 77 without the first "O" in "Occupation."

Stamps of Gold Coast Overprinted in London

TOGO
ANGLO-FRENCH
OCCUPATION

1916, Apr.

Ordinary Paper

80 A7 ½p green	.20	.85
81 A8 1p scarlet	.20	.65
a. Inverted overprint		
82 A7 2p gray	.30	.40
83 A7 2½p ultra	.40	1.25

Chalky Paper

84 A7 3p violet, *yel*	.45	.60
85 A7 6p dl vio & red vio	.45	.85
86 A7 1sh black, *grn*	1.25	1.75
a. 1sh black, *emerald*	175.00	300.00
b. 1sh black, *bl grn*, ol back	3.25	5.00
87 A7 2sh vio & ultra, *bl*	3.75	6.00
88 A7 2sh6p blk & red, *bl*	3.75	5.50
89 A7 5sh grn & red, *yel*	6.50	20.00
90 A7 10sh grn & red, *bl grn*, ol back	13.00	42.50
a. 10sh green & red, *grn*	20.00	50.00
91 A7 20sh vio & blk, *red*	110.00	67.50
Nos. 80-91 (12)	140.25	147.85

The overprint on Nos. 80 to 91 is in heavier letters than on Nos. 66 to 78 and the 2nd and 3rd lines are each ½mm longer. The letter "O" on Nos. 80 to 91 is narrower and more oval.

TOKELAU

'tō-kə-,laù

(Union Islands)

LOCATION — Pacific Ocean 300 miles north of Apia, Western Samoa
GOVT. — A dependency of New Zealand
AREA — 4 sq. mi.
POP. — 1,572 (est. 1981)

The Tokelau islands consist of three atolls: Atafu, Nukunono and Fakaofo, which span 100 miles of ocean.

12 Pence = 1 Shilling
100 Cents = 1 Dollar (1967)

Catalogue values for all unused stamps in this country are for Never Hinged items.

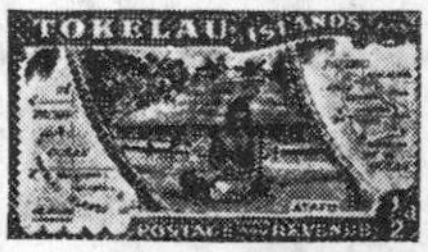
Map and Scene on Atafu — A1

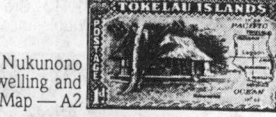

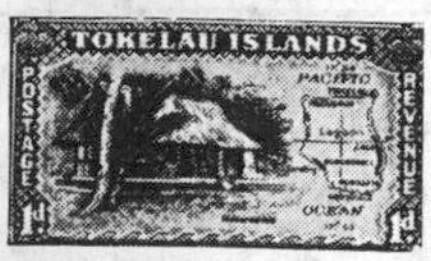
Nukunono Dwelling and Map — A2

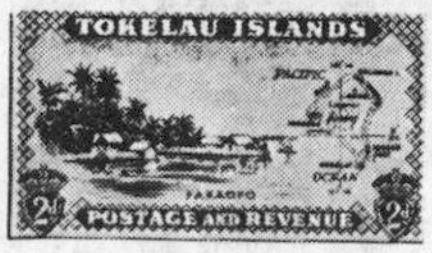
Fakaofo Shore Line and Map — A3

Perf. 13½x13

1948, June 22 Wmk. 253 Engr.

1 A1 ½p red brown & rose lilac	.18	.18
2 A2 1p dp green & orange brn	.30	.30
3 A3 2p deep ultra & green	.55	.55
Nos. 1-3 (3)	1.03	1.03

For surcharges see Nos. 5, 9-11.

Coronation Issue

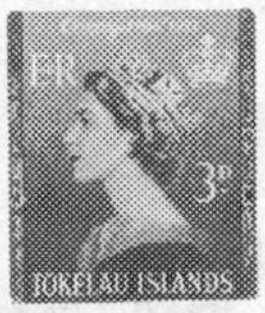

Queen Elizabeth II — A3a

1953, May 25 Photo. *Perf. 14x14½*
4 A3a 3p brown 6.00 8.00

No. 1 Surcharged in Black:

ONE SHILLING

Perf. 13½x13
1956, Mar. 27 Engr. Wmk. 253
5 A1 1sh on ½p 4.00 5.50

Postal-Fiscal Type of New Zealand, 1950, Surcharged **6D TOKELAU ISLANDS**

Wmk. 253
1966, Nov. Typo. *Perf. 14*
6 A109 6p light blue 1.50 .75
7 A109 8p light green 2.75 1.50
8 A109 2sh pink 5.00 3.75
Nos. 6-8 (3) 9.25 6.00

Nos. 1-3 Surcharged with New Value and Dots Obliterating Old Denomination

1967, July 10 Engr. *Perf. 13½x13*
9 A2 1c on 1p .45 .45
10 A3 2c on 2p 1.10 1.10
11 A1 10c on ½p 3.50 3.50
Nos. 9-11 (3) 5.05 5.05

The 1c and 2c surcharges include two dots, the 10c surcharge has only one.

Postal Fiscal Type of New Zealand, 1950, Surcharged **5c TOKELAU ISLANDS**

1967, July 10 Typo. *Perf. 14*
12 A109 3c light lilac .60 .60
13 A109 5c light blue 1.10 1.10
14 A109 7c light green 1.75 1.75
15 A109 20c pink 4.50 4.50
Nos. 12-15 (4) 7.95 7.95

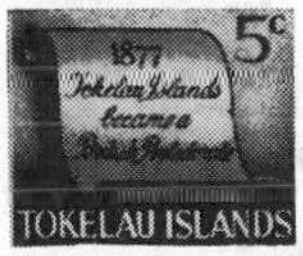

1877, British Protectorate — A4

History of Tokelau: 10c, 1916, part of Gilbert and Ellice Islands Colony. 15c, 1925, administration transferred to New Zealand. 20c, 1948, New Zealand Territory.

Perf. 13x12½
1969, Aug. 8 Litho. Wmk. 253
16 A4 5c ultra, yellow & blk .80 .80
17 A4 10c rose red, yel & blk 1.50 1.50
18 A4 15c dull grn, yel & blk 2.50 2.50
19 A4 20c brown, yel & blk 3.00 3.00
Nos. 16-19 (4) 7.80 7.80

Tokelau stamps can be mounted in the Scott New Zealand Dependencies album.

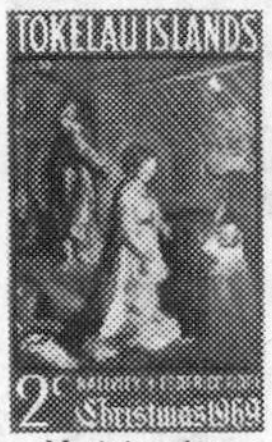

Nativity, by Federico Fiori — A4a

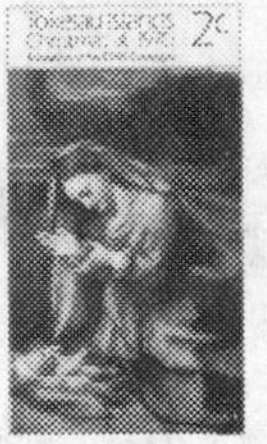
Adoration, by Correggio — A4b

1969, Oct. 1 Photo. *Perf. 13½x14*
20 A4a 2c multicolored .50 .50

Christmas.

Perf. 12½
1970, Oct. 1 Unwmk. Litho.
21 A4b 2c multicolored .50 .50

Christmas.

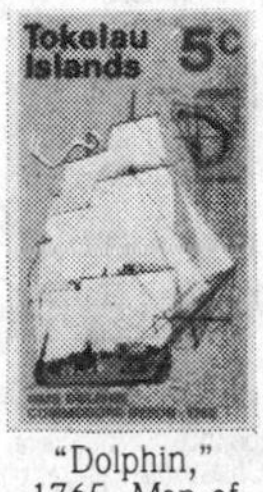

"Dolphin," 1765, Map of Atafu — A5

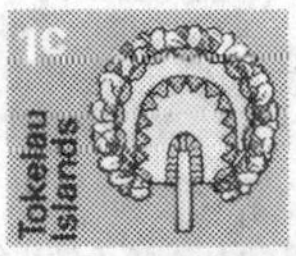

Fan — A6

Designs: 10c, "Pandora," 1791, and map of Nukunono. 25c, "General Jackson," 1835, and map of Fakaofo, horiz.

1970, Dec. 9 Unwmk. *Perf. 13½*
22 A5 5c yellow & multi 1.40 1.10
23 A5 10c multicolored 2.75 2.25
24 A5 25c pink & multi 7.00 5.75
Nos. 22-24 (3) 11.15 9.10

Discovery of Tokelau Islands.

1971, Oct. 20 Litho. *Perf. 14*

Native Handicrafts: 2c, Round vessel. 3c, Hexagonal box. 5c, Shoulder bag. 10c, Handbag. 15c, Jewelry box with beads. 20c, Outrigger canoe model. 25c, Fish hooks.

25 A6 1c olive & multi .20 .15
26 A6 2c red & multi .28 .16
27 A6 3c dk violet & multi .40 .28
28 A6 5c dull blue & multi .65 .40
29 A6 10c dp orange & multi 1.40 .80
30 A6 15c emerald & multi 2.00 1.40
31 A6 20c multicolored 2.75 1.75
32 A6 25c violet blue & multi 3.25 2.25
Nos. 25-32 (8) 10.93 7.19

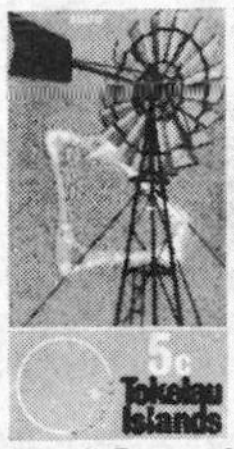

Windmill Pump, Map of Atafu — A7

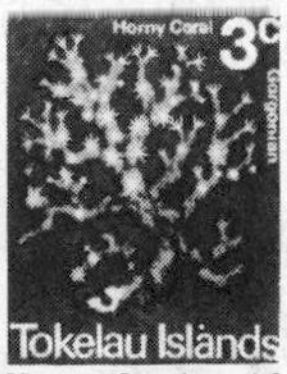

Horny Coral — A8

South Pacific Commission Emblem and: 10c, Community well, map of Fakaofo. 15c, Eradication of rhinoceros beetle, map of Nukunono. 20c, members.

1972, Sept. 6 Litho. *Perf. 14x13½*
33 A7 5c lt blue grn & multi .75 .55
34 A7 10c grnsh blue & multi 1.65 1.00
35 A7 15c lilac & multi 2.50 1.40
36 A7 20c violet bl & multi 3.25 2.00
Nos. 33-36 (4) 8.15 4.95

South Pacific Commission, 25th anniversary. On 15c, "PACIFIC" reads "PACFIC."

1973, Sept. 12 Litho. *Perf. 13x13½*
37 A8 3c shown .75 .50
38 A8 5c Soft coral 1.10 .75
39 A8 15c Mushroom coral 4.00 2.50
40 A8 25c Staghorn coral 6.25 4.00
Nos. 37-40 (4) 12.10 7.75

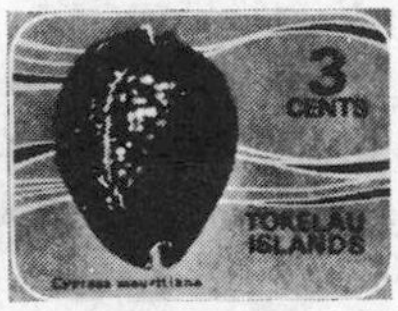

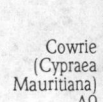

Cowrie (Cypraea Mauritiana) A9

Cowrie shells: 5c, Cypraea tigris. 15c, Cypraea talpa. 25c, Cypraea argus.

1974, Nov. 13 Litho. *Perf. 14*
41 A9 3c apple grn & multi .80 .40
42 A9 5c dk blue & multi 1.10 .60
43 A9 15c blue & multi 4.00 2.00
44 A9 25c green & multi 6.25 3.25
Nos. 41-44 (4) 12.15 6.25

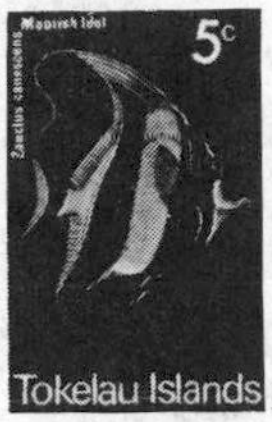

Moorish Idol — A10

Fish: 10c, Long-nosed butterflyfish. 15c, Lined butterflyfish. 25c, Red firefish.

1975, Nov. 19 Litho. *Perf. 14*
45 A10 5c blue & multi .70 .52
46 A10 10c brown & multi 1.50 .90
47 A10 15c lilac & multi 2.50 1.50
48 A10 25c multicolored 4.25 2.75
Nos. 45-48 (4) 8.95 5.67

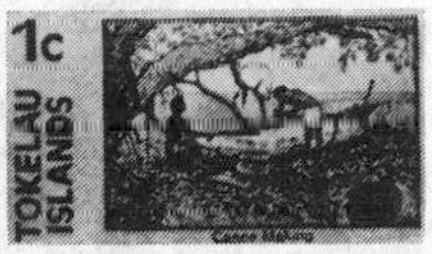

Canoe Making A11

Designs: 2c, Reef fishing. 3c, Woman preparing pandanus leaves for weaving. 5c, Communal kitchen (umu). 9c, Wood carving. 20c, Husking coconuts. 50c, Wash day. $1, Meal time. 9c, 20c, 50c, $1, vertical.

1976, Oct. 27 Litho. *Perf. 14*
49 A11 1c pink & multi .15 .15
50 A11 2c multicolored .15 .15
51 A11 3c lt blue & multi .15 .15
52 A11 5c yellow & multi .15 .15
53 A11 9c bister & multi .15 .15
54 A11 20c multicolored .32 .32
55 A11 50c tan & multi .65 .65
56 A11 $1 multicolored 1.25 1.25
Nos. 49-56 (8) 2.97 2.97

1981, July 17 *Perf. 15*
49a A11 1c .15 .15
51a A11 3c .15 .15
52a A11 5c .15 .15
53a A11 9c .15 .15
54a A11 20c .32 .32
55a A11 50c .65 .65
56a A11 $1 1.25 1.25
Nos. 49a-56a (7) 2.82 2.82

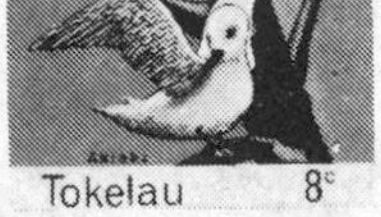

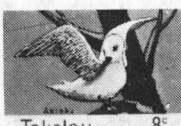

White Tern — A12

Birds of Tokelau: 10c, Turnstone. 15c, White-capped noddy. 30c, Brown noddy.

1977, Nov. 16 Litho. *Perf. 14½x15*
57 A12 8c multicolored .42 .32
58 A12 10c multicolored .55 .42
59 A12 15c multicolored .80 .70
60 A12 30c multicolored 1.75 1.50
Nos. 57-60 (4) 3.52 2.94

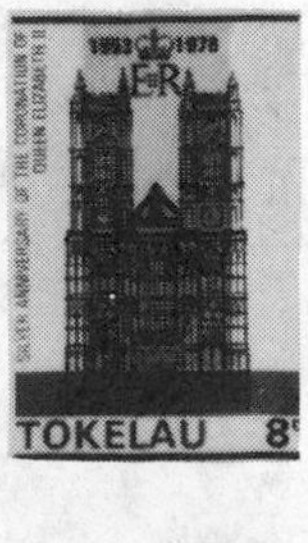

Westminster Abbey — A13

Designs: 10c, King Edward's Chair. 15c, Scepter, Crown, Orb, Bible and Staff of State. 30c, Elizabeth II.

1978, June 28 Litho. *Perf. 14*
61 A13 8c multicolored .28 .28
62 A13 10c multicolored .40 .40
63 A13 15c multicolored .60 .60
64 A13 30c multicolored 1.10 1.10
Nos. 61-64 (4) 2.38 2.38

25th anniv. of coronation of Elizabeth II.

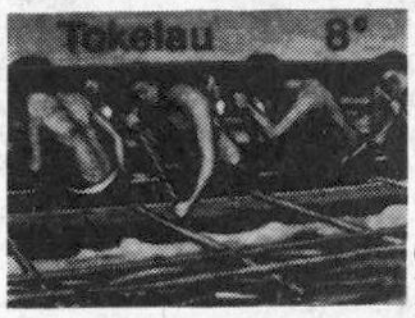

Canoe Racing — A14

Designs: Various canoe races.

1978, Nov. 8 Litho. *Perf. 13½x14*
65 A14 8c multicolored .40 .16
66 A14 12c multicolored .52 .26
67 A14 15c multicolored .55 .32
68 A14 30c multicolored .90 .55

1979, Nov. 7 Photo. *Perf. 14*
69 A14 10c Rugby .24 .16
70 A14 15c Cricket .38 .25
71 A14 20c Rugby, diff. .45 .38
72 A14 30c Cricket, diff. .90 .50

1980, Nov. 5 Litho. *Perf. 13½*
73 A14 10c Surfing .16 .16
74 A14 20c Surfing, diff. .30 .30
75 A14 30c Swimming .42 .42
76 A14 50c Swimming, diff. .75 .75

1981, Nov. 4 Photo. *Perf. 14*
77 A14 10c High jump, vert. .16 .16
78 A14 20c Volleyball, vert. .30 .30
79 A14 30c Running, vert. .42 .42
80 A14 50c Volleyball, vert., diff. .75 .75
Nos. 65-80 (16) 7.60 5.84

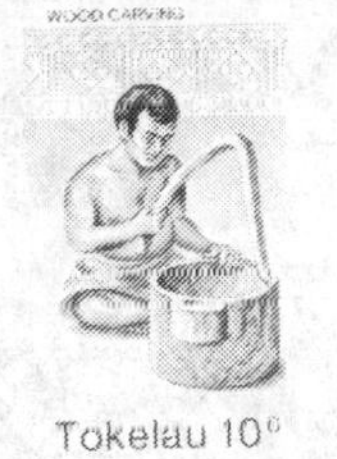

Wood Carving — A15

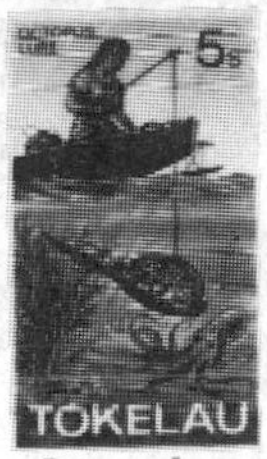

Octopus Lure Fishing — A16

1982, May 5 Litho. *Perf. 13½x13*
81 A15 10s shown .15 .15
82 A15 22s Bow-drilling sea shells .25 .25
83 A15 34s Bowl finishing .42 .42
84 A15 60s Basket weaving .85 .85
Nos. 81-84 (4) 1.67 1.67

1982, Nov. 3 Litho. *Perf. 14*

Designs: Fishing Methods.

85 A16 5s shown .15 .15
86 A16 18s Multiple-hook .20 .20
87 A16 23s Ruvettus .28 .28
88 A16 34s Netting flying fish .40 .40
89 A16 63s Noose .65 .65
90 A16 75s Bonito .80 .80
Nos. 85-90 (6) 2.48 2.48

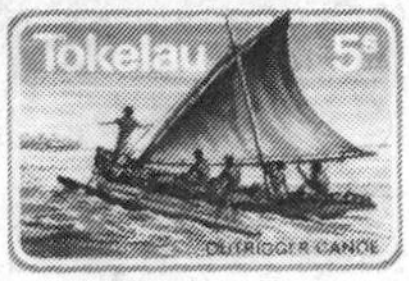

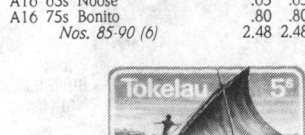

Outrigger Canoe — A17

1983, May 4 Litho. *Perf. 13½x14*
91 A17 5s shown .15 .15
92 A17 18s Whale boat .20 .20
93 A17 23s Aluminium whale boat .28 .28
94 A17 34s Alia fishing boat .40 .40
95 A17 63s Cargo ship .65 .65
96 A17 75s Seaplane .80 .80
Nos. 91-96 (6) 2.48 2.48

Traditional Games A18

1983, Nov. 2   Litho.   Perf. 14
97	A18	5s Javelin throwing	.15	.15
98	A18	18s Tifaga string game	.20	.20
99	A18	23s Fire making	.28	.28
100	A18	34s Shell throwing	.40	.40
101	A18	63s Handball	.65	.65
102	A18	75s Mass wrestling	.80	.80
		Nos. 97-102 (6)	2.48	2.48

Planting, Harvesting Copra — A19

Copra Industry: b, Husking, splitting. c, Drying, cutting. d, Bagging, weighing. e, Shipping. Continuous design.

1984, May 2   Litho.   Perf. 13½x13
103	Strip of 5	2.75	2.75
a.-e.	A19 48s any single	.55	.55

1984, Dec. 5   Litho.   Perf. 14½x14
104	A20	1c Manini	.15	.15
105	A20	2c Hahave	.15	.15
106	A20	5c Uloulo	.15	.15
107	A20	9c Ume Ihu	.15	.15
108	A20	23c Lifilafi	.30	.30
109	A20	34c Fagamea	.35	.35
110	A20	50c Kakahi	.48	.48
111	A20	75c Palu Po	.70	.70
112	A20	$1 Mokoha	.90	.90
113	A20	$2 Hakula	1.75	1.75
		Nos. 104-113 (10)	5.08	5.08

Trees, Fruits and Herbs — A21

1985, June 26   Litho.   Perf. 13½
114	A21	5c Mati	.15	.15
115	A21	18c Nonu	.25	.25
116	A21	32c Ulu	.40	.40
117	A21	48c Fala	.65	.65
118	A21	60c Kanava	.80	.80
119	A21	75c Niu	1.00	1.00
		Nos. 114-119 (6)	3.25	3.25

Public Buildings and Churches A22

Designs: 5c, Administration Center, Atafu. 18c, Administration Center, Nukunonu. 32c, Administration Center, Fakaofo. 48c, Congregational Church, Atafu. 60c, Catholic Church, Nukunonu. 75c, Congregational Church, Fakaofo.

1985, Dec. 4
120	A22	5c multicolored	.15	.15
121	A22	18c multicolored	.22	.22
122	A22	32c multicolored	.38	.38
123	A22	48c multicolored	.60	.60
124	A22	60c multicolored	.70	.70
125	A22	75c multicolored	.90	.90
		Nos. 120-125 (6)	2.95	2.95

Hospitals and Schools A23

Designs: 5c, Atafu Hospital. 18c, St. Joseph's Hospital, Nukunonu. 32c, Fenuafala Hospital, Fakaofo. 48c, Matauala School, Atafu. 60c, Matiti School, Nukunonu. 75c, Fenuafala School, Fakaofo.

1986, May 7   Perf. 13½
126	A23	5c multicolored	.15	.15
127	A23	18c multicolored	.20	.20
128	A23	32c multicolored	.35	.35
129	A23	48c multicolored	.55	.55
130	A23	60c multicolored	.68	.68
131	A23	75c multicolored	.85	.85
		Nos. 126-131 (6)	2.78	2.78

Fauna A24

1986, Dec. 3   Litho.   Perf. 14
132	A24	5c Coconut crab	.15	.15
133	A24	18c Pigs	.25	.25
134	A24	32c Chickens	.45	.45
135	A24	48c Turtles	.65	.65
136	A24	60c Goats	.85	.85
137	A24	75c Ducks	1.00	1.00
		Nos. 132-137 (6)	3.35	3.35

Flora — A25

1987, May 6
138	A25	5c Gahu	.15	.15
139	A25	18c Puka	.25	.25
140	A25	32c Higano	.42	.42
141	A25	48c Tialetiale	.65	.65
142	A25	60c Gagie	.85	.85
143	A25	75c Puapua	1.10	1.10
		Nos. 138-143 (6)	3.42	3.42

Olympic Sports A26

1987, Dec. 2   Litho.   Perf. 14x14½
144	A26	5c Javelin	.15	.15
145	A26	18c Shot put	.30	.30
146	A26	32c Long jump	.50	.50
147	A26	48c Hurdles	.80	.80
148	A26	60c Running	1.00	1.00
149	A26	75c Wrestling	1.25	1.25
		Nos. 144-149 (6)	4.00	4.00

Australia Bicentennial, SYDPEX '88 — A27

Re-enactment of the arrival of the First Fleet in Sydney Harbor, Jan. 26, 1988 (in a continuous design): a, Ships in harbor, building (LL). b, Ships in harbor, tall ship (LR). c, Ships in harbor, Sydney Opera House. d, Bridge. e, North Sydney.

1988, July 30   Litho.   Perf. 13½x13
150	Strip of 5	4.50	4.50
a.-e.	A27 50c any single	.90	.90

Political Development — A28

Designs: 5c, Transfer of administration from the New Zealand Department of Maori and Island Affairs to the Ministry of Foreign Affairs, 1975. 18c, The General Fono empowered as the decision-making body of Tokelau, 1977. 32c, 1st Visit of New Zealand's prime minister, 1985. 48c, 1st Visit of UN representatives, 1976. 60c, 1st Tokelau delegation to go to the UN, 1987. 75c, 1st Tokelau appointed to the office of Official Secretary, 1987.

1988, Aug. 10   Perf. 14½
151	A28	5c multicolored	.15	.15
152	A28	18c multicolored	.28	.28
153	A28	32c multicolored	.48	.48
154	A28	48c multicolored	.70	.70
155	A28	60c multicolored	.88	.88
156	A28	75c multicolored	1.10	1.10
		Nos. 151-156 (6)	3.59	3.59

Island Christmas A29

Designs: 5c, Three Wise Men (Na Makoi). 20c, Holy family (He Tala). 40c, Escape into Egypt (Fakagagalo ki Aikupito). 60c, Christmas presents (Meaalofa Kilihimahi). 70c, Christ child (Pepe ko Iesu). $1, Christmas parade (Holo Tamilo).

1988, Dec. 7   Litho.   Perf. 13½
157	A29	5c multicolored	.15	.15
158	A29	20c multicolored	.28	.28
159	A29	40c multicolored	.55	.55
160	A29	60c multicolored	.80	.80
161	A29	70c multicolored	.95	.95
162	A29	$1 multicolored	1.35	1.35
		Nos. 157-162 (6)	4.08	4.08

Food Gathering A30

Fishing and gathering coconuts. Printed se-tenant in continuous designs.
No. 163: a, Launching outrigger canoe. b, Outrigger canoe and sailboat starboard side. c, Outrigger canoe and sailboat stern.
No. 164: a, Outrigger and sailboat port side. b, Islander carrying baskets of coconuts. c, Gathering coconuts from palm trees.

1989, June 28   Litho.   Perf. 14x14½
163	Strip of 3	1.95	1.95
a.-c.	A30 50c any single	.65	.65
164	Strip of 3	1.95	1.05
a.-c.	A30 50c any single	.65	.65

Women's Work and Leisure — A31

1990, May 2   Litho.   Perf. 14½
165	A31	5c Weavers	.15	.15
166	A31	20c Washing clothes	.23	.23
167	A31	40c Resting among palm trees	.46	.46
168	A31	60c Weaving mat	.70	.70
169	A31	80c Weaving, diff.	.92	.92
170	A31	$1 Basket weaver	1.15	1.15
		Nos. 165-170 (6)	3.61	3.61

Souvenir Sheet

Penny Black, 150th Anniv. — A32

1990, May 3   Litho.   Perf. 11½
171	A32	$3 multicolored	6.00	6.00

Men's Handicrafts — A33

1990, Aug. 1   Photo.   Perf. 13
172	A33	50c shown	.60	.60
173	A33	50c Carving pots	.60	.60
174	A33	50c Tying rope on pot	.60	.60
a.		Strip of 3, #172-174	1.80	1.80
175	A33	50c Finishing pots	.60	.60
176	A33	50c Shaping a canoe	.60	.60
177	A33	50c Three men working	.60	.60
a.		Strip of 3, #175-177	1.80	1.80
		Nos. 172-177 (6)	3.60	3.60

1992 Summer Olympics, Barcelona — A34

1992, July 8   Litho.   Perf. 13½
178	A34	40c Swimming	.45	.45
179	A34	60c Long jump	.70	.70
180	A34	$1 Volleyball	1.15	1.15
181	A34	$1.80 Running	2.00	2.00
		Nos. 178-181 (4)	4.30	4.30

Discovery of America, 500th Anniv. A35

1992, Dec. 18
182	A35	40c Santa Maria	.45	.45
183	A35	60c Columbus	.70	.70
184	A35	$1.20 Columbus' fleet	1.35	1.35
185	A35	$1.80 Landfall	2.00	2.00
		Nos. 182-185 (4)	4.50	4.50

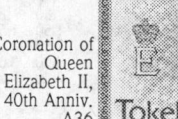

Coronation of Queen Elizabeth II, 40th Anniv. A36

1993, July 8   Litho.   Perf. 13½
186	A36	25c Queen, early portrait	.28	.28
187	A36	40c Prince Philip	.45	.45
188	A36	$1 Queen, recent portrait	1.10	1.10
189	A36	$2 Queen & Prince Philip	2.25	2.25
		Nos. 186-189 (4)	4.08	4.08

Birds — A37

Designs: 25c, Numenius tahitiensis. 40c, Phaethon rubricauda. $1, Egretta sacra. $2, Pluvialis fulva.

1993-94 Litho. *Perf. 13½*

190	A37	25c multicolored	.30	.30
191	A37	40c multicolored	.45	.45
192	A37	$1 multicolored	1.25	1.25
193	A37	$2 multicolored	2.25	2.25
a.		Souvenir sheet of 4, #190-193, perf. 14x14½	4.25	4.25
		Nos. 190-193 (4)	4.25	4.25

No. 193a contains Hong Kong '94 emblem, inscription in Chinese and English in sheet margin and sold for $20 HK at the show.

Issued: #190-193, 12/15/93; #193a, 2/1/94.

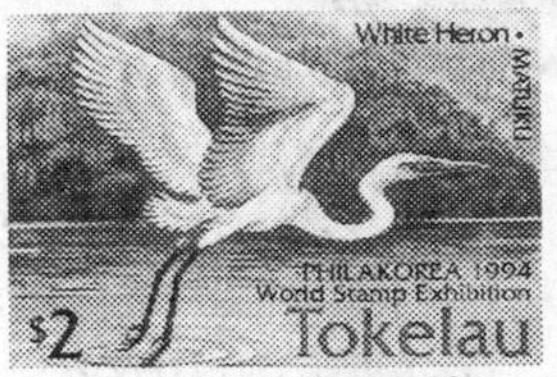

PHILAKOREA '94 — A38

1994, Aug. 16 Litho. *Perf. 12*

194	A38	$2 White heron	2.50	2.50
a.		Souvenir sheet of 1	2.50	2.50

No. 194a has a continuous design.

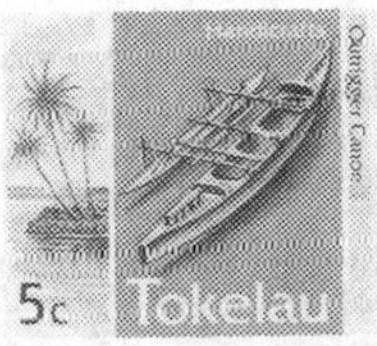

Handicrafts A39

1995 Litho. *Perf. 13½*

195	A39	5c Outrigger canoe	.15	.15
196	A39	25c Plaited fan	.32	.32
197	A39	40c Plaited baskets	.50	.50
198	A39	50c Fishing box	.65	.65
199	A39	80c Water bottle	1.00	1.00
200	A39	$1 Fishing hook	1.25	1.25
201	A39	$2 Coconut gourds	2.50	2.50
202	A39	$5 Shell necklace	6.25	6.25
		Nos. 195-202 (8)	12.62	12.62

Souvenir Sheet

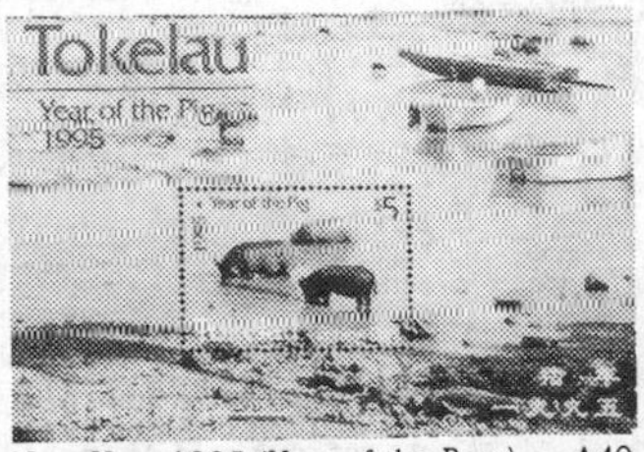

New Year 1995 (Year of the Boar) — A40

Illustration reduced.

1995, Feb. 3 Litho. *Perf. 14*

203	A40	$5 multicolored	6.25	6.25
a.		Ovptd. in sheet margin	6.25	6.25

No. 203a ovptd. in red in sheet margin "POST'X 95 / 3-6 February / 1995 / AUCKLAND" surrounded by simulated perforations.

No. 203 Ovptd. in Red in Sheet Margin

1995 Litho. *Perf. 14*

203b	Ovptd. in red	7.50	7.50

No. 203b ovptd. in red in sheet margin with Singapore '95 exhibition emblem.

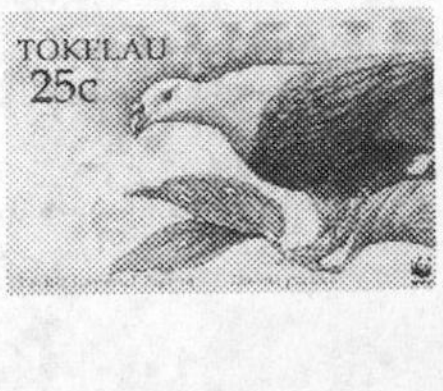

Pacific Imperial Pigeon A41

1995, Apr. 27 Litho. *Perf. 13½*

204	A41	25c shown	.32	.32
205	A41	40c Full view	.50	.50
206	A41	$1 In tree, red berries	1.25	1.25
207	A41	$2 Nesting	2.50	2.50
		Nos. 204-207 (4)	4.57	4.57

World Wildlife Fund.

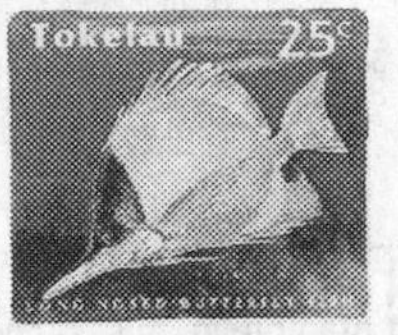

Reef Fish — A42

Designs: 25c, Long nosed butterfly fish. 40c, Emperor angelfish. $1, Moorish idol. $2, Lined butterfly fish.

$3, Red fire fish.

1995, Sept. 1 Litho. *Perf. 12*

208	A42	25c multicolored	.40	.40
209	A42	40c multicolored	.60	.60
210	A42	$1 multicolored	1.50	1.50
211	A42	$2 multicolored	3.00	3.00
		Nos. 208-211 (4)	5.50	5.50

Souvenir Sheet

212	A42	$3 multicolored	4.50	4.50

No. 212 contains one 40x35mm stamp and is inscribed in sheet margin for Singapore '95.

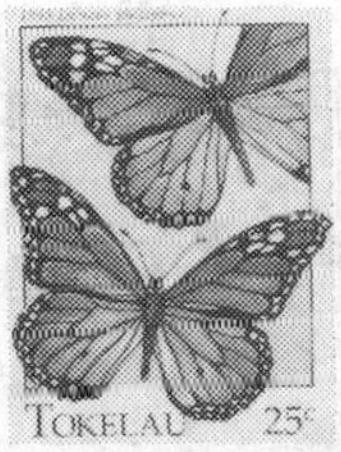

Butterflies — A43

Designs: 25c, Danaus plexippus. 40c, Precis villida samoensis. $1, Hypolimnas bolina. $2, Euploea lewenii.

1995, Oct. 16 Litho. *Perf. 12*

213	A43	25c multicolored	.40	.40
214	A43	40c multicolored	.60	.60
215	A43	$1 multicolored	1.50	1.50
216	A43	$2 multicolored	3.00	3.00
		Nos. 213-216 (4)	5.50	5.50

TONGA

'täŋ–gə

LOCATION — A group of islands in the south Pacific Ocean, south of Samoa

GOVT. — Kingdom in British Commonwealth

AREA — 289 sq. mi.

POP. — 98,750 (est. 1983)

CAPITAL — Nuku'alofa

This group, also known as the Friendly Islands, became a British Protectorate in 1900 under the Anglo-German Agreement of 1899. On June 4, 1970, the United Kingdom ceased to have any responsibility for the external relations of Tonga.

12 Pence = 1 Shilling
20 Shillings = 1 Pound
100 Seniti = 1 Pa'anga (1967)

Catalogue values for unused stamps in this country are for Never Hinged items, beginning with Scott 87 in the regular postage section, Scott B1 in the semi-postal section, Scott C1 in the air post section Scott CE1 in the air post special delivery section, Scott CO1 in the air post official section, and Scott O11 in the officials section.

Watermarks

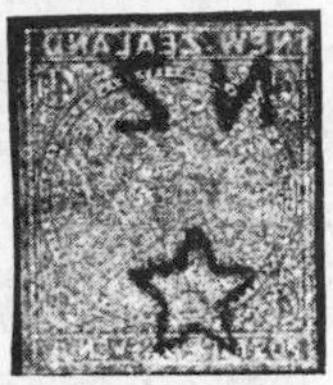

Wmk. 62- NZ and Small Star Wide Apart

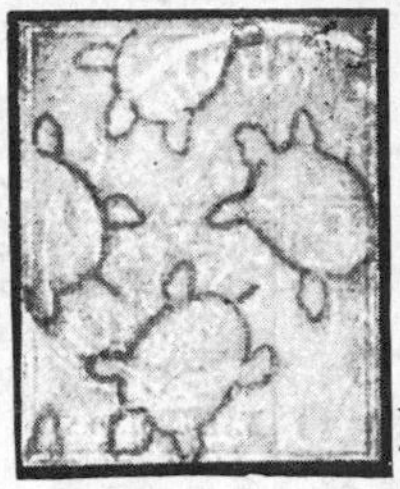

Wmk. 79- Turtles

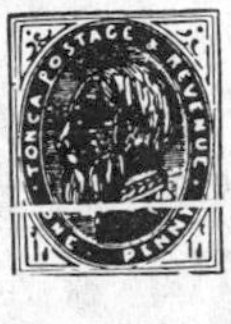

King George I — A1

Perf. 12x11½

1886-92 Typo. **Wmk. 62**

1	A1	1p car rose ('87)	11.00	6.00
a.		Perf. 12½	250.00	15.00
b.		Perf. 12½x10		
2	A1	2p violet ('87)	25.00	3.00
a.		Perf. 12½	40.00	12.00
3	A1	6p ultra ('88)	40.00	3.00
a.		Perf. 12½	47.50	3.00
4	A1	6p org yel ('92)	12.00	*25.00*
5	A1	1sh blue grn ('88)	45.00	6.75
a.		Perf. 12½	75.00	4.00
b.		Half used as 6p on cover		
		Nos. 1-5 (5)	133.00	*43.75*

For surcharges and overprints see #6-9, 24.

Nos. 1 and 2 Surcharged or Overprinted in Black:

FOUR PENCE. (a)   ✱ (b)

1891, Nov. 10 *Perf. 12x11½*

6	A1(a)	4p on 1p car rose	2.50	10.00
a.		No period after "PENCE"	42.50	*85.00*
7	A1(a)	8p on 2p violet	40.00	70.00

1891, Nov. 23 *Perf. 12½*

Two types of overprint:
I - Solid stars, rays pointed and short.
II - Open-center stars, rays blunt and long.

8	A1(b)	1p car rose (I)	32.50	45.00
a.		Overprinted with 3 stars (I)	225.00	
b.		Overprinted with 4 stars (I)	300.00	
c.		Overprinted with 5 stars (I)	425.00	
d.		Type II	27.50	27.50
e.		Perf. 12x11½ (I or II)	120.00	90.00
9	A1(b)	2p violet (I)	50.00	*40.00*
a.		Type II	50.00	*55.00*
b.		Perf. 12x11½ (I or II)	250.00	

Coat of Arms A4

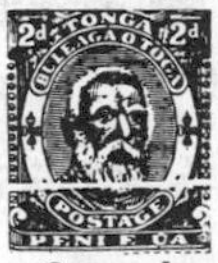

George I A5

1892, Nov. 10 Typo. *Perf. 12x11½*

10	A4	1p rose	12.00	16.00
a.		Diagonal half used as ½p on cover		500.00
11	A5	2p olive gray	13.00	*15.00*
12	A4	4p red brown	37.50	50.00
13	A5	8p violet	50.00	90.00
14	A5	1sh brown	70.00	90.00
		Nos. 10-14 (5)	182.50	261.00

For surcharges and overprints see Nos. 15-23, 25-28, 36-37, O1-O10.

Types A4 and A5 Surcharged in Carmine or Black:

½d. (c)   2½d. (d)   7½d. (f)

FIVE PENCE.

1893

15	A4	½p on 1p ultra (C)	22.50	22.50
a.		Surcharge omitted		
16	A4	½p on 1p ultra	45.00	47.50
17	A5	2½p on 2p blue grn (C)	15.00	12.00
18	A5	2½p on 2p blue grn	18.00	18.00
a.		Double surcharge		675.00
19	A4	5p on 4p org yel (C)	5.00	4.50
20	A5	7½p on 8p rose (C)	35.00	60.00
		Nos. 15-20 (6)	140.50	164.50

Stamps of 1886-92 Surcharged in Blue or Black:

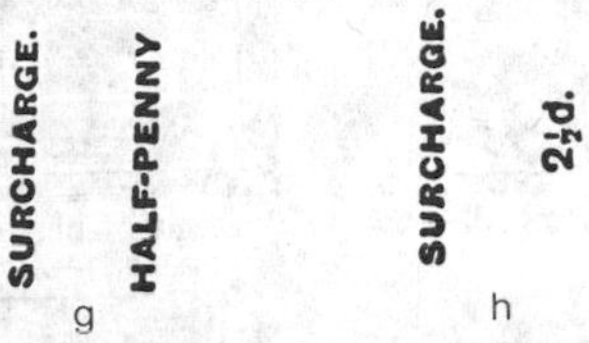

SURCHARGE. HALF-PENNY (g)   SURCHARGE. 2½d. (h)

1894

21	A4	½p on 4p red brn (Bl)	3.00	*7.00*
a.		"SURCHARCE"	7.00	*17.00*
b.		Pair, one without surcharge		
c.		"HALF PENNY" omitted		
22	A5	½p on 1sh brown (Bk)	3.50	*10.00*
a.		Double surcharge	300.00	
b.		"SURCHARCE"	10.00	35.00
c.		As "b," double surcharge	850.00	
23	A5	2½p on 8p violet (Bk)	6.50	*7.50*
a.		No period after "SURCHARGE"	30.00	45.00
24	A1	2½p on 1sh blue grn (Bk)	35.00	20.00
a.		No period after "SURCHARGE"	110.00	
b.		Perf. 12x11½	15.00	30.00
		Nos. 21-24 (4)	48.00	*44.50*

Type A5 with Same Surcharges in Carmine

1895 **Unwmk.**

25	A5(g)	1p on 2p lt blue	32.50	20.00
26	A5(h)	1½p on 2p lt bl, perf. 12x11	35.00	25.00
a.		Perf. 12	45.00	25.00
27	A5(h)	2½p on 2p lt blue	40.00	45.00
b.		Without period	225.00	225.00
28	A5(h)	7½p on 2p lt bl, perf. 12x11	55.00	47.50
a.		Perf. 12	150.00	
		Nos. 25-28 (4)	162.50	137.50

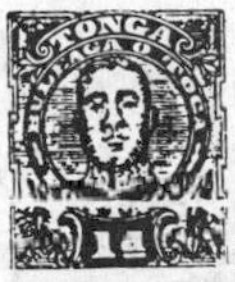

King George II — A13

1895, Aug. 16 *Perf. 12*

29	A13	1p gray green	20.00	25.00
a.		Diagonal half used as ½p on cover		*650.00*
b.		Horiz. pair, imperf. btwn.	*750.00*	*5,500.*
30	A13	2½p dull rose	20.00	20.00
31	A13	5p brt blue, perf. 12x11	15.00	35.00
a.		Perf. 12	15.00	35.00
b.		Perf. 11	325.00	
32	A13	7½p yellow	21.00	*35.00*
		Nos. 29-32 (4)	76.00	*115.00*

Type A13 Redrawn and Surcharged "g" or "h" in Black

33	A13(g)	½p on 2½p red	30.00	*32.50*
a.		"SURCHARCE"	70.00	
b.		Period after "Postage"	80.00	
34	A13(g)	1p on 2½p red	40.00	*25.00*
a.		Period after "Postage"	85.00	
35	A13(h)	7½p on 2½p red	45.00	45.00
a.		Period after "Postage"	85.00	
		Nos. 33-35 (3)	115.00	*102.50*

Nos. 26 and 28 with Additional Surcharge in Violet and Black

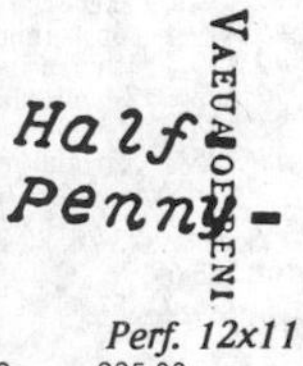

Half Penny-   VAEUA 'AE PENI

1896, May *Perf. 12x11*

36	A5	½p on 1½p on 2p	225.00	
a.		Tongan surcharge reading upwards	240.00	

b. Perf. 12 225.00 *250.00*
c. As "a," perf. 12 240.00 *275.00*
d. "Haalf" 600.00
37 A5 ½p on 7½p on 2p 27.50 *40.00*
a. "Half penny" inverted 900.00
b. "Half penny" double
c. Tongan surcharge reading upwards 27.50 *40.00*
d. Tongan surcharge as "c" and double
e. "Hafl Penny" 450.00 *600.00*
f. "Hafl" only 600.00
g. "Hwlf"
h. Periods instead of hyphens after words 225.00
j. Perf. 12 275.00

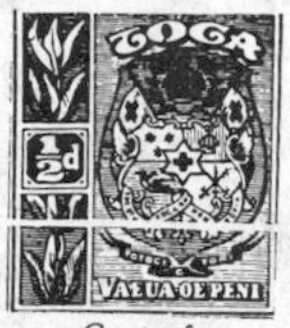
Coat of Arms — A17

Ovava Tree — A18

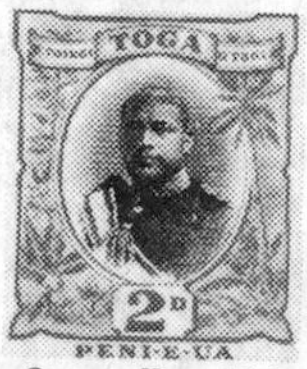
George II — A19

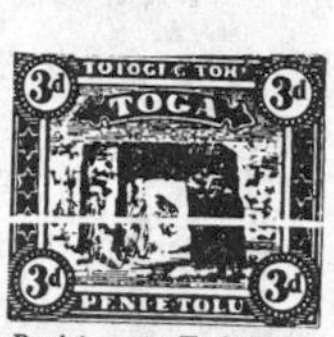
Prehistoric Trilithon, Tongatabu — A20

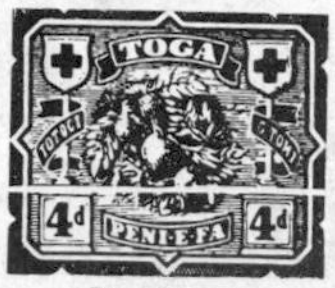
Breadfruit A21

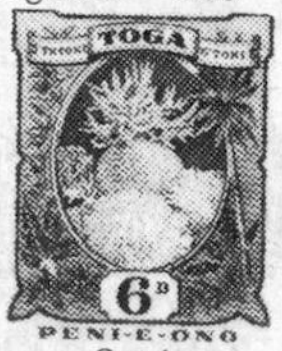
Coral Formations A22

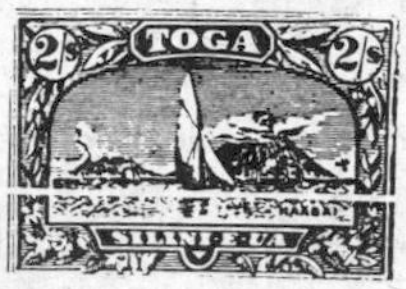
View of Haabai — A23

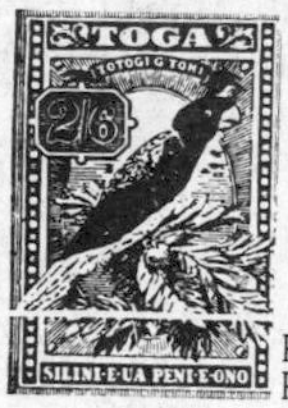
Red-breasted Musk Parrot — A24

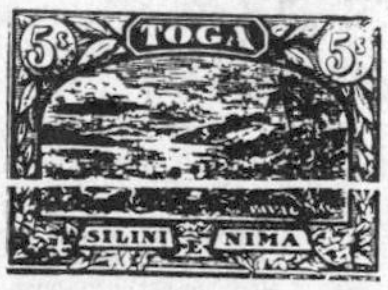
View of Vavau — A25

Two types of 2p:
I - Top of sword hilt shows above "2."
II - No hilt shows.

1897-1934 Engr. Wmk. 79 *Perf. 14*

38 A17 ½p dark blue 1.65 1.75
39 A17 ½p green ('34) .30 .80
40 A18 1p dp red & blk .55 .55
41 A19 2p bister & blk (I) 7.75 2.25
a. Type II 7.00 2.00
42 A19 2½p lt blue & blk 3.25 .60
a. "½" without fraction bar 60.00 55.00
43 A20 3p ol grn & blk 2.50 *2.75*
44 A21 4p dull vio & grn 2.50 2.75
45 A19 5p orange & blk 17.00 7.00
46 A22 6p red 6.00 2.50
47 A19 7½p green & blk 6.25 13.00
a. Center inverted 3,500.
48 A19 10p carmine & blk 18.00 20.00
49 A19 1sh red brown & blk 7.75 4.50
50 A23 2sh dk ultra & blk 35.00 40.00
51 A24 2sh6p dk violet 32.50 20.00
52 A25 5sh dull red & blk 30.00 27.50
Nos. 38-52 (15) 171.00 145.95

See Nos. 73-74, 77-78, 80-81. For surcharges see Nos. 63-69.

Stamp of 1897 Overprinted in Black

T - L

1 June. 1899.

1899, June 1

53 A18 1p red & black 30.00 50.00
a. "1889" instead of "1899" 250.00 250.00
b. Comma omitted after June
c. Double overprint

Marriage of George II to Lavinia, June 1, 1899. The letters "T L" are the initials of Taufa'ahau, the King's family name, and Lavinia.

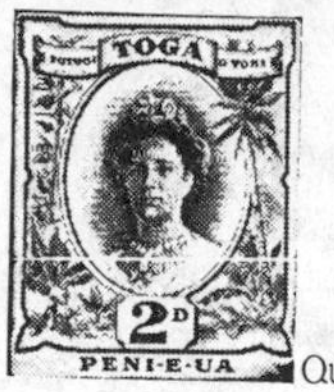
Queen Salote — A26

Dies of 2p:
Die I - Ball of "2" smaller.
Die II - Ball of "2" larger. "U" has spur at left.

1920-35 Engr. Wmk. 79

54 A26 1½p gray blk ('35) .25 *.85*
55 A26 2p violet & sepia 4.50 7.50
56 A26 2p dl vio & blk (I) ('24) 1.50 1.10
a. Die II 3.00 2.50
57 A26 2½p blue & black 2.75 *17.50*
58 A26 2½p ultra ('34) 1.50 1.40
59 A26 5p red org & blk 3.00 4.00
60 A26 7½p green & blk 1.50 1.40
61 A26 10p carmine & blk 2.75 *4.25*
62 A26 1sh red brown & blk 2.25 3.00
Nos. 54-62 (9) 20.00 41.00

See Nos. 75-76, 79.

Stamps of 1897 Surcharged in Dark Blue or Red

TWO PENCE

PENI-E-UA

1923

63 A19 2p on 5p org & blk .85 1.00
64 A19 2p on 7½p grn & blk 16.00 20.00
65 A19 2p on 10p car & blk 12.50 *16.00*
66 A19 2p on 1sh red brn & blk 25.00 25.00
67 A23 2p on 2sh ultra & blk (R) 5.50 *10.00*
68 A24 2p on 2sh6p dk vio (R) 6.50 8.25
69 A25 2p on 5sh dull red & blk (R) 4.00 5.00
Nos. 63-69 (7) 70.35 85.25

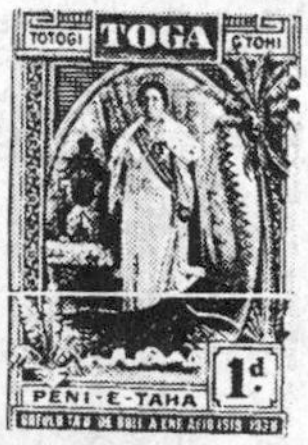
Queen Salote — A27

Inscribed "1918-1938"

1938, Oct. 12 *Perf. 14*

70 A27 1p carmine & blk .35 .90
71 A27 2p violet & blk 2.50 2.75
72 A27 2½p ultra & blk 2.50 2.75
Nos. 70-72 (3) 5.35 6.40

20th anniv. of the accession of Queen Salote Tupou.
See Nos. 82-86.

Types of 1897-1920

1942 Engr. Wmk. 4

Die III of 2p:
Foot of "2" longer than in Die II, extending beyond curve of loop.

73 A17 ½p green .15 .15
74 A18 1p scarlet & blk .30 .70
75 A26 2p dull vio & blk (II) .30 .40
a. Die III 3.75 3.75
76 A26 2½p ultra .40 .55
77 A20 3p green & black .30 .75
78 A22 6p orange red .90 1.50
79 A26 1sh red brown & gray blk .80 1.40
80 A24 2sh6p dk violet 7.50 17.00
81 A25 5sh dull red & brn blk 10.00 22.50
Nos. 73-81 (9) 20.65 44.95

Type of 1938, Inscribed "1918-1943"

1944, Jan. 28

82 A27 1p rose car & blk .15 .25
83 A27 2p purple & blk .15 .25
84 A27 3p dk yel grn & blk .15 .25
85 A27 6p red orange & blk .30 .50
86 A27 1sh dk red brn & blk .40 .50
Nos. 82-86 (5) 1.15 1.75

25th anniv. of the accession of Queen Salote.

Catalogue values for unused stamps in this section, from this point to the end of the section, are for Never Hinged items.

UPU Issue
Common Design Types
Engr.; Name Typo. on 3p, 6p
Perf. 13½, 11x11½

1949, Oct. 10 Wmk. 4

87 CD306 2½p ultra .20 .28
88 CD307 3p deep olive .32 .40
89 CD308 6p deep carmine .48 .50
90 CD309 1sh red brown 1.00 1.10
Nos. 87-90 (4) 2.00 2.28

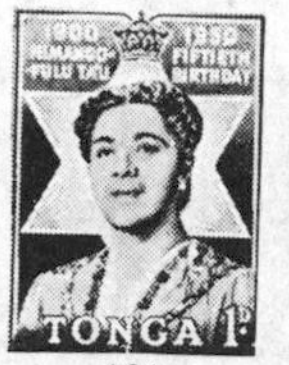
A28

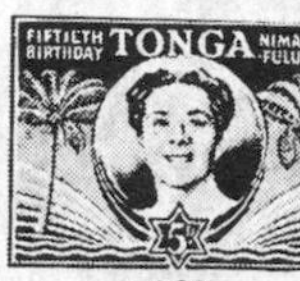
A29

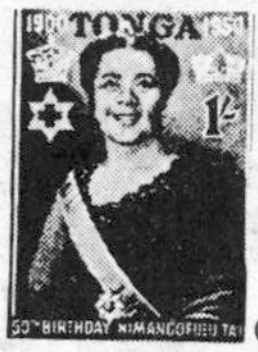
Queen Salote — A30

1950, Nov. 1 Photo. *Perf. 12½*

91 A28 1p cerise .16 .16
92 A29 5p green .40 .40
93 A30 1sh violet .50 .50
Nos. 91-93 (3) 1.06 1.06

50th anniv. of the birth of Queen Salote.

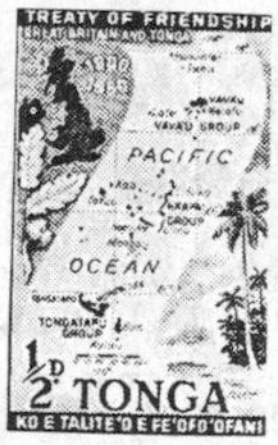
Map and Island Scene — A31

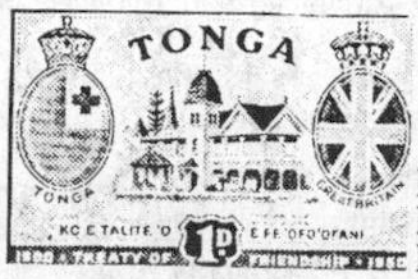
Badges and Royal Palace — A32

Designs: 2½p, Queen Salote and coastal scene. 3p, Queen Salote and ship "Bellona." 5p, Flag of Tonga, island view. 1sh, Arms of Tonga and Great Britain.

Perf. 13x13½ (1p), 13½x13, 12½ (3p)

1951, July 2 Engr. Wmk. 4

94 A31 ½p deep green .18 .18
95 A32 1p carmine & black .25 .25
96 A32 2½p choc & dp grn .60 .60
97 A31 3p ultra & org yel .80 .80
98 A32 5p dp green & car 1.00 1.00
99 A32 1sh purple & orange 1.75 1.75
Nos. 94-99 (6) 4.58 4.58

50th anniv. of the treaty of friendship between Tonga and Great Britain.

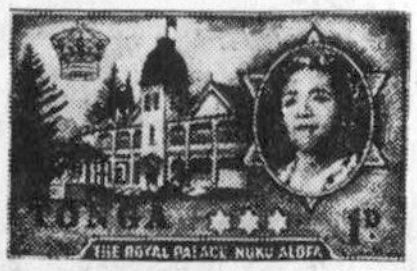
Royal Palace, Nukualofa A33

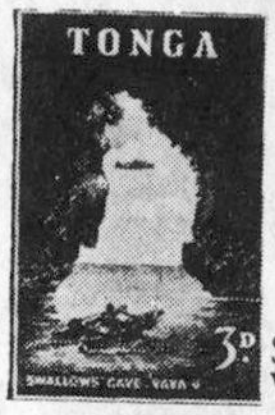
Swallows' Cave, Vavau — A34

Designs: 1½p, Fisherman. 2p, Canoe and schooners. 3½p, Map of Tongatabu. 4p, Vavau harbor. 5p, Post Office, Nukualofa. 6p, Fuaamotu airport. 8p, Wharf, Nukualofa. 1sh, Map of Tonga Islands. 2sh, Beach at Lifuka, Haapai. 5sh, Mutiny on the Bounty. 10sh, Queen Salote. £1, Arms of Tonga.

Perf. 11½x11, 11x11½

1953, July 1 Wmk. 79

100 A33 1p chocolate & blk .15 .15
101 A33 1½p emerald & ultra .15 .15
102 A33 2p black & aqua .15 .15
103 A34 3p dk green & ultra .15 .15
104 A33 3½p carmine & yel .18 .15
105 A33 4p rose car & yel .18 .15
106 A33 5p choc & ultra .20 .18
107 A33 6p black & dp ultra .25 .22
108 A33 8p purple & emer .30 .25
109 A34 1sh black & ultra .45 .38
110 A33 2sh choc & ol grn 1.00 .90
111 A33 5sh purple & yel 2.50 2.50
112 A34 10sh black & yellow 5.50 5.25
113 A34 £1 ultra, car & yel 11.00 10.50
Nos. 100-113 (14) 22.16 21.08

For surcharges and overprints see Nos. 119-126, 158-174, 182-202, 210-215, 218-221, 237, 269-273, C34-C39, C47-C54, C87-C91CO4-CO6, CO11-CO20, CO27-CO43.

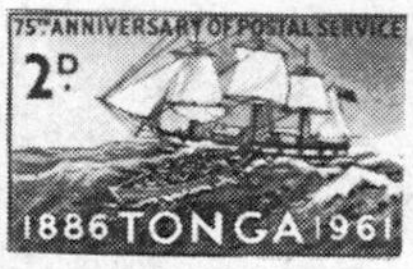
Whaling Ship and Longboat A35

Designs: 1p, Stamp of 1886. 4p, Post Office, Customs and Treasury Building and Queen Salote. 5p, Diesel-driven ship Aoniu. 1sh, Plane over Tongatabu.

Perf. 14½x13½

1961, Dec. 1 Photo.

114 A35 1p brn org & car rose .16 .16
115 A35 2p ultra .16 .16
116 A35 4p bright green .20 .20
117 A35 5p purple .28 .28
118 A35 1sh red brown .60 .60
Nos. 114-118 (5) 1.40 1.40

75th anniversary of postal service.
For surcharges & overprints see #146-151, 216-221, C16-C21, C55-C57, CO1-CO3, CO9-CO10.

Stamps of 1953 and 1961 Overprinted in Red: "1862 / TAU'ATAINA / EMANCIPATION / 1962"

Perf. 11½x11, 11x11½, 14½x13
Engr.; Photo. (4p)

1962, Feb. 7 Wmk. 79

119 A33 1p choc & blk .20 .20
120 A35 4p brt green .35 .35
121 A33 5p choc & ultra .35 .35
122 A33 6p black & dp ultra .50 .50
123 A33 8p purple & emer .55 .55
124 A34 1sh black & ultra .65 .65
125 A34 2sh on 3p dk grn & ultra 1.10 1.10
126 A33 5sh purple & yellow 2.75 2.75
Nos. 119-126 (8) 6.45 6.45

Cent. of emancipation. See Nos. CO1-CO6.

Freedom from Hunger Issue
Common Design Type with Portrait of Queen Salote
Perf. 14x14½

1963, June 4 Wmk. 79 Photo.

127 CD314 11p ultra .45 .45

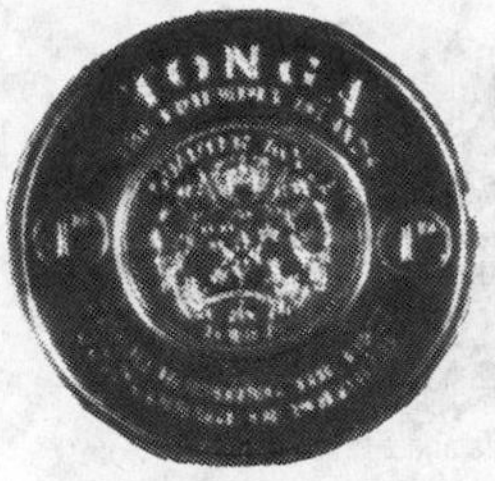

Coat of Arms, 1/4 Koula Coin, Reverse A36

Designs: 2p, 9p, 2sh, Queen Salote (head), 1/4-koula coin, obverse.

Litho.; Embossed on Gilt Foil
1963, July 15 Unwmk. *Imperf.*
Diameter: 40mm

128	A36	1p dp carmine	.15	.15
129	A36	2p violet blue	.15	.15
130	A36	6p dp green	.30	.30
131	A36	9p magenta	.35	.35
132	A36	1sh6p violet	.75	.75
133	A36	2sh emerald	.80	.80
		Nos. 128-133,C1-C6,CO7 (13)	13.60	13.60

1st gold coinage of Polynesia. Backed with paper inscribed in salmon-colored alternating rows: "TONGA" and "THE FRIENDLY ISLANDS" in multiple.

For surcharges see #140-145, C11-C15, CO8.

Red Cross Centenary Issue
Common Design Type with Portrait of Queen Salote
Wmk. 79
1963, Sept. 2 Litho. *Perf. 13*

134	CD315	2p black & red	.15	.15
135	CD315	11p ultra & red	.50	.50

Queen Salote on 1/4-Koula Coin A37

Litho.; Embossed on Gilt Foil
1964, Oct. 19 Unwmk. *Imperf.*

136	A37	3p pink	.15	.15
137	A37	9p light blue	.15	.15
138	A37	2sh yellow green	.38	.38
139	A37	5sh pale lilac	.90	.90
		Nos. 136-139,C7-C10 (8)	3.71	3.71

Pan-Pacific and Southeast Asia Women's Association Conf., Nukualofa, Aug. 1964. See note on paper backing after No. 133.

For surcharges & overprints see #152-157, 263-268.

Nos. 128-133 Surcharged in Red, White or Black

1965, Mar. 18

140	A36	1sh3p on 1sh6p (R)	.16	.16
141	A36	1sh9p on 9p (W)	.22	.22
142	A36	2sh6p on 6p (R)	.40	.40
143	A36	5sh on 1p	14.00	14.00
144	A36	5sh on 2p	2.25	2.25
145	A36	5sh on 2sh	1.00	1.00
		Nos. 140-145,C11-C15,CO8 (12)	66.05	66.05

Nos. 114-115 Overprinted and Surcharged in Purple or Red

1866-1966
TUPOU COLLEGE
& SECONDARY
EDUCATION

3d XX

Perf. 14 1/2x13 1/2
1966, June 18 Photo. Wmk. 79

146	A35	1p (P)	.15	.15
147	A35	3p on 1p (P)	.15	.15
148	A35	6p on 2p (R)	.15	.15
149	A35	1sh2p on 2p (R)	.22	.22
150	A35	2sh on 2p (R)	.40	.40
151	A35	3sh on 2p (R)	.60	.60
		Nos. 146-151,C16-C21,CO9-CO10 (14)	8.97	8.97

Centenary of Tupou College and of secondary eucation.

Nos. 136-137 Overprinted and Surcharged in Silver on Black or Ultramarine

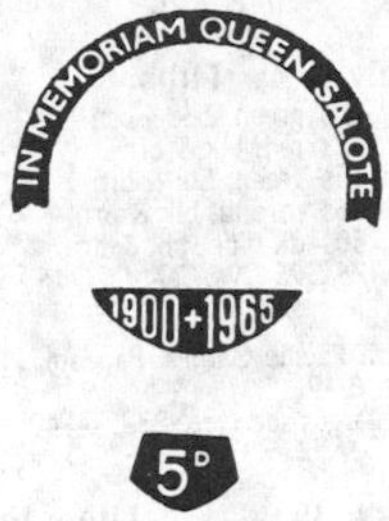

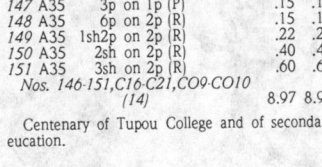

Illustration reduced.

Litho.; Embossed on Gilt Foil
1966, Dec. 16 Unwmk. *Imperf.*

152	A37	3p pink (U)	.15	.15
153	A37	5p on 9p lt blue	.15	.15
154	A37	9p lt bl	.15	.15
155	A37	1sh7p on 3p pink (U)	.30	.30
156	A37	3sh6p on 9p lt blue	.60	.60
157	A37	6sh6p on 3p pink (U)	1.10	1.10
		Nos. 152-157,C22-C26 (11)	5.80	5.80

Nos. 100-110, 147 and 151 Surcharged in Black or Red

4 SENITI 4

Perf. 11 1/2x11, 11x11 1/2, 14 1/2x13 1/2
1967, Mar. 25 Wmk. 79

158	A33	1s on 1p	.15	.15
159	A33	2s on 4p	.15	.15
160	A33	3s on 5p	.15	.15
161	A33	4s on 5p	.15	.15
162	A33	5s on 3 1/2p	.15	.15
163	A33	6s on 8p	.15	.15
164	A33	7s on 1 1/2p	.16	.16
165	A33	8s on 6p	.20	.20
166	A34	9s on 3p	.22	.22
167	A34	10s on 1sh	.25	.25
168	A35	11s on 3p on 1p	.32	.32
169	A35	21s on 3sh on 2p	.55	.55
170	A33	23s on 1p	.60	.60
171	A33	30s on 2sh (R) (1-line surcharge)	1.20	1.20
172	A33	30s on 2sh (R) (3-line surcharge)	1.40	1.40
173	A33	50s on 6p (R)	1.60	1.60
174	A33	60s on 2p (R)	2.00	2.00
		Nos. 158-174 (17)	9.40	9.40

The size, typeface and arrangement of surcharge vary on the different denominations.

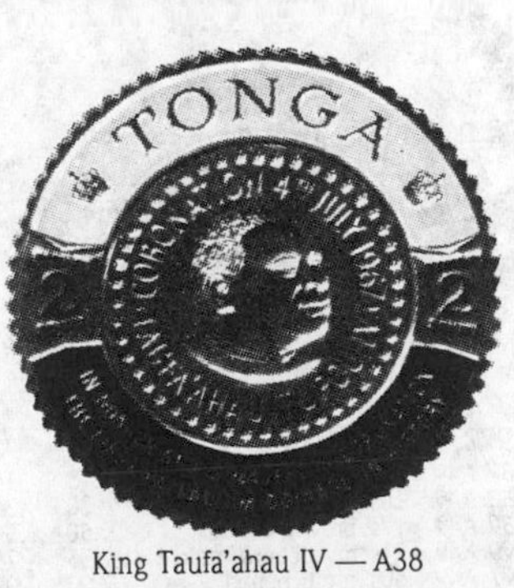

King Taufa'ahau IV — A38

Designs: 1s, 4s, 28s, 1pa, Coat of Arms, reverse of new palladium coins.

Litho.; Embossed on Palladium Foil
1967, July 4 Unwmk. *Imperf.*

Diameter: 1s, 44mm; 2s, 50s, 52mm; 4s, 59mm; 15s, 68mm; 28s, 40mm; 1pa, 74mm

175	A38	1s orange & brt bl	.15	.15
176	A38	2s brt blue & dp mag	.15	.15
177	A38	4s emerald & mag	.15	.15
178	A38	15s blue grn & vio	.35	.35
179	A38	28s black & brt red lil	.68	.68
180	A38	50s red & vio bl	1.20	1.20
181	A38	1pa ultra & brt rose	2.50	2.50
		Nos. 175-181,C27-C33 (14)	12.51	12.51

Coronation of King Taufa'ahau IV, July 4, 1967. Backed with paper inscribed in yellow alternating rows: "Tonga The Friendly Islands" and "Historically The First Palladium Coinage."

For surcharges and overprints see Nos. 203-209, C40-C46, CO21-CO24,

Types of Regular Issue, 1953, Surcharged

The Friendly Islands welcome the United States Peace Corps

8

Wmk. 79
1967, Dec. 15 Engr. *Imperf.*

182	A33	1s on 1p yellow & blk	.15	.15
183	A33	2s on 2p carmine & ultra	.15	.15
184	A34	3s on 3p brown org & yel	.15	.15
185	A33	4s on 4p purple & yel	.15	.15
186	A33	5s on 5p green & yel	.18	.18
187	A34	10s on 10p rose red & yel	.35	.35
188	A33	20s on 2sh carmine & ultra	.70	.70
189	A33	50s on 5sh sepia & yel	1.75	1.75
190	A34	1pa on 10sh orange yel	3.50	3.50
		Nos. 182-190 (9)	7.08	7.08

Arrival of US Peace Corps.

Nos. 100-111 Surcharged in Red, Black or Ultramarine

1 SENITI 1

Perf. 11 1/2x11, 11x11 1/2
1968, Apr. 6 Engr. Wmk. 79

191	A33	1s on 1p (R)	.15	.15
192	A33	2s on 4p	.15	.15
193	A34	3s on 3p (U)	.15	.15
194	A33	4s on 5p (R)	.15	.15
195	A33	5s on 2p (R)	.15	.15
196	A33	6s on 6p (R)	.18	.18
197	A33	7s on 1 1/2p (R)	.18	.18
198	A33	8s on 8p (R)	.22	.22
199	A33	9s on 3 1/2p	.22	.22
200	A34	10s on 1sh (R)	.28	.28
201	A33	20s on 5sh (R)	.55	.55
202	A33	2pa on 2sh (R)	5.50	5.50
		Nos. 191-202,C37-C39,CO15-CO18 (19)	20.23	20.23

Surcharge on 3s and 10s is vertical.

Nos. 175-181 Overprinted: "H.M'S BIRTHDAY / 4 July 1968" in Gold on Red Panel on 1s, 4s, 28s and 1pa. "HIS MAJESTY'S 50th BIRTHDAY" in Silver on Blue Panel on 2s, 15s and 50s

Litho.; Embossed on Palladium Foil
1968, July 4 Unwmk. *Imperf.*

203	A38	1s orange & brt bl	.15	.15
204	A38	2s brt blue & dp mag	.15	.15
205	A38	4s emerald & mag	.15	.15
206	A38	15s blue grn & vio	.55	.55
207	A38	28s black & brt red lil	1.00	1.00
208	A38	50s red & vio bl	1.60	1.60
209	A38	1pa ultra & brt rose	3.25	3.25
		Nos. 203-209,C40-C46,CO21-CO24 (18)	34.47	34.47

Types of 1953 Surcharged in Red, Black or Green: "Friendly Islands / Field & Track Trials / South Pacific Games / Port Moresby 1969"

Designs as before.

Wmk. 79
1968, Dec. 19 Engr. *Imperf.*

210	A33	5s on 5p green & yel (R)	.15	.15
211	A34	10s on 1sh cer & buff	.20	.20
212	A33	15s on 2sh rose car & bl	.30	.30
213	A33	25s on 2p rose car & bl	.50	.50
214	A33	50s on 1p yel & blk	1.00	1.00
215	A34	75s on 10sh org (G)	1.50	1.50
		Nos. 210-215,C47-C54,CO19-CO20 (16)	9.76	9.76

Issued to publicize the field and track trials for the third South Pacific Games, Port Moresby, 1969. The overprint is in 5 lines on the horizontal stamps, in 7 lines on vertical stamps. On the vertical stamps "Trial" is printed on the line ahead of "Field & Track." On #215 the denomination is spelled out.

Nos. 149-150 and Types of 1953 Surcharged

Perf. 14 1/2x13 1/2
1968 Photo. Wmk. 79

216	A35	1s on 1sh2p on 2p	.45	.45
217	A35	1s on 2sh on 2p	.45	.45

Engr. *Imperf.*

218	A33	1s on 6p yellow & blk	.15	.15
219	A33	2s on 3 1/2p dk blue	.15	.15
220	A33	3s on 1 1/2p lt green	.22	.25
221	A33	4s on 8p black & pale grn	.30	.30
		Nos. 216-221,C55-C57 (9)	3.07	3.10

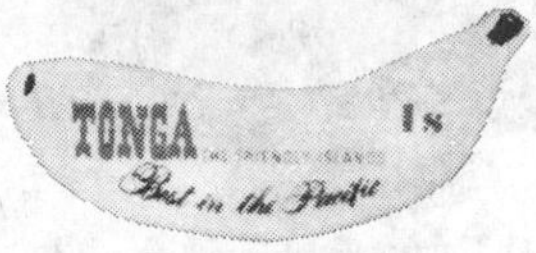

Banana A39

Unwmk.
1969, Apr. 21 Typo. *Imperf.*
Self-adhesive

222	A39	1s yellow, black & red	.15	.15
223	A39	2s yellow, black & emer	.20	.15
224	A39	3s yellow, black & lil	.35	.25
225	A39	4s yellow, black & ultra	.50	.40
226	A39	5s yellow, black & ol grn	.60	.50
		Nos. 222-226 (5)	1.80	1.45

Packed in boxes of 200. See Nos. 248-252, 297-301, O11-O15.

Peelable Backing Inscribed
Starting in 1969, self-adhesive stamps are attached to peelable paper backing printed with "TONGA where time begins" in multiple rows and various colors, unless otherwise stated.

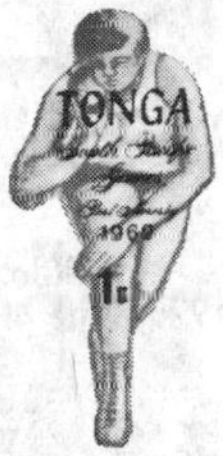

Shot-putter — A40

1969, Aug. 13 Litho. *Imperf.*
Self-adhesive

227	A40	1s bister, red & blk	.15	.15
228	A40	3s bister, red & emer	.15	.15
229	A40	6s bister, red & blue	.22	.22
230	A40	10s bister, red & pur	.35	.35
231	A40	30s bister, red & blue	1.00	1.00
		Nos. 227-231,C58-C62,CO25-CO26 (12)	14.25	14.25

3rd Pacific Games, Port Moresby, Papua and New Guinea, Aug. 13-23.

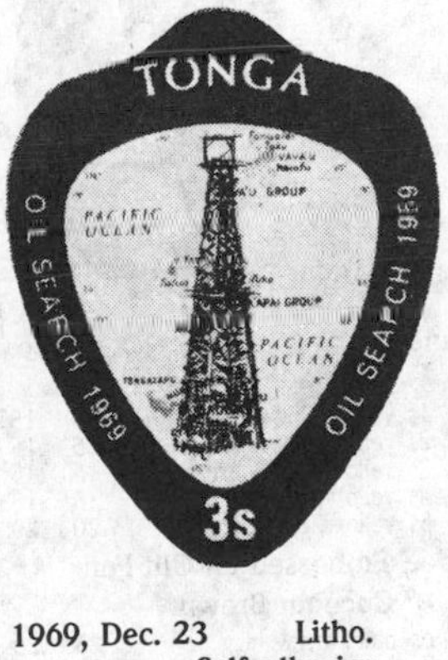

Oil Derrick and Map of Tonga Islands A41

1969, Dec. 23 Litho. *Imperf.*
Self-adhesive

232	A41	3s brown & multi	.15	.15
233	A41	7s brt blue & multi	.20	.20
234	A41	20s multicolored	.60	.60
235	A41	25s orange & multi	.90	.90
236	A41	35s henna brn & multi	1.20	1.20

Type of Regular Issue, 1953, Surcharged in Red: "1969 / OIL / SEARCH / T$1.10" and Oil Derrick Obliterating Old Denomination

Wmk. 79 *Imperf.*

237	A34	1.10pa on £1 green & multi	4.00	4.00
		Nos. 232-237,C63-C67,CO27 (12)	14.00	14.00

First scientific search for oil in Tonga.

British and Tongan Royal Families — A42

Litho.; Gold Embossed
1970, Mar. 7   Self-adhesive   *Imperf.*

238	A42	3s multicolored	.15	.15
239	A42	5s multicolored	.20	.20
240	A42	10s multicolored	.40	.40
241	A42	25s multicolored	.90	.90
242	A42	50s multicolored	2.00	2.00

Nos. 238-242,C68-C72,CO28-CO30
(13)   19.80   19.80

Visit of Elizabeth II, Prince Philip and Princess Anne, Mar. 1970.

Open Book, George Tupou I and II, Salote Tupou III, Taufa'ahau Tupou IV and Tonga Flag — A43

Litho.; Gold Embossed
1970, June 4   *Imperf.*
Self-adhesive

243	A43	3s multicolored	.15	.15
244	A43	7s multicolored	.25	.25
245	A43	15s multicolored	.55	.55
246	A43	25s multicolored	.90	.90
247	A43	50s multicolored	2.00	2.00

Nos. 243-247,C73-C77,CO31-CO33
(13)   18.95   18.95

Tonga's independence and entry into the British Commonwealth of Nations.
For surcharges see Nos. CO49-CO51, CO71.

Banana Type of 1969 redrawn and

Coconut — A44

1970, June 9   Typo.
Self-adhesive

248	A39	1s yellow, blk & mag	.15	.15
249	A39	2s yellow, blk & bl	.15	.15
250	A39	3s yellow, blk & brn	.15	.15
251	A39	4s yellow, blk & grn	.18	.18
252	A39	5s yellow, blk & org	.20	.20

Typo.; Embossed on Gilt Foil
Coconut Brown

253	A44	6s blue, grn & mag	.25	.25
254	A44	7s purple & green	.30	.30
255	A44	8s gold, grn & vio bl	.35	.35
256	A44	9s carmine & green	.40	.40
257	A44	10s gold, grn & org	.45	.45

Nos. 248-257,O11-O20 (20)   5.18   5.18

Nos. 248-252 have no white shading in upper part of the banana, Nos. 222-226 have white shading. Nos. 253-256 have self-adhesive control numbers in lower left corner of paper backing. Paper backing is green on Nos. 253-257.
See Nos. 302-306, O26-O30.

Red Cross and Arms of Tonga A45

1970, Oct. 17   Litho.   *Imperf.*
Self-adhesive

258	A45	3s red, black & grn	.15	.15
259	A45	7s red, black & vio blue	.25	.25
260	A45	15s red, black & red lil	.55	.55
261	A45	25s red, black & brt grn	.90	.90
262	A45	75s red, black & brn	3.00	3.00

Nos. 258-262,C78-C82,CO34-CO36
(13)   22.55   22.55

Centenary of the British Red Cross.

Nos. 153, 152
Surcharged

Litho.; Embossed on Gilt Foil
1971, Jan. 31   *Imperf.*

263	A37	2s on 9p lt blue	.15	.15
264	A37	3s on 9p lt blue	.15	.15
265	A37	5s on 3p pink	.25	.15
266	A37	15s on 9p lt blue	.75	.62
267	A37	25s on 3p pink	1.10	.95
268	A37	50s on 3p pink	2.50	.90

Nos. 263-268,C83-C86,CO37-CO40
(14)   24.90   18.10

In memory of Queen Salote (1900-65). The "In Memoriam" inscription is in silver on black panel on the 2s, 3s and 15s; in silver on ultramarine panel on the 5s, 25s and 50s. The dates and denominations are all on black panels in silver and metallic red, green, bronze, magenta or gold respectively.

3s ■

Type of Regular Issue, 1953, Surcharged in Red and Black

PHILATOKYO '71

1971   Engr.   Wmk. 79   *Imperf.*

269	A33	3s on 8p black & pale grn	.18	.15
270	A33	7s on 4p purple & yel	.30	.25
271	A33	25s on 1p yellow & blk	1.10	.95
272	A33	75s on 2sh carmine & ultra	3.75	3.25

Nos. 269-272,C87-C89,CO41-CO43
(10)   18.73   14.61

Philatokyo 71, Philatelic Exposition, Tokyo, Apr. 19-29.

HONOURING JAPANESE POSTAL CENTENARY 1871-1971

15s ■

Type of Regular Issue, 1971, Surcharged

1971

273	A34	15s on 1sh carmine & buff	.30	.30

Centenary of Japanese postal service. See Nos. C90-C91.

Self-adhesive & Imperf.
Starting with Nos. 274-278, all issues are self-adhesive and imperforate, unless otherwise stated.

Pole Vault — A46

Gold Medal of Merit — A47

1971, July   Litho.   Unwmk.

274	A46	3s green, blk & brn	.15	.15
275	A46	7s red, blk & brn	.30	.30
276	A46	15s green, blk & brn	.62	.62
277	A46	25s rose lil, blk & brn	.95	.95
278	A46	50s dk blue, blk & brn	1.90	1.90

Nos. 274-278,C92-C96,CO44-CO46
(13)   15.92   15.92

4th South Pacific Games, Papeete, French Polynesia, Sept. 8-19.
For surcharges see Nos. 332, C140.

1971, Oct. 30   Litho; Embossed

Designs: 24s, Silver Medal of Merit. 38s, Bronze Medal of Merit, obverse (King Taufa'ahau IV).

279	A47	3s gold & multi	.15	.15
280	A47	24s silver & multi	.80	.80
281	A47	38s bronze & multi	1.25	1.25

Nos. 279-281,C99-C101,CO49-CO51 (9)   16.52   16.52

First investiture of Tongan Medal of Merit.
For surcharges see Nos. 333-336.

Juggler, UNICEF Emblem A48

1971, Dec.   Litho.

282	A48	2s violet & multi	.15	.15
283	A48	4s multicolored	.15	.15
284	A48	8s blue & multi	.32	.32
285	A48	16s emerald & multi	.70	.70
286	A48	30s lilac rose & multi	1.25	1.25

Nos. 282-286,C102-C106,CO52-CO54 (13)   19.60   19.60

25th anniv. of UNICEF.

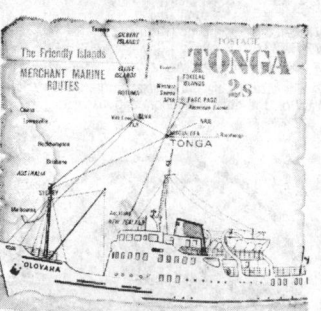

Merchant Marine Routes from Tonga and "Olovaha" — A49

1972, Apr. 14

287	A49	2s blue & multi	.15	.15
288	A49	10s magenta & multi	.30	.30
289	A49	17s brown & multi	.50	.50
290	A49	21s dk green & multi	.75	.75
291	A49	60s multicolored	2.00	2.00

Nos. 287-291,C107-C111,CO55-CO57 (13)   17.20   17.20

Togan Merchant Marine publicity
For surcharges see Nos. C124, CO66-CO69.

King Taufa'ahau IV Coronation Coin, ¼ Hau — A50

Litho.; Embossed on Metallic Foil
1972, July 15

292	A50	5s silver & multi	.25	.25
293	A50	7s silver & multi	.32	.32
294	A50	10s silver & multi	.40	.40
295	A50	17s silver & multi	.75	.75
296	A50	60s silver & multi	2.75	2.75

Nos. 292-296,C112-C116,CO58-CO60 (13)   22.54   22.54

Coronation of King Taufa'ahau IV, 5th anniv.

Coconut Type of 1970 and

Banana A51

Watermelon — A52

1972, Sept. 30   Typo.

297	A51	1s brt yel, red & blk	.15	.15
298	A51	2s brt yel, blue & blk	.15	.15
299	A51	3s brt yel, emer & blk	.15	.15
300	A51	4s brt yel & blk	.15	.15
301	A51	5s brt yel & brn blk	.16	.16
302	A44	6s brown, org & grn	.18	.18
303	A44	7s brown, ultra & grn	.20	.20
304	A44	8s brown, mag & grn	.25	.25
305	A44	9s brown, red & grn	.30	.30
306	A44	10s brown, blue & grn	.35	.35
307	A52	15s green, org brn & ultra	.55	.55
308	A52	20s green, blue & red	.70	.70
309	A52	25s green, red & brn	.85	.85
310	A52	40s green, blue & org	1.40	1.40
311	A52	50s green, dk bl & yel	1.50	1.50

Nos. 297-311,O21-O35 (30)   13.93   13.93

Paper backing is brown on Nos. 302-311. Nos. 302-306 have self-adhesive control number in lower left corner of paper backing.

Flag Raising, Minerva Reef — A53

1972, Dec. 9   Litho.

312	A53	5s black & multi	.15	.15
313	A53	7s green & multi	.20	.20
314	A53	10s purple & multi	.35	.35
315	A53	15s orange & multi	.50	.50
316	A53	40s ultra & multi	1.25	1.25

Nos. 312-316,C119-C123,CO63-CO65 (13)   15.40   15.40

Tonga's proclamation of sovereignty over the Minerva Reefs, June 1972.

Tongan Coins and Bank Building — A54

1973, Mar. 30   Litho.
317	A54	5s silver & multi	.18 .18
318	A54	7s silver & multi	.25 .25
319	A54	10s silver & multi	.38 .38
320	A54	20s silver & multi	.75 .75
321	A54	30s silver & multi	1.10 1.10

Nos. 317-321,C125-C129,CO66-
CO68 (13)   20.70 20.70

Establishment of Bank of Tonga.

Handshake, Outrigger Canoe — A55

1973, June 29
322	A55	5s silver & multi	.48 .48
323	A55	7s silver & multi	.72 .72
324	A55	15s silver & multi	1.80 1.80
325	A55	21s silver & multi	2.50 2.50
326	A55	65s silver & multi	6.25 6.25

Nos. 322-326,C130-
C134,CO69-CO71 (13)   183.45 140.95

Tongan Boy Scout Movement, 25th anniv.

Capt. Cook's Report and Tongan
Rulers — A56

Litho.; Embossed on Gilt Foil
1973, Oct. 2
327	A56	6s multicolored	.38 .38
328	A56	8s multicolored	.50 .50
329	A56	11s multicolored	.62 .62
330	A56	35s multicolored	1.50 1.50
331	A56	40s multicolored	1.90 1.90

Nos. 327-331,C135-C139,CO72-
CO74 (13)   38.90 38.90

Bicentenary of Capt. Cook's arrival. Design is
from the manuscript in British Museum.

Nos. 278, 281, C100-C101 and 280
Surcharged and Overprinted in Silver or
Gold on Red (12s, 14s) or Black Panels
(5s, 20s, 50s): "Commonwealth Games
Christchurch 1974"

1973, Dec. 19   Litho.
332	A46	5s on 50s multi (G)	.25 .25

Litho.; Embossed
333	A47	12s on 38s bronze (S)	.55 .55
334	A47	14s on 75s silver (G)	.65 .65
335	A47	20s on 1pa brnz & multi (G)	1.00 1.00
336	A47	50s on 24s sil & multi (S)	2.50 2.50

Nos. 332-336,C140-C144,CO75-
CO77 (13)   22.92 22.92

10th British Commonwealth Games, Christchurch, N.Z., Jan. 24-Feb. 2, 1974.

Letter Addressed to Tonga, Names of UPU
Members — A57

1974, June 20   Typo.
337	A57	5s tan & multi	.20 .20
338	A57	10s tan & multi	.42 .42
339	A57	15s tan & multi	.85 .85
340	A57	20s tan & multi	.50 .50
341	A57	50s tan & multi	1.25 1.25

Nos. 337-341,C154-C158,CO87-
CO89 (13)   17.92 17.92

Centenary of Universal Postal Union.

Girl Guide Badges — A58

1974, Sept. 11   Litho.
342	A58	5s multicolored	.28 .28
343	A58	10s multicolored	.52 .52
344	A58	20s multicolored	1.10 1.10
345	A58	40s multicolored	2.25 2.25
346	A58	60s multicolored	3.00 3.00

Nos. 342-346,C159-C163,CO90-
CO92 (13)   26.78 26.78

Girl Guides of Tonga.
For surcharges see Nos. C189, C192.

Sailing Ship
and Anchors
A59

1974, Dec. 11
347	A59	5s blue & multi	.20 .15
348	A59	10s blue & multi	.40 .40
349	A59	25s blue & multi	.90 .75
350	A59	50s blue & multi	1.80 1.50
351	A59	75s blue & multi	2.75 2.25

Nos. 347-351,C164-C168,CO93-
CO95 (13)   21.50 16.60

Establishment of Royal Marine Institute.

Dateline Hotel, Nukualofa — A60

1975, Mar. 11
352	A60	5s blue & multi	.20 .20
353	A60	10s green & multi	.40 .40
354	A60	15s scarlet & multi	.60 .60
355	A60	30s purple & multi	1.10 1.10
356	A60	1pa orange & multi	4.00 4.00

Nos. 352-356,C169-C173,CO96-
CO98 (13)   18.33 18.33

First meeting of South Pacific area Prime Ministers. See note after No. 226.

Boxing and Games' Emblem — A61

1975, June 11   Litho.
357	A61	5s black & multi	.25 .25
358	A61	10s green & multi	.32 .32
359	A61	20s brown & multi	.65 .65
360	A61	25s orange & multi	1.50 1.50
361	A61	65s violet & multi	2.75 2.75

Nos. 357-361,C174-C178,CO99-
CO101 (13)   18.35 18.35

5th South Pacific Games, Guam, Aug. 1-10. See
note after No. 226.
For surcharges see Nos. 412, 482.

King
Taufa'ahau IV
Coin — A62

Designs (FAO Coins): 5s, Chicken. 20s, like 1pa,
(small coin, 27mm). 50s, School of fish. 2pa, Animals and plants on reverse, King on obverse (large
coin, 42mm.).

1975, Sept. 3
362	A62	5s red, sil & blk	.22 .22
363	A62	20s ultra, grn, sil & blk	.65 .65
364	A62	50s blue, sil & blk	1.50 1.50
365	A62	1pa silver & black	3.25 3.25
366	A62	2pa silver & black	7.50 7.50

Nos. 362-366,C179-C183 (10)   19.50 19.50

Coinage issued for the benefit of the FAO. Size of
paper backing of 2pa: 82x50mm; others 45x45mm.
See note after No. 226.
For surcharge see Nos. 413.

Coat of Arms, 5pa Coin, Reverse — A63

George Tupou I Coin, Reverse and
Obverse — A64

Coins: 20s, King Taufa'ahau IV. 50s, King
George Tupou II, 50pa obverse and reverse. 75s,
20pa reverse.

Litho.; Embossed on Gilt Foil
1975, Nov. 4
Pink Background
367	A63	5s black, sil & vio bl	.15 .15
368	A64	10s gold, blk & red	.25 .25
369	A63	20s black, sil & grn	.50 .50
370	A64	50s gold, blk & vio	.90 .90
371	A63	75s black, sil & red lil	1.40 1.40

Nos. 367-371,C184-C188,CO102-
CO104 (13)   10.47 10.47

Centenary of Constitution of Tonga. Size of
paper backing of Nos. 367 and 369: 65x60mm; of
No. 371, 87x78mm. See note after No. 226.
For surcharges see Nos. C232, C296.

Montreal Olympic Games Emblem — A65

1976, Feb. 24   Litho.
372	A65	5s red, ultra & blk	.20 .15
373	A65	10s red, green & blk	.40 .30
374	A65	25s black, sil & blk	.90 .75
375	A65	35s red, lilac & blk	1.25 1.00
376	A65	70s red, bister & blk	2.50 2.00

Nos. 372-376,C189-C193,CO105-
CO107 (13)   18.75 15.00

21st Olympic Games, Montreal, Canada, July 17-
Aug. 1. See note after No. 226.
For surcharges see Nos. 414, 478.

William Hooper, William Floyd, John
Penn, Francis Lightfoot Lee — A66

Signers of Declaration of Independence, Flags of
US and Tonga: 10s, Benjamin Franklin, Thomas
Nelson, Jr., Benjamin Harrison, William Ellery. 15s,
Oliver Wolcott, Lyman Hall, William Whipple,
Carter Braxton. 25s, George Taylor, Thomas Stone,
Arthur Middleton, Richard Stockton. 75s, Stephen
Hopkins, Eldridge Gerry, James Wilson, Francis
Hopkinson.

1976, May 26   Litho.
377	A66	9s buff & multi	.50 .38
378	A66	10s buff & multi	.50 .38
379	A66	15s buff & multi	.75 .55
380	A66	25s buff & multi	1.10 .90
381	A66	75s buff & multi	6.25 5.50

Nos. 377-381,C194-C198,CO108-
CO110 (13)   33.40 27.83

American Bicentennial. Printed on peelable buff
paper backing, inscribed in carmine with facsimile
of Declaration of Independence.
For surcharges see #481, C233, C236-C237,
C297.

Nathaniel Turner and John Thomas — A67

1976, Aug. 25
382	A67	5s yellow & multi	.15 .15
383	A67	10s multicolored	.25 .25
384	A67	20s multicolored	.50 .50

385 A67 25s multicolored   .55   .55
386 A67 85s multicolored   1.50   1.50
Nos. 382-386,C199-C203,CO111-
CO113 (13)   10.34 10.34

Sesquicentennial of the arrival of Methodist missionaries and establishment of Christianity in Tonga. Printed on peelable paper backing inscribed in manuscript with segments of John Thomas's Tonga diary.
For surcharges see Nos. 415-416, 479-480.

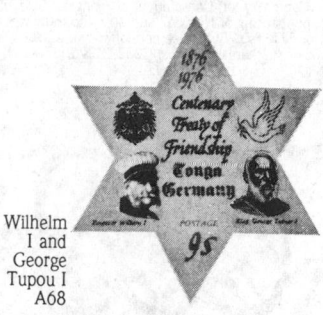

Wilhelm I and George Tupou I A68

1976, Nov. 1
387 A68   9s yellow & multi   .30   .30
388 A68 15s yellow & multi   .50   .50
389 A68 22s yellow & multi   .70   .70
390 A68 50s yellow & multi   1.20   1.20
391 A68 73s yellow & multi   1.75   1.75
Nos. 387-391,C204-C208,CO114-
CO116 (13)   13.42 13.42

Tonga-Germany Friendship Treaty, centenary. Printed on peelable paper backing showing reproduction of original treaty.

Queen Salote in Coronation Procession, 1953 — A69

1977, Feb. 7   Litho.
392 A69 11s blue & multi   1.40   1.40
393 A69 20s green & multi   1.65   1.65
394 A69 30s vio blue & multi   1.00   1.00
395 A69 50s lt green & multi   1.50   1.50
396 A69 75s violet & multi   2.50   2.50
Nos. 392-396,C209-C213,CO117-
CO119 (13)   63.65 28.40

25th anniv. of the reign of Elizabeth II. Printed on peelable paper backing showing replica of handwritten Proclamation of Accession.
For surcharge see No. 417.

Various Coins — A70

1977, July 4
397 A70 10s multicolored   .35   .30
398 A70 15s multicolored   .48   .45
399 A70 25s multicolored   .85   .75
400 A70 50s multicolored   1.75   1.50
401 A70 75s multicolored   2.75   2.25
Nos. 397-401,C214-C218,CO120-
CO122 (13)   18.13 15.25

10th anniversary of coronation of King Taufa'ahau IV. Printed on peelable paper backing showing multicolored replicas of Tongan stamps.

Capt. Cook's Resolution A71

1977, Sept. 27   Litho.
402 A71 10s multicolored   .65   .50
403 A71 17s multicolored   1.75   1.25
404 A71 25s multicolored   1.20   .90
405 A71 30s multicolored   2.00   1.50
406 A71 40s multicolored   2.00   1.50
Nos. 402-406,C219-C223,CO123-
CO125 (13)   47.45 26.55

Bicentenary of Capt. Cook's farewell voyage.

Humpback Whale — A72

1977, Dec. 16
407 A72 15s ultra & black   .35   .25
408 A72 22s green & black   .50   .35
409 A72 31s orange & black   .75   .50
410 A72 38s lilac & black   1.00   .60
411 A72 64s red & black   1.10   1.00
Nos. 407-411,C224-C228,CO126-
CO128 (13)   12.55   8.63

Whale protection.

Stamps of 1975-77 Surcharged in Black, Green, Brown or Black on Silver

1978
412 A61 15s on 20s (#359;B)   .75   .75
413 A62 15s on 5s (#362;B)   .75   .75
414 A65 15s on 10s (#373;G)   .75   .75
415 A67 15s on 5s (#382;Br)   .75   .75
416 A67 15s on 10s (#383;B)   .75   .75
417 A69 15s on 11s (#392;B on
             S)   3.75   3.75
418 OA11 15s on 38s (#CO99;B)   .75   .75
Nos. 412-416,418 (6)   4.50   4.50

The surcharge on No. 413 is only the "1," and on No. 418 includes "postage."

Flags of Canada and Tonga A73

1978, May 5   Litho.
419 A73 10s red & multi   .30   .30
420 A73 15s red & multi   .42   .42
421 A73 20s red & multi   .60   .60
422 A73 25s red & multi   .75   .75
423 A73 45s red & multi   1.25   1.25
Nos. 419-423,C239-C243,CO129-
CO131 (13)   14.97 14.97

11th Commonwealth Games, Edmonton, Canada, Aug. 3-12. See note after No. 226.

King Taufa'ahau IV — A74

1978, July 4
424 A74   2s multicolored   .15   .15
425 A74   5s multicolored   .15   .15
426 A74 10s multicolored   .30   .30
427 A74 25s multicolored   .75   .75
428 A74 75s multicolored   2.25   2.25
Nos. 424-428,C244-C248,CO132-
CO134 (13)   15.10 15.10

60th birthday of King Taufa'ahau IV. See note after No. 226.

Two Bananas A75

Coconut A76

Designs: 1s to 5s, Bananas. 6s to 10s, Coconuts. 15s to 1pa, Pineapples.

1978, Sept. 29   Typo.
429 A75   1s yellow & black   .15   .15
430 A75   2s yellow & dk blue   .15   .15
431 A75   3s multicolored   .15   .15
432 A75   4s multicolored   .15   .15
433 A75   5s multicolored   .15   .15
434 A76   6s multicolored   .15   .15
435 A76   7s multicolored   .18   .18
436 A76   8s multicolored   .20   .20
437 A76   9s multicolored   .22   .22
438 A76 10s brown & green   .24   .24
439 A76 15s green & lt brown   .35   .35
440 A76 20s multicolored   .48   .48
441 A76 30s multicolored   .70   .70
442 A76 50s multicolored   1.20   1.20
443 A76 1pa multicolored   2.40   2.40
Nos. 429-443,O36-O50 (30)   12.69 12.69

Nos. 429-443 issued in coils; self-adhesive control numbers on paper backing, except on 1s and 5s. See note after No. 226.
See No. 529.

Whale A77

1978, Dec. 15   Litho. & Typo.
444 A77 15s shown   .70   .70
445 A77 18s Bat   .90   .90
446 A77 25s Turtle   1.25   1.25
447 A77 28s Parrot   1.30   1.30
448 A77 60s like 15s   2.75   2.75
Nos. 444-448,C249-C253,CO150-
CO152 (13)   24.05 24.05

Wildlife conservation. See note after No. 226.

Introduction of Metric System — A78

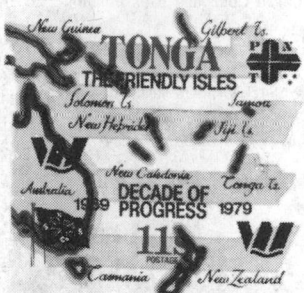

Shipping Routes, South Pacific Map — A79

Peace Corps — A80

Designs: 22s, New church buildings. 50s, Air routes to Auckland, Suva, Apia and Pago Pago.

1979, Feb. 16   Litho.
449 A78   5s multicolored   .18   .18
450 A79 11s multicolored   .38   .38
451 A80 18s multicolored   .70   .70
452 A79 22s multicolored   .75   .75
453 A79 50s multicolored   1.75   1.75
Nos. 449-453,C254-C258,CO153-
CO155 (13)   18.21 18.21

Decade of Progress. Paper backing shows map of Tonga.

Tongan First Day Covers — A81

1979, June 1
454 A81   5s multicolored   .15   .15
455 A81 10s multicolored   .24   .24
456 A81 25s multicolored   .60   .60
457 A81 50s multicolored   1.20   1.20
458 A81 1pa multicolored   1.80   1.80
Nos. 454-458 (5)   3.99   3.99

10th anniversary of introduction of self-adhesive stamps and for Bernard Mechanick, inventor of self-adhesive, free-form stamps; death centenary of Sir Rowland Hill.
Printed on peelable paper backing showing advertisement.
For surcharges and overprints see Nos. 469-473.

Eua Island through Camera Lens A82

1979, Nov. 23   Litho.
459	A82 10s multicolored	.24	.24
460	A82 18s multicolored	.45	.45
461	A82 31s multicolored	.75	.75
462	A82 50s multicolored	1.20	1.20
463	A82 60s multicolored	1.45	1.45
	Nos. 459-463,C275-C279,CO170-		
	CO172 (13)	12.09	12.09

Printed on peelable paper backing showing film and camera.

King George Tupou I, Admiral du Bouzet, Map of Tonga A83

1980, Jan. 9   Litho.
464	A83 7s multicolored	.16	.16
465	A83 10s multicolored	.24	.24
466	A83 14s multicolored	.35	.35
467	A83 50s multicolored	1.20	1.20
468	A83 75s multicolored	1.80	1.80
	Nos. 464 468 (5)	3.75	3.75

Tongan-French Friendship Treaty, 125th anniversary. Printed on peelable paper; multicolored backing shows map of Tonga.

Nos. 454-458 Surcharged and Overprinted in Black on Silver: "1980 OLYMPIC GAMES," Moscow '80 and Bear Emblems

1980, Apr. 30   Litho.
469	A81 13s on 5s multi	.32	.32
470	A81 20s on 10s multi	.48	.48
471	A81 25s multicolored	.60	.60
472	A81 33s on 50s multi	.80	.80
473	A81 1pa multicolored	2.40	2.40
	Nos. 469 473,C285-C289,CO176-		
	CO178 (13)	12.08	12.08

Boy Scout Cooking over Campfire — A84

1980, Sept. 30   Litho.
474	A84 9s multicolored	.30	.30
475	A84 13s multicolored	.45	.45
476	A84 15s multicolored	.50	.50
477	A84 30s multicolored	1.00	1.00
	Nos. 474-477,C290-C293,CO179-		
	CO180 (10)	16.40	16.40

Boy Scout Jamboree; Rotary Intl., 75th anniv. Peelable backing shows map of Tonga.

Nos. 361, 375, 380, 384-385 Surcharged

1980, Dec. 3   Litho.
478	A65 9s on 35s multi	.22	.22
479	A67 13s on 20s multi	.32	.32
480	A67 13s on 25s multi	.32	.32
481	A66 19s on 25s multi	.45	.45
482	A61 1pa on 65s multi	2.40	2.40
	Nos. 478-482,C294-C299,CO181		
	(12)	13.77	13.77

Intl. Year of the Disabled — A85

1981, Sept. 9   Litho.
483	A85 2pa multicolored	6.00	6.00
484	A85 3pa multicolored	9.00	9.00
	Nos. 483-484,C300-C302 (5)	18.35	18.35

Prince Charles and Lady Diana — A86

Designs: 13s, Charles, King Taufa'ahau. 47s, 1.50pa, Couple, diff.

1981, Oct. 21   Litho.
485	A86 13s multicolored	.32	.32
486	A86 47s multicolored	1.00	1.00
487	A86 1.50pa multicolored	3.60	3.60
488	A86 3pa multicolored	7.25	7.25
	Nos. 485-488 (4)	12.17	12.17

Royal Wedding and Gt. Britain-Tonga Friendship Treaty centenary. Issued in sheets of 20 (2x10) and 5 labels in vert. center row.
For surcharge see No. B1.

Bicentenary of Discovery of Vavau by Francisco Maurelle — A87

Designs: 18th century Spanish engravings and maps.

1981, Nov. 25   Litho.
489	A87 9s multicolored	.20	.20
490	A87 13s multicolored	.32	.32
491	A87 47s multicolored	1.00	1.00
492	A87 1pa multicolored	2.40	2.40
a.	Souvenir sheet, imperf.	3.50	3.50
	Nos. 489-492 (4)	3.92	3.92

No. 492a contains one No. 492 (32x25mm).

Biblo Class, 1830 Print A88

1981, Nov. 25
493	A88 9s Open book	.20	.20
494	A88 13s Book, diff.	.32	.32
495	A88 32s Type	.80	.80
496	A88 47s shown	1.00	1.00
	Nos. 493-496 (4)	2.32	2.32

Christmas 1981 and sesquicentennial of books printed in Tonga.

175th Anniv. of Capture of The Port-au-Prince — A89

1981, Dec. 16   Litho.
497	A89 29s Battle	.70	.70
498	A89 32s Battle, diff.	.80	.80
499	A89 47s Map	1.10	1.10
500	A89 47s Sinking ship	1.10	1.10
a.	Pair, #499-500	2.25	
501	A89 1pa Ship	2.40	2.40
	Nos. 497-501 (5)	6.10	6.10

Nos. CO179-CO180 Surcharged

1982, Jan. 4   Litho.
502	OA19 5pa on 25s multi	10.00	10.00
503	OA19 5pa on 2pa multi	10.00	10.00

Scouting Year — A90

1982, Feb. 22   Litho.
504	A90 29s Brownsea Isld. Camp, 1907	.55	.55
505	A90 32s Baden-Powell, horse	.60	.60
506	A90 47s Imperial Jamboree, 1924	.90	.90
507	A90 1.50pa "Scouting for Boys"	2.75	2.75
508	A90 2.50pa Mafeking stamp	4.50	4.50
	Nos. 504-508 (5)	9.30	9.30

1982 World Cup — A91

Designs: Various soccer players, map showing match sites.

1982, July 7   Litho.
509	A91 32s multicolored	.60	.60
510	A91 47s multicolored	.90	.90
511	A91 75s multicolored	1.40	1.40
512	A91 1.50pa multicolored	2.75	2.75
	Nos. 509-512 (4)	5.65	5.65

Inter-island Transport A92

Designs: 9s, 13s, Ferry Olovaha. 47s, 1pa SPIA Twin Otter (Niuatoputapu Airport opening).

1982, Aug. 11
513	A92 9s multicolored	.15	.15
514	A92 13s multicolored	.25	.25
515	A92 47s multicolored	.90	.90
516	A92 1pa multicolored	1.75	1.75
	Nos. 513-516 (4)	3.05	3.05

Tin Can Mail Centenary A93

Designs: 13s, 32s, 47s, Collecting mail. 2pa, Map. Nos. 517-519 form continuous design.

1982, Sept. 29   Litho.
517	A93 13s multicolored	.25	.25
518	A93 32s multicolored	.55	.55
519	A93 47s multicolored	.90	.90
a.	Souv. sheet of 3 (13s, 32s, 47s)	1.75	1.75
520	A93 2pa multicolored	4.00	4.00
a.	Souvenir sheet of 1	4.00	4.00
	Nos. 517-520 (4)	5.70	5.70

No. 520 comes with different labels. For surcharges see Nos. 526-528.

Tonga College Centenary — A94

1982, Oct. 25   Size: 42x30mm (5s)
521	A94 5s Students	.16	.16
522	A94 29s King George Tupou I	1.00	1.00
523	A94 29s Monument	1.00	1.00
a.	Pair, #522-523	2.00	2.00
	Nos. 521-523 (3)	2.16	2.16

Nos. 521-523 inscribed in English or Tongan.

12th Commonwealth Games, Brisbane, Australia, Sept. 30-Oct. 9 — A95

1982, Oct. 25
524	A95 32s Decathlon, vert.	.50	.50
525	A95 1.50pa Opening ceremony	2.25	2.25

Nos. 517 519 Overprinted in Red or Silver in 1 or 2 Lines: "Christmas / Greetings / 1982"

1982, Nov. 17
526	A93 13s multicolored	.32	.32
527	A93 32s multicolored	.80	.80
528	A93 47s multicolored	1.10	1.10
	Nos. 526-528 (3)	2.22	2.22

Pineapple Type of 1978 and

Fruit — A96

1982, Nov. 17
529	A76 13s multicolored	.25	.25
530	A96 2pa multicolored	4.00	4.00
531	A96 3pa multicolored	6.00	6.00
	Nos. 529-531 (3)	10.25	10.25

Capt. Cook's Resolution, 1777 and Canberra, 1983 A96a

Designs: 32s, like 29s. 47s, 1.50pa, Montgolfier Bros. balloon, 1783, Concorde. 2.50pa, Concorde, Canberra. 29s se-tenant with label showing Resolution.

1983, Feb. 22   Litho.
532	A96a 29s multicolored	.50	.50
533	A96a 32s multicolored	.60	.60
534	A96a 47s multicolored	.90	.90
535	A96a 1pa multicolored	2.50	2.50
	Nos. 532-535 (4)	4.50	4.50

Souvenir Sheet
536	A96a 2.50pa multicolored	4.50	4.50

Pacific Forum of Sea and Air Transport (29s, 32s, 2.50pa); manned flight bicentenary (47s, 1.50pa). For overprints see Nos. O68-O70.

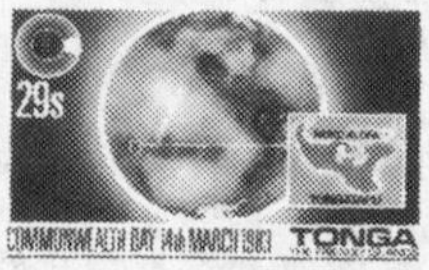

A96b

1983, Mar. 14

537 A96b 29s Map 1.40 1.40
538 A96b 32s Dancers 1.60 1.60
539 A96b 47s Fishermen 2.25 2.25
540 A96b 1.50pa King Taufa'ahau IV, flag 7.00 7.00
Nos. 537-540 (4) 12.25 12.25

Commonwealth Day.

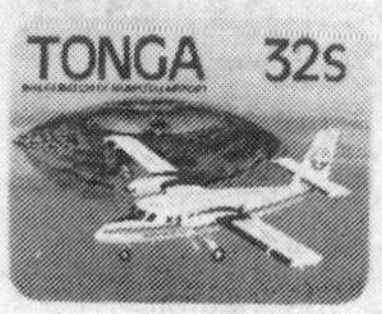

Niuafo'ou Airport Opening A97

1983, May 11 **Litho.**

541 A97 32s De Havilland Otter .60 .60
542 A97 47s like 32s .90 .90
543 A97 1pa Boeing 707 1.75 1.75
544 A97 1.50pa like 1pa 2.75 2.75
Nos. 541-544 (4) 6.00 6.00

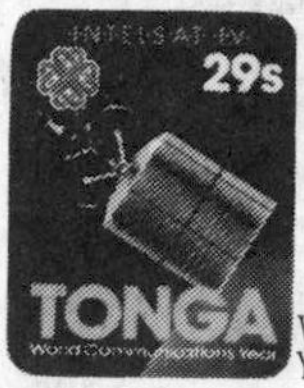

World Communications Year — A98

1983, June 22 **Litho.**

545 A98 29s Intelsat IV .70 .70
546 A98 32s Intelsat IV-A .80 .80
547 A98 75s Intelsat V 1.75 1.75

Size: 45x32mm

548 A98 2pa Apollo 15 Moon post cover 4.75 4.75
Nos. 545-547 (3) 3.25 3.25

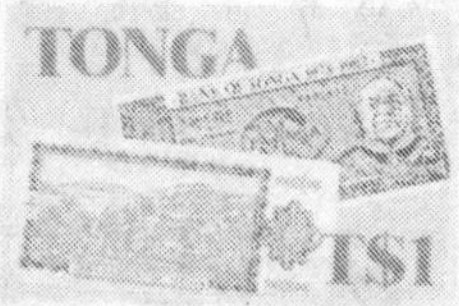

10th Anniv. of Bank of Tonga A99

Various banknotes.

1983, Aug. 3 **Litho.**

549 A99 1pa multicolored 1.75 1.75
550 A99 2pa multicolored 3.50 3.50

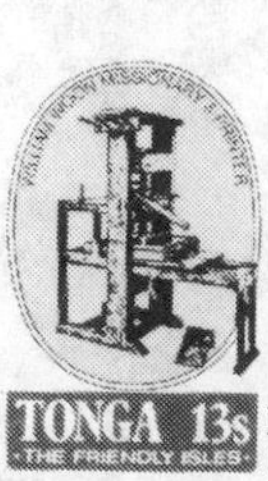

Printing Press, 1830 — A100

1983, Sept. 22 **Litho.**

551 A100 13s shown .22 .22
552 A100 32s Woon's arrival, 1831 .60 .60
553 A100 1pa Print 1.60 1.60
554 A100 2pa Tonga Chronicle 3.50 3.50
Nos. 551-554 (4) 5.92 5.92

Sesquicentennial of printing in Tonga (by missionary William Woon).

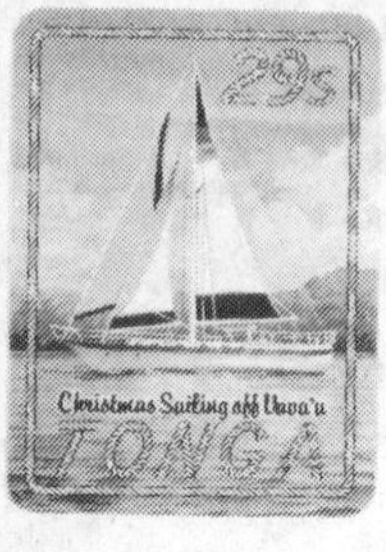

Christmas 1983 — A101

Designs: Various sailboats off Vava'u.

1983, Nov. 17 **Litho.**

555 A101 29s multicolored .50 .50
556 A101 32s multicolored .60 .60
557 A101 1.50pa multicolored 2.50 2.50
558 A101 2.50pa multicolored 4.50 4.50
Nos. 555-558 (4) 8.10 8.10

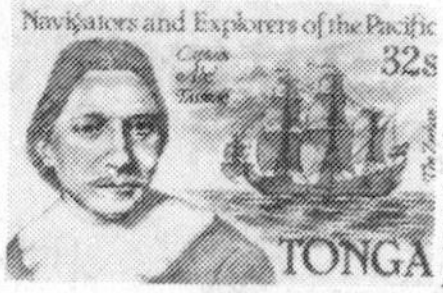

Abel Tasman, Discoverer of Tonga, and his Zeehan A102

Navigators and Explorers of the Pacific and their Ships.

1984, Mar. 12 **Litho.**

559 A102 32s shown .70 .70
560 A102 47s Samuel Wallis, Dolphin .90 .90
561 A102 90s William Bligh, Bounty 1.75 1.75
562 A102 1.50pa James Cook, Resolution 3.00 3.00
Nos. 559-562 (4) 6.35 6.35

See Nos. 593-596.

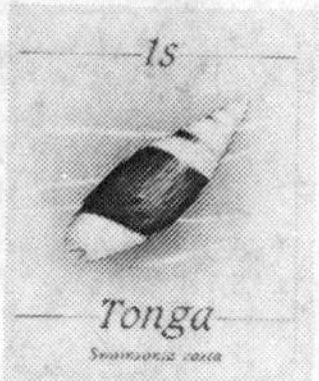

Swainsonia Casta — A103

Shells, fish.

1984-85 **Litho.**

563 A103 1s shown .15 .15
564 A103 2s Porites (coral) .15 .15
565 A103 3s Holocentrus ruber .15 .15
566 A103 5s Cypraea mappa viridis .15 .15
567 A103 6s Dardanus megistos (crab) .15 .15
568 A103 9s Stegostoma fasciatum .15 .15
a. Perf. 14½ ('85) .15 .15
569 A103 10s Conus bullatus .16 .16
570 A103 13s Pterois volitans .22 .22
571 A103 15s Conus textile .25 .25
572 A103 20s Dascyllus aruanus .32 .32
573 A103 29s Conus aulicus .50 .50
574 A103 32s Acanthurus leucosternon .50 .50
575 A103 47s Lambis truncata .80 .80

Size: 39x25mm

576 A103 1pa Millepora dichotama (coral) 1.60 1.60
577 A103 2pa Birgus latro (crab) 3.25 3.25
578 A103 3pa Chicoreus palmarosae 5.00 5.00
579 A103 5pa Thunnus albacares 8.25 8.25
Nos. 563-579 (17) 21.75 21.75

See Nos. 682-692, 701-709, 756-759. For surcharges and overprints see Nos. 618-625, 808, 810, O52-O67, O71-O77.

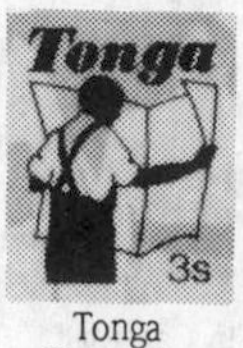

Tonga Chronicle, 20th Anniv. — A104

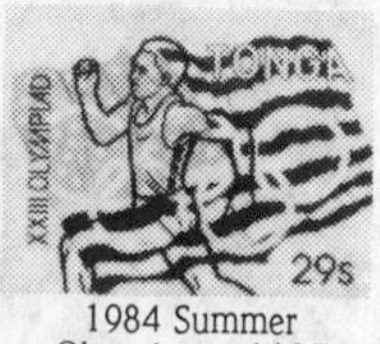

1984 Summer Olympics — A105

1984, June 26

580 A104 3s multicolored .15 .15
a. Sheet of 12 .75
581 A104 32s multicolored .60 .60
a. Sheet of 12 7.25

Nos. 580-581 issued in sheets of 12; sheet backgrounds show pages of Chronicle, giving each stamp different background.

1984, July 23

582 A105 29s Running .55 .55
583 A105 47s Javelin .90 .90
584 A105 1.50pa Shot put 2.75 2.75
585 A105 3pa Torch 5.50 5.50
Nos. 582-585 (4) 9.70 9.70

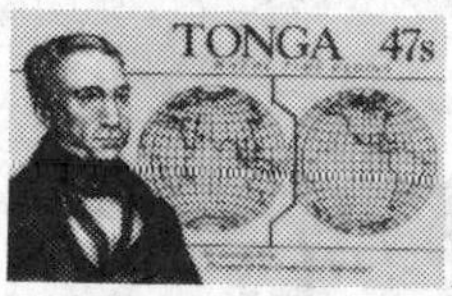

Intl. Dateline Centenary A106

1984, Aug. 20

586 A106 47s George Airy, Greenwich Meridian pioneer .75 .75
587 A106 2pa Sandford Fleming, time zone pioneer 3.25 3.25

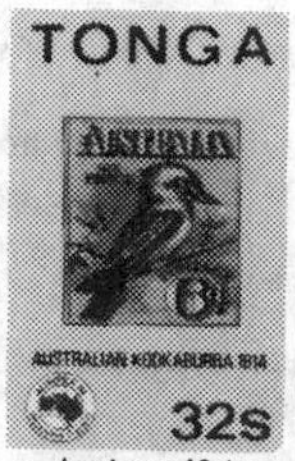

Ausipex '84 A107

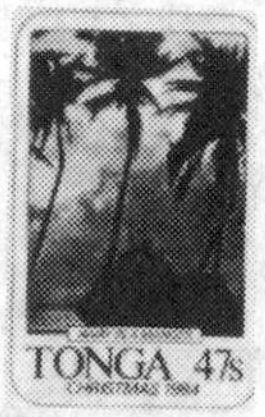

Christmas 1984 A108

1984, Sept. 17

588 A107 32s Australia #18 .50 .50
589 A107 1.50pa Tonga #51 2.50 2.50

Souvenir Sheet

589A Sheet of 2, #588-589 3.00 3.00

Nos. 588-589 each printed se-tenant with label showing exhibition emblem.

No. 589A contains two imperf. stamps similar to Nos. 588-589, but with denomination replacing logo. No. 589A without denominations was not valid for postage.

1984, Nov. 12 **Litho.**

Christmas Carols in local settings.

590 A108 32s Silent Night .50 .50
591 A108 47s Away in a Manger .75 .75
592 A108 1pa I Saw Three Ships 1.60 1.60
Nos. 590-592 (3) 2.85 2.85

Famous Mariners

Designs: 32s, Willem Schouten (c. 1580-1625), The Eendracht, 1616. 47s, Jakob Le Maire (1585-1616), The Hoorn, 1615. 90s, Lt. Fletcher Christian, The Bounty, 1789. 1.50pa, Francisco Maurelle, La Princessa, 1781.

1985, Feb. 27 **Litho.** ***Imperf.***

593 A102 32s multicolored .55 .55
a. Perf. 14 .55 .55
594 A102 47s multicolored .85 .85
595 A102 90s multicolored 1.50 1.50
596 A102 1.50pa multicolored 2.75 2.75
Nos. 593-596 (4) 5.65 5.65

Nos. 593-596 each printed se-tenant with self-adhesive label picturing anchor.

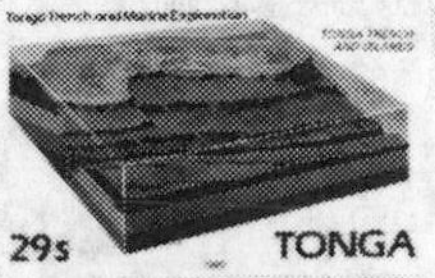

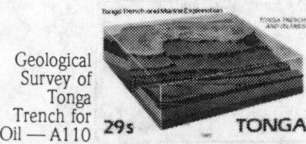

Geological Survey of Tonga Trench for Oil — A110

Designs: 29s, Tonga Trench and islands. 32s, Marine exploration, seismic surveying. 47s, Search for oil off Tongatapu, vert. No. 600, Exploration of sea bed, vert. No. 601, Angler fish.

1985, Apr. 10

597 A110 29s multicolored .42 .42
598 A110 32s multicolored .45 .45
599 A110 47s multicolored .68 .68
600 A110 1.50pa multicolored 2.15 2.15
Nos. 597-600 (4) 3.70 3.70

Souvenir Sheet

601 A110 1.50pa multicolored 2.50 2.50

Nos. 597-600 printed in sheets of 40, 2 panes of 20 separated by labels inscribed "Proof 1," etc.

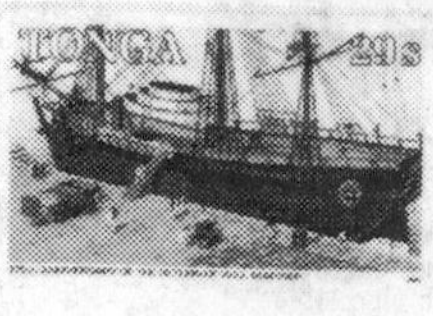

Adventures of Will Mariner A111

Designs: 29s, Readying Port au Prince for sail, Gravesend, 1805. 32s, Captured and set afire, 1806. 47s, Mariner taken prisoner by Chief Finow, Tonga. 1.50pa, Passage to China aboard brig Favourite. 2.50pa, Returning to England aboard East Indiaman Cuffnells, 1810.

1985, June 18 ***Imperf.***

602 A111 29s multicolored .42 .42
a. Perf. 14 .42 .42
603 A111 32s multicolored .45 .45
a. Perf. 14 .45 .45
604 A111 47s multicolored .68 .68
a. Perf. 14 .68 .68
605 A111 1.50pa multicolored 2.15 2.15
a. Perf. 14 2.15 2.15
606 A111 2.50pa multicolored 3.50 3.50
a. Perf. 14 3.50 3.50
Nos. 602-606 (5) 7.20 7.20

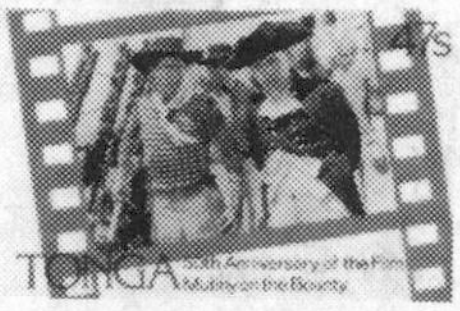

Mutiny on the Bounty, Film 50th Anniv. A112

Designs: a, Byron Russell (Quintal), Stanley Fields (Muspratt) and Charles Laughton (Capt. Bligh). b, Laughton, Donald Crisp (Burkitt), Eddie Quillon (Ellison) and David Thursby (Maxwell). c, Clark Gable (Fletcher Christian). d, Russell, Alec Craig (McCoy), Laughton and Fields. e, Laughton and Franchot Tone (Roger Byam).

1985, July 16 ***Perf. 14***

607 Strip of 5 3.40 3.40
a.-e. A112 47s, any single .68 .68

Sheets consist of four strips of 5 and a central strip of labels showing film credits.

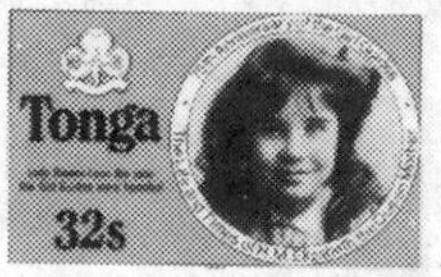

Queen Mother, 85th Birthday A113

Designs: 32s, Age 10. 47s, At Hadfield Girl Guides rally, 1931. 1.50pa, In Guide uniform. 2.50pa, Portrait by Norman Parkinson, 1985.

1985, Aug. 20 ***Imperf.***

608 A113 32s multicolored .45 .45
a. Perf. 14 .45 .45
609 A113 47s multicolored .68 .68
a. Perf. 14 .68 .68
610 A113 1.50pa multicolored 2.15 2.15
a. Perf. 14 2.15 2.15
611 A113 2.50pa multicolored 3.50 3.50
a. Perf. 14 3.50 3.50
Nos. 608-611 (4) 6.78 6.78
Nos. 608a-611a (4) 6.78 6.78

Girl Guides movement, 75th anniv.

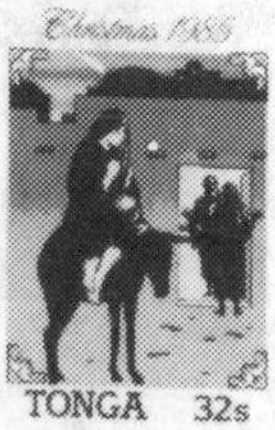

Christmas — A114

1985, Nov. 12

612 A114 32s No room at the inn .45 .45
613 A114 42s Shepherds follow star .60 .60

614 A114 1.50pa The three kings 2.15 2.15
615 A114 2.50pa Holy family 3.50 3.50
Nos. 612-615 (4) 6.70 6.70

Self-adhesive Discontinued
In 1986, imperforate self-adhesive stamps attached to peelable paper backing were no longer issued, unless otherwise stated.

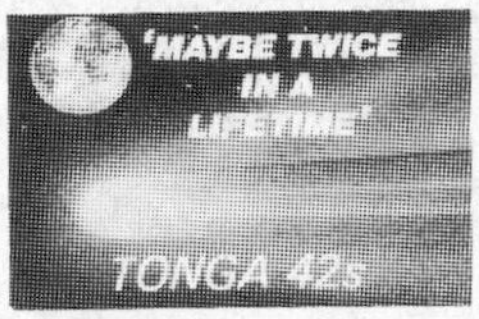

Halley's Comet A115

Designs: Nos. 616a, 617a, Comet. Nos. 616b, 617b, Edmond Halley. Nos. 616c, 617c, Solar system. Nos. 616d, 617d, Telescope. Nos. 616e, 617e, Giotto space probe.

1986, Mar. 26 *Perf. 14*
616 Strip of 5 3.00 3.00
a.-e. A115 42s, any single .60 .60
617 Strip of 5 4.00 4.00
a.-e. A115 57s, any single .80 .80

Nos. 564, 570, 565, 568, 567, 572, 577 and 579 Surcharged

1986, Apr. 16 **Litho.** *Imperf.*
Self-adhesive
618 A103 4s on 2s, #564 .15 .15
619 A103 4s on 13s, #570 .15 .15
620 A103 42s on 3s, #565 .60 .60
621 A103 42s on 9s, #568 .60 .60
622 A103 57s on 6s, #567 .82 .82
623 A103 57s on 20s, #572 .82 .82
624 A103 2.50pa on 2pa, #577 3.50 3.50
625 A103 2.50pa on 5pa, #579 3.50 3.50
Nos. 618-625 (8) 10.14 10.14

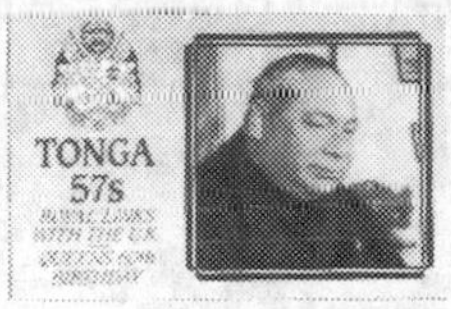

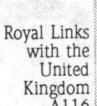

Royal Links with the United Kingdom A116

1986, May 22 *Perf. 14*
626 A116 57s Taufa'ahau IV .80 .80
627 A116 57s Elizabeth II .80 .80
a. Pair, #626-627 1.60 1.60

Size: 40x40mm
628 A116 2.50pa King and queen 3.50 3.50
Nos. 626-628 (3) 5.10 5.10

Queen Elizabeth II, 60th birthday. No. 628 printed in sheets of 5 plus one label.

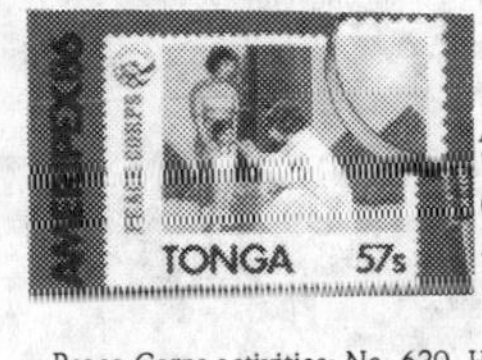

AMERIPEX '86, Chicago, May 22-June 1 — A117

Peace Corps activities: No. 629, Health care. No. 630, Education.

1986, May 22
629 A117 57s multicolored .80 .80
630 A117 1.50pa multicolored 2.15 2.15
a. Souv. sheet of 2, #629, 630, imperf. 3.00 3.00
b. Pair, #629-630 3.00 3.00

Peace Corps in Tonga, 20th anniv.

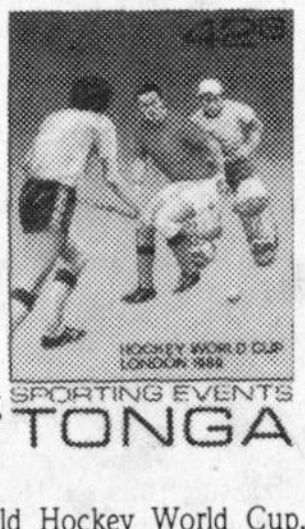

Intl. Sporting Events — A118

Designs: 42s, 1986 Field Hockey World Cup, London. 57s, Women's basketball, 13th Commonwealth Games, Scotland. 1pa, Boxing, Commonwealth Games. 2.50pa, 1986 World Cup Soccer Championships, Mexico.

1986, July 23 **Litho.** *Perf. 14*
631 A118 42s multicolored .60 .60
632 A118 57s multicolored .82 .82
633 A118 1pa multicolored 1.40 1.40
634 A118 2.50pa multicolored 3.50 3.50
Nos. 631-634 (4) 6.32 6.32

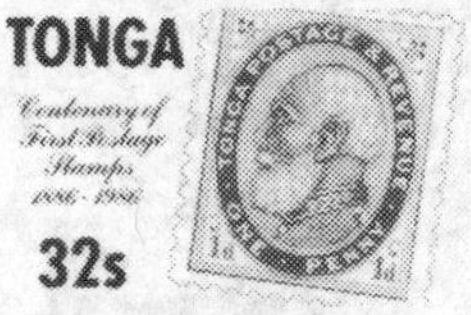

Postage Stamp Cent. A119

Stamps on stamps: No. 635, #1. No. 636, #47a. No. 637, #91. No. 638, #628. No. 639a, #40, UL portion of #C29. No. 639b, UR portion of #C29, left side #245. No. 639c, Center of #245, Type AP10. No. 639d, Left side #245, #C148. No. 639e, LL portion of #C29, #429, #440. No. 639f, LR portion of #C29, #C135. No. 639g, #507. No. 639h, #514. Nos. 639a-639h, vert.

1986, Aug. 27
635 A119 32s multicolored .45 .45
636 A119 42s multicolored .60 .60
637 A119 57s multicolored .82 .82
638 A119 2.50pa multicolored 3.50 3.50
Nos. 635-638 (4) 5.37 5.37

Souvenir Sheet
639 Sheet of 8 5.60 5.60
a.-h. A119 50s, any single .70 .70

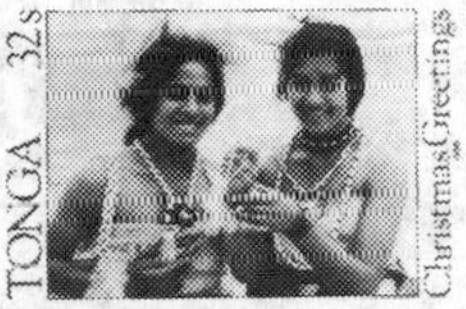

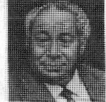

Christmas A120

Designs: 32s, Girls wearing shell jewelry. 42s, Boy, totem poles, vert. 57s, Folk dancers, vert. 2pa, outrigger canoe.

1986, Nov. 12 **Litho.** *Perf. 14*
640 A120 32s multicolored .45 .45
641 A120 42s multicolored .60 .60
642 A120 57s multicolored .82 .82
643 A120 2pa multicolored 2.85 2.85
Nos. 640-643 (4) 4.72 4.72

Nos. 641-642 Ovptd. with Jamboree Emblem and "BOY SCOUT / JAMBOREE / 5th-10th DEC '86" in Silver

1986, Dec. 2 **Litho.** *Perf. 14*
644 A120 42s multicolored .60 .60
645 A120 57s multicolored .82 .82

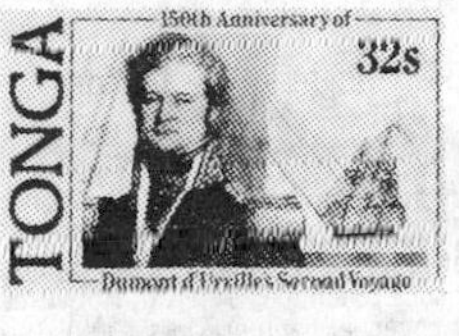

Dumont d'Urville's Second Voyage A121

Designs: 32s, D'Urville and ship Astrolabe. 42s, Four Tongan girls, detail fron D'Urville's engraving, Voyage au Pole et dans l'Oceanie. 1pa, Map of voyage. 2.50pa, Wreck of the Astrolabe.

1987, Feb. 24
646 A121 32s multicolored .45 .45
647 A121 42s multicolored .60 .60
648 A121 1pa multicolored 1.40 1.40
649 A121 2.50pa multicolored 3.50 3.50
Nos. 646-649 (4) 5.95 5.95

Dumont d'Urville (1790-1842), explorer and admiral.

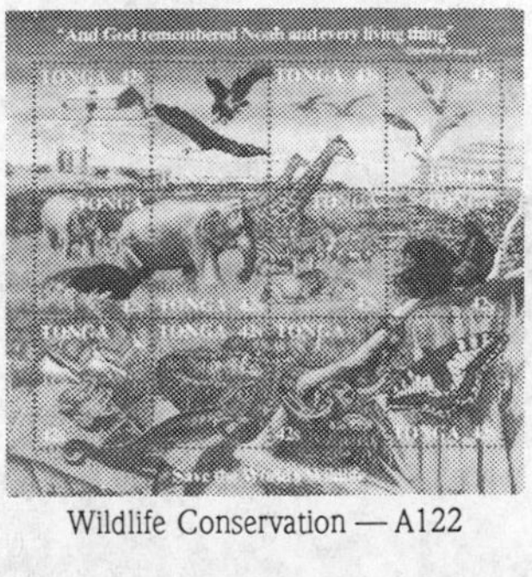

Wildlife Conservation — A122

Fauna: a, Noah's Ark. b, Eagles. c, Giraffes, birds. d, Seagulls. e, Elephants, ostriches. f, Elephant. g, Lions, zebras, antelopes. h, Chimpanzees. i, Antelope, frogs. j, Tigers, lizard. k, Tiger, snake. l, Butterfly.

1987, May 6 *Perf. 13½*
650 Sheet of 12 7.25 7.25
a.-l. A122 42s any single .60 .60

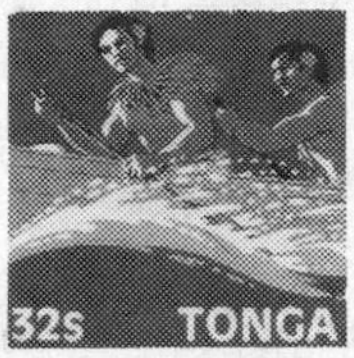

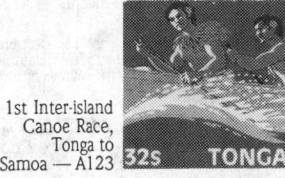

1st Inter-island Canoe Race, Tonga to Samoa — A123

1987, July 1 *Perf. 14*
651 A123 32s Two paddlers .45 .45
652 A123 42s Five paddlers .60 .60
653 A123 57s Three paddlers .80 .80
654 A123 1.50pa Two, diff. 2.15 2.15
a. Souvenir sheet of 4, #651-654 4.00 4.00
Nos. 651-654 (4) 4.00 4.00

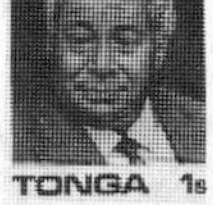

Coronation of King Taufa'ahau IV, 20th Anniv. — A124

Booklet Stamps

1987-88 *Imperf.*
Self-Adhesive
655 A124 1s green & yel grn .15 .15
655A A124 2s blk & pale yel org .15 .15
656 A124 5s black & brt pink .15 .15
a. Bklt. pane of 12 (6 5s plus 1 5s, 2 10s, 3 15s with gutter between) 1.00
657 A124 10s black & bluish lil .15 .15
658 A124 15s brn blk & org ver .22 .22
a. Bklt. pane of 12 (1s, 2 2s, 3 10s, plus 2 5s, 10s, 3 15s with gutter between) ('88) 1.55
659 A124 32s Prus blue & aqua .45 .45
a. Bklt. pane of 12 (4 32s, 2 15s plus 4 10s, 2 1s with gutter between) 2.95
b. Bklt. pane of 12 (6 32s plus 2 2s, 4 1s with gutter between) ('88) 3.00
Set value .98 .98

Issued: 2s, July 4, 1988; others, July 1, 1987.

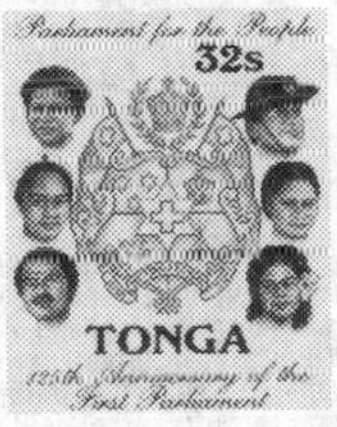

Parliament, 125th Anniv. — A125

1987, Sept. 2 **Litho.** *Perf. 14½*
660 A125 32s multicolored .50 .50
661 A125 42s multicolored .65 .65
662 A125 75s multicolored 1.15 1.15
663 A125 2pa multicolored 3.00 3.00
Nos. 660-663 (4) 5.30 5.30

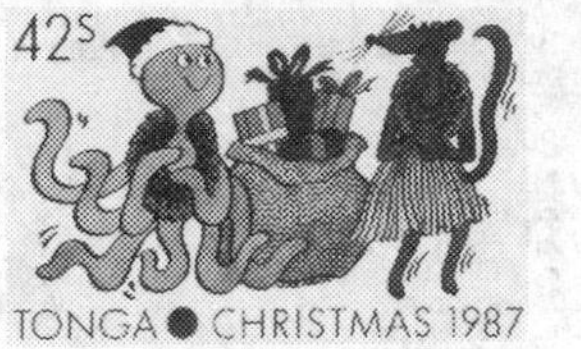

Christmas 1987 — A126

Cartoons featuring Octopus as Santa Claus and mouse as his helper.

1987, Nov. 18 **Litho.** *Perf. 14*
664 A126 42s Sack of gifts .68 .68
665 A126 57s Delivering them by canoe .92 .92
666 A126 1pa By automobile 1.60 1.60
667 A126 3pa Sipping tropical drinks 4.85 4.85
Nos. 664-667 (4) 8.05 8.05

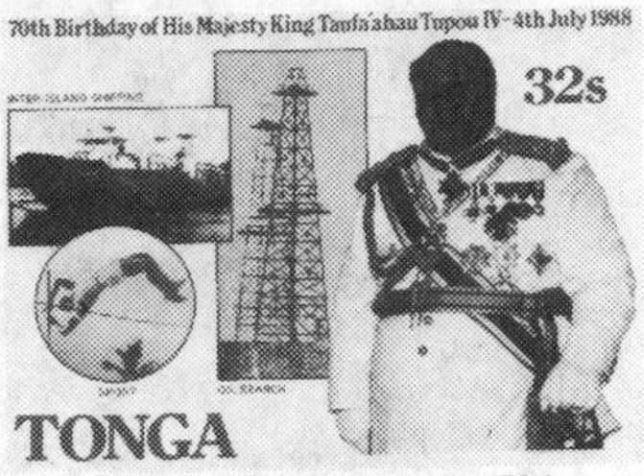

King Taufa'ahau Tupou IV, 70th Birthday — A127

Portrait and: 32s, M.V. *Olovaha* inter-island ship, athlete pole vaulting and offshore oil derrick. 42s, Banknote and coins, Ha'Amonga Trilithon and traditional craftsman. 57s, Rowing, Red Cross nurse and communications satellite. 2.50pa, Tonga Scouts emblem, No. 506 and Friendly Islands Airways passenger plane.

1988, July 4 **Litho.** *Perf. 11½*
668 A127 32s multicolored .48 .48
669 A127 42s multicolored .60 .60
670 A127 57s multicolored .82 .82
671 A127 2.50pa multicolored 3.60 3.60
Nos. 668-671 (4) 5.50 5.50

See Nos. 744-747 for stamps inscribed for the silver jubilee.

Souvenir Sheet

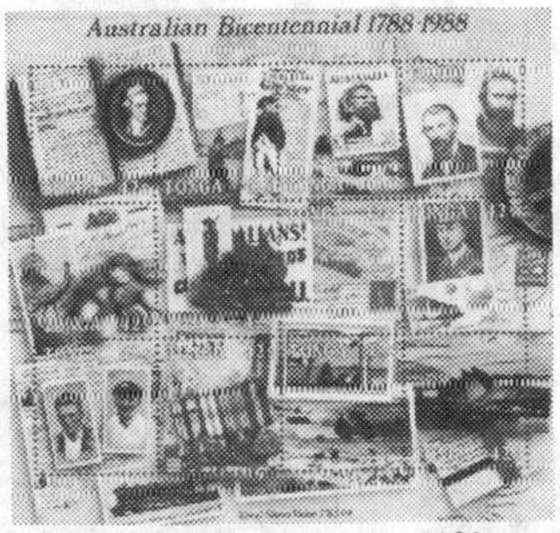

Australia Bicentennial — A128

Designs: a, Cook and his journal. b, List of stores shipped aboard the *Lady Juliana*, the ship, Arthur Philip, 1st gov. of New South Wales, 1788, and left half of the list of sentences of all the prisoners tried at Glo'ster Assizes. c, Right half of list of sentences, Australia Type A59 redrawn and aerial view of an early settlement. d, Robert O'Hara Burke (1820-61) and W.J. Wills (1834-61), the 1st explorers to cross Australia from south to north. e, Emu pictured on a Player's cigarette card, U.R. Stuart's (gold) prospecting license and opals. f, Australian Commonwealth Military Forces emblem, WW I recruit on cigarette card, and war poster. g, Souv. card commemorating 1st overland mail delivery by transcontinental railway, and Australia Type A4 on cover. h, Hand-canceled cover commemorating the 1st England-Australia transcontinental airmail flight, Nov. 12-Dec.10, 1919, aviator Capt. Ross Smith (1892-1922) and Great Britain #588. i, Don Bradman and Harold Larwood, cricket champions of the 1930s, on cigarette cards, and era newspaper frontispiece. j, Frontispiece of Hulton's natl. weekly *Picture Post* Victory Special issue, and WW II campaign medals. k, Australia #676 and a sheep station. l, Sydney Harbor Bridge, Opera House and theater tickets to *The Bartered Bride*.

1988, July 11 **Litho.** *Perf. 13½*
672 A128 Sheet of 12 7.25 7.25
a.-l. 42s any single .60 .60

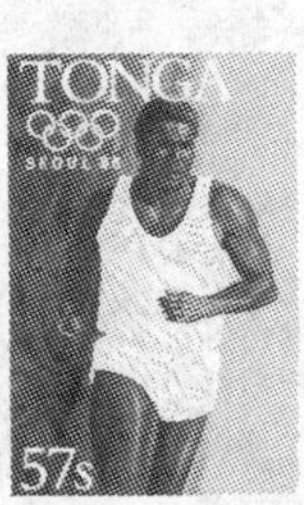

1988 Summer Olympics, Seoul — A129

1988, Aug. 11 *Perf. 14*
673 A129 57s Running .82 .82
674 A129 75s Yachting 1.05 1.05
675 A129 2pa Cycling 2.85 2.85
676 A129 3pa Women's tennis 4.25 4.25
Nos. 673-676 (4) 8.97 8.97

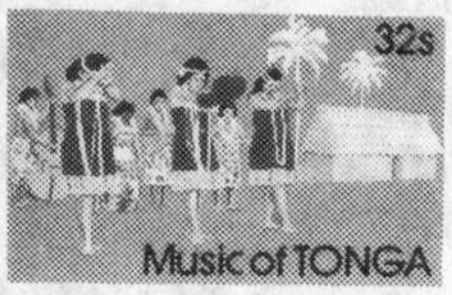

Music of Tonga
A130

1988, Sept. 9 Litho. *Perf. 14*

677 A130 32s shown .45 .45
678 A130 42s Choir .60 .60
679 A130 57s Tonga Police Band .82 .82
680 A130 2.50pa The Jets 3.50 3.50
Nos. 677-680 (4) 5.37 5.37

Souvenir Sheet

681 Sheet of 2 1.65 1.65
a. A130 57s like 2.50pa .82 .82
b. A130 57s Olympic eternal flame .82 .82

SPORT AID '88.

Marine Type of 1984

1988 Litho. *Perf. 14½*

Size: 27x34mm

682 A103 1s like No. 563 .15 .15
683 A103 2s like No. 564 .15 .15
684 A103 5s like No. 566 .15 .15
685 A103 6s like No. 567 .15 .15
686 A103 10s like No. 569 .18 .18
687 A103 15s like No. 571 .26 .26
688 A103 20s like No. 572 .35 .35
689 A103 32s like No. 574 .55 .55
690 A103 42s Fregata ariel .75 .75
691 A103 57s Sula leucogaster 1.00 1.00

Size: 41x27mm

Perf. 14

692 A103 3pa Like No. 578 5.25 5.25
Nos. 682-692 (11) 8.94 8.94

Issue dates: 1s, 5s, 10s, 20s, 32s, Oct. 4; 2s, 6s, 15s, 42s, 57s, 3pa, Oct. 18.

Nos. 683-684, 686, 689 exist inscribed "1990." See Nos. 701-709. For surcharge see No. 808.

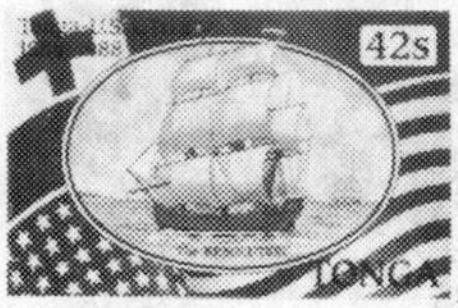

Tonga-US Treaty, Cent.
A131

1988, Oct. 20 *Perf. 14*

693 A131 42s *Resolution* .75 .75
694 A131 57s *Santa Maria* 1.00 1.00
695 A131 2pa Capt. Cook, Columbus 3.50 3.50
a. Souvenir sheet of 3, #693-695 5.25 5.25
Nos. 693-695 (3) 5.25 5.25

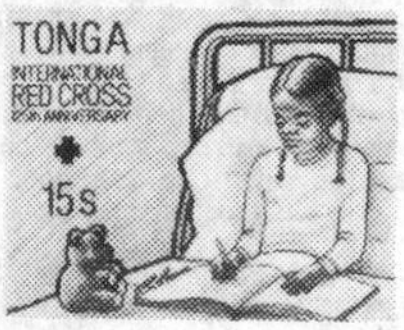

Christmas
A132

Designs (a, Intl. Red Cross, b, Natl. Red Cross): 15s, Girl, teddy bear. 32s, Nurse reading to child. 42s, Checking pulse. 57s, Tucking child into bed. 1.50pa, Boy in wheelchair.

1988, Nov. 17 Litho. *Perf. 14½*

696 Pair, #a.-b. .60 .60
697 Pair, #a.-b. 1.30 1.30
698 Pair, #a.-b. 1.70 1.70
699 Pair, #a.-b. 2.30 2.30
700 Pair, #a.-b. 6.00 6.00
Nos. 696-700 (5) 11.90 11.90

Intl. Red Cross 125th anniv. and 25th anniv. of the natl. Red Cross.

Marine Type of 1984

1989, Mar. 2 Litho. Size: 27x34mm

701 A103 4s like No. 570 .15 .15
702 A103 7s Diomedea exulans .15 .15
703 A103 35s Hippocampus 1.40 1.40
704 A103 50s like No. 573 2.00 2.00

Size: 41x27mm

Perf. 14

705 A103 1pa Chelonia mydas 4.00 4.00
706 A103 1.50pa Megaptera novaeangliae 6.00 6.00
707 A103 2pa like No. 577 3.35 3.35
709 A103 5pa like No. 579 8.25 8.25
Nos. 701-709 (8) 25.30 25.30

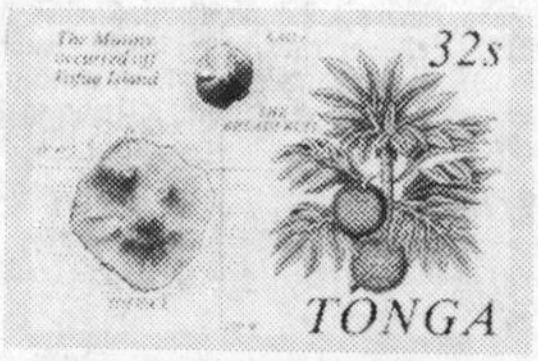

Mutiny on the *Bounty*, Bicent. — A133

Designs: 32s, Map of Tofua and Kao Isls., breadfruit. 42s, *Bounty*, chronometer. 57s, William Bligh and castaways in longboat. 2pa, Mutineers on the *Bounty*, vert. 3pa, Castaways.

Perf. 13½x14, 14x13½

1989, Apr. 28 Photo.

710 A133 32s multicolored .58 .58
711 A133 42s multicolored .75 .75
712 A133 57s multicolored 1.00 1.00
Nos. 710-712 (3) 2.33 2.33

Souvenir Sheet

713 Sheet of 2 8.75 8.75
a. A133 2pa multicolored 3.50 3.50
b. A133 3pa multicolored 5.25 5.25

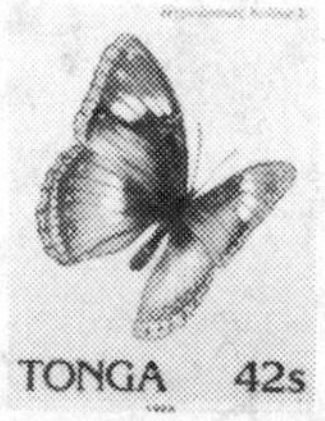

Butterflies — A134

1989, May 15 Litho. *Perf. 14½*

714 A134 42s *Hypolimnas bolina* .72 .72
715 A134 57s *Jamides bochus* .98 .98
716 A134 1.20pa *Melanitis leda solandra* 2.10 2.10
717 A134 2.50pa *Danaus plexippus* 4.30 4.30
Nos. 714-717 (4) 8.10 8.10

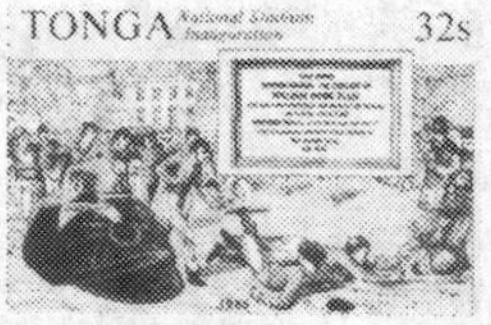

Opening of the Natl. Sports Stadium and the South Pacific Mini Games, Aug. 22
A135

Rugby (No. 718): a, Rugby Public School, 1870. b, Dave Gallaher and the Springboks vs. East Midlands, 1906. c, King George V inspecting Cambridge team of 1922 and Wavell Wakefield, captain of England. d, Ernie Crawford, captain of Ireland, Danie Craven demonstrating the dive pass and cigarette cards from the 1930's. e, Sioni Mafi, captain of Tonga, and match scene.

Tennis (No. 719): a, Royal tennis, 1659. b, Walter Clopton Wingfield and game of lawn tennis, 1873. c, Oxford and Cambridge teams of 1884. d, Bunny Ryan in 1910 and cigarette cards. e, Tennis players, 1980's.

Cricket (No. 720): a, Match in 1743 and bronze memorial to Fuller Pilch. b, W.G. Grace, 19th cent. c, *The Boys Own Paper*, 1909. d, Australian team of 1909 and cigarette cards. e, The Ashes trophy and modern match scene.

1989, Aug. 22 Litho. *Perf. 14*

718 Strip of 5 2.75 2.75
a.-e. A135 32s any single .55 .55
719 Strip of 5 3.60 3.60
a.-e. A135 42s any single .72 .72
720 Strip of 5 4.90 4.90
a.-e. A135 57s any single .98 .98
Nos. 718-720 (3) 11.25 11.25

Printed in sheets of 10 containing descriptions and emblem.

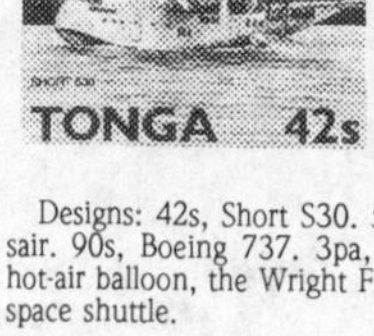

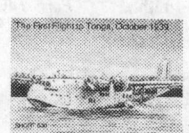

Natl. Aviation History — A136

Designs: 42s, Short S30. 57s, Vought F4U Corsair. 90s, Boeing 737. 3pa, Montgolfier brothers' hot-air balloon, the Wright Flyer, Concorde jet and space shuttle.

1989, Oct. 23 Litho. *Perf. 14½x14*

721 A136 42s multicolored .78 .78
722 A136 57s multicolored 1.05 1.05
723 A136 90s multicolored 1.65 1.65

Size: 97x126½mm

724 A136 3pa multicolored 5.50 5.50
Nos. 721-724 (4) 8.98 8.98

1st Flight to Tonga, 1939 (42s); military base on the island, 1943 (57s); civil aviation, Fua'amotu Airport (90s); aviation through the ages (3pa).

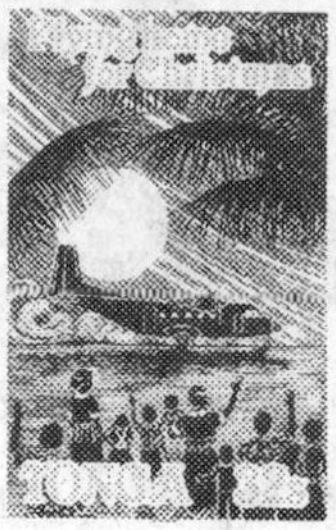

Flying Home for Christmas
A137

1989, Nov. 9 *Perf. 14x13½*

725 A137 32s Aircraft landing .60 .60
726 A137 42s Islanders waving, aircraft .78 .78
727 A137 57s Tongan in outrigger canoe, aircraft 1.05 1.05
728 A137 3pa Islanders waving, aircraft, diff. 5.50 5.50
Nos. 725-728 (4) 7.93 7.93

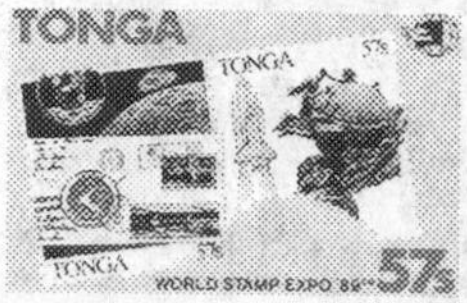

World Stamp Expo '89
A138

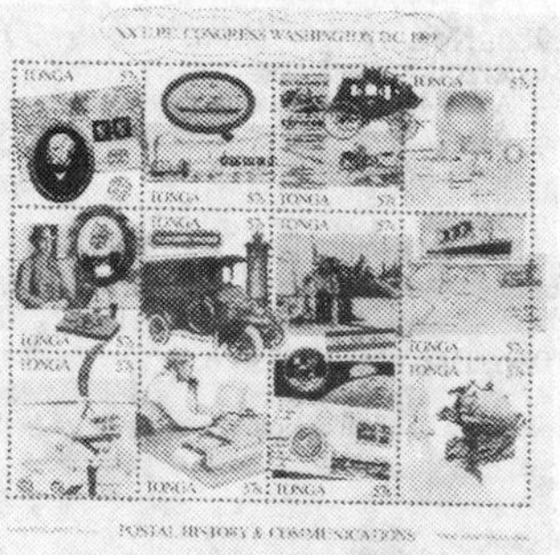

20th UPU Congress, Washington, DC — A139

Postal history and communications (No. 730): a, Sir Rowland Hill, penny blacks on Mulready envelope. b, Clipper ship, early train. c, Pony Express advertisement, stagecoach, post rider. d, Hot-air balloon and flight cover. e, Samuel Morse, miniature, telegraph key. f, Early Royal Mail truck, mailbox. g, Biplane and early aviators. h, Zeppelin flight cover, HMS *Queen Mary*. i, Helicopter, truck. j, Computer operator, facsimile machine. k, Apollo 11 mission emblem, flight cover, planetary bodies. l, American space shuttle, UPU monument.

1989, Nov. 17 Litho. *Perf. 14*

729 A138 57s Pair, #730k-730 l .98 .98

Souvenir Sheet

Perf. 13½

730 A139 Sheet of 12 12.00 12.00
a.-l. A139 57s any single .98 .98

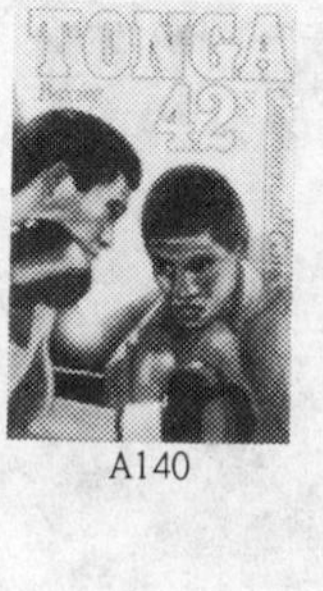

A140

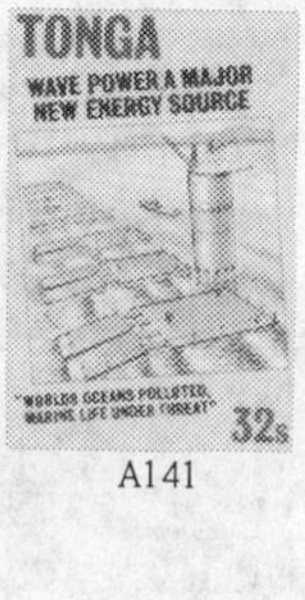

A141

1990, Feb. 14 Litho. *Perf. 14*

731 A140 42s Boxing .70 .70
732 A140 57s Archery 1.00 1.00
733 A140 1pa Bowls 1.75 1.75
734 A140 2pa Swimming 3.50 3.50
Nos. 731-734 (4) 6.95 6.95

1990 Commonwealth Games.

1990, Apr. 11 Litho. *Perf. 14*

Protect the Environment: 32s, Wave power, ocean pollution. 57s, Wind power, acid rain. $1.20, Solar power, ozone layer. $2.50, Green earth, rain forests.

735 A141 32s multicolored .55 .55
736 A141 57s multicolored .95 .95
737 A141 1.20pa multicolored 2.00 2.00
Nos. 735-737 (3) 3.50 3.50

Souvenir Sheet

738 A141 2.50pa multicolored 4.50 4.50

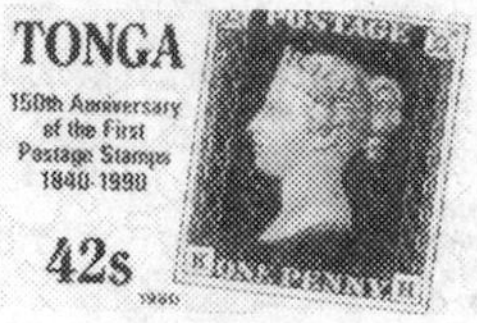

First Postage Stamps, 150th Anniv.
A142

1990 Litho. *Perf. 14*

739 A142 42s G. B. #1 .75 .75
740 A142 42s G. B. #2 .75 .75
a. Pair, #739-740 1.50 1.50
741 A142 57s Tonga #1 1.00 1.00
742 A142 1.50pa Tonga #CO180 2.60 2.60
743 A142 2.50pa Tonga #736 4.25 4.25
Nos. 739-743 (5) 9.35 9.35

King's Birthday Type of 1988 Inscribed "Silver Jubilee of His Majesty King Taufa'ahau Tupou IV 1965-1990"

1990, July 4 Litho. *Perf. 11½*

744 A127 32s like No. 668 .60 .60
745 A127 42s like No. 669 .80 .80
746 A127 57s like No. 670 1.05 1.05
747 A127 2.50pa like No. 671 4.75 4.75
Nos. 744-747 (4) 7.20 7.20

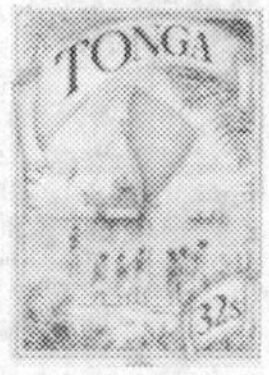

Native Catamaran — A143

1990, June 6 *Perf. 14½*

748 A143 32s buff & green .60 .60
749 A143 42s buff & blue, diff. .80 .80
750 A143 1.20pa buff & brn, diff. 2.25 2.25
751 A143 3pa buff & vio, diff. 5.50 5.50
Nos. 748-751 (4) 9.15 9.15

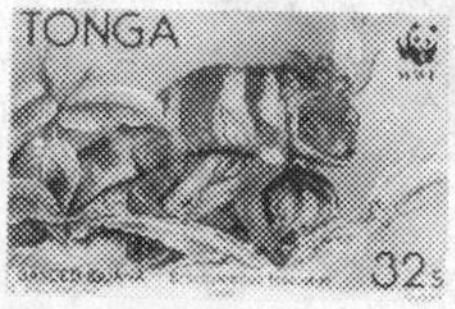

Banded Iguana
A144

1990, Sept. 12 Litho. *Perf. 14*

752 A144 32s multicolored .60 .60
753 A144 42s multi, diff. .80 .80
754 A144 57s multi, diff. 1.00 1.00
755 A144 1.20pa multi, diff. 2.25 2.25
Nos. 752-755 (4) 4.65 4.65

Marine Type of 1984

1990, July 6 Litho. *Perf. 14*

Size: 20x22mm

756 A103 2s like No. 564 .15 .15
a. Booklet pane of 10 .50 .50
757 A103 5s like No. 566 .15 .15
a. Booklet pane of 10 1.00 1.00
758 A103 10s like No. 569 .20 .20
a. Booklet pane of 10 2.00 2.00
759 A103 32s like No. 574 .60 .60
a. Booklet pane of 10 6.00 6.00
Set value .95 .95

Nos. 756-758 exist inscribed "1992."
For surcharge see No. 810.
Issue date: #756a-759a, Sept. 4.

UN Development Program, 40th
Anniv. — A145

1990, Oct. 25		Litho.		Perf. 14	
760	A145	57s Tourism		1.00	1.00
761	A145	57s Agriculture, fisheries		1.00	1.00
a.		Pair, #760-761		2.00	2.00
762	A145	3pa Education		5.35	5.35
763	A145	3pa Healthcare		5.35	5.35
a.		Pair, #762-763		10.75	10.75
		Nos. 760-763 (4)		12.70	12.70

Rotary Intl. — A146

Accident Prevention — A147

1990, Nov. 28					
764	A146	32s shown		.55	.55
765	A146	42s Two boys		.75	.75
766	A146	2pa Three children		3.50	3.50
767	A146	2pa Two girls		5.35	5.35
		Nos. 764-767 (4)		10.15	10.15

1991, Apr. 10   Litho.   Perf. 14½

No. 768: a, d, Care at work; hard hats save lives.
b, c, Keep matches and medicines out of children's reach.

No. 769: a, d, Don't drink and drive. b, c, Crash helmets save lives; mind cyclists and children.

No. 770: a, d, Listen to forecasts; learn to swim. b, c, Swim from safe beaches; beware of broken glass.

"a" and "b" have English inscriptions, denominations at top; "c" and "d" have Tongan inscriptions, denominations at bottom.

Strips of 4 + Label

768	A147	32s #a.-d.		2.40	2.40
769	A147	42s #a.-d.		3.20	3.20
770	A147	57s #a.-d.		4.00	4.00
		Nos. 768-770 (3)		9.60	9.60

Center label is a progressive proof.
For surcharge see No. 811.

A148

A149

1991, July 2		Litho.		Perf. 14½	
771	A148	42s Fish		.80	.80
772	A148	57s Island, boat		1.00	1.00
773	A148	2pa Fruit, island		3.50	3.50
774	A148	3pa Turtle, beach		5.50	5.50
		Nos. 771-774 (4)		10.80	10.80

Heilala week.

1991, July 2

Racing yachts: a, Red spinnaker. b, Yellow spinnaker. c, Green striped spinnaker. d, Yacht at sunset. e, Yacht, moon.

Miniature Sheet of 5 + Label

775	A149	1pa #775a-775e		9.00	9.00

Around the world yacht race.

Church of Jesus Christ
of Latter Day Saints in
Tonga, Cent. — A150

1991, Aug. 19					
776	A150	42s Tonga Temple		.80	.80
777	A150	57s Temple at night		1.00	1.00

Rowing Festival
A151

The Siu'a'alo

1991, Oct. 29		Litho.		Perf. 14	
778	A151	42s Women's coxed eight		.75	.75
779	A151	57s Men's longboat		1.05	1.05
780	A151	1pa Outrigger		1.85	1.85
781	A151	2pa Bow of large canoe		3.75	3.75
782	A151	2pa Stern of large canoe		3.75	3.75
a.		Pair, #781-782		7.50	7.50
		Nos. 778-782 (5)		11.15	11.15

For surcharges see Nos. 898-899C.

Telecommunications — A152

Designs: No. 783a, Recording television program. b, Communications Satellite. c, Watching television program.

No. 784a, Man on telephone, woman at computer. b, Communications satellite, diff. c, Man in city on telephone.

No. 785a, Seaman on sinking ship broadcasting SOS. b, Man on telephone, satellite relay station. c, Rescue missions.

No. 786a, Weather satellite. b, Men at computers. c, Television weather report, storm.

1991, Oct. 15		Litho.		Perf. 14½	
783	A152	15s Strip of 3, #a.-c.		.80	.80
784	A152	32s Strip of 3, #a.-c.		1.75	1.75
785	A152	42s Strip of 3, #a.-c.		2.25	2.25
786	A152	57s Strip of 3, #a.-c.		3.15	3.15
		Nos. 783-785 (3)		4.80	4.80

Christmas
A153

Designs: 32s, Turtles pulling Santa's sleigh. 42s, Santa on roof. 57s, Family with presents. 3.50pa, Waving goodbye to Santa.

1991, Nov. 11					
787	A153	32s multicolored		.58	.58
788	A153	42s multicolored		.75	.75
789	A153	57s multicolored		1.05	1.05
790	A153	3.50pa multicolored		6.50	6.50
		Nos. 787-790 (4)		8.88	8.88

Armed
Forces — A154   **TONGA 42**

1991, Dec. 15

791	A154	42s Royal Tonga Marine		.75	.75
792	A154	42s Patrol boat Pangai		.75	.75
a.		Pair, #791-792		1.50	1.50
793	A154	57s Patrol boat Neiafu		1.05	1.05
794	A154	57s Tonga Royal Guards		1.05	1.05
a.		Pair, #793-794		2.10	2.10
795	A154	2pa King Tupou IV, military parade		3.75	3.75
796	A154	2pa Patrol boat Savea		3.75	3.75
a.		Pair, #795-796		7.50	7.50
		Nos. 791-796 (6)		11.10	11.10

Miniature Sheet

Discovery of America,
500th Anniv. — A155

Designs: a, Columbus. b, Monastery of Santa Maria de la Chevas. c, Obverse and reverse of coin of Ferdinand and Isabella. d, Spain #C48, #426. e, Compass, astrolabe. f, Santa Maria. g, Map, Columbus' signature. h, Columbus arriving in New World. i, Lucayan artifacts, parrot. j, Pineapple, artifacts. k, Columbus announcing his discovery. l, Medal of Columbus, signature.

1992, Apr. 28		Litho.		Perf. 13½	
797	A155	57s Sheet of 12, #a.-l.		12.50	12.50

Marine Type of 1984 and

A155a   **TONGA 1s**

Perf. 13x13½, 14 (15s, 20s, 10pa)

1992-93				Litho.	
798	A155a	1s Swainsonia casta		.15	.15
799	A155a	3s Holocentrus ruber		.15	.15
800	A155a	5s Cypraea mappa viridis		.15	.15
801	A155a	10s Conus bullatus		.16	.16
802	A103	15s like #567		.28	.28
803	A155a	20s Dascyllus aruanus		.32	.32
804	A155a	45s Lambis truncata		.72	.72
805	A155a	60s Conus aulicus		.95	.95
806	A155a	80s Pterois volitans		1.30	1.30

Size: 27x41mm

807	A103	10pa like #568		18.00	18.00
		Nos. 798-807 (10)		22.18	22.18

Issued: 1s, 3s, 5s, 10s, 20s, 45s, 60s, 80s, May 12, 1993. 15s, 10pa, May 5, 1992.

See Nos. 874-884. Area covered by background colors on Nos. 874, 876 879 has been reduced in size.

For overprints see Nos. O78-O82.

XXX

1s   **45s** **45s**

No. 688   No. 759
Surcharged   Surcharged

No. 769 Surcharged in Red
and Black   **60**

1992		Litho.		Perf. 14½, 14	
808	A103	1s on 20s #688		.15	.15
810	A103	45s on 32s #759		.30	.30
811	A147	60s on 42s Strip of 4, #a.-d. + label		3.60	3.60
		Nos. 808-811 (3)		4.05	4.05

Issued: 1s, May 19; 45s, 60s, Aug. 11.

World
War II in
Pacific,
50th
Anniv.
A156

Designs: a, Newspaper headline, Japanese attack on Pearl Harbor. b, Map of Bataan, Corregidor, and Manila, pilot's wings, airplanes. c, Newspaper headline, troops landing in Gilbert Islands, Marine Corps emblem, dogtags. d, Uniform patch, B-29 "Enola Gay," troops landing on Iwo Jima. e, Map of Battle of Midway, Admiral Nimitz. f, Southwest Pacific campaign map, Gen. MacArthur. g, Map of Saipan and Tinian, Lt. Gen. Holland Smith. h, Map outling bombing of Japan, Maj. Gen. Curtis Lemay. i, Mitsubishi A6M Zero. j, Douglas SBD Dauntless. k, Grumman F4F Wildcat. l, Supermarine Seafire.

1992, May 26		Litho.		Perf. 14	
814	A156	42s Sheet of 12, #a.-l.		9.25	9.25

1992 Summer
Olympics,
Barcelona — A157

1992, June 16					
815	A157	42s Boxing		.78	.78
816	A157	57s Diving		1.05	1.05
817	A157	1.50pa Tennis		2.75	2.75
818	A157	3pa Cycling		5.50	5.50
		Nos. 815-818 (4)		10.08	10.08

King Taufa'ahau
IV, 25th Anniv.
of Coronation
A158

Designs: 45s, 2pa, King, Queen Halaevalu. No. 820a, King, crown. b, Extract from investiture ceremony. c, King, #C33.

1992, July 4				Perf. 13½x13	
819	A158	45s multicolored		.85	.85

Size: 51x38mm

Perf. 12½x12

820	A158	80s Strip of 3, #a.-c.		4.50	4.50
821	A158	2pa multicolored		3.65	3.65
		Nos. 819-821 (3)		9.00	9.00

Sacred Bats of
Kolovai — A159

Designs: No. 822a, Bats in flight. b, Close-up of flying bat. c, Flying bats, tree. d, Bats hanging in tree. e, Bat hanging from tree limb.

Origin of sacred bats: No. 823a, 45s, Kula leaving for Upolu to be tattooed as Tongan chief. b, 45s, Kula looking through path of fires. c, 2pa, Kula walking down path, Hina. d, 2pa, Hina waving. e, 2pa, Kula leaving with pet fruit bats.

Nos. 823a-823d are horiz.

1992, Oct. 20		Litho.		Perf. 14	
822	A159	60s Strip of 5, #a.-e.		5.25	5.25

Souvenir Sheet
Perf. 14½

823	A159	Sheet of 4, #a.-d.		8.50	8.50

Christmas
A160

1992, Nov. 10   *Perf. 14*
824 A160 60s Pearls   1.05 1.05
825 A160 80s Reef fish   1.40 1.40
826 A160 2pa Pacific orchids   3.50 3.50
827 A160 3pa Eua parrots   5.25 5.25
     Nos. 824-827 (4)   11.20 11.20

For surcharges see Nos. 894-897.

Anniversaries
and Events
A161

Designs: 60s, Tonga flag, Rotary emblem. 80sh, John F. Kennedy, Peace Corps emblem. 1.50pa, FAO, WHO emblems. 3.50pa, Globe, Rotary Foundation emblem.

1992, Dec. 15   *Perf. 14½*
828 A161   60s multicolored   1.05 1.05
829 A161   80s multicolored   1.40 1.40
830 A161 1.50pa multicolored   2.65 2.65
831 A161 3.50pa multicolored   6.15 6.15
     Nos. 828-831 (4)   11.25 11.25

Rotary Intl. in Tonga, 25th anniv. (#828). Peace Corps in Tonga, 25th anniv. (#829). Intl. Conference of FAO and WHO (#830). Rotary Foundation of Rotary Intl., 75th anniv. (#831).
For overprint see No. 868.

Family
Planning — A163

Outdoor silhouette scenes: No. 832, Mother, girl, butterflies. No. 833, Child on tricycle pulling kite. No. 834, Girl, kittens. No. 835, Adult, child playing chess.

1993, Jan. 26   *Perf. 14x13½*
832 A163 15s Pair, #a.-b.   1.10 1.10
833 A163 45s Pair, #a.-b.   1.60 1.60
834 A163 60s Pair, #a.-b.   2.10 2.10
835 A163 2pa Pair, #a.-b.   7.00 7.00
     Nos. 832-835 (4)   11.80 11.80

Nos. 832a-835a have Tongan inscriptions. Nos. 832b-835b have English inscriptions and are mirror images of Nos. 832a-835a.

Health and Fitness — A164

Designs: 60s, Fresh fruit, fish, anti-smoking and anti-drug symbols. 80s, Anti-smoking symbol, weight training. 1.50pa, Anti-drug symbol, water sports. 2.50pa, Fresh fruit, fish, cyclist, jogger. Illustration reduced.

1993, Mar. 16   Litho.   *Perf. 14*
836 A164   60s multicolored   1.05 1.05
837 A164   80s multicolored   1.40 1.40
838 A164 1.50pa multicolored   2.60 2.60
839 A164 2.50pa multicolored   4.35 4.35
     Nos. 836-839 (4)   9.40 9.40

Tonga Fire
Service,
25th
Anniv.
A165

1993, May 18   Litho.   *Perf. 14*
840 A165 45s Fireman's badge   .78 .78
841 A165 45s Police van, badge   .78 .78
842 A165 60s Police band   1.05 1.05
843 A165 60s Putting out fire   1.05 1.05
    a.   Pair, #842-843   2.10 2.10
844 A165 2pa Fire truck at station   3.50 3.50
845 A165 2pa Policeman, police
         dog   3.50 3.50
    a.   Pair, #844-845   7.00 7.00
     Nos. 840-845 (6)   10.66 10.66

Tonga Police Training College, 25th anniv. (#841-842, 845).

A166   A167

Abel Tasman's Voyage to Eua, 350th Anniv.: 30s, Map of islands. 60s, Sailing ships, Heemskirk and Zeehaen. 80s, Sailing ships, natives in canoes. 3.50pa, Landing on Eua.

1993, June 21
846 A166 30s multicolored   .52 .52
847 A166 60s multicolored   1.05 1.05
848 A166 80s multicolored   1.40 1.40
849 A166 3.50pa multicolored   6.00 6.00
     Nos. 846-849 (4)   8.97 8.97

1993, July 1   Litho.   *Perf. 13x13½*
King Taufa'ahau IV, 75th Birthday: 45s, 2pa, Musical instruments.
No. 851a, Sporting events. b, Ancient landmarks. c, Royal Palace.

850 A167 45s multicolored   .78 .78
     Perf. 12x12½
     Size: 37x48mm
851 A167 80s Strip of 3, #a.-c.   4.25 4.25
852 A167 2pa multicolored   3.50 3.50
     Nos. 850-852 (3)   8.53 8.53

A168   A168a

Children's Stamp Designs: Nos. 853a, 854a, Beach scene. Nos. 853b, 854b, "Maui-The Fisher of the Islands." Nos. 853c, 854c, Raft on ocean. Nos. 853d, 854d, Woman with hands in mixing bowl. Nos. 853e, 854e, "Maui and his Hook." Nos. 853f, 854f, "Communication in the South Pacific."

1993, Dec. 1   Litho.   *Perf. 14*
853 A168 10s Strip of 6, #a.-f.   1.10 1.10
854 A168 80s Strip of 6, #a.-f.   8.75 8.75

1993, Nov. 10   Litho.   *Perf. 14*
Christmas traditions: 60s, Festive dinner. 80s, Shooting cannon. 1.50pa, Musicians. 3pa, Going to church.

855 A168a   60s multicolored   1.10 1.10
856 A168a   80s multicolored   1.40 1.40
857 A168a 1.50pa multicolored   2.75 2.75
858 A168a 3pa multicolored   5.50 5.50
     Nos. 855-858 (4)   10.75 10.75

Miniature Sheet

Kindness to
Animals — A169

Designs: a, 80s, Boy holding puppy. b, 80s, Girl holding kitten. c, 60s, Boy holding rooster (b). d, 60s, Girl with butterfly. e, 60s, Three dogs. f, 60s, Boy, puppy.

1994, Jan. 14   *Perf. 14½*
859 A169   Sheet of 6, #a.-f.   6.25 6.25
For overprint see No. 868.

Game Fishing — A170

1994, Feb. 28   Litho.   *Perf. 12*
860 A170   60s Tiger Shark   1.10 1.10
861 A170   80s Dolphin fish   1.50 1.50
862 A170 1.50pa Yellow fin tuna   3.00 3.00
863 A170 2.50pa Pacific blue marlin   4.75 4.75
     Nos. 860-863 (4)   10.35 10.35

1994 World Cup Soccer Championships,
US — A171

Designs: No. 864a, Player's legs. No. 864b, World Cup trophy. No. 865a, American player in red, white, & blue. No. 865b, German player in black shorts, white shirt.

1994, June 1   *Perf. 14x14½*
864 A171 80s Pair, #a.-b.   3.00 3.00
865 A171 2pa Pair, #a.-b.   7.75 7.75

Pan Pacific & South
East Asia Women's
Assoc.
Conference — A172

Career women: No. 866a, Lawyer. No. 866b, Policewoman. No. 867a, Doctor. No. 867b, Nurse.

1994, Aug. 18   Litho.   *Perf. 14*
866 A172 45s Pair, #a.-b.   1.75 1.75
867 A172 2.50pa Pair, #a.-b.   9.50 9.50

Nos. 859a, 859c-859f Ovptd. "MERRY /
CHRISTMAS"
No. 859b Ovptd. "KILISIMASI FIEFIA"

1994, Nov. 10   Litho.   *Perf. 14½*
868 A169   Sheet of 6, #a.-f.   7.75 7.75

No. 831 Ovptd. in Dark Blue

1994, Nov. 17   Litho.   *Perf. 14½*
869 A161 60s on 3.50pa multi   .90 .90

Types of 1969-85 and

Tongastar 1
Satelite
A173

Design: a, 10s, Type A39 banana, size 22x11mm. b, 25s, Type AP12. c, Booklet pane, 12 #870a, 3 #870b. d, 45s, like #608. e, 45s, like #609. f, 45s, like #610. g, 45s, like #611. h, Booklet pane of 3 each #870d-870e, 2 #870f, 1 #870g. i, 60s, Type A72. j, 60s, Type OA19. k, 80s, Type OA17. l, Booklet pane, #870i-870k. m, 2pa, Tongastar 1. n, Booklet pane of 1 #870m.

     Unwmk.
1994, Dec. 14   Litho.   *Die Cut*
     Self-adhesive
870 A173   Souvenir booklet   20.00

First full-scale production of self-adhesive stamps by Tonga, 25th anniv. (#870). Satellite communications network for Tongan Islands (#870m).
No. 870b is airmail. Nos. 870j-870k are air post official stamps.
No. 870m contains a holographic image. Soaking in water may affect the hologram.

Marine Type of 1992-93 Redrawn
1994-95   Litho.   *Perf. 14*
874 A155a 10s like #799A   .15 .15
876 A155a 30s like #801   .30 .30
877 A155a 45s like #803   .70 .70
878 A155a 60s like #804   .95 .95
879 A155a 80s like #805   1.25 1.25
     Size: 41x27mm, 41x27mm
880 A155a 1pa like #705, horiz.   1.90 1.90
881 A155a 2pa like #577, horiz.   3.75 3.75
882 A155a 3pa like #578, horiz.   5.75 5.75
883 A155a 5pa like #706   9.50 9.50
884 A155a 5pa like #568   20.00 20.00
     Nos. 874-884 (10)   44.25 44.25

Area covered by background colors on Nos. 874, 876-879 has been reduced in size.
Issued: 1pa, 2pa, 3pa, 6/21/94; 5pa, 9/21/94; 10pa, 1/18/95; 10s, 20s, 45s, 60s, 80s, 9/25/95. This is an expanding set. Numbers may change.

FAO, 50th
Anniv.
A174

1995, May 16   Litho.   *Perf. 14*
886 A174 5pa multicolored   9.50 9.50

Tonga's Entry into British Commonwealth,
25th Anniv. — A175

Children with bicycles from parts of Commonwealth.

1995, June 6
887 A175   45s Polynesia   .90 .90
888 A175   60s Asia   1.25 1.25
889 A175   80s Africa   1.50 1.50
890 A175   2pa India   3.75 3.75
891 A175 2.50pa Europe   4.75 4.75
     Nos. 887-891 (5)   12.15 12.15

1995 Rugby World Cup, South Africa — A176

Designs: No. 892a, Player running right with ball, two others. b, Two players. No. 893a, Three players. b, Player ready to catch ball.

1995, June 20   *Perf. 14½*
892 A176 80s Pair, #a.-b.   3.00 3.00
893 A176 2pa Pair, #a.-b.   7.50 7.50

Nos. 892-893 were each issued in sheets of 4 stamps.

Nos. 824-827 Surcharged

60

WHERE TIME BEGINS
i

60

THE 21st CENTURY STARTS HERE
j

1995, June 30   Litho.   *Perf. 14*
894   60s Pair   1.40 1.40
  a. A160(i) on #824   .70 .70
  b. A160(j) on #824   .70 .70
895   60s Pair   1.40 1.40
  a. A160(i) on 80s #825   .70 .70
  b. A160(j) on 80s #825   .70 .70
896   60s Pair   1.40 1.40
  a. A160(i) on 2pa #826   .70 .70
  b. A160(j) on 2pa #826   .70 .70
897   60s Pair   1.40 1.40
  a. A160(i) on 3pa #827   .70 .70
  b. A160(j) on 3pa #827   .70 .70
       Nos. 894-897 (4)   5.60 5.60

Nos. 779-782 Surcharged

80

VISIT SOUTH PACIFIC YEAR 95

1995, June 30   Litho.   *Perf. 14*
898 A151 60s on 57s #779   1.40 1.40
899 A151 80s on 2pa #781   1.75 1.75
899A A151 80s on 2pa #782   1.75 1.75
  b.   Pair, #899-899A   3.50 3.50
899C A151 1pa on #780   2.25 2.25
       Nos. 898-899C (4)   7.15 7.15

Victory in the Pacific, 50th Anniv. — A177

Nos. 900, 901: a, Soldier climbing from rope ladder. b, Ship, soldiers. c, Ship, landing craft with

troops, soldiers up close. d, Ship, landing craft with troops. e, Map.

1995, Aug. 1   Litho.   *Perf. 14x14½*
900 A177 60s Strip of 5, #a.-e.   6.25 6.25
901 A177 80s Strip of 5, #a.-e.   7.50 7.50

Nos. 900-901 are continuous designs and were issued together in sheet containing ten stamps.

WORLD STAMP EXHIBITION
Singapore '95 — A178

Designs: No. 902a, 45s, #887. b, 60s, #888. 2pa, Boy cycling in Singapore.

1995, Sept. 1   Litho.   *Perf. 12*
902 A178   Pair, #a.-b.   1.65 1.65

Souvenir Sheet
903 A178 2pa multicolored   3.25 3.25

Souvenir Sheet

Beijing Intl. Coin & Stamp Show '95 — A179

Design: 1.40pa, Mount Song, Henan Province, China. Illustration reduced.

1995, Sept. 14   *Perf. 14½*
904 A179 1.40pa multicolored   2.25 2.25

End of World War II, UN, 50th Anniv. — A180

No. 905a, Holocaust survivors. b, UN emblem, "50." c, Children of Holocaust survivors in celebration.
No. 906a, Mushroom cloud from atom bomb explosion. b, Like #905b. c, Space shuttle.

1995, Oct. 20   *Perf. 13*
905 A180 60s Strip of 3, #a.-c.   2.75 2.75
906 A180 80s Strip of 3, #a.-c.   3.75 3.75

Nos. 905b, 906b are 23x31mm.

─────────────

SEMI-POSTAL STAMP

Catalogue values for unused stamps in this section are for Never Hinged items.

No. 488 Surcharged in Silver for Cyclone Relief

1982, Apr. 14   Litho.
B1 A86 3pa + 50s multi   8.50 8.50

─────────────

AIR POST STAMPS

Catalogue values for unused stamps in this section are for Never Hinged items.

Type of Regular Gold Coin Issue

Designs: 10p, 1sh1p, Queen Salote standing, ½-koula coin, obverse. 11p, Coat of arms, ½-koula coin, reverse. 2sh1p, 2sh9p, Queen Salote standing, 1-koula coin, obverse. 2sh4p, Coat of arms, 1-koula coin, reverse.

Litho.; Embossed on Gilt Foil
1963, July 15   Unwmk.   *Imperf.*
          Diameter: 54mm
C1 A36 10p dp carmine   .40 .40
C2 A36 11p green   .60 .60
C3 A36 1sh6p violet blue   .60 .60
          Diameter: 80mm
C4 A36 2sh1p magenta   1.00 1.00
C5 A36 2sh4p emerald   1.00 1.00
C6 A36 2sh9p violet   1.50 1.50
       Nos. C1-C6 (6)   5.10 5.10

See note after No. 133.

Map of Tongatabu and ¼-Koula Coin — AP1

Litho.; Embossed on Gilt Foil
1964, Oct. 19
C7   AP1 10p deep green   .15 .15
C8   AP1 1sh2p black   .18 .18
C9   AP1 3sh6p carmine   .60 .60
C10 AP1 6sh6p purple   1.20 1.20
       Nos. C7-C10 (4)   2.13 2.13

Pan-Pacific and Southeast Asia Women's Association Conf., Nukualofa, Aug. 1964. See note after No. 133.

Nos. C1-C2, C4-C6 Surcharged like Regular Issue, 1965, in Black, White or Red

1965, Mar. 18
C11 A36 2sh3p on 10p dp car (B) .42 .42
C12 A36 2sh9p on 11p green (W)   .60 .60
C13 A36 4sh6p on 2sh1p magenta 14.00 14.00
C14 A36 4sh6p on 2sh4p emerald 14.00 14.00
C15 A36 4sh6p on 2sh9p violet   14.00 14.00
       Nos. C11-C15 (5)   43.02 43.02

Nos. 114-115, 117-118 Overprinted or Surcharged

AIRMAIL
1866 CENTENARY 1966
TUPOU COLLEGE
&
SECONDARY EDUCATION
10d   **XX**

                      Perf. 14½x13½
1966, June 18   Wmk. 79
C16 A35 5p purple   .15 .15
C17 A35 10p on 1p brn org & car rose .15 .15
C18 A35 1sh red brown   .15 .15
C19 A35 2sh9p on 2p ultra   .40 .40
C20 A35 3sh6p on 5p purple   .55 .55
C21 A35 4sh6p on 1sh red brown   .65 .65
       Nos. C16-C21 (6)   2.05 2.05

Centenary of Tupou College and secondary education. The overprint or surcharge is spaced differently on other values.

Nos. C7-C8 Overprinted and Surcharged in Silver or Gold on Black, or in Black on Gold

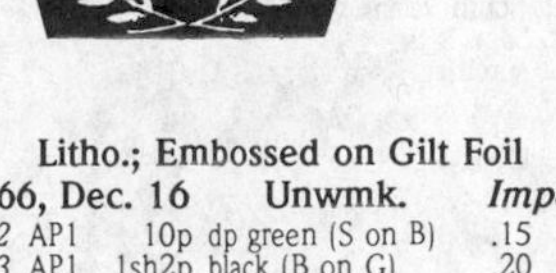

Litho.; Embossed on Gilt Foil
1966, Dec. 16   Unwmk.   *Imperf.*
C22 AP1 10p dp green (S on B)   .15 .15
C23 AP1 1sh2p black (B on G)   .20 .20
C24 AP1 4sh on 10p dp green (S on B) .65 .65
C25 AP1 5sh6p on 1sh2p black (B on G) .85 .85

C26 AP1 10sh6p on 1sh2p black (G on B) 1.50 1.50
       Nos. C22-C26 (5)   3.35 3.35

In memory of Queen Salote (1900-65).

King Taufa'ahau Type of Regular Issue, 1967

Designs: 7s, 11s, 23s, 2pa, Taufa'ahau IV, obverse of new palladium coins. 9s, 21s, 29s, Coat of Arms, reverse.

Litho.; Embossed on Palladium Foil
1967, July 4

Diameter: 7s, 44mm; 9s, 29s, 52mm; 11s, 59mm; 21s, 68mm; 23s, 40mm; 2pa, 74mm.

C27 A38 7s red & black   .16 .16
C28 A38 9s maroon & emer   .25 .25
C29 A38 11s brt blue & org   .32 .32
C30 A38 21s black & emer   .55 .55
C31 A38 23s magenta & emer   .60 .60
C32 A38 29s vio blue & emer   .70 .70
C33 A38 2pa magenta & orange   4.75 4.75
       Nos. C27-C33 (7)   7.33 7.33

See note after No. 181.

Type of Regular Issue, 1953 Surcharged in Red or Black

The Friendly Islands welcome the United States Peace Corps
AIRMAIL 21s

Wmk. 79
1967, Dec. 15   Engr.   *Imperf.*
C34 A33 11s on 3½p ultra (R)   .42 .42
C35 A33 21s on 1½p emerald   .70 .70
C36 A33 23s on 3½p ultra (R)   .90 .90
       Nos. C34-C36 (3)   2.02 2.02

Arrival of the United States Peace Corps.

No. 112 Surcharged in Red

AIRMAIL 11 SENITI 11

1968, Apr. 6   Engr.   *Perf. 11x11½*
C37 A34 11s on 10sh black & yellow .35 .35
C38 A34 21s on 10sh black & yellow .65 .65
C39 A34 23s on 10sh black & yellow .80 .80
       Nos. C37-C39 (3)   1.80 1.80

Nos. C27-C33 Overprinted: "HIS MAJESTY'S 50th BIRTHDAY" in Silver on Blue Panel on 7s, 11s, 23s and 2pa. "H.M.'s BIRTHDAY / 4 . JULY . 1968" in Gold on Red Panel on 9s, 21s and 29s

Litho.; Embossed on Palladium Foil
1968, July 4   Unwmk.   *Imperf.*
C40 A38 7s red & black   .25 .25
C41 A38 9s maroon & emerald   .32 .32
C42 A38 11s brt blue & orange   .40 .40
C43 A38 21s black & emerald   .85 .85
C44 A38 23s magenta & emerald   1.00 1.00
C45 A38 29s vio blue & emerald 1.40 1.40
C46 A38 2pa magenta & orange   8.00 8.00
       Nos. C40-C46 (7)   12.22 12.22

50th birthday of King Taufa'ahau IV.

Types of 1953 Surcharged: "Friendly Islands / Field & Track Trials / South Pacific Games / Port Moresby 1969 / AIRMAIL"

Designs as before.

1968, Dec. 19   Engr.   Wmk. 79
C47 A33 6s on 6p yellow & black .15 .15
C48 A33 7s on 4p purple & yellow .15 .15
C49 A33 8s on 8p black & lt green .15 .15
C50 A33 9s on 1½p emerald   .16 .16
C51 A34 11s on 3p brown org & yel .20 .20
C52 A33 21s on 3½p dk blue   .40 .40
C53 A33 38s on 5sh sepia & yel   .80 .80
C54 A34 1pa on 10sh orange yel 2.00 2.00
       Nos. C47-C54 (8)   4.01 4.01

Issued to publicize the field and track trials for the third South Pacific Games, Port Moresby, 1969. The overprint is in 5 lines on the horizontal stamps, in 7 lines on the vertical stamps. On the vertical stamps "Trial" is printed on the line ahead of "Field

& Track". On No. C54 the denomination is spelled out.

Nos. C19-C21 Surcharged
Perf. 14½x13½

1968	Photo.		Wmk. 79	
C55	A35	1s on 2sh9p on 2p ultra	.45	.45
C56	A35	1s on 3sh6p on 5p purple	.45	.45
C57	A35	1s on 4sh6p on 1sh red brown	.45	.45
	Nos. C55-C57 (3)		1.35	1.35

Pacific Games Type of Regular Issue
Design: Boxer.

1969, Aug. 13   Litho.   Imperf.
Self-adhesive

C58	A40	9s orange, blk & pur	.35	.35
C59	A40	11s orange, blk & dk bl	.38	.38
C60	A40	20s orange, blk & yel grn	.65	.65
C61	A40	60s orange, blk & scar	2.00	2.00
C62	A40	1pa orange, blk & grn	3.50	3.50
	Nos. C58-C62 (5)		6.88	6.88

See note after No. 231.

Oil Derrick on Map of Tongatabu and King Taufa'ahau IV — AP2

1969, Dec. 23   Litho.; Gold Embossed
Self-adhesive

C63	AP2	9s multicolored	.30	.30
C64	AP2	10s multicolored	.30	.30
C65	AP2	24s multicolored	.75	.75
C66	AP2	29s multicolored	.90	.90
C67	AP2	38s multicolored	1.20	1.20
	Nos. C63-C67 (5)		3.45	3.45

1st scientific search for oil in Tonga.

King Taufa'ahau IV and Queen Elizabeth II — AP3

1970, Mar. 7   Litho.; Gold Embossed
Self-adhesive

C68	AP3	7s multicolored	.30	.30
C69	AP3	9s multicolored	.35	.35
C70	AP3	24s multicolored	.90	.90
C71	AP3	29s multicolored	1.10	1.10
C72	AP3	38s multicolored	1.50	1.50
	Nos. C68-C72 (5)		4.15	4.15

See note after No. 242.

King Taufa'ahau Tupou IV Medal — AP4

Litho.; Gold Embossed
1970, June 4   Self-adhesive

C73	AP4	9s grnsh bl, ver & gold	.35	.35
C74	AP4	10s lilac, bl & gold	.35	.35
C75	AP4	24s yel, grn & gold	.90	.90
C76	AP4	29s ultra, org & gold	1.25	1.25
C77	AP4	38s ocher, emer & gold	2.00	2.00
	Nos. C73-C77 (5)		4.85	4.85

See note after No. 247.

Red Cross Type of Regular Issue Without Coat of Arms

1970, Oct. 17   Litho.   Imperf.
Self-adhesive

C78	A45	9s red & silver	.35	.35
C79	A45	10s red & magenta	.35	.35
C80	A45	18s red & brt green	.75	.75
C81	A45	38s red & brt blue	1.50	1.50
C82	A45	1pa red & green	4.50	4.50
	Nos. C78-C82 (5)		7.45	7.45

Centenary of the British Red Cross.

Nos. C22-C24 Surcharged

Lithographed; Embossed on Gilt Foil
1971, Jan. 31   Imperf.

C83	AP1	9s on #C22 (S on B)	.50	.38
C84	AP1	24s on #C24 (G on B)	1.10	.95
C85	AP1	29s on #C23 (R on B)	1.50	1.10
C86	AP1	38s on #C23 (G on B)	2.50	1.50
	Nos. C83-C86 (4)		5.60	3.93

In memory of Queen Salote (1900-1965).

Type of Regular Issue, 1953, Surcharged in Red and Black

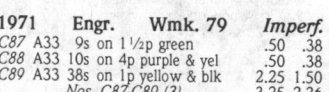

1971	Engr.	Wmk. 79		Imperf.
C87	A33	9s on 1½p green	.50	.38
C88	A33	10s on 4p purple & yel	.50	.38
C89	A33	38s on 1p yellow & blk	2.25	1.50
	Nos. C87-C89 (3)		3.25	2.26

See note after No. 272.

Types of Regular Issue Surcharged in Purple or Black: "AIRMAIL," New Denomination and "HONOURING JAPANESE POSTAL CENTENARY 1871-1971"

1971				
C90	A34	18s on 1sh car & buff (P)	.40	.40
C91	A33	1pa on 2sh car & ultra	2.25	2.25

Surcharge on #C90 in 6 lines, on #C91 in 4.

Self-adhesive & Imperf.
Starting with Nos. C92-C96, all airmail issues are self-adhesive and imperforate, unless otherwise stated.

High Jump AP5

1971, July		Litho.		Unwmk.
C92	AP5	9s brown, mag & blk	.25	.25
C93	AP5	10s brown, blue & blk	.30	.30
C94	AP5	24s brown, dk grn & blk	.60	.60
C95	AP5	29s brown, vio & blk	.90	.90
C96	AP5	38s brown, red & blk	1.20	1.20
	Nos. C92-C96 (5)		3.25	3.25

4th South Pacific Games, Papeete, French Polynesia, Sept. 8-19.
For surcharges see Nos. C141-C142.

Prehistoric Trilithon, King's Watch and Portrait AP6

1971, July 20   Litho. and Embossed

C97	AP6	14s dk brown & multi	.65	.65
C98	AP6	21s ocher & multi	.90	.90

2nd anniversary of man's first landing on the moon and the placement of a Bulova Accutron there. See Nos. C117-118, CO47-CO48, CO61-CO62. Advertisement on peelable paper backing.

Medal Type of Regular Issue
Designs: 10s, Gold Medal of Merit, obverse (King Taufa'ahau IV). 75s, Silver Medal of Merit, obverse (King Taufa'ahau IV). 1pa, Bronze Medal of Merit, reverse.

1971, Oct. 30   Litho. & Embossed

C99	A47	10s gold & multi	.32	.32
C100	A47	75s silver & multi	2.50	2.50
C101	A47	1pa bronze & multi	3.25	3.25
	Nos. C99-C101 (3)		6.07	6.07

Girl with Blocks and UNICEF Emblem — AP7

1971, Dec.   Litho.

C102	AP7	10s multicolored	.38	.38
C103	AP7	15s multicolored	.55	.55
C104	AP7	25s multicolored	.95	.95
C105	AP7	50s multicolored	1.90	1.90
C106	AP7	1pa multicolored	3.75	3.75
	Nos. C102-C106 (5)		7.53	7.53

25th anniversary of UNICEF.

Ship Type of Regular Issue
Design: Map of Merchant Marine routes from Tonga and cargo ship "Niuvakai."

1972, Apr. 14

C107	A49	9s ver & multi	.25	.25
C108	A49	12s multicolored	.35	.35
C109	A49	14s dk purple & multi	.40	.40
C110	A49	75s olive & multi	2.50	2.50
C111	A49	90s black & multi	3.00	3.00
	Nos. C107-C111 (5)		6.50	6.50

For surcharge and overprint see No. C124.

Coin Type of Regular Issue
Design: Coins on top; panel at bottom inscribed "5th anniversary world's first palladium coinage."

Litho.; Embossed on Metallic Foil
1972, July 15

C112	A50	9s silver & multi	.40	.40
C113	A50	12s silver & multi	.52	.52
C114	A50	14s silver & multi	.65	.65
C115	A50	21s silver & multi	1.00	1.00
C116	A50	75s silver & multi	3.25	3.25
	Nos. C112-C116 (5)		5.82	5.82

Watch Type of 1971

1972, July 20   Litho. and Embossed

C117	AP6	17s multicolored	.75	.75
C118	AP6	38s multicolored	1.50	1.50

Advertisement on peelable paper backing.

Proclamation of Sovereignty — AP8

1972, Dec. 9   Litho.

C119	AP8	9s ultra & multi	.30	.30
C120	AP8	12s red brown & multi	.40	.40
C121	AP8	14s magenta & multi	.50	.50
C122	AP8	38s brn org & multi	1.25	1.25
C123	AP8	1pa olive & multi	3.00	3.00
	Nos. C119-C123 (5)		5.45	5.45

Tonga's proclamation of sovereignty over the Minerva Reefs, June 1972.

No. C107
Surcharged   **NOVEMBER 1972 INAUGURAL Internal Airmail Nuku'alofa — Vava'u**

1972, Nov.   Litho.

C124	A49	7s on 9s multicolored	1.50	1.50

Inauguration of internal airmail service Nuku-alofa-Vavau, Nov. 1972.

Tongan Bank Notes and Bank Building — AP9

1973, Mar. 30   Litho.

C125	AP9	9s multicolored	.32	.32
C126	AP9	12s ultra & multi	.45	.45
C127	AP9	17s dp car & multi	.62	.62
C128	AP9	50s lt blue & multi	2.25	2.25
C129	AP9	90s multicolored	3.75	3.75
	Nos. C125-C129 (5)		7.39	7.39

Establishment of Bank of Tonga.

Boy Scout Emblem — AP10

1973, June 29   Litho.

C130	AP10	9s silver & multi	.90	.90
C131	AP10	12s silver & multi	1.50	1.50
C132	AP10	14s silver & multi	1.80	1.80
C133	AP10	17s silver & multi	2.00	2.00
C134	AP10	1pa silver & multi	21.00	21.00
	Nos. C130-C134 (5)		27.20	27.20

See note after No. 326.
For surcharges see Nos. C143-C144.

"Resolution" AP11

1973, Oct. 2 Litho.
C135	AP11 9s multicolored	1.10	1.10
C136	AP11 14s multicolored	1.90	1.90
C137	AP11 29s multicolored	5.50	5.50
C138	AP11 38s multicolored	9.00	9.00
C139	AP11 75s multicolored	5.00	5.00
	Nos. C135-C139 (5)	22.50	22.50

Bicentenary of Capt. Cook's arrival.

Nos. 277, C96, C94, C130 and C132
Surcharged in Silver, Violet or Black:
"Commonwealth Games Christchurch 1974"

1973, Dec. 19
C140	A46 7s on 25s multi (S)	.32	.32
C141	AP5 9s on 38s multi (V)	.40	.40
C142	AP5 24s multicolored (B)	1.25	1.25
C143	AP10 29s on 9s multi (V)	1.50	1.50
C144	AP10 40s on 14s multi (B)	2.00	2.00
	Nos. C140-C144 (5)	5.47	5.47

10th British Commonwealth Games, Christchurch, New Zealand, Jan. 24-Feb. 2, 1974. No. C140 is overprinted "AIRMAIL" in black; the silver surcharge and overprint are on black panels.

Parrot of Eua — AP12

1974, Mar. 20 Litho.
C145	AP13 7s multicolored	.25	.25
C146	AP12 9s multicolored	.30	.30
C147	AP12 12s multicolored	.30	.30
C148	AP12 14s multicolored	.45	.45
C149	AP12 17s multicolored	.50	.50
C150	AP12 29s multicolored	.90	.90
C151	AP12 38s multicolored	1.20	1.20
C152	AP12 50s multicolored	1.50	1.50
C153	AP12 75s multicolored	2.25	2.25
	Nos. C145-C153 (9)	7.65	7.65

Printed in rolls of 500. Self-adhesive rose red control number in upper left corner.

Carrier Pigeon Scattering Letters over Tonga — AP13

1974, June 20 Typo.
C154	AP13 14s lt blue & multi	.55	.55
C155	AP13 21s lt blue & multi	.75	.75
C156	AP13 60s lt blue & multi	1.40	1.40
C157	AP13 75s lt blue & multi	2.00	2.00
C158	AP13 1pa lt blue & multi	5.00	5.00
	Nos. C154-C158 (5)	9.70	9.70

Centenary of Universal Postal Union.

Girl Guide Leaders — AP14

1974, Sept. 11 Litho.
C159	AP14 14s blue & multi	.48	.48
C160	AP14 16s blue & multi	.75	.75
C161	AP14 29s blue & multi	1.50	1.50
C162	AP14 31s blue & multi	1.90	1.90
C163	AP14 75s blue & multi	4.00	4.00
	Nos. C159-C163 (5)	8.63	8.63

Girl Guides of Tonga.
For surcharges and overprints see Nos. C190-C191, C193.

Freighter "James Cook" and List of Tongan Merchantmen — AP15

1974, Dec. 11
C164	AP15 9s blue & multi	.40	.30
C165	AP15 14s blue & multi	.60	.45
C166	AP15 17s blue & multi	.70	.55
C167	AP15 60s blue & multi	2.50	2.00
C168	AP15 90s blue & multi	4.00	3.00
	Nos. C164-C168 (5)	8.20	6.30

Establishment of Royal Marine Institute.

Beach AP16

Designs: 12s, 14s, like 9s. 17s, 38s, Surf.

1975, Mar. 11 Litho.
C169	AP16 9s gold & multi	.40	.40
C170	AP16 12s gold & multi	.48	.48
C171	AP16 14s gold & multi	.60	.60
C172	AP16 17s gold & multi	.65	.65
C173	AP16 38s gold & multi	1.50	1.50
	Nos. C169-C173 (5)	3.63	3.63

First meeting of South Pacific area Prime Ministers. See note after No. 226.
For surcharges see Nos. C229, C298.

Women's Discus and Games' Emblem AP17

1975, June 11
C174	AP17 9s multicolored	.40	.40
C175	AP17 12s multicolored	.48	.48
C176	AP17 14s multicolored	.50	.50
C177	AP17 17s black & multi	.75	.75
C178	AP17 90s olive & multi	3.00	3.00
	Nos. C174-C178 (5)	5.13	5.13

5th South Pacific Games, Guam, Aug. 1-10. See note after No. 226.
For surcharges see Nos. C230-C231.

FAO Type of 1975

Designs (FAO Coins): 12s, Coins showing cattle, corn and pig. 14s, Cornucopias; coins showing king, family planning emblem and melons. 25s, Bananas and treasure chest. 50s, King Taufa'ahau. 1pa, Palms.

1975, Sept. 3
C179	A62 12s multicolored	.38	.38
C180	A62 14s blue & multi	.45	.45
C181	A62 25s silver, blk & org	.80	.80
C182	A62 50s car, sil & blk	1.50	1.50
C183	A62 1pa silver & black	3.25	3.25
	Nos. C179-C183 (5)	6.38	6.38

Size of paper backing of 14s: 82x50mm; others 45x45mm. See note after No. 226.

Coin Type of 1975

Coins: 9s, King Taufa'ahau IV, obverse. 12s, Queen Salote III, 75pa reverse and obverse. 14s, 10pa reverse. 38s, King Taufa'ahau IV, 10pa reverse and observe. 1pa, Heads of four constitutional monarchs.

1975, Nov. 4
Light Blue Background
C184	A63 9s black, sil & red	.22	.22
C185	A63 12s gold, blk & grn	.30	.30
C186	A63 14s black, sil & ol	.35	.35
C187	A63 38s gold, blk & org	.90	.90
C188	A63 1pa black, sil & blue	2.25	2.25
	Nos. C184-C188 (5)	4.02	4.02

Size of paper backing of 1pa: 87x78mm, others 65x60mm. See note after No. 226.

Nos. 344-345, C160, C163 Surcharged and Overprinted in Carmine on Silver, Green or Gold

a

b

1976, Feb. 24 Litho.
C189	A58 (a) 12s on 20s (S)	.50	.35
C190	AP14 (b) 14s on 16s (Gr)	.60	.45
C191	AP14 (b) 16s (G)	.65	.50
C192	A58 (b) 38s on 40s (G)	1.50	1.25
C193	AP14 (b) 75s (S)	3.00	2.50
	Nos. C189-193 (5)	6.25	5.05

21st Olympic Games, Montreal, Canada, July 17-Aug. 1. See note after No. 226.

Bicentennial Type of 1976

Signers of Declaration of Independence, Flags of US and Tonga: 12s, Abraham Clark, George Ross, Thomas Lynch, Jr., Charles Carroll, Roger Sherman

(no flags). 14s, Robert Treat Paine, Thomas Jefferson, Thomas McKean, John Adams. 17s, Button Gwinnett, Lewis Morris, Caesar Rodney, Richard Henry Lee. 38s, John Hart, Samuel Huntington, Philip Livingstone, John Morton. 1pa, John Hancock, Joseph Hewes, Josiah Bartlett, John Witherspoon.

1976, May 26
C194	A66 12s buff & multi	.75	.55
C195	A66 14s buff & multi	.80	.62
C196	A66 17s buff & multi	.90	.80
C197	A66 38s buff & multi	3.75	3.25
C198	A66 1pa buff & multi	6.25	5.00
	Nos. C194-C198 (5)	12.45	10.22

See note after No. 381.

Missionary Ship "Triton" — AP18

1976, Aug. 25 Litho.
C199	AP18 9s pink & multi	.22	.22
C200	AP18 12s multicolored	.30	.30
C201	AP18 14s multicolored	.35	.35
C202	AP18 17s buff & multi	.42	.42
C203	AP18 38s multicolored	.75	.75
	Nos. C199-C203 (5)	2.04	2.04

See note after No. 386.
For surcharges see Nos. C234, C294, C299.

Treaty Signing Ceremony, Nukualofa — AP19

1976, Nov. 1
C204	AP19 11s multicolored	.40	.40
C205	AP19 17s multicolored	.55	.55
C206	AP19 18s multicolored	.60	.60
C207	AP19 31s multicolored	1.00	1.00
C208	AP19 39s multicolored	1.25	1.25
	Nos. C204-C208 (5)	3.80	3.80

See note after No. 391.
For surcharges see Nos. C235, C295.

Elizabeth II and Taufa'ahau IV — AP20

1977, Feb. 7
C209	AP20 15s gray & multi	.65	.65
C210	AP20 17s gray & multi	1.00	1.00
C211	AP20 22s gray & multi	32.50	6.50

C212	AP20	31s gray & multi	1.65 1.65
C213	AP20	39s gray & multi	1.65 1.65
		Nos. C209-C213 (5)	37.45 11.45

See note after No. 396.

Coronation Coin — AP21

1977, July 4   Litho.
C214	AP21	11s multicolored	.35 .30
C215	AP21	17s multicolored	.65 .55
C216	AP21	18s multicolored	.75 .60
C217	AP21	39s multicolored	1.50 1.25
C218	AP21	1pa multicolored	3.50 3.00
		Nos. C214-C218 (5)	6.75 5.70

See note after No. 401.
See Nos. CO120-CO122.

Capt. Cook Medal and Journal
Quotation — AP22

1977, Sept. 27
C219	AP22	15s multicolored	.55 .45
C220	AP22	22s multicolored	.90 .60
C221	AP22	31s multicolored	2.00 1.25
C222	AP22	50s multicolored	6.00 3.00
C223	AP22	1pa multicolored	12.00 6.00
		Nos. C219-C223 (5)	21.45 11.30

Bicentenary of Capt. Cook's farewell voyage.
See Nos. CO123-CO125.

Sei and Fin Whales — AP23

1977, Dec. 16
C224	AP23	11s black, vio & blue	.25 .18
C225	AP23	17s black, red & blue	1.10 .85
C226	AP23	18s black, grn & blue	.50 .30
C227	AP23	39s black, brn & blue	1.80 .65
C228	AP23	50s black, mag & blue	1.10 .80
		Nos. C224-C228 (5)	4.75 2.78

Whale protection.
See Nos. CO126-CO128.

Stamps of 1975-77 Surcharged in Various
Colors

1978
C229	AP16	17s on 38s (#C173;Gr)	.90 .90
C230	AP17	17s on 9s (#C174;B)	.90 .90
C231	AP17	17s on 12s (#C175;DBl)	.90 .90
C232	A63	17s on 38s (#C187;B)	.90 .90
C233	A66	17s on 12s (#C194; R on G)	.90 .90
C234	AP18	17s on 9s (#C199; B)	.90 .90
C235	AP19	17s on 18s (#C206; G on Brn)	.90 .90
C236	A66	1pa on 75s (#381; Gr on S)	9.00 9.00
C237	A66	1pa on 38s (#C197; DBl on G)	9.00 9.00
C238	OA15	1pa on 1.10pa (#CO119; S on DBl)	52.00 52.00

Edmonton Games Type of 1978

Design: Canadian Maple leaf and Tongan coat of arms.

1978, May 5   Litho.
C239	A73	17s red & multi	.55 .55
C240	A73	35s red & multi	1.10 1.10
C241	A73	38s red & multi	1.20 1.20
C242	A73	40s red & multi	1.25 1.25
C243	A73	65s red & multi	1.90 1.90
		Nos. C239-C243 (5)	6.00 6.00

See note after No. 423.

King Type of 1978

Design: Head of King Taufa'ahau IV within 6-pointed star.

1978, July 4
C244	A74	11s multicolored	.30 .30
C245	A74	15s multicolored	.45 .45
C246	A74	17s multicolored	.55 .55
C247	A74	39s multicolored	1.20 1.20
C248	A74	1pa multicolored	3.00 3.00
		Nos. C244-C248 (5)	5.50 5.50

See note after No. 226.

Wildlife Type of 1978

1978, Dec. 15   Litho. & Typo.
C249	A77	17s Whale	.90 .90
C250	A77	22s Bat	1.00 1.00
C251	A77	31s Turtle	1.50 1.50
C252	A77	39s Parrot	2.00 2.00
C253	A77	45s like 17s	2.25 2.25
		Nos. C249-C253 (5)	7.65 7.65

Wildlife conservation. See note after No. 226.

Types of 1979

Designs: 15s, like No. 453. 17s, like No. 450. 31s, Rotary emblem. 39s, Ministry and tourism buildings, Bank of Tonga, GPO. 1pa, Dish antenna and map of Tonga.

1979, Feb. 16   Litho.
C254	A79	15s multicolored	.50 .50
C255	A79	17s multicolored	.70 .70
C256	A78	31s vio blue & gold	1.10 1.10
C257	A79	39s multicolored	1.50 1.50
C258	A79	1pa multicolored	3.50 3.50
		Nos. C254-C258 (5)	7.30 7.30

Decade of Progress. Paper backing shows map of Tonga.

Type of 1979

Design: Tongan self-adhesive, free-form stamps.

1979, June 1
C259	A81	15s multicolored	.35 .35
C260	A81	17s multicolored	.45 .45
C261	A81	18s multicolored	.48 .48
C262	A81	31s multicolored	.75 .75
C263	A81	39s multicolored	.95 .95
		Nos. C259-C263 (5)	2.98 2.98

See note after No. 458.

Jet — AP24

1979, Aug. 17
C264	AP24	5s multicolored	.15 .15
C265	AP24	11s multicolored	.25 .25
C266	AP24	14s multicolored	.34 .34
C267	AP24	17s multicolored	.35 .35
C268	AP24	17s multicolored	.45 .45
C269	AP24	18s multicolored	.48 .48
C270	AP24	22s multicolored	.52 .52
C271	AP24	31s multicolored	.75 .75
C272	AP24	39s multicolored	.95 .95
C273	AP24	75s multicolored	1.75 1.75
C274	AP24	1pa multicolored	2.40 2.40
		Nos. C264-C274 (11)	8.39 8.39

Nos. C264-C274 issued in coils; self-adhesive control number in lower left corner of paper backing except on 14s, 18s, 22s, 75s. See note after No. 226.
See Nos. C303-C305.

View Type of 1979

Design: Kao Island. See note after No. 463.

1979, Nov. 23
C275	A82	5s multicolored	.15 .15
C276	A82	15s multicolored	.35 .35
C277	A82	17s multicolored	.45 .45
C278	A82	39s multicolored	.95 .95
C279	A82	75s multicolored	1.75 1.75
		Nos. C275-C279 (5)	3.65 3.65

Friendship Treaty Type of 1980

Design: George Tupou I, Admiral du Bouzet, Adventure. See notes over No. 464 and after No. 468.

1980, Jan. 9   Litho.
C280	A83	15s multicolored	.35 .35
C281	A83	17s multicolored	.45 .45
C282	A83	22s multicolored	.52 .52
C283	A83	31s multicolored	.75 .75
C284	A83	39s multicolored	.95 .95
		Nos. C280-C284 (5)	3.02 3.02

Nos. C259-C263 Surcharged and Overprinted in Black on Silver: "1980 OLYMPIC GAMES," Moscow '80 and Bear Emblems

1980, Apr. 30   Litho.
C285	A81	9s on 15s multi	.22 .22
C286	A81	16s on 17s multi	.38 .38
C287	A81	29s on 18s multi	.70 .70
C288	A81	32s on 31s multi	.78 .78
C289	A81	47s on 39s multi	1.15 1.15
		Nos. C285-C289 (5)	3.23 3.23

22nd Summer Olympic Games, Moscow, July 19-Aug. 3.

Scouting Activities in Rotary
Emblem — AP25

1980, Sept. 30   Litho.
C290	AP25	29s multicolored	1.00 1.00
C291	AP25	32s multicolored	1.10 1.10
C292	AP25	47s multicolored	1.50 1.50
C293	AP25	1pa multicolored	3.25 3.25
		Nos. C290-C293 (4)	6.85 6.85

Boy Scout Jamboree; Rotary International, 75th anniversary. Peelable backing shows map of Tonga.

Nos. C170, C185, C195, C200-C201, C208 Surcharged

1980, Dec. 3   Litho.
C294	AP18	29s on 14s multi	.70 .70
C295	AP19	29s on 39s multi	.70 .70
C296	A63	32s on 12s multi	.78 .78
C297	A66	32s on 12s multi	.78 .78
C298	AP16	47s on 12s multi	1.15 1.15
C299	AP18	47s on 12s multi	1.15 1.15
		Nos. C294-C299 (6)	5.26 5.26

IYD Type of 1981

1981, Sept. 9   Litho.
Size: 25x32mm
C300	A85	29s multicolored	.85 .85
C301	A85	32s multicolored	1.00 1.00
C302	A85	47s multicolored	1.50 1.50
		Nos. C300-C302 (3)	3.35 3.35

Jet Type of 1979

1982, Nov. 17   Litho.
C303	AP24	29s pink & black	.85 .85
C304	AP24	32s pale yel & blk	1.00 1.00
C305	AP24	47s lt brown & blk	1.50 1.50
		Nos. C303-C305 (3)	3.35 3.35

AIR POST SPECIAL DELIVERY

Catalogue values for unused stamps in this section are for Never Hinged items.

Owl — APSD1

1990, Feb. 21   Litho.   Perf. 11½
CE1	APSD1	10pa multi	17.00 17.00

AIR POST OFFICIAL STAMPS

Catalogue values for unused stamps in this section are for Never Hinged items.

Nos. 115, 117-118, 111-113 Overprinted "OFFICIAL AIR MAIL / 1862 / TAU'ATAINA / EMANCIPATION / 1962" in Red
Engr.; Photo. (A35)

1962, Feb. 7   Wmk. 79
CO1	A35	2p ultra	17.50
CO2	A35	5p purple	17.50
CO3	A35	1sh red brown	12.50
CO4	A33	5sh purple & yel	100.00
CO5	A34	10sh black & yel	45.00
CO6	A34	£1 ultra, car & yel	55.00
		Nos. CO1-CO6 (6)	247.50

Centenary of emancipation.

Type of Regular Gold Coin Issue

Design: 15sh, Queen Salote standing, 1-koula coin, obverse.

Litho.; Embossed on Gilt Foil
1963, July 15   Unwmk.   Imperf.
Diameter: 80mm
CO7	A36	15sh black	6.00 6.00

Note after No. 133 also applies to No. CO7.

No. CO7 Surcharged like Regular Issue of 1965 in Black

1965, Mar. 18
CO8	A36	30sh on 15sh black	5.00 5.00

No. 116 Surcharged in Italic Letters Similarly to Nos. C16-C21
Perf. 14½x13½

1966, June 18   Wmk. 79
CO9	A35	10sh on 4p brt green	1.75 1.75
CO10	A35	20sh on 4p brt green	3.50 3.50

Centenary of Tupou College and secondary education.

No. 111 Surcharged in Red: "OFFICIAL / AIRMAIL / ONE PA'ANGA"

1967, Mar. 25   Engr.   Perf. 11½x11
CO11	A33	1p on 5sh purple & yel	3.00 3.00

Type of Regular
Issue Surcharged

The Friendly Islands welcome the United States Peace Corps Official Airmail 30s

1967, Dec. 15   Wmk. 79   Imperf.
CO12	A34	30s on £1 multi	1.10 1.10
CO13	A34	70s on £1 multi	2.50 2.50
CO14	A34	1.50pa on £1 multi	5.25 5.25
		Nos. CO12-CO14 (3)	8.85 8.85

Arrival of US Peace Corps.

No. 113 Surcharged with New Value and "OFFICIAL/AIRMAIL"

1968, Apr. 6   Engr.   Perf. 11x11½
CO15	A34	40s on £1 multi	.90 .90
CO16	A34	60s on £1 multi	1.40 1.40
CO17	A34	1pa on £1 multi	2.75 2.75
CO18	A34	2pa on £1 multi	5.50 5.50
		Nos. CO15-CO18 (4)	10.55 10.55

Type of 1953 Surcharged: "Friendly Islands / Trials / Field & Track / South Pacific / Games / Port Moresby / 1969 / OFFICIAL AIRMAIL"
Wmk. 79

			1968, Dec. 19	Engr.	Imperf.
CO19	A34	20s on £1 grn & multi		.35	.35
CO20	A34	1pa on £1 grn & multi		1.75	1.75

No. 176 Overprinted and Surcharged in Gold on Colored Panels (Green, Emerald, Violet or Lilac) like Nos. 203-209.

Litho.; Embossed on Palladium Foil

1968			Unwmk.
CO21	A38	40s on 2s (G)	1.40 1.40
CO22	A38	60s on 2s (E)	2.00 2.00
CO23	A38	1pa on 2s (V)	4.00 4.00
CO24	A38	2pa on 2s (L)	8.00 8.00
	Nos. CO21-CO24 (4)		15.40 15.40

50th birthday of King Taufa'ahau IV.

Pacific Games Type of Regular Issue
Design: Boxer.

1969, Aug. 13   Litho.   Imperf.
Self-adhesive

CO25	A40	70s gray, red & green	2.50 2.50
CO26	A40	80s gray, red & orange	3.00 3.00

See note after No. 231.

Type of Regular Issue, 1953, Surcharged: "OFFICIAL AIRMAIL / 1969 OIL / SEARCH / 90s" and Oil Derrick Obliterating Old Denomination

1969, Dec. 23   Imperf.

CO27 A34 90s on £1 grn & multi   3.50 3.50

First scientific search for oil in Tonga.

Type of Regular Issue, 1953, Surcharged: "Royal Visit / MARCH / 1970 / OFFICIAL / AIRMAIL" in Black, Violet Blue or Emerald

1970, Mar. 7   Engr.   Wmk. 79

CO28	A34	75s on 1sh	3.00 3.00
CO29	A34	1pa on 1sh (VBl)	4.00 4.00
CO30	A34	1.25pa on 1sh (E)	5.00 5.00
	Nos. CO28-CO30 (3)		12.00 12.00

See note after No. 242.

Type of Regular Issue Surcharged in Black, Red or Emerald

1970, June 4   Wmk. 79   Imperf.

CO31	A33	50s on 5sh (B)	1.75 1.75
CO32	A33	90s on 5sh (R)	3.00 3.00
CO33	A33	1.50pa on 5sh (E)	5.50 5.50
	Nos. CO31-CO33 (3)		10.25 10.25

See note after No. 247.

Type of Regular Issue, 1953, Surcharged in Red and Purple or Black:

1970, Oct. 17   Engr.   Imperf.

CO34	A33	30s on 1½p (B & R)	1.50 1.50
CO35	A33	80s on 5sh (P & R)	4.00 4.00
CO36	A33	90s on 5sh (P & R)	4.75 4.75
	Nos. CO34-CO36 (3)		10.25 10.25

Centenary of the British Red Cross.

Type of Regular Issue, 1953, Surcharged in Black, Purple, Blue or Green

1965 IN MEMORIAM 1970

1971, Jan. 31   Engr.   Imperf.

CO37	A34	20s on 10sh (Bk)	.90 .75
CO38	A34	30s on 10sh (P)	1.50 1.10
CO39	A34	50s on 10sh (Bl)	2.50 1.90
CO40	A34	2pa on 10sh (G)	9.50 7.50
	Nos. CO37-CO40 (4)		14.40 11.25

In memory of Queen Salote (1900-1965).

Type of Regular Issue, 1953, Surcharged in Red and Blue, Black or Purple

1971   Engr.   Wmk. 79   Imperf.
Colors: Green & Yellow

CO41	A33	30s on 5p (R & Bl)	1.90 1.25
CO42	A33	80s on 5p (R & Bk)	3.75 3.25
CO43	A33	90s on 5p (R & P)	4.50 3.25
	Nos. CO41-CO43 (3)		10.15 7.75

See note after No. 272.

Self-adhesive & Imperf.
Starting with Nos. CO44-CO46, all airmail official issues are self-adhesive and imperforate, unless otherwise stated.

Soccer Ball — OA1

1971, July   Litho.   Unwmk.

CO44	OA1	50s multicolored	1.50 1.50
CO45	OA1	90s multicolored	2.75 2.75
CO46	OA1	1.50pa multicolored	4.50 4.50
	Nos. CO44-CO46 (3)		8.75 8.75

4th South Pacific Games, Papeete, French Polynesia, Sept. 8-19.
For overprints see Nos. CO75-CO77.

Watch Type of Air Post Issues

1971, July 20   Litho. and Embossed

CO47	AP6	14s brown & multi	.65 .65
CO48	AP6	21s brown red & multi	.90 .90

Advertisement on peelable paper backing.

Nos. 243-244, 246 Surcharged

INVESTITURE   1971
OFFICIAL   60s   AIRMAIL

Reduced illustration.

Litho.; Gold Embossed

1971, Oct. 30

CO49	A43	60s on 3s multi	2.00 2.00
CO50	A43	80s on 25s multi	2.75 2.75
CO51	A43	1.10pa on 7s multi	3.50 3.50
	Nos. CO49-CO51 (3)		8.25 8.25

First investiture of Tongan Medal of Honor.

"UNICEF" — OA2

1971, Dec.   Litho.

CO52	OA2	70s black & multi	2.75 2.75
CO53	OA2	80s multicolored	3.25 3.25
CO54	OA2	90s multicolored	3.50 3.50
	Nos. CO52-CO54 (3)		9.50 9.50

25th anniversary of UNICEF.
For overprint see No. CO70.

Ship Type of Regular Issue

Design: Map of Merchant Marine routes from Tonga and tanker "Aoniu."

1972, Apr. 14

CO55	A49	20s multicolored	.75 .75
CO56	A49	50s multicolored	1.75 1.75
CO57	A49	1.20pa multicolored	4.50 4.50
	Nos. CO55-CO57 (3)		7.00 7.00

Coin Type of Regular Issue

Design: Coins in center, inscription panel above, date below coins.

Litho.; Embossed on Metallic Foil

1972, July 15

CO58	A50	50s silver & multi	2.50 2.50
CO59	A50	70s silver & multi	3.25 3.25
CO60	A50	1.50pa silver & multi	6.50 6.50
	Nos. CO58-CO60 (3)		12.25 12.25

Watch Type of Air Post Issue

1972, July 20   Litho.; Embossed

CO61	AP6	17s multicolored	.60 .60
CO62	AP6	38s ocher & multi	1.25 1.25

Advertisement on peelable paper backing

Flags and Map of Tonga Islands — OA3

1972, Dec. 9   Litho.

CO63	OA3	25s black & multi	.75 .75
CO64	OA3	75s multicolored	2.25 2.25
CO65	OA3	1.50pa multicolored	4.50 4.50
	Nos. CO63-CO65 (3)		7.50 7.50

Tonga's proclamation of sovereignty over the Minerva Reefs, June 1972.

No. 290 Surcharged in Black, Ultramarine or Green

1973
ESTABLISHMENT BANK OF TONGA 40s OFFICIAL AIRMAIL

1973, Mar. 30   Litho.

CO66	A49	40s on 21s (B)	1.90 1.90
CO67	A49	85s on 21s (U)	3.75 3.75
CO68	A49	1.25pa on 21s (G)	5.00 5.00
	Nos. CO66-CO68 (3)		10.65 10.65

Establishment of Bank of Tonga.

Nos. CO55, CO53 and 247 Overprinted or Surcharged in Silver:

No. CO69: New value, 4 wavy lines, fleur-de-lis and "SILVER JUBILEE/ TONGAN SCOUTING / 1948-1973"

No. CO70: "SILVER / JUBILEE" (vertically), fleur-de-lis and "1948 1973"

No. CO71: Silver surcharge and overprint on dark blue panels "OFFICIAL AIRMAIL / T$1.40," "1948-1973" "SILVER / JUBILEE/ TONGAN / SCOUTING," "1948-1973" in dark blue

---

1973, June 29

CO69	A49	30s on 20s	12.00 12.00
CO70	OA2	80s multi	42.50 30.00
CO71	A43	1.40pa on 50s	90.00 60.00
	Nos. CO69-CO71 (3)		144.50 102.00

25th anniv. of Tongan Boy Scout movement.

Tanker James Cook and Cook Medal — OA4

1973, Oct. 2   Litho.

CO72	OA4	25s multicolored	1.25 1.25
CO73	OA4	80s multicolored	4.00 4.00
CO74	OA4	1.30pa multicolored	6.25 6.25
	Nos. CO72-CO74 (3)		11.50 11.50

Bicentenary of Capt. Cook's arrival.

Nos. CO44-CO46 Overprinted in Dark Blue, Black or Green with Games' Emblems and: "1974 / Commonwealth / Games / Christchurch"

1973, Dec. 19

CO75	OA1	50s multicolored (DBl)	2.00 2.00
CO76	OA1	90s multicolored (B)	4.00 4.00
CO77	OA1	1.50pa multicolored (G)	6.50 6.50
	Nos. CO75-CO77 (3)		12.50 12.50

10th British Commonwealth Games, Christchurch, N.Z., Jan. 24-Feb. 2, 1974.

Peace Dove OA5

1974, Mar. 20   Litho.

CO78	OA5	7s multicolored	.25 .25
CO79	OA5	9s multicolored	.30 .30
CO80	OA5	12s multicolored	.30 .30
CO81	OA5	14s multicolored	.45 .45
CO82	OA5	17s multicolored	.50 .50
CO83	OA5	29s multicolored	.90 .90
CO84	OA5	38s multicolored	1.20 1.20
CO85	OA5	50s multicolored	1.50 1.50
CO86	OA5	75s multicolored	2.25 2.25
	Nos. CO78-CO86 (9)		7.65 7.65

Printed in rolls of 500. Self-adhesive lilac control number in upper left corner.

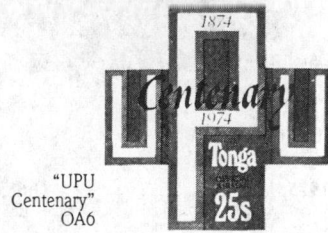

"UPU Centenary" OA6

1974, June 20   Typo.

CO87	OA6	25s red, green & blk	1.25 1.25
CO88	OA6	35s yel, red lil & blk	1.25 1.25
CO89	OA6	70s dp org, blue & blk	2.50 2.50
	Nos. CO87-CO89 (3)		5.00 5.00

Centenary of Universal Postal Union.

Lady Baden-
Powell
OA7

1974, Sept. 11   Litho.
CO90	OA7	45s emerald & multi	2.50	2.50
CO91	OA7	55s emerald & multi	3.50	3.50
CO92	OA7	1pa emerald & multi	5.00	5.00
	Nos. CO90-CO92 (3)		11.00	11.00

Girl Guides of Tonga.
For overprints see Nos. CO105-CO107.

Handshake and Institute's Emblem — OA8

Institute's Emblem and Banknotes — OA9

1974, Dec. 11
CO93	OA8	30s multicolored	1.50	1.00
CO94	OA8	35s multicolored	1.75	1.25
CO95	OA9	80s red & multi	4.00	3.00
	Nos. CO93-CO95 (3)		7.25	5.25

Establishment of Royal Marine Institute.

Arch
and
Palms
OA10

Designs: 75s, 1.25pa, Dawn over lagoon.

1975, Mar. 11   Litho.
CO96	OA10	50s multi	1.65	1.65
CO97	OA10	75s multi	2.50	2.50
CO98	OA10	1.25pa multi	4.25	4.25
	Nos. CO96-CO98 (3)		8.40	8.40

First meeting of South Pacific area Prime Ministers. See note after No. 226.

Track and Games' Emblem — OA11

1975, June 11
CO99	OA11	38s multicolored	1.25	1.25
CO100	OA11	75s multicolored	2.50	2.50
CO101	OA11	1.20pa multicolored	4.00	4.00
	Nos. CO99-CO101 (3)		7.75	7.75

5th South Pacific Games, Guam, Aug. 1-10. See note after No. 226.
For surcharge see No. 418.

Four Constitutional Monarchs — OA12

Litho.; Embossed on Gilt Foil
1975, Nov. 4
CO102	OA12	17s multicolored	.40	.40
CO103	OA12	60s multicolored	1.10	1.10
CO104	OA12	90s multicolored	1.75	1.75
	Nos. CO102-CO104 (3)		3.25	3.25

No. CO90-
CO92
Overprinted in
Carmine on
Blue, Silver or
Gold

1976, Feb. 24   Litho.
CO105	OA7	45s multicolored (B)	1.50	1.25
CO106	OA7	55s multicolored (S)	1.75	1.50
CO107	OA7	1pa multicolored (G)	4.00	3.00
	Nos. CO105-CO107 (3)		7.25	5.75

21st Olympic Games, Montreal, Canada, July 17-Aug. 1. See note after No. 226.

Bicentennial Type of 1976

Signers of Declaration of Independence: 20s, William Paca, Francis Lewis, George Read, Edward Rutledge, Thomas Heyward, Jr. 50s, George Walton, Matthew Thornton, Robert Morris, William Williams, James Smith. 1.15pa, Benjamin Rush, Samuel Adams, Samuel Chase, George Wythe, George Clymer.

1976, May 26
CO108	A66	20s buff & multi	1.10	.90
CO109	A66	50s buff & multi	3.25	2.75
CO110	A66	1.15pa buff & multi	7.50	6.25
	Nos. CO108-CO110 (3)		11.85	9.90

See note after No. 381.

Inside View of Lifuka Chapel — OA13

1976, Aug. 25   Litho.
CO111	OA13	65s multicolored	1.50	1.50
CO112	OA13	85s multicolored	1.60	1.60
CO113	OA13	1.15pa multicolored	2.25	2.25
	Nos. CO111-CO113 (3)		5.35	5.35

See note after No. 386.
For surcharge see No. CO181.

OA14

1976, Nov. 1
CO114	OA14	30s silver & multi	.72	.72
CO115	OA14	60s silver & multi	1.45	1.45
CO116	OA14	1.25pa silver & multi	3.00	3.00
	Nos. CO114-CO116 (3)		5.17	5.17

See note after No. 391.

Flags and Arms of Great Britain and
Tonga — OA15

1977, Feb. 7   Litho.
CO117	OA15	35s multi	12.50	3.25
CO118	OA15	45s multi	1.65	1.65
CO119	OA15	1.10pa multi	4.00	4.00
	Nos. CO117-CO119 (3)		18.15	8.90

See note after No. 396.
For surcharge see No. C238.

Coin Type of Air Post Stamps 1977

Design: Coronation coin, inscriptions in round upper panel.

1977, July 4
CO120	AP21	20s multicolored	.70	.60
CO121	AP21	40s multicolored	1.50	1.20
CO122	AP21	80s multicolored	3.00	2.50
	Nos. CO120-CO122 (3)		5.20	4.30

See note after No. 401.

Capt. Cook Type of Air Post Stamps 1977

Design: Inscription and flying dove.

1977, Sept. 27
CO123	AP22	20s gold & multi	.90	.60
CO124	AP22	55s on 20s multi	5.50	3.00
CO125	AP22	85s on 20s multi	12.00	6.00
	Nos. CO123-CO125 (3)		18.40	9.60

Printed on peelable paper backing showing dark brown replica of entry in Capt. Cook's diary.

Whale Type of Air Post Stamps 1977

Design: Blue whale.

1977, Dec. 16
CO126	AP23	45s multicolored	1.00	.75
CO127	AP23	65s multicolored	1.10	.90
CO128	AP23	85s multicolored	2.00	1.50
	Nos. CO126-CO128 (3)		4.10	3.15

Whale protection.

Games' Emblem and
Athletes
OA16

1978, May 5   Litho.
CO129	OA16	30s red & multi	.90	.90
CO130	OA16	60s red & multi	1.75	1.75
CO131	OA16	1pa red & multi	3.00	3.00
	Nos. CO129-CO131 (3)		5.65	5.65

See note after No. 423.

King Type of 1978

Design: Head of King Taufa'ahau IV on medal.

1978, July 4
CO132	A74	26s multicolored	.75	.75
CO133	A74	85s multicolored	2.50	2.50
CO134	A74	90s multicolored	2.75	2.75
	Nos. CO132-CO134 (3)		6.00	6.00

See note after No. 226.

Wildlife Type of 1978

1978, Dec. 15   Litho. & Typo.
CO150	A77	40s Whale	2.00	2.00
CO151	A77	50s Bat	2.50	2.50
CO152	A77	1.10pa Turtle	5.00	5.00
	Nos. CO150-CO152 (3)		9.50	9.50

Wildlife conservation. See note after No. 226.

Types of 1979

Designs: 38s, Red Cross and star. 74s, like No. 451. 80s, like No. 450.

1979, Feb. 16   Litho.
CO153	A78	38s multicolored	1.40	1.40
CO154	A80	74s multicolored	2.75	2.75
CO155	A79	80s multicolored	3.00	3.00
	Nos. CO153-CO155 (3)		7.15	7.15

Decade of Progress. Paper backing shows map of Tonga.

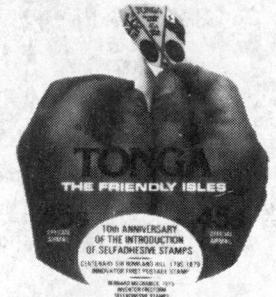

Hands Peeling off No. CO118 — OA17

1979, June 1
CO156	OA17	45s multicolored	1.10	1.10
CO157	OA17	65s multicolored	1.50	1.50
CO158	OA17	80s multicolored	1.90	1.90
	Nos. CO156-CO158 (3)		4.50	4.50

See note after No. 458.
For surcharges see Nos. CO176-CO178.

Parrot — OA18

1979, Aug. 1
CO159	OA18	5s multicolored	.15	.15
CO160	OA18	11s multicolored	.25	.25
CO161	OA18	14s multicolored	.34	.34
CO162	OA18	15s multicolored	.35	.35
CO163	OA18	17s multicolored	.45	.45
CO164	OA18	18s multicolored	.48	.48
CO165	OA18	22s multicolored	.52	.52
CO166	OA18	31s multicolored	.75	.75
CO167	OA18	39s multicolored	.95	.95

CO168 OA18 75s multicolored 1.75 1.75
CO169 OA18 1pa multicolored 2.40 2.40
Nos. CO159-CO169 (11) 8.39 8.39

Nos. CO159-CO169 issued in coils. See note after No. 226.

The 5s exists with denomination in magenta and the leaves behind the bird missing. This seems to be a special printing that was not available for postal purposes.

View Type of 1979

Design: Niuatoputapu and Tafahi Islands. See note after No. 463.

1979, Nov. 23 **Litho.**
CO170 A82 35s multicolored .85 .85
CO171 A82 45s multicolored 1.10 1.10
CO172 A82 1pa multicolored 2.40 2.40
Nos. CO170-CO172 (3) 4.35 4.35

Friendship Treaty Type of 1980

Design: Church. See note after No. 468.

1980, Jan. 9 **Litho.**
CO173 A83 40s multicolored 1.00 1.00
CO174 A83 55s multicolored 1.25 1.25
CO175 A83 1.25pa multicolored 3.00 3.00
Nos. CO173-CO175 (3) 5.25 5.25

Nos. CO156-CO158 Surcharged and Overprinted in Black on Silver: "1980 OLYMPIC GAMES," Moscow '80 and Bear Emblems

1980, Apr. 30 **Litho.**
CO176 OA17 26s on 45s .65 .65
CO177 OA17 40s on 65s .95 .95
CO178 OA17 1.10pa on 80s 2.65 2.65
Nos. CO176-CO178 (3) 4.25 4.25

22nd Summer Olympic Games, Moscow, July 19-Aug. 3.

Tents and Rotary Emblem — OA19

1980, Sept. 30 **Litho.**
CO179 OA19 25s multicolored .80 .80
CO180 OA19 2pa multicolored 6.50 6.50

Boy Scout Jamboree; Rotary Intl., 75th anniv. Peelable backing shows map of Tonga.
For surcharges see Nos. 502-503.

No. CO111 Surcharged

1980, Dec. 3 **Litho.**
CO181 OA13 2pa on 65s multi 4.80 4.80

OFFICIAL STAMPS

Types of Postage Issue of 1892 Overprinted in Carmine **G.F.B.**

Perf. 12x11½

1893, Feb. 13 **Wmk. 62**
O1 A4 1p ultra 9.00 *25.00*
a. Half used as ½p on cover
O2 A5 2p ultra 15.00 *30.00*
O3 A4 4p ultra 32.50 *62.50*
O4 A5 8p ultra 80.00 *175.00*
O5 A5 1sh ultra 87.50 *200.00*
Nos. O1-O5 (5) 224.00 *492.50*

Values are for copies of good color. Faded and discolored copies sell for much less.

The overprinted initials stand for "Gaue Faka Buleaga" (On Government Service).

Nos. O1-O5 with Additional Surcharge Handstamped in Black **1D. ½**

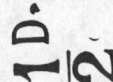

1893
O6 A4 ½p on 1p ultra 12.50 *35.00*
O7 A5 2½p on 2p ultra 17.50 *32.50*
O8 A4 5p on 4p ultra 17.50 *32.50*
O9 A5 7½p on 8p ultra 17.50 *40.00*
O10 A5 10p on 1sh ultra 20.00 *47.50*
Nos. O6-O10 (5) 85.00 *187.50*

Catalogue values for unused stamps in this section, from this point to the end of the section, are for Never Hinged items.

Redrawn Banana and Coconut Types of Regular Issue, 1970, Inscribed "Official Post"

1970, June 9 **Typo.** ***Imperf.***
Self-adhesive
O11 A39 1s yel, blk & dp car .15 .15
O12 A39 2s yel, blk & blue .15 .15
O13 A39 3s yel, blk & brn .15 .15
O14 A39 4s yel, blk & emer .20 .20
O15 A39 5s yel, blk & org .20 .20

Litho.; Embossed on Gilt Foil
O16 A44 6s brown & multi .25 .25
O17 A44 7s brown & multi .30 .30
O18 A44 8s brown & multi .35 .35
O19 A44 9s brown & multi .40 .40
O20 A44 10s brown & multi .45 .45
Nos. O11-O20 (10) 2.60 2.60

Nos. O13, O17-O18 and O20 have self-adhesive control numbers in lower left corner of paper backing.

Types of Regular Issue 1970-72

1972, Sept. 30 **Typo.**
Self-adhesive
O21 A51 1s yel, red & brn .15 .15
O22 A51 2s yel, grn & brn .15 .15
O23 A51 3s yel, emer & brn .15 .15
O24 A51 4s yel, blk & brn .15 .15
O25 A51 5s yellow & brn .16 .16
O26 A44 6s brown & green .18 .18
O27 A44 7s brown & green .20 .20
O28 A44 8s brown & green .25 .25
O29 A44 9s brown & green .30 .30
O30 A44 10s brown & green .35 .35
O31 A52 15s green & ultra .55 .55
O32 A52 20s green & ver .70 .70
O33 A52 25s green & dk brn .85 .85
O34 A52 40s green & org 1.25 1.25
O35 A52 50s green & vio bl 1.50 1.50
Nos. O21-O35 (15) 6.89 6.89

Paper backing is brown on Nos. O26-O35. Nos. O30-O35 have self-adhesive control number in lower left corner, Nos. O21-O29 lower right corner.

Types of Regular Issue 1978

Designs: 1s-5s, Bananas (similar to type A75). 6s-10s, Coconuts. 15s-1pa, Pineapples.

1978, Sept. 29 **Typo.**
O36 A75 1s yellow & lilac .15 .15
O37 A75 2s yellow & brown .15 .15
O38 A75 3s multicolored .15 .15
O39 A75 4s multicolored .15 .15
O40 A75 5s multicolored .15 .15
O41 A76 6s multicolored .15 .15
O42 A76 7s multicolored .15 .15
O43 A76 8s multicolored .16 .16
O44 A76 9s multicolored .18 .18
O45 A76 10s multicolored .20 .20
O46 A76 15s multicolored .28 .28
O47 A76 20s multicolored .40 .40
O48 A76 30s multicolored .55 .55
O49 A76 50s multicolored 1.00 1.00
O50 A76 1pa multicolored 2.00 2.00
Nos. O36-O50 (15) 5.82 5.82

Nos. O36-O50 issued in coils; self-adhesive control numbers on paper backing except on 1s. See note after No. 226.

Type of 1984 Overprinted "OFFICIAL"

1984-85 **Litho.** ***Imperf.***
O52 A103 1s multicolored .15 .15
O53 A103 2s multicolored .15 .15
O54 A103 3s multicolored .15 .15
O55 A103 5s multicolored .15 .15
O56 A103 6s multicolored .15 .15
O57 A103 9s multicolored .15 .15
a. Perf. 14½ ('85) .15 .15
O58 A103 10s multicolored .15 .15
O59 A103 13s multicolored .18 .18
O60 A103 15s multicolored .20 .20
O61 A103 20s multicolored .25 .25
O62 A103 29s multicolored .40 .40
O63 A103 32s multicolored .45 .45
O64 A103 47s multicolored .65 .65
O65 A103 1pa multicolored 1.25 1.25
O66 A103 2pa multicolored 2.75 2.75
O67 A103 5pa multicolored ('85) 7.50 7.50
Nos. O52-O67 (16) 14.68 14.68

Nos. 532-534 Ovptd. "OFFICIAL"

1983, Feb. 22 **Litho.** ***Imperf.***
O68 A96a 29s multicolored *2.50 2.50*
O69 A96a 32s multicolored *2.50 2.50*
O70 A96a 47s multicolored *2.50 2.50*
Nos. O68-O70 (3) *7.50 7.50*

O68-O70 handstamped.

Nos. 564-565, 567-568, 570, 572 and 577 Surcharged "OFFICIAL"

1986, Apr. 16 **Litho.** ***Imperf.***
Self-adhesive
O71 A103 4s on 2s, #564 .15 .15
O72 A103 4s on 13s, #570 .15 .15
O73 A103 42s on 3s, #565 .60 .60
O74 A103 42s on 9s, #568 .60 .60
O75 A103 57s on 6s, #567 .82 .82
O76 A103 57s on 20s, #572 .82 .82
O77 A103 2.50pa on 2pa, #577 3.50 3.50
Nos. O71-O77 (7) 6.64 6.64

Nos. 874, 876-879 Inscribed "POSTAGE & REVENUE" and "OFFICIAL"

1995, Sept. 25 **Litho.** ***Perf. 14***
O78 A155a 10s multicolored .15 .15
O79 A155a 20s multicolored .30 .30
O80 A155a 45s multicolored .70 .70
O81 A155a 60s multicolored .95 .95
O82 A155a 80s multicolored 1.25 1.25
Nos. O78-O82 (5) 3.35 3.35

NIUAFO'OU

Tin Can Island

Catalogue values for all unused stamps in this country are for Never Hinged items.

Nos. 1-62 are self-adhesive stamps on peelable inscribed backing paper and imperforate.

Niuafo'ou Airport Type of Tonga

1983, May 11 **Litho.** ***Imperf.***
1 A97 29s multicolored .60 .60
2 A97 1pa multicolored 2.00 2.00

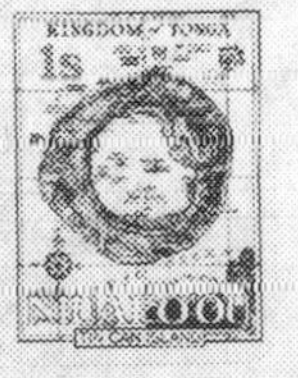

Map of Niuafo'ou — A1

1983, May 11
3 A1 1s buff, blk & red .15 .15
4 A1 2s buff, blk & brt green .15 .15
5 A1 3s buff, blk & brt blue .15 .15
6 A1 3s buff, blk & brn org .15 .15
7 A1 5s buff, blk & deep rose lil .15 .15
8 A1 6s buff, blk & grnsh blue .15 .15
9 A1 9s buff, blk & lt ol grn .18 .18
10 A1 10s buff, blk & brt bl .20 .20
11 A1 13s buff, blk & brt grn .25 .25
12 A1 15s buff, blk & brn org .30 .30
13 A1 20s buff, blk & grnsh blue .40 .40
14 A1 29s buff, blk & deep rose lil .60 .60
15 A1 32s buff, blk & lt ol grn .65 .65
16 A1 47s buff, blk & red .95 .95
Nos. 3-16 (14) 4.43 4.43

See Nos. 19-22.

Tonga No. 520 Surcharged or Ovptd. in Purple or Gold "NIUAFO'OU / Kingdom of Tonga"

1983, May 11
17 A93 1pa on 2pa multi (P) 1.75 1.75
18 A93 2pa multicolored (G) 3.50 3.50

Nos. 17-18 exist se-tenant with label.

Map Type of 1983
Value Typo. in Violet Blue

1983, May 30
19 A1 3s buff & black .15 .15
20 A1 5s buff & black .15 .15
21 A1 32s buff & black .55 .55
22 A1 2pa buff & black 3.50 3.50
Nos. 19-22 (4) 4.35 4.35

The denomination on Nos. 19-22 added like a surcharge and is larger than on Nos. 5-7, 15, covering part of the design.

Nos. 19-22 exist se-tenant with label.

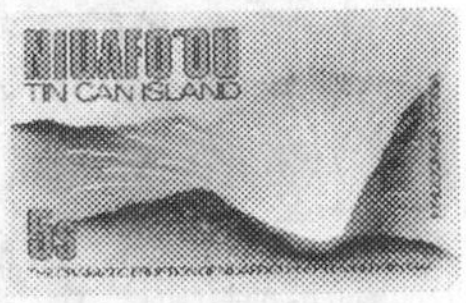

Eruption of Niuafo'ou, Sept. 9, 1946
A2

1983, Sept. 29
23 A2 5s shown .15 .15
24 A2 29s Lava flow .52 .52
25 A2 32s Moving to high ground .55 .55
26 A2 1.50pa Evacuation to Eua 2.75 2.75
Nos. 23-26 (4) 3.97 3.97

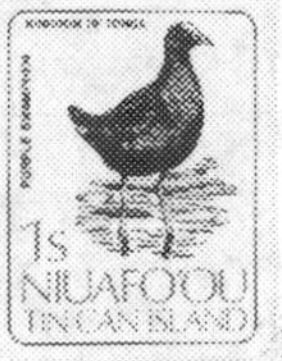

Birds — A3

1983, Nov. 15
27 A3 1s Purple swamphen .15 .15
28 A3 2s White-collared kingfisher .15 .15
29 A3 3s Red-headed parrotfinch .15 .15
30 A3 5s Banded rail .15 .15
31 A3 6s Niuafo'ou megapode .15 .15
32 A3 9s Giant forest honeyeater .16 .16
33 A3 10s Purple swamphen, drinking .18 .18
34 A3 13s Banded rail, diff. .25 .25
35 A3 15s Niuafo'ou megapode, diff. .28 .28

Size: 25x39mm

36 A3 20s like #34 .35 .35
37 A3 29s Red-headed parrotfinch, diff. .52 .52
38 A3 32s White-collared kingfisher, diff. .55 .55
39 A3 47s like #35 .85 .85

Size: 32x42mm

40 A3 1pa like #33 1.75 1.75
41 A3 2pa like #35 3.50 3.50
Nos. 27-41 (15) 9.14 9.14

Nos. 34-36, 39 and 41 horiz.
For surcharges see Nos. 66-73.

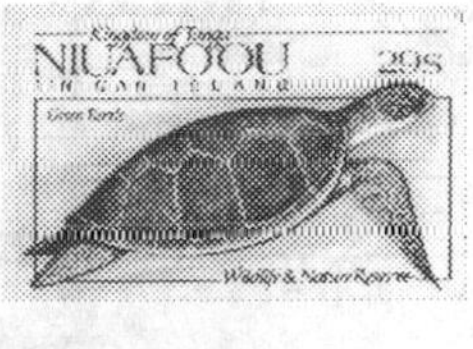

Wildlife
A4

1984, Mar. 7
42 A4 29s Green turtle .52 .52
43 A4 32s Flying fox, vert. .55 .55
44 A4 47s Humpback whale .85 .85
45 A4 1.50pa Niuafo'ou megapode, vert. 2.75 2.75
Nos. 42-45 (4) 4.67 4.67

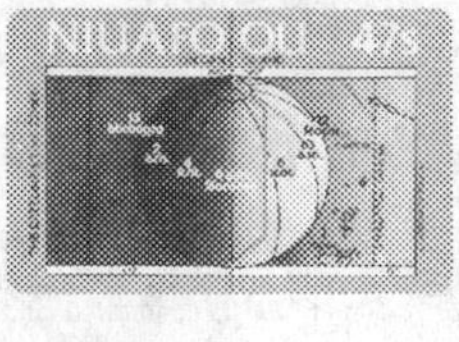

Intl. Date Line, Cent. — A5

1984, Aug. 20
46 A5 47s shown .85 .85
47 A5 2pa Map 3.50 3.50

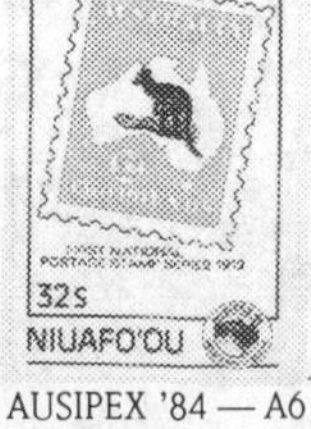

AUSIPEX '84 — A6

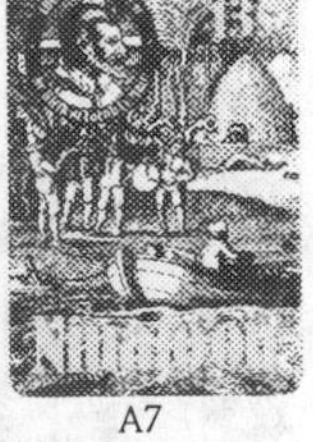

A7

1984, Sept. 17
48 A6 32s Australia No. 15 .55 .55

49 A6 1.50pa No. 10 2.75 2.75

Souvenir Sheet

50 Sheet of 2 3.30 3.30

No. 50 contains two imperf. stamps similar to Nos. 48-49, but with denomination replacing logo. No. 50 without denominations was not valid for postage.

1985, Feb. 20

Jacob Le Maire, 400th Birth Anniv.: 13s, Dutch band entertaining natives. 32s, Natives preparing kava. 47s, Native outrigger canoes. 1.50pa, Le Maire's ship at anchor.

51 A7 13s multicolored .24 .24
52 A7 32s multicolored .55 .55
53 A7 47s multicolored .85 .85
54 A7 1.50pa multicolor 2.75 2.75
Nos. 51-54 (4) 4.39 4.39

Souvenir Sheet

55 A7 1.50pa multicolored 2.75 2.75

Mail Ships — A8

1985, May 22 *Imperf.*

56 A8 9s Ysabel, 1902 .16 .16
a. Perf. 14 .16 .16
57 A8 13s Tofua I, 1908 .24 .24
a. Perf. 14 .24 .24
58 A8 47s Mariposa, 1934 .85 .85
a. Perf. 14 .85 .85
59 A8 1.50pa Matua, 1936 2.75 2.75
a. Perf. 14 2.75 2.75
Nos. 56-59 (4) 4.00 4.00
Nos. 56a-59a (4) 4.00 4.00

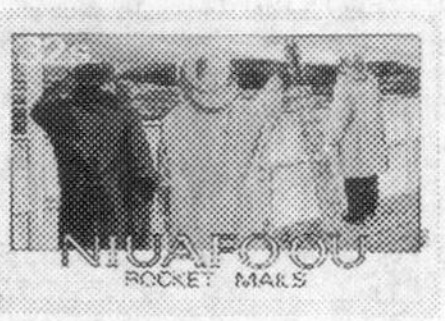

Rocket Mail — A9

Designs: 32s, Preparing to fire rocket. 42s, Rocket airborne. 57s, Captain watching rocket's progress. 1.50pa, Islanders reading mail.

1985, Nov. 5

60 A9 32s multicolored .55 .55
61 A9 42s multicolored .75 .75
62 A9 57s multicolored 1.00 1.00
63 A9 1.50pa multicolored 2.75 2.75
Nos. 60-63 (4) 5.05 5.05

Self-adhesive stamps discontinued.

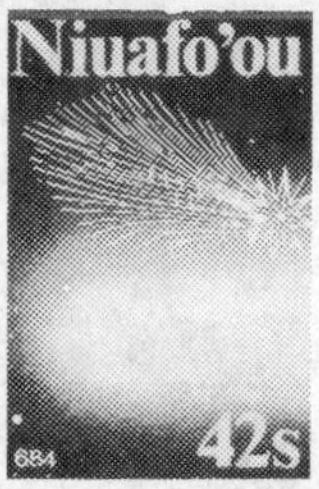

Halley's Comet — A10

Nos. 64, 65: a, Drawing of Comet in 684. b, Comet shown in Bayeux Tapestry, 1066. c, Edmond Halley. d, Comet, 1910. e, Infrared photography, 1986.

1986, Mar. 26 *Perf. 14*

64 A10 42s Strip of #a.-e. 3.75 3.75
65 A10 57s Strip of #a.-e. 5.00 5.00

Nos. 32-39 Surcharged in Blue

42s

X X

1986, Apr. 16 *Imperf.*

Self-Adhesive

66 A3 4s on 9s #32 .15 .15
67 A3 4s on 10s #33 .15 .15
68 A3 42s on 13s #34 .75 .75
69 A3 42s on 15s #35 .75 .75
70 A3 57s on 29s #37 1.00 1.00
71 A3 57s on 32s #38 1.00 1.00
72 A3 2.50pa on 20s #36 4.50 4.50
73 A3 2.50pa on 47s #39 4.50 4.50
Nos. 66-73 (8) 12.80 12.80

Placement of surcharge varies.

AMERIPEX '86 Type of Tonga

1986, May 22 *Perf. 14*

74 A117 57s Surveying 1.00 1.00
75 A117 1.50pa Agriculture 2.75 2.75
a. Souv. sheet of 2, #74-75, imperf. 4.00 4.00

Peace Corps in Tonga, 25th anniv.

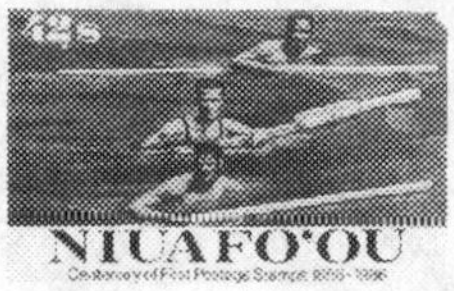

First Tongan Postage Stamps, Cent. A11

1986, Aug. 27

76 A11 42s Swimmers with mail .75 .75
77 A11 57s Loading tin can mail into canoe 1.00 1.00
78 A11 1pa Rocket mail 1.75 1.75
79 A11 2.50pa Outrigger canoe 4.50 4.50
Nos. 76-79 (4) 8.00 8.00

Souvenir Sheet

80 A11 2.50pa Outrigger canoe, diff. 4.75 4.75

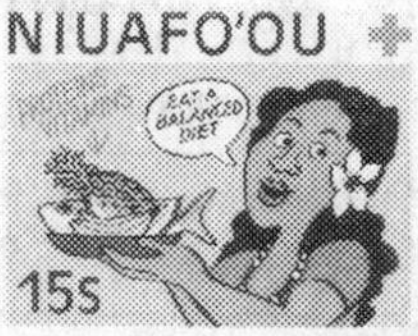

Red Cross — A12

1987, Mar. 11 *Perf. 14x14½*

81 A12 15s Balanced diet .25 .25
82 A12 42s Post-natal care .75 .75
83 A12 1pa Insects spread disease 1.75 1.75
84 A12 2.50pa Fight against drugs, alcohol, smoking 4.50 4.50
Nos. 81-84 (4) 7.25 7.25

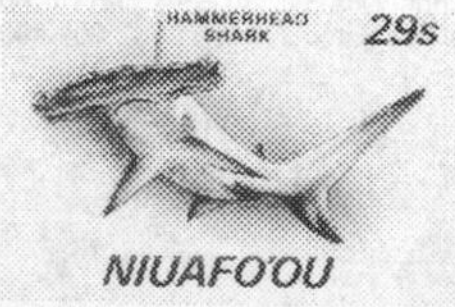

Sharks A13

1987, Apr. 29 *Perf. 14*

85 A13 29s Hammerhead .52 .52
86 A13 32s Tiger .55 .55
87 A13 47s Gray nurse .85 .85
88 A13 1pa Great white 1.75 1.75
Nos. 85-88 (4) 3.67 3.67

Souvenir Sheet

89 A13 2pa Shark attack 3.50 3.50

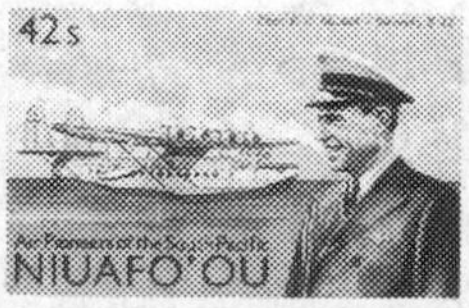

Aviators and Aircraft A14

Designs: 42s, Capt. E. C. Musick and Sikorsky S-42. 57s, Capt. J.W. Burgess and Shorts S-30. 1.50pa, Sir Charles Kingsford Smith and Fokker F.VIIb-3m. 2pa, Amelia Earhart and Lockheed Electra 10A.

1987, Sept. 2

90 A14 42s multicolored .75 .75
91 A14 57s multicolored 1.00 1.00
92 A14 1.50pa multicolored 2.75 2.75
93 A14 2pa multicolored 3.50 3.50
Nos. 90-93 (4) 8.00 8.00

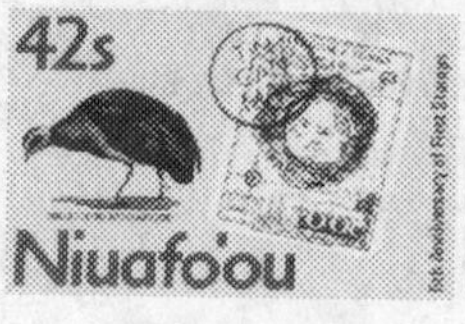

First Niuafo'ou Postage Stamps, 5th Anniv. A15

Designs: 42s, 57s, Niuafo'ou megapode, No. 15. 1pa, 2pa, Concorde, No. 1.

1988, May 18

94 A15 42s multicolored .75 .75
95 A15 57s multicolored 1.00 1.00
96 A15 1pa multicolored 1.75 1.75
97 A15 2pa multicolored 3.50 3.50
Nos. 94-97 (4) 7.00 7.00

#96-97, Niuafo'ou Airport Inauguration, 5th anniv.

Settlement of Australia, Bicent. Type of Tonga Miniature Sheet

Designs: a, Arrival of First Fleet, Sydney Cove, Jan. 1788. b, Aborigines. c, Early settlement. d, Soldier on guard. e, Herd of sheep. f, Horseman. g, Locomotive, kangaroos. h, Train, kangaroos. i, Flying doctor service. j, Cricket players. k, Stadium, batsman guarding wicket. l, Sydney Harbor Bridge, Opera House.

1988, July 11 *Perf. 13½*

98 A128 42s Sheet of 12, #98a-98 l 9.00 9.00

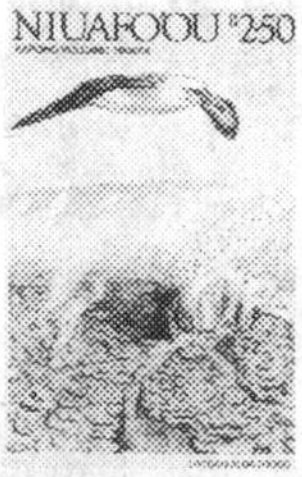

Polynesian Islands — A16

Birds and landmarks: 42s, Audubon's shearwater, blowholes at Houma, Tonga. 57s, Kiwi, Akaroa Harbor, New Zealand. 90s, Red-tailed tropicbird, Rainmaker Mountain, Samoa. 2.50pa, Laysan albatross, Kapoho Volcano, Hawaii.

1988, Aug. 18 *Perf. 14*

99 A16 42s multicolored .75 .75
100 A16 57s multicolored 1.00 1.00
101 A16 90s multicolored 1.65 1.65
102 A16 2.50pa multicolored 4.50 4.50
Nos. 99-102 (4) 7.90 7.90

Miniature Sheet

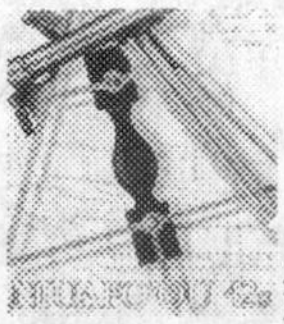

Mutiny on the Bounty, Bicent. — A17

Designs: a, Sextant. b, William Bligh. c, Royal Navy lieutenant. d, Midshipman. e, Contemporary newspaper, Tahitian girl. f, Breadfruit. g, *Mutiny on the Bounty* excerpt, pistol grip. h, Pistol barrel, illustration of Bounty castaways. i, Tahitian girl, newsprint. j, Bligh's and Fletcher Christian's signatures. k, Christian, Pitcairn Island. l, Tombstone of John Adams.

1989, Apr. 28 *Perf. 13½*

103 A17 42s Sheet of 12, #a.-l. 9.00 9.00

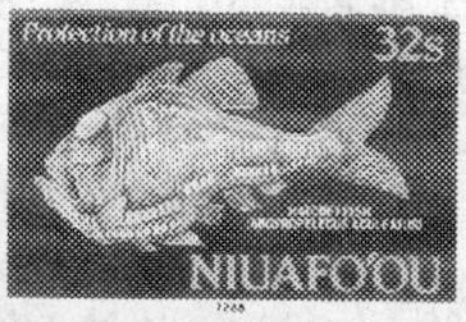

Marine Conservation — A18

1989, June 2 *Perf. 14*

104 A18 32s Hatchet fish .55 .55
105 A18 42s Snipe eel .75 .75
106 A18 57s Viper fish 1.00 1.00
107 A18 1.50pa Angler fish 2.75 2.75
Nos. 104-107 (4) 5.05 5.05

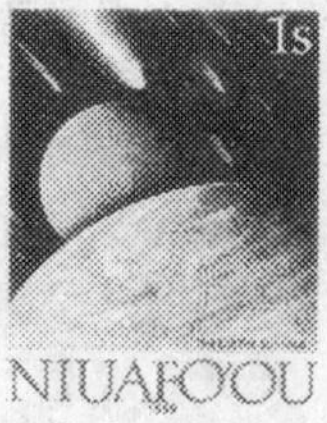

Evolution of the Earth — A19

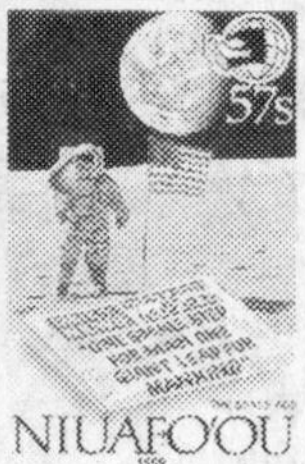

A20

Designs: 1s, Formation of the crust. 2s, Cross-section of crust. 5s, Volcanism. 10s, Surface cools. 13s, Gem stones. 15s, Oceans form. 20s, Mountains develop. 32s, River valley. 42s, Silurian Era plant life. 50s, Trilobites, Cambrian Era marine life. 45s, Early marine life. 57s, Carboniferous Era forest, coal seams. 60s, Dinosaurs feeding. 80s, Dinosaurs fighting. 1pa, Carboniferous Era insect, amphibians. 1.50pa, Stegosaurus, Jurassic Era. Birds and mammals, Jurassic Era. 5pa, Hominid family, Pleistocene Era. 10pa, Mammoth, saber tooth tiger.

1989-93 *Perf. 14½*

108 A19 1s multicolored .15 .15
109 A19 2s multicolored .15 .15
110 A19 5s multicolored .15 .15
111 A19 10s multicolored .18 .18
111A A19 13s multicolored .22 .22
112 A19 15s multicolored .28 .28
113 A19 20s multicolored .35 .35
114 A19 32s multicolored .55 .55
115 A19 42s multicolored .75 .75
115A A19 45s multicolored .78 .78
116 A19 50s multicolored .90 .90
117 A19 57s multicolored 1.00 1.00
117A A19 60s multicolored 1.05 1.05
117B A19 80s multicolored 1.40 1.40

Size: 26x40mm

Perf. 14

118 A19 1pa multicolored 1.75 1.75
119 A19 1.50pa multicolored 2.75 2.75
120 A19 2pa multicolored 3.50 3.50
121 A19 5pa multicolored 9.00 9.00

Perf. 14

121A A19 10pa multicolored 18.00 18.00
Nos. 108-121A (19) 42.91 42.91

Issued: 1s-10s, 15s-42s, 50s-57s, 6/6/89; 13s, 45s, 60s, 80s, 5/3/93; 10pa, 9/14/93; others, 8/1/89.

1990, Nov. 17 *Perf. 14*

122 A20 57s multicolored 1.00 1.00

Miniature Sheet

Nos. 108-121 with UPU emblem: Nos. 123a-123e, #108-112, Nos. 123f-123j, #113-117, Nos. 123k-123n, #118-121.

123 Sheet of 15, #a.-n., 122 11.50 11.50
a.-e. A19 32s any single, perf. 14½ .55 .55
f.-j. A19 42s any single, perf. 14½ .75 .75
k.-n. A19 57s any single, perf. 14 1.00 1.00

Miniature Sheet

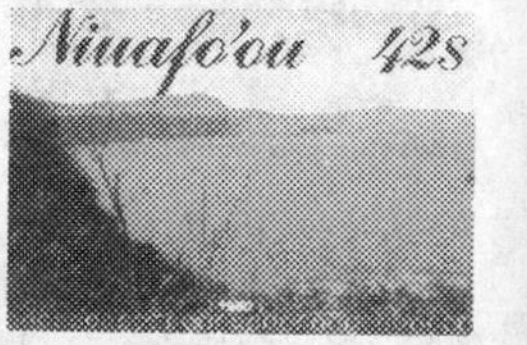

Lake Vai Lahi, Niuafo'ou A21

Designs: a, d, Left part of lake. b, e, Small islands in center of lake. c, f, Small islet in right side of lake.

1990, Apr. 4 *Perf. 14*

124 Sheet of 6 7.75 7.75
a.-c. A21 42s any single .75 .75
d.-f. A21 1pa any single 1.75 1.75

Nos. 124a-124c and 124d-124f printed in continuous designs.

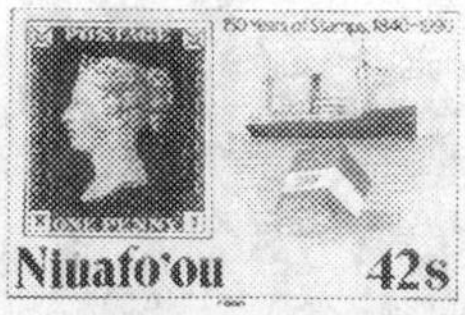

Penny Black, 150th Anniv. A22

Tin Can Mail and: 42s, Penny Black. 57s, US #2. 75s, Western Australia #1. 2.50pa, Cape of Good Hope #178.

1990, May 1

125 A22 42s multicolored .75 .75
126 A22 57s multicolored 1.00 1.00
127 A22 75s multicolored 1.25 1.25
128 A22 2.50pa multicolored 4.50 4.50
Nos. 125-128 (4) 7.50 7.50

Polynesian Whaling — A23

Designs: 15s, Whale surfacing. 42s, Whale diving beneath outrigger canoe. 57s, Tail flukes. 1pa, 2pa, Old man, two whales.

1990   **Perf. 11½**
129	A23	15s multicolored	.25	.25
130	A23	42s multicolored	.75	.75
131	A23	57s multicolored	1.00	1.00
132	A23	2pa multicolored	3.50	3.50
		Nos. 129-132 (4)	5.50	5.50

Souvenir Sheet
Perf. 14x14½
133	A23	1pa multicolored	1.75	1.75

Issue dates: No. 133, Sept. 4, others, June 6.
The entire souvenir sheet, No. 133, shows a modified No. 132. The 37½x30½mm stamp shows the two whales.
For surcharges see Nos. 139, 174-178.

UN Development Program, 40th Anniv. — A24

Designs: No. 134a, Agriculture and fisheries. No. 134b, Education. No. 135a, Health care. No. 135b, Communications.

1990, Oct. 25   **Perf. 14**
134	A24	57s Pair, #134a-134b	2.00	2.00
135	A24	2.50pa Pair, #135a-135b	9.00	9.00

Charting of Niuafo'ou, Bicent. — A24a

Designs: No. 136a, 32s, The Bounty. b, 42s, Chart showing location of Niuafo'ou and Tonga. c, 57s, The Pandora.
No. 137a, 2pa, Capt. Edwards of the Pandora. b, 2pa, Capt. Bligh of the Bounty.

1991, July 25   **Litho.**   **Perf. 14½**
136	A24a	Strip of 3, #a.-c.	2.00	2.00

Souvenir Sheet
137	A24a	Sheet of 2, #a.-b.	7.50	7.50

No. 133 Surcharged in Dark Blue Violet

X X

1991 ORNITHOLOGICAL AND
SCIENTIFIC EXPEDITION.

T$1

1991, July 31   **Litho.**   **Perf. 14x14½**
139	A23	1pa on 1pa #133	1.75	1.75

Ceresium
Unicolor — A25

1991, Sept. 11   **Perf. 14½x14**
140	A25	42s Larva stage	.75	.75
141	A25	57s Mature beetle	1.00	1.00
142	A25	1.50pa Larva stage, diff.	2.75	2.75
143	A25	2.50pa Mature beetle on tree limb	4.50	4.50
		Nos. 140-143 (4)	9.00	9.00

Christmas
A26

Legend of the origin of the coconut tree: 15s, No. 146a, Heina bathing in lake being watched by eel. 42s, No. 146b, Heina weeping over plant growing from eel's grave. No. 146c, 1.50pa, Heina's boy climbing coconut tree. No. 146d, 3pa, "Eel's face" on coconut.

1991, Nov. 12   **Litho.**   **Perf. 14½**
144	A26	15s multicolored	.22	.22
145	A26	42s multicolored	.65	.65
146	A26	Sheet of 4, #a.-d.	11.00	11.00
		Nos. 144-146 (3)	11.87	11.87

Nos. 144-145 inscribed "Christmas Greetings 1991." No. 146 contains Nos. 144-145, 146a-146d inscribed "A Love Story."

Miniature Sheet

Discovery of America,
500th Anniv. — A27

Designs: a, Columbus. b, Queen Isabella, King Ferdinand. c, Columbus being blessed by Abbot of Palos. d, Men in boat, 15th century compass. e, Wooden traverse, wind rose, Nina. f, Bow of Santa Maria. g, Stern of Santa Maria. h, Pinta. i, Two men raising cross. j, Explorers, natives. k, Columbus kneeling before King and Queen. l, Columbus' second coat of arms.

1992, Apr. 28   **Litho.**   **Perf. 13½**
147	A27	57s Sheet of 12, #a.-l.	12.50	12.50

Miniature Sheet

World War II in Pacific, 50th Anniv. A28

Newspaper headline and: a, Battleship ablaze at Pearl Harbor. b, Destroyed aircraft. c, Japanese A6M Zero fighter. d, Declaration of war, Pres. Franklin D. Roosevelt. e, Japanese T95 tank. Gen. MacArthur. f, Japanese naval ensign. g, Douglas SBD Dauntless dive bomber, Admiral Nimitz. g, Bren gun, Gen. Sir Thomas Blamey. h, Australian mortar crew, Kokoda Trail. i, US battleship, Maj. Gen. Julian C. Smith. j, Aircraft carrier USS Enterprise. k, American soldier, flag, Maj. Gen. Curtis Lemay. l, B-29 bomber, surrender ceremony on USS Missouri in Tokyo bay.

1992, May 12   **Perf. 14**
148	A28	42s Sheet of 12, #a.-l.	9.25	9.25

King Taufa'ahau IV, 25th Anniv. of Coronation A29

Designs: 45s, 2pa, King, Queen Halaevalu during coronation. No. 150a, King, Tongan national anthem. b, Extract from investiture ceremony. c, Tongan national anthem, singers.

1992, July 4   **Perf. 13½x13**
149	A29	45s multicolored	.85	.85

Size: 51x38mm
Perf. 12½x12
150	A29	80s Strip of 3, #a.-c.	4.50	4.50
151	A29	2pa multicolored	3.65	3.65
		Nos. 149-151 (3)	9.00	9.00

Megapodius Pritchardii — A30

1992, Sept. 15   **Litho.**   **Perf. 14**
152	A30	45s Female & male	.68	.68
153	A30	60s Female with egg	.90	.90
154	A30	80s Chick	1.20	1.20
155	A30	1.50pa Head of male	2.25	2.25
		Nos. 152-155 (4)	5.03	5.03

World Wildlife Fund.

First Niuafo'ou
Postage
Stamps, 10th
Anniv. — A31

1993, May 3   **Litho.**   **Perf. 14x14½**
156	A31	60s Nos. 4, 117A	1.05	1.05
157	A31	80s Nos. 7, 117B	1.40	1.40

Aviation in Niuafo'ou, 10th Anniv. — A32

Airplanes of: 1pa, South Pacific Island Airways. 2.50pa, Friendly Islands Airways.

1993, May 3
158	A32	1pa multicolored	1.75	1.75
159	A32	2.50pa multicolored	4.35	4.35

King's 75th Birthday Type of Tonga
King and: 45s, 2pa, Patrol boat Pangai.
No. 161a, Sporting events. b, Aircraft and communications. c, Musical instruments.

1993, July 1   **Perf. 13x13½**
160	A167	45s multicolored	.80	.80

Perf. 12x12½
Size: 37x48mm
161	A167	80s Strip of 3, #a.-c.	4.25	4.25
162	A167	2pa multicolored	3.50	3.50
		Nos. 160-162 (3)	8.55	8.55

Wildlife — A33

Designs: a, Two parrots. b, Bird with fish. c, Butterfly, beetle. d, Birds, dragonfly, butterfly. e, Bird in flight, two on ground.

1993, Aug. 10   **Litho.**   **Perf. 14**
163	A33	60s Strip of 5, #a.-e.	5.50	5.50

No. 163 is a continuous design.

Beetles
A35

1994, Mar. 15   **Litho.**   **Perf. 14**
168	A35	60s Scarabaeidea	1.10	1.10
169	A35	80s Coccinellidea	1.40	1.40
170	A35	1.50pa Cerambycidea	2.50	2.50
171	A35	2.50pa Pentatomidae	4.50	4.50
		Nos. 168-171 (4)	9.50	9.50

A36   A37

Sailing Ships: a, Stern of HMS Bounty. b, Bow of HMS Bounty. c, HMS Pandora. d, Whaling ship. e, Trading schooner.

1994, June 21   **Litho.**   **Perf. 14**
172	A36	80s Strip of 5, #a.-e.	7.00	7.00

No. 172 is a continuous design.

1994, Sept. 21   **Litho.**   **Perf. 14½**

1946 Volcanic Eruption: a, Blue-crowned lorikeet, lava flow. b, Black Pacific ducks, lava flow. c, Megapodes, palm trees (b). d, White-tailed tropic birds, people evacuating island (c). e, People wading out to sailboats, Pacific reef heron.

173	A37	80s Strip of 5, #a.-e.	7.50	7.50

No. 173 is a continuous design.

Nos. 129-133
Surcharged in Blue

1995, June 30   **Litho.**   **Perf. 11½**
174	A23	60s on 42s #130	1.10	1.10
175	A23	80s on 15s #129	1.50	1.50
176	A23	80s on 57s #131	1.65	1.65
177	A23	2pa on #132	4.00	4.00
		Nos. 174-177 (4)	8.25	8.25

Souvenir Sheet
178	A23	1.50pa on 1pa #133	3.00	3.00

Size and location of surcharge varies. Surcharge on No. 178 includes "COME WHALE WATCHING / IN THE SOUTH PACIFIC."

Victory in the Pacific Type of Tonga
Nos. 179, 180: a, Soldier holding rifle. b, Soldier aiming rifle, tank. c, Front of tank. d, Troops coming off boat, firing weapons. e, Troops on beach.

1995, Aug. 1   **Litho.**   **Perf. 14x14½**
179	A177	60s Strip of 5, #a.-e.	6.25	6.25
180	A177	80s Strip of 5, #a.-e.	7.50	7.50

Nos. 179-180 are continuous designs and were issued together in sheets containing 10 stamps.

Singapore '95 Type of Tonga
Designs, vert: No. 181a, 45s, like #117A. b, 60s, like #117B.
2pa, Plesiosaurus.

1995, Sept. 1   **Litho.**   **Perf. 12**
181	A178	Pair, #a.-b.	1.65	1.65

Souvenir Sheet
182	A178	2pa multicolored	3.25	3.25

Beijing Intl. Coin & Stamp Show '95
Type of Tonga
Souvenir Sheet
Design: 1.40pa, The Great Wall of China.

1995, Sept. 14   **Perf. 14½**
183	A179	1.40pa multicolored	2.25	2.25

End of World War II, UN, 50th Anniv.
Type of Tonga
No. 184: a, London blitz. b, UN emblem, "50." c, Concorde.
No. 185: a, Building of Siam-Burma Railway by Allied prisoners of war. b, Like #184b. c, Japanese bullet train.

VISIT SOUTH PACIFIC TANK '95 60

1995, Oct. 20 Litho. *Perf. 14*

184 A180 60s Strip of 3, #a.-c. 2.75 2.75
185 A180 80s Strip of 3, #a.-c. 3.75 3.75

Nos. 184b, 185b are 23x31mm.

TRANSVAAL

tran(t)s-'väl

(South African Republic)

LOCATION — Southern Africa
GOVT. — A former British Colony
AREA — 110,450 sq. mi.
POP. — 1,261,736 (1904)
CAPITAL — Pretoria

Transvaal was known as the South African Republic until 1877 when it was occupied by the British. The republic was restored in 1884 and continued until 1900 when it was annexed to Great Britain and named "The Transvaal."

Although issued by an independent state, the stamps of the South African Republic are included in this section in accord with established philatelic practice.

12 Pence = 1 Shilling
20 Shillings = 1 Pound

Most unused stamps between Nos. 1-96, 119-122 and 136-137 were issued with gum, but do not expect gum on scarcer stamps as few examples retain their original gum. In many cases removal of the remaining gum may enhance the preservation of the stamps. Otherwise, values for unused stamps are for examples with original gum as defined in the catalogue introduction.

Very fine imperforate stamps will have adequate to large margins. However, rouletted stamps are valued as partly rouletted, with straight edges, and rouletted just into the design, as the rouletting methods were quite inaccurate.

First Republic

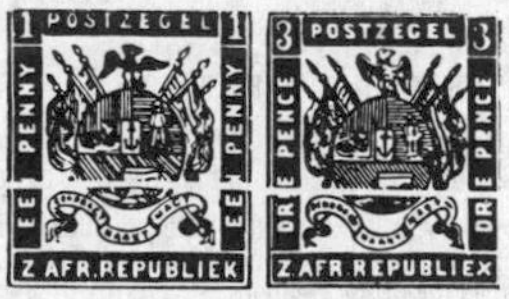

Coat of Arms
A1 A2

Mecklenburg Printings
By Adolph Otto, Gustrow
Fine Impressions
Thin Paper

A1 has spread wings on eagle.

1869 Unwmk. *Imperf.*

1 A1 1p brown lake 350.00
a. 1p red 350.00 350.00
2 A1 6p ultra 125.00 *150.00*
3 A1 1sh dark green 450.00 450.00
a. Tete beche pair *10,000.*

Rouletted 15½, 16

4 A1 1p red 70.00
a. 1p brown lake 65.00
5 A1 6p ultra 65.00
6 A1 1sh blue green 75.00 *125.00*
a. 1sh yellow green 95.00
b. 1sh deep green 125.00

Nos. 1-6 were printed from 2 sets of plates, differing in the spacing between the stamps.

See Nos. 9-24, 26-33, 35-36, 38-39, 41-42, 43-49, 119, 122. For overprints see Nos. 53-61, 63-66, 68-72, 75-78, 81-83, 86-87, 90-91, 94.

1871-74

7 A2 3p lilac 75.00 75.00
a. 3p violet 75.00 75.00
8 A2 6p brt ultra ('74) 55.00 37.50
a. Half used as 3p on cover —

So-called reprints and trial impressions of the stamps in types A1 and A2 are counterfeits. This applies to Nos. 1-96. All copies in other than the issued colors are known to be forgeries. Many forgeries exist in colors duller or lighter than he genuine stamps.

In forgeries of type A1, all values, the "D" of "EENDRAGT" is not noticeably larger than the other letters and does not touch the top of the ribbon. In type A1 genuine stamps, the "D" is large and touches the ribbon top. The eagle's eye is a dot and its face white on the genuine stamps; the eye is a loop or blob attached to the beak, and the beak is strongly hooked, on the forgeries. Many forgeries of the 1sh have the top line of the ribbon broken above "EENDRAGT."

Forgeries of type A2 usually can be detected only by color.

A sharply struck cancellation of a numeral in three rings is found on many of these forgeries. The similar genuine cancellation is always roughly or heavily struck.

Tete beche pairs of the 6p and 1sh are known both genuine and counterfeit.

See Nos. 25, 34, 437, 40, 42B, 120-121. For overprints see Nos. 50-52, 62, 67, 73-74, 79-80, 84-85, 88-89, 92-93, 95-96.

Local Printings
(A) By M. J. Viljoen, Pretoria
Poor Impressions,
Overinked and Spotted
Thin Soft Paper

1870 *Imperf.*

9 A1 1p carmine 55.00
a. 1p rose red 70.00
b. 1p pink 60.00
10 A1 6p dull ultra 200.00 100.00
a. Tete beche pair *6,500.*

Rouletted 15½, 16

11 A1 1p carmine 500.00 225.00
a. Rouletted 6½ 750.00
12 A1 6p dull ultra 200.00 125.00

Hard Paper, Thick to Medium
Imperf

13 A1 1p carmine 55.00 55.00
14 A1 6p ultra
15 A1 1sh gray green 70.00 70.00
a. 1sh dark green *650.00* *300.00*
b. Tete beche pair *8,250.* *6,500.*
c. Half used as 6p on cover

Rouletted 15½, 16

16 A1 1p carmine 45.00 45.00
a. 1p light carmine 55.00 40.00
17 A1 6p ultra 70.00 60.00
a. Tete beche pair *6,500.* *4,750.*
18 A1 1sh dark green 80.00 60.00
a. 1sh gray green 300.00 165.00

Copies of Nos. 16 to 18 are sometimes so heavily inked as to be little more than blots of color.

(B) By J. P. Borrius, Potchefstroom
Clearer Impressions Though Often Overinked
Thick Porous Paper

1870 *Imperf.*

19 A1 1p black 110.00 95.00
20 A1 6p indigo 250.00

Rouletted 15½, 16

21 A1 1p black 14.00 17.50
22 A1 6p gray blue 80.00 55.00
a. 6p indigo 100.00 60.00
b. 6p bright ultra

Thin Transparent Paper

23 A1 1p black 150.00 *450.00*
24 A1 1p brt carmine 90.00 45.00
a. 1p deep carmine 90.00 45.00
25 A2 3p gray lilac 70.00 35.00
26 A1 6p ultra 90.00 40.00
27 A1 1sh yellow green 70.00 45.00
a. 1sh deep green 70.00 45.00
b. Half used as 6p on cover —

Thick Soft Paper

28 A1 1p dull rose 325.00 65.00
a. 1p brown rose 350.00 75.00
b. Printed on both sides
29 A1 6p dull blue 75.00 40.00
a. 6p bright blue 140.00 40.00
b. 6p ultramarine 150.00 50.00
c. Rouletted 6½
30 A1 1sh yellow green 700.00 550.00

The paper of Nos. 28 to 30 varies considerably in thickness.

(C) By P. Davis & Son, Natal
Thin to Medium Paper

1874 *Perf. 12½*

31 A1 1p red 75.00 40.00
a. 1p brownish red 75.00 40.00
32 A1 6p deep blue 90.00 45.00
a. 6p blue 90.00 45.00
b. Horiz. pair, imperf. between

(D) By the Stamp Commission, Pretoria
Pelure Paper

1875-76 *Imperf.*

33 A1 1p pale red 35.00 12.50
a. 1p orange red 35.00 12.50
b. 1p brown red 40.00 15.00
c. Pin perf. 500.00 225.00
34 A2 3p gray lilac 42.50 25.00
a. 3p dull violet 50.00 27.50
b. Pin perf. 200.00

35 A1 6p blue 45.00 37.50
a. 6p pale blue 45.00 45.00
b. 6p dark blue 50.00 42.50
c. Tete beche pair *7,500.* *6,000.*
d. Pin perf. 200.00

Rouletted 15½, 16

36 A1 1p orange red 325.00 110.00
a. Rouletted 6½ 650.00 140.00
37 A2 3p dull violet 350.00 125.00
a. Rouletted 6½ 180.00
38 A1 6p blue 165.00 90.00
a. Rouletted 6½ 725.00 75.00

The paper of this group varies slightly in thickness and is sometimes divided into pelure and semipelure. We believe there was only one lot of the paper and that the separation is not warranted.

Thick Hard Paper
Imperf

39 A1 1p orange red ('76) 19.00 13.00
40 A2 3p lilac
41 A1 6p deep blue 85.00 18.00
a. 6p blue 85.00 18.00
b. Tete beche pair *5,500.*

Rouletted 15½, 16

42 A1 1p orange red ('76) 325.00 100.00
a. Rouletted 6½ ('75) 450.00 100.00
42B A2 3p lilac 240.00
43 A1 6p deep blue *600.00* 85.00
a. 6p blue *600.00* 120.00
b. Rouletted 6½ ('75) *650.00* 135.00

Soft Porous Paper
Imperf

44 A1 1p orange red 90.00 40.00
45 A1 6p deep blue 140.00 45.00
a. 6p dull blue 275.00 80.00
46 A1 1sh yellow green 200.00 80.00

Rouletted 15½, 16

47 A1 1p orange red 200.00
a. Rouletted 6½ 200.00
48 A1 6p deep blue 37.50
a. Rouletted 6½
49 A1 1sh yellow grn 575.00 150.00
a. Rouletted 6½
b. Rouletted 15½-16x16½ 500.00 325.00

First British Occupation

V. R.

Stamps and Types of 1875 Overprinted

TRANSVAAL.

Red Overprint
Pelure Paper

1877 Unwmk. *Imperf.*

50 A2 3p lilac 900.00 100.00
a. Overprinted on back 3,000.
b. Double ovpt., red and black *7,500.*

Rouletted 15½, 16

51 A2 3p lilac *8,000.* 1,700.
a. Rouletted 6½ *8,000.* 1,700.

Thin Hard Paper
Imperf

52 A2 3p lilac 1,400. 300.00

Soft Porous Paper

53 A1 6p blue 1,500. 200.00
a. 6p deep blue 275.00
b. Inverted overprint *5,750.*
c. Double overprint *4,900.*
54 A1 1sh yellow grn 425.00 225.00
a. Inverted overprint *3,750.*
b. Half used as 6p on cover *1,900.*

Rouletted 15½, 16

55 A1 6p blue *6,000.* 1,700.
a. Rouletted 6½ *7,000.* 1,700.
56 A1 1sh yellow grn 1,500. 600.00
a. Rouletted 6½ 2,250. 900.00

Black Overprint
Pelure Paper
Imperf

57 A1 1p red 175.00 100.00

Rouletted 15½, 16

58 A1 1p red 5,500. 1,500.

Thick Hard Paper
Imperf

59 A1 1p red 18.00 18.00
a. Inverted overprint 500.00 375.00

Rouletted 15½, 16

60 A1 1p red 150.00 50.00
a. Rouletted 6½ 450.00 275.00
b. Inverted overprint
c. Double overprint

Soft Porous Paper
Imperf

61 A1 1p red 16.00 18.00
a. Double overprint *1,500.*
62 A2 3p lilac 50.00 37.50
a. 3p deep lilac 125.00 50.00
b. Inverted overprint *3,500.*
63 A1 6p dull blue 75.00 27.50
a. 6p bright blue 125.00 27.50
b. 6p dark blue 125.00 27.50
c. Tete beche pair *5,000.*
d. Inverted overprint 2,000. 400.00
e. Double overprint *5,000.*

64 A1 6p blue, *rose* 40.00 20.00
a. Tete beche pair *3,750.*
b. Inverted overprint 45.00 20.00
c. Overprint omitted *4,000.*
d. Half used as 3p on cover
65 A1 1sh yellow grn 60.00 25.00
a. Tete beche pair *5,000.*
b. Inverted overprint 1,400. 250.00
c. Half used as 6p on cover 1,650.

Rouletted 15½, 16

66 A1 1p red 47.50 40.00
a. Rouletted 6½ 650.00 185.00
67 A2 3p lilac 55.00 50.00
a. Rouletted 6½ 500.00
68 A1 6p dull blue 150.00 42.50
a. Inverted overprint *5,000.* 600.00
b. Rouletted 6½ *5,000.* 600.00
c. As "a," rouletted 6½
69 A1 6p blue, *rose* 140.00 40.00
a. Inverted overprint 500.00 70.00
b. Rouletted 6½
c. Tete beche pair
d. Overprint omitted
e. As "a," rouletted 6½
f. As "d," rouletted 6½
70 A1 1sh yellow grn 150.00 60.00
a. Inverted overprint 1,000. 575.00
b. Rouletted 6½ 350.00 100.00
c. As "a," rouletted 6½ 1,700. 550.00

In this issue the space between "V. R." and "TRANSVAAL" is normally 8½mm but occasionally it is 12mm. In this and the following issues there are numerous minor varieties of the overprint, missing periods, etc.

V. R.

Types A1 and A2 Overprinted

Transvaal

1877-79 *Imperf.*

71 A1 1p red, *blue* 30.00 15.00
a. "Transvral" *6,000.* *3,000.*
b. Inverted overprint *600.00* 350.00
c. Double overprint *4,500.*
d. Overprint omitted
72 A1 1p red, *org* ('78) 14.00 15.00
a. Printed on both sides
b. Pin perf.
73 A2 3p lilac, *buff* 37.50 22.50
a. Inverted overprint 600.00
b. Pin perf.
74 A2 3p lilac, *grn* ('79) 125.00 22.50
a. Inverted overprint 1,500.
b. Double overprint
c. Pin perf.
75 A1 6p blue, *grn* 70.00 25.00
a. Tete beche pair *3,250.*
b. Inverted overprint 1,100.
c. Half used as 3p on cover
d. Pin perf.
76 A1 6p blue, *bl* ('78) 42.50 20.00
a. Tete beche pair
b. Overprint omitted 2,500.
c. Inverted overprint 750.00
d. Half used as 3p on cover 600.00
e. Double overprint 2,750.
f. Pin perf.
Nos. 71-76 (6) 319.00 120.00

Rouletted 15½, 16

77 A1 1p red, *blue* 60.00 25.00
a. "Transvral" *3,000.*
b. Inverted overprint
c. Double overprint
78 A1 1p red, *org* ('78) 25.00 20.00
a. Horiz. pair, imperf. vert.
b. Rouletted 6½ 275.00 125.00
79 A2 3p lilac, *buff* 75.00 20.00
a. Inverted overprint *3,000.*
b. Vert. pair, imperf. horiz.
c. Rouletted 6½ 100.00
80 A2 3p lilac, *grn* ('79) 400.00 110.00
a. Inverted overprint
b. Rouletted 6½ 250.00
81 A1 6p blue, *green* 140.00 40.00
a. Inverted overprint 500.00
b. Overprint omitted 3,250.
c. Tete beche pair
d. Half used at 3p on cover 600.00
e. Rouletted 6½ *4,000.* 900.00
82 A1 6p blue, *bl* ('78) 47.50 22.50
a. Inverted overprint *3,000.* 1,000.
b. Overprint omitted *6,000.* 3,000.
c. Tete beche pair
d. Horiz. pair, imperf. vert.
e. Half used as 3p on cover 600.00
f. Double overprint
g. Rouletted 6½ 250.00
h. As "a," rouletted 6½
Nos. 77-82 (6) 747.50 237.50

V. R.

Types A1 and A2 Overprinted

Transvaal

Imperf

83 A1 1p red, *org* ('78) 37.50 27.50
84 A2 3p lilac, *buff* ('78) 50.00 32.50
a. Pin perf.
85 A2 3p lilac, *grn* ('79) 95.00 32.00
a. Inverted overprint *1,500.*
b. Overprint omitted *2,600.*
c. Printed on both sides

86 A1 6p blue, *bl* ('78) 110.00 27.50
a. Tete beche pair 10,000.
b. Inverted overprint 325.00
Nos. 83-86 (4) 292.50 119.50

Rouletted 15½, 16

87 A1 1p red, *org* ('78) 87.50
a. Rouletted 6½ 275.00
88 A2 3p lilac, *buff* ('78) 150.00 65.00
a. Vert. pair, imperf. horiz.
b. Rouletted 6½ 275.00
89 A2 3p lilac, *grn* ('79) 425.00 110.00
a. Inverted overprint
b. Overprint omitted
c. Rouletted 6½ ('97) 300.00
90 A1 6p blue, *bl* ('78) 110.00
a. Tete beche pair
b. Inverted overprint 4,000. 850.00
d. Rouletted 6½ 425.00
e. As "b," rouletted 6½

Types A1 and A2 Overprinted

V. R.
Transvaal

1879 ***Imperf.***

91 A1 1p red, *orange* 35.00 22.50
a. 1p red, *yellow* 37.50 32.50
b. Small capital "T" 200.00 165.00
92 A2 3p lilac, *green* 75.00 20.00
a. Small capital "T" 225.00 165.00
93 A2 3p lilac, *blue* 37.50 20.00
a. Small capital "T" 165.00 75.00
Nos. 91-93 (3) 147.50 62.50

Rouletted 15½, 16

94 A1 1p red, *yellow* 200.00
a. 1p red, *orange* 325.00
b. Small capital "T" 775.00 265.00
c. Rouletted 6½ 650.00
d. Pin perf. 500.00
95 A2 3p lilac, *green* 825.00 200.00
a. Small capital "T"
b. Rouletted 6½
96 A2 3p lilac, *blue* 115.00
a. Small capital "T" 800.00
b. Rouletted 6½
c. Pin perf.

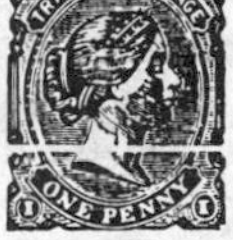

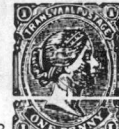

Queen Victoria — A3

1878-80 **Engr.** ***Perf. 14, 14½***

97 A3 ½p vermilion ('80) 17.00 42.50
98 A3 1p red brown 8.00 2.00
99 A3 3p claret 9.50 2.00
100 A3 4p olive green 12.00 5.50
101 A3 6p slate 6.00 2.75
a. Half used as 3p on cover
102 A3 1sh green 90.00 30.00
103 A3 2sh blue 125.00 70.00
Nos. 97-103 (7) 267.50 154.75

For surcharges see Nos. 104-118, 138-139.

No. 101 Surcharged in Red or Black:

(a) Surcharged **1 PENNY**

1879

104 A3 1p on 6p slate (R) 82.50 65.00
105 A3 1p on 6p slate (Bk) 35.00 24.00

(b) Surcharged **1 Penny**

106 A3 1p on 6p slate (R) 350.00 275.00
107 A3 1p on 6p slate (Bk) 165.00 85.00

(c) Surcharged **1 Penny**

108 A3 1p on 6p slate (R) 200.00 115.00
109 A3 1p on 6p slate (Bk) 65.00 32.50

(d) Surcharged **1 Penny**

110 A3 1p on 6p slate (R) 225.00 125.00
111 A3 1p on 6p slate (Bk) 55.00 50.00
a. Pair, one without surcharge

(e) Surcharged ***1 Penny***

112 A3 1p on 6p slate (R) 350.00 225.00
113 A3 1p on 6p slate (Bk) 145.00 75.00

(f) Surcharged **1 Penny**

114 A3 1p on 6p slate (R) 325.00 145.00
115 A3 1p on 6p slate (Bk) 90.00 55.00

(g) Surcharged **1 Penny**

116 A3 1p on 6p slate (R) 1,500.
117 A3 1p on 6p slate (Bk) 500.00 145.00

Surcharge distinctions: a, "PENNY" in gothic capitals. b, "1" has heavy serif at base; "P," thin serif at base. c, No serif at base of "1." d, Heavy serifs at base of "1" and "p." e, Italics. f, "1" has long, sloping serif at top, thin serif at base. g, Tail of "y" missing.

Second Republic

No. 100 Surcharged **EEN PENNY**

1882 **Unwmk.** ***Perf. 14, 14½***

118 A3 1p on 4p olive grn 7.00 4.25
a. Inverted surcharge 250.00 250.00

1883 ***Perf. 12***

119 A1 1p black 3.00 1.10
a. Imperf.
b. Vert. pair, imperf. horiz.
c. Horiz. pair, imperf. vert.
120 A2 3p red 6.00 2.00
a. Horiz. pair, imperf. vert.
b. Half used as 1p on cover
121 A2 3p black, *rose* 15.00 2.50
a. Half used as 1p on cover 750.00
122 A1 1sh green 25.00 3.00
a. Tete beche pair 450.00 115.00
b. Half used as 6p on cover 400.00
Nos. 119-122 (4) 49.00 8.60

The so-called reprints of this issue are forgeries. They were made from the counterfeit plates described in the note following No. 8, plus a new false plate for the 3p. The false 3p plate has many small flaws and defects.

Forgeries of No. 120 are in dull orange red, clearly printed on whitish paper, and those of No. 121 in brownish or grayish black on bright rose. Genuine copies of No. 120 lack the orange tint and the paper is yellowish; genuine copies of No. 121 are in black without gray or brown shade, on dull lilac rose paper.

A 6p in slate on white, apparently of this issue, is a late print from the counterfeit plate.

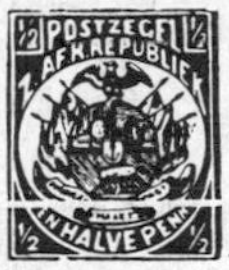

A4

Perf. 13½, 11½x12, 12½, 12½x12

1885-93 **Typo.**

123 A4 ½p gray .20 .15
124 A4 1p rose .20 .15
125 A4 2p brown 1.00 .75
126 A4 2p olive bis ('87) .40 .15
127 A4 2½p purple ('93) 1.10 .40
128 A4 3p violet 1.10 .50
129 A4 4p bronze green 2.00 .40
130 A4 6p blue 2.75 1.75
a. Imperf.
131 A4 1sh green 2.25 .25
132 A4 2sh6p yellow 3.00 1.25
133 A4 5sh steel blue 4.25 2.00
134 A4 10sh pale brown 22.50 4.50
135 A4 £5 dark green ('92)
Nos. 123-134 (12) 40.75
Set value 2.00

Reprints of Nos. 123-137, 140-163, 166-174 closely resemble the originals. Paper is whiter, perf. 12½, large holes.

Excellent counterfeits of No. 135 exist.

For overprint and surcharges see Nos. 140-147, 163, 213.

Nos. 120, 122 Surcharged

HALVE PENNY

1885 ***Perf. 12***

136 A2 ½p on 3p red 3.00 5.00
a. Surcharge reading down 3.00 5.00
137 A1 ½p on 1sh green 7.00 15.00
a. Surcharge reading down 7.00 15.00
b. Tete beche pair 450.00 250.00

Nos. 101, 128 Surcharged in Red or Black

HALVE PENNY Z. A. R.

HALVE PENNY

Perf. 14

138 A3 ½p on 6p slate 15.00 27.50
139 A3 2p on 6p slate 2.25 2.50
a. Horiz. pair, imperf. vert.

Perf. 11½x12, 12½x12

140 A4 ½p on 3p vio (Bk) 1.75 1.75
a. "PRNNY" 50.00
b. 2nd "N" of "PENNY" invtd. 125.00

2d

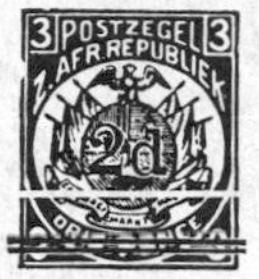

No. 141 No. 142

1887

141 A4 2p on 3p violet .50 .90
a. Double surcharge 150.00
142 A4 2p on 3p violet 4.00 4.00
a. Double surcharge 225.00

Nos. 126, 130, 131 Surcharged

Halve Penny 2½ Pence

Nos. 143-144 Nos. 145-146

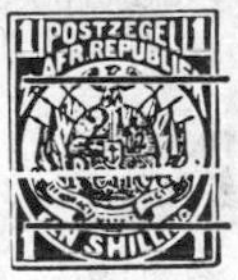

No. 147

Red Surcharge

1893

143 A4 ½p on 2p olive bis .50 .50
a. Inverted surcharge 2.25 2.25
b. Bars 14mm apart 1.30 1.30
c. As "b," inverted 6.50 6.50

Black Surcharge

144 A4 ½p on 2p olive bis .50 .50
a. Inverted surcharge 4.25 4.25
b. Bars 14mm apart 1.30 1.30
c. As "b," inverted 13.00 11.00
145 A4 1p on 6p blue .30 .30
a. Inverted surcharge 1.30 1.30
b. Double surcharge 50.00 50.00
c. Pair, one without surcharge 175.00
d. Bars 14mm apart .55 .55
e. As "d," inverted 5.50 5.50
f. As "d," double 90.00
146 A4 2½p on 1sh green .60 .90
a. Inverted surcharge 5.00 6.00
b. Fraction line misplaced "2/½" 27.50 27.50
c. As "b," inverted 325.00 275.00
d. Bars 14mm apart 1.50 1.50
e. As "d," inverted 7.25 10.00
147 A4 2½p on 1sh green 2.00 2.00
a. Inverted surcharge 6.50 6.50
b. Bars 14mm apart 5.00 5.00
c. As "b," inverted 32.50 20.00
d. Double surcharge 60.00 75.00
Nos. 143-147 (5) 3.90 4.20

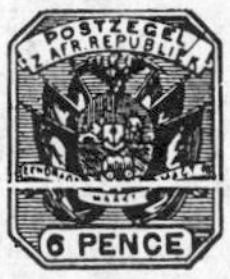

A13

Wagon with Two Shafts

1894 **Typo.** ***Perf. 12½***

148 A13 ½p gray .15 .15
149 A13 1p rose .15 .15
150 A13 2p olive bister .15 .15
151 A13 6p blue .70 .40
152 A13 1sh yellow grn 4.00 5.00
Nos. 148-152 (5) 5.15 5.85

Counterfeits of #148-152 are plentiful.
See note following No. 135 for reprints.

1895-96 **Wagon with Pole**

153 A13 ½p gray .15 .15
154 A13 1p rose .15 .15
155 A13 2p olive bister .15 .15
156 A13 3p violet .15 .15
157 A13 4p slate .85 .45
158 A13 6p blue .75 .30
159 A13 1sh green .85 .45
160 A13 5sh slate blue ('96) 8.00 11.00
161 A13 10sh red brown ('96) 8.00 2.25
Nos. 153-161 (9) 19.05 15.05

Most of the unused specimens of Nos. 153 to 161 now on the market are reprints.

See Nos. 166-174. For surcharge and overprints see Nos. 162, 214-220, 232-235.

See note following No. 135 for reprints.

Nos. 159, 127 Surcharged in Red or Green

Halve Penny **1d.**

1895

162 A13 ½p on 1sh green (R) .15 .15
a. Inverted surcharge 5.25 5.25
b. "Pennij" instead of "Penny" 60.00 60.00
c. Double surcharge 60.00 60.00
163 A4 1p on 2½p pur (G) .15 .15
a. Inverted surcharge 27.50 27.50
b. Surcharge sideways
c. Surcharge on back
d. Space between "1" and "d" 1.30 1.30
Set value .15 .15

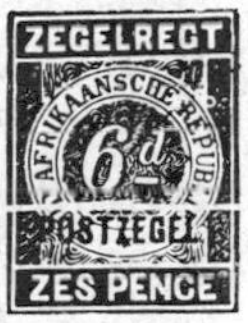

A16

1895 ***Perf. 11½***

164 A16 6p rose (G) .65 .65
a. Vertical pair, imperf. between

Counterfeits of No. 164 are on the 6p dark red revenue stamp of 1898, and have a shiny green ink for the overprint. The false overprint is also found on other revenue denominations, though only the 6p rose was converted to postal use.

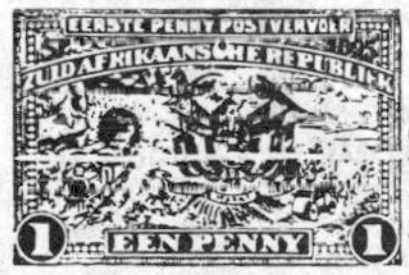

Coat of Arms, Wheat Field and Railroad Train — A17

1895, Sept. 6 **Litho.**

165 A17 1p red .20 .20
a. Imperf.
b. Vertical pair, imperf. between 25.00 25.00

Penny Postage in Transvaal.
For overprint see No. 245.

With Pole

1896 **Typo.** ***Perf. 12½***

166 A13 ½p green .15 .15
167 A13 1p rose & grn .15 .15
168 A13 2p brown & grn .15 .15
169 A13 2½p ultra & grn .20 .15
170 A13 3p red vio & grn .50 .50
171 A13 4p olive & grn .50 .50
172 A13 6p violet & grn .25 .15
173 A13 1sh bister & grn .30 .15
174 A13 2sh6p lilac & grn 1.00 1.00
Nos. 166-174 (9) 3.20 2.90

See note following No. 135 for reprints.

For overprints and surcharges see Nos. 202-212, 214-235, 237-244, 246-251, Cape of Good Hope Nos. N5-N8.

Pietersburg Issue

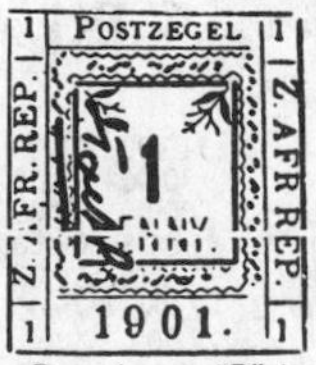

Date large; "P" in Postzegel large — A18

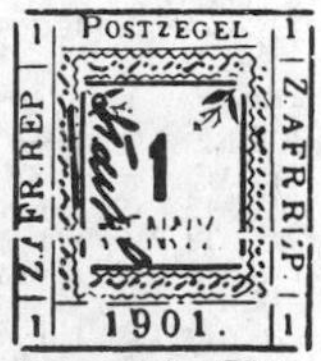

Date small; "P" in Postzegel large — A19

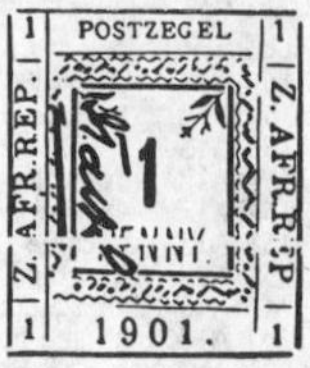

Date small; "P" in Postzegel small — A20

1901 **Typeset** *Imperf.*

Initials in Red

175 A18 ½p black, *green* 37.50
a. Initials omitted 125.00
b. Initials in black 45.00
176 A19 ½p black, *green* 50.00
a. Initials omitted 125.00
b. Initials in black 45.00
177 A20 ½p black, *green* 50.00
a. Initials omitted 125.00
b. Initials in black 45.00

Initials in Black

178 A18 1p black, *rose* 10.00
179 A19 1p black, *rose* 13.00
180 A20 1p black, *rose* 16.00
181 A18 2p black, *orange* 15.00
182 A19 2p black, *orange* 20.00
183 A20 2p black, *orange* 22.50
184 A18 4p black, *dull blue* 25.00
185 A19 4p black, *dull blue* 30.00
186 A20 4p black, *dull blue* 40.00
187 A18 6p black, *green* 32.50
188 A19 6p black, *green* 47.50
189 A20 6p black, *green* 65.00
190 A18 1sh black, *yellow* 75.00
191 A19 1sh black, *yellow* 55.00
192 A20 1sh black, *yellow* 140.00

Perf. 11½

Initials in Red

193 A18 ½p black, *green* 13.00
194 A19 ½p black, *green* 15.00
195 A20 ½p black, *green* 20.00

Initials in Black

196 A18 1p black, *rose* 10.00
a. Horiz. pair, imperf. vert. 125.00
197 A19 1p black, *rose* 13.00
a. Horiz. pair, imperf. vert. 150.00
198 A20 1p black, *rose* 13.00
a. Horiz. pair, imperf. vert. 150.00
199 A18 2p black, *orange* 15.00
200 A19 2p black, *orange* 17.00
201 A20 2p black, *orange* 17.00

Nos. 193 to 201 inclusive are always imperforate on one side.

The setting consisted of 12 stamps of type A18, 6 of type A19, and 6 of type A20. The first printings, for all values, were without errors; but many errors found their way into the later printings of the ½p, 1p, 2p and 4p stamps. The perforated stamps are from the first printing and were put into use first. Used copies are not valued as all seen show evidence of having been canceled to order.

Second British Occupation
Issued under Military Authority

Nos. 166-174, 160-161, 135 Overprinted **V. R. I.**

1900 **Unwmk.** ***Perf. 12½***

202 A13 ½p green .15 .15
a. "V.I.R." 650.00
203 A13 1p rose & grn .15 .15
204 A13 2p brown & grn 1.00 .40
a. "V.I.R." 650.00
205 A13 2½p ultra & grn .40 .40
206 A13 3p red vio & grn .40 .15
207 A13 4p olive & grn .75 .15
a. "V.I.R." 650.00
208 A13 6p violet & grn .75 .40
209 A13 1sh bister & grn .80 .80
210 A13 2sh6p hel & grn 1.25 2.25
211 A13 5sh slate blue 3.00 4.00
212 A13 10sh red brown 4.50 4.50
213 A4 £5 dark green
Nos. 202-212 (11) 13.15 13.35

Nos. 202 to 213 have been extensively counterfeited. The overprint on the forgeries is clear and clean, with small periods and letters showing completely. In the genuine, letters are worn and lack many or all serifs; the periods are large and oval.

The genuine overprint exists inverted; double; with period missing after "V," after "R," after "I," etc.

Issued in Lydenburg

Overprinted in Black **V.R.I.**

1900

214 A13 ½p green 110.00 110.00
215 A13 1p rose & grn 80.00 80.00
216 A13 2p brown & grn 800.00 700.00
217 A13 2½p ultra & grn 800.00
218 A13 4p olive & grn 2,250. 650.00
219 A13 6p violet & grn 2,250. 575.00
220 A13 1sh bister & grn 2,500.

Beware of counterfeits.

No. 167 Surcharged **V.R.I. 3d.**

221 A13 3p on 1p rose & green 45.00 45.00

Issued in Rustenburg

Nos. 166-170, 172-174 Handstamped in Violet **V.R.**

1900 ***Perf. 12½***

223 A13 ½p green 100.00 100.00
224 A13 1p rose & grn 95.00 60.00
225 A13 2p brown & grn 200.00 190.00
226 A13 2½p ultra & grn 120.00 80.00
227 A13 3p red vio & grn 190.00 110.00
229 A13 6p violet & grn 650.00 500.00
230 A13 1sh bister & grn 1,300. 650.00
231 A13 2sh6p hel & grn *4,250.*

Issued in Schweizer Reneke

Nos. 166-168 and 172 Handstamped "BESIEGED" in Black

1900 **Typo.** ***Perf. 12½***

232 A13 ½p green 250.00
233 A13 1p rose & green 275.00
234 A13 2p brown & green 440.00
235 A13 6p violet & green 900.00
Nos. 232-235 (4) 1,865.

Same Overprint on Cape of Good Hope No. 59 and Type of 1893

Perf. 14

236 A15 ½p green 650.00
236A A15 1p carmine 650.00

In 1902 five revenue stamps overprinted "V.R.I." are said to have been used postally in Volksrust. There seems to be some doubt that this issue was properly authorized for postal use.

Issued in Wolmaransstad

Nos. 166-173 Handstamped in Blue or Red **Cancelled V-R-I.**

1900

237 A13 ½p green 175.00
238 A13 1p rose & grn 165.00 *175.00*
239 A13 2p brown & grn 1,400. *1,400.*
240 A13 2½p ultra & grn (R) 2,000. *2,000.*
241 A13 3p red vio & grn 2,500.
242 A13 4p olive & grn 3,000. *3,750.*
243 A13 6p violet & grn 2,750. *4,250.*
244 A13 1sh bister & grn

No. 165 Overprinted in Blue **Cancelled V-R-I.**

245 A17 1p red 165.00 *150.00*

Regular Issues

No. 166-168, 170-171, 174 Surcharged or Overprinted

E. R. I. Half Penny **E. R. I.**

1901-02

246 A13 ½p on 2p brn & grn .15 .15
247 A13 ½p green .15 .15
248 A13 1p rose & grn .15 .15
a. Overprint "E" omitted 65.00
249 A13 3p red vio & grn .25 .25
250 A13 4p olive & grn .32 .32
251 A13 2sh6p hel & grn 3.50 3.50
Nos. 246-251 (6) 4.52 4.52

Excellent counterfeits of Nos. 246 to 251 are plentiful. See note after No. 213 for the recognition marks of the counterfeits.

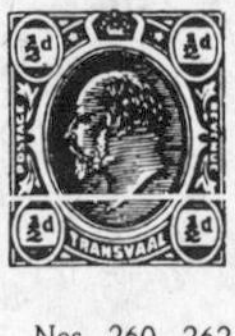

Edward VII — A27

Nos. 260, 262 to 267 and 275 to 280 have "POSTAGE" at each side; the other stamps of type A27 have "REVENUE" at the right.

Wmk. Crown and C A (2)

1902-03 **Typo.** ***Perf. 14***

252 A27 ½p gray grn & blk .70 .15
253 A27 1p rose & blk .70 .15
254 A27 2p violet & blk 1.40 .20
255 A27 2½p ultra & blk 2.00 .80
256 A27 3p ol grn & blk 3.25 .30
257 A27 4p choc & blk 3.25 .35
258 A27 6p brn org & blk 1.50 .50
259 A27 1sh ol grn & blk 7.50 3.25
260 A27 1sh red brn & blk 5.00 1.00
261 A27 2sh brown & blk 14.00 18.00
262 A27 2sh yel & blk 8.00 *7.00*
263 A27 2sh6p black & vio 10.00 6.50
264 A27 5sh vio & blk, *yel* 13.00 13.00
265 A27 10sh vio & blk, *red* 30.00 17.00
266 A27 £1 violet & grn 110.00 75.00
267 A27 £5 violet & org 1,000. 525.00
Nos. 252-266 (15) 210.30 143.20

Issue dates: 3p, 4p, Nos. 260, 262, £1, £5, 1903. Others, Apr. 1, 1902.

1904-09 **Wmk. 3**

268 A27 ½p gray grn & blk 2.25 1.00
269 A27 1p rose & blk 2.25 .15
270 A27 2p violet & blk 3.00 .30
271 A27 2½p ultra & blk 4.00 2.25
272 A27 3p ol grn & blk 2.25 .20
273 A27 4p choc & blk 2.25 .20
274 A27 6p brn org & blk 2.25 .20
275 A27 1sh red brn & blk 2.25 .15
276 A27 2sh yellow & blk 11.00 3.00
277 A27 2sh6p blk & red vio 20.00 1.50
278 A27 5sh vio & blk, *yel* 10.00 1.25
279 A27 10sh vio & blk, *red* 24.00 2.00
280 A27 £1 violet & grn 110.00 16.00
Nos. 268-280 (13) 195.50 28.20

The 2p and 3p are on chalky paper, the 2½p, 4p, 6p and £1 on both chalky and ordinary, and the other values on ordinary paper only.

Issue years: ½p, 1p, 5sh, 1904. 2½p, 6p, 1sh, 1905. 2p, 3p, 4p, 2sh, 1906. 10sh, 1907. £1, 1908. 2sh6p, 1909.

1905-10

281 A27 ½p green 1.10 .15
a. Booklet pane of 6
282 A27 1p carmine .85 .15
a. Wmk. 16 (error) ('07) 300.00
b. Booklet pane of 6
283 A27 2p dull vio ('10) 2.50 .20
284 A27 2½p ultra ('10) 7.00 2.00
Nos. 281-284 (4) 11.45
Set value .84

Some of the above stamps are found with the overprint "C. S. A. R." for use by the Central South African Railway, the control mark being applied after the stamps had left the post office.

POSTAGE DUE STAMPS

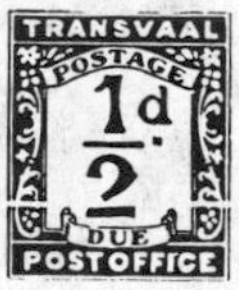

D1

Wmk. Multiple Crown and C A (3)

1907 **Typo.** ***Perf. 14***

J1 D1 ½p green & blk 2.00 1.10
J2 D1 1p carmine & blk 2.75 .70
J3 D1 2p brown & org 3.00 1.00
J4 D1 3p blue & blk 3.00 2.75
J5 D1 5p violet & blk 1.50 10.00
J6 D1 6p red brown & blk 4.00 11.00
J7 D1 1sh black & car 7.00 4.50
Nos. J1-J7 (7) 23.25 31.05

Most canceled copies of #J1-J7 were used outside the Transvaal under the Union of South Africa administration in 1910-16.

The stamps of Transvaal were replaced by those of South Africa.

TRISTAN DA CUNHA

ˌtris-tən-də-ˈkü-nə

LOCATION — Group of islands in the south Atlantic Ocean midway between the Cape of Good Hope and South America
GOVT. — A dependency of St. Helena
AREA — 40 sq. mi.
POP. — 325 (1982)

12 Pence = 1 Shilling
100 Cents = 1 Rand (1961)
12 Pence = 1 Shilling (1963)
20 Shillings = 1 Pound
100 Pence = 1 Pound (1971)

Catalogue values for all unused stamps in this country are for Never Hinged items.

Stamps of St. Helena, 1938-49, Overprinted in Black **TRISTAN DA CUNHA**

1952, Jan. 1 **Wmk. 4** ***Perf. 12½***

1 A24 ½p purple .35 .22
2 A24 1p blue grn & blk .45 .32
3 A24 1½p car rose & blk .55 .40
4 A24 2p carmine & blk .80 .55
5 A24 3p gray 1.10 1.70
6 A24 4p ultra 1.50 .90
7 A24 6p gray blue 2.00 1.25
8 A24 8p olive 2.50 1.65
9 A24 1sh sepia 2.75 *3.25*
10 A24 2sh6p deep claret 10.50 *10.00*
11 A24 5sh brown 27.50 *22.50*
12 A24 10sh violet 60.00 *52.50*
Nos. 1-12 (12) 110.00 *95.24*

Coronation Issue
Common Design Type

1953, June 2 **Engr.** ***Perf. 13½x13***

13 CD312 3p dk green & black 1.50 2.00

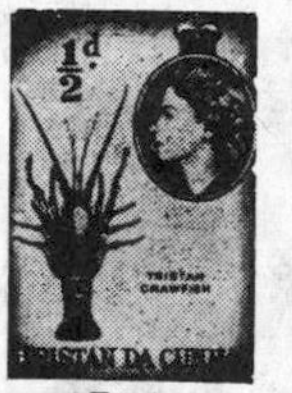

Tristan Crayfish — A1

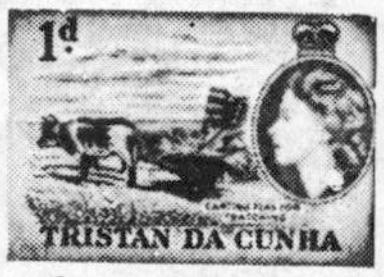

Carting Flax — A2

Designs: 1½p, Rockhopper penguin. 2p, Factory. 2½p, Mollymauk. 3p, Island boat. 4p, View of Tristan. 5p, Potato patches. 6p, Inaccessible Island. 9p, Nightingale Island. 1sh, St. Mary's Church. 2sh 6p, Elephant seal. 5sh, Flightless rail. 10sh, Island spinning wheel.

1954-58 ***Perf. 12½***

14 A1 ½p chocolate & red .25 .18
a. Bklt. pane of 4 ('58) 2.50
15 A2 1p green & choc .45 .22
a. Bklt. pane of 4 ('58) 4.00
16 A1 1½p dp plum & black .50 .25
a. Bklt. pane of 4 ('58) 6.00
17 A2 2p orange & vio blue .60 .30
18 A2 2½p carmine & blk .60 .30
19 A1 3p olive grn & ultra .65 .32
a. Bklt. pane of 4 ('58) 9.00
20 A2 4p dp blue & aqua .70 .35
a. Bklt. pane of 4 ('58) 11.00
21 A2 5p gray & blue grn 1.00 .50
22 A2 6p violet & dk ol grn 1.25 .60
23 A2 9p henna brn & rose lil 2.00 1.00
24 A2 1sh chocolate & ol grn 2.50 1.25
25 A2 2sh6p blue & choc 12.00 6.00
26 A2 5sh red orange & blk 27.50 13.00
27 A2 10sh red violet & org 55.00 27.50
Nos. 14-27 (14) 105.00 51.77

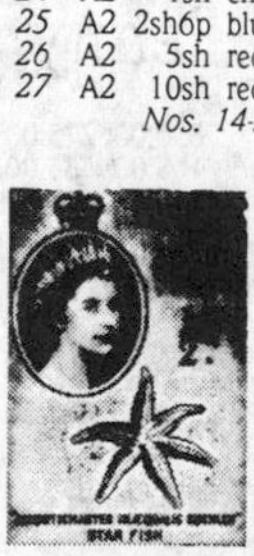

Starfish — A3

Fish: 1p, Concha. 1½p, Klipfish. 2p, Heron fish (saury). 2½p, Snipefish ("swordfish"). 3d, Tristan crawfish. 4p, Soldier fish. 5p, Five finger fish. 6p, Mackeral scad. 9p, Stumpnose. 1sh, Bluefish. 2sh6p, Snoek (snake mackerel). 5sh, Shark. 10sh, Atlantic right whale.

Perf. 12½x13

1960, Feb. 1 **Engr.** **Wmk. 314**

28 A3 ½p orange & black .24 .16
a. Booklet pane of 4 1.75
29 A3 1p rose lilac & blk .32 .18
a. Booklet pane of 4 3.00
30 A3 1½p grnsh blue & blk .45 .28
a. Booklet pane of 4 3.50

31	A3	2p green & black	.55	.30
32	A3	2½p brown & black	.60	.32
33	A3	3p rose red & black	.65	.38
a.		Booklet pane of 4	4.75	
34	A3	4p gray olive & blk	.85	.45
a.		Booklet pane of 4	5.25	
35	A3	5p orange yel & blk	1.00	.55
36	A3	6p blue & black	1.10	.65
37	A3	9p rose car & blk	2.00	.90
38	A3	1sh brown org & blk	2.50	1.10
39	A3	2sh6p vio blue & blk	6.50	3.75
40	A3	5sh emerald & blk	24.00	11.00
41	A3	10sh violet & blk	50.00	26.00
		Nos. 28-41 (14)	90.76	46.02

1961, Apr. 15 *Perf. 12½x13*

42	A3	½c like No. 28	.15	.15
43	A3	1c like No. 29	.15	.15
44	A3	1½c like No. 30	.20	.15
45	A3	2c like No. 32	.26	.16
46	A3	2½c like No. 33	.35	.20
47	A3	3c like No. 34	.45	.28
48	A3	4c like No. 35	.60	.35
49	A3	5c like No. 36	.85	.48
50	A3	7½c like No. 37	1.25	.80
51	A3	10c like No. 38	2.00	1.25
52	A3	25c like No. 39	10.00	6.00
53	A3	50c like No. 40	21.00	13.00
54	A3	1r like No. 41	52.50	30.00
		Nos. 42-54 (13)	89.76	52.97

Nos. 46, 49-51 surcharged for "Tristan Relief" are listed as St. Helena Nos. B1-B4.

Types of St. Helena, 1961 Overprinted **TRISTAN DA CUNHA RESETTLEMENT 1963**

Perf. 11½x12, 12x11½

1963, Apr. 12 Photo. Wmk. 4

55	A29	1p rose, ultra, yel & grn	.15	.15
56	A29	1½p bis, sep, yel & grn	.15	.15
57	A29	2p gray & red	.15	.15
58	A30	3p dk bl, rose & grnsh bl	.15	.15
a.		Double overprint		
59	A29	4½p slate, brn & grn	.15	.15
60	A29	6p cit, brn & dp car	.22	.16
61	A29	7p vio, blk & red brn	.28	.18
62	A29	10p blue & dp claret	.35	.22
63	A29	1sh red brn, grn & yel	.70	.45
64	A29	1sh6p gray bl & blk	1.10	.75
65	A29	2sh6p grnsh bl, yel & red	2.50	1.65
66	A29	5sh green, brn & yel	5.00	3.50
67	A29	10sh gray bl, blk & sal	11.00	7.25
		Nos. 55-67 (13)	21.90	14.91

Freedom from Hunger Issue
Common Design Type
Perf. 14x14½
1963, Oct. 2 Photo. Wmk. 314

68	CD314	1sh6p rose carmine	2.25	1.40

Red Cross Centenary Issue
Common Design Type
1964, Jan. 2 Litho. *Perf. 13*

69	CD315	3p black & red	.28	.20
70	CD315	1sh6p ultra & red	2.50	1.50

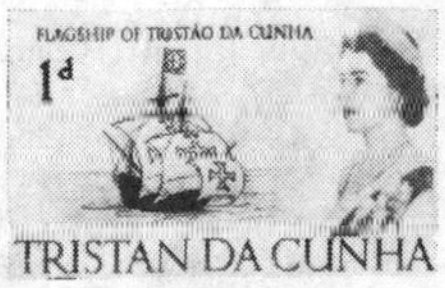

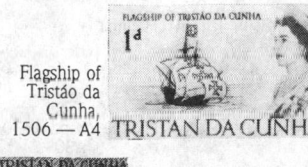

Flagship of Tristáo da Cunha, 1506 — A4

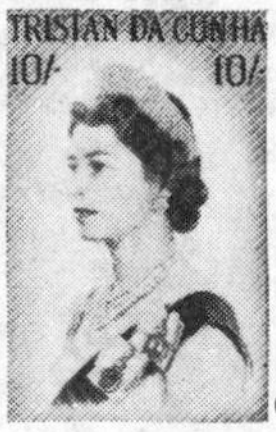

Queen Elizabeth II — A5

Designs: ½p, Map of South Atlantic Ocean. 1½p, Dutch ship Heemstede, first landing, 1643. 2p, New England whaler. 3p, Confederate ship Shenandoah. 4½p, H.M.S. Galatea, 1867. 6p, H.M.S. Cilicia, 1942. 7p, H.M. Royal Yacht Britannia, 1957. 10p, H.M.S. Leopard, Evacuation, 1961. 1sh, Dutch ship Tjisadane, 1961. 1sh6p, M.V. Tristania. 2sh6p, M.V. Boissevain, returning islanders, 1963. 5sh, M.S. Bornholm, returning islanders, 1963.

Perf. 11x11½
1965, Feb. 17 Engr. Wmk. 314

71	A4	½p black & dk blue	.15	.15
a.		Booklet pane of 4	.28	
72	A4	1p black & emerald	.15	.15
a.		Booklet pane of 4	.50	
73	A4	1½p black & ultra	.18	.15
a.		Booklet pane of 4	.75	
74	A4	2p black & lilac	.20	.15
75	A4	3p black & grnsh blue	.30	.18
a.		Booklet pane of 4	1.25	
76	A4	4½p black & brown	.60	.35
77	A4	6p black & green	.48	.30
a.		Booklet pane of 4	2.00	
78	A4	7p black & ver	.70	.40
79	A4	10p black & dk brn	.90	.50
80	A4	1sh black & lil rose	1.00	.60
81	A4	1sh6p black & olive	2.00	1.25
82	A4	2sh6p black & brn org	3.50	2.00
83	A4	5sh black & violet	6.75	4.00

Perf. 11½x11

84	A5	10sh lilac rose & dk bl	8.75	5.00
		Nos. 71-84 (14)	25.66	15.18

See Nos. 113-115. For surcharges see Nos. 108, 141-152. For overprints see Nos. 132.

ITU Issue
Common Design Type
1965, May 11 Litho. *Perf. 11x11½*

85	CD317	3p vermilion & gray	.95	.50
86	CD317	6p purple & orange	1.75	1.00

Intl. Cooperation Year Issue
Common Design Type
1965, Oct. 25 Wmk. 314 *Perf. 14½*

87	CD318	1p blue grn & claret	.35	.18
88	CD318	6p lt violet & green	2.25	1.25

Common Design Types pictured in section before Great Britain.

Churchill Memorial Issue
Common Design Type
Wmk. 314
1966, Jan. 24 Photo. *Perf. 14*
Design in Black, Gold and Carmine Rose

89	CD319	1p bright blue	.15	.15
90	CD319	3p green	.55	.24
91	CD319	6p brown	2.35	1.00
92	CD319	1sh6p violet	7.25	3.25
		Nos. 89-92 (4)	10.20	4.64

World Cup Soccer Issue
Common Design Type
1966 Litho. *Perf. 14*

93	CD320	3p multicolored	.40	.20
94	CD321	2sh6p multicolored	2.25	1.25

Nos. 93-94 were issued Oct. 1 in Tristan da Cunha, but on July 1 in St. Helena.

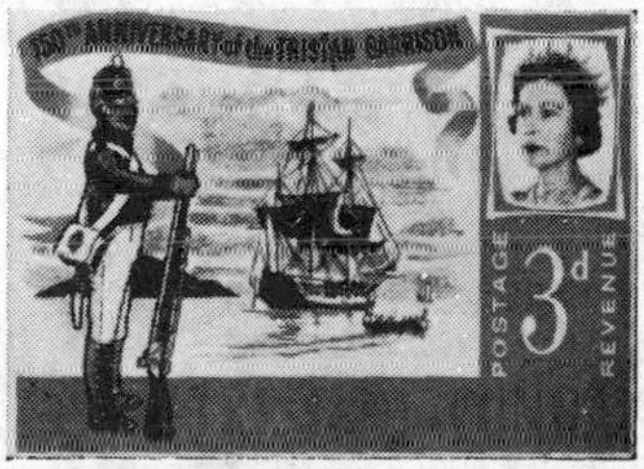

Light Dragoon of 19th Century and Sailing Ship — A6

Perf. 14½
1966, Aug. 15 Litho. Wmk. 314

95	A6	3p pale green & multi	.15	.15
96	A6	6p tan & multi	.35	.16
97	A6	1sh6p gray & multi	.90	.55
98	A6	2sh6p multicolored	1.50	.85
		Nos. 95-98 (4)	2.90	1.71

150th anniv. of the establishment of a garrison on Tristan da Cunha.

WHO Headquarters Issue
Common Design Type
1966, Oct. 1 Litho. *Perf. 14*

99	CD322	6p multicolored	.50	.30
100	CD322	5sh multicolored	2.50	1.50

UNESCO Anniversary Issue
Common Design Type
1966, Dec. 1 Litho. *Perf. 14*

101	CD323	10p "Education"	.50	.30
102	CD323	1sh6p "Science"	1.10	.60
103	CD323	2sh6p "Culture"	2.00	1.10
		Nos. 101-103 (3)	3.60	2.00

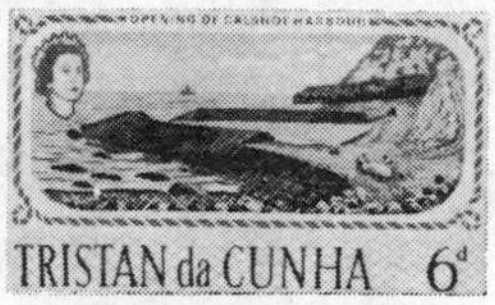

Calshot Harbor A7

Perf. 14x14½
1967, Jan. 2 Litho. Unwmk.

104	A7	6p dull green & multi	.15	.15
105	A7	10p brown & multi	.16	.15
106	A7	1sh6p dull blue & multi	.28	.22
107	A7	2sh6p orange brn & multi	.48	.40
		Nos. 104-107 (4)	1.07	.92

Opening of the artificial Calshot Harbor.

No. 76 Surcharged with New Value and Three Bars

Perf. 11x11½
1967, May 10 Engr. Wmk. 314

108	A4	4p on 4½p blk & brn	.30	.30

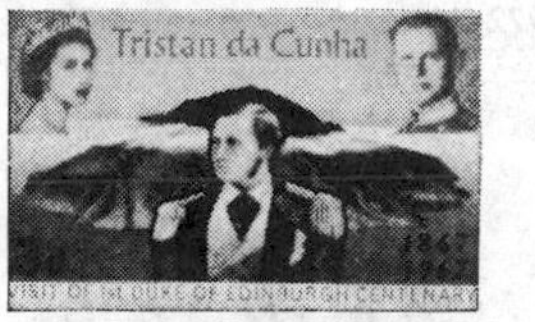

Tristan da Cunha, Prince Alfred, Queen Elizabeth II and Prince Philip — A8

1967, July 10 Litho. *Perf. 14x14½*

109	A8	3p blue grn, dk grn & blk	.15	.15
110	A8	6p dk carmine & blk	.15	.15
111	A8	1sh6p brt grn, gray grn & blk	.30	.25
112	A8	2sh6p dull ultra, sep & blk	.50	.45
		Nos. 109-112 (4)	1.10	1.00

Cent. of the visit of Prince Alfred, First Duke of Edinburgh, to Tristan da Cunha.

Types of 1965

Designs: 4p, H.M.S. Challenger, 1870. 10sh, South African research vessel, R.S.A. £1, Queen Elizabeth II.

Perf. 11x11½
1967, Sept. 1 Engr. Wmk. 314

113	A4	4p black & orange	1.00	.55
114	A4	10sh black & dull grn	26.00	14.00

Perf. 11½x11

115	A5	£1 brn org & dk blue	22.50	14.00
		Nos. 113-115 (3)	49.50	28.55

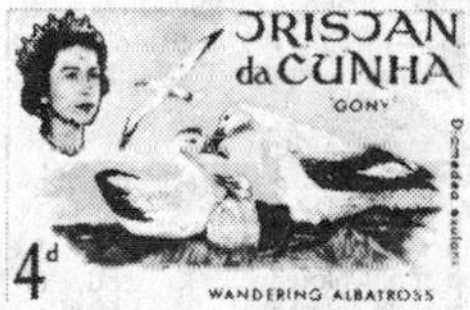

Wandering Albatross Nest — A9

Birds: 1sh, Big-billed buntings. 1sh6p, Tristan thrushes. 2sh6p, Great shearwaters.

Perf. 14x14½
1968, May 15 Photo. Wmk. 314

116	A9	4p multicolored	.16	.15
117	A9	1sh multicolored	.52	.30
118	A9	1sh6p multicolored	.95	.52
119	A9	2sh6p multicolored	1.50	.85
		Nos. 116-119 (4)	3.13	1.82

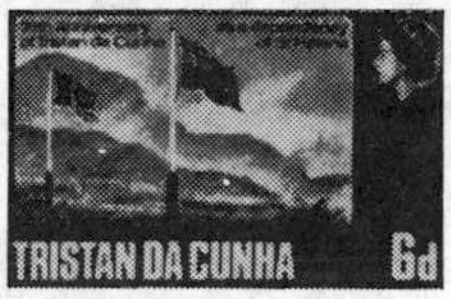

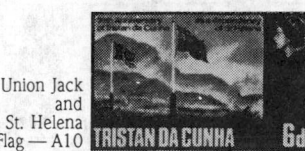

Union Jack and St. Helena Flag — A10

Design: 9p, 2sh6p, Map showing locations of St. Helena and Tristan da Cunha.

1968, Nov. 1 Litho. Wmk. 314

120	A10	6p violet & multi	.16	.15
121	A10	9p brn, bl grn & vio bl	.30	.22
122	A10	1sh6p green & multi	.55	.45
123	A10	2sh6p dp car, bl grn & vio bl	1.00	.80
		Nos. 120-123 (4)	2.01	1.62

30th anniv. of Tristan da Cunha as a Dependency of St. Helena.

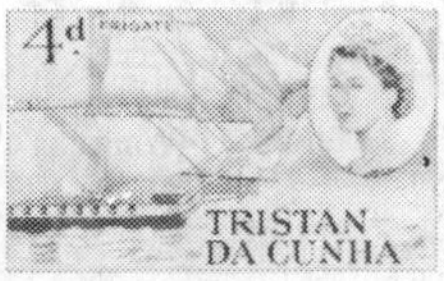

Frigate A11

Designs: 1sh, Cape Horner. 1sh6p, Barque. 2sh6p, Tea Clipper.

Perf. 11x11½
1969, June 1 Engr. Wmk. 314

124	A11	4p brt blue	.26	.16
125	A11	1sh rose carmine	.55	.48
126	A11	1sh6p green	.80	.65
127	A11	2sh6p sepia	1.40	1.10
		Nos. 124-127 (4)	3.01	2.39

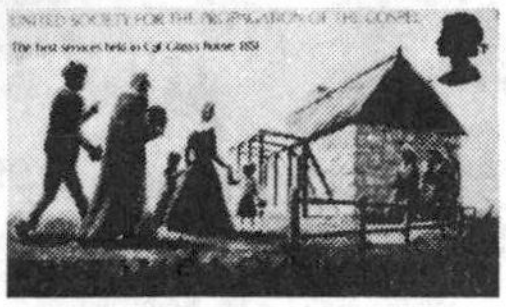
Islanders Going to First Religious Service, 1851 A12

Designs: 4p, Tristan da Cunha, birds and ship. 1sh6p, Landing at the beach. 2sh6p, St. Mary's Church, 1969, and procession.

Perf. 14½x14
1969, Nov. 1 Litho. Wmk. 314

128	A12	4p multicolored	.16	.15
129	A12	9p multicolored	.35	.22
130	A12	1sh6p multicolored	.65	.45
131	A12	2sh6p multicolored	1.25	.85
		Nos. 128-131 (4)	2.41	1.67

Issued to honor the work of the United Society for the Propagation of the Faith.

No. 77 Overprinted in Deep Orange: "NATIONAL / SAVINGS"

Perf. 11x11½
1970, May 15 Engr. Wmk. 314

132	A4	6p black & green	.35	.35

Issued to promote national savings. No. 132 also used as savings stamp.

In 1971, No. 132 was locally surcharged "2½p" and 3 short bars by means of a rubber handstamp.

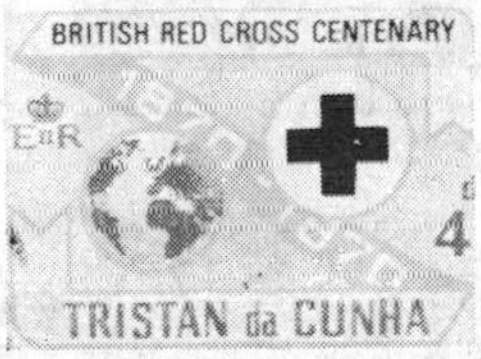

Globe and Red Cross A13

Design: 1sh9p, 2sh6p, British and Red Cross flags, vert.

Perf. 13½x13, 13x13½
1970, June 1 Litho.

133	A13	4p emer, red & grnsh bl	.16	.15
134	A13	9p bister, red & grnsh bl	.38	.22
135	A13	1sh9p gray, vio bl & red	1.10	.60
136	A13	2sh6p rose cl, vio bl & red	1.65	.95
		Nos. 133-136 (4)	3.29	1.92

Centenary of the British Red Cross Society.

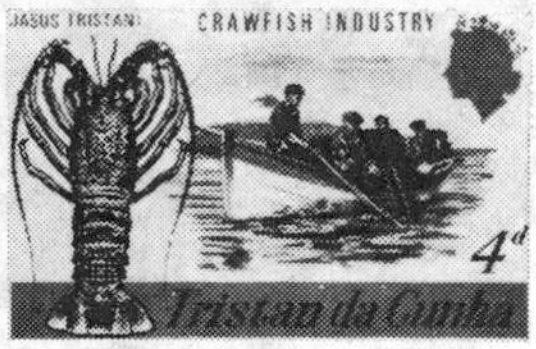

Rock Lobster and Lobster Men Placing Trap A14

Designs: 10p, 2sh6p, Workers in processing plant and side view of rock lobster (jasus tristani).

Perf. 12½x13
1970, Nov. 1 Litho. Wmk. 314

137	A14	4p lilac rose & multi	.18	.15
138	A14	10p dull yel & multi	.45	.22
139	A14	1sh6p brown org & multi	1.25	.60
140	A14	2sh6p olive & multi	1.90	.95
		Nos. 137-140 (4)	3.78	1.92

Issued to publicize the Tristan da Cunha rock lobster (crawfish) industry.

Nos. 72-74, 77-83, 113-114 Surcharged with New Value and Three Bars

Perf. 11x11½

1971, Feb. 15 Engr. Wmk. 314

141 A4 ½p on 1p .15 .15
142 A4 1p on 2p .15 .15
143 A4 1½p on 4p .15 .15
144 A4 2½p on 6p .20 .15
145 A4 3p on 7p .28 .22
146 A4 4p on 10p .40 .25
147 A4 5p on 1sh .50 .35
148 A4 7½p on 1sh6p .85 .55
149 A4 12½p on 2sh6p 1.75 1.10
150 A4 15p on 1½p 2.50 1.75
151 A4 25p on 5sh 3.25 2.25
152 A4 50p on 10sh 9.50 7.00
Nos. 141-152 (12) 19.68 14.07

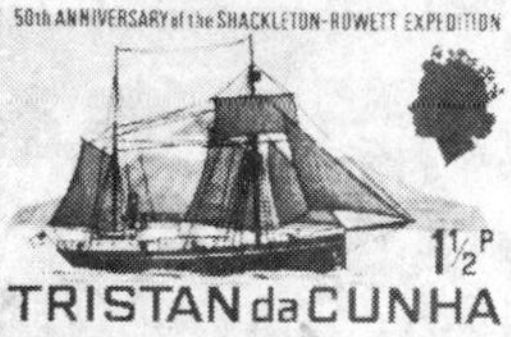

"Quest" A15

Designs: 4p, Presentation of Scout Troop flag in front of Tristan school. 7½p, Great Britain No. 167a with Tristan da Cunha cancellation. 12½c, Sir Ernest Henry Shackleton, boat and expedition cancellations.

Perf. 13½x14

1971, June 1 Litho. Wmk. 314

153 A15 1½p lt blue & multi .25 .15
154 A15 4p buff, yel grn & blk .75 .35
155 A15 7½p pale grn, rose lil & blk 1.75 .90
156 A15 12½p buff & multi 3.00 1.50
Nos. 153-156 (4) 5.75 2.90

50th anniversary of the Shackleton-Rowett South Atlantic expedition.

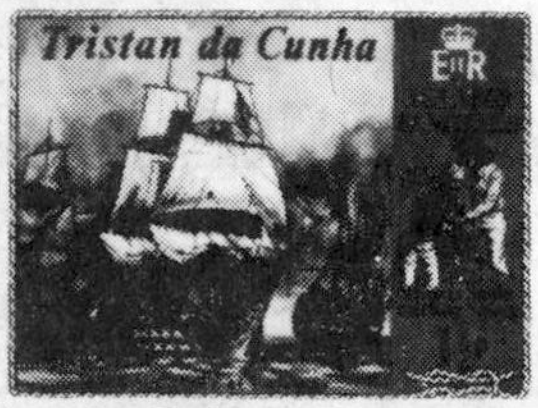

"Victory" at Trafalgar and Thomas Swain Catching Nelson — A16

Ships and Island Families: 2½p, "Emily of Stonington" and inscribed P. W. Green, 1836. 4p, "Italia" and inscribed Gaetano Lavarello, 1892, and Andrea Repetto. 7½p, "Falmouth" and Corp. William Glass, 1816. 12½p, American Whaler and inscribed 1836 Joshua Rogers, 1849, Capt. Andrew Hangan.

1971, Nov. 1

157 A16 1½p bister & multi .28 .30
158 A16 2½p multicolored .55 .62
159 A16 4p gray & multi 1.10 1.25
160 A16 7½p multicolored 1.75 2.00
161 A16 12½p blue & multi 2.75 3.00
Nos. 157-161 (5) 6.43 7.17

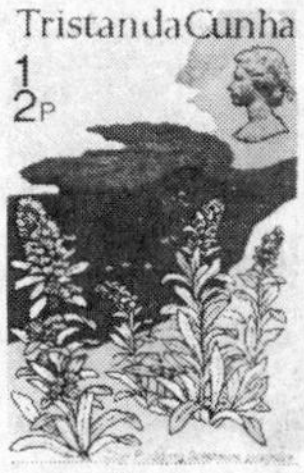

Cow Pudding — A17

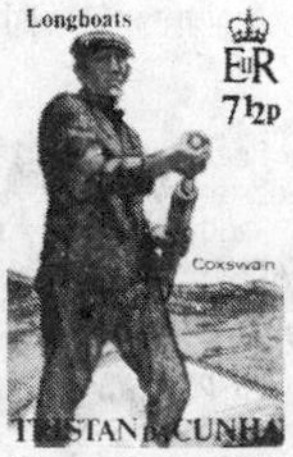

Coxswain — A18

Native Flora: 1p, Peak berry and crater lake. 1½p, Sand flower, horiz. 2½p, New Zealand flax, horiz. 3p, Island tree. 4p, Bog fern and snow-capped mountain. 5p, Dog catcher and albatrosses. 7½p, Celery and terns. 12½p, Pepper tree and waterfall. 25p, Foul berry, horiz. 50p, Tussock and penguins. £1, Tussac and islands, horiz.

Perf. 13½x13, 13x13½

1972, Feb. 26 Wmk. 314

162 A17 ½p gray & multi .15 .15
163 A17 1p salmon & multi .15 .15
164 A17 1½p green & multi .16 .15
165 A17 2½p multicolored .22 .22
166 A17 3p multicolored .26 .26
167 A17 4p lemon & multi .30 .30
168 A17 5p yel grn & multi .38 .35
169 A17 7½p dull yel & multi .52 .52
170 A17 12½p multicolored .85 .85
171 A17 25p gray & multi 1.75 1.75

Litho. and Engr.

172 A17 50p multicolored 4.25 4.00
173 A17 £1 lt blue & multi 7.50 7.50
Nos. 162-173 (12) 16.49 16.20

1972, June 1 Litho. *Perf. 14*

Designs: 2½p, Launching longboat, horiz. 4p, Men rowing longboat, horiz. 12½p, Longboat under sail.

174 A18 2½p multicolored .30 .20
175 A18 4p multicolored .45 .35
176 A18 7½p multicolored .90 .70
177 A18 12½p multicolored 1.50 1.10
Nos. 174-177 (4) 3.15 2.35

Silver Wedding Issue, 1972

Common Design Type

Design: Queen Elizabeth II, Prince Philip, thrush and wandering albatrosses.

Perf. 14x14½

1972, Nov. 20 Photo. Wmk. 314

178 CD324 2½p multicolored .35 .30
179 CD324 7½p ultra & multi .85 .75

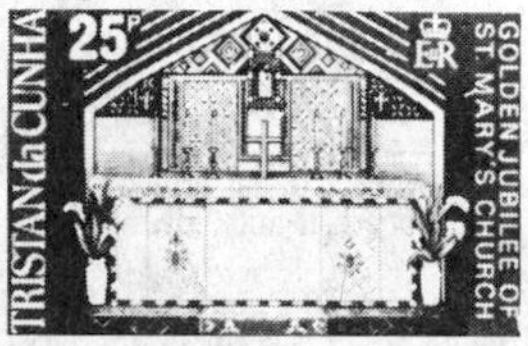

Altar, St. Mary's Church A19

1973, July 8 Litho. *Perf. 13½*

180 A19 25p dk blue & multi 2.50 2.50

50th anniversary of St. Mary's Church, Tristan da Cunha.

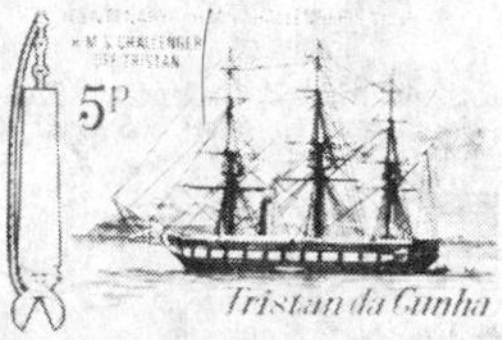

"Challenger" off Tristan, Steil's Sounding Instrument — A20

Designs: 4p, Challenger's laboratory. 7½p, Challenger off Nightingale Island. 12½p, Map of Challenger's voyage. Each stamp shows an instrument for deep sea soundings.

Perf. 13½x14

1973, Oct. 15 Wmk. 314

181 A20 4p multicolored .30 .30
182 A20 5p multicolored .50 .50
183 A20 7½p multicolored .80 .80
184 A20 12½p multicolored 1.50 1.50
a. Souvenir sheet of 4, #181-184, perf. 13½ 4.00 4.00
Nos. 181-184 (4) 3.10 3.10

Centenary of "Challenger's" visit to Tristan da Cunha during oceanographic exploration world trip, 1872-76.

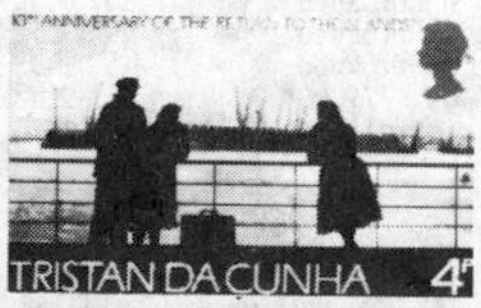

View of English Port from Shipboard A21

Designs: 5p, Inspectors at volcano rim. 7½p, Islanders disembarking from "Bornholm." 12½p, Islanders on board ship approaching Tristan da Cunha.

1973, Nov. 10 *Perf. 14½*

185 A21 4p yellow, blk & gold .45 .32
186 A21 5p multicolored .55 .42
187 A21 7½p multicolored .80 .60
188 A21 12½p multicolored 1.10 .85
Nos. 185-188 (4) 2.90 2.19

10th anniversary of return of islanders to Tristan da Cunha.

Princess Anne's Wedding Issue

Common Design Type

1973, Nov. 14 Wmk. 314 *Perf. 14*

189 CD325 7½p multicolored .28 .28
190 CD325 12½p blue grn & multi .45 .45

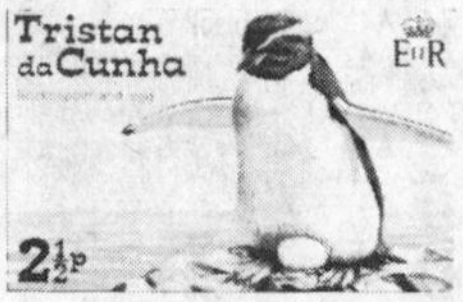

Rockhopper Penguin A22

Designs: Rockhopper penguins.

1974, May 1 Litho.

191 A22 2½p shown 2.75 1.25
192 A22 5p Colony 3.25 1.65
193 A22 7½p Penguins fishing 3.75 2.00
194 A22 25p Penguin and fledgling 8.75 5.00
Nos. 191-194 (4) 18.50 9.90

Souvenir Sheet

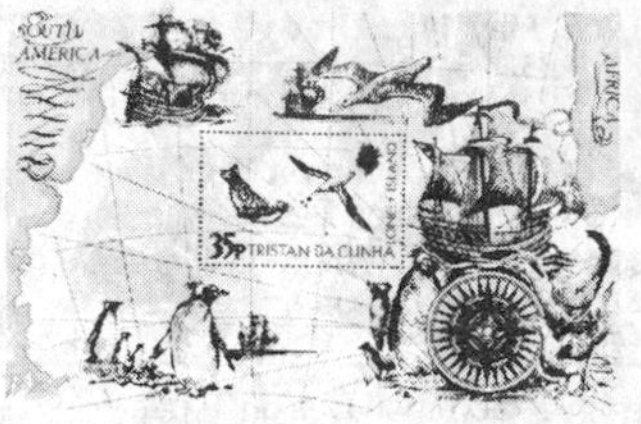

Map of Tristan da Cunha, Penguin and Sea Gull — A23

1974, Oct. 1 Wmk. 314 *Perf. 13½*

195 A23 35p multicolored 3.50 2.25

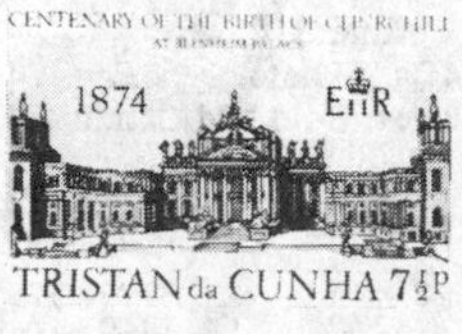

Blenheim Palace A24

Design: 25p, Churchill and Queen Elizabeth II.

Wmk. 373

1974, Nov. 30 Litho. *Perf. 14*

196 A24 7½p black & yellow .30 .28
197 A24 25p black & brown .75 .70
a. Souvenir sheet of 2, #196-197 1.50 1.25

Sir Winston Churchill (1874-1965).

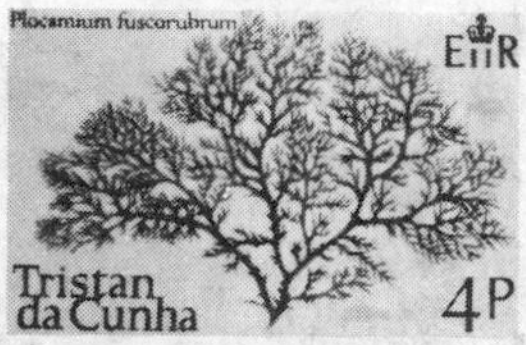

Plocamium Fuscorubrum — A25

Aquatic Plants: 5p, Ulva lactuca. 10p, Epymenia flabellata. 20p, Macrocystis pyrifera.

1975, Apr. 16 Wmk. 314 *Perf. 13x14*

198 A25 4p lilac & multi .26 .22
199 A25 5p ultra & multi .35 .28
200 A25 10p yellow & multi .65 .55
201 A25 20p lt green & multi 1.25 1.10
Nos. 198-201 (4) 2.51 2.15

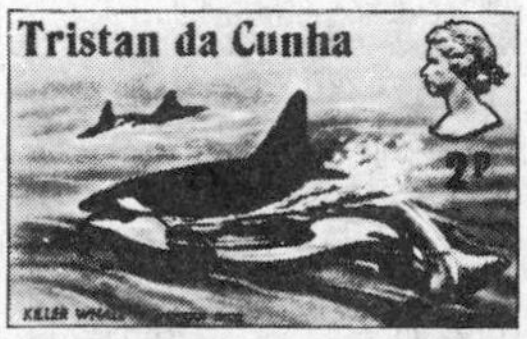

Killer Whales A26

Perf. 13½

1975, Nov. 1 Litho. Wmk. 314

202 A26 2p shown .28 .16
203 A26 3p Rough-toothed dolphins .42 .22
204 A26 5p Atlantic right whale 1.25 .60
205 A26 20p Finback whales 3.00 1.40
Nos. 202-205 (4) 4.95 2.38

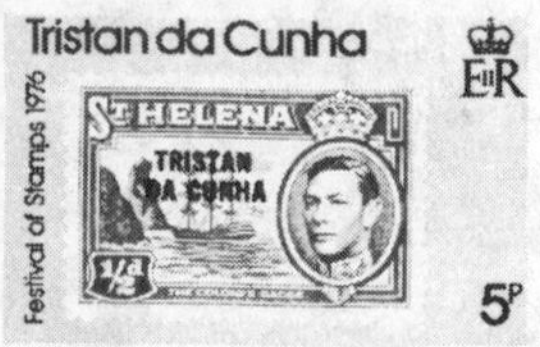

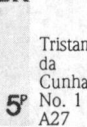

Tristan da Cunha No. 1 A27

Designs: 9p, Tristan da Cunha #13, vert. 25p, Freighter Tristania II.

Perf. 13½x14, 14x13½

1976, May 4 Litho. Wmk. 373

206 A27 5p lilac, vio & blk .25 .25
207 A27 9p bluish gray, grn & blk .40 .40
208 A27 25p multicolored 1.25 1.25
Nos. 206-208 (3) 1.90 1.90

Festival of Stamps 1976. For souvenir sheet containing No. 208 see Ascension No. 214a.

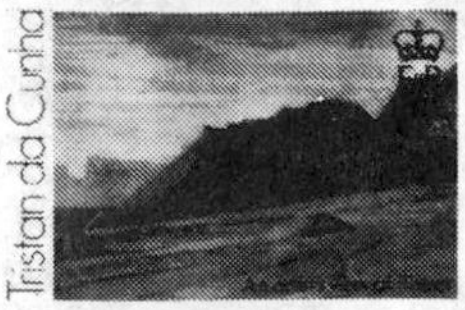

The Patches A28

Views, by Roland Svensson: 3p, Tristan house, vert. 10p, Tristan Settlement and Cliffs. 20p, Huts at Nightingale, vert.

1976, Oct. 4 Litho. *Perf. 14*

209 A28 3p multicolored .20 .16
210 A28 5p multicolored .28 .20
211 A28 10p multicolored .55 .45
212 A28 20p multicolored 1.25 .85
a. Souvenir sheet of 4, #209-211 3.00 2.25
Nos. 209-212 (4) 2.28 1.66

An artist's view of Tristan da Cunha. See Nos. 234-237.

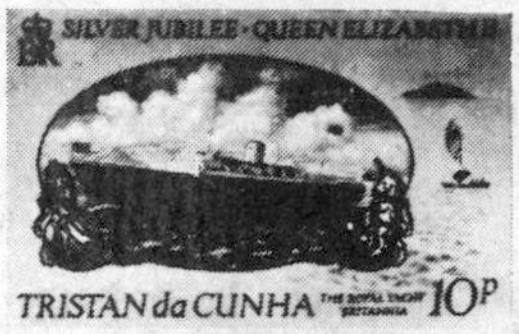

Royal Yacht Britannia — A29

Designs: 15p, Royal standard. 25p, Royal family.

1977, Feb. 7 Wmk. 373 *Perf. 13*

213 A29 10p multicolored .65 .52
214 A29 15p multicolored .52 .42
215 A29 25p multicolored .85 .70
Nos. 213-215 (3) 2.02 1.64

25th anniv. of the reign of Elizabeth II. For surcharges see Nos. 220-221.

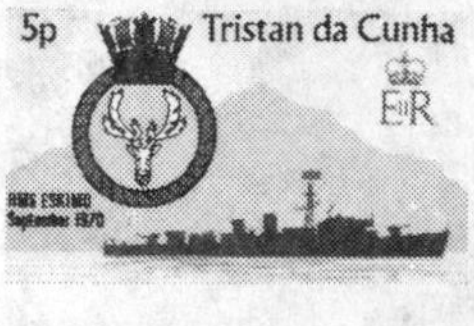

H.M.S. Eskimo, Sept. 1970 A30

Royal Naval Ships and Arms: 10p, Naiad, Nov. 1968. 15p, Jaguar, Mar. 1964. 20p, London, Dec. 1964. Dates of visits to island.

1977, Oct. 1 Litho. *Perf. 14½*

216 A30 5p multicolored .22 .18
217 A30 10p multicolored .45 .35
218 A30 15p multicolored .70 .55
219 A30 20p multicolored .90 .70
a. Souvenir sheet of 4, #216-219 3.00 2.50
Nos. 216-219 (4) 2.27 1.78

Nos. 214-215 Surcharged with New Value and Bar

1977, Oct. 13 Wmk. 373 *Perf. 13*

220 A29 4p on 15p multi 7.00 6.25
221 A29 7½p on 25p multi 7.00 6.25

Tristan da Cunha stamps can be mounted in the Scott British Africa album.

Giant
Fulmars — A31

Perf. 13½x14, 14x13½

1977, Dec. 1   Litho.

Design A31

222	1p	Pterodroma macroptera	.15	.15
223	2p	Fregetta marina	.15	.15
224	3p	Macronectes giganteus	.15	.15
225	4p	Pterodroma mollis	.15	.15
226	5p	Diomedea exulans	.16	.15
227	10p	Pterodroma brevirostris	.32	.18
228	15p	Sterna vittata	.50	.28
229	20p	Puffinus gravis	.60	.35
230	25p	Pachyptila vittata	.80	.45
231	50p	Catharacta skua	1.50	.90
232	£1	Pelecanoides urinatrix	2.50	1.25
233	£2	Diomedea chlororynchos	5.50	3.00
		Nos. 222-233 (12)	12.48	7.16

For overprints see Nos. 318-319.

Painting Type of 1976

Views by Roland Svensson: 5p, St. Mary's Church. 10p, Longboats. 15p, A Tristan home. 20p, Harbor, 1970.

Perf. 14½

1978, Mar. 1   Wmk. 373   Litho.

234	A28	5p multicolored	.25	.16
235	A28	10p multicolored	.50	.30
236	A28	15p multicolored	.80	.45
237	A28	20p multicolored	1.25	.65
a.		Souvenir sheet of 4, #234-237	3.00	2.50
		Nos. 234-237 (4)	2.80	1.56

An artist's view of Tristan da Cunha.

Elizabeth II Coronation Anniversary

Common Design Types

Souvenir Sheet

1978, Apr. 21   Unwmk.   Perf. 15

238		Sheet of 6	3.50	3.75
a.	CD326	25p King's Bull	.65	.65
b.	CD327	25p Elizabeth II	.65	.65
c.	CD328	25p Tristan crawfish	.65	.65

No. 238 contains 2 se-tenant strips of Nos. 238a-238c, separated by horizontal gutter with commemorative and descriptive inscriptions and showing central part of coronation procession with coach.

Sodalite — A32

Local Minerals: 5p, Aragonite. 10p, Sulphur. 20p, Lava containing pyroxene crystal.

Perf. 13½x14

1978, June 9   Litho.   Wmk. 373

239	A32	3p multicolored	.20	.15
240	A32	5p multicolored	.32	.20
241	A32	10p multicolored	.65	.40
242	A32	20p multicolored	1.25	.80
		Nos. 239-242 (4)	2.42	1.55

Fish
A33

1978, Sept. 29   Litho.   Perf. 14

243	A33	5p Klipfish	.22	.16
244	A33	10p Fivefinger	.45	.30
245	A33	15p Concha	.70	.45
246	A33	20p Soldier	.85	.55
		Nos. 243-246 (4)	2.22	1.46

Orangeleaf and
Navy
Flag — A34

Royal Fleet Auxiliary Vessels: 10p, Tarbatness. 20p, Tidereach. 25p, Reliant.

1978, Nov. 24   Litho.   Perf. 12½

247	A34	5p multicolored	.18	.15
248	A34	10p multicolored	.35	.24
249	A34	20p multicolored	.75	.48
250	A34	25p multicolored	.95	.60
a.		Souvenir sheet of 4, #247-250	3.50	3.50
		Nos. 247-250 (4)	2.23	1.47

Fur Seals — A35

Wildlife conservation: 5p, Elephant seal. 15p, Tristan thrush. 20p, Tristan buntings.

Wmk. 373

1979, Jan. 3   Litho.   Perf. 14

251	A35	5p multicolored	.20	.18
252	A35	10p multicolored	.42	.35
253	A35	15p multicolored	.60	.52
254	A35	20p multicolored	.85	.70
		Nos. 251-254 (4)	2.07	1.75

Tristan
Longboat
A36

Ships: 10p, Queen Mary. 15p, Queen Elizabeth. 20p, QE II. 25p, QE II, longboat, view of Tristan.

1979, Feb. 8   Perf. 14½

255	A36	5p multicolored	.32	.28
256	A36	10p multicolored	.42	.38
257	A36	15p multicolored	.60	.55
258	A36	20p multicolored	.85	.75
		Nos. 255-258 (4)	2.19	1.96

Souvenir Sheet

259	A36	25p multicolored	5.00	4.00

Visit of cruise ship QE II, Feb. 8.

Tristan da
Cunha
5p No. 12
A37

Tristan da Cunha Stamps: 10p, No. 26. 25p, No. 58, vert. 50p, 1p-local "potatoe" stamp.

Perf. 14½x14, 14x14½

1979, Aug. 27   Litho.   Wmk. 373

260	A37	5p multicolored	.16	.16
261	A37	10p multicolored	.28	.28
262	A37	25p multicolored	.70	.70
		Nos. 260-262 (3)	1.14	1.14

Souvenir Sheet

263	A37	50p multicolored	1.10	1.10

Sir Rowland Hill (1795-1879), originator of penny postage.

The Padre's
House, IYC
Emblem
A38

IYC Emblem, Children's Drawings: 10p, "Houses in the Village." 15p, "St. Mary's Church." 20p, "Rockhopper Penguins."

1979, Nov. 26   Litho.   Perf. 14

264	A38	5p multicolored	.15	.15
265	A38	10p multicolored	.25	.25
266	A38	15p multicolored	.40	.40
267	A38	20p multicolored	.52	.52
		Nos. 264-267 (4)	1.32	1.32

International Year of the Child.

Stoltenhoff
Island
A39

Views (Sketches by Roland Svensson): 10p, Nightingale from the East. 15p, The Administrator's abode, vert. 20p, "Ridge where the goat jumped off," vert.

1980, Feb.   Litho.   Perf. 14

268	A39	5p multicolored	.16	.15
269	A39	10p multicolored	.30	.20
270	A39	15p multicolored	.45	.28
271	A39	20p multicolored	.60	.40
a.		Souvenir sheet of 4, #268-271	1.50	1.50
		Nos. 268-271 (4)	1.51	1.03

Mail Pickup
Boat — A40

Golden
Hinde — A41

1980, May 6   Litho.   Perf. 14

272	A40	5p shown	.15	.15
273	A40	10p Unloading mail	.24	.20
274	A40	15p Truck transport	.35	.30
275	A40	20p Delivery bell	.48	.40
276	A40	25p Distribution	.60	.50
		Nos. 272-276 (5)	1.82	1.55

London 80 Intl. Stamp Exhib., May 6-14.

Queen Mother Elizabeth Birthday Issue

Common Design Type

1980, Aug. 11   Litho.   Perf. 14

277	CD330	14p multicolored	.35	.35

1980, Sept. 6   Perf. 14½

278	A41	5p shown	.15	.15
279	A41	10p Drake's route	.26	.16
280	A41	20p Sir Francis Drake	.50	.35
281	A41	25p Queen Elizabeth I	.60	.42
		Nos. 278-281 (4)	1.51	1.08

Sir Francis Drake's circumnavigation, 400th anniversary.

Humpty
Dumpty
A42

Perf. 13½

1980, Oct. 31   Litho.   Wmk. 373

282		Sheet of 9	3.50	2.25
a.	A42	15p shown	.35	.22
b.	A42	15p Mary had a Little Lamb	.35	.22
c.	A42	15p Little Jack Horner	.35	.22
d.	A42	15p Hey Diddle Diddle	.35	.22
e.	A42	15p London Bridge	.35	.22
f.	A42	15p Old King Cole	.35	.22
g.	A42	15p Sing a Song of Sixpence	.35	.22
h.	A42	15p Tom Tom the Piper's Son	.35	.22
i.	A42	25p The Owl and the Pussy Cat	.35	.22

Christmas 1980.

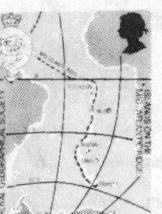

Islands on Mid-
Atlantic Ridge,
Society
Emblem — A43

Royal Geographical Soc., 150th Anniv. (Maps and Expeditions): 10p, Tristan da Cunha, Francis Beaufort, 1806. 15p, Tristan Island, Norwegian expedition, 1937-1938. 20p, Gough Island, scientific survey, 1955-1956.

1980, Dec. 15

283	A43	5p multicolored	.16	.15
284	A43	10p multicolored	.30	.26
285	A43	15p multicolored	.45	.40
286	A43	20p multicolored	.60	.50
		Nos. 283-286 (4)	1.51	1.31

Rev. Edwin
Dodgson
A44

Wmk. 373

1981, Mar. 23   Litho.   Perf. 14

287	A44	10p portrait, vert.	.30	.20
288	A44	20p shown	.60	.40
289	A44	30p Dodgson preaching, vert.	.90	.65
a.		Souvenir sheet of 3, #287-289	1.75	1.50
		Nos. 287-289 (3)	1.80	1.25

Centenary of arrival of Rev. Edwin H. Dodgson, who saved population from starvation.

Map of Tristan da Cunha showing L'heure du Berger Route, 1767 (Dalrymple's Map, 1781) — A45

Early Maps and Charts By: 5p, 21p, Capt. Denham, 1853 (diff.). 35p, Ivan Keulen, 1700.

1981, May 22

290	A45	5p multicolored	.15	.20
291	A45	14p multicolored	.55	.40
292	A45	21p multicolored	.65	.85
		Nos. 290-292 (3)	1.35	1.45

Souvenir Sheet

293	A45	35p multicolored	1.00	.70

Royal Wedding Issue

Common Design Type

Wmk. 373

1981, July 22   Litho.   Perf. 14

294	CD331	5p Bouquet	.15	.15
295	CD331	20p Charles	.52	.45
296	CD331	50p Couple	1.25	1.10
		Nos. 294-296 (3)	1.92	1.70

Hiking — A46

1981, Sept. 14

297	A46	5p shown	.16	.15
298	A46	10p Camping	.28	.18
299	A46	20p Map reading	.55	.35
300	A46	25p Prince Philip	.65	.42
		Nos. 297-300 (4)	1.64	1.10

Duke of Edinburgh's Awards, 25th anniv.

Inaccessible Island Rail — A47

1981, Nov. 1   Litho.   Perf. 13¹/₂x14
301   Strip of 4   1.40 1.10
  a. A47 10p Nest   .35   .25
  b. A47 10p Eggs   .35   .25
  c. A47 10p Chicks   .35   .25
  d. A47 10p Adult rail   .35   .25

Six-gilled
Shark — A48

1982, Feb. 8   Litho.   Perf. 13¹/₂x14
302 A48 5p shown   .16   .15
303 A48 14p Porbeagle shark .42   .28
304 A48 21p Blue shark   .65   .45
305 A48 35p Hammerhead shark 1.00 .70
    Nos. 302-305 (4)   2.23 1.58

Marcella — A49

1982, Apr. 5   Litho.   Perf. 14
306 A49 5p shown   .15   .15
307 A49 15p Eliza Adams   .40   .32
308 A49 30p Corinthian   .85   .70
309 A49 50p Samuel & Thomas 1.25 1.10
    Nos. 306-309 (4)   2.65 2.27
       See Nos. 324-327.

Princess Diana Issue
Common Design Type
Perf. 14¹/₂x14
1982, July 1   Litho.   Wmk. 373
310 CD333 5p Arms   .15   .15
311 CD333 15p Diana   .35   .28
312 CD333 30p Wedding   .75   .55
313 CD333 50p Portrait   1.10 .90
    Nos. 310-313 (4)   2.35 1.88

Scouting Year — A50

Perf. 13¹/₂x13, 13x13¹/₂
1982, Aug. 23   Litho.
314 A50 5p Baden-Powell, vert. .16 .15
315 A50 20p Brownsea Isld. camp,
           1907, vert.   .55 .45
316 A50 50p Saluting   1.25 1.10
    Nos. 314-316 (3)   1.96 1.70

Souvenir Sheet
Perf. 14
317 A50 50p Tree illustration, vert. 1.25 1.10

Nos. 226, 230 Overprinted: "1st
PARTICIPATION / COMMONWEALTH /
GAMES 1982"
Perf. 13¹/₂x14
1982, Sept. 28   Litho.   Wmk. 373
318 A31 5p multicolored   .15   .15
319 A31 50p multicolored   .75   .65

12th Commonwealth Games, Brisbane, Australia, Sept. 30-Oct. 9.

Formation of
Volcanic
Island — A51

1982, Nov. 1   Perf. 14x14¹/₂
320 A51 5p shown   .15   .15
321 A51 15p Surface cinder cones .40 .32
322 A51 25p Eruption   .65   .55
323 A51 35p 1961 eruption   .90   .75
    Nos. 320-323 (4)   2.10 1.77

Ship Type of 1982

1983, Feb. 1   Litho.   Perf. 14
324 A49 5p Islander, vert.   .15   .15
325 A49 20p Roscoe   .52   .52
326 A49 30p Columbia   .90   .75
327 A49 50p Emeline, vert.   1.25 1.10
    Nos. 324-327 (4)   2.82 2.52

Tractor
Pulling
Trailer
A52

1983, May 2   Litho.   Perf. 14
328 A52 5p shown   .15   .15
329 A52 15p Pack mules   .42   .30
330 A52 30p Oxen pulling cart .80 .65
331 A52 50p Jeep   1.25 1.00
    Nos. 328-331 (4)   2.62 2.10

Map of
South
Atlantic
A53

Island History.

Wmk. 373
1983, Aug. 1   Litho.   Perf. 14
332 A53 1p shown   .15   .15
333 A53 3p Tristao d'Acunha's
           flagship   .15   .15
334 A53 4p Landing, 1643   .15   .15
335 A53 5p 17th cent. views .15   .15
336 A53 10p Landing party, 1815 .28 .22
337 A53 15p Settlement   .40   .35
338 A53 18p Governor Glass's
           house   .50   .40
339 A53 20p Rev. W.F. Taylor, Pe-
           ter Green   .55   .45
340 A53 25p Three-master John
           and Elizabeth   .65   .55
341 A53 50p Dependency declara-
           tion of St. Helena,
           1938   1.40 1.10
342 A53 £1 Commissioning cere-
           mony   2.75 2.25
343 A53 £2 Evacuation, 1961 5.50 4.50
    Nos. 332-343 (12)   12.63 10.42

Raphael, 500th Birth
Anniv. — A54

1983, Oct. 27   Litho.   Perf. 14¹/₂
344 A54 10p multicolored   .25   .22
345 A54 25p multicolored   .65   .52
346 A54 40p multicolored   1.10 .90
    Nos. 344-346 (3)   2.00 1.64
Souvenir Sheet
347 A54 50p multi, horiz.   1.50 1.25
    Details from Christ's Charge to St. Peter.

St. Helena Colony Sesquicentenary — A55

1984, Jan. 3   Litho.   Perf. 14
348 A55 10p No. 7   .25   .20
349 A55 15p No. 9   .40   .30
350 A55 25p No. 10   .65   .50
351 A55 60p No. 12   1.65 1.25
    Nos. 348-351 (4)   2.95 2.25

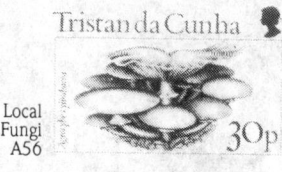

Local
Fungi
A56

1984, Mar. 26
352 A56 10p Agrocybe praecox, vert. .32 .25
353 A56 20p Laccaria tetraspora,
           vert.   .65   .50
354 A45 30p Agrocybe cylindracea 1.00 .75
355 A56 50p Sarcoscypha coccinea 1.65 1.25
    Nos. 352-355 (4)   3.62 2.75

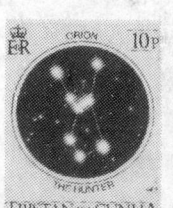

Constellations — A57   Sheep
                            Shearing — A58

1984, July 30   Perf. 14¹/₂
356 A57 10p Orion   .25   .22
357 A57 20p Scorpius   .52   .45
358 A57 25p Canis Major   .65   .55
359 A57 50p Crux   1.25 1.10
    Nos. 356-359 (4)   2.67 2.32

1984, Oct. 1
360 A58 9p shown   .24   .20
361 A58 17p Carding wool   .45   .38
362 A58 29p Spinning   .75   .65
363 A58 45p Knitting   1.25 1.00
  a. Souvenir Sheet of 4, #360-363 2.75 2.25
    Nos. 360-363 (4)   2.69 2.23

Christmas
1984 — A59

1984, Dec. 3   Perf. 14
364 A59 10p Three angels, Christmas
           dinner   .25   .24
365 A59 20p Two angels, cart .50 .48
366 A59 30p Candles, sailboat .80 .70
367 A59 50p Trees, Nativity 1.25 1.10
    Nos. 364-367 (4)   2.80 2.52

Shipwrecks — A60

1985, Feb. 4   Perf. 14x13¹/₂, 13¹/₂x14
368 A60 10p HMS Julia, 1817, vert. .32 .25
369 A60 25p Bell from Mabel Clark,
           1878, vert.   .80   .65
370 A60 35p Barque Glenhuntley,
           1898   1.10 .85
    Nos. 368-370 (3)   2.22 1.75

Souvenir Sheet
371 A60 60p Map of shipwreck sites 2.00 1.65
No. 371 contains one 48x32mm stamp.

See Nos. 393-396, 412-415.

Queen Mother 85th Birthday
Common Design Type
Perf. 14¹/₂x14
1985, June 7   Litho.   Wmk. 384
372 CD336 10p With Prince Charles,
             1954   .30   .30
373 CD336 20p With Margaret at
             Ascot   .60   .60
374 CD336 30p Queen Mother   .90   .90
375 CD336 50p Holding Prince Hen-
             ry   1.10 1.10
    Nos. 372-375 (4)   2.90 2.90
Souvenir Sheet
376 CD336 80p With Anne   2.75 2.75

Flags — A61

Designs: 10p, Jonathan Lambert and flag of
1811, Isles of Refreshment. 15p, Cannon and flag
of 21st Light Dragoons, 1816-17, Fort Malcolm.
25p, HMS Falmouth, 1816, and flag of HMS Atlantic Isle, HMS JOB 9, 1942-46. 60p, View of Tristan
and Union Jack, 1816 to date.

1985, Sept. 30   Wmk. 373   Perf. 14
377 A61 10p multicolored   .28   .28
378 A61 15p multicolored   .42   .42
379 A61 30p multicolored   .72   .72
380 A61 60p multicolored   1.75 1.75
    Nos. 377-380 (4)   3.17 3.17
       Nos. 378-380 vert.

Loss of The
Lifeboat,
Cent. — A62

1985, Nov. 28
381 A62 10p Lifeboat, barque West
           Riding   .30   .30
382 A62 30p Map   .90   .90
383 A62 50p Death toll   1.50 1.50
    Nos. 381-383 (3)   2.70 2.70

Halley's
Comet
A63

1986, Mar. 3   Wmk. 384
384 A63 10p Bayeux Tapestry,
           c. 1092   .28   .28
385 A63 20p Trajectory around Earth .55 .55
386 A63 30p Comet over Inaccessi-
           ble Is.   .80   .80
387 A63 50p Ship Paramour   1.40 1.40
    Nos. 384-387 (4)   3.03 3.03

Queen Elizabeth II 60th Birthday
Common Design Type
Designs: 10p, With Prince Charles, 1950. 15p,
Birthday Parade, wearing uniform of Scots Guards,
1976. 25p, At Westminster Abbey, London, 1972,
wearing mantle and robes of the Most Noble Order
of Bath. 45p, Silver Jubilee Tour, Canada, 1977.
65p, Visiting Crown Agents' offices, 1983.

1986, Apr. 21   Perf. 14¹/₂
388 CD337 10p scarlet, blk & sil .28 .28
389 CD337 15p ultra & multi .40   .40
390 CD337 25p green & multi .65   .65
391 CD337 45p violet & multi 1.25 1.25
392 CD337 65p rose vio & multi 1.65 1.65
    Nos. 388-392 (5)   4.23 4.23

For overprints see Nos. 429-433.

Shipwrecks Type of 1985

1986, June 2   *Perf. 13½*
393 A60 9p SV Allanshaw, 1893   .28 .28
394 A60 20p Church font from Edward Vittery, 1881   .65 .65
395 A60 40p Figurehead, 1940   1.40 1.40
    Nos. 393-395 (3)   2.33 2.33

Souvenir Sheet
Perf. 13½x13
396 A60 65p Barque Italia, 1892   2.50 2.50
    Nos. 394-395 vert.

Royal Wedding Issue, 1986
Common Design Type

Designs: 10p, Informal portrait. 40p, Andrew operating helicopter.

1986, July 23   *Perf. 14*
397 CD338 10p multicolored   .25 .25
398 CD338 40p multicolored   1.10 1.10

A64   A65

1986, Sept. 30
399 A64 5p Wandering albatross   .16 .16
400 A64 10p Daisy   .35 .35
401 A64 20p Vanessa butterfly   .70 .70
402 A64 25p Wilkins's bunting   .85 .85
403 A64 50p Ring-eye   1.75 1.75
    Nos. 399-403 (5)   3.81 3.81

Flora & fauna of Inaccessible Island.

Indigenous Flightless Species and Habitats: 10p, Flightless moth, Edinburgh Settlement. 25p, Strapwinged fly, Crater Lake. 35p, Flightless rail, Inaccessible Island. 50p, Gough Island moorhen, Gough Island.

1987, Jan. 23   *Perf. 14½*
404 A65 10p multicolored   .32 .32
405 A65 25p multicolored   .80 .80
406 A65 35p multicolored   1.10 1.10
407 A65 50p multicolored   1.65 1.65
    Nos. 404-407 (4)   3.87 3.87

Rockhopper Penguins — A66

1987, June 22
408 A66 10p Swimming   .35 .35
409 A66 20p Nesting   .75 .75
410 A66 30p Adult and young   1.10 1.10
411 A66 50p Adult's head   2.00 2.00
    Nos. 408-411 (4)   4.20 4.20

Shipwrecks Type of 1985

Designs: 11p, Castaways attacking sea elephant, vert. 17p, Henry A. Paull, 1879, Sandy Point. 45p, Gustav Stoltenhoff, Stoltenhoff Is., vert. 70p, Map of wrecks off Inaccessible Is.

1987, Apr. 2   *Perf. 14*
412 A60 11p olive gray & blk   .32 .32
413 A60 17p dark violet & blk   .50 .50
414 A60 45p myrtle green & blk   1.35 1.35
    Nos. 412-414 (3)   2.17 2.17

Souvenir Sheet
415 A60 70p light blue, royal blue & apple grn   2.10 2.10

Norwegian Scientific Expedition, 50th Anniv. — A67

Designs: 10p, Microscope and textbooks symbolic of expedition results. 20p, Scientists tagging a mollymawk. 30p, Expedition headquarters on the island. 50p, S.S. Thorshammer.

Wmk. 384
1987, Dec. 7   Litho.   *Perf. 14*
416 A67 10p multicolored   .38 .38
417 A67 20p multicolored   .75 .75

Wmk. 373
418 A67 30p multicolored   1.15 1.15
419 A67 50p multicolored   1.90 1.90
    Nos. 416-419 (4)   4.18 4.18

Fauna of Nightingale Island — A68

1988, Mar. 21   Wmk. 384   *Perf. 14*
420 A68 5p Tristan bunting   .20 .20
421 A68 10p Tristan thrush   .38 .38
422 A68 20p Yellow-nosed albatross   .75 .75
423 A68 25p Great shearwater   .92 .92
424 A68 50p Elephant seal   1.85 1.85
    Nos. 420-424 (5)   4.10 4.10

Handicrafts A69

1988, May 30   *Perf. 14½*
425 A69 10p Painted penguin eggs   .38 .38
426 A69 15p Moccasins   .55 .55
427 A69 35p Woolen clothing   1.30 1.30
428 A69 50p Model canvas boats   1.85 1.85
    Nos. 425-428 (4)   4.08 4.08

Nos. 388-392 Ovptd. "40TH WEDDING ANNIVERSARY" in Silver

1988, Mar. 9
429 CD337 10p scar, blk & sil   .30 .30
430 CD337 15p ultra & multi   .45 .45
431 CD337 25p green & multi   .70 .70
432 CD337 45p violet & multi   1.25 1.25
433 CD337 65p rose vio & multi   2.00 2.00
    Nos. 429-433 (5)   4.70 4.70

19th Cent. Whaling A70

1988, Oct. 6   *Perf. 14x14½*
434 A70 10p "Trying out" blubber   .38 .38
435 A70 20p Harpoon guns   .75 .75
436 A70 30p Scrimshaw   1.15 1.15
437 A70 50p Ships   1.90 1.90
    Nos. 434-437 (4)   4.18 4.18

Souvenir Sheet
438 A70 £1 Right whale   3.50 3.50

Lloyds of London, 300th Anniv.
Common Design Type

Designs: 10p, Lloyds's new building, 1988. 25p, Cargo ship Tristania II, horiz. 35p, Supply ship St. Helena, horiz. 50p, Square-rigger Kobenhavn, lost at sea.

1988, Nov. 7   *Perf. 14*
439 CD341 10p multicolored   .35 .35
440 CD341 25p multicolored   .85 .85
441 CD341 35p multicolored   1.20 1.20
442 CD341 50p multicolored   1.70 1.70
    Nos. 439-442 (4)   4.10 4.10

Paintings of the Island, 1824, by Augustus Earle (1793-1838) — A71

Designs: 1p, Government House. 3p, Squall off Tristan. 4p, Rafting Blubber. 5p, Tristan. 10p, Man Killing an Albatross. 15p, View on the Summit. 20p, Nightingale Island. 25p, Tristan, diff. 35p, "Solitude," Watching the Horizon. 50p, North Eastern. £1, Tristan, diff. £2, Governor Glass and His Companions.

1988, Dec. 10
443 A71 1p multicolored   .15 .15
444 A71 3p multicolored   .15 .15
445 A71 4p multicolored   .15 .15
446 A71 5p multicolored   .16 .16
447 A71 10p multicolored   .32 .32
448 A71 15p multicolored   .45 .45
449 A71 20p multicolored   .60 .60
450 A71 25p multicolored   .75 .75
451 A71 35p multicolored   1.10 1.10
452 A71 50p multicolored   1.50 1.50
453 A71 £1 multicolored   3.00 3.00
454 A71 £2 multicolored   6.00 6.00
    Nos. 443-454 (12)   14.33 14.33

Gough Is. Fauna — A72   Ferns — A73

1989, Feb. 6   Litho.   Wmk. 384
455 A72 5p Giant petrel   .18 .18
456 A72 10p Gough moorhen   .35 .35
457 A72 20p Gough bunting   .75 .75
458 A72 25p Sooty albatross   .90 .90
459 A72 50p Amsterdam fur seal   1.80 1.80
    Nos. 455-459 (5)   3.98 3.98

1989, May 22   Wmk. 373   *Perf. 14*
460 A73 10p Eriosorus cheilanthoides   .35 .35
461 A73 25p Asplenium alvarezense   .90 .90
462 A73 35p Elaphoglossum hybridum   1.25 1.25
463 A73 35p Ophioglossum opacum   1.80 1.80
    Nos. 460-463 (4)   4.30 4.30

A74

1989, Nov. 20   Wmk. 384
464 A74 10p Cattle egret   .42 .42
465 A74 25p Spotted sandpiper   1.00 1.00
466 A74 35p Purple gallinule   1.50 1.50
467 A74 50p Barn swallow   2.00 2.00
    Nos. 464-467 (4)   4.92 4.92

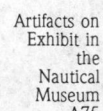 

Artifacts on Exhibit in the Nautical Museum A75

1989, Sept. 25
468 A75 10p Surgeon's mortar   .32 .32
469 A75 20p Parts of a harpoon   .65 .65
470 A75 30p Compass with binnacle hood   .98 .98
471 A75 60p Rope-twisting device   1.90 1.90
    Nos. 468-471 (4)   3.85 3.85

10p Moths A76

1990, Feb. 1   *Perf. 14*
472 A76 10p Peridroma saucia   .35 .35
473 A76 15p Ascalapha odorata   .55 .55
474 A76 35p Agrius cingulata   1.25 1.25
475 A76 60p Eumorpha labruscae   2.25 2.25
    Nos. 472-475 (4)   4.40 4.40

Starfish (Echinoderms) — A77

1990, June 12   *Perf. 14x13½*
476 A77 10p shown   .32 .32
477 A77 20p multi, diff.   .65 .65
478 A77 35p multi, diff.   .95 .95
479 A77 60p multi, diff.   1.90 1.90
    Nos. 476-479 (4)   3.82 3.82

Queen Mother, 90th Birthday
Common Design Types

1990, Aug. 4   Wmk. 384   *Perf. 14x15*
480 CD343 25p Queen Mother at the Coliseum   .85 .85

Perf. 14½
481 CD344 £1 Broadcasting to women of the empire, 1939   3.40 3.40

Dunnottar Castle, 1942 — A78

Designs: 15p, RMS St. Helena, 1977-1990. 35p, Launching new RMS St. Helena, 1989. 60p, Duke of York launching new RMS St. Helena. £1, New RMS St. Helena.

1990, Sept. 13   Wmk. 373   *Perf. 14½*
482 A78 10p multicolored   .35 .35
483 A78 15p multicolored   .52 .52
484 A78 35p multicolored   1.25 1.25
485 A78 60p multicolored   2.10 2.10
    Nos. 482-485 (4)   4.22 4.22

Souvenir Sheet
486 A78 £1 multicolored   3.50 3.50

See Ascension Nos. 493-497, St. Helena Nos. 535-539.

Royal Navy Warships A79

Perf. 14½x14
1990, Nov. 30   Litho.   Wmk. 373
487 A79 10p Pyramus, 1829   .40 .40
488 A79 25p Penguin, 1815   1.00 1.00
489 A79 35p Thalia, 1886   1.40 1.40
490 A79 50p Sidon, 1858   2.00 2.00
    Nos. 487-490 (4)   4.80 4.80

See Nos. 547-550.

1991, Feb. 4
491 A79 10p Milford, 1938   .40 .40
492 A79 25p Dublin, 1923   1.00 1.00
493 A79 35p Yarmouth, 1919   1.40 1.40
494 A79 50p Carlisle, 1938   2.00 2.00
    Nos. 491-494 (4)   4.80 4.80

Souvenir Sheet

Royal Viking Sun — A80

Wmk. 384

1991, Apr. 1   Litho.   Perf. 14
495 A80 £1 multicolored   3.75 3.75

Prince Philip, 70th Birthday A81

Designs: 10p, HMS Galatea, Prince Alfred. 25p, Royal Visit, 1957. 30p, HMY Britannia, Prince Philip. 50p, Settlement of Edinburgh, Prince Philip.

1991, June 10   Wmk. 373
496 A81 10p multicolored   .40   .40
497 A81 25p multicolored   1.00 1.00
498 A81 30p multicolored   1.20 1.20
499 A81 50p multicolored   2.00 2.00
      Nos. 496-499 (4)   4.60 4.60

Birds A82

1991, Oct. 1
500 A82 8p Gough moorhens   .32   .32
501 A82 10p Gough bunting   .40   .40
502 A82 12p Gough moorhen in nest   .50   .50
503 A82 15p Gough bunting with
              chicks   .60   .60
      Nos. 500-503 (4)   1.82 1.82

World Wildlife Fund.

Discovery of America, 500th Anniv. — A83

1992, Jan. 23
504 A83 10p STV Eye of the Wind   .40   .40
505 A83 15p STV Soren Larsen   .60   .60
506 A83 35p STV Pinta, Nina, Santa
              Maria   1.40 1.40
507 A83 60p Columbus, Santa Maria   2.40 2.40
      Nos. 504-507 (4)   4.80 4.80

World Columbian Stamp Expo '92, Chicago and Genoa '92 Intl. Philatelic Exhibitions.

Queen Elizabeth II's Accession to the Throne, 40th Anniv.
Common Design Type

1992, Feb. 6
508 CD349 10p multicolored   .35   .35
509 CD349 20p multicolored   .70   .70
510 CD349 25p multicolored   .85   .85
511 CD349 35p multicolored   1.20 1.20
512 CD349 65p multicolored   2.20 2.20
      Nos. 508-512 (5)   5.30 5.30

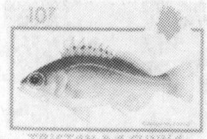

Fish — A84

Designs: 10p, Caesioperca coatsii. 15p, Mendosoma lineatum. 35p, Physiculus karrerae. 60p, Decapterus longimanus.

1992, June 1
513 A84 10p multicolored   .35   .35
514 A84 15p multicolored   .55   .55
515 A84 35p multicolored   1.20 1.20
516 A84 60p multicolored   2.10 2.10
      Nos. 513-516 (4)   4.20 4.20

Wreck of the Italia, Cent. A85

Designs: 10p, Italia leaving Greenock. 45p, In mid-Atlantic. 65p, Driving ashore on Stony Beach. £1, Italia in peaceful waters.

1992, Sept. 18   Perf. 13½x14
517 A85 10p multicolored   .35   .35
518 A85 45p multicolored   1.60 1.60
519 A85 65p multicolored   2.30 2.30
      Nos. 517-519 (3)   4.25 4.25

Souvenir Sheet
520 A85 £1 multicolored   3.50 3.50

Genoa '92 Intl. Philatelic Exhibition (#520).

Insects — A86

Designs: 15p, Stenoscelis hylastoides. 45p, Trogloscaptomyza brevilamellata. 60p, Senilites tristanicola.

Perf. 14x13½
1993, Feb. 2   Litho.   Wmk. 384
521 A86 15p multicolored   .52   .52
522 A86 45p multicolored   1.60 1.60
523 A86 60p multicolored   2.10 2.10
      Nos. 521-523 (3)   4.22 4.22

Coronation of Queen Elizabeth II, 40th Anniv. — A87

Designs: 10p, Ampulla, spoon. 15p, Orb. 35p, Imperial State Crown. 60p, St. Edward's Crown.

1993, June 14   Perf. 14½
524 A87 10p green & black   .28   .28
525 A87 15p red vio & black   .42   .42
526 A87 35p purple & black   1.00 1.00
527 A87 60p blue & black   1.70 1.70
      Nos. 524-527 (4)   3.40 3.40

Resettlement to Tristan, 30th Anniv. — A88

Ships: No. 528, Tristania, Frances Repetto. No. 529, Boissevain. 50p, Bornholm.

1993, Nov. 10   Perf. 13½x14
528 A88 35p multicolored   1.00 1.00
529 A88 35p multicolored   1.00 1.00
   a. Pair, #528-529   2.00 2.00
530 A88 50p multicolored   1.40 1.40
      Nos. 528-530 (3)   3.40 3.40

Christmas — A89

Entire paintings or details: 5p, Madonna with Child, School of Botticelli. 15p, The Holy Family, by Daniel Gran. 35p, The Holy Virgin and Child, by Rubens. 65p, The Mystical Marriage of St. Catherine with the Holy Child, by Jan Van Balen.

1993, Nov. 30   Wmk. 373   Perf. 13
531 A89 5p multicolored   .15   .15
532 A89 15p multicolored   .42   .42
533 A89 35p multicolored   1.00 1.00
534 A89 65p multicolored   1.75 1.75
      Nos. 531-534 (4)   3.32 3.32

Ships A90

Designs: 1p, Duchess of Atholl, 1929. 3p, Empress of Australia, 1935. 5p, Anatolia, 1937. 8p, Viceroy of India, 1939. 10p, Rangitata, 1943. 15p, Caronia, 1950. 20p, Rotterdam, 1960. 25p, Leonardo da Vinci, 1972. 35p, Vistafjord, 1974. £1, World Discoverer, 1984. £2, Astor, 1984. £5, RMS St. Helena, 1992.

1994, Feb. 3   Wmk. 384   Perf. 14
535 A90 1p multicolored   .15   .15
536 A90 3p multicolored   .15   .15
537 A90 5p multicolored   .15   .15
538 A90 8p multicolored   .22   .22
539 A90 10p multicolored   .28   .28
540 A90 15p multicolored   .40   .40
541 A90 20p multicolored   .55   .55
542 A90 25p multicolored   .70   .70
543 A90 35p multicolored   .95   .95
544 A90 £1 multicolored   2.75 2.75
545 A90 £2 multicolored   5.50 5.50
546 A90 £5 multicolored   14.00 14.00
      Nos. 535-546 (12)   25.80 25.80

Royal Navy Warships Type of 1990

1994, May 2   Wmk. 373
547 A79 10p HMS Nigeria, 1948   .30   .30
548 A79 25p HMS Phoebe, 1949   .75   .75
549 A79 35p HMS Liverpool, 1949   1.00 1.00
550 A79 50p HMS Magpie, 1955   1.50 1.50
      Nos. 547-550 (4)   3.55 3.55

Sharks A91

1994, Aug.   Wmk. 384
551 A91 10p Blue shark   .35   .35
552 A91 45p Seven-gill shark   1.50 1.50
553 A91 65p Mako shark   2.00 2.00
      Nos. 551-553 (3)   3.85 3.85

Farm Animals — A92

1994, Nov.   Wmk. 373
554 A92 10p Donkeys   .30   .30
555 A92 20p Cattle   .60   .60
556 A92 35p Ducks, geese   1.10 1.10
557 A92 60p Girl feeding lamb   1.90 1.90
      Nos. 554-557 (4)   3.90 3.90

Local Transport A93

Designs: 15p, Pick-up truck. 20p, Leyland Daf Sherpa van. 45p, Yamaha motorcycle, scooter. 60p, Administrator's Landrover.

Wmk. 384
1995, Feb. 27   Litho.   Perf. 14
558 A93 15p multicolored   .48   .48
559 A93 20p multicolored   .65   .65
560 A93 45p multicolored   1.40 1.40
561 A93 60p multicolored   1.90 1.90
      Nos. 558-561 (4)   4.43 4.43

End of World War II, 50th Anniv.
Common Design Types

Designs: 15p, Lewis gun instruction, 1943. 20p, Tristan defense volunteers, 1943-46. 45p, Radio, weather stations. 60p, HNS Birmingham, 1942. £1, Reverse of War Medal, 1939-45.

Perf. 13x13½
1995, June 19   Litho.   Wmk. 373
562 CD351 15p multicolored   .50   .50
563 CD351 20p multicolored   .65   .65
564 CD351 45p multicolored   1.40 1.40
565 CD351 60p multicolored   1.90 1.90
      Nos. 562-565 (4)   4.45 4.45

Souvenir Sheet
Perf. 14
566 CD352 £1 multicolored   3.25 3.25

Souvenir Sheet

Queen Mother, 95th Birthday — A94

Perf. 14½x14
1995, Aug. 4   Litho.   Wmk. 373
567 A94 £1.50 multicolored   4.75 4.75

UN, 50th Anniv.
Common Design Type

Designs: 20p, Bedford 4-ton truck. 30p, Saxon armored personnel carrier. 45p, Mi26 heavy lift helicopter. 50p, RFA Sir Tristram transporting UN vehicles.

Perf. 13½x13
1995, Oct. 24   Litho.   Wmk. 373
568 CD353 20p multicolored   .65   .65
569 CD353 30p multicolored   1.00 1.00
570 CD353 45p multicolored   1.40 1.40
571 CD353 50p multicolored   1.65 1.65
      Nos. 568-571 (4)   4.70 4.70

Seals A95

Sub Antarctic fur seal: 10p, On rock. 35p, Coming out of water with young.
Southern elephant seal: 45p, On beach with young. 50p, In water.

Perf. 13½
1995, Nov. 3   Litho.   Wmk. 373
572 A95 10p multicolored   .30   .30
573 A95 35p multicolored   1.10 1.10
574 A95 45p multicolored   1.50 1.50
575 A95 50p multicolored   1.65 1.65
      Nos. 572-575 (4)   4.55 4.55

POSTAGE DUE STAMPS

Type of Barbados 1934-47

1957, Feb. 1 Wmk. 4 Typo. Perf. 14
Chalky Paper

J1	D1	1p rose red	3.25	5.25
J2	D1	2p orange yellow	4.25	7.00
J3	D1	3p green	4.50	8.50
J4	D1	4p ultramarine	5.50	10.00
J5	D1	5p deep claret	7.00	12.00
		Nos. J1-J5 (5)	24.50	42.75

Numeral — D2

Perf. 13½x14

1976, Sept. 3 Litho. Wmk. 373

J6	D2	1p lilac rose	.45	.35
J7	D2	2p grayish green	.55	.55
J8	D2	4p violet	.60	.75
J9	D2	5p light blue	.85	1.25
J10	D2	10p brown	2.25	3.00
		Nos. J6-J10 (5)	4.70	5.90

1976, May 31 Wmk. 314

J6a	D2	1p lilac rose	.18	.18
J7a	D2	2p grayish green	.38	.38
J8a	D2	4p violet	.75	.75
J9a	D2	5p light blue	.95	.95
J10a	D2	10p brown	2.50	2.50
		Nos. J6a-J10a (5)	4.76	4.76

Outline Map of Tristan da Cunha — D3

Perf. 15x14

1986, Nov. 20 Litho. Wmk. 384

J11	D3	1p pale yel brn & brn	.15	.15
J12	D3	2p orange & brown	.15	.15
J13	D3	5p crimson rose & brn	.15	.15
J14	D3	7p lt lilac & black	.22	.22
J15	D3	10p pale ultra & blk	.30	.30
J16	D3	25p lt green & blk	.75	.75
		Nos. J11-J16 (6)	1.72	1.72

TRUCIAL STATES

'trü-shǝl 'stāts

LOCATION — Qatar Peninsula, Persian Gulf
GOVT. — Sheikdoms under British Protection
AREA — 32,300 sq. mi.
POP. 86,000
CAPITAL — Dubai

The Trucial States are: Abu Dhabi, Ajman, Dubai, Fujeira, Ras al Khaima, Sharjah and Kalba, and Umm al Qiwain.
Stamps inscribed "Trucial States" were issued and used only in Dubai. Beginning Aug. 1972 all Trucial States used the stamps of United Arab Emirates.

100 Naye Paise = 1 Rupee

Catalogue values for all unused stamps in this country are for Never Hinged items.

7 Palm Trees — A1   Dhow — A2

Perf. 14½x14

1961, Jan. 7 Photo. Unwmk.

1	A1	5np emerald	.15	.15
2	A1	15np red brown	.15	.15
3	A1	20np ultra	.16	.15
4	A1	30np orange	.22	.20

5	A1	40np purple	.30	.28
6	A1	50np brown olive	.38	.38
7	A1	75np gray	.60	.50

		Engr.	Perf. 13x12½	
8	A2	1r emerald	1.10	.90
9	A2	2r black	2.00	2.00
10	A2	5r rose red	6.50	6.50
11	A2	10r violet blue	12.50	12.50
		Nos. 1-11 (11)	24.06	23.71

Stamps inscribed "Trucial States" were withdrawn in June, 1963, when the individual states began issuing their own stamps.

TUVALU

tü-'vä-(,)ü

LOCATION — A group of islands in the Pacific Ocean northeast of Australia.
GOVT. — Independent state in the British Commonwealth
AREA — 9½ sq. mi.
POP. — 7,349 (1979)
CAPITAL — Fongafale

Tuvalu, formerly Ellice Islands, consists of nine islands.

Catalogue values for all unused stamps in this country are for Never Hinged items.

Watermark

Wmk. 380- "POST OFFICE"

Gilbert and Ellice Islands Types of 1971 Overprinted "TUVALU" and Bar in Violet Blue or Silver (35c)

Wmk. 373

1976, Jan. 1 Litho. Perf. 14

1	A18	1c	.15	.15
2	A19	2c	.15	.15
a.		Wmk. 314 sideways	100.00	35.00
b.		Wmk. 314 upright	725.00	140.00
3	A19	3c Wmk. 314	.15	.15
a.		Wmk. 373	.15	.15
4	A19	4c	.20	.20
5	A19	5c Wmk. 314	.20	.20
6	A18	6c	.30	.30
7	A18	8c Wmk. 314	.35	.35
8	A18	10c Wmk. 314	.45	.45
9	A18	15c	.45	.45
10	A19	20c	.60	.60
11	A19	35c Wmk. 314	.95	.95
a.		Wmk. 373	.95	.95
12	A19	35c	1.50	1.25
13	A18	50c	3.50	2.75
a.		Wmk. 314	26.00	14.00
14	A18	$1	7.50	6.00
a.		Wmk. 314	60.00	52.50
15	A18	$2	20.00	15.00
		Nos. 1-15 (15)	36.45	28.95

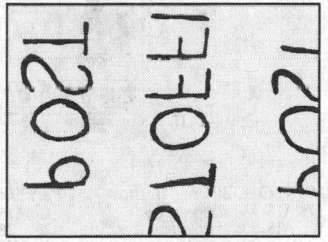

Men from Gilbert and Ellice — A1

Designs: 10c, Map of Gilbert and Ellice Islands, vert. 35c, Gilbert and Ellice canoes.

1976, Jan. 1 Wmk. 373

16	A1	4c multicolored	.40	.30
17	A1	10c multicolored	1.10	.75
18	A1	35c multicolored	3.00	1.75
		Nos. 16-18 (3)	4.50	2.80

Separation of the Gilbert and Ellice Islands.

50c Coin and Octopus — A2

New coinage: 10c, 10c-coin and red-dyed crab. 15c, 20c-coin and flyingfish. 35c, $1-coin and green turtle.

Wmk. 373

1976, Apr. 21 Litho. Perf. 14

19	A2	5c bister & multi	.40	.25
20	A2	10c ultra & multi	1.00	.75
21	A2	15c blue & multi	1.65	1.10
22	A2	35c lt green & multi	2.50	2.25
		Nos. 19-22 (4)	5.55	4.35

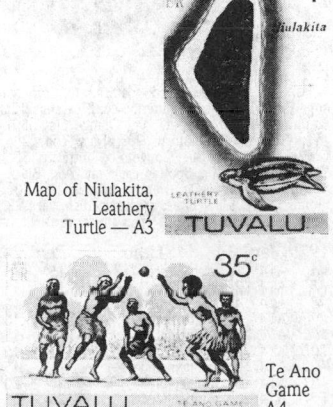

Map of Niulakita, Leathery Turtle — A3

Te Ano Game — A4

Designs: 2c, Map of Nukulaelae and sleeping mat. 4c, Map of Nui and talo vegetable. 5c, Map of Nanumanga and grass dancing skirt. 6c, Map of Nukufetau and coconut crab. 8c, Map of Funafuti and banana tree. 10c, Map of Tuvalu Islands. 15c, Map of Niutao and flyingfish. 20c, Map of Vaitupu and maneapa (house). 25c, Map of Nanumea and palu fish hook. 50c, Canoe pole fishing. $1, Reef fishing by flare. $2, House. $5, Colony Ship M.V. Nivanga.

1976 Wmk. 373 Litho. Perf. 13½

23	A3	1c multicolored	.20	.20
24	A3	2c multicolored	.18	.15
25	A3	4c multicolored	.20	.15
26	A3	5c multicolored	.40	.35
27	A3	6c multicolored	.20	.15
28	A3	8c multicolored	.35	.25
29	A3	10c multicolored	.40	.35
30	A3	15c multicolored	.35	.25
31	A3	20c multicolored	.40	.35
32	A3	25c multicolored	4.00	2.00
33	A4	35c multicolored	.65	.50
34	A4	50c multicolored	1.00	.90
35	A4	$1 multicolored	2.50	2.00
36	A4	$2 multicolored	5.00	4.00
37	A4	$5 multicolored	45.00	15.00
		Nos. 23-37 (15)	60.83	26.60

Issue dates: $5, Sept. 1, others July 1.
See #58-77. For overprints see #85-91.

New Testament — A5

Designs: 20c, Lotolelei Church, Nanumea. 25c, Kelupi Church, Nui. 30c, Mataloa o Tuvalu Church, Vaitupu. 35c, Palataiso o Keliso Church, Nanumanga.

1976, Oct. 6 Litho. Wmk. 373

38	A5	5c multicolored	.40	.22
39	A5	20c multicolored	1.40	1.00
40	A5	25c multicolored	1.75	1.25
41	A5	30c multicolored	2.25	1.40
42	A5	35c multicolored	2.75	2.25
		Nos. 38-42 (5)	8.55	6.12

Christmas 1976. Printed in sheets of 10 stamps and 2 labels.

Prince Philip Carried Ashore at Vaitupu — A6

Designs: 15c, Queen and Prince Philip on Buckingham Palace balcony. 50c, Queen Leaving Buckingham Palace for coronation.

1977, Feb. 9 Litho. Perf. 13½x14

43	A6	15c multicolored	1.50	1.10
44	A6	35c multicolored	2.00	1.25
45	A6	50c multicolored	2.25	1.50
a.		Souv. sheet of 3, #43-45, perf. 15	8.50	7.00
		Nos. 43-45 (3)	5.75	3.85

25th anniv. of the reign of Elizabeth II.

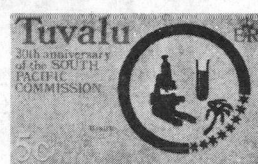

Health (Microscope) — A7

Designs: 20c, Education (blackboard). 30c, Fruit growing (palm). 35c, Map of South Pacific Territory.

1977, May 4 Litho. Perf. 13½x14

46	A7	5c lilac & multi	.45	.32
47	A7	20c orange & multi	.85	.65
48	A7	30c yellow grn & multi	.95	.85
49	A7	35c lt blue & multi	1.00	1.10
		Nos. 46-49 (4)	3.25	2.92

South Pacific Commission, 30th anniv.

Swearing-in Ceremony and Scout Emblem — A8

Designs (Scout Emblem and): 20c, Scouts in outrigger canoe. 30c, Scouts under sun shelter. 35c, Lord Baden-Powell.

Perf. 13½x14

1977, Aug. 10 Litho. Wmk. 373

50	A8	5c multicolored	.45	.35
51	A8	20c multicolored	.90	.70
52	A8	30c multicolored	1.10	1.00
53	A8	35c multicolored	1.10	1.25
		Nos. 50-53 (4)	3.55	3.30

Scouting in Tuvalu (Ellice Islands), 50th anniv.

Hurricane Beach and Coral — A9

Designs: 20c, Boring apparatus on "Porpoise," vert. 30c, Map of islands showing line of dredgings to prove Darwin's theory, vert. 35c, Charles Darwin and "Beagle."

Perf. 13½

1977, Nov. 2 Unwmk. Litho.

54	A9	5c multicolored	.25	.22
55	A9	20c multicolored	.80	.65
56	A9	30c multicolored	1.10	1.00
57	A9	35c multicolored	1.25	1.10
		Nos. 54-57 (4)	3.40	2.97

1896-97 Royal Soc. of London Expeditions to explore coral reefs by dredging and boring.

Types of 1976

Designs: 30c, Fatele, local dance. 40c, Screw pine. Others as before.

1977-78 Unwmk. Perf. 13½

58	A3	1c multicolored	.15	.15
59	A3	2c multicolored	.15	.15
60	A3	4c multicolored	.15	.15

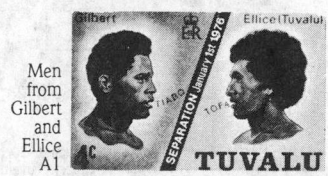

61	A3	5c multicolored	.20	.20
62	A3	6c multicolored	.20	.20
63	A3	8c multicolored	.25	.20
64	A3	10c multicolored	.35	.30
66	A3	20c multicolored	5.00	4.00
67	A3	25c multicolored	.55	.45
68	A4	30c multicolored	.65	.55
69	A4	40c multicolored	.70	.65
70	A4	$5 multicolored	7.50	7.50
		Nos. 58-70 (12)	15.85	14.50

Issued: #58, 61, 67, 72, 1977; others, 1978.

Pacific
Pigeon — A10

Wild Birds of Tuvalu: 20c, Reef heron. 30c, Fairy
tern. 40c, Lesser frigate bird.

Perf. 14x13½

1978, Jan. 25   Litho.   Unwmk.
73	A10	8c lilac & multi	1.10	.45
74	A10	20c ocher & multi	1.75	1.40
75	A10	30c dull green & multi	2.25	1.75
76	A10	40c brt green & multi	2.75	2.25
		Nos. 73-76 (4)	7.85	5.85

Lawedua — A11

Ships: 20c, Tug Wailacia. 30c, Freighter Cenpac
Rounder. 40c, Pacific Explorer.

1978, Apr. 5   Unwmk.   Perf. 13½x14
77	A11	8c multicolored	.24	.20
78	A11	20c multicolored	.60	.52
79	A11	30c multicolored	.90	.75
80	A11	40c multicolored	1.10	1.00
		Nos. 77-80 (4)	2.84	2.47

Canterbury Cathedral — A12

Designs: 30c, Salisbury Cathedral. 40c, Wells
Cathedral. $1, Hereford Cathedral.

1978, June 2   Litho.   Perf. 13½x14
81	A12	8c multicolored	.15	.15
82	A12	30c multicolored	.22	.22
83	A12	40c multicolored	.30	.30
84	A12	$1 multicolored	.70	.70
a.		Souvenir sheet of 4, #81-84, perf. 15	1.50	1.50
		Nos. 81-84 (4)	1.37	1.37

25th anniv. of coronation of Elizabeth II.
#81-84 were also issued in booklet panes of 2.

Types of 1976 Overprinted:
"INDEPENDENCE 1ST OCTOBER 1978"
Wmk. 373, Unwmkd.

1978, Oct. 1   Litho.   Perf. 13½
85	A3	8c multicolored	.15	.15
86	A3	10c multicolored	.15	.15
87	A3	15c multicolored	.15	.15
88	A3	20c multicolored	.16	.16
89	A4	30c multicolored	.25	.25
90	A4	35c multicolored	.28	.28
91	A4	40c multicolored	.35	.35
		Nos. 85-91 (7)	1.49	1.49

Independence, Oct. 1, 1978. Overprint in 3 lines
on vertical stamps, one line on horizontal.

White
Frangipani — A13

Wild Flowers: 20c, Zephyrantes rosea. 30c, Gardenia taitensis. 40c, Clerodendron inerme.

1978, Oct. 4   Unwmk.   Perf. 14
92	A13	8c multicolored	.15	.15
93	A13	20c multicolored	.24	.22
94	A13	30c multicolored	.40	.35
95	A13	40c multicolored	.55	.50
		Nos. 92-95 (4)	1.34	1.22

Squirrelfish
A14

Fish: 2c, Yellow-banded goatfish. 4c, Imperial
angelfish. 5c, Rainbow butterfly. 6c, Blue angelfish.
8c, Blue striped snapper. 10c, Orange clownfish.
15c, Chevroned coralfish. 20c, Fairy cod. 25c,
Clown triggerfish. 30c, Long-nosed butterfly. 35c,
Yellowfin tuna. 40c, Spotted eagle ray. 45c, Black-
tipped rock cod. 50c, Hammerhead shark. 70c,
Lionfish, vert. $1, White-barred triggerfish, vert. $2,
Beaked coralfish, vert. $5, Tiger shark, vert.

1979, Jan. 24   Litho.   Perf. 14
96	A14	1c multicolored	.15	.15
97	A14	2c multicolored	.15	.15
98	A14	4c multicolored	.15	.15
99	A14	5c multicolored	.15	.15
100	A14	6c multicolored	.15	.15
101	A14	8c multicolored	.15	.15
102	A14	10c multicolored	.15	.15
103	A14	15c multicolored	.20	.20
104	A14	20c multicolored	.25	.25
105	A14	25c multicolored	.28	.28
106	A14	30c multicolored	.32	.32
107	A14	35c multicolored	.40	.40
108	A14	40c multicolored	.45	.45
108A	A14	45c multicolored ('81)	.55	.55
109	A14	50c multicolored	.70	.70
110	A14	70c multicolored	.80	.80
111	A14	$1 multicolored	1.10	1.10
112	A14	$2 multicolored	2.50	2.50
113	A14	$5 multicolored	6.00	6.00
		Nos. 96-113 (19)	14.60	14.60

No. 108A issued June 16, 1981.
For surcharge & overprints see #150, O1-O19.

Capt.
Cook — A15

Designs: 30c, Flag raising on new island. 40c,
Observation of transit of Venus. $1, Death of Capt.
Cook.

1979, Feb. 14   Perf. 14x14½
114	A15	8c multicolored	.15	.15
115	A15	30c multicolored	.42	.32
116	A15	40c multicolored	.55	.48
117	A15	$1 multicolored	1.40	1.10
a.		Strip of 4, #114-117	3.00	3.00

Bicentenary of death of Capt. James Cook (1728-
1779). Nos. 114-117 printed se-tenant horizontally
in sheets of 12 (4x3) with gutters between horizontal rows.

Grumman Goose over Nukulaelae — A16

Grumman Goose over: 20c, Vaitupu. 30c, Nui.
40c, Funafuti.

1979, May 16   Litho.   Perf. 14x13½
118	A16	8c multicolored	.15	.15
119	A16	20c multicolored	.22	.22
120	A16	30c multicolored	.55	.55
121	A16	40c multicolored	.70	.70
		Nos. 118-121 (4)	1.62	1.62

Inauguration of internal air service.

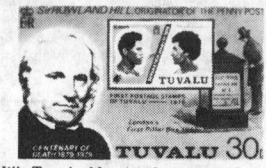

Hill, Tuvalu No. 16, Letterbox, London,
1855 — A17

Hill, Stamps of Tuvalu and: 40c, No. 17, Penny
Black. $1, No. 18, mail coach.

1979, Aug. 20   Litho.   Perf. 13½x14
122	A17	30c multicolored	.18	.18
123	A17	40c multicolored	.25	.25
124	A17	$1 multicolored	.65	.65
a.		Souvenir sheet of 3, #122-124	1.65	1.65
		Nos. 122-124 (3)	1.08	1.08

Sir Rowland Hill (1795-1879), originator of
penny postage.

Boy — A18

Designs: Children of Tuvalu.

1979, Oct. 20   Litho.   Perf. 14
125	A18	8c multicolored	.15	.15
126	A18	20c multicolored	.28	.28
127	A18	30c multicolored	.40	.40
128	A18	40c multicolored	.55	.55
		Nos. 125-128 (4)	1.38	1.38

International Year of the Child.

Cowry
Shells
A19

1980, Feb.   Litho.   Perf. 14
129	A19	8c Cypraea Argus	.15	.15
130	A19	20c Cypraea scurra	.28	.28
131	A19	30c Cypraea carneola	.42	.42
132	A19	40c Cypraea aurantium	.55	.55
		Nos. 129-132 (4)	1.40	1.40

Philatelic Bureau, Funafuti, Tuvalu No. 28,
Arms, London 1980 Emblem — A20

Coat of Arms, London 1980 Emblem and: 20c,
Gilbert and Ellice #41, Nukulaelae cancel, Tuvalu
#24. 30c, US airmail cover. $1, Map of Tuvalu.

1980, Apr. 30   Litho.   Perf. 13½x14
133	A20	10c multicolored	.15	.15
134	A20	20c multicolored	.16	.16
135	A20	30c multicolored	.25	.25
136	A20	$1 multicolored	.80	.80
a.		Souvenir sheet of 4, #133-136	1.50	1.50
		Nos. 133-136 (4)	1.36	1.36

London 80 Intl. Stamp Exhib., May 6-14.

Queen Mother
Elizabeth, 80th
Birthday — A21

1980, Aug. 14   Litho.   Perf. 14
137	A21	50c multicolored	.75	.52

Issued in sheets of 10 plus 2 labels.

Aethaloessa
Calidalis
A22

1980, Aug. 20   Litho.   Perf. 14
138	A22	8c shown	.15	.15
139	A22	20c Parotis suralis	.28	.28
140	A22	30c Dudua aprobola	.42	.42
141	A22	40c Decadarchis simulans	.55	.55
		Nos. 138-141 (4)	1.40	1.40

Air Pacific Heron (First Regular Air Service
to Tuvalu, 1964)
A23

Aviation Anniversaries: 20c, Hawker Siddeley
748 (air service to Tuvalu). 30c, Sunderland Flying
Boat (War time service to Funafuti, 1945. 40c,
Orville Wright and Flyer (Wright brothers' first
flight, 1903).

1980, Nov. 5   Litho.   Perf. 14
142	A23	8c multicolored	.15	.15
143	A23	20c multicolored	.28	.28
144	A23	30c multicolored	.42	.42
145	A23	40c multicolored	.55	.55
		Nos. 142-145 (4)	1.40	1.40

Hypolimnas
Bolina
Elliciana
A24

1981, Feb. 3   Litho.   Perf. 14½
146	A24	8c shown	.15	.15
147	A24	20c Hypolimnas, diff.	.28	.28
148	A24	30c Hypolimnas, diff.	.42	.42
149	A24	40c Junonia vallida	.55	.55
		Nos. 146-149 (4)	1.40	1.40

No. 109 Surcharged

1981, Feb. 24   Litho.   Perf. 14
150	A14	45c on 50c multicolored	.60	.60

Elizabeth,
1809 — A25

Wmk. 373

1981, May 13   Litho.   Perf. 14
151	A25	10c shown	.15	.15
152	A25	25c Rebecca, 1819	.30	.30
153	A25	35c Independence II, 1821	.42	.42
154	A25	45c Basilisk, 1872	.45	.45
155	A25	45c Royalist, 1890	.55	.55
156	A25	50c Olivebank, 1920	.60	.60
		Nos. 151-156 (6)	2.47	2.47

See Nos. 216-221, 353-356, 410-413.

Prince Charles, Lady Diana, Royal Yacht Charlotte A25a

Prince Charles and Lady Diana — A25b

Illustration A25b is reduced.

Wmk. 380
1981, July 10   Litho.   Perf. 14
157	A25a	10c Couple, Carolina	.15	.15
a.		Blkt. pane of 4, perf. 12, unwmkd.	.60	
158	A25b	10c Couple	.15	.15
159	A25a	45c Victoria and Albert III	.52	.52
160	A25b	45c like #158	.52	.52
a.		Blkt. pane of 2, perf. 12, unwmkd.	1.40	
161	A25a	$2 Britannia	2.25	2.25
162	A25b	$2 like #158	2.25	2.25
		Nos. 157-162 (6)	5.84	5.84

Royal wedding. Issued in sheets of 7 (6 type A25a; 1 type A25b).

Souvenir Sheet
1981, Dec.   Litho.   Perf. 12
163	A25b	$1.50 Couple	2.50	2.50

Admission to UPU — A26

Wmk. Harrison's, London
1981, Nov. 19   Engr.   Perf. 14½x14
164	A26	70c dark blue	.65	.65
165	A26	$1 dark red brown	.95	.95
a.		Souv. sheet of 2, #164-165, unwmkd.	1.75	1.75

Amatuku Maritime School — A27

1982, Feb. 17   Litho.   Perf. 13½x14
166	A27	10c Map	.15	.15
167	A27	25c Motorboat	.28	.28
168	A27	35c School, dock	.40	.40
169	A27	45c Flag, ship	.55	.55
		Nos. 166-169 (4)	1.38	1.38

A27a

Wmk. 380
1982, May 19   Litho.   Perf. 14
170	A27a	10c Caroline of Brandenburg-Ansbach, 1714	.15	.15
171	A27a	45c Brandenburg-Ansbach arms	.45	.45
172	A27a	$1.50 Diana	1.75	1.75
		Nos. 170-172 (3)	2.35	2.35

21st birthday of Princess Diana, July 1.

#170-172 Overprinted: "ROYAL BABY"
1982, July 14   Perf. 14
173	A27a	10c multicolored	.15	.15
174	A27a	45c multicolored	.48	.48
175	A27a	$1.50 multicolored	1.65	1.65
		Nos. 173-175 (3)	2.28	2.28

Birth of Prince William of Wales, June 21.

Scouting Year — A28

1982, Aug. 18
176	A28	10c Emblems	.18	.18
177	A28	25c Campfire	.48	.48
178	A28	35c Parade	.65	.65
179	A28	45c Scout	.85	.85
		Nos. 176-179 (4)	2.16	2.16

Visit of Queen Elizabeth II and Prince Philip — A29

1982, Oct. 26   Litho.   Perf. 14
180	A29	25c Arms, Duke of Edinburgh's Personal Standard	.28	.28
181	A29	45c Flags	.48	.48
182	A29	50c Queen Elizabeth II, maps	.60	.60
a.		Souvenir sheet of 3, #180-182	1.75	1.75
		Nos. 180-182 (3)	1.36	1.36

Handicrafts A30

1983, Mar. 14   Litho.   Perf. 14
183	A30	1c Fisherman's hat, lures, hooks	.15	.15
184	A30	2c Cowrie shell handbags	.15	.15
185	A30	5c Wedding and baby food baskets	.15	.15
186	A30	10c Canoe model	.22	.22
186A	A30	15c Women's sun hats ('84)	.25	.25
187	A30	20c Climbing rope	.30	.30
188	A30	25c Pandanus baskets	.35	.35
188A	A30	30c Tray, coconut stands	.32	.32
189	A30	35c Pandanus pillows, shell necklaces	.55	.55
190	A30	40c Round baskets, fans	.60	.60
191	A30	45c Reef sandals, fish trap	.70	.70
192	A30	50c Rat trap, vert.	.75	.75
192A	A30	60c Waterproof boxes	.65	.65
193	A30	$1 Pump drill, adze, vert.	1.50	1.50
194	A30	$2 Fisherman's hat, canoe bailers, vert.	3.00	3.00
195	A30	$5 Fishing rod, lures, scoop nets, vert.	7.50	7.50
		Nos. 183-195 (16)	17.14	17.14

For surcharges & overprints see #207, 230, O20-O32.

Commonwealth Day — A31

Wmk. 373
1983, Mar. 14   Litho.   Perf. 14
196	A31	20c Fishing industry	.32	.32
197	A31	35c Traditional dancing	.55	.55
198	A31	45c Satellite view	.70	.70
199	A31	50c First container ship	.75	.75
		Nos. 196-199 (4)	2.32	2.32

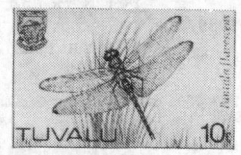

Dragonflies A32

1983, May 25   Wmk. 380
200	A32	15c Pantala flavescens	.15	.15
201	A32	35c Anax guttatus	.55	.55
202	A32	40c Tholymis tillarga	.60	.60
203	A32	50c Diplacodes bipunctata	.75	.75
		Nos. 200-203 (4)	2.05	2.05

Boys Brigade Centenary — A33

1983, Aug. 10   Wmk. 373
204	A33	10c Running, emblem	.18	.18
205	A33	35c Canoeing	.48	.48
206	A33	$1 Officer, boys	1.40	1.40
		Nos. 204-206 (3)	2.06	2.06

No. 193 Surcharged in Black
1983, Aug. 26   Wmk. 380
207	A30	60c on $1 multi	1.00	1.00

First Manned Flight Bicentenary A34

1983, Sept. 21   Wmk. 373
208	A34	25c Montgolfier balloon, vert.	.35	.35
209	A34	35c McKinnon Turbo Goose	.52	.52
210	A34	45c Beechcraft Super King Air 200	.65	.65
211	A34	50c Double Eagle II Balloon, vert.	.70	.70
a.		Souvenir sheet of 4, #208-211	2.50	2.50
		Nos. 208-211 (4)	2.22	2.22

World Communications Year — A35

1983, Nov. 18   Wmk. 380
212	A35	25c Conch Shell Trumpet, vert.	.35	.35
213	A35	35c Radio Operator, vert.	.52	.52
214	A35	45c Teleprinter	.60	.60
215	A35	50c Transmitting station	.70	.70
		Nos. 212-215 (4)	2.17	2.17

Ship Type of 1981
1984, Feb. 16   Wmk. 380
216	A25	10c Titus, 1897	.15	.15
217	A25	20c Malaita, 1905	.25	.25
218	A25	25c Aymeric, 1906	.32	.32
219	A25	35c Anshun, 1905	.45	.45
220	A25	45c Beaverbank, 1970	.55	.55
221	A25	50c Benjamin Bowring, 1981	.65	.65
		Nos. 216-221 (6)	2.37	2.37

Leaders of the World
Large quantities of some Leaders of the World issues were sold at a fraction of face value when the printer was liquidated.

Historic Locomotives A36

Locomotives from side view and on tracks.

Perf. 12½x13
1984, Feb. 29   Se-tenant Pairs   Unwmk.
222		1c Class GS-4, US, 1941	.15	.15
223		15c AD-60, Australia, 1952	.30	.30
224		40c C38, Australia, 1943	.85	.85
225		60c Achilles England, 1892	1.30	1.30
		Nos. 222-225 (4)	2.60	2.60

See Nos. 235-246, 291-294, 320-323.

No. 191 Surcharged
Wmk. 380
1984, Feb. 1   Litho.   Perf. 14
230	A30	30c on 45c multi	.45	.45

For overprint see No. O25.

Beach Flowers A38

1984, May 30
231	A38	25c Ipomoea pes-caprae	.35	.35
232	A38	45c Ipomoea macrantha	.60	.60
233	A38	50c Triumfetta procumbens	.70	.70
234	A38	60c Portulaca quadrifida	.85	.85
		Nos. 231-234 (4)	2.50	2.50

Train Type of 1984
Designs A36-A37
1984   Litho.   Perf. 12½x13
Se-tenant Pairs
235		1c Class 9700, Japan, 1897	.15	.15
236		10c Casey Jones, US, 1896	.15	.15
237		15c Class 2310K, France, 1909	.30	.30
238		15c Triplex, US, 1914	.30	.30
239		20c Class 370, Gt. Britain, 1981	.45	.45
240		25c Class 4F, Gt. Britain, 1924	.50	.50
241		30c Glass 640, Italy, 1907	.65	.65
242		40c Tornado, Gt. Britain, 1888	.85	.85
243		50c Broadlands, Gt. Britain, 1967	1.10	1.10
244		60c Locomotion, Gt. Britain, 1825	1.40	1.40
245		$1 C57, Japan, 1937	2.00	2.00
246		$1 Class 4500, France, 1906	2.00	2.00
		Nos. 235-246 (12)	9.85	9.85

Issued: #235, 237, 241, 245, 10/4; others, 6/27.

15th South Pacific Forum A38a

1984, Aug. 21   Litho.   Perf. 14
255	A38a	60c National flag	.70	.70
256	A38a	60c Tuvalu crest	.70	.70

Ausipex '84 — A38b

1984, Aug. 21   *Perf. 14*
257 A38b 60c Exhib. emblem .70 .70
258 A38b 60c Royal Exhibi. Building .70 .70

A. Shrewsbury
Playing
Cricket — A39

Cricket players in action or portrait.

1984, Nov. 5 Litho. *Perf. 12½*
Se-tenant Pairs
259 A39 5c shown .15 .15
260 A39 30c H. Verity .75 .75
261 A39 50c E.H. Hendren 1.20 1.20
262 A39 60c J. Briggs 1.60 1.60
 Nos. 259-262 (4) 3.70 3.70

Drawings,
Christmas
1984 — A40

1984, Nov. 14 Litho. *Perf. 14½x14*
267 A40 15c By Eli Faalata .22 .22
268 A40 40c By Toakai Niutao .55 .55
269 A40 50c By Falesa Teuila .70 .70
270 A40 60c By Piuani Talie .90 .90
 Nos. 267-270 (4) 2.37 2.37

Classic
Automobiles
A41

Sketch listed first followed by angled view.

1984, Dec. 7 Litho. *Perf. 12½x13*
Se-tenant Pairs
271 A41 1c Morris Minor, 1949 .15 .15
272 A41 15c Studebaker Avanti,
    1963 .35 .35
273 A41 50c Chevrolet International
    Six, 1929 1.10 1.10
274 A41 $1 Allard J2, 1950 2.25 2.25
 Nos. 271-274 (4) 3.85 3.85

See Nos. 299-302, 332-339, 396-396E, 414-425.

John J.
Audubon — A42

1985, Feb. 12 Litho. *Perf. 12½*
279 A42 1c Common flicker .15 .15
280 A42 1c Say's phoebe .15 .15
281 A42 25c Townsend's warbler .35 .35
282 A42 25c Bohemian waxwing .35 .35
283 A42 50c Prothonotary warbler .65 .65
284 A42 50c Worm-eating warbler .65 .65
285 A42 70c Broad-winged hawk .90 .90
286 A42 70c Northern harrier .90 .90
 Nos. 279-286 (8) 4.10 4.10

Stamps of the same denomination se-tenant.

Birds and
Eggs — A43

1985, Feb. 27   *Perf. 14*
287 A43 15c Black-naped tern .30 .30
288 A43 40c Black noddy .70 .70
289 A43 50c White-tailed tropicbird .85 .85
290 A43 60c Sooty tern 1.10 1.10
 Nos. 287-290 (4) 2.95 2.95

Train Type of 1984
Designs A36-A37

1985, Mar. 19 *Perf. 12½*
Se-tenant Pairs
291 5c Churchward, U.K. .15 .15
292 10c Class K.F., China .25 .25
293 30c Class 99.77, East Germany .70 .70
294 $1 Pearson, U.K. 2.25 2.25
 Nos. 291-294 (4) 3.35 3.35

Automobile Type of 1984

1985, Apr. 3
Se-tenant Pairs
299 A41 1c Rickenbacker, 1923 .15 .15
300 A41 20c Detroit-Electric, 1914 .45 .45
301 A41 50c Packard Clipper, 1941 1.10 1.10
302 A41 70c Audi Quattro, 1982 1.50 1.50
 Nos. 299-302 (4) 3.20 3.20

World War
II Aircraft
A44

1985, May 29 Litho. *Perf. 14*
307 A44 15c Curtiss P-40N .20 .20
308 A44 40c Consolidated B-24D
    Liberator .55 .55
309 A44 50c Lockheed PV-1 Ventura .70 .70
310 A44 60c Douglas C-54
    Skymaster .80 .80
a. Souvenir sheet of 4, #307-310 2.25 2.25
 Nos. 307-310 (4) 2.25 2.25

Queen Mother, 85th
Birthday — A45

Photographs.

1985, July 4 Litho. *Perf. 12½*
311 A45 5c Facing right .15 .15
312 A45 5c Facing left .15 .15
313 A45 30c Facing right, diff. .32 .32
314 A45 30c Facing front .32 .32
315 A45 60c Waving to crowd .65 .65
316 A45 60c Facing front, diff. .65 .65
317 A45 $1 Facing front, diff. 1.10 1.10
318 A45 $1 Facing left, diff. 1.10 1.10
 Nos. 311-318 (8) 4.44 4.44

Souvenir Sheets
319 Sheet of 2 2.00 2.00
a.-b. A45 $1.20 any single .90 .90
319C Sheet of 2 ('86) 3.50 3.50
e. A45 $2 like #315 1.65 1.65
f. A45 $2 like #316 1.65 1.65
319D Sheet of 2 ('86) 5.00 5.00
g. A45 $3 like #313 2.50 2.50
h. A45 $3 like #314 2.50 2.50

Stamps of same denomination se-tenant.
No. 319 contains 2 stamps picturing black &
white photographs of the Queen Mother as a young
woman and as Queen Consort.
Nos. 319C-319D issued June 10, 1986.

Train Type of 1984
Designs A36-A37

1985, Sept. 18
320 10c 1936 Green Arrow, U.K. .20 .20
321 40c 1982 G.M. (EMD) SD-50,
   USA .80 .80
322 65c 1932 DRG Flying
   Hamburger, Germany 1.30 1.30
323 $1 1908 JNR Class 1070, Ja-
   pan 2.00 2.00
 Nos. 320-323 (4) 4.30 4.30

Girl Guides, 75th
Anniv. — A46

1985, Aug. 28 Litho. *Perf. 15*
328 A46 15c Playing guitar .20 .20
329 A46 40c Camping .55 .55
330 A46 50c Flag bearer .65 .65
331 A46 60c Guides' salute .85 .85
a. Souvenir sheet of 4, #328-331 2.40 2.40
 Nos. 328-331 (4) 2.25 2.25

Car Type of 1984

1985, Oct. 8 *Perf. 12½*
Se-tenant Pairs
332 A41 5c 1929 Cord L-29,
    US .15 .15
333 A41 10c 1932 Horch 670
    V-12, Germany .20 .20
334 A41 15c 1901 Lanchester,
    UK .30 .30
335 A41 35c 1950 Citroen 2
    CV, France .70 .70
336 A41 40c 1957 MGA, UK .85 .85
337 A41 55c 1962 Ferrari 250-
    GTO, Italy 1.10 1.10
338 A41 $1 1932 Ford V-8, US 2.25 2.25
339 A41 $1.50 1977 Aston Mar-
    tin-Lagonda, UK 3.25 3.25
 Nos. 332-339 (8) 8.80 8.80

Crabs
A47

1986, Jan. 7 *Perf. 15*
348 A47 15c Stalk-eyed ghost .22 .22
349 A47 40c Red and white painted .55 .55
350 A47 50c Red-spotted .70 .70
351 A47 60c Red hermit .85 .85
 Nos. 348-351 (4) 2.32 2.32

Souvenir Sheet

Events — A48

Designs: No. 352a, American and Soviet flags,
chess board and knight. No. 352b, Rotary Intl.
emblem.

1986, Mar. 19 Litho. *Perf. 13x12½*
352 Sheet of 2 8.00 8.00
a.-b. A48 $3 any single 4.00 4.00

Fischer and Karpov, world chess champions;
Rotary Intl., 80th anniv.
No. 352 exists with plain or decorated border.

Ship Type of 1981

1986, Apr. 14 *Perf. 15*
353 A25 15c Messenger of Peace .22 .22
354 A25 40c John Wesley .60 .60
355 A25 50c Duff .75 .75
356 A25 60c Triton .85 .85
 Nos. 353-356 (4) 2.42 2.42

Queen Elizabeth II, 60th Birthday — A49

Various portraits.

1986, Apr. 21 *Perf. 12½*
357 A49 10c multicolored .15 .15
358 A49 90c multicolored 1.25 1.25
359 A49 $1.50 multicolored 2.00 2.00
360 A49 $3 multi, vert. 4.00 4.00
 Nos. 357-360 (4) 7.40 7.40
Souvenir Sheet
361 A49 $4 multicolored 5.00 5.00

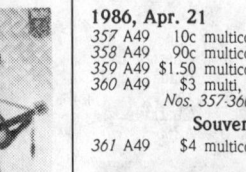

Peace Corps,
25th Anniv.
A50

1986, May 22 *Perf. 14*
362 A50 50c multicolored .75 .75

For overprint see No. 374.

A51   A52

1986, May 22 *Perf. 14x13½*
363 A51 60c multicolored .90 .90

AMERIPEX '86.

1986, June 30 Litho. *Perf. 15*
Players and teams.
364 A52 1c So. Korea .15 .15
365 A52 5c France .15 .15
366 A52 10c W. Germany, 1974 .15 .15
367 A52 40c Italy .45 .45
Size: 60x40mm
Perf. 13x12½
368 A52 60c W. Germany vs. Hol-
    land, 1974 .60 .60
369 A52 $1 Canada 1.00 1.00
370 A52 $2 No. Ireland 2.00 2.00
371 A52 $3 England 3.00 3.00
 Nos. 364-371 (8) 7.50 7.50
Souvenir Sheets
372 A52 $1.50 like #369 1.65 1.65
373 A52 $2.50 like #370 2.75 2.75

1986 World Cup Soccer Championships. Nos.
366 and 368 picture emblem; others picture character trademark.

No. 362 Ovptd. with STAMPEX '86
Emblem

1986, Aug. 4 Litho. *Perf. 14*
374 A50 50c multicolored .75 .75

Wedding of Prince Andrew and Sarah
Ferguson — A53

Perf. 12½
1986, July 18 Litho. Unwmk.
382 A53 60c Andrew, vert. .65 .65
383 A53 60c Couple, vert. .65 .65
384 A53 $1 Andrew, diff. 1.10 1.10
385 A53 $1 Princess Diana, Sarah 1.10 1.10
 Nos. 382-385 (4) 3.50 3.50

Stamps of the same denomination printed se-
tenant. No. 384 pictures Westminster Abbey in LR.
For overprints see Nos. 392-395.

Geckos
A54

1986, July 30   Litho.   Perf. 14
386 A54 15c Mourning gecko .22 .22
387 A54 40c Oceanic stump-toed .55 .55
388 A54 50c Azure-tailed skink .70 .70
389 A54 60c Moth skink 1.00 1.00
Nos. 386-389 (4) 2.47 2.47

Souvenir Sheet

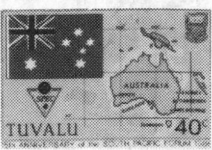

South Pacific
Forum, 15th
Anniv.
A55

Flags and maps: a, Australia. b, Cook Islands. c, Micronesia. d, Fiji. e, Kiribati. f, Nauru. g, New Zealand. h, Niue. i, Papua New Guinea. j, Solomon Islands. k, Tonga. l, Tuvalu. m, Vanuatu. n, Western Samoa.

Wmk. 380
1986, Aug. 4   Litho.   Perf. 15
390   Sheet of 14 + label 7.00 7.00
a.-n.   A55 40c any single .50 .50

No. 390 has center label picturing Executive Committee headquarters, Suva, Fiji.

Souvenir Sheet

Wedding of Prince Andrew and Sarah Ferguson — A56

1986   Litho.   Perf. 13x12½
391 A56 $6 Newlyweds 7.00 7.00

Nos. 382-385 Ovptd. "Congratulations to T.R.H. The Duke & Duchess of York" in Silver

1986   Unwmk.   Perf. 12½
392 A53 60c No. 382 .75 .75
393 A53 60c No. 383 .75 .75
394 A53 $1 No. 384 1.25 1.25
395 A53 $1 No. 385 1.25 1.25
Nos. 392-395 (4) 4.00 4.00

Stamps of the same denomination exist printed tete beche and se tenant.

Car Type of 1984

1986, Oct.   Litho.   Perf. 12½
396 A41 15c 1953 Cooper, UK .30 .30
396A A41 40c 1964 Rover 2000, UK .80 .80
396B A41 50c 1930 Ruxton, US 1.00 1.00
396C A41 60c 1950 Jowett Jupiter, UK 1.20 1.20
396D A41 90c 1964 Cobra Daytona Coupe, US 1.75 1.75
396E A41 $1.50 1903 Packard Model F "Old Pacific," US 3.00 3.00
Nos. 396-396E (6) 8.05 8.05

Marine
Life — A57

1986, Nov. 5   Unwmk.   Perf. 14
397 A57 15c Sea star .24 .24
398 A57 40c Pencil urchin .65 .65
399 A57 50c Fragile coral .85 .85
400 A57 60c Pink coral 1.00 1.00
Nos. 397-400 (4) 2.74 2.74

See Nos. 465-468, 524-527.

Souvenir Sheets

Statue of Liberty, Cent. — A58

Various views of the statue.

1986, Nov. 24
401 A58 $1.25 multicolored 1.50 1.50
402 A58 $1.50 multicolored 1.75 1.75
403 A58 $1.80 multicolored 2.25 2.25
404 A58 $2 multicolored 2.50 2.50
405 A58 $2.25 multicolored 2.75 2.75
406 A58 $2.50 multicolored 3.00 3.00
407 A58 $3 multicolored 3.50 3.50
408 A58 $3.25 multicolored 4.00 4.00
409 A58 $3.25 multicolored 4.25 4.25
Nos. 401-409 (9) 25.50 25.50

Ships Type of 1981

1987, Feb. 4   Unwmk.   Perf. 14
410 A25 15c Southern Cross IV .22 .22
411 A25 40c John Williams VI .60 .60
412 A25 50c John Williams IV .75 .75
413 A25 60c M.S. Southern Cross .90 .90
Nos. 410-413 (4) 2.47 2.47

Car Type of 1984
Perf. 12½
1987, May 7   Litho.   Unwmk.
Se-tenant Pairs
414 A41 1c 1938 Talbot-Lago, France .15 .15
415 A41 2c 1930 Dupont Model G, US .15 .15
416 A41 5c 1950 Riley RM, U.K. .15 .15
417 A41 10c 1915 Chevrolet Baby Grand, US .20 .20
418 A41 20c 1968 Shelby Mustang GT 500 KR, US .40 .40
419 A41 30c 1952 Ferrari 212 Export Barchetta, Italy .60 .60
420 A41 40c 1912 Peerless Model 48-Six, US .80 .80
421 A41 50c 1954 Sunbeam Alpine, U.K. 1.00 1.00
422 A41 60c 1969 Matra-Ford MS80, France 1.20 1.20
423 A41 70c 1934 Squire 1-Litre, U.K. 1.40 1.40
424 A41 75c 1931 Talbot 105, U.K. 1.50 1.50
425 A41 $1 1928 Plymouth Model Q, US 2.00 2.00
a.   Souvenir sheet of 2 2.75 2.75
Nos. 414-425 (12) 9.55 9.55

Ferns — A59

1987, July 7   Wmk. 380   Perf. 14
438 A59 15c Nephrolepis saligna .16 .16
439 A59 40c Asplenium nidus .42 .42
440 A59 50c Microsorum scolopendria .52 .52
441 A59 60c Pteris tripartita .65 .65
Nos. 438-441 (4) 1.75 1.75
Souvenir Sheet
442 A59 $1.50 Psilotum nudum 1.65 1.65

Flowers and Women Wearing Fous — A60

1987, Aug. 12   Wmk. 380
443 A60 15c Flowers .20 .20
444 A60 15c Woman wearing fou .20 .20
445 A60 40c Woman wearing fou, diff. .52 .52
446 A60 40c Flowers, diff. .52 .52
447 A60 50c Flowers, diff. .65 .65
448 A60 50c Woman wearing fou, diff. .65 .65
449 A60 60c Woman wearing fou, diff. .80 .80
450 A60 60c Flowers, diff. .80 .80
Nos. 443-450 (8) 4.34 4.34

Crayfish
and
Coconut
Crabs
A61

Wmk. 380
1987, Nov. 11   Litho.   Perf. 14
451 A61 40c Coconut crabs .60 .60
452 A61 50c Painted crayfish .75 .75
453 A61 60c Ocean crayfish .88 .88
Nos. 451 453 (3) 2.23 2.23

Photograph
of Queen
Victoria,
1897, by
Downey
A62

Designs: 60c, Elizabeth and Philip on their wedding day, 1947. 80c, Elizabeth, Charles, Philip, c. 1950. $1, Elizabeth, Anne, 1950. $2, Elizabeth, 1970. $3, Elizabeth, children, 1950.

1987, Nov. 20   Unwmk.   Perf. 15
454 A62 40c olive green & blk .55 .55
455 A62 60c dull blue grn & blk .80 .80
456 A62 80c dark blue & blk 1.10 1.10
457 A62 $1 rose magenta & blk 1.40 1.40
458 A62 $2 multicolored 2.75 2.75
Nos. 454-458 (5) 6.60 6.60

Souvenir Sheet
459 A62 $3 red orange & blk 4.00 4.00

Accession of Queen Victoria to the throne of England, sesquicentennial; wedding of Queen Elizabeth II and Prince Philip, 40th anniv.

16th World Scout Jamboree, Australia, 1987-88 — A63

Jamboree and Australia bicentennial emblems plus: 40c, Aborigine, Ayer's Rock. 60c, Capt. Cook, by Dance, and HMS Endeavor. $1, Scout and Scout Park Arch. $1.50, Koala and kangaroo. $2.50, Lord and Lady Baden-Powell.

Perf. 13x12½
1987, Dec. 2   Litho.   Unwmk.
460 A63 40c multicolored .60 .60
461 A63 60c multicolored .90 .90
462 A63 $1 multicolored 1.50 1.50
463 A63 $1.50 multicolored 2.20 2.20
Nos. 460-463 (4) 5.20 5.20

Souvenir Sheet
464 A63 $2.50 multicolored 3.70 3.70

Marine Life Type of 1986

Unwmk.
1988, Feb. 29   Litho.   Perf. 15
465 A57 15c Spanish dancer .25 .25
466 A57 40c Hard corals .60 .60
467 A57 50c Feather stars .75 .75
468 A57 60c Staghorn corals .90 .90
Nos. 465-468 (4) 2.50 2.50

Birds — A64

1988, Mar. 2   Perf. 15
469 A64 5c Jungle fowl .15 .15
470 A64 10c White tern .15 .15
471 A64 15c Brown noddy .20 .20
472 A64 20c Phoenix petrel .30 .30
473 A64 25c Pacific golden plover .40 .40
474 A64 30c Crested tern .45 .45
475 A64 35c Sooty tern .50 .50
476 A64 40c Bristle-thighed curlew .55 .55
477 A64 45c Eastern bar-tailed godwit .65 .65
478 A64 50c Reef heron .75 .75
479 A64 55c Greater frigatebird .80 .80
480 A64 60c Red-footed booby .90 .90
481 A64 70c Red-necked stint 1.10 1.10
482 A64 $1 New Zealand long-tailed cuckoo 1.65 1.65
483 A64 $2 Red-tailed tropicbird 3.00 3.00
484 A64 $5 Banded rail 7.50 7.50
Nos. 469-484 (16) 19.05 19.05

For overprints see Nos. 676-679, O33-O48.

Intl. Red Cross and Red Crescent Organizations, 125th Annivs. — A65

Perf. 12½
1988, May 9   Litho.   Unwmk.
485 A65 15c Jean-Henri Dunant .25 .25
486 A65 40c Junior Red Cross .60 .60
487 A65 50c Care for the handicapped .75 .75
488 A65 60c First aid training .90 .90
Nos. 485-488 (4) 2.50 2.50

Souvenir Sheet
489 A65 $1.50 Lecture 2.25 2.25

A66

Voyages of Capt. Cook — A67

Designs: 20c, HMS *Endeavour* (starboard side). 40c, *Endeavour* (stern). 50c, Landing, Tahiti, 1769, vert. 60c, Maori chief, vert. 80c, *Resolution* and native Hawaiian sail ship. $1, Cook, by Sir Nathaniel Dance-Holland (1735-1811), vert. $2.50, Antarctic icebergs surrounding the *Resolution*.

1988, June 15   **Litho.**   *Perf. 12½*
490 A66	20c shown		.35	.35
491 A66	40c multicolored		.70	.70
492 A66	50c multicolored		.85	.85
493 A66	60c multicolored		1.00	1.00
494 A66	80c multicolored		1.30	1.30
495 A66	$1 multicolored		1.65	1.65
	Nos. 490-495 (6)		5.85	5.85

Souvenir Sheet
496 A67	$2.50 shown	4.25	4.25

For surcharges see Nos. B1-B2.

Fungi — A68

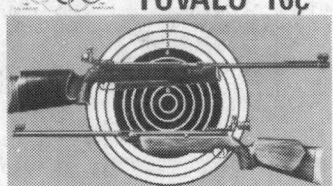

1988, July 25   **Litho.**   *Perf. 15*
497 A68	40c Ganoderma applanatum	.65	.65
498 A68	50c Pseudoepicoccum cocos	.85	.85
499 A68	60c Rigidoporus zonalis	1.00	1.00
500 A68	90c Rigidoporus microporus	1.50	1.50
	Nos. 497-500 (4)	4.00	4.00

See Nos. 520-523.

1988 Summer Olympics, Seoul — A69

Perf. 12½
1988, Aug. 19   **Litho.**   **Unwmk.**
501 A69	10c Rifles, target	.15	.15
502 A69	20c Judo	.30	.30
503 A69	40c One-man kayak	.65	.65
504 A69	60c Swimming	1.00	1.00
505 A69	80c Yachting	1.25	1.25
506 A69	$1 Balance beam	1.65	1.65
	Nos. 501-506 (6)	5.00	5.00

Natl. Independence, 10th Anniv. — A70

Wmk. 380
1988, Sept. 28   **Litho.**   *Perf. 14*
507 A70	60c Queen Elizabeth in boat	1.00	1.00
a.	Souvenir sheet of 1	1.00	1.00
508 A70	90c In sedan chair	1.40	1.40
a.	Souvenir sheet of 1	1.40	1.40
509 A70	$1 shown	1.65	1.65
a.	Souvenir sheet of 1	1.65	1.65
510 A70	$1.20 Seated at dais	1.90	1.90
a.	Souvenir sheet of 1	1.90	1.90
	Nos. 507-510 (4)	5.95	5.95

Nos. 507-508 and 510 vert.

Christmas
A71

Unwmk.
1988, Dec. 5   **Litho.**   *Perf. 14*
511 A71	15c Mary	.30	.30
512 A71	40c Christ child	.70	.70
513 A71	60c Joseph	1.10	1.10
	Nos. 511-513 (3)	2.10	2.10

Souvenir Sheet
514 A71	$1.50 Heraldic angel	2.75	2.75

Palm-frond or Pandanus-leaf Skirts — A72

1989, Mar. 31   **Litho.**   *Perf. 14*
515 A72	40c multi	.70	.70
516 A72	50c multi, diff.	.80	.80
517 A72	60c multi, diff.	1.00	1.00
518 A72	90c multi, diff.	1.50	1.50
	Nos. 515-518 (4)	4.00	4.00

Souvenir Sheet
519 A72	$1.50 multi, vert.	2.50	2.50

Fungi Type of 1988
1989, May 24   **Litho.**   *Perf. 14*
520 A68	40c Trametes muelleri	.60	.60
521 A68	50c Pestalotiopsis palmarum	.75	.75
522 A68	60c Trametes cingulata	.90	.90
523 A68	90c Schizophyllum commune	1.40	1.40
	Nos. 520-523 (4)	3.65	3.65

Marine Life Type of 1986
1989, July 31   **Litho.**   *Perf. 14*
524 A57	40c Pennant coralfish	.60	.60
525 A57	50c Anemone fish	.80	.80
526 A57	60c Batfish	.90	.90
527 A57	90c Threadfin coralfish	1.40	1.40
a.	Miniature sheet of 4, #524-527	3.75	3.75
	Nos. 524-527 (4)	3.70	3.70

Souvenir Sheet

Maiden Voyage of M.V. *Nivaga II*, 1988 — A73

1989, Oct. 9   **Litho.**   *Perf. 14*
528 A73	$1.50 multicolored	2.25	2.25

Christmas — A74   Tropical Trees — A75

Unwmk.
1989, Nov. 29   **Litho.**   *Perf. 14*
529 A74	40c Conch shell	.60	.60
530 A74	50c Flower bouquet	.80	.80
531 A74	60c Germinated coconut	.95	.95
532 A74	90c Shell jewelry	1.40	1.40
	Nos. 529-532 (4)	3.75	3.75

1990, Feb. 28   **Litho.**   *Perf. 14½*
533 A75	15c Cocus nucifera	.25	.25
534 A75	30c Rhizophora samoensis	.45	.45
535 A75	40c Messerschmidia argentea	.60	.60
536 A75	50c Pandanus tectorius	.75	.75
537 A75	60c Hernandia nymphaeifolia	.90	.90
538 A75	90c Pisonia grandis	1.40	1.40
	Nos. 533-538 (6)	4.35	4.35

Penny Black, 150th Anniv. A76

1990, May 3   **Litho.**   *Perf. 14*
539 A76	15c multicolored	.25	.25
540 A76	60c multicolored	.65	.65
541 A76	90c multicolored	1.50	1.50
	Nos. 539-541 (3)	2.40	2.40

Souvenir Sheet
542 A76	$2 multicolored	3.25	3.25

Stamp World London '90.

World War II Ships A77

Designs: 15c, Japanese merchant conversion, 1940. 30c, USS Unimak, seaplane tender, 1944. 40c, Amagari, Japanese Hubuki class, 1942. 50c, AO-24 USS Platte, Nov. 1, 1943. 60c, Japanese Shumushu Class (Type A) escort. 90c, CV-22 USS Independence.

1990
543 A77	15c multicolored	.25	.25
544 A77	30c multicolored	.50	.50
545 A77	40c multicolored	.65	.65
546 A77	50c multicolored	.80	.80
547 A77	60c multicolored	1.00	1.00
548 A77	90c multicolored	1.50	1.50
	Nos. 543-548 (6)	4.70	4.70

Flowers — A78

1990, Sept. 21   **Litho.**   *Perf. 14½*
549 A78	15c Erythrina fusca	.25	.25
550 A78	30c Capparis cordifolia	.50	.50
551 A78	40c Portulaca pilosa	.65	.65
552 A78	50c Cordia subcordata	.80	.80
553 A78	60c Scaevola taccada	1.00	1.00
554 A78	90c Suriana maritima	1.50	1.50
	Nos. 549-554 (6)	4.70	4.70

UN Development Program, 40th Anniv. — A79

1990, Nov. 20   **Litho.**   *Perf. 14*
555 A79	40c Surveyor	.65	.65
556 A79	60c Communications station	1.00	1.00
557 A79	$1.20 Fishing boat *Te Tautai*	1.90	1.90
	Nos. 555-557 (3)	3.55	3.55

Christmas — A80   Seashells — A81

1990, Nov. 20
558 A80	15c Mary and Joseph	.25	.25
559 A80	40c Nativity	.65	.65
560 A80	60c Shepherds	1.00	1.00
561 A80	90c Three Kings	1.50	1.50
	Nos. 558-561 (4)	3.40	3.40

1991, Jan. 18   **Litho.**   *Perf. 14*
562 A81	40c Murex ramosus	.65	.65
563 A81	50c Conus marmoreus	.80	.80
564 A81	60c Trochus niloticus	1.00	1.00
565 A81	$1.50 Cypraea mappa	2.30	2.30
	Nos. 562-565 (4)	4.75	4.75

Insects A82

1991, Mar. 22   **Litho.**   *Perf. 14*
566 A82	40c Cylas formicarius	.65	.65
567 A82	50c Heliothis armiger	.80	.80
568 A82	60c Spodoptera litura	1.00	1.00
569 A82	$1.50 Agrius convolvuli	2.25	2.25
	Nos. 566-569 (4)	4.70	4.70

A83   A84

Endangered marine life.

1991, May 31   **Litho.**   *Perf. 14*
570 A83	40c Green turtle	.65	.65
571 A83	50c Humpback whale	.80	.80
572 A83	60c Hawksbill turtle	1.00	1.00
573 A83	$1.50 Sperm whale	2.25	2.25
	Nos. 570-573 (4)	4.70	4.70

1991, July 31   **Litho.**   *Perf. 14*
574 A84	40c Soccer	.65	.65
575 A84	50c Volleyball	.80	.80
576 A84	60c Lawn tennis	1.00	1.00
577 A84	$1.50 Cricket	2.25	2.25
	Nos. 574-577 (4)	4.70	4.70

9th South Pacific Games.

World War II Ships A85

1991, Oct. 15   **Litho.**   *Perf. 14*
578 A85	40c USS Tennessee	.65	.65
579 A85	50c IJN Haguro	.80	.80
580 A85	60c HMS Achilles	1.00	1.00
581 A85	$1.50 USS North Carolina	2.50	2.50
	Nos. 578-581 (4)	4.95	4.95

A86   A87

Christmas: various traditional dance costumes.

1991, Dec. 13
582 A86	40c multicolored	.65	.65
583 A86	50c multicolored	.80	.80
584 A86	60c multicolored	1.00	1.00
585 A86	$1.50 multicolored	2.50	2.50
	Nos. 582-585 (4)	4.95	4.95

1992, Jan. 29 — Litho. — Perf. 14

Constellations.

586	A87	40c Southern Fish	.65	.65
587	A87	50c Scorpio	.80	.80
588	A87	60c Sagittarius	.95	.95
589	A87	$1.50 Southern Cross	2.25	2.25
		Nos. 586-589 (4)	4.65	4.65

British Annexation of the Gilbert & Ellice Islands, Cent. A88

1992, Mar. 23 — Litho. — Perf. 14

590	A88	40c King George VI	.60	.60
591	A88	50c King George V	.75	.75
592	A88	60c King Edward VII	.90	.90
593	A88	$1.50 Queen Victoria	2.25	2.25
		Nos. 590-593 (4)	4.50	4.50

Discovery of America, 500th Anniv. A89

Columbus and: 40c, Queen Isabella & King Ferdinand of Spain. 50c, Polynesians. 60c, South American Indians. $1.50, North American Indians.

1992, May 22 — Litho. — Perf. 14

594	A89	40c black & dk blue	.60	.60
595	A89	50c black & dk plum	.75	.75
596	A89	60c black & dk green	.90	.90
597	A89	$1.50 black & dk purple	2.25	2.25
		Nos. 594-597 (4)	4.50	4.50

World Columbian Stamp Expo '92, Chicago.

Fish A90

Designs: 15c, Bluespot butterflyfish. 20c, Pink parrotfish. 25c, Stripe surgeonfish. 30c, Moon wrasse. 35c, Harlequin filefish. 40c, Bird wrasse. 45c, Black-finned pigfish. 50c, Blue-green chromis. 60c, Hump-headed Maori wrasse. 70c, Ornate coralfish, vert. 90c, Saddled butterflyfish, vert. $1, Vagabond butterflyfish, vert. $2, Longfin bannerfish, vert. $3, Moorish idol, vert.

1992, July 15

598	A90	15c multicolored	.25	.25
599	A90	20c multicolored	.30	.30
600	A90	25c multicolored	.40	.40
601	A90	30c multicolored	.50	.50
602	A90	35c multicolored	.60	.60
603	A90	40c multicolored	.65	.65
604	A90	45c multicolored	.70	.70
605	A90	50c multicolored	.80	.80
606	A90	60c multicolored	1.00	1.00
607	A90	70c multicolored	1.10	1.10
608	A90	90c multicolored	1.40	1.40
609	A90	$1 multicolored	1.65	1.65
610	A90	$2 multicolored	3.25	3.25
611	A90	$3 multicolored	4.75	4.75
		Nos. 598-611 (14)	17.35	17.35

For overprints see Nos. 629-632.

1992 Summer Olympics, Barcelona — A91

1992, July 27 — Litho. — Perf. 14

612	A91	40c Discus	.60	.60
613	A91	50c Javelin	.75	.75
614	A91	60c Shotput	.90	.90
615	A91	$1.50 Track & field	2.25	2.25
		Nos. 612-615 (4)	4.50	4.50

Souvenir Sheet

616	A91	$2 Olympic stadium	3.00	3.00

Blue Coral A92

Various views of blue coral.

1992, Sept. 1

617	A92	10c multicolored	.15	.15
618	A92	25c multicolored	.38	.38
619	A92	30c multicolored	.45	.45
620	A92	35c multicolored	.50	.50
		Nos. 617-620 (4)	1.48	1.48

World Wildlife Fund.

Wild Flowers of

Christmas — A93   Wild Flowers — A94

Designs: 40c, Fishermen seeing angel. 50c, Fishermen sailing canoes toward island. 60c, Adoration of the fishermen. $1.50, Flowers, shell necklaces.

1992, Dec. 25 — Litho. — Perf. 14

621	A93	40c multicolored	.55	.55
622	A93	50c multicolored	.70	.70
623	A93	60c multicolored	.80	.80
624	A93	$1.50 multicolored	2.00	2.00
		Nos. 621-624 (4)	4.05	4.05

1993, Feb. 2 — Litho. — Perf. 14

625	A94	40c Calophyllum inophyllum	.60	.60
626	A94	50c Hibiscus tiliaceus	.70	.70
627	A94	60c Lantana camara	.85	.85
628	A94	$1.50 Plumeria rubra	2.00	2.00
		Nos. 625-628 (4)	4.15	4.15

Nos. 601, 603, & 605-606 Ovptd.

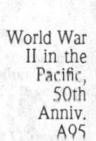

1992, Sept. 1 — Litho. — Perf. 14

629	A90	30c on #601	.50	.50
630	A90	40c on #603	.65	.65
631	A90	50c on #605	.80	.80
632	A90	60c on #606	1.00	1.00
		Nos. 629-632 (4)	2.95	2.95

World War II in the Pacific, 50th Anniv. A95

1993, Apr. 23 — Litho. — Perf. 14

633	A95	40c Japanese bombers	.60	.60
634	A95	50c Anti-aircraft gun, vert.	.70	.70
635	A95	60c Using flame thrower	.85	.85
636	A95	$1.50 Map of Funafuti Atoll, vert.	2.25	2.25
		Nos. 633-636 (4)	4.40	4.40

Indopex '93 — A96

1993, May 29 — Perf. 14x14½

637	A96	$1.50 Cepora perimale	2.25	2.25

Marine Life — A97

1993, June 29 — Litho. — Perf. 14

638	A97	40c Giant clam	.55	.55
639	A97	50c Anemone crab	.70	.70
640	A97	60c Octopus	.85	.85
641	A97	$1.50 Green turtle	2.00	2.00
		Nos. 638-641 (4)	4.10	4.10

Coronation of Queen Elizabeth II, 40th Anniv. A98

Queen: 40c, Riding in parade with Prince Phillip. 50c, Drinking coconut milk. 60c, Holding umbrella. $1.50, With natives. $2, Coronation ceremony.

1993, July 5

642	A98	40c multicolored	.55	.55
643	A98	50c multicolored	.70	.70
644	A98	60c multicolored	.85	.85
645	A98	$1.50 multicolored	2.00	2.00
		Nos. 642-645 (4)	4.10	4.10

Souvenir Sheet

646	A98	$2 multicolored	2.75	2.75

Souvenir Sheet

Taipei '93 — A99

Illustration reduced.

Perf. 14½x14

1993, Aug. 14 — Litho. & Typo.

647	A99	$1.50 Geoffroyi godart	2.00	2.00

Souvenir Sheet

Bangkok '93 — A100

Illustration reduced.

1993, Oct. 1 — Litho. — Perf. 14x14½

648	A100	$1.50 Paradisea staudinger	2.00	2.00

Greenhouse Effect — A101   Christmas — A102

Beach scene with: 40c, Sun at UR. 50c, Sun at UL. 60c, Crab on beach. $1.50, Sea gull in flight.

1993, Nov. 2 — Litho. — Perf. 13½

649	A101	40c multicolored	.50	.50
650	A101	50c multicolored	.65	.65
651	A101	60c multicolored	.80	.80
652	A101	$1.50 multicolored	2.00	2.00
a.		Souvenir sheet of 4, #649-652, perf. 14½x14	4.00	4.00
		Nos. 649-652 (4)	3.95	3.95

1993, Dec. 6 — Litho. — Perf. 13½

653	A102	40c shown	.55	.55
654	A102	50c Candle, flowers	.70	.70
655	A102	60c Angel, flowers	.85	.85
656	A102	$1.50 Palm tree, candles	2.00	2.00
		Nos. 653-656 (4)	4.10	4.10

Souvenir Sheet

Hong Kong '94 — A103

Illustration reduced.

1994, Feb. 18 — Perf. 14½x14

657	A103	$2 Monarch	2.75	2.75

Scenic Views A104

1994, Feb. 18 — Litho. — Perf. 14

658	A104	40c shown	.60	.60
659	A104	50c Beach, trees, diff.	.70	.70
660	A104	60c Boats, ocean	.85	.85
661	A104	$1.50 Boats, beach	2.25	2.25
		Nos. 658-661 (4)	4.40	4.40

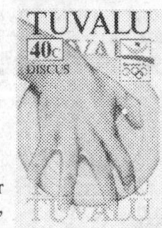

New Year 1994 (Year
of the Dog) — A105

1994, Apr. 23   Litho.   Perf. 14
662 A105 40c Irish setter   .60   .60
663 A105 50c Golden retriever   .70   .70
664 A105 60c West Highland terri-
er   .85   .85
665 A105 $1.50 German shepherd   2.25 2.25
    Nos. 662-665 (4)   4.40 4.40

A106   Seashells — A107

1994, June 7
666 A106 40c Australia   .60   .60
667 A106 50c England   .75   .75
668 A106 60c Argentina   .90   .90
669 A106 $1.50 Germany   2.25 2.25
    Nos. 666-669 (4)   4.50 4.50

Souvenir Sheet
670 A106 $2 US   3.00 3.00
1994 World Cup Soccer Championships, US.

1994, Aug. 16   Litho.   Perf. 14
671 A107 40c Umbonium gigante-
um   .60   .60
672 A107 50c Turbo petholatus   .75   .75
673 A107 60c Planaxis savignyi   .90   .90
674 A107 $1.50 Hydatina physis   2.25 2.25
    Nos. 671-674 (4)   4.50 4.50

Souvenir Sheet

PHILAKOREA '94 — A108

Illustration reduced.

1994, Aug. 16
675 A108 $1.50 Pekinese dog   2.25 2.25

Nos. 469-470, 476-477
Ovptd.

1994, Aug. 31   Litho.   Perf. 15
676 A64 5c multicolored   .15   .15
677 A64 10c multicolored   .15   .15
678 A64 40c multicolored   .60   .60
679 A64 45c multicolored   .65   .65
    Nos. 676-679 (4)   1.55 1.55

First Manned Moon
Landing, 25th
Anniv. — A109

Designs: a, 40c, Saturn V. b, 50c, Apollo 11. c,
60c, Neil Armstrong. d, $1.50, Splash-down.

1994, Oct. 31   Perf. 14
680 A109 Strip of 4, #a.-d.   4.50 4.50

Christmas
A110

Designs: 40c, Boys playing in water. 50c, Islanders, fish being gathered. 60c, People seated under
canopy, food. $1.50, Traditional dancers.

1994, Dec. 15   Litho.   Perf. 14
681 A110 40c multicolored   .60   .60
682 A110 50c multicolored   .75   .75
683 A110 60c multicolored   .90   .90
684 A110 $1.50 multicolored   2.25 2.25
    Nos. 681-684 (4)   4.50 4.50

New Year
1995 (Year of
the
Boar) — A111

Designs: 40c, One pig. 50c, Pig, piglet. 60c,
Three pigs. $1.50, Sow nursing litter.

1995, Jan. 30   Litho.   Perf. 14
685 A111 40c multicolored   .60   .60
686 A111 50c multicolored   .75   .75
687 A111 60c multicolored   .90   .90
688 A111 $1.50 multicolored   2.25 2.25
    Nos. 685-688 (4)   4.50 4.50

FAO, 50th
Anniv.
A112

Designs: 40c, Men with vegetables in wheelbarrow. 50c, Man with sack of vegetables. 60c, Girl
cleaning vegetables. $1.50, Girl mixing food.

1995, Mar. 31   Litho.   Perf. 14
689 A112 40c multicolored   .52   .52
690 A112 50c multicolored   .65   .65
691 A112 60c multicolored   .80   .80
692 A112 $1.50 multicolored   2.00 2.00
    Nos. 689-692 (4)   3.97 3.97

Visit South
Pacific Year
A113

1995, May 26   Litho.   Perf. 14
693 A113 40c shown   .60   .60
694 A113 50c Sailboat   .75   .75
695 A113 60c Hut   .90   .90
696 A113 $1.50 Home, beach   2.25 2.25
    Nos. 693-696 (4)   4.50 4.50

Pacific
Coastal
Orchids
A114

Designs: 40c, Dendrobium comptonii. 50c, Dendrobium aff. involutum. 60c, Dendrobium rarum.
$1.50, Grammatophyllum scriptum.

1995, July 28   Litho.   Perf. 14
697 A114 40c multicolored   .60   .60
698 A114 50c multicolored   .75   .75
699 A114 60c multicolored   .90   .90
700 A114 $1.50 multicolored   2.25 2.25
    Nos. 697-700 (4)   4.50 4.50

No. 701 not assigned.

Souvenir Sheet

Jakarta '95, Asian World Stamp
Exhibition — A116

Illustration reduced.

1995, Aug. 19   Litho.   Perf. 12
702 A116 $1 Traditional dancer   1.50 1.50

Souvenir Sheet

Singapore '95 World Stamp
Exhibition — A117

Illustration reduced.

1995, Sept. 1
703 A117 $1 Phalaenopsis amabillis 1.50 1.50

End of
World War
II, 50th
Anniv.
A118

Designs: 40c, Soldier with sub-machine gun,
map of Japan, Tuvalu. 50c, Soldier holding rifle,
landing exercise on beach. 60c, US Marine, offshore air and sea battle. $1.50, Soldier firing rifle,
atomic mushroom cloud.

1995, Aug. 19   Litho.   Perf. 14
704 A118 40c multicolored   .60   .60
705 A118 50c multicolored   .75   .75
706 A118 60c multicolored   .90   .90
707 A118 $1.50 multicolored   2.25 2.25
    Nos. 704-707 (4)   4.50 4.50

Souvenir Sheet

UN, 50th Anniv. — A119

Designs: a, Rowing in outrigger canoes. b, UN
New York headquarters. Illustration reduced.

1995, Oct. 24   Perf. 14½
708 A119 $1 Sheet of 2, #a.-b.   3.00 3.00

SEMI-POSTAL STAMPS

Nos. 159-160 Surcharged and Overprinted:
"TONGA CYCLONE / RELIEF / 1982" in
1 or 3 Lines
Wmk. 380
1982, May 20   Litho.   Perf. 14
B1 A66 45c + 20c multi   1.25 1.25
B2 A67 45c + 20c multi   1.25 1.25

POSTAGE DUE STAMPS

Arms of Tuvalu — D1

1981, May 13   Litho.   Perf. 14
J1 D1 1c brt rose lil & blk   .15   .15
J2 D1 2c grnsh bl & blk   .15   .15
J3 D1 5c yellow brn & blk   .15   .15
J4 D1 10c blue grn & blk   .20   .20
J5 D1 20c chocolate & blk   .25   .25
J6 D1 30c orange & blk   .38   .38
J7 D1 40c ultra & blk   .50   .50
J8 D1 50c yellow grn & blk   .65   .65
J9 D1 $1 brt lilac & blk   1.25 1.25
    Nos. J1-J9 (9)   3.68 3.68

1982-83   Perf. 14x15
J1a D1 1c bright rose lilac & black   .15 .15
J2a D1 2c greenish blue & black   .15 .15
J3a D1 5c yellow brown & black   .15 .15
J4a D1 10c blue green & black   .20 .20
J5a D1 20c chocolate & black   .25 .25
J6a D1 30c orange & black   .38 .38
J7a D1 40c ultra & black   .50 .50
J8a D1 50c yellow green & black   .65 .65
J9a D1 $1 bright lilac & black   1.25 1.25
    Nos. J1a-J9a (9)   3.68 3.68

Issue dates: 1c-20c, Nov. 25 1982, inscribed
"1982." 30c-$1, May 25, 1983, inscribed "1983."

OFFICIAL STAMPS

Nos. 96-113 Overprinted: "OFFICIAL"
1981   Litho.   Unwmk.   Perf. 14
O1 A14 1c multicolored   .15   .15
O2 A14 2c multicolored   .15   .15
O3 A14 4c multicolored   .15   .15
O4 A14 5c multicolored   .15   .15
O5 A14 6c multicolored   .15   .15
O6 A14 8c multicolored   .15   .15
O7 A14 10c multicolored   .15   .15
O8 A14 15c multicolored   .25   .25
O9 A14 20c multicolored   .35   .35
O10 A14 25c multicolored   .45   .45
O11 A14 30c multicolored   .55   .55
O12 A14 35c multicolored   .65   .65
O13 A14 40c multicolored   .75   .75
O14 A14 45c multicolored   .90   .90
O15 A14 50c multicolored   .95   .95
O16 A14 70c multicolored   1.25 1.25
O17 A14 $1 multicolored   1.90 1.90
O18 A14 $2 multicolored   3.75 3.75
O19 A14 $5 multicolored   9.00 9.00
    Nos. O1-O19 (19)   21.80 21.80

No. 193 Surcharged and Overprinted
"OFFICIAL"
Wmk. 380
1983, Aug.   Litho.   Perf. 14
O20 A30 60c on $1 multi   1.00 1.00

Nos. 185-186A, 188, 230, 188A-195
Overprinted: "OFFICIAL"
1984   Litho.   Wmk. 380   Perf. 14
O21 A30 5c multicolored   .15   .15
O22 A30 10c multicolored   .15   .15
O23 A30 15c multicolored   .20   .20
O24 A30 25c multicolored   .32   .32
O25 A30 30c on 45c multi   .40   .40
O25A A30 35c multicolored   .40   .40
O26 A30 35c multicolored   .45   .45
O27 A30 40c multicolored   .50   .50
O28 A30 45c multicolored   .55   .55
O29 A30 50c multicolored   .65   .65
O29A A30 60c multicolored   .80   .80
O30 A30 $1 multicolored   1.25 1.25
O31 A30 $2 multicolored   2.50 2.50
O32 A30 $5 multicolored   6.25 6.25
    Nos. O21-O32 (14)   14.57 14.57

Issued: #O23, O29A, Apr. 30; others Feb. 1.

Nos. 469-484 Overprinted "OFFICIAL"

1989, Feb. 22 Litho. *Perf. 15*

O33 A64 5c multicolored .15 .15
O34 A64 10c multicolored .15 .15
O35 A64 15c multicolored .22 .22
O36 A64 20c multicolored .30 .30
O37 A64 25c multicolored .38 .38
O38 A64 30c multicolored .45 .45
O39 A64 35c multicolored .52 .52
O40 A64 40c multicolored .60 .60
O41 A64 45c multicolored .68 .68
O42 A64 50c multicolored .75 .75
O43 A64 55c multicolored .82 .82
O44 A64 60c multicolored .90 .90
O45 A64 70c multicolored 1.05 1.05
O46 A64 $1 multicolored 1.50 1.50
O47 A64 $2 multicolored 3.00 3.00
O48 A64 $5 multicolored 7.50 7.50
Nos. O33-O48 (16) 18.97 18.97

For the following islands all are types of Tuvalu unless otherwise specified.
See note following Tuvalu No. 221.

Leaders of the World
Large quantities of some Leaders of the World sets, including unissued stamps, were sold at a fraction of face value when the printer was liquidated.

FUNAFUTI

Catalogue values for all unused stamps in this country are for Never Hinged items.

Locomotive Type of 1984
Tuvalu Designs A36-A37
Perf. 12½x13

1984-86 Litho. Unwmk.

Se-tenant Pairs

1 5c 1919 Class C51, Japan .15 .15
2 5c 1935 F.C.C. Andes Class, Peru .15 .15
3 15c 1934 Kolhapur Class, UK .30 .30
4 15c 1941 V.R. Class H, Australia .30 .30
5 15c 1885 S.A.R. Class Y, Australia .30 .30
6 20c 1951 Class 4, UK .42 .42
7 20c 1928 Class U, UK .42 .42
8 25c 1923 Eryri Cog, UK .55 .55
9 30c 1927 Royal Scot Class, UK .65 .65
10 35c 1828 Lancashire Witch, UK .75 .75
11 35c 1906 NY, NH & H RR Class EP-1, US .75 .75
12 40c 1942 Springbok Class B1, UK .85 .85
13 40c 1827 Royal George, UK .85 .85
14 40c 1926 Northern Pacific Class A5, US .85 .85
15 40c 1900 Aberdare Class 2600, UK .85 .85
16 50c 1829 Sans Pareil, UK 1.10 1.10
17 50c 1924 EST Class 241A, France 1.10 1.10
18 55c 1911 Class 8K, UK 1.25 1.25
19 60c 1913 Sir Gilbert Claughton, UK 1.40 1.40
20 60c 1920 Sherlock Holmes, UK 1.40 1.40
21 60c 1949 Class K1, UK 1.40 1.40
22 $1 1925 Class P1, UK 2.25 2.25
23 $1 1940 SNCF Class 232R, France 2.25 2.25
24 $1.50 1904 B&O Class DD-1 3.25 3.25
Nos. 1-24 (24) 23.54 23.54

Issue dates: Nos. 3, 6, 9, 12, 16, 19, Apr. 16, 1984; 1, 4, 8, 10, 13, 18, 20, 22, Dec. 24, 1984; 2, 5, 11, 14, 17, 23, Apr. 29, 1985; 7, 15, 21, 24, Dec. 30, 1986.
1986 stamps not inscribed "Leaders of the World."

Automobile Type of 1984
Tuvalu Design A41

1984-87

Se-tenant Pairs

25 1c 1957 Triumph TR3A, UK .15 .15
26 1c 1932 Nash Special 8 Convertible, US .15 .15
27 10c 1937 Cord 812 Supercharged, US .15 .15
28 10c 1925 AC Six, UK .15 .15
29 20c 1924 Alfa Romeo P2, Italy .42 .42
30 30c 1935 Aston Martin Ulster, UK .60 .60
31 40c 1948 Morgan 4+4, UK .85 .85
32 40c 1906 Renault GP, France .85 .85
33 55c 1903 Cadillac Model A 1.10 1.10
34 60c 1971 Porsche 917K, Germany 1.25 1.25
35 60c 1913 Simplex 75HP, US 1.25 1.25
36 75c 1939 Delahaye Type 165, France 1.50 1.50
37 80c 1938 Opel Admiral, Germany 1.65 1.65
38 $1 1936 Jaguar SS 100, UK 2.00 2.00
39 $1 1965 Aston Martin DB5, UK 2.00 2.00
40 $1.50 1977 Porsche 935 3.25 3.25
Nos. 25-40 (16) 17.32 17.32

Issues dates: Nos. 25, 27, 31, 38, Sept. 13, 1984; 26, 30, 33, 34, Feb. 8, 1985; 28-29, 32, 35-37, 39-40, Aug. 27, 1987.
1987 stamps not inscribed "Leaders of the World."

Queen Mother Type of 1985

1985-86 *Perf. 13x12½*

41 A45 5c Blue feathered hat .15 .15
42 A45 5c White hat .15 .15
43 A45 25c Pink hat .28 .28
44 A45 25c Tiara .28 .28
45 A45 80c Blue hat .90 .90
46 A45 80c Blue hat with veil covering face .90 .90
47 A45 $1.05 Blue hat, diff. 1.10 1.10
48 A45 $1.05 Tiara, diff. 1.10 1.10
Nos. 41-48 (8) 4.86 4.86

Souvenir Sheets

49 Sheet of 2 2.25 2.25
a. A45 $1.05 Headband 1.10 1.10
b. A45 $1.05 Hat 1.10 1.10
50 Sheet of 2 4.50 4.50
a. A45 $2 like #43 2.25 2.25
b. A45 $2 like #44 2.25 2.25
51 Sheet of 2 6.50 6.50
a. A45 $3 like #45 3.25 3.25
b. A45 $3 like #46 3.25 3.25

Issued: #41-49, Aug. 26; #50-51, Jan. 3, 1986.
Stamps of same denomination se-tenant.

Elizabeth II 60th Birthday Type
Perf. 13x12½, 12½x13

1986, Apr. 21

52 A49 10c Trooping the colors .15 .15
53 A49 50c Tiara .60 .60
54 A49 $1.50 As young woman, 1952 1.90 1.90
55 A49 $3.50 Tiara, diff., vert. 4.25 4.25
Nos. 52-55 (4) 6.90 6.90

Souvenir Sheet

56 A49 $5 Scarf 6.25 6.25

Royal Wedding Type of 1986

1986, July 23

57 A53 60c Andrew holding rifle, vert. .60 .60
58 A53 60c Sarah Ferguson, vert. .60 .60
59 A53 $1 Couple 1.00 1.00
60 A53 $1 Prince Philip and Andrew 1.00 1.00
Nos. 57-60 (4) 3.20 3.20

Souvenir Sheet

61 A56 $4 Newlyweds 4.00 4.00

Stamps of same denomination se-tenant.

Nos. 57-60 Ovptd. in Silver "Congratulations to T.R.H. The Duke & Duchess of York"

1986, July 23

62 A53 60c On No. 57 .70 .70
63 A53 60c On No. 58 .70 .70
64 A53 $1 On No. 59 1.10 1.10
65 A53 $1 On No. 60 1.10 1.10
Nos. 62-65 (4) 3.60 3.60

Stamps of same denomination se-tenant.

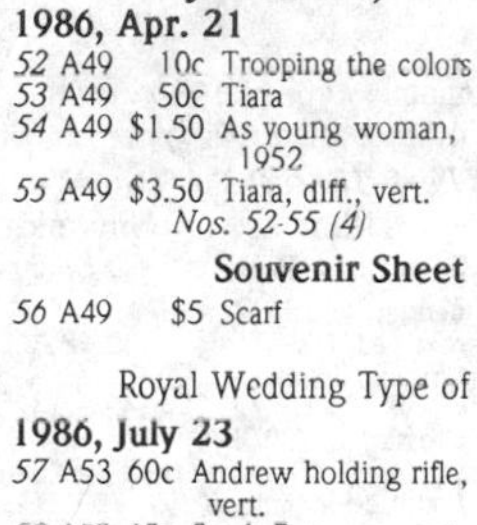

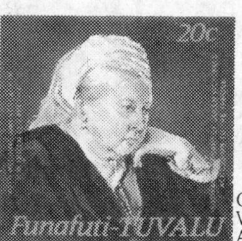

Queen Victoria
A1

1987 *Perf. 15*

66 A1 20c shown .22 .22
67 A1 50c George VI, Family .55 .55
68 A1 75c Elizabeth .85 .85
69 A1 $1.20 Elizabeth, Philip 1.40 1.40
70 A1 $1.75 Elizabeth, diff. 2.00 2.00
Nos. 66-70 (5) 5.02 5.02

Souvenir Sheet

71 A1 $3 Elizabeth, Family 3.25 3.25

Elizabeth's 40th wedding anniv., Queen Victoria's accession to the throne, sesquicentennial.

Summer Olympics Type of 1988

1988, Aug. 19 *Perf. 13x12½*

72 A69 10c Hurdles .15 .15
73 A69 20c High jump .25 .25
74 A69 40c Running .50 .50
75 A69 50c Discus .60 .60
76 A69 80c Pole vault 1.00 1.00
77 A69 90c Javelin 1.10 1.10
Nos. 72-77 (6) 3.60 3.60

NANUMAGA

Automobile Type of 1984
Tuvalu Design A41
Perf. 12½x13

1984-87 Litho. Unwmk.

Se-tenant Pairs

1 5c 1903 De Dion-Bouton Single Cylinder .15 .15
2 5c 1955 Ford Thunderbird .15 .15
3 5c 1966 Lotus Elan, UK .15 .15
4 10c 1915 Stutz Bearcat .20 .20
5 10c 1915 Dodge 4-Cylinder Touring Car .20 .20
6 10c 1976 Jaguar XJ-S, UK .20 .20
7 10c 1928 Morgan Super Sports, UK .20 .20
8 15c 1906 Spyker, Holland .30 .30
9 20c 1957 Dual-Ghia, US .42 .42
10 25c 1966 Lamborghini P400 Miura Coupe, Italy .50 .50
11 25c 1947 Kaiser Traveler, US .50 .50
12 25c 1951 Lancia Aurelia, Italy .50 .50
13 30c 1963 Chevrolet Corvette Coupe .60 .60
14 40c 1949 Jaguar XK 120, UK .85 .85
15 40c 1930 Renault Reinastella, France .85 .85
16 50c 1938 Alvis Speed 25, UK 1.00 1.00
17 60c 1956 Studebaker Golden Hawk 1.25 1.25
18 75c 1909 Alco, US 1.50 1.50
19 $1 1966 Shelby GT-350 Coupe, US 2.00 2.00
20 $1 1968 Mercedes 300 SEL, Germany 2.00 2.00
21 $1 1953 BRM V-16, UK 2.00 2.00
22 $1 1910 Lozier Briarcliff, US 2.00 2.00
Nos. 1-22 (22) 17.52 17.52

Issue dates: Nos. 1, 4, 10, 14, 19, June 11, 1984; 2, 5, 16, 20, Dec. 24, 1984; 6, 11, 18, 21, July 23, 1985; 3, 7-9, 12, 15, 17, 22, Aug. 6, 1987.
1987 stamps not inscribed "Leaders of the World."

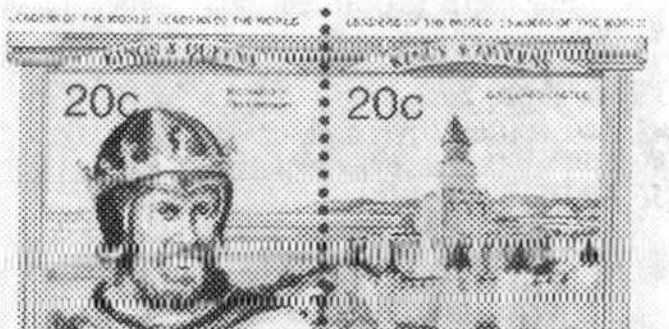

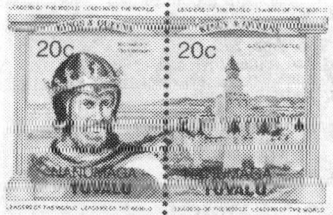

British Monarchs — A2

1984, Nov. 27 *Perf. 13x12½*

Se-tenant Pairs

23 A2 10c Richard I .25 .25
24 A2 20c Richard I, diff. .50 .50
25 A2 30c Third Crusade .75 .75
26 A2 40c Alfred the Great 1.00 1.00
27 A2 50c Alfred, diff. 1.20 1.20
28 A2 $1 Battle of Edington 2.50 2.50
Nos. 23-28 (6) 6.20 6.20

Locomotive Type of 1984
Tuvalu Designs A36-A37

1985, Apr. 3 *Perf. 12½x13*

Se-tenant Pairs

29 10c 1906 NYC & HR Class S .20 .20
30 25c 1884 T.R. Class B, Australia .55 .55
31 50c 1902 Decapod, UK 1.00 1.00
32 60c 1846 Coppernob, UK 1.25 1.25
Nos. 29-32 (4) 3.00 3.00

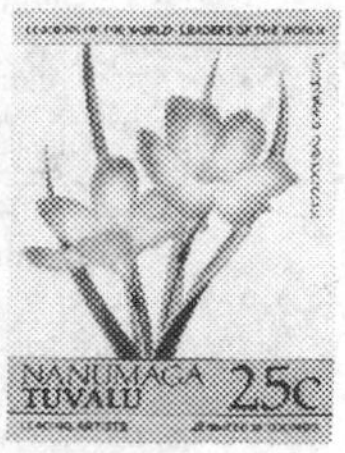

Flowers — A3

1985, May 3 *Perf. 13x12½*

33 A3 25c Tecophilaea cyanocrocus .32 .32
34 A3 25c Lilium pardalinum .32 .32
35 A3 30c Canarina abyssinica .38 .38
36 A3 30c Vanda coerulea .38 .38
37 A3 40c Lathyrus maritimus .50 .50
38 A3 40c Narcissus tazetta .50 .50
39 A3 50c Bauera sessiflora .60 .60
40 A3 50c Thelymitra venosa .60 .60
Nos. 33-40 (8) 3.60 3.60

Stamps of same denomination se-tenant.

Queen Mother Type of 1985
Tuvalu Design A45

1985-86

41 15c White hat .16 .16
42 15c Blue feathered hat .16 .16
43 55c Violet blue wide-brimmed hat .60 .60
44 55c Blue green wide-brimmed hat .60 .60
45 65c Tiara .70 .70
46 65c Light blue hat .70 .70
47 90c Dark blue hat .95 .95
48 90c Black hat .95 .95
Nos. 41-48 (8) 4.82 4.82

Souvenir Sheets

49 Sheet of 2 2.75 2.75
a. $1.15 As young girl 1.25 1.25
b. $1.15 As young woman 1.25 1.25
50 Sheet of 2 4.50 4.50
a. $2.10 Like #43 2.25 2.25
b. $2.10 Like #44 2.25 2.25
51 Sheet of 2 5.50 5.50
a. $2.50 Like #45 2.75 2.75
b. $2.50 Like #46 2.75 2.75

Issue dates: #41-49, Sept. 5; 50-51, Jan. 3, 1986.
Stamps of same denomination se-tenant.

Elizabeth II 60th Birthday Type
Perf. 13x12½, 12½x13

1986, Apr. 21

52 A49 5c White hat .15 .15
53 A49 $1 As young woman 1.25 1.25
54 A49 $1.75 Tam 2.25 2.25
55 A49 $2.50 Tiara, vert. 3.00 3.00
Nos. 52-55 (4) 6.65 6.65

Souvenir Sheet

56 A49 $4 Portrait 5.00 5.00

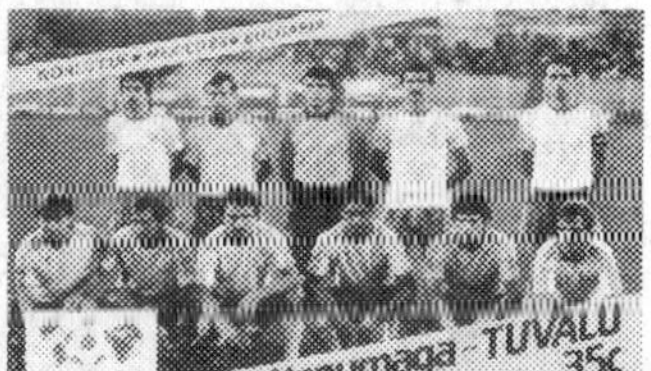

World Cup Soccer Championships, Mexico — A4

Players and teams from participating countries.

Perf. 12½x13, 13x12½

1986, June 30

57 A4 1c Uruguay, vert. .15 .15
58 A4 5c Morocco, vert. .15 .15
59 A4 5c Hungary, vert. .15 .15
60 A4 10c Poland, vert. .15 .15
61 A4 20c Argentina, vert. .25 .25
62 A4 35c Bulgaria .45 .45
63 A4 50c Portugal, vert. .60 .60
64 A4 60c Belgium .75 .75
65 A4 75c France .95 .95
66 A4 $1 Canada, vert. 1.25 1.25
67 A4 $2 Germany 2.50 2.50
68 A4 $4 Scotland, vert. 5.00 5.00
Nos. 57-68 (12) 12.35 12.35

Royal Wedding Type of 1986

1986, July 23

69	A53	60c Prince Andrew, vert.	.60	.60
70	A53	60c Sarah Ferguson, vert.	.60	.60
71	A53	$1 Prince Philip, Andrew	1.00	1.00
72	A53	$1 Prince Andrew	1.00	1.00
		Nos. 69-72 (4)	3.20	3.20

Souvenir Sheet

73	A56	$4 Couple	4.00	4.00

Stamps of same denomination se-tenant.

Nos. 69-72 Ovptd. in Silver "Congratulations to T.R.H. The Duke & Duchess of York"

1986, Oct. 26

74	A53	60c multicolored	.70	.70
75	A53	60c multicolored	.70	.70
76	A53	$1 multicolored	1.10	1.10
77	A53	$1 multicolored	1.10	1.10
		Nos. 74-77 (4)	3.60	3.60

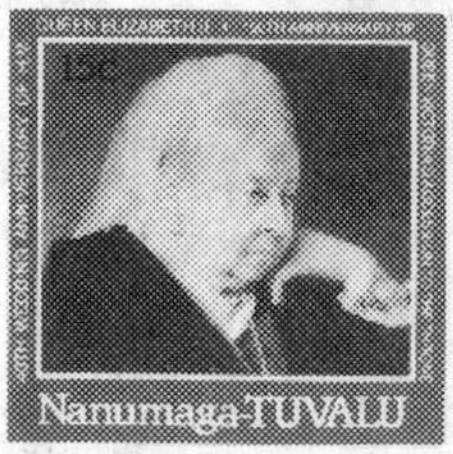

Queen Victoria A5

1987, Oct. 15 *Perf. 15*

78	A5	15c shown	.16	.16
79	A5	35c Princesses Margaret and Elizabeth	.40	.40
80	A5	60c Elizabeth holding Princess Anne	.70	.70
81	A62	$1.50 Elizabeth, Philip	1.75	1.75
82	A62	$1.75 Elizabeth wearing tiara	2.00	2.00
		Nos. 78-82 (5)	5.01	5.01

Souvenir Sheet

83	A5	$3 Elizabeth	3.25	3.25

Elizabeth's 40th wedding anniv. and Queen Victoria's accession to the throne, sesquicentennial.

NANUMEA

Locomotive Type of 1984
Tuvalu Designs A36-A37

Perf. 12½x13

1984-85 **Litho.** **Unwmk.**

Se-tenant Pairs

1	1c 1940 Class E94, Germany	.15	.15
2	15c 1946 Class 2251, UK	.30	.30
3	20c 1941 Bantam Cock Class V4, UK	.42	.42
4	30c 1902 Class C1, UK	.65	.65
5	35c 1952 S.N.C.F. CC 7121, France	.75	.75
6	40c 1903 La France Frenchmen Class, UK	.85	.85
7	50c 1929 5700 Class, UK	1.10	1.10
8	50c 1954 S.N.C.F. Class BB 1200, France	1.10	1.10
9	60c 1881 Fairlight Class G, UK	1.25	1.25
10	60c 1928 V.R. Class S, Australia	1.25	1.25
	Nos. 1-10 (10)	7.82	7.82

Issued: #2-4, 6-7, 9, 4/30/84; #1, 5, 8, 10, 2/8/85.

Cricket Players Type of 1984
Tuvalu Design A39

1984, Oct. 9 *Perf. 13x12½*

Se-tenant Pairs

11	1c J.A. Snow	.15	.15
12	10c C.J. Tavare	.25	.25
13	40c G.B. Stevenson	1.00	1.00
14	$1 P. Carrick	2.50	2.50
	Nos. 11-14 (4)	3.90	3.90

Automobile Type of 1984
Tuvalu Design A41

1985-86 *Perf. 12½x13*

Se-tenant Pairs

15	5c 1965 Humber Supersnipe, UK	.15	.15
16	10c 1934 Singer 9, UK	.20	.20
17	15c 1948 Holden FX 2.1 Liter Sedan, Australia	.30	.30
18	20c 1953 Buick Skylark	.42	.42
19	20c 1951 Simca Aronde, France	.42	.42
20	35c 1967 Toyota 2000 GT, Japan	.75	.75
21	40c 1960 Elva Courier, UK	.85	.85
22	50c 1952 Bentley Continental, UK	1.10	1.10
23	50c 1938 Hispano-Suiza V12 Saoutchik Cabriolet, Spain/France	1.10	1.10
24	50c 1913 Peugeot Bebe, France	1.10	1.10
25	60c 1935 Bluebird V (LSR), UK	1.25	1.25
26	60c 1978 Mazda RX7, Japan	1.25	1.25
27	75c 1970 Lola T70, UK	1.50	1.50
28	$2 1908 Locomobile, US	4.25	4.25
	Nos. 15-28 (14)	14.64	14.64

Issued: #15, 21-22, 25, Jan. 14; #17-18, 23, 26, Feb. 22; #16, 19-20, 24, 27-28, Dec. 30, 1986.

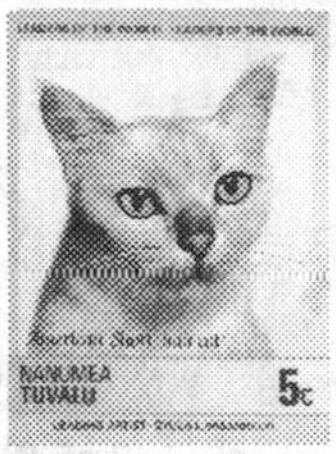

Cats — A6

1985, May 28 *Perf. 13x12½*

29	A6	5c American short-hair	.15	.15
30	A6	5c Turkish Angora	.15	.15
31	A6	30c Korat	.38	.38
32	A6	30c American Maine Coon	.38	.38
33	A6	50c Himalayan	.60	.60
34	A6	50c Shaded Cameo	.60	.60
35	A6	$1 Long-haired ginger	1.25	1.25
36	A6	$1 Siamese Seal Point	1.25	1.25
		Nos. 29-36 (8)	4.76	4.76

Stamps of same denomination se-tenant.

Queen Mother Type of 1985

1985-86

37	A45	5c Light gray hat	.15	.15
38	A45	5c Light blue hat	.15	.15
39	A45	30c Lavender hat	.32	.32
40	A45	30c Blue hat	.32	.32
41	A45	75c Purple hat	.85	.85
42	A45	75c Pink hat	.85	.85
43	A45	$1.05 Blue hat, diff.	1.10	1.10
44	A45	$1.05 Blue flowered hat	1.10	1.10
		Nos. 37-44 (8)	4.84	4.84

Souvenir Sheets

45	Sheet of 2	2.75	2.75
a.	A45 $1.20 Feathered hat	1.25	1.25
b.	A45 $1.20 Veiled hat	1.25	1.25
46	Sheet of 2	2.25	2.25
a.	A45 $1 Like #43	1.10	1.10
b.	A45 $1 Like #44	1.10	1.10
47	Sheet of 2	8.75	8.75
a.	A45 $4 Like #37	4.25	4.25
b.	A45 $4 Like #38	4.25	4.25

Issue dates: Nos. 38-45, Sept. 5, 1985, 46-47, Jan. 10, 1986.

Stamps of same denomination se-tenant.

Elizabeth II 60th Birthday Type

Perf. 13x12½, 12½x13

1986, Apr. 21

48	A49	10c As teenager	.15	.15
49	A49	80c As young woman	1.00	1.00
50	A49	$1.75 Red hat	2.25	2.25
51	A49	$3 Tiara, vert.	3.75	3.75
		Nos. 48-51 (4)	7.15	7.15

Souvenir Sheet

52	A49	$4 Green print hat	5.00	5.00

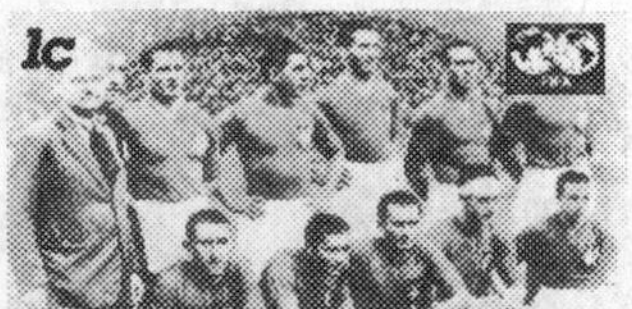

1986 World Cup Soccer Championships, Mexico — A7

1986, June 10 *Perf. 13x12½*

53	A7	1c Italy, 1934	.15	.15
54	A7	2c Italy, 1938	.15	.15
55	A7	5c Uruguay, 1950	.15	.15
56	A7	10c Brazil, 1958	.15	.15
57	A7	25c Argentina vs. Holland, 1978	.25	.25
58	A7	40c Brazil vs. Czechoslovakia, 1962	.40	.40
59	A7	50c Uruguay vs. Argentina, 1930	.52	.52
60	A7	75c West Germany vs. Hungary, 1954	.75	.75
61	A7	90c Brazil, 1970	.90	.90
62	A7	$1 West Germany, 1974	1.00	1.00
63	A7	$2.50 Italy vs. West Germany, 1982	2.50	2.50
64	A7	$4 England, 1966	4.00	4.00
		Nos. 53-64 (12)	10.92	10.92

Royal Wedding Type of 1986

Perf. 13x12½, 12½x13

1986, July 23

65	A53	60c Prince Andrew in jeep, vert.	.60	.60
66	A53	60c Sarah Ferguson, vert.	.60	.60
67	A53	$1 Couple	1.00	1.00
68	A53	$1 Prince Andrew, Princess Anne and parents	1.00	1.00
		Nos. 65-68 (4)	3.20	3.20

Souvenir Sheet

69	A56	$4 Newlyweds	4.00	4.00

Nos. 65-68 Ovptd. in Silver "Congratulations to T.R.H. The Duke & Duchess of York"

1986, Oct. 28

70	A53	60c multicolored	.70	.70
71	A53	60c multicolored	.70	.70
72	A53	$1 multicolored	1.10	1.10
73	A53	$1 multicolored	1.10	1.10
		Nos. 70-73 (4)	3.60	3.60

Elizabeth 40th Wedding Anniv. Type

1987, Oct. 15 *Perf. 15*

74	A62	40c Victoria	.45	.45
75	A62	60c Elizabeth & Philip, wedding portrait	.70	.70
76	A62	80c Elizabeth, Philip & Prince Charles	.90	.90
77	A62	$1 Elizabeth, Princess Anne	1.10	1.10
78	A62	$2 Elizabeth	2.25	2.25
		Nos. 74-78 (5)	5.40	5.40

Souvenir Sheet

79	A62	$3 Royal family, diff.	3.25	3.25

Queen Victoria's accession to the throne, 150th anniv.

NIUTAO

Automobile Type of 1984
Tuvalu Design A41

Perf. 12½x13

1984-85 **Litho.** **Unwmk.**

Se-tenant Pairs

1	15c 1930 Bentley 4½ Liter Supercharged, UK	.30	.30
2	20c 1935 Wolseley Hornet Special, UK	.42	.42
3	25c 1920 Crossley 25/30HP, UK	.52	.52
4	30c 1976 Cadillac Eldorado 7-Liter V-8	.60	.60
5	40c 1968 Austin Mini Cooper, UK	.85	.85
6	40c 1958 BMW 507 Cabriolet, W. Germany	.85	.85
7	50c 1963 Porsche 365C Cabriolet, W. Germany	1.10	1.10
8	60c 1971 Tyrrell Ford 001, UK	1.25	1.25
	Nos. 1-8 (8)	5.89	5.89

Issued: #1, 4-5, 7, 4/16/84; #2-3, 6, 8, 5/2/85.

Locomotive Type of 1984
Tuvalu Designs A36-A37

1984-85

Se-tenant Pairs

9	5c 1830 Planet, UK	.15	.15
10	10c 1863 Prince, UK	.22	.22
11	10c 1943 Gordon Austerity Class, UK	.22	.22
12	20c 1830 Northumbrian, UK	.42	.42
13	30c 1879 Merddin Emrys, UK	.65	.65
14	40c 1829 Agenoria, UK	.85	.85
15	45c 1909 Atchison, Topeka & Santa Fe, 1301	.95	.95
16	50c 1897 Class 6200, Japan	1.10	1.10
17	60c 1938 F.M.S.R. Class O, Malaya	1.25	1.25
18	75c 1880 1F, UK	1.65	1.65
19	$1 1908 Class E550, Italy	2.25	2.25
20	$1.20 1914 J.N.R. Class 6760, Japan	2.50	2.50
	Nos. 9-20 (12)	12.21	12.21

Issue dates: Nos. 9-10, 12, 14, 16, 19, Sept. 17; Nos. 11, 13, 15, 18, 20, Aug. 21, 1985.

Cricket Players Type of 1984
Tuvalu Design A39

1985, Jan. 7 *Perf. 13x12½*

Se-tenant Pairs

21	1c S.G. Hinks	.15	.15
22	15c C. Penn	.35	.35
23	50c T.M. Alderman	1.30	1.30
24	$1 K.B.S. Jarvis	2.50	2.50
	Nos. 21-24 (4)	4.30	4.30

Audubon Bicentennial Type

1985, Apr. 4

25	A42	5c Purple finch	.15	.15
26	A42	5c White-throated sparrow	.15	.15
27	A42	15c Anna's hummingbird	.18	.18
28	A42	15c Smith's longspur	.18	.18
29	A42	25c White-tailed kite	.32	.32
30	A42	25c Harris' hawk	.32	.32
31	A42	$1 Northern oriole	1.25	1.25
32	A42	$1 Great crested flycatcher	1.25	1.25
		Nos. 25-32 (8)	3.80	3.80

Stamps of same denomination se-tenant.

Queen Mother Type of 1985

1985-86

33	A45	15c Light blue hat	.16	.16
34	A45	15c Yellow hat	.16	.16
35	A45	35c Black hat	.40	.40
36	A45	35c Blue hat	.40	.40
37	A45	70c Tiara	.80	.80
38	A45	70c Pink hat	.80	.80
39	A45	95c White hat	1.10	1.10
40	A45	95c Blue hat, diff.	1.10	1.10
		Nos. 33-40 (8)	4.92	4.92

Souvenir Sheets

41	Sheet of 2	2.50	2.50
a.	A45 $1.05 As young woman	1.10	1.10
b.	A45 $1.05 Feathered hat	1.10	1.10
42	Sheet of 2	3.50	3.50
a.	A45 $1.50 Like #39	1.65	1.65
b.	A45 $1.50 Like #40	1.65	1.65
43	Sheet of 2	8.75	8.75
a.	A45 $4 Like #35	4.25	4.25
b.	A45 $4 Like #36	4.25	4.25

Issued: #33-41, Sept. 4; #42-43, Jan. 10, 1986.

Stamps of same denomination se-tenant.

Elizabeth II 60th Birthday Type

Perf. 13x12½, 12½x13

1986, Apr. 21

44	A49	5c White & gray hat	.15	.15
45	A49	60c Infant	.75	.75
46	A49	$1.50 Flowered white hat	1.90	1.90
47	A49	$3.50 Tiara, vert.	4.50	4.50
		Nos. 44-47 (4)	7.30	7.30

Souvenir Sheet

48	A49	$5 With tiara, diff.	6.25	6.25

For overprints see Nos. 58-62.

Royal Wedding Type

Perf. 12½x13, 13x12½

1986, July 23

49	A53	50c Couple, vert.	.50	.50
50	A53	50c Sarah Ferguson, vert.	.50	.50
51	A53	$1 Prince Andrew	1.00	1.00
52	A53	$1 Sarah in evening gown	1.00	1.00
		Nos. 49-52 (4)	3.00	3.00

Souvenir Sheet

53	A56	$4 Newlyweds	4.00	4.00

Stamps of same denomination se-tenant.

Nos. 49-52 Ovptd. in Silver "Congratulations to T.R.H. The Duke & Duchess of York"

1986, Oct. 28

54	A53	60c multicolored	.70	.70
55	A53	60c multicolored	.70	.70
56	A53	$1 multicolored	1.10	1.10
57	A53	$1 multicolored	1.10	1.10
		Nos. 54-57 (4)	3.60	3.60

Nos. 44-48 Ovptd. in Gold "40th WEDDING ANNIVERSARY OF H.M. QUEEN ELIZABETH II"

1987, Mar. *Perf. 13x12½, 12½x13*

58	A49	5c multicolored	.15	.15
59	A49	60c multicolored	.75	.75
60	A49	$1.50 multicolored	1.90	1.90
61	A49	$3.50 multicolored	4.50	4.50
		Nos. 58-61 (4)	7.30	7.30

Souvenir Sheet

62	A49	$5 multicolored	6.25	6.25

NUI

Locomotives Type of 1984
Tuvalu Designs A36-A37

1984-88 Litho. *Perf. 12½x13*

Se-tenant Pairs

1 5c 1911 Class 8800, Japan .15 .15
2 5c 1932 Soviet Union Railways Class SU .15 .15
3 10c 1847 Jenny Lind Type, UK .22 .22
4 10c 1907 Victorian Government Railways Class A2, Australia .22 .22
5 15c same, 1950 Class R .30 .30
6 15c 1913 Class 9600, Japan .30 .30
7 20c 1934 LMS Stanier Tilbury Class 4P, UK .42 .42
8 25c 1924 Jinty Class 3, UK .55 .55
9 25c 1928 Boston & Albany Class D12 .55 .55
10 25c 1847 Iron Duke Class, UK .55 .55
11 25c 1917 Wabash Railroad Class L .55 .55
12 30c 1943 South Australian Government Railways 520 Class .65 .65
13 35c 1885 Tennant Class 1463, UK .75 .75
14 40c 1947 No. 10000, UK .85 .85
15 40c 1848 Padarn Railway Fire Queen, UK .85 .85
16 50c 1935 Princess Margaret Rose Class 8P, UK 1.10 1.10
17 50c 1932 Soviet Union Railways Class IS 1.10 1.10
18 60c 1973 D.B. Class ET403, W. Germany 1.25 1.25
19 60c 1916 E. Tenn. & W. N. Carolina R.R. No. 10 1.25 1.25
20 75c 1973 D.B. Class 151, W. Germany 1.65 1.65
21 75c 1909 Tasmanian Government Railways Class K Garratt 1.65 1.65
22 $1 1937 B&O President Class 2.25 2.25
23 $1 1832 Mohawk & Hudson Railroad Experiment 2.25 2.25
24 $1.25 1934 Union Pacific Railroad, M-10000 Streamliner 2.75 2.75
Nos. 1-24 (24) 22.31 22.31

Issued: #5, 8, 12, 16, Mar. 19, 1984; #1, 6, 9, 22, Feb. 22, 1985; #3, 10, 14, 18, 20, 24, Aug. 7, 1987; #2, 4, 7, 11, 15, 17, 19, 21, Jan. 29, 1988.
1987 and 1988 stamps not inscribed "Leaders of the World."

British Monarchs Type of Nanumaga

1984, July 18 *Perf. 13x12½*

Se-tenant Pairs

25 A2 1c Queen Anne .15 .15
26 A2 5c Henry V .15 .15
27 A2 15c Henry V, diff. .35 .35
28 A2 40c Queen Anne, diff. 1.00 1.00
29 A2 50c Queen Anne, diff. 1.30 1.30
30 A2 $1 Henry V, diff. 2.50 2.50
Nos. 25-30 (6) 5.45 5.45

Automobile Type of 1984
Tuvalu Design A41

1985 *Perf. 12½x13*

Se-tenant Pairs

31 5c 1909 Buick .15 .15
32 15c 1966 Oldsmobile Toronado .30 .30
33 25c 1947 Railton Mobil Special, UK .55 .55
34 30c 1924 Opel Laubfrosch, Germany .60 .60
35 40c 1966 Jensen FF, UK .85 .85
36 40c 1963 Lotus-Climax GP MK 25, UK .85 .85
37 50c 1910 Delaunay Belleville, France 1.10 1.10
38 60c 1956 Jensen 541, UK 1.25 1.25
39 90c 1924 Hispano-Suiza H6 Boulogne, France 1.75 1.75
40 $1.10 1972 Citroen-Maserati S.M. Coupe, France 2.25 2.25
Nos. 31-40 (10) 9.65 9.65

Issue dates: #33-35, 37, Apr. 2; #31-32, 36, 38-40, Oct. 9, 1985.

Cricket Players Type of 1984
Tuvalu Design A39

1985, May 27 *Perf. 13x12½*

Se-tenant Pairs

41 1c S.C. Goldsmith .15 .15
42 40c S.N.V. Waterton 1.00 1.00
43 60c A. Sidebottom 1.50 1.50
44 70c A.A. Metcalfe 1.80 1.80
Nos. 41-44 (4) 4.45 4.45

Queen Mother Type of 1985

1985-86

45 A45 5c Purple hat .15 .15
46 A45 5c Tiara .15 .15
47 A45 50c Light blue hat .55 .55
48 A45 50c Lavender hat .55 .55
49 A45 75c Violet hat .85 .85
50 A45 75c White hat .85 .85
51 A45 85c Light blue hat, diff. .95 .95
52 A45 85c Tiara, diff. .95 .95
Nos. 45-52 (8) 5.00 5.00

Souvenir Sheets

53 Sheet of 2 2.75 2.75
a. A45 $1.15 White hat, diff. 1.25 1.25
b. A45 $1.15 Black hat 1.25 1.25
54 Sheet of 2 3.25 3.25
a. A45 $1.50 Like #45 1.50 1.50
b. A45 $1.50 Like #46 1.50 1.50
55 Sheet of 2 7.75 7.75
a. A45 $3.50 Like #51 3.75 3.75
b. A45 $3.50 Like #52 3.75 3.75

Issue dates: #45-53, Sept. 4; 54-55, Jan. 8, 1986.
Stamps of same denomination se-tenant.

Elizabeth II 60th Birthday Type

Perf. 13x12½, 12½x13

1986, Apr. 21

56 A49 10c Feathered hat .15 .15
57 A49 80c As young woman 1.00 1.00
58 A49 $1.75 Tiara 2.25 2.25
59 A49 $3 Tiara, diff., vert. 3.75 3.75
Nos. 56-59 (4) 7.15 7.15

Souvenir Sheet

60 A49 $4 Portrait 5.00 5.00

Royal Wedding Type of 1986

Perf. 12½x13, 13x12½

1986, July 23

61 A53 60c Couple, vert. .60 .60
62 A53 60c Prince Andrew, vert. .60 .60
63 A53 $1 Couple, Queen Elizabeth II 1.00 1.00
64 A53 $1 Andrew as young boy 1.00 1.00
Nos. 61-64 (4) 3.20 3.20

Souvenir Sheet

65 A56 $4 Sarah in wedding dress 4.00 4.00

Stamps of same denomination se-tenant.

Nos. 61-64 Ovptd. in Silver
"Congratulations to T.R.H. The Duke & Duchess of York"

1986, Oct. 28

66 A53 60c multi, vert. .70 .70
67 A53 60c multi, vert. .70 .70
68 A53 $1 multicolored 1.10 1.10
69 A53 $1 multicolored 1.10 1.10
Nos. 66-69 (4) 3.60 3.60

Elizabeth 40th Wedding Anniv. Type of Funafuti

1987, Oct. 15 *Perf. 15*

70 A1 20c Queen Victoria .22 .22
71 A1 50c George VI, Family .60 .60
72 A1 75c Elizabeth .85 .85
73 A1 $1.20 Elizabeth, Philip 1.40 1.40
74 A1 $1.75 Elizabeth, diff. 2.00 2.00
Nos. 70-74 (5) 5.07 5.07

Souvenir Sheet

75 A1 $3 Elizabeth, Family 3.50 3.50

Queen Victoria's accession to the throne, sesquicentennial.

NUKUFETAU

Automobile Type of 1984
Tuvalu Design A41

Perf. 12½x13

1984-85 Litho. Unwmk.

Se-tenant Pairs

1 5c 1904 Mercedes 28 PS, Germany .15 .15
2 10c 1966 Ford GT40 Mark II .20 .20
3 10c 1911 Vauxhall Prince Henry, UK .20 .20
4 15c 1956 Lincoln Continental Mark II .30 .30
5 20c 1950 Bristol 400, UK .42 .42
6 25c 1913 Morris Oxford "Bullnose," UK .55 .55
7 30c 1923 Austin Seven Tourer .60 .60
8 50c 1921 Bugatti Type 13 "Brescia," France 1.10 1.10
9 50c 1967 Monteverdi, Switzerland 1.10 1.10
10 60c 1925 Lancia Lambda, Italy 1.25 1.25
11 60c 1938 Panhard Dynamic, France 1.25 1.25
12 75c 1960 A.C. Ace, UK 1.50 1.50
13 $1.50 1950 Land Rover Model 80, UK 3.25 3.25
Nos. 1-13 (13) 11.87 11.87

Issued; #2, 6-8, 10, May 23; #1, 3-5, 9, 11-13, June 26, 1985.

British Monarchs Type of Nanumaga

1984, Nov. 27 *Perf. 13x12½*

Se-tenant Pairs

14 A2 1c Mary II .15 .15
15 A2 10c Mary II, diff. .25 .25
16 A2 30c Mary II, diff. .75 .75
17 A2 50c Henry IV 1.30 1.30
18 A2 60c Henry IV, diff. 1.50 1.50
19 A2 $1 Henry IV, diff. 2.50 2.50
Nos. 14-19 (6) 6.45 6.45

Cricket Players Type of 1984
Tuvalu Design A39

1985, Jan. 7

Se-tenant Pairs

20 1c D.G. Aslett .15 .15
21 10c N.R. Taylor .25 .25
22 55c S. Oldham 1.40 1.40
23 $1 C.W.J. Athey 2.50 2.50
Nos. 20-23 (4) 4.30 4.30

Locomotive Type of 1984

1985-88

Se-tenant Pairs

24 1c 1900 Class XV, Germany .15 .15
25 5c 1859 ECR Class Y, UK .15 .15
26 10c 1923 Nord Super Pacific, France .22 .22
27 10c 1905 LNWR Experiment Class, UK .22 .22
28 15c 1941 SR Merchant Navy Class, UK .30 .30
29 20c 1830 S. Carolina Railroad Best Friend of Charleston .42 .42
30 25c 1941 SR No. 1, UK .55 .55
31 30c 1987 Class 89, UK .65 .65
32 40c 1923 Southern Pacific Railroad Class 4300, US .85 .85
33 50c 1956 New South Wales Government Railways Class 46 1.10 1.10
34 60c 1953 D.B. Class V200, Germany 1.25 1.25
35 60c 1936 Union Railroad Class S-7, US 1.25 1.25
36 60c 1877 Phildelphia & Reading Railroad Camelback 1.25 1.25
37 70c 1968 J.N.R. Class 381, Japan 1.50 1.50
38 $1 1933 Rio Grande Southern Railroad Galloping Goose Railcar, US 2.25 2.25
a. Souvenir sheet of 2 2.50 2.50
39 $1.50 1935 Chicago, Milwaukee, St. Paul & Pacific Class A 3.25 3.25
Nos. 24-39 (16) 15.36 15.36

Issue dates: #24, 26, 34, 37, Apr. 2, 1985; #29, 32, 35, 39, Mar. 20, 1986; #25, 27-28, 30-31, 33, 36, 38, 38a, Sept. 10, 1987.
1986 and 1987 stamps not inscribed "Leaders of the World."

Queen Mother Type of 1985

1985, Sept. 5 *Perf. 13x12½*

40 A45 10c Wide-brimmed blue hat .15 .15
41 A45 10c Tiara .15 .15
42 A45 45c Tiara, diff. .48 .48
43 A45 45c Lavender hat .48 .48
44 A45 65c Blue hat .70 .70
45 A45 65c White stole .70 .70
46 A45 $1 White hat 1.10 1.10
47 A45 $1 Blue hat, diff. 1.10 1.10
Nos. 40-47 (8) 4.86 4.86

Souvenir Sheets

48 Sheet of 2 2.50 2.50
a. A45 $1.10 White hat, diff. 1.10 1.10
b. A45 $1.10 Wide-brimmed hat 1.10 1.10
49 Sheet of 2 4.00 4.00
a. A45 $1.75 Like #48a 2.00 2.00
b. A45 $1.75 Like #48b 2.00 2.00
50 Sheet of 2 6.50 6.50
a. A45 $3 Like #46 3.25 3.25
b. A45 $3 Like #47 3.25 3.25

Issue dates: #24, 26, 34, 37, Apr. 2, 1985; #29, 32, 35, 39, Mar. 20, 1986; #25, 27-28, 30-31, 33, 36, 38, 38a, Sept. 10, 1987. Stamps of same denomination se-tenant.

Elizabeth II 60th Birthday Type

Perf. 13x12½, 12½x13

1986, Apr. 21

51 A49 5c Scarf .15 .15
52 A49 40c Tiara .50 .50
53 A49 $2 Bareheaded 2.50 2.50
54 A49 $4 Tiara, vert. 5.00 5.00
Nos. 51-54 (4) 8.15 8.15

Souvenir Sheet

55 A49 $5 Blue hat 6.25 6.25

For overprints see Nos. 65-69.

Royal Wedding Type of 1986

1986, July 22

56 A53 60c Couple, vert. .60 .60
57 A53 60c Andrew, vert. .60 .60
58 A53 $1 Andrew, parents 1.00 1.00
59 A53 $1 Andrew 1.00 1.00
Nos. 56-59 (4) 3.20 3.20

Souvenir Sheet

60 A56 $4 Wedding ceremony 4.00 4.00

Stamps of same denomination se-tenant.

Nos. 56-59 Ovptd. in Silver
"Congratulations to T.R.H. The Duke & Duchess of York"

1986, Oct. 28

61 A53 60c multicolored .70 .70
62 A53 60c multicolored .70 .70
63 A53 $1 multicolored 1.10 1.10
64 A53 $1 multicolored 1.10 1.10
Nos. 61-64 (4) 3.60 3.60

Nos. 51-55 Ovptd. in Gold
"40th WEDDING ANNIVERSARY OF H.M. QUEEN ELIZABETH II"

1987, Oct. 15

65 A49 5c multicolored .15 .15
66 A49 40c multicolored .50 .50
67 A49 $2 multicolored 2.50 2.50
68 A49 $4 multicolored 5.00 5.00
Nos. 65-68 (4) 8.15 8.15

Souvenir Sheet

69 A49 $5 multicolored 6.25 6.25

NUKULAELAE

Locomotive Type of 1984
Tuvalu Designs A36-A37

Perf. 12½x13

1984-86 Litho. Unwmk.

Se-tenant Pairs

1 5c 1891 Calbourne Class 02, UK .15 .15
2 5c 1912 K.P.E.V. Class T18, Germany .15 .15
3 10c 1942 SNCF Class 141P, France .22 .22
4 10c 1962 Class 47, UK .22 .22
5 15c 1941 Union Pacific Big Boy, US .30 .30
6 15c 1955 DRB 83-10, Germany .30 .30
7 20c 1940 S.N.C.F. 160-A-1, France .42 .42
8 25c 1901 Class AEG High Speed Railcar, Germany .55 .55
9 25c 1839 Albion Railroad Samson, Canada .55 .55
10 40c 1907 Saint Class, UK .85 .85
11 40c 1900 Nord De Glehn Atlantic, France .85 .85
12 40c 1851 Folkstone Class, UK .85 .85
13 50c 1914 J.N.R. Class 8620, Japan 1.10 1.10
14 50c 1936 Class 8F, UK 1.10 1.10
15 80c 1857 Shannon, UK 1.75 1.75
16 $1 1948 Class A1, UK 2.25 2.25
17 $1 1955 E.A.R. Class 59, Kenya 2.25 2.25
18 $1 1897 V.R. Class Na, Australia 2.25 2.25
19 $1 1859 Undine Class, UK 2.25 2.25
20 $1.50 1935 Turbomotive, UK 3.25 3.25
Nos. 1-20 (20) 21.61 21.61

Issue dates: #1, 5, 10, 16, May 23; #2, 7, 11, 17, Dec. 12; #3, 8, 13, 18, Mar. 24, 1985; #4, 6, 9, 12, 15, 19-20, July 11, 1986.
1986 stamps not inscribed "Leaders of the World."

Cricket Players Type of 1984
Tuvalu Design A39

1984, Aug. 8 *Perf. 13x12½*

Se-tenant Pairs

21 5c D.B. Close .15 .15
22 15c G. Boycott .35 .35
23 30c D.L. Bairstow .75 .75
24 $1 T.G. Evans 2.50 2.50
Nos. 21-24 (4) 3.75 3.75

Automobile Type of 1984
Tuvalu Design A41

1985 *Perf. 12½x13*

Se-tenant Pairs

25 5c 1924 Bugatti Type 35, France .15 .15
26 10c 1908 Sizaire-Naudin, France .20 .20
27 25c 1965 Sunbeam Tiger, UK .55 .55
28 35c 1907 Napier 60HP Touring Car, UK .75 .75
29 35c 1975 BMW 2002 TII, Germany .75 .75
30 50c 1910 Austro-Daimler Prince Henry, Austria 1.10 1.10
31 50c 1927 La Salle, US 1.10 1.10
32 70c 1901 Oldsmobile Curved Dash Buckboard 1.50 1.50
33 75c 1955 Rover 90, UK 1.65 1.65
34 $1 1948 Chrysler Town & Country 2.00 2.00
Nos. 25-34 (10) 9.75 9.75

Issue dates: #25, 28, 30, 32, Feb. 8; #26-27, 29, 31, 33-34, July 23.

Animal Type of Nanumea

1985, Apr. 30

35 A6 5c Hungarian vizsla .15 .15
36 A6 5c Bearded collie .15 .15
37 A6 20c Bernese mountain dog .25 .25
38 A6 20c Boxer .25 .25
39 A6 50c Labrador retriever .65 .65
40 A6 50c Shetland sheepdog .65 .65
41 A6 70c Welsh springer spaniel .90 .90
42 A6 70c Scottish terrier .90 .90
Nos. 35-42 (8) 3.90 3.90

Stamps of same denomination se-tenant.

Queen Mother Type of 1985

1985-86

43 A45 5c Purple hat .15 .15
44 A45 5c Blue hat .15 .15
45 A45 25c Tiara .28 .28
46 A45 25c Lavender hat .28 .28
47 A45 85c Pink hat .95 .95
48 A45 85c Dark blue hat .95 .95
49 A45 $1 Light purple hat 1.10 1.10
50 A45 $1 Light blue hat 1.10 1.10
Nos. 43-50 (8) 4.96 4.96

Souvenir Sheets

51 Sheet of 2 2.75 2.75
a. A45 $1.20 As young girl 1.25 1.25
b. A45 $1.20 Lace hat 1.25 1.25
52 Sheet of 2 2.75 2.75
a. A45 $1.20 Like #45 1.25 1.25
b. A45 $1.20 Like #46 1.25 1.25
53 Sheet of 2 8.00 8.00
a. A45 $3.50 Like #47 4.00 4.00
b. A45 $3.50 Like #48 4.00 4.00

Issue dates: #43-51, Sept. 4; 52-53, Jan. 8, 1986.
Stamps of same denomination se-tenant.

Elizabeth II 60th Birthday Type
Perf. 13x12½, 12½x13

1986, Apr. 21

54 A49 10c White hat .15 .15
55 A49 $1 As young woman 1.25 1.25
56 A49 $1.50 In orange dress 1.90 1.90
57 A49 $3 Tiara, vert. 3.75 3.75
Nos. 54-57 (4) 7.05 7.05

Souvenir Sheet

58 A49 $4 In brown dress 5.00 5.00

Royal Wedding Type of 1986
Perf. 12½x13, 13x12½

1986, July 23

59 A53 60c Andrew, vert. .60 .60
60 A53 60c Couple, vert. .60 .60
61 A53 $1 Sarah Ferguson and Princess Diana 1.00 1.00
62 A53 $1 Andrew, diff. 1.00 1.00
Nos. 59-62 (4) 3.20 3.20

Souvenir Sheet

63 A56 $4 Sarah in wedding dress 4.00 4.00

Stamps of same denomination se-tenant.

Nos. 59-62 Ovptd. in Silver
"Congratulations to T.R.H. The Duke & Duchess of York"

1986, Oct. 28

64 A53 60c multicolored .70 .70
65 A53 60c multicolored .70 .70
66 A53 $1 multicolored 1.10 1.10
67 A53 $1 multicolored 1.10 1.10
Nos. 64-67 (4) 3.60 3.60

Queen Elizabeth II 40th Wedding Anniv.
Type of Nanumaga

1987, Oct. 15 *Perf. 15*

68 A5 15c Queen Victoria .16 .16
69 A5 35c Princesses Margaret and Elizabeth .40 .40
70 A5 60c Elizabeth holding Princess Anne .65 .65
71 A5 $1.50 Elizabeth, Philip 1.75 1.75
72 A5 $1.75 Elizabeth wearing tiara 2.00 2.00
Nos. 68-72 (5) 4.96 4.96

Souvenir Sheet

73 A5 $3 Elizabeth 3.50 3.50

Queen Victoria's accession to the throne, sesquicentennial.

VAITUPU

Automobile Type of 1984
Tuvalu Design A41
Perf. 12½x13

1984-85 **Litho.** **Unwmk.**

Se-tenant Pairs

1 5c 1961 Lotus Elite, UK .15 .15
2 15c 1950 MG TD Midget, UK .30 .30
3 15c 1932 Hillman Minx, UK .30 .30
4 15c 1905 White Model E Steam Car, US .30 .30
5 25c 1935 Auburn Supercharged 851, US .52 .52
6 25c 1981 Renault RE20, France .52 .52
7 30c 1928 Lea-Francis Hyper .60 .60
8 30c 1940 Packard Darrin .60 .60
9 30c 1938 Graham, US .60 .60
10 40c 1968 Chevrolet Camaro .85 .85
11 40c 1957 Renault Dauphine-Gordini, France .85 .85
12 50c 1930 Packard Eight 1.10 1.10
13 50c 1926 Miller Special, US 1.10 1.10
14 60c 1950 Healey Silverstone, UK 1.25 1.25
15 60c 1970 De Tomaso Pantera, Italy 1.25 1.25
16 $1 1927 Bentley 3-Liter, UK 2.00 2.00
Nos. 1-16 (16) 12.29 12.29

Issued: #2, 5, 7, 12, Mar. 19; #1, 3, 6, 8, 10, 13-14, 16, Dec. 12; #4, 9, 11, 15, Apr. 4, 1985.

British Monarchs Type of Nanumaga

1984, July 18 *Perf. 13x12½*

Se-tenant Pairs

17 A2 1c Richard III .15 .15
18 A2 5c Charles I .15 .15
19 A2 15c Charles I, diff. .35 .35
20 A2 40c Richard III, diff. 1.00 1.00
21 A2 50c Richard III, diff. 1.30 1.30
22 A2 $1 Charles I, diff. 2.50 2.50
Nos. 17-22 (6) 5.45 5.45

Locomotive Type of 1984
Tuvalu Designs A36-A37

1985-87 *Perf. 12½x13*

Se-tenant Pairs

23 5c 1929 D.R.G. V3201, Germany .15 .15
24 10c 1841 G.W.R. Leo Class, UK .22 .22
25 10c 1937 New York Central Railroad Class J3a .22 .22
26 15c 1949 Richmond, Fredericksburg & Potomac Railroad Class E8 .30 .30
27 25c 1845 Columbine, UK .55 .55
28 25c 1954 BR Class 2MT, UK .55 .55
29 25c 1980 Amtrak Class AEM-7 .55 .55
30 35c 1981 Via Rail LRC Class MPA-27a, Canada .75 .75
31 45c 1983 British Columbia Railway Class GF6C .95 .95
32 50c 1888 D&H Class B, India 1.10 1.10
33 60c 1936 D.R. Class 45, Germany 1.25 1.25
34 65c 1904 Northern Pacific Railway Class W, US 1.40 1.40
35 80c 1855 W. & A. R.R. General, US 1.75 1.75
36 85c 1938 Chicago & North Western Railway Class E-4 1.90 1.90
37 $1 1911 J.N.R. Class 9020 Mallet, Japan 2.25 2.25
38 $1 1977 Chicago Regional Transportation Authority Class F40 2.25 2.25
Nos. 23-38 (16) 16.14 16.14

Issued: #24, 27, 32-33, 3/7/85; #23, 28, 35, 37, 1/16/86; #25-26, 29-31, 34, 36, 38, 9/10/87.
1986 and 1987 stamps not inscribed "Leaders of the World."

Animal Type of Nanumea

Butterfly illustrations by Roger V. Vigurs.

1985, Mar. 12 *Perf. 13x12½*

39 A6 5c Marpesia petreus .15 .15
40 A6 5c Pseudolycaena marsyas .15 .15
41 A6 15c Charaxes jasius .18 .18
42 A6 15c Junonia coenia .18 .18
43 A6 50c Palaeochrysophanus hippothoe .65 .65
44 A6 50c Sticopthalma camadeva .65 .65
45 A6 75c Phoebis avellaneda .95 .95
46 A6 75c Apatura iris .95 .95
Nos. 39-46 (8) 3.86 3.86

Stamps of same denomination printed se-tenant.

Queen Mother Type of 1985

1985-86

47 A45 15c Light blue hat .16 .16
48 A45 15c White hat .16 .16
49 A45 40c Tiara .45 .45
50 A45 40c Lavender hat .45 .45
51 A45 65c Violet hat .70 .70
52 A45 65c Green hat .70 .70
53 A45 95c Blue hat 1.10 1.10
54 A45 95c Pink hat 1.10 1.10
Nos. 47-54 (8) 4.82 4.82

Souvenir Sheets

55 Sheet of 2 2.75 2.75
a. A45 $1.10 Looking up 1.25 1.25
b. A45 $1.10 Looking forward 1.25 1.25
56 Sheet of 2 4.50 4.50
a. A45 $2 Like #51 2.25 2.25
b. A45 $2 Like #52 2.25 2.25
57 Sheet of 2 5.75 5.75
a. A45 $2.50 Like #47 2.75 2.75
b. A45 $2.50 Like #48 2.75 2.75

Issued: #47-55, 8/28/85; 56-57, 1/8/86.
Stamps of same denomination se-tenant.

Elizabeth II 60th Birthday Type
Perf. 13x12½, 12½x13

1986, Apr. 21

58 A49 5c Green hat .15 .15
59 A49 60c As young woman .75 .75
60 A49 $2 Flowered hat 2.50 2.50
61 A49 $3.50 Tiara, vert. 4.50 4.50
Nos. 58-61 (4) 7.90 7.90

Souvenir Sheet

62 A49 $5 Straw hat 6.25 6.25

For overprints see Nos. 72-76.

Royal Wedding Type of 1986
Perf. 12½x13, 13x12½

1986, July 18

63 A53 60c Andrew, vert. .60 .60
64 A53 60c Sarah Ferguson, vert. .60 .60
65 A53 $1 Charles, Andrew 1.00 1.00
66 A53 $1 Couple 1.00 1.00
Nos. 63-66 (4) 3.20 3.20

Souvenir Sheet

67 A56 $4 Newlyweds 4.00 4.00

Stamps of same denomination se-tenant.

Nos. 63-66 Ovptd. in Silver
"Congratulations to T.R.H. The Duke & Duchess of York"

1986, Oct. 28

68 A53 60c multicolored .70 .70
69 A53 60c multicolored .70 .70
70 A53 $1 multicolored 1.10 1.10
71 A53 $1 multicolored 1.10 1.10
Nos. 68-71 (4) 3.60 3.60

Nos. 58-62 Ovptd. in Gold
"40th WEDDING ANNIVERSARY OF H.M. QUEEN ELIZABETH II"
Perf. 13x12½, 12½x13

1987, Oct. 15

72 A49 5c multicolored .15 .15
73 A49 60c multicolored .75 .75
74 A49 $2 multicolored 2.50 2.50
75 A49 $3 multicolored 3.75 3.75
Nos. 72-75 (4) 7.15 7.15

Souvenir Sheet

76 A49 $5 multicolored 6.25 6.25

UGANDA

ü-'gan-də

LOCATION — East Africa, at the Equator and separated from the Indian Ocean by Kenya and Tanzania
GOVT. — Independent state
AREA — 91,343 sq. mi.
POP. — 13,990,000 (est. 1983)
CAPITAL — Kampala

Stamps of 1898-1902 were replaced by those issued for Kenya, Tanganyika and Uganda. Uganda became independent October 9, 1962.

Cowries (50 = 4 Pence)
16 Annas = 1 Rupee (1896)
100 Cents = 1 Shilling (1962)

Catalogue values for unused stamps in this country are for Never Hinged items, beginning with Scott 79 in the regular postage section and Scott J1 in the postage due section.

Unused values for Nos. 2-68 are for copies without gum. Very fine examples will be evenly cut and will show at least two full typewritten framelines.

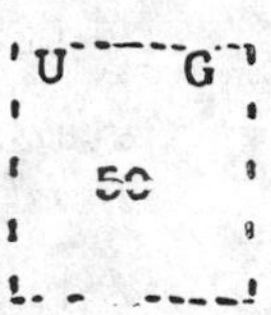
A1

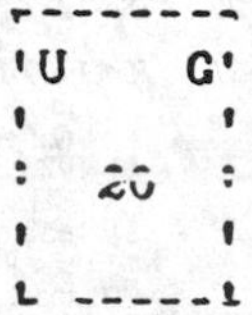
A2

Nos. 2-53 were produced with a typewriter by Rev. Ernest Millar of the Church Missionary Society. They were 20-26mm wide, with nine stamps in a horizontal row. Later two more were added to each row, and the stamps became narrower, 16-18mm.

Rev. Millar got a new typewriter in 1895, and the stamps he typed on it have a different appearance. A violet ribbon in the machine, inserted late in 1895, resulted in Nos. 35-53.

Nos. 2-53 are on thin, tough, white paper, laid horizontally with traces of a few vertical lines.

Forgeries of Nos. 2-53 are known.

Without Gum
Wide Letters
Typewritten on Thin Laid Paper
Stamps 20 to 26mm wide

1895 **Unwmk.** ***Imperf.***

2 A1 10(c) black 2,000. —
4 A1 20(c) black 3,000. 1,500.
6 A1 30(c) black 1,400. 1,350.
7 A1 40(c) black 2,000. —
8 A1 50(c) black 1,200. 1,200.
9 A1 60(c) black 1,500. —

Surcharged with New Value in Black, Pen-written

10 A1 10 on 50(c) black —
11 A1 15 on 10(c) black —
12 A1 15 on 20(c) black —
13 A1 15 on 40(c) black —
14 A1 15 on 50(c) black —
15 A1 25 on 50(c) black —
16 A1 50 on 60(c) black —

Stamps 16 to 18mm wide

17 A1 5(c) black 1,400. 1,200.
18 A1 10(c) black 950. 875.
19 A1 15(c) black 800. 800.
20 A1 20(c) black 800. 800.
21 A1 25(c) black 800. 800.
22 A1 30(c) black 4,000. 4,000.
23 A1 40(c) black 4,750. 4,750.
24 A1 50(c) black 2,250. 2,250.
25 A1 60(c) black 3,000. 3,000.

Narrow Letters
Stamps 16 to 18mm wide

26 A2 5(c) black 450.
27 A2 10(c) black 450.
28 A2 15(c) black 500.
29 A2 20(c) black 375.
30 A2 25(c) black 450.
31 A2 30(c) black 575.

32	A2	40(c) black	525.	
33	A2	50(c) black	450.	
34	A2	60(c) black	850.	
35	A2	5(c) violet	450.	450.
36	A2	10(c) violet	450.	450.
37	A2	15(c) violet	550.	450.
38	A2	20(c) violet	450.	375.
39	A2	25(c) violet	500.	500.
40	A2	30(c) violet	500.	500.
41	A2	40(c) violet	600.	500.
42	A2	50(c) violet	500.	—
43	A2	100(c) violet	2,250.	—

As a favor to a philatelist, 35c and 45c denominations were made in black and violet. They were not intended for postal use and no rate called for those denominations.

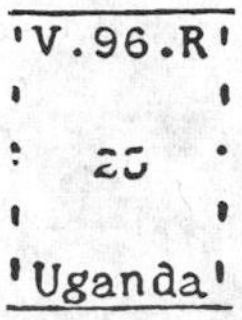

A3

A4

1896

44	A3	5(c) violet	325.	325.
45	A3	10(c) violet	325.	300.
46	A3	15(c) violet	325.	325.
47	A3	20(c) violet	325.	200.
48	A3	25(c) violet	400.	
49	A3	30(c) violet	400.	450.
50	A3	40(c) violet	400.	450.
51	A3	50(c) violet	400.	450.
52	A3	60(c) violet	1,250.	
53	A3	100(c) violet	1,500.	—

Overprinted "L" in Black

1896 Typeset White Paper

54	A4	1a black (thin "1")	125.00	70.00
a.		Small "O" in "POSTAGE"	500.00	
55	A4	2a black	42.50	60.00
a.		Small "O" in "POSTAGE"	150.00	175.00
56	A4	3a black	110.00	110.00
a.		Small "O" in "POSTAGE"	675.00	
57	A4	4a black	70.00	80.00
a.		Small "O" in "POSTAGE"	175.00	

Yellowish Paper

58	A4	8a black	125.00	165.00
a.		Small "O" in "POSTAGE"	450.00	
59	A4	1r black	225.00	225.00
a.		Small "O" in "POSTAGE"	625.00	
60	A4	5r black		

Without Overprint

White Paper

61	A4	1a black (thin "1")	72.50	70.00
a.		Small "O" in "POSTAGE"	200.00	200.00
62	A4	1a black (thick "1")	13.00	13.00
a.		Small "O" in "POSTAGE"	40.00	40.00
63	A4	2a black	15.00	15.00
a.		Small "O" in "POSTAGE"	40.00	45.00
64	A4	3a black	15.00	15.00
a.		Small "O" in "POSTAGE"	45.00	50.00
65	A4	4a black	15.00	15.00
a.		Small "O" in "POSTAGE"	45.00	50.00

Yellowish Paper

66	A4	8a black	22.50	22.50
a.		Small "O" in "POSTAGE"	85.00	85.00
67	A4	1r black	55.00	65.00
a.		Small "O" in "POSTAGE"	150.00	175.00
68	A4	5r black	125.00	200.00
a.		Small "O" in "POSTAGE"	425.00	425.00

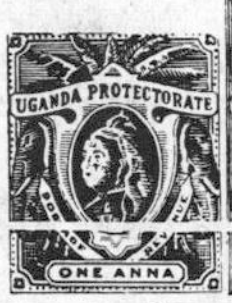

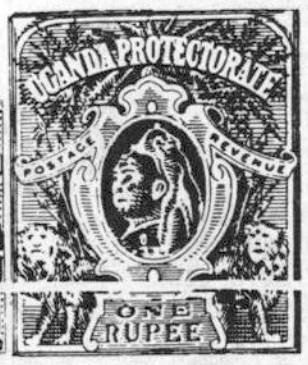

Queen Victoria
A5 A6

1898-1902 Engr. Wmk. 2 Perf. 14

69	A5	1a red	.60	.50
70	A5	1a car rose ('02)	.50	.45
71	A5	2a brown	.40	2.00
72	A5	3a gray	3.50	9.00
73	A5	4a dark green	1.25	4.00
74	A5	8a olive gray	3.00	15.00

Wmk. 1

75	A6	1r ultra	11.00	22.50
76	A6	5r brown	50.00	60.00
		Nos. 69-76 (8)	70.25	113.45

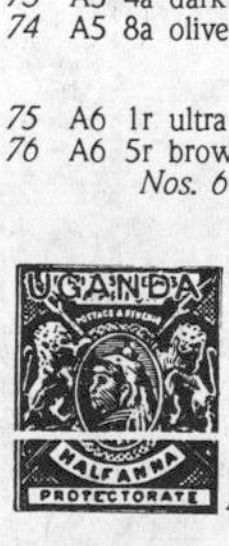

A7

1902 Wmk. 2 Black Overprint

77	A7	½a yellow green	.80	.50
a.		Inverted overprint	1,100.	
b.		Double overprint	1,200.	
c.		Pair, one without overprint	2,000.	

Red Overprint

78	A7	2½a dark blue	.80	1.25
a.		Double overprint	1,000.	

Catalogue values for unused stamps in this section, from this point to the end of the section, are for Never Hinged items.

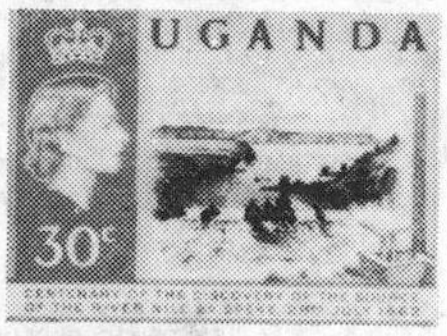

Ripon Falls and Speke Monument A8

Wmk. 314

1962, July 28 Engr. Perf. 14

79	A8	30c vermilion & blk	.15	.15
80	A8	50c violet & blk	.15	.15
81	A8	1.30sh green & blk	.20	.20
82	A8	2.50sh ultra & blk	.60	.60
		Nos. 79-82 (4)	1.10	1.10

Cent. of the discovery of the source of the Nile by John Hanning Speke.

Independent State

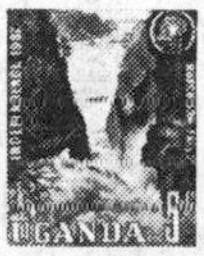

Murchison Falls — A9

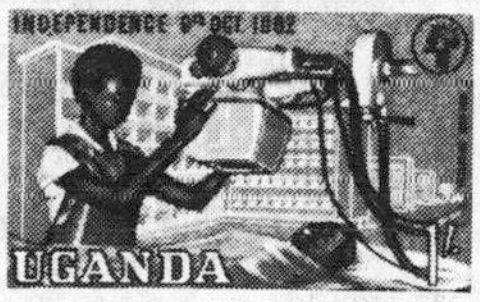

Mulago Hospital, X-Ray Service A10

Designs: 10c, Tobacco growing. 15c, Coffee growing. 20c, Ankole cattle. 30c, Cotton growing. 50c, Mountains of the Moon. 1.30sh, Rubaga and Namirembe Cathedrals and Kibuli Mosque. 2sh, Makerere College and students. 5sh, Copper mining. 10sh, Cement factory. 20sh, Parliament.

Perf. 14½x14, 14x14½

1962, Oct. 9 Photo. Unwmk.

83	A9	5c Prus green	.15	.15
84	A9	10c red brown	.15	.15
85	A9	15c green, blk & car	.15	.15
86	A9	20c bister & pur	.15	.15
87	A9	30c brt blue	.15	.15
88	A9	50c bluish grn & blk	.15	.15
89	A10	1sh bl grn, sep & red	.20	.15
90	A10	1.30sh pur & ocher	.35	.15
91	A10	2sh grnsh bl, blk & dk car	.45	.25
92	A10	5sh dk green & red	1.10	.55
93	A10	10sh red brn & slate	2.25	1.10
94	A10	20sh blue & pale brn	6.25	3.00
		Nos. 83-94 (12)	11.50	6.10

Uganda's independence, Oct. 9, 1962.

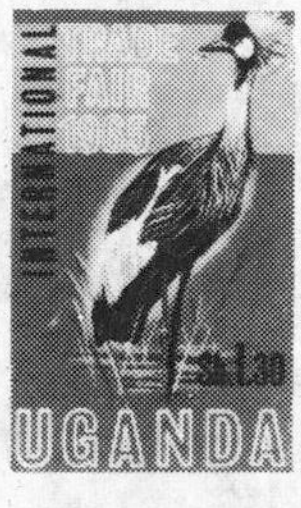

Crowned Crane — A11

1965, Feb. 20 Photo. Perf. 14½

95	A11	30c bl grn, blk, yel & red	.25	.15
96	A11	1sh30c ultra, blk, yel & red	.75	.50

Intl. Trade Fair at Lugogo Stadium, Kampala, Feb. 20-28.

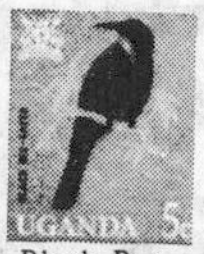

Black Bee-eater — A12

African Jacana — A13

Arms of Uganda and Birds: 15c, Orange weaver. 20c, Narina trogon. 30c, Sacred ibis. 40c, Blue-breasted kingfisher. 50c, Whale-headed stork. 65c, Black-winged red bishop. 1sh, Ruwenzori turaco. 1.30sh, African fish eagle. 2.50sh, Great blue turaco. 5sh, Lilac-breasted roller. 10sh, Black-collared lovebird. 20sh, Crowned crane.

Perf. 14½x14, 14x14½

1965, Oct. 9 Photo. Unwmk.

Birds in Natural Colors

Size: 17x21mm, 21x17mm

97	A12	5c lt vio bl & blk	.15	.15
98	A13	10c dull blue & red	.15	.15
99	A12	15c dk brown & org	.15	.15
100	A12	20c bister & brt grn	.15	.15
101	A13	30c hn brn & blk	.15	.15
102	A12	40c lt yel grn & red	.30	.15
103	A12	50c dp pur & gray	.35	.15
104	A13	65c gray & brick red	1.00	.75

Perf. 14½

Size: 41x25mm, 25x41mm

105	A13	1sh lt blue & blk	.65	.15
106	A12	1.30sh yel & red brn	2.00	.20
107	A13	2.50sh brt yel grn & blk	3.00	.50
108	A12	5sh lil gray & vio bl	5.00	.90
109	A13	10sh lt brown & blk	8.00	2.25
110	A13	20sh olive grn & blk	15.00	4.75
		Nos. 97-110 (14)	36.05	10.55

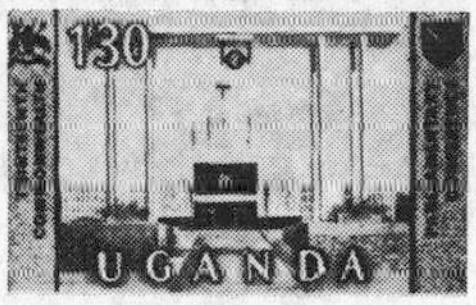

Parliament Building A14

13th Commonwealth Parliamentary Assoc. Conf.: 30c, Animal carvings from entrance hall of Uganda Parliament. 50c, Arms of Uganda. 2.50sh, Parliament Chamber.

1967, Oct. 26 Photo. Perf. 14½

111	A14	30c multicolored	.15	.15
112	A14	50c multicolored	.16	.15
113	A14	1.30sh multicolored	.35	.32
114	A14	2.50sh multicolored	.70	.60
		Nos. 111-114 (4)	1.36	1.22

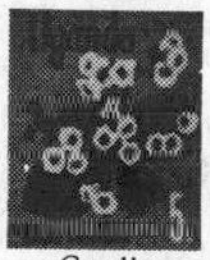
Cordia Abyssinica A15

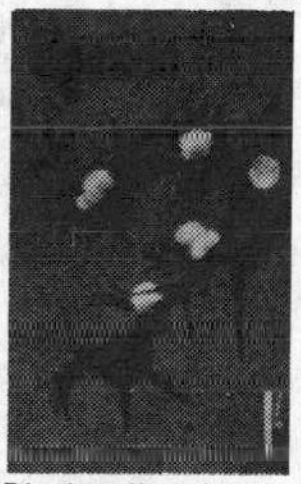
Black-galled Acacia A16

Flowers: 10c, Grewia similis. 15c, Cassia didymobotrya. 20c, Coleus barbatus. 30c, Ochna ovata. 40c, Ipomoea spathulata (morning glory). 50c, Spathodea nilotica (flame tree). 60c, Oncoba spinosa. 70c, Carissa edulis. 1.50sh, Clerodendrum myricoides (blue butterfly bush). 2.50sh, Acanthus arboreus. 5sh, Kigelia aethiopium (sausage tree). 10sh, Erythrina abyssinica (Uganda coral). 20sh, Monodora myristica.

Perf. 14½x14

1969, Oct. 9 Photo. Unwmk.

115	A15	5c multicolored	.15	.15
116	A15	10c multicolored	.15	.15
117	A15	15c multicolored	.15	.15
118	A15	20c multicolored	.15	.15
119	A15	30c multicolored	.15	.15
120	A15	40c gray & multi	.15	.15
121	A15	50c tan & multi	.15	.15
122	A15	60c multicolored	.18	.15
123	A15	70c multicolored	.22	.15

Perf. 14

124	A16	1sh multicolored	.38	.15
125	A16	1.50sh multicolored	.55	.15
126	A16	2.50sh multicolored	.70	.15
127	A16	5sh multicolored	1.25	.18
128	A16	10sh multicolored	3.00	.55
129	A16	20sh tan & multi	7.75	1.25
		Nos. 115-129 (15)	15.08	
		Set value		2.75

Values of Nos. 124-129 are for canceled-to-order stamps. Cancellations were printed on Nos. 128-129. Postally used copies sell for higher prices.

Nos. 125-126, 129 Surcharged

1975, Sept. 29 Photo. Perf. 14

130	A16	2sh on 1.50sh multi	.95	.95
131	A16	3sh on 2.50sh multi	19.00	19.00
132	A16	40sh on 20sh multi	7.75	7.75
		Nos. 130-132 (3)	27.70	27.70

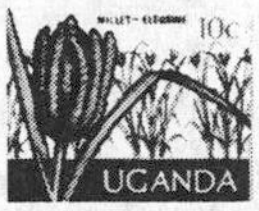

Millet — A17

Ugandan Crops: 20c, Sugar cane. 30c, Tobacco. 40c, Onions. 50c, Tomatoes. 70c, Tea. 80c, Bananas. 1sh, Corn. 2sh, Pineapple. 3sh, Coffee. 5sh, Oranges. 10sh, Peanuts. 20sh, Cotton. 40sh, Beans.

1975, Oct. 9 Photo. Perf. 14x14½

Size: 21x17mm

Multicolored, Name Panel as follows

133	A17	10c lt brown	.15	.15
134	A17	20c blue	.15	.15
135	A17	30c vermilion	.15	.15
136	A17	40c lilac	.15	.15
137	A17	50c olive	.15	.15
138	A17	70c brt green	.18	.15
139	A17	80c purple	.22	.15

Perf. 14½

Size: 41x25mm

140	A17	1sh ocher	.25	.15
141	A17	2sh slate	.50	.28
142	A17	3sh blue	.75	.40
143	A17	5sh yellow green	1.00	.55
144	A17	10sh brown red	2.00	1.10
145	A17	20sh rose lilac	4.00	2.25
146	A17	40sh orange	8.00	4.25
		Nos. 133-146 (14)	17.65	10.03

See Nos. 195-198. For surcharge and overprints see Nos. 175, 203-206, 227-244, 253-257.

Communications Type of Kenya 1976

Designs: 50c, Microwave tower. 1sh, Cordless switchboard and operators, horiz. 2sh, Telephones of 1880, 1930 and 1976. 3sh, Message switching center, horiz.

1976, Apr. 15 Litho. Perf. 14½

147	A5	50c blue & multi	.15	.15
148	A5	1sh red & multi	.25	.22
149	A5	2sh yellow & multi	.50	.40
150	A5	3sh multicolored	.75	.60
a.		Souvenir sheet of 4	2.25	2.25
		Nos. 147-150 (4)	1.65	1.37

Telecommunications development in East Africa. No. 150a contains 4 stamps similar to Nos. 147-150 with simulated perforations.

Olympics Type of Kenya 1976

Designs: 50c, Akii Bua, Ugandan hurdler. 1sh, Filbert Bayi, Tanzanian runner. 2sh, Steve Muchoki, Kenyan boxer. 3sh, Olympic torch, flags of Kenya, Tanzania and Uganda.

1976, July 5 Litho. Perf. 14½

151	A6	50c blue & multi	.15	.15
152	A6	1sh red & multi	.28	.20
153	A6	2sh yellow & multi	.52	.45
154	A6	3sh blue & multi	.80	.65
a.		Souv. sheet of 4, #151-154, perf. 13	7.50	5.25
		Nos. 151-154 (4)	1.75	1.45

21st Olympic Games, Montreal, Canada, July 17-Aug. 1.

Railway Type of Kenya 1976

Designs: 50c, Tanzania-Zambia Railway. 1sh, Nile Bridge, Uganda. 2sh, Nakuru Station, Kenya. 3sh, Class A locomotive, 1896.

1976, Oct. 4 Litho. Perf. 14

155	A7	50c lilac & multi	.20	.15
156	A7	1sh emerald & multi	.40	.20
157	A7	2sh brt rose & multi	.80	.45
158	A7	3sh yellow & multi	1.25	.65
a.		Souv. sheet of 4, #155-158, perf. 13	3.75	3.75
		Nos. 155-158 (4)	2.65	1.45

Rail transport in East Africa.

Fish Type of Kenya 1977

1977, Jan. 10 Litho. Perf. 14½

159	A8	50c Nile perch	.15	.15
160	A8	1sh Tilapia	.32	.15
161	A8	3sh Sailfish	.85	.60

162	A8	5sh Black marlin	1.25	1.00
a.		Souvenir sheet of 4, #159-162	3.25	2.75
		Nos. 159-162 (4)	2.57	1.90

Festival Type of Kenya 1977

Festival Emblem and: 50c, Masai tribesmen bleeding cow. 1sh, Dancers from Uganda. 2sh, Makonde sculpture, Tanzania. 3sh, Tribesmen skinning hippopotamus.

1977, Jan. 15 *Perf. 13½x14*

163	A9	50c multicolored	.15	.15
164	A9	1sh multicolored	.28	.20
165	A9	2sh multicolored	.52	.45
166	A9	3sh multicolored	.80	.70
a.		Souvenir sheet of 4, #163-166	2.25	2.25
		Nos. 163-166 (4)	1.75	1.50

2nd World Black and African Festival, Lagos, Nigeria, Jan. 15-Feb. 12.

Rally Type of Kenya 1977

Safari Rally Emblem and: 50c, Automobile passing through village. 1sh, Winner at finish line. 2sh, Car passing through washout. 5sh, Car, elephants and Mt. Kenya.

1977, Apr. 5 Litho. *Perf. 14*

167	A10	50c multicolored	.15	.15
168	A10	1sh multicolored	.25	.15
169	A10	2sh multicolored	.50	.30
170	A10	5sh multicolored	1.25	.85
a.		Souvenir sheet of 4, #167-170	2.25	2.25
		Nos. 167-170 (4)	2.15	1.45

25th Safari Rally, Apr. 7-11.

Church Type of Kenya 1977

Designs: 50c, Rev. Canon Apolo Kivebulaya. 1sh, Uganda Cathedral. 2sh, Early grass-topped Cathedral. 5sh, Early tent congregation, Kigezi.

1977, June 30 Litho. *Perf. 14*

171	A11	50c multicolored	.15	.15
172	A11	1sh multicolored	.24	.15
173	A11	2sh multicolored	.45	.30
174	A11	5sh multicolored	1.25	.75
a.		Souvenir sheet of 4, #171-174	2.25	2.25
		Nos. 171-174 (4)	2.09	1.35

Church of Uganda, centenary.

Type of 1975 Surcharged with New Value and 2 Bars

1977, Aug. 22 Photo. *Perf. 14x14½*

175	A17	80c on 60c bananas	.24	.20

No. 175 was not issued without surcharge.

Wildlife Type of Kenya 1977

Wildlife Fund Emblem and: 50c, Pancake tortoise. 1sh, Nile crocodile. 2sh, Hunter's hartebeest. 3sh, Red colobus monkey. 5sh, Dugong.

1977, Sept. 26 Litho. *Perf. 14x13½*

176	A13	50c multicolored	.15	.15
177	A13	1sh multicolored	.25	.15
178	A13	2sh multicolored	.75	.30
179	A13	3sh multicolored	1.00	.48
180	A13	5sh multicolored	1.65	.75
a.		Souvenir sheet of 4, #177-180	4.00	3.25
		Nos. 176-180 (5)	3.80	1.83

Endangered species.

Soccer Type of Kenya

Soccer Cup and: 50c, Soccer scene and Joe Kadenge. 1sh, Mohammed Chuma receiving trophy, and his portrait. 2sh, Shot on goal and Omari S. Kidevu. 5sh, Backfield defense and Polly Ouma.

1978, May 3 Litho. *Perf. 14x13½*

181	A17	50c green & multi	.15	.15
182	A17	1sh lt brown & multi	.24	.15
183	A17	2sh lilac & multi	.45	.30
184	A17	5sh dk blue & multi	1.25	.75
a.		Souvenir sheet of 4, #181-184	2.25	2.25
		Nos. 181-184 (4)	2.09	1.35

World Soccer Cup Championships, Argentina, June 1-25.

Crop Type of 1975

Designs as before.

1978, June Litho. *Perf. 14½*

Size: 41x25mm

Multicolored, Name Panel as follows

195	A17	5sh blue	1.00	.52
196	A17	10sh rose lilac	1.90	1.00
197	A17	20sh brown	3.75	2.00
198	A17	40sh deep orange	7.75	4.25
		Nos. 195-198 (4)	14.40	7.77

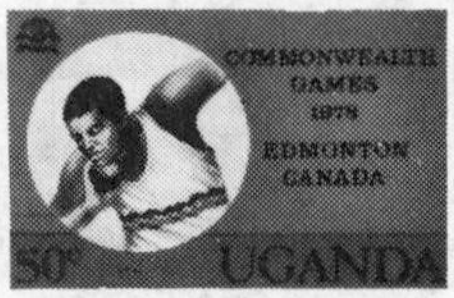

Shot Put — A18

1978, July 10 Litho. *Perf. 14*

199	A18	50c shown	.16	.16
200	A18	1sh Broad jump	.26	.26
201	A18	2sh Running	.52	.52
202	A18	5sh Boxing	1.25	1.25
a.		Souv. sheet of 4, #199-202, perf. 12	3.00	3.00
		Nos. 199-202 (4)	2.19	2.19

Commonwealth Games, Edmonton, Canada, Aug. 3-12.
For overprints see Nos. 249-252.

Soccer Type of 1978 Inscribed: "WORLD CUP 1978"

Designs: 50c, Backfield defense and Polly Ouma. 2sh, Shot on goal and Omari S. Kidevu. 5sh, Soccer scene and Joe Kadenge. 10sh, Mohammed Chuma receiving trophy, and his portrait.

1978, Sept. 11 *Perf. 14x13½*

203	A17	50c dk blue & multi	.15	.15
204	A17	2sh lilac & multi	.45	.35
205	A17	5sh green & multi	1.00	.90
206	A17	10sh lt brown & multi	2.00	1.75
a.		Souv. sheet of 4, #203-206, perf. 12	4.00	4.00
		Nos. 203-206 (4)	3.60	3.15

World Cup Soccer Championship winners.

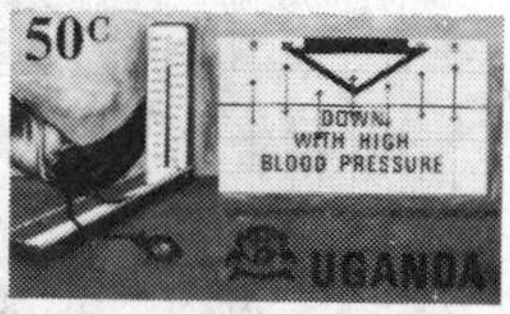

Blood Pressure Gauge and Chart A19

1978, Sept. 25 Litho. *Perf. 14*

207	A19	50c shown	.15	.15
208	A19	1sh Heart	.22	.18
209	A19	2sh Retina	.45	.38
210	A19	5sh Kidneys	1.10	.95
a.		Souvenir sheet of 4, #207-210	2.00	2.00
		Nos. 207-210 (4)	1.92	1.66

World Health Day and Hypertension Month.

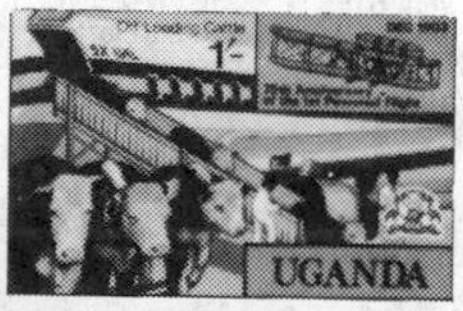

Cattle Unloaded from Plane A20

Flyer 1 and: 1.50sh, "Islander" on runway, Kampala. 2.70sh, Coffee loaded on transport jet. 10sh, Concorde.

1978, Dec. 16

211	A20	1sh multicolored	.22	.18
212	A20	1.50sh multicolored	.32	.28
213	A20	2.70sh multicolored	.55	.50
214	A20	10sh multicolored	2.25	1.75
a.		Souvenir sheet of 4, #211-214	3.50	3.50
		Nos. 211-214 (4)	3.34	2.71

75th anniversary of 1st powered flight.
For overprints see Nos. 258-261.

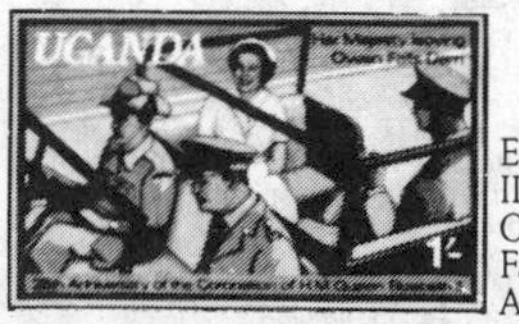

Elizabeth II Leaving Owen Falls Dam A21

Designs: 1.50sh, Coronation regalia. 2.70sh, Coronation ceremony. 10sh, Royal family on balcony of Buckingham Palace.

1979, Feb. 15 Litho. *Perf. 12½x12*

215	A21	1sh multicolored	.20	.15
216	A21	1.50sh multicolored	.30	.24
217	A21	2.70sh multicolored	.50	.45
218	A21	10sh multicolored	2.00	1.65
a.		Souvenir sheet of 4, #215-218	3.50	3.50
		Nos. 215-218 (4)	3.00	2.49

25th anniv. of coronation of Elizabeth II.
For overprints see Nos. 245-248.

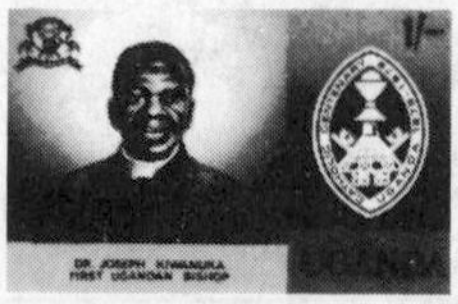

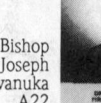

Bishop Joseph Kiwanuka A22

Designs: 1.50sh, Lubaga Cathedral. 2.70sh, Ugandan pilgrims and St. Peter's, Rome. 10sh, Friar Lourdel-Mapeera, missionary.

1979, Feb. 15 *Perf. 14*

219	A22	1sh multicolored	.20	.15
220	A22	1.50sh multicolored	.30	.24
221	A22	2.70sh multicolored	.50	.45
222	A22	10sh multicolored	2.00	1.65
a.		Souvenir sheet of 4, #219-222	3.50	3.50
		Nos. 219-222 (4)	3.00	2.49

Ugandan Catholic Church, centenary.
See No. 274. For overprints see Nos. 262-265.

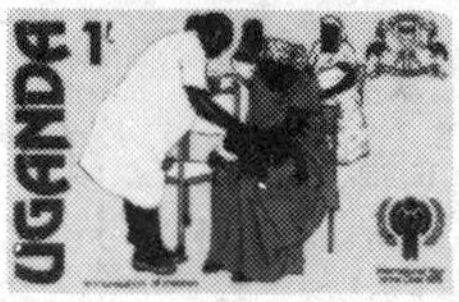

Child Receiving Vaccination A23

IYC Emblem and: 1.50sh, Handicapped children playing. 2.70sh, Ugandan IYC emblem. 10sh, Teacher and pupils.

1979, June 28 Litho. *Perf. 14*

223	A23	1sh multicolored	.22	.18
224	A23	1.50sh multicolored	.32	.28
225	A23	2.70sh multicolored	.55	.50
226	A23	10sh multicolored	2.25	1.75
a.		Souvenir sheet of 4, #223-226	3.50	3.50
		Nos. 223-226 (4)	3.34	2.71

International Year of the Child.
For overprints see Nos. 266-269.

Nos. 133-146, 195-198, 215-218 Overprinted: "UGANDA / LIBERATED / 1979"

1979, July 12 Photo. *Perf. 14x14½*

Size: 21x17mm

227	A17	10c multicolored	.15	.15
228	A17	20c multicolored	.15	.15
229	A17	30c multicolored	.15	.15
230	A17	40c multicolored	.15	.15
231	A17	50c multicolored	.15	.15
232	A17	70c multicolored	.15	.15
233	A17	80c multicolored	.18	.15

Perf. 14½

Size: 41x25mm

234	A17	1sh multicolored	.22	.18
235	A17	2sh multicolored	.45	.38
236	A17	3sh multicolored	.65	.55
237	A17	5sh multicolored	.95	.80
238	A17	10sh multicolored	1.90	1.50
239	A17	20sh multicolored	3.75	3.25
240	A17	40sh multicolored	7.75	6.50
		Nos. 227-240 (14)	16.75	14.21

1979 Litho. *Perf. 14½*

Multicolored, name panel as follows

241	A17	5sh blue	1.25	1.00
242	A17	10sh rose lilac	2.50	2.00
243	A17	20sh brown	4.75	4.00
244	A17	40sh deep orange	9.50	8.00
		Nos. 241-244 (4)	18.00	15.00

1979, July 12 Litho. *Perf. 12½x12*

245	A21	1sh multicolored	.22	.18
246	A21	1.50sh multicolored	.32	.30
247	A21	2.70sh multicolored	.50	.60
248	A21	15sh on 10sh multi	3.25	2.25
a.		Souvenir sheet of 4	4.25	
		Nos. 245-248 (4)	4.29	3.33

No. 248a contains Nos. 245-247 and a 15sh in design of No. 218. Issued Aug. 1.

Nos. 199-202; 203, 204-206; 211-214; 219-222, 223-226 Overprinted: "UGANDA LIBERATED 1979"

1979, Aug. 1 Litho. *Perf. 14*

249	A18	50c multicolored	.15	.15
250	A18	1sh multicolored	.20	.16
251	A18	2sh multicolored	.45	.35
252	A18	5sh multicolored	1.10	.95

Type A17 of Kenya

1979, Aug. 1 *Perf. 14x13½*

253	A17	50c multicolored	.15	.15
255	A17	2sh multi (#204)	.48	.40
256	A17	5sh multicolored	1.25	1.00
257	A17	10sh multicolored	2.50	2.00

Overprint exists on No. 183.

1979, Aug. 1 *Perf. 14*

258	A20	1sh multicolored	.25	.22
259	A20	1.50sh multicolored	.38	.32
260	A20	2.70sh multicolored	.70	.60
261	A20	10sh multicolored	2.50	2.00

1979, Aug. 1

262	A22	1sh multicolored	.20	.16
263	A22	1.50sh multicolored	.30	.25
264	A22	2.70sh multicolored	.55	.48
265	A22	10sh multicolored	2.00	1.75

1979, Aug. 16

266	A23	1sh multicolored	.20	.16
267	A23	1.50sh multicolored	.30	.25
268	A23	2.70sh multicolored	.55	.48
269	A23	10sh multicolored	2.00	1.75
a.		Souvenir sheet of 4, #266-269	3.25	3.25
		Nos. 249-269 (20)	16.21	13.58

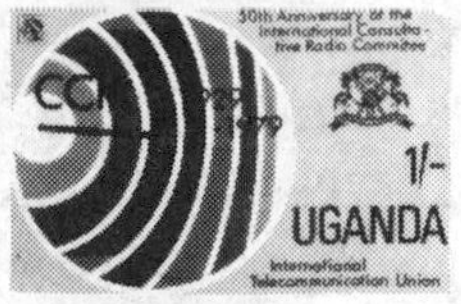

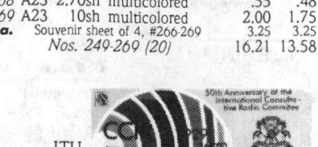

ITU Emblem, Radio Waves A24

1979, Sept. 11

270	A24	1sh lt gray & multi	.20	.16
271	A24	1.50sh orange & multi	.30	.25
272	A24	2.70sh yellow & multi	.55	.48
273	A24	10sh blue & multi	2.00	1.75
		Nos. 270-273 (4)	3.05	2.64

50th anniv. of Intl. Radio Consultative Committee (CCIR) of the ITU.

No. 222a Redrawn and Inscribed: FREEDOM OF WORSHIP DECLARED Souvenir Sheet

1979, Sept. *Perf. 12*

274		Sheet of 4	3.25	3.25
a.		A22 1sh No. 219	.20	.16
b.		A22 1.50sh No. 220	.30	.25
c.		A22 2.70sh No. 221	.55	.48
d.		A22 10sh No. 222	2.00	1.75

In top panel of margin scrolls and coat of arms have been replaced by inscription.

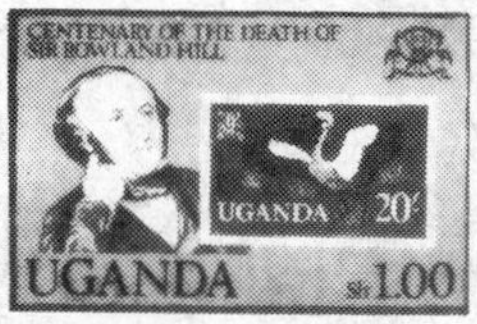

A25

1979, Nov. 12 Litho. *Perf. 14*

275	A25	1sh #110	.20	.16
276	A25	1.50sh #112	.30	.25
277	A25	2.70sh #94	.55	.48
278	A25	10sh #69	2.00	1.75
a.		Souvenir sheet of 4, #275-278	3.50	3.50
		Nos. 275-278 (4)	3.05	2.64

Sir Rowland Hill (1795-1879), originator of penny postage.
For overprints see Nos. 293-296.

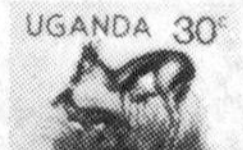

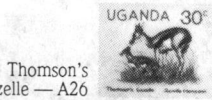

Thomson's Gazelle — A26

Designs: 10c, Impalas. 20c, Large-spotted genet. 50c, Bush babies. 80c, Wild hunting dogs. 1sh, Lions. 1.50sh, Mountain gorillas. 2sh, Zebras. 2.70sh, Leopards. 3.50sh, Black rhinoceroses. 5sh, Defassa waterbucks. 10sh, African black buffaloes. 20sh, Hippopotami. 40sh, African elephants.

1979, Dec. 3 Litho. *Perf. 14*

Size: 21x17mm

279	A26	10c multicolored	.15	.15
280	A26	20c multicolored	.15	.15
281	A26	30c multicolored	.15	.15
282	A26	50c multicolored	.15	.15
283	A26	80c multicolored	.18	.18

Size: 39x25mm

284	A26	1sh multicolored	.22	.18
285	A26	1.50sh multicolored	.26	.22
286	A26	2sh multicolored	.35	.26
287	A26	2.70sh multicolored	.42	.40
288	A26	3.50sh multicolored	.55	.48
289	A26	5sh multicolored	.80	.70
290	A26	10sh multicolored	1.50	1.40
291	A26	20sh multicolored	3.25	2.75
292	A26	40sh multicolored	6.75	5.50
		Nos. 279-292 (14)	14.88	12.67

Nos. 284, 286, 289 reissued inscribed 1982. See Nos. 400-406. For surcharges see Nos. 386-392.

Nos. 275-278a Overprinted: "LONDON 1980"

1980, May 6 Litho. *Perf. 14*

293 A25 1sh multicolored .20 .16
294 A25 1.50sh multicolored .30 .25
295 A25 2.70sh multicolored .55 .48
296 A25 10sh multicolored 2.00 2.00
a. Souvenir sheet of 4, #293-296 3.50 3.50
Nos. 293-296 (4) 3.05 2.89

London 80 Intl. Stamp Exhib., May 6-14.

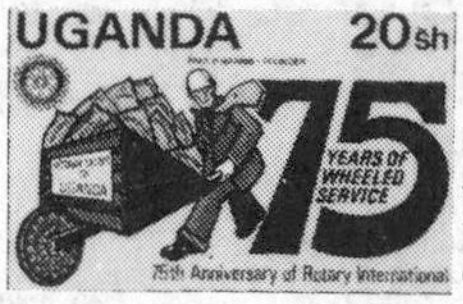

Paul Harris Wheeling Rotary Cart — A27

1980, Aug. Litho. *Perf. 14*

297 A27 1sh Rotary emblem, vert. .20 .15
298 A27 20sh shown 4.00 3.25
a. Souvenir sheet of 2, #297-298 4.25

Rotary International, 75th anniversary.

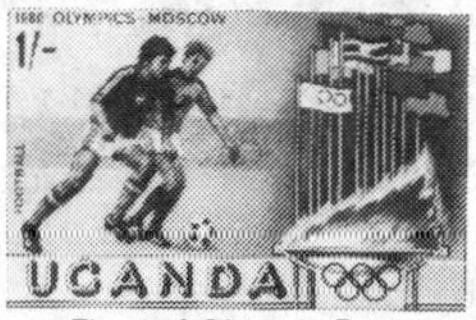

Soccer, Flags of Olympic Participants, Flame — A28

1980, Dec. 29 Litho. *Perf. 14*

299 A28 1sh shown .20 .15
300 A28 2sh Relay race .40 .32
301 A28 10sh Hurdles 2.00 2.00
302 A28 20sh Boxing 4.00 4.00
Nos. 299-302 (4) 6.60 6.47

Souvenir Sheet

303 Sheet of 4 7.75 7.75
a. A28 2.70sh like #299 .55 .50
b. A28 3sh like #300 .60 .52
c. A28 5sh like #301 1.00 .90
d. A28 25sh like 302 5.25 4.50

22nd Summer Olympic Games, Moscow, July 19-Aug. 3.

Nos. 299-303 Overprinted with Sport, Winner and Country

1980, Dec. 29

304 A28 1sh multicolored .20 .15
305 A28 2sh multicolored .40 .32
306 A28 10sh multicolored 2.00 1.65
307 A28 20sh multicolored 4.00 3.25
Nos. 304-307 (4) 6.60 5.37

Souvenir Sheet

308 Sheet of 4 7.75 7.75
a. A28 2.70sh like #304 .55 .50
b. A28 3sh like #305 .60 .52
c. A28 5sh like #306 1.00 .90
d. A28 25sh like #307 5.25 4.50

Souvenir Sheet

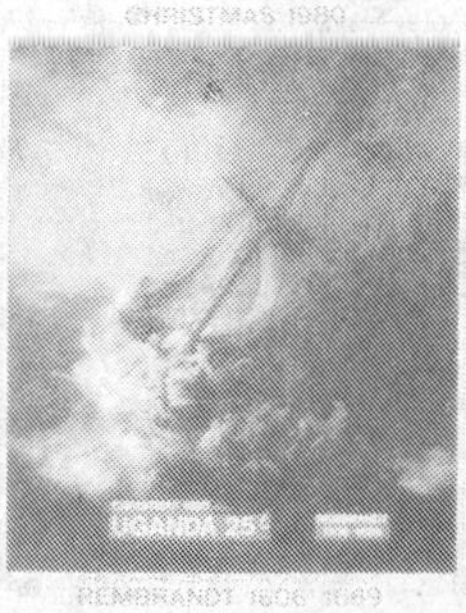

Christ in the Storm on the Sea of Galilee, by Rembrandt — A29

1980, Dec. 31 *Imperf.*

309 A29 25sh multicolored 5.50 4.50

Christmas 1980.

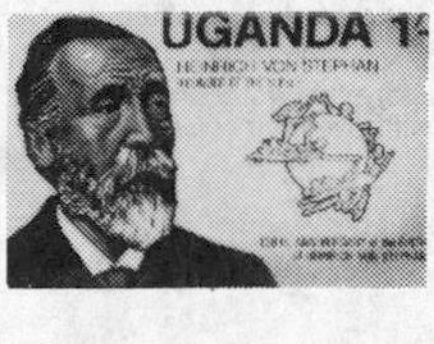

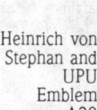

Heinrich von Stephan and UPU Emblem A30

1981, June 2 Litho. *Perf. 14*

310 A30 1sh shown .22 .18
311 A30 2sh UPU headquarters .45 .38
312 A30 2.70sh Mail plane, 1935 .60 .52
313 A30 10sh Mail train, 1927 2.25 1.90
a. Souvenir sheet of 4, #310-313 3.75 3.75
Nos. 310-313 (4) 3.52 2.98

Von Stephan (1831-97), UPU founder.

Royal Wedding Issue
Common Design Type

1981 Litho. *Perf. 14*

314 CD331 10sh Couple .22 .18
a. 10sh on 1sh .22 .18
315 CD331 50sh Tower of London 1.10 .95
a. 50sh on 5sh 1.10 .95
316 CD331 200sh Prince Charles 4.50 3.75
a. 200sh on 20sh 4.50 3.75
Nos. 314-316 (3) 5.82 4.88
Nos. 314a-316a (3) 5.82 4.88

Souvenir Sheet

317 CD331 250sh Royal mews 5.00 4.00
a. 250sh on 25sh, light orange 5.00 4.00

Royal wedding. Issue dates: surcharges, July 13; others, July 29. Nos. 314-316 also issued in sheets of 5 plus label, perf. 12, in changed colors.
For overprints see Nos. 342-345.

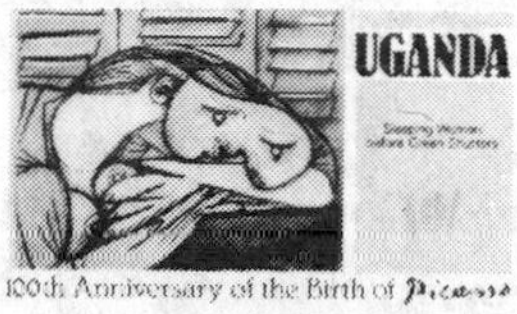

Sleeping Woman Before Green Shutters, by Picasso — A31

Picasso Birth Centenary: 20sh, Bullfight. 30sh, Nude Asleep on a Landscape. 200sh, Interior with a Girl Drawing. 250sh, Minotaur.

1981, Sept. 21 Litho. *Perf. 14*

318 A31 10sh multicolored .22 .18
319 A31 20sh multicolored .45 .38
320 A31 30sh multicolored .65 .55
321 A31 200sh multicolored 4.50 3.75

Size: 120x146mm

Imperf

322 A31 250sh multicolored 6.00 5.00
Nos. 318-322 (5) 11.82 9.86

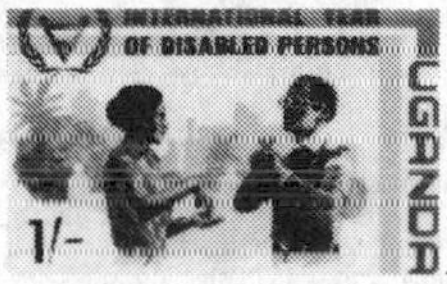

Intl. Year of the Disabled A32

1981, Dec. *Perf. 15*

323 A32 1sh Sign language .15 .15
324 A32 10sh Teacher in wheelchair .22 .18
325 A32 50sh Retarded children 1.10 .95
326 A32 200sh Blind man 4.50 3.75
a. Souvenir sheet of 4, #323-326 6.25 5.50
Nos. 323-326 (4) 5.97 5.03

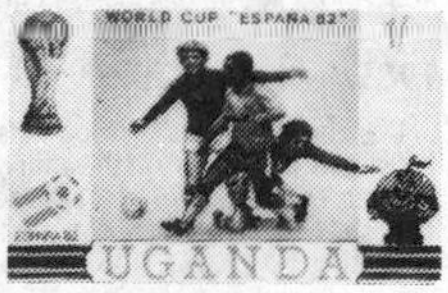

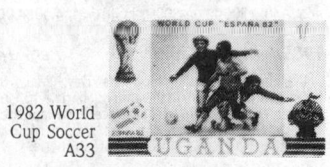

1982 World Cup Soccer A33

Designs: Various soccer players.

1982, Jan. 11 Litho. *Perf. 14*

327 A33 1sh multicolored .15 .15
328 A33 10sh multicolored .22 .18
329 A33 50sh multicolored 1.10 .95
330 A33 200sh multicolored 4.50 3.75
Nos. 327-330 (4) 5.97 5.03

Souvenir Sheet

331 A33 250sh World Cup 6.00 6.00

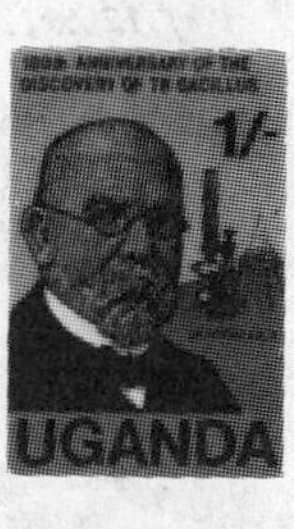

TB Bacillus Centenary — A34

1982, June 14 Litho.

332 A34 1sh Koch .15 .15
333 A34 10sh Microscope .22 .18
334 A34 50sh Inoculation 1.10 .95
335 A34 100sh Virus under microscope 2.25 1.90
Nos. 332-335 (4) 3.72 3.18

Souvenir Sheet

336 A34 150sh Medical School 3.75 3.00

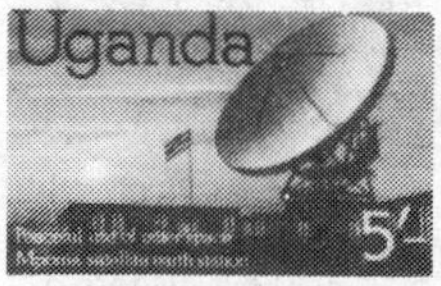

Peaceful Uses of Outer Space — A35

1982, May 17 Litho. *Perf. 15*

337 A35 5sh Mpoma Satellite Earth Station .15 .15
338 A35 10sh Pioneer II .20 .15
339 A35 50sh Columbia space shuttle 1.00 .85
340 A35 100sh Voyager II, Saturn 2.00 1.65
Nos. 337-340 (4) 3.35 2.80

Souvenir Sheet

341 A35 150sh Columbia shuttle 3.50 3.00

Nos. 314-317 Overprinted: "21st BIRTHDAY / HRH Princess of Wales / JULY 1 1982"

1982, July 7 *Perf. 14*

342 CD331 10sh multicolored .20 .15
343 CD331 50sh multicolored 1.00 .85
344 CD331 200sh multicolored 4.00 3.25
Nos. 342-344 (3) 5.20 4.25

Souvenir Sheet

345 CD331 250sh multicolored 5.25 4.50

Also issued in sheets of 5 + label in changed colors, perf. 12x12½.

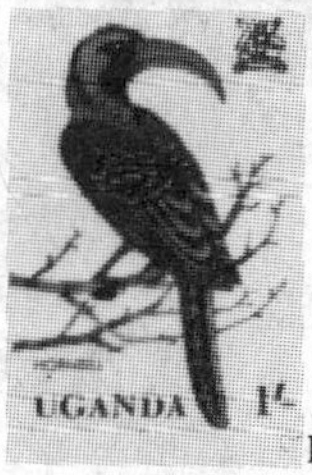

Hornbill — A36

1982, July 12

346 A36 1sh shown .20 .20
347 A36 20sh Superb starling .55 .45
348 A36 50sh Bateleur eagle 1.25 1.10
349 A36 100sh Saddle-bill stork 2.50 2.25
Nos. 346-349 (4) 4.50 4.00

Souvenir Sheet

350 A36 200sh Laughing dove 5.00 4.00

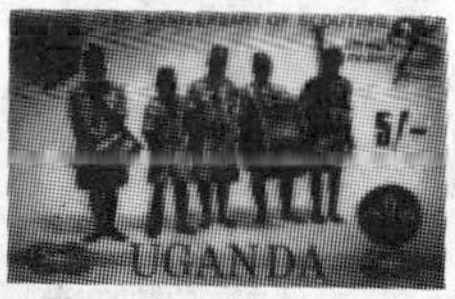

Scouting Year — A37

1982, Aug. 23

351 A37 5sh Scouts .15 .15
352 A37 20sh Trophy presentation .45 .38
353 A37 50sh Helping disabled 1.10 .95
354 A37 100sh First aid instruction 2.25 1.90
Nos. 351-354 (4) 3.95 3.38

Souvenir Sheet

355 A37 150sh Baden-Powell 3.50 3.00

For overprints see Nos. 376-380.

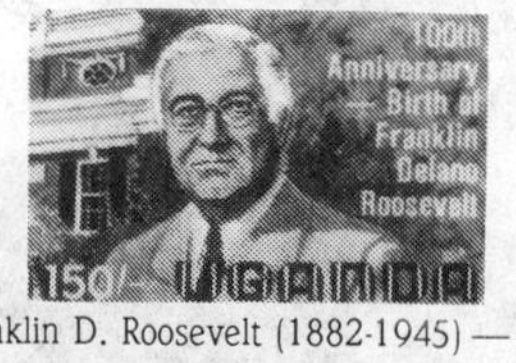

Franklin D. Roosevelt (1882-1945) — A38

Roosevelt and Washington: 50sh, 200sh, Inaugurations. No. 358, Mount Vernon. No. 359, Hyde Park.

1982, Sept. Litho.

356 A38 50sh multicolored .90 .75
357 A38 200sh multicolored 3.50 3.00

Souvenir Sheets

358 A38 150sh multicolored 3.00 2.75
359 A38 150sh multicolored 3.00 2.75

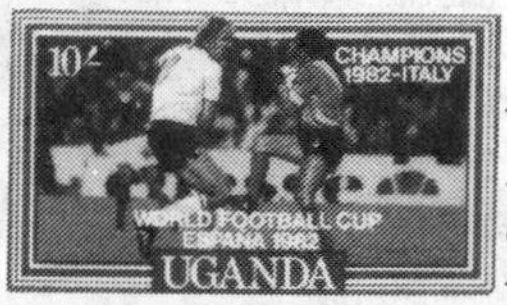

Italy's Victory in 1982 World Cup A39

1982, Oct. Litho. *Perf. 14½*

359A A39 10sh Players .20 .20
359B A39 200sh Team 4.25 4.25

Souvenir Sheet

359C A39 250sh Globe 3.50 3.50

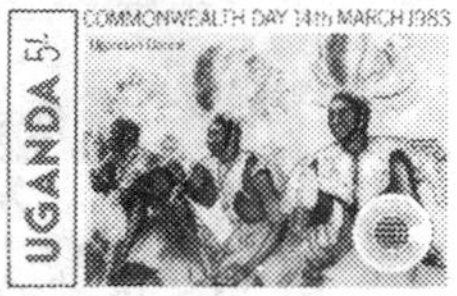

A39a

1983, Mar. 14 Litho. *Perf. 14*

360 A39a 5sh Dancers .15 .15
361 A39a 20sh Traditional currency .35 .35
362 A39a 50sh Village .90 .90
363 A39a 100sh Drums 1.75 1.75
Nos. 360-363 (4) 3.15 3.15

Commonwealth Day.

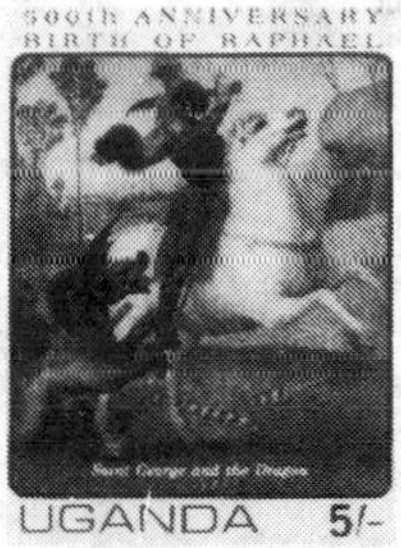

St. George and the Dragon, by Raphael — A40

1983, Apr.

364 A40 5sh shown .15 .15
365 A40 20sh St. George and the Dragon, 1505 .35 .35
366 A40 50sh Moses Parts the Red Sea .90 .90
367 A40 200sh Expulsion of Heliodorus 3.50 3.50
Nos. 364-367 (4) 4.90 4.90

Souvenir Sheet

368 A40 250sh Leo the Great and Attila, 1513 4.25 4.25

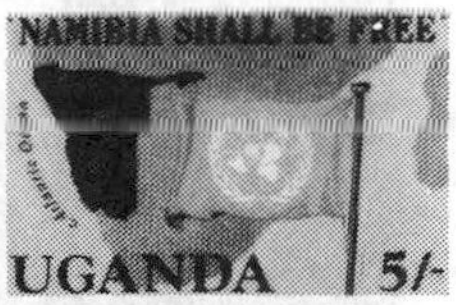

A41

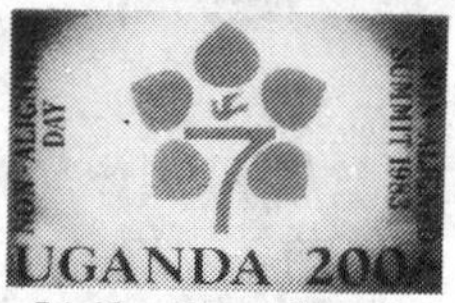

7th Non-aligned Summit Conference — A42

1983, Aug. 15 Litho. *Perf. 14½*

369 A41 5sh multicolored .15 .15
370 A42 200sh multicolored 2.50 2.50

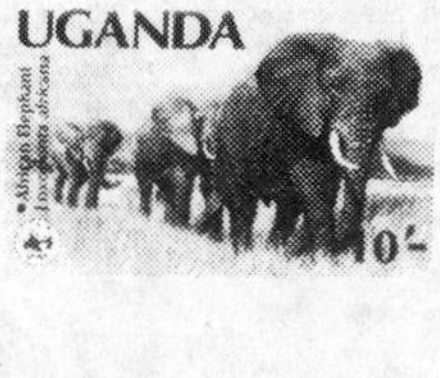

African Elephants and World Wildlife Emblem A43

5sh, 10sh, 30sh, 70sh Various African elephants. 300sh, Zebras, vert.

1983, Aug. 22 *Perf. 15*

371 A43 5sh multicolored .15 .15
372 A43 10sh multicolored .15 .15
373 A43 30sh multicolored .35 .35
374 A43 70sh multicolored .85 .85
Nos. 371-374 (4) 1.50 1.50

Souvenir Sheet

375 A43 300sh multicolored 3.75 3.75

Nos. 351-355 Overprinted or Surcharged: "BOYS BRIGADE CENTENARY 1883-1983"

1983, Sept. 19 Litho. *Perf. 14*

376 A37 5sh multicolored .15 .15
377 A37 20sh multicolored .22 .22
378 A37 50sh multicolored .55 .55
379 A37 400sh on 100sh multi 4.50 4.50
Nos. 376-379 (4) 5.42 5.42

Souvenir Sheet

380 A37 150sh multicolored 1.75 1.75

World Communications Year — A44

Designs: 20sh, Mpoma Satellite Earth Station. 50sh, Railroad, Computer Operator. 70sh, Filming Lions. 100sh, Pilots, Radio Communications. 300sh, Communications Satellite.

1983, Oct. 3 Litho. *Perf. 15*

381 A44 20sh multicolored .15 .15
382 A44 50sh multicolored .60 .60
383 A44 70sh multicolored .85 .85
384 A44 100sh multicolored 1.25 1.25
Nos. 381-384 (4) 2.85 2.85

Souvenir Sheet

385 A44 300sh multicolored 3.50 3.50

Nos. 279, 281-285, 289 Surcharged

1983, Nov. 7 Litho. *Perf. 14*

386 A26 100sh on 10c multi
387 A26 135sh on 1sh multi
388 A26 175sh on 30c multi
389 A26 200sh on 50c multi
390 A26 400sh on 80c multi
391 A26 700sh on 5sh multi
392 A26 1000sh on 1.50sh
Nos. 386-392 (7) 15.00 15.00

World Food Day — A45

1984, Jan. 12 Litho. *Perf. 14*

393 A45 10sh Plowing .15 .15
394 A45 200sh Banana crop 2.25 2.25

Christmas A46

1983, Dec. 12 Litho. *Perf. 14*

395 A46 10sh Navitity .15 .15
396 A46 50sh Sheperds and Angel .38 .38
397 A46 175sh Flight into Egypt 1.25 1.25
398 A46 400sh Angels Blowing Trumpets 3.00 3.00
Nos. 395-398 (4) 4.78 4.78

Souvenir Sheet

399 A46 300sh Three Kings 2.25 2.25

Animal Type of 1979

1983, Dec. 19

400 A26 100sh like No. 284 .60 .60
401 A26 135sh like No. 285 .75 .75
402 A26 175sh like No. 286 1.00 1.00
403 A26 200sh like No. 287 1.35 1.35
404 A26 400sh like No. 288 2.75 2.75
405 A26 700sh like No. 292 4.50 4.50
406 A26 1000sh like No. 291 6.50 6.50
Nos. 400-406 (7) 17.45 17.45

1984 Summer Olympics A48

1983 *Perf. 14½*

417 A48 5sh Ruth Kyalisiima .15 .15
418 A48 115sh Javelin .65 .65
419 A48 155sh Wrestling .80 .80
420 A48 175sh Rowing 1.10 1.10
Nos. 417-420 (4) 2.70 2.70

Souvenir Sheet

421 A48 500sh Akii-Bua 3.00 3.00

For overprints see Nos. 458-462.

Intl. Civil Aviation Org., 40th Anniv. A49

1984, Sept.

422 A49 5sh Passenger service .15 .15
423 A49 115sh Cargo service .70 .70
424 A49 155sh Police airwing .90 .90
425 A49 175sh Soroti Flying School plane 1.25 1.25
Nos. 422-425 (4) 3.00 3.00

Souvenir Sheet

426 A49 250sh Hot air balloon 1.75 1.75

Butterflies A50

1984, Oct. Litho. *Perf. 14½*

427 A50 5sh Silver-barred Charaxes .15 .15
428 A50 115sh Western Emperor Swallowtail .70 .70
429 A50 155sh African Giant Swallowtail .95 .95
430 A50 175sh Blue Salamis 1.25 1.25
Nos. 427-430 (4) 3.05 3.05

Souvenir Sheet

431 A50 250sh Veinted Yellow 1.75 1.75

Freshwater Fish — A51

1985 Litho. *Perf. 15*

432 A51 5sh Nothobran-chius taeniopygus .15 .15
433 A51 10sh Bagrus dogmac .15 .15
434 A51 50sh Polypterus senegalus .15 .15
435 A51 100sh Clarias .26 .26
436 A51 135sh Mormyrus kannume .35 .35
437 A51 175sh Synodontis victoriae .45 .45
438 A51 205sh Haplochromis brownae .55 .55
439 A51 400sh Lates niloticus 1.10 1.10
440 A51 700sh Protopterus aethiopicus 1.75 1.75
441 A51 1000sh Barbus radcliffii 3.00 3.00
442 A51 2500sh Malapterus electricus 7.00 7.00
Nos. 432-442 (11) 14.91 14.91

Issue dates: Nos. 432-435, 437-441, Apr. 1. Nos. 436, 442, June 10.

For overprints see Nos. 490-494.

Easter — A52

1985, May 13 Litho. *Perf. 14*

443 A52 5sh The Last Supper .15 .15
444 A52 115sh Jesus confronts doubting Thomas .42 .42
445 A52 155sh Crucifixion .60 .60
446 A52 175sh Pentecost .65 .65
Nos. 443-446 (4) 1.82 1.82

Souvenir Sheet

447 A52 250sh Last prayer in garden 1.00 1.00

UN Child Survival Campaign A53

1985, July 1

448 A53 5sh Mother breastfeeding .15 .15
449 A53 115sh Growth monitorization .42 .42
450 A53 155sh Immunization .60 .60
451 A53 175sh Oral rehydration therapy .65 .65
Nos. 448-451 (4) 1.82 1.82

Souvenir Sheet

452 A53 500sh Expectant Mother, food 1.90 1.90

Audubon Birth Bicent. — A54

UN Decade for Women — A56

1985, July

453 A54 115sh Acrocephalus schoenobaenus .42 .42
454 A54 155sh Ardeola ibis .65 .65
455 A54 175sh Galerida gristata .65 .65
456 A54 500sh Aythya fuligula 1.90 1.90
Nos. 453-456 (4) 3.62 3.62

Souvenir Sheet

457 A54 1000sh Strix aluco 4.00 4.00

See Nos. 469-473.

Nos. 417-421 Ovptd. or Surcharged with Winners Names, Medals and Countries in Gold

Gold medalists: 5sh, Benita Brown-Fitzgerald, US, 100-meter hurdles. 115sh, Arto Haerkoenen, Finland, javelin. 155sh, Atsuji Miyahara, Japan, 115-pound Greco-Roman wrestling. 100sh, West Germany, quadruple sculls. 1200sh, Edwin Moses, US, 400-meter hurdles.

1985, July *Perf. 15*

458 A48 5sh multicolored .15 .15
459 A48 115sh multicolored .28 .28
460 A48 155sh multicolored .38 .38
461 A48 1000sh on 175sh multi 2.40 2.40
Nos. 458-461 (4) 3.21 3.21

Souvenir Sheet

462 A48 1200sh on 500sh multi 4.00 4.00

1985 Litho. *Perf. 14*

Designs: 5sh, Natl. Women's Day, Mar. 8. 115sh, Girl Guides 75th anniv., horiz. 155sh, Mother Theresa, 1979 Nobel Peace Prize laureate. 1000sh, Queen Mother. No. 467, Queen Mother inspecting troops. No. 468, like 115sh, horiz.

463 A56 5sh multicolored .15 .15
464 A56 115sh multicolored .35 .35
465 A56 155sh multicolored .48 .48
466 A56 1000sh multicolored 3.25 3.25
Nos. 463-466 (4) 4.23 4.23

Souvenir Sheets

467 A56 1500sh multicolored 5.00 5.00
468 A56 1500sh multicolored 5.00 5.00

Issue dates: #466-467, Aug. 21; others, Nov. 1.

Audubon Type of 1985

1985, Dec. 23 *Perf. 12½x12*

469 A54 5sh Rock ptarmigan .15 .15
470 A54 155sh Sage grouse .55 .55
471 A54 175sh Lesser yellowlegs .60 .60
472 A54 500sh Brown-headed cowbird 1.75 1.75
Nos. 469-472 (4) 3.05 3.05

Souvenir Sheet

Perf. 14

473 A54 1000sh Whooping crane 3.75 3.75

UN, 40th Anniv. — A57

Designs: 10sh, Forest resources, vert. 180sh, UN Peace-keeping Force. 200sh, Emblem, UN Development Project. 250sh, Intl. Peace Year. 2000sh, Natl., UN flags, vert. 2500sh, Flags, UN Building, New York, vert.

1986, Feb. *Perf. 15*

474 A57 10sh multicolored .15 .15
475 A57 180sh multicolored .28 .28
476 A57 200sh multicolored .32 .32
477 A57 250sh multicolored .40 .40
478 A57 2000sh multicolored 3.25 3.25
Nos. 474-478 (5) 4.40 4.40

Souvenir Sheet

479 A57 2500sh multicolored 4.00 4.00

1986 World Cup Soccer Championships, Mexico — A58

Various soccer plays.

1986, Mar. *Perf. 14*

480 A58 10sh multicolored .15 .15
481 A58 180sh multicolored .28 .28
482 A58 250sh multicolored .40 .40
483 A58 2500sh multicolored 3.50 3.50
Nos. 480-483 (4) 4.33 4.33

Souvenir Sheet

484 A58 3000sh multicolored 4.50 4.50

No. 484 contains vert. stamp.

For overprints see Nos. 514-518.

A59

Halley's Comet A60

Designs: 50sh, Arecibo radio telescope, Puerto Rico, and Tycho Brahe (1546-1601), Danish astronomer. 100sh, Recovery of Astronaut John Glenn, US space capsule, Caribbean, 1962. 140sh, Adoration of the Magi, 1301, by Giotto (1276-1337). 2500sh, Sighting, 1835, Davy Crockett at The Alamo.

1986, Mar. Litho. *Perf. 14*

485 A59 50sh multicolored .15 .15
486 A59 100sh multicolored .15 .15
487 A59 140sh multicolored .22 .22
488 A59 2500sh multicolored 3.75 3.75
Nos. 485-488 (4) 4.27 4.27

Souvenir Sheet

489 A60 3000sh multicolored 4.75 4.75

For overprints see Nos. 519-523.

Nos. 437, 440-442 and 468 Ovptd. "NRA LIBERATION / 1986" in Silver or Black

1986, Apr. *Perf. 15*

490 A51 175sh multi .28 .28
491 A51 700sh multi 1.10 1.10
492 A51 1000sh multi (Bk) 1.50 1.50
493 A51 2500sh multi (Bk) 3.75 3.75
Nos. 490-493 (4) 6.63 6.63

Souvenir Sheet

Perf. 14

494 A56 1500sh multi (Bk) 3.00 3.00

No. 494 ovptd. in one line in margin. A 400sh also exists with silver overprint. All stamps exist with overprint colors transposed.

Queen Elizabeth II, 60th Birthday
Common Design Type

1986, Apr. 21 *Perf. 14*

495 CD339 100sh At London Zoo, c. 1938 .15 .15
496 CD339 140sh At the races, 1970 .22 .22
497 CD339 2500sh Sandringham, 1982 3.75 3.75
Nos. 495-497 (3) 4.12 4.12

Souvenir Sheet

498 CD339 3000sh Engagement, 1947 4.75 4.75

AMERIPEX '86 — A61

1986, May 22 *Perf. 15*

499 A61 50sh Niagara Falls .15 .15
500 A61 100sh Jefferson Memorial .15 .15
501 A61 250sh Liberty Bell .35 .35
502 A61 1000sh The Alamo 1.35 1.35
503 A61 2500sh George Washington Bridge 3.50 3.50
Nos. 499-503 (5) 5.50 5.50

Souvenir Sheet

504 A61 3000sh Grand Canyon 4.10 4.10

Statue of Liberty, cent.

A62

Statue of Liberty, Cent. — A63

Tall ships, Operation Sail: 50sh, Gloria, Colombia, vert. 100sh, Mircea, Romania, vert. 140sh, Sagres II, Portugal. 2500sh, Gazela Primero, US.

1986, July *Perf. 14*

505 A62 50sh multicolored .15 .15
506 A62 100sh multicolored .15 .15
507 A62 140sh multicolored .20 .20
508 A62 2500sh multicolored 3.50 3.50
Nos. 505-508 (4) 4.00 4.00

Souvenir Sheet

509 A63 3000sh multicolored 4.10 4.10

Royal Wedding Issue, 1986
Common Design Type

Designs: 50sh, Prince Andrew and Sarah Ferguson. 140sh, Andrew and Princess Anne. 2500sh, At formal affair. 3000sh, Couple diff.
Nos. 510-512 horiz.

1986, July 23

510 CD340 50sh multicolored .15 .15
511 CD340 140sh multicolored .20 .20
512 CD340 2500sh multicolored 3.50 3.50
Nos. 510-512 (3) 3.85 3.85

Souvenir Sheet

513 CD340 3000sh multicolored 4.10 4.10

Nos. 480-484 Ovptd. or Surcharged "WINNERS Argentina 3 W. Germany 2" in Gold in 2 or 3 Lines

1986, Sept. 15 Litho. *Perf. 14*

514 A58 50sh on 10sh multi .15 .15
515 A58 180sh multicolored .25 .25
516 A58 250sh multicolored .35 .35
517 A58 2500sh multicolored 3.50 3.50
Nos. 514-517 (4) 4.25 4.25

Souvenir Sheet

518 A58 3000sh multicolored 3.75 4.25

Nos. 485-489 Ovptd. with Halley's Comet Emblem

1986, Oct. 15 Litho. *Perf. 14*

519 A59 50sh multicolored .15 .15
520 A59 100sh multicolored .15 .15
521 A59 140sh multicolored .20 .20
522 A59 2500sh multicolored 3.50 3.50
Nos. 519-522 (4) 4.00 4.00

Souvenir Sheet

523 A60 3000sh multicolored 4.25 4.25

Christian Martyrs A64

Designs: 50sh, St. Kizito. 150sh, St. Kizito educating Ganda converts. 200sh, Execution of Bishop James Hannington. 1000sh, Mwanga's execution of converts, cent. 1500sh, King Mwanga sentencing Christians to death.

1986, Oct. 15

524 A64 50sh multicolored .15 .15
525 A64 150sh multicolored .22 .22
526 A64 200sh multicolored .30 .30
527 A64 1000sh multicolored 1.50 1.50
Nos. 524-527 (4) 2.17 2.17

Souvenir Sheet

528 A64 1500sh multicolored 2.25 2.25

A65

Christmas A66

Paintings by Albrecht Durer and Titian: 50sh, Madonna of the Cherries. 150sh, Madonna and Child, vert. 200sh, Assumption of the Virgin, vert. 2500sh, Praying Hands, vert. No. 533, Adoration of the Magi. No. 534, Presentation of the Virgin in the Temple.

1986, Nov. 26 Litho. *Perf. 14*

529 A65 50sh multicolored .15 .15
530 A65 150sh multicolored .24 .24
531 A65 200sh multicolored .32 .32
532 A65 2500sh multicolored 3.50 3.50
Nos. 529-532 (4) 4.21 4.21

Souvenir Sheets

533 A66 3000sh multicolored 4.00 4.00
534 A66 3000sh multicolored 4.00 4.00

Birds and Animals A67

1987 *Perf. 15*

535 A67 2sh Red-billed firefinch .15 .15
536 A67 5sh African pygmy kingfisher .18 .18
537 A67 10sh Scarlet-chested sunbird .32 .32
538 A67 25sh White rhinoceros .85 .85
539 A67 35sh Lion 1.25 1.25
540 A67 45sh Cheetahs 1.50 1.50
541 A67 50sh Cordon bleu 1.65 1.65
542 A67 100sh Giant eland 3.25 3.25
Nos. 535-542 (8) 9.15 9.15

Souvenir Sheets

543 A67 150sh Carmine bee-eaters 5.00 5.00
544 A67 150sh Cattle egret, zebra 5.00 5.00

Issue dates: Nos. 535-537, 541, 543, Nov. 2; Nos. 538-540, 542-544, July 22.

Transportation Innovations — A68

1987, Aug. 14

545 A68 2sh Eagle, 1987 .15 .15
546 A68 3sh Bremen, 1928 .15 .15
547 A68 5sh Winnie Mae, 1933 .16 .16
548 A68 10sh Voyager, 1986 .32 .32
549 A68 15sh Chanute biplane glider, 1896 .48 .48
550 A68 25sh Norge, 1926 .80 .80
551 A68 35sh Curtis biplane, USS Pennsylvania, 1911 1.10 1.10
552 A68 45sh Freedom 7, 1961 1.40 1.40
553 A68 100sh Concorde, 1976 3.25 3.25
Nos. 545-553 (9) 7.81 7.81

1988 Summer Olympics, Seoul A69

Flags and athletes.

1987, Oct. 5 *Perf. $14^1/_2$x14*

554 A69 5sh Torch bearer .18 .18
555 A69 10sh Swimming .32 .32
556 A69 50sh Cycling 1.65 1.65
557 A69 100sh Gymnastic rings 3.35 3.35
Nos. 554-557 (4) 5.50 5.50

Souvenir Sheet

558 A69 150sh Boxing 5.00 5.00

A70

Natl. Independence, 25th Anniv. — A71

1987, Oct. 8

559 A70 5sh shown .18 .18
560 A70 10sh Mulago Hospital .35 .35
561 A70 25sh Independence Monument .82 .82
562 A70 50sh High Court 1.65 1.65
Nos. 559-562 (4) 3.00 3.00

Souvenir Sheet

563 A71 100sh shown 3.50 3.50

A72

Science and Space — A73

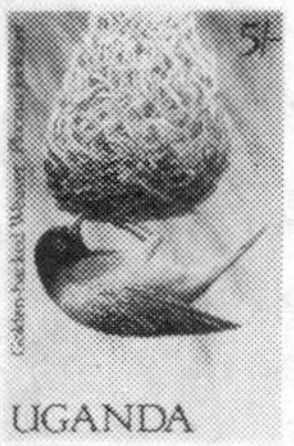

Birds — A74

Designs: 5sh, Hippocrates, father of modern medicine, caduceus and surgeons. 25sh, Albert Einstein and Theory of Relativity equation. 35sh, Sir Isaac Newton and Optics Theory. 45sh, Karl Benz (1844-1929), German engineer, automobile pioneer, and the Velocipede, Mercedes-Benz sports coupe and manufacturers' emblems.

1987, Nov. 2 *Perf. $14^1/_2$x14*

564 A72 5sh multicolored .18 .18
565 A72 25sh multicolored .85 .85
566 A72 35sh multicolored 1.20 1.20
567 A72 45sh multicolored 1.50 1.50
Nos. 564-567 (4) 3.73 3.73

Souvenir Sheet

Perf. 14x$14^1/_2$

568 A73 150sh shown 5.00 5.00

1987, Nov. 2 Litho. *Perf. 14*

569 A74 5sh Golden-backed weaver .18 .18
570 A74 10sh Hoopoe .35 .35
571 A74 15sh Red-throated bee-eater .50 .50
572 A74 25sh Lilac-breasted roller .85 .85
573 A74 35sh Pygmy goose 1.20 1.20
574 A74 45sh Scarlet-chested sunbird 1.50 1.50
575 A74 50sh Crowned crane 1.70 1.70
576 A74 100sh Long-tailed fiscal shrike 3.35 3.35
Nos. 569-576 (8) 9.63 9.63

Souvenir Sheets

577 A74 150sh African barn owl, horiz. 5.00 5.00
578 A74 150sh African fish-eagle, horiz. 5.00 5.00

14th World Boy Scout Jamboree, Australia, 1987-88 A75

Activities: 5sh, Stamp collecting, Uganda Nos. 84 and 116. 25sh, Planting trees, Natl. flag. 35sh, Canoeing on Lake Victoria. 45sh, Hiking and camping. 150sh, Logo of 1987 jamboree and natl. Boy Scout organization emblem.

1987, Nov. 20

579 A75 5sh multicolored .18 .18
580 A75 25sh multicolored .85 .85
581 A75 35sh multicolored 1.20 1.20
582 A75 45sh multicolored 1.50 1.50
Nos. 579-582 (4) 3.73 3.73

Souvenir Sheet

583 A75 150sh multicolored 5.00 5.00

Christmas A76

The life of Christ and the Virgin pictured on bas-reliefs, c. 1250, and a tapestry from France: 5sh, The Annunciation. 10sh, The Nativity. 50sh, Flight into Egypt. 100sh, The Adoration of the Magi. 150sh, The Mystic Wine Tapestry.

1987, Dec. 18

584 A76 5sh multicolored .18 .18
585 A76 10sh multicolored .35 .35
586 A76 50sh multicolored 1.70 1.70
587 A76 100sh multicolored 3.35 3.35
Nos. 584-587 (4) 5.58 5.58

Souvenir Sheet

588 A76 150sh multicolored 5.00 5.00

Locomotives A77

Designs: 5sh, Class 12 2-6-2T light shunter. 10sh, Class 92 1Co-Co1 diesel electric. 15sh, Class 2-8-2. 25sh, Class 2-6-2T light shunter. 35sh, Class 4-8-0. 45sh, Class 4-8-2. 50sh, Class 4-8-4+4-8-4 Garratt. 100sh, Class 87 1Co-Co1 diesel electric. No. 597, Class 59 4-8-2+2-8-4 Garratt. No. 598, Class 31 2-8-4.

1988, Jan. 18

589 A77 5sh multicolored .18 .18
590 A77 10sh multicolored .35 .35
591 A77 15sh multicolored .55 .55

592	A77	25sh	multicolored	.82	.82
593	A77	35sh	multicolored	1.20	1.20
594	A77	45sh	multicolored	1.50	1.50
595	A77	50sh	multicolored	1.65	1.65
596	A77	100sh	multicolored	3.50	3.50
			Nos. 589-596 (8)	9.75	9.75

Souvenir Sheets

597	A77	150sh	multicolored	5.00	5.00
598	A77	150sh	multicolored	5.00	5.00

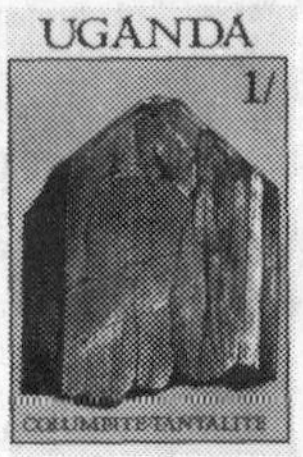

Minerals — A78

1988, Jan. 18

599	A78	1sh	Columbite-tantalite	.15	.15
600	A78	2sh	Galena	.15	.15
601	A78	5sh	Malachite	.18	.18
602	A78	10sh	Cassiterite	.35	.35
603	A78	35sh	Ferberite	1.20	1.20
604	A78	50sh	Emerald	1.70	1.70
605	A78	100sh	Monazite	3.35	3.35
606	A78	150sh	Microcline	5.00	5.00
			Nos. 599-606 (8)	12.08	12.08

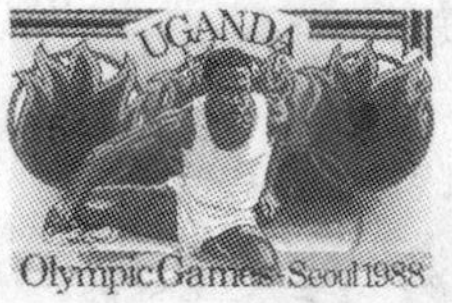

1988 Summer Olympics, Seoul A79

1988, May 16 Litho. *Perf. 14*

607	A79	5sh	Hurdles	.18	.18
608	A79	25sh	High jump	.85	.85
609	A79	35sh	Javelin	1.20	1.20
610	A79	45sh	Long jump	1.50	1.50
			Nos. 607-610 (4)	3.73	3.73

Souvenir Sheet

611	A79	150sh	Medals, five-ring emblem	5.00	5.00

For overprints see Nos. 651-655.

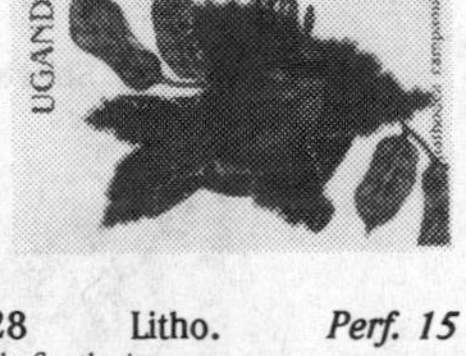

Flowers A80

1988, July 28 Litho. *Perf. 15*

612	A80	5sh	Spathodea campanulata	.16	.16
613	A80	10sh	Gloriosa simplex	.32	.32
614	A80	20sh	Thevetica peruviana, vert.	.65	.65
615	A80	25sh	Hibiscus schizopetalus	.82	.82
616	A80	35sh	Aframomum sceptrum	1.15	1.15
617	A80	45sh	Adenium obesum	1.50	1.50
618	A80	50sh	Kigelia africana, vert.	1.65	1.65
619	A80	100sh	Clappertonia ficifolia	3.30	3.30
			Nos. 612-619 (8)	9.55	9.55

Souvenir Sheets

620	A80	150sh	Costus spectabilis	5.00	5.00
621	A80	150sh	Canarina abyssinica, vert.	5.00	5.00

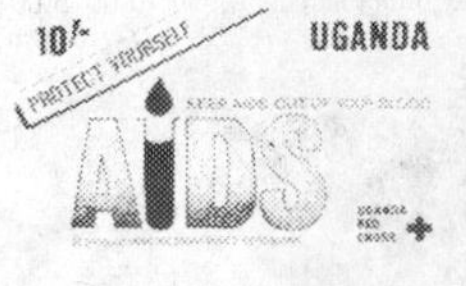

Intl. Red Cross, 125th Anniv. A81

1988, Oct. 28 Litho. *Perf. 14*

622	A81	10sh	"AIDS"	.15	.15
623	A81	40sh	Immunize children	.50	.50
624	A81	70sh	Relief distribution	.90	.90
625	A81	90sh	First aid	1.25	1.25
			Nos. 622-625 (4)	2.80	2.80

Souvenir Sheet

626	A81	150sh	Jean-Henri Dunant, vert.	2.00	2.00

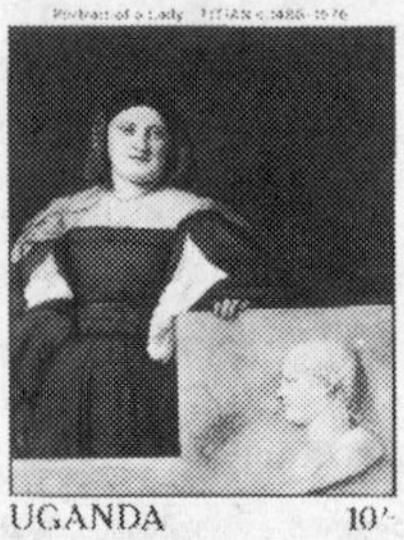

Paintings by Titian — A82

Designs: 10sh, Portrait of a Lady, c. 1508. 20sh, Portrait of a Man, 1507. 40sh, Portrait of Isabella d'Este, c. 1534. 50sh, Portrait of Vincenzo Mosti, 1520. 70sh, Pope Paul III Farnese, c. 1545. 90sh, Violante, 1515. 100sh, Lavinia, Titian's Daughter, c. 1565. 250sh, Portrait of Dr. Parma, c. 1515. No. 635, The Speech of Alfonso D'Avalos, c. 1540. No. 636, Cain and Abel.

1988, Oct. 31 *Perf. 14*

627	A82	10sh	multicolored	.15	.15
628	A82	20sh	multicolored	.18	.18
629	A82	40sh	multicolored	.55	.55
630	A82	50sh	multicolored	.68	.68
631	A82	70sh	multicolored	.95	.95
632	A82	90sh	multicolored	1.20	1.20
633	A82	100sh	multicolored	1.35	1.35
634	A82	250sh	multicolored	3.40	3.40
			Nos. 627-634 (8)	8.46	8.46

Souvenir Sheets

635	A82	150sh	multicolored	3.00	3.00
636	A82	350sh	multicolored	4.75	4.75

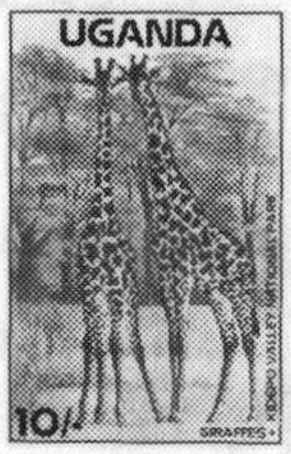

Game Preserves — A83

Designs: 10sh, Giraffes, Kidepo Valley Natl. Park. 25sh, Zebras, Lake Mburo Natl. Park. 100sh, African buffalo, Murchison Falls Natl. Park. 250sh, Pelicans, Queen Elizabeth Natl. Park. 350sh, Roan antelopes, Lake Mburo Natl. Park.

1988, Nov. 18 Litho. *Perf. 14*

637	A83	10sh	multicolored	.15	.15
638	A83	25sh	multicolored	.32	.32
639	A83	100sh	multicolored	1.35	1.35
640	A83	250sh	multicolored	3.35	3.35
			Nos. 637-640 (4)	5.17	5.17

Souvenir Sheet

641	A83	350sh	multicolored	4.75	4.75

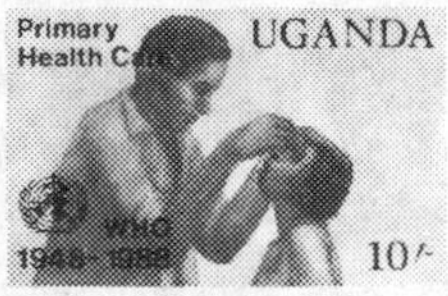

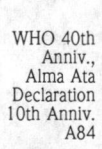

WHO 40th Anniv., Alma Ata Declaration 10th Anniv. A84

1988, Dec. 1

642	A84	10sh	Primary health care	.15	.15
643	A84	25sh	Mental health	.35	.35
644	A84	45sh	Rural health care	.60	.60
645	A84	100sh	Dental care	1.35	1.35
646	A84	200sh	Postnatal care	2.70	2.70
			Nos. 642-646 (5)	5.15	5.15

Souvenir Sheet

647	A84	350sh	Conference Hall, Alma-Ata, USSR	4.75	4.75

Miniature Sheet

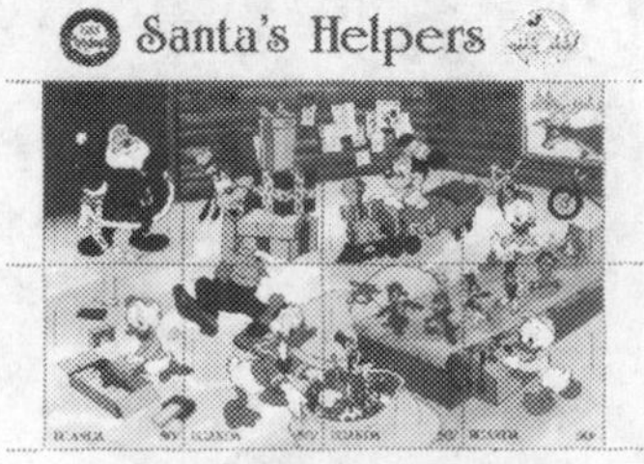

Christmas, Mickey Mouse 60th Birthday — A85

Walt Disney characters: No. 648a, Santa Claus. b, Goofy. c, Mickey Mouse. d, Huey at conveyor belt. e, Dewey packing building blocks. f, Donald Duck. g, Chip-n-Dale. h, Louie at conveyor belt controls. No. 649, Preparing reindeer for Christmas eve flight. No. 650, Mickey loading sleigh with toys, horiz.

1988, Dec. 2 *Perf. 13½x14, 14x13½*

648			Sheet of 8	5.50	5.50
a.-h.	A85	50sh	any single	.68	.68

Souvenir Sheets

649	A85	350sh	multicolored	4.75	4.75
650	A85	350sh	multicolored	4.75	4.75

Nos. 607-611 Ovptd. or Surcharged to Honor Olympic Winners

5sh: "110 M HURDLES / R. KINGDOM / USA"

25sh: "HIGH JUMP / G. AVDEENKO / USSR"

35sh: "JAVELIN / T. KORJUS / FINLAND"

300sh: "LONG JUMP / C. LEWIS / USA"

1989, Jan. 30 Litho. *Perf. 14*

651	A79	5sh	multicolored	.15	.15
652	A79	25sh	multicolored	.35	.35
653	A79	35sh	multicolored	.48	.48
654	A79	300sh	on 45sh multi	4.00	4.00
			Nos. 651-654 (4)	4.98	4.98

Souvenir Sheet

655	A79	350sh	on 150sh multi	4.75	4.75

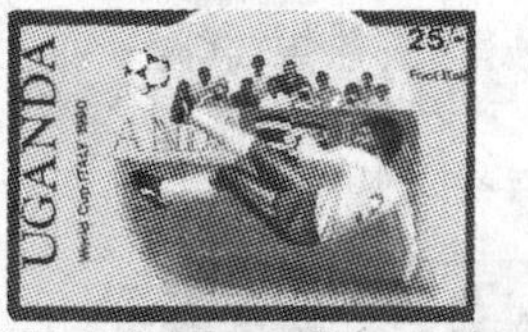

1990 World Cup Soccer Championships, Italy — A86

Various action scenes.

1989, Apr. 24 Litho. *Perf. 14*

656	A86	10sh	multi, vert.	.15	.15
657	A86	25sh	multicolored	.35	.35
658	A86	75sh	multicolored	1.00	1.00
659	A86	200sh	multi, vert.	2.65	2.65
			Nos. 656-659 (4)	4.15	4.15

Souvenir Sheet

660	A86	300sh	multicolored	4.00	4.00

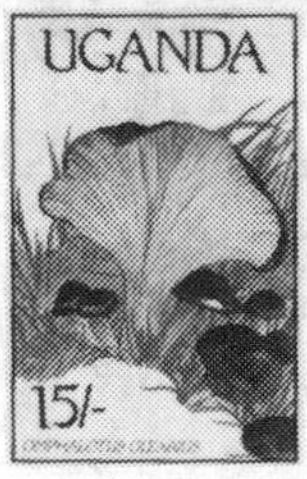

Mushrooms — A87

1989, Aug. 14 Litho. *Perf. 14*

661	A87	10sh	Suillus granulatus	.15	.15
662	A87	15sh	Omphalotus olearius	.20	.20
663	A87	45sh	Oudemansiella radicata	.60	.60
664	A87	50sh	Clitocybe nebularis	.68	.68
665	A87	60sh	Macrolepiota rhacodes	.80	.80
666	A87	75sh	Lepista nuda	1.00	1.00
667	A87	150sh	Suillus luteus	2.00	2.00
668	A87	200sh	Agaricus campestris	2.65	2.65
			Nos. 661-668 (8)	8.08	8.08

Souvenir Sheets

669	A87	350sh	Schizophyllum commune	4.00	4.00
670	A87	350sh	Bolbitius vitellinus	4.00	4.00

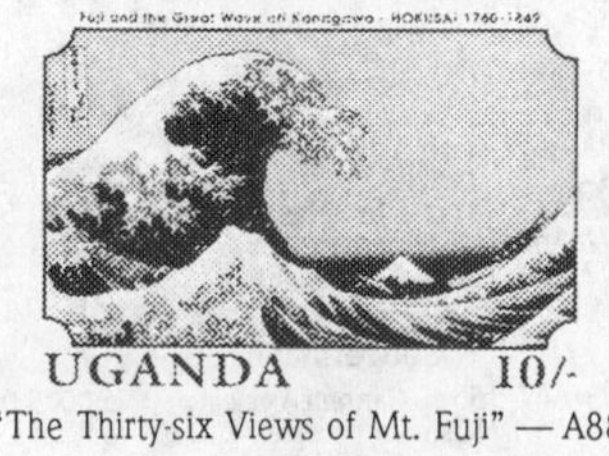

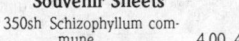

"The Thirty-six Views of Mt. Fuji" — A88

Prints by Hokusai (1760-1849): 10sh, Fuji and the Great Wave off Kanagawa. 15sh, Fuji from Lake Suwa. 20sh, Fuji from Kajikazawa. 60sh, Fuji from Shichirigahama. 90sh, Fuji from Ejiri in Sunshu. 120sh, Fuji Above Lightning. 200sh, Fuji from Lower Meguro in Edo. 250sh, Fuji from Edo. No. 679, The Red Fuji from the Foot. No. 680, Fuji from Umezawa.

1989, May 15 Litho. *Perf. 14x13½*

671	A88	10sh	multicolored	.15	.15
672	A88	15sh	multicolored	.15	.15
673	A88	20sh	multicolored	.20	.20
674	A88	60sh	multicolored	.60	.60
675	A88	90sh	multicolored	.90	.90
676	A88	120sh	multicolored	1.20	1.20
677	A88	200sh	multicolored	2.00	2.00
678	A88	250sh	multicolored	2.50	2.50
			Nos. 671-677 (7)	5.20	5.20

Souvenir Sheets

679	A88	500sh	multicolored	5.00	5.00
680	A88	500sh	multicolored	5.00	5.00

Hirohito (1901-1989), Showa emperor, and Akihito, Heisei emperor of Japan.

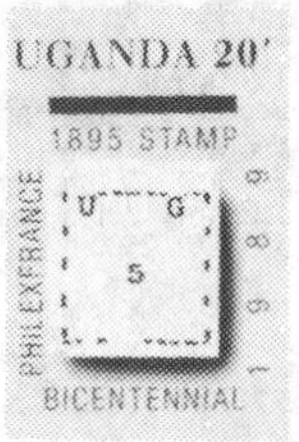

PHILEXFRANCE '89 — A89

1989, July 7 Litho. *Perf. 14*

681	A89	20sh	No. 1	.20	.20
682	A89	70sh	No. 10	.70	.70
683	A89	100sh	No. 48	1.00	1.00
684	A89	250sh	No. 67	2.50	2.50
a.			Souv. sheet of 4, #681-684	5.00	5.00
			Nos. 681-684 (4)	4.40	4.40

No. 684a sold for 500sh.

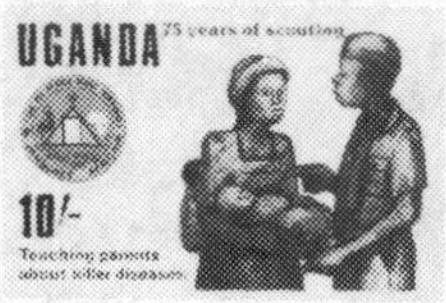

2nd All African Scout Jamboree, Aug. 3-15 — A90

1989, Aug. 3 Litho. *Perf. 14*

685	A90	10sh	Fatal child ailments	.15	.15
686	A90	70sh	Raising poultry	.70	.70
687	A90	90sh	Immunization	.90	.90
688	A90	100sh	Brick-making	1.00	1.00
			Nos. 685-688 (4)	2.75	2.75

Souvenir Sheet

689	A90	500sh	Natl. emblem, vert.	5.00	5.00

Scouting, 75th anniv.

For surcharges see Nos. 1301-1304.

Miniature Sheet

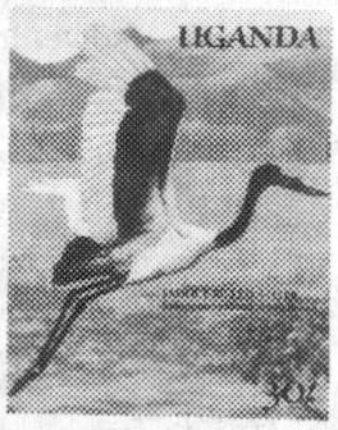

Wildlife at Waterhole — A91

Designs: a, Saddle-billed stork. b, White pelican. c, Marabou stork. d, Egyptian vulture, giraffes. e, Bateleur eagle, antelope. f, African elephant. g, Giraffe. h, Goliath heron. i, Black rhinoceros, zebras. j, Zebras, oribi. k, African fish eagle. l, Hippopotamus. m, Black-backed jackal, white pelican. n, Cape buffalo. o, Olive baboon. p, Bohor reedbuck. q, Lesser flamingo, serval. r, Shoebill stork. s, Crowned crane. t, Impala. No. 691, Lion. No. 692, Long-crested eagle.

1989, Sept. 12 *Perf. 14½x14*

690			Sheet of 20	6.00	6.00
a.-t.	A91	30sh	any single	.30	.30

Souvenir Sheets

691	A91	500sh	multicolored	5.00	5.00
692	A91	500sh	multicolored	5.00	5.00

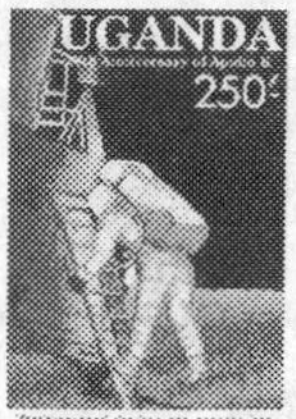

1st Moon Landing, 20th Anniv. — A92

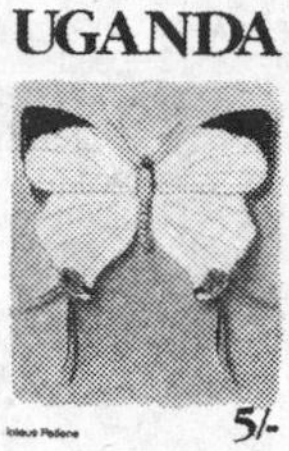

Butterflies — A93

Quotations and scenes from the Apollo 11 mission.

1989, Oct. 20 Litho. *Perf. 14*

693	A92	10sh	Launch vehicle, Moon	.15	.15
694	A92	20sh	Eagle lower stage on Moon	.20	.20
695	A92	30sh	Columbia	.30	.30
696	A92	50sh	Eagle landing	.50	.50
697	A92	70sh	Aldrin on Moon	.70	.70
698	A92	250sh	Armstrong on ladder	2.50	2.50
699	A92	300sh	Eagle ascending	3.00	3.00
700	A92	350sh	Aldrin, diff.	3.50	3.50
			Nos. 693-700 (8)	10.85	10.85

Souvenir Sheets

701	A92	500sh	Liftoff	5.00	5.00
702	A92	500sh	Parachute landing	5.00	5.00

Nos. 693-697 and 699 horiz.

1989, Nov. 13

"UGANDA" in Black

703	A93	5sh	Ioalus pallene	.15	.15
704	A93	10sh	Hewitsonia boisduvali	.15	.15
705	A93	20sh	Euxanthe wakefeildi	.20	.20
706	A93	30sh	Papilio echerioides	.30	.30
707	A93	40sh	Acraea semivitrca	.40	.40
708	A93	50sh	Colotis antevippe	.50	.50
709	A93	70sh	Acraea perenna	.70	.70
710	A93	90sh	Charaxes cynthia	.90	.90
711	A93	100sh	Euphaedra neophroa	1.00	1.00
712	A93	150sh	Cymothoe beckeri	1.50	1.50
713	A93	200sh	Vanessula milca	2.00	2.00
714	A93	400sh	Mimacraea marshalli	4.00	4.00
715	A93	500sh	Axiocerses amanga	5.00	5.00
716	A93	1000sh	Precis hierta	10.00	10.00
			Nos. 703-716 (14)	26.80	26.80

See Nos. 826-839 for "UGANDA" in blue.

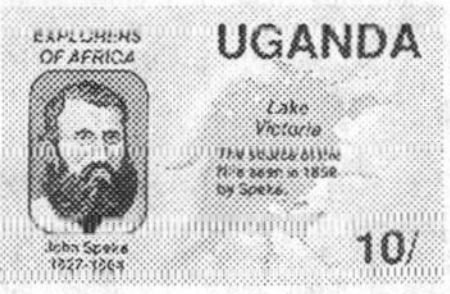

Explorers of Africa A94

Designs: 10sh, John Speke (1827-64), satellite view of Lake Victoria. 25sh, Sir Richard Burton (1821-90), satellite view of Lake Tanganyika. 40sh, Richard Lander (1804-34), bronze ritual figure of the Bakota tribe. 90sh, Rene Caillie (1799-1838), mosque. 125sh, Dorcas gazelle and Sir Samuel Baker (1821-93), discoverer of Lake Albert. 150sh, Phoenician galley and Necho II (d. 595 B.C.), king of Egypt credited by Herodotus with sending an expedition to circumnavigate Africa. 250sh, Vasco da Gama (c. 1460-1524), 1st European to sail around the Cape of Good Hope, and caravel. 300sh, Sir Henry Stanley (1841-1904), discoverer of Lake Edward, and Lady Alice . No. 725, Dr. David Livingstone (1813-73), discoverer of Victoria Falls, and steam launch Ma-Robert. No. 726, Mary Kingsley (1862-1900), ethnologist, and tail-spot climbing perch.

1989, Nov. 15 Litho. *Perf. 14*

717	A94	10sh	multicolored	.15	.15
718	A94	25sh	multicolored	.25	.25
719	A94	40sh	multicolored	.40	.40
720	A94	90sh	multicolored	.90	.90
721	A94	125sh	multicolored	1.25	1.25
722	A94	150sh	multicolored	1.50	1.50
723	A94	250sh	multicolored	2.50	2.50
724	A94	300sh	multicolored	3.00	3.00
			Nos. 717-724 (8)	9.95	9.95

Souvenir Sheets

725	A94	500sh	multicolored	5.00	5.00
726	A94	500sh	multicolored	5.00	5.00

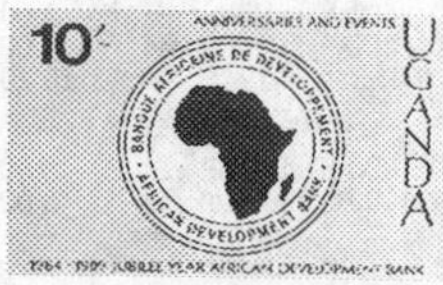

Anniversaries and Events — A95

1989, Dec. 12

727	A95	10sh	Bank emblem	.15	.15
728	A95	20sh	Satellite dishes, arrows	.20	.20
729	A95	75sh	Nehru	.75	.75
730	A95	90sh	Pan-American Dixie Clipper	.90	.90
731	A95	100sh	Locomotion, Stephenson	1.00	1.00
732	A95	150sh	Concorde cockpit	1.50	1.50
733	A95	250sh	Wapen von Hamburg, Leopoldus Primus	2.50	2.50
734	A95	300sh	Concorde cockpit, crew	3.00	3.00
			Nos. 727-734 (8)	10.00	10.00

Souvenir Sheets

735	A95	500sh	Storming of the Bastille	5.00	5.00
736	A95	500sh	Emperor Frederick I Barbarossa, charter	5.00	5.00

African Development Bank 25th anniv. (10sh); World Telecommunications Day, May 17 (20sh); Birth cent. of Jawaharlal Nehru, 1st prime minister of independent India (75sh); 1st scheduled transatlantic airmail flight, 50th anniv. (90sh); 175th anniv. of the invention of the 1st steam locomotive by George Stephenson and opening of the Stockton & Darlington Railway in 1825 (100sh); 1st test flight of the Concorde, 20th anniv. (150sh, 300sh); Port of Hamburg, 800th anniv. (250sh, No. 736); and French revolution bicent. (No. 735).

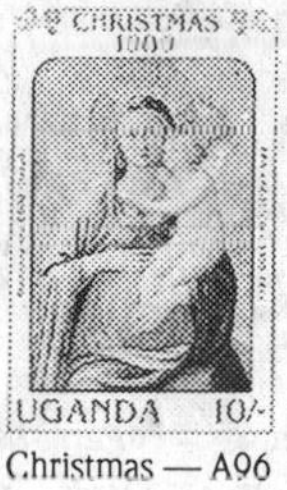

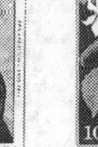

Christmas — A96

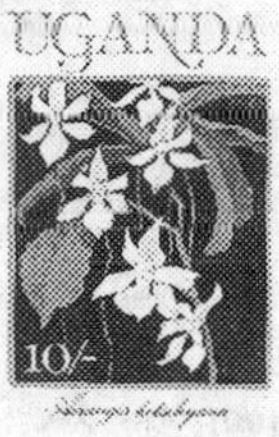

Orchids — A97

Religious paintings by Fra Angelico: 10sh, Madonna and Child. 20sh, Adoration of the Magi. 40sh, Virgin and Child Enthroned with Saints. 75sh, The Annunciation. 100sh, St. Peter Martyr triptych center panel. 150sh, Virgin and Child Enthroned with Saints, diff. 250sh, Virgin and Child Enthroned. 350sh, Annalena Altarpiece. No. 745, Bosco ai Frati Altarpiece. No. 746, Madonna and Child with Twelve Angels.

1989, Dec. 18

737	A96	10sh	multicolored	.15	.15
738	A96	20sh	multicolored	.20	.20
739	A96	40sh	multicolored	.40	.40
740	A96	75sh	multicolored	.75	.75
741	A96	100sh	multicolored	1.00	1.00
742	A96	150sh	multicolored	1.50	1.50
743	A96	250sh	multicolored	2.50	2.50
744	A96	350sh	multicolored	3.50	3.50
			Nos. 737-744 (8)	10.00	10.00

Souvenir Sheets

745	A96	500sh	multicolored	5.00	5.00
746	A96	500sh	multicolored	5.00	5.00

1989, Dec. 18

747	A97	10sh	Aerangis kotschyana	.15	.15
748	A97	15sh	Angraecum infundibulare	.15	.15
749	A97	45sh	Cyrtorchis chailluana	.45	.45
750	A97	50sh	Aerangis rhodosticta	.50	.50
751	A97	100sh	Eulophia speciosa	1.00	1.00
752	A97	200sh	Calanthe sylvatica	2.00	2.00
753	A97	250sh	Vanilla imperialis	2.50	2.50
754	A97	350sh	Polystachya vulcanica	3.50	3.50
			Nos. 747-754 (8)	10.25	10.25

Souvenir Sheets

755	A97	500sh	Ansellia africana	5.00	5.00
756	A97	500sh	Ancistrochilus rothschildianus	5.00	5.00

For overprints see Nos. 782-786A.

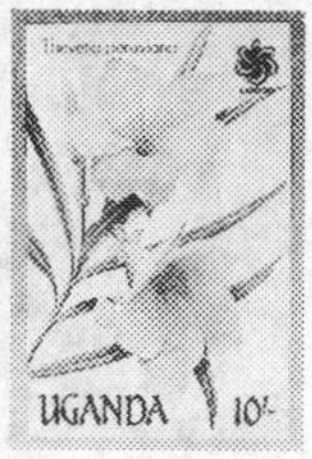

EXPO '90, Osaka — A98

Flowering trees.

1990, Apr. 17 Litho. *Perf. 14*

757	A98	10sh	*Thevetia peruviana*	.15	.15
758	A98	20sh	*Acanthus eminens*	.15	.15
759	A98	90sh	*Gnidia glauca*	.52	.52
760	A98	150sh	*Oncoba spinosa*	.85	.85
761	A98	175sh	*Hibiscus rosa-sinensis*	1.00	1.00
762	A98	400sh	*Jacaranda mimosifolia*	2.25	2.25
763	A98	500sh	*Erythrina abyssinica*	2.85	2.85
764	A98	700sh	*Bauhinia purpurea*	4.00	4.00
			Nos. 757-764 (8)	11.77	11.77

Souvenir Sheets

765	A98	1000sh	*Delonix regia*	5.75	5.75
766	A98	1000sh	*Cassia didymobatrya*	5.75	5.75

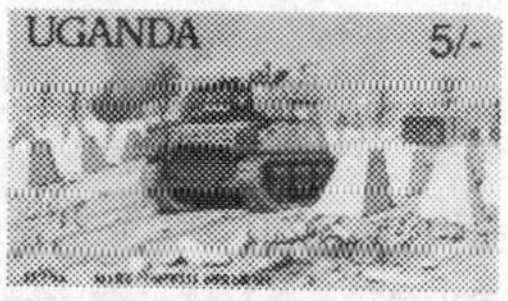

World War II Milestones — A99

Designs: 5sh, Allies penetrate west wall, Dec. 3, 1944. 10sh, VE Day, May 8, 1945. 20sh, US forces capture Okinawa, June 22, 1945. 75sh, DeGaulle named commander of all Free French forces, Apr. 4, 1944. 100sh, US troops invade Saipan, June 15, 1944. 150sh, Allied troops launch Operation Market Garden, Sept. 17, 1944. 200sh, Gen. MacArthur returns to Philippines, Oct. 20, 1944. 300sh, US victory at Coral Sea, May 8, 1942. 350sh, First battle of El Alamein, July 1, 1942. 500sh, Naval battle at Guadalcanal, Nov. 12, 1942. 1000sh, Battle of Britain.

1990, June 8 Litho. *Perf. 14*

767	A99	5sh	multicolored	.15	.15
768	A99	10sh	multicolored	.15	.15
769	A99	20sh	multicolored	.15	.15
770	A99	75sh	multicolored	.42	.42
771	A99	100sh	multicolored	.56	.56
772	A99	150sh	multicolored	.85	.85
773	A99	200sh	multicolored	1.15	1.15
774	A99	300sh	multicolored	1.70	1.70
775	A99	350sh	multicolored	2.00	2.00
776	A99	500sh	multicolored	2.80	2.80
			Nos. 767-776 (10)	9.93	9.93

Souvenir Sheet

777	A99	1000sh	multicolored	5.75	5.75

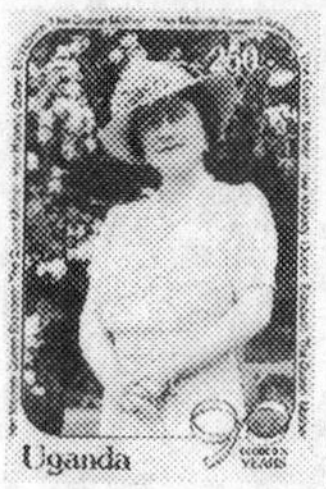

Queen Mother, 90th Birthday — A100

1990, July 5

778	A100	250sh	shown	1.45	1.45
779	A100	250sh	Facing left	1.45	1.45
780	A100	250sh	Holding dog	1.45	1.45
			Nos. 778-780 (3)	4.35	4.35

Souvenir Sheet

781	A100	1000sh	like No. 778	5.75	5.75

Nos. 747-754 Ovptd. in Silver

Nos. 755-756 Ovptd. in Silver

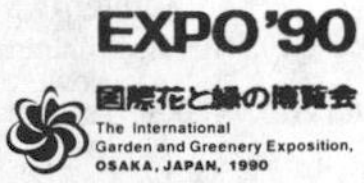
EXPO'90
The International Garden and Greenery Exposition, OSAKA, JAPAN, 1990

1990 Litho. *Perf. 14*

782	A97	10sh	on No. 747	.15	.15
782A	A97	15sh	on No. 748	.15	.15
782B	A97	45sh	on No. 749	.22	.22
783	A97	50sh	on No. 750	.25	.25
783A	A97	100sh	on No. 751	.50	.50
784	A97	200sh	on No. 752	1.00	1.00
785	A97	250sh	on No. 753	1.25	1.25
785A	A97	350sh	on No. 754	1.75	1.75
			Nos. 782-785A (8)	5.27	5.27

Souvenir Sheet

786	A97	500sh	on No. 755	2.50	2.50
786A	A97	500sh	on No. 756	2.50	2.50

Overprints on Nos. 786-786A are in sheet margin.

Issue dates: 15sh, 45sh, 100sh, 350sh, No. 786A, Nov.; others, July 30.

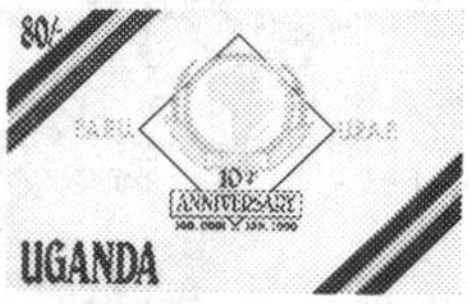

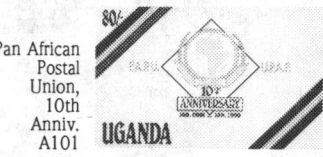

Pan African Postal Union, 10th Anniv. A101

Designs: 750sh, UN Conference on the least developed countries, Paris, Sept. 3-14.

1990, Aug. 3 Litho. *Perf. 14*

787	A101	80sh	multicolored	.40	.40

Souvenir Sheet

788	A101	750sh	multicolored	3.75	3.75

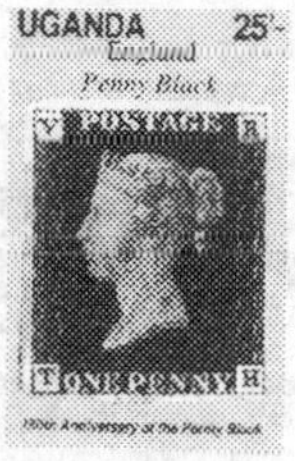

Great Britain No. O1 — A102

Designs: 50sh, Canada #12. 100sh, Baden #4b. 150sh, Switzerland #3L1. 200sh, US #C3a. 300sh, Western Australia #1. 500sh, Uganda #29. 600sh, Great Britain #2. No. 797, Uganda #29. No. 798, Sir Rowland Hill.

1990, Aug. 6 Litho. *Perf. 14*

789	A102	25sh	multicolored	.15	.15
790	A102	50sh	multicolored	.25	.25
791	A102	100sh	multicolored	.50	.50
792	A102	150sh	multicolored	.75	.75
793	A102	200sh	multicolored	1.00	1.00
794	A102	300sh	gray & black	1.50	1.50
795	A102	500sh	multicolored	2.50	2.50
796	A102	600sh	multicolored	3.00	3.00
			Nos. 789-796 (8)	9.65	9.65

Souvenir Sheets

Size: 108x77mm

797	A102	1000sh	multicolored	5.00	5.00

Size: 119x85mm

798	A102	1000sh	scarlet & blk	5.00	5.00

Penny Black, 150th anniversary. Nos. 797-798, Stamp World London '90.

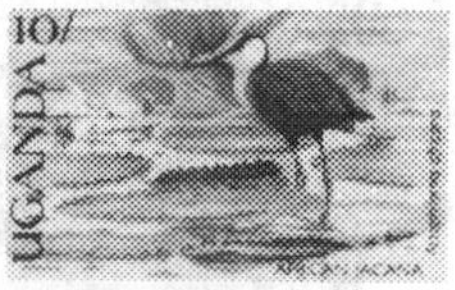

Birds A103

1990, Sept. 3 Litho. *Perf. 14*

799	A103	10sh	African jacana	.15	.15
800	A103	15sh	Ground hornbill	.15	.15
801	A103	45sh	Kori bustard, vert.	.22	.22
802	A103	50sh	Secretary bird	.25	.25
803	A103	100sh	Egyptian geese	.50	.50
804	A103	300sh	Goliath heron, vert.	1.50	1.50
805	A103	500sh	Ostrich, vert.	2.50	2.50
806	A103	650sh	Saddlebill stork, vert.	3.25	3.25
			Nos. 799-806 (8)	8.52	8.52

Souvenir Sheets

807	A103	1000sh	Volturine guinea fowl, vert.	5.00	5.00
808	A103	1000sh	Lesser flamingo, vert.	5.00	5.00

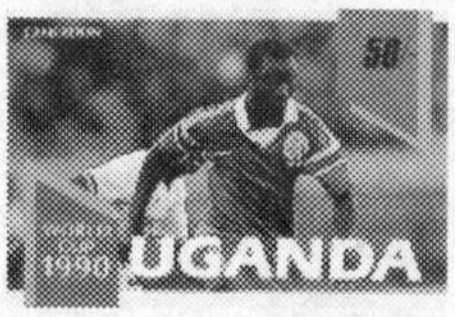

World Cup Soccer Championships, Italy — A104

Players from various national teams.

1990, Sept. 24

809	A104	50sh	Cameroun	.25	.25
810	A104	100sh	Egypt	.50	.50
811	A104	250sh	Ireland	1.25	1.25
812	A104	600sh	West Germany	3.00	3.00
			Nos. 809-812 (4)	5.00	5.00

Souvenir Sheets

813	A104	1000sh	Sweden	5.00	5.00
814	A104	1000sh	Scotland	5.00	5.00

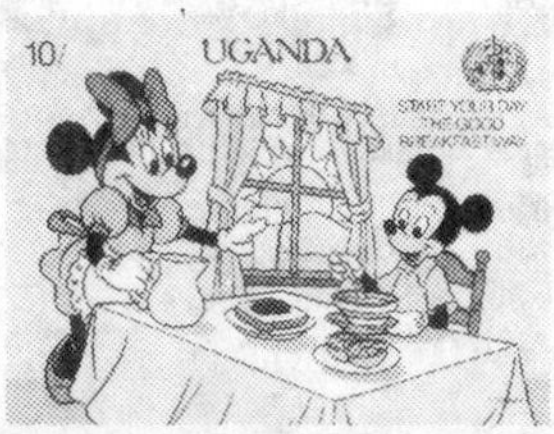

WHO, Promote Better Health — A105

Walt Disney characters in scenes promoting improved health: 10sh, Mickey, Minnie Mouse having a good breakfast. 20sh, Huey, Dewey and Louie looking before crossing street. 50sh, Mickey, Donald Duck against smoking. 90sh, Mickey saving Donald from choking. 100sh, Mickey, Goofy using seat belts. 250sh, Mickey, Minnie avoiding drugs. 500sh, Donald, Daisy exercising. 600sh, Mickey showing bicycle safety. No. 823, Mickey, friends at doctor's office. No. 824, Mickey, friends walking.

1990, Oct. 19 Litho. *Perf. 13½x13*

815	A105	10sh	multicolored	.15	.15
816	A105	20sh	multicolored	.15	.15
817	A105	50sh	multicolored	.25	.25
818	A105	90sh	multicolored	.45	.45
819	A105	100sh	multicolored	.50	.50
820	A105	250sh	multicolored	1.25	1.25
821	A105	500sh	multicolored	2.50	2.50
822	A105	600sh	multicolored	3.00	3.00
			Nos. 815-822 (8)	8.25	8.25

Souvenir Sheets

823	A105	1000sh	multicolored	5.00	5.00
824	A105	1000sh	multicolored	5.00	5.00

Butterfly Type of 1989
"Uganda" in Blue

1990-92 Litho. *Perf. 14*

826	A93	10sh	like #704	.15	.15
827	A93	20sh	like #705	.15	.15
828	A93	30sh	like #706	.15	.15
829	A93	40sh	like #707	.20	.20
830	A93	50sh	like #708	.15	.15
831	A93	70sh	like #709	.35	.35
832	A93	90sh	like #710	.45	.45
833	A93	100sh	like #711	.50	.50
834	A93	150sh	like #712	.75	.75
835	A93	200sh	like #713	1.00	1.00
836	A93	400sh	like #714	1.15	1.15
837	A93	500sh	like #715	1.40	1.40
838	A93	1000sh	like #716	2.85	2.85
839	A93	2000sh	like #716	10.00	10.00
839A	A93	3000sh	Euphaedra eusemoides	15.00	15.00
839B	A93	4000sh	Acraea natalica	20.00	20.00
839C	A93	5000sh	Euphaedra themis	15.00	15.00
			Nos. 826-839C (17)	69.25	69.25

Issue dates: 50sh, 400sh, 500sh, 1000sh, 1991. 3000sh, 4000sh, Jan. 2, 1992. Nos. 827, 833, 835 and 839 exist dated 1991.

This is an expanding set, numbers may change.

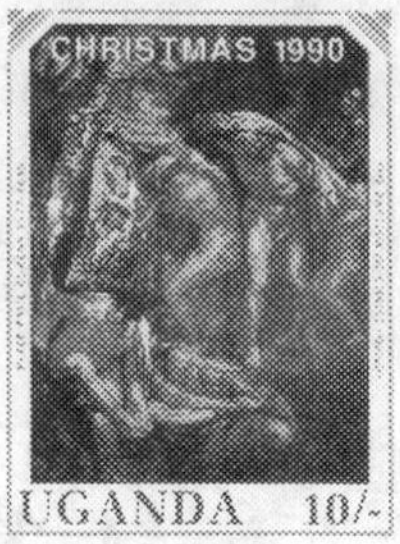

Christmas A106

Details from paintings by Rubens: 10sh, 500sh, The Baptism of Christ. 20sh, 150sh, 400sh, 600sh, St. Gregory the Great and Other Saints. 100sh, Saints Nereus, Domitilla and Achilleus. 300sh, Saint Augustine. No. 853, Victory of Eucharistic Truth Over Heresy, horiz. No. 854, Triumph of Faith, horiz.

1990, Dec. 17 Litho. *Perf. 14*

845	A106	10sh	multicolored	.15	.15
846	A106	20sh	multicolored	.15	.15
847	A106	100sh	multicolored	.50	.50
848	A106	150sh	multicolored	.75	.75
849	A106	300sh	multicolored	1.50	1.50
850	A106	400sh	multicolored	2.00	2.00
851	A106	500sh	multicolored	2.50	2.50
852	A106	600sh	multicolored	3.00	3.00
			Nos. 845-852 (8)	10.55	10.55

Souvenir Sheets

853	A106	1000sh	multicolored	5.00	5.00
854	A106	1000sh	multicolored	5.00	5.00

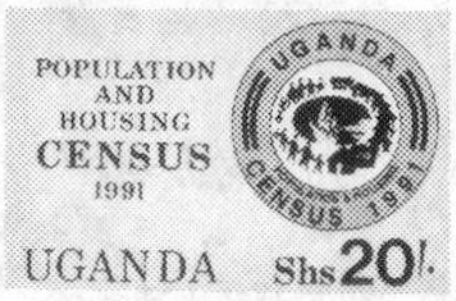

Natl. Census A107

Design: 1000sh, Counting on fingers, houses, people.

1990, Dec. 28 Litho. *Perf. 14*

855	A107	20sh	multicolored	.15	.15

Souvenir Sheet

856	A107	1000sh	multicolored	5.00	5.00

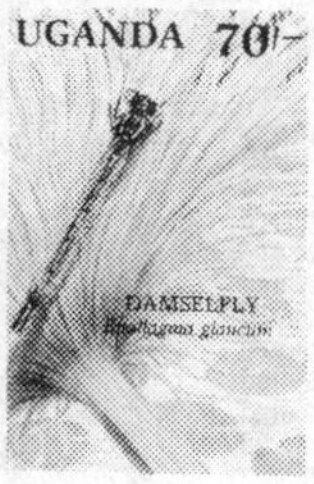

Wetlands Fauna — A108

Designs: No. 857a, Damselfly. b, Purple gallinule. c, Sitatunga. d, Purple heron. e, Bushpig. f, Vervet monkey. g, Long reed frog. h, Malachite kingfisher. i, Marsh mongoose. j, Painted reed frog. k, Jacana. l, Charaxes butterfly. m, Nile crocodile. n, Herald snake. o, Dragonfly. p, Lungfish.

No. 858, Nile monitor, horiz.

1991, Jan. 1 Litho. *Perf. 14*

857	A108	70sh	Min. sheet, #a.-p.	5.60	5.60
858	A108	1000sh	Souv. sheet of 1	5.00	5.00

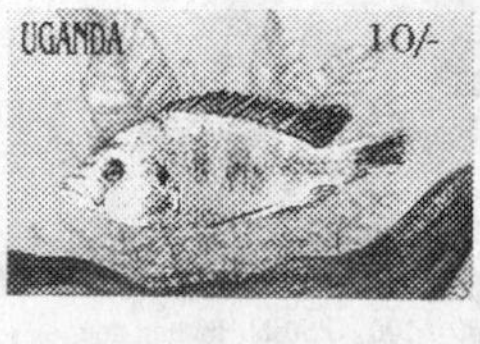

Fish A109

Designs: 10sh, Haplochromis limax. 20sh, Notobranchius palmqvisti. 40sh, Distichodus affinis. 90sh, Haplochromis sauvagei. 100sh, Aphyosemion calliurum. 350sh, Haplochromis johnstoni. 600sh, Haplochromis dichrourus. 800sh, Hemichromis bimaculatus. No. 867, Haplochromis sp. No. 868, Aphyosemion striatum.

1991, Jan. 18 Litho. *Perf. 14*

859	A109	10sh	multicolored	.15	.15
860	A109	20sh	multicolored	.15	.15
861	A109	40sh	multicolored	.20	.20
862	A109	90sh	multicolored	.45	.45
863	A109	100sh	multicolored	.50	.50
864	A109	350sh	multicolored	1.75	1.75
865	A109	600sh	multicolored	3.00	3.00
866	A109	800sh	multicolored	4.00	4.00
			Nos. 859-866 (8)	10.20	10.20

Souvenir Sheets

867	A109	1000sh	multicolored	5.00	5.00
868	A109	1000sh	multicolored	5.00	5.00

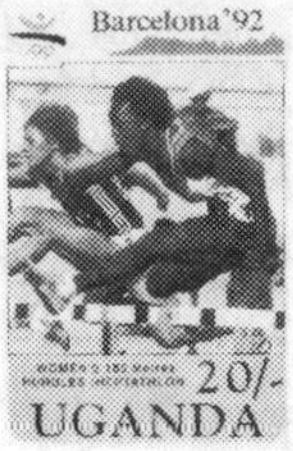

1992 Summer Olympics, Barcelona — A110

1991, Feb. 25 Litho. *Perf. 14*

869	A110	20sh	Women's hurdles	.15	.15
870	A110	40sh	Long jump	.20	.20
871	A110	125sh	Table tennis	.62	.62
872	A110	250sh	Soccer	1.25	1.25
873	A110	500sh	800-meter race	2.50	2.50
			Nos. 869-873 (5)	4.72	4.72

Souvenir Sheets

874	A110	1200sh	Women's 4x100-meter relay, horiz.	6.00	6.00
875	A110	1200sh	Opening ceremony, horiz.	6.00	6.00

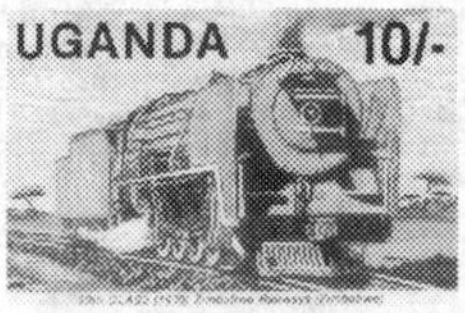

Trains A111

Designs: 10sh, 10th Class, Zimbabwe. 20sh, 12th Class, Zimbabwe. 80sh, Tribal class, Tanzania and Zambia. 200sh, 4-6-0 Type, Egypt. 300sh, Mikado, Sudan. 400sh, Mountain class Garrat, Uganda. 500sh, Mallet Type, Uganda. 1000sh, 5 F 1 Electric locomotive, South Africa. No. 884, 4-8-2 Type, Zimbabwe. No. 885, Atlantic type, Egypt. No. 886, 4-8-2 Type, Angola. No. 887, Mallet Compound Type, Natal.

1991, Apr. 2 Litho. *Perf. 14*

876	A111	10sh	multicolored	.15	.15
877	A111	20sh	multicolored	.15	.15
878	A111	80sh	multicolored	.40	.40
879	A111	200sh	multicolored	1.00	1.00
880	A111	300sh	multicolored	1.50	1.50
881	A111	400sh	multicolored	2.00	2.00
882	A111	500sh	multicolored	2.50	2.50
883	A111	1000sh	multicolored	5.00	5.00
			Nos. 876-883 (8)	12.70	12.70

Souvenir Sheets

884	A111	1200sh	multicolored	6.00	6.00
885	A111	1200sh	multicolored	6.00	6.00
886	A111	1200sh	multicolored	3.50	3.50
887	A111	1200sh	multicolored	3.50	3.50

Even though Nos. 886-887 have the same issue date as Nos. 876-885, their dollar value was lower when they were released.

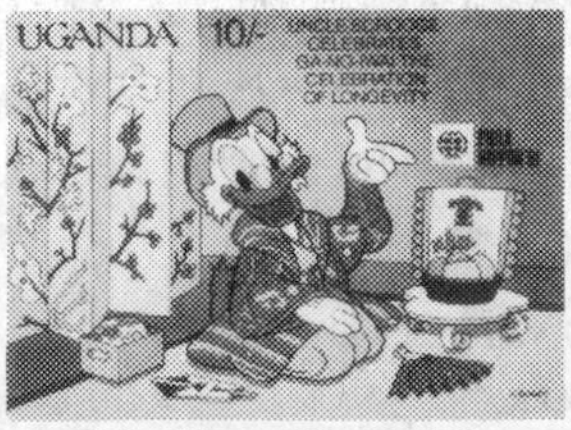

Phila Nippon '91 — A112

Walt Disney characters in Japan: 10sh, Scrooge McDuck celebrating Ga-No-Iwai. 20sh, Mickey removes shoes before entering Minnie's home. 70sh, Cartman Goofy leading horse. 80sh, Daisy, Minnie exchange gifts. 300sh, Minnie kneels at entrance to home. 400sh, Mickey, Donald in volcanic sand bath. 500sh, Clarabelle Cow enjoys incense burning. 1000sh, Mickey, Minnie writing New Year cards. No. 896, Mickey, Donald and Goofy in public bath. No. 897, Mickey and friends playing Japanese music.

1991, May 29 Litho. *Perf. 14x13½*

888	A112	10sh	multicolored	.15	.15
889	A112	20sh	multicolored	.15	.15
890	A112	70sh	multicolored	.35	.35
891	A112	80sh	multicolored	.40	.40
892	A112	300sh	multicolored	1.50	1.50
893	A112	400sh	multicolored	2.00	2.00
894	A112	500sh	multicolored	2.50	2.50
895	A112	1000sh	multicolored	5.00	5.00
			Nos. 888-895 (8)	12.05	12.05

Souvenir Sheets

896	A112	1200sh	multicolored	6.00	6.00
897	A112	1200sh	multicolored	6.00	6.00

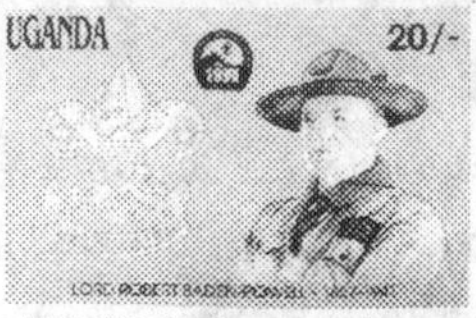

17th World Scout Jamboree, Korea — A113

Designs: 20sh, Lord Baden-Powell. 80sh, Scouts collecting stamps. 100sh, Scout encampment, NY World's Fair, 1939. 150sh, Cover of first Scout Handbook. 300sh, Cooking over campfire. 400sh, Neil Armstrong, Edwin Aldrin, first scouts on moon. 500sh, Hands raised for Scout Pledge. 1000sh, Statue to Unknown Scout, Gilwell Park, England. No. 906, William D. Boyce, Lord Baden-Powell, Rev. L. Hadley. No. 907, 17th Jamboree Emblem.

1991, May 27 *Perf. 14*

898	A113	20sh	multicolored	.15	.15
899	A113	80sh	multicolored	.40	.40
900	A113	100sh	multicolored	.50	.50
901	A113	150sh	grn & blk	.75	.75
902	A113	300sh	multicolored	1.50	1.50
903	A113	400sh	multicolored	2.00	2.00
904	A113	500sh	multicolored	2.50	2.50
905	A113	1000sh	multicolored	5.00	5.00
			Nos. 898-905 (8)	12.80	12.80

Souvenir Sheets

906	A113	1200sh	multicolored	6.00	6.00
907	A113	1200sh	cream & blk	6.00	6.00

For surcharge see No. 1305.

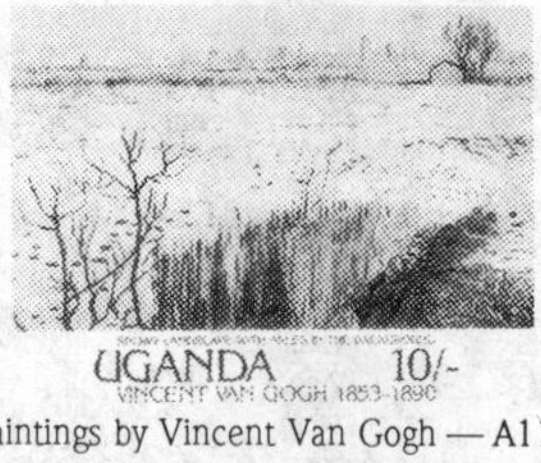

Paintings by Vincent Van Gogh — A114

Paintings: 10sh, Snowy Landscape with Arles in the Background. 20sh, Peasant Woman Binding Sheaves, vert. 60sh, The Drinkers. 80sh, View of Auvers. 200sh, Mourning Man, vert. 400sh, Still Life: Vase with Roses. 800sh, The Raising of Lazarus. 1000sh, The Good Samaritan, vert. No. 916, First Steps. No. 917, Village Street and Steps in Auvers with Figures.

1991, June 26 Litho. *Perf. 13½*

908	A114	10sh	multicolored	.15	.15
909	A114	20sh	multicolored	.15	.15
910	A114	60sh	multicolored	.30	.30
911	A114	80sh	multicolored	.40	.40
912	A114	200sh	multicolored	1.00	1.00
913	A114	400sh	multicolored	2.00	2.00
914	A114	800sh	multicolored	4.00	4.00
915	A114	1000sh	multicolored	5.00	5.00
			Nos. 908-915 (8)	13.00	13.00

Size: 102x76mm

Imperf

916	A114	1200sh	multicolored	6.00	6.00
917	A114	1200sh	multicolored	6.00	6.00

Royal Family Birthday, Anniversary
Common Design Type

1991, July 5 Litho. *Perf. 14*

918	CD347	20sh	multi	.15	.15
919	CD347	70sh	multi	.35	.35
920	CD347	90sh	multi	.45	.45
921	CD347	100sh	multi	.50	.50
922	CD347	200sh	multi	1.00	1.00
923	CD347	500sh	multi	2.50	2.50
924	CD347	600sh	multi	3.00	3.00
925	CD347	1000sh	multi	5.00	5.00
			Nos. 918-925 (8)	12.95	12.95

Souvenir Sheets

926	CD347	1200sh	Elizabeth, Philip	6.00	6.00
927	CD347	1200sh	Sons, Diana, Charles	6.00	6.00

20sh, 100sh, 200sh, 1000sh, No. 927, Charles and Diana, 10th wedding anniversary. Others, Queen Elizabeth II, 65th birthday.

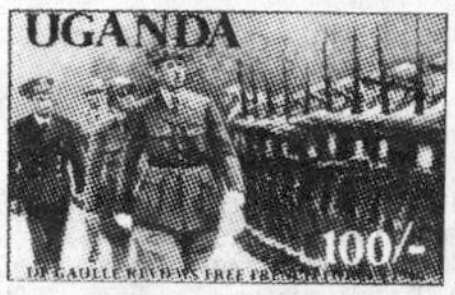

Charles de Gaulle, Birth Cent. A115

Designs: 20sh, Portrait, vert. 70sh, Liberation of Paris, 1944, vert. 90sh, With King George VI, 1940, vert. 100sh, Reviewing Free French forces, 1940. 200sh, Making his appeal on BBC, 1940. 500sh, In Normandy, 1944. 600sh, At Albert Hall, 1940. 1000sh, Becoming President of France, 1959, vert. No. 936, Entering Paris, 1944, vert. No. 937, With Eisenhower, 1942.

1991, July 15 *Perf. 14*

928 A115 20sh multicolored .15 .15
929 A115 70sh multicolored .35 .35
930 A115 90sh multicolored .45 .45
931 A115 100sh multicolored .50 .50
932 A115 200sh multicolored 1.00 1.00
933 A115 500sh multicolored 2.50 2.50
934 A115 600sh multicolored 3.00 3.00
935 A115 1000sh multicolored 5.00 5.00
Nos. 928-935 (8) 12.95 12.95

Souvenir Sheets

936 A115 1200sh multicolored 6.00 6.00
937 A115 1200sh multicolored 6.00 6.00

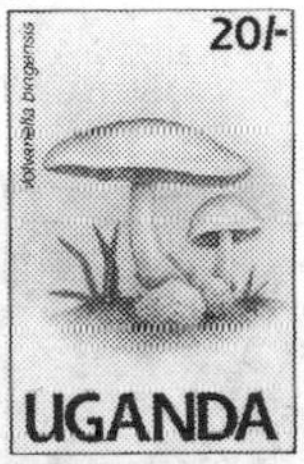

Mushrooms — A116

Designs: 20sh, Volvariella bingensis. 70sh, Agrocybe broadwayi. 90sh, Camarophyllus olidus. 140sh, Marasmius arborescens. 180sh, Marasmiellus subcinereus. 200sh, Agaricus campestris. 500sh, Chlorophyllum molybdites. 1000sh, Agaricus bingensis. No. 946, Leucocoprinus cepaestipes, horiz. No. 947, Laccaria lateritia, horiz.

1991, July 19 **Litho.** *Perf. 14*

938 A116 20sh multicolored .15 .15
939 A116 70sh multicolored .35 .35
940 A116 90sh multicolored .45 .45
941 A116 140sh multicolored .70 .70
942 A116 180sh multicolored .90 .90
943 A116 200sh multicolored 1.00 1.00
944 A116 500sh multicolored 2.50 2.50
945 A116 1000sh multicolored 5.00 5.00
Nos. 938-945 (8) 11.05 11.05

Souvenir Sheets

946 A116 1200sh multicolored 6.00 6.00
947 A116 1200sh multicolored 6.00 6.00

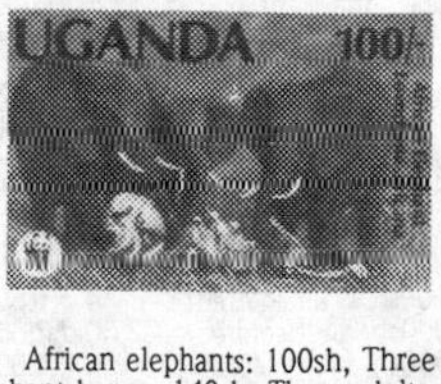

African Animals A117

African elephants: 100sh, Three adults with elephant bones. 140sh, Three adults walking. 200sh, Elephants standing in water hole. 600sh, Adults with calf.

1991, Aug. 1

948 A117 100sh multicolored .50 .50
949 A117 140sh multicolored .70 .70
950 A117 200sh multicolored 1.00 1.00
951 A117 600sh multicolored 3.00 3.00
Nos. 948-951 (4) 5.20 5.20

Souvenir Sheets

Perf. 13x12½

952 A117 1200sh Giraffe 6.00 6.00
953 A117 1200sh Rhinoceros 6.00 6.00

World Wildlife Fund.

Miniature Sheet

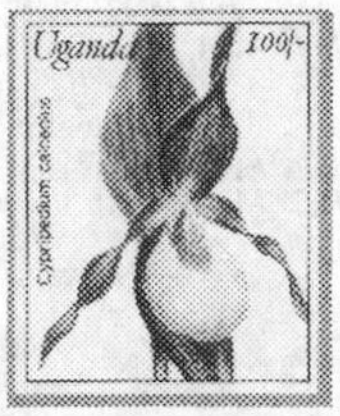

Flowers in Royal Botanical Gardens, Kew — A118

Designs: No. 954a, Cypripedium calceolus. b, Rhododendron thomsonii. c, Ginkgo biloba. d, Magnolia campbellii. e, Wisteria sinensis. f, Clerodendrum ugandense. g, Eulophia horsfallii. h, Aerangis rhodosticta. i, Abelmoschus moschatus. j, Gloriosa superba. k, Carissa edulis. l, Ochna kirkii. m, Canarina abyssinica. n, Nymphaea caerulea. o, Ceropegia succulenta. p, Strelitzia reginae. q, Strongylodon macrobotrys. r, Victoria amazonica. s, Orchis militaris. t, Sophora microphylla. No. 956, The Pagoda, Kew.

Royal Botanic Gardens, Melbourne, Australia: No. 955a, Anigozanthos manglesii. b, Banksia grandis. c, Clianthus formosus. d, Gossypium sturtianum. e, Callistemon lanceolatus. f, Saintpaulia ionantha. g, Calodendrum capense. h, Aloe ferox. i, Bolusanthus speciousus. j, Lithops schwantesii k, Protea repens. l, Plumbago capensis. m, Clerodendrum thomsoniae. n, Thunbergia alata. o, Schotia latifolia. p, Epacris impressa. q, Acacia pycnantha. r, Telopea speciosissima. s, Wahlenbergia gloriosa. t, Eucalyptus globulus. No. 957, Temple of the Winds, Melbourne.

1991, Nov. 25 **Litho.** *Perf. 14½*

954 A118 100sh Sheet of 20, #a.-t. 8.00 8.00
955 A118 90sh Sheet of 20, #a.-t. 5.25 5.25

Souvenir Sheets

956 A118 1400sh multicolored 5.60 5.60
957 A118 1400sh multicolored 4.00 4.00

No. 956 contains one 30x38mm stamp.

While Nos. 955 and 957 have the same issue date as Nos. 954 and 956, their dollar value was lower when released. Numbers have been reserved for additional values in this set.

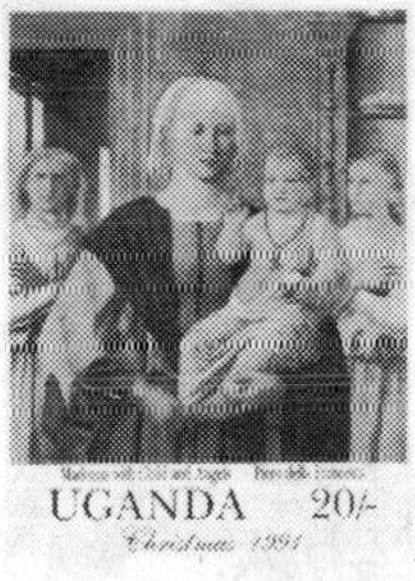

Christmas A120

Paintings by Piero Della Francesca: 20sh, Madonna with Child and Angels. 50sh, The Baptism of Christ. 80sh, Polyptych of Mercy. 100sh, The Madonna of Mercy. 200sh, The Legend of the True Cross: The Annunciation. 500sh, Pregnant Madonna. 1000sh, Polyptych of St. Anthony: The Annunciation. 1500sh, The Nativity. No. 968, The Brera Altarpiece. No. 969, Polyptych of St. Anthony.

1991, Dec. 18 **Litho.** *Perf. 12*

960 A120 20sh multicolored .15 .15
961 A120 50sh multicolored .25 .25
962 A120 80sh multicolored .40 .40
963 A120 100sh multicolored .50 .50
964 A120 200sh multicolored 1.00 1.00
965 A120 500sh multicolored 2.50 2.50
966 A120 1000sh multicolored 5.00 5.00
967 A120 1500sh multicolored 7.50 7.50
Nos. 960-967 (8) 17.30 17.30

Souvenir Sheets

Perf. 14½

968 A120 1800sh multicolored 9.00 9.00
969 A120 1800sh multicolored 9.00 9.00

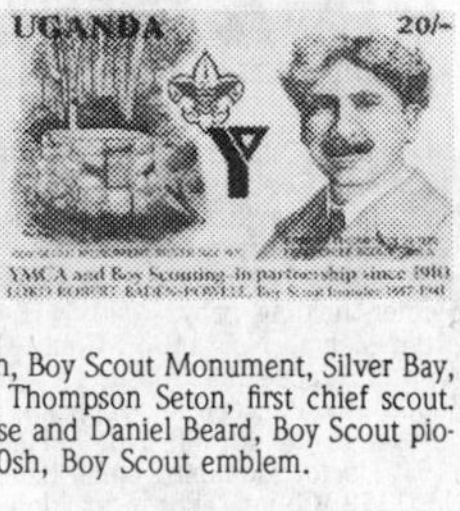

Boy Scouts A121

Designs: 20sh, Boy Scout Monument, Silver Bay, NY and Ernest Thompson Seton, first chief scout. 50sh, Tree house and Daniel Beard, Boy Scout pioneer, vert. 1500sh, Boy Scout emblem.

1992, Jan. 6 **Litho.** *Perf. 14*

970 A121 20sh multicolored .15 .15
971 A121 50sh multicolored .25 .25

Souvenir Sheet

972 A121 1500sh multicolored 7.50 7.50

YMCA-Boy Scouts partnership, Lord Robert Baden-Powell, 50th death anniv. in 1991 (#970) and 17th World Scout Jamboree, Korea (#971-972).

A number has been reserved for an additional value in this set.

Miniature Sheet

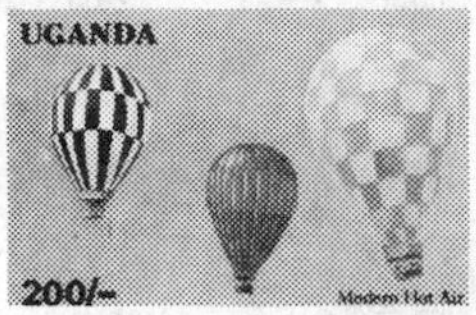

Balloons A122

Balloons: a, Modern Hot Air. b, Sport. c, Pro Juventute. d, Blanchard's. e, Nadar's Le Geant. f, First trans-Pacific balloon crossing. g, Montgolfier's. h, Paris, Double Eagle II, used in first trans-Atlantic balloon crossing. i, Tethered.

1992, Jan. 6 **Litho.** *Perf. 14*

974 A122 200sh Sheet of 9, #a.-i. 5.25 5.25

Miniature Sheet

Japanese Attack on Pearl Harbor, 50th Anniv. (in 1991) A123

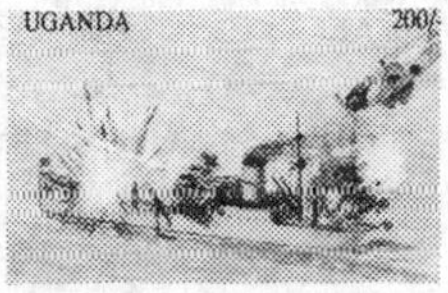

Designs: a, Japanese bombers attack USS Vestal. b, Japanese Zero fighter. c, Zeros over burning USS Arizona. d, Battleship Row, USS Nevada under way. e, Japanese Val dive bomber. f, US Dauntless dive bomber attacking Hiryu. g, Japanese planes over Midway Island. h, US Buffalo fighter plane. i, US Wildcat fighters over carrier. j, USS Yorktown and Hammann torpedoed by Japanese submarine.

1992, Jan. 6 *Perf. 14½x15*

975 A123 200sh Sheet of 10, #a.-j. 5.80 5.80

Battle of Midway, 50th anniv. (#975f-975j). Inscription for No. 975i incorrectly describes fighters as Hellcats.

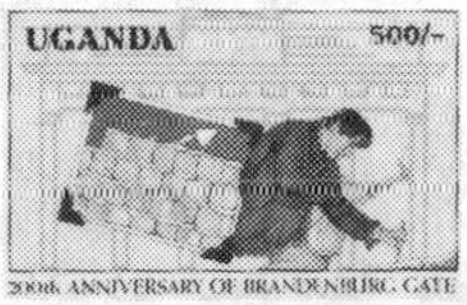

Anniversaries and Events — A124

Designs: 400sh, Glider No. 8. 500sh, Man breaking pieces from Berlin Wall. 700sh, Portrait of Mozart and scene from "The Magic Flute." 1200sh, Electric locomotive.

1992, Jan. 6 **Litho.** *Perf. 14*

976 A124 400sh multicolored 2.00 2.00
977 A124 500sh multicolored 2.50 2.50
978 A124 700sh multicolored 3.50 3.50
Nos. 976-978 (3) 8.00 8.00

Souvenir Sheet

979 A124 1200sh multicolored 6.00 6.00

Otto Lillienthal, hang glider, cent. (in 1991) (#976). Brandenburg Gate, Bicent. (#977), Wolfgang Amadeus Mozart, death bicent. (#978), Trans-Siberian Railway, cent. (#979).

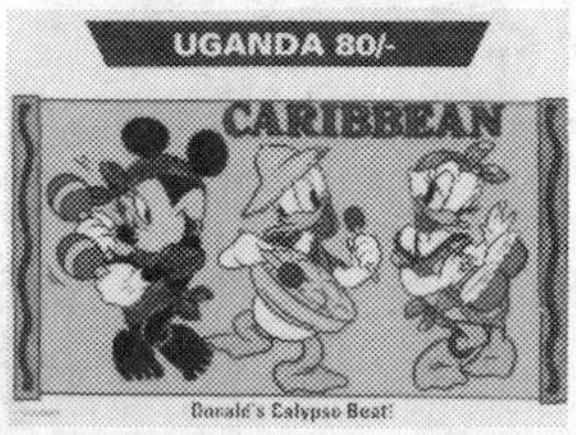

Walt Disney Characters on World Tour — A125

Designs: 20sh, Safari surprise in Africa. 50sh, Pluto's tail of India. 80sh, Donald's calypso beat in Caribbean. 200sh, Goofy pulling rickshaw in China. 500sh, Minnie, Mickey on camel in Egypt. 800sh, Wrestling, Japanese style. 1000sh, Goofy bullfighting in Spain. 1500sh, Mickey scoring in soccer game. No. 988, Daisy singing opera in Germany, vert. No. 989, Mickey and Pluto as Cossack dancers in Moscow, vert.

1992, Feb. *Perf. 13*

980 A125 20sh multicolored .15 .15
981 A125 50sh multicolored .15 .15
982 A125 80sh multicolored .20 .20
983 A125 200sh multicolored .52 .52
984 A125 500sh multicolored 1.25 1.25
985 A125 800sh multicolored 2.00 2.00
986 A125 1000sh multicolored 2.50 2.50
987 A125 1500sh multicolored 3.75 3.75
Nos. 980-987 (8) 10.52 10.52

Souvenir Sheets

988 A125 2000sh multicolored 5.00 5.00
989 A125 2000sh multicolored 5.75 5.75

Queen Elizabeth II's Accession to the Throne, 40th Anniv.

Common Design Type

1992, Feb. 6 **Litho.** *Perf. 14*

990 CD348 100sh multicolored .50 .50
991 CD348 200sh multicolored 1.00 1.00
992 CD348 500sh multicolored 2.50 2.50
993 CD348 1000sh multicolored 5.00 5.00
Nos. 990-993 (4) 9.00 9.00

Souvenir Sheets

994 CD348 1800sh Queen, waterfalls 9.00 9.00
995 CD348 1800sh Queen, dam 9.00 9.00

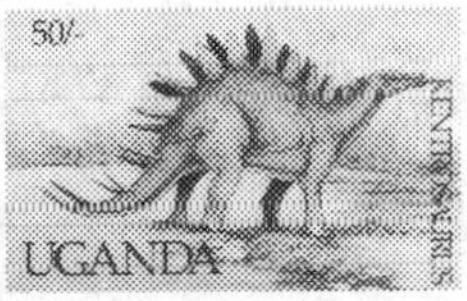

Dinosaurs A126

1992, Apr. 8 **Litho.** *Perf. 14*

996 A126 50sh Kentrosaurus .15 .15
997 A126 200sh Iguanodon .40 .40
998 A126 250sh Hypsilophodon .70 .70
999 A126 300sh Brachiosaurus .60 .60
1000 A126 400sh Peloneustes 1.15 1.15
1001 A126 500sh Pteranodon 1.00 1.00
1002 A126 800sh Tetra- lophodon 1.60 1.60
1003 A126 1000sh Megalosaurus 2.85 2.85
Nos. 996-1003 (8) 8.45 8.45

Souvenir Sheets

1004 A126 2000sh like #1003 5.75 5.75
1005 A126 2000sh like #998 4.00 4.00

Nos. 1004-1005 printed in continuous design.

While Nos. 997, 999, 1001-1002, 1005 have the same release date as Nos. 996, 998, 1000, 1003-1004, their value in relation to the dollar was lower when they were released.

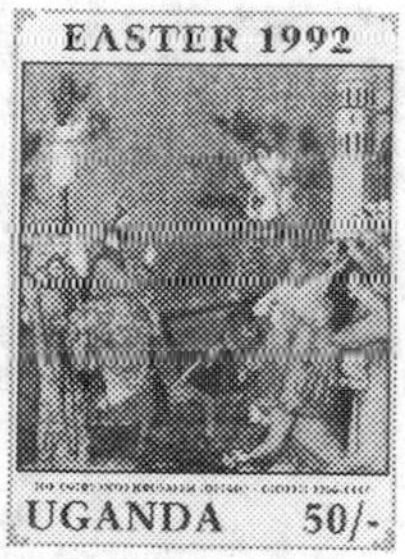

Easter — A127

Paintings: 50sh, The Entry into Jerusalem (detail), by Giotto. 100sh, Pilate and the Watch from psalter of Robert de Lisle. 200sh, The Kiss of Judas (detail), by Giotto. 250sh, Christ Washing the Feet of the Disciples, illumination from Life of Christ. 300sh, Christ Seized in the Garden from Melissande Psalter. 500sh, Doubting Thomas, illumination from Life of Christ. 1000sh, The Marys at the Tomb (detail), artist unknown. 2000sh, The Ascension, from 14th century Florentine illuminated manuscript.

Limoge enamels: No. 1014, Agony at Gethsemane. No. 1015, The Piercing of Christ's Side.

1992 **Litho.** *Perf. 13½x14*

1006 A127 50sh multi .15 .15
1007 A127 100sh multi .28 .28
1008 A127 200sh multi .58 .58
1009 A127 250sh multi .70 .70
1010 A127 300sh multi .85 .85
1011 A127 500sh multi 1.40 1.40
1012 A127 1000sh multi 2.85 2.85
1013 A127 2000sh multi 5.75 5.75
Nos. 1006-1013 (8) 12.56 12.56

Souvenir Sheets

1014 A127 2500sh multi 7.10 7.10
1015 A127 2500sh multi 7.10 7.10

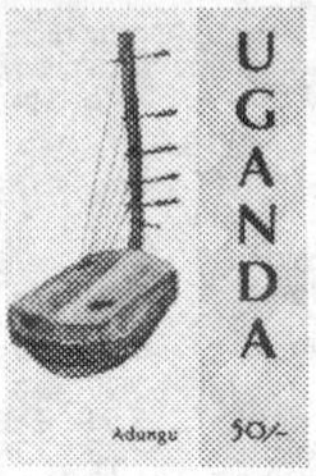

Musical Instruments — A128

1992, July 20 **Litho.** ***Perf. 14***

1016	A128	50sh	Adungu	.15	.15
1017	A128	100sh	Endingidi	.28	.28
1018	A128	200sh	Akogo	.58	.58
1019	A128	250sh	Nanga	.70	.70
1020	A128	300sh	Engoma	.85	.85
1021	A128	400sh	Amakondere	1.15	1.15
1022	A128	500sh	Akakyenkye	1.40	1.40
1023	A128	1000sh	Ennanga	2.85	2.85
			Nos. 1016-1023 (8)	7.96	7.96

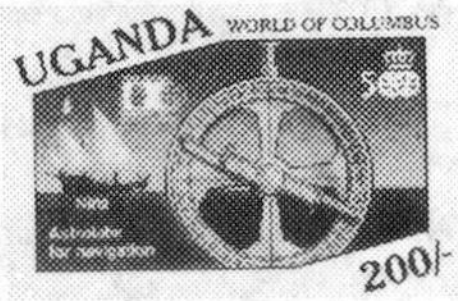

Discovery of America, 500th Anniv. A129

Designs: 50sh, World map, 1486. 100sh, Map of Africa, 1508. 150sh, New World, 1500. 200sh, Nina, astrolabe. 600sh, Quadrant, Pinta. 800sh, Hour glass. 900sh, 15th century compass. 2000sh, World map, 1492. No. 1032, 1490 Map by Henricus Martellus, 1490, vert. No. 1033, Sections of 1492 globe.

1992, July 24 **Litho.** ***Perf. 14***

1024	A129	50sh	multicolored	.15	.15
1025	A129	100sh	multicolored	.15	.15
1026	A129	150sh	multicolored	.15	.15
1027	A129	200sh	multicolored	.58	.58
1028	A129	600sh	multicolored	1.75	1.75
1029	A129	800sh	multicolored	2.30	2.30
1030	A129	900sh	multicolored	2.60	2.60
1031	A129	2000sh	multicolored	2.00	2.00
			Nos. 1024-1031 (8)	9.68	9.68

Souvenir Sheets

1032	A129	2500sh	multicolored	7.25	7.25
1033	A129	2500sh	multicolored	5.00	5.00

World Columbian Stamp Expo '92, Chicago.

While Nos. 1024-1026, 1031 and 1033 have the same issue date as Nos. 1027-1030 and 1032, their value in relation to the dollar was lower when they were released.

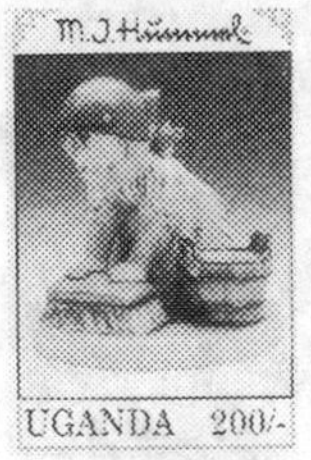

Hummel Figurines — A130

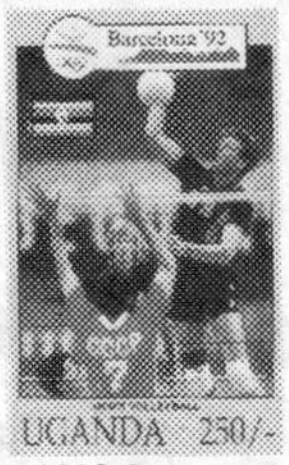

1992 Summer Olympics, Barcelona — A131

Designs: No. 1042a, like #1034. b, like #1035. c, like #1036. d, like #1037.

No. 1043a, like #1039. b, like #1038. c, like #1040. d, like #1041.

1992, Aug. 28 **Litho.** ***Perf. 14***

1034	A130	50sh	Little Laundry Girl	.15	.15
1035	A130	200sh	Scrub Girl	.58	.58
1036	A130	250sh	Sweeper Girl	.70	.70
1037	A130	300sh	Little Mother	.85	.85
1038	A130	600sh	Little Mountaineer	1.20	1.20
1039	A130	900sh	Little Knitter	1.80	1.80
1040	A130	1000sh	Little Cowboy	2.00	2.00
1041	A130	1500sh	Little Astronomer	4.30	4.30
			Nos. 1034-1041 (8)	11.58	11.58

Souvenir Sheets of 4

1042	A130	500sh	#a.-d.	5.70	5.70
1043	A130	500sh	#a.-d.	4.00	4.00

While Nos. 1034, 1038-1040, 1043 have the same issue date as Nos. 1035-1037, 1041-1042, their value in relation to the dollar was lower when they were released.

1992 **Litho.** ***Perf. 14***

1044	A131	50sh	Javelin	.15	.15
1045	A131	100sh	High jump, horiz.	.20	.20
1046	A131	200sh	Pentathlon (Fencing)	.40	.40
1047	A131	250sh	Volleyball	.50	.50
1048	A131	300sh	Women's platform diving	.60	.60
1049	A131	500sh	Team cycling	1.00	1.00
1050	A131	1000sh	Tennis	2.00	2.00
1051	A131	2000sh	Boxing, horiz.	4.00	4.00
			Nos. 1044-1051 (8)	8.85	8.85

Souvenir Sheets

1052	A131	2500sh	Baseball	5.00	5.00
1053	A131	2500sh	Basketball	5.00	5.00

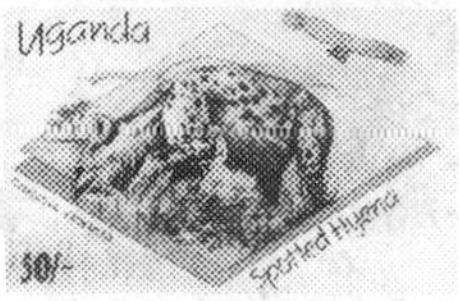

Wild Animals A132

1992, Sept. 25 **Litho.** ***Perf. 14***

1054	A132	50sh	Spotted hyena	.15	.15
1055	A132	100sh	Impala	.20	.20
1056	A132	200sh	Giant forest hog	.40	.40
1057	A132	250sh	Pangolin	.50	.50
1058	A132	300sh	Golden monkey	.60	.60
1059	A132	800sh	Serval	1.60	1.60
1060	A132	1000sh	Bush genet	2.00	2.00
1061	A132	3000sh	Defassa waterbuck	6.00	6.00
			Nos. 1054-1061 (8)	11.45	11.45

Souvenir Sheets

1062	A132	2500sh	Mountain gorilla	5.00	5.00
1063	A132	2500sh	Hippopotamus	5.00	5.00

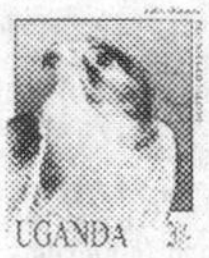

Birds — A133

Designs: 20sh, Red necked falcon. 30sh, Yellow-billed hornbill. 50sh, Purple heron. 100sh, Regal sunbird. 150sh, White-brown robin chat. 200sh, Shining-blue kingfisher. 250sh, Great blue turaco. 300sh, Emerald cuckoo. 500sh, Abyssinian roller. 800sh, Crowned crane. 1000sh, Doherty's bush shrike. 2000sh, Splendid glossy starling. 3000sh, Little bee eater. 4000sh, Red-headed lovebird.

1992, Aug. **Litho.** ***Perf. 15x14***

1064	A133	20sh	multi	.15	.15
1065	A133	30sh	multi	.15	.15
1066	A133	50sh	multi	.15	.15
1067	A133	100sh	multi	.20	.20
1068	A133	150sh	multi	.30	.30
1069	A133	200sh	multi	.40	.40
1070	A133	250sh	multi	.50	.50
1071	A133	300sh	multi	.60	.60
1072	A133	500sh	multi	1.00	1.00
1073	A133	800sh	multi	1.60	1.60
1074	A133	1000sh	multi	2.00	2.00
1075	A133	2000sh	multi	4.00	4.00
1076	A133	3000sh	multi	6.00	6.00
1076A	A133	4000sh	multicolored	8.00	8.00
			Nos. 1064-1076A (14)	25.05	25.05

Issued: 3000sh, Oct.; others, Aug.?

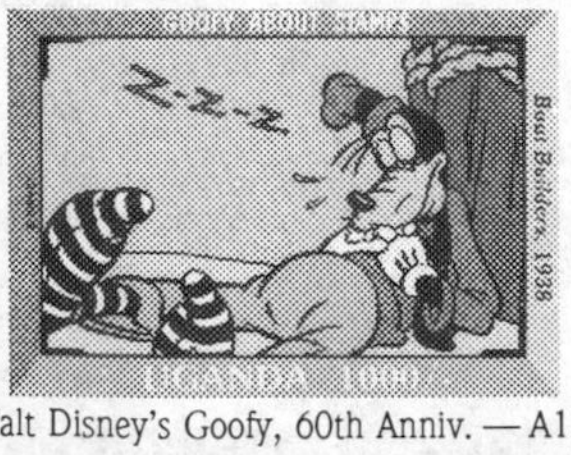

Walt Disney's Goofy, 60th Anniv. — A134

Scenes from Disney animated films: 50sh, Hawaiian Holiday, 1937, vert. 100sh, The Nifty Nineties, 1941, vert. 200sh, Mickey's Fire Brigade, 1935, vert. 250sh, The Art of Skiing, 1941. 300sh, Mickey's Amateurs, 1937. 1000sh, Boat Builders, 1938. 1500sh, The Olympic Champ, 1942, vert. 2000sh, The Olympic Champ, 1942, vert. No. 1085, Goofy and Wilbur, 1939. No. 1086, Goofy's family tree, vert.

Perf. 13¹/₂x14, 14x13¹/₂

1992, Nov. 2 **Litho.**

1077	A134	50sh	multicolored	.15	.15
1078	A134	100sh	multicolored	.20	.20
1079	A134	200sh	multicolored	.40	.40
1080	A134	250sh	multicolored	.50	.50
1081	A134	300sh	multicolored	.60	.60
1082	A134	1000sh	multicolored	2.00	2.00
1083	A134	1500sh	multicolored	3.00	3.00
1084	A134	2000sh	multicolored	4.00	4.00
			Nos. 1077-1084 (8)	10.85	10.85

Souvenir Sheets

1085	A134	3000sh	multicolored	6.00	6.00
1086	A134	3000sh	multicolored	6.00	6.00

Souvenir Sheet

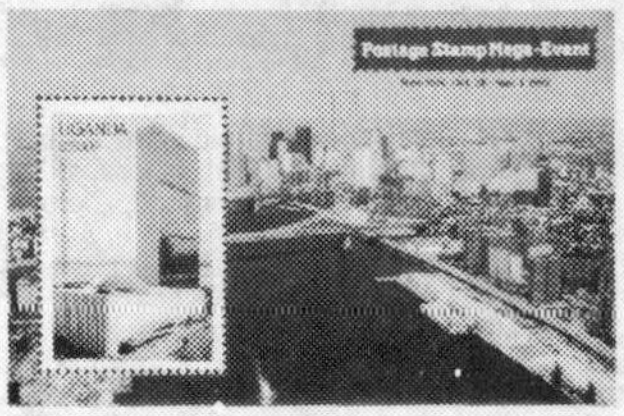

UN Headquarters, New York City — A135

1992, Oct. 28 **Litho.** ***Perf. 14***

1087	A135	2500sh	multicolored	5.00	5.00

Postage Stamp Mega Event '92, New York City.

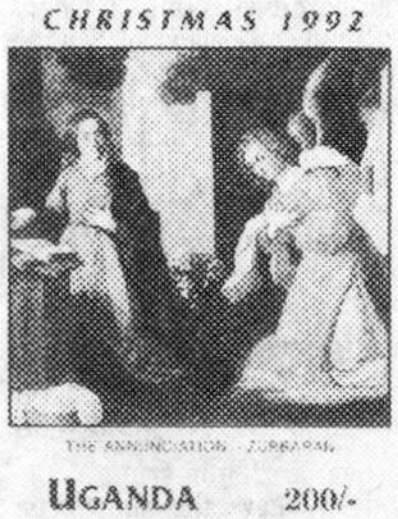

Christmas A136

Details or entire paintings by Zurbaran: 50sh, The Annunciation (angel at left). 200sh, The Annunciation (angel at right). 250sh, The Virgin of the Immaculate Conception. 300sh, The Virgin of the Immaculate Conception (detail). 800sh, 900sh, The Holy Family with Saints Anne, Joachim and John the Baptist (800sh, entire, 900sh, detail). 1000sh, Adoration of the Magi (entire). 2000sh, Adoration of the Magi. No. 1096, The Virgin of the Immaculate Conception (Virgin with arms outstretched). No. 1097, The Virgin of the Immaculate Conception (Virgin with arms folded).

1992, Nov. 16 **Litho.** ***Perf. 13¹/₂x14***

1088	A136	50sh	multicolored	.15	.15
1089	A136	200sh	multicolored	.40	.40
1090	A136	250sh	multicolored	.50	.50
1091	A136	300sh	multicolored	.60	.60
1092	A136	800sh	multicolored	1.60	1.60
1093	A136	900sh	multicolored	1.80	1.80
1094	A136	1000sh	multicolored	2.00	2.00
1095	A136	2000sh	multicolored	4.00	4.00
			Nos. 1088-1095 (8)	11.05	11.05

Souvenir Sheets

1096	A136	2500sh	multicolored	5.00	5.00
1097	A136	2500sh	multicolored	5.00	5.00

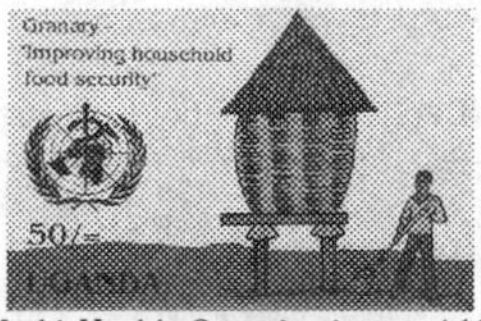

World Health Organization — A137

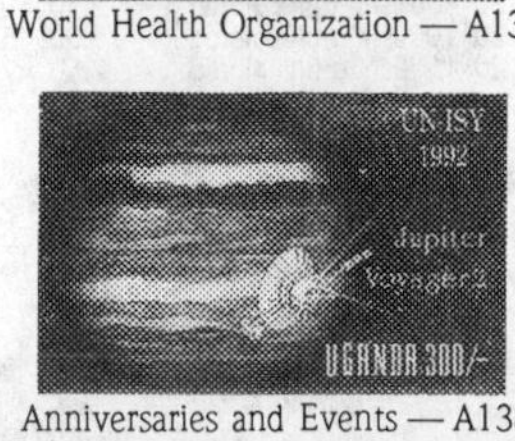

Anniversaries and Events — A138

Designs: 50sh, Improving household food security. 200sh, Continue to breastfeed. 250sh, At four months old, give breast milk and soft food. No. 1101, Drink water from a safe and protected source. No. 1102, Jupiter, Voyager 2. No. 1103, Mother holding baby. No. 1104, Impala. No. 1105, Zebra. No. 1106, Count Ferdinand von Zeppelin, zeppelin. 2000sh, Neptune, Voyager 2. 3000sh, Count Zeppelin, zeppelin, diff. No. 1109, Voyager 2, Jupiter, diff. No. 1110, Wart hog. No. 1111, Doctor examining child, Lions Intl. emblem. No. 1112, Count Zeppelin, balloon.

1992 **Litho.** ***Perf. 14***

1098	A137	50sh	multicolored	.15	.15
1099	A137	200sh	multicolored	.40	.40
1100	A137	250sh	multicolored	.50	.50
1101	A137	300sh	multicolored	.60	.60
1102	A138	300sh	multicolored	.60	.60
1103	A137	800sh	multicolored	1.60	1.60
1104	A138	800sh	multicolored	1.60	1.60
1105	A138	1000sh	multicolored	2.00	2.00
1106	A138	1000sh	multicolored	2.00	2.00
1107	A138	2000sh	multicolored	4.00	4.00
1108	A138	3000sh	multicolored	6.00	6.00
			Nos. 1098-1108 (11)	19.45	19.45

Souvenir Sheets

1109	A138	2500sh	multicolored	5.00	5.00
1110	A138	2500sh	multicolored	5.00	5.00
1111	A138	2500sh	multicolored	5.00	5.00
1112	A138	2500sh	multicolored	5.00	5.00

WHO (#1098-1101, 1103). Intl. Space Year (#1102, 1107, 1109). Earth Summit, Rio de Janeiro (#1104-1105, 1110). Count Zeppelin, 75th anniv. of death (#1106, 1108, 1112). Lions Intl., 75th anniv. (#1111).

Issue dates: Nos. 1098-1103, 1106, 1109, 1112, Nov.; others, Dec.

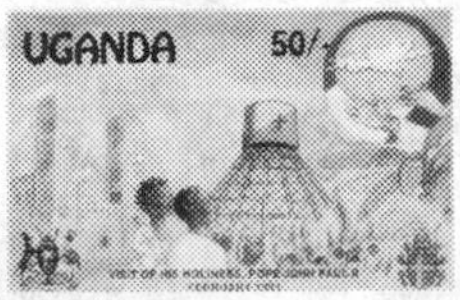

1993 Visit of Pope John Paul II to Uganda A139

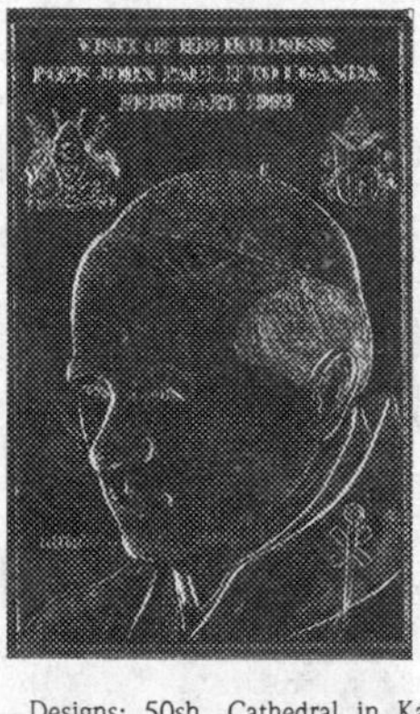

A139a

Designs: 50sh, Cathedral in Kampala, site of Papal Mass, Kampala, hands releasing doves. 200sh, Site of Papal Mass, Pope. 250sh, Ugandan man, Pope. 300sh, Three Ugandan Catholic leaders, Pope. 800sh, Pope waving, Ugandan map and flag. 900sh, Ugandan woman, Pope wearing mitre. 1000sh, Pope, Ugandan flag, site of Papal Mass. 2000sh, Ugandan flag, Pope waving.

No. 1121, Pope at door of airplane, vert. No. 1122, Pope delivering message at podium, vert.

No. 1123, Pope John Paul II. No. 1124, Pope with hands raised.

1993, Feb. 1 **Litho.** ***Perf. 14***

1113	A139	50sh	multicolored	.15	.15
1114	A139	200sh	multicolored	.40	.40
1115	A139	250sh	multicolored	.50	.50
1116	A139	300sh	multicolored	.60	.60
1117	A139	800sh	multicolored	1.60	1.60
1118	A139	900sh	multicolored	1.80	1.80
1119	A139	1000sh	multicolored	2.00	2.00
1120	A139	2000sh	multicolored	4.00	4.00
			Nos. 1113-1120 (8)	11.05	11.05

Souvenir Sheets

1121	A139	3000sh	multicolored	6.00	6.00
1122	A139	3000sh	multicolored	6.00	6.00

Embossed

Embossed ***Perf. 12***

1123	A139a	5000sh	gold

Souvenir Sheet

Imperf

1124	A139a	5000sh	gold

Demand, as well as supply, determine a stamp's market value.

Miniature Sheet

Louvre Museum, Bicent. A140

Details or entire paintings by Rembrandt: No. 1125a, Self-Portrait with an Easel. b, Birds of Paradise. c, The Beef Carcass. d, The Supper at Emmaus. e, Hendrickje Stoffels. f, Titus, Son of the Artist. g, The Holy Family (left). h, The Holy Family (right).
2500sh, Philosopher in Meditation, horiz.

1993, Apr. 5   Litho.   Perf. 12
1125 A140 500sh Sheet of 8, #a.-h.
           + label   8.00 8.00
Souvenir Sheet
Perf. 14¹/₂
1126 A140 2500sh multicolored   4.25 4.25

Dogs A141

1993, May 28   Litho.   Perf. 14
1127 A141   50sh Afghan hound   .15 .15
1128 A141 100sh Newfoundland   .18 .18
1129 A141 200sh Siberian huskies .35 .35
1130 A141 250sh Briard   .45 .45
1131 A141 300sh Saluki   .58 .58
1132 A141 800sh Labrador retriev-
                 er, vert.   1.50 1.50
1133 A141 1000sh Greyhound   1.75 1.75
1134 A141 1500sh Pointer   2.85 2.85
     Nos. 1127-1134 (8)   7.81 7.81
Souvenir Sheets
1135 A141 2500sh Cape hunting dog 4.25 4.25
1136 A141 2500sh Norwegian elk-
                 hound   4.25 4.25

Miniature Sheet

Coronation of Queen Elizabeth II, 40th Anniv. A142

Designs: No. 1137a, 50sh, Official coronation photograph. b, 200sh, Orb, Rod of Equity and Mercy. c, 500sh, Queen during coronation ceremony. d, 1500sh, Queen Elizabeth II, Princess Margaret.
2500sh, The Crown, by Grace Wheatley, 1959.

1993, June 2   Litho.   Perf. 13¹/₂x14
1137 A142 Sheet, 2 each #a.-d.   7.50 7.50
Souvenir Sheet
Perf. 14
1138 A142 2500sh multicolored   4.25 4.25
     No. 1138 contains one 28x42mm stamp.

Miniature Sheet

Taipei '93 — A143

Funerary objects: No. 1139a, Tomb guardian god. b, Civil official. c, Tomb guardian god, diff. d, Civil official, diff. e, Chimera. f, Civil official, diff.
2500sh, Statue of Sacred Mother, Ceremonial Hall, Taiyuan, Shanxi.

1993, Sept. 22   Litho.   Perf. 14x13¹/₂
1139 A143 600sh Sheet of 6, #a.-f. 6.00 6.00
Souvenir Sheet
1140 A143 2500sh multicolored   4.25 4.25

With Bangkok '93 Emblem

Thai sculpture: No. 1141a, Standing Buddha, 13th-15th cent. b, Crowned Buddha, 13th cent. c, Thepanom, 15th cent. d, Crowned Buddha, 12th cent. e, Four-armed Avalokitesvara, 9th cent. f, Lop Buri standing Buddha, 13th cent.
2500sh, Buddha, interior of Wat Mahathat.

1993, Sept. 22
1141 A143 600sh Sheet of 6, #a.-f. 6.00 6.00
Souvenir Sheet
1142 A143 2500sh multicolored   4.25 4.25

With Indopex '93 Emblem
Miniature Sheet

Japanese Wayang Puppets, Indonesia: No. 1143a, Bupati karma, Prince of Wangga. b, Rahwana. c, Sondjeng Sandjata. d, Raden Damar Wulan. e, Klitik figure. f, Hanaman. 2500sh, Candi Mendut in Kedu Plain, Java, Indonesia.

1993, Sept. 22   Litho.   Perf. 13¹/₂x14
1143 A143 600sh Sheet of 6, #a.-f. 6.00 6.00
Souvenir Sheet
1144 A143 2500sh multicolored   4.25 4.25

A144   A145

1993, Oct. 1   Litho.   Perf. 14
1145 A144   50sh Gutierrez, Voeller .15 .15
1146 A144 200sh Tomas Brolin   .35 .35
1147 A144 250sh Gary Lineker   .45 .45
1148 A144 300sh Munoz, Bu-
                 tragueno   .52 .52
1149 A144 800sh Carlos Valder-
                 rama   1.40 1.40
1150 A144 900sh Diego Maradona   1.50 1.50
1151 A144 1000sh Pedro Troglio   1.75 1.75
1152 A144 2000sh Enzo Scifo   3.50 3.50
     Nos. 1145-1152 (8)   9.62 9.62
Souvenir Sheets
1153 A144 2500sh Brazil coaches   4.25 4.25
1154 A144 2500sh De Napoli,
                 Skuhravy, horiz. 4.25 4.25

1994 World Cup Soccer Championships, US.

1993, Nov. 3   Perf. 14
Cathedrals of the World: 50sh, York Minster, England. 100sh, Notre Dame, Paris. 200sh, Little Metropolis, Athens. 250sh, St. Patrick's, New York. 300sh, Ulm, Germany. 800sh, St. Basil's, Moscow. 1000sh, Roskilde, Denmark. 2000sh, Seville, Spain. No. 1163, Namirembe, Uganda. No. 1163A, St. Peter's, Vatican City.

1155 A145   50sh multicolored   .15 .15
1156 A145 100sh multicolored   .18 .18
1157 A145 200sh multicolored   .35 .35
1158 A145 250sh multicolored   .42 .42
1159 A145 300sh multicolored   .52 .52
1160 A145 800sh multicolored   1.40 1.40
1161 A145 1000sh multicolored   1.75 1.75
1162 A145 2000sh multicolored   3.50 3.50
     Nos. 1155-1162 (8)   8.27 8.27

Souvenir Sheets
1163 A145 2500sh multicolored   4.25 4.25
1163A A145 2500sh multicolored   4.25 4.25

Christmas A146

Details or entire woodcut, The Virgin with Carthusian Monks, by Durer: 50sh, 200sh, 300sh, 2000sh.
Details or entire paintings by Raphael: 100sh, 800sh, Sacred Family. 250sh, The Virgin of the Rose. 1000sh, Holy Family (Virgin with Beardless Joseph).
No. 1172, The Virgin with Carthusian Monks, by Durer. No. 1173, Sacred Family, by Raphael.

1993, Nov. 19   Litho.   Perf. 13¹/₂x14
1164-1171 A146 Set of 8   8.50 8.50
Souvenir Sheets
1172-1173 A146 2500sh Set of 2   8.50 8.50

Mickey Mouse, Friends with Dinosaurs — A147

Disney characters depicted with: 50sh, Stegosaurus. 100sh, Pteranodon. 200sh, Mamenchisaurus. 250sh, Rock painting. 300sh, Dino "sails." 500sh, Diplodocus. 800sh, Mamenshisaurus, diff. 1000sh, Triceratops.
No. 1182, Tyrannosaurus rex, Mickey. No. 1183, Minnie, Mickey, mamenchisaurus, diff.

1993, Dec. 22   Litho.   Perf. 14x13¹/₂
1174-1181 A147 Set of 8   5.00 5.00
Souvenir Sheets
1182-1183 A147 2500sh Set of 2   8.00 8.00

Rinderpest Campaign — A148   Picasso (1881-1973) — A149

1993, Dec. 29   Perf. 14
1184 A148 200sh multicolored   .35 .35

1993, Dec. 29
Paintings: 100sh, Woman in Yellow, 1907. 250sh, Gertrude Stein, 1906. 2500sh, Woman by a Window, 1956.
1185-1186 A149 Set of 2   .50 .50
Souvenir Sheet
1187 A149 2500sh multicolored   4.25 4.25

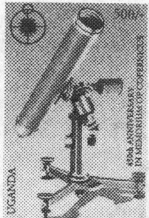 

Copernicus (1473-1543) A150   Polska '93 A151

Telescopes: 500sh, Early. 1000sh, Modern. 2500sh, Copernicus.

1993, Dec. 29
1188-1189 A150 Set of 2   2.50 2.50
Souvenir Sheet
1190 A150 2500sh multicolored   4.25 4.25

1993, Dec. 29
Paintings: 800sh, Creation of the World, by S. I. Witkiewicz par J. Gloqowski, 1921. 1000sh, For the Right to Work, by Andrezej Strumillo, 1952. 2500sh, Temptation of St. Anthony I, by S. I. Witkiewicz (1908-21), horiz.
1191-1192 A151 Set of 2   3.00 3.00
Souvenir Sheet
1193 A151 2500sh multicolored   4.25 4.25

World Meteorological Day — A152   Fruits and Crops — A153

Designs: 50sh, Weather station, horiz. 200sh, Observatory at Meteorological Training School, Entebbe. 250sh, Satellite receiver at National Meteorological Center, horiz. 300sh, Reading temperatures, National Center, Entebbe, horiz. 400sh, Automatic weather station. 800sh, Destruction by hail storm, horiz. 2500sh, Barograph, horiz.

1993, Dec. 29
1194-1199 A152 Set of 6   3.75 3.75
Souvenir Sheet
1200 A152 2500sh multicolored   4.25 4.25

1993, Dec. 29
Designs: 50sh, Passiflora edulis. 100sh, Helianthus annus. 150sh, Musa sapientum. 200sh, Vanilla fragrans. 250sh, Ananas comosus. 300sh, Artocarpus heterophyllus. 500sh, Sorghum boicolor. 800sh, Zea mays.
No. 1209, Sesamum indicum. No. 1210, Coffea canephora.
1201-1208 A153 Set of 8   4.50 4.50
Souvenir Sheets
1209-1210 A153 2000sh Set of 2   8.50 8.50

Automotive Anniversaries — A154

Designs: No. 1211a, 1903 Model A Ford, Henry Ford. b, Model T Snowmobile at 1932 Winter Olympics, Jack Shea. c, Lee Iacocca, Ford Mustang at New York World's Fair. d, Jim Clark, Lotus-Ford winning 1965 Indianapolis 500 race.
No. 1212a, 1994 Mercedes Benz S600 Coupe. b, 1955 Mercedes Benz W196 Grand Prix Champion car, Juan Manuel Fangio. c, 1938 Mercedes Benz W125 road speed record holder, Rudolph Caracciola. d, Carl Benz, 1893 Benz Viktoria.
No. 1213, Carl Benz, vert. No. 1214, Henry Ford, vert.

1994, Jan. 18   Litho.   Perf. 14
1211 A154 700sh Strip of 4, #a.-d. 6.25 6.25

1212 A154 800sh Strip of 4, #a.-d. 7.25 7.25

Souvenir Sheets

1213 A154 2500sh multicolored 4.50 4.50
1214 A154 2500sh multicolored 4.50 4.50

First Ford motor, cent. (#1211, #1214). First Benz four-wheel car, cent. (#1212, #1213).

A155

Hong Kong '94 — A156

Stamps, religious shrines, Repulse Bay: No. 1215, Hong Kong #531. No. 1216, #1163.
Snuff boxes, Qing Dynasty: No. 1217a, Glass painted enamel with pavilion. b, Porcelain with floral design. c, Porcelain with quail design. d, Porcelain with openwork design. e, Agate with pair of dogs. f, Agate with man on donkey.

1994, Feb. 18 Litho. Perf. 14
1215 A155 500sh multicolored .90 .90
1216 A155 500sh multicolored .90 .90
 a. Pair, #1215-1216 1.75 1.75

Miniature Sheet

1217 A155 200sh Sheet of 6, #a.-f. 2.25 2.25

Nos. 1215-1216 issued in sheets of 5 pairs. No. 1216a is continuous design.
New Year 1994 (Year of the Dog) (#1217e).

Miniature Sheet

1994 World Cup Soccer Championships, US — A157

Designs: No. 1218a, Georges Grun, Belgium. b, Oscar Ruggeri, Argentina. c, Frank Rijkaard, Holland. d, Magid "Tyson" Musisi, Uganda. e, Donald Keeman, Holland. f, Igor Shallmov, Russia.
No. 1219, RFK Stadium, Washington DC. No. 1220, Ruud Gullit, Holland.

1994, June 27 Litho. Perf. 14
1218 A157 500sh Sheet of 6, #a.-f. 5.50 5.50

Souvenir Sheets

1219-1220 A157 2500sh each 4.50 4.50

Heifer Project Intl., 50th Anniv. A158

1994, June 29 Litho. Perf. 14
1221 A158 100sh multicolored .20 .20

Moths — A159   Native Crafts — A160

Designs: 100sh, Lobobunaea goodii. 200sh, Bunaeopsis hersilia. 300sh, Rufoglanis rosea. 350sh, Acherontia atropos. 400sh, Rohaniella pygmaea. 450sh, Euchloron megaera. 500sh, Epiphora rectifascia. 1000sh, Polyphychus coryndoni.
Lobobunaea goodii: No. 1230, Wings down. No. 1231, Wings extended.

1994, July 13
1222-1229 A159 Set of 8 6.75 6.75

Souvenir Sheets

1230-1231 A159 2500sh each 5.00 5.00

1994, July 18

Designs: 100sh, Wood stool. 200sh, Wood & banana fiber chair. 250sh, Raffia & palm leaves basket. 300sh, Wool tapestry showing tree planting. 450sh, Wool tapestry showing hair grooming. 500sh, Wood sculpture, drummer. 800sh, Decorated gourds. 1000sh, Lady's bag made from bark cloth.
No. 1240, Raffia baskets. No. 1241, Papyrus hats.

1232-1239 A160 Set of 8 7.00 7.00

Souvenir Sheets

1240-1241 A160 2500sh each 5.00 5.00

Cats — A161   ILO, 75th Anniv. — A162

Cat, historic landmark: 50sh, Turkish angora, Blue Mosque, Turkey, horiz. 100sh, Japanese bobtail, Mt. Fuji, Japan, horiz. 200sh, Norwegian forest cat, windmill, Holland, horiz. 300sh, Egyptian mau, pyramids, Egypt. 450sh, Rex, Stonehenge, England. 500sh, Chartreux, Eiffel Tower, France, horiz. 1000sh, Burmese, Shwe Dagon Pagoda, Burma. 1500sh, Maine coon, Pemaquid Point Lighthouse, Maine.
No. 1250, Russian blue, horiz. No. 1251, Manx, horiz.

1994, July 22
1242-1249 A161 Set of 8 8.25 8.25

Souvenir Sheets

1250-1251 A161 2500sh each 5.00 5.00

1994, July 29
1252 A162 350sh multicolored .70 .70

PHILAKOREA '94 — A163

Designs: 100sh, Eight story Sari pagoda, Paekyangsa. 350sh, Ch'omsongdae (Natl. treasure). 1000sh, Pulguksa Temple exterior.
2500sh, Bronze mural, Pagoda Park, Seoul.

1994, Aug. 8
1253-1255 A163 Set of 3 3.00 3.00

Souvenir Sheet

1256 A163 2500sh multicolored 5.00 5.00

Intl. Year of the Family A164

1994, Aug. 11
1257 A164 100sh multicolored .20 .20

D-Day, 50th Anniv. A165

Designs: 300sh, Mulberry Harbor pierhead moves into position. 1000sh, Mulberry Harbor floating bridge lands armor.
2500sh, Ships, Mulberry Harbor.

1994, Aug. 11
1258 A165 300sh multicolored .60 .60
1259 A165 1000sh multicolored 2.00 2.00

Souvenir Sheet

1260 A165 2500sh multicolored 5.00 5.00

A166

Intl. Olympic Committee, Cent. — A167

Designs: 350sh, John Akii-bua, Uganda, 100-meter hurdles, 1972. 900sh, Heike Herkel, Germany, high jump, 1992.
2500sh, Aleksei Urmanov, Russia, figure skating, 1994.

1994, Aug. 11
1261 A166 350sh multicolored .70 .70
1262 A167 900sh multicolored 1.75 1.75

Souvenir Sheet

1263 A166 2500sh multicolored 5.00 5.00

Miniature Sheet of 7

First Manned Moon Landing, 25th Anniv. A168

Project Mercury astronauts: No. 1264a, 50sh, Alan B. Shepard, Jr., Freedom 7. b, 100sh, M. Scott Carpenter, Aurora 7. c, 200sh, Virgil I. Grissom, Liberty Bell 7. d, 300sh, L. Gordon Cooper, Jr., Faith 7. e, 400sh, Walter M. Schirra, Jr., Sigma 7. f, 500sh, Donald K. Slayton, Apollo-Soyuz, 1975. g, John H. Glenn, Jr., Friendship 7.
3000sh, Apollo 11 anniv. emblem.

1994, Aug. 11
1264 A168 #a.-g., + 2 labels 4.25 4.25

Souvenir Sheet

1265 A168 3000sh multicolored 6.00 6.00

Miniature Sheets of 9

Disney's The Lion King — A169a

Designs: No. 1266a, Baby Simba. b, Mufasa, Simba, Sarabi. c, Young Simba, Nala. d, Timon. e, Rafiki. f, Pumbaa. g, Hyenas. h, Scar. i, Zazu.
No. 1267a, Rafiki, Mufasa. b, Rafiki, Mufasa, Sarabi. c, Rafiki, Simba. d, Scar, Zazu. e, Rafiki seeing vision. f, Simba, Scar. g, Simba, Nala. h, Simba trying on mane. i, Simba, Nala, Zazu.
No. 1268a, Scar plots evil plan. b, Mufasa rescues Simba. c, Destroying Mufasa. d, Simba escaping hyenas. e, Timon, Pumbaa, Simba. f, Simba, Timon, Pumbaa sing Hakuna Matata. g, Rafiki. h, Simba, Nala. i, Simba seeing reflection.
No. 1269, Simba, Timon. No. 1270, Characters of the Lion King, vert. No. 1271, Simba's colorful animal kingdon.
No. 1271A, Mufasa, Simba. No. 1271B, Mufasa, Simba on back, standing on rock.
Illustration A169a reduced.

Perf. 14x13¹/₂, 13¹/₂x14

1994, Sept. 30
1266 A169 100sh #a.-i. 1.75 1.75
1267 A169 200sh #a.-i. 3.75 3.75
1268 A169 250sh #a.-i. 4.50 4.50
 Nos. 1266-1268 (3) 10.00 10.00

Souvenir Sheets

1269-1271 A169 2500sh each 5.00 5.00

Litho. & Embossed
Perf. 11¹/₂

1271A A169a 5000sh gold
1271B A169a 5000sh gold

Miniature Sheets of 7 or 8

Sierra Club, Cent. — A170

Various animals: No. 1272, horiz, a, 200sh, Cheetahs. b, 250sh, Cheetah kittens. c-d, 300sh, 500sh, African wild dog. e, 600sh, Grevy's zebra. f, 800sh, Chimpanzee. g, 1000sh, Grevy's zebra.
No. 1273a-1273b, 100sh, 200sh, Chimpanzee. c, 250sh, African wild dog. d, 300sh, Cheetah. e-f, 500sh, 600sh, Gelada baboon. g, 800sh, Grevy's zebra. h, 1000sh, Gelada baboon.

1994, Nov. 9
1272 A170 #a.-g. + label 8.00 8.00
1273 A170 #a.-h. 8.25 8.25

ICAO, 50th Anniv. A171

Designs: 100sh, Entebbe Intl. Airport terminal building. 250sh, Entebbe control tower.

1994, Nov. 14 Litho. Perf. 14
1274 A171 100sh multicolored .20 .20
1275 A171 250sh multicolored .55 .55

Environmental Protection — A172

Designs: 100sh, Stop poaching. 250sh, Waste disposals. 350sh, Overfishing is a threat. 500sh, Deforestation.

1994, Nov. 15
1276-1279 A172 Set of 4 2.50 2.50

Christmas
A173

Paintings: 100sh, Adoration of the Christ Child, by Fillipino Lippi. 200sh, The Holy Family Rests on the Flight into Egypt, by Annibale Carracci. 300sh, Madonna with Christ Child ant St. John, by Piero di Cosimo. 350sh, The Conestabile Madonna, by Raphael. 450sh, Madonna and Child with Angels, after Antonio Rossellino. 500sh, Madonna and Child with St. John, by Raphael. 900sh, Madonna and Child, by Luca Signorelli. 1000sh, Madonna with the Child Jesus, St. John and an Angel, in style of Pier Francesco Fiorentino.
No. 1288, The Madonna of the Magnificat, by Sandro Botticelli. No. 1289, Adoration of the Magi, by Fra Angelico & Filippo Lippi.

1994, Dec. 5   Litho.   Perf. 13½x14
1280-1287 A173 Set of 8   8.50 8.50
Souvenir Sheets
1288-1289 A173 2500sh each   5.50 5.50

Tintoretto
(1518-94)
A174

Details or entire paintings: 100sh, Self-portrait. 300sh, A Philosopher. 400sh, The Creation of the Animals, horiz. 450sh, The Feast of Belshazzar, horiz. 500sh, The Raising of the Brazen Serpent. 1000sh, Elijah Fed by the Angel.
No. 1296, Finding of Moses. No. 1297, Moses Striking Water from a Rock.

1995, Feb. 7   Litho.   Perf. 13½
1290-1295 A174   5.75 5.75
Souvenir Sheets
1296-1297 A174 2000sh each   4.25 4.25

Miniature Sheet of 16

Birds
A175

Designs: a, White-faced tree duck. b, European shoveler. c, Hartlaub's duck. d, Milky eagle-owl. e, Avocet. f, African fish eagle. g, Spectacled weaver. h, Black-headed gonolek. i, Great crested grebe. j, Red-knobbed coot. k, Woodland kingfisher. l, Pintail. m, Squacco heron. n, Purple gallinule. o, African darter. p, African jacana.
No. 1299, Fulvous tree duck. No. 1300, Pygmy goose.

1995, Apr. 24   Litho.   Perf. 14
1298 A175 200sh #a.-p.   7.00 7.00
Souvenir Sheets
1299-1300 A175 2500sh each   5.50 5.50

Nos. 685-688, 906 Surcharged

18th World Scout Jamboree
Mondial, Holland, August 1995

 450/-

1995, June 1   Litho.   Perf. 14
1301 A90 100sh on #688 multi   .22 .22
1302 A90 450sh on 70sh #686   1.00 1.00
1303 A90 800sh on 90sh #687   1.75 1.75
1304 A90 1500sh on 10sh #685   3.25 3.25
  Nos. 1301-1304 (4)   6.22 6.22
Souvenir Sheet
1305 A113 2500sh on 1200sh multi   5.50 5.50

UN, 50th
Anniv. — A176

Designs: 1000sh, Hands releasing butterflies, dragonfly, dove.
No. 1308, Infant's hand holding adult's finger.

1995, July 6   Litho.   Perf. 14
1306 A176 450sh shown   1.25 1.25
1307 A176 1000sh multicolored   2.75 2.75
Souvenir Sheet
1308 A176 2000sh multicolored   4.50 4.50

FAO, 50th
Anniv. — A177

Husking corn: No. 1309a, 350sh, Young woman. b, 500sh, Old woman, girl. c, 1000sh, Woman with baby on back.
2000sh, Boy beside bore well for livestock, irrigation.

1995, July 6
1309 A177 Strip of 3, #a.-c.   4.00 4.00
Souvenir Sheet
1310 A177 2000sh multicolored   4.50 4.50

Miniature Sheets of 6 or 8

A178

End of World
War II, 50th
Anniv.
A179

No. 1311: a, Russian 152mm gun fires into center of Berlin. b, Soviets capture Moltke Bridge. c, Emperor William Memorial Church, now war memorial. d, Brandenburg Gate falls to Russian tanks. e, US B-17's continue to devastate industrial Germany. f, Soviet tanks enter Berlin. g, Hitler's chancellery lies in ruins. h, Reichstag burns.
Flags of countries each forming "V]:" No. 1312a, Australia. b, Great Britain. c, New Zealand. d, US. e, China. f, Canada.
No. 1313, Waving Soviet flag from atop building in Berlin. No. 1314, US flag, combat soldier.

1995, July 6
1311 A178 500sh #a.-h. + label   9.00 9.00
1312 A179 600sh #a.-f. + label   8.00 8.00
Souvenir Sheets
1313 A178 2500sh multicolored   5.50 5.50
1314 A179 2500sh multicolored   5.50 5.50

No. 1313 contains one 56x42mm stamp.

Rotary Intl., 90th
Anniv. — A180

Rotary emblem and: No. 1315, Paul Harris. No. 1316, Natl. flag.

1995, July 6   Litho.   Perf. 14
1315 A180 2000sh multicolored   4.50 4.50
Souvenir Sheet
1316 A180 2000sh multicolored   4.50 4.50

Queen Mother,
95th
Anniv. — A181

No. 1317: a, Drawing. b, Waving. c, Formal portrait. d, Green blue outfit.
2500sh, Pale blue outfit.

1995, July 6   Perf. 13½x14
1317 A181 500sh Block or strip of
  4, #a.-d.   4.50 4.50
Souvenir Sheet
1318 A181 2500sh multicolored   5.50 5.50
No. 1317 was issued in sheets of 8 stamps.

Dinosaurs — A182

Designs: 150sh, Veloceraptor. 200sh, Psittacosaurus. 350sh, Dilophosaurus. 400sh, Kentrosaurus. 500sh, Stegosaurus. 1500sh, Pterodaustro.
No. 1325, vert.: a, Archaeopteryx. b, Quetzalcoatlus. c, Pteranodon (b, d). d, Brachiosa (g, h). e, Tsintaosaur. f, Allosaur (g-h). g, Tyranosaur (f, i-k). h, Apatosaur (l). i, Giant dragonfly. j, Dimorphodon. k, Triceratops (l). l, Compsognathus.
No. 1326, Parasaurolophus. No. 1327, Shunosaurus.

1995, July 15   Perf. 14
1319-1324 A182 Set of 6   6.75 6.75
Miniature Sheet of 12
1325 A182 300sh #a.-l.   8.00 8.00
Souvenir Sheets
1326-1327 A182 2000sh each   4.50 4.50

Reptiles — A183

1995   Litho.   Perf. 14x15
1328 50sh Rough scaled bush
             viper   .15 .15
1329 100sh Pygmy python   .20 .20
1330 150sh Three horned cha-
             meleon   .30 .30
1331 200sh African rock python   .40 .40
1332 350sh Nile monitor   .70 .70
1333 400sh Savannah monitor   .85 .85
1334 450sh Bush viper   .95 .95
1335 500sh Nile crocodile   1.00 1.00

Size: 38x24mm
Perf. 14
1336 700sh Bell's hinged tor-
             toise   1.40 1.40
1337 900sh Rhinoceros viper   1.90 1.90
1338 1000sh Gaboon viper   2.00 2.00
1339 2000sh Spitting cobra   4.00 4.00
1340 3000sh Leopard tortoise   6.25 6.25
1341 4000sh Puff adder   8.25 8.25
1341A 5000sh Common house
             gecko   10.00 10.00
1341B 6000sh Dwarf chamele-
             on   12.00 12.00
1341C 10,000sh Boomslang   20.00 20.00
  Nos. 1328-1341C (17)   70.35 70.35
  Issued: 5000sh, 6000sh, 10,000sh, 11/20/; others, 8/21.

Nsambya
Church
A184

Designs: 450sh, Namilyango College. 500sh, Intl. Cooperative Alliance, cent. 1000sh, UN Volunteers, 25th anniv.

1995, Sept. 7   Litho.   Perf. 14
1342-1345 A184 Set of 4   4.50 4.50
Mill Hill Missionaries in Uganda, cent. (#1342-1343).

Scenic
Landscapes
& Waterfalls
of Uganda
A185

Designs: No. 1346, 50sh, Bwindi Forest. No. 1347, 50sh, Sipi Falls, vert. No. 1348, 100sh, Karamoja. No. 1349, 100sh, Murchison Falls. No. 1350, 450sh, Sunset, Lake Mburo Natl. Park. No. 1351, 450sh, Bujagali Falls. No. 1352, 500sh, Sunset, Gulu District. No. 1353, 500sh, Two Falls, Murchison. No. 1354, 900sh, Kabale District. No. 1355, 900sh, Falls, Rwenzoris, vert. No. 1356, 1000sh, Rwenzori Mountains. No. 1357, 1000sh, Falls, Rwenzoris, diff., vert.

1995, Sept. 14
1346-1357 A185 Set of 12   12.50 12.50

1996 Summer Olympics, Atlanta — A186

Athletes: 50sh, Peter Rono, runner. 350sh, Reiner Klimke, dressage. 450sh, German cycling team. 500sh, Grace Birungi, runner. 900sh, Francis Ogola, track. 1000sh, Nyakana Godfrey, welterweight boxer.
No. 1364, Rolf Dannenberg, discus, vert. No. 1365, Sebastian Coe, runner.

1995, Sept. 21
1358-1363 A186 Set of 6   7.25 7.25
Souvenir Sheets
1364-1365 A186 2500sh each   5.50 5.50

Miniature Sheet of 16

Domestic
Animals
A187

No. 1366: a, Peafowl (e). b, Pouter pigeon. c, Rock dove. d, Rouen duck. e, Guinea fowl. f, Donkey. g, Shetland pony. h, Palomino. i, Pigs. j, Border collie. k, Merino sheep. l, Milch goat. m, Black dutch rabbit. n, Lop rabbit. o, Somali cat (p). p, Asian cat.
No. 1367, Saddle bred horses. No. 1368, Oxen.

1995, Oct. 2
1366 A187 200sh #a.-p. 7.00 7.00

Souvenir Sheets

1367-1368 A187 2500sh each 5.50 5.50

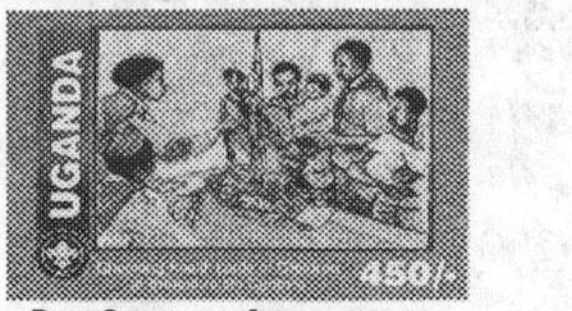
UGANDA
450/-

Boy Scouts at Immunization Centers — A188

Designs: 150sh, Dressing children for weighing, vert. 350sh, Helping mothers carry children, vert. 450sh, Checking health cards. 800sh, Assisting in immunization. 1000sh, Weighing children, vert.

1995, Oct. 18 Litho. *Perf. 14*
1369-1373 A188 Set of 5 6.00 6.00

Miniature Sheets of 12

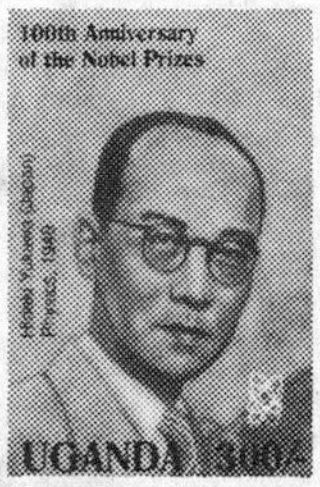
100th Anniversary
of the Nobel Prizes
UGANDA 300/-

Nobel Prize Fund Established, Cent. — A189

Recipients: No. 1374a, Hideki Yukawa, physics, 1949. b, F.W. DeKlerk, peace, 1993. c, Nelson Mandela, peace, 1993. d, Odysseus Elytis, literature, 1979. e, Ferdinand Buisson, peace, 1927. f, Lev Landau, physics, 1962. g, Halldor Laxness, literature, 1955. h, Wole Soyinka, literature, 1986. i, Desmond Tutu, peace, 1984. j, Susumu Tonegawa, physiology or medicine, 1987. k, Louis de Broglie, physics, 1929. l, George Seferis, literature, 1963.

No. 1375: a, Hermann Staudinger, chemistry, 1953. b, Fritz Haber, chemistry, 1918. c, Bert Sakmann, physiology or medicine, 1991. d, Adolf O.R. Windaus, chemistry, 1928. e, Wilhelm Wien, physics, 1911. f, Ernest Hemingway, literature, 1954. g, Richard M. Willstätter, chemistry, 1915. h, Stanley Cohen, physiology or medicine, 1986. i, J. Hans D. Jensen, physics, 1963. j, Otto H. Warburg, physiology or medicine, 1931. k, Heinrich O. Wieland, chemistry, 1927. l, Albrecht Kossel, physiology or medicine, 1910.

No. 1376, Werner Forssmann, physiology or medicine, 1956. No. 1377, Nelly Sachs, literature, 1966.

1995, Oct. 31
1374-1375 A189 300sh #a.-l., each 8.00 8.00

Souvenir Sheets

1376-1377 A189 2000sh each 4.50 4.50

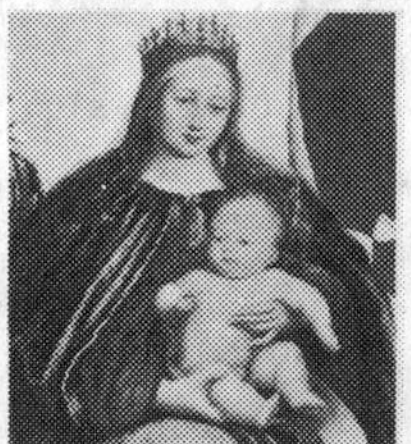
Christmas 1995
Uganda
150/-

Christmas A190

Details or entire paintings of the Madonna and Child, by: 150sh, Hans Holbein the Younger. 350sh, Procaccini. 500sh, Pisanello. 1000sh, Crivelli. 1500sh, Le Nain.

No. 1383, The Holy Family, by Andrea Del Sarto. No. 1384, Madonna and Child, by Bellini.

1995, Nov. 30 Litho. *Perf. 13¹/₂x14*
1378-1382 A190 Set of 5 7.75 7.75

Souvenir Sheets

1383-1384 A190 2500sh each 5.00 5.00

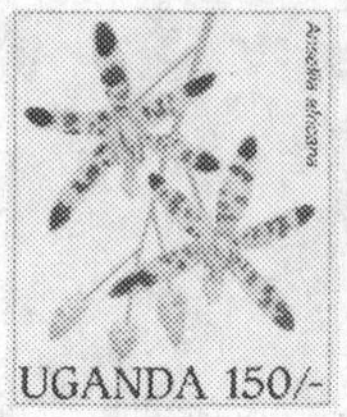
UGANDA 150/-

Orchids — A191

Designs: 150sh, Ansellia africana. 450sh, Satyricum crassicaule. 500sh, Polystachya cultriformis. 800sh, Disa erubescens.

No. 1389: a, Aerangis iuteoalba. b, Satyrium saccculatum. c, Bolusiella maudiae. d, Habenaria attenuata. e, Cyrtorchis arcuata. f, Eulophia angolensis. g, Tridactyle bicaudata. h, Eulophia horsfallii. i, Diaphananthe fragrantissima.

No. 1390, Diaphananthe pulchella. No. 1391, Rangaeris amaniensis.

1995, Dec. 8 *Perf. 14*
1385-1388 A191 Set of 4 3.75 3.75

Miniature Sheet

1389 A191 350sh Sheet of 9, #a.-i. 6.25 6.25

Souvenir Sheets

1390-1391 A191 2500sh each 5.00 5.00

POSTAGE DUE STAMPS

Catalogue values for unused stamps in this section are for Never Hinged items.

Type of Kenya, 1967
Perf. 14x13¹/₂

1967, Jan. 3 Litho. Unwmk.
J1 D1 5c red .15 .15
J2 D1 10c green .15 .15
J3 D1 20c dark blue .25 .25
J4 D1 30c reddish brown .35 .35
J5 D1 40c red lilac .60 .60
J6 D1 1sh orange 1.50 1.50
Nos. J1-J6 (6) 3.00 3.00

1970, Mar. 31 *Perf. 14x15*
J1a D1 5c red .15 .15
J2a D1 10c green .15 .15
J3a D1 20c dark blue .22 .22
J4a D1 30c reddish brown .30 .30
J5a D1 40c red lilac .50 .50
Nos. J1a-J5a (5) 1.32 1.32

1973 *Perf. 15*
J1b D1 5c red .15 .15
J2b D1 10c green .15 .15
J3b D1 20c dark blue .22 .22
J4b D1 30c reddish brown .30 .30
J5b D1 40c red lilac .50 .50
J6b D1 1sh orange 1.25 1.25
Nos. J1b-J6b (6) 2.57 2.57

Nos. J1-J6 Overprinted in Black: "LIBERATED / 1979"

1979, Dec. Litho. *Perf. 14*
J7 D1 5c red .15 .15
J8 D1 10c green .15 .15
J9 D1 20c violet blue .15 .15
J10 D1 30c reddish brown .20 .15
J11 D1 40c red lilac .24 .15
J12 D1 1sh orange .60 .50
Set value 1.25 .85

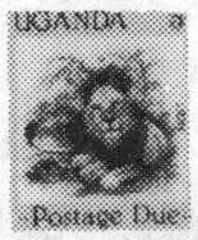
UGANDA
Postage Due

Wildlife — D2

1985, Mar. 11 Litho. *Perf. 15x14*
J13 D2 5sh Lion .15 .15
J14 D2 10sh African buffalo .15 .15
J15 D2 20sh Kob antelope .15 .15
J16 D2 40sh Elephant .16 .16
J17 D2 50sh Zebra .20 .20
J18 D2 100sh Rhinoceros .38 .38
Set value .95 .95

VANUATU

ˌvan-ˌwä-ˈtü

LOCATION — Island group in south Pacific Ocean northeast of New Caledonia
GOVT. — Republic
AREA — 5,700 sq. mi.
POP. — 117,000 (est. 1980)
CAPITAL — Vila

The Anglo-French condominium of New Hebrides (Vol. 1 and Vol. 3) became the independent state of Vanuatu July 30, 1980.

Hebrides franc Vatu (1981)

Catalogue values for all unused stamps in this country are for Never Hinged items.

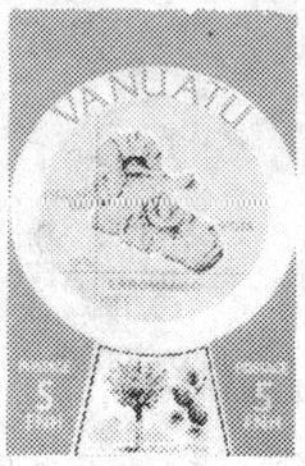
VANUATU
5
5

Erromango Is. and Kaori Tree — A44

Designs: 10fr, Archipelago and man making copra. 15fr, Espiritu Santo Island and cattle. 20fr, Efate Island and Post Office, Vila. 25fr, Malakula Island and headdresses. 30fr, Aoba and Maewo Islands and pig tusks. 35fr, Pentecost Island and land diving. 40fr, Tanna Island and Prophet John Frum's Red Cross. 50fr, Shepherd Island and canoe with sail. 70fr, Banks Island and dancers. 100fr, Ambrym Island and carvings. 200fr, Aneityum Island and decorated baskets. 500fr, Torres Islands and fishing with bow and arrow.

Wmk. 373

1980, July 30 Litho. *Perf. 14*
280 A44 5fr multicolored .15 .15
281 A44 10fr multicolored .15 .15
282 A44 15fr multicolored .18 .18
283 A44 20fr multicolored .25 .25
284 A44 25fr multicolored .32 .32
285 A44 30fr multicolored .40 .40
286 A44 35fr multicolored .45 .45
287 A44 40fr multicolored .50 .50
288 A44 50fr multicolored .65 .65
289 A44 70fr multicolored .90 .90
290 A44 100fr multicolored 1.25 1.25
291 A44 200fr multicolored 2.50 2.50
292 A44 500fr multicolored 6.50 6.50
Nos. 280-292 (13) 14.20 14.20

Inscribed in French

Unwmk.

280a A44 5fr multicolored .15 .15
281a A44 10fr multicolored .15 .15
282a A44 15fr multicolored .18 .18
283a A44 20fr multicolored .25 .25
284a A44 25fr multicolored .32 .32
285a A44 30fr multicolored .40 .40
286a A44 35fr multicolored .45 .45
287a A44 40fr multicolored .50 .50
288a A44 50fr multicolored .65 .65
289a A44 70fr multicolored .90 .90
290a A44 100fr multicolored 1.25 1.25
291a A44 200fr multicolored 2.50 2.50
292a A44 500fr multicolored 6.50 6.50
Nos. 280a-292a (13) 14.20 14.20

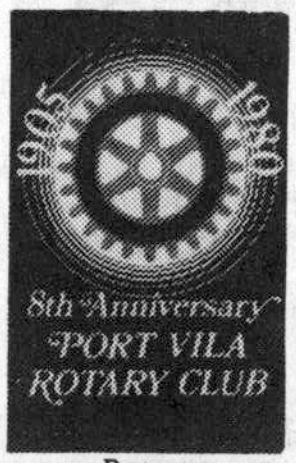
1905
1980
8th Anniversary
PORT VILA
ROTARY CLUB

Rotary Emblem — A52

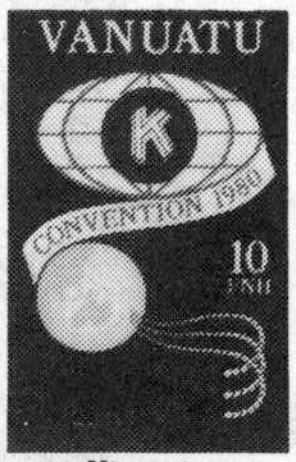
VANUATU
K
CONVENTION 1980
10

Kiwanis Emblem — A53

1980, Sept. 16 Wmk. 373
293 A52 10fr Emblem, horiz. .15 .15
294 A52 40fr shown .65 .65

Inscribed in French

Unwmk.

293a A52 10fr multicolored .20 .20
294a A52 40fr multicolored .85 .85

75th anniv. of Rotary Intl. and 8th anniv. of Port Vila Rotary Club (40fr).

1980, Sept. 16 Wmk. 373
295 A53 10fr shown .16 .16
296 A53 40fr Emblem, horiz. .65 .65

Inscribed in French

Unwmk.

295a A53 10fr multicolored .20 .20
296a A53 40fr multicolored .85 .85

New Zealand District Kiwanis Convention, Port Vila, Sept. 16-18.

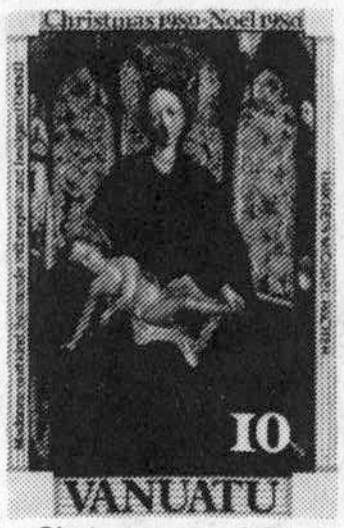
Christmas 1980 - Noel 1980
10
VANUATU

Christmas — A54

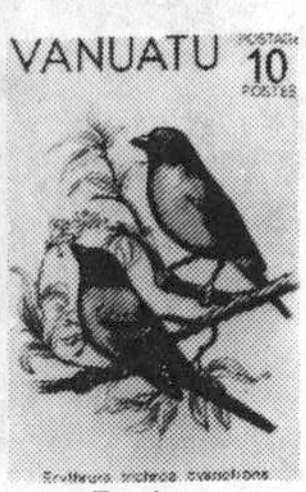
VANUATU
10

Erythrura Trichroa — A55

Paintings: 10fr, Virgin and Child, by Michael Pacher. 15fr, Virgin and Child, by Hans Memling. 30fr, Rest on the Flight to Egypt, by Adriaen van der Werff.

1980, Nov. 12 Wmk. 373
297 A54 10fr multicolored .18 .18
298 A54 15fr multicolored .28 .28
299 A54 30fr multicolored .55 .55
Nos. 297-299 (3) 1.01 1.01

1981, Feb. 18
300 A55 10fr shown .25 .20
301 A55 20fr Chalcophaps indica .45 .40
302 A55 30fr Pachycephala pectoralis .70 .65
303 A55 40fr Ptilinopus tannensis .85 .85
Nos. 300-303 (4) 2.25 2.10

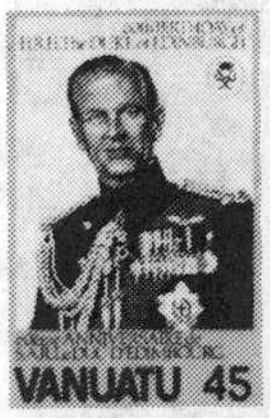
VANUATU 45

Duke of Edinburgh's 60th Birthday — A56

1981, June 10 *Perf. 14x14¹/₂*
304 A56 15v Tribesman, portrait .20 .20
305 A56 25v Portrait .35 .35
306 A56 35v Family .50 .50
307 A56 45v shown .70 .70
Nos. 304-307 (4) 1.75 1.75

Royal Wedding Issue

Common Design Type

1981, July 29
308 CD331 15v Bouquet .26 .26
309 CD331 45v Charles .60 .60
310 CD331 75v Couple .90 .90
Nos. 308-310 (3) 1.76 1.76

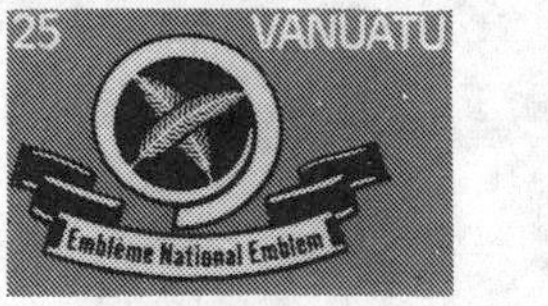
25
VANUATU
Emblème National Emblem

First Anniv. of Independence — A57

1981, July 19
311 A57 15v Map, flag, vert. .24 .24
312 A57 25v Emblem .32 .32
313 A57 45v Anthem .60 .60
314 A57 75v Arms, vert. .90 .90
Nos. 311-314 (4) 2.06 2.06

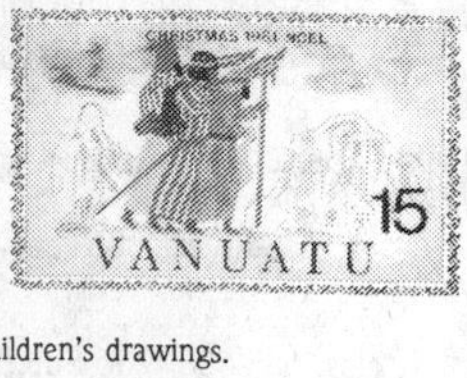
15
VANUATU

Christmas A58

Designs: Children's drawings.

Wmk. 373

1981, Nov. 11 Litho. *Perf. 14*
315 A58 15v Three kings .26 .26
316 A58 25v Girl holding lamb, vert. .40 .40
317 A58 35v Butterfly-angel .55 .55
318 A58 45v Gift bearer, vert. .80 .80
a. Souvenir sheet, #315-318 2.00 2.00
Nos. 315-318 (4) 2.01 2.01

Broadbills — A59   Orchids — A60

1982, Feb. 8   *Perf. 14¹/₂x14*
319 A59 15v shown   .42 .42
320 A59 20v Rainbow lorries .55 .55
321 A59 25v Buff-bellied flycatchers .70 .70
322 A59 45v Fantails   1.25 1.25
    Nos. 319-322 (4)   2.92 2.92

Perf. 14x13¹/₂, 13¹/₂x14
1982, June 15
323 A60 1v Flickengeria comata .15 .15
324 A60 2v Calanthe triplicata .15 .15
325 A60 10v Dendrobium sladei   .26 .26
326 A60 15v Dendrobium moh-
         lianum   .28 .28
327 A60 20v Dendrobium
         macrophyllum   .32 .32
328 A60 25v Dendrobium
         purpureum   .42 .42
329 A60 30v Robiquetia mimus   .52 .52
330 A60 35v Dendrobium moore-
         anum   .60 .60
331 A60 45v Spathoglottis plicata .80 .80
332 A60 50v Dendrobium
         seemannii   .85 .85
333 A60 75v Dendrobium
         conanthum   1.10 1.10
334 A60 100v Dendrobium
         Macranthum   1.65 1.65
335 A60 200v Coelogyne lamellata 3.25 3.25
336 A60 500v Bulbophyllum
         longiscapum   8.75 8.75
    Nos. 323-336 (14)   19.10 19.10

Nos. 330-333, 336 horiz.
For surcharges see Nos. 383, 512, 551-554, 586-589, B1.

Scouting Year A61

Wmk. 373
1982, Sept. 1   Litho.   Perf. 14
337 A61 15v Around campfire .30 .30
338 A61 20v First aid   .35 .35
339 A61 25v Signal tower   .45 .45
340 A61 45v Building raft   .85 .85
341 A61 75v Scout sign   1.25 1.25
    Nos. 337-341 (5)   3.20 3.20

Christmas A62

Designs: Details from Nativity painting. 35v, 45v horiz.

1982, Nov. 16
342 A62 15v multicolored   .28 .28
343 A62 20v multicolored   .40 .40
344 A62 35v multicolored   .60 .60
345 A62 45v multicolored   .80 .80
 a. Souvenir sheet of 4, #342-345 2.25 2.25
    Nos. 342-345 (4)   2.08 2.08

Hypolimnas Octocula A63

1983, Jan. 17   *Perf. 14¹/₂*
346   Pair   .60 .60
 a. A63 15v shown   .30 .30
 b. A63 15v cuploea sylvester .30 .30
347   Pair   .75 .75
 a. A63 20v Polyura sacco   .35 .35
 b. A63 20v Papilio canopus .35 .35

348   Pair   1.00 1.00
 a. A63 25v Parantica pumila .50 .50
 b. A63 25v Luthrodes cleotas .50 .50
    Nos. 346-348 (3)   2.35 2.35

A64

1983, Mar. 14   *Perf. 13¹/₂x14*
349 A64 15v Pres. Sokomanu   .24 .24
350 A64 20v Fisherman   .32 .32
351 A64 25v Herdsman, cattle .35 .35
352 A64 75v Flags, map   1.10 1.10
    Nos. 349-352 (4)   2.01 2.01

Commonwealth Day. 20v, 75v inscribed in French.

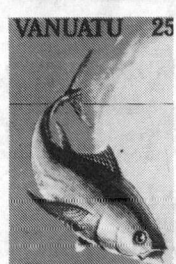

Economic Zone — A65

Designs: a, Thunnus albacares. b, Map. c, Matthew Isld. d, Hunter Isld. e, Epinephelus morrhua, etelis carbunculus. f, Katsuwonus pelamis.

Perf. 14x13¹/₂
1983, May 23   Litho.   Wmk. 373
353   Sheet of 6   3.00 3.00
 a.-f. A65 25v multicolored .48 .48

Manned Flight Bicentenary — A66

Balloons or Airships: 15v, Montgolfiere, 1783. 20v, J.A.C. Charles first hydrogen balloon, 1783. 25v, Blanchard and Jeffries first English Channel crossing, 1785. 35v, H. Giffard's first mechanically powered airship, 1852. 40v, Renard and Krebs' airship, 1884. 45v, Graf Zeppelin's first transworld flight, 1929. 15v, 20v, 25v, vert.

1983, Aug. 4   Litho.   Perf. 14
354 A66 15v multicolored   .30 .30
355 A66 20v multicolored   .35 .35
356 A66 25v multicolored   .45 .45
357 A66 35v multicolored   .60 .60
358 A66 40v multicolored   .70 .70
359 A66 45v multicolored   .85 .85
    Nos. 354-359 (6)   3.25 3.25

For overprint see No. 372.

World Communications Year — A67

1983, Oct. 10   Litho.   Wmk. 373
360 A67 15v Mail transport,
         Bauerfield Airport   .28 .28
361 A67 20v Switchboard operator .35 .35
362 A67 25v Telex operator   .48 .48
363 A67 45v Satellite earth station .90 .90
 a. Souv. sheet of 4, #360-363 + 3 labels 2.50 2.50
    Nos. 361-364 (4)   2.08 2.08

No. 363a issued for WCY and 75th anniv. of New Hebrides stamps.

Local Fungi — A68

1984, Jan. 9   Litho.   Perf. 14
364 A68 15v Cymatoderma elegans,
         vert.   .35 .35
365 A68 25v Lignosus rhinoceros,
         vert.   .60 .60
366 A68 35v Stereum ostrea   .85 .85
367 A68 45v Ganoderma boninenze,
         vert.   1.10 1.10
    Nos. 364-367 (4)   2.90 2.90

Lloyd's List Issue
Common Design Type

1984, Apr. 30   Litho.   Perf. 14¹/₂x14
368 CD335 15v Port Vila   .35 .35
369 CD335 20v Induna   .45 .45
370 CD335 25v Air Vanuatu jet .60 .60
371 CD335 45v Brahman Express 1.10 1.10
    Nos. 368-371 (4)   2.50 2.50

No. 359 Overprinted "UPU CONGRESS / HAMBURG"

1984, June 11   Wmk. 373   Perf. 14
372 A66 45v multicolored   .90 .90

Cattle A69

1984, July 3   Litho.   Perf. 14
373 A69 15v Charolais   .28 .28
374 A69 25v Charolais-Afrikaner .45 .45
375 A69 45v Friesian   .85 .85
376 A69 75v Charolais-Brahman 1.40 1.40
    Nos. 373-376 (4)   2.98 2.98

Ausipex '84 A70

Ships.

1984, Sept. 7
377 A70 25v Makambo   .45 .45
378 A70 45v Rockton   .80 .80
379 A70 100v Waroonga   1.75 1.75
 a. Souvenir sheet of 3, #377-379 3.00 3.00
    Nos. 377-379 (3)   3.00 3.00

Christmas A71

1984, Nov. 19   Litho.   Wmk. 373
380 A71 25v Father Christmas, child
         in hospital   .50 .50
381 A71 45v Nativity   .90 .90
382 A71 75v Father Christmas, chil-
         dren   1.50 1.50
    Nos. 380-382 (3)   2.90 2.90

No. 323 Surcharged with 2 Black Bars
1985, Jan. 22   Litho.   Perf. 14x13¹/₂
383 A60 5v on 1v multi   .15 .15

Ceremonial Dance Costumes — A71a   Audubon Birth Bicent. — A72

1985, Jan. 22   *Perf. 14*
384 A71a 20v Ambrym Island   .38 .38
385 A71a 25v Pentecost Island .48 .48
386 A71a 45v Women's Grade Cere-
         mony, S.W. Malakula .85 .85
387 A71a 75v Same, men's   1.50 1.50
    Nos. 384-387 (4)   3.21 3.21

Wmk. 373
1985, Mar. 26   Litho.   Perf. 14
Peregrine falcons.
388 A72 20v multicolored   .48 .48
389 A72 35v multicolored   .85 .85
390 A72 45v multicolored   1.10 1.10
391 A72 100v multicolored   2.50 2.50
    Nos. 388-391 (4)   4.93 4.93

Queen Mother 85th Birthday
Common Design Type
Perf. 14¹/₂x14
1985, June 7   **Wmk. 384**
392 CD336 5v Wedding photo   .15 .15
393 CD336 20v 80th birthday cele-
         bration   .40 .40
394 CD336 35v At Ancona, Italy .70 .70
395 CD336 55v Holding Prince
         Henry   1.10 1.10
    Nos. 392-395 (4)   2.35 2.35

Souvenir Sheet
396 CD336 100v At Covent Garden
         Opera   2.00 2.00

EXPO '85, Tsukuba A73

Designs: 35v, Mala naval patrol boat. 45v, Japanese fishing fleet, Port Vila. 55v, Mobile Force Band. 100v, Prime Minister Walter H. Lini.

1985, July 26   Wmk. 373   Perf. 14
397 A73 35v multicolored   .55 .55
398 A73 45v multicolored   .80 .80
399 A73 55v multicolored   1.00 1.00
400 A73 100v multicolored   1.90 1.90
 a. Souvenir sheet of 4, #397-400 4.25 4.25
    Nos. 397-400 (4)   4.25 4.25

Natl. independence, 5th anniv.

Intl. Youth Year — A74

Children's drawings.

1985, Sept. 16   Wmk. 373   Perf. 14
401 A74 20v Alain Lagaliu   .40 .40
402 A74 30v Peter Obed   .60 .60
403 A74 50v Mary Estelle   1.00 1.00
404 A74 100v Abel M rani   2.00 2.00
    Nos. 401-404 (4)   4.00 4.00

Natl. and UN Flags, Map A75

1985, Sept. 24   Litho.   Perf. 14
405 A75 45v multicolored   .90 .90

Admission of Vanuatu to UN, 4th anniv.

Sea Slugs — A76   Scuba Diving — A77

1985, Nov. 11 Wmk. 373 *Perf. 14½*

406 A76 20v Chromodoris elisa bethina .35 .35
407 A76 35v Halgerda aurantiomaculata .65 .65
408 A76 55v Chromodoris kuniei 1.00 1.00
409 A76 100v Notodoris minor 1.75 1.75
Nos. 406-409 (4) 3.75 3.75

Nos. 407-408 horiz. See Nos. 497-500.

1986, Jan. 22 Wmk. 384 *Perf. 14*

410 A77 30v shown .60 .60
411 A77 35v Volcanic eruption .70 .70
412 A77 55v Land diving 1.10 1.10
413 A77 100v Wind surfing 2.00 2.00
Nos. 410-413 (4) 4.40 4.40

See No. 479.

Queen Elizabeth II 60th Birthday Common Design Type

Designs: 20v, With Prince Charles and Princess Anne, 1951. 35v, At christening of Prince William, the Music Room, Buckingham Palace, 1982. 45v, State visit, 1985. 55v, State visit to Mexico, 1974. 100v, Visiting Crown Agents' offices, 1983.

1986, Apr. 21 Litho. *Perf. 14x14½*

414 CD337 20v scar, blk & sil .38 .38
415 CD337 35v ultra & multi .65 .65
416 CD337 45v green & multi .80 .80
417 CD337 55v violet & multi 1.00 1.00
418 CD337 100v multicolored 1.90 1.90
Nos. 414-418 (5) 4.73 4.73

For overprints & surcharges see #465-469, B2-B6.

AMERIPEX '86 — A78

1986, May 19 Wmk. 373 *Perf. 14*

419 A78 45v SS President Coolidge .80 .80
420 A78 55v As troop ship, 1942 1.00 1.00
421 A78 135v Site of sinking, 1942 2.50 2.50
a. Souvenir sheet of 3, #419-421 4.50 4.50
Nos. 419-421 (3) 4.30 4.30

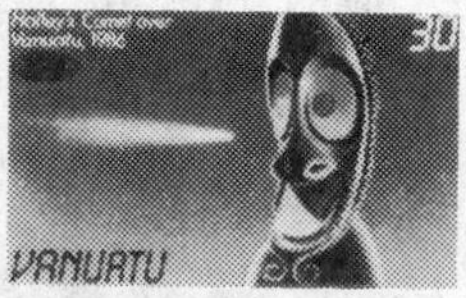

Halley's Comet A79

1986, June 23 Wmk. 384 *Perf. 14½*

422 A79 30v Comet, deity statue .60 .60
423 A79 45v Family sighting comet .90 .90
424 A79 55v Comet over SW Pacific 1.10 1.10
425 A79 100v Edmond Halley, manuscript 2.00 2.00
Nos. 422-425 (4) 4.60 4.60

Coral A80

1986, Oct. 27 Wmk. 373 *Perf. 14*

426 A80 20v Daisy .40 .40
427 A80 45v Organ pipe .90 .90
428 A80 55v Sea fan 1.10 1.10
429 A80 135v Soft 2.75 2.75
Nos. 426-429 (4) 5.15 5.15

Intl. Peace Year — A81

1986, Nov. 3 Litho. *Perf. 14*

430 A81 30v Children of the world .60 .60
431 A81 45v Child praying .90 .90
432 A81 55v UN building, negotiators 1.10 1.10
433 A81 135v Peoples working in harmony 2.70 2.70
Nos. 430-433 (4) 5.30 5.30

Automotives A82

1987, Jan. 22

434 A82 20v Datsun 240Z, 1969 .38 .38
435 A82 45v Model A Ford, 1927 .85 .85
436 A82 55v Unic, 1924-25 .95 .95
437 A82 135v Citroen DS19, 1975 2.25 2.25
Nos. 434-437 (4) 4.43 4.43

IRHO Coconut Research Station, 25th Anniv. A83

1987, May 13 *Perf. 14½x14*

438 A83 35v Nursery .60 .60
439 A83 45v Cocos nucifera tree .80 .80
440 A83 100v Cocos nucifera fruit 1.75 1.75
441 A83 135v Station 2.50 2.50
Nos. 438-441 (4) 5.65 5.65

Fish — A84

Perf. 14x14½

1987, July 15 Wmk. 384

442 A84 1v Cirrhitichthys aprinus .15 .15
443 A84 5v Zanclus cornutus .15 .15
444 A84 10v Canthigaster cinctus .16 .16
445 A84 15v Amphiprion rubrocinctus .25 .25
446 A84 20v Acanthurus lineatus .35 .35
447 A84 30v Thalassoma hardwicki .50 .50
448 A84 35v Anthias tuka .60 .60
449 A84 40v Adioryx microstomus .65 .65
450 A84 45v Balistoides conspicillum .75 .75
451 A84 50v Xyrichtys taeniouris .80 .80
452 A84 55v Hemitaurichthys polyepis .90 .90
453 A84 65v Pterois volitans 1.00 1.00
454 A84 100v Paracirrhites forsteri 1.65 1.65
455 A84 300v Balistapus undulatus 5.00 5.00
456 A84 500v Chaetodon ephippium 8.00 8.00
Nos. 442-456 (15) 20.91 20.91

Insects — A85

1987, Sept. 22 Wmk. 373 *Perf. 14*

457 A85 45v Xylotrupes gideon .85 .85
458 A85 55v Phyllodes imperialis 1.00 1.00
459 A85 65v Cyphogaster 1.25 1.25
460 A85 100v Othreis fullonia 1.90 1.90
Nos. 457-460 (4) 5.00 5.00

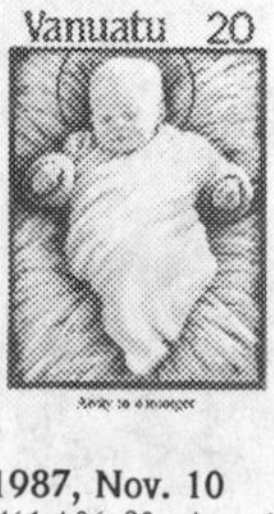

Christmas Carols — A86

1987, Nov. 10 *Perf. 13½x14*

461 A86 20v Away in a Manger .40 .40
462 A86 45v Once in Royal David's City .90 .90
463 A86 55v While Shepherds Watched Their Flocks 1.10 1.10
464 A86 65v We Three Kings of Orient Are 1.30 1.30
Nos. 461-464 (4) 3.70 3.70

Nos. 414-418 Ovptd. in Silver: "40TH WEDDING ANNIVERSARY"

Perf. 14x14½

1987, Dec. 9 Litho. Wmk. 384

465 CD337 20v scar, blk & sil .35 .35
466 CD337 35v ultra & multi .65 .65
467 CD337 45v green & multi .85 .85
468 CD337 55v violet & multi .95 .95
469 CD337 100v multicolored 1.75 1.75
Nos. 465-469 (5) 4.55 4.55

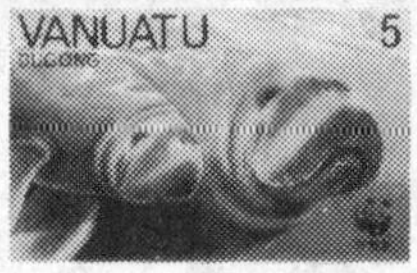

World Wildlife Fund — A87

Dugongs.

1988, Feb. 29 *Perf. 13x13½*

470 A87 5v Mother, calf .20 .20
471 A87 10v Adult .40 .40
472 A87 20v Two adults .80 .80
473 A87 45v Herd 1.65 1.65
Nos. 470-473 (4) 3.05 3.05

Australia Bicentennial A88

Burns Philip emblem, bicent. emblem and steamships.

1988, May 18 Wmk. 373 *Perf. 12*

474 A88 20v S.S. Tambo .32 .32
475 A88 45v S.S. Induna .75 .75
476 A88 55v S.S. Morinda .90 .90
477 A88 65v S.S. Marsina 1.00 1.00
Nos. 474-477 (4) 2.97 2.97

Capt. James Cook (1728-1779), Explorer — A89

Perf. 14 on 2 or 3 Sides

1988, July 29 Wmk. 384

478 A89 45v black & red .80 .80

SYDPEX '88. No. 478 printed in panes of 10 plus 5 center labels picturing a map of Vanuatu, HMS Resolution, exhibition emblem, HMS Endeavour or a map of Australia.

Tourism Type of 1986
Souvenir Sheet

Wmk. 373

1988, Aug. 24 Litho. *Perf. 14*

479 Sheet of 2 3.00 3.00
a. A77 55v like No. 412 1.00 1.00
b. A77 100v like No. 413 2.00 2.00

EXPO '88. Nos. 479a-479b are dated 1988 and "Vanuatu" is inscribed in violet blue.

1988 Summer Olympics, Seoul — A90

1988, Sept. 19 *Perf. 13½x14*

480 A90 20v Boxing .35 .35
481 A90 45v Track events .80 .80
482 A90 55v Signing Olympic agreement 1.00 1.00
483 A90 65v Soccer 1.10 1.10
Nos. 480-483 (4) 3.25 3.25

Souvenir Sheet

484 A90 150v Tennis 2.75 2.75

Intl. Tennis Federation, 75th anniv. (150v).

Lloyds of London, 300th Anniv.

Common Design Type

Designs: 20v, Lloyds new building, 1988. 55v, Cargo ship Shirrabank, horiz. 65v, Adela, horiz. 145v, Excursion steamer General Slocum on fire in New York Harbor, 1904.

1988, Oct. 25 Wmk. 384 *Perf. 14*

485 CD341 20v multicolored .35 .35
486 CD341 55v multicolored .95 .95
487 CD341 65v multicolored 1.10 1.10
488 CD341 145v multicolored 2.50 2.50
Nos. 485-488 (4) 4.90 4.90

FAO — A91

Perf. 14½x14, 14x14½

1988, Nov. 14

489 A91 45v Tending crops .75 .75
490 A91 55v Fishing, vert. .95 .95
491 A91 65v Animal husbandry, vert. 1.10 1.10
492 A91 120v Produce market 2.00 2.00
Nos. 489-492 (4) 4.80 4.80

Christmas A92

Carols: 20v, Silent Night, Holy Night. 45v, Angels From the Realms of Glory. 65v, O Come All Ye Faithful. 155v, In That Poor Stable How Charming Jesus Lies.

1988, Dec. 1 Litho. *Perf. 14½x14*

493 A92 20v multicolored .35 .35
494 A92 45v multicolored .75 .75
495 A92 65v multicolored 1.10 1.10
496 A92 155v multicolored 2.75 2.75
Nos. 493-496 (4) 4.95 4.95

Marine Life Type of 1985

Shrimp.

1989, Feb. 1 *Perf. 14*

497 A76 20v Periclimenes brevicarpalis .35 .35
498 A76 45v Lysmata grabhami .80 .80
499 A76 65v Rhynchocinetes 1.10 1.10
500 A76 150v Stenopus hispidus 2.50 2.50
Nos. 497-500 (4) 4.75 4.75

Economic & Social Commission for Asia and the Pacific (ESCAP) A93

Perf. 12x12½

1989, Apr. 5 Litho. Wmk. 373

501 A93 20v Consolidated Catalina .38 .38
502 A93 45v Douglas DC-3 .85 .85
503 A93 55v Embraer EMB110 Bandeirante 1.05 1.05
504 A93 200v Boeing 737-300 3.75 3.75
Nos. 501-504 (4) 6.03 6.03

Inauguration of the Sydney-Noumea-Espiritu Santo Service, 1948 (20v).

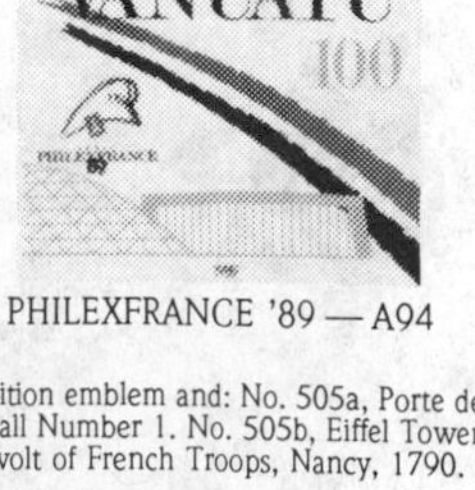

PHILEXFRANCE '89 — A94

Exhibition emblem and: No. 505a, Porte de Versailles Hall Number 1. No. 505b, Eiffel Tower. No. 506, Revolt of French Troops, Nancy, 1790.

1989, July 5 Wmk. 373 *Perf. 12*

505 Pair 3.75 3.75
a.-b. A94 100v any single 1.85 1.85

Souvenir Sheet
Perf. 14
Wmk. 384

506 A94 100v multicolored   1.85 1.85
  French revolution, bicent.

Moon Landing, 20th Anniv.
Common Design Type

Apollo 17: 45v, Command module in space. 55v, Harrison Schmitt, Gene Cerman and Ron Evans. 65v, Mission emblem. 120v, Liftoff. 100v, Recovery of Apollo 11 crew after spashdown.

1989, July 20 Wmk. 384 Perf. 14
Size of Nos. 508-509: 29x29mm

507 CD342 45v multicolored   .85 .85
508 CD342 55v multicolored   1.00 1.00
509 CD342 65v multicolored   1.20 1.20
510 CD342 120v multicolored   2.25 2.25
  Nos. 507-510 (4)   5.30 5.30

Souvenir Sheet
511 CD342 100v multicolored   1.85 1.85

No. 324 Surcharged

100

Perf. 14x13½
1989, Oct. 18 Litho. Wmk. 373
512 A60 100v on 2v multi   1.70 1.70
  STAMPSHOW '89, Melbourne.

World Stamp Expo '89 — A95

Perf. 14x13½
1989, Nov. 6 Litho. Wmk. 384
513 A95 65v New Hebrides #256   1.10 1.10

Souvenir Sheet
514   Sheet of 2   2.80 2.80
a. A95 65v New Hebrides #254   1.10 1.10
b. A95 100v The White House (detail)   1.70 1.70

Flora — A96

Perf. 12½x12
1990, Jan. 5 Wmk. 373
515 A96 45v Alocasia macrorrhiza   .75 .75
516 A96 55v Acacia spirorbis   .92 .92
517 A96 65v Metrosideros collina   1.10 1.10
518 A96 145v Hoya australis   2.45 2.45
  Nos. 515-518 (4)   5.22 5.22

Stamp World London '90 — A97

Exhibition emblem and simulated stamps or stamps on stamps: 45v, Kava (simulated stamps). 65v, Luganville P.O. exterior, interior (simulated stamps). 100v, Propeller plane, 19th cent. packet (simulated stamps). 150v, New Hebrides #187-188, first day cancellation. 200v, Great Britain #1, Vanuatu #281.

1990, Apr. 30 Perf. 13x13½
519 A97 45v multicolored   .75 .75
520 A97 65v multicolored   1.10 1.10
521 A97 100v multicolored   1.70 1.70
522 A97 200v multicolored   3.35 3.35
  Nos. 519-522 (4)   6.90 6.90

Souvenir Sheet
523 A97 150v multicolored   2.50 2.50
  Penny Black, 150th anniv. No. 523 margin pictures first day cancel and cachet.

Independence, 10th Anniv. — A98

Designs: 25v, Natl. Council of Women Emblem. 50v, Pres. Frederick Kalomuana Timakata. 55v, Preamble to Constitution. 65v, Vanuaaku Pati flag. 80v, Reserve Bank. 150v, Prime Minister Walter H. Lini.

1990, July 30 Perf. 14
524 A98 25v multicolored   .42 .42
525 A98 50v multicolored   .85 .85
526 A98 55v multicolored   .95 .95
527 A98 65v multicolored   1.10 1.10
528 A98 80v multicolored   1.35 1.35
  Nos. 524-528 (5)   4.67 4.67

Souvenir Sheet
529 A98 150v multi   2.50 2.50

Minature Sheet

Charles De Gaulle (1890-1970) — A99

Wmk. 373
1990, Nov. 22 Litho. Perf. 14
530   Sheet of 10 + 2 labels (2 each #530c-530f)   7.75 7.75
a. A99 20v At Bayeux, after D-day landing   .35 .35
b. A99 25v Alsace, 1945   .42 .42
c. A99 30v Portrait   .55 .55
d. A99 45v Spitfire, Biggin Hill, 1942   78 78
e. A99 55v Casablanca, 1943   .95 .95
f. A99 65v Day of Glory, Paris, 1944   1.15 1.15

Christmas — A100

1990, Dec. 5 Wmk. Perf. 13
531   Strip of 5   5.00 5.00
a. A100 25v Angel facing right   .42 .42
b. A100 50v Shepherds   .85 .85
c. A100 65v Nativity   1.10 1.10
d. A100 70v The Three Kings   1.20 1.20
e. A100 80v Angel facing left   1.35 1.35

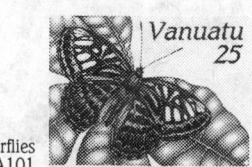
Butterflies A101

1991, Jan. 9 Perf. 14x14½
532 A101 25v Parthenos sylvia   .42 .42
533 A101 55v Euploea nemertes   .95 .95
534 A101 80v Lampides boeticus   1.35 1.35
535 A101 150v Danaus plexippus   2.60 2.60
  Nos. 532-535 (4)   5.32 5.32

Art Festival — A102

Phila Nippon '91 — A103

Perf. 13½
1991, May 2 Litho. Wmk. 373
536 A102 25v Dance   .42 .42
537 A102 65v Weaving   1.15 1.15
538 A102 80v Carving   1.40 1.40
539 A102 150v Music   2.65 2.65
  Nos. 536-539 (4)   5.62 5.62

Elizabeth & Philip, Birthdays
Common Design Types
Perf. 14½
1991, June 17 Litho. Wmk. 384
540 CD345 65v multicolored   1.05 1.05
541 CD346 70v multicolored   1.15 1.15
a.   Pair, #540-541 + label   2.20 2.20

Perf. 14½
1991, Nov. 15 Litho. Wmk. 373
Birds: 50v, White-collared kingfisher. 55v, Green palm lorikeet. 80v, Scarlet robin. 100v, Pacific swallow. 150v, Reef heron.

542 A103 50v multicolored   .85 .85
543 A103 55v multicolored   .95 .95
544 A103 80v multicolored   1.35 1.35
545 A103 100v multicolored   1.70 1.70
  Nos. 542-545 (4)   4.85 4.85

Souvenir Sheet
546 A103 150v multicolored   2.55 2.55

Fight Against AIDS A104

Designs: 25v, Multiple partners, unsafe sex can spread AIDS. 65v, AIDS victim and care giver. 80v, AIDS kills, shark. 150v, Children's playground.

1991, Nov. 29 Wmk. 384 Perf. 14
547 A104 25v multicolored   .45 .45
548 A104 55v multicolored   1.10 1.10
549 A104 80v multicolored   1.35 1.35
550 A104 150v multicolored   2.55 2.55
  Nos. 547-550 (4)   5.45 5.45

Nos. 324-326 & 329 Surcharged
20

Perf. 14x13½
1991, June 12 Litho. Wmk. 373
551 A60 20v on 2v #324   .32 .32
552 A60 60v on 10v #325   1.00 1.00
553 A60 70v on 15v #326   1.20 1.20
554 A60 80v on 30v #329   1.35 1.35
  Nos. 551-554 (4)   3.87 3.87

Queen Elizabeth II's Accession to the Throne, 40th Anniv.
Common Design Type
1992, Feb. 6 Wmk. 384 Perf. 14
555 CD349 20v multicolored   .32 .32
556 CD349 25v multicolored   .42 .42
557 CD349 60v multicolored   1.00 1.00
558 CD349 65v multicolored   1.10 1.10

Wmk. 373
559 CD349 70v multicolored   1.15 1.15
  Nos. 555-559 (5)   3.99 3.99

New Hebrides Participation in World War II — A105

Designs: 50v, Grumman F4F-4 Wildcat. 55v, Douglas SBD-3 Dauntless. 65v, Consolidated PBY-5A Catalina. 80v, USS Hornet. 200v, Vought-Sikorsky OS2U-3.

Perf. 13½x14
1992, May 22 Litho. Wmk. 373
560 A105 50v multicolored   .85 .85
561 A105 55v multicolored   .90 .90
562 A105 65v multicolored   1.05 1.05
563 A105 80v multicolored   1.30 1.30
  Nos. 560-563 (4)   4.10 4.10

Souvenir Sheet
564 A105 200v multicolored   3.20 3.20
  World Columbian Stamp Expo, Chicago (No. 564).
  See Nos. 590-594, 664-667.

Vanuatu's Membership in the World Meteorological Organization, 10th Anniv. — A106

Designs: 25v, Meteorological station, Port Vila. 60v, Cyclone near Vanuatu seen by Japanese satellite GMS 4. 80v, Weather chart showing cyclone. 105v, Cyclone warning broadcast by radio.

Wmk. 373
1992, June 20 Litho. Perf. 14
565 A106 25v multicolored   .42 .42
566 A106 60v multicolored   1.00 1.00
567 A106 80v multicolored   1.30 1.30
568 A106 105v multicolored   1.65 1.65
  Nos. 565-568 (4)   4.37 4.37

1992 Melanesian Cup — A107

Perf. 13½x14
1992, July 20 Litho. Wmk. 373
569 A107 20v Soccer team, trophy   .35 .35
570 A107 65v Soccer players   1.10 1.10
571 A107 70v Men's track   1.20 1.20
572 A107 80v Women's track   1.35 1.35
  Nos. 569-572 (4)   4.00 4.00

1992 Summer Olympics, Barcelona (#571-572). For surcharges see Nos. 621-622.

World Food Day — A108

Designs: 20v, "Breast is best." 70v, Central Hospital, Port Vila. 80v, "Give your children a healthy future." 150v, Nutritious food.

Wmk. 384
1992, Oct. 16 Litho. Perf. 14
573 A108 20v green & brown   .35 .35
574 A108 70v brown & green   1.20 1.20
575 A108 80v green & brown   1.35 1.35
576 A108 150v brown & green   2.50 2.50
  Nos. 573-576 (4)   5.40 5.40

Turtles A109

Perf. 14x14½
1992, Dec. 15 Litho. Wmk. 384
577 A109 55v Leatherback turtle   1.00 1.00
578 A109 65v Loggerhead turtle   1.15 1.15
579 A109 70v Hawksbill turtle   1.25 1.25
580 A109 80v Green turtle   1.40 1.40
  Nos. 577-580 (4)   4.80 4.80

Souvenir Sheet
581 A109 200v Green turtle hatchlings   3.50 3.50

Hibiscus — A110

Designs: 25v, Light pink hibiscus rosa-sinensis.
55v, Hibiscus tiliaceus. 80v, Red hibiscus rosa-
sinensis. 150v, Dark pink hibiscus rosa-sinensis.

Wmk. 384
1993, Mar. 3   Litho.   Perf. 14
582 A110 25v multicolored   .45   .45
583 A110 55v multicolored   1.00 1.00
584 A110 80v multicolored   1.40 1.40
585 A110 150v multicolored   2.60 2.60
        Nos. 582-585 (4)   5.45 5.45

Nos. 331, 333-335 Surcharged

WORLD ORCHID
CONFERENCE 1993

40
═

Perf. 13½x14, 14x13½
1993, Apr. 21   Litho.   Wmk. 373
586 A60 40v on 45v #331   .75   .75
587 A60 55v on 75v #333   1.00 1.00
588 A60 65v on 100v #334   1.15 1.15
589 A60 150v on 200v #335   2.70 2.70
        Nos. 586-589 (4)   5.60 5.60

Size and location of surcharge varies.

World War II Type of 1992
Designs: 20v, Grumman F6F-3 Hellcat. 55v,
Lockheed P-38F Lightning. 65v, GrummanTBF-1
Avenger. 80v, USS Essex. 200v, Douglas C-47
Dakota.

1993, June 30   Perf. 13½
590 A105 20v multicolored   .35   .35
591 A105 55v multicolored   1.00 1.00
592 A105 65v multicolored   1.20 1.20
593 A105 80v multicolored   1.45 1.45
        Nos. 590-593 (4)   4.00 4.00

Souvenir Sheet
594 A105 200v multicolored   3.65 3.65

Island Scenes
A111

Designs: 5v, Iririki Island, Port Vila. 10v, Iririki
Island, yachts. 15v, Court House, Port Vila. 20v,
Two girls, Pentecost Island. 25v, Women dancers,
Tanna Island. 30v, Market, Port Vila. 45v, Man
with canoe, Erakor Island, vert. 50v, Coconut trees,
Champagne Beach. 55v, Coconut trees, North Efate
Islands. 60v, Fish (Banks Group). 70v, Sea fan,
Tongoa Island, vert. 75v, Espiritu Santo Island. 80v,
Sailboat at sunset, Port Vila Bay, vert. 100v, Mele
Waterfall, vert. 300v, Yasur Volcano, Tanna Island,
vert. 500v, Erakor Island.

Perf. 14x14½, 14½x14
1993, July 7   Litho.   Wmk. 373
595 A111   5v multicolored   .15   .15
596 A111 10v multicolored   .16   .16
597 A111 15v multicolored   .24   .24
598 A111 20v multicolored   .32   .32
599 A111 25v multicolored   .40   .40
600 A111 30v multicolored   .48   .48
601 A111 45v multicolored   .75   .75
602 A111 50v multicolored   .80   .80
603 A111 55v multicolored   .90   .90
604 A111 60v multicolored   1.00 1.00
605 A111 70v multicolored   1.15 1.15
606 A111 75v multicolored   1.20 1.20
607 A111 80v multicolored   1.30 1.30
608 A111 100v multicolored   1.60 1.60
609 A111 300v multicolored   4.75 4.75
610 A111 500v multicolored   8.00 8.00
        Nos. 595-610 (16)   23.20 23.20

For surcharges see Nos. 619-620.

Trochus niloticus 1993

VANUATU 55 Shells — A112

Perf. 14½
1993, Sept. 15   Litho.   Wmk. 373
611 A112 55v Trochus niloticus   .90   .90
612 A112 65v Lioconcha castrensis 1.10 1.10
613 A112 80v Turbo petholatus   1.40 1.40
614 A112 150v Pleuroploca trapezi-
           um   2.50 2.50
        Nos. 611-614 (4)   5.90 5.90

See Nos. 632-635, 654-657.

Louvre
Museum,
Bicent.
A113

Paintings by De La Tour: 25v, St. Joseph the
Carpenter. 55v, The Newborn. 80v, Adoration of
the Shepherds (detail). 150v, Adoration of the Shepherds (entire).

Wmk. 373
1993, Nov. 10   Litho.   Perf. 14
615 A113 25v multicolored   .40   .40
616 A113 55v multicolored   .90   .90
617 A113 80v multicolored   1.25 1.25
618 A113 150v multicolored   2.50 2.50
        Nos. 615-618 (4)   5.05 5.05

Nos. 570, 572, 598, 600 Surcharged

SOUTH PACIFIC MINI GAMES
PORT VILA DECEMBER 1993

1993, Dec. 6   Litho.   Wmk. 373
Perfs. as Before
619 A111 15v on 20v #598   .25   .25
620 A111 25v on 30v #600   .40   .40
621 A107 55v on 65v #570   .90   .90
622 A107 70v on 80v #572   1.10 1.10
        Nos. 619-622 (4)   2.65 2.65

Service
Organizations
A114

Intl. Year of the
Family
A115

Hong Kong '94: 25v, Kiwanis Intl., Charity
Races, vert. 60v, Lions Intl. Twin Otter on mercy
mission. 75v, Rotary Intl. fighting malaria, vert.
150v, Red Cross blood donar service. 200v,
Emblems of service organizations.

Perf. 14x15, 15x14
1994, Feb. 18   Litho.   Wmk. 373
623 A114 25v multicolored   .42   .42
624 A114 60v multicolored   1.00 1.00
625 A114 75v multicolored   1.25 1.25
626 A114 150v multicolored   2.50 2.50
        Nos. 623-626 (4)   5.17 5.17

Souvenir Sheet
627 A114 200v multicolored   3.25 3.25

1994, Mar. 2   Perf. 14
628 A115 25v violet & rose brown   .42   .42
629 A115 60v vermilion & dk green 1.00 1.00
630 A115 90v green & sepia   1.50 1.50
631 A115 150v brown & violet blue 2.50 2.50
        Nos. 628-631 (4)   5.42 5.42

Shell Type of 1993
1994, May 31   Litho.   Perf. 12
632 A112 60v Cyprea argus   1.00 1.00
633 A112 70v Conus marmoreus   1.25 1.25
634 A112 85v Lambis chiragra   1.50 1.50
635 A112 155v Chicoreus brunneus 2.75 2.75
        Nos. 632-635 (4)   6.50 6.50

Tourism — A116

Designs: a, 25v, Slit gong (drum), traditional hut.
b, 75v, Volcano, boats. c, 90v, Sailboats, airplane,
green palm lorikeet. d, 200v, Helicopter, woman
with tray of fruit.

1994, July 27   Litho.   Perf. 13½
636 A116 Strip of 4, #a.-d.   6.75 6.75

VANUATU 55

Anemonefish — A117

1994, Aug. 16   Litho.   Perf. 12
637 A117 55v Pink   .95   .95
638 A117 70v Clark's   1.25 1.25
639 A117 80v Red & black   1.40 1.40
640 A117 140v Orange-fin   2.50 2.50
  a. Souvenir sheet of 1   2.50 2.50
        Nos. 637-640 (4)   6.10 6.10

Philakorea '94 (#640a).

VANUATU 25

ICAO, 50th
Anniv. — A118

Designs: 25v, 1950 Qantas Catalina. 60v, 1956
Tai Douglas DC3. 75v, 1966 New Herbrides Airways Drover. 90v, 1994 Air Vanuatu Boeing 737.

1994, Dec. 7
641 A118 25v multicolored   .42   .42
642 A118 60v multicolored   1.00 1.00
643 A118 75v multicolored   1.25 1.25
644 A118 90v multicolored   1.50 1.50
        Nos. 641-644 (4)   4.17 4.17

VANUATU 1995 25 Hibiscus
A119

1995, Feb. 1   Litho.   Perf. 12
645 A119 25v The Path   .45   .45
646 A119 60v Old Frankie   1.10 1.10
647 A119 90v Fijian white   1.65 1.65
648 A119 200v Surf rider   3.50 3.50
        Nos. 645-648 (4)   6.70 6.70

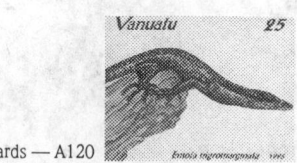

Vanuatu 25

Lizards — A120

Designs: 25v, Emoia nigromarginata. 55v, Nac-
tus multicarinatus. 70v, Lepidodactylus. 80v, Emoia
caerulocauda. 140v, Emoia sanfordi.

1995, Apr. 12
649 A120 25v multicolored   .45   .45
650 A120 55v multicolored   1.00 1.00
651 A120 70v multicolored   1.25 1.25

652 A120 80v multicolored   1.40 1.40
653 A120 140v multicolored   2.50 2.50
        Nos. 649-653 (5)   6.60 6.60

Shell Type of 1993
1995, June 1
654 A112 25v Epitonium scalare   .45   .45
655 A112 55v Strombus latissimus 1.00 1.00
656 A112 90v Conus bullatus   1.65 1.65
657 A112 200v Pterynotus pinnatus 3.50 3.50
        Nos. 654-657 (4)   6.60 6.60

Anniversaries — A121

Designs: 25v, Girls wearing traditional head
pieces. 55v, Stylized picture of natives dancing,
vert. 60v, Children, doves, natl. flag, UN flag, vert.
75v, Embroidered tapestry of native, vert. 90v,
Troops parading. 140v, Group in traditional
ceremony.

Perf. 14x13½, 13½x14
1995, July 28   Litho.
658 A121 25v multicolored   .45   .45
659 A121 55v multicolored   1.00 1.00
660 A121 60v multicolored   1.10 1.10
661 A121 75v multicolored   1.40 1.40
662 A121 90v multicolored   1.65 1.65
663 A121 140v multicolored   2.50 2.50
        Nos. 658-663 (6)   8.10 8.10

UN, 50th anniv. (#660). Others, independence,
15th anniv.

World War II Type of 1992
1995, Sept. 1   Litho.   Perf. 12½
664 A105 60v SB2C Helldiver   1.10 1.10
665 A105 70v Spitfire Mk VIII 1.25 1.25
666 A105 75v F4U-1A Corsair   1.30 1.30
667 A105 80v PV1 Ventura   1.40 1.40
        Nos. 664-667 (4)   5.05 5.05

VANUATU Artifacts — A122

Ambae money mat and: a, 25sh, Rambaramp
mortuary effigy, Malakula. b, 60sh, Wusi pot, Espiritu Santo. c, 75sh, Slit gong, Efate Island. d, 90sh,
Tapa cloth, Erromango Island.

1995, Nov. 22   Litho.   Perf. 13½x13
668 A122 Strip of 4, #a.-d.   4.50 4.50

SEMI POSTAL STAMPS

Nos. 324 and 414-418 Surcharged
"Hurricane Relief Fund"
Wmk. 373 (No. B1), 384
Perf. 14x13½, 14x14½
1987, May 12   Litho.
B1 A60   20v +10v on 2v   .55   .55
B2 CD337 20v +10v   .55   .55
B3 CD337 35v +15v   .95   .95
B4 CD337 45v +20v   1.10 1.10
B5 CD337 55v +25v   1.50 1.50
B6 CD337 100v +50v   2.75 2.75
        Nos. B1-B6 (6)   7.40 7.40

Old value of #B1 obliterated by 2 horizontal bars.
Surcharge indicated by text "Surcharge +10."

VICTORIA

vik-ʹtōr-ē-ə

LOCATION — In the extreme southeastern
part of Australia
GOVT. — A former British Colony

AREA — 87,884 sq. mi.
POP. — 1,201,341 (1901)
CAPITAL — Melbourne

Victoria was one of the six former British colonies which united on Jan. 1, 1901, to form the Commonwealth of Australia.

12 Pence = 1 Shilling
20 Shillings = 1 Pound

Unused values for Nos. 1-16 are for stamps without gum as these stamps are seldom found with original gum. Otherwise, unused values are for stamps with original gum as defined in the catalogue introduction.

Very fine examples of all rouletted, perforated and serrate perforated stamps from Nos. 9-109 and F2 will have roulettes, perforations or serrate perforations touching the design. Examples clear on four sides range from scarce to rare and will command higher prices.

Watermarks

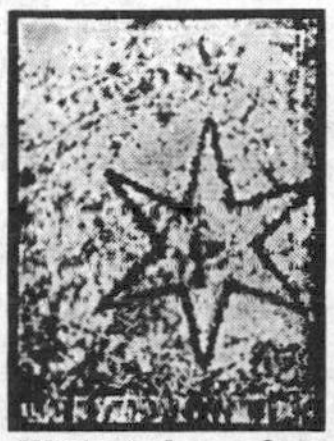
Wmk. 6- Large Star

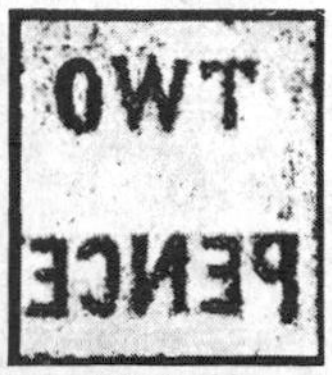
Wmk. 80

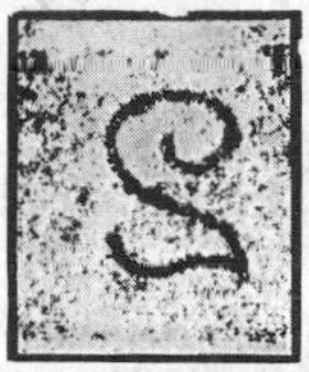
Wmk. 50

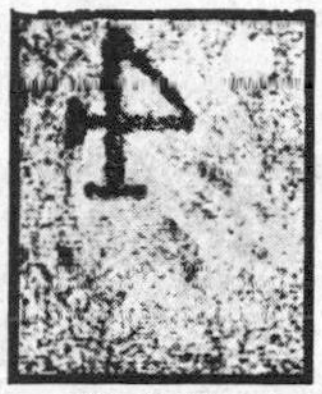
Wmk. 80a

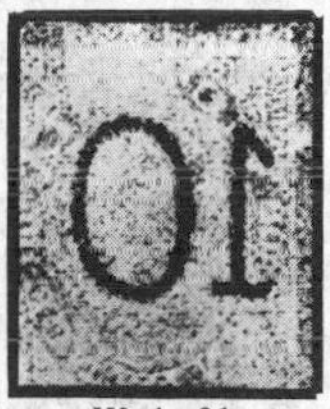
Wmk. 81

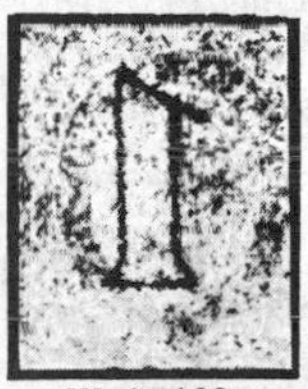
Wmk. 139

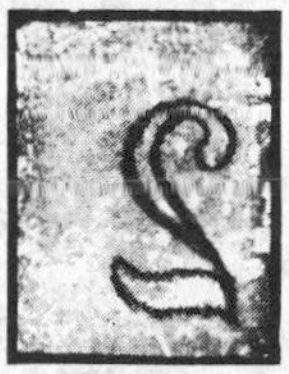
Wmk. 49

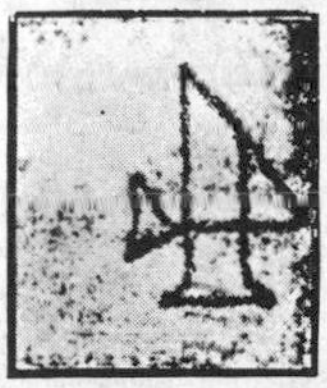
Wmk. 75

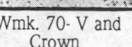

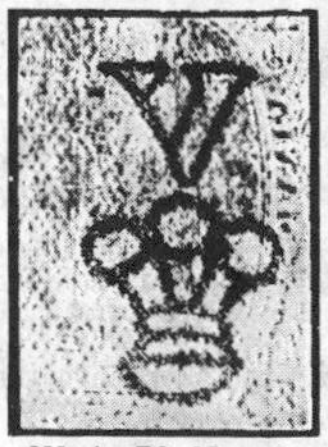
Wmk. 70- V and Crown

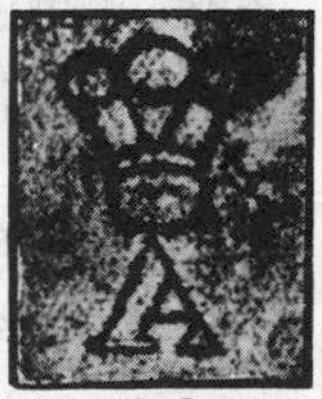
Wmk. 13- Crown & Double-lined A

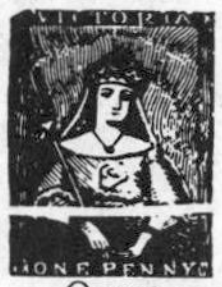

Queen Victoria
A1

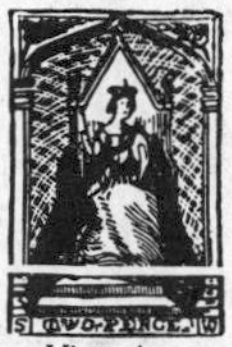
Victoria on Throne
A2

1850 Litho. Unwmk. *Imperf.*
1 A1 1p dull red 875.00 90.00
a. 1p vermilion 600.00 125.00
2 A1 1p rose 375.00 75.00
a. 1p pink 410.00 85.00
3 A1 3p blue 600.00 50.00
a. 3p light blue 550.00 50.00
4 A1 3p indigo 625.00 50.00
Nos. 1-4 (4) 2,475. 265.00

Nos. 1-4 exist with and without frame line.

THREE TYPES OF 2p:
Type I - Border, two sets of nine wavy lines crisscrossing. Background, 22 groups of wavy triple lines below "VICTORIA."
Type II - Border, same. Background, 15 groups of wavy triple lines below "VICTORIA."
Type III - Border, two sets of five wavy lines crisscrossing. Background, same as type II.

5 A1 2p lilac, I *3,000.* 300.00
a. 2p brn lilac, I *3,750.* 325.00
6 A1 2p brn lilac, II 875.00 90.00
a. 2p gray lilac, II 925.00 90.00
7 A1 2p brn lilac, III 875.00 80.00
a. 2p gray lilac, III 875.00 90.00
b. Value omitted, III 2,500.
8 A1 2p yel brn, III 650.00 55.00

Rouletted 7
10 A1 3p blue 140.00
a. 3p deep blue 1,600. 190.00

Perf. 12
12 A1 3p blue *2,000.* 125.00
a. 3p deep blue *2,000.* 125.00

1852 Engr. *Imperf.*
14 A2 2p reddish brown 160.00 35.00

#14 was reprinted on paper with watermark 70, imperf. & perf. 12½, overprinted "REPRINT."

1854 Litho.
15 A2 2p gray brown 220.00 35.00
16 A2 2p brown lilac 200.00 30.00
a. 2p red lilac 250.00 35.00

Fifty varieties.

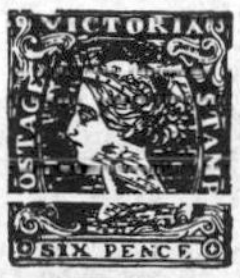

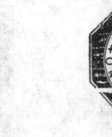

A3

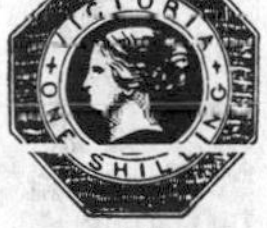

A4

1854-58 Typo.
17 A3 6p orange 150.00 27.50
a. 6p red orange 180.00 25.00

See Nos. 19-20, 22-24A, 26-28

Lithographed
18 A4 1sh blue 450.00 20.00

See Nos. 21, 25.

Typographed
19 A3 2sh green 1,100. 125.00

1857-58 *Rouletted 7, 9½*
20 A3 6p orange 525.00 60.00

Lithographed
21 A4 1sh blue 1,500. 90.00

Typographed
22 A3 2sh green ('58) *4,000.* 225.00

Small Serrate Perf. 19
23 A3 6p orange *1,200.* 100.00

Large Serpentine Perf. 10½
24 A3 6p orange 800.00 55.00

Serrate x Serpentine Perf.
24A A3 6p orange 125.00

1859 Litho. *Perf. 12*
25 A4 1sh blue 180.00 14.00

Typographed
26 A3 2sh green 260.00 37.50

1861 Wmk. "SIX PENCE" (80)
27 A3 6p black 260.00 50.00

Wmk. Single-lined "2" (50)
1864 *Perf. 12, 13*
28 A3 2sh blue, *green* 250.00 8.50

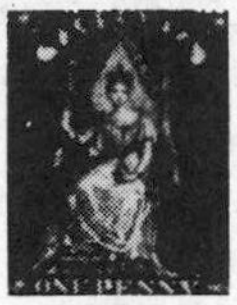
A5

Wmk. Large Star (6)
1856, Oct. Engr. *Imperf.*
29 A5 1p green 125.00 30.00

1858 *Rouletted 5½-6½*
30 A5 6p blue 125.00 7.00

Nos. 29 and 30 have been reprinted on paper watermarked V and Crown. They are imperforate and overprinted "REPRINT."

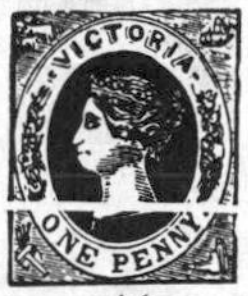

A6

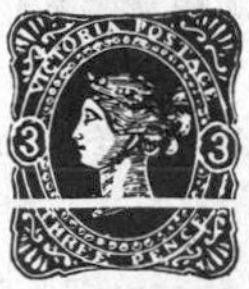
A7

1857-61 Typo. *Imperf.*
31 A6 1p yellow green 90.00 12.00
a. Printed on both sides *900.00*
32 A6 4p vermilion 275.00 15.00
a. Printed on both sides *900.00*
33 A6 4p rose 200.00 11.50

Rouletted 7 to 9½
34 A6 1p yellow green 325.00 125.00
35 A6 4p rose 525.00 40.00

Perf. 12
36 A6 1p yellow green 600.00 325.00

Unwmk. *Imperf.*
37 A6 1p blue green 300.00 18.00
38 A6 2p lilac 240.00 15.00
39 A6 4p rose *500.00* 40.00

Copies of No. 39 printed in dull carmine on thin paper are regarded as printer's waste and of little value. They are also found printed on both sides.

Rouletted 7 to 9½
40 A6 1p blue green 300.00 10.00
a. 1p yellow green 400.00 32.50
b. Horiz. pair, imperf. btwn. *1,000.*
41 A6 2p lilac 1,200. 32.50
42 A6 4p rose 300.00 8.00
a. Horiz. pair, imperf. btwn. *1,000.*

Perf. 12
43 A6 1p blue green 160.00 10.00
a. 1p yellow green 200.00 15.00
b. Horiz. pair, imperf. btwn. *650.00*
44 A6 2p lilac 90.00
45 A6 4p rose 180.00 5.00
b. Vert. pair, imperf. btwn.

Serrate Perf. 19
45A A6 2p lilac 600.00 250.00

Laid Paper
Imperf
46 A6 4p rose 600.00 25.00

Rouletted 5 to 7
47 A6 2p dark lilac 200.00 8.00
a. 2p brown lilac 225.00 8.00
b. 2p violet 150.00 5.00
48 A6 4p rose 160.00 5.50

Perf. 12
49 A6 1p green 240.00 14.00
50 A6 4p rose 150.00 11.00

Wove Paper
1860 Wmk. Value in Words (80)
51 A6 1p yellow green 60.00 8.00
a. Wmk. "FOUR PENCE" (error) *2,000.*
52 A6 2p gray lilac 140.00 7.50
a. 2p brown lilac 400.00 24.00

Wmk. "THREE PENCE" (80)
53 A6 2p gray lilac 240.00 10.00

Single-lined "2" (50)
54 A6 2p lilac 160.00 16.00
a. 2p gray lilac 160.00 16.00
b. 2p brown lilac 160.00 16.00
c. As "b," wmkd. single-lined "6" *4,500.*

1860 Unwmk. Laid Paper
56 A7 3p deep blue 360.00 45.00

Wmk. Value in Words (80)
Perf. 11½ to 12
1860-62 Wove Paper
57 A7 3p blue 175.00 10.00
58 A7 3p claret 175.00 35.00
a. Perf. 13 190.00 40.00
59 A7 4p rose 175.00 4.50
60 A7 6p orange *3,000.* 325.00
61 A7 6p black 250.00 8.00

Wmk. "FIVE SHILLINGS" (80)
62 A7 4p rose 1,500. 20.00

Wmk. Single-lined "4" (80a)
1863 *Imperf.*
63 A7 4p rose *1,200.* *135.00*

Rouletted
64 A7 4p rose *2,400.* 200.00

Perf. 11½ to 12
65 A7 4p rose 100.00 8.00

1863 Unwmk. *Perf. 12*
66 A7 4p rose 450.00 10.50

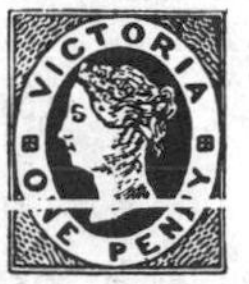

A8

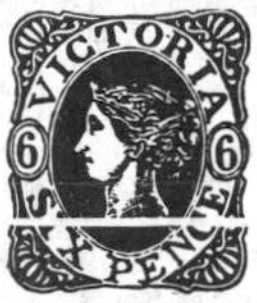

A9

1861-63 Wmk. 80 *Perf. 11½ to 12*
67 A8 1p green 90.00 9.00
68 A9 6p black 175.00 7.50

Wmk. Double-lined "1" (139)
69 A8 1p green 200.00 13.00

Wmk. Single-lined Figures (50)
70 A8 1p green 45.00 6.50
71 A9 6p black 175.00 6.50

The 1p and 6p of 1861-63 are known on paper without watermark but were probably impressions on the margins of watermarked sheets.

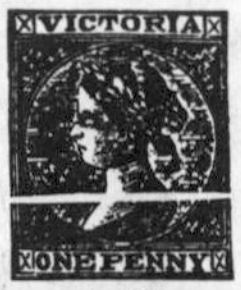
A10

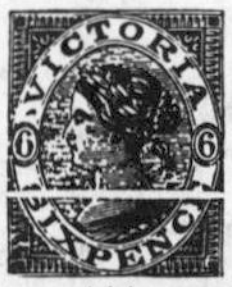
A11

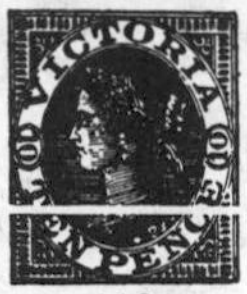
A12

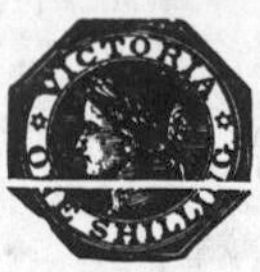
A13

Wmk. Single-lined Figures (50, 80a, 81)

1863-67 *Perf. 11½ to 13*

74	A10 1p green	70.00	4.00
a.	Double impression		900.00
75	A10 2p gray lilac	75.00	4.00
a.	2p violet	50.00	2.75
76	A10 4p rose	110.00	3.00
a.	Double impression		900.00
77	A11 6p blue	87.50	3.00
78	A10 8p orange	300.00	50.00
79	A12 10p brn, *rose*	150.00	4.50
80	A13 1sh blue, *blue*	150.00	3.00
	Nos. 74-80 (7)	942.50	71.50

See Nos. 81-82, 84-96, 99-101, 108-112, 115-119, 124-126, 144, 188. Compare type A11 with type A54.

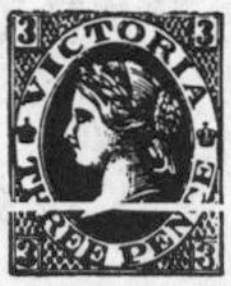
A14

Wmk. Double-lined "1" (139)

81	A10 1p green	95.00	5.00
82	A10 2p gray lilac	250.00	8.00
83	A14 3p lilac	200.00	35.00
84	A11 6p blue	65.00	6.00
	Nos. 81-84 (4)	610.00	54.00

See Nos. 97, 113, 155, 186. Compare type A14 with type A51.

Wmk. Double-lined "2" (49)

85	A11 6p blue		*3,250.*

Wmk. Single-lined "4" (80a)

86	A10 1p green	150.00	11.00
87	A10 2p gray lilac	200.00	7.00
88	A11 6p blue		*1,500.*

Wmk. Double-lined "4" (75)

89	A10 1p green	1,300.	145.00
90	A10 2p gray lilac	200.00	6.00
91	A10 4p rose	225.00	7.00
92	A11 6p blue	325.00	18.00

Wmk. Single-lined "6" (50)

93	A10 1p green	250.00	10.00
94	A10 2p gray lilac	225.00	5.75

Wmk. Single-lined "8" (50)

95	A10 1p green	200.00	15.00
96	A10 2p gray lilac	250.00	6.50
97	A14 3p lilac	200.00	30.00
99	A12 10p slate	400.00	120.00

Wmk. "SIX PENCE" (80)

100	A10 1p green	750.00	21.00
101	A11 6p blue	350.00	15.00

All values of the 1864-67 series except the 3p and 8p are known on unwatermarked paper. They are probably varieties from watermarked sheets which have been so placed on the printing press that some of the stamps escaped the watermark.

One copy of the 2p gray lilac, type A10, is reported to exist with only "PENCE" of watermark 80 showing. Some believe this is part of the "SIX PENCE" watermark.

1870 **Wmk. "THREE PENCE" (80)**

108	A11 6p blue	225.00	6.25

Wmk. "FOUR PENCE" (80)

109	A11 6p blue	500.00	40.00

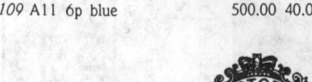

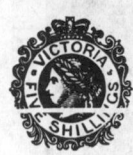

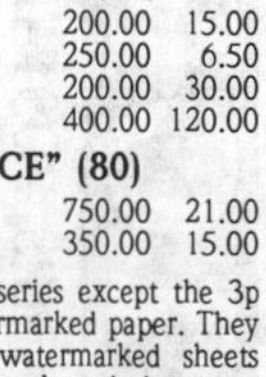
A15

1867-78 Wmk. (70) *Perf. 11½ to 13*

110	A10 1p green	60.00	2.00
111	A10 2p lilac	85.00	3.25
a.	2p gray lilac	62.50	2.00
112	A10 2p lilac, *lilac*	90.00	10.00
113	A14 3p red lilac	300.00	18.00
a.	3p lilac	350.00	20.00
114	A14 3p orange	22.50	2.00
a.	3p yellow	62.50	2.00
115	A10 4p rose	90.00	3.50
116	A11 6p blue	25.00	2.50
117	A11 6p ultra	27.50	2.50
a.	6p lilac blue	62.50	2.25
118	A10 8p brn, *rose*	125.00	5.00
119	A13 1sh bl, *blue*	250.00	10.00
120	A15 5sh bl, *yel*	1,250.	450.00
121	A15 5sh bl & rose	125.00	15.00
a.	Without blue line under crown	140.00	17.00
122	A15 5sh ultra & rose	175.00	20.00

See #126, 144, 188. For surcharge see #124.
For additional stamps of type A15, see No. 191. Compare type A15 with type A58.

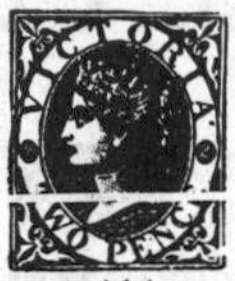
A16

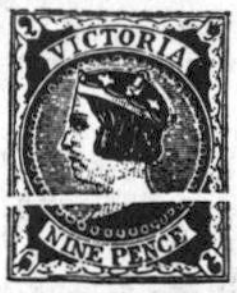
A19

1870 *Perf. 13*

123	A16 2p lilac	40.00	2.00
a.	Perf. 12	40.00	1.25

No. 110 Surcharged in Red

½ ½
HALF

1873, July 19 *Perf. 13, 12*

124	A10 ½p on 1p green	35.00	10.00

No. 79 Surcharged in Blue

9 9
NINEPENCE

1871 **Wmk. Single-lined "10" (81)**

125	A12 9p on 10p brn, *rose*	350.00	11.00
a.	Double surcharge		*1,200.*

1873-78 **Typo.**

126	A10 8p brown, *rose* ('78)	125.00	6.50
127	A19 9p brown, *rose*	125.00	6.50

For additional stamps of type A19, see Nos. 128-129, 174-175. Compare type A19 with type A55.

1875 **Wmk. V and Crown (70)**

128	A19 9p brown, *rose*	140.00	11.00

No. 128 Surcharged in Black

8d 8d
EIGHTPENCE

1876

129	A19 8p on 9p brn, *rose*	175.00	14.00

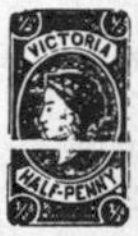
A21

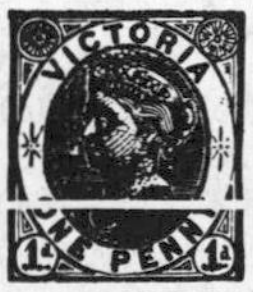
A22

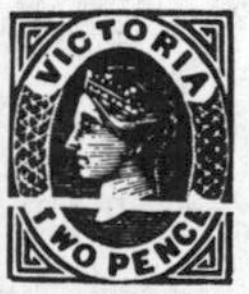
A23

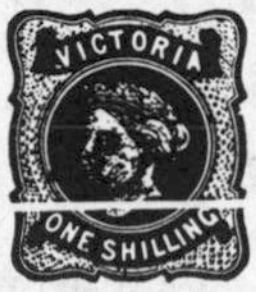
A24

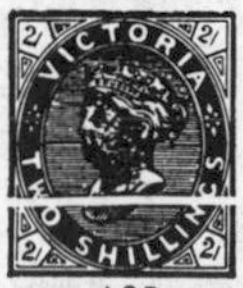
A25

1873-81 *Perf. 13, 12*

130	A21 ½p rose ('74)	5.50	.35
131	A21 ½p rose, *rose* ('78)	20.00	8.00
132	A22 1p grn ('75)	15.00	1.00
133	A22 1p grn, *gray* ('78)	90.00	60.00
134	A22 1p grn, *yel* ('78)	40.00	15.00
135	A23 2p violet	15.00	.25
136	A23 2p vio, *grnsh* ('78)	125.00	15.00
137	A23 2p vio, *buff* ('78)	125.00	15.00
137A	A23 2p vio, *lil* ('78)		340.00
138	A24 1sh bl, *bl* ('76)	55.00	4.00
139	A25 2sh bl, *grn* ('81)	175.00	20.00

See Nos. 140, 156A-159, 184, 189-190. Compare type A21 with type A46, A24 with A56, A25 with A57.

1878

Double-lined Outer Oval

140	A23 2p violet	20.00	.25
a.	Imperf., pair		400.00

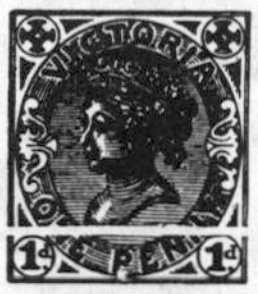
A26

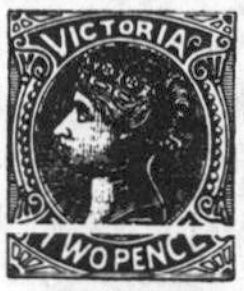
A27

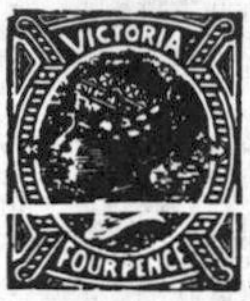
A28

1881-83 *Perf. 12½*

141	A26 1p green ('83)	14.00	.90
142	A27 2p brown	27.50	.25
143	A27 2p lilac	12.00	.15
144	A10 4p car rose	200.00	2.75
145	A28 4p car rose	30.00	1.50
	Nos. 141-145 (5)	283.50	5.55

See Nos. 156, 185, 187. Compare type A26 with type A47, A27 with A49, A28 with A52.

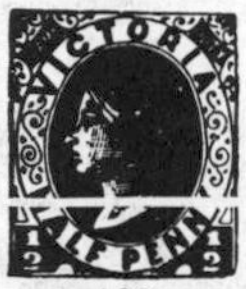
A29

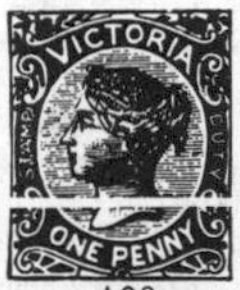
A30

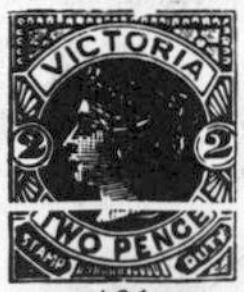
A31

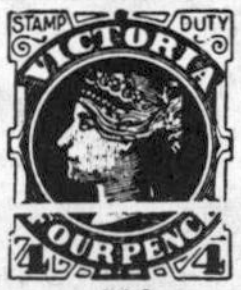
A32

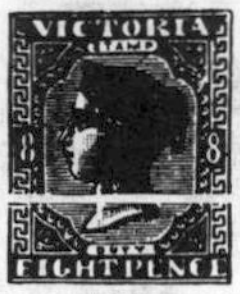
A33

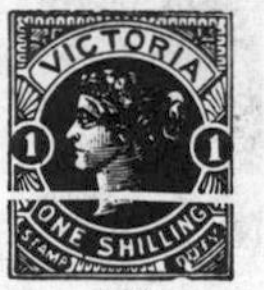
A34

1884-86

146	A29 ½p rose	6.00	.40
147	A30 1p green	6.00	.20
148	A31 2p violet	4.75	.15
a.	2p lilac rose	10.50	.16
149	A30 3p bister	8.00	.50
a.	3p ocher	6.50	.50
150	A32 4p magenta	32.50	2.25
a.	4p violet (error)	*4,000.*	400.00
151	A30 6p gray blue	42.50	1.40
a.	6p ultramarine	35.00	1.40
152	A33 8p rose, *rose*	22.50	4.50
153	A34 1sh blue, *yel*	47.50	3.25
154	A33 2sh olive, *grn*	22.50	2.00
	Nos. 146-154 (9)	192.25	14.65

See Nos. 177-178, 192A. Compare types A31-A32 with types A37-A38.

Nos. 114, 145, 138-139 Overprinted "STAMP / DUTY" Vertically in Blue or Black

1885

155	A14 3p orange (Bl)	60.00	21.00
156	A28 4p car rose (Bl)	50.00	12.50
156A	A24 1sh bl, *bl* (Bl)		1,250.
157	A24 1sh bl, *bl* (Bk)	95.00	22.50
158	A25 2sh bl, *grn* (Bk)	75.00	20.00
	Nos. 155-156,157-158 (4)	280.00	76.00

Reprints of 4p and 1sh have brighter colors than originals. They lack the overprint "REPRINT."

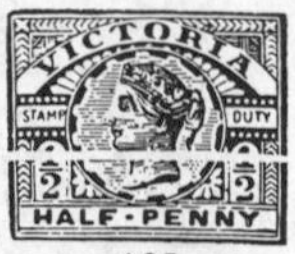
A35

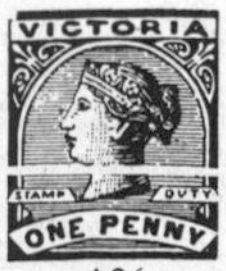
A36

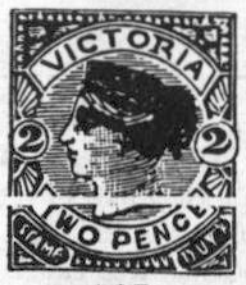
A37

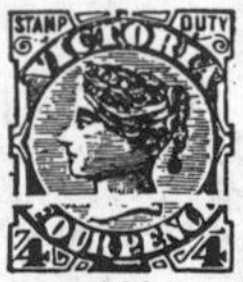
A38

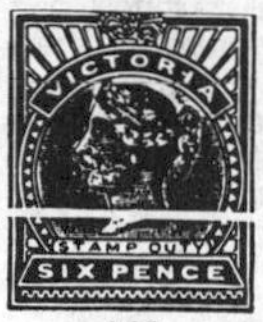
A39

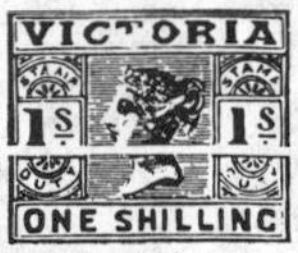
A40

1886-87 *Perf. 12½*

159	A35 ½p lilac	16.00	3.00
160	A35 ½p rose	4.50	.15
160A	A35 ½p scarlet	5.00	.15
161	A36 1p green	5.00	.15
162	A37 2p violet	3.00	.15
a.	2p red lilac	2.00	.15
b.	Imperf.		
163	A38 4p red	6.00	.60
164	A39 6p blue	7.50	.40
165	A39 6p ultra	7.50	.15
166	A40 1sh lilac brown	22.50	1.50
	Nos. 159-166 (9)	77.00	6.25

See No. 180.

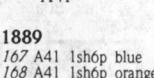

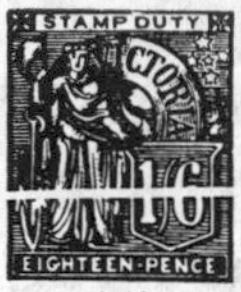
A41

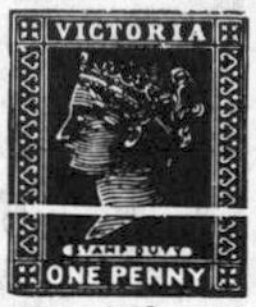
A42

1889

167	A41 1sh6p blue	110.00	62.50
168	A41 1sh6p orange	15.00	4.00

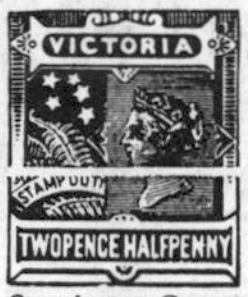
Southern Cross
A43

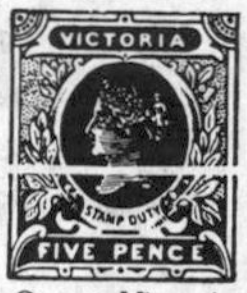
Queen Victoria
A44

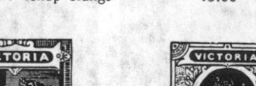

1890-95 *Perf. 12½*

169	A42 1p org brn	2.25	.15
a.	1p chocolate brown	2.75	.15
170	A42 1p yel brn	2.00	.15
171	A42 1p brn org, *pink* ('91)	1.65	.50
172	A43 2½p brn red, *yel*	6.00	.50
173	A44 5p choc ('91)	7.00	.50
174	A19 9p green ('92)	20.00	5.00
175	A19 9p rose red	13.00	1.50
a.	9p rose ('95)	13.00	1.50
176	A40 1sh deep claret	15.00	.50
a.	1sh red brown	13.00	.38
b.	1sh maroon	20.00	1.00
177	A33 2sh yel grn	25.00	10.00
178	A33 2sh emerald	20.00	6.00
	Nos. 169-178 (10)	111.90	24.80

In 1891 many stamps of the early issues were reprinted. They are on paper watermarked V and Crown, perforated 12, 12½, and overprinted "REPRINT."

See Nos. 181, 183, 192. Compare type A43 with type A50, A44 with A53.

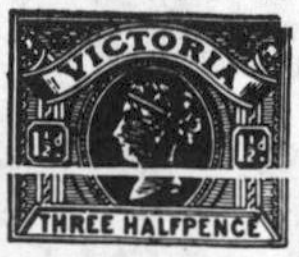
A45

1897

179	A45 1½p yellow green	4.00	1.75

See No. 182. Compare type A45 with type A48.

1899

180 A35	1/2p emerald		5.00	.20
181 A42	1p brt rose		4.00	.15
182 A45	1 1/2p red, *yel*		2.75	1.50
183 A43	2 1/2p dark blue		6.50	1.25
	Nos. 180-183 (4)		18.25	3.10

1901

184 A21	1/2p blue green	1.90	.50
a.	"VICTCRIA"	65.00	25.00
185 A27	2p violet	4.50	.15
186 A14	3p brown org	14.00	1.50
187 A28	4p bister	25.00	5.00
188 A11	6p emerald	9.00	2.75
189 A24	1sh orange yel	30.00	10.00
190 A25	2sh blue, *rose*	40.00	11.00
191 A15	5sh rose red & bl	60.00	20.00
	Nos. 184-191 (8)	184.40	50.90

1901

192 A42	1p olive green	6.50	5.00
192A A30	3p sage green	21.00	12.00

Nos. 192-192A were available for postal use until June 30, 1901, and thereafter restricted to revenue use.

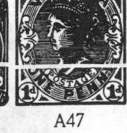

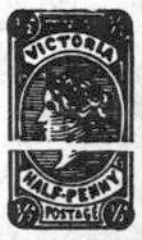
A46

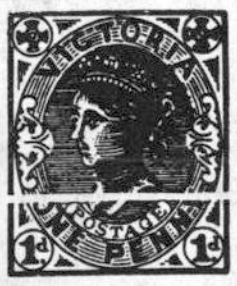
A47

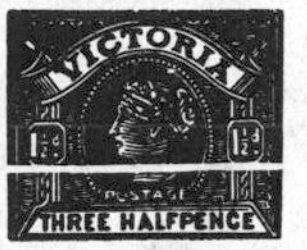
A48

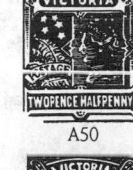

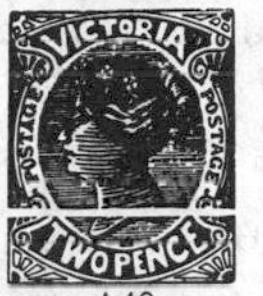
A49

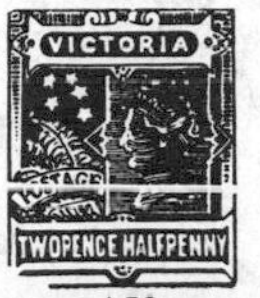
A50

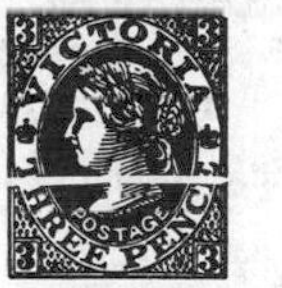
A51

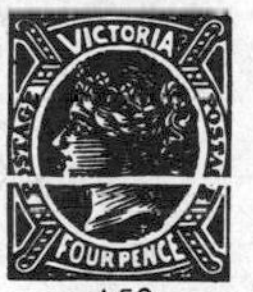
A52

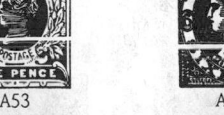

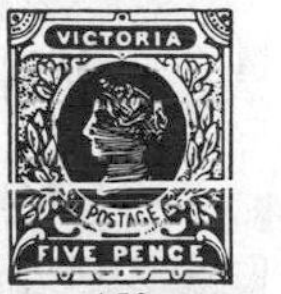
A53

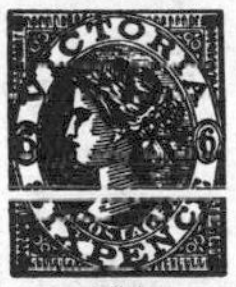
A54

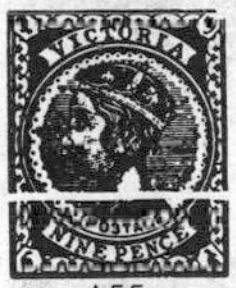
A55

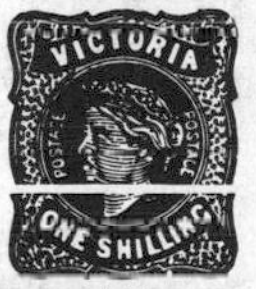
A56

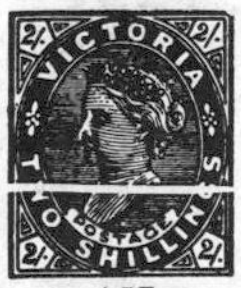
A57

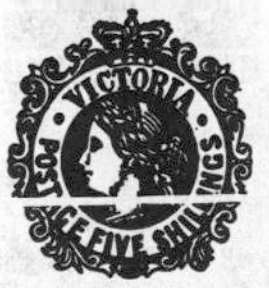
A58

1901 ***Perf. 11, 12 1/2 and Compound***

193 A46	1/2p blue green	1.50	.15
194 A47	1p rose red	1.25	.15
a.	1p rose	1.25	.15
195 A48	1 1/2p red, *yellow*	2.25	.50
a.	Perf. 11	50.00	32.50
196 A49	2p violet	2.75	.15
197 A50	2 1/2p blue	3.25	.15
198 A51	3p brown org	6.00	.30
199 A52	4p bister	6.00	.35
200 A53	5p chocolate	5.25	.25
201 A54	6p emerald	8.00	.50
202 A55	9p rose	10.00	.75
203 A56	1sh org yel	11.50	.75
204 A57	2sh blue, *rose*	21.00	2.25
205 A58	5sh rose red & bl	65.00	12.50
a.	5sh carmine & blue	65.00	9.00
	Nos. 193-205 (13)	143.75	18.75

See Nos. 209-229, 232.

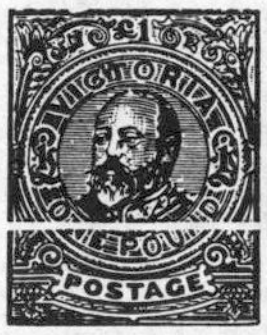

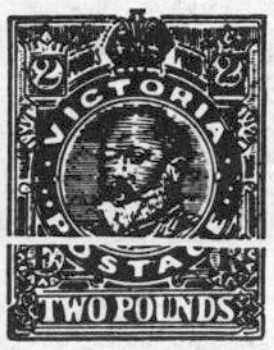

King Edward VII
A59 A60

1901-05

206 A59	£1 deep rose	300.00	125.00
a.	Perf. 11 ('05)	325.00	140.00
208 A60	£2 dk blue ('02)	750.00	200.00
a.	Perf. 11 ('05)	850.00	600.00

See Nos. 230-231.

1903 **Redrawn**

209 A56	1sh yellow	15.00	1.40
a.	1sh orange	13.00	1.40

No. 209 has the network lighter than No. 203. In the latter the "P" and "E" of "POSTAGE" are in a position more nearly horizontal than on No. 209.

Perf. 11, 12x12 1/2, 12 1/2, 12 1/2x11
1905-10 **Wmk. 13**

218 A46	1/2p blue green	1.25	.60
219 A47	1p rose red	1.00	.15
a.	1p carmine rose	2.00	.15
220 A49	2p violet	3.25	.15
a.	2p purple	3.25	.15
221 A50	2 1/2p blue	3.50	.25
222 A51	3p brown org	4.50	.30
a.	3p dull yellow	5.25	.25
223 A52	4p bister	6.50	.40
224 A53	5p chocolate	6.00	.32
225 A54	6p emerald	8.25	.48
226 A55	9p brown rose	13.00	1.10
a.	9p orange brown	10.00	1.10
227 A55	9p car rose	10.00	1.10
228 A56	1sh yellow ('08)	10.00	1.00
229 A58	5sh rose red & ultra	70.00	12.50
a.	5sh orange red & ultra	62.50	12.50
230 A59	£1 pale red ('07)	325.00	110.00
a.	£1 rose ('10)	325.00	100.00
231 A60	£2 dull blue	750.00	300.00
	Nos. 218-229 (12)	137.25	18.35

No. 220 Surcharged in Red **ONE PENNY**

1912, July 1

232 A49	1p on 2p violet	.32	.20

POSTAL-FISCAL STAMPS

On Jan. 1, 1884, all postage and fiscal stamps were made available for either purpose. Therefore all stamps inscribed "Stamp Duty" on hand at that date or issued thereafter can be considered as postage stamps.

Values for used are for postally canceled.

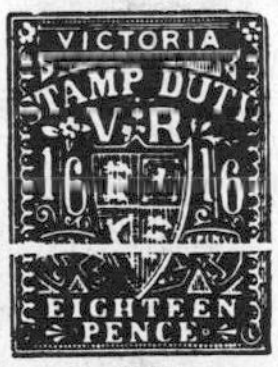
PF5

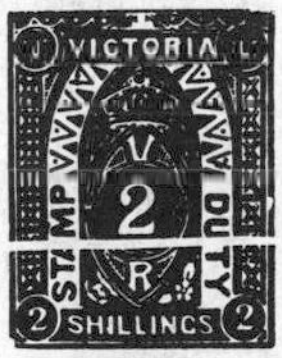
PF6

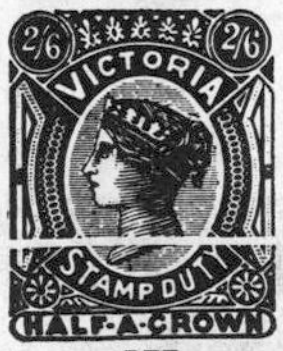
PF7

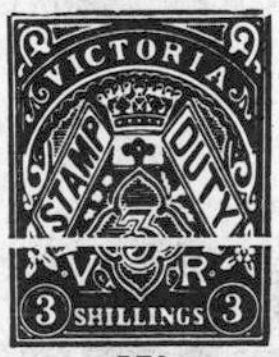
PF8

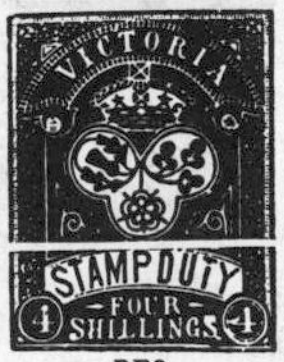
PF9

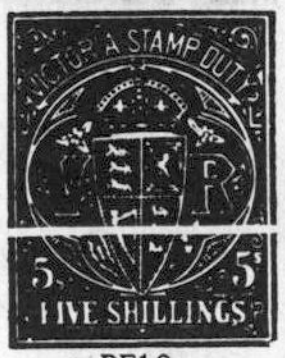
PF10

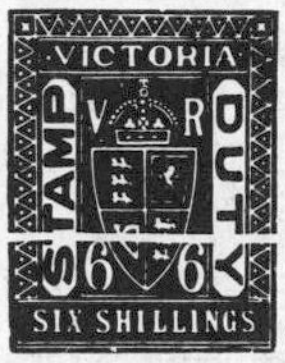
Coat of Arms — PF11

Wmk. V and Crown (70)
1884-96 **Typo.** ***Perf. 12 1/2***

AR1	PF5	1sh6p rose	150.00	15.00
AR2	PF6	2sh bl, *grn*	150.00	12.00
AR3	PF7	2sh6p orange	150.00	30.00
AR4	PF8	3sh bister	87.50	15.00

Lithographed

AR5	PF8	3sh vio, *bl*	275.00	30.00
AR6	PF9	4sh orange	85.00	5.75
a.		4sh vermilion	85.00	5.75

Typographed

AR7	PF10	5sh claret, *yel*	70.00	10.00
AR8	PF10	5sh car rose ('96)	130.00	6.75
AR9	PF11	6sh yel grn	275.00	22.50
		Nos. AR1-AR9 (9)	1,372.	147.00

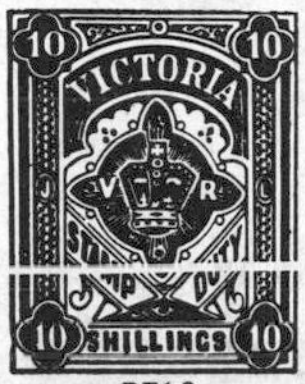
PF12

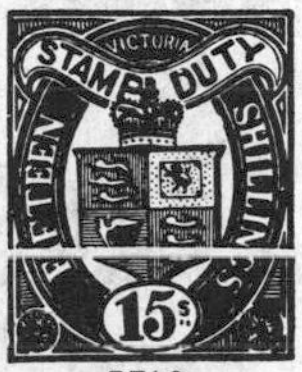
PF13

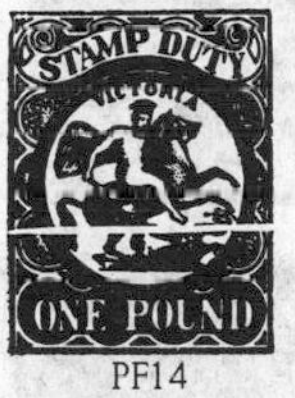
PF14

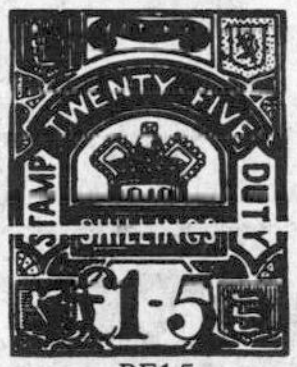
PF15

PF16

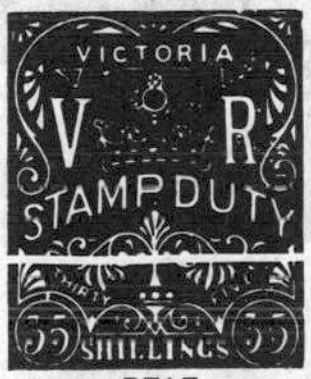
PF17

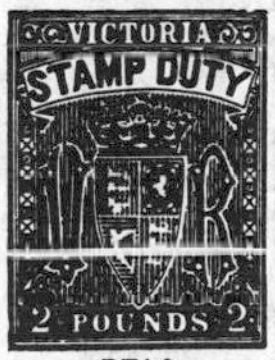
PF18

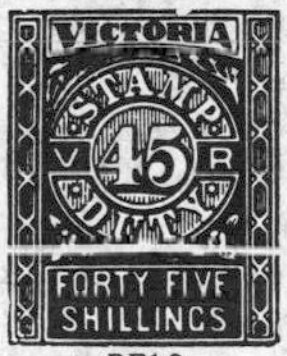
PF19

AR10	PF12	10sh brown	250.00	100.00
AR11	PF12	10sh gray grn	240.00	17.50

Lithographed

AR12	PF13	15sh lilac		250.00

Typographed

AR13	PF13	15sh pale brn	500.00	150.00

Lithographed

AR14	PF14	£1 org, *yel*	*500.00*	47.50
AR15	PF15	£1 5sh pink	*1,350.*	90.00
AR16	PF16	£1 10sh ol grn	1,000.	22.50
AR17	PF17	35sh violet		
		Revenue cancellation		250.00

Typographed

AR18	PF18	£2 blue	1,200.	65.00
AR19	PF19	45sh gray lilac	*2,000.*	250.00

Victoria stamps can be mounted in the Scott Australia album.

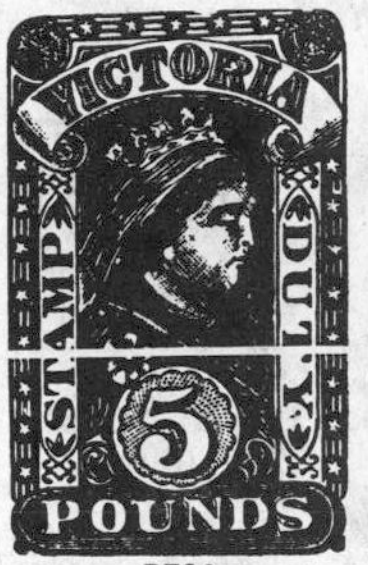
PF20

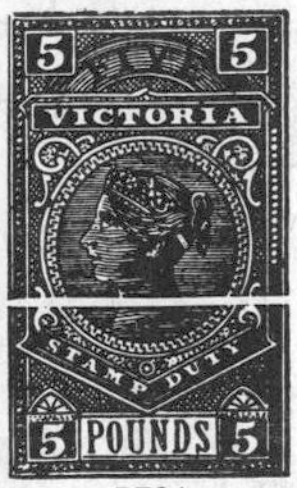
PF21

Litho.

AR20	PF20	£5 rose		200.00

Typographed

AR21	PF21	£5 claret & ultra	*1,200.*	60.00

SEMI-POSTAL STAMPS

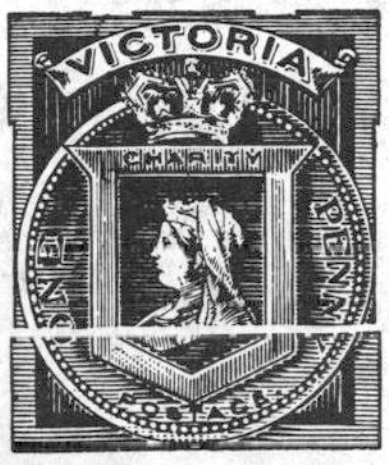
SP1

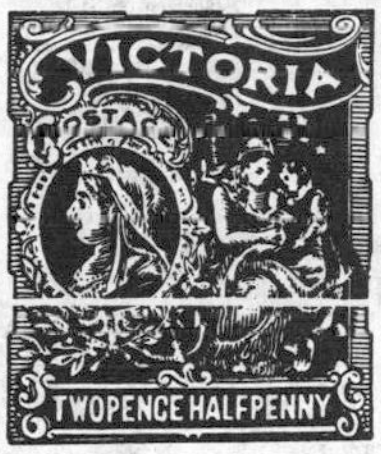
Queen Victoria and Figure of Charity — SP2

Wmk. V and Crown (70)
1897, Oct. **Typo.** ***Perf. 12 1/2***

B1	SP1	1p deep blue	8.50	18.00
B2	SP2	2 1/2p red brown	110.00	110.00

These stamps were sold at 1sh and 2sh6p respectively. The premium was given to a charitable institution.

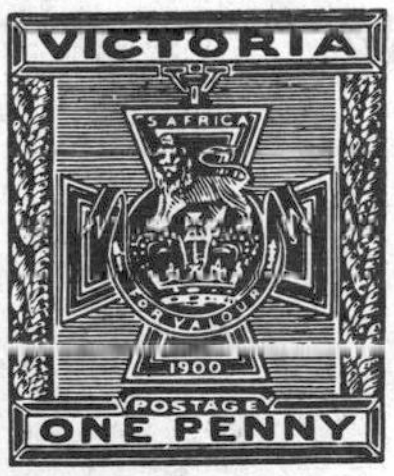
Victoria Cross — SP3

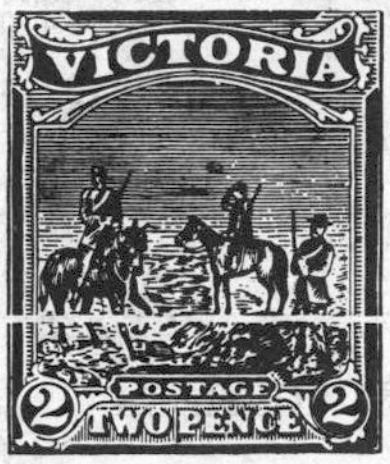
Scout Reporting — SP4

1900

B3	SP3	1p brown olive	70.00	70.00
B4	SP4	2p emerald	140.00	140.00

These stamps were sold at 1sh and 2sh respectively. The premium was given to a patriotic fund in connection with the South African War.

REGISTRATION STAMPS

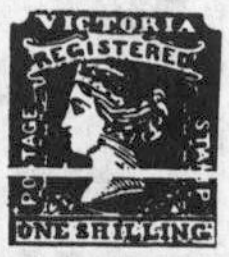
R1

1854, Dec. 1 Typo. Unwmk. *Imperf.*

F1	R1	1sh rose & blue	1,000.	100.00

1857 ***Rouletted 7***

F2	R1	1sh rose & blue	5,000.	150.00

LATE FEE STAMP

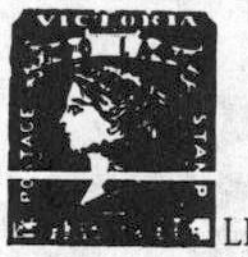
LF1

1855, Jan. 1 Typo. Unwmk. *Imperf.*

I1	LF1	6p lilac & green	650.00	150.00

POSTAGE DUE STAMPS

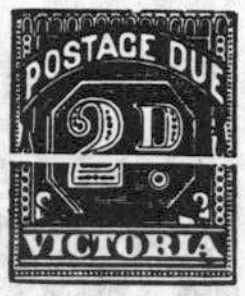
D1

Wmk. V and Crown (70)

1890 Typo. *Perf. 12½*

J1	D1	½p claret & blue	2.00	1.65
J2	D1	1p claret & blue	3.25	1.25
J3	D1	2p claret & blue	5.00	1.50
J4	D1	4p claret & blue	6.00	1.75
J5	D1	5p claret & blue	5.50	1.65
J6	D1	6p claret & blue	6.25	1.50
J7	D1	10p claret & blue	60.00	32.50
J8	D1	1sh claret & blue	35.00	5.00
J9	D1	2sh claret & blue	92.50	42.50
J10	D1	5sh claret & blue	140.00	90.00
		Nos. J1-J10 (10)	355.50	179.30

1891

J11	D1	½p lake & blue	2.50	2.00
J12	D1	1p brown red & blue	4.25	1.25
J13	D1	2p brown red & blue	4.25	.90
J14	D1	4p lake & blue	6.50	4.50
		Nos. J11-J14 (4)	17.50	8.65

1894

J15	D1	½p bl grn & rose	1.65	1.40
J16	D1	1p bl grn & rose	.70	.35
J17	D1	2p bl grn & rose	1.50	.30
J18	D1	4p bl grn & rose	3.50	1.25
J19	D1	5p bl grn & rose	4.00	2.25
J20	D1	6p bl grn & rose	4.00	2.50
J21	D1	10p bl grn & rose	10.00	8.50
J22	D1	1sh bl grn & rose	5.00	2.75
J23	D1	2sh green & rose	60.00	20.00
J24	D1	5sh green & rose	100.00	35.00
		Nos. J15-J24 (10)	190.35	74.30

1906 **Wmk. 13**

J25	D1	½p yel grn & rose	1.65	1.65
J26	D1	1p yel grn & rose	3.00	.65
J27	D1	2p yel grn & rose	6.50	1.50
J28	D1	4p yel grn & rose	13.00	10.00
		Nos. J25-J28 (4)	24.15	13.80

WESTERN AUSTRALIA

ˈwes–tərn o–ˈstrāl–yə

LOCATION — Western part of Australia, occupying about a third of that continent
GOVT. — A former British Colony
AREA — 975,920 sq. mi.
POP. — 184,124 (1901)
CAPITAL — Perth

Western Australia was one of the six British colonies that united on January 1, 1901, to form the Commonwealth of Australia.

12 Pence = 1 Shilling
20 Shillings = 1 Pound

Unused values for Nos. 1-10 are for stamps without gum as these stamps are seldom found with original gum. Otherwise, unused values are for stamps with original gum as defined in the catalogue introduction.

Very fine examples of all rouletted and perforated stamps from Nos. 6-34 have roulettes or perforations touching the design. Examples clear on all four sides range from scarce to rare and will command higher prices.

Watermarks

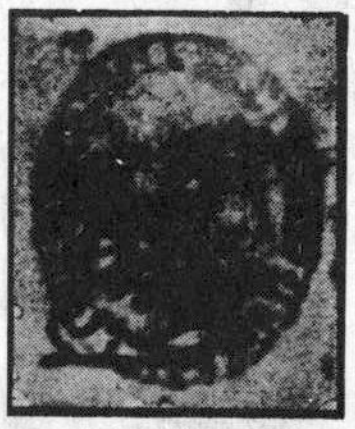
Wmk. 82- Swan

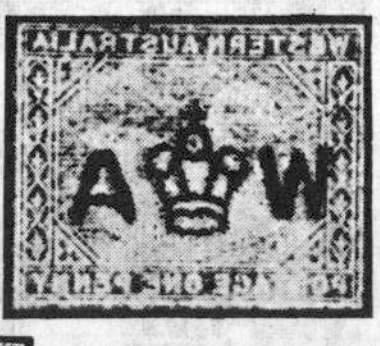
Wmk. 83- Crown and W A

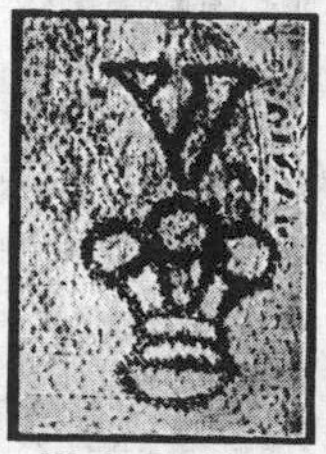
Wmk. 70- V and Crown

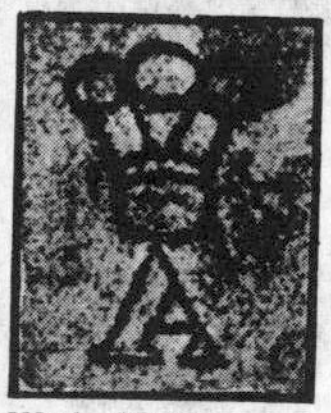
Wmk. 13- Crown & Double-lined A

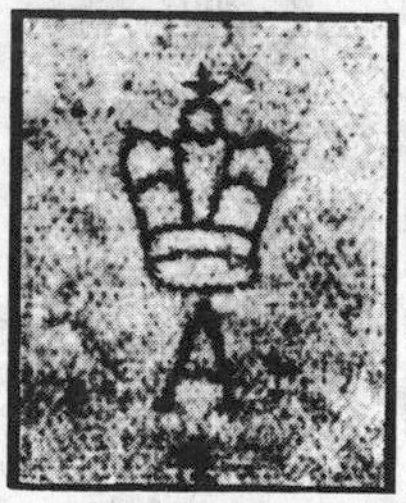
Wmk. 74- Crown and Single-lined A

A1

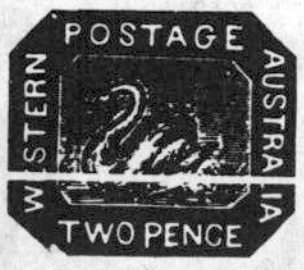
A2

Swan

1854-57 Engr. Wmk. 82 *Imperf.*

1	A1	1p black	750.	190.

Litho.

2	A2	2p brown, *red* ('57)	1,300.	425.
a.		2p brown, *deep red* ('57)	1,500.	475.
b.		Printed on both sides	1,500.	750.

See Nos. 4, 6-7, 9, 14-39, 44-52, 54, 59-61. For surcharges see Nos. 41, 55-56.

Western Australia stamps can be mounted in the Scott Australia album.

A3

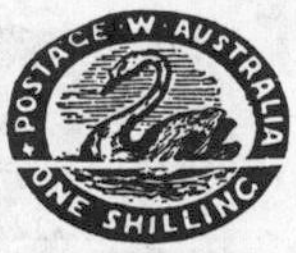
A4

3	A3	4p blue	275.	150.
a.		Frame inverted		*60,000.*
		As "a," cut to shape		*16,000.*
b.		4p slate blue	1,000.	575.
4	A2	6p bronze ('57)	3,000.	600.
5	A4	1sh pale brown	400.	225.
a.		1sh dark brown	500.	375.
b.		1sh dark red brown	800.	400.
c.		1sh pale red brown		1,800.

Engraved

Rouletted

6	A1	1p black	1,750.	500.

Lithographed

7	A2	2p brown, *red* ('57)	3,250.	1,200.
a.		Printed on both sides		
8	A3	4p blue	1,400.	600.
9	A2	6p bronze ('57)	3,500.	1,000.
10	A4	1sh brown	2,000.	700.

The 2p, 4p and 6p are known with pin-perforation but this is believed to be unofficial.

1860 Engr. *Imperf.*

14	A1	2p vermilion	100.00	87.50
a.		2p pale orange	95.00	60.00
15	A1	4p blue	185.00	*800.00*
16	A1	6p dull green	1,100.	600.00

Rouletted

17	A1	2p vermilion	600.00	200.00
a.		2p pale orange	600.00	200.00
18	A1	4p deep blue	2,500.	—
19	A1	6p dull green	—	400.00

1861 ***Clean-Cut Perf. 14 to 16***

20	A1	1p rose	330.00	80.00
a.		Imperf.		
21	A1	2p blue	70.00	25.00
a.		Imperf., pair		
b.		Horiz. pair, imperf. vert.		
22	A1	4p vermilion	265.00	150.00
a.		Imperf.		
23	A1	6p purple brn	175.00	35.00
a.		Imperf.		
24	A1	1sh green	300.00	45.00
a.		Imperf.		

Rough Perf. 14 to 16

24B	A1	1p rose	200.00	27.50
24C	A1	6p pur brn, *bluish*	750.00	50.00
24D	A1	1sh deep green	1,200.	350.00

Perf. 14

25	A1	1p rose	140.00	45.00
25A	A1	2p blue	70.00	30.00
25B	A1	4p vermilion	200.00	85.00

Unwmk. ***Perf. 13***

26	A1	1p lake	40.00	5.50
28	A1	6p violet	90.00	32.50

1865-79 Wmk. 1 *Perf. 12½*

29	A1	1p bister	40.00	2.00
30	A1	1p yel ocher	60.00	5.50
31	A1	2p yellow	45.00	.60
a.		2p lilac (error) ('79)	*7,500.*	*3,750.*
32	A1	4p carmine	50.00	5.50
a.		Double impression	*6,000.*	
33	A1	6p violet	62.50	6.00
a.		6p lilac	130.00	6.00
b.		6p red lilac	120.00	6.00
c.		Double impression		
34	A1	1sh bright green	85.00	10.50
a.		1sh sage green	140.00	18.00
		Nos. 29-34 (6)	342.50	30.10

1872-78 ***Perf. 14***

35	A1	1p bister	50.00	2.00
36	A1	1p yellow ocher	40.00	.48
37	A1	2p yellow	40.00	.40
38	A1	4p carmine	200.00	65.00
39	A1	6p lilac	80.00	4.00
		Nos. 35-39 (5)	410.00	71.88

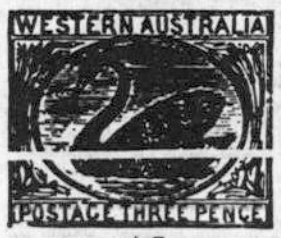
A5

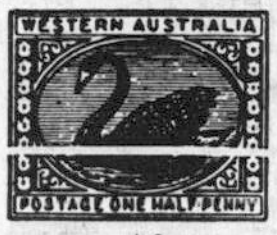
A8

1872 **Typo.**

40	A5	3p red brown	26.00	3.75
a.		3p brown	26.00	3.75

See #53, 92. For surcharges see #57, 69-72A.

No. 31 Surcharged in Green ONE PENNY

1875 Engr. *Perf. 12½*

41	A1	1p on 2p yellow	200.00	45.00
a.		Pair, one without surcharge		
b.		"O" of "ONE" omitted		
c.		Triple surcharge		

Forged surcharges exist.

1882 Wmk. 2 *Perf. 12*

44	A1	1p ocher yellow	85.00	1.65
46	A1	2p yellow	110.00	1.10
47	A1	4p carmine	160.00	27.50
48	A1	6p pale violet	275.00	27.50
		Nos. 44-48 (4)	630.00	57.75

1882 ***Perf. 14***

49	A1	1p ocher yellow	13.00	.20
50	A1	2p yellow	18.00	.20
51	A1	4p carmine	72.50	11.50
52	A1	6p pale violet	80.00	2.50
a.		6p violet	47.50	2.50

Typographed

53	A5	3p red brown	8.50	.70
a.		3p brown	12.50	.45
		Nos. 49-53 (5)	192.00	15.10

1883 Engr. *Perf. 12x14*

54	A1	1p ocher yellow	1,650.	300.00

Nos. 44 and 49 Surcharged in Red **1/2**

1884 ***Perf. 12***

55	A1	½p on 1p ocher yel	9.00	12.00

Perf. 14

56	A1	½p on 1p ocher yel	13.00	15.00

No. 40 Surcharged in Green **1d.**

1885 Typo. Wmk. 1

57	A5	1p on 3p red brown	27.50	8.50
a.		1p on 3p brown	12.00	6.00
b.		"1" with straight top	27.50	11.00

Wmk. Crown and C A (2)

1885 Typo. *Perf. 14*

58	A8	½p green	2.00	.15

See No. 89.

1888 **Engr.**

59	A1	1p rose	12.00	.70
60	A1	2p slate	25.00	2.00
61	A1	4p red brown	82.50	17.00
		Nos. 59-61 (3)	119.50	19.70

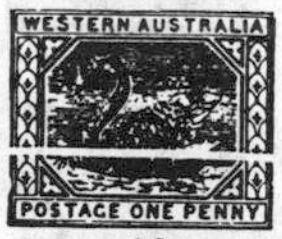
A9

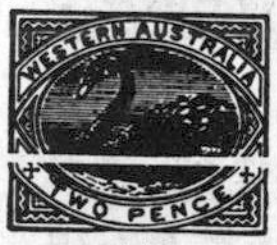
A10

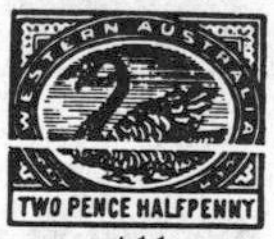
A11

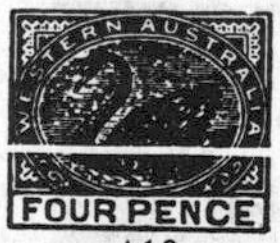
A12

1890-93 **Typo.**

62	A9	1p carmine rose	6.50	.15
63	A10	2p slate	10.00	.15
64	A11	2½p blue	6.00	.50
65	A12	4p orange brown	6.00	.50
66	A12	5p bister	8.25	.65
67	A12	6p violet	14.00	.50
68	A12	1sh olive green	16.00	1.40
		Nos. 62-68 (7)	66.75	3.85

See Nos. 73-74, 76, 80, 90, 94.

Nos. 40 and 53a Surcharged in Green **ONE PENNY**

1893 Wmk. Crown and C C (1)

69	A5	1p on 3p red brown	8.50	4.00
a.		1p on 3p brown	8.00	3.25
b.		Double surcharge	*725.00*	

Wmkd. Crown and C A (2)

70	A5	1p on 3p brown	40.00	9.00

Nos. 40a and 53a Surcharged in Green **Half-penny**

1895   **Wmk. Crown and C C (1)**
71   A5   ½p on 3p brown   6.00   2.75
   a.   Double surcharge   700.00

Green and Red Surcharge
72   A5   ½p on 3p brown   125.00

Wmk. Crown and C A (2)
72A   A5   ½p on 3p brown   70.00

After the supply of paper watermarked Crown and C C was exhausted, No. 72A was printed. Ostensibly this was to provide samples for Postal Union distribution, but a supply for philatelic demands was also made.

Types of 1890-93 and

A15

1899-1901   **Typo.**   **Wmk. 83**
73   A9   1p carmine rose   3.00   .15
74   A10   2p yellow   8.00   .15
75   A15   2½p blue ('01)   5.00   .20
   Nos. 73-75 (3)   16.00   .50

A16   A17

A18   A19

A20   A21

A22   Southern Cross — A23

Queen Victoria
A24   A25

Perf. 12½, 12x12½
1902-05   **Wmk. 70**
76   A9   1p carmine rose   6.50   .15
   a.   1p salmon
   b.   Perf. 11   100.00   5.00
   c.   Perf. 12½x11   180.00
77   A16   2p yellow   3.25   .20
   a.   Perf. 11   125.00   5.50
   b.   Perf. 12½x11   220.00
79   A17   4p orange brn   6.00   .80
   a.   Perf. 11   375.00   110.00
80   A12   5p olive bis ('05)   72.50   40.00
   a.   Perf. 11   45.00   21.00
81   A18   8p pale yel grn   20.00   2.75
82   A19   9p orange   26.00   4.00
   b.   Perf. 11   60.00   40.00
83   A20   10p red   27.50   5.50
84   A21   2sh red, yel   42.50   8.25
   a.   Perf. 11   125.00   55.00
85   A22   2sh6p dk bl, rose   37.50   7.75
86   A23   5sh blue green   70.00   19.00
87   A24   10sh violet   165.00   60.00
88   A25   £1 brown org   475.00   225.00
   Nos. 76-88 (12)   951.75   373.40

Perf. 12½, 12x12½
1905-12   **Wmk. 13**
89   A8   ½p dp green ('10)   2.25   .35
90   A9   1p rose   3.00   .20
   e.   Perf. 11   4.50
   f.   Perf. 12½x11   200.00   82.50
91   A16   2p yellow   3.00   .15
   a.   Perf. 11   11.00   4.50
   b.   Perf. 12½x11   230.00   95.00

92   A5   3p brown   6.50   .40
   a.   Perf. 11   12.00   2.75
   b.   Perf. 12½x11   265.00   82.50
93   A17   4p orange brn   8.00   1.50
     4p bister brown   8.00   1.50
   b.   Perf. 11   465.00   90.00
94   A12   5p olive bis   10.00   .70
   b.   Perf. 11   25.00   8.50
95   A18   8p pale yel grn ('12)   16.00   17.00
96   A19   9p orange   21.00   3.00
   b.   Perf. 11   65.00   55.00
97   A20   10p red orange   21.00   10.00
98   A23   5s blue green   140.00   60.00
   Nos. 89-98 (10)   230.75   73.30

For surcharge see No. 103.

A26   A27

1906-07   **Wmk. 83**   **Perf. 14**
99   A26   6p bright violet   15.00   .70
100   A27   1sh olive green   25.00   6.00

1912   **Wmk. 74**   **Perf. 11½x12**
101   A26   6p bright violet   11.00   3.00
102   A27   1sh gray green   22.50   4.00
   a.   Perf. 12½

No. 91 Surcharged **ONE PENNY**

1912   **Wmk. 13**   **Perf. 12½**
103   A16   1p on 2p yellow   .75   .40

Stamps of Western Australia were replaced by those of Australia.

ZAMBIA

ˈzam–bē–ə

LOCATION — Southern Africa
GOVT. — Republic
AREA — 290,586 sq. mi.
POP. — 6,242,000 (est. 1982)
CAPITAL — Lusaka

The former British protectorate of Northern Rhodesia became an independent republic Oct. 24, 1964, taking the name Zambia. See Northern Rhodesia; see Rhodesia and Nyasaland.

12 Pence = 1 Shilling
20 Shillings = 1 Pound
100 Ngwee = 1 Kwacha (1968)

Catalogue values for all unused stamps in this country are for Never Hinged items.

Pres. Kenneth D. Kaunda, Victoria Falls — A1   College of Further Education, Lusaka — A2

Perf. 14½x14, 14x14½
1964, Oct. 24   **Photo.**   **Unwmk.**
1   A1   3p shown   .15   .15
2   A2   6p shown   .15   .15
3   A1   1sh3p Barotse dancer   .30   .30
   Nos. 1-3 (3)   .60   .60

Zambia's independence, Oct. 24, 1964.

Farmer and Silo   X-Ray Technician
A3   A4

Designs: 2p, Chinyau dancer. 3p, Woman picking cotton. 4p, Angoni bull. 6p, Communications by drum and teletype. 9p, Redwood blossoms and factory. 1sh, Night fishing on Lake Tanganyika. 1sh3p, Woman tobacco worker. 2sh, Tonga basket maker and child. 2sh6p, Elephants in Luangwa Valley Game Reserve. 5sh, Child and school. 10sh, Copper mining. £1, Makishi dancer.

1964, Oct. 24   **Photo.**   **Perf. 14½**
Size: 23x19mm, 19x23mm
4   A3   ½p emerald, blk & red   .15   .15
5   A4   1p ultra, blk & brn   .15   .15
6   A4   2p orange, brn & red   .15   .15
7   A4   3p red & black   .15   .15
8   A4   4p orange & black   .15   .15

Perf. 13½x14½, 14½x13½
Size: 32x23mm, 23x32mm
9   A3   6p Prus grn, brn & org   .15   .18
10   A3   9p ultra, brn & dk car rose   .15   .15
11   A3   1sh blue, bis & blk   .20   .15
12   A4   1sh3p dk bl, ver, blk & yel   .22   .15
13   A4   2sh org, blk, brn & ultra   .40   .28
14   A3   2sh6p org ycl & blk   .45   .32
15   A3   5sh emerald, blk & yel   1.00   .60
16   A3   10sh orange & blk   2.00   1.50
17   A4   £1 red, blk, brn & yel   4.00   2.50
   Nos. 4-17 (14)   9.32   6.58

ITU Emblem, Old and New Communication Equipment — A5

1965, July 26   **Photo.**   **Perf. 14**
18   A5   6p brt lilac & gold   .18   .15
19   A5   2sh6p gray & gold   .65   .52

Cent. of the ITU.

ICY Emblem
A6

1965, July 26   **Perf. 14**
20   A6   3p grnsh blue & gold   .16   .15
21   A6   1sh3p ultra & gold   .40   .35

International Cooperation Year, 1965.

Pres. Kaunda and State House, Lusaka   Clematopsis
A7   A8

Designs: 6p, Fireworks over Independence Stadium. 2sh6p, Tithonia diversifolia.

Perf. 13½x14½
1965, Oct. 18   **Unwmk.**
22   A7   3p multicolored   .15   .15
23   A7   6p ind, yel & brt pink   .15   .15

Perf. 14
24   A8   1sh3p pink, yel & brn   .20   .20
25   A8   2sh6p brt grn, dp org & brn   .38   .38
   Nos. 22-25 (4)   .88   .88

1st anniv. of independence, Oct. 24.

Inauguration of WHO Headquarters, Geneva — A9

1966, May 18   **Perf. 14**
26   A9   3p rose brn, brt bl & gold   .15   .15
27   A9   1sh3p vio bl, brt bl & gold   .42   .42
   Set value   .50   .50

University of Zambia — A10

1966, July 12   **Photo.**   **Perf. 14**
28   A10   3p brt green & gold   .15   .15
29   A10   1sh3p brt purple & gold   .42   .42
   Set value   .50   .50

University of Zambia opening, Mar. 17.

National Assembly Building
A11

1967, May 2   **Unwmk.**   **Perf. 14**
30   A11   3p slate & bronze   .15   .15
31   A11   6p yellow grn & bronze   .24   .24
   Set value   .30   .30

Completion of National Assembly Building.

Lusaka Airport — A12

1967, Oct. 2   **Photo.**   **Perf. 13½x14½**
32   A12   6p vio blue & bronze   .15   .15
33   A12   2sh6p brown & bronze   .42   .42
   Set value   .50   .50

Opening of Lusaka International Airport.

Symbols of Agriculture — A13   Radio, Telephone and Television — A14

Designs: 4p, Emblem of Zambia Youth Service. 1sh, Map showing locations of Zambia coalfields. 1sh6p, Map showing Zambia-Tanzania Road.

Perf. 14½x13½, 13½x14½
1967, Oct. 23
34   A14   4p gray, red & gold   .15   .15
35   A13   6p lt vio bl, gold & blk   .15   .15
36   A14   9p dull blue, sil & blk   .15   .15
37   A13   1sh gold, red, blk & vio bl   .18   .18
38   A13   1sh6p bl grn, ultra, gold & blk   .30   .30
   Set value   .80   .80

Issued to publicize National Development.

Lusaka
Cathedral — A15

Baobab
Tree — A16

Designs: 3n, Zambia Airways plane. 5n, National Museum, Livingstone. 8n, Vimbuza dancer. 10n, Woman tobacco picker. 15n, Nudaurelia zambesina butterfly. 20n, Crowned cranes. 25n, Angoni warrior. 50n, Chokwe dancer. 1k, Railroad bridge, Kafue River. 2k, Eland.

Perf. 13¹/₂x14¹/₂, 14¹/₂x13¹/₂
1968, Jan. 16   **Photo.**
Size: 26x22mm, 22x26mm

39	A15	1n bronze & multi	.15	.15
a.		Booklet pane of 6	.20	
b.		Booklet pane of 4	.15	
40	A16	2n bronze & multi	.15	.15
41	A16	3n bronze & multi	.15	.15
a.		Booklet pane of 6	.60	
b.		Booklet pane of 4	.40	
42	A16	5n sepia & bronze	.15	.15
43	A16	8n bronze & multi	.20	.15
44	A16	10n bronze & multi	.24	.15

Size: 32x26mm, 26x32mm

45	A15	15n bronze & multi	.35	.16
46	A16	20n bronze & multi	.50	.28
47	A16	25n bronze & multi	.55	.35
48	A15	50n brone, org & blk	1.25	.35
49	A15	1k dk blue & brnz	2.00	.90
50	A15	2k copper & blk	5.00	2.00
		Nos. 39-50 (12)	10.69	4.94

Used values of Nos. 48-50 are for canceled-to-order stamps. Postally used copies sell for more.

Map of Zambia,
Arrow Pointing to
Ndola — A17

Perf. 14¹/₂x14
1968, June 29   **Photo.**   **Unwmk.**
51	A17	15n brt green & gold	.30	.30

Zambia Trade Fair at Ndola.

Children and
Human Rights
Flame — A18

WHO
Emblem — A19

Children — A20

Photogravure; Gold Impressed
1968, Oct. 23   **Perf. 14¹/₂x14**
52	A18	3n ultra, dk bl & gold	.15	.15
53	A19	10n brt violet & gold	.20	.20
54	A20	25n brt blue, blk & gold	.52	.52
		Nos. 52-54 (3)	.87	.87

Intl. Human Rights Year; 20th anniv. of WHO; 21st anniv. of UNICEF (25n).

Copper
Miner — A21

Map of Africa with
Zambia — A22

Design: 25n, Worker poling furnace, horiz.

Perf. 14¹/₂x13¹/₂
1969, June 18   **Photo.**
55	A21	3n dp violet & copper	.15	.15
56	A21	25n yellow, blk & copper	.65	.65
		Set value	.70	.70

50th anniv. of the ILO.

Perf. 13¹/₂x14, 14x13¹/₂
1969, Oct. 23   **Photo.**

Designs: 10n, Waterbucks, Kafue National Park, horiz. 15n, Golden perch, Kasaba Bay, horiz. 25n, Carmine bee-eater, Luangwa Valley.

57	A22	5n ultra, yel & copper	.15	.15
58	A22	10n copper & multi	.24	.24
59	A22	15n copper & multi	.38	.38
60	A22	25n copper & multi	.60	.60
		Nos. 57-60 (4)	1.37	1.37

International Year of African Tourism.

Nimbus III
Weather
Satellite — A23

1970, Mar. 23   **Litho.**   **Perf. 13x11**
61	A23	15n multicolored	.50	.50

Issued for World Meteorological Day.

"Clean
Water" — A24

Designs: 15n, "Nutrition" (infant on scale). 25n, Children's immunization and Edward Jenner, M.D.

1970, July 4   **Litho.**   **Perf. 13x12¹/₂**
62	A24	3n multicolored	.15	.15
63	A24	15n multicolored	.50	.50
64	A24	25n multicolored	.85	.85
		Nos. 62-64 (3)	1.50	1.50

Issued to publicize preventive medicine and the "Under Five" children's clinics.

Mural by
Gabriel
Ellison — A25

1970, Sept. 8   **Litho.**   **Perf. 14x14¹/₂**
65	A25	15n multicolored	.35	.35

Opening of the Conf. of Non-Aligned Nations in Mulungushi Hall (decorated with murals by Mrs. Ellison) in Zambia.

Ceremonial
Axe — A26

Traditional Crafts: 5n, Clay pipe bowl with antelope head. 15n, Makishi mask, vert. 25n, The Kuomboka Ceremony (dancers and ceremonial boat).

1970, Nov. 30   **Litho.**   **Perf. 14x14¹/₂**
Size: 34x25mm
66	A26	3n dp lil rose & multi	.15	.15
67	A26	5n dp org, blk & sepia	.15	.15

Perf. 13x13¹/₂
Size: 30x45¹/₂mm
68	A26	15n dp lil rose & multi	.45	.45

Perf. 12¹/₂
Size: 71¹/₂x23¹/₂mm
69	A26	25n violet, blue & multi	.75	.75
a.		Souvenir sheet of 4, #66-69	6.00	6.00
		Nos. 66-69 (4)	1.50	1.50

Dag Hammarskjold and UN General
Assembly — A27

Hammarskjold and: 10n, Downed plane. 15n, Dove with olive branch. 25n, Plaque and flowers.

1971, Sept. 18   **Perf. 13¹/₂**
70	A27	4n brown & multi	.15	.15
71	A27	10n yellow grn & multi	.18	.18
72	A27	15n blue & multi	.28	.28
73	A27	25n plum & multi	.45	.45
		Nos. 70-73 (4)	1.06	1.06

10th anniv. of the death of Dag Hammarskjold, (1905-61) Secretary-General of the UN, near Ndola, Zambia.

Red-Breasted Bream — A28

1971, Dec. 10
74	A28	4n shown	.20	.18
75	A28	10n Green-headed bream	.60	.50
76	A28	15n Tigerfish	1.25	.75
		Nos. 74-76 (3)	2.05	1.43

Christmas.

Cheetah — A29

Soil Conservation
A30

1972, Mar. 15   **Perf. 13¹/₂x14**
77	A29	4n shown	.28	.18
78	A29	10n Lechue	.70	.55

79	A30	15n Cape porcupine	1.10	.85
80	A30	25n Elephant	2.75	1.40
		Nos. 77-80 (4)	4.83	2.98

Conservation Year.

1972, June 30   **Litho.**   **Perf. 14x13¹/₂**
Size: 18¹/₂x45mm
81	A30	4n shown	.25	.25
82	A30	10n Forest conservation	.75	.75

Perf. 13¹/₂x14
83	A29	15n Water conservation (river view)	1.10	1.10
84	A29	25n Woman in corn field	1.90	1.90
		Nos. 81-84 (4)	4.00	4.00

Souvenir Sheet
85		Sheet of 4	7.25	7.25
a.	A30	10n Giraffe and zebra	1.40	
b.	A30	10n Rhinoceros	1.40	
c.	A30	10n Hippopotamus and deer	1.40	
d.	A30	10n Lion	1.40	

Conservation Year. Stamp size: 27x50mm.

1972, Sept. 22   **Perf. 13¹/₂x14**

Designs: All horizontal.

Size: 48x35mm
86	A30	4n Zambian flowers	.80	.50
87	A30	10n Citrus swallowtails and roses	1.65	1.40
88	A30	15n Bee	3.00	2.00
89	A30	25n Locusts in corn field	4.50	3.00
		Nos. 86-89 (4)	9.95	6.90

Conservation Year.

Mary and
Joseph
Going to
Bethlehem
A31

1972, Dec. 1   **Litho.**   **Perf. 14**
90	A31	4n shown	.15	.15
91	A31	9n Holy Family	.25	.25
92	A31	15n Adoration of the shepherds	.42	.42
93	A31	25n Kings following the star	.75	.75
		Nos. 90-93 (4)	1.57	1.57

Christmas.

Broken Hill
Man — A32

Designs: 4n, Oudenodon and rubidgea (artist's conception; vert.). 10n, Zambiasaurus. 15n, Skull of Luangwa Drysdalli. 25n, Glossoptoris (seed).

Perf. 14x13¹/₂, 14
1973, Feb. 1   **Litho.**
Size: 29x45mm
94	A32	4n org ver & multi	.65	.32

Size: 37¹/₂x21mm
95	A32	9n org ver & multi	1.00	.65
96	A32	10n apple grn & multi	1.10	.85
97	A32	15n lilac & multi	1.50	1.10
98	A32	25n orange brn & multi	2.75	2.75
		Nos. 94-98 (5)	7.00	5.67

Fossils from Luangwa area (except 9n), over 200 million years old.

Meeting of Stanley and Livingstone at
Ujiji — A33

Designs: 4n, Livingstone, the missionary. 9n, Livingstone at Victoria Falls. 10n, Livingstone stopping slave traders. 15n, Livingstone, the physician. 25n, Portrait and tree in Chitumbu, marking burial place of heart.

1973, May 1   **Perf. 13x13¹/₂**
99	A33	3n multicolored	.20	.20
100	A33	4n multicolored	.30	.30
101	A33	9n multicolored	.60	.60
102	A33	10n multicolored	.75	.75

103 A33	15n multicolored	1.10 1.10
104 A33	25n multicolored	1.75 1.75
	Nos. 99-104 (6)	4.70 4.70

Dr. David Livingstone (1813-73), medical missionary and explorer.

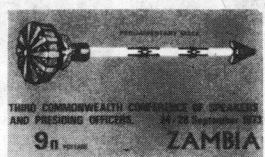

Parliamentary Mace — A34

1973, Sept. 24   Litho.   Perf. 13½x14

105 A34	9n tan & multi	.75 .75
106 A34	15n gray & multi	1.40 1.40
107 A34	25n brt green & multi	1.90 1.90
	Nos. 105-107 (3)	4.05 4.05

Third Commonwealth Conference of Speakers and Presiding Officers, Lusaka.

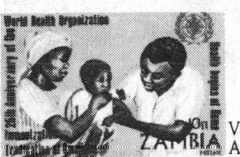

Vaccination A35

WHO Emblem and: 4n, Mother washing infant, vert. 9n, Nurse weighing infant, vert. 15n, Child eating cereal and fruit.

1973, Oct. 16   Litho.   Perf. 14

108 A35	4n blue & multi	67.50 25.00
109 A35	9n orange & multi	.30 .30
110 A35	10n brt green & multi	.40 .40
111 A35	15n violet & multi	.50 .50
	Nos. 108-111 (4)	68.70 26.20

WHO, 25th anniv.

A36   A37

Birth of the Second Republic: 4n, UNIP flag. 9n, United National Independence Party Headquarters, Lusaka. 10n, Army band. 15n, Women dancing and singing. 25n, President's parliamentary chair.

1973, Dec. 13   Litho.   Perf. 14x13½

112 A36	4n multicolored	24.00 5.00
113 A36	9n multicolored	.22 .22
114 A36	10n multicolored	.30 .30
115 A36	15n multicolored	.45 .45
116 A37	25n multicolored	.75 .75
	Nos. 112-116 (5)	25.72 6.72

Pres. Kaunda and his Home During
Struggle for Independence — A38

Designs: 4n, Pres. Kaunda at Mulungushi, vert. 15n, Pres. Kaunda holding torch of freedom.

1974, Apr. 28   Litho.   Perf. 14½x14

117 A38	4n multicolored	.70 .70
118 A38	9n multicolored	.90 .90
119 A38	15n multicolored	1.40 1.40
	Nos. 117-119 (3)	3.00 3.00

50th birthday of Pres. Kenneth Kaunda.

- Nakambla Sugar Estate — A39

Designs: 4n, Local market. 9n, Kapiri glass factory. 10n, Kafue hydroelectric plant. 15n, Kafue Bridge. 25n, Conference of Non-aligned Nations, Lusaka, 1970.

1974, Oct. 24   Litho.   Perf. 13½x14

120 A39	3n multicolored	.15 .15
121 A39	4n multicolored	.18 .18
122 A39	9n multicolored	.40 .40
123 A39	10n multicolored	.45 .45
124 A39	15n multicolored	.70 .70
125 A39	25n multicolored	1.10 1.10
	Nos. 120-125 (6)	2.98 2.98

Souvenir Sheet

126	Sheet of 4	7.00 7.00
a.	A39 15n Academic education	1.50
b.	A39 15n Teacher Training College	1.50
c.	A39 15n Technical education	1.50
d.	A39 15n University of Zambia	1.50

10th anniversary of independence.

Mobile Post Office A40

UPU Emblem and: 9n, Rural mail service by Zambia Airways. 10n, Modern Post Office, Chipata. 15n, Ndola Postal Training Center.

1974, Nov. 15

127 A40	4n multicolored	.15 .15
128 A40	9n multicolored	.25 .16
129 A40	10n multicolored	.28 .18
130 A40	15n multicolored	.45 .28
	Nos. 127-130 (4)	1.13 .77

Centenary of Universal Postal Union.

Radar by Day A41

Designs: 9n, Radar by night. 15n, Radar at dawn. 25n, Radar Station.

1974, Dec. 16

131 A41	4n multicolored	.24 .16
132 A41	9n multicolored	.52 .40
133 A41	15n multicolored	1.00 .70
134 A41	25n multicolored	1.75 1.25
	Nos. 131-134 (4)	3.51 2.51

Inauguration of Mwembeshi Earth Station, Oct. 21, 1974.

Rhinoceros and
Calf — A42

Peanut Harvest A43

1975, Jan. 3   Litho.   Perf. 13½x14

135 A42	1n shown	.15 .15
136 A42	2n Guinea fowl	.15 .15
137 A42	3n Zambian dancers	.15 .15
138 A42	4n Fish eagle	.15 .15
139 A42	5n Bridge, Victoria Falls	.15 .15
140 A42	8n Sitatunga	.15 .15
141 A42	9n Elephant, Kasaba Bay Resort	.15 .15
142 A42	10n Giant pangolin	.18 .15

Perf. 13

143 A43	15n Zambezi River source, Monument	.28 .15
144 A43	20n shown	.38 .22
145 A43	25n Tobacco field	.45 .32
146 A43	50n Flying doctor service	.90 .65
147 A43	1k Lady Ross's touraco	1.75 1.25
148 A43	2k Village scene	3.50 2.50
	Nos. 135-148 (14)	8.49 6.29

For surcharges see #188-191, 319, 371.

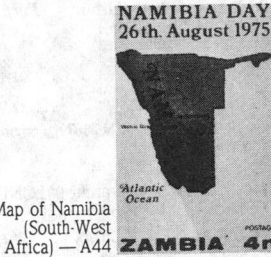

Map of Namibia
(South-West
Africa) — A44

1975, Aug. 26   Litho.   Perf. 14x13½

149 A44	4n green & dk green	.15 .15
150 A44	9n dk blue & gray bl	.24 .24
151 A44	15n yellow & orange	.42 .42
152 A44	25n orange & dp orange	.70 .70
	Nos. 149-152 (4)	1.51 1.51

Namibia Day.

Sprinkler Irrigation — A45

Designs: 9n, Sprinkler irrigation over rows of vegetables. 15n, Furrow irrigation.

1975, Dec. 16   Litho.   Perf. 13

153 A45	4n multicolored	.22 .22
154 A45	9p multicolored	.50 .50
155 A45	15n multicolored	.80 .80
	Nos. 153-155 (3)	1.52 1.52

Intl. Commission on Irrigation and Drainage, 25th anniv.

Julbernardia Paniculata — A46

Trees of Zambia: 4n, Sycamore fig. 9n, Baikiaea plurijuga. 10n, Colophospermum. 15n, Uapaca kirkiana. 25n, Pterocarpus angolensis.

1976, Mar. 22   Litho.   Perf. 13

156 A46	3n multicolored	.15 .15
157 A46	4n multicolored	.15 .15
158 A46	9n multicolored	.28 .28
159 A46	10n multicolored	.32 .32
160 A46	15n multicolored	.48 .48
161 A46	25n multicolored	.80 .80
	Nos. 156-161 (6)	2.18 2.18

World Forestry Day, Mar. 21.

TAZARA Passenger Train — A47

Designs: 9n, Train carrying copper. 10n, Clearing the bush. No. 164, Train carrying heavy machinery. No. 166b, Track laying. 20n, Reinforcing railroad track. No. 165, Train carrying various goods. No. 166d, Completed tracks.

1976, Dec. 10   Litho.   Perf. 13

162 A47	4n multicolored	.20 .20
163 A47	9n multicolored	.45 .45
164 A47	15n multicolored	.80 .80
165 A47	25n multicolored	1.40 1.40
	Nos. 162-165 (4)	2.85 2.85

Souvenir Sheet
Perf. 13½x14

166	Sheet of 4	4.00 4.00
a.	A47 10n multicolored	.40 .28
b.	A47 15n multicolored	.60 .45
c.	A47 20n multicolored	.70 .50
d.	A47 25n multicolored	1.00 .65

Completion of Tanzania-Zambia Railroad.

Kayowe Dance A48

1977, Jan. 18   Litho.   Perf. 13½x14

167 A48	4n shown	.15 .15
168 A48	9n Lilombola dance	.24 .16
169 A48	15n Initiation ceremony	.45 .40
170 A48	25n Munkhwele dance	.75 .48
	Nos. 167-170 (4)	1.59 1.19

2nd World Black and African Festival, Lagos, Nigeria, Jan. 15-Feb. 12.

Grimwood's
Longclaw — A49

Birds of Zambia: 9n, Shelley's sunbird. 10n, Black-cheeked lovebird. 15n, Locust finch. 20n, White-chested tinkerbird. 25n, Chaplin's barbet.

1977, July 1   Litho.   Perf. 14½

171 A49	4n multicolored	.35 .18
172 A49	9n multicolored	.60 .42
173 A49	10n multicolored	.70 .48
174 A49	15n multicolored	.95 .70
175 A49	20n multicolored	1.50 .95
176 A49	25n multicolored	1.90 1.25
	Nos. 171-176 (6)	6.00 3.98

Children
Playing with
Blocks
A50

Designs: 9n, Women of various races dancing in circle. 15n, Black and white girls with young bird.

1977, Oct. 20   Litho.   Perf. 14x14½

177 A50	4n multicolored	.15 .15
178 A50	9n multicolored	.20 .20
179 A50	15n multicolored	.35 .35
	Nos. 177-179 (3)	.70 .70

Combat racism and racial discrimination.

"Glory to
God in the
Highest"
A51

Christmas: 9n, Nativity. 10n, Three Kings and camel. 15n, Presentation at the Temple.

1977, Dec. 20   Litho.   Perf. 14

180 A51	4n multicolored	.15 .15
181 A51	9n multicolored	.24 .24
182 A51	10n multicolored	.24 .24
183 A51	15n multicolored	.35 .35
	Nos. 180-183 (4)	.98 .98

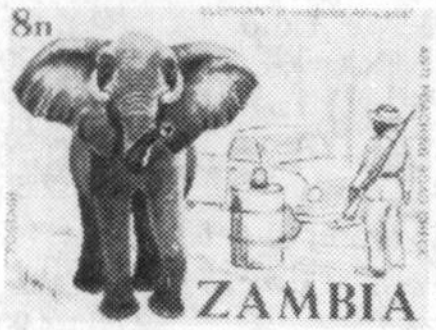

Elephant and Road Check A52

Designs: 18n, Waterbuck and Kafue River boat patrol. 28n, Warthog and helicopter surveillance of National Parks. 32n, Cheetah and armed wildlife guards in Parks and Game Management Areas.

1978, Aug. 1 Litho. *Perf. 14x14½*

184 A52 8n multicolored .22 .22
185 A52 18n multicolored .50 .50
186 A52 28n multicolored .85 .85
187 A52 32n multicolored .90 .90
Nos. 184-187 (4) 2.47 2.47

Anti-poaching Campaign of Zambia Wildlife Conservation Society, Aug. 1978.

Nos. 141, 137, 145 and 143 Surcharged with New Value and 2 Bars

1979, Mar. 15 *Perf. 13½x14, 13*

188 A42 8n on 9n multi .18 .18
189 A42 10n on 3n multi .20 .20
190 A43 18n on 25n multi .38 .38
191 A43 28n on 15n multi .60 .60
Nos. 188-191 (4) 1.36 1.36

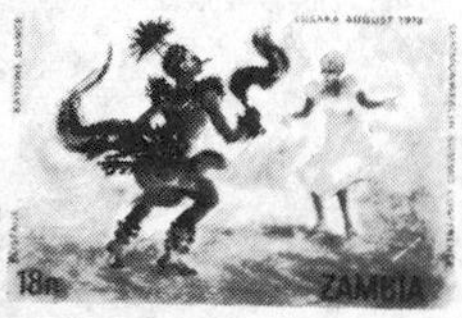

Kayowe Dance A53

Designs: 32n, Kutambala dance. 42n, Chitwansombo drummers. 58n, Lilombola dance.

1979, Aug. 1

192 A53 18n multicolored .40 .40
193 A53 32n multicolored .70 .70
194 A53 42n multicolored .90 .90
195 A53 58n multicolored 1.25 1.25
Nos. 192-195 (4) 3.25 3.25

Commonwealth Summit Conf., Lusaka, Aug. 1-9.

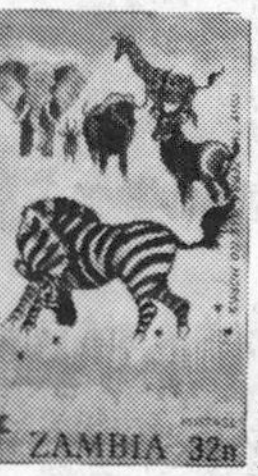

"Why the Zebra is Hornless" — A54

Children's Stories: 18n, Kalulu and the Tug of War. 42n, How the Tortoise got his Shell. 58n, Kalulu and the Lion.

1979, Sept. 21 Litho. *Perf. 14*

196 A54 18n multicolored .38 .38
197 A54 32n multicolored .65 .65
198 A54 42n multicolored .80 .80
199 A54 58n multicolored 1.10 1.10
a. Souvenir sheet of 4, #196-199 3.25 3.25
Nos. 196-199 (4) 2.93 2.93

International Year of the Child.

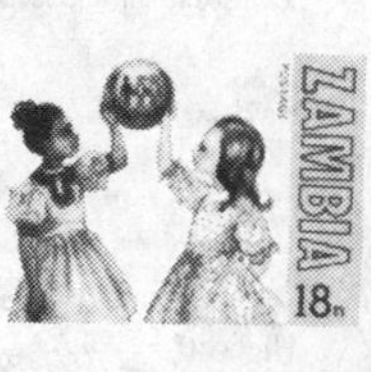

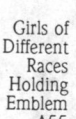

Girls of Different Races Holding Emblem A55

Anti-Apartheid Year (1978): 32n, Boys and toy car. 42n, Infants and butterfly. 58n, Children and microscope.

1979, Nov. 16 Litho. *Perf. 14½x15*

200 A55 18n multicolored .38 .38
201 A55 32n multicolored .65 .65
202 A55 42n multicolored .80 .80
203 A55 58n multicolored 1.10 1.10
Nos. 200-203 (4) 2.93 2.93

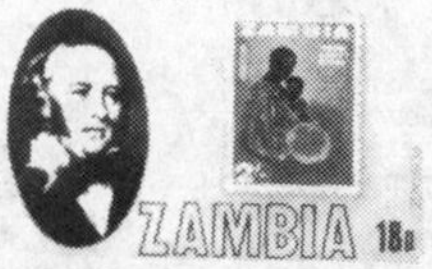

Hill, Zambia No. 13 A56

Hill and: 32n, Mailman & bicycle. 42n, No. Rhodesia #75. 58n, Mailman & oxcart.

1979, Dec. 20 Litho. *Perf. 14½*

204 A56 18n multicolored .38 .38
205 A56 32n multicolored .65 .65
206 A56 42n multicolored .80 .80
207 A56 58n multicolored 1.10 1.10
a. Souvenir sheet of 4, #204-207 3.25 3.25
Nos. 204-207 (4) 2.93 2.93

Sir Rowland Hill (1795-1879), originator of penny postage.

Nos. 204-207a Overprinted "LONDON 1980"

1980, Mar 6 Litho. *Perf. 15*

208 A56 18n multicolored .38 .38
209 A56 32n multicolored .65 .65
210 A56 42n multicolored .80 .80
211 A56 58n multicolored 1.10 1.10
a. Souvenir sheet of 4 3.25 3.25
Nos. 208-211 (4) 2.93 2.93

London 80 Intl. Stamp Exhib., May 6-14.

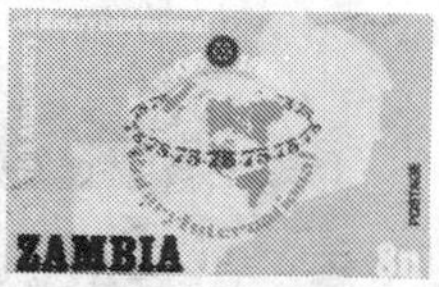

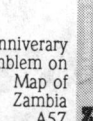

Anniverary Emblem on Map of Zambia A57

1980, June 18 Litho. *Perf. 14*

212 A57 8n multicolored .16 .16
213 A57 32n multicolored .65 .65
214 A57 42n multicolored .80 .80
215 A57 58n multicolored 1.10 1.10
a. Souvenir sheet of 4, #212-215 3.00 3.00
Nos. 212-215 (4) 2.71 2.71

Rotary International, 75th anniversary.

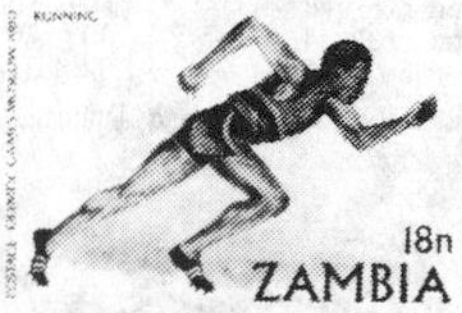

Running A58

1980, July 19 Litho. *Perf. 13*

216 A58 18n shown .40 .40
217 A58 32n Boxing .70 .70
218 A58 42n Soccer .90 .90
219 A58 58n Swimming 1.25 1.25
a. Souvenir sheet of 4, #216-219 3.50 3.50
Nos. 216-219 (4) 3.25 3.25

22nd Summer Olympic Games, Moscow, July 19-Aug. 3.

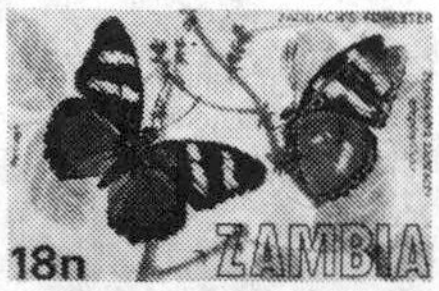

Zaddach's Forester A59

1980, Sept. 22

220 A59 18n shown .45 .45
221 A59 32n Northern highflier .80 .80
222 A59 42n Zambezi skipper 1.00 1.00
223 A59 58n Modest blue 1.50 1.50
a. Souvenir sheet of 4, #220-223 3.75 3.75
Nos. 220-223 (4) 3.75 3.75

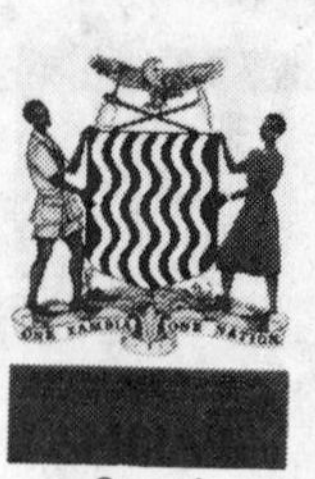

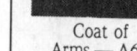

Coat of Arms — A60

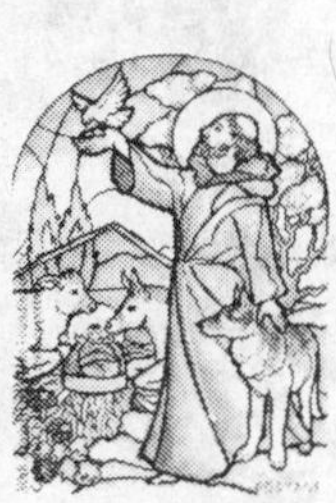

A61

1980, Sept. 27 Litho. *Perf. 14½*

224 A60 18n multicolored .40 .40
225 A60 32n multicolored .70 .70
226 A60 42n multicolored .95 .95
227 A60 58n multicolored 1.25 1.25
Nos. 224-227 (4) 3.30 3.30

26th Commonwealth Parliamentary Association Conference, Lusaka.

1980, Oct. Litho. *Perf. 14*

Nativity and St. Francis of Assisi (stained glass window), Ndola Church.

228 A61 8n multicolored .18 .18
229 A61 28n multicolored .60 .60
230 A61 32n multicolored .70 .70
231 A61 42n multicolored .95 .95
Nos. 228-231 (4) 2.43 2.43

Christmas and 50th anniv. of Catholic Church in Copperbelt (central Zambia).

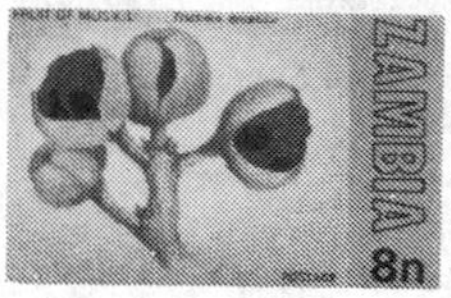

Trichilia Emetica Seed Pods, Musikili A62

Designs: Seed Pods.

1981, Mar. 21 Litho. *Perf. 14*

232 A62 8n shown .18 .18
233 A62 18n Afzelia quanzensis, Mupapa .40 .40
234 A62 28n Erythrina abyssinica, Mulunguti .60 .60
235 A62 32n Combretum collinum, Mulama .70 .70
Nos. 232-235 (4) 1.88 1.88

World Forestry Day.

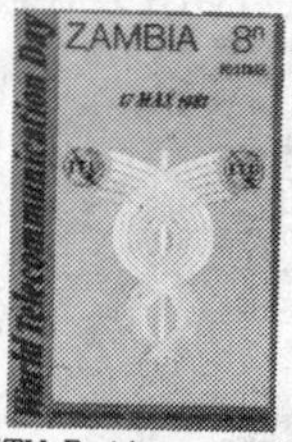

ITU Emblem — A63

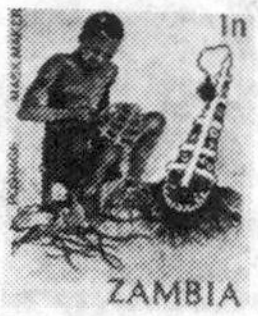

Mask Maker — A64

Designs: 18n, 32n, WHO emblem.

1981, May 15 Litho. *Perf. 14½*

236 A63 8n multicolored .16 .16
237 A63 18n multicolored .38 .38
238 A63 28n multicolored .55 .55
239 A63 32n multicolored .65 .65
Nos. 236-239 (4) 1.74 1.74

13th World Telecommunications Day (8n, 28n).

1981-83

240 A64 1n shown .15 .15
241 A64 2n Blacksmiths .15 .15
242 A64 5n Potter .15 .15
243 A64 8n Straw basket fishing .15 .15
244 A64 10n Roof thatching .20 .20
244A A64 12n Picking mushrooms ('83) .18 .18
245 A64 18n Millet grinding .28 .28
246 A64 28n Royal Barge paddler .45 .45
247 A64 30n Makishi tightrope dancer .48 .48
248 A64 35n Tonga-ila granary, house .52 .52
249 A64 42n Cattle herding .65 .65

Perf. 14

Size: 37x25mm

250 A64 50n Traditional healer .75 .75
251 A64 75n Carrying water jugs ('83) 1.10 1.10
252 A64 1k Grinding corn ('83) 1.50 1.50
253 A64 2k Woman smoking pipe 3.50 3.50
Nos. 240-253 (15) 10.21 10.21

For surcharges see Nos. 358, 372, 499-506, 596.

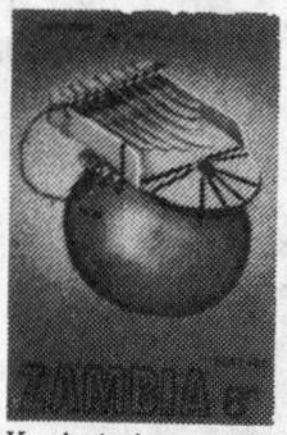

Kankobele — A65

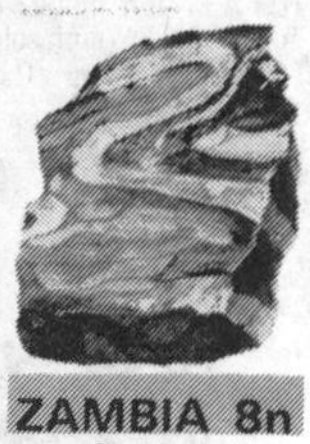

Banded Ironstone — A66

Designs: Traditional musical instruments.

1981, Sept. 30 Litho. *Perf. 14½*

254 A65 8n shown .15 .15
255 A65 18n Inshingili .32 .32
256 A65 28n Ilimba .55 .55
257 A65 32n Bango .60 .60
Nos. 254-257 (4) 1.62 1.62

1982, Jan. 5 Litho. *Perf. 14*

258 A66 8n shown .15 .15
259 A66 18n Cobaltocalcite .42 .42
260 A66 28n Amazonite .65 .65
261 A66 32n Tourmaline .75 .75
262 A66 42n Uranium ore 1.00 1.00
Nos. 258-262 (5) 2.97 2.97

1982, July 1 Litho. *Perf. 14*

263 A66 8n Bornite .30 .30
264 A66 18n Chalcopyrite .85 .85
265 A66 28n Malachite 1.25 1.25
266 A66 32n Azurite 1.50 1.50
267 A66 42n Vanadinite 2.25 2.25
Nos. 263-267 (5) 6.15 6.15

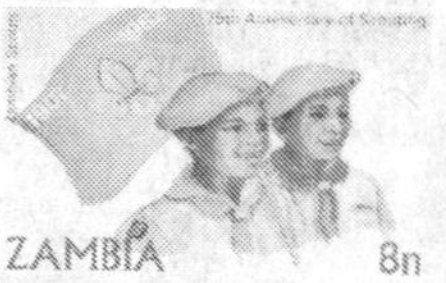

Scouting Year A67

1982, Mar. 30 Litho. *Perf. 14*

268 A67 8n Scouts, flag .15 .15
269 A67 18n Baden-Powell .32 .32
270 A67 28n Horned buffalo, patrol pennat .55 .55
271 A67 1k Eagle, conservation badge 1.75 1.75
a. Souvenir sheet of 4, #268-271 3.25 3.25
Nos. 268-271 (4) 2.77 2.77

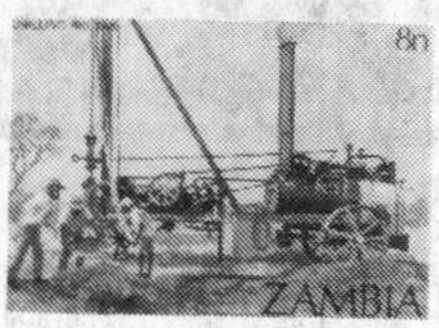

Drilling Rig, 1926 — A68

Steam locomotives.

1983, Jan. 26 *Perf. 14x14½*

272 A68 8n shown .22 .22
273 A68 18n Class B6, 1910 .50 .50
274 A68 28n Borsig engine, 1925 .85 .85
275 A68 32n 7th class, 1900 .90 .90
Nos. 272-275 (4) 2.47 2.47

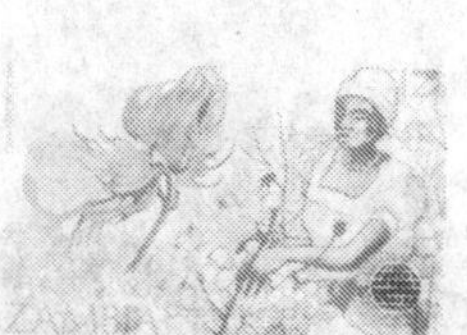

Commonwealth Day — A68a

1983, Mar. 10 Litho. *Perf. 14*

276 A68a 12n Cotton picking .20 .20
277 A68a 18n Miners .30 .30
278 A68a 28n Ritual pot, dancers .50 .50
279 A68a 1k Victoria Falls, purple-crested lorie 1.65 1.65
Nos. 276-279 (4) 2.65 2.65

Local Flowers — A69

1983, May 26   Litho.   *Perf. 14*
280 A69 12n Eulophia cucullata .20 .20
281 A69 28n Kigelia africana .50 .50
282 A69 35n Protea gaguedi .60 .60
283 A69 50n Leonotis nepotifolia .85 .85
   a.   Souvenir sheet of 4, #280-283, perf.
     12x12¹/₂   2.25 2.25
     Nos. 280-283 (4)   2.15 2.15

Thornicroft's Giraffes A70

1983, July 21   Litho.   *Perf. 14*
284 A70 12n shown .16 .16
285 A70 28n Cookson's wildebeest .45 .45
286 A70 35n Black lechwe .52 .52
287 A70 1k Yellow backed duiker 1.50 1.50
     Nos. 284-287 (4)   2.63 2.63

Tiger Fish — A71

1983, Sept. 29   Litho.   *Perf. 14*
288 A71 12n shown .16 .16
289 A71 28n Silver Barbel .45 .45
290 A71 35n Spotted Squeaker .52 .52
291 A71 38n Red Breasted Bream .55 .55
     Nos. 288-291 (4)   1.68 1.68

Christmas — A72

1983, Dec. 12   Litho.   *Perf. 14x14¹/₂*
292 A72 12n Annunciation .16 .16
293 A72 28n Shepherds .45 .45
294 A72 35n Three Kings .52 .52
295 A72 38n Flight into Egypt .55 .55
     Nos. 292-295 (4)   1.68 1.68

40th Anniv. of Intl. Civil Aviation Org. — A73

1984, Jan. 26   Litho.   *Perf. 14*
296 A73 12n Boeing 737, 1983 .16 .16
297 A73 28n Beaver, 1954 .35 .35
298 A73 35n Short Solent Flying
     Boat, 1948 .45 .45
299 A73 1k DH-66, 1931 1.25 1.25
     Nos. 296-299 (4)   2.21 2.21

60th Birthday of Pres. Kaunda A74

Perf. 14¹/₂x14, 14x14¹/₂
1984, Apr. 28   Litho.
300 A74 12n Receiving greetings .15 .15
301 A74 28n Swearing in, 1983,
     vert. .32 .32
302 A74 60n Planting cherry tree .65 .65
303 A74 1k Opening Natl. Assem-
     bly, vert. 1.10 1.10
     Nos. 300-303 (4)   2.22 2.22

1984 Summer Olympics — A75

1984, July 18   Litho.   *Perf. 14*
304 A75 12n Soccer .18 .18
305 A75 28n Running .45 .45
306 A75 35n Hurdles .55 .55
307 A75 50n Boxing .80 .80
     Nos. 304-307 (4)   1.98 1.98

Reptiles A76

1984, Sept. 5   Litho.   *Perf. 14*
308 A76 12n Gabon viper .15 .15
309 A76 28n Chameleon .35 .35
310 A76 35n Nile crocodile .45 .45
311 A76 1k Blue-headed agama 1.25 1.25
   a.   Souvenir sheet of 4, #308-311 2.25 2.25
     Nos. 308-311 (4)   2.20 2.20

20th Anniv. of Independence — A77

1984, Oct. 22   Litho.   *Perf. 14*
312 A77 12n Pres. Kaunda,
     Mulungushi Rock .15 .15
313 A77 28n Freedom Statue .35 .35
314 A77 1k Produce 1.25 1.25
     Nos. 312-314 (3)   1.75 1.75

Local Mushrooms — A78

1984, Dec. 12   Litho.   *Perf. 14x14¹/₂*
315 A78 12n Amanita flammeola .22 .22
316 A78 28n Amanita zambiana .45 .45
317 A78 32n Termitomyces letestui .52 .52
318 A78 75n Cantharellus miniates-
     cens 1.25 1.25
     Nos. 315-318 (4)   2.44 2.44

No. 146 Surcharged with New Value and Two Bars
1985, Mar. 5   Litho.   *Perf. 13¹/₂*
319 A43 5k on 50n multi 4.25 4.25

Primates A79

1985, Apr. 25   Litho.   *Perf. 14*
320 A79 12n Chacma baboon .15 .15
321 A79 20n Moloney's monkey .18 .18
322 A79 45n Blue monkey .40 .40
323 A79 1k Vervet monkey .90 .90
     Nos. 320-323 (4)   1.63 1.63

SADCC, 5th Anniv. A80

1985, July 9   Litho.   *Perf. 14*
324 A80 20n Map .18 .18
325 A80 45n Mining .38 .38
326 A80 1k Mulungushi Hall .90 .90
     Nos. 324-326 (3)   1.46 1.46

Southern African Development Coordination Conference.

Queen Mother, 85th Birthday A81

Designs: 25n, Portrait in blue, age 80, vert. 45n, Queen Consort at Clarence House, 1963, vert. 55n, With Elizabeth II and Princess Margaret. 5k, With royal family, christening of Prince Henry, 1984.

1985, Aug. 2
327 A81 25n multicolored .20 .20
328 A81 45n multicolored .38 .38
329 A81 55n multicolored .50 .50
330 A81 5k multicolored 4.25 4.25
     Nos. 327-330 (4)   5.33 5.33

For surcharges see Nos. 401, 406, 410, 414, 611.

Postal and Telecommunications Corp., 10th Anniv. — A82

1985, Dec. 12   *Perf. 13¹/₂x13*
331 A82 20n Lusaka P.O., 1958 .15 .15
332 A82 45n Livingstone P.O., 1950 .15 .15
333 A82 55n Kalomo P.O., 1902 .22 .22
334 A82 5k Transcontinental Tele-
     graph, 1900 2.00 2.00
     Nos. 331-334 (4)   2.52 2.52

For surcharges see Nos. 590-593.

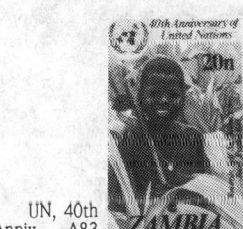

UN, 40th Anniv. — A83

1985, Dec. 19   *Perf. 14*
335 A83 20n Boy in cornfield .15 .15
336 A83 45n Emblem .15 .15
337 A83 1k Pres. Kaunda, 1970 .40 .40
338 A83 2k Charter signing, 1945 .80 .80
     Nos. 335-338 (4)   1.50 1.50

For surcharge see No. 594.

Beetles A84

1986, Mar. 20
339 A84 35n Mylabris tricolor .15 .15
340 A84 1k Phasgonocnema me-
     lanianthe .30 .30
341 A84 1.70k Amaurodes passerinii .50 .50
342 A84 5k Ranzania petersiana 1.50 1.50
     Nos. 339-342 (4)   2.45 2.45

Queen Elizabeth II 60th Birthday
Common Design Type

Designs: 35n, At the Flower Ball, Savoy Hotel, London, 1951. 1.25k, With Prince Andrew at

---

Lusaka Airport, Commonwealth Conf., 1979. 1.70k, With Dr. Kaunda observing natl. anthem. 1.95k, Wearing Queen Mary tiara, state visit to Luxembourg, 1976. 5k, Visiting Crown Agents' offices, 1983.

1986, Apr. 21   Wmk. 384   *Perf. 14*
343 CD337 35n scar, blk & sil .15 .15
344 CD337 1.25k ultra & multi .40 .40
345 CD337 1.70k grn, blk & sil .55 .55
346 CD337 1.95k vio & multi .62 .62
347 CD337 5k rose vio & multi 1.60 1.60
     Nos. 343-347 (5)   3.32 3.32

For surcharges see Nos. 402, 405, 407, 411, 415.

Royal Wedding Issue, 1986
Common Design Type

Designs: 1.70k, Sarah Ferguson kissing Prince Andrew. 5k, Andrew in informal dress.

1986, July 23   Litho.   *Perf. 14*
348 CD338 1.70k multicolored .55 .55
349 CD338 5k multicolored 1.60 1.60

1986 World Cup Soccer Championships, Mexico — A85

Various soccer plays.

1986, June 27   Litho.   *Perf. 14¹/₂*
350 A85 35n multicolored .15 .15
351 A85 1.25k multicolored .32 .32
352 A85 1.70k multicolored .45 .45
353 A85 5k multicolored 1.25 1.25
     Nos. 350-353 (4)   2.17 2.17

For surcharges see Nos. 403, 408, 412, 416.

Halley's Comet A86

Designs: 1.25k, Edmond Halley (1656-1742), by Henry Pegram. 1.70k, Giotto space probe approaching comet. 2k, Youth, astronomer. 5k, Halley's map of the southern constellations.

1986, July 4
354 A86 1.25k multicolored .35 .35
355 A86 1.70k multicolored .50 .50
356 A86 2k multicolored .60 .60
357 A86 5k multicolored 1.50 1.50
     Nos. 354-357 (4)   2.95 2.95

For surcharges see Nos. 404, 409, 413, 417.

#244A Surchd. in Light Red Brown
1986, July   Litho.   *Perf. 14¹/₂*
358 A64 20n on 12n multi .15 .15

Christmas A87

Children's drawings.

1986, Dec. 15   Litho.   *Perf. 14*
359 A87 35n Nativity .15 .15
360 A87 1.25k Magi .22 .22
361 A87 1.60k Nativity .28 .28
362 A87 5k Angel, house, tree .90 .90
     Nos. 359-362 (4)   1.55 1.55

Tazara Railroad, 10th Anniv. A88

Locomotive traveling various railway lines.

1986, Dec. 22

363 A88	35n Overpass, Kasama	.15	.15
364 A88	1.25k Tunnel 21 vicinity	.20	.20
365 A88	1.70k Tunnels 6-7	.28	.28
366 A88	5k Mpika Station grade separation	.80	.80
	Nos. 363-366 (4)	1.43	1.43

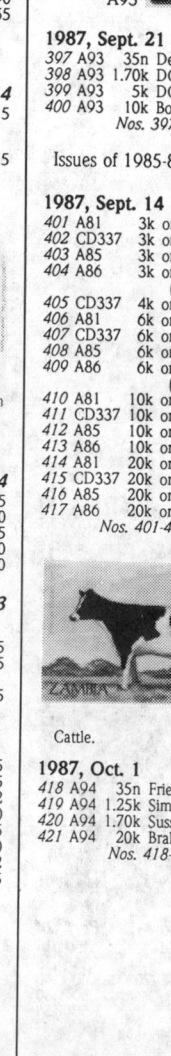

University of Zambia A89

Designs: 35n, Pres. Kaunda shaking council member's hand. 1.25k, University crest, vert. 1.60k, University statue. 5k, Kaunda laying university building cornerstone, vert.

1987, Jan. 27   Litho.   Perf. 14

367 A89	35n multicolored	.15	.15
368 A89	1.25k multicolored	.22	.22
369 A89	1.60k multicolored	.28	.28
370 A89	5k multicolored	.90	.90
	Nos. 367-370 (4)	1.55	1.55

Nos. 137, 243 Surcharged in Black or Blue

1987   Perf. 13¹/₂x14

| 371 A42 | 10n on 3n multi | .15 | .15 |

Perf. 14¹/₂

| 372 A64 | 25n on 8n multi (Bl) | .15 | .15 |

ZAMBIA

Kitwe Coat-of-Arms   35n

Municipal Arms — A90

ZAMBIA   25n

Birds — A91

1987, Mar. 26   Perf. 14

373 A90	35n Kitwe	.15	.15
374 A90	1.25k Ndola	.20	.20
375 A90	1.70k Lusaka	.25	.25
376 A90	20k Livingstone	3.00	3.00
	Nos. 373-376 (4)	3.60	3.60

1987-88   Perf. 11x13

Size: 20x25¹/₂mm

377 A91	25n Long-toed fluff tail	.15	.15
378 A91	30n Miombo pied barbet	.15	.15
379 A91	35n Black-and-rufous swallow	.15	.15

Size: 25x38¹/₂mm
Perf. 14

380 A91	50n Slaty egret	.15	.15
381 A91	1k Bradfield's hornbill	.25	.25
382 A91	1.25k Margaret's batis	.32	.32
383 A91	1.60k Red-and-blue sunbird	.40	.40
384 A91	1.70k Boehm's bee-eater	.45	.45
385 A91	1.95k Gorgeous bush shrike	.50	.50
386 A91	2k Shoebill	.52	.52
387 A91	5k Taita falcon	1.25	1.25

Surcharged

K1.65
=

Size: 20x25¹/₂mm
Perf. 11x13

388 A91	20n on 1n Yellow swamp warbler	.15	.15
389 A91	75n on 2n Olive-flanked robin	.20	.20
390 A91	1.65k on 30n #378	.42	.42

Size: 25x38¹/₂mm
Perf. 14

391 A91	10k on 50n #380	2.50	2.50
392 A91	20k on 2k #386	5.00	5.00
	Nos. 377-392 (16)	12.56	12.56

Issued: #377, 379, 381-385, 387, 9/14/87; #391-392, 3/10/88; others 10/8/87.
Nos. 388-389 not issued without overprint.
See Nos. 433-435, 527-547. For surcharges see Nos. 490, 492-498.

Look-out Tree, Livingstone A92

1987, June 30   Perf. 14

393 A92	35n shown	.15	.15
394 A92	1.25k Rafting, Zambezi River	.28	.28
395 A92	1.70k Walking safari, Luangwa Valley	.40	.40
396 A92	10k White pelicans	2.25	2.25
	Nos. 393-396 (4)	3.08	3.08

Zambia Airways, 20th Anniv. A93

1987, Sept. 21

397 A93	35n De Havilland Beaver	.15	.15
398 A93	1.70k DC-10	.42	.42
399 A93	5k DC-3	1.20	1.20
400 A93	10k Boeing 707	2.45	2.45
	Nos. 397-400 (4)	4.22	4.22

Issues of 1985-86 Surcharged in Gold or Black

1987, Sept. 14   Perfs. as Before

401 A81	3k on 25n #327 (G)	.75	.75
402 CD337	3k on 35n #343	.75	.75
403 A85	3k on 35n #350	.75	.75
404 A86	3k on 1.25k #354 (G)	.75	.75
405 CD337	4k on 1.25k #344	1.00	1.00
406 A81	6k on 45n #328	1.50	1.50
407 CD337	6k on 1.70k #345	1.50	1.50
408 A85	6k on 1.25k #351	1.50	1.50
409 A86	6k on 1.70k #355 (G)	1.50	1.50
410 A81	10k on 55n #329 (G)	2.50	2.50
411 CD337	10k on 1.95k #346	2.50	2.50
412 A85	10k on 1.70k #352	2.50	2.50
413 A86	10k on 2k #356 (G)	2.50	2.50
414 A81	20k on 5k #330 (G)	5.00	5.00
415 CD337	20k on 5k #347	5.00	5.00
416 A85	20k on 5k #353	5.00	5.00
417 A86	20k on 5k #357 (G)	5.00	5.00
	Nos. 401-417 (17)	40.00	40.00

World Food Day — A94

Cattle.

1987, Oct. 1   Perf. 14¹/₂x15

418 A94	35n Friesian-Holstein	.15	.15
419 A94	1.25k Simmental	.25	.25
420 A94	1.70k Sussex	.35	.35
421 A94	20k Brahma	4.00	4.00
	Nos. 418-421 (4)	4.75	4.75

Traditional Heritage — A95

Zambian people.

1987, Oct. 20   Perf. 13x12¹/₂

422 A95	35n Mpoloto Ne Mikobango	.15	.15
423 A95	1.25k Zintaka	.32	.32
424 A95	1.70k Mufuluhi	.42	.42
425 A95	10k Ntebwe	2.50	2.50
426 A95	20k Kubangwa Aa Mbulunga	5.00	5.00
	Nos. 422-426 (5)	8.39	8.39

World Wildlife Fund — A96   Wild Cats — A97

1987, Dec. 21   Litho.   Perf. 14

427 A96	50n Black lechwe drinking water	.15	.15
428 A96	2k Adults and young, horiz.	.50	.50
429 A96	2.50k Running, horiz.	.62	.62
430 A96	10k Male, diff.	2.50	2.50
	Nos. 427-430 (4)	3.77	3.77

Souvenir Sheets

| 431 A97 | 20k Cheetah | 5.00 | 5.00 |
| 432 A97 | 20k Caracal | 5.00 | 5.00 |

Bird Type of 1987

1987   Litho.   Perf. 11x13

433 A91	5n Black-tailed cisticola	.15	.15
434 A91	10n White-winged starling	.15	.15
435 A91	40n Wattled crane	.15	.15
	Set value	.22	.22

For surcharge see No. 491.

Intl. Fund for Agricultural Development (IFAD), 10th Anniv. — A98

1988, Apr. 2   Perf. 14

436 A98	50n Cassava crop	.15	.15
437 A98	2.50k Net fishing	.65	.65
438 A98	2.85k Cattle breeding	.75	.75
439 A98	10k Coffee picking	2.60	2.60
	Nos. 436-439 (4)	4.15	4.15

A99   A100

1988, Sept. 12   Litho.   Perf. 12¹/₂

440 A99	50n Breast-feeding	.15	.15
441 A99	2k Growth monitoring	.52	.52
442 A99	2.85k Immunization	.75	.75
443 A99	10k Oral rehydration	2.60	2.60
	Nos. 440-443 (4)	4.02	4.02

UN child survival campaign.

1988, Oct. 10   Litho.   Perf. 12¹/₂x13

444 A100	50n Asbestos cement	.15	.15
445 A100	2.35k Textiles	.60	.60
446 A100	2.50k Tea	.65	.65
447 A100	10k Poultry	2.60	2.60
	Nos. 444-447 (4)	4.00	4.00

Preferential Trade Area Fair.

Intl. Red Cross and Red Crescent Organizations, 125th Anniv. — A101

1988, Oct. 20   Perf. 14

448 A101	50n Famine relief	.15	.15
449 A101	2.50k Giving first aid	.62	.62
450 A101	2.85k Teaching first aid	.72	.72
451 A101	10k Jean-Henri Dunant	2.60	2.60
	Nos. 448-451 (4)	4.09	4.09

Endangered Species A102

1988, Dec. 5   Litho.   Perf. 14

452 A102	50n Aardvark	.15	.15
453 A102	2k Pangolin	.52	.52
454 A102	2.85k Wild dog	.75	.75
455 A102	20k Black rhinoceros	5.25	5.25
	Nos. 452-455 (4)	6.67	6.67

1988 Summer Olympics, Seoul A103

1988, Dec. 30   Litho.   Perf. 14

456 A103	50n Boxing	.15	.15
457 A103	2k Running	.52	.52
458 A103	2.50k Hurdling	.65	.65
459 A103	20k Soccer	5.25	5.25
	Nos. 456-459 (4)	6.57	6.57

Souvenir Sheets

| 460 A103 | 30k Tennis | 6.50 | 6.50 |
| 461 A103 | 30k Martial arts | 6.50 | 6.50 |

Frogs and Toads A104

1989, Jan. 25   Litho.   Perf. 12¹/₂

462 A104	50n Red toad	.15	.15
463 A104	2.50k Puddle frog	.50	.50
464 A104	2.85k Marbled reed frog	.58	.58
465 A104	10k Young reed frogs	2.00	2.00
	Nos. 462-465 (4)	3.23	3.23

Bats — A105

1989, Mar. 22   Litho.   Perf. 12¹/₂x13

466 A105	50n Common slit-faced	.15	.15
467 A105	2.50k Little free-tailed	.50	.50
468 A105	2.85k Hildebrandt's horseshoe	.58	.58
469 A105	10k Peter's epauletted fruit	2.00	2.00
	Nos. 466-469 (4)	3.23	3.23

A106   A107

1989, May 2   Litho.   Perf. 12¹/₂

470 A106	50n Map of Zambia	.15	.15
471 A106	6.85k Peace dove	1.35	1.35
472 A106	7.85k Papal arms	1.60	1.60
473 A106	10k Victoria Falls	2.00	2.00
	Nos. 470-473 (4)	5.10	5.10

State visit of Pope John Paul II, May 2-4.
For surcharge see No. 616.

1989, July 26   Litho.   Perf. 14¹/₂x15

Edible wild fruits.

474 A107	50n Parinari curatellifolia	.15	.15
475 A107	6.50k Uapaca kirkiana	1.30	1.30
476 A107	6.85k Ficus capensis	1.35	1.35
477 A107	10k Borassus aethiopum	2.00	2.00
	Nos. 474-477 (4)	4.80	4.80

For surcharge see No. 613.

Grasshoppers — A108

1989, Nov. 8 Litho. *Perf. 14x13½*
478 A108 70n Phamphagid .15 .15
479 A108 10.40k Pyrgomorphid 1.25 1.25
480 A108 12.50k Brown katydid 1.50 1.50
481 A108 15k Bush locust 1.85 1.85
Nos. 478-481 (4) 4.75 4.75

Christmas — A109

Flowers.

1989, Dec. 6 Litho. *Perf. 14½*
482 A109 70n Fireball .15 .15
483 A109 10.40k Flame lily 1.20 1.20
484 A109 12.50k Foxglove lily 1.45 1.45
485 A109 20k Vlei lily 2.30 2.30
Nos. 482-485 (4) 5.10 5.10

Stamp World London '90 A110

Designs: 1.20k, Lusaka Main P.O., van, mailman, bicycle. 19.50k, Zambia #220. 20.50k, Rhodesia and Nyasaland #164A, No. Rhodesia #1. 50k, Great Britain #1, Maltese Cross cancel in red.

Unwmk.
1990, May 2 Litho. *Perf. 14*
486 A110 1.20k multicolored .15 .15
487 A110 19.50k multicolored 1.00 1.00
488 A110 20.50k multicolored 1.10 1.10
489 A110 50k multicolored 2.75 2.75
Nos. 486-489 (4) 5.00 5.00

Nos. 379, 381 387, 433 Surcharged **K8.00**

1989, July 1 *Perf. 11x13*
490 A91 70n on 35n #379 .15 .15
491 A91 3k on 5n #433 .15 .15

Size: 25x38½mm
Perf. 14
492 A91 8k on 1.25k #382 .40 .40
493 A91 9.90k on 1.70k #384 .50 .50
494 A91 10.40k on 1.60k #383 .52 .52
495 A91 12.50k on 1k #381 .62 .62
496 A91 15k on 1.95k #385 .75 .75
497 A91 20k on 2k #386 1.00 1.00
498 A91 20.35k on 5k #387 1.05 1.05
Nos. 490-498 (9) 5.14 5.14

Nos. 242, 244-245, 247-248 251, 253 Surcharged in Black, Orange Brown, Red Brown, or Violet

K1.20 (a) K3.75 (b) K18.50 (c)

1989 *Perf. 14½*
Size: 22x26mm
499 A64(a) 1.20k on 35n #248 (OB) .15 .15
500 A64(b) 3.75k on 5n #242 .18 .18
501 A64(b) 8.11k on 10n #244 .40 .40
502 A64(b) 9k on 30n #247 .45 .45

Size: 37x25mm
Perf. 14
503 A64(b) 10k on 75n #251 .50 .50
504 A64(c) 18.50k on 2k #253 .90 .90

Size: 22x26mm
Perf. 14½
505 A64(a) 19.50k on 12n #244A (RB) .98 .98
506 A64(a) 20.50k on 18n #245 (V) 1.00 1.00
Nos. 499-506 (8) 4.56 4.56

Issued: #500-504, 7/1; others, 11/1.

World Cup Soccer Championships, Italy — A111

Soccer players in various positions.

1990, July 7 Litho. *Perf. 14*
507 A111 1.20k multicolored .15 .15
508 A111 18.50k multicolored .90 .90
509 A111 19.50k multicolored 1.00 1.00
510 A111 20.50k multicolored 1.05 1.05
Nos. 507-510 (4) 3.10 3.10

Souvenir Sheet
510A A111 50k multicolored 2.50 2.50

Southern African Development Co-ordination Conf. (SADCC), 10th Anniv. A112

Map of SADCC members and: 1.20k, Truck. 19.50k, Telecommunications. 20.50k, Regional cooperation. 50k, Coal transport by cable car.

1990, July 23 *Perf. 12½*
511 A112 1.20k multicolored .15 .15
512 A112 19.50k multicolored 1.00 1.00
513 A112 20.50k multicolored 1.05 1.05
514 A112 50k multicolored 2.50 2.50
Nos. 511-514 (4) 4.70 4.70

Independence, 26th Anniv. — A113

1990, Oct. 23 Litho. *Perf. 14*
515 A113 1.20k Agriculture .15 .15
516 A113 19.50k Shoe factory 1.00 1.00
517 A113 20.50k Satellite communications 1.05 1.05
518 A113 50k Mother and child statue 2.50 2.50
Nos. 515-518 (4) 4.70 4.70

Small Carnivores A114

1990, Nov. 12
519 A114 1.20k Genet .15 .15
520 A114 18.50k Civet .90 .90
521 A114 19.50k Serval 1.00 1.00
522 A114 20.50k African wild cat 1.05 1.05
Nos. 519-522 (4) 3.10 3.10

Intl. Literacy Year — A115

Soy Beans — A116

Children's stories.

1991, Jan. 11 Litho. *Perf. 14*
523 A115 1.20k Bird and the Snake .15 .15
524 A115 18.50k Hare and the Leopard .90 .90
525 A115 19.50k Mouse and Lion 1.00 1.00
526 A115 20.50k Hare and the Hippo 1.05 1.05
Nos. 523-526 (4) 3.10 3.10

Bird Type of 1987

1990-91 Litho. *Perf. 11x13*
527 A91 10n Livingstone's flycatcher .15 .15
528 A91 15n Bar-winged weaver .15 .15
529 A91 30n Purple-throated cuckoo shrike .15 .15
530 A91 50n Red-billed helmet shrike .15 .15
521 A91 50n like #527 .15 .15
532 A91 1k like #528 .15 .15
533 A91 1.20k Western bronze-naped pigeon .15 .15
534 A91 2k like #529 .15 .15
535 A91 3k like #530 .15 .15
536 A91 5k like #533 .20 .20

Size: 25x38½mm
Perf. 14
537 A91 15k Corn crake .60 .60
538 A91 20k Dickinson's grey kestrel .80 .80
539 A91 20.50k like #538 .82 .82
540 A91 50k Denham's bustard 2.00 2.00
Nos. 527-540 (14) 5.77 5.77

Issued: #533, 1k, 2k, 3k, 5k, 20k, 5/7/91; others, 10/30.

1991, June 28 Litho. *Perf. 13½*
548 A116 1k Woman cooking .15 .15
549 A116 2k Soy bean seed .15 .15
550 A116 5k Woman feeding child .20 .20
551 A116 20k Malnourished, healthy children .80 .80
552 A116 50k Pres. Kaunda, child 2.00 2.00
Nos. 548-552 (5) 3.30 3.30

United Church of Zambia / Rotary Foundation Project.

St. Ignatius of Loyola (1491-1556), Founder of Jesuit Order — A117

Designs: 1k, Chilubula Church near Kasama. 2k, Chikuni Church near Monze. 20k, Bishop Joseph Du Pont.

1991, July 18 Litho. *Perf. 13½*
553 A117 1k multicolored .15 .15
554 A117 2k multicolored .15 .15
555 A117 20k multicolored .80 .80
556 A117 50k shown 2.00 2.00
Nos. 553-556 (4) 3.10 3.10

Flowering Trees — A118

1991, Nov. 29 Litho. *Perf. 13½*
557 A118 1k Baobab .15 .15
558 A118 2k Dichrostachys cinerea .15 .15
559 A118 10k Sterospermum kunthianum .40 .40
560 A118 30k Azanza garckeana 1.20 1.20
Nos. 557-560 (4) 1.90 1.90

Queen Elizabeth II's Accession to the Throne, 40th Anniv.
Common Design Type
Perf. 14x13½

1992, Feb. 2 Litho. Wmk. 373
561 CD349 4k multicolored .16 .16
562 CD349 32k multicolored 1.30 1.30
563 CD349 35k multicolored 1.40 1.40
564 CD349 38k multicolored 1.55 1.55
565 CD349 50k multicolored 2.00 2.00
Nos. 561-565 (5) 6.41 6.41

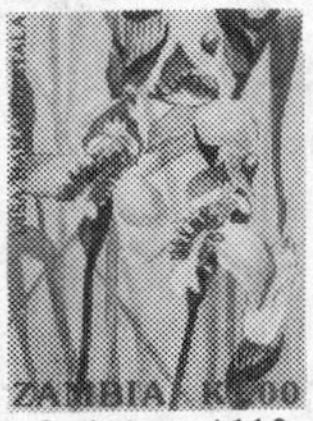

Orchids — A119

Masks — A120

Perf. 13x13½
1992, Feb. 28 Unwmk.
566 A119 1k Disa hamatopetala .15 .15
567 A119 2k Eulophia paivaeana .15 .15
568 A119 5k Eulophia quartiniana .20 .20
569 A119 20k Aerangis verdickii .80 .80
Set value 1.12 1.12

1992, Mar. 10
570 A120 1k Kasinja .15 .15
571 A120 2k Chizaluke .15 .15
572 A120 10k Mwanapweu .40 .40
573 A120 30k Maliya 1.20 1.20
Nos. 570-573 (4) 1.90 1.90

Antelopes A121

1992, Sept. 14 Litho. *Perf. 14*
574 A121 4k Bushbuck .15 .15
575 A121 40k Eland .42 .42
576 A121 45k Roan antelope .48 .48
577 A121 100k Sable antelope 1.05 1.05
Nos. 574-577 (4) 2.10 2.10

Airmail Services, 75th Anniv. A122

1992, Nov. 24 Litho. *Perf. 14*
578 A122 4k DH66 Hercules .15 .15
579 A122 40k VC10 .40 .40
580 A122 45k C Class flying boat .45 .45
581 A122 100k DC10 1.00 1.00
Nos. 578-581 (4) 2.00 2.00

1992 Summer Olympics, Barcelona — A123

1992, Dec. 28
582 A123 10k 400-meter hurdles .15 .15
583 A123 40k Boxing .40 .40
584 A123 80k Judo .80 .80
585 A123 100k Cycling 1.00 1.00
Nos. 582-585 (4) 2.35 2.35

Christmas — A124

1992, Dec. 23 Litho. *Perf. 14*
586 A124 10k Wise men .15 .15
587 A124 80k Nativity scene .80 .80
588 A124 90k Angels singing .90 .90
589 A124 100k Angel, shepherds 1.00 1.00
a. Souvenir sheet of 4, #586-589 2.85 2.85
Nos. 586-589 (4) 2.85 2.85

K2

Nos. 331-334 Surcharged

=

1991, Mar. 4   Litho.   Perf. 13½x13
590 A82 2k on 20n #331
591 A82 2k on 45n #332
592 A82 2k on 55n #333
593 A82 2k on 5k #334

=

Stamps of 1981-89 Surcharged **K2**

1991, July 5   Litho.   Perfs. as Before
594 A83 2k on 20n #335
596 A64 2k on 28n #246
611 A81 2k on 5k #330
613 A107 2k on 6.50k #475
616 A106 2k on 7.85k #472

Numbers have been reserved for additional surcharges in this set.

Waterfalls
A125

1993, Sept. 30   Litho.   Perf. 13½
617 A125 50k Nkundalila   .20   .20
618 A125 200k Chishimba   .80   .80
619 A125 250k Chipoma   1.00 1.00
620 A125 300k Lumangwe   1.20 1.20
    Nos. 617-620 (4)   3.20 3.20

Healthy
Hearts — A126

1993, Oct. 20   Litho.   Perf. 14½
621 A126 O Runner   .20   .20
622 A126 P Heart   .32   .32

No. 621 sold for 50k and No. 622 sold for 80k on date of issue.

Sunbirds
A127

Designs: 20k, Bronze. 50k, Violet-backed. No. 624, Marico. No. 625, Eastern double-collared. 100k, Scarlet-chested. 150k, Bannerman's blue-headed. 200k, Oustalet's. 250k, Red and blue. 300k, Olive. 350k, Green-headed. 400k, Scarlet tufted malachite. 500k, Yellow-bellied. 800k, Copper. 1000k, Orange-tufted. 1500k, Black. 2000k, Green-throated.

1993, May 30   Litho.   Perf. 13
623 A127 20k multicolored   .15   .15
624 A127 50k multicolored   .28   .28
625 A127 O multicolored   .28   .28
626 A127 P multicolored   .45   .45
627 A127 100k multicolored   .60   .60
628 A127 150k multicolored   .85   .85
629 A127 200k multicolored   1.10 1.10
630 A127 250k multicolored   1.40 1.40
631 A127 300k multicolored   1.75 1.75
632 A127 350k multicolored   2.00 2.00
633 A127 400k multicolored   2.25 2.25
634 A127 500k multicolored   2.75 2.75
635 A127 800k multicolored   4.50 4.50
636 A127 1000k multicolored   5.75 5.75
637 A127 1500k multicolored   8.75 8.75
638 A127 2000k multicolored 11.50 11.50
    Nos. 623-638 (16)   44.36 44.36

Nos. 625 sold for 50k and 626 sold for 80k on date of issue.

Snakes — A128

1994, Sept. 28   Litho.   Perf. 14
639 A128 50k Tiger snake   .15   .15
640 A128 200k Egyptian cobra   .60   .60
641 A128 300k African python   .90   .90
642 A128 500k Green mamba   1.50 1.50
    Nos. 639-642 (4)   3.15 3.15

ILO, 75th
Anniv.
A129

1995, Apr. 3   Litho.   Perf. 14
643 A129 100k Road rehabilitation   .30   .30
644 A129 450k Block making   1.40 1.40

Christmas
Angels
A130

1995, Aug. 29   Perf. 14½x14
645 A130 100k shown   .30   .30
646 A130 300k With animals   .90   .90
647 A130 450k Blowing horn, birds 1.40 1.40
648 A130 500k Playing drum   1.50 1.50
    Nos. 645-648 (4)   4.10 4.10

UN, 50th
Anniv. — A131

1995, Dec. 30   Litho.   Perf. 11½
Granite Paper
649 A131 700k multicolored   1.50 1.50

POSTAGE DUE STAMPS

Type of Northern Rhodesia
Perf. 12½
1964, Oct. 24   Litho.   Unwmk.
J1 D1 1p orange   .15   .15
J2 D1 2p dark blue   .18   .18
J3 D1 3p rose claret   .25   .25
J4 D1 4p violet blue   .35   .35
J5 D1 6p purple   .50   .50
J6 D1 1sh emerald   1.50 1.50
    Nos. J1-J6 (6)   2.93 2.93

ZANZIBAR

ˈzan-zə-ˌbär

LOCATION — Group of islands about twenty miles off the coast of Tanganyika in East Africa
GOVT. — Republic
AREA — 1,044 sq. mi. (approx.)
POP. — 354,360 (est. 1967)
CAPITAL — Zanzibar

Before 1895, unoverprinted stamps of India were used in Zanzibar.

Zanzibar was a British protectorate until Dec. 10, 1963, when it became independent. After a revolt in January, 1964, a

republic was established. Zanzibar joined Tanganyika Apr. 26, 1964, to form the United Republic of Tanganyika and Zanzibar (later renamed Tanzania). See Tanzania.

12 Pies = 1 Anna
16 Annas = 1 Rupee
100 Cents = 1 Rupee (1908)
100 Cents = 1 Shilling (1935)

Watermarks

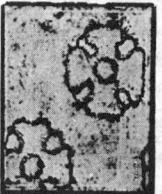 

Wmk. 47- Multiple   Wmk. 71- Rosette
Rosette

Stamps of British India Overprinted
Zanzibar

On Stamps of 1882-95
1895   Wmk. Star (39)   Perf. 14
Blue Overprint
1 A17 ½a green   6,500. 1,400.
2 A19 1a violet brown 1,500. 575.
   a. "Zanzidar"   6,000.

1895-96

Black Overprint
3 A17 ½a green   2.00 1.50
   a. "Zanzibar"   800.00 550.00
   b. "Zanibar"   850.00 1,000.
   c. "Zapzibar"
4 A19 1a violet brn   2.00 1.65
   a. "Zanzibar"   1,000. 1,000.
   b. "Zanibar"
5 A20 1a6p bister brn 2.00 1.65
   a. "Zanzibar"   1,500. 750.00
   b. "Zanibar"   1,400.
   c. "Zanzibar"   900.00 1,000.
6 A21 2a ultra   2.00 2.00
   a. "Zanzibar"   1,750. 1,250.
   b. "Zanibar"   1,500. 1,000.
   c. "Zapzibar"
   d. Double overprint 325.00
7 A28 2a6p green   2.75 2.00
   a. "Zanzibar"   1,500. 900.00
   b. "Zanibar"   375.00 750.00
   c. "Zapzibar"
   d. "Zanzipar"   900.00
8 A22 3a orange   4.00 4.00
   a. "Zanzibar"   450.00 750.00
   b. "Zanibar"   2,250. 2,250.
9 A23 4a olive grn   5.25 5.25
   a. "Zanzibar"   2,750. 2,000.
10 A25 8a red vio   10.00 10.00
   a. "Zanzibar"   3,000. 3,000.
11 A26 12a vio, red   10.00 7.50
   a. "Zanzibar"   3,000. 3,000.
12 A27 1r gray   90.00 70.00
   a. "Zanzibar"   3,500. 3,000.
13 A29 1r car rose & grn 7.50 12.50
   a. Vertical overprint 400.00
14 A30 2r brn & rose 25.00 40.00
   a. "Zanzibar"   4,000. 4,000.
   b. Inverted "r"   2,250. 2,250.
   c. Pair, one without overprint
15 A30 3r grn & brn   25.00 40.00
   a. "Zanzibar"   4,000.
   b. Inverted "r"   2,250. 2,250.
16 A30 5r vio & blue 25.00 35.00
   a. "Zanzibar"   4,000.
   b. Inverted "r"   1,600. 2,000.
   c. Dbl. ovpt., one invtd. 750.00

On Stamp of 1873-76
Wmk. Elephant's Head (38)
17 A14 6a bister   2.75 2.75
   a. "Zanzidar"   2,500. 2,000.
   b. "Zanzibarr"   2,000. 2,000.
   c. "Zanibar"   550.00 1,000.
   e. Double overprint
   Nos. 3-17 (15)   215.25 235.80

Nos. 4-6 Surcharged:

2½ a   **2½** b   **2½** c

2½ d   **2½** e   **2½** f

1896   Wmk. Star (39)
Black Surcharge
18 (a) 2½a on 1a   140.00 100.00
19 (b) 2½a on 1a   400.00 250.00
20 (c) 2½a on 1a   150.00 100.00
Red Surcharge
21 (a) 2½a on 1a   225.00 400.00
22 (b) 2½a on 1a   425.00 600.00
23 (c) 2½a on 1a   250.00 400.00
24 (a) 2½a on 1a6p   37.50 30.00
   a. "Zanzibar"   1,000. 1,000.
   b. "Zanibar"   2,000. 1,500.
24C (b) 2½a on 1a6p   160.00 300.00
25 (c) 2½a on 1a6p   100.00 165.00
26 (d) 2½a on 1a6p   125.00 80.00
27 (e) 2½a on 1a6p   375.00 275.00
27A (f) 2½a on 1a6p   7,000. 3,500.
28 (a) 2½a on 2a   85.00 150.00
28A (b) 2½a on 2a   160.00 300.00
29 (c) 2½a on 2a   95.00 175.00
30 (d) 2½a on 2a   37.50 25.00
31 (e) 2½a on 2a   125.00 70.00
31A (f) 2½a on 2a   2,750. 1,000.

Certain type varieties are found in the word "Zanzibar" on Nos. 1 to 31A viz: Inverted "q" for "b," broken "p" for "n," "i" without dot, small second "z" and tall second "z." These varieties are found on all values from ½a to 1r inclusive and the tall "z" is also found on the 2r, 3r and 5r.

Stamps of British East Africa, 1896,   **Zanzibar**
Overprinted in Black or Red

1896   Wmk. Crown and C A (2)
32 A8 ½a yellow grn   22.50 14.00
33 A8 1a carmine   20.00 15.00
34 A8 2½a dk blue (R) 67.50 35.00
35 A8 4½a orange   30.00 30.00
36 A8 5a dark ocher   35.00 19.00
37 A8 7½a lilac   22.50 22.50
   Nos. 32-37 (6)   197.50 135.50

Sultan Seyyid Hamed-bin-Thwain
A2   A3

1896, Sept. 20   Engr.   Wmk. 71
38 A2 ½a yel grn & red   1.90   .80
39 A2 1a indigo & red   .85 1.25
40 A2 2a red brn & red   1.10   .60
41 A2 2½a ultra & red   5.50   .80
42 A2 3a slate & red   3.50 3.00
43 A2 4a dk green & red 3.50 2.50
44 A2 4½a orange & red   2.00 3.00
45 A2 5a bister & red   1.90 2.00
   a. Half used as 2½a on cover   1,000.
46 A2 7½a lilac & red   1.90 2.00
47 A2 8a ol gray & red   5.00 5.25
48 A3 1r ultra & red   7.75 8.00
49 A3 2r green & red   14.00 8.50
50 A3 3r violet & red   17.00 8.50
51 A3 4r lake & red   12.00 12.00
52 A3 5r blk brn & red 17.00 12.00
   Nos. 38-52 (15)   94.90 70.20

No. 43 Surcharged in Red
1897
53 A2 (a) 2½a on 4a   50.00 30.00
54 A2 (b) 2½a on 4a   150.00 60.00
55 A2 (c) 2½a on 4a   60.00 40.00
   Nos. 53-55 (3)   260.00 130.00

1898   Engr.   Wmk. 47
56 A2 ½a yel grn & red   .65   .30
57 A2 1a indigo & red   .65   .50
58 A2 2a red brn & red 1.65   .70
58A A2 2½a ultra & red   .90   .30
59 A2 3a slate & red   2.25   .55
60 A2 4a dk grn & red   1.25   .90
60A A2 4½a orange & red 3.00   .65
61 A2 5a bister & red   6.75 1.65
61A A2 7½a lilac & red   2.50 2.50
61B A2 8a ol gray & red 4.50 2.00
   Nos. 56-61B (10)   24.10 10.05

Sultan Seyyid Hamoud-bin-Mahommed-bin-Said
A4 A5

1899-1901

62	A4	½a yel grn & red	.80	.25
63	A4	1a indigo & red	1.50	.20
64	A4	1a car & red ('01)	.65	.15
65	A4	2a red brn & red	.90	.35
66	A4	2½a ultra & red	.90	.40
67	A4	3a slate & red	1.00	1.10
68	A4	4a dk green & red	1.25	.85
69	A4	4½a orange & red	3.50	1.90
70	A4	4½a ind & red ('01)	6.00	6.25
71	A4	5a bister & red	1.25	1.10
72	A4	7½a lilac & red	1.75	3.00
73	A4	8a ol gray & red	1.75	3.75

Wmk. 71

74	A5	1r ultra & red	12.00	10.00
75	A5	2r green & red	12.00	12.50
76	A5	3r violet & red	20.00	21.00
77	A5	4r lilac rose & red	27.50	35.00
78	A5	5r gray brown & red	35.00	*40.00*
		Nos. 62-78 (17)	127.75	*137.80*

For surcharges see Nos. 94-98.

Monogram of Sultan Ali bin Hamoud
A6 A7

1904, June 8 Typo. Wmk. 47

79	A6	½a emerald	.85	.40
80	A6	1a rose red	.85	.15
81	A6	2a bister brown	1.10	.30
82	A6	2½a ultra	1.90	.25
83	A6	3a gray	1.50	.90
84	A6	4a blue green	1.90	.90
85	A6	4½a black	2.50	1.75
86	A6	5a ocher	2.75	.90
87	A6	7½a violet	3.25	4.00
88	A6	8a olive green	3.25	1.75
89	A7	1r ultra & red	14.00	6.00
90	A7	2r green & red	12.00	*20.00*
91	A7	3r violet & red	32.50	*45.00*
92	A7	4r magenta & red	35.00	*57.50*
93	A7	5r olive & red	35.00	*60.00*
		Nos. 79-93 (15)	148.35	*199.80*

Nos. 69-70, 72-73 Surcharged in Black or Lake:

One *g* **Two** *h* **Two & Half** *i*

1904

94	A4 (g)	1a on 4½a	1.25	*2.75*
95	A4 (g)	1a on 4½a (L)	3.75	*12.00*
96	A4 (h)	2a on 4a (L)	12.00	13.00
97	A4 (i)	2½a on 7½a	11.00	14.00
a.		"Hlaf"		*1,000.*
98	A4 (i)	2½a on 8a	12.50	*22.50*
a.		"Hlaf"		*1,000.*
		Nos. 94-98 (5)	40.50	*64.25*

Sultan Ali bin Hamoud
A8 A9

A10

Palace of the Sultan — A11

1908-09 Engr. Wmk. 47

99	A8	1c gray ('09)	.25	.15
100	A8	3c yellow grn	.65	.20
101	A8	6c carmine	2.50	.20
102	A8	10c org brn ('09)	1.10	2.00
103	A8	12c violet	2.00	.50
104	A9	15c ultra	2.00	.70
105	A9	25c brown	2.00	.80
106	A9	50c dp green	3.00	2.75
107	A9	75c slate ('09)	5.00	*7.50*
108	A10	1r yellow green	10.00	5.00
109	A10	2r violet	12.50	9.00
110	A10	3r yellow brown	24.00	*35.00*
111	A10	4r red	27.50	*55.00*
112	A10	5r blue	35.00	37.50
113	A11	10r brn & dk grn	75.00	80.00
114	A11	20r yel grn & blk	140.00	250.00
115	A11	30r dk brn & blk	225.00	375.00
116	A11	40r org brn & blk	400.00	
117	A11	50r lilac & blk	325.00	
118	A11	100r blue & blk	700.00	
119	A11	200r black & brn	1,000.	
		Nos. 99-112 (14)	127.50	*156.30*

It is probable that Nos. 118 and 119 were used only for fiscal purposes.

Sultan Khalifa bin Harub — A12

Dhow — A13

Dhow — A14

1913 ***Perf. 14***

120	A12	1c gray	.15	.15
121	A12	3c yellow grn	.30	.15
122	A12	6c carmine	.80	.15
123	A12	10c brown	.70	.90
124	A12	12c violet	.65	.20
125	A12	15c ultra	.90	.35
126	A12	25c black brn	.70	.45
127	A12	50c dk green	2.00	2.75
128	A12	75c dk gray	1.50	1.50
129	A13	1r yellow grn	3.00	*4.00*
130	A13	2r dk violet	7.00	*18.00*
131	A13	3r orange	10.00	*25.00*
132	A13	4r red	17.50	*45.00*
133	A13	5r blue	25.00	*37.50*
134	A14	10r brown & grn	60.00	*100.00*
135	A14	20r yel grn & blk	85.00	*175.00*
136	A14	30r dk brn & blk	100.00	*250.00*
137	A14	40r orange & blk	200.00	*350.00*
138	A14	50r dull vio & blk	225.00	*350.00*
139	A14	100r blue & blk	350.00	*350.00*
140	A14	200r black & brn	600.00	*600.00*
		Nos. 120-134 (15)	130.20	*226.10*

1914-22 Wmk. 3

141	A12	1c gray	.20	.25
142	A12	3c yellow grn	.70	.15
143	A12	6c carmine	.70	.15
144	A12	8c vio, *yel* ('22)	.65	*2.25*
145	A12	10c dk grn, *yel* ('22)	.55	.40
146	A12	15c ultra	.75	*2.50*
148	A12	50c dark green	4.00	*4.50*
149	A12	75c deep gray	2.50	*17.00*
150	A13	1r yellow grn	4.00	2.50
151	A13	2r dark violet	4.00	*7.00*
152	A13	3r brown org	13.00	*22.50*
153	A13	4r red	14.00	*60.00*
154	A13	5r blue	15.00	*45.00*
155	A14	10r brown & grn	60.00	*175.00*
		Nos. 141-155 (14)	120.05	*339.20*

1921-29 Wmk. 4

156	A12	1c gray	.15	7.00
157	A12	3c yellow grn	.18	2.00
158	A12	3c orange ('22)	.20	.15
159	A12	4c green ('22)	.40	.40
160	A12	6c carmine	.30	.40
161	A12	6c vio, *bl* ('22)	.50	.15
162	A12	10c lt brown	.70	5.00
163	A12	12c violet	.50	.35
164	A12	12c carmine ('22)	.50	.50
165	A12	15c ultra	.70	4.50
166	A12	20c dk blue ('22)	.75	.70
167	A12	25c black brn	.85	6.50
168	A12	50c blue green	1.00	1.50
169	A12	75c dark gray	2.00	30.00
170	A13	1r yellow grn	2.00	1.65
171	A13	2r dk violet	2.00	5.00
172	A13	3r ocher	3.50	6.00
173	A13	4r red	8.00	25.00
174	A13	5r blue	13.00	45.00
175	A14	10r brown & grn	45.00	125.00
176	A14	20r green & blk	110.00	*200.00*
177	A14	30r dk brn & blk ('29)	150.00	*300.00*
		Nos. 156-175 (20)	82.23	266.80

Sultan Khalifa bin Harub ("CENTS" with Serifs) — A15

1926-27

184	A15	1c brown	.15	.15
185	A15	3c yellow org	.22	.15
186	A15	4c deep green	.25	.25
187	A15	6c dark violet	.35	.15
188	A15	8c slate	.75	1.65
189	A15	10c olive green	.60	.25
190	A15	12c deep red	1.25	.16
191	A15	20c ultra	.60	.25
192	A15	25c violet, *yel*	3.00	1.00
193	A15	50c claret	.80	.40
194	A15	75c olive brown	5.25	7.00
		Nos. 184-194 (11)	13.22	11.41

Catalogue values for unused stamps in this section, from this point to the end of the section, are for Never Hinged items.

"CENTS" without Serifs — A16

Dhow — A17

Dhow — A18

1936 ***Perf. 14***

201	A16	5c deep green	.15	.15
202	A16	10c black	.15	.15
203	A16	15c carmine	.18	.18
204	A16	20c brown org	.24	.18
205	A16	25c violet, *yel*	.35	.30
206	A16	30c ultra	.42	.35
207	A16	40c black brown	.42	.42
208	A16	50c claret	.60	.60
209	A17	1sh yellow grn	.75	.65
210	A17	2sh dark violet	1.40	.95
211	A17	5sh red	4.50	4.50
212	A17	7.50sh blue	5.75	9.00
213	A18	10sh brown & green	7.25	7.25
		Nos. 201-213 (13)	22.16	24.68

For overprints see Nos. 222-223.

Sultan Khalifa bin Harub — A19

1936, Dec. 9

214	A19	10c olive grn & blk	.50	.50
215	A19	20c red violet & blk	.55	.55
216	A19	30c deep ultra & blk	.55	.55
217	A19	50c red orange & blk	.85	.85
		Nos. 214-217 (4)	2.45	2.45

Reign of Sultan Khalifa bin Harub, 25th anniv.

Dhow and Map Showing Zanzibar and Muscat — A20

Wmk. 4

1944, Nov. 20 Engr. ***Perf. 14***

218	A20	10c violet blue	.15	.15
219	A20	20c brown orange	.18	.18
220	A20	50c Prus green	.25	.25
221	A20	1sh dull purple	.45	.45
		Nos. 218-221 (4)	1.03	1.03

200th anniv. of the Al Busaid Dynasty.

Nos. 202 and 206 Overprinted in Red

VICTORY ISSUE
8TH JUNE 1946

1946, Nov. 11

222	A16	10c black	.15	.15
223	A16	30c ultra	.30	.30

Victory of the Allied Nations in WW II.

Silver Wedding Issue
Common Design Types

1949, Jan. 10 Photo. ***Perf. 14x14½***

224	CD304	20c orange	.75	.75

Engraved; Name Typographed
Perf. 11½x11

225	CD305	10sh light brown	11.00	11.00

UPU Issue
Common Design Types
Engr.; Name Typo. on 30c, 50c
Perf. 13½, 11x11½

1949, Oct. 10 Wmk. 4

226	CD306	20c red orange	.20	.15
227	CD307	30c indigo	.25	.20
228	CD308	50c red lilac	.50	.40
229	CD309	1sh blue green	.75	.65
		Nos. 226-229 (4)	1.70	1.40

Sultan Khalifa bin Harub A21

Seyyid Khalifa Schools A22

Perf. 12x12½, 13x12½

1952, Aug. 26 Engr.

230	A21	5c black	.15	.15
231	A21	10c red orange	.15	.15
232	A21	15c green	.15	.15
233	A21	20c carmine	.18	.15
234	A21	25c plum	.22	.18
235	A21	30c blue green	.22	.18
236	A21	35c ultra	.25	.24
237	A21	40c chocolate	.42	.35
238	A21	50c purple	.42	.30
239	A22	1sh choc & bl grn	.48	.42
240	A22	2sh claret & ultra	1.10	.90
241	A22	5sh carmine & blk	1.90	1.75
242	A22	7.50sh emerald & gray	6.00	9.00
243	A22	10sh gray blk & rose red	4.25	3.75
		Nos. 230-243 (14)	15.89	17.67

Sultan Khalifa bin Harub — A23

1954, Aug. 26 ***Perf. 12½x12***

244	A23	15c green	.18	.18
245	A23	20c scarlet	.22	.22
246	A23	30c ultra	.25	.25

247 A23 50c purple .38 .38
248 A23 1.25sh brown orange .95 .95
Nos. 244-248 (5) 1.98 1.98

The frames differ on Nos. 245 and 247. Sultan Khalifa bin Harub, 75th birth anniv.

Cloves — A24 Sultan's Barge — A26

Dhows A25

Malindi Minaret Mosque — A27 Kibweni Palace — A28

Sultan Khalifa bin Harub and: 25c, 35c, and 50c Map showing location of Zanzibar. 1sh, 2sh, Dimbani Mosque.

Perf. 11½ (A24), 11x11½ (A25), 14x13½ (A26), 13½x14 (A27), 13x13½ (A28)

1957, Aug. 26   Engr.   Wmk. 314
249 A24 5c dull grn & org .15 .15
250 A24 10c rose car & brt grn .15 .15
251 A25 15c dk brn & grn .15 .15
252 A26 20c ultra .15 .15
253 A26 25c blk & brn org .15 .15
254 A25 30c int blk & rose car .15 .15
255 A26 35c brt grn & indigo .15 .15
256 A27 40c int blk & redsh brn .20 .18
257 A26 50c dull green & blue .30 .22
258 A27 1sh int blk & brt car .38 .30
259 A25 1.25sh rose car & dk grn .55 .45
260 A27 2sh dull grn & orange .75 .65
261 A28 5sh ultra 1.65 1.25
262 A28 7.50sh green 2.75 5.75
263 A28 10sh rose carmine 3.75 3.25
Nos. 249-263 (15) 11.38 13.10

Sultan Seyyid Abdulla bin Khalifa — A29

Designs as before with portrait of Sultan Seyyid Abdulla bin Khalifa.

Perf. 11½ (A29), 11x11½ (A25), 14x13½ (A26), 13½x14 (A27)

1961, Oct. 17   Engr.   Wmk. 314
264 A29 5c dull grn & org .15 .15
265 A29 10c rose car & brt grn .15 .15
266 A25 15c dk brown & grn .15 .15
267 A26 20c ultra .15 .15
268 A26 25c blk & brn org .15 .15
269 A25 30c int blk & rose car .15 .15
270 A26 35c brt grn & indigo .15 .15
271 A27 40c int blk & redsh brn .15 .15
272 A26 50c dull grn & bl .20 .20
273 A27 1sh int blk & brt car .30 .25
274 A25 1.25sh rose car & dk grn .60 .50
275 A27 2sh dull grn & org .65 .65

Perf. 13x13½
276 A28 5sh ultra 1.25 1.10
277 A28 7.50sh green 2.75 2.75
278 A28 10sh rose carmine 3.25 3.25
279 A28 20sh dk brown 8.00 8.00
Nos. 264-279 (16) 18.20 17.90

For overprints see Nos. 285-300.

Freedom from Hunger Issue
Common Design Type with Portrait of Sultan Seyyid Abdulla bin Khalifa
1963, June 4   Photo.   Perf. 14x14½
280 CD314 1.30sh sepia .55 .55

Independent State

Sultan Seyyid Jamshid bin Abdulla and Zanzibar Clove — A30

Designs: 50c, "To Prosperity," arch and sun. 1.30sh, "Religious Tolerance," composite view of churches and mosques, horiz. 2.50sh, "Towards the Light," Mangapwani Cave.

Perf. 12½
1963, Dec. 10   Photo.   Unwmk.
281 A30 30c multicolored .15 .15
282 A30 50c multicolored .28 .28
283 A30 1.30sh multicolored .42 .42
284 A30 2.50sh multicolored .65 .65
Nos. 281-284 (4) 1.50 1.50

Zanzibar's independence, Dec. 10, 1963.
For overprints see Nos. 301-304.

Republic
Nos. 264-279
Overprinted   **JAMHURI 1964**

1964, Feb. 28   As Before
285 A29 5c dull grn & org .15 .15
286 A29 10c rose car & brt grn .15 .15
287 A25 15c dk brn & grn .15 .15
288 A26 20c ultra .15 .15
289 A26 25c blk & brn org .15 .15
290 A25 30c int blk & rose car .15 .15
291 A26 35c brt grn & ind .15 .15
292 A27 40c int blk & redsh brn .15 .15
293 A26 50c dull grn & blue .15 .15
294 A27 1sh int blk & brt car .18 .18
295 A25 1.25sh rose car & dk grn .20 .20
296 A27 2sh dull grn & org .35 .35
297 A28 5sh ultra .95 .95
298 A28 7.50sh green 1.50 1.50
299 A28 10sh rose carmine 1.90 1.90
300 A28 20sh dark brown 3.50 3.50
Nos. 285-300 (16) 9.93 9.93

The overprint was applied in England. It is in 2 lines on 40c and 1sh to 20sh. "Jamhuri" means "republic."

Overprint Handstamped
285a A29 5c .25 .25
286a A29 10c .25 .25
287a A25 15c .25 .25
288a A26 20c .25 .25
289a A26 25c .25 .25
290a A25 30c .25 .25
291a A26 35c .25 .25
292a A27 40c .25 .25
293a A26 50c .25 .25
294a A27 1sh .25 .25
295a A25 1.25sh .30 .30
296a A27 2sh 1.50 1.50
297a A28 5sh 3.50 3.50
298a A28 7.50sh 6.00 6.00
299a A28 10sh 6.50 6.50
300a A28 20sh 8.00 8.00
Nos. 285a-300a (16) 28.30 28.30

This overprint was applied locally. It has one line of serifed letters. These are found diagonal, vertical, horizontal, double and inverted. See Nos. 301a-304b. Other stamps with this overprint, including postage dues, were unofficial.

JAMHURI
Nos. 281-284
Overprinted
1964

1964, Feb. 28   As Before
301 A30 30c multi .20 .20
302 A30 50c multi .30 .30
303 A30 1.30sh multi .45 .45
304 A30 2.50sh multi .75 .75
a. Green omitted 60.00
Nos. 301-304 (4) 1.70 1.70

One-line overprint on 1.30sh.

Overprint Handstamped
301a A30 30c .20 .20
302a A30 50c .30 .30
303a A30 1.30sh .45 .45
304b A30 2.50sh .75 .75
Nos. 301a-304b (4) 1.70 1.70

See note after No. 300a.

Moorish Arch, Ax, Sword and Spear — A31

Designs: 10c, 20c, Arch and arrow piercing chain. 25c, 40c, Man with rifle. 30c, 50c, Man breaking chain. 1sh, Man, flag and sun. 1.30sh, Hands breaking chain and cloves, horiz. 2sh, Hands waving flag, horiz. 5sh, Map of Zanzibar and Pemba and flag, horiz. 10sh, Flag and map of Zanzibar and Pemba. 20sh, Flag of Zanzibar, horiz.

Perf. 13x13½, 13½x13
1964, June 21   Litho.   Unwmk.
305 A31 5c multi .15 .15
306 A31 10c multi .15 .15
307 A31 15c multi .15 .15
308 A31 20c multi .15 .15
309 A31 25c multi .15 .15
310 A31 30c multi .15 .15
311 A31 40c multi .16 .15
312 A31 50c multi .20 .16
313 A31 1sh multi .24 .24
314 A31 1.30sh multi .28 .28
315 A31 2sh multi .45 .45
316 A31 5sh multi 1.10 1.10
317 A31 10sh multi 2.00 2.00
318 A31 20sh multi 4.25 4.25
Nos. 305-318 (14) 9.58 9.53

Soldier and Maps of Zanzibar and Pemba A32  Reconstruction A33

Perf. 13½x13, 13x13½
1965, Jan. 12   Unwmk.
319 A32 20c green & yel grn .15 .15
320 A33 30c dk brown & ocher .15 .15
321 A32 1.30sh vio blue & blue .30 .30
322 A33 2.50sh purple & rose .55 .55
Nos. 319-322 (4) 1.15 1.15

First anniversary of the revolution.

Zanzibar and Tanzania

Rice Planting A34

Design: 3c, 1.30sh, Hands holding rice.

Perf. 13x12½
1965, Oct. 17   Litho.   Unwmk.
323 A34 2c blue & blk brn .15 .15
324 A34 3c brt pink & blk brn .15 .15
325 A34 1.30sh org & blk brn .30 .30
326 A34 2.50sh emer & blk brn .60 .60
Nos. 323-326 (4) 1.20 1.20

Issued to publicize agricultural development.

Symbols of Trade, Agriculture, Industry and Education A35 Pres. Abeid Amani Karume and Vice-Pres. Abdulla Kassim Hanga A36

Designs: 50c, 2.50sh, Soldier and sunburst.

1966, Jan. 12   Litho.   Perf. 12½x13
327 A35 20c ultra, red & gray .15 .15
328 A35 50c black & yel .15 .15
329 A35 1.30sh multicolored .35 .35
330 A35 2.50sh black & org .55 .55
Nos. 327-330 (4) 1.20 1.20

2nd anniv. of the revolution of Jan. 12, 1964.

1966, Apr. 26   Photo.   Perf. 13½x13
Design: 50c, 1.30sh, Flag, laurel and hands holding Flame of the Union (inscribed: Jamhuri Tanzania Zanzibar).
331 A36 30c multicolored .15 .15
332 A36 50c multicolored .15 .15
333 A36 1.30sh multicolored .30 .30
334 A36 2.50sh multicolored .55 .55
Nos. 331-334 (4) 1.15 1.15

Union of Tanganyika and Zanzibar, 2nd anniv.

Logging A37

Designs: 10c, 1sh, Clove trees and man. 15c, 40c, Cabinetmaker. 20c, 5sh, Lumumba College and book. 25c, 1.30sh, Farmer and tractor. 30c, 2sh, Volunteer farm workers. 50c, 10sh, Street scene, vert.

Perf. 13x12½, 12½x13
1966, June 5   Litho.
335 A37 5c lemon & vio brn .15 .15
336 A37 10c brt grn & vio brn .15 .15
337 A37 15c vio bl & brn bl .15 .15
338 A37 20c vio bl & org .15 .15
339 A37 25c vio brn & yel .15 .15
340 A37 30c vio brn & dl yel .15 .15
341 A37 40c vio brn & rose .15 .15
342 A37 50c green & yel .15 .15
343 A37 1sh ultra & vio brn .24 .24
344 A37 1.30sh lt bl grn & vio brn .35 .35
345 A37 2sh grn & vio brn .50 .50
346 A37 5sh ver & gray 1.25 1.25
347 A37 10sh red brn & yel 2.50 2.50
348 A37 20sh brt pink & vio brn 5.00 5.00
Nos. 335-348 (14) 11.04 11.04

Symbols of Education A38

1966, Sept. 25   Perf. 13½x13
349 A38 50c blue, blk & org .15 .15
350 A38 1.30sh blue, blk & yel grn .30 .30
351 A38 2.50sh blue, blk & pink .55 .55
Nos. 349-351 (3) 1.00 1.00

Introduction of free education.

People and Flag A39

Design: 50c, 1.30sh, Vice-President Abdulla Kassim Hanga, flag and crowd, vert.

Perf. 14x14½, 14½x14
1967, Feb. 5   Litho.   Unwmk.
352 A39 30c multicolored .15 .15
353 A39 50c multicolored .15 .15
354 A39 1.30sh multicolored .30 .30
355 A39 2.50sh multicolored .55 .55
Nos. 352-355 (4) 1.15 1.15

10th anniversary of Afro-Shirazi Party.

Volunteer Workers A40

Perf. 12½x12
1967, Aug. 20   Photo.   Unwmk.
356 A40 1.30sh multicolored .30 .30
357 A40 2.50sh multicolored .55 .55
Volunteer (Young) Workers Brigade.

All Zanzibar stamps were withdrawn July 1, 1968, and replaced with current Kenya, Uganda and Tanzania stamps.

POSTAGE DUE STAMPS

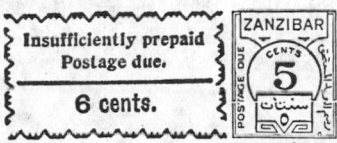

Insufficiently prepaid. Postage due. 1 cent. D1

			Rouletted 10	
1931		Typeset	Unwmk.	
		Thin Paper		
		Without Gum		
J1	D1	1c blk, *orange*	7.50	
J2	D1	2c blk, *orange*	2.25	
J3	D1	3c blk, *orange*	3.00	
J3A	D1	6c blk, *orange*		
J4	D1	9c blk, *orange*	2.00	
J4A	D1	12c blk, *orange*		
J4B	D1	12c blk, *green*	800.00	500.00
J5	D1	15c blk, *orange*	2.00	6.50
J6	D1	18c blk, *orange*	8.00	
a.		18c black, *salmon*	4.00	
J7	D1	20c blk, *orange*	4.00	
J8	D1	21c blk, *orange*	2.75	
J8A	D1	25c blk, *orange*		
J8B	D1	25c blk, *magenta*	1,750.	1,100.
J9	D1	31c blk, *orange*	8.00	
J10	D1	50c blk, *orange*	20.00	
J11	D1	75c blk, *orange*	50.00	

The variety "cent.s" occurs once on each sheet of Nos. J3 to J11 inclusive.

Insufficiently prepaid Postage due. 6 cents. D2

ZANZIBAR CENTS 5 POSTAGE DUE D3

1931-33			Rouletted 5	
		Thick Paper		
J12	D2	2c blk, *salmon*	3.00	
J13	D2	3c blk, *rose*	2.75	
J14	D2	6c blk, *yellow*	2.75	
J15	D2	12c blk, *blue*	4.00	
J16	D2	25c blk, *pink*	9.00	
J17	D2	25c blk, *dull violet*	7.50	
		Nos. J12-J17 (6)	29.00	

Catalogue values for unused stamps in this section, from this point to the end of the section, are for Never Hinged items.

1936		Typo.	Wmk. 4	Perf. 14	
J18	D3	5c violet		.15	.15
J19	D3	10c carmine		.30	.30
J20	D3	20c green		.45	.45
J21	D3	30c brown		.75	.75
J22	D3	40c ultra		.90	.90
J23	D3	1sh gray		2.25	2.25
		Nos. J18-J23 (6)		4.80	4.80

Chalky paper was introduced in 1956 for the 5c, 30c, 40c, 1sh, and in 1962 for the 10c, 20c. See note after No. 300a.

ZIMBABWE

zim-'bä-bwē

LOCATION — Southeastern Africa, bordered by Zambia, Mozambique, South Africa, and Botswana
GOVT. — Republic
AREA — 150,699 sq. mi.
POP. — 7,532,000 (1982)
CAPITAL — Harare

Rhodesia became Zimbabwe December 31, 1978. The Republic of Zimbabwe was established April 18, 1980.

100 Cents = 1 Dollar

Catalogue values for all unused stamps in this country are for Never Hinged items.

Morganite A69

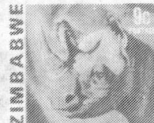

Black Rhinoceros A70

Odzani Falls — A71

Perf. 14½, 14½x14 (A70)

1980			Litho.		
414	A69	1c shown		.15	.15
415	A69	3c Amethyst		.15	.15
416	A69	4c Garnet		.15	.15
417	A69	5c Citrine		.15	.15
418	A69	7c Blue topaz		.15	.15
419	A70	9c shown		.18	.18
420	A70	11c Lion		.22	.22
421	A70	13c Warthog		.25	.25
422	A70	15c Giraffe		.30	.30
423	A70	17c Zebra		.32	.32
424	A71	21c shown		.40	.40
425	A71	25c Goba Falls		.45	.45
426	A71	30c Inyangombe Falls		.55	.55
426A	A71	40c Bundi Falls		.65	.65
427	A71	$1 Bridal Veil Falls		1.75	1.75
428	A71	$2 Victoria Falls		3.25	3.25
		Nos. 414-428 (16)		9.07	9.07

Rotary International, 75th Anniversary — A72

1980, June 18			Perf. 14½		
429	A72	4c multicolored		.15	.15
430	A72	13c multicolored		.25	.25
431	A72	21c multicolored		.40	.40
432	A72	25c multicolored		.50	.50
a.		Souvenir sheet of 4, #429-432		1.50	1.50
		Nos. 429-432 (4)		1.30	1.30

Olympic Rings A73

1980, July 19					
433	A73	17c multicolored		.35	.35

22nd Summer Olympic Games, Moscow, July 19-Aug. 3.

Gatooma Post Office, 1912 A74

Post Offices: 7c, Salisbury, 1912. 9c, Umtali, 1901. 17c, Bulawayo, 1895.

1980			Litho.	Perf. 14½	
434	A74	5c multicolored		.15	.15
435	A74	7c multicolored		.18	.18
436	A74	9c multicolored		.25	.25
437	A74	17c multicolored		.40	.40
a.		Souvenir sheet of 4, #434-437		1.00	1.00
		Nos. 434-437 (4)		.98	.98

Post Office Savings Bank, 75th anniv.

Intl. Year of the Disabled — A75

Natl. Tree Day — A76

Designs: Various disabilities. Nos. 438-441 form a continuous design.

1981, Sept. 23			Litho.	Perf. 14½	
438	A75	5c multicolored		.15	.15
439	A75	7c multicolored		.15	.15
440	A75	11c multicolored		.24	.24
441	A75	17c multicolored		.35	.35
		Nos. 438-441 (4)		.89	.89

1981, Dec. 4					
442	A76	5c Msasa		.15	.15
443	A76	7c Mopane		.15	.15
444	A76	21c Flat-crowned acacia		.50	.50
445	A76	30c Pod mahogany		.60	.60
		Nos. 442-445 (4)		1.40	1.40

Rock Paintings A77

Designs: 9c, Khoisan figures, Gwamgwadza Cave. 11c, Kudus, human figures, Epworth Mission. 17c, Diana's Vow, Rusape. 21c, Giraffes, Gwamgwadza Cave. 25c, Warthog, Mucheka Cave. 30c, Hunters, Shinzwini Shelter.

1982, Mar. 17			Litho.	Perf. 14½	
446	A77	9c multicolored		.35	.35
447	A77	11c multicolored		.42	.42
448	A77	17c multicolored		.60	.60
449	A77	21c multicolored		.90	.90
450	A77	25c multicolored		.90	.90
451	A77	30c multicolored		1.25	1.25
		Nos. 446-451 (6)		4.42	4.42

Scouting Year — A78

1982, July 21					
452	A78	9c Emblem		.30	.30
453	A78	11c Campfire		.30	.30
454	A78	17c Map reading		.65	.65
455	A78	30c Baden Powell		.85	.85
		Nos. 452-455 (4)		2.10	2.10

TB Bacillus Centenary A79

1982, Nov. 17				Perf. 14½	
456	A79	11c Koch		.50	.50
457	A79	30c Scientist examining slide		1.00	1.00

Commonwealth Day — A80

Sculptures: 9c, Wing Woman, by Henry Mudzengerere, vert. 11c, Telling Secrets, by Joseph Ndandarika. 30c, Hornbill Man, by John Takawira. $1, The Chief, by Nicholas Mukomberanwa, vert.

1983, Mar. 14				Perf. 14½	
458	A80	9c multicolored		.15	.15
459	A80	11c multicolored		.15	.15
460	A80	30c multicolored		.45	.45
461	A80	$1 multicolored		1.50	1.50
		Nos. 458-461 (4)		2.25	2.25

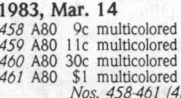

World Plowing Contest, May A81

Various plowing scenes. Stamps of same denomination in continuous design.

1983, May 13			Litho.	Perf. 14½	
462		Pair		.65	.65
a.-b.		A81 21c, any single		.32	.32
463		Pair		.85	.85
a.-b.		A81 30c, any single		.42	.42

World Communications Year — A82

Means of communication and transportation. Nos. 464-467 vert.

1983, Oct. 12			Litho.	Perf. 14½	
464	A82	9c Mailman		.15	.15
465	A82	11c Signaling airplane		.15	.15
466	A82	15c Telephone operators		.20	.20
467	A82	17c Reading newspapers		.25	.25
468	A82	21c Truck on highway		.30	.30
469	A82	30c Train		.45	.45
		Nos. 464-469 (6)		1.50	1.50

Zimbabwe Intl. Trade Fair, Bulawayo, May 5-13 — A83

1984, Apr. 11			Litho.	Perf. 14½	
470	A83	9c shown		.18	.18
471	A83	11c Globe		.22	.22
472	A83	30c Emblem		.55	.55
		Nos. 470-472 (3)		.95	.95

1984 Summer Olympics A84

Children's Drawings.

1984, July 18			Litho.	Perf. 14½	
473	A84	11c Bicycling		.15	.15
474	A84	21c Swimming		.25	.25
475	A84	30c Running		.40	.40
476	A84	40c Hurdles		.55	.55
		Nos. 473-476 (4)		1.35	1.35

Heroes' Day — A85

1984, Aug. 8 Litho. *Perf. 14½*

477	A85	9c	Heroes	.15	.15
478	A85	11c	Monument, vert.	.18	.18
479	A85	17c	Statue, vert.	.30	.30
480	A85	30c	Bas-relief	.52	.52
			Nos. 477-480 (4)	1.15	1.15

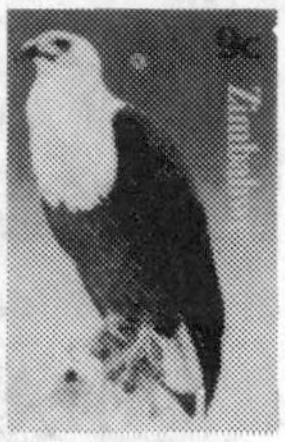

Fish Eagle — A86

1984, Oct. 10 Litho. *Perf. 14½*

481	A86	9c	shown	.40	.40
482	A86	11c	Long crested eagle	.48	.48
483	A86	13c	Bateleur	.60	.60
484	A86	17c	Black eagle	.85	.85
485	A86	21c	Martial eagle	1.10	1.10
486	A86	30c	African hawk eagle	1.50	1.50
			Nos. 481-486 (6)	4.93	4.93

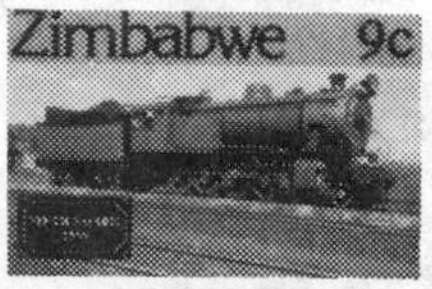

Superheat Engine No. 86, Mashonaland Railways, 1918 — A87

Steam locomotives: 11c, Engine No. 190, North British Locomotive Co., 1926. 17c, Engine No. 424, Beyer Peacock & Co., 1950. Engine No. 726, Beyer Peacock & Co., 1957.

1985, May 15 Litho.

487	A87	9c	multicolored	.42	.42
488	A87	11c	multicolored	.52	.52
489	A87	17c	multicolored	.85	.85
490	A87	30c	multicolored	1.50	1.50
			Nos. 487-490 (4)	3.29	3.29

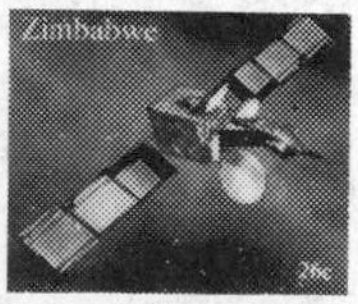

INTELSAT V
A88

Design: 57c, Mazowe Earth Satellite Station.

Perf. 14½x14, 14½

1985, July 8 Litho.

491	A88	26c	multicolored	.85	.85

Size: 62x23mm

492	A88	57c	multicolored	1.90	1.90

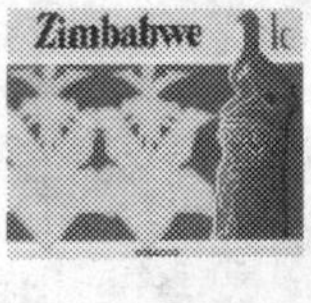

Zimbabwe Bird and Tobacco — A89

Agriculture and industry.

1985, Aug. 21 Litho. *Perf. 15*

493	A89	1c	shown	.15	.15
494	A89	3c	Corn	.15	.15
495	A89	4c	Cotton	.15	.15
496	A89	5c	Tea	.15	.15
497	A89	10c	Cattle	.15	.15
498	A89	11c	Birchenough Bridge	.15	.15
499	A89	12c	Stamp mill	.15	.15
500	A89	13c	Gold production	.15	.15
501	A89	15c	Coal mining	.15	.15
502	A89	17c	Amethyst mining	.16	.16
503	A89	18c	Electric train	.18	.18
504	A89	20c	Kariba Dam	.20	.20
505	A89	23c	Elephants	.22	.22
506	A89	25c	Zambezi River sunset	.24	.24
507	A89	26c	Baobab tree	.25	.25
508	A89	30c	Great Zimbabwe ruins	.30	.30
509	A89	35c	Folk dancing	.32	.32
510	A89	45c	Crushing corn	.45	.45
511	A89	57c	Wood carving	.55	.55
512	A89	$1	Mbira drum	.95	.95
513	A89	$2	Mule-drawn scotch cart	1.90	1.90
514	A89	$5	Natl. coat of arms	5.00	5.00
			Nos. 493-514 (22)	12.07	12.07

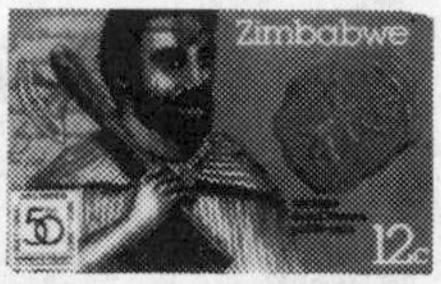

Natl. Archives, 50th Anniv.
A90

Designs: 12c, Gatsi Rusere (c. 1589-1623), ruler of Mashonaland and Zambezi area; mutapa, 17th cent. 18c, Lobengula, ruler of Ndebele State (1870-94), sketch by E. A. Maund, 1889; 1888 Moffat Treaty and elephant seal. 26c, Archives exhibition hall. 35c, Archives building.

1985, Sept. 18 *Perf. 14½*

515	A90	12c	multicolored	.15	.15
516	A90	18c	multicolored	.22	.22
517	A90	26c	multicolored	.32	.32
518	A90	35c	multicolored	.45	.45
			Nos. 515-518 (4)	1.14	1.14

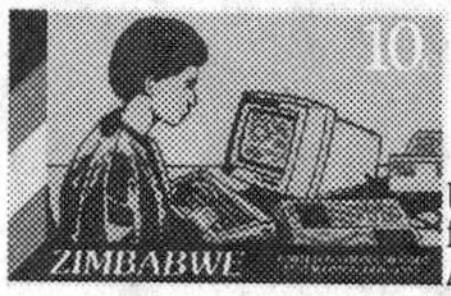

UN Decade for Women
A91

1985, Nov. 13

519	A91	10c	Computer operator	.24	.24
520	A91	17c	Nurse, child	.40	.40
521	A91	26c	Engineer	.60	.60
			Nos. 519-521 (3)	1.24	1.24

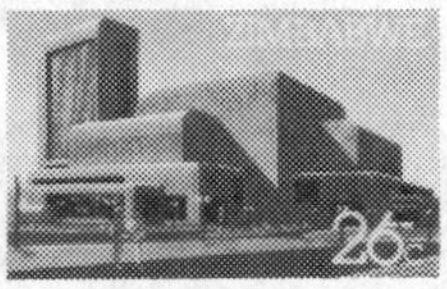

Harare Conference Center
A92

1986, Jan. 29 Litho. *Perf. 14½*

523	A92	26c	Facade	.35	.35
524	A92	35c	Interior	.45	.45

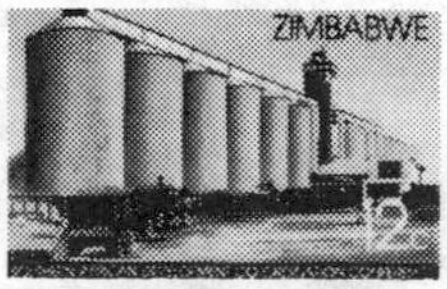

Southern African Development Coordination Conference — A93

1986, Apr. 1 *Perf. 14½*

525	A93	12c	Grain elevators	.30	.30
526	A93	18c	Rhinoceros	.45	.45
527	A93	26c	Map, jet	.65	.65
528	A93	35c	Map, flags	.85	.85
			Nos. 525-528 (4)	2.25	2.25

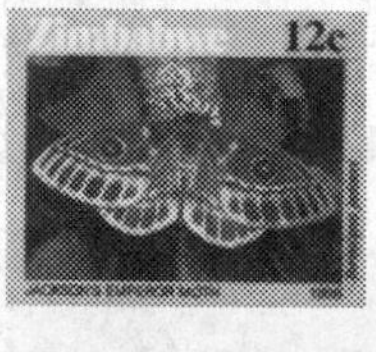

Moths — A94

1986, June 18 Litho. *Perf. 14½x14*

529	A94	12c	Jackson's emperor	.52	.52
530	A94	18c	Oleander hawk	.75	.75
531	A94	26c	Zaddach's emperor	1.10	1.10
532	A94	35c	Southern marbled emperor	1.50	1.50
			Nos. 529-532 (4)	3.87	3.87

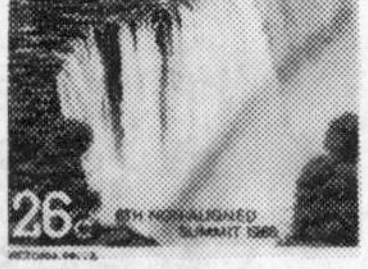

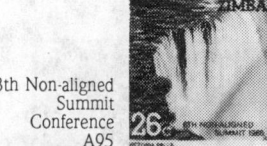

8th Non-aligned Summit Conference
A95

1986, Aug. 28 Litho. *Perf. 14½x14*

533	A95	26c	Victoria Falls	.50	.50

Size: 66x26mm

Perf. 14½

534	A95	$1	Great Zimbabwe Enclosure	2.00	2.00

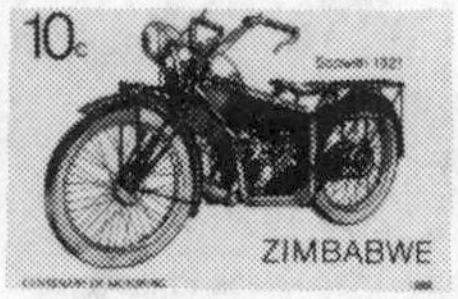

Motoring Cent.
A96

1986, Oct. 8 *Perf. 14½*

535	A96	10c	Sopwith, 1921	.28	.28
536	A96	12c	Gladiator, 1902	.35	.35
537	A96	17c	Douglas, 1920	.48	.48
538	A96	26c	Ford Model-A, 1930	.75	.75
539	A96	35c	Schacht, 1909	.95	.95
540	A96	40c	Benz Velocipede, 1886	1.10	1.10
			Nos. 535-540 (6)	3.91	3.91

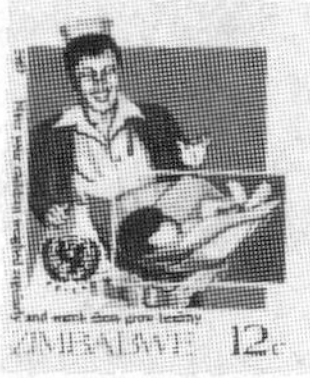

A97

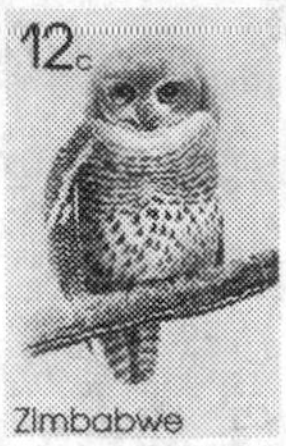

A98

UN Child Survival Campaign: a, Growth monitoring. b, Breast-feeding. c, Oral rehydration. d, Immunization.

1987, Feb. 11 Litho. *Perf. 14x14½*

541	Block of 4		1.75	1.75
a.-d.	A97 12c any single		.42	.42

1987, Apr. 15 *Perf. 14½*

Indigenous owls.

542	A98	12c	Barred	.65	.65
543	A98	18c	Pearl-spotted	1.25	1.25
544	A98	26c	White-faced	1.40	1.40
545	A98	35c	Scops	1.90	1.90
			Nos. 542-545 (4)	5.20	5.20

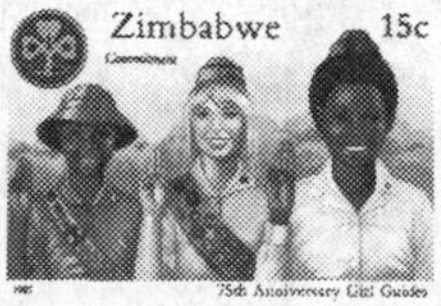

Natl. Girl Guides Movement, 75th Anniv.
A99

1987, June 24

546	A99	15c	Commitment	.20	.20
547	A99	23c	Adventure	.30	.30
548	A99	35c	Service	.45	.45
549	A99	$1	Intl. friendship	1.25	1.25
			Nos. 546-549 (4)	2.20	2.20

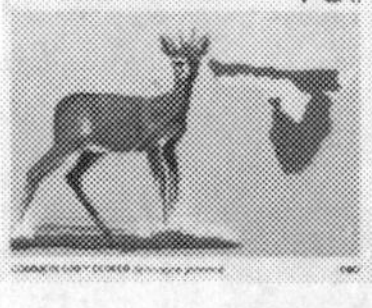

Duikers and Population Maps — A100

1987, Oct. 7 *Perf. 14½x14*

550	A100	15c	Common gray	.16	.16
551	A100	23c	Zebra	.24	.24
552	A100	25c	Yellow-backed	.26	.26
553	A100	30c	Blue	.32	.32
554	A100	35c	Jentink's	.38	.38
555	A100	38c	Red	.40	.40
			Nos. 550-555 (6)	1.76	1.76

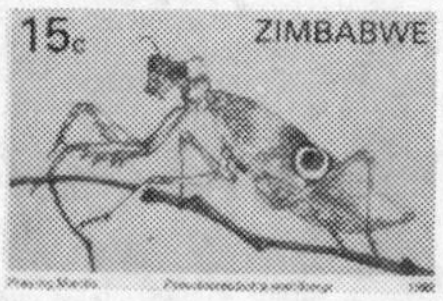

Insects
A101

1988, Jan. 12 Litho. *Perf. 14½*

556	A101	15c	Praying mantis	.20	.20
557	A101	23c	Scarab beetle	.28	.28
558	A101	35c	Short-horned grasshopper	.45	.45
559	A101	45c	Giant shield bug	.58	.58
			Nos. 556-559 (4)	1.51	1.51

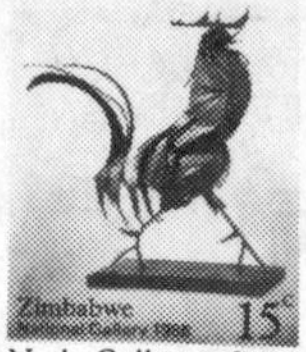

Natl. Gallery of Art, 30th Anniv.
A102

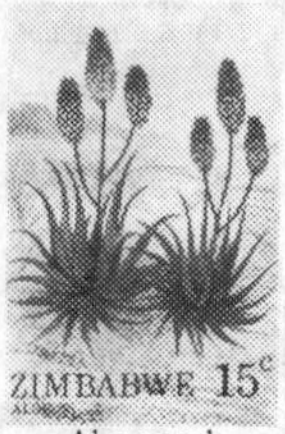

Aloes and Succulents
A103

Sculpture and paintings: 15c, Cockerel, by Arthur Azevedo. 23c, Changeling, by Bernard Matemera. 30c, Spirit Python, by Henry Munyaradzi. 35c, Spirit Bird Carrying People, by Thomas Mukarobgwa, horiz. 38c, The Song of the Shepherd Boy, by George Nene, horiz. 45c, War Victim, by Joseph Muzondo, horiz.

Perf. 14x14½, 14½x14

1988, Apr. 14 Litho.

560	A102	15c	multicolored	.18	.18
561	A102	23c	multicolored	.25	.25
562	A102	30c	multicolored	.32	.32
563	A102	35c	multicolored	.40	.40
564	A102	38c	multicolored	.42	.42
565	A102	45c	multicolored	.52	.52
			Nos. 560-565 (6)	2.09	2.09

1988, July 14 *Perf. 14½*

566	A103	15c	Aloe cameronii bondana	.20	.20
567	A103	23c	Orbeopsis caudata	.28	.28
568	A103	25c	Euphorbia wildii	.32	.32
569	A103	30c	Euphorbia fortissima	.38	.38
570	A103	35c	Aloe aculeata	.45	.45
571	A103	38c	Huernia zebrina	.48	.48
			Nos. 566-571 (6)	2.11	2.11

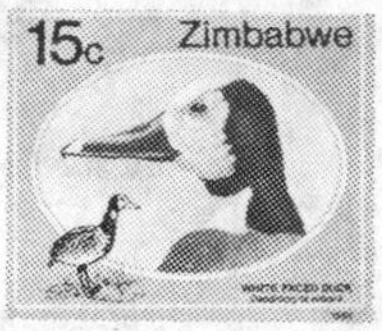

A104

1988, Oct. 6 Litho. *Perf. 14½x14*

572	A104	15c	White-faced duck	.16	.16
573	A104	23c	Pygmy goose	.25	.25
574	A104	30c	Hottentot teal	.32	.32
575	A104	35c	Knob-billed duck	.38	.38
576	A104	38c	White-backed duck	.40	.40
577	A104	45c	Maccoa	.48	.48
			Nos. 572-577 (6)	1.99	1.99

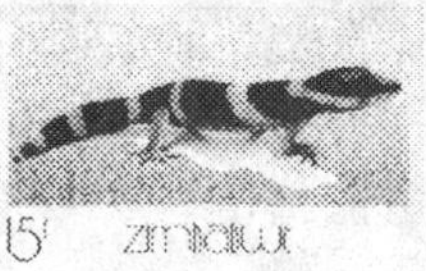

Geckos
A105

1989, Jan. 10 Litho. *Perf. 14½*

578	A105	15c	O'Shaughnessy's banded	.16	.16
579	A105	23c	Tiger rock	.25	.25
580	A105	35c	Tasman's	.38	.38
581	A105	45c	Bibron's	.48	.48
			Nos. 578-581 (4)	1.27	1.27

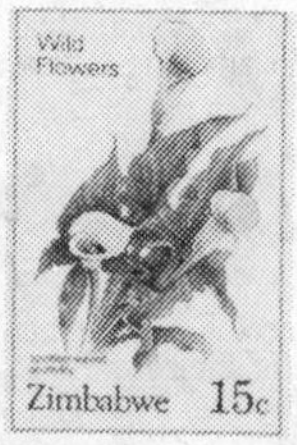

Wildflowers — A106

1989, Apr. 12 Litho. *Perf. 14½*

582	A106	15c	Spotted-leaved arum-lily	.16	.16
583	A106	23c	Grassland vlei-lily	.25	.25
584	A106	30c	Manica protea	.32	.32
585	A106	35c	Flame lily	.38	.38
586	A106	38c	Poppy hibiscus	.40	.40
587	A106	45c	Blue sesbania	.48	.48
			Nos. 582-587 (6)	1.99	1.99

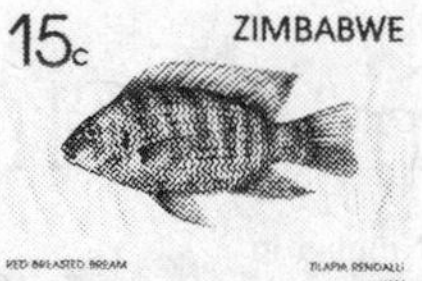

Fish — A107

1989, July 12 Litho. *Perf. 14½*

588 A107 15c	Red-breasted bream	.25	.25
589 A107 23c	Chessa	.40	.40
590 A107 30c	Eastern bottle-nose	.52	.52
591 A107 35c	Vundu	.60	.60
592 A107 38c	Largemouth black bass	.65	.65
593 A107 45c	Tiger fish	.80	.80
	Nos. 588-593 (6)	3.22	3.22

See Nos. 696-701.

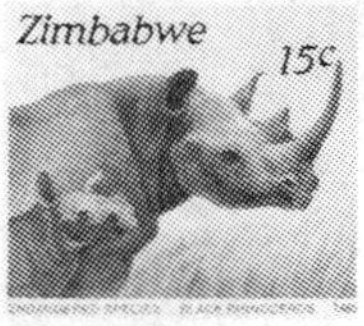

Endangered Species — A108

1989 Litho. *Perf. 14½x14*

594 A108 15c	Black rhinoceros	.25	.25
595 A108 23c	Cheetah	.40	.40
596 A108 30c	Wild dog	.52	.52
597 A108 35c	Pangolin	.60	.60
598 A108 38c	Brown hyena	.65	.65
599 A108 45c	Roan antelope	.80	.80
	Nos. 594-599 (6)	3.22	3.22

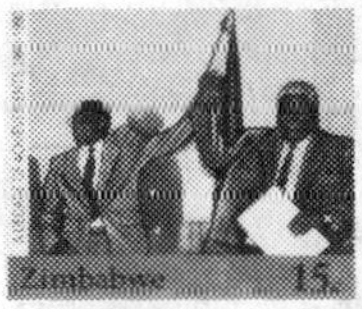

Achievements, 1980-1990 A109

1990, Apr. 17 Litho. *Perf. 14½x14*

600 A109 15c	Unity accord	.15	.15
601 A109 23c	Conference center	.24	.24
602 A109 30c	Education	.30	.30
603 A109 35c	Satellite dish	.35	.35
604 A109 38c	Sports stadium	.38	.38
605 A109 45c	Agriculture	.45	.45
	Nos. 600-605 (6)	1.87	1.87

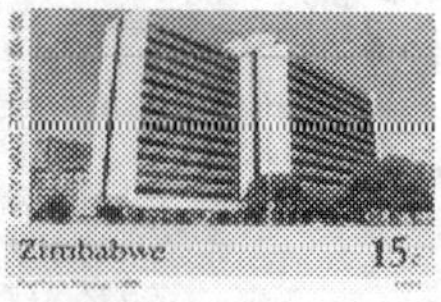

City of Harare, Cent. A110

1990, July 11 Litho. *Perf. 14½*

606 A110 15c	Runhare house, 1986	.15	.15
607 A110 23c	Market hall, 1894	.23	.23
608 A110 30c	Charter house, 1959	.30	.30
609 A110 35c	Supreme Court, 1927	.35	.35
610 A110 38c	Standard Chartered Bank, 1911	.38	.38
611 A110 45c	Town house, 1933	.45	.45
	Nos. 606-611 (6)	1.86	1.86

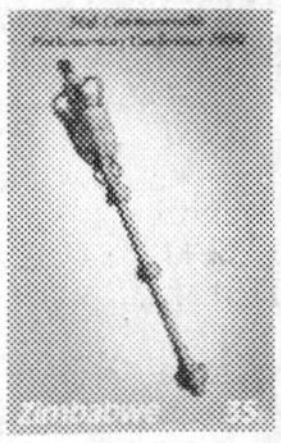

36th Commonwealth Parliamentary Conf. — A111

1990, Sept. 17

612 A111 35c	Speaker's mace	.35	.35
613 A111 $1	Speaker's chair	1.00	1.00

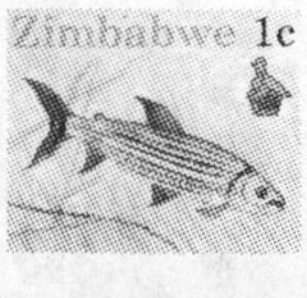

Animals — A112

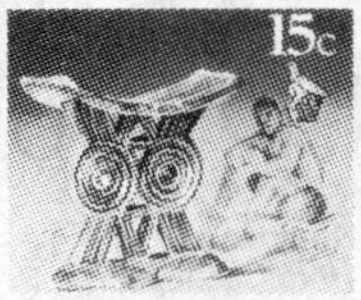

Hand Crafts — A113

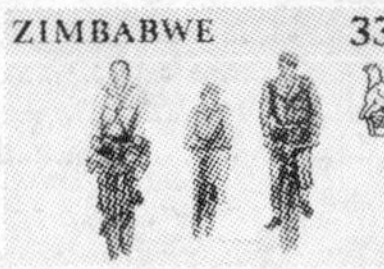

Transportation — A114

1990, Jan. 2 Litho. *Perf. 14*

614 A112 1c	Tiger fish	.15	.15
615 A112 2c	Helmeted guineafowl	.15	.15
616 A112 3c	Scrub hare	.15	.15
617 A112 4c	Pangolin	.15	.15
618 A112 5c	Greater kudu	.15	.15
619 A112 9c	Black rhinoceros	.15	.15
620 A113 15c	Head rest	.15	.15
621 A113 20c	Hand axe	.18	.18
622 A113 23c	Gourd, water pot	.20	.20
623 A113 25c	Snuff box	.20	.20
624 A113 26c	Winnowing basket	.22	.22
625 A113 30c	Grinding stone	.25	.25
626 A114 33c	Riding bicycles	.30	.30
627 A114 35c	Buses	.30	.30
628 A114 38c	Train	.35	.35
629 A114 45c	Motorcycle, trailer	.38	.38
630 A114 $1	Jet	.85	.85
631 A114 $2	Tractor-trailer truck	1.75	1.75
	Nos. 614-631 (18)	6.03	6.03

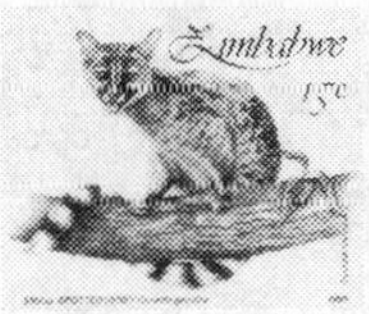

Animals — A115

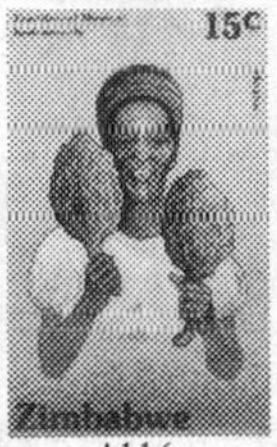

A116

1991, Jan. 15 Litho. *Perf. 14½x14*

632 A115 15c	Small-spotted genet	.15	.15
633 A115 23c	Red squirrel	.24	.24
634 A115 35c	Night ape	.35	.35
635 A115 45c	Bat-eared fox	.45	.45
	Nos. 632-635 (4)	1.19	1.19

1991, Apr. 16 Litho. *Perf. 14½*

Traditional musical instruments.

636 A116 15c	Hosho	.15	.15
637 A116 23c	Mbira	.24	.24
638 A116 30c	Ngororombe	.30	.30
639 A116 35c	Chipendani	.35	.35
640 A116 38c	Marimba	.38	.38
641 A116 45c	Ngoma	.45	.45
	Nos. 636-641 (6)	1.87	1.87

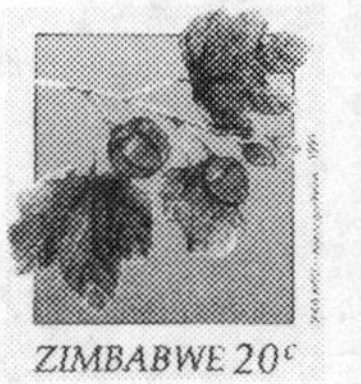

Wild Fruits — A117

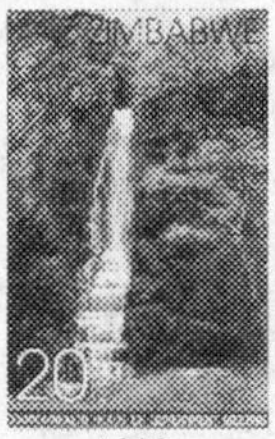

A118

1991, July 17 Litho. *Perf. 14x14½*

642 A117 20c	Snot-apple	.15	.15
643 A117 39c	Marula	.28	.28
644 A117 51c	Mobola plum	.35	.35
645 A117 60c	Water berry	.42	.42
646 A117 65c	Northern dwaba berry	.45	.45
647 A117 77c	Mahobohobo	.52	.52
	Nos. 642-647 (6)	2.17	2.17

1991, Oct. 16 Litho. *Perf. 14½*

648 A118 20c	Bridal Veil Falls	.15	.15
649 A118 39c	Conference Emblem	.28	.28
650 A118 51c	Chinhoyi Caves	.35	.35
651 A118 60c	Kariba Dam Wall	.42	.42
652 A118 65c	Victoria Falls	.45	.45
653 A118 77c	Balancing Rocks	.52	.52
	Nos. 648-653 (6)	2.17	2.17

Commonwealth Heads of Government meeting, Harare.

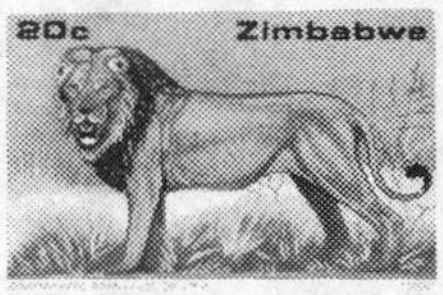

Wild Cats A119

1992, Jan. 8 Litho. *Perf. 14½*

654 A119 20c	Lion	.15	.15
655 A119 39c	Leopard	.28	.28
656 A119 60c	Cheetah	.42	.42
657 A119 77c	Serval	.52	.52
	Nos. 654-657 (4)	1.37	1.37

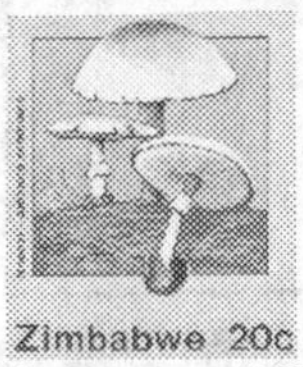

Mushrooms — A120

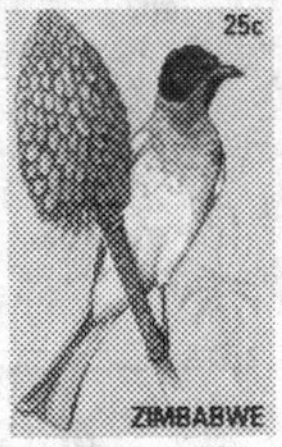

Birds — A121

Designs: 20c, Amanita zambiana. 39c, Boletus edulis. 51c, Termitomyces. 60c, Cantharellus densifolius. 65c, Cantharellus longisporus. 77c, Cantharellus cibarius.

1992, Apr. 8 Litho. *Perf. 14x14½*

658 A120 20c	multicolored	.15	.15
659 A120 39c	multicolored	.25	.25
660 A120 51c	multicolored	.34	.34
661 A120 60c	multicolored	.40	.40
662 A120 65c	multicolored	.42	.42
663 A120 77c	multicolored	.52	.52
	Nos. 658-663 (6)	2.08	2.08

1992, July 17 Litho. *Perf. 14½*

664 A121 25c	Blackeyed bulbul	.15	.15
665 A121 59c	Fiscal shrike	.40	.40
666 A121 77c	Forktailed drongo	.52	.52
667 A121 90c	Cardinal woodpecker	.60	.60
668 A121 98c	Yellowbilled hornbill	.65	.65
669 A121 $1.16	Crested francolin	.78	.78
	Nos. 664-669 (6)	3.10	3.10

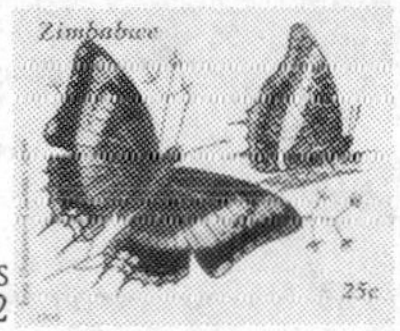

Butterflies A122

1992, Oct. 15 Litho. *Perf. 14½x14*

670 A122 25c	Foxy charaxes	.15	.15
671 A122 59c	Orange & lemon	.28	.28
672 A122 77c	Emperor swallowtail	.35	.35
673 A122 90c	Blue pansy	.42	.42
674 A122 90c	African monarch	.45	.45
675 A122 $1.16	Gaudy commodore	.55	.55
	Nos. 670-675 (6)	2.20	2.20

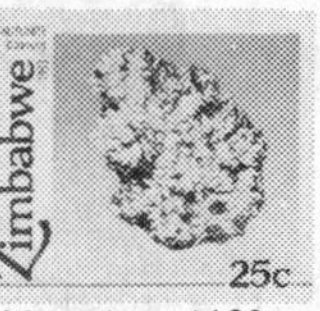

Minerals — A123

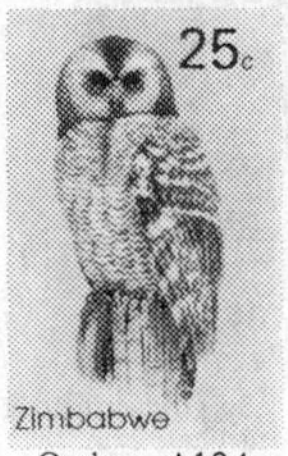

Owls — A124

1993, Jan. 12 Litho. *Perf. 14½x14*

676 A123 25c	Autunite	.15	.15
677 A123 59c	Chromite	.28	.28
678 A123 77c	Azurite	.35	.35
679 A123 90c	Coal	.42	.42
680 A123 98c	Gold	.45	.45
681 A123 $1.16	Emerald	.55	.55
	Nos. 676-681 (6)	2.20	2.20

1993, Apr. 6 Litho. *Perf. 14½*

682 A124 25c	Wood owl	.15	.15
683 A124 59c	Pels fishing owl	.22	.22
684 A124 90c	Spotted eagle owl	.35	.35
685 A124 $1.16	Giant eagle owl	.45	.45
	Nos. 682-685 (4)	1.17	1.17

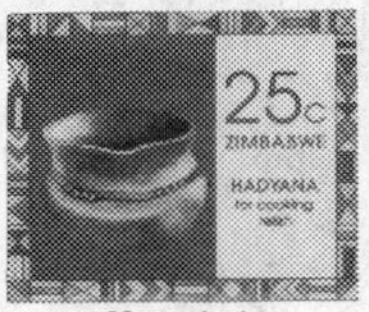

Household Pottery — A125

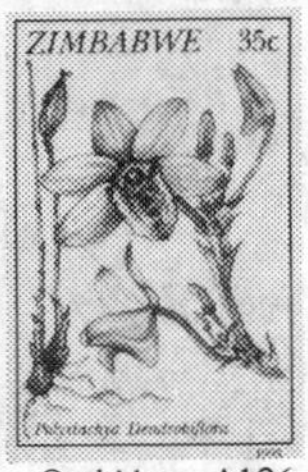

Orchids — A126

1993, July 13 Litho. *Perf. 14½x14*

686 A125 25c	Hadyana	.15	.15
687 A125 59c	Chirongo	.22	.22
688 A125 77c	Mbiya	.30	.30
689 A125 90c	Pfuko	.35	.35
690 A125 98c	Tsaya	.38	.38
691 A125 $1.16	Gate	.45	.45
	Nos. 686-691 (6)	1.85	1.85

1993, Oct. 12 Litho. *Perf. 14½*

692 A126 35c	Polystachya dendrobiflora	.15	.15
693 A126 $1	Diaphananthe subsimplex	.38	.38
694 A126 $1.50	Ansellia gigantea	.60	.60
695 A126 $1.95	Vanilla polyepis	.75	.75
	Nos. 692-695 (4)	1.88	1.88

Fish Type of 1989

1994, Jan. 20 Litho. *Perf. 14½*

696 A107 35c	Hunyani salmon	.15	.15
697 A107 $1	Barbel	.38	.38
698 A107 $1.30	Rainbow trout	.50	.50
699 A107 $1.50	Mottled eel	.60	.60
700 A107 $1.65	Mirror carp	.65	.65
701 A107 $1.95	Robustus bream	.75	.75
	Nos. 696-701 (6)	3.03	3.03

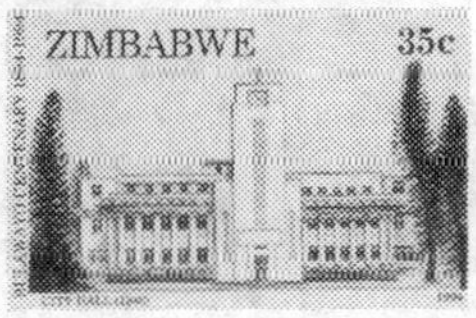

City of Bulawayo, Cent. A127

1994, Apr. 5 Litho. *Perf. 14½*

702 A127 35c	City Hall	.15	.15
703 A127 80c	Cresta Churchill Hotel	.20	.20
704 A127 $1.15	High Court	.28	.28
705 A127 $1.75	Douslin House	.42	.42
706 A127 $1.95	Goldfields Building	.48	.48
707 A127 $2.30	Parkade Centre	.55	.55
	Nos. 702-707 (6)	2.08	2.08

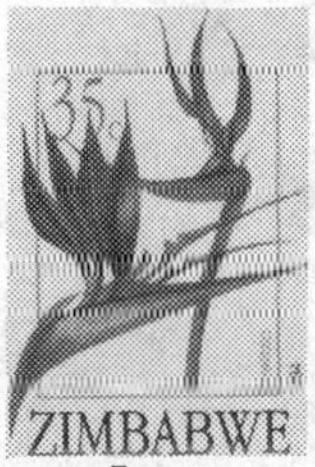

Export Flowers — A128

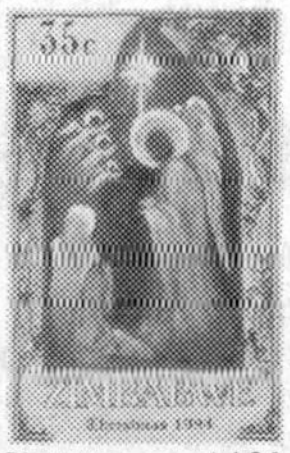

Christmas — A129

1994, July 12 Litho. *Perf. 14½*

708 A128 35c	Strelitzia	.15	.15
709 A128 80c	Protea	.20	.20
710 A128 $1.15	Phlox	.28	.28
711 A128 $1.75	Chrysanthemum	.45	.45
712 A128 $1.95	Lilium	.48	.48
713 A128 $2.30	Rose	.60	.60
	Nos. 708-713 (6)	2.16	2.16

1994, Oct. 11 Litho. *Perf. 14½*

Designs: 35c, Archangel Gabriel, Virgin Mary. 80c, Mary, Joseph on way to Bethlehem. $1.15, Nativity scene. $1.75, Angel pointing way to shepherds. $1.95, Magi following star. $2.30, Madonna and child.

714 A129 35c	multicolored	.15	.15
715 A129 80c	multicolored	.20	.20
716 A129 $1.15	multicolored	.28	.28
717 A129 $1.75	multicolored	.42	.42
718 A129 $1.95	multicolored	.48	.48
719 A129 $2.30	multicolored	.55	.55
	Nos. 714-719 (6)	2.08	2.08

A130

1995, Jan. 17   Litho.   Perf. 14

720	A130	1c	Corn	.15 .15
721	A130	2c	Sugar cane	.15 .15
722	A130	3c	Sunflowers	.15 .15
723	A130	4c	Sorghum	.15 .15
724	A130	5c	Mine workers	.15 .15
725	A130	10c	Underground mining	.15 .15
726	A130	20c	Coal mining	.15 .15
727	A130	30c	Chrome smelting	.15 .15
728	A130	40c	Opencast mining	.15 .15
729	A130	50c	Gold smelting	.15 .15
730	A130	70c	Boggie Clock Tower	.18 .18
731	A130	80c	Masvingo Watchtower	.20 .20
732	A130	$1	Hanging tree	.25 .25
733	A130	$2	Cecil House	.50 .50
734	A130	$5	The Toposcope	1.25 1.25
735	A130	$10	Paper House	2.50 2.50
			Set value	5.30 5.30

Insects
A131

1995, Apr. 4   Litho.   Perf. 14½

736	A131	35c	Spider-hunting wasp	.15 .15
737	A131	$1.15	Emperor dragonfly	.28 .28
738	A131	$1.75	Foxy charaxes	.42 .42
739	A131	$2.30	Antlion	.55 .55
			Nos. 736-739 (4)	1.40 1.40

6th All Africa
Games,
Harare — A132

1995, July 11   Litho.   Perf. 14x14½

740	A132	35c	Soccer	.15 .15
741	A132	80c	Track	.20 .20
742	A132	$1.15	Boxing	.30 .30
743	A132	$1.75	Swimming	.40 .40
744	A132	$1.95	Field hockey	.45 .45
745	A132	$2.30	Volleyball	.55 .55
			Nos. 740-745 (6)	2.05 2.05

UN, 50th
Anniv. — A133

1995, Oct. 17   Litho.   Perf. 14½

746	A133	35c	Health	.15 .15
747	A133	$1.15	Environment	.30 .30
748	A133	$1.75	Food distribution	.40 .40
749	A133	$2.30	Education	.55 .55
			Nos. 746-749 (4)	1.40 1.40

POSTAGE DUE STAMPS

D1   D2

1981   Litho.   Perf. 14½

J20	D1	1c	emerald	.15 .15
J21	D1	2c	ultramarine	.15 .15
J22	D1	5c	lilac	.15 .15
J23	D1	6c	yellow	.18 .18
J24	D1	10c	red	.45 .45
			Set value	.82 .82

For surcharge see No. J30.

1985, Aug. 21   Litho.   Perf. 14½

J25	D2	1c	pale orange	.15 .15
J26	D2	2c	lilac rose	.15 .15
J27	D2	6c	light green	.15 .15
J28	D2	10c	tan	.15 .15
J29	D2	13c	bright blue	.18 .18
			Set value	.50 .50

No. J24 Surcharged

1990, Jan. 2   Litho.   Perf. 14½
J30 D1 25c on 10c #J24   10.00 10.00

D3

1995, Jan. 17   Litho.   Perf. 14½

J31	D3	1c	yellow	.15 .15
J32	D3	2c	yellow orange	.15 .15
J33	D3	5c	rose lilac	.15 .15
J34	D3	10c	pale blue	.15 .15
J35	D3	25c	violet	.15 .15
J36	D3	40c	green	.15 .15
J37	D3	60c	orange	.18 .18
J38	D3	$1	brown	.30 .30
			Set value	.70 .70

ZULULAND

'zü–(‚)lü–‚land

LOCATION — Northeastern part of Natal, South Africa
GOVT. — British Colony, 1887-1897
AREA — 10,427 sq. mi.
POP. — 230,000 (estimated 1900)
CAPITAL — Eshowe

12 Pence = 1 Shilling
20 Shillings = 1 Pound

Stamps of Great Britain **ZULULAND**
Overprinted

1888-93   Wmk. 30   Perf. 14

1	A54	½p	vermilion	2.00	2.50
2	A40	1p	violet	20.00	4.25
3	A56	2p	green & red	10.00	17.00
4	A57	2½p	vio, bl ('91)	13.00	18.00
5	A58	3p	violet, yel	21.00	22.00
6	A59	4p	green & brn	27.50	40.00
7	A61	5p	lil & bl ('93)	70.00	90.00
8	A62	6p	vio, rose	10.00	16.00
9	A63	9p	blue & lil ('92)	62.50	70.00
10	A65	1sh	green ('92)	85.00	95.00

Wmk. 31

11	A51	5sh	rose ('92)	600.00	475.00
			Nos. 1-10 (10)	321.00	374.75

Natal No. 66 Overprinted **ZULULAND.**

1888-94   Wmk. 2

12	A14	½p	green, no period	18.00	30.00
a.		Period after "Zululand"		60.00	60.00
b.		As "a," double overprint		1,000.	1,050.
c.		As "a," invtd. overprint		1,200.	
d.		As "a," pair, one without ovpt.		4,500.	4,500.
e.		As No. 12, double overprint		1,500.	1,500.

Natal No. 71 Ovptd. Like Nos. 1-11

13	A11	6p	violet ('94)	47.50	50.00

A1   A2

1891

14	A1	1p	lilac		2.25 2.00

By proclamation of the Governor of Zululand, dated June 27th, 1891, No. 14 was declared to be a postage stamp.

1894-96   Typo.

15	A2	½p	lilac & grn	1.10	3.25
16	A2	1p	lilac & rose	4.00	.90
17	A2	2½p	lilac & blue	13.00	7.00
18	A2	3p	lilac & brn	7.25	4.00
19	A2	6p	lilac & blk	17.00	17.00
20	A2	1sh	green	27.50	32.50
21	A2	2sh6p	grn & blk ('96)	65.00	75.00
22	A2	4sh	grn & car rose	90.00	150.00
23	A2	£1	violet, red	600.00	550.00
24	A2	£5	vio & blk, red	4,250.	1,750.
			Nos. 15-22 (8)	224.85	289.65

Numerals of #19-24 are in color on plain tablet.
Purple or violet cancellations are not necessarily revenue cancels.

Zululand was annexed to Natal in Dec. 1897 and separate stamps discontinued June 30th, 1898.

1997 Vol. 1B Number Changes

Number in 1996 Catalogue	Number in 1997 Catalogue
Great Britain	
27b, 28b	Added
39d, 39e	Added
59b	Added
61a	Deleted
Australia	
415a	Added
628a	Added
788a	Added
Bangkok	
12b, 16a, 18a	Footnoted
Bechuanaland	
31a, 31b, 31c	Added
35a	Deleted
38d, 39d	Added
British East Africa	
14b, 14c	14c, 14d
14b, 14e	Added
Burma	
2N6a	Footnoted
Cape of Good Hope	
5	5, 5a
5a/5b	5b/5c
5c	5d
7	7/7b
7b	7c/7d
9	9/9a/9b
9a	9c
9b	9f/9g
9c	9d
Ceylon	
44a	Added
152e-152h	Added
Cocos Islands	
250-255A	249-255
258A-259	259-260
Cook Islands	
1a	5a
Fiji	
38a, 39a	Added
Gambia	
3a, 4a, 4b	Added
10a, 18c, 18d	Added
14	14b
14a	Deleted
14	Added
Gold Coast	
6b, 7b, 8b	Added
Griqualand West	
2a	Added
Heligoland	
5	5b
5	Added
19	19a
19	Added
20	20a
20a	20
25a	Deleted
Hong Kong	
1a	Added
69b, 70a	Added
India	
840c	Deleted
Kenya, Uganda, Tanganyika	
41D-41F	Added

Number in 1996 Catalogue	Number in 1997 Catalogue
Maldive Islands	
1622-1624	1624-1626
1630-1635A	1629-1635
Mauritius	
3e, 3f, 4h, 4i	Added
5e, 5f, 6g, 6h	Added
New South Wales	
45a, 46a	Added
New Zealand	
648	648a
648b	648
7f	Added
Niue	
13	13b
13b	13
Pakistan	
612-613A, 614	613-616
Rhodesia & Nyasaland	
J4a	Added
Sarawak	
27a	Deleted
Singapore	
675A (Apr. 95)	675D
South Africa	
371a	378A
J24a	J24
J24	J24a
Bophuthatswana	
157	155
160-163	156-159
Southern Rhodesia	
1c, 2c, 2d	Added
6a, 11a, 13a	Deleted
32b	Added
South West Africa	
J80a, J83a	Added
Tonga	
798A	799
799-799A	800-801
800-801	802-803
803-806	804-807
Tuvalu	
222-229	222-225
235-258	235-246
258A-258D	255-258
259-266	259-262
271-278	271-274
291-298	291-294
299-306	299-302
320-327	320-323
332-347	332-339
396-396K	396-396E
414-437	414-425
Uganda	
1122-1123	1121-1122
1121	1123
Victoria	
9	Deleted
Zambia	
530	529
532-533A	530-532
534-536	533-535
538	536
542	537
544-546	538-540

Dies of British Colonial Stamps Referred to in the Catalogue

DIE A

DIE B

DIE I

DIE II

DIE A:
1. The lines in the groundwork vary in thickness and are not uniformly straight.
2. The seventh and eighth lines from the top, in the groundwork, converge where they meet the head.
3. There is a small dash in the upper part of the second jewel in the band of the crown.
4. The vertical color line in front of the throat stops at the sixth line of shading on the neck.

DIE B:
1. The lines in the groundwork are all thin and straight.
2. All the lines of the background are parallel.
3. There is no dash in the upper part of the second jewel in the band of the crown.
4. The vertical color line in front of the throat stops at the eighth line of shading on the neck.

DIE I:
1. The base of the crown is well below the level of the inner white line around the vignette.
2. The labels inscribed "POSTAGE" and "REVENUE" are cut square at the top.
3. There is a white "bud" on the outer side of the main stem of the curved ornaments in each lower corner.
4. The second (thick) line below the country name has the ends next to the crown cut diagonally.

DIE Ia.	DIE Ib.
1 as die II.	1 and 3 as die II.
2 and 3 as die I.	2 as die I.

DIE II:
1. The base of the crown is aligned with the underside of the white line around the vignette.
2. The labels curve inward at the top inner corners.
3. The "bud" has been removed from the outer curve of the ornaments in each corner.
4. The second line below the country name has the ends next to the crown cut vertically.

Wmk. 1
Crown and C C

Wmk. 2
Crown and C A

Wmk. 3
Multiple Crown
and C A

Wmk. 4
Multiple Crown
and Script C A

Wmk. 4a

Wmk. 314
St. Edward's Crown
and C A Multiple

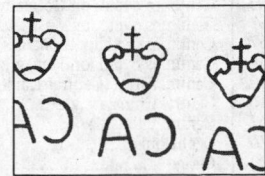
Wmk. 373

Wmk. 384

British Colonial and Crown Agents Watermarks

Watermarks 1 to 4, 314, 373, and 384, common to many British territories, are illustrated here to avoid duplication.

The letters "CC" of Wmk. 1 identify the paper as having been made for the use of the Crown Colonies, while the letters "CA" of the others stand for "Crown Agents." Both Wmks. 1 and 2 were used on stamps printed by De La Rue & Co.

Wmk. 3 was adopted in 1904; Wmk. 4 in 1921; Wmk. 314 in 1957; Wmk. 373 in 1974; and Wmk. 384 in 1985.

In Wmk. 4a, a non-matching crown of the general St. Edwards type (bulging on both sides at top) was substituted for one of the Wmk. 4 crowns which fell off the dandy roll. The non-matching crown occurs in 1950-52 printings in a horizontal row of crowns on certain regular stamps of Johore and Seychelles, and on various postage due stamps of Barbados, Basutoland, British Guiana, Gold Coast, Grenada, Northern Rhodesia, St. Lucia, Swaziland and Trinidad and Tobago. A variation of Wmk. 4a, with the non-matching crown in a horizontal row of crown-CA-crown, occurs on regular stamps of Bahamas, St. Kitts-Nevis and Singapore.

Wmk. 314 was intentionally used sideways, starting in 1966. When a stamp was issued with Wmk. 314 both upright and sideways, the sideways varieties usually are listed also – with minor numbers. In many of the later issues, Wmk. 314 is slightly visible.

Wmk. 373 is usually only faintly visible.

Index and Identifier

All page numbers shown are those in
this Volume 1B.

Postage stamps that do not have English
words on them are shown in the Identifier
which begins on page 852.

Illustrated Identifier

This section pictures stamps or parts of stamp designs that will help identify postage stamps that do not have English words on them.

Many of the symbols that identify stamps of countries are shown here as well as typical examples of their stamps.

See the Index and Identifier on the previous pages for stamps with inscriptions such as "sen," "posta," "Baja Porto," "Helvetia," "K.S.A.", etc.

Linn's Stamp Identifier is now available. The 144 pages include more 2,000 inscriptions and over 500 large stamp illustrations. Available from Linn's Stamp News, P.O. Box 29, Sidney, OH 45365-0029.

HEADS, PICTURES AND NUMERALS

GREAT BRITAIN

Great Britain stamps never show the country name, but, except for postage dues, show a picture of the reigning monarch.

Victoria

Edward VII   George V   Edward VIII

George VI

Elizabeth II

Some George VI and Elizabeth II stamps are surcharged in annas, new paisa or rupees. These are listed under Oman.

10ᴾ

Silhouette (sometimes facing right, generally at the top of stamp)

11ᴾ

The silhouette indicates this is a British stamp. It is not a U.S. stamp.

VICTORIA

Queen Victoria

INDIA

Other stamps of India show this portrait of Queen Victoria and the words "Service" and "Annas."

AUSTRIA

YUGOSLAVIA

(Also BOSNIA & HERZEGOVINA if imperf.)

BOSNIA & HERZEGOVINA

Denominations also appear in top corners instead of bottom corners.

HUNGARY

Another stamp has posthorn facing left

BRAZIL

AUSTRALIA

 Kangaroo and Emu

GERMANY

Mecklenburg-Vorpommern

SWITZERLAND

ORIENTAL INSCRIPTIONS

CHINA

Any stamp with this one character is from China (Imperial, Republic or People's Republic). This character appears in a four-character overprint on stamps of Manchukuo. These stamps are local provisionals, which are unlisted. Other overprinted Manchukuo stamps show this character, but have more than four characters in the overprints. These are listed in People's Republic of China.

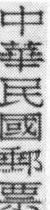 

Some Chinese stamps show the Sun.

Most stamps of Republic of China show this series of characters.

Stamps with the China character and this character are from People's Republic of China.

Calligraphic form of People's Republic of China

Chinese stamps without China character

REPUBLIC OF CHINA

PEOPLE'S REPUBLIC OF CHINA

Mao Tse-tung

MANCHUKUO

Temple   The first 3 characters   Emperor
          are common to many   Pu-Yi
          Manchukuo stamps.

The last 3 characters are common to
other Manchukuo stamps.

Orchid Crest

Manchukuo
stamp with-
out these
elements

JAPAN

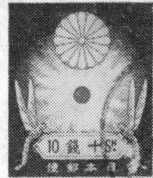 

Chrysanthemum Crest   Country Name

Japanese stamps without these elements

RYUKYU ISLANDS

Country Name

PHILIPPINES
(Japanese Occupation)

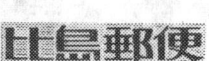

Country Name

NORTH BORNEO
(Japanese Occupation)

 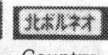

Indicates Japanese   Country
Occupation   Name

MALAYA
(Japanese Occupation)

Indicates Japanese Occupation

 Country Name

BURMA
(Japanese Occupation)

Indicates Japanese Occupation

 Country Name

Other Burma Japanese Occupation stamps
without these elements

Burmese Script

KOREA

These two characters, in any order, are common
to stamps from the Republic of Korea (South
Korea) or the unlisted stamps of the People's
Democratic Republic of Korea (North Korea).

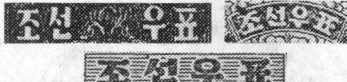

This series of four characters can be found
on the stamps of both Koreas.

Yin Yang appears on some stamps.

Indicates Republic of Korea (South Korea)

THAILAND

Country Name

King Prajadhipok and Chao P'ya Chakri

CENTRAL AND EASTERN ASIAN INSCRIPTIONS

INDIA - FEUDATORY STATES

Alwar   Bhor

Bundi

Similar stamps come with different designs in corners and differently drawn daggers (at center of circle).

Faridkot

Hyderabad

Similar stamps exist with straight line frame around stamp, and also with different central design which is inscribed "Postage" or "Post & Receipt."

Indore   **Jammu & Kashmir**

Jhalawar   Nowanuggur

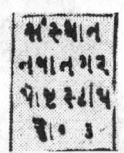

Rajpeepla   Soruth

BANGLADESH

NEPAL

Similar stamps are smaller, have squares in upper corners and have five or nine characters in central bottom panel.

TANNU TUVA   **ISRAEL**

GEORGIA

ARMENIA

The four characters are found somewhere on pictorial stamps. On some stamps only the middle two are found.

ARABIC INSCRIPTIONS

AFGHANISTAN

Many early Afghanistan stamps show Tiger's head, many of these have ornaments protruding from outer ring, others show inscriptions in black.

Arabic Script

Mosque Gate & Crossed Cannons

BAHRAIN

EGYPT

IRAN

Country Name

Note Crown

Lion with Sword

JORDAN

LEBANON

Similar types have denominations at top and slightly different design.

LIBYA

Country Name in various styles

Other Libya stamps show Eagle and Shield (head facing either direction) or Red, White and Black Shield (with or without eagle in center).

SAUDI ARABIA

Note Tughra (Central design)

20 H   ٥٢٠

Palm Tree and Swords

SYRIA

THRACE   YEMEN

PAKISTAN - Bahawalpur

Country Name in top panel,
star and crescent

TURKEY

Star & Crescent

 Tughra (similar tughras can be
found on stamps of Afghanistan
and Saudi Arabia)

Mohammed V

Mustafa Kemal

Plane, Star
and Crescent

TURKEY IN ASIA

Other Turkey in Asia pictorials show
star & crescent.

GREEK INSCRIPTIONS

GREECE

Country Name in various styles
(Some Crete stamps overprinted with the Greece
country name are listed in Crete.)

Lepta

Drachma   Drachmas   Lepton

Abbreviated Country Name   ΕΛΛ

Other forms of Country Name

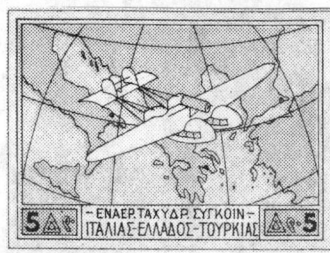

No country name

CRETE

Country Name

These words are on other stamps

Grosion

Crete stamps with a surcharge that have the year "1922" are listed under Greece.

EPIRUS
Country Name

IONIAN ISLANDS

CYRILLIC INSCRIPTIONS

RUSSIA
Postage Stamp

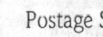

Imperial Eagle

Postage in various styles

Abbreviation for Kopeck

 Abbreviation for Ruble

 Russia

Abbreviation for Russian Soviet Federated Socialist Republic

Abbreviation for Union of Soviet Socialist Republics

RUSSIA - Army of the North

"OKCA"

RUSSIA - Wenden

RUSSIAN OFFICES IN THE TURKISH EMPIRE

These letters appear on other stamps of the Russian offices.

The unoverprinted version of this stamp and a similar stamp were overprinted by various countries (see below).

ARMENIA

FAR EASTERN REPUBLIC
Country Name

SOUTH RUSSIA
Country Name

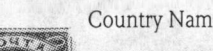

FINLAND

Circles and Dots
on stamps similar
to Imperial
Russia issues

BATUM

Forms of Country Name

TRANSCAUCASIAN FEDERATED REPUBLICS

Abbreviation for
Country Name

KAZAKHSTAN

Country Name

KYRGYZSTAN   ROMANIA

КЫРГЫЗСТАН
Counrty Name

TADJIKISTAN

Counrty Name & Abbreviation

UKRAINE

Country Name in various forms

The trident
appears on many
stamps, usually
as an overprint.

Abbreviation for
Ukrainian Soviet
Socialist Republic

WESTERN UKRAINE

Abbreviation for
Country Name

AZERBAIJAN

AZƏRBAYCAN

Country Name

Azerbaijan Soviet
Socialist Republic

MONTENEGRO

Country Name in various forms

Abbreviation for
country name

No country name
(A similar Montene-
gro stamp without
country name has
same vignette.)

SERBIA

Country Name in various forms

Abbreviation for country name

YUGOSLAVIA

Showing country name

No Country Name

MACEDONIA

Country Name

BULGARIA

Country Name   Postage

Stotinka   Abbreviation for Stotinki

Stotinki (plural)

Country Name in various forms and styles

НР България

No country name

Abbreviation for Lev, leva

MONGOLIA

Country name in one word

Tugrik in Cyrillic

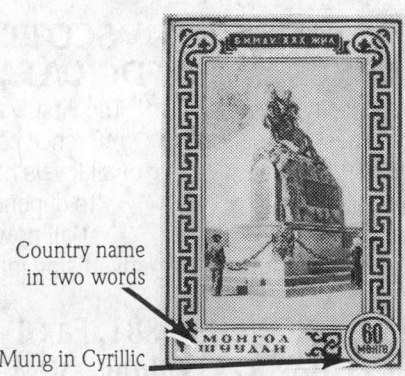

Country name in two words

Mung in Cyrillic

Mung in Mongolian

Tugrik in Mongolian

Arms

No Country Name

INDEX TO ADVERTISERS – 1997 VOLUME 1B

1997
VOLUME 1B
DEALER DIRECTORY
YELLOW PAGE LISTINGS

This section of your Scott Catalogue contains
advertisements to help you conveniently find
what you need,
when you need it...!

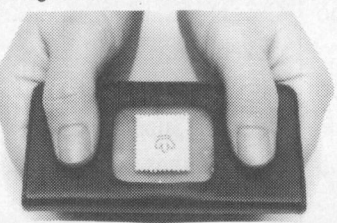

Channel Islands

WEST NISSOURI STAMP COMPANY
P.O. Box 4641-A
London, Ontario N5W 5L7
CANADA
519-432-0080 or 519-432-0286
d.jorgensen3@genie.com e-mail

China

MICHAEL ROGERS, INC.
199 E. Welbourne Avenue
Winter Park, FL 32789
407-644-2290
407-645-4434 FAX

Collections

SHARI'S STAMPS
104-3 Old Highway 40 #130
O'Fallon, MO 63366
800-382-3597

Covers

JUDNICK POSTCARDS & COVERS
P.O. Box 12248
Columbus, OH 43212-0248
614-278-9399

Covers - First Day

ROSS WETREICH INC.
P.O. Box 1300
Valley Stream, NY 11582-1300
516-825-8974

Czechoslovakia

SOCIETY FOR CZECHOSLOVAK PHILATELY INC.
Tom Cossaboom, SCP Secretary
Box 25332
Scott Air Force Base, IL 62225
USA

Discount Supplies

VERUS DISCOUNT STAMP CO.
P.O. Box 187
West Chicago, IL 60186
708-896-8938

Duck Stamps

TRENTON STAMP & COIN CO.
1804 RT. 33
Trenton, NJ 08690
800-446-8664
609-587-8664 FAX

Great Britain

AMERICAN COIN & STAMP EXCHANGE
330 So. Gallatin Road
Madison, TN 37115
615-865-8791

NOVA PHILATELIC SALES
Box 161
Lakeside, N.S. B3T 1M6
CANADA
902-826-2165

WEST NISSOURI STAMP COMPANY
P.O. Box 4641-A
London, Ontario N5W 5L7
CANADA
519-432-0080 or 519-432-0286
d.jorgensen3@genie.com e-mail

Hong Kong

THE STAMP ACT
P.O. Box 1136
Belmont, CA 94002
415-592-3315
415-508-8104 FAX
BChang@IX.NETCOM.COM
Internet address

Ireland

ROSEMOOR STAMP & COIN CO.
2021 Ridge Road
Homewood, IL 60430
708-799-0880

Inverted Centers - World

MARTIN SELLINGER
Box 47
White Plains, NY 10602
914-948-4246
914-682-7384 FAX

Literature

ROSEMOOR STAMP & COIN CO.
2021 Ridge Road
Homewood, IL 60430
708-799-0880

Lots & Collections

DAVE ALLEGO
P.O. Box 13
Ambridge, PA 15003-0013
412-266-4255

BOB & MARTHA FRIEDMAN STAMPS
624 Homestead
Joliet, IL 60435
805-725-6666
708-281-1532 FAX

DR. ROBERT FRIEDMAN & SONS STAMPS & COINS
7451 S. Woodward #108
Woodridge, IL 60517-2665
708-241-1515
708-241-1532 FAX

RANDY SCHOLL STAMP COMPANY
Southampton Square
7460 Jager Court
Cincinnati, OH 45230-4344
513-624-6800
513-624-6440 FAX

Mail Bid Sales

CONNEXUS
P.O. Box 130
Tryon, NC 28782
704-859-5882
704-859-2702 FAX

QUEST INTERNATIONAL
P.O. Box 139A,
Thames Ditton,
Surrey, KT7 OER
UNITED KINGDOM
44-181-398-7740
44-181-398-4661 FAX

Mail Order

ALMAZ CO., DEPT. VY
P.O. Box 100-812
Vanderveer Station
Brooklyn, NY 11210
718-241-6360 TELEPHONE & FAX

Mail Order

B & D HOBBIES
P.O. Box 4
Gladstone, OR 97027
503-656-3149

BOB BECK
Box 3209 Harbourtown Station
Hilton Head Island, SC 29928
803-671-3241

LOG HOUSE PHILATELIST
Box 267
Harju Road
Grand Marais, MI 49839

ROBERT'S STAMP EXCHANGE
P.O. Box 362
Carpentersville, IL 60110
708-695-6568

SHARI'S STAMPS
104-3 Old Highway 40 #130
O'Fallon, MO 63366
800-382-3597

Middle East - Arab

THE PERFECT PERF
P.O. Box 16127
Pittsburgh, PA 15242
412-429-1618
412-561-0660 FAX

Mounts

VIDIFORMS COMPANY INC.
Showgard House
110 Brenner Drive
Congers, NY 10920
914-268-4005
914-268-5324 FAX

New Issues

DAVIDSON'S STAMP SERVICE
P.O. Box 20502
Indianapolis, IN 46220
317-255-9408

New Issues - Retail

BOMBAY PHILATELIC CO., INC.
P.O. Box 7719
Delray Beach, FL 33482-7719
561-499-7990
561-499-7553 FAX

STANLEY M. PILLER
3351 Grand Ave.
Oakland, CA 94610
510-465-8290
510-465-7121 FAX

New Issues - Wholesale

BOMBAY PHILATELIC CO., INC.
P.O. Box 7719
Delray Beach, FL 33482-7719
561-499-7990
561-499-7553 FAX

New Zealand

JAY'S STAMP CO.
Box 28484
Dept. S
Philadelphia, PA 19149
215-743-0207 TELEPHONE & FAX

New Zealand - Ducks

METROPOLITAN STAMP CO. OF CHICAGO, INC.
P.O. Box 1133
Chicago, IL 60690-1133
815-439-0142
815-439-0143 FAX

New Zealand - New Issues

NEW ZEALAND STAMP AGENCY IN NORTH AMERICA
One Unicover Center
Cheyenne, WY 82008-0014
800-443-4225
800-628-3132 FAX

Postal History

INTERSTAMP
312 S. Cedros Avenue
Suite 326
Solana Beach, CA 92075
619-755-2259
619-755-9113 FAX

Postcards

JUDNICK POSTCARDS & COVERS
P.O. Box 12248
Columbus, OH 43212-0248
614-278-9399

Price Lists

JAY'S STAMP CO.
Box 28484
Dept. S
Philadelphia, PA 19149
215-743-0207 TELEPHONE & FAX

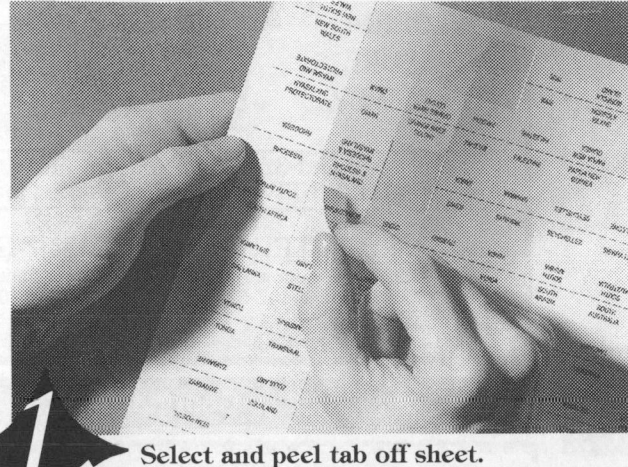
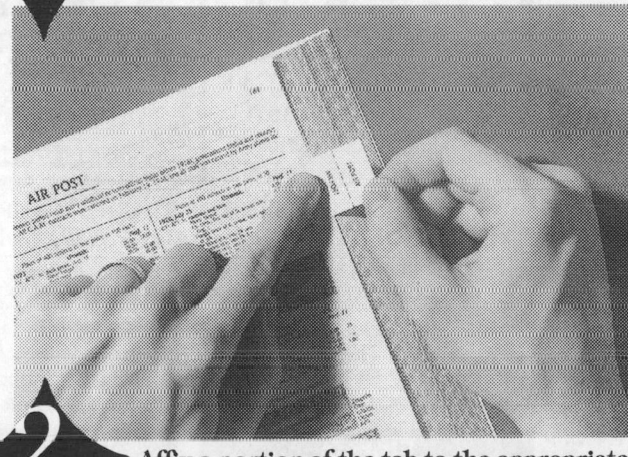
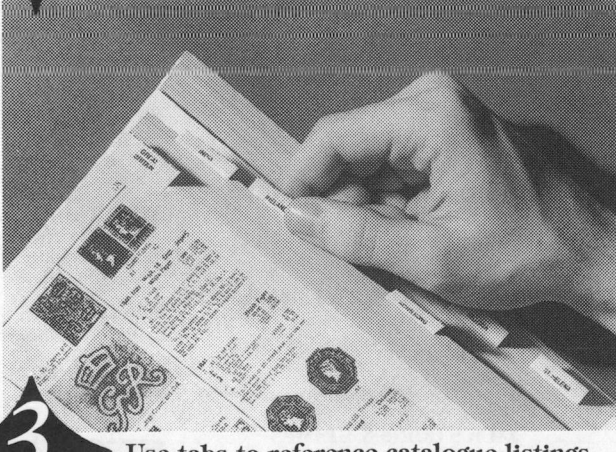

Publications / Collector

AMERICAN PHILATELIST
Dept. TZ
P.O. Box 8000
State College, PA 16803
814-237-3803
814-237-6128 FAX

GLOBAL STAMP NEWS
P.O. Box 97
Sidney, OH 45365-0097
513-492-3183
513-492-6514 FAX

MEKEEL'S WEEKLY STAMP NEWS
Box 5050-sy
White Plains, NY 10602
800-MEKEEL-1
914-997-7261 FAX

Safes - Stamps

KINGSBERY MANUFACTURING CORP.
715 West Zavala Street
Crystal City, TX 78839
800-445-0763

Stamp Shows

ATLANTIC COAST EXHIBITIONS
Division of Beach Philatelics
P.O. Box 150
Virginia Beach, VA 23458-0150
804-425-8566 TELEPHONE & FAX

HIGHTSTOWN SECOND SATURDAY BOURSE
Monmouth St.(RTE.633) opposite
Ramada Inn
Exit 8 New Jersey Turnpike
Hightstown, NJ 08520

AL SOTH
P.O. Box 22081
Milwaukie, OR 97269
503-794-0956

S T A M P   S T O R E S

Arizona

B.J.'S STAMPS / BARBARA J. JOHNSON
6342 W. Bell Road
Glendale, AZ 85308
602-878-2080
602-412-3456 FAX

California

ASHTREE STAMP & COIN
2410 N. Blackstone
Fresno, CA 93703
209-227-7167

BREWART STAMPS
1015 N. Euclid
Anaheim, CA 92801
714-533-0400
714-533-2701 FAX

BROSIUS STAMP & COIN
2105 Main Street
Santa Monica, CA 90405
310-396-7480

FISCHER - WOLK PHILATELICS
24771 "G" Alicia Parkway
Laguna Hills, CA 92653
714-837-2932

HERB'S STAMP CENTER
11748 Washington Place
West Los Angeles, CA 90066
310-397-3883

KENRICH CO.
9418-A Las Tunas Drive
Temple City, CA 91780
818-286-3888
818-286-6035 FAX

NATICK STAMPS & HOBBIES
405 S. Myrtle Avenue
Monrovia, CA 91016
818-305-7333
818-305-7335 FAX

STANLEY M. PILLER
3351 Grand Ave.
Oakland, CA 94610
510-465-8290
510-465-7121 FAX

THE STAMP GALLERY
1515 Locust Street
Walnut Creek, CA 94596
510-944-9111

STAMPCRAFT
P.O. Box 2425
Santa Clara, CA 95055
800-245-5389
408-241-4440 FAX

Colorado

ACKLEY'S ROCKS & STAMPS
3230 N. Stone Ave.
Colorado Springs, CO 80907
719-633-1153

AURORA STAMPS & COINS
9818 E. Colfax Avenue
Aurora, CO 80010
303-364-3223

SHOWCASE STAMPS
3865 Wadsworth Blvd.
Wheat Ridge, CO 80033
303-425-9252
303-425-7410 FAX

Connecticut

MILLER'S STAMP SHOP
41 New London Turnpike
Uncasville, CT 06382
860-848-0468 TELEPHONE & FAX

SILVER CITY COINS & J & B STAMPS
41 Colony Street
Meriden, CT 06451
203-235-7634

Delaware

AUREL STAMP SHOPPE
Bobby Leiter
104 Market Street
Bridgeville, DE 19933-1127
302-337-7855

Florida

ARLINGTON STAMP & COIN CO.
1350 University Blvd., North
Jacksonville, FL 32211-5226
904-743-1776

BEACH STAMP & COIN
971 E. Eau Gallie Blvd.
and Highway A1A Suite G
Melbourne Beach, FL 32937
407-777-1666

CLARK'S CORNER
4223 Bee Ridge Road
Sarasota, FL 34233
941-377-6909
941-377-6604 FAX

S T A M P   S T O R E S

Florida

WHEN VISITING CENTRAL FLORIDA BE SURE TO STOP BY...

Send 32¢ long SASE for our MONTHLY NEWSLETTER of stamps for sale!

Michael Rogers - Alvin Hintz

 WINTER PARK STAMP SHOP
199 E. Welbourne Ave., 2nd floor, Winter Park, FL 32789
Phone 407-628-1120 • FAX 407-628-0091
1-800-845-1819
Open Mon. through Fri. 10am-6pm • Sat. 10am-3pm (4 miles North of Orlando)

Georgia

BLUE RIDGE STAMP CO.

801 E. MAIN STREET
POST OFFICE BOX 2230
BLUE RIDGE, GA 30513
1-800-61-STAMP
FAX 706-632-3908

WE OFFER A FULL LINE OF STAMPS & SUPPLIES FOR THE BEGINNER AND THE ADVANCED COLLECTOR.

WE OFFER A NEW ISSUE SERVICE UNIQUE FROM OTHERS:
NO MINIMUMS AND WE STOCK THE COUNTRIES WE SERVICE.

G.P.S. Our 4000 Sq. Ft. Store Is Located In The N. Georgia Mtns. Surrounded By Antique, Craft, and Specialty Shops. B.I.A. CSA

Florida

CORBIN STAMP & COIN
115-A East Brandon Blvd.
Brandon, FL 33511
813-651-3266

HAUSER'S COIN & STAMP
3425 S. Florida Ave.
Lakeland, FL 33803
941-647-2052
941-644-5738 FAX

HUGO'S STAMP EMPORIUM
P.O. Box 5527
Lake Worth, FL 33466
407-966-7517

INTERCONTINENTAL / RICARDO DEL CAMPO
7379 Coral Way
Miami, FL 33155-1402
305-264-4983
305-262-2919 FAX

JACK'S COINS & STAMPS
801 Northlake Blvd.
North Palm Beach, FL 33408
407-844-7710

JERRY SIEGEL / STAMPS FOR COLLECTORS
1920 E. Hallandale Beach Blvd.
Suite 507
Hallandale, FL 33009
954-457-0422 TELEPHONE & FAX

Florida

NEW ENGLAND STAMP
4987 Tamiami Trail East
Village Falls Professional Ctr
Naples, FL 33962
941-732-8000
941-732-7701 FAX

ST. JOHN'S STAMP SHOP
2 Aviles Street
St. Augustine, FL 32084
904-829-9673

THE STAMP PLACE
576 First Avenue North
St. Petersburg, FL 33701
813-894-4082

WINTER PARK STAMP SHOP
199 E. Welbourne Ave.
Suite 201
Winter Park, FL 32789
800-845-1819
407-628-0091 FAX

Georgia

STAMPS UNLIMITED OF GEORGIA
133 Carnegie Way
Room 250
Atlanta, GA 30303
404-688-9161

STAMP STORES

Illinois

DON CLARK'S STAMPS
937 1/2 W. Galena Blvd.
Aurora, IL 60506
708-896-4606

DR. ROBERT FRIEDMAN & SONS STAMPS & COINS
7451 S. Woodward #108
Woodridge, IL 60517-2665
708-241-1515
708-241-1532 FAX

H.C. STAMP & COIN CO.
10 Crystal Lake Plaza
Crystal Lake, IL 60014
815-459-3940

MARSHALL FIELD'S STAMP DEPT.
111 N. State Street
Chicago, IL 60602
312-781-4237

ROSEMOOR STAMP & COIN CO.
2021 Ridge Road
Homewood, IL 60430
708-799-0880

STAMP KING / RICHARD E. DREWS AUCTIONS
7139 W. Higgins Road
Chicago, IL 60656
312-775-2100
312-792-9116 FAX

WHITE HOUSE JEWELERS
54 N. Main
Canton, IL 61520
309-647-2777

Indiana

J & J COINS & STAMPS
7019 Calumet Avenue
Hammond, IN 46324
219-932-5818

KNIGHT STAMP & COIN COMPANY
301 Main Street
Hobart, IN 46342
800-634-2646

VILLAGE STAMP AND COIN
40 E. Cedar
Zionsville, IN 46077
317-873-6762

Kentucky

COLLECTORS STAMPS LTD.
4012 DuPont Circle #313
Louisville, KY 40207
502-897-9045

TREASURE ISLAND COINS & STAMPS
232 W. Broadway
Louisville, KY 40202
502-583-1222

Maryland

BALTIMORE COIN & STAMP EXCHANGE INC.
10194 Baltimore National Pike
Unit 104
Ellicott City, MD 21042
410-418-8282
410-418-4813 FAX

BULLDOG STAMP CO.
4641 Montgomery Ave.
Bethesda, MD 20814
301-654-1138

Maryland

STAMP & COIN WORLD
511-A Delaware Avenue
Towson, MD 21286
410-828-4465 or 800-452-4560
410-828-4560 FAX

Massachusetts

FALMOUTH STAMP & COIN
11 Town Hall Square
Falmouth, MA 02540
508-548-7075 or 800-341-3701

J & N FORTIER
484 Main Street
Worcester, MA 01608
508-757-3657

KAPPY'S COINS & STAMPS
534 Washington St.
Norwood, MA 02062
617-762-5552
617-762-3292 FAX

Michigan

AMERICA'S STAMP STOP
23333 Orchard Lake Rd.
Farmington, MI 48336
810-474-4460

BIRMINGHAM COIN AND JEWELRY
1287 S. Woodward
Birmingham, MI 48009
810-642-1234
810-642-4207 FAX

MEL COON STAMPS
3833 Twelve Mile
Berkley, MI 48072
810-398-6085
810-398-4549 FAX

THE MOUSE AND SUCH
696 N. Mill Street
Plymouth, MI 48170
313-454-1515

Minnesota

CROSSROADS STAMP SHOP
2211 West 54th Street
Minneapolis, MN 55419-1515
612-928-0119

JW STAMP COMPANY
5300 250th Street
Saint Cloud, MN 56301
320-252-2996

Missouri

KNIGHT'S COINS & STAMPS
323 South Ave.
Springfield, MO 65806
417-862-3018

REGENCY STAMPS, LTD.
Le Chateau Village #106
10411 Clayton Road
St. Louis, MO 63131
800-782-0066
314-997-2231 FAX

Nebraska

TUVA ENTERPRISES
209 So. 72nd Street
Omaha, NE 68114
402-397-9937

New Hampshire

BRUNELLE STAMPS & COINS
25 East Broadway
Derry, NH 03038
603-432-2658
603-437-7279 FAX

New Jersey

AALLSTAMPS
38 N. Main Street
P.O. Box 249
Milltown, NJ 08850
908-247-1093
908-247-1094 FAX

A.D.A STAMP CO., INC.
910 Boyd Street
Toms River, NJ 08753
908-240-1131
908-240-2620 FAX

BERGEN STAMPS & COLLECTABLES
717 American Legion Dr.
Teaneck, NJ 07666
201-836-8987

CHARLES STAMP SHOP
47 Old Post Road
Edison, NJ 08817
908-985-1071
908-819-0549 FAX

COLONIAL COINS & STAMPS
1865 Rt. #35
Wall Township, NJ 07719
908-449-4549

FAIRIDGE STAMP INC.
447 Broadway
Westwood, NJ 07675
201-666-8869

RON RITZER STAMPS, INC.
Millburn Mall
2933 Vauxhall Road
Union, NJ 07088
908-687-0007 TELEPHONE & FAX

SCRIVENER'S STAMPS & COLLECTIBLES
178 Maplewood Avenue
P.O. Box 1035
Maplewood, NJ 07040
201-762-5650
201-762-6709 FAX

TRENTON STAMP & COIN CO.
1804 RT. 33
Trenton, NJ 08690
800-446-8664
609-587-8664 FAX

New York

B.B.C. STAMP & COIN INC.
185 East Main St.
P.O. Box 2141
Setauket, NY 11733-0715
516-751-5662

CHAMPION STAMP CO.
432 West 54th Street
New York, NY 10019
212-489-8130
212-581-8130 FAX

JOHN'S COINS, CARDS & STAMPS INC.
36 West 34th Street
2nd Floor
New York, NY 10001
212-244-2646

LINCOLN COIN & STAMP
33 West Tupper Street
Buffalo, NY 14202
716-856-1884

New York

SUBURBAN STAMPS, COINS AND COLLECTIBLES
120 Kreischer Road
North Syracuse, NY 13212
315-452-0593

VILLAGE STAMPS & COINS
22 Oriskany Blvd.
Yorkville Plaza
Yorkville, NY 13495
315-736-1007 or 800-490-1007

North Dakota

THE COLLECTORS DEN / L.V. FISCHER
P.O. Box 9303
Fargo, ND 58106-9303
701-241-7747 TELEPHONE & FAX

Ohio

CROWN & EAGLE
5303 N. High Street
Columbus, OH 43214
614-436-2042

FEDERAL COIN INC.
39 The Arcade
Cleveland, OH 44114
216-861-1160
216-861-5960 FAX

HILLTOP STAMP SERVICE
P.O. Box 626
Wooster, OH 44691
330-262-5378

J L F STAMP STORE
3041 E. Waterloo Road
Akron, OH 44312
330-628-8343

LAZARUS STAMP DEPT.
141 S. High St.
5th Floor
Columbus, OH 43215
614-463-3214

THE LINK STAMP CO.
3461 E. Livingston Ave.
Columbus, OH 43227
614-237-4125 or 800-546-5726

NEWARK STAMP COMPANY
49 North Fourth Street
Newark, OH 43055
614-349-7900

RANDY SCHOLL STAMP COMPANY
Southampton Square
7460 Jager Court
Cincinnati, OH 45230-4344
513-624-6800
513-624-6440 FAX

Oregon

AL'S STAMP & COIN
2132 West 6th
Eugene, OR 97402
503-343-0091

UNIQUE ESTATE APPRAISALS
1937 NE Broadway
Portland, OR 97232
503-287-4200 or 800-646-1147

STAMP STORES

Pennsylvania

KAUFMANN'S STAMP DEPT.
400 Fifth Ave.
Pittsburgh, PA 15219
412-232-2598

LARRY LEE STAMPS
322 S. Front Street
Wormleysburg, PA 17043
717-763-7605

PENNSYLVANIA STAMP CO.
229 Sixth Street
McKeesport, PA 15132
800-545-6604

PHILLY STAMP & COIN CO. INC.
1804 Chestnut Street
Philadelphia, PA 19103
215-563-7341
215-563-7382 FAX

WORLD OF STAMPS & COINS
Route 611
Fountain Court Mall
Bartonsville, PA 18321
717-688-9829

Rhode Island

PODRAT COIN EXCHANGE INC.
769 Hope Street
Providence, RI 02906
401-861-7640
401-272-3032 FAX

Tennessee

HERRON HILL, INC.
5007 Black Road
Suite 140
Memphis, TN 38117-4505
901-683-9644

Texas

ALAMO HEIGHTS STAMP SHOP
1201 Austin Hwy
Suite 128
San Antonio, TX 78209
800-214-9526
800-495-5255 FAX

AUSTIN STAMP & COIN
13107 F M 969
Austin, TX 78724
512-276-7793

DALLAS STAMP GALLERY
1002 North Central Expressway
Suite 501
Richardson, TX 75080
800-759-9109
214-669-4742 FAX

Virginia

ALAN BLAIR STAMPS / AUCTIONS
5520A Lakeside Avenue
Richmond, VA 23228
800-689-5602 TELEPHONE & FAX

CENTURY STAMPS & COINS
6436 Brandon Ave.
Springfield, VA 22150
703-569-0739

KENNEDY'S STAMPS & COINS
7059 Brookfield Plaza
Springfield, VA 22150
703-569-7300

LATHEROW & CO. INC.
5054 Lee Highway
Arlington, VA 22207
703-538-2727

PRINCE WILLIAM STAMP & COIN CO.
14011-H St. Germain Dr.
Centreville, VA 22020
703-830-4669

Washington

HIDDEN TREASURES INC.
9960 NW Silverdale Way #11
Silverdale, WA 98383
360-692-1999 or 800-322-1993
360-698-1905 FAX

TACOMA MALL BLVD. COIN & STAMP
5225 Tacoma Mall Blvd. E-101
Tacoma, WA 98409
206-472-9632

THE STAMP & COIN PLACE
1310 Commercial
Bellingham, WA 98225
360-676-8720
360-647-6947 FAX

West Virginia

DAVID HILL LTD.
6433 U.S. Route 60 E
Barboursville, WV 25504
304-736-4383

Wisconsin

HERITAGE STAMPS
11400 W. Bluemound Rd.
Milwaukee, WI 53226-4049
800-231-6080
414-369-0741 FAX

JIM LUKES' STAMP & COIN
815 Jay Street
P.O. Box 1780
Manitowoc, WI 54221
414-682-2324

Supplies

VIDIFORMS COMPANY INC.
Showgard House
110 Brenner Drive
Congers, NY 10920
914-268-4005
914-268-5324 FAX

Supplies & Accessories

BEACH PHILATELICS
P.O. Box 150
Virginia Beach, VA 23458-0150
804-425-8566 TELEPHONE & FAX

GLOBAL STAMP & COIN
460 Ridge Street
Lewiston, NY 14092
800-368-4328
716-754-8513 FAX

THE STAMP ACT
Rt. 1 P.O. Box 93
East Orland, ME 04431
800-743-7832

Supplies - Mail Order

GOPHER SUPPLY CO.
1973 Sloan Place #20
Maplewood, MN 55117
612-771-8840 or 800-815-3868
612-771-8850 FAX

STAMPCRAFT
P.O. Box 2425
Santa Clara, CA 95055
800-245-5389
408-241-4440 FAX

Supplies - Stamps & Coins

M.A. STORCK CO.
652 Congress Street
Portland, ME 04104
800-734-7271

Topicals

GERSON-REITER INC.
610 SW Alder St.
Suite 500
Portland, OR 97205
503-228-5233
503-228-5288 FAX

Topicals - Biology

EASTERN SHORE STAMP CO.
P.O. Box 298
Fruitland, MD 21826
410-742-7221

Topicals - Columbus

MR. COLUMBUS
Box 1492
Frankenmuth, MI 48734

Topicals - Miscellaneous

BOMBAY PHILATELIC CO., INC.
P.O. Box 7719
Delray Beach, FL 33482-7719
561-499-7990
561-499-7553 FAX

DISCOUNT TOPICALS
P.O. Box 74-7435
Rego Park, NY 11374
212-726-8075

EASTERN SHORE STAMP CO.
P.O. Box 298
Fruitland, MD 21826
410-742-7221

MEKEEL'S WEEKLY STAMP NEWS
Box 5050-sy
White Plains, NY 10602
800-MEKEEL-1
914-997-7261 FAX

MINI - ARTS
Estherville, IA 51334
712-362-4710

United Kingdom - Ducks

METROPOLITAN STAMP CO. OF CHICAGO, INC.
P.O. Box 1133
Chicago, IL 60690-1133
815-439-0142
815-439-0143 FAX

United Nations

BEACH PHILATELICS
P.O. Box 150
Virginia Beach, VA 23458-0150
804-425-8566 TELEPHONE & FAX

Topicals - Worldwide

WE SELL TOPICALS
TOPICALS
TOPICALS
TOPICALS
TOPICALS

Draw from our extensive worldwide stocks covering more than....... 100 TOPICS!!!

Write or call us TODAY with your requests to join our approval services for all your ....TOPICAL NEEDS

Westminster Stamp Gallery Ltd.
Don Palazzo - Managing Director
P.O. Box 456, Foxboro, MA 02035
PH. 508-384-6157 • FAX 508-384-3130
ASDA
SEE OUR LARGE AD IN THE 1997 SCOTT VOL. 1A YELLOW PAGES.

United States

BEACH PHILATELICS
P.O. Box 150
Virginia Beach, VA 23458-0150
804-425-8566 TELEPHONE & FAX

BOB & MARTHA FRIEDMAN STAMPS
624 Homestead Place
Joliet, IL 60435
805-725-6666
708-281-1532 FAX

DR. ROBERT FRIEDMAN & SONS STAMPS & COINS
7451 S. Woodward #108
Woodridge, IL 60517-2665
708-241-1515
708-241-1532 FAX

United States - Plate Blocks

BEACH PHILATELICS
P.O. Box 150
Virginia Beach, VA 23458-0150
804-425-8566 TELEPHONE & FAX

United States - Price Lists

ROBERT E. BARKER
P.O. Box 888063
Dunwoody, GA 30356
800-833-0217
770-671-8918 FAX

United States Stamps & Covers - Supplies

QUALITY STAMPS
22669 Remington Court
Elkhart, IN 46514-4675

Want Lists

BOMBAY PHILATELIC CO., INC.
P.O. Box 7719
Delray Beach, FL 33482-7719
561-499-7990
561-499-7553 FAX

GERSON - REITER INC.
610 SW Alder Street
Suite 500
Portland, OR 97205
503-228-5233
503-228-5288 FAX

CHARLES P. SCHWARTZ
P.O. Box 165
Mora, MN 55051
612-679-4705

Want Lists - Worldwide

ST. JOHN'S STAMP SHOP
2 Aviles Street
St. Augustine, FL 32084
904-829-9673

Wanted - Estates

TOWN & COUNTRY STAMPS LTD.
P.O. Box 13542-S
St. Louis, MO 63138
314-869-7063
314-869-7851 FAX

Wholesale - British Commonwealth

LAKESIDE PHILATELICS
3935 Lakeside Rd. Ste. 7A
Comp. 4 RR# 2
Penticton, BC V2A 6J7
CANADA
604-493-5239
604-493-3324 FAX
http://vvv.com/~greek
Internet home page #
greek@tnet.net e-mail

Wholesale - Canada

LAKESIDE PHILATELICS
3935 Lakeside Rd. Ste. 7A
Comp. 4 RR# 2
Penticton, BC V2A 6J7
CANADA
604-493-5239
604-493-3324 FAX
http://vvv.com/~greek
Internet home page #
greek@tnet.net e-mail

Wholesale Collections

A.D.A STAMP CO., INC.
910 Boyd Street
Toms River, NJ 08753
908-240-1131
908-240-2620 FAX

Wholesale Philatelic & Numismatic Accessories

ECONOMICAL WHOLESALE CO.
6 King Philip Road
Worcester, MA 01606
508-853-3127

HARRY EDELMAN
111-37 Lefferts Blvd.
P.O.Box 20140
So. Ozone Park, NY 11420
718-641-2710
718-641-0737 FAX

M. C. CLAYTON
290 East Grand Avenue
S. San Francisco, CA 94080
415-873-7577
415-873-7573 FAX

CHARLES R. HEISLER INC.
500 Oak Grove Drive
Lancaster, PA 17601
800-784-6886
717-299-2366 FAX

LEDO SUPPLY CO.
P.O. Box 1749
Sandpoint, ID 83864
800-257-8331

M.A. STORCK CO.
652 Congress Street
Portland, ME 04104
800-734-7271

POLLARD COIN & STAMP SUPPLY CO., INC.
5220 E. 23rd Street
Indianapolis, IN 46218
317-547-1306
317-547-1311 FAX

SCOTT WESTERN
5670 Schaefer Ave. No. L
Chino, CA 91710
909-590-5030
909-465-6368 FAX

Wholesale Supplies

DOUBLE J. STAMPS
P.O. Box 1127
Arlington Heights, IL 60006
847-843-8700
847-843-2878 FAX

JOHN VAN ALSTYNE STAMPS & SUPPLIES
1787 Tribute Rd. Suite J
Sacramento, CA 95815
916-565-0600
916-565-0539 FAX

Worldwide

DAVE ALLEGO
P.O. Box 13
Ambridge, PA 15003-0013
412-266-4255

AMERICAN STAMP & COIN CO.
7225 N. Oracle Rd.
Suite #102
Tucson, AZ 85704
520-297-3456

MEL COON STAMPS
3833 Twelve Mile
Berkley, MI 48072
810-398-6085
810-398-4549 FAX

GERSON - REITER INC.
610 SW Alder Street
Suite 500
Portland, OR 97205
503-228-5233
503-228-5288 FAX

HERITAGE STAMPS
11400 W. Bluemound Rd.
Milwaukee, WI 53226-4049
800-231-6080
414-369-0741 FAX

Worldwide - Collections

BOB & MARTHA FRIEDMAN STAMPS
624 Homestead Place
Joliet, IL 60435
805-725-6666
708-281-1532 FAX

DR. ROBERT FRIEDMAN & SONS STAMPS & COINS
7451 S. Woodward #108
Woodridge, IL 60517-2665
708-241-1515
708-241-1532 FAX

Worldwide - Price Lists

HALL'S STAMPS (ITEX)
P.O. Box 8095
Spokane, WA 99203
509-838-1903 TELEPHONE & FAX

Worldwide - Romania

GEORGE ARGHIR, PHILATELISTS
Detunata Str. 17-27
P.O. Box 521
RO-3400 Cluj-Napoca 9
ROMANIA
40-64-414036 TELEPHONE & FAX

Worldwide - Year Sets

BOMBAY PHILATELIC CO., INC.
P.O. Box 7719
Delray Beach, FL 33482-7719
561-499-7990
561-499-7553 FAX

WALLACE STAMPS
Box 82
Port Washington, NY 11050
516-883-5578